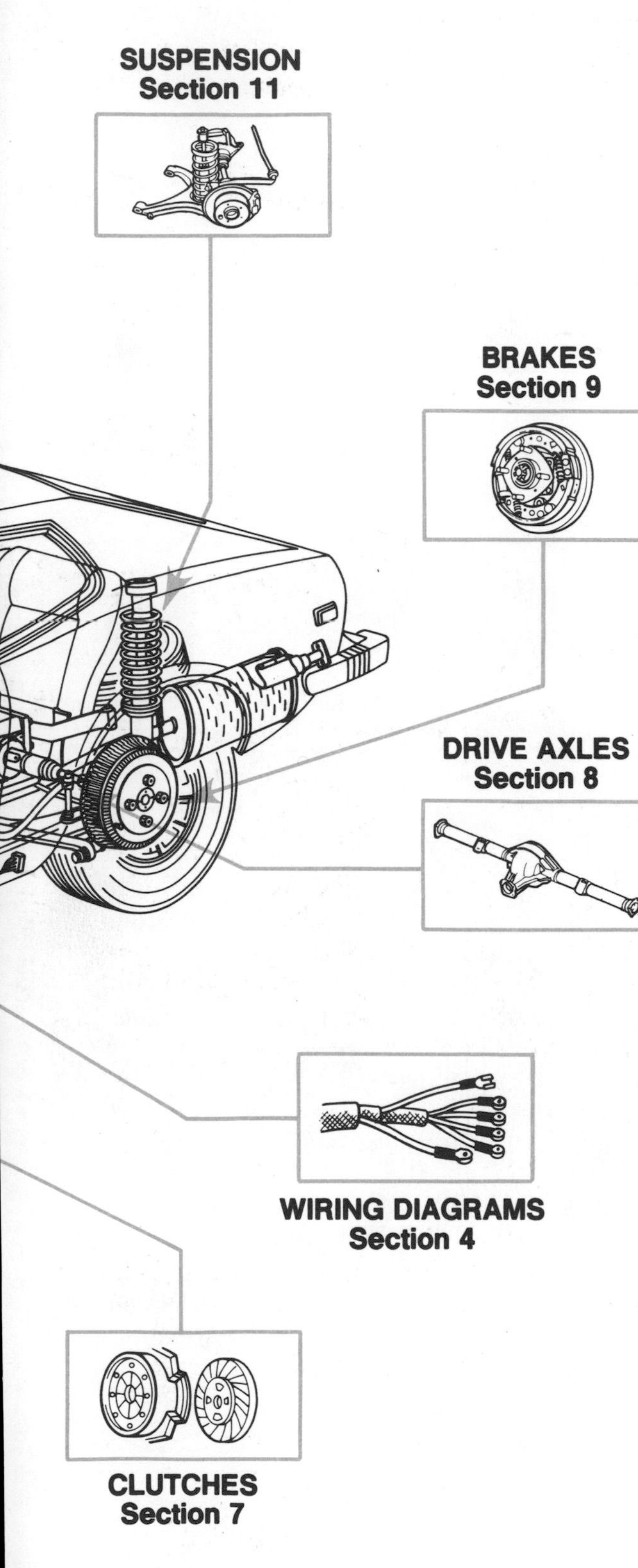
SUSPENSION
Section 11
BRAKES
Section 9
DRIVE AXLES
Section 8
WIRING DIAGRAMS
Section 4
CLUTCHES
Section 7

PREFACE

This is the 1983 edition of Mitchell Manuals' Imported Car Tune-Up/Mechanical Service and Repair Manual. This book, like the many Mitchell publications which have preceded it, represents our commitment to professionalism. in the automotive service market.

The automotive industry advances every year, and Mitchell Manuals pledges to advance and improve its products as we maintain the quality and usefulness of all Mitchell Manuals' publications.

We cordially acknowledge the good will and mutual goals that exist in the automotive business, and it is in this spirit that we thank the automotive manufacturers, distributors, dealers and the entire automotive industry for their fine cooperation and assistance which have made this publication possible.

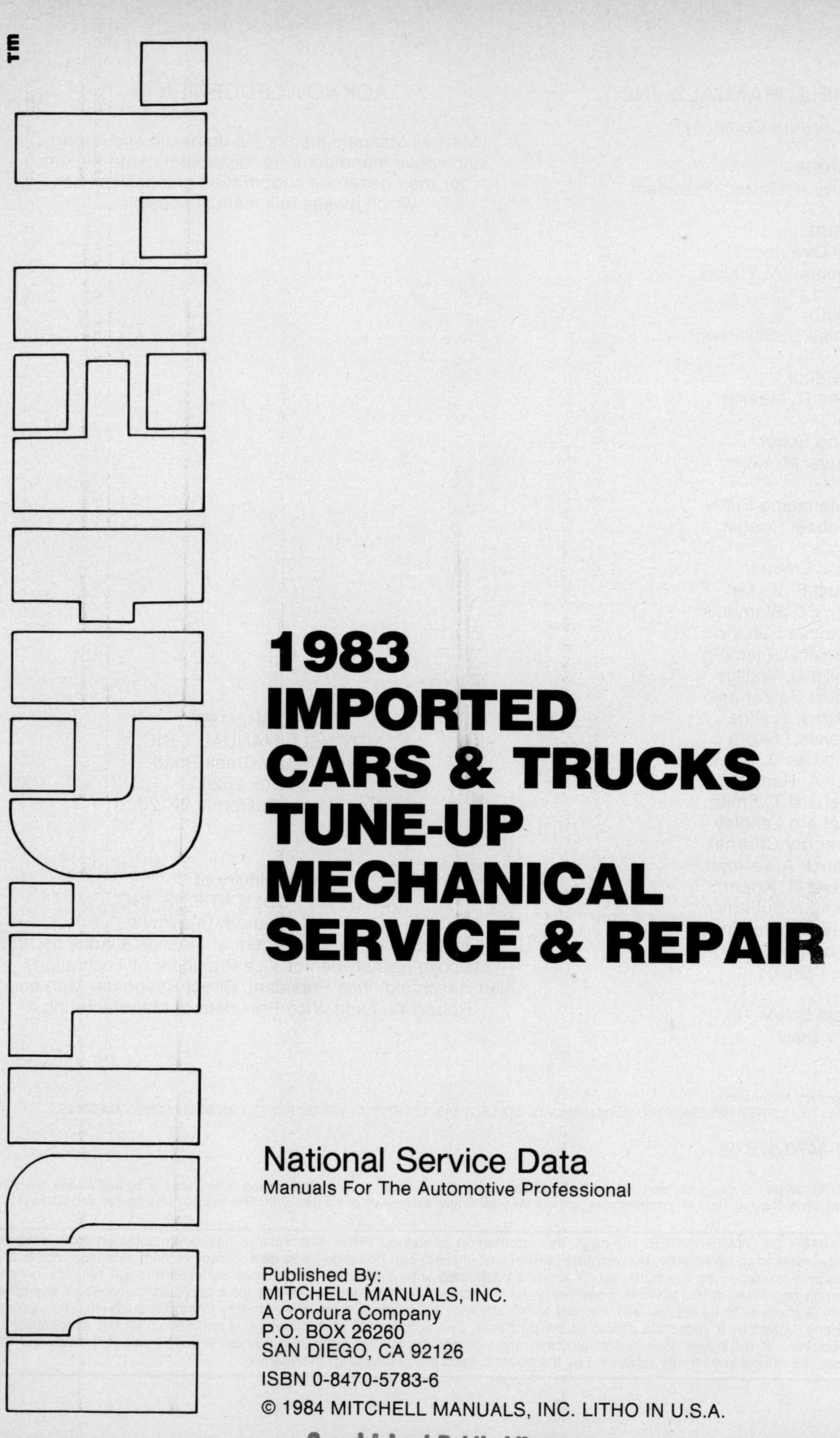

1983 IMPORTED CARS & TRUCKS TUNE-UP MECHANICAL SERVICE & REPAIR

National Service Data
Manuals For The Automotive Professional

Published By:
MITCHELL MANUALS, INC.
A Cordura Company
P.O. BOX 26260
SAN DIEGO, CA 92126

ISBN 0-8470-5783-6

MITCHELL MANUALS, INC.

A Cordura Company

PUBLISHER

Barry A. Norton, President

EDITORIAL

Editorial Director
Kenneth A. Young

Art Director
Eloise S. Stiverson

Detroit Editor
Lynn D. Meeker

Managing Editor
Daniel M. Kelley

Ass't. Managing Editor
Michael Roeder

Technical Editors
Daryl F. Visser
Terry L. Blomquist
Thomas L. Landis
Daniel D. Fleming
Philip G. Wallan
Eddie Santangelo
Patrick T. Rice
David L. Skora
Thomas G. Meyer
Jay A. Hannibal
Richard T. Smith
Richard Langley
Gregory Chornak
Chuck Ackerman
David R. Koontz
Ramiro Gutierrez
Dave Costantino
John Edward von Euen
Ron Brezic

Electrical Editor
Erv Deis

ACKNOWLEDGEMENT

Mitchell Manuals thanks the domestic and import automotive manufacturers, distributors, and dealers for their generous cooperation and assistance which makes this manual possible.

PUBLISHED BY
MITCHELL MANUALS, INC.
9889 Willow Creek Road
P.O. Box 26260
San Diego, California 92126

a subsidiary of
CORDURA PUBLICATIONS, INC.
George C. Evanoff, President
John Opelt, Senior Vice President of Finance & Administration
Malcolm Ferrier, Senior Vice President of Technology
Alan Hirschfeld, Vice President, Direct Response Marketing
Robert W. Ladd, Vice President of Manufacturing

For Subscription Information:
CALL TOLL FREE 800-854-7030. In California CALL COLLECT 619-578-8770. Or WRITE: P.O. Box 26260, San Diego, CA 92126

ISBN 0-8470-5783-6

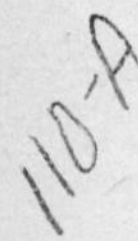

SECTION I

GENERAL INDEX

CONTENTS

1983 General Index

A

B

Cont.

1983 General Index

C

Cont.

1983 General Index

Cont.

1983 General Index

D

Cont.

1983 General Index

Cont.

1983 General Index

Cont.

1983 General Index

Cont.

1983 General Index

Cont.

1983 General Index

Cont.

1983 General Index

F

Cont.

1983 General Index

Cont.

1983 General Index

Cont.

1983 General Index

Cont.

1983 General Index

J

L

Cont.

1983 General Index

Cont.

1983 General Index

Cont.

1983 General Index

Cont.

1983 General Index

Cont.

1983 General Index

Cont.

1983 General Index

Cont.

1983 General Index

W

Cont.

1983 General Index

Cont.

1983 General Index

SECTION T

QUICK-CHECK TUNE-UP SPECIFICATIONS

CONTENTS

TUNE-UP SPECIFICATIONS

NOTE: ALSO SEE GENERAL INDEX.

1983 Tune-Up Specifications

TUNE-UP SPECIFICATIONS

MODEL	SPARK PLUGS Type	SPARK PLUGS Gap	FUEL SYSTEM Make & Model	VALVE CLEARANCE Intake	VALVE CLEARANCE Exhaust	IGNITION SYSTEM Make	No.
ALFA ROMEO	Lodge						
Spider 2.0	HLE	Not Required	Bosch AFC Fuel Inj.	.017" C	.019" C	Bosch	1
GTV-6 2.5	HLE	Not Required	Bosch AFC Fuel Inj.	.019" C	.009" C [1]	Bosch	2
AUDI							
4000	Bosch						
4-Cylinder	W7D [1]	.028"	Bosch CIS Fuel Inj.	.010" H	.018" H	Bosch	3
5-Cylinder	W7D [1]	.028"	Bosch CIS Fuel Inj.	.010" H	.018" H	Bosch	4
5000	W7D [1]	.028"	Bosch CIS Fuel Inj.	.010" H	.018" H	Bosch	5
5000 Turbo	WR7DS	.028"	Bosch CIS Fuel Inj.	.010" H	.018" H	Bosch	6
Coupe	W7D [1]	.028"	Bosch CIS Fuel Inj.	.010" H	.010" H	Bosch	7
BMW	Bosch						
318i	WR9DS	.024"	Bosch AFC Fuel Inj.	.008" C	.008" C	Bosch	8
320i	WR9DS	.024"	Bosch CIS Fuel Inj.	.007" C	.007" C	Bosch	9
528e	WR9LS	.027"	Bosch AFC Fuel Inj. [2]	.010" C	.010" C	Bosch [2]	10
533i	WR9DS	.027"	Bosch AFC Fuel Inj. [2]	.012" C	.012" C	Bosch [2]	11
633CSi & 733i	WR9DS	.024"	Bosch AFC Fuel Inj. [2]	.012" C	.012" C	Bosch [2]	12
CHRYSLER CORP.							
IMPORTS	NGK						
1.4L	BPR-6ES11	.041"	Solex 28-32 DIDTA	.006" H [1]	.010" H	Mitsubishi	13
1.6L	BPR-6ES11	.041"	Solex 28-32 DIDTA	.006" H [1]	.010" H	Mitsubishi	14
2.0L	BPR-6EA11	.041"	Solex 32-35 DIDTA	.006" H [1]	.010" H	Mitsubishi	15
2.6L	BPR-5ES11	.041"	Solex 32-35 DIDTA [4]	.006" H [1]	.010" H	Mitsubishi	16
DATSUN/NISSAN	NGK						
Maxima	BPR-6ES11	.041"	Bosch AFC Fuel Inj.	.010" H	.012" H	Hitachi	17
Pickup	BPR-6ES [3]	.033"	Hitachi DCR 342	.012" H	.012" H	Hitachi	18
Pulsar	BPR-5ES11	.041"	Hitachi DCZ 328 [5]	.011" H	.011" H	Hitachi	19
Sentra							
MPG	BPR-6ES11	.041"	Hitachi DCR 306	.011" H	.011" H	Hitachi	20
Exc. MPG	BPR-5ES11	.041"	Hitachi DCR 306	.011" H	.011" H	Hitachi	21
Stanza	BPR-6ES [6]	.041"	Hitachi DCR 342	.012" H	.012" H	Hitachi	22
200SX	BPR-6ES [3]	.033"	Bosch AFC Fuel Inj.	.012" H	.012" H	Hitachi	23
280ZX	BPR-6ES11	.041"	Bosch AFC Fuel Inj.	.010" H	.012" H	Hitachi	24
280ZX Turbo	BPR-6ES11	.041"	Bosch AFC Fuel Inj.	Hyd.	Hyd.	Hitachi [7]	25
HONDA	NGK						
Accord	BR-6EBL11	.041"	Keihin 2-Bbl.	.006" C [1]	.011" C	Hitachi [2]	26
Civic							
1.3L with 4-Spd.	BR-6EB11	.041"	Keihin 2-Bbl.	.006" C [1]	.008" C	Hitachi	27
1.3L with 5-Spd.	BR-6EB11	.041"	Keihin 2-Bbl.	.006" C [1]	.008" C	Hitachi	28
1.5L	BR-6EB11	.041"	Keihin 2-Bbl.	.006" C [1]	.008" C	Hitachi	29
Prelude	BUR-6EB11	.041"	Two Keihin 1-Bbls.	.006" C [1]	.011" C	Hitachi [2]	30
ISUZU	NGK						
I-Mark	BPR-6ES11	.040"	Hitachi DCH 340	.006" C	.010" C	Nippondenso	31
Impulse	BPR-6ES11	.040"	I-Tec EFI	.006" C	.010" C	I-Tec Electronic	32
P'UP	BPR-6ES11	.040"	Hitachi DCH 340	.006" C	.010" C	Nippondenso	33

1983 Tune-Up Specifications

TUNE-UP SPECIFICATIONS (Cont.)

No.	IGNITION TIMING At Idle	HOT IDLE SPEED Man.	HOT IDLE SPEED Auto.	FAST IDLE RPM	EXHAUST CO READING At Idle	REMARKS
1	11° BTDC	800-1000	.....	.....	0.5-0.7% [2]	[1] – At cam. Set to .013" at valve. [2] – With oxygen sensor disconnected. [3] – 2° BTDC for Calif. (50 State) models.
2	5° ATDC [3]	800-1000	.....	.....	0.5-0.7% [2]	
3	3° ATDC [2]	850-1000	850-1000	.....	0.3-1.2%	[1] – WR7DS on Calif. models. [2] – 6° BTDC for Man. Trans. [3] – At 3000 RPM.
4	3° ATDC [2]	775-925	850-1000	.....	0.3-1.2%	
5	3° ATDC [2]	850-1000	850-1000	.....	0.3-1.2%	
6	21° BTDC [3]	.....	790-910	.....	0.4-1.2%	
7	3° ATDC [2]	850-1000	850-1000	.....	0.3-1.2%	
8	15° BTDC [1]	700-800	700-800	.....	.....	[1] – Timing at 2000-2200 RPM. [2] – Part of Motronic system. [3] – ISC controlled.
9	25° BTDC [1]	850-950	800-900	.....	0.2-1.2%	
10	[2]	650-750 [3]	650-750 [3]	[3]	0.2-1.2%	
11	[2]	650-750 [3]	650-750 [3]	.....	0.2-1.2%	
12	[2]	650-750 [3]	650 750 [3]	.....	0.2-1.2%	
13	5° BTDC	650	.....	.....	0.5% [2]	[1] – Set jet valves to .006" H. [2] – Air injection disconnected. [3] – 700 RPM for Federal models with 5-Spd. Man. Trans. [4] – Challenger & Sapporo use Solex 30-35 DIDTA.
14	5° BTDC	650	750	.....	0.5% [2]	
15	5° BTDC	750	750	.....	0.5% [2]	
16	7° BTDC	750 [3]	800	.....	0.5% [2]	
17	8° BTDC [1]	550-750	550-750	.....	.0-.3% [2]	[1] – Auto. Trans. in "D". [2] – With O_2 sensor connected. [3] – Uses BPR-5ES on exhaust side. [4] – 700-900 RPM on 4WD models. [5] – Hitachi DFC 328 on Calif. models. [6] – Uses BPR-5ES11 on exhaust side. [7] – Part of Datsun ECCS system.
18	3° BTDC [1]	550-750 [4]	550-750	.....	.0-.3% [2]	
19	5° ATDC [1]	700-800	600-700	.....	.0-.3% [2]	
20	2° ATDC [1]	650-750	.....	2400-3200	.0-.3% [2]	
21	5° ATDC [1]	700-800	600-700	.....	.0-.3% [2]	
22	0° TDC [1]	550-750	550-750	.....	.0-.3% [2]	
23	8° BTDC [1]	650-850	600-800	.....	.0-.3% [2]	
24	8° BTDC [1]	550-750	550-750	.....	.0-.3% [2]	
25	24° BTDC [1]	650-750	600-700	.....	.0-.3% [2]	
26	16° BTDC [3]	700-800	650-750	2000-3000	0-0.1%	[1] – Set aux. valves to .006" C. [2] – Some models use Toyo Denso. [3] – 12° BTDC on Calif. Man. Trans. [4] – Transmission in "D". [5] – 10° BTDC on Fed. Man.Trans.
27	20° BTDC	650-750	.....	3000	0-0.1%	
28	18° BTDC	600-700	.....	3000	0-0.1%	
29	18° BTDC	650-750	650-750 [4]	3000	0-0.1%	
30	12° BTDC [5]	750-850	700-800	1500-2500	0-0.1%	
31	6° BTDC	850-950	850-950	3200	.....	[1] – 750-850 RPM on Fed. Man. Trans.
32	12° BTDC	850-950	850-950	.....	.....	
33	6° BTDC	850-950 [1]	850-950	3200	.....	

1983 Tune-Up Specifications

TUNE-UP SPECIFICATIONS

MODEL	SPARK PLUGS		FUEL SYSTEM	VALVE CLEARANCE		IGNITION SYSTEM	
	Type	Gap	Make & Model	Intake	Exhaust	Make	No.
JAGUAR	Champion						
XJ6	N12Y	.035"	Bosch AFC Fuel Inj.	.013" C	.013" C	Lucas	34
XJS	BN5	.025"	Lucas Dig. Fuel Inj.	.011" C	.011" C	Lucas	35
MAZDA	NGK						
B2000	BPR-5ES	.031"	Nikki 2-Bbl.	.012" H	.012" H	Mitsubishi	36
GLC	BPR-5ES	.031"	Hitachi 2-Bbl.	.010" H	.012" H	Mitsubishi	37
RX7	BR-8EQ14	.055"	Nikki 4-Bbl.	.....	.....	Mitsubishi	38
626	BPR-5ES	.031"	Nikki 2-Bbl.	.012" H	.012" H	Mitsubishi	39
MERCEDES-BENZ	Bosch						
380 Series	W9D	.032"	Bosch CIS Fuel Inj.	Hyd.	Hyd.	Bosch	40
MITSUBISHI	NGK						
Cordia	BUR-6EA11	.041"	32-35 DIDTA	.006" H [1]	.010" H	Mitsubishi	41
Montero	BP-5ES11	.041"	32-35 DIDTA	.006" H [1]	.010" H	Mitsubishi	42
Pickup							
2.0L	BUR-6EA11	.041"	32-35 DIDTA	.006" H [1]	.010" H	Mitsubishi	43
2.6L	BPR-5ES11	.041"	32-35 DIDTA	.006" H [1]	.010" H	Mitsubishi	44
Starion	BUR-6EA11	.041"	Mitsubishi Fuel Inj.	.006" H [1]	.010" H	Mitsubishi	45
Tredia	BUR-6EA11	.041"	32-35 DIDTA	.006" H [1]	.010" H	Mitsubishi	46
PEUGEOT	Bosch						
505	WR7DS	.024"	Bosch CIS Fuel Inj.	.004" C	.010" C	Ducellier	47
PORSCHE	Bosch						
911SC	W225T30	.028"	Bosch CIS Fuel Inj.	.004" C	.004" C	Bosch	48
928	WR8DS	.028"	Bosch AFC Fuel Inj.	Hyd.	Hyd.	Bosch	49
944	WR8DS	.028"	Bosch AFC Fuel Inj.	Hyd.	Hyd.	Bosch	50
RENAULT	Bosch						
Fuego	WR7DS	.026"	Bosch AFC Fuel Inj.	.008" C	.010" C	Ducellier	51
Fuego Turbo	RN3G [1]	.024"	Bosch AFC Fuel Inj.	.008" C	.010" C	Ducellier [2]	52
LeCar	WR9DS [4]	.024"	Weber 32 DIR	.006" C	.008" C	Ducellier	53
18i	WR7DS	.026"	Bosch AFC Fuel Inj.	.008" C	.010" C	Ducellier	54
SAAB	NGK						
900	BP-6ES	.026"	Bosch CIS Fuel Inj.	.009" C	.017" C	Bosch	55
900 Turbo	BP-7ES	.026"	Bosch CIS Fuel Inj.	.009" C	.018" C	Bosch	56

1983 Tune-Up Specifications

TUNE-UP SPECIFICATIONS (Cont.)

No.	IGNITION TIMING At Idle	HOT IDLE SPEED Man.	HOT IDLE SPEED Auto.	FAST IDLE RPM	EXHAUST CO READING At Idle	REMARKS
34	17° BTDC [1]	.....	800	.....	0.5-1.5% [2]	[1] – Vacuum hose disconnected.
35	18° BTDC [3]	.....	750	.....	1.0-2.0% [4]	[2] – Oxygen sensor disconnected.
						[3] – Vac. hose disconnected at 3000 RPM.
						[4] – Air injection disconnected.
36	8° BTDC	650	.....	3000-4000	.....	[1] – 8° BTDC on GLC Wagon.
37	6° BTDC [1]	850 [2]	750 [3]	3000-4000	.....	[2] – 800 RPM on GLC Wagon.
38	TDC [4]	750	750 [3]	3000-4000	.....	[3] – Transmission in "D".
39	6° BTDC [5]	750	700 [3]	3000-4000	.....	[4] – Trailing timing is 20° ATDC.
						[5] – Vacuum line disconnected and plugged (Exc. Calif.).
40	5° BTDC	.....	500-600	.....	.....	
41	5° BTDC	550-750 [2]	650-850	1250-1350 [3]	0.5%	[1] – Set jet valves to .006" H.
42	7° BTDC	650-850	.....	850-950 [3]	0.5%	[2] – 4 x 2 transaxle is 600-800 RPM.
						[3] – With A/C on.
43	5° BTDC	600-800 [4]	650-850	850-950 [3]	0.5%	[4] – Fed. 5-Spd.; Fed. 4-Spd. is 650-850 RPM.
44	7° BTDC	650-850	700-900	850-950 [3]	0.5%	
45	10° BTDC	750-950	.....	.....	.....	
46	5° BTDC	550-750 [2]	650-850	1250-1350 [3]	0.5%	
47	8° BTDC	800-850	800-850	.....	0.3-1.3%	
48	5° BTDC [1]	900-1000	.....	.....	0.4-0.8% [2]	[1] – Vacuum hoses disconnected.
49	20° BTDC [1] [3]	700-800	700-800	.....	0.4-0.8% [2]	[2] – Oxygen sensor disconnected.
50	3-7° BTDC [4]	850-950	850-950	.....	0.4-0.8% [2]	[3] – At 3000 RPM.
						[4] – Electronically controlled.
						[1] – Champion number.
51	10° BTDC	750-850	600-700	.....	0.4-1.0%	[2] – Computer controlled.
52	10° BTDC [3]	700-800	.....	.....	.....	[3] – Not adjustable; electronic control.
53	3° BTDC	700-800	.....	.....	0.5-2.1% [5]	[4] – Fed. models – Champion RN12Y.
54	10° BTDC	750-850	600-700	.....	0.4-1.0%	[5] – Air injection disconnected. Not measured on Calif. models.
55	20° BTDC [1]	800-950	800-950	.....	.....	[1] – Vacuum hoses disconnected; engine at 2000 RPM.
56	20° BTDC [1]	800-950	800-950	.....	.....	

1983 Tune-Up Specifications

TUNE-UP SPECIFICATIONS

MODEL	SPARK PLUGS		FUEL SYSTEM	VALVE CLEARANCE		IGNITION SYSTEM	
	Type	Gap	Make & Model	Intake	Exhaust	Make	No.
SUBARU	NGK						
1.6L	BPR-6ES11	.041"	Hitachi DCP 306	.010" C	.014" C	Nippondenso	57
1.8L	BPR-6ES11	.041"	Hitachi DCP 306 [3]	.010" C [4]	.014" C [4]	Nippondenso [5]	58
1.8L Turbo	BPR-6ES11	.041"	Bosch AFC Fuel Inj.	Hyd.	Hyd.	Hitachi	59
TOYOTA	NGK						
Camry	BPR5EA-L11	.043"	Bosch AFC Fuel Inj.	Hyd.	Hyd.	Nippondenso	60
Celica	BPR-5EY	.031"	Aisan 2-Bbl. [2]	.008" H	.012" H	Nippondenso	61
Corolla	BPR-5EAL11	.043"	Aisan 2-Bbl.	.008" H	.012" H	Nippondenso	62
Cressida	BPR-5EP11	.043"	Bosch AFC Fuel Inj.	Hyd.	Hyd.	Nippondenso	63
Land Cruiser	BPR-4EY	.031"	Aisan 2-Bbl.	.008" H	.014" H	Nippondenso	64
Pickup	BPR-5EY	.031"	Aisan 2-Bbl.	.008" H	.012" H	Nippondenso	65
Starlet							
4-Speed	BPR-5EP11	.043"	Bosch AFC Fuel Inj.	Hyd. [7]	Hyd. [7]	Nippondenso	66
5-Speed	BPR-529Y11	.043"	Bosch AFC Fuel Inj.	Hyd. [7]	Hyd. [7]	Nippondenso	67
Supra	BPR-5EP11	.043"	Bosch AFC Fuel Inj.	Hyd.	Hyd.	Nippondenso	68
Tercel							
4-Speed	BPR-5EA11 [9]	.043"	Aisan 2-Bbl.	.008" H	.012" H	Nippondenso	69
5-Speed	BPR-5EA11 [9]	.043"	Aisan 2-Bbl.	.008" H	.012" H	Nippondenso	70
VOLKSWAGEN	Bosch						
Jetta & Scirocco	W175T30 [1]	.028"	Bosch CIS Fuel Inj.	.010" H	.018" H	Bosch	71
Quantum							
4- or 5-Cylinder	W175T30 [1]	.028"	Bosch CIS Fuel Inj.	.010" H	.018" H	Bosch	72
Rabbit & Convert.	W175T30 [1]	.028"	Bosch CIS Fuel Inj. [3]	.010" H	.018" H	Bosch	73
Rabbit GTI	WR7DS	.028"	Bosch CIS Fuel Inj. [3]	.010" H	.018" H	Bosch	74
Rabbit Pickup							
Federal	W175T30 [1]	.028"	Bosch CIS Fuel Inj. [3]	.010" H	.018" H	Bosch	75
Calif.	W175T30 [1]	.028"	Bosch CIS Fuel Inj. [3]	.010" H	.018" H	Bosch	76
Vanagon							
Air-Cooled							
Federal	W145M2	.028"	Bosch AFC Fuel Inj.	Hyd.	Hyd.	Bosch [6]	77
Calif.	W145M2	.028"	Bosch AFC Fuel Inj.	Hyd.	Hyd.	Bosch	78
Water-Cooled	W7C0	.030"	Bosch AFC Fuel Inj.	Hyd.	Hyd.	Bosch	79
VOLVO	Bosch						
4-Cylinder	WR7DS	.030"	LH-Jetronic Fuel Inj. [1]	.015" C	.015" C	Volvo [2]	80
V6	HR6DS	.028"	Bosch CIS Fuel Inj.	.005" C	.011" C	Bosch	81

1983 Tune-Up Specifications

TUNE-UP SPECIFICATIONS (Cont.)

No.	IGNITION TIMING At Idle	HOT IDLE SPEED Man.	HOT IDLE SPEED Auto.	FAST IDLE RPM	EXHAUST CO READING At Idle	REMARKS
57	8° BTDC	600-800	700-900 [1]	.....	0-0.5% [2]	[1] – In Neutral. [2] – Air hose on. 1.0-3.0% for Man. Trans. or 0.5-2.5% for Auto. Trans. [3] – Some 2WD Fed. Man. Trans. models use Carter-Weber TYF 1-Bbl. [4] – 1800 Auto. Trans. models have hydraulic lifters. [5] – Some 4WD models use Hitachi.
58	8° BTDC	600-800	700-900	.....	0-0.5% [2]	
59	15° BTDC	.....	750-850	.....	0-0.1%	
60	5° BTDC [1]	650-750	700-800		.....	[1] – At 950 RPM, or less. [2] – EFI models use Bosch AFC Fuel Inj. [3] – 750 RPM EFI models. [4] – Carbureted models only. [5] – With power steering, 800 RPM. [6] – With power steering, 900 RPM. [7] – One turn past zero lash. [8] – With A/C on, 900 RPM in Neutral. [9] – Federal model. Calif. BPR5EA-L11
61	5° BTDC [1]	700 [3]	700 [3]	2600 [4]	....	
62	5° BTDC [1]	650 [5]	800 [6]	3000	.....	
63	10° BTDC [1]	650	650	.....	.....	
64	7° BTDC [1]	650	650	1800	.....	
65	5° BTDC [1]	700	750	2600	.....	
66	5° BTDC [1]	700	700	.....	.....	
67	5° BTDC [1]	700	700	.....	.....	
68	10° BTDC	650 [8]	650 [8]	.....	.....	
69	5° BTDC [1]	550	800 [6]	3000	.....	
70	5°BTDC [1]	650 [5]	800 [6]	3000	.....	
71	6° BTDC [2]	850-1000	850-1000	.....	0.3-1.2%	[1] – WR7DS on Calif. models. [2] – 3° ATDC for Auto. Trans. [3] – Some use Carter/Weber TYF 1-BBl. [4] – With Carter/Weber TYF 1-BBl. [5] – 7.5° BTDC@800-1000 RPM on carb. models. [6] – Uses breaker point system.
72	6° BTDC [2]	850-1000	850-1000	.....	0.3-1.2%	
73	6° BTDC [2] [5]	850-1000	850-1000	2600-3000 [4]	0.3-1.2%	
74	6° BTDC [2]	850-1000	850-1000	.....	0.3-1.2%	
75	3° ATDC [2] [5]	850-1000	850-1000	2600-3000 [4]	1.0-2.0%	
76	6° BTDC [2]	850-1000	850-1000	.....	0.3-1.5%	
77	7.5° BTDC	800-950	850-1000	.....	0.5-1.5%	
78	5° ATDC	850-950	850-950	.....	0.3-1.1%	
79	5° ATDC	800-900	800-900	.....	0.3-1.1%	
80	12° BTDC	750 [3]	750 [3]	.....	0.4-0.8% [4]	[1] – Turbo models use Bosch CIS. [2] – Bosch on Turbo CIS engine. [3] – Turbo models – 900 RPM. [4] – Turbo is 0.7-1.3%. [5] – 2500 RPM, Vac. Reg. disconnected.
81	23° BTDC [5]	900	900	.....	0.7-1.3%	

SECTION 1

TUNE-UP

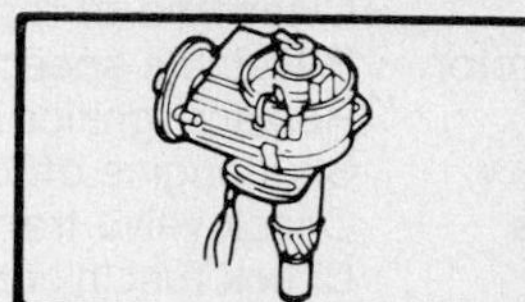

NOTE: ALSO SEE GENERAL INDEX.

Tune-Up

TUNE-UP TROUBLE SHOOTING

CONDITION	POSSIBLE CAUSE	CORRECTION
SPARK PLUG DIAGNOSIS		
Normal Spark Plug Condition	Light Tan or Gray deposits on insulator Electrode not burned or fouled Gap tolerance not changed	
Cold Fouling or Carbon Deposits	Over-rich air/fuel mixture Faulty choke Clogged air filter Incorrect idle speed or dirty carburetor Faulty ignition wiring Prolonged operation at idle Sticking valves or worn valve seals Fuel injection operation	Adjust air/fuel mixture, see TUNE-UP Replace choke assembly, see FUEL SYSTEMS Clean and/or replace air filter Reset idle speed and/or clean carburetor Replace ignition wiring Shut engine off during long idle Check valve train Check fuel injection, see FUEL SYSTEMS
Wet Fouling or Oil Deposits	Worn rings and pistons Excessive cylinder wear Worn or loose bearings	Install new rings and pistons Rebore or replace block Tighten or replace bearings
Gap Bridged	Deposits in combustion chamber becoming fused to electrode	Clean combustion chanber of deposits
Blistered Electrode	Engine overheating Wrong type of fuel Loose spark plugs Over-advanced ignition timing	Check cooling system Replace with correct fuel Re-tighten spark plugs Reset ignition timing, see TUNE-UP
Pre-Ignition or Melted Electrodes	Incorrect type of fuel Incorrect ignition timing Burned valves Engine overheating Wrong type of spark plug, too hot	Replace with correct fuel Reset ignition timing, see TUNE-UP Replace valves Check cooling system Replace with correct spark plug, see TUNE-UP
Chipped Insulators	Severe detonation Improper gapping procedure	Check for over-advanced timing or combustion chamber deposits Re-gap spark plugs
Rust Colored Deposits	Additives in unleaded fuel Water in combustion chamber	Try different fuel brand These deposits do not affect plug performance
ELECTRONIC IGNITION DIAGNOSIS		
Before diagnosing an electronic ignition system, ensure that all wiring is properly connected between distributor, wiring connector and spark plugs. Ignition problems will show up either as: Engine Will Not Start or Engine Runs Rough.		
Engine Won't Start	Open circuits in the following locations: Between distributor and bulkhead connector Between bulkhead connector and ignition switch Between ignition switch and starter solenoid	 Repair circuit Repair circuit Repair circuit
Engine Runs Rough	Fuel lines leaking or clogged Ignition timing incorrect Distributor advance malfunction Defective spark plugs, or wiring	Tighten fitting, remove restriction Reset ignition timing, see TUNE-UP Check distributor advance, see ELECTRICAL Replace plugs or plug wiring
Component Failure	Spark arc-over on rotor, coil or cap Defective pick-up coil Defective ignition coil Defective vacuum unit Defective control module	Replace rotor, cap or coil Replace pick-up coil, see ELECTRICAL Replace ignition coil Replace vacuum unit, see ELECTRICAL Replace control module

TUNE-UP TROUBLE SHOOTING (Cont.)

CONDITION	POSSIBLE CAUSE	CORRECTION
	ELECTRONIC IGNITION DIAGNOSIS BY OSCILLOSCOPE PATTERN	
Firing Voltage Lines are the Same, But Abnormally High	Retarded ignition timing	Reset ignition timing, see TUNE-UP
	Fuel mixture too lean	Re-adjust fuel system, see TUNE-UP
	High resistance in coil wire	Replace coil wire
	Corrosion in coil tower terminal	Clean and/or replace coil
	Corrosion in distributor coil terminal	Clean or replace distributor cap
Firing Voltage Lines are the Same, But Abnormally Low	Fuel mixture too rich	Re-adjust fuel system, see TUNE-UP
	Breaks in coil wire causing arcing	Replace coil wire
	Cracked coil tower causing arcing	Replace coil
	Low coil output	Replace coil
	Low engine compression	Determine cause and repair
Several Firing Voltage Lines Higher Than Others	Fuel system idle mixture not balanced	Re-adjust idle mixture, see TUNE-UP
	EGR valve stuck open	Inspect and/or replace EGR valve
	High resistance in spark plug wire	Replace spark plug wires
	Cracked or broken spark plug insulator	Replace spark plugs
	Intake vacuum leak	Repair leak
	Defective spark plugs	Replace spark plugs
	Corroded spark plug terminals	Replace spark plugs
Several Firing Voltage Lines Lower Than Others	Curb idle mixture not balanced	Re-adjust idle mixture, see TUNE-UP
	Breaks in plug wires causing arcing	Replace spark plug wires
	Cracked coil tower causing arcing	Replace coil
	Low compression	Determine cause and repair
	Defective or fouled spark plugs	Replace spark plugs
Cylinders Not Firing	Cracked distributor cap terminals	Replace distributor cap
	Shorted spark plug wire	Determine cause of short and replace wire
	Mechanical problem in engine	Determine problem and correct
	Defective spark plugs	Replace spark plugs
	Spark plugs fouled	Replace spark plugs
	GENERAL DIAGNOSIS	
Hard Starting	Binding carburetor linkage	Eliminate binding
	Binding choke assembly	Eliminate binding
	No fuel delivery	Check fuel system
	Restricted choke vacuum	Check vacuum lines for blockage
	Worn or dirty needle valve and seat	Clean carburetor, see FUEL SYSTEMS
	Float sticking	Re-adjust or replace float, see FUEL SYSTEMS
	Incorrect choke adjustment	Reset choke adjustment, see TUNE-UP
	Defective coil	Replace coil
	Improper spark plug gap	Re-gap spark plugs
	Incorrect ignition timing	Reset ignition timing, see TUNE-UP
Detonation	Over-advanced ignition timing	Reset ignition timing, see TUNE-UP
	Defective spark plugs	Replace spark plugs
	Fuel lines clogged	Clean out fuel lines
	EGR system malfunction	Check EGR system
	PCV system malfunction	Check PCV system
	Vacuum leaks	Check and repair vacuum system
	Loose fan belts	Tighten or replace fan belts, see TUNE-UP
	Restricted air flow	Remove restriction
	Vacuum advance malfunction	Check distributor operation, see ELECTRICAL
	Overheating	Check cooling system

Tune-Up

TUNE-UP TROUBLE SHOOTING (Cont.)

CONDITION	POSSIBLE CAUSE	CORRECTION
	GENERAL DIAGNOSIS (Cont.)	
Dieseling	Binding carburetor linkage	Free carburetor linkage
	Overheating	Check cooling system
	Binding choke linkage or fast idle cam	Free binding linkage
	Defective idle solenoid	Replace solenoid, see FUEL SYSTEMS
	Improper base idle speed	Reset idle speed, see TUNE-UP
	Incorrect ignition timing	Reset ignition timing, see TUNE-UP
	Incorrect idle mixture setting	Reset idle mixture setting, see TUNE-UP
Faulty Acceleration	Incorrect ignition timing	Reset ignition timing, see TUNE-UP
	Engine cold and choke too lean	Adjust choke and allow engine to warm-up
	Defective spark plugs	Replace spark plugs
	Defective coil	Replace coil
	Restricted exhaust	Check with vacuum gauge
Faulty Low Speed Operation	Clogged idle transfer slots	Clean idle transfer slots, see FUEL SYSTEMS
	Restricted idle air bleeds and passages	Clean carburetor, see FUEL SYSTEMS
	Improper fuel injection operation	Check system, see FUEL SYSTEMS
	Clogged air cleaner filter	Replace air cleaner
	Defective spark plugs	Replace spark plugs
	Defective ignition wires	Replace ignition wires, see TUNE-UP
	Defective distributor cap	Replace distributor cap
Faulty High Speed Operation	Incorrect ignition timing	Reset ignition timing, see TUNE-UP
	Defective distributor advance	Check mechanism, see ELECTRICAL
	Defective electronic advance	Check electronic control, see ELECTRICAL
	Incorrect spark plugs or plug gap	Check gap and/or replace spark plugs
	Faulty choke operation	Check choke and repair as required
	Defective fuel injection operation	Check system, see FUEL SYSTEMS
	Clogged vacuum passages	Remove restrictions
	Improper size or clogged main jet	Check jet size or clean, see FUEL SYSTEMS
	Restricted air cleaner	Check filter and replace as required
	Restricted fuel filter	Check filter and replace as required
	Defective distributor cap, rotor or coil	Replace cap, rotor or coil
	Worn distributor shaft	Replace distributor
Misfire At All Speeds	Defective spark plugs or wires	Replace spark plugs or wires
	Defective distributor cap, rotor or coil	Replace cap, rotor, or coil
	Cracked or broken vacuum hoses	Replace vacuum hoses
	Vacuum leaks	Seal leaks
	Fuel lines clogged	Remove restriction
Hesitation	Cracked or broken vacuum hoses	Replace vacuum hoses
	Vacuum leaks	Repair leaks
	Binding carburetor linkage	Eliminate binding
	Binding choke linkage or fast idle cam	Eliminate binding
	Improper float setting	Re-adjust float setting, see FUEL SYSTEMS
	Cracked or broken ignition wires	Replace ignition wires
Rough Idle, Missing or Stalling	Incorrect curb idle or fast idle speed.	Reset idle speeds, see TUNE-UP
	Incorrect basic timing	Reset ignition timing, see TUNE-UP
	Improper idle mixture adjustment	Reset idle mixture adjustment, see TUNE-UP
	Improper feedback system operation	Check feedback system, see FUEL SYSTEMS
	Incorrect spark plug gap	Reset spark plug gap, see TUNE-UP
	Moisture in ignition components	Dry components
	Damaged distributor cap or rotor	Replace cap or rotor
	Faulty ignition coil or wires	Replace coil or wires
	Fuel filter clogged or worn	Replace fuel filter
	Improper fast idle cam adjustment	Reset fast idle cam adjustment, see TUNE-UP
	Improper EGR valve operation	Replace EGR valve
	Faulty PCV valve air flow	Replace PCV valve

TUNE-UP TROUBLE SHOOTING (Cont.)

CONDITION	POSSIBLE CAUSE	CORRECTION
	GENERAL DIAGNOSIS (Cont.)	
Rough Idle, Missing or Stalling (Cont.)	Choke binding, or improper setting	Reset choke and eliminate binding
	Vacuum leak	Eliminate leak
	Improper float bowl fuel level	Reset float adjustment, see FUEL SYSTEMS
	Clogged air bleed or idle passages	Clean carburetor passages, see FUEL SYSTEMS
	Clogged or worn air cleaner filter	Replace air filter
	Faulty choke vacuum diaphragm	Replace diaphragm, see FUEL SYSTEMS
	Exhaust manifold heat valve inoperative	Replace heat valve
	Improper distributor spark advance	Check distributor operation, see ELECTRICAL
	Leaking valves or valve components	Check valve train
	Improper carburetor mounting	Remove and remount carburetor
	Excessive play in distributor shaft	Replace distributor, see ELECTRICAL
	Loose or corroded wiring connections	Repair or replace as required
	Faulty feedback system	See COMPUTERIZED ENGINE CONTROL
Engine Surges	Improper PCV valve air flow	Replace PCV valve
	Vacuum leaks	Eliminate leaks
	Clogged main jets	Remove restriction
	Clogged air bleeds	Remove restriction
	EGR valve malfunction	Replace EGR valve
	Restricted air cleaner filter	Replace air filter
	Cracked or broken vacuum hoses	Repair or replace hoses
	Cracked or broken ignition wires	Replace ignition wires
	Ignition advance malfunction	Check units and replace if required
	Defective or fouled spark plugs	Replace spark plugs
Ping or Spark Knock	Incorrect ignition timing	Reset ignition timing, see TUNE-UP
	Distributor centrifugal, vacuum or electronic advance malfunction	Check operation amd replace as required
	Carburetor setting too lean	Re-adjust mixture setting, see TUNE-UP
	Vacuum leak	Eliminate leak
	EGR valve malfunction	Replace EGR valve
Poor Gasoline Mileage	Cracked or broken vacuum hoses	Replace vacuum hoses
	Vacuum leaks	Eliminate leaks
	Defective ignition wires	Replace wires
	Incorrect choke setting	Re-adjust setting, see FUEL SYSTEMS
	Defective advance	Check ignition advance, see ELECTRICAL
	Defective spark plugs	Replace spark plugs
	Binding carburetor power piston	Eliminate binding
	Dirt in carburetor jets	Clean jets and/or replace, see FUEL SYSTEMS
	Incorrect float adjustment	Re-adjust float setting, see FUEL SYSTEMS
	Defective power valves	Replace power valve, see FUEL SYSTEMS
	Fuel pressure regulator	Check line pressure, see FUEL SYSTEMS
Engine Stalls	Incorrect idle speed	Re-adjust idle speed, see TUNE-UP
	Improper float level	Re-adjust float level, see FUEL SYSTEMS
	Leaking needle valve and seat	Replace needle valve and seat, see FUEL SYSTEMS
	Vacuum leaks	Eliminate leaks

1983 Alfa Romeo 4 Tune-Up

TUNE-UP

Spider 2.0

ENGINE IDENTIFICATION

Engine number is located on left rear side of engine block.

ENGINE CODE

Application	Code
Spider 2.0	AR01544

VALVE CLEARANCE

1) Adjust valves with engine cold. Using a feeler gauge, measure clearance at point shown in *Fig. 1.*

Fig. 1: Adjusting Alfa Romeo Valve Clearance

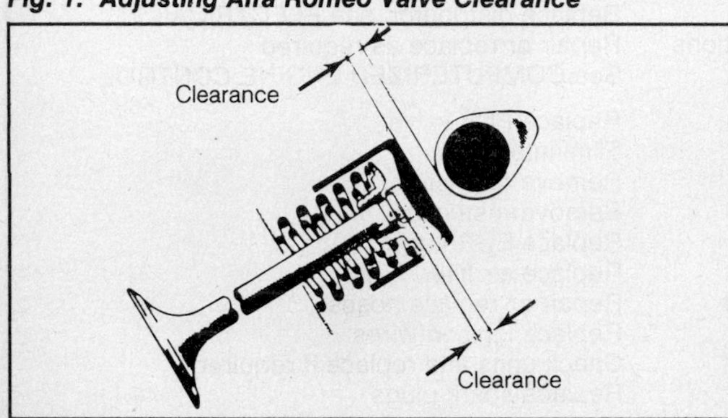
Clearance
Clearance

VALVE CLEARANCE SPECIFICATIONS

Application	In. (mm)
Intake	.016-.018 (.40-.45)
Exhaust	.018-.020 (.45-.50)

2) If clearance is not within specifications, remove camshafts and valve cups. Measure thickness of adjusting pad on each valve stem. Replace it with pad of correct thickness to return clearance within specifications.

3) Pads are available in thickness from .051-.138" (1.3-3.5 mm) in increments of .001" (.025 mm). Install camshafts, aligning timing marks correctly. Adjust timing chain tension.

VALVE ARRANGEMENT

Right Side — All Intake
Left Side — All Exhaust

SPARK PLUGS

SPARK PLUG TYPE

Application	Lodge	Champion
All Models	HLE	RN5C

SPARK PLUG SPECIFICATIONS

Application	Gap In. (mm)	Torque Ft. Lbs. (N.m)
All Models	[1] .023-.027 (.6-.7)	18-25 (25-38)

[1] — Gap is for Champion spark plug. Lodge spark plug has 4 points and central electrode, requiring no gap adjustment.

DISTRIBUTOR

All models use a computerized, digital, electronic ignition system. The distributor's only function is supplying spark to the appropriate spark plug.

Fig. 2: Firing Order and Distributor Rotation

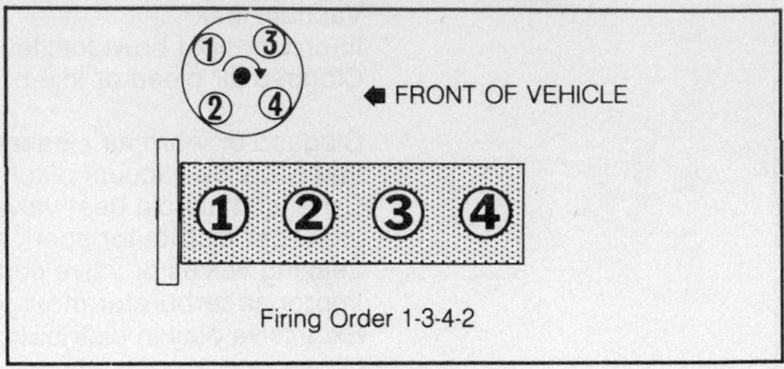
FRONT OF VEHICLE
Firing Order 1-3-4-2

IGNITION TIMING

The Spider 2.0 uses a computerized, digital electronic, ignition system. With this system ignition timing is controlled electronically and no timing adjustment is possible.

IGNITION TIMING SPECIFICATIONS (Degrees BTDC@RPM)

Application	Timing
Spider 2.0	11@900

IDLE SPEED & MIXTURE

IDLE SPEED

1) The idle speed adjustment must be made with engine at operating temperature, transmission in Neutral, and all accessories off. To adjust, loosen idle adjuster lock nut. *See Fig. 3.*

2) Turn adjuster ring until idle speed is 800-1000 RPM. Retighten lock nut.

IDLE MIXTURE

NOTE: Mixture control adjustment screw opening is plugged to prevent tampering. Adjustment is not a normal tune-up procedure and should not be performed unless mixture control unit is replaced or vehicle fails emissions testing.

1) Disconnect wire from oxygen sensor at connector inside the engine compartment. Remove exhaust tap plug and connect exhaust analyzer. With engine idling, CO should be 0.5-0.7% (oxygen sensor disconnected).

NOTE: Testing must be done at tap upstream of catalytic converter.

2) If CO exceeds 0.5-0.7%, remove air flow sensor. Place unit in holding fixture or vise, taking care not to damage housing. Drill hole into adjustment plug, but do not drill through completely. Blow out chips with air. Twist in tap into drilled hole and pull plug out. *See Fig. 4.*

TUNE-UP (Cont.)

Fig. 3: Spider 2.0 Idle Speed Adjustment Location

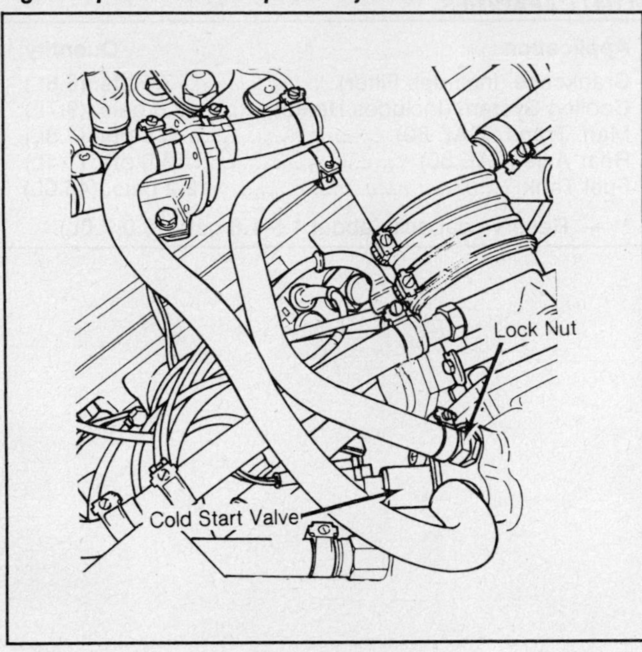

Lock Nut
Cold Start Valve

Fig. 4: Spider 2.0 Mixture Adjusting Plug

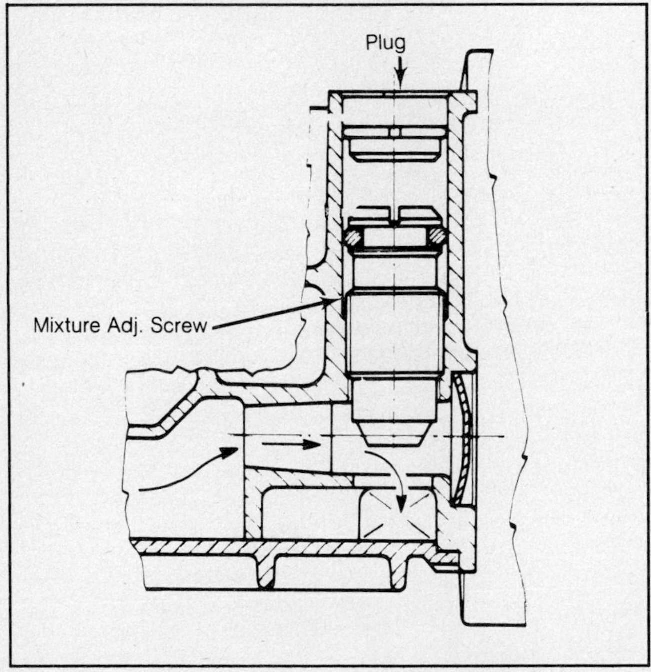

Plug
Mixture Adj. Screw

3) Adjustment screw is now accessible. Reinstall air sensor on vehicle. With engine idling (800-1000 RPM) at operating temperature, adjust CO. Press in new plug seal, and readjust idle speed if necessary. Install exhaust test port plug, and connect oxygen sensor wire.

IDLE SPEED & CO LEVEL SPECIFICATIONS

Application	Idle RPM	[1] CO%
Spider 2.0	800-1000	0.5-0.7

[1] — With oxygen sensor disconnected.

OXYGEN SENSOR

SENSOR REPLACEMENT

1) Oxygen sensor must be replaced at 30,000 miles on Spider 2.0. Disconnect oxygen sensor electrical lead in engine compartment. From underneath vehicle, loosen clamp and cover. Remove oxygen sensor.

2) Coat new oxygen sensor threads with anti-seize compound before installation. Tighten oxygen sensor and reconnect the electrical lead.

NOTE: Do not apply anti-seize compound to the slotted part of the oxygen sensor.

OXYGEN SENSOR LIGHT

Mileage counter is located in engine compartment on left side. To reset, remove plastic cover by drilling through shank of attaching screws. Remove cover, then rotate and press button. *See Fig. 5*. Reinstall cover using new screws.

Fig. 5: Spider 2.0 Oxygen Counter

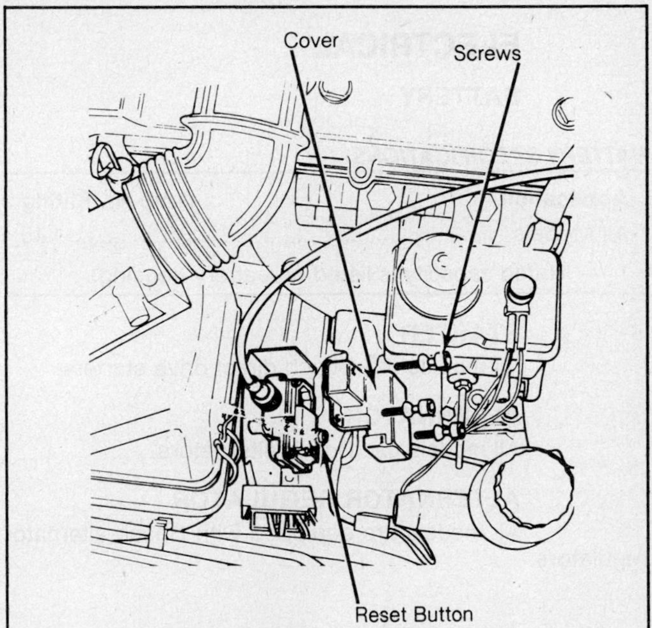

Cover
Screws
Reset Button

Counter located left side of engine compartment

FUEL PUMP

FUEL PUMP PERFORMANCE

Application	Pressure psi (kg/cm²)	Vol. in 30 Sec. Pints (Liters)
All Models	33-38	[1]
	(2.3-2.7)	[1]

[1] – Information not available from manufacturer.

EMISSION CONTROL SYSTEMS

See Mitchell Manuals' Emission Control Manual

1983 Alfa Romeo 4 Tune-Up

GENERAL SERVICING

IGNITION

DISTRIBUTOR

All models are equipped with a computerized, digital, electronic ignition system. Distributor's only function is spark distribution.

IGNITION COIL

IGNITION COIL RESISTANCE — Ohms @ 68°F (20°C)

Application	Primary	Secondary
All Models	0.6-1.0	3000-5000

FUEL SYSTEMS

FUEL INJECTION

All models are equipped with Bosch AFC fuel injection system.

ELECTRICAL

BATTERY

BATTERY SPECIFICATIONS

Application	Amp Hr. Rating
All Models	[1] 45

[1] — Rated capacity is listed on battery housing.

STARTER

All models use Bosch direct drive starters.

ALTERNATOR

All models use Bosch alternators.

ALTERNATOR REGULATOR

All models are equipped with Bosch alternator regulators.

SERVICE SPECIFICATIONS

BELT ADJUSTMENT

Application	Deflection In. (mm)
Alternator Belt	[1] 1/2 (13)
Air Conditioner Belt	[2] 1/2 (13)

[1] — Measured with 18 lbs. (8 kg) pressure applied at midpoint of longest belt run.

[2] — With hand pressure at belt midpoint.

REPLACEMENT INTERVALS

Component	Interval (Miles)
Oil Filter	7500
Air Filter	30,000
Spark Plugs	30,000
Oxygen Sensor	30,000

FLUID CAPACITIES

Application	Quantity
Crankcase (Includes Filter)	7.1 qts. (6.6L)
Cooling System (Includes Heater)	2.5 gals. (9.7L)
Man. Trans. (SAE 80)	3.8 pts. (1.8L)
Rear Axle (SAE 80)	3.0 pts. (1.4L)
Fuel Tank	[1] 12.2 gals. (46.0L)

[1] — Reserve capacity about 1.5-1.8 gals. (6.0-7.0L)

TUNE-UP

GTV-6 2.5

ENGINE IDENTIFICATION

Engine identification number is located on the rear side of the engine block, near the left bank cylinder head.

ENGINE CODE

Application	Code
2.5L Engine	AR01911

ENGINE COMPRESSION

COMPRESSION SPECIFICATIONS

Compression Ratio	9.0:1

VALVE CLEARANCE

1) Remove necessary wires and hoses to remove valve covers. Attach a dial indicator to adjusting tool (C.6. 0178). Zero dial indicator with tool (C.6. 0182). Rotate crankshaft until it is possible to locate adjusting tool on cam of valve to be adjusted. Read intake valve clearance.

2) If adjustment is required, rotate crankshaft until "P-F" mark on engine pulley aligns with reference pin. Marks on camshafts should then align with marks on bearing caps. Remove covers from plastic timing belt housing.

3) Using camshaft holding tool (A.2. 0361) and a wrench, unscrew camshaft pulley nut. Loosen 3 screws. Using tool (A.3. 0521), remove hub and toothed pulley. Remove camshaft bearing caps. Lift off camshaft (at rear first).

4) Remove valve cups and adjusting pads below them. Measure thickness of each pad used, and replace with pads that will bring valve clearance within specifications.

Fig. 1: Measuring Intake and Exhaust Valve Clearance

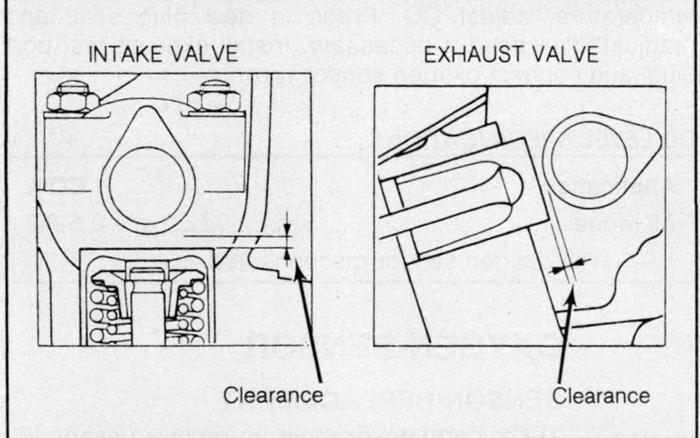
INTAKE VALVE
EXHAUST VALVE
Clearance
Clearance

5) To adjust exhaust valve clearance, use adjusting tool (A.5. 0220). Loosen lock nut by rotating tool's lever. Rotate wrench portion of tool until specified clearance is obtained. Tighten nut and recheck valve clearance.

VALVE CLEARANCE SPECIFICATIONS

Application	In. (mm)
Intake Valves	.0187-.0197 (.48-.50)
Exhaust Valves	
On Cam	.0088-.0098 (.23-.25)
On Valve	.0122-.0134 (.31-.34)

VALVE ARRANGEMENT

BOTH BANKS

Inner Valves — All Intake
Outer Valves — All Exhaust

SPARK PLUGS

SPARK PLUG TYPE

Application	Lodge	Champion
All Models	HLE (Silver)	RN11YC

SPARK PLUG SPECIFICATIONS

Application	Gap In. (mm)	Torque Ft. Lbs. (N.m)
Lodge HLE	[1]	18-25 (24-34)
Champion	.030 (.75 mm)	18-25 (24-34)

[1] — Spark plugs have surface gap with 4 points and central electrode. No adjustment necessary.

DISTRIBUTOR

A Bosch computerized, digital electronic ignition system is used. A distributor sensor provides engine speed information to the electronic control unit.

Fig. 2: Firing Order and Distributor Rotation

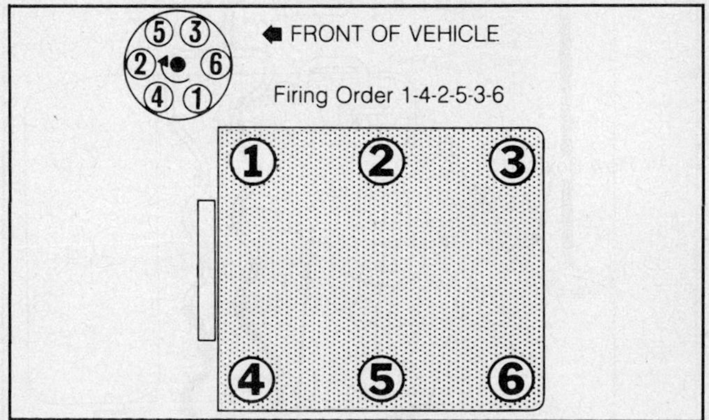
5 3
2 6
4 1
FRONT OF VEHICLE
Firing Order 1-4-2-5-3-6
1 2 3
4 5 6

IGNITION TIMING

FEDERAL (49 STATES) MODEL

1) The GTV-6 2.5 Federal ignition system is similar to that of the Spider 2.0, but ignition timing is adjustable. Check ignition timing with engine idling at normal operating temperature and distributor vacuum hoses connected.

2) At idle speed, pulley mark "R" (5° ATDC) should be aligned within .079" (2 mm) of reference pin.

TUNE-UP (Cont.)

With engine running at 5000 RPM and upper vacuum pipe disconnected, pulley mark "M" (26-29° BTDC) should be aligned within .118" (3 mm) with reference pin . To adjust timing, loosen clamp and turn distributor.

CALIF. (50 STATES) MODEL ALSO SOLD FEDERALLY

With engine at normal operating temperature, transmission in Neutral, and engine idling at 900 RPM, pulley mark "F" should align with reference pin.

CAUTION: **Do not attempt to adjust ignition timing by rotating the distributor or very serious damage may occur.**

IGNITION TIMING SPECIFICATIONS (Degrees @ RPM)

Application	[1] Timing @ 900 RPM	[2] Timing @ 5000 RPM
Federal	5°ATDC	26-29°BTDC
Calif. (50 State)	2°BTDC	.....

[1] — With vacuum hoses connected.
[2] — With upper vacuum pipe disconnected.

IDLE SPEED & MIXTURE

IDLE SPEED

1) The idle speed adjustment must be made with engine at operating temperature, transmission in Neutral, and all accessories off. To adjust, loosen idle bypass adjuster lock nut. *See Fig. 3.*

Fig. 3: GTV-6 2.5 Idle Speed Adjustment Location

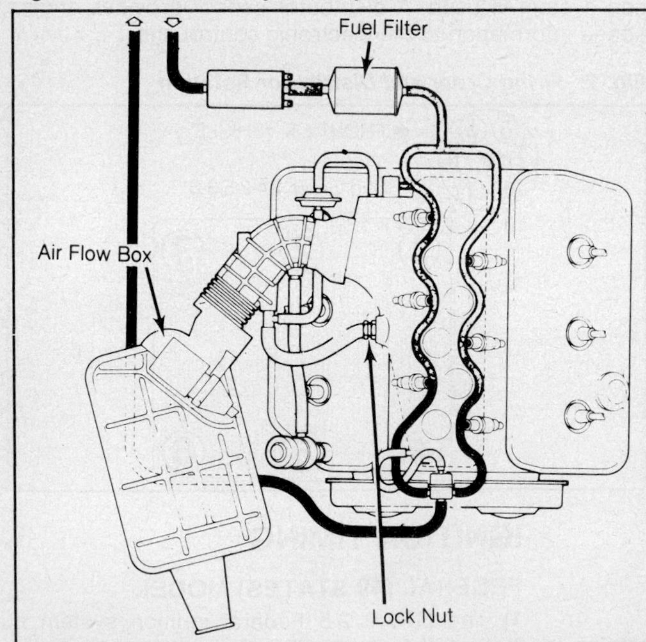
Fuel Filter
Air Flow Box
Lock Nut

2) Turn adjuster ring until idle speed is to specifications. Retighten lock nut.

IDLE SPEED SPECIFICATIONS

Application	RPM
All Models	800-1000

IDLE MIXTURE

NOTE: **Mixture control adjustment screw opening is plugged to prevent tampering. Adjustment is not a normal tune-up procedure and should not be performed unless mixture control unit is replaced or vehicle fails emissions testing.**

1) Disconnect wire from oxygen sensor at connector inside the engine compartment. Remove exhaust tap plug and connect exhaust analyzer. With engine idling, CO should be 0.5-0.7% (oxygen sensor disconnected).

2) If CO exceeds 0.5-0.7%, remove air flow sensor. Place unit in holding fixture or vise, taking care not to damage housing. Drill hole into adjustment plug, but do not drill through completely. Blow out chips with air. Twist in tap into drilled hole and pull plug out.

Fig. 4: GTV-6 2.5 Mixture Adjusting Plug

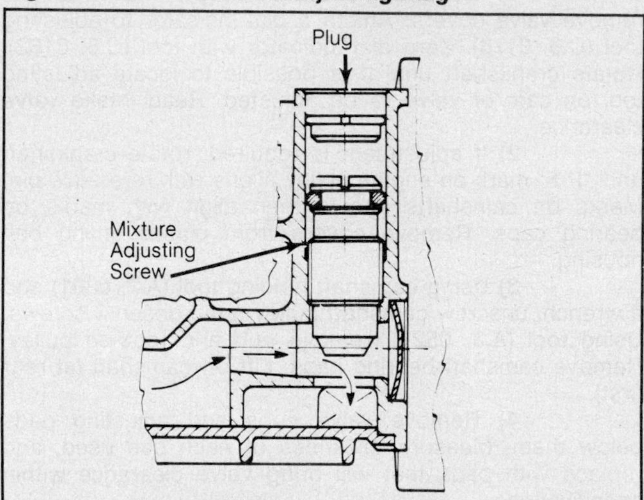
Plug
Mixture
Adjusting
Screw

3) Adjustment screw is now accessible. Reinstall air sensor on vehicle. With engine idling at operating temperature, adjust CO. Press in new plug seal, and readjust idle speed if necessary. Install exhaust test port plug, and connect oxygen sensor wire.

CO LEVEL SPECIFICATIONS

Application	[1] CO%
All Models	0.5-0.7

[1] — With oxygen sensor disconnected.

OXYGEN SENSOR

SENSOR REPLACEMENT

1) Oxygen sensor must be replaced every 30,000 miles on Federal models; every 60,000 miles on Calif. models. Disconnect oxygen sensor electrical lead in engine compartment. From underneath vehicle, loosen clamp and cover. Remove oxygen sensor.

TUNE-UP (Cont.)

2) Coat new oxygen sensor threads with anti-seize compound before installation. Tighten oxygen sensor and reconnect the electrical lead.

NOTE: Do not apply anti-seize compound to the slotted part of the oxygen sensor.

OXYGEN SENSOR LIGHT

Mileage counter is located at the right fender skirt under the dash board cowl. Remove the control unit cover panel and the passenger parcel shelf by loosening the side screws. Reset the counter by pressing the White button.

FUEL PUMP

FUEL PUMP PERFORMANCE

Application	Pressure psi (kg/cm²)	Volume in 30 Sec. Pints (Liters)
All Models	33-39 (2.35-2.75)	1.6-2.1 (.75-1.0L)

EMISSION CONTROL SYSTEMS

See Mitchell Manuals Emission Control Manual.

GENERAL SERVICING

IGNITION

DISTRIBUTOR

A Bosch computerized, digital electronic ignition system is used. A distributor sensor provides engine speed information to the electronic control unit. Ignition timing cannot be adjusted on California (50 States) models.

FUEL SYSTEMS

All models use a Bosch AFC Fuel Injection System, with an oxygen sensor.

ELECTRICAL

BATTERY

BATTERY SPECIFICATIONS

Application	Amp Hr. Rating
All Models	45

STARTER

All models use Bosch starters.

STARTER SPECIFICATIONS (Full Load) [1]

Application	Volts	Amps	Test RPM
All Models	9	290	1200 Min.

[1] — Developing torque of 5.8 ft. lbs. (7.9 N.m)

ALTERNATORS

All models are equipped Bosch alternators with integral voltage regulators.

ALTERNATOR SPECIFICATIONS

Application	Rated Amp Output
All Models	65

ALTERNATOR REGULATOR

All models are equipped with Bosch integral alternator regulators.

SERVICE SPECIFICATIONS

BELT ADJUSTMENT

Application	[1] Deflection In. (mm)
All Belts	1/2 (13)

[1] — Measured with 18 lbs. (8 kg) pressure applied at midpoint of longest belt run.

REPLACEMENT INTERVALS

Component	Interval (Miles)
Oil Filter	7500
Air Filter	30,000
Spark Plugs	30,000
Oxygen Sensor	30,000

FLUID CAPACITIES

Application	Quantity
Crankcase (Including Filter)	7.1 qts. (6.0L)
Cooling System	12.8 qts. (12.0L)
Man. Trans. & Differential (SAE 80)	3.0 qts. (2.6L)
Fuel Tank [1]	17.6 gals. (67.0L)

[1] — Does not include 2.1-2.6 gal. (8-10L) reserve.

1983 Audi 4 Tune-Up

TUNE-UP

4000

ENGINE IDENTIFICATION

Engine number is stamped on left side of engine block near distributor.

ENGINE CODE

Application	Code
4000	WT

ENGINE COMPRESSION

Check compression with engine warm, all spark plugs removed and throttle wide open. Crank engine at least 6 strokes per cylinder to determine engine compression.

NOTE: Connect coil high tension wire to ground before cranking engine for compression test.

COMPRESSION SPECIFICATIONS

Compression Ratio	8.2:1
Compression Pressure	
Normal (New Engine)	131-174 psi (9-12 kg/cm²)
Minimum	102 psi (7 kg/cm²)
Max. Variation Between Cylinders	44 psi (3 kg/cm²)

VALVE CLEARANCE

1) Adjust valves with engine at normal operating temperature. Clearance adjustments are to be checked and made according to firing order sequence. Rotate crankshaft until cam lobes for No. 1 cylinder valves point upward. Measure valve clearances of No. 1 cylinder.

CAUTION: To avoid timing belt slip when adjusting valves, only rotate engine CLOCKWISE.

2) If adjustment is necessary, use tappet depressor (VW546) and disc remover (10-208) to remove and install adjusting discs. Rotate camshaft until cam lobes no longer rest on adjusting discs of cylinder.

3) Turn tappet until notches are at 90° to camshaft. Insert depressor (VW546) and depress tappet. Using disc remover (10-208), hold tappet disc and rotate it out from under camshaft.

4) Thickness is stamped on bottom side of disc. Use clearance measurement to determine thickness of adjusting disc needed. Discs are available in .002" (.05 mm) increments from .118-.167" (3.0-4.2 mm).

5) Reverse removal procedures to install proper disc. Repeat procedure as required for remaining valves.

VALVE CLEARANCE SPECIFICATIONS

Application	In. (mm)
Intake	.008-.012 (.2-.3)
Exhaust	.016-.020 (.4-.5)

VALVE ARRANGEMENT

E-I-E-I-I-E-I-E (Front-to-rear)

SPARK PLUGS

SPARK PLUG TYPE

Application	Bosch	Champion
Federal	W7D	N8Y
Calif.	WR7DS	N8GY

SPARK PLUG SPECIFICATIONS

Application	Gap In. (mm)	Torque Ft. Lbs. (N.m)
All Models	.028 (.7)	22 (29)

HIGH TENSION WIRE RESISTANCE

Carefully remove ends of wire from spark plug and distributor. Using an ohmmeter, check resistance while gently twisting wire. If resistance is incorrect, or fluctuates from infinity to any value, replace wire.

HIGH TENSION WIRE RESISTANCE

Application	Ohms
Spark Plug Wire Only	800-1400
Spark Plug Wire With Connector	800-7400
Coil Wire	1600-2400

DISTRIBUTOR

All models are equipped with breakerless electronic ignition systems that use a Hall Effect pick-up and an idle stablizer unit.

Fig. 1: Firing Order and Distributor Rotation

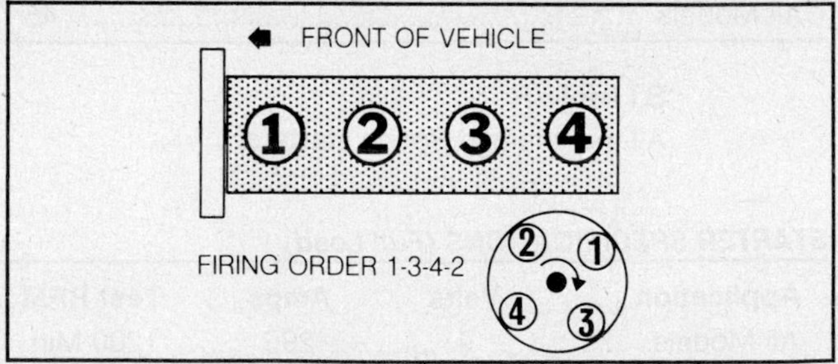
FRONT OF VEHICLE
1
2
3
4
FIRING ORDER 1-3-4-2

IGNITION TIMING

CAUTION: Do not connect any test instruments to terminal 15 (+) of ignition coil. Use fuse 10 terminal for connection.

1) Warm engine to normal operating temperature. Stop engine and disconnect oxygen sensor. Discon-

TUNE-UP (Cont.)

nect both plugs from idle stabilizer and connect them together.

2) Pull PCV hose from valve cover. Adjust idle speed, and check ignition timing. Adjust timing by turning distributor. All vacuum hoses must remain connected.

NOTE: **Electric cooling fan must not run while adjustments are made.**

IGNITION TIMING

Application	Degrees@RPM
4-Cylinder	
Man. Trans.	6° BTDC@850-1000
Auto. Trans.	3° ATDC@850-1000

Fig. 2: Ignition Timing Mark Location

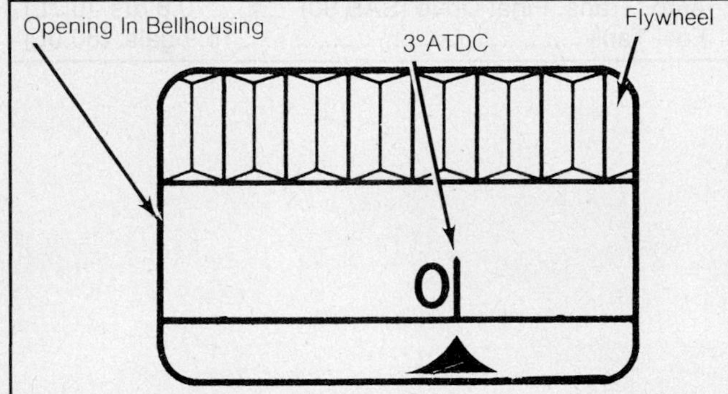

Opening In Bellhousing
Flywheel
3°ATDC
0

Timing mark is located at 3° ATDC.

IDLE SPEED & MIXTURE

IDLE SPEED

1) With engine at normal operating temperature, turn headlights on high beam and turn air conditioning switch to "OFF" position.

2) Disconnect and plug crankcase breather hose at cylinder head. Also, disconnect hose between charcoal canister and air cleaner.

3) Check and adjust ignition timing as necessary. Adjust idle speed to specified RPM using adjusting screw on side of throttle valve housing.

IDLE SPEED SPECIFICATIONS

Application	Idle RPM
4000	850-1000

IDLE MIXTURE

NOTE: **Mixture adjustment is not a part of normal tune-up procedure and should not be performed unless fuel injection components are replaced or vehicle fails emission tests.**

NOTE: **Oxygen sensor system was designed to be maintenance free and no adjustments are normally required. However, if a performance problem does occur, the system can be checked using the following procedure. A dwell meter (VW 1367) is required to adjust the duty cycle produced by oxygen sensor control unit. A CO meter is used only to verify that system is operating properly. DO NOT disconnect oxygen sensor for this procedure.**

1) Remove both connectors from idle stabilizer and connect them together. Run engine until temperature is above 175°F (80°C). Radiator fan must have come on at least once.

2) Remove both PCV hoses from valve cover. Place hoses so fresh air can be drawn into system. Remove cap from "T" piece in charcoal canister vent hose near right fender well.

3) Connect CO meter to CO test point using adapter hose (US 4492). Connect dwell meter to oxygen sensor test connection. The duty cycle should fluctuate between 25-65% or 23-59° on dwell meter.

4) If duty cycle is out of range, remove plug from air sensor housing. Insert adjusting tool (P377) and adjust duty cycle with mixture adjusting screw to 44-56% or 40-50°.

5) Duty cycle should fluctuate within specified range. If it does not, there is a problem with oxygen sensor.

6) Check CO value. It should be 0.3-1.2% with oxygen sensor connected. Recheck and adjust idle speed, if necessary. Stop engine and reconnect all hoses and idle stabilizer.

IDLE CO LEVEL SPECIFICATIONS

Application	Idle CO%
4000	0.3-1.2

Fig. 3: Adjusting Idle Speed & Mixture

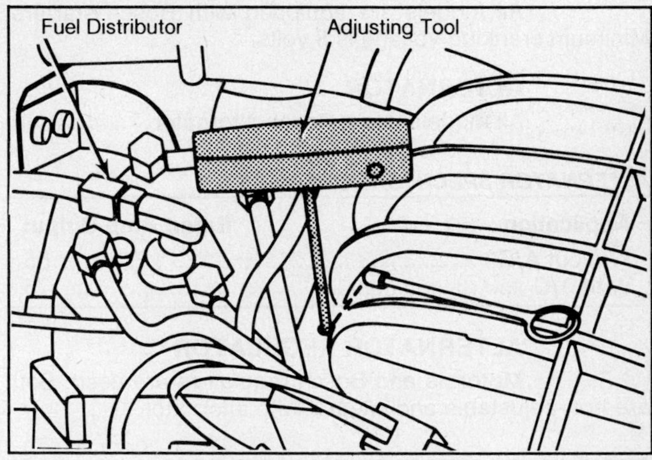

Fuel Distributor
Adjusting Tool

Always adjust idle mixture from lean to rich.

FUEL PUMP

FUEL PUMP PERFORMANCE

Application	Pressure psi (kg/cm^2)	Volume in 30 sec. Pints (Liters)
All Models	64-74 (4.5-5.2)	2 (.9)

EMISSION CONTROL SYSTEMS

See Michell Manuals' Emission Control Manual.

1983 Audi 4 Tune-Up

GENERAL SERVICING

IGNITION

DISTRIBUTOR

All models are equipped with Bosch breakerless electronic ignition with idle stabilizer unit.

IGNITION COIL

RESISTANCE — Ohms @ 68°F (20°C)

Application	Primary	Secondary
All Models	.52-.76	2400-3500

FUEL SYSTEMS

FUEL INJECTION

All models are equipped wih Bosch (CIS) Continuous Injection System. All models use an oxygen sensor system.

ELECTRICAL

BATTERY

BATTERY SPECIFICATIONS

Application	Amp Hr. Rating
Without A/C	45
With A/C	63

STARTER

All models are equipped with Bosch starters. Minimum cranking voltage is 8 volts.

ALTERNATOR

All models use a Bosch alternator.

ALTERNATOR SPECIFICATIONS

Application	Rated Amp Output
Without A/C	55
With A/C	75

ALTERNATOR REGULATOR

Motorola and Bosch regulators are used. Both are non-adjustable and integral with alternator.

REGULATOR OPERATING VOLTAGE @ 68°F (20°C)

Application	Voltage
All Models	13.5-14.5

SERVICE SPECIFICATIONS

BELT ADJUSTMENT

Application	[1] Deflection In. (mm)
All Belts	.3-.5 (10-15)

[1] - With moderate pressure applied midway between pulleys.

REPLACEMENT INTERVALS

Component	Interval (Miles)
Oil Filter	7500
Air Filter	30,000
Fuel Filter	15,000
PCV Valve	30,000
Oxygen Sensor	30,000
Spark Plugs	15,000

FLUID CAPACITIES

Application	Quantity
Crankcase (Includes Filter)	3.5 qts. (3.0L)
Cooling System	7.4 qts. (7.0L)
Man. Trans. (SAE 80W-90)	1.7 qts. (1.6L)
Auto. Trans. (Dexron)	3.2 qts. (3.0L)
Auto. Trans. Final Drive (SAE 90)	0.8 qts. (0.7L)
Fuel Tank	15.9 gals. (60.0L)

1983 Audi 5 Tune-Up

TUNE-UP

Coupe, 4000, 5000, 5000 Turbo

ENGINE IDENTIFICATION

Engine number is stamped on left side of block near No. 3 cylinder.

ENGINE CODE

Application	Code
Coupe, 4000, 5000	WE
5000 Turbo	WK

ENGINE COMPRESSION

Check compression with engine warm, all spark plugs removed and throttle wide open. Crank engine through at least 6 compression strokes per cylinder to determine engine compression.

COMPRESSION SPECIFICATIONS

Compression Ratio	
Coupe	8.2:1
4000	8.2:1
5000	8.0:1
5000 Turbo	7.0:1
Compression Pressure	
All Except Turbo	
Normal (New Engine)	131-174 psi (9-12 kg/cm²)
Minimum	102 psi (7 kg/cm²)
Turbo	
Normal (New Engine)	100-131 psi (7-9 kg/cm²)
Minimum	72 psi (5 kg/cm²)
Max. Variation Between Cylinders	
All Except Turbo	44 psi (3 kg/cm²)
Turbo	28 psi (2 kg/cm²)

VALVE CLEARANCE

1) Adjust valves with engine at normal operating temperature. Remove accelerator linkage and cylinder head cover. Clearance adjustments are to be checked and made according to firing order sequence.

2) Rotate crankshaft until cam lobes for No. 1 cylinder valves point upward. Measure valve clearances of No. 1 cylinder.

CAUTION: To avoid timing belt slip when adjusting valves, only rotate engine CLOCKWISE.

3) If adjustment is necessary, use disc remover (US4476) and tappet depressor (2078) to remove and install adjusting discs. Turn tappet until notches are at 90° to camshaft.

4) Insert depressor (2078) and depress tappet. Using disc remover (US4476), grasp tappet disc and rotate it out from under camshaft.

5) Thickness is stamped on bottom side of disc. Use clearance measurement to choose adjusting disc. Discs are available in .002" (.05 mm) increments from .118-.167" (3.0-4.3 mm). Repeat procedure as required for remaining valves.

VALVE CLEARANCE SPECIFICATIONS

Application	In. (mm)
All Models	
Intake	.008-.012 (.2-.3)
Exhaust	.016-.020 (.4-.5)

VALVE ARRANGEMENT

E-I-E-I-I-E-I-E-I-E (Front-to-rear)

SPARK PLUGS

SPARK PLUG TYPE

Application	Bosch	Champion
Coupe, 4000, 5000		
Federal	W7D	N8Y
Calif.	WR7DS	N8GY
5000 Turbo	WR7DS	N8GY

SPARK PLUG SPECIFICATIONS

Application	Gap In. (mm)	Torque Ft. Lbs. (N.m)
All Models	.028 (.7)	22 (30)

HIGH TENSION WIRE RESISTANCE

Carefully remove ends of wire from spark plug and distributor. Using an ohmmeter, check resistance of wire while gently twisting wire. If resistance is incorrect or fluctuates from infinity to any value, replace wire.

NOTE: Wire resistance cannot be measured if the wires are marked with this symbol:

HIGH TENSION WIRE RESISTANCE

Application	Ohms
Spark Plug Wire Only	800-1400
Spark Plug Wire With Connector	4000-6000
Coil Wire	
Coupe, 4000	600-2400
5000	800-1200

Fig. 1: Firing Order and Distributor Rotation

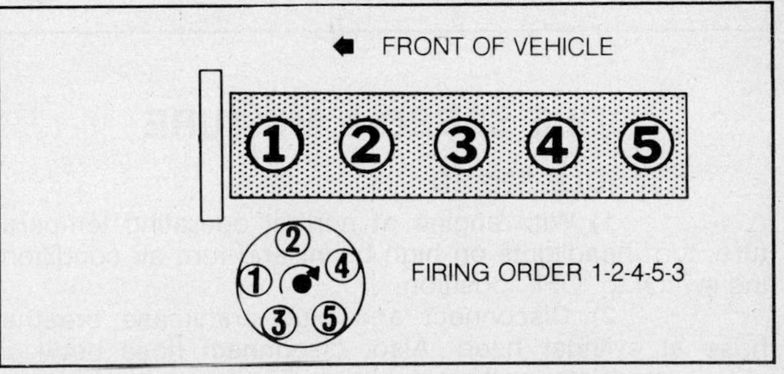
FRONT OF VEHICLE
1
2
3
4
5
FIRING ORDER 1-2-4-5-3

1983 Audi 5 Tune-Up

TUNE-UP (Cont.)

DISTRIBUTOR

All models are equipped with an electronic, breakerless ignition system. All California and Turbo models, have an idle stabilizer unit, which adjusts ignition timing to maintain a constant idle speed.

IGNITION TIMING

NOTE: On vehicles equipped with Digital Idle Stabilizer (DIS), it is necessary to by-pass the DIS unit. Disconnect both plugs from the unit and connect them together while checking or adjusting timing.

COUPE, 4000, 5000

Disconnect 2 plugs at idle stabilizer unit, if equipped, and connect them together. Leave vacuum hoses connected at distributor. With engine idling, adjust ignition timing by turning distributor. Reconnect idle stabilizer unit.

5000 TURBO

Disconnect and plug both hoses at distributor. With engine at 3000 RPM, adjust timing by turning distributor.

IGNITION TIMING (Degrees BTDC@RPM)

Application	Degrees@RPM
Coupe, 4000, 5000	
Man. Trans.	6°@775-925
Auto. Trans.	[1] 3°@850-1000
5000 Turbo	21°@3000

[1] – Degrees ATDC.

Fig. 2: Coupe, 4000, 5000 Ignition Timing Mark Location

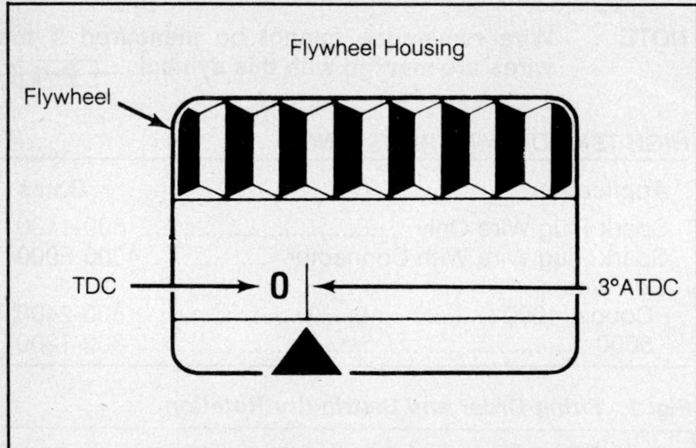
Flywheel Housing
Flywheel
TDC
0
3°ATDC

IDLE SPEED & MIXTURE

IDLE SPEED

1) With engine at normal operating temperature, turn headlights on high beam and turn air conditioning switch to "OFF" position.

2) Disconnect and plug crankcase breather hose at cylinder head. Also, disconnect hose between charcoal canister and air cleaner.

3) Check and adjust ignition timing as necessary. Adjust idle speed to specified RPM using adjusting screw on side of throttle valve housing.

IDLE SPEED SPECIFICATION

Application	RPM
Coupe, 4000 & 5000	
Man. Trans.	775-925
Auto. Trans.	850-1000
5000 Turbo	790-910

IDLE MIXTURE

NOTE: Mixture adjustment is not a part of normal tune-up procedures and should not be performed unless fuel injection components are replaced or vehicle fails emission tests.

NOTE: Oxygen sensor system was designed to be maintenance free and no adjustments are normally required. However, if a performance problem does occur, the system can be checked using the following procedure. A dwell meter is required to adjust the duty cycle produced by oxygen sensor control unit. A CO meter is used only to verify that system is operating properly. DO NOT disconnect oxygen sensor, if (VW 1367) dwell meter is used. Disconnect oxygen sensor, if any other type of dwell meter is used.

1) Remove both connectors from idle stabilizer and connect them together. Run engine until temperature is above 175°F (80°C). Radiator fan must come on at least once.

2) Remove PCV hose from valve cover and plug hose. On Coupe and 4000 models, remove cap from "T" piece in charcoal caniser vent hose near right fender well. On 5000, remove canister purge hose and plug hose.

3) Connect CO meter to CO test point using adapter hose (US 4492). Connect dwell meter to oxygen sensor test plug connection. The duty cycle should fluctuate (between 25-65% or 23-59° with VW 1367 dwell meter). Reading will vary, if any other type of dwell meter is used.

4) If dwell meter does not cycle, or is out of range, remove plug from air sensor housing. Insert adjusting tool (P377) and adjust duty cycle with mixture adjusting screw to (44-56% or 40-50° on VW dwell meter). Duty cycle should fluctuate within specified range. If not, there is a problem with oxygen sensor.

5) Check CO value. It should be 0.3-1.2% with oxygen sensor connected or .3-3.0% with oxygen sensor disconnected. Recheck and adjust idle speed, if necessary. Stop engine and reconnect all hoses and idle stabilizer.

IDLE CO LEVEL SPECIFICATION

Application	CO%
Coupe, 4000 & 5000	
Man. Trans.	0.3-1.2
Auto. Trans.	0.3-1.2
5000 Turbo	0.4-1.2

1983 Audi 5 Tune-Up

TUNE-UP (Cont.)

FUEL PUMP

FUEL PUMP PERFORMANCE

Application	Pressure psi (kg/cm²)	Volume in 30 sec. Pints (Liters)
Coupe, 4000 & 5000	64-74 (4.5-5.2)	1.0 (.47)
5000 Turbo	72-82 (4.9-5.6)	1.0 (.47)

EMISSION CONTROL SYSTEMS

See Mitchell Manuals' Emission Control Manual.

GENERAL SERVICING

IGNITION

DISTRIBUTOR

All models are equipped with electronic ignition. All models use an idle stabilizer in addition to the Hall Effect ignition system.

IGNITION COIL

RESISTANCE – OHMS @ 68°F (20°C)

Application	Primary	Secondary
All Models	.52-.76	2400-3500

FUEL SYSTEMS

FUEL INJECTION

All models are equipped with Bosch (CIS) Continuous Injection System.

ELECTRICAL

BATTERY

BATTERY SPECIFICATIONS

Application	Amp Hr. Rating
All Models	63

STARTER

All models are equipped with Bosch starters.

ALTERNATOR

All models use a Bosch alternator.

ALTERNATOR SPECIFICATIONS

Application	Rated Amp Output
Coupe	75
5000, 5000 Turbo	90

ALTERNATOR REGULATOR

All models use Bosch, non-adjustable regulators which are integral with the alternator.

ALTERNATOR OPERATING VOLTAGE @ 80°F (27°C)

Application	Voltage
All Models	13.5-14.5

SERVICE SPECIFICATIONS

BELT ADJUSTMENT

Application	[1] Deflection In. (mm)
All Belts	.3-.5 (10-15 mm)

[1] – With a 20 lb. (9 kg) load applied at the midway point on the belt.

REPLACEMENT INTERVALS

Component	Interval (Miles)
Oil Filter [1]	15,000
Air Filter	30,000
Fuel Filter	15,000
PCV Valve	30,000
Oxygen Sensor	30,000
Spark Plugs	30,000

[1] – Turbo models have 2 oil filters. Change both every 15,000 miles.

FLUID CAPACITIES

Application	Quantity
Crankcase (Includes Filter)	
4000 (4-Cylinder)	3.2 qts. (3.0L)
Coupe & 4000 (5-Cylinder)	4.0 qts. (3.5L)
5000 & 5000 Turbo	5.0 qts. (4.5L)
Cooling System (Includes Heater)	
4000 (4-Cylinder)	7.4 qts. (7.0L)
Coupe, 4000 & 5000 (5-Cylinder)	8.6 qts. (8.1L)
5000 Turbo	10.0 qts. (9.4L)
Man. Trans. (SAE 80W-90)	
Coupe & 4000	1.7 qts. (1.6L)
5000	2.7 qts. (2.5L)
Auto. Trans. (Dexron)	3.2 qts. (3.0L)
Auto. Trans. Final Drive (SAE 90)	
Coupe & 4000	0.8 qts. (0.7L)
5000 & 5000 Turbo	1.1 qts. (1.0L)
Fuel Tank	
Coupe & 4000	15.9 gals. (63.6L)
5000 & 5000 Turbo	19.8 gals. (74.8L)

1983 Audi Diesel 4 & 5 Tune-Up

TUNE-UP

4000 Turbo Diesel &
5000 Turbo Diesel

ENGINE IDENTIFICATION

Engine number is stamped into left side of block near No. 3 cylinder.

ENGINE CODE

Application	Code
4000 Turbo (4-Cyl.)	CY
5000 Turbo (5-Cyl.)	DE

ENGINE COMPRESSION

1) Engine must be operating temperature. Remove electrical wire from fuel shut-off solenoid on injection pump. Remove injector pipes, injector and heat shields. Insert oil heat shield into head.

2) Insert adapter (US 1110/2A) and compression tester. Check compression while cranking engine through at least 6 strokes.

COMPRESSION SPECIFICATIONS

Compression Ratio	23.0:1
Compression Pressure	
Normal (New Engine)	493 psi (34 kg/cm²)
Minimum	406 psi (28 kg/cm²)
Max. Variation Between Cylinders	73 psi (5 kg/cm²)

VALVE CLEARANCE

1) Turn engine clockwise until camshaft lobes for No. 1 cylinder valves point upward. Check valve clearance. If not within tolerance, adjusting disc must be changed.

2) Turn crankshaft 1/4 turn after TDC valves will not hit piston top. Depress cam followers with depressor tool (VW2078). Remove disc with special pliers (VW4476).

3) Calculate thickness of disc needed, coat with oil and install with marks down. Replacement discs are available in thicknesses of .120-.167" (3.00-4.25 mm), in increments of .002" (.05 mm).

4) Check valve clearance on remaining cylinders. Check in same sequence as firing order. Be sure to check valve clearance at TDC, then turn 1/4 turn after TDC before depressing valves.

VALVE CLEARANCE SPECIFICATIONS

Application	In. (mm)
Intake	.008-.012 (.2-.3)
Exhaust	.016-.020 (.4-.5)

VALVE ARRANGEMENT

4000 — E-I-E-I-I-E-I-E (Front-to-rear).
5000 — E-I-E-I-I-E-I-E-I-E (Front-to-rear).

Fig. 1: Audi 4-Cylinder Turbo Diesel Firing Order

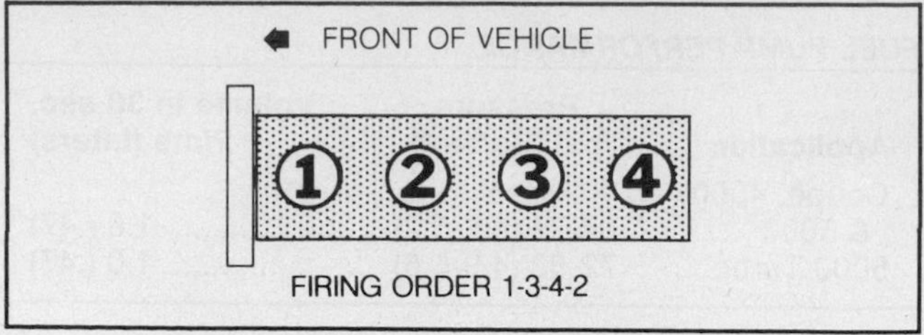

FRONT OF VEHICLE
1
2
3
4
FIRING ORDER 1-3-4-2

Fig. 2: Audi 5-Cylinder Turbo Diesel Firing Order

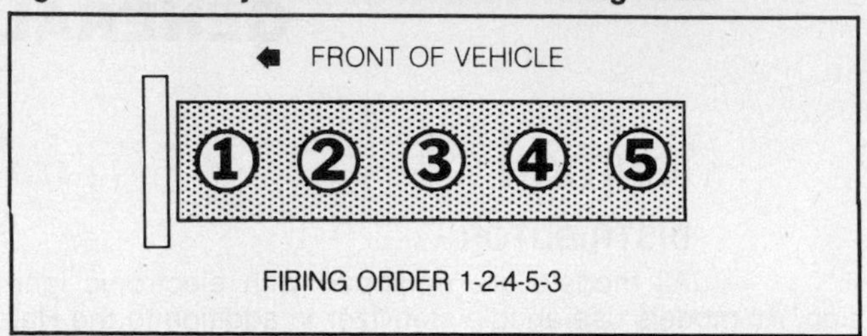

FRONT OF VEHICLE
1
2
3
4
5
FIRING ORDER 1-2-4-5-3

GLOW PLUGS

GLOW PLUG TYPE

Application	Bosch
All Models	N 019 100 6

IDLE SPEED

1) With the engine at normal operating temperature, turn idle speed control knob on dash panel counterclockwise to stop.

2) Connect diesel tachometer (VW 1367) according to manufacturer instructions. Adjust idle speed with idle adjusting screw. Tighten lock nut. *See Fig. 3.*

3) Open throttle fully and quickly adjust maximum speed to 5050-5150 RPM using maximum RPM screw. Tighten lock nut.

Fig. 3: Adjusting Idle & Maximum Speed Settings

Idle Screw
Max. RPM Screw

Adjust maximum speed setting quickly to avoid unnecessary strain on engine.

TUNE-UP (Cont.)

IDLE SPEED SPECIFICATIONS

Application	Idle RPM
4000	900-1000
5000	700-800

INJECTION PUMP TIMING

NOTE: **Before starting timing procedure, check valve timing and drive belt tension.**

1) Set crankshaft to TDC on No. 1 cylinder and align marks on flywheel and clutch housing. Check marks on injection pump sprocket and mounting plate.

2) If timing adjustment is necessary, remove plug from injection pump cover and install adapter and dial indicator in place of plug. Push in cold start device completely.

3) Preload dial indicator (2066) to .097" (2.5 mm). Slowly turn engine counterclockwise until dial indicator needle stops moving. Zero indicator.

4) Turn engine clockwise until TDC mark on flywheel lines up with reference mark. Check dial indicator reading. *See Diesel Fuel Injection Pump Timing Specifications.*

5) If necessary, loosen bolts on mounting plate and support. Turn pump to adjust timing and tighten bolts. Recheck dial indicator readings.

EMISSION CONTROL SYSTEMS

See Mitchell Manuals' Emission Control Manual.

GENERAL SERVICING

FUEL SYSTEMS

FUEL INJECTION

All models use the Bosch mechanical diesel fuel injection system.

DIESEL FUEL INJECTION TIMING

Application	Degrees BTDC	Plunger Travel In. (mm)
All Models	0	.035 (.88)

ELECTRICAL

BATTERY SPECIFICATIONS

Application	Amp Hr. Rating
4000	63
5000	88

STARTER

Some models equipped with Bosch starters. Some models are equipped with Mitsubishi starters.

ALTERNATOR

All models equipped with Bosch alternators.

ALTERNATOR SPECIFICATIONS

Application	Rated Amp Output
All Models	90

ALTERNATOR REGULATOR

All models are equipped with Bosch non-adjustable voltage regulators.

REGULATOR OPERATING VOLTAGE @ 68°F (20°C)

Application	Voltage
All Models	13.9-14.8

SERVICE SPECIFICATIONS

BELT ADJUSTMENT

Application	[1] Deflection In. (mm)
All Belts	.3-.5 (10-15 mm)

[1] — With moderate pressure applied halfway between pulleys.

REPLACEMENT INTERVALS

Component	Interval (Miles)
Oil Filter	15,000
Fuel Filter	7500
Air Filter	30,000
PCV Valve	30,000

FLUID CAPACITIES

Application	Quantity
Crankcase (Includes Filter)	4.5 qts. (4.2L)
Cooling System (Includes Heater)	10.0 qts. (9.3L)
Manual Transaxle (SAE 80)	2.0 qts. (1.9L)
Automatic Transaxle (Dexron)	3.2 qts. (3.0L)
Fuel Tank	
4000	16.0 gals. (60.0L)
5000	20.0 gals. (37.0L)

TUNE-UP

318i & 320i

ENGINE IDENTIFICATION

Engine number is stamped into engine block above starter. Engine can also be identified by first 4 numbers in chassis code, located on right front wheel sill.

ENGINE CODE

Application	Code
318i	
Man. Trans.	1733
Auto. Trans.	1743
320i	
Man.Trans.	1074
Auto. Trans.	1084

ENGINE COMPRESSION

Remove fuel pump relay. Pull plug on transistor ignition control (TCI) unit. Check compression with engine warm, battery fully charged, throttle fully open and engine at cranking speed.

COMPRESSION SPECIFICATIONS

Compression Ratio	
318i	9.3:1
320i	8.8:1
Compression Pressure	142-146 psi (9.9-10.2 kg/cm²)
Max. Variation Between Cylinders	15%

VALVE CLEARANCE

Adjust valves with engine cold. Remove valve cover, loosen nut on rocker arm and check clearance between eccentric and valve. Adjust valves in firing order sequence at TDC of compression stroke.

VALVE ADJUSTMENT SEQUENCE

Adjust Cylinder @ TDC	When Valves of Cylinder Overlap
No. 1	No. 4
No. 3	No. 2
No. 4	No. 1
No. 2	No. 3

VALVE CLEARANCE SPECIFICATIONS

Application	In. (mm)
318i	
Intake & Exhaust (Cold)	.008 (.20)
Intake & Exhaust (Hot)	.010 (.25)
320i	
Intake & Exhaust (Cold)	.007 (.18)

VALVE ARRANGEMENT

Left Side — All Intake
Right Side — All Exhaust

SPARK PLUGS

SPARK PLUG TYPE

Application	Bosch No.
All Models	WR9DS

SPARK PLUG SPECIFICATIONS

Application	Gap In. (mm)	Torque Ft. Lbs. (N.m)
All Models	.024 (.7)	18 (24)

HIGH TENSION WIRE RESISTANCE

Carefully remove ends of wire from spark plug and distributor. Using an ohmmeter, check resistance of wire while gently twisting wire. If resistance is incorrect or fluctuates from infinity to any value, replace wire.

HIGH TENSION WIRE RESISTANCE

Application	Ohms
318i	4500-5500
320i	800-1200

DISTRIBUTOR

All BMW models are equipped with Bosch transistorized electronic ignition. Distributor pick-up coil air gap is preset and nonadjustable.

Fig. 1: Firing Order and Distributor Rotation

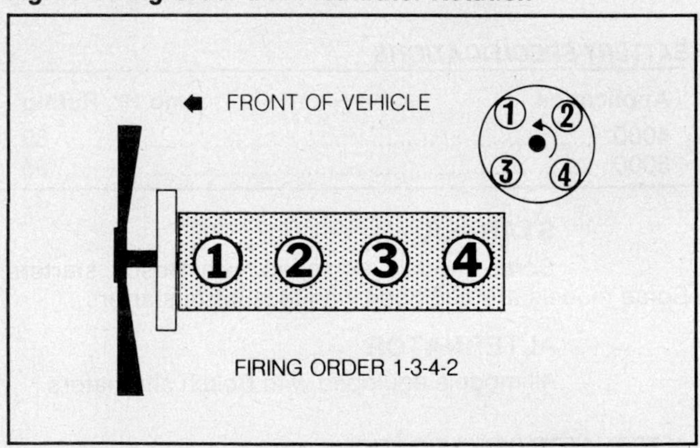
FRONT OF VEHICLE
1
2
3
4
FIRING ORDER 1-3-4-2

IGNITION TIMING

1) Check or adjust ignition timing with engine at normal operating temperature and distributor vacuum hoses disconnected. Connect timing light and tachometer, start engine and increase engine speed to specified RPM.

2) Aim timing light at steel ball embedded in flywheel. Timing is correct if ball is aligned with pointer located near hole in flywheel housing.

3) Loosen distributor clamp, turn distributor until specified timing is obtained and tighten clamp. Connect distributor vacuum hoses and set idle speed.

1983 BMW 4 Tune-Up

TUNE-UP (Cont.)

Fig. 2: Ignition Timing Mark Location

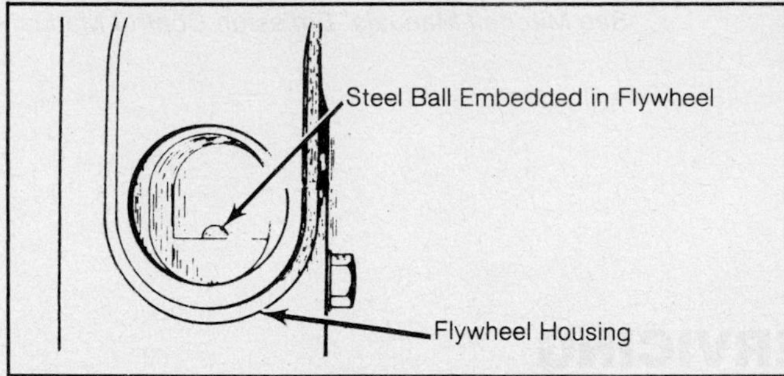
Steel Ball Embedded in Flywheel
Flywheel Housing

IGNITION TIMING (Degrees BTDC @ RPM)

Application	Timing
318i	15@2000
320i	25@2200

IDLE SPEED & MIXTURE

IDLE SPEED

NOTE: The following adjustments must be made with air filter clean, ignition timing and valve clearance adjusted to specification and engine at normal operating temperature.

318i & 320i

1) Idle speed is controlled by an idle speed control unit. Connect dwell/tachometer to engine. Check idle speed. If idle is not as specified, check idle speed control unit and replace if required.

2) The 318i also has an idle valve located on the intake manifold. To test valve, engine must be at normal operating temperature. Unplug wire connector from idle valve. Idle speed should rise to 2000 RPM. Connect wire and RPM should drop to below idle speed. Replace valve if it does not perform as indicated.

IDLE SPEED SPECIFICATIONS

Application	Idle RPM
318i	700-800
320i	
Man. Trans.	850-950
Auto. Trans	800-900

Fig. 3: Idle Speed Adjusting Location at Throttle Housing

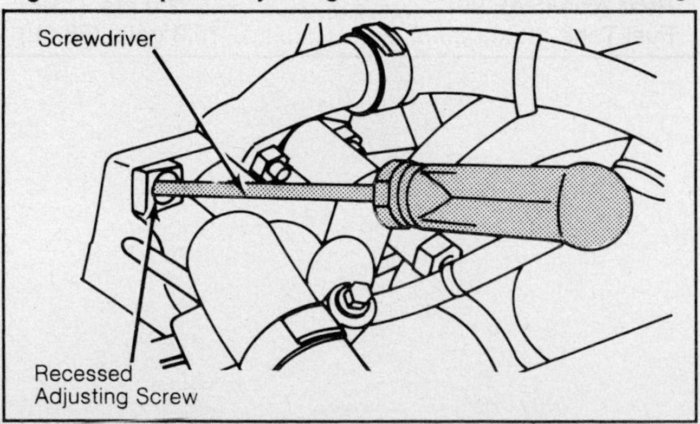
Screwdriver
Recessed
Adjusting Screw

Make adjustments before setting CO adjustment.

IDLE MIXTURE

NOTE: Mixture adjustment is not a part of normal tune-up procedure and should not be performed unless fuel injection components are replaced or vehicle fails emission testing.

320i

1) Disconnect charcoal canister-to-throttle housing hose but do not plug hose or port. Connect tachometer to engine.

2) Install CO meter at test points in exhaust manifold. Set idle speed to specified RPM by turning air screw on throttle valve housing.

3) Read and record CO value. Disconnect oxygen sensor wire at right rear corner of engine compartment. CO reading should not change after sensor is disconnected.

4) If CO value is incorrect or changes when sensor is disconnected, remove plug near fuel distributor. Use Allen wrench to carefully adjust CO level, but do not accelerate engine with adjusting wrench in place.

5) Check CO readings and adjust until values are within specifications and do not change when sensor is disconnected. Replace plugs, reconnect canister purge hose and remove test equipment.

318i

1) Set idle speed to proper RPM. Remove hose from collector to carbon canister. Connect special tool (13 0 070) with adapter (13 0 100) on exhaust manifold. Connect CO tester. Check CO value.

2) Do not attempt to change CO level at idle speed by pulling off oxygen sensor wire. To adjust CO level, drill a hole in anti-tamper plug on air flow sensor using removal tool (13 11 092).

3) Screw removal tool (13 1 094) into anti-tamper plug. Knock tool and anti-tamper plug out of air flow sensor with sharp impact. Insert adjuster tool (13 1 060) into anti-tamper lock hole, and adjust engine speed by turning control screw. After completion, install new anti-tamper plug.

CO LEVEL SPECIFICATIONS

Application	CO%
318i & 320i	0.2-1.2

Fig. 4: 320i CO Level Adjustment Location

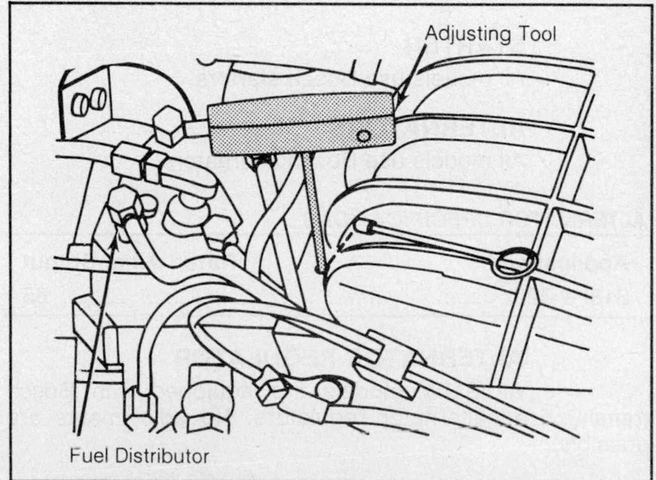
Adjusting Tool
Fuel Distributor

Do not accelerate while making adjustments.

TUNE-UP (Cont.)

FUEL PUMP

FUEL PUMP PERFORMANCE

Application	Pressure psi (kg/cm²)	Volume in 30 sec. Pints (Liters)
318i & 320i	40.6-46.4	1.6
	(2.8-3.2)	(.75)

EMISSION CONTROL SYSTEMS

See Mitchell Manuals' Emission Control Manual.

GENERAL SERVICING

IGNITION

DISTRIBUTOR

All models are equipped with Bosch electronic ignition. Units are self-contained and require no adjustments.

IGNITION COIL

IGNITION COIL RESISTANCE — Ohms @ 68°F (20°C)

Application	Primary	Secondary
318i & 320i	.82	8250

FUEL SYSTEMS

FUEL INJECTION

All 320i models are equipped with Bosch Lambda CIS fuel injection with oxygen sensor. On 318i models, the Bosch AFC fuel injection system is used.

ELECTRICAL

BATTERY

BATTERY SPECIFICATIONS

Application	Amp Hr. Rating
318i & 320i	55

STARTER

All models use Bosch starters.

ALTERNATORS

All models use Bosch alternators.

ALTERNATOR SPECIFICATIONS

Application	Rated Amp. Output
318i & 320i	65

ALTERNATOR REGULATOR

All BMW models are equipped with Bosch transistorized alternator regulators. No adjustments are possible.

REGULATOR OPERATING VOLTAGE @ 68°F (20°C)

Application	Voltage
318i & 320i	13.9-14.5

SERVICE SPECIFICATIONS

BELT ADJUSTMENT

Application	[1] Deflection In. (mm)
Alternator Belt	.2-.4 (5-10)
Air Conditioning Belt	.5 (12)

[1] — Measured with moderate hand pressure applied midway between pulleys on longest belt run.

REPLACEMENT INTERVALS

Component	Interval (Miles)
Oil Filter	7500
Air Filter	30,000
Fuel Filter	30,000
Spark Plugs	30,000
Oxygen Sensor	30,000

FLUID CAPACITIES

Application	Quantity
Crankcase (Includes Filter)	4.3 qts. (4.0L)
Cooling System (Includes Heater)	7.4 qts. (7.0L)
Man. Trans. (SAE 80)	2.4 pts. (1.2L)
Auto. Trans. (Dexron)	4.2 qts. (2.0L)
Rear Axle (SAE 90)	2.0 pts. (1.0L)
Fuel Tank	15.3 gals. (58.0L)

TUNE-UP

528e, 533i, 633CSi & 733i

ENGINE IDENTIFICATION

All engines have a serial number stamped on left side of block above starter motor. Engines can also be identified by first 4 numbers in chassis code, stamped on sill above right front wheel on 528e and 533i, and on firewall on 633CSi and 733i.

ENGINE CODE

Application	Code
528e	
Man. Trans.	4073
Auto. Trans.	4083
533i	
Man. Trans.	4274
Auto. Trans.	4284
633CSi	
Man. Trans	5274
Auto. Trans.	5284
733i	
Man. Trans.	6674
Auto. Trans.	6684

ENGINE COMPRESSION

Deactivate fuel injection system by removing main relay prior to compression test. With battery fully charged, engine at normal operating temperature, throttle fully open and engine at cranking speed, compression pressure should be as follows:

COMPRESSION SPECIFICATIONS

Compression Ratio	
528e	9.0:1
533i, 633CSi & 733i	8.8:1
Compression Pressure	
All Engines	142-156 psi (10-11 kg/cm²)

VALVE CLEARANCE

1) Adjust valves with engine COLD. Remove valve cover. Loosen nut on rocker arm and adjust position of eccentric cam to obtain proper clearance.

2) Adjust valves in same sequence as firing order (1-5-3-6-2-4), with valve being adjusted at TDC of compression stroke. Use a feeler gauge to measure clearance between rocker arm eccentric and valve stem.

VALVE CLEARANCE SPECIFICATIONS

Application	In. (mm)
528e	
Intake & Exhaust	.010 (.25)
533i, 633CSi & 733i	
Intake & Exhaust	.012 (.30)

VALVE ARRANGEMENT

Left Side — All Intake
Right Side — All Exhaust

SPARK PLUGS

SPARK PLUG TYPE

Application	Bosch
All Except 528e	WR9DS
528e	WR9LS

SPARK PLUG SPECIFICATIONS

Application	Gap In. (mm)	Torque Ft. Lbs. (N.m)
All Models	.027 (.66)	18-22 (24-30)

HIGH TENSION WIRE RESISTANCE

Carefully remove ends of wire from spark plug and distributor. Check resistance by connecting ohmmeter leads to each end of wire. Check resistance of wire while gently twisting wire. If resistance is not to specification, or fluctuates from infinity to any value, replace wire.

HIGH TENSION WIRE RESISTANCE

Application	Ohms
All Models	800-1200

DISTRIBUTOR

All models use an electronic breakerless ignition system. The ignition system is computer controlled by the Motronic system. The distributor has no spark timing function, other than to distribute spark to the proper spark plug. Therefore, no maintenance or adjustments to the distributor are necessary.

Fig. 1: Firing Order and Distributor Rotation

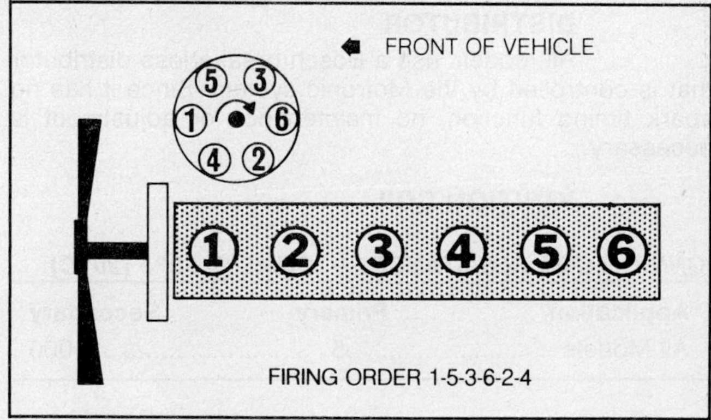
FRONT OF VEHICLE
5
3
1
6
4
2
1 2 3 4 5 6
FIRING ORDER 1-5-3-6-2-4

Illustration applies to all models.

IGNITION TIMING

NOTE: **Ignition timing on 528e, 533i, 633CSi, and 733i models is controlled by an electronic control unit which processes input from engine sensors and computes correct timing. No ignition timing adjustments are possible.**

1983 BMW 6 Tune-Up

TUNE-UP (Cont.)

IGNITION TIMING (Degrees BTDC @ RPM)

Application	Timing
528e	4@700
5331, 633CSi & 733i	6@700

IDLE SPEED & MIXTURE

NOTE: The following adjustments must be made with air filter clean, ignition timing, and valve clearance adjusted to specification and engine at normal operating temperature.

IDLE SPEED

Idle speed is controlled by an idle speed control unit. Connect dwell/tachometer to engine. Check idle speed. If specification is not correct, check idle speed control unit and replace if required.

IDLE SPEED SPECIFICATIONS

Application	RPM
528e & 533i	650-750
633CSi & 733i	650-750

IDLE MIXTURE

NOTE: Mixture adjustment is not a part of normal tune-up procedure and should not be performed unless fuel injection components are replaced or vehicle fails emission testing.

1) Remove hose from collector to carbon canister. Connect special tool (13 0 070) with adapter (13 0 100) on exhaust manifold. Special tool (13 0 070) is designed to connect a CO tester directly to the exhaust manifold. Connect CO tester and check value. *See CO Level Specifications*.

CO LEVEL SPECIFICATIONS

Application	CO%
All Models	0.2-1.2

2) CO level at idle speed should NOT be changed by pulling plug off oxygen sensor. To adjust CO level, drill a hole in plug on air flow sensor using removal tool (13 11 092).

3) Screw removal tool (13 1 094) into plug. Knock tool and plug out of air flow sensor with sharp impact.

4) Insert adjuster tool (13 1 060) into plug hole, and adjust engine speed by turning control screw. After completion, install new plug.

FUEL PUMP

FUEL PUMP PERFORMANCE

Application	Pressure psi (kg/cm²)	Volume in 30 sec. Pints (Liters)
All Models	43 (3.0)	4.6 (2.2)

EMISSION CONTROL SYSTEMS

See Mitchell Manuals' Emission Control Manual.

GENERAL SERVICING

IGNITION

DISTRIBUTOR

All models use a Bosch breakerless distributor that is controlled by the Motronic system. Since it has no spark timing function, no maintenance or adjustment is necessary.

IGNITION COIL

IGNITION COIL RESISTANCE — OHMS @ 68°F (20°C)

Application	Primary	Secondary
All Models	.5	6000

FUEL SYSTEM

All models are equipped with Bosch L-Jetronic (AFC) fuel injection which is controlled by the Motronic Control Unit.

ELECTRICAL

BATTERY

BATTERY SPECIFICATIONS

Application	Amp Hr. Rating
All Models	65

STARTER

Bosch starters are used on all models. Test specifications are not available from manufacturer.

ALTERNATOR

Bosch alternators are used on all models.

ALTERNATOR SPECIFICATIONS

Application	Rated Amp Output
All Models	80

GENERAL SERVICING (Cont.)

ALTERNATOR REGULATOR

All BMW models are equipped with Bosch alternator regulators.

REGULATOR OPERATING VOLTAGE @ 68°F (20°C)

Application	Volts
All Models	13.5-14.6

SERVICE SPECIFICATIONS

BELT ADJUSTMENT

Application	[1] Deflection In. (mm)
Air Conditioning Belt	.5 (13)
All Other Belts	.2-.4 (5-10)

[1] — When depressed with firm hand pressure midway between pulleys.

REPLACEMENT INTERVALS

Component	Interval (Miles)
Oil Filter	7500
Air Filter	30,000
Fuel Filters	30,000
Oxygen Sensor	30,000
Spark Plugs	30,000

FLUID CAPACITIES

Application	Quantity
Crankcase (Includes Filter)	
528e	4.5 qts. (4.25L)
All Others	6.1 qts. (5.8L)
Cooling System	12.7 qts. (12.0L)
Man. Trans. (SAE 80)	3.5 pts. (1.6L)
Auto. Trans. (Dexron)	4.2 pts. (2.0L)
Rear Axle (SAE 90)	3.8 pts. (1.8L)
Fuel Tank	
All (Exc. 733i)	16.5 gals. (63.0L)
733i	22.5 gals. (85.0L)

TUNE-UP

Challenger, Colt, Colt Pickup, Ram-50 Pickup, Sapporo

ENGINE IDENTIFICATION

Engine code numbers are stamped on top edge of right front side of cylinder block.

ENGINE CODE

Application	Code
1.4L	G12B
1.6L	G32B
2.0L	G63B
2.6L	G54B

ENGINE COMPRESSION

Check compression pressure with engine at normal operating temperature, choke and throttle valves wide open and engine at cranking speed (250 RPM). Crank engine at least 6 "puffs" per cylinder to determine engine compression.

COMPRESSION SPECIFICATIONS

Compression Ratio	
1.4L	8.8:1
1.6L & 2.0L	8.5:1
2.6L	8.2:1
Compression Pressure	149 psi (10.5 kg/cm²)
Maximum Variation Between Cylinders	10%

VALVE CLEARANCE

NOTE: Jet valve clearance must be adjusted before adjusting intake valve clearance. Loosen intake valve adjusting screw at least 2 full turns before adjusting jet valve.

Check or adjust valve clearance with engine off, at normal operating temperature and with coil wire to distributor disconnected. To adjust valves, loosen lock nut and turn adjusting screw until specified clearance is obtained.

VALVE CLEARANCE SPECIFICATIONS

Application	In. (mm)
Jet	.006 (.15)
Intake	.006 (.15)
Exhaust	.010 (.25)

VALVE ARRANGEMENT

Left Side – All Intake
Right Side – All Exhaust

SPARK PLUGS

SPARK PLUG TYPE

Application	NGK	Champion
1.4L & 1.6L	BPR6ES-11	RN-9Y
2.0L	BPR6EA-11	RN-9Y
2.6L	BPR5ES-11	RN-12Y

SPARK PLUG SPECIFICATIONS

Application	Gap In. (mm)	Torque Ft. Lbs. (N.m)
All Models	.041 (1.0)	20 (27)

HIGH TENSION WIRE RESISTANCE

Carefully remove high tension wires from spark plugs and distributor cap. Twist wire gently while measuring resistance with ohmmeter. If resistance is greater than specified value, or fluctuates from infinity to any value, replace wire.

HIGH TENSION WIRE RESISTANCE

Application	Ohms
All Models	Less Than 22,000

DISTRIBUTOR

All models use Mitsubishi electronic, breakerless ignition systems with an electronic control unit.

Fig. 1: Firing Order and Distributor Rotation All Engines

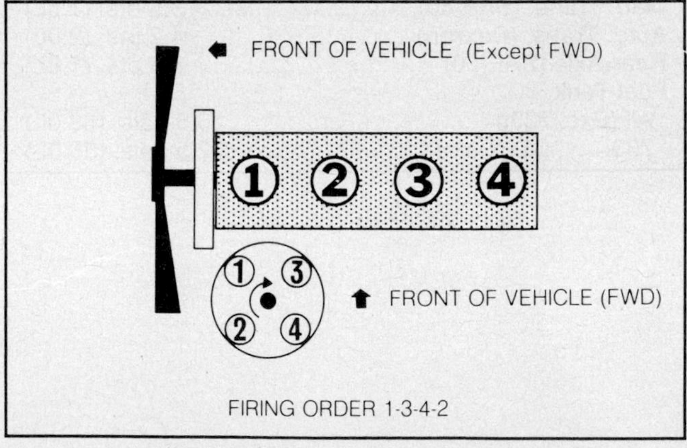
FRONT OF VEHICLE (Except FWD)
1
2
3
4
1
3
2
4
FRONT OF VEHICLE (FWD)
FIRING ORDER 1-3-4-2

IGNITION TIMING

1) Turn lights and all accessories off. Position transmission in Neutral. Run engine at idle speed until normal operating temperature is reached. Stop engine and connect tachometer and timing light. On 1.4L and 1.6L engines with A/C, remove A/C belt.

TUNE-UP (Cont.)

Fig. 2: Ignition Timing Mark Location

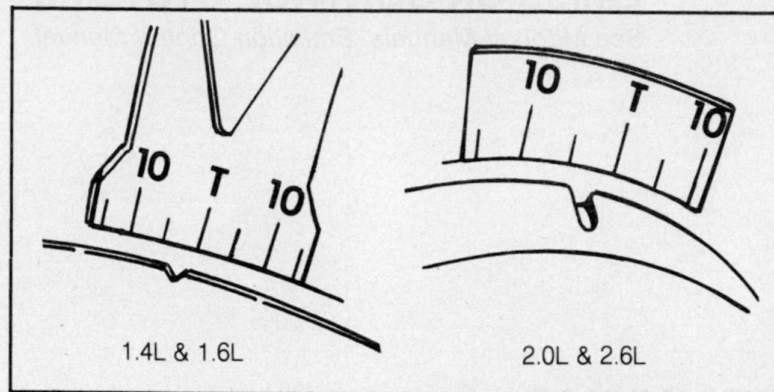
10
T
10
1.4L & 1.6L
2.0L & 2.6L

2) Start engine and run at curb idle speed. On 1.4L 4-speed Man. Trans. models, disconnect White striped hose from distributor. On 2.0L 5-speed Man. Trans. Federal models, disconnect vacuum hoses from distributor and temporarily seal ends of hoses.

3) On all models, adjust ignition timing by loosening distributor hold down nut and rotating distributor.

IGNITION TIMING SPECIFICATIONS (Degrees BTDC@RPM)

Application	Man. Trans.	Auto Trans.
1.4L	5@700	.....
1.6L	5@700	5@750
2.0L	5@750 [1]	5@750
2.6L	7@750	7@800

[1] – Set Federal 5-Speed. Man. Trans. to 5@700.

AIR CONDITIONING IDLE SPEED

1) Turn lights and accessories off, place transmission in neutral. Run engine until normal operating temperature is reached. On 1.4L and 1.6L engines, electric fan must be off. Make sure that curb idle is within specifications. If necessary reset idle speed to specifications.

2) On 2.0L and 2.6L engines turn A/C on. On 1.4L and 1.6L engines turn A/C off, and disconnect vacuum hose from throttle opener nipple. Connect vacuum pump to nipple and apply 19 in. Hg.

Fig. 3: Air Conditioning Idle Speed Screw Location

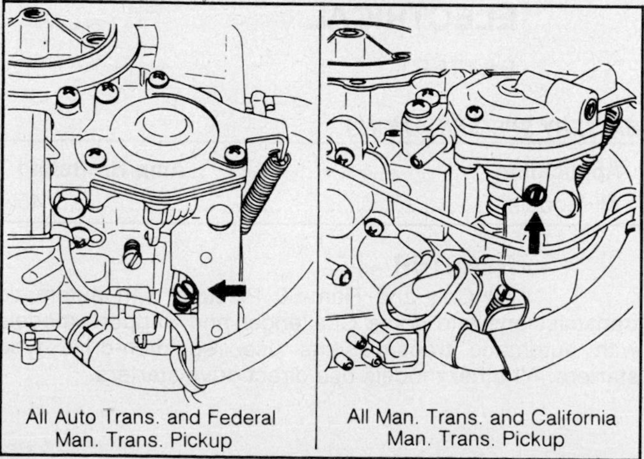
All Auto Trans. and Federal Man. Trans. Pickup — All Man. Trans. and California Man. Trans. Pickup

3) Adjust engine speed to specification with throttle opener screw. *See Fig. 3.* After adjustment reconnect vacuum hose on 1.4L and 1.6L engines.

AIR CONDITIONING IDLE SPEED SPECIFICATIONS

Application	RPM
1.4L & 1.6L	
Man. Trans.	1050-1150
Auto. Trans.	1100-1200
2.0L & 2.6L	
Pickup	850-950
All Others	1000-1100

IDLE MIXTURE

NOTE: Mixture adjustment is NOT a part of normal tune-up procedure and should not be performed unless carburetor is disassembled or vehicle fails emission testing.

1) Remove carburetor from engine and clamp in a vise with the adjusting screw facing up. Be careful to protect gasket surface from vise jaws.

2) Drill a 5/64" (2 mm) pilot hole in the casting surrounding the idle mixture adjusting screw. Redrill hole to 1/8" (3 mm). *See Fig. 4.* Insert a blunt punch into the hole and drive out the concealment plug. Reinstall carburetor.

Fig. 4: Removing Concealment Plug

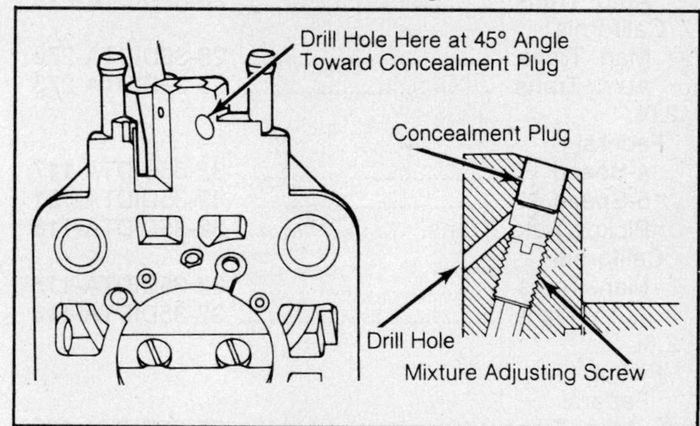
Drill Hole Here at 45° Angle Toward Concealment Plug
Concealment Plug
Drill Hole
Mixture Adjusting Screw

3) Turn lights and accessories off, place transmission in neutral. Run engine until normal operating temperature is reached. Disconnect and plug hose from air cleaner to pulse air feeder.

4) Run engine for more than 5 seconds at 2000-3000 RPM. Run engine at idle speed for more than two minutes. Set engine idle speed and idle CO to specified values by adjusting the idle speed screw and the idle mixture screw.

5) Unplug hose and reconnect to air cleaner. If engine idle speed is outside specified speed range reset speed to correct value using the idle speed screw. Reinstall concealment plug to seal idle mixture screw.

CO LEVEL SPECIFICATIONS AT IDLE

Application	[1] CO%
All Models	0.5

[1] – With air injection disconnected.

TUNE-UP (Cont.)

FUEL PUMP

FUEL PUMP PERFORMANCE

Application	Pressure psi (kg/cm^2)	Volume in 30 Sec. Pints (Liters)
1.4L	3.7-5.1 (.26-.36)	1.4 (.7)
1.6L	3.7-5.1 (.26-.36)	1.7 (.8)
2.0L	4.6-6.0 (.32-.42)	2.1 (1.0)
2.6L	4.6-6.0 (.32-.42)	2.1 (1.0)

EMISSION CONTROL SYSTEMS

See Mitchell Manuals' Emission Control Manual.

GENERAL SERVICING

FUEL SYSTEMS

CARBURETOR APPLICATIONS

Application	[1] Part No.
1.4L	
Federal	
4-Speed	28-32DIDTA-276
4x2-Speed	28-32DIDTA-271
California	28-32DIDTA-270
1.6L	
Federal	
Man. Trans.	28-32DIDTA-274
Auto. Trans.	28-32DIDTA-275
California	
Man. Trans.	28-32DIDTA-272
Auto. Trans.	28-32DIDTA-273
2.0L	
Federal	
4-Speed	32-35DIDTA-117
5-Speed	32-35DIDTA-121
Pickup Auto. Trans.	32-35DIDTA-118
California	
Man. Trans.	32-35DIDTA-115
Auto. Trans	32-35DIDTA-116
2.6L	
Pickup	
Federal	
Man. Trans.	32-35DIDTA-106
Auto. Trans.	32-35DIDTA-107
California	
Man. Trans.	32-35DIDTA-104
Auto. Trans.	32-35DIDTA-105
Challenger & Sapporo	
Federal	
Man. Trans.	30-35DIDTA-102
Auto. Trans.	30-35DIDTA-103
California	
Man. Trans.	30-35DIDTA-100
Auto. Trans.	30-35DIDTA-101

[1] – Solex (Mikuni) carburetors.

IGNITION

DISTRIBUTOR

All models use Mitsubishi electronic, breakerless ignition systems with electronic control unit.

TOTAL SPARK ADVANCE @ 2800 RPM

Application	W/Vac. Advance	W/O Vac. Advance
1.4L & 1.6L	43°	[1] 20°
2.0L		
Federal		
Man. Trans.		
4-Speed	38°	12°
5-Speed.	38°	12°
Auto. Trans.	32°	12°
California	23.6°	12°
2.6L		
Federal	20°	12°
California	19°	12°

[1] – 1.4L and 1.6L at 4400 RPM.

DISTRIBUTOR PICK-UP COIL RESISTANCE

Application	Ohms
All Models	920-1120

IGNITION COIL

IGNITION COIL RESISTANCE – Ohms @ 68°F (20°C)

Application	Primary	Secondary
Pickups	1.04-1.27	7100-9600
Other Models	.70-.85	9000-11,000

ELECTRICAL

BATTERY

BATTERY SPECIFICATIONS

Application	Amp Hr. Rating
All Models	45

STARTER

All Colt and Ram-50 Pickups with automatic transmissions and some Challenger and Sapporo models with automatic transmissions use reduction-drive type starters. All other models use direct drive starters.

GENERAL SERVICING (Cont.)

STARTER SPECIFICATIONS

Application	Volts	Amps	Test RPM
1.4L & 1.6L			
Man. Trans.	11.5	60	6500
Auto. Trans.	11.5	60	6600
2.0L & 2.6L			
Man. Trans.	11.5	60	6600
Auto. Trans.	11.5	90	3300

ALTERNATORS

All models use Mitsubishi alternators.

ALTERNATOR SPECIFICATIONS

Application	Rated Amp. Output
Challenger & Sapporo	50
All Others	45

ALTERNATOR REGULATORS

All models use Mitsubishi alternator regulators which are integral with the alternator.

REGULATOR OPERATING VOLTAGE @ 68°F (20°C)

Application	Voltage
All Models	14.1-14.7

SERVICE SPECIFICATIONS

BELT ADJUSTMENT

Application	[1] Deflection In. (mm)
Alternator Belt	1/4-3/8 (7-10)

[1] – Measured with 22 lbs. (10 kg) pressure applied midway between pulleys on longest belt run.

REPLACEMENT INTERVALS

Components	Miles
Oil Filter	15,000
Fuel Filter	50,000
Air Filter	30,000
Canister Filter	50,000
PCV Valve	30,000
Spark Plugs	30,000

FLUID CAPACITIES

Application	Quantity
Crankcase (Includes Filter)	
1.4L	3.7 qts. (3.5L)
1.6L	4.2 qts. (4.0L)
2.0L	
4WD Pickups	5.2 qts. (5.0L)
All Except 4WD Pickups	4.2 qts. (4.0L)
2.6L	
4WD Pickups	6.1 qts. (5.8L)
All Except 4WD Pickups	5.2 qts. (5.0L)
Cooling System (Includes Heater)	
1.4L & 1.6L	5.0 qts. (4.8L)
2.0L	9.5 qts. (9.0L)
2.6L	
Pickups	9.5 qts. (9.0L)
Challenger & Sapporo	9.7 qts. (9.2L)
Manual Transaxle (SAE 80)	4.8 pts. (2.3L)
Manual Transmission (SAE 90)	
2.0L	4.4 pts. (2.1L)
2.6L	4.9 pts. (2.3L)
Transfer Case (4WD Pickups)	4.6 pts. (2.2L)
Automatic Transaxle (Dexron)	12.0 pts. (5.8L)
Automatic Transmission (Dexron)	14.4 pts. (6.8L)
Rear Axle (SAE 80W-90)	
Challenger & Sapporo	2.8 pts. (1.3L)
Pickups	3.2 pts. (1.5L)
All Other Models	3.0 pts. (1.4L)
Front Axle (4WD Pickups)	2.8 pts. (1.3L)
Fuel Tank	
Colt & Ram-50 Pickups	[1] 18.0 gals. (68.0L)
Challenger & Sapporo	15.8 gals. (60.0L)
Colt	
Luxury & Rally Sports	13.2 gals. (50.0L)
All Others	10.6 gals. (40.0L)

[1] – Some 2WD models, 15.1 gals. (57.2L).

TUNE-UP

Colt Pickup, Ram-50 Pickup

ENGINE IDENTIFICATION

The engine model number and serial number are located on the left side of the engine, just to the rear of the dipstick.

ENGINE CODE

Application	Code
2.3L Turbo Diesel	4D55

ENGINE COMPRESSION

Warm engine to normal operating temperature. Operate starter at 250 RPM and read compression.

COMPRESSION SPECIFICATIONS

Compression Ratio	21:1
Compression Pressure	384 psi (27 kg/cm²)

VALVE CLEARANCE

1) Run engine until coolant reaches normal operating temperature of 176-194°F (80-90°C). Place piston in No. 1 cylinder at TDC on compression stroke to adjust valve clearances marked "1".

Fig. 1: Adjusting Valve Clearance of Chrysler Corp. Imports Diesel Engine

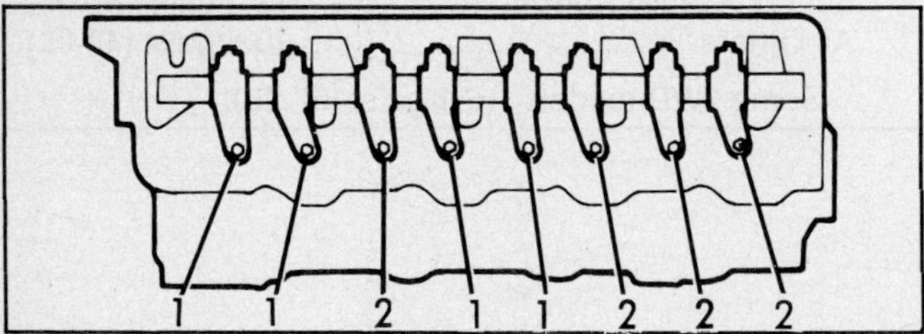
1 1 2 1 1 2 2 2

2) Loosen nut and adjust to specifications with adjusting screw. Retighten nut. Check valve clearance again. Place piston of No. 4 cylinder at TDC of compression stroke to adjust valve clearances marked "2". Adjust valve clearance in same manner as for valves marked "1".

3) Check idle speed and readjust valve clearance if necessary.

VALVE CLEARANCE SPECIFICATIONS

Application	In. (mm)
Intake and Exhaust (Hot)	.010 (.25)

VALVE ARRANGEMENT

E-I-E-I-E-I-E-I (Front-to-rear)

GLOW PLUGS

GLOW PLUG TORQUE SPECIFICATIONS

Application	Ft. Lbs. (N.m)
All Models	11-14 (15-19)

Fig. 2: Diesel Firing Order Illustration

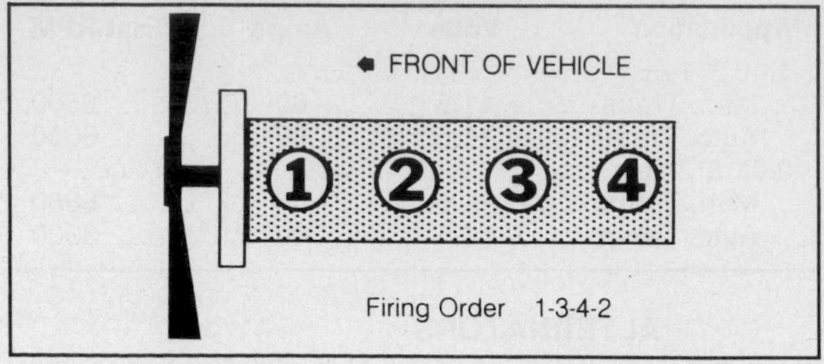
FRONT OF VEHICLE
1 2 3 4
Firing Order 1-3-4-2

IDLE SPEED

1) Turn all lights and accessories off, and place transmission in neutral. Operate cold engine at fast idle until coolant temperature reaches 185-205°F (85-95°C). Run engine at 2000-3000 RPM for more than 5 seconds.

Fig. 3: Diesel Idle Speed Adjusting Screw

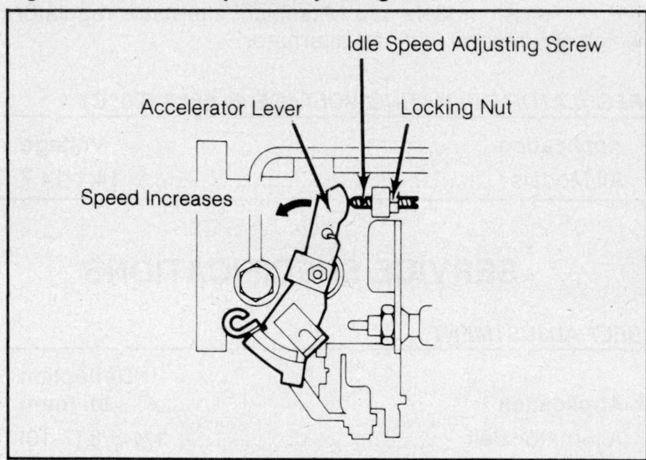
Idle Speed Adjusting Screw
Accelerator Lever
Locking Nut
Speed Increases

2) Run engine at idle speed for 2 minutes. Using a tachometer, read idle speed. If not to specifications, readjust speed using idle speed adjusting screw. Do not disturb other screws.

IDLE SPEED SPECIFICATIONS

Application	Idle RPM
All Models	700-850

FUEL SYSTEM BLEEDING

Loosen the air vent screw on top of fuel filter housing. Pull out the priming pump knob by turning it to the left. Pump the priming pump until fuel flowing out of vent hole is free of air bubbles. Tighten the air vent screw.

EMISSION CONTROL SYSTEMS

See Mitchell Manual's Emission Control Manual.

GENERAL SERVICING

FUEL SYSTEMS

FUEL INJECTION

All Chrysler Corp. Import diesel models use a Bosch VE diesel fuel injection system.

DIESEL FUEL INJECTION TIMING [1]

Application	Degrees
High Altitude	TDC
All Other Models	2°ATDC

[1] — Measured in degrees at .0394" (1 mm) plunger travel.

ELECTRICAL

BATTERY

BATTERY SPECIFICATIONS

Application	Amp Hr. Rating
All Models	[1] 80

[1] — Cranking capacity at 0°F (—17°C) is 600 amps.

STARTER

Mitsubishi reduction drive starters are used on all models.

STARTER SPECIFICATIONS

Application	Volts	Amps	Test RPM
All Models	11	130	4000

ALTERNATOR

Mitsubishi alternators, equipped with a vacuum pump to generate vacuum for the brake booster, are used on all models.

ALTERNATOR SPECIFICATIONS

Application	Rated Amp Output
All Models	50

ALTERNATOR REGULATOR

All Diesel models use Mitsubishi IC alternator regulators.

REGULATOR OPERATING VOLTAGE @ 68°F (20°C)

Application	Voltage
All Models	13.9-14.9

GLOW PLUGS

GLOW PLUG SYSTEM RESISTANCE @ 68°F (20°C)

Application	Ohms
Glow Plugs	0.10
Dropping Resistor	0.13

SERVICE SPECIFICATIONS

BELT ADJUSTMENT

Application	[1] Deflection In. (mm)
All Belts	3/8 - 1/2 (10-13)

[1] — With force of 22 lbs. (10 kg) pressure applied midway between pulleys on longest belt run.

REPLACEMENT INTERVALS

Component	Interval (Miles)
Oil Filter	6000
Fuel Filter	30,000
Air Filter	30,000
Turbo Air Intake Hose	30,000
Turbo Oil Hose	50,000

FLUID CAPACITIES

Application	Quantity
Crankcase, Including Filter (API CD)	
2WD	5.0 qts. (4.8L)
4WD	6.3 qts. (6.1L)
Cooling System [1]	8.5 qts. (8.0L)
4-Speed Man. Trans. (SAE 75W-85W)	
2WD	4.4 pts. (2.1L)
4WD	4.6 pts. (2.2L)
5-Speed Man. Trans. (SAE 75W-85W)	
2WD	4.9 pts. (2.3L)
4WD	4.6 pts. (2.2L)
Transfer Case (SAE 80)	4.6 pts. (2.2L)
Front Axle (SAE 90)	2.3 pts. (1.1L)
Rear Axle (SAE 90)	3.2 pts. (1.5L)
Fuel Tank	
2WD Standard	15.0 gals. (57.0L)
2WD Optional	18.0 gals. (68.0L)
4WD	18.0 gals. (68.0L)

[1] – Includes heater and coolant reserve system.

1983 Datsun/Nissan 4 Tune-Up

TUNE-UP

Pickup, Pulsar, Sentra, Stanza & 200SX

ENGINE IDENTIFICATION

On Pickup and 200SX models, engine code and serial number is stamped on left side of cylinder block below No. 2 and No. 3 spark plugs. For Stanza, Sentra and Pulsar models, engine code is on left rear side of cylinder block, just below cylinder head mating surface.

ENGINE CODE

Application	Code
Pickup	
Calif.	Z24
Federal	Z20
Pulsar & Sentra	E16
Sentra M.P.G.	E15
Stanza	CA20
200SX	Z22E

ENGINE COMPRESSION

Check compression pressure with engine at normal operating temperature, all spark plugs removed, electrical lead to anti-dieseling solenoid disconnected and choke and throttle valves wide open.

Crank engine at least 6 revolutions to determine engine compression. Lowest cylinder pressure should be at least 80% that of the highest cylinder.

COMPRESSION SPECIFICATIONS

Compression Pressure	
Pickup, Stanza & 200SX	128-171 psi (9.0-12.0 kg/cm²)
Pulsar & Sentra	142-181 psi (10.0-12.7 kg/cm²)

VALVE CLEARANCE

NOTE: **On all models, start and run engine to normal operating temperature. Turn engine off, remove valve cover and adjust clearances immediately. Do not allow engine to cool before or during adjustment, or incorrect valve clearances may be obtained.**

PICKUP & 200SX

1) Rotate crankshaft to bring No. 1 cylinder to TDC on compression stroke. Adjust intake valves on cylinders No. 1 and No. 2, and exhaust valves on cylinders No. 1 and No. 3.

2) Rotate crankshaft 360° to bring the first cam lobe to a straight up position. Adjust remaining valves.

PULSAR & SENTRA

1) Rotate crankshaft to bring No. 1 piston to TDC on compression stroke. Adjust intake valves on cylinders No. 1 and No. 2 and adjust exhaust valves on cylinders No. 1 and No. 3.

2) Rotate crankshaft 360° to bring No. 4 piston to TDC on compression stroke. Adjust intake valves on cylinders No. 3 and No. 4 and adjust exhaust valves on cylinders No. 2 and No. 4.

STANZA

1) Rotate engine so that high point of No. 1 cam lobe points straight down. Adjust clearance on No. 1 and 2 intake valves and No. 3 and 4 exhaust valves.

2) Turn crankshaft so that No. 1 cam lobe is straight up. Adjust intake valves on No. 3 and 4 cylinders and exhaust valves on No. 1 and 2 cylinders.

VALVE CLEARANCE SPECIFICATIONS

Application	[1] Clearance In. (mm)
Pickup, Stanza & 200SX	.012 (.30)
Pulsar & Sentra	.011 (.28)

[1] — Adjust valves with engine hot.

VALVE ARRANGEMENT

Right Side — All Intake
Left Side — All Exhaust

SPARK PLUGS

SPARK PLUG TYPE

Application	NGK No.
Pickup & 200SX	
Intake Side	BPR6ES
Exhaust Side	BPR5ES
Pulsar & Sentra (Exc. M.P.G.)	BPR5ES-11
Sentra M.P.G.	BPR6ES-11
Stanza	
Intake Side	BPR6ES-11
Exhaust Side	BPR5ES-11

SPARK PLUG SPECIFICATIONS

Application	Gap In. (mm)	Torque Ft. Lbs. (N.m)
Pickup, 200SX	.033 (.85)	11-14 (15-20)
Pulsar, Sentra, Stanza	.041 (1.05)	11-14 (15-20)

HIGH TENSION WIRE RESISTANCE

Remove distributor cap from distributor but do not disconnect high tension wires from cap. Disconnect high tension wires from spark plugs. Using an ohmmeter, check resistance from contact at spark plug end of wires to contact inside of distributor cap. *See High Tension Wire Resistance Chart.* If resistance is higher, disconnect wire from cap and recheck resistance. Replace wire if resistance is still to high.

HIGH TENSION WIRE RESISTANCE

Application	Ohms
All Models	30,000 Max.

DISTRIBUTOR

All models use Hitachi breakerless, transistorized ignition systems. Pickup, Stanza and 200SX models

TUNE-UP (Cont.)

have 2 spark plugs per cylinder. The distributor is equipped with 8 secondary wires and a dual level rotor which fires both spark plugs at the same time.

Fig. 1: Firing Order and Distributor Rotation for Pickup, Stanza and 200SX

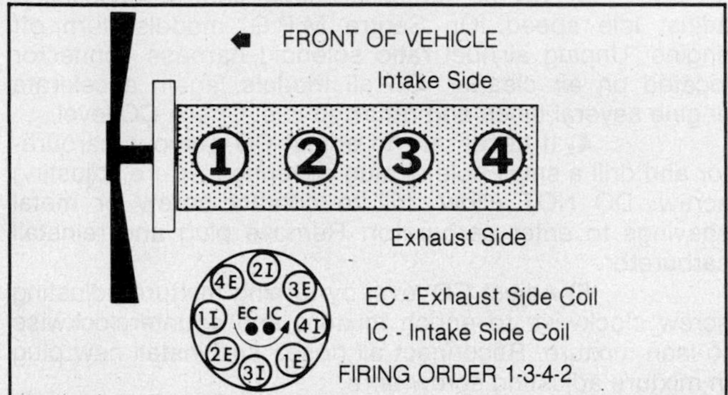
FRONT OF VEHICLE
Intake Side
1
2
3
4
Exhaust Side
EC - Exhaust Side Coil
IC - Intake Side Coil
FIRING ORDER 1-3-4-2

Fig. 2: Firing Order and Distributor Rotation for Pulsar & Sentra

FRONT OF VEHICLE
1
2
3
4
FIRING ORDER 1-3-4-2

IGNITION TIMING

NOTE: Pickup, Stanza, and 200SX models use dual electronic ignition system. Firing order is 1-3-4-2 and rotor is designed with 135° offset to fire both plugs simultaneously.

1) Warm engine to normal operating temperature. Turn air conditioning off (if equipped). Place transmission in Neutral (Man. Trans.) or in "D" (Auto. Trans.). Set idle speed to specifications. Disconnect and plug distributor vacuum hoses.

2) Connect timing light to engine. Loosen distributor clamp bolt and turn distributor until specified ignition timing is obtained. Retighten distributor clamp bolt.

IGNITION TIMING (Degrees BTDC@RPM)

Application	Man. Trans.	[1] Auto. Trans.
Pickup		
2WD	3°@550-750	3°@550-750
4WD	3°@700-900	3°@550-750
Pulsar	[2] 5°@700-800	[2] 5°@600-700
Sentra		
M.P.G.	[2] 2°@650-750	
Exc. M.P.G.	[2] 5°@700-800	[2] 5°@600-700
Stanza	0°@550-750	0°@550-750
200SX	8°@650-850	8°@600-800

[1] – With Auto. Trans. selector in "D" position.
[2] – Degrees are ATDC.

Fig. 3: Ignition Timing Mark Location for Pickup, Stanza and 200SX

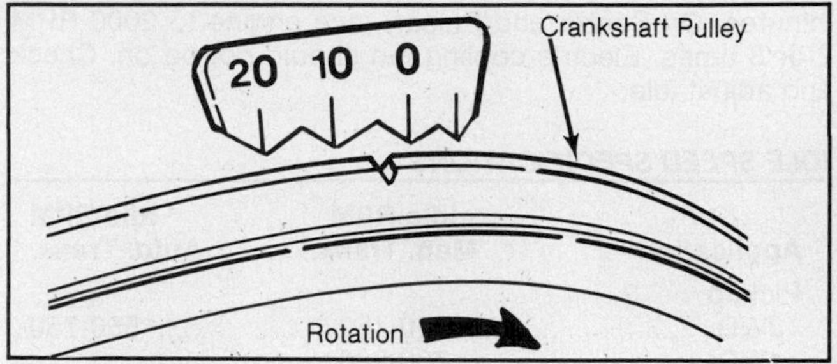
Crankshaft Pulley
20
10
0
Rotation

Fig. 4: Ignition Timing Mark Location for Pulsar & Sentra

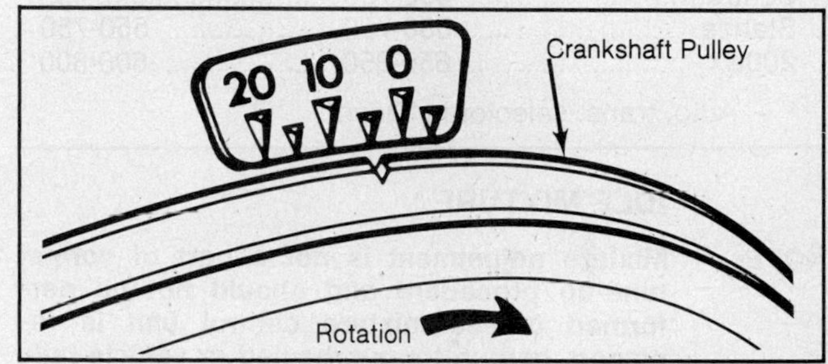
Crankshaft Pulley
20
10
0
Rotation

IDLE SPEED & MIXTURE

NOTE: The following adjustment procedures should be performed with engine at normal operating temperature, air conditioning "OFF" (if equipped), ignition timing set to specifications and air cleaner installed. Set parking brake, block drive wheels and on models with automatic transmission, place gear selector in "D" position.

IDLE SPEED

200SX

Connect a tachometer to engine and run at 2000 RPM for 5 minutes to stabilize operating condition. Accelerate engine 2-3 times and return to idle. Turn idle speed adjusting screw to obtain specified idle RPM. *See Fig. 5.*

Fig. 5: Adjusting 200SX Idle Speed

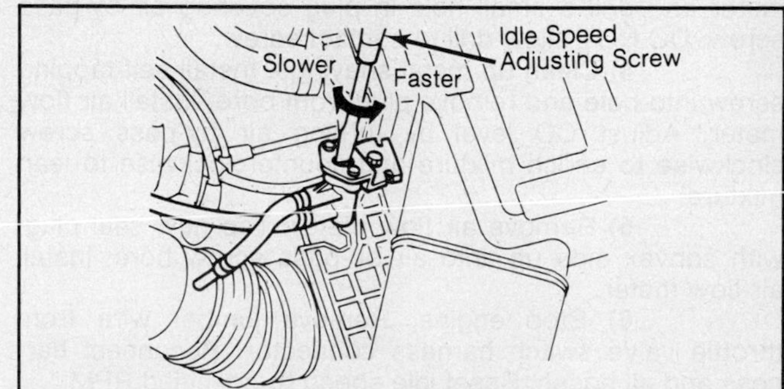
Idle Speed
Adjusting Screw
Slower
Faster

Engine must be at operating temperature.

TUNE-UP (Cont.)

Pickup, Pulsar, Sentra & Stanza

Connect a tachometer to engine. On Pickup and Stanza models, run engine at 2000 RPM for 2 minutes. On Sentra and Pulsar, race engine to 2000 RPM 2 or 3 times. Electric cooling fan should not be on. Check and adjust idle.

IDLE SPEED SPECIFICATIONS

Application	Idle RPM Man. Trans.	[1] Idle RPM Auto. Trans.
Pickup		
2WD	550-750	550-750
4WD	700-900	.....
Pulsar	700-800	600-700
Sentra	700-800	600-700
Sentra M.P.G.	650-750	.....
Stanza	550-750	550-750
200SX	650-850	600-800

[1] – Auto. trans. selector in "Drive".

IDLE MIXTURE

NOTE: **Mixture adjustment is not a part of normal tune-up procedure and should not be performed unless mixture control unit is replaced, carburetor overhauled or vehicle fails emissions testing.**

200SX

1) Turn ignition switch off. Unplug throttle valve switch harness connector. Unplug exhaust gas sensor harness connector. Connect a jumper wire between throttle valve switch harness connector terminals No. 24 and No. 30. Install CO meter probe into tailpipe at least 16".

NOTE: **Connecting jumper wire between connector terminals signals the control unit of a full throttle condition which allows the idle mixture to run at full load enrichment. This step is necessary to enrichen the CO% level at idle enough to be read by the CO meter.**

2) Start engine, accelerate 2-3 times and allow to idle for 1 minute. Check and, if necessary, adjust ignition timing and idle speed. On models with altitude switch, unplug switch harness connector. With engine idling, check CO level.

3) If necessary to adjust CO, remove air flow meter and drill a small hole in plug covering air by-pass screw. DO NOT allow drill to contact screw.

4) Clean up metal shavings. Install self tapping screw into hole and remove plug from bore. Install air flow meter. Adjust CO level by turning air by-pass screw clockwise to enrich mixture and counterclockwise to lean mixture.

5) Remove air flow meter. Tap new seal plug, with convex side up, into air by-pass screw bore. Install air flow meter.

6) Stop engine. Remove jumper wire from throttle valve switch harness connector. Reconnect harness and all hoses. Reset idle speed to specified RPM.

Pickup, Pulsar, Sentra, & Stanza

1) Install CO meter probe 16" or more into tailpipe. Disconnect and plug distributor vacuum and air induction hoses. Unplug and cap air induction hoses (if equipped). Accelerate engine to 2000-3000 RPM several times under no load.

2) Return engine to idle speed for 1 minute. Check and, if necessary, adjust ignition timing. On Pulsar, Sentra, and Stanza models, reconnect distributor vacuum hoses.

3) On all models, check and, if necessary, adjust idle speed. On Sentra M.P.G. models, turn off engine. Unplug air/fuel ratio solenoid harness connector located on air cleaner. On all models, again accelerate engine several times and return to idle. Check CO level.

4) If necessary to adjust CO, remove carburetor and drill a small hole in plug covering mixture adjusting screw. DO NOT allow drill to contact screw or metal shavings to enter carburetor. Remove plug and reinstall carburetor.

5) Adjust CO level by turning mixture adjusting screw clockwise to enrich mixture and counterclockwise to lean mixture. Reconnect all hoses and install new plug in mixture adjusting screw bore.

IDLE CO LEVEL SPECIFICATIONS

Application	CO Level
Pickup & Stanza	.3-2.5%
Pulsar, Sentra, Sentra M.P.G. & 200SX	.8-2.5%

COLD (FAST) IDLE RPM

NOTE: **The fast idle on 200SX models is controlled by the Cold Start Enrichment System. No adjustment is necessary.**

PULSAR & SENTRA

Adjust fast idle speed with engine at normal operating temperature, transmission in neutral and fast idle speed screw on 2nd highest step of fast idle cam.

FAST IDLE RPM

Application	Man.Trans.	Auto. Trans.
Pulsar & Sentra		
Federal	2400-3200	2700-3500
California	2600-3400	2900-3700
Sentra M.P.G.	2400-3200	.....

PICKUP & STANZA

Carburetor must be removed from vehicle to set fast idle. Place upper side of fast idle screw on 2nd step of fast idle cam. Measure throttle valve clearance between throttle plate and throttle bore. *See Throttle Bore Clearance Specifications.*

THROTTLE BORE CLEARANCE SPECIFICATIONS

Application	Man. Trans. In. (mm)	Auto. Trans. In. (mm)
Pickup	.81-.95 (.032-.037)	.97-1.11 (.038-.044)
Stanza	.66-.80 (.026-.032)	.81-.95 (.032-.037)

TUNE-UP (Cont.)

DASHPOT ADJUSTMENT

PICKUP & STANZA

Automatic Transmission Models

1) Engine must be at normal operating temperature, idle speed and mixture correctly set and A/C OFF. Turn throttle valve by hand and read engine speed when dashpot just contacts adjusting screw on stop lever.

2) Turn adjusting screw on stop lever to obtain an engine speed of 1400-1600 RPM. Accelerate engine and release. When dashpot plunger contacts stop lever, engine should decelerate smoothly from 2000 RPM to 1000 RPM in about 3 seconds.

3) On Stanza models, turn A/C on, place transmission in "D" and fan on "HI". Engine speed should be 600-650 RPM.

FUEL PUMP

FUEL PUMP PERFORMANCE

Application	Pressure psi (kg/cm²)	Volume in 30 Sec. Pints (Liters)
Pickup	3.4 (.24)	1.6 (.75)
Pulsar & Sentra	3.4 (.24)	1.4 (.65)
200SX	30 (2.1)	....
Pickup		
Mechanical	3.4 (.24)	1.8 (.85)
Electric	3.4 (.24)	1.5 (.7)

EMISSION CONTROL SYSTEMS

See Mitchell Manuals' Emission Control Manual.

GENERAL SERVICING

IGNITION

DISTRIBUTOR

All models are equipped with Hitachi breakerless, transistorized ignition systems.

DISTRIBUTOR PICK-UP COIL AIR GAP

Application	In. (mm)
All Models	.012-.020 (.3-.5)

IGNITION COIL

IGNITION COIL RESISTANCE — Ohms @ 68°F (20°C)

Application	Primary	Secondary
Stanza	.84-1.02	8200-12,400
All Others	1.04-1.27	7300-11,000

FUEL SYSTEMS

CARBURETORS

All Pulsar and Sentra (including M.P.G.) models use a Hitachi DFC 328 carburetor on California models. On Federal models, the Hitachi DCZ 328 carburetor is used. All Stanza and Pickup models use a Hitachi DCR 342 carburetor.

FUEL INJECTION

All 200SX models are equipped with Bosch AFC electronic fuel injection.

ELECTRICAL

BATTERY

BATTERY SPECIFICATIONS

Application	Amp Hr. Rating
Pickup Diesel	80
All Others	60

STARTER

All models use a Hitachi solenoid actuated starter with an overrunning clutch.

STARTER SPECIFICATIONS

Application	Volts	Amps	Test RPM
Pulsar & Sentra	11.5	60	7000
Pickup			
Man. Trans.	11.5	60	6000
Auto. Trans.	11.5	60	7000
Stanza			
Non-Reduction	11.5	60	7000
Reduction	11	100	3900
200SX			
Man. Trans.	11.5	60	7000
Auto. Trans.	11.5	60	6000

ALTERNATOR

All models use Hitachi alternators.

ALTERNATOR SPECIFICATIONS

Application	Rated Amp Output
Pulsar	50
Pickup	
Standard	50
Option	60
Sentra	
Standard	50
Option	60
Stanza & 200SX	60

ALTERNATOR REGULATOR

All models use a Hitachi IC regulator, integral with alternator.

REGULATOR OPERATING VOLTAGE @ 68°F (20°C)

Application	Voltage
All Models	14.4-15.0

GENERAL SERVICING (Cont.)

SERVICE SPECIFICATIONS

FLUID CAPACITIES

Application	Quantity
Crankcase (Includes Filter)	
Pickup	
2WD	4.4 qts. (4.1L)
4WD	4.5 qts. (4.2L)
Pulsar & Sentra	3.9 qts. (3.7L)
Stanza	4.1 qts. (3.9L)
200SX	4.5 qts. (4.2L)
Cooling System (Includes Heater)	
Pickup	10.5 qts. (9.9L)
Pulsar	6.0 qts. (5.7L)
Sentra	5.3 qts. (5.0L)
Stanza	7.5 qts. (7.1L)
200SX	10.0 qts. (9.5L)
Man. Transaxle (SAE 80W-90/API GL-4)	
Pulsar & Sentra	
4-Speed	4.9 pt. (2.3L)
5-Speed	5.8 pt. (2.7L)
Stanza	5.8 pt. (2.7L)
Man. Transmission (SAE 80W-90/API GL-4)	
Pickup & 200SX	4.3 pt. (2.0L)
Auto. Transaxle (Dexron)	
All Models	6.4 qts. (6.1L)
Auto. Transmission (Dexron)	
All Models	5.9 qts. (5.5L)
Differential (SAE 80W-90/API GL-5)	
Pickup	
Front	2.1 pts. (1.0L)
Rear	2.6 pts. (1.3L)
200SX	2.4 pts. (1.1L)
Transfer Case	1.5 qts. (1.4L)
Fuel Tank	
Pickup	
Shortbed	
2WD	13.3 gals. (50.0L)
4WD	15.9 gals. (60.0L)
Longbed	
2WD	16.9 gals. (64.0L)
4WD	19.9 gals. (75.0L)
Pulsar & Sentra	13.3 gals. (50.0L)
Stanza	14.3 gals. (54.0L)
200SX	
Hardtop	14.0 gals. (53.0L)
Hatchback	15.9 gals. (60.0L)

REPLACEMENT INTERVALS

Component	Interval (Miles)
Oil & Filter	7,500
Air Filter	30,000
Fuel Filter	30,000
Spark Plugs	30,000

BELT ADJUSTMENT

Application	[1] Deflection In. (mm)
Alternator	.5 (13)
A/C Compressor	
Sentra & Pulsar	.4 (10)
Pickup	.3 (8)
Stanza	.2 (5)
200SX	.5 (12)
Power Steering	
Sentra & Pulsar	.3 (8)
Pickup & 200SX	.6 (16)
Stanza	.3 (8)
Idler Pulley	.3 (8)

[1] — Deflection is with 22 lbs. (10 kg) pressure applied midway on longest belt run.

TUNE-UP

Pickup & Sentra

ENGINE IDENTIFICATION

Engine serial number is stamped into left rear side of block on Sentra (CD17) models. Serial number is preceded by engine model number.

Pickup (SD22) models have the engine serial number stamped on the right side of block below the No. 2 injector. Engine code is stamped below the No. 1 injector.

ENGINE CODE

Application	Code
Sentra	CD17
Pickup	SD22

ENGINE COMPRESSION

1) Check compression pressure with engine at normal operating temperature. Remove injection tube on nozzle side, spill tube assembly and nozzle assemblies with washers.

2) On Sentra models, disconnect fuel cut solenoid wire. On both models, place a compression gauge adapter in cylinder. Hand tighten bleeder screw on gauge. Crank engine at least 6 revolutions and check compression.

3) Install nozzle assemblies with washers, spill tube assembly, and injection tube. Bleed fuel system. *See Fuel System Bleeding.*

COMPRESSION SPECIFICATIONS

Sentra	427-469 psi (30-33 kg/cm²)
Pickup	356-427 psi (25-30 kg/cm²)
Max. Variation Between Cylinders	
Sentra	71 psi (5 kg/cm²)
Pickup	43 psi (3 kg/cm²)

VALVE CLEARANCE

PICKUP

1) Warm engine to normal operating temperature. Turn engine off. Remove valve cover. Rotate crankshaft to bring No. 1 piston to TDC on compression stroke. Adjust intake valves on cylinder No. 1 and 2, and exhaust valves on cylinder No. 1 and 3.

2) Rotate crankshaft to bring No. 4 piston to TDC on compression stroke. Adjust intake valves on cylinder No. 3 and 4, and exhaust valves on cylinder No. 2 and 4.

SENTRA

1) The CD17 engine uses bucket type valve lifters. Clearance is adjusted by replacement of lifter plates (shims). Bring engine to operating temperature. Set No. 1 cylinder on TDC of compression stroke.

2) Measure clearance between camshaft and lifter plates on No. 1 cylinder. If clearance is not within specifications, select the appropriate size lifter plate. Plates can be changed using special tool (KV11102600).

3) Lifter plates are available from .12" (3 mm) to .165" (4.2 mm) in increments of .002" (.05 mm). Use same procedure to adjust remaining valves. Install lifter plate with identification number facing DOWN.

VALVE CLEARANCE SPECIFICATIONS

Application	[1] In. (mm)
Pickup	
Intake & Exhaust	.014 (.35)
Sentra	
Intake	.013 (.32)
Exhaust	.014 (.36)

[1] — Adjust valves with engine hot.

Fig. 1: Firing Order

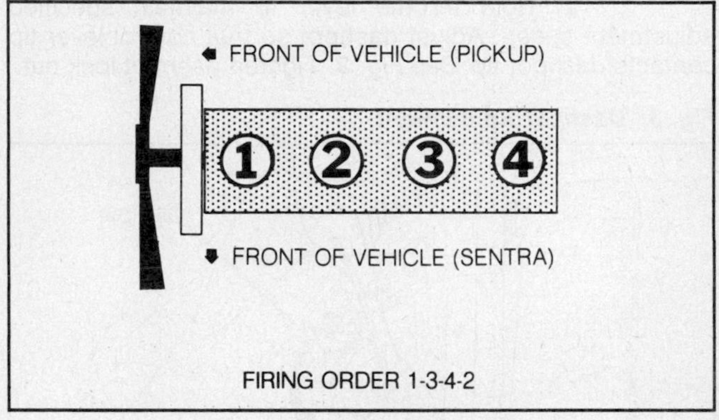
FRONT OF VEHICLE (PICKUP)
1
2
3
4
FRONT OF VEHICLE (SENTRA)
FIRING ORDER 1-3-4-2

VALVE ARRANGEMENT

PICKUP

E-I-I-E-E-I-I-E (Front-to-rear)

SENTRA

E-I-E-I-I-E-I-E (Front-to-rear)

IDLE SPEED ADJUSTMENT

1) With transmission in neutral, parking brake applied and all wheels blocked, warm up engine to normal operating temperature. Connect a tachometer to engine. On pickups, push in throttle control knob under dash panel.

Fig. 2: Idle Speed Adjustment

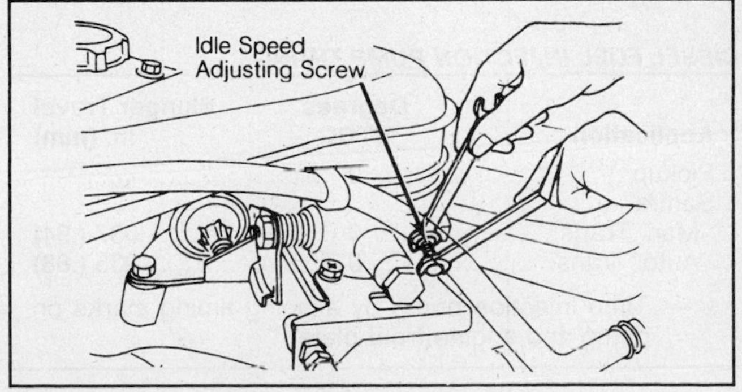
Idle Speed
Adjusting Screw

Tighten lock nut after adjustment.

TUNE-UP (Cont.)

2) On both models, race engine 2 or 3 times and check idle. Loosen idle adjusting screw lock nut. Start engine and adjust idle by turning idle adjusting screw. *See Fig. 2*. Tighten idle adjusting screw lock nut.

IDLE SPEED SPECIFICATIONS

Application	RPM
Pickup & Sentra	650-800

DASHPOT ADJUSTMENT

PICKUP

1) Warm up engine to normal operating temperature. Connect tachometer to engine.

2) Hold throttle lever to maintain specified adjustment speed. Adjust dashpot so that control lever tip contacts dashpot tip. *See Fig. 3*. Tighten dashpot lock nut.

Fig. 3: Dashpot Adjustment

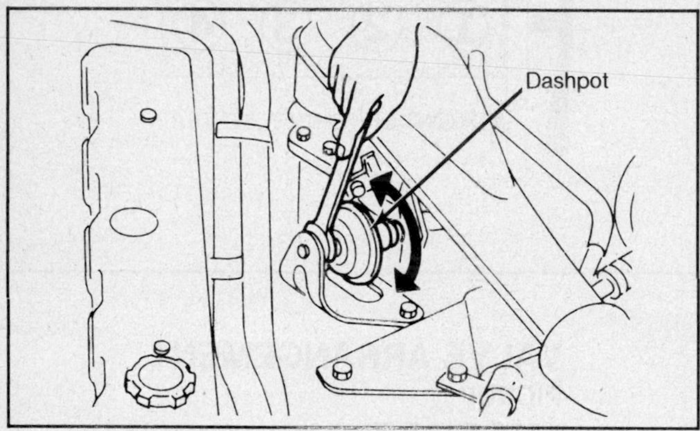
Dashpot

DASHPOT ADJUSTMENT SPECIFICATIONS

Application	RPM
Pickup	1280-1350

FUEL SYSTEM BLEEDING

PICKUP

1) Priming pump is located on side of injection pump housing. Bleed fuel system by removing primary pump cap and loosening air vent screw. Turn priming pump counterclockwise and move up and down until no air comes out air vent screws.

2) Tighten air vent screws. Push and turn priming pump clockwise. Install cap. Wipe off excess fuel. *See Fig. 4*.

Fig. 4: Bleeding Pickup Fuel System

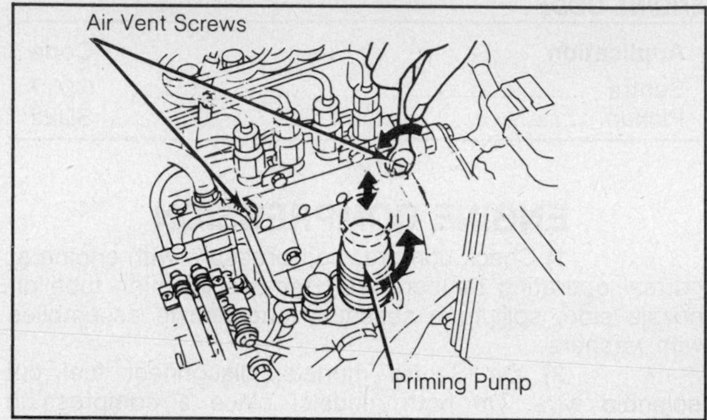
Air Vent Screws
Priming Pump

Loosen both air vent screws while bleeding.

SENTRA

1) Priming pump is located above the fuel filter. Loosen priming pump vent screw and pump until fuel comes out of vent. Disconnect fuel return hose on fuel line side and check for fuel flow.

2) If engine will not start, loosen injection tubes at nozzle side and crank engine until fuel overflows from injection tubes.

EMISSION CONTROL SYSTEMS

See Mitchell Manuals' Emission Control Manual.

GENERAL SERVICING

FUEL SYSTEMS

FUEL INJECTION

Pickup and Sentra use Kiki (Bosch) mechanical pump-type diesel fuel injection.

DIESEL FUEL INJECTION PUMP TIMING

Application	Degrees BTDC	Plunger Travel In. (mm)
Pickup [1]	0	....
Sentra		
Man. Trans.	0	.037 (.94)
Auto. Trans.	0	.035 (.88)

[1] — Time injection pump by aligning timing marks on pump and engine front plate.

ELECTRICAL

BATTERY

BATTERY SPECIFICATIONS

Application	Amp Hr. Rating
Pickup & Sentra	80

STARTER

Pickup and Sentra models are equipped with a Hitachi gear reduction, solenoid actuated starter using an overrunning clutch.

GENERAL SERVICING (Cont.)

STARTER SPECIFICATIONS

Application	Volts	Amps	Test RPM
Pickup	12	150	3500
Sentra	11	100	3900

ALTERNATOR

All models are equipped with Hitachi alternators using an integral IC voltage regulator.

ALTERNATOR SPECIFICATIONS

Application	Rated Amp Output
Pickup	50
Sentra	
Federal	50
California	60

ALTERNATOR REGULATOR

All models use a Hitachi IC voltage regulator that is integral with alternator.

REGULATOR OPERATING VOLTAGE @ 68°F (20°F)

Application	Voltage
All Models	14.4-15.0

SERVICE SPECIFICATIONS

FLUID CAPACITIES

Application	Quantity
Crankcase (Includes Filter)	
Pickup	5.4 qts. (5.1L)
Sentra	4.4 qts. (4.1L)
Cooling System (Includes Heater)	
Pickup	10.1 qts. (10.5L)
Sentra	7.4 qts. (7.0L)
Manual Transaxle (SAE 80W-90/API GL-4)	
4-Speed	4.9 qts. (2.3L)
5-Speed	5.8 qts. (2.7L)
Manual Transmission (SAE 80W-90/API GL-4)	
Pickup	4.3 pts. (2.0L)
Differential (SAE 80W-90/API GL-5)	
Rear Axle	2.6 pts. (1.3L)
Front Axle	2.1 pts. (1.0L)
Fuel Tank	
Pickup	
Short Bed [1]	
2WD	13.3 gals. (50.0L)
4WD	16.0 gals. (60.0L)
Long Bed	17.0 gals. (64.0L)
2WD	17.0 gals. (64.0L)
4WD	20.0 gals. (75.0L)
Sentra	13.3 gals. (50.0L)

[1] – Includes King Cab model.

BELT ADJUSTMENT

Application	[1] Deflection In. (mm)
All Belts	.4 (10)

[1] — Deflection is with 22 lbs. (10 kg) pressure applied midway on longest belt run.

REPLACEMENT INTERVALS

Component	Interval (Miles)
Engine Oil	3000
Oil Filter	6000
Fuel Filter	15,000
Air Filter	30,000

1983 Datsun/Nissan 6 Tune-Up

TUNE-UP

Maxima, 280ZX & 280ZX Turbo

ENGINE IDENTIFICATION

Engine serial number is stamped on right rear side of cylinder block at cylinder head contact surface. Serial number is preceded by engine model number.

ENGINE CODE

Application	Code
Maxima	L24E
280ZX	L28E
280ZX Turbo	L28ET

ENGINE COMPRESSION

Test compression with engine at normal operating temperature, spark plugs removed, all injector connectors and cold start valve disconnected, throttle valve fully open and engine at cranking speed (350 RPM).

COMPRESSION SPECIFICATIONS

Maxima	
Compression Ratio	8.9:1
Compresion Pressure	128 psi (9.0 kg/cm²)
280ZX	
Compression Ratio	8.8:1
Compression Pressure	171 psi (12.0 kg/cm²)
280ZX Turbo	
Compression Ratio	7.4:1
Compression Pressure	142 psi (10.0 kg/cm²)
Max. Variation Between Cylinders	20%

VALVE CLEARANCE

NOTE: **The L28ET (turbocharged) engine uses hydraulic lifters. No valve adjustment is necessary.**

1) Adjust valves with engine off and at normal operating temperature. Remove rocker cover. Set No. 1 cylinder to TDC of compression stroke. Adjust intake valves on cylinder No. 2, 4 and 6 and exhaust valves on cylinder No. 1, 4 and 5.

2) Rotate crankshaft 360° so that No. 1 cam lobe points down. Adjust intake valves on cylinder No. 1, 3, and 5 and exhaust valves on cylinder No. 2, 3 and 6.

VALVE CLEARANCE SPECIFICATIONS

Application	[1] In. (mm)
Intake	.010 (.25)
Exhaust	.012 (.30)

[1] — Adjust valves with engine hot.

VALVE ARRANGEMENT

E-I-I-E-I-E-E-I-E-I-I-E (Front-to-rear)

SPARK PLUGS

SPARK PLUG TYPE

Application	NGK No.
All Models	BPR6ES-11

SPARK PLUG SPECIFICATIONS

Application	Gap In. (mm)	Torque Ft. Lbs. (N.m)
All Models	.041 (1.05)	13 (17)

Fig. 1: Firing Order and Distributor Rotation

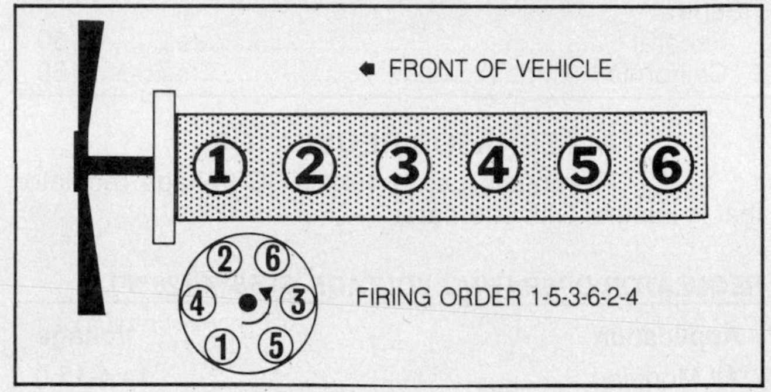
FRONT OF VEHICLE
1 2 3 4 5 6
2 6 4 3 1 5
FIRING ORDER 1-5-3-6-2-4

HIGH TENSION WIRE RESISTANCE

Remove distributor cap from distributor but do not disconnect high tension wires from cap. Disconnect high tension wires from spark plugs. Using an ohmmeter, check resistance from contact at spark plug end of wires to contact inside of distributor cap.

Resistance should be as specified. If resistance is higher, disconnect wire from cap and recheck resistance. Replace wire if resistance still exceeds specifications.

HIGH TENSION WIRE RESISTANCE

Application	Ohms
All Models	30,000

DISTRIBUTOR

All models use a single pick-up transistor ignition system with no point set. The only adjustment needed is for air gap between the reluctor and pick-up coil.

Measure air gap using non-magnetic feeler gauge. If gap is not to specifications, loosen pick-up coil screws and adjust gap.

DISTRIBUTOR PICK-UP COIL AIR GAP

Application	In. (mm)
All Models	.012-.020 (.3-.5)

TUNE-UP (Cont.)

IGNITION TIMING

1) With engine at normal operating temperature, connect a timing light and tachometer to engine. With Man. Trans. in neutral or Auto. Trans. in "D", check and, if necessary, adjust air gap and idle speed.

2) On all models except 280ZX Turbo, turn off engine and unplug harness connector from distributor. On all models, start engine and disconnect and plug distributor vacuum hose.

Fig. 2: Ignition Timing Mark Location

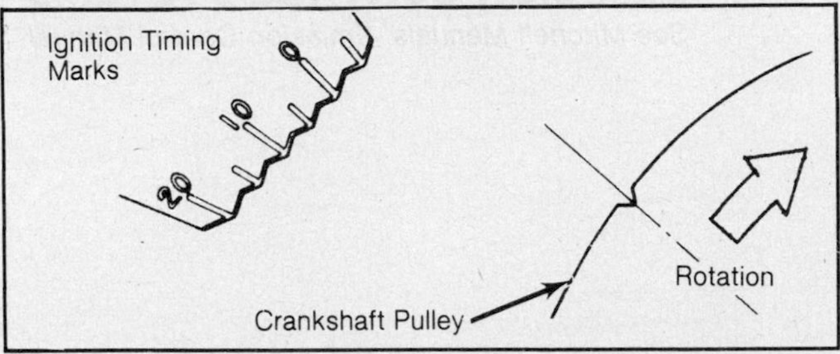

Ignition Timing Marks
10
20
Rotation
Crankshaft Pulley

3) Adjust timing by loosening set screw and rotating distributor until timing is set. Tighten set screw and recheck timing. Connect all hoses and wiring.

IGNITION TIMING (Degrees BTDC@RPM)

Application	Man. Trans.	[1] Auto. Trans.
Maxima	8@550-750	8@500-700
280ZX	8@550-750	8@550-750
280ZX Turbo	24@650-750	24@600-700

[1] — Transmission in "D"

IDLE SPEED & MIXTURE

NOTE: Regular idle speed and mixture adjustment are not necessary on 280ZX Turbo models.

Fig. 3: Adjusting Maxima and 280ZX Idle Speed

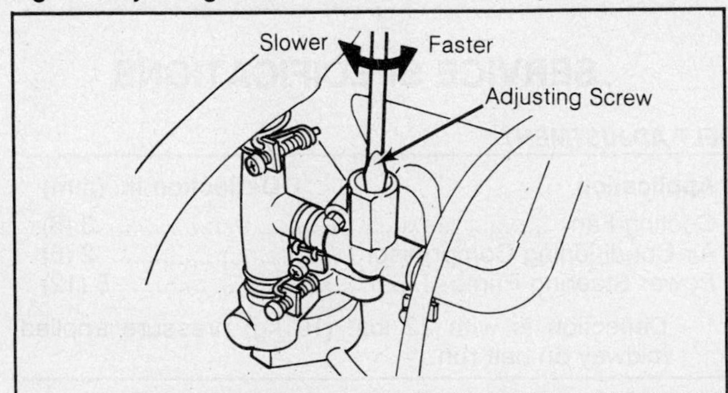

Slower
Faster
Adjusting Screw

IDLE SPEED

1) The following adjustment procedures should be performed with engine at operating temperature, A/C "OFF", ignition timing set to specifications and air cleaner installed. Set parking brake and on models with automatic transmission, place gear selector in "D" position.

2) Connect a tachometer to engine and run at 2000 RPM for about 5 minutes to stabilize operating condition. Accelerate engine 2-3 times and return to idle. Turn idle speed adjusting screw to obtain specified idle RPM.

IDLE SPEED SPECIFICATIONS

Application	RPM
Maxima	
Man. Trans.	5500-750
Auto. Trans.	[1] 550-750
280ZX	
Man. Trans.	550-750
Auto. Trans.	[1] 550-750
280ZX Turbo	
Man. Trans.	650-750
Auto. Trans.	[1] 600-700

[1] – Auto. Trans. in "Drive".

IDLE MIXTURE

NOTE: Mixture adjustment is not a part of normal tune-up procedure and should not be performed unless mixture control unit is replaced or vehicle fails emissions testing.

1) Adjust idle speed. Turn ignition switch off and disconnect throttle valve switch harness connector. Position harness connector at least 4" away from any secondary ignition wires.

2) Connect a jumper wire between throttle valve switch harness connector terminals No. 24 and No. 30.

NOTE: Connecting jumper wire between connector terminals signals the control unit of a full throttle condition which allows the idle mixture to run at full load enrichment. This step is necessary to enrichen the CO% level at idle enough to be read by the CO meter.

3) Disconnect and plug distributor vacuum hose. Disconnect air induction hose and canister purge hose at intake manifold. Plug air induction pipe and purge hose fitting on intake manifold.

Fig. 4: Idle Mixture Adjustment (CO%)

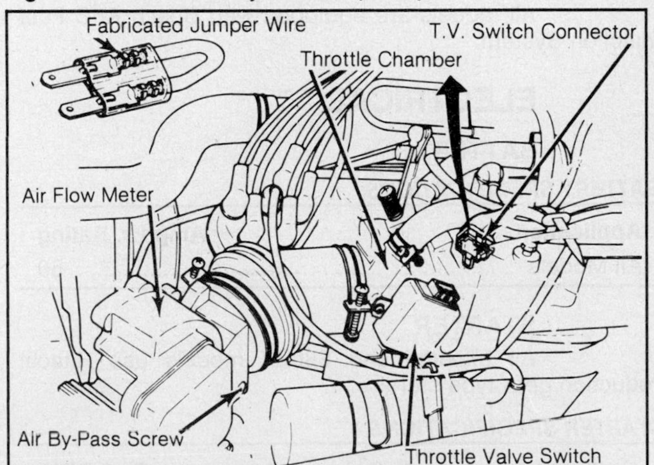

Fabricated Jumper Wire
T.V. Switch Connector
Throttle Chamber
Air Flow Meter
Air By-Pass Screw
Throttle Valve Switch

TUNE-UP (Cont.)

4) Start engine, accelerate 2-3 times and allow to idle for 1 minute. Check and, if necessary, adjust ignition timing. *See Fig. 2*. Insert CO meter probe into tail pipe at least 16".

5) With engine idling, check CO level. If necessary to adjust CO, remove air flow meter and drill a small hole in plug covering air by-pass screw. DO NOT allow drill to contact screw. Clean up metal shavings. Install self-tapping screw, and pull plug from bore.

6) Install air flow meter. Adjust CO level by turning air by-pass screw clockwise to richen mixture and counterclockwise to lean mixture. Reset idle speed to specified RPM.

7) Stop engine and remove jumper wire from throttle valve switch harness connector. Remove air flow meter. Tap new seal plug, with convex side up, into air by-pass screw bore. Install air flow meter. Reconnect harness and all hoses.

IDLE CO LEVEL SPECIFICATIONS

Application	Max. CO%
Maxima	2.7
280ZX	2.7

FUEL PUMP

FUEL PUMP PERFORMANCE

Application	Pressure psi (kg/cm²)
All Models	
At Idle	30 (2.1)
Wide Open Throttle	36.3 (2.6)

EMISSION CONTROL SYSTEMS

See Mitchell Manuals' Emission Control Manual.

GENERAL SERVICING

IGNITION

DISTRIBUTOR

Maxima and 280ZX are equipped with Hitachi Transistor Ignition System. The 280ZX Turbo distributor is part of the Electronic Concentrated Engine Control System.

IGNITION COIL RESISTANCE — Ohms @ 68°F (20°C)

Application	Primary	Secondary
280ZX & Maxima	.84-1.02	8200-12,400
280ZX Turbo	.63-.77	7000-8600

FUEL SYSTEMS

FUEL INJECTION

All models are equipped with Bosch AFC Fuel Injection System.

ELECTRICAL

BATTERY

BATTERY SPECIFICATIONS

Application	Amp Hr. Rating
All Models	60

STARTER

All Maxima and 280ZX models use Hitachi reduction gear type starters.

STARTER SPECIFICATIONS

Application	Volts	Amps	Test RPM
All Models	11	100	3900

ALTERNATORS

All models use a Hitachi alternator.

ALTERNATOR SPECIFICATIONS

Application	Rated Amp Output
Maxima & 280ZX	60
280ZX Turbo	70

ALTERNATOR REGULATOR

All models use a Hitachi alternator regulator.

REGULATOR OPERATING VOLTAGE @ 68°F (20°C)

Application	Voltage
All Models	14.5-15.0

SERVICE SPECIFICATIONS

BELT ADJUSTMENT

Application	[1] Deflection In. (mm)
Cooling Fan	.3 (8)
Air Conditioning Compressor	.2 (6)
Power Steering Pump	.5 (12)

[1] - Deflection is with 22 lbs. (10 kg) pressure applied midway on belt run.

REPLACEMENT INTERVALS

Component	Service Interval (Miles)
Oil Filter	7500
Air Filter	30,000
Spark Plugs	30,000

GENERAL SERVICING (Cont.)

FLUID CAPACITIES

Application	Quantity
Crankcase (Includes Filter)	
280ZX & 280ZX Turbo	5.1 qts. (4.9L)
Maxima	5.3 qts. (5.0L)
Cooling System (Includes Heater)	
280ZX & 280ZX Turbo	11.1 qts. (10.5L)
Maxima	11.6 qts. (11.0L)
Man. Trans. (API GL-5/SAE 80)	4.3 pts. (2.0L)
Auto. Trans. (Dexron)	
Maxima	7.4 qts. (7.0L)
280ZX	
Turbo	5.9 qts. (5.5L)
Non Turbo	6.5 qts. (6.1L)
Rear Axle (API GL-5/SAE 80-90)	
280ZX	
Model R180	2.1 pts. (1.0L)
Model R200	2.8 pts. (1.3L)
280ZX Turbo	2.8 pts. (1.3L)
Maxima	2.1 pts. (1.0L)
Fuel Tank	
280ZX & 280ZX Turbo	21.1 gals. (80.0L)
Maxima	
Sedan	16.4 gals. (62.0L)
Station Wagon	15.9 gals. (60.0L)

TUNE-UP

Maxima

ENGINE IDENTIFICATION

Engine number is stamped into right side of cylinder block near the dipstick. First 4 digits indicate engine code.

ENGINE CODE

Application	Code
All Models	LD28

ENGINE COMPRESSION

1) Warm engine to normal operating temperature. Stop engine. Remove spill tube assembly, injection tubes on nozzle side and nozzle assemblies taking care to remove nozzle washer with tweezers.

2) Install compression gauge adapter on cylinder head. Close bleeder screw on compression gauge. Crank engine and note compression reading as quickly as possible.

COMPRESSION SPECIFICATIONS

Min. Compression Pressure	356-455 psi (25-32 kg/cm²)
Max. Variation Between Cylinders	71 psi (5 kg/cm²)

VALVE CLEARANCE

1) Adjust valves with engine off and at normal operating temperature. Remove rocker cover. Place No. 1 cylinder on TDC of compression stroke. Adjust intake valves on cylinder No. 1, 2, and 4 and exhaust valves on cylinder No. 1, 3, and 5.

2) Rotate crankshaft so that No. 1 cam lobe points down. Adjust remaining valves. Install rocker cover.

VALVE CLEARANCE SPECIFICATIONS

Application	[1] In. (mm)
Intake	.010 (.25)
Exhaust	.012 (.30)

[1] — Adjust valves with engine hot.

VALVE ARRANGEMENT

E-I-I-E-I-E-E-I-E-I-I-E (Front-to-rear)

Fig. 1: Diesel Firing Order Illustration

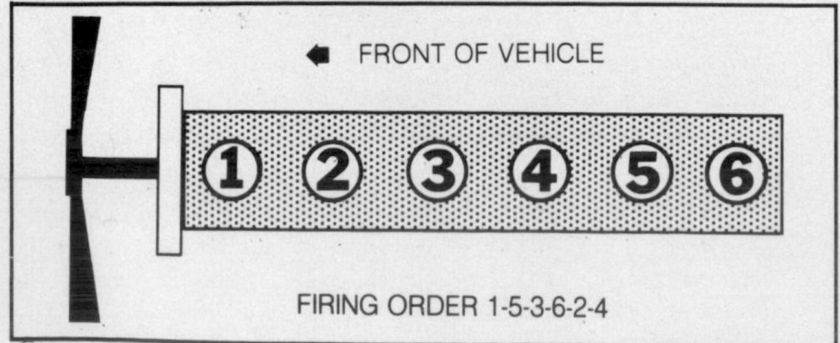
FRONT OF VEHICLE
1 2 3 4 5 6
FIRING ORDER 1-5-3-6-2-4

GLOW PLUGS

GLOW PLUG TORQUE SPECIFICATIONS

Application	Ft. Lbs. (N.m)
All Models	14-18 (20-25)

IDLE SPEED ADJUSTMENT

1) With engine at normal operating temperature and all electrical accessories off, attach tachometer. Start engine and run at 2000 RPM for 2 minutes. Return engine to idle for 1 minute. Check that idle speed is to specification (Auto. Trans. in "D").

2) If adjustment is required, loosen idle adjusting screw lock nut on idle adjusting screw. Turn screw until proper idle RPM is obtained. Tighten lock nut. *See Fig. 2.*

Fig. 2: Idle Adjusting Screw Location

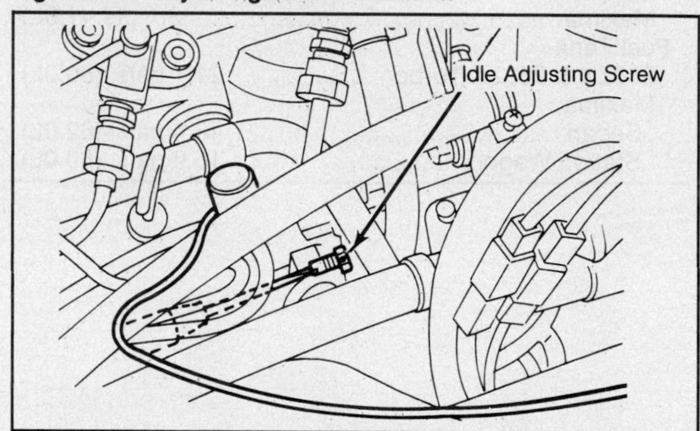
Idle Adjusting Screw

Tighten lock nut after adjusting.

3) With engine idling and air conditioning turned on (if so equipped), set fast idle speed. Locate Fast Idle Control Device (F.I.C.D.) diaphragm. Turn adjusting screw on accelerator drum until fast idle speed is to specification. *See Fig. 3.*

Fig. 3: Fast Idle Control Device

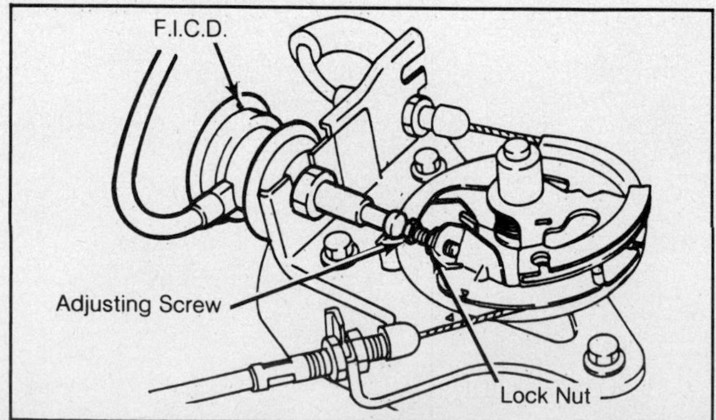
F.I.C.D.
Adjusting Screw
Lock Nut

Set fast idle with A/C on (if equipped).

IDLE SPEED SPECIFICATIONS

Application	Idle RPM	Fast Idle RPM
All Models	600-750	800

TUNE-UP (Cont.)

FUEL SYSTEM BLEEDING

1) Loosen priming pump vent screw on fuel filter. Pump the priming pump until fuel flows out of vent hole free of air bubbles. Tighten pump vent screw.

2) Disconnect fuel return hose and pump priming pump until fuel flows out of hose. Connect fuel return hose.

EMISSION CONTROL SYSTEMS

See Mitchell Manuals' Emission Control Manual.

GENERAL SERVICING

FUEL SYSTEMS

FUEL INJECTION

All models use Bosch mechanical pump-type diesel fuel injection.

DIESEL FUEL INJECTION TIMING

Application	Degrees BTDC	Plunger Travel In. (mm)
Maxima	0	.034 (.86)

ELECTRICAL

BATTERY SPECIFICATIONS

Application	Amp Hr. Rating
All Models	80

STARTER

All models are equipped with Hitachi starters.

STARTER SPECIFICATIONS

Application	Volts	Amps	Test RPM
All Models	11	140	3900

ALTERNATOR

All models are equipped with Hitachi alternators using an integral IC voltage regulator.

ALTERNATOR SPECIFICATIONS

Application	Rated Amp Output
All Models	60

ALTERNATOR REGULATOR

All models are equipped with Hitachi IC alternator regulators.

REGULATOR OPERATING VOLTAGE @ 68°F (20°C)

Application	Voltage
All Models	14.5-15.0

SERVICE SPECIFICATIONS

BELT ADJUSTMENT

Application	[1] Deflection In. (mm)
Alternator	.4 (10)
Air Conditioning Compressor	.4 (10)
Power Steering Pump	.3 (8)

[1] — Deflection is with 22 lbs. (10 kg) pressure applied midway on belt run.

REPLACEMENT INTERVALS

Component	Interval (Miles)
Oil & Filter	5000
Air Filter	30,000
Fuel Filter	30,000

FLUID CAPACITIES

Application	Quantity
Crankcase (Includes Filter)	6.5 qts. (6.2L)
Cooling System	11.0 qts. (10.4L)
Auto. Trans. (Dexron)	7.4 qts. (7.0L)
Differential (API GL-5/SAE 80-90)	2.1 pts. (1.0L)
Fuel Tank	
Sedan	16.4 gals. (62.0L)
Station Wagon	15.9 gals. (60.2L)

TUNE-UP

Accord, Civic, Prelude

ENGINE IDENTIFICATION

Engine serial number is stamped on a machined surface at right rear of engine, near the starter. Engine serial number is preceded by a 3-character code denoting engine type.

ENGINE CODE

Application	Code
Accord	EK1
Civic	
1.3L	EJ1
1.5L	EM1
Prelude	ES1

ENGINE COMPRESSION

Check compression with engine at normal operating temperature, air cleaner and spark plugs removed, throttle and choke valve wide open and engine at normal cranking speed (300 RPM). Crank engine at least 6 "puffs" per cylinder to determine engine compression.

COMPRESSION SPECIFICATIONS

Compression Ratio	
Accord	8.8:1
Civic	9.3:1
Prelude	9.4:1
Compression Pressure	
Accord	185 psi (13 kg/cm²)
Civic & Prelude	192 psi (13.5 kg/cm²)
Max. Variation Between Cylinders	28 psi (2 kg/cm²)

VALVE CLEARANCE

1) Adjust valves with engine cold. Remove valve cover. Place No. 1 piston at TDC to adjust valves of No. 1 cylinder.

2) On Civic and Accord models, the notched cutaway in the camshaft pulley should be at top, and TDC groove on back side of pulley should align with top of cylinder head surface. On Prelude, "UP" mark on camshaft pulley should be at top, and TDC grooves on back side of pulley should align with cylinder head surface.

3) Repeat procedure for remaining valves in firing order sequence. Rotate crankshaft 180° counterclockwise after each adjustment to position next piston in firing order for adjustment.

VALVE CLEARANCE SPECIFICATIONS

Application	In. (mm)
Accord & Prelude	
Intake & Auxiliary	.005-.007 (.12-.17)
Exhaust	.010-.012 (.25-.30)
Civic	
Intake & Auxiliary	.005-.007 (.12-.17)
Exhaust	.007-.009 (.17-.22)

VALVE ARRANGEMENT

ACCORD

Left Side — E-I-E-I-I-E-I-E (Front-to-rear)
Right Side — All Auxiliary Intake

CIVIC

Left Side — I-E-E-I-I-E-E-I (Front-to-rear)
Right Side — All Auxiliary Intake

PRELUDE

Left Side — All Intake
Right Side — Exhaust & Auxiliary Intake

SPARK PLUGS

SPARK PLUG TYPE

Application	Nippondenso	NGK
Accord	W21ESR-L11	BR6EB-L-11
Civic	W20ESR-L11	BR6EB-11
Prelude	W20EKR-S11	BUR6EB-11

SPARK PLUG SPECIFICATIONS

Application	Gap In. (mm)	Torque Ft. Lbs. (N.m)
All Models	.041 (1.0)	13 (18)

HIGH TENSION WIRE RESISTANCE

Carefully remove ends of wire from spark plug and distributor cap. Using an ohmmeter, check resistance of wire while gently twisting wire. If resistance exceeds 25,000 ohms replace wire.

DISTRIBUTOR

All Honda models are equipped with electronic breakerless ignition systems and no adjustments are necessary. Although Hitachi distributors are available on all 3 models, some Accord and Prelude models may have Toyo Denso systems.

Fig. 1: Accord & Civic Firing Order and Distributor Rotation

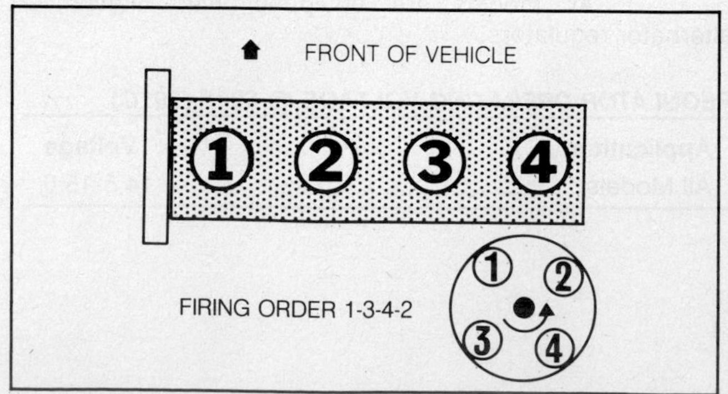
FRONT OF VEHICLE
1
2
3
4
FIRING ORDER 1-3-4-2
1
2
3
4

1983 Honda 4 Tune-Up

TUNE-UP (Cont.)

Fig. 2: Prelude Firing Order and Distributor Rotation

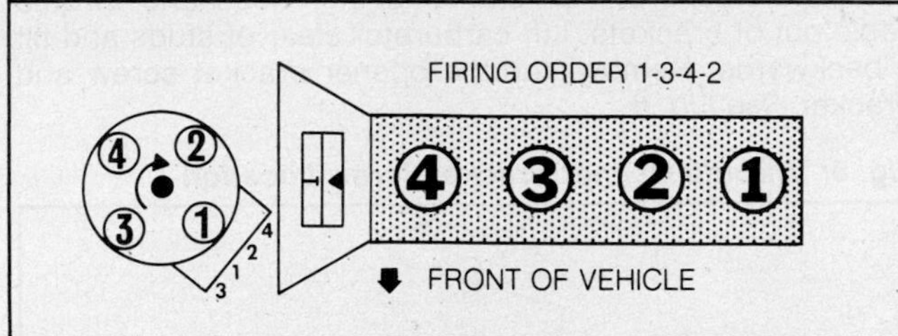
FIRING ORDER 1-3-4-2
4
2
3
1
4 3 2 1
FRONT OF VEHICLE

IGNITION TIMING

1) Remove rubber inspection cap from window on cylinder block. Attach timing light. Engine should be idling at normal operating temperature.

2) Timing is correct if specified mark on flywheel is aligned with index pointer on crankcase. To adjust, loosen distributor bolt and turn body counterclockwise to retard timing and clockwise to advance timing.

IGNITION TIMING SPECIFICATIONS (Degrees BTDC@RPM)

Application	Man. Trans.	Auto. Trans.
Accord		
California	12°@750	16°@700
Federal & Hi. Alt.	16°@750	16°@700
Civic		
1.3L	[1] 20°@700	
1.5L	18°@700	18°@700
Prelude		
Calif.	12°@800	12°@750
Federal	10°@800	12°@750

[1] – With 4-speed. With 5-speed, 18°BTDC@650.

Fig. 3: Prelude Timing Marks

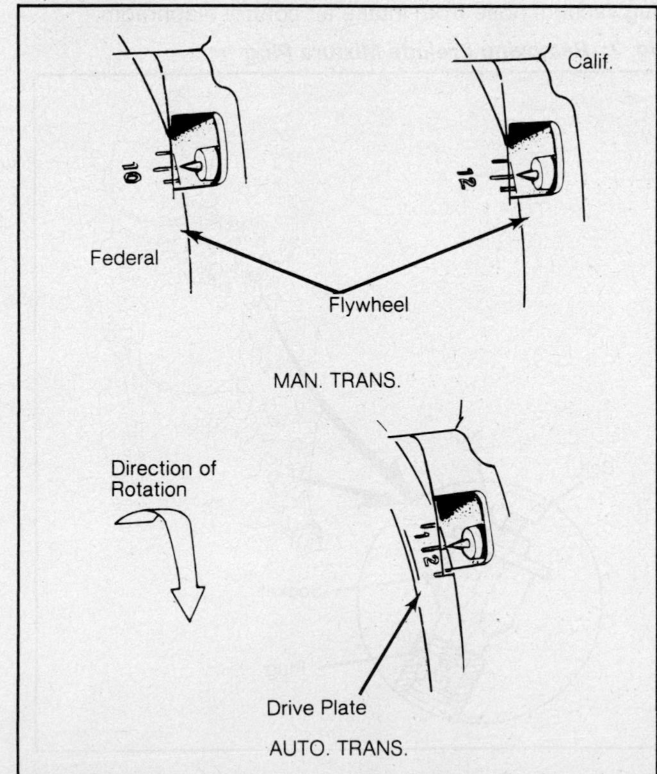
Calif.
10
12
Federal
Flywheel
MAN. TRANS.
Direction of Rotation
Drive Plate
AUTO. TRANS.

Fig. 4: Accord Timing Marks

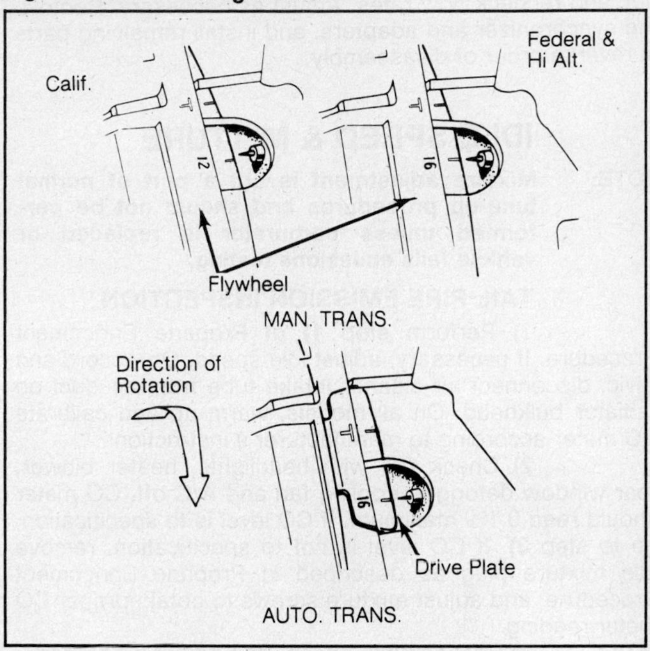
Calif.
Federal & Hi Alt.
12
16
Flywheel
MAN. TRANS.
Direction of Rotation
16
Drive Plate
AUTO. TRANS.

Fig. 5: Civic Timing Marks

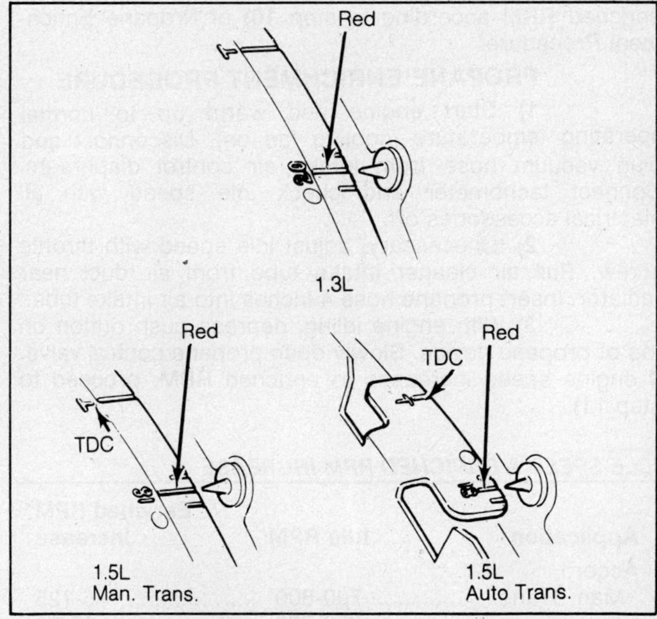
Red
1.3L
Red
Red
TDC
TDC
1.5L
Man. Trans.
1.5L
Auto Trans.

CARBURETOR SYNCHRONIZATION

PRELUDE

1) Remove the air cleaner cover and element. Remove air intake screens and air intake flanges. Install synchronization adapters (0750-SB00000). Connect a tachometer. Start the engine and allow it to reach operating temperature. Measure the flow rate through both adapters using the carburetor synchronizer.

2) If flow rates are different, loosen the adjusting screw lock nut, and adjust as necessary. If flow rates can't be balanced, check for air leaks or carbon

TUNE-UP (Cont.)

build-up on throttle valve. Tighten adjusting screw lock nut, and recheck flow rates. Adjust as necessary. Remove the synchronizer and adapters, and install remaining parts in reverse order of disassembly.

IDLE SPEED & MIXTURE

NOTE: Mixture adjustment is not a part of normal tune-up procedures and should not be performed unless carburetor is replaced or vehicle fails emissions testing.

TAIL PIPE EMISSION INSPECTION

1) Perform step **1)** of Propane Enrichment Procedure. If necessary, adjust idle speed. On Accord and Civic, disconnect air cleaner intake tube from air duct on radiator bulkhead. On all models, warm up and calibrate CO meter according to manufacturer's instructions.

2) Check CO with headlights, heater blower, rear window defogger, cooling fan and A/C off. CO meter should read 0.1% maximum. If CO level is to specification, go to step **3)**. If CO level is not to specification, remove idle mixture plug as described in Propane Enrichment Procedure, and adjust mixture screws to obtain proper CO meter reading.

3) Recheck idle speed, and adjust if necessary by turning throttle stop screw. Then recheck CO level and adjust if necessary. On Prelude, check and adjust propane enriched RPM according to step **10)** of Propane Enrichment Procedure.

PROPANE ENRICHMENT PROCEDURE

1) Start engine and warm up to normal operating temperature (cooling fan on). Disconnect and plug vacuum hose from intake air control diaphragm. Connect tachometer and check idle speed with all electrical accessories off.

2) If necessary, adjust idle speed with throttle screw. Pull air cleaner intake tube from air duct near radiator. Insert propane hose 4 inches into air intake tube.

3) With engine idling, depress push button on top of propane device. Slowly open propane control valve. If engine speed increases to enriched RPM, proceed to step **11)**.

IDLE SPEED & ENRICHED RPM INCREASE

Application	Idle RPM	Enriched RPM Increase
Accord		
Man. Trans.	700-800	75-125
Auto. Trans.	650-750	30-70
Civic		
Man. Trans.		
1.3L 4-Speed	650-750	85-135
1.3L 5-Speed	600-700	85-135
1.5L	650-750	75-125
Auto. Trans.	650-750	30-70
Prelude		
Man. Trans.	750-850	75-125
Auto. Trans.	700-800	10-50

4) If engine speed does not increase to enriched RPM, remove air cleaner. Disconnect vacuum hose to fast idle unloader. Remove bolts holding throttle opener bracket to rear edge of carburetor.

5) On Accord and Civic, remove carburetor nuts and washers. Pull brake booster hose and throttle cable out of brackets. Lift carburetor clear of studs and tilt it backwards. Remove throttle opener bracket screw and bracket. *See Fig. 6.*

Fig. 6: Throttle Opener Bracket Screw Location

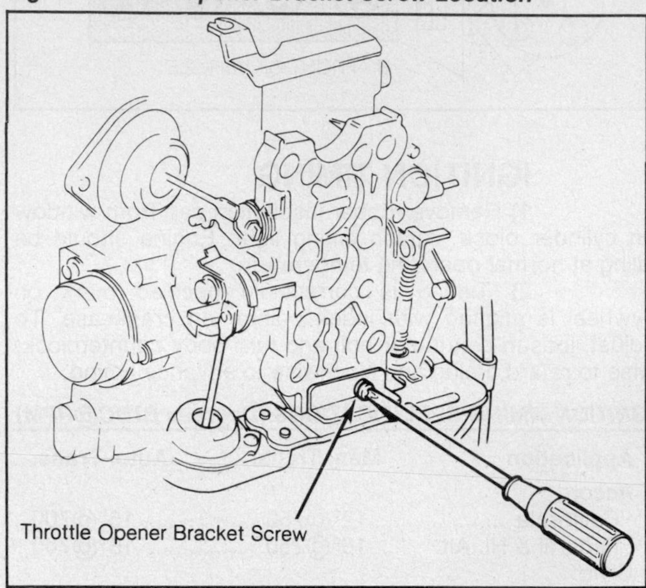
Throttle Opener Bracket Screw

Location is for Accord and Civic models only.

6) Remove mixture adjusting screw hole cap from throttle opener bracket. Reinstall bracket. Using new "O" rings on insulator and new gaskets for heat shield, reinstall carburetor.

7) Reconnect vacuum hose to fast idle unloader. Install air cleaner. Start engine and warm up to normal operating temperature (cooling fan on). Disconnect and plug vacuum hose from intake air control diaphragm.

Fig. 7: Removing Prelude Mixture Plug

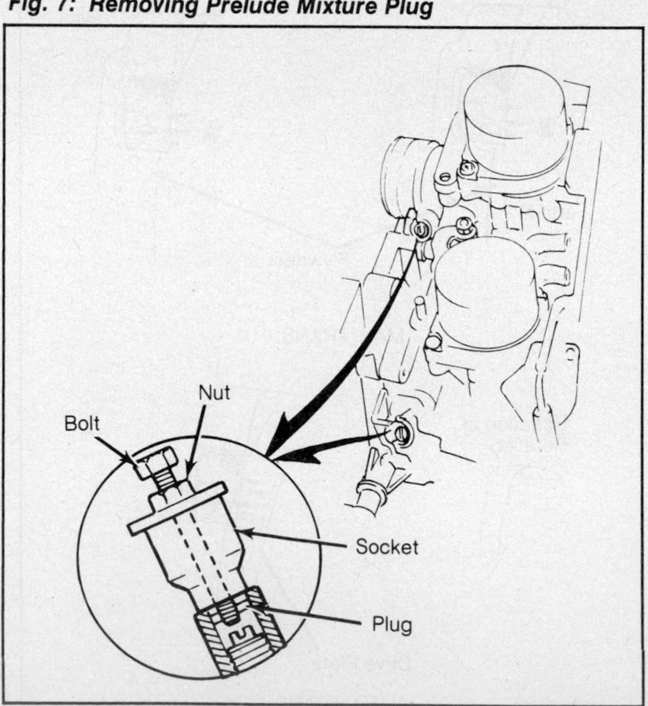
Nut
Bolt
Socket
Plug

TUNE-UP (Cont.)

8) On Prelude, disconnect all vacuum hoses and lines from carburetors. Disconnect throttle cable and vacuum hose from throttle opener diaphragm. Disconnect automatic choke lead. Drain coolant and disconnect hoses. Remove carburetors.

9) Place a drill stop on a 4 mm drill bit (5/32" from end). Drill through center of mixture screw hole plug. Tap the hole with a 5 mm tap and blow out metal chips. Make a plug puller using a 5 mm bolt, 1/4" drive socket and flat washer. Turn the nut to remove plug. *See Fig. 7.* Reinstall carburetors in reverse order of removal and replace coolant.

10) On all models, reinstall propane enrichment kit and recheck maximum propane enriched RPM. If enriched RPM is low, lean out mixture. If high, enrich mixture. Turn mixture screw clockwise to increase RPM; counterclockwise to lower RPM.

11) Run engine at 2500 RPM for 10 seconds to stabilize mixture. Close propane control valve and recheck idle speed. Repeat procedure until idle RPM and enriched RPM are correct. Remove propane enrichment kit. Reconnect air cleaner intake tube.

COLD (FAST) IDLE ADJUSTMENT

ACCORD & CIVIC

1) With engine at normal operating temperature, connect tachometer to engine. Disconnect and plug inside vacuum hose to fast idle unloader.

2) With engine off, hold choke valve closed. Open and close throttle to engage fast idle cam. Start engine, run 1 minute, and check idle RPM. If not within specifications, adjust by turning fast idle screw.

PRELUDE

1) With engine at operating temperature, connect tachometer to engine. Remove "E" clip and flat washer from wax linkage. Slide out linkage until its tab is clear of the fast idle cam. Be careful not to bend linkage.

2) Hold throttle open and turn fast idle cam counterclockwise until fast idle lever is aligned on third cam step. Without opening the throttle, start the engine. Check the idle speed. Adjust idle speed, if necessary, by turning fast idle screw.

3) Stop engine and reconnect the thermowax linkage. Start engine and check that idle speed decreases as engine speed increases. If not, spray linkage with carburetor cleaner, and check for damaged or stuck parts.

FAST IDLE SPEED

Application	Fast Idle RPM
Accord	2000-3000
Civic	3000
Prelude	1500-2500

FUEL PUMP

FUEL PUMP PERFORMANCE

Application	Pressure psi (kg/cm²)	Volume in 30 sec. Pints (Liters)
Accord & Prelude	2-3 (.14-.20)	.7 (.34)
Civic	2-3 (.14-.21)	.5 (.2)

EMISSION CONTROL SYSTEMS

See Mitchell Manuals' Emission Control Manual.

GENERAL SERVICING

IGNITION

DISTRIBUTOR

All Civic models are equipped with Hitachi electronic ignition systems. Accord and Prelude models may be fitted with either Hitachi or Toyo Denso electronic ignition systems.

IGNITION COIL

IGNITION COIL RESISTANCE — Ohms @ 68°F (20°C)

Application	Primary	Secondary
Accord & Prelude	1.06-1.24	7400-11,000
Civic	1.00-1.30	7400-11,000

FUEL SYSTEM

CARBURETORS

Application	Model
Accord & Civic	Keihin 2-Bbl.
Prelude	Two Synchronized Keihin 1-Bbls.

ELECTRICAL

BATTERY

BATTERY SPECIFICATIONS

Application	Amp Hr. Rating
Accord & Civic	47
Prelude	50

ALTERNATOR

All models use Nippondenso alternators.

ALTERNATOR SPECIFICATIONS

Application	Rated Amp Output
Accord & Prelude	60
Civic	45

ALTERNATOR REGULATOR

Nippondenso alternator regulators are used on all models.

GENERAL SERVICING (Cont.)

REGULATOR OPERATING VOLTAGE @ 68°F (20°C)

Application	Voltage
Accord & Prelude	14.5-15.1
Civic	13.5-14.5

STARTER

Civic Calif. models use Hitachi and Nippondenso direct drive starters. Other Civic models, all Prelude models, and some Accord models use Nippondenso reduction drive starters. Some Accord models are equipped with Mitsuba Denki direct drive starters.

STARTER SPECIFICATIONS

Application	Volts	Amps	Test RPM
Accord & Prelude	11.5	90	3500
Civic			
Calif.			
Nippondenso	11.0	50	5000
Hitachi	11.0	70	6000
All Others	11.5	90	3000

SERVICE SPECIFICATIONS

REPLACEMENT INTERVALS

Component	Interval (Miles)
Oil Filter	7500
Air Filter	30,000
Fuel Filters	60,000
Spark Plugs	30,000

FLUID CAPACITIES

Application	Quantity
Crankcase (Includes Filter)	3.7 qts. (3.5L)
Cooling System	
Accord	6.3 qts. (6.0L)
Civic	
1.3L	4.9 qts. (4.6L)
1.5L	5.7 qts. (5.4L)
Prelude	
With Man. Transaxle	7.2 qts. (6.8L)
With Auto. Transaxle	7.9 qts. (7.5L)
Man. Transaxle (SAE 10W-40)	5.3 pts. (2.5L)
Auto. Transaxle (Dexron)	
Accord	
Drain & Refill	5.9 pts. (2.8L)
Overhaul	11.8 pts. (5.6L)
Civic	
Drain & Refill	5.3 pts. (2.5L)
Overhaul	10.4 pts. (4.9L)
Prelude	
Drain & Refill	5.9 pts. (2.8L)
Overhaul	12.3 pts. (5.8L)
Fuel Tank	
Accord & Prelude	15.9 gals. (60.0L)
Civic	
Hatchback & Wagon	10.8 gals. (41.0L)
Sedan	12.2 gals. (46.0L)

BELT ADJUSTMENT

Application	[1] Deflection In. (mm)
Accord	
Alternator Belt	.6-.7 (14-17)
Air Conditioning Belt	.5-.6 (12-16)
Power Steering Belt	.7-.9 (17-22)
Civic	
Alternator Belt	.5-.7 (12-17)
Air Conditioning Belt	.3-.4 (8-10)
Prelude	
Alternator Belt	.3-.4 (7-10)
Air Conditioning Belt	.4-.5 (10-12)
Power Steering Belt	.7-.9 (17-22)

[1] — 22 Lbs. (10 kg) pressure applied midway between pulleys on longest belt run.

TUNE-UP

I-Mark, Impulse & P'UP

ENGINE IDENTIFICATION

I-Mark and Impulse engine serial numbers are stamped on the top right front corner of the cylinder block. P'UP engine serial number is stamped on the right side of the cylinder block near the distributor.

ENGINE CODE

Application	Code
I-Mark 1.8L	G180Z
P'UP 1.9L	G200Z
Impulse 1.9L	G200Z

ENGINE COMPRESSION

Test compression with engine at normal operating temperature, spark plugs removed, throttle valve wide open and engine at cranking speed (300 RPM).

COMPRESSION SPECIFICATIONS

Compression Ratio	
I-Mark	8.5:1
Impulse	9.3:1
P'UP	8.4:1
Compression Pressure	
New Engine	
I-Mark & P'UP	170 psi (12 kg/cm²)
Impulse	178 psi (12.5 kg/cm²)
Minimum	
I-Mark & P'UP	120 psi (8.4 kg/cm²)
Impulse	125 psi (8.8 kg/cm²)
Maximum Variation Between Cylinders	
I-Mark & P'UP	9 psi (0.6 kg/cm²)
Impulse	7 psi (0.5 kg/cm²)

VALVE CLEARANCE

NOTE: Before adjusting valve clearance, ensure rocker arm shaft brackets are properly tightened to 16 ft. lbs. (22 N.m).

1) Adjust valves every 15,000 miles with engine cold. Measure valve clearance between rocker arm and valve stem.

2) Position No. 1 piston on TDC of compression stroke and adjust valves listed in table. Turn crankshaft one full turn (No. 4 piston on TDC of compression stroke) to adjust remaining valves.

VALVE ADJUSTMENT SEQUENCE

Piston On TDC	Adjust Int. Nos.	Adjust Exh. Nos.
1	1, 2	1, 3
4	3, 4	2, 4

VALVE CLEARANCE SPECIFICATIONS

Application	In. (mm)
Intake (Cold)	.006 (.15)
Exhaust (Cold)	.010 (.25)

VALVE ARRANGEMENT

Right Side — All Intake
Left Side — All Exhaust

SPARK PLUGS

SPARK PLUG TYPE

Application	NGK No.
All Models	BPR6ES11

SPARK PLUG SPECIFICATIONS

Application	Gap In. (mm)	Torque Ft. Lbs. (N.m)
All Models	.040 (1.05)	18-25 (24-34)

HIGH TENSION WIRE RESISTANCE

Carefully remove high tension wire from spark plugs and from distributor cap. Using an ohmmeter, check resistance of wire while gently twisting wire. If resistance is not within specifications, or fluctuates from infinity to any value, replace wire.

HIGH TENSION WIRE RESISTANCE

Application	Ohms
All Models	31,500-73,500 per foot

DISTRIBUTOR

I-Mark and P'UP are equipped with a Nippondenso electronic distributor. Impulse models are equipped with I-TEC electronic ignition system.

Fig. 1: Firing Order and Distributor Rotation

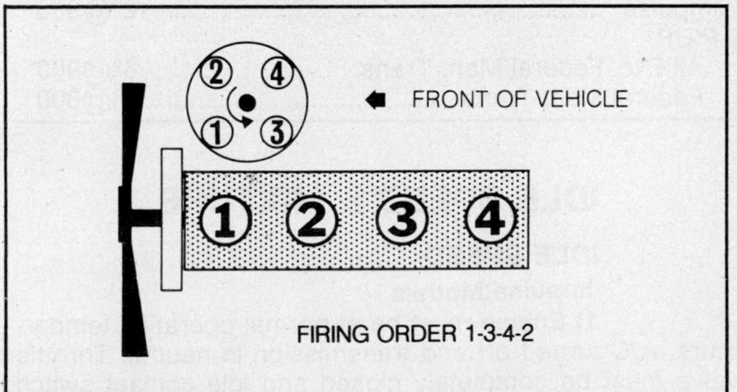
2
4
1
3
FRONT OF VEHICLE
1
2
3
4
FIRING ORDER 1-3-4-2

1983 Isuzu 4 Tune-Up

TUNE-UP (Cont.)

The Impulse's photoelectric type distributor has a built-in crank angle sensor, which detects engine speed and position of piston in each cylinder. The Impulse distributor is not serviceable.

DISTRIBUTOR PICK-UP AIR GAP

Application	In (mm.)
I-Mark & P'UP	.008-.016 (.2-.4)

IGNITION TIMING

1) Ensure engine is warmed up to normal operating temperature, A/C is turned off and transmission is in "Neutral". Connect timing light to either No. 1 or No. 4 cylinder.

3) On Impulse models, throttle valve must be completely closed and idle contact on. Harness of pressure regulator vacuum switching valve must be disconnected.

3) On all models, loosen distributor clamping bolts and turn distributor in either direction until timing is within specifications. *See Fig. 2.*

Fig. 2: Isuzu Timing Mark Location

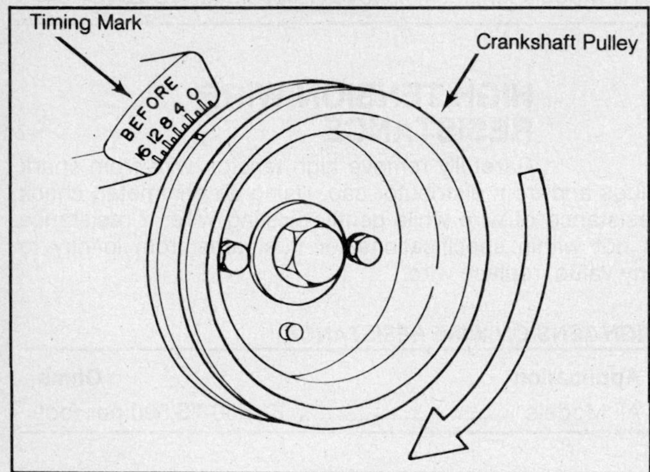
Timing Mark
Crankshaft Pulley
BEFORE
16 12 8 4 0

Adjust ignition timing with engine at proper idle RPM.

IGNITION TIMING (Degrees BTDC@RPM)

Application	Setting
I-Mark	6°@900
Impulse	12°@900
P'UP	
All Exc. Federal Man. Trans.	6°@900
Federal Man. Trans.	6°@800

IDLE SPEED & MIXTURE

IDLE SPEED

Impulse Models

1) Engine must be at normal operating temperature, A/C turned off and transmission in neutral. Throttle valve must be completely closed and idle contact switch closed. Disconnect pressure regulator vacuum switching valve harness.

CAUTION: Check and clean idle ports as restrictions in the port cause fluctuations in idle speed.

2) Adjust idle speed with the idle adjust screw on the throttle body. After adjustment, connect the vacuum switching valve harness. *See Fig. 3.*

Fig. 3: Adjusting Impulse Idle Speed

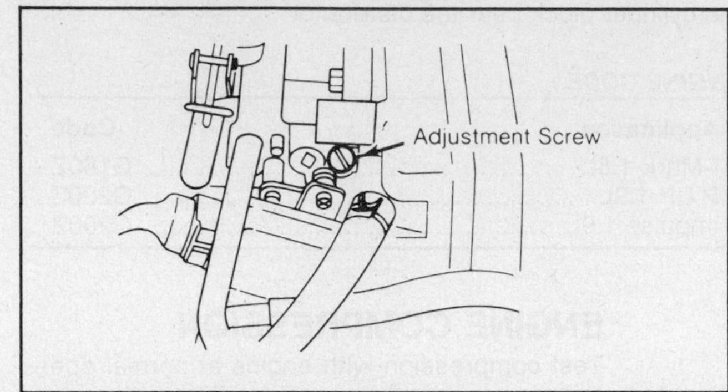
Adjustment Screw

Ensure throttle valve is fully closed.

I-Mark & P'UP Models

1) Set parking brake and block drive wheels. Place transmission in Neutral. Be sure engine is at operating temperature, choke open, A/C off (if equipped) and air cleaner installed.

2) Disconnect and plug distributor vacuum hose, canister purge line and EGR control hose. Disable idle compensator vacuum line by bending rubber hose.

3) Turn throttle (idle) adjusting screw until specified idle RPM is reached. If equipped with A/C, turn to maximum cooling and high blower.

4) Open throttle about one-third and let it close to allow speed-up solenoid to reach full travel. Turn solenoid speed screw to reach 850-950 RPM.

IDLE SPEED SPECIFICATIONS

Application	Idle RPM
I-Mark	850-950
Impulse	850-950
P'UP	
All Exc. Fed. Man. Trans.	850-950
Fed. Man. Trans.	750-850

IDLE MIXTURE

NOTE: Mixture adjustment is NOT a part of a normal tune-up procedure and should not be performed unless carburetor is overhauled, fuel injection system components are replaced, or vehicle fails emissions testing.

Impulse Models

Idle mixture is controlled electronically by the I-TEC fuel injection system. No adjustments are possible.

I-Mark & California P'UP Models

1) Set parking brake and block drive wheels. Place transmission in Neutral. Remove carburetor from vehicle. Insert a screwdriver into the slit on the carburetor lower flange and remove idle mixture screw plug. *See Fig. 4.* Reinstall carburetor.

2) Disconnect and plug distributor vacuum hose, canister purge line and EGR vacuum line. Disable

TUNE-UP (Cont.)

Fig. 4: Removing Mixture Screw Plug

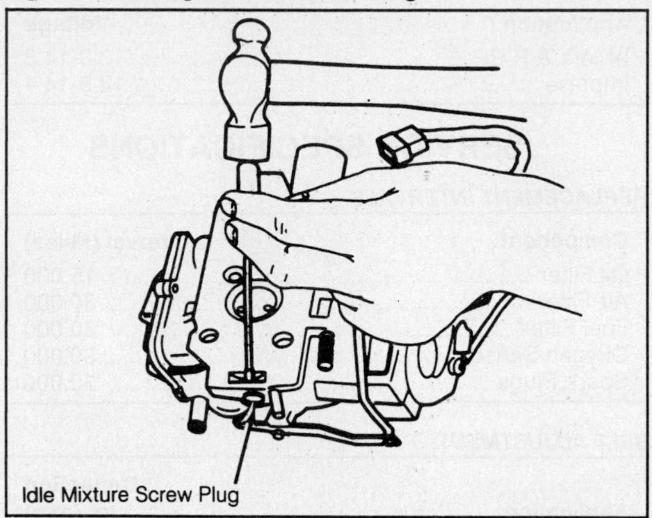
Idle Mixture Screw Plug

Carefully remove plug from recess in throttle body to gain access to mixture screw.

idle compensator vacuum line by pinching rubber hose. With engine at normal operating temperature, choke open and A/C off (if equipped), adjust idle speed.

3) Connect positive lead of dwell meter or duty meter to duty monitor and ground negative terminal. Turn idle mixture screw all the way in and then back out 1 1/2 turns.

4) Adjust throttle adjusting screw to 850-950 RPM. Check meter and ensure that dwell is varying. Adjust setting of idle mixture screw to obtain an average dwell or duty as specified.

5) Reset throttle adjusting screw. Put idle mixture screw plug back in place. If equipped with A/C, follow steps **3)** and **4)** of Idle Speed adjustment.

I-MARK & CALIFORNIA P'UP DWELL METER SETTING

Application	Setting
Dwell Meter	36°
Duty Meter	40%

Federal P'UP Models

1) Set parking brake and block drive wheels. Place transmission in Neutral. Remove carburetor. Insert screwdriver in slit on carburetor lower flange and remove idle mixture screw plug. *See Fig. 4.* Reinstall carburetor.

2) Disconnect and plug distributor vacuum hose, canister purge line and EGR vacuum line. Disable idle compensator vacuum line by bending rubber hose. With engine at normal operating temperature, choke open and A/C off (if equipped), adjust idle speed.

3) Adjust throttle screw to 750-850 RPM on manual transmissions or 850-950 RPM on automatic transmissions.

4) Turn idle mixture screw all the way in and then back out 3 turns. Adjust throttle screw to 800 RPM on manual transmissions and 900 RPM on automatic transmissions.

5) Adjust idle mixture screw to achieve maximum speed. Reset throttle adjusting screw to 850 RPM on manual transmissions and 950 RPM on automatic transmissions.

6) Turn idle mixture adjusting screw clockwise (lean) until engine speed is down to 750-850 RPM on manual transmissions and 850-950 RPM on automatic transmissions.

7) Replace idle mixture screw plug. If equipped with A/C, follow steps **3)** and **4)** of Idle Speed procedures.

COLD (FAST) IDLE SPEED

Impulse Models

Engine fast idle speed must be slightly higher than normal immediately after starting engine. Idle speed should normalize as engine reaches operating temperature. No adjustment is possible.

I-Mark & P'UP Models

1) Fast idle speed is determined by opening angle of throttle valve on carburetor. It is not set by adjusting engine speed.

2) Remove carburetor from engine. Turn throttle stop screw all the way in before measuring clearance. Adjust throttle valve opening with fast idle screw on first step of fast idle cam.

3) Close choke valve completely and measure primary throttle valve opening angle. Adjust opening angle with fast idle adjusting screw. Install carburetor.

4) With engine at normal operating temperature, distributor, idle compensator and EGR valve vacuum hoses disconnected and plugged, fast idle speed should be about 3200 RPM.

FAST IDLE SPEED SPECIFICATIONS

Application	Throttle Valve Opening Angle
I-Mark & P'UP	
Man. Trans.	15-17°
Auto. Trans.	17-19°

HIGH ALTITUDE ADJUSTMENT

Federal vehicles, not originally designed for high altitude applications, can be adjusted to operate at high altitudes by performing the following procedure:

1) Engine timing should be advanced up to 4° from the recommended setting. However, timing should not be advanced if spark knock occurs at high altitude.

2) Engine speeds should be adjusted to the specification shown on the emission control decal.

FUEL PUMP PRESSURE

FUEL PUMP PERFORMANCE

Application	Pressure psi (kg/cm²)
I-Mark & P'UP	3.56 (.25)
Impulse [1]	28.4 (2.0)

[1] — Pressure regulator vacuum hose connected and engine at 900 RPM.

EMISSION CONTROL SYSTEMS

See Mitchell Manuals' Emission Control Manual.

GENERAL SERVICING

IGNITION

DISTRIBUTOR

I-Mark and P'UP are equipped with a Nippondenso electronic distributor. Impulse is equipped with I-TEC electronic photoelectric type distributor.

DISTRIBUTOR PICK-UP COIL RESISTANCE

Application	(Ohms)
I-Mark & P'UP	140-180

IGNITION COIL

IGNITION COIL RESISTANCE — Ohms @ 68°F (20°C)

Application	Primary	Secondary
All Models	1.13-1.53	10,200-13,800

FUEL SYSTEM

CARBURETOR

CARBURETOR SPECIFICATIONS

Application	Model
I-Mark & P'UP	Hitachi DCH 340 2-Bbl.

FUEL INJECTION

Impulse uses the I-TEC Fuel Injection system.

ELECTRICAL

STARTER

All models are equipped with Hitachi starters.

STARTER SPECIFICATIONS

Application	Volts	Amps	Test RPM
All Models	12	70	6000

ALTERNATOR

All models use Hitachi alternators.

ALTERNATOR SPECIFICATIONS

Application	Rated Amp Output
I-Mark & P'UP	50
Impulse	60

BATTERY

BATTERY SPECIFICATIONS

Application	Amp. Hr. Rating
All Models	50

ALTERNATOR REGULATOR

All models use Hitachi alternator regulators.

REGULATOR OPERATING VOLTAGE @ 68°F (20°C)

Application	Voltage
I-Mark & P'UP	13.8-14.8
Impulse	13.8-14.4

SERVICE SPECIFICATIONS

REPLACEMENT INTERVALS

Component	Interval (Miles)
Oil Filter	15,000
Air Filter	30,000
Fuel Filter	30,000
Oxygen Sensor	30,000
Spark Plugs	30,000

BELT ADJUSTMENT

Application	[1] Deflection In. (mm)
All Belts	.4 (10)

[1] - Moderate hand pressure applied midway between pulleys on longest belt run.

FLUID CAPACITIES

Application	Quantity
Crankcase (Includes Filter)	
I-Mark	3.8 qts. (3.6L)
Impulse	3.8 qts. (3.6L)
P'UP	3.8 qts. (3.6L)
Cooling System	
I-Mark	
Man. Trans.	7.2 qts. (6.8L)
Auto. Trans.	7.1 qts. (6.7L)
Impulse	
Man. Trans.	6.7 qts. (6.3L)
Auto. Trans.	6.6 qts. (6.2L)
P'UP	
Man. Trans.	8.4 qts. (8.0L)
Auto. Trans.	8.2 qts. (7.8L)
Auto. Trans. (Dexron II)	
I-Mark & Impulse	6.7 qts. (6.3L)
P'UP	6.4 qts. (6.0L)
Man. Trans. (SAE 30 [1])	
4-Speed	
I-Mark & P'UP	2.7 pts. (1.3L)
5-Speed	
All Models	3.3 pts. (1.6L)
Rear Axle (SAE 90)	
I-Mark	2.5 pts. (1.2L)
Impulse	2.1 pts. (1.0L)
P'UP	2.7 pts. (1.3L)
Front Axle (SAE 90)	
P'UP	1.7 pts. (0.8L)
Transfer Case (SAE 30)	
P'UP	5.2 pts. (2.5L)
Fuel Tank	
I-Mark	13.7 gals. (52.0L)
Impulse	15.0 gals. (57.0L)
P'UP	
Long Bed	19.1 gals. (72.6L)
All Others	13.2 gals. (50.2L)

[1] – Impulse uses SAE 40.

TUNE-UP

I-Mark, P'UP

ENGINE IDENTIFICATION

The first 4 digits of engine serial number are used to identify engine models. I-Mark engine serial number is stamped on left rear corner of the cylinder block. P'UP engine serial number is stamped on front side of the cylinder block near the water pump.

ENGINE CODE

Application	Code
I-Mark (1.8L)	4FBI
P'UP (2.2L)	C223

ENGINE COMPRESSION

Warm engine to normal operating temperature. Remove sensing resistor, glow plug connectors, glow plugs and fuel cut solenoid connector. Disconnect fusible link wire of "Quick Start" system at harness connector.

Install compression gauge adapter (J-29762) and compression gauge. Operate starter and read compression at 200 RPM.

COMPRESSION SPECIFICATIONS

Compression Ratio	
I-Mark	22.0:1
P'UP	21.0:1
Compression Pressure	
Normal (New Engine)	441 psi (31 kg/cm²)
Minimum	
I-Mark	370 psi (26 kg/cm²)
P'UP	398 psi (28 kg/cm²)

VALVE CLEARANCE

CAUTION: Before adjusting valves, check rocker arm shaft bracket bolts for looseness. Tighten as necessary: I-Mark — 15-22 ft. lbs. (20-30 N.m); P'UP — 9-17 ft. lbs. (13-23 N.m).

1) Rotate crankshaft until No. 1 piston is at TDC of compression stroke. Measure valve clearance between adjusting screw and valve stem end cap. With No. 1 piston at TDC, adjust intake valves on cylinders No. 1 and 2, and exhaust valves on cylinders No. 1 and 3.

2) Rotate crankshaft 1 complete revolution until No. 4 piston is at TDC of compression stoke. Adjust intake valves on cylinders No. 3 and 4, and exhaust valves on cylinders No. 2 and 4.

VALVE CLEARANCE SPECIFICATIONS

Application	Intake In. (mm)	Exhaust In. (mm)
I-Mark		
Hot & Cold	.010 (.25)	.014 (.35)
P'UP		
Hot	.015 (.37)	.015 (.37)
Cold	.016 (.40)	.016 (.40)

VALVE ARRANGEMENT

I-MARK

I-E-I-E-I-E-I-E (Front-to-rear)

P'UP

E-I-I-E-E-I-I-E (Front-to-rear)

Fig. 1: Diesel Firing Order Illustration

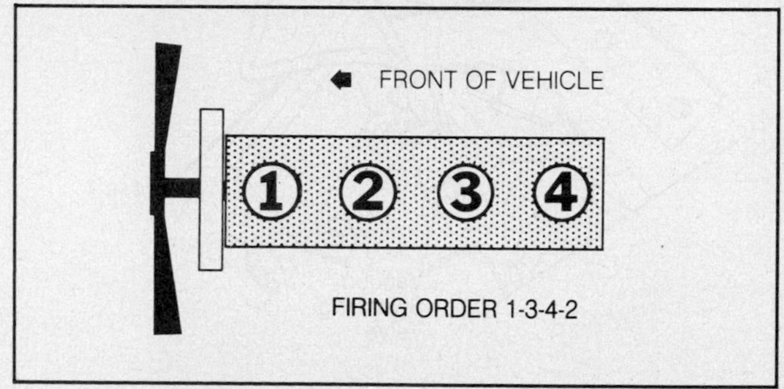

FRONT OF VEHICLE
1
2
3
4
FIRING ORDER 1-3-4-2

IDLE SPEED

P'UP

1) Set parking brake, block drive wheels and place transmission in Neutral. Start engine and run until it reaches normal operating temperature.

2) Connect tachometer and check idle speed. If idle speed is incorrect, loosen idle speed adjusting screw lock nut and turn adjusting screw to reach correct idle speed. Tighten lock nut.

I-MARK

1) Set parking brake and block drive wheels. Place transmission in Neutral. Start engine and run until it reaches normal operating temperature. Connect tachometer to engine.

2) Check that idle adjusting bolt is in contact with accelerator lever. If idle speed is not to specification, turn idle adjusting bolt to obtain proper specification.

3) Adjust setting of outer cable to adjust accelerator control inner cable play. If setting of idle control lever is incorrect, adjust with outer cable.

IDLE SPEED SPECIFICATIONS

Application	RPM
I-Mark	
Auto. Trans.	675-775
Man. Trans.	575-675
P'UP	700-800

FAST IDLE

1) Start engine and run until it reaches normal operating temperature. Connect tachometer (J-28885).

2) Disconnect hoses 1 and 2 from vacuum switch valve. *See Fig. 2.* Connect hoses together using a pipe or tube.

TUNE-UP (Cont.)

Fig. 2: Isuzu Diesel Fast Idle Vacuum Hose Removal

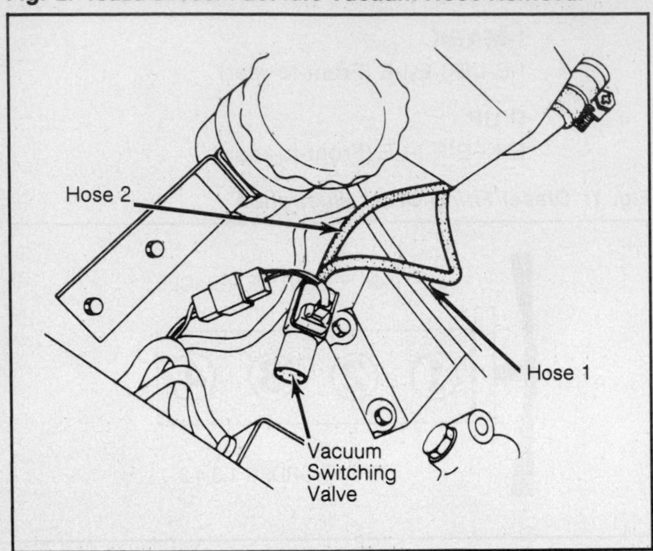
Hose 2
Hose 1
Vacuum
Switching
Valve

3) Check fast idle speed. If fast idle speed is incorrect, loosen adjusting lock nut 4 and adjust idle speed by moving adjusting nut 3. *See Fig. 3.*

Fig. 3: Isuzu Diesel Fast Idle Speed Adjustment Locations

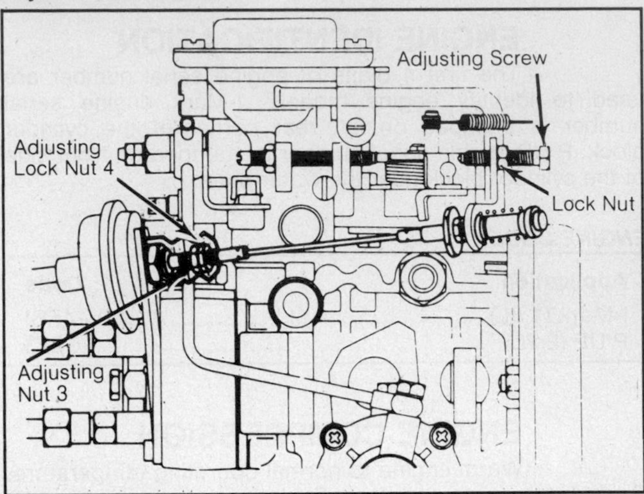
Adjusting Screw
Adjusting
Lock Nut 4
Lock Nut
Adjusting
Nut 3

FAST IDLE SPEED SPECIFICATIONS

Application	Idle RPM
All Models	900-950

GENERAL SERVICING

FUEL SYSTEMS

FUEL INJECTION

All Isuzu models use Bosch mechanical diesel fuel injection.

ELECTRICAL

BATTERY

BATTERY SPECIFICATIONS

Application	Amp Hr. Rating
All Models	80

STARTER

All models use Hitachi starters.

STARTER SPECIFICATIONS

Application	Volts	Amps	Test RPM
All Models	11.5	120	4000

ALTERNATOR

All models use Hitachi alternators.

ALTERNATOR SPECIFICATIONS

Application	Rated Amp Output
All Models	50

ALTERNATOR REGULATOR

All models use Hitachi alternator regulators.

REGULATOR OPERATING VOLTAGE @ 68°F (20°C)

Application	Voltage
All Models	14.0-14.6

SERVICE SPECIFICATIONS

BELT ADJUSTMENT

Application	[1] Deflection In. (mm)
All Belts	0.4 (10)

[1] — Measured between longest span and depressed with firm thumb pressure.

REPLACEMENT INTERVALS

Component	Interval (Miles)
Oil Filter	7500
Air Filter	30,000
Fuel Filter	30,000

GENERAL SERVICING (Cont).

FLUID CAPACITIES

Application	Quantity
Crankcase (Includes Filter)	
I-Mark	5.8 qts. (5.5L)
P'UP	6.3 qts. (6.0L)
Cooling System	
I-Mark	7.4 qts. (7.0L)
P'UP	
Man.Trans.	9.5 qts. (9.0L)
Auto. Trans.	11.2 qts. (10.6L)
Man. Trans. (SAE 30)	
4-Speed	2.7 pts. (1.3L)
5-Speed	3.3 pts. (1.6L)
Auto. Trans. (Dexron II)	
I-Mark & P'UP	6.7 qts. (6.3L)
Transfer Case (SAE 30)	5.3 pts. (2.5L)
Rear Differential (SAE 90)	
I-Mark	2.5 pts. (1.2L)
P'UP	2.7 pts. (1.3L)
Front Differential (SAE 90)	1.7 pts. (0.8L)
Fuel Tank	
I-Mark	13.7 gals. (52.0L)
P'UP	
Short Bed	13.2 gals. (50.0L)
Long Bed	19.1 gals. (72.4L)

TUNE-UP

XJ6

ENGINE IDENTIFICATION

Engine number is stamped on top of cylinder block at rear of engine. Number is also stamped on Commission Plate which is located in the engine compartment.

ENGINE COMPRESSION

Check compression pressure with engine at normal operating temperature, throttle valve wide open, all spark plugs removed and coil wire disconnected.

COMPRESSION SPECIFICATIONS

Application	Specification
Compression Ratio	8.1:1
Compression Pressure	[1]
Max. Variation Between Cylinders	5 psi (.35 kg/cm²)

[1] — Compression pressures vary from engine to engine. The critical factor is pressure variation between cylinders.

VALVE CLEARANCE

1) With camshaft covers removed, rotate camshafts and record clearance between heel of each cam lobe and its respective tappet. If adjustment is necessary, rotate camshaft and align with valve timing gauge (C 3993) before removing final camshaft retaining nut. Disconnect sprockets from camshafts.

NOTE: **DO NOT rotate engine while camshaft sprockets are disconnected.**

2) Remove camshaft bearing caps and lift off camshaft. Remove each tappet that required adjustment, and note its location for reassembly in its original position. Remove adjusting pad and measure thickness.

Fig. 1: Position of Valve Timing Gauge

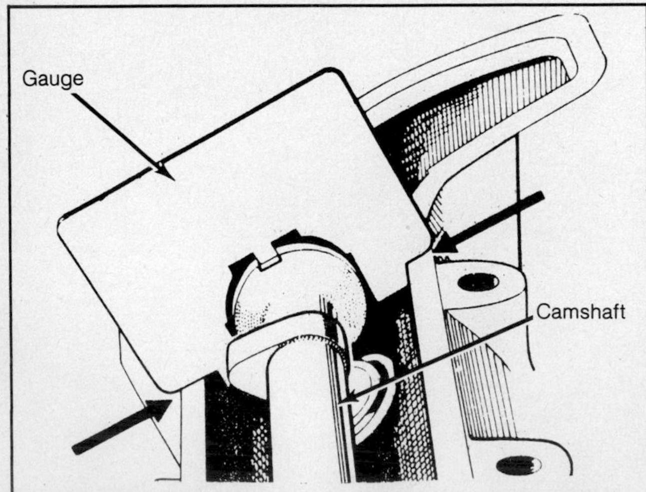
Gauge
Camshaft

Use gauge to position camshaft before final sprocket removal and installation.

3) Use measured pad thickness and difference between measured valve clearance and specified clearance to calculate required thickness of new adjusting pad. Adjusting pads are available in increments of .001" (.03 mm) from .085" (2.16 mm) to .110" (2.79 mm) and are marked with letters from "A" to "Z", respectively.

4) Insert correct adjusting pads and install tappets. Install camshafts and align with timing gauge. Torque camshaft bearing cap nuts to 9 ft. lbs. (12.2 N.m). Connect camshaft sprockets and install camshaft covers.

VALVE CLEARANCE SPECIFICATIONS

Application	[1] In. (mm)
Intake & Exhaust	.012-.014 (.30-.35)

[1] — Clearance measured with engine cold.

VALVE ARRANGEMENT

Left Side — All Exhaust
Right Side — All Intake

SPARK PLUGS

SPARK PLUG TYPE

Application	Champion No.
All Models	N12Y

SPARK PLUG SPECIFICATIONS

Application	Gap In. (mm)	Torque Ft. Lbs. (N.m)
All Models	.035 (.89)	27 (36)

HIGH TENSION WIRE RESISTANCE

Carefully remove high tension wires from plugs and distributor cap. Using an ohmmeter, check resistance of each wire while gently twisting wire. If resistance is incorrect, or fluctuates from infinity to any value, replace wire.

HIGH TENSION WIRE RESISTANCE

Application	Ohms
All Models	30,000

DISTRIBUTOR

All models are equipped with a Lucas breakerless, electronic ignition systems. Under normal operating conditions, no adjustments are necessary. If distributor has been disassembled or parts have been replaced, check gap between the timing rotor and pick-up module and adjust as needed.

1983 Jaguar 6 Tune-Up

TUNE-UP (Cont.)

DISTRIBUTOR PICK-UP COIL AIR GAP

Application	In. (mm)
All Models	.008-.014 (.20-.35)

Fig. 2: Firing Order and Distributor Rotation

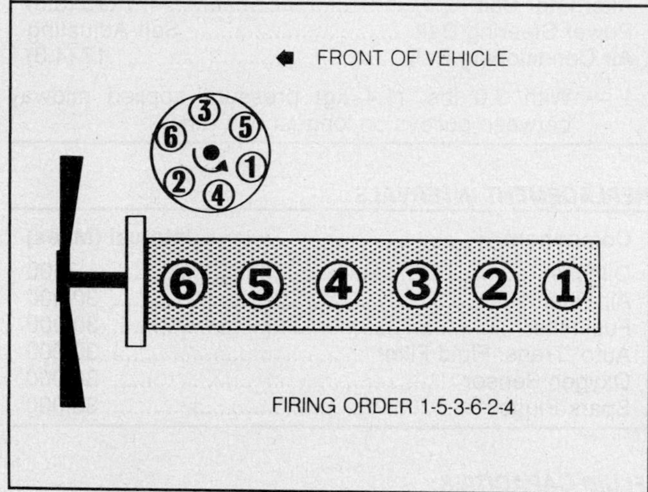
FRONT OF VEHICLE
3 5 6 1 2 4
6 5 4 3 2 1
FIRING ORDER 1-5-3-6-2-4

IGNITION TIMING

1) Check or adjust ignition timing with engine at normal operating temperature, idle speed set to specification and distributor vacuum line disconnected.

Fig. 3: Ignition Timing Mark Location

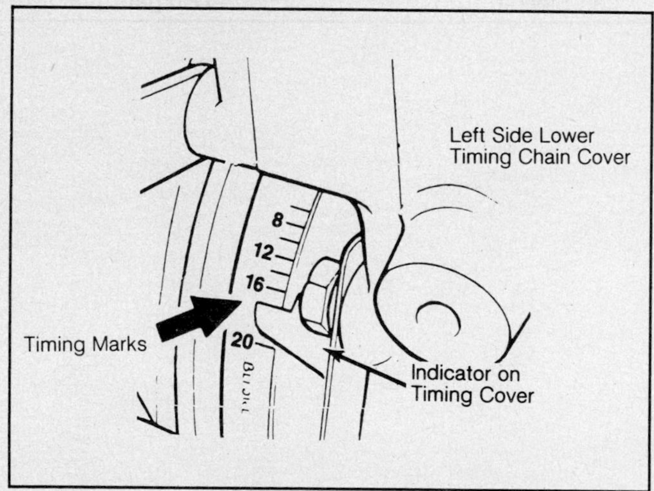
Left Side Lower
Timing Chain Cover
8
12
16
20
Timing Marks
Indicator on
Timing Cover

2) If timing is not correct, loosen distributor clamp bolt and rotate distributor until correct timing is obtained. Tighten clamp bolt.

IGNITION TIMING (Degrees BTDC@RPM)

Application	Timing
All Models	17@800

IDLE SPEED & MIXTURE

IDLE SPEED

1) The following adjustments must be performed with engine at normal operating temperature, air filter in good condition and ignition timing and valve clearance adjusted to specifications. Check that throttle linkage is operating properly, and that return springs are secure and operating.

2) Start engine and run for 2-3 minutes. Turn idle speed adjusting screw to obtain proper specification. Idle speed screw is located on air distribution block on XJ6.

IDLE SPEED SPECIFICATIONS

Application	Idle RPM
XJ6	800

IDLE MIXTURE

NOTE: **Mixture adjustment is not a part of normal tune-up procedure. It should not be performed unless fuel injection parts are replaced or vehicle fails emissions testing.**

1) Connect special tools (BLT 1044 & 1047) to exhaust downpipe test points. With engine idling at 800 RPM, disconnect oxygen sensor and allow 1 minute for engine to stablize.

2) Using an infrared analyzer, check CO reading. Reading should be 0.5-1.5%. If not, adjust by turning mixture adjusting screw on air flow meter housing.

3) Turn mixture screw clockwise to richen mixture and counterclockwise to lean mixture. If correct setting cannot be attained, check that all electrical connections and all hoses are in good condition and properly located.

4) Replace oxygen sensor lead and disconnect test instruments.

CO LEVEL SPECIFICATIONS

Application	[1] CO%
All Models	.5-1.5

[1] — With oxygen sensor disconnected.

FUEL PUMP

FUEL PUMP PERFORMANCE

Application	Pressure psi (kg/cm²)
All Models	36 (2.5)

EMISSION CONTROL SYSTEMS

See Mitchell Manuals' Emission Control Manual.

1983 Jaguar 6 Tune-Up

GENERAL SERVICING

IGNITION

DISTRIBUTOR

All models are equipped with Lucas Constant Energy Ignition System.

DISTRIBUTOR PICK-UP COIL RESISTANCE

Application	Ohms
All Models	2.2-4.8

FUEL SYSTEMS

FUEL INJECTION

All models are equipped with Lucas-Bosch L-Jetronic (AFC) fuel injection.

ELECTRICAL

BATTERY SPECIFICATIONS

Application	Amp Hr. Rating
All Models	75

STARTER

All 6-cylinder models are equipped with Lucas pre-engaged starters.

STARTER SPECIFICATIONS

Application	Amps	Test RPM
All Models	100	5500

ALTERNATORS

ALTERNATOR SPECIFICATIONS

Application	Rated Amp Output
Lucas 25ACR	66
Motorola 9AR 25 12P	70

ALTERNATOR REGULATOR

All models use Lucas or Motorola regulators.

REGULATOR OPERATING VOLTAGE @ 68°F (20°C)

Application	Voltage
Lucas	13.6-14.4
Motorola	13.7-14.7

SERVICE SPECIFICATIONS

BELT ADJUSTMENT

Application	[1] Deflection In. (mm)
Alternator Belt	.15 (3.8)
Power Steering Belt	Self-Adjusting
Air Conditioning Belt	.17 (4.3)

[1] — With 3.0 lbs. (1.4 kg) pressure applied midway between pulleys on longest belt run.

REPLACEMENT INTERVALS

Component	Interval (Miles)
Oil Filter	7500
Air Filter	30,000
Fuel Filter	30,000
Auto. Trans. Fluid Filter	30,000
Oxygen Sensor	30,000
Spark Plugs	30,000

FLUID CAPACITIES

Application	Quantity
Crankcase (Includes Filter)	7.5 qts. (7.3L)
Cooling System	19.5 qts. (18.2L)
Auto. Trans. (ATF Type F)	16.8 pts. (8.0L)
Rear Axle (SAE 90)	3.3 pts. (1.6L)
Fuel Tank	
Right Side	12.0 gals. (48.0L)
Left Side	12.0 gals. (48.0L)

1983 Jaguar V12 Tune-Up

TUNE-UP

XJS

ENGINE IDENTIFICATION

Engine number is stamped on top rear of cylinder block, between cylinder heads.

ENGINE COMPRESSION

Check compression pressure with battery fully charged, engine at normal operating temperature, throttle fully open and engine at cranking speed.

COMPRESSION SPECIFICATIONS

Compression Pressure	[1] 225 psi (15.8 kg/cm²)
Maximum Variation	5 psi (.4 kg/cm²)

[1] — Use as guideline only.

VALVE CLEARANCE

1) Adjust valves with engine cold. Remove valve covers, and check that camshaft bearing caps are tightened to correct torque. Check clearance between heel of cam and valve tappet.

2) Subtract correct valve clearance from clearance obtained. See Valve Clearance Specifications table. Select adjusting pads equal to measurement and install under tappet.

3) Adjusting pads are available in widths from .085-.110" (2.16-2.79 mm) in increments of .001" (.03 mm). Pads are coded with letters A to Z, each letter corresponding to a thickness increase of 1 size.

VALVE CLEARANCE SPECIFICATIONS

Application	In. (mm)
Intake & Exhaust (Cold)	.010-.012 (.25-.30)

VALVE ARRANGEMENT

RIGHT SIDE

E-I-E-I-E-I-I-E-I-E-I-E (Front-to-rear)

LEFT SIDE

E-I-E-I-E-I-I-E-I-E-I-E (Front-to-rear)

SPARK PLUGS

SPARK PLUG TYPE

Application	Champion No.
All Models	BN5

SPARK PLUG SPECIFICATIONS

Application	Gap In. (mm)	Torque Ft. Lbs. (N.m)
All Models	.025 (.64)	27 (37)

DISTRIBUTOR

All models are equipped with Lucas Constant Energy Ignition System. Under normal operating conditions, no adjustments are necessary. However, if the unit has been disassembled, check air gap between reluctor and pick-up module and adjust as needed.

DISTRIBUTOR PICK-UP COIL AIR GAP

Application	In. (mm)
All Models	.008-.014 (.20-.35)

Fig. 1: Firing Order and Distributor Rotation

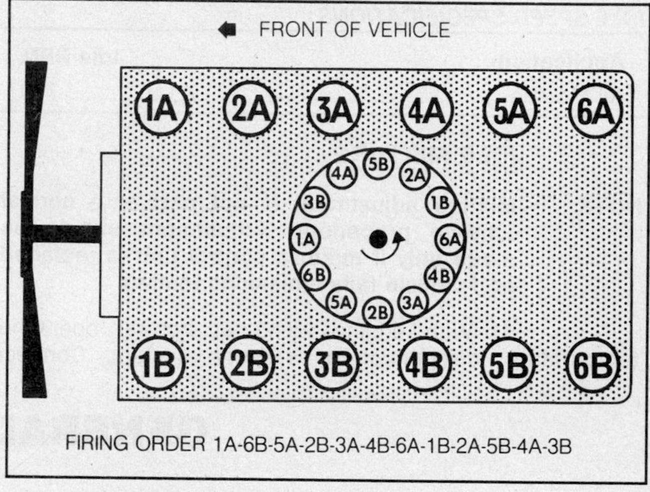
FRONT OF VEHICLE
1A
2A
3A
4A
5A
6A
5B
2A
1B
6A
4B
3A
2B
5A
6B
1A
3B
4A
1B
2B
3B
4B
5B
6B
FIRING ORDER 1A-6B-5A-2B-3A-4B-6A-1B-2A-5B-4A-3B

IGNITION TIMING

With engine at normal operating temperature, disconnect vacuum pipe. Connect timing light and tachometer to vehicle. Run engine at 3000 RPM and check timing. Adjust timing by loosening distributor lock nut and rotating distributor.

IGNITION TIMING (Degrees BTDC@RPM)

Application	Timing
All Models	18@3000

Fig. 2: Ignition Timing Mark Location

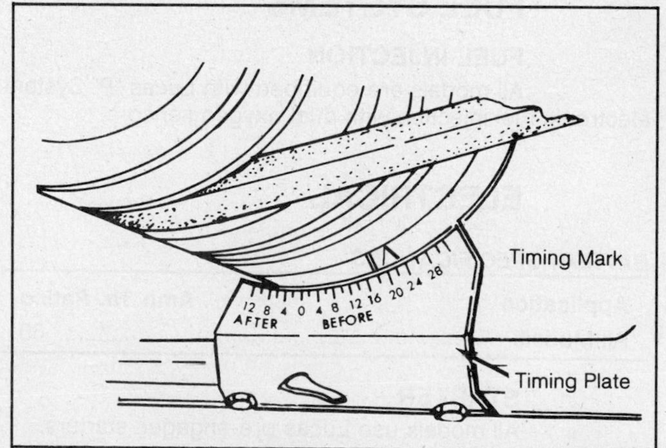
Timing Mark
AFTER
BEFORE
Timing Plate

TUNE-UP (Cont.)

IDLE SPEED & MIXTURE

IDLE SPEED

1) The following adjustments must be performed with engine at normal operating temperature, air filter in good condition and ignition timing and valve clearance adjusted to specifications.

2) Check that throttle linkage is operating properly and that return springs are secure and operating. Start engine and run for 2-3 minutes.

3) Turn idle speed adjusting screw to obtain proper specification. Idle speed screw is located in auxiliary air valve.

IDLE SPEED SPECIFICATIONS

Application	Idle RPM
All Models	750

IDLE MIXTURE

NOTE: **Mixture adjustment is not part of a normal tune-up procedure. Adjustment should be made only if mixture control unit is replaced or if vehicle fails emissions testing.**

1) With engine idling at normal operating temperature, disconnect air injection system. Connect Feedback Meter (60973066) to plug next to electronic control unit, located in trunk.

2) Re-activate oxygen sensor circuit by removing plug from fly lead, located close to feedback checking point. Observe meter lights, and ensure they agree with unit operating instructions for CO checking. CO level should be 1.0-2.0%.

CO LEVEL SPECIFICATIONS

Application	Idle RPM	CO%
All Models	750	1.0-2.0

FUEL PUMP

FUEL PUMP PERFORMANCE

Application	Pressure psi (kg/cm²)
All Models	36 (2.5)

EMISSION CONTROL SYSTEMS

See Mitchell Manuals' Emission Control Manual.

GENERAL SERVICING

IGNITION

DISTRIBUTOR

All models are equipped with Lucas Constant Energy Ignition System. Under normal operating conditions, no adjustments are necessary.

IGNITION COIL

IGNITION COIL RESISTANCE — Ohms @ 68°F (20°C)

Application	Primary	Secondary
All Models	.9-1.1	.....

FUEL SYSTEMS

FUEL INJECTION

All models are equipped with Lucas "P" System electronic fuel injection with dual oxygen sensors.

ELECTRICAL

BATTERY SPECIFICATIONS

Application	Amp Hr. Rating
All Models	60

STARTER

All models use Lucas pre-engaged starters.

ALTERNATORS

All models use Lucas or Motorola alternators.

ALTERNATOR SPECIFICATIONS

Application	Rated Amp Output
Lucas 25ACR	66
Motorola 9AR 2533P	70

ALTERNATOR REGULATOR

REGULATOR OPERATING VOLTAGE @ 68°F (20°C)

Application	Voltage
Lucas	13.6-14.4
Motorola	13.7-14.7

SERVICE SPECIFICATIONS

BELT ADJUSTMENT

Application	Pressure Lbs. (kg)	[1] Deflection In. (mm)
Alternator Belt	3.2 (7.0)	.15 (3.8)
Air Conditioning Belt	2.9 (6.4)	.17 (4.3)
Air Pump Belt	6.9 (15.2)	.22 (5.6)
Power Steering Belt	6.4 (14.1)	.16 (4.1)

[1] — With indicated pressure applied midway between pulleys on longest belt run.

GENERAL SERVICING (Cont.)

REPLACEMENT INTERVALS

Component	Interval (Miles)
Oil Filter	7500
Air Filter	30,000
Fuel Filter	30,000
Auto. Trans. Fluid Filter	30,000
Oxygen Sensor	30,000
Spark Plugs	30,000

FLUID CAPACITIES

Application	Quantity
Crankcase (Includes Filter)	11.4 qts. (10.3L)
Cooling System (Includes Heater)	21.0 qts. (19.5L)
Auto. Trans. (Dexron)	19.2 pts. (9.1L)
Rear Axle (SAE 90)	3.3 pts. (1.6L)
Fuel Tank	25 gal. (90L)

TUNE-UP

B2000 Pickup, GLC, GLC Wagon & 626

ENGINE IDENTIFICATION

On B2000 and GLC Wagon models, engine serial number and model code are stamped on right front upper wall of cylinder block. The engine serial number for 626 models is stamped on the upper left hand corner of the cylinder block.

On GLC models, the serial number is located on the right rear of the cylinder block. It is above the transaxle mating surface.

ENGINE COMPRESSION

Check compression pressure with engine at normal operating temperature, spark plugs removed, throttle valve wide open and engine at cranking speed. Crank engine until maximum pressure is reached at each cylinder.

COMPRESSION SPECIFICATIONS

Normal Compression Pressure	
GLC Wagon	164 psi (11 kg/cm²)
All Others	171 psi (12 kg/cm²)
Min. Compression Pressure	
GLC Wagon	114 psi (8 kg/cm²)
All Others	128 psi (9 kg/cm²)
Max. Variation	28 psi (2 kg/cm²)

VALVE CLEARANCE

Adjust valves with engine at normal operating temperature.

VALVE CLEARANCE SPECIFICATIONS

Application	[1] In. (mm)
Intake	
GLC & GLC Wagon	.010 (.25)
626 & B2000	.012 (.30)
Exhaust	.012 (.30)

[1] — Measured between valve and rocker arm.

VALVE ARRANGEMENT

GLC, GLC WAGON & 626

Right Side — All Intake
Left Side — All Exhaust

B2000

Right Side — All Exhaust
Left Side — All Intake

SPARK PLUGS

SPARK PLUG TYPE

Application	NGK No.
All Models	BPR-5ES or BPR-6ES

SPARK PLUG SPECIFICATIONS

Application	Gap In. (mm)	Torque Ft. Lbs. (N.m)
All Models	.031 (0.8)	13 (18)

HIGH TENSION WIRE RESISTANCE

Carefully remove high tension wires from spark plugs and distributor cap. Using an ohmmeter, check resistance of wires while gently twisting wire. If resistance is not to specification, or fluctuates from infinity to any value, replace wire.

HIGH TENSION WIRE RESISTANCE

Application	Ohms
All Models	4880 per ft.

Fig. 1: B2000 & GLC Wagon Firing Order & Distributor Rotation

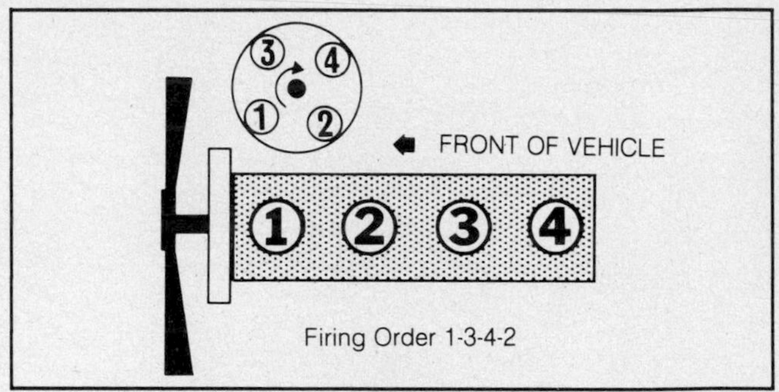
3
4
1
2
FRONT OF VEHICLE
1 2 3 4
Firing Order 1-3-4-2

Fig. 2: GLC Firing Order and Distributor Rotation

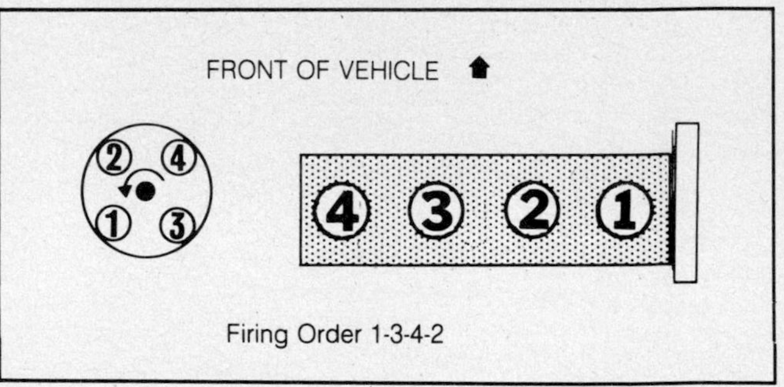
FRONT OF VEHICLE
2
4
1
3
4 3 2 1
Firing Order 1-3-4-2

Fig. 3: 626 Firing Order and Distributor Rotation

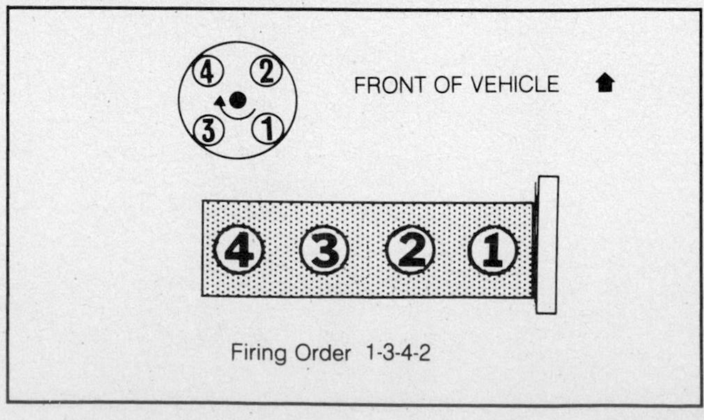
4
2
3
1
FRONT OF VEHICLE
4 3 2 1
Firing Order 1-3-4-2

TUNE-UP (Cont.)

Fig. 4: Mazda Piston Engine Timing Marks

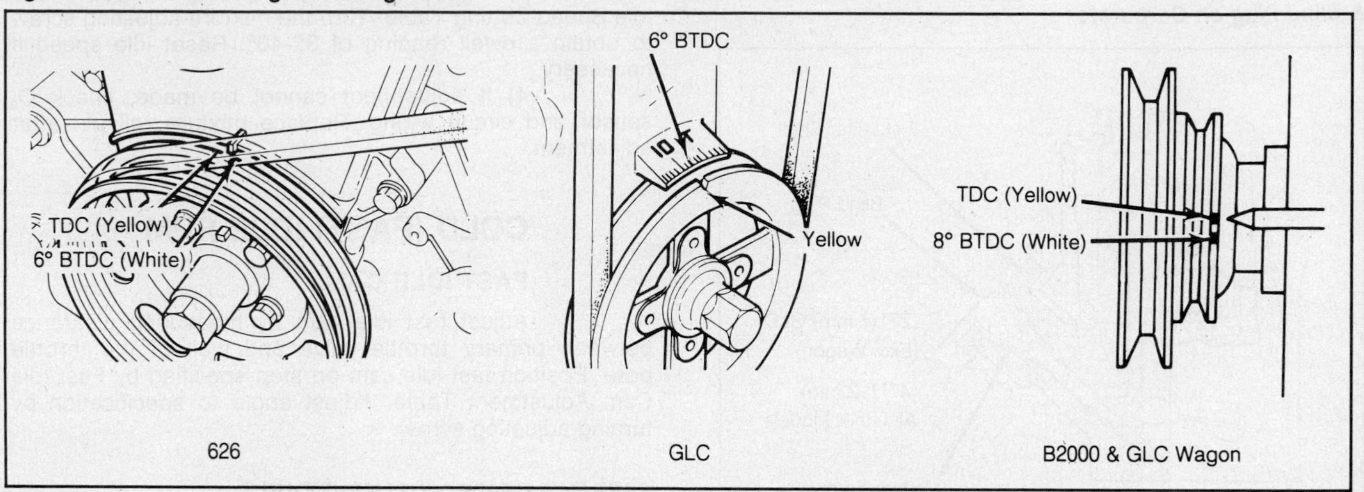
TDC (Yellow)
6° BTDC (White)
626
6° BTDC
Yellow
GLC
TDC (Yellow)
8° BTDC (White)
B2000 & GLC Wagon

DISTRIBUTOR

All models are equipped with a Mitsubishi breakerless electronic ignition system and no adjustments are needed.

IGNITION TIMING

1) With engine at normal operating temperature, set transmission in "D" (Auto. Trans.) or Neutral (Man. Trans.).

2) Unplug wiring connector to engine cooling fan (if equipped). Be sure idle speed is set to specifications. Connect timing light and set timing as required.

IGNITION TIMING (Degrees BTDC@RPM)

Application	Man. Trans.	[1] Auto. Trans.
B2000	8@650	......
GLC	6@850	6@750
GLC Wagon	8@800	8@750
626	6@750	6@700

[1] – Auto. Trans. in "D".

IDLE SPEED AND MIXTURE

IDLE SPEED

1) Switch off all accessories. Set parking brake and block drive wheels. Connect tachometer to engine. Warm engine to normal operating temperature.

2) Place automatic transmission in "D". Unplug electric fan motor connector (if equipped). Adjust idle speed to specification by turning throttle adjusting screw.

IDLE SPEED SPECIFICATIONS

Application	Man. Trans. RPM	[1] Auto. Trans. RPM
B2000	650	....
GLC	850	750
GLC Wagon	800	750
626	750	700

[1] — Auto. Trans. in "D".

Fig. 5: Carburetor Adjustment Screw Location

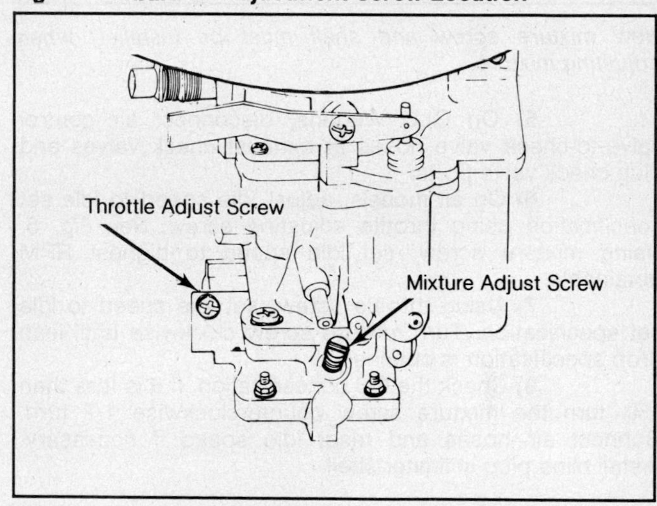
Throttle Adjust Screw
Mixture Adjust Screw

IDLE MIXTURE

NOTE: **Mixture adjustment is not a part of normal tune-up procedure and should not be performed unless carburetor is disassembled or vehicle fails emission testing.**

B2000 & GLC Wagon

1) Remove carburetor from engine. Separate carburetor main body and throttle body. Using a hacksaw, cut through limiter shell (from cap end) .27" (7 mm) on GLC Wagons or .47" (12 mm) on B2000 model. *See Fig. 6.*

2) Remove and discard limiter shell, mixture spring and screw. Install new limiter shell with flat portion facing up. To install new mixture screw, tighten screw lightly and insure it is fully seated.

3) Back screw out 3 turns on B2000 models and 4 turns on GLC Wagons for preliminary adjustment. Reinstall carburetor with new gaskets and warm engine to normal operating temperature. Connect exhaust gas analyzer. Switch off all accessories.

4) On Federal B2000 models, disconnect air cleaner-to-reed valve hose at reed valve port. On Calif. B2000 models, disconnect air by-pass valve-to-check valve hose at check valve and plug check valve port.

TUNE-UP (Cont.)

Fig. 6: Idle Mixture Limiter Shell & Blind Plug on Carburetor

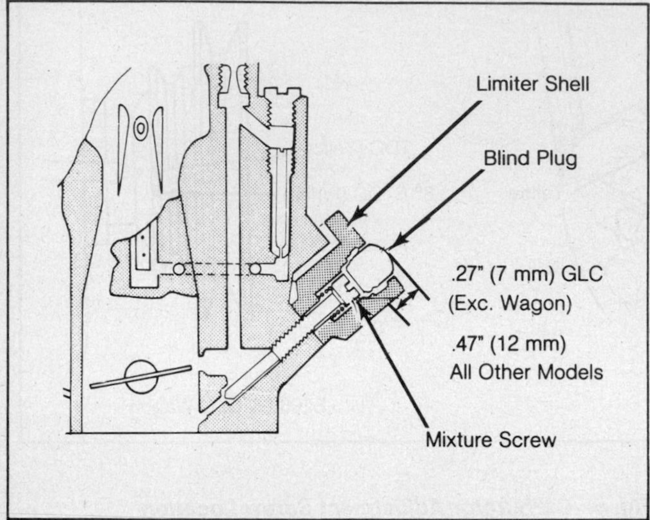
Limiter Shell
Blind Plug
.27" (7 mm) GLC
(Exc. Wagon)
.47" (12 mm)
All Other Models
Mixture Screw

New mixture screw and shell must be installed when adjusting mixture.

5) On GLC Wagons, disconnect air control valve-to-check valve hoses at exhaust check valves and plug check valve ports.

6) On all models, adjust idle speed to idle set specification using throttle adjusting screw. *See Fig. 5.* Using mixture screw, set idle speed to highest RPM obtainable.

7) Using throttle screw, set idle speed to idle set specification. Turn mixture screw clockwise until lean drop specification is obtained.

8) Check the CO concentration. If it is less than 1%, turn the mixture screw counterclockwise 1/2 turn. Connect air hoses and reset idle speed if necessary. Install blind plug in limiter shell.

IDLE MIXTURE SPECIFICATIONS [1]

Application	Idle Set RPM	Lean Drop RPM
B2000		
California	620	600
Federal	670	650
GLC Wagon		
Man. Trans.	830	800
Auto. Trans.	1030	1000

[1] — Auto. Trans. in neutral.

GLC & 626

1) Remove carburetor from engine. Drive out mixture screw roll pin. Install carburetor on engine. Install air cleaner and connect hoses to idle compensator, thermo-sensor and reed valves.

2) Warm engine to operating temperature. Connect a dwell meter (4-cylinder setting) to the service connector for the carburetor Air/Fuel Solenoid Valve. On 626 models, the connector is a Brown/Yellow wire. On GLC models, the connector is Yellow wire.

3) Adjust the idle speed to specification. See Idle Speed Setting Table. Turn the mixture adjusting screw to obtain a dwell reading of 32-40°. Reset idle speed if necessary.

4) If adjustment cannot be made, check O_2 sensor and circuit wiring. Replace mixture roll pin after adjustment.

COLD (FAST) IDLE RPM

FAST IDLE CAM

Adjust fast idle cam by measuring clearance between primary throttle valve and wall of the throttle bore. Position fast idle cam on step specified by Fast Idle Cam Adjustment Table. Adjust angle to specification by turning adjusting screw.

FAST IDLE CAM ADJUSTMENT TABLE

Application	[1] Fast Idle Cam Step	Throttle Bore Clearance In. (mm)
B2000	1	.051-.059 (1.5-1.3)
GLC	3	.031-.039 (.78-.96)
GLC Wagon	3	.031-.038 (.78-.96)
626	2	.028-.043 (.70-1.1)

[1] — The highest cam step is the 1st step.

FAST IDLE SPEED

1) Warm engine to operating temperature and set idle speed. Remove the air cleaner and plug the idle compensator, thermo-sensor and reed valve hoses.

2) While holding the throttle valve slightly open, close the choke valve. Release the choke valve after releasing the throttle. Start the engine but do not touch the accelerator pedal.

3) Engine speed should be between 3000-4000 RPM. If not, turn fast idle adjusting screw.

FUEL PUMP

FUEL PUMP PERFORMANCE

Application	Pressure psi (kg/cm²)	Volume in 30 Sec. Pints (Liters)
B2000 & GLC	2.8-3.6 (.2-.3)	.8 (.40)
GLC Wagon	2.8-3.8 (.2-.3)	.5 (.35)
626	2.8-4.3 (.2-.3)	.9 (.43)

EMISSION CONTROL SYSTEMS

See Mitchell Manuals' Emission Control Manual.

GENERAL SERVICING

IGNITION

DISTRIBUTOR

All models are equipped with a Mitsubishi breakerless electronic ignition system. No adjustments are necessary.

IGNITION COIL

IGNITION COIL RESISTANCE — Ohms @ 68°F (20°C)

Application	Primary	Secondary
GLC, GLC Wagon & 626	1.15	.....
B2000	.90	7000

FUEL SYSTEMS

All GLC models use Hitachi 2-bbl. carburetors. All other models use Nikki 2-bbl. carburetors.

ELECTRICAL

BATTERY

BATTERY SPECIFICATIONS

Application	Amp Hr. Rating
B2000 & 626	[1] 45
GLC & GLC Wagon	60

[1] — 70 amp battery also available on B2000.

STARTER

All models are equipped with a Mitsubishi starter that uses an overrunning clutch.

STARTER SPECIFICATIONS

Application	Volts	Amps	Test RPM
626 Auto. Trans.	11.5	60	6600
All Other Models	11.5	53	6800

ALTERNATOR

All models use Mitsubishi alternators.

ALTERNATOR SPECIFICATIONS

Application	Rated Amp. Output
B2000	50
GLC & GLC Wagon	30
626	60

ALTERNATOR REGULATOR

All alternators are equipped with a solid state Mitsubishi regulator. No adjustments are possible.

REGULATOR OPERATING VOLTAGE @ 68°F (20°C)

Application	Voltage
All Models	14.1-15.0

SERVICE SPECIFICATIONS

BELT ADJUSTMENT

Application	[1] Deflection In. (mm)
Air Conditioner Belt	.6-.7 (15-18)
Air Pump Belt	
GLC	.63-.70 (16-18)
GLC Wagon	.3-.4 (8-10)
626 & B2000	.4-.6 (10-15)
Alternator Belt	
GLC	.47-.50 (12-13)
All Others	.3-.4 (8-10)

[1] — Deflection is with 22 lbs. (10 kg) pressure applied midway on longest belt run.

REPLACEMENT INTERVALS

Component	Interval (Miles)
Oil Filter	7500
Air Filter	30,000
Fuel Filter (B2000)	15,000
Spark Plugs	30,000

FLUID CAPACITIES

Application	Quantity
Crankcase (Includes Filter)	
B2000	6.2 qts. (5.8L)
GLC & Wagon	3.5 qts. (3.3L)
626	4.1 qts. (3.9L)
Cooling System (Includes Heater)	
B2000	7.6 qts. (7.2L)
GLC & GLC Wagon	5.8 qts. (5.5L)
626	7.3 qts. (7.0L)
Manual Transaxle (ATF Type "F")	3.4 qts. (3.2L)
Manual Transmission (SAE 80W-90)	
4-Speed	
B2000	1.5 qts. (1.4L)
GLC Wagon	1.4 qts. (1.3L)
5-Speed	1.8 qts. (1.7L)
Automatic Transaxle (ATF Type "F")	6.0 qts. (5.7L)
Automatic Transmission (ATF Type "F")	
GLC Wagon	6.0 qts. (5.7L)
Rear Axle (SAE 80W-90)	
B2000	2.8 pts. (1.3L)
GLC Wagon	1.6 pts. (.8L)
Fuel Tank	
B2000	
Standard Bed	14.8 gals. (56.0L)
Long Bed	17.4 gals. (65.9L)
GLC	11.1 gals. (42.0L)
GLC Wagon	11.9 gals. (45.0L)
626	15.8 gals. (60.0L)

1983 Mazda Diesel 4 Tune-Up

TUNE-UP

B2200 Pickup

ENGINE IDENTIFICATION

Engine number is stamped into the front left side of the engine block.

ENGINE COMPRESSION

1) Run engine until it reaches normal operating temperature. Remove the injection nozzles and holders from cylinders. Attach adapter fitting (49 1456 010) to nozzle opening on 1 cylinder. Connect a compression gauge capable of reading more than 427 psi (30 kg/cm²) to adapter.

2) Disconnect wire from fuel cut solenoid. Crank engine until maximum compression pressure is reached and note reading. Repeat procedure for remaining cylinders. Reinstall injection nozzles and fuel cut solenoid wire after completing compression test.

COMPRESSION SPECIFICATIONS

Normal Compression Pressure	427 psi (30 kg/cm²)
Min. Compression Pressure	384 psi (27 kg/cm²)
Max. Variation	42.7 psi (3 kg/cm²)

VALVE CLEARANCE

1) Engine must be at normal operating temperature. Remove valve cover. Set No.1 cylinder at TDC of compression stroke. Check clearance of intake valves on cylinders No. 1 and 2 and of exhaust valves on cylinders No. 1 and 3.

2) Turn the crankshaft 360° so that cylinder No. 4 is at TDC of compression stroke. Check clearance of intake valves on cylinders No. 3 and 4 and of exhaust valves on cylinders 2 and 4.

VALVE CLEARANCE SPECIFICATIONS

Application	In. (mm)
Intake & Exhaust	.012 (.30)

VALVE ARRANGEMENT

I-E-I-E-I-E-I-E (Front-to-rear)

GLOW PLUGS

GLOW PLUG TORQUE SPECIFICATIONS

Application	Ft. Lbs. (N.m)
All Models	7-11 (10-15)

Fig. 1: B2200 Firing Order

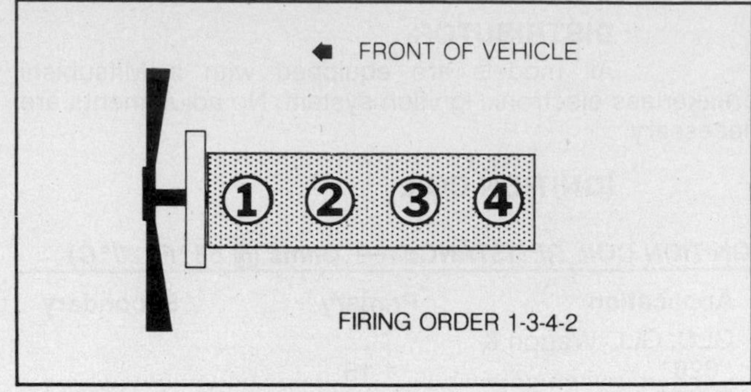
FRONT OF VEHICLE
1
2
3
4
FIRING ORDER 1-3-4-2

IDLE SPEED

1) Check that end play of accelerator cable is within .04-.12" (1.0-3.0 mm). If adjustment is necessary, loosen lock nut of the idle adjusting bolt and adjust play by turning the idle adjusting bolt.

NOTE: Idle speed will increase when adjusting bolt is turned right and decrease when turned left.

2) After adjustment, race engine 2 or 3 times to inspect the return of the accelerator cable.

IDLE SPEED SPECIFICATIONS

Application	RPM
All Models	700

Fig. 2: B2200 Diesel Fuel Injection Pump

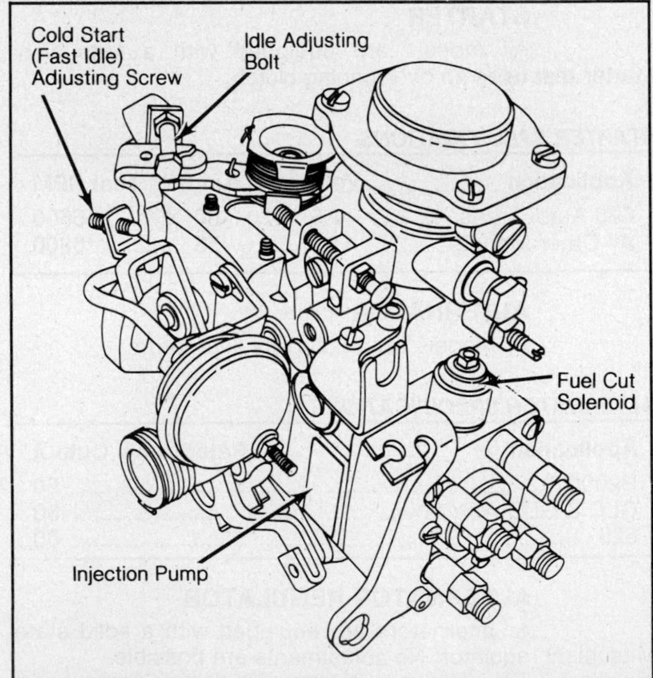
Cold Start
(Fast Idle)
Adjusting Screw
Idle Adjusting
Bolt
Fuel Cut
Solenoid
Injection Pump

TUNE-UP (Cont.)

COLD START SPEED

Pull cold start knob on dashboard to fully extended position. Connect a tachometer to engine. Start engine and note engine RPM. Adjust speed by turning cold start adjusting screw.

COLD START SPEED

Application	RPM
All Models	1150-1250

FUEL SYSTEM BLEEDING

Loosen the fuel filter air vent plug. Pump the head of the fuel filter until fuel flowing from the air vent hole is free of air bubbles. Close the air vent plug.

EMISSION CONTROL SYSTEMS

See Mitchell Manuals' Emission Control Manual.

GENERAL SERVICING

FUEL SYSTEMS

FUEL INJECTION

All models use a Diesel Kiki VE type mechanical fuel injection pump.

DIESEL FUEL INJECTION TIMING

Application	Degrees ATDC	Plunger Travel In. (mm)
B2200	2	.04 (1)

ELECTRICAL

BATTERY

BATTERY SPECIFICATIONS

Application	Amp Hr. Rating
All Models	80

STARTER

All models use a Mitsubishi starter.

STARTER SPECIFICATIONS

Application	Volts	Amps	Test RPM
All Models	11.0	180	3800

ALTERNATORS

All models use a Mitsubishi alternator.

ALTERNATOR SPECIFICATIONS

Application	Rated Amp Output
All Models	40

ALTERNATOR REGULATOR

All models are equipped with a Mitsubishi electronic voltage regulator.

REGULATOR OPERATING VOLTAGE @ 68°F (20°C)

Application	Voltage
All Models	14.1-14.7

SERVICE SPECIFICATIONS

BELT ADJUSTMENT

Application	[1] Deflection In. (mm)
Fan Belt	.3-.4 (9-11)

[1] — With moderate pressure applied midway between pulleys on longest belt run.

REPLACEMENT INTERVALS

Component	Interval (Miles)
Oil & Filter	3750
Air Cleaner	30,000
Fuel Filter	30,000

FLUID CAPACITIES

Application	Quantity
Crankcase (Includes Filter)	6.2 qts. (5.8L)
Cooling System (Includes Heater)	11.1 qts. (10.5L)
Man. Trans. (SAE 90)	
4-Speed	1.5 qts. (1.4L)
5-Speed	1.8 qts. (1.7L)
Rear Axle (SAE 90)	1.4 qts. (1.3L)
Fuel Tank	
Short Bed	14.8 gals. (56.0L)
Long Bed	17.4 gals. (65.9L)

1983 Mazda Rotary Tune-Up

TUNE-UP

RX7

ENGINE IDENTIFICATION

Engine type code is stamped on rear rotor housing, to the rear of oil filter. Engine serial number is stamped on front rotor housing behind distributor.

ENGINE COMPRESSION

The manufacturer recommends using a special compression tester (49 0820 280K). Compression testers for piston engines will read only the highest pressure of the 3 combustion chambers in the rotor housing.

COMPRESSION SPECIFICATIONS

Min. Compression Pressure	86 psi (6.0 kg/cm²)
Max. Variation	21 psi (1.5 kg/cm²)

SPARK PLUGS

SPARK PLUG TYPE

Application	Nippondenso No.	NGK No.
All Models	W25EDR14	BR8EQ14

SPARK PLUG SPECIFICATIONS

Application	Gap In. (mm)	Torque Ft. Lbs. (N.m)
All Models	.055 (1.4)	11 (15)

HIGH TENSION WIRE RESISTANCE

Carefully remove high tension wires from spark plugs and distributor cap. Using an ohmmeter, measure resistance of wires while gently twisting wires. If resistance is not to specifications, or fluctuates from infinity to any value, replace high tension wire(s).

HIGH TENSION WIRE RESISTANCE

Application	Ohms
All Models	4880 per Foot

DISTRIBUTOR

All models are equipped with Mitsubishi electronic ignition with 2 pick-up coils. Air gap is non-adjustable.

IGNITION TIMING

NOTE: **On vehicles equipped with automatic transmission, place selector lever in "D" position and block the wheels.**

Fig. 1: Firing Order and Distributor Rotation

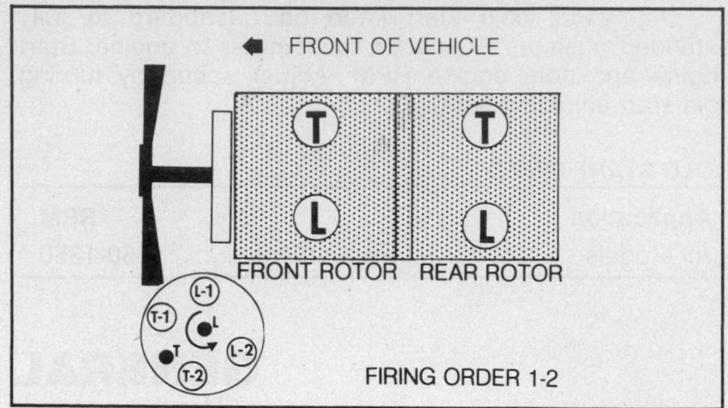

FRONT OF VEHICLE
T
T
L
L
FRONT ROTOR
REAR ROTOR
L-1
T-1
L-2
T-2
FIRING ORDER 1-2

1) Warm engine to normal operating temperature. Connect a tachometer, then connect timing light to leading (lower) spark plug of front rotor. Start engine and run at idle speed.

2) Check ignition timing and rotate distributor to correct if necessary. Tighten distributor lock nut and recheck timing.

3) Connect timing light to trailing (upper) plug of front rotor. Start engine and check timing. If not correct, loosen vacuum unit attaching screws and move vacuum unit in or out to adjust trailing timing. Remove test equipment.

Fig. 2: Connecting Timing Light

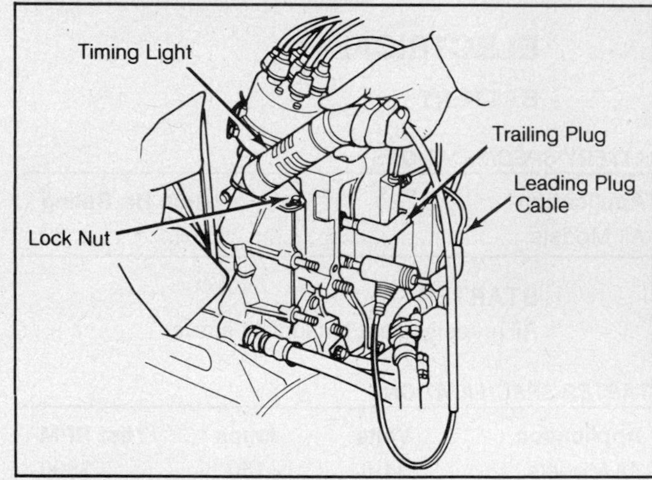

Timing Light
Trailing Plug
Leading Plug Cable
Lock Nut

Check leading plug timing first.

Fig. 3: Ignition Timing Mark Location

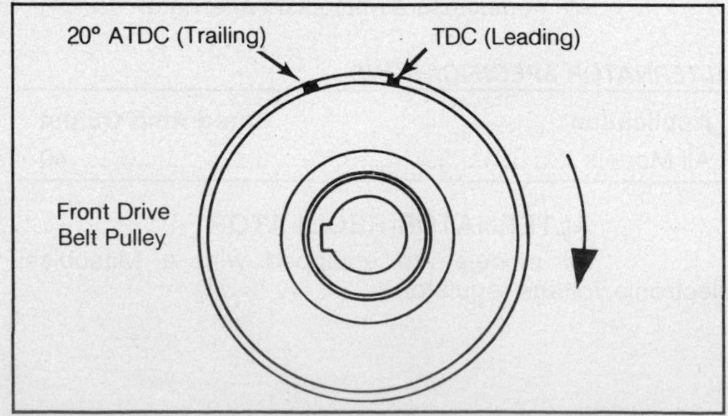

20° ATDC (Trailing)
TDC (Leading)
Front Drive Belt Pulley

TUNE-UP (Cont.)

IGNITION TIMING (Degrees ATDC @ RPM)

Application	Timing
Leading	TDC@750
Trailing	20@750

IDLE SPEED & MIXTURE

IDLE SPEED

1) Switch off all accessories. Remove fuel filler cap. Disconnect and plug idle compensator tube at air cleaner. Connect tachometer to engine. Ensure parking brake is engaged and wheels are blocked.

2) On manual transmission models, make sure dashpot rod does not keep throttle lever from returning to stop. On air conditioned models, make sure throttle opener does not keep throttle lever from returning to stop.

3) Warm engine to normal operating temperature. Place automatic transmission in "D". Check idle speed. Adjust curb idle speed to specification by turning throttle adjusting screw.

IDLE MIXTURE

NOTE: **Mixture adjustment is not part of normal tune-up procedure and should not be performed unless carburetor is overhauled or vehicle fails emissions testing.**

1) Idle mixture adjustment requires removal of carburetor to remove limiter cap. Using a hacksaw, cut through limiter cap and mixture screw 0.4" (10 mm) from cap end. Remove mixture screw and install new mixture screw.

2) To install new mixture screw, tighten screw lightly and ensure it is fully seated. Back screw out 3 turns for preliminary adjustment. Reinstall carburetor with new gaskets and warm engine to normal operating temperature.

3) To adjust idle mixture, set idle speed to idle set specification by turning throttle set screw (automatic transmission in "N"). Set idle speed to highest RPM obtainable by turning mixture screw. Reset idle speed to idle set specification by turning throttle screw. *See Fig. 4*.

4) Turn mixture screw until lean drop specification is obtained (automatic transmission in "N"). On automatic transmission, shift transmission to "D" and set idle speed to curb idle specification by turning throttle screw.

IDLE SPEED & MIXTURE SPECIFICATIONS

Application	Curb Idle RPM	Idle Set RPM	Lean Drop RPM
Man. Trans.	750	770	750
Auto. Trans.	[1] 750	[2] 870	[2] 840

[1] — Transmission in "D".
[2] — Transmission in "N".

Fig. 4: Carburetor Adjusting Screw Locations

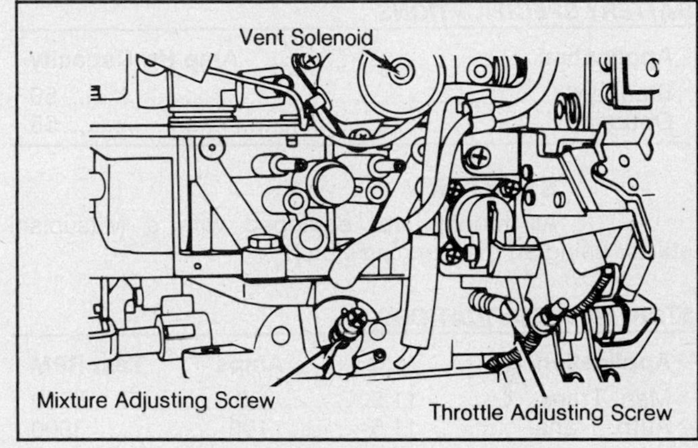
Vent Solenoid
Mixture Adjusting Screw
Throttle Adjusting Screw

COLD (FAST) IDLE RPM

NOTE: **Carburetor must be removed to check and/or adjust fast idle.**

Adjust fast idle by setting angle of primary throttle valve with choke valve fully closed. Clearance between primary throttle valve and throttle bore should be .040-.047" (1.0-1.2 mm). If not to specification, bend fast idle rod until correct clearance is obtained.

FUEL PUMP

FUEL PUMP PERFORMANCE

Application	Pressure psi (kg/cm²)	Volume in 30 Sec. Pints (Liters)
All Models	2.8-3.6 (.2-.3)	1.5 (.7)

EMISSION CONTROL SYSTEMS

See Mitchell Manuals' Emission Control Manual.

GENERAL SERVICING

IGNITION

DISTRIBUTOR

All models are equipped with Mitsubishi electronic ignition with 2 pick-up coils. Air gap is non-adjustable.

IGNITION COIL

IGNITION COIL RESISTANCE — Ohms @ 68°F (20°C)

Application	Primary	Secondary
All Models	1.2-1.5	.....

GENERAL SERVICING (Cont.)

FUEL SYSTEMS

CARBURETOR

All models use a Nikki 4-Bbl. carburetor.

ELECTRICAL

BATTERY

BATTERY SPECIFICATIONS

Application	Amp Hr. Capacity
Standard	50
Optional	55

STARTER

All models are equipped with a Mitsubishi starter using an overrunning clutch.

STARTER SPECIFICATIONS

Application	Volts	Amps	Test RPM
Man. Trans.	11.5	60	6500
Auto. Trans.	11.5	100	3500

ALTERNATOR

All models are equipped with a Mitsubishi alternator.

ALTERNATOR SPECIFICATIONS

Application	Rated Amp Output
All Models	50

ALTERNATOR REGULATOR

All models are equipped with a Mitsubishi voltage regulator.

REGULATOR OPERATING VOLTAGE @ 68°F (20°C)

Application	Voltage
All Models	13.5

SERVICE SPECIFICATIONS

BELT ADJUSTMENT

Application	[1] Deflection In. (mm)
Alternator Belt	.5-.7 (13-17)
Air Pump Belt	.43-.51 (11-13)
A/C Belt	.39-.47 (10-12)

[1] — Deflection is with 22 lbs. (10 kg) pressure applied midway on longest belt run.

REPLACEMENT INTERVALS

Component	Interval (Miles)
Engine Oil	7500
Oil Filter	15,000
Air Filter	30,000
Spark Plugs	30,000

FLUID CAPACITIES

Application	Quantity
Crankcase (Includes Filter)	4.9 qts. (4.6L)
Cooling System (Includes Heater)	10.0 qts. (9.5L)
Man. Trans. (SAE 90)	2.1 qts. (1.9L)
Auto Trans. (ATF Type F)	6.6 qts. (6.2L)
Rear Axle (SAE 90)	
Standard	2.6 pts. (1.2L)
Limited Slip	3.4 pts. (1.6L)
Fuel Tank	16.6 gals. (63L)

TUNE-UP

240D, 300 Turbo Diesel Series

ENGINE IDENTIFICATION

First six digits of engine identification number, located on a tag at the rear, left side of engine crankcase, identify engines as follows:

ENGINE CODE

Application [1]	Code
4-Cylinder	
240D	616.912
5-Cylinder	
300D	617.952
300CD	617.952
300SD	617.951
300TD	617.952

[1] — All models except 240D are turbocharged.

ENGINE COMPRESSION

Check compression pressure with engine at normal operating temperature and throttle valve fully open. Crank engine through at least 8 revolutions.

COMPRESSION SPECIFICATIONS

Compression Ratio	
240D	21.0:1
All Other Models	21.5:1
Compression Pressure	
Normal	
240D	319-348 psi (22.4-24.5 kg/cm²)
All Other Models	348-435 psi (24.4-30.6 kg/cm²)
Minimum	218 psi (15.3 kg/cm²)
Maximum Variation	
Between Cylinders	44 psi (3.1 kg/cm²)

VALVE CLEARANCE

Valves must be adjusted at ignition TDC and in firing order of individual cylinders. With engine cold, measure clearance between rocker arm and base circle of cam. Adjust valves to following specifications:

VALVE CLEARANCE SPECIFICATIONS

Application	[1] In. (mm)
240D (4-Cyl.)	
Intake	.004 (.10)
Exhaust	.012 (.30)
All Other Models (5-Cyl.)	
Intake	.004 (.10)
Exhaust	.014 (.35)

[1] — Valves are adjusted with engine cold.

VALVE ARRANGEMENT

240D

E-I-I-E-E-I-I-E (Front-to-rear)

ALL OTHER MODELS

E-I-I-E-E-I-I-E-E-I (Front-to-rear)

Fig. 1: 240D Firing Order Illustration

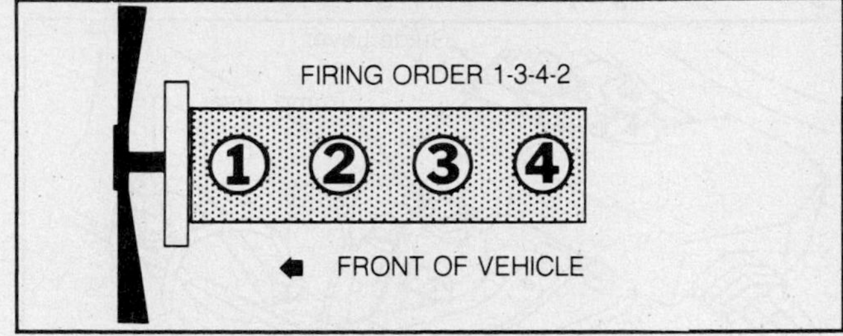
FIRING ORDER 1-3-4-2
1
2
3
4
FRONT OF VEHICLE

Fig. 2: 300 Series Firing Order Illustration

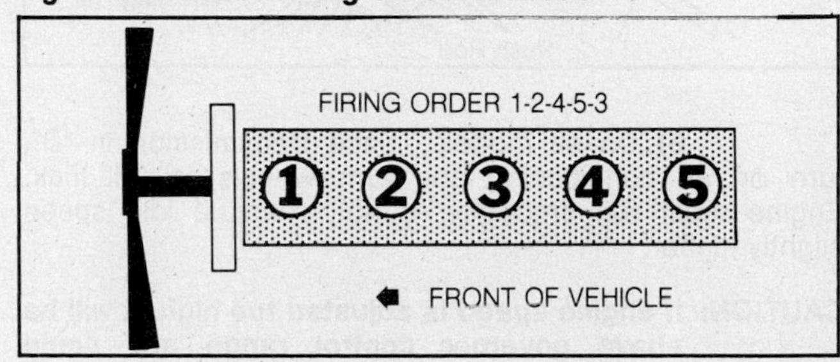
FIRING ORDER 1-2-4-5-3
1
2
3
4
5
FRONT OF VEHICLE

GLOW PLUGS

GLOW PLUG SPECIFICATIONS

Make & Type	Bosch 0 100 221 107
Tightening Torque	15-22 ft. lbs. (20-30 N.m)

IDLE SPEED ADJUSTMENT

1) Start engine and run until normal operating temperature is reached, at least 176°F (80°C) oil temperature. If equipped, turn idle adjusting knob on dashboard clockwise to stop.

2) Disconnect throttle linkage push rod at angle lever. Check idle speed. If necessary, loosen lock nut and adjust with idle adjusting screw.

Fig. 3: Idle Adjusting Screw Location

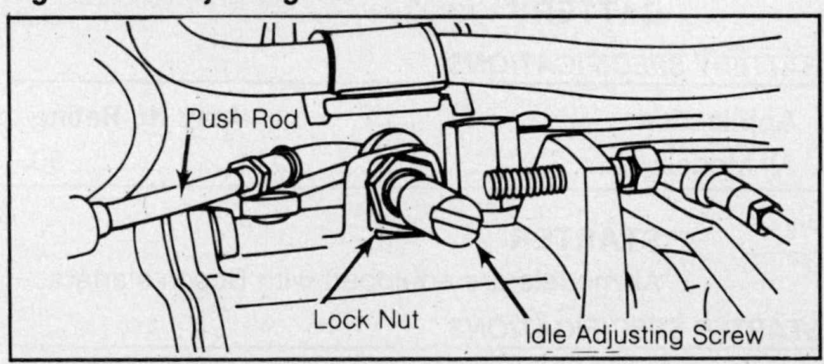
Push Rod
Lock Nut
Idle Adjusting Screw

3) On non-turbo models, adjust push rod so guide lever cam is just resting against switch-over valve lever (free of tension). Injection pump lever should be resting against idle speed stop.

4) Push shutoff ("STOP") lever and ensure cruise control cable is not too tight. Adjust by turning cable nut. When lever is released, a slight amount of clearance should be present. *See Fig. 4*.

5) On turbo models, adjust push rod so roller in guide lever rests, free of tension, against end stop. Disconnect cruise control connecting rod and push lever against idle speed stop. Reattach connecting rod so lever has .039" (1 mm) clearance from stop. *See Fig. 5*.

TUNE-UP (Cont.)

Fig. 4: Adjusting Injection Linkage on Non-Turbo Models

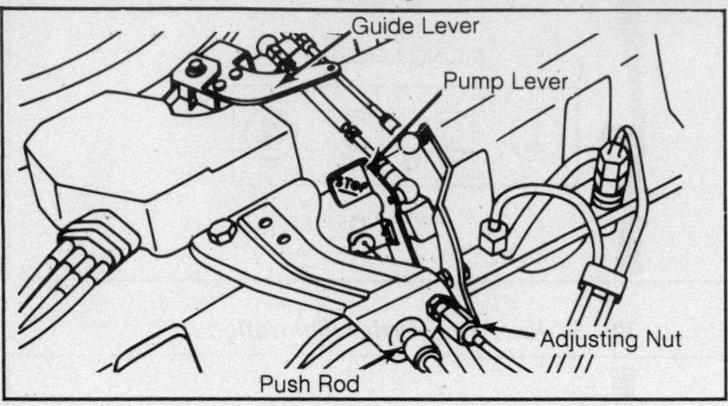
Guide Lever
Pump Lever
Adjusting Nut
Push Rod

Fig. 5: Injection Linkage Adjustment (Turbo Models)

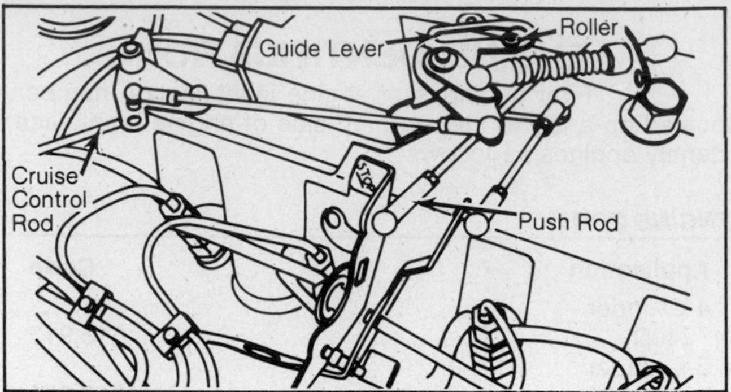
Roller
Guide Lever
Cruise Control Rod
Push Rod

6) On all models, place transmission in "D", turn on air conditioning and turn wheels to full lock. Engine must run smoothly. If not, readjust idle speed slightly higher.

CAUTION: If engine speed is adjusted too high, it will be above governor control range and could increase to maximum RPM when engine is not loaded.

IDLE SPEED SPECIFICATIONS

Application	Idle RPM
240D (4-Cyl.)	700-800
All Other Models (5-Cyl.)	650-850

EMISSION CONTROL SYSTEMS

See Mitchell Manuals' Emission Control Manual.

GENERAL SERVICING

FUEL SYSTEM

All models are equipped with Bosch diesel fuel injection systems.

DIESEL FUEL INJECTION TIMING

Application	Degrees BTDC
All Models	24

ELECTRICAL

BATTERY

BATTERY SPECIFICATIONS

Application	Amp Hr. Rating
All Models	90

STARTER

All models are equipped with Bosch starters.

STARTER SPECIFICATIONS

Application	Volts	Amps	Test RPM
All Models	11.5	65-95	6500

ALTERNATOR

All models are equipped with Bosch alternators, which have integral regulators.

ALTERNATOR SPECIFICATIONS

Application	Rated Amp Output
All Models	55

ALTERNATOR REGULATOR

All models are equipped with Bosch alternator regulators, which are integral with alternator and non-adjustable.

REGULATOR OPERATING VOLTAGE @ 68°F (20°C)

Application	Voltage
All Models	13.0-14.5

SERVICE SPECIFICATIONS

BELT ADJUSTMENT

Application	[1] Deflection In. (mm)
Power Steering Belt	.4 (10)
All Other Belts	.2 (5)

[1] — Deflection with a pressure of 13 lbs. (6 kg) applied midway on longest belt run.

REPLACEMENT INTERVALS

Application	Interval (Miles)
Oil Filter	5000
Air Filter	30,000
Fuel Filter	30,000
Auto. Trans. Filter	30,000

GENERAL SERVICING (Cont.)

FLUID CAPACITIES

Application	Quantity
Crankcase (Includes Filter)	
240D (4-Cyl.)	6.9 qts. (6.5L)
All Other Models (5-Cyl.)	7.9 qts. (7.5L)
Cooling System	
240D (4-Cyl.)	10.6 qts. (10.0L)
All Other Models (5-Cyl.)	13.2 qts. (12.5L)
Man. Trans. (SAE 10W-20)	2.8 pts. (1.3L)
Auto. Trans. (Dexron)	
240D (4-Cyl.)	10.2 pts. (4.8L)
All Other Models (5-Cyl.)	13.2 pts. (6.2L)
Rear Axle (SAE 90)	2.2 pts. (1.0L)
Power Steering (Dexron)	
300SD	2.6 pts. (1.2L)
All Other Models	3.0 pts. (1.4L)
Fuel Tank	
240D	17.0 gals. (65.0L)
300CD & 300D	21.0 gals.(80.0L)
300SD	20.0 gals.(77.0L)
300TD	18.5 gals.(70.0L)

TUNE-UP

380 Series

ENGINE IDENTIFICATION

The engine identification number is located on left rear side of engine crankcase.

ENGINE CODE

Application	Code
380SL	116.962
380SEL & 380SEC	116.963

ENGINE COMPRESSION

Check compression pressure with engine at normal operating temperature, throttle valve fully open and all spark plugs removed. Crank engine at least 8 revolutions per cylinder.

COMPRESSION SPECIFICATIONS

Compression Ratio	8.3:1
Compression Pressure	
Normal	123 psi (8.6 kg/cm²)
Minimum	109 psi (7.7 kg/cm²)
Maximum Variation	
Between Cylinders	22 psi (1.5 kg/cm²)

VALVE CLEARANCE

Mercedes-Benz V8 engines use hydraulic valve lifters and no adjustment is necessary.

VALVE ARRANGEMENT

Right Bank — E-I-E-I-E-I-I-E (Front-to-rear)
Left Bank — E-I-I-E-I-E-I-E (Front-to-rear)

SPARK PLUGS

SPARK PLUG TYPE

Application	Bosch	Champion
All Models	W9D	N12Y

SPARK PLUG SPECIFICATIONS

Application	Gap In. (mm)	Torque Ft. Lbs. (N.m)
All Models	.032 (.81)	22 (30)

HIGH TENSION WIRE RESISTANCE

Carefully remove high tension wires from spark plugs and distributor cap. Using an ohmmeter, check resistance of wires while gently twisting wire.

Resistance should be 25,000-30,000 ohms. If resistance is not as specified, or fluctuates from infinity to any value, replace wire(s).

DISTRIBUTOR

All models are equipped with a Bosch breakerless transistorized distributor. No regular maintenance or adjustments are necessary.

Fig. 1: Firing Order and Distributor Rotation

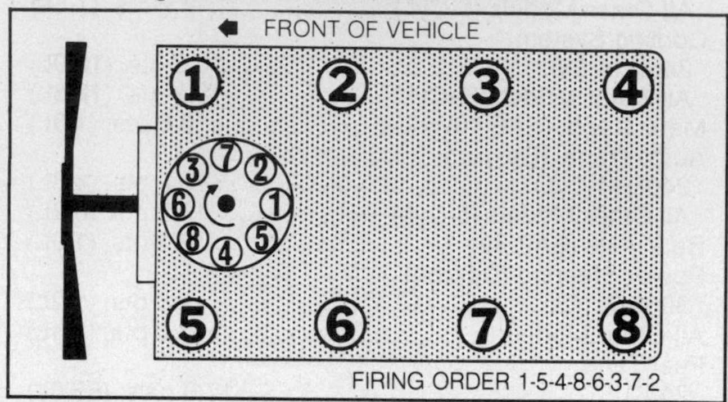
FRONT OF VEHICLE
1
2
3
4
5
6
7
8
FIRING ORDER 1-5-4-8-6-3-7-2

Illustration applies to all models.

IGNITION TIMING

Check or adjust ignition timing with engine at normal operating temperature, idle speed set to specifications and distributor vacuum lines connected.

IGNITION TIMING (Degrees BTDC @ RPM)

Application	Auto. Trans.
All Models	5@500

Fig. 2: Ignition Timing Mark Location

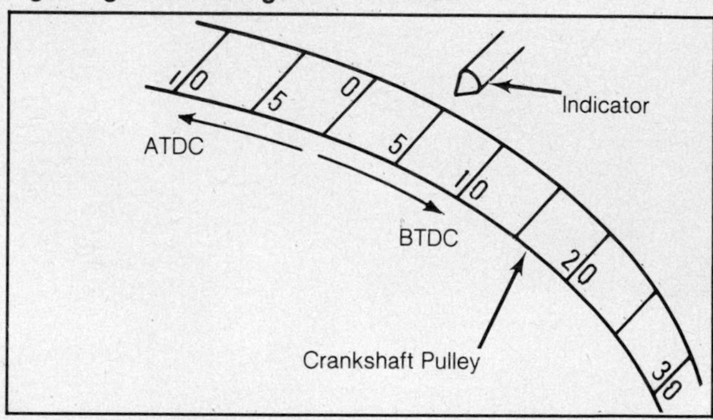
Indicator
ATDC
BTDC
Crankshaft Pulley
10
5
0
5
10
20
30

IDLE SPEED & MIXTURE

IDLE SPEED

All models are equipped with electronic idle speed control and no adjustments are necessary.

IDLE SPEED SPECIFICATIONS

Application	Idle RPM
All Models [1]	
Engine Cold	750
Engine Warm	500-600

[1] – Non-adjustable.

TUNE-UP (Cont.)

IDLE MIXTURE

NOTE: **Mixture control unit adjustment screw opening is plugged to prevent tampering. Adjustment is not a normal maintenance procedure and should not be performed unless mixture control unit is replaced or vehicle fails emissions testing.**

1) Warm engine to normal operating temperature and adjust timing. Remove cover from diagnostic plug (on fender panel near hood hinge). Connect voltmeter negative lead to pin 3 of plug, and positive lead to battery voltage.

2) Disconnect oxygen sensor plug (near sensor under vehicle). Observe voltmeter reading and place a piece of tape on voltmeter dial to indicate needle position. Needle should not be moving.

NOTE: **Oxygen sensor plug is inside a holder. Remove holder bolt (if necessary), push plug out of holder, and disconnect.**

3) Reconnect oxygen sensor. Needle should vibrate and vibrations should be centered around mark on voltmeter. If not, adjustment is necessary.

4) Remove plug from mixture control unit. Insert Allen wrench and adjust mixture screw carefully until needle is centered around mark on voltmeter dial. Remove test equipment and plug adjustment opening.

FUEL PUMP

FUEL PUMP PERFORMANCE

Application	Pressure psi (kg/cm²)	Volume in 30 Sec. Pints (Liters)
All Models	72-81 (5.0-5.6)	2 (.9)

EMISSION CONTROL SYSTEMS

See Mitchell Manuals' Emission Control Manual.

GENERAL SERVICING

IGNITION

DISTRIBUTOR

All models are equipped with a Bosch breakerless transistorized distributor. No regular maintenance or adjustments are necessary.

IGNITION COIL

IGNITION COIL RESISTANCE — Ohms @ 68°F (20°C)

Application	Primary	Secondary
All Models	.38-.42	8000-11,000

FUEL SYSTEMS

FUEL INJECTION

All models use Bosch Lambda Continuous Injection System fuel injection.

ELECTRICAL

BATTERY

BATTERY SPECIFICATIONS

Application	Amp Hr. Rating
380SEC & 380SEL	66
380 SL	88

STARTER

All models are equipped with Bosch starters.

STARTER SPECIFICATIONS

Application	Volts	Amps	Test RPM
All Models	11.5	50-80	8300

ALTERNATOR

All models are equipped with Bosch integrally regulated alternators.

ALTERNATOR SPECIFICATIONS

Application	Rated Amp Output
380 SEC & 380 SEL	80
380 SL	70

ALTERNATOR REGULATOR

All models are equipped with Bosch integral alternator regulators.

REGULATOR OPERATING VOLTAGE @ 68°F (20°C)

Application	Volts
All Models	13.0-14.5

SERVICE SPECIFICATIONS

BELT ADJUSTMENT

Application	[1] Deflection In. (mm)
Power Steering Belt	.4 (10)
All Other Belts	.2 (5)

[1] — With moderate thumb pressure applied midway between pulleys.

REPLACEMENT INTERVALS

Component	Interval (Miles)
Oil & Filter	7500
Air Filter	30,000
Auto. Trans. Filter	30,000
Spark Plugs	30,000
Oxygen Sensor	30,000
Fuel Filter	60,000

GENERAL SERVICING (Cont.)

FLUID CAPACITIES

Application	Quantity
Crankcase (Includes Filter)	8.5 qts. (8.0L)
Cooling System	13.2 qts. (12.5L)
Auto. Trans. (Dexron)	8.0 qts. (7.7L)
Rear Axle (SAE 90)	2.8 pts. (1.3L)
Power Steering (Dexron)	
380SL	3.0 pts. (1.5L)
380SEC & 380SEL	2.6 pts. (1.2L)
Fuel Tank	
380SL	22.5 gals. (85.0L)
380SEC & 380SEL	24.0 gals. (90.0L)

TUNE-UP

Cordia, Montero, Pickup, Starion (Turbo) & Tredia

ENGINE IDENTIFICATION

The engine model and serial number is stamped on the upper right front of the cylinder block. The model number is a 4 digit code beginning with "G". The serial number is a 6 or 8 digit code stamped below the model number.

ENGINE CODE

Application	Code
Cordia & Tredia 1.8L	G62B
Montero & Starion 2.6L	G54B
Pickup	
2.0L	G63B
2.6L	G54B

ENGINE COMPRESSION

Check compression pressure with engine at normal operating temperature, choke and throttle valves wide open and engine at cranking speed (250 RPM). Crank engine at least 6 revolutions per cylinder to determine engine compression.

COMPRESSION SPECIFICATIONS

Compression Ratio	
1.8L & 2.0L	8.5:1
2.6L	
Montero & Pickup	8.2:1
Starion	7.0:1
Compression Pressure	149 psi (10.5 kg/cm²)
Maximum Variation Between Cylinders	10%

VALVE CLEARANCE

NOTE: Jet valve clearance must be adjusted before adjusting intake valve clearance. Loosen intake valve adjusting screw at least 2 full turns before adjusting jet valve.

Check or adjust valve clearance with engine off, at normal operating temperature and with coil wire to distributor disconnected. To adjust valves, loosen lock nut and turn adjusting screw until specified clearance is obtained.

VALVE CLEARANCE SPECIFICATIONS

Application	In. (mm)
Jet	.006 (.15)
Intake	.006 (.15)
Exhaust	.010 (.25)

VALVE ARRANGEMENT

Left Side — All intake
Right Side — All exhaust

SPARK PLUGS

SPARK PLUG TYPE

Application	NGK	Nippondenso
Cordia, Starion		
Tredia	BUR6EA-11	W20EPR-S11
Montero	BP5ES-11	W16EPR-U10
Pickup		
2.0L	BUR6EA-11	W20EPR-S11
2.6L	BPR5ES-11	W16EPR-11

SPARK PLUG SPECIFICATIONS

Application	Gap In. (mm)	Torque Ft. Lbs. (N.m)
All Models	.041 (1.0)	19 (26)

HIGH TENSION WIRE RESISTANCE

Carefully remove high tension wires from spark plugs and distributor cap. Twist wire gently while measuring resistance with ohmmeter. If resistance is greater than specified value, or fluctuates from infinity to any value, replace wire.

HIGH TENSION WIRE RESISTANCE

Application	Ohms
All Models	4880 per Foot.

DISTRIBUTOR

All models use a Mitsubishi breakerless electronic ignition system. No adjustments are necessary.

Fig. 1: 1.8L Firing Order & Distributor Rotation

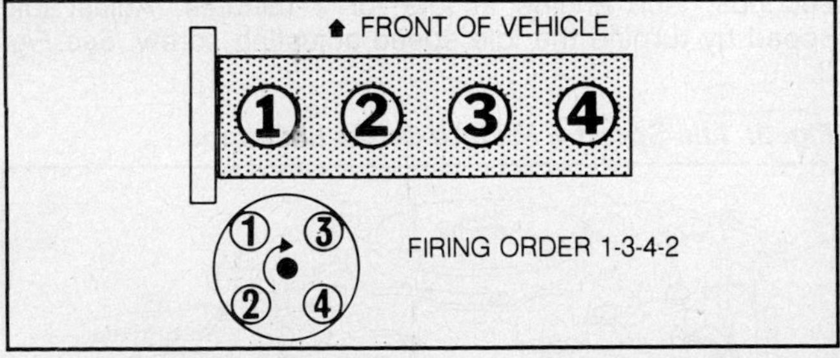
FRONT OF VEHICLE
1 2 3 4
1 3
2 4
FIRING ORDER 1-3-4-2

Fig. 2: 2.0L & 2.6L Firing Order & Distributor Rotation

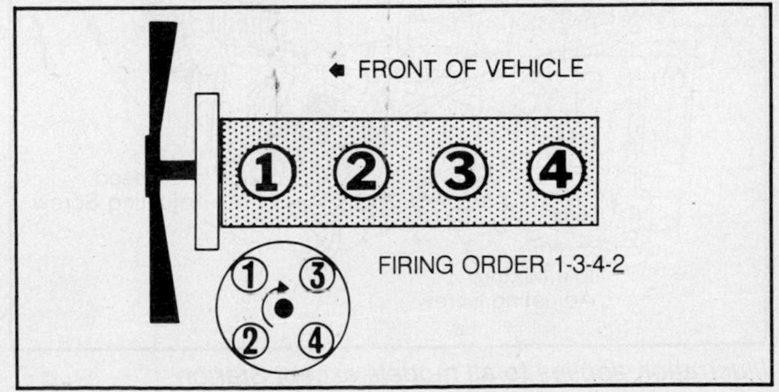
FRONT OF VEHICLE
1 2 3 4
1 3
2 4
FIRING ORDER 1-3-4-2

TUNE-UP (Cont.)

IGNITION TIMING

1) Turn lights and all accessories off. Disconnect electric cooling fan, if equipped. Position transmission in Neutral. Run engine at fast idle until normal operating temperature is obtained. Stop engine and connect tachometer and timing light.

2) On 1.8L and Federal 2.0L engines with 5-speed manual transmissions, disconnect and plug vacuum hoses at distributor. On Montero models, disconnect and plug White striped hose at distributor. Start engine and run at curb idle speed.

3) On all models, adjust ignition timing by loosening distributor hold down nut and rotating distributor. Stop engine. Unplug and reconnect vacuum hoses. Remove test equipment and reconnect electric cooling fan, if equipped.

IGNITION TIMING (Degrees BTDC@RPM)

Application	Man. Trans.	Auto. Trans.
1.8L	5@650 [1]	5@750
2.0L	5@750 [2]	5@750
2.6L		
Starion	10@850 [3]	.....
All Others	7@750	7@800

[1] — Set 4x2-Speed to 5@700.
[2] — Set Federal 5-Speed to 5@700.
[3] — Idle speed controlled by computer.

IDLE SPEED AND MIXTURE

IDLE SPEED

All Except Starion

1) Engine must be at normal operating temperature with all electrical accessories turned off. Place transmission in neutral.

2) Run engine at 2000-3000 RPM for 5 seconds. Run engine at idle for 2 minutes. Adjust idle speed by turning the idle speed adjusting screw. *See Fig. 3.*

Fig. 3: Idle Speed & Mixture Screw Locations

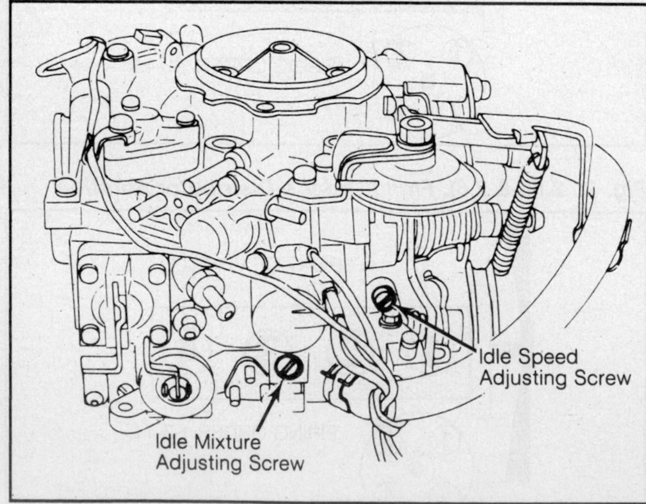
Idle Speed
Adjusting Screw
Idle Mixture
Adjusting Screw

Illustration applies to all models except Starion.

Starion

1) Start and warm engine to 176-194°F (80-90°C). Turn all lights and accessories off. Place transmission in Neutral. Accelerate engine 2 or 3 times at 2000-3000 RPM.

2) Allow engine to return to idle and check ignition timing. Adjust timing to specifications, if necessary.

3) Remove rubber cap from idle switch without disconnecting cable connector. Adjust idle speed to specifications by turning idle switch. *See Fig. 4.*

4) If idle switch is turned more than 1 turn during adjustment, disconnect connector and connect it to the dummy terminal.

Fig. 4: Idle Speed Adjustment for Starion

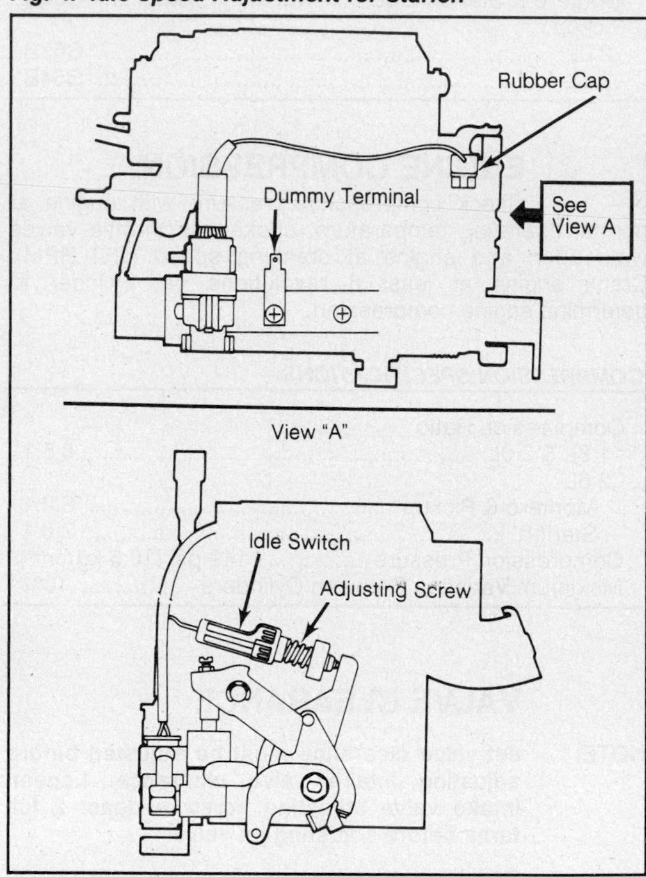
Rubber Cap
Dummy Terminal
See
View A
View "A"
Idle Switch
Adjusting Screw

If idle switch is turned more than 1 turn, disconnect connector and connect it to dummy terminal.

IDLE SPEED SPECIFICATIONS

Application	Man. Trans. RPM	Auto. Trans. RPM
1.8L	[1] 550-750	650-850
2.0L	[2] 650-850	650-850
2.6L		
Starion	750-850	.....
All Others	650-850	700-900

[1] - Set 4x2-Speed to 700 RPM.
[2] - Set Federal 5-Speed to 700 RPM.

TUNE-UP (Cont.)

THROTTLE OPENER SYSTEM

Engines With A/C Only

1) Turn lights and accessories off, place transmission in Neutral. Run engine until normal operating temperature is obtained. Disconnect electric cooling fan, if equipped.

2) Make sure that curb idle speed is within specifications. If necessary, reset idle speed to specifications.

3) On 1.8L engines, turn A/C off and disconnect vacuum hose from throttle opener nipple. Connect vacuum pump to nipple and apply 20 in. Hg. On all other engines, turn A/C on.

4) On all models, adjust engine speed to specification by turning throttle opener screw. *See Fig. 5.* After adjustment, reconnect vacuum hose and electric cooling fan, if equipped.

Fig. 5: Adjusting Throttle Opener System

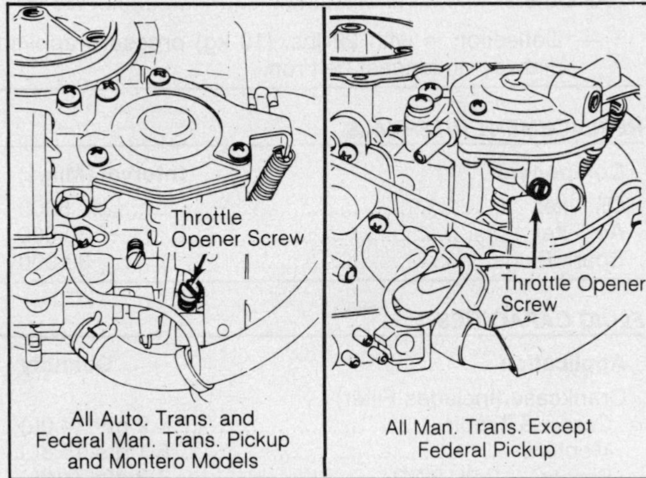
Throttle
Opener Screw
Throttle Opener
Screw
All Auto. Trans. and
Federal Man. Trans. Pickup
and Montero Models
All Man. Trans. Except
Federal Pickup

This adjustment is only for gasoline engines with A/C.

THROTTLE OPENER SPEED SPECIFICATIONS

Application	RPM
1.8L	1250-1350
All Others	850-950

IDLE MIXTURE

NOTE: **Idle mixture is not a part of a normal tune-up procedure and should not be performed unless carburetor is overhauled, fuel injection components are replaced, or vehicle fails emissions testing.**

All Except Starion

1) Remove carburetor from engine and clamp in vise with mixture adjusting screw facing up. Protect gasket surface from damage of vise jaws.

2) Drill a 5/64" pilot hole in throttle body casting surrounding idle mixture adjusting screw. Redrill hole to 1/8". *See Fig. 6.* Insert a blunt punch into hole just drilled and drive out concealment plug. Reinstall the carburetor.

Fig. 6: Removing Mixture Screw Concealment Plug

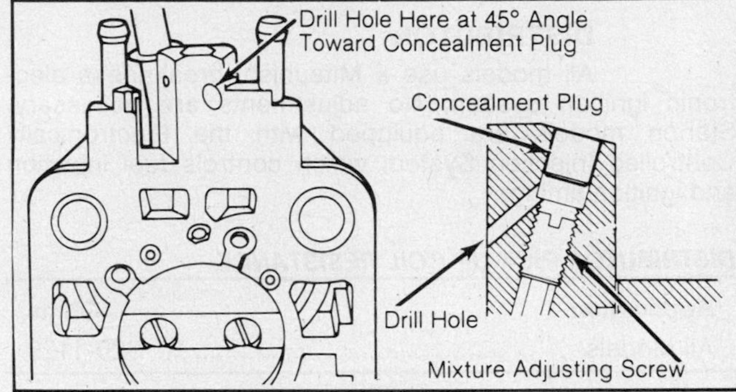
Drill Hole Here at 45° Angle
Toward Concealment Plug
Concealment Plug
Drill Hole
Mixture Adjusting Screw

Protect gasket surface from damage.

3) Turn lights and accessories off. Place transmission in Neutral and turn off electric cooling fan, if equipped. Start and run engine until normal operating temperature is obtained. Disconnect and plug hose from air cleaner to pulse air feeder (secondary air hose).

4) Run engine for more than 5 seconds at 2000-3000 RPM. Run engine at idle speed for 2 minutes. Set engine idle speed and idle CO to specified values by turning idle speed and idle mixture screws.

5) Unplug and reconnect hose to air cleaner. If engine idle speed is not to specification, reset speed by turning idle speed screw. Reinstall idle mixture screw concealment plug.

Starion

Idle mixture on Starion models is controlled electronically and is non-adjustable.

CO LEVEL SPECIFICATIONS

Application	[1] CO%
All Models	0.5

[1] — With air injection disconnected.

COLD (FAST) IDLE RPM

All models with carburetors are equipped with a factory sealed, tamper proof automatic choke. All choke related parts are factory adjusted. Fast idle on Starion models is controlled by the electronic fuel injection system.

FUEL PUMP

FUEL PUMP PERFORMANCE

Application	Pressure psi (kg/cm²)	Volume in 30 Sec. Pints (Liters)
2.0L & 2.6L	4.6-6.0 (.32-.42)	2.1 (1.0)
Starion 2.6L	35-47 (2.5-3.3)	.....

EMISSION CONTROL SYSTEMS

See Mitchell Manuals' Emission Control Manual.

1983 Mitsubishi 4 Tune-Up

GENERAL SERVICING

IGNITION

DISTRIBUTOR

All models use a Mitsubishi breakerless electronic ignition system. No adjustments are necessary. Starion models are equipped with the Electronically Controlled Injection System which controls fuel injection and ignition timing.

DISTRIBUTOR PICK-UP COIL RESISTANCE

Application	Ohms
All Models	920-1120

IGNITION COIL

IGNITION COIL RESISTANCE — Ohms @ 68°F (20°C)

Application	Primary	Secondary
All Models	1.04-1.27	7100-9600

FUEL SYSTEMS

All vehicles except Starion are equipped with Solex (Mikuni) model 32-35 DIDTA 2-barrel carburetors. The Starion model is equipped with the Electronically Controlled Injection System (ECI), a throttle body type of fuel injection system.

ELECTRICAL

BATTERY

BATTERY SPECIFICATIONS

Application	Amp Hr. Rating
All Models	45

STARTER

All models are equipped with a Mitsubishi starter using an overrunning clutch.

STARTER SPECIFICATIONS

Application	Volts	Amps	Test RPM
Pickup			
Auto. Trans.	11.5	100	3000
All Others	11.5	60	6500

ALTERNATOR

All models use a Mitisubishi alternator with an integral regulator.

ALTERNATOR SPECIFICATIONS

Application	Rated Amp Output
Cordia, Starion & Tredia	65
Montero & Pickup	45

ALTERNATOR REGULATOR

All models are with Mitsubishi solid state voltage regulators.

REGULATOR OPERATING VOLTAGE @ 68°F (20°C)

Application	Volts
Cordia, Starion & Tredia	14.1-14.7
Montero & Pickup	13.9-14.9

SERVICE SPECIFICATIONS

BELT ADJUSTMENT

Application	[1] Deflection In. (mm)
Air Conditioner	
Cordia, Tredia & Pickup	.35 (8)
Montero & Starion	.7 (17)
Alternator	.35 (8)
Power Steering	
Montero	.40 (9)
All Others	.35 (8)

[1] — Deflection is with 22 lbs. (10 kg) pressure applied midway on longest belt run.

REPLACEMENT INTERVALS

Component	Interval (Miles)
Oil Filter	6000
Air Filter	30,000
Spark Plugs	30,000

FLUID CAPACITIES

Application	Quantity
Crankcase (Includes Filter)	
Cordia & Tredia	4.2 qts. (4.0L)
Montero	6.1 qts. (5.8L)
Pickup – 2.0L 2WD	4.2 qts. (4.0L)
Pickup – 2.0L 4WD & 2.6L 4WD	5.2 qts. (5.0L)
Pickup – 2.6L 4WD	6.1 qts. (5.8L)
Starion	4.5 qts. (4.3L)
Cooling System	
Cordia & Tredia	7.4 qts. (7.0L)
Montero	8.5 qts. (8.0L)
Pickup	9.5 qts. (9.0L)
Starion	9.7 qts. (9.2L)
Manual Transaxle (75W-85W)	4.4 pts. (2.1L)
Manual Transmission (75W-85W)	
Montero	4.6 pts. (2.2L)
Pickup – 2WD 4-Speed	4.4 pts. (2.1L)
Pickup – 2WD 5-Speed	4.9 pts. (2.4L)
Pickup – 4WD	4.6 pts. (2.2L)
Starion	4.8 pts. (2.3L)
Automatic Transaxle (Dexron)	12.2 pts. (5.8L)
Automatic Transmission (Dexron)	14.4 pts. (6.8L)
Rear Axle (85W-90)	
Montero	3.8 pts. (1.8L)
Pickup	3.2 pts. (1.5L)
Starion	2.7 pts. (1.3L)
Front Axle (85W-90)	2.3 pts. (1.1L)
Transfer Case (75W-85W)	4.6 pts. (2.2L)
Fuel Tank	
Cordia & Tredia	13.0 gals. (50.0L)
Montero	16.0 gals. (60.0L)
Pickup – 2WD	15.0 gals. (57.0L)
Pickup – 4WD	18.0 gals. (68.0L)
Starion	20.0 gals. (75.0L)

TUNE-UP

Pickup

ENGINE IDENTIFICATION

The engine model number and serial number are located on the left side of the engine, just to the rear of the dipstick.

ENGINE CODE

Application	Code
2.3L Turbo Diesel	4D55

ENGINE COMPRESSION

Warm engine to normal operating temperature. Operate starter at 250 RPM and read compression.

COMPRESSION SPECIFICATIONS

Compression Ratio	21:1
Compression Pressure	384 psi (27 kg/cm²)

VALVE CLEARANCE

1) Run engine until coolant reaches normal operating temperature of 176-194°F (80-90°C). Place piston in No. 1 cylinder at TDC on compression stroke to adjust valve clearances marked "1".

Fig. 1: Adjusting Valve Clearance of Mitsubishi Diesel

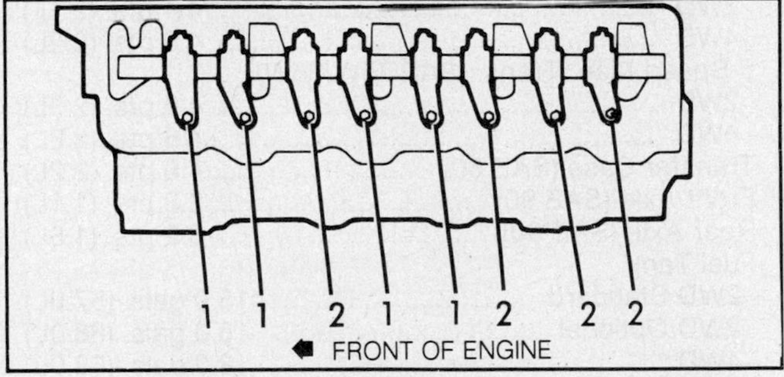
1 1 2 1 1 2 2 2
FRONT OF ENGINE

2) Loosen nut and adjust to specifications with adjusting screw. Retighten nut. Check valve clearance again. Place piston of No. 4 cylinder at TDC of compression stroke to adjust valve clearances marked "2".

3) Adjust valve clearance in same manner as for valves marked "1". Check idle speed and readjust clearance if necessary.

VALVE CLEARANCE SPECIFICATIONS

Application	In. (mm)
Intake and Exhaust (Hot)	.010 (.25)

VALVE ARRANGEMENT

E-I-E-I-E-I-E-I (Front-to-rear)

GLOW PLUGS

GLOW PLUG TORQUE SPECIFICATIONS

Application	Ft. Lbs. (N.m)
All Models	11-14 (15-19)

Fig. 2: Mitsubishi Diesel Firing Order Illustration

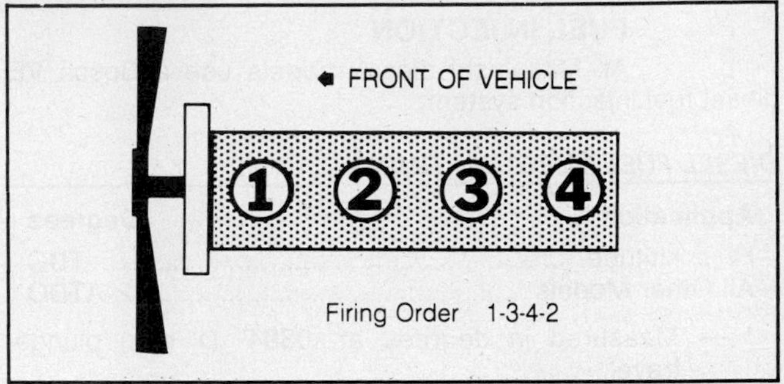
FRONT OF VEHICLE
1
2
3
4
Firing Order 1-3-4-2

IDLE SPEED

1) Turn all lights and accessories off, and place transmission in neutral. Operate cold engine at fast idle until coolant temperature reaches 185-205°F (85-95°C). Run engine at 2000-3000 RPM for more than 5 seconds.

Fig. 3: Diesel Idle Speed Adjusting Screw

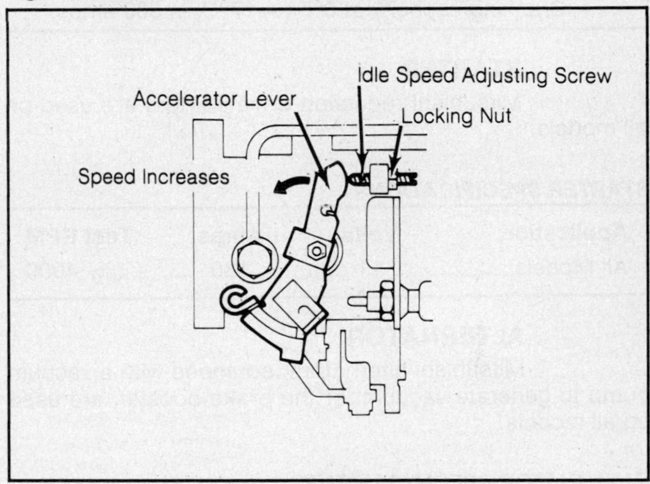
Idle Speed Adjusting Screw
Accelerator Lever
Locking Nut
Speed Increases

2) Run engine at idle speed for 2 minutes. Using a tachometer, read idle speed. If not to specifications, readjust speed using idle speed adjusting screw. Do not disturb other screws.

IDLE SPEED SPECIFICATIONS

Application	Idle RPM
All Models	700-850

FUEL SYSTEM BLEEDING

Loosen the air vent screw on top of fuel filter housing. Pull out the priming pump knob by turning it to the left. Pump the priming pump until fuel flowing out of vent hole is free of air bubbles. Tighten the air vent screw.

EMISSION CONTROL SYSTEMS

See Mitchell Manual's Emission Control Manual.

1983 Mitsubishi Diesel 4 Tune-Up

GENERAL SERVICING

FUEL SYSTEMS

FUEL INJECTION

All Mitsubishi diesel models use a Bosch VE diesel fuel injection system.

DIESEL FUEL INJECTION TIMING [1]

Application	Degrees
High Altitude	TDC
All Other Models	2°ATDC

[1] — Measured in degrees at .0394" (1 mm) plunger travel.

ELECTRICAL

BATTERY

BATTERY SPECIFICATIONS

Application	Amp Hr. Rating
All Models	[1] 80

[1] — Cranking capacity at 0°F (—17°C) is 600 amps.

STARTER

Mitsubishi reduction drive starters are used on all models.

STARTER SPECIFICATIONS

Application	Volts	Amps	Test RPM
All Models	11	130	4000

ALTERNATOR

Mitsubishi alternators, equipped with a vacuum pump to generate vacuum for the brake booster, are used on all models.

ALTERNATOR SPECIFICATIONS

Application	Rated Amp Output
All Models	50

ALTERNATOR REGULATOR

All models are equipped with Mitsubishi IC alternator regulators.

REGULATOR OPERATING VOLTAGE @ 68°F (20°C)

Application	Voltage
All Models	13.9-14.9

GLOW PLUGS

GLOW PLUG SYSTEM RESISTANCE @ 68°F (20°C)

Application	Ohms
Glow Plugs	0.10
Dropping Resistor	0.13

SERVICE SPECIFICATIONS

BELT ADJUSTMENT

Application	[1] Deflection In. (mm)
All Belts	3/8 - 1/2 (10-13)

[1] — With force of 22 lbs. (10 kg) pressure applied midway between pulleys on longest belt run.

REPLACEMENT INTERVALS

Component	Interval (Miles)
Oil Filter	6000
Fuel Filter	30,000
Air Filter	30,000
Turbo Air Intake Hose	30,000
Turbo Oil Hose	50,000

FLUID CAPACITIES

Application	Quantity
Crankcase, Including Filter (API CD)	
2WD	5.0 qts. (4.8L)
4WD	6.3 qts. (6.1L)
Cooling System [1]	
2WD	8.5 qts. (8.0L)
4WD	8.5 qts. (8.0L)
Engine Oil Cooler	0.3 pts. (0.5L)
4-Speed Man. Trans. (SAE 75W-85W)	
2WD	4.4 pts. (2.1L)
4WD	4.6 pts. (2.2L)
5-Speed Man. Trans. (SAE 75W-85W)	
2WD	4.9 pts. (2.3L)
4WD	4.6 pts. (2.2L)
Transfer Case (SAE 80)	4.6 pts. (2.2L)
Front Axle (SAE 90)	2.3 pts. (1.1L)
Rear Axle (SAE 90)	3.2 pts. (1.5L)
Fuel Tank	
2WD Standard	15.0 gals. (57.0L)
2WD Optional	18.0 gals. (68.0L)
4WD	18.0 gals. (68.0L)

[1] - Includes heater and coolant reserve system.

TUNE-UP

505

ENGINE IDENTIFICATION

The gas engine in all 505 models is referred to as XN6 version. Engine codes are stamped on camshaft tunnel on left side of block.

ENGINE CODE

Application	Code
505	
Man. Trans.	M5 BVM
Auto. Trans.	A3 BVA

ENGINE COMPRESSION

Check compression with battery fully charged and engine at normal cranking speed.

COMPRESSION SPECIFICATIONS

Compression Ratio	8.4:1

VALVE CLEARANCE

Valves must be set with engine cold. To adjust valves, remove valve cover and rotate crankshaft until valve listed in 1st column of table is fully open. Adjust valves listed in 2nd column of table. Replace valve cover.

NOTE: **Valves and cylinders are numbered from rear to front.**

VALVE ADJUSTMENT SEQUENCE

Exhaust Valve Open	Valves to Adjust
No. 1	No. 3 Int. & No. 4 Exh.
No. 3	No. 4 Int. & No. 2 Exh.
No. 4	No. 2 Int. & No. 1 Exh.
No. 2	No. 1 Int. & No. 3 Exh.

VALVE CLEARANCE SPECIFICATIONS

Application	Intake In. (mm)	Exhaust In. (mm)
All Models [1]	.004 (.10)	.010 (.25)

[1] — Set valves with engine cold.

VALVE ARRANGEMENT

Right Side — All Exhaust
Left Side — All Intake

SPARK PLUGS

SPARK PLUG TYPE

Application	Bosch No.
All Models	WR7DS

SPARK PLUG SPECIFICATIONS

Application	Gap In. (mm)	Torque Ft. Lbs. (N.m)
All Models	.024 (.61)	15 (20)

HIGH TENSION WIRE RESISTANCE

Carefully remove high tension wires from spark plugs and distributor cap. Using an ohmmeter, check high tension wire resistance while gently twisting wire. If resistance is not to specification or fluctuates from infinity to any value, replace wire(s).

HIGH TENSION WIRE RESISTANCE

Application	Ohms
All Models	6000

DISTRIBUTOR

All models use a Ducellier single pick-up breakerless distributor in conjunction with an AC Delco coil and transistorized amplifier module.

The only adjustment provided is for air gap between the reluctor and pick-up coil in the distributor. Measure gap using a non-magnetic feeler gauge.

DISTRIBUTOR AIR GAP SPECIFICATIONS

Application	In. (mm)
All Models	.012-.020 (.30-.50)

Fig. 1: 505 Firing Order & Distributor Rotation

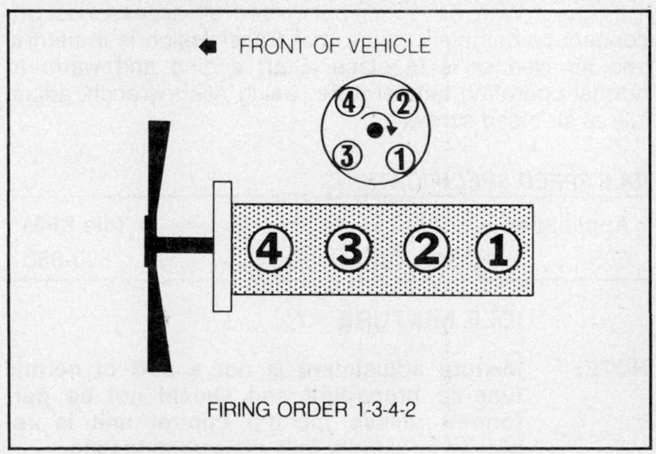
FRONT OF VEHICLE
4
2
3
1
4
3
2
1
FIRING ORDER 1-3-4-2

IGNITION TIMING

1) Disconnect and plug distributor vacuum line. Connnect a timng light to No. 1 cylinder. Start engine and warm to normal operating temperature.

2) With engine idling at 800 RPM, check ignition timing. If timing is not correct, loosen distributor flange and rotate distributor to adjust timing to correct specification. When timing is correct, tighten distributor flange and reconnect distributor vacuum hose.

TUNE-UP (Cont.)

IGNITION TIMING (Degrees BTDC@RPM)

Application	Timing
505	[1] 8@800

[1] — Transmission in Neutral

Fig. 2: Ignition Timing Marks

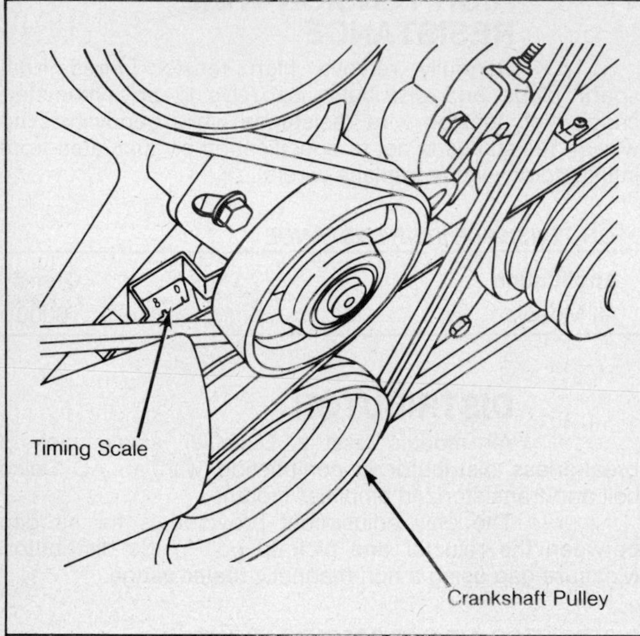
Timing Scale
Crankshaft Pulley

IDLE SPEED & MIXTURE

IDLE SPEED

With air conditioning and all accessories off, connect tachometer. Insure that transmission is in neutral and air cleaner is in place. Start engine and warm to normal operating temperature. Using Allen wrench, adjust idle at air bleed screw.

IDLE SPEED SPECIFICATIONS

Application	Idle RPM
505	800-850

IDLE MIXTURE

NOTE: **Mixture adjustment is not a part of normal tune-up procedure and should not be performed unless mixture control unit is replaced or vehicle fails emissions testing.**

1) Adjust idle speed. Connect CO meter to front tap in catalytic converter. Disconnect wire 47C from thermovalve and ground it. Disconnect and plug vacuum supply hose to canister purge valve and air injection hose at diverter valve.

2) Check CO reading. If reading is not to specification given in table, proceed with mixture adjustment. Stop engine and disconnect battery.

3) Remove mixture control unit and set it upside down. Pull out plug at mixture adjustment opening. Push anti-stall stop into control unit. Reinstall mixture control unit and reconnect battery.

4) Start engine and warm to normal operating temperature. If necessary, readjust idle at air bleed screw. Using Allen wrench adjust fuel mixture to obtain correct CO specification. Accelerate engine and recheck CO reading. If not correct, repeat adjustment procedure.

5) Remove testing equipment and reconnect thermovalve wire 47C, canister purge and air injection hoses. Install new plug in mixture adjustment opening.

CO LEVEL SPECIFICATIONS

Application	CO%
505	[1] 0.3-1.3

[1] — With air injection disconnected.

COLD (FAST) IDLE RPM

1) With engine at operating temperature and idle correctly adjusted, place transmission in neutral and turn off all accessories. Stop engine.

2) Disconnect hose with green ring from vacuum "T" near Solex valve (right fender panel). Disconnect hose with red ring from Solex valve and connect it to "T". This applies vacuum to idle speed diaphragm.

3) Remove domed nut "1" shown in *Fig. 3*. Loosen lock nut "2" and start engine. Engine speed should be as specified.

4) If engine speed is not correct, adjust screw "3" to specification, using a 3 mm Allen wrench. Tighten lock nut "2" and install domed nut "1", making sure gasket is in place.

Fig. 3 Adjusting Fast Idle at Deceleration Vacuum Unit

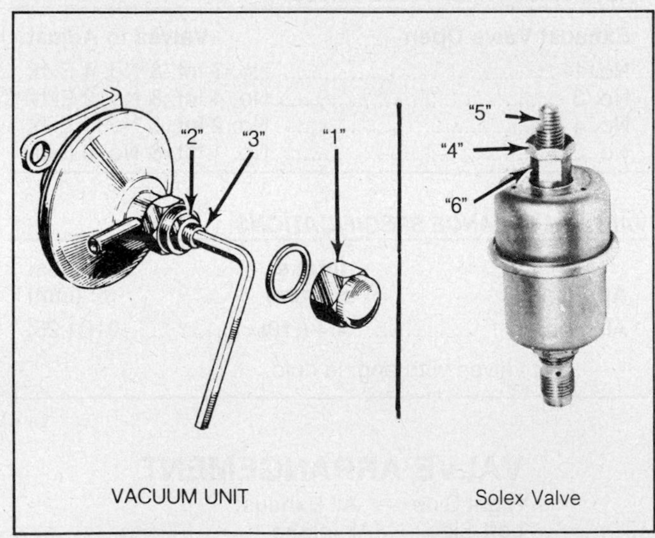
"2"
"3"
"1"
"5"
"4"
"6"
VACUUM UNIT
Solex Valve

5) Return vacuum hoses to original locations. Loosen lock nut "4" on Solex valve (not vacuum unit). Screw in threaded rod "5" to obtain 1500 RPM idle.

NOTE: **Always hold nut with wrench when loosening or tightening lock nut on deceleration valve, so as not to exert force on diaphragm.**

TUNE-UP (Cont.)

6) Increase engine speed to 3000 RPM without load, and allow engine speed to decrease. Unscrew threaded rod "5" one-half turn at a time until normal idle (800 RPM) is obtained.

7) Unscrew threaded rod one additional half turn and tighten lock nut.

FAST IDLE SPEED

Application	RPM
All Models	1500-1550

FUEL PUMP

FUEL PUMP PERFORMANCE

Application	Pressure psi (kg/cm²)	Volume in 30 Sec. Pints (Liters)
505	65-76 (4.5-5.3)	1.6 (.75)

EMISSION CONTROL SYSTEMS

See Mitchell Manuals' Emission Control Manual.

GENERAL SERVICING

IGNITION

DISTRIBUTOR

All 4-cylinder models are equipped with Ducellier breakerless electronic ignition systems.

IGNITION COIL

IGNITION COIL RESISTANCE — Ohms @ 68°F (20°C)

Application	Primary	Secondary
All Models	.48-.61	9000-11,000

FUEL SYSTEMS

FUEL INJECTION

All models are equipped with Bosch Lambda Continuous Injection System (CIS) fuel injection with oxygen sensor.

ELECTRICAL

BATTERY

BATTERY SPECIFICATIONS

Application	Amp Hour Rating
All Models	60

STARTER

All models use Paris-Rhone starters.

ALTERNATOR

All models use Paris-Rhone alternators.

ALTERNATOR SPECIFICATIONS

Application	Rated Amp Output
All Models	75

ALTERNATOR REGULATOR

A solid state, integral alternator regulator is used on all models.

BELT ADJUSTMENT

1) Loosen idler pulley mounting bolts and apply 36 ft. lbs. (48 N.m) to pivot nut above idler pulley. Tighten bolts, then turn engine 1 revolution. Loosen bolts and apply 58 ft. lbs. (77 N.m) to pivot nut. Tighten idle pulley mounting bolts.

2) Air conditioning belt is tightened by pivoting compressor. The belt from crankshaft pulley to water pump is a force-fit and no adjustment is possible.

SERVICE SPECIFICATIONS

REPLACEMENT INTERVALS

Component	Interval (Miles)
Oil Filter	7500
Fuel Filter	60,000
Air Filter	30,000
Spark Plugs	30,000
Oxygen Sensor	30,000

FLUID CAPACITIES

Application	Quantity
Crankcase (Includes Filter)	4.2 qts. (4.0L)
Cooling System	
Man. Trans.	7.5 qts. (7.1L)
Auto. Trans.	7.7 qts. (7.3L)
Man. Trans. (SAE10W-40)	3.4 pts. (1.6L)
Auto. Trans. (Dexron)	5.4 qts. (5.2L)
Rear Axle (SAE80W-90)	3.3 pts. (1.5L)
Fuel Tank	18.0 gals. (68.0L)

1983 Peugeot Diesel 4 Tune-Up

TUNE-UP

504, 505, 505 Turbo, 604 Turbo

ENGINE IDENTIFICATION

Engine number is stamped on left side of block just below cylinder head and is followed by VIN number.

ENGINE CODE

Application	Code
Diesel	XD2C
Turbo Diesel	XD2S

ENGINE COMPRESSION

With engine at normal operating temperature, disconnect injection lines. Remove return lines and nozzle holders. Lock pump stop control in off position. Connect pressure gauge and crank for 4 seconds at 200 RPM. Compression pressure should be as follows:

COMPRESSION SPECIFICATIONS

Compression Ratio	
Diesel	23:1
Turbo Diesel	21:1
Compression Pressure	Min. 261 psi (18.3 kg/cm²)
Max. Variation Between Cylinders	18%

VALVE CLEARANCE

Valves must be set with engine cold. To adjust valves rotate crankshaft until valve listed in first column of table is fully open, then adjust valves listed in second column of table.

CAUTION: Note that valves (and cylinders) are numbered from REAR to FRONT.

VALVE ADJUSTMENT SEQUENCE

Exh. Valve Open	Valves to Adjust
No. 1	No. 3 Int. & No. 4 Exh.
No. 3	No. 4 Int. & No. 2 Exh.
No. 4	No. 2 Int. & No. 1 Exh.
No. 2	No. 1 Int. & No. 3 Exh.

VALVE CLEARANCE SPECIFICATIONS

Application	Intake In. (mm)	Exhaust In. (mm)
Diesel [1]	.010 (.25)	.010 (.25)
Turbo Diesel [1]	.006 (.15)	.010 (.25)

[1] — Set valves with engine cold.

VALVE ARRANGEMENT

ALL MODELS

I-E-E-I-I-E-E-I (Rear-to-front)

Fig. 1: Diesel Firing Order Illustration

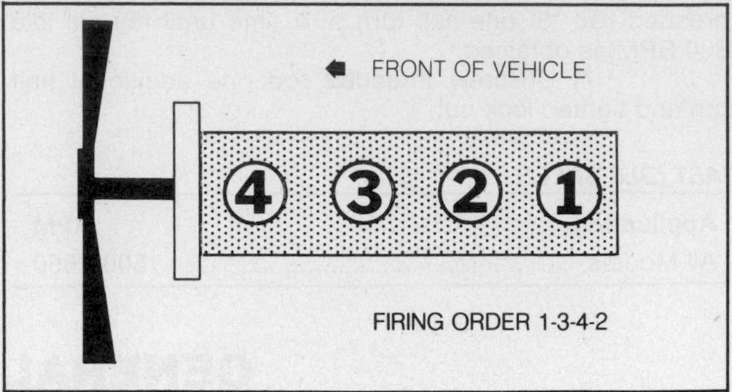
FRONT OF VEHICLE
4
3
2
1
FIRING ORDER 1-3-4-2

GLOW PLUGS

All models use Bosch glow plugs.

GLOW PLUG SPECIFICATIONS

Application	Bosch Part No.	Ft. Lbs. (N.m)
All Models	1018	33 (45)

IDLE SPEED ADJUSTMENT

1) Idle is adjusted on a warm engine after the engagement of the clutch fan. Check that accelerated idle stop is not in contact with throttle lever and that accelerator cable is released.

Fig. 2: Diesel Idle Adjustment Locations

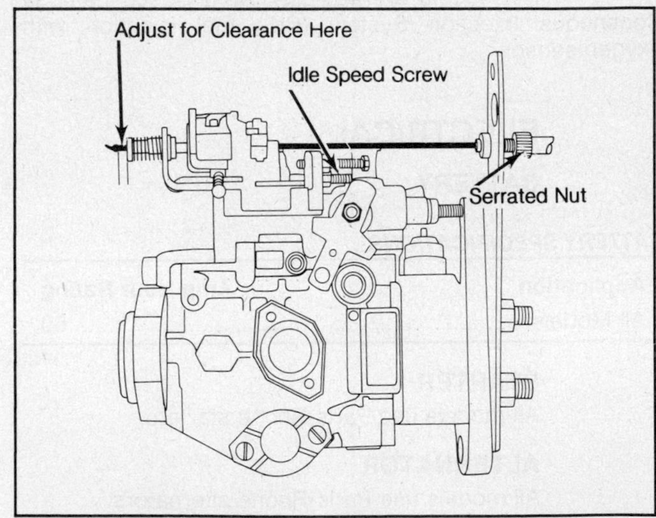
Adjust for Clearance Here
Idle Speed Screw
Serrated Nut

Adjustments are made after engine reaches operating temperatures.

2) Adjust the set screw to obtain proper RPM. *See Fig. 2.* Turn fast idle cable sleeve nut to obtain a clearance of .04" (1 mm) between fast idle cable end and fast idle stop.

3) Start engine and warm to operating temperature. Compress the fast idle stop and check idle speed. Engine speed should be 1200-1400 RPM. Adjust if necessary. Adjust cable and clearance.

TUNE-UP (Cont.)

IDLE SPEED SPECIFICATIONS

Application	Idle RPM
504, 505 Diesel	
With A/C	830-860
Without A/C	780-830
505, 604 Turbo Diesel	
With A/C	830-860
Without A/C	780-840

FUEL SYSTEM BLEEDING

1) Loosen bleed screw at bottom of filter bowl. Pump lever or button on top of filter to force out water. Retighten bleed screw and loosen air bleed screw. Pump button until resistance is felt, then tighten air bleed screw.

2) Bleed filter every 3000 miles, or more often if necessary. If vehicle has run out of fuel and injector pump is dry, continue to pump fuel filter button approximately 40 times. Turn key on and activate starter for 15 seconds, then press accelerator until engine starts.

Fig. 3: Peugeot Fuel Filter Bowl System

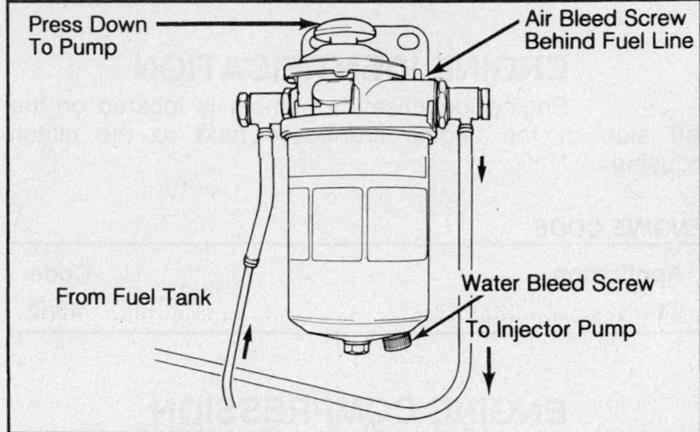
Press Down
To Pump
Air Bleed Screw
Behind Fuel Line
From Fuel Tank
Water Bleed Screw
To Injector Pump

Illustration is showing bleeding locations.

EMISSION CONTROL SYSTEMS

See Mitchell Manuals' Emission Control Manual.

GENERAL SERVICING

FUEL SYSTEMS

FUEL INJECTION

All models use Bosch Diesel Injection Systems with the VE4/9 F2250 R50 pump.

DIESEL FUEL INJECTION TIMING

Application	Degrees BTDC	Plunger Travel In. (mm)
Standard Diesel	11	.019 (.50)
Turbo Diesel	7	.019 (.50)

[1] — Timed on No. 4 cylinder.

ELECTRICAL

BATTERY

BATTERY SPECIFICATIONS

Application	Amp Hour. Rating
All Models	90

STARTER

Bosch, Ducellier and Paris-Rhone are all used on Peugeot diesel models.

ALTERNATOR

All models use Paris-Rhone alternators.

ALTERNATOR SPECIFICATIONS

Application	Rated Amp Output
All Models	75

ALTERNATOR REGULATOR

All diesel models use Paris-Rhone integral alternator regulator.

SERVICE SPECIFICATIONS

BELT ADJUSTMENT

Using a "Krikit" gauge (Part No. 9797.09) check belt tension for the following values:

BELT ADJUSTMENT

Belt	New Lbs. (kg)	Used Lbs. (kg)
Vacuum Pump	44-66	33
	(20-30)	(15)
All Other Belts	88-110	44
	(40-50)	(20)

REPLACEMENT INTERVALS

Component	Interval (Miles)
Air Filter	
Diesel	15,000
Turbo Diesel	30,000
Oil Filter	3000
Fuel Filter	30,000

FLUID CAPACITIES

Application	Quantity
Crankcase (Includes Filter)	5.3 qts. (5.0L)
Cooling System	10.5 qts. (10.0L)
Man. Trans. (SAE 10W-40)	
504	2.4 pts. (1.0L)
505 & 604	
4-Speed	2.4 pts. (1.0L)
5-Speed	3.4 pts. (1.6L)
Auto Trans. (Dexron)	11.0 pts. (5.2L)
Rear Axle (SAE 80W-90) [1]	3.3 pts. (1.5L)
Fuel Tank	18.0 gals. (68.0L)

[1] – All models equipped with limited slip differential.

TUNE-UP

944

ENGINE IDENTIFICATION

Engine identification number is located on the left side of the engine crankcase next to the clutch housing.

ENGINE CODE

Applicaton	Code
944	43 D

ENGINE COMPRESSION

Check compression with engine at normal operating temperature, fully open throttle, all spark plugs removed and at normal cranking speed. Crank engine at least 12 revolutions per cylinder.

COMPRESSION SPECIFICATIONS

Compression Ratio	9.5:1

VALVE CLEARANCE

The 944 model uses hydraulic valve lifters. Valve adjustment is not necessary.

VALVE ARRANGEMENT

I-E-I-E-I-E-I-E (Front-to-rear)

SPARK PLUGS

SPARK PLUG TYPE

Application	Bosch No.	Champion No.
944	WR8DS	RN10GY

SPARK PLUG SPECIFICATIONS

Application	Gap In. (mm)	Torque Ft. Lbs. (N.m)
944	.028 (0.7)	20 (27)

HIGH TENSION WIRE RESISTANCE

CAUTION: DO NOT touch any part of ignition system on 944 while engine is running. Extremely high voltages could be fatal.

Carefully remove high tension wires from distributor cap. Using an ohmmeter, check resistance of high tension wires while gently twisting wire. If resistance is not to specification, or fluctuates from infinity to any value, replace high tension wires.

HIGH TENSION WIRE RESISTANCE

Application	Ohms
944	3000

Fig. 1: Firing Order and Distributor Rotation

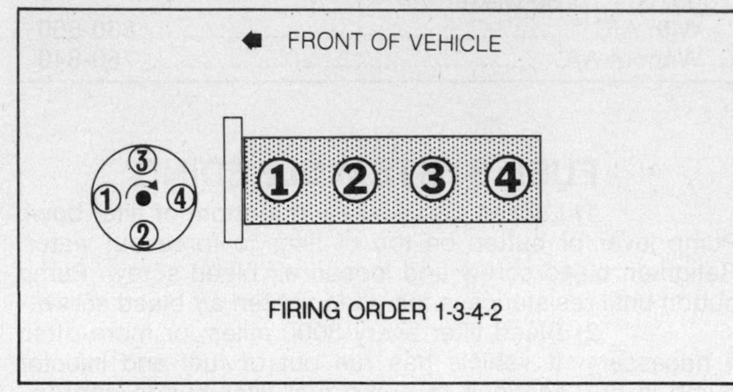
FRONT OF VEHICLE
1
2
3
4
3
1
4
2
FIRING ORDER 1-3-4-2

DISTRIBUTOR

The 944 model uses a digital engine electronics (DME) system to control ignition and AFC fuel injection. DME system uses flywheel speed and reference sensors.

IGNITION TIMING

The 944 model uses digital engine electronics (DME). With this system ignition timing is controlled electronically and no timing adjustment is necessary.

IGNITION TIMING SPECIFICATIONS

Application	Timing RPM	Setting
944	850-950	[1] 3-7° BTDC

[1] — No adjustment necessary.

IDLE SPEED & MIXTURE

NOTE: Idle mixture and speed should be performed with engine at normal operating temperature and timing properly set. If equipped, electric cooling fan and A/C must be turned off.

IDLE SPEED

With radiator fan switched OFF, turn control screw or by-pass screw on throttle housing until specified speed is reached.

IDLE SPEED SPECIFICATIONS

Application	Idle RPM
944	850-950

IDLE MIXTURE

NOTE: Mixture adjustment is not a part of normal tune-up procedure and should not be performed unless fuel injection components are replaced or vehicle fails emission tests.

TUNE-UP (Cont.)

1) Connect exhaust gas test line to test point on catalytic converter. Connect CO tester and tachometer. Engine must be at operating temperature. Adjust idle speed by turning adjusting screw in the by-pass port of the throttle housing.

2) Pull off rubber cap on plug for oxygen sensor. Detach plug. If CO level is not correct, correct setting on the air flow sensor. Connect plug for oxygen sensor. Coat threads of capped nut on test connection with molybdenum paste and install.

CO LEVEL SPECIFICATIONS

Application	CO%
944	0.4-0.8

FUEL PUMP

On 944, an electric fuel pump is mounted in right rear fender.

FUEL PUMP PERFORMANCE

Application	Pressure psi (kg/cm^2)	Volume in 30 sec. Pints (Liters)
944	33-39 (2.3-2.7)	1.8 (.85)

EMISSION CONTROL SYSTEM

See Mitchell Manuals' Emission Control Manual.

GENERAL SERVICING

IGNITION

DISTRIBUTOR

The 944 model uses a computerized engine control system. It is equipped with a breakerless electronic ignition system. Distributors are used only to distribute the spark to the proper spark plug.

IGNITION COIL

IGNITION COIL RESISTANCE — Ohms @ 68°F (20°C)

Application	Primary	Secondary
944	.4-.6	5000-7200

FUEL SYSTEMS

FUEL INJECTION

The 944 model is equipped with Bosch AFC fuel injection with oxygen sensor.

ELECTRICAL

BATTERY

BATTERY SPECIFICATIONS

Application	Amp Hr. Rating
944	63

ALTERNATOR

ALTERNATOR SPECIFICATIONS

Application	Rated Amp Output
944	90

ALTERNATOR REGULATOR

All models are equipped with Bosch alternator regulators, integral with alternator. Test regulator with rear window defogger and headlights turned on, and engine at about 2000 RPM.

REGULATOR OPERATING VOLTAGE @ 68°F (20°C)

Application	Voltage
944	13.5-14.5

SERVICE SPECIFICATIONS

BELT ADJUSTMENT

Application	[1] Deflection In. (mm)
944	
Power Steering	.2 (.5)
Alternator, A/C Compressor	[2] 9.2-9.8

[1] — Deflection is measured with firm thumb pressure in center of longest belt run.

[2] — Using special tool (9201). Value given is not in inches or mm.

REPLACEMENT INTERVALS

Component	Interval (Miles)
Oil Filter	15,000
Air Filter	30,000
Fuel Filter	30,000
Spark Plugs	30,000
Oxygen Sensor	30,000

FLUID CAPACITIES

Application	Quantity
Crankcase (Includes Filter)	5.8 qts. (5.5L)
Cooling System	8.2 qts. (7.8L)
Man. Trans. & Differential (80W-90)	2.7 qts. (2.6L)
Auto. Trans. (Dexron II)	
Drain & Refill	3.0 qts. (2.8L)
Overhaul	6.4 qts. (6.0L)
Fuel Tank	17.5 gals. (66.0L)

1983 Porsche 6 Tune-Up

TUNE-UP

911SC

ENGINE IDENTIFICATION

Engine identification number is stamped on left of engine crankcase near fan housing. The first 3 digits in engine number identify engine type and year. The last 4 digits are the engine serial number.

ENGINE CODE

Application	Code
911SC	64D

ENGINE COMPRESSION

Perform compression test with wide open throttle and oil temperature not less than 140°F (60°C). Remove all spark plugs and allow about 12 piston strokes per cylinder test.

COMPRESSION SPECIFICATIONS

Compression Ratio	9.3:1
Compression Pressure	
Normal	142-184 psi (10-13 kg/cm²)
Minimum	107 psi (7.5 kg/cm²)
Max. Variation	
Between Cylinders	22 psi (1.5 kg/cm²)

VALVE CLEARANCE

Adjust the valve clearance to specification with the engine cold.

VALVE CLEARANCE SPECIFICATIONS

Application	In. (mm)
Intake & Exhaust (Cold)	.004 (.1)

VALVE ARRANGEMENT

Engine cylinders have individual heads and contain one intake and one exhaust valve per head. Upper valves are intake and lower valves are exhaust.

SPARK PLUGS

SPARK PLUG TYPE

Application	Bosch No.
911SC	W 225 T 30

SPARK PLUG SPECIFICATIONS

Application	Gap In. (mm)	Torque Ft. Lbs. (N.m)
911SC	.028 (.7)	22 (30)

HIGH TENSION WIRE RESISTANCE

Carefully remove high tension wires from spark plugs and distributor cap. Using an ohmmeter, check high tension wire resistance while gently twisting wires. If resistance is incorrect, or fluctuates from infinity to any value, replace high tension wire(s).

HIGH TENSION WIRE RESISTANCE

Application	Ohms
All Models	25,000-30,000

DISTRIBUTOR

All models use Bosch breakerless electronic distributors. No adjustments are necessary.

Fig. 1: Firing Order and Distributor Rotation

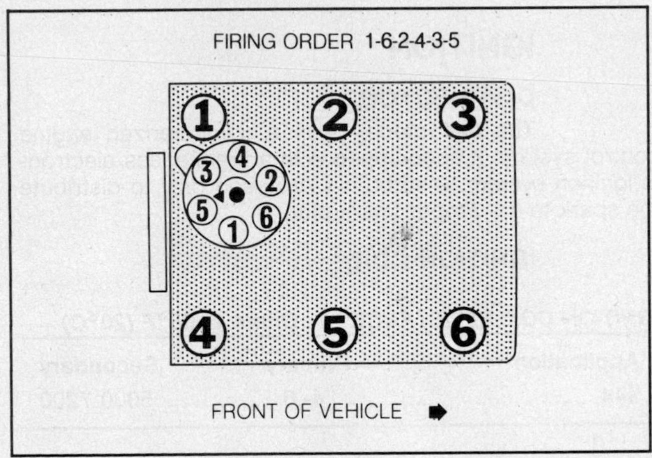

FIRING ORDER 1-6-2-4-3-5
1
2
3
4
5
6
FRONT OF VEHICLE

IGNITION TIMING

Warm engine to normal operating temperature and disconnect distributor vacuum lines. Connect a tachometer and timing light. With engine idling, rotate distributor until mark on pulley is lined up with reference mark on blower housing.

Fig. 2: Ignition Timing Mark Location

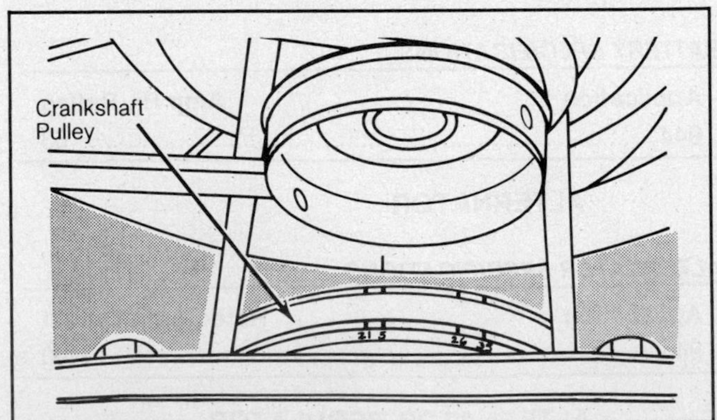

Crankshaft
Pulley

TUNE-UP (Cont.)

IGNITION TIMING (Degrees BTDC@RPM)

Application	Timing
911SC	[1] 5@950

[1] — Distributor vacuum lines disconnected.

IDLE SPEED & MIXTURE

NOTE: Mixture adjustment is not a part of normal tune-up procedure and should not be performed unless fuel injection components are replaced or vehicle fails emission testing.

1) Connect exhaust pickup line on the test connection of catalytic converter. Connect CO tester according to equipment instructions. Disconnect plug for oxygen sensor in engine compartment on left side.

NOTE: Make sure that oil tank cap and seal fit properly prior to checking or adjusting idle speed. Leaks at oil tank cap cause incorrect measurement.

2) Turn control screw or by-pass screw on throttle housing until idle RPM is obtained. Check CO level. If adjustment is necessary, remove plug from mixture control unit between fuel distributor unit and venturi, and insert adjusting tool (P 377 or equivalent).

NOTE: Do not force or press down on adjusting tool during adjustments or engine will stall. Turn adjusting screw in very small increments as the slightest adjustment will change the CO level considerably.

3) Remove adjusting tool and accelerate engine briefly. Allow engine to return to stabilized idle and recheck both CO level and idle speed. Correct if necessary and insert plug in mixture control unit.

4) Connect electric plug for oxygen sensor. Coat threads of cap nut for testing connection with molybdenum paste and install on catalytic converter.

IDLE SPEED & CO LEVEL SPECIFICATIONS

Application	Idle RPM	CO%
911SC	950	0.4-0.8

FUEL PUMP

FUEL PUMP PERFORMANCE

Application	Pressure psi (kg/cm²)	Volume in 30 Sec. Pints (Liters)
All Models	65-75 (4.5-5.2)	1.0 (2.2)

EMISSION CONTROL SYSTEMS

See Mitchell Manuals' Emission Control Manual.

GENERAL SERVICING

IGNITION

DISTRIBUTOR

All models use Capacitive Discharge Ignition systems with Bosch breakerless distributors.

IGNITION COIL

IGNITION COIL RESISTANCE Ohms @ 68°F (20°C)

Application	Primary	Secondary
911SC	0.4-0.6	600-790

FUEL SYSTEMS

FUEL INJECTION

All models are equipped with Bosch Lambda Continuous Injection System (CIS) with oxygen sensor.

ELECTRICAL

BATTERY

Battery is located on left in front luggage compartment, under the floor mat.

BATTERY SPECIFICATIONS

Application	Amp Hr. Rating
911SC	[1] 66

[1] — 88 amp hr. battery is optional.

ALTERNATORS

All models use a Bosch alternator.

ALTERNATOR SPECIFICATIONS

Application	Rated Amp Output
911SC	75

ALTERNATOR REGULATOR

All models are equipped with Bosch or Motorola alternator regulators.

REGULATOR OPERATING VOLTAGE @ 68°F (20°C)

Application	Volts
911SC	[1] 13.5-14.5

[1] — Voltage at 2500 RPM.

GENERAL SERVICING (Cont.)

STARTER

All models are equipped with Bosch starters with overrunning clutch.

SERVICE SPECIFICATIONS

BELT ADJUSTMENT

Application	[1] Deflection In. (mm)
All Belts	.2-.5 (6-13)

[1] — Light pressure applied halfway between pulleys.

REPLACEMENT INTERVALS

Component	Interval (Miles)
Oil Filter	15,000
Air Filter	30,000
Fuel Filter	30,000
PCV Valve	30,000
Oxygen Sensor	30,000
Spark Plugs	30,000

FLUID CAPACITIES

Application	Quantity
Crankcase (Includes Filter)	
Total	13.7 qts. (13.0L)
Oil Change	10.6 qts. (10.0L)
Transaxle (SAE 90)	3.2 qts. (3.0L)
Fuel Tank	[1] 21 gals. (80.0L)

[1] — Includes 2.1 gals. (8.0L) in reserve.

TUNE-UP

928S

ENGINE IDENTIFICATION

The engine identification number is stamped on the front reinforcing rib in the top half of the crankcase. The first 3 digits in engine number identify type and model year.

ENGINE CODE

Application	Code
928S	813

ENGINE COMPRESSION

With engine at normal operating temperature, remove all plugs and allow 12 compression strokes per cylinder.

COMPRESSION SPECIFICATIONS

Compression Ratio	9:1
Compression Pressure	
Normal	142-199 psi (10-14 kg/cm²)
Minimum	114 psi (8 kg/cm²)
Max. Variation	
Between Cylinders	21 psi (1.5 kg/cm²)

VALVE CLEARANCE

Porsche 928 models are equipped with self-adjusting hydraulic valve lifters.

VALVE ARRANGEMENT

Both Banks — I-E-I-E-I-E-I-E (Front-to-rear)

SPARK PLUGS

SPARK PLUG TYPE

Application	Bosch No.
All Models	WR8DS

SPARK PLUG SPECIFICATIONS

Application	Gap In. (mm)	Torque Ft. Lbs. (N.m)
All Models	.028 (.7)	18 (24)

HIGH TENSION WIRE RESISTANCE

Carefully remove high tension wires from spark plugs and distributor cap. Using an ohmmeter, check high tension wire resistance while gently twisting wires. If resistance is incorrect, or fluctuates from infinity to any value, replace wires.

HIGH TENSION WIRE RESISTANCE

Application	Ohms
All Models	2500

DISTRIBUTOR

All models use Bosch breakerless electronic ignition. No adjustments are necessary.

Fig. 1: Firing Order and Distributor Rotation

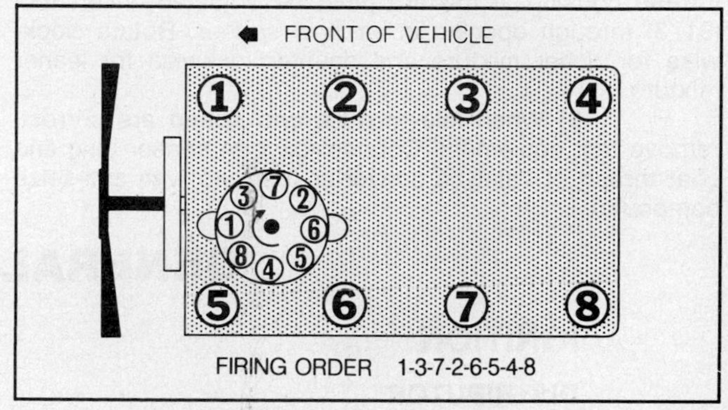
FRONT OF VEHICLE
1
2
3
4
5
6
7
8
FIRING ORDER 1-3-7-2-6-5-4-8

IGNITION TIMING

1) With engine at normal operating temperature, disconnect and plug hoses at distributor advance unit. Stop engine and connect timing light to No. 1 cylinder. Connect tachometer to connection stud above ignition control unit in engine compartment.

CAUTION: Dangerously high voltage exists in ignition system. Ignition must be off when attaching or removing testing equipment, or severe shock may occur.

2) Start engine and accelerate. Adjust timing as necessary by turning distributor. Return engine to idle, and connect vacuum hoses. Recheck timing. Timing should read TDC to 7° BTDC. If not to specification, distributor should be removed and tested.

Fig. 2: Ignition Timing Mark Location

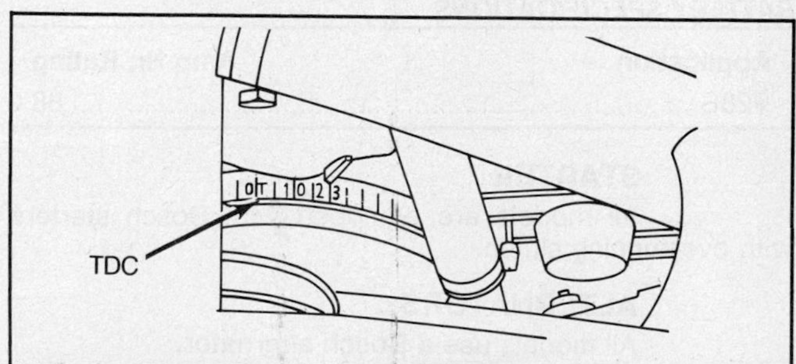
TDC

IGNITION TIMING (Degrees BTDC@RPM)

Application	Timing
All Models	[1] 20@3000

[1] — With distributor vacuum advance hoses disconnected and plugged.

1983 Porsche V8 Tune-Up

TUNE-UP (Cont.)

IDLE SPEED & MIXTURE

NOTE: **Mixture adjustment is not a part of normal tune-up procedure and should not be performed unless fuel injection components are replaced or vehicle fails emission testing.**

1) Fold up foot support on passenger side under dashboard. Disconnect plug from oxygen sensor (left side of footwell). Connect CO meter to test point on catalytic converter and connect tachometer.

2) Adjust idle speed using screw in front of throttle housing. If mixture must be adjusted, insert tool (9178) through opening in air flow sensor. Rotate clockwise for richer mixture and counterclockwise for leaner mixture.

3) When idle mixture and speed are correct, remove test equipment. Connect oxygen sensor plug and coat thread of catalytic converter test cap with anti-seize compound.

IDLE SPEED & CO LEVEL SPECIFICATIONS

Application	Idle RPM	CO%
928S	700-800	[1] 0.4-0.8

[1] — With oxygen sensor disconnected.

FUEL PUMP

FUEL PUMP PERFORMANCE

Application	Pressure psi (kg/cm²)	Volume in 30 Sec. Pints (Liters)
All Models	26-32 (1.8-2.2)	1.2 (.6)

EMISSION CONTROL SYSTEMS

See Mitchell Manuals' Emission Control Manual.

GENERAL SERVICING

IGNITION

DISTRIBUTOR

All models are equipped with Bosch transistorized ignition system with breakerless distributor.

IGNITION COIL

IGNITION COIL RESISTANCE Ohms @ 68°F (20°C)

Application	Primary	Secondary
928S	0.4-0.6	650-790

FUEL SYSTEMS

FUEL INJECTION

All models are equipped with Bosch AFC Lambda fuel injection system with oxygen sensor.

ELECTRICAL

BATTERY SPECIFICATIONS

Application	Amp Hr. Rating
928S	88

STARTER

All models are equipped with Bosch starters with overrunning clutch.

ALTERNATORS

All models use a Bosch alternator.

ALTERNATOR SPECIFICATIONS

Application	Rated Amp Output
928S	90

ALTERNATOR REGULATOR

All models are equipped with Bosch or Motorola solid state alternator regulators.

REGULATOR OPERATING VOLTAGE @ 68°F (20°C)

Application	Volts
928S	13.5-14.8

SERVICE SPECIFICATIONS

BELT ADJUSTMENT

Application	[1] Deflection In. (mm)
Alternator	[2] 8.4
All Others	.4 (10)

[1] — With moderate pressure applied midway on longest belt run.

[2] — Tension measured with special tool (9201) midway on longest belt run. Value given is not inches or mm.

REPLACEMENT INTERVALS

Component	Interval (Miles)
Oil Filter	15,000
Air Filter	30,000
Fuel Filter	30,000
PCV Valve	30,000
Oxygen Sensor	30,000
Spark Plugs	30,000

FLUID CAPACITIES

Application	Quantity
Crankcase (Includes Filter)	8.0 qts. (7.5L)
Cooling System	17.0 qts. (16.0L)
Man. Trans. (SAE 75W-90)	4.0 qts. (3.8L)
Auto. Trans. (Dexron II)	5.8 qts. (5.5L)
Differential (SAE 90)	2.1 qts. (2.0L)
Fuel Tank	23.0 gals. (86.0L)

1983 Renault 4 Tune-Up

TUNE-UP

Fuego, Fuego Turbo, Le Car & 18i

ENGINE IDENTIFICATION

Type of vehicle and engine number are marked on a number plate, riveted to the left rear side of the engine block. Plate is located just below cylinder head mating surface. First group of digits indicate engine type.

Engine Code

Application	Code
Fuego & 18i	
Man. Trans.	843-7-18
Auto. Trans.	843-7-19
Fuego Turbo	
Man. Trans.	A7L-7-23
Le Car	847-25

ENGINE COMPRESSION

Check engine compression with battery fully charged and engine at normal cranking speed.

COMPRESSION SPECIFICATIONS

Compression Ratio	
Fuego & 18i	8.6:1
Fuego Turbo	8.0:1
Le Car	8.8:1

VALVE CLEARANCE

Valves must be set with engine cold. To adjust valves, rotate crankshaft until valve listed in first column of table is fully open, then adjust valves listed in second column of table.

VALVE ADJUSTMENT SEQUENCE

Exhaust Valve Open	Valves to Adjust
No. 1	No. 3 Int. & No. 4 Exh.
No. 3	No. 4 Int. & No. 2 Exh.
No. 4	No. 2 Int. & No. 1 Exh.
No. 2	No. 1 Int. & No. 3 Exh.

VALVE CLEARANCE SPECIFICATIONS (COLD)

Application	Intake In. (mm)	Exhaust In. (mm)
Fuego, Fuego Turbo & 18i	.008 (.20)	.010 (.25)
Le Car	.006 (.15)	.008 (.20)

VALVE ARRANGEMENT

Left Side — All Exhaust
Right Side — All Intake

SPARK PLUGS

SPARK PLUG TYPE

Application	Bosch No.	Champion No.
Fuego & 18i	WR7DS	.....
Fuego Turbo	.....	RN3G
Le Car		
Calif.	WR9DS	.....
Federal	.....	RN12Y

SPARK PLUG SPECIFICATIONS

Application	Gap In. (mm)	Torque Ft. Lbs. (N.m)
Fuego & 18i	.026 (.66)	20 (27)
Fuego Turbo	.024 (.61)	20 (27)
Le Car	.024 (.61)	20 (27)

HIGH TENSION WIRE RESISTANCE

Carefully remove high tension wires from spark plugs and distributor cap. Using an ohmmeter, check resistance of high tension wires while gently twisting wires. If resistance is not to specification, or fluctuates from infinity to any value, replace high tension wire(s).

HIGH TENSION WIRE RESISTANCE

Application	Resistance (Ohms)
All Models	25,000-30,000

DISTRIBUTOR

FUEGO TURBO

Fuego Turbo uses a computerized electronic ignition control system. Its Ducellier distributor has no spark timing function. With this system, ignition timing at idle can be checked, but not adjusted.

ALL OTHER MODELS

All other models are equipped with Ducellier dual pick-up electronic ignition distributors. Trigger plate air gap is adjustable.

Fig. 1: Le Car Firing Order & Distributor Rotation

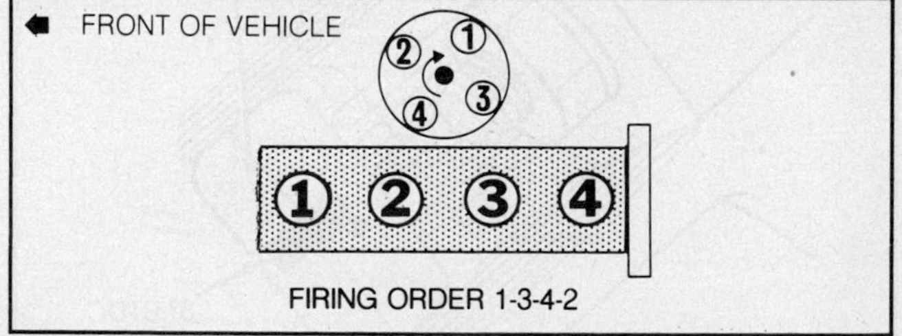
FRONT OF VEHICLE
1
2
3
4
FIRING ORDER 1-3-4-2

1983 Renault 4 Tune-Up

TUNE-UP (Cont.)

DISTRIBUTOR AIR GAP SPECIFICATIONS

Application	In. (mm)
All Models Except Fuego Turbo	.012-.024 (.3-.6)

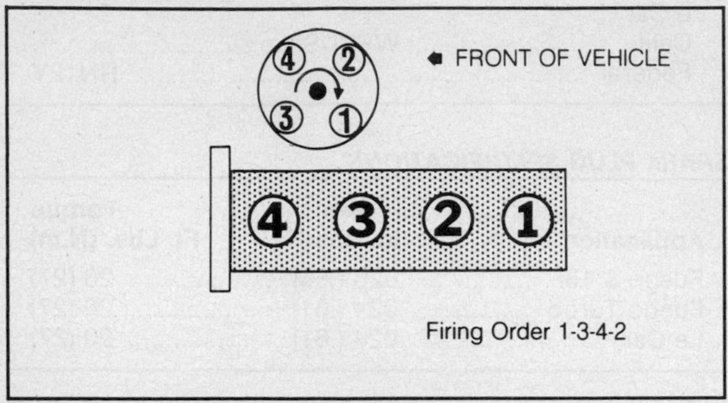

FRONT OF VEHICLE
4
3
2
1
Firing Order 1-3-4-2

Fig. 2: Fuego, Fuego Turbo & 18i Firing Order & Distributor Rotation

IGNITION TIMING

FUEGO TURBO

Fuego Turbo uses a computerized electronic ignition control system. Ignition timing is therefore not adjustable.

ALL OTHER MODELS

Check or adjust ignition timing with vacuum line disconnected and plugged and engine running at idle speed. To adjust, turn distributor until specified mark on flywheel is aligned with specified graduation mark on clutch housing. Reconnect distributor vacuum hose.

IGNITION TIMING (Degrees BTDC@RPM)

Application	Timing
Fuego & 18i	
Man. Trans.	10@800
Auto. Trans. [1]	10@650
Fuego Turbo	Not Adjustable
Le Car	3@750

[1] - With transmission in "D".

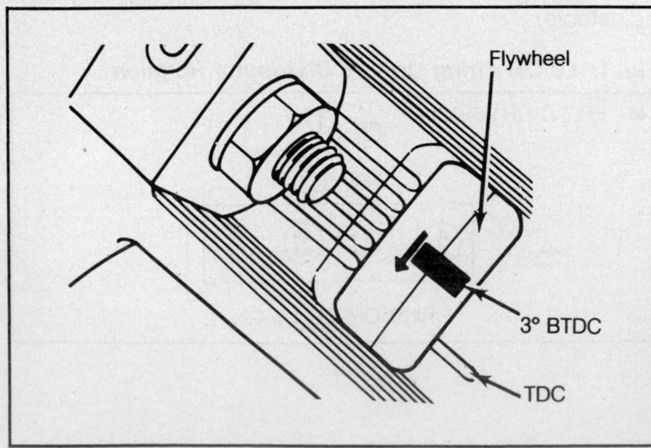

Flywheel
3° BTDC
TDC

Fig. 3: Le Car Timing Mark Location

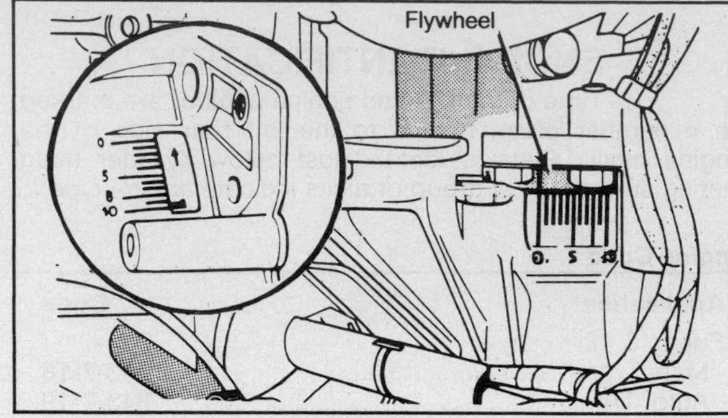

Flywheel

Fig. 4: Fuego, Fuego Turbo & 18i Timing Mark Location

Illustration shows manual transmission location.

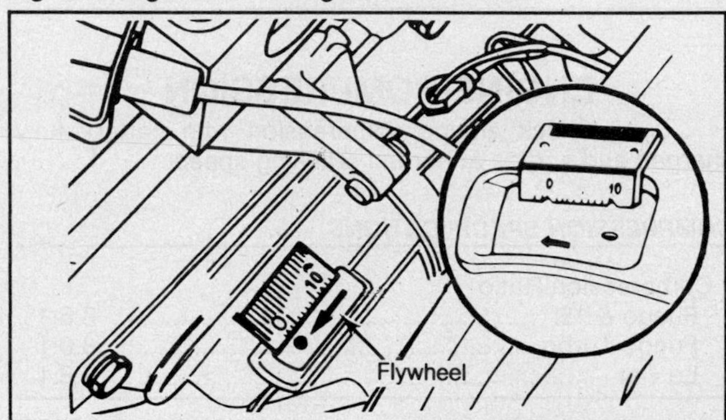

Flywheel

Fig. 5: Fuego & 18i Timing Mark Location

Illustration shows automatic transmission location.

IDLE SPEED & MIXTURE

NOTE: Mixture adjustment is not a part of normal tune-up procedure and should not be performed unless fuel injection components or carburetor is disassembled or vehicle fails emission testing.

CARBURETED MODELS

Federal Le Car

1) Clamp, or disconnect and plug air pump hose to injection manifold. Connect tachometer.

2) Adjust idle speed screw to obtain 700-725 RPM idle. Remove cap and adjust fuel metering screw to obtain 0.5-2.0% CO level. Repeat procedure if necessary to have both speed and mixture correct.

3) Reconnect air injection. Idle speed must be 700-800 RPM. If not, adjust with idle speed screw. Remove test equipment.

California Le Car

1) Start engine and bring to normal operating temperature. Using a "T" connector, connect accurate vacuum gauge to line between carburetor and vacuum solenoid regulator.

2) Start engine and adjust idle speed with fuel metering screw to 700-800 RPM. Vacuum gauge should indicate .3-2.7 in. Hg.

3) If vacuum reading is not correct, remove brass cap from mixture screw. Adjust carefully until

TUNE-UP (Cont.)

vacuum reading is within specifications. Remove test equipment.

Fig. 6: Federal Carburetor Adjustment Locations

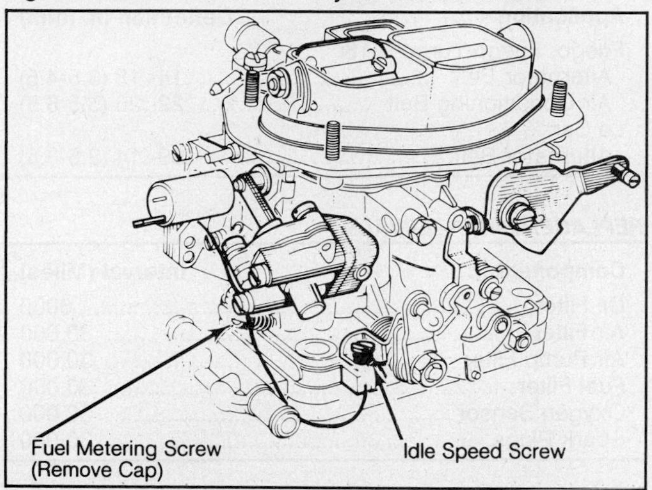
Fuel Metering Screw
(Remove Cap)
Idle Speed Screw

Fig. 7: California Carburetor Adjustment Locations

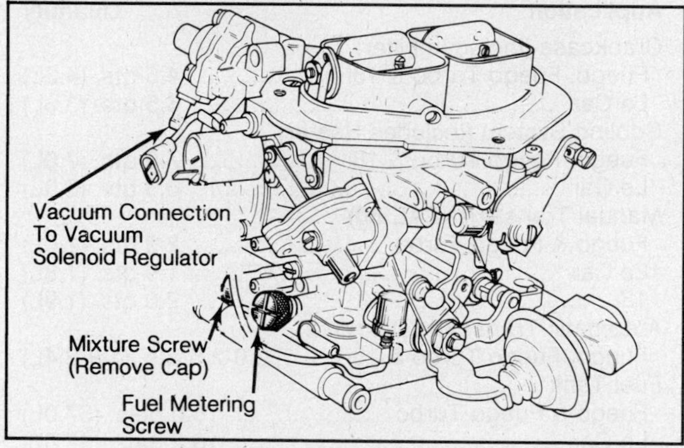
Vacuum Connection
To Vacuum
Solenoid Regulator
Mixture Screw
(Remove Cap)
Fuel Metering
Screw

FUEL INJECTED MODELS

Fuego Turbo

1) Warm engine to normal operating temperature and attach tachometer. Connect voltmeter negative lead to terminal 2 and voltmeter positive lead to terminal 8 of diagnostic socket. Voltage reading should fluctuate ±.5 volts.

2) If voltage remains stable around 6.4 volts, warm up engine at 3000 RPM to energize oxygen sensor. Adjust throttle housing idle speed screw to set idle speed.

3) Adjust flow meter idle mixture screw to obtain voltage reading of 6.5-7.5 volts. If necessary to turn screw more than one full turn, check for manifold leaks or grounded oxygen sensor wire.

All Except Fuego Turbo

1) Warm engine to normal operating temperature and attach tachometer. Place shift selector lever in "D" on automatic transmission models. Adjust throttle plate by-pass screw to set idle speed.

2) With idle speed set, disconnect oxygen sensor wire. Do not allow wire to ground on any metal objects. Locate fuel injection diagnostic socket (near right front shock absorber).

3) Connect voltmeter negative lead to terminal 2 and voltmeter positive lead to terminal 8 of diagnostic connector. Voltage should measure 6.5 volts.

4) Reconnect oxygen sensor wire. Voltage should remain at 6.5 volts. If not, adjust mixture screw to obtain reading as close to 6.5 volts as possible.

IDLE SPEED & CO LEVEL SPECIFICATIONS

Application	Idle RPM	CO%
Fuego & 18i		
Man.Trans. [1]	750-850	0.4-1.0
Auto.Trans. [1] [2]	600-700	0.4-1.0
Fuego Turbo		
Man. Trans.	700-800	[3]
Le Car [1]	700-800	0.5-2.1

[1] - Air injection disconnected.
[2] - Transmission in "D".
[3] - Voltmeter reading of 6.5-7.5 volts.

COLD (FAST) IDLE RPM

FEDERAL LE CAR

Connect intake manifold vacuum directly to throttle plate opener or connect a vacuum pump. Apply a vacuum of at least 4.5 in. Hg or accelerate to 2500 RPM. Slowly release accelerator. If adjustment is necessary, turn fast idle adjusting screw.

CALIFORNIA LE CAR

Apply intake manifold vacuum directly to vacuum regulator (or apply 6 in. Hg vacuum on throttle plate opener diaphragm). Set throttle plate opener to achieve fast idle speed.

FAST IDLE RPM

Application	RPM
Le Car	
Federal Models	1800-2000
Calif. Models	1400-1600

FUEL PUMP

FUEL PUMP PERFORMANCE

Application	Pressure psi (kg/cm²)	Volume in 30 sec. Pints (Liters)
Fuego, Fuego Turbo & 18i [1]	25.0-31.0 (1.8-2.2)	1 (.5)
Le Car	2.5-3.5 (.18-.24)	....

[1] — Vacuum connected. If vacuum is disconnected, 33.0-39.0 psi (2.3-2.7 kg/cm²).

EMISSION CONTROL SYSTEMS

See Mitchell Manuals' Emission Control Manual.

1983 Renault 4 Tune-Up

GENERAL SERVICING

IGNITION

DISTRIBUTOR

All models are equipped with Ducellier electronic distributors. However, the distributor used on Fuego Turbo models has no spark timing function.

IGNITION COIL

On Fuego Turbo models, the ignition coil is built into the same metal housing as the computer. On all other models, the ignition coil is mounted in the same aluminum housing as the electronic control module.

FUEL SYSTEMS

CARBURETORS

CARBURETOR TYPE

Application	Model
Le Car	
Federal	Weber 32 DIR 87
Calif.	Weber 32 DIR 80

FUEL INJECTION

All Fuego, Fuego Turbo and 18i models use Bosch AFC fuel injection systems.

ELECTRICAL

BATTERY

BATTERY SPECIFICATIONS

Application	Amp Hr. Rating
Fuego, Fuego Turbo & 18i	[1] 45
Le Car	50

[1] — 60 amp with air conditioning.

STARTER

All models use Paris-Rhone starters.

ALTERNATOR

Le Car models use Paris-Rhone alternators; Fuego Turbo, Fuego and 18i models may be equipped with Motorola, Paris-Rhone, SEV Marchal, or Ducellier alternators.

ALTERNATOR SPECIFICATIONS

Application	Rated Amp Output
All Models	[1] 50

[1] - 70 amp with air conditioning.

ALTERNATOR REGULATOR

Most alternators have built-in regulators.

SERVICE SPECIFICATIONS

BELT ADJUSTMENT

Application	Deflection In. (mm)
Fuego, Fuego Turbo & 18i	
Alternator Belt	.14-.18 (3.5-4.5)
Air Conditioning Belt	.22-.26 (5.5-6.5)
Le Car	
Alternator Belt	.09-.14 (2.5-3.5)

REPLACEMENT INTERVALS

Component	Interval (Miles)
Oil Filter	6000
Air Filter	30,000
Air Pump Filter	30,000
Fuel Filter	30,000
Oxygen Sensor	30,000
Spark Plugs	30,000

FLUID CAPACITIES

Application	Quantity
Crankcase (Includes Filter)	
Fuego, Fuego Turbo & 18i	4.5 qts. (4.3L)
Le Car	3.5 qts. (3.3L)
Cooling System (Includes Heater)	
Fuego, Fuego Turbo & 18i	7.5 qts. (7.0L)
Le Car	6.3 qts. (6.0L)
Manual Transaxle (SAE 80) [1]	
Fuego & Fuego Turbo	2.2 qts. (2.0L)
Le Car	1.9 qts. (1.8L)
18i	2.0 qts. (1.9L)
Automatic Transaxle (Dexron II) [1]	
Fuego, Fuego Turbo & 18i	2.0-2.5 qts. (1.9-2.4L)
Fuel Tank	
Fuego & Fuego Turbo	15.0 gals. (57.0L)
Le Car	10.0 gals. (38.0L)
18i	
Sedan	14.0 gals. (53.0L)
Station Wagon	15.0 gals. (57.0L)

[1] - Refill capacity shown.

1983 Saab 4 Tune-Up

TUNE-UP

900 & 900 Turbo

ENGINE IDENTIFICATION

Engine number is stamped on a machined pad on engine block below CIS throttle housing.

ENGINE CODE

Application	Code
900	
Man. Trans.	B 20 I M UC D
Auto. Trans.	B 20 I A UC D
900 Turbo (APC)	
Man. Trans.	B 20 S M UC D
Auto. Trans.	B 20 S A UC D

ENGINE COMPRESSION

Check compression with battery fully charged, engine at normal operating temperature, throttle fully open and engine at cranking speed.

COMPRESSION SPECIFICATIONS

Compression Ratio	
900	9.3:1
900 Turbo (APC)	8.5:1

VALVE CLEARANCE

1) Run engine until warm and let cool 30 minutes before checking valves. Position cam lobe opposite valve depressor. Install measuring tool (8391450) with dial indicator to valve depressor. With measuring point of dial indicator resting on tip of cam, zero dial indicator.

2) Lift valve depressor with special tool. Note movement of dial indicator, indicating present valve clearance. Any valve not within specifications should be adjusted as follows.

3) Remove camshaft, valve depressors and adjusting pads of valves needing adjustment. Measure thickness of adjusting pad with micrometer and calculate thickness of new pad required to bring valve clearance within specifications.

VALVE CLEARANCE SPECIFICATIONS

Application	In. (mm)
Checking Tolerance	
900	
Intake	.006-.012 (.15-.30)
Exhaust	.014-.020 (.35-.50)
900 Turbo (APC)	
Intake	.006-.012 (.15-.30)
Exhaust	.016-.020 (.40-.50)
Adjustment Range	
900	
Intake	.008-.010 (.20-.25)
Exhaust	.016-.018 (.40-.45)
900 Turbo (APC)	
Intake	.008-.010 (.20-.25)
Exhaust	.018-.020 (.45-.50)

4) Measured valve clearance, plus adjusting pad thickness, equals total distance between valve and cam. This total distance, less the specified valve clearance, determines thickness of new adjusting pad to be installed.

5) Install new adjusting pad, valve depressors, and camshaft. Recheck that clearances are correct.

VALVE ARRANGEMENT

E-I-I-E-E-I-I-E (Front-to-rear)

SPARK PLUGS

SPARK PLUG TYPE

Application	Champion No.	NGK No.
Turbo (APC)	N-7Y	BP7ES
All Other Models	N-9Y	BP6ES

SPARK PLUG SPECIFICATIONS

Application	Gap In. (mm)	Torque Ft. Lbs. (N.m)
All Models	.024-028 (.6-.7)	18-22 (24-30)

HIGH TENSION WIRE RESISTANCE

Carefully remove high tension wires from spark plugs and distributor cap. Using an ohmmeter, check high tension wire resistance while gently twisting wires. If resistance is not to specifications, or fluctuates from infinity to any value, replace high tension wire(s).

HIGH TENSION WIRE RESISTANCE

Application	Ohms
All Models	
Spark Plug-to-Distributor Cap	2000-4000
Coil-to-Distributor	500-1500

DISTRIBUTOR

All models are equipped with Bosch Hall Effect breakerless, electronic ignition systems. No adjustments are required for distributor. Air gap and pick-up coil resistance are not measurable.

Fig. 1: Firing Order and Distributor Rotation

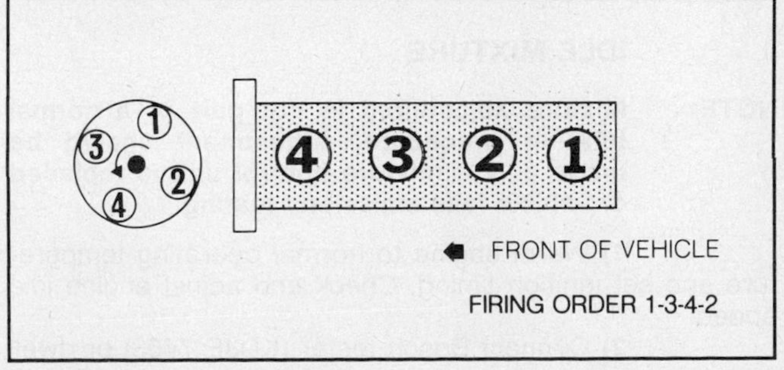

1
3
2
4
4
3
2
1
FRONT OF VEHICLE
FIRING ORDER 1-3-4-2

1983 Saab 4 Tune-Up

TUNE-UP (Cont.)

IGNITION TIMING

1) Connect tachometer and timing light. Disconnect and plug vacuum advance hose. Place transmission in neutral position.

2) With engine at normal operating temperature and running at specified speed, line on flywheel must align with specified mark on flywheel housing.

Fig. 2: Saab Ignition Timing Marks

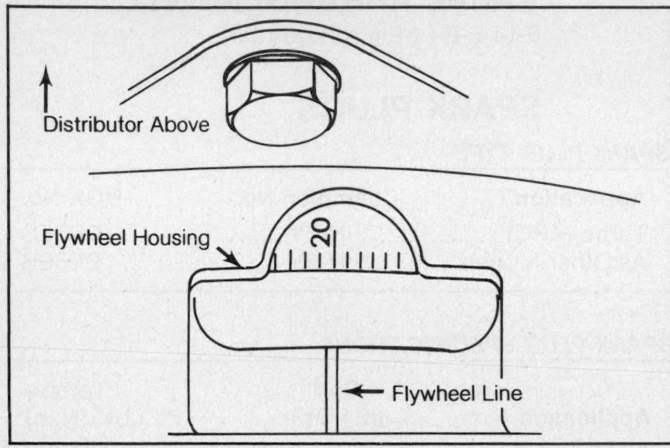

Distributor Above
Flywheel Housing
20
Flywheel Line

Align mark on flywheel housing with line on flywheel.

3) If not within specifications, loosen distributor retaining screw and rotate distributor housing until timing is set to specifications. Reconnect vacuum advance hose and adjust engine idle speed.

IGNITION TIMING SPECIFICATIONS
(Degrees BTDC@RPM)

Application	Timing
All Models	20@2000

[1] — Disconnect and plug vacuum advance hose.

IDLE SPEED & MIXTURE

IDLE SPEED

1) Warm engine to operating temperature and set ignition timing.

2) Check and adjust engine idling speed, using idle adjusting screw on throttle valve housing. *See Fig. 3.*

IDLE SPEED SPECIFICATIONS

Application	RPM
All Models	800-950

IDLE MIXTURE

NOTE: Mixture adjustment is not part of a normal tune-up procedure. Adjustment should be made only if mixture control unit is replaced or vehicle fails emissions testing.

1) Warm engine to normal operating temperature and set ignition timing. Check and adjust engine idle speed.

2) Connect Bosch tester (KDJE 7453) or dwell meter to test connector in front of fuse box. *See Fig. 4.*

Fig. 3: Adjusting Idle Speed

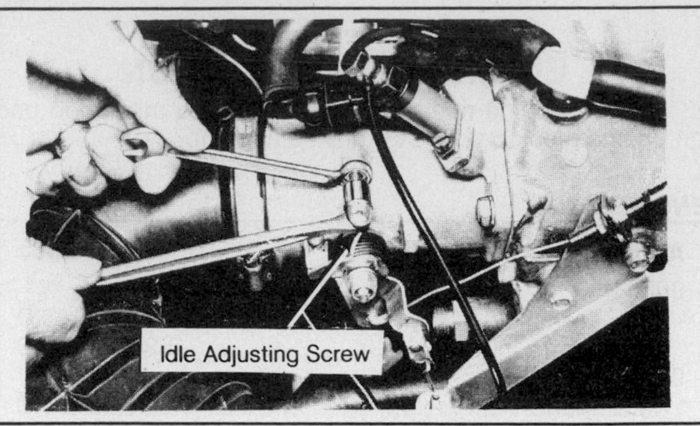

Idle Adjusting Screw

Start engine and observe scale on tester. If needle fluctuates between 10-90% on Bosch tester or 10-80° on dwell meter (4-cyl. scale), no adjustment is needed.

Fig. 4: Mixture Adjustment Tester Connections

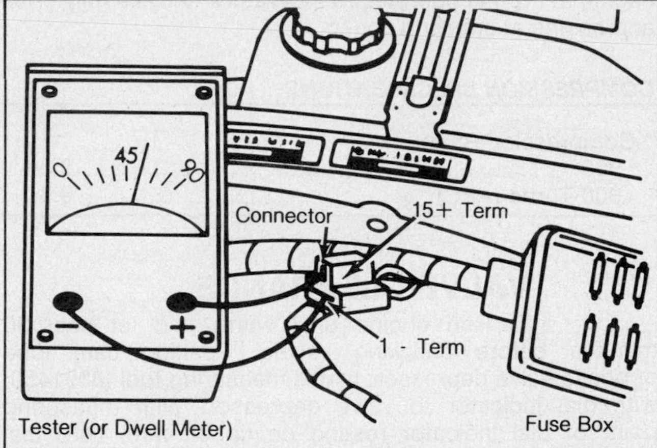

45
0
90
Connector
15+ Term
1 - Term
Tester (or Dwell Meter)
Fuse Box

Use Bosch tester (KDJE 7453) or dwell meter.

3) If adjustment is necessary, remove mixture control unit from vehicle. Disassemble sensor plate and lever. Drive out mixture adjustment opening plug with punch. Reassemble mixture control unit and install on vehicle.

4) With engine idling, adjust mixture with hex head wrench until tester indicates 45-55%. Dwell meter will show 40-50° on 4-cyl. scale. Accelerate engine and recheck adjustment, then reinstall plug. Remove test equipment.

DASHPOT ADJUSTMENT

AUTO. TRANS. MODELS

NOTE: For vehicles with manual transmissions, decel fuel shutoff system engages above 1575 RPM, and cuts out below 1375 RPM, when throttle is closed against contact. Calibration is fixed by relay (85 74 899).

1) Bring engine to normal operating temperature. On Turbo models, disconnect and plug EGR hose. On all other models, disconnect and plug vacuum advance. Connnect tachometer and check idle speed. Adjust if necessary.

TUNE-UP (Cont.)

2) Rotate throttle lever and check that dashpot rod strikes the stop at 2100-2300 RPM on Turbo models, or 2400-2600 RPM on all others. If not, adjust by turning dashpot.

3) Accelerate engine to 3000 RPM and measure time from release of throttle until engine reaches idle speed. Deceleration time should be 3-6 seconds. If not, turn dashpot in toward stop to lengthen delay, or away from stop to shorten delay time.

FUEL PUMP

FUEL PUMP PERFORMANCE

Application	Pressure psi (kg/cm²)	Volume in 30 sec. Pints (Liters)
All Models	64-72 (4.5-5.1)	[1] 1.9 (.90)

[1] — Measured at return fuel line.

EMISSION CONTROL SYSTEMS

See Mitchell Manuals' Emission Control Manual.

GENERAL SERVICING

IGNITION

DISTRIBUTOR

All models are equipped with Bosch Hall Effect breakerless, electronic distributors.

IGNITION COIL

IGNITION COIL RESISTANCE Ohms @ 68°F (20°C)

Application	Primary	Secondary
All Models	1.05-1.35	5500-8500

FUEL SYSTEMS

FUEL INJECTION

Saab uses Bosch Lambda (CIS) fuel injection.

ELECTRICAL

BATTERY

BATTERY SPECIFICATIONS

Application	Amp. Hr. Rating
All Models	60

STARTER

All models use Bosch starters.

STARTER SPECIFICATIONS

Application	Volts	Amps	Test RPM
All Models	11.5	35-55	6500-8500

ALTERNATOR

All models use Motorola or Bosch alternators.

ALTERNATOR SPECIFICATIONS

Application	Rated Amp Output
Bosch	55
Bosch	65
Bosch	70
Motorola	70

ALTERNATOR REGULATOR

All alternators have built-in regulators which require no adjustment.

SERVICE SPECIFICATIONS

BELT ADJUSTMENT

Application	[1] Deflection In. (mm)
Alternator Belt	.2 (5)

[1] — Deflection is with 3.3 Lbs. (1.5 kg) pressure applied midway on longest belt run.

REPLACEMENT INTERVALS

Components	Interval (Miles)
Oil Filter	
Turbo (APC)	5000
All Other Models	7500
Air Filter	30,000
Fuel Filter	30,000
Spark Plugs	30,000
Oxygen Sensor	30,000
Canister	60,000

FLUID CAPACITIES

Application	Quantity
Crankcase (Includes Filter)	
Turbo (APC)	4.5 qts. (4.3L)
All Other Models	3.7 qts. (3.5L)
Cooling System	
All Models	10.6 qts. (10.0L)
Man. Trans. (SAE 10W-30) [1]	3.0 qts. (2.9L)
Auto. Trans. (ATF Type F)	8.5 qts. (8.1L)
Auto. Trans. Final Drive (SAE 80)	1.3 qts. (1.2L)
Fuel Tank	16.6 gals. (63.0L)

[1] — Including Final Drive.

TUNE-UP

1600, 1800, 1800 Turbo

ENGINE IDENTIFICATION

Engine can be identified by a combination letter-number code stamped on machined pad on front right side of engine, near distributor.

ENGINE CODE

Application	Code
1600	
4-Speed Man. Trans.	EA71A
5-Speed Man. Trans.	EA71G
1800	
2WD	
5-Speed Man. Trans.	EA81G
Auto.Trans.	EA81T
4WD	
4-Speed Man. Trans.	
DL & Standard	EA81W
GL	EA81P
1800 & 1800 Turbo	
4WD	
Auto. Trans.	EA81X

ENGINE COMPRESSION

Check pressure with engine warm, plugs removed, throttle valve wide open and engine at cranking speed.

COMPRESSION SPECIFICATIONS

Compression Ratio	
1.6L	9.0:1
1.8L	8.7:1
1800 Turbo (1.8L)	7.7:1
Compression Pressure	
1.6L	175 psi (12.3 kg/cm²)
1.8L	171 psi (12.0 kg/cm²)
1800 Turbo (1.8L)	156 psi (11.0 kg/cm²)
Minimum Compression Pressure	
1800 Turbo	117 psi (8.2 kg/cm²)
Other Models	128 psi (9.0 kg/cm²)
Max. Variation	28 psi (2.0 kg/cm²)

VALVE CLEARANCE

1) With engine cold, bring piston of the cylinder to be checked to top dead center of compression stroke. Insert feeler gauge between valve stem and rocker arm.

2) Loosen lock nuts and turn adjusting screws to proper clearance. Adjust valves in firing order sequence using valve clearance adjusting tool (498767000) or equivalent.

VALVE CLEARANCE SPECIFICATIONS

Application	[1] In. (mm)
Intake	.010 (.25)
Exhaust	.014 (.35)

[1] — Adjust valves with engine cold.

NOTE: Hydraulic lifters are used on 1800 and 1800 Turbo models with automatic transmissions.

VALVE ARRANGEMENT

I-E-E-I (Both banks, front-to-rear)

SPARK PLUGS

SPARK PLUG TYPE

Application	NGK No.	Champion No.
All Models	BPR-6ES-11	RN11YC-4

SPARK PLUG SPECIFICATIONS

Application	Gap In. (mm)	Torque Ft. Lbs. (N.m)
All Models	.041 (1.0)	15 (20)

HIGH TENSION WIRE RESISTANCE

1) Carefully remove high tension wires from spark plugs and ignition coil. Remove distributor cap with wires still in place.

2) Using an ohmmeter, check high tension wire resistance between free end of wire and distributor cap electrode. If resistance is not correct, or fluctuates from infinity to any value, replace high tension wires.

HIGH TENSION WIRE RESISTANCE

Application	Ohms
All Models	25,000

DISTRIBUTOR

All models are equipped with breakerless, electronic ignition systems. Nippondenso distributors are used in 2WD models and in 4WD 1800 models with automatic transmissions. Hitachi distributors are used in 4WD 1800 models with manual transmissions and 4WD 1800 Turbo models with automatic transmissions.

Distributors for 1800 Turbo models retard timing during turbocharger operation, and permit normal advance at other times.

Fig. 1: Firing Order and Distributor Rotation

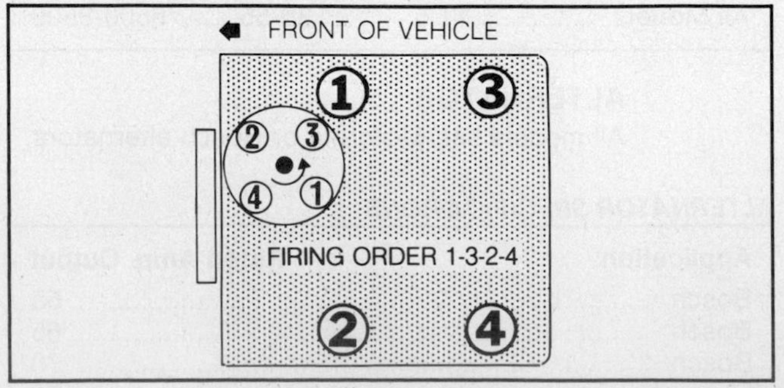
FRONT OF VEHICLE
1
3
2
3
4
1
FIRING ORDER 1-3-2-4
2
4

TUNE-UP (Cont.)

AIR GAP SPECIFICATIONS

Application	Gap In. (mm)
Hitachi	.012-.020 (.3-.5)
Nippondenso	.008-.016 (.2-.4)

IGNITION TIMING

Check or adjust ignition timing with engine at normal operating temperature, and transmission in Neutral. Disconnect and plug distributor vacuum hoses. Run engine at idle speed.

Fig. 2: Subaru Timing Mark Location

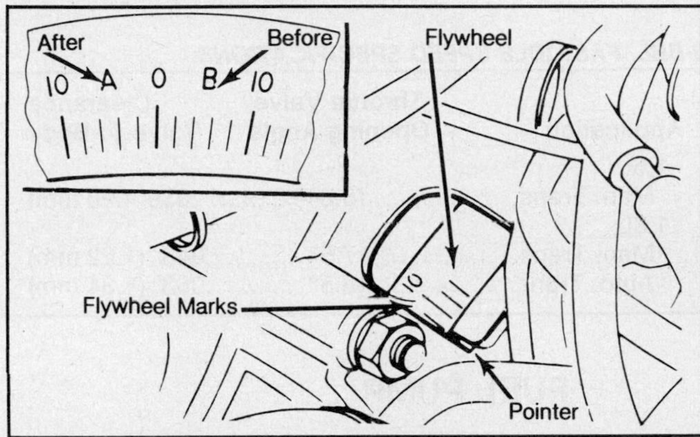
After
Before
10 A 0 B 10
Flywheel
Flywheel Marks
Pointer

NOTE: **Ignition timing marks are visible through opening in flywheel cover on right side of engine.**

IGNITION TIMING SPECIFICATIONS (Degrees BTDC@RPM)

Application	Man. Trans.	Auto. Trans.
1800 Turbo		15°@800
All Other Models	[1] 8@700	[1] 8@800

[1] — High altitude is 12° BTDC.

IDLE SPEED & MIXTURE

NOTE: **Ignition timing and valve clearances must be correct and engine must be at normal operating temperature prior to adjusting idle speed and mixture.**

IDLE SPEED

1800 Turbo

1) Be sure all vacuum hoses, blow-by hoses, valve cover, and oil filler cap are securely attached. Warm engine and oxygen sensor by running engine at 2500 RPM for approximately 1 minute after engine reaches normal operating temperature.

2) Be sure auxiliary air valve is completely closed. Adjust idle speed with idle adjusting screw located on the throttle body.

All Other Models

Disconnect canister purge hose at check valve near intake manifold. Plug hose. Start engine and warm up for at least 5 minutes. Adjust idle speed with transmission in Neutral.

IDLE SPEED SPECIFICATIONS (RPM)

Application	Man. Trans.	[1] Auto. Trans.
1800 Turbo		750-850
All Other Models	600-800	700-900

[1] — In Neutral or Park.

IDLE MIXTURE

NOTE: **Mixture adjustment is not a part of normal tune-up procedure and should not be performed unless carburetor is disassembled or vehicle fails emission testing.**

1800 Turbo Models

1) Adjust both ignition timing and idle speed. Check CO content of exhaust gas. It is not necessary to adjust the CO adjusting screw of the air flow meter, as the air-fuel ratio is feedback-controlled.

2) If CO level is not to specifications, eliminate problem by checking the following: Ignition system, valve clearance and engine compression. Turn ignition off and attach jumper wire across 2 test connectors above brake pedal. Start engine and run at idle speed. If fuel injection system is operating properly ECS lamp on instrument panel should flash.

3) If problem still exists, check fuel pressure, fuel injectors and air cleaner element. A degraded catalyst, faulty exhaust system, or use of leaded gasoline could be other causes of high CO content.

1800 TURBO CO LEVEL SPECIFICATIONS

Application	Max. CO%
1800 Turbo	0.1

Federal 1800 4WD Models

1) Start and run engine until it reaches normal operating temperature. Check idle speed and exhaust gas CO percentage. Disconnect air injection hose at the air cleaner.

2) Plug air injection hose. Recheck idle speed and exhaust gas CO while air injection hose is plugged. If idle speed and CO are not to specifications, leave air injection hose plugged and adjust by turning both the idle speed screw and idle mixture screw.

3) After obtaining correct idle speed and CO with air injection hose disconnected and plugged, reconnect hose and recheck adjustments.

FEDERAL 1800 4WD CO LEVEL SPECIFICATIONS

Application	Man. Trans.	Auto. Trans.
Air Hose On	0-0.5%	0-0.5%
Air Hose Off	1.0-3.0%	0.5-2.5%

All Other Models

1) Connect a dwell meter to Green/White wire in Pink main duty cycle solenoid connector. Set meter on 4-cylinder scale and observe needle movement with engine idling. *See Fig. 3.*

2) Dwell meter needle should move up and down within a 30-40° range. If not moving, run engine at 2000-3000 RPM for at least 2 minutes, then recheck.

1983 Subaru 4 Tune-Up

TUNE-UP (Cont.)

Fig. 3: Idle Mixture Test Connections

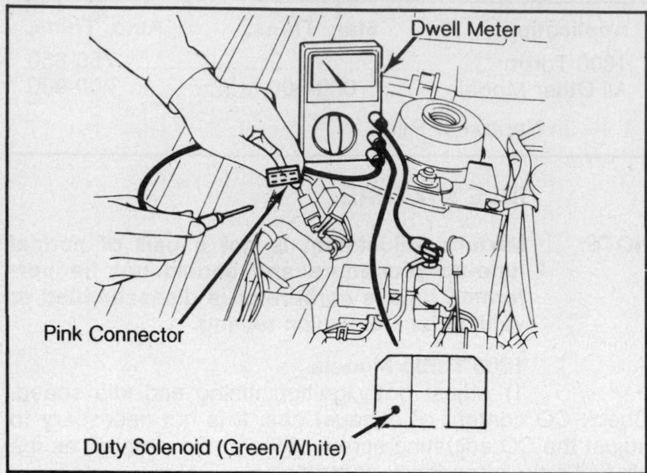
Dwell Meter
Pink Connector
Duty Solenoid (Green/White)

3) If dwell meter needle movement is not within specified range, adjust idle mixture screw until needle movement is correct. Recheck idle speed and readjust if necessary. Remove test equipment, reconnect purge hose and install roll pin.

CARBURETOR DUTY CYCLE SOLENOID RATIO

Application	Dwell Reading
High Alt. (W/Hitachi Carb.)	50°
All Others	32°

FAST IDLE ADJUSTMENT

1-BBL. CARBURETOR MODELS

1) Check idle speed and mixture prior to adjusting fast idle speed. Start and run engine until it reaches normal operating temperature. Ensure that automatic choke is fully opened.

2) Place fast idle adjusting screw on 3rd (middle) step of fast idle cam. Adjust fast idle speed to specifications.

1-BBL. FAST IDLE SPEED SPECIFICATIONS

Application	RPM
All Models	2000

2-BBL. CARBURETOR MODELS

With cam adjusting lever on first step of fast idle cam, primary throttle valve opening angle and clearance should be as specified. If not, adjust fast idle screw.

2-BBL. FAST IDLE SPEED SPECIFICATIONS

Application	Throttle Valve Opening Angle	Clearance Valve-to-Body
1.6L		
Man. Trans.	15.0°	.039" (.98 mm)
1.8L		
Man. Trans.	17.5°	.048" (1.22 mm)
Auto. Trans.	18.5°	.053" (1.34 mm)

FUEL PUMP

FUEL PUMP PERFORMANCE

Application	Pressure psi (kg/cm²)	Volume in 30 Sec. Pints (Liters)
1800 Turbo	43.4 (3.1)	1.7 (.80)
Other Models	1.7 (.12)	.5 (.24)

EMISSION CONTROL SYSTEMS

See Mitchell Manuals' Emission Control Manual.

GENERAL SERVICING

IGNITION

DISTRIBUTOR

Breakerless, electronic ignition systems are used on all models. Hitachi systems are used on 1800 4WD models with manual transmission and 1800 Turbo models with automatic transmissions. Nippondenso systems are used on all other models. Distributors for 1800 Turbo have advance-retard diaphragm, permitting timing retard during turbocharger operation.

IGNITION COIL

IGNITION COIL RESISTANCE — Ohms @ 68°F (20°C)

Application	Primary	Secondary
Hitachi		
1800	1.04-1.27	7360-11,040
1800 Turbo	.84-1.02	8,000-10,000
Nippondenso	1.13-1.38	10,795-14,605

FUEL SYSTEMS

CARBURETORS

All models equipped with a 1-Bbl. carburetor use a Carter TYF type carburetor. All models with 2-Bbl. carburetors use a Hitachi DCP306 type carburetor.

FUEL INJECTION

The Bosch AFC fuel injection system is used on 1800 Turbo. Subaru refers to it as the Electronic-Controlled Gasoline Injection (EGI) system.

ELECTRICAL

STARTER

All models use Nippondenso starters. 1800 and 1800 Turbo models use a gear reduction-type starter.

GENERAL SERVICING (Cont.)

STARTER SPECIFICATIONS

Application	Volts	Amps	Test RPM
1.6L	11.0	50	5000
1.8L			
Man. Trans.	11.5	90	3000
Auto. Trans.	11.5	90	4100

BATTERY

BATTERY SPECIFICATIONS

Application	Amp Hr. Rating
Without Power Steering	60
With Power Steering	65

ALTERNATOR

All models use a Hitachi alternator.

ALTERNATOR SPECIFICATIONS

Application	Rated Amp Output
All Models	55

ALTERNATOR REGULATOR

All models are equipped with Hitachi alternator regulators.

REGULATOR OPERATING VOLTAGE @ 68°F (20°C)

Application	Voltage
All Models	14.2-14.8

SERVICE SPECIFICATIONS

BELT ADJUSTMENT

Application	[1] Deflection In. (mm)
1800 Turbo	
Without A/C	.28-.35 (7-9)
With A/C	.24-.31 (6-8)
All Other Models	
Alternator Belt	.51-.55 (13-14)
Power Steering Belt	.59-.79 (15-20)

[1] – With 22 lbs. (10 kg) pressure applied midway on longest belt run.

REPLACEMENT INTERVALS

Component	Interval (Miles)
Oil Filter	7500
Air Filter	30,000
Fuel Filter	15,000
Spark Plugs	30,000

FLUID CAPACITIES

Application	Quantity
Crankcase (Includes Filter)	
1.6L	3.7 qts. (3.5L)
1.8L	4.2 qts. (4.0L)
Cooling System	
1.6L	5.6 qts. (5.3L)
1.8L	5.8 qts. (5.5L)
Man. Transaxle (SAE 85W-90)	
2WD	2.9 qts. (2.7L)
4WD	3.2 qts. (3.0L)
Auto. Transaxle (Dexron)	4.2 qts. (4.0L)
Differential (SAE 85W-90)	
Front	2.6 pts. (1.2L)
Rear (4WD)	1.6 pts. (0.8L)
Fuel Tank	
Hatchback	
2WD	13.0 gals. (50.0L)
4WD	12.0 gals. (45.0L)
All Other Models	
2WD	16.0 gals. (60.0L)
4WD	14.5 gals. (55.0L)

1983 Toyota 4 Tune-Up

TUNE-UP

Camry, Celica, Corolla, Pickup, Starlet, Tercel

ENGINE IDENTIFICATION

Each of the engine serial numbers contains an identifying code for engine identification. On Starlet models, the serial number is located on the right side of the engine block.

All other models have the number stamped on the left side of engine block. Engine codes are also provided on decal at front edge of valve cover.

ENGINE CODE

Application	Code
Camry	2S-E
Celica & Pickup	[1] 22R
Corolla	4A-C
Starlet	4K-E
Tercel	3A-C

[1] – Celica fuel injected models use the 22R-E engine.

ENGINE COMPRESSION

CARBURETED MODELS

Run engine until it reaches normal operating temperature. Remove all spark plugs and coil high tension wire. Hold throttle valve wide open and operate engine at cranking speed, when checking compression.

FUEL INJECTED MODELS

1) Engine must be at normal operating temperature. Unplug fuel injection solenoid resistor wire connector. Solenoid resistor is located on the front of the left shock tower on Camry and Starlet models. On Celica models, it is on the right front shock tower.

2) Remove spark plugs and coil wire. Ground coil wire. Check compression with throttle wide open and at cranking speed.

COMPRESSION SPECIFICATIONS

Compression Ratio	
Camry	8.6:1
Celica, Corolla, Pickup & Tercel	9.0:1
Starlet	9.5:1
Normal Compression Pressure	
Camry, Celica & Pickup	171 psi (12.0 kg/cm²)
Corolla & Tercel	178 psi (12.5 kg/cm²)
Starlet	185 psi (13.0 kg/cm²)
Min. Compression Pressure	128 psi (9.0 kg/cm²)
Max. Variation	14 psi (1.0 kg/cm²)

VALVE CLEARANCE

CAMRY & STARLET

The Camry and Starlet models use hydraulic lifters. No adjustments are necessary.

CELICA, COROLLA, PICKUP & TERCEL

1) Check or adjust valve clearance with engine at normal operating temperature. Remove valve cover and set No. 1 cylinder at TDC. Check that rocker arms for No.1 cylinder are loose and for No. 4 cylinder are tight.

2) Adjust intake valve on cylinders No. 1 and No. 2 and exhaust valve on cylinders No. 1 and No. 3. Turn crankshaft 360°. Adjust intake valve on cylinders No. 3 and No. 4 and exhaust valve on cylinders No. 2 and No. 4.

VALVE CLEARANCE SPECIFICATIONS

Application	[1] In. (mm)
Intake	.008 (.20)
Exhaust	.012 (.30)

[1] – Adjust valve clearance with engine hot.

Fig. 1: Camry Firing Order and Distributor Rotation

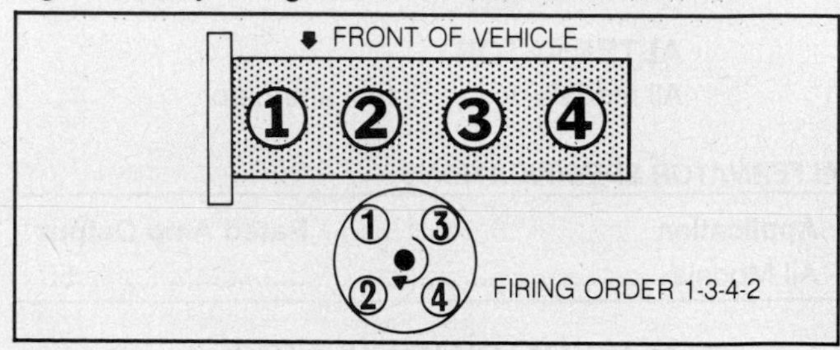
FRONT OF VEHICLE
1 2 3 4
FIRING ORDER 1-3-4-2

Fig. 2: Celica and Pickup Firing Order and Distributor Rotation

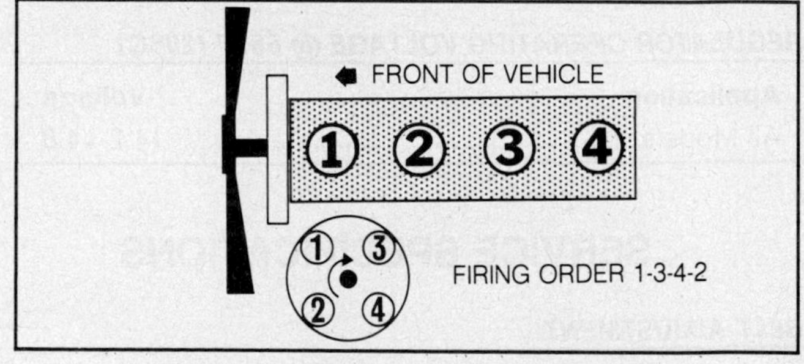
FRONT OF VEHICLE
1 2 3 4
FIRING ORDER 1-3-4-2

Fig. 3: Corolla and Tercel Firing Order and Distributor Rotation

FRONT OF VEHICLE
20 15 10 5 0 5
1 2 3 4
FIRING ORDER 1-3-4-2

Fig. 4: Starlet Firing Order and Distributor Rotation

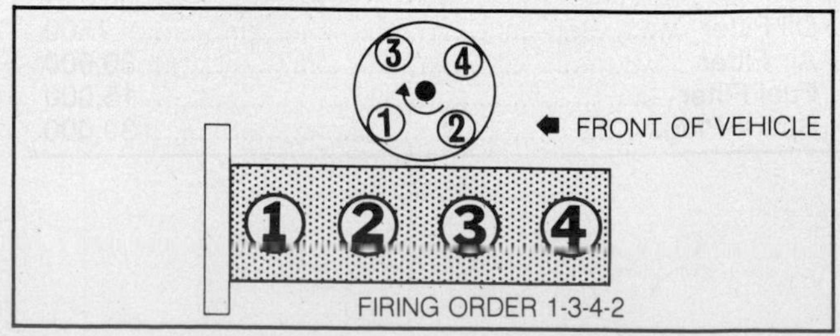
FRONT OF VEHICLE
1 2 3 4
FIRING ORDER 1-3-4-2

TUNE-UP (Cont.)

VALVE ARRANGEMENT

CAMRY
I-E-I-E-E-I-E-I (Front-to-rear)

STARLET
E-I-I-E-E-I-I-E (Front-to-rear)

TERCEL
I-E-E-I-I-E-E-I (Front-to-rear)

ALL OTHER MODELS
Right Side – All Intake
Left Side – All Exhaust

SPARK PLUGS

SPARK PLUG TYPE

Application	NGK No.	Nippondenso No.
Camry	BPR5EA-L11	W16EXR-U11
Celica & Pickup	BPR5EY	W16EXR-U
Corolla	BPR5EA-L11	W16EXR-U11
Starlet		
4-Speed	BPR5EP11	P16R
5-Speed	BRE529Y11	J16BR-U11
Tercel	BPR5EA-L11	W16EXR-U11

SPARK PLUG SPECIFICATIONS

Application	Gap In. (mm)	Torque Ft. Lbs. (N.m)
Camry, Corolla Starlet & Tercel	.043 (1.1)	11-15 (15-20)
Celica & Pickup	.031 (.8)	11-15 (15-20)

HIGH TENSION WIRE RESISTANCE

Carefully remove high tension wires from spark plugs and distributor cap. Using an ohmmeter, check high tension wire resistance while gently twisting wires. If resistance is not to specifications, or fluctuates from infinity to any value, replace high tension wire(s).

HIGH TENSION WIRE RESISTANCE

Application	Ohms
All Models	25,000

DISTRIBUTOR

All models use transistorized ignition which eliminates breaker points. Reluctor-to-pick-up air gap is the only adjustment. Measure air gap with a non-magnetic feeler gauge and move pick-up if necessary to correct air gap.

DISTRIBUTOR PICK-UP COIL AIR GAP

Application	In. (mm)
All Models	.008-.016 (.2-.4)

IGNITION TIMING

1) Engine must be at operating temperature. Connect tachometer and timing light to engine. Connect test probe of tachometer to negative (–) terminal of coil, or to the service connector on distributor (if equipped). Adjust idle speed to specifications.

2) On 3A-C and 4A-C engines (Tercel and Corolla), disconnect and plug INBOARD distributor vacuum line only. On all other engines, disconnect and plug both distributor vacuum lines. On all models, adjust timing by turning distributor.

IGNITION TIMING (Degrees BTDC@RPM)

Application	Timing Vac. Plugged	Timing Vac. Connected
Camry	5°@950	16°@950
Celica	5°@950	....
Corolla	5°@950	....
Pickup (Gas)	5°@950	12°@950
Starlet	5°@950	18°@950
Tercel		
Man. Trans.	5°@950	13°@Idle
Auto. Trans.	5°@950	13°@Idle

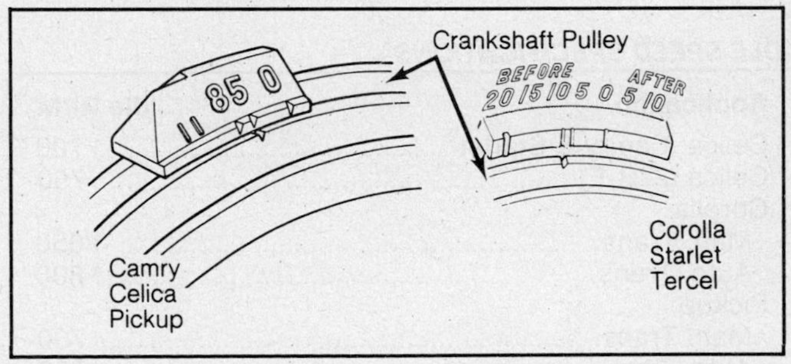
Crankshaft Pulley
85 0
BEFORE
20 15 10 5 0 5 10
AFTER
Camry
Celica
Pickup
Corolla
Starlet
Tercel
Fig. 5: Ignition Timing Marks

IDLE SPEED & MIXTURE

IDLE SPEED

Carbureted Models

1) Engine must be at normal operating temperature. Adjust idle speed under the following conditions: air cleaner installed, choke fully open, all accessories off, engine cooling fan off, transmission in "N", and all emission system vacuum lines connected.

2) Connect tachometer to engine. Check and adjust timing. Set idle speed to specifications using the adjusting screw. *See Fig. 6.*

Idle Speed Screw
Fast Idle Screw
Idle Mixture Screw
Fig. 6: Carburetor Adjusting Screws

TUNE-UP (Cont.)

Fuel Injected Models

1) Adjust idle under the following conditions: air cleaner installed, all air intake system hoses connected, all vacuum lines connected, EFI system wiring connectors tight, transmission in neutral, and all accessories and engine cooling fan off.

2) Engine must be at normal operating temperature. Connect a tachometer to engine. Race engine at 2500 RPM for 2 minutes. Set the idle by turning the idle speed adjusting screw. *See Fig. 7.*

Fig. 7: Adjusting Idle Speed On Fuel Injected Models

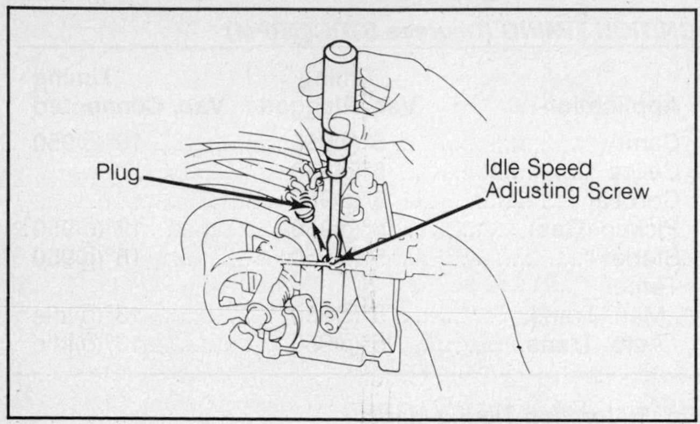
Plug
Idle Speed
Adjusting Screw

IDLE SPEED SPECIFICATIONS

Application	Idle RPM
Celica, Camry & Starlet	[1] 700
Celica (22R-E)	750
Corolla	
Man. Trans.	[2] 650
Auto. Trans.	[3] 800
Pickup	
Man. Trans.	700
Auto. Trans.	750
Tercel	
Man. Trans.	
4-Speed	550
5 & 6-Speed	[2] 650
Auto. Trans.	[2] 800

[1] – Camry with Auto. Trans. set to 750.
[2] – Models with power steering set to 800.
[3] – Models with power steering set to 900.

IDLE MIXTURE

NOTE: **On fuel injected models, idle mixture is controlled electronically and is not adjustable.**

NOTE: **Mixture adjustment is not a part of normal tune-up procedure and should not be performed unless carburetor is disassembled or vehicle fails emissions testing.**

Carbureted Models

1) Place transmission in neutral and ensure fuel level in carburetor sight glass is about mid-way. Remove carburetor from engine. Carefully drill a .256" (6.5 mm) hole in the center of the idle mixture screw plug. Use a .295" (7.5 mm) drill to pry out the plug.

CAUTION: **There is only .04" (1 mm) clearance between the plug and screw.**

2) Remove the mixture screw. If the drill has damaged the top or the tapered portion is damaged, replace the screw.

3) Install and fully seat the mixture screw. Back out the screw 3-4 turns. Install the carburetor. Start engine and adjust idle speed. Adjust to the maximum (lean drop) RPM by turning the idle mixture screw.

4) Set idle speed using the idle speed adjusting screw. Continue adjustments until maximum (lean drop) speed will not rise any further. Adjust idle RPM by turning in the idle mixture screw. *See Idle Mixture Specifications Chart.* Install replacement mixture screw cap and protective cover, if so equipped.

5) On Corolla and Tercel models, use idle speed screw to reset idle speed to specification, after idle mixture adjustment. *See Idle Speed Specifications Chart.*

IDLE MIXTURE SPECIFICATIONS

Application	Lean Drop RPM	Idle RPM
Celica		
Man. Trans.	740	700
Auto. Trans.	790	750
Corolla	700	650
Pickup		
Man. Trans.	740	700
Auto. Trans.	790	750
Tercel	700	650

COLD (FAST) IDLE RPM

CELICA & PICKUP

1) After setting idle and mixture, stop engine. Remove air cleaner. Disconnect and plug hoses at distributor vacuum advance, choke opener diaphragm and EGR valve.

2) Hold throttle valve slightly open. Push choke valve closed and release throttle valve. Without touching accelerator, start engine. Set fast idle to specifications by turning fast idle adjusting screw.

COROLLA & TERCEL

1) After setting idle and mixture, stop engine. Remove air cleaner. Disconnect and plug hose from EGR valve. On Calif. models, disconnect hoses for hot idle compensation system, and plug both air suction hoses at the reed valve on the air cleaner.

2) Hold throttle valve slightly open. Push choke valve closed and release throttle valve. Without touching accelerator, start engine. Set fast idle to specifications by turning fast idle adjusting screw.

FAST IDLE SPEED SPECIFICATIONS

Application	RPM
Celica	2600
Corolla	3000
Pickup	2600
Tercel	3000

TUNE-UP (Cont.)

THROTTLE POSITIONER

COROLLA & TERCEL

1) With engine at operating temperature, connect tachometer, remove air cleaner and disconnect and plug vacuum hose to "M" port of thermostatic vacuum switching valve (TVSV).

2) Ensure choke valve is fully open, idle speed is correct and check sight glass for proper fuel level. Disconnect and plug vacuum hose to throttle positioner diaphragm and start engine.

3) Adjust engine speed to 1400 RPM by turning throttle positioner adjustment screw. *See Fig. 8.* Reconnect vacuum hose to diaphragm and ensure engine speed returns to idle.

Fig. 8: Throttle Positioner Adjustment

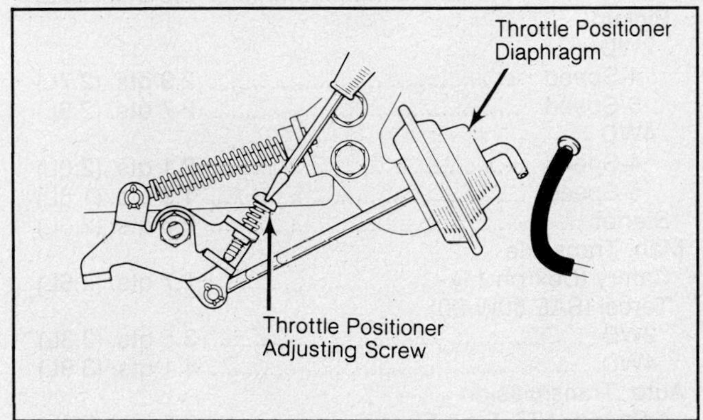
Throttle Positioner
Diaphragm
Throttle Positioner
Adjusting Screw

FUEL PUMP

FUEL PUMP PERFORMANCE

Application	Pressure psi (kg/cm²)
Celica, Pickup	2.8-4.3 (.2-.3)
Corolla, Tercel	2.5-3.5 (.18-.25)
Fuel Injection	
All Models	[1] 28 (2.0)

[1] – With pressure regulator vacuum hose disconnected, pressure is 36-38 (2.5-2.7 kg/cm²).

EMISSION CONTROL SYSTEM

See Mitchell Manuals' Emission Control Manual.

GENERAL SERVICING

IGNITION

DISTRIBUTOR

All models are equipped with a Nippondenso transistorized ignition system.

IGNITION COIL

IGNITION COIL RESISTANCE – Ohms @ 68°F (20°C)

Application	Primary	Secondary
Camry, Corolla & Tercel	.4-.5	7700-10,400
Celica & Pickup Type IV	.8-1.1	10,700-14,500
Pickup Type III	.4-.5	8500-11,500
Starlet	1.3-1.6	10,700-14,500

FUEL SYSTEMS

CARBURETORS

Celica (22R), Corolla, Pickup and Tercel models use Aisan 2-Bbl. carburetors.

FUEL INJECTION

Camry, Starlet and Celica (22R-E) are equipped with electronic fuel injection.

ELECTRICAL

BATTERY

BATTERY SPECIFICATIONS

Application	Amp Hr. Rating
Standard	50
Optional	60

STARTER

All models are equipped with Nippondenso solenoid-actuated starters.

STARTER SPECIFICATIONS

Application	Volts	Amps	Test RPM
Camry & Celica	11.5	90	3000
Corolla & Pickup			
1.0kW	11.5	90	3000
1.4kW	11.5	90	3500
Starlet & Tercel			
Conventional	11.0	50	5000
Reduction	11.5	90	3000

GENERAL SERVICING (Cont.)

ALTERNATORS

All models are equipped with Nippondenso alternators.

ALTERNATOR SPECIFICATIONS

Application	Rated Amp Output
Camry	70
Celica	60
Corolla	50
Pickup	40, 55 or 60
Starlet	50 or 55
Tercel	50 or 55

ALTERNATOR REGULATOR

All models are equipped with Nippondenso alternator regulators.

REGULATOR OPERATING VOLTAGE @ 68°F (20°C)

Application	Voltage
All Models	13.8-14.8

SERVICE SPECIFICATIONS

BELT ADJUSTMENT
Lbs. (Kg) of Tension Using Borroughs Tension Gauge

Application	New Belt	Used Belt
Camry		
Alternator		
Without A/C	125 (57)	95 (43)
With A/C	175 (79)	130 (59)
Power Steering	125 (57)	80 (36)
All Others	125 (57)	80 (36)

REPLACEMENT INTERVALS

Component	Interval (Miles)
Oil Filter	10,000
Air Filter	30,000
Fuel Filter	60,000
Spark Plugs	30,000

FLUID CAPACITIES

Application	Quantity
Crankcase (Includes Filter)	
Camry	4.2 qts. (4.0L)
Celica & Pickup	5.0 qts. (4.6L)
Corolla & Tercel	3.5 qts. (3.3L)
Starlet	3.7 qts. (3.5L)
Cooling System (Includes Heater)	
Camry	7.4 qts. (7.0L)
Celica & Pickup	8.9 qts. (8.4L)
Corolla	[1] 5.7 qts. (5.4L)
Starlet	5.5 qts. (5.2L)
Tercel	5.6 qts. (5.3L)
Man. Transmission (SAE 80W-90)	
Celica	2.5 qts. (2.4L)
Corolla	1.8 qts. (1.7L)
Pickup	
2WD	
4-Speed	2.9 qts. (2.7L)
5-Speed	2.7 qts. (2.6L)
4WD	
4-Speed	2.1 qts. (2.0L)
5-Speed	1.9 qts. (1.8L)
Starlet	2.6 qts. (2.5L)
Man. Transaxle	
Camry (Dexron 11)	2.7 qts. (2.6L)
Tercel (SAE 80W-90)	
2WD	3.5 qts. (3.3L)
4WD	4.1 qts. (3.9L)
Auto. Transmission	
4-Speed (ATF Type F)	2.5 qts. (2.4L)
5-Speed (Dexron II)	2.5 qts. (2.4L)
Auto. Transaxle (Dexron II)	
Camry	2.5 qts. (2.4L)
Tercel	2.3 qts. (2.2L)
Transfer Case (SAE 80W-90)	3.4 pts. (1.7L)
Differential (SAE 80W-90)	
Camry	
Front With Auto. Transaxle	[2] 4.2 pts. (2.0L)
Celica	
Banjo-Type	2.8 pts. (1.3L)
Unitized-Type	2.2 pts. (1.0L)
Corolla & Starlet	2.2 pts. (1.0L)
Pickup	
2WD	
7.5"	3.6 pts. (1.7L)
8.0"	3.8 pts. (1.8L)
4WD (Front and Rear)	4.6 pts. (2.2L)
Tercel (Front with Auto. Transaxle)	2.0 pts. (.9L)
4WD (Rear Diff.)	2.2 pts. (1.0L)
Fuel Tank	
Camry	14.5 gals. (55.0L)
Celica	16.0 gals. (61.0L)
Corolla	
Exc. Station Wagon	13.0 gals. (50.0L)
Station Wagon	12.5 gals. (47.0L)
Pickup	
Short Bed	13.5 gals. (51.0L)
Long Bed	16.0 gals. (61.0L)
Starlet	10.5 gals. (40.0L)
Tercel	
2WD	12.0 gals. (45.0L)
4WD	13.0 gals. (50.0L)

[1] – 6.6 qts. (6.2L) with Auto. Trans.
[2] – Use Dexron II fluid.

TUNE-UP

Pickup

ENGINE IDENTIFICATION

The engine serial number is stamped on the left side of the cylinder block. Engine code is located on decal at front edge of valve cover.

ENGINE CODE

Application	Code
All Models	LN44D

ENGINE COMPRESSION

With engine at normal operating temperature, remove all glow plugs. Install special tool (Toyota 09992-00021) in glow plug mounting hole and attach a compression gauge. Disconnect wire at fuel cut solenoid. Crank engine at 250 RPM and measure compression.

NOTE: **Make sure glow plug wiring does not ground. Count number of revolutions necessary for No. 1 cylinder to reach maximum compression reading and use same number of revolutions to determine compression on remaining cylinders.**

COMPRESSION SPECIFICATIONS

Min. Compression Pressure	427 psi (30 kg/cm²)
Max. Variation Between Cylinders	71 psi (5 kg/cm²)

VALVE CLEARANCE

1) With engine at normal operating temperature, remove valve cover and rotate crankshaft until No. 1 cylinder is at TDC on compression stroke.

2) If No. 1 cylinder is at TDC on compression stroke, rocker arms will be loose on No. 1 cylinder and tight on No. 4 cylinder. Adjust intake valves on cylinder No.1 and 2, and exhaust valves on cylinder No. 1 and 3.

3) Rotate crankshaft 360°. Adjust intake valves on cylinder No. 3 and 4, and exhaust valves on cylinder No. 2 and 4. Recheck clearance. Replace valve cover.

VALVE CLEARANCE SPECIFICATIONS

Application	[1] In. (mm)
Intake	.010 (.25)
Exhaust	.014 (.36)

[1] – With engine at operating temperature.

Fig. 1: Toyota Diesel Firing Order

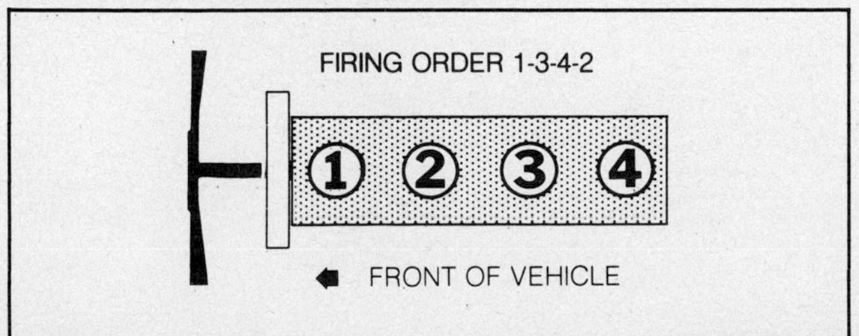
FIRING ORDER 1-3-4-2
1
2
3
4
FRONT OF VEHICLE

VALVE ARRANGEMENT

E-I-E-I-E-I-E-I (Front-to-rear)

IDLE SPEED

1) With engine at normal operating temperature, air cleaner installed, turn all accessories off. Place transmission in neutral and turn idle adjusting knob counterclockwise. Ensure that idle knob fully returns to the unlocked position.

2) Remove the accelerator connection rod. Connect a tachometer to engine. Start engine and check idle speed. If necessary, adjust by turning idle speed adjusting screw on injection pump. *See Fig. 2.*

IDLE SPEED SPECIFICATIONS

Application	Idle RPM
All Models	700

MAXIMUM SPEED

1) Install tachometer and run engine until normal operating temperature is obtained. Remove wire seal on maximum speed adjusting screw, if seal is present.

Fig. 2: Idle Speed and Maximum Speed Adjusting Screws

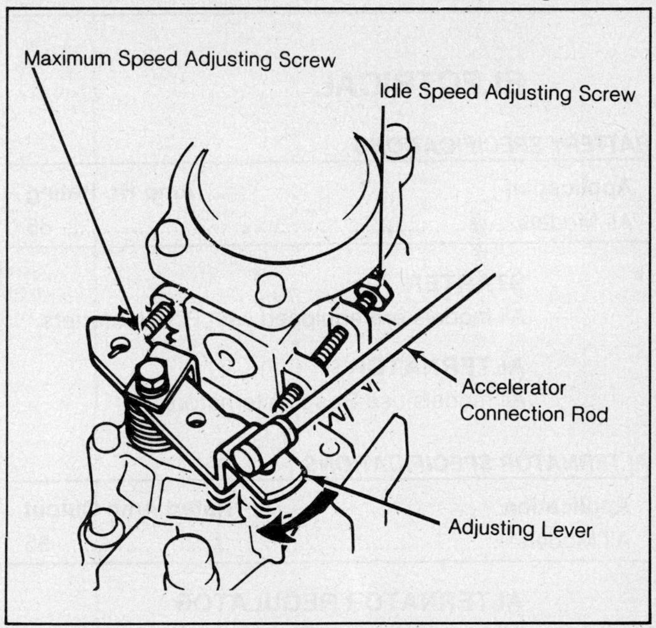
Maximum Speed Adjusting Screw
Idle Speed Adjusting Screw
Accelerator Connection Rod
Adjusting Lever

2) Using special socket tool (09275-54020) or equivalent, loosen lock nut on adjusting scew and adjust maximum speed by turning adjusting screw. *See Fig. 2.*

3) Fully depress accelerator pedal, checking to see that adjusting lever is stopped by maximum speed adjusting screw. Adjust accelerator pedal with the stop bolt. Tighten lock nut at adjusting screw, and remove tachometer.

NOTE: **Be sure engine speed increases when idle adjusting knob is pulled out and turned clockwise and returns to idle when turned fully counterclockwise.**

TUNE-UP (Cont.)

MAXIMUM SPEED SPECIFICATIONS

Application	Maximum RPM
All Models	4900

FUEL SYSTEM BLEEDING

Bleed air from the fuel system by pumping the priming pump on the top of the water separator. Fuel system must be bled whenever any fuel system components are repaired or replaced.

EMISSION CONTROL SYSTEMS

See Mitchell Manuals' Emission Control Manual.

GENERAL SERVICING

FUEL SYSTEM

FUEL INJECTION

All models use Kiki-Bosch mechanical type fuel injection.

DIESEL FUEL INJECTION TIMING

Application	Degrees BTDC	Plunger Travel In. (mm)
Pickup	0	.04 (1.0)

ELECTRICAL

BATTERY SPECIFICATIONS

Application	Amp Hr. Rating
All Models	65

STARTER

All models are equipped with Bosch starters.

ALTERNATORS

All models use Bosch alternators.

ALTERNATOR SPECIFICATIONS

Application	Rated Amp Output
All Models	55

ALTERNATOR REGULATOR

All models use Bosch regulator which is integral with alternator.

REGULATOR OPERATING VOLTAGE @ 68°F (20°C)

Application	Volts
All Models	13.8-14.4

SERVICE SPECIFICATIONS

BELT ADJUSTMENT
Lbs. (Kg) of Tension Using Borroughs Tension Gauge

Application	New Belt Lbs. (Kg)	Used Belt Lbs. (Kg)
Drive Belt	125 (57)	80 (36)

REPLACEMENT INTERVALS

Component	Interval (Miles)
Oil Filter	3750
Air Filter	30,000
Fuel Filter	30,000

FLUID CAPACITIES

Application	Quantity
Crankcase (Includes Filter)	6.0 qts. (5.8L)
Cooling System	11.0 qts. (10.5L)
Man. Trans. (SAE 80W-90)	4.6 pts. (2.2L)
Differential (SAE 90W)	3.6 pts. (1.7L)
Fuel Tank	
Short Bed	13.5 gals. (51.0L)
Long Bed	16.0 gals. (60.5L)

TUNE-UP

Cressida, Land Cruiser, Supra

ENGINE IDENTIFICATION

Engines can be identified by prefix of engine serial number, stamped on right side of engine block. Engine code can also be found on front of valve cover.

ENGINE CODE

Application	Code
Cressida & Supra	5M-GE
Land Cruiser	2F

ENGINE COMPRESSION

Check compression pressure with engine at normal operating temperature. Remove all spark plugs and coil high tension wire. Hold throttle valve wide open and operate engine at cranking speed.

COMPRESSION SPECIFICATIONS

Normal Compression Pressure	
Cressida & Supra	164 psi (11.5 kg/cm²)
Land Cruiser	149 psi (10.5 kg/cm²)
Min. Compression Pressure	
Cressida & Supra	128 psi (9.0 kg/cm²)
Land Cruiser	114 psi (8.0 kg/cm²)
Max. Variation	14 psi (1.0 kg/cm²)

VALVE CLEARANCE

NOTE: **Valve lash on Cressida and Supra models is controlled by hydraulic lifters. No adjustment is necessary.**

LAND CRUISER

Engine must be at operating temperature. Remove valve cover. Adjust from front to rear. Recheck clearance. Feeler gauge should have slight drag when pulled between valve stem and rocker arm.

VALVE CLEARANCE SPECIFICATIONS

Application	[1] In. (mm)
Land Cruiser	
Intake	.008 (.21)
Exhaust	.014 (.36)
Cressida & Supra	Hydraulic Lifters

[1] — Adjust valves with engine hot.

VALVE ARRANGEMENT

CRESSIDA & SUPRA

Left Side — All Intake
Right Side — All Exhaust

LAND CRUISER

E-I-I-E-E-I-I-E-E-I-I-E (Front-to-rear)

SPARK PLUGS

SPARK PLUG TYPE

Application	NGK No.	Nippondenso No.
Cressida & Supra	BPR5EP11	P16R
Land Cruiser	BPR4EY	W14EXR-U

SPARK PLUG SPECIFICATIONS

Application	Gap In. (mm)	Torque Ft. Lbs. (N.m)
Cressida & Supra	.043 (1.1)	11-15 (15-20)
Land Cruiser	.031 (0.8)	11-15 (15-20)

Fig. 1: Firing Order and Distributor Rotation for Cressida & Supra

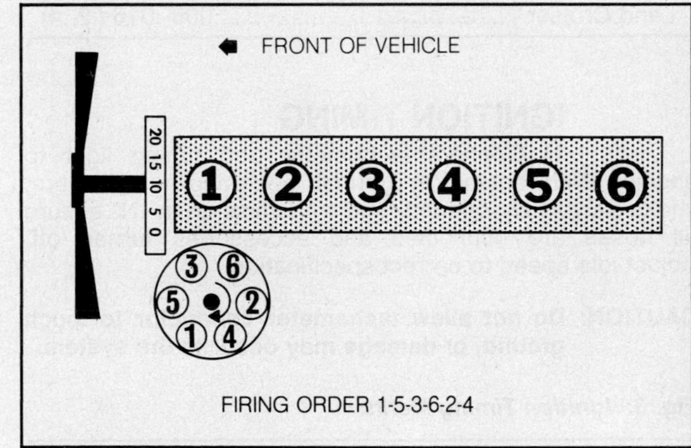
FRONT OF VEHICLE
20 15 10 5 0
1 2 3 4 5 6
3 6 5 2 1 4
FIRING ORDER 1-5-3-6-2-4

Fig. 2: Firing Order and Distributor Rotation for Land Cruiser

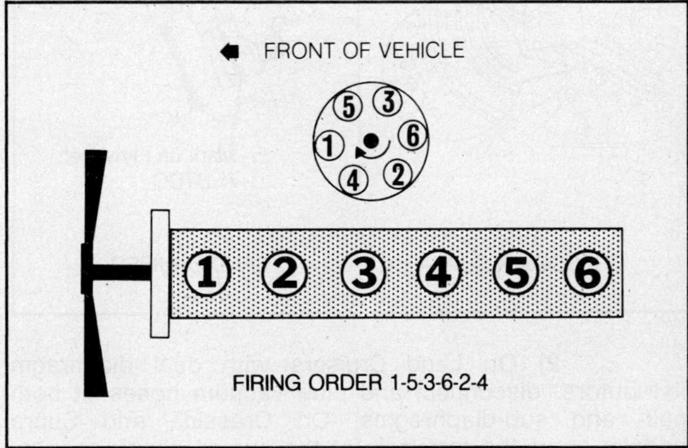
FRONT OF VEHICLE
5 3 1 6 4 2
1 2 3 4 5 6
FIRING ORDER 1-5-3-6-2-4

HIGH TENSION WIRE RESISTANCE

Carefully remove high tension wires from spark plugs and distributor cap. Using an ohmmeter, check high tension wire resistance while gently twisting wires. If resistance is not to specifications, or fluctuates from infinity to any value, replace high tension wire(s).

TUNE-UP (Cont.)

HIGH TENSION WIRE RESISTANCE

Application	Ohms
All Models	16,000-25,000

DISTRIBUTOR

Land Cruisers with 6-cylinder engines are fitted with Nippondenso Transistorized Electronic Ignition Systems. The only distributor adjustment possible is to set the air gap.

Cressida and Supra models are equipped with the Electronic Spark Advance (ESA) ignition system. No adjustments are necessary, but distributor pick-up coil resistance can be checked.

DISTRIBUTOR PICK-UP COIL AIR GAP

Application	In. (mm)
Land Cruiser	.008-.016 (.2-.4)

IGNITION TIMING

1) Connect tachometer and timing light to engine. With engine at normal operating temperature, choke valve fully opened, and transmission in "N" ensure all hoses are connected and accessories turned off. Adjust idle speed to correct specification.

CAUTION: Do not allow tachometer connector to touch ground, or damage may occur to the system.

Fig. 3: Ignition Timing Marks

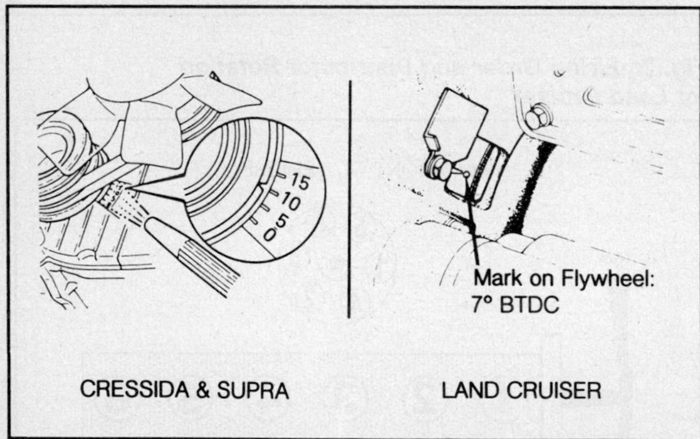
15
10
5
0
Mark on Flywheel:
7° BTDC
CRESSIDA & SUPRA
LAND CRUISER

2) On Land Cruisers with dual diaphragm distributors, disconnect and plug vacuum hoses at both main and sub-diaphragms. On Cressida and Supra models, short the terminals of the engine check connector. *See Fig. 4*.

3) On all models, adjust timing by turning distributor. Reconnect hoses to distributor diaphragms.

NOTE: On Federal low altitude Land Cruiser models, flywheel timing mark should move when vacuum hose between HAC valve and distributor sub-diaphragm is pinched near valve. On high altitude models, timing mark should move when sub-diaphragm hose is reconnected.

IGNITION TIMING (Degrees BTDC@RPM)

Application	Setting
Cressida & Supra	10@650
Land Cruiser	7@650

Fig. 4: Adjusting Ignition Timing on Cressida & Supra

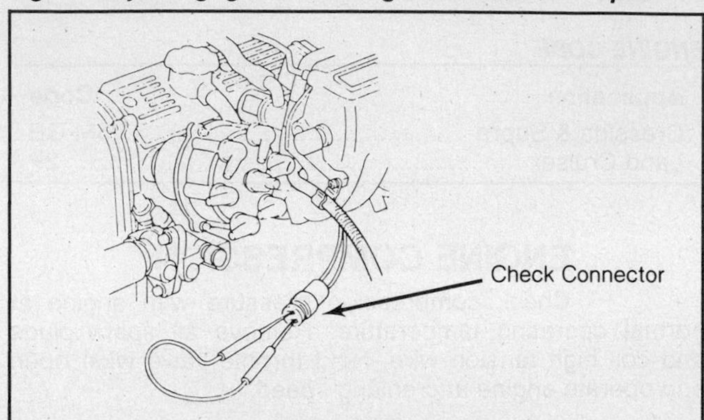
Check Connector

Short out check connector while adjusting timing.

IDLE SPEED & MIXTURE

IDLE SPEED

Land Cruiser

1) Adjust idle speed with air cleaner installed, engine at normal operating temperature, choke fully open, all accessories off and vacuum lines connected.

NOTE: Attach tachometer positive terminal to coil negative terminal. Do not allow tachometer connector to touch ground, or damage may occur to system.

2) Set transmission in neutral and check to see that fuel level in carburetor sight glass is midway between marks. Remove idle speed screw limiter caps, if installed, and adjust idle speed RPM as specified.

Fig. 5: Carburetor Adjustment Screw Locations

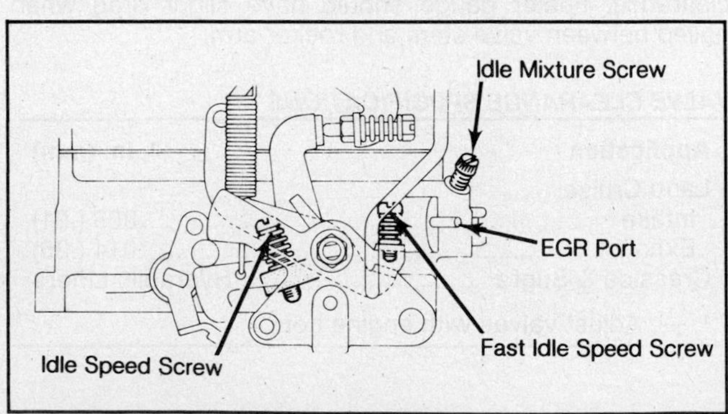
Idle Mixture Screw
EGR Port
Fast Idle Speed Screw
Idle Speed Screw

Cressida & Supra

1) With air cleaner installed, engine at normal operating temperature, all wiring connectors, vacuum lines, pipes and hoses connected and all accessories off, be sure timing is at correct specification.

2) Set transmission in neutral. Start engine and run at idle. Pinch air valve hose to ensure engine RPM does not drop more than 50 RPM.

TUNE-UP (Cont.)

3) Remove rubber cap from 4-terminal service connector at left front fender. Connect voltmeter positive probe to "VF" and negative probe to "E1" using a pigtail connector. *See Fig. 6.* Do not damage connector terminals with voltmeter probes.

Fig. 6: Idle Speed Service Connections

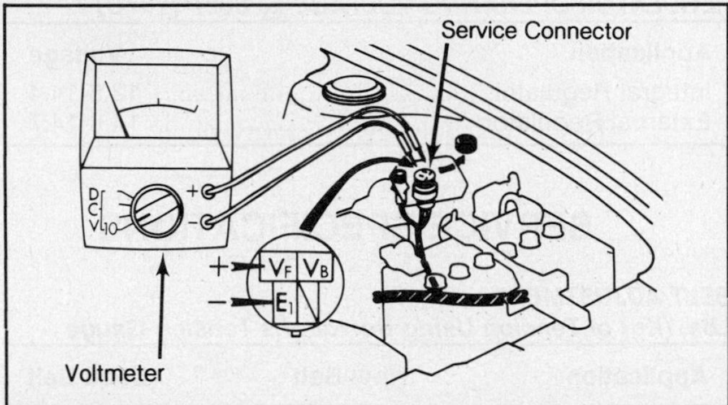
Service Connector
DC V 10
+
−
VF VB
E1
Voltmeter

Illustration applies to fuel injected models.

4) Warm up engine at 2500 RPM for about 2 minutes. Voltmeter needle should fluctuate 8 times or more in 10 seconds. If it does not, check fuel injection system and replace oxygen sensor, if necessary.

5) Set idle speed as specified with idle speed adjusting screw. Voltmeter reading should now be 1.25-3.75 volts. If out of specification, check air intake system for leaks.

IDLE SPEED SPECIFICATIONS

Application	RPM
Cressida & Supra	650
Land Cruiser	650

IDLE MIXTURE

NOTE: Mixture adjustment is not possible on fuel-injected vehicles. If voltmeter fluctuates properly in idle speed check, mixture should be correct. If not, air flow meter or other components must be replaced. Mixture adjustment screw is plugged and has very little effect on mixture ratio.

Land Cruiser

1) If adjustment is necessary, drill out and remove idle mixture screw cap. Remove metal shavings created by drilling. Remove idle mixture screw and check for damage. Reinstall mixture screw by turning in until fully seated. Unscrew mixture screw 2 full turns.

2) Start engine and adjust idle. Turn idle mixture adjusting screw to obtain maximum RPM. Now, turn idle speed screw until lean drop RPM is obtained. Repeat adjustments again, turning idle mixture screw to maximum RPM, then turn idle speed screw to lean drop RPM.

3) Once lean drop RPM is set after the highest possible speed is obtained using this procedure, turn in idle mixture adjusting screw until idle speed RPM is obtained. Install replacement mixture screw caps and protective cover, if so equipped.

IDLE MIXTURE SPECIFICATIONS

Application	Lean Drop RPM	Idle RPM
Land Cruiser	690	650

COLD (FAST) IDLE RPM

NOTE: There is no fast idle speed adjustment for Electronic Fuel Injection equipped vehicles.

LAND CRUISER

1) After setting idle speed and mixture, stop engine. Pull choke knob fully out. Disconnect and plug the vacuum supply hoses from distributor vacuum advance and from evaporation ports of the VCV and EGR valves.

2) Start engine and adjust fast idle speed to specification with fast idle adjusting screw. Engine should return to normal idle when choke knob is pushed in fully.

FAST IDLE SPEED SPECIFICATIONS

Application	RPM
Land Cruiser	[1] 1800

[1] – EGR, EVAP, and distributor diaphragm disconnected.

DASHPOT ADJUSTMENT

CRESSIDA & SUPRA

1) Run engine until it reaches operating temperature. Check and adjust idle speed. Connect a tachometer to engine. While maintaining an engine speed of 3000 RPM, pinch off vacuum hose leading to dashpot. Release throttle lever and note engine speed.

2) If engine speed is not as specified, adjust dashpot stop screw on throttle lever. Release dashpot vacuum hose. Engine should return to idle speed within 1 second. If not, thermal vacuum valve requires servicing.

DASHPOT SETTING SPEED

Application	RPM
Cressida & Supra	2000

FUEL PUMP

FUEL PUMP PERFORMANCE

Application	Pressure psi (kg/cm²)	Vol. in 30 Sec. Pints (Liters)
Cressida & Supra	[1] 35-38 (2.5-2.7)	.....
Land Cruiser	4.1 (.29)	2.5 (1.2)

[1] — Measured with vacuum hose at pressure regulator disconnected and plugged. With hose connected, 28 psi (2.0 kg/cm²).

EMISSION CONTROL SYSTEMS

See Mitchell Manuals' Emission Control Manual.

GENERAL SERVICING

IGNITION

DISTRIBUTOR

Land Cruisers are equipped wih Nippondenso Transistorized Electronic Ignition Systems. Cressida and Supra models use the Electronic Spark Advance (ESA) ignition system.

DISTRIBUTOR PICK-UP COIL RESISTANCE

Application	Ohms
Cressida & Supra	140-180

IGNITION COIL

IGNITION COIL RESISTANCE Ohms @ 68°F (20°C)

Application	Primary	Secondary
Cressida & Supra	.4-.5	8500-11,500
Land Cruiser	.5-.7	11,000-15,500

FUEL SYSTEMS

CARBURETORS

Land Cruiser models are equipped with Aisan 2-Bbl. carburetors.

FUEL INJECTION

Cressida and Supra models are equipped with Bosch AFC fuel injection with oxygen sensor.

ELECTRICAL

BATTERY

BATTERY SPECIFICATIONS

Application	Amp Hr. Rating
All Models	70

STARTER

All models are equipped with Nippondenso solenoid-actuated starters.

STARTER SPECIFICATIONS

Application	Volts	Amps	Test RPM
Cressida & Supra	11.5	90	3500
Land Cruiser	11.0	50	5000

ALTERNATORS

All models are equipped with Nippondenso alternators.

ALTERNATOR SPECIFICATIONS

Application	Rated Amp Ouput
Cressida & Supra	65
Land Cruiser	55

ALTERNATOR REGULATOR

All models are equipped with Nippondenso alternator regulators. Some alternators are equipped with integrated circuit regulators (mounted integrally with alternator).

REGULATOR OPERATING VOLTAGE @ 68°F (20°C)

Application	Voltage
Integral Regulator	13.8-14.4
External Regulator	14.0-14.7

SERVICE SPECIFICATIONS

BELT ADJUSTMENT
Lbs. (Kg) of Tension Using Borroughs Tension Gauge

Application	New Belt	Used Belt
Cressida & Supra	125 (57)	80 (36)
Land Cruiser		
A/C Belt	125 (57)	70 (32)
All Others	145 (66)	100 (45)

REPLACEMENT INTERVALS

Component	Interval (Miles)
Oil Filter	10,000
Air Filter	30,000
Fuel Filter	60,000
Spark Plugs	
Cressida & Supra	60,000
Land Cruiser	30,000

FLUID CAPACITIES

Application	Quantity
Crankcase (Includes Filter)	
Cressida & Supra	5.4 qts. (5.1L)
Land Cruiser	8.2 qts. (7.8L)
Cooling System	
Cressida	9.5 qts. (9.0L)
Land Cruiser	17.0 qts. (16.0L)
Supra	8.5 qts. (8.0L)
Man. Trans. (SAE 80W-90)	
Cressida & Supra	5.0 pts. (2.4L)
Land Cruiser	6.6 pts. (3.1L)
Auto. Trans. (ATF Type F)	2.5 qts. (2.4L)
Differential (SAE 90)	
Cressida & Supra	3.0 pts. (1.4L)
Land Cruiser	5.2 pts. (2.5L)
Transfer Case (SAE 90)	5.2 pts. (2.5L)
Fuel Tank	
Cressida	17.0 gals. (65.0L)
Land Cruiser	
Station Wagon	24.0 gals. (90.0L)
All Others	22.5 gals. (85.0L)
Supra	16.0 gals. (61.0L)

TUNE-UP

Jetta, Quantum, Rabbit, Rabbit GTI, Rabbit Pickup, Scirocco, Vanagon

ENGINE IDENTIFICATION

Engine can be identified by prefixes to engine serial number. On Vanagon, engine serial number is stamped on right side of crankcase directly in front of the fan housing. On all other models, serial number is stamped on left side of engine near ignition distributor.

ENGINE CODE

Application	Code
Jetta, Rabbit, Rabbit Pickup & Scirocco (1.7L)	EN
Quantum (1.7L)	WT
Rabbit GTI (1.8L)	JH
Vanagon	
Air-Cooled (2.0L)	CV
Water-Cooled (1.9L)	DU

ENGINE COMPRESSION

Check compression with engine warm, all spark plugs removed and throttle wide open. Crank engine through at least 6 compression strokes per cylinder to determine engine compression.

CAUTION: On models with electronic ignition, connect coil high tension wire to ground before cranking engine.

COMPRESSION SPECIFICATIONS

Compression Ratio	
Rabbit GTI	8.5:1
Vanagon	
Air-Cooled	7.3:1
Water-Cooled	8.6:1
All Others	8.2:1
Compression Pressure	
Vanagon	
Air-Cooled	
Maximum	145-189 psi (10.0-13.0 kg/cm²)
Minimum	116 psi (8.0 kg/cm²)
Water-Cooled	
Maximum	85-135 psi (6.0-9.5 kg/cm²)
Minimum	71 psi (5.0 kg/cm²)
All Others	
Maximum	131-174 psi (9.0-12.0 kg/cm²)
Minimum	102 psi (7.0 kg/cm²)
Max. Variation Between Cylinders	
All Models	44 psi (3.0 kg/cm²)

VALVE CLEARANCE

1) On Vanagon, no adjustment is needed as engine is equipped with hydraulic valve lifters. On all other models, valve clearance is between the cam lobe and cam follower.

2) Clearance is adjusted by replaceable discs. Discs are available in 26 thicknesses from .119-.166" (3.0-4.25 mm). Discs most frequently used are .140-.150" (3.55-3.80 mm).

3) To adjust, warm engine to normal operating temperature. Using wrench on center bolt of crankshaft pulley, hand turn crankshaft clockwise until cam lobes for cylinder being tested are pointing upward. Use feeler gauge to check valve clearance.

4) Use special depressor tool (2078) to press down cam follower, so that adjusting disc can be readily removed with special pliers (US 4476). When depressing cam followers, turn so that openings are at a 90° angle to cam.

VALVE CLEARANCE SPECIFICATIONS

Application	In. (mm)
All Models Except Vanagon (Hot)	
Intake	.008-.012 (.20-.30)
Exhaust	.016-.020 (.40-.50)

VALVE ARRANGEMENT

Vanagon – E-I-I-E (Both banks)
All Others – E-I-E-I-I-E-I-E (Front-to-rear)

SPARK PLUGS

SPARK PLUG TYPE SPECIFICATIONS

Application	Bosch No.	Champion No.
Vanagon		
Air-Cooled	W145M2	N288
Water-Cooled	W7C0	N288
All Other Models		
Federal [1]	W7D	N8Y
Calif.	WR7DS	N8GY

[1] – Federal Rabbit GTI Uses WR7DS (Bosch) or N8GY (Champion).

SPARK PLUG SPECIFICATIONS

Application	Gap In. (mm)	Torque Ft. Lbs. (N.m)
Vanagon		
Air-Cooled	.025 (.64)	14 (22)
Water-Cooled	.030 (.76)	14 (22)
All Other Models	.028 (.70)	14 (22)

HIGH TENSION WIRE RESISTANCE

Remove distributor cap and disconnect high tension wires from spark plugs (not distributor cap). Using an ohmmeter, measure resistance from cap terminal to other end of wire. If resistance is not to specifications, or fluctuates when wire is twisted gently, replace wire(s).

NOTE: High tension wire resistance cannot be measured if wire ends are marked with the following symbol: —▶◀—

TUNE-UP (Cont.)

HIGH TENSION WIRE RESISTANCE SPECIFICATIONS

Application	Ohms
All Models	5000-7000

DISTRIBUTOR

All models except Federal Vanagon with air-cooled engine use Bosch Hall Effect ignition systems. No adjustments are required. Federal Vanagon models use conventional Bosch single point distributor. Set point gap to approximately .016" (.40 mm) so that dwell reads 44-50°.

Fig. 1: Vanagon Firing Order & Distributor Rotation

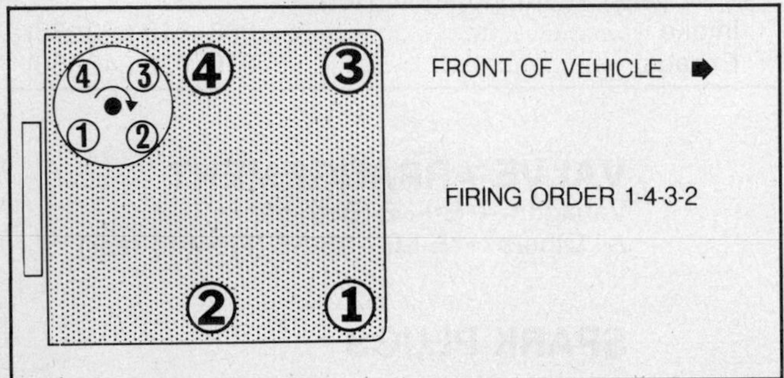
4
3
1
2
4
3
FRONT OF VEHICLE
FIRING ORDER 1-4-3-2
2
1

Fig. 2: Firing Order & Distributor Rotation for All Models Except Vanagon

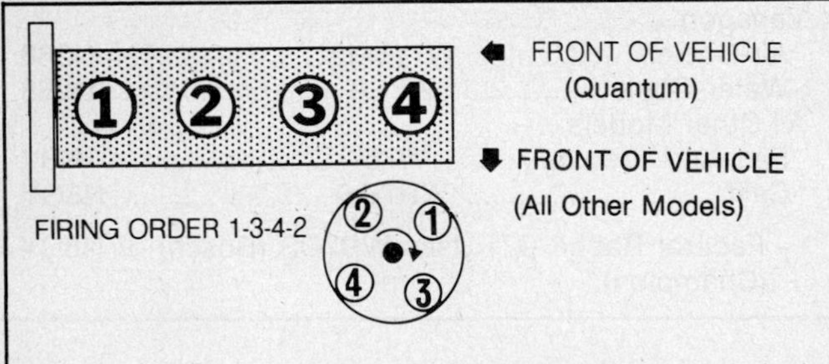
1
2
3
4
FRONT OF VEHICLE (Quantum)
FRONT OF VEHICLE (All Other Models)
FIRING ORDER 1-3-4-2
2
1
4
3

IGNITION TIMING

CALIFORNIA VANAGON WITH AIR- OR WATER-COOLED ENGINE

CAUTION: DO NOT connect any test equipment on terminal 15 (+) of ignition coil. This could damage electronic ignition parts. Use fuse No. 10 for connection.

1) Connect tachometer and timing light. Disconnect plugs from idle stabilizer (squeeze connector to loosen) and connect together.

2) With engine at normal operating temperature and correct idle, check timing. If timing is not to specifications, correct by turning distributor.

FEDERAL VANAGON WITH AIR-COOLED ENGINE ONLY

1) Warm engine to normal operating temperature. Turn engine off. Disconnect and plug distributor vacuum lines. Connect timing light. Start engine.

2) With engine at correct idle speed, check timing. If timing is not to specifications, correct by turning distributor.

Fig. 3: Ignition Timing Mark Locations

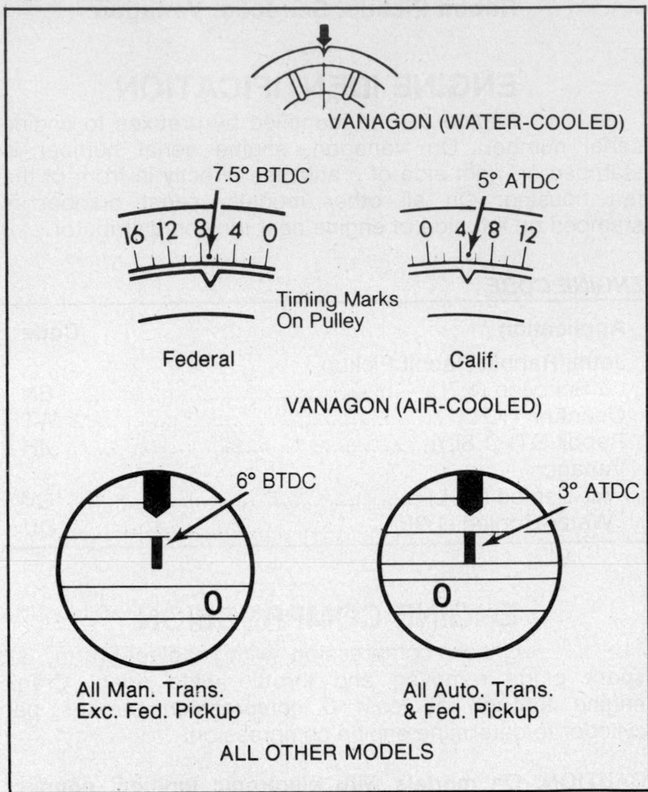
VANAGON (WATER-COOLED)
7.5° BTDC
5° ATDC
16 12 8 4 0
0 4 8 12
Timing Marks On Pulley
Federal
Calif.
VANAGON (AIR-COOLED)
6° BTDC
3° ATDC
0
0
All Man. Trans. Exc. Fed. Pickup
All Auto. Trans. & Fed. Pickup
ALL OTHER MODELS

Adjust timing by turning distributor.

ALL OTHER MODELS

1) Make sure engine oil temperature is at least 140°F (60°C) and distributor vacuum hoses are connected. Attach timing light to engine. Disconnect idle stabilizer control unit connectors, and connect them together.

2) Make sure idle speed and timing are set to specifications. If timing is not to specifications, adjust by turning distributor. Reconnect idle stabilizer connectors and remove test equipment.

IGNITION TIMING SPECIFICATIONS
Degrees ATDC@RPM

Application	Man. Trans.	Auto. Trans.
Vanagon		
Air-Cooled		
Federal	[1] 7.5@800-950	[1] 7.5@850-1000
Calif.	5@850-950	5@850-950
Water-Cooled	5@800-900	5@800-900
Rabbit		
Pickup [2]		
Federal	3@850-1000	3@850-1000
Calif.	[1] 6@850-1000	3@850-1000
All Others [2]	[1] 6@850-1000	3@850-1000

[1] – BTDC.
[2] – Ignition timing is 7.5°BTDC@800-1000 RPM on carbureted models.

IDLE SPEED & MIXTURE

NOTE: Mixture adjustment is not a part of normal tune-up procedure and should not be per-

TUNE-UP (Cont.)

formed unless carburetor or mixture control unit is replaced or vehicle fails emissions testing.

VANAGON

1) With engine at normal operating temperature, connect CO tester at probe receptacle on exhaust pipe in front of catalytic converter. Connect a tachometer to engine.

2) Adjust idle screw until idle speed is correct. Check CO reading. If incorrect, turn engine off and disconnect oxygen sensor plug. Disconnect idle stabilizer plugs (if equipped) and connect together.

3) Remove intake air sensor. Center punch the plug in CO adjusting hole. Using a 3/32" drill bit, drill hole 5/32" deep in center of plug. Remove any metal shavings.

4) Screw in a sheet metal screw and remove plug with screw, using pliers. Reinstall intake air sensor. Start engine and adjust CO. Turn engine off and drive in new adjusting hole plug flush with air intake sensor. Reconnect other plugs and remove test equipment.

RABBIT CARBURETED MODEL

All Models (Exc. A/C Equipped)

1) Run engine until oil temperature is a minimum of 176°F (80°C). Be sure choke is fully open. Remove PCV valve from valve cover. Turn off all electrical equipment.

2) Connect tachometer, timing light and dwell meter to engine. Be sure dwell meter is connected to test receptacle on left strut tower. Start engine and accelerate to 2000 RPM for 5 seconds. Check idle speed and dwell. Dwell will fluctuate between 18-45°.

3) If idle speed is incorrect, disconnect both idle stabilizer plugs and connect plugs together. Remove vacuum advance and retard hoses at distributor and plug hoses.

4) Adjust idle by turning idle adjustment screw, located on throttle lever, adjacent to solenoid plunger. Adjust engine idle speed at 820-900 RPM, with solenoid energized and engine at operating temperature.

5) If dwell is incorrect, remove carburetor and remove tamper-proof plug from idle mixture screw. Reinstall carburetor and adjust idle mixture screw to obtain a 28-50° dwell. (Turning screw clockwise, lowers duty cycle, turning counterclockwise raises reading). Install new tamper-proof plug.

Solvac (Air Conditioned Models Only)

1) Solvac is a 2-stage solenoid, controlled electrically and by vacuum. Electrical stage is a solenoid that de-energizes when ignition switch is turned off, preventing engine "dieseling."

2) Vacuum stage is a diaphragm, activated by vacuum from a solenoid, energized when A/C is on and clutch is engaged. Diaphragm increases idle speed to compensate for added engine load.

3) Adjust idle by turning idle adjustment screw, located on throttle lever near solenoid plunger. Set engine idle to 820-900 RPM, with A/C clutch disengaged and engine at operating temperature. *See Fig. 4.*.

4) Once idle has been adjusted, shut engine off, disconnect test equipment and reconnect all hoses.

Fig. 4: Idle Speed and Solvac Adjustment

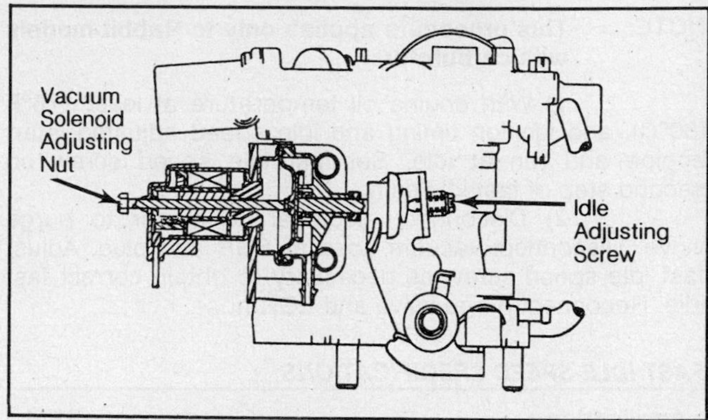
Vacuum
Solenoid
Adjusting
Nut
Idle
Adjusting
Screw

Adjustment screw location for carbureted models only.

ALL OTHER MODELS

NOTE: **The CO meter is no longer used to adjust the idle mixture. Instead, mixture is adjusted using the VW 1367 dwell meter. The CO meter is used only to verify that oxygen sensor system operates properly.**

1) Remove both connectors from idle stabilizer and connect them together. Run engine until oil temperature is above 176°F (80°C). Disconnect and plug PCV hose so fresh air can enter system. Turn off all electrical equipment.

2) On Rabbit and Scirocco models, remove charcoal canister vent hose at elbow below intake boot. On Quantum models, remove cap from "T" piece in charcoal canister vent hose near right fender well.

3) Connect CO meter to CO test point on engine using adapter hose (US 4492). Start engine and briefly accelerate. Check idle speed and adjust as necessary. Check ignition timing and adjust.

4) Remove plug from air sensor housing. Insert adjusting tool (P377) and adjust dwell with mixture adjusting screw. The dwell reading will fluctuate. Adjust so reading displays 38-52°. If dwell does not fluctuate check oxygen sensor system.

5) Check CO value. If value is too high, check for leaks in intake system and exhaust system. Also check fuel system for a malfunction. Reconnect tester and recheck idle speed. Adjust if necessary.

6) Stop engine, reconnect PCV hoses, charcoal canister hose and idle stabilizer.

IDLE SPEED AND CO LEVEL SPECIFICATIONS

Application	Idle RPM	CO%
Vanagon		
Air-Cooled		
Federal		
Man. Trans.	800-950	0.5-1.5
Auto. Trans.	850-1000	0.5-1.5
Calif.	850-950	0.3-1.1
Water-Cooled	800-900	0.3-1.1
Federal Pickup	850-1000	1.0-2.0
All Others	850-1000	0.3-1.2

TUNE-UP (Cont.)

FAST (COLD) IDLE

NOTE: This procedure applies only to Rabbit models with carburetors.

1) With engine oil temperature at least 176°F (80°C), and ignition timing and idle speed adjusted, start engine and run at idle. Set fast idle speed screw on second step of fast idle cam.

2) Disconnect electrical connector to purge valve. Disconnect vacuum hose at EGR and plug. Adjust fast idle speed screw as necessary to obtain correct fast idle. Reconnect purge valve and EGR hose.

FAST IDLE SPEED SPECIFICATIONS

Application	RPM
Rabbit (Carbureted Models Only)	2600-3000

FUEL PUMP

1) To test fuel pump on Vanagon, connect ammeter in series with pump and current supply. Turn on ignition. Open air sensor flap. Ammeter should read 6.5-8.5 amps.

CAUTION: Do not touch positive connection to ground.

2) On all other models, disconnect fuel output line and apply 12 volts to fuel pump.

FUEL PUMP PERFORMANCE SPECIFICATIONS

Application	Pressure psi (kg/cm²)	Volume in 30 sec. Pints (Liters)
Vanagon	33-39 (2.3-2.7)	4.2 (0.5)
All Others	[1] 68-78 (4.8-5.5)	8.4 (1.0)

[1] – Fuel pressure for carbureted models is 4.0-5.3 psi (.28-.37 kg/cm²).

EMISSION CONTROL SYSTEMS

See Mitchell Manuals' Emission Control Manual.

GENERAL SERVICING

IGNITION

DISTRIBUTOR

All models except Federal Vanagon with air-cooled engine use Bosch Hall Effect ignition systems. Federal Vanagon models use conventional Bosch single point distributor.

IGNITION COIL

IGNITION COIL RESISTANCE (OHMS) SPECIFICATIONS

Application	Primary	Secondary
All Models	.52-.76	2400-3500

FUEL SYSTEMS

CARBURETOR

Some Rabbit models use a Carter/Weber TYF 1-barrel carburetor.

FUEL INJECTION

Vanagon models use Bosch AFC fuel injection (California and Water-Cooled models have an oxygen sensor). All other models use Bosch Lambda CIS fuel injection with oxygen sensor.

ELECTRICAL

STARTER

All models are equipped with Bosch starters.

BATTERY SPECIFICATIONS

Application	Amp Hr. Rating
Jetta, Quantum, Rabbit Convertible & Scirocco	45
Rabbit, Rabbit GTI, Rabbit Pickup & Vanagon	54

ALTERNATORS

All models are equipped with Bosch or Motorola alternators with integral voltage regulators.

ALTERNATOR SPECIFICATIONS

Application	Rated Amp Output
Rabbit Pickup	55
All Other Models	65

ALTERNATOR REGULATOR

All models are equipped with Bosch or Motorola alternator regulators. Regulators are not adjustable.

GENERAL SERVICING (Cont.)

SERVICE SPECIFICATIONS

BELT ADJUSTMENT

Application	[1] Deflection In. (mm)
Vanagon (Water-Cooled)	
Water Pump	.4-.6 (10-15)
All Other Models	
A/C Belt	.4-.6 (10-15)
Alternator Belt	.08-.2 (2-5)

[1] – Deflection is measured with moderate thumb pressure applied midway on longest belt run.

REPLACEMENT INTERVALS

Component	Service Interval (Miles)
Oil Filter	15,000
Air Filter	30,000
Fuel Filter	
Quantum [1] & Scirocco	60,000
All Others	15,000
Spark Plugs	30,000

[1] – Discard Mini-Fuel filter at 1000 mile maintenance. Install new copper gaskets.

FLUID CAPACITIES

Application	Quantity
Crankcase (Including Filter)	
Quantum	3.5 qts. (3.0L)
Vanagon	
Air-Cooled	3.7 qts. (3.5L)
Water-Cooled	4.8 qts. (4.5L)
All Other Models	4.8 qts. (4.5L)
Cooling System	
Jetta & Scirocco	5.1 qts. (4.8L)
Quantum	5.5 qts. (5.2L)
Rabbit, Rabbit GTI & Rabbit Pickup	6.9 qts. (6.5L)
Vanagon	18.5 qts. (17.5L)
Man. Transaxles (SAE 80W-90)	
Vanagon	6.4 pts. (3.0L)
All Other Models	
4-Speed	3.2 pts. (1.5L)
5-Speed	4.2 pts. (2.0L)
Auto. Transaxle (Dexron)	6.4 pts. (3.0L)
Auto. Transaxle Differential (SAE 90)	
Vanagon	3.0 pts. (1.4L)
All Other Models	1.6 pts. (0.8L)
Fuel Tank	
Jetta & Scirocco	10.5 gals. (40.0L)
Quantum & Vanagon	16.0 gals. (60.0L)
Rabbit & Rabbit GTI	10.0 gals. (38.0L)
Rabbit Pickup	15.0 gals. (57.0L)

TUNE-UP

Jetta, Quantum, Rabbit, Rabbit Pickup, & Vanagon

ENGINE IDENTIFICATION

First 2 letters of engine identification code are used to identify engine models. Code is stamped on cylinder block below No. 3 glow plug.

ENGINE CODE

Application	Code
Rabbit & Rabbit Pickup	JK
Vanagon	CS
Jetta, Rabbit & Quantum Turbo Diesels	CY

ENGINE COMPRESSION

1) Remove electrical wire from fuel shut-off solenoid on injection pump. Insulate wire end and remove injection pipes. Disconnect fuel return hoses. Remove injectors with removal tool (US 2775 or equivalent).

2) Remove heat shields from injectors and place in cylinder being tested. Install test gauge adapter (VW 1323/2) and test gauge (VW 1323) to injector hole, operate starter and read compression. Install new injector heat shields when reinstalling injectors.

COMPRESSION SPECIFICATIONS

Compression Ratio	23.0:1
Compression Pressure	
Normal	493 psi (34.6 kg/cm²)
Minimum	406 psi (28.5 kg/cm²)
Maximum Variation	73 psi (5.1 kg/cm²)

VALVE CLEARANCE

NOTE: When adjusting valves, pistons MUST NOT be at TDC. Turn crankshaft 1/4 turn past TDC so valves do not hit pistons when tappets are depressed. Do NOT rotate crankshaft by turning camshaft pulley. This will stretch the drive belt. Place vehicle in 4th gear and push to turn crankshaft.

1) Valves must be checked with engine warm. Coolant temperature must be above 95°F (35°C). Check valve clearance in firing order, 1-3-4-2.

2) Measure between cam lobes and adjusting dics, when both lobes to be checked point upward. Adjust clearance by changing disc thickness. Twenty six discs are available in .118-.167" (3.00-4.25 mm) thicknesses.

3) To remove adjusting discs, use special removal tool (US-4476), while holding cam follower down with compression tool (VW546).

VALVE CLEARANCE SPECIFICATIONS

Application	In. (mm)
Intake (Hot)	.008-.012 (.20-.30)
Exhaust (Hot)	.016-.020 (.40-.50)

VALVE ARRANGEMENT

E-I-E-I-I-E-I-E (Front-to-rear)

Fig. 1: Diesel Firing Order Illustration

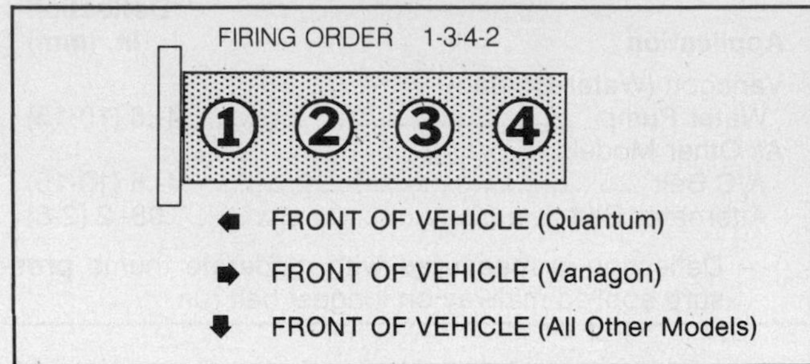
FIRING ORDER 1-3-4-2
1
2
3
4
FRONT OF VEHICLE (Quantum)
FRONT OF VEHICLE (Vanagon)
FRONT OF VEHICLE (All Other Models)

IDLE SPEED ADJUSTMENT

1) Run engine until warm. Mount tachometer sensor (US 1324) on valve cover and connect to battery. Attach tachometer to sensor and check idle speed.

2) If adjustment is needed, loosen lock nut on idle screw. Turn in to increase idle, out to decrease. Apply thread sealer and tighten lock nut.

IDLE SPEED SPECIFICATIONS

Application	Idle RPM
Vanagon	800-850
All Other Models	810-950

Fig. 2: Idle and Maximum Speed Adjustment

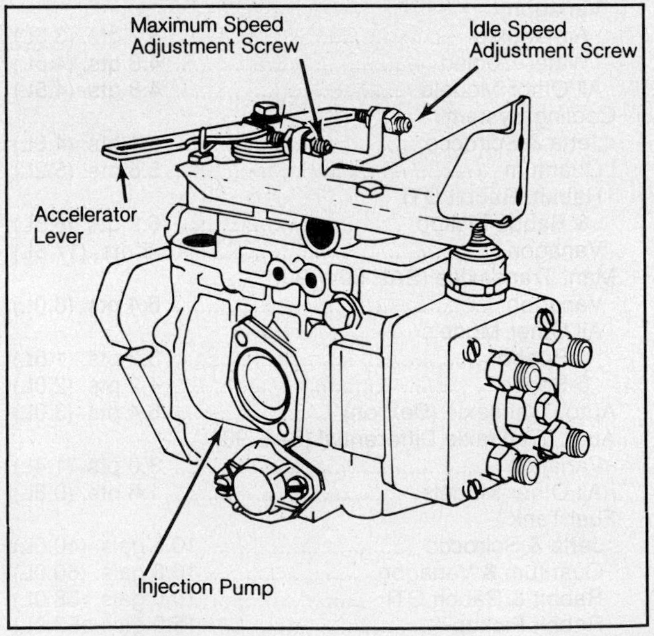
Maximum Speed Adjustment Screw
Idle Speed Adjustment Screw
Accelerator Lever
Injection Pump

MAXIMUM SPEED ADJUSTMENT

1) Run engine until warm and install tachometer sensor (US 1324). Connect tachometer and set idle speed. Accelerate engine briefly to full throttle.

TUNE-UP (Cont.)

2) If maximum speed does not match specifications, loosen lock nut on maximum speed adjustment screw and adjust. Turning screw out raises speed, turning screw in lowers speed. Apply thread sealer and tighten lock nut.

MAXIMUM SPEED SPECIFICATIONS

Application	Maximum RPM
Turbo	5050-5150
Vanagon	4750-4850
All Other Models	5300-5400

FUEL INJECTION TIMING

NOTE: Before adjusting injection timing push in cold start device completely

1) Remove plug from injection pump cover. Install adaptor (2066) and dial gauge (US 1026) to 0-.118" (0-3 mm) in place of plug. Preload gauge to approx. .097" (2.5 mm).

2) Turn engine slowly counterclockwise until gauge needle stops moving. Zero gauge. Turn engine clockwise until TDC mark on flywheel is aligned with boss on bell housing.

3) If adjustment is necessary slighty loosen bolts on pump mounting plate. Turn pump to get correct Dial gauge reading. Tighten bolts. Recheck injection timing.

4) When reinstalling plug, torque to 10-14 ft. lbs. (14-20 N.m) with copper seal (Reddish-Brown in color) or 14-18 ft. lbs. (20-24 N.m) with bronze seal (Yellow-Brown in color).

CAUTION: To avoid fuel leaks, always replace seal for plug

FUEL INJECTION TIMING SPECIFICATIONS

Application	Dial Gauge Reading In. (mm)
Rabbit & Rabbit Pickup	.035-.039 (.90-1.00)
Turbo	.037-.041 (.95-1.05)
Vanagon	.033-.035 (.84-.88)

FUEL SYSTEM BLEEDING

VANAGON

Disconnect negative battery cable. Loosen water drain plug from bottom of fuel filter. Drain until fuel is pure. Reconnect battery cable. Start engine and accelerate a few times to clear air bubbles from fuel lines.

ALL EXCEPT VANAGON

1) Disconnect negative battery cable. Open vent screw on fuel filter flange. Lift filter straight up off mount. Loosen water drain plug from bottom of fuel filter. Drain until fuel is pure.

2) Reinstall filter onto mount. Close vent screw. Reconnect battery cable. Start engine and accelerate a few times to clear air bubbles from fuel lines.

EMISSION CONTROL SYSTEMS

See Mitchell Manuals' Emission Control Manual.

GENERAL SERVICING

FUEL SYSTEMS

FUEL INJECTION

All models use Bosch Diesel Fuel Injection.

ELECTRICAL

BATTERY

BATTERY SPECIFICATIONS

Application	Amp Hr. Rating
All Models	63

STARTER

All models are equipped with Bosch starters.

ALTERNATOR

All models use Bosch or Motorola alternators.

ALTERNATOR SPECIFICATIONS

Application	Rated Amp Output
Jetta, Quantum, Rabbit & Vanagon	65
Rabbit Pickup	55

ALERNATOR REGULATOR

All models use Bosch or Motorola regulators, integral with alternator. Regulators are not adjustable.

SERVICE SPECIFICATIONS

BELT ADJUSTMENT

Application	[1] Deflection In. (mm)
All Belts	3/8-9/16 (10-15)

[1] — Measured in center of longest span and depressed with firm thumb pressure.

GENERAL SERVICING (Cont.)

REPLACEMENT INTERVALS

Component	Service Interval (Miles)
Oil Filter	7500
Fuel Filter	10,000
Air Filter	15,000

FLUID CAPACITIES

Application	Quantity
Crankcase (Includes Filter)	
Jetta & Quantum	4.0 qts. (3.8L)
Rabbit & Rabbit Pickup	4.7 qts. (4.4L)
Vanagon	4.2 qts. (4.0L)
Cooling System	
Jetta, Rabbit & Rabbit Pickup	6.9 qts. (6.5L)
Quantum	6.5 qts. (6.2L)
Vanagon	16.9 qts. (16.0L)
Auto Transaxle (Dexron)	6.4 pts. (3.1L)
Manual Transaxle (SAE80W-90)	
Vanagon	8.4 pts. (4.0L)
All Other Models	
4-Speed	3.1 pts. (1.5L)
5-Speed	4.2 pts. (2.0L)
Fuel Tank	
Jetta	10.5 gals. (40.0L)
Rabbit	11.0 gals. (42.0L)
Rabbit Pickup	15.0 gals. (57.0L)
Quantum & Vanagon	16.0 gals. (60.0L)

TUNE-UP

Quantum GL

ENGINE IDENTIFICATION

Engine number is stamped on left side of block near No. 3 cylinder.

ENGINE CODE

Application	Code
Quantum GL 2.2L	WE

ENGINE COMPRESSION

Check compression with engine warm, all spark plugs removed and throttle wide open. Crank engine through at least 6 compression strokes per cylinder to determine engine compression.

COMPRESSION SPECIFICATIONS

Compression Ratio	8.2:1
Compression Pressure	
Maximum	131-174 psi (9-12 kg/cm²)
Minimum	102 psi (7 kg/cm²)
Max. Variation Between Cylinders	44 psi (3 kg/cm²)

VALVE CLEARANCE

1) Adjust valves with engine at normal operating temperature. Remove accelerator linkage and cylinder head cover. Clearance adjustments are to be checked and made according to firing order sequence.

2) Rotate crankshaft until cam lobes for No. 1 cylinder valves point upward. Measure valve clearances of No. 1 cylinder.

CAUTION: To avoid timing belt slip when adjusting valves, only rotate engine CLOCKWISE.

3) If adjustment is necessary, use disc remover (US 4476) and tappet depressor (2078) to remove and install adjusting discs. Turn tappet until notches are at 90° to camshaft.

4) Insert depressor (2078) and depress tappet. Using disc remover (US 4476), grasp tappet disc and rotate it out from under camshaft.

5) Thickness is stamped on bottom side of disc. Use clearance measurement to choose adjusting disc. Discs are available in .002" (.05 mm) increments from .118-.167" (3.0-4.3 mm). Repeat procedure as required for remaining valves.

VALVE CLEARANCE SPECIFICATIONS

Application	In. (mm)
Intake	.008-.012 (.2-.3)
Exhaust	.016-.020 (.4-.5)

VALVE ARRANGEMENT

E-I-E-I-I-E-I-E-I-E (Front-to-rear)

SPARK PLUGS

SPARK PLUG TYPE

Application	Bosch	Champion
Federal	W7D	N8Y
Calif.	WR7DS	N8GY

SPARK PLUG SPECIFICATIONS

Application	Gap In. (mm)	Torque Ft. Lbs. (N.m)
All Models	.028 (.7)	14 (22)

HIGH TENSION WIRE RESISTANCE

Carefully remove ends of wire from spark plug and distributor. Using an ohmmeter, check resistance of wire while gently twisting wire. If resistance is incorrect or fluctuates from infinity to any value, replace wire.

NOTE: **Wire resistance cannot be measured if the wires are marked with this symbol:** ⧓

HIGH TENSION WIRE RESISTANCE

Application	Ohms
Spark Plug Wire Only	800-1400
Spark Plug Wire With Connector	4800-7400
Coil Wire	1600-2400

Fig. 1: Firing Order and Distributor Rotation

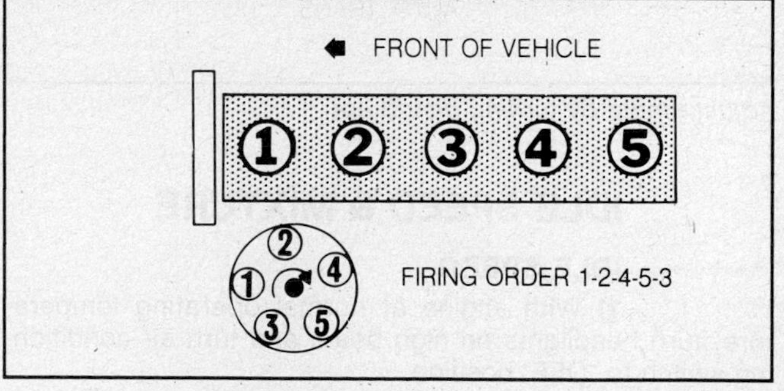
FRONT OF VEHICLE
1 2 3 4 5
FIRING ORDER 1-2-4-5-3

DISTRIBUTOR

All models are equipped with a Bosch Hall Effect electronic, breakerless ignition system. All California models have an idle stabilizer unit, which adjusts ignition timing to maintain a constant idle speed.

IGNITION TIMING

Disconnect 2 plugs at idle stabilizer unit, if equipped, and connect them together. Leave vacuum hoses connected at distributor. With engine idling, adjust ignition timing by turning distributor. Reconnect idle stabilizer unit.

TUNE-UP (Cont.)

IGNITION TIMING

Application	Timing@RPM
Man. Trans.	6° BTDC@850-1000
Auto. Trans.	3° ATDC@850-1000

Fig. 2: Ignition Timing Mark Location

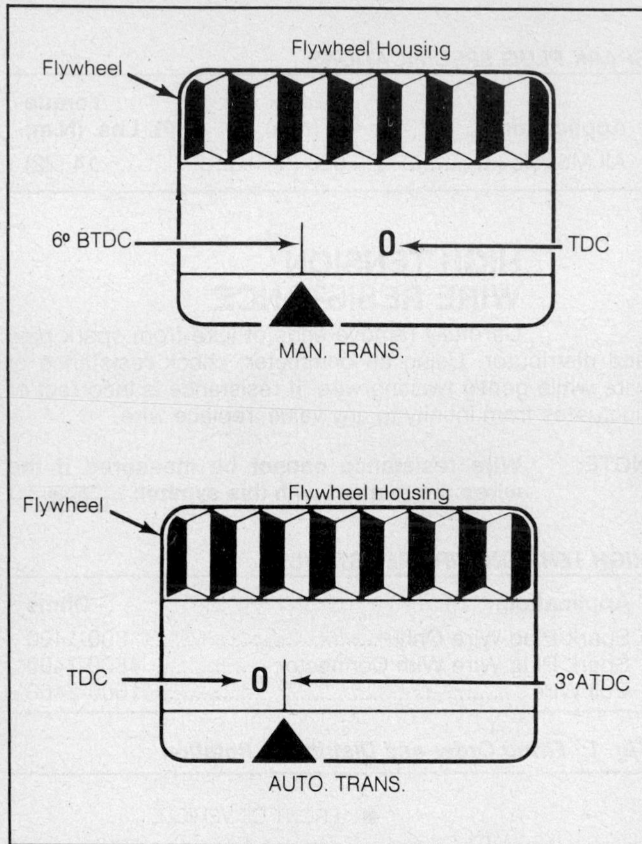

Flywheel Housing
Flywheel
6° BTDC
0
TDC
MAN. TRANS.
Flywheel Housing
Flywheel
TDC
0
3°ATDC
AUTO. TRANS.

Adjust timing by turning distributor.

IDLE SPEED & MIXTURE

IDLE SPEED

1) With engine at normal operating temperature, turn headlights on high beam and turn air conditioning switch to "OFF" position.

2) Disconnect and plug crankcase breather hose at cylinder head. Also, disconnect hose between charcoal canister and air cleaner.

3) Check and adjust ignition timing as necessary. Adjust idle speed to specified RPM, using adjusting screw on side of throttle valve housing.

IDLE SPEED SPECIFICATION

Application	RPM
All Models	850-1000

IDLE MIXTURE

NOTE: Mixture adjustment is not a part of normal tune-up procedure. It should not be performed unless fuel injection parts are replaced or vehicle fails emissions testing.

NOTE: Oxygen sensor system was designed to be maintenance free and no adjustments are normally required. However, if a performance problem does occur, the system can be checked using the following procedure. A dwell meter (VW 1367) is required to adjust the duty cycle produced by oxygen sensor control unit. A CO meter is used only to verify that system is operating properly. DO NOT disconnect oxygen sensor for this procedure.

1) Remove both connectors from idle stabilizer, and connect them together. Run engine until temperature is above 175°F (80°C). Radiator fan must have come on at least once.

2) Remove PCV hose from valve cover and plug hose. Remove cap from "T" piece in charcoal canister vent hose near right fender well.

3) Connect CO meter to CO test point using adapter hose (US 4492). Connect dwell meter to oxygen sensor test connection. The duty cycle should fluctuate between 25-65% or 23-59° on dwell meter.

4) If duty cycle is out of range, remove plug from air sensor housing. Insert adjusting tool (P377) and adjust duty cycle with mixture adjusting screw to 44-56% or 40-50°. Duty cycle should fluctuate within specified range. If not, there is a problem with oxygen sensor.

5) Check CO value. It should be 0.3-1.2% with oxygen sensor connected. Recheck and adjust idle speed, if necessary. Stop engine and reconnect all hoses and idle stabilizer.

CO LEVEL SPECIFICATIONS

Application	CO%
All Models	0.3-1.2

FUEL PUMP

FUEL PUMP PERFORMANCE

Application	Pressure psi (kg/cm²)	Volume in 30 sec. Pints (Liters)
All Models	65-74 (4.5-5.2)	1.0 (.47)

EMISSION CONTROL SYSTEMS

See Mitchell Manuals' Emission Control Manual.

GENERAL SERVICING

IGNITION

DISTRIBUTOR

Quantum GL is equipped with electronic ignition. All California models use an idle stabilizer in addition to the Hall Effect ignition system.

IGNITION COIL

IGNITION COIL RESISTANCE — OHMS @ 68°F (20°C)

Application	Primary	Secondary
All Models	.52-.76	2400-3500

FUEL SYSTEMS

FUEL INJECTION

Quantum GL is equipped with Bosch (CIS) Continuous Injection System.

ELECTRICAL

BATTERY

BATTERY SPECIFICATIONS

Application	Amp Hr. Rating
All Models	63

STARTER

Quantum GL is equipped with a Bosch starter.

ALTERNATOR

Quantum GL uses a Bosch alternator.

ALTERNATOR SPECIFICATIONS

Application	Rated Amp Output
All Models	65

ALTERNATOR REGULATOR

Quantum GL is equipped with Bosch, non-adjustable voltage regulator which is integral with the alternator.

ALTERNATOR OPERATING VOLTAGE @ 80°F (27°C)

Application	Voltage
All Models	13.5-14.5

SERVICE SPECIFICATIONS

BELT ADJUSTMENT

Application	[1] Deflection In. (mm)
All Models	
A/C Belt	.4-.6 (10-15)
Alternator Belt	.08-.2 (2-5)

[1] — Deflection is measured with moderate thumb pressure applied midway on longest belt run.

REPLACEMENT INTERVALS

Component	Interval (Miles)
Oil Filter	15,000
Air Filter	30,000
Fuel Filter [1]	15,000
PCV Valve	30,000
Oxygen Sensor	30,000
Spark Plugs	30,000

[1] — Discard Mini-fuel filter at 1000-mile maintenance. Install new copper gaskets.

FLUID CAPACITIES

Application	Quantity
Crankcase (Includes Filter)	4.0 qts. (3.5L)
Cooling System (Includes Heater)	5.0 qts. (4.7L)
Man. Trans. (SAE 80W-90)	4.2 pts. (2.0L)
Auto. Trans. (Dexron)	3.2 qts. (3.0L)
Auto. Trans. Final Drive (SAE 90)	1.6 pts. (0.8L)
Fuel Tank	16.0 gals. (60.0L)

1983 Volvo 4 Tune-Up

TUNE-UP

GL, Turbo

ENGINE IDENTIFICATION

Identification number for B21F Turbo and B23F type engine is stamped on left side of engine block near the distributor.

ENGINE CODE

Application	Code
Non-Turbo	
Man. Trans.	499-802
Auto. Trans.	499-803
Turbo	
Man. Trans.	499-800
Auto. Trans.	499-801

ENGINE COMPRESSION

Check compression with engine at normal operating temperature, all spark plugs removed, throttle valve wide open and at normal cranking speed (250-300 RPM). Crank engine at least 6 "puffs" per cylinder.

COMPRESSION SPECIFICATIONS

Compression Ratio	
Turbo	7.5:1
Non-Turbo	10.3:1
Compression Pressure	
Turbo	[1]
Non-Turbo	128-156 psi (9-11 kg/cm²)

[1] – Information not available from manufacturer.

VALVE CLEARANCE

1) Valve clearance is adjusted with engine shut off and either warm or cold. Remove valve cover. Turn crankshaft center bolt until camshaft is in position for firing No. 1 cylinder. Both cam lobes should point up at equally large angles. Pulley timing mark should be at 0°.

2) Check valve clearance of No. 1 cylinder, using a feeler gauge between camshaft lobe and adjusting discs. Intake and exhaust valves have same clearance.

3) If clearances are incorrect adjust by changing thickness of discs, which are available in .002" (.05 mm) increments from .130" (3.30 mm) to .177" (4.50 mm). Use tools 5022 and 5026 to depress and remove disc.

4) After valves for No. 1 cylinder are properly adjusted, rotate crankshaft to firing position for No. 3, No. 4 and No. 2 cylinders in sequence and complete adjustment.

VALVE CLEARANCE SPECIFICATIONS

Application	Cold In. (mm)	Hot In. (mm)
Intake and Exhaust		
Checking	.012-.016 (.30-.40)	.014-.018 (.35-.45)
Setting	.014-.016 (.35-.40)	.010-.010 (.40-.45)

VALVE ARRANGEMENT

E-I-E-I-E-I-E-I (Front-to-rear)

SPARK PLUGS

SPARK PLUG TYPE

Application	Bosch No.
All Models	WR7DS

SPARK PLUG SPECIFICATIONS

Application	Gap In. (mm)	Torque Ft. Lbs. (N.m)
All Models	.030 (.75)	7-11 (10-14)

DISTRIBUTOR

All models except Turbo are equipped with a Volvo Breakerless Ignition System, featuring computer-controlled spark advance and a Hall Effect distributor. Turbo models are equipped with a Bosch Electronic Ignition System. For both systems, no adjustments are required.

Fig. 1: Firing Order and Distributor Rotation

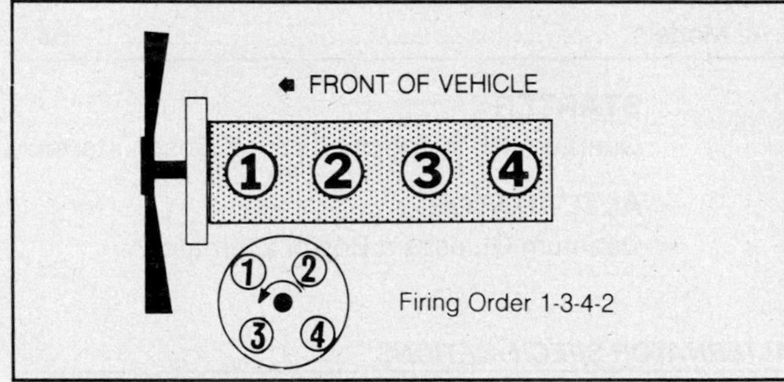
FRONT OF VEHICLE
1
2
3
4
1
2
3
4
Firing Order 1-3-4-2

IGNITION TIMING

Check or adjust ignition timing with engine at normal operating temperature, distributor vacuum hose disconnected, air conditioning "OFF" (if equipped), and engine speed set to specification. If possible, use magnetic timing device to set ignition timing on all models.

IGNITION TIMING SPECIFICATIONS (Degrees BTDC@RPM)

Application	Timing
Turbo	12@900
Non-Turbo	12@750

IDLE SPEED & MIXTURE

IDLE SPEED

NOTE: **Idle adjustment for Turbo models is factory-sealed and no adjustment is required.**

TUNE-UP (Cont.)

Fig. 2: Volvo 4-Cylinder Timing Mark Location

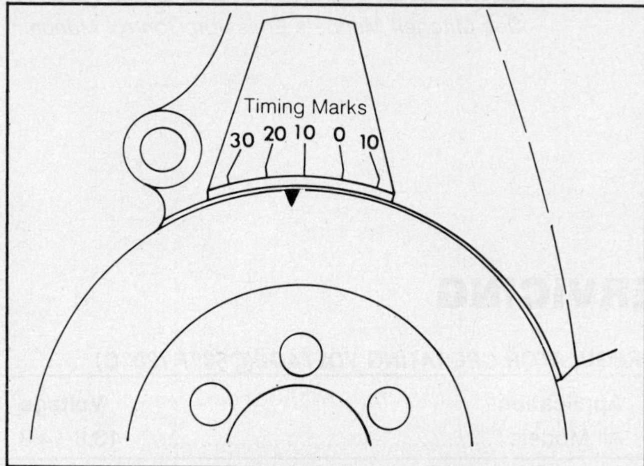
Timing Marks
30 20 10 0 10

On Non-Turbo models, ground Blue/White wire of test point at left front wheel housing. Adjust idle speed with idle screw to 720 RPM. Remove ground at test point. Engine speed should increase to 730-770 RPM.

IDLE MIXTURE

NOTE: **Mixture control adjustment screw opening is plugged to prevent tampering. Adjustment is not a normal tune-up procedure and should not be performed unless mixture control unit is replaced or vehicle fails emissions testing.**

Turbo Models

1) Remove mixture control unit, separate control unit and drive out mixture plug (steel ball) with a punch. Reassemble control unit and reinstall.

2) Disconnect oxygen sensor electrical connector. Remove plug in exhaust pipe in front of catalytic converter and insert CO probe.

3) If CO reading is not within specifications, insert adjusting wrench (5015) into adjustment hole and adjust CO reading to specifications.

4) Reconnect oxygen sensor electrical connector and check CO reading. Repeat adjustment procedure if necessary. *See Fig. 3.*

Fig. 3: Turbo Idle Mixture Adjustment

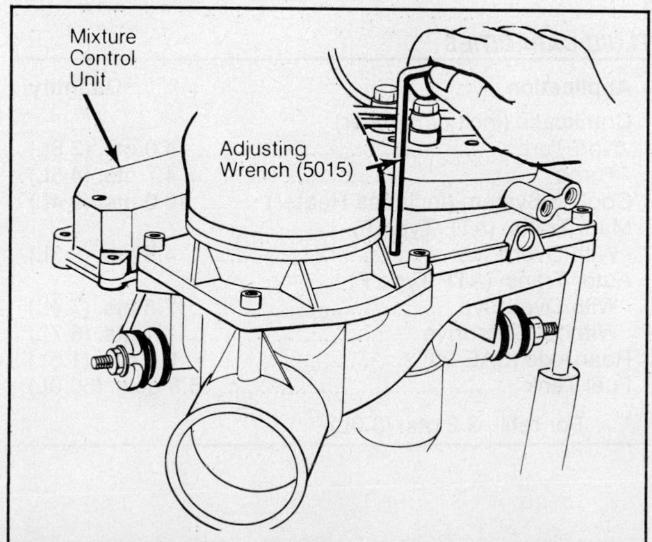
Mixture Control Unit
Adjusting Wrench (5015)

5) After each adjustment, remove adjusting wrench, and cover adjustment hole. This will prevent a lean mixture while checking CO level.

6) After CO adjustment, remove test equipment. Insert exhaust pipe plug and seal mixture adjustment hole.

Non-Turbo Models

1) Ground Blue/White wire of test point at left front wheel housing. Adjust idle speed with idle screw to 720 RPM. Remove ground at test point. Engine speed should increase to 730-770 RPM. Disconnect oxygen sensor.

2) Insert probe and check CO level. If CO level is outside of check value, switch off engine, drill two 5/16" holes in adjustment seal and pull out plug with snap ring pliers. Start engine and adjust CO level. *See Fig. 4.*

Fig. 4: Non-Turbo Idle Mixture Adjustment

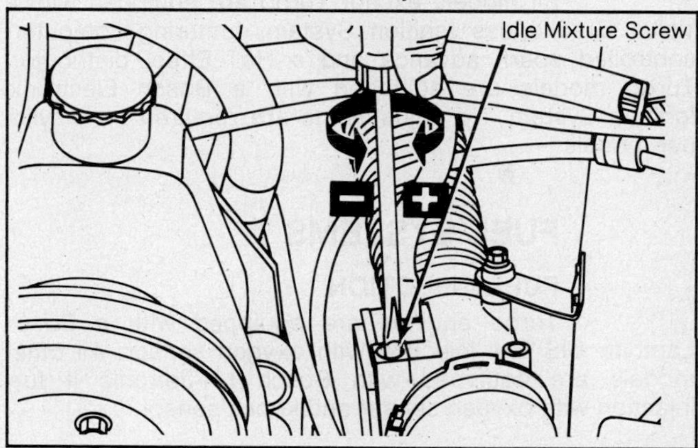
Idle Mixture Screw
−
+

3) Turning screw counterclockwise decreases CO level, turning screw clockwise increases level. Reconnect oxygen sensor. CO level should decrease. Seal CO adjustment with a new plug.

IDLE SPEED & CO LEVEL SPECIFICATIONS

Application	Idle RPM	CO%
Turbo	850-950	[1] 0.7-1.3
Non-Turbo	730-770	[1] 0.4-0.8

[1] – With oxygen sensor disconnected. Less than 1.0% with oxygen sensor connected.

OXYGEN SENSOR REPLACEMENT

1) Disconnect oxygen sensor electrical leads and remove oxygen sensor. Coat new oxygen sensor threads with anti-seize compound before installing oxygen sensor.

NOTE: **Do not apply anti-seize compound to the slotted part of the oxygen sensor.**

2) Tighten oxygen sensor to 36-44 ft. lbs. (50-60 N.m). Reconnect the electrical lead.

FUEL PUMP

Check fuel pump with full battery charge and clean fuel filter.

TUNE-UP (Cont.)

FUEL PUMP PERFORMANCE

Application	Pressure psi (kg/cm²)	Volume in 30 sec. Pints (Liters)
Turbo	75-83 (5.2-5.8)	2.1 (1.0)
Non-Turbo	64-76 (4.5-5.3) [1]	1.7 (0.8)

[1] – Line pressure above intake manifold pressure 35 (psi) 2.5 (kg/cm²).

EMISSION CONTROL SYSTEMS

See Mitchell Manuals Emission Control Manual.

GENERAL SERVICING

IGNITION

DISTRIBUTOR

All models except Turbo are equipped with a Volvo Breakerless Ignition System, featuring computer-controlled spark advance and a Hall Effect distributor. Turbo models are equipped with a Bosch Electronic Ignition System. No adjustments are required on 4-cylinder models.

FUEL SYSTEMS

FUEL INJECTION

Turbo engines are equipped with a Bosch Lambda CIS fuel injection with oxygen sensor. All other models are equipped with Bosch LH-Jetronic II fuel injection with oxygen sensor and knock sensor.

ELECTRICAL

BATTERY SPECIFICATIONS

Application	Amp Hour Rating
All Models	60

STARTER

All models are equipped with Bosch overrunning clutch starters.

STARTER SPECIFICATIONS

Application	Volts	Amps	Test RPM
All Models	11.5	30-50	5500-7500

ALTERNATOR

All models are equipped with Bosch alternators with integral voltage regulators.

ALTERNATOR SPECIFICATIONS

Application	Rated Amp. Output
All Models	[1] 70

[1] – Some Turbo models may have 55 amp alternators.

ALTERNATOR REGULATOR

All models are equipped with Bosch alternator regulators.

REGULATOR OPERATING VOLTAGE@68°F (20°C)

Application	Voltage
All Models	13.8-14.8

SERVICE SPECIFICATIONS

BELT ADJUSTMENT

Application	[1] Deflection In. (mm)
All Belts	.2-.4 (5-10)

[1] – Deflection is measured with moderate thumb pressure applied midway on longest belt run.

REPLACEMENT INTERVALS

Component	Interval (Miles)
Oil Filter	
Non-Turbo	7500
Turbo	3750
Air Filter	30,000
Fuel Filter	
Non-Turbo	45,000
Turbo	30,000
Fuel Tank Filter	60,000
PCV Valve	15,000
Oxygen Sensor	30,000
Spark Plugs	30,000

FLUID CAPACITIES

Application	Quantity
Crankcase (Including Filter)	
Non-Turbo	4.0 qts. (3.8L)
Turbo	4.7 qts. (4.5L)
Cooling System (Includes Heater)	10.0 qts. (9.4L)
Man. Trans. (ATF Type F)	
With Overdrive	4.8 pts. (2.3L)
Auto. Trans. (ATF Type F) [1]	
With Overdrive	7.8 qts. (7.4L)
Without Overdrive	7.1 qts. (6.7L)
Rear Axle (SAE 90)	3.4 pts. (1.6L)
Fuel Tank	15.8 gals. (60.0L)

[1] – For refill, 3.2 qts. (3.0L)

1983 Volvo V6 Tune-Up

TUNE-UP

760 GLE

ENGINE IDENTIFICATION

B28F engine identification number is stamped in lower left front corner of block above front cover of oil pan.

ENGINE COMPRESSION

Check compression with engine at normal operating temperature, spark plugs removed, throttle valve wide open and at normal cranking speed (250-300 RPM). Crank engine at least 6 "puffs" per cylinder.

COMPRESSION SPECIFICATIONS

Compression Ratio	8.8:1
Compression Pressure	114-156 psi (8-11 kg/cm²)

VALVE CLEARANCE

1) Adjust valves with engine cold. Rotate crankshaft so that No. 1 cylinder is at TDC of ignition stroke (both rocker arms for No. 1 cylinder have clearance).

NOTE: **Crank pulley has 2 notches. When No. 1 cylinder is at TDC, upper notch will align with "0" notch on timing marker and lower crank pulley notch will be 150° counterclockwise from upper notch. (Second notch is TDC for No. 6 cylinder when aligned with "0" on timing marker).**

2) Adjust intake valves of cylinder Nos. 1, 2 and 4 and exhaust valves of cylinder Nos. 1, 3 and 6. Rotate crankshaft 360°. This will set No. 1 cylinder at TDC of exhaust stroke (rocker arms for No. 1 cylinder with no clearance). Adjust intake valves of cylinder Nos. 3, 5 and 6 and exhaust valves of cylinder Nos. 2, 4 and 5.

VALVE CLEARANCE SPECIFICATIONS

Application	Intake In. (mm)	Exhaust In. (mm)
All Models	.004-.006 (.10-.15)	.010-.012 (.25-.30)

VALVE ARRANGEMENT

Right Bank — E-I-E-I-E-I (Front-to-rear)
Left Bank — I-E-I-E-I-E (Front-to-rear)

SPARK PLUGS

SPARK PLUG SPECIFICATIONS

Application	Gap In. (mm)	Torque Ft. Lbs. (N.m)
All Models	.028 (.70)	9 (12)

SPARK PLUG TYPE

Application	Bosch No.
All Models	HR6DS

Fig. 1: Firing Order and Distributor Rotation

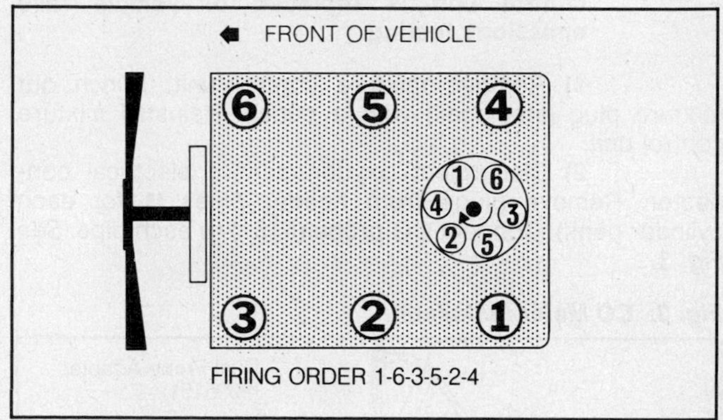
FRONT OF VEHICLE
6 5 4
1 6 4 3 2 5
3 2 1
FIRING ORDER 1-6-3-5-2-4

DISTRIBUTOR

All models are equipped with Bosch Electronic Ignition Systems. No adjustments are required.

IGNITION TIMING

Check or adjust ignition timing with engine at normal operating temperature, distributor vacuum hose disconnected, air conditioning "OFF" (if equipped), and engine speed set to specification. If possible, use magnetic timing device to set ignition timing on all models.

IGNITION TIMING SPECIFICATIONS (Degrees BTDC@RPM)

Application	[1] Timing
All Models	23@2500

[1] — With distributor vacuum hose disconnected and plugged.

Fig. 2: Ignition Timing Mark Location

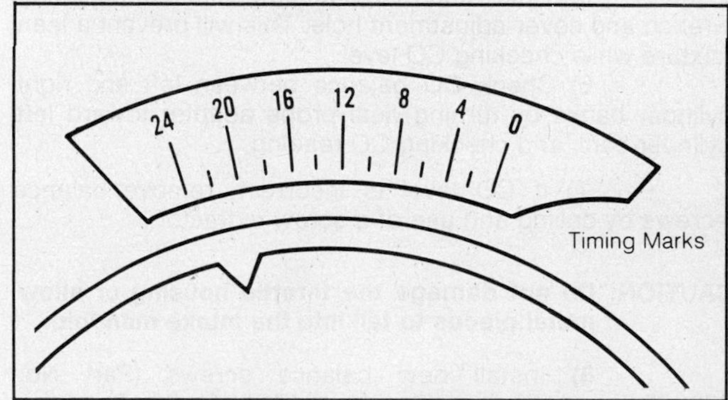
24 20 16 12 8 4 0
Timing Marks

IDLE SPEED & MIXTURE

IDLE SPEED

NOTE: **Idle adjustment is electronically-controlled and no adjustment is possible or required.**

TUNE-UP (Cont.)

IDLE MIXTURE

NOTE: Mixture control adjustment screw opening is plugged to prevent tampering. Adjustment is not a normal maintenance procedure and should not be performed unless mixture control unit is replaced or vehicle fails emissions testing.

1) Remove mixture control unit. Punch out mixture plug (steel ball) with a punch. Reinstall mixture control unit.

2) Disconnect oxygen sensor electrical connector. Remove plugs from header pipes (1 for each cylinder bank). Connect CO probe (5151) to each pipe. *See Fig. 3.*

Fig. 3: CO Meter Installation

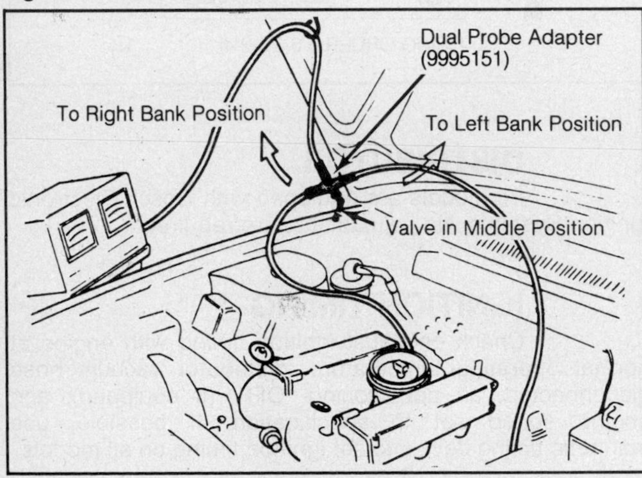
Dual Probe Adapter
(9995151)
To Right Bank Position
To Left Bank Position
Valve in Middle Position

3) Turn dual probe adapter to center position. In this position exhaust gases are admitted from both cylinder banks for total CO reading. Cover mixture adjustment hole and read CO level.

4) With CO meter and tachometer still installed, install air cleaner and connect hoses. To adjust CO level, insert adjusting wrench (5102) into adjustment hole and adjust CO to specifications. *See Fig. 4.*

5) After each adjustment, remove adjusting wrench and cover adjustment hole. This will prevent a lean mixture while checking CO level.

6) Check CO balance between left and right cylinder banks by turning dual probe adapter toward left cylinder bank and checking CO reading.

7) If CO level is incorrect, remove balance screws by drilling and use of a screw extractor.

CAUTION: Do not damage the throttle housing or allow metal pieces to fall into the intake manifold.

8) Install new balance screws (Part No. 269835-5) and "O" rings (Part No. 947114-5). *See Fig. 5.*

9) Turn all balance screws to bottom position. Unscrew balance screw "1" (1 turn) and balance screw "2" (5 turns). *See Fig. 5.*

CAUTION: DO NOT turn air adjusting screw.

Fig. 4: Idle Mixture Adjustment

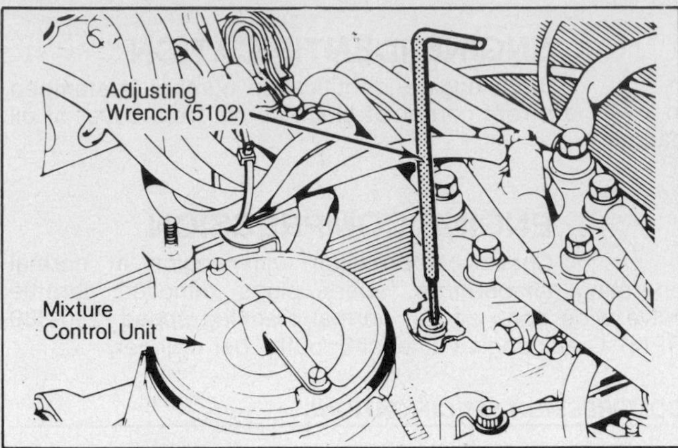
Adjusting
Wrench (5102)
Mixture
Control Unit

NOTE: Left balance screw goes to right side manifold and right balance screw goes to left side manifold.

Fig. 5: Balance and Air Adjusting Screw Location

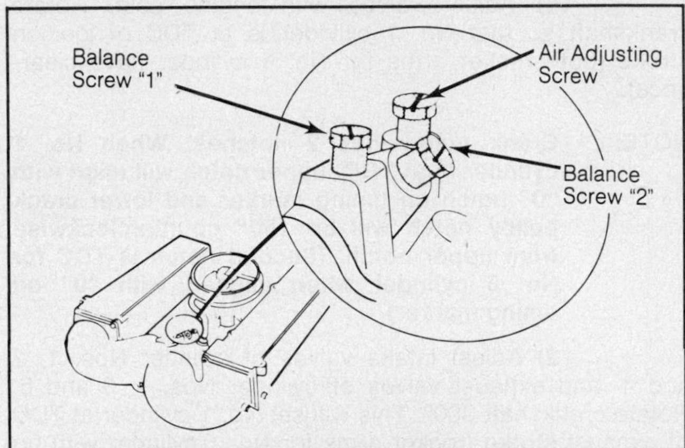
Balance
Screw "1"
Air Adjusting
Screw
Balance
Screw "2"

10) If left bank CO level is not within specifications, correct by adjusting balance screw "2". *See Fig. 5.*

11) Turn dual probe adapter toward right cylinder bank and check CO reading (should be equal for both banks and correct for total system).

12) If right bank CO level is not within specifications, correct by adjusting balance screw "1". *See Fig. 5.*

13) Recheck CO level with dual probe adapter in center position. If necessary, repeat adjustment procedure. Reconnect oxygen sensor electrical connector.

14) After CO adjustment, remove test equipment, insert exhaust pipe plugs and seal mixture adjustment hole.

IDLE SPEED & CO LEVEL SPECIFICATIONS

Application	Idle RPM	CO%
All Models	900	[1] 0.7-1.3

[1] — With oxygen sensor disconnected. With oxygen sensor connected, CO level should be below 1.0%.

TUNE-UP (Cont.)

OXYGEN SENSOR

1) Disconnect oxygen sensor electrical leads and remove oxygen sensor. Coat new oxygen sensor threads with anti-seize compound before installing oxygen sensor.

NOTE: **Do not apply anti-seize compound to the slotted part of the oxygen sensor.**

2) Tighten oxygen sensor to 36-44 ft. lbs. (50-60 N.m), then reconnect the electrical lead.

FUEL PUMP

FUEL PUMP PERFORMANCE

Application	Pressure psi (kg/cm²)	Volume in 30 sec. Pints (Liters)
All Models	64-75 (4.5-5.3)	2.1 (1.0)

EMISSION CONTROL SYSTEM

See Mitchell Manuals' Emission Control Manual.

GENERAL SERVICING

IGNITION

DISTRIBUTOR

All models are equipped with Bosch Electronic Ignition Systems. No adjustments are required.

IGNITION COIL

IGNITION COIL RESISTANCE – OHMS @ 68°F (20°C)

Application	Primary	Secondary
All Models	.5	9500

FUEL SYSTEM

FUEL INJECTION

All models are equipped with Bosch Lambda CIS fuel injection system with oxygen sensor.

ELECTRICAL

BATTERY

BATTERY SPECIFICATIONS

Application	Amp. Hr. Rating
All Models	66

STARTER

All models are equipped with Bosch overrunning clutch starters.

STARTER SPECIFICATION

Application	Volts	Amps	Test RPM
All Models	11.5	70	7500

ALTERNATOR

All models are equipped with Bosch alternators with integral voltage regulators.

ALTERNATOR SPECIFICATIONS

Application	Rated Amp. Output
All Models	70

ALTERNATOR REGULATOR

All models are equipped with Bosch alternator regulators, integral with alternator.

REGULATOR OPERATING VOLTAGE

Application	Voltage
All Models	13.4-14.8

SERVICE SPECIFICATIONS

BELT ADJUSTMENT

Application	[1] Deflection In. (mm)
All Belts	.2-.4 (5-10)

[1] – Deflection is measured with moderate thumb pressure applied at midpoint of longest belt run.

REPLACEMENT INTERVALS

Component	Interval (Miles)
Oil Filter	7500
Air Filter	30,000
Fuel Filter	30,000
PCV Valve	60,000
Spark Plugs	30,000
Oxygen Sensor	30,000

FLUID CAPACITIES

Application	Quantity
Crankcase (Including Filter)	7.0 qts. (6.5L)
Cooling System (Including Heater)	10.5 qts. (10.0L)
Auto. Trans. (ATF Type F) [1]	8.0 qts. (7.5L)
Rear Axle (SAE 90)	1.7 qts. (1.6L)
Fuel Tank	16.0 gals. (60.0L)

[1] – For refill, 3.5 qts. (3.3L)

1983 Volvo Diesel 6 Tune-Up

TUNE-UP

DL & GL Diesel, 760 GLE Turbo Diesel

ENGINE IDENTIFICATION

D24 and D24T diesel engine identification numbers are stamped on left side of block under vacuum pump.

ENGINE CODE

Application	Code
D24	
Man. Trans.	498-704
Auto. Trans.	498-705
D24T	
Man. Trans.	498-726
Auto. Trans.	498-733

ENGINE COMPRESSION

Disconnect wire at stop valve on injection pump. Remove vacuum pump and pump plunger. Clean fuel delivery pipes, remove pipes, and plug all openings. Remove injectors and heat shields. Place heat shield back in injector opening, followed by compression tester adapter 5191. Connect compression tester and test compression.

COMPRESSION SPECIFICATIONS

Compression Ratio	23.0:1
Normal Compression Pressure	455 psi (32.0 kg/cm²)
Minimum Pressure	341 psi (24.0 kg/cm²)
Maximum Variation Between Cylinders	114 psi (8.0 kg/cm²)

VALVE CLEARANCE

1) Using wrench on crankshaft pulley, turn engine until No. 1 cylinder is at TDC on compression stroke. Remove valve cover. Both cam lobes should point upward at equal angles.

VALVE CLEARANCE SPECIFICATIONS

Application	In. (mm)
Checking	
Cold	
Intake	.006-.010 (.15-.25)
Exhaust	.014-.018 (.35-.45)
Warm	
Intake	.008-.012 (.20-.30)
Exhaust	.016-.020 (.40-.50)
Adjustment	
Cold	
Intake	.008 (.20)
Exhaust	.016 (.40)
Warm	
Intake	.010 (.25)
Exhaust	.018 (.45)

2) Check valve clearance for No. 1 cylinder. If not correct, turn crankshaft 1/4 turn ATDC (so valves will not hit piston top). Depress cam followers with compression tool (5196). Using special pliers (tool 5195), remove disc. Calculate thickness of disc needed, coat with oil, and install.

NOTE: New discs are available in thicknesses from .130-167" (3.30-4.25 mm) in increments of .002" (.05 mm). New discs should be positioned with marks down.

3) Check valve clearance on remaining cylinders, proceeding in firing order. Be sure to check valve clearance at TDC and turn 1/4 turn after TDC before depressing valves.

VALVE ARRANGEMENT

E-I-E-I-E-I-I-E-I-E-I-E (Front-to-rear)

Fig. 1: Firing Order Illustration

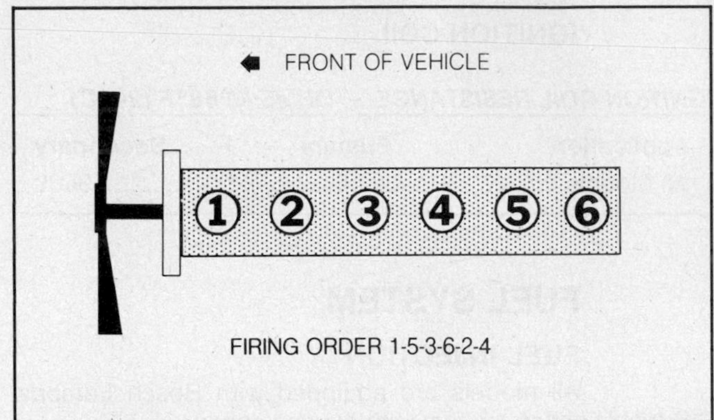
FRONT OF VEHICLE
1
2
3
4
5
6
FIRING ORDER 1-5-3-6-2-4

GLOW PLUGS

GLOW PLUG TYPE

Application	Volvo Part No.
All Models	1257141-0

IDLE SPEED ADJUSTMENT

1) Connect tachometer. Warm engine to normal operating temperature. Adjust low idle speed with idle speed screw. Check maximum engine speed and adjust if necessary with maximum speed screw. *See Fig. 2.*

2) Stop engine and disconnect link rod at lever on injection pump. Adjust throttle cable by turning cable sheath nut. Cable should be tight but not move pulley. Depress accelerator pedal and ensure that pulley touches full speed stop.

3) On automatic transmission models, depress accelerator to floor. Kickdown cable should move 2.05" (52 mm) between end positions. In idle position, cable should be stretched and clearance between clip and cable sheath should be .01-.04" (.25-1.0 mm).

1983 Volvo Diesel 6 Tune-Up

TUNE-UP (Cont.)

Fig. 2: Adjusting Idle Speed and Throttle Linkage

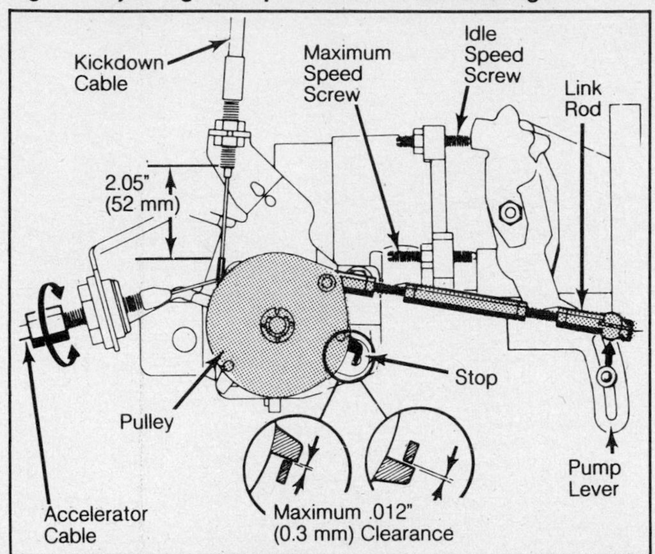
Kickdown Cable
Maximum Speed Screw
Idle Speed Screw
Link Rod
2.05" (52 mm)
Stop
Pulley
Pump Lever
Accelerator Cable
Maximum .012" (0.3 mm) Clearance

4) Connect link rod to injection pump lever. Turn pulley to maximum throttle position, and adjust length of link (by rotating) until lever touches maximum speed screw.

5) Return pulley to idle position, and move link rod ball joint in lever slot until lever touches idle adjusting screw. Recheck adjustments and repeat if necessary until idle speed and throttle positions are correct.

NOTE: A clearance of .012" (.3 mm) is permissible between pulley and stop.

IDLE SPEED SPECIFICATIONS

Application	Idle RPM	Maximum RPM
All Models	700-800	5100-5300

EMISSION CONTROL SYSTEMS

See Mitchell Manuals' Emission Control Manual.

GENERAL SERVICING

FUEL SYSTEM

FUEL INJECTION

All models use Bosch diesel fuel injection.

DIESEL FUEL INJECTION TIMING

Application	Degrees ATDC	Plunger Travel In. (mm)
D24	0	.032-.035 (.82-.90)
D24T	0	.031-.034 (.78-.85)

ELECTRICAL

BATTERY

BATTERY SPECIFICATIONS

Application	Amp Hr. Rating
All Models	90

STARTER

All models are equipped with Bosch starters.

ALTERNATOR

All models are equipped with Bosch alternators with integral voltage regulator.

ALTERNATOR SPECIFICATIONS

Application	Rated Amp Output
All Models	55

ALTERNATOR REGULATOR

All models are equipped with Bosch non-adjustable voltage regulators.

REGULATOR OPERATING VOLTAGE @ 68°F (20°C)

Application	Voltage
All Models	13.4-14.8

SERVICE SPECIFICATIONS

BELT ADJUSTMENT

Application	[1] Deflection In. (mm)
All Belts	.2-.4 (5-10)

[1] – Deflection is measured with moderate thumb pressure applied at midpoint of longest belt run.

REPLACEMENT INTERVALS

Component	Interval (Miles)
Oil Filter	[1] 15,000
Fuel Filter	[1] 15,000
Air Filter	30,000

[1] — Drain every 7,500 miles.

FLUID CAPACITIES

Application	Quantity
Crankcase (Includes Filter)	7.4 qts. (7.0L)
Cooling System (Includes Heater)	
760 GLE Model	
Man. Trans.	11.5 qts. (11.0L)
Auto. Trans.	10.5 qts. (10.0L)
All Other Models	
Man. Trans.	10.0 qts. (9.5L)
Auto. Trans.	9.8 qts. (9.3L)
Man. Trans. (ATF Type F)	2.4 qts. (2.3L)
Auto. Trans. (ATF Type F)	7.1 qts. (6.7L)
Rear Axle (SAE 90)	3.4 pts. (1.6L)
Fuel Tank	15.8 gals. (60.0L)

SECTION 1a

COMPUTERIZED ENGINE CONTROLS

CONTENTS

NOTE: ALSO SEE GENERAL INDEX.

Computerized Engine Controls

BMW MOTRONIC EMISSION CONTROL SYSTEM

528e, 533i, 633CSi, 733i

DESCRIPTION

The Motronic Emission Control System is an electronically controlled, computerized engine system which controls fuel injection and ignition timing as well as air/fuel ratio.

The Motronic Control Unit (MCU) is the "brain" of the system. Various engine sensors supply the MCU with operating information including air flow, air temperature, throttle position, coolant temperature, engine speed, piston position and oxygen content of exhaust gases.

The MCU uses this information to determine engine operating conditions, and adjusts timing and fuel ratio accordingly. The MCU is located behind the speaker in the right kick panel of 633CSi and 733i models and in the glove compartment of the 528e and 533i.

Fig. 1: Motronic Emission Control System Schematic

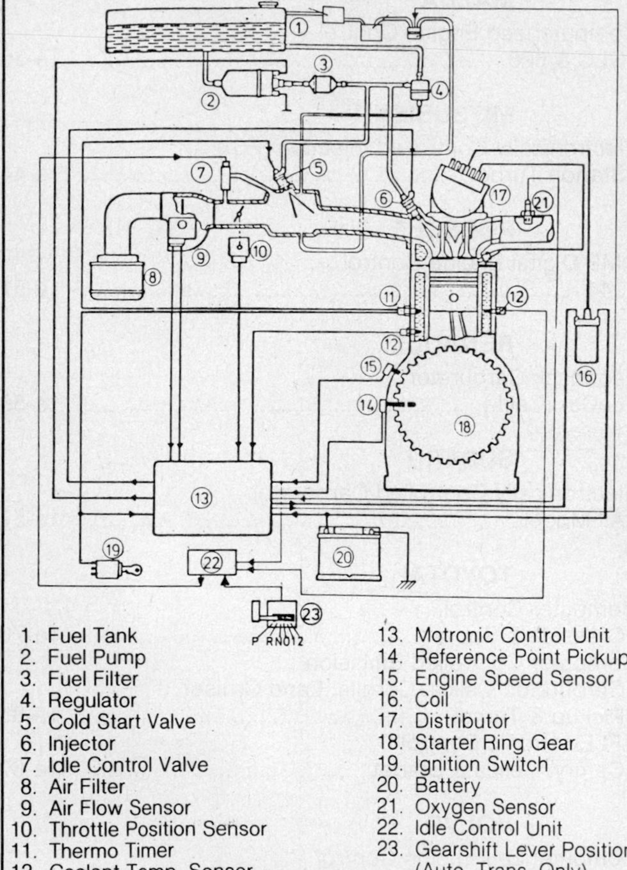
1. Fuel Tank
2. Fuel Pump
3. Fuel Filter
4. Regulator
5. Cold Start Valve
6. Injector
7. Idle Control Valve
8. Air Filter
9. Air Flow Sensor
10. Throttle Position Sensor
11. Thermo Timer
12. Coolant Temp. Sensor
13. Motronic Control Unit
14. Reference Point Pickup
15. Engine Speed Sensor
16. Coil
17. Distributor
18. Starter Ring Gear
19. Ignition Switch
20. Battery
21. Oxygen Sensor
22. Idle Control Unit
23. Gearshift Lever Position (Auto. Trans. Only)

OPERATION

MOTRONIC CONTROL UNIT (MCU)

The MCU receives electronic input signals from several engine sensors. Information supplied by these sensors is used to determine optimum ignition and fuel injection timing under various engine operating conditions.

An ideal air/fuel ratio of 14.7:1 is maintained under most driving conditions. This is the ratio at which the catalytic converter operates most efficiently to reduce exhaust emissions.

OXYGEN SENSOR

Oxygen content of exhaust gases is detected by the Oxygen Sensor located in the exhaust manifold. This sensor converts the percentage of oxygen present in exhaust gases into an electrical signal which is transmitted to the MCU. MCU uses this information to determine air/fuel ratio and adjusts injection pulse width to obtain the desired 14.7:1 ratio.

AIR FLOW SENSOR

Intake air flow is detected by the Air Flow Sensor. It is located in the intake passage between the air filter and the intake manifold and informs the MCU of rate of air intake. Incorporated into the Air Flow Sensor is the Air Temperature Sensor. This sensor informs the MCU of ambient temperature of incoming air.

THROTTLE POSITION SENSOR

The Throttle Position Sensor is located on the throttle linkage at the intake butterfly valve where it detects position of the throttle valve. This information is converted into an electrical signal and sent to the MCU. The MCU interprets the signal as either full throttle, idle or normal operating condition and makes adjustments accordingly.

ENGINE SPEED SENSOR

The Engine Speed Sensor (ESS) is mounted on the bellhousing, adjacent to the starter ring gear. A steel ball, embedded in the ring gear, causes an electronic pulse in the ESS with each engine revolution. These pulses are converted into an electrical signal which is sent to the MCU. The MCU uses this information to determine engine RPM.

REFERENCE POINT PICKUP

This sensor is located in the bellhousing, next to the ESS. It supplies the MCU with piston position information. When the MCU has determined optimum ignition timing (based on input from various sources) information supplied by the Reference Point Pickup is used to signal ignition firing.

COOLANT TEMPERATURE SENSORS

There are 3 components which supply coolant temperature information to the MCU. They are the Coolant Temperature Switch, Coolant Temperature Sensor and the Thermo Timer. All 3 devices are located in the water jacket of the engine block. They supply coolant temperature information to the MCU in the form of electrical signals.

The MCU interprets these signals as cold or normal operating temperatures. During cold operating conditions, the air/fuel mixture is enriched by the Cold Start Valve. This valve is located in the intake manifold, downstream from the butterfly valve. It supplies additional fuel to the inlet charge when signaled by the MCU. Extra rich conditions are maintained until normal operating temperature is attained.

BMW MOTRONIC EMISSION CONTROL SYSTEM (Cont.)

TESTING

PRELIMINARY TESTING

The Motronic system may be suspected when problems arise which are related to driveability, fuel economy or excess emissions. However, before beginning diagnosis ensure that all other systems are operating properly. Any engine system which would normally be checked in a vehicle not equipped with the Motronic system should be checked and approved before beginning Motronic testing.

When all other engine systems have been checked out, Motronic diagnosis may begin. Determine which component or area is the most probable source of performance difficulty and begin testing there. Many component failures may be traced to faults in the wiring circuit. Therefore, before beginning other diagnostic procedures, check the appropriate circuit for breaks or shorts and be sure that all electrical connections are clean and tight.

TEST EQUIPMENT

In addition to a standard volt/ohm meter, jumper wires and connectors, some special testing equipment is required for proper diagnosis of the Motronic system. The "BMW Service Test" kit, Bosch L-Jetronic Fuel Injection testing procedures, and BMW Test Meter (22 13 100) are required to properly test Motronic systems. This equipment will be refered to throughout the following test procedures and must be used as indicated. Failure to do so may result in unnecessary replacement of good component parts.

TEST 1: FUEL PRESSURE

No Fuel Pressure

1) Check fuel pump fuse and replace if defective. If fuse is okay, pull off electrical connector on fuel pump. Connect voltmeter between the 2 wires in connector and start engine. Voltmeter should read battery voltage. If voltage is correct, replace fuel pump.

2) If voltage reading is incorrect, check ground (Brown) wire: Connect ohmmeter between wire and ground. Resistance should be zero. If not, repair wire. If resistance is correct, check power (Green/Violet) wire: Disconnect Relay 1 and connect ohmmeter between power wire and connector 87 of relay socket. Resistance should be zero. If value is incorrect, repair wire.

3) If resistance is correct, check power supply from Relay 1: Connect voltmeter between wire 30 (Green/Yellow) on relay socket and ground. Turn ignition on. Meter should read battery voltage. If not, repair wire.

4) If voltage is correct, check power supply to Relay 1: Connect voltmeter between wire 86 (Red/White) of plug and ground. Start engine. Voltmeter should show battery voltage. If not, connect a voltmeter between wire 87 (Red/White) of Relay 2 and ground (relay still connected). Turn on ignition. Voltmeter should read battery voltage. If reading is incorrect, repair wire.

5) If power supply to Relay 1 is correct, check Relay 1 ground: Connect ohmmeter between wire 85 (Brown/Green) on socket and ground. Start engine. Resistance should be about zero. If resistance is correct, replace Relay 1.

6) If voltage in last part of step **4)** is correct, or if resistance is incorrect in step **5)**, check resistance of Brown/Green wire between connector 85 on Relay 1 plug and pin 20 of MCU connector. Resistance should be about zero. If not, repair wire. If resistance is correct, go to Test 3 for Motronic Control Unit.

Fuel Pressure Too High

1) Check the vacuum connection of the fuel pressure regulator and vacuum hoses for leaks or kinks. Repair or replace as needed.

2) Check for defective pressure regulator and replace if faulty. Check the fuel return line for bends, pinches or clogs. Repair or replace as needed.

Fuel Pressure Too Low

Fuel feed is probably restricted. Check for kinked, bent or clogged fuel line. Repair or re-route as needed. Check fuel filter for excessive restriction and replace if dirty. Clean filter screen in fuel intake. Check pressure regulator operation and replace if defective.

TEST 2: FUEL INJECTORS

1) Check for fuel delivery at injectors. If one or more injectors are not operating correctly, start engine and check for movement of needles in injectors. Movement can be felt with finger.

2) If no movement is detected, check power lines and coil of fuel injectors according to procedures in BMW Service Test, L-Jetronic step **5)**. If test value is incorrect, check wiring for shorts, breaks or poor connections and repair as needed. If wiring is okay, replace defective fuel injectors.

3) If test value is correct, check power supply to injectors: Connect a voltmeter between wire 87 (Red/Blue) on Relay 2 and ground (relay plugged in). Meter should read battery voltage. If not, go to Test 3 for Motronic Control Unit.

4) If voltage is correct, check activation of injectors (BMW Service Test, L-Jetronic step **2)**. If test value is incorrect, replace MCU.

TEST 3: MOTRONIC CONTROL UNIT

1) Check power supply to Motronic Control Unit (MCU): Connect BMW Service Test unit and perform L-Jetronic Test step **1)**. If values are correct, replace MCU.

2) If voltage value between wire 18/35 and 5, or 4 and 5 is insufficient or incorrect, connect voltmeter between wire 4 on disconnected MCU plug and ground. Start engine. If voltmeter does not show battery voltage, trace circuit and repair wiring. *See Fig. 2.*

3) Check wire 18 and 35 for breaks or poor connections. Connect ohmmeter between wire 5 on MCU plug and ground. Resistance should be zero. Connect ohmmeter between wire 18 or 35 on MCU plug, and wire 87 on plug of Relay 2. Resistance should be zero. If either test shows resistance, repair wiring.

4) If resistance values are correct, check power supply to Relay 2: Disconnect Relay 1 and connect voltmeter between terminal 86 on relay socket and ground. Turn ignition on. Voltmeter should read battery voltage. If not, trace circuit and repair wiring. *See Fig. 2.*

5) If voltage is correct, check ground of Relay 2: Pull off relay and check resistance between connector 85 and ground. Resistance should be zero. If not, trace circuit and repair wiring. *See Fig. 2.*

6) If resistance is correct, check power supply of Relay 2: Pull off relay and connect voltmeter between connector 30 of relay socket and ground. Voltmeter should read battery voltage. If not, trace circuit and repair wiring. If voltage reading is correct, replace Relay 2.

Computerized Engine Controls

BMW MOTRONIC EMISSION CONTROL SYSTEM (Cont.)

Fig. 2: BMW Motronic Emission Control System Wiring Diagram

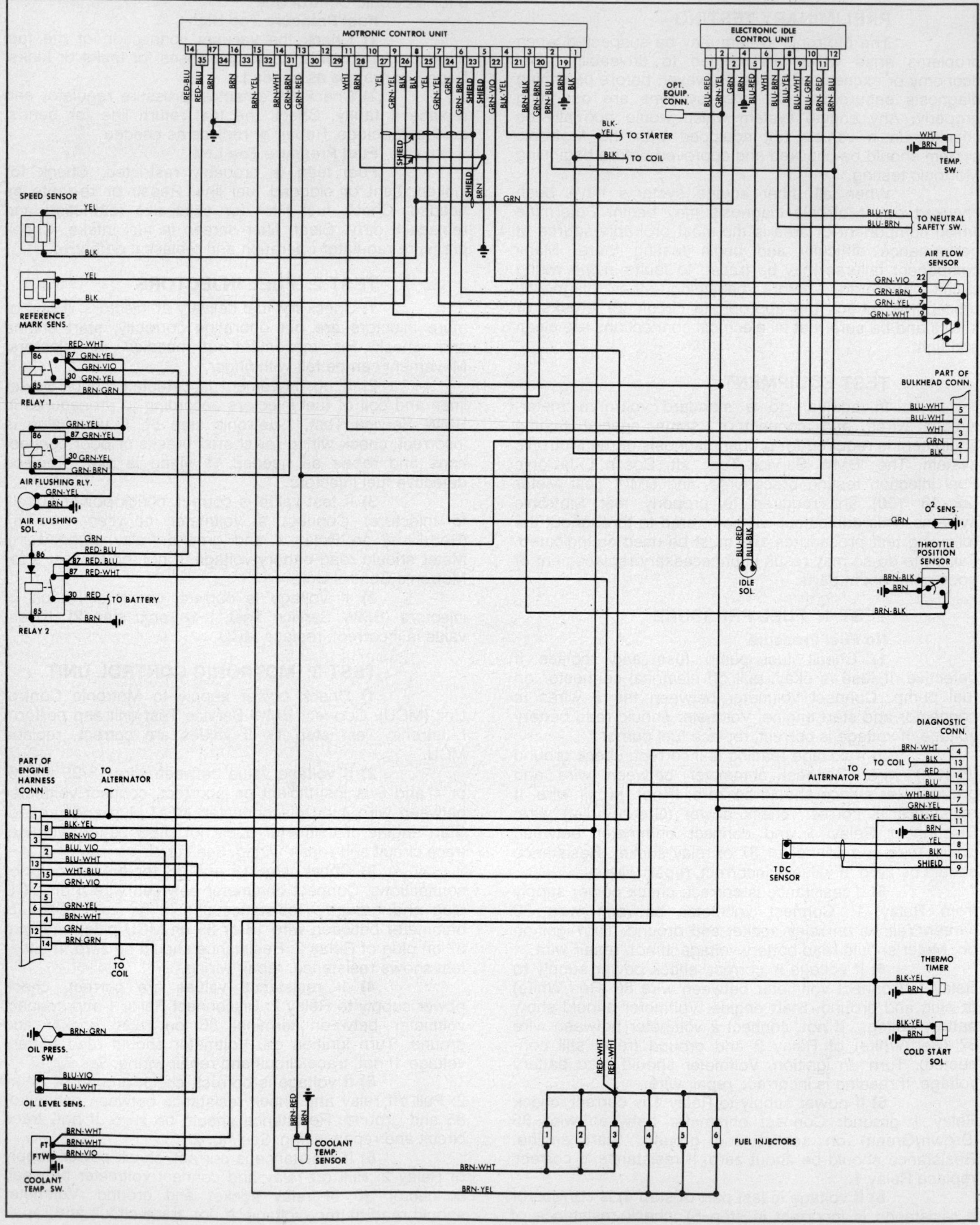

MOTRONIC CONTROL UNIT
ELECTRONIC IDLE CONTROL UNIT
OPT. EQUIP. CONN.
TO STARTER
TO COIL
TEMP. SW.
TO NEUTRAL SAFETY SW.
SPEED SENSOR
AIR FLOW SENSOR
REFERENCE MARK SENS.
RELAY 1
PART OF BULKHEAD CONN.
AIR FLUSHING RLY.
AIR FLUSHING SOL.
O² SENS.
THROTTLE POSITION SENSOR
IDLE SOL.
TO BATTERY
RELAY 2
DIAGNOSTIC CONN.
PART OF ENGINE HARNESS CONN.
TO ALTERNATOR
TDC SENSOR
TO COIL
THERMO TIMER
OIL PRESS. SW
COLD START SOL.
OIL LEVEL SENS.
COOLANT TEMP. SENSOR
FUEL INJECTORS
COOLANT TEMP. SW.

BMW MOTRONIC EMISSION CONTROL SYSTEM (Cont.)

TEST 4: COLD START VALVE

Valve Does Not Open

1) Remove valve, leaving fuel lines connected. Supply battery voltage to valve with jumper wire and be sure valve is properly grounded. Pull off Relay 1. Apply battery voltage to connector 87 in relay plug and check that fuel pump runs. Cold start valve should deliver fuel. If not, replace valve.

2) If valve functions properly, check power supply to valve: Pull plug off valve and connect voltmeter between wires of plug. Start engine. Meter should read battery voltage while cranking engine. If not, trace circuit and repair wiring. *See Fig. 2.*

3) Check Thermo Timer as in Test 12 and replace if resistance values are not correct.

Valve Leaks

Check valve operation as in first Cold Start Valve test. If valve operates properly (fuel is delivered), remove jumper wire to battery voltage and check that fuel delivery stops. If fuel is still delivered, or leaks, or seeps out, replace valve.

TEST 5: IDLE CONTROL VALVE

1) Valve should be open when vehicle is at rest (no voltage to valve). When voltage is applied to valve (engine on), valve should close. Remove 2 valve hoses and observe valve operation. If valve does not operate as described, replace valve.

2) If valve operates properly, pull off connector plug and connect voltmeter between the 2 wires in plug. Start engine and turn A/C on. Voltmeter should read battery voltage. If it does not, check Idle Control Unit. *See Test 6.*

TEST 6: IDLE CONTROL UNIT

1) Check power supply to Idle Control Unit (ICU): Pull connector plug off of ICU and connect voltmeter between terminal 2 of plug and ground. Start engine. Voltmeter should read battery voltage. If not, repair circuit.

2) If voltage is correct, check ground connection of ICU: Connect ohmmeter between terminal 4 of plug and ground. Ohmmeter should read zero. If not, trace circuit and repair wiring.

3) If resistance is correct, check speed signal to ICU at terminal 3 of plug with BMW test meter (22 13 100). If signal is not correct, trace circuit and repair wiring.

4) If signal is correct, check for ground at terminal 6 of ICU: Connect ohmmeter between terminal 6 of ICU plug and ground. With coolant temperature below 106°F (41°C), resistance should be zero. With coolant temperature above 117°F (47°C), resistance should be infinite. If values are incorrect, check Coolant Temperature Switch. *See Test 11.* If switch is good, trace Idle Control Unit circuit and repair wiring. If resistance values are correct, go to next step.

5) On automatic transmission equipped vehicles, check for battery voltage at terminal 7 of plug with ignition on and transmission shift lever in "N". If voltage is absent, trace circuit and repair wiring. If voltage is present at terminal 7, check for battery voltage at terminal 8 with shift lever in "P". If voltage is absent, trace circuit and repair wiring. If reading is correct, go to next step.

6) On vehicles with air conditioning, check for battery voltage at terminal 9 of plug with air conditioner "ON". Trace circuit and repair wiring if voltage is incorrect. If reading is correct, go to next step.

7) On all models, check for battery voltage at terminal 10 of ICU plug with ignition on. Voltage should be present with air temperature below 41°F (5°C), and absent at higher temperatures. If values are incorrect, check Air Temperature Sensor. *See Test 13.* Replace if faulty. If sensor is okay, repair wiring.

8) If voltage readings are correct, check for ground at terminal 12 of ICU: Connect ohmmeter between terminal 12 of plug and ground. Resistance should be zero with throttle closed, and infinite with throttle open. If values are incorrect, check Throttle Position Sensor. *See Test 9.* Replace or adjust as needed. If switch is good, repair wiring.

9) If resistance values are correct, check ground connection at terminal 11 of ICU: Connect ohmmeter between terminal 11 and ground. Resistance value should be zero. If not, check Coolant Temperature Sensor. *See Test 10.* Replace sensor if faulty. If sensor is good, repair wiring.

10) If resistance values are correct, and Idle Control Valve is good (Test 5), replace Idle Control Unit.

TEST 7: ENGINE SPEED SENSOR & REFERENCE POINT PICKUP

1) Check sensor and pickup general condition. Ensure that they are installed in the proper position and firmly seated. Electrical contacts must be clean and tight. Check that sensor plugs are not reversed. Plugs are color coded for identification.

2) Install BMW test meter (22 13 100). Connect terminals 8 and 27 and check for speed signal. Connect terminals 25 and 26 and check for reference signal. If signals are not correct, repair wiring. Remove terminal connections and recheck signals. If either signal is absent, replace sensor and/or pickup as needed.

TEST 8: AIR FLOW SENSOR

1) Check that sensor is properly installed and firmly seated. Ensure that sensor plate moves freely.

2) Run L-Jetronic test 4 to check air flow value. If value is incorrect, repair wiring. Check resistance at terminals 7 and 9 of sensor. Resistance should be checked with sensor plate in several different positions.

TEST 9: THROTTLE POSITION SENSOR

Check that sensor is properly installed and firmly seated. Run L-Jetronic Test 3 to determine throttle sensor values. If values are incorrect, adjust or replace sensor as needed.

TEST 10: COOLANT TEMP. SENSOR

Check that sensor is properly installed and firmly seated. Check that cooling system is full. Bleed system. Check resistance between switch connections. If resistance is incorrect, replace sensor. If resistance is correct, trace sensor circuit and repair wiring.

TEST 11: COOLANT TEMP. SWITCH

Switch must be tightly installed. Check that cooling system is full. Bleed system. Check resistance between switch contacts. Resistance below 106°F (41°C) should be zero. At higher temperatures, resistance should

BMW MOTRONIC EMISSION CONTROL SYSTEM (Cont.)

be infinite. If values are correct, trace circuit and repair wiring. If values are incorrect, replace switch.

TEST 12: THERMO TIMER

1) Check that timer is properly installed and firmly seated. Check radiator for correct coolant level. Bleed cooling system.

2) Disconnect timer and check resistance values between plug terminals "G" and "W", "G" and ground, and "W" and ground. If values are correct, trace timer circuit and repair wiring. If values are incorrect, replace timer. *See Thermo Timer Resistance Specifications.*

THERMO TIMER RESISTANCE SPECIFICATIONS

Circuit Tested	Resistance
"G" to Ground	40-70 Ohms
"G" to "W" & "W" to Ground	
Above 60°F (15°C)	Infinite
Below 60°F (15°C)	Zero

TEST 13: AIR TEMPERATURE SENSOR

1) Check electrical connections on sensor. Use L-Jetronic test 4 to check Air Temperature Sensor values. If values are incorrect, remove connector from sensor and attach ohmmeter. Check resistance between terminals 22 and 6 and compare with table. *See Air Temp. Sensor Resistance Specifications.*

2) If resistance values are correct, trace sensor circuit and repair wiring. If values are incorrect, replace Air Flow Sensor.

AIR TEMP. SENSOR RESISTANCE SPECIFICATIONS

Air Temperature °F (°C)	Resistance Ohms
66-70 (19-21)	2280-2720
120-124 (49-51)	760-910

ADJUSTMENTS

OXYGEN SENSOR

1) After 30,000 miles of vehicle operation, a warning light in the dash will come on, indicating that oxygen sensor service is required. Trace wire from oxygen sensor to plug and disconnect. On 528e, pull off protective metal plate.

2) On all models, remove oxygen sensor. With a light coat of copper paste applied to threads, install new sensor. On all except 528e, reset interval switch by pressing White button. On 528e, switch cannot be reset. Bulb must be removed from display panel to deactivate oxygen light.

Computerized Engine Controls

DATSUN/NISSAN ELECTRONIC CONCENTRATED ENGINE CONTROL SYSTEM

280ZX Turbo

DESCRIPTION

The Electronic Concentrated Engine Control System (ECCS) is a computerized emission, ignition, and fuel control system. A single control unit monitors a variety of sensors, including the following:

- Air Conditioning Switch
- Air Flow Meter
- Air Temperature Sensor
- Barometric Pressure Sensor
- Crankshaft Angle Sensor
- Cylinder Head Temperature Sensor
- Detonation Sensor
- Oxygen Sensor
- Park/Neutral Switch
- Throttle Valve Switch
- Vehicle Speed Sensor

The computer processes information from these sensors and controls these engine functions:

- EGR Operation
- Engine Idle Speed
- Fuel Injectors
- Fuel Pump Operation
- Ignition Timing and Dwell

OPERATION

ECCS CONTROL UNIT

The control unit is located on driver's side kick panel. It is not serviceable and should not be opened. A monitor lamp is provided on lower side of unit so system operation can be checked. The control unit contains memory and logic circuits that enable it to interpret sensor inputs and control different engine systems.

ENGINE SENSORS

Air Flow Meter & Temperature Sensor

The air flow meter measures incoming air so fuel mixture can be determined and injection time controlled by ECCS control unit. It is a standard AFC flow meter, but incorporates a temperature sensor which is also used for ECCS input. The sensor cannot be serviced separately.

Barometric Pressure Sensor

This sensor is built into the ECCS control unit and cannot be serviced separately. It allows the control unit to compensate for altitude changes.

Crankshaft Angle Sensor

The crankshaft angle sensor, which is built into the distributor, has 2 diodes and a wave-forming circuit. When a signal rotor plate passes the space between light emitting diode (LED) and photo diode, the slit to the signal rotor plate alternately cuts the light which is sent to the photo diode from the LED This causes an alternative

Fig. 1: 280ZX Turbo ECCS Component Locations

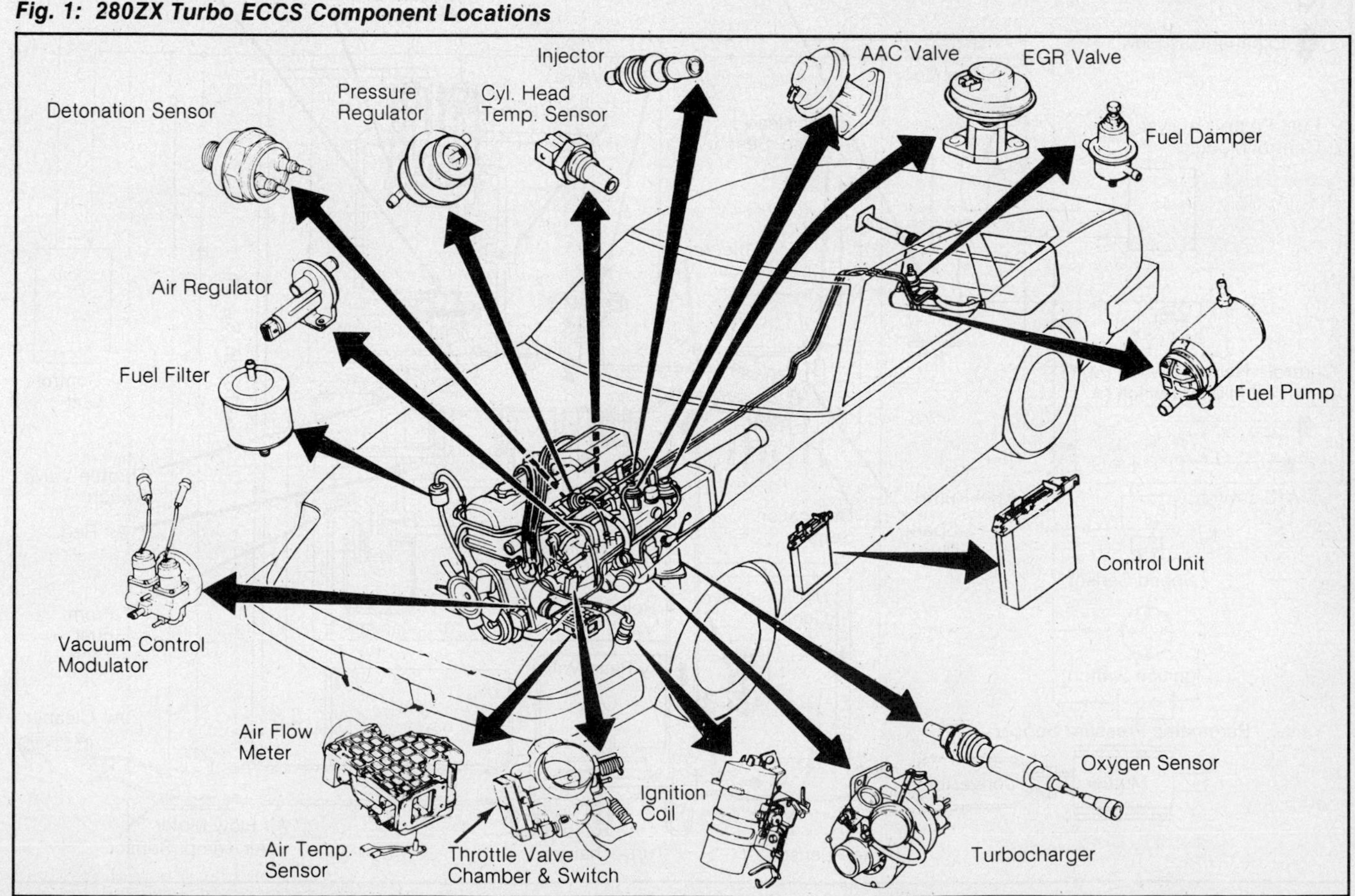
Injector
AAC Valve
EGR Valve
Detonation Sensor
Pressure Regulator
Cyl. Head Temp. Sensor
Fuel Damper
Air Regulator
Fuel Filter
Fuel Pump
Control Unit
Vacuum Control Modulator
Air Flow Meter
Ignition Coil
Oxygen Sensor
Air Temp. Sensor
Throttle Valve Chamber & Switch
Turbocharger

DATSUN/NISSAN ELECTRONIC CONCENTRATED ENGINE CONTROL SYSTEM (Cont.)

voltage which is converted into an on-off pulse by the wave-forming circuit and sent to the control unit.

Cylinder Head Temperature Sensor

The cylinder head temperature sensor is located in the right rear corner of the head and provides a varying resistance measurement as cylinder head temperature changes.

Detonation Sensor

The detonation sensor is located near the oil dipstick and sends a signal when "knocking" occurs. The control unit modifies ignition timing to reduce detonation.

Oxygen Sensor

This component measures the amount of unburned oxygen in the exhaust and provides a voltage signal which is used to adjust fuel mixture (amount of injection time).

Throttle Valve Switch

The throttle valve switch is open when the throttle is being moved and closed when the engine is idling. The switch also contains a set of full throttle contacts, but these are not used in this system.

ENGINE CONTROLS

EGR Operation

Exhaust gas recirculation is controlled by the ECCS. A signal is sent to the vacuum control modulator, which provides a regulated vacuum supply to open the EGR valve. EGR operation is affected by cylinder head temperature, throttle valve position and ignition switch position. Recirculation takes place only when the engine is operating above idle with cylinder head temperature between 135-239°F (57-115°C).

Engine Idle Speed

Auxiliary Air Control (AAC) valve is used to control idle speed. Valve is operated by a vacuum signal from vacuum control modulator and works much like an EGR valve does. It allows extra air into throttle chamber, which increases idle speed. Control unit monitors speed with crankshaft angle sensor and continually corrects idle speed by operating vacuum control modulator.

Fuel Injection

The control unit determines how long voltage is provided to each injector. The injection time will determine how much fuel is injected. For more information, see the appropriate *Bosch AFC Fuel Injection article in FUEL SYSTEMS Section.*

Fuel Pump

The ECCS control unit operates electric fuel pump. When ignition is turned to "ON" or "START" position, the fuel pump operates. If ignition is on and no signal is received from crank sensor 120° pick-up for more than 1 second, the fuel pump stops. It will operate

Fig. 2: 280ZX Turbo ECCS Schematic & Vacuum Diagram

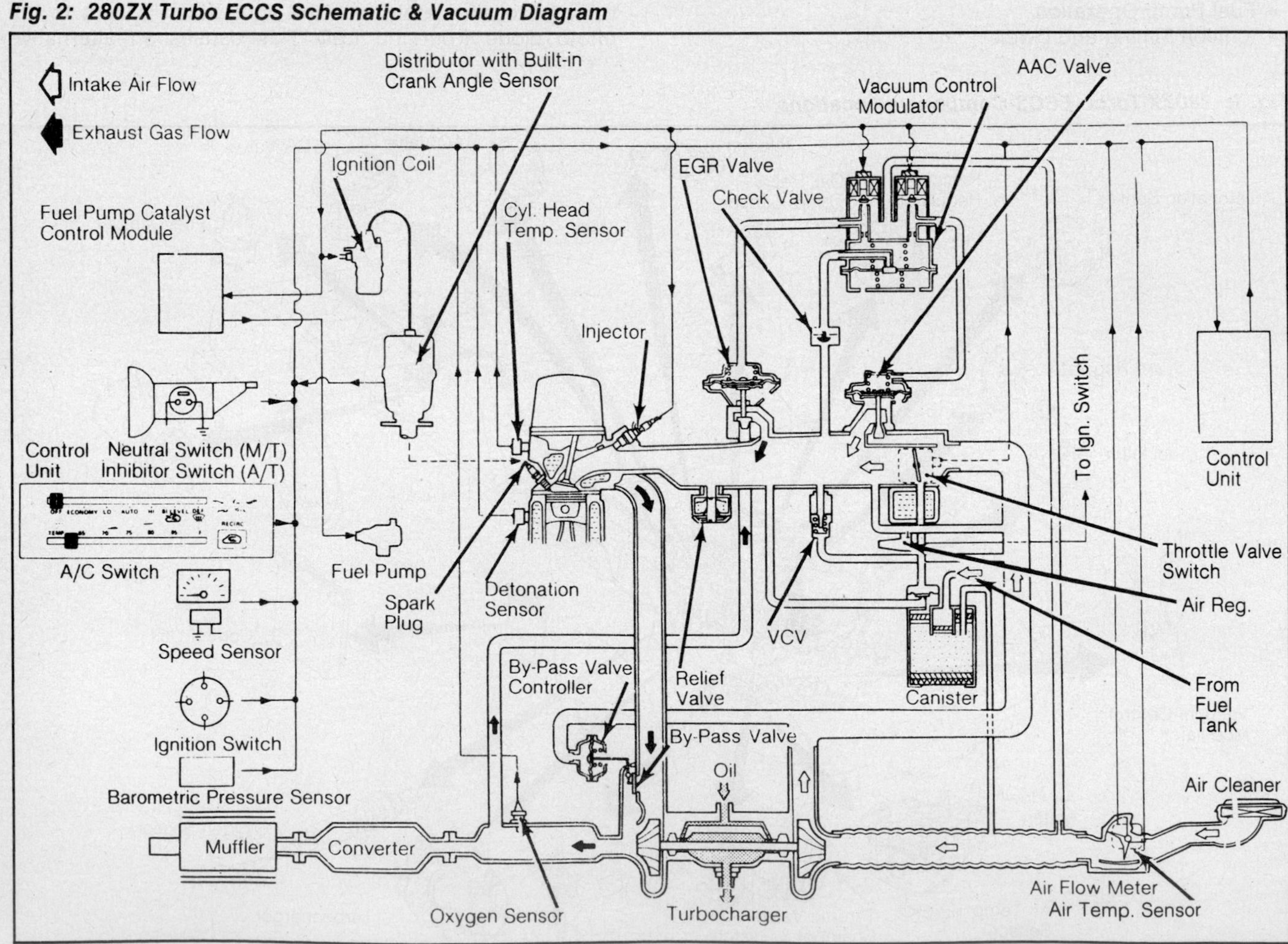
Intake Air Flow
Exhaust Gas Flow
Distributor with Built-in Crank Angle Sensor
AAC Valve
Vacuum Control Modulator
Ignition Coil
EGR Valve
Check Valve
Fuel Pump Catalyst Control Module
Cyl. Head Temp. Sensor
Injector
To Ign. Switch
Control Unit
Neutral Switch (M/T)
Inhibitor Switch (A/T)
Control Unit
A/C Switch
Fuel Pump
Spark Plug
Detonation Sensor
Throttle Valve Switch
Air Reg.
VCV
Speed Sensor
By-Pass Valve Controller
Relief Valve
Canister
From Fuel Tank
Ignition Switch
By-Pass Valve
Oil
Barometric Pressure Sensor
Air Cleaner
Muffler
Converter
Air Flow Meter
Air Temp. Sensor
Oxygen Sensor
Turbocharger

Note direction of flow.

DATSUN/NISSAN ELECTRONIC CONCENTRATED ENGINE CONTROL SYSTEM (Cont.)

for 5 seconds before engine is cranked, and will then stop if engine is not cranked over at 20 RPM or more.

Ignition Timing

The ECCS control unit uses sensor input to determine correct timing. It sends a signal to a power transistor located on coil, which permits current to flow through coil. Timing is advanced and retarded by control unit based on sensor input, built-in programming and detonation sensor signals.

TESTING

NOTE: The ECCS system requires a special tester (Datsun ECCS Analyzer - J28835) to be fully diagnosed. However, some checks of individual components may be made using regular shop test equipment.

CAUTION: Be sure ignition switch is off when disconnecting connectors from control unit. While testing, be careful not to bend any pins and do not touch more than 1 pin at a time with meter lead as meter or control unit could be damaged.

PREPARATION FOR TESTING

1) Turn ignition off. Disconnect battery ground cable and disconnect wire from terminal "S" at starter motor.

2) Remove air cleaner and position air flow meter so flap can be moved by hand from air cleaner side. Disconnect all 3 connectors at control unit.

COMPONENT TESTING

Air Conditioning Switch

Connect voltmeter between control unit connector terminal 22 and ground. With switch "ON", 12 volts should be measured. With switch "OFF", 0 volts should be measured. If not correct, check harness or replace switch.

Air Flow Meter

1) Connect ohmmeter across pins 26 and 33 in control unit connector. Resistance should be 280-400 ohms. If not, disconnect harness at meter and check

Fig. 3: Air Flow Meter Test Locations

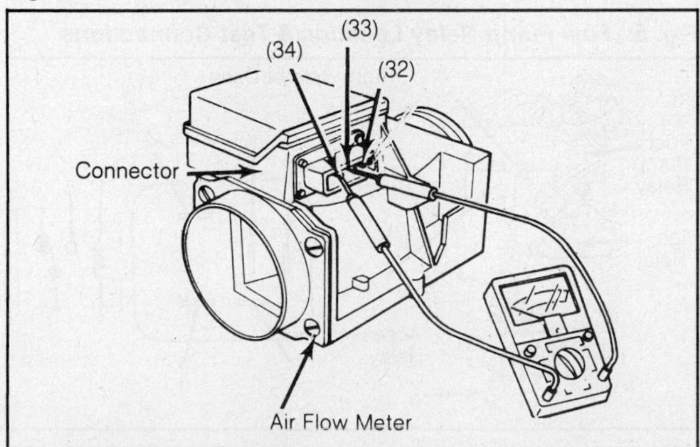
(33)
(34)
(32)
Connector
Air Flow Meter

Connect ohmmeter as shown.

resistance between pins 34 and 33. *See Fig. 3.* Resistance should be 280-400 ohms. If not correct, repair harness or replace air flow meter.

2) Connect ohmmeter across pins 33 and 31 in control unit connector. Resistance should measure any value between infinity and zero. If not, disconnect harness at meter and check resistance between pins 34 and 32. If okay at meter, repair harness. If not, replace air flow meter.

3) Connect 1 lead of ohmmeter to ground and other lead to connector pin 26, then 31, then 33 on control unit. Infinite resistance should be shown in all cases. If not, replace air flow meter.

4) Operate air flow meter flap by hand to ensure it moves smoothly without binding. If okay, meter is functioning properly. If not, replace air flow meter.

Air Regulator

1) Connect ohmmeter between pin 108 in control unit connector and ground. Resistance should be 25-90 ohms.

2) Connect ECCS harness connectors to control unit. Turn ignition "ON". Fuel pump should operate for 5 seconds. If pump is not heard, check pump relay. If pump is heard, check air regulator.

3) Start engine and pinch hose between throttle chamber and air regulator. Engine speed should decrease during warm-up, but not when engine is at operating temperature.

4) Disconnect hoses from both ends of regulator and see if flap opens. It should move smoothly. Check resistance across terminals on regulator. If continuity exists, regulator is good. If not, replace regulator.

Air Temperature Sensor

1) Connect ohmmeter across pins 30 and 33 in control unit connector. With air temperature below 68°F (20°C), resistance should be 2100 or more ohms. With air temperature above 68°F (20°C), resistance should be below 2900 ohms.

2) If resistance is not correct, repeat test at air flow meter terminals 34 and 25. If resistance is still not correct, repair harness or replace meter as necessary. *See Fig. 3*

3) Connect ohmmeter between ground and pin 30 at connector. No continuity should be present. Repeat check at air flow meter terminal 25 and body. Repair harness or replace meter as necessary.

Control Unit Ground Circuits

Measure resistance between ground and the following control unit connector terminals: 28, 36, 107, 109, 112 and 113. Continuity should be present in all cases. If not, repair harness.

Cylinder Head Temperature Sensor

1) Connect ohmmeter across pins 23 and 26 in control unit connector. With air temperature below 68°F (20°C), resistance should be 2100 or more ohms. With air temperature above 68°F (20°C), resistance should be below 2900 ohms.

2) If resistance is not correct, remove sensor from head. Dip end of sensor into water. Heat water and observe resistance across terminals. Resistance should be the same as listed in step **1)**. If not, repair harness or replace sensor.

DATSUN/NISSAN ELECTRONIC CONCENTRATED ENGINE CONTROL SYSTEM (Cont.)

EFI Relay

1) With battery cables connected and ignition on, measure voltage between control unit connector pin 35 and ground. Battery voltage should be present.

2) If not, check EFI relay operation. Relay is located under a cover in engine compartment. *See Fig. 4.*

Fig. 4: EFI Relay Location & Test Connections

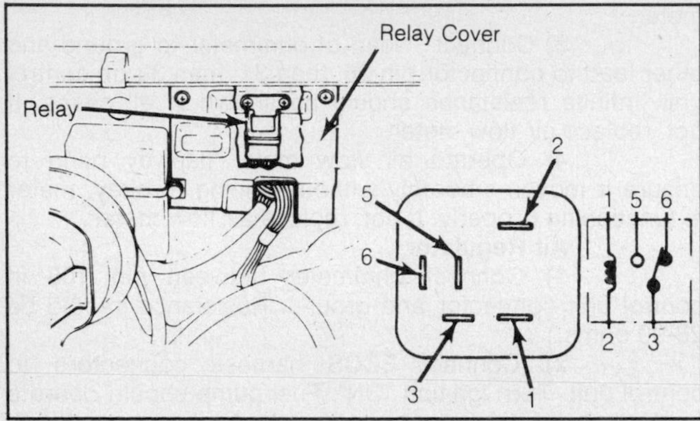

Relay Cover
Relay
2
5
1 5 6
6
2 3
3
1

3) Continuity should exist across terminals 1 and 2, and 3 and 6. With battery voltage applied to terminals 1 and 2, continuity should exist across terminals 3 and 5. If not, replace relay.

Fuel Injectors

NOTE: **Never turn the selecting switch of the tester to the "Ohmmeter" or "Ammeter" position during these tests as it may burn out the injectors and circuit.**

1) Connect battery ground cable. Use a voltmeter to measure between ground and the following terminals at control unit connector: 101, 102, 103, 104, 105, and 106. Battery voltage should be present at all terminals.

2) If battery voltage was not present at terminal, check the appropriate injector. Disconnect battery ground cable and remove connectors at injector. Continuity should exist across terminals on injector. If not, replace injector.

NOTE: **Injector circuits are numbered according to cylinder number. For example, injector power circuit 103 goes to cylinder 3, etc.**

Fuel Pump Relay

1) Fuel pump relay is mounted on right side of dashboard. Remove relay and check continuity. It should be present to terminals 1 and 2, and terminals 3 and 5.

2) With 12 volts applied to terminals 1 and 2, continuity should be present across terminals 3 and 5. If test is okay, check harness. If not okay, replace relay. *See Fig. 5.*

Ignition Signal Circuit

1) Disconnect starter motor "S" terminal and connect battery ground cable. Turn ignition switch to "START".

2) Measure voltage between control unit connector pin 9 and ground. If battery voltage is not present, check harness and ignition coil.

Oxygen Sensor

1) Connect all wiring and battery cables. Start engine and warm to normal operating temperature. Open hood and run engine at 2000 RPM for 5 minutes.

2) If engine does not run smoothly, check air flow meter, cylinder head temperature sensor, and air temperature sensor.

3) Accelerate engine several times, then check idle. If not 600-700 RPM in "D" (650-750 RPM for manual transmission), check idle speed control system and vacuum control modulator.

NOTE: **Special ECCS tester is required for idle speed control system check.**

4) Check and adjust timing, if required. Adjust to 21-27° BTDC by turning distributor (loosen bolt first). Accelerate engine several times.

5) Using a mirror, check that inspection lamp on bottom of control unit goes on and off more than 5 times in 10 seconds with engine running at 2000 RPM in "N".

6) If so, sensor is okay. If not, check oxygen sensor harness. If harness if okay, replace oxygen sensor.

Oxygen Sensor Harness

Disconnect harness from sensor at oxygen sensor (in exhaust pipe) and connect to ground with jumper wire. Measure resistance between ground and pin 24 in control unit connector. Continuity should be measured. If not present, repair harness.

Park/Neutral Switch

Connect ohmmeter between control unit connector pin 10 and ground. With transmission lever in "N" or "P", zero ohms should be present. If not, check harness or replace switch.

Throttle Valve Switch

1) Connect ohmmeter across pins 18 and 25 in control unit connectors. With throttle depressed, no continuity should be present. With throttle released, continuity should be present. If not correct, adjust throttle switch. *See ADJUSTMENTS in this article.*

2) Connect ohmmeter to terminal 18 and ground, then 25 and ground. *See Fig. 6.* Infinite ohm reading should be present in both positions. If not, repair short to ground in harness, or replace throttle valve switch.

Fig. 5: Fuel Pump Relay Location & Test Connections

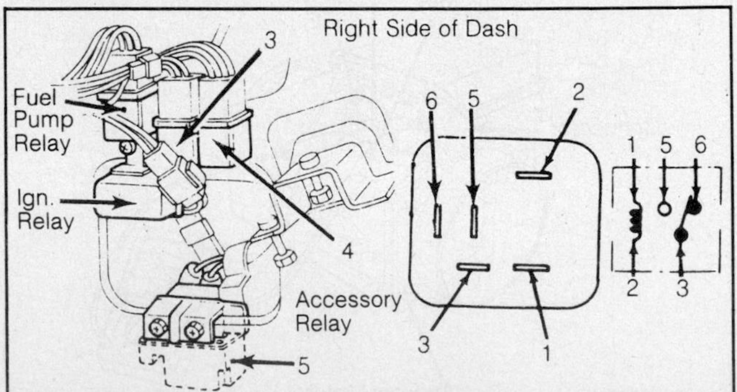

Right Side of Dash
3
Fuel
Pump
Relay
Ign.
Relay
4
Accessory
Relay
5
6 5
2
1 5 6
2 3
3
1

DATSUN/NISSAN ELECTRONIC CONCENTRATED ENGINE CONTROL SYSTEM (Cont.)

Vacuum Control Modulator

1) Connect battery ground cable and turn ignition "ON". Measure voltage between control unit connector terminal 2 and ground. Battery voltage should be present.

2) Check for battery voltage between terminal 4 and ground. If voltage is present in both checks, modulator solenoid valves are okay. If not, disconnect both connectors at modulator.

3) Check resistance between terminals for each solenoid valve on modulator. Resistance should be 40 ohms for each valve. If not, replace vacuum control modulator.

ADJUSTMENTS

THROTTLE VALVE SWITCH

Disconnect throttle valve switch connector. Connect ohmmeter across terminals 18 and 25, ensuring that continuity exists. Allow engine to run at idle and adjust switch so continuity is lost at about 900 RPM. *See Fig. 6.*

Fig. 6: Throttle Valve Switch Adjustment

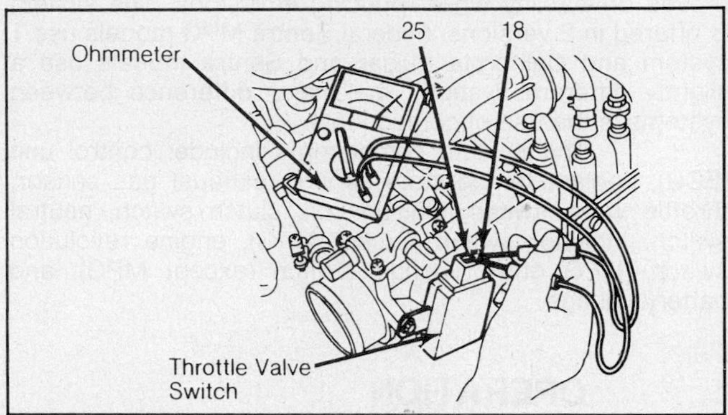
25
18
Ohmmeter
Throttle Valve
Switch

Connect ohmmeter across terminals as shown.

Fig. 7: Datsun 280ZX Turbo ECCS Wiring Diagram

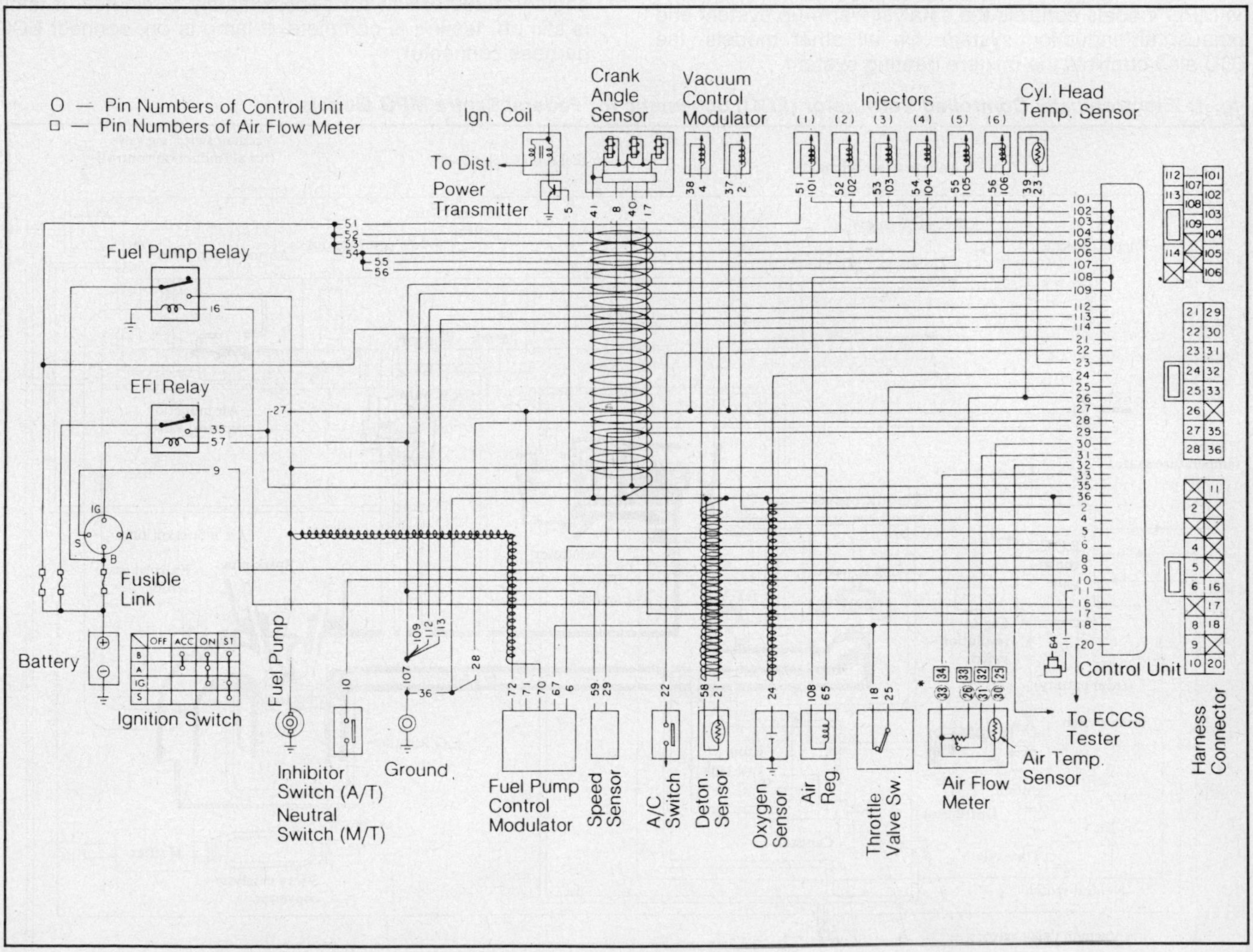

O — Pin Numbers of Control Unit
□ — Pin Numbers of Air Flow Meter
Ign. Coil
To Dist.
Power Transmitter
Crank Angle Sensor
Vacuum Control Modulator
Injectors (1) (2) (3) (4) (5) (6)
Cyl. Head Temp. Sensor
Fuel Pump Relay
EFI Relay
Fusible Link
Battery
Ignition Switch
Fuel Pump
Inhibitor Switch (A/T) Neutral Switch (M/T)
Ground
Fuel Pump Control Modulator
Speed Sensor
A/C Switch
Deton. Sensor
Oxygen Sensor
Air Reg.
Throttle Valve Sw.
Air Flow Meter
Air Temp. Sensor
To ECCS Tester
Control Unit
Harness Connector

DATSUN/NISSAN ELECTRONICALLY CONTROLLED CARBURETOR

Pulsar, Sentra

DESCRIPTION

The electronically controlled carburetor improves driveability while reducing emissions. The system is offered in 2 versions: Federal Sentra MPG models use 1 system and California Pulsar and Sentra models use a slightly different system. The major difference between systems is the use of components.

The system components include: control unit (ECU), coolant temperature sensor, exhaust gas sensor, throttle valve switch, ignition coil, clutch switch, neutral switch, inhibitor switch (except MPG), engine revolution switch (MPG only), vacuum switch (except MPG), and battery voltage.

OPERATION

The electronic control unit (ECU), which incorporates a microprocessor, receives impulses from various sensors and switches. On both systems, it controls the air/fuel ratio and fuel shut-off system. In addition, the ECU on MPG models controls the catalyst warm-up system and exhaust air induction system. On all other models, the ECU also controls the mixture heating system.

TESTING

SYSTEM CHECK

1) Visually check clamps at all air intake components and vacuum hoses for leakage. Check air cleaner and fuel filters for clogging. Start engine and warm to normal operating temperature.

2) Check for leaks at dipstick, anti-backfire valve, and air induction hoses (MPG only). Check intake manifold, EGR valve gaskets, valve cover, and oil filter cap. Check operation of EGR valve seat, air induction control valve (MPG only), and anti-backfire valve.

3) Check fuel lines for leaks. With engine idling, check that fuel level centers on mark on carburetor sight glass. Make sure ignition system voltage, ignition timing, idle RPM, and mixture are to specifications. *See DATSUN/NISSAN TUNE-UP SERVICE PROCEDURES article in TUNE-UP Section.*

4) Turn engine off. Disconnect ECC harness connector. Turn ignition switch "ON". Check that ECC inspection lamp (located on instrument panel) is on. If not replace bulb.

5) Start engine. Check that lamp turns off. Run engine at 2000 RPM for approximately 5 minutes. If lamp is still off, testing is complete. If lamp is on, connect ECC harness connector.

Fig. 1: Electronically Controlled Carburetor (ECC) Schematic for Federal Sentra MPG Models

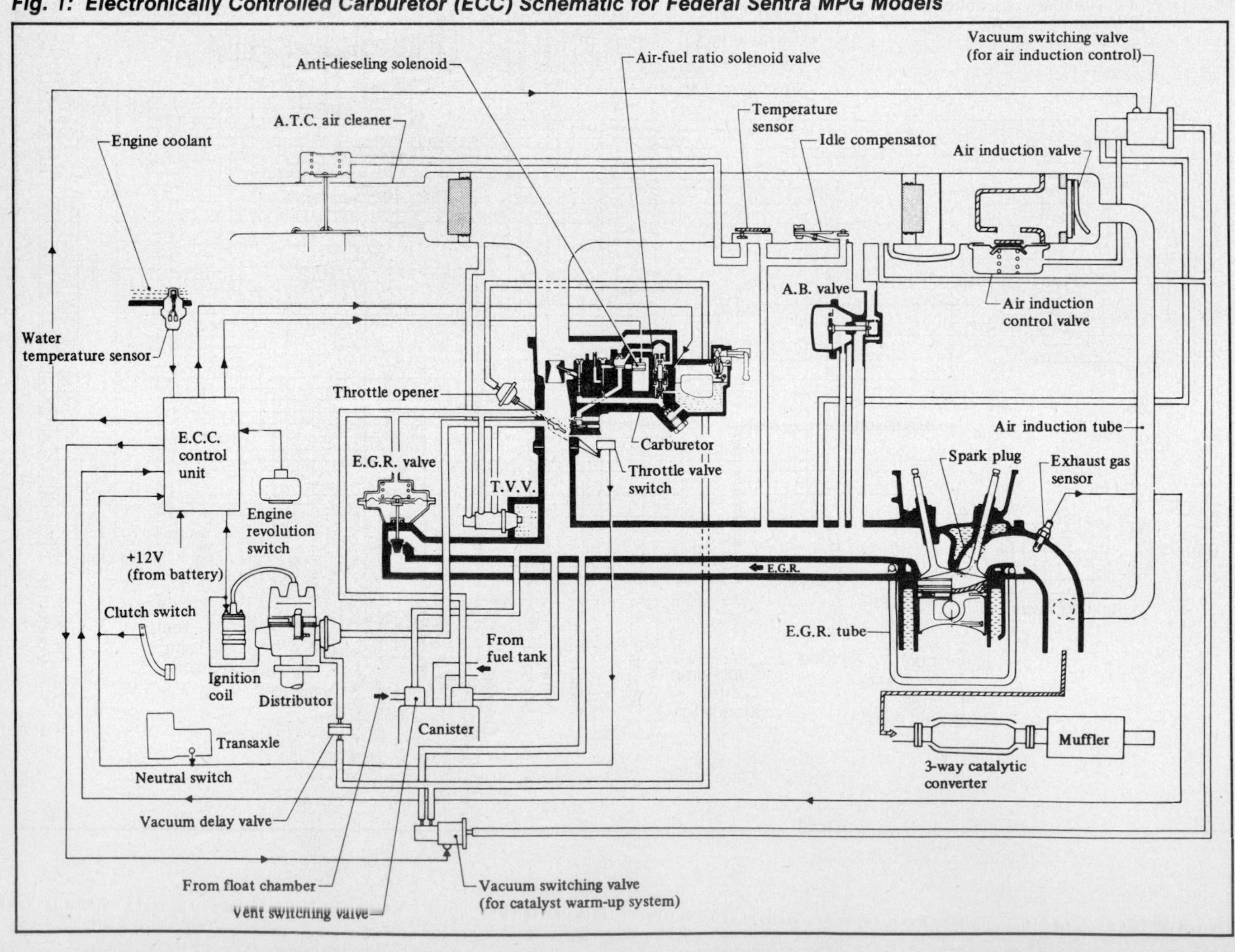
Anti-dieseling solenoid
Air-fuel ratio solenoid valve
Vacuum switching valve (for air induction control)
A.T.C. air cleaner
Temperature sensor
Idle compensator
Engine coolant
Air induction valve
A.B. valve
Air induction control valve
Water temperature sensor
Throttle opener
Air induction tube
E.C.C. control unit
Carburetor
Spark plug
Exhaust gas sensor
E.G.R. valve
T.V.V.
Throttle valve switch
Engine revolution switch
+12V (from battery)
E.G.R.
Clutch switch
E.G.R. tube
From fuel tank
Ignition coil
Distributor
Canister
Transaxle
Muffler
Neutral switch
3-way catalytic converter
Vacuum delay valve
From float chamber
Vacuum switching valve (for catalyst warm-up system)
Vent switching valve

DATSUN/NISSAN
ELECTRONICALLY CONTROLLED CARBURETOR (Cont.)

6) If lamp stays on and momentarily flashes off, turn ignition switch "OFF". Using ohmmeter, check that resistance of air/fuel ratio solenoid is 30-50 ohms and anti-dieseling solenoid, catalyst warm-up vacuum switching solenoid (MPG only), and air induction vacuum switching solenoid (MPG only) is 25-45 ohms.

7) If any solenoid is not within specification, replace it. Disconnect 10-pin connector from ECC control unit. Turn ignition switch on. Using voltmeter, check that there is 12-14 volts between terminals F and G (also I and J on MPG) and ground. If not, repair or replace harness. If okay, replace control unit.

8) If lamp stays off and momentarily flashes on, turn ignition switch "OFF". Check that each harness connector is connected securely. Disconnect ECC 20-pin connector from control unit.

9) Disconnect exhaust gas sensor harness connector. Using jumper wire, connect terminal for exhaust gas sensor to ground. Check for continuity between terminal No. 2 of ECC 20-pin connector and ground.

10) If continuity exists, replace exhaust gas sensor. If not, repair or replace ECC harness. If lamp still momentarily flashes on, remove coolant temperature sensor. Immerse sensor end and thermometer into container of water.

11) With water temperature below 68°F (20°C), check that resistance is 2100-2900 ohms. Heat water to 122°F (50°C). Check that resistance is 680-1000 ohms. If okay, repair or replace ECC harness. If not, replace coolant temperature sensor.

FUEL SHUT-OFF SYSTEM

1) Turn ignition switch "OFF". Disconnect ECC 20-pin connector. Check that there is continuity between terminal 5 and ground with clutch disengaged. If not, replace clutch switch.

2) Check that there is continuity between terminal 4 and ground with transmission in Neutral. If not, replace neutral switch.

Fig. 2: Electronically Controlled Carburetor (ECC) Schematic for California Pulsar and Sentra Models

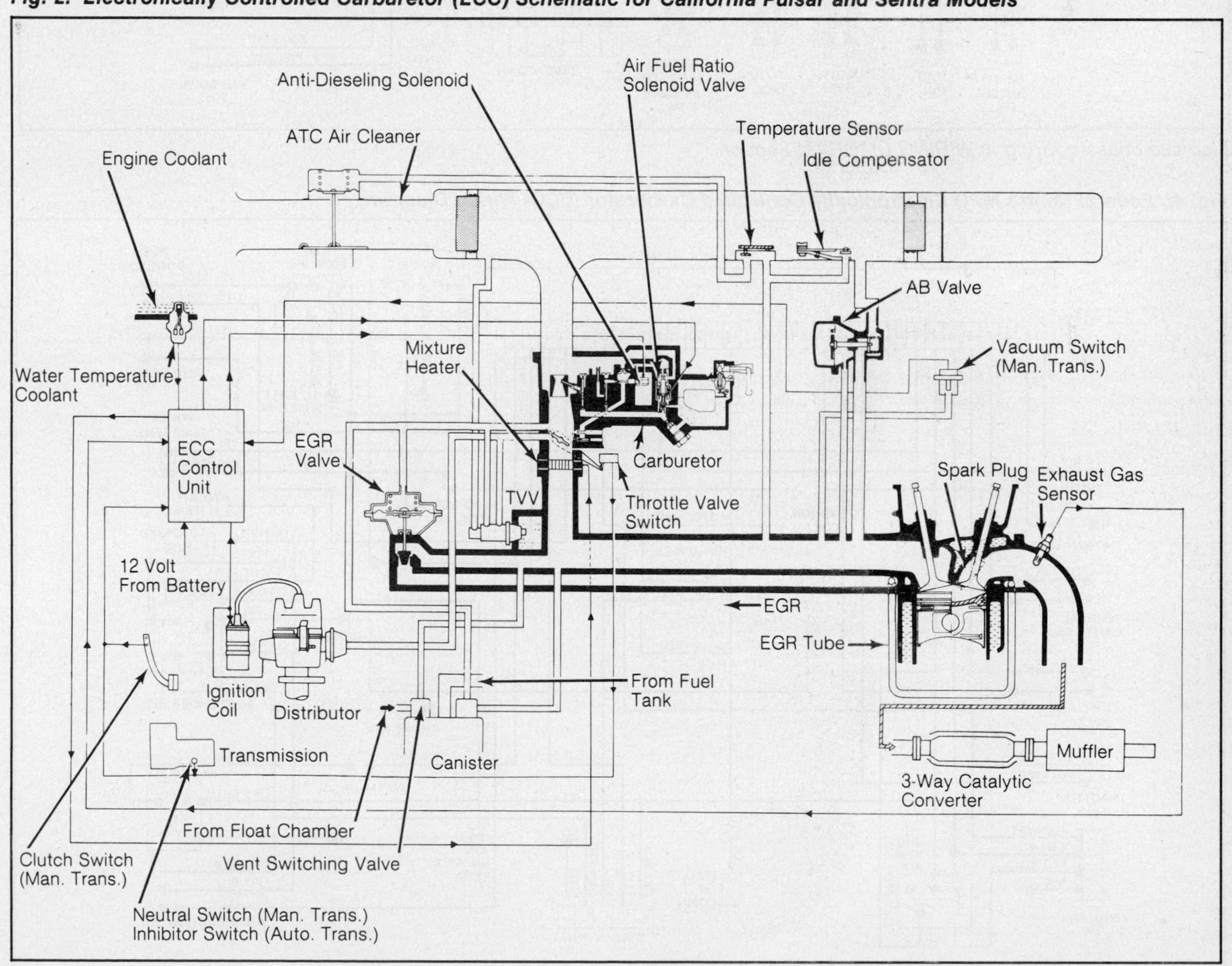

Anti-Dieseling Solenoid
Air Fuel Ratio
Solenoid Valve
ATC Air Cleaner
Temperature Sensor
Idle Compensator
Engine Coolant
AB Valve
Mixture
Heater
Vacuum Switch
(Man. Trans.)
Water Temperature
Coolant
ECC
Control
Unit
EGR
Valve
TVV
Carburetor
Throttle Valve
Switch
Spark Plug
Exhaust Gas
Sensor
12 Volt
From Battery
EGR
EGR Tube
Ignition
Coil
Distributor
From Fuel
Tank
Transmission
Canister
Muffler
3-Way Catalytic
Converter
From Float Chamber
Clutch Switch
(Man. Trans.)
Vent Switching Valve
Neutral Switch (Man. Trans.)
Inhibitor Switch (Auto. Trans.)

DATSUN/NISSAN
ELECTRONICALLY CONTROLLED CARBURETOR (Cont.)

Fig. 3: California Pulsar & Sentra Electronically Controlled Carburetor (ECC) Wiring Diagram

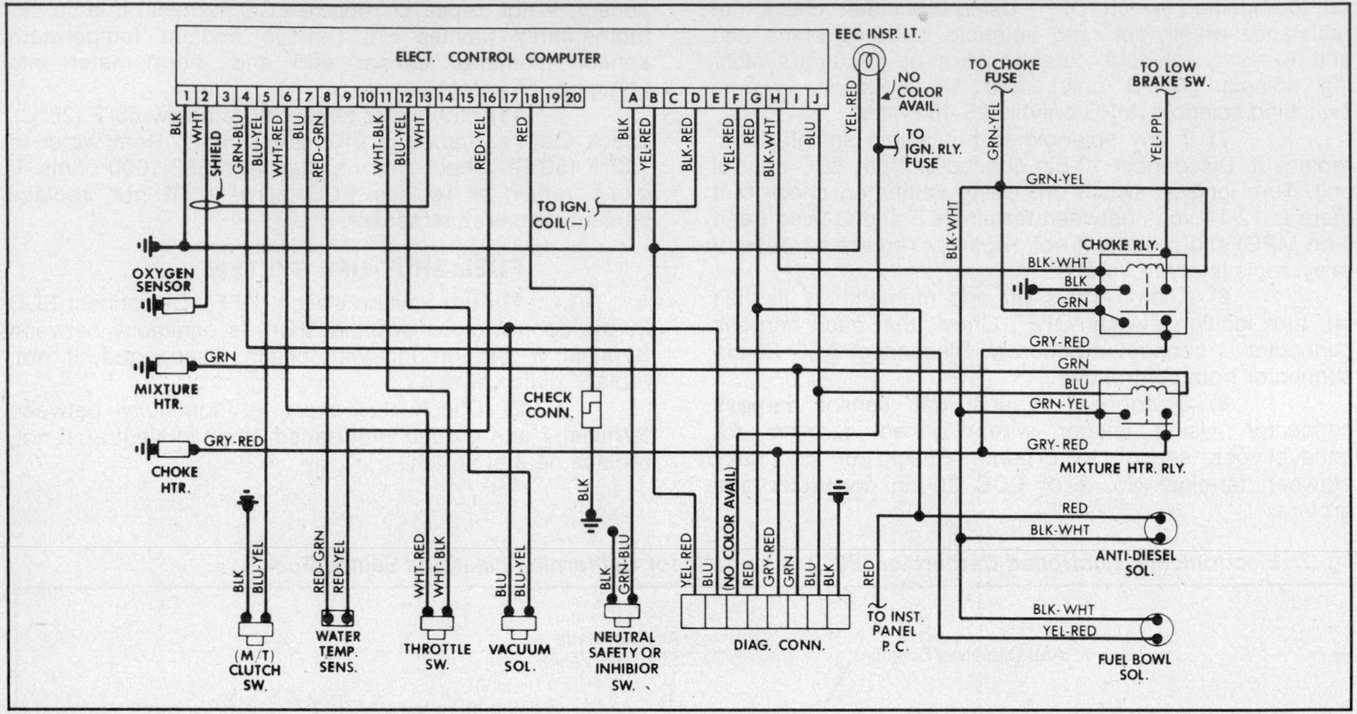

ELECT. CONTROL COMPUTER
1 2 3 4 5 6 7 8 9 10 11 12 13 14 15 16 17 18 19 20
A B C D E F G H I J
EEC INSP. LT.
NO COLOR AVAIL.
TO IGN. RLY. FUSE
TO CHOKE FUSE
TO LOW BRAKE SW.
BLK
WHT
SHIELD
GRN-BLU
BLU-YEL
WHT-RED
BLU
RED-GRN
WHT-BLK
BLU-YEL
WHT
RED-YEL
RED
YEL-RED
BLK-RED
BLK-WHT
GRN-YEL
YEL-PPL
TO IGN. COIL(−)
OXYGEN SENSOR
CHOKE RLY.
GRN
GRY-RED
MIXTURE HTR.
CHECK CONN.
CHOKE HTR.
MIXTURE HTR. RLY.
ANTI-DIESEL SOL.
(NO COLOR AVAIL)
(M/T) CLUTCH SW.
WATER TEMP. SENS.
THROTTLE SW.
VACUUM SOL.
NEUTRAL SAFETY OR INHIBIOR SW.
DIAG. CONN.
TO INST. PANEL P.C.
FUEL BOWL SOL.

Also see chassis wiring in WIRING DIAGRAM Section.

Fig. 4: Federal Sentra MPG Electronically Controlled Carburetor (ECC) Wiring Diagram

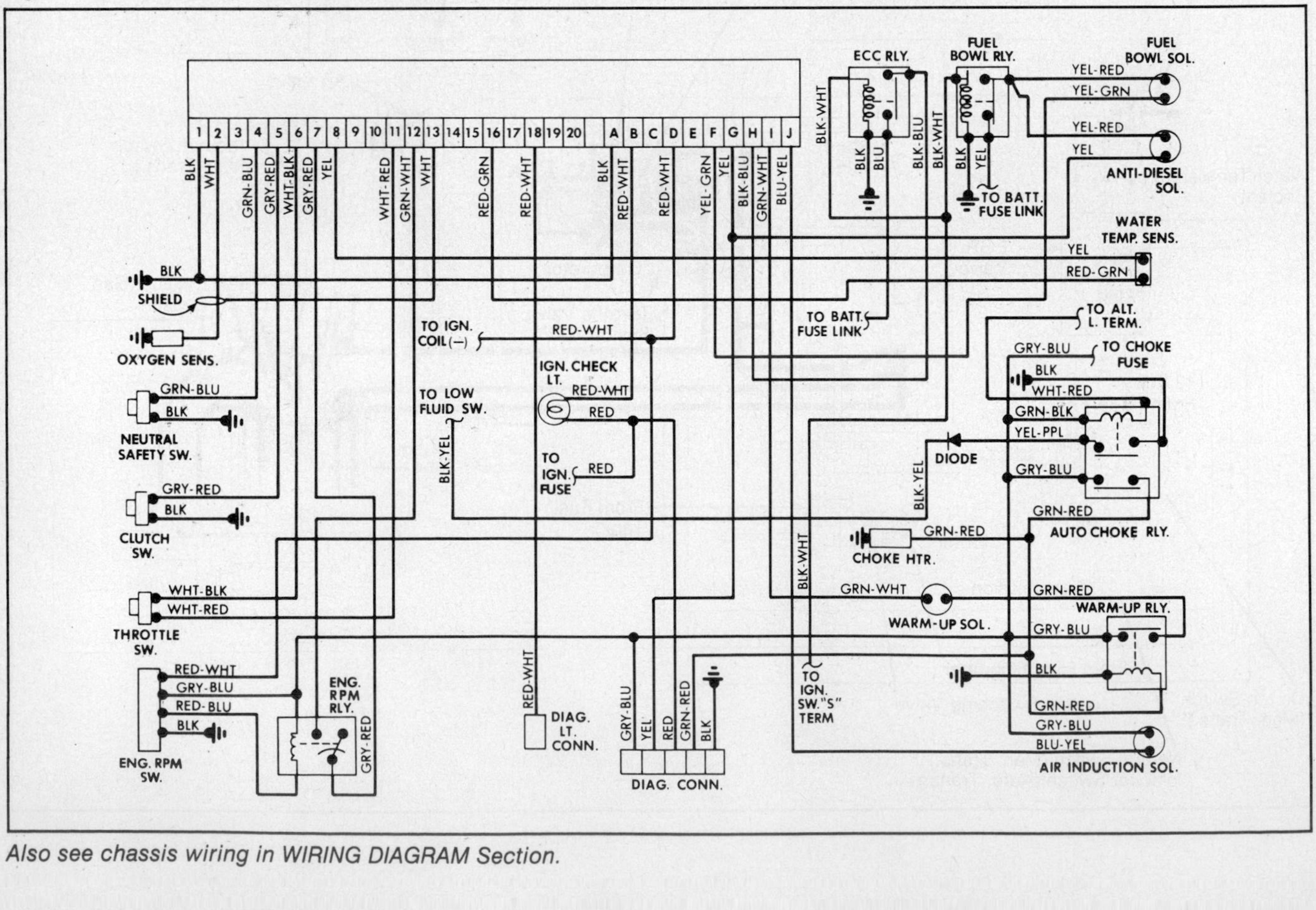

ECC RLY.
FUEL BOWL RLY.
FUEL BOWL SOL.
ANTI-DIESEL SOL.
WATER TEMP. SENS.
TO BATT. FUSE LINK
TO ALT. L. TERM.
TO CHOKE FUSE
SHIELD
OXYGEN SENS.
TO IGN. COIL(−)
IGN. CHECK LT.
TO LOW FLUID SW.
TO IGN. FUSE
NEUTRAL SAFETY SW.
CLUTCH SW.
THROTTLE SW.
ENG. RPM RLY.
ENG. RPM SW.
DIAG. LT. CONN.
DIAG. CONN.
DIODE
AUTO CHOKE RLY.
CHOKE HTR.
WARM-UP SOL.
WARM-UP RLY.
TO IGN. SW. "S" TERM
AIR INDUCTION SOL.

Also see chassis wiring in WIRING DIAGRAM Section.

ISUZU CLOSED LOOP EMISSION SYSTEM

Isuzu I-Mark, P'UP

DESCRIPTION

The Closed Loop Emission control system is an electronically controlled system that is used on California I-Mark and P'UP engines. It monitors various engine/vehicle functions to control engine operation and lower exhaust emissions while maintaining good fuel economy and driveability.

The Electronic Control Module (ECM) is the brain of the system. The ECM controls the engine-related systems to constantly adjust engine operation to maintain good vehicle performance under all normal driving conditions. The system consists of the ECM, various engine sensors, a feedback carburetor and a catalytic converter.

Fig. 1: Isuzu Closed Loop Emission Control System

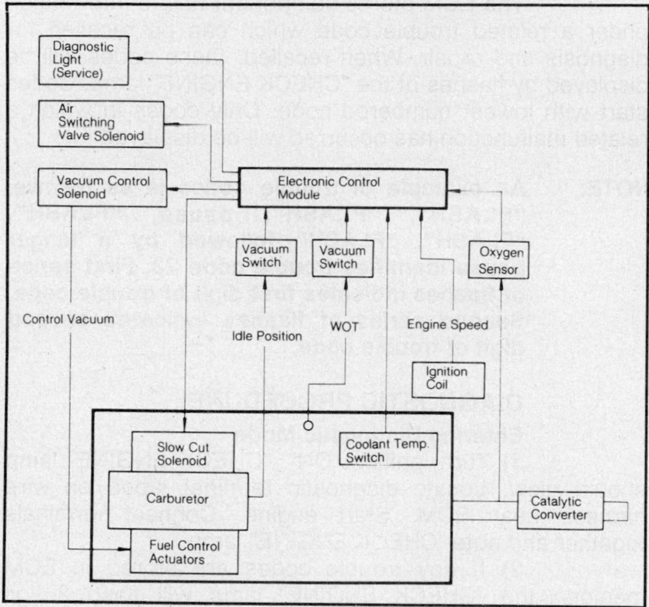

Diagnostic Light (Service)
Air Switching Valve Solenoid
Vacuum Control Solenoid
Electronic Control Module
Vacuum Switch
Vacuum Switch
Oxygen Sensor
Control Vacuum
Idle Position
WOT
Engine Speed
Ignition Coil
Slow Cut Solenoid
Carburetor
Fuel Control Actuators
Coolant Temp. Switch
Catalytic Converter

OPERATION

The primary objective of the system is to maintain an ideal air/fuel ratio of 14.7:1 under all operating conditions. When an ideal ratio is maintained, the catalytic converter can effectively control engine pollutants.

FUEL CONTROLS

The engine is equipped with a feedback carburetor which contains vacuum-operated fuel control actuators. The ECM, responding to inputs from the data sensors, constantly adjusts the air/fuel ratio to maintain engine performance. The ECM sends electrical signals to a vacuum control valve. The vacuum control valve converts the ECM signals to vacuum signals to operate the actuators.

The vacuum control valve consists of a vacuum regulator and a vacuum control solenoid. The regulator changes the inconsistent vacuum levels from the intake manifold into constant vacuum levels. The solenoid, controlled by the ECM, uses the vacuum from the regulator to operate the fuel control actuators.

When the ECM responds to signals received from oxygen sensor, the system is in closed loop operation. Under certain operating conditions, the ECM may ignore inputs from various data sensors and use a pre-programmed calibration control to operate the engine under that particular condition.

During cold engine starts, the vacuum control solenoid is turned off by the ECM to provide a rich mixture. Operating conditions which cause the ECM to ignore oxygen sensor signals cause the system to operate in the open loop mode.

OXYGEN SENSOR

This sensor is mounted in the exhaust manifold. It supplies a low voltage when fuel mixture is lean (too much oxygen) and a higher voltage when fuel mixture is rich (not enough oxygen). Oxygen sensor must be hot to function properly. The oxygen sensor measures quantity of oxygen only.

NOTE: **No attempt should be made to measure oxygen sensor voltage output. Current drain of voltmeter could permanently damage sensor, shift sensor calibration range and/or render sensor unusable. Do not connect jumper wire, test leads or other electrical connectors to sensor. Use these devices only on ECM side of harness after disconnecting from sensor.**

COOLANT TEMPERATURE SENSOR

The CTS is located in the engine coolant stream to supply coolant temperature information to ECM. This information is used by ECM to determine when system is ready to go into closed loop and to determine operation of the secondary air injection system.

IDLE POSITION SWITCH

This switch is a vacuum controlled switch mounted on a bracket on right side of engine compartment. This switch senses intake manifold vacuum and sends an electrical signal to ECM in relation to amount of manifold vacuum. The ECM uses this information to distinguish between closed throttle (idle) and open throttle positions.

WIDE OPEN THROTTLE SWITCH

This switch is mounted on the same bracket in the engine compartment as the idle position switch. This switch senses intake manifold vacuum and sends an electrical signal to the ECM when engine is at wide open throttle. This information is used by the ECM to distinguish between closed throttle (idle) and wide open throttle positions.

ELECTRONIC CONTROL MODULE

The ECM controls all functions of the closed loop system. The ECM sends an electrical signal to the vacuum control solenoid which controls the air/fuel mixture by vacuum signals. This control signal is constantly cycling the solenoid between "ON" and "OFF" time (duty cycle) as a function of the input voltages from the data sensors.

The control signal generated by the ECM is selected from 4 operational modes. These modes include: Inhibit Mode, Enrichment Mode, Open Loop Mode and Closed Loop Mode. A brief description of each mode is as follows:

ISUZU CLOSED LOOP EMISSION SYSTEM (Cont.)

Inhibit Mode

No electrical signals are sent to the vacuum control solenoid by the ECM in this mode.

Enrichment Mode

In this mode a fixed, pre-programmed duty cycle electrical signal is sent to the vacuum control solenoid by the ECM. This signal is sent to the solenoid when fuel enrichment is necessary for cold engine starts or sudden acceleration.

Open Loop Mode

In this mode the ECM sends electrical signals to the vacuum control solenoid based on information stored within the ECM. This information has been calculated and used by the ECM to operate the engine at optimum efficiency for that particular operating condition of the engine, without any input from the sensors. Open loop mode is used when the engine has not reached operating temperature.

Closed Loop Mode

In this mode the ECM sends an electrical signal to the vacuum control solenoid based on input from the oxygen sensor and other data sensors. In closed loop, the air/fuel mixture is controlled directly by the ECM in response to oxygen sensor signals.

During any operational mode, the ECM maintains the current duty cycle being used within its memory; for either idle or off-idle operation. When the ECM receives a change in idle position, as signaled by the Idle Position Switch or Wide Open Throttle Switch, the ECM retrieves data from its memory to operate the engine at the duty cycle last recorded for optimum operation.

After the initial change in idle position, the ECM then controls the system in one of the four operational modes. The ECM also controls the operation of the slow cut solenoid valve incorporated in the carburetor. When the ECM senses a coasting condition it opens the circuit to the slow cut solenoid valve (engine speed above a predetermined value).

The circuit to the slow cut solenoid valve is cut off only when the vacuum signal of the vacuum switch is below specified vacuum and the engine speed exceeds a predetermined speed.

DIAGNOSTIC SYSTEM

The ECM of the Closed Loop Emission Control system is equipped with a self-diagnostic system which detects system failures or abnormalities. When a malfunction occurs, the ECM will light the amber "CHECK ENGINE" lamp located on the instrument panel. When a malfunction is detected and lamp is turned on, a corresponding trouble code is stored in ECM memory.

As a bulb and system check, the "CHECK ENGINE" lamp will glow when ignition switch is on and engine is not running. When engine is started, the lamp should go out after 1-4 seconds. If not, a malfunction has been detected in the Closed Loop Emission system.

NOTE: **Trouble codes will be recorded at various operating times. Some codes require operation of sensor or switch for 5 seconds; others require operation for 5 minutes or more.**

DIAGNOSIS & TESTING

Diagnosis of the Closed Loop Emission system is done in the following order:

1) Ensure all engine systems NOT related to the system are fully operational. Do not proceed with testing unless all other problems have been corrected. Ensure that all electrical and vacuum connections are correct and in good condition.

2) Enter diagnostic mode and record trouble codes flashed by "CHECK ENGINE" lamp. Exit diagnostic mode.

3) Distinguish between fixed or intermittent trouble codes.

4) If trouble codes were displayed, go to Diagnostic Circuit Check chart. Follow instructions given in chart.

5) If no trouble codes were recorded, go to Driver Complaint chart and follow instructions given there.

6) After any repairs are made, perform System Performance Check. Clear any trouble codes.

The ECM stores component failure information under a related trouble code which can be recalled for diagnosis and repair. When recalled, these codes will be displayed by flashes of the "CHECK ENGINE" lamp. Codes start with lowest numbered code. Only codes in which a related malfunction has occurred will be displayed.

NOTE: **An example of trouble codes is as follows: "FLASH", "FLASH", pause, "FLASH", "FLASH", "FLASH" followed by a longer pause identifies trouble code 23. First series of flashes indicates first digit of trouble code. Second series of flashes indicates second digit of trouble code.**

DIAGNOSTIC PROCEDURE

Entering Diagnostic Mode

1) Turn ignition "ON". "CHECK ENGINE" lamp should glow. Locate diagnostic terminal taped on wire harness near ECM. Start engine. Connect terminals together and note "CHECK ENGINE" lamp.

2) If any trouble codes are stored in ECM memory, the "CHECK ENGINE" lamp will flash 2-digit codes. Trouble codes will be displayed from lowest to highest numbered code (3 times each) and be repeated as long as the diagnostic terminals are connected.

I-MARK ECM TROUBLE CODE IDENTIFICATION

Code	Circuit Affected
12	Idle Position Switch - High Output
13	Idle Position Switch - Low Output
14	Wide Open Throttle Switch - High Output
15	Wide Open Throttle Switch - Low Output
21	Vacuum Control Solenoid - High Output
22	Vacuum Control Solenoid - Low Output
23	Incorrect Oxygen Sensor Reading
24	Incorrect Coolant Temperature Switch Reading
25	RAM Error

ISUZU CLOSED LOOP EMISSION SYSTEM (Cont.)

P'UP ECM TROUBLE CODE IDENTIFICATION

Code	Problem
12	No Ignition Reference Pulse to ECM
13	Oxygen Sensor Circuit
14	Shorted Coolant Sensor Circuit
15	Open Coolant Sensor Circuit
21	Idle Switch Circuit Open or WOT Switch Circuit Shorted
22	Fuel Cut Solenoid Circuit Open or Grounded
23	Vacuum Control Solenoid Circuit Open or Grounded
25	Air Switching Solenoid Circuit Open or Grounded
31	No Ignition Reference Pulse to ECM
44	Lean Oxygen Sensor Indication
45	Rich System Indication
51	Shorted Fuel Cut Solenoid Circuit and/or Faulty ECM
52	Faulty ECM (RAM Problem in ECM)
53	Shorted Air Switching Solenoid and/or Faulty ECM
54	Shorted Vacuum Control Solenoid and/or Faulty ECM
55	Faulty ECM (A/D Converter in ECM)

Clearing Trouble Codes

To clear memory of trouble codes, turn ignition "ON" and connect diagnostic terminals together. Turn ignition "OFF" and remove positive battery cable from battery. Disconnect diagnostic terminals.

Exiting Diagnostic Mode

To exit diagnostic mode, turn engine off and disconnect diagnostic terminals.

NOTE: The term "Enter Diagnostics" and "Exit Diagnostics" will be used periodically throughout this section. Follow the procedure for entering diagnostic mode when instructed to "Enter Diagnostics". Follow the procedure for exiting diagnostic mode when instructed to "Exit Diagnostics".

Diagnostic Circuit Check

If complaint is "CHECK ENGINE" lamp related, this check will lead to most likely problem area, if malfunction exists. Enter diagnostics and record stored trouble codes. Begin diagnosis with lowest numbered code which is displayed and refer to appropriate trouble code chart.

Driver Complaint Sheet

1) If complaint is not "CHECK ENGINE" lamp related, this check will lead to most likely problem area. However, first make checks that would normally be made for the complaint on vehicle without Closed Loop Emission Control system.

2) Follow instructions in diagnostic chart and repair malfunction. After repair, perform System Performance Check.

System Performance Check

1) This check verifies that system is functioning properly. This check should always be made after any repair on the system.

2) When performing this check, always engage parking brake and block drive wheels. Transmission should be in Neutral (man. trans.) or "P" (auto. trans.).

Diagnostic Tools

1) The Closed Loop Emission Control system does not require special tools for diagnosis. A dwell meter, tachometer, test light, ohmmeter, digital voltmeter with 10 megohms impedance (minimum), vacuum pump, vacuum gauge and jumper wires are the only tools necessary for diagnosis.

2) A test light, rather than a voltmeter, must be used where indicated in diagnostic chart. A dwell meter is used to measure the time that the vacuum control solenoid is on or off. This gives an indication of how the system is working and how rich or lean the mixture. The dwell meter is set for 4-cyl. scale.

3) Dwell meter is connected to Green connector located near carburetor. This connector will not be connected to any circuit EXCEPT when testing with the dwell meter. Do not allow terminal wire to come in contact with any ground source, including rubber hoses.

NOTE: If engine operation seems to change when dwell meter is connected to Green wire, remove dwell meter and use another type. A few brands are not compatible with the electronic emission system.

4) When engine is at operating temperature and idling, dwell meter needle will move up and down the scale. This indicates the system is in closed loop operation. If the needle does not move, the system is in open loop operation.

Fig. 2: I-Mark Electronic Control Module Terminal Identification

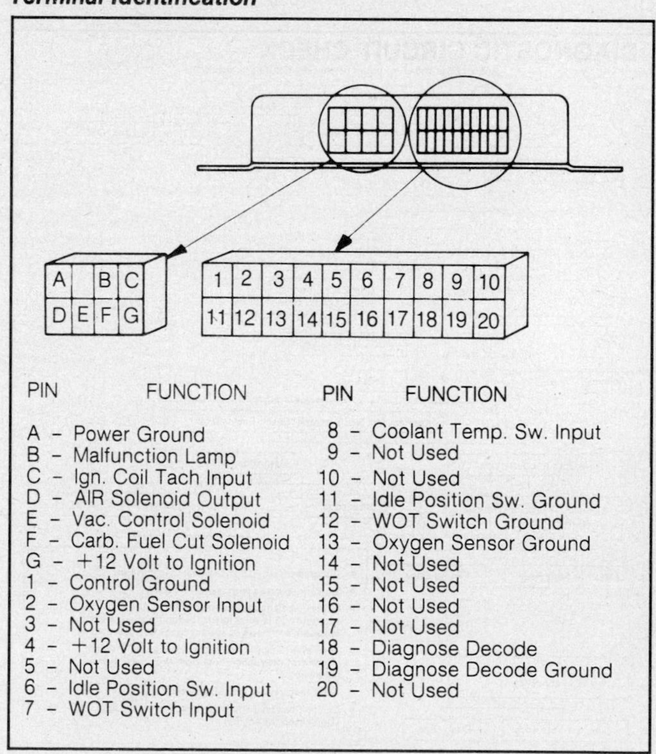

A B C
D E F G
1 2 3 4 5 6 7 8 9 10
11 12 13 14 15 16 17 18 19 20

PIN	FUNCTION	PIN	FUNCTION
A	Power Ground	8	Coolant Temp. Sw. Input
B	Malfunction Lamp	9	Not Used
C	Ign. Coil Tach Input	10	Not Used
D	AIR Solenoid Output	11	Idle Position Sw. Ground
E	Vac. Control Solenoid	12	WOT Switch Ground
F	Carb. Fuel Cut Solenoid	13	Oxygen Sensor Ground
G	+12 Volt to Ignition	14	Not Used
1	Control Ground	15	Not Used
2	Oxygen Sensor Input	16	Not Used
3	Not Used	17	Not Used
4	+12 Volt to Ignition	18	Diagnose Decode
5	Not Used	19	Diagnose Decode Ground
6	Idle Position Sw. Input	20	Not Used
7	WOT Switch Input		

ISUZU CLOSED LOOP EMISSION SYSTEM (Cont.)

1983 I-MARK TEST CHARTS

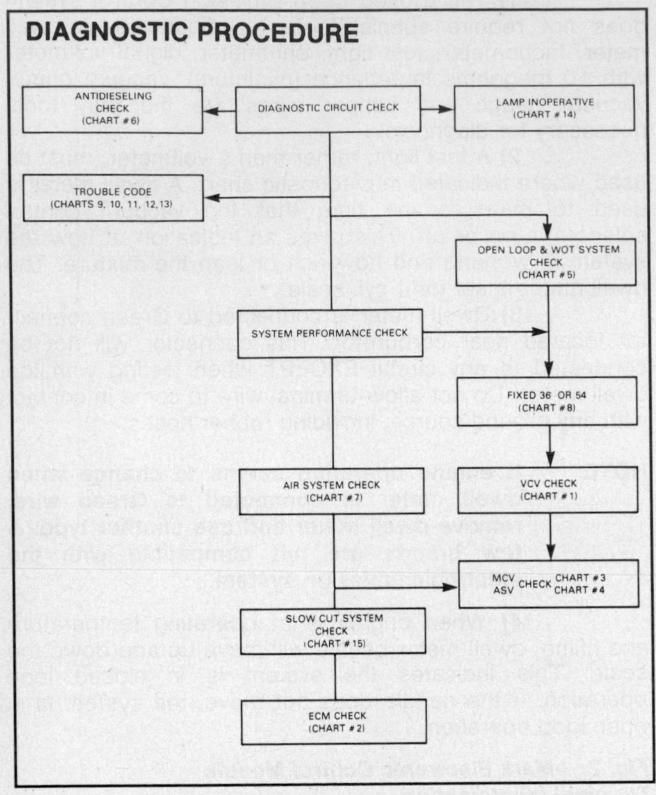
DIAGNOSTIC PROCEDURE
ANTIDIESELING CHECK (CHART #6)
DIAGNOSTIC CIRCUIT CHECK
LAMP INOPERATIVE (CHART #14)
TROUBLE CODE (CHARTS 9, 10, 11, 12,13)
OPEN LOOP & WOT SYSTEM CHECK (CHART #5)
SYSTEM PERFORMANCE CHECK
FIXED 36 OR 54 (CHART #8)
AIR SYSTEM CHECK (CHART #7)
VCV CHECK (CHART #1)
MCV ASV CHECK CHART #3 CHART #4
SLOW CUT SYSTEM CHECK (CHART #15)
ECM CHECK (CHART #2)

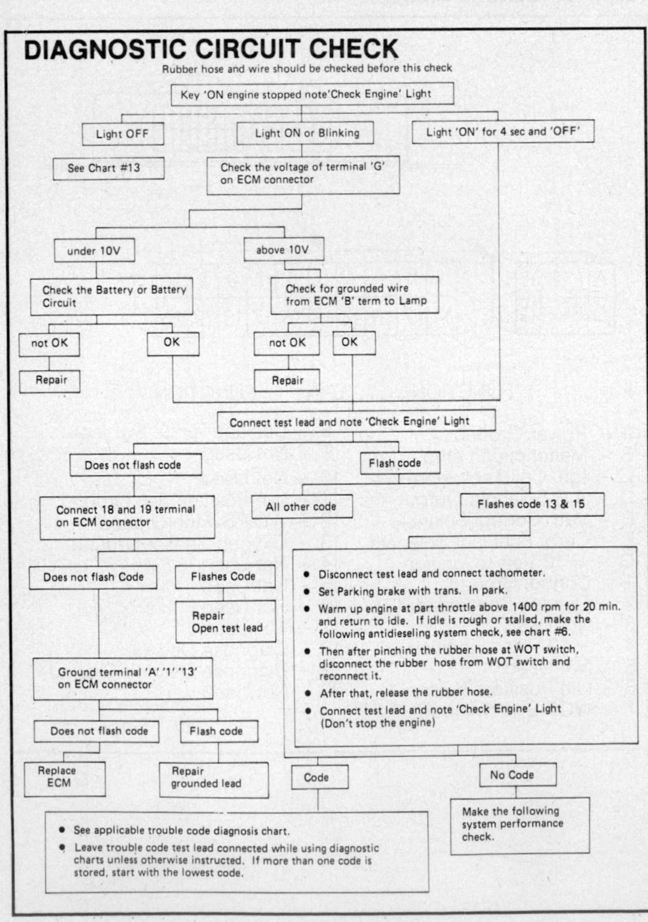
DIAGNOSTIC CIRCUIT CHECK
Rubber hose and wire should be checked before this check
Key 'ON engine stopped note 'Check Engine' Light
Light OFF
Light ON or Blinking
Light 'ON' for 4 sec and 'OFF'
See Chart #13
Check the voltage of terminal 'G' on ECM connector
under 10V
above 10V
Check the Battery or Battery Circuit
Check for grounded wire from ECM 'B' term to Lamp
not OK
OK
not OK
OK
Repair
Repair
Connect test lead and note 'Check Engine' Light
Does not flash code
Flash code
Connect 18 and 19 terminal on ECM connector
All other code
Flashes code 13 & 15
Does not flash Code
Flashes Code
Repair Open test lead
Disconnect test lead and connect tachometer.
Set Parking brake with trans. In park.
Warm up engine at part throttle above 1400 rpm for 20 min. and return to idle. If idle is rough or stalled, make the following antidieseling system check, see chart #6.
Then after pinching the rubber hose at WOT switch, disconnect the rubber hose from WOT switch and reconnect it.
After that, release the rubber hose.
Connect test lead and note 'Check Engine' Light (Don't stop the engine)
Ground terminal 'A' '1' '13' on ECM connector
Does not flash code
Flash code
Replace ECM
Repair grounded lead
Code
No Code
Make the following system performance check.
See applicable trouble code diagnosis chart.
Leave trouble code test lead connected while using diagnostic charts unless otherwise instructed. If more than one code is stored, start with the lowest code.

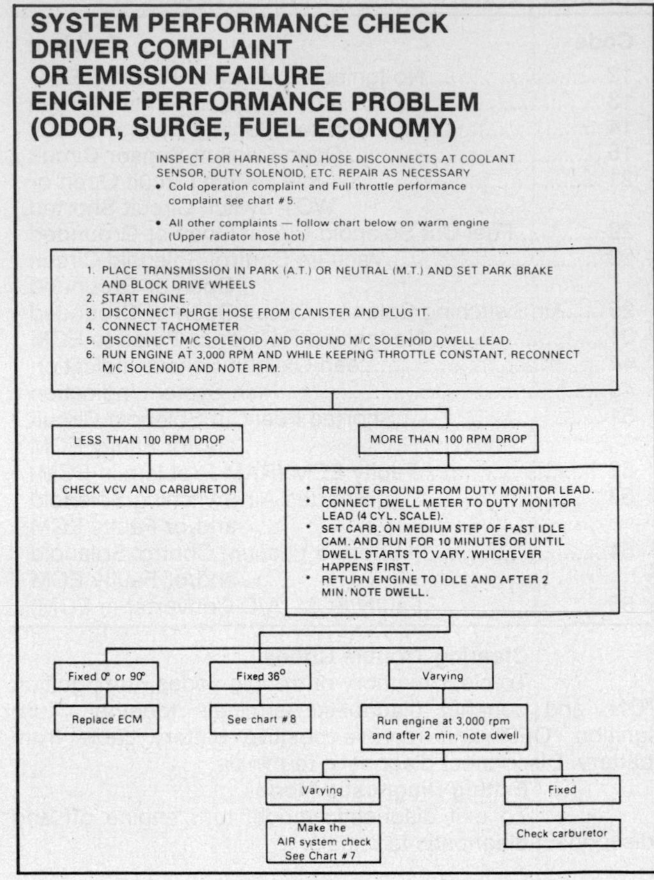
SYSTEM PERFORMANCE CHECK
DRIVER COMPLAINT
OR EMISSION FAILURE
ENGINE PERFORMANCE PROBLEM
(ODOR, SURGE, FUEL ECONOMY)
INSPECT FOR HARNESS AND HOSE DISCONNECTS AT COOLANT SENSOR, DUTY SOLENOID, ETC. REPAIR AS NECESSARY
Cold operation complaint and Full throttle performance complaint see chart #5.
All other complaints — follow chart below on warm engine (Upper radiator hose hot)
1. PLACE TRANSMISSION IN PARK (A.T.) OR NEUTRAL (M.T.) AND SET PARK BRAKE AND BLOCK DRIVE WHEELS
2. START ENGINE.
3. DISCONNECT PURGE HOSE FROM CANISTER AND PLUG IT.
4. CONNECT TACHOMETER
5. DISCONNECT M/C SOLENOID AND GROUND M/C SOLENOID DWELL LEAD.
6. RUN ENGINE AT 3,000 RPM AND WHILE KEEPING THROTTLE CONSTANT, RECONNECT M/C SOLENOID AND NOTE RPM.
LESS THAN 100 RPM DROP
MORE THAN 100 RPM DROP
CHECK VCV AND CARBURETOR
REMOTE GROUND FROM DUTY MONITOR LEAD.
CONNECT DWELL METER TO DUTY MONITOR LEAD (4 CYL. SCALE).
SET CARB. ON MEDIUM STEP OF FAST IDLE CAM. AND RUN FOR 10 MINUTES OR UNTIL DWELL STARTS TO VARY, WHICHEVER HAPPENS FIRST.
RETURN ENGINE TO IDLE AND AFTER 2 MIN. NOTE DWELL.
Fixed 0° or 90°
Fixed 36°
Varying
Replace ECM
See chart #8
Run engine at 3,000 rpm and after 2 min, note dwell
Varying
Fixed
Make the AIR system check See Chart #7
Check carburetor

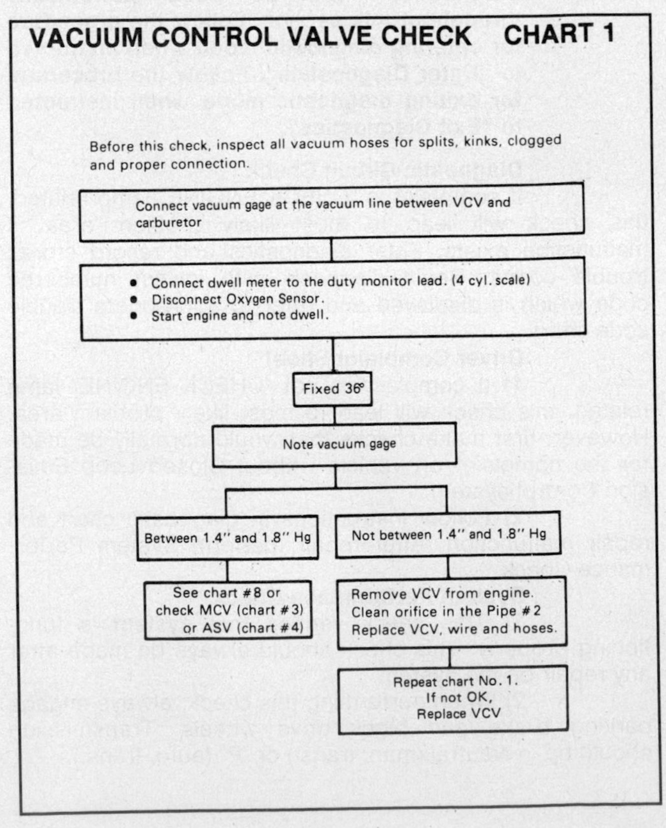
VACUUM CONTROL VALVE CHECK CHART 1
Before this check, inspect all vacuum hoses for splits, kinks, clogged and proper connection.
Connect vacuum gage at the vacuum line between VCV and carburetor
Connect dwell meter to the duty monitor lead. (4 cyl. scale)
Disconnect Oxygen Sensor.
Start engine and note dwell.
Fixed 36°
Note vacuum gage
Between 1.4" and 1.8" Hg
Not between 1.4" and 1.8" Hg
See chart #8 or check MCV (chart #3) or ASV (chart #4)
Remove VCV from engine. Clean orifice in the Pipe #2 Replace VCV, wire and hoses.
Repeat chart No. 1. If not OK, Replace VCV

ISUZU CLOSED LOOP EMISSION SYSTEM (Cont.)

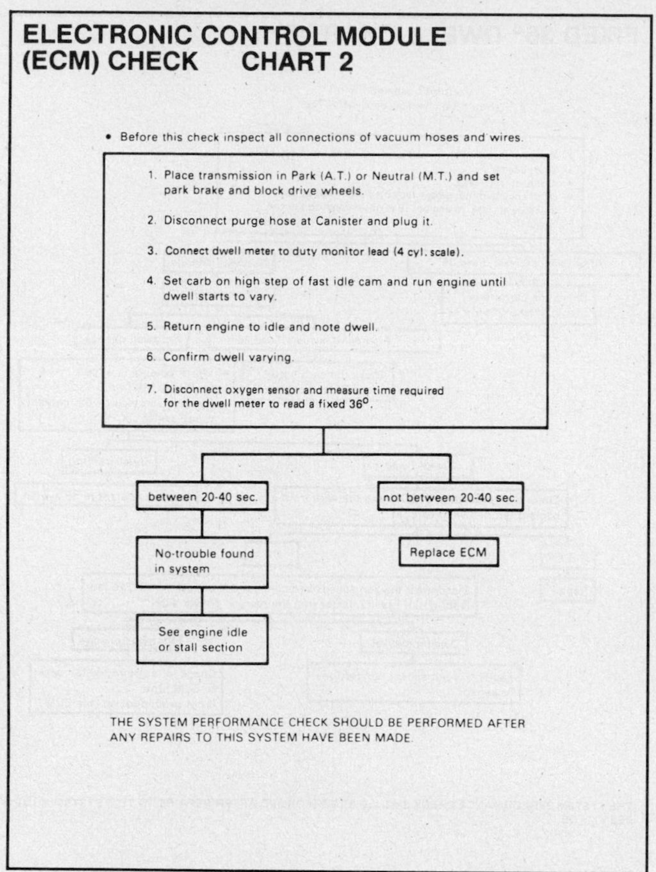
ELECTRONIC CONTROL MODULE (ECM) CHECK CHART 2
• Before this check inspect all connections of vacuum hoses and wires.
1. Place transmission in Park (A.T.) or Neutral (M.T.) and set park brake and block drive wheels.
2. Disconnect purge hose at Canister and plug it.
3. Connect dwell meter to duty monitor lead (4 cyl. scale).
4. Set carb on high step of fast idle cam and run engine until dwell starts to vary.
5. Return engine to idle and note dwell.
6. Confirm dwell varying.
7. Disconnect oxygen sensor and measure time required for the dwell meter to read a fixed 36°.
between 20-40 sec.
not between 20-40 sec.
No-trouble found in system
Replace ECM
See engine idle or stall section
THE SYSTEM PERFORMANCE CHECK SHOULD BE PERFORMED AFTER ANY REPAIRS TO THIS SYSTEM HAVE BEEN MADE.

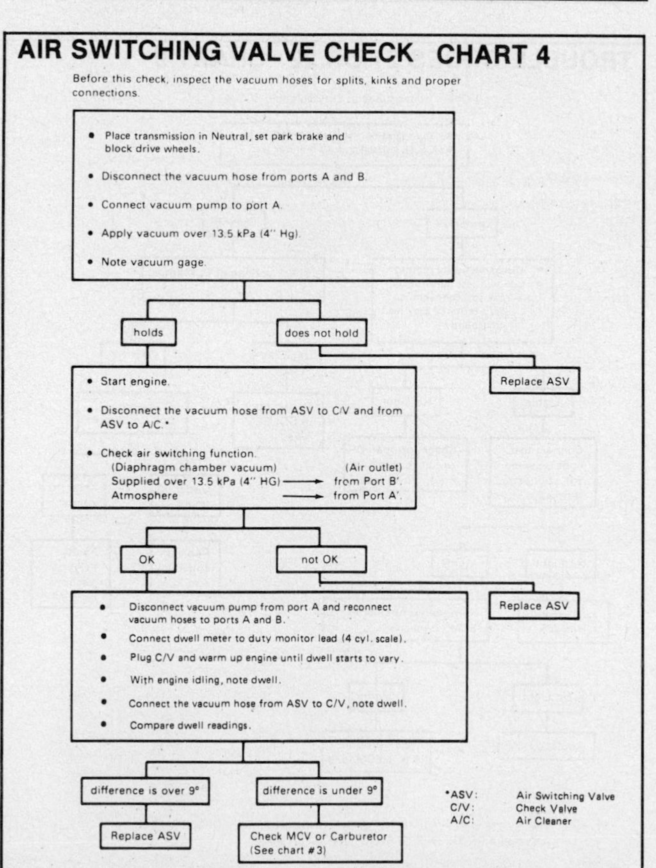
AIR SWITCHING VALVE CHECK CHART 4
Before this check, inspect the vacuum hoses for splits, kinks and proper connections.
• Place transmission in Neutral, set park brake and block drive wheels.
• Disconnect the vacuum hose from ports A and B.
• Connect vacuum pump to port A.
• Apply vacuum over 13.5 kPa (4" Hg).
• Note vacuum gage.
holds
does not hold
Replace ASV
• Start engine.
• Disconnect the vacuum hose from ASV to C/V and from ASV to A/C.*
• Check air switching function.
(Diaphragm chamber vacuum) (Air outlet)
Supplied over 13.5 kPa (4" HG) → from Port B'
Atmosphere → from Port A'
OK
not OK
Replace ASV
• Disconnect vacuum pump from port A and reconnect vacuum hoses to ports A and B.
• Connect dwell meter to duty monitor lead (4 cyl. scale).
• Plug C/V and warm up engine until dwell starts to vary.
• With engine idling, note dwell.
• Connect the vacuum hose from ASV to C/V, note dwell.
• Compare dwell readings.
difference is over 9°
difference is under 9°
Replace ASV
Check MCV or Carburetor (See chart #3)
*ASV: Air Switching Valve
C/V: Check Valve
A/C: Air Cleaner

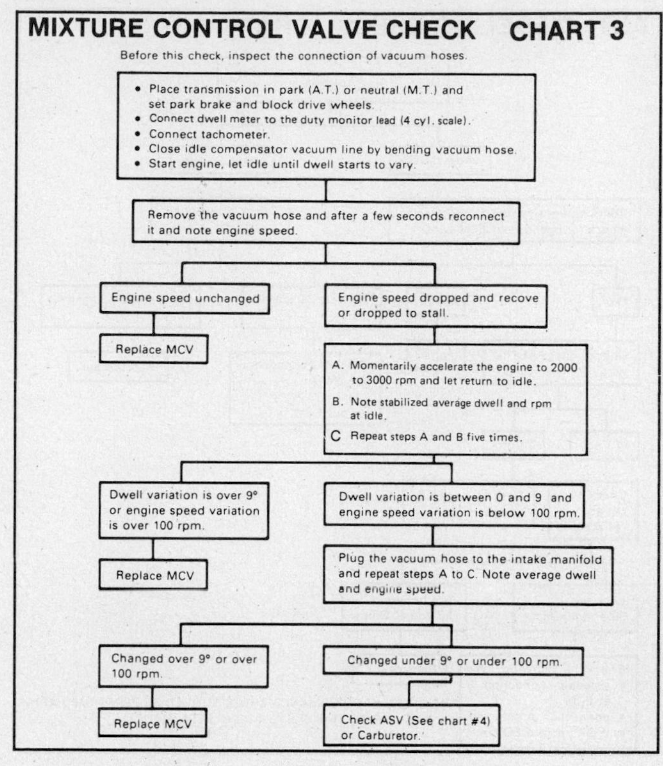
MIXTURE CONTROL VALVE CHECK CHART 3
Before this check, inspect the connection of vacuum hoses.
• Place transmission in park (A.T.) or neutral (M.T.) and set park brake and block drive wheels.
• Connect dwell meter to the duty monitor lead (4 cyl. scale).
• Connect tachometer.
• Close idle compensator vacuum line by bending vacuum hose.
• Start engine, let idle until dwell starts to vary.
Remove the vacuum hose and after a few seconds reconnect it and note engine speed.
Engine speed unchanged
Engine speed dropped and recove or dropped to stall.
Replace MCV
A. Momentarily accelerate the engine to 2000 to 3000 rpm and let return to idle.
B. Note stabilized average dwell and rpm at idle.
C Repeat steps A and B five times.
Dwell variation is over 9° or engine speed variation is over 100 rpm.
Dwell variation is between 0 and 9 and engine speed variation is below 100 rpm.
Replace MCV
Plug the vacuum hose to the intake manifold and repeat steps A to C. Note average dwell and engine speed.
Changed over 9° or over 100 rpm.
Changed under 9° or under 100 rpm.
Replace MCV
Check ASV (See chart #4) or Carburetor.

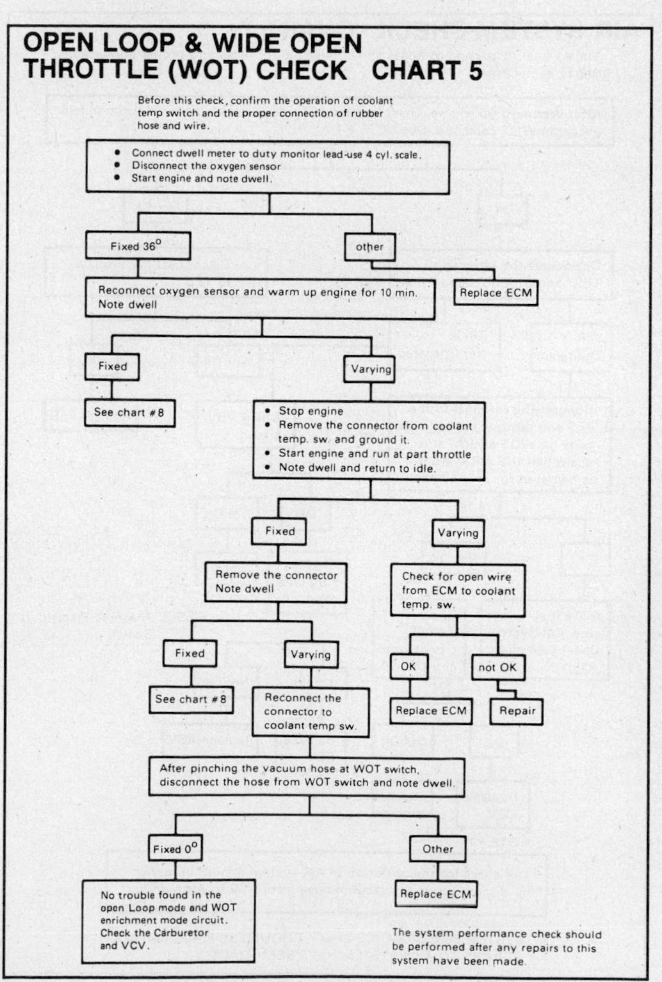
OPEN LOOP & WIDE OPEN THROTTLE (WOT) CHECK CHART 5
Before this check, confirm the operation of coolant temp switch and the proper connection of rubber hose and wire.
• Connect dwell meter to duty monitor lead-use 4 cyl. scale.
• Disconnect the oxygen sensor
• Start engine and note dwell.
Fixed 36°
other
Replace ECM
Reconnect oxygen sensor and warm up engine for 10 min. Note dwell
Fixed
Varying
See chart #8
• Stop engine
• Remove the connector from coolant temp. sw. and ground it.
• Start engine and run at part throttle
• Note dwell and return to idle.
Fixed
Varying
Remove the connector Note dwell
Check for open wire from ECM to coolant temp. sw.
Fixed
Varying
OK
not OK
See chart #8
Reconnect the connector to coolant temp sw.
Replace ECM
Repair
After pinching the vacuum hose at WOT switch, disconnect the hose from WOT switch and note dwell.
Fixed 0°
Other
No trouble found in the open Loop mode and WOT enrichment mode circuit. Check the Carburetor and VCV.
Replace ECM
The system performance check should be performed after any repairs to this system have been made.

Computerized Engine Controls

ISUZU CLOSED LOOP EMISSION SYSTEM (Cont.)

ANTI-DIESELING CHECK CHART 6

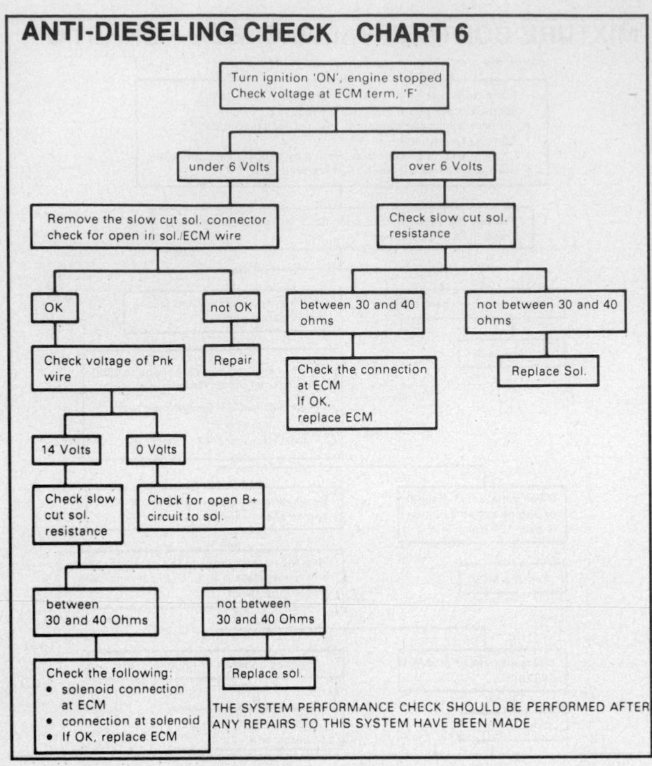

Turn ignition 'ON', engine stopped Check voltage at ECM term. 'F'
under 6 Volts
over 6 Volts
Remove the slow cut sol. connector check for open in sol./ECM wire
Check slow cut sol. resistance
OK
not OK
between 30 and 40 ohms
not between 30 and 40 ohms
Check voltage of Pnk wire
Repair
Check the connection at ECM If OK, replace ECM
Replace Sol.
14 Volts
0 Volts
Check slow cut sol. resistance
Check for open B+ circuit to sol.
between 30 and 40 Ohms
not between 30 and 40 Ohms
Check the following:
• solenoid connection at ECM
• connection at solenoid
• If OK, replace ECM
Replace sol.
THE SYSTEM PERFORMANCE CHECK SHOULD BE PERFORMED AFTER ANY REPAIRS TO THIS SYSTEM HAVE BEEN MADE

AIR SYSTEM CHECK CHART 7

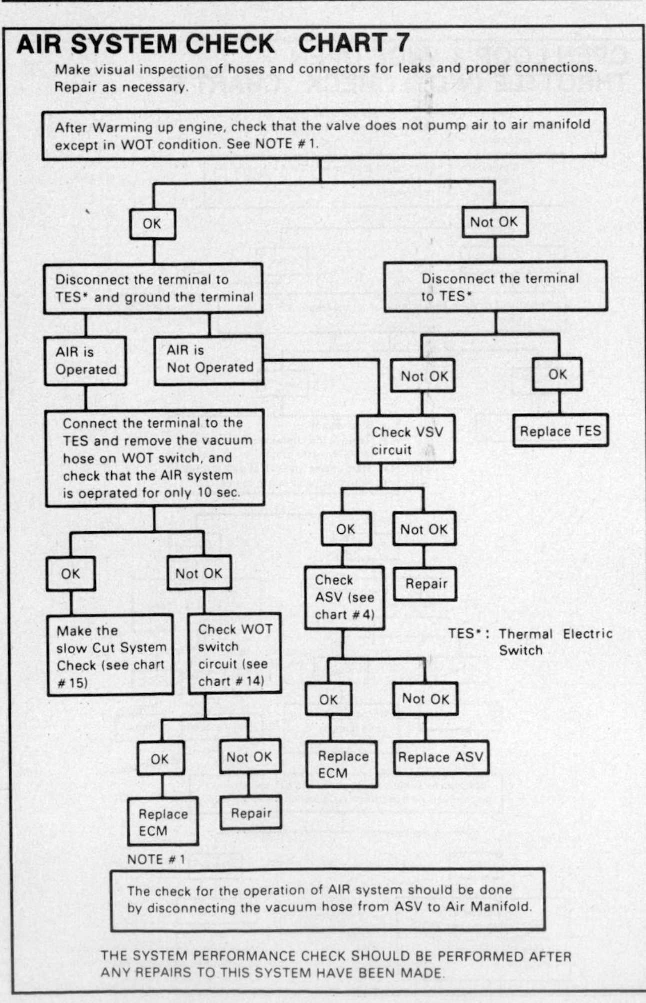

Make visual inspection of hoses and connectors for leaks and proper connections. Repair as necessary.
After Warming up engine, check that the valve does not pump air to air manifold except in WOT condition. See NOTE # 1.
OK
Not OK
Disconnect the terminal to TES* and ground the terminal
Disconnect the terminal to TES*
AIR is Operated
AIR is Not Operated
Not OK
OK
Connect the terminal to the TES and remove the vacuum hose on WOT switch, and check that the AIR system is oeprated for only 10 sec.
Check VSV circuit
Replace TES
OK
Not OK
OK
Not OK
Check ASV (see chart #4)
Repair
Make the slow Cut System Check (see chart # 15)
Check WOT switch circuit (see chart # 14)
TES*: Thermal Electric Switch
OK
Not OK
OK
Not OK
Replace ECM
Replace ASV
Replace ECM
Repair
NOTE # 1
The check for the operation of AIR system should be done by disconnecting the vacuum hose from ASV to Air Manifold.
THE SYSTEM PERFORMANCE CHECK SHOULD BE PERFORMED AFTER ANY REPAIRS TO THIS SYSTEM HAVE BEEN MADE.

FIXED 36° DWELL CHART 8

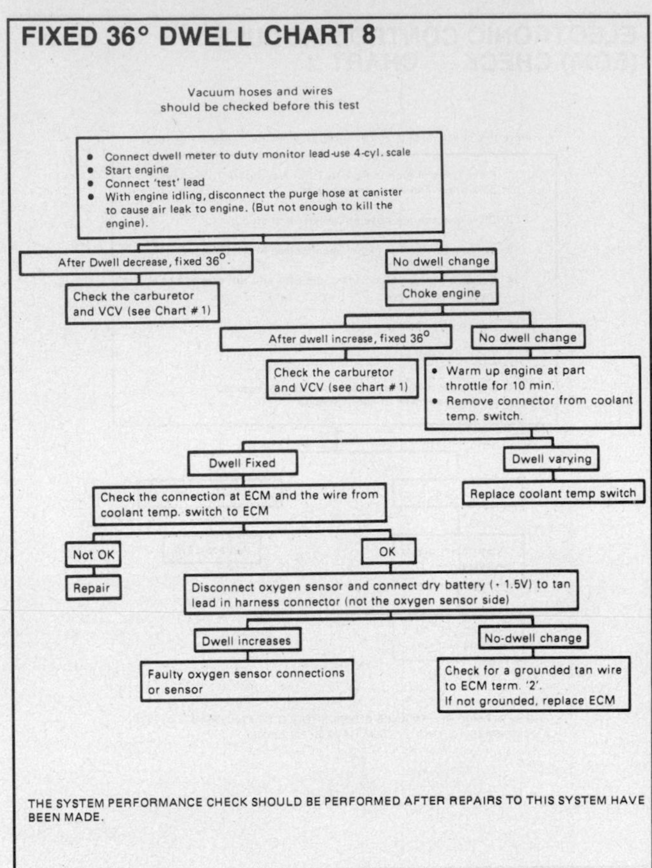

Vacuum hoses and wires should be checked before this test
• Connect dwell meter to duty monitor lead-use 4-cyl. scale
• Start engine
• Connect 'test' lead
• With engine idling, disconnect the purge hose at canister to cause air leak to engine. (But not enough to kill the engine).
After Dwell decrease, fixed 36°.
No dwell change
Check the carburetor and VCV (see Chart # 1)
Choke engine
After dwell increase, fixed 36°
No dwell change
Check the carburetor and VCV (see chart # 1)
• Warm up engine at part throttle for 10 min.
• Remove connector from coolant temp. switch.
Dwell Fixed
Dwell varying
Check the connection at ECM and the wire from coolant temp. switch to ECM
Replace coolant temp switch
Not OK
OK
Repair
Disconnect oxygen sensor and connect dry battery (+ 1.5V) to tan lead in harness connector (not the oxygen sensor side)
Dwell increases
No-dwell change
Faulty oxygen sensor connections or sensor
Check for a grounded tan wire to ECM term. '2'. If not grounded, replace ECM
THE SYSTEM PERFORMANCE CHECK SHOULD BE PERFORMED AFTER REPAIRS TO THIS SYSTEM HAVE BEEN MADE.

TROUBLE CODES 21 OR 22 CHART 9

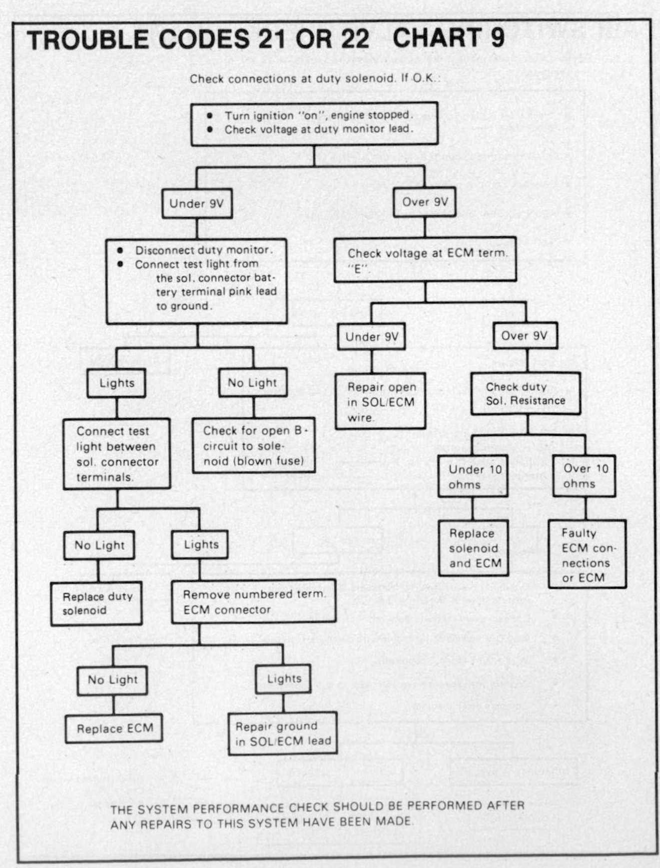

Check connections at duty solenoid. If O.K.:
• Turn ignition "on", engine stopped.
• Check voltage at duty monitor lead.
Under 9V
Over 9V
• Disconnect duty monitor.
• Connect test light from the sol. connector battery terminal pink lead to ground.
Check voltage at ECM term. "E".
Under 9V
Over 9V
Lights
No Light
Repair open in SOL/ECM wire.
Check duty Sol. Resistance
Connect test light between sol. connector terminals.
Check for open B+ circuit to solenoid (blown fuse)
Under 10 ohms
Over 10 ohms
No Light
Lights
Replace solenoid and ECM
Faulty ECM connections or ECM
Replace duty solenoid
Remove numbered term. ECM connector
No Light
Lights
Replace ECM
Repair ground in SOL/ECM lead
THE SYSTEM PERFORMANCE CHECK SHOULD BE PERFORMED AFTER ANY REPAIRS TO THIS SYSTEM HAVE BEEN MADE.

ISUZU CLOSED LOOP EMISSION SYSTEM (Cont.)

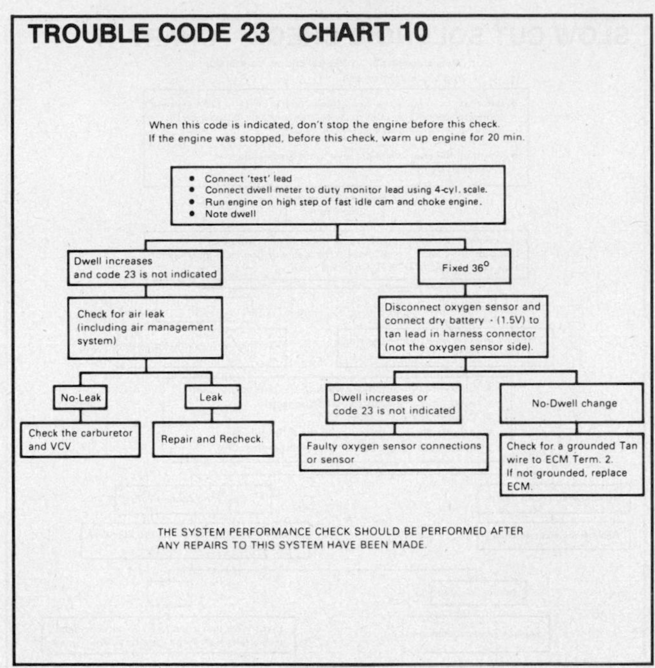

TROUBLE CODE 23 CHART 10
When this code is indicated, don't stop the engine before this check.
If the engine was stopped, before this check, warm up engine for 20 min.
• Connect 'test' lead
• Connect dwell meter to duty monitor lead using 4-cyl. scale.
• Run engine on high step of fast idle cam and choke engine.
• Note dwell
Dwell increases and code 23 is not indicated
Fixed 36°
Check for air leak (including air management system)
Disconnect oxygen sensor and connect dry battery - (1.5V) to tan lead in harness connector (not the oxygen sensor side).
No-Leak
Leak
Dwell increases or code 23 is not indicated
No-Dwell change
Check the carburetor and VCV
Repair and Recheck.
Faulty oxygen sensor connections or sensor
Check for a grounded Tan wire to ECM Term. 2. If not grounded, replace ECM.
THE SYSTEM PERFORMANCE CHECK SHOULD BE PERFORMED AFTER ANY REPAIRS TO THIS SYSTEM HAVE BEEN MADE.

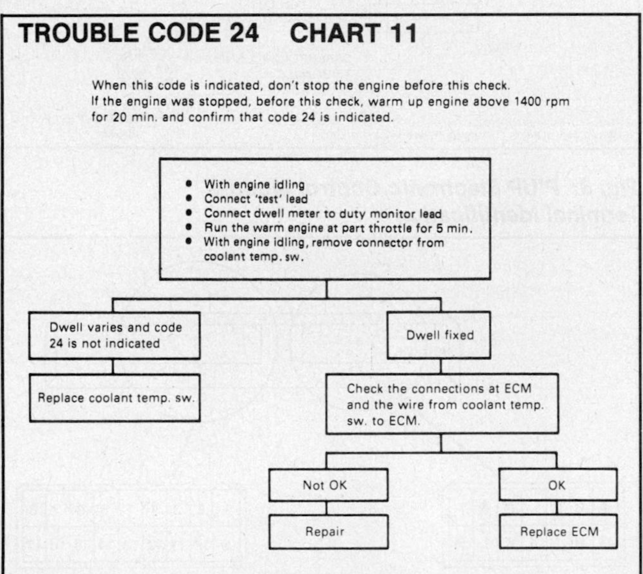

TROUBLE CODE 24 CHART 11
When this code is indicated, don't stop the engine before this check.
If the engine was stopped, before this check, warm up engine above 1400 rpm for 20 min. and confirm that code 24 is indicated.
• With engine idling
• Connect 'test' lead
• Connect dwell meter to duty monitor lead
• Run the warm engine at part throttle for 5 min.
• With engine idling, remove connector from coolant temp. sw.
Dwell varies and code 24 is not indicated
Dwell fixed
Replace coolant temp. sw.
Check the connections at ECM and the wire from coolant temp. sw. to ECM.
Not OK
OK
Repair
Replace ECM

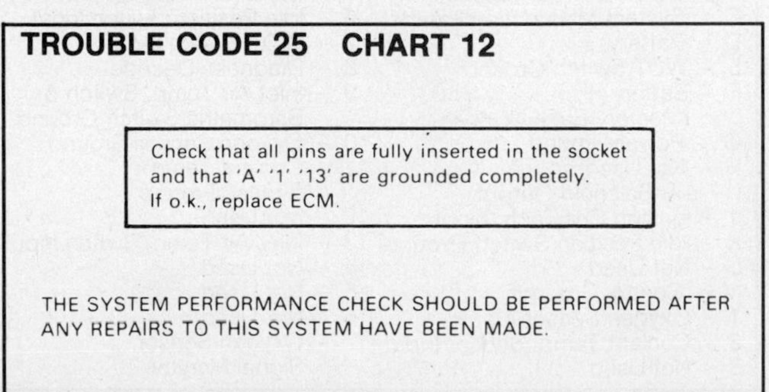

TROUBLE CODE 25 CHART 12
Check that all pins are fully inserted in the socket and that 'A' '1' '13' are grounded completely.
If o.k., replace ECM.
THE SYSTEM PERFORMANCE CHECK SHOULD BE PERFORMED AFTER ANY REPAIRS TO THIS SYSTEM HAVE BEEN MADE.

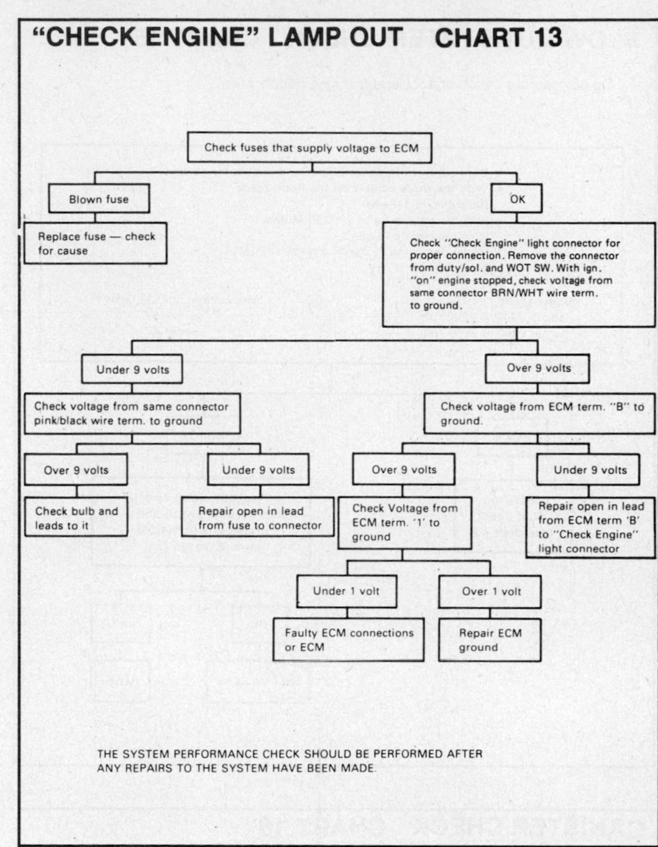

"CHECK ENGINE" LAMP OUT CHART 13
Check fuses that supply voltage to ECM
Blown fuse
OK
Replace fuse — check for cause
Check "Check Engine" light connector for proper connection. Remove the connector from duty/sol. and WOT SW. With ign. "on" engine stopped, check voltage from same connector BRN/WHT wire term. to ground.
Under 9 volts
Over 9 volts
Check voltage from same connector pink/black wire term. to ground
Check voltage from ECM term. "B" to ground.
Over 9 volts
Under 9 volts
Over 9 volts
Under 9 volts
Check bulb and leads to it
Repair open in lead from fuse to connector
Check Voltage from ECM term. '1' to ground
Repair open in lead from ECM term 'B' to "Check Engine" light connector
Under 1 volt
Over 1 volt
Faulty ECM connections or ECM
Repair ECM ground
THE SYSTEM PERFORMANCE CHECK SHOULD BE PERFORMED AFTER ANY REPAIRS TO THE SYSTEM HAVE BEEN MADE.

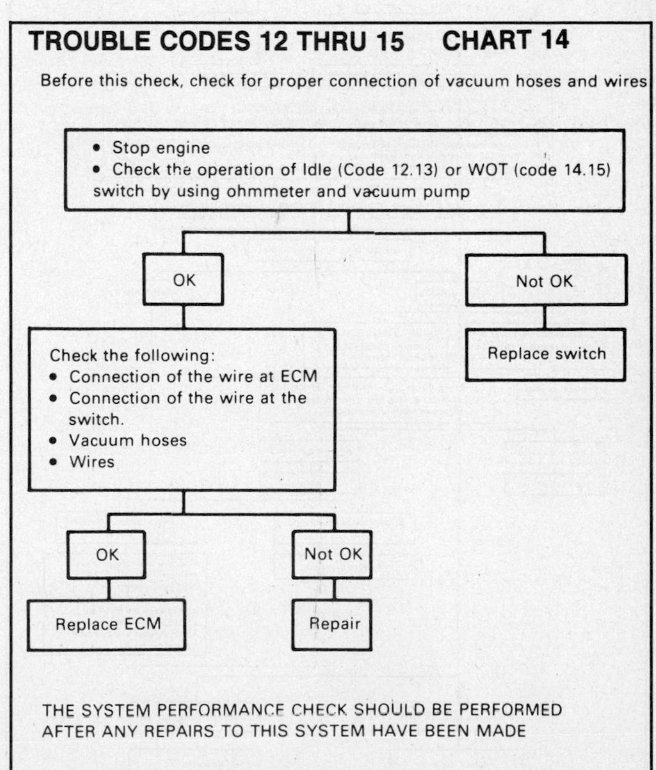

TROUBLE CODES 12 THRU 15 CHART 14
Before this check, check for proper connection of vacuum hoses and wires
• Stop engine
• Check the operation of Idle (Code 12.13) or WOT (code 14.15) switch by using ohmmeter and vacuum pump
OK
Not OK
Check the following:
• Connection of the wire at ECM
• Connection of the wire at the switch.
• Vacuum hoses
• Wires
Replace switch
OK
Not OK
Replace ECM
Repair
THE SYSTEM PERFORMANCE CHECK SHOULD BE PERFORMED AFTER ANY REPAIRS TO THIS SYSTEM HAVE BEEN MADE

Computerized Engine Controls

ISUZU CLOSED LOOP EMISSION SYSTEM (Cont.)

SLOW CUT SYSTEM CHECK CHART 15

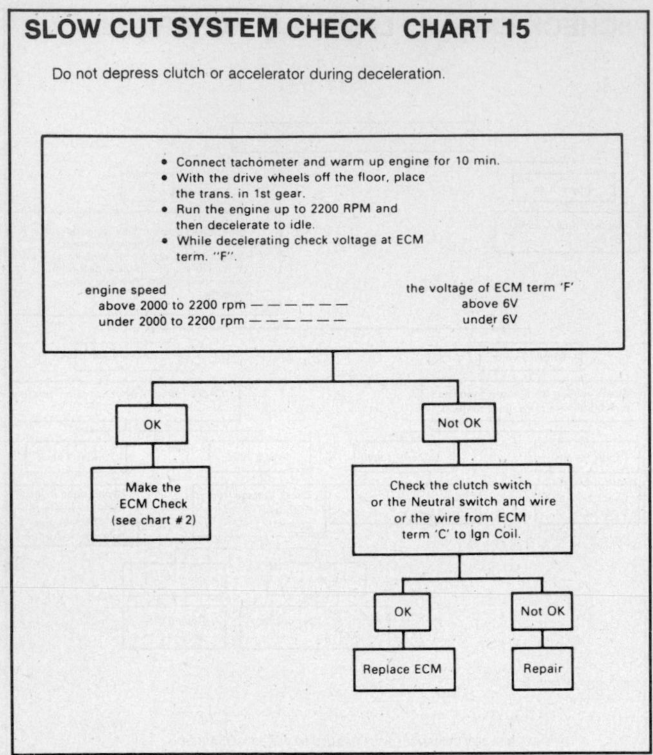

Do not depress clutch or accelerator during deceleration.
• Connect tachometer and warm up engine for 10 min.
• With the drive wheels off the floor, place the trans. in 1st gear.
• Run the engine up to 2200 RPM and then decelerate to idle.
• While decelerating check voltage at ECM term. "F".
engine speed
above 2000 to 2200 rpm
under 2000 to 2200 rpm
the voltage of ECM term 'F'
above 6V
under 6V
OK
Not OK
Make the ECM Check (see chart #2)
Check the clutch switch or the Neutral switch and wire or the wire from ECM term 'C' to Ign Coil.
OK
Not OK
Replace ECM
Repair

CANISTER CHECK CHART 16

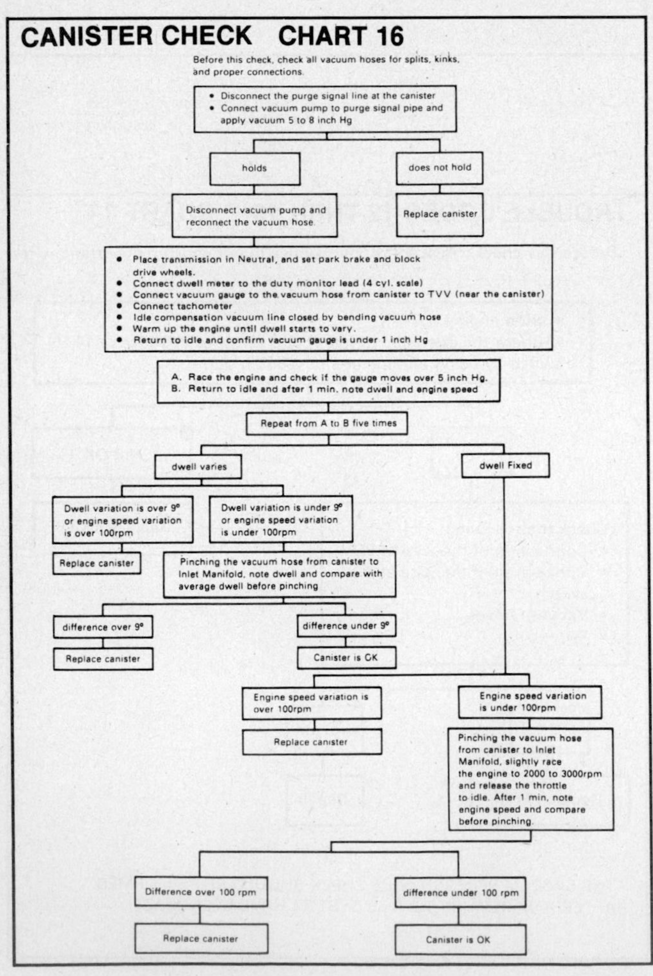

Before this check, check all vacuum hoses for splits, kinks, and proper connections.
• Disconnect the purge signal line at the canister
• Connect vacuum pump to purge signal pipe and apply vacuum 5 to 8 inch Hg
holds
does not hold
Disconnect vacuum pump and reconnect the vacuum hose
Replace canister
• Place transmission in Neutral, and set park brake and block drive wheels.
• Connect dwell meter to the duty monitor lead (4 cyl. scale)
• Connect vacuum gauge to the vacuum hose from canister to TVV (near the canister)
• Connect tachometer
• Idle compensation vacuum line closed by bending vacuum hose
• Warm up the engine until dwell starts to vary.
• Return to idle and confirm vacuum gauge is under 1 inch Hg
A. Race the engine and check if the gauge moves over 5 inch Hg.
B. Return to idle and after 1 min. note dwell and engine speed
Repeat from A to B five times
dwell varies
dwell Fixed
Dwell variation is over 9° or engine speed variation is over 100rpm
Dwell variation is under 9° or engine speed variation is under 100rpm
Replace canister
Pinching the vacuum hose from canister to Inlet Manifold, note dwell and compare with average dwell before pinching
difference over 9°
difference under 9°
Replace canister
Canister is OK
Engine speed variation is over 100rpm
Engine speed variation is under 100rpm
Replace canister
Pinching the vacuum hose from canister to Inlet Manifold, slightly race the engine to 2000 to 3000rpm and release the throttle to idle. After 1 min. note engine speed and compare before pinching.
Difference over 100 rpm
difference under 100 rpm
Replace canister
Canister is OK

SLOW CUT SOLENOID CHECK CHART 17

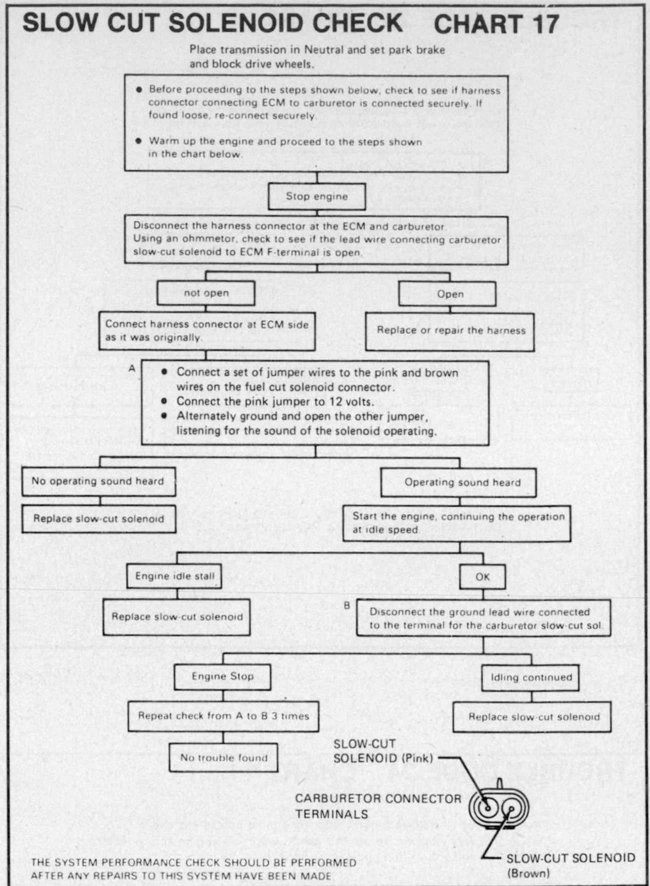

Place transmission in Neutral and set park brake and block drive wheels.
• Before proceeding to the steps shown below, check to see if harness connector connecting ECM to carburetor is connected securely. If found loose, re-connect securely.
• Warm up the engine and proceed to the steps shown in the chart below.
Stop engine
Disconnect the harness connector at the ECM and carburetor. Using an ohmmetor, check to see if the lead wire connecting carburetor slow-cut solenoid to ECM F-terminal is open.
not open
Open
Connect harness connector at ECM side as it was originally.
Replace or repair the harness
A
• Connect a set of jumper wires to the pink and brown wires on the fuel cut solenoid connector.
• Connect the pink jumper to 12 volts.
• Alternately ground and open the other jumper, listening for the sound of the solenoid operating.
No operating sound heard
Operating sound heard
Replace slow-cut solenoid
Start the engine, continuing the operation at idle speed.
Engine idle stall
OK
Replace slow-cut solenoid
B
Disconnect the ground lead wire connected to the terminal for the carburetor slow-cut sol.
Engine Stop
Idling continued
Repeat check from A to B 3 times
Replace slow-cut solenoid
No trouble found
SLOW-CUT SOLENOID (Pink)
CARBURETOR CONNECTOR TERMINALS
SLOW-CUT SOLENOID (Brown)
THE SYSTEM PERFORMANCE CHECK SHOULD BE PERFORMED AFTER ANY REPAIRS TO THIS SYSTEM HAVE BEEN MADE

Fig. 3: P'UP Electronic Control Module Terminal Identification

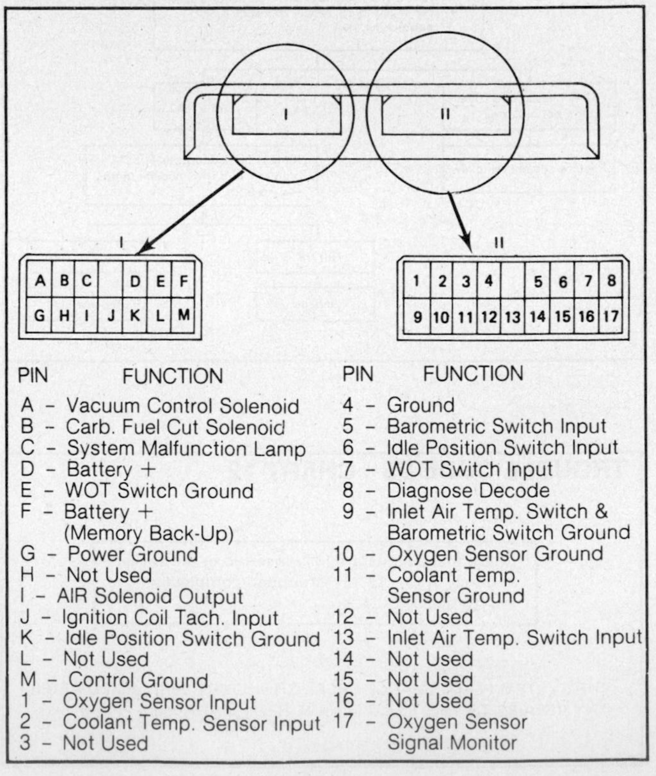

I
II
I
A B C D E F
G H I J K L M
II
1 2 3 4 5 6 7 8
9 10 11 12 13 14 15 16 17
PIN FUNCTION
A – Vacuum Control Solenoid
B – Carb. Fuel Cut Solenoid
C – System Malfunction Lamp
D – Battery +
E – WOT Switch Ground
F – Battery + (Memory Back-Up)
G – Power Ground
H – Not Used
I – AIR Solenoid Output
J – Ignition Coil Tach. Input
K – Idle Position Switch Ground
L – Not Used
M – Control Ground
1 – Oxygen Sensor Input
2 – Coolant Temp. Sensor Input
3 – Not Used
PIN FUNCTION
4 – Ground
5 – Barometric Switch Input
6 – Idle Position Switch Input
7 – WOT Switch Input
8 – Diagnose Decode
9 – Inlet Air Temp. Switch & Barometric Switch Ground
10 – Oxygen Sensor Ground
11 – Coolant Temp. Sensor Ground
12 – Not Used
13 – Inlet Air Temp. Switch Input
14 – Not Used
15 – Not Used
16 – Not Used
17 – Oxygen Sensor Signal Monitor

ISUZU CLOSED LOOP EMISSION SYSTEM (Cont.)

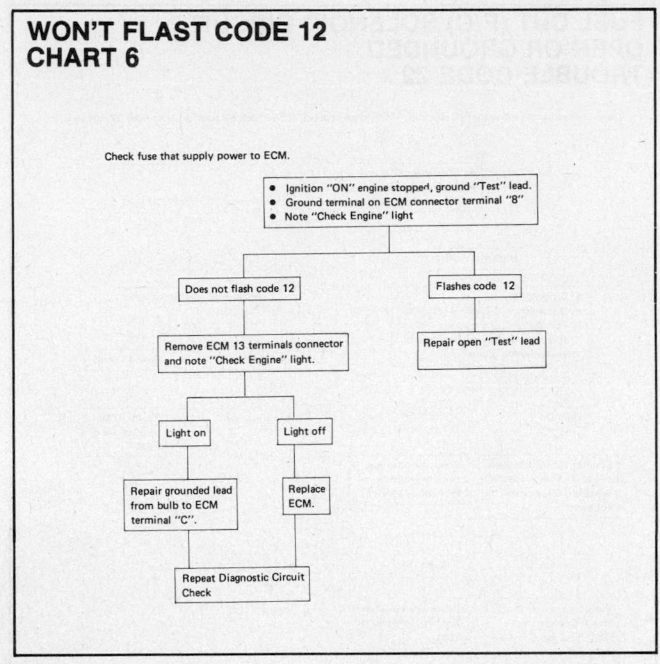
WON'T FLAST CODE 12
CHART 6
Check fuse that supply power to ECM.
• Ignition "ON" engine stopped, ground "Test" lead.
• Ground terminal on ECM connector terminal "8"
• Note "Check Engine" light
Does not flash code 12
Flashes code 12
Remove ECM 13 terminals connector and note "Check Engine" light.
Repair open "Test" lead
Light on
Light off
Repair grounded lead from bulb to ECM terminal "C".
Replace ECM.
Repeat Diagnostic Circuit Check

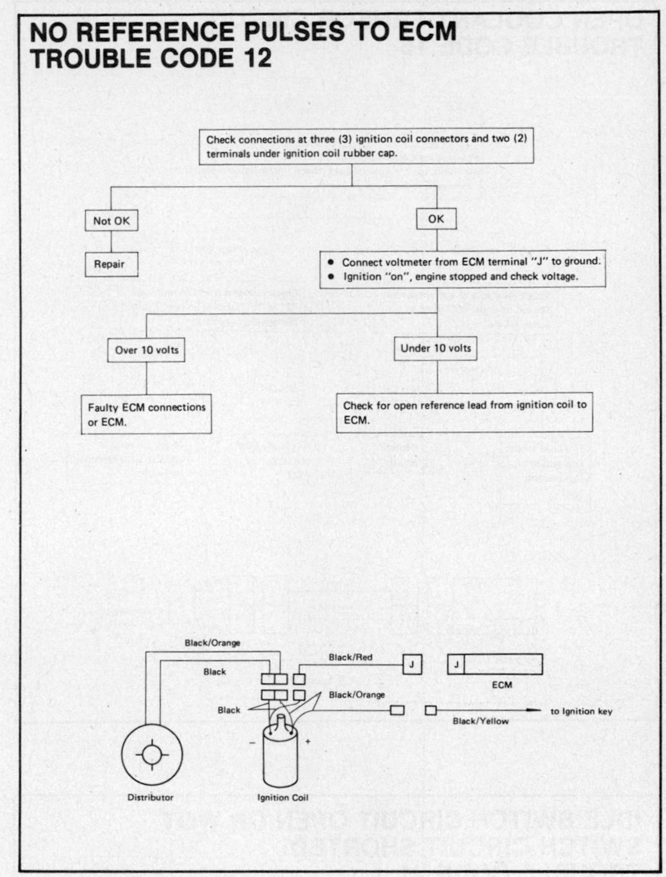
NO REFERENCE PULSES TO ECM
TROUBLE CODE 12
Check connections at three (3) ignition coil connectors and two (2) terminals under ignition coil rubber cap.
Not OK
OK
Repair
• Connect voltmeter from ECM terminal "J" to ground.
• Ignition "on", engine stopped and check voltage.
Over 10 volts
Under 10 volts
Faulty ECM connections or ECM.
Check for open reference lead from ignition coil to ECM.
Black/Orange
Black
Black/Red
J
J
ECM
Black/Orange
Black
Black/Yellow
to Ignition key
Distributor
Ignition Coil

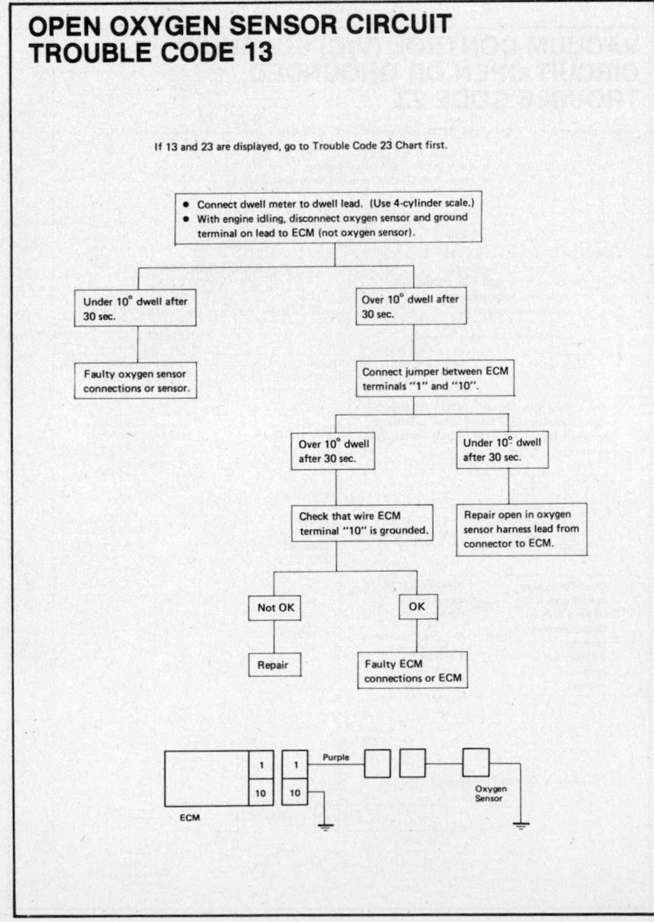
OPEN OXYGEN SENSOR CIRCUIT
TROUBLE CODE 13
If 13 and 23 are displayed, go to Trouble Code 23 Chart first.
• Connect dwell meter to dwell lead. (Use 4-cylinder scale.)
• With engine idling, disconnect oxygen sensor and ground terminal on lead to ECM (not oxygen sensor).
Under 10° dwell after 30 sec.
Over 10° dwell after 30 sec.
Faulty oxygen sensor connections or sensor.
Connect jumper between ECM terminals "1" and "10".
Over 10° dwell after 30 sec.
Under 10° dwell after 30 sec.
Check that wire ECM terminal "10" is grounded.
Repair open in oxygen sensor harness lead from connector to ECM.
Not OK
OK
Repair
Faulty ECM connections or ECM
1
10
1
10
Purple
Oxygen Sensor
ECM

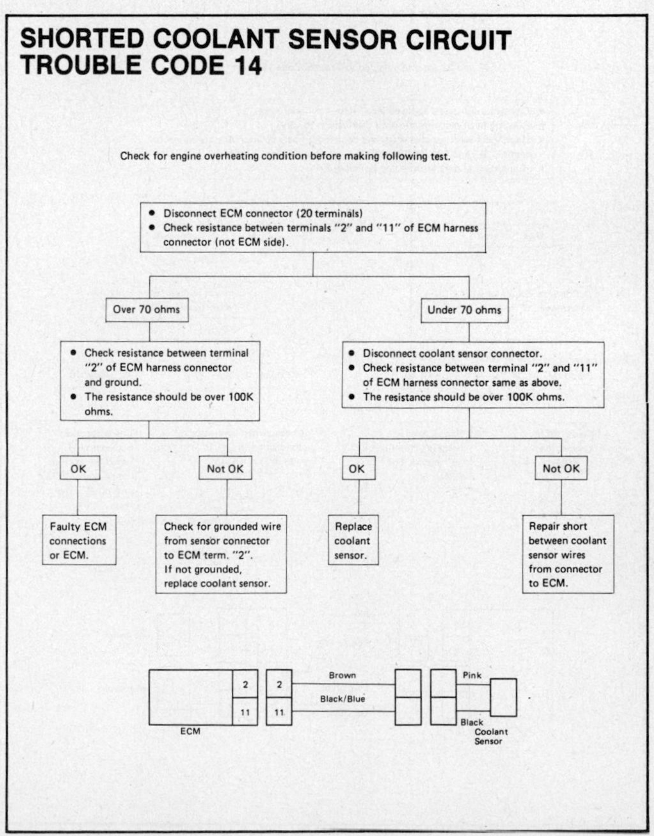
SHORTED COOLANT SENSOR CIRCUIT
TROUBLE CODE 14
Check for engine overheating condition before making following test.
• Disconnect ECM connector (20 terminals)
• Check resistance between terminals "2" and "11" of ECM harness connector (not ECM side).
Over 70 ohms
Under 70 ohms
• Check resistance between terminal "2" of ECM harness connector and ground.
• The resistance should be over 100K ohms.
• Disconnect coolant sensor connector.
• Check resistance between terminal "2" and "11" of ECM harness connector same as above.
• The resistance should be over 100K ohms.
OK
Not OK
OK
Not OK
Faulty ECM connections or ECM.
Check for grounded wire from sensor connector to ECM term. "2". If not grounded, replace coolant sensor.
Replace coolant sensor.
Repair short between coolant sensor wires from connector to ECM.
2
11
2
11
Brown
Black/Blue
Pink
Black
ECM
Coolant Sensor

ISUZU CLOSED LOOP EMISSION SYSTEM (Cont.)

OPEN COOLANT SENSOR CIRCUIT TROUBLE CODE 15

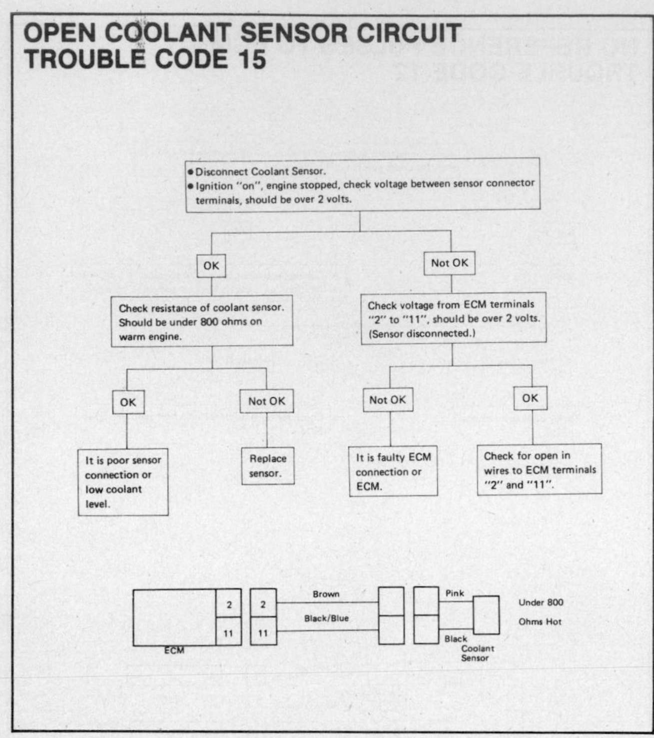
• Disconnect Coolant Sensor.
• Ignition "on", engine stopped, check voltage between sensor connector terminals, should be over 2 volts.
OK
Not OK
Check resistance of coolant sensor. Should be under 800 ohms on warm engine.
Check voltage from ECM terminals "2" to "11", should be over 2 volts. (Sensor disconnected.)
OK
Not OK
Not OK
OK
It is poor sensor connection or low coolant level.
Replace sensor.
It is faulty ECM connection or ECM.
Check for open in wires to ECM terminals "2" and "11".
2
11
2
11
ECM
Brown
Black/Blue
Pink
Black
Under 800 Ohms Hot
Coolant Sensor

IDLE SWITCH CIRCUIT OPEN OR WOT SWITCH CIRCUIT SHORTED TROUBLE CODE 21

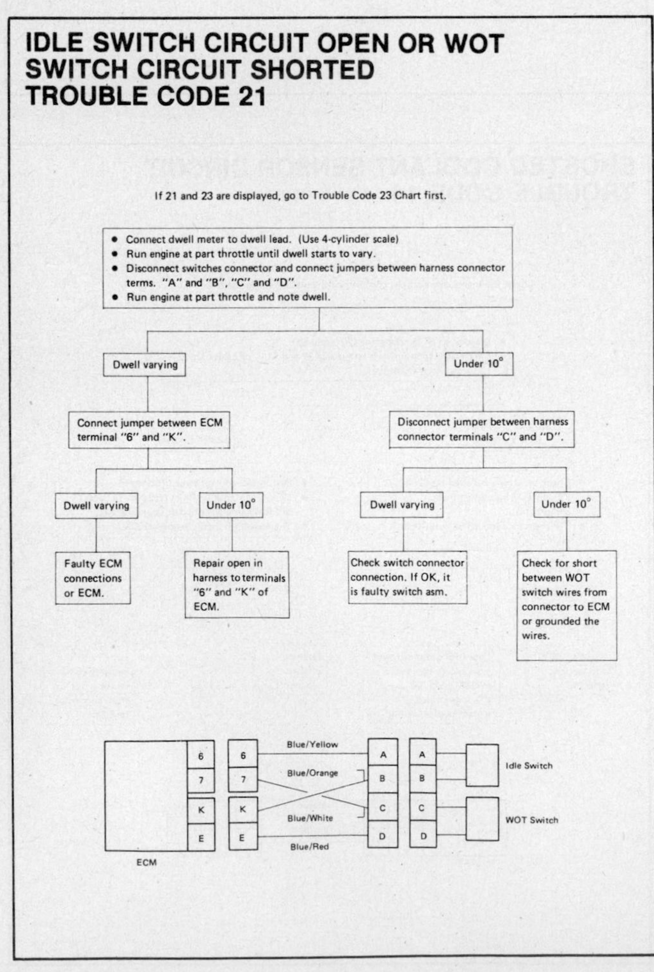
If 21 and 23 are displayed, go to Trouble Code 23 Chart first.
• Connect dwell meter to dwell lead. (Use 4-cylinder scale)
• Run engine at part throttle until dwell starts to vary.
• Disconnect switches connector and connect jumpers between harness connector terms. "A" and "B", "C" and "D".
• Run engine at part throttle and note dwell.
Dwell varying
Under 10°
Connect jumper between ECM terminal "6" and "K".
Disconnect jumper between harness connector terminals "C" and "D".
Dwell varying
Under 10°
Dwell varying
Under 10°
Faulty ECM connections or ECM.
Repair open in harness to terminals "6" and "K" of ECM.
Check switch connector connection. If OK, it is faulty switch asm.
Check for short between WOT switch wires from connector to ECM or grounded the wires.
6
7
K
E
6
7
K
E
ECM
Blue/Yellow
Blue/Orange
Blue/White
Blue/Red
A
B
C
D
A
B
C
D
Idle Switch
WOT Switch

FUEL CUT (F/C) SOLENOID CIRCUIT OPEN OR GROUNDED TROUBLE CODE 22

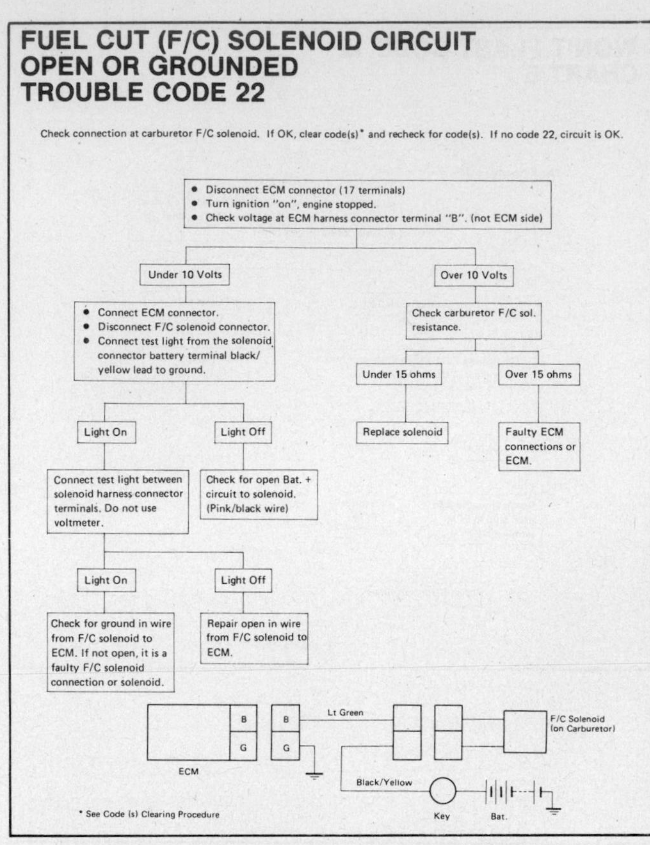
Check connection at carburetor F/C solenoid. If OK, clear code(s)* and recheck for code(s). If no code 22, circuit is OK.
• Disconnect ECM connector (17 terminals)
• Turn ignition "on", engine stopped.
• Check voltage at ECM harness connector terminal "B". (not ECM side)
Under 10 Volts
Over 10 Volts
• Connect ECM connector.
• Disconnect F/C solenoid connector.
• Connect test light from the solenoid connector battery terminal black/yellow lead to ground.
Check carburetor F/C sol. resistance.
Under 15 ohms
Over 15 ohms
Replace solenoid
Faulty ECM connections or ECM.
Light On
Light Off
Connect test light between solenoid harness connector terminals. Do not use voltmeter.
Check for open Bat. + circuit to solenoid. (Pink/black wire)
Light On
Light Off
Check for ground in wire from F/C solenoid to ECM. If not open, it is a faulty F/C solenoid connection or solenoid.
Repair open in wire from F/C solenoid to ECM.
B
G
B
G
ECM
Lt Green
Black/Yellow
F/C Solenoid (on Carburetor)
Key
Bat.
* See Code (s) Clearing Procedure

VACUUM CONTROL (V/C) SOLENOID CIRCUIT OPEN OR GROUNDED TROUBLE CODE 23

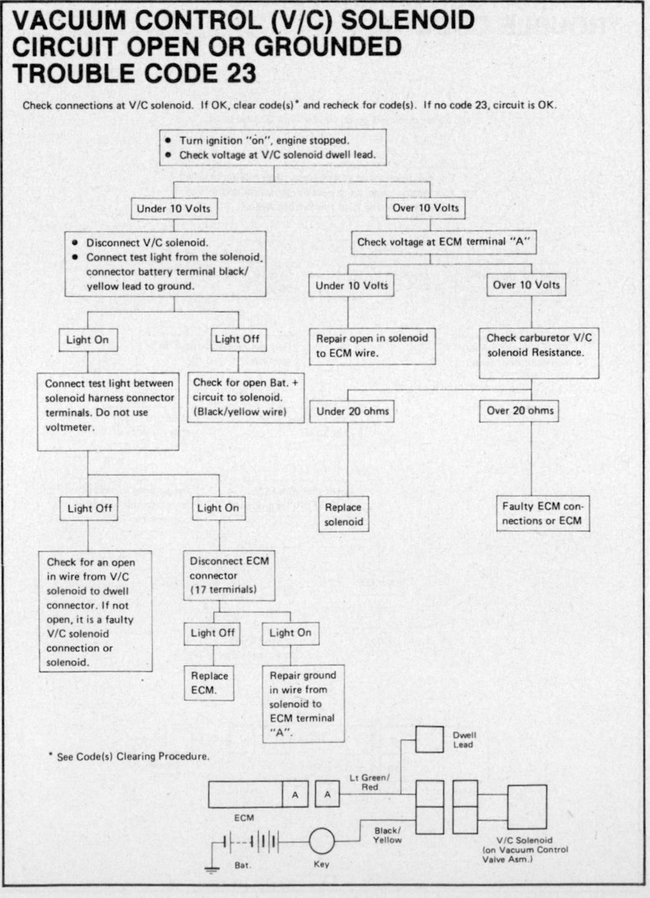
Check connections at V/C solenoid. If OK, clear code(s)* and recheck for code(s). If no code 23, circuit is OK.
• Turn ignition "on", engine stopped.
• Check voltage at V/C solenoid dwell lead.
Under 10 Volts
Over 10 Volts
• Disconnect V/C solenoid.
• Connect test light from the solenoid connector battery terminal black/yellow lead to ground.
Check voltage at ECM terminal "A"
Under 10 Volts
Over 10 Volts
Light On
Light Off
Repair open in solenoid to ECM wire.
Check carburetor V/C solenoid Resistance.
Connect test light between solenoid harness connector terminals. Do not use voltmeter.
Check for open Bat. + circuit to solenoid. (Black/yellow wire)
Under 20 ohms
Over 20 ohms
Light Off
Light On
Replace solenoid
Faulty ECM connections or ECM
Check for an open in wire from V/C solenoid to dwell connector. If not open, it is a faulty V/C solenoid connection or solenoid.
Disconnect ECM connector (17 terminals)
Light Off
Light On
Replace ECM.
Repair ground in wire from solenoid to ECM terminal "A".
* See Code(s) Clearing Procedure.
Dwell Lead
A
A
ECM
Lt Green/Red
Black/Yellow
Bat.
Key
V/C Solenoid (on Vacuum Control Valve Asm.)

ISUZU CLOSED LOOP EMISSION SYSTEM (Cont.)

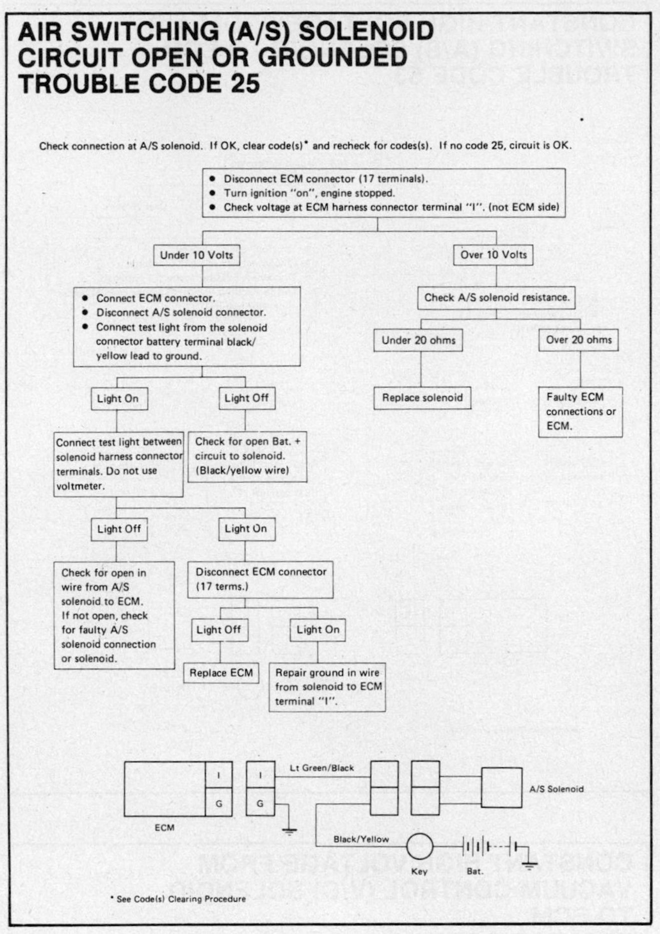

AIR SWITCHING (A/S) SOLENOID
CIRCUIT OPEN OR GROUNDED
TROUBLE CODE 25
Check connection at A/S solenoid. If OK, clear code(s)* and recheck for code(s). If no code 25, circuit is OK.
• Disconnect ECM connector (17 terminals).
• Turn ignition "on", engine stopped.
• Check voltage at ECM harness connector terminal "I". (not ECM side)
Under 10 Volts
Over 10 Volts
• Connect ECM connector.
• Disconnect A/S solenoid connector.
• Connect test light from the solenoid connector battery terminal black/yellow lead to ground.
Check A/S solenoid resistance.
Under 20 ohms
Over 20 ohms
Replace solenoid
Faulty ECM connections or ECM.
Light On
Light Off
Connect test light between solenoid harness connector terminals. Do not use voltmeter.
Check for open Bat. + circuit to solenoid. (Black/yellow wire)
Light Off
Light On
Check for open in wire from A/S solenoid to ECM. If not open, check for faulty A/S solenoid connection or solenoid.
Disconnect ECM connector (17 terms.)
Light Off
Light On
Replace ECM
Repair ground in wire from solenoid to ECM terminal "I".
ECM
I
G
Lt Green/Black
A/S Solenoid
Black/Yellow
Key
Bat.
* See Code(s) Clearing Procedure

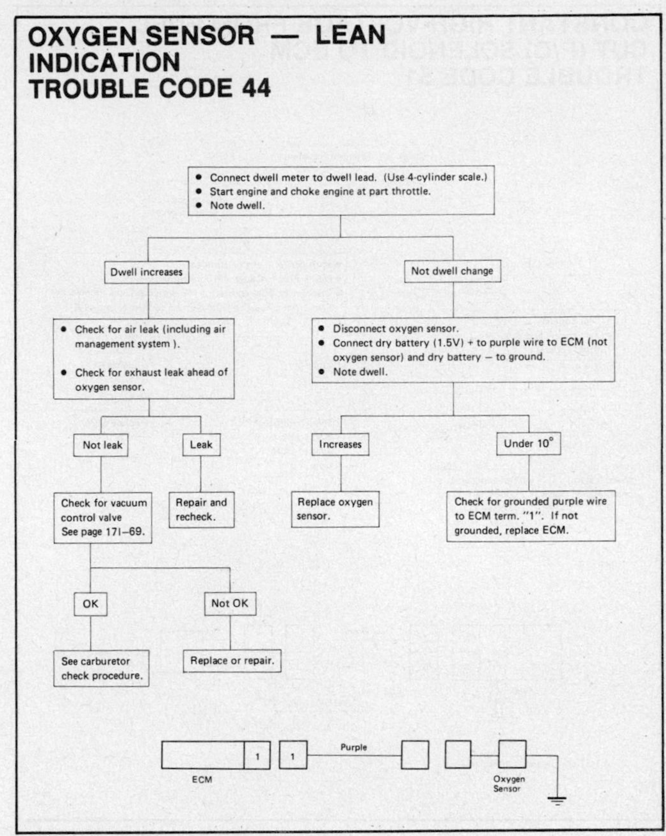

OXYGEN SENSOR — LEAN
INDICATION
TROUBLE CODE 44
• Connect dwell meter to dwell lead. (Use 4-cylinder scale.)
• Start engine and choke engine at part throttle.
• Note dwell.
Dwell increases
Not dwell change
• Check for air leak (including air management system).
• Check for exhaust leak ahead of oxygen sensor.
• Disconnect oxygen sensor.
• Connect dry battery (1.5V) + to purple wire to ECM (not oxygen sensor) and dry battery – to ground.
• Note dwell.
Not leak
Leak
Increases
Under 10°
Check for vacuum control valve See page 17I–69.
Repair and recheck.
Replace oxygen sensor.
Check for grounded purple wire to ECM term. "1". If not grounded, replace ECM.
OK
Not OK
See carburetor check procedure.
Replace or repair.
ECM
1
Purple
Oxygen Sensor

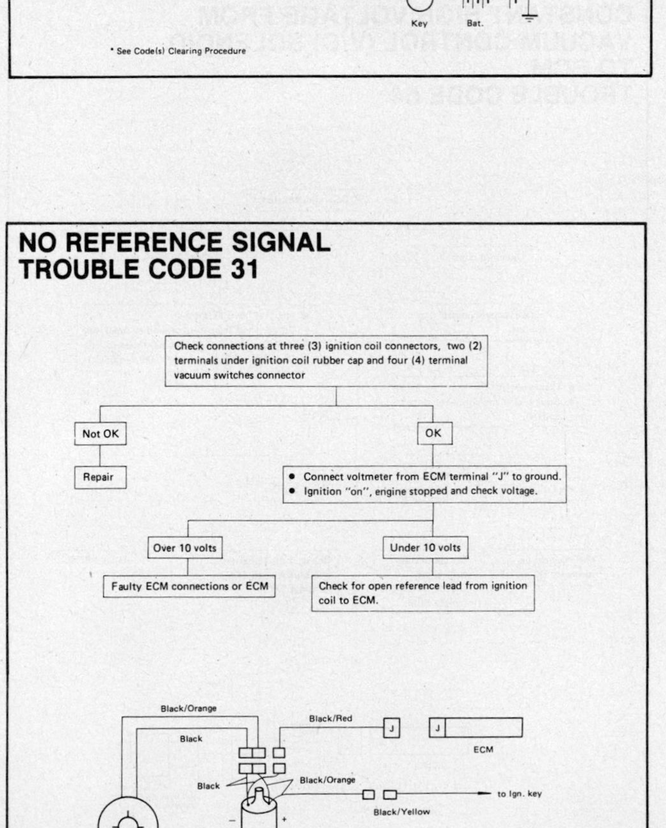

NO REFERENCE SIGNAL
TROUBLE CODE 31
Check connections at three (3) ignition coil connectors, two (2) terminals under ignition coil rubber cap and four (4) terminal vacuum switches connector
Not OK
OK
Repair
• Connect voltmeter from ECM terminal "J" to ground.
• Ignition "on", engine stopped and check voltage.
Over 10 volts
Under 10 volts
Faulty ECM connections or ECM
Check for open reference lead from ignition coil to ECM.
Black/Orange
Black
Black/Red
J
ECM
Black
Black/Orange
to Ign. key
Black/Yellow
Distributor
Ign. Coil

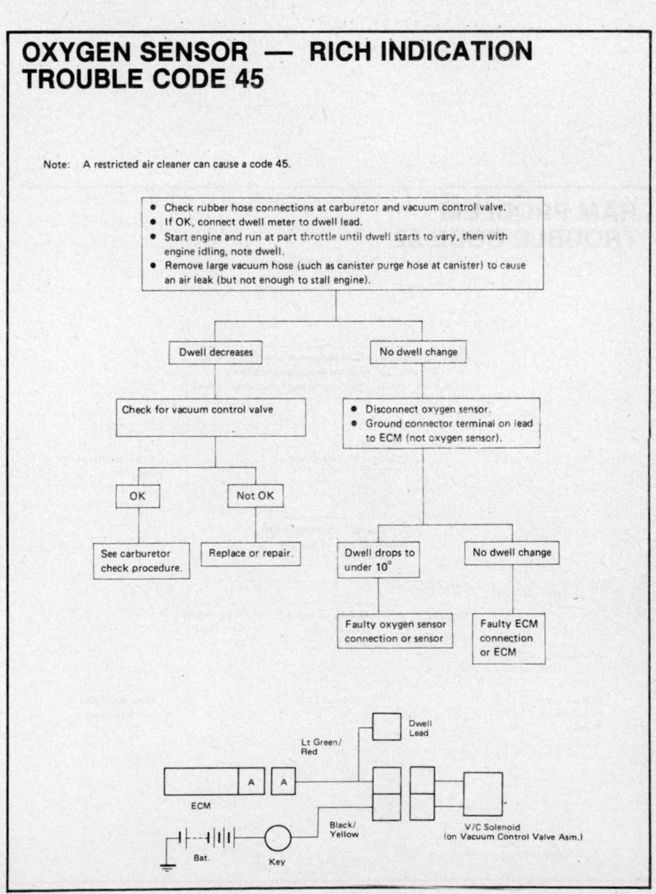

OXYGEN SENSOR — RICH INDICATION
TROUBLE CODE 45
Note: A restricted air cleaner can cause a code 45.
• Check rubber hose connections at carburetor and vacuum control valve.
• If OK, connect dwell meter to dwell lead.
• Start engine and run at part throttle until dwell starts to vary, then with engine idling, note dwell.
• Remove large vacuum hose (such as canister purge hose at canister) to cause an air leak (but not enough to stall engine).
Dwell decreases
No dwell change
Check for vacuum control valve
• Disconnect oxygen sensor.
• Ground connector terminal on lead to ECM (not oxygen sensor).
OK
Not OK
See carburetor check procedure.
Replace or repair.
Dwell drops to under 10°
No dwell change
Faulty oxygen sensor connection or sensor
Faulty ECM connection or ECM
Dwell Lead
Lt Green/Red
ECM
A
Black/Yellow
V/C Solenoid (on Vacuum Control Valve Asm.)
Bat.
Key

Computerized Engine Controls

ISUZU CLOSED LOOP EMISSION SYSTEM (Cont.)

CONSTANT HIGH VOLTAGE FROM FUEL CUT (F/C) SOLENOID TO ECM TROUBLE CODE 51

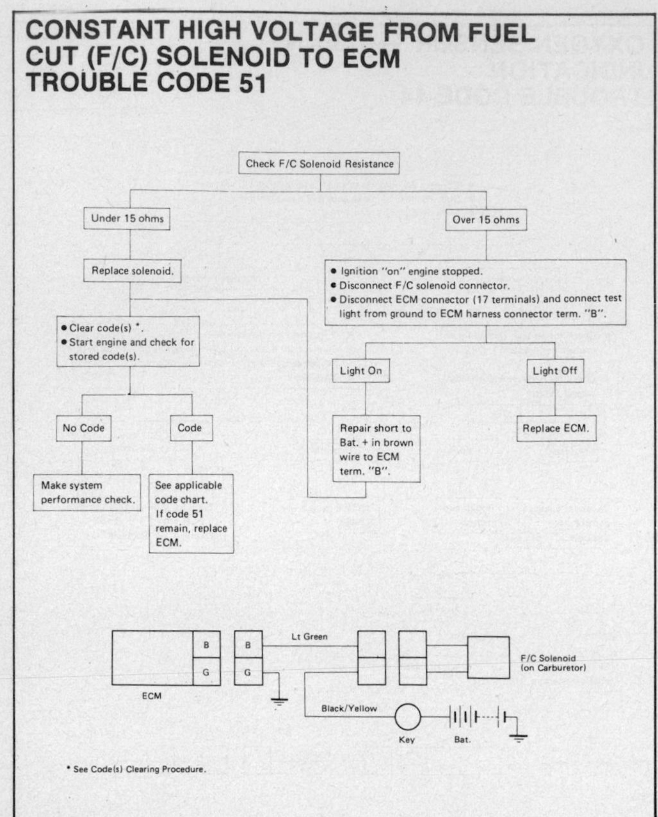
Check F/C Solenoid Resistance
Under 15 ohms
Over 15 ohms
Replace solenoid.
• Ignition "on" engine stopped.
• Disconnect F/C solenoid connector.
• Disconnect ECM connector (17 terminals) and connect test light from ground to ECM harness connector term. "B".
• Clear code(s) *.
• Start engine and check for stored code(s).
Light On
Light Off
No Code
Code
Repair short to Bat. + in brown wire to ECM term. "B".
Replace ECM.
Make system performance check.
See applicable code chart. If code 51 remain, replace ECM.
Lt Green
B
G
ECM
F/C Solenoid (on Carburetor)
Black/Yellow
Key
Bat.
* See Code(s) Clearing Procedure.

RAM PROBLEM TROUBLE CODE 52

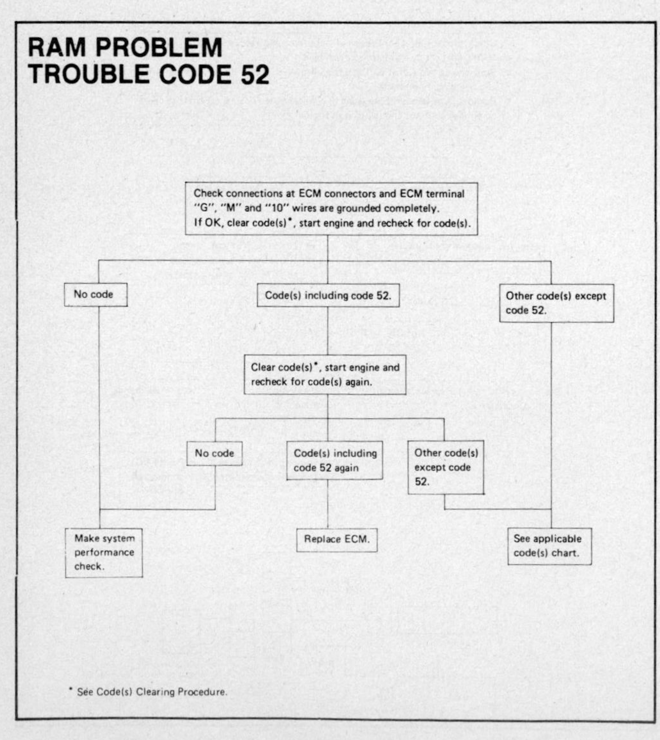
Check connections at ECM connectors and ECM terminal "G", "M" and "10" wires are grounded completely. If OK, clear code(s)*, start engine and recheck for code(s).
No code
Code(s) including code 52.
Other code(s) except code 52.
Clear code(s)*, start engine and recheck for code(s) again.
No code
Code(s) including code 52 again
Other code(s) except code 52.
Make system performance check.
Replace ECM.
See applicable code(s) chart.
* See Code(s) Clearing Procedure.

CONSTANT HIGH VOLTAGE FROM AIR SWITCHING (A/S) SOLENOID TO ECM TROUBLE CODE 53

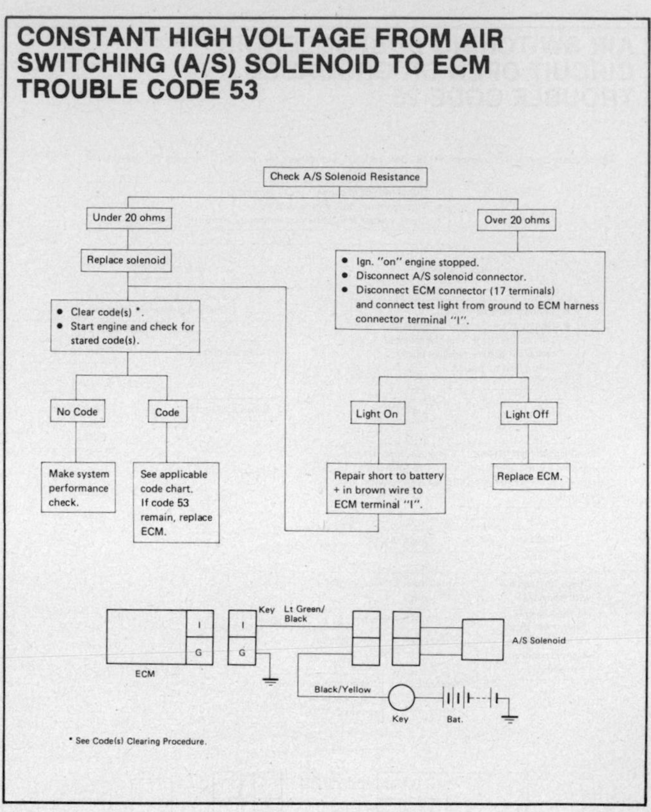
Check A/S Solenoid Resistance
Under 20 ohms
Over 20 ohms
Replace solenoid
• Ign. "on" engine stopped.
• Disconnect A/S solenoid connector.
• Disconnect ECM connector (17 terminals) and connect test light from ground to ECM harness connector terminal "I".
• Clear code(s) *.
• Start engine and check for stared code(s).
No Code
Code
Light On
Light Off
Make system performance check.
See applicable code chart. If code 53 remain, replace ECM.
Repair short to battery + in brown wire to ECM terminal "I".
Replace ECM.
Key
Lt Green/ Black
I
G
ECM
A/S Solenoid
Black/Yellow
Key
Bat.
* See Code(s) Clearing Procedure.

CONSTANT HIGH VOLTAGE FROM VACUUM CONTROL (V/C) SOLENOID TO ECM TROUBLE CODE 54

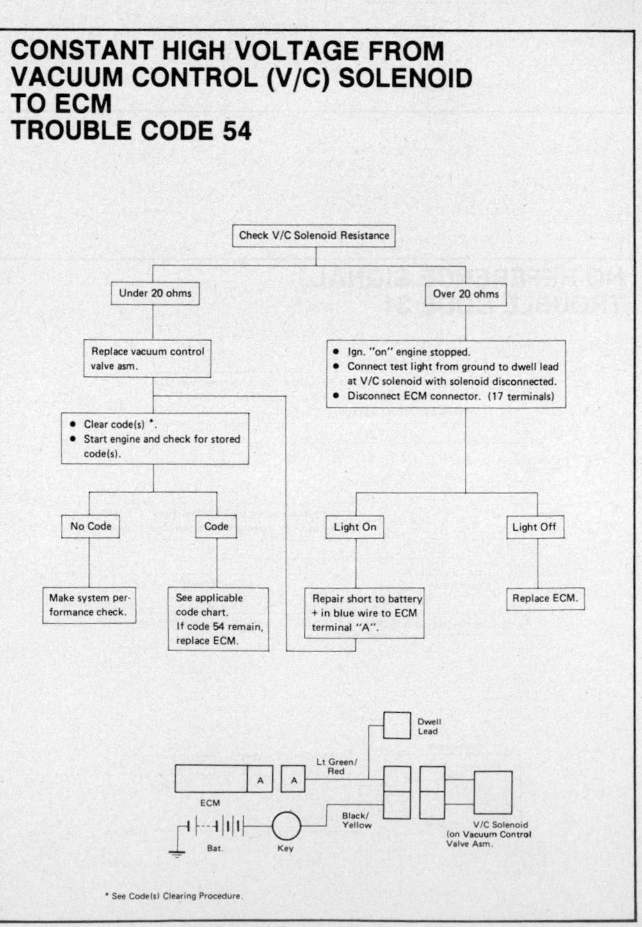
Check V/C Solenoid Resistance
Under 20 ohms
Over 20 ohms
Replace vacuum control valve asm.
• Ign. "on" engine stopped.
• Connect test light from ground to dwell lead at V/C solenoid with solenoid disconnected.
• Disconnect ECM connector. (17 terminals)
• Clear code(s) *.
• Start engine and check for stored code(s).
No Code
Code
Light On
Light Off
Make system performance check.
See applicable code chart. If code 54 remain, replace ECM.
Repair short to battery + in blue wire to ECM terminal "A".
Replace ECM.
Dwell Lead
Lt Green/ Red
A
ECM
Black/ Yellow
Bat.
Key
V/C Solenoid (on Vacuum Control Valve Asm.
* See Code(s) Clearing Procedure.

ISUZU CLOSED LOOP EMISSION SYSTEM (Cont.)

A/C CONVERTER PROBLEM TROUBLE CODE 55

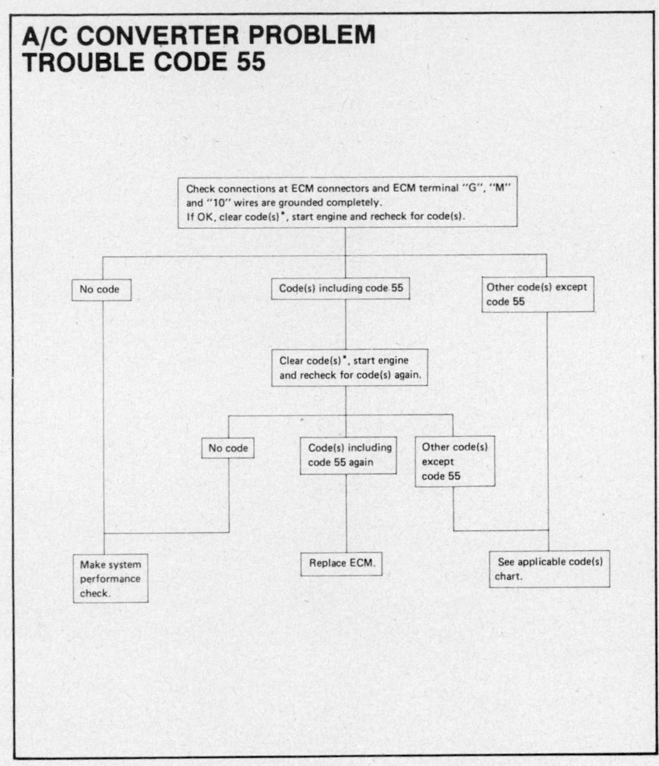

Check connections at ECM connectors and ECM terminal "G", "M" and "10" wires are grounded completely.
If OK, clear code(s)*, start engine and recheck for code(s).
No code
Code(s) including code 55
Other code(s) except code 55
Clear code(s)*, start engine and recheck for code(s) again.
No code
Code(s) including code 55 again
Other code(s) except code 55
Make system performance check.
Replace ECM.
See applicable code(s) chart.

IDLE AND WOT SWITCHES ASM. CHECK

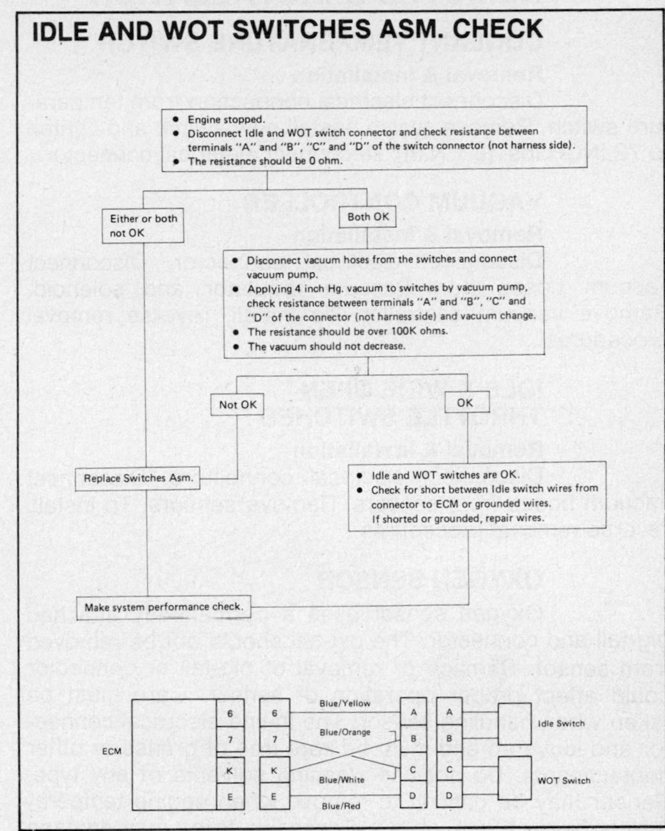

• Engine stopped.
• Disconnect Idle and WOT switch connector and check resistance between terminals "A" and "B", "C" and "D" of the switch connector (not harness side).
• The resistance should be 0 ohm.
Either or both not OK
Both OK
• Disconnect vacuum hoses from the switches and connect vacuum pump.
• Applying 4 inch Hg. vacuum to switches by vacuum pump, check resistance between terminals "A" and "B", "C" and "D" of the connector (not harness side) and vacuum change.
• The resistance should be over 100K ohms.
• The vacuum should not decrease.
Not OK
OK
Replace Switches Asm.
• Idle and WOT switches are OK.
• Check for short between Idle switch wires from connector to ECM or grounded wires. If shorted or grounded, repair wires.
Make system performance check.
ECM
6
7
K
E
Blue/Yellow
Blue/Orange
Blue/White
Blue/Red
A
B
C
D
Idle Switch
WOT Switch

AIR MANAGEMENT CHECK

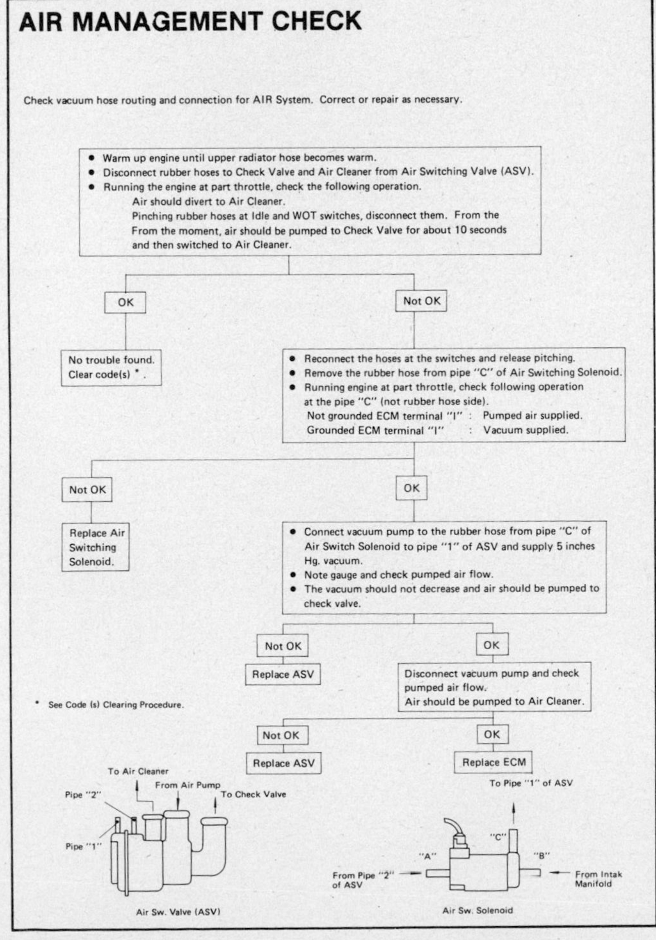

Check vacuum hose routing and connection for AIR System. Correct or repair as necessary.
• Warm up engine until upper radiator hose becomes warm.
• Disconnect rubber hoses to Check Valve and Air Cleaner from Air Switching Valve (ASV).
• Running the engine at part throttle, check the following operation.
Air should divert to Air Cleaner.
Pinching rubber hoses at Idle and WOT switches, disconnect them. From the From the moment, air should be pumped to Check Valve for about 10 seconds and then switched to Air Cleaner.
OK
Not OK
No trouble found. Clear code(s)*.
• Reconnect the hoses at the switches and release pitching.
• Remove the rubber hose from pipe "C" of Air Switching Solenoid.
• Running engine at part throttle, check following operation at the pipe "C" (not rubber hose side).
Not grounded ECM terminal "I" : Pumped air supplied.
Grounded ECM terminal "I" : Vacuum supplied.
Not OK
OK
Replace Air Switching Solenoid.
• Connect vacuum pump to the rubber hose from pipe "C" of Air Switch Solenoid to pipe "1" of ASV and supply 5 inches Hg. vacuum.
• Note gauge and check pumped air flow.
• The vacuum should not decrease and air should be pumped to check valve.
Not OK
OK
Replace ASV
Disconnect vacuum pump and check pumped air flow.
Air should be pumped to Air Cleaner.
Not OK
OK
Replace ASV
Replace ECM
* See Code (s) Clearing Procedure.
To Air Cleaner
From Air Pump
Pipe "2"
To Check Valve
Pipe "1"
Air Sw. Valve (ASV)
To Pipe "1" of ASV
"C"
"A"
"B"
From Pipe "2" of ASV
From Intake Manifold
Air Sw. Solenoid

VACUUM CONTROL VALVE (VCV) CHECK

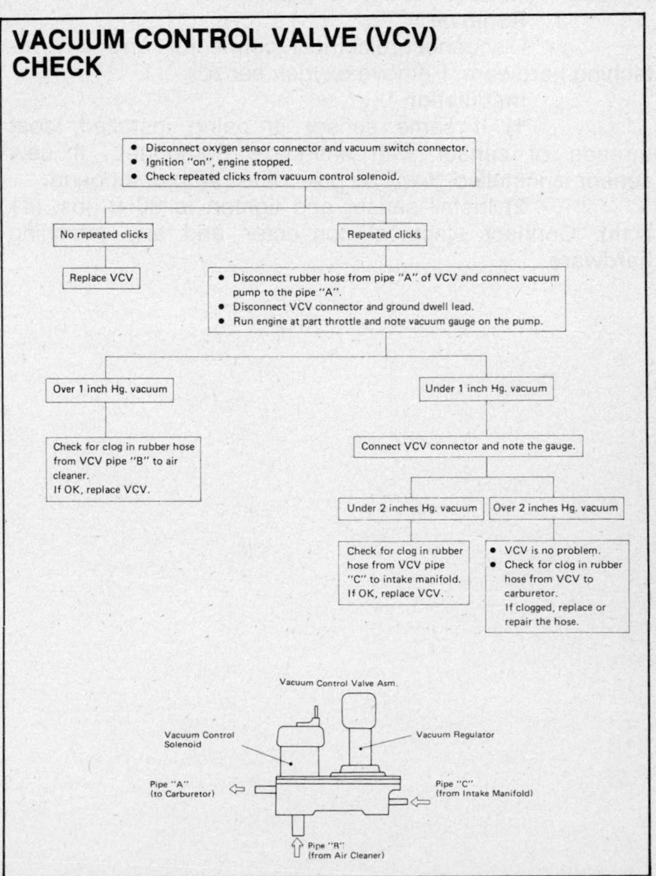

• Disconnect oxygen sensor connector and vacuum switch connector.
• Ignition "on", engine stopped.
• Check repeated clicks from vacuum control solenoid.
No repeated clicks
Repeated clicks
Replace VCV
• Disconnect rubber hose from pipe "A" of VCV and connect vacuum pump to the pipe "A".
• Disconnect VCV connector and ground dwell lead.
• Run engine at part throttle and note vacuum gauge on the pump.
Over 1 inch Hg. vacuum
Under 1 inch Hg. vacuum
Check for clog in rubber hose from VCV pipe "B" to air cleaner.
If OK, replace VCV.
Connect VCV connector and note the gauge.
Under 2 inches Hg. vacuum
Over 2 inches Hg. vacuum
Check for clog in rubber hose from VCV pipe "C" to intake manifold.
If OK, replace VCV.
• VCV is no problem.
• Check for clog in rubber hose from VCV to carburetor.
If clogged, replace or repair the hose.
Vacuum Control Valve Asm.
Vacuum Control Solenoid
Vacuum Regulator
Pipe "A" (to Carburetor)
Pipe "C" (from Intake Manifold)
Pipe "B" (from Air Cleaner)

ISUZU CLOSED LOOP EMISSION SYSTEM (Cont.)

REMOVAL & INSTALLATION

COOLANT TEMPERATURE SWITCH

Removal & Installation

Disconnect electrical connection from temperature switch. Remove switch. Install new switch and tighten to 72 INCH lbs. (8.1 N.m). Reconnect electrical connector.

VACUUM CONTROLLER

Removal & Installation

Disconnect electrical connector. Disconnect vacuum hoses from vacuum regulator and solenoid. Remove vacuum controller. To install, reverse removal procedures.

IDLE & WIDE OPEN THROTTLE SWITCHES

Removal & Installation

Disconnect electrical connectors. Disconnect vacuum hoses from sensors. Remove sensors. To install, reverse removal procedures.

OXYGEN SENSOR

Oxygen sensor uses a permanently attached pig-tail and connector. The pig-tail should not be removed from sensor. Damage or removal of pig-tail or connector could affect proper operation of sensor. Care must be taken when handling sensor. The in-line electrical connector and louvered end must be kept free of grease or other contaminants. Do not use cleaning solvents of any type. Sensor may be difficult to remove when engine temperature is below 120°F (48°C). Excessive force may damage threads in exhaust manifold or pipe.

Removal

Disconnect electrical connector and any attaching hardware. Remove oxygen sensor.

Installation

1) If same sensor is being installed, coat threads of sensor with anti-sieze compound. If new sensor is installed, it will be pre-coated with compound.

2) Install sensor and tighten to 30 ft. lbs. (41 N.m). Connect electrical connector and any attaching hardware.

ISUZU I-TEC CONTROL SYSTEM

Impulse

DESCRIPTION

The I-TEC control system is an electronically controlled system used on Isuzu Impulse. It monitors the engine and controls engine operation. This lowers emissions while maintaining fuel economy and driveability.

The Microcomputer Control Unit (MCU) is the "brain" of the system. The MCU controls fuel and ignition systems, constantly adjusting engine operation. The system consists of the MCU, various engine sensors, fuel injectors and a transistorized ignition coil.

Fig. 1: Impulse I-TEC System

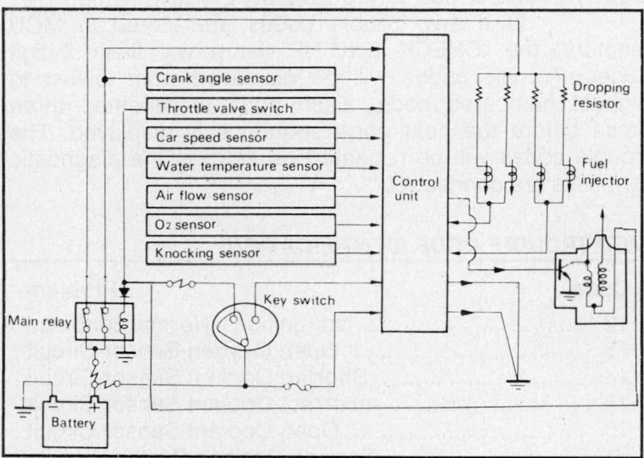
Crank angle sensor
Throttle valve switch
Car speed sensor
Water temperature sensor
Air flow sensor
O2 sensor
Knocking sensor
Control unit
Dropping resistor
Fuel injector
Key switch
Main relay
Battery

OPERATION

The I-TEC system consists of the following subsystems: Fuel Control system, Data Sensors (engine sensors), Microcomputer Control Unit (MCU), Electronic Spark Control and Fuel Cutoff.

FUEL CONTROL

Fuel control system consists of an electric fuel pump, control relay, fuel filter, 4 fuel injectors, fuel lines, pressure regulator and vacuum switching valve. The injectors are located in the intake manifold and electrically pulsed (timed). The MCU varies the rate of fuel based on engine load information supplied by the data sensors.

The MCU controls the length of time that injectors are open. The pressure regulator receives commands from the vacuum switching valve (VSV), to control fuel pressure. The VSV is located in the engine compartment near the ignition coil. The VSV controls the fuel pressure regulator according to intake manifold vacuum and the MCU.

Because the fuel pressure is precisely controlled, the MCU only has to control the length of time that injectors are open in order to control mixture.

DATA SENSORS

The sensors provide electrical impulses to MCU by monitoring vacuum, temperature, pressure, and other engine operating conditions. Location and operation of each sensor is as follows:

Air Flow Sensor

The air flow sensor is located in a housing between the air filter and throttle valve. The sensor measures the rate of air intake (volume). This information is required for MCU to compute fuel injector duration.

Throttle Position Switch

The throttle position switch is located on the throttle linkage at the throttle body. It detects throttle valve position at engine idle, part throttle and wide open throttle. This information is converted into an electrical signal which is used to determine engine speed.

Oxygen Sensor

This sensor is mounted in the exhaust manifold. An electrical signal is produced, proportional to unburned oxygen in the exhaust gases. The MCU receives the signal from the oxygen sensor. The fuel injection duration rate is then altered by the MCU to provide the proper air/fuel mixture under all engine conditions.

Coolant Temperature Sensor (CTS)

The CTS is located in engine coolant passage of the block, under the intake manifold. It sends coolant temperature information to MCU. This information is used by MCU to determine engine temperature for calculating required air/fuel mixture.

Crank Angle Sensor

This sensor is located inside the distributor housing. The engine speed and relative position of each piston in its cylinder are detected. From these parameters, MCU calculates proper ignition timing and dwell angle. The MCU then sends a signal to the transistorized ignition coil, to create a spark.

Detonation Sensor

The detonation sensor is located on the cylinder head. The sensor sends electrical impulses to the MCU when "knocking" occurs. If "knocking" occurs, MCU retards timing to reduce detonation.

Vehicle Speed Sensor

The MCU receives electrical impulses from the vehicle speed sensor. The sensor is connected to the back of the speedometer.

MICROCOMPUTER CONTROL UNIT (MCU)

The MCU is located under the instrument panel. The MCU analyzes all electrical data signals from the sensors. It controls the ignition coil, fuel injection impulses and the vacuum switching valve.

FUEL CUT SYSTEM

Fuel is shut off during vehicle deceleration when the engine is warm, to reduce exhaust emissions. With engine warm, vehicle at cruising speed and throttle position switch returned to idle position, MCU reduces impulses to fuel injectors.

DIAGNOSTIC SYSTEM

The MCU is equipped with a self-diagnostic system which detects system failures or abnormalities. When a malfunction occurs, the MCU will store a code in its memory. MCU will also turn on a "CHECK ENGINE" lamp located on the instrument panel.

As a bulb and system check, the "CHECK ENGINE" lamp will glow when ignition switch is on and engine is not running. When engine is started, the lamp should go out after 4 seconds. If not, a malfunction has been detected in the I-TEC system.

ISUZU I-TEC CONTROL SYSTEM (Cont.)

NOTE: **The MCU self-diagnosis system is capable of troubleshooting the electrical circuits in the I-TEC system only. The MCU can not detect problems in the data sensors, secondary ignition system, fuel delivery system or engine mechanical conditions.**

Diagnosis of the I-TEC system is done in the following order:

1) Ensure all engine systems NOT related to the system are fully operational. Do not proceed with testing unless all other problems have been corrected. Ensure that all electrical and vacuum connections are correct and in good condition. All I-TEC wires must be at least 4" (100 mm) from any high voltage cables.

2) Ensure all fuel hoses are tight and in good order. Check fuel pump operation. Pressure should be 36 psi (2.5 kg/cm²) when vacuum hose is disconnected from the pressure regulator. Be sure there is no water in fuel tank or any other part of system.

3) Check fuel injection system for proper operation and leakage. Measure the resistance of the dropping resistor. Inspect air regulator electrical connection, cold idle speed and hoses. Check and adjust throttle position switch. *See appropriate fuel injection article in FUEL SYSTEMS Section.*

4) Check and adjust idle speed and ignition timing. *See appropriate Tune-Up Service article in TUNE-UP Section.*

5) Display trouble codes in the MCU memory. To do this, follow procedure given for Entering Diagnostic Mode. The MCU will "FLASH" the trouble codes in the "CHECK ENGINE" lamp.

6) If trouble codes were displayed, go to Diagnostic Circuit Check chart. Follow instructions given in chart.

7) After any MCU circuit repairs are made, clear any trouble codes. Road test vehicle, making sure "CHECK ENGINE" lamp remains off.

Fig. 2: Impulse I-TEC Diagnostic Leads Location

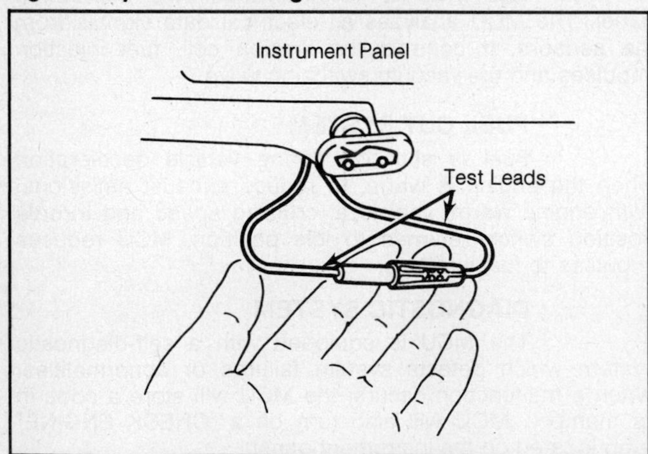
Instrument Panel
Test Leads

DIAGNOSIS & TESTING

The MCU stores circuit failure information under a related trouble code which can be recalled for diagnosis and repair. When recalled, these codes will be displayed by flashes of the "CHECK ENGINE" lamp. Codes start with lowest numbered code. Only codes in which a related malfunction has occurred will be displayed.

NOTE: **An example of trouble codes is as follows: "FLASH", "FLASH", pause, "FLASH", "FLASH", "FLASH" followed by a longer pause identifies trouble code 23. First series of flashes indicates first digit of trouble code. Second series of flashes indicates second digit of trouble code.**

DIAGNOSTIC PROCEDURE

Entering Diagnostic Mode

1) Turn ignition "ON". "CHECK ENGINE" lamp should glow. Locate diagnostic terminal wires near MCU. Connect diagnostic terminal leads together (Brown and Black/Yellow wires) found near MCU. MCU will start to display trouble codes, in the "CHECK ENGINE" lamp.

2) If any trouble codes are stored in MCU memory, the "CHECK ENGINE" lamp will flash 2-digit codes. Trouble codes will be displayed from lowest to highest numbered code. Each code is repeated three times before the next code sequence is displayed. The trouble codes will be repeated as long as the diagnostic terminals are connected.

MCU TROUBLE CODE IDENTIFICATION

Code	Problem
12	No Ignition - Normal condition
13	Open Oxygen Sensor Circuit
14	Shorted Coolant Sensor Circuit
15	Incorrect Coolant Sensor Circuit
16	Open Coolant Sensor Circuit
21	Throttle Position Switch Circuits Connected at Same Time
22	Starter Signal Circuit
23	Output Terminal to Ignition Coil Grounded
25	Output Terminal to Vacuum Switching Solenoid Circuit Open or Grounded
33	Open or Shorted Fuel Injector Circuit
35	Ignition Power Transistor Open
41	Bad Signal From Crank Angle Sensor
43	No Idle Position Signal
44	Lean Oxygen Sensor Indication
45	Rich System Indication
51	Faulty MCU
52	Faulty MCU
53	Vacuum Switching Valve
54	Bad Ignition Transistor or Ground
55	Faulty MCU
61	Circuit to Air Flow Sensor Bad
62	Circuit to Air Flow Sensor Bad
63	No Vehicle Speed Sensor Signal
64	Fuel Injector Transistor or Ground
65	Continuous Signal From Throttle Position Switch
66	Open or Shorted Knock Sensor Circuit

Clearing Trouble Codes

To clear memory of trouble codes, disconnect No. 4 fuse in the fuse box. Connect diagnostic terminals together, turn ignition "ON" and make sure that only code 12 is displayed. Disconnect diagnostic terminals.

NOTE: **Disconnecting the 13 pole connector from the MCU will also clear the memory. Removing No. 4 fuse will also stop clock and other electrical equipment.**

ISUZU I-TEC CONTROL SYSTEM (Cont.)

Fig. 3: Impulse I-TEC System Wiring Diagram

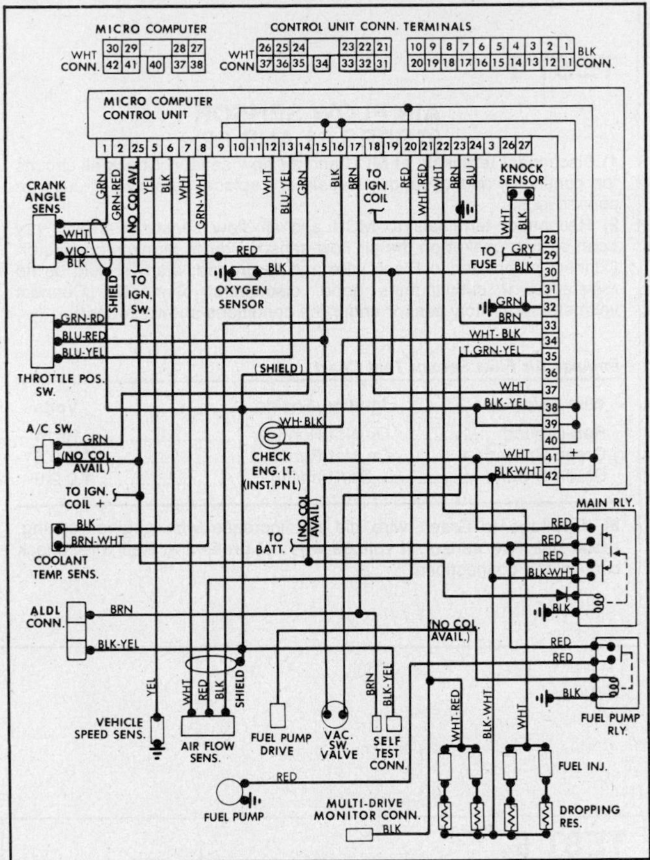
MICRO COMPUTER
CONTROL UNIT CONN. TERMINALS
WHT CONN.
BLK CONN.
MICRO COMPUTER CONTROL UNIT
CRANK ANGLE SENS.
KNOCK SENSOR
TO IGN. COIL
OXYGEN SENSOR
TO IGN. SW.
THROTTLE POS. SW.
A/C SW.
TO IGN. COIL +
CHECK ENG. LT. (INST. PNL)
COOLANT TEMP. SENS.
TO BATT.
MAIN RLY.
ALDL CONN.
VEHICLE SPEED SENS.
AIR FLOW SENS.
FUEL PUMP DRIVE
VAC. SW. VALVE
SELF TEST CONN.
FUEL PUMP RLY.
FUEL INJ.
FUEL PUMP
MULTI-DRIVE MONITOR CONN.
DROPPING RES.

Also see Chassis Wiring in WIRING DIAGRAMS Section.

Diagnostic Tools

The I-TEC system does not require special tools for diagnosis. A tachometer, ohmmeter, voltmeter, jumper wires and a 1.5 volt battery are the only tools necessary for diagnosis.

Circuit Inspection

1) Disconnect all three connectors from I-TEC system to the MCU before turning ignition switch on.

2) When connecting test leads to I-TEC circuit harness, insert wire at back side of connector.

3) Carefully note the terminal number to avoid a direct battery connection when the ignition is turned on.

Fig. 4: Isuzu I-TEC Terminal Identification

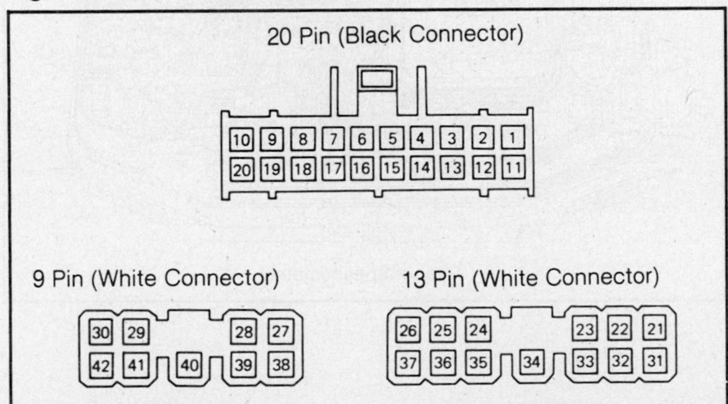
20 Pin (Black Connector)
10 9 8 7 6 5 4 3 2 1
20 19 18 17 16 15 14 13 12 11
9 Pin (White Connector)
30 29 28 27
42 41 40 39 38
13 Pin (White Connector)
26 25 24 23 22 21
37 36 35 34 33 32 31

4) Disconnect wiring at MCU, sensor or output device when testing for shorts or continuity. If trouble can not be corrected by test procedures, clear memory. Reconnect all circuits, road test vehicle and recheck trouble code display. If trouble can not be found, test MCU by installing a known good MCU unit.

1983 TEST CHARTS

TEST 1

POWER SUPPLY CHECK

1) Disconnect MCU control terminals at MCU. Turn ignition on, and check for battery voltage at terminals 29 and 41. If battery voltage is present, go to step **2)**. If no voltage at terminals, check main relay, starter switch, fuses, fusible link and circuits.

2) Check for continuity between terminals 38 and 39 and ground. If ohmmeter does not show continuity to ground, check ground connection, terminal ends and wires.

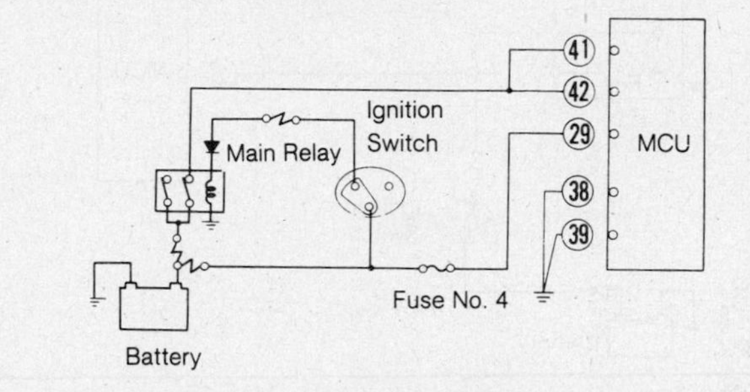
41
42
29
38
39
MCU
Ignition Switch
Main Relay
Fuse No. 4
Battery

TEST 2

OXYGEN SENSOR (CODES 13, 44 AND 45)

1) Disconnect MCU control terminals at MCU. Disconnect oxygen sensor at connector. Check for continuity and grounds between terminal 30 and oxygen sensor connector. If circuits are good, go to step **2)**.

CAUTION: A voltmeter with internal resistance of at least 20,000 ohms must be used to check the oxygen sensor. Damage to the oxygen sensor may result if any other test meter is used.

2) Connect a test wire to the oxygen sensor terminal, and reconnect sensor terminal to I-TEC wiring. Connect the positive lead of the tester to the test wire and the negative lead to ground. Start engine, and check for voltage variations between 0 and .8 volts when engine speed is momentarily increased. Replace oxygen sensor if no voltage variation is noted.

TEST 3

WATER TEMPERATURE SENSOR (CODES 14, 15 AND 16)

1) Disconnect MCU control terminals at MCU. Disconnect terminal connector from water temperature sensor. Check circuits 6 and 8 between the MCU terminal and water temperature sensor for shorts and grounds.

2) Measure the resistance across the water temperature sensor terminals. Compare sensor resistance to coolant temperature.

Impulse Water Temperature Sensor Resistance

Temperature	Resistance
15 F° (-10 C°)	7—12 ohms
50 F° (10 C°)	3—5 ohms
70 F° (21 C°)	2—3 ohms
125 F° (52 C°)	0.7—1 ohms
175 F° (80 C°)	0.2—0.4 ohms

3) Replace water temperature sensor if resistance does not meet specifications.

ISUZU I-TEC CONTROL SYSTEM (Cont.)

TEST 4

THROTTLE POSITION SWITCH (CODES 21, 43 AND 65)

1) Disconnect MCU control terminals at MCU. Disconnect terminal at throttle position switch. Check circuits between MCU terminals 2 and 13 and throttle position switch for continuity and grounds. Repair any faulty wiring or terminal connectors.
2) Check throttle position switch contacts at idle, cruise and full throttle positions. Test terminal I and terminal B for continuity at idle position. Test terminal F and terminal B for continuity at full throttle position. Check that no continuity is present between terminals I, F or B when throttle control is in any cruise position. If switch fails above tests, replace throttle position switch.

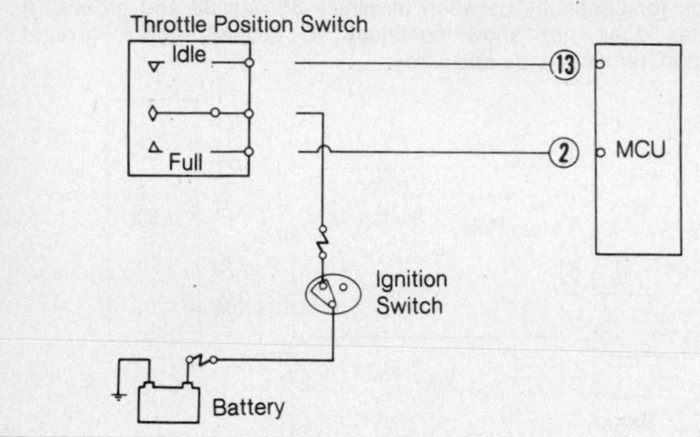
Throttle Position Switch
Idle
Full
13
2
MCU
Ignition Switch
Battery

TEST 5

STARTER SIGNAL (CODE 22)

Disconnect MCU control terminals at MCU. Connect voltmeter positive lead to terminal 25 and negative lead to ground. Check for starter signal when ignition switch is turned to start position. If no signal, check circuits to ignition switch and ignition switch.

TEST 6

CRANK ANGLE SENSOR (CODE 41)

1) Disconnect terminals at MCU and crank angle sensor connector at distributor. Check all circuits for continuity and grounds. Replace any defective circuits or connections.
2) If circuits tested are good, replace distributor assembly.

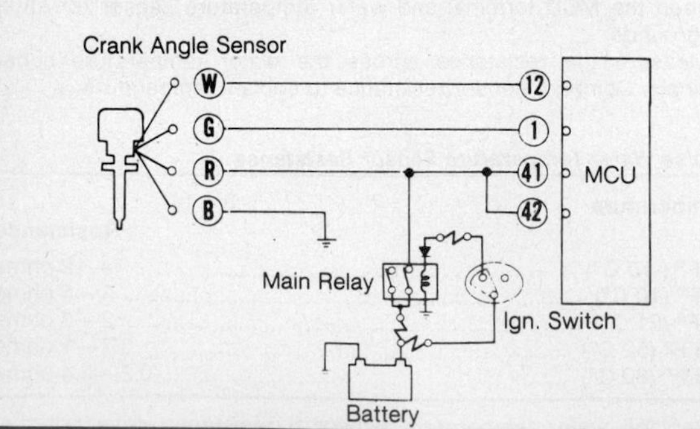
Crank Angle Sensor
W
G
R
B
12
1
41
42
MCU
Main Relay
Ign. Switch
Battery

TEST 7

AIR FLOW SENSOR (CODES 61 AND 62)

1) Disconnect terminals at MCU and air flow sensor. Check all circuits for continuity and grounds. Repair or replace defective circuits or connections.
2) Reconnect terminals to MCU and air flow sensor. Carefully pry open sealing gasket on the air flow sensor side of terminal connector. Connect ohmmeter to Black wire and to ground; there should be no resistance. If circuit tests good, disconnect ohmmeter. Connect voltmeter to air flow sensor under the conditions shown in chart.

Impulse Air Flow Sensor Test Chart

Wire Color	Ignition/Engine	Volts
Red-Ground	On/Not Running	10-14
Green-Ground	On/Not Running	0.2-0.6
Green-Ground	On/Running	1.0-2.0

3) If voltage in Green wire did not increase with engine running, replace air flow sensor. If voltage was not present at Red wire, check circuits and connections.

TEST 8

VEHICLE SPEED SENSOR (CODE 63)

1) Disconnect MCU control terminals at MCU. Connect ohmmeter between terminal 5 and ground. Disconnect speedometer cable from transmission and turn inner cable slowly. If vehicle speed sensor circuit is good, ohmmeter will show open and closed circuit alternately.
2) If no signal pulses are found in step **1)**. Disconnect 10 pin connector from back of speedometer gauge. Locate Yellow wire at terminal number 4. Check circuit between terminal 5 and terminal 4 for shorts and grounds.
3) If trouble cannot be located, replace speedometer assembly.

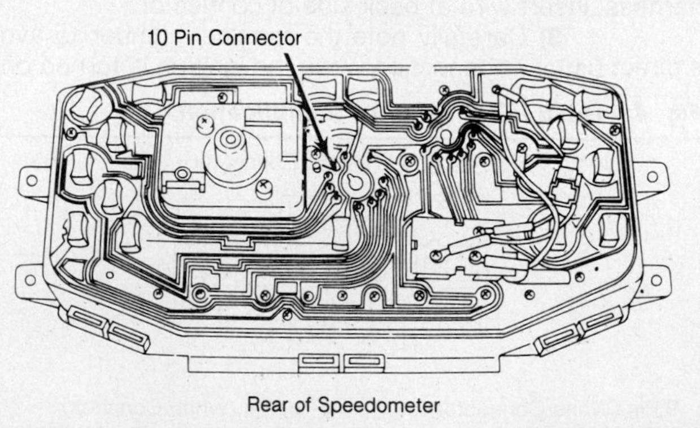
10 Pin Connector
Rear of Speedometer

ISUZU I-TEC CONTROL SYSTEM (Cont.)

TEST 9

DETONATION SENSOR (CODE 66)

1) Disconnect terminals at MCU and at detonation sensor. Check circuits for shorts and grounds.
2) The resistance across the detonation sensor terminals should be 650 — 800 ohms. Replace sensor if ohms reading is different.

TEST 10

MCU (CODES 51, 52 AND 55)

Remove MCU terminals and check all connectors. Reconnect MCU terminals and road test vehicle. Check to see if trouble codes have been corrected. If trouble codes are still present, replace MCU control unit.

TEST 11

POWER TRANSISTOR SYSTEM (CODES 23, 35 AND 54)

1) Disconnect terminal connector near coil (lead connects to pin 24 of MCU connector). Disconnect high tension wire between coil and center of distributor cap. Hold high tension lead 1/4" (6mm) away from good metal ground. Turn ignition switch on. Use jumper wire to connect "Y" terminal of transistor to positive side of 1.5 volt battery. Negative side of battery has to be touching ground. Disconnect jumper lead from 1.5 volt battery. Check to see if a spark is created from the high tension lead to ground. If spark is not created, replace the power transistor and bracket assembly.
2) Disconnect MCU terminal connectors at MCU, and ignition coil. Check circuit from pin 24 to ignition coil for continuity or shorts. Check pins 23 and 33 for good ground. Repair or replace defective wires or connections.

Lead From Transistor
Jumper Wire
Coil
High Tension Lead
1.5 Volt Battery

TEST 12

VACUUM SWITCHING VALVE (CODE 25 AND 53)

1) Disconnect MCU terminal connectors at MCU, and at vacuum switching valve. Check circuit between pin 35 and LT. Green/Yellow wire for continuity and grounds. Repair or replace defective wires or connections.
2) Check vacuum switching valve. *See Isuzu I-TEC EFI article in Fuel Systems Section.*

TEST 13

FUEL INJECTOR CIRCUITS (CODE 33)

1) Disconnect MCU terminal connectors at MCU, and fuel injectors. Check circuits between pin 21 and injectors A and B. Check circuits between pin 22 and injectors C and D. Repair or replace circuits that do not have continuity or are grounded.
2) Turn ignition on. Check for 12 volts at dropping resistor side of fuel injector terminals. If voltage is not present, check dropping resistor, main relay and ignition switch.

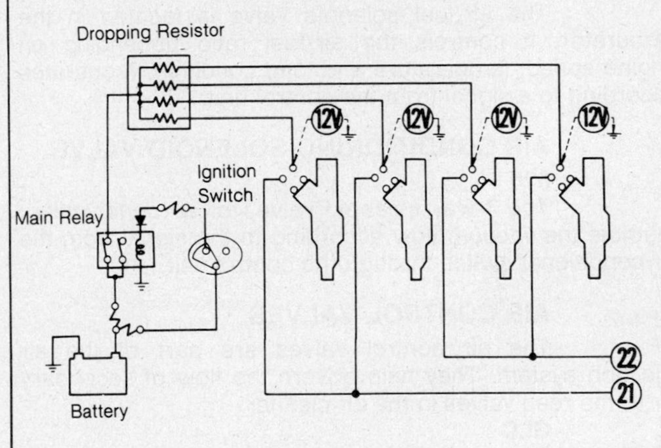
Dropping Resistor
12V
12V
12V
12V
Ignition Switch
Main Relay
Battery
22
21

TEST 14

INJECTOR TRANSISTOR GROUND CIRCUIT (CODE 64)

Disconnect MCU terminal connectors at MCU. Check pins 31 and 32 for continuity to ground. Repair defects to circuits or connections.

MAZDA PISTON ENGINE COMPUTERIZED ENGINE CONTROL

GLC & 626

DESCRIPTION

The Mazda GLC and 626 models use a computerized engine control system to reduce exhaust emissions and maintain good fuel economy.

The main function of the system is the control of the EGR control valve and air/fuel ratio under all operating conditions. All system functions are governed by an electronic control unit located behind the right kick panel in the passenger compartment.

OPERATION

CONTROL UNIT

Through various sensors, the control unit detects the following: Engine speed, intake manifold vacuum, coolant temperature, oxygen concentration in exhaust system, EGR control valve position (626), throttle opening, in-gear position and air conditioner ON/OFF condition.

The control unit governs the operation of the feedback-type carburetor, EGR system and air injection system.

AIR/FUEL SOLENOID VALVE

The air/fuel solenoid valve is located in the carburetor. It controls the air/fuel ratio depending on engine speed, temperature and load condition. It operates according to a signal from the control unit.

AIR CONDITIONING SOLENOID VALVE

626

The 3-way solenoid valve, for air conditioning, restricts the vacuum flow according to the signal from the air conditioner switch through the control unit.

AIR CONTROL VALVES

The air control valves are part of the air injection system. They help govern the flow of secondary air to the reed valves in the air cleaner.

GLC

An air control valve is used on Federal models only. It controls the flow of secondary air to the exhaust manifold, upstream of the front catalytic converter. It is controlled by the ACV solenoid which in turn is governed by the control unit.

626

The No. 1 air control valve controls flow of secondary air to reed valve "A" according to intake manifold vacuum. It also supplies air when 3-way solenoid valve is "ON".

The No. 2 air control valve (Federal models only) is used in conjunction with the No.1 valve to control air flow to reed valve "A". No. 2 air control valve is vacuum actuated. The vacuum signal is controlled by the ACV solenoid valve which in turn is governed by the control unit.

ALTITUDE COMPENSATOR

Federal vehicles are equipped with an altitude compensator which maintains the air/fuel mixture in the intake manifold. It adds air to carburetor air bleeds when atmospheric pressure drops due to elevation. On GLC models, the altitude compensator also helps govern the operation of the EGR valve.

COASTING RICHER SOLENOID VALVE

626

The coasting richer solenoid valve is located in the carburetor secondary fuel circuit. It functions after 1 second when engine speed is 1400-2000 RPM and the idle, neutral and clutch switch are off.

CLUTCH & NEUTRAL SWITCH

The clutch and neutral switches detect in-gear condition. The neutral switch is on in neutral and off in all other ranges. The clutch switch is on when the clutch pedal is depressed and off when pedal is released.

DUTY SOLENOID VALVES

626

The duty solenoid valves consist of the vent and vacuum valves. Their purpose is to control vacuum to the EGR valve. The duty solenoid valves are controlled by signals from the control unit.

The vent valve is connected to the air cleaner and controls fresh air flow to the duty solenoid valve. The vacuum valve controls intake manifold vacuum flow.

EGR SYSTEM

EGR Control Valve

The EGR valve supplies exhaust gas to the intake manifold. It operates during acceleration and constant speed driving. The EGR valve is vacuum actuated. The vacuum signal is governed by the control unit.

EGR Modulator Valve (GLC)

The EGR modulator valve helps control the operation of the EGR valve. The modulator valve senses carburetor ported vacuum and exhaust gas pressure.

EGR Position Sensor (626)

The EGR position sensor detects the lift of the EGR valve and sends the signal to the control unit.

EGR Thermo Valve (GLC)

The EGR thermo valve prevents the flow of exhaust gas to the EGR control valve until the engine is at operating temperature.

IDLE UP SYSTEM

626

The idle-up system increases engine RPM at idle on models equipped with air conditioning and/or power steering.

IDLE SWITCH

The idle switch, located on the carburetor, detects throttle opening for the control unit. The idle switch is off at idle and on at 1200-1300 RPM in neutral.

OXYGEN SENSOR

The oxygen sensor is part of a closed loop system which consists of the control unit and the sensor. The sensor detects the exhaust manifold oxygen concentration and sends the signal to the control unit.

MAZDA PISTON ENGINE
COMPUTERIZED ENGINE CONTROL (Cont.)

Fig. 1: 626 Emission Control Component Location

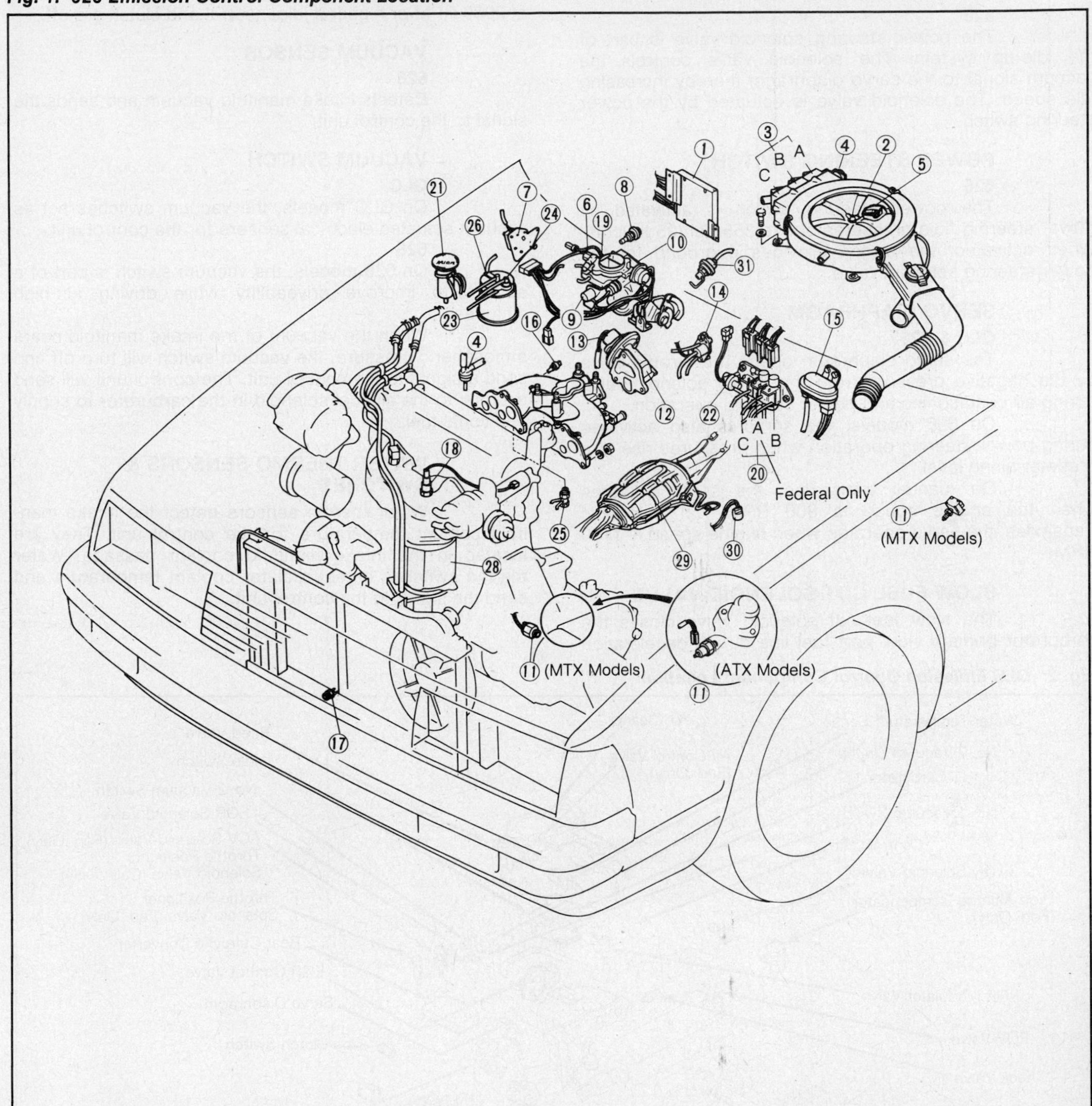
A
B
C
Federal Only
(MTX Models)
(MTX Models)
(ATX Models)

1. Control Unit
2. Air Cleaner
3. Reed Valve
4. No.1 ACV
   No.2 ACV (Fed. Only)
5. Idle Compensator Valve
6. Air Vent Solenoid Valve
7. Idle Switch
8. Dash Pot
9. Coasting Richer Solenoid
10. Slow Fuel Cut Solenoid Valve
11. Clutch Switch & Neutral Switch
12. EGR Valve
13. EGR Position Sensor
14. Duty Solenoid Valve
15. Vacuum Sensor
16. Water Thermo Sensor
17. Water Thermo Switch
18. O_2 Sensor
19. A/F Solenoid Valve
20. 3-Way Solenoid Valve
21. Altitude Compensator (Fed. Only)
22. Vacuum Switch
23. Canister
24. No. 1 Purge Control Valve
25. Water Thermo Valve
26. No. 2 Purge Control Valve
27. Check Valve
28. Front Catalyst
29. Rear Catalyst
30. Power Steering Switch
31. Servo Diaphragm

MAZDA PISTON ENGINE
COMPUTERIZED ENGINE CONTROL (Cont.)

POWER STEERING SOLENOID VALVE

626

The power steering solenoid valve is part of the idle-up system. The solenoid valve controls the vacuum signal to the servo diaphragm thereby increasing idle speed. The solenoid valve is actuated by the power steering switch.

POWER STEERING SWITCH

626

The power steering switch is activated by power steering fluid pressures above 355 psi (25 kg/cm²). When activated, the switch provides a ground for the power steering solenoid valve.

SERVO DIAPHRAGM

GLC & 626

The servo diaphragm opens the throttle valve by the negative pressure from the 3-way solenoid valve during air conditioning and power steering operation.

On 626 models, the servo is also activated during power steering operation when pressures rise to a predetermined level.

On manual transaxles, the servo operates when the engine speed is 900 RPM. On automatic transaxles, the servo operates when engine speed is 1150 RPM.

SLOW FUEL CUT SOLENOID VALVE

The slow fuel cut solenoid valve closes the carburetor primary slow port fuel line during deceleration and when the ignition switch is off. The valve will function at 2000 RPM or higher if idle, neutral and clutch are off.

VACUUM SENSOR

626

Detects intake manifold vacuum and sends the signal to the control unit.

VACUUM SWITCH

GLC

On GLC models, the vacuum switches act as vacuum actuated electrical sensors for the control unit.

626

On 626 models, the vacuum switch is part of a system to improve driveability while driving at high altitudes.

When the vacuum of the intake manifold nears atmospheric pressure, the vacuum switch will turn off and send a signal to the control unit. The control unit will send a signal to the air/fuel solenoid in the carburetor to supply additional fuel.

WATER THERMO SENSORS & SWITCHES

Water thermo sensors detect the intake manifold coolant temperature for the control unit. They are located in the intake manifold coolant passage. Water thermo switches detect radiator coolant temperature and send the signal to the control unit.

Fig. 2: GLC Emission Control Component Location

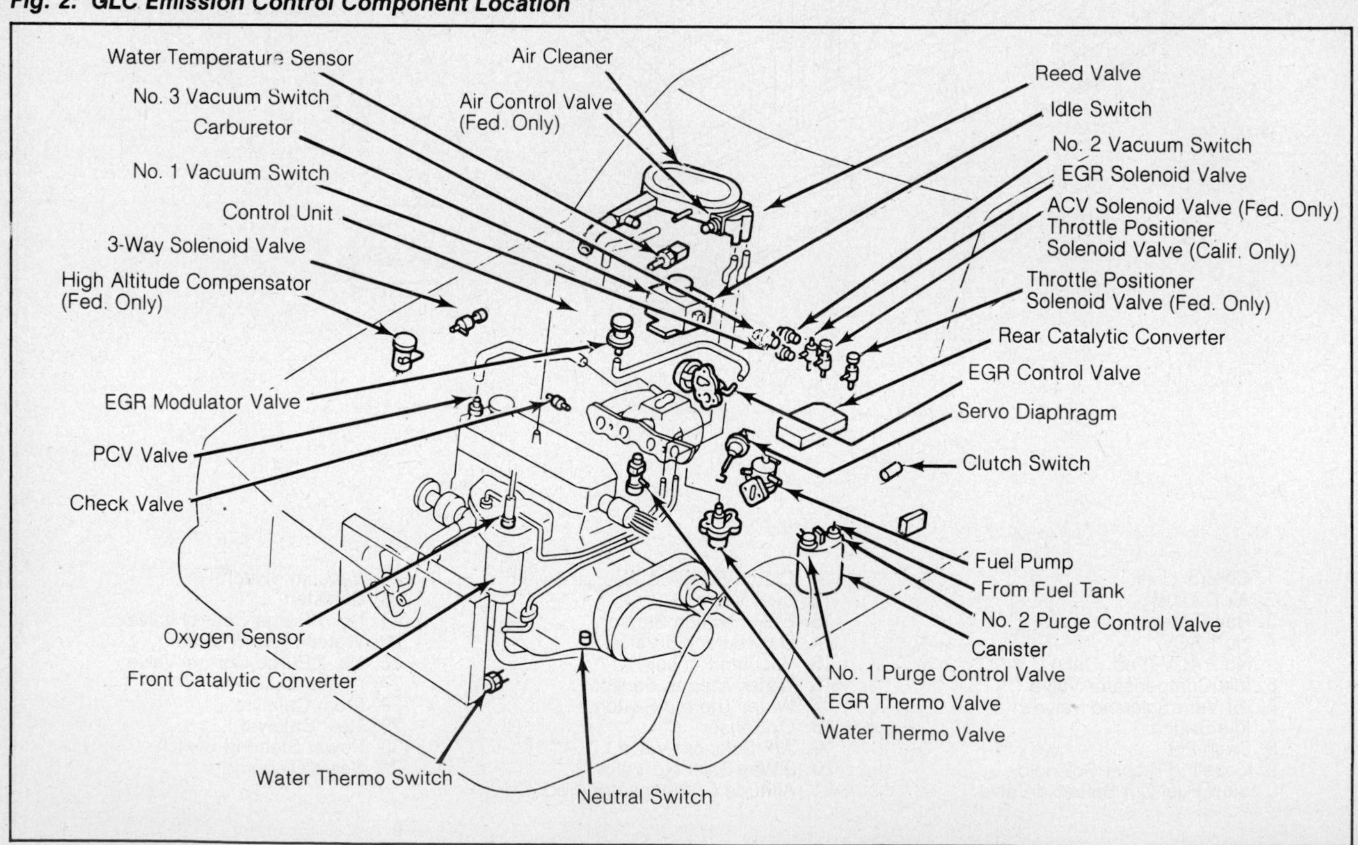
Water Temperature Sensor
Air Cleaner
No. 3 Vacuum Switch
Air Control Valve
(Fed. Only)
Carburetor
No. 1 Vacuum Switch
Control Unit
3-Way Solenoid Valve
High Altitude Compensator
(Fed. Only)
EGR Modulator Valve
PCV Valve
Check Valve
Oxygen Sensor
Front Catalytic Converter
Water Thermo Switch
Neutral Switch
Reed Valve
Idle Switch
No. 2 Vacuum Switch
EGR Solenoid Valve
ACV Solenoid Valve (Fed. Only)
Throttle Positioner
Solenoid Valve (Calif. Only)
Throttle Positioner
Solenoid Valve (Fed. Only)
Rear Catalytic Converter
EGR Control Valve
Servo Diaphragm
Clutch Switch
Fuel Pump
From Fuel Tank
No. 2 Purge Control Valve
Canister
No. 1 Purge Control Valve
EGR Thermo Valve
Water Thermo Valve

MAZDA PISTON ENGINE COMPUTERIZED ENGINE CONTROL (Cont.)

TESTING & ADJUSTMENT

NOTE: Testing of the Air/Fuel Solenoid Valve will be found in the appropriate article in FUEL SYSTEMS Section.

ALTITUDE COMPENSATOR

GLC

All ports on the altitude compensator should be open at elevations of 984-2295 ft. (300-700 m). All air passages should be blocked at higher elevations.

626

At altitudes of 3609 ft. (1100 m) or above, the altitude compensator passages should be blocked. Air passages should be open at lower elevations.

Fig. 3: Altitude Compensator Systems

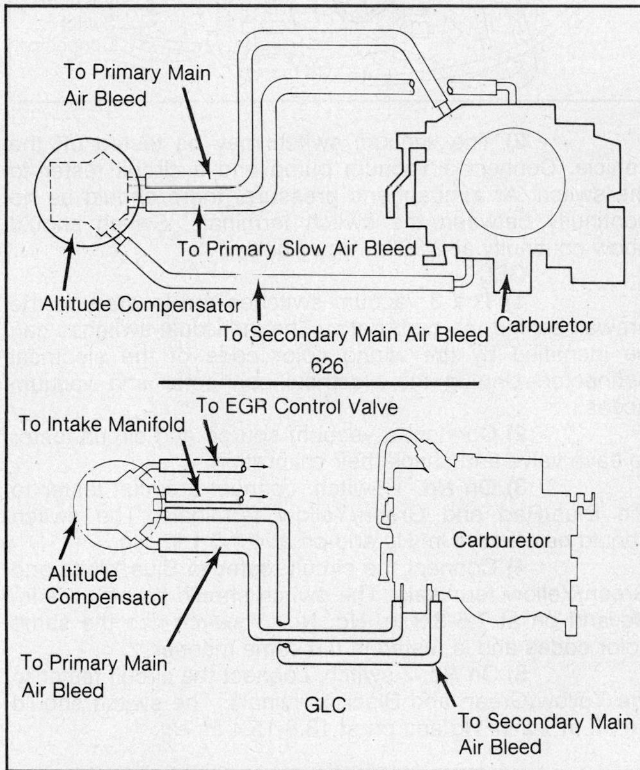
To Primary Main Air Bleed
To Primary Slow Air Bleed
Altitude Compensator
To Secondary Main Air Bleed
Carburetor
626
To EGR Control Valve
To Intake Manifold
Carburetor
Altitude Compensator
To Primary Main Air Bleed
GLC
To Secondary Main Air Bleed

Illustration applies to Federal vehicles only.

IDLE UP SYSTEM

System Check

1) Warm engine to operating temperature and run at idle. Turn air conditioner on and check that servo diaphragm stem is raised.

2) The servo diaphragm is activated when the air conditioner is on and engine speed is 1300 RPM for 626 models and 1200 RPM on GLC models.

3) Turn air conditioner off. On 626 models, turn steering wheel all the way to the right or left and ensure servo diaphragm stem is raised. If system does not respond as described, check the 3-way solenoid valves, servo diaphragm and control unit signal.

3-Way Solenoid Valves

1) On 626 models, unplug connector from air conditioning solenoid valve. Ground the Black/Red terminal and apply 12V to Black/White terminal. With power applied, the solenoid valve should be open.

2) Unplug connector from power steering solenoid valve. Ground the Green/Red terminal and apply 12V to Black/White terminal. Solenoid valve should be open. *See Fig. 4.*

Fig. 4: Idle Up System 3-Way Solenoid Valves for 626

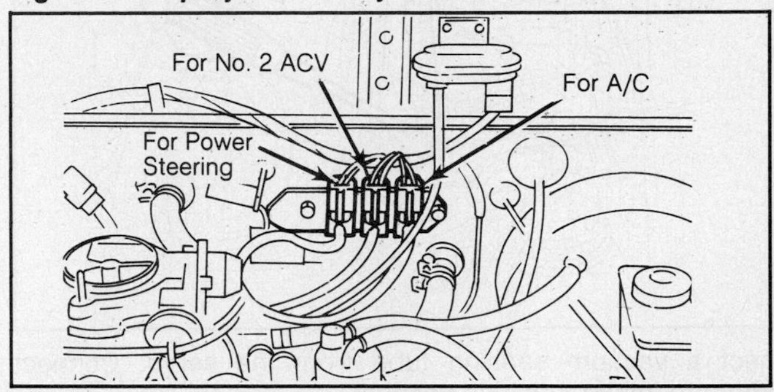
For No. 2 ACV
For A/C
For Power Steering

3) On GLC models, unplug connector from throttle positioner solenoid valve. Valve is located on the firewall behind the carburetor. Apply battery power to Yellow/Black terminal and ground the Light Green/Red terminal.

4) The throttle positioner solenoid should be open to manifold vacuum signal. Replace if it does not respond as described.

Power Steering Switch

1) Start engine and run at idle. Unplug the power steering switch connector from the steering gear housing. Turn the steering wheel all the way to the left or right. Ensure there is continuity between the switch terminals.

2) When the oil pressure is above 355 psi (25 kg/cm²), the switch should be on. At pressures below 355 psi (25 kg/cm²), the switch should be off.

Servo Diaphragm Adjustment (626)

1) Remove the air cleaner. Plug the hoses of the idle compensator, thermo sensor and the reed valves. Warm up engine to operating temperature. All accessories should be off. Do not adjust while the electric fan motor is running.

2) On models with air conditioner only, disconnect the A/C solenoid valve-to-servo vacuum sensing tube from the servo diaphragm. Apply manifold vacuum to the servo diaphragm. Engine speed should increase to 1200-1400 RPM. If not, turn adjusting screw. *See Fig. 5.*

3) If vehicle is equipped with A/C and power steering, follow procedures outlined in steps **1)** and **2)** before continuing. On power steering models, disconnect power steering solenoid valve-to-servo vacuum sensing tube.

4) Apply manifold vacuum to the servo. Engine speed should increase to 800-1000 RPM on manual transaxle models and 1050-1250 RPM on automatic transaxle models.

5) If engine speed must be adjusted, turn the adjusting screw on the servo diaphragm head. Recheck engine speed.

Servo Diaphragm Adjustment (GLC)

1) Remove the air cleaner. Warm up engine to operating temperature and connect a tachometer. Discon-

MAZDA PISTON ENGINE
COMPUTERIZED ENGINE CONTROL (Cont.)

Fig. 5: Adjusting Servo Diaphragm (A/C Models)

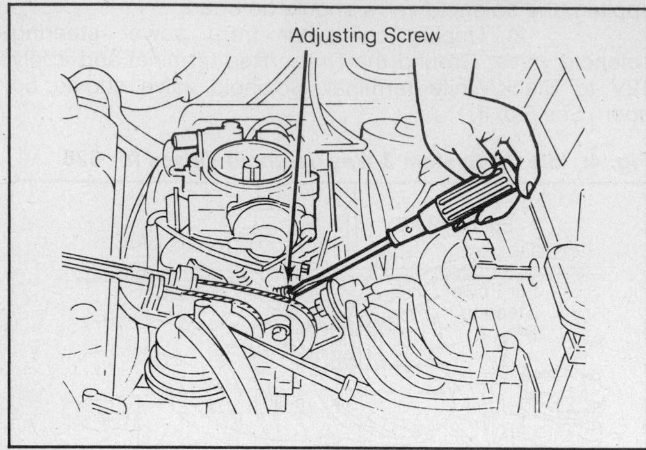
Adjusting Screw

nect a vacuum sensing tube from the servo. Connect servo to intake manifold vacuum.

2) Increase engine speed to 2000 RPM and release throttle. Engine speed should be within 1100-1300 RPM. If engine speed is not within specification, adjust servo screw.

Fig. 6: Idle Up System

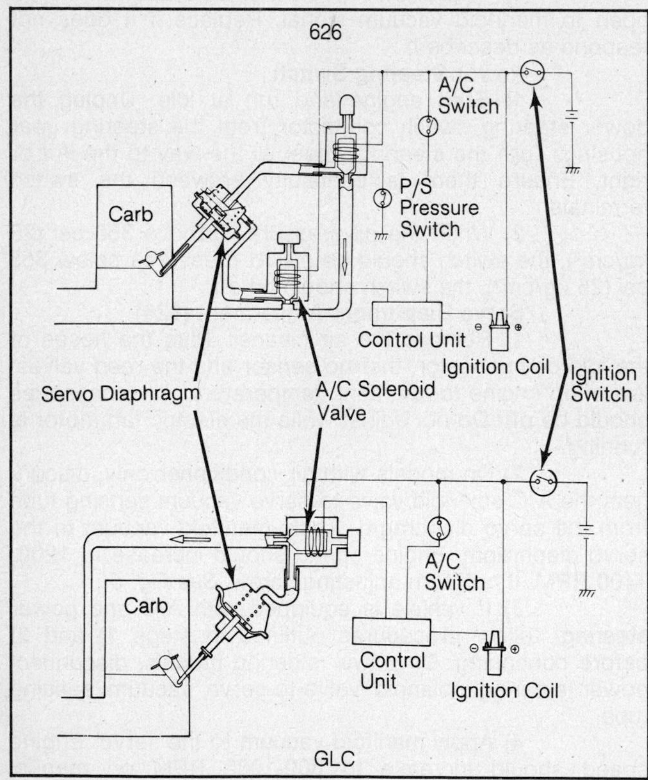
626
A/C Switch
P/S Pressure Switch
Carb
Control Unit
Ignition Coil
Ignition Switch
Servo Diaphragm
A/C Solenoid Valve
A/C Switch
Carb
Control Unit
Ignition Coil
GLC

OXYGEN SENSOR

No testing procedure is provided by the manufacturer for the oxygen sensor.

VACUUM SWITCH

626

1) Run the engine at idle. Connect a voltmeter to the vacuum switch connector Green terminal. Voltmeter should read below 1.5V. Disconnect and plug vacuum sensing tube from the vacuum switch. Voltmeter should read 12V. *See Fig. 7* .

Fig. 7: Testing Vacuum Switch for 626

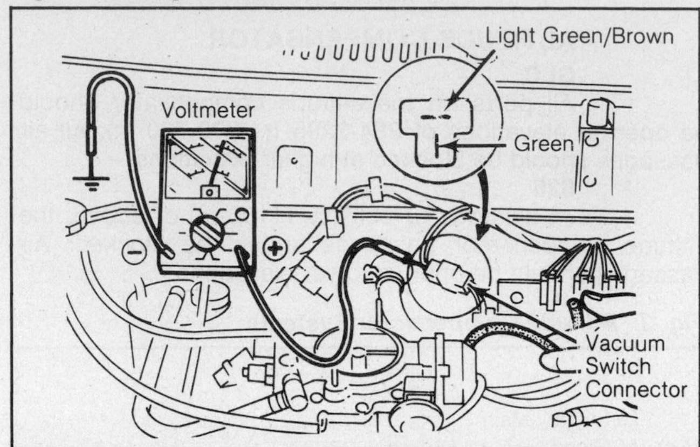
Light Green/Brown
Voltmeter
Green
Vacuum Switch Connector

2) The vacuum switch may be tested off the vehicle. Connect a vacuum pump and a circuit tester to the switch. At atmospheric pressure, there should be no continuity between the switch terminals. Switch should show continuity at 2.36 in. Hg or below.

GLC

1) The 3 vacuum switches are located on the firewall behind the carburetor. The individual switches can be identified by the wiring color code of the electrical connector. Unplug the electrical connector and vacuum hoses.

2) Connect a vacuum source and circuit tester to each valve and check their calibration.

3) On No. 1 switch, connect a circuit tester to the Blue/Red and Green/Yellow terminals. The switch should be off at .8 in. Hg and on at 4.3-5.1 in. Hg.

4) Connect the circuit tester to Blue/White and Green/Yellow terminals. The switch should be off at .9 in. Hg and on at 7.5-8.3 in. Hg. No. 3 switch has the same color codes and is tested in the same manner.

5) On No. 2 switch, connect the circuit tester to the Yellow/Green and Black terminals. The switch should be off at 1.2 in. Hg and on at 13.8-15.4 in. Hg.

WATER THERMO SWITCHES

GLC & 626

1) Remove switch from lower left hand corner of radiator. On GLC models, the switch will have Green/Red and Black wires attached to it. On 626 models, Green/Black and Black wires are attached to the switch.

2) Place the switch in water with a thermometer and heat up water gradually. Check the temperature at which continuity exists between both terminals of the switch.

3) The switch should show continuity at 59.4-66.6°F (15-19°C). Replace the switch if it does not agree with standard value.

WATER THERMO SENSOR

626

Remove water thermo sensor from the intake manifold. Sensor will have Blue/Red and Blue/Yellow

MAZDA PISTON ENGINE
COMPUTERIZED ENGINE CONTROL (Cont.)

wires attached. Place sensor in water with a thermometer and heat up water gradually. Check calibration of the sensor. *See Water Thermo Sensor Calibration table*.

WATER THERMO SENSOR CALIBRATION

Water Temperature °F (°C)	Resistance (Ohms)
68 (20)	2210-2690
176 (80)	288-352

GLC & 626 CONTROL UNITS

1) The control unit may be tested with a voltmeter. Engine must be at operating temperature. For testing, ignition switch must be "ON" and engine not running. Measure voltage at each terminal and compare values to appropriate Control Unit Testing chart.

2) On 626 models, the control unit has a built-in fail safe mechanism. If certain malfunctions occur during driving, the control unit will automatically initiate a command so driving performance will not be affected. *See 626 Control Unit Malfunction chart*.

626 CONTROL UNIT MALFUNCTION CHART

Malfunction	Control Unit Action
Water Thermo Sensor	Outputs a constant 176°F (80°C) command
Oxygen Sensor	Holds A/F solenoid to duty 20%
Vacuum Sensor	Prevents operation of EGR valve; holds A/F solenoid to duty 0%
EGR Position Sensor	Prevents operation of EGR valve

CONTROL UNIT TESTING – GLC

Terminal	Connection	Voltage	Checking Condition
A	Ignition Signal	12V	Ignition Switch "ON"
B	Battery Power	12V	Ignition Switch "ON"
C	Air Conditioner Signal	12V	Air conditioner "ON" (all engine speeds)
D	Slow Fuel Cut Solenoid	12V	At 2500 RPM with terminals m and o disconnected.
E, l, n	Not Necessary to Check		
F	Air/Fuel Solenoid	0-12V	At idle speed
H	Throttle Positioner Solenoid	12V	At 1700 RPM
K	EGR Solenoid	12V	At 2500 RPM
M	ACV Solenoid	12V	At idle speed
N, p, r	Ground	0V	Ignition Switch "ON"
a	O_2 Sensor	0-1V	At idle speed
b	O_2 Sensor (Sealed)	0V	Ignition Switch "ON"
c	Water Temperature Sensor	1.2V	At idle speed
d	Ground (Water Temp. Sensor)	0V	Ignition Switch "ON"
i	Power Steering Signal	12V	Power steering "OFF"
k, l	Vacuum Switch	10V	Ignition Switch "ON"
m	Neutral & Clutch Switch	0V	At idle speed
o	Idle Switch	10V	At idle speed
q	Water Thermo Switch	0V	At idle speed

MAZDA PISTON ENGINE COMPUTERIZED ENGINE CONTROL (Cont.)

CONTROL UNIT TESTING — MAZDA 626

Terminal	CHECKING CONDITION — Engine at normal operating temperature and ignition switch "ON"	
	Connection	Voltage
A	Ignition Coil Negative Terminal	12V
B	Ignition Power Supply	12V
C	Air Conditioner Relay	12V with A/C "ON"
E, I	System Check Terminal	E: 12V; below 1.5V after .4 sec. I: below 1.5V after 2 sec.
F	Air/Fuel Solenoid Valve	12V
H	Coasting Richer Solenoid Valve	12V
D	Slow-Fuel-Cut Sol. Valve	Below 1.5V
J	Air Conditioner Solenoid	12V
K, L	Duty Solenoid Valve	12V
M	Solenoid Valve for ACV	12V
N, R	Ground	0V
a, b	O_2 Sensor	Below 1.5V
c	Water Thermo-Sensor	3.4V at 68°F (20°C); 1.1V at 176°F (80°C)
d	Water Thermo-Sensor Ground	Below 1.5V
e	Vacuum Sensor	4V
f	Vacuum Sensor Ground	Below 1.5V
g	Vacuum Sensor	5V
h, j	EGR Position Sensor	Below 1.5V
l	EGR Position Sensor	5V
k	Vacuum Switch	12V
m	Clutch & Neutral Switch	12V
n	Ignition Switch "Start" Terminal	Below 1.5V; 10V at "START"
o	Idle Switch	12V
p	Idle & Vacuum Switch Ground	Below 1.5V
q	Water Thermo Switch	Below 1.5V at 63°F (17°C)

MAZDA PISTON ENGINE COMPUTERIZED ENGINE CONTROL (Cont.)

Fig. 8: Mazda GLC Computerized Engine Control Wiring Diagram

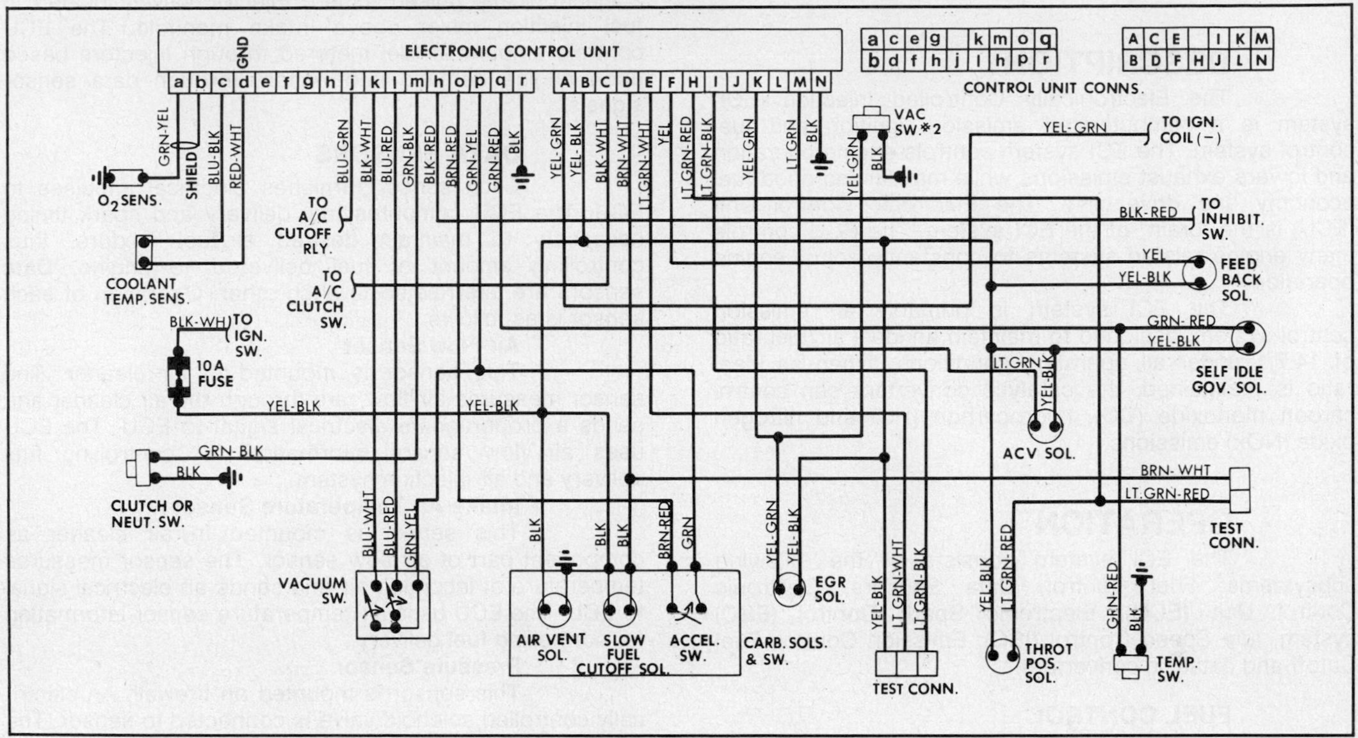
ELECTRONIC CONTROL UNIT
GND
a b c d e f g h j k l m h o p q r
A B C D E F H I J K L M N
a c e g k m o q
b d f h j l h p r
A C E I K M
B D F H J L N
CONTROL UNIT CONNS.
GRN-YEL
SHIELD
BLU-BLK
RED-WHT
O2 SENS.
COOLANT TEMP. SENS.
BLU-GRN
BLU-WHT
BLU-RED
GRN-BLK
BLK-RED
BRN-RED
GRN-YEL
GRN-RED
BLK
YEL-GRN
YEL-BLK
BLK-WHT
BRN-WHT
LT.GRN-WHT
YEL
LT.GRN-RED
LT.GRN-BLK
YEL-GRN
LT.GRN
BLK
TO A/C CUTOFF RLY.
TO A/C CLUTCH SW.
VAC SW.#2
YEL-GRN
BLK
YEL-GRN
TO IGN. COIL (−)
BLK-RED
TO INHIBIT. SW.
YEL
YEL-BLK
FEED BACK SOL.
GRN-RED
YEL-BLK
SELF IDLE GOV. SOL.
LT.GRN
YEL-BLK
ACV SOL.
BLK-WH
TO IGN. SW.
10A FUSE
YEL-BLK
YEL-BLK
GRN-BLK
BLK
CLUTCH OR NEUT. SW.
BLU-WHT
BLU-RED
GRN-YEL
BLK
VACUUM SW.
BLK
BLK
BRN-RED
GRN
AIR VENT SOL.
SLOW FUEL CUTOFF SOL.
ACCEL. SW.
CARB. SOLS. & SW.
YEL-GRN
YEL-BLK
EGR SOL.
YEL-BLK
LT.GRN-WHT
LT.GRN-BLK
TEST CONN.
YEL-BLK
LT.GRN-RED
THROT POS. SOL.
GRN-RED
BLK
TEMP. SW.
BRN-WHT
LT.GRN-RED
TEST CONN.

Fig. 9: Mazda 626 Computerized Engine Control Wiring Diagram

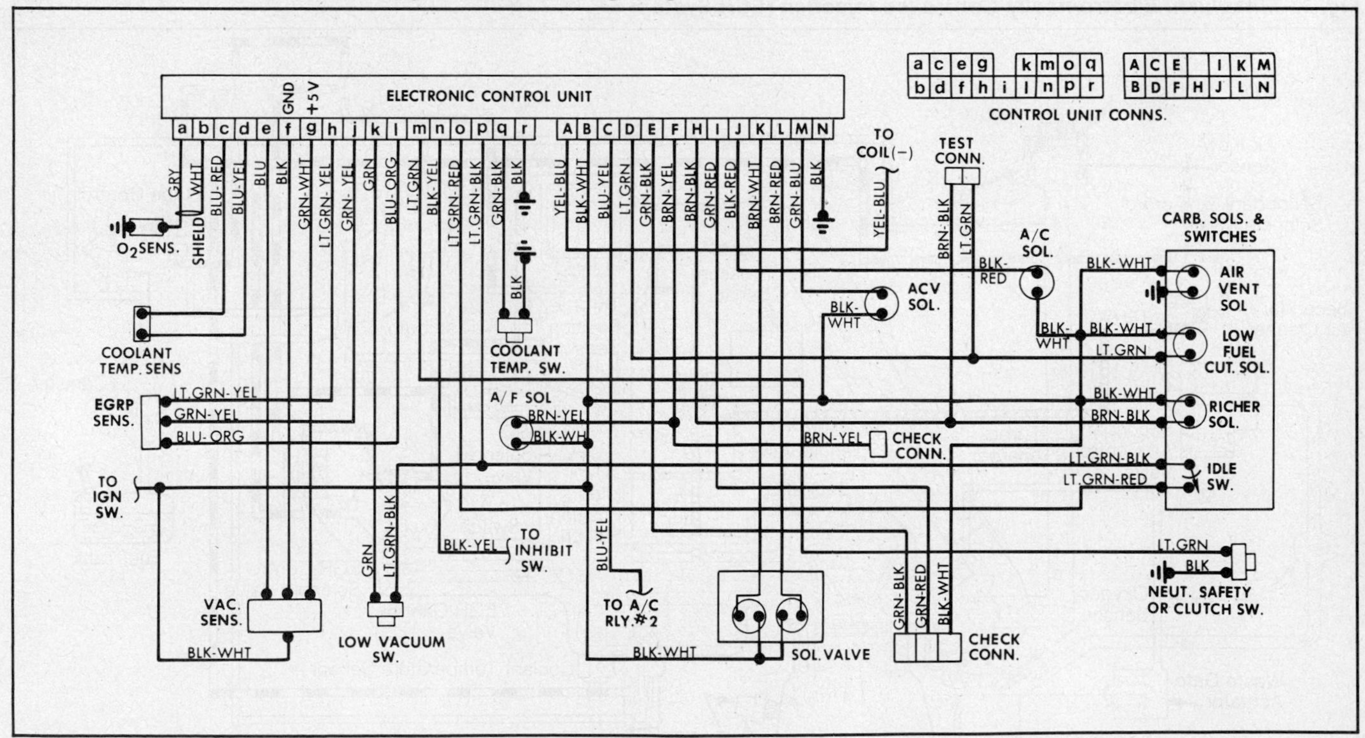
ELECTRONIC CONTROL UNIT
GND
+5V
a b c d e f g h j k l m n o p q r
A B C D E F H I J K L M N
a c e g k m o q
b d f h i l n p r
A C E I K M
B D F H J L N
CONTROL UNIT CONNS.
GRY
WHT
SHIELD
BLU-RED
BLU-YEL
BLU
BLK
GRN-WHT
LT.GRN-YEL
GRN-YEL
GRN
BLU-ORG
LT.GRN
BLK-YEL
LT.GRN-RED
LT.GRN-BLK
GRN-BLK
BLK
YEL-BLU
BLK-WHT
BLU-YEL
LT.GRN
GRN-BLK
BRN-YEL
BRN-BLK
GRN-BLK
BLK-RED
BRN-WHT
BRN-RED
GRN-BLU
BLK
O2 SENS.
COOLANT TEMP. SENS
BLK
COOLANT TEMP. SW.
TO COIL (−)
YEL-BLU
TEST CONN.
BRN-BLK
LT.GRN
A/C SOL.
BLK-RED
ACV SOL.
BLK-WHT
CARB. SOLS. & SWITCHES
BLK-WHT
AIR VENT SOL
BLK-WHT
BLK-WHT
LT.GRN
LOW FUEL CUT. SOL.
BLK-WHT
BRN-BLK
RICHER SOL.
EGRP SENS.
LT.GRN-YEL
GRN-YEL
BLU-ORG
A/F SOL
BRN-YEL
BLK-WH
BRN-YEL
CHECK CONN.
LT.GRN-BLK
LT.GRN-RED
IDLE SW.
TO IGN SW.
LT.GRN-BLK
BLK-YEL
TO INHIBIT SW.
BLU-YEL
TO A/C RLY.#2
GRN
LT.GRN
BLK
NEUT. SAFETY OR CLUTCH SW.
GRN-BLK
GRN-RED
BLK-WHT
CHECK CONN.
VAC. SENS.
BLK-WHT
LOW VACUUM SW.
BLK-WHT
SOL. VALVE

MITSUBISHI ELECTRONICALLY CONTROLLED INJECTION (ECI) SYSTEM

Starion Turbo

DESCRIPTION

The Electronically Controlled Injection (ECI) system is a computerized emission, ignition and fuel control system. The ECI system controls engine operation and lowers exhaust emissions while maintaining good fuel economy and driveability. The Electronic Control Unit (ECU) is the "brain" of the ECI system. The ECU controls many engine related systems to constantly adjust engine operation.

The ECI system is primarily an emission control system, designed to maintain an ideal air/fuel ratio of 14.7:1 under all operating conditions. When an ideal ratio is maintained, the catalytic converters can control carbon monoxide (CO), hydrocarbon (HC) and nitrogen oxide (NOx) emissions.

OPERATION

The ECI system consists of the following subsystems: Fuel Control, Data Sensors, Electronic Control Unit (ECU), Electronic Spark Control (ESC) system, Idle Speed Control (ISC), Emission Control, Fuel Cutoff and catalytic converters.

FUEL CONTROL

Fuel control system consists of an electric fuel pump, control relay, fuel filter, fuel injectors, fuel pressure regulator and fuel lines. Fuel is supplied to engine through 2 electronically pulsed (timed) injector valves located in fuel injection mixer above intake manifold. The ECU controls amount of fuel metered through injectors based upon engine demand information, through data sensor signals.

DATA SENSORS

Each sensor furnishes electrical impulses to ECU. The ECU computes fuel delivery and spark timing necessary to maintain desired air/fuel mixture, thus controlling amount of fuel delivered to engine. Data sensors are interrelated to each other. Operation of each sensor is as follows:

Air Flow Sensor

This sensor is mounted in air cleaner. The sensor measures air flow rate through the air cleaner and sends a proportionate electrical signal to ECU. The ECU uses air flow sensor information for controlling fuel delivery and air injection system.

Intake Air Temperature Sensor

This sensor is mounted in air cleaner as component part of air flow sensor. The sensor measures temperature of incoming air and sends an electrical signal to ECU. The ECU uses air temperature sensor information for controlling fuel delivery.

Pressure Sensor

This sensor is mounted on firewall. An electrically controlled solenoid valve is connected to sensor. The

Fig. 1: Mitsubishi Electronically Controlled Injection (ECI) System

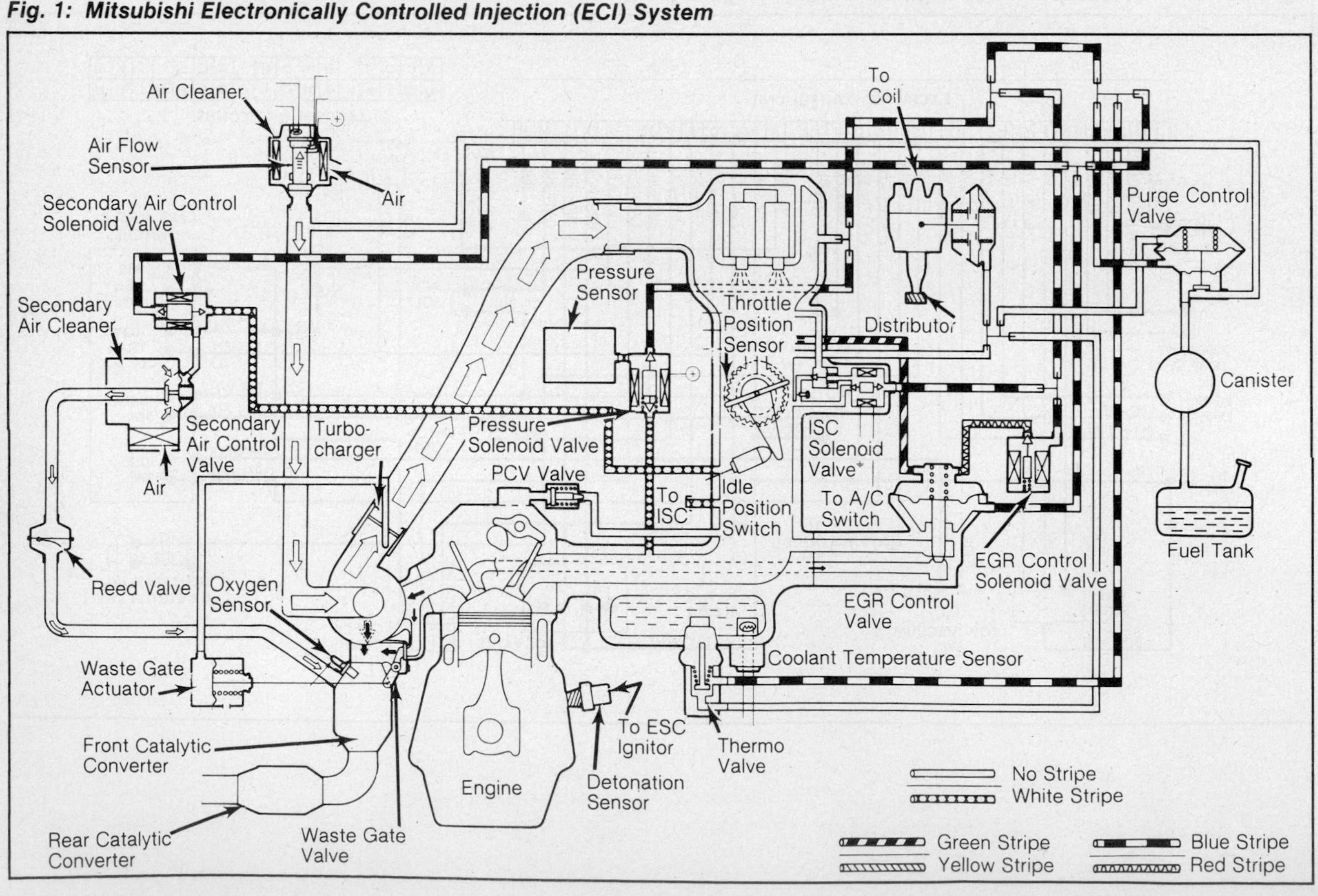
Air Cleaner
Air Flow Sensor
Air
Secondary Air Control Solenoid Valve
Secondary Air Cleaner
Secondary Air Control Valve
Air
Turbo-charger
Pressure Sensor
Pressure Solenoid Valve
PCV Valve
To ISC
Idle Position Switch
Throttle Position Sensor
To Coil
Distributor
ISC Solenoid Valve*
To A/C Switch
Purge Control Valve
Canister
Fuel Tank
EGR Control Solenoid Valve
EGR Control Valve
Reed Valve
Oxygen Sensor
Waste Gate Actuator
Coolant Temperature Sensor
Front Catalytic Converter
To ESC Ignitor
Thermo Valve
Engine
Detonation Sensor
Rear Catalytic Converter
Waste Gate Valve
No Stripe
White Stripe
Green Stripe
Yellow Stripe
Blue Stripe
Red Stripe

MITSUBISHI ELECTRONICALLY CONTROLLED INJECTION (ECI) SYSTEM (Cont.)

solenoid valve has 2 hoses connected to it; one hose connects above throttle valve and other hose connects below throttle valve.

The solenoid valve is activated by ECU whenever ignition switch is turned to "ON" or "START" positions, for a specific period of time. When activated, the solenoid measures ambient barometric pressure from above throttle valve. Ambient barometric pressure changes due to weather and/or altitude. This information is sent to ECU for controlling fuel delivery time.

After a predetermined period of time, solenoid valve is deactivated by ECU. When deactivated, the solenoid measures intake manifold pressure below throttle valve. The ECU compares barometric pressure and intake manifold pressure and an absolute value is used to determine fuel delivery and ignition timing.

The pressure sensor and solenoid valve are also used for altitude compensation. These components inform ECU of altitude. The ECU calculates air/fuel ratio necessary for engine operation in high altitude areas.

Fig. 2: Mitsubishi Pressure Sensor

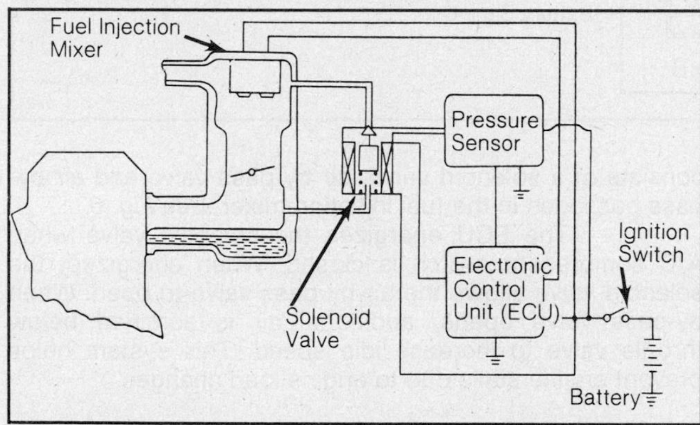
Fuel Injection
Mixer
Pressure
Sensor
Ignition
Switch
Electronic
Control
Unit (ECU)
Solenoid
Valve
Battery

Note solenoid valve and pressure sensor locations.

Coolant Temperature Sensor (CTS)

The coolant temperature sensor is installed in intake manifold. This sensor is a thermistor which converts temperature of engine coolant to electrical signal for use by ECU. The ECU uses coolant temperature information for controlling fuel delivery time, EGR and air injection system.

Engine Speed

Engine speed signal is received from ignition coil. Electrical signals from ignition coil are sent to ECU where time between signals is used to calculate engine speed. This information is used by ECU for controlling fuel delivery time, EGR and air injection system.

Oxygen Sensor

This sensor is mounted in exhaust system between turbocharger and front catalytic converter. Output voltage of oxygen sensor varies with oxygen content in exhaust gas stream.

When oxygen sensor signal is being interpreted by ECU, information is used to control fuel delivery time; this is called closed loop mode of operation. When oxygen sensor signals are not being interpreted by ECU, this is open loop mode of operation.

Throttle Position Sensor

This sensor is mounted on fuel injection mixer. The sensor, a rotary potentiometer, signals ECU of changes in throttle valve position. This information is used for controlling fuel delivery time.

Idle Position Switch

This switch is mounted on fuel injection mixer. When throttle valve is closed (idle position), the switch is activated. When throttle valve is at any other position, the switch is deactivated. This information is used by the ECU for controlling fuel delivery time (during deceleration) and air injection system. This switch is also used as an idle speed adjusting device.

Fig. 3: Idle Position Switch

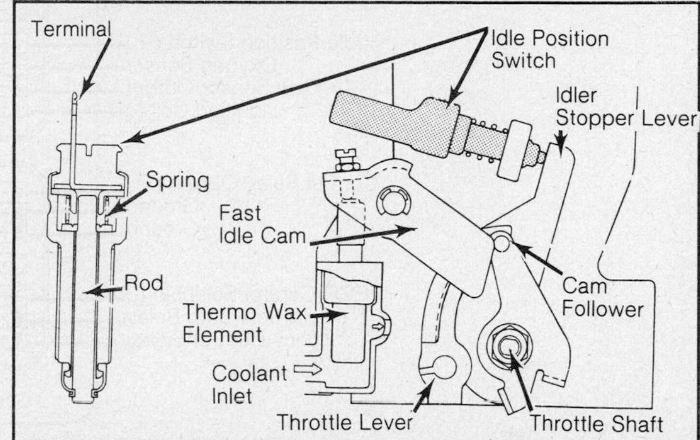
Terminal
Idle Position
Switch
Idler
Stopper Lever
Spring
Fast
Idle Cam
Rod
Cam
Follower
Thermo Wax
Element
Coolant
Inlet
Throttle Lever
Throttle Shaft

This switch is also used for adjusting idle speed.

Detonation Sensor

The detonation sensor (knock sensor) is located in cylinder block. This sensor converts engine vibration (knock) into an electrical signal. This signal is processed by the Electronic Spark Control (ESC) ignitor and relayed to ECU for determining amount of ignition timing retard. The ECU sends a signal to ESC ignitor to modify ignition timing. Ignition timing is retarded only during period of knock.

CAUTION: Detonation sensor is strong enough to withstand engine vibration, but excessive impact with hammer, wrench, etc., can damage sensor.

ELECTRONIC CONTROL UNIT (ECU)

The ECU is mounted behind passenger kick panel and controls all ECI functions. The ECU consists of a printed circuit board enclosed within a metal box. The ECU receives various signals from sensors and switches. These signals are processed by the ECU for controlling fuel delivery, EGR, ignition timing, and air injection systems.

During closed loop operation, the ECU stores the mean values of feedback signals used to maintain 14.7:1 air fuel ratio. During open loop operation, the ECU uses these mean values to modify pre-programmed information. By doing this, the ECU can more closely control exhaust emissions even when engine is in open loop mode of operation.

ELECTRONIC SPARK CONTROL

Electronic Spark Control (ESC) system is a closed loop system that controls engine detonation by adjusting spark timing. This system consists of ignition system, ESC ignitor, detonation sensor, pressure sensor and control relay.

MITSUBISHI ELECTRONICALLY CONTROLLED INJECTION (ECI) SYSTEM (Cont.)

Fig. 4: Electronic Control Unit Terminal Identification

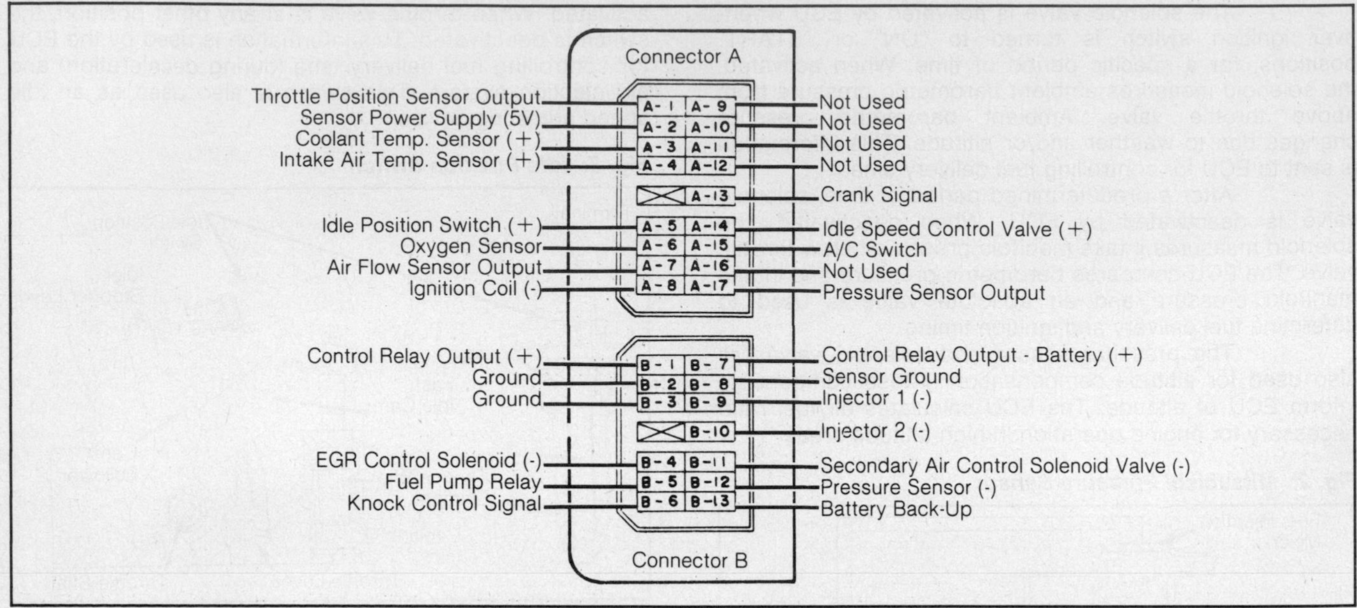

Connector A
Throttle Position Sensor Output
Sensor Power Supply (5V)
Coolant Temp. Sensor (+)
Intake Air Temp. Sensor (+)
A-1
A-2
A-3
A-4
A-9
A-10
A-11
A-12
A-13
Not Used
Not Used
Not Used
Not Used
Crank Signal
Idle Position Switch (+)
Oxygen Sensor
Air Flow Sensor Output
Ignition Coil (-)
A-5
A-6
A-7
A-8
A-14
A-15
A-16
A-17
Idle Speed Control Valve (+)
A/C Switch
Not Used
Pressure Sensor Output
Control Relay Output (+)
Ground
Ground
B-1
B-2
B-3
B-7
B-8
B-9
B-10
Control Relay Output - Battery (+)
Sensor Ground
Injector 1 (-)
Injector 2 (-)
EGR Control Solenoid (-)
Fuel Pump Relay
Knock Control Signal
B-4
B-5
B-6
B-11
B-12
B-13
Secondary Air Control Solenoid Valve (-)
Pressure Sensor (-)
Battery Back-Up
Connector B

The detonation sensor detects presence (or absence) and intensity of detonation by vibration characteristics of engine. Detonation sensor sends electrical signal to ignitor. The ECU monitors signal and issues a command signal to ignitor to adjust ignition timing.

The distributor receives commands from controller, and spark timing is delayed during detonation, thus providing required retard. The amount of retard is a function of degree of detonation.

Fig. 5: Mitsubishi Electronic Spark Control (ESC) System

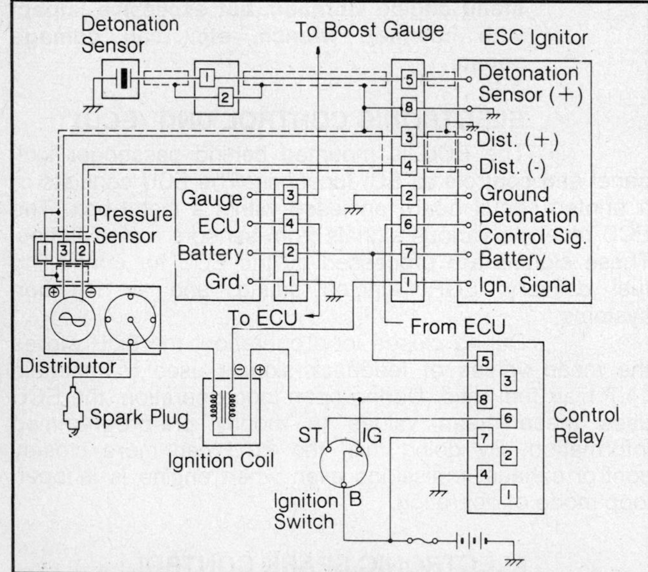

Detonation Sensor
To Boost Gauge
ESC Ignitor
Detonation Sensor (+)
Dist. (+)
Dist. (-)
Ground
Detonation Control Sig.
Battery
Ign. Signal
Pressure Sensor
Gauge
ECU
Battery
Grd.
To ECU
From ECU
Distributor
Spark Plug
Ignition Coil
ST
IG
Ignition Switch
B
Control Relay

Note interrelationship of components.

IDLE SPEED CONTROL (ISC)

The Idle Speed Control (ISC) system increases engine idle speed when A/C compressor is operated, without changing throttle valve position. The system consists of a solenoid valve, air by-pass valve and air by-pass passages in the fuel injection mixer. *See Fig. 6.*

The ECU energizes the solenoid valve when A/C compressor switch is closed. When energized, the solenoid valve allows the air by-pass valve to open. When by-pass valve opens, additional air is admitted below throttle valve to increase idle speed. This system helps prevent engine stalls due to engine load changes.

Fig. 6: Mitsubishi Idle Speed Control (ISC) System

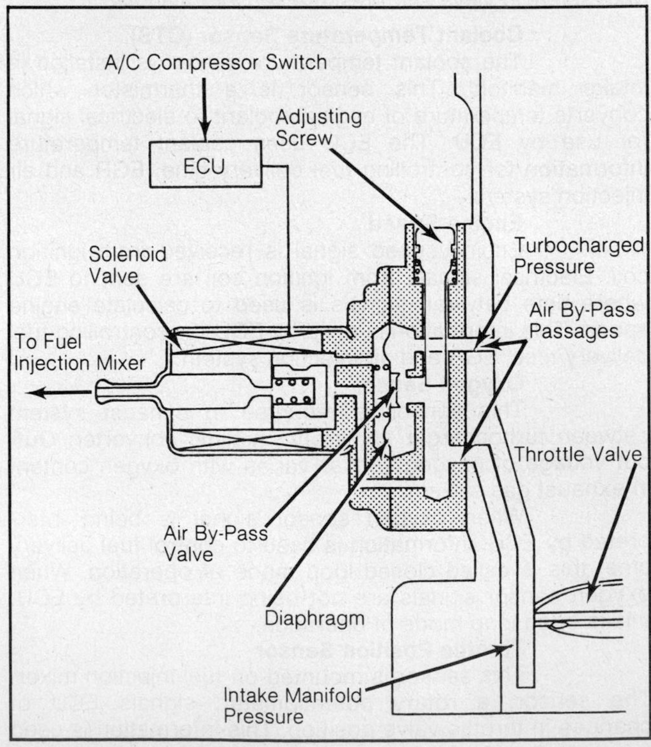

A/C Compressor Switch
ECU
Adjusting Screw
Turbocharged Pressure
Solenoid Valve
Air By-Pass Passages
To Fuel Injection Mixer
Throttle Valve
Air By-Pass Valve
Diaphragm
Intake Manifold Pressure

Note position of adjusting screw.

MITSUBISHI ELECTRONICALLY CONTROLLED INJECTION (ECI) SYSTEM (Cont.)

EMISSION CONTROL

Air Injection System (Secondary Air Supply)

The ECU controls the air injection system. The air injection system consists of a secondary air filter, reed valve, secondary air control valve and secondary air solenoid valve. *See Fig. 7.* This system reduces exhaust emissions by promoting oxidation of exhaust gases.

The ECU monitors engine speed, intake air flow, coolant temperature and idle position. When all required conditions are met, the ECU activates the solenoid valve to supply secondary air to exhaust manifold during engine warm-up, hot-start and deceleration modes of operation.

When the ECU activates the solenoid valve, intake manifold vacuum opens the secondary air control valve. The control valve allows additional air to enter the exhaust manifold. The reed valve, actuated by vacuum pulsations in exhaust manifold, controls the amount of additional air entering the exhaust manifold.

Fig. 7: Air Injection (Secondary Air Supply) System

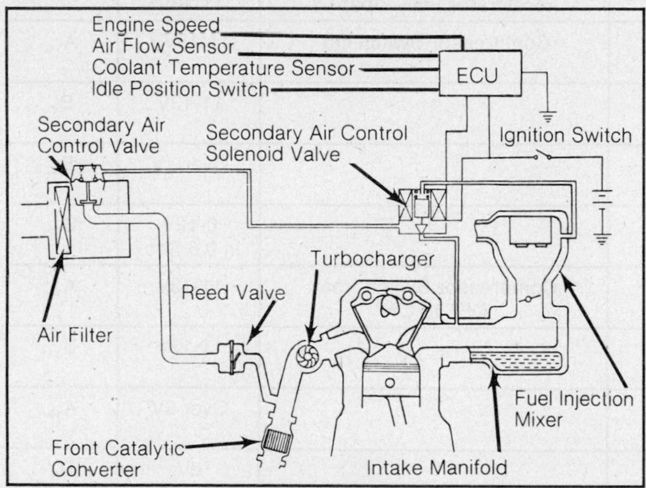
Engine Speed
Air Flow Sensor
Coolant Temperature Sensor
Idle Position Switch
ECU
Secondary Air Control Valve
Secondary Air Control Solenoid Valve
Ignition Switch
Turbocharger
Reed Valve
Air Filter
Fuel Injection Mixer
Front Catalytic Converter
Intake Manifold

ECU monitors engine and controls air injection.

EGR System

An EGR system is used to reduce oxides of nitrogen (NOx) emissions in vehicle exhaust gases. Exhaust gas is partially recirculated from an exhaust port in cylinder head into an intake manifold port below fuel injection mixer. The EGR system is controlled by the ECU and consists of an EGR control solenoid valve and EGR control valve. *See Fig. 8.*

The ECU monitors engine speed and coolant temperature. When conditions are met, the ECU de-energizes the EGR solenoid valve. When solenoid is de-energized, EGR control valve is opened (aided by throttle ported vacuum) and EGR flow occurs.

When EGR solenoid is energized by ECU, control valve closes due to combined forces of throttle ported pressure and turbocharged pressure.

EGR flow is suspended during engine idle and wide open throttle operation. The ECU does not allow EGR flow if engine conditions do not meet predetermined criteria.

FUEL CUTOFF

Two different fuel cutoff systems are used to change fuel delivery rate to engine:

Fig. 8: Mitsubishi EGR System

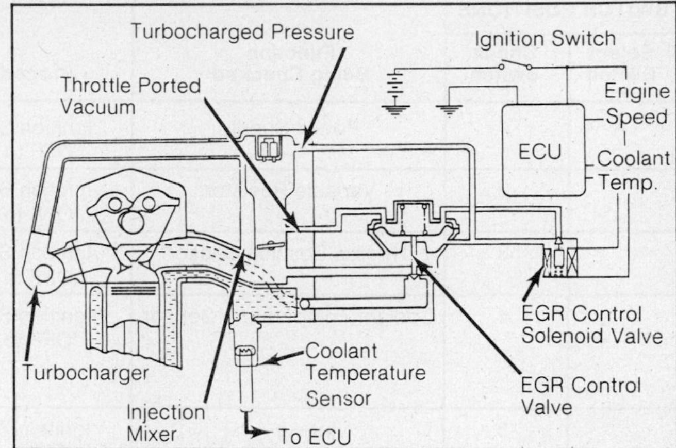
Turbocharged Pressure
Ignition Switch
Throttle Ported Vacuum
Engine Speed
ECU
Coolant Temp.
EGR Control Solenoid Valve
Turbocharger
Coolant Temperature Sensor
EGR Control Valve
Injection Mixer
To ECU

ECU monitors engine and controls EGR flow.

Deceleration Fuel Cutoff

During vehicle operation, idle position switch not at idle position, fuel delivery is determined by ECU responding to throttle valve closing speeds.

To decrease HC emissions during vehicle deceleration, fuel delivery time is decreased by ECU changing injection interval. When engine is operated under predetermined conditions, injection interval is changed from once every 3 pulses of air flow sensor to once every 6 pulses of air flow sensor.

Over Boost Fuel Cutoff

This fuel cutoff system protects the engine during turbocharger operation. When the pressure sensor detects higher manifold pressure than the predetermined value stored in ECU memory, the ECU changes fuel delivery rate. When pressure value is exceeded, the fuel injectors are energized according to ignition spark timing.

TESTING

NOTE: **The Mitsubishi ECI system requires a special tester (Mitsubishi ECI Checker - MD998406) to be fully diagnosed. However, some checks of individual components may be made using regular shop test equipment.**

CAUTION: **Be sure ignition switch is off when disconnecting connectors from control unit. While testing, be careful not to bend any pins and do not touch more than 1 pin at a time with meter lead as meter or ECU could be damaged.**

PRETESTING INSPECTION

If ECI system components fail, interruption of fuel supply or failure to supply proper amount of fuel for engine operation will result. The following conditions will result: engine is hard to start or does not start at all, unstable idle and/or poor driveability. Before testing ECI system, perform basic engine checks first (ignition system, incorrect engine adjustments, etc.).

MITSUBISHI ELECTRONICALLY CONTROLLED INJECTION (ECI) SYSTEM (Cont.)

ECI SYSTEM CHECK PROCEDURE CHART

ECI CHECKER SWITCH POSITIONS						
Select Switch	Check Switch	Function Being Checked	Procedure	Condition	Normal Reading	Terminal No.
A	1	Power Supply	Ignition Switch "OFF to ON"		11-13V	B_1
	2	Variable Resistor	Ignition Switch "OFF to ON"		.....	A_{10}
	3	Throttle Position Sensor	Ignition Switch "OFF to ON"	Accelerator Fully Closed Accelerator Fully Opened	0-0.6V 4-5V [1]	A_1
	4	Coolant Temperature Sensor	Ignition Switch "OFF to ON"	32°F (0°C) 68°F (20°C) 104°F (40°C) 176°F (80°C)	3.5V 2.6V 1.8V 0.6V	A_3
	5	Intake Air Temperature Sensor	Ignition Switch "OFF to ON"	32°F (0°C) 68°F (20°C) 104°F (40°C) 176°F (80°C)	3.5V 2.6V 1.8V 0.7V	A_4
	6	Idle Position Switch	Ignition Switch "OFF to ON"	Accelerator Fully Closed Accelerator Fully Opened	0V [2] 11-13V	A_5
	7	Idle Speed Control Solenoid Valve	Ignition Switch "OFF to ON"	Compressor Switch Off	11-13V [3]	A_{14}
	8	EGR Control Solenoid Valve	Ignition Switch "OFF to ON"		11-13V	B_4
	9	Spark Retard Signal	Ignition Switch "OFF to ON"		Over 4V	B_6
	10	Pressure Solenoid Valve	Ignition Switch "OFF to ON"		0-12V In 0.6 Sec.	B_{12}
	11	Compressor Switch	Ignition Switch "OFF to ON"	Compressor Switch from "OFF to ON"	11-13V	A_{15}
	12	Secondary Air Control Solenoid Valve	Ignition Switch "OFF to ON"		11-13V	B_{11}
B	1	Cranking Signal	Ignition Switch "OFF to START"		Over 8V	A_{13}
	2	Control Relay	Idling		0V	B_5
	3	Idle Speed Control Solenoid Valve	Idling	Cooler Switch "OFF" Cooler Switch "OFF to ON"	12V 0V	A_{14}
	4	Ignition Pulse	Idling		12-14V	A_8
	5	Air Flow Sensor	Idling 3000 RPM		3V 3V	A_7
	6	Injector 1 Pulse	Idling 3000 RPM		13-14V 13V	B_9
	7	Injector 2 Pulse	Idling 3000 RPM		13-14V 13V	B_{10}
	8	Oxygen Sensor	After Warm-Up Above 1300 RPM	To Heat Up Sensor	0-1-2.7V	A_6
	9	EGR Control Solenoid Valve	Idling 800-3000 RPM Above 3000 RPM	After Warm-Up	0V 12-15V 0V	B_4
	10	Pressure Sensor	Ignition Switch "ON to OFF" Idling	Engine Stopped	1.5-2.6V 0.2-1.2V	A_{17}
	11	Spark Retard Signal	Idling		Over 4V	B_6
	12	Secondary Air Control Solenoid Valve	Idling	Water Temp. Above 131°F (55°C)	0-12-15V In 30 sec.	B_{11}

[1] — Cold engine, fast idle operating = 2-3V. [2] — Cold engine, fast idle operating = 12-13V. [3] — Non-A/C equipped models = 0V.

MITSUBISHI ELECTRONICALLY CONTROLLED INJECTION (ECI) SYSTEM (Cont.)

COMPONENT TESTING

Air Temperature Sensor

1) Disconnect electrical connector from sensor. Measure resistance of sensor by connecting positive lead of ohmmeter to terminal 4 and negative lead to terminal 1.

2) Resistance should be 2200 ohms at 77°F (25°C). If not, replace sensor and repeat ECI check.

Fig. 9: Measuring Air Temperature Sensor Resistance

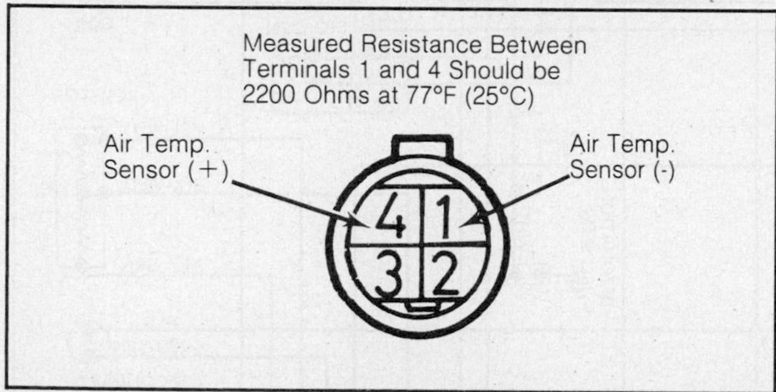
Measured Resistance Between
Terminals 1 and 4 Should be
2200 Ohms at 77°F (25°C)
Air Temp.
Sensor (+)
Air Temp.
Sensor (-)
4
1
3
2

Make sure leads are properly connected.

Throttle Position Sensor

1) Disconnect electrical connector from sensor. Connect ohmmeter leads between terminals 1 and 3. When throttle valve is slowly operated from idle to wide open throttle, resistance value should change smoothly.

2) Total resistance measured at terminals 1 and 3 of sensor should be 4000-6000 ohms. If not, replace sensor and repeat ECI check.

Fig. 10: Measuring Throttle Position Sensor Resistance

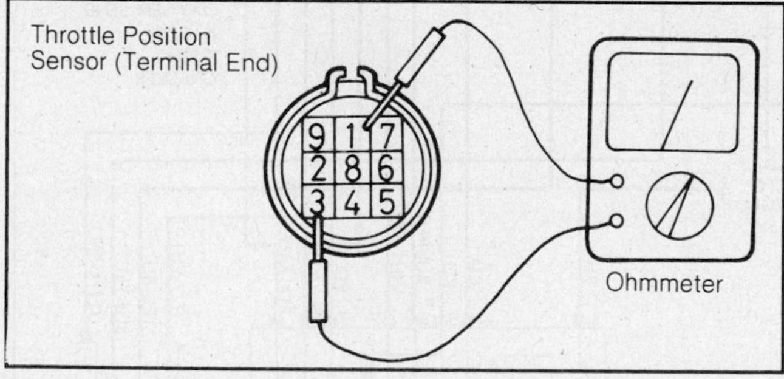
Throttle Position
Sensor (Terminal End)
9 1 7
2 8 6
3 4 5
Ohmmeter

Make sure leads are properly connected.

Coolant Temperature Sensor

1) Remove coolant temperature sensor from intake manifold and dip end of sensor into water. Do not allow sensor to touch container. Terminal connector portion of sensor should be .12" (3 mm) above water.

2) Gradually heat water and read resistance values at terminal connectors. Resistance should be as shown in Coolant Temperature Sensor Resistance chart. If not, replace sensor.

COOLANT TEMPERATURE SENSOR RESISTANCE

Temperature °F (°C)	Resistance (Ohms)
68 (20)	2450
176 (80)	296

Resistor

1) Disconnect electrical connector from resistor. Measure resistance across terminals 1 and 2 and 1 and 3. If resistance is about 6 ohms, resistor is good.

2) If resistance measures 0 or infinity, resistor has short circuit or open circuit. Replace resistor.

Control Relay

1) Control relay is mounted on top of ECU. Disconnect electrical harness and test continuity between terminals 1 and 7 and 3 and 7. If there is no continuity, relay is good. If continuity is measured, replace control relay.

2) Apply battery voltage to terminals 8 (positive) and 4 (negative). Measure continuity between terminals 3 and 7. If continuity is measured, relay is good. If not, replace relay.

3) Apply battery voltage across terminals 6 (positive) and 4 (negative) while testing continuity between terminals 1 and 7. If there is continuity, relay is good. If not, replace relay.

4) Apply battery voltage across terminals 5 (positive) and 2 (negative) while testing continuity between terminals 1 and 7. If there is continuity, relay is good. If not, replace relay.

EGR Control Solenoid Valve

1) Start engine and run at idle until normal operating temperature is obtained. Disconnect Green stripe hose from fuel injection mixer and connect vacuum pump to hose.

2) Disconnect electrical connector from solenoid valve and apply 9.8 in. Hg to Green stripe hose. If idle becomes unstable or engine stalls, EGR system is operating properly.

3) Reconnect electrical connector and repeat step **2)**. Engine idle should not be affected. If idle becomes unstable or engine stalls, solenoid valve is remaining closed. Replace solenoid valve.

ADJUSTMENTS

IDLE SPEED CONTROL SYSTEM

1) To adjust idle speed control system, start engine and allow to idle until coolant temperature reaches 185-205°F (85-96°C). Turn all lights and accessories off and place transmission in neutral. Electric cooling fan must be off during adjustment.

2) Check curb idle speed and adjust if necessary. Turn A/C system on. Adjust engine speed to 1000-1100 RPM by turning adjusting screw on idle speed control system solenoid valve. *See Fig. 6.*

MITSUBISHI ELECTRONICALLY CONTROLLED INJECTION (ECI) SYSTEM (Cont.)

Fig. 11: Mitsubishi ECI System Wiring Diagram

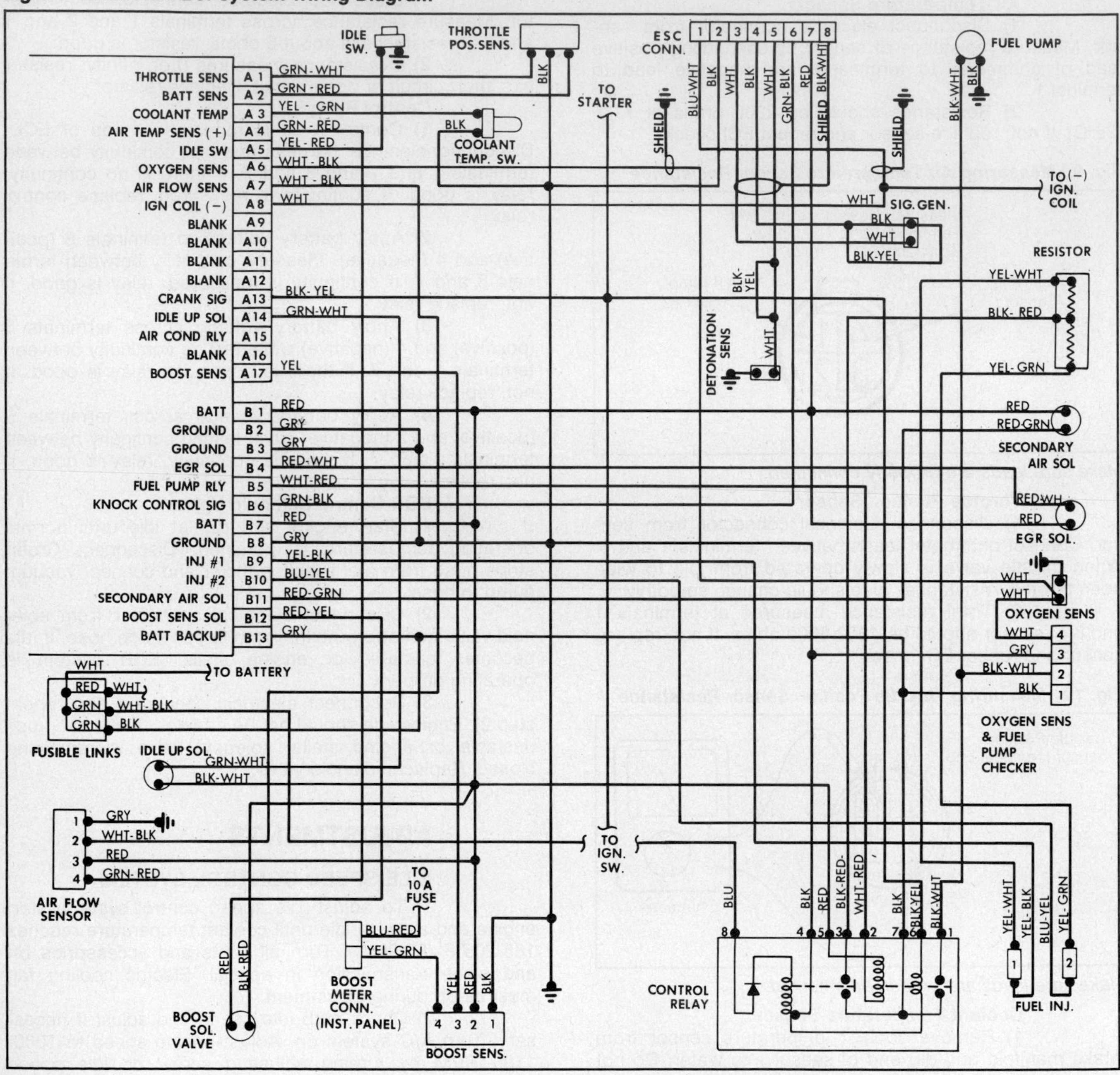

THROTTLE SENS A 1 GRN-WHT
BATT SENS A 2 GRN-RED
COOLANT TEMP A 3 YEL-GRN
AIR TEMP SENS (+) A 4 GRN-RED
IDLE SW A 5 YEL-RED
OXYGEN SENS A 6 WHT-BLK
AIR FLOW SENS A 7 WHT-BLK
IGN COIL (−) A 8 WHT
BLANK A 9
BLANK A10
BLANK A11
BLANK A12
CRANK SIG A13 BLK-YEL
IDLE UP SOL A14 GRN-WHT
AIR COND RLY A15
BLANK A16
BOOST SENS A17 YEL
BATT B 1 RED
GROUND B 2 GRY
GROUND B 3 GRY
EGR SOL B 4 RED-WHT
FUEL PUMP RLY B5 WHT-RED
KNOCK CONTROL SIG B6 GRN-BLK
BATT B7 RED
GROUND B8 GRY
INJ #1 B9 YEL-BLK
INJ #2 B10 BLU-YEL
SECONDARY AIR SOL B11 RED-GRN
BOOST SENS SOL B12 RED-YEL
BATT BACKUP B13 GRY
IDLE SW.
THROTTLE POS.SENS.
BLK
COOLANT TEMP. SW.
TO STARTER
ESC CONN.
1 2 3 4 5 6 7 8
SHIELD
BLU-WHT
BLK
WHT
BLK
WHT
GRN-BLK
RED
BLK-WHT
FUEL PUMP
TO (−) IGN. COIL
SIG. GEN.
BLK-YEL
DETONATION SENS
RESISTOR
YEL-WHT
BLK-RED
YEL-GRN
RED-GRN
SECONDARY AIR SOL
REDWH
EGR SOL.
OXYGEN SENS
OXYGEN SENS & FUEL PUMP CHECKER
TO BATTERY
FUSIBLE LINKS
IDLE UP SOL
AIR FLOW SENSOR
TO IGN. SW.
TO 10 A FUSE
BLU-RED
YEL-GRN
BOOST METER CONN. (INST. PANEL)
BOOST SOL. VALVE
BOOST SENS.
4 3 2 1
BLU
BLK
RED
BLK-RED-
WHT-RED
BLK-YEL
CONTROL RELAY
YEL-BLK
BLU-YEL
FUEL INJ.

PORSCHE 944 DME DIGITAL ENGINE CONTROL

DESCRIPTION

The Porsche 944 is equipped with the Bosch DME digital electronic engine control system. The DME system uses various data sensors that monitor intake air volume, speed, crankshaft position, coolant temperature, intake air temperature, and throttle position.

Signals from these sensors, as well as a start signal and oxygen sensor signal, are sent to the electronic control unit.

The electronic control unit (ECU) is a microcomputer, and is the "brain" of the DME system. Using information obtained from data sensors, the ECU determines the correct amount of fuel and optimum ignition timing.

The DME control unit switches from open loop to closed loop operation when the coolant temperature is above 113°F (45°C), and when the oxygen sensor temperature is above 480°F (250°C).

OPERATION

The DME system consists of 4 sub-systems: Fuel Control, Data Sensors, Electronic Control Unit (ECU), and Spark Timing.

FUEL CONTROL

The Porsche 944 is equipped with the Bosch Air Flow Controlled (AFC) fuel injection system. The AFC system is electronically controlled by the ECU, which is programed to regulate fuel injection based upon information received from various data sensors. It also considers the specific data for the 944 engine (stored in computer memory).

The ECU generates control signals for the fuel pump relay, auxiliary air valve, cold start injector coil, and the cylinder port injector coils. These devices control cold idle, curb idle speed and mixture, air/fuel ratio and fuel supply.

SPARK CONTROL

Spark control allows the electronic control unit (ECU) to determine the exact instant that ignition is required, based upon information received from data sensors.

At the optimum time, the ECU breaks the primary circuit of the ignition coil, producing a high voltage at coil center tower. This voltage surge fires the spark plug at the proper time for most efficient combustion, eliminating the need for vacuum and/or centrifugal advance.

Fig. 1: Schematic of DME Engine Control System

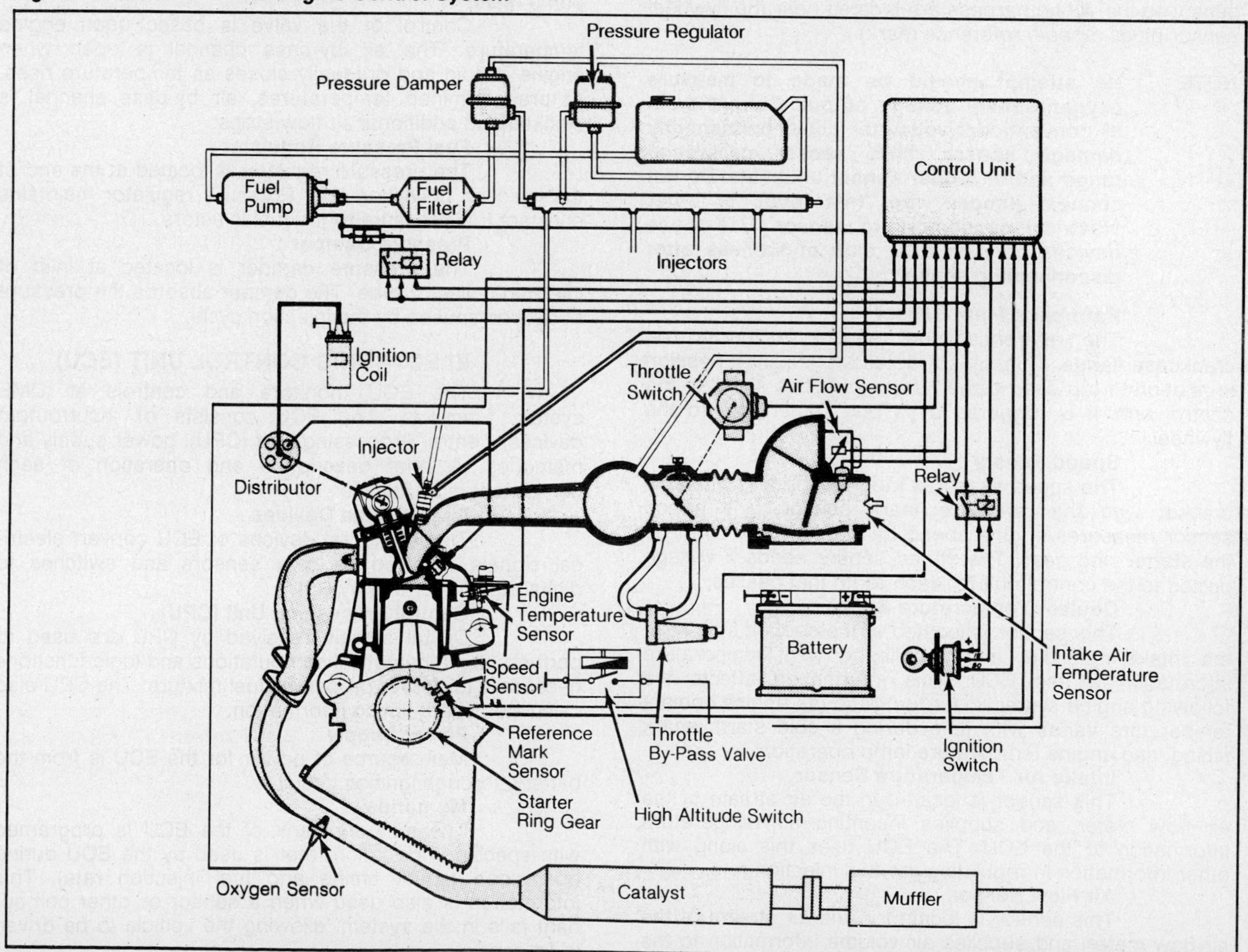
Pressure Regulator
Pressure Damper
Control Unit
Fuel Pump
Fuel Filter
Relay
Injectors
Ignition Coil
Throttle Switch
Air Flow Sensor
Injector
Distributor
Relay
Engine Temperature Sensor
Battery
Intake Air Temperature Sensor
Speed Sensor
Reference Mark Sensor
Throttle By-Pass Valve
Ignition Switch
Starter Ring Gear
High Altitude Switch
Oxygen Sensor
Catalyst
Muffler

The DME system consists of 4 sub-systems.

PORSCHE 944 DME DIGITAL ENGINE CONTROL (Cont.)

DATA SENSORS

Each sensor furnishes electronic impulses to the ECU. Using this information, the ECU computes spark timing, and correct amount of fuel necessary to maintain proper engine operation.

The function of each sensor is closely related in maintaining proper engine operation. Operation of each sensor is as follows:

Oxygen Sensor

This sensor is mounted in engine exhaust stream, in front of catalytic converter. It supplies a low voltage (under 1/2 volt) when fuel mixture is lean (too much oxygen) and a higher voltage (up to 1 volt) when fuel mixture is rich (not enough oxygen).

Oxygen sensor must be hot (over 480°F/250°C) to function properly and to allow ECU to accept its electrical signals. The oxygen sensor measures quantity of oxygen only.

California vehicles are equipped with a special electrically heated oxygen sensor. This oxygen sensor reaches operating temperature sooner and also begins to function earlier. The heated oxygen sensor has 3 wires, 2 for the heater element (power & ground), and a single wire for the oxygen sensor signal.

The heating begins with ignition on (via fuel pump & DME relay terminal 87). The plugs from the sensor to the wiring harness are located near the flywheel sensor plugs (speed, reference mark).

NOTE: **No attempt should be made to measure oxygen sensor voltage output. Current drain of conventional voltmeter could permanently damage sensor, shift sensor calibration range and/or render sensor unusable. Do not connect jumper wire, test leads or other electrical connectors to sensor. Use these devices only on ECU side of harness after disconnecting sensor.**

Reference Mark Sensor

The reference mark sensor is located on crankcase flange. This sensor detects crankshaft position in relation to top dead center, and sends this signal to the control unit. It is triggered by a bolt cemented into the flywheel.

Speed Sensor

The speed sensor is mounted on an adjustable bracket with the reference mark sensor. The speed sensor measures engine speed by counting the teeth on the starter ring gear. The speed sensor sends 2 voltage pulses to the control unit for each tooth that passes.

Coolant Temperature Sensor

This sensor is located in the coolant stream of the intake manifold, and supplies coolant temperature information to the ECU. This information affects the following engine systems: Air/fuel ratio (as engine coolant temperature varies with time during a cold start), spark timing, and engine temperature lamp operation.

Intake Air Temperature Sensor

This sensor is located in the air stream of the air flow meter, and supplies incoming air temperature information to the ECU. The ECU uses this along with other information in regulating the fuel injection rate.

Air Flow Sensor

This sensor is located in the air stream of the air flow meter, and supplies air volume information to the ECU. The ECU uses this and other information in regulating the fuel injection rate.

The air flow meter incorporates a measuring flap, that opens against pressure of a spiral spring, and is connected to a potentiometer. The potentiometer transmits an electrical signal determined by position of the measuring flap, to inform the ECU of engine load.

Throttle Switch

A contact-type throttle switch is located on the throttle body. It converts throttle position into electrical signals to inform ECU of throttle position.

The potentiometer within the air flow meter prevents loss of engine power during sudden acceleration/deceleration by signaling the ECU of necessary fuel enrichment requirements.

High Altitude Switch

Switch is mounted under the dashboard, on driver's side of vehicle. In altitudes higher than 3300 ft. (1000 m) The high altitude switch closes, signaling the ECU to lean the fuel mixture.

Auxiliary Air Valve

Auxiliary air valve provides additional air during cold engine starts and warm-up. It is located next to throttle body. The valve consists of an electrically heated bi-metel strip, movable disc and air by-pass channel. The heater coil on the bi-metel strip is energized by the fuel pump relay.

Control of the valve is based upon engine temperature. The air by-pass channel is open when engine is cold and gradually closes as temperature rises. At predetermined temperatures, air by-pass channel is blocked and additional air flow stops.

Fuel Pressure Regulator

The pressure regulator is located at the end of the injection collection line. Pressure regulator maintains constant fuel pressure to the fuel injectors.

Pressure Damper

The pressure damper is located at inlet of injection collector tube. The damper absorbs the pressure oscillation caused by the injection cycle.

ELECTRONIC CONTROL UNIT (ECU)

The ECU monitors and controls all DME system functions. The ECU consists of input/output devices, Central Processing Unit (CPU), power supply and memories. A brief description and operation of each component is as follows:

Input/Output Devices

These integral devices of ECU convert electrical signals received by data sensors and switches to digital signals for use by CPU.

Central Processing Unit (CPU)

Digital signals received by CPU are used to perform all mathematical computations and logic functions necessary to deliver proper air/fuel mixture. The CPU also calculates spark timing information.

Power Supply

Main source of power for the ECU is from the battery, through ignition circuit.

Memories

The memory bank of the ECU is programed with specific information, that is used by the ECU during open loop (spark timing and fuel injection rate). This information is also used when a sensor or other component fails in the system, allowing the vehicle to be driven in for repairs.

PORSCHE 944 DME DIGITAL ENGINE CONTROL (Cont.)

ADJUSTMENTS

SPEED SENSOR CLEARANCE

NOTE: **Adjusting speed sensor automatically adjusts reference mark sensor. They cannot be adjusted separately.**

1) The speed sensor bracket is mounted on the crankcase flange with 2 bolts. To adjust clearance, loosen bolts and turn sensor holder. Clearance should be .030-034" (.75-.85 mm).

2) To adjust clearance with engine installed in vehicle, remove speed sensor. Usng a depth gauge, measure distance from sensor holder's upper surface to tooth head on starter ring gear.

3) Measure length of speed sensor. Subtract speed sensor length from holder-to-flywheel tooth distance. Difference should be .030-.034" (.75-.85 mm).

4) If not to specification, loosen screws and turn holder until holder-to-flywheel tooth distance is equal to the length of the sensor plus the specified clearance. Tighten screws, and install speed sensor in holder.

IDLE SPEED

Idle speed is adjusted by turning adjusting screw, located at by-pass port of throttle housing.

DIAGNOSIS & TESTING

CAUTION: **DME ignition system voltage is extremely high. Contact with current-carrying parts while engine is running could prove fatal. Always turn ignition switch "OFF" or remove battery ground cable when connecting testers or replacing system components. High voltage is particularly present at spark plug, distributor, and ignition coil connections and at terminal 1 of the control unit. Do not attempt to check ignition system by a sparking test of spark plugs. This may destroy ignition coil or control unit.**

NOTE: **Complete testing of the DME system requires an oscilloscope, voltmeter, ohmmeter and special test leads to insert in multiple pin control unit connector. Therefore, system testing is limited.**

ELECTRICAL CONNECTIONS

1) Check that all electrical connections are free of corrosion and securely attached. Check DME ground wire on engine flange and on clutch housing near speed and reference mark sensors. Be sure connections have good contact and are tight.

2) Particularly check 9-pin connector above brake booster, 4-pin connector on air flow sensor, 3-pin connector on throttle switch, 35-pin connector on control unit, 2-pin connector at temperature sensor, 1-pin connector for oxygen sensor (on firewall above flywheel sensors), and two 3-pin connectors for flywheel sensors (attached to No. 4 cylinder intake manifold).

NOTE: **Control unit connector is held in place by a catch. Push catch to the right and pull off plug with a downward motion.**

3) In addition, on California vehicles, check 2-pin connector for oxygen sensor heating element.

IGNITION CIRCUIT POWER CHECK

With ignition turned "ON", but with engine not running, connect positive voltmeter lead to terminal 1 of control unit harness connector. Connect negative lead to ground. Voltmeter should register battery voltage. If not, check wiring back to battery.

SPEED SENSOR CHECK

NOTE: **This is an alternate test when an oscilloscope is not available.**

1) Secure a Fresnel lens front LED from an electronics store or use Part No. 171 919 061B. Connect a 220-ohm-1/4 watt resistor in series with one of the LED terminals.

2) Connect positive LED test lead to terminal 8 of control unit harness connector. Connect negative LED test lead to terminal 27 of same connector. Do not start engine, but operate starter. L.E.D. will flicker dimly if speed sensor is sending a signal.

REFERENCE MARK SENSOR CHECK

NOTE: **This is an alternate test when an oscilloscope is not available.**

1) Using same LED tester as used for speed sensor, connect positive lead to control unit harness connector terminal 25 and negative lead to terminal 26.

2) Do not start engine, but operate starter. If sensor is sending a signal, LED should flicker dimly.

IGNITION COIL RESISTANCE CHECK

Primary Resistance

1) With ignition switch "OFF", disconnect wires from primary terminals of ignition coil to isolate it from the system. Set ohmmeter for x1 scale. Connect ohmmeter leads to 2 primary terminals.

2) Reading should be .4-.6 ohm. If not, replace ignition coil.

Secondary Resistance

1) With ignition switch still "OFF", remove wire from coil tower. Set ohmmeter at x1000 scale. Connect ohmmeter leads to ignition coil positive terminal and coil tower.

2) Reading should be 5,000-7,200 ohms. If not within specifications, replace ignition coil.

IGNITION RESISTANCE CHECKS

Shielded resistance of spark plug connectors should be 3,000 ohms. Shielded resistance of distributor rotor, and of all distributor cap connections should be 1000 ohms.

PORSCHE 944 DME DIGITAL ENGINE CONTROL (Cont.)

Fig. 2: Cutaway View of DME System Distributor

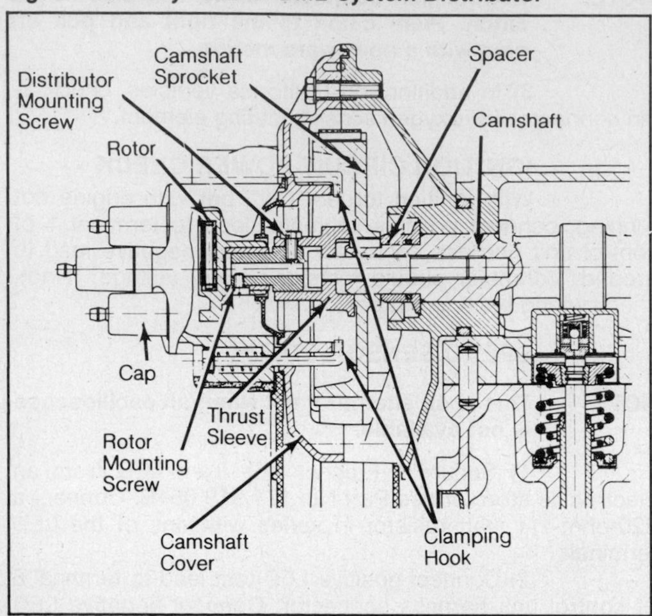
Camshaft Sprocket
Spacer
Distributor Mounting Screw
Camshaft
Rotor
Cap
Thrust Sleeve
Rotor Mounting Screw
Camshaft Cover
Clamping Hook

Align distributor cap with its locking boss facing up.

REMOVAL & INSTALLATION

DISTRIBUTOR CAP

Removal

1) Make a tool from a 4 1/2-6" long screwdriver, having a tip about 5/16" wide. Heat screwdriver and bend to a 90° angle about 3 1/2" from end.

2) Push in lower clamping hook with a screwdriver, and turn to the right (clockwise). Push in on upper clamping hook and turn it to the right, and remove cap.

Installation

1) Before installing cap, remove cable for No. 3 cylinder to provide access to clamping hook. Align distributor cap with its locking boss facing up.

2) Align clamping hooks in distributor cap so they are positioned horizontally and facing toward left side when viewed from front. Guide hooks into both slots and engage distributor cap by turning back and forth slightly. Watch position of dust cap.

Fig. 3: Wiring Diagram for Porsche DME System

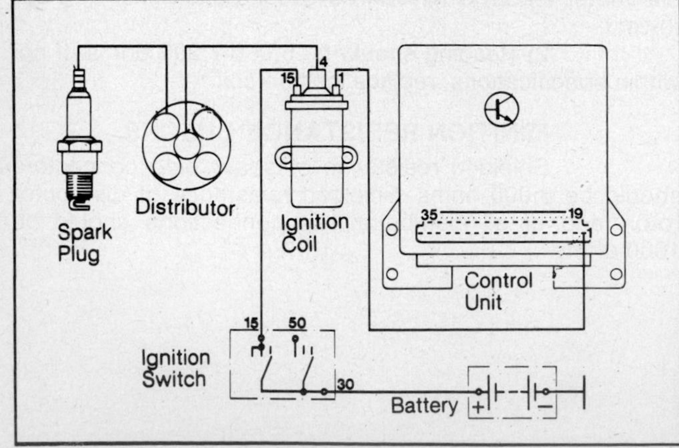
4
15
1
Spark Plug
Distributor
Ignition Coil
35
19
1
Control Unit
15
50
Ignition Switch
30
Battery

3) Turn both clamping hooks against left stop. Press in on hooks far enough so that they can be turned counterclockwise approximately 1/4 turn and engage when released.

4) Check that distributor cap fits tightly. Be sure hooks are firmly engaged. Reinstall cable for No. 3 cylinder on distributor cap.

RENAULT FEEDBACK CARBURETOR SYSTEM

Le Car (Calif. Only)

DESCRIPTION & OPERATION

California Le Car models use a feedback carburetor system to achieve good fuel economy and reduce emissions. The system includes a modified Weber 2-Bbl. carburetor, a vacuum solenoid regulator, electronic control unit, oxygen sensor, and sensor replacement reminder counter.

Fig. 1: Le Car Feedback Carburetor Main Jet

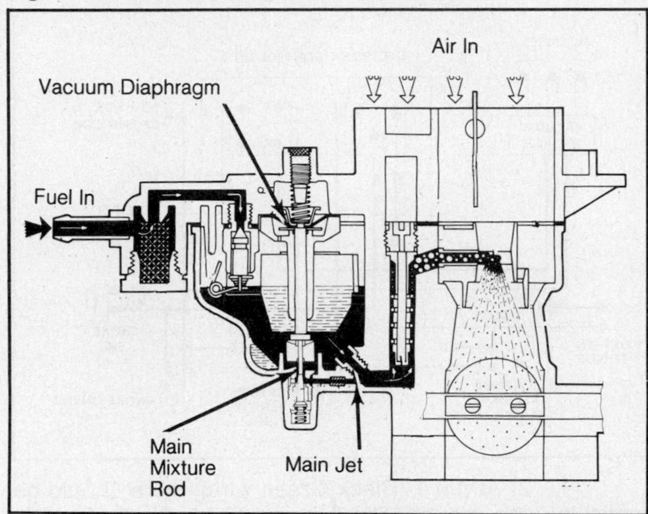
Air In
Vacuum Diaphragm
Fuel In
Main
Mixture
Rod
Main Jet

FEEDBACK CARBURETOR

The specially calibrated carburetor has 2 metering rods which vary idle and main fuel mixtures when they are moved. The rods are attached to vacuum diaphragms controlled by a signal from the vacuum regulator. The idle mixture rod controls an air bleed, and the main mixture rod controls a fuel passage.

Fig. 2: Le Car Feedback Carburetor Idle Circuit

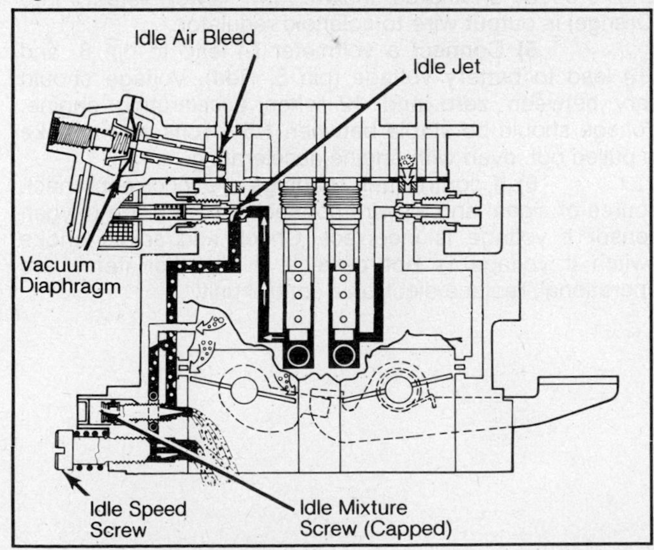
Idle Air Bleed
Idle Jet
Vacuum
Diaphragm
Idle Speed
Screw
Idle Mixture
Screw (Capped)

OXYGEN SENSOR

The oxygen sensor generates a small voltage when oxygen is present in the exhaust gases. When the mixture is lean, the sensor produces a voltage less than 100mv. When the mixture is rich, the voltage will be more than 600mv. The sensor gradually deteriorates and must be replaced after 30,000 miles or if leaded gasoline has been used.

Fig. 3: Le Car Oxygen Sensor

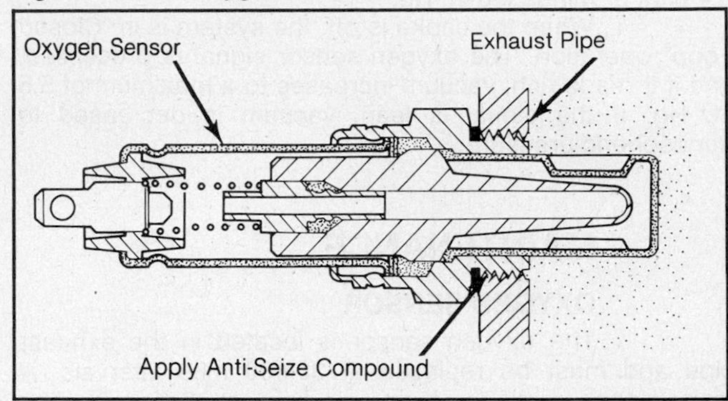
Oxygen Sensor
Exhaust Pipe
Apply Anti-Seize Compound

VACUUM SOLENOID REGULATOR

The regulator provides the vacuum signal to the feedback carburetor. A solenoid and regulator are combined in one housing. When the solenoid is de-energized, the output port is blocked and vacuum is vented to atmosphere. When the solenoid is energized, vacuum passes to the carburetor. The average "ON" time versus "OFF" time determines the vacuum level provided.

When the oxygen sensor and control unit sense a rich mixture, the solenoid is "ON" longer, producing a higher vacuum signal. This allows more air through the idle circuit, and less fuel through the main mixture circuit. For lean conditions, the vacuum signal is lower.

Fig. 4: Le Car Vacuum Solenoid Regulator

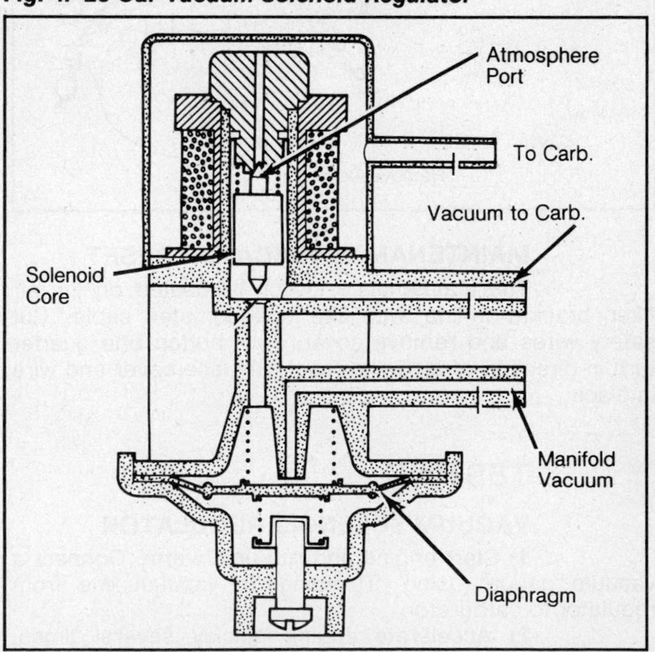
Atmosphere
Port
To Carb.
Vacuum to Carb.
Solenoid
Core
Manifold
Vacuum
Diaphragm

ELECTRONIC CONTROL UNIT

The electronic control unit processes inputs from the oxygen sensor, ignition coil (engine speed), and

RENAULT FEEDBACK CARBURETOR SYSTEM (Cont.)

choke. It is also connected to battery voltage and ground. An output signal is sent from the control unit to the vacuum regulator to control mixture ratio.

When the choke is pulled out, the control unit is in "Open Loop" operation. The vacuum regulator then operates at a constant 40% of maximum vacuum, which is 2.4 plus or minus 0.8 in. Hg.

When the choke is off, the system is in "Closed Loop" operation. The oxygen sensor signal is processed, and if it reads rich, vacuum increases to a maximum of 5.5 in. Hg. If the signal is lean, vacuum is decreased to atmospheric pressure.

MAINTENANCE

OXYGEN SENSOR

The oxygen sensor is located in the exhaust pipe and must be replaced at 30,000 mile intervals. A maintenance reminder lamp will light at that time. The threads of the new sensor must be coated with anti-seize compound when it is installed.

Fig. 5: Oxygen Sensor Indicator Reset

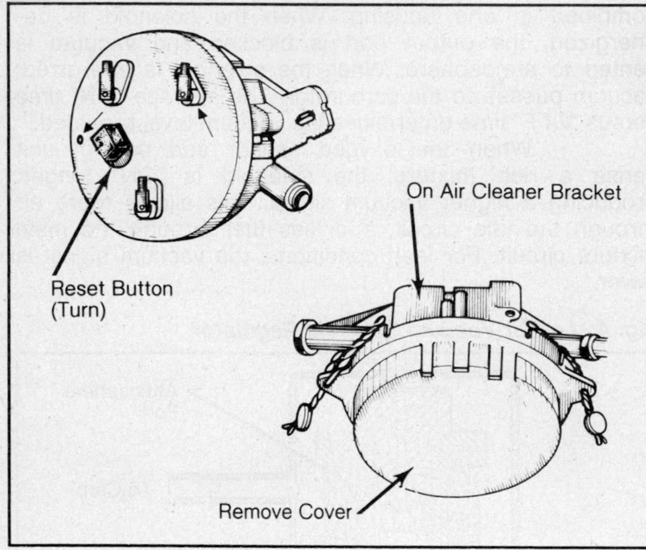
On Air Cleaner Bracket
Reset Button
(Turn)
Remove Cover

MAINTENANCE INDICATOR RESET

The maintenance switch is located on the air filter bracket in-line with the speedometer cable. Cut safety wires and remove cover. Turn button one quarter turn in direction of arrow to reset. Replace cover and wire in place.

TESTING

VACUUM SOLENOID REGULATOR

1) Start engine and run until warm. Connect a vacuum gauge (using "T" fitting) to vacuum line from regulator to carburetor.

2) Accelerate engine quickly several times. Vacuum should increase quickly to 5.5 in. Hg.

3) Pull choke knob out slightly until choke light comes on. Vacuum should quickly stabilize between 1.8-3.0 in. Hg.

4) If regulator does not work properly, check vacuum hose connections, check for presence of vacuum at inlet line from manifold, and be sure all electrical connections are clean and tight. If electronic control unit functions properly when tested, replace vacuum regulator.

ELECTRONIC CONTROL UNIT

1) Pull back rubber sleeves to expose wire terminals, but do not disconnect wires. Connect a 20,000 ohms/volt multimeter to the following wires:

Fig. 6: Feedback Carburetor Wiring Diagram

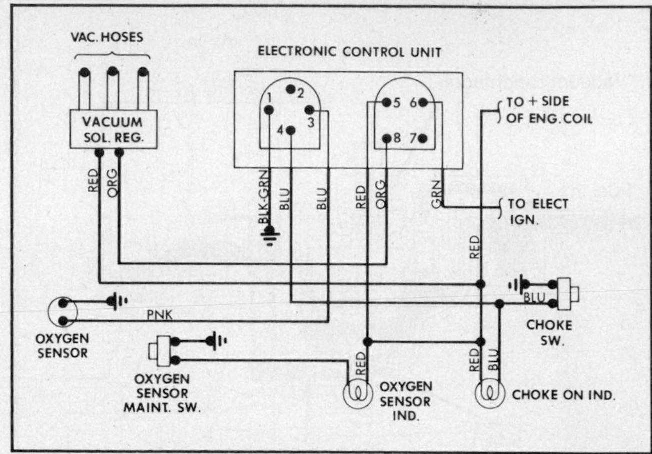
VAC. HOSES
ELECTRONIC CONTROL UNIT
VACUUM SOL. REG.
1
2
3
4
5
6
8
7
TO + SIDE OF ENG. COIL
RED
ORG
BLK-GRN
BLU
BLU
RED
ORG
GRN
TO ELECT IGN.
RED
PNK
BLU
CHOKE SW.
OXYGEN SENSOR
OXYGEN SENSOR MAINT. SW.
RED
OXYGEN SENSOR IND.
RED
BLU
CHOKE ON IND.

2) At pin 1 (Black/Green wire), there should be continuity with ground. Pin 2 is not used. Pin 3 (Pink) is connected to oxygen sensor. With engine warm and choke knob pulled out, there should be more than 600mv at Pink wire. With choke in, accelerate engine quickly several times. Voltage should vary between zero and more than 600mv.

3) Pin 4 (Blue) is connected to choke. With knob in, 12 volts should be present. With knob out, no voltage. Pin 5 (Red) should show battery voltage.

4) Connect a tachometer to pin 6 (Green). Engine speed should be shown. Pin 7 is not tested. Pin 8 (Orange) is output wire to solenoid regulator.

5) Connect a voltmeter (-) lead to pin 8, and (+) lead to battery voltage (pin 5, Red). Voltage should vary between zero and 12 when accelerating engine. Voltage should be stable between 1.5-5 volts when choke is pulled out, even with engine accelerating.

6) If control unit readings are incorrect, check source of signal and all wire connections. Replace oxygen sensor if voltage is incorrect. Check and adjust choke switch if voltage is not correct. If all other items are operational, replace electronic control unit.

SUBARU ELECTRONICALLY CONTROLLED CARBURETOR

All Models

DESCRIPTION

The Electronically Controlled Carburetor (ECC) system is a computerized emission and fuel control system. The system is used on all Federal models without 4WD and all California models.

Two versions of the ECC system are used on Subaru models, depending upon carburetor application. One system is used with Hitachi carburetors and another system is used with Carter carburetors. All California models are equipped with Hitachi 2-barrel carburetors. Federal models without 4WD can be equipped with Carter 1-barrel or Hitachi 2-barrel carburetors.

The ECC system controls engine operation and lowers exhaust emissions while maintaining good fuel economy and driveability. The Electronic Control Module (ECM) is the "brain" of the ECC system. The ECM controls many engine related systems to constantly adjust engine operation.

Fig. 1: ECC System Used With Hitachi Carburetor

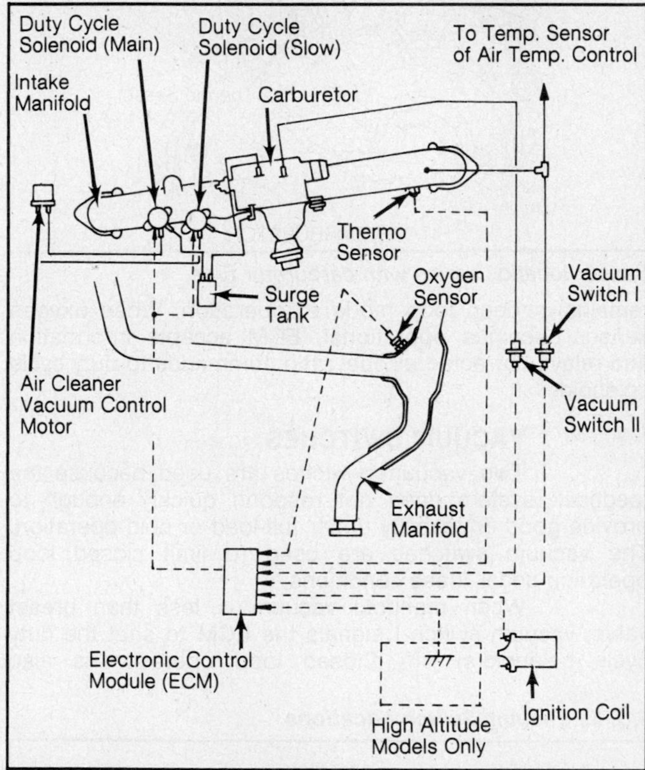
Duty Cycle
Solenoid (Main)
Duty Cycle
Solenoid (Slow)
To Temp. Sensor
of Air Temp. Control
Intake
Manifold
Carburetor
Thermo
Sensor
Surge
Tank
Oxygen
Sensor
Vacuum
Switch I
Air Cleaner
Vacuum Control
Motor
Vacuum
Switch II
Exhaust
Manifold
Electronic Control
Module (ECM)
High Altitude
Models Only
Ignition Coil

This carburetor is used on Federal models without 4WD and all California models.

The ECC system is primarily an emission control system, designed to maintain an ideal air/fuel ratio of 14.7:1 under all operating conditions. When an ideal ratio is maintained, the catalytic converters can control carbon monoxide (CO), hydrocarbon (HC) and nitrogen oxide (NOx) emissions.

OPERATION

The ECC system consists of the following sub-systems: Fuel Control, Data Sensors, Vacuum Switches, Electronic Control Module (ECM), Emission Control, catalytic converters and diagnostic system.

FUEL CONTROL

All models equipped with ECC use feedback carburetors. Feedback carburetors use duty cycle solenoids to control air/fuel ratio. The air/fuel ratio is determined by the ECM in response to data sensor and vacuum switch signals.

Fig. 2: ECC System Used With Carter Carburetor

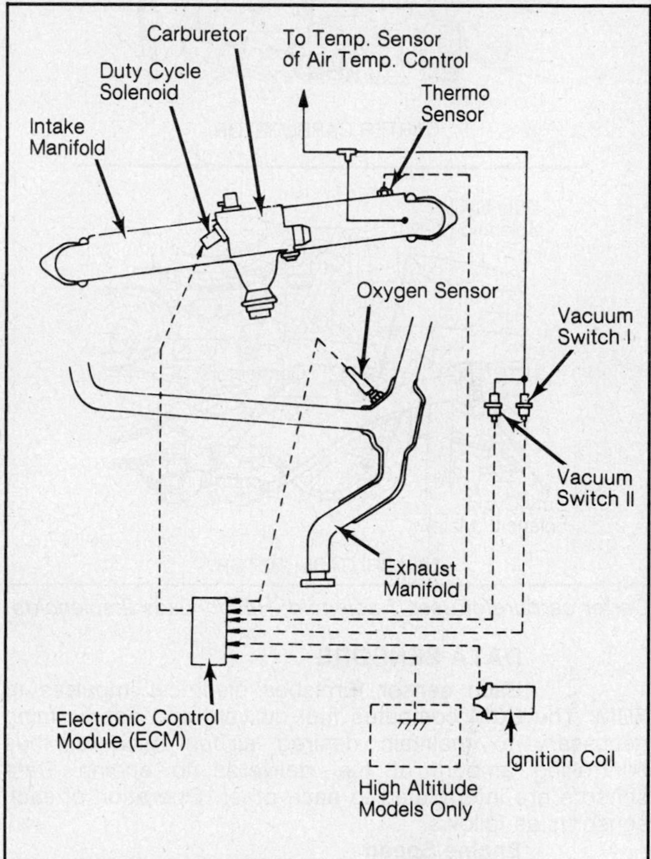
Carburetor
To Temp. Sensor
of Air Temp. Control
Duty Cycle
Solenoid
Thermo
Sensor
Intake
Manifold
Oxygen Sensor
Vacuum
Switch I
Vacuum
Switch II
Exhaust
Manifold
Electronic Control
Module (ECM)
High Altitude
Models Only
Ignition Coil

This carburetor is used only on Federal models without 4WD.

The ECM monitors various engine operating conditions and calculates appropriate air/fuel ratio. The duty cycle ratio (time that solenoid is energized compared against time that solenoid is de-energized) is dependent upon coolant temperature, oxygen sensor signals, engine speed, engine load (intake manifold vacuum), and altitude.

When the ECM is changing air/fuel ratio based upon oxygen sensor information, the system is operating in closed loop mode. In closed loop, air/fuel ratio is dependent upon oxygen content of exhaust gases.

When coolant temperature and oxygen sensor temperature do not meet preset values, the system operates in open loop mode of operation. In open loop mode, the ECM issues air/fuel ratio commands to duty cycle solenoid based upon pre-programmed information.

Models equipped with Carter carburetors use 1 solenoid and models with Hitachi carburetors use 2 solenoids (slow and main circuits). The solenoid for Carter carburetors is an integral part of carburetor. The solenoids for Hitachi carburetors are externally mounted on

SUBARU ELECTRONICALLY CONTROLLED CARBURETOR (Cont.)

intake manifold and are connected to the carburetor by air hoses. *See Fig. 3.*

Fig. 3: Duty Cyle Solenoid Locations

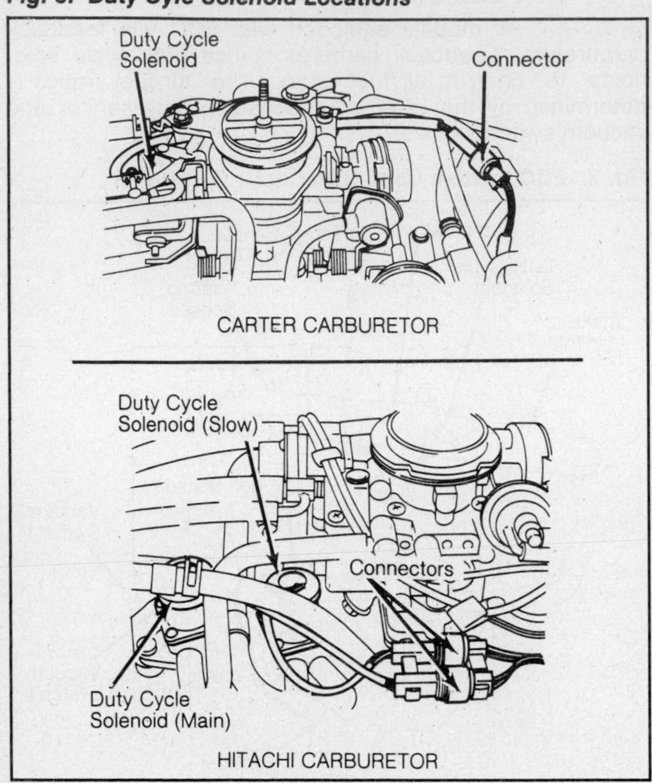
Duty Cycle Solenoid
Connector
CARTER CARBURETOR
Duty Cycle Solenoid (Slow)
Connectors
Duty Cycle Solenoid (Main)
HITACHI CARBURETOR

Carter carburetor uses 1 solenoid; Hitachi uses 2 solenoids.

DATA SENSORS

Each sensor furnishes electrical impulses to ECM. The ECM computes fuel delivery and spark timing necessary to maintain desired air/fuel mixture, thus controlling amount of fuel delivered to engine. Data sensors are interrelated to each other. Operation of each sensor is as follows:

Engine Speed

Engine speed signal is received from ignition coil. Electrical signals from ignition coil are sent to ECM where time between signals is used to calculate engine speed. This information is used by ECM for controlling fuel mixture, EGR and air injection system.

Thermo Sensor

The thermo sensor is installed in intake manifold on all models. *See Fig. 4.* This sensor is a thermistor which converts temperature of engine coolant to electrical signal for use by ECM. The ECM uses coolant temperature information for controlling air/fuel mixture, EGR and air injection systems.

Oxygen Sensor

The oxygen sensor is installed in exhaust manifold. Output voltage of sensor varies with oxygen content of exhaust gases in exhaust gas stream. High output voltage to ECM signals that mixture is too rich; ECM issues lean command to duty cycle solenoid. Low output voltage to ECM signals that mixture is too lean; ECM issues rich command to duty cycle solenoid.

The ECM does not accept oxygen sensor information until sensor has warmed to about 600°F (316°C). Until oxygen sensor is fully operational, ECM

Fig. 4: Thermo Sensor Location

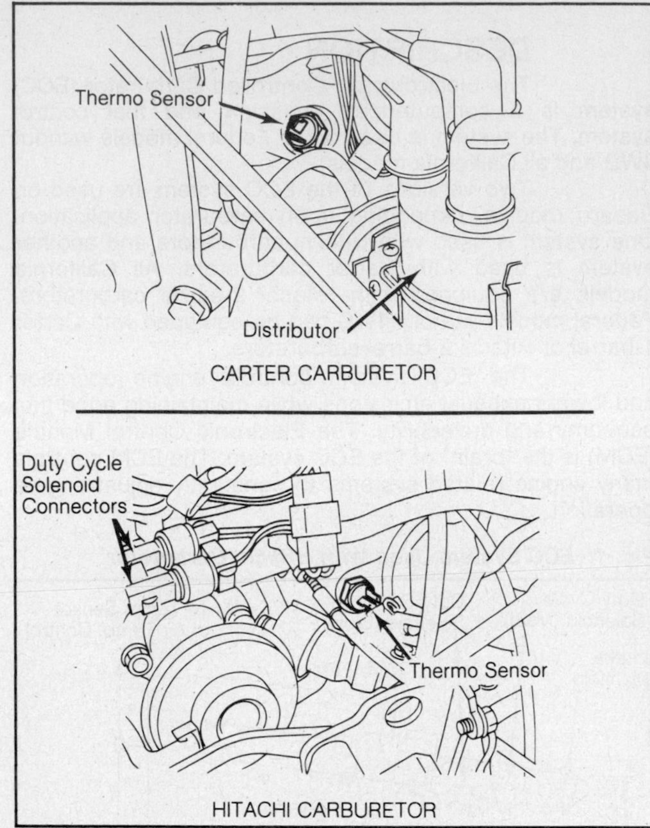
Thermo Sensor
Distributor
CARTER CARBURETOR
Duty Cycle Solenoid Connectors
Thermo Sensor
HITACHI CARBURETOR

Sensor location varies with carburetor type.

remains in open loop mode of operation. When oxygen sensor becomes operational, ECM accepts information and relays corrected air/fuel ratio commands to duty cycle solenoid.

VACUUM SWITCHES

Two vacuum switches are used because the feedback system does not respond quickly enough to provide good driveability under full-load or cold operation. The vacuum switches are used to limit closed loop operation under these conditions.

When manifold vacuum is less than preset value, vacuum switch I signals the ECM to shut the duty cycle solenoid(s) off. Closed loop operation is also

Fig. 5: Vacuum Switch Locations

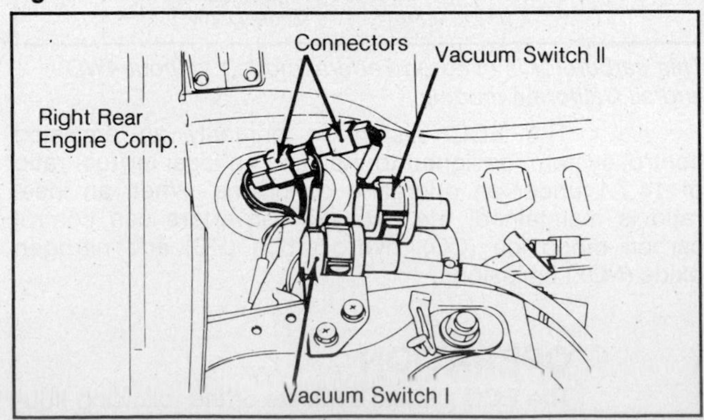
Connectors
Vacuum Switch II
Right Rear Engine Comp.
Vacuum Switch I

This applies to all models with ECC.

SUBARU ELECTRONICALLY CONTROLLED CARBURETOR (Cont.)

prevented by vacuum switch II, when the engine is warm and vacuum falls below a preset value (during acceleration/deceleration). After a lapse of about 5 seconds, the switch returns control of duty cycle solenoid(s) to ECM.

ELECTRONIC CONTROL MODULE

The ECM monitors and controls all ECC system functions. The ECM is a digital computer housed in a metal box. The ECM receives electrical signals from various sensors and switches to maintain good driveability and low emissions.

The ECM is located below the steering column in the passenger compartment. A small lamp (oxygen sensor monitor) is provided on the control module to assist in trouble shooting.

Fig. 6: Electronic Control Module (ECM) Location

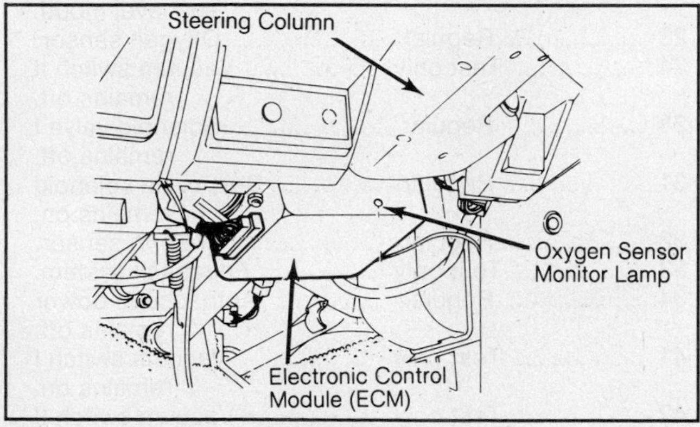
Steering Column
Oxygen Sensor
Monitor Lamp
Electronic Control
Module (ECM)

This applies to all models with ECC.

EMISSION CONTROL

Air Injection System

All Federal models without 4WD and all California models are equipped with computer-controlled air injection systems. The ECM monitors coolant temperature and activates a timer.

When coolant temperature is below 95°F (35°C), the ECM issues a command to solenoid valve I. The solenoid valve opens, admitting intake manifold vacuum to open the air suction valve(s) through the cutoff valve(s) for about 2 minutes.

After the time has elapsed, the ECM issues a command to solenoid valve I to close the vacuum passage. The solenoid valve closes and this closes the cutoff valve(s).

CATALYTIC CONVERTERS

All models equipped with the ECC system use two 3-way catalytic converters. Each catalytic converter contains platinum and rhodium as basic material. This type of converter is used to reduce CO, HC and NOx emissions and permits simultaneous oxidation and reduction.

DIAGNOSTIC SYSTEM

The ECM of the ECC system is equipped with a self-diagnostic system which detects system failures or abnormalities. When a malfunction occurs, ECM will light the "ECS" lamp located on the instrument panel. When a malfunction is detected and lamp is turned on, a corresponding trouble code is stored in ECM memory.

As a bulb and system check, the "ECS" lamp will glow when ignition switch is turned on and engine is not running. When engine is started, the lamp should go out. If not, a malfunction has been detected in ECC system.

DIAGNOSIS & TESTING

DIAGNOSTIC TOOLS

The ECC system does not require special tools for diagnosis. A dwell meter (set on 4-cylinder scale), volt/ohmmeter, 1.5 volt flashlight battery and a stethoscope or listening tube are the only tools required for diagnosis.

The dwell meter is used to check operation of the duty cycle solenoid. *See appropriate TUNE-UP article for procedure.*

ECC DIAGNOSIS

Diagnosis of the ECC system is done in the following order:

1) Ensure that all engine systems NOT related to ECC are fully operational. Do not proceed with testing unless you are sure that all other problems have been corrected.

2) ECC diagnosis is performed in 2 modes: Regular mode and test mode. Most of the trouble codes can be activated in regular mode test. Some codes require that the test mode option be entered to activate display of codes. To enter test mode, the test mode connector must be connected together. *See Fig. 7.*

NOTE: The test mode connector must not be connected together unless specific tests require that it be connected. Connector must be disconnected after performing any tests.

Fig. 7: ECC Test Connector Locations

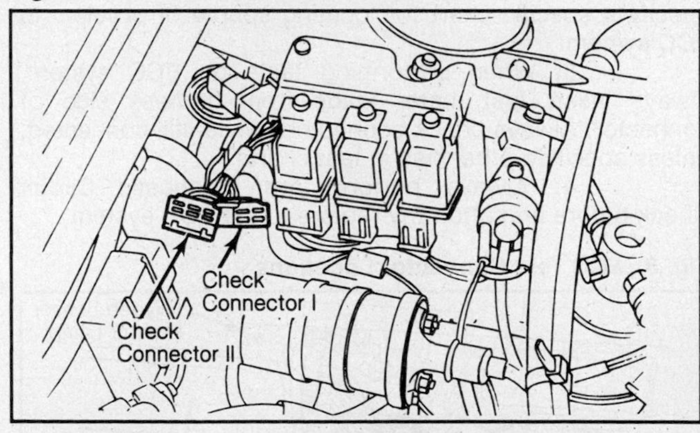
Check
Connector I
Check
Connector II

These connectors are located below steering column.

3) When a malfunction occurs in the ECC system, the ECM lights the "ECS" lamp on the instrument panel and causes the oxygen sensor monitor lamp to flash a trouble code. Trouble codes are displayed in numerical order from lowest code to highest code.

4) Trouble codes are displayed by flashes of the oxygen sensor monitor lamp on the ECM. In regular mode or test mode, a trouble code will be displayed by the oxygen sensor monitor lamp only when the "ECS" lamp is on. Trouble codes are 2-digit numbers.

SUBARU ELECTRONICALLY CONTROLLED CARBURETOR (Cont.)

5) An example of trouble codes is as follows: "FLASH", "FLASH", pause, "FLASH", "FLASH", "FLASH" followed by a longer pause identifies trouble code "23". The first series of flashes indicates first digit of trouble code; second series of flashes indicates second digit of trouble code.

6) The first digit is flashed for about 1.2 seconds with a 0.3 second pause between each flash. The second digit is flashed for about 0.2 seconds with a 0.3 second pause between each flash. Each trouble code is separated by a 1.8 second pause. Trouble codes display repeatedly until malfunction is repaired.

Entering Diagnostic Mode

Turn ignition on (engine off). In regular mode, "ECS" lamp will glow and trouble codes will be displayed on oxygen sensor monitor lamp. Turn ignition off and connect test mode connector to enter test mode. In test mode, "ECS" lamp will glow and trouble codes will be displayed on oxygen sensor monitor lamp. Disconnect test mode connector.

Clearing Trouble Codes

Trouble codes will be cleared from ECM memory only after malfunction has been repaired. Always perform diagnostic test after any repair to make sure that no other malfunction exists and that repairs solved original problem.

Exiting Diagnostic Mode

Regular mode test is always active in ECC system. Only test mode can be selected by technicians. Disconnect test mode connector to exit test mode.

DIAGNOSTIC PROCEDURE

1) The ECC system should be considered as a possible source of trouble on engine performance, fuel economy and exhaust emission complaints ONLY after normal checks (which apply to vehicles without ECC) have been performed.

2) Diagnosis of the ECC system consists of 1 initial check: Diagnostic Circuit Check. This check will specify a specific chart for locating source of problem in ECC system.

3) When performing tests on ECC system, always insert test meter leads from harness side of connector. Always check connectors while still connected, unless specified otherwise in test charts.

4) Always perform the Diagnostic Circuit Check before and after any repairs to the ECC system.

Fig. 8: ECC Test Connector Locations

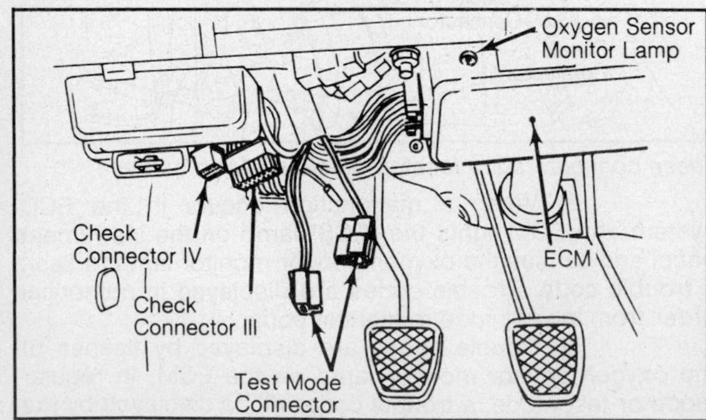

Oxygen Sensor
Monitor Lamp
Check
Connector IV
Check
Connector III
ECM
Test Mode
Connector

These connectors are located near ignition coil in engine compartment.

ECM TROUBLE CODE IDENTIFICATION

Trouble Code	Test Mode	Circuit Affected
11	Regular	Carter carb. high altitude mode.
12	Regular	Carter carb. sea level mode.
13	Regular	Duty cycle solenoid remains off.
14	Test only	Vacuum switch I remains off.
15	Regular	Solenoid valve III remains off.
21	Regular	Hitachi carb. high altitude mode.
22	Regular	Hitachi carb. sea level mode.
23	Regular	Oxygen sensor.
24	Test only	Vacuum switch II remains off.
25	Regular	Solenoid valve I remains off.
31	Regular	Duty cycle solenoid remains on.
32	Regular	Thermo sensor.
33	Test only	Feedback system.
34	Regular	Auto. choke power remains off.
41	Test only	Vacuum switch I remains on.
42	Test only	Vacuum switch II remains on.
43	Regular	Auto. choke power remains on.
51	Regular	Solenoid valve III remains on.
52	Regular	Solenoid valve I remains on.

SUBARU ELECTRONICALLY CONTROLLED CARBURETOR (Cont.)

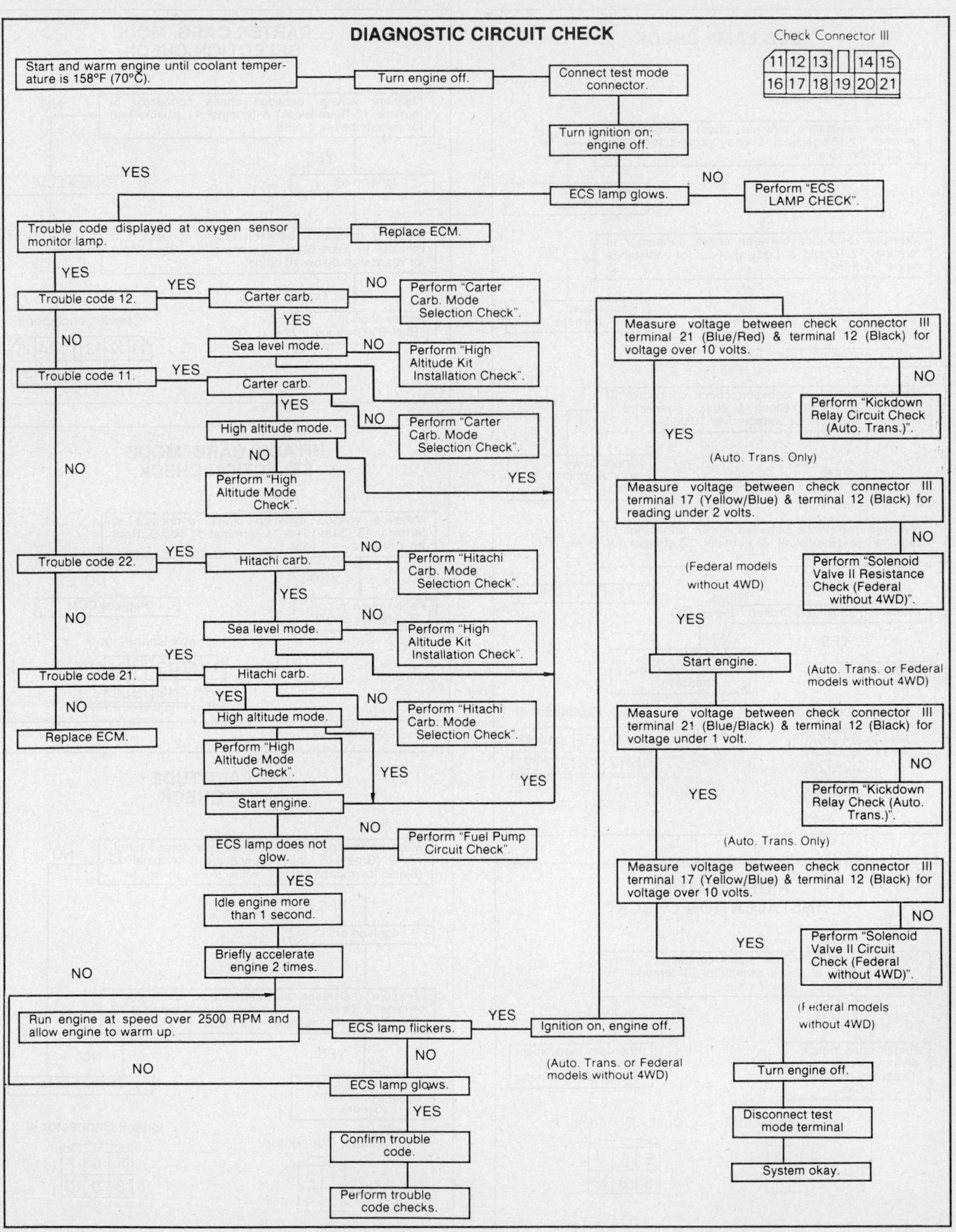
DIAGNOSTIC CIRCUIT CHECK
Check Connector III
11 12 13 14 15
16 17 18 19 20 21
Start and warm engine until coolant temperature is 158°F (70°C).
Turn engine off.
Connect test mode connector.
Turn ignition on; engine off.
ECS lamp glows.
YES
NO
Perform "ECS LAMP CHECK".
Trouble code displayed at oxygen sensor monitor lamp.
Replace ECM.
Trouble code 12.
Carter carb.
Perform "Carter Carb. Mode Selection Check".
Sea level mode.
Perform "High Altitude Kit Installation Check".
Trouble code 11.
Carter carb.
High altitude mode.
Perform "Carter Carb. Mode Selection Check".
Perform "High Altitude Mode Check".
Trouble code 22.
Hitachi carb.
Perform "Hitachi Carb. Mode Selection Check".
Sea level mode.
Perform "High Altitude Kit Installation Check".
Trouble code 21.
Hitachi carb.
High altitude mode.
Perform "Hitachi Carb. Mode Selection Check".
Replace ECM.
Perform "High Altitude Mode Check".
Start engine.
ECS lamp does not glow.
Perform "Fuel Pump Circuit Check".
Idle engine more than 1 second.
Briefly accelerate engine 2 times.
Run engine at speed over 2500 RPM and allow engine to warm up.
ECS lamp flickers.
Ignition on, engine off.
(Auto. Trans. or Federal models without 4WD)
ECS lamp glows.
Confirm trouble code.
Perform trouble code checks.
Measure voltage between check connector III terminal 21 (Blue/Red) & terminal 12 (Black) for voltage over 10 volts.
Perform "Kickdown Relay Circuit Check (Auto. Trans.)".
(Auto. Trans. Only)
Measure voltage between check connector III terminal 17 (Yellow/Blue) & terminal 12 (Black) for reading under 2 volts.
Perform "Solenoid Valve II Resistance Check (Federal without 4WD)".
(Federal models without 4WD)
Start engine.
(Auto. Trans. or Federal models without 4WD)
Measure voltage between check connector III terminal 21 (Blue/Black) & terminal 12 (Black) for voltage under 1 volt.
Perform "Kickdown Relay Check (Auto. Trans.)".
(Auto. Trans. Only)
Measure voltage between check connector III terminal 17 (Yellow/Blue) & terminal 12 (Black) for voltage over 10 volts.
Perform "Solenoid Valve II Circuit Check (Federal without 4WD)".
(Federal models without 4WD)
Turn engine off.
Disconnect test mode terminal
System okay.

SUBARU ELECTRONICALLY CONTROLLED CARBURETOR (Cont.)

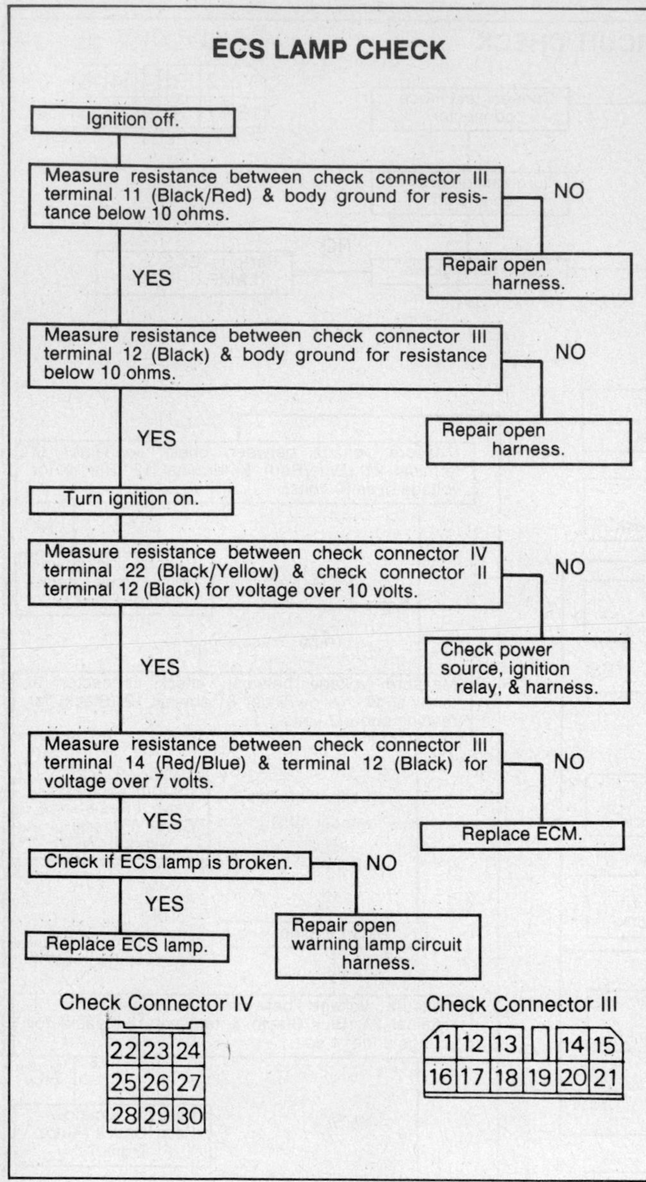
ECS LAMP CHECK
Ignition off.
Measure resistance between check connector III terminal 11 (Black/Red) & body ground for resistance below 10 ohms.
NO
Repair open harness.
YES
Measure resistance between check connector III terminal 12 (Black) & body ground for resistance below 10 ohms.
NO
Repair open harness.
YES
Turn ignition on.
Measure resistance between check connector IV terminal 22 (Black/Yellow) & check connector II terminal 12 (Black) for voltage over 10 volts.
NO
Check power source, ignition relay, & harness.
YES
Measure resistance between check connector III terminal 14 (Red/Blue) & terminal 12 (Black) for voltage over 7 volts.
NO
Replace ECM.
YES
Check if ECS lamp is broken.
NO
Repair open warning lamp circuit harness.
YES
Replace ECS lamp.
Check Connector IV
22 23 24
25 26 27
28 29 30
Check Connector III
11 12 13 14 15
16 17 18 19 20 21

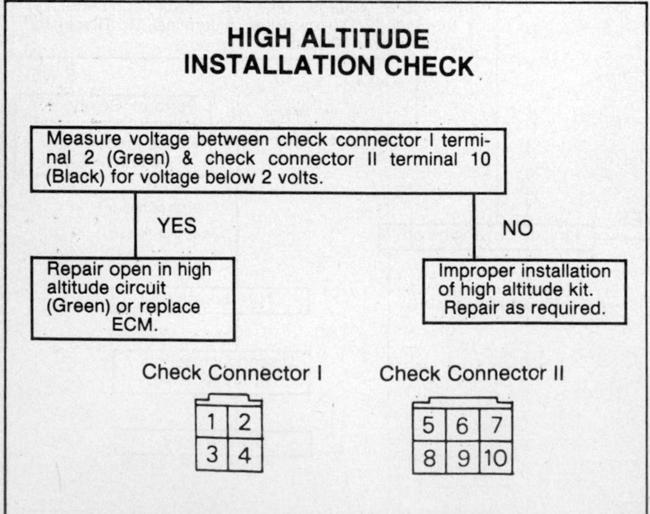
HIGH ALTITUDE INSTALLATION CHECK
Measure voltage between check connector I terminal 2 (Green) & check connector II terminal 10 (Black) for voltage below 2 volts.
YES
Repair open in high altitude circuit (Green) or replace ECM.
NO
Improper installation of high altitude kit. Repair as required.
Check Connector I
1 2
3 4
Check Connector II
5 6 7
8 9 10

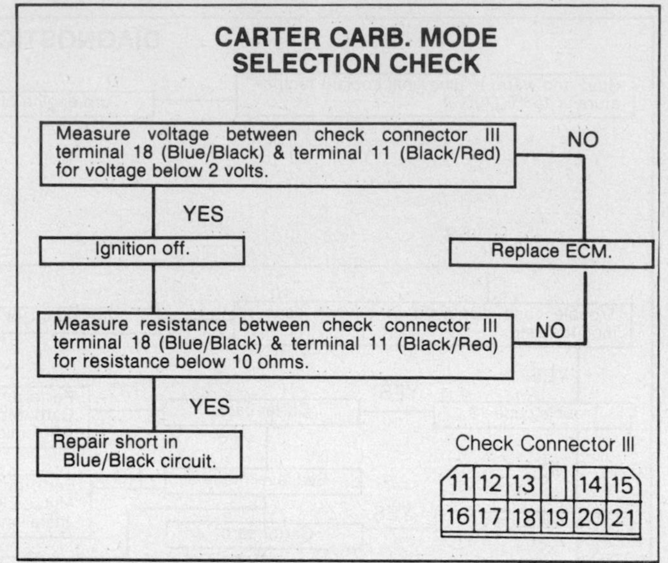
CARTER CARB. MODE SELECTION CHECK
Measure voltage between check connector III terminal 18 (Blue/Black) & terminal 11 (Black/Red) for voltage below 2 volts.
NO
Replace ECM.
YES
Ignition off.
Measure resistance between check connector III terminal 18 (Blue/Black) & terminal 11 (Black/Red) for resistance below 10 ohms.
NO
YES
Repair short in Blue/Black circuit.
Check Connector III
11 12 13 14 15
16 17 18 19 20 21

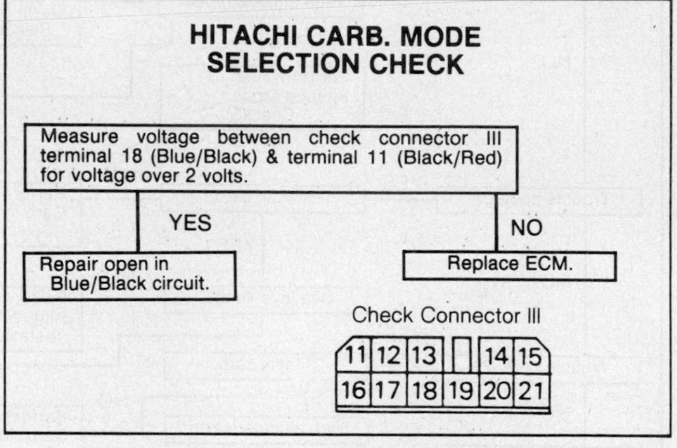
HITACHI CARB. MODE SELECTION CHECK
Measure voltage between check connector III terminal 18 (Blue/Black) & terminal 11 (Black/Red) for voltage over 2 volts.
YES
Repair open in Blue/Black circuit.
NO
Replace ECM.
Check Connector III
11 12 13 14 15
16 17 18 19 20 21

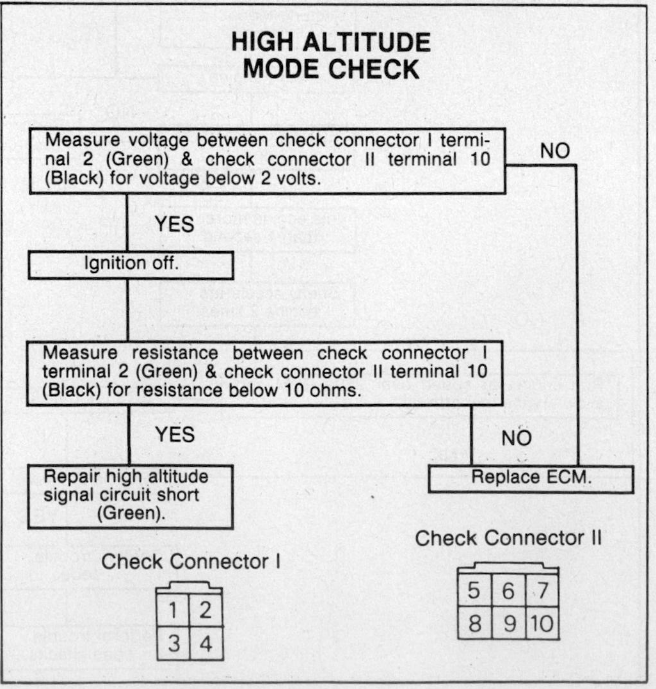
HIGH ALTITUDE MODE CHECK
Measure voltage between check connector I terminal 2 (Green) & check connector II terminal 10 (Black) for voltage below 2 volts.
NO
YES
Ignition off.
Measure resistance between check connector I terminal 2 (Green) & check connector II terminal 10 (Black) for resistance below 10 ohms.
YES
Repair high altitude signal circuit short (Green).
NO
Replace ECM.
Check Connector I
1 2
3 4
Check Connector II
5 6 7
8 9 10

SUBARU ELECTRONICALLY CONTROLLED CARBURETOR (Cont.)

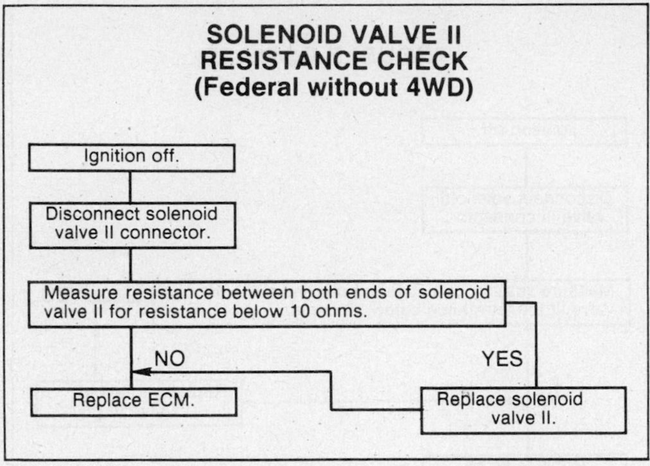
SOLENOID VALVE II
RESISTANCE CHECK
(Federal without 4WD)
Ignition off.
Disconnect solenoid valve II connector.
Measure resistance between both ends of solenoid valve II for resistance below 10 ohms.
NO
YES
Replace ECM.
Replace solenoid valve II.

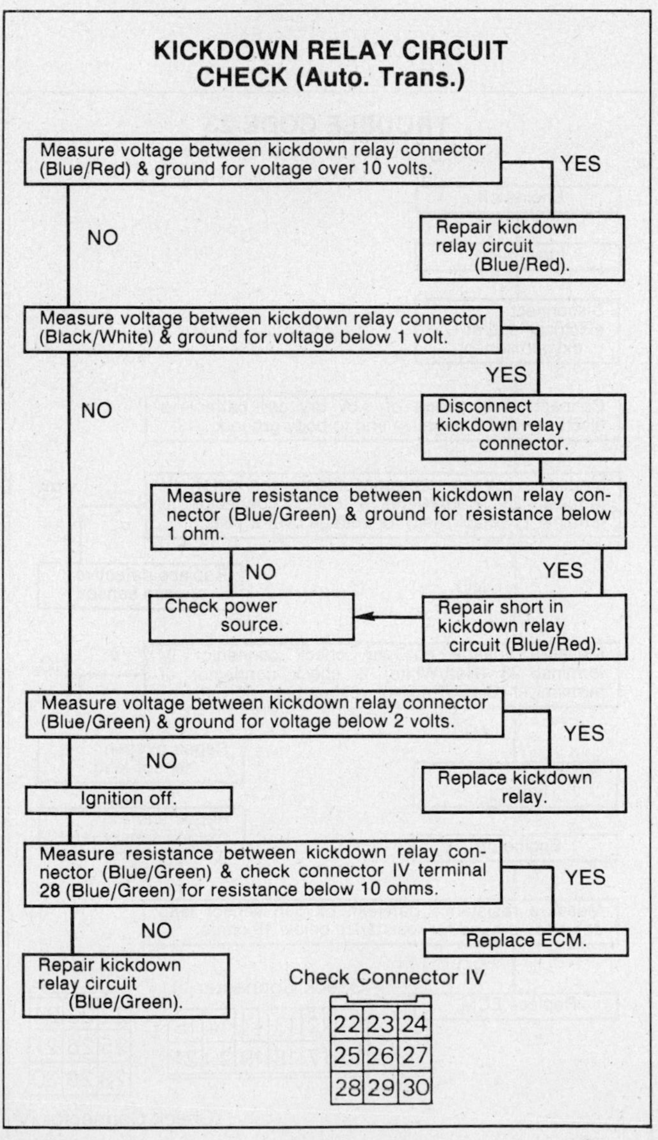
KICKDOWN RELAY CIRCUIT
CHECK (Auto. Trans.)
Measure voltage between kickdown relay connector (Blue/Red) & ground for voltage over 10 volts.
YES
Repair kickdown relay circuit (Blue/Red).
NO
Measure voltage between kickdown relay connector (Black/White) & ground for voltage below 1 volt.
YES
Disconnect kickdown relay connector.
NO
Measure resistance between kickdown relay connector (Blue/Green) & ground for resistance below 1 ohm.
NO
YES
Check power source.
Repair short in kickdown relay circuit (Blue/Red).
Measure voltage between kickdown relay connector (Blue/Green) & ground for voltage below 2 volts.
YES
Replace kickdown relay.
NO
Ignition off.
Measure resistance between kickdown relay connector (Blue/Green) & check connector IV terminal 28 (Blue/Green) for resistance below 10 ohms.
YES
Replace ECM.
NO
Repair kickdown relay circuit (Blue/Green).
Check Connector IV
22 23 24
25 26 27
28 29 30

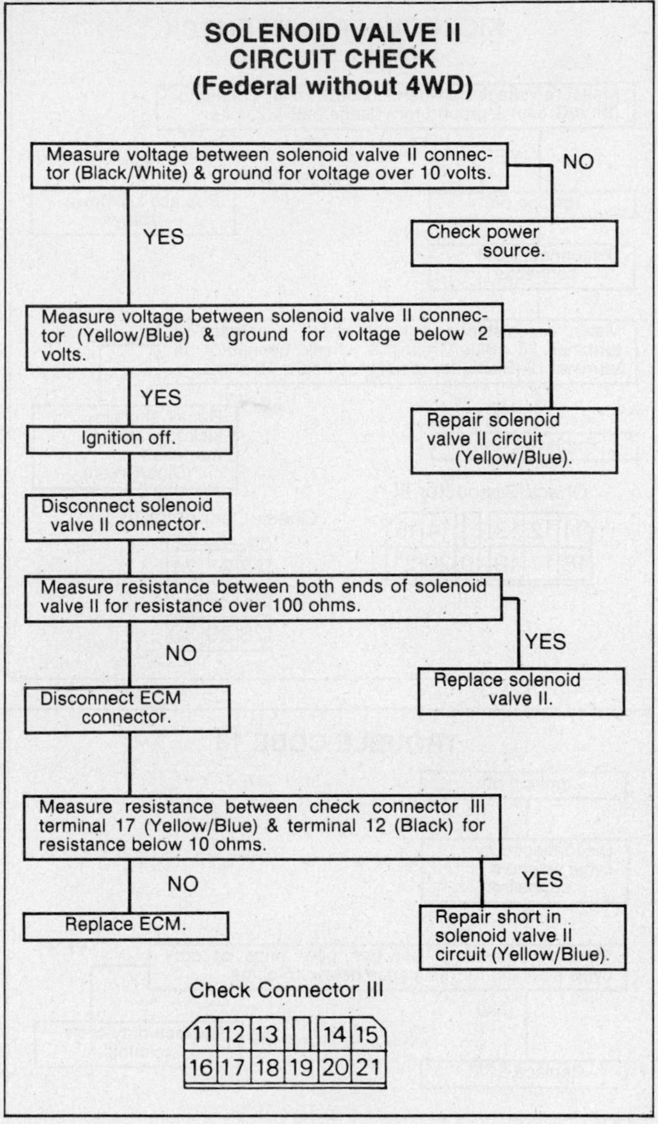
SOLENOID VALVE II
CIRCUIT CHECK
(Federal without 4WD)
Measure voltage between solenoid valve II connector (Black/White) & ground for voltage over 10 volts.
NO
Check power source.
YES
Measure voltage between solenoid valve II connector (Yellow/Blue) & ground for voltage below 2 volts.
YES
Ignition off.
Repair solenoid valve II circuit (Yellow/Blue).
Disconnect solenoid valve II connector.
Measure resistance between both ends of solenoid valve II for resistance over 100 ohms.
YES
NO
Replace solenoid valve II.
Disconnect ECM connector.
Measure resistance between check connector III terminal 17 (Yellow/Blue) & terminal 12 (Black) for resistance below 10 ohms.
NO
YES
Replace ECM.
Repair short in solenoid valve II circuit (Yellow/Blue).
Check Connector III
11 12 13 14 15
16 17 18 19 20 21

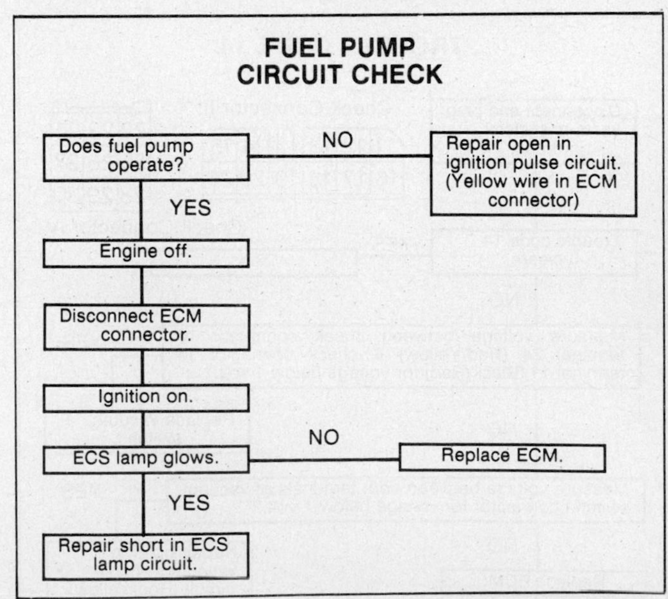
FUEL PUMP
CIRCUIT CHECK
Does fuel pump operate?
NO
Repair open in ignition pulse circuit. (Yellow wire in ECM connector)
YES
Engine off.
Disconnect ECM connector.
Ignition on.
ECS lamp glows.
NO
Replace ECM.
YES
Repair short in ECS lamp circuit.

SUBARU ELECTRONICALLY CONTROLLED CARBURETOR (Cont.)

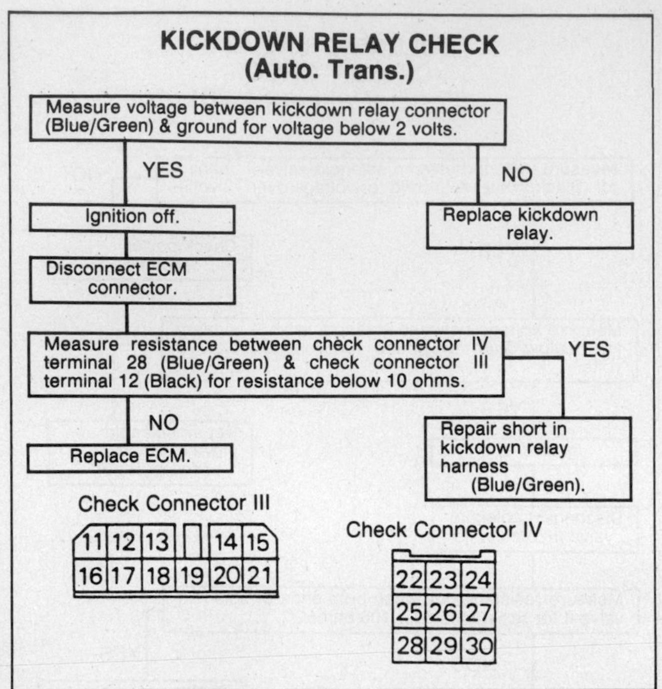
KICKDOWN RELAY CHECK
(Auto. Trans.)
Measure voltage between kickdown relay connector (Blue/Green) & ground for voltage below 2 volts.
YES
NO
Ignition off.
Replace kickdown relay.
Disconnect ECM connector.
Measure resistance between check connector IV terminal 28 (Blue/Green) & check connector III terminal 12 (Black) for resistance below 10 ohms.
YES
NO
Replace ECM.
Repair short in kickdown relay harness (Blue/Green).
Check Connector III
11 12 13 14 15
16 17 18 19 20 21
Check Connector IV
22 23 24
25 26 27
28 29 30

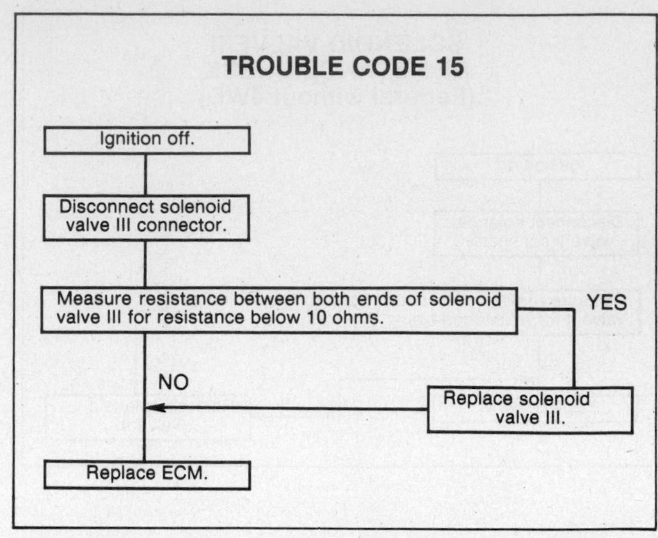
TROUBLE CODE 15
Ignition off.
Disconnect solenoid valve III connector.
Measure resistance between both ends of solenoid valve III for resistance below 10 ohms.
YES
NO
Replace solenoid valve III.
Replace ECM.

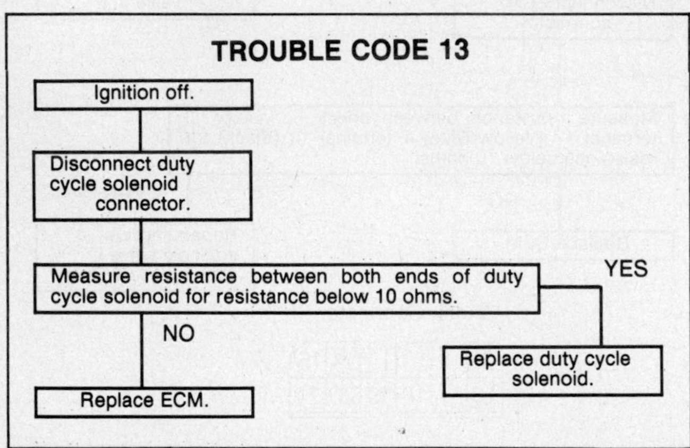
TROUBLE CODE 13
Ignition off.
Disconnect duty cycle solenoid connector.
Measure resistance between both ends of duty cycle solenoid for resistance below 10 ohms.
YES
NO
Replace duty cycle solenoid.
Replace ECM.

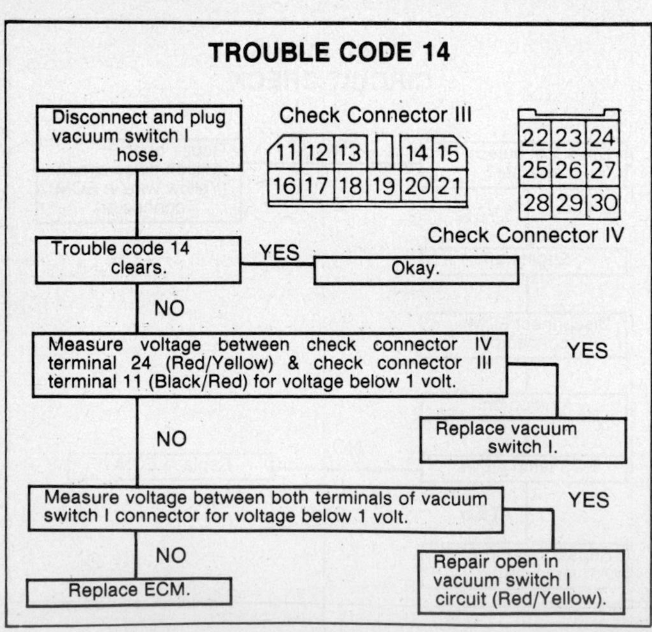
TROUBLE CODE 14
Disconnect and plug vacuum switch I hose.
Check Connector III
11 12 13 14 15
16 17 18 19 20 21
22 23 24
25 26 27
28 29 30
Check Connector IV
Trouble code 14 clears.
YES
Okay.
NO
Measure voltage between check connector IV terminal 24 (Red/Yellow) & check connector III terminal 11 (Black/Red) for voltage below 1 volt.
YES
NO
Replace vacuum switch I.
Measure voltage between both terminals of vacuum switch I connector for voltage below 1 volt.
YES
NO
Replace ECM.
Repair open in vacuum switch I circuit (Red/Yellow).

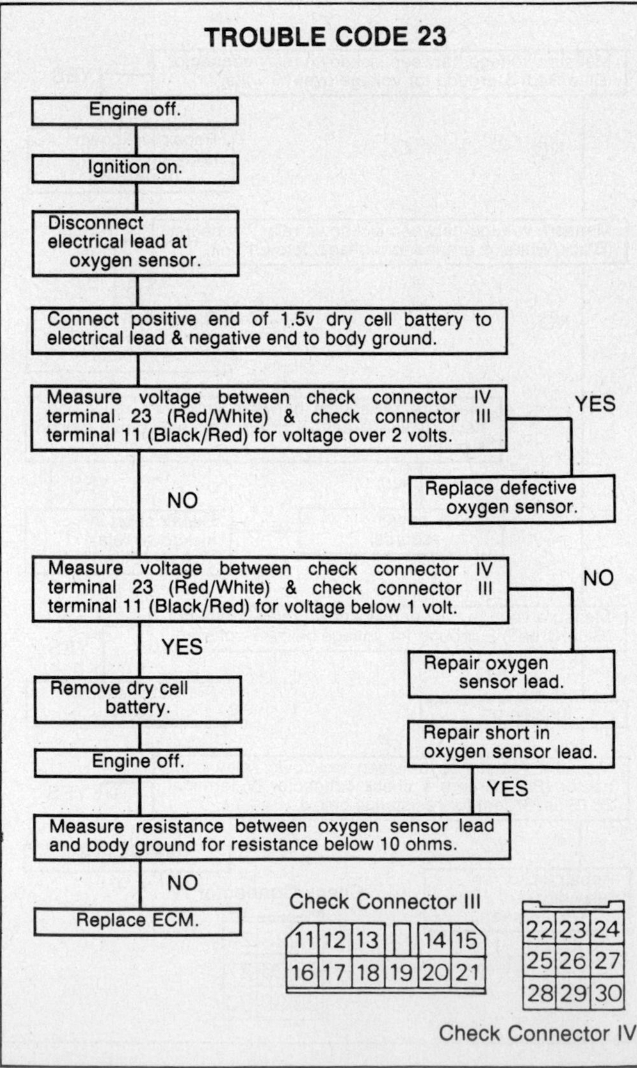
TROUBLE CODE 23
Engine off.
Ignition on.
Disconnect electrical lead at oxygen sensor.
Connect positive end of 1.5v dry cell battery to electrical lead & negative end to body ground.
Measure voltage between check connector IV terminal 23 (Red/White) & check connector III terminal 11 (Black/Red) for voltage over 2 volts.
YES
Replace defective oxygen sensor.
NO
Measure voltage between check connector IV terminal 23 (Red/White) & check connector III terminal 11 (Black/Red) for voltage below 1 volt.
NO
YES
Repair oxygen sensor lead.
Remove dry cell battery.
Repair short in oxygen sensor lead.
Engine off.
YES
Measure resistance between oxygen sensor lead and body ground for resistance below 10 ohms.
NO
Replace ECM.
Check Connector III
11 12 13 14 15
16 17 18 19 20 21
22 23 24
25 26 27
28 29 30
Check Connector IV

SUBARU ELECTRONICALLY CONTROLLED CARBURETOR (Cont.)

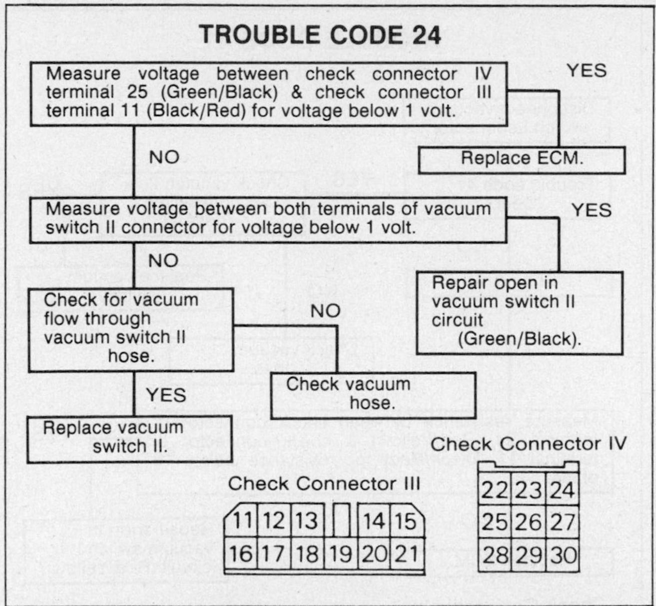

TROUBLE CODE 24
Measure voltage between check connector IV terminal 25 (Green/Black) & check connector III terminal 11 (Black/Red) for voltage below 1 volt.
YES
Replace ECM.
NO
Measure voltage between both terminals of vacuum switch II connector for voltage below 1 volt.
YES
Repair open in vacuum switch II circuit (Green/Black).
NO
Check for vacuum flow through vacuum switch II hose.
NO
Check vacuum hose.
YES
Replace vacuum switch II.
Check Connector IV
22 23 24
25 26 27
28 29 30
Check Connector III
11 12 13 14 15
16 17 18 19 20 21

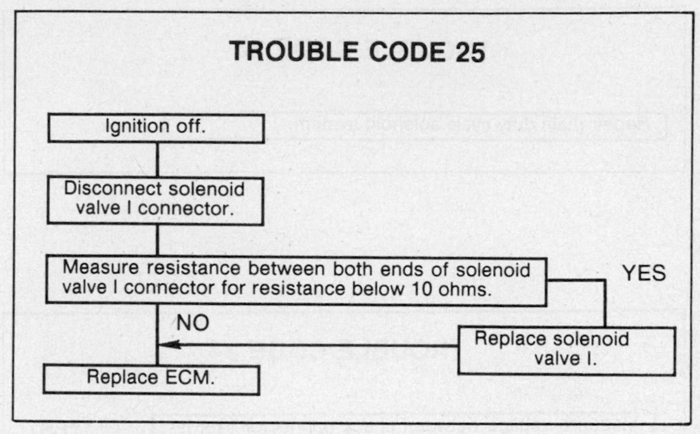

TROUBLE CODE 25
Ignition off.
Disconnect solenoid valve I connector.
Measure resistance between both ends of solenoid valve I connector for resistance below 10 ohms.
YES
Replace solenoid valve I.
NO
Replace ECM.

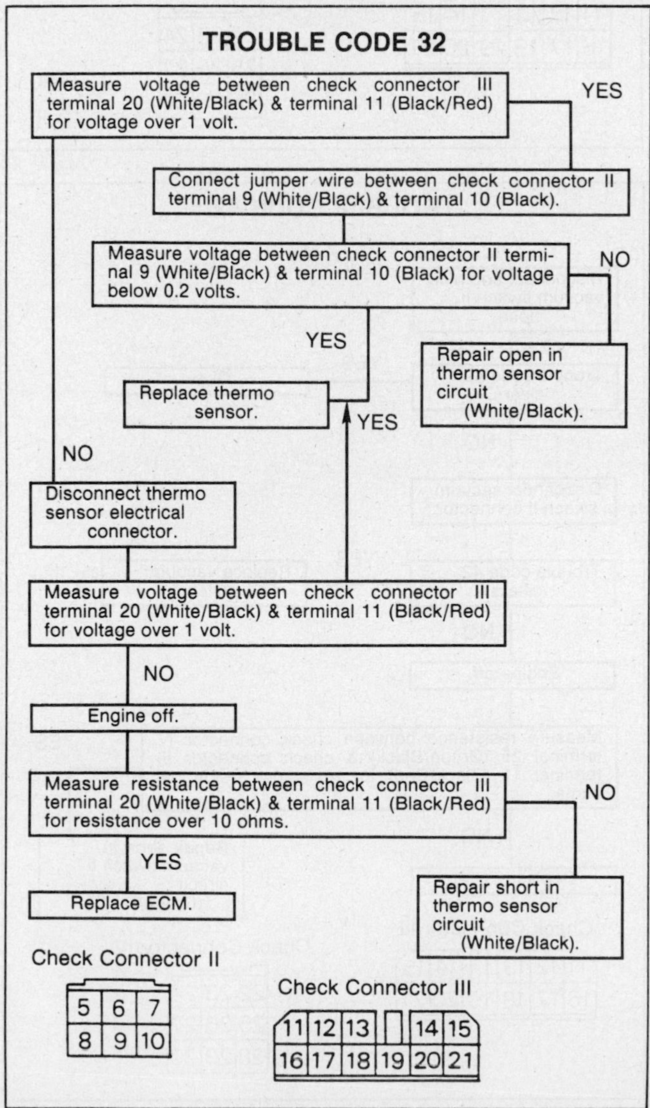

TROUBLE CODE 32
Measure voltage between check connector III terminal 20 (White/Black) & terminal 11 (Black/Red) for voltage over 1 volt.
YES
Connect jumper wire between check connector II terminal 9 (White/Black) & terminal 10 (Black).
Measure voltage between check connector II terminal 9 (White/Black) & terminal 10 (Black) for voltage below 0.2 volts.
NO
Repair open in thermo sensor circuit (White/Black).
YES
Replace thermo sensor.
YES
NO
Disconnect thermo sensor electrical connector.
Measure voltage between check connector III terminal 20 (White/Black) & terminal 11 (Black/Red) for voltage over 1 volt.
NO
Engine off.
Measure resistance between check connector III terminal 20 (White/Black) & terminal 11 (Black/Red) for resistance over 10 ohms.
NO
Repair short in thermo sensor circuit (White/Black).
YES
Replace ECM.
Check Connector II
5 6 7
8 9 10
Check Connector III
11 12 13 14 15
16 17 18 19 20 21

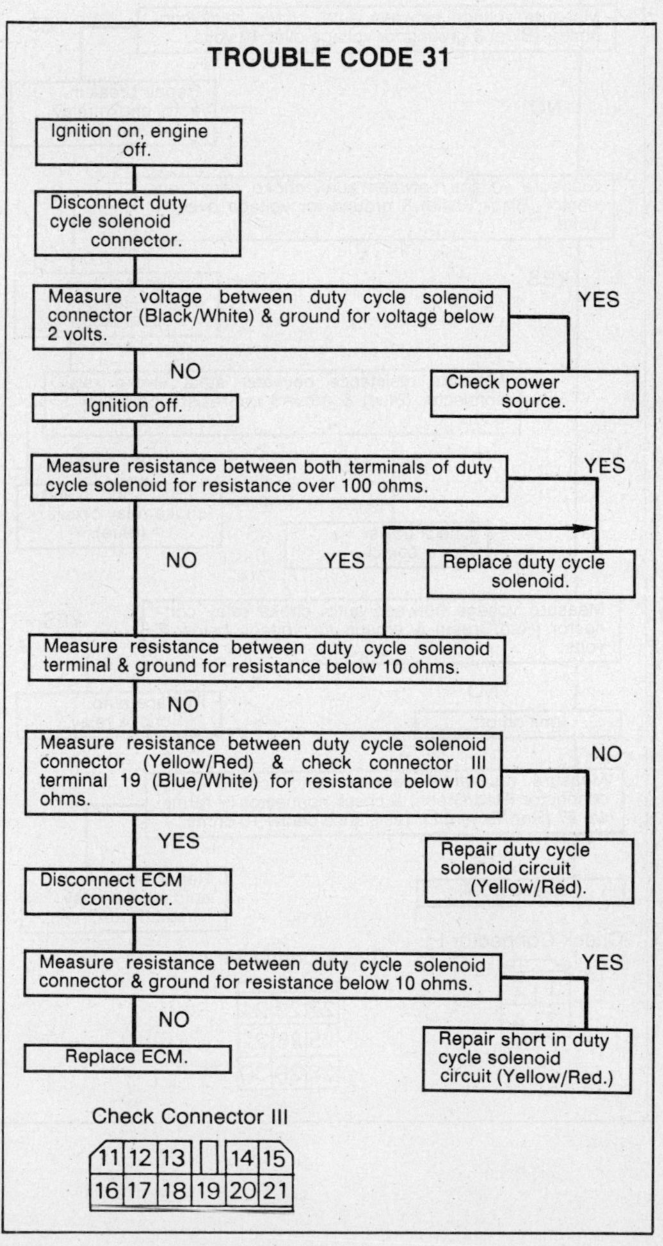

TROUBLE CODE 31
Ignition on, engine off.
Disconnect duty cycle solenoid connector.
Measure voltage between duty cycle solenoid connector (Black/White) & ground for voltage below 2 volts.
YES
Check power source.
NO
Ignition off.
Measure resistance between both terminals of duty cycle solenoid for resistance over 100 ohms.
YES
Replace duty cycle solenoid.
NO
YES
Measure resistance between duty cycle solenoid terminal & ground for resistance below 10 ohms.
NO
Measure resistance between duty cycle solenoid connector (Yellow/Red) & check connector III terminal 19 (Blue/White) for resistance below 10 ohms.
NO
Repair duty cycle solenoid circuit (Yellow/Red).
YES
Disconnect ECM connector.
Measure resistance between duty cycle solenoid connector & ground for resistance below 10 ohms.
YES
Repair short in duty cycle solenoid circuit (Yellow/Red.)
NO
Replace ECM.
Check Connector III
11 12 13 14 15
16 17 18 19 20 21

SUBARU ELECTRONICALLY CONTROLLED CARBURETOR (Cont.)

TROUBLE CODE 33

Repair main duty cycle solenoid system.

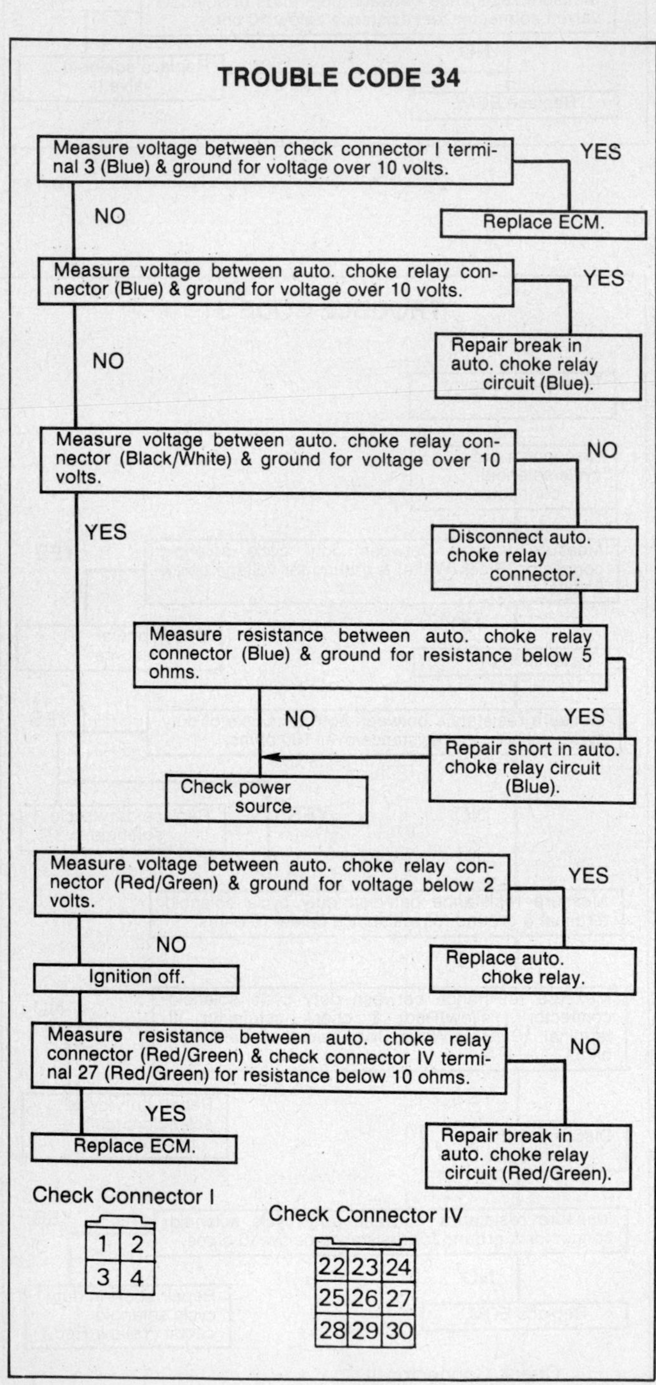
TROUBLE CODE 34
Measure voltage between check connector I terminal 3 (Blue) & ground for voltage over 10 volts.
YES
Replace ECM.
NO
Measure voltage between auto. choke relay connector (Blue) & ground for voltage over 10 volts.
YES
Repair break in auto. choke relay circuit (Blue).
NO
Measure voltage between auto. choke relay connector (Black/White) & ground for voltage over 10 volts.
NO
Disconnect auto. choke relay connector.
Measure resistance between auto. choke relay connector (Blue) & ground for resistance below 5 ohms.
NO
YES
Repair short in auto. choke relay circuit (Blue).
Check power source.
YES
Measure voltage between auto. choke relay connector (Red/Green) & ground for voltage below 2 volts.
YES
Replace auto. choke relay.
NO
Ignition off.
Measure resistance between auto. choke relay connector (Red/Green) & check connector IV terminal 27 (Red/Green) for resistance below 10 ohms.
NO
Repair break in auto. choke relay circuit (Red/Green).
YES
Replace ECM.
Check Connector I
1 2
3 4
Check Connector IV
22 23 24
25 26 27
28 29 30

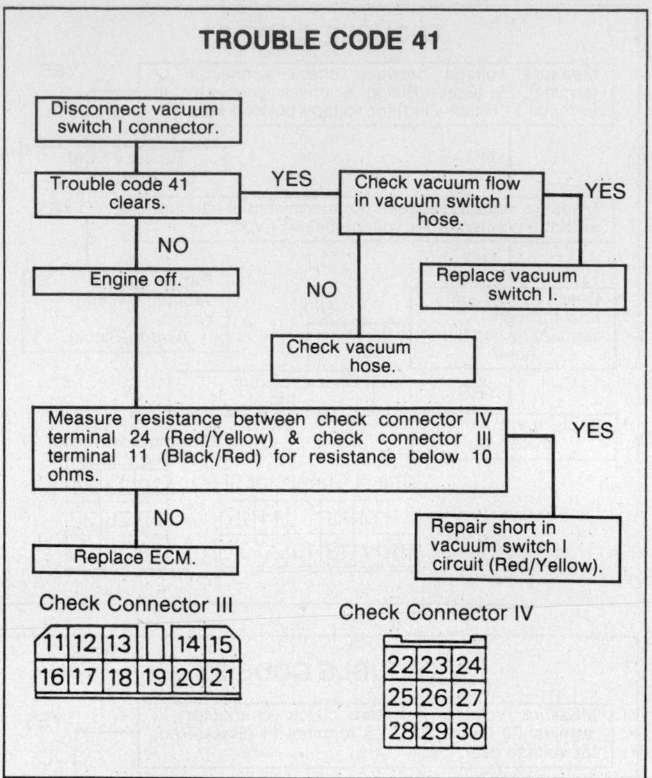
TROUBLE CODE 41
Disconnect vacuum switch I connector.
Trouble code 41 clears.
YES
Check vacuum flow in vacuum switch I hose.
YES
Replace vacuum switch I.
NO
Check vacuum hose.
NO
Engine off.
Measure resistance between check connector IV terminal 24 (Red/Yellow) & check connector III terminal 11 (Black/Red) for resistance below 10 ohms.
YES
Repair short in vacuum switch I circuit (Red/Yellow).
NO
Replace ECM.
Check Connector III
11 12 13 14 15
16 17 18 19 20 21
Check Connector IV
22 23 24
25 26 27
28 29 30

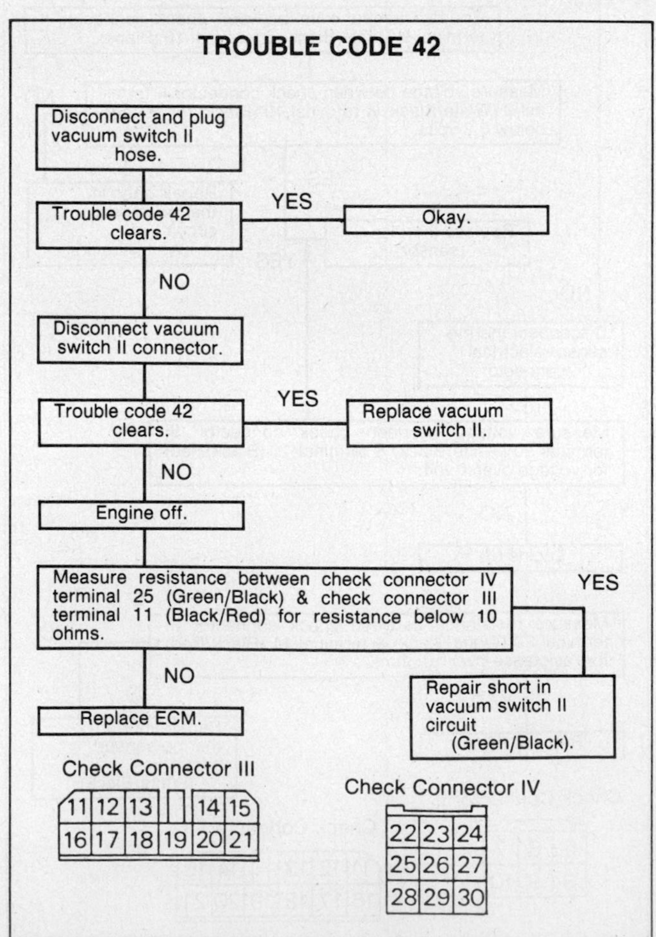
TROUBLE CODE 42
Disconnect and plug vacuum switch II hose.
Trouble code 42 clears.
YES
Okay.
NO
Disconnect vacuum switch II connector.
Trouble code 42 clears.
YES
Replace vacuum switch II.
NO
Engine off.
Measure resistance between check connector IV terminal 25 (Green/Black) & check connector III terminal 11 (Black/Red) for resistance below 10 ohms.
YES
Repair short in vacuum switch II circuit (Green/Black).
NO
Replace ECM.
Check Connector III
11 12 13 14 15
16 17 18 19 20 21
Check Connector IV
22 23 24
25 26 27
28 29 30

SUBARU ELECTRONICALLY CONTROLLED CARBURETOR (Cont.)

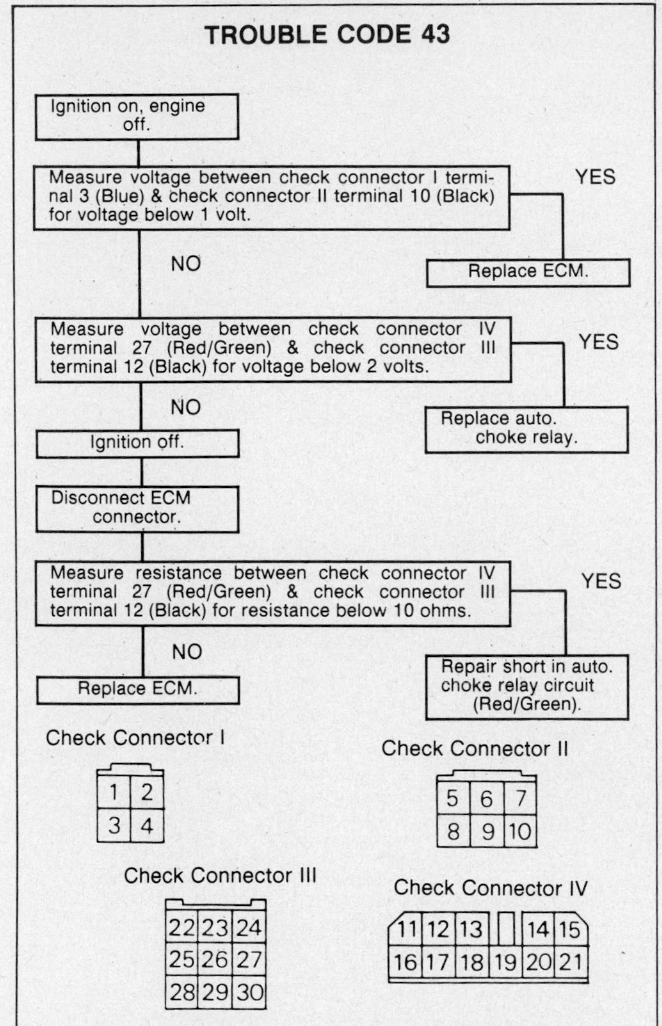
TROUBLE CODE 43
Ignition on, engine off.
Measure voltage between check connector I terminal 3 (Blue) & check connector II terminal 10 (Black) for voltage below 1 volt.
YES
Replace ECM.
NO
Measure voltage between check connector IV terminal 27 (Red/Green) & check connector III terminal 12 (Black) for voltage below 2 volts.
YES
Replace auto. choke relay.
NO
Ignition off.
Disconnect ECM connector.
Measure resistance between check connector IV terminal 27 (Red/Green) & check connector III terminal 12 (Black) for resistance below 10 ohms.
YES
Repair short in auto. choke relay circuit (Red/Green).
NO
Replace ECM.
Check Connector I
1 2 3 4
Check Connector II
5 6 7 8 9 10
Check Connector III
22 23 24 25 26 27 28 29 30
Check Connector IV
11 12 13 14 15 16 17 18 19 20 21

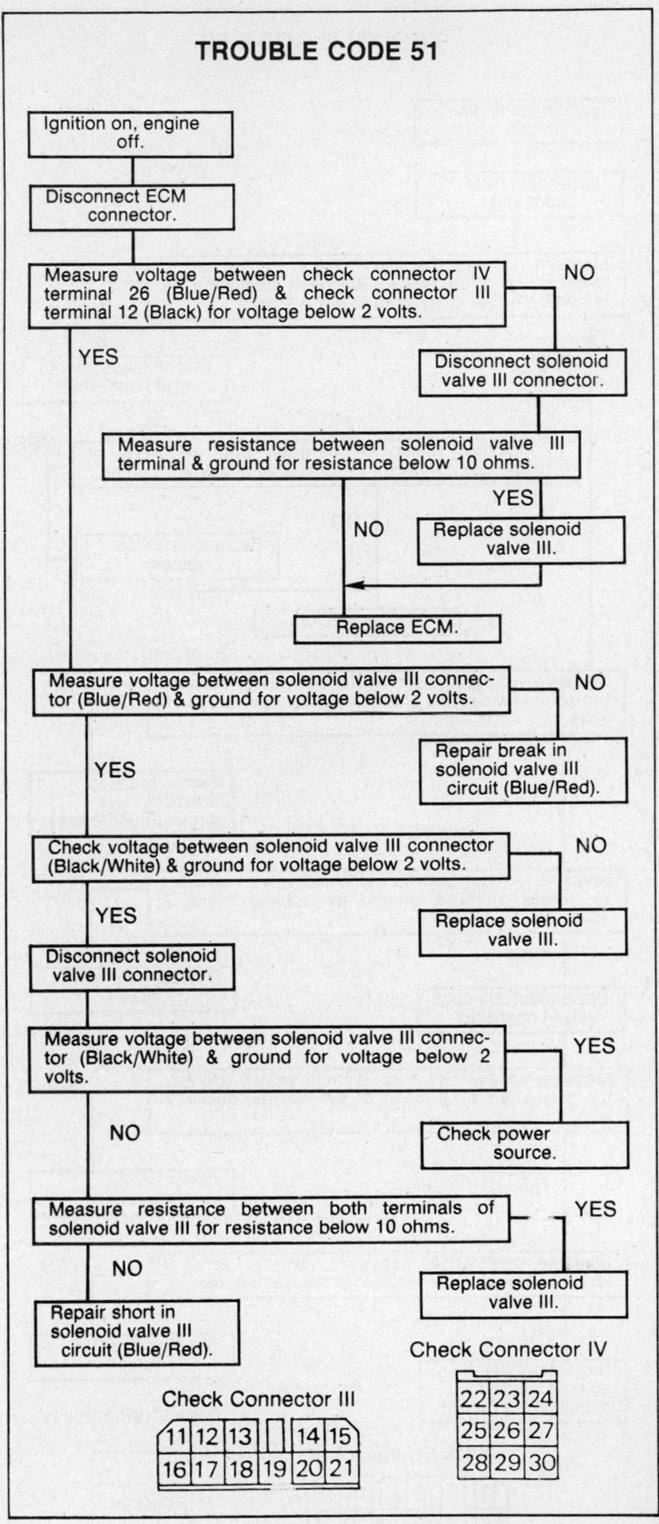
TROUBLE CODE 51
Ignition on, engine off.
Disconnect ECM connector.
Measure voltage between check connector IV terminal 26 (Blue/Red) & check connector III terminal 12 (Black) for voltage below 2 volts.
NO
Disconnect solenoid valve III connector.
Measure resistance between solenoid valve III terminal & ground for resistance below 10 ohms.
YES
Replace solenoid valve III.
NO
Replace ECM.
YES
Measure voltage between solenoid valve III connector (Blue/Red) & ground for voltage below 2 volts.
NO
Repair break in solenoid valve III circuit (Blue/Red).
YES
Check voltage between solenoid valve III connector (Black/White) & ground for voltage below 2 volts.
NO
Replace solenoid valve III.
YES
Disconnect solenoid valve III connector.
Measure voltage between solenoid valve III connector (Black/White) & ground for voltage below 2 volts.
YES
Check power source.
NO
Measure resistance between both terminals of solenoid valve III for resistance below 10 ohms.
YES
Replace solenoid valve III.
NO
Repair short in solenoid valve III circuit (Blue/Red).
Check Connector IV
22 23 24 25 26 27 28 29 30
Check Connector III
11 12 13 14 15 16 17 18 19 20 21

SUBARU ELECTRONICALLY CONTROLLED CARBURETOR (Cont.)

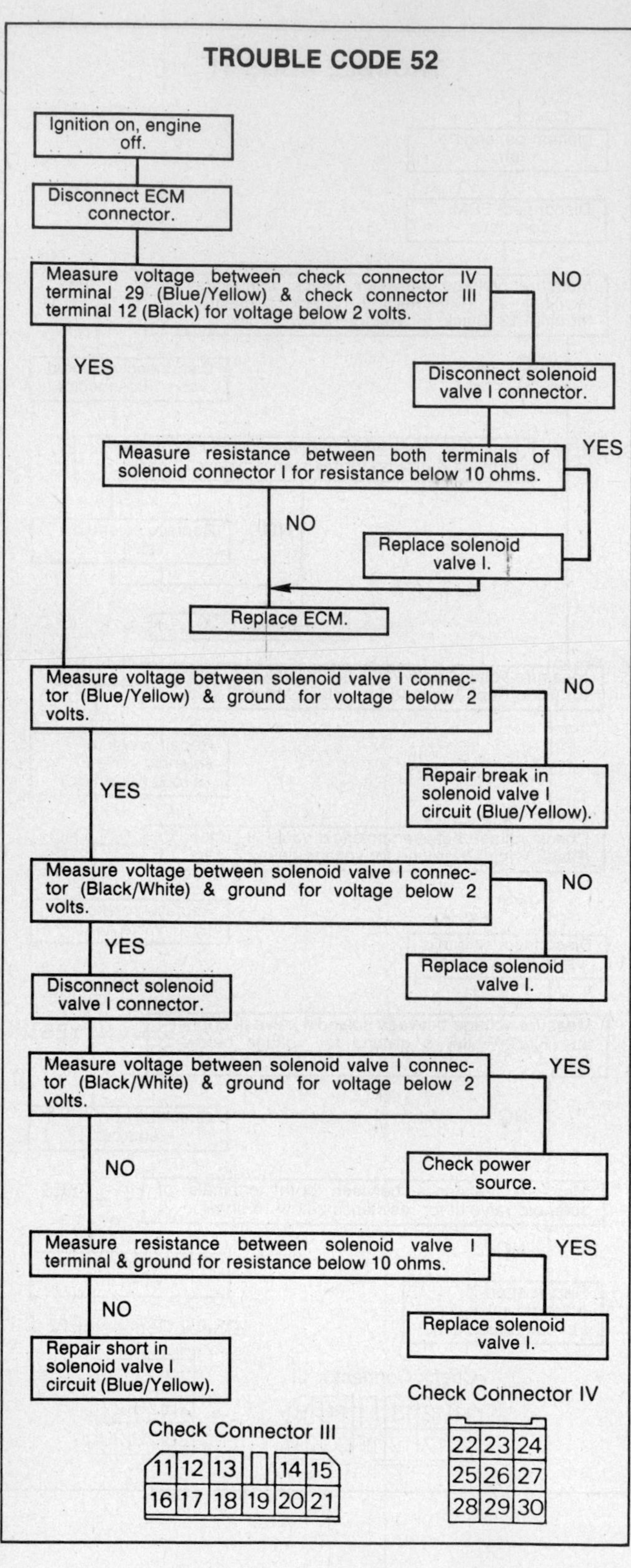
TROUBLE CODE 52
Ignition on, engine off.
Disconnect ECM connector.
Measure voltage between check connector IV terminal 29 (Blue/Yellow) & check connector III terminal 12 (Black) for voltage below 2 volts.
NO
YES
Disconnect solenoid valve I connector.
Measure resistance between both terminals of solenoid connector I for resistance below 10 ohms.
YES
NO
Replace solenoid valve I.
Replace ECM.
Measure voltage between solenoid valve I connector (Blue/Yellow) & ground for voltage below 2 volts.
NO
YES
Repair break in solenoid valve I circuit (Blue/Yellow).
Measure voltage between solenoid valve I connector (Black/White) & ground for voltage below 2 volts.
NO
YES
Replace solenoid valve I.
Disconnect solenoid valve I connector.
Measure voltage between solenoid valve I connector (Black/White) & ground for voltage below 2 volts.
YES
NO
Check power source.
Measure resistance between solenoid valve I terminal & ground for resistance below 10 ohms.
YES
NO
Replace solenoid valve I.
Repair short in solenoid valve I circuit (Blue/Yellow).
Check Connector IV
Check Connector III
11 12 13 14 15
16 17 18 19 20 21
22 23 24
25 26 27
28 29 30

SUBARU ELECTRONICALLY CONTROLLED CARBURETOR (Cont.)

Fig. 9: Subaru ECC Wiring Diagram

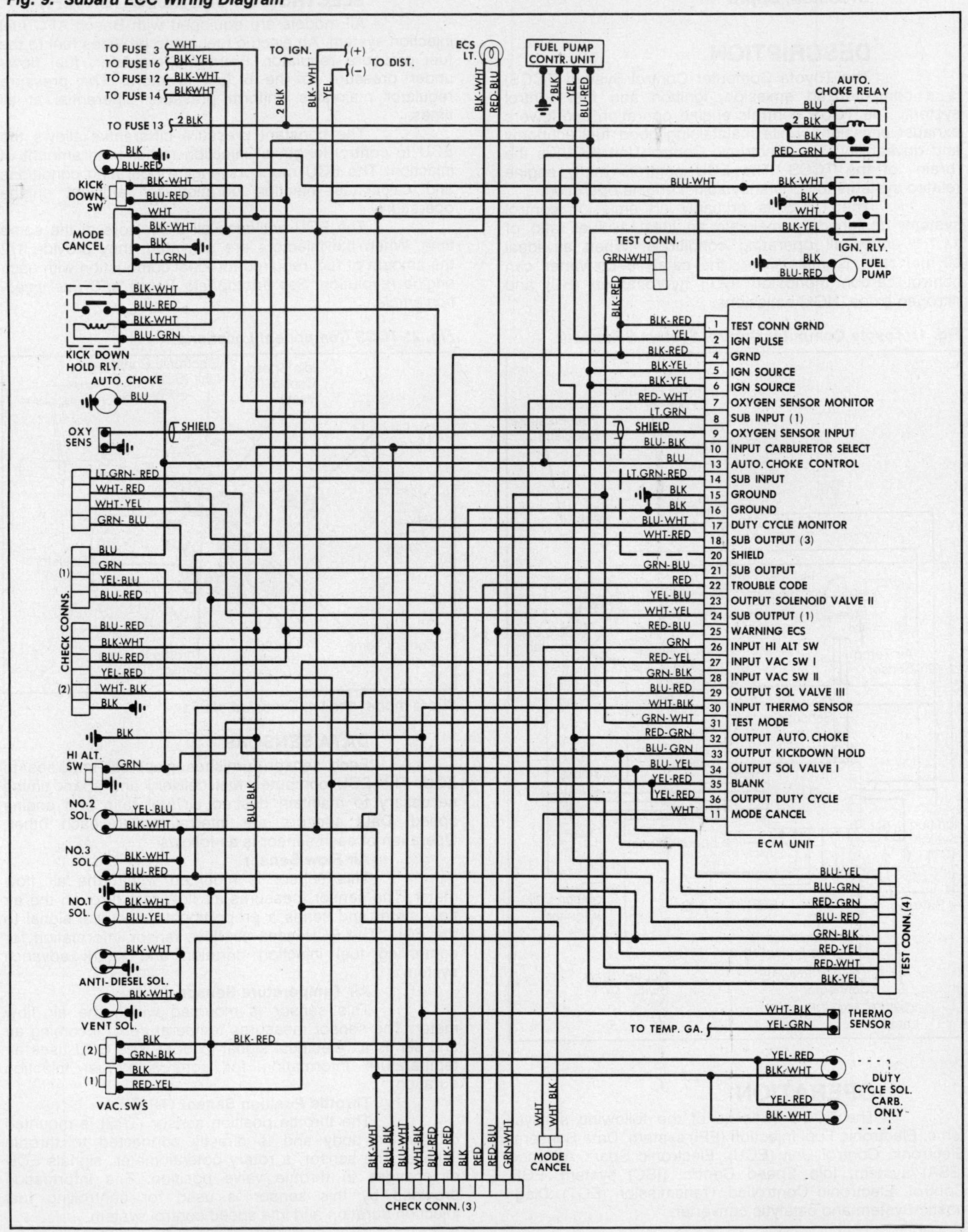
TO FUSE 3 WHT
TO FUSE 16 BLK-YEL
TO FUSE 12 BLK-WHT
TO FUSE 14 BLKWHT
TO FUSE 13 2 BLK
TO IGN.
(+)
(−)
TO DIST.
ECS LT.
FUEL PUMP CONTR. UNIT
AUTO. CHOKE RELAY
IGN. RLY.
FUEL PUMP
TEST CONN.
KICK DOWN SW
MODE CANCEL
KICK DOWN HOLD RLY.
AUTO. CHOKE
OXY SENS
SHIELD
CHECK CONNS.
(1)
(2)
HI ALT. SW
NO.2 SOL.
NO.3 SOL.
NO.1 SOL.
ANTI-DIESEL SOL.
VENT SOL.
VAC. SW'S
1 TEST CONN GRND
2 IGN PULSE
4 GRND
5 IGN SOURCE
6 IGN SOURCE
7 OXYGEN SENSOR MONITOR
8 SUB INPUT (1)
9 OXYGEN SENSOR INPUT
10 INPUT CARBURETOR SELECT
13 AUTO. CHOKE CONTROL
14 SUB INPUT
15 GROUND
16 GROUND
17 DUTY CYCLE MONITOR
18 SUB OUTPUT (3)
20 SHIELD
21 SUB OUTPUT
22 TROUBLE CODE
23 OUTPUT SOLENOID VALVE II
24 SUB OUTPUT (1)
25 WARNING ECS
26 INPUT HI ALT SW
27 INPUT VAC SW I
28 INPUT VAC SW II
29 OUTPUT SOL VALVE III
30 INPUT THERMO SENSOR
31 TEST MODE
32 OUTPUT AUTO. CHOKE
33 OUTPUT KICKDOWN HOLD
34 OUTPUT SOL VALVE I
35 BLANK
36 OUTPUT DUTY CYCLE
11 MODE CANCEL
ECM UNIT
TEST CONN.(4)
TO TEMP. GA.
THERMO SENSOR
DUTY CYCLE SOL. CARB. ONLY
MODE CANCEL
CHECK CONN.(3)

TOYOTA COMPUTER CONTROL SYSTEM

Cressida, Supra

DESCRIPTION

The Toyota Computer Control System (TCCS) is a computerized emission, ignition and fuel control system. The TCCS controls engine operation and lowers exhaust emissions while maintaining good fuel economy and driveability. The Electronic Control Unit (ECU) is the "brain" of the TCCS. The ECU controls many engine related systems to constantly adjust engine operation.

The TCCS is primarily an emission control system, designed to maintain an ideal air/fuel ratio of 14.7:1 under all operating conditions. When an ideal air/fuel ratio is maintained, the catalytic converter can control carbon monoxide (CO), hydrocarbon (HC) and nitrogen oxide (NOx) emissions.

Fig. 1: Toyota Computer Control System Schematic

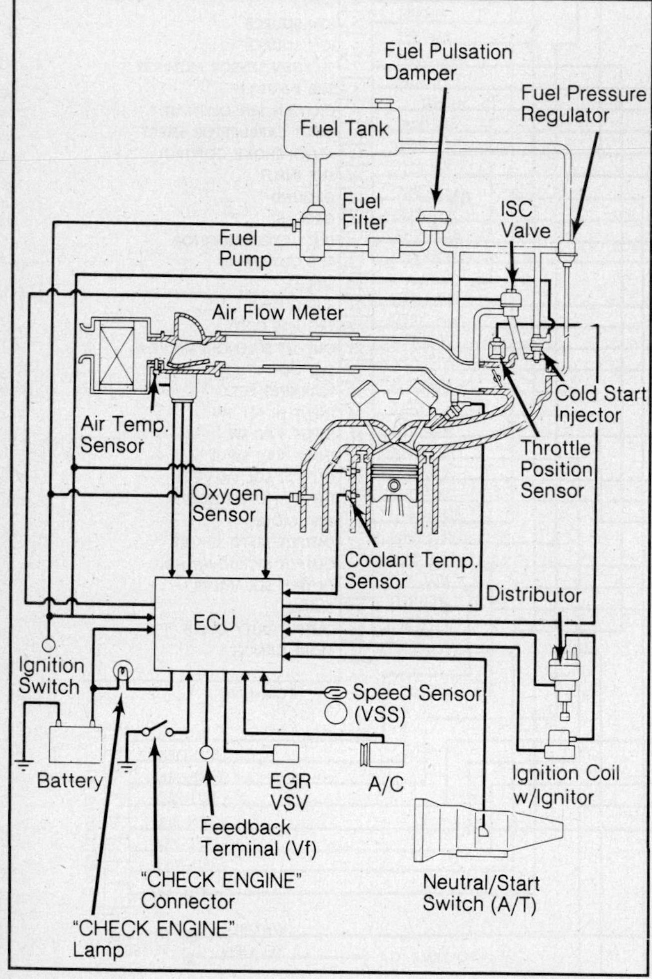
Fuel Pulsation Damper
Fuel Pressure Regulator
Fuel Tank
Fuel Filter
ISC Valve
Fuel Pump
Air Flow Meter
Cold Start Injector
Air Temp. Sensor
Throttle Position Sensor
Oxygen Sensor
Coolant Temp. Sensor
Distributor
ECU
Ignition Switch
Speed Sensor (VSS)
Battery
EGR VSV
A/C
Ignition Coil w/Ignitor
Feedback Terminal (Vf)
"CHECK ENGINE" Connector
Neutral/Start Switch (A/T)
"CHECK ENGINE" Lamp

OPERATION

The TCCS consists of the following subsystems: Electronic Fuel Injection (EFI) system, Data Sensors, Electronic Control Unit (ECU), Electronic Spark Advance (ESA) system, Idle Speed Control (ISC) system, EGR Control, Electronic Controlled Transmission (ECT), Diagnostic System and catalytic converter.

ELECTRONIC FUEL INJECTION (EFI)

All models are equipped with Bosch AFC fuel injection system. An electric fuel pump provides fuel to the fuel pressure regulator. From the regulator, fuel flows under pressure to the 6 fuel injectors. The pressure regulator maintains uniform pressure differential at all times.

The constant pressure differential allows the ECU to control length of injection rather than amount of injection. The ECU monitors engine operating conditions and calculates injection duration for efficient engine operation.

The ECU activates all 6 injectors at the same time. When the injectors are activated, they provide 1/2 the amount of fuel required for ideal combustion with each engine revolution. *See appropriate Bosch AFC Fuel Injection article.*

Fig. 2: TCCS Component Locations

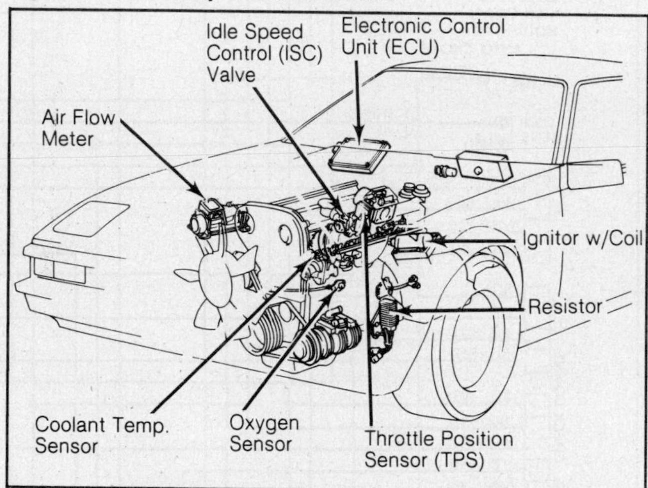
Idle Speed Control (ISC) Valve
Electronic Control Unit (ECU)
Air Flow Meter
Ignitor w/Coil
Resistor
Coolant Temp. Sensor
Oxygen Sensor
Throttle Position Sensor (TPS)

Supra model shown, Cressida similar.

DATA SENSORS

Each sensor furnishes electrical impulses to ECU. The ECU computes fuel delivery and spark timing necessary to maintain desired air/fuel ratio and engine speed. Data sensors are interrelated to each other. Operation of each sensor is as follows:

Air Flow Sensor

This sensor is mounted within the air flow meter. The sensor measures air flow rate through the air flow meter and sends a proportionate electrical signal to the ECU. The ECU uses air flow sensor information for controlling fuel injection duration and spark advance system.

Air Temperature Sensor

This sensor is mounted within the air flow meter. The sensor measures temperature of incoming air and sends an electrical signal to ECU. The ECU uses air temperature information for controlling fuel injection duration.

Throttle Position Sensor (TPS)

The throttle position sensor (TPS) is mounted on throttle body and is directly connected to throttle linkage. The sensor, a rotary potentiometer, signals ECU of changes in throttle valve position. The information provided by this sensor is used for controlling fuel injection duration and idle speed control system.

Coolant Temperature Sensor

The coolant temperature sensor is installed in intake manifold. This sensor is a thermistor which converts temperature of engine coolant to electrical signal for use by ECU. The ECU uses coolant temperature information for controlling fuel injection duration, spark advance system, idle speed control system and EGR system.

Oxygen Sensor

The oxygen sensor is installed in exhaust manifold. Output voltage of oxygen sensor varies with oxygen content of exhaust gases. The ECU uses exhaust gas oxygen content information for determining fuel injection duration.

Vehicle Speed Sensor (VSS)

This sensor is mounted in the instrument panel and is a component of the speedometer. Vehicle speed information is used by the ECU for cruise control and electronic control of automatic transmission.

Engine Speed

Engine speed signal information is received from the ignition coil. These signals are used by the ECU for fuel injection duration control and spark advance system.

A/C Switch

A signal is sent to ECU when the air conditioner is activated. The ECU requires this input for controlling idle speed during A/C operation.

Neutral/Start Switch

A switch is installed on automatic transmission models to inform the ECU of transmission selection position. This information is used by the ECU to allow starter operation. This information is also relayed to the ECT computer. Manual transmission models are equipped with a clutch switch.

ELECTRONIC CONTROL UNIT (ECU)

The ECU is mounted behind glove compartment under instrument panel. The ECU controls all functions of the TCCS. The ECU consists of a printed circuit board enclosed within a metal box. The ECU receives signals from the data sensors and switches. These signals are processed by the ECU for controlling EFI, ESA, ISC, EGR and ECT systems.

The TCCS has a "fail-safe" feature designed into the ECU. If the ECU malfunctions, a back-up circuit is activated to assist in getting the vehicle to a service facility. During this mode of operation, driveability will be minimal. The "CHECK ENGINE" lamp will also be lit when the computer malfunctions.

ELECTRONIC SPARK ADVANCE (ESA) SYSTEM

The ECU contains preprogrammed information which has all the data necessary for maintaining optimum ignition timing under all operating conditions. Input from the various data sensors allows the ECU to deliver spark at exactly the right moment.

IDLE SPEED CONTROL (ISC) SYSTEM

Engine idle speed is controlled by the ECU. The ECU contains preprogrammed information which contains specific engine speed values for different engine operating conditions.

The ECU receives signals from such sensors as the coolant temperature sensor and air conditioner sensor. Using this information, the ECU transmits a command signal to the ISC valve in the throttle body.

The ISC valve opens and closes the idle air bypass to control the amount of air which by-passes throttle valve. The greater the amount of air which is by-passed around the throttle valve, the greater the engine idle speed.

EGR CONTROL

The EGR control system prevents recirculation of exhaust gases when coolant temperature is below 135°F (57°C). The coolant temperature sensor constantly monitors and informs the ECU of coolant temperature.

Fig. 3: Electronic Control Unit Electrical Connector Identification

E_{01}	No. 10	STA	EGR	N/C
E_{02}	No. 20	IGt	E_1	

ISC 1	ISC 2	G⊖		G	Ne		IGf	THW
ISC 3	ISC 4	VF	T	PSW	IDL		O_2	E_2

O_2			M-REL	SPD	S_1	THA	Vs	Vc	BAT	IG S/W
E_2	E_1	ECT		A/C	W	OIL	S_2		+B	+B

Symbol	Terminal	Symbol	Terminal	Symbol	Terminal
E_{01}	Engine Ground	G⊖	Engine Speed Sensor	SPD	Speedometer
E_{02}	Engine Ground	Vf	EFI Service Connector	W	Warning Lamp
No. 10	Injector	G	Engine Speed Sensor	THA	Air Temp. Sensor
No. 20	Injector	T	"CHECK ENGINE" Connector	Vs	Air Flow Meter
STA	Neutral/Start Switch	PSW	Throttle Position Sensor	Vc	Air Flow Meter
IGt	Ignitor	Ne	Engine Speed Sensor	BAT	Positive Side of Battery
EGR	EGR Vacuum Switching Valve	IDL	Throttle Position Sensor	IG S/W	Ignition Switch
E_1	Engine Ground	IGf	Ignitor	+B	Main Relay
N/C	Neutral/Start Switch (A/T)	O_2	Oxygen Sensor	ECT	ECT Computer
	Clutch Switch (M/T)	THW	Coolant Temp. Switch	S_1	ECT Computer
ISC_1	ISC Control Valve No. 1	E_2	Sensor Ground	S_2	ECT Computer
ISC_2	ISC Control Valve No. 2	E_1	Engine Ground	OIL	Oil Pressure Switch
ISC_3	ISC Control Valve No. 3			M-REL	EFI Main Relay
ISC_4	ISC Control Valve No. 4			A/C	A/C Compressor Switch

TOYOTA COMPUTER CONTROL SYSTEM (Cont.)

When the temperature is below the specified value, the ECU opens the vacuum switching valve (VSV) to prevent EGR flow.

When coolant temperature exceeds the specified value, the ECU closes the VSV to allow EGR flow. The vacuum modulator opens at idle speeds to prevent EGR flow when coolant temperature exceeds the specified value.

ELECTRONIC CONTROLLED TRANSMISSION (ECT)

Automatic transmission models are equipped with an electronic control unit to control transmission operation. The ECU of the TCCS provides signals on engine operation to the ECU of the ECT system. This information is used by the ECT computer to prevent shift up to 3rd gear or overdrive during cold engine operation.

NOTE: **The ECU of the TCCS is not interchangeable with the ECU of the ECT system.**

DIAGNOSTIC SYSTEM

The ECU of the TCCS is equipped with a self-diagnostic system which detects system failures or abnormalities. When a malfunction occurs, the ECU lights the "CHECK ENGINE" lamp located on instrument panel. At the same time, a corresponding trouble code is stored in ECU memory. Interpretation of the trouble codes can be performed by using an analog voltmeter.

All codes, except code "51", are stored in memory from the time of detection until the codes are cleared from the memory. The "CHECK ENGINE" lamp will go out as soon as the malfunction is cleared; but the code will remain in memory (except code "51"). Code "11" will NOT have any other code stored in memory with it.

Some trouble codes are recorded in ECU memory without causing the "CHECK ENGINE" lamp to glow. These codes are minor malfunctions which do not have a detrimental effect upon the system.

As a bulb and system check, the "CHECK ENGINE" lamp will glow when ignition switch is turned on and engine is not running. When engine is started, the lamp should go out after a short period of time. If not, a malfunction has been detected in the TCCS.

CATALYTIC CONVERTER

All models are equipped with 3-way catalytic converters. This type of converter changes CO, HC, and NOx exhaust emissions into carbon dioxide, water vapor and nitrogen gas. The converter is a monolithic type.

DIAGNOSIS & TESTING

DIAGNOSIS

Diagnose TCCS system in the following order:

1) Ensure that all engine systems NOT related to TCCS are fully operational. Do not proceed with testing until you are sure that all other problems have been fixed. Always check fuses, fusible links and wire connectors before condemning the ECU.

2) Enter diagnostic mode and record trouble codes. Exit diagnostic mode. If no trouble codes were displayed, go to Diagnostic Circuit Check chart. Follow instructions given there.

3) If no trouble codes were displayed after performing Diagnostic Circuit Check, perform voltage and resistance checks. If trouble codes are displayed, perform tests to confirm cause of malfunction which set the corresponding trouble code.

4) After any repairs are made, clear trouble codes and perform Diagnostic Circuit Check. Normal system operation code should be displayed if repair solved cause of malfunction.

NOTE: **The following paragraphs explain the procedures involved in performing the steps outlined above.**

RECALLING TROUBLE CODES

The ECU stores component failure information for TCCS under a related trouble code which can be recalled for diagnosis and repair. When recalled, these codes will be displayed by voltage pulsations on an analog voltmeter.

Codes are displayed starting with lowest numbered code. Only codes in which a related malfunction has occured will be displayed.

Entering Diagnostic Mode

1) Prior to entering diagnostic mode, the following conditions must be met: Engine must be at normal operating temperature, battery voltage above 11 volts, transmission in "P" or Neutral, throttle valve fully closed and A/C off.

2) Turn ignition on, but do NOT start engine. Remove rubber cap from "CHECK ENGINE" connector, located near distributor. Using a jumper wire, jumper both terminals of the connector together. *See Fig. 4.*

Fig. 4: Jumpering "CHECK ENGINE" Connector

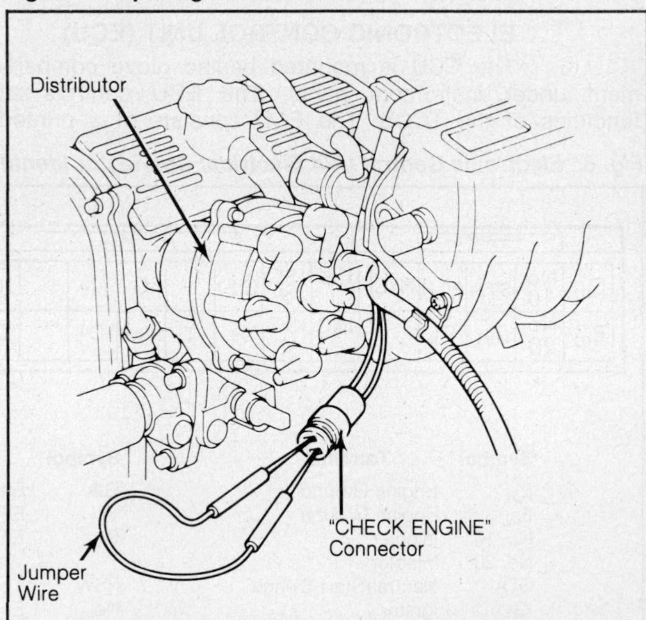
Distributor
"CHECK ENGINE"
Connector
Jumper
Wire

Insert jumper wire in "CHECK ENGINE" connector.

3) Remove rubber cap from "EFI" service connector, located near battery. Using an adapter harness (SST 09842-14010), connect adapter to service connector. Connect positive probe of an analog voltmeter to Red lead of adapter harness and negative probe to Black lead. *See Fig. 5.*

TOYOTA COMPUTER CONTROL SYSTEM (Cont.)

Fig. 5: Connecting Voltmeter to "EFI" Connector

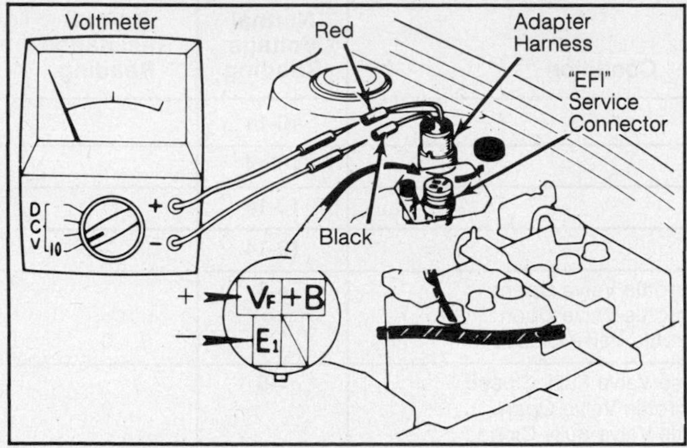
Voltmeter
Red
Adapter Harness
"EFI" Service Connector
Black
DCV 10
+
−
VF
+B
E1

Make sure leads are properly connected.

Diagnostic Code Output

1) After entering diagnostic mode, the voltmeter needle should indicate 5 volts for 2 seconds; then 2.5 volts for 2 seconds. This code ("start code") signifies the start of diagnostic code output. *See Fig. 6.*

Fig. 6: Example of Trouble Code Output

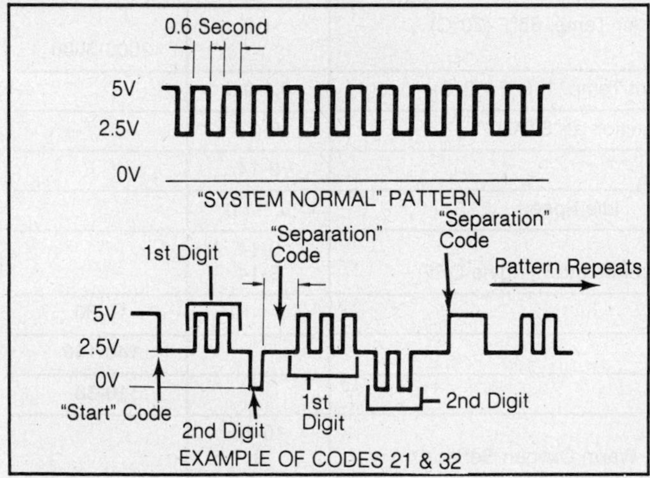
0.6 Second
5V
2.5V
0V
"SYSTEM NORMAL" PATTERN
1st Digit
"Separation" Code
"Separation" Code
Pattern Repeats
5V
2.5V
0V
"Start" Code
2nd Digit
1st Digit
2nd Digit
EXAMPLE OF CODES 21 & 32

Output is in form of voltmeter needle fluctuations.

2) If no trouble codes are stored in ECU memory, the "start code" will be displayed, followed by the "system normal" code. The "system normal" code consists of a series of needle fluctuations between 5 volts and 2.5 volts at 0.6 second intervals.

3) Trouble codes are displayed in the following manner: After the "start code", the voltmeter needle will deflect a number of times between 2.5 volts and 5 volts at 0.6 second intervals. This is the first digit of the trouble code.

4) The needle will then indicate 2.5 volts for 2 seconds ("separator code"). Next, the needle will fluctuate between 2.5 volts and 0 volt at 0.6 second intervals. This is the second digit of the trouble code.

5) Trouble codes will be displayed from lowest to highest numbered code. Output of the diagnostic codes will continue as long as the diagnostic mode is activated. A "separator code" follows display of first and second digit of trouble codes, and separates each trouble code. A "start code" will be displayed at the beginning of each pass through the output.

TCCS TROUBLE CODE IDENTIFICATION

Code No. (Pattern)	Circuit Affected	"CHECK ENGINE" Lamp
.....	System normal	OFF
11	ECU power source	OFF
12	RPM signal	ON
13	RPM signal	ON
14	Ignition signal	ON
21	Oxygen sensor signal	ON
22	Coolant temp. signal	ON
23	Intake air temp. signal	OFF
31	Air flow meter signal	ON
32	Air flow meter signal	ON
41	TPS signal	OFF
42	VSS signal	OFF
43	Starter signal	OFF
51	Switch signal [1]	OFF

[1] — A/C switch or Neutral/Start switch.

Clearing Trouble Codes

After any repairs are performed, clear ECU memory of all stored trouble codes. To clear memory, turn ignition off and remove 15A "STOP" fuse from fuse panel for 30 seconds. The lower the ambient (outside) temperature, the longer the fuse must be left out. Replace fuse and exit diagnostic mode.

Exiting Diagnostic Mode

To exit diagnostic mode, remove voltmeter and adapter harness from "EFI" service connector. Remove jumper wire from "CHECK ENGINE" connector. Turn ignition off. Replace rubber caps over connectors.

SYSTEM TESTING

TCCS Voltage Tests

The TCCS can be checked using a voltmeter. Before making voltage tests, make sure battery voltage is at least 11 volts. Perform voltage tests with harness connectors connected to ECU and ignition switch on. Connect probes to each wire cavity of ECU connectors. If voltage values are not as specified, perform resistance tests.

TCCS Resistance Tests

The TCCS can be checked using an ohmmeter. Before making resistance tests, turn ignition off and disconnect wiring connectors at ECU. Insert ohmmeter probes into wiring connectors from wire side. Measure resistance at connector terminals, NOT ECU terminals.

Computerized Engine Controls

TOYOTA COMPUTER CONTROL SYSTEM (Cont.)

TCCS VOLTAGE AND RESISTANCE SPECIFICATION CHART [1]

Terminals	Position of Connectors at ECU	Procedure	Condition	Normal Voltage Reading	Normal Resistance Reading
BAT - E_1	Connected			10-14	
+B - E_1	Connected	Ignition ON		10-14	
IG S/W - E_1	Connected	Ignition ON		10-14	
M-REL - E_1	Connected	Ignition ON		10-14	
IDL - E_1	Connected	Ignition ON	Throttle Valve Open	4-6	
	Disconnected	Ignition OFF	Throttle Valve Open		∞
			Throttle Valve Closed		0
PSW - E_1	Connected	Ignition ON	Throttle Valve Fully Closed	4-6	
	Disconnected	Ignition OFF	Throttle Valve Open		0
			Throttle Valve Fully Closed		∞
Vc - E_2	Connected	Ignition ON		4-6	
	Disconnected	Ignition OFF			200-400
Vs - E_2	Connected	Ignition ON	Air Flap Fully Closed	4-5	
			Air Flap Fully Open	0.02-0.08	
			Idle Speed	2-4	
			3000 RPM	0.3-1.0	
	Disconnected	Ignition OFF	Air Flap Fully Closed		20-400
			Air Flap Fully Open		20-1000
THA - E_2	Connected	Ignition ON	Intake Air Temp. 68°F (20°C)	1-2	
	Disconnected	Ignition OFF			2000-3000
THW - E_1	Connected	Ignition ON	Coolant Temp. 176°F (80°C)	0.1-0.5	
STA - E_1	Connected		Ignition at "START"	6-12	
No. 10 & No. 20 - E_1	Connected	Ignition ON		9-14	
IGt - E_1	Connected	Ignition ON	Idle Speed	0.7-1.0	
ISC_1 thru ISC_4 - E_1	Connected	Ignition ON		9-14	
			2-3 Seconds after Engine OFF	9-14	
ISC_1 thru ISC_4 - +B	Disconnected	Ignition OFF			10-30
G - G⊖	Disconnected	Ignition OFF			140-180
Ne - G⊖	Disconnected	Ignition OFF			10-30
+B - EGR	Connected	Ignition ON		10-13	
			Start & Warm Oxygen Sensor	0	
N/C - E_1	Connected	Ignition ON	"P" or "N" (Auto. Trans.)	0	
			Clutch Not Engaged (Man. Trans.)		
			Except "P" or "N" (Auto. Trans.)	4-6	
			Clutch Engaged (Man. Trans.)		
			Engine Cranking	9-11	
T - E_1	Connected	Ignition ON	"CHECK ENGINE" Connector NOT Jumpered	4-6	
			"CHECK ENGINE" Connector Jumpered	0	
OIL - E_1	Connected	Ignition ON	Engine "OIL" Light ON	4-6	
			Start Engine; "OIL" Light OFF	0	
A/C - E_1	Connected	Ignition ON	A/C Switch ON	10-13	
			A/C Switch OFF	0	
Vf - E_1	Connected	Ignition ON	Start Engine (Throttle Open)	0-5	
W - E_1	Connected	Ignition ON		0	
			Start Engine	10-13	
ECT - E_1	Connected	Ignition ON	Coolant Temp. Under 95°F (35°C)	2-3	
			Coolant Temp. 95-140°F (35-60°C)	0	
			Coolant Temp. Above 140°F (60°C)	4-6	

[1] — Do NOT allow probes of volt/ohmmeter to touch terminals O_2 and Vf (unless instructed).

TOYOTA COMPUTER CONTROL SYSTEM (Cont.)

TROUBLE CODES & PROBABLE CAUSE FOR CODES

Code No.	Probable Cause
11	Main Relay or Circuit, ECU.
12 & 13	Distributor or Circuit, Starter Signal Circuit, ECU.
14	Ignitor or Circuit, ECU.
21	Oxygen Sensor or Circuit, ECU.
22	Coolant Temp. Sensor or Circuit, ECU.
23	Intake Air Temp. Sensor or Circuit, ECU.
31 & 32	Air Flow Meter or Circuit, ECU.
41	Throttle Position Sensor or Circuit, ECU.
42	Vehicle Speed Sensor or Circuit, Slipping Torque Converter, ECU.
43	Main Relay Circuit, Starter Circuit, Ignition Circuit, ECU.
51	Neutral/Start Switch, A/C Switch, ECU.

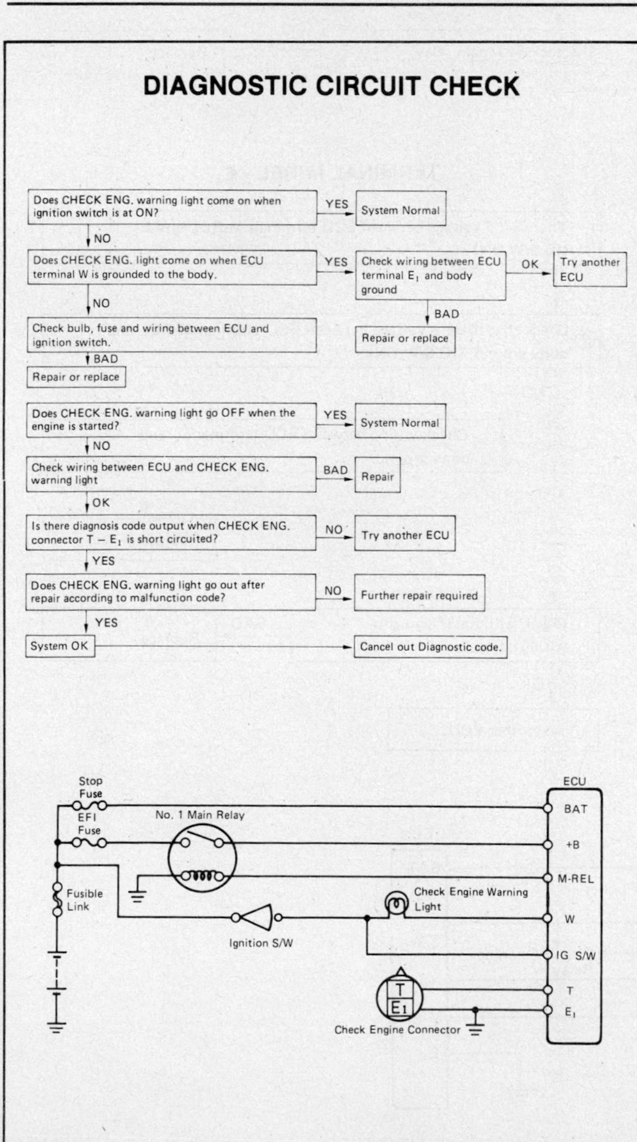

DIAGNOSTIC CIRCUIT CHECK
Does CHECK ENG. warning light come on when ignition switch is at ON?
YES
System Normal
NO
Does CHECK ENG. light come on when ECU terminal W is grounded to the body.
YES
Check wiring between ECU terminal E1 and body ground
OK
Try another ECU
BAD
Repair or replace
NO
Check bulb, fuse and wiring between ECU and ignition switch.
BAD
Repair or replace
Does CHECK ENG. warning light go OFF when the engine is started?
YES
System Normal
NO
Check wiring between ECU and CHECK ENG. warning light
BAD
Repair
OK
Is there diagnosis code output when CHECK ENG. connector T – E1 is short circuited?
NO
Try another ECU
YES
Does CHECK ENG. warning light go out after repair according to malfunction code?
NO
Further repair required
YES
System OK
Cancel out Diagnostic code.
Stop Fuse
EFI Fuse
No. 1 Main Relay
Fusible Link
Check Engine Warning Light
Ignition S/W
Check Engine Connector
ECU
BAT
+B
M-REL
W
IG S/W
T
E1

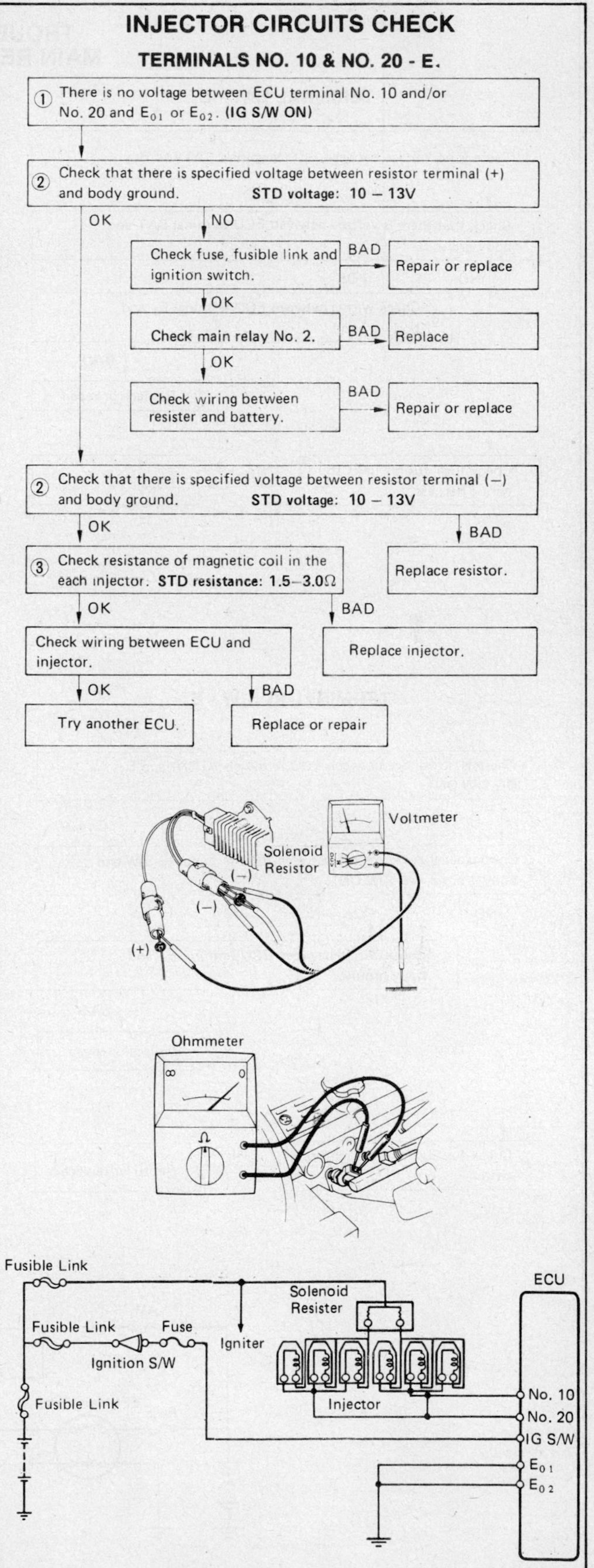

INJECTOR CIRCUITS CHECK
TERMINALS NO. 10 & NO. 20 - E.
① There is no voltage between ECU terminal No. 10 and/or No. 20 and E01 or E02. (IG S/W ON)
② Check that there is specified voltage between resistor terminal (+) and body ground. STD voltage: 10 – 13V
OK
NO
Check fuse, fusible link and ignition switch.
BAD
Repair or replace
OK
Check main relay No. 2.
BAD
Replace
OK
Check wiring between resister and battery.
BAD
Repair or replace
② Check that there is specified voltage between resistor terminal (–) and body ground. STD voltage: 10 – 13V
OK
BAD
③ Check resistance of magnetic coil in the each injector. STD resistance: 1.5–3.0Ω
Replace resistor.
OK
BAD
Check wiring between ECU and injector.
Replace injector.
OK
BAD
Try another ECU.
Replace or repair
Voltmeter
Solenoid Resistor
(–)
(–)
(+)
Ohmmeter
Fusible Link
Solenoid Resister
Fusible Link
Fuse
Igniter
Ignition S/W
Fusible Link
Injector
ECU
No. 10
No. 20
IG S/W
E01
E02

Computerized Engine Controls

TOYOTA COMPUTER CONTROL SYSTEM (Cont.)

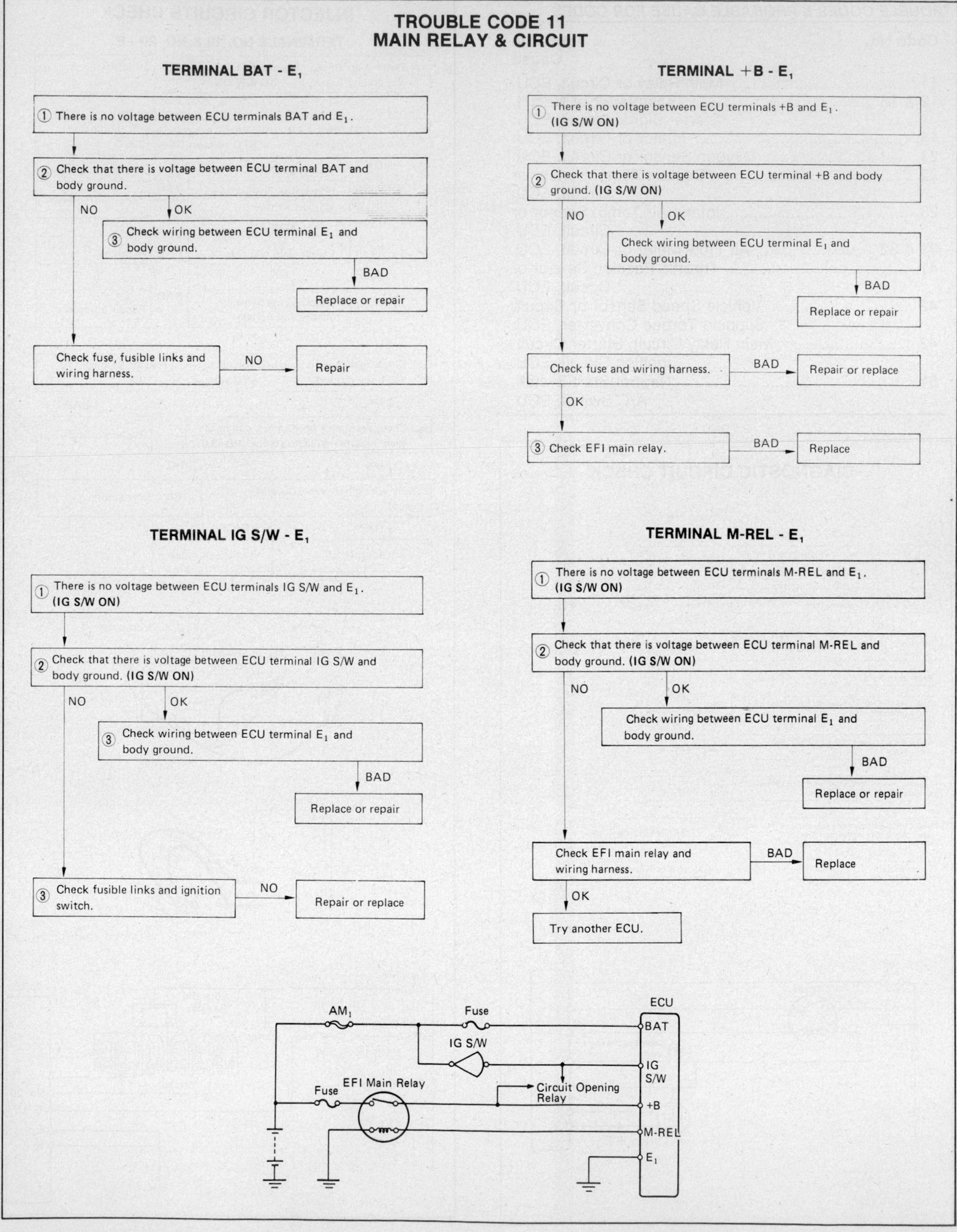
TROUBLE CODE 11
MAIN RELAY & CIRCUIT
TERMINAL BAT - E1
① There is no voltage between ECU terminals BAT and E1.
② Check that there is voltage between ECU terminal BAT and body ground.
NO
OK
③ Check wiring between ECU terminal E1 and body ground.
BAD
Replace or repair
Check fuse, fusible links and wiring harness.
NO
Repair
TERMINAL +B - E1
① There is no voltage between ECU terminals +B and E1. (IG S/W ON)
② Check that there is voltage between ECU terminal +B and body ground. (IG S/W ON)
NO
OK
Check wiring between ECU terminal E1 and body ground.
BAD
Replace or repair
Check fuse and wiring harness.
BAD
Repair or replace
OK
③ Check EFI main relay.
BAD
Replace
TERMINAL IG S/W - E1
① There is no voltage between ECU terminals IG S/W and E1. (IG S/W ON)
② Check that there is voltage between ECU terminal IG S/W and body ground. (IG S/W ON)
NO
OK
③ Check wiring between ECU terminal E1 and body ground.
BAD
Replace or repair
③ Check fusible links and ignition switch.
NO
Repair or replace
TERMINAL M-REL - E1
① There is no voltage between ECU terminals M-REL and E1. (IG S/W ON)
② Check that there is voltage between ECU terminal M-REL and body ground. (IG S/W ON)
NO
OK
Check wiring between ECU terminal E1 and body ground.
BAD
Replace or repair
Check EFI main relay and wiring harness.
BAD
Replace
OK
Try another ECU.
AM1
Fuse
ECU
BAT
IG S/W
IG S/W
Fuse
EFI Main Relay
Circuit Opening Relay
+B
M-REL
E1

TOYOTA COMPUTER CONTROL SYSTEM (Cont.)

TROUBLE CODES 12 & 13
RPM SIGNAL

DISTRIBUTOR CHECK

Check distributor cap and rotor for cracks, carbon tracks and burnt or corroded terminals.

Check distributor center contact for wear.

If problem is found, replace component.

Using an ohmmeter, check resistance of both pick-up coils. (G - G⊖ and Ne - G⊖).

If resistance is not correct, replace distributor.

IGNITOR CHECK

Ignition ON.

Disconnect Brown and Yellow wire connector.

Using a voltmeter, connect positive lead to Brown connector on wiring harness side and negative lead to ignitor body ground. (About 12V.)

Reconnect connector.

Disconnect coil wire from distributor.

Disconnect Pink and White wire connector.

Using a dry cell flashlight battery, connect positive end to Pink wire terminal and negative end to ignitor body ground. (Voltage greater than 5V would destroy diodes.)

Spark should be produced at coil wire within 1 second.

If not, replace ignitor.

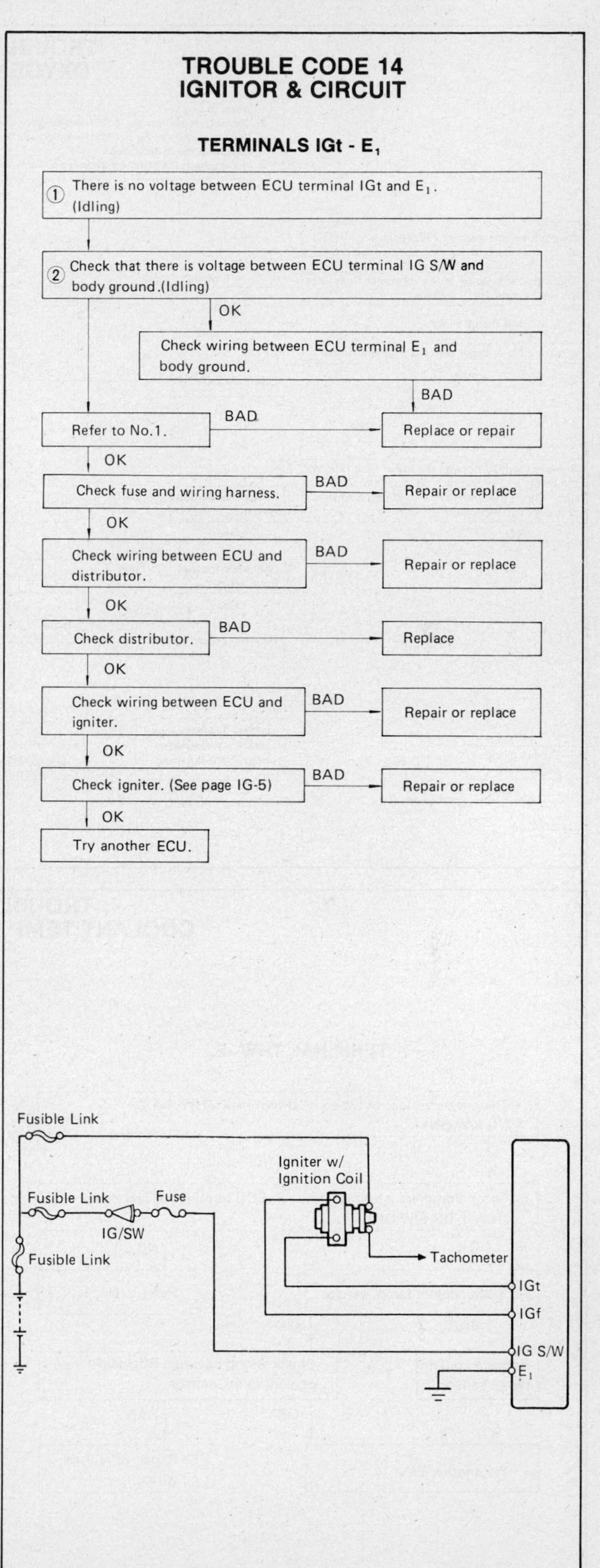
TROUBLE CODE 14
IGNITOR & CIRCUIT
TERMINALS IGt - E1
① There is no voltage between ECU terminal IGt and E1. (Idling)
② Check that there is voltage between ECU terminal IG S/W and body ground.(Idling)
OK
Check wiring between ECU terminal E1 and body ground.
BAD
Refer to No.1.
BAD
Replace or repair
OK
Check fuse and wiring harness.
BAD
Repair or replace
OK
Check wiring between ECU and distributor.
BAD
Repair or replace
OK
Check distributor.
BAD
Replace
OK
Check wiring between ECU and igniter.
BAD
Repair or replace
OK
Check igniter. (See page IG-5)
BAD
Repair or replace
OK
Try another ECU.
Fusible Link
Igniter w/ Ignition Coil
Fusible Link
Fuse
IG/SW
Fusible Link
Tachometer
IGt
IGf
IG S/W
E1

TOYOTA COMPUTER CONTROL SYSTEM (Cont.)

TROUBLE CODE 21 OXYGEN SENSOR

1. Warm up engine.
2. Connect adapter harness to "EFI" service connector.
3. Connect positive probe of voltmeter to Red wire of adapter and negative probe to Black wire.
4. Run engine at 2500 RPM for 2 minutes to warm up oxygen sensor.

Maintain engine speed at 2,500 rpm.

Check that the needle of the voltmeter fluctuates 8 times or more in 10 seconds.

8 times or more → Normal

Zero → Less than 2.5V?

less than 8 times → Is there 2.5V or more with the engine running?

YES → Repair

NO → Remove the PCV hose on the lower flow side of the throttle valve and race the engine to 2,500 rpm. Check that the needle fluctuates 8 times or more in 10 seconds.

YES → Check the ignition system.

NO → Replace oxygen sensor.

Less than 2.5V? NO → Measure voltage.

Less than 2.5V? YES → Check the ignition system.

Check the ignition system. BAD → Repair

OK → Check for fouled spark plugs.

Several dirty Plugs → Replace injector.

All dirty → Repair

OK → Re-warm oxygen sensor.

Is there 0V when oxygen sensor is disconnected while engine is running?

NO → Repair

YES → Replace ECU

Measure voltage.

Less than 2.5V → After turning off the engine, re-start without depressing the accelerator pedal.

More than 2.5V → Re-warm oxygen sensor.

Is there 2.5V or more with the engine running?

YES → Repair

NO → Check for short or open circuit in wiring between oxygen sensor and ECU.

Short, Open → Repair

OK → After turning off the engine, re-start without depressing the accelerator pedal.

Lean → Replace ECU.

Open Circuit → Replace oxygen sensor.

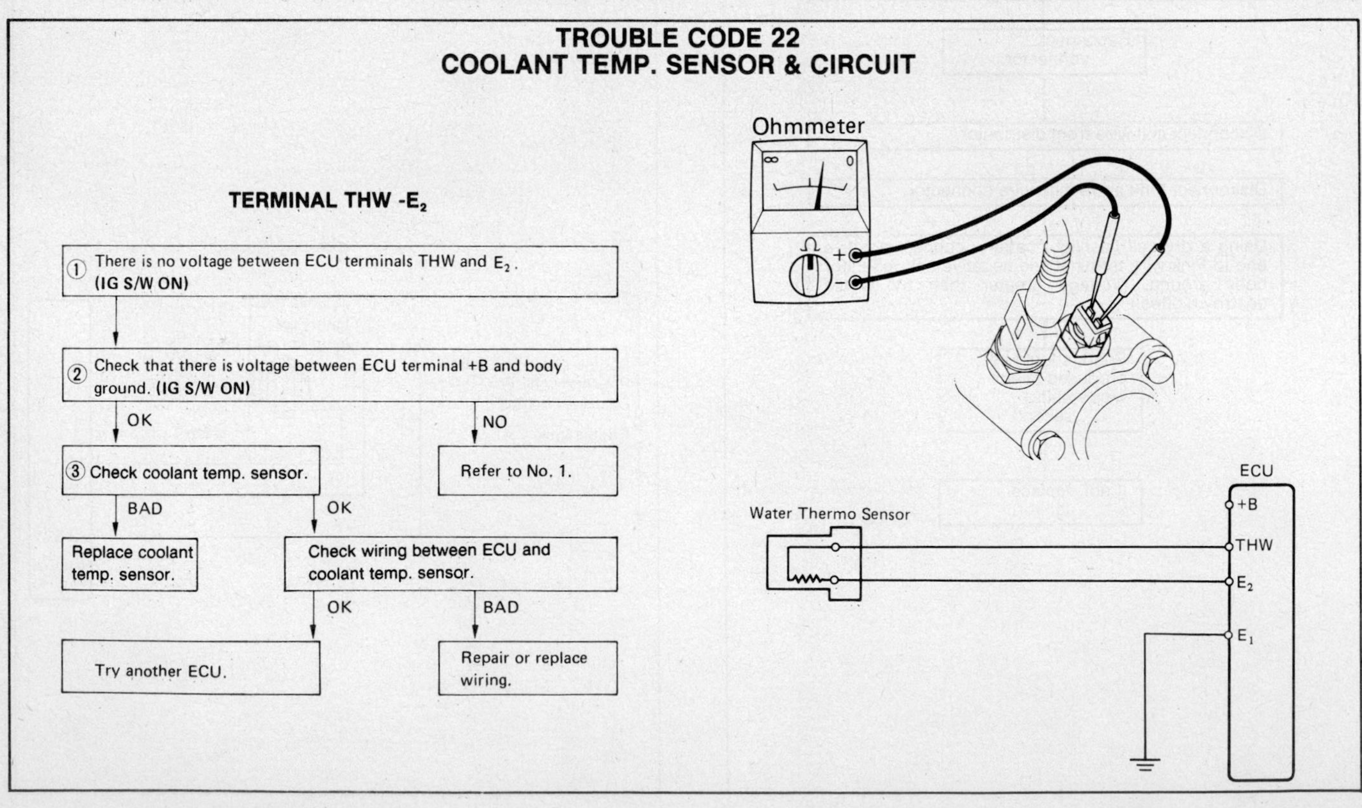
TROUBLE CODE 22
COOLANT TEMP. SENSOR & CIRCUIT
TERMINAL THW -E2
① There is no voltage between ECU terminals THW and E2. (IG S/W ON)
② Check that there is voltage between ECU terminal +B and body ground. (IG S/W ON)
OK
NO
③ Check coolant temp. sensor.
Refer to No. 1.
BAD
OK
Replace coolant temp. sensor.
Check wiring between ECU and coolant temp. sensor.
OK
BAD
Try another ECU.
Repair or replace wiring.
Ohmmeter
Water Thermo Sensor
ECU
+B
THW
E2
E1

TOYOTA COMPUTER CONTROL SYSTEM (Cont.)

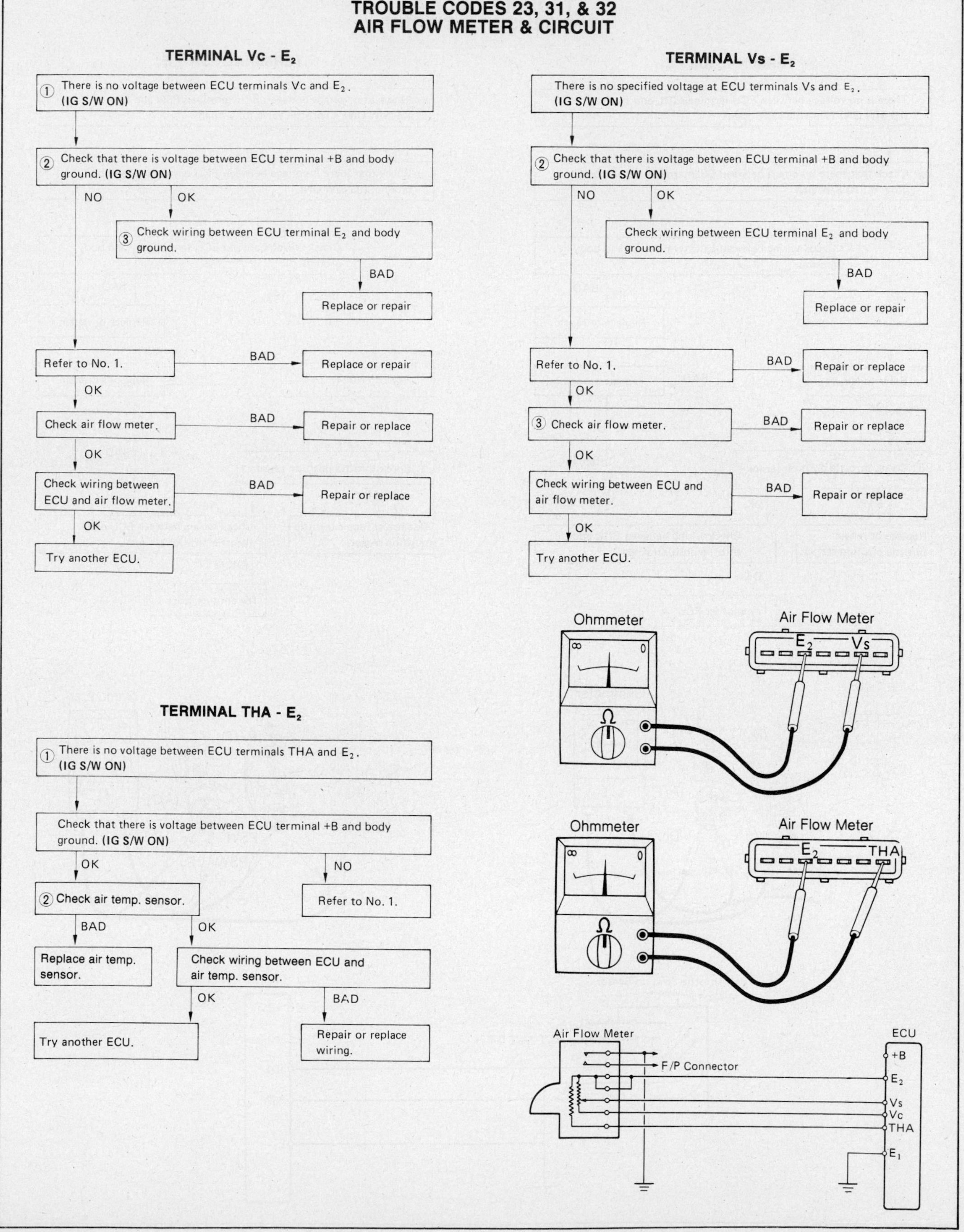

TROUBLE CODES 23, 31, & 32
AIR FLOW METER & CIRCUIT
TERMINAL Vc - E2
① There is no voltage between ECU terminals Vc and E2. (IG S/W ON)
② Check that there is voltage between ECU terminal +B and body ground. (IG S/W ON)
NO
OK
③ Check wiring between ECU terminal E2 and body ground.
BAD
Replace or repair
Refer to No. 1.
BAD
Replace or repair
OK
Check air flow meter.
BAD
Repair or replace
OK
Check wiring between ECU and air flow meter.
BAD
Repair or replace
OK
Try another ECU.
TERMINAL Vs - E2
There is no specified voltage at ECU terminals Vs and E2. (IG S/W ON)
② Check that there is voltage between ECU terminal +B and body ground. (IG S/W ON)
NO
OK
Check wiring between ECU terminal E2 and body ground.
BAD
Replace or repair
Refer to No. 1.
BAD
Repair or replace
OK
③ Check air flow meter.
BAD
Repair or replace
OK
Check wiring between ECU and air flow meter.
BAD
Repair or replace
OK
Try another ECU.
Ohmmeter
Air Flow Meter
E2
Vs
TERMINAL THA - E2
① There is no voltage between ECU terminals THA and E2. (IG S/W ON)
Check that there is voltage between ECU terminal +B and body ground. (IG S/W ON)
OK
NO
② Check air temp. sensor.
Refer to No. 1.
BAD
OK
Replace air temp. sensor.
Check wiring between ECU and air temp. sensor.
OK
BAD
Try another ECU.
Repair or replace wiring.
Ohmmeter
Air Flow Meter
E2
THA
Air Flow Meter
F/P Connector
ECU
+B
E2
Vs
Vc
THA
E1

TOYOTA COMPUTER CONTROL SYSTEM (Cont.)

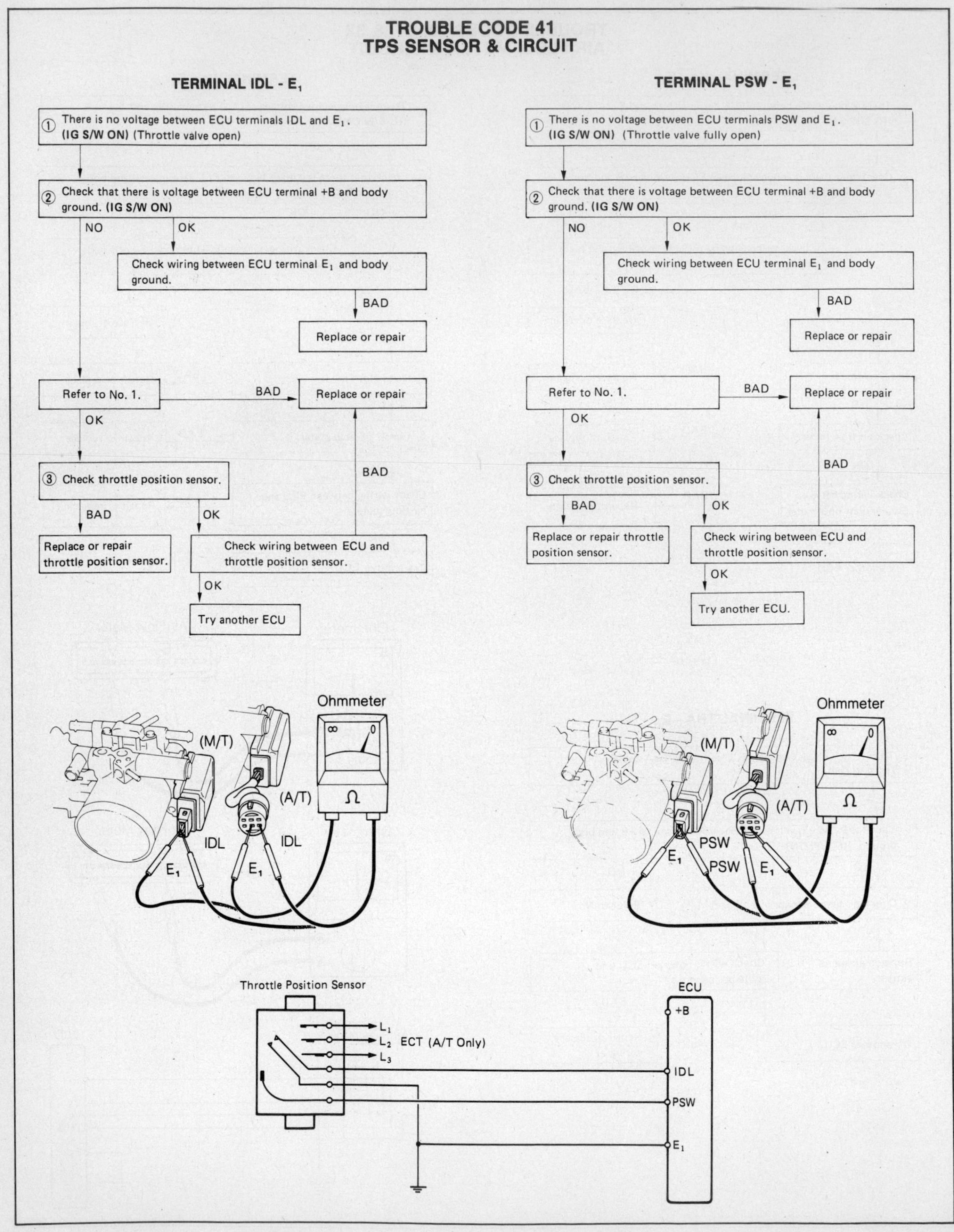
TROUBLE CODE 41
TPS SENSOR & CIRCUIT
TERMINAL IDL - E1
① There is no voltage between ECU terminals IDL and E1. (IG S/W ON) (Throttle valve open)
② Check that there is voltage between ECU terminal +B and body ground. (IG S/W ON)
NO
OK
Check wiring between ECU terminal E1 and body ground.
BAD
Replace or repair
Refer to No. 1.
BAD
Replace or repair
OK
BAD
③ Check throttle position sensor.
BAD
OK
Replace or repair throttle position sensor.
Check wiring between ECU and throttle position sensor.
OK
Try another ECU
TERMINAL PSW - E1
① There is no voltage between ECU terminals PSW and E1. (IG S/W ON) (Throttle valve fully open)
② Check that there is voltage between ECU terminal +B and body ground. (IG S/W ON)
NO
OK
Check wiring between ECU terminal E1 and body ground.
BAD
Replace or repair
Refer to No. 1.
BAD
Replace or repair
OK
BAD
③ Check throttle position sensor.
BAD
OK
Replace or repair throttle position sensor.
Check wiring between ECU and throttle position sensor.
OK
Try another ECU.
Ohmmeter
(M/T)
(A/T)
IDL
IDL
E1
E1
Ohmmeter
(M/T)
(A/T)
PSW
PSW
E1
E1
Throttle Position Sensor
L1
L2 ECT (A/T Only)
L3
ECU
+B
IDL
PSW
E1

TOYOTA COMPUTER CONTROL SYSTEM (Cont.)

TROUBLE CODE 43
IGNITION & STARTER CIRCUITS

TERMINAL STA - E_1

(1) There is no voltage between ECU terminals STA and E_1. **(IG S/W ST)**

Check starter operation.
- OK → Check wiring between ECU and starter terminal 50.
  - BAD → Repair or replace
  - OK → Check wiring between ECU terminal E_1 and body ground.
    - BAD → Repair or replace
- BAD → Check fusible link, battery, wiring and ignition switch.
  - BAD → Repair or replace
  - OK → (2) Check that there is voltage at STA (50) terminal of starter. **(IG S/W ST)** **STD voltage: 9 – 11V**
    - OK → Check starter
    - NO → Check wiring between ignition switch ST terminal and starter STA (50) terminal.

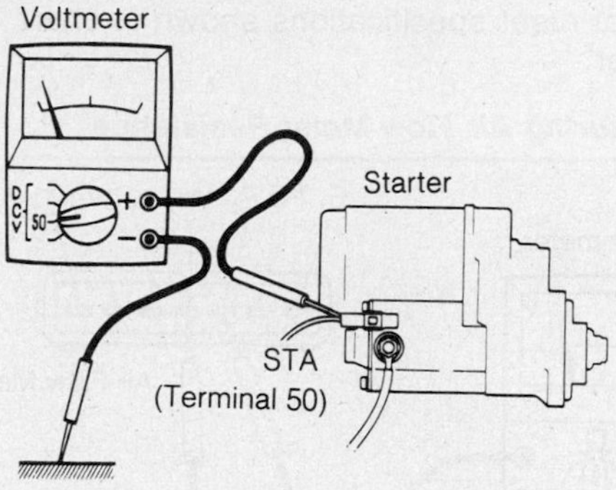

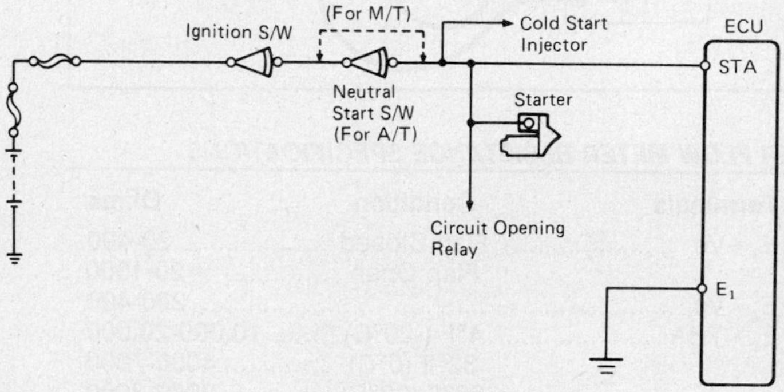

Voltmeter
Starter
STA
(Terminal 50)
Ignition S/W
(For M/T)
Cold Start
Injector
ECU
STA
Neutral
Start S/W
(For A/T)
Starter
Circuit Opening
Relay
E_1

ISC & CIRCUIT CHECK

ISC_1 thru ISC_4 - E_1

(1) There is no voltage between ECU terminals ISC_1 – ISC_4 and E_1. **(IG S/W ON)**

(2) Check that there is voltage between ECU terminal +B and body ground. **(IG S/W ON)**
- OK → Check wiring between computer terminal E_1 and body ground.
  - OK → Try another ECU.
  - BAD → Replace or repair
- NO → Refer to No. 1.
  - NO → Repair or replace
  - OK → Check wiring between No. 1 main relay and Battery.
    - BAD → Repair or replace
    - OK → Check wiring between EFI main relay and Battery.
      - BAD → Repair or replace
      - → (3) Check ISC valve

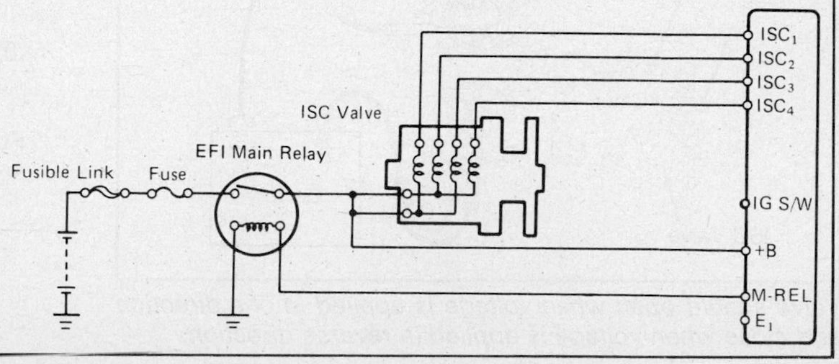

S_1
S_3
S_4
S_2
B_2
B_1
ISC_1
ISC_2
ISC_3
ISC_4
ISC Valve
EFI Main Relay
Fusible Link
Fuse
IG S/W
+B
M-REL
E_1

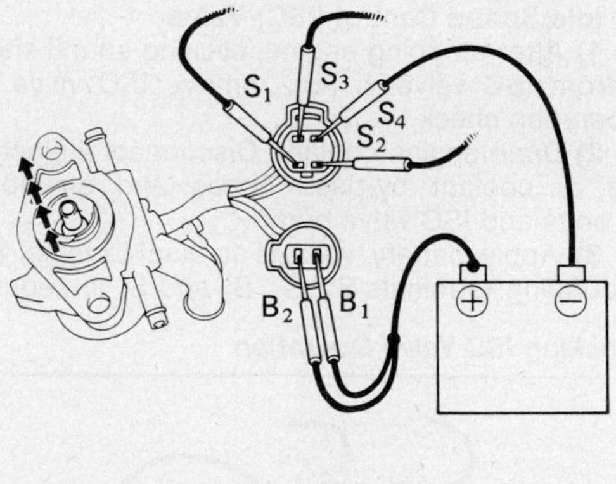

TOYOTA COMPUTER CONTROL SYSTEM (Cont.)

COMPONENT TESTING

Air Flow Meter

Turn ignition off. Disconnect wiring connector from air flow meter. Using an ohmmeter, measure resistance between each terminal. *See Fig. 7.* If resistance values do not meet specifications shown in chart, replace air flow meter.

Fig. 7: Measuring Air Flow Meter Resistance

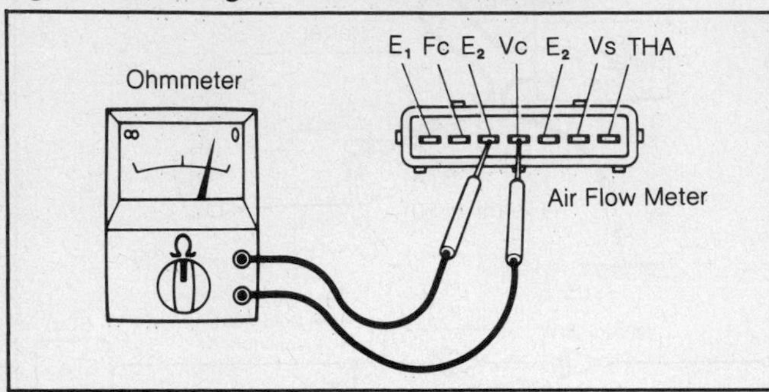

E1 Fc E2 Vc E2 Vs THA
Ohmmeter
Air Flow Meter

AIR FLOW METER RESISTANCE SPECIFICATIONS

Terminals	Condition	Ohms
E_2 - Vs	Flap Closed	20-400
	Flap Open	[1] 20-1000
E_2 - Vc		200-400
E_2 - THA	4°F (-20°C)	10,000-20,000
	32°F (0°C)	4000-7000
	68°F (20°C)	2000-3000
	104°F (40°C)	900-1300
	140°F (60°C)	400-700
E_1 - Fc	Flap Closed	Infinity (∞)
	Flap Open	Zero

[1] — Resistance changes with flap position.

Idle Speed Control (ISC) Valve

1) After stopping engine, clicking sound should be heard from ISC valve. If not, remove ISC valve and perform operation check.

2) Drain engine coolant. Disconnect 2 electrical connectors, 2 coolant by-pass hoses and air hoses. Remove 2 bolts and ISC valve body.

3) Apply battery voltage to dual-terminal connector. Grounding terminals S_1, S_2, S_3 and S_4 in sequence should cause valve to open. *See Fig. 8.* With battery voltage still connected, grounding terminals in reverse sequence (S_4, S_3, S_2 and S_1) should cause valve to close. If not, perform resistance check.

Fig. 8: Checking ISC Valve Operation

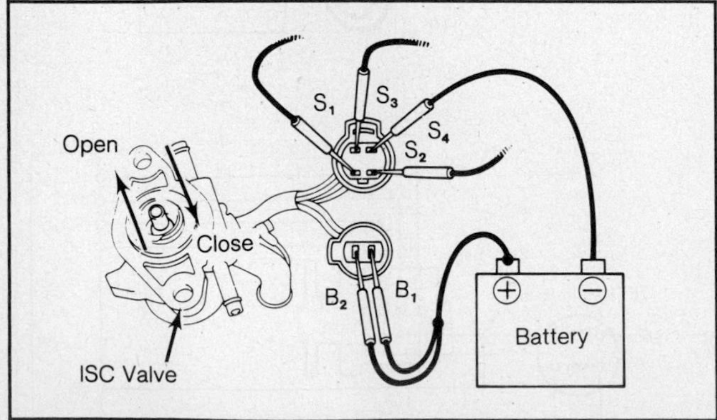

S1
S3
S4
S2
Open
Close
B2
B1
Battery
ISC Valve

Valve should open when voltage is applied in one direction and close when voltage is applied in reverse direction.

4) Check resistance values of ISC valve. Check resistance with ignition off and ISC electrical connector disconnected. If resistance is not as specified in chart, replace ISC valve.

IDLE SPEED CONTROL VALVE (ISC) RESISTANCE

Terminals	Ohms
B_1-S_1 or S_2	10-30
B_2-S_2 or S_4	10-30

Throttle Position Sensor (TPS)

Turn ignition off and disconnect electrical connector at TPS. Insert a thickness gauge between throttle stop screw and throttle lever. Using an ohmmeter, check resistance values. *See Fig. 9.* If values are not as specified in chart, adjust or replace TPS.

Fig. 9: Checking Throttle Position Sensor

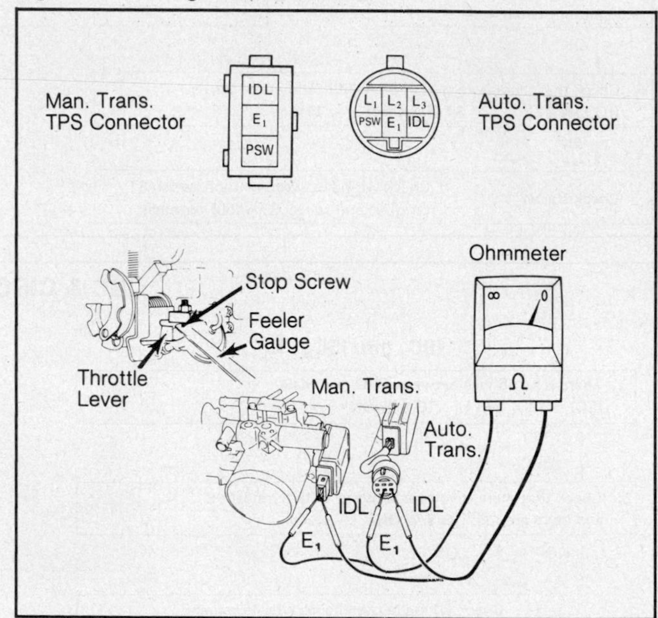

Man. Trans.
TPS Connector
IDL
E1
PSW
L1 L2 L3
PSW E1 IDL
Auto. Trans.
TPS Connector
Ohmmeter
Stop Screw
Feeler
Gauge
Throttle
Lever
Man. Trans.
Auto.
Trans.
IDL
IDL
E1
E1

Perform adjustment before replacing.

TPS RESISTANCE SPECIFICATIONS

Throttle Clearance	Terminals	Ohmmeter Reading
.024" (.60 mm)	IDL - E_1	Low Value
	Psw - E_1	Infinity
	IDL - Psw	Infinity
.037" (.95 mm)	IDL - E_1	Infinity
	Psw - E_1	Infinity
	IDL - Psw	Infinity
Fully Open	IDL - E_1	Infinity
	Psw - E_1	Low Value
	IDL - Psw	Infinity

TOYOTA COMPUTER CONTROL SYSTEM (Cont.)

ADJUSTMENTS

THROTTLE POSITION SENSOR (TPS)

1) Loosen 2 TPS retaining screws. Insert a .030" (.75 mm) thickness gauge between throttle stop screw and throttle. With ignition off and electrical connector disconnected, connect ohmmeter between terminals IDL and E_1. *See Fig. 9.*

2) Gradually turn TPS counterclockwise until ohmmeter needle deflects. Secure TPS retaining screws.

Fig. 10: Cressida TCCS Wiring Diagram

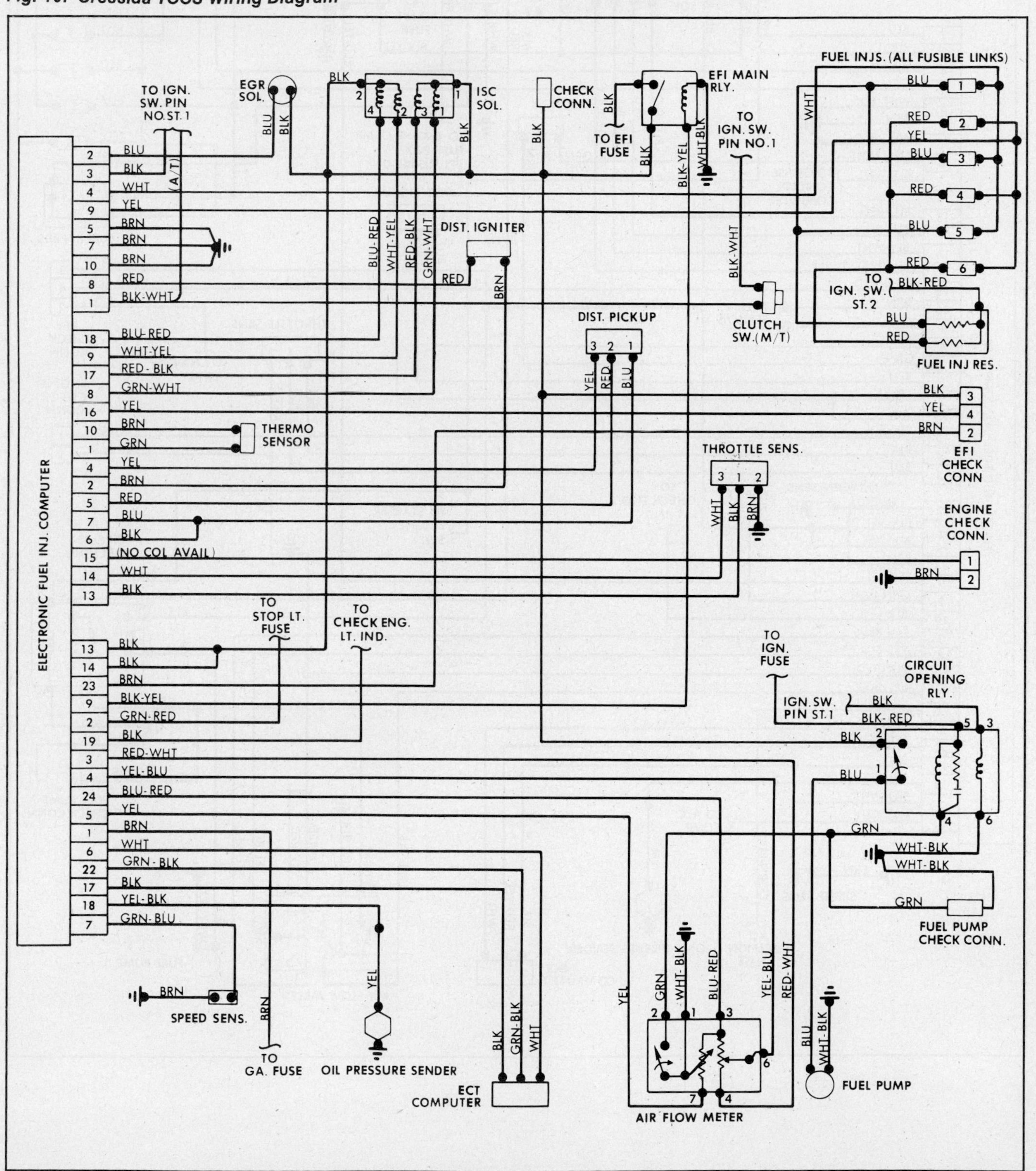

ELECTRONIC FUEL INJ. COMPUTER
TO IGN. SW. PIN NO. ST. 1
(A/T)
EGR SOL.
ISC SOL.
CHECK CONN.
EFI MAIN RLY.
TO EFI FUSE
TO IGN. SW. PIN NO. 1
FUEL INJS. (ALL FUSIBLE LINKS)
DIST. IGNITER
DIST. PICKUP
TO IGN. SW. ST. 2
CLUTCH SW. (M/T)
FUEL INJ RES.
THERMO SENSOR
THROTTLE SENS.
EFI CHECK CONN
ENGINE CHECK CONN.
(NO COL AVAIL)
TO STOP LT. FUSE
TO CHECK ENG. LT. IND.
TO IGN. FUSE
CIRCUIT OPENING RLY.
IGN. SW. PIN ST. 1
FUEL PUMP CHECK CONN.
SPEED SENS.
TO GA. FUSE
OIL PRESSURE SENDER
ECT COMPUTER
AIR FLOW METER
FUEL PUMP

Computerized Engine Controls

TOYOTA COMPUTER CONTROL SYSTEM (Cont.)

Fig. 11: Supra TCCS Wiring Diagram

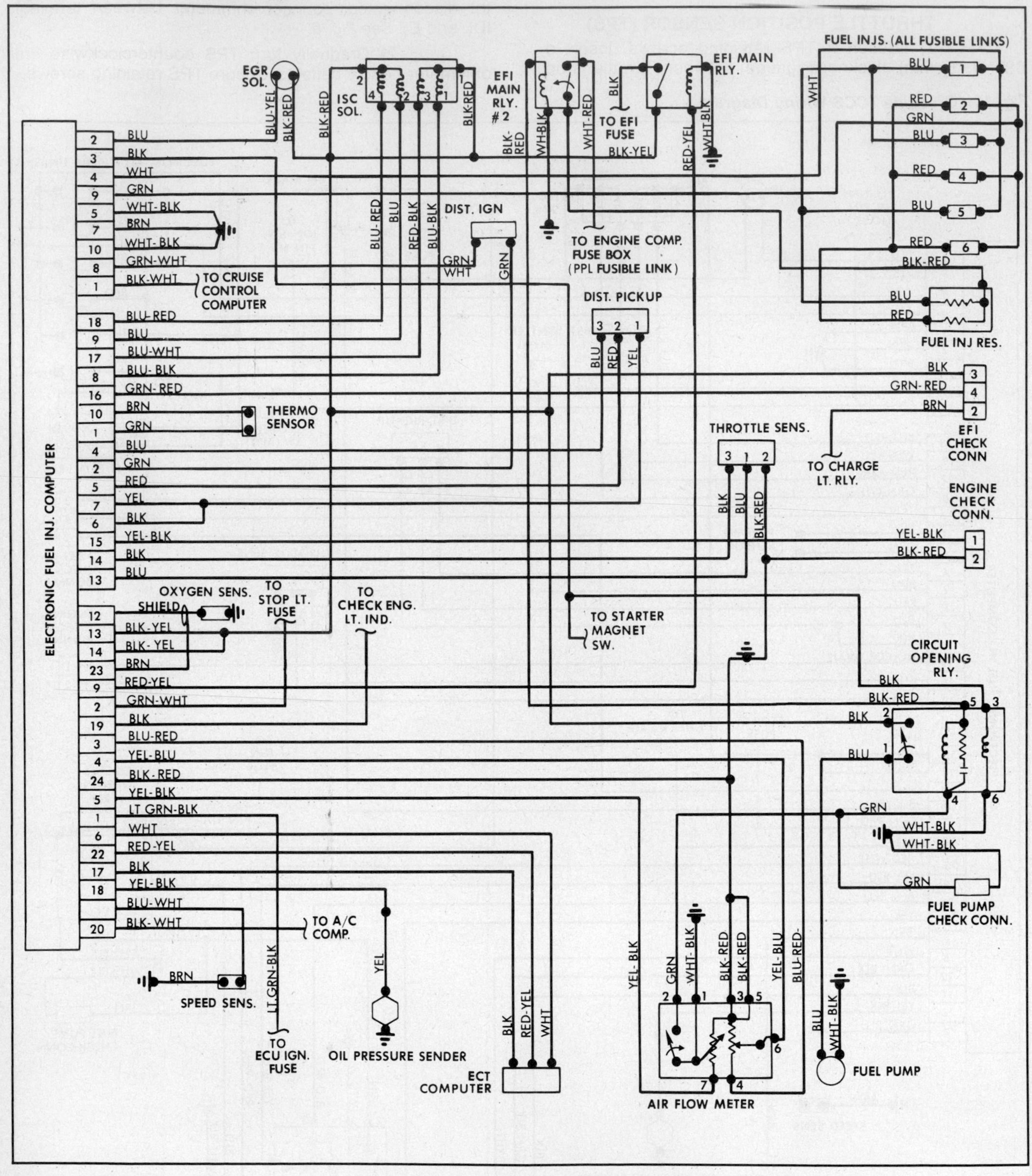

ELECTRONIC FUEL INJ. COMPUTER
EGR SOL.
ISC SOL.
EFI MAIN RLY. #2
EFI MAIN RLY.
TO EFI FUSE
FUEL INJS. (ALL FUSIBLE LINKS)
DIST. IGN
TO ENGINE COMP. FUSE BOX (PPL FUSIBLE LINK)
TO CRUISE CONTROL COMPUTER
DIST. PICKUP
FUEL INJ RES.
THERMO SENSOR
EFI CHECK CONN
THROTTLE SENS.
TO CHARGE LT. RLY.
ENGINE CHECK CONN.
OXYGEN SENS.
SHIELD
TO STOP LT. FUSE
TO CHECK ENG. LT. IND.
TO STARTER MAGNET SW.
CIRCUIT OPENING RLY.
FUEL PUMP CHECK CONN.
TO A/C COMP.
SPEED SENS.
TO ECU IGN. FUSE
OIL PRESSURE SENDER
ECT COMPUTER
AIR FLOW METER
FUEL PUMP

TOYOTA COMPUTER CONTROLLED EMISSION SYSTEM

Celica (Carbureted), Corolla, Land Cruiser, Pickup & Tercel

DESCRIPTION

The Computer Controlled Emission (CCE) system is a computerized emission control system. The CCE monitors engine operation and to lower exhaust emissions. The Electronic Control Unit (ECU) is the "brain" of the CCE system.

OPERATION

The CCE system consists of various sensors and switches that provide the ECU with engine operating conditions. From this information, the ECU issues electrical command signals to vacuum valves, solenoids or other devices. The systems controlled by the ECU are as follows:

Fuel Evaporation System

On all models, the ECU monitors coolant temperature and engine speed. The ECU compares these inputs with preprogrammed memory and properly routes fuel vapors.

Air Injection with Feedback

Celica, Land Cruiser and Pickup (Calif. only) models are equipped with an electronically controlled air injection system. This system helps control air/fuel ratio.

The ECU receives information from an oxygen sensor, catalytic converter temperature sensor and coolant temperature sensor. Depending upon coolant temperature, converter temperature and oxygen content of exhaust gases, the ECU directs additional air into the intake manifold or catalytic converter.

Air Bleed with Feedback

On Corolla and Tercel models, the ECU monitors oxygen content of exhaust gases with an oxygen sensor. When oxygen content is high, the air bleed passage is closed, allowing a richer mixture. When oxygen content is low, the air bleed passage is opened to allow more air into intake manifold.

Exhaust Gas Recirculation (EGR)

Land Cruiser models are equipped with an electronically controlled EGR system. The ECU monitors engine speed and engine coolant temperature to determine correct time to allow EGR flow.

Deceleration Fuel Cut System

Land Cruiser and Pickup models are equipped with an electronically controlled deceleration fuel cut system. The ECU monitors engine speed to control the fuel cut system during deceleration.

Cold Mixture Heater

All models are equipped with a cold mixture heater. When coolant temperature is low, the ECU activates a heater in the intake manifold which warms the air/fuel mixture. This system promotes starting in cold weather.

DIAGNOSIS & TESTING

Diagnosis and testing information for the various Toyota emission systems is thoroughly covered in the 1983 Mitchell Manuals Emission Control Service and Repair Manual for Imported Cars and Trucks. No diagnosis or testing information for the ECU is available. Helpul wiring diagrams for the systems are included here for your assistance.

Fig. 1: Carbureted Celica Computer Controlled Emission System Wiring Diagram

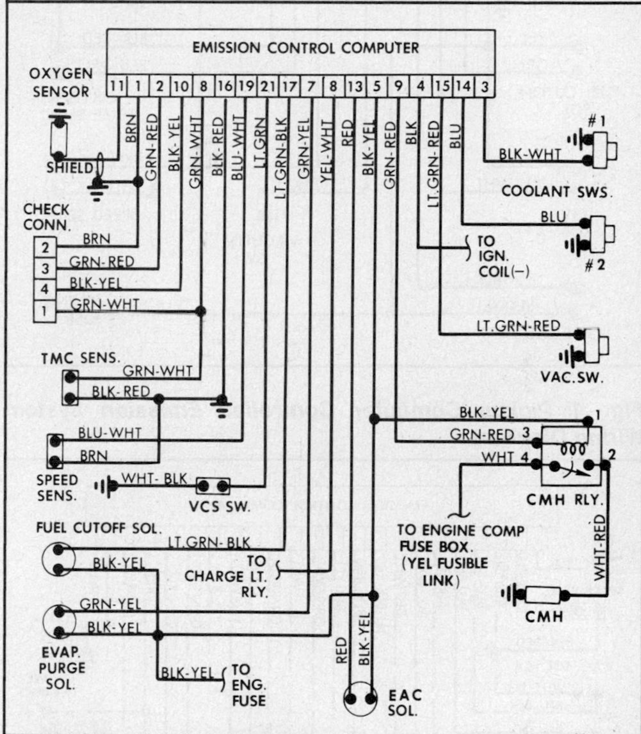
EMISSION CONTROL COMPUTER
OXYGEN SENSOR
11 1 2 10 8 16 19 21 17 7 8 13 5 9 4 15 14 3
BRN
GRN-RED
BLK-YEL
GRN-WHT
BLK-RED
BLU-WHT
LT.GRN
LT.GRN-BLK
GRN-YEL
YEL-WHT
RED
BLK-YEL
GRN-RED
BLK
LT.GRN-RED
BLU
SHIELD
CHECK CONN.
#1
BLK-WHT
COOLANT SWS.
TO IGN. COIL(–)
#2
VAC.SW.
TMC SENS.
SPEED SENS.
WHT-BLK
VCS SW.
FUEL CUTOFF SOL.
TO CHARGE LT. RLY.
WHT 4
CMH RLY.
TO ENGINE COMP FUSE BOX. (YEL FUSIBLE LINK)
WHT-RED
CMH
EVAP. PURGE SOL.
TO ENG. FUSE
EAC SOL.

Fig. 2: Corolla Computer Controlled Emission System Wiring Diagram

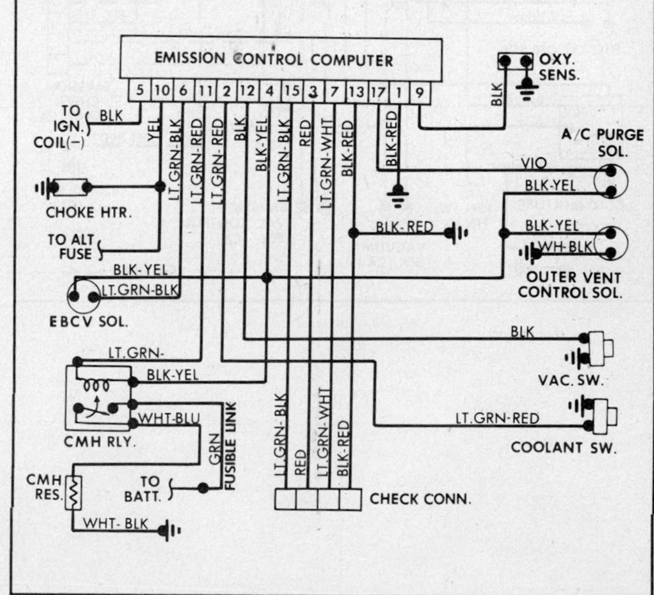
EMISSION CONTROL COMPUTER
5 10 6 11 2 12 4 15 3 7 13 17 1 9
OXY. SENS.
TO IGN. COIL(–)
BLK
YEL
LT.GRN-BLK
LT.GRN-RED
BLK-YEL
RED
LT.GRN-WHT
BLK-RED
A/C PURGE SOL.
VIO
CHOKE HTR.
TO ALT FUSE
WH-BLK
OUTER VENT CONTROL SOL.
EBCV SOL.
VAC. SW.
CMH RLY.
WHT-BLU
GRN FUSIBLE LINK
COOLANT SW.
CMH RES.
TO BATT.
WHT-BLK
CHECK CONN.

TOYOTA COMPUTER CONTROLLED EMISSION SYSTEM (Cont.)

Fig. 3: Land Cruiser Computer Controlled Emission System Wiring Diagram

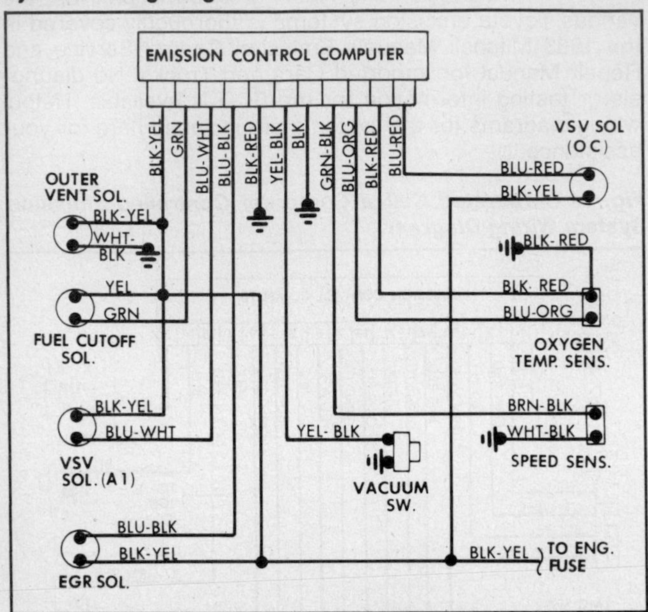
EMISSION CONTROL COMPUTER
VSV SOL (OC)
OUTER VENT SOL.
FUEL CUTOFF SOL.
OXYGEN TEMP. SENS.
VSV SOL. (A1)
VACUUM SW.
SPEED SENS.
EGR SOL.
TO ENG. FUSE

Fig. 4: Pickup Computer Controlled Emission System Wiring Diagram

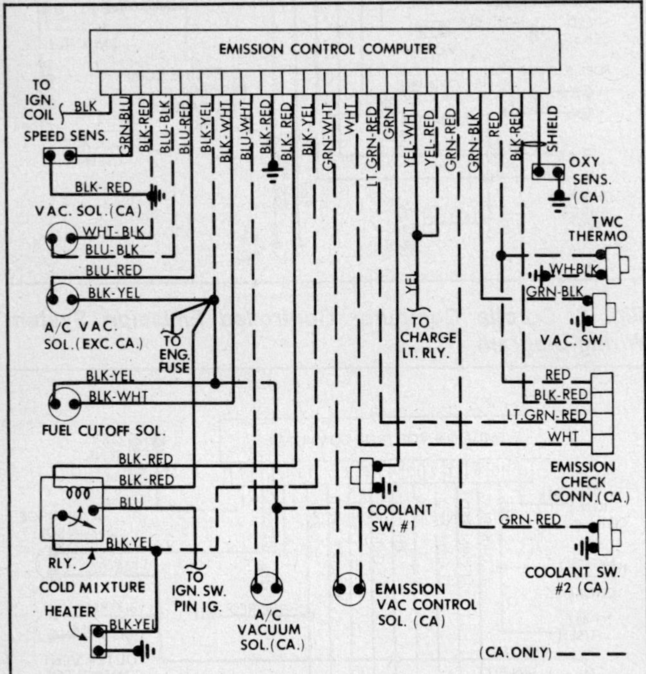
EMISSION CONTROL COMPUTER
TO IGN. COIL
SPEED SENS.
VAC. SOL. (CA)
OXY SENS. (CA)
TWC THERMO
A/C VAC. SOL. (EXC. CA.)
TO ENG. FUSE
TO CHARGE LT. RLY.
VAC. SW.
FUEL CUTOFF SOL.
EMISSION CHECK CONN. (CA.)
COOLANT SW. #1
RLY.
COLD MIXTURE HEATER
TO IGN. SW. PIN IG.
A/C VACUUM SOL. (CA.)
EMISSION VAC CONTROL SOL. (CA)
COOLANT SW. #2 (CA)
(CA. ONLY)

Fig. 5: Tercel Computer Controlled Emission System Wiring Diagram

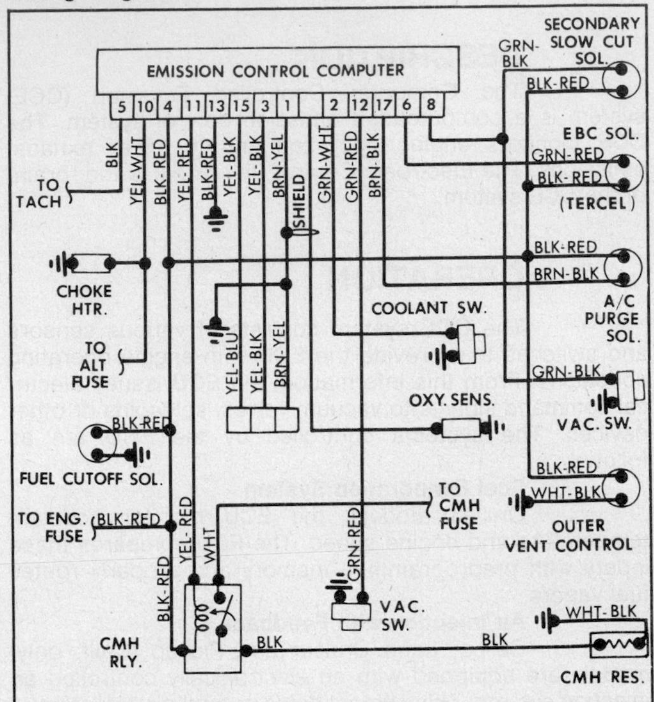
EMISSION CONTROL COMPUTER
SECONDARY SLOW CUT SOL.
EBC SOL.
(TERCEL)
TO TACH
CHOKE HTR.
A/C PURGE SOL.
COOLANT SW.
TO ALT FUSE
OXY. SENS.
VAC. SW.
FUEL CUTOFF SOL.
TO CMH FUSE
OUTER VENT CONTROL
TO ENG. FUSE
VAC. SW.
CMH RLY.
CMH RES.

TOYOTA EFI ELECTRONIC CONTROL SYSTEM

Camry, Celica, Starlet

DESCRIPTION

The Toyota EFI Electronic Control System (ECS) is a computerized fuel control system. Starlet models with 5-speed manual transmissions use a Mechatro Spark Control (MS) system to control ignition timing. The ECS controls engine operation and lowers exhaust emissions while maintaining good fuel economy and driveability. The Electronic Control Unit (ECU) is the "brain" of the ECS. The ECU controls many engine related systems to constantly adjust engine operation.

The ECS is primarily an emission control system, designed to maintain an ideal air/fuel ratio of 14.7:1 under all operating conditions. When an ideal air/fuel ratio is maintained, the catalytic converter can control carbon monoxide (CO), hydrocarbon (HC) and nitrogen oxide (NOx) emissions.

Fig. 1: Camry Electronic Control System Schematic

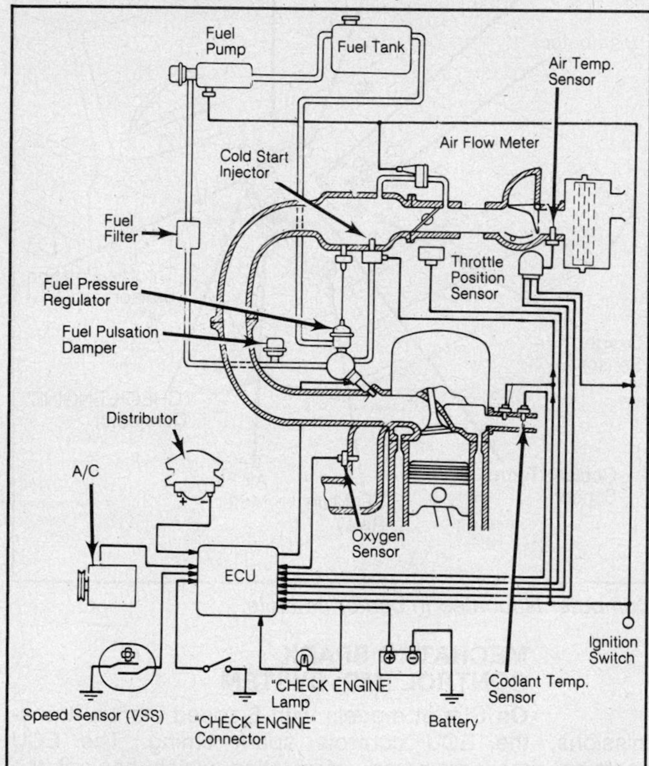
Fuel Pump
Fuel Tank
Air Temp. Sensor
Air Flow Meter
Cold Start Injector
Fuel Filter
Throttle Position Sensor
Fuel Pressure Regulator
Fuel Pulsation Damper
Distributor
A/C
Oxygen Sensor
ECU
Ignition Switch
"CHECK ENGINE" Lamp
Coolant Temp. Sensor
Speed Sensor (VSS)
"CHECK ENGINE" Connector
Battery

OPERATION

The ECS consists of the following subsystems: Electronic Fuel Injection (EFI) system, Data Sensors, Electronic Control Unit (ECU), Mechatro Spark Control (MS) system (Starlet with 5-speed man. trans.), Electronic Controlled Transmission (ECT) on Camry models, Fuel Cut System, Charge Warning System (Camry models), Diagnostic System and catalytic converter.

ELECTRONIC FUEL INJECTION (EFI)

All models are equipped with Bosch AFC fuel injection system. An electric fuel pump provides fuel to the fuel pressure regulator. From the regulator, fuel flows under pressure to the fuel injectors. The pressure regulator maintains uniform pressure differential at all times.

The constant pressure differential allows the ECU to control length of injection rather than amount of injection. The ECU monitors engine operating conditions and calculates injection duration for efficient engine operation.

The ECU activates all the injectors at the same time. When the injectors are activated, they provide 1/2 the amount of fuel required for ideal combustion with each engine revolution. *See appropriate Bosch AFC Fuel Injection article.*

Fig. 2: Celica Electronic Control System Schematic

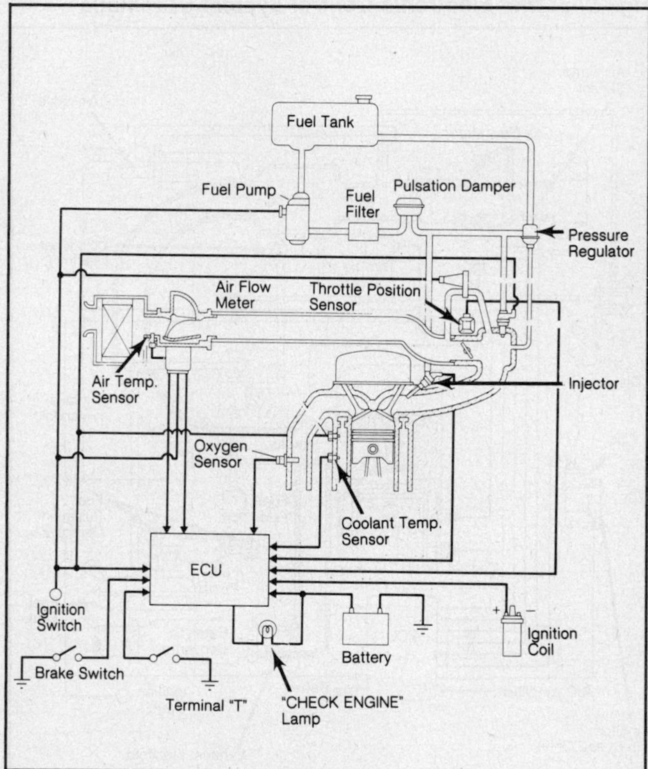
Fuel Tank
Fuel Pump
Fuel Filter
Pulsation Damper
Pressure Regulator
Air Flow Meter
Throttle Position Sensor
Air Temp. Sensor
Injector
Oxygen Sensor
Coolant Temp. Sensor
ECU
Ignition Switch
Brake Switch
Terminal "T"
"CHECK ENGINE" Lamp
Battery
Ignition Coil

DATA SENSORS

Each sensor furnishes electrical impulses to ECU. The ECU computes fuel delivery and spark timing (Starlet 5-speed models) necessary to maintain desired air/fuel ratio and engine speed. Data sensors are interrelated to each other. Operation of each sensor is as follows:

Air Flow Sensor

This sensor is mounted within the air flow meter. The sensor measures air flow rate through the air flow meter and sends a proportionate electrical signal to the ECU. The ECU uses air flow sensor information for controlling fuel injection duration.

Air Temperature Sensor

This sensor is mounted within the air flow meter. The sensor measures temperature of incoming air and sends an electrical signal to ECU. The ECU uses air temperature information for controlling fuel injection duration.

TOYOTA EFI ELECTRONIC CONTROL SYSTEM (Cont.)

Throttle Position Sensor (TPS)

The throttle position sensor (TPS) is mounted on throttle body and is directly connected to throttle linkage. The sensor, a rotary potentiometer, signals ECU of changes in throttle valve position. The information provided by this sensor is used for controlling fuel injection duration.

Coolant Temperature Sensor

The coolant temperature sensor is installed in engine block (intake manifold on Camry models). This sensor is a thermistor which converts temperature of engine coolant to electrical signal for use by ECU. The ECU uses coolant temperature information for controlling fuel injection duration.

Fig. 3: Starlet Electronic Control System Schematic

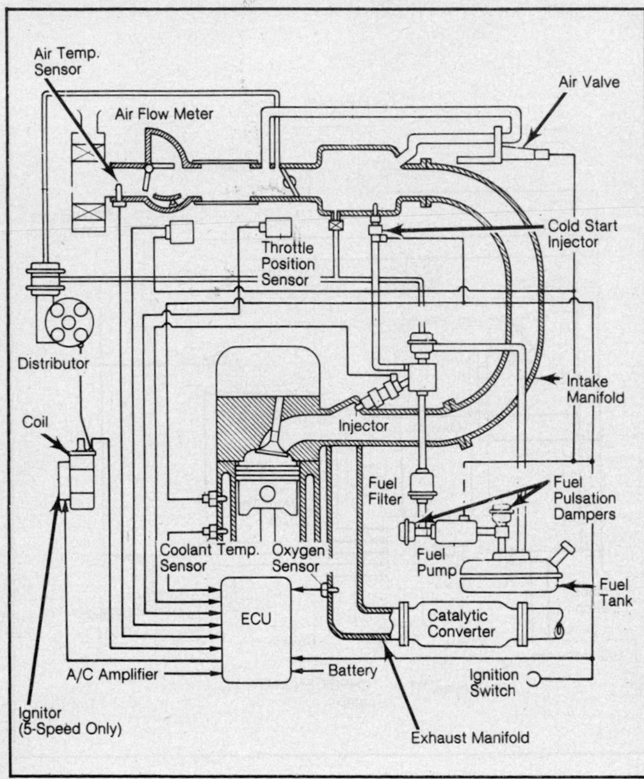

Air Temp. Sensor
Air Flow Meter
Air Valve
Cold Start Injector
Throttle Position Sensor
Distributor
Intake Manifold
Coil
Injector
Fuel Filter
Fuel Pulsation Dampers
Coolant Temp. Sensor
Oxygen Sensor
Fuel Pump
Fuel Tank
ECU
Catalytic Converter
A/C Amplifier
Battery
Ignition Switch
Ignitor (5-Speed Only)
Exhaust Manifold

Oxygen Sensor

The oxygen sensor is installed in exhaust manifold. Output voltage of oxygen sensor varies with oxygen content of exhaust gases. The ECU uses exhaust gas oxygen content information for determining fuel injection duration.

Vehicle Speed Sensor (VSS)

This sensor is mounted in the instrument panel and is a component of the speedometer on Camry models only. Vehicle speed information is used by the ECU for electronic control of automatic transmission.

Engine Speed

Engine speed signal information is received from the ignition coil. These signals are used by the ECU for fuel injection duration control and MS system (5-speed Starlet models).

A/C Switch

On Camry and Starlet models, a signal is sent to ECU when the air conditioner is activated. The ECU requires this input to increase idle speed during A/C operation.

Brake Light Switch

The brake light switch on Celica models is routed through the ECU.

ELECTRONIC CONTROL UNIT (ECU)

The ECU is mounted in center console under instrument panel (behind glove compartment on Celica models). The ECU controls all functions of the ECS. The ECU consists of a printed circuit board enclosed within a metal box. The ECU receives signals from the data sensors and switches. These signals are processed by the ECU for controlling various engine functions.

Fig. 4: Camry ECS Component Locations

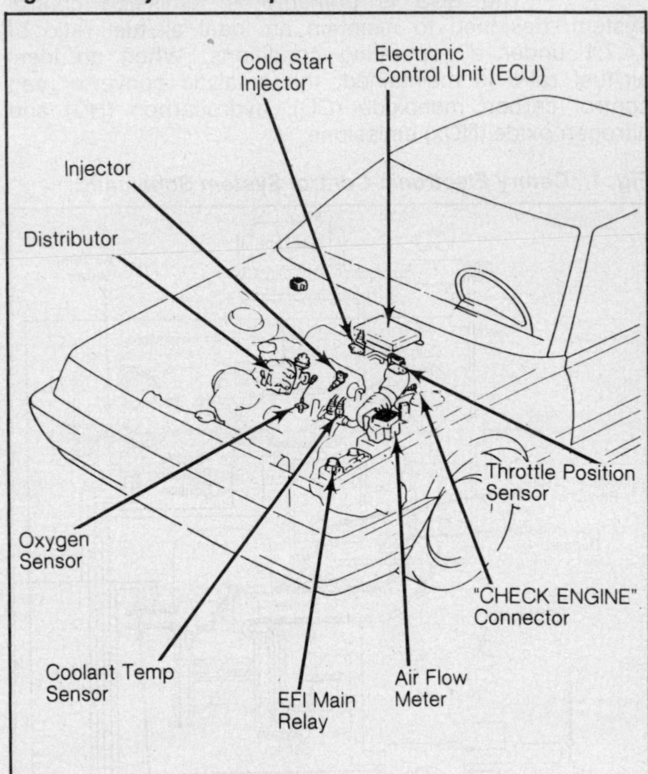

Cold Start Injector
Electronic Control Unit (ECU)
Injector
Distributor
Throttle Position Sensor
Oxygen Sensor
"CHECK ENGINE" Connector
Coolant Temp Sensor
EFI Main Relay
Air Flow Meter

Computer is located in center console.

MECHATRO SPARK CONTROL (MS) SYSTEM

On Starlet models with 5-speed manual transmissions, the ECU controls spark timing. The ECU contains preprogrammed information which has all the data necessary for maintaining optimum ignition timing under all operating conditions. Input from the various data sensors allows the ECU to deliver spark at exactly the right moment.

ELECTRONIC CONTROLLED TRANSMISSION (ECT)

Automatic transmission Camry models are equipped with an electronic control unit to control transmission operation. The ECU of the ECS provides signals on engine operation to the ECU of the ECT system. This information is used by the ECT computer to prevent shift up to 3rd gear or overdrive during cold engine operation.

NOTE: **The ECU of the ECS is not interchangeable with the ECU of the ECT system.**

TOYOTA EFI ELECTRONIC CONTROL SYSTEM (Cont.)

Fig. 5: Celica ECS Component Locations

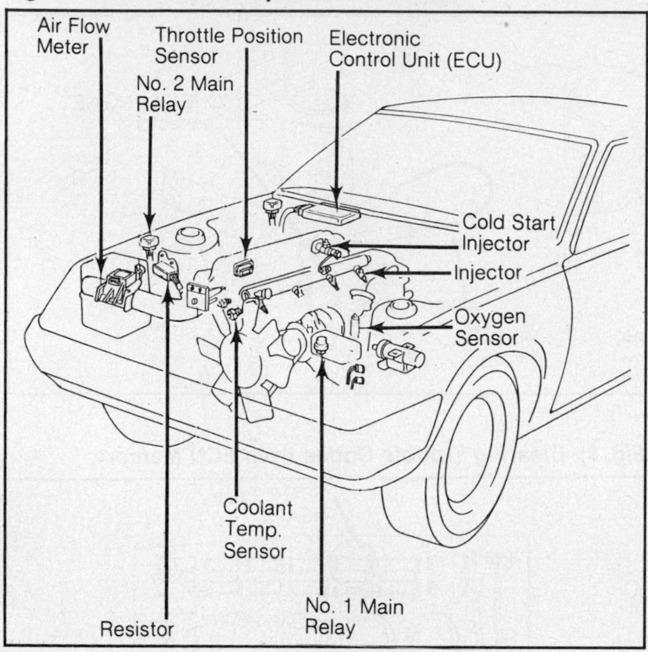
Air Flow Meter
Throttle Position Sensor
Electronic Control Unit (ECU)
No. 2 Main Relay
Cold Start Injector
Injector
Oxygen Sensor
Coolant Temp. Sensor
No. 1 Main Relay
Resistor

Computer is located behind glove compartment.

FUEL CUT SYSTEM

All models are equipped with an electronically controlled fuel cut system. During sudden deceleration, the ECU adjusts fuel injection duration to prevent overloading the engine with fuel. The system also maintains smooth engine operation to prevent backfiring.

CHARGE WARNING SYSTEM

Camry models are equipped with a charge warning system. The ECU monitors alternator output. If a problem is detected in charging system or alternator output is not to specifications, the "CHARGE" warning light will be lit.

Fig. 6: Starlet ECS Component Locations

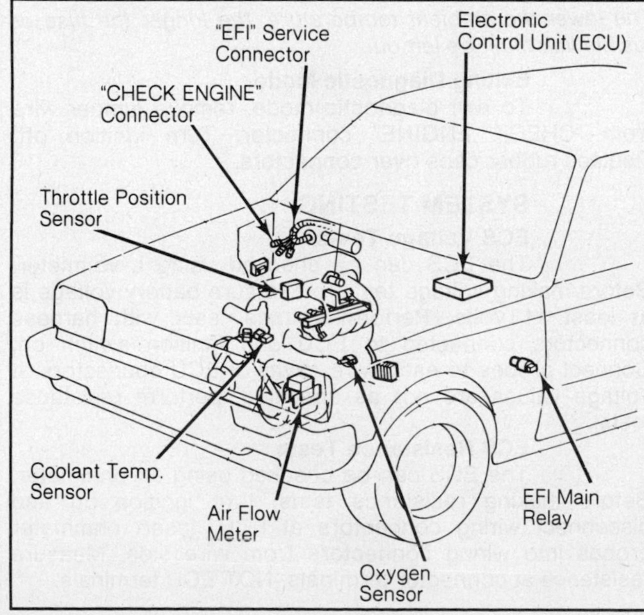
"EFI" Service Connector
Electronic Control Unit (ECU)
"CHECK ENGINE" Connector
Throttle Position Sensor
Coolant Temp. Sensor
Air Flow Meter
EFI Main Relay
Oxygen Sensor

Computer is located in center console.

DIAGNOSTIC SYSTEM

The ECU of the ECS is equipped with a self-diagnostic system which detects system failures or abnormalities. When a malfunction occurs, the ECU lights the "CHECK ENGINE" lamp located on instrument panel. At the same time, a corresponding trouble code is stored in ECU memory. Interpretation of the trouble codes can be performed by observing number of flashes of "CHECK ENGINE" lamp.

All codes are stored in memory from the time of detection until the codes are cleared from the memory. The "CHECK ENGINE" lamp will go out as soon as the malfunction is cleared; but the code will remain in memory.

As a bulb and system check, the "CHECK ENGINE" lamp will glow when ignition switch is turned on and engine is not running. When engine is started, the lamp should go out after a short period of time. If not, a malfunction has been detected in the ECS.

CATALYTIC CONVERTER

All models are equipped with 3-way catalytic converters (2 converters on Starlet models). This type of converter changes CO, HC, and NOx exhaust emissions into carbon dioxide, water vapor and nitrogen gas. All converters are monolithic type.

DIAGNOSIS & TESTING

DIAGNOSIS

Diagnose ECS in the following order:

1) Ensure that all engine systems NOT related to ECS are fully operational. Do not proceed with testing until you are sure that all other problems have been fixed. Always check fuses, fusible links and wire connectors before condemning the ECU.

2) Enter diagnostic mode and record trouble codes. Exit diagnostic mode. If no trouble codes were displayed, go to Diagnostic Circuit Check chart. Follow instructions given there.

3) If no trouble codes were displayed after performing Diagnostic Circuit Check, perform voltage and resistance checks. If trouble codes are displayed, perform tests to confirm cause of malfunction which set the corresponding trouble code.

4) After any repairs are made, clear trouble codes and perform Diagnostic Circuit Check. Normal system operation code should be displayed if repair solved cause of malfunction.

NOTE: **The following paragraphs explain the procedures involved in performing the steps outlined above.**

RECALLING TROUBLE CODES

The ECU stores component failure information for ECS under a related trouble code which can be recalled for diagnosis and repair. When recalled, these codes will be displayed by flashes of the "CHECK ENGINE" lamp.

Codes are displayed starting with lowest numbered code. Only codes in which a related malfunction has occured will be displayed.

TOYOTA EFI ELECTRONIC CONTROL SYSTEM (Cont.)

Fig. 7: Jumpering "CHECK ENGINE" Connector

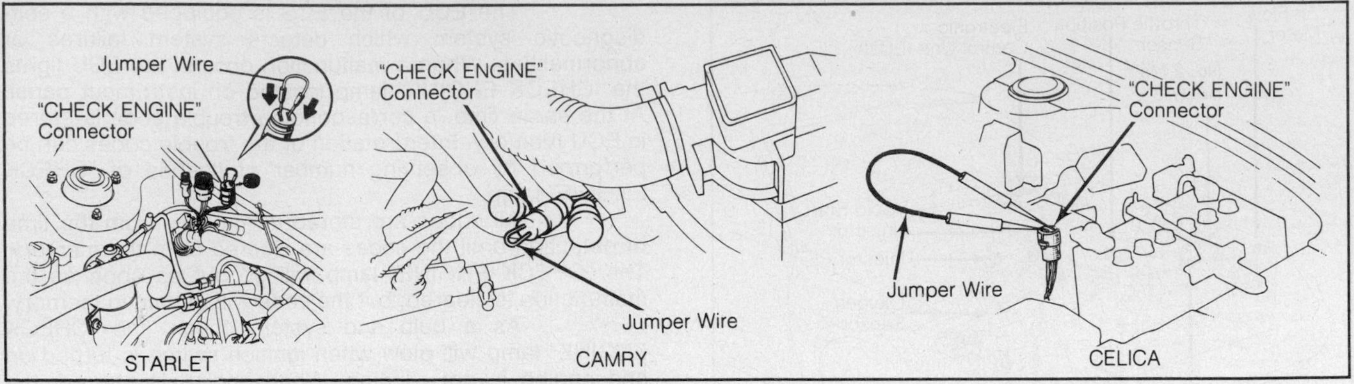
Jumper Wire
"CHECK ENGINE" Connector
"CHECK ENGINE" Connector
Jumper Wire
STARLET
CAMRY
"CHECK ENGINE" Connector
Jumper Wire
CELICA

Insert jumper wire in "CHECK ENGINE" connector.

Entering Diagnostic Mode

1) Prior to entering diagnostic mode, the following conditions must be met: Engine must be at normal operating temperature, battery voltage above 11 volts, transmission in Neutral, throttle valve fully closed and A/C off.

2) Turn ignition on, but do NOT start engine. Remove rubber cap from "CHECK ENGINE" connector. *See Fig. 7.* Using a jumper wire, jumper both terminals of the connector together.

Diagnostic Code Output

1) After entering diagnostic mode, the "CHECK ENGINE" lamp should flash a code. If no trouble codes are stored in memory, the lamp should flash once every 3 seconds. This is the "system normal" code.

2) If trouble codes are stored in ECU memory, the "CHECK ENGINE" lamp will flash once every second. If code "6" is stored in memory, the lamp will flash 6 times in 6 seconds.

3) Trouble codes will be displayed from lowest to highest numbered code. Output of the diagnostic codes will continue as long as the diagnostic mode is activated. A 3-second delay follows display of each code.

ECS TROUBLE CODE IDENTIFICATION

Code No. (Pattern)	Circuit Affected
11	System normal
2	Air flow meter signal
3	Air flow meter signal
4	Coolant temp. sensor signal
5	Oxygen sensor signal
6	No ignition signal
7	[1] Throttle position signal

[1] — All models except 5-speed Starlet.

Clearing Trouble Codes

After any repairs are performed, clear ECU memory of all stored trouble codes. To clear memory, turn ignition off and remove appropriate fuse from fuse panel for 30 seconds. Disconnect fusible link on Starlet models. *See Fig. 8.* The lower the ambient (outside) temperature, the longer the fuse (fusible link) must be left out. Replace fuse or fusible link and exit diagnostic mode.

Fig. 8: Clearing Trouble Codes from ECU Memory

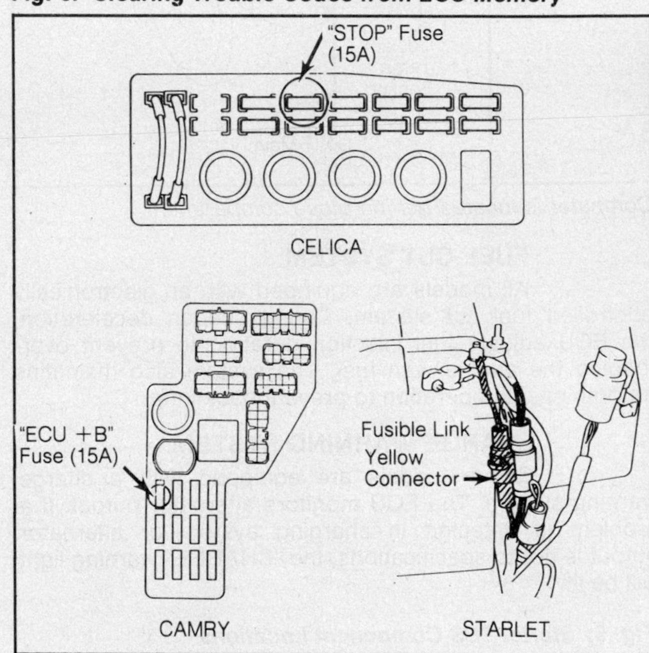
"STOP" Fuse (15A)
CELICA
"ECU +B" Fuse (15A)
Fusible Link
Yellow Connector
CAMRY
STARLET

The lower the ambient temperature, the longer the fuse or fusible link must be left out.

Exiting Diagnostic Mode

To exit diagnostic mode, remove jumper wire from "CHECK ENGINE" connector. Turn ignition off. Replace rubber caps over connectors.

SYSTEM TESTING

ECS Voltage Tests

The ECS can be checked using a voltmeter. Before making voltage tests, make sure battery voltage is at least 11 volts. Perform voltage tests with harness connectors connected to ECU and ignition switch on. Connect probes to each wire cavity of ECU connectors. If voltage values are not as specified, perform resistance tests.

ECS Resistance Tests

The ECS can be checked using an ohmmeter. Before making resistance tests, turn ignition off and disconnect wiring connectors at ECU. Insert ohmmeter probes into wiring connectors from wire side. Measure resistance at connector terminals, NOT ECU terminals.

TOYOTA EFI ELECTRONIC CONTROL SYSTEM (Cont.)

Fig. 9: Toyota Electronic Control Unit Connector Identification

E_2	V_S	V_C	BAT	THA		STA	A/C	Ox	THW	IDL	V_F	T	No 10	E01
IG	E_3	W	+B		SPD	L	CHG		E_1	TL	P_{SW}		No 20	E02

CAMRY MODELS

Symbol	Terminal	Symbol	Terminal	Symbol	Terminal
E_2	Engine Ground	Vs	Air Flow Meter	Vc	Air Flow Meter
Bat	Positive Side of Battery	THA	Air Temp. Sensor	STA	Neutral/Start Switch
A/C	A/C Compressor Switch	Ox	Oxygen Sensor	THW	Coolant Temp. Sensor
IDL	Throttle Position Sensor	Vf	EFI Service Connector	T	"CHECK ENGINE" Connector
No. 10	Injector	E01	.....	IG	Ignitor
E_3	Engine Ground	W	"CHECK ENGINE" Lamp	+B	Main Relay
SPD	Speedometer	L	Alternator	CHG	Charge Warning Lamp
E_1	Engine Ground	TL	Throttle Position Sensor	PSW	Throttle Position Sensor
No. 20	Injector			E02	.....

E_2	Vs	Vc	BAT	THA	B/R	STA		Ox	THW	Idl	V_F	T	#10	E_{01}
IG	E_1	W	+B						E_1	TL	Psw		#20	E_{02}

CELICA MODELS

Symbol	Terminal	Symbol	Terminal	Symbol	Terminal
E_2	Engine Ground	Vs	Air Flow Meter	Vc	Air Flow Meter
Bat	Positive Side of Battery	THA	Air Temp. Sensor	B/R	Brake Light Switch
STA	Neutral/Start Switch	Ox	Oxygen Sensor	THW	Coolant Temp. Sensor
IDL	Throttle Position Sensor	Vf	EFI Service Connector	T	"CHECK ENGINE" Connector
# 10	Injector	E01	.....	IG	Ignitor
E_3	Engine Ground	W	"CHECK ENGINE" Lamp	+B	Main Relay
E_1	Engine Ground	TL	Throttle Position Sensor	PSW	Throttle Position Sensor
# 20	Injector			E02	.....

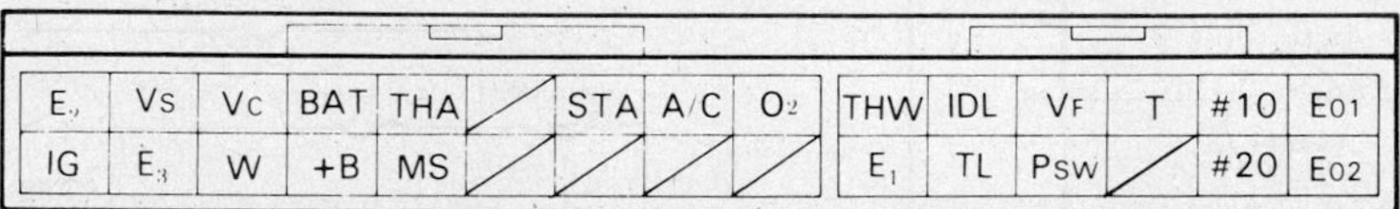
E2
Vs
Vc
BAT
THA
STA
A/C
O2
THW
IDL
VF
T
#10
E01
IG
E3
W
+B
MS
E1
TL
Psw
#20
E02

STARLET MODELS

Symbol	Terminal	Symbol	Terminal	Symbol	Terminal
E_2	Engine Ground	Vs	Air Flow Meter	Vc	Air Flow Meter
Bat	Positive Side of Battery	THA	Air Temp. Sensor	STA	Neutral/Start Switch
A/C	A/C Compressor Switch	O_2	Oxygen Sensor	THW	Coolant Temp. Sensor
IDL	Throttle Position Sensor	Vf	EFI Service Connector	T	"CHECK ENGINE" Connector
# 10	Injector	E01	.....	IG	Ignitor
E_3	Engine Ground	W	Warning Lamp	+B	Main Relay
MS	Mechatro Signal	E_1	Engine Ground	TL	Throttle Position Sensor
PSW	Throttle Position Sensor	# 20	Injector	E02	.....

Computerized Engine Controls

TOYOTA EFI ELECTRONIC CONTROL SYSTEM (Cont.)

TROUBLE CODES & PROBABLE CAUSE FOR CODES

Code No.	Probable Cause
2 & 3	Air Flow Meter or Circuit, ECU.
4	Coolant Temp. Sensor or Circuit, ECU.
5	Oxygen Sensor or Circuit, ECU.
6	Ignition System Circuit, Distributor, Coil, Ignitor, ECU.
7	Throttle Position Sensor or Circuit, ECU.

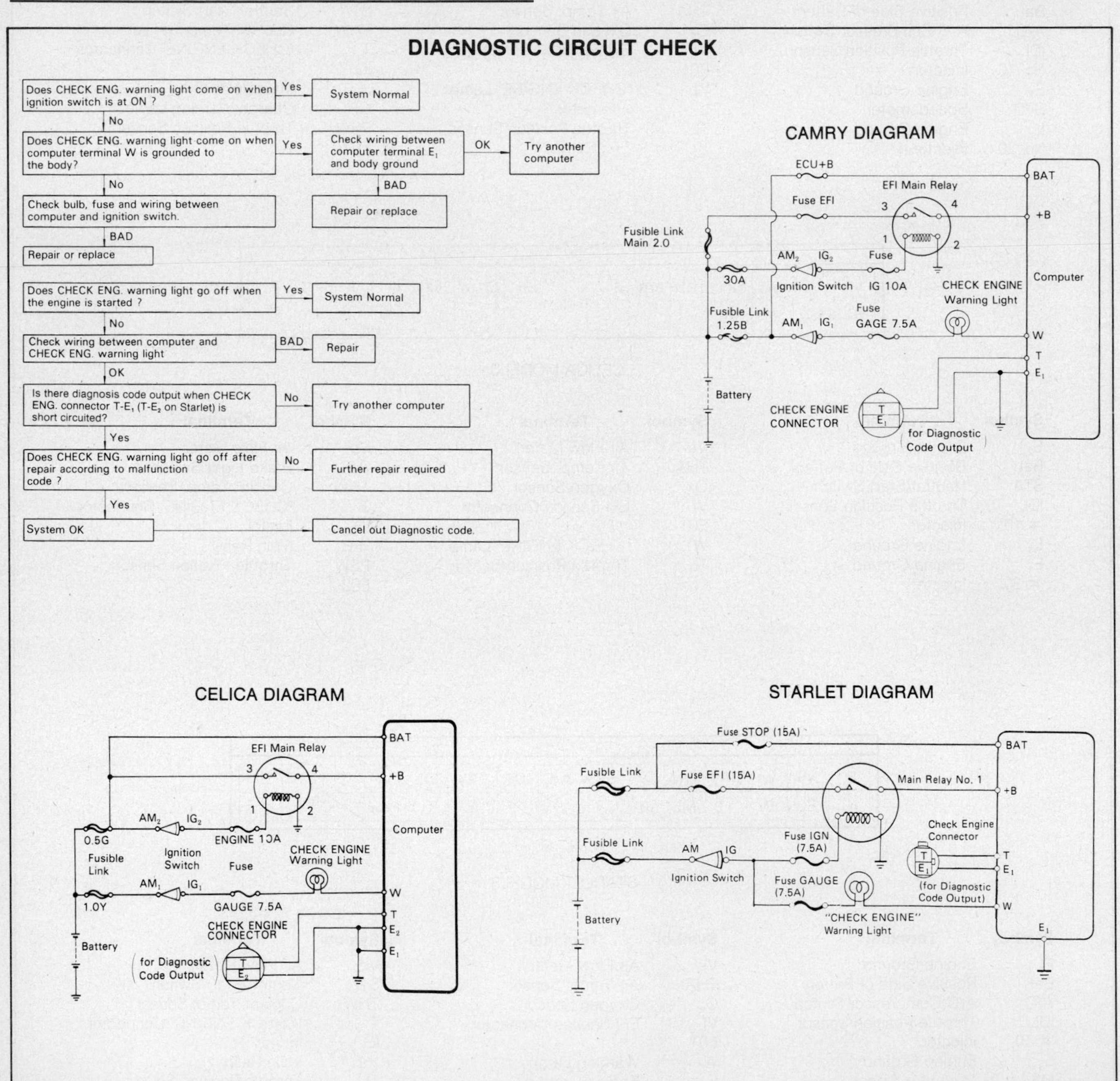
DIAGNOSTIC CIRCUIT CHECK
Does CHECK ENG. warning light come on when ignition switch is at ON ?
Yes
System Normal
No
Does CHECK ENG. warning light come on when computer terminal W is grounded to the body?
Yes
Check wiring between computer terminal E_1 and body ground
OK
Try another computer
BAD
Repair or replace
No
Check bulb, fuse and wiring between computer and ignition switch.
BAD
Repair or replace
Does CHECK ENG. warning light go off when the engine is started ?
Yes
System Normal
No
Check wiring between computer and CHECK ENG. warning light
BAD
Repair
OK
Is there diagnosis code output when CHECK ENG. connector T-E_1 (T-E_2 on Starlet) is short circuited?
No
Try another computer
Yes
Does CHECK ENG. warning light go off after repair according to malfunction code ?
No
Further repair required
Yes
System OK
Cancel out Diagnostic code.
CAMRY DIAGRAM
ECU+B
BAT
EFI Main Relay
Fuse EFI
+B
Fusible Link Main 2.0
AM_2
IG_2
Fuse
30A
Ignition Switch
IG 10A
Computer
CHECK ENGINE Warning Light
Fusible Link 1.25B
AM_1
IG_1
Fuse GAGE 7.5A
W
T
E_1
Battery
CHECK ENGINE CONNECTOR
(for Diagnostic Code Output)
CELICA DIAGRAM
BAT
EFI Main Relay
+B
AM_2
IG_2
0.5G
Fusible Link
Ignition Switch
ENGINE 10A
Fuse
Computer
CHECK ENGINE Warning Light
AM_1
IG_1
1.0Y
GAGE 7.5A
W
CHECK ENGINE CONNECTOR
T
E_2
E_1
Battery
(for Diagnostic Code Output)
STARLET DIAGRAM
Fuse STOP (15A)
BAT
Fusible Link
Fuse EFI (15A)
Main Relay No. 1
+B
Check Engine Connector
Fusible Link
AM
IG
Fuse IGN (7.5A)
T
E_1
Ignition Switch
Fuse GAUGE (7.5A)
(for Diagnostic Code Output)
W
Battery
"CHECK ENGINE" Warning Light
E_1

TOYOTA EFI ELECTRONIC CONTROL SYSTEM (Cont.)

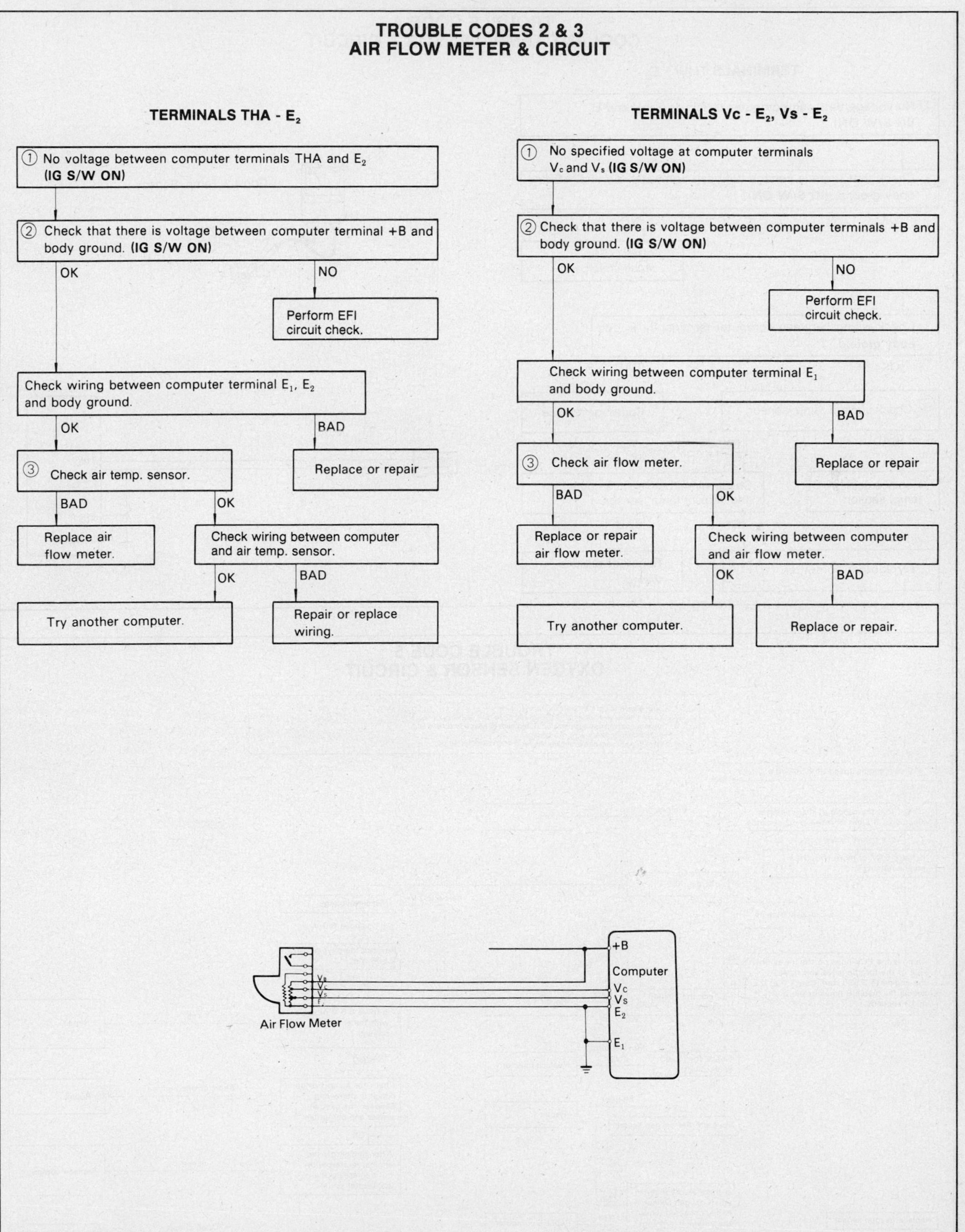
TROUBLE CODES 2 & 3
AIR FLOW METER & CIRCUIT
TERMINALS THA - E2
① No voltage between computer terminals THA and E2 (IG S/W ON)
② Check that there is voltage between computer terminal +B and body ground. (IG S/W ON)
OK
NO
Perform EFI circuit check.
Check wiring between computer terminal E1, E2 and body ground.
OK
BAD
③ Check air temp. sensor.
Replace or repair
BAD
OK
Replace air flow meter.
Check wiring between computer and air temp. sensor.
OK
BAD
Try another computer.
Repair or replace wiring.
TERMINALS Vc - E2, Vs - E2
① No specified voltage at computer terminals Vc and Vs (IG S/W ON)
② Check that there is voltage between computer terminals +B and body ground. (IG S/W ON)
OK
NO
Perform EFI circuit check.
Check wiring between computer terminal E1 and body ground.
OK
BAD
③ Check air flow meter.
Replace or repair
BAD
OK
Replace or repair air flow meter.
Check wiring between computer and air flow meter.
OK
BAD
Try another computer.
Replace or repair.
Air Flow Meter
VB
VC
VS
E2
+B
Computer
Vc
Vs
E2
E1

TOYOTA EFI ELECTRONIC CONTROL SYSTEM (Cont.)

TROUBLE CODE 4
COOLANT TEMP. SENSOR & CIRCUIT

TERMINALS THW - E_2

① No voltage between computer terminals THW and E_2 **(IG S/W ON)**

② Check that there is voltage between computer terminal +B and body ground. **(IG S/W ON)**
- NO → Perform EFI circuit check.
- OK → Check wiring between computer terminal E_1, E_2 and body ground.
  - BAD → Repair or replace
  - OK → ③ Check coolant temp. sensor.
    - BAD → Replace coolant temp. sensor.
    - OK → Check wiring between computer and coolant temp. sensor.
      - OK → Try another computer.
      - BAD → Repair or replace wiring.

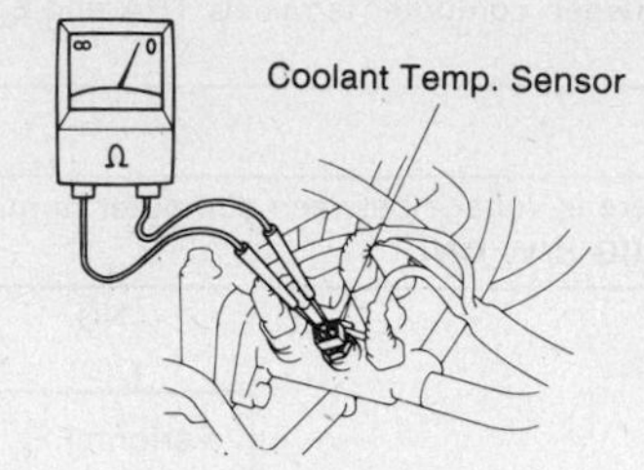

Coolant Temp. Sensor

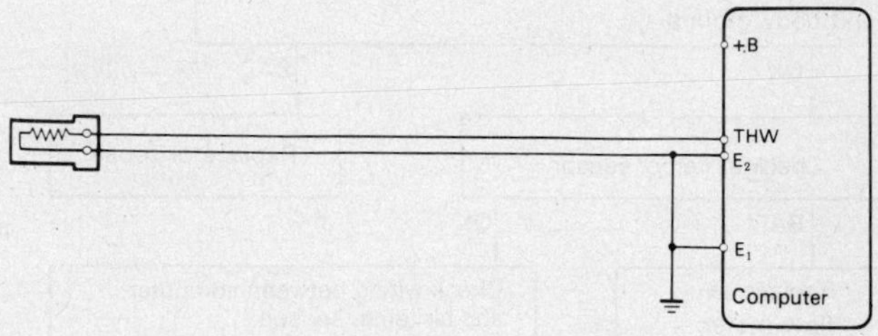

+B
THW
E_2
E_1
Computer

TROUBLE CODE 5
OXYGEN SENSOR & CIRCUIT

1. Warm engine to normal operating temperature.
2. Connect harness adapter (SST 09842-14010) to "EFI" service connector.
3. Connect positive lead of voltmeter to Red wire of adapter harness and negative lead to Black wire of adapter.
4. Warm oxygen sensor by running engine at 2500 RPM for 90 seconds.

Maintain engine speed at 2,500 rpm.

Check that the needle of the voltmeter fluctuates 8 times or more in 10 seconds
- 8 times or more → Normal
- Less than 8 times → Is there 6.0V or more with the engine running?
  - Yes → Repair
  - No → Remove the PCV hose on the lower flow side of the throttle valve and race the engine to 2,500 rpm. Check that the needle fluctuates 8 times or more in 10 seconds.
    - No → Replace oxygen sensor.
    - Yes → Check the ignition system.
- Zero → Less than 6.0 V?
  - NO → Measure voltage
  - Yes → Check the ignition system.

Check the ignition system.
- BAD → Repair
- OK → Check for fouled spark plugs.
  - Several dirty plugs → Replace injector.
  - All dirty → Repair
  - OK → Re-warm the oxygen sensor.
    - Is there zero voltage when oxygen sensor is disconnected while the engine is running?
      - No → Repair
      - Yes → Replace computer

Measure voltage
- below 6.0 V → After turning off the engine, re-start without depressing the accelerator pedal.
- above 6.0 V → Rewarm the oxygen sensor 2,500 rpm.
  - Is there 6.0 V or more with the engine running?
    - Yes → Repair
    - NO → Check for a short or open circuit in the wiring between the oxygen sensor and computer.
      - Short or open circuit → Repair
      - OK → After turning off the engine, re-start without depressing the accelerator pedal.
        - Lean → Replace computer.
        - Open circuit → Replace oxygen sensor.

TOYOTA EFI ELECTRONIC CONTROL SYSTEM (Cont.)

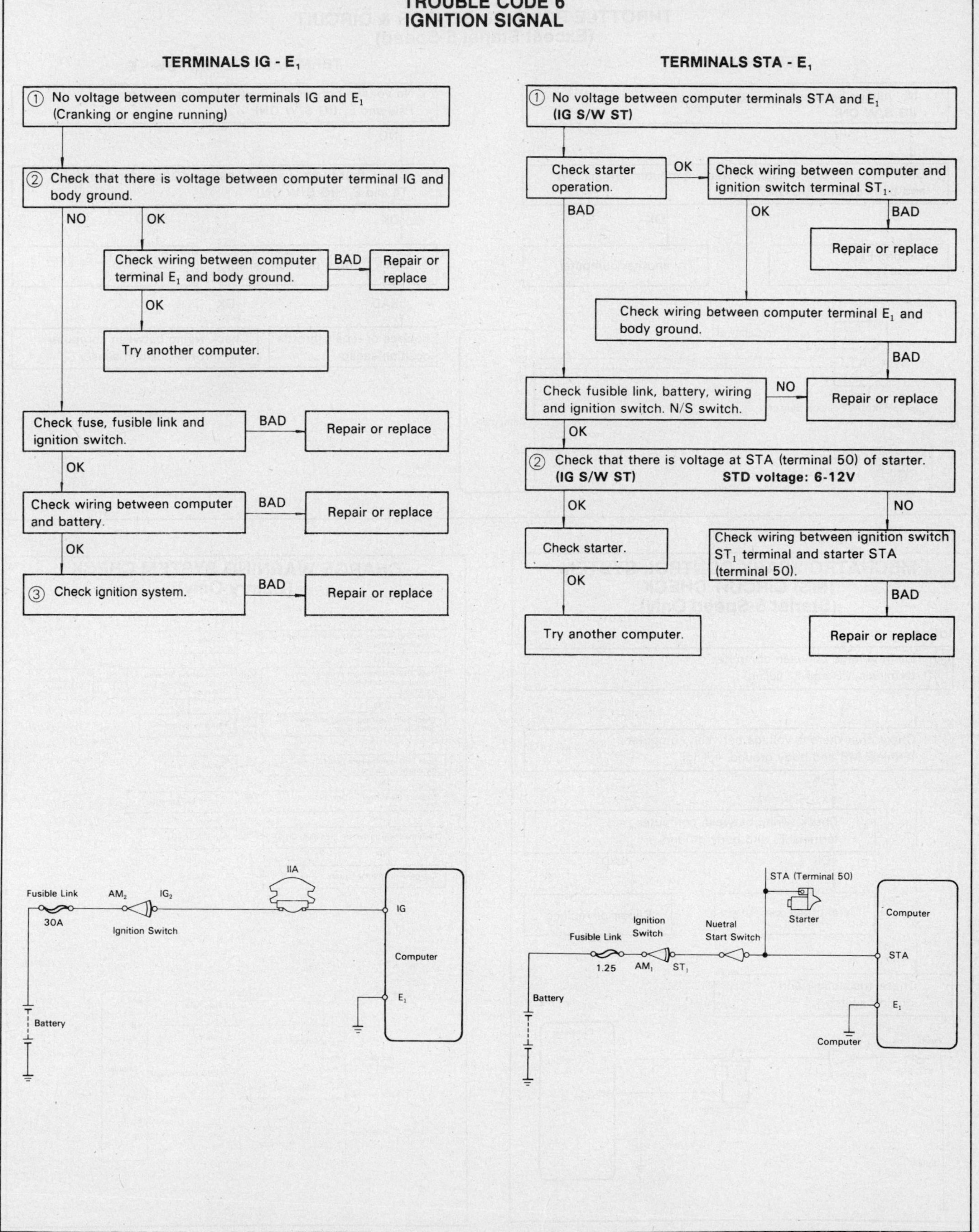

TROUBLE CODE 6
IGNITION SIGNAL
TERMINALS IG - E_1
① No voltage between computer terminals IG and E_1 (Cranking or engine running)
② Check that there is voltage between computer terminal IG and body ground.
NO
OK
Check wiring between computer terminal E_1 and body ground.
BAD
Repair or replace
OK
Try another computer.
Check fuse, fusible link and ignition switch.
BAD
Repair or replace
OK
Check wiring between computer and battery.
BAD
Repair or replace
OK
③ Check ignition system.
BAD
Repair or replace
TERMINALS STA - E_1
① No voltage between computer terminals STA and E_1 (IG S/W ST)
Check starter operation.
OK
Check wiring between computer and ignition switch terminal ST_1.
BAD
OK
BAD
Repair or replace
Check wiring between computer terminal E_1 and body ground.
BAD
Check fusible link, battery, wiring and ignition switch. N/S switch.
NO
Repair or replace
OK
② Check that there is voltage at STA (terminal 50) of starter. (IG S/W ST) STD voltage: 6-12V
OK
NO
Check starter.
Check wiring between ignition switch ST_1 terminal and starter STA (terminal 50).
OK
BAD
Try another computer.
Repair or replace
Fusible Link
30A
AM_2
IG_2
Ignition Switch
IIA
IG
Computer
E_1
Battery
STA (Terminal 50)
Starter
Computer
Fusible Link
1.25
Ignition Switch
AM_1
ST_1
Nuetral Start Switch
STA
E_1
Battery
Computer

TOYOTA EFI ELECTRONIC CONTROL SYSTEM (Cont.)

TROUBLE CODE 7
THROTTLE POSITION SENSOR & CIRCUIT
(Except Starlet 5-Speed)

TERMINALS TL - E_1

① No voltage between computer terminals TL and E_1 **(IG S/W ON)**

② Check that there is voltage between computer terminal +B and body ground. **(IG S/W ON)**
- NO: Perform EFI circuit test.
- OK: Try another computer.

TERMINALS IDL - E_1, PSW - E_1

① No voltage between computer terminals IDL or Psw and E_1 **(IG S/W ON)**
- NO

① Check that there is voltage between computer terminals TL and E_1. **(IG S/W ON)**
- OK: ③ Check throttle position sensor
  - BAD: Replace or repair throttle position sensor.
  - OK: Check wiring between computer and throttle position sensor.
- NO: Refer to TL-E_1 throttle section.

L_1, L_2, L_3 } To Camry ECT (A/T)

+B, IDL, TL, P_{SW}, Computer, E_1

Throttle Position Sensor

M/T: PSW, TL, IDL

A/T: L_1, L_2, L_3, PSW, TL, IDL — Camry A/T Connector

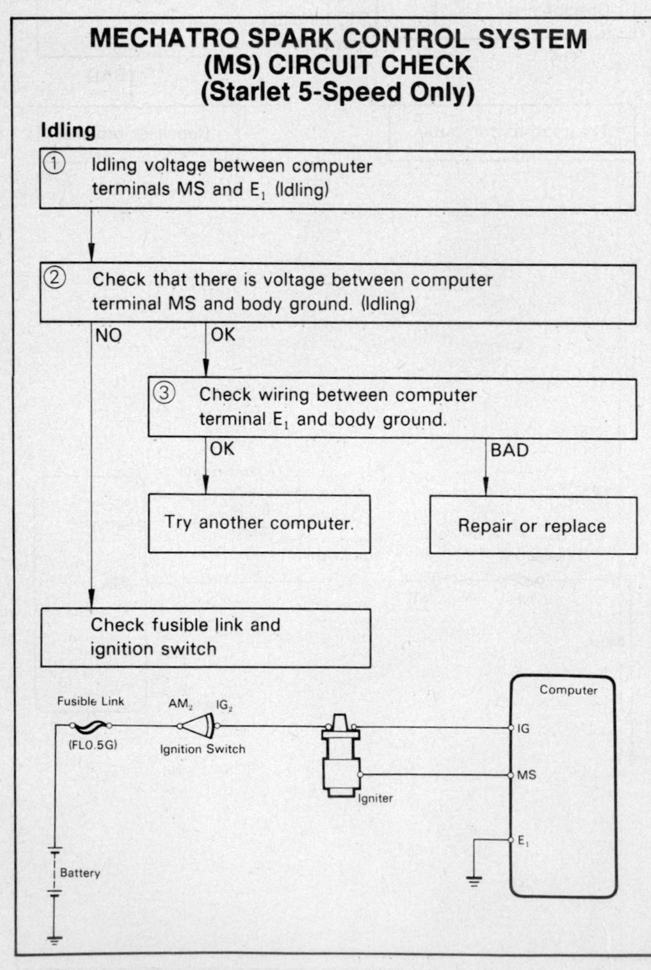
MECHATRO SPARK CONTROL SYSTEM
(MS) CIRCUIT CHECK
(Starlet 5-Speed Only)
Idling
① Idling voltage between computer terminals MS and E1 (Idling)
② Check that there is voltage between computer terminal MS and body ground. (Idling)
NO
OK
③ Check wiring between computer terminal E1 and body ground.
OK
BAD
Try another computer.
Repair or replace
Check fusible link and ignition switch
Fusible Link
(FLO.5G)
AM2
IG2
Ignition Switch
Igniter
Computer
IG
MS
E1
Battery

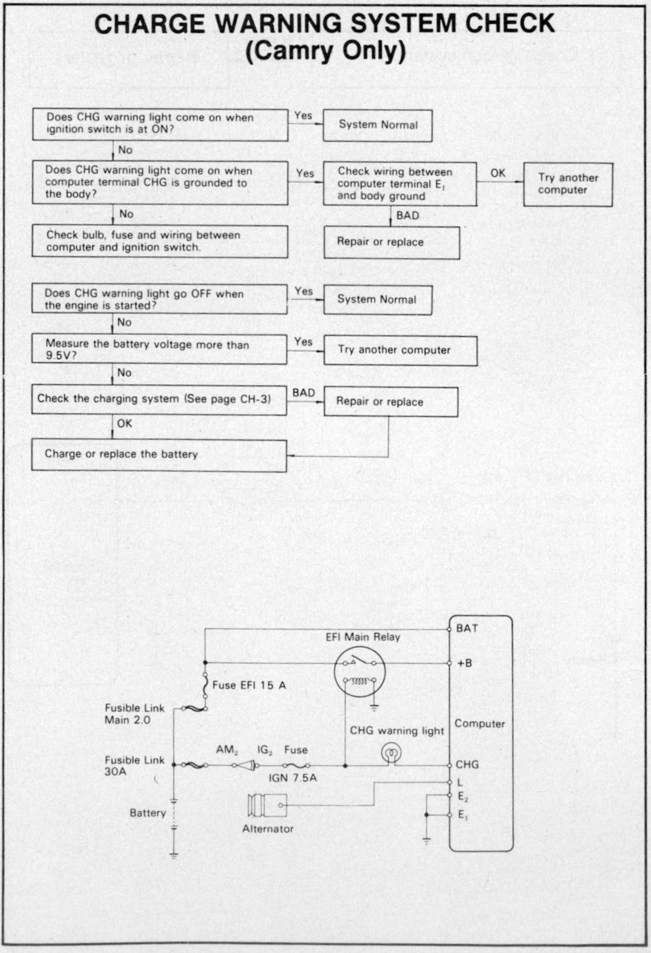
CHARGE WARNING SYSTEM CHECK
(Camry Only)
Does CHG warning light come on when ignition switch is at ON?
Yes
System Normal
No
Does CHG warning light come on when computer terminal CHG is grounded to the body?
Yes
Check wiring between computer terminal E1 and body ground
OK
Try another computer
BAD
Repair or replace
No
Check bulb, fuse and wiring between computer and ignition switch.
Does CHG warning light go OFF when the engine is started?
Yes
System Normal
No
Measure the battery voltage more than 9.5V?
Yes
Try another computer
No
Check the charging system (See page CH-3)
BAD
Repair or replace
OK
Charge or replace the battery
BAT
EFI Main Relay
+B
Fuse EFI 15 A
Fusible Link
Main 2.0
Computer
CHG warning light
AM2
IG2
Fuse
Fusible Link
30A
CHG
IGN 7.5A
L
E2
E1
Battery
Alternator

TOYOTA EFI ELECTRONIC CONTROL SYSTEM (Cont.)

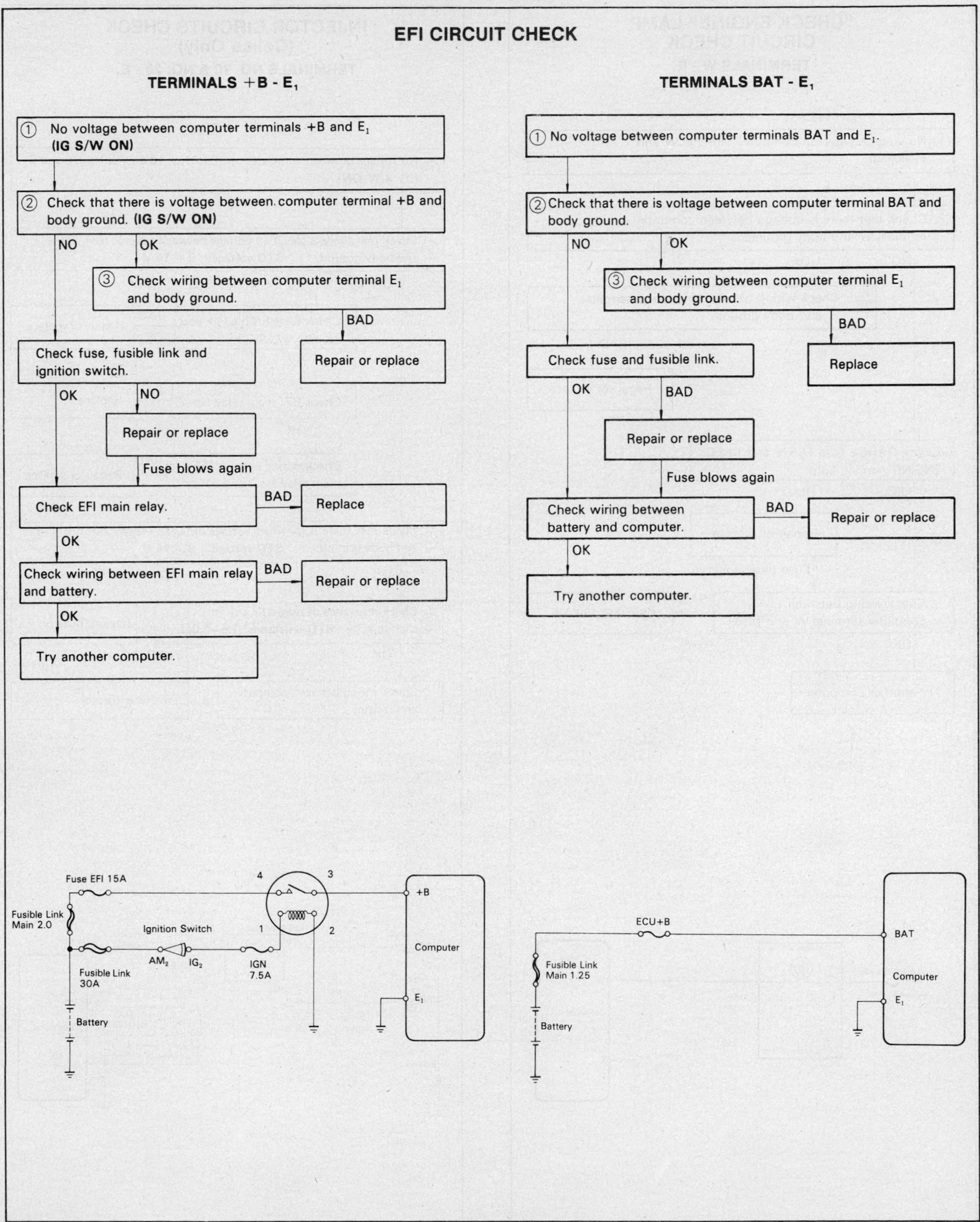
EFI CIRCUIT CHECK
TERMINALS +B - E1
① No voltage between computer terminals +B and E1 (IG S/W ON)
② Check that there is voltage between computer terminal +B and body ground. (IG S/W ON)
NO
OK
③ Check wiring between computer terminal E1 and body ground.
BAD
Check fuse, fusible link and ignition switch.
Repair or replace
OK
NO
Repair or replace
Fuse blows again
Check EFI main relay.
BAD
Replace
OK
Check wiring between EFI main relay and battery.
BAD
Repair or replace
OK
Try another computer.
TERMINALS BAT - E1
① No voltage between computer terminals BAT and E1.
② Check that there is voltage between computer terminal BAT and body ground.
NO
OK
③ Check wiring between computer terminal E1 and body ground.
BAD
Check fuse and fusible link.
Replace
OK
BAD
Repair or replace
Fuse blows again
Check wiring between battery and computer.
BAD
Repair or replace
OK
Try another computer.
Fuse EFI 15A
4
3
+B
Fusible Link Main 2.0
Ignition Switch
1
2
Computer
AM2
IG2
IGN 7.5A
Fusible Link 30A
E1
Battery
ECU+B
BAT
Fusible Link Main 1.25
Computer
E1
Battery

TOYOTA EFI ELECTRONIC CONTROL SYSTEM (Cont.)

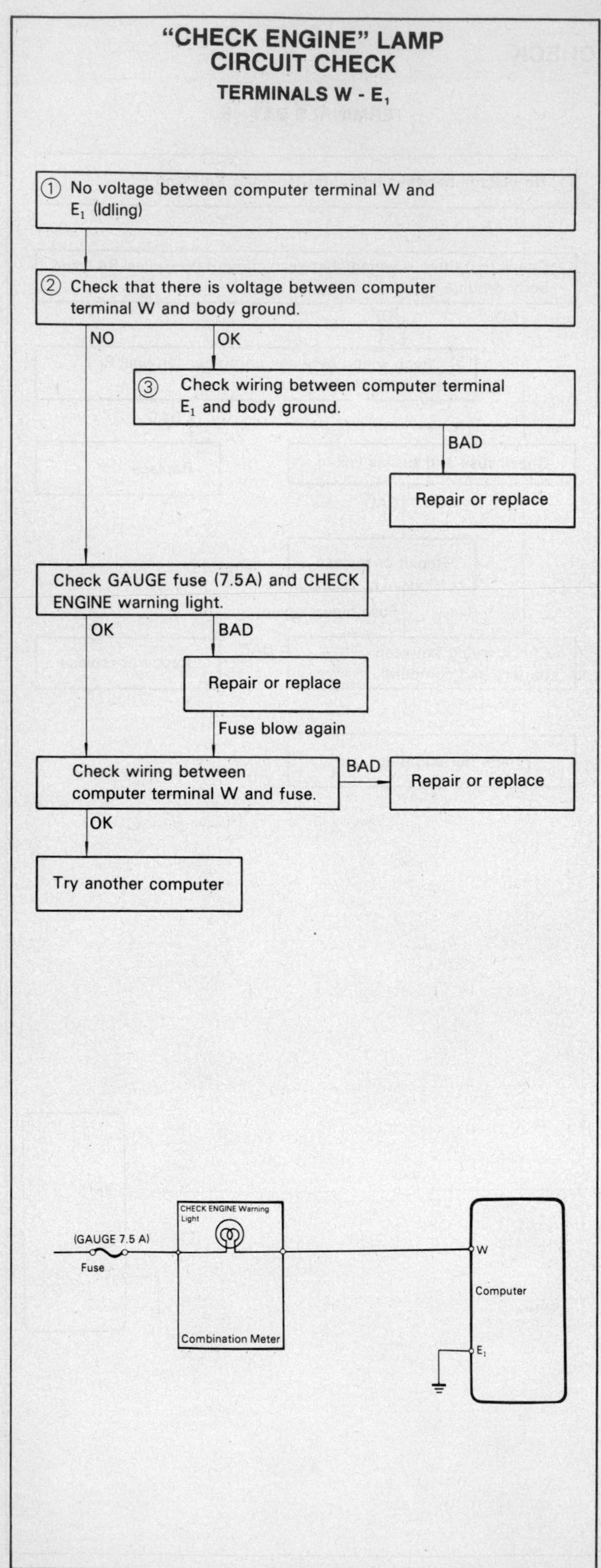
"CHECK ENGINE" LAMP
CIRCUIT CHECK
TERMINALS W - E_1
① No voltage between computer terminal W and E_1 (Idling)
② Check that there is voltage between computer terminal W and body ground.
NO
OK
③ Check wiring between computer terminal E_1 and body ground.
BAD
Repair or replace
Check GAUGE fuse (7.5A) and CHECK ENGINE warning light.
OK
BAD
Repair or replace
Fuse blow again
Check wiring between computer terminal W and fuse.
BAD
Repair or replace
OK
Try another computer
CHECK ENGINE Warning Light
(GAUGE 7.5 A)
Fuse
Combination Meter
W
Computer
E_1

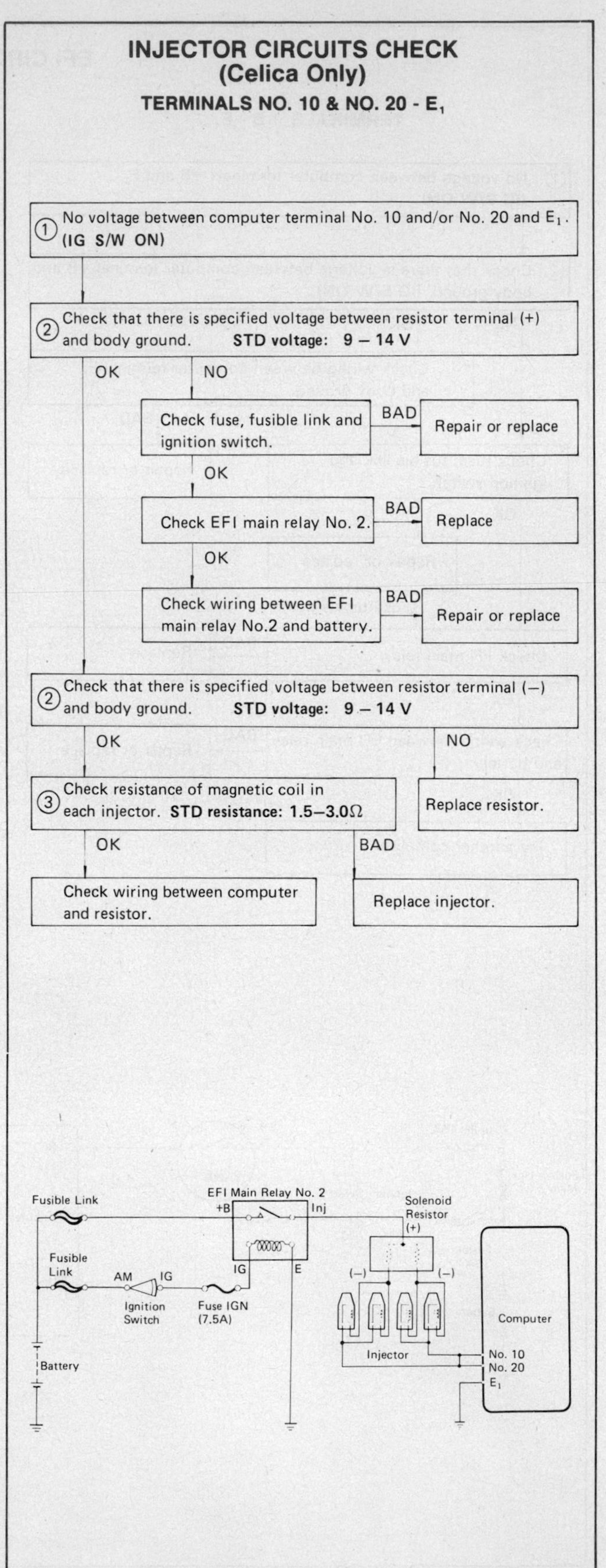
INJECTOR CIRCUITS CHECK
(Celica Only)
TERMINALS NO. 10 & NO. 20 - E_1
① No voltage between computer terminal No. 10 and/or No. 20 and E_1. (IG S/W ON)
② Check that there is specified voltage between resistor terminal (+) and body ground. STD voltage: 9 – 14 V
OK
NO
Check fuse, fusible link and ignition switch.
BAD
Repair or replace
OK
Check EFI main relay No. 2.
BAD
Replace
OK
Check wiring between EFI main relay No.2 and battery.
BAD
Repair or replace
② Check that there is specified voltage between resistor terminal (–) and body ground. STD voltage: 9 – 14 V
OK
NO
③ Check resistance of magnetic coil in each injector. STD resistance: 1.5–3.0Ω
Replace resistor.
OK
BAD
Check wiring between computer and resistor.
Replace injector.
Fusible Link
EFI Main Relay No. 2
+B
Inj
Solenoid Resistor
(+)
Fusible Link
AM
IG
IG
E
(–)
(–)
Ignition Switch
Fuse IGN (7.5A)
Battery
Injector
Computer
No. 10
No. 20
E_1

TOYOTA EFI ELECTRONIC CONTROL SYSTEM (Cont.)

A/C SWITCH CHECK (Camry & Starlet Only)

TERMINALS A/C - E_1

① No voltage between computer terminals A/C and E_1 (Air conditioning ON)

② Check that there is voltage between computer terminal A/C and body ground.

- OK → ③ Check wiring between computer E_1 and body ground.
  - OK → Try another computer
  - BAD → Repair or replace
- NO → Check compressor running
  - OK → Check wiring between computer terminal A/C and amplifier
    - BAD → Repair or replace
  - BAD → Check that there is voltage between amplifier terminal and body ground
    - BAD → Repair or replace
    - OK → Check wiring between amplifier and computer or compressor.

A/C Amplifier
A/C
Computer
E_1
A/C Compressor

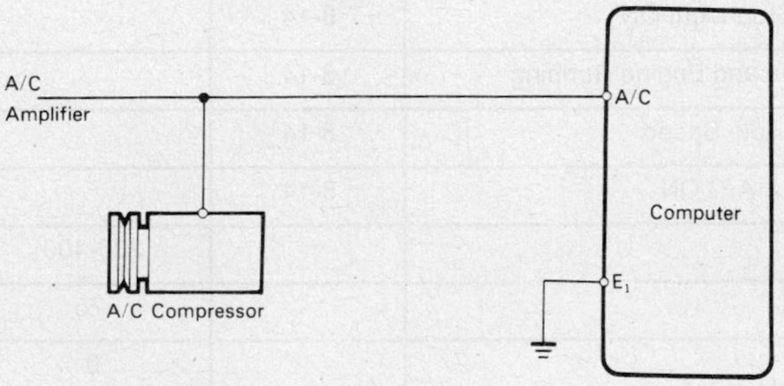

INJECTOR CIRCUITS CHECK (Camry & Starlet Only)

TERMINALS NO. 10 & NO. 20 - E_1

① No voltage between computer terminal No. 10 and/or No. 20 and E_1 **(IG S/W ON)**

② Check that there is specified voltage between resistor terminal (+B) and body ground. **STD voltage: 9-14V**

- NO → Check fuse, fusible link and ignition switch.
- OK → ② Check that there is specified voltage between resistor terminal (No.10 or No.20) and body ground. **STD voltage: 9-14V**
  - NO → Replace resistor
  - OK → ③ Check resistance of magnetic coil in the each injector. **STD resistance: 1.5-3.0Ω**
    - BAD → Replace injector
    - OK → Check wiring between computer and resistor.
      - BAD → Repair or replace wiring.
      - OK → Try another computer.

Fusible Link 30A
AM_2
IG_2
Ingition Switch
+B
Solenoid Resistor
No.10
No.20
Injector
Computer
Battery
No. 10
No. 20
E_1

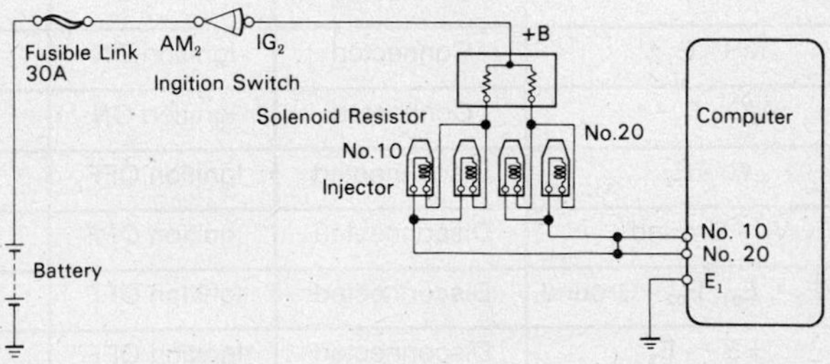

TOYOTA EFI ELECTRONIC CONTROL SYSTEM (Cont.)

ECS VOLTAGE AND RESISTANCE SPECIFICATION CHART [1]

Terminals	Position of Connectors at ECU	Procedure	Condition	Normal Voltage Reading	Normal Resistance Reading
BAT - E_1	Connected			10-14	
+B - E_1	Connected	Ignition ON		10-14	
IG - E_1	Connected	Ignition ON	Engine Cranking; Engine Running	Above 3	
IDL - E_1	Connected	Ignition ON	Throttle Valve Fully Closed	8-14	
IDL - Ground	Disconnected	Ignition OFF			∞
PSW - E_1	Connected	Ignition ON	Throttle Valve Fully Open	8-14	
PSW - Ground	Disconnected	Ignition OFF			∞
TL - E_1	Connected	Ignition ON		8-14	
TL - IDL	Disconnected	Ignition OFF	Throttle Valve Fully Closed Throttle Valve Fully Open		0 ∞
TL - PSW	Disconnected	Ignition OFF	Throttle Valve Fully Closed Throttle Valve Fully Open		∞ 0
TL - Ground	Disconnected	Ignition OFF			∞
Vc - E_2	Connected Disconnected	Ignition ON Ignition OFF		4-9	 100-300
Vc - Ground	Disconnected	Ignition OFF			∞
Vs - E_2	Connected Disconnected	Ignition ON Ignition OFF	Air Flap Fully Closed Air Flap Fully Open Idle Speed Air Flap Fully Closed Air Flap Fully Open	0.5-2.5 5-8 2.5-5.5	 20-400 20-1000
Vs - Ground	Disconnected	Ignition OFF			∞
THA - E_2	Connected Disconnected	Ignition ON Ignition OFF	Intake Air Temp. 68°F (20°C)	2-6	 2000-3000
THA - Ground	Disconnected	Ignition OFF			∞
THW - E_2	Connected Disconnected	Ignition ON Ignition OFF	Coolant Temp. 176°F (80°C)	0.5-2.5	 200-400
THW - Ground	Disconnected	Ignition OFF			∞
STA - E_1	Connected		Engine Cranking	6-12	
No. 10 & No. 20 - E_1	Connected	Ignition ON		9-14	
L, CHG - E_1 [2]	Connected	Ignition ON	Idle Speed	9-14	
B/R [3]	Connected	Ignition ON	Stop Light ON	8-14	
W - E_1 [2,4]	Connected		No Trouble and Engine Running	8-14	
MS - E_1 [4]	Connected	Ignition ON	Idle Speed	8-14	
A/C - E_1 [2,4]	Connected	Ignition ON	A/C ON	8-14	
Vb - E_2	Disconnected	Ignition OFF			200-400
Vb - Ground	Disconnected	Ignition OFF			∞
E_1, E_2 [3], E_{01}, E_{02} - Ground	Disconnected	Ignition OFF			0
+B [3] - E_2	Disconnected	Ignition OFF			200-400
+B [3] - Ground	Disconnected	Ignition OFF			∞
Vb - E_2 [2,4]	Disconnected	Ignition OFF			200-400
Vb - Ground [2,4]	Disconnected	Ignition OFF			∞

[1] — Do NOT allow probes of volt/ohmmeter to touch ECU terminals.
[2] — Camry models only.
[3] — Celica models only.
[4] — Starlet models only.

TOYOTA EFI ELECTRONIC CONTROL SYSTEM (Cont.)

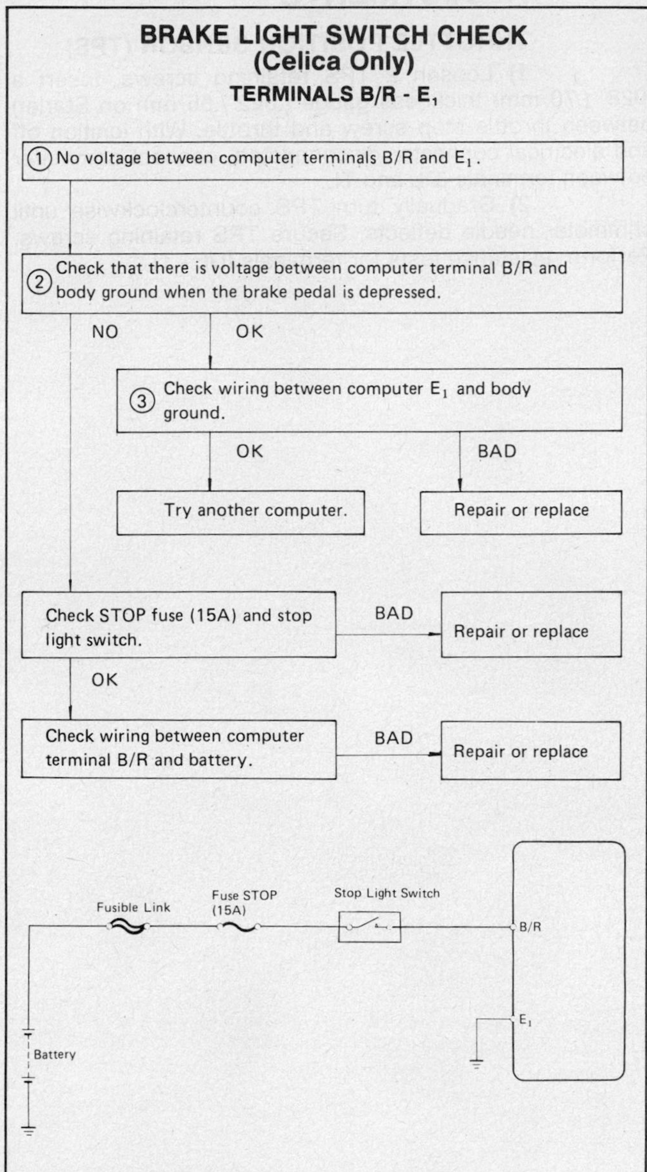
BRAKE LIGHT SWITCH CHECK
(Celica Only)
TERMINALS B/R - E1
① No voltage between computer terminals B/R and E1.
② Check that there is voltage between computer terminal B/R and body ground when the brake pedal is depressed.
NO
OK
③ Check wiring between computer E1 and body ground.
OK
BAD
Try another computer.
Repair or replace
Check STOP fuse (15A) and stop light switch.
BAD
Repair or replace
OK
Check wiring between computer terminal B/R and battery.
BAD
Repair or replace
Fusible Link
Fuse STOP (15A)
Stop Light Switch
B/R
E1
Battery

COMPONENT TESTING

Air Flow Meter

Turn ignition off. Disconnect wiring connector from air flow meter. Using an ohmmeter, measure resistance between each terminal. *See Fig. 10.* If resistance values do not meet specifications shown in chart, replace air flow meter.

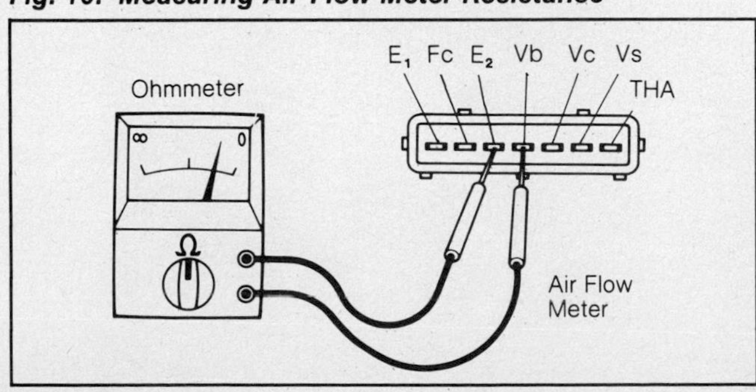
E1 Fc E2 Vb Vc Vs
THA
Ohmmeter
Air Flow
Meter

Fig. 10: Measuring Air Flow Meter Resistance

AIR FLOW METER RESISTANCE SPECIFICATIONS

Terminals	Condition	Ohms
E_2 - Vs	Flap Closed	20-400
	Flap Open	[1] 20-1000
E_2 - Vc		100-300
E_2 - Vb		200-400
E_2 - THA	4°F (-20°C)	10,000-20,000
	32°F (0°C)	4000-7000
	68°F (20°C)	2000-3000
	104°F (40°C)	900-1300
	140°F (60°C)	400-700
E_1 - Fc	Flap Closed	Infinity (∞)
	Flap Open	Zero

[1] — Resistance changes with flap position.

Throttle Position Sensor (TPS)

Turn ignition off and disconnect electrical connector at TPS. Insert a thickness gauge between throttle stop screw and throttle lever. Using an ohmmeter, check resistance values. *See Fig. 11.* If values are not as specified in chart, adjust or replace TPS.

Fig. 11: Checking Throttle Position Sensor

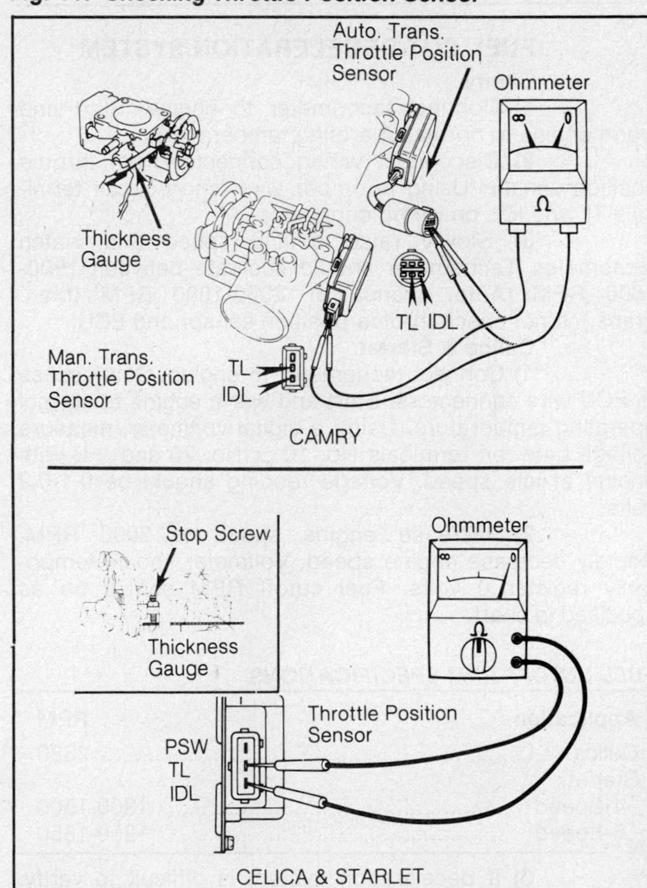
Auto. Trans.
Throttle Position
Sensor
Ohmmeter
Thickness
Gauge
TL IDL
Man. Trans.
Throttle Position
Sensor
TL
IDL
CAMRY
Stop Screw
Ohmmeter
Thickness
Gauge
Throttle Position
Sensor
PSW
TL
IDL
CELICA & STARLET

Perform adjustment before replacing.

TOYOTA EFI ELECTRONIC CONTROL SYSTEM (Cont.)

TPS RESISTANCE SPECIFICATIONS

Throttle Clearance	Terminals	Ohmmeter Reading
Camry & Celica		
.020" (.50 mm)	IDL - TL	Low Value
	PSW - TL	Infinity
	IDL - PSW	Infinity
Camry		
.035" (.90 mm)	IDL - TL	Infinity
	PSW - TL	Infinity
	IDL - PSW	Infinity
Celica & Starlet		
.028" (.70 mm)	IDL - E_1	Infinity
	PSW - TL	Infinity
	IDL - PSW	Infinity
Starlet		
.013" (.34 mm)	IDL - TL	Low Value
	PSW - TL	Infinity
	IDL - PSW	Infinity
All Models		
Fully Open	IDL - TL	Infinity
	PSW - TL	Low Value
	IDL - PSW	Infinity

FUEL CUT DECELERATION SYSTEM

Camry

1) Connect tachometer to engine. Start and warm engine to normal operating temperature.

2) Disconnect wiring connector from throttle position sensor. Using a jumper wire, short-circuit terminals TL and IDL on wiring connector.

3) Slowly raise engine speed and watch tachometer. Tachometer should fluctuate between 1900-1600 RPM (Auto. Trans.) or 2000-1600 RPM (Man. Trans.). If not check throttle position sensor and ECU.

Celica & Starlet

1) Connect tachometer to engine. Gain access to ECU wire connectors. Start and warm engine to normal operating temperature. Using a digital voltmeter, measure voltage between terminals No. 10 or No. 20 and +B with engine at idle speed. Voltage reading should be 0.1-0.2 volts.

2) Increase engine speed to 3000 RPM. Rapidly decrease engine speed. Voltmeter should temporarily register 0 volts. Fuel cutoff RPM should be as specified in chart.

FUEL CUTOFF RPM SPECIFICATIONS

Application	RPM
Celica	2380
Starlet	
4-Speed	1300-1500
5-Speed	1250-1550

3) If deceleration system is difficult to verify, check by performing road test. If accurate testing was performed and system does not operate properly, check throttle position sensor. Remove test equipment and replace ECU.

ADJUSTMENTS

THROTTLE POSITION SENSOR (TPS)

1) Loosen 2 TPS retaining screws. Insert a .028" (.70 mm) thickness gauge (.022"/.55 mm on Starlet) between throttle stop screw and throttle. With ignition off and electrical connector disconnected, connect ohmmeter between terminals IDL and TL.

2) Gradually turn TPS counterclockwise until ohmmeter needle deflects. Secure TPS retaining screws. Perform resistance tests for terminals IDL - TL.

TOYOTA EFI ELECTRONIC CONTROL SYSTEM (Cont.)

Fig. 12: Camry ECS Wiring Diagram

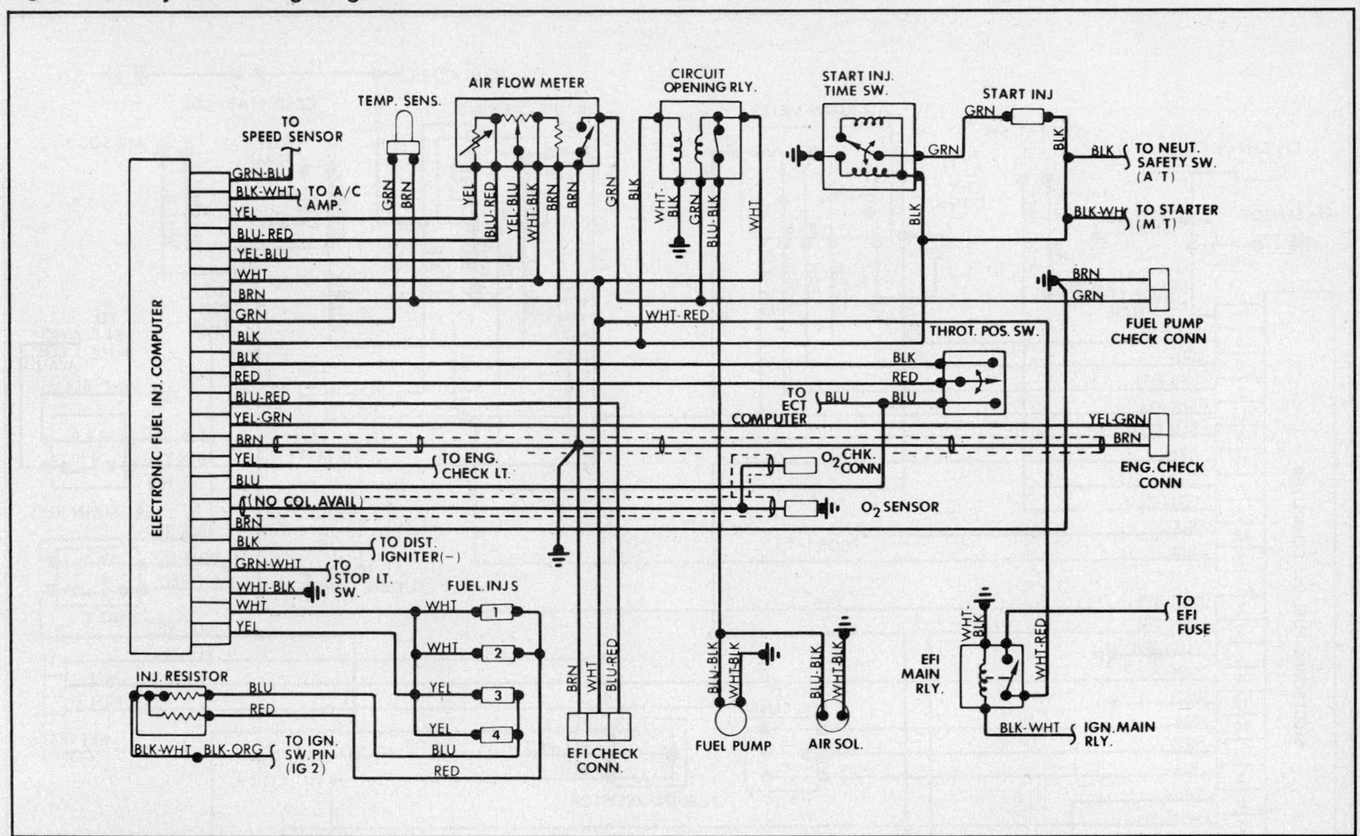

ELECTRONIC FUEL INJ. COMPUTER
TO SPEED SENSOR
TEMP. SENS.
AIR FLOW METER
CIRCUIT OPENING RLY.
START INJ. TIME SW.
START INJ
TO NEUT. SAFETY SW. (A/T)
TO STARTER (M/T)
TO A/C AMP.
FUEL PUMP CHECK CONN
THROT. POS. SW.
TO ECT COMPUTER
ENG. CHECK CONN
TO ENG. CHECK LT.
O2 CHK. CONN
O2 SENSOR
(NO COL. AVAIL)
TO DIST. IGNITER(−)
TO STOP LT. SW.
FUEL INJ S
TO EFI FUSE
EFI MAIN RLY.
IGN. MAIN RLY.
INJ. RESISTOR
TO IGN. SW. PIN (IG 2)
EFI CHECK CONN.
FUEL PUMP
AIR SOL.

Fig. 13: Starlet ECS Wiring Diagram

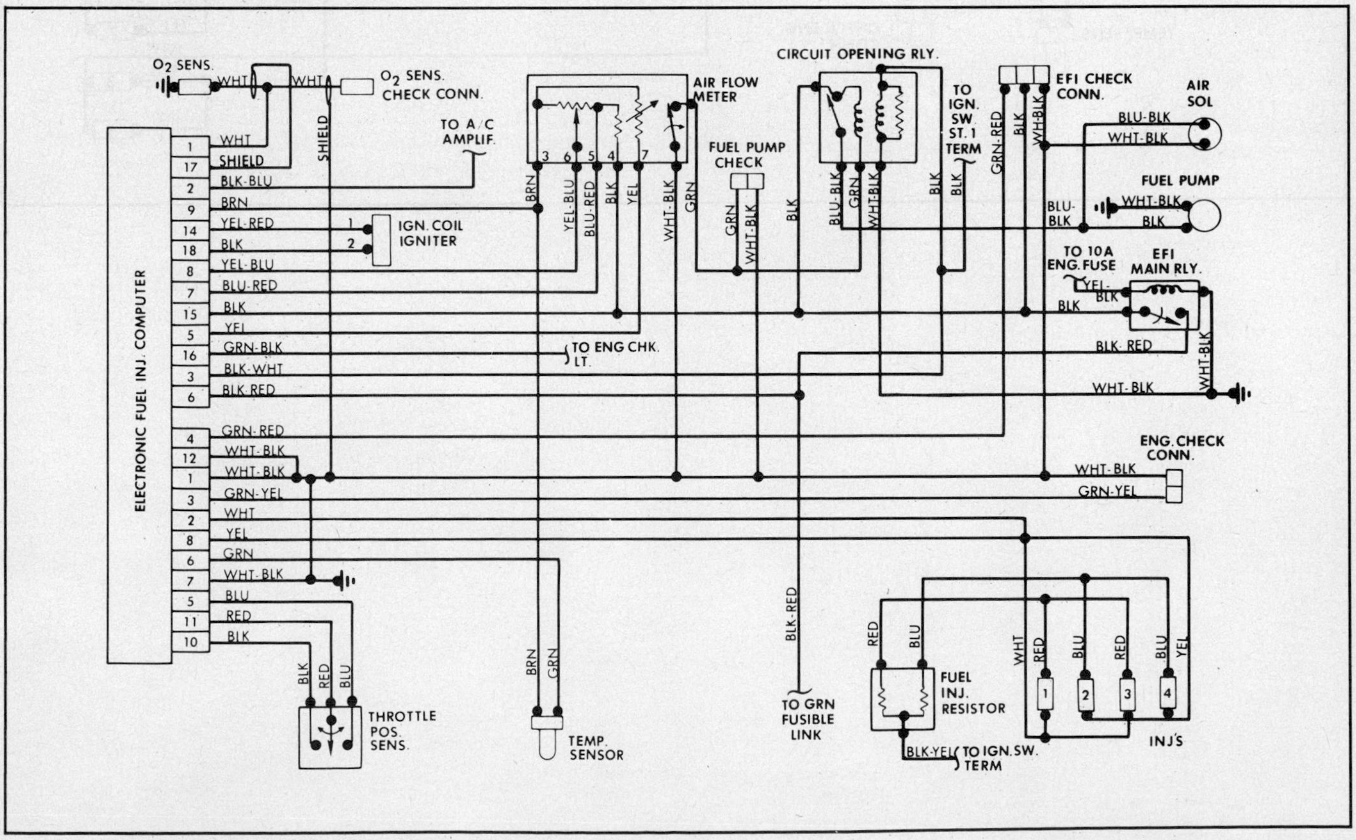

O2 SENS.
O2 SENS. CHECK CONN.
TO A/C AMPLIF.
AIR FLOW METER
CIRCUIT OPENING RLY.
TO IGN. SW. ST. 1 TERM
EFI CHECK CONN.
AIR SOL
FUEL PUMP
FUEL PUMP CHECK
IGN. COIL IGNITER
ELECTRONIC FUEL INJ. COMPUTER
TO 10A ENG. FUSE
EFI MAIN RLY.
TO ENG CHK. LT.
ENG. CHECK CONN.
THROTTLE POS. SENS.
TEMP. SENSOR
TO GRN FUSIBLE LINK
FUEL INJ. RESISTOR
TO IGN. SW. TERM
INJ'S

TOYOTA EFI ELECTRONIC CONTROL SYSTEM (Cont.)

Fig. 14: Celica ECS Wiring Diagram

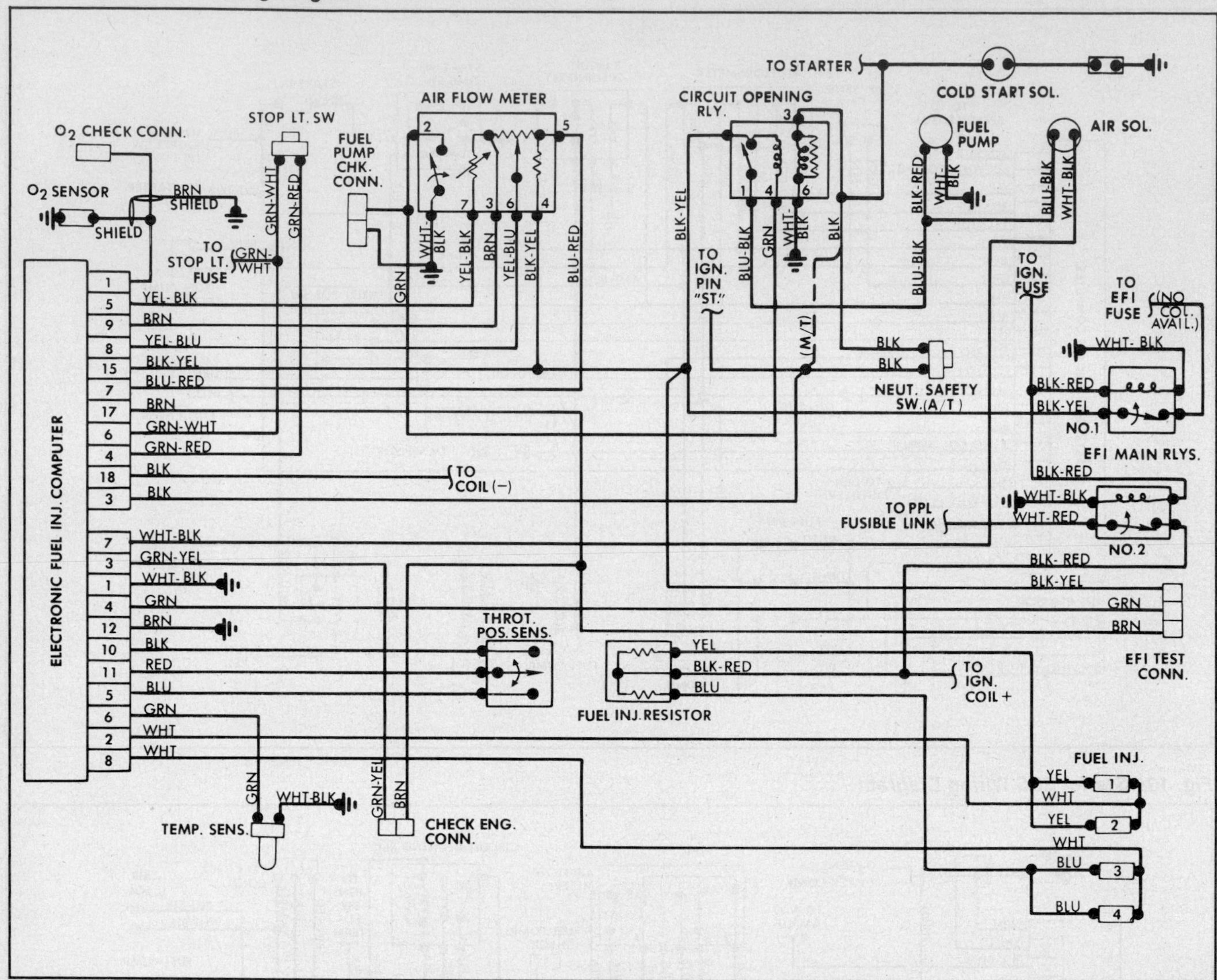

TO STARTER
COLD START SOL.
CIRCUIT OPENING RLY.
AIR FLOW METER
STOP LT. SW
O2 CHECK CONN.
FUEL PUMP CHK. CONN.
FUEL PUMP
AIR SOL.
O2 SENSOR
BRN SHIELD
SHIELD
TO STOP LT. FUSE
GRN-WHT
GRN-RED
WHT-BLK
YEL-BLK
BRN
YEL-BLU
BLK-YEL
BLU-RED
BLK-YEL
BLU-BLK
GRN
BLK
TO IGN. PIN "ST."
(M/T)
BLK-RED
BLU-BLK
WHT-BLK
TO IGN. FUSE
TO EFI FUSE
(NO COL. AVAIL.)
NEUT. SAFETY SW.(A/T)
BLK-RED
BLK-YEL
NO.1
EFI MAIN RLYS.
TO PPL FUSIBLE LINK
WHT-RED
NO.2
ELECTRONIC FUEL INJ. COMPUTER
TO COIL (−)
GRN-YEL
RED
BLU
WHT
THROT. POS. SENS.
YEL
BLK-RED
FUEL INJ. RESISTOR
TO IGN. COIL +
EFI TEST CONN.
FUEL INJ.
TEMP. SENS.
CHECK ENG. CONN.

VOLVO COMPUTERIZED ENGINE CONTROL

DL, GL

DESCRIPTION

The Volvo Computerized Engine Control System is used on all Volvo 4-cylinder engines except GLT Turbo. It consists of a computer controlled electronic ignition system and Bosch LH-Jetronic II fuel system with integrated Constant Idle Speed system.

The computer controlled ignition system consists of Volvo breakerless distributor, an electronic control unit, ignition coil, ignition switch, throttle switch and knock sensor. The distributor contains no vacuum or centrifugal advance mechanisms. The rotor and armature are a single unit. *See Fig. 1*.

Fig. 1: Disassembled View of Volvo Electronic Distributor

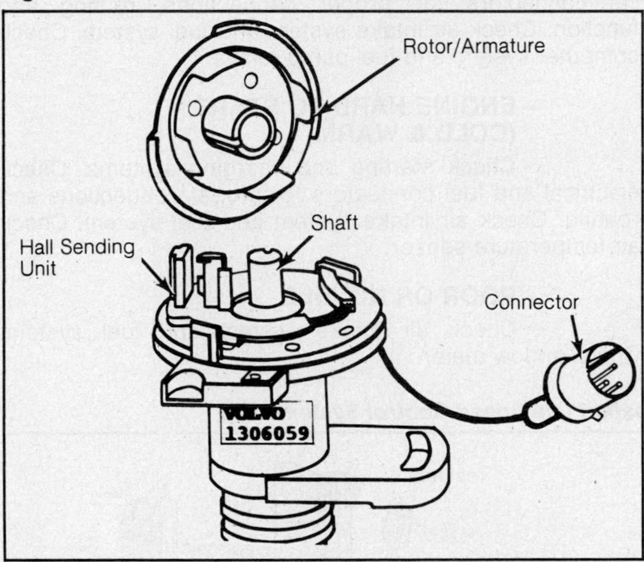
Rotor/Armature
Shaft
Hall Sending Unit
Connector
VOLVO
1306059

Distributor contains Hall sending unit.

A Hall Effect sending unit in the distributor provides engine speed signals to the electronic control unit. The distributor also consists of necessary connecting wiring and a distributor cap.

The fuel system includes an electronic control unit, ignition coil, ignition switch, system relay, fuel system components, A/C switch, airflow meter, air control valve, starter motor, throttle switch, coolant temperature sensor, oxygen sensor and connecting wiring and hoses.

NOTE: Only those components directly used in the Constant Idle Speed system will be covered in this section. For information on fuel injection system, refer to appropriate article in FUEL SYSTEMS Section.

OPERATION

COMPUTER CONTROLLED IGNITION

As the engine turns the distributor shaft, the shutter blades of the rotor/armature assembly pass through the Hall Effect sending unit's pick-up coil. A signal is then sent to the electronic control unit.

In addition to receiving engine speed information from the distributor, the electronic control unit receives engine load information from the intake manifold. Speed and vacuum signals are processed in the electronic control unit to control spark advance and dwell.

A throttle switch (located on the airflow meter) provides throttle information. Under normal conditions, the throttle position signal is sent to the electronic control unit.

The manifold vacuum signal is also processed by the control unit to control ignition timing. When the throttle is closed, (during deceleration and idle) the circuit is closed, and no signal is sent to the control unit.

Fig. 2: Volvo Computer Controlled Ignition System

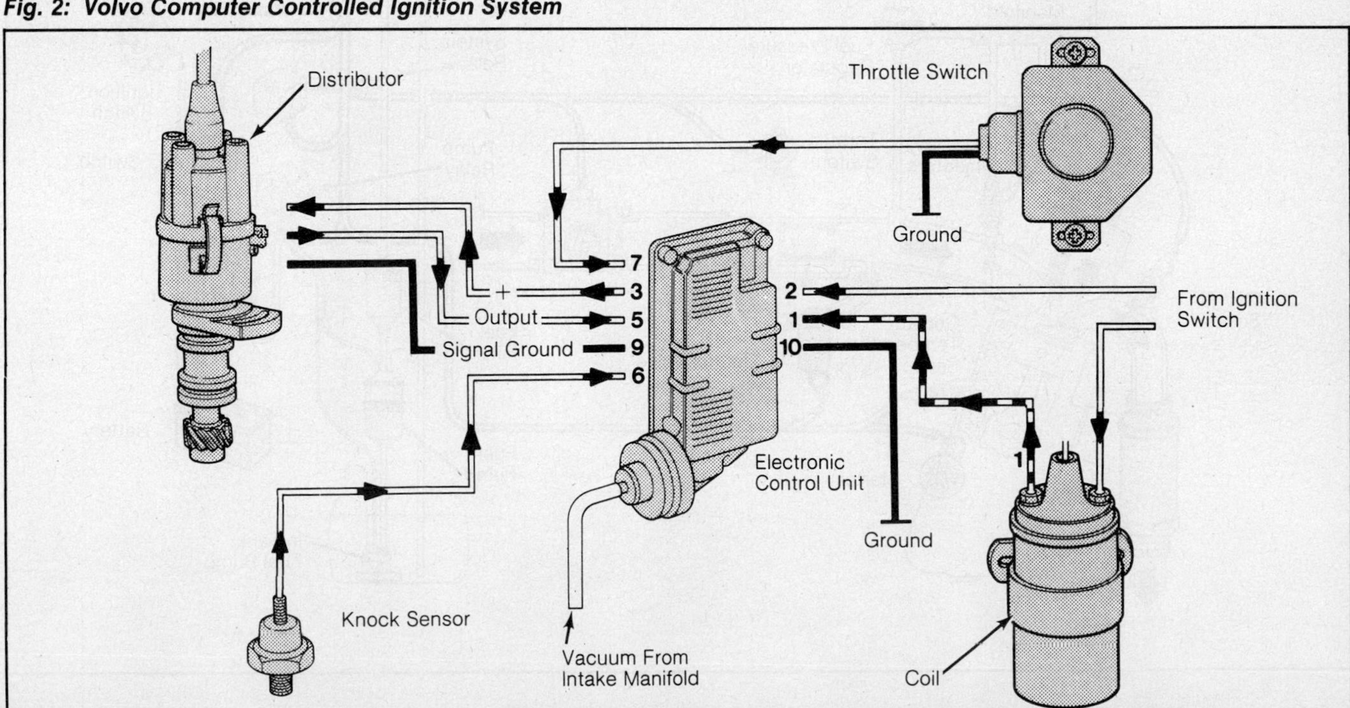
Distributor
Throttle Switch
Ground
7
+
3
Output
5
Signal Ground
9
6
2
1
10
From Ignition Switch
1
Electronic Control Unit
Ground
Knock Sensor
Vacuum From Intake Manifold
Coil

VOLVO COMPUTERIZED ENGINE CONTROL (Cont.)

The electronic control unit analyzes all information, and interrupts the signal to the ignition coil primary circuit. This causes a high voltage surge in the secondary circuit, firing the spark plugs at the proper time.

The knock sensor detects engine detonation. The electronic control unit receives a signal from the knock sensor during engine detonation and then retards timing. Timing is retarded 2° every 20 milliseconds until maximum retard of 6° is obtained, or detonation stops. Timing is then advanced in 1° increments every 20 milliseconds, until normal timing is achieved or detonation begins again.

CONSTANT IDLE SPEED SYSTEM

Electronic Control Unit

The electronic control unit processes information it receives from the engine coolant temperature sensor, throttle switch and distributor. After receiving information on coolant temperature, throttle position and engine speed, the control unit sends electrical impulses to air control valve to regulate idle speed.

Air Control Valve

The air control valve consists of a small electrical motor mounted between connecting hoses at the throttle valve. The motor rotates clockwise or counterclockwise to increase or decrease the amount of air which is injected into intake manifold.

Throttle Switch

Throttle switch is a small electrical switch activated by the throttle lever. The switch provides control unit with idle and full throttle position information.

Coolant Temperature Sensor

Coolant temperature sensor provides an electrical impulse to the electronic control unit at low coolant temperatures. At low temperatures, the control unit activates the air control valve to provide more air to increase engine speed.

A/C Switch

When air conditioner is activated, the control unit increases idle speed to compensate for the additional load caused by the air conditioning system.

TROUBLE SHOOTING

ENGINE DOES NOT START

Check fuse No. 12 in fuse block and fuel pump fuse at rear of engine compartment. Check ignition system, starting system, charging system, and all electrical connectors for proper connections, routing and function. Check air intake system and fuel system. Check computer system and fuel pump relays.

ENGINE HARD TO START (COLD & WARM)

Check starting and charging systems. Check electrical and fuel connectors for proper connections and routing. Check air intake system and fuel system. Check air temperature sensor.

POOR OR NO IDLE

Check air intake system and fuel system. Check airflow meter.

Fig. 3: Bosch Electronic Fuel Injection System With Integral Constant Idle Speed Control System

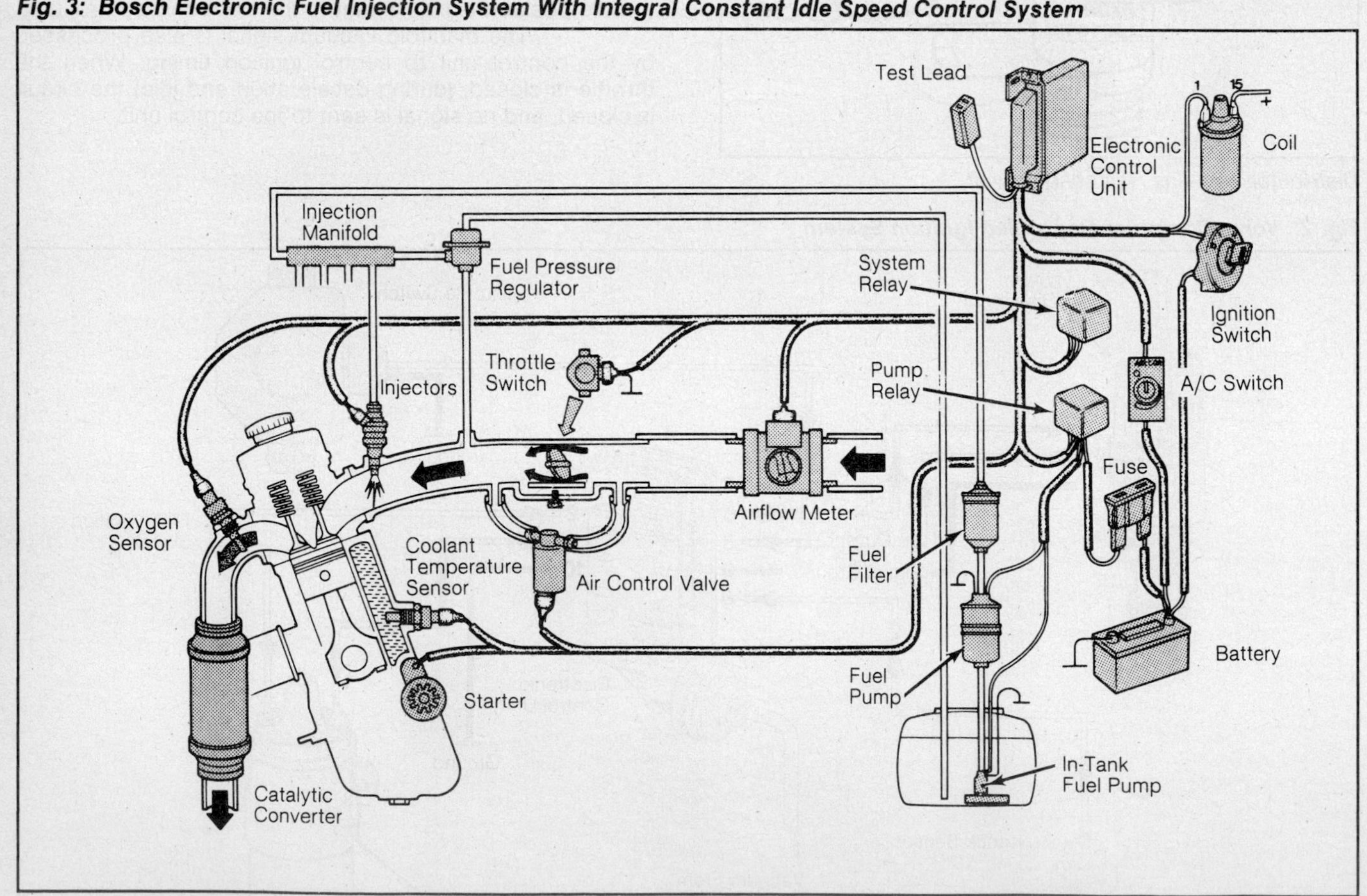
Test Lead
Electronic Control Unit
Coil
1
15
+
Injection Manifold
Fuel Pressure Regulator
System Relay
Ignition Switch
Throttle Switch
Injectors
Pump Relay
A/C Switch
Fuse
Oxygen Sensor
Airflow Meter
Coolant Temperature Sensor
Air Control Valve
Fuel Filter
Battery
Fuel Pump
Starter
In-Tank Fuel Pump
Catalytic Converter

VOLVO COMPUTERIZED ENGINE CONTROL (Cont.)

EXCESSIVE FUEL CONSUMPTION

Check fuel system for excessive pressure and leaks. Check throttle valve switch and mixture adjustment.

POOR PERFORMANCE (LOW TOP SPEED)

Check air intake system, fuel pressure, and fuel pump. Check throttle valve switch and mixture adjustment.

ERRATIC IDLE

Check air intake system and fuel injectors. Check air control valve hose for proper connection and blockage. Check throttle valve adjustment and attaching screws.

IDLE SPEED TOO HIGH

Check throttle valve and throttle valve switch. Check idle speed. Check air temperature sensor.

IDLE SPEED TOO LOW (ENGINE COLD)

Check air temperature sensor and air control valve. Check idle speed control system.

JERKING, POOR ACCELERATION

Check acceleration enrichment.

DIAGNOSIS & TESTING

NOTE: **Only components directly related to Constant Idle Speed system will be covered in this article. Information not available for ignition system testing. Refer to appropriate article in FUEL SYSTEMS Section for fuel system components.**

CAUTION: **Before testing components, be sure that the battery is properly charged, and that all wires are sound and connections are secure. Inspect the distributor cap and rotor for cracks and carbon tracking. When connecting test equipment, connecting or disconnecting electronic control unit, or when replacing parts, turn ignition switch off.**

ELECTRONIC CONTROL UNIT (CONSTANT IDLE SPEED SYSTEM)

1) Turn ignition off and remove passenger kick panel. Push latch to side and disconnect electrical connector from control unit by pulling connector down from top. Remove screw in end of connector cover and separate connector block from cover.

NOTE: **Always check terminals through holes in side of connector. Terminal numbers are stamped on side of connector.**

2) To check ground connections, connect ohmmeter between terminal 11 and ground, then 25 and ground. Resistance should be zero ohms. If not, check ground points on intake manifold.

3) To check power supply, turn ignition on. Connect voltmeter between terminal 18 and ground. Battery voltage should be registered. If not, check wire for short or open. Turn ignition off.

4) To check system relay, connect voltmeter between terminal 9 and ground. Using a jumper wire, jumper terminal 21 to ground. Relay should energize and battery voltage should be indicated. If not, check for short or ground. If wiring is okay, replace system relay.

THROTTLE SWITCH

1) Connect ohmmeter between ground and terminal 3 at electronic control unit connector. With ignition off, depress accelerator pedal. Zero resistance should be measured at idle position and infinite resistance should be measured at all other positions.

2) Connect ohmmeter between ground and terminal 12 at electronic control unit connector. Repeat step **1)**. Infinite resistance should be measured at idle position and zero resistance should be measured at all other positions.

3) If resistance readings are not as specified in steps **1)** and **2)**, check throttle switch ground at intake manifold. If ground connection is okay, replace throttle switch.

A/C SWITCH

Connect ohmmeter between ground and terminal 16 at electronic control unit connector. As A/C knob is rotated, resistance should decrease. If not, replace A/C switch.

COOLANT TEMPERATURE SENSOR

Using a thermometer, record coolant temperature. Connect ohmmeter between ground and terminal 2 at electronic control unit connector. If reading is not as specified, replace sensor. *See Coolant Temperature Sensor Resistance table.* Extremely high resistance value indicates open circuit and zero resistance indicates short circuit.

COOLANT TEMPERATURE SENSOR RESISTANCE

Temperature	(Ohms)
68°F (20°C)	2280-2720
175°F (80°C)	290-364

AIR CONTROL VALVE

1) Connect ohmmeter between fuel pump relay terminal 87 and electronic control unit connecter terminal 10. Then connect ohmmeter between same fuel pump relay terminal and electronic control unit connecter terminal 23. Resistance should be about 20 ohms for both connections.

2) If not, replace fuel pump relay and repeat test. If resistance is still not correct, repair short or open circuit.

ADJUSTMENT

THROTTLE SWITCH

1) Before adjusting switch, open throttle valve slightly and listen. If a "click" is heard when throttle valve is opened, throttle switch is properly adjusted. If sound is not heard, adjust switch.

2) To adjust throttle switch, loosen 2 switch retaining screws. Lightly turn switch clockwise. Then turn switch counterclockwise to contact stop, but before throttle valve begins to open. Tighten retaining screws and repeat step **1)**.

SECTION 2
FUEL SYSTEMS

CONTENTS

NOTE: **ALSO SEE GENERAL INDEX.**

1983 Fuel Systems

CARBURETOR TROUBLE SHOOTING

CONDITION	POSSIBLE CAUSE	CORRECTION
Engine Won't Start	Choke not closing Choke linkage bent	Check choke operation, see FUEL Check linkage, see FUEL
Engine Starts, Then Dies	Choke vacuum kick setting too wide Fast idle RPM too low Fast idle cam index incorrect Vacuum leak Low fuel pump outlet Low carburetor fuel level	Check setting and adjust, see FUEL Reset RPM to specification, see TUNE-UP Reset fast idle cam index, see FUEL Inspect vacuum system for leaks Repair or replace pump, see FUEL Check float setting, see FUEL
Engine Quits Under Load	Choke vacuum kick setting incorrect Fast idle cam index incorrect Incorrect hot fast idle speed RPM	Reset vacuum kick setting, see FUEL Reset fast idle cam index, see FUEL Reset fast idle RPM, see TUNE-UP
Engine Starts, Runs Up, Then Idles Slowly With Black Smoke	Choke vacuum kick set too narrow Fast idle cam index incorrect Hot fast idle RPM too low	Reset vacuum kick, see FUEL Reset fast idle cam index, see FUEL Reset fast idle RPM, see TUNE-UP
	HOT STARTING SYMPTOMS	
Engine Won't Start	Engine flooded	Allow fuel to evaporate
	COLD ENGINE DRIVEABILITY SYMPTOMS	
Engine Stalls in Gear	Choke vacuum kick setting incorrect Fast idle RPM incorrect Fast idle cam index incorrect	Reset choke vacuum kick, see FUEL Reset fast idle RPM, see TUNE-UP Reset fast idle cam index, see FUEL
Acceleration Sag or Stall	Defective choke control switch Choke vacuum kick setting incorrect Float level incorrect (too low) Accelerator pump defective Secondary throttles not closed	Replace choke control switch Reset choke vacuum kick, see FUEL Adjust float level, see FUEL Repair or replace pump, see FUEL Inspect lockout adjustment, see FUEL
Sag or Stall After Warmup	Defective choke control switch Defective accelerator pump (low output) Float level incorrect (too low)	Replace choke control switch, see FUEL Replace pump, see FUEL Adjust float level, see FUEL
Backfiring & Black Smoke	Plugged heat crossover system	Remove restriction
	WARM ENGINE DRIVEABILITY SYMPTOM	
Hesitation With Small Amount of Gas Pedal Movement	Vacuum leak Accelerator pump weak or inoperable Float level setting too low Metering rods sticking or binding Carburetor idle or transfer system plugged Frozen or binding heated air inlet	Inspect vacuum lines Replace pump, see FUEL Reset float level, see FUEL Inspect and/or replace rods, see FUEL Inspect system and remove restrictions Inspect heated air door for binding
Hesitation With Heavy Gas Pedal Movement	Defective accelerator pump Metering rod carrier sticking or binding Large vacuum leak Float level setting too low Defective fuel pump, lines or filter Air door setting incorrect	Replace pump, see FUEL Remove restriction Inspect vacuum system and repair leak Reset float level, see FUEL Inspect pump, lines and filter Adjust air door setting, see FUEL

1983 Fuel Systems

DIESEL FUEL INJECTION TROUBLE SHOOTING

CONDITION	POSSIBLE CAUSE	CORRECTION
Engine Won't Start	No voltage to fuel solenoid	Check electrical connections
	Faulty glow plugs or glow plug controls	Check and/or replace glow plugs or controller
	Plugged fuel return system	Remove restrictions
	No fuel to nozzles	Inspect fuel delivery system
	No fuel to injecton pump	Inspect fuel delivery system
	Clogged fuel tank filter	Replace filter, see FUEL
	Incorrect or contaminated fuel	Remove and replace fuel
	Incorrect pump timing	Reset pump timing, see FUEL
Engine Stalls at Idle	Incorrect slow idle adjustment	Reset idle adjustment, see TUNE-UP
	Faulty fast idle solenoid	Replace solenoid, see FUEL
	Plugged fuel return system	Remove restrictions
	Glow plugs turn off too soon	Check glow plug system, see FUEL
	Incorrect pump timing	Check and reset timing, see FUEL
	Limited fuel to injection pump	Check fuel delivery system
	Air in injection lines to nozzles	Check line fittings
	Incorrect or contaminated fuel	Remove and replace fuel
	Faulty injection pump	Remove and replace pump, see FUEL
	Fuel solenoid closes in RUN position	Check solenoid operation, see FUEL
Engine Starts, Idles Rough WITHOUT Unusual Noise or Smoke	Incorrect slow idle adjustment	Reset slow idle adjustment, see TUNE-UP
	Leaking injection line	Check fittings and/or replace line
	Plugged fuel return line	Remove restrictions
	Air in lines to nozzles	Check line fittings
	Air in injection pump	Check pump fittings and pump operation
	Faulty nozzle	Replace nozzle, see FUEL
	Improper or contaminated fuel	Remove and replace fuel
	Uneven fuel distribution	Check fuel delivery system
Engine Starts and Idles WITH Excessive Noise and/or Smoke	Incorrect pump timing	Reset injection pump timing, see FUEL
	Air in injection lines to nozzles	Check fittings on lines
	Faulty nozzle	Replace nozzle, see FUEL
	Improperly installed high pressure lines	Remove and reinstall properly
Engine Idles Okay but Misfires Above Idle	Plugged fuel filter	Remove restrictions and/or replace filter
	Incorrect pump timing	Reset injection pump timing, see FUEL
	Incorrect or contaminated fuel	Remove and replace fuel
Engine Will Not Idle	Linkage binding or misadjusted	Remove binding and readjust linkage
	Defective injection pump	Replace injection pump, see FUEL
Fuel Leaks With No Other Engine Malfunction	Loose or broken fuel line or connection	Check all fuel line fittings and correct
	Internal seal leak in injection pump	Remove and replace injection pump
Low Engine Power	Restricted air intake	Remove restrictions
	Plugged fuel filter	Remove restriction and/or replace filter
	Restricted fuel return system	Remove restrictions
	Restricted tank-to-pump fuel supply	Check fuel delivery system
	Incorrect or contaminated fuel	Remove and replace fuel
	Restricted fuel tank filter	Replace filter
	Nozzle or glow plug compression leaks	Check fittings and replace as required
	Plugged nozzle	Remove restriction and/or replace nozzle
"Rapping" Noise From One or More Cylinders	Air in fuel system	Check fuel delivery system for leaks
	Air in high pressure lines	Check fittings for leaks
	Nozzle sticking in open position	Inspect nozzle and/or replace
	Low nozzle opening pressure	Check nozzle operation, see FUEL
	Filter in nozzle broken or loose	Remove and replace filter, see FUEL

1983 Fuel Systems

DIESEL FUEL INJECTION TROUBLE SHOOTING (Cont.)

CONDITION	POSSIBLE CAUSE	CORRECTION
Excessive Combustion Noise With Black Smoke	Incorrect pump timing	Reset injection pump timing, see FUEL
	Incorrect pump housing pressure	Check pump for internal leaks, FUEL
	Defective injection pump	Replace injection pump, see FUEL
Engine Will Not Shut Off With Key	Injection pump fuel solenoid does not return to off position	Check solenoid operation, see FUEL

TURBOCHARGER TROUBLE SHOOTING

CONDITION	POSSIBLE CAUSE	CORRECTION
Engine Detonation	Malfunction in spark advance or retard system	Check distributor and ignition
	EGR system defect	Check EGR system
	Carburetor/throttle body or turbocharger air inlet restrictions	Remove restrictions
	Actuator allows too much boost	Check boost pressure and adjust
	Defect in carburetor/throttle body power system	Inspect and repair carburetor/throttle body, see FUEL
	Internal turbocharger defect	Replace turbocharger, see FUEL
Low Engine Power	Air inlet restriction	Remove restriction in inlet
	Exhaust system restriction	Remove restriction
	Malfunction in spark advance or retard system	Check distributor and ignition
	EFE system defect	Check EFE system operation
	EGR system defect	Check EGR system
Engine Noise	EFE system defect	Check EFE system
	Loose exhaust system or leak	Check exhaust mounting and connections
	AIR system defect	Check AIR system
	Restricted turbocharger oil supply	Check oil delivery system
Engine Surges	ESC malfunction	Check ESC system
	Defective vacuum switch	Replace defective switch
	EGR system defect	Check EGR system
	Loose turbocharger bolts on compressor side	Check mounting bolts and tighten
Excessive Oil Consumption (Blue Exhaust Smoke)	Leak at turbocharger oil inlet	Check fittings and repair
	Turbocharger oil drain hose leaks or stopped up	Check drain hose for restrictions or loose fittings
	Turbocharger seals leaking	Replace seals, see FUEL

1983 Aisan Carburetors

AISAN 2-BARREL – TOYOTA 2F ENGINE

Land Cruiser

DESCRIPTION

Carburetor is a 2-barrel, downdraft type with vacuum operated choke breaker to improve cold engine operation. A secondary slow port helps fuel mixing at start of secondary valve opening. Improvement of operation is noticed during low speed load. A piston type accelerator pump is incorporated into the primary barrel.

Other equipment includes a diaphragm to open secondary valve at high speed and full throttle operation. A throttle stop solenoid is also used to prevent dieseling during engine shut down.

CARBURETOR IDENTIFICATION

Application	Carb. No.
All Models	21100-61141

ADJUSTMENTS

NOTE: For all on-vehicle adjustments not covered in this article, see the appropriate TUNE-UP SERVICE PROCEDURES article.

NOTE: Manufacturer recommends using carburetor adjustment kits 09240-00014 and 09240-00020 to make the following adjustments and measurements.

FLOAT LEVEL

Invert air horn and measure clearance between upper surface of float and gasket surface of air horn. Clearance should be .236" (6.0 mm). Bend center float tab "A" to adjust. *See Fig. 1.*

Fig. 1: Float Level Adjustment

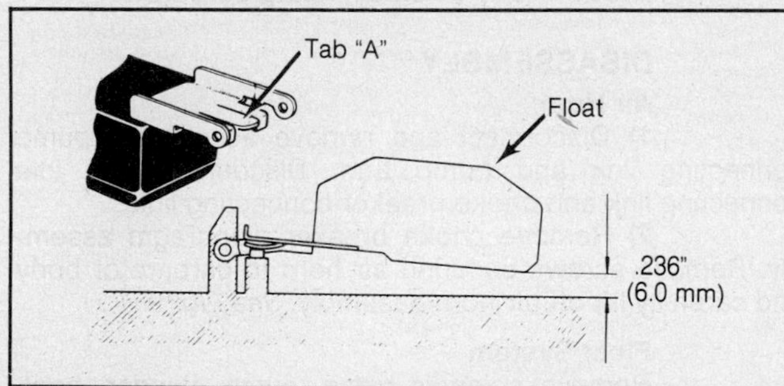
Tab "A"
Float
.236"
(6.0 mm)

Adjust by bending float tab "A".

Fig. 2: Float Drop Adjustment

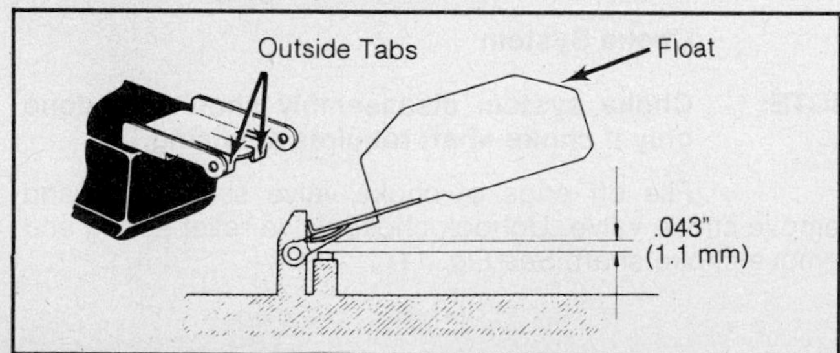
Outside Tabs
Float
.043"
(1.1 mm)

Adjust by bending both outside float tabs.

FLOAT DROP

Invert air horn, gently lift up float assembly and measure clearance between needle valve and center float tab. Clearance should be .043" (1.1 mm). Bend both outside float tabs to adjust. *See Fig. 2.*

PRIMARY & SECONDARY THROTTLE VALVES

Invert carburetor, insert angle gauge and separately measure angle of primary and secondary throttle valves at full throttle. Angle should be 90° from horizontal plane for primary and secondary throttle valves. Adjust by bending the respective throttle lever stop.

FAST IDLE

Bench Adjustment

Fully close choke valve and using gauge (09240-00020), measure clearance between carburetor flange and primary throttle valve. Clearance should be .051" (1.3 mm). Adjust by turning fast idle adjusting screw. *See Fig. 3.*

Fig. 3: Fast Idle Adjustment

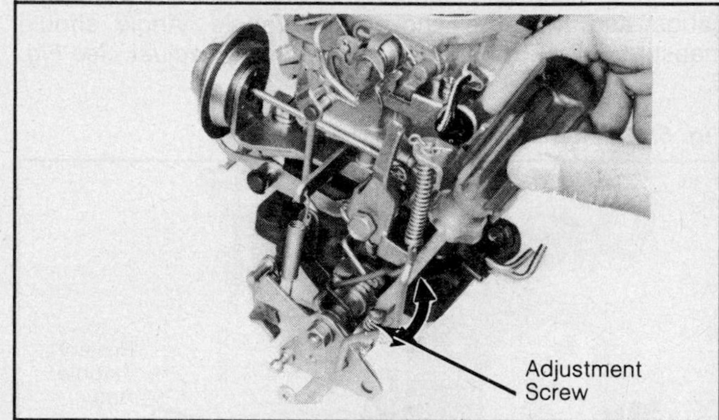
Adjustment
Screw

Adjust by turning fast idle adjustment screw.

CHOKE BREAKER

Apply vacuum to choke breaker diaphragm. Insert angle gauge and measure choke valve angle while closing choke valve by hand. Angle should be 45°. Bend choke breaker link at existing bend to adjust. *See Fig. 4.*

Fig. 4: Choke Breaker Adjustment

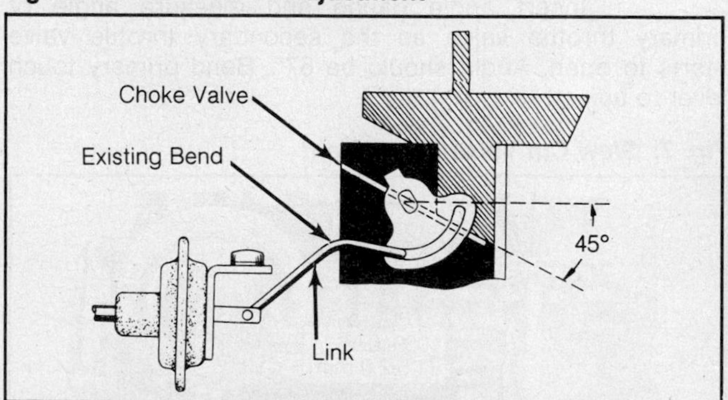
Choke Valve
Existing Bend
45°
Link

Adjust by bending link at existing bend.

CHOKE OPENER

Fully close choke valve, apply vacuum to opener diaphragm, insert angle gauge and measure choke

1983 Aisan Carburetors

AISAN 2-BARREL – TOYOTA 2F ENGINE (Cont.)

valve angle. Angle should be 75°. Bend choke shaft stopper to adjust. *See Fig. 5.*

Fig. 5: Choke Opener Adjustment

Choke
Shaft
Stopper

Bend choke shaft stopper to adjust.

CHOKE UNLOADER

Fully open primary throttle valve, insert angle gauge and measure choke valve angle. Angle should measure 50°. Bend primary throttle arm to adjust. *See Fig. 6.*

Fig. 6: Choke Unloader Adjustment

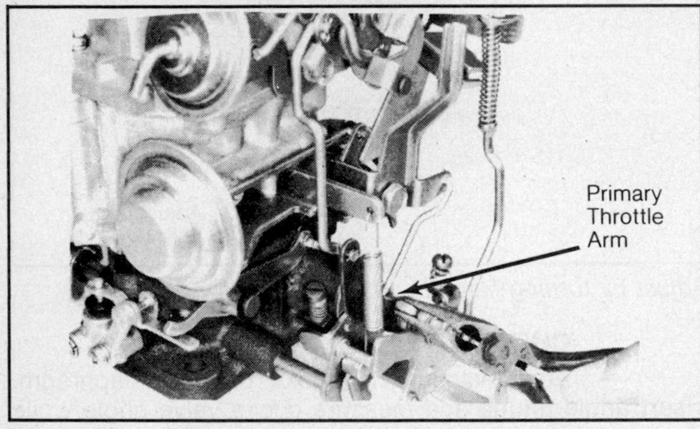
Primary
Throttle
Arm

Bend primary throttle arm to adjust.

SECONDARY TOUCH ANGLE

Insert angle gauge and measure angle of primary throttle valve as the secondary throttle valve starts to open. Angle should be 67°. Bend primary touch lever to adjust.

Fig. 7: Slow Cut Valve Adjustment

.059-.079"
(1.5-2.0 mm)

Bend actuating lever to adjust.

SLOW CUT VALVE

Ensure secondary touch angle is correct and measure slow cut valve stroke. Stroke should be .059-.079" (1.5-2.0 mm). Bend actuating lever to adjust. *See Fig. 7.*

SECONDARY KICK-UP

Fully open primary throttle valve and measure angle of secondary throttle valve. Angle should be 25°. Bend secondary throttle lever to adjust. *See Fig. 8.*

Fig. 8: Secondary Kick-Up Adjustment

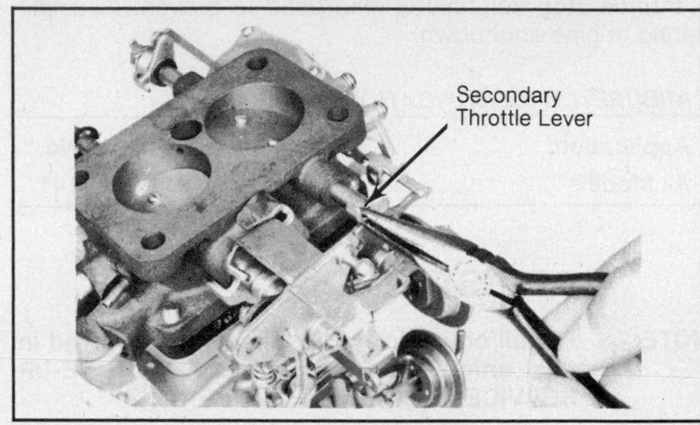
Secondary
Throttle Lever

Bend secondary throttle lever to adjust.

ACCELERATOR PUMP STROKE

Place a straightedge on top of air horn, fully open choke valve and measure full travel of pump plunger. Plunger travel should be .374" (9.5 mm). Adjust pump stroke by bending connecting link at existing bend.

OVERHAUL

NOTE: Manufacturer recommends using driver kit 09860-11011 when servicing carburetor.

DISASSEMBLY

Air Horn

1) Disconnect and remove accelerator pump connecting link and pump arm. Disconnect fast idle connecting link and choke breaker connecting link.

2) Remove choke breaker diaphragm assembly. Remove screws securing air horn to carburetor body and carefully lift off air horn assembly. *See Fig. 9.*

Float System

Remove solenoid valve, pump plunger, boot, float pin and float. Remove air horn gasket, needle valve, spring and pin. Remove needle valve seat, power piston retainer, power piston and spring. *See Fig. 10.*

Choke System

NOTE: Choke system disassembly should be done only if choke shaft requires servicing.

File off ends of choke valve set screws and remove choke valve. Unhook choke valve relief spring and remove choke shaft. *See Fig. 11.*

AISAN 2-BARREL – TOYOTA 2F ENGINE (Cont.)

Fig. 9: Exploded View of Carburetor Air Horn

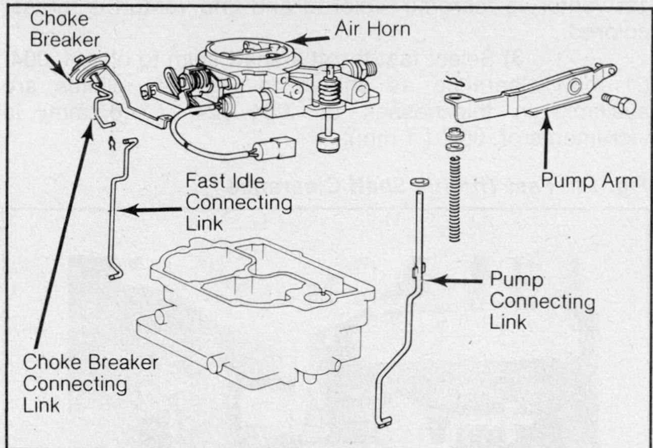
Choke Breaker
Air Horn
Fast Idle Connecting Link
Pump Arm
Pump Connecting Link
Choke Breaker Connecting Link

Fig. 10: Exploded View of Carburetor Float System

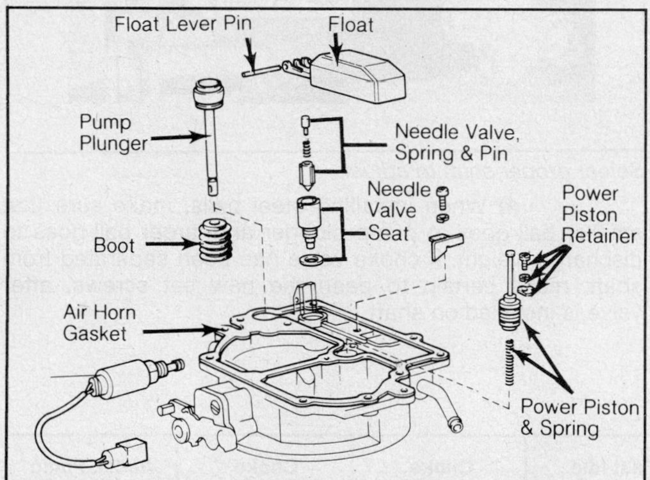
Float Lever Pin
Float
Pump Plunger
Needle Valve, Spring & Pin
Needle Valve Seat
Power Piston Retainer
Boot
Air Horn Gasket
Power Piston & Spring

Fig. 11: Exploded View of Carburetor Choke Assembly

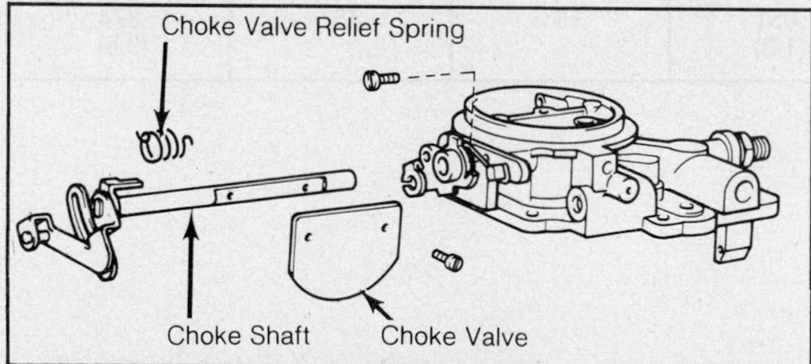
Choke Valve Relief Spring
Choke Shaft
Choke Valve

Main Body & Carburetor Flange

1) Remove discharge weight, spring, steel ball and pump damping spring. Using tweezers, remove check ball retainer, then remove steel ball for pump plunger. *See Fig. 12.*

2) Remove 1st and 2nd slow jets, power valve and 1st and 2nd main jets. Remove small venturi, sight glass gauge, and secondary diaphragm.

3) Remove choke cable clamp, throttle return spring, choke opener lever and choke opener. Remove vacuum passage bolt and slow cut valve. *See Fig. 13.*

Fig. 12: Exploded View of Carburetor Main Body

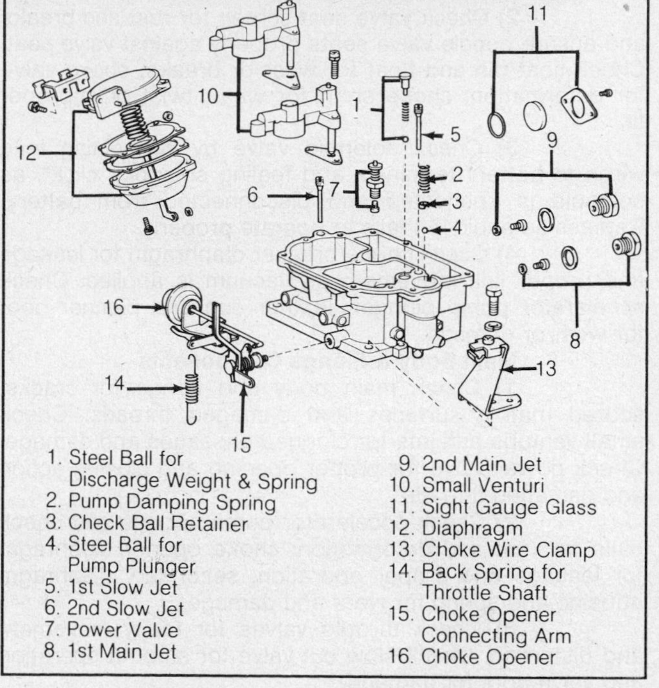
11
10
1
5
12
9
2
6
7
3
4
16
8
13
14
15

1. Steel Ball for Discharge Weight & Spring
2. Pump Damping Spring
3. Check Ball Retainer
4. Steel Ball for Pump Plunger
5. 1st Slow Jet
6. 2nd Slow Jet
7. Power Valve
8. 1st Main Jet
9. 2nd Main Jet
10. Small Venturi
11. Sight Gauge Glass
12. Diaphragm
13. Choke Wire Clamp
14. Back Spring for Throttle Shaft
15. Choke Opener Connecting Arm
16. Choke Opener

CLEANING

NOTE: Do not immerse synthetic parts, electrical components or diaphragm assemblies in carburetor cleaner.

Clean cast parts with carburetor cleaner. Clean jets, fuel passages and vacuum ports with compressed air. Do not use wire or similar metal objects. Clean all other parts with solvent and soft brush.

INSPECTION

Air Horn Components

1) Check air horn for cracks, damaged threads and worn choke shaft bores; power piston spring for rust

Fig. 13: Exploded View of Carburetor Flange Parts

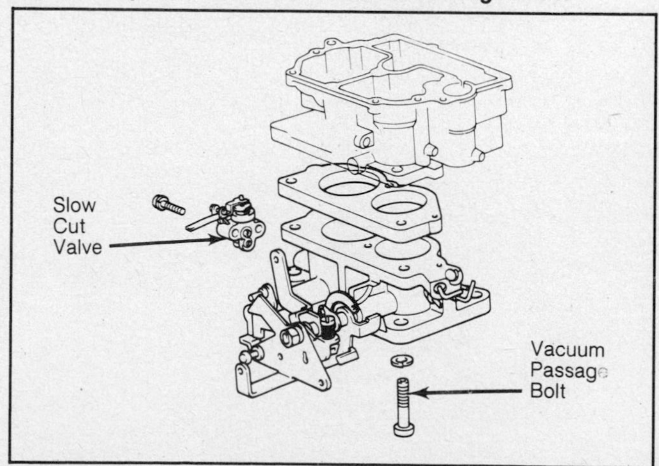
Slow Cut Valve
Vacuum Passage Bolt

1983 Aisan Carburetors

AISAN 2-BARREL – TOYOTA 2F ENGINE (Cont.)

or distortion; power piston and piston bore for wear or damage.

2) Check valve seat screen for rust and breaks and ensure needle valve seats properly against valve seat. Check float pin and float for wear or breaks; choke valve for deformation; choke shaft for wear, twist or improper fit.

3) Check solenoid valve by connecting lead wires to battery terminals and feeling solenoid "click", as solenoid is connected and disconnected from battery. Replace solenoid if it fails to operate properly.

4) Check choke breaker diaphragm for leakage and proper link movement as vacuum is applied. Check accelerator pump plunger, leather cup and plunger boot for wear or damage.

Main Body & Flange Components

1) Check main body and flange for cracks, scored mating surfaces and damaged threads. Check small venturis and jets for clogged passages and damage. Check power valve for proper opening and closing action and damaged threads.

2) Check accelerator pump springs and check balls for rust and deformation; choke opener diaphragm for leakage and proper operation; secondary diaphragm housing and spring for wear and damage.

3) Check throttle valves for faulty movement and distortion. Check slow cut valve for smooth operation and valve boot for damage.

REASSEMBLY

1) Assemble by reversing the disassembly procedure, using new gaskets. When installing 1st and 2nd main jets, 1st jet is "brass" colored and 2nd jet is "chrome" colored.

2) When installing 1st and 2nd small venturies, 1st venturi is "chrome" colored and 2nd venturi is "brass" colored.

3) Select fast throttle shaft shim to obtain .004" (.1 mm) clearance as shown in *Fig. 14.*. Shims are available in thicknesses of .004-.024" (.1-.6 mm) in increments of .004" (.1 mm).

Fig. 14: Fast Throttle Shaft Clearance

Clearance
.004" (.1 mm)

Select proper shim to adjust.

4) When installing steel balls, make sure that smaller ball goes to pump plunger and larger ball goes to discharge weight. If choke valve has been separated from shaft, make certain to peen the new set screws, after valve is installed on shaft.

CARBURETOR ADJUSTMENT SPECIFICATIONS

Application	Float Level In. (mm)	Float Drop In. (mm)	Fast Idle Opening In. (mm)	Choke Opener Angle	Choke Breaker Angle	Accel. Pump Stroke In. (mm).
Land Cruiser	.236 (6.0)	.043 (1.1)	.051 (1.3)	75°	45°	.374 (9.5)

AISAN 2-BARREL – TOYOTA 3A-C ENGINE

Tercel

DESCRIPTION

Carburetor is a 2-barrel, downdraft design, equipped with an automatic choke consisting of a bi-metallic coil and an electrically-operated ceramic heater. A piston type accelerator pump is incorporated into the primary barrel and an auxiliary accelerator pump system aids in cold engine acceleration.

Other equipment includes diaphragms which open secondaries at high speed and full throttle operation. Other features include throttle positioner, mixture control, choke breaker, choke opener, deceleration fuel cut, hot idle compensation and high altitude compensation (Federal option) devices.

CARBURETOR IDENTIFICATION

Application	Part. No.
All Models	21100-15280

ADJUSTMENTS

NOTE: **For all on-vehicle adjustments not covered in this article, see the appropriate TUNE-UP SERVICE PROCEDURES article.**

NOTE: **Manufacturer recommends using carburetor adjustment kits 09240-00014 and 09240-00020 to make the following adjustments and measurements.**

Fig. 1: Float Level Measurement

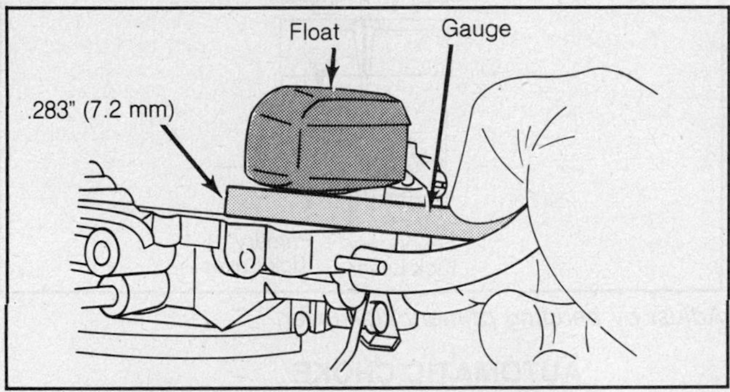
Float
Gauge
.283" (7.2 mm)

Fig. 2: Float Level Adjustment

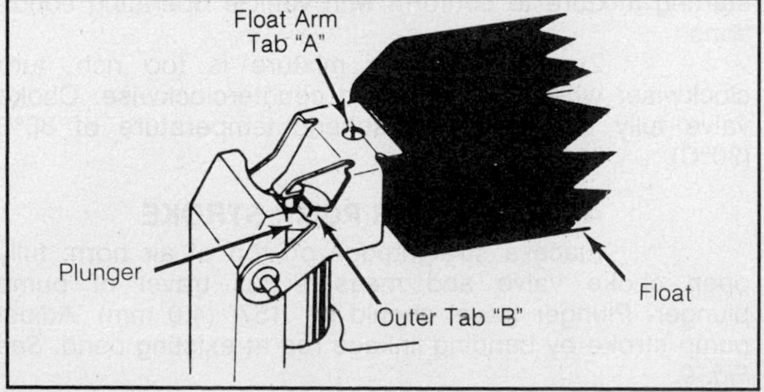
Float Arm
Tab "A"
Plunger
Outer Tab "B"
Float

Adjust gap by inserting tool in hole.

FLOAT LEVEL ADJUSTMENT

NOTE: **Remove needle valve wire clip and install new inlet seat gasket before adjusting float.**

Remove air horn gasket, invert air horn and allow float to hang by its own weight. Measure clearance between top of float and air horn. *See Fig. 1.* Clearance should be .283" (7.2 mm). Adjust clearance by bending float arm at tab "A". *See Fig. 2.*

FLOAT DROP ADJUSTMENT

1) Invert air horn and gently lift up float. Using gauge No. (09240-00014), measure clearance between needle valve and float arm. *See Fig. 3.*

2) Clearance adjustment should be .066-.078" (1.67-1.99 mm). Adjust clearance by bending outer float tab "B". *See Fig. 4.* Install needle valve clip after completing float adjustments.

Fig. 3: Float Drop Measurement

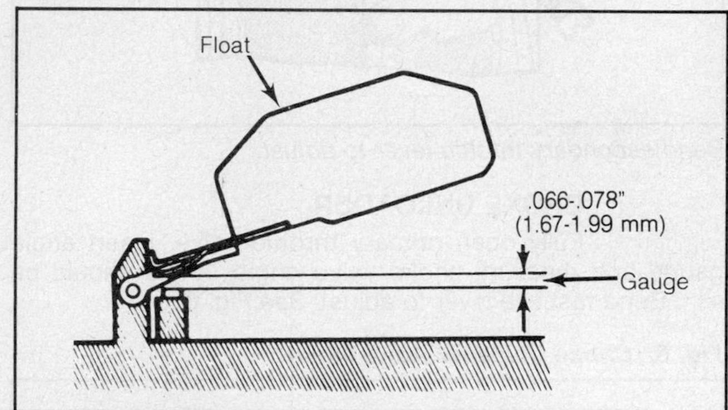
Float
.066-.078"
(1.67-1.99 mm)
Gauge

Fig. 4: Float Drop Adjustment

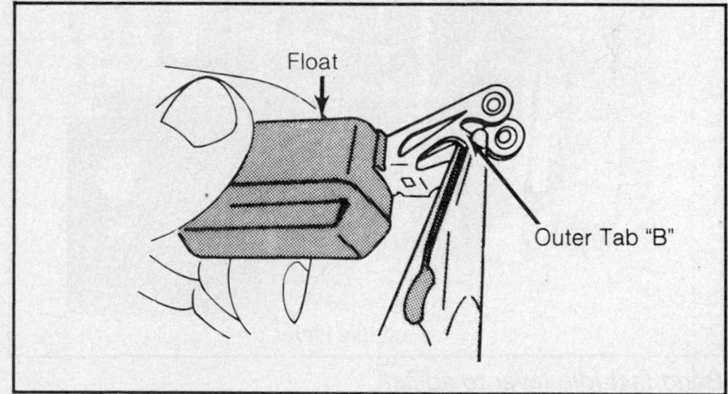
Float
Outer Tab "B"

Bend outer tab "B" to adjust.

PRIMARY & SECONDARY THROTTLE VALVES

Invert carburetor, insert angle gauge and separately measure angle of primary and secondary throttle valves at full throttle. Angle should be 90° from horizontal plane for primary, 75° for secondary. Adjust by bending the respective throttle lever stop.

FAST IDLE

Bench Adjustment

Position throttle shaft lever to high (first) step of fast idle cam. Close choke valve and measure primary throttle valve angle. Angle should be 20°. Adjust by turning fast idle adjustment screw.

1983 Aisan Carburetors

AISAN 2-BARREL – TOYOTA 3A-C ENGINE (Cont.)

SECONDARY KICK-UP

Fully open primary throttle valve. Measure clearance between secondary throttle valve and the body. Clearance should be .0043-.0087" (.11-.22 mm). Adjust by bending secondary throttle lever. *See Fig. 5.*

Fig. 5: Secondary Kick-Up Adjustment

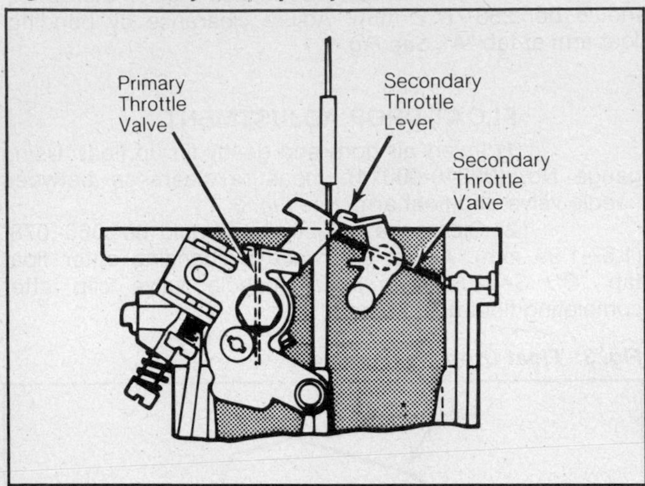
Primary
Throttle
Valve
Secondary
Throttle
Lever
Secondary
Throttle
Valve

Bend secondary throttle lever to adjust.

CHOKE UNLOADER

Fully open primary throttle valve, insert angle gauge and measure choke valve angle. Angle should be 41°. Bend fast idle lever to adjust. *See Fig. 6.*

Fig. 6: Choke Unloader Adjustment

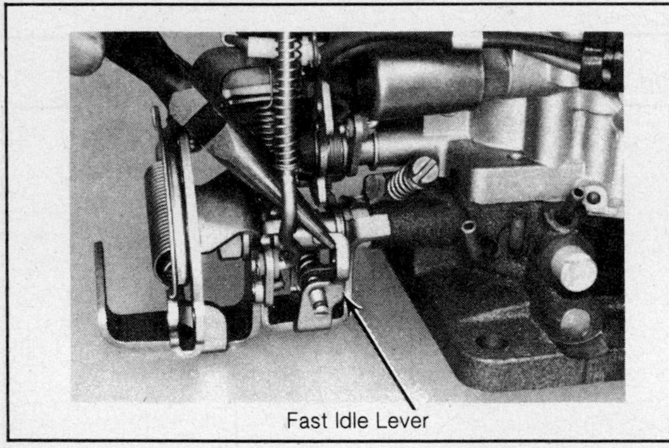
Fast Idle Lever

Bend fast idle lever to adjust.

CHOKE BREAKER

1) Fully close choke valve. Apply vacuum to choke breaker diaphragm "A" and measure choke valve angle. Angle should be 38°.

2) Adjust by bending tang on relief lever, connecting breaker diaphragm link to choke valve shaft.

3) Apply vacuum to choke breaker diaphragms "A" and "B" and measure choke valve angle. Angle should be 52°. Adjust by turning diaphragm adjustment screw. *See Fig. 7.*

CHOKE OPENER

1) Set fast idle cam, open throttle slightly and gently push choke valve closed. Keeping choke valve closed, release throttle valve.

Fig. 7: Choke Breaker Adjustment

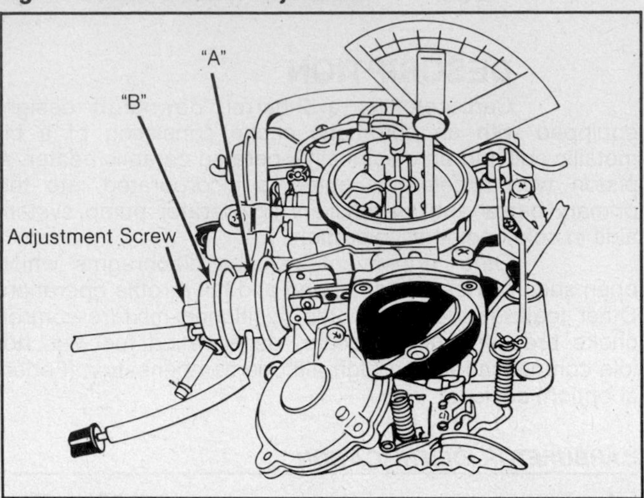
"A"
"B"
Adjustment Screw

2) Apply vacuum to choke opener diaphragm and measure choke valve angle. Angle should be 77°. Adjust by bending tang on relief lever, connecting choke opener link to choke valve shaft.

SECONDARY TOUCH ANGLE

Check primary throttle valve opening angle at the same time primary kick lever touches secondary kick lever. Angle should be 45°. Adjust by bending primary kick lever. *See Fig. 8.*

Fig. 8: Secondary Touch Angle Adjustment

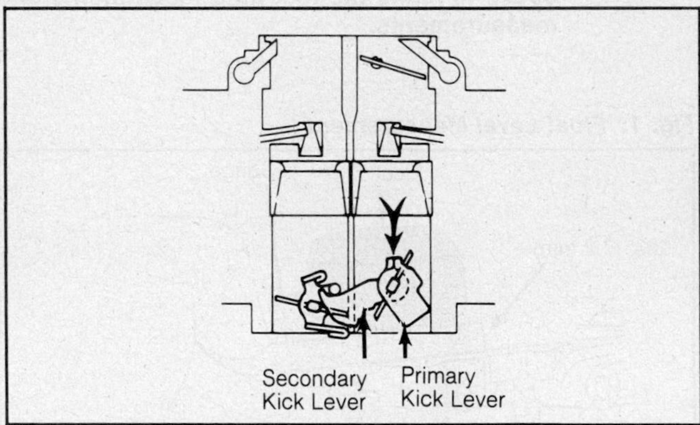
Secondary
Kick Lever
Primary
Kick Lever

Adjust by bending primary kick lever.

AUTOMATIC CHOKE

1) Set coil housing scale to center line of thermostat case. Turn coil housing and adjust engine starting mixture to conform with vehicle operating conditions.

2) When starting mixture is too rich, turn clockwise; when too lean, turn counterclockwise. Choke valve fully closes at atmospheric temperature of 86°F (30°C).

ACCELERATOR PUMP STROKE

Place a straightedge on top of air horn, fully open choke valve and measure full travel of pump plunger. Plunger travel should be .157" (4.0 mm). Adjust pump stroke by bending linkage rod at existing bend. *See Fig. 9.*

AISAN 2-BARREL – TOYOTA 3A-C ENGINE (Cont.)

Fig. 9: Accelerator Pump Stroke Adjustment

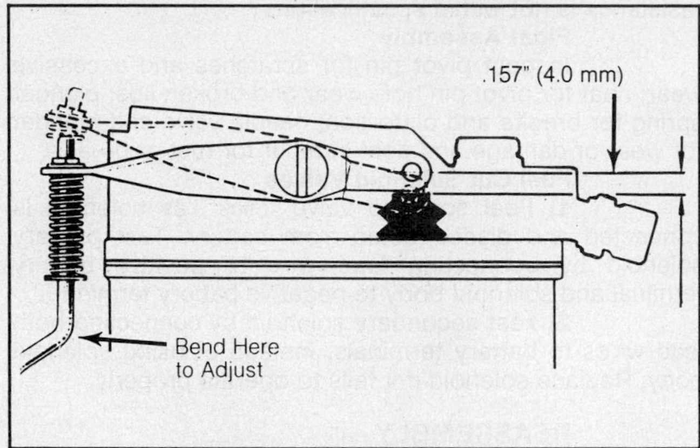
.157" (4.0 mm)
Bend Here to Adjust

Bend linkage rod at existing bend to adjust.

OVERHAUL

NOTE: Manufacturer recommends using carburetor driver kit 09860-11011 to service carburetor.

DISASSEMBLY

Air Horn

1) Disconnect choke link and accelerator pump connecting rod. Remove pump arm pivot screw and pump arm. Remove fuel line and union and 8 air horn screws.

2) Disconnect the choke opener link and remove air horn with gasket from body. Disconnect wiring and remove solenoid valves from body. Remove float pivot pin, float and needle valve assembly.

Fig. 10: Exploded View of Carburetor Air Horn

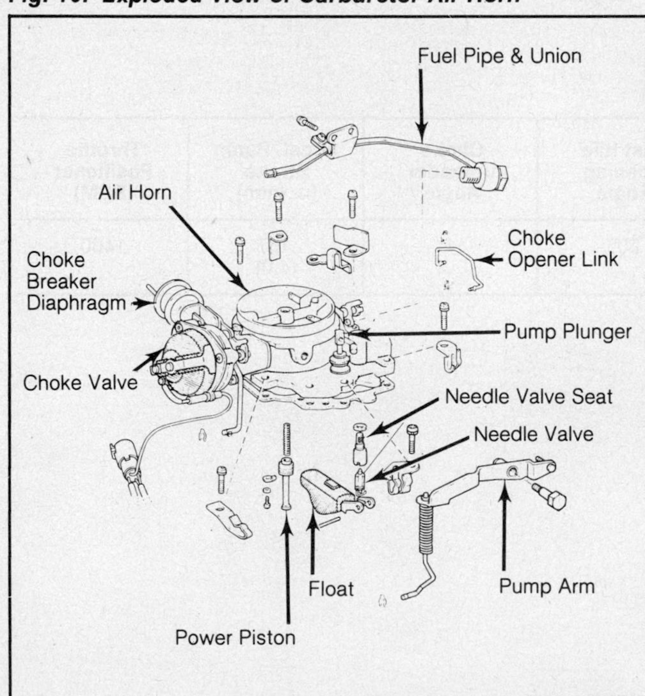
Fuel Pipe & Union
Air Horn
Choke Opener Link
Choke Breaker Diaphragm
Pump Plunger
Choke Valve
Needle Valve Seat
Needle Valve
Float
Pump Arm
Power Piston

3) Remove air horn gasket, power piston retainer, power piston and spring. Remove pump plunger and boot. *See Fig. 11.* Remove coil housing and gasket.

4) Remove following air horn parts only if choke shaft or choke breaker require servicing. Remove thermostat housing, disconnect breaker link and remove choke breaker diaphragm.

5) Remove choke lever, choke breaker relief lever, washers and fast idle lever. File off peened portion of set screws. Remove set screws and choke valve.

Fig. 11: Exploded View of Carburetor Main Body

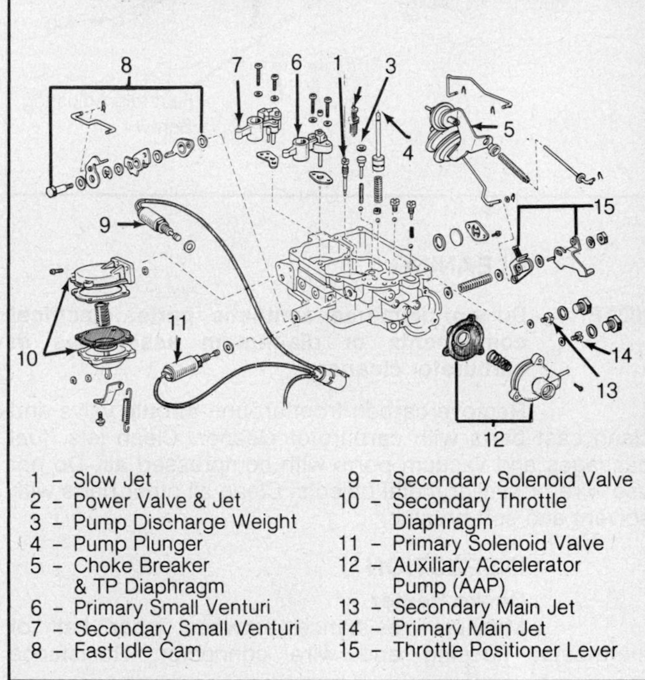
8
7
6
1
3
4
5
9
15
11
10
14
13
12
1 – Slow Jet
2 – Power Valve & Jet
3 – Pump Discharge Weight
4 – Pump Plunger
5 – Choke Breaker & TP Diaphragm
6 – Primary Small Venturi
7 – Secondary Small Venturi
8 – Fast Idle Cam
9 – Secondary Solenoid Valve
10 – Secondary Throttle Diaphragm
11 – Primary Solenoid Valve
12 – Auxiliary Accelerator Pump (AAP)
13 – Secondary Main Jet
14 – Primary Main Jet
15 – Throttle Positioner Lever

Main Body

1) Disconnect throttle positioner links and remove bracket attaching bolts. Remove accelerator pump retainer gasket and remove pump discharge weight, spring and check ball. *See Fig. 12.*

2) Remove pump dampening spring and using tweezers, remove retainer and check ball. Remove slow jet, power valve with jet and throttle lever. Remove primary and secondary main passage plugs, primary main jet and gasket.

3) Remove AAP housing, diaphragm and spring. Remove AAP inlet plug and check ball. Remove outlet plug, short spring and check ball. Remove primary and secondary small venturies.

4) Remove sight glass retainer, sight glass and "O" ring. Remove throttle lever return spring and back spring. Remove the throttle lever and fast idle cam subassembly.

5) Disconnect link, and remove secondary throttle valve diaphragm assembly and gasket. Remove the 3 body-to-flange bolts, vacuum passage bolt and separate body from flange. *See Fig. 13.*

1983 Aisan Carburetors

AISAN 2-BARREL – TOYOTA 3A-C ENGINE (Cont.)

Fig. 12: Exploded View of Carburetor Flange

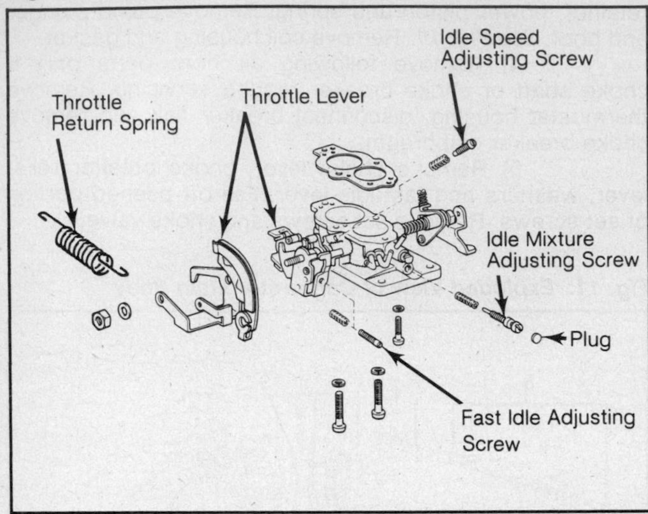
Idle Speed
Adjusting Screw
Throttle
Return Spring
Throttle Lever
Idle Mixture
Adjusting Screw
Plug
Fast Idle Adjusting
Screw

CLEANING

NOTE: Do not immerse synthetic parts, electrical components or diaphragm assemblies in carburetor cleaner.

Remove carbon from around throttle valve and clean cast parts with carburetor cleaner. Clean jets, fuel passages and vacuum ports with compressed air. Do not use wire or similar metal objects. Clean all other parts with solvent and soft brush.

INSPECTION

Choke Heater

Measure resistance between inner half of thermostat housing and wire connector. Resistance should be 19-24 ohms at 68°F (20°C). Replace air horn, if resistance is not within specifications.

Float Assembly

Inspect pivot pin for scratches and excessive wear; float for pivot pin hole wear and broken lips; plunger spring for breaks and distortion; needle valve and plunger for wear or damage and seat strainer for rust or breaks.

Fuel Cut Solenoid Valves

1) Feel solenoid valve "click", as solenoid is connected and disconnected from battery. Test primary solenoid by connecting lead wire to positive battery terminal and solenoid body to negative battery terminal.

2) Test secondary solenoid by connecting both lead wires to battery terminals, instead of using solenoid body. Replace solenoid if it fails to operate properly.

REASSEMBLY

Reassemble by reversing the disassembly procedure, using new gaskets and "O" rings.

1) When assembling flange parts, ensure vacuum passage bolt is installed in correct position. Ensure springs are installed in proper location and check balls are located in appropriate orifices.

2) When installing pump discharge weight and outlet valve assembly, ensure all components are installed in correct order. After installing power piston, check piston for smooth operation.

3) If choke valve has been separated from shaft, make certain to peen the new retaining screws, after valve is installed on shaft. When installing air horn tighten air horn screws gradually and alternately to prevent distortion.

CARBURETOR ADJUSTMENT SPECIFICATIONS

Application	Float Level In. (mm)	Float Drop In. (mm)	Fast Idle Opening Angle	Choke Unloader Angle	Accel. Pump Stroke In. (mm)	Throttle Positioner (RPM)
Tercel	.283 (7.2)	.066-.078 (1.67-1.99)	20°	41°	.157 (4.0)	1400

1983 Aisan Carburetors

AISAN 2-BARREL – TOYOTA 4A-C ENGINE

Corolla

DESCRIPTION

Carburetor is a 2-barrel, downdraft design, equipped with an automatic choke consisting of a bi-metallic coil and an electrically-operated ceramic heater. A piston type accelerator pump is incorporated into the primary barrel and an auxiliary accelerator pump system (AAP), aids in cold engine acceleration.

Other features include diaphragms which open secondaries at high speed and full throttle operation, throttle positioner, choke opener, choke breaker, deceleration fuel cut, and hot idle compensation devices.

CARBURETOR IDENTIFICATION

Application	Part No.
All Models	21100-16010

ADJUSTMENTS

NOTE: **For all on-vehicle adjustments not covered in this article, see the appropriate TUNE-UP SERVICE PROCEDURES article.**

NOTE: **Manufacturer recommends using carburetor service kit 09860-11011 to make carburetor adjustments and measurements.**

FLOAT LEVEL

NOTE: **Remove needle valve wire clip and install new inlet seat gasket before adjusting float.**

Fig. 1: Float Level Measurement

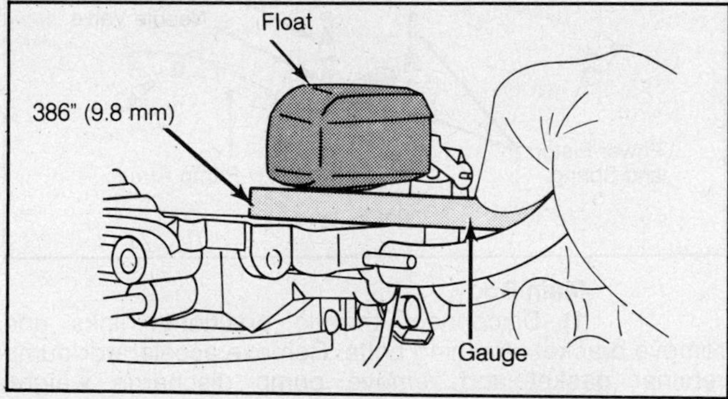
Float
386" (9.8 mm)
Gauge

Fig. 2: Float Level Adjustment

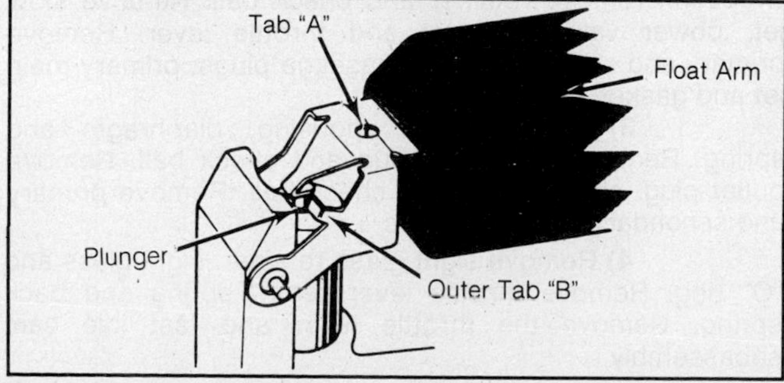
Tab "A"
Float Arm
Plunger
Outer Tab "B"

Adjust gap by bending float arm at tab "A".

Remove air horn gasket, invert air horn and allow float to hang by its own weight. Measure clearance between top of float and air horn. *See Fig. 1.* Clearance should be .386" (9.8 mm). Adjust clearance by bending float arm at tab "A". *See Fig. 2.*

FLOAT DROP

1) Invert air horn, gently lift up float and measure clearance between needle valve and float arm. *See Fig. 3.* Clearance should be .066-.078" (1.67-1.99 mm).

2) Adjust clearance by bending outer float tab "B". *See Fig. 4.* Install needle valve clip after completing float adjustments.

Fig. 3: Float Drop Measurement

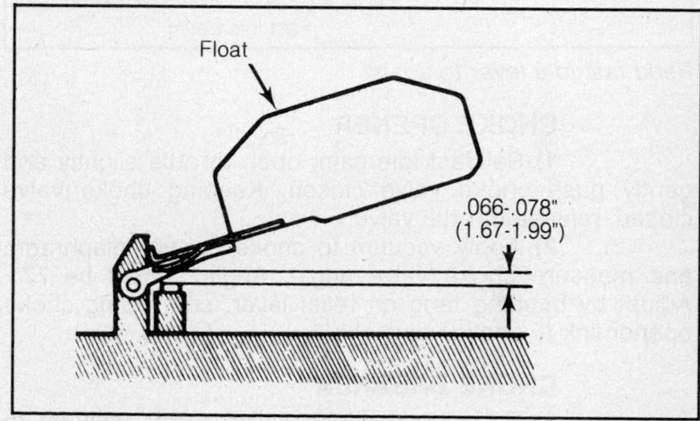
Float
.066-.078"
(1.67-1.99")

Fig. 4: Float Drop Adjustment

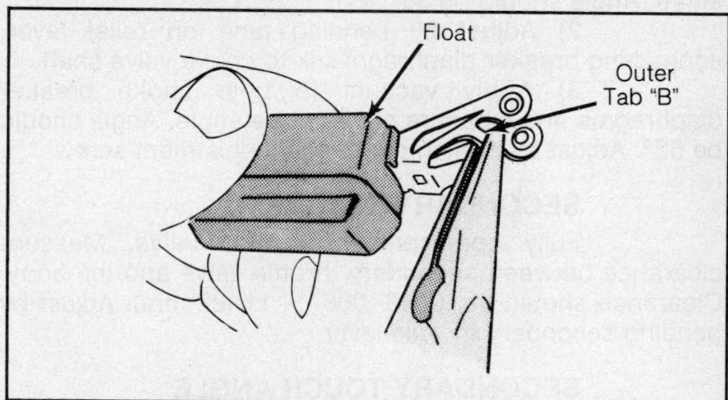
Float
Outer
Tab "B"

Bend outer tab "B" to adjust.

PRIMARY & SECONDARY THROTTLE VALVES

Invert carburetor, insert angle gauge and separately measure angle of primary and secondary throttle valves at full throttle. Angle should be 90° from horizontal plane for primary, 75° for secondary. Adjust by bending the respective throttle lever stop.

FAST IDLE

Bench Adjustment

Position throttle shaft lever to high (first) step of fast idle cam. Close choke valve and measure primary throttle valve angle. Angle should be 20°. Adjust by turning fast idle adjustment screw.

CHOKE UNLOADER

Fully open primary throttle valve, insert angle gauge and measure choke valve angle. Angle should be 41°. Bend fast idle lever to adjust. *See Fig. 5.*

1983 Aisan Carburetors

AISAN 2-BARREL – TOYOTA 4A-C ENGINE (Cont.)

Fig. 5: Choke Unloader Adjustment

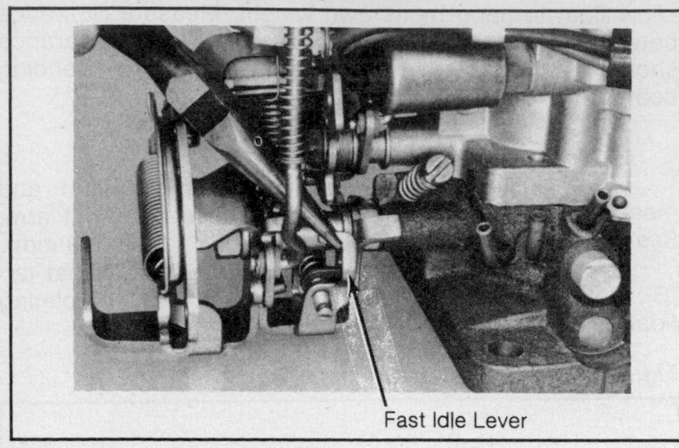
Fast Idle Lever

Bend fast idle lever to adjust

CHOKE OPENER

1) Set fast idle cam, open throttle slightly and gently push choke valve closed. Keeping choke valve closed, release throttle valve.

2) Apply vacuum to choke opener diaphragm and measure choke valve angle. Angle should be 77°. Adjust by bending tang on relief lever, connecting choke opener link to choke valve shaft.

CHOKE BREAKER

1) Fully close choke valve. Apply vacuum to choke breaker inner diaphragm and measure choke valve angle. Angle should be 38°.

2) Adjust by bending tang on relief lever, connecting breaker diaphragm link to choke valve shaft.

3) Apply vacuum to both choke breaker diaphragms and measure choke valve angle. Angle should be 52°. Adjust by turning diaphragm adjustment screw.

SECONDARY KICK-UP

Fully open primary throttle valve. Measure clearance between secondary throttle valve and the body. Clearance should be .0043-.0087" (.11-.22 mm). Adjust by bending secondary throttle lever.

SECONDARY TOUCH ANGLE

Check primary throttle valve opening angle as the primary kick lever touches the secondary kick lever. Angle should be 45°. Adjust by bending primary kick lever.

ACCELERATOR PUMP STROKE

Place a straightedge on top of air horn, fully open choke valve and measure full travel of pump plunger. Plunger travel should be .157" (4.0 mm). Adjust pump stroke by bending linkage rod at existing bend. *See Fig. 6.*

Fig. 6: Accelerator Pump Stroke Adjustment

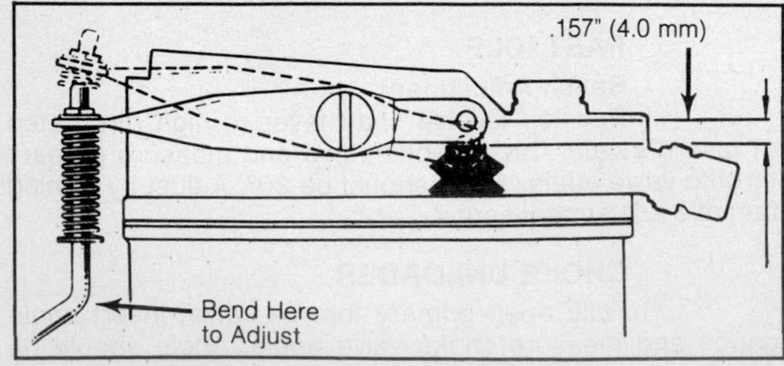
.157" (4.0 mm)
Bend Here
to Adjust

Bend linkage rod at existing bend to adjust.

OVERHAUL

NOTE: **Manufacturer recommends using carburetor driver kit 09860-11011 to service carburetor.**

DISASSEMBLY

Air Horn

1) Disconnect choke link and accelerator pump connecting rod. Remove pump arm pivot screw and pump arm. Remove fuel line and union and 8 air horn screws.

2) Disconnect the choke opener link and remove air horn with gasket from body. Disconnect wiring and remove primary and secondary solenoid valves from body.

3) Remove float pivot pin, float and needle valve assembly. Remove air horn gasket, power piston retainer, power piston and spring. Remove pump plunger and boot. *See Fig. 7.*

Fig. 7: Exploded View of Air Horn Assembly

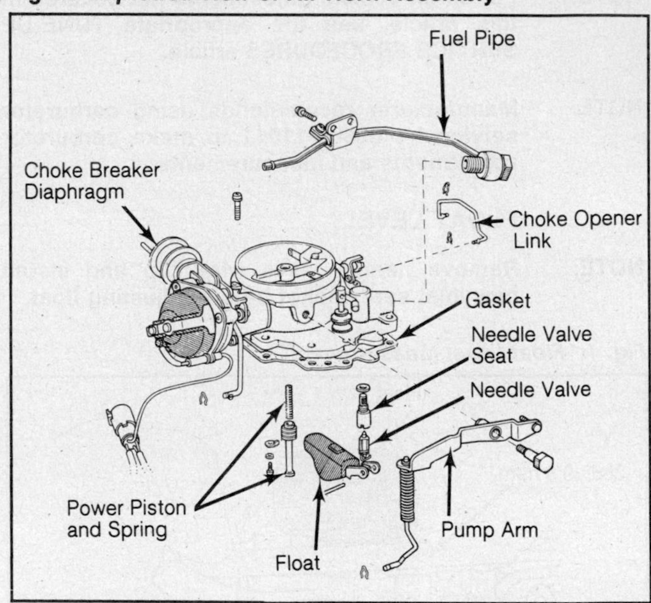
Fuel Pipe
Choke Breaker
Diaphragm
Choke Opener
Link
Gasket
Needle Valve
Seat
Needle Valve
Power Piston
and Spring
Pump Arm
Float

Main Body

1) Disconnect throttle positioner links and remove bracket attaching bolts. Remove accelerator pump retainer gasket and remove pump discharge weight, spring and check ball. *See Fig. 8.*

2) Remove pump dampening spring and using tweezers, remove retainer and check ball. Remove slow jet, power valve with jet and throttle lever. Remove primary and secondary main passage plugs, primary main jet and gasket.

3) Remove AAP housing, diaphragm and spring. Remove AAP inlet plug and check ball. Remove outlet plug, short spring and check ball. Remove primary and secondary small venturies.

4) Remove sight glass retainer, sight glass and "O" ring. Remove throttle lever return spring and back spring. Remove the throttle lever and fast idle cam subassembly.

1983 Aisan Carburetors

AISAN 2-BARREL – TOYOTA 4A-C ENGINE (Cont.)

Fig. 8: Exploded View of Carburetor Main Body

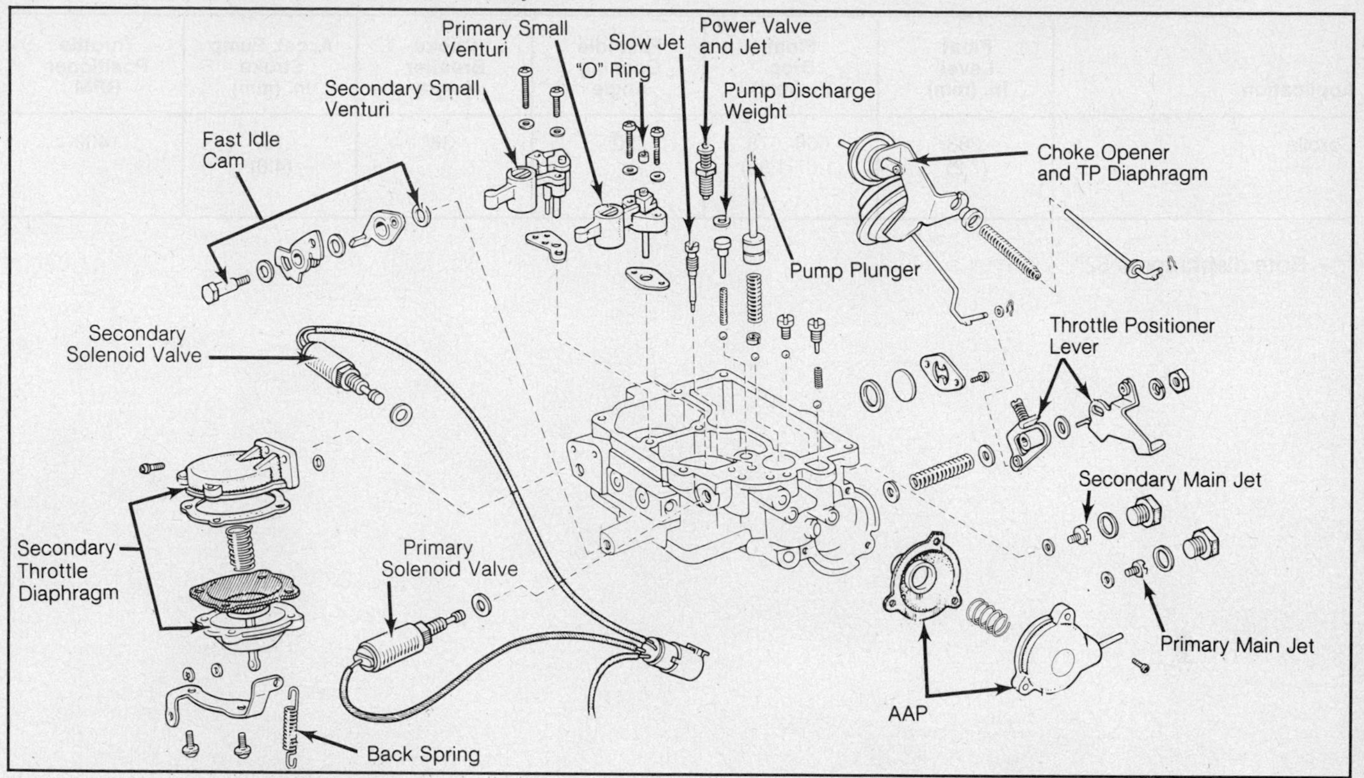
Primary Small Venturi
Power Valve and Jet
Slow Jet
"O" Ring
Secondary Small Venturi
Pump Discharge Weight
Fast Idle Cam
Choke Opener and TP Diaphragm
Pump Plunger
Secondary Solenoid Valve
Throttle Positioner Lever
Secondary Main Jet
Secondary Throttle Diaphragm
Primary Solenoid Valve
Primary Main Jet
AAP
Back Spring

5) Disconnect link, and remove secondary throttle valve diaphragm assembly and gasket. Remove the 3 body-to-flange bolts, vacuum passage bolt and separate body from flange. *See Fig. 9.*

Fig. 9: Exploded View of Carburetor Flange

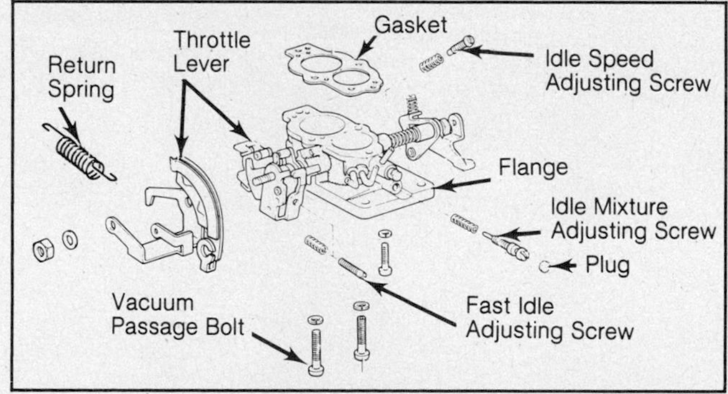
Gasket
Throttle Lever
Return Spring
Idle Speed Adjusting Screw
Flange
Idle Mixture Adjusting Screw
Plug
Vacuum Passage Bolt
Fast Idle Adjusting Screw

CLEANING

NOTE: **Do not immerse synthetic parts, electrical components or diaphragm assemblies in carburetor cleaner.**

Remove carbon from around throttle valve and clean cast parts with carburetor cleaner. Clean jets, fuel passages and vacuum ports with compressed air. Do not use wire or similar metal objects. Clean all other parts with solvent and soft brush.

INSPECTION

Choke Heater

Measure resistance between inner half of thermostat housing and wire connector. Resistance should be 19-24 ohms at 68°F (20°C). Replace air horn, if resistance is not within specifications.

Float Assembly

Inspect pivot pin for scratches and excessive wear; float for pivot pin hole wear and broken lips; plunger spring for breaks and distortion; needle valve and plunger for wear or damage and seat strainer for rust or breaks.

Fuel Cut Solenoid Valves

1) Feel solenoid valve "click", as solenoid is connected and disconnected from battery. Test primary solenoid by connecting lead wire to positive battery terminal and solenoid body to negative battery terminal.

2) Test secondary solenoid by connecting both lead wires to battery terminals, instead of using solenoid body. Replace solenoid if it fails to operate properly.

REASSEMBLY

Reassemble by reversing the disassembly procedure, using new gaskets and "O" rings, noting the following:

1) When assembling flange parts, ensure vacuum passage bolt is installed in correct position. Ensure springs are installed in proper location and check balls are located in appropriate orifices.

2) When installing pump discharge weight and outlet valve assembly, ensure all components are installed in correct order. After installing power piston, check piston for smooth operation.

3) If choke valve has been separated from shaft, make certain to peen the new retaining screws after valve is installed on shaft. When installing air horn, tighten air horn screws gradually and alternately to prevent distortion.

1983 Aisan Carburetors

AISAN 2-BARREL – TOYOTA 4A-C ENGINE (Cont.)

CARBURETOR ADJUSTMENT SPECIFICATIONS

Application	Float Level In. (mm)	Float Drop In. (mm)	Fast Idle Opening Angle	Choke Breaker Angle	Accel. Pump Stroke In. (mm)	Throttle Positioner RPM
Corolla	.283 (7.2)	.066-.078 (1.67-1.99)	20°	[1] 38°	.157 (4.0)	1400

[1] – Both diaphragms 52°.

1983 Aisan Carburetors

AISAN 2-BARREL – TOYOTA 22R ENGINE

Celica, Pickup

DESCRIPTION

Carburetor is a 2-barrel downdraft design with primary and secondary venturi. An automatic choke containing a bi-metallic spring, controlled by a ceramic heater, provides proper air/fuel mixture control during engine warm-up.

Secondary throttle valve is actuated by a vacuum diaphragm unit with a kick-up (open) lever. Secondary valve begins to open when primary throttle valve opening exceeds 50°.

A thermostatic valve provides air flow under secondary throttle valve, when ambient air temperature is high, to maintain proper combustion. Other features include a choke opener, an auxiliary accelerator pump (AAP), a secondary slow circuit fuel cut system, a fast idle cam breaker, a deceleration fuel cut system, and a solenoid valve.

CARBURETOR IDENTIFICATION

Application	Carburetor No.
Celica	21100-35210
Pickup	
Calif. Man. Trans.	21100-35210
Calif. Auto. Trans.	21100-35230
Federal Man. Trans.	21100-35240
Federal Auto. Trans.	21100-35250

ADJUSTMENTS

NOTE: **For all on-vehicle adjustments not covered in this article, see the appropriate TUNE-UP SERVICE PROCEDURES article.**

NOTE: **Manufacturer recommends using carburetor adjustment kit No. 09240-00014 for carburetor measurements and adjustments.**

FLOAT LEVEL

Remove air horn gasket, invert air horn, and allow float to hang by its own weight. Measure clearance between top of float and air horn. Clearance should be .386" (9.8 mm). Adjust clearance by bending float arm at tab "A". *See Fig. 1.*

Fig. 1: Float Level Adjustment

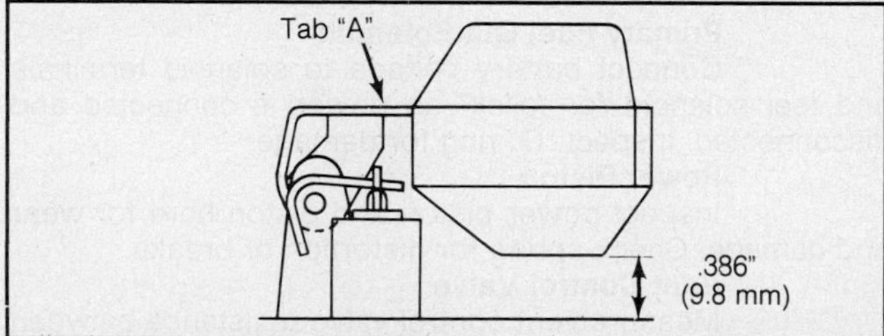
Tab "A"
.386"
(9.8 mm)

Adjust by bending float arm at tab "A".

FLOAT DROP

Remove air horn gasket, position air horn upright and let float hang by its own weight. Measure distance between bottom of float and air horn. Float drop measurement should be 1.89" (48 mm). Adjust clearance by bending float tab "B". *See Fig. 2.*

Fig. 2: Float Drop Adjustment

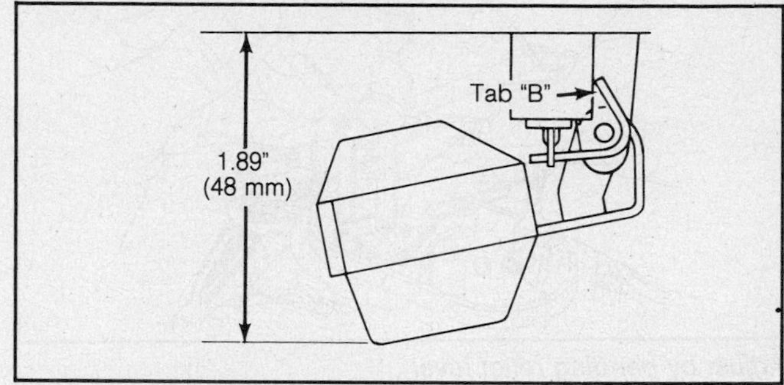
Tab "B"
1.89"
(48 mm)

Adjust by bending float tab "B".

UNLOADER

Fully open primary throttle valve, insert angle gauge, and measure choke valve angle. Choke valve angle should measure 50°. Adjust by bending first throttle arm at "A". *See Fig. 3.*

Fig. 3: Choke Unloader and Throttle Valve Adjustment

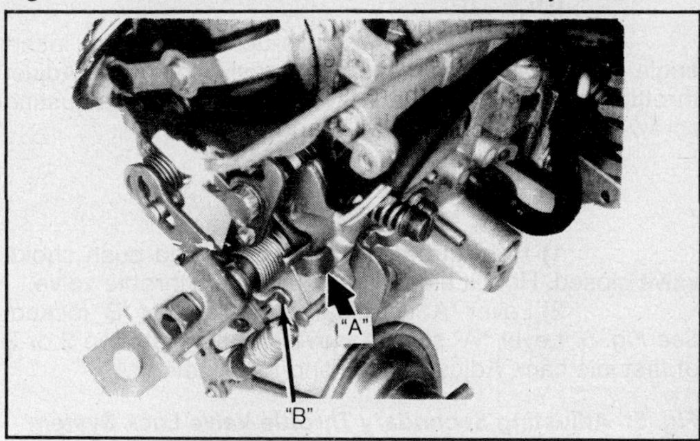
"A"
"B"

THROTTLE VALVE OPENING

1) Invert carburetor and fully open throttle valves. Measure angle of primary and secondary throttle valves, using angle gauge.

2) Angle of throttle valves should measure 90°. Adjust by bending the respective first throttle arm at "A" for primary, "B" for secondary. *See Fig. 3.*

SECONDARY TOUCH ANGLE

Measure the primary throttle valve angle as secondary throttle valve just begins to open. Primary throttle angle should measure 59°.

FAST IDLE

Bench Adjustment

Set throttle lever to high (first) step of fast idle cam. Fully close choke valve, insert angle gauge and adjust primary throttle valve angle by turning fast idle adjusting screw. Angle adjustment is 22°.

CHOKE BREAKER

Apply vacuum to choke breaker diaphragm. Close choke valve by hand, insert angle gauge, and measure choke valve angle. *See Fig. 4.* Choke valve angle should measure 42°. Adjust by bending relief lever.

1983 Aisan Carburetors

AISAN 2-BARREL – TOYOTA 22R ENGINE (Cont.)

Fig. 4: Choke Breaker Adjustment

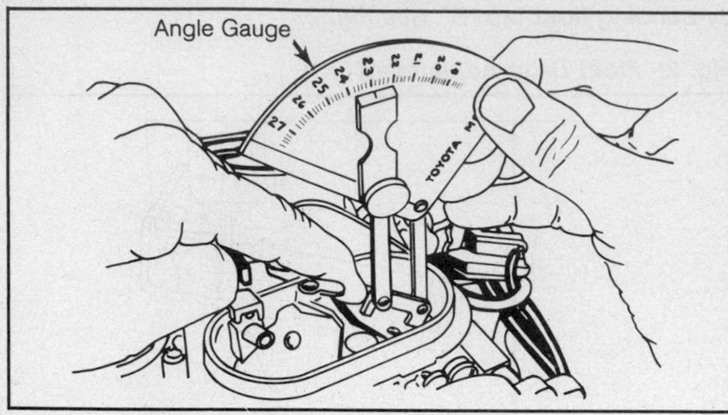
Angle Gauge
TOYOTA

Adjust by bending relief lever

CHOKE OPENER

1) Apply vacuum to choke opener diaphragm. Check that fast idle cam is released to fourth step. If not, adjust by bending choke opener lever.

2) Close choke valve, and set fast idle lever to first step. Ensure there is clearance between choke opener lever and fast idle cam.

IDLE-UP

Apply vacuum to idle-up diaphragm, insert angle gauge, and measure throttle valve opening. Adjust throttle valve opening angle to 16.5° by turning adjusting screw.

SECONDARY THROTTLE VALVE LOCK SYSTEM

1) Hold throttle slightly open, and push choke valve closed. Hold it closed as you release throttle valve.

2) Lever "A" should be holding lever "B" locked. *See Fig. 5.* Lever "A" should move smoothly at step 2 or 3 of fast idle cam. Adjust by bending top of lever "A".

Fig. 5: Adjusting Secondary Throttle Valve Lock System

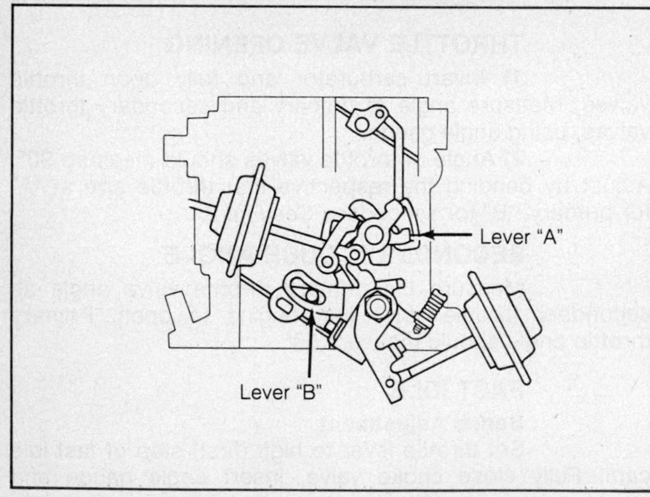
Lever "A"
Lever "B"

3) While holding throttle slightly open and choke valve closed, rotate lever "B" until it makes contact with lever "A". Measure clearance between secondary valve and bore. Check for .020" (.5 mm) clearance.

4) With choke valve opened above 52°, check that lever "A" unlocks when throttle valve is opened. Repeat step **1)**. Apply vacuum to choke opener and check that lever "A" withdraws and that lever "B" unlocks.

OVERHAUL

DISASSEMBLY

Air Horn

1) Remove metering needle, and disconnect fast idle link and air valve connecting rod. Remove the 5 air horn screws, lift air horn from body, and place next to body.

2) Loosen solenoid valve, and remove from body by rotating body counterclockwise. Remove float pivot pin and float with the needle valve. Remove needle valve seat.

3) Loosen power piston retaining screw, hold piston, rotate retainer, and remove piston and spring. Loosen the 3 screws, and remove the outer vent control valve.

Main Body

1) Remove slow jet using tool (SST 09922-00010). Remove power valve with jet, metering needle guide, and secondary main jet.

2) Remove plug and primary main jet. Remove main and auxiliary acceleration pump housings, springs, and diaphragms.

3) Disconnect idle-up diaphragm link and diaphragm. Disconnect choke opener link, and remove choke opener. Remove 3 body-to-flange screws and remove flange from body.

CLEANING

NOTE: **Do not immerse diaphragm valves, electrical components, or synthetic parts in carburetor cleaner.**

Clean cast parts in carburetor cleaner and blow dry. Do not clean jets or other passages with wire or similar metal objects. Inspect all parts for wear or damage and replace necessary parts.

INSPECTION

Choke Heater

Measure choke heater resistance between terminal and housing. Resistance should measure 19-23 ohms.

Choke Breaker, Choke Opener & Idle-Up Diaphragm

Apply vacuum to diaphragm and check for leakage. Ensure link or valve moves as vacuum is applied.

Float & Needle Valve

Inspect pivot pin for scratches and wear. Check float for wear in pivot pin holes and for broken lips. Inspect needle valve and seat for wear and damage and strainer for rust or breaks.

Primary Fuel Cut Solenoid

Connect battery voltage to solenoid terminals and feel solenoid for "click" as power is connected and disconnected. Inspect "O" ring for damage.

Power Piston

Inspect power piston and piston bore for wear and damage. Check spring for distortion or breaks.

Vent Control Valve

Measure vent control valve resistance between terminal and solenoid body. Resistance should measure 63-73 ohms at 68°F (20° C).

REASSEMBLY

Reassemble carburetor by reversing disassembly procedure, using new gaskets where required. Check for smooth operation of all valves and linkage.

AISAN 2-BARREL – TOYOTA 22R ENGINE (Cont.)

Fig. 6: Exploded View of Carburetor

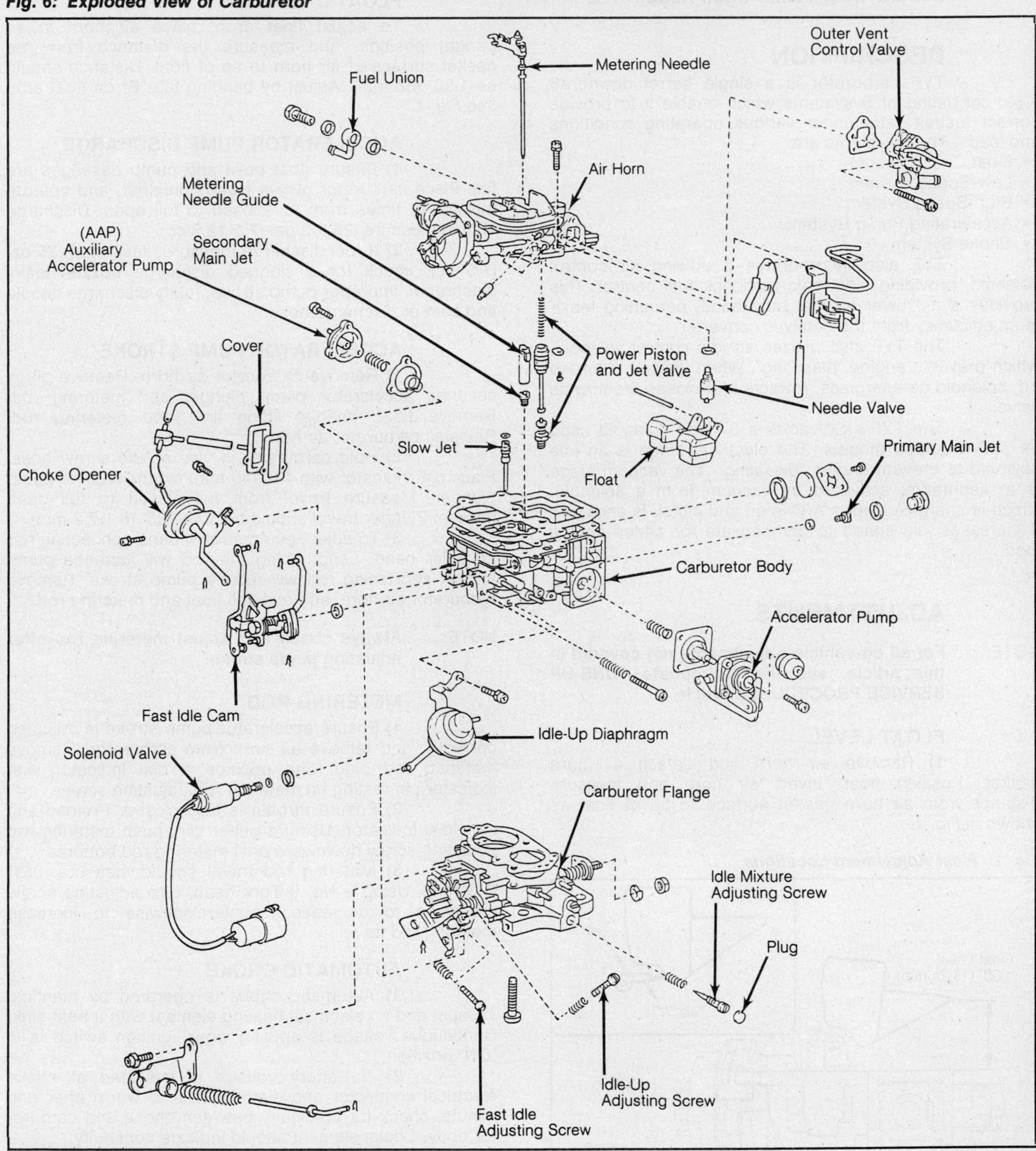
Outer Vent
Control Valve
Metering Needle
Fuel Union
Air Horn
Metering
Needle Guide
(AAP)
Auxiliary
Accelerator Pump
Secondary
Main Jet
Cover
Power Piston
and Jet Valve
Needle Valve
Slow Jet
Primary Main Jet
Choke Opener
Float
Carburetor Body
Accelerator Pump
Fast Idle Cam
Idle-Up Diaphragm
Solenoid Valve
Carburetor Flange
Idle Mixture
Adjusting Screw
Plug
Idle-Up
Adjusting Screw
Fast Idle
Adjusting Screw

CARBURETOR ADJUSTMENT SPECIFICATIONS

Application	Float Level In. (mm)	Float Drop In. (mm)	Choke Opener In. (mm)	Choke Breaker Angle	Throttle Positioner Angle
Celica & Pickup	.386 (9.8)	1.89 (48)	.....	42°	16.5°

1983 Carter-Weber Carburetors

TYF SINGLE BARREL

Subaru 1.8L, Volkswagen Rabbit 1.7L

DESCRIPTION

TYF carburetor is a single barrel downdraft type, consisting of 5 systems which enable it to provide correct fuel/air ratio under various operating conditions and loads. The 5 systems are:

- Float Circuit System
- Low-Speed System
- High-Speed System
- Accelerating Pump System
- Choke System

TYF also incorporates a pulsing air control solenoid, providing electronic feedback fuel control. This provides a narrower air/fuel ratio band, permitting maximum efficiency from the catalytic converter.

The TYF also utilizes an idle control solenoid, which prevents engine "dieseling". When ignition is turned off, solenoid de-energizes, retracts and closes the throttle valve.

The TYF's Solvac is a 2-stage solenoid used on A/C-equipped models. The electrical stage is an idle solenoid to prevent engine "dieseling". The vacuum stage is a diaphragm, activated by vacuum from a solenoid, which is energized when A/C is on and clutch is engaged. It increases idle speed to compensate for added engine load.

ADJUSTMENTS

NOTE: **For all on-vehicle adjustments not covered in this article, see the appropriate TUNE-UP SERVICE PROCEDURES article.**

FLOAT LEVEL

1) Remove air horn and detach air horn gasket. Position float, invert air horn and measure distance from air horn gasket surface to tip of float as shown in *Fig. 1.*

Fig. 1: Float Adjustment Locations

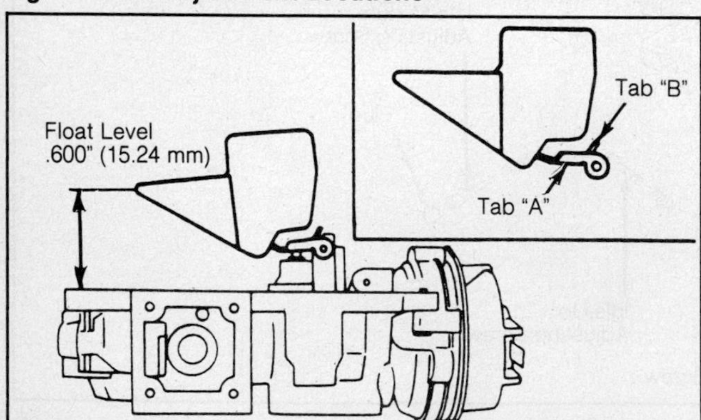

Tab "B"
Float Level
.600" (15.24 mm)
Tab "A"

Bend float arm at tab "A" to adjust float level, bend tab "B" to adjust float drop.

NOTE: **Applying pressure to the needle valve while bending float tabs will damage needle tip.**

2) If distance is not within specifications, bend tab "A" to adjust. After distance has been properly adjusted, proceed to float drop adjustment.

FLOAT DROP

To adjust float drop, place air horn in an upright position, and measure the distance from the gasket surface of air horn to tip of float. Distance should be 1.50" (38 mm). Adjust by bending tab "B" on float arm. *See Fig. 1.*

ACCELERATOR PUMP DISCHARGE

1) Ensure float bowl and pump passages are full. Place carburetor over a clean container, and operate throttle 10 times from full closed to full open. Discharge should measure .25-.42 oz. (7.5-12.5 cc).

2) If fuel discharge measures less than .25 oz. (7.5 cc), check for a clogged discharge nozzle, leaky diaphragm, improper pump stroke, faulty discharge needle and seat or discharge hose.

ACCELERATOR PUMP STROKE

1) Remove carburetor air horn. Remove plugs covering accelerator pump plunger and metering rod. Remove float, needle, lifting link, and metering rod. Reinstall carburetor air horn.

2) Hold carburetor in vise at idle screw boss. Place dial indicator with 1.6" (40 mm) extension over pump plunger. Measure travel from full closed to full open throttle. Plunger travel should be .240-285" (6.1-7.2 mm).

3) To adjust pump stroke, bend connecting rod at lower bend. Lengthening the rod will increase pump stroke, shortening rod will reduce pump stroke. Remove carburetor air horn, and reinstall float and metering rod.

NOTE: **Always check and adjust metering rod after adjusting pump stroke.**

METERING ROD

1) Ensure accelerator pump stroke is adjusted correctly, and remove air horn from carburetor. Remove metering rod plug, and position a dial indicator with indicator pin resting on metering rod adjusting screw.

2) Ensure throttle is fully closed. Preload and zero dial indicator. Using a paper clip, push metering rod adjusting screw downward until metering rod bottoms.

3) Metering rod travel should measure .051" (1.3 mm). Using a No. 9 Torx head, turn adjusting screw clockwise to decrease, counterclockwise to increase metering rod travel.

AUTOMATIC CHOKE

1) Automatic choke is operated by manifold vacuum and an electrical heating element with a heat sink. Continuous voltage is applied when ignition switch is in "ON" position.

2) If battery voltage is indicated at choke electrical connector and element fails to warm after one minute, check for continuity between choke and carburetor body. Choke element should indicate continuity.

3) Adjust Volkswagon models, by locating choke housing notch and index retainer to left of fuel inlet fitting. On Suburu models, cover locates one notch to rich side.

CHOKE CAM INDEX

NOTE: **Cam index adjustment must be made with engine at operating temperature.**

1983 Carter-Weber Carburetors

TYF SINGLE BARREL (Cont.)

1) Set adjusting screw for fast idle speed on the fifth step of fast idle cam, with adjusting screw shoulder touching ramp of fourth step.

2) Apply vacuum to pull-down diaphragm. Slowly push choke closed until increased resistance is felt, without changing position of adjusting screw.

3) A gap of .005-.035" (.13-.89 mm) should be indicated between fast idle arm and fast idle cam. If necessary, adjust by bending fast idle arm. *See Fig. 2.*

Fig. 2: Checking and Adjusting Choke Cam Index

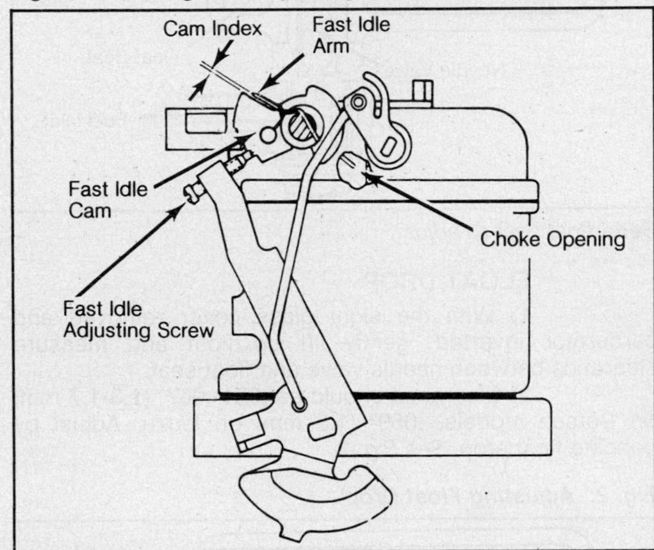
Cam Index
Fast Idle
Arm
Fast Idle
Cam
Choke Opening
Fast Idle
Adjusting Screw

Adjust by bending fast idle arm.

CHOKE UNLOADER

Hold throttle valve in wide open position. Close choke valve, without applying force. There should be .164" (4.2 mm) clearance between lower edge of choke valve and inner wall of air horn. Adjust by bending tang on throttle lever.

CHOKE PULL-DOWN

1) Set adjusting screw for fast idle speed on top step of fast idle cam. Connect manually operated vacuum pump to pull-down unit, and apply vacuum. Pressing gently, close choke valve slightly.

2) Check gap between lower end of choke valve and inner wall of the air horn. Gap should be .164" (4.2 mm). Adjust gap at adjustment screw located under plug in pull-down diaphragm cover. After adjustment, install a new plug.

Fig. 3: Exploded View of the Carter-Weber TYF Carburetor

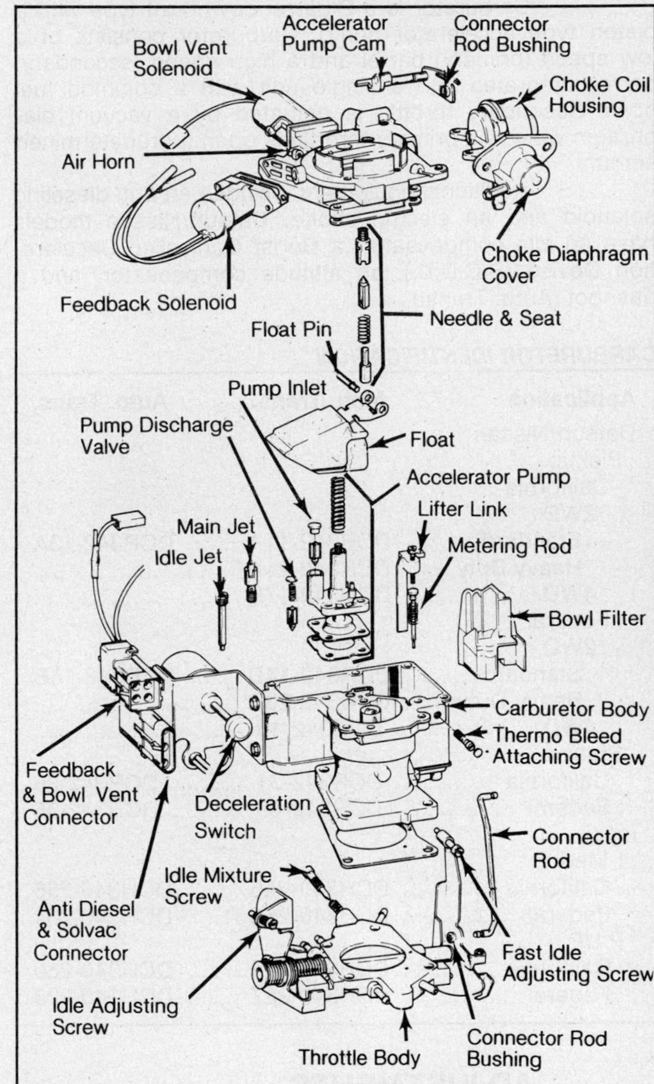
Accelerator
Pump Cam
Connector
Rod Bushing
Bowl Vent
Solenoid
Choke Coil
Housing
Air Horn
Choke Diaphragm
Cover
Feedback Solenoid
Needle & Seat
Float Pin
Pump Inlet
Pump Discharge
Valve
Float
Accelerator Pump
Lifter Link
Main Jet
Idle Jet
Metering Rod
Bowl Filter
Carburetor Body
Thermo Bleed
Attaching Screw
Feedback
& Bowl Vent
Connector
Deceleration
Switch
Connector
Rod
Idle Mixture
Screw
Anti Diesel
& Solvac
Connector
Fast Idle
Adjusting Screw
Idle Adjusting
Screw
Connector Rod
Bushing
Throttle Body

CARBURETOR ADJUSTMENT SPECIFICATIONS

Application	Float Level	Choke Unloader	Choke Pull-Down	Fast Idle	Auto. Choke
Subaru	.670" (17.02 mm)	.152" (3.8 mm)	.152" (3.8 mm)	2000	1 Notch Rich .....
Volkswagen Rabbit	.570-630" (14.3-15.8 mm)	.164" (4.2 mm)	.164" (4.2 mm)	2600-3000	....

1983 Hitachi Carburetors

HITACHI DCH 340 & DCR 342 2-BARREL

Datsun/Nissan Pickup, Stanza;
Isuzu I-Mark, P'UP

DESCRIPTION

Carburetor is a 2-barrel downdraft type with a piston type accelerator pump. Carburetor consists of a low speed (primary) barrel and a high speed (secondary) barrel integrated into a single unit with a common fuel bowl. Secondary throttle is actuated by a vacuum diaphragm when the primary throttle is open a predetermined amount.

Additional equipment includes an anti-dieseling solenoid and an electric choke. Datsun/Nissan models have an idle compensator, a Boost Controlled Deceleration Device (B.C.D.D.), an altitude compensator, and a dashpot (Auto. Trans.)

CARBURETOR IDENTIFICATION

Application	Man. Trans.	Auto. Trans.
Datsun/Nissan		
Pickup		
California		
2WD		
Standard	DCR342-11A	DCR342-13A
Heavy Duty	DCR342-21A	.....
4WD	DCR342-17B	.....
Federal		
2WD		
Standard	DCR342-14B	DCR342-16B
Heavy Duty	DCR342-23B	.....
4WD	DCR342-19	.....
Stanza		
California	DCR342-31	DCR342-38
Federal	DCR342-33	DCR342-36
Isuzu		
I-Mark		
California	DCH340-255	DCH340-256
Federal	DCH340-253	DCH340-254
P'UP		
California	DCH340-229	DCH340-230
Federal	DCH340-227	DCH340-228

ADJUSTMENTS

NOTE: **For all on-vehicle adjustments not covered in this article, see the appropriate TUNE-UP SERVICE PROCEDURES article.**

FLOAT LEVEL

NOTE: **Line on fuel bowl sight glass indicates proper fuel level. If adjustment is necessary, use following procedures.**

Datsun/Nissan

With sight glass cover removed and carburetor inverted, measure clearance between top of float and float bowl. Clearance should be .283" (7.2 mm). Adjust by bending float seat. *See Fig. 1.*

Isuzu

With sight glass cover removed and carburetor inverted, check float position in relation to being parallel with top of fuel bowl. Bend float seat to make necessary adjustment. *See Fig. 1.*

Fig. 1: Adjusting Float Level

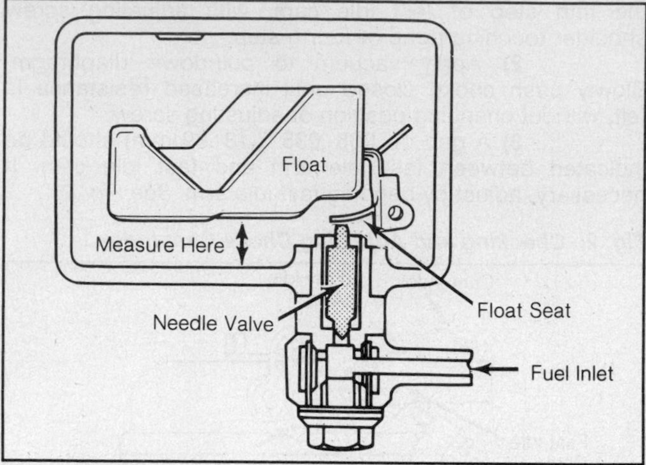
Float
Measure Here
Float Seat
Needle Valve
Fuel Inlet

Bend float seat to adjust.

FLOAT DROP

1) With the sight glass cover removed and carburetor inverted, gently lift up float and measure clearance between needle valve and float seat.

2) Clearance should be .051-.067" (1.3-1.7 mm) on Datsun models, .059" (1.5 mm) on Isuzu. Adjust by bending float stop. *See Fig. 2.*

Fig. 2: Adjusting Float Drop

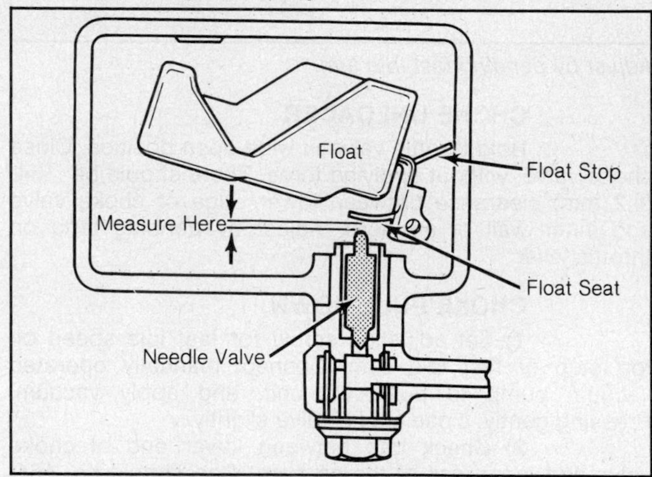
Float
Float Stop
Measure Here
Float Seat
Needle Valve

Bend float stop to adjust.

VACUUM BREAK

Datsun/Nissan

1) Close choke valve and hold in place with a rubber band attached to vacuum break lever and stationary part of carburetor.

2) Apply vacuum to vacuum break diaphragm and measure clearance between choke valve and inner wall of air horn. Adjust by bending vacuum break rod. *See Fig. 3.*

CHOKE UNLOADER

Datsun/Nissan

1) Close choke valve and hold in place with a rubber band attached to the vacuum break lever and stationary part of carburetor.

1983 Hitachi Carburetors

HITACHI DCH 340 & DCR 342 2-BARREL (Cont.)

Fig. 3: Adjusting Vacuum Break on Datsun

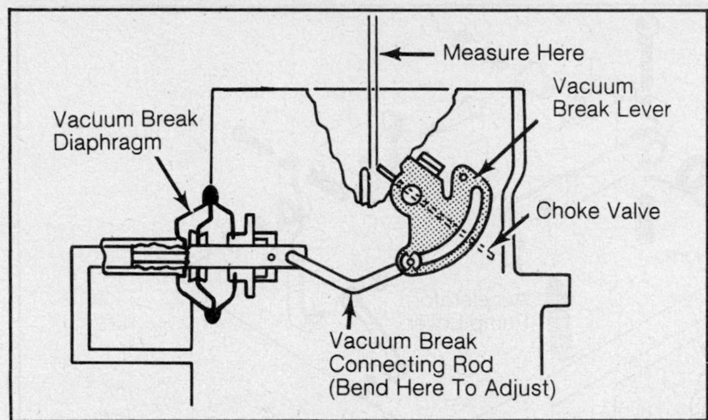
Measure Here
Vacuum Break Lever
Vacuum Break Diaphragm
Choke Valve
Vacuum Break
Connecting Rod
(Bend Here To Adjust)

Bend vacuum break rod to adjust.

2) Fully open throttle valve and measure clearance between the choke valve and air horn wall. Clearance should be .081-.112" (2.1-2.9 mm). Bend unloader tang to adjust.

NOTE: Ensure primary throttle valve opens fully when carburetor is installed on vehicle. If throttle fails to open completely, unloader becomes inoperative.

SECONDARY THROTTLE CLEARANCE

1) When primary throttle valve opens 50° (47° on Isuzu), the lockout lever which is interlocked with primary throttle shaft, contacts kick lever and prevents secondary throttle opening.

2) Further opening of throttle valve releases the lockout lever, permitting secondary throttle operation.

3) To check, measure clearance between primary throttle valve and wall of throttle chamber when lockout arm contacts kick lever tang.

4) Clearance should be .29-.33" (7.4-8.4 mm) on Datsun, .24-.30" (6.1-7.6 mm) on Isuzu. Adjust by bending kick lever tang. *See Fig. 4.*

Fig. 4: Adjusting Secondary Throttle Clearance

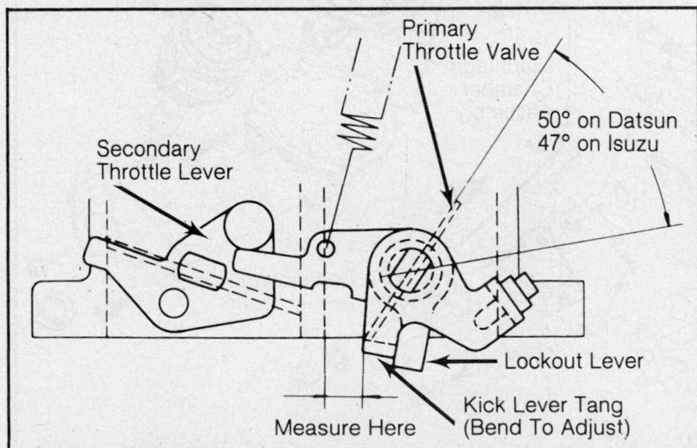
Primary
Throttle Valve
50° on Datsun
47° on Isuzu
Secondary
Throttle Lever
Lockout Lever
Kick Lever Tang
(Bend To Adjust)
Measure Here

Bend kick lever tang to adjust.

CHOKE LINKAGE (FAST IDLE OPENING ANGLE)

1) Close choke valve to position fast idle screw on first (high) step of fast idle cam on Isuzu models, slightly open choke valve to position screw on second step on Datsun models. *See Fig. 5.*

2) Measure clearance between throttle valve and wall of throttle chamber. On Isuzu models, angle of throttle valve can also be used to determine if adjustment is correct.

3) Clearance on Datsun models should be .81-.95" (.032-.037 mm) with manual transmission, .97-1.11" (.038-.044" mm) with automatic transmission. Clearance on Isuzu models should be .050-.059" (1.28-1.51" mm).

4) On Isuzu models, if throttle valve angle is being used to determine proper adjustment, angle should be 15°-17° on models with manual transmission, 17°-19° with automatic transmission.

Fig. 5: Choke Linkage Adjustment (Fast Idle Opening Angle)

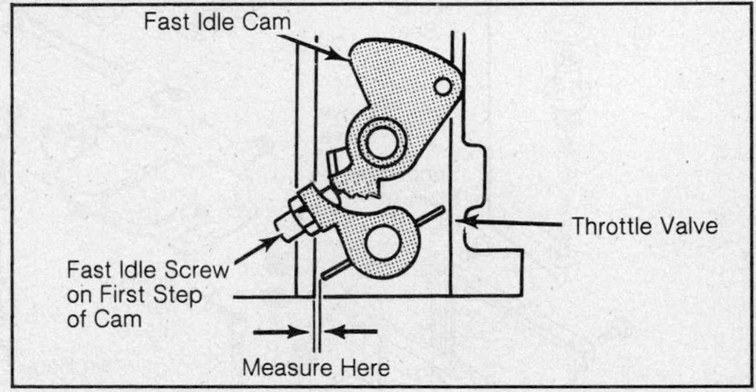
Fast Idle Cam
Throttle Valve
Fast Idle Screw
on First Step
of Cam
Measure Here

Turn fast idle screw to adjust.

OVERHAUL

CAUTION: Use properly fitting screwdrivers and wrenches when servicing. Using improper tools can damage parts and alter carburetor calibration.

DISASSEMBLY

NOTE: Slow and main actuators are factory adjusted and should not be disassembled.

1) Disconnect accelerator pump lever. Remove throttle return spring, choke thermostat housing and lead wire, fuel pipe nipple and strainer. Remove retaining clip and disconnect choke rod from counter lever.

2) Disconnect choke vacuum hose from float chamber. Remove attaching screws and remove choke chamber from float chamber. Remove diaphragm rod-to-secondary throttle lever retaining clip. Remove diaphragm retaining screws and diaphragm.

3) Separate float chamber from throttle valve body. Remove slow actuator if equipped. Remove accelerator pump plunger assembly, float needle valve assembly, sight glass cover and float assembly.

4) Remove screws attaching diaphragm cover, diaphragm cover, spring and diaphragm. Remove all jets from upper part of float chamber and remove small venturi from both primary and secondary venturi.

5) Remove injector weight plug, weight and ball. Remove power jet, main jet plugs, main jets, and primary slow air bleed from choke chamber. Do not remove throttle valves or choke valve unless components are damaged.

1983 Hitachi Carburetors

HITACHI DCH 340 & DCR 342 2-BARREL (Cont.)

Fig. 6: Exploded View of Hitachi DCR Carburetor Assembly

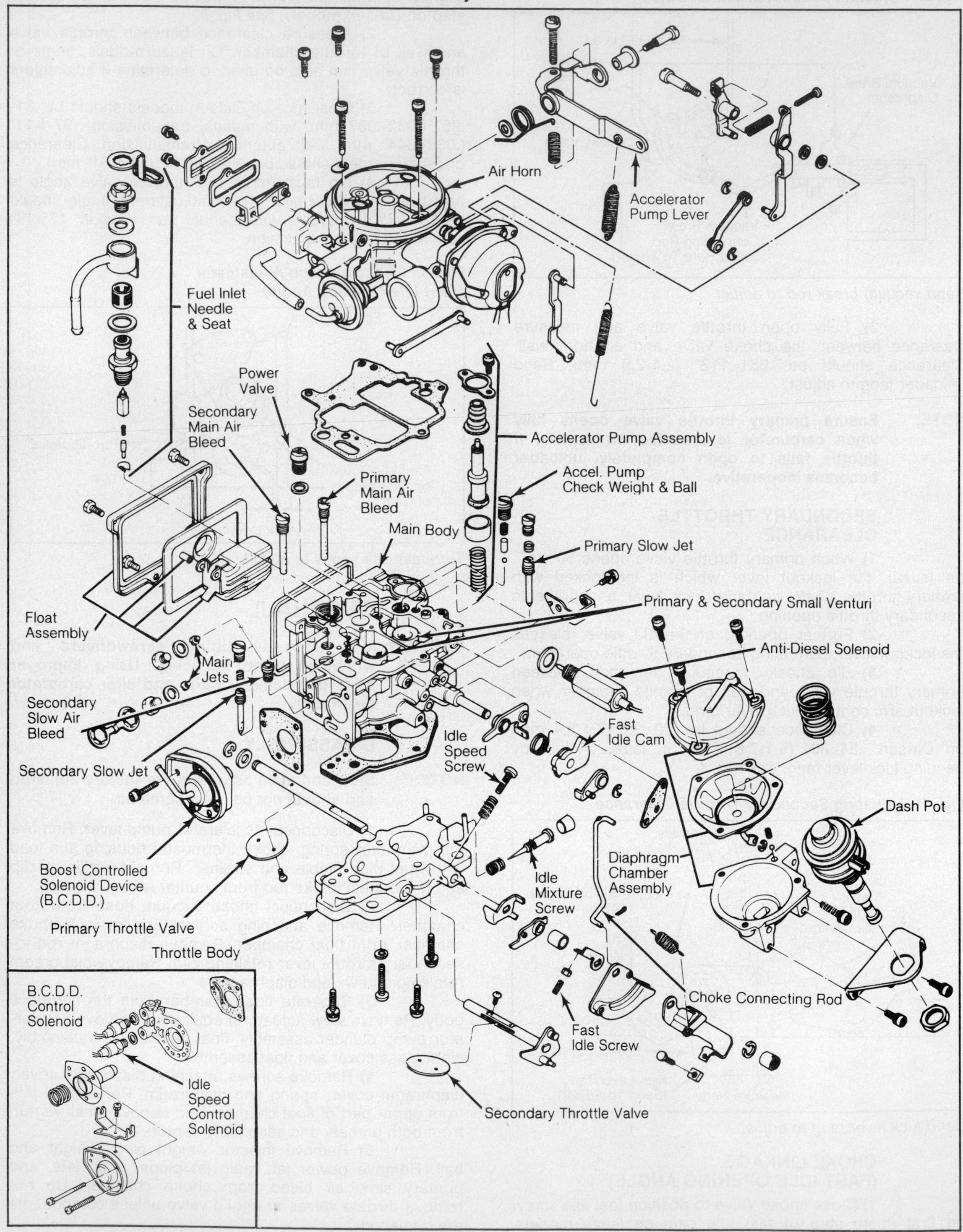

Air Horn
Accelerator
Pump Lever
Fuel Inlet
Needle
& Seat
Power
Valve
Secondary
Main Air
Bleed
Accelerator Pump Assembly
Accel. Pump
Check Weight & Ball
Primary
Main Air
Bleed
Main Body
Primary Slow Jet
Float
Assembly
Primary & Secondary Small Venturi
Anti-Diesel Solenoid
Main
Jets
Secondary
Slow Air
Bleed
Fast
Idle Cam
Idle
Speed
Screw
Secondary Slow Jet
Dash Pot
Boost Controlled
Solenoid Device
(B.C.D.D.)
Idle
Mixture
Screw
Diaphragm
Chamber
Assembly
Primary Throttle Valve
Throttle Body
B.C.D.D.
Control
Solenoid
Choke Connecting Rod
Fast
Idle Screw
Idle
Speed
Control
Solenoid
Secondary Throttle Valve

Shown in inset is Datsun/Nissan Boost Controlled Deceleration Device (B.C.D.D.).

1983 Hitachi Carburetors

HITACHI DCH 340 & DCR 342 2-BARREL (Cont.)

Fig. 7: Exploded View of Hitachi DCH Carburetor Assembly

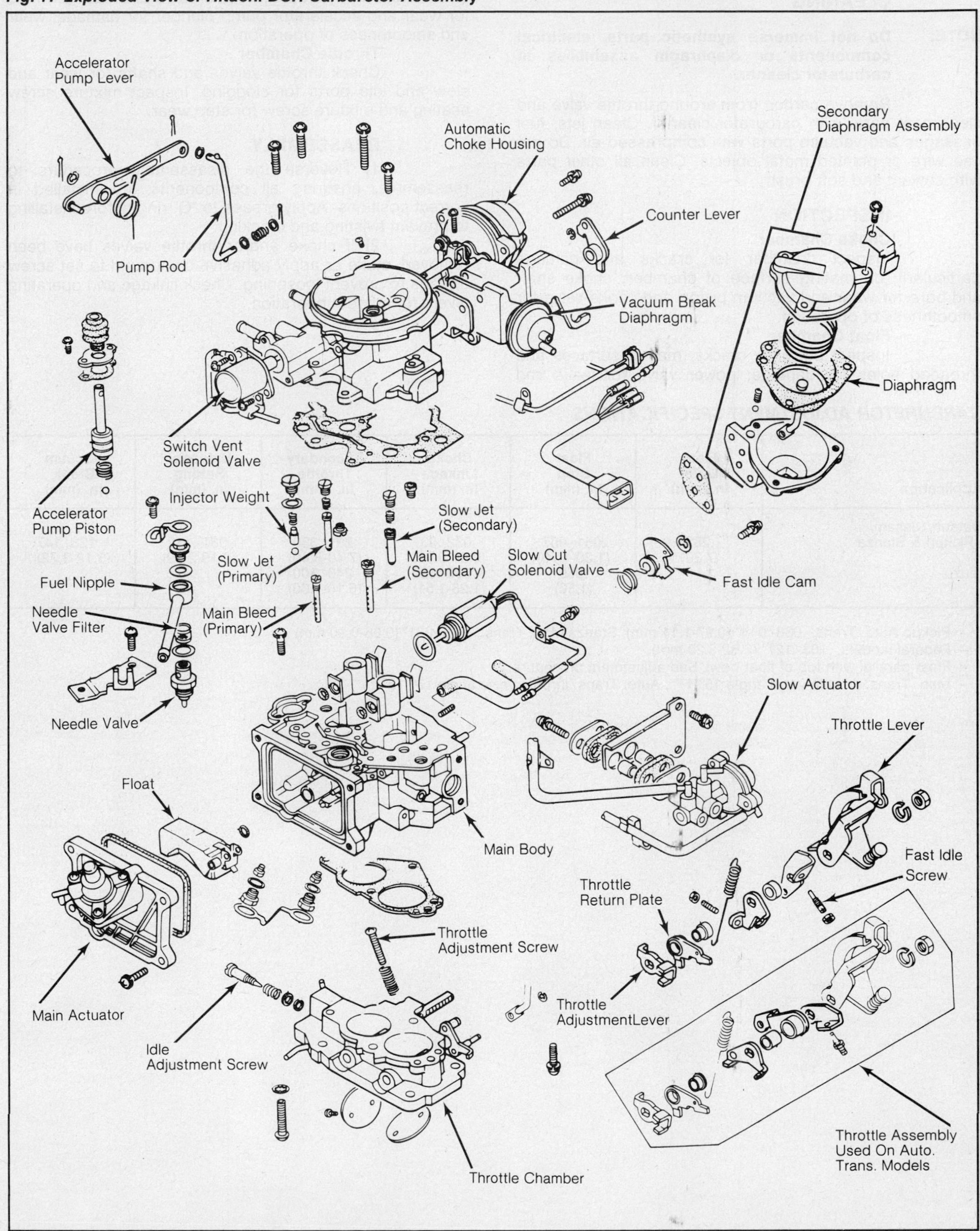
Accelerator Pump Lever
Pump Rod
Automatic Choke Housing
Secondary Diaphragm Assembly
Counter Lever
Vacuum Break Diaphragm
Diaphragm
Switch Vent Solenoid Valve
Accelerator Pump Piston
Injector Weight
Slow Jet (Secondary)
Slow Jet (Primary)
Main Bleed (Secondary)
Slow Cut Solenoid Valve
Fast Idle Cam
Fuel Nipple
Needle Valve Filter
Main Bleed (Primary)
Needle Valve
Slow Actuator
Throttle Lever
Float
Main Body
Fast Idle Screw
Throttle Return Plate
Throttle Adjustment Screw
Main Actuator
Throttle AdjustmentLever
Idle Adjustment Screw
Throttle Assembly Used On Auto. Trans. Models
Throttle Chamber

Used on Isuzu I-Mark and P'UP

1983 Hitachi Carburetors

HITACHI DCH 340 & DCR 342 2-BARREL (Cont.)

CLEANING

NOTE: **Do not immerse synthetic parts, electrical components or diaphragm assemblies in carburetor cleaner.**

Remove carbon from around throttle valve and clean cast parts with carburetor cleaner. Clean jets, fuel passages and vacuum ports with compressed air. Do not use wire or pointed metal objects. Clean all other parts with solvent and soft brush.

INSPECTION

Choke Chamber

Inspect chamber for cracks and damage particularly on mating surface of chamber; choke shaft and bore for wear and vacuum piston and choke valve for smoothness of operation.

Float Chamber

Inspect body for cracks, mating surfaces and threaded holes for damage; power valve for leaks and smoothness of operation; needle valve and float pin hole for wear and accelerator pump plunger for damage, wear and smoothness of operation.

Throttle Chamber

Check throttle valves and shafts for wear and slow and idle ports for clogging. Inspect mixture screw seating and mixture screw for step wear.

REASSEMBLY

1) Reverse the disassembly procedure to reassemble, ensuring all components are installed in correct positions. Apply grease to "O" ring before installing to prevent twisting and cracking.

2) If choke and/or throttle valves have been removed, stake or apply adhesive compound to set screw threads to prevent loosening. Check linkage and operating levers for smooth operation.

CARBURETOR ADJUSTMENT SPECIFICATIONS

Application	Float Level In. (mm)	Float Drop In. (mm)	Choke Linkage In. (mm)	Secondary Throttle In. (mm)	Unloader Setting In. (mm)	Vacuum Break In. (mm)
Datsun/Nissan Pickup & Stanza	.283 (7.20)	.051-.067 (1.30-1.70)	[1] .032-.037 (0.81-0.95)	.291-.330 (7.40-8.40)	.081-.112 (2.10-2.90)	[2] .123-.147 (3.12-3.72)
Isuzu	[3]	.059 (1.50)	[4] .050-.059 (1.28-1.51)	.240-.300 (6.10-7.60)	.....	.....

[1] – Pickup Auto. Trans, .038-.044" (0.97-1.11 mm); Stanza Man. Trans., .026-.031" (0.66-0.80 mm)
[2] – Federal models, .103-.127" (2.62-3.22 mm).
[3] – Float parallel with top of float bowl. See adjustment procedure.
[4] – Man. Trans. throttle valve angle 15°-17°; Auto. Trans. throttle valve angle 17°-19°.

1983 Hitachi Carburetors

HITACHI DCZ 328, DCP 306, DFC 328 & DFP 306 2-BARREL

Datsun/Nissan Pulsar & Sentra, Mazda GLC, Subaru

DESCRIPTION

Carburetor is a 2-barrel downdraft design with primary and secondary throttle system. A choke valve and idle circuit are used in primary system only. Both primary and secondary venturis have main fuel nozzles.

A mechanical accelerator pump and a vacuum operated power valve are used for increased fuel requirements. An anti-dieseling solenoid valve is used to stop fuel flow in idle circuit (on some models) when ignition switch is turned off. All models use an electric choke system.

Some models use an altitude compensator device to maintain optimum air/fuel ratio at higher altitudes. On FWD Mazda models, the carburetor includes a duty (air flow) solenoid that is controlled by computer to maintain optimum air/fuel ratio. Datsun/Nissan uses an air/fuel ratio control solenoid control valve in conjunction with E.C.C. (electronic-controlled carburetors) on California models and Sentra MPG models.

CARBURETOR IDENTIFICATION

Application	Man. Trans.	Auto. Trans.
Datsun/Nissan		
Sentra		
California	DFC328-1	DFC328-2
Federal	DCZ328-1	DCZ328-2
MPG	DFP306-2	....
Pulsar		
California	DFC328-1	DFC328-2
Federal	DCZ328-1	DCZ328-2
Mazda [1]		
FWD	E563-13-600	E563-13-600
RWD	D501-13-600	E501-13-600
Subaru		
1600	DCP306-17	....
1800		
Fed. 4WD	DCP306-21	DCP306-22
All Others	DCP306-18	DCP306-19

[1] – Number listed is Mazda part number.

ADJUSTMENTS

NOTE: **For all on-vehicle adjustments not covered in this article, see the appropriate TUNE-UP SERVICE PROCEDURES Article.**

FLOAT LEVEL

NOTE: **If fuel is not within mark on float chamber sight glass, with engine idling, remove air horn and adjust using following procedures.**

Invert air horn, let float hang by its own weight and measure distance between float and air horn gasket surface (gasket removed). If necessary, bend tab "A" to adjust. *See Fig. 1.*

FLOAT DROP

1) After checking float level, gently lift float until float stop contacts air horn projection. Hold float up in this position.

2) On all except Mazda, measure clearance between float tab and needle valve. On Mazda, measure from bottom of float to air horn. On all models, adjust by bending float stop. *See Fig. 2.*

Fig. 1: Float Level Adjustment

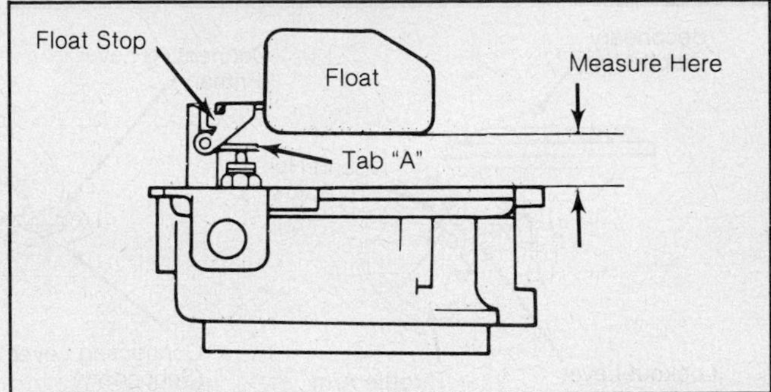
Float Stop
Float
Measure Here
Tab "A"

Bend tab "A" to adjust.

Fig. 2: Float Drop Adjustment

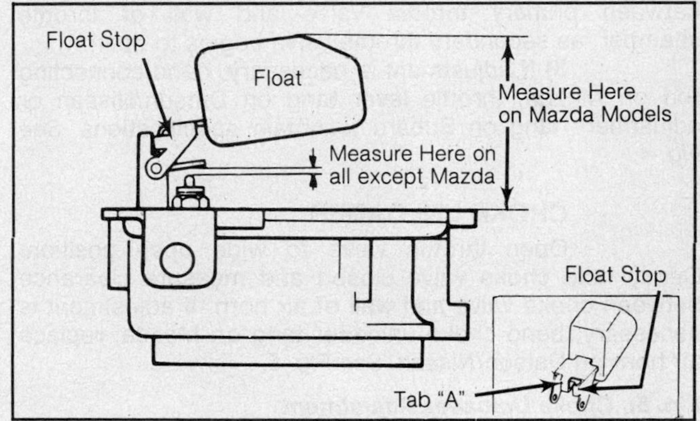
Float Stop
Float
Measure Here on Mazda Models
Measure Here on all except Mazda
Float Stop
Tab "A"

Bend float stop to adjust.

FAST IDLE

Bench Adjustment

1) Close choke valve. Position fast idle lever on first (high) step of fast idle cam on Subaru models, on second step on Datsun/Nissan and on third step on Mazda.

2) Measure clearance between primary throttle valve and wall of throttle chamber. Adjust by turning fast idle adjustment screw.

Fig. 3: Fast Idle Bench Adjustment

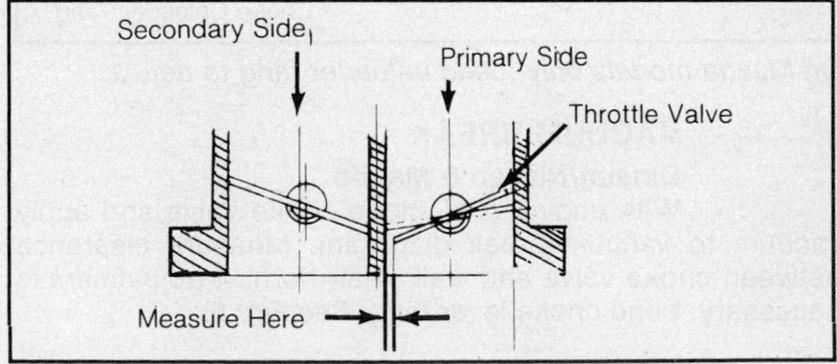
Secondary Side
Primary Side
Throttle Valve
Measure Here

SECONDARY THROTTLE CLEARANCE

1) Secondary throttle valve begins to opens when primary throttle valve opens 57° on Mazda, 49° on Datsun/Nissan and Subaru.

1983 Hitachi Carburetors

HITACHI DCZ 328, DCP 306, DFC 328 & DFP 306 2-BARREL (Cont.)

Fig. 4: Secondary Throttle Clearance Adjustment

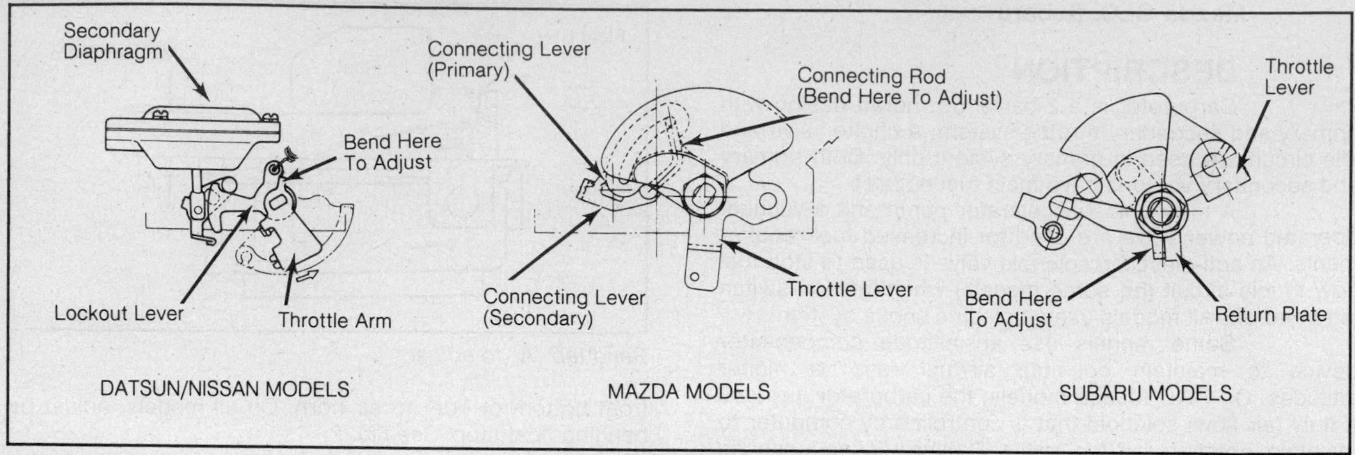
Secondary Diaphragm
Bend Here To Adjust
Lockout Lever
Throttle Arm
DATSUN/NISSAN MODELS
Connecting Lever (Primary)
Connecting Rod (Bend Here To Adjust)
Connecting Lever (Secondary)
Throttle Lever
MAZDA MODELS
Throttle Lever
Bend Here To Adjust
Return Plate
SUBARU MODELS

2) To check adjustment, measure clearance between primary throttle valve and wall of throttle chamber, as secondary throttle valve begins to open.

3) If adjustment is necessary, bend connecting rod on Mazda, throttle lever tang on Datsun/Nissan or adjustment tang on Subaru to obtain specifications. *See Fig. 4.*

CHOKE UNLOADER

Open throttle valve to wide open position. Gently hold choke valve closed and measure clearance between choke valve and wall of air horn. If adjustment is necessary, bend choke unloader tang on Mazda, replace air horn on Datsun/Nissan. *See Fig. 5.*

Fig. 5: Choke Unloader Adjustment

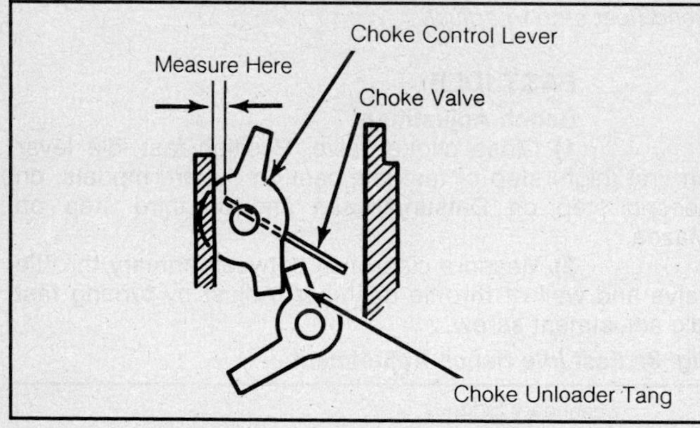
Choke Control Lever
Measure Here
Choke Valve
Choke Unloader Tang

On Mazda models only, bend unloader tang to adjust.

VACUUM BREAK

Datsun/Nissan & Mazda

With engine cold, close choke valve and apply vacuum to vacuum break diaphram. Measure clearance between choke valve and wall of air horn. If adjustment is necessary, bend choke lever tang. *See Fig. 6.*

CHOKE VALVE

Mazda Only

1) With fast idle cam adjusted correctly, place the fast idle cam on second step and close the choke valve by finger. Measure clearance between choke valve and the wall of air horn.

2) Clearance should be .035-.051" (.88-1.28 mm). Adjust clearance by bending tang on fast idle cam. If large adjustment is required, choke rod should be bent.

ACCELERATOR LINKAGE

Mazda Only

1) Check the freeplay of the cable at the carburetor. If play is not within range of .04-.12" (1-3 mm) adjust with adjusting nut.

2) On FWD models, fully depress accelerator pedal and check that throttle valves open completely. Adjust pedal stop bolt if necessary.

OVERHAUL

DISASSEMBLY

NOTE: **Disassembly and reassembly procedures for Datsun/Nissan models were not available from manufacturer.**

Subaru

1) Remove throttle return spring, pump lever shaft, pump lever, spring and spring washer. Disconnect cam connecting rod, cotter pins and washers. Remove return spring of return plate. Unclamp harness at 2 points.

2) Remove anti-dieseling switch. Remove the choke chamber, being careful not to damage the float.

Fig. 6: Vacuum Break Adjustment

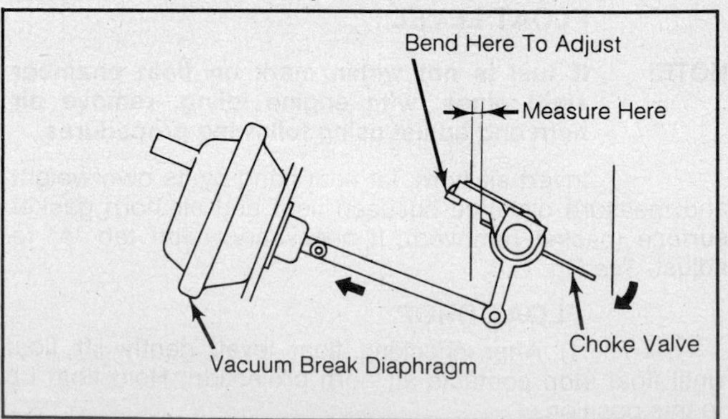
Bend Here To Adjust
Measure Here
Choke Valve
Vacuum Break Diaphragm

Bend choke lever tang to adjust.

1983 Hitachi Carburetors

HITACHI DCZ 328, DCP 306, DFC 328 & DFP 306 2-BARREL (Cont.)

Remove secondary diaphragm snap ring, secondary diaphragm, gasket and screws.

3) Separate float chamber, throttle chamber, accelerating pump piston and pump cover. Remove float shaft, float and needle valve. Remove primary and secondary slow air bleeds.

4) Remove switch vent solenoid valve, gasket and screws. Remove piston return spring, ball and injector weight. Remove primary and secondary main air bleeds. Remove primary and secondary plugs and slow jets.

5) Remove lock plate, float chamber drain plugs and primary and secondary main jets and power valve. Remove throttle adjusting screw and spring and idle adjusting screw and spring. Remove nuts and parts on throttle valve shaft.

Mazda (FWD)

1) Remove the accelerator pump lever and disconnect choke rod and lead wire from automatic choke heater. Remove air vent solenoid valve, air horn and gasket, float, needle valve and accelerator pump.

2) Invert the main body and remove pump return spring, pump injector weight, pump outlet check ball and pump inlet check ball. Remove all jets and air bleeds.

3) Note the size and position of all bleeds so they may be installed in correct positions. Remove jets, idle switch, secondary diaphragm and slow fuel cut solenoid valve.

4) Remove bolt located between throttle valves and separate throttle body from main body. Do not remove throttle valve and shaft, venturi, choke valve and shaft. Remove mixture adjusting screw after removing spring pin with a drift.

Mazda (RWD)

1) Remove accelerator pump connecting rod and lever, throttle return spring and disconnect choke rod. Spread clip and disconnect automatic choke heater and slow fuel cut solenoid valve leads.

2) Separate air horn and automatic choke assembly from main body. Remove accelerator pump piston and boot, float and float pin and needle valve. Remove primary and secondary slow air bleeds.

3) Drill out rivets and remove choke thermostat cover. Invert main body and remove accelerator pump return spring and inlet check ball. Remove discharge weight, slow fuel cut solenoid and gasket and accelerator switch.

4) Remove the secondary diaphragm pin, attaching screws, diaphragm and gasket. Remove bolt located between throttle valves and separate throttle body from main body.

5) Remove diaphragm cover, spring and diaphragm and spring and ball. Remove all air jets and bleeds, noting positioning and sizes for reassembly. Remove power valve, throttle hanger and throttle adjustment screw.

6) Pull out out mixture adjusting screw shell or cut the shell with a hacksaw to remove mixture adjusting screw.

CLEANING

NOTE: **Do not immerse synthetic parts, electrical components or diaphragm assemblies in carburetor cleaner.**

Replace all parts contained in service overhaul kits. Clean cast parts with carburetor cleaner. Clean jets, fuel passages and vacuum ports with compressed air. Do not use wire or pointed metal objects. Clean all other parts with solvent and soft brush.

INSPECTION

1) Inspect air horn, throttle body and main body for cracks, nicks or burrs on gasket surfaces; float for damage, wear or deformation; needle valve for wear and improper seating and seat strainer for rust or breaks.

2) Inspect jets and air bleeds for clogged orifices, damaged threads, heads slots and installation holes. Check thermostat cover for continuity between wire connector and heater housing. Replace heater if no continuity.

3) Inspect accelerator pump piston assembly for wear on sliding portion and leather cup and rust and spring for rust. Inspect secondary diaphragm for wear or damage and throttle valves for smooth movement and shaft wear.

4) Check diaphragm assemblies for leaks and proper operation. Apply battery voltage to terminals of solenoid valves and electric switches, listen for operating sound as terminals are connected and disconnected.

REASSEMBLY

1) To reassemble, reverse the disassembly procedure using all new gaskets, taking care not to mistake primary and secondary barrel parts.

2) On Mazda RWD models, install a new mixture adjustment screw and shell if old mixture screw was removed. Lightly seat screw and back-out 4 turns to obtain prelimary adjustment.

3) Set float level and adjust linkage when required and ensure smooth operation of system after completing adjustments. On Subaru, install piston return spring with hook portion facing downward.

1983 Hitachi Carburetors

HITACHI DCZ 328, DCP 306, DFC 328 & DFP 306 2-BARREL (Cont.)

Fig. 7: Exploded View of Datsun/Nissan Pulsar and Sentra Standard Carburetor

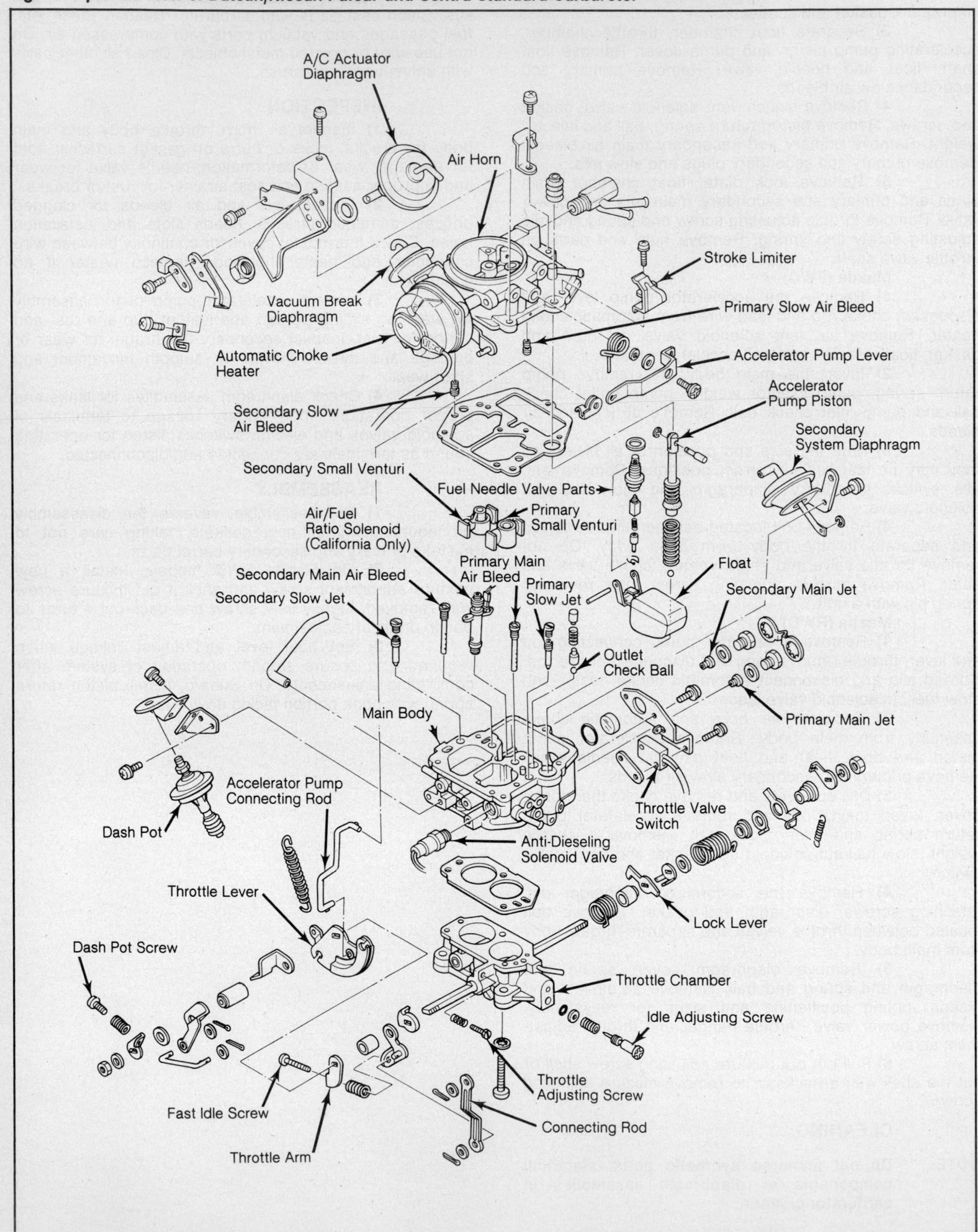

A/C Actuator Diaphragm
Air Horn
Stroke Limiter
Vacuum Break Diaphragm
Primary Slow Air Bleed
Automatic Choke Heater
Accelerator Pump Lever
Accelerator Pump Piston
Secondary Slow Air Bleed
Secondary System Diaphragm
Secondary Small Venturi
Fuel Needle Valve Parts
Air/Fuel Ratio Solenoid (California Only)
Primary Small Venturi
Primary Main Air Bleed
Float
Secondary Main Air Bleed
Secondary Slow Jet
Primary Slow Jet
Secondary Main Jet
Outlet Check Ball
Main Body
Primary Main Jet
Accelerator Pump Connecting Rod
Dash Pot
Throttle Valve Switch
Anti-Dieseling Solenoid Valve
Throttle Lever
Lock Lever
Dash Pot Screw
Throttle Chamber
Idle Adjusting Screw
Throttle Adjusting Screw
Fast Idle Screw
Connecting Rod
Throttle Arm

1983 Hitachi Carburetors

HITACHI DCZ 328, DCP 306, DFC 328 & DFP 306 2-BARREL (Cont.)

Fig. 8: Exploded View of Datsun/Nissan Sentra MPG Carburetor

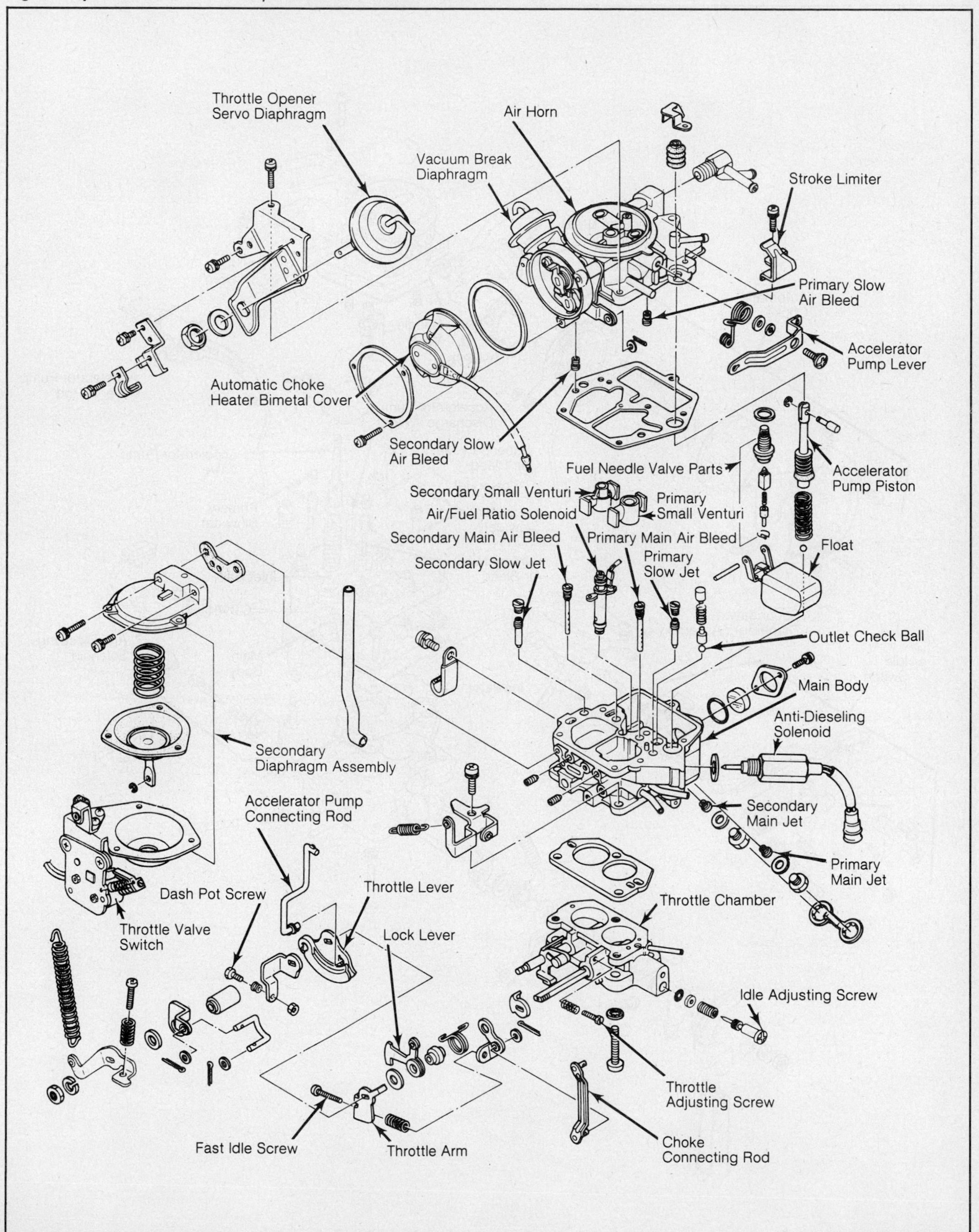
Throttle Opener
Servo Diaphragm
Air Horn
Vacuum Break
Diaphragm
Stroke Limiter
Primary Slow
Air Bleed
Accelerator
Pump Lever
Automatic Choke
Heater Bimetal Cover
Secondary Slow
Air Bleed
Fuel Needle Valve Parts
Accelerator
Pump Piston
Secondary Small Venturi
Primary
Small Venturi
Air/Fuel Ratio Solenoid
Secondary Main Air Bleed
Primary Main Air Bleed
Float
Secondary Slow Jet
Primary
Slow Jet
Outlet Check Ball
Main Body
Anti-Dieseling
Solenoid
Secondary
Diaphragm Assembly
Accelerator Pump
Connecting Rod
Secondary
Main Jet
Primary
Main Jet
Dash Pot Screw
Throttle Lever
Throttle Chamber
Throttle Valve
Switch
Lock Lever
Idle Adjusting Screw
Throttle
Adjusting Screw
Choke
Connecting Rod
Fast Idle Screw
Throttle Arm

1983 Hitachi Carburetors

HITACHI DCZ 328, DCP 306, DFC 328 & DFP 306 2-BARREL (Cont.)

Fig. 9: Exploded View of Typical Mazda GLC Carburetor

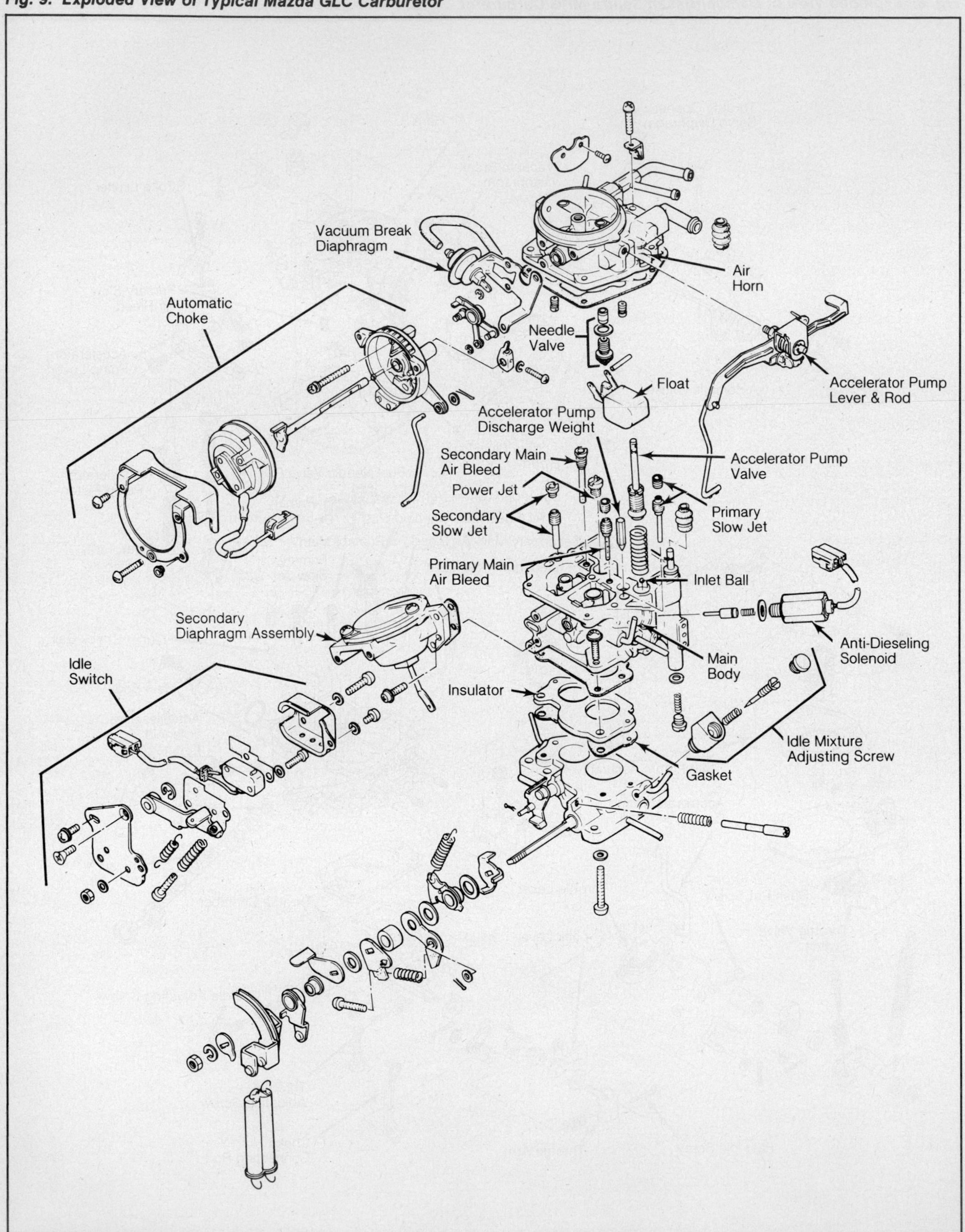
Vacuum Break
Diaphragm
Air
Horn
Automatic
Choke
Needle
Valve
Float
Accelerator Pump
Lever & Rod
Accelerator Pump
Discharge Weight
Secondary Main
Air Bleed
Accelerator Pump
Valve
Power Jet
Secondary
Slow Jet
Primary
Slow Jet
Primary Main
Air Bleed
Inlet Ball
Secondary
Diaphragm Assembly
Anti-Dieseling
Solenoid
Idle
Switch
Main
Body
Insulator
Idle Mixture
Adjusting Screw
Gasket

1983 Hitachi Carburetors

HITACHI DCZ 328, DCP 306, DFC 328 & DFP 306 2-BARREL (Cont.)

Fig. 10: Exploded View of Subaru Carburetor

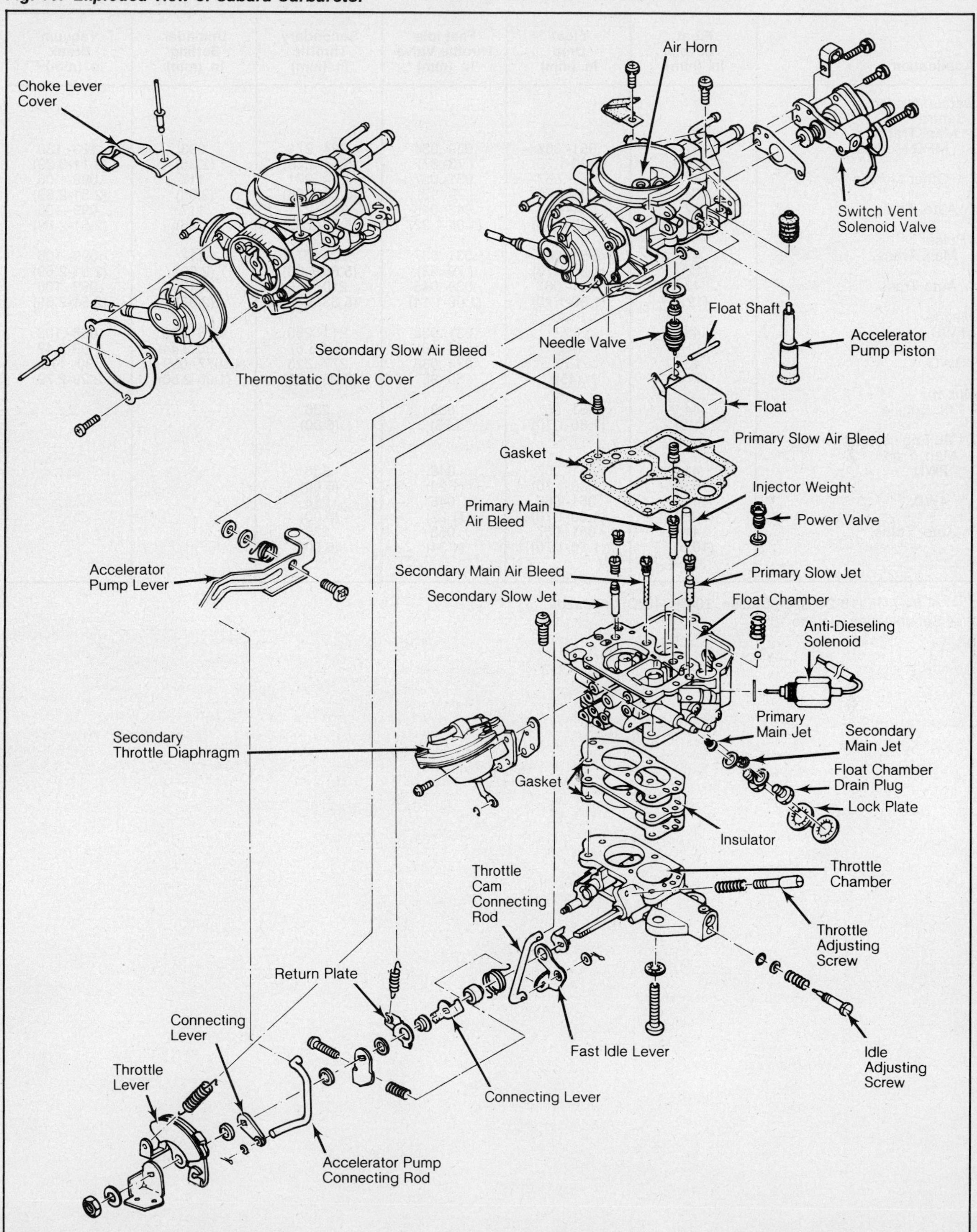

Choke Lever Cover
Air Horn
Switch Vent Solenoid Valve
Float Shaft
Accelerator Pump Piston
Needle Valve
Secondary Slow Air Bleed
Thermostatic Choke Cover
Float
Primary Slow Air Bleed
Gasket
Injector Weight
Primary Main Air Bleed
Power Valve
Accelerator Pump Lever
Secondary Main Air Bleed
Primary Slow Jet
Secondary Slow Jet
Float Chamber
Anti-Dieseling Solenoid
Primary Main Jet
Secondary Main Jet
Secondary Throttle Diaphragm
Float Chamber Drain Plug
Gasket
Lock Plate
Insulator
Throttle Cam Connecting Rod
Throttle Chamber
Throttle Adjusting Screw
Return Plate
Connecting Lever
Fast Idle Lever
Idle Adjusting Screw
Throttle Lever
Connecting Lever
Accelerator Pump Connecting Rod

1983 Hitachi Carburetors

HITACHI DCZ 328, DCP 306, DFC 328 & DFP 306 2-BARREL (Cont.)

CARBURETOR ADJUSTMENT SPECIFICATIONS

Application	Float Level In. (mm)	Float Drop In. (mm)	Fast Idle Throttle Valve In. (mm)	Secondary Throttle In. (mm)	Unloader Setting In. (mm)	Vacuum Break In. (mm) [1]
Datsun/Nissan						
Sentra						
Man. Trans.						
MPG Models	.47 (12)	.051-.067 (1.30-1.70)	.029-.034 (.73-.87)	.224-.271 (5.68-6.88)	.093 (2.36)	.123-.130 (3.11-3.29)
Other Models	.47 (12)	.051-.067 (1.30-1.70)	.031-.037 (.79-.93)	.224-.271 (5.68-6.88)	.117 (2.96)	.099-1.06 (2.51-2.69)
Auto. Trans.	.47 (12)	.051-.067 (1.30-1.70)	.043-.048 (1.08-1.22)	.224-.271 (5.68-6.88)	.117 (2.96)	.099-.106 (2.51-2.69)
Pulsar						
Man. Trans.	.47 (12)	.051-.067 (1.30-1.70)	.031-.037 (.79-.93)	.224-.271 (5.68-6.88)	.117 (2.96)	.099-.106 (2.51-2.69)
Auto Trans.	.47 (12)	.051-.067 (1.30-1.70)	.039-.045 (1.00-1.14)	.210-.250 (5.33-6.33)	.117 (2.96)	.099-.106 (2.51-2.69)
Mazda						
FWD	.43 (11)	1.77 (45)	.031-.038 (.78-.96)	.211-.260 (5.4-6.6)	.075-.096 (1.90-2.44)	.068-.108 1.99-2.49
RWD	.43 (11)	1.77 (45)	.024-.038 (.60-.96)	.277-.325 (7.05-8.25)	.077-.099 (1.96-2.50)	.90-.110 2.29-2.79
Subaru						
1.6L Engine	.44 (11.3)	.051-.067 (1.30-1.70)	.039 (.98)	.236 (6.00)	[2]	.....
1.8L Engine						
Man. Trans.						
2WD	.41 (10.5)	.051-.067 (1.30-1.70)	.048 (1.22)	.236 (6.00)	[2]	.....
4WD	.41 (10.5)	.051-.067 (1.30-1.70)	.048 (1.22)	.236 (6.00)	[2]	.....
Auto. Trans.	.41 (10.5)	.051-.067 (1.30-1.70)	.053 (1.34)	.236 (6.00)	[2]	.....

[1] – At 64-77°F (18-24°C) on Datsun, 104°F (40°C) on Mazda.

[2] – Set unloader angle to 16°.

1983 Keihin Carburetors

KEIHIN 1-BARREL — HONDA

Prelude

DESCRIPTION

Prelude models use a pair of 1-barrel, side draft carburetors. A small third carburetor is located between the main carburetors to feed the prechambers. Carburetor components include electrically heated automatic choke, thermowax valve, fuel cut solenoid valves and idle boost diaphragm.

ADJUSTMENTS

NOTE: For all on-vehicle adjustments not covered in this article, see the appropriate TUNE-UP SERVICE PROCEDURES article.

FLOAT LEVEL

1) With carburetors removed, remove float chambers. Using the float level gauge (07401-0010000), measure the float level with the float tip lightly contacting the float valve and the carburetor float chamber surface inclined about 30° from vertical. Float level shoud be .56-.64" (15-17 mm). Adjust as necessary.

2) Remove the float chamber for the subcarburetor. Using the float level gauge, measure the float level of the subcarburetor in the same manner as the main carburetors. Float level should be .63-.71" (16-18 mm). Float level is not adjustable. If incorrect, replace carburetor float as a unit.

THROTTLE CABLE

1) Check that throttle cable operates smoothly with no binding or sticking. Repair as necessary. Check cable free-play at throttle linkage. Cable deflection should be 3/16-3/8" (4-10 mm).

2) If not, loosen lock nut and turn adjusting nut until cable can be deflected as specified. Tighten lock nut. With cable adjusted, check throttle valve to be sure it opens fully when accelerator pedal is pushed to floor.

CHOKE LINKAGE

1) Remove air cleaner. Remove choke cover. Disconnect the upper choke opener hose to the thermovalve and leave open to the atmosphere. Disconnect the lower hose and attach a hand vacuum pump. Apply 8 in. Hg vacuum. If vacuum drops below 8 in. Hg, repump to maintain level.

2) Turn the choke drive lever counterclockwise until it touches choke opener lever and measure the clearance between choke valve and casting. Clearance should be .059-.065" (1.51-1.65 mm) for manual transmission models, .053-.059" (1.36-1.51 mm) for automatic transmission models. Adjust clearance by bending tab "A". *See Fig. 1.*

Fig. 1: Choke Linkage Adjustment

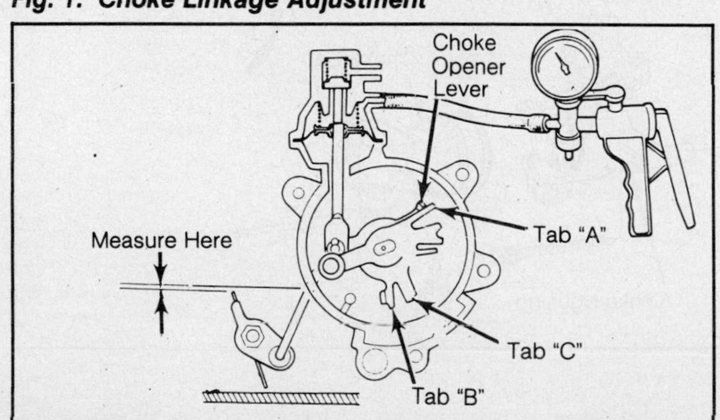
Choke
Opener
Lever
Tab "A"
Measure Here
Tab "C"
Tab "B"

3) Clamp off the upper vacuum hose and pull choke opener rod to the full extended position by using the hand vacuum pump until it shows 6-7 in. Hg vacuum. Turn the choke drive lever counterclockwise until tab "A" seats against the choke opener lever. Measure the clearance between the choke valve and casting.

4) Clearance should be 2.29-2.47" (.090-.098 mm) for manual transmission models and .077-.085 (1.96-2.14 mm) for automatic transmission models. Adjust by bending tab "B". While holding the opener lever against the tab, turn the choke drive lever until tab "C" touches the spring and measure clearance at choke valve.

5) Clearance should be .352-.370" (8.92-9.40 mm) for manual transmission models and .372-.390" (9.45-9.93 mm) for automatic transmission models. Adjust clearance by bending tab "C".

THERMOWAX VALVE

1) Disconnect the lower coolant hose from the thermowax valve. Insert a thermometer into the open coolant fitting. Measure and record coolant temperature. Refer to the chart shown in *Fig. 2.* Draw a line straight up from the measured temperature specification to intersect the diagonal line on the chart.

Fig. 2: Thermowax Valve Coolant Temperature Chart

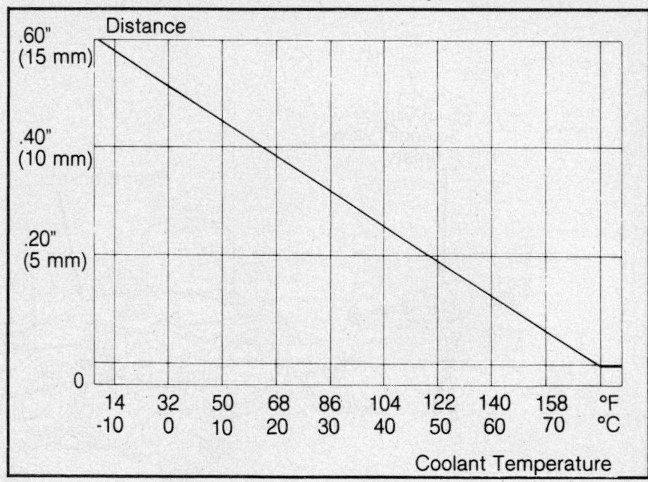
Distance
.60"
(15 mm)
.40"
(10 mm)
.20"
(5 mm)
0
14 32 50 68 86 104 122 140 158 °F
-10 0 10 20 30 40 50 60 70 °C
Coolant Temperature

2) Distance specification to the left of the intersection should correspond with measured distance

Fig. 3: Thermowax Valve Adjustment Point

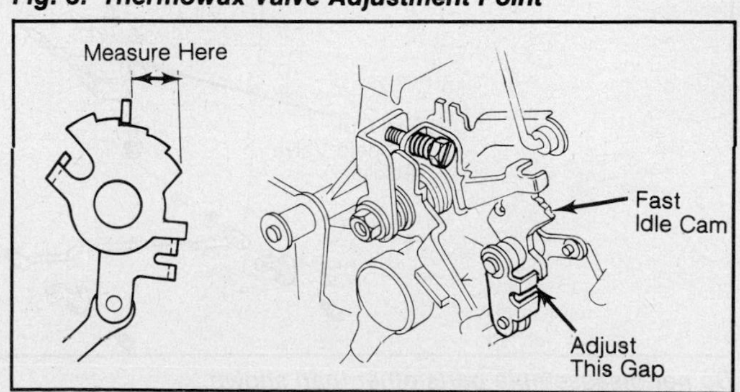
Measure Here
Fast
Idle Cam
Adjust
This Gap

KEIHIN 1-BARREL — HONDA (Cont.)

from the end of the fast idle cam to the end of fast idle lever. If measurement doesn't correspond, spread or narrow the gap in the tabs as necessary and recheck. *See Fig. 3.*

OVERHAUL

NOTE: The sub-carburetor is synchronized to the primary carburetors at the factory. It cannot be re-synchronized if the front and rear brackets have been removed at the same time. Do not disassemble other than as shown in Fig. 4.

Disassembly

1) With carburetors removed from vehicle, remove 2 attaching bolts and remove thermowax valve. Remove choke cap and automatic choke. Remove attaching screws and remove auxiliary fuel cut solenoid valve and primary fuel cut solenoid valve.

2) Remove cotter pins from idle boost diaphragm and remove front bracket through bolts. Remove any other attaching hardware and remove front bracket. *See Fig. 4.*

3) Remove attaching screws from piston chambers and remove chamber. Remove vacuum piston and jet needle as an assembly. Remove attaching screws

Fig. 4: Removal of Carburetor External Components

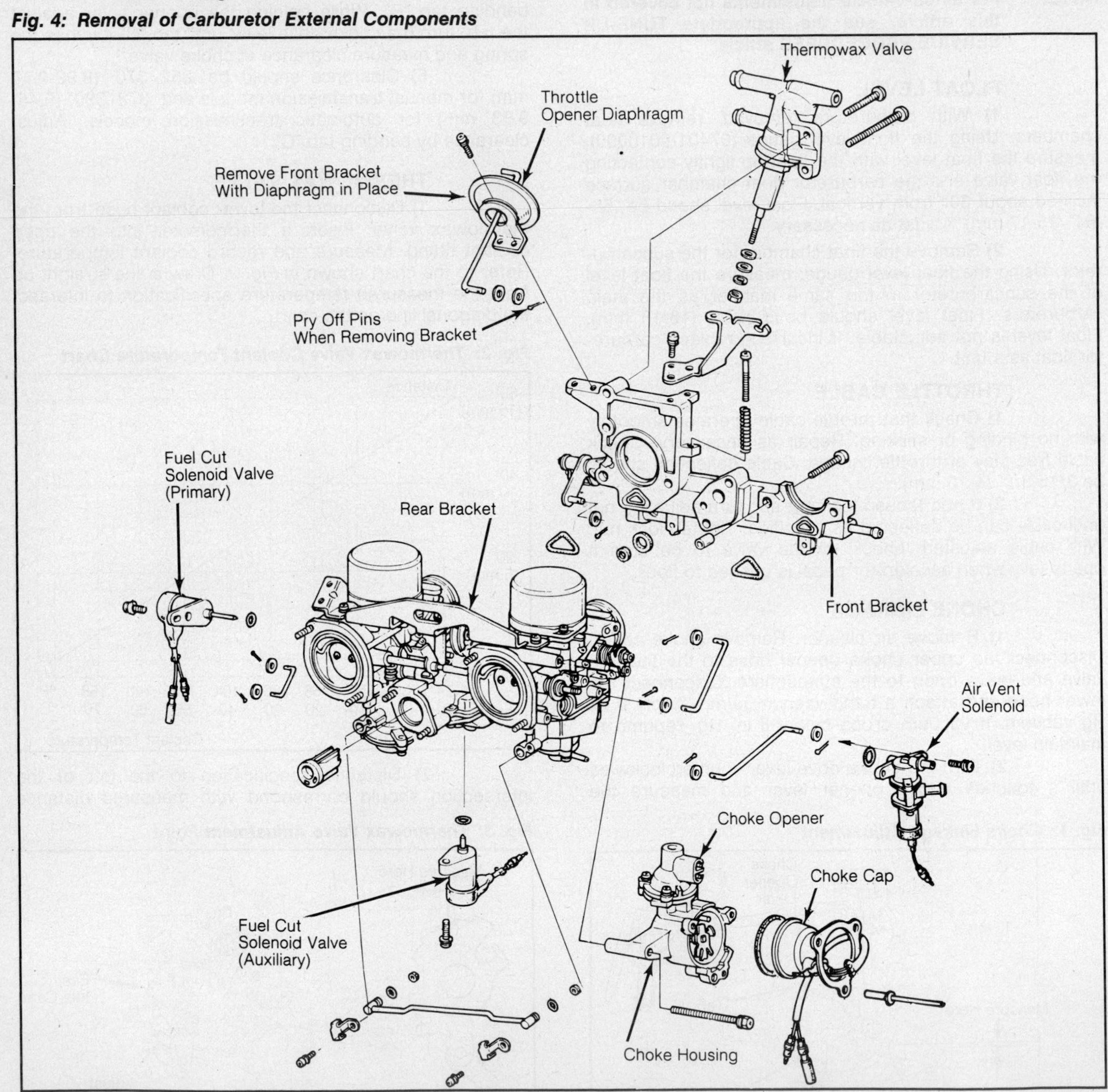
Thermowax Valve
Throttle
Opener Diaphragm
Remove Front Bracket
With Diaphragm in Place
Pry Off Pins
When Removing Bracket
Fuel Cut
Solenoid Valve
(Primary)
Rear Bracket
Front Bracket
Air Vent
Solenoid
Choke Opener
Choke Cap
Fuel Cut
Solenoid Valve
(Auxiliary)
Choke Housing

Do not disassemble parts other than shown.

KEIHIN 1-BARREL — HONDA (Cont.)

from float chamber and remove float chamber and accelerator pump as an assembly. *See Fig. 5.*

Reassembly

To reassemble carburetors, reverse the disassembly procedure.

Fig. 5: Exploded View Carburetor Assembly

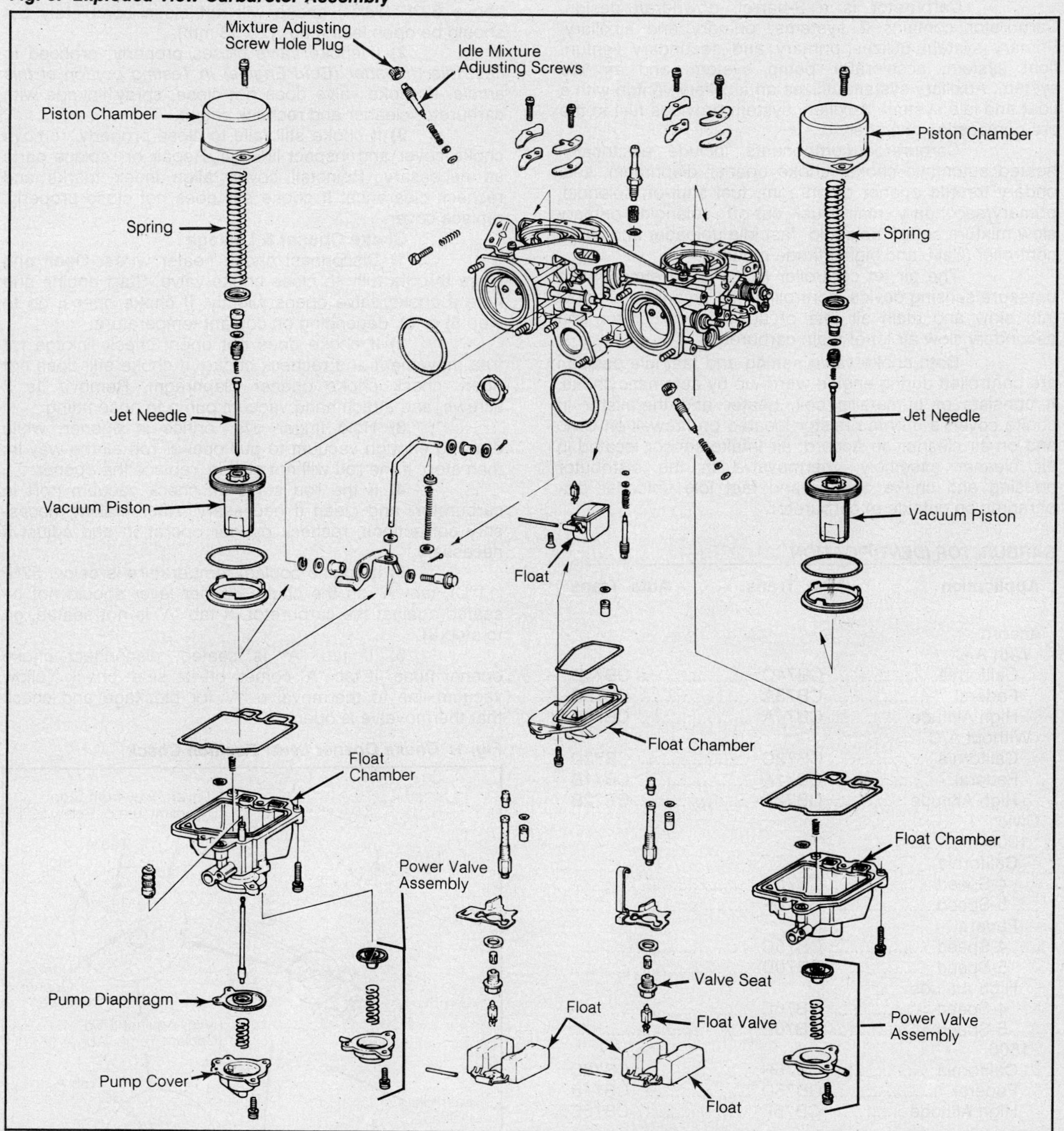
Mixture Adjusting
Screw Hole Plug
Idle Mixture
Adjusting Screws
Piston Chamber
Piston Chamber
Spring
Spring
Jet Needle
Jet Needle
Vacuum Piston
Vacuum Piston
Float
Float Chamber
Float
Chamber
Float Chamber
Power Valve
Assembly
Valve Seat
Pump Diaphragm
Float
Float Valve
Power Valve
Assembly
Pump Cover
Float

KEIHIN 3-BARREL – HONDA

Accord, Civic

DESCRIPTION

Carburetor is a 3-barrel, downdraft design. Carburetor contains 2 systems, primary and auxiliary. Primary system utilizes primary and secondary venturi, float system, accelerator pump system, and an idle system. Auxiliary system utilizes an auxiliary venturi with a float and idle system. Auxiliary system provides fuel to the pre-combustion chamber.

Carburetor components include electrically-heated automatic choke, choke opener diaphragm, secondary throttle opener diaphragm, fuel shut-off solenoid, primary/secondary main fuel cut-off solenoid, primary slow mixture cut-off solenoid, fast idle unloader and air jet controller (Calif. and high altitude models).

The air jet controller (AJC) is an atmospheric pressure sensing device, controlling the amount of air flow into slow and main air jets of auxiliary carburetor and secondary slow air jet of main carburetor.

Both choke valve setting and fast idle position are controlled during engine warm-up by automatic choke. It consists of bi-metallic coil, heater and thermistor in choke cover; a 5 ohm resistor located on firewall on Civic and on air cleaner on Accord; air intake sensor located in air cleaner assembly; thermovalve in the distributor housing and choke opener and fast idle unloader diaphragms on outside of carburetor.

CARBURETOR IDENTIFICATION

Application	Man. Trans.	Auto. Trans
Accord		
With A/C		
California	CB74C	CB74D
Federal	CB73A	CB73B
High Altitude	CB74A	CB74B
Without A/C		
California	CB72C	CB72D
Federal	CB71A	CB71B
High Altitude	CB72A	CB72B
Civic		
1300		
California		
4-Speed	CB76G	.....
5-Speed	CB70F	.....
Federal		
4-Speed	CB75C	.....
5-Speed	CB70D	.....
High Altitude		
4-Speed	CB76E	.....
5-Speed	CB70E	.....
1500		
California	CB76H	CB78D
Federal	CB75D	CB77B
High Altitude	CB76F	CB78C

ADJUSTMENTS

NOTE: For all on-vehicle adjustments not covered in this article, see the appropriate TUNE-UP SERVICE PROCEDURES article.

AUTOMATIC CHOKE

Choke Coil Tension & Linkage

1) Remove air cleaner and open and close throttle fully to close the choke valve. If temperature is above 82°F (28°C) choke will not close completely but should be open less than .125" (3 mm).

2) If choke valve closes properly, proceed to *Fast Idle Unloader (Cold Engine) in Testing portion of this article.* If choke valve does not close, spray linkage with carburetor cleaner and recheck choke.

3) If choke still fails to close properly, remove choke cover and inspect linkage. Repair or replace parts as necessary. Reinstall cover, align index marks and recheck clearance. If choke still does not close properly, replace cover.

Choke Opener & Linkage

1) Disconnect choke heater wires. Open and close throttle fully to close choke valve. Start engine and note if choke valve opens slightly. If choke opens, go to step **5)** or **8)**, depending on coolant temperature.

2) If choke does not open, check linkage for free movement and recheck choke. If choke still does not open, check choke opener diaphragm. Remove its 2 screws, and attach hand vacuum pump to hose fitting.

3) Hold finger over orifice in opener, while drawing enough vacuum to pull opener rod all the way in; then stop. If the rod will not stay in, replace the opener.

4) If the rod stays in, check vacuum port in carburetor, and clean if necessary. After making necessary corrections, recheck opener operation and adjust if necessary.

5) If engine coolant temperature is below 52°F (11°C), tab "A" on the choke opener lever should not be seated against the carburetor. If tab "A" is not seated, go to step **8)**.

6) If tab "A" is seated, disconnect choke opener hose. If tab "A" comes off its seat, check Yellow vacuum line to thermovalve "A" for blockage and check that thermovalve is open.

Fig. 1: Choke Opener Lever Position Check

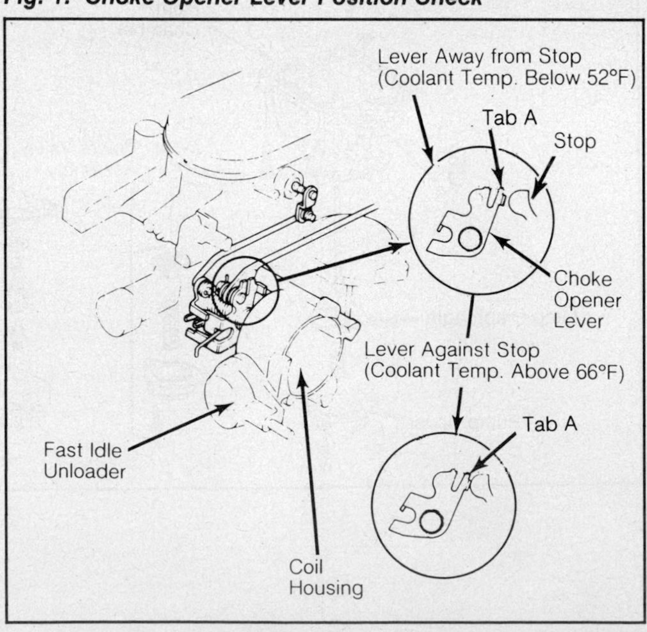
Lever Away from Stop
(Coolant Temp. Below 52°F)
Tab A
Stop
Choke
Opener
Lever
Lever Against Stop
(Coolant Temp. Above 66°F)
Tab A
Fast Idle
Unloader
Coil
Housing

7) If tab "A" does not come off its seat, press down on the choke opener lever until it does. If it won't

KEIHIN 3-BARREL – HONDA (Cont.)

stay off, clean out the choke opener fitting with a No. 76 (.5 mm) drill bit and recheck. If tab "A" still does not come off its seat, replace the choke opener.

8) If coolant temperature is above 66°F (19°C), tab "A" on choke opener lever should be seated against the carburetor. If tab "A" is seated, reconnect the choke heater wire and proceed to *Choke Coil Heater in Testing portion of this article.* If tab "A" is not seated, check vacuum line to thermovalve "A" and check that thermovalve "A" is closed.

Choke Valve Opening

1) Remove choke cover. While holding the choke valve closed, open and close the throttle fully to engage the choke and fast idle linkage.

2) Disconnect the choke opener hose from thermovalve "A" and attach a check valve. Apply 15-85 psi (1-6 kg/cm²) compressed air to choke opener.

3) Push choke opener rod toward the opener diaphragm until it stops. Pull choke drive lever down against choke opener lever.

4) Measure clearance between choke valve and carburetor body. Adjust first stage clearance specification by bending tab "D". *See Fig. 2.*

Fig. 2: Choke Valve Clearance Measurement

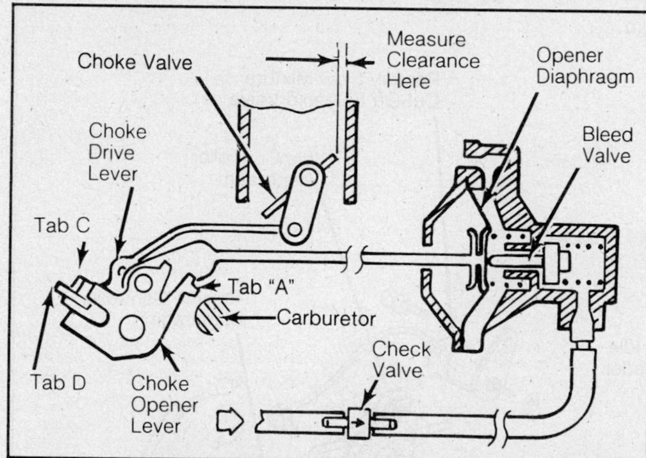
Choke Valve
Measure Clearance Here
Opener Diaphragm
Choke Drive Lever
Bleed Valve
Tab C
Tab "A"
Carburetor
Check Valve
Tab D
Choke Opener Lever

5) Remove the check valve, and reconnect the choke opener hose. Hold both levers together, and push toward opener diaphragm until tab "A" seats against carburetor.

6) Measure choke valve clearance. Adjust second stage clearance by bending tab "A". While holding choke opener lever, release choke drive lever and measure choke valve clearance.

7) Tab "C" on the drive lever should stay seated against the spring loop. If not, open and close throttle to engage choke and fast idle linkage and recheck. Adjust third stage clearance specification by bending tab "C".

FLOAT LEVEL

1) Ensure vehicle is on level ground. Start engine and warm to normal operating temperature. Snap throttle between idle and 3000 RPM several times, and then let idle.

2) With fuel level stabilized, check that it touches dot on the inspection windows. Adjust by turning external adjusting screws. *See Fig. 3.*

3) Do not turn adjusting screws more than 1/8 turn every 15 seconds. When correct float level is

Fig. 3: Float Level Adjustment

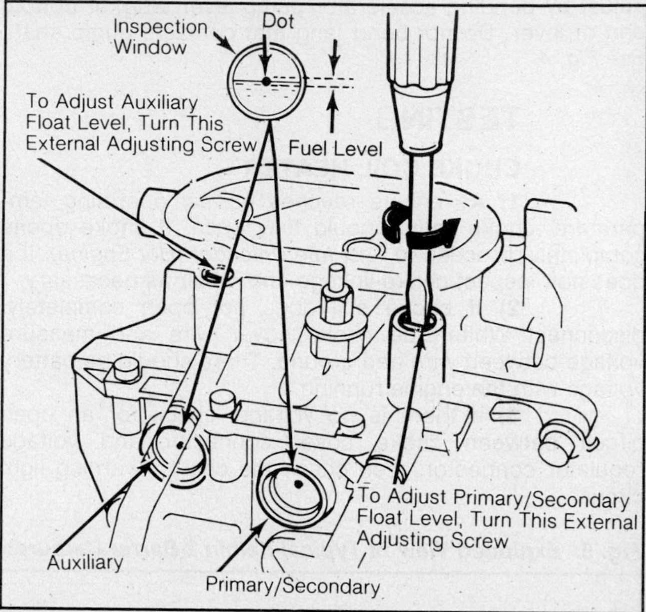
Inspection Window
Dot
To Adjust Auxiliary Float Level, Turn This External Adjusting Screw
Fuel Level
To Adjust Primary/Secondary Float Level, Turn This External Adjusting Screw
Auxiliary
Primary/Secondary

achieved, paint adjusting screws to keep adjustment from changing.

THROTTLE CABLE

1) Check throttle cable for smooth operation, with no binding or sticking. Check cable free play at linkage. Adjust cable deflection to .16-.40" (4-10 mm) by turning adjusting nut.

2) Secure by tightening lock nut. Throttle valve should open fully when accelerator pedal is depressed and return to idle position when pedal is released.

ACCELERATOR PUMP

1) Check accelerator linkage to ensure pump shaft travels freely throughout pump stroke and pump lever is in contact with pump shaft. Measure gap between bottom end of pump lever and stop tab.

Fig. 4: Accelerator Pump Adjustment

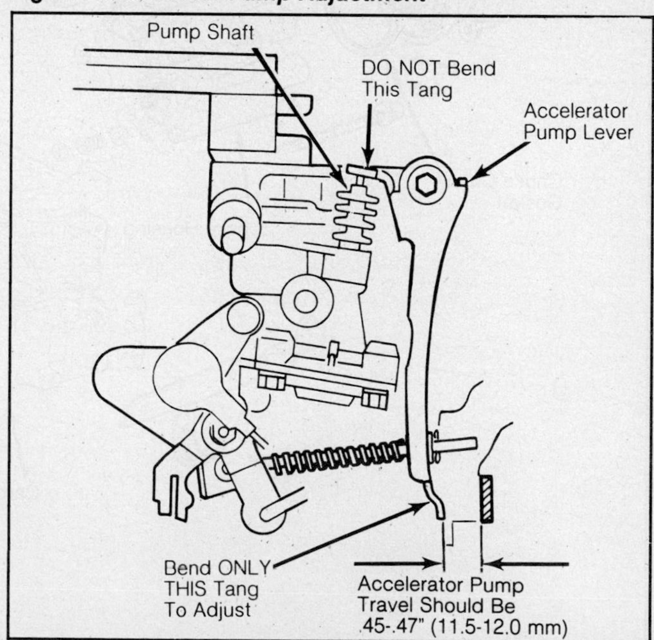
Pump Shaft
DO NOT Bend This Tang
Accelerator Pump Lever
Bend ONLY THIS Tang To Adjust
Accelerator Pump Travel Should Be .45-.47" (11.5-12.0 mm)

KEIHIN 3-BARREL – HONDA (Cont.)

2) If clearance is not .45-.47" (11.5-12.0 mm), adjust by bending accelerator pump lever tang, at bottom end of lever. Do not bend tang that contacts pump shaft. *See Fig. 4.*

TESTING

CHOKE COIL HEATER

1) As engine reaches normal operating temperature, choke valve should fully open. If choke opens completely, proceed to *Fast Idle Unloader (Hot Engine).* If it does not, inspect choke linkage and repair as necessary.

2) If choke still does not open completely, disconnect White/Blue choke cover wire and measure voltage between wire and ground. There should be battery voltage with the engine running.

3) If there is no voltage, check for an open circuit between choke cover connector and voltage regulator connector, then check the charge warning light circuit.

4) If the voltmeter reads battery voltage, connect the Blue/White wire, disconnect the air temperature connector and measure the voltage from the Red choke cover wire to ground. Leave choke cover wires connected. Voltmeter should read 2-4 volts.

5) If the voltmeter reads 0 volts, choke heater has an open circuit. Replace the choke cover. If the voltmeter reads battery voltage, check for an open circuit in the external resistor or its wiring. If the resistor circuit is okay, check for a short in choke heater.

FAST IDLE UNLOADER (COLD ENGINE)

1) Disconnect 2 vacuum hoses from fast idle unloader. Open and close throttle fully to engage fast idle cam and start engine. If engine has fast idle, proceed to *Fast Idle Unloader (Hot Engine).*

2) If engine fails to run at fast idle, stop engine, remove choke cover and check operation of fast idle cam.

Fig. 5: Exploded View of Typical Keihin 2-Barrel Carburetor

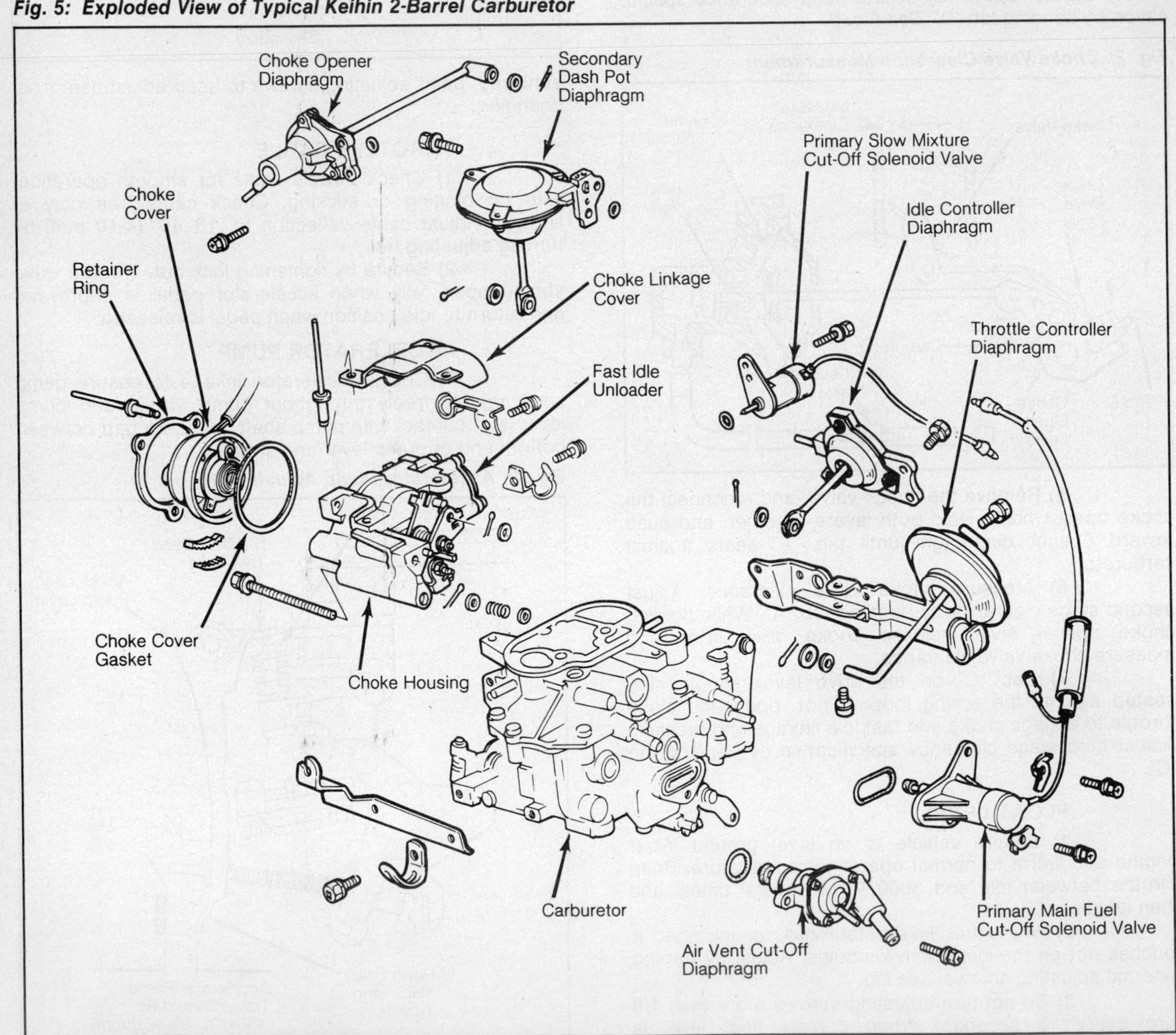
Choke Opener Diaphragm
Secondary Dash Pot Diaphragm
Choke Cover
Retainer Ring
Choke Linkage Cover
Fast Idle Unloader
Primary Slow Mixture Cut-Off Solenoid Valve
Idle Controller Diaphragm
Throttle Controller Diaphragm
Choke Cover Gasket
Choke Housing
Carburetor
Air Vent Cut-Off Diaphragm
Primary Main Fuel Cut-Off Solenoid Valve

KEIHIN 3-BARREL – HONDA (Cont.)

Apply vacuum to inside fitting of unloader, and start engine. If idle speed drops, proceed to *Fast Idle Unloader (Hot Engine)*.

3) If idle fails to drop, check unloader for leaks, blockage or damaged diaphragm. Remove choke cover. Check unloader rod for free movement. Repair or replace as necessary and reconnect vacuum hoses.

FAST IDLE UNLOADER (HOT ENGINE)

1) Warm engine to normal operating temperature. Do not manually open throttle. If speed drops below 1400 RPM, as engine warms, adjust fast idle speed.

2) If not, disconnect 2 unloader hoses and check for vacuum. If vacuum is present, check diaphragm for leaks and free movement of unloader rod and recheck. If no vacuum is present, check thermovalve.

THERMOVALVE

1) Drain engine coolant until level is below distributor holder. Remove the distributor holder and thermovalve. Attach vacuum pump and apply vaccum to thermovalve.

NOTE: **Install additional vacuum hose on open vacuum port to prevent water from entering valve.**

2) Suspend thermovalve in cold water. Slowly heat water and note temperature and vacuum readings. Make certain thermometer does not contact bottom of container.

3) Thermovalve "A" should open below 60°F (15°C) and not hold vacuum. Valve should close above 77°F (25°C) and hold vacuum. Thermovalve "B" should open below 104°F (40°C) and close above 122°F (50°C).

CRANKING LEAK SOLENOID VALVE

1) Ground coil wire, disconnect inside hose from fast idle unloader and turn ignition switch to "START" position. If vacuum is present, check for voltage at cranking leak solenoid valve.

2) If no voltage, check wiring and fuse. If both are okay, replace starter relay on fuse/relay panel and recheck. If there is voltage, replace solenoid valve and recheck. Connect coil wire when finished.

AIR TEMPERATURE SENSOR

1) Disconnect and remove sensor from air cleaner. Check for continuity across sensor lead wires. Sensor should have continuity if air temperature is above 73°F (23°C).

2) Sensor should have no continuity if temperature is below 40°F (4.5°C). Replace air temperature sensor if not to specifications.

CARBURETOR ADJUSTMENT SPECIFICATIONS

Application	1st Stage Clearance In. (mm)		2nd Stage Clearance In. (mm)		3rd Stage Clearance In. (mm)	
	Man. Trans.	Auto. Trans.	Man. Trans.	Auto. Trans.	Man. Trans.	Auto. Trans.
Accord & Civic	[1] .040-.046 (1.02-1.16)	[2] .034-.040 (.863-1.02 mm)	.072-.080 (1.83-2.03)	.072-.080 (1.83-2.03)	[3] .151-.169 (3.84-3.29)	.151-1.69 (3.84-4.29)

[1] – Accord Hi. Alt. model is .046-.052" (1.16-1.32 mm).
[2] – Accord Calif. and Hi. Alt. and Civic 1500 cc Hi. Alt. models are .040-.046" (1.02-1.16 mm).
[3] – Accord Hi. Alt. model is .161-.179" (4.08-4.55 mm).

1983 Nikki Carburetors

NIKKI 2-BARREL – MAZDA B2000

DESCRIPTION

Carburetor is a 2-barrel, downdraft type, 2-stage design with an electric automatic choke. The primary stage includes a curb idle system, accelerator pump system, idle transfer system, main metering system and power enrichment system. The secondary stage includes an idle transfer system and main metering system.

CARBURETOR IDENTIFICATION

Application	Part No.
California	
Man. Trans.	8397-13-600
Auto. Trans.	HE94-13-600
Federal	
Man. Trans.	8387-13-600
Auto. Trans.	HE90-13-600

ADJUSTMENTS

NOTE: **For all on-vehicle adjustments not covered in this article, see the appropriate TUNE-UP SERVICE PROCEDURES article.**

FLOAT LEVEL

1) With engine running, check fuel level in fuel bowl sight glass. If fuel level is not to specified mark on sight glass, remove carburetor from vehicle.

2) Remove fuel bowl sight glass cover, invert carburetor and allow float to hang by its own weight. Measure clearance between top of float and fuel bowl. Bend float tab "A" to adjust. *See Fig. 1.*

Fig. 1: Float Level Adjustment

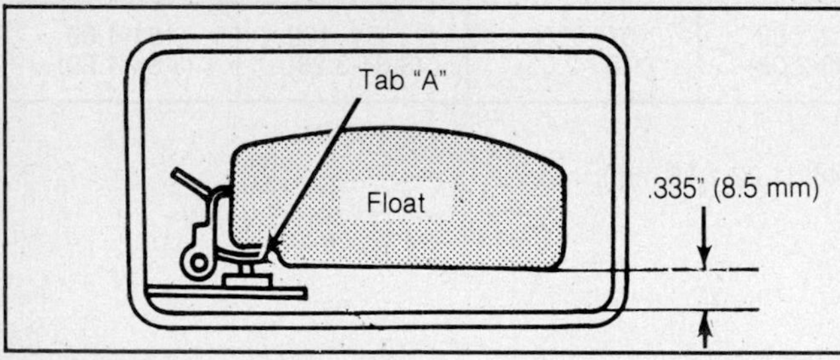
Tab "A"
Float
.335" (8.5 mm)

Bend float tab "A" to adjust.

FLOAT DROP

1) Position carburetor upright and allow float to hang by its own weight. Measure clearance between bottom of float and fuel bowl. Bend float tab "B" to adjust. *See Fig. 2.*

Fig. 2: Float Drop Adjustment

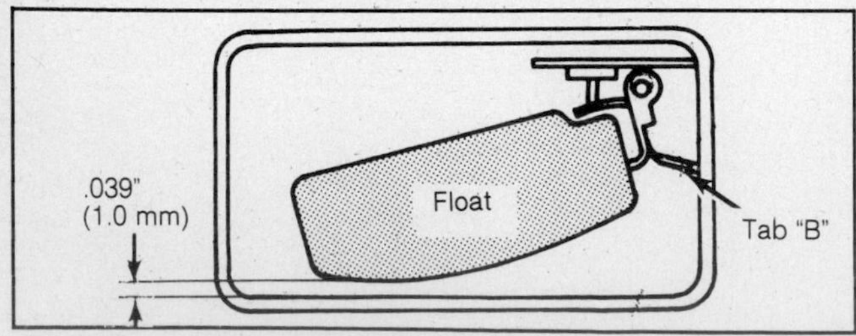
.039"
(1.0 mm)
Float
Tab "B"

Bend float tab "B" to adjust.

2) Install fuel bowl sight glass cover and install carburetor on engine. Operate engine and make sure fuel level is at specified mark in sight glass.

CHOKE LINKAGE (FAST IDLE OPENING ANGLE)

Fully close choke valve. Place fast idle adjusting screw on first (high) step of fast idle cam. Measure clearance between primary throttle valve and wall of throttle bore. Clearance should be .051-.059" (1.3-1.5 mm). Adjust by turning fast idle adjusting screw. *See Fig. 3.*

Fig. 3: Choke Linkage Adjustment (Fast Idle Opening Angle)

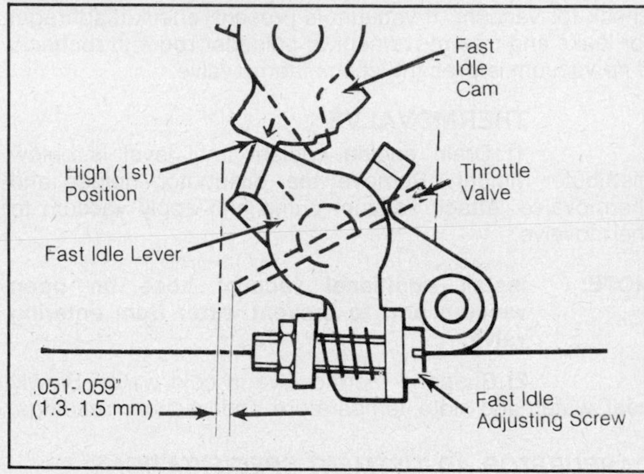
Fast
Idle
Cam
High (1st)
Position
Throttle
Valve
Fast Idle Lever
.051-.059"
(1.3- 1.5 mm)
Fast Idle
Adjusting Screw

Turn fast idle adjusting screw to adjust.

CHOKE VALVE OPENING

Place fast idle screw on second step of fast idle cam. Measure clearance between choke valve and air horn. Adjust by bending starting arm. If large adjustment is required, bend choke rod. *See Fig. 4.*

Fig. 4: Choke Valve Opening Adjustment

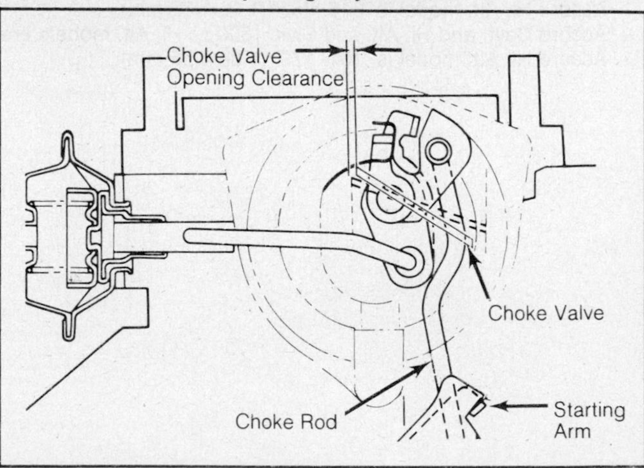
Choke Valve
Opening Clearance
Choke Valve
Choke Rod
Starting
Arm

Bend starting arm for small adjustment, choke rod if large adjustment is required.

NIKKI 2-BARREL – MAZDA B2000 (Cont.)

Fig. 5: Exploded View of Nikki 2-Barrel Carburetor

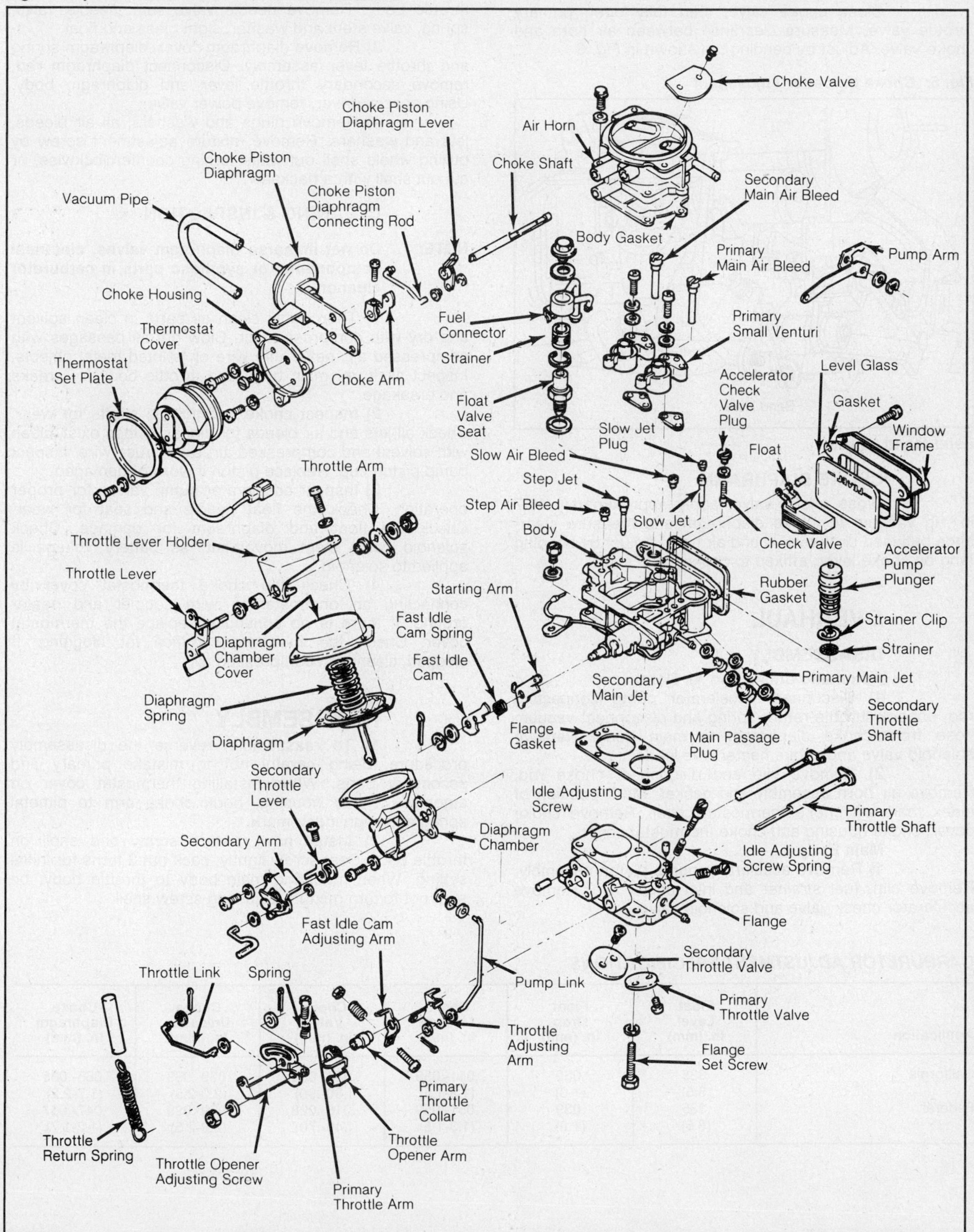
Choke Valve
Air Horn
Choke Piston Diaphragm Lever
Choke Shaft
Choke Piston Diaphragm
Secondary Main Air Bleed
Vacuum Pipe
Choke Piston Diaphragm Connecting Rod
Body Gasket
Pump Arm
Primary Main Air Bleed
Choke Housing
Fuel Connector
Primary Small Venturi
Thermostat Cover
Strainer
Thermostat Set Plate
Choke Arm
Level Glass
Accelerator Check Valve Plug
Float Valve Seat
Gasket
Window Frame
Slow Jet Plug
Float
Slow Air Bleed
Throttle Arm
Step Jet
Step Air Bleed
Slow Jet
Body
Check Valve
Throttle Lever Holder
Accelerator Pump Plunger
Throttle Lever
Rubber Gasket
Starting Arm
Fast Idle Cam Spring
Strainer Clip
Diaphragm Chamber Cover
Strainer
Fast Idle Cam
Primary Main Jet
Secondary Main Jet
Diaphragm Spring
Secondary Throttle Shaft
Flange Gasket
Main Passage Plug
Diaphragm
Secondary Throttle Lever
Idle Adjusting Screw
Primary Throttle Shaft
Diaphragm Chamber
Secondary Arm
Idle Adjusting Screw Spring
Flange
Fast Idle Cam Adjusting Arm
Secondary Throttle Valve
Throttle Link
Spring
Pump Link
Primary Throttle Valve
Throttle Adjusting Arm
Flange Set Screw
Primary Throttle Collar
Throttle Return Spring
Throttle Opener Arm
Throttle Opener Adjusting Screw
Primary Throttle Arm

1983 Nikki Carburetors

NIKKI 2-BARREL – MAZDA B2000 (Cont.)

CHOKE UNLOADER

Close choke valve, then fully open primary throttle valve. Measure clearance between air horn and choke valve. Adjust by bending tab shown in *Fig. 6.*

Fig. 6: Choke Unloader Adjustment

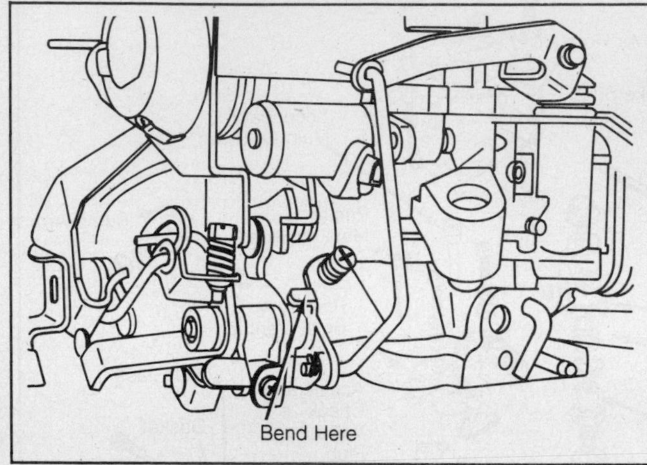
Bend Here

Bend tab to adjust.

CHOKE DIAPHRAGM

Close choke valve, apply approximately 15.7 in. Hg vacuum to choke diaphragm and measure clearance between choke valve and air horn. Adjust by bending tang on choke lever, affixed to choke valve shaft.

OVERHAUL

DISASSEMBLY

Automatic Choke and Air Horn

1) Disconnect accelerator pump connecting rod, unhook throttle return spring and disconnect vacuum hose from choke diaphragm to main body. Remove solenoid valve and choke heater wire leads.

2) Remove clip and disconnect choke rod. Remove air horn assembly and gasket. Mark position of index mark on choke thermostat cover. Remove choke cover, choke housing and choke thermostat cover.

Main Body

1) Remove accelerator pump piston assembly. Remove clip, fuel strainer and inlet check ball. Remove accelerator check valve and solenoid valve.

2) Invert carburetor and remove carburetor throttle body. Remove needle valve seat, needle valve, spring, valve stem and washer, sight glass and float.

3) Remove diaphragm cover, diaphragm spring and throttle lever assembly. Disconnect diaphragm rod, remove secondary throttle lever and diaphragm body. Using special driver, remove power valve.

4) Remove plugs and washers, all air bleeds, jets and washers. Remove mixture adjustment screw by pulling whole shell out while turning counterclockwise, or cut out shell with a hacksaw.

CLEANING & INSPECTION

NOTE: **Do not immerse diaphragm valves, electrical components, or synthetic parts in carburetor cleaner.**

1) Thoroughly clean all parts in clean solvent and dry with compressed air. Blow out all passages with compressed air, never use wire or pointed metal objects. Inspect air horn, main body and throttle body for cracks and breakage.

2) Inspect choke and throttle shafts for wear. Check all jets and air bleeds for clogs. If clogs exist, clean with solvent and compressed air. Do not use wire. Inspect pump piston cup. Replace piston if worn or damaged.

3) Inspect accelerator pump valves for proper operation. Check the float needle and seat for wear. Check the float and diaphragm for damage. Check solenoid valve stem movement, as battery voltage is applied to solenoid.

4) Check the choke thermostat cover by connecting an ohmmeter to wire coupler and heater ground. If there is no continuity, replace the thermostat cover. Check the fuel return orifice for clogging. If clogged, clean with compressed air.

REASSEMBLY

1) To reassemble, reverse the disassembly procedure, being careful not to mistake primary and secondary parts. When installing thermostat cover on automatic choke housing, hook choke arm to bimetal spring and align index mark.

2) Install new mixture screw and shell on throttle body. Seat screw lightly, back out 3 turns for initial setting. When mounting main body to throttle body, be sure not to turn mixture adjusting screw shell.

CARBURETOR ADJUSTMENT SPECIFICATIONS

Application	Float Level In. (mm)	Float Drop In. (mm)	Choke Linkage In. (mm)	Choke Valve In. (mm)	Choke Unloader In. (mm)	Choke Diaphragm In. (mm)
California	.335 (8.5)	.039 (1.0)	.051-.059 (1.3-1.5)	.024-.036 (.60-.90)	.079-.099 (2.0-2.5)	.065-.085 (1.7-2.2)
Federal	.335 (8.5)	.039 (1.0)	.051-.059 (1.3-1.5)	.016-.028 (.40-.70)	.079-.099 (2.0-2.5)	.047-.067 (1.2-1.7)

1983 Nikki Carburetors

NIKKI 2-BARREL – MAZDA 626

DESCRIPTION

Carburetor is a 2-barrel downdraft type. It is equipped with an electric automatic choke, coasting richer system, air vent solenoid, slow fuel cut solenoid, and computer controlled air/fuel (A/F) solenoid. A double venturi provides for high air flow velocity at the venturi under all operating conditions, resulting in more efficient atomization of fuel for smooth combustion.

ADJUSTMENTS

NOTE: For all on-vehicle adjustments not covered in this article, see the appropriate TUNE-UP SERVICE PROCEDURES article.

FLOAT LEVEL

Remove air horn from carburetor. Invert air horn and allow float to hang by its own weight. Measure clearance between float and air horn gasket surface, with gasket removed. If clearance is not .394" (10 mm), bend float seat to adjust. *See Fig. 1.*

Fig. 1: Float Level Adjustment

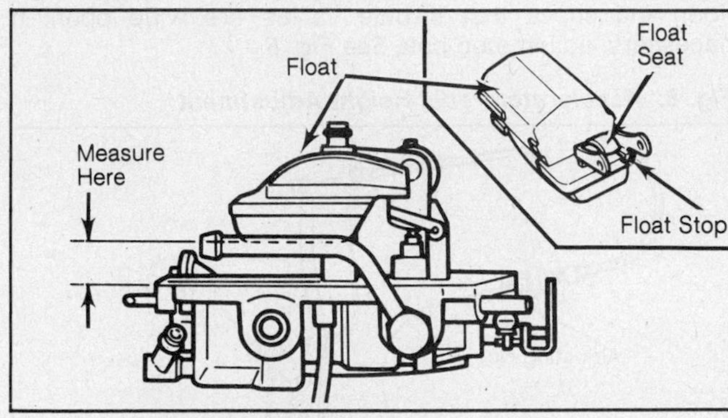
Float
Float Seat
Measure Here
Float Stop

Bend float seat to adjust.

FLOAT DROP

Turn air horn upright and allow float to hang by its own weight. *See Fig. 2.* Measure distance between bottom of float and air horn. If distance is not 1.93" (49 mm), bend float stop to adjust.

Fig. 2: Float Drop Adjustment

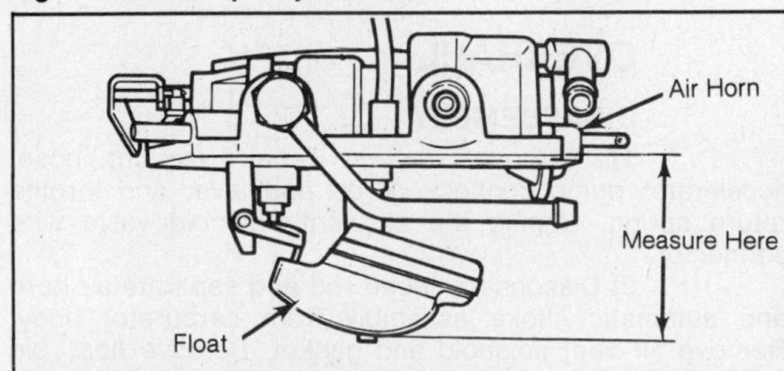
Air Horn
Measure Here
Float

Bend float stop to adjust.

CHOKE LINKAGE (FAST IDLE OPENING ANGLE)

Fully close choke valve. Position fast idle lever on second step of fast idle cam. Measure clearance between throttle valve and wall of throttle bore. Clearance should be .028-.043" (.70-1.1 mm). Adjust by turning fast idle adjustment screw. *See Fig. 3.*

Fig. 3: Choke Linkage Adjustment (Fast Idle Opening Angle)

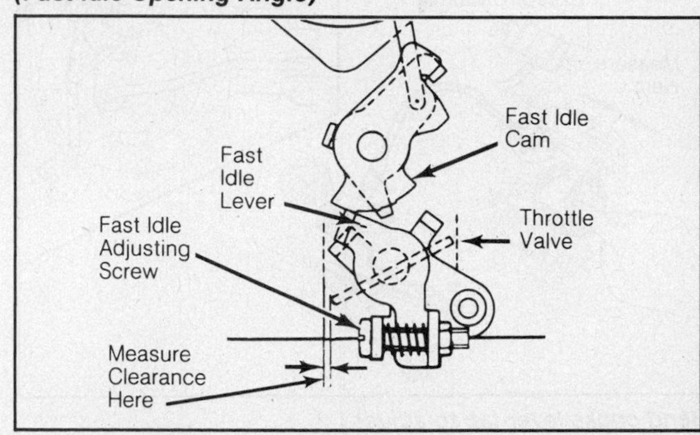
Fast Idle Cam
Fast Idle Lever
Throttle Valve
Fast Idle Adjusting Screw
Measure Clearance Here

Turn fast idle adjustment screw to adjust.

CHOKE VALVE OPENING

1) Check choke linkage adjustment, then place fast idle lever on second step of fast idle cam. Measure clearance between choke valve and air horn.

2) Choke valve clearance should be .023-.039" (.60-1.00 mm). Adjust clearance by bending starting arm. If large adjustment is necessary, bend choke rod. *See Fig. 4.*

Fig. 4: Choke Valve Opening Adjustment

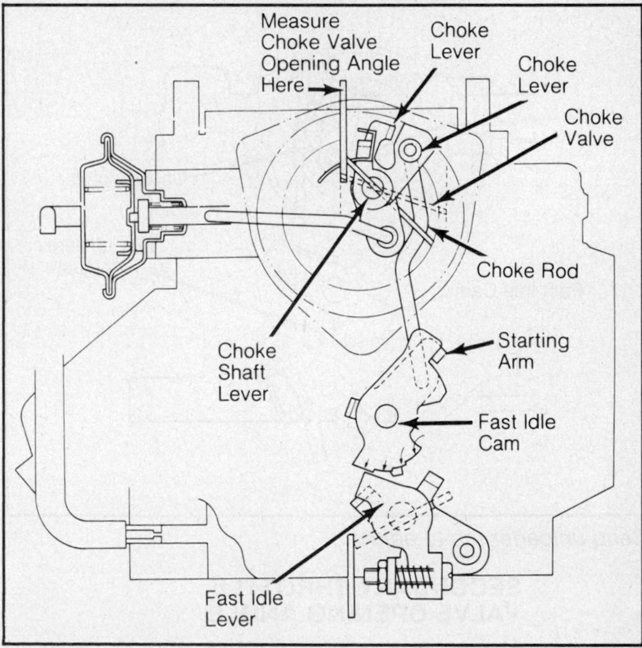
Measure Choke Valve Opening Angle Here
Choke Lever
Choke Lever
Choke Valve
Choke Rod
Choke Shaft Lever
Starting Arm
Fast Idle Cam
Fast Idle Lever

Bend starting arm for small adjustment, choke rod if large adjustment is necessary.

CHOKE DIAPHRAGM

1) Apply approximately 15.7 in. Hg vacuum to choke diaphragm vacuum tube. Fast idle lever should be on first (high) step of cam.

2) Gently press choke valve closed and measure clearance between upper edge of choke valve

NIKKI 2-BARREL – MAZDA 626 (Cont.)

and air horn. Bend choke lever tab until clearance is .067-.087" (1.70-2.20 mm). *See Fig. 5.*

Fig. 5: Choke Diaphragm Adjustment

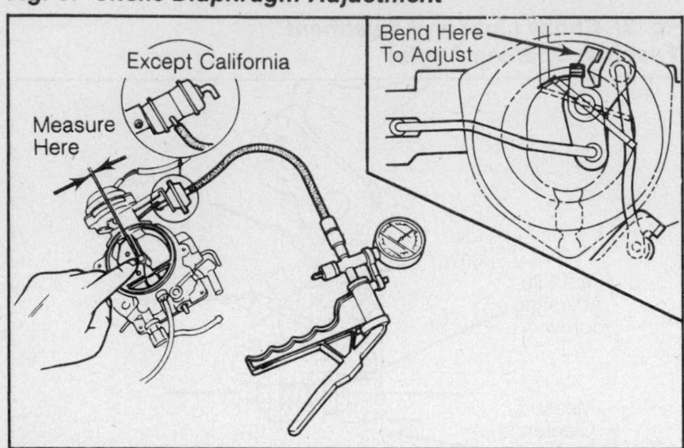
Except California
Measure Here
Bend Here To Adjust

Bend choke lever tab to adjust.

CHOKE UNLOADER

Fully close choke valve, open primary throttle valve completely and measure clearance between upper edge of choke valve and air horn. Adjust clearance to .112-.144" (2.85-3.65 mm) by bending unloader tab. *See Fig. 6.*

Fig. 6: Choke Unloader Adjustment

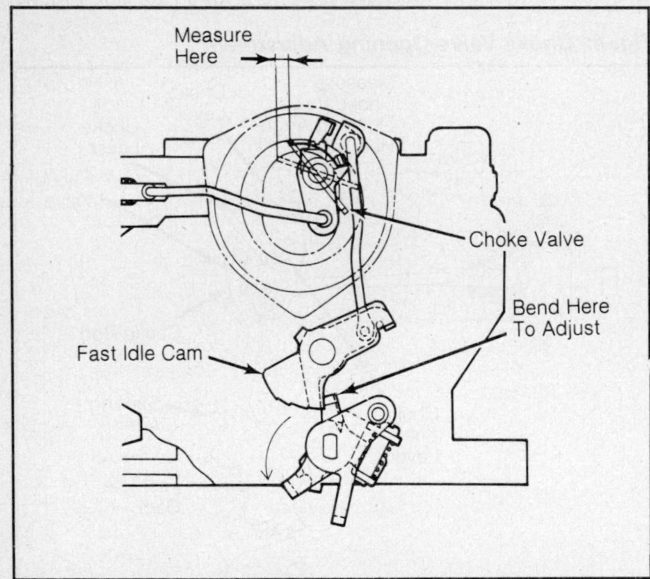
Measure Here
Choke Valve
Bend Here To Adjust
Fast Idle Cam

Bend unloader tab to adjust.

SECONDARY THROTTLE VALVE OPENING ANGLE

1) Secondary throttle valve should begin to open when primary throttle valve opens 48-52° and should be fully open when primary valve is fully open.

2) Check clearance of primary throttle valve and wall of throttle bore as secondary throttle valve begins to open. Bend throttle arm tab until clearance is .244-.283" (6.2-7.2 mm). *See Fig. 7.*

Fig. 7: Secondary Throttle Valve Opening Adjustment

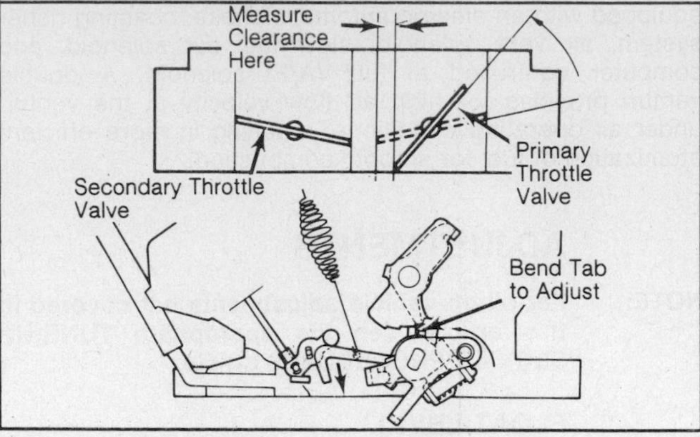
Measure Clearance Here
Primary Throttle Valve
Secondary Throttle Valve
Bend Tab to Adjust

Bend throttle arm tab to adjust.

ACCELERATOR LINKAGE

1) Accelerator pedal cable free play at carburetor should be .04-.12" (1-3 mm). If free play is not to specifications, adjust cable adjusting nut.

2) To check pedal height, depress pedal to the floor and check that throttle valves are wide open. If necessary, adjust stop bolt. *See Fig. 8.*

Fig. 8: Accelerator Pedal Height Adjustment

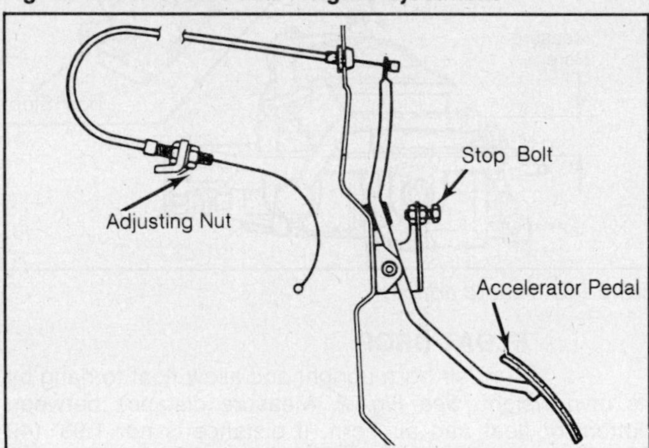
Stop Bolt
Adjusting Nut
Accelerator Pedal

Turn adjusting nut to adjust cable; stop bolt to adjust pedal height.

OVERHAUL

DISASSEMBLY

1) Remove vacuum break vacuum hose, accelerator pump connecting rod and lever and throttle return spring. Unplug the air vent solenoid valve wire connector.

2) Disconnect choke rod and separate air horn and automatic choke assembly from carburetor body. Remove air vent solenoid and gasket. Remove float, pin and gasket.

3) Remove needle valve assembly. Remove coasting richer solenoid valve and idle switch. Remove fuel cut solenoid valve and gasket. Remove dash pot bracket and dash pot.

NIKKI 2-BARREL – MAZDA 626 (Cont.)

4) Remove accelerator pump plunger assembly and spring. Remove retaining clip and check valve plug. Invert body, remove strainer and accelerator pump inlet check ball.

5) Remove accelerator pump outlet check ball and spring. Disconnect throttle link, vacuum diaphragm connecting rod and separate throttle body from main body.

NOTE: **One of the bolts attaching main body is in throttle body between throttle valves.**

6) Remove diaphragm cover mounting screws, cover, spring and diaphragm. Remove throttle lever hanger mounting screws. Remove fuel bowl sight glass mounting screws.

7) Remove cover, gasket, glass and rubber gasket. Remove all air bleeds and jets from main body. Note size and position of all jets and bleeds for installation in original position. *See Fig. 9.*

Fig. 9: Air Bleed and Jet Removal

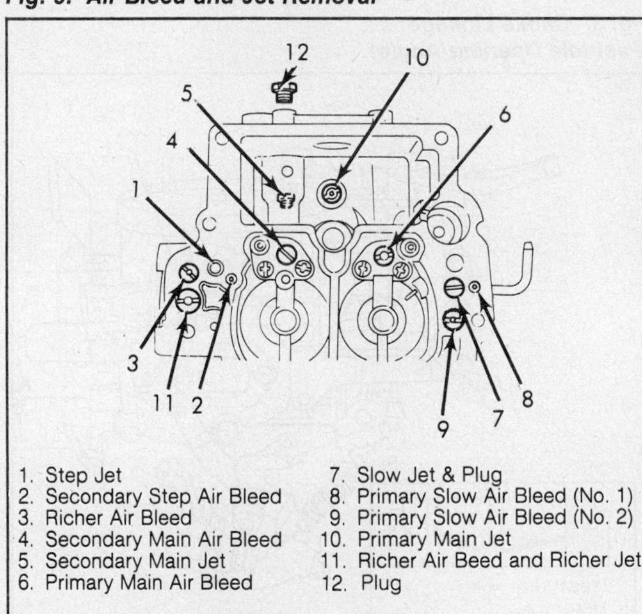
12
10
5
6
4
1
3
11
2
8
7
9

1. Step Jet
2. Secondary Step Air Bleed
3. Richer Air Bleed
4. Secondary Main Air Bleed
5. Secondary Main Jet
6. Primary Main Air Bleed
7. Slow Jet & Plug
8. Primary Slow Air Bleed (No. 1)
9. Primary Slow Air Bleed (No. 2)
10. Primary Main Jet
11. Richer Air Beed and Richer Jet
12. Plug

8) Remove throttle hanger and other levers, but do not remove throttle valve and shaft, venturi or choke valve and shaft from throttle body. When removing mixture adjusting screw, press out the spring pin as shown in *Fig. 10.*

Fig. 10: Throttle Body Assembly

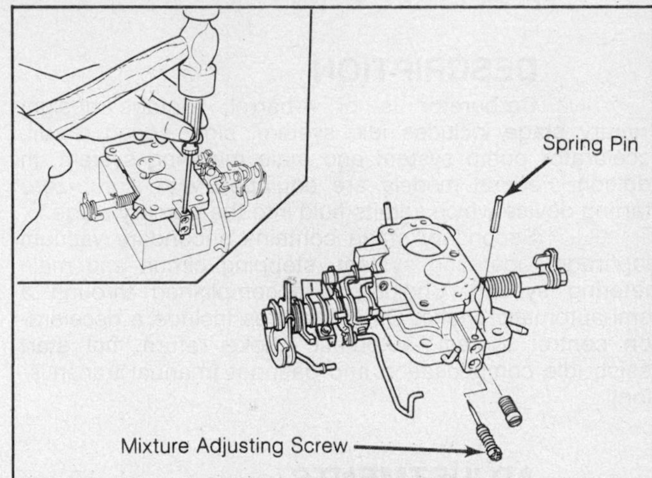
Spring Pin
Mixture Adjusting Screw

CLEANING & INSPECTION

1) Wash all parts in clean gasoline and blow out fuel passages with compressed air. Never use wire for cleaning jets. Inspect air horn, main body and throttle body for cracks and breakage.

2) Check float needle and seat for wear and float for damage. Inspect choke shaft and throttle shaft for wear. Examine all jets and air bleeds for clogs. Inspect accelerator pump plunger for wear or damage.

3) Check diaphragms and inspect mixture adjusting screws. Test solenoid valve operation by grounding body while touching terminal to battery positive post. Valve stem should pull into solenoid body.

4) Check for continuity between choke heater coupler and ground with ohmmeter. If there is no continuity, replace heater. Connect one A/F solenoid valve lead wire to positive terminal of battery, other to ground.

5) Blow air through valve to ensure it is working properly. When current is applied, air should not pass through valve. When current is not applied, air should pass through valve.

REASSEMBLY

To reassemble, reverse disassembly procedure, being careful not to mistake primary and secondary parts. Do not secure the spring pin to lock the mixture adjusting screw until idle adjustment has been completed.

CARBURETOR ADJUSTMENT SPECIFICATIONS

Application	Float Level In. (mm)	Float Drop In. (mm)	Choke Linkage In. (mm)	Accel. Cable Free Play In. (mm)	Choke Valve Opening In. (mm)
626	.394 (10.0)	1.93 (49.0)	.028-.043 (0.7-1.1)	.04-.12 (1.0-3.0)	.023-.039 (.60-1.0)

1983 Nikki Carburetors

NIKKI 4-BARREL

Mazda RX7

DESCRIPTION

Carburetor is of 4-barrel, 2-stage design. Primary stage includes idle system, slow speed circuit, accelerator pump system and main metering system. In addition, Federal models are equipped with a sub-zero starting device which admits fluid into the primary stage.

Secondary stage contains secondary vacuum diaphragm operating system, stepping circuit and main metering system. Choking is accomplished through a semi-automatic choke. Other features include a deceleration control system, automatic choke return, hot start assist, idle compensation and dashpot (manual transmission).

ADJUSTMENTS

NOTE: **For all on-vehicle adjustments not covered in this article, see the appropriate TUNE-UP SERVICE PROCEDURES article.**

FLOAT LEVEL

1) Before assembling air horn to main body, adjust float level. Invert air horn and allow float to hang by its own weight.

2) Measure clearance between float and air horn gasket. *See Fig. 1.* Clearance should be .61-.65" (15.5-16.5 mm). If not within specifications, bend float seat to adjust.

Fig. 1: Float Level Adjustment

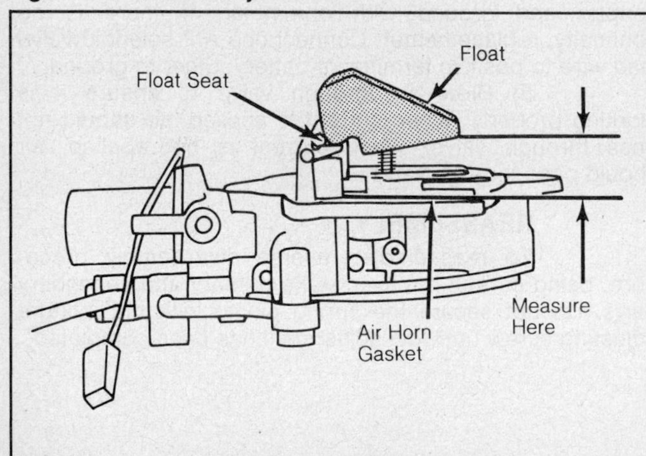
Float
Float Seat
Measure
Here
Air Horn
Gasket

FLOAT DROP

Turn air horn upright and allow float to hang by its own weight. Measure distance between bottom of float and air horn gasket. *See Fig. 2.* Distance should be 1.98-2.02" (50.5-51.5 mm). If not, bend float stop to adjust.

CHOKE LINKAGE (FAST IDLE OPENING ANGLE)

Close choke valve fully and measure clearance between primary throttle valve and wall of throttle bore. Set clearance to .040-.047" (1.0-1.2 mm) by bending fast idle rod. *See Fig. 3.*

Fig. 2: Float Drop Adjustment

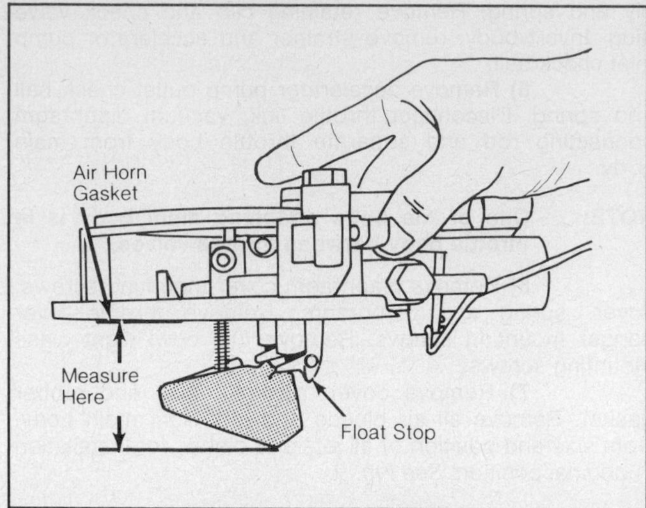
Air Horn
Gasket
Measure
Here
Float Stop

Fig. 3: Choke Linkage (Fast Idle Opening Angle)

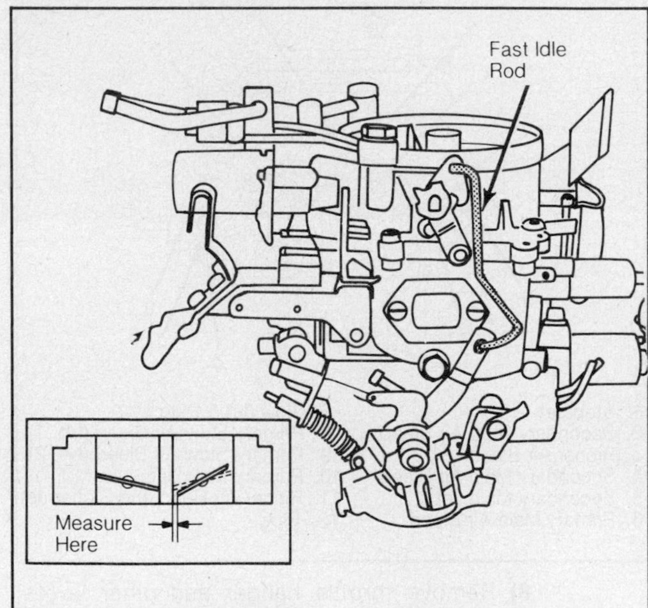
Fast Idle
Rod
Measure
Here

Bend fast idle rod to adjust.

CHOKE VALVE OPENING ANGLE

NOTE: **Choke diaphragm No. 1 is the dual diaphragm assembly, choke diaphragm No. 2 is the single diaphragm assembly.**

1) Disconnect both vacuum sensing tubes from No. 1 vacuum diaphragms. Pull choke lever link out fully and hold in place. Apply more than 19.7 in. Hg to inner diaphragm. *See Fig. 4.*

2) Clearance should be .22-.24" (5.5-6.2 mm). Apply more than 19.7 in. Hg to both diaphragms and measure clearance again. Clearance should be .45-.51" (11.5-13.0 mm).

NO. 2 CHOKE DIAPHRAGM

1) Disconnect vacuum sensing tube from No. 2 vacuum diaphragm. Pull choke lever link out fully and hold

NIKKI 4-BARREL (Cont.)

in place. Choke valve should close fully. (Cool bi-metal coil if necessary).

2) Apply more than 19.7 in. Hg to vacuum diaphragm and measure clearance between choke valve and wall of air horn. Clearance should be .057-.070" (1.46-1.80 mm).

Fig. 4: Choke Valve Opening Angle Adjustment

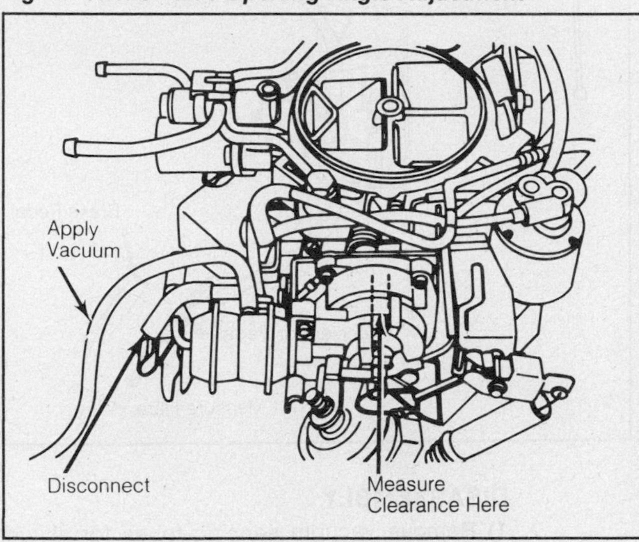
Apply
Vacuum
Disconnect
Measure
Clearance Here

CHOKE DIAPHRAGM OPERATION (NO. 1 & NO. 2 DIAPHRAGMS)

Remove air cleaner. Start engine and run at idle. Disconnect both vacuum sensing tubes from No. 1 diaphragm and one from the No. 2 diaphragm. Each diaphragm shaft should move outward from diaphragm.

CHECKING CHOKE DELAY VALVE OPERATION

NOTE: Automatic transmission must be in Neutral.

1) Warm engine to normal operating temperature. Stop engine and remove air cleaner assembly. Disconnect inner vacuum sensing tube from choke diaphragm No. 1.

2) Start the engine and run at idle speed. Diaphragm shaft should move fully inward within 10-20 seconds after reconnecting vacuum sensing tube to choke diaphragm.

Fig. 5: Checking Automatic Choke Release

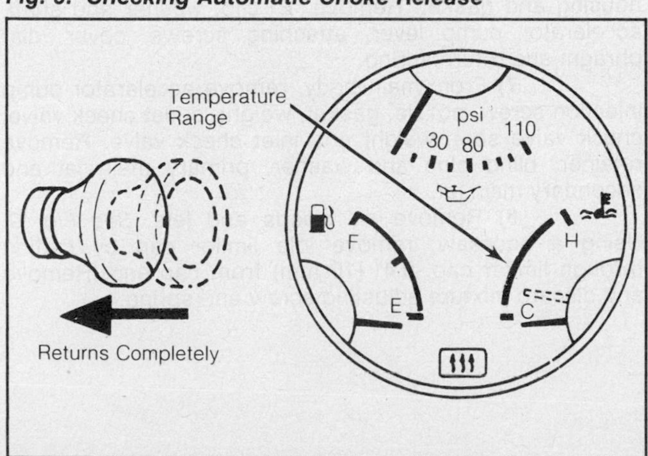
Temperature
Range
psi
30
80
110
F
H
E
C
Returns Completely

CHECKING AUTOMATIC CHOKE RELEASE

1) With engine cold and ignition "OFF", pull choke knob out fully and release. Knob should return automatically and freely. Connect tachometer to engine.

2) Start engine and set engine speed at 2000 RPM with choke knob. As engine temperature reaches range indicated in *Fig. 5.*, choke knob should return automatically and freely.

CHECKING CARBURETOR HEATER

1) Disconnect electrical connector from No. 1 water temperature switch and connect jumper wire to both terminals of connector. Connect tachometer to engine.

2) Disconnect carburetor heater electrical connector and connect voltmeter to connector. Start engine and set engine speed at 2000 RPM with choke knob.

3) With choke knob pulled out, current should flow to carburetor heater lead. Current should not flow to heater lead with choke knob pushed in.

4) Connect ohmmeter between carburetor heater lead and carburetor body. If ohmmeter shows no movement, carburetor heater is defective and must be replaced.

HOT START ASSIST CABLE

1) Remove lock spring of hot start assist cable from cable bracket. Slowly pull outer cable until hot start lever just touches stop lever.

2) Check clearance between cable bracket and lock nut on cable. *See Fig. 6.* Clearance should be .02-.08" (0.5-2.0 mm). Adjust by turning lock nut, then install lock spring securely on cable.

Fig. 6: Hot Start Assist Cable Adjustment

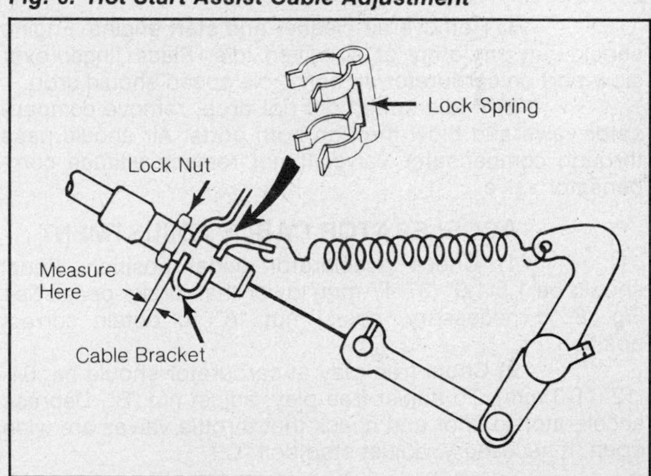
Lock Spring
Lock Nut
Measure
Here
Cable Bracket

THROTTLE OPENER

A/C Models Only

1) Turn off all accessories. Remove fuel filler cap. Disconnect and plug idle compensator tube at air cleaner. Connect tachometer to engine and warm engine to normal operating temperature.

2) Disconnect electrial connector from air switching solenoid valve (Gray color). Disconnect and plug vacuum sensing tubes from leading vacuum control units on distributor.

NIKKI 4-BARREL (Cont.)

Fig. 7: Throttle Opener Adjustment (A/C Models Only)

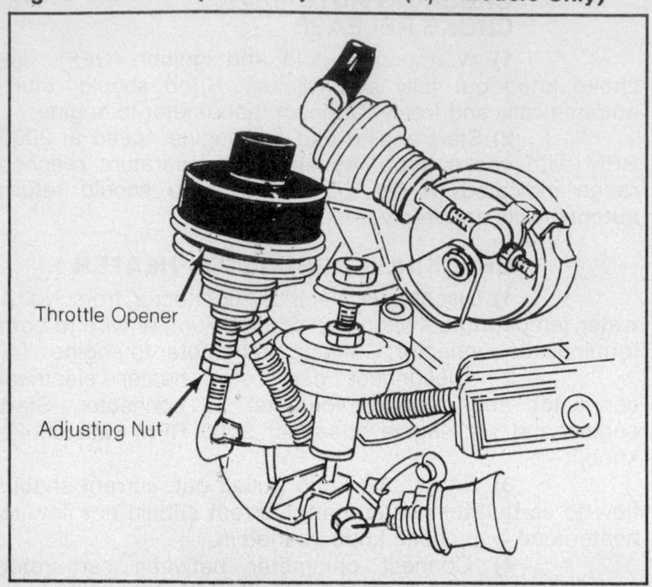
Throttle Opener
Adjusting Nut

3) Turn off air conditioner switch. Disconnect electrical connector from air conditioner solenoid. Connect battery power to one terminal in connector and ground other terminal.

4) Throttle opener should operate and engine speed should increase to 1150-1250 RPM in Neutral. If engine speed is not to specification, turn adjusting nut shown in *Fig. 7*.

CHECKING ALTITUDE COMPENSATOR

NOTE: Altitude compensator must be checked at altitudes of 1640-4920 feet.

1) Remove air cleaner and start engine. Engine should run smoothly at specified idle. Place finger over slow port on carburetor air horn; idle speed should drop.

2) If idle speed did not drop, remove compensator valve and blow through both ports. Air should pass through compensator valve. If not replace altitude compensator valve.

ACCELERATOR CABLE ADJUSTMENT

1) Check accelerator pedal position. Pedal should be 1.5-1.9" (37-47 mm) lower than brake pedal. *See Fig. 8.* If necessary, adjust nut "A" to obtain correct position.

2) Cable free play at carburetor should be .04-.12" (1-3 mm). To adjust free play, adjust nut "B". Depress accelerator to floor and check that throttle valves are wide open. If necessary, adjust stop bolt "C".

OVERHAUL

NOTE: Disassembly and assembly procedures will vary from vehicle to vehicle due to emissions equipment and type of transmission. Some carburetors may not have all parts referred to in the following procedures.

Fig. 8: Accelerator Cable and Pedal Height Adjustment

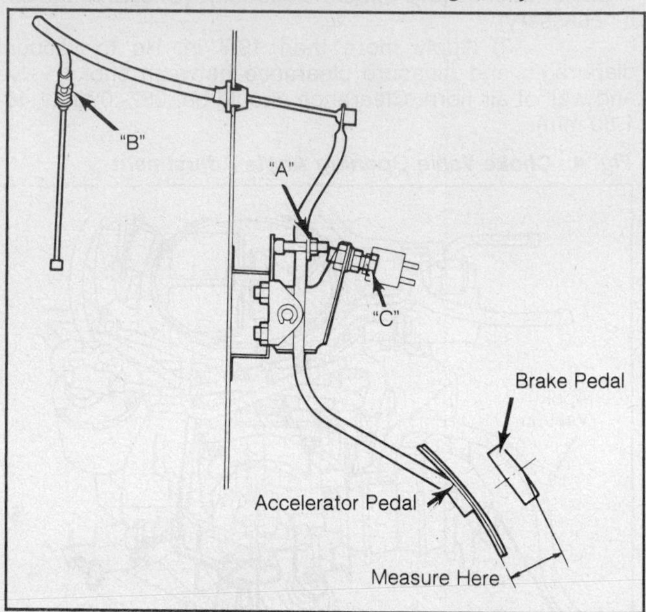
"B"
"A"
"C"
Brake Pedal
Accelerator Pedal
Measure Here

DISASSEMBLY

1) Remove vacuum sensing tubes for altitude compensator valve and choke delay valve. Remove choke heater lead, choke diaphragm No. 2 vacuum sensing tube and altitude compensator valve.

2) Remove throttle opener and bracket assembly, No. 1 choke diaphragm vacuum sensing tube, dashpot diaphragm and bracket assembly (Man. Trans. only) and throttle return spring.

3) Remove sub-return spring, return spring bracket, bi-metal spring housing and bracket assembly. Remove split pin and fast idle rod, hot start assist lever spring and bracket assembly and choke lever.

4) Remove the choke return diaphragm and bracket, No. 2 choke diaphragm and air horn assembly from main body. Disconnect float pin and remove float, needle valve, spring, valve stem and retainer.

5) From main body, remove accelerator pump rod, secondary throttle valve rod, throttle sensor and main body attaching bolts. Remove main body from throttle body.

6) Remove secondary throttle attaching screws, cover, return spring, pin and clip, diaphragm, housing and gasket. Remove "E" clip, washer and shaft, accelerator pump lever, attaching screws, cover, diaphragm and return spring.

7) From main body, remove accelerator pump injection screw, nozzle, gasket, weight, outlet check valve, check valve seat, weight and inlet check valve. Remove retainer, blind plug and washer, primary main jet and secondary main jet.

8) Remove air bleeds and jets. *See Fig. 9.* Using a hacksaw, remove idle limiter cap by cutting through limiter cap, 0.4" (10 mm) from cap end. Remove and discard mixture adjusting screw and spring.

1983 Nikki Carburetors

NIKKI 4-BARREL (Cont.)

Fig. 9: Removing Jets and Air Bleeds

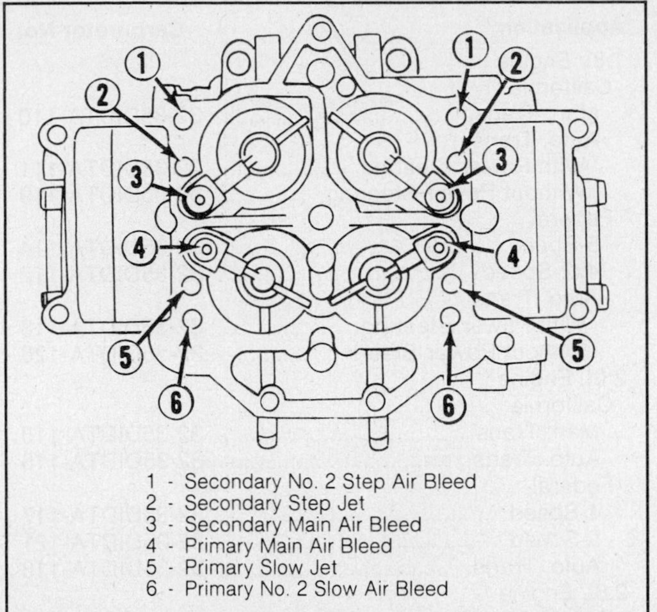
1
2
3
4
5
6
1
2
3
4
5
6

1 - Secondary No. 2 Step Air Bleed
2 - Secondary Step Jet
3 - Secondary Main Air Bleed
4 - Primary Main Air Bleed
5 - Primary Slow Jet
6 - Primary No. 2 Slow Air Bleed

CLEANING & INSPECTION

1) Wash all parts in clean solvent and clear all passages using compressed air. Never use wire for cleaning jets, orifices or passages. Inspect air horn, main body and throttle body for cracks or breakage.

2) Inspect choke shaft and throttle shaft for wear, linkage and connecting rods for bends, and return springs for damage. Inspect float, needle valve and seat and strainer for damage.

3) To check air vent solenoid for proper operation, apply battery voltage to solenoid valve, valve stem should pull into valve body. Replace solenoid if it fails to operate properly.

REASSEMBLY

1) To reassemble, reverse the disassembly procedure, using new gaskets. Avoid mixing primary and secondary system parts having similar shape. When installing new mixture screw, seat lightly and back out 3 turns for initial adjustment.

2) When installing bi-metal spring housing, fit choke shaft lever to bi-metal spring by closing choke valve and pulling vacuum diaphragm shaft. Before installing air horn, make necessary float adjustments.

CARBURETOR ADJUSTMENT SPECIFICATIONS

Application	Float Level In. (mm)	Float Drop In. (mm)	Choke Linkage In. (mm)	Accel. Cable Free Play In. (mm)	Choke Valve Opening In. (mm)
RX7	.61-.65 (15.5-16.5)	1.98-2.02 (50.5-51.5)	.040-.047 (1.0-1.2)	.04-.12 (1.0-3.0)	.22-.24 (5.5-6.2)

1983 Solex Carburetors

SOLEX (MIKUNI) DIDTA 2-BARREL

Chrysler Corp. Imports: Challenger, Colt, Colt Pickup, Ram-50 Pickup, Sapporo
Mitsubishi: Cordia, Montero, Pickup, Tredia

DESCRIPTION

Solex (Mikuni) 28-32 DIDTA carburetor is used on all Colt models, 30-35 DIDTA on all Challenger and Sapporo models, and 32-35 DIDTA on Colt Pickup, RAM-50 Pickup and all Mitsubishi models.

These 2-barrel, 2-stage carburetors use primary and secondary circuits. Carburetor components include conventional accelerator pump, vacuum-actuated secondary throttle diaphragm, sub-EGR valve system, fully automatic choke, coasting air valve, fuel cut-off solenoid (except Pickups with 2.0L engine), anti-overfill device, and air switching valve.

A jet air control valve, bowl vent valve and dashpot are used on all manual transmission models except the Pickups.

CHRYSLER CORP. IMPORT CARBURETOR IDENTIFICATION

Application	Carburetor No.
1.4L Engine	
California	28-32DIDTA-270
Federal	
4-Speed	28-32DIDTA-276
4x2-Speed	28-32DIDTA-271
1.6L Engine	
California	
Man. Trans.	28-32DIDTA-272
Auto. Trans.	28-32DIDTA-273
Federal	
Man. Trans.	28-32DIDTA-274
Auto. Trans.	28-32DIDTA-275
2.0L Engine	
California	
Man. Trans.	32-35DIDTA-115
Auto. Trans.	32-35DIDTA-116
Federal	
4-Speed	32-35DIDTA-117
5-Speed	32-35DIDTA-121
Auto. Trans.	32-35DIDTA-118
2.6L Engine	
Challenger & Sapporo	
California	
Man. Trans.	30-35DIDTA-100
Auto. Trans.	30-35DIDTA-101
Federal	
Man. Trans.	30-35DIDTA-102
Auto. Trans.	30-35DIDTA-103
Colt Pickup & Ram-50 Pickup	
California	
Man. Trans.	32-35DIDTA-104
Auto. Trans.	32-35DIDTA-105
Federal	
Man. Trans.	32-35DIDTA-106
Auto. Trans.	32-35DIDTA-107

MITSUBISHI CARBURETOR IDENTIFICATION

Application	Carburetor No.
1.8L Engine	
California	
Man. Trans.	32-35DIDTA-110
Auto. Trans.	
With Power Steering	32-35DIDTA-111
Without Power Steering	32-35DIDTA-119
Federal	
5-Speed	32-35DIDTA-114
4x2-Speed	32-35DIDTA-112
Auto. Trans.	
With Power Steering	32-35DIDTA-113
Without Power Steering	32-35DIDTA-120
2.0L Engine	
California	
Man. Trans.	32-35DIDTA-115
Auto. Trans.	32-35DIDTA-116
Federal	
4-Speed	32-35DIDTA-117
5-Speed	32-35DIDTA-121
Auto. Trans.	32-35DIDTA-118
2.6L Engine [1]	
California	
Man. Trans.	32-35DIDTA-104
Auto. Trans.	32-35DIDTA-105
Federal	
Man. Trans.	32-35DIDTA-106
Auto. Trans.	32-35DIDTA-107

[1] – Montero uses 32-35DIDTA-106 on all models.

ADJUSTMENTS

NOTE: **For all on-vehicle adjustments not covered in this article, see the appropriate TUNE-UP SERVICE PROCEDURES article.**

FACTORY ADJUSTMENTS ONLY

The automatic choke, choke breaker (vacuum kick), fast idle, secondary throttle opener, accelerator pump and sub-EGR valve have all been factory-calibrated and should not be changed for any reason.

FUEL LEVEL ADJUSTMENT

NOTE: **Fuel level is adjusted by changing thickness of needle valve shims. Shims are available in a set of 3 thicknesses: .008" (0.2 mm), .012" (0.3 mm) and .02" (0.5 mm).**

Model 28-32 Carburetor

1) Check that fuel level is nearly in the middle of dot on float chamber sight glass. If fuel level is either .16" (4 mm) above or below dot on sight glass window, fuel level is okay.

2) If float level is not within specified range, adjust by increasing or decreasing the number of needle valve shims. *See Fig. 1.* Adding or subtracting a shim will

SOLEX (MIKUNI) DIDTA 2-BARREL (Cont.)

change fuel level about 3 times the thickness of shim. Adding shims lowers level.

Fig. 1: Model 28-32 Fuel Level Adjustment

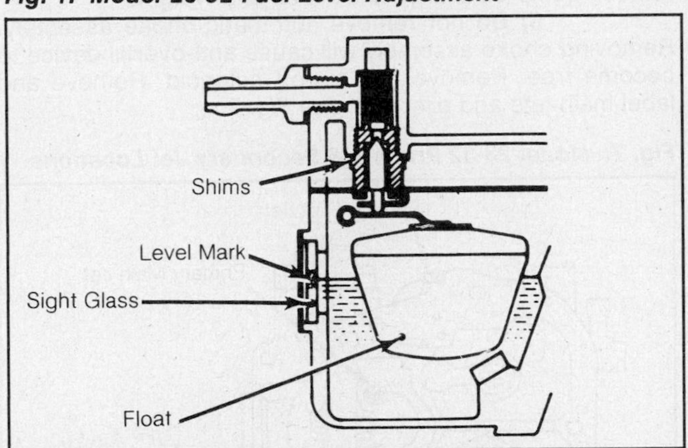

Shims
Level Mark
Sight Glass
Float

Specified level is .16" (4 mm) above or below dot on sight glass window.

Model 30-35 & 32-35 Carburetors

1) Start and run engine at idle speed. Remove plug and washer from fuel level check hole on cover assembly. *See Fig. 2.*

Fig. 2: Model 30-35 & 32-35 Fuel Level Check Hole Location

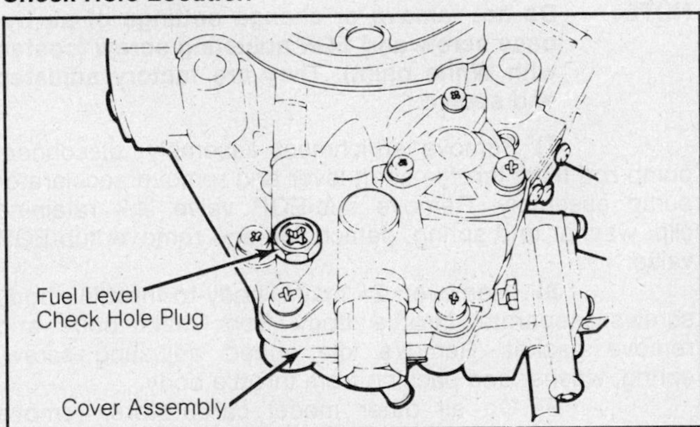

Fuel Level
Check Hole Plug
Cover Assembly

Remove plug with engine at idle speed.

2) Turn guide collar on fuel level gauge (MD998161) so that 4 lines are above bold line. This will set fuel level gauge at midpoint of specified fuel level of .08"-.16" (2-4 mm). Turning guide collar 1 full turn moves gauge .04" (1 mm). *See Fig. 3.*

3) Insert fuel level gauge into check hole until bottom of collar touches plug seat. Do not tilt gauge. Push squirt head to determine if fuel is drawn into fuel level gauge.

4) If fuel does not come up fuel level gauge, remove gauge and turn collar 1/2 turn clockwise. Repeat this and step **3)** until fuel is drawn into gauge.

5) When fuel does enter fuel gauge, remove gauge and turn collar 1/2 turn counterclockwise to determine actual fuel level height. If fuel level is too high or too low, remove cover assembly and change needle valve seat shims.

6) Reduce shim thickness if fuel level is low; increase if too high. Adding or subtracting a shim will change fuel level about 3 times the thickness of shim. Recheck fuel level.

Fig. 3: Presetting & Using Fuel Level Gauge

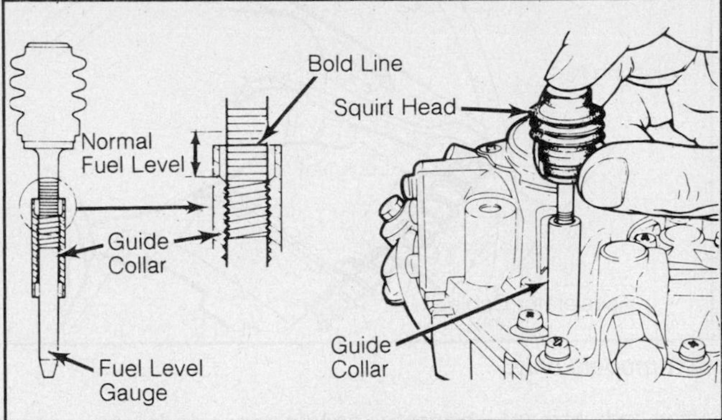

Bold Line
Squirt Head
Normal
Fuel Level
Guide
Collar
Guide
Collar
Fuel Level
Gauge

This gauge is used to set fuel level on model 30-35 & 32-35 carburetors.

ACCELERATOR PEDAL & CABLE ADJUSTMENT

Exc. Colt, Cordia & Tredia Models

1) With engine at normal operating temperature, slide accelerator cable holder to the position at which the throttle lever will begin to operate.

2) Check that inner cable has no more than .04" (1 mm) of free play. After adjustment, operate accelerator pedal to make sure that throttle valve operates smoothly from fully closed to fully opened position. *See Fig. 4.*

Fig. 4: Accelerator Cable Adjustment

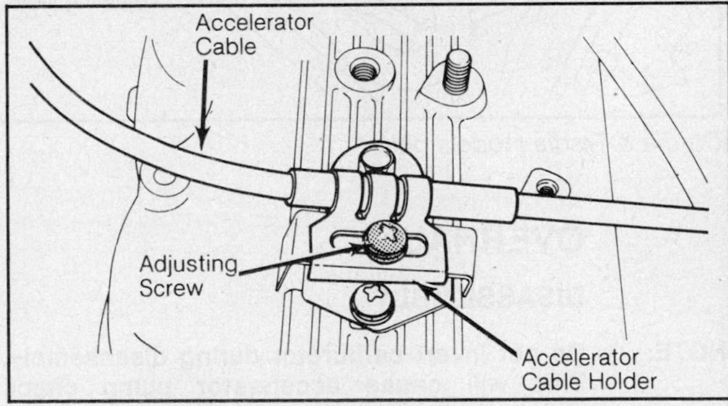

Accelerator
Cable
Adjusting
Screw
Accelerator
Cable Holder

All except Colt, Cordia & Tredia models.

Colt

1) With engine at normal operating temperature, adjust accelerator cable so that there is no more than .04" (1 mm) of free play. Adjust cable free play adjusting nut and tighten lock nut after adjustment is made. *See Fig. 5.*

2) After adjustment is made, operate accelerator pedal to make sure that throttle valve operates smoothly from fully closed to fully opened position.

Cordia & Tredia

1) With engine at normal operating temperature, adjust accelerator cable so that there is no more than .08" (2 mm) of free play. Loosen adjusting nuts to free throttle lever. Remove any sharp bends from cable.

2) Position adjusting nuts on cable so specified play exists between inner and outer cable. *See Fig. 6.*

1983 Solex Carburetors

SOLEX (MIKUNI) DIDTA 2-BARREL (Cont.)

Fig. 5: Accelerator Cable Adjustment

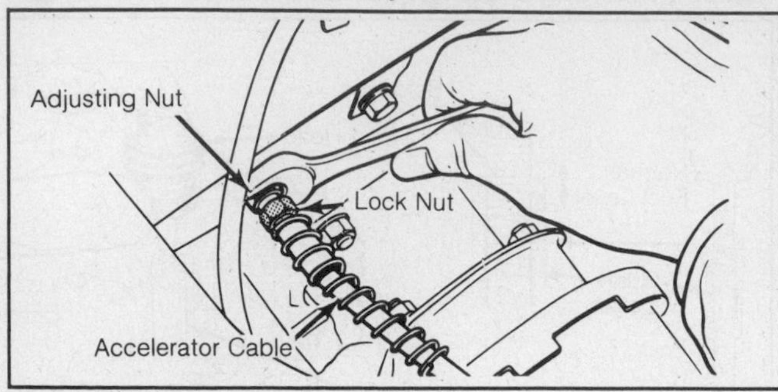
Adjusting Nut
Lock Nut
Accelerator Cable

Colt models only.

After adjustment, operate accelerator pedal to ensure throttle valve operates smoothly from fully closed to fully opened position.

Fig. 6: Accelerator Cable Adjustment

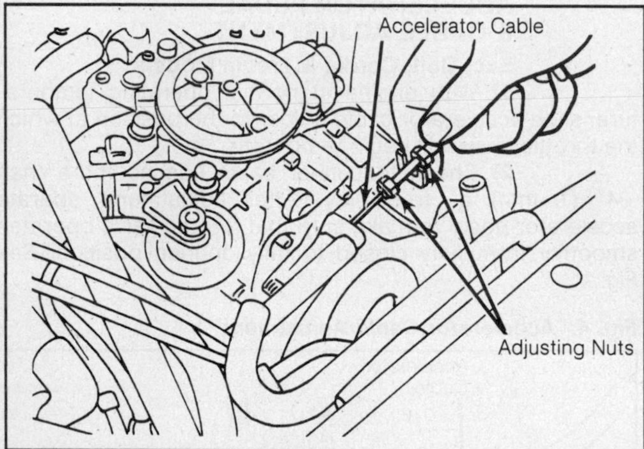
Accelerator Cable
Adjusting Nuts

Cordia & Tredia models only.

OVERHAUL

DISASSEMBLY

NOTE: **Do not invert carburetor during disassembly. This will cause accelerator pump check weight and ball, and steel ball for anti-overfill device to fall out.**

1) Disconnect water hose from throttle body to choke chamber. Grind heads off choke cover lock screws and remove cover. Disconnect ground wire from fuel cut-off solenoid at cover assembly.

2) Remove throttle return spring and damper spring. On model 28-32 carburetors, remove throttle adjuster lever spring and secondary return spring. Disconnect lower end of throttle opener link from lever.

3) Remove 2 attaching screws and remove throttle opener assembly. Remove choke unloader link retaining clip and disconnect link. Disconnect vacuum hose and lower end of diaphragm link.

4) Remove top diaphragm nut, without deforming diaphragm bracket, and remove diaphragm. Remove 2 attaching screws and remove air switching valve. Remove 5 attaching screws and remove float chamber cover assembly.

5) Remove gasket, float lever pin, float assembly, needle valve assembly, gasket and filter. Remove coasting air valve screws and valve. Invert main body and remove pump discharge check ball and weight.

6) Do not remove automatic choke assembly. Removing choke assembly will cause anti-overfill device to become free. Remove fuel cut-off solenoid. Remove and label main jets and pilot jets. *See Fig. 7.*

Fig. 7: Model 28-32 Primary & Secondary Jet Locations

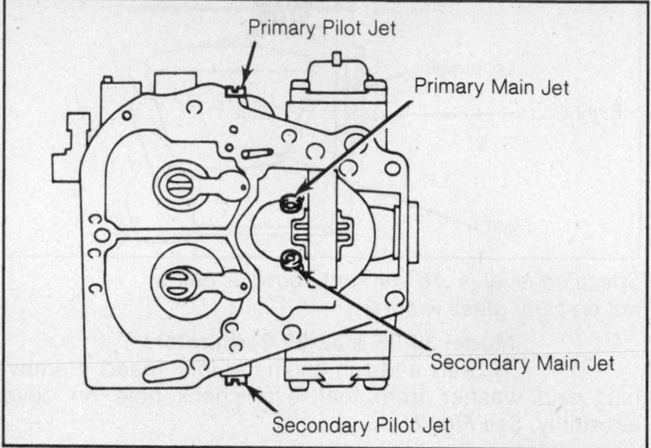
Primary Pilot Jet
Primary Main Jet
Secondary Main Jet
Secondary Pilot Jet

Label jets for correct installation.

NOTE: **Do not remove or change settings of air by-pass screw and EGR adjusting screw (coated with White paint). They are factory adjusted and sealed.**

7) Remove enrichment assembly, disconnect pump rod from throttle shaft lever and remove accelerator pump assembly. Remove sub-EGR valve link retaining clip, washer and spring, detach link and remove sub-EGR valve.

8) Remove 2 main body-to-throttle body screws, separate throttle body from main body and remove gasket. Remove idle speed adjusting screw, spring, washer and packing from throttle body.

9) On all other model carburetors, remove vacuum hose connecting depression chamber to throttle body; accelerator pump rod from throttle lever and dashpot rod (man. trans.) or throttle opener rod (auto. trans.) from free lever.

10) Remove depression chamber rod from secondary throttle lever. Remove 6 cover assembly screws. Four screws connecting cover assembly to main body and 2 connecting to throttle body. *See Fig. 9.*

11) Remove only main body by lifting cover assembly. Cover cannot be removed because choke unloader rod is connected to throttle shaft. Remove "E" clip where choke unloader rod connects to throttle shaft.

12) Do not remove devices connected to float chamber unless necessary, especially automatic choke system. Remove float pin and float. Remove needle valve by removing screw and retainer that hold needle valve in place.

13) Remove accelerator pump and fuel cut-off solenoid. Further disassembly of carburetor is not required. Do not remove throttle valves or change settings of idle speed or dashpot adjusting screws.

SOLEX (MIKUNI) DIDTA 2-BARREL (Cont.)

Fig. 8: Exploded View of Solex (Mikuni) DIDTA 2-Barrel Carburetor

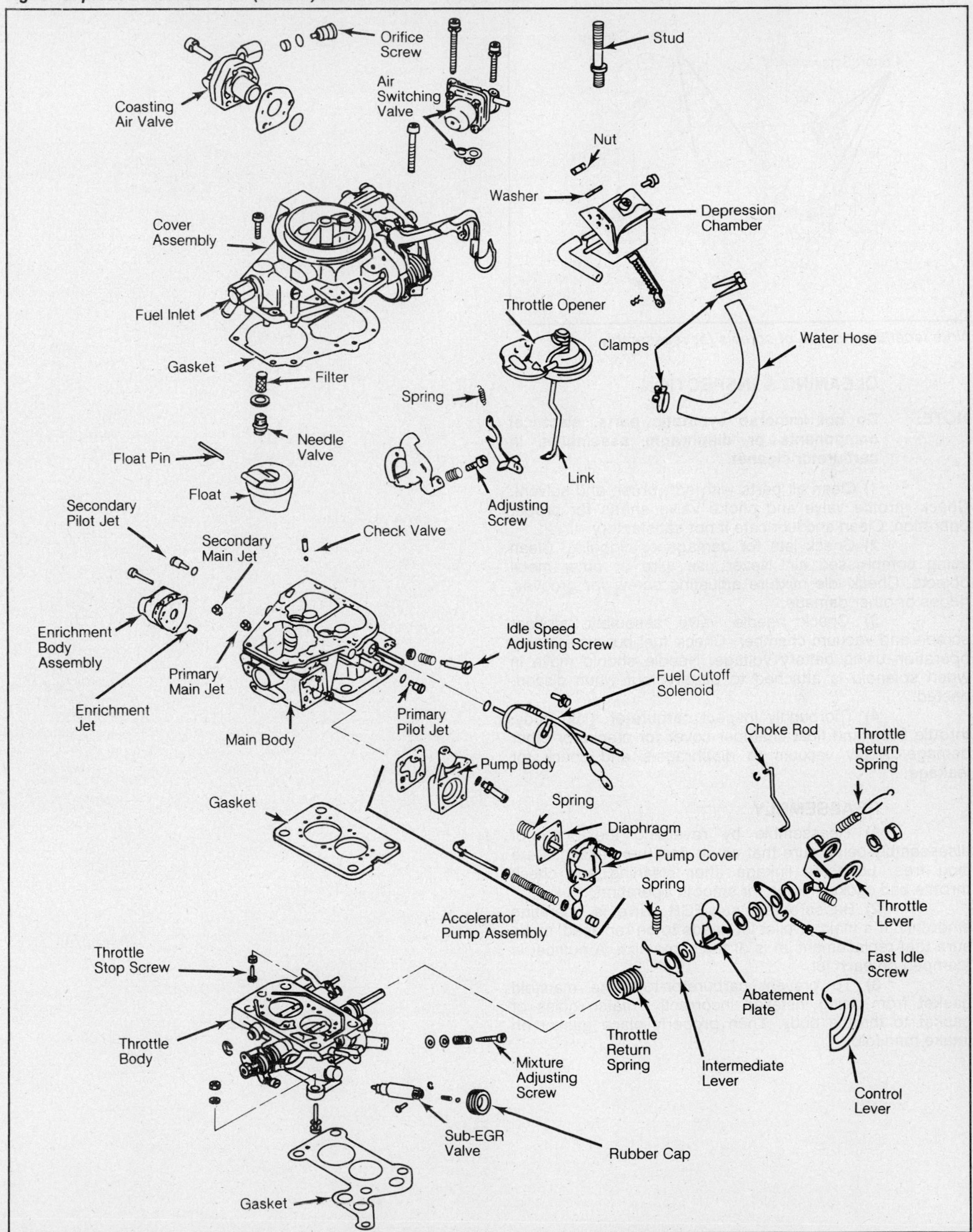
Orifice Screw
Stud
Coasting Air Valve
Air Switching Valve
Nut
Washer
Depression Chamber
Cover Assembly
Fuel Inlet
Throttle Opener
Clamps
Water Hose
Gasket
Filter
Spring
Needle Valve
Float Pin
Link
Float
Adjusting Screw
Secondary Pilot Jet
Secondary Main Jet
Check Valve
Enrichment Body Assembly
Idle Speed Adjusting Screw
Primary Main Jet
Fuel Cutoff Solenoid
Enrichment Jet
Primary Pilot Jet
Main Body
Choke Rod
Throttle Return Spring
Pump Body
Gasket
Spring
Diaphragm
Pump Cover
Spring
Throttle Lever
Accelerator Pump Assembly
Fast Idle Screw
Throttle Stop Screw
Abatement Plate
Throttle Body
Throttle Return Spring
Mixture Adjusting Screw
Intermediate Lever
Control Lever
Sub-EGR Valve
Rubber Cap
Gasket

1983 Solex Carburetors

SOLEX (MIKUNI) DIDTA 2-BARREL (Cont.)

Fig. 9: Model 30-35 & 32-35 Cover Assembly Screws

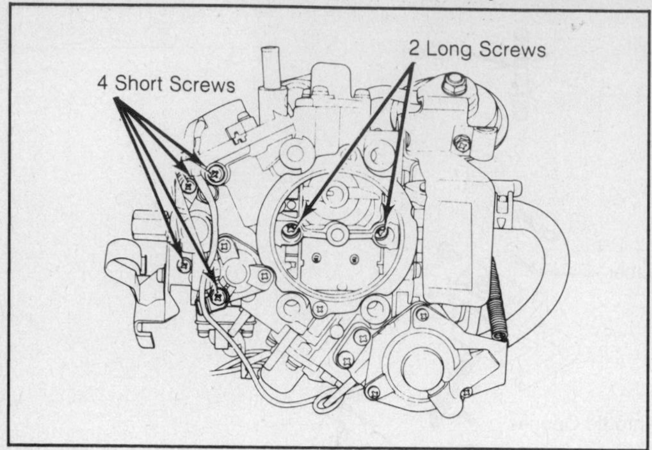
2 Long Screws
4 Short Screws

Note location and size of screws for reassembly.

CLEANING & INSPECTION

NOTE: **Do not immerse synthetic parts, electrical components or diaphragm assemblies in carburetor cleaner.**

1) Clean all parts with soft brush and solvent. Check throttle valve and choke valve shafts for proper operation. Clean and lubricate if not satisfactory.

2) Check jets for damage or clogging. Clean using compressed air. Never use wire or other metal objects. Check idle mixture adjusting screw for grooves, ridges or other damage.

3) Check needle valve assembly, strainer screen and vacuum chamber. Check fuel cut-off solenoid operation using battery voltage. Needle should move in when solenoid is attached to battery; out when disconnected.

4) Thoroughly inspect carburetor main body, throttle body and float chamber cover for cracks or other damage. Apply vacuum to diaphragms and check for leakage.

REASSEMBLY

1) Reassemble by reversing the order of disassembly being sure that all air and fuel passages are clog free. Lubricate linkage after cleaning and check throttle and choke linkage for smooth operation.

2) Be sure that sub-EGR valve is operating smoothly. If a main or pilot jet needs to be replaced, make sure that replacement jet is of the same size. A number is stamped on each jet.

3) To prevent carburetor-to-intake manifold gasket from being installed incorrectly, match holes of gasket to throttle body. Then properly place gasket on intake manifold.

1983 Weber Carburetors

WEBER 32 DIR 2-BARREL

Renault Le Car

DESCRIPTION

The Weber 32 DIR carburetor is a 2-barrel downdraft type. The carburetor base is heated by engine coolant flowing through it.

The California model has a fuel feedback system, a fast idle (throttle opener) system, a dashpot, an idle cut-off system, an electromagnetic vent cut-off valve, and a cold start system (manual choke).

The Federal model has a throttle plate opener, an electromagnetic vent valve, idle cut-off and manual choke, but has no dashpot or fuel feedback system.

CARBURETOR IDENTIFICATION

Application	Carb. No.
Le Car	
California	32 DIR 80
Federal	32 DIR 87

ADJUSTMENTS

NOTE: **For all on-vehicle adjustments not covered in this article, see appropriate TUNE-UP SERVICE PROCEDURES article.**

FLOAT LEVEL & FLOAT DROP (TRAVEL)

California Models

1) Hold the fuel bowl top vertically with its gasket in place so that the float weight closes the needle without pushing the ball inward.

2) Check dimension (dimension "A") between bowl gasket and float against specifications. *See Fig. 1.*

Fig. 1: Float Level and Drop (Travel) Adjustment

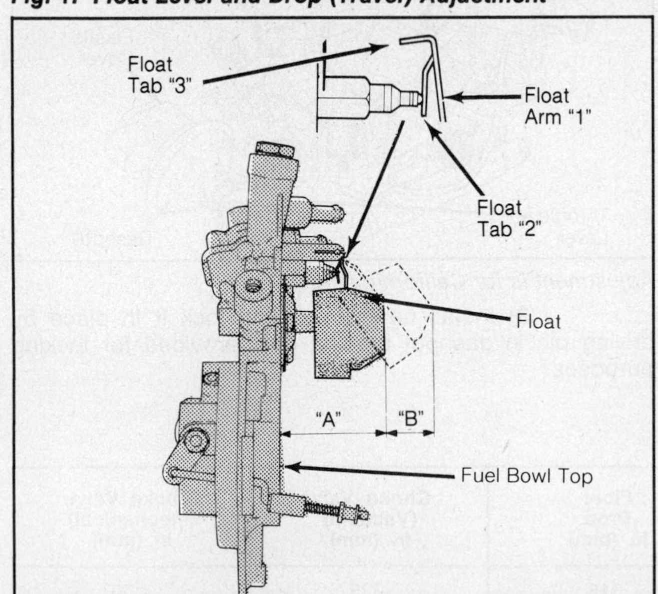
Float
Tab "3"
Float
Arm "1"
Float
Tab "2"
Float
"A"
"B"
Fuel Bowl Top

California models shown.

3) To adjust, bend float arm "1" until inner tab "2" resting against needle, is perpendicular to needle. Tab "3" should permit float travel (dimension "B") as noted in specifications.

Federal Models

1) Remove float bowl and hold top in vertical position. *See Fig. 2.* Allow weight of float to close needle without allowing ball to enter valve.

Fig. 2: Float Level and Drop (Travel) Adjustment

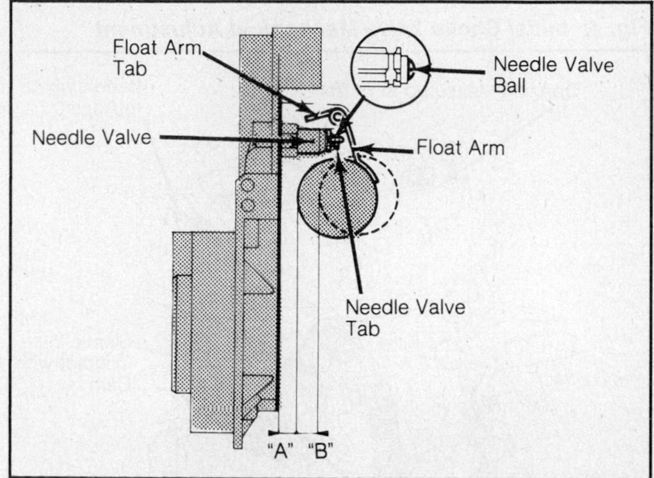
Float Arm
Tab
Needle Valve
Ball
Needle Valve
Float Arm
Needle Valve
Tab
"A"
"B"

Federal models shown.

2) Measure dimension "A" to check float level. *See Fig. 2.* If necessary, adjust by bending float arm. Measure dimension "B" for float drop or travel. If necessary, adjust float tab.

INITIAL THROTTLE VALVE OPENING

1) Put choke lever in cold start position. Measure initial opening of first barrel throttle, using feeler gauges.

2) To adjust, remove plastic cap and turn adjusting screw until specification is reached. *See Fig. 3.* After adjustment, tighten lock nut (if equipped) and install new plastic cap over adjusting screw.

Fig. 3: Initial Throttle Valve Opening Adjustment

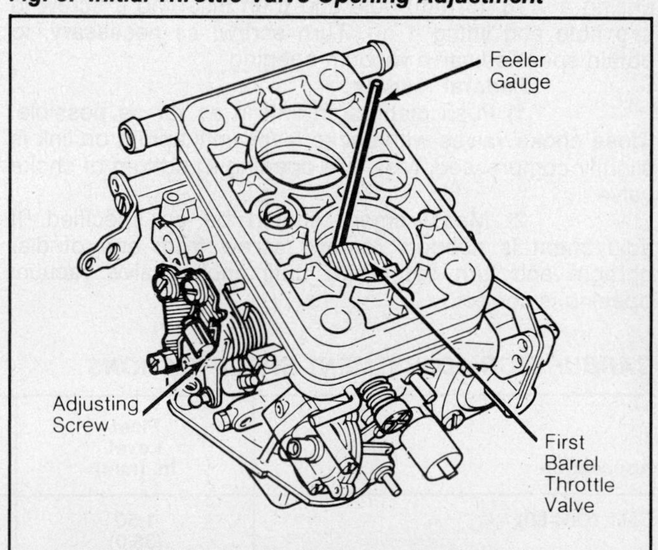
Feeler
Gauge
Adjusting
Screw
First
Barrel
Throttle
Valve

California models shown; Federal models similar.

1983 Weber Carburetors

WEBER 32 DIR 2-BARREL (Cont.)

INITIAL CHOKE VALVE MECHANICAL OPENING

1) With choke valve fully closed, push on sleeve until it contacts cam lever. Measure opening at bottom of choke valve.

2) Measurement should be as noted in specifications. If adjustment is needed, bend link as shown. *See Fig. 4.*

Fig. 4: Initial Choke Valve Mechanical Adjustment

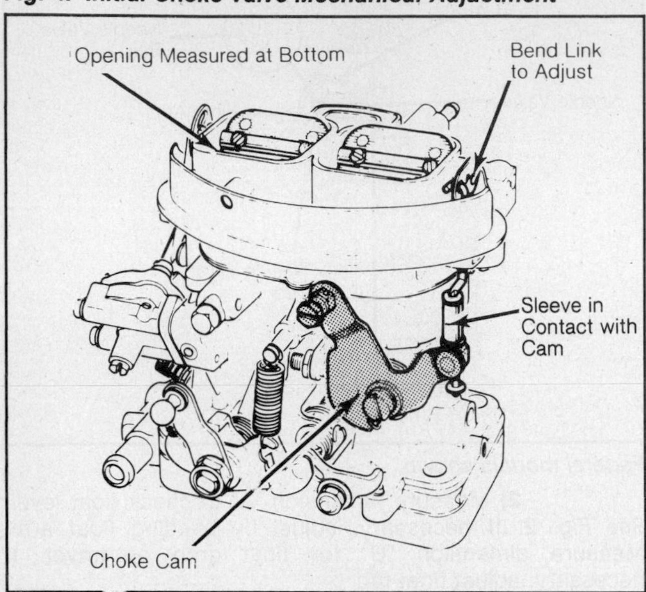

Opening Measured at Bottom
Bend Link to Adjust
Sleeve in Contact with Cam
Choke Cam

Federal models shown; California models similar.

INITIAL CHOKE VALVE VACUUM OPENING

California Models

1) Place choke lever in cold start position. Push in diaphragm link until it is against stop. Measure initial opening of choke valve on the large section side. Measure at bottom of valve.

2) Remove brass cap from adjusting screw by drilling a .118" (3 mm) hole and then inserting a screw in cap hole and lifting it off. Turn screw, as necessary, to obtain specified valve vacuum opening.

Federal Models

1) Push diaphragm link in as far as possible. Close choke valves with choke lever until spring on link is slightly compressed. Measure opening at bottom of choke valve.

2) Measurement should be as specified. If adjustment is needed, remove screw from end of diaphragm and turn set screw until choke valve vacuum opening is correct.

Fig. 5: Initial Choke Valve Vacuum Adjustment

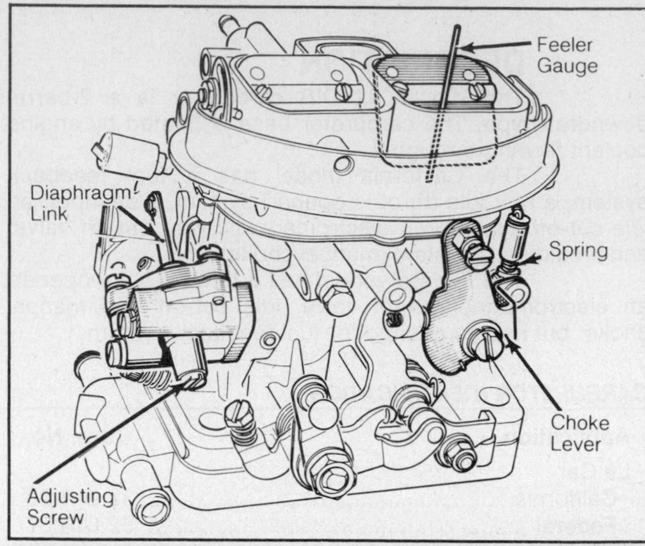

Feeler Gauge
Diaphragm Link
Spring
Choke Lever
Adjusting Screw

California models shown.

DASHPOT ADJUSTMENT

California Models Only

1) Install .059" (1.5 mm) feeler gauge as shown to maintain the initial opening of the first barrel throttle plate. *See Fig. 3.*

2) Cut plastic cover off dashpot assembly to gain access to adjustment screw. Position dashpot so that it just contacts the throttle lever. *See Fig. 6.*

Fig. 6: Dashpot Adjustment

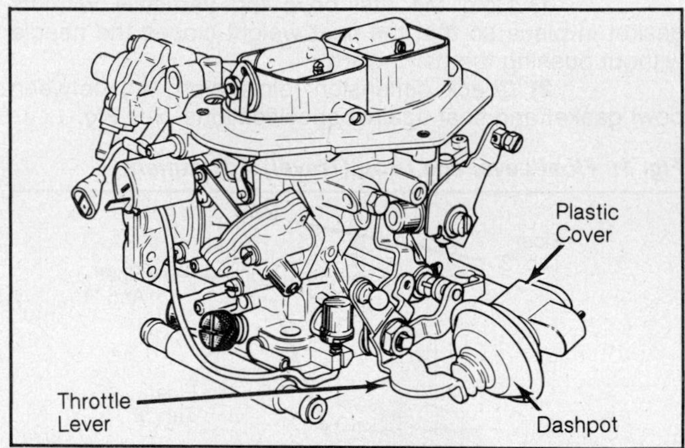

Plastic Cover
Throttle Lever
Dashpot

Adjustment is for California models only.

3) Install new cover, and lock it in place by driving pin in dashpot bracket hole provided for locking purposes.

CARBURETOR ADJUSTMENT SPECIFICATIONS

Application	Float Level In. (mm)	Float Drop In. (mm)	Choke Valve (Vacuum) In. (mm)	Choke Valve (Mechanical) In. (mm)
Calif. (DIR 80)	1.50 (38.0)	.315 (8.0)	.393 (10.0)	.250 (6.5)
Federal (DIR 87)	.276 (7.0)	.315 (8.0)	.354 (9.0)	.236 (6.0)

BOSCH AFC - DIGIJET

Volkswagen Vanagon
(1.9L Water-Cooled Engine Only)

DESCRIPTION & OPERATION

The Bosch AFC Digijet system is similar to the standard AFC system used on other Volkswagen models. However, the Digijet system is not equipped with a cold start system (cold start injector and thermo time switch). Testing procedures are also different for both fuel injection system. For information on theory, see the *Bosch AFC-European Models article in this section.*

TESTING

SYSTEM CHECK

The entire system may be checked at the multi-pin connector of the control unit. Turn ignition switch off. Unplug multi-pin connector from control unit. Using an ohmmeter and voltmeter, check system at terminal noted. *See Vanagon AFC Digijet System Ohmmeter and Voltmeter* charts. Turn ignition on when testing system.

CAUTION: To prevent damage to ohmmeter when testing system, connect ohmmeter leads only to terminals specified in charts.

FUEL PUMP

Delivery Rate

1) Disconnect fuel return line at pressure regulator and plug line. Attach hose to return line fitting and place other end of hose in measuring container.

2) Remove fuel pump relay. Place jumper wire across terminals 30 and 87 for 30 seconds. Minimum delivery rate should be 16.9 ozs. (500 cc).

FUEL PRESSURE REGULATOR

Using "T" fitting, connect fuel pressure gauge in fuel delivery line. Run engine at idle speed. Pressure should be 29 psi (2.04 kg/cm²) with pressure regulator vacuum line connected. Pressure should be 36 psi (2.53 kg/cm²) with vacuum hose connected.

FUEL INJECTORS

CAUTION: Do not disconnect terminal No. 1 at ignition coil when operating starter.

Spray Pattern

1) Remove a pair of injectors from one side of engine. Leave electrical plugs and fuel lines connected. Unplug connector from fuel injectors which are still installed.

2) Hold injectors over jar or pan. Operate starter briefly. Spray pattern must be an even, cone-shaped spray. Repeat test for remaining injectors.

Leak Test

Remove injectors from engine. Leave fuel lines connected but unplug electrical connectors. Turn ignition on for about 5 seconds. No more than 2 drops should leak from each injector in 1 minute. Replace sealing rings when installing injectors.

CAUTION: To prevent control unit damage when checking injector voltage supply, do not short-circuit connector contacts.

Voltage Supply

Unplug electrical connectors from injectors. Connect test lamp across harness plug connector. Test lamp should flicker when operating starter. If not, check relays, ground connections at cylinder head, and Hall control unit.

AIR FLOW METER

1) Turn ignition switch off. Unplug air hose and electrical connector from air flow meter. Connect ohmmeter to terminals 3 and 4 of air flow meter. Resistance should be approximately 560 ohms. Terminals 6 and 9 have the same resistance.

2) Connect ohmmeter to terminals 2 and 3. Resistance should change when moving sensor plate. Test result should be the same for terminals 7 and 9. Replace air flow meter if it fails any resistance test.

Air Temperature Sensor

Connect an ohmmeter between terminals 6 and 22. Ohmmeter reading should correspond to specifications. *Temperature Sensor Resistance Test* table. If not, replace air temperature sensor.

TEMPERATURE SENSOR RESISTANCE TEST

Temperature °F (°C)	Ohms
50 (10)	3700
68 (20)	2500
86 (30)	1700
121 (50)	900
130 (55)	700
157 (70)	450
175 (80)	325
193 (90)	250
212 (100)	200

COOLANT TEMPERATURE SENSOR

Coolant temperature sensor is located on intake air distributor. Sensor resistance depends on coolant temperature. *See Temperature Sensor Resistance Test* table. Coolant temperature sensor resistance varies the same as the air temperature sensor.

AUXILIARY AIR REGULATOR

1) Engine must be cold to perform this test. Start engine and run at idle speed. Pinch air regulator-to-intake manifold hose. RPM must drop.

2) Run engine at idle speed for about 5 minutes more. Repeat test. RPM should not drop.

3) If RPM changes when engine is warm, unplug electrical connector from air regulator. Check for voltage with engine running. If good, replace auxiliary air regulator.

THROTTLE VALVE SWITCHES

CAUTION: Do not connect test light to throttle valve switch connectors if control unit is connected.

Deceleration/Idle Switch

1) Unplug deceleration/idle switch connectors on throttle body. Connect ohmmeter to switch contacts. Switch should show continuity with throttle valve closed and infinity with throttle valve open.

1983 Fuel Injection

BOSCH AFC - DIGIJET (Cont.)

VANAGON AFC DIGIJET SYSTEM VOLTMETER CHECKS

Voltmeter To Terminal	Components Checked [1]	Specifications
No. 1 & No. 7	AEG type Hall control unit	Turn ignition on. Battery voltage or slightly less. 1.5 volts or slightly less when center wire of ignition distributor connector is grounded.
No. 1 & ignition coil terminal 15	Fairchild type Hall control unit	Turn ignition on. Battery voltage or slightly less. 1.5 volts or slightly less when center wire of ignition distributor connector is grounded.
No. 13 & No. 7	Left relay	Battery voltage
No. 21 & No. 7	Starter enrichment signal and wiring	Pull injector plugs off. Cranking voltage should be present when cranking engine.
No. 20 [2] & No. 25	Right relay	Place jumper wire across terminals. Turn ignition on and fuel pump must run.
No. 20 & No. 25	Auxiliary air regulator	Battery voltage must be present at auxiliary air regulator with ignition on.

1 – All system checks are performed with ignition switch on.
2 – Never connect test lamp to this terminal if multi-pin plug is connected to control unit.

VANAGON AFC DIGIJET SYSTEM OHMMETER CHECKS

Ohmmeter To Terminal	Components Checked [1]	Specifications
No. 2 & No. 7	Coolant temperature sensor	2300-2700 ohms at 68°F (20°C)
No. 4 [2] & No. 7	Idle and full throttle enrichment switch	0 ohms
No. 5 & No. 7	Oxygen sensor	0 ohms with O_2 sensor disconnected and grounded, infinity with sensor connected
No. 6 & No. 19	Air flow meter potentiometer	Approximately 560 ohms
No. 7 & No. 25	Control unit ground connection	0 ohms
No. 11 & No. 7	No. 4 cylinder fuel injector and wiring	Approximately 16-16.4 ohms
No. 12 & No. 7	No. 3 cylinder fuel injector and wiring	Approximately 16-16.4 ohms
No. 14 & No. 6	Intake air temperature sensor	2300-2700 ohms at 68°F (20°C)
No. 15 & No. 19	Air flow meter potentiometer	Resistance must change as sensor plate is moved
No. 23 & No. 7	No. 1 cylinder fuel injector and wiring	Approximately 16-16.4 ohms
No. 24 & No. 7	No. 2 cylinder fuel injector and wiring	Approximately 16-16.4 ohms
No. 25 & No. 7	Control unit ground connection	0 ohms

1 – System checks are performed with ignition switch turned on. To prevent ohmmeter damage, only check terminals specified.

2) Run engine at idle speed for a short time. Stop engine and turn ignition on. Unplug connectors from deceleration/idle and full throttle enrichment switches. Voltage between connectors of throttle valve idle switch should be 1/2 volt. If not, check for defective control unit or wiring.

3) To check deceleration function of switch, test results of step **1)** and **2)** must be positive. Plug in all throttle valve switch connectors. Temperature at coolant sensor must be at 140°F (60°C) or more and resistance below 550 ohms.

4) Accelerate engine slowly. At the same time, operate deceleration/idle switch by hand. Engine speed must fluctuate. If not, replace control unit.

Full Throttle Enrichment Switch

1) Unplug both throttle valve switches. Full throttle enrichment switch should have no continuity with throttle closed and continuity with throttle fully open.

2) Run engine at idle for a short time. Stop engine and turn ignition on. With both throttle valve switches unplugged, check for 1/2 volt between connectors of full throttle enrichment switch harness. If not, check for defective wiring or control unit.

3) If enrichment switch, wiring, and control unit are good, check full throttle enrichment in the following manner. Bring engine to normal operating temperature. Connect a CO tester and tachometer to engine.

4) Run engine for about 2 minutes at idle speed. Increase idle speed slowly until tachometer reads about 4000 RPM. CO should be between .3 to 1.1%.

5) With engine at about 4000 RPM, operate full throttle enrichment switch by hand for about 15 seconds. CO must increase above 1.5%. If not, control unit is defective.

BOSCH AFC - DIGIJET (Cont.)

RELAYS

CAUTION: Do not connect test lamp to terminal 86 of fuel pump relay if control unit is plugged in.

1) The power supply and fuel pump relays are located in the engine compartment. They are both in a plastic box on the firewall. The fuel pump relay is mounted on the right side of the box and power supply relay on the left.

2) Unplug all electrical connectors to injectors. To check power to relays, turn ignition switch on. Use test lamp to check for voltage at terminal 30 and 85 of both relays. Power supply relay should also have voltage at terminal 85. If not, check wiring.

3) Terminal 87 of fuel pump relay should have voltage when starter is operated. If not, check wiring. If wiring is good, check relay. If relay is good, replace control unit.

Power Supply Relay

Turn ignition switch on. Connect test lamp to terminals 30 and 86. Test lamp should light. If not, check wiring. Connect test lamp between terminals 86 and 87. If test lamp does not light, replace power supply relay.

Fuel Pump Relay

1) Connect test lamp between terminals 30 and 86. Test lamp should light while cranking engine. If not, check wiring to terminal 20 of control unit. If wiring is good, replace control unit.

2) Connect test lamp to terminal 87. Test lamp should light while cranking engine. If not, replace fuel pump relay.

ADJUSTMENTS

IDLE SPEED

See the appropriate Volkswagen article in the TUNE-UP Section.

DECELERATION/IDLE SWITCH

Close throttle valve. Turn adjusting screw so that switch just closes. From this position, turn adjusting screw exactly 1 turn farther in. Secure screw with sealant.

FULL THROTTLE ENRICHMENT SWITCH

Loosen switch retaining screw. Open throttle valve fully. Move switch until cut-in position is reached. Roller should be nearly in center of cam disk. Tighten retaining screws.

Fig. 1: Vanagon Bosch AFC Digijet Fuel Injection Wiring Diagram

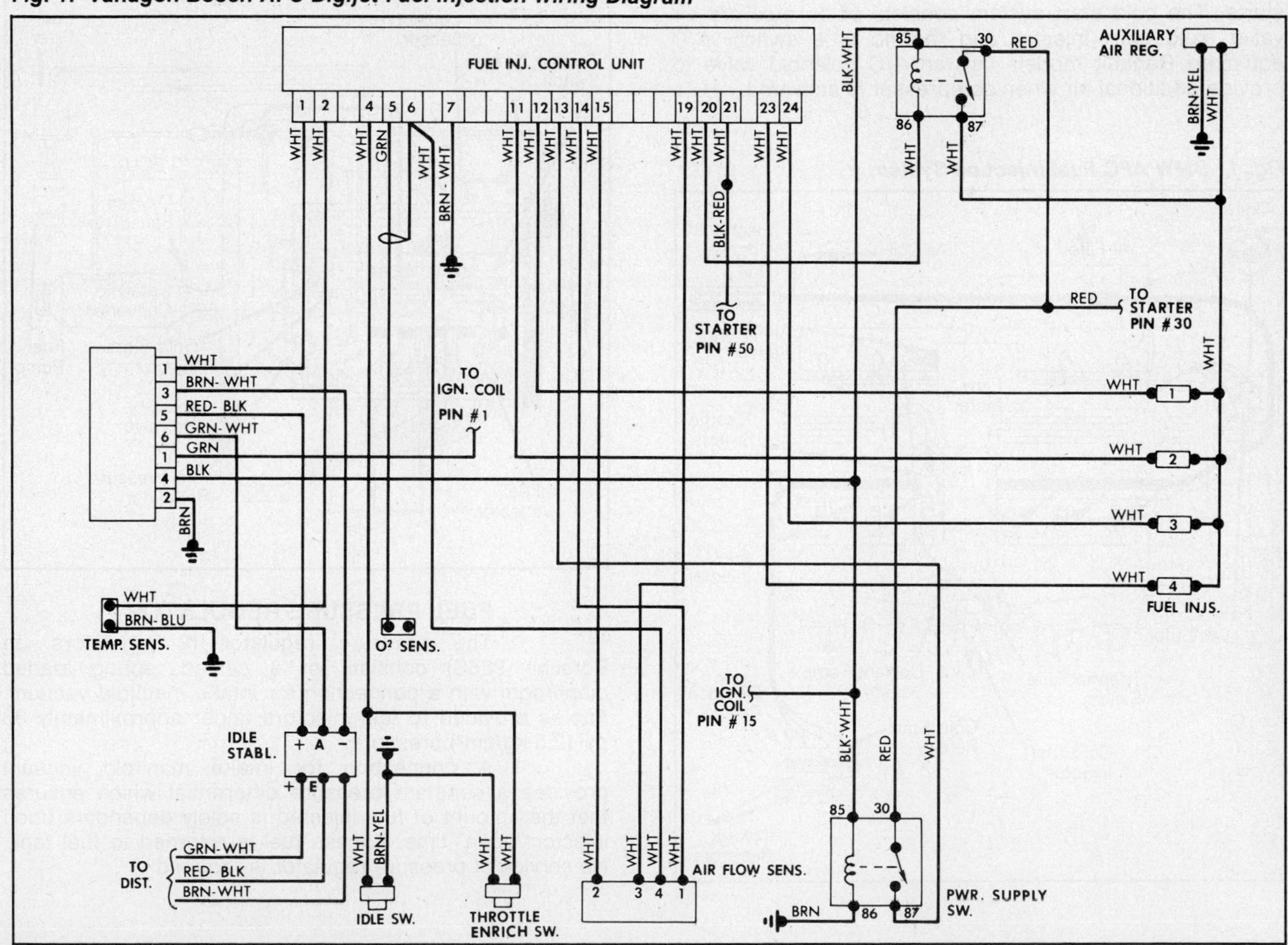

FUEL INJ. CONTROL UNIT
1 2 4 5 6 7 11 12 13 14 15 19 20 21 23 24
WHT
GRN
BRN-WHT
BLK-RED
BLK-WHT
RED
85
30
86
87
AUXILIARY AIR REG.
BRN-YEL
TO STARTER PIN #50
TO STARTER PIN #30
TO IGN. COIL PIN #1
RED-BLK
GRN-WHT
BLK
BRN
FUEL INJS.
WHT
BRN-BLU
TEMP. SENS.
O² SENS.
TO IGN. COIL PIN #15
IDLE STABL.
TO DIST.
IDLE SW.
THROTTLE ENRICH SW.
AIR FLOW SENS.
PWR. SUPPLY SW.

Also see chassis wiring in WIRING DIAGRAM Section.

1983 Fuel Injection

BOSCH AFC — EUROPEAN MODELS

Alfa Romeo GTV-6 2.5, Spider 2.0; BMW 528e, 533i, 633CSi, 733i; Porsche 928S, 944; Renault Fuego, Fuego Turbo, 18i; Volkswagen Vanagon

NOTE: **This article covers the Bosch AFC fuel injection system in general, with manufacturer's differences noted. For information on the Volkswagen Vanagon equipped with water-cooled engine, see BOSCH AFC-DIGIJET article in this Section.**

DESCRIPTION

The Bosch Air Flow Controlled (AFC) fuel injection system is an electronically controlled system operated by incoming air flow. The AFC fuel injection system also contains a feedback system which measures oxygen content of exhaust gases and, using this information, maintains the air/fuel ratio at about 14.7:1.

The fuel injection system consists of an electric fuel pump, fuel pressure regulator, fuel injectors, Electronic Control Unit (ECU), air flow meter, air temperature sensor, throttle switch, coolant temperature switch (cylinder head temperature switch on Volkswagen), oxygen sensor, catalytic converter and electrical relays.

In addition, all models except Porsche 944 are equipped with a cold start system to aid in cold engine starts. The cold start system consists of an auxiliary air valve, cold start injector and thermo time switch. A/C equipped Renault models use an A/C solenoid valve to provide additional air when compressor is activated.

Fig. 1: BMW AFC Fuel Injection System

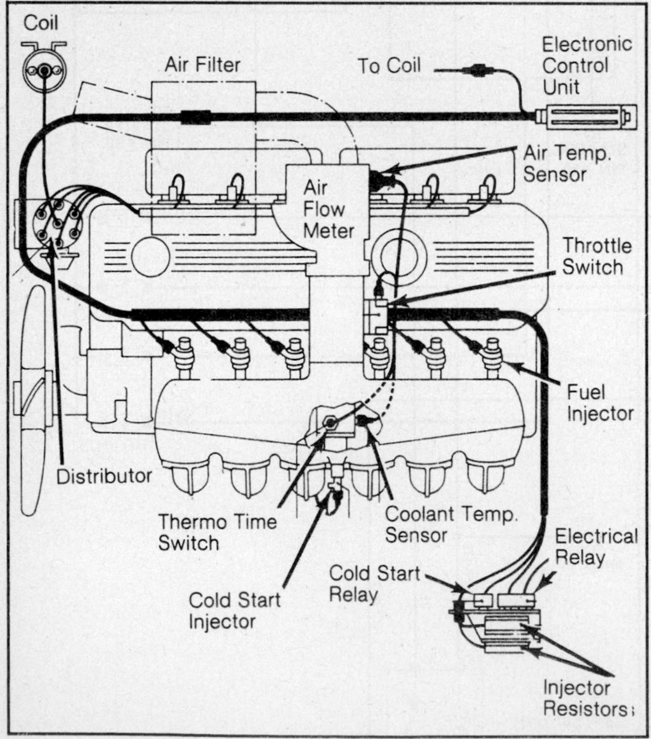
Coil
Air Filter
To Coil
Electronic Control Unit
Air Temp. Sensor
Air Flow Meter
Throttle Switch
Fuel Injector
Distributor
Thermo Time Switch
Coolant Temp. Sensor
Electrical Relay
Cold Start Relay
Cold Start Injector
Injector Resistors

California Volkwagen models are equipped with a speed limit switch between throttle switch and ECU which deactivates the oxygen sensor at engine speeds in excess of 3000 RPM.

BMW, Porsche 944 and Renault Fuego Turbo models are equipped with electronic engine control. On these vehicles the ECU controls ignition timing in addition to fuel injection. Spider 2.0 models are equipped with digital electronic ignition systems with separate control units.

ELECTRIC FUEL PUMP

The fuel pump (2 on Spider 2.0 models) provides fuel under pressure to the fuel pressure regulator. Power for operation during cranking mode is provided from starter relay via the fuel pump relay. After the engine has started, control of the fuel pump is by a fuel pump circuit in the air flow meter.

The first movement of the air flow meter air measuring flap (about 5°) closes the fuel pump contacts and provides power to fuel pump after engine has started. With engine stopped, no air flow is present, measuring flap closes and fuel pump contacts are opened to cut power to fuel pump. This circuit reduces the risk of fire in a collision. The fuel pump is a sealed unit. No service is required.

Fig. 2: Porsche 928S AFC Fuel Injection System

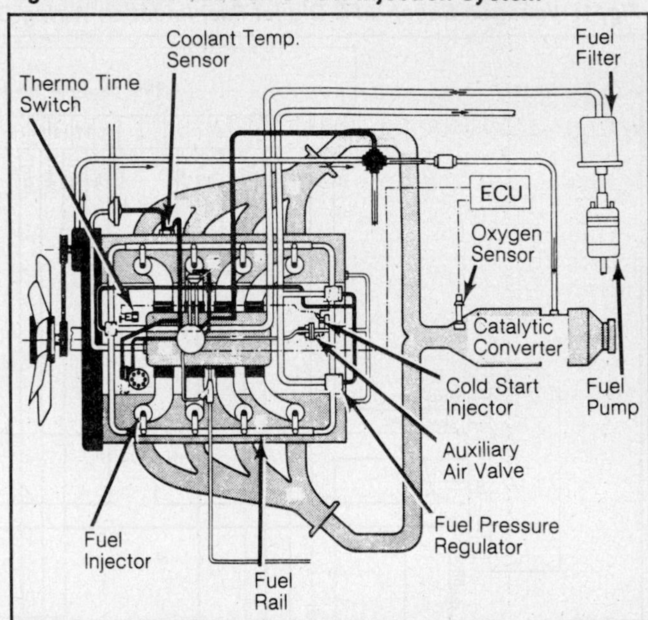
Coolant Temp. Sensor
Fuel Filter
Thermo Time Switch
ECU
Oxygen Sensor
Catalytic Converter
Cold Start Injector
Fuel Pump
Auxiliary Air Valve
Fuel Pressure Regulator
Fuel Injector
Fuel Rail

FUEL PRESSURE REGULATOR

The pressure regulator (2 regulators on Porsche 928S) consists of a sealed, spring loaded diaphragm with a connection for intake manifold vacuum. Fuel is provided to fuel injectors under approximately 36 psi (2.5 kg/cm²) pressure.

A connection for intake manifold vacuum provides a constant pressure differential which ensures that the amount of fuel injected is solely dependent upon injector "open" time. Excess fuel is returned to fuel tank. No service of pressure regulator is required.

Fig. 3: Renault 18i AFC Fuel Injection System

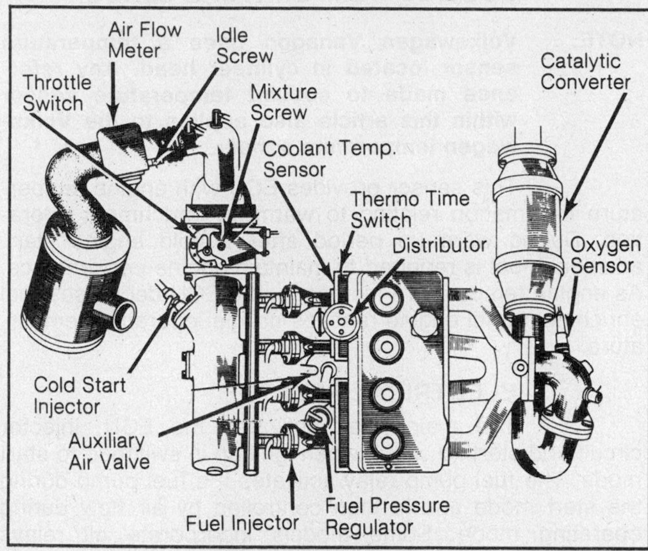
Air Flow Meter
Idle Screw
Throttle Switch
Mixture Screw
Catalytic Converter
Coolant Temp. Sensor
Thermo Time Switch
Distributor
Oxygen Sensor
Cold Start Injector
Auxiliary Air Valve
Fuel Injector
Fuel Pressure Regulator

FUEL INJECTORS

A fuel rail links the fuel pressure regulator with the fuel injectors. Each cylinder is provided with a solenoid-operated injector which sprays fuel towards back of each inlet valve. Each injector is energized through the ignition coil and grounded through the ECU to complete the circuit.

Each injector is linked to a resistor (resistor may be external or integral with injector or ECU) to reduce operating voltage to 3 volts and to protect injectors from power surges. The ECU controls the length of time each injector is open.

The "open" time of the injector governs the amount of fuel delivered. The injectors deliver 1/2 the amount of fuel required for an operating cycle each time they open (twice per cycle).

Fig. 4: Volkswagen AFC Fuel Injection System

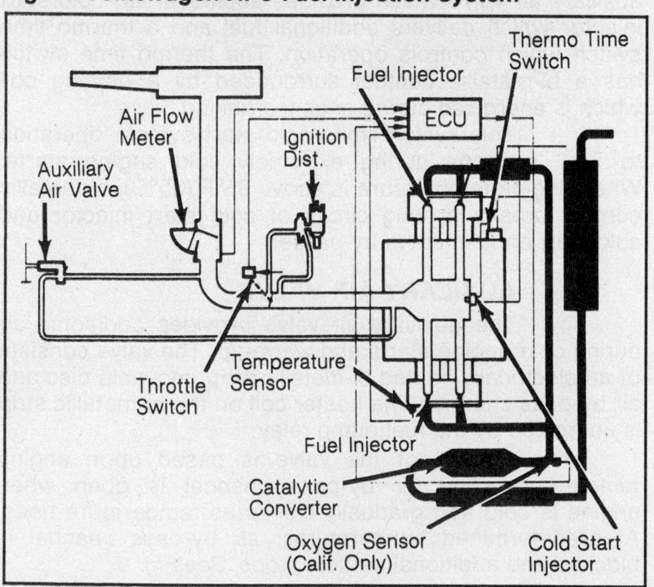
Thermo Time Switch
Fuel Injector
ECU
Air Flow Meter
Ignition Dist.
Auxiliary Air Valve
Temperature Sensor
Throttle Switch
Fuel Injector
Catalytic Converter
Oxygen Sensor (Calif. Only)
Cold Start Injector

ELECTRONIC CONTROL UNIT (ECU)

All components of the control system are electrically connected to the ECU. *See Fig. 5.* The ECU is a preprogrammed computer which receives and interprets data from various sensors. It calculates the amount of fuel required by the engine to maintain efficiency with minimum exhaust emissions.

Impulses from the oxygen sensor inform the ECU of oxygen content of exhaust gases and the ECU constantly adjusts the air/fuel ratio by controlling the injector "open" time.

The ECU provides fuel enrichment whenever engine is cranked, regardless of engine temperature. This is activated by a direct electrical connection from the starter circuit to the ECU. On BMW, Porsche 944 and Renault Fuego Turbo models, the ECU also controls ignition timing. The ECU is a sealed unit. No service is required.

NOTE: The injection system ECU of Spider 2.0 models is not interchangeable with the electronic ignition system ECU. DO NOT confuse these 2 ECUs.

Fig. 5: Electronic Control Unit (ECU)

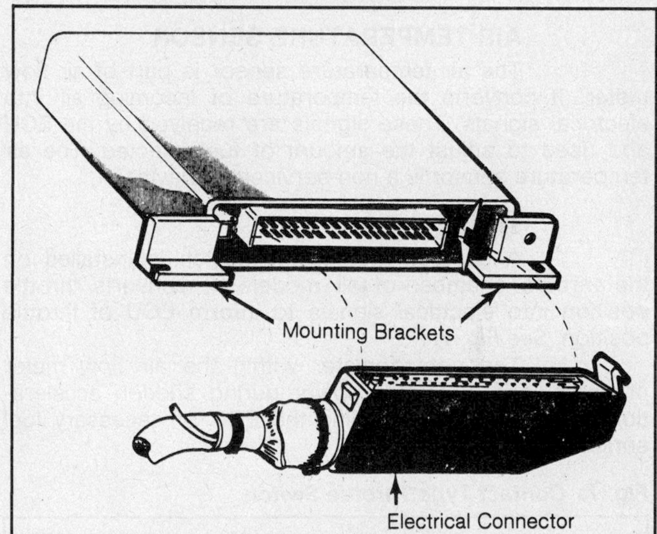
Mounting Brackets
Electrical Connector

AIR FLOW METER

All engine air is drawn through the air flow meter. The meter contains a tunnel with measuring flap and dampening flap (offset 90° on same casting). The measuring flap swings in air stream against pressure of a spiral spring and is connected to a potentiometer.

The potentiometer transmits an electrical signal determined by measuring flap position to inform the ECU of engine load. *See Fig. 6.* In addition to monitoring the air flow, the meter also controls fuel pump operation and idling. At idle, the measuring flap is almost closed due to spiral spring pressure.

An idle air by-pass receives air from main air flow through a small hole, the size of which is controlled by the idle mixture screw. This adjustable air by-pass influences CO levels at low engine speeds.

1983 Fuel Injection

BOSCH AFC — EUROPEAN MODELS (Cont.)

Fig. 6: Bosch AFC Air Flow Meter

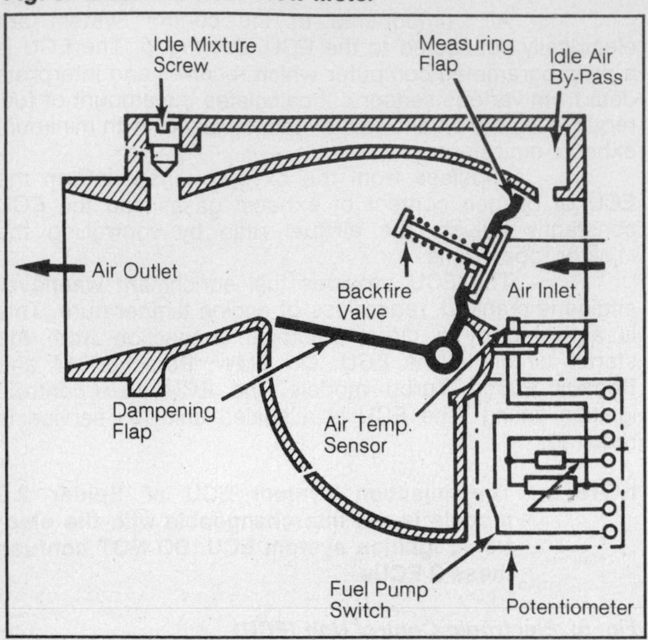

Idle Mixture Screw
Measuring Flap
Idle Air By-Pass
Air Outlet
Backfire Valve
Air Inlet
Dampening Flap
Air Temp. Sensor
Fuel Pump Switch
Potentiometer

AIR TEMPERATURE SENSOR

The air temperature sensor is part of air flow meter. It converts the temperature of incoming air into electrical signals. These signals are received by the ECU and used to adjust the amount of fuel injected. The air temperature sensor is a non-serviceable device.

THROTTLE SWITCH

A contact-type throttle switch is installed on the throttle chamber of all models. It converts throttle position into electrical signals to inform ECU of throttle position. *See Fig. 7.*

The potentiometer within the air flow meter prevents loss of engine power during sudden acceleration/deceleration by signaling the ECU of necessary fuel enrichment requirements.

Fig. 7: Contact Type Throttle Switch

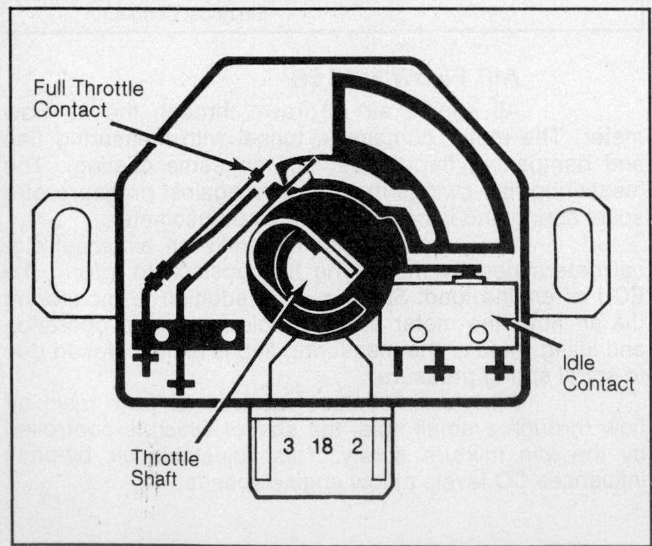

Full Throttle Contact
Idle Contact
Throttle Shaft
3 18 2

Illustration applies to all models except Volkswagen.

COOLANT TEMPERATURE SENSOR

NOTE: **Volkswagen Vanagon uses a temperature sensor located in cylinder head. Any reference made to coolant temperature sensor within this article also applies to the Volkswagen temperature sensor.**

This sensor provides ECU with engine temperature information relating to warm-up enrichment operation. During warm-up period after a cold engine start, additional fuel is required to maintain engine performance. As engine temperature increases, the ECU decreases fuel enrichment until engine reaches normal operating temperature.

ELECTRICAL RELAYS

The main relay activates the ECU, injector circuit and starting circuit when ignition is switched to start mode. The fuel pump relay activates the fuel pump during the start mode and is then controlled by air flow during operating mode. Some models incorporate all relays within a single relay set or dual relay. The cold start system is also activated through the relay set.

Relay set is located in following positions:

- Alfa Romeo GTV-6 2.5, right side of firewall; Spider 2.0, under floor behind passenger seat.
- BMW 528e and 533i, bracket above left wheel well; 633CSi, behind coolant reservoir; 733i, right side of firewall.
- Renault Fuego, Fuego Turbo and 18i, passenger seat.
- Volkswagen Vanagon, left side of firewall.

COLD START SYSTEM

NOTE: **Porsche 944 does not use cold start system. Instead, additional fuel for cold starts is supplied through injectors.**

The cold start system provides additional air and fuel during cold engine starts. It consists of an auxiliary air valve which provides additional air, cold start injector which delivers additional fuel and a thermo time switch which controls operation. The thermo time switch has a bi-metallic contact surrounded by a heating coil which is energized during engine cranking.

This switch limits cold start system operation to 5-12 seconds during extremely cold engine starts. When engine temperature is above 95°F (35°C), bi-metallic contact breaks ground circuit of cold start injector and cold start enrichment is by-passed.

AUXILARY AIR VALVE

The auxiliary air valve provides additional air during cold engine starts and warm-up. The valve consists of an electrically heated bi-metallic strip, movable disc and air by-pass channel. The heater coil on the bi-metallic strip is energized by the fuel pump relay.

Control of the valve is based upon engine temperature. The air by-pass channel is open when engine is cold and gradually closes as temperature rises. At predetermined temperatures, air by-pass channel is blocked and additional air flow stops. *See Fig. 8.*

BOSCH AFC — EUROPEAN MODELS (Cont.)

Fig. 8: Auxiliary Air Valve

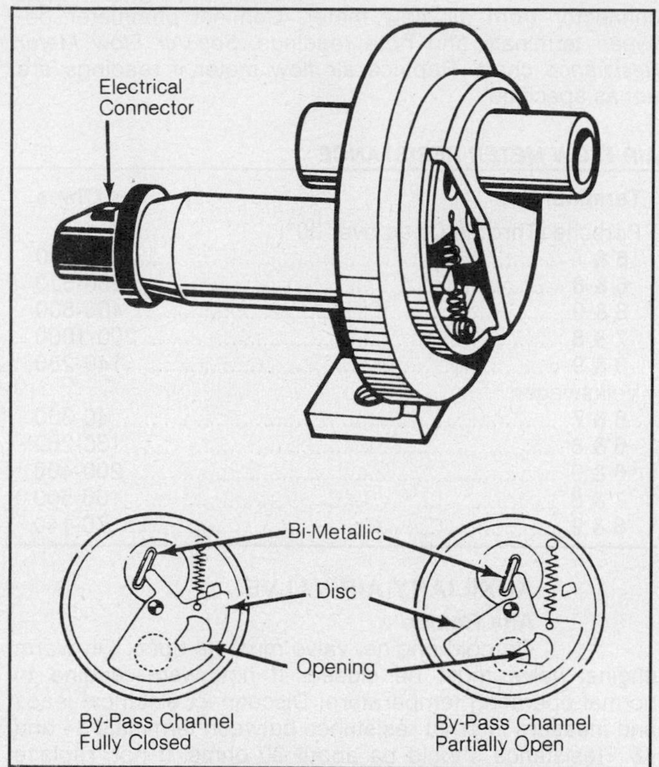
Electrical
Connector
Bi-Metallic
Disc
Opening
By-Pass Channel
Fully Closed
By-Pass Channel
Partially Open

By-pass channel closes as engine temperature rises.

AIR CONDITIONING SOLENOID VALVE

(Renault Only)

On vehicles equipped with A/C, a solenoid valve delivers additional air to compensate for drop in idle speed when air conditioner is activated. The solenoid is electrically actuated through the compressor clutch circuit to apply vacuum to a circuit behind throttle plate.

The applied vacuum opens the vacuum diaphragm which opens the additional air circuit. The diameter of the air circuit on manual transmission models is 0.12" (3.0 mm) and 0.14" (3.5 mm) on automatic transmission models. *See Fig. 9.*

Fig. 9: Renault Air Conditioning Solenoid Valve

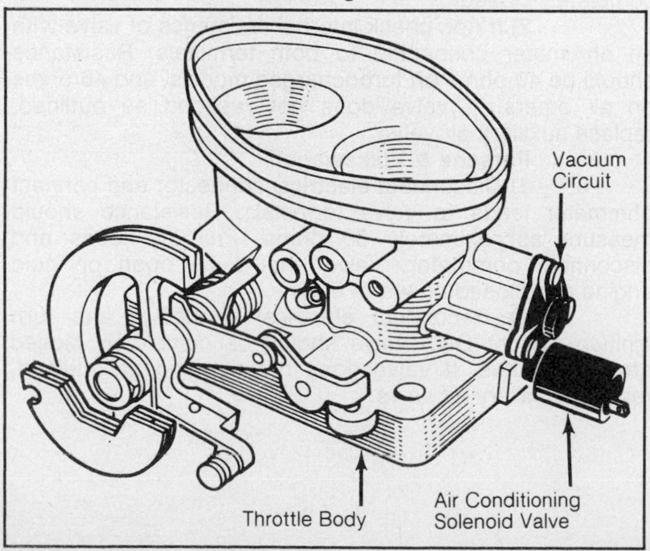
Vacuum
Circuit
Throttle Body
Air Conditioning
Solenoid Valve

ACCESSORIES

Alfa Romeo Spider 2.0

Spider 2.0 models use a different control unit for the digital ignition system. Its components include vacuum sensor (Black connector), temperature sensor (White connector), ignition ECU, revolution transmitter and reference point transmitter.

Porsche 944

Electronic engine control (control of both fuel injection and ignition timing) on these vehicles requires additional devices. These devices include speed sensor and reference sensors on flywheel, a pressure damper located at inlet of injector collector tube, and a high altitude switch.

Renault Fuego Turbo

Electronic engine control (control of both fuel injection and ignition timing) on turbo models requires additional devices. These devices include magnetic position sensor on clutch housing, vacuum sensor on electronic control unit, and spark knock detector on cylinder head.

TESTING

NOTE: **The Bosch AFC fuel injection system maintains constant fuel pressure in fuel lines and component parts at all times. Be sure to relieve pressure before attempting to open system at any point for testing. For further testing of related components on BMW vehicles, see BMW MOTRONIC EMISSION CONTROL SYSTEM in Computerized Engine Controls Section.**

ELECTRONIC CONTROL UNIT

Do not attempt to test ECU, as permanent damage could result. It is possible to check plug wires for continuity. The ECU should only be judged faulty after compression is checked, ignition system has been tested and found free of problems, and all other fuel injection components have been thoroughly tested (including wiring).

FUEL PRESSURE

Porsche

1) Remove capped nut from test connection on fuel rail without damaging seal. Connect fuel pressure gauge to test connection. Working inside passenger compartment, fold up passenger foot support (if equipped) and unplug fuel pump relay from central electric board.

2) Fuel pump relay is second box from right side on bottom row on 928S, second box from left in row furthest from fuses on 944. Using jumper wire, connect together terminals 30 and 87 for 928S, 30 and 87b on 944. Fuel pump should run. Fuel pressure should be as specified. If not, replace fuel pump.

Fuego Turbo

1) Release fuel system pressure. Remove fuel supply line at cold start injector and connect fuel pressure gauge. Turn ignition on. Jump terminal Nos. 2 and 8 of tachometer relay. Fuel pump pressure should be as specified. If not, check fuel pump, fuel filter and fuel pump circuit.

1983 Fuel Injection

BOSCH AFC — EUROPEAN MODELS (Cont.)

2) Turn off ignition. Disconnect vacuum hose from pressure regulator and connect hand vacuum pump. Turn ignition on. Reading should drop about 7 psi (0.5 kg/cm²). If not, check pressure regulator.

All Other Models

1) Release fuel system pressure. Remove fuel supply line at cold start injector and connect fuel pressure gauge. Disconnect vacuum hose from pressure regulator and connect hand vacuum pump to regulator. Turn ignition on and check pressure reading. *See Fuel Pressure Specifications* chart.

2) Apply 16 in. Hg to pressure regulator. Reading should drop about 7 psi (0.5 kg/cm²). If pressure is too low, check fuel pump delivery rate. If pressure is too high, check fuel return line. If readings are still not as specified, replace regulator.

FUEL PRESSURE SPECIFICATIONS

Application	psi (kg/cm²)
All Models	33-39 (2.3-2.8)

FUEL PUMP CIRCUIT

Renault Fuego & 18i,
Alfa Romeo GTV-6 2.5

1) Remove electrical connector from air flow meter. Connect terminals 36 and 39 with jumper wire. Disconnect fuel input line at fuel pressure regulator and place in container. Turn ignition on and push air measuring flap open.

2) Fuel should flow into container. If fuel does not flow but clicking sound is heard, replace fuel pump. Fuel circuit is good. If no clicking sound is heard, replace air flow meter assembly and repeat test.

Volkswagen

1) Turn ignition off and disconnect electrical connector at ECU. Using a voltmeter, connect probes between terminal No. 20 and ground.

2) Turn ignition on and open air flow meter flap. Voltage reading should be 12 volts. If not, check air flow meter and relays.

AIR TEMPERATURE SENSOR

NOTE: Testing procedure not available for Porsche or Renault.

Turn ignition switch off. Disconnect electrical connector at air flow meter and connect ohmmeter between terminals 6 and 22 on BMW, 6 and 27 on all others. Readings should be as follows. If not, replace temperature sensor and air flow meter as an assembly.

TEMPERATURE/RESISTANCE RELATIONSHIP

Temperature	Ohms
68°F (20°C)	2,000-3,000
122°F (50°C)	760-970

AIR FLOW METER POTENTIOMETER

NOTE: Testing procedures not available for Renault models. Alfa Romeo and BMW models require use of Bosch tester.

Turn ignition switch off. Unplug electrical connector from air flow meter. Connect ohmmeter between terminals and note readings. *See Air Flow Meter Resistance* chart. Replace air flow meter if readings are not as specified.

AIR FLOW METER RESISTANCE

Terminal No.	Ohms
Porsche (Throttle Open over 30°)	
6 & 7	80-600
6 & 8	260-520
6 & 9	400-800
7 & 8	200-1000
8 & 9	140-280
Volkswagen	
6 & 7	40-300
6 & 8	130-260
6 & 9	200-400
7 & 8	100-500
8 & 9	70-140

AUXILIARY AIR VALVE

Alfa Romeo

On cold engine, valve must be open. On warm engine, valve must be closed. If not, warm engine to normal operating temperature. Disconnect electrical leads and measure internal resistance between terminals 34 and 48. Resistance should be about 30 ohms. If not, replace auxiliary air valve.

BMW

1) With engine at normal operating temperature and idle speed set to specifications, turn air conditioner on. Connect ohmmeter to Black wire of valve connector.

2) Voltage should be registered and air should flow through valve. Turn air conditioner off. No voltage or air should flow through valve. If valve does not respond as outlined, replace auxiliary air valve.

Renault

1) Warm engine to temperature of about 68°F (20°C) and stop engine. Disconnect air hoses and electrical connector from valve. Visually check that diaphragm is partially open. Connect battery power to valve terminals. After 8 minutes, diaphragm should be completely closed.

2) If not, check internal resistance of valve with an ohmmeter connected to both terminals. Resistance should be 40 ohms on turbocharged models, and 46 ohms on all others. If valve does not respond as outlined, replace auxiliary air valve.

Porsche & Volkswagen

1) Disconnect electrical connector and connect ohmmeter leads to valve terminals. Resistance should measure approximately 30 ohms. Pull off hoses and disconnect ohmmeter. Valve should be open on cold engine and closed on warm engine.

2) Reconnect electrical connector and turn ignition switch "ON". Valve should be completely closed after 5 minutes. If valve does not respond as outlined, replace auxiliary air valve.

BOSCH AFC — EUROPEAN MODELS (Cont.)

THERMO TIME SWITCH

Porsche & Volkswagen

1) With engine cold and air temperature below 68°F (20°C), disconnect electrical connector from cold start injector and connect test lamp to connector terminals. Disconnect electrical connector from No. 1 ignition coil terminal.

2) Operate starter. Test lamp should glow brightly. After 11 seconds (maximum), test lamp should dim or go out. If not, replace thermo time switch.

All Other Models

1) Remove thermo time switch and install plug to prevent loss of coolant. Cool thermo time switch by immersing in cold water. Connect positive wire of switch to a test lamp and battery positive terminal. Connect battery negative terminal to switch body. Test lamp should glow. *See Fig. 10.*

Fig. 10: Testing Thermo Time Switch

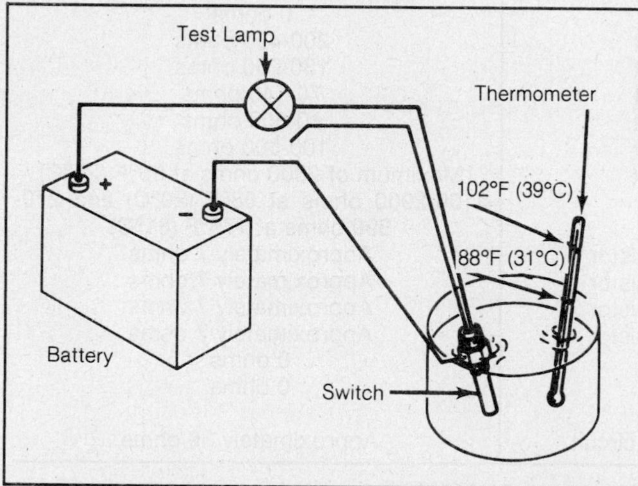
Test Lamp
Thermometer
102°F (39°C)
88°F (31°C)
+
−
Battery
Switch

Test applies to all models, except Porsche & Volkswagen.

2) Insert thermometer in water and gradually heat water. Test lamp should glow until temperature reaches 88-102°F (31-39°C). If switch does not respond as outlined, continue testing as follows:

3) Cool switch to temperature below that stamped on side of switch. Connect ohmmeter between terminals shown in table and note readings. Heat switch to temperature above 104°F (40°C) and again note readings in table. If readings are not to specifications, replace thermo time switch.

THERMO TIME SWITCH RESISTANCE
(All Models, Except Porsche & Volkswagen)

Temperature °F (°C)	Terminal Numbers	Ohms
Below 86 (30)	G & Ground	25-40
	W & Ground	0
	G & W	25-40
Above 104 (40)	G & Ground	50-80
	W & Ground	100-160
	G & W	50-80

COLD START INJECTOR

All Models

1) Disconnect electrical connector from cold start valve. Connect voltmeter leads between harness terminals and crank engine. Voltage readings should be battery voltage when engine is cold and zero volts when engine is warm. If not, check thermo time switch and electrical circuit.

2) Turn engine off and remove voltmeter. Measure resistance of cold start injector. Resistance should be about 4-5 ohms. If not, replace cold start injector.

COOLANT TEMPERATURE SENSOR

All Models

1) Warm engine to normal operating temperature and stop engine. Using a thermometer, measure temperature of coolant (oil on Volkswagen models). Disconnect electrical connector from temperature sensor and connect 1 lead of ohmmeter to terminal in sensor and other lead to ground. Ohmmeter readings should be as specified in table. If not, replace temperature sensor.

2) On Volkswagen models, if resistance reading is too high, touch ground lead of ohmmeter to sensor body. If resistance is as specified in table, corrosion is present between sensor and cylinder head. If resistance is still not as specified, replace temperature sensor.

TEMPERATURE/RESISTANCE RELATIONSHIP

Temperature	Ohms
14°F (-10°C)	7,000-12,000
68°F (20°C)	2,000-3,000
176°F (80°C)	250-400

SPEED LIMIT SWITCH

Calif. Volkswagen Vanagon

Remove speed limit switch from firewall and connect positive voltmeter lead to terminal 8 and negative voltmeter lead to terminal 6. Start engine and accelerate to 3000 RPM. Voltmeter should indicate battery voltage. If not, replace speed limit switch.

Fig. 11: Testing Speed Limit Switch

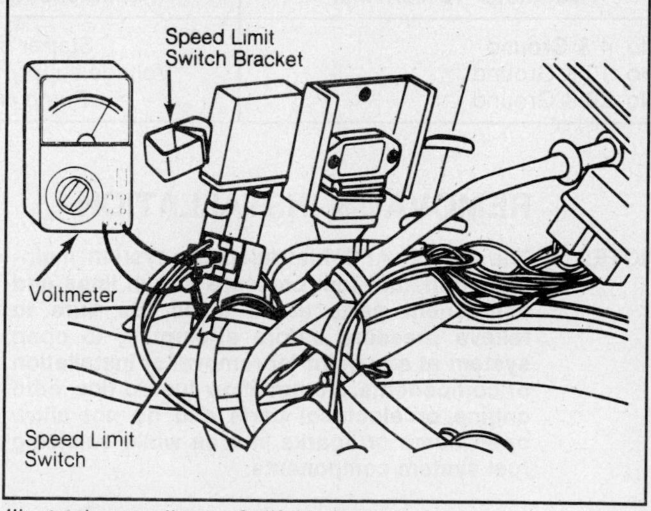
Speed Limit
Switch Bracket
Voltmeter
Speed Limit
Switch

Illustration applies to Calif. Vanagon only.

BOSCH AFC — EUROPEAN MODELS (Cont.)

INJECTORS

Volkswagen Vanagon

1) Pull connector off injector and place ohmmeter across terminals. Resistance should be 2-3 ohms. If not, replace injector.

2) Unplug connector from series resistor on firewall. Connect one ohmmeter lead to center pin of connector and touch other lead to each side pin. Resistance for each must be 5.5-6.5 ohms. If not, replace series resistor.

NOTE: **On California Vanagon models, series resistor is built in control unit and cannot be checked.**

SYSTEM CHECK

Volkswagen Vanagon

Turn ignition switch off. Unplug control unit connector. Using an ohmmeter and voltmeter, check system components and circuits. *See Vanagon AFC System Ohmmeter and Voltmeter Checks* charts.

VANAGON AFC SYSTEM OHMMETER CHECKS

Ohmmeter To Terminal	Components Checked	Specifications
No. 1 & Ground	Wire to No. 1 terminal on coil	Infinity with White coil wire disconnected and 0 when wire is grounded.
No. 3 & No. 18	Full throttle enrichment circuit	0 ohms with accelerator pedal fully down
No. 5 & Ground	Ground circuit	0 ohms
No. 6 & No. 9	Air sensor circuit	200-400 ohms
No. 6 & No. 8	Air sensor circuit	130-260 ohms
No. 8 & No. 9	Air sensor circuit	70-140 ohms
No. 6 & No. 7	Air sensor circuit	40-300 ohms
No. 7 & No. 8	Air sensor circuit	100-500 ohms
No. 6 & No. 27	Air sensor circuit	Maximum of 2800 ohms at 68°F (20°C)
No. 13 & Ground	Head sensor	2100-2900 ohms at 68°F (20°C) and 270-390 ohms at 176°F (81°C)
No. 14 & No. 10	Injector wire and resistor	Approximately 7 ohms
No. 15 & No. 10	Injector wire and resistor	Approximately 7 ohms
No. 32 & No. 10	Injector wire and resistor	Approximately 7 ohms
No. 33 & No. 10	Injector wire and resistor	Approximately 7 ohms
No. 16 & Ground	Ground circuit	0 ohms
No. 17 & Ground	Ground circuit	0 ohms
No. 34 at control unit and No. 37 at double relay on firewall	Auxiliary air regulator circuit	Approximately 30 ohms

VANAGON AFC SYSTEM VOLTMETER CHECKS

Voltmeter To Terminal	Components Checked	Specifications
No. 4 & Ground	Starter signal	0 volts normally, 12 volts during cranking
No. 10 & Ground	Voltage supply to computer	12 volts with key on, 0 volts with key off
No. 20 & Ground	Pump circuit	12 volts with key on and sensor flap open

REMOVAL & INSTALLATION

NOTE: **The Bosch AFC fuel injection system maintains constant fuel pressure in fuel lines and component parts at all times. Be sure to relieve pressure before attempting to open system at any point for removal or installation of components. Do not allow fuel to flow onto engine or electrical parts and do not allow open flame or sparks in area while servicing fuel system components.**

ELECTRONIC CONTROL UNIT

1) Disconnect battery ground cable. On Alfa Romeo Spider and Renault models, remove passenger seat and fold back carpet. On all models, disconnect electrical connector retaining clamps or press back on clip located on wire end of connector.

2) Disconnect electrical connector, swinging to right if necessary to remove. Remove ECU retaining screws and remove ECU. To install, reverse removal procedure. ECU is located as follows:

- Alfa Romeo GTV-6 2.5 – Right kick panel.
- Alfa Romeo Spider – Under carpet, behind right seat.
- BMW 528e, 533i, & 633CSi – Glove compartment.
- BMW 733i – Right kick panel, behind speaker.
- Porsche 928S – Right kick panel.
- Porsche 944 – Under dash.
- Renault – Under carpet, under right seat.
- Volkswagen – Right side of engine compartment.

BOSCH AFC — EUROPEAN MODELS (Cont.)

Fig. 12: Alfa Romeo Spider 2.0 AFC Fuel Injection Wiring Diagram

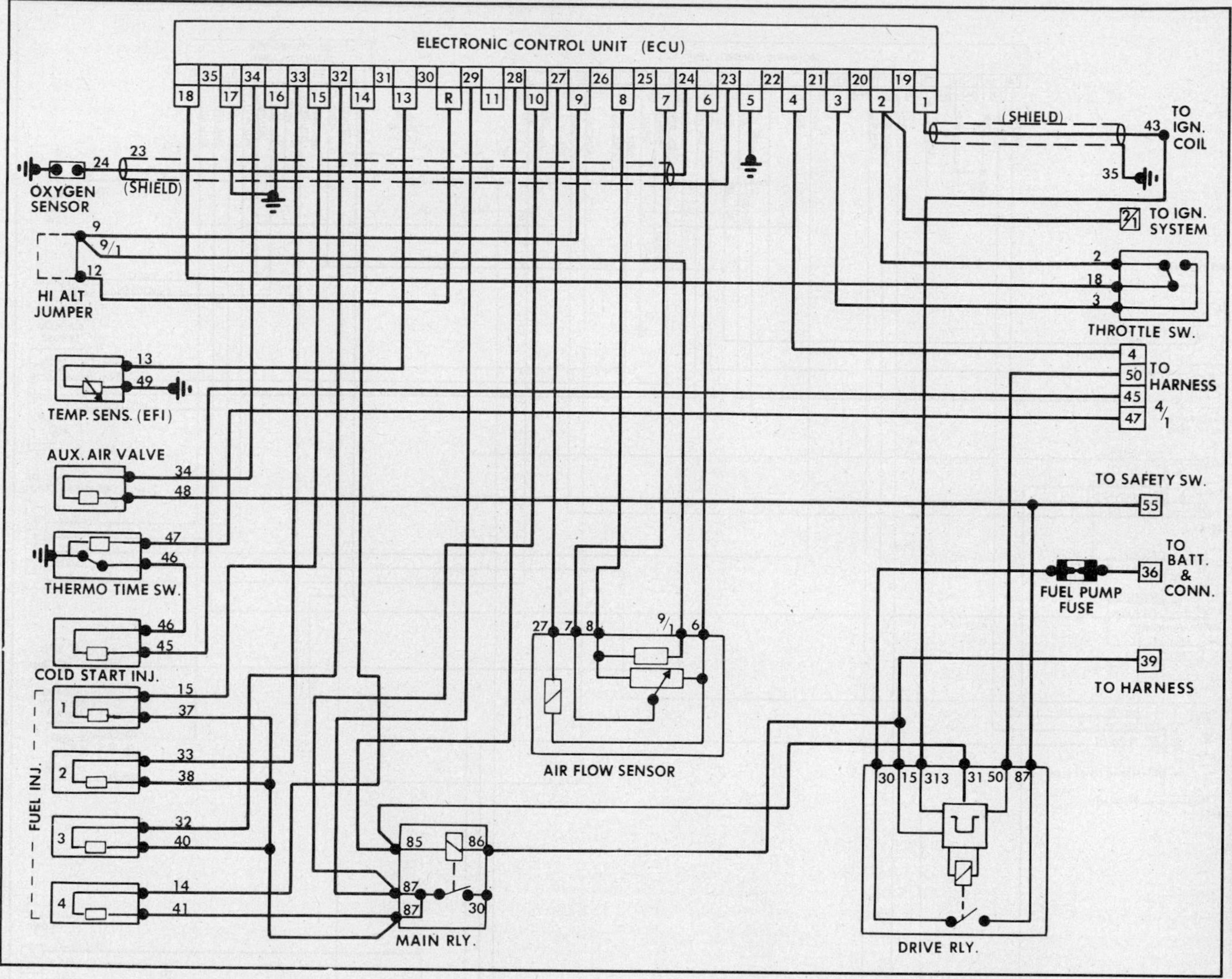

ELECTRONIC CONTROL UNIT (ECU)
OXYGEN SENSOR
(SHIELD)
HI ALT JUMPER
TEMP. SENS. (EFI)
AUX. AIR VALVE
THERMO TIME SW.
COLD START INJ.
FUEL INJ.
AIR FLOW SENSOR
MAIN RLY.
DRIVE RLY.
TO IGN. COIL
TO IGN. SYSTEM
THROTTLE SW.
TO HARNESS
TO SAFETY SW.
TO BATT. & CONN.
FUEL PUMP FUSE
TO HARNESS

AIR FLOW METER

NOTE: **Removal and installation procedures not available for Porsche or Volkswagen models.**

Alfa Romeo & BMW

Unscrew hose clamp. Remove cover attaching nuts. Pull out plug for electrical connector. Pull air flow meter out of air cleaner housing and remove. To install, reverse removal procedure.

Renault

Disconnect battery ground cable. Disconnect electrical connector from air flow meter. Separate air hoses from air flow meter. Unclip retaining hook and remove air flow meter. To install, reverse removal procedure and make sure retaining hook is secured.

THROTTLE SWITCH

Disconnect battery ground cable. Disconnect throttle switch electrical connector. Remove 2 screws (bolts) securing throttle switch to housing. Remove switch by slowly pulling switch off throttle shaft. To install, reverse removal procedure. Make sure switch is aligned on throttle shaft after replacement. Perform Throttle Switch adjustment. *See Adjustments in this article.*

COLD START INJECTOR

Disconnect battery ground cable. Remove electrical connector from cold start injector. Release fuel system pressure and remove fuel supply line from injector. Remove injector retaining bolts and remove injector. To install, reverse removal procedure.

AUXILIARY AIR VALVE

NOTE: **Replacement of auxiliary air valve requires that immediate replacement be available or draining cooling system below level of valve (oil on Volkswagen models).**

Disconnect battery ground cable. Remove electrical connector and air hoses from air valve. Remove 2 bolts securing valve to cylinder head and remove valve. To install, reverse removal procedure.

1983 Fuel Injection

BOSCH AFC — EUROPEAN MODELS (Cont.)

Fig. 13: BMW AFC Fuel Injection Wiring Diagram

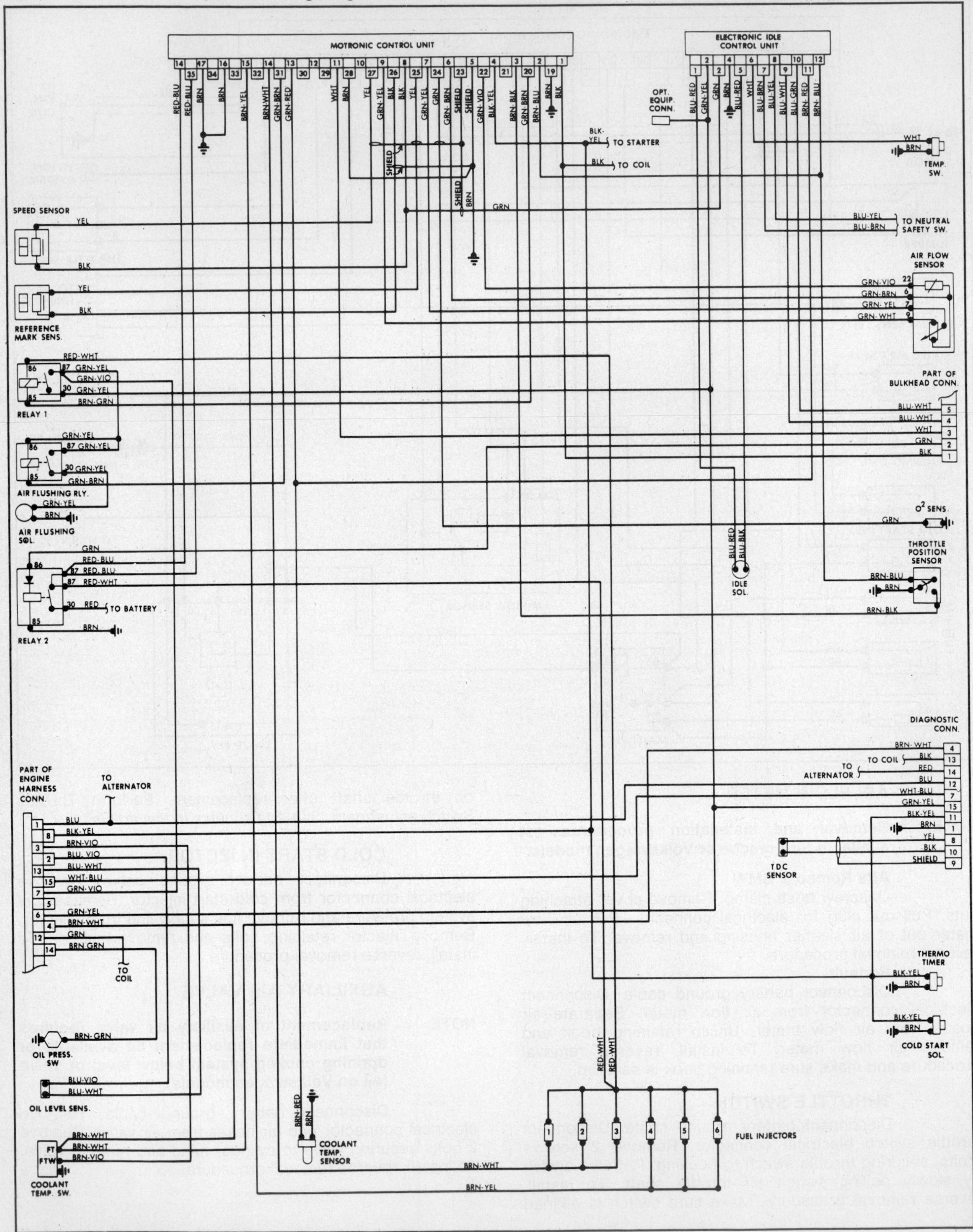

MOTRONIC CONTROL UNIT
ELECTRONIC IDLE CONTROL UNIT
OPT. EQUIP. CONN.
TO STARTER
TO COIL
TEMP. SW.
SPEED SENSOR
REFERENCE MARK SENS.
TO NEUTRAL SAFETY SW.
AIR FLOW SENSOR
PART OF BULKHEAD CONN.
RELAY 1
AIR FLUSHING RLY.
AIR FLUSHING SOL.
O2 SENS.
THROTTLE POSITION SENSOR
IDLE SOL.
TO BATTERY
RELAY 2
DIAGNOSTIC CONN.
TO ALTERNATOR
PART OF ENGINE HARNESS CONN.
TDC SENSOR
THERMO TIMER
COLD START SOL.
OIL PRESS. SW
OIL LEVEL SENS.
COOLANT TEMP. SENSOR
FUEL INJECTORS
COOLANT TEMP. SW.

BOSCH AFC — EUROPEAN MODELS (Cont.)

COOLANT TEMPERATURE SENSOR

NOTE: **Replacement of temperature sensor should be done only on a cold engine. Removal of sensor requires having replacement sensor ready for immediate installation or draining cooling system below level of sensor (oil on Volkswagen).**

Disconnect battery ground cable. Drain coolant as required. Disconnect electrical connector from sensor. Loosen and remove sensor. To install, reverse removal procedure using sealer on sensor threads. Replace sealing washers (if equipped).

THERMO TIME SWITCH

NOTE: **Thermo time switch removal should be done only when engine is cold. Removal of switch requires having replacement ready for immediate installation or draining cooling system below level of switch (oil on Volkswagen).**

Disconnect battery ground cable and drain cooling system as required. Disconnect or remove components as required to gain access to thermo time switch. Disconnect electrical connector from switch. Loosen and remove switch. To install, reverse removal procedure, using sealer on switch threads.

FUEL PRESSURE REGULATOR

Disconnect battery ground cable and relieve fuel system pressure. Disconnect or remove components as required to gain access to regulator. Disconnect fuel lines and vacuum line at regulator. Remove pressure regulator, separating from bracket (if used). To install, reverse removal procedure.

FUEL INJECTORS

BMW, Porsche & Volkswagen

1) Disconnect battery ground cable and relieve fuel system pressure. Unscrew mounting bolts of injection tube. Push up injection tube until injectors have been taken out of guide on intake manifold.

2) Pull off electrical connector on fuel injector. Lift off lock from injector and pull injector out of injection tube. To install, reverse removal procedure, replacing seals.

All Other Models

1) Disconnect battery ground cable and relieve fuel system pressure. Disconnect or remove all components, wiring and vacuum hoses as required to gain access to injectors. Remove intake manifold on Alfa Romeo GTV-6 2.5 models.

2) Disconnect electrical connectors from injectors. On Alfa Romeo GTV-6 2.5 models, loosen injector retainers and remove fuel rail and injectors as an assembly. Remove injector seals and lock rings (if equipped).

3) On all models, remove injector clamps at fuel rail. Remove injectors from fuel rail by melting hose lengthwise with a soldering gun until injector can be removed from rail. Thoroughly clean fuel rail of rubber.

4) To install, reverse removal procedure. Install injectors on fuel rail with new hose and ensure hose is

Fig. 14: Renault 18i AFC Fuel Injection Wiring Diagram (Fuego Similar)

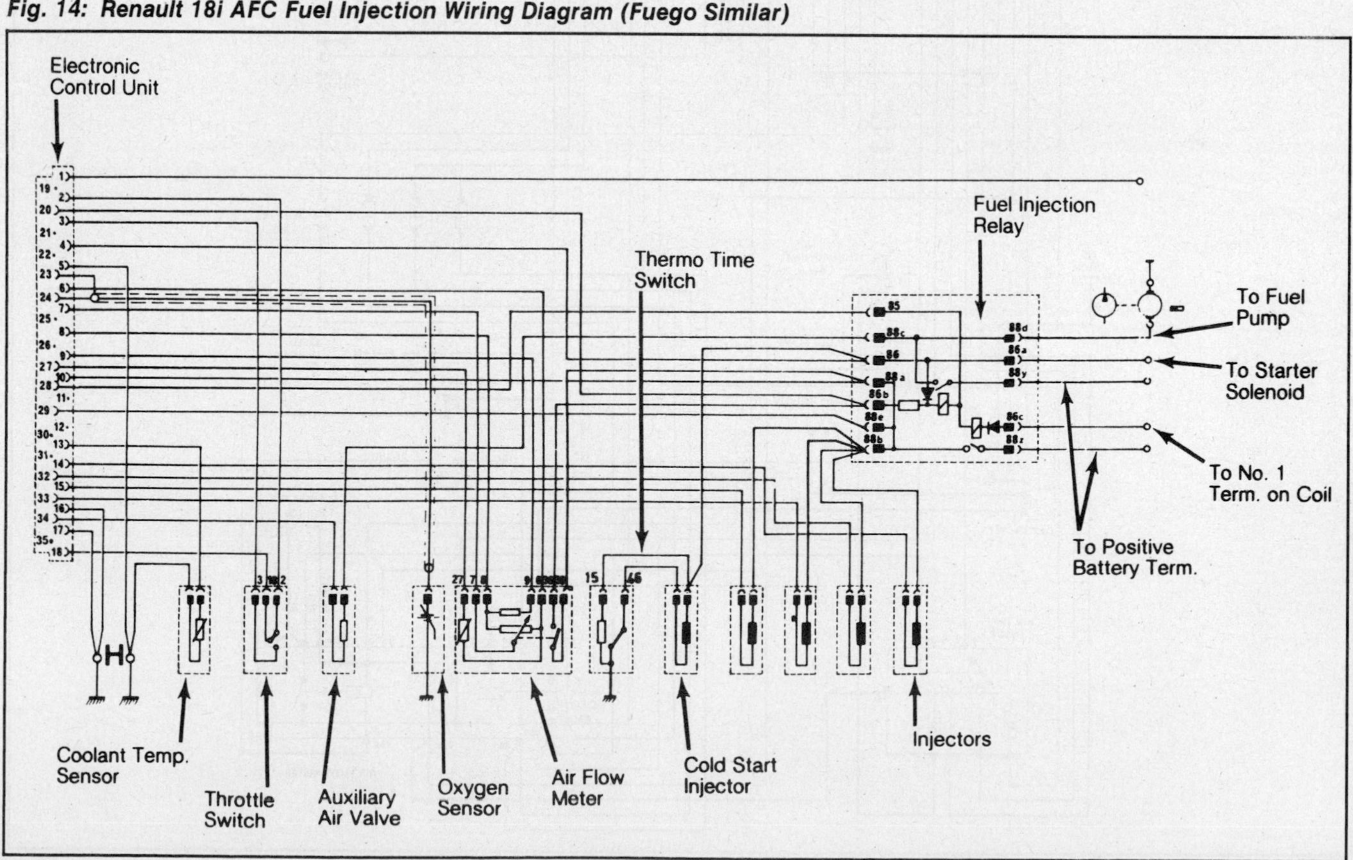
Electronic
Control Unit
Fuel Injection
Relay
Thermo Time
Switch
To Fuel
Pump
To Starter
Solenoid
To No. 1
Term. on Coil
To Positive
Battery Term.
Coolant Temp.
Sensor
Throttle
Switch
Auxiliary
Air Valve
Oxygen
Sensor
Air Flow
Meter
Cold Start
Injector
Injectors

BOSCH AFC — EUROPEAN MODELS (Cont.)

fully seated on injector and fuel rail. Connect hose with a clamp. Ensure injector seals are properly installed.

ADJUSTMENTS

NOTE: **For all on-vehicle adjustments not covered in this article, see appropriate TUNE-UP SERVICE PROCEDURES article.**

THROTTLE SWITCH

NOTE: **Adjustment procedure not available for Alfa Romeo Spider 2.0 or Porsche 928S models. BMW models require use of tester.**

Alfa Romeo GTV-6 2.5

1) Disconnect electrical connector at throttle switch and connect test lamp. Turn ignition on.

2) Slowly rotate throttle plate from closed position. Test lamp should glow when throttle plate is rotated 58° from fully closed position. If not, loosen screws and rotate switch until lamp glows when throttle plate is 58° from fully closed position. Tighten retaining screws.

Renault

1) Loosen throttle switch retaining screws. With the throttle plate against the idle stop, slowly rotate throttle switch to wide open position until inner stop can be felt. Tighten switch retaining screws.

2) Disconnect electrical connector from throttle switch and connect ohmmeter leads between terminal Nos. 7 and 9. With ignition off, resistance should be 0 ohms when throttle plate is fully closed and 15,000 ohms (minimum) when throttle is wide open.

3) Move ohmmeter leads to terminals 9 and 10. Ohmmeter resistance should be 0 ohms when throttle plate is wide open and 15,000 ohms (minimum) when throttle plate is fully closed. If not, readjust throttle switch.

Volkswagen

1) Disconnect electrical connector at throttle switch. Zero ohmmeter and connect ohmmeter leads to both terminals on switch. With throttle valve closed, ohmmeter reading should be infinity. Slowly open throttle. Just before reaching stop, ohmmeter reading should be 0 ohms.

2) If switch does not respond as described, fully depress and hold accelerator pedal. Loosen throttle switch and move switch until ohmmeter reading changes from infinity reading to 0 ohms. Tighten switch.

3) Roller of switch should be centered on curved arm of throttle lever. If switch cannot be adjusted as described, replace throttle switch.

Fig. 15: Volkswagen Vanagon AFC Fuel Injection Wiring Diagram (Air Cooled Engine)

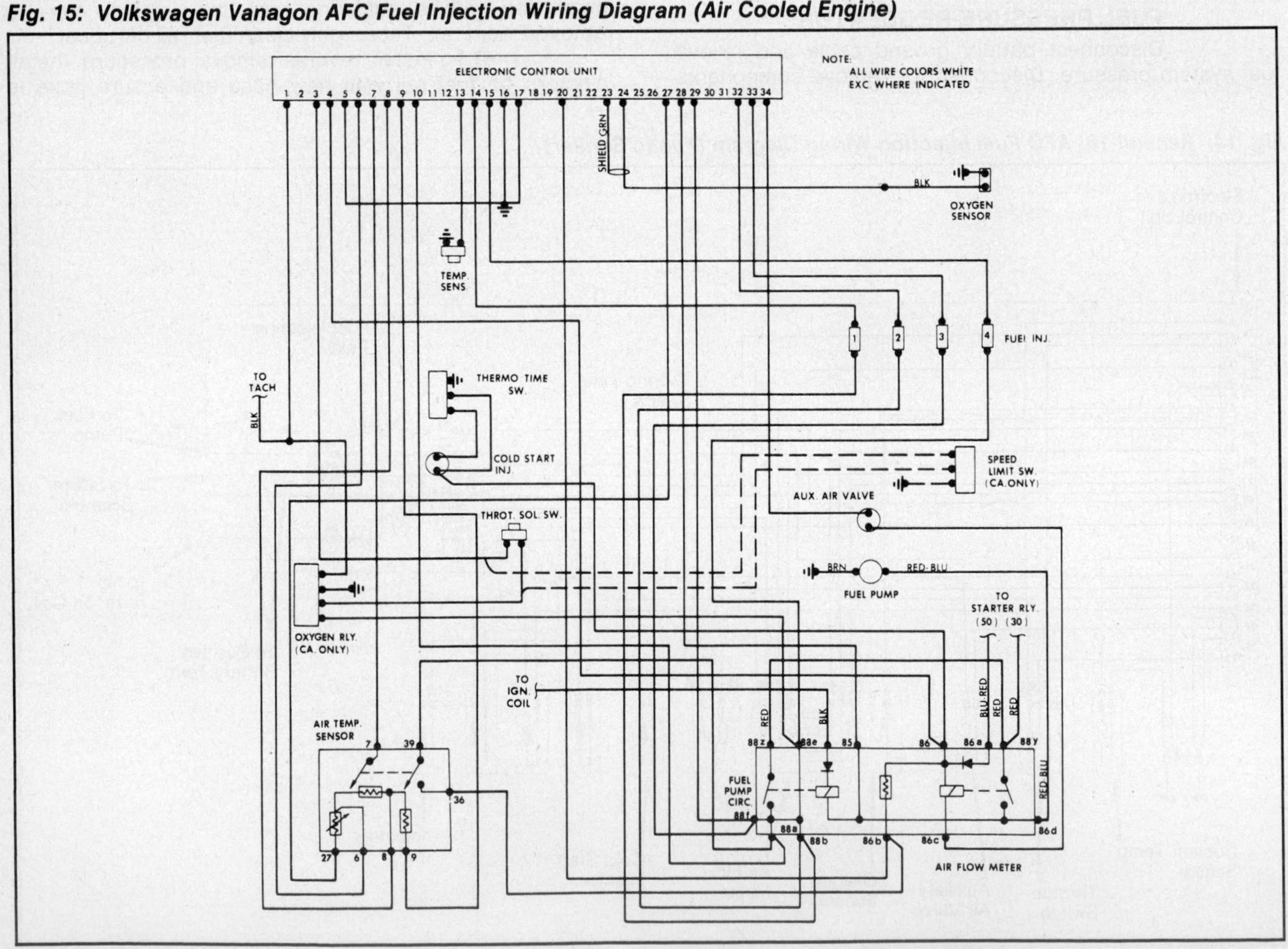
ELECTRONIC CONTROL UNIT
1 2 3 4 5 6 7 8 9 10 11 12 13 14 15 16 17 18 19 20 21 22 23 24 25 26 27 28 29 30 31 32 33 34
NOTE:
ALL WIRE COLORS WHITE
EXC. WHERE INDICATED
SHIELD GRN
BLK
OXYGEN SENSOR
TEMP. SENS.
1
2
3
4
FUEL INJ.
TO TACH
BLK
THERMO TIME SW.
COLD START INJ.
SPEED LIMIT SW. (CA ONLY)
AUX. AIR VALVE
THROT. SOL. SW.
BRN
RED-BLU
FUEL PUMP
TO STARTER RLY.
(50) (30)
OXYGEN RLY. (CA ONLY)
TO IGN. COIL
AIR TEMP. SENSOR
7
39
36
27
6
8
9
RED
BLK
BLU-RED
RED
RED
RED-BLU
88z
88e
85
86
86a
88y
FUEL PUMP CIRC.
88f
88a
88b
86b
86c
86d
AIR FLOW METER

1983 Fuel Injection

BOSCH AFC – EUROPEAN MODELS (Cont.)

Fig. 16: Alfa Romeo GTV-6 2.5 AFC Fuel Injection Wiring Diagram

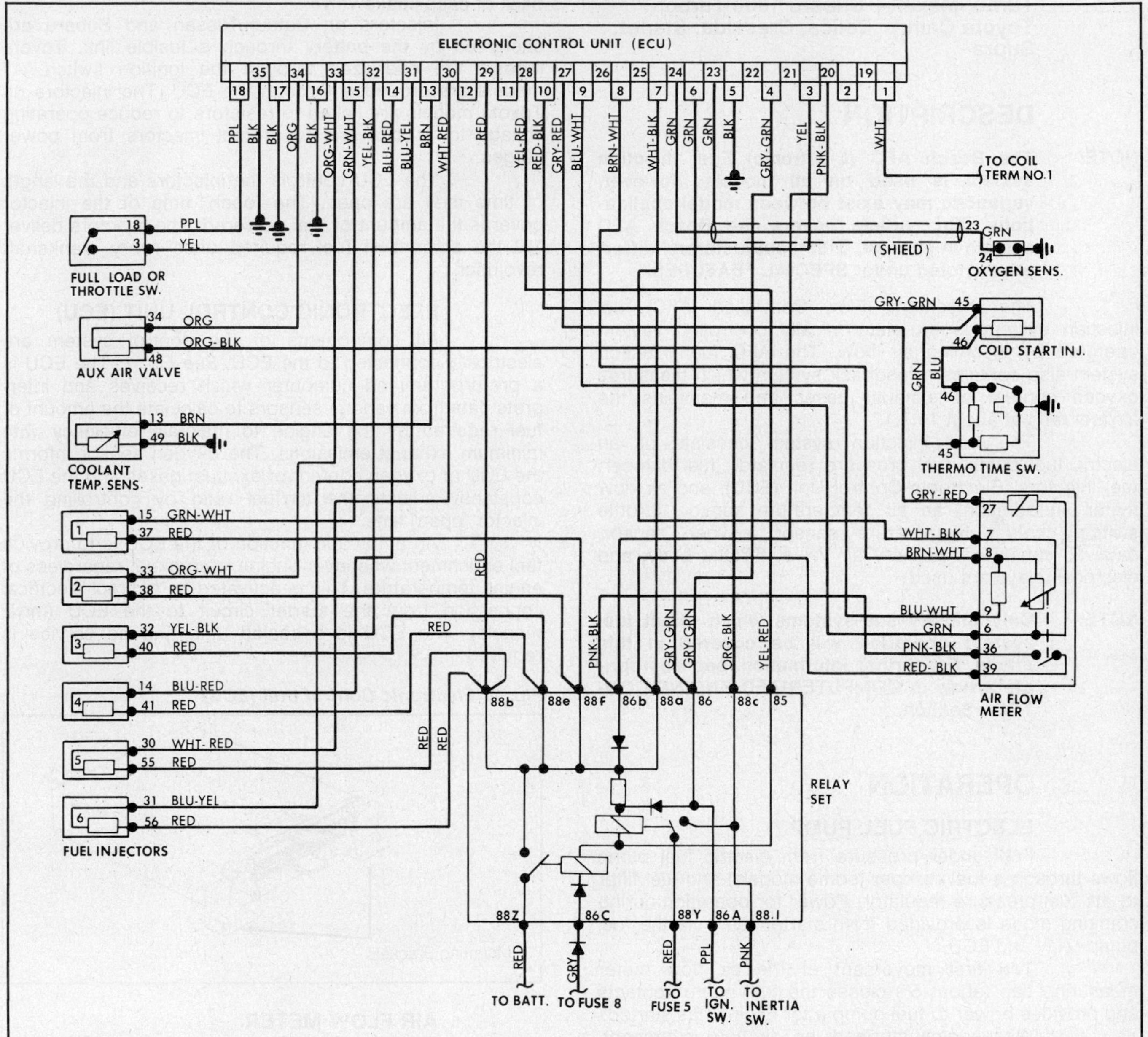

ELECTRONIC CONTROL UNIT (ECU)
TO COIL TERM NO. 1
(SHIELD)
OXYGEN SENS.
FULL LOAD OR THROTTLE SW.
AUX AIR VALVE
COLD START INJ.
THERMO TIME SW.
COOLANT TEMP. SENS.
AIR FLOW METER
FUEL INJECTORS
RELAY SET
TO BATT.
TO FUSE 8
TO FUSE 5
TO IGN. SW.
TO INERTIA SW.

1983 Fuel Injection

BOSCH AFC – JAPANESE MODELS

Datsun/Nissan 200SX, 280ZX, 280ZX Turbo, Maxima, Subaru 1800 Turbo; Toyota Camry, Celica, Cressida, Starlet, Supra

DESCRIPTION

NOTE: **The Bosch AFC (L-Jetronic) Fuel Injection system is used on all models; however, variations may exist between model applications. This article covers the Bosch AFC system in general, with manufacturers' differences noted under SPECIAL FEATURES.**

The Bosch Air Flow Controlled (AFC) fuel injection system is an electronically controlled system operated by incoming air flow. The AFC fuel injection system also contains a feedback system which measures oxygen content of exhaust gases and maintains the air/fuel ratio at about 14.7:1.

The fuel injection system consists of an electric fuel pump, fuel pressure regulator, fuel damper, fuel injectors, Electronic Control Unit (ECU), and air flow meter. In addition, an air temperature sensor, throttle switch, coolant temperature sensor, oxygen sensor, catalytic converter, auxiliary air valve, throttle body, and electrical relays are used.

NOTE: **Only primary sub-systems which affect fuel system operation will be covered in this article. For further information, see appropriate article in COMPUTERIZED ENGINE CONTROL Section.**

OPERATION

ELECTRIC FUEL PUMP

Fuel under pressure from electric fuel pump flows through a fuel damper (some models) and fuel filter to the fuel pressure regulator. Power for operation during cranking mode is provided from starter relay via the fuel pump relay and ECU.

The first movement of the air flow meter measuring flap (about 5°) closes the fuel pump contacts and provides power to fuel pump after engine has started.

With engine stopped, no air flow is present, measuring flap closes and fuel pump contacts are opened to cut power to fuel pump. This method reduces the risk of fire, in case of a collision.

FUEL PRESSURE REGULATOR

The pressure regulator consists of a sealed, spring loaded diaphragm with a connection for intake manifold vacuum. Fuel is provided to fuel injectors under approximately 36 psi (2.5 kg/cm²) pressure.

A connection for intake manifold vacuum provides a constant pressure differential which ensures that the amount of fuel injected is solely dependent upon injector "open" time. Excess fuel is returned to fuel tank. No service of pressure regulator is required.

FUEL INJECTORS

A fuel rail links the fuel pressure regulator with the fuel injectors. Each cylinder is provided with a solenoid-operated injector which sprays fuel toward the back of each intake valve.

Injectors on Datsun/Nissan and Subaru are energized by the battery through a fusible link. Toyota models are energized through the ignition switch. All models are grounded through the ECU. The injectors on Toyota models are linked to resistors to reduce operating voltage to 3 volts and to protect injectors from power surges.

The ECU controls the injectors and the length of time they are open. The "open" time of the injector governs the amount of fuel delivered. The injectors deliver 1/2 the amount of fuel required once every crankshaft revolution.

ELECTRONIC CONTROL UNIT (ECU)

All components of the control system are electrically connected to the ECU. *See Fig. 1.* The ECU is a pre-programmed computer which receives and interprets data from various sensors to calculate the amount of fuel required by the engine to maintain efficiency with minimum exhaust emissions. The oxygen sensor informs the ECU of oxygen content of exhaust gases and the ECU constantly adjusts the air/fuel ratio by controlling the injector "open" time.

An automatic function of the ECU is to provide fuel enrichment whenever engine is cranked, regardless of engine temperature. This is activated by a direct electrical connection from the starter circuit to the ECU (most models). The ECU is a sealed unit, and no service is required.

Fig. 1: Electronic Control Unit (ECU)

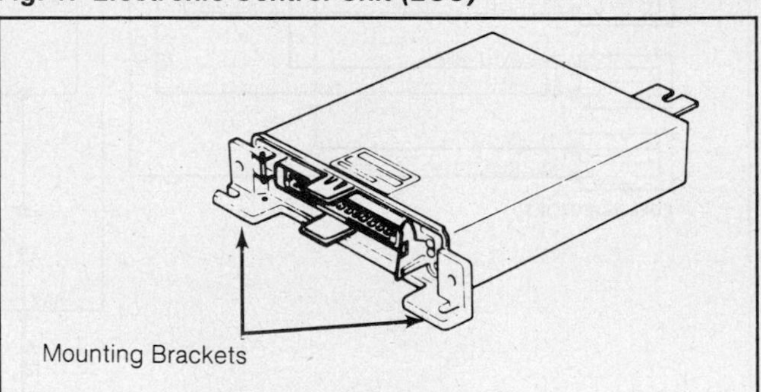
Mounting Brackets

AIR FLOW METER

All engine air is drawn through the air flow meter. The meter is basically a tunnel with similarly shaped measuring flap and dampening flap (offset 90° on same casting). The measuring flap swings on an axis in air stream against pressure of a spiral spring and is connected to a potentiometer. The potentiometer transmits an electrical signal to inform the ECU of engine load. *See Fig. 2.*

In addition to monitoring the air flow, it controls engine idle. At idle, the measuring flap is almost closed due to spring pressure. An idle air by-pass receives air from main air flow through a small hole, the size of which is controlled by the idle mixture screw. This adjustable air by-pass influences CO levels at low engine speeds.

BOSCH AFC – JAPANESE MODELS (Cont.)

Fig. 2: Bosch AFC Air Flow Meter

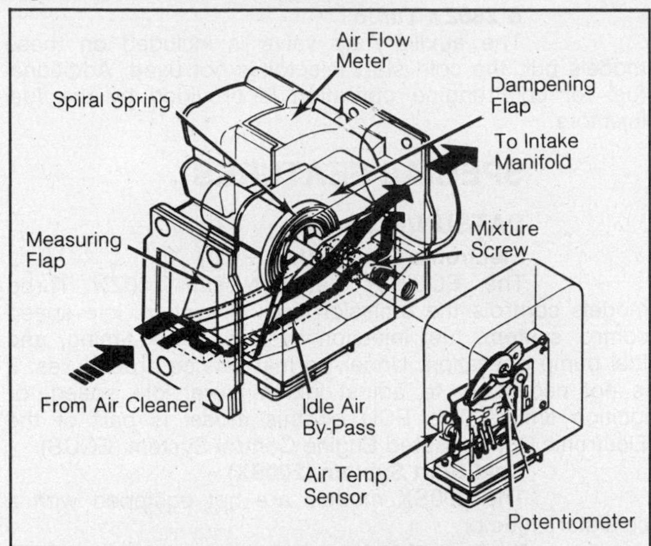
Air Flow Meter
Spiral Spring
Dampening Flap
To Intake Manifold
Measuring Flap
Mixture Screw
From Air Cleaner
Idle Air By-Pass
Air Temp. Sensor
Potentiometer

AIR TEMPERATURE SENSOR

The air temperature sensor is an integral component of the air flow meter which converts temperature of incoming air into electrical signals. These signals are received by the ECU and processed to adjust the amount of fuel delivered by the injectors. The air temperature sensor is not serviceable.

THROTTLE BODY

The throttle body controls the intake air flow in response to accelerator pedal movement. Located between the air flow meter and the intake manifold, the throttle body shaft is connected to throttle switch.

Throttle bodies on Subaru models contain an idle adjustment screw and a fast idle solenoid. The fast idle solenoid opens a by-pass passage during air conditioner operation to maintain engine idle speed. *See Fig. 3.*

Fig. 3: Subaru Throttle Body

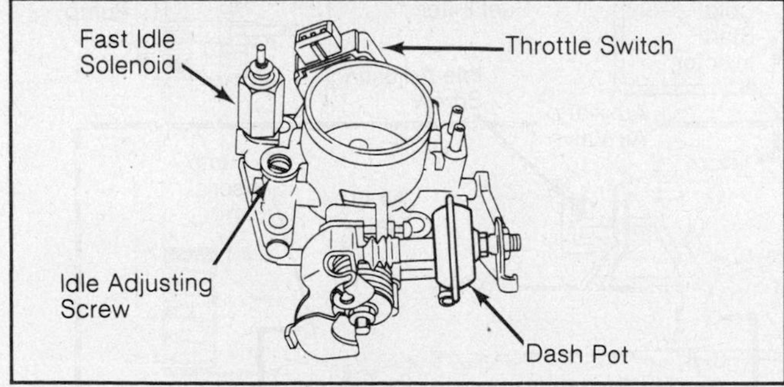
Fast Idle Solenoid
Throttle Switch
Idle Adjusting Screw
Dash Pot

THROTTLE SWITCH

A contact type throttle switch is installed on the throttle chamber of all models. It converts throttle position into electrical signals to inform ECU of throttle position. Signals are sent to ECU when throttle is fully open or at idle. *See Fig. 4*. The potentiometer prevents loss of power during sudden acceleration/deceleration by signaling the ECU of necessary fuel enrichment requirements.

NOTE: Datsun/Nissan 200SX and Subaru models with automatic transmissions are also equipped with a dashpot to prevent abrupt closing of throttle valve.

Fig. 4: Contact Type Throttle Switch

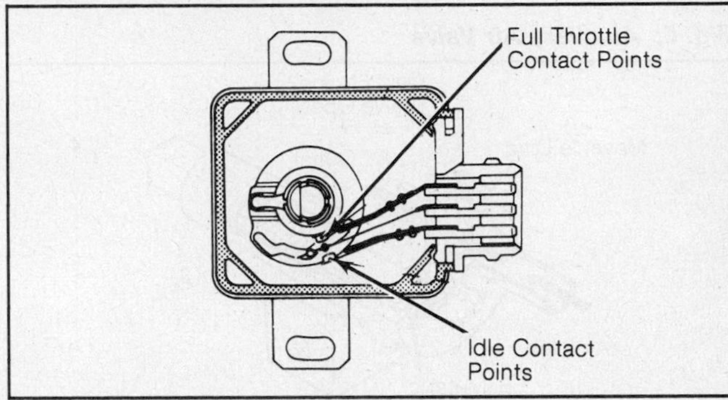
Full Throttle Contact Points
Idle Contact Points

COOLANT TEMPERATURE SENSOR

This sensor provides ECU with engine temperature information relating to warm-up enrichment operation. During warm-up period after a cold engine start, additional fuel is required to maintain engine performance. As engine temperature increases, the ECU decreases fuel enrichment until engine reaches normal operating temperature.

ELECTRICAL RELAYS

The various relays used with the electronic controls of the AFC injection system control power to injectors, fuel pump, ECU, and cold start system. The electrical relays may consist of 1 component for all relays or a combination of individual relays.

COLD START SYSTEM

Toyota & Datsun/Nissan Maxima & 280ZX

The cold start system provides additional air and fuel during cold engine starts. The cold start system consists of the following. Auxiliary air valve which provides additional air, cold start injector which delivers additional fuel, and a thermo time switch which controls operation of the cold start system. The Toyota Cressida and Supra models use an Idle Air Control (IAC) valve in place of the auxiliary air valve used on other vehicles.

The thermal time switch has a bi-metallic contact surrounded by a heating coil which is energized during engine cranking. This switch limits cold start injection to 1-12 seconds under extreme cold engine starts in relation to engine temperature. When engine temperature rises above a specified point, bi-metallic contact breaks ground circuit of cold start injector and cold start enrichment is by-passed.

The auxiliary air valve provides additional air during cold engine starts and warm-up periods. The valve consists of an electrically heated bi-metallic strip, movable disc, and air by-pass channel. The heater coil on the bi-metallic strip is energized by the fuel pump relay. Control of the valve is based upon engine temperature; the air by-pass channel is open when engine is cold and gradually closes as temperature rises. At predetermined temperatures, air by-pass channel is blocked and additional air flow stops. *See Fig. 5*.

The IAC valve on Toyota Cressida and Supra models performs the same function as the auxiliary air valve. Mounted on the throttle body, the IAC is a solenoid-

1983 Fuel Injection

BOSCH AFC – JAPANESE MODELS (Cont.)

actuated valve which provides additional air during cold engine operation. It also maintains idle speed during air conditioner operation. The IAC is controlled directly by the ECU.

Fig. 5: Auxiliary Air Valve

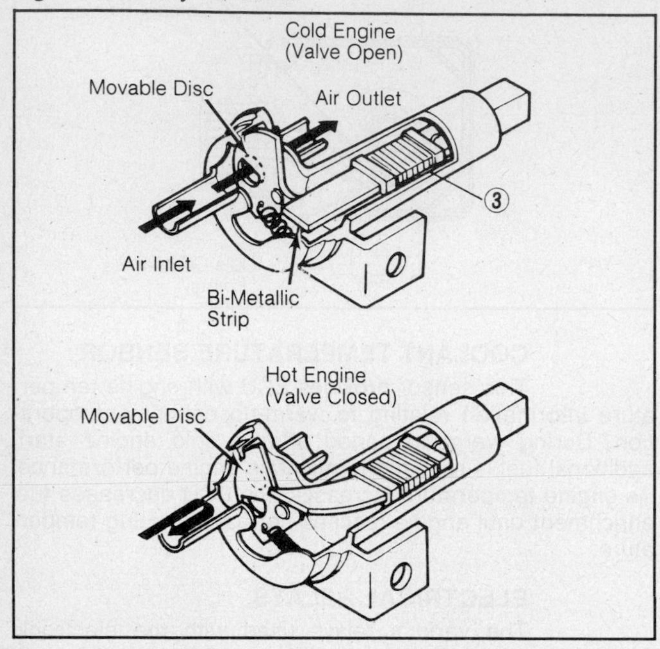
Cold Engine
(Valve Open)
Movable Disc
Air Outlet
3
Air Inlet
Bi-Metallic
Strip
Hot Engine
(Valve Closed)
Movable Disc

Subaru & Datsun/Nissan 200SX & 280ZX Turbo

The auxiliary air valve is included on these models but, the cold start injector is not used. Additional fuel for cold engine operation is provided by the fuel injectors.

SPECIAL FEATURES

DATSUN/NISSAN

Electronic Control Unit (ECU)

The ECU of Datsun/Nissan 280ZX Turbo models controls the emission control system, idle speed control system, fuel injection system, spark timing, and fuel pump operation. Under normal service procedures, it is not necessary to adjust idle mixture, idle speed, or ignition timing. The ECU on this model is part of the Electronic Concentrated Engine Control System (ECCS).

Cold Start System (200SX)

The 200SX models are not equipped with a cold start injector.

Dashpot (200SX)

A dashpot is installed on the throttle body on vehicles equipped with automatic transmissions. The dashpot prevents engine stalls due to abrupt closing of the throttle.

Electric Fuel Pump

Power for operation during cranking mode is provided by the ECU through the fuel pump relay. After

Fig. 6: Datsun/Nissan Maxima & 280ZX Fuel Injection System

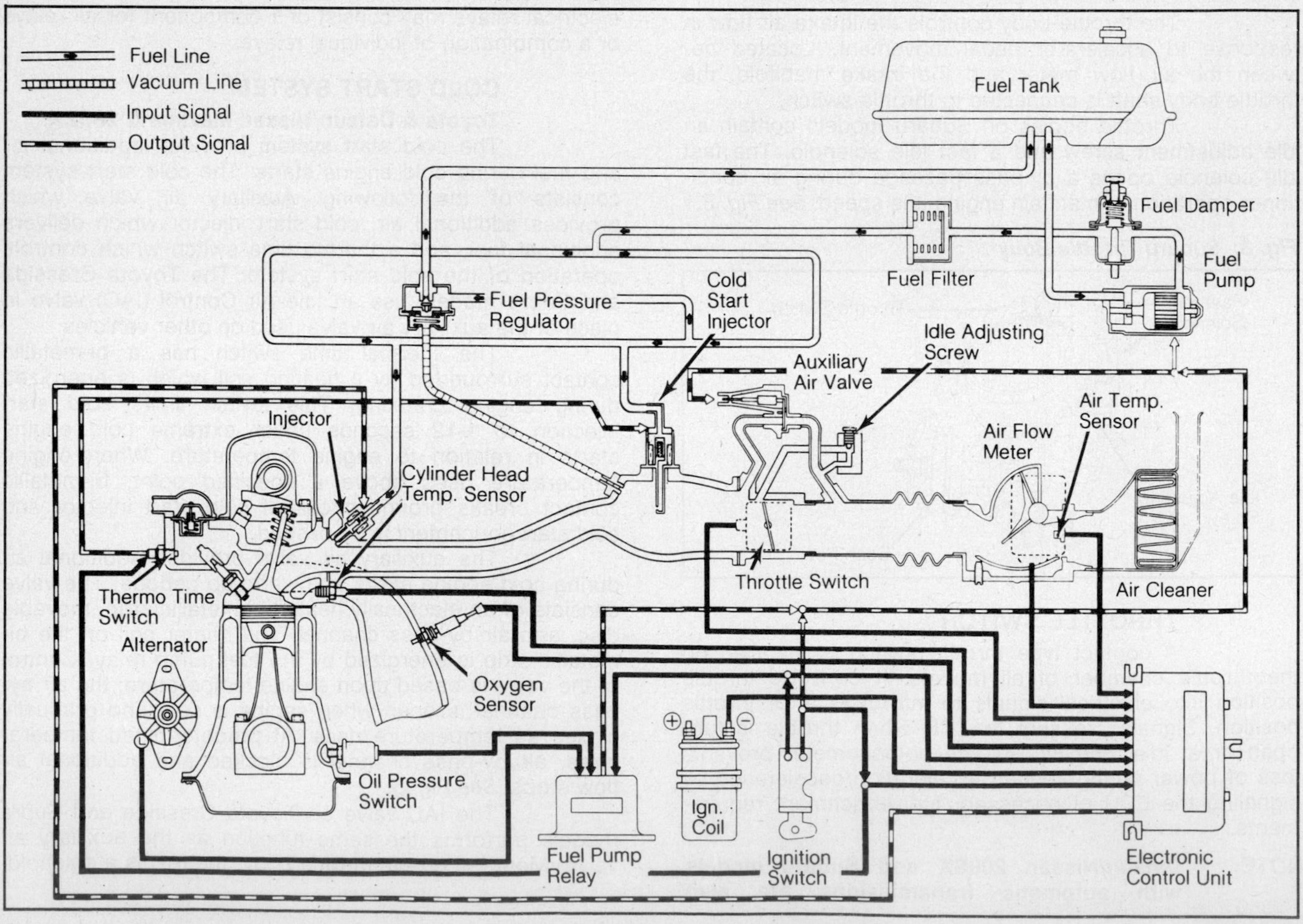

Fuel Line
Vacuum Line
Input Signal
Output Signal
Fuel Tank
Fuel Damper
Fuel Filter
Fuel Pump
Fuel Pressure
Regulator
Cold
Start
Injector
Idle Adjusting
Screw
Auxiliary
Air Valve
Air Temp.
Sensor
Air Flow
Meter
Injector
Cylinder Head
Temp. Sensor
Throttle Switch
Air Cleaner
Thermo Time
Switch
Alternator
Oxygen
Sensor
Oil Pressure
Switch
Ign.
Coil
Fuel Pump
Relay
Ignition
Switch
Electronic
Control Unit

1983 Fuel Injection

BOSCH AFC – JAPANESE MODELS (Cont.)

the engine has started, control of the fuel pump is by the charging system and oil pressure switch. Power to fuel pump is stopped if alternator does not generate a charge and oil pressure decreases. This method reduces risk of fire, in the case of a collision.

TOYOTA

Electric Fuel Pump

After the engine has started, control of the fuel pump is by a fuel pump circuit in the air flow meter. The air flow meter also controls fuel pump operation, and idling.

Idle Speed Control (IAC) Valve

On Cressida and Supra models, the IAC performs the same function as the auxiliary air valve on other vehicles. It controls air flow through the throttle body air by-pass passage to maintain idle speed when engine is cold or during air conditioner operation.

SUBARU

Throttle Body

Subaru throttle bodies are equipped with an idle speed adjusting screw and a fast idle solenoid. The fast idle solenoid opens an air by-pass passage during air conditioner operation to maintain engine idle speed. Throttle bodies are also equipped with dashpots to prevent engine stall during deceleration.

Fig. 7: Datsun/Nissan 200SX Fuel Injection System

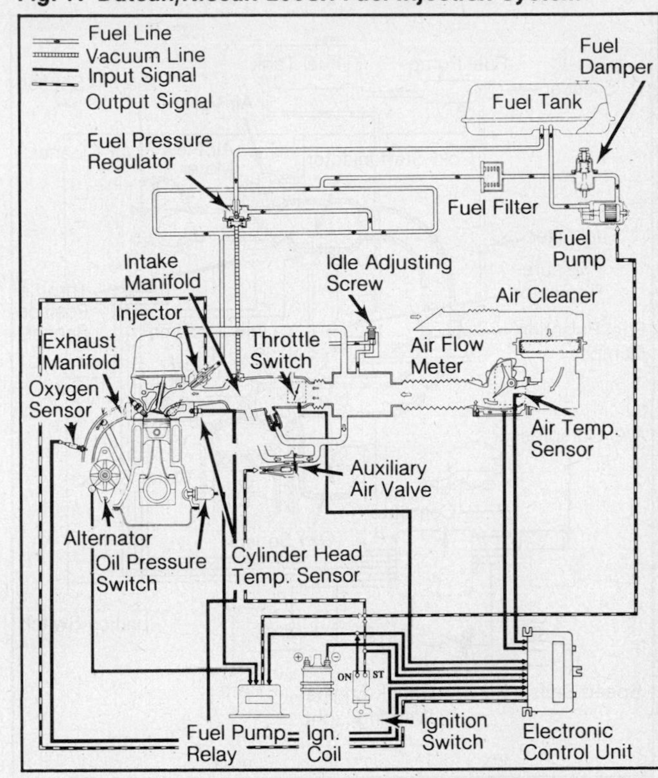
Fuel Line
Vacuum Line
Input Signal
Output Signal
Fuel Damper
Fuel Tank
Fuel Pressure Regulator
Fuel Filter
Fuel Pump
Intake Manifold
Idle Adjusting Screw
Air Cleaner
Injector
Exhaust Manifold
Throttle Switch
Air Flow Meter
Oxygen Sensor
Air Temp. Sensor
Auxiliary Air Valve
Alternator
Oil Pressure Switch
Cylinder Head Temp. Sensor
Fuel Pump Relay
Ign. Coil
Ignition Switch
Electronic Control Unit

Fig. 8: Datsun/Nissan 280ZX Turbo Fuel Injection System

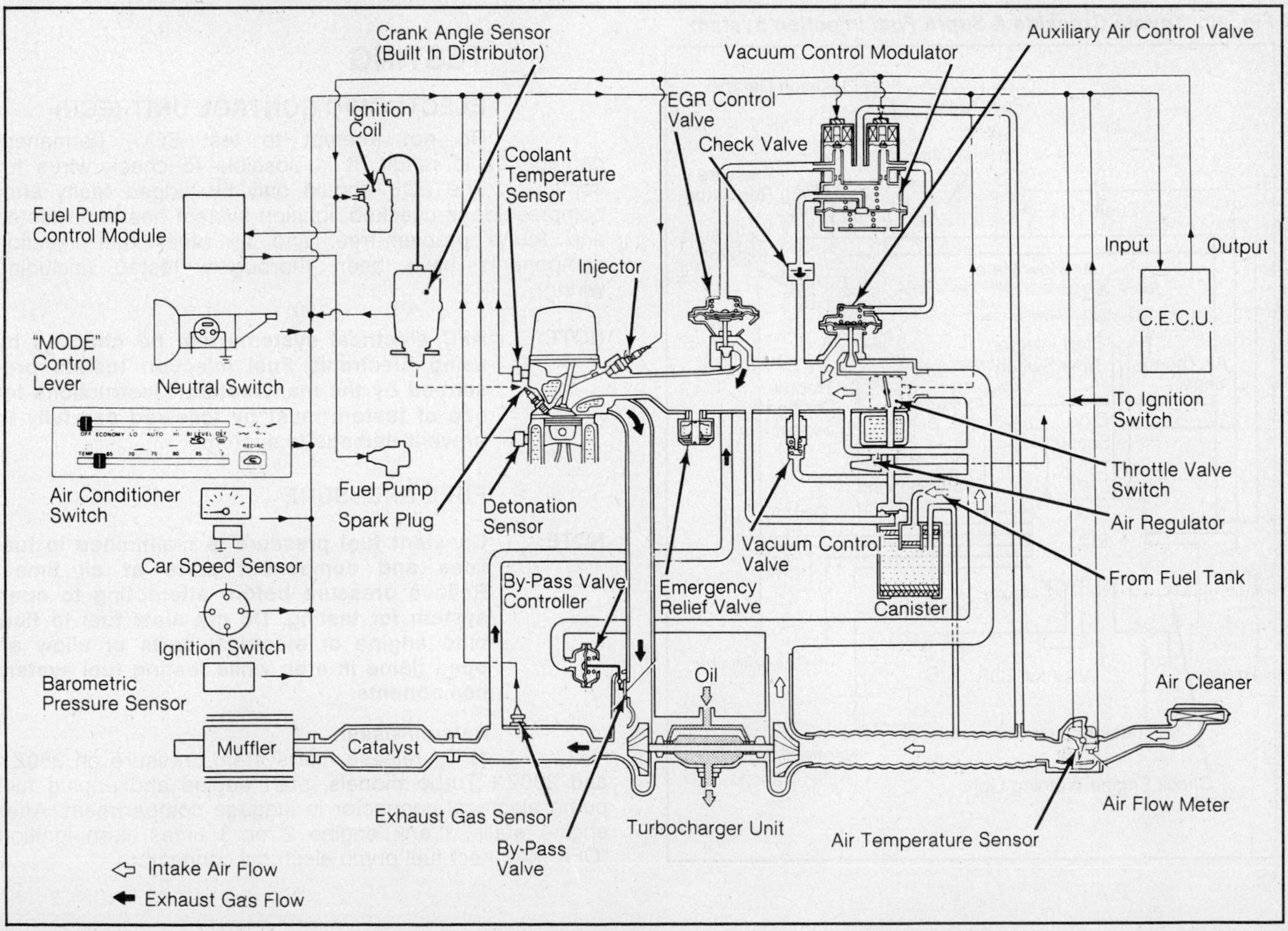

Crank Angle Sensor (Built In Distributor)
Vacuum Control Modulator
Auxiliary Air Control Valve
Ignition Coil
EGR Control Valve
Check Valve
Coolant Temperature Sensor
Fuel Pump Control Module
Input
Output
Injector
C.E.C.U.
"MODE" Control Lever
Neutral Switch
To Ignition Switch
Throttle Valve Switch
Air Conditioner Switch
Fuel Pump
Spark Plug
Detonation Sensor
Air Regulator
Vacuum Control Valve
Car Speed Sensor
From Fuel Tank
By-Pass Valve Controller
Emergency Relief Valve
Canister
Ignition Switch
Oil
Air Cleaner
Barometric Pressure Sensor
Muffler
Catalyst
Air Flow Meter
Exhaust Gas Sensor
Turbocharger Unit
Air Temperature Sensor
By-Pass Valve
Intake Air Flow
Exhaust Gas Flow

1983 Fuel Injection

BOSCH AFC – JAPANESE MODELS (Cont.)

Fig. 9: Toyota Camry Fuel Injection System

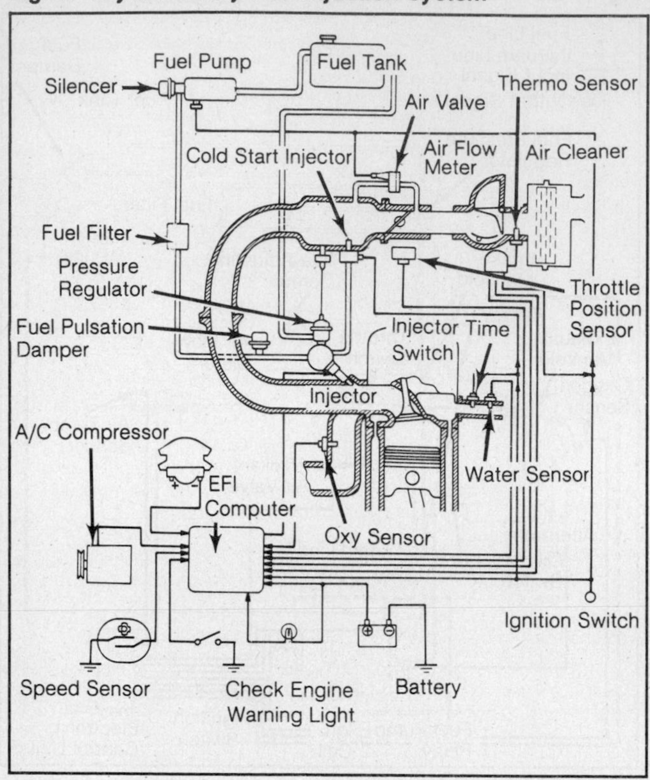
Fuel Pump
Fuel Tank
Silencer
Thermo Sensor
Air Valve
Cold Start Injector
Air Flow Meter
Air Cleaner
Fuel Filter
Pressure Regulator
Throttle Position Sensor
Fuel Pulsation Damper
Injector Time Switch
Injector
A/C Compressor
Water Sensor
EFI Computer
Oxy Sensor
Ignition Switch
Speed Sensor
Check Engine Warning Light
Battery

Fig. 10: Toyota Cressida & Supra Fuel Injection System

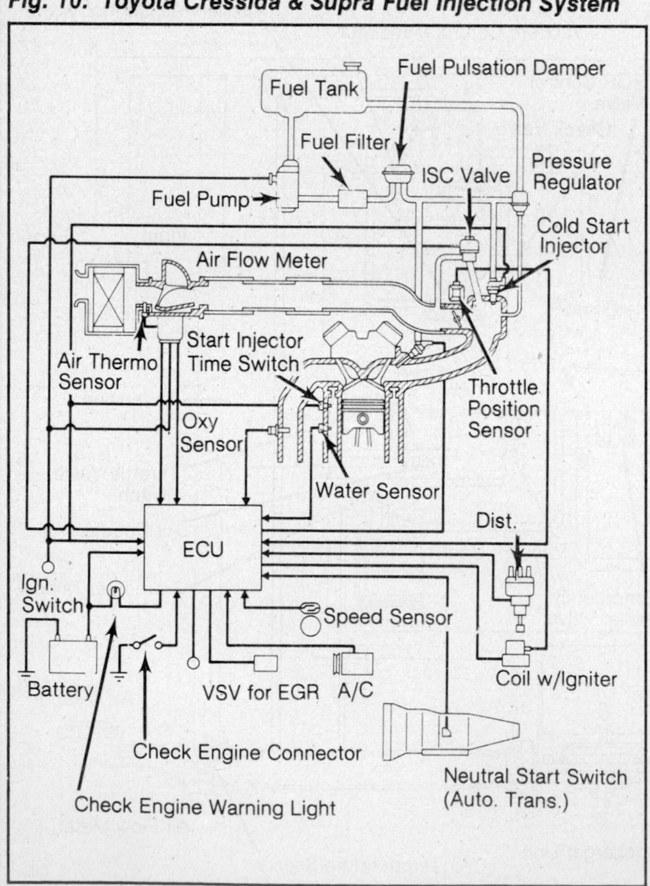
Fuel Tank
Fuel Pulsation Damper
Fuel Filter
Pressure Regulator
ISC Valve
Fuel Pump
Cold Start Injector
Air Flow Meter
Start Injector Time Switch
Air Thermo Sensor
Throttle Position Sensor
Oxy Sensor
Water Sensor
Dist.
ECU
Ign. Switch
Speed Sensor
Battery
VSV for EGR
A/C
Coil w/Igniter
Check Engine Connector
Neutral Start Switch (Auto. Trans.)
Check Engine Warning Light

Fig. 11: Toyota Starlet Fuel Injection System

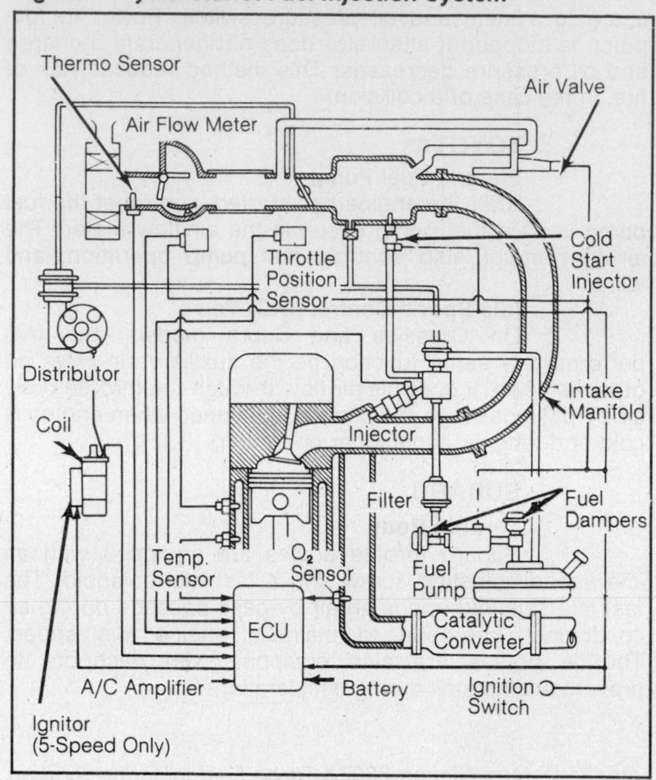
Thermo Sensor
Air Valve
Air Flow Meter
Cold Start Injector
Throttle Position Sensor
Distributor
Intake Manifold
Coil
Injector
Filter
Fuel Dampers
Temp. Sensor
O2 Sensor
Fuel Pump
ECU
Catalytic Converter
A/C Amplifier
Battery
Ignition Switch
Ignitor (5-Speed Only)

TESTING

ELECTRONIC CONTROL UNIT (ECU)

Do not attempt to test ECU, permanent damage could result. It is possible to check wires for continuity. The ECU should only by judged faulty after compression is checked, ignition system has been tested and found problem-free, and all other fuel injection components have been thoroughly tested (including wiring).

NOTE: **AFC electrical systems can be checked by using Electronic Fuel Injection testers prescribed by the manufacturer. Instructions for use of testers must by followed carefully to prevent damage to system.**

FUEL PRESSURE

NOTE: **Constant fuel pressure is maintained in fuel lines and component parts at all times. Relieve pressure before attempting to open system for testing. Do not alow fuel to flow onto engine or electrical parts or allow an open flame in area while testing fuel system components.**

Datsun/Nissan

1) To release fuel system pressure on 280ZX and 280ZX Turbo models, start engine and unplug fuel pump electrical connector in luggage compartment. After engine stalls, crank engine 2 or 3 times, turn ignition "OFF". Connect fuel pump electrical connector.

BOSCH AFC – JAPANESE MODELS (Cont.)

2) On Maxima and 200SX models, start engine, disconnect fuel pump relay. Fuel pump relay is located on the right front fender. After engine stalls, crank engine 2 or 3 times, turn ignition "OFF". Connect No. 2 fuel pump relay.

3) Remove fuel filter-to-fuel rail hose and connect a pressure gauge using a "T" fitting. Start engine and read fuel pressure at idle. If pressure is not as specified, replace pressure regulator and repeat test.

4) Disconnect vacuum line from fuel pressure regulator and connect a hand vacuum pump. On 280ZX and 280ZX Turbo models, disconnect the fuel pump connector and apply battery power. On Maxima and 200SX models, remove fuel pump relay and place jumper wire between Light Green/Red and Black/White wire in harness connector. Turn ignition "ON".

5) On all models, as vacuum is applied to pressure regulator, pressure reading should decrease. *See Datsun/Nissan Fuel Pressure Specifications* table. If pressure and vacuum readings do not conform to specifications, replace fuel pressure regulator.

DATSUN FUEL PRESSURE SPECIFICATIONS

Condition In. Hg	Pressure psi (kg/cm²)
Idle [1]	30 (2.1)
0	36-37 (2.5-2.6)
5	33-35 (2.3-2.5)
10	31-32 (2.2-2.3)
15	29-30 (2.0-2.1)
20	26-28 (1.8-2.0)

[1] – Vacuum hose connected at pressure regulator.

Subaru

1) To relieve fuel system pressure, unplug fuel pump connect and crank engine more than 5 seconds. Run engine until it stalls. Disconnect fuel hose at pressure regulator and install fuel pressure gauge using "T" fitting.

2) Start engine and check fuel pressure at idle. Fuel pressure should be 26-30 psi (1.8-2.1 kg/cm²). Increase engine RPM and make sure fuel pressure increases correspondingly.

Toyota

1) Disconnect negative battery cable. Unplug cold start injector electrical connector. Place container under fuel rail at union bolt of cold start injector hose.

2) Remove union bolt and drain fuel rail. Remove cold start injector hose from union bolt and install fuel pressure gauge with hose to union bolt. Install gauge and bolt to fuel rail with a gasket on each side of gauge fitting.

3) Connect battery cable and start engine. Disconnect vacuum line from fuel pressure regulator and pinch line closed. Gauge reading should be 33-38 psi (2.3-2.7 kg/cm²). If pressure is too high, replace fuel pressure regulator; if too low check fuel system for leaks.

4) Connect vacuum line to pressure regulator. Pressure reading should decrease to 28 psi (2.0 kg/cm²) with engine at idle speed. If not, replace fuel pressure regulator. Stop engine. If pressure drops quickly, check fuel pump, pressure regulator, and injectors.

FUEL PUMP CIRCUIT

Datsun/Nissan

1) On 280ZX Turbo models, turn ignition "ON" and listen for fuel pump operation. Pump should operate for 5 seconds after ignition switch is turned on.

2) On all other models, turn ignition "ON", disconnect oil pressure switch electrical harness or alternator terminal "L". Fuel pump operation should be heard.

3) On all models, if fuel pump does not operate, check relays, fuel pump, alternator terminal "L" (if used) and oil pressure switch (if used).

Toyota

1) Turn ignition "ON". Remove cap from fuel pump test connector. Using a jumper wire, jump both terminals of connector. Connector is located below air flow meter on Camry, Cressida, and Supra models. On Celica models it is located next to the throttle body. Starlet check connector is on wiring harness on left side of engine.

2) Fuel pressure should be felt at cold start injector hose and noise of fuel returning to tank should be heard at fuel pressure regulator.

3) Remove jumper wire, install connector cap and turn ignition "OFF". If none of the above conditions were met, check fusible link, engine fuse, fuel injection fuse, circuit opening relay, fuel pump, and all electrical connectors.

AIR TEMPERATURE SENSOR

Datsun/Nissan & Toyota

1) With ignition "OFF", unplug electrical connector at air flow meter. Connect an ohmmeter between terminals 30 and 33 (280ZX Turbo), terminals E2 and "THA" (Toyota) or terminals 25 and 34 (all other models). Measure and record air temperature.

2) Ohmmeter readings should be as specified. *See Temperature/Resistance Relationship* charts. If not, check insulation resistance with ohmmeter between terminal 30 (280ZX Turbo), terminal "THA" (Toyota) or terminal 25 (all other models) and ground. Use air flow meter as ground.

3) Infinity ohmmeter reading should be obtained. If values are not as specified, replace electrical harness or air flow meter assembly, as required.

DATSUN TEMPERATURE/RESISTANCE RELATIONSHIP

Temperature °F(°C)	Ohms
68 (20) or Above	Below 2900
Below 68 (20)	2100 or Above

TOYOTA TEMPERATURE/RESISTANCE RELATIONSHIP

Temperature °F(°C)	Ohms
32 (0)	4000-7000
68 (20)	2000-3000
104 (40)	9000-13,000

Subaru

Ignition switch must be turned off. Unplug air flow meter connector. Measure resistance between Light Green/Yellow and Yellow/Blue wires. If ohmmeter reads 0 or infinity, replace air flow meter.

AIR FLOW METER POTENTIOMETER

Turn ignition switch off. Unplug electrical connector from air flow meter. Connect ohmmeter between terminals and note readings. *See Air Flow Meter Resistance* tables. If readings are not to specifications, replace air flow meter.

BOSCH AFC – JAPANESE MODELS (Cont.)

DATSUN AIR FLOW METER RESISTANCE

Application	Terminals	Ohms
Maxima, 200SX, 280ZX	33-34	100-400
	34-35	200-500
	[1] 32-34	[2]
280ZX Turbo	33-34	280-400
	[1] 32-34	[2]

[1] – While moving measuring flap.
[2] – Any value except 0 or infinity.

SUBARU AIR FLOW METER RESISTANCE

Terminal Wire Colors	Ohms
Green-Yellow/Blue	300
Blue/Yellow-Yellow/Blue	200
Yellow/Red-Yellow/Blue	[1] 50

[1] – Flap fully open. With flap closed, 500 ohms.

TOYOTA AIR FLOW METER RESISTANCE

Application	Terminals	Ohms	Measuring Flap
Camry, Starlet	E2-Vc	100-300	
	E2-Vb	200-400	
	E2-Vs	20-400	Closed
	E2-Vs	1000	Full Open
Celica	E2-Vc	100-300	
	E2-Vb	200-400	
	E2-Vs	20-100	Closed
	E2-Vs	1000	Full Open
Cressida, Supra	E2-Vc	200-400	
	E2-Vs	20-400	Closed
	E2-Vs	1000	Full Open
All Models	E1-Fc	Infinity	Closed
	E1-Fc	0	Open
	E2-THA	[1] 2-3 K	

[1] – At 68°F (20°C). Resistance will be higher at low temperatures and lower at high temperatures.

Fig. 12: Toyota Air Flow Meter Terminal Identification

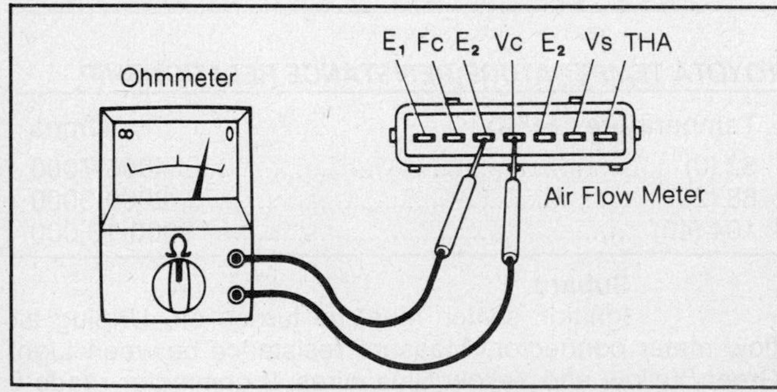
E1 Fc E2 Vc E2 Vs THA
Ohmmeter
Air Flow Meter

AUXILIARY AIR VALVE

Ensure engine is cold, then start engine. Pinch rubber hose between air valve and throttle chamber. Engine speed should decrease. After engine reaches operating temperature, pinch hose again. Engine speed should not decrease more than 50 RPM. If valve does not operate as outlined, replace auxiliary air valve.

IAC VALVE

Cressida & Supra

See TOYOTA EFI COMPUTER CONTROL SYSTEM in COMPUTERIZED ENGINE CONTROL Section.

THERMO TIME SWITCH

Datsun/Nissan
(Except 200SX & 280ZX Turbo)

1) Disconnect negative battery cable and switch connector. Connect ohmmeter between terminal 45 and switch body (ground). Reading should be 40-70 ohms. Connect ohmmeter between terminal 46 and ground.

2) At coolant temperature below 57°F (14°C), reading should be 0 ohms; above 77°F (25°C), reading should be infinity. Between 57-77°F (14-25°C), reading should be infinity or 0. If readings are not as specified, replace thermo time switch.

Toyota

Disconnect negative battery cable and switch connector. Using ohmmeter, check resistance between terminals. *See Toyota Thermo Time Switch Resistance* chart. If readings are not as specified, replace thermo time switch.

TOYOTA THERMO TIME SWITCH RESISTANCE

Model	Terminals	Ohms	Coolant Temp. °F (C°)
Camry	STA-STJ	30-50	Below 95 (35)
	STA-STJ	70-90	Above 95 (35)
	STA-Gnd.	30-90	
Celica	STA-STJ	25-35	Below 72 (22)
	STA-STJ	64-76	Above 72 (22)
Cressida, Supra	STA-STJ	30-50	Below 72 (22)
	STA-STJ	70-90	Above 72 (22)
	STA-Gnd.	30-90	
Starlet	STA-Gnd.	25-35	Below 95 (35)
	STA-Gnd.	64-76	Above 95 (35)

Fig. 13: Toyota Thermo Time Switch Terminal Identification

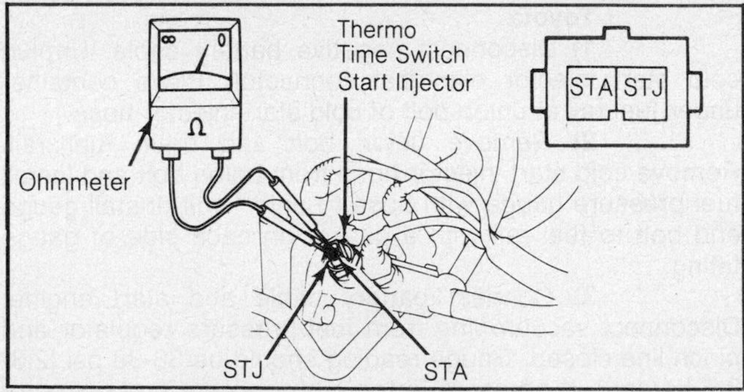
Thermo
Time Switch
Start Injector
STA STJ
Ohmmeter
STJ
STA

COLD START INJECTOR

(Except 200SX, 280ZX Turbo, & Subaru)

1) Disconnect negative battery cable, and cold start injector connector. Remove cold start injector (with fuel supply connected) and place over glass container.

2) Connect battery power to injector terminals. Fuel should spray from injector. If not, replace cold start injector.

CAUTION: Perform this test within the shortest possible time.

BOSCH AFC — JAPANESE MODELS (Cont.)

3) On Toyota models, disconnect test harness from cold start injector and check for fuel leakage from injector. Maximum leakage is less than 1 drop of fuel per minute. Resistance between cold start injector terminals should be 3-5 ohms.

COOLANT TEMPERATURE SENSOR

1) Warm engine to normal operating temperature and stop engine. Using a thermometer, measure temperature of coolant. Disconnect negative battery cable and sensor electrical connector.

2) Connect ohmmeter leads to both terminals of sensor. Readings should be as specified for corresponding temperatures. *See Coolant Temperature Sensor Resistance* chart. If not, replace coolant temperature sensor.

COOLANT TEMPERATURE SENSOR RESISTANCE

Temperature °F(°C)	Ohms
68 (20)	2100-2900
122 (50)	700-1000
176 (80)	400-600

REMOVAL & INSTALLATION

NOTE: **The fuel injection system maintains constant fuel pressure in fuel lines and component parts at all times. Always relieve fuel pressure before attempting to open system for testing or replacement of components. Do not allow fuel to flow onto engine or electrical parts. Do not allow open flame or sparks in area while servicing components. Disconnect negative battery cable before disconnecting any electrical component.**

ELECTRONIC CONTROL UNIT (ECU)

Removal & Installation

1) Disconnect negative battery cable. Clear area for access to ECU. Disconnect electrical connector lock lever (if used) and carefully remove connector. Remove ECU retaining screws and remove ECU. To install, reverse removal procedure.

2) On Celica, Cressida, and Supra models, ECU is located behind glove compartment. On Camry and Starlet models it is located under center of instrument panel. The ECU on Subaru vehicles is located under driver's side of instrunent panel.

3) On 280ZX and 280ZX Turbo models, ECU is located behind kick panel on driver's side. The Maxima ECU is under the front passenger's seat.

AIR FLOW METER

Removal & Installation

Disconnect negative battery cable. Disconnect air ducts and hoses connecting air cleaner and air flow meter. Remove air cleaner cover, if required. Remove air flow meter retaining bolts. Unplug air flow meter electrical connector and remove air flow meter. To install, reverse removal procedure.

THROTTLE SWITCH

Removal & Installation

1) Disconnect negative battery cable. Unplug throttle switch electrical connector. Remove 2 screws securing throttle switch to housing. Remove switch by slowly pulling switch off throttle shaft.

2) To install, reverse removal procedure. Make sure switch is aligned on throttle shaft and after replacement, perform throttle switch adjustment. *See Adjustments in this article.*

COLD START INJECTOR

Removal & Installation

Disconnect negative battery cable and remove electrical connector from cold start injector. Relieve fuel system pressure and remove fuel supply line from injector. Remove injector retaining bolts and remove injector. To install, reverse removal procedure.

AUXILIARY AIR VALVE

NOTE: **Replacement of auxiliary air valve on Toyota models requires that immediate replacement be available or cooling system be drained below level of valve.**

Removal & Installation

Disconnect negative battery cable and remove electrical connector from air valve. Drain engine coolant, if required. Remove air hoses and coolant hoses (if equipped). Remove retaining bolts and remove air valve. To install, reverse removal procedure.

COOLANT TEMPERATURE SENSOR

NOTE: **Replacement of temperature sensor on Toyota models requires that immediate replacement be available or cooling system be drained below level of sensor.**

Removal & Installation

Disconnect negative battery cable and remove electrical connector from coolant sensor. Drain engine coolant, if required. Remove sensor. To install, reverse removal procedure.

THERMO TIME SWITCH

NOTE: **Thermo time switch removal should be done only when engine is cold. Removal of switch requires having replacement switch ready for immediate installation or cooling system be drained below level of switch.**

Removal & Installation

Disconnect negative battery cable and electrical connector from switch. Drain cooling system as required. Remove switch. To install, reverse removal procedure.

FUEL PRESSURE REGULATOR

Removal & Installation

1) Disconnect negative battery cable and relieve fuel system pressure. Disconnect fuel lines and vacuum line at regulator. Remove pressure regulator.

2) To remove pressure regulator on Datsun/Nissan 200SX models, remove fuel rail. *See Fuel Injectors.* To install, reverse removal procedure.

1983 Fuel Injection

BOSCH AFC — JAPANESE MODELS (Cont.)

FUEL INJECTORS

NOTE: No information is available from manufacturer on Subaru fuel injector removal.

Removal (Datsun/Nissan)

1) Release fuel system pressure and disconnect negative battery cable. Unplug electrical connectors from cold start injector and fuel injectors. Disconnect fuel injection wiring harness from clip on fuel rail.

2) Clear fuel rail and injectors by disconnecting all air, vacuum, fuel supply, and fuel return lines. Remove cold start injector fuel rail and fuel injector retaining bolts.

3) Remove fuel rail, cold start injector and fuel injectors as an assembly. Remove fuel supply hose retaining clip from cold start injector and each fuel injector and remove injectors.

4) To replace injector fuel supply hose, cut hose with soldering iron just enough to remove hose. Do not touch any part of injector with soldering iron, or mount injector in a vise.

Installation

To install, reverse removal procedure. Coat inside of new fuel hose with gasoline and slide onto injector.

Removal (Toyota)

1) Release fuel system pressure and disconnect negative battery cable. Drain cooling system. Clear fuel rail and intake air chamber by disconnecting all air hoses, coolant hoses, vacuum hoses, and fuel hoses.

2) Remove EGR valve and pipe and intake air duct. Remove intake air chamber and support bracket. Disconnect fuel injection wiring harness from all connectors near fuel rail and place harness on top of engine.

3) Remove fuel rail retaining bolts. Remove fuel rail, injectors and fuel pressure regulator as an assembly.

4) Separate fuel injectors from fuel rail by pulling injectors. Discard sealing grommet and "O" ring. Remove insulators from injector holes in intake manifold.

Installation

1) To install, reverse removal procedure. Install new insulators in injector holes in intake manifold. Install new grommets and "O" rings on fuel injectors.

2) Coat grommets and "O" rings with gasoline and push injectors onto fuel rail. Coat insulators and injector tips with gasoline prior to installation of injectors. Ensure injectors rotate freely.

ADJUSTMENTS

IDLE ADJUSTMENTS

See the appropriate article in the TUNE-UP Section.

THROTTLE SWITCH

Datsun/Nissan

1) With engine running at idle RPM, unplug throttle switch electrical connector. Connect ohmmeter leads to terminals 18 and 25 (280ZX Turbo) or 29 and 30 (all others) of throttle switch.

NOTE: Do not connect ohmmeter leads to electrical connector of harness or damage to ohmmeter may result.

2) Loosen throttle switch retaining screws. Adjust position of throttle switch so that ohmmeter reading changes from 0 ohms to infinity reading when engine speed is about 900 RPM.

3) To adjust with engine off, set clearance between throttle valve shaft lever and stopper screw to.012" (0.3 mm). Adjust throttle switch position until ohmmeter reading goes from 0 ohms to infinity. If switch does not perform as described, replace throttle valve switch.

4) To check full throttle contact, stop engine and disconnect negative battery cable. Connect ohmmeter between terminals 24 and 30 (18 and 25 280ZX Turbo).

5) Continuity should not exist when throttle valve is in idle position. Depress accelerator to full throttle position; continuity should exist. If not, replace throttle switch.

Subaru

Loosen throttle switch mounting screws. Insert a .92" (23.37 mm) feeler gauge between stopper and stopper screw. *See Fig. 14.* Connect ohmmeter between terminals "A" and "C". Adjust switch position so ohmmeter reading changes from 0 to infinity with feeler gauge in position.

Fig. 14: Adjusting Subaru Throttle Valve Switch

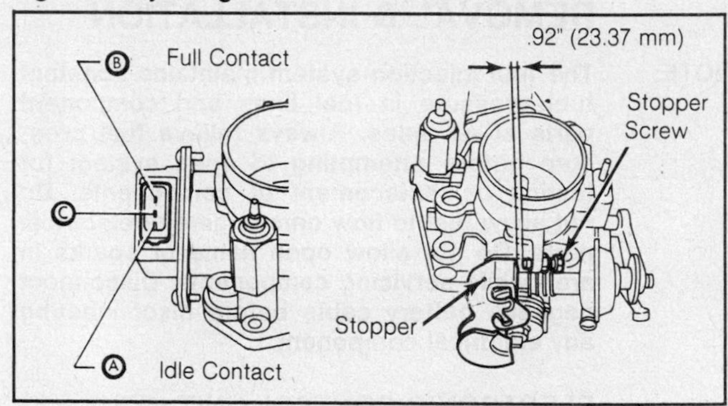

B
Full Contact
.92" (23.37 mm)
Stopper
Screw
C
Stopper
A
Idle Contact

Toyota

To adjust throttle angle switch on Toyota it will be necessary to construct a throttle angle gauge. *See Fig. 15.* For adjustment procedures, *see Toyota EFI article in COMPUTERIZED ENGINE CONTROL Section.*

BOSCH AFC — JAPANESE MODELS (Cont.)

Fig. 15: Adjusting Toyota Throttle Switch

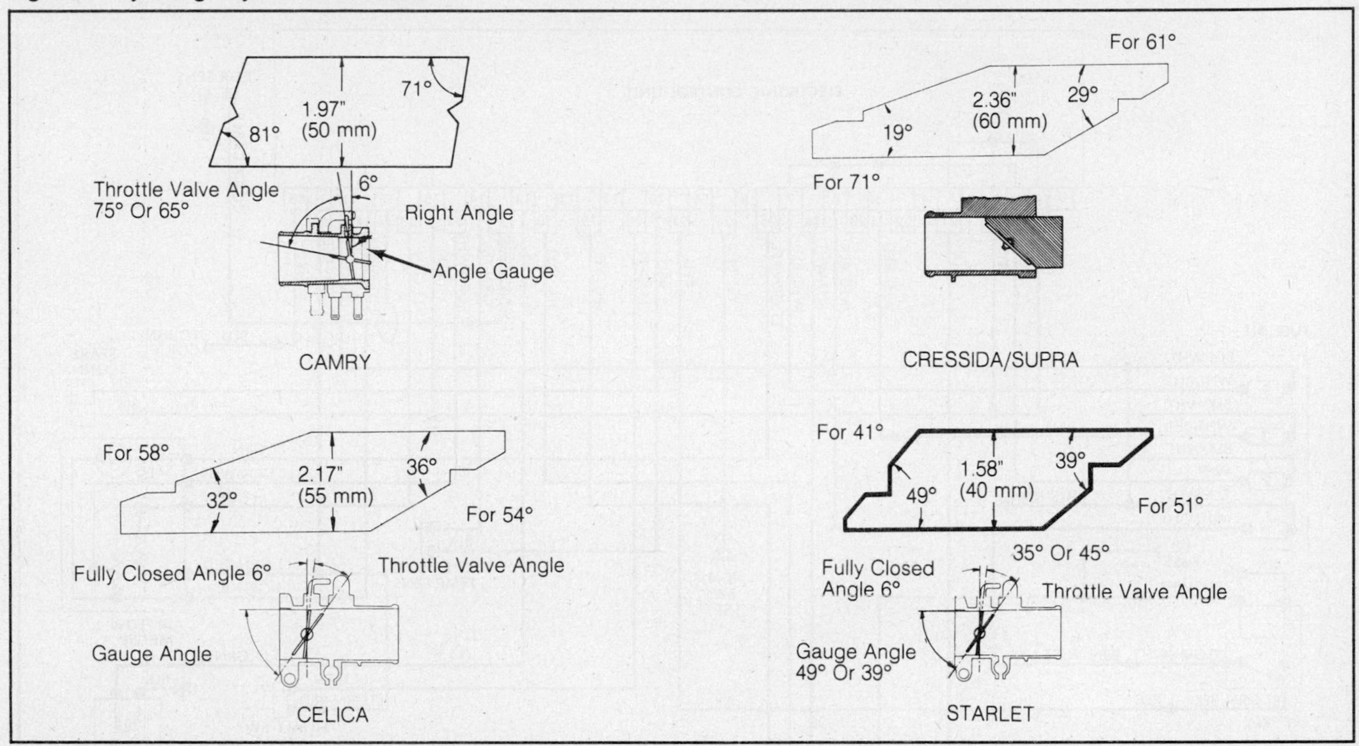

71°
1.97"
(50 mm)
81°
Throttle Valve Angle
75° Or 65°
6°
Right Angle
Angle Gauge
CAMRY
For 61°
2.36"
(60 mm)
29°
19°
For 71°
CRESSIDA/SUPRA
For 58°
2.17"
(55 mm)
36°
32°
For 54°
Fully Closed Angle 6°
Throttle Valve Angle
Gauge Angle
CELICA
For 41°
1.58"
(40 mm)
39°
49°
For 51°
35° Or 45°
Fully Closed
Angle 6°
Throttle Valve Angle
Gauge Angle
49° Or 39°
STARLET

Construct angle gauge to dimensions shown.

Fig. 16: Datsun/Nissan Maxima Fuel Injection Wiring Diagram

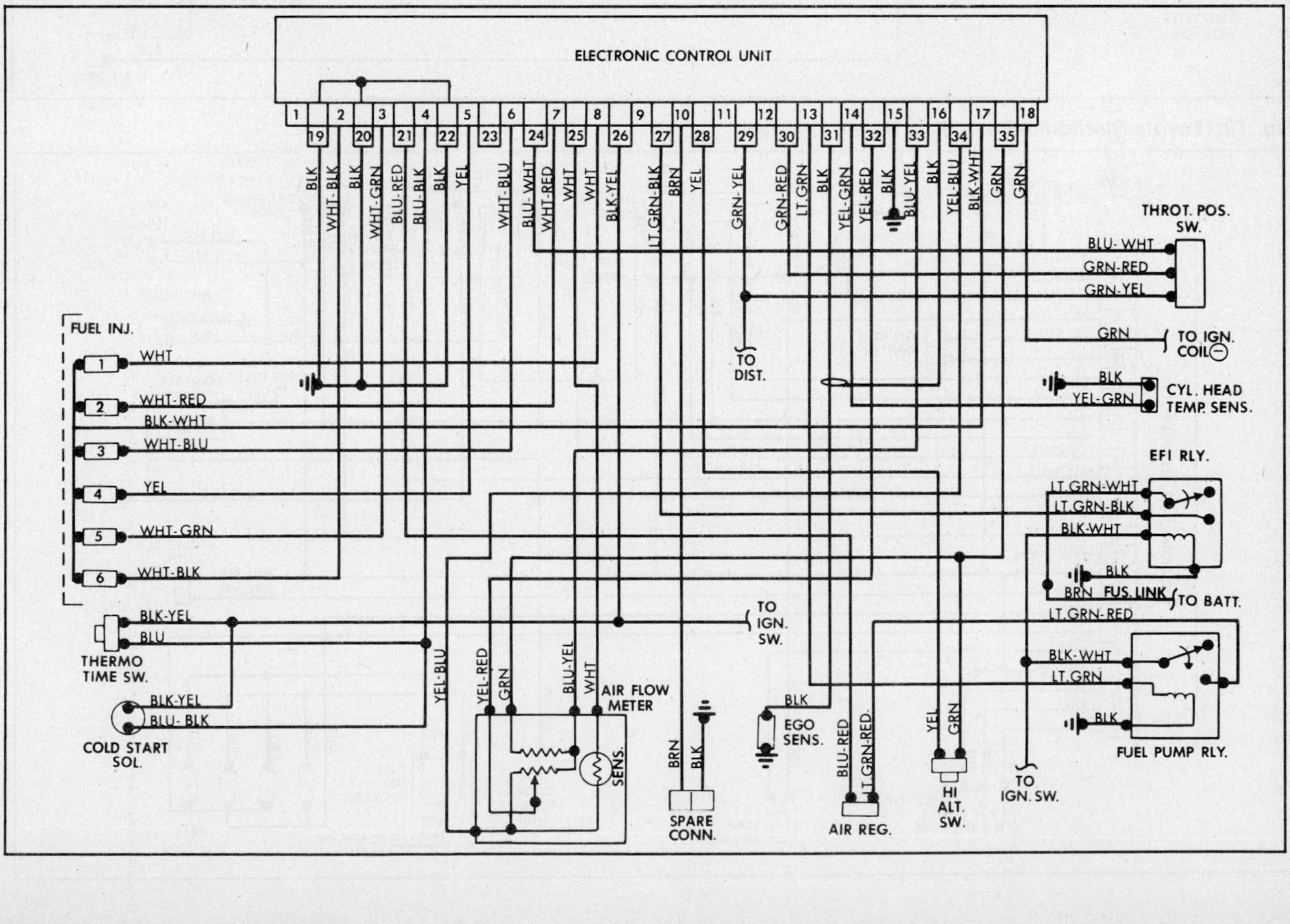

ELECTRONIC CONTROL UNIT
1 2 3 4 5 6 7 8 9 10 11 12 13 14 15 16 17 18
19 20 21 22 23 24 25 26 27 28 29 30 31 32 33 34 35
BLK WHT-BLK BLK WHT-GRN BLU-RED BLU-BLK BLK YEL WHT-BLU BLU-WHT WHT-RED WHT WHT BLK-YEL LT.GRN-BLK BRN YEL GRN-YEL GRN-RED LT.GRN BLK YEL-GRN YEL-RED BLK BLU-YEL BLK YEL-BLU BLK-WHT GRN GRN
THROT. POS. SW.
BLU-WHT
GRN-RED
GRN-YEL
GRN
TO IGN. COIL ⊖
TO DIST.
BLK
YEL-GRN
CYL. HEAD TEMP. SENS.
EFI RLY.
LT.GRN-WHT
LT.GRN-BLK
BLK-WHT
BLK
BRN
FUS. LINK
TO BATT.
LT.GRN-RED
BLK-WHT
LT.GRN
BLK
FUEL PUMP RLY.
FUEL INJ.
1 WHT
2 WHT-RED
BLK-WHT
3 WHT-BLU
4 YEL
5 WHT-GRN
6 WHT-BLK
BLK-YEL
BLU
THERMO TIME SW.
TO IGN. SW.
BLK-YEL
BLU-BLK
COLD START SOL.
YEL-BLU
YEL-RED
GRN
BLU-YEL
WHT
AIR FLOW METER
SENS.
BRN
BLK
SPARE CONN.
BLK
EGO SENS.
BLU-RED
LT.GRN-RED
AIR REG.
YEL
GRN
HI ALT. SW.
TO IGN. SW.

1983 Fuel Injection

BOSCH AFC — JAPANESE MODELS (Cont.)

Fig. 17: Datsun/Nissan 200SX Fuel Injection Wiring Diagram

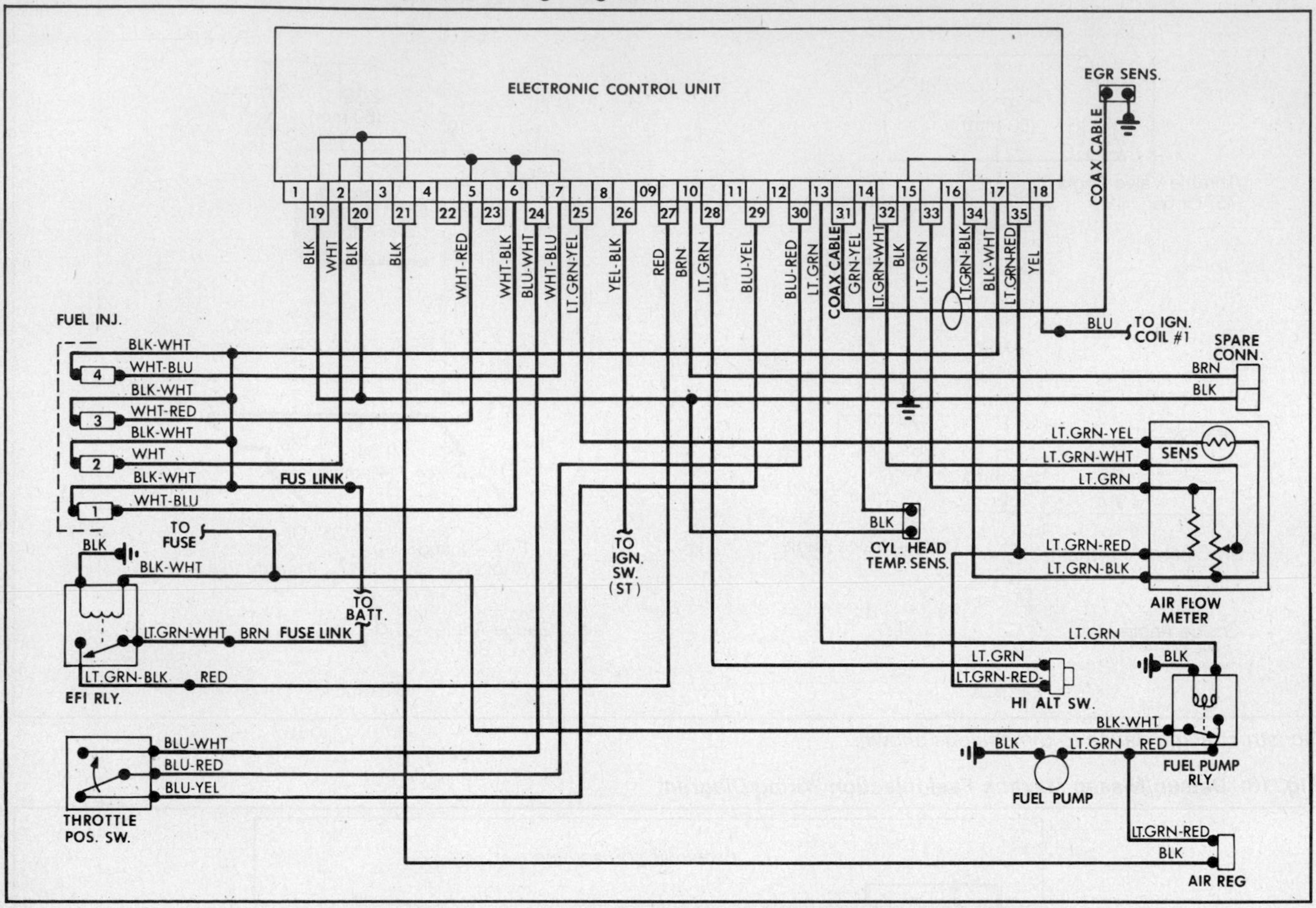

Fig. 18: Toyota Starlet Fuel Injection Wiring Diagram

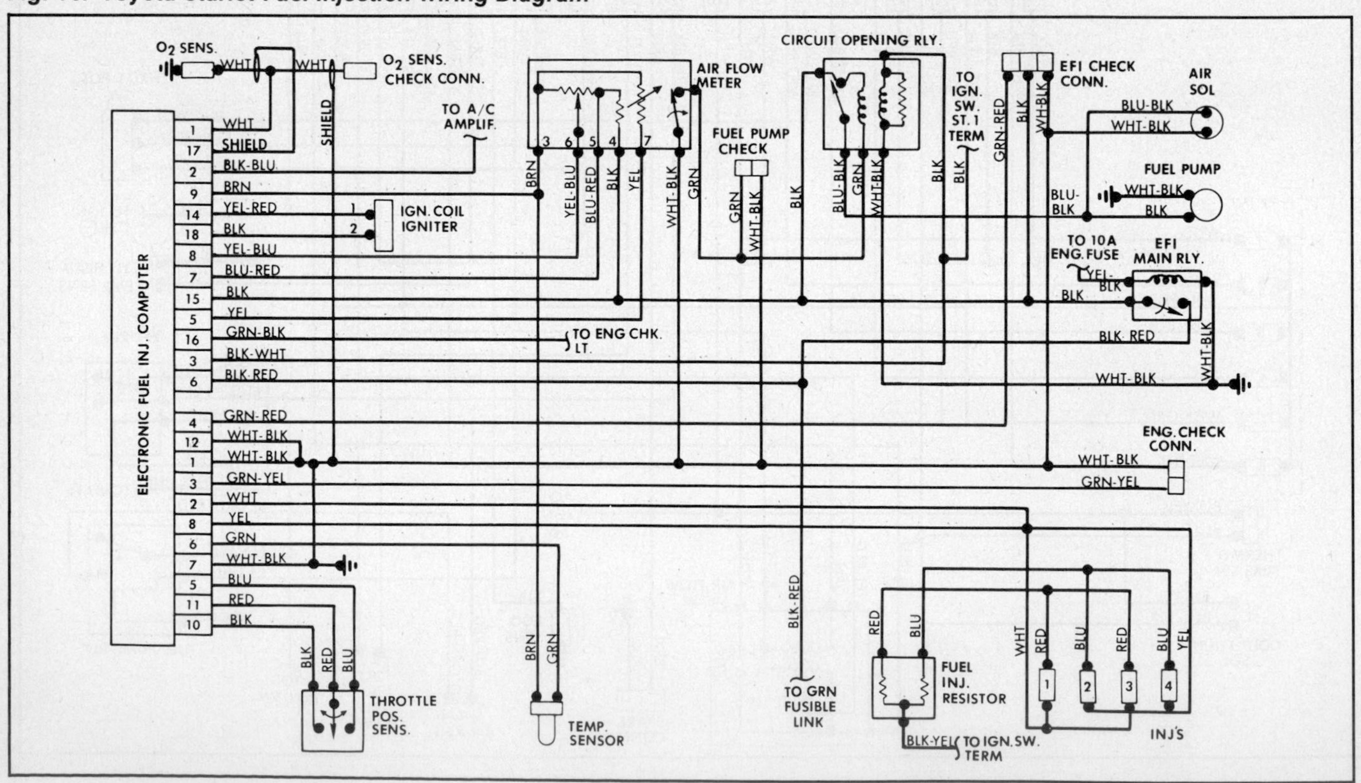
O2 SENS.
O2 SENS. CHECK CONN.
SHIELD
TO A/C AMPLIF.
AIR FLOW METER
FUEL PUMP CHECK
CIRCUIT OPENING RLY.
TO IGN. SW. ST. 1 TERM
EFI CHECK CONN.
AIR SOL
FUEL PUMP
IGN. COIL IGNITER
ELECTRONIC FUEL INJ. COMPUTER
TO ENG CHK. LT.
TO 10A ENG. FUSE
EFI MAIN RLY.
ENG. CHECK CONN.
THROTTLE POS. SENS.
TEMP. SENSOR
TO GRN FUSIBLE LINK
FUEL INJ. RESISTOR
TO IGN. SW. TERM
INJ'S

BOSCH AFC — JAPANESE MODELS (Cont.)

Fig. 19: Datsun/Nissan 280ZX (Except Turbo) Fuel Injection Wiring Diagram

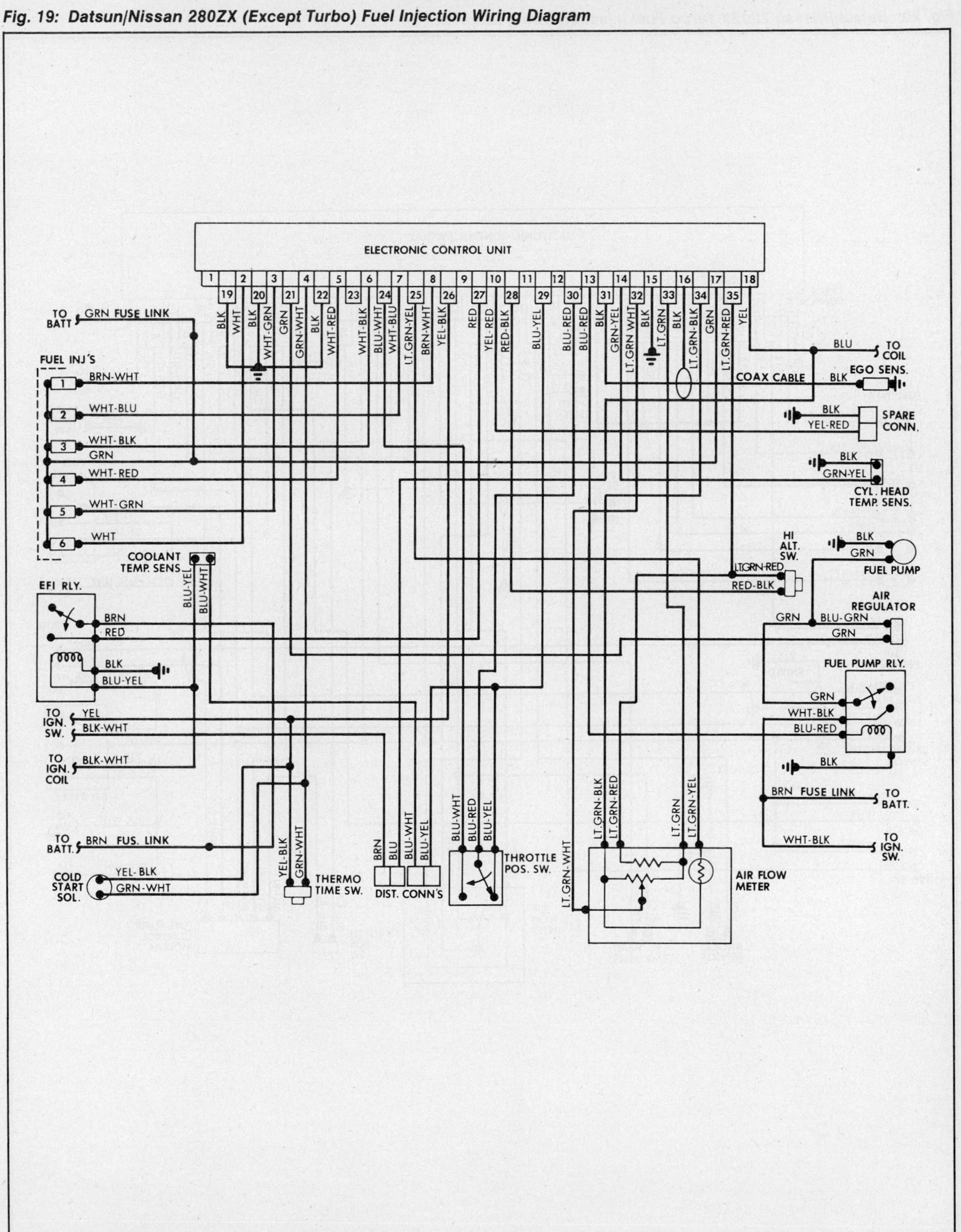
ELECTRONIC CONTROL UNIT
TO BATT GRN FUSE LINK
FUEL INJ'S
BRN-WHT
WHT-BLU
WHT-BLK
GRN
WHT-RED
WHT-GRN
WHT
COOLANT TEMP. SENS.
BLU-YEL
BLU-WHT
EFI RLY.
BRN
RED
BLK
BLU-YEL
TO IGN. SW. YEL
BLK-WHT
TO IGN. COIL BLK-WHT
TO BATT. BRN FUS. LINK
COLD START SOL.
YEL-BLK
GRN-WHT
THERMO TIME SW.
BRN
BLU
BLU-WHT
BLU-YEL
DIST. CONN'S
BLU-WHT
BLU-RED
BLU-YEL
THROTTLE POS. SW.
LT.GRN-WHT
LT.GRN-BLK
LT.GRN-RED
LT.GRN
LT.GRN-YEL
AIR FLOW METER
BLK
WHT
BLK
WHT-GRN
GRN
GRN-WHT
BLK
WHT-RED
WHT-BLK
BLU-WHT
WHT-BLU
LT.GRN-YEL
BRN-WHT
YEL-BLK
RED
YEL-RED
RED-BLK
BLU-YEL
BLU-RED
BLU-RED
BLK
GRN-YEL
LT.GRN WHT
BLK
LT.GRN
BLK
LT.GRN-BLK
GRN
LT.GRN-RED
YEL
BLU
TO COIL
COAX CABLE
BLK
EGO SENS.
BLK
YEL-RED
SPARE CONN.
BLK
GRN-YEL
CYL. HEAD TEMP. SENS.
HI ALT. SW.
LT.GRN-RED
RED-BLK
BLK
GRN
FUEL PUMP
AIR REGULATOR
GRN
BLU-GRN
GRN
FUEL PUMP RLY.
GRN
WHT-BLK
BLU-RED
BLK
BRN FUSE LINK
TO BATT.
WHT-BLK
TO IGN. SW.

1983 Fuel Injection

BOSCH AFC — JAPANESE MODELS (Cont.)

Fig. 20: Datsun/Nissan 280ZX Turbo Fuel Injection Wiring Diagram

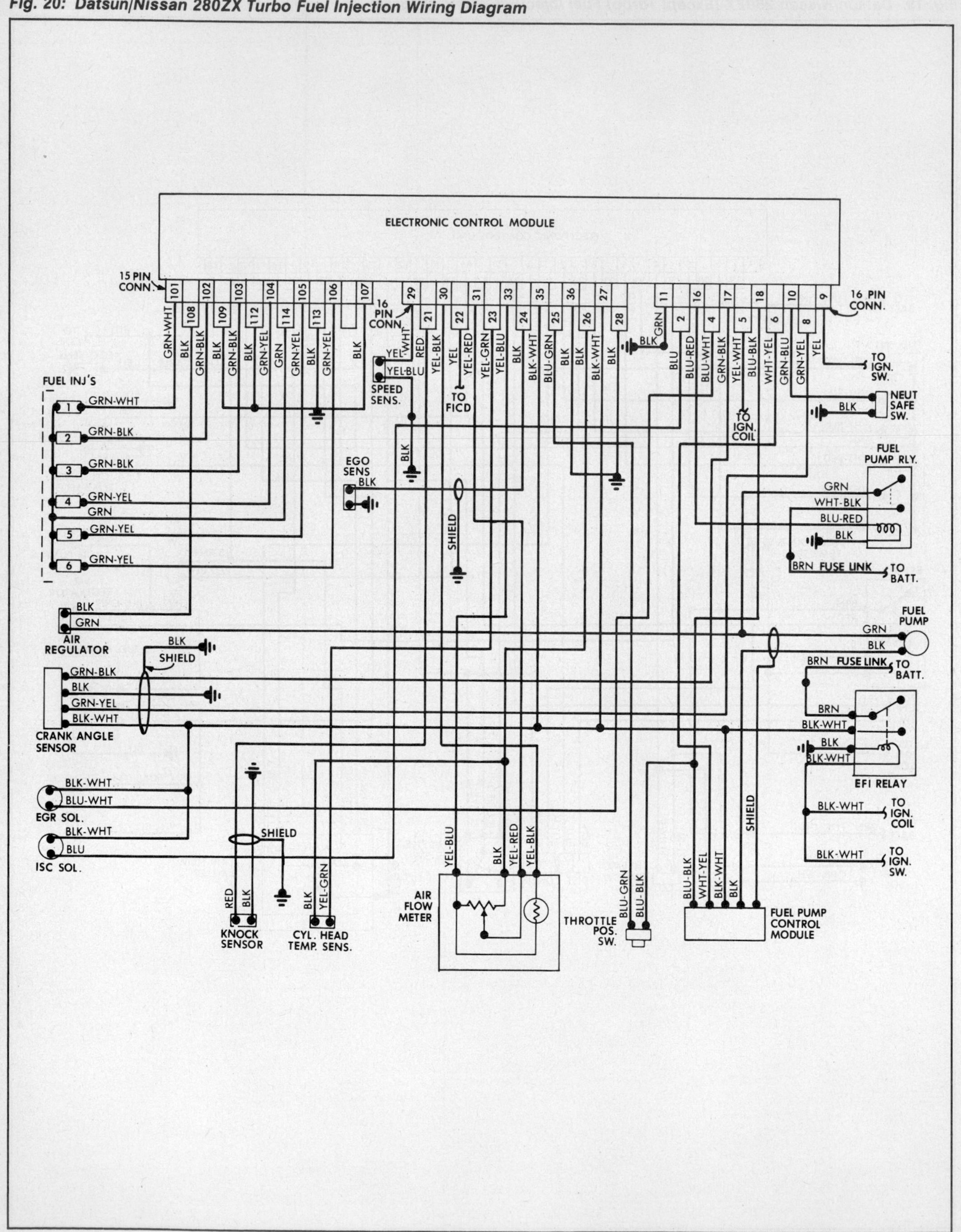
ELECTRONIC CONTROL MODULE
15 PIN CONN.
16 PIN CONN.
16 PIN CONN.
101
102
103
104
105
106
107
108
109
112
114
113
29
30
31
33
35
36
27
21
22
23
24
25
26
28
11
16
17
18
10
9
2
4
5
6
8
GRN-WHT
BLK
GRN-BLK
GRN-YEL
GRN
YEL-WHT
YEL-BLU
RED
YEL-BLK
YEL
YEL-RED
YEL-GRN
BLK-WHT
BLU-GRN
BLU
BLU-RED
BLU-WHT
YEL-WHT
BLU-BLK
WHT-YEL
GRN-BLU
FUEL INJ'S
SPEED SENS.
TO FICD
TO IGN. SW.
NEUT SAFE SW.
TO IGN. COIL
FUEL PUMP RLY.
EGO SENS
SHIELD
WHT-BLK
BRN
FUSE LINK
TO BATT.
AIR REGULATOR
FUEL PUMP
CRANK ANGLE SENSOR
EFI RELAY
EGR SOL.
ISC SOL.
KNOCK SENSOR
CYL. HEAD TEMP. SENS.
AIR FLOW METER
THROTTLE POS. SW.
FUEL PUMP CONTROL MODULE

1983 Fuel Injection

BOSCH AFC — JAPANESE MODELS (Cont.)

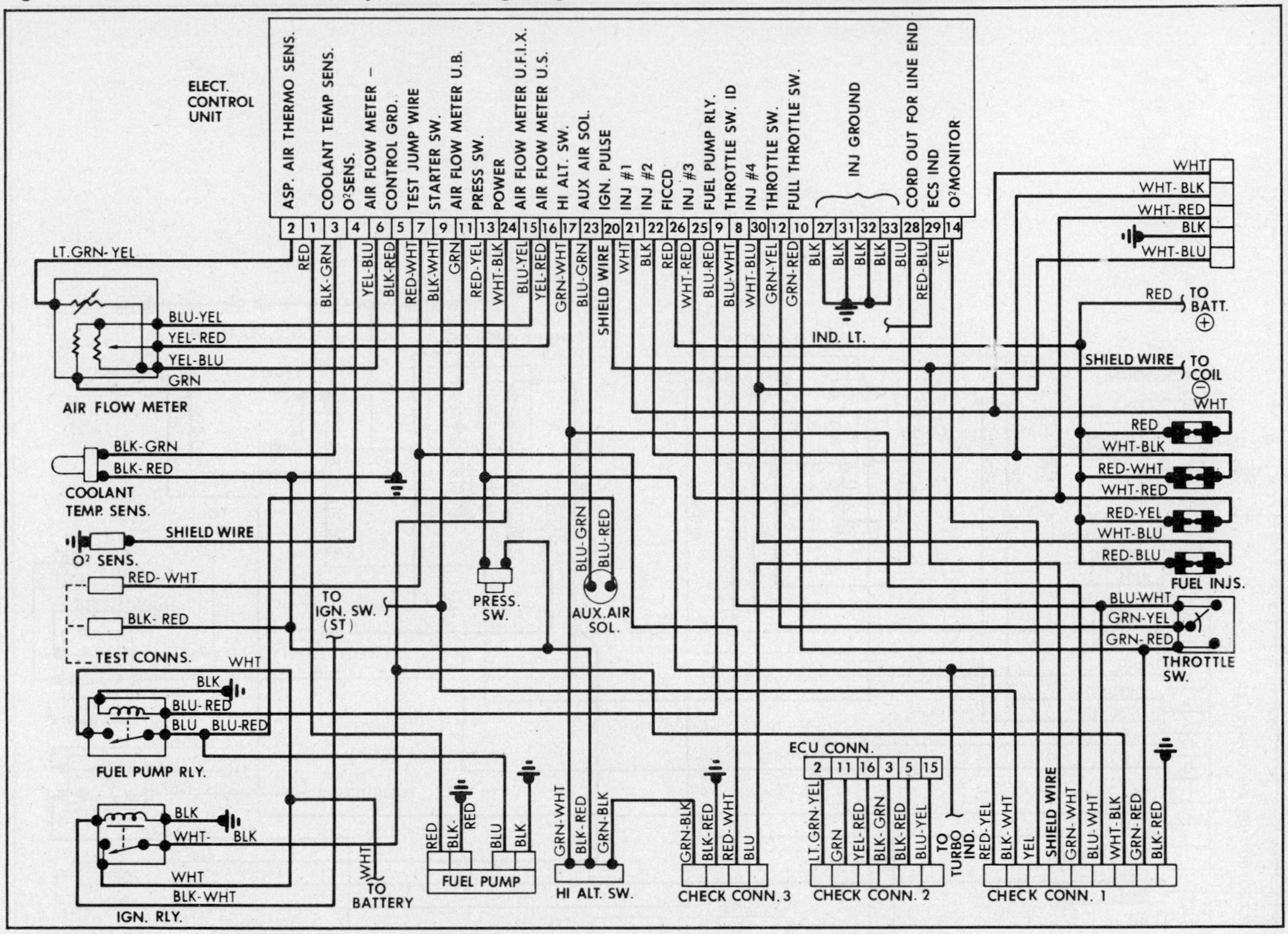

Fig. 21: Subaru 1800 Turbo Fuel Injection Wiring Diagram

Fig. 22: Toyota Camry Fuel Injection Wiring Diagram

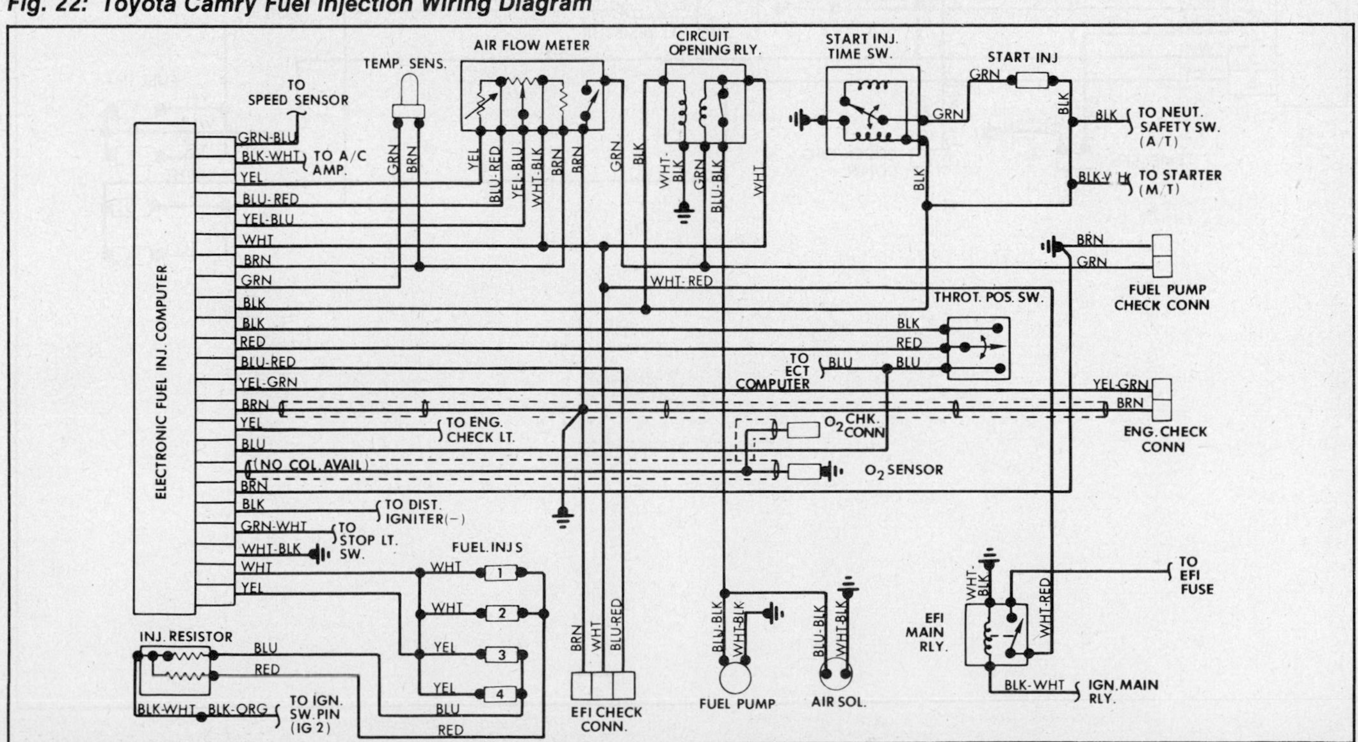
ELECTRONIC FUEL INJ. COMPUTER
TO SPEED SENSOR
TEMP. SENS.
AIR FLOW METER
CIRCUIT OPENING RLY.
START INJ. TIME SW.
START INJ
TO NEUT. SAFETY SW. (A/T)
TO STARTER (M/T)
GRN-BLU
BLK-WHT
TO A/C AMP.
YEL
BLU-RED
YEL-BLU
WHT
BRN
GRN
BLK
RED
YEL-GRN
TO ENG. CHECK LT.
BLU
(NO COL. AVAIL)
TO DIST. IGNITER(−)
GRN-WHT
WHT-BLK
TO STOP LT. SW.
WHT-RED
FUEL PUMP CHECK CONN
THROT. POS. SW.
TO ECT COMPUTER
ENG. CHECK CONN
O2 CHK. CONN
O2 SENSOR
FUEL. INJS
INJ. RESISTOR
BLK-ORG
TO IGN. SW. PIN (IG 2)
EFI CHECK CONN.
FUEL PUMP
AIR SOL.
EFI MAIN RLY.
TO EFI FUSE
IGN. MAIN RLY.

1983 Fuel Injection

BOSCH AFC — JAPANESE MODELS (Cont.)

Fig. 23: Toyota Celica Fuel Injection Wiring Diagram

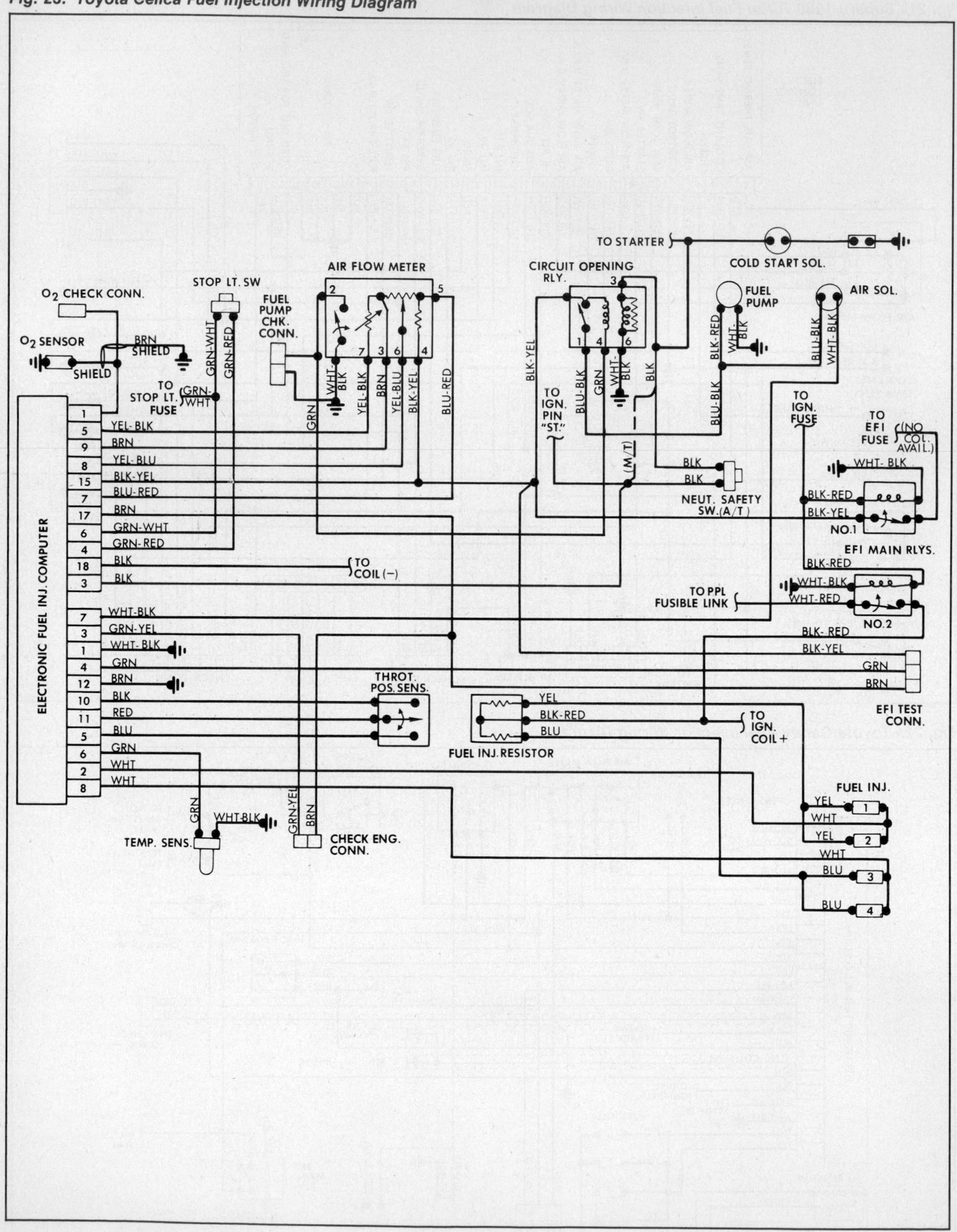
TO STARTER
COLD START SOL.
AIR FLOW METER
CIRCUIT OPENING RLY.
FUEL PUMP
AIR SOL.
STOP LT. SW
FUEL PUMP CHK. CONN.
O2 CHECK CONN.
O2 SENSOR
SHIELD
BRN SHIELD
TO STOP LT. FUSE
TO IGN. PIN "ST."
TO IGN. FUSE
TO EFI FUSE
(NO COL. AVAIL.)
NEUT. SAFETY SW. (A/T)
(M/T)
NO.1
EFI MAIN RLYS.
TO PPL FUSIBLE LINK
NO.2
EFI TEST CONN.
ELECTRONIC FUEL INJ. COMPUTER
TO COIL (−)
THROT. POS. SENS.
FUEL INJ. RESISTOR
TO IGN. COIL +
FUEL INJ.
TEMP. SENS.
CHECK ENG. CONN.
YEL-BLK
BRN
YEL-BLU
BLK-YEL
BLU-RED
GRN-WHT
GRN-RED
BLK
WHT-BLK
GRN-YEL
GRN
RED
BLU
WHT
YEL
BLK-RED
WHT-RED
BLU-BLK
WHT-BLK

Fig. 24: Toyota Cressida Fuel Injection Wiring Diagram

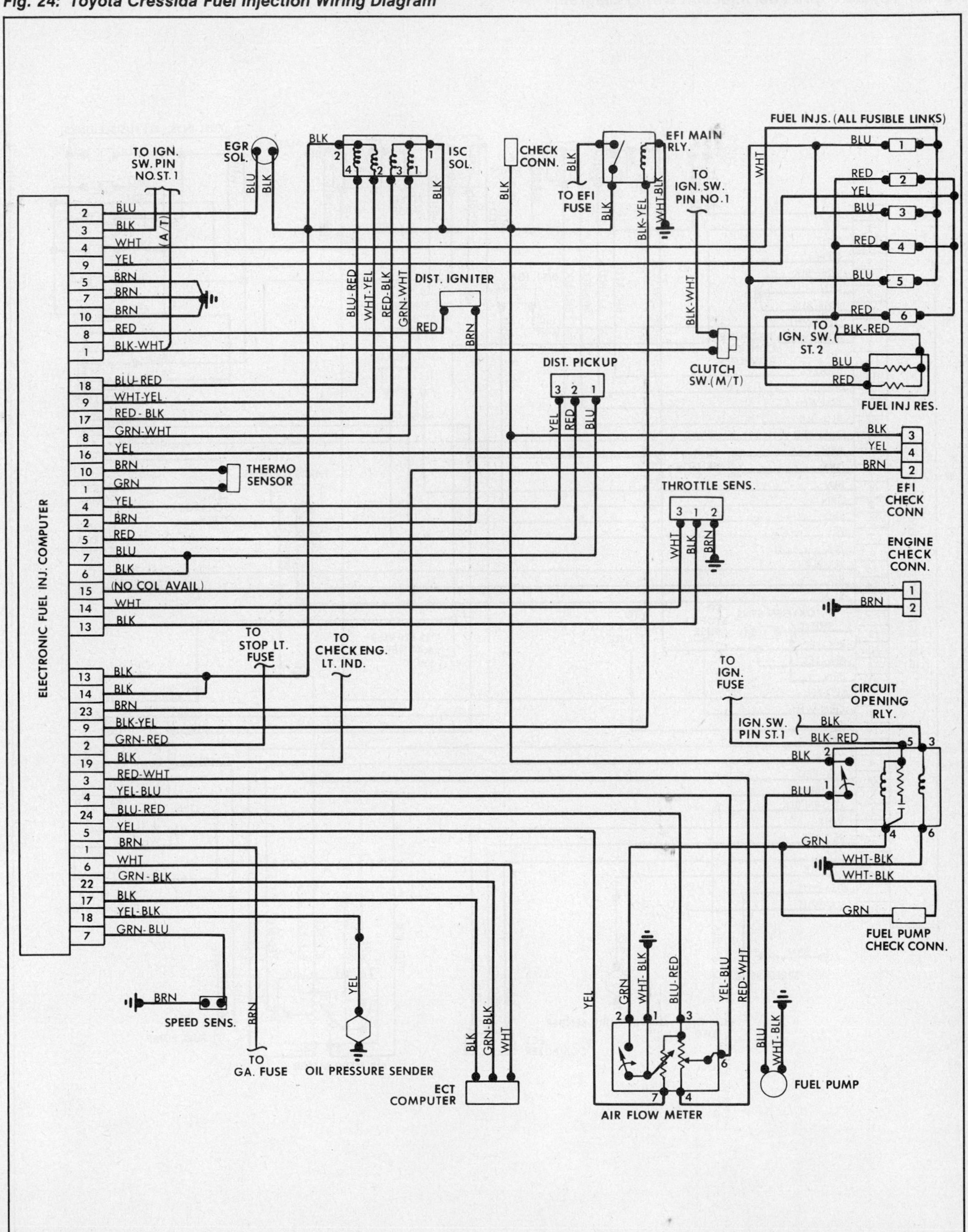
TO IGN. SW. PIN NO. ST. 1
EGR SOL.
BLU
BLK
ISC SOL.
CHECK CONN.
TO EFI FUSE
EFI MAIN RLY.
TO IGN. SW. PIN NO. 1
FUEL INJS. (ALL FUSIBLE LINKS)
(A/T)
DIST. IGNITER
BLU-RED
WHT-YEL
RED-BLK
GRN-WHT
BLK-YEL
WHT-BLK
BLK-WHT
TO IGN. SW. ST. 2
CLUTCH SW. (M/T)
FUEL INJ RES.
DIST. PICKUP
THERMO SENSOR
EFI CHECK CONN
THROTTLE SENS.
ENGINE CHECK CONN.
ELECTRONIC FUEL INJ. COMPUTER
(NO COL AVAIL)
TO STOP LT. FUSE
TO CHECK ENG. LT. IND.
TO IGN. FUSE
CIRCUIT OPENING RLY.
IGN. SW. PIN ST. 1
BLK-RED
RED-WHT
YEL-BLU
GRN-RED
GRN-BLK
YEL-BLK
GRN-BLU
FUEL PUMP CHECK CONN.
SPEED SENS.
TO GA. FUSE
OIL PRESSURE SENDER
ECT COMPUTER
AIR FLOW METER
FUEL PUMP

1983 Fuel Injection

BOSCH AFC — JAPANESE MODELS (Cont.)

Fig. 25: Toyota Supra Fuel Injection Wiring Diagram

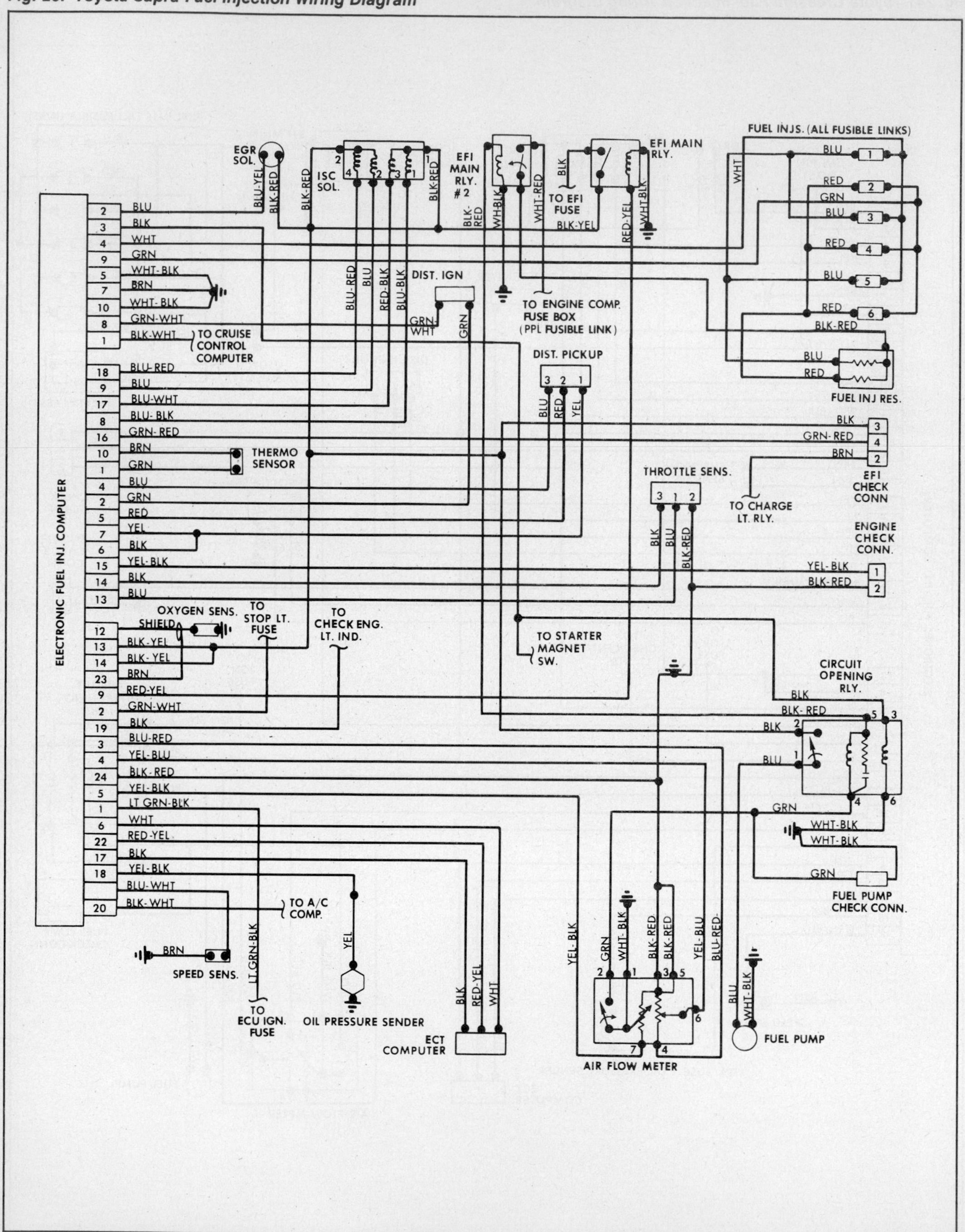
ELECTRONIC FUEL INJ. COMPUTER
EGR SOL.
ISC SOL.
EFI MAIN RLY. #2
TO EFI FUSE
EFI MAIN RLY.
FUEL INJS. (ALL FUSIBLE LINKS)
FUEL INJ RES.
DIST. IGN
TO ENGINE COMP. FUSE BOX (PPL FUSIBLE LINK)
DIST. PICKUP
TO CRUISE CONTROL COMPUTER
THERMO SENSOR
EFI CHECK CONN
TO CHARGE LT. RLY.
THROTTLE SENS.
ENGINE CHECK CONN.
OXYGEN SENS.
SHIELD
TO STOP LT. FUSE
TO CHECK ENG. LT. IND.
TO STARTER MAGNET SW.
CIRCUIT OPENING RLY.
FUEL PUMP CHECK CONN.
TO A/C COMP.
SPEED SENS.
TO ECU IGN. FUSE
OIL PRESSURE SENDER
ECT COMPUTER
AIR FLOW METER
FUEL PUMP

1983 Bosch Fuel Injection

BOSCH CIS (LAMBDA) FUEL INJECTION

Audi Coupe, 4000, 5000, 5000 Turbo; BMW 320i; Mercedes-Benz 380; Peugeot 505; Porsche 911SC; Saab 900, 900 Turbo; Volkswagen Jetta, Rabbit, Scirocco, Pickup, Quantum; Volvo (Exc. LH-Jetronic)

DESCRIPTION

The Bosch Continuous Injection System (CIS) is a hydraulic-type fuel injection system which uses an air flow sensor, that is mechanically connected to a hydraulic valve, to control injection quantity.

The Lambda system is a feedback control capable of measuring air/fuel ratios and constantly correcting them. The combination of the two systems makes it possible to obtain both economy and performance, while minimizing exhaust emissions. *See Fig. 1.*

The system consists of the mixture control unit (air-flow sensor and fuel distributor), control pressure regulator, auxiliary air valve, cold start valve, thermo-time switch, injector nozzles, fuel pump, filter, oxygen sensor, electronic control unit, frequency valve, and catalytic converter.

Some models use additional components, such as a thermo-vacuum valve, hot start pulse relay, or a constant idle speed control system.

OPERATION

MIXTURE CONTROL UNIT

The air-flow sensor contains a plate, mounted on a hinged lever, which moves in a cone-shaped venturi. All engine air is drawn past this sensor. The plate moves as air is drawn into the engine, moving the hinged lever up or down.

Fig. 1: Bosch CIS Lambda Fuel Injection System Diagram

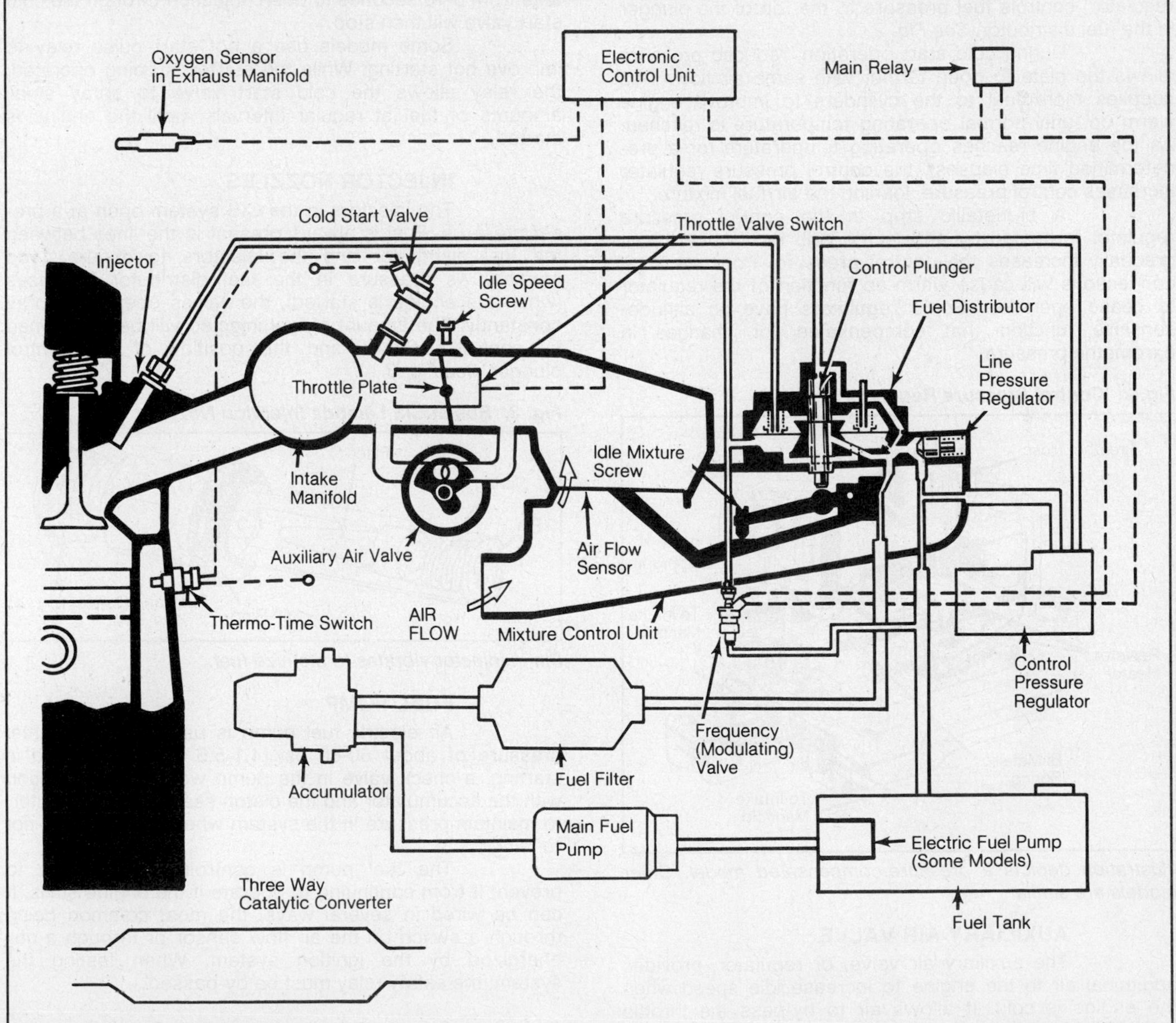
Oxygen Sensor
in Exhaust Manifold
Electronic
Control Unit
Main Relay
Cold Start Valve
Throttle Valve Switch
Injector
Idle Speed
Screw
Control Plunger
Fuel Distributor
Line
Pressure
Regulator
Throttle Plate
Idle Mixture
Screw
Intake
Manifold
Auxiliary Air Valve
Air Flow
Sensor
Thermo-Time Switch
AIR
FLOW
Mixture Control Unit
Control
Pressure
Regulator
Frequency
(Modulating)
Valve
Fuel Filter
Accumulator
Main Fuel
Pump
Electric Fuel Pump
(Some Models)
Three Way
Catalytic Converter
Fuel Tank

This illustration is typical of all models. Specific details among models may vary.

BOSCH CIS (LAMBDA) FUEL INJECTION (Cont.)

Movement of the sensor plate raises or lowers a fuel control plunger in the fuel distributor, which meters the amount of fuel injected into each cylinder. The movement of the plate is controlled by air flow, cone shape of venturi, a balance weight, and fuel pressure.

NOTE: **Air flows UP through the sensor on most inline engines, and DOWN through the sensor on V6, V8 and turbocharged engines. The direction of air flow does not affect system operation. It is changed for convenience of routing air flow.**

Fuel distribution can be equal only if the pressure to each injector is equal. Pressure regulating valves in the fuel distributor equalize system pressure. These valves are adjusted during assembly of fuel distributor and cannot be adjusted in service.

CONTROL PRESSURE REGULATOR

The control pressure regulator (or warm-up regulator) controls fuel pressure to the top of the plunger in the fuel distributor. *See Fig. 2.*

During cold start operation, reduced pressure allows the plate to open farther with same air flow. This supplies more fuel to the cylinders to improve engine warm up, until normal operating temperature is reached. As the engine reaches operating temperature (or a pre-determined time elapses), the control pressure regulator increases control pressure, leaning the air/fuel mixture.

A bi-metallic strip in the control pressure regulator is heated by an electric coil. As it heats up, it gradually increases the control pressure. Poor electrical connections will cause warm-up function of the regulator to cease operation. Some regulators have an altitude-sensitive function that compensates for changes in barometric pressure.

Fig. 2: Control Pressure Regulator

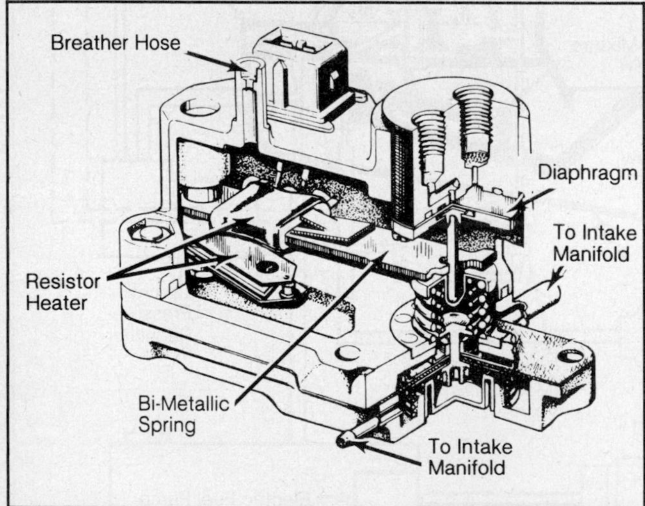
Breather Hose
Diaphragm
To Intake Manifold
Resistor Heater
Bi-Metallic Spring
To Intake Manifold

Illustration depicts a pressure-compensated model. Other models are similar.

AUXILIARY AIR VALVE

The auxiliary air valve, or regulator, provides additional air to the engine to increase idle speed when the engine is cold. It allows air to by-pass the throttle valves which are closed at idle.

A heating coil in the valve is connected to the fuel pump circuit. As the coil warms up, it gradually closes the air passage. The valve is calibrated to maintain a smooth idle without a large engine speed change as the engine is warming up.

COLD START VALVE

The cold start valve is mounted on the intake manifold and sprays fuel during starting. It enrichens the mixture so the engine will start easily. The valve is powered through the starter circuit and grounded through the thermo-time switch so it operates for only a short time while the engine is being cranked.

THERMO-TIME SWITCH & HOT START RELAY

The thermo-time switch controls opening time of cold start valve. It is affected by engine temperature and starter current. Depending on coolant temperature (or engine temperature on air-cooled engines), the switch will take from 3-10 seconds to open. Injection through the cold start valve will then stop.

Some models use a hot start pulse relay to improve hot starting. While the starter is being operated, the relay allows the cold start valve to spray small amounts of fuel at regular intervals, until the engine is started.

INJECTOR NOZZLES

The injectors in the CIS system open at a pre-set pressure. Fuel is always present in the lines between the fuel distributor and the injectors to ensure good starting. As pressure in the fuel distributor increases (when the engine is started), the valves open and spray constantly. The amount of fuel injected will be determined by control pressure and the position of the control plunger. *See Fig. 3.*

Fig. 3: Bosch CIS Lambda Injection Nozzle

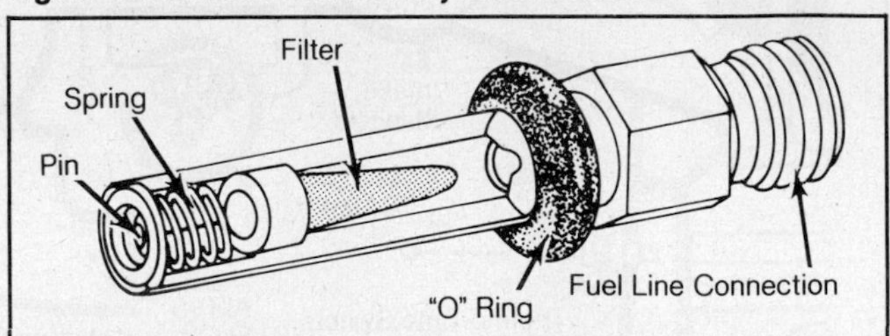
Filter
Spring
Pin
"O" Ring
Fuel Line Connection

Pin in injector vibrates to atomize fuel.

FUEL PUMP

An electric fuel pump is used to provide fuel pressure of about 60-80 psi (4.1-5.5 kg/cm²). To aid in starting, a check valve in the pump works in conjunction with the accumulator and the piston seal in fuel distributor, to maintain pressure in the system when the engine is not running.

The fuel pump is controlled by a relay to prevent it from continuing to operate if the engine stalls. It can be wired in several ways, the most common being through a switch on the air flow sensor or through a coil energized by the ignition system. When testing the system, the safety relay must be by-passed.

BOSCH CIS (LAMBDA) FUEL INJECTION (Cont.)

OXYGEN SENSOR

The oxygen sensor is located in the exhaust manifold and measures the amount of unburned oxygen in the exhaust gas. If oxygen is low (rich mixture) a high voltage will be generated by the sensor. If oxygen is high (lean mixture) low voltage will be generated. The voltage signal from the oxygen sensor is sent to an electronic control unit which controls fuel mixture.

ELECTRONIC CONTROL UNIT & FREQUENCY VALVE

The electronic control unit is designed to continually correct air/fuel mixture, based on signals from the oxygen sensor. It sends a series of pulses to a frequency valve. The frequency valve is located in a fuel line that connects the upper and lower halves of the fuel distributor. *See Fig. 4.*

When the frequency valve is closed, fuel pressure to the injectors is determined by a spring in each pressure regulating valve. When the frequency valve is open, fuel pressure decreases in the lower half of the fuel distributor, the tension on the spring is relieved, and more fuel is directed to the cylinders.

Fig. 4: Bosch CIS Lambda Electronic Control Unit

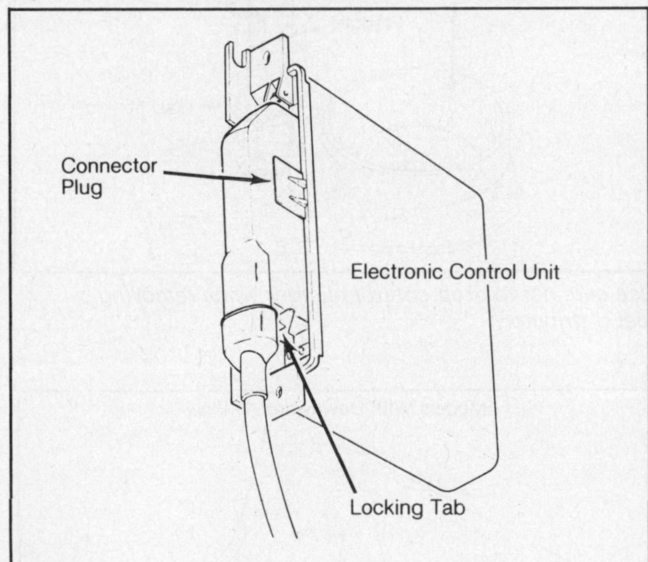
Connector Plug
Electronic Control Unit
Locking Tab

The electronic control unit opens and closes the frequency valve many times a second to ensure a smooth regulation of fuel pressure and mixture. When the engine is cold, the ratio of valve open to valve closed is about 50%.

After the engine warms up, the voltage produced by the oxygen sensor determines the amount of time the frequency valve must be open or closed. This ratio can be read with a special tester or with a dwell meter (on most models). A dwell reading of 45° indicates a ratio of 50% open, 50% closed.

CATALYTIC CONVERTER

CIS Lambda systems can control air/fuel ratios within .02%. This close regulation allows the use of a 3-way catalyst that can decrease NOx, HC, and CO emissions. The converter can be damaged by improper adjustment of the system or by the use of leaded fuels.

IDLE SPEED CONTROL SYSTEMS

Mercedes-Benz Electronic Idle Speed Control

The system controls a variable air bleed into the intake system. Idle speed is held constant by increasing or decreasing the amount of extra air injected through an insulating sleeve around each fuel injector.

A high idle speed is maintained when engine temperature is below 107°F (40°C), then idle speed drops to a constant low idle RPM when engine temperature is above 107°F (40°C).

The idle speed control system consists of an idle speed adjuster, intake air distributor and an electronic control unit.

Volvo Electronic Idle Speed Control

This system maintains a constant idle speed by varying the amount of air by-passing the throttle valve. This air is controlled by the air control valve.

The air control valve is operated by the electronic idle speed control unit which receives engine information from the throttle switch, coolant temperature sensor, and the ignition coil.

TESTING

NOTE: Testing procedures described below will apply to all models using the CIS Lambda system unless otherwise noted. Not all models will use all components.

PREPARATION FOR TESTING

1) All CIS systems are very sensitive to air leaks. Check condition of rubber boots, hoses, and gaskets. Other areas of leakage are injectors, cold start valve, and PCV system (filler cap and dipstick).

2) Install a pressure gauge to perform fuel pressure tests. On all models, pressure gauge is installed between the control pressure regulator and the center fitting on fuel distributor. *See Fig. 5.*

Fig. 5: Pressure Gauge Installation

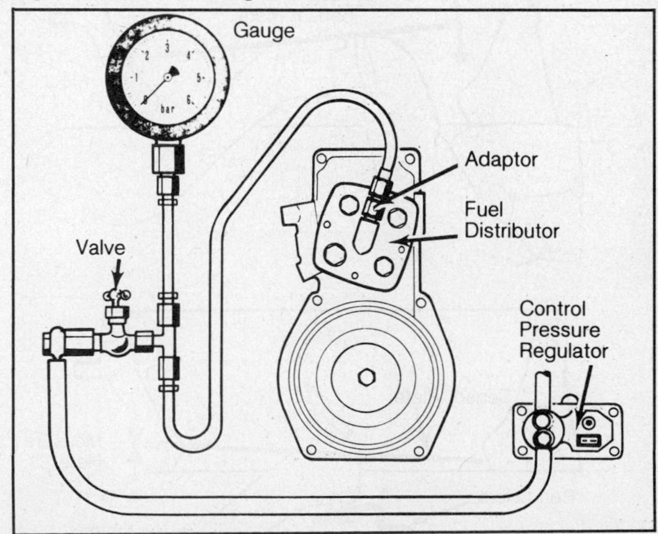
Gauge
Adaptor
Fuel Distributor
Valve
Control Pressure Regulator

After installation, bleed pressure gauge by opening and closing valve several times.

1983 Bosch Fuel Injection

BOSCH CIS (LAMBDA) FUEL INJECTION (Cont.)

3) To operate fuel pump with engine not running, disconnect fuel pump relay from relay panel (VW, Porsche, Audi, Saab, Mercedes-Benz). Insert a jumper wire into sockets that correspond to terminals 30 and 87 on relay. *See Fig. 6.*

4) On Peugeot models, remove steering wheel and lower left dash panel. Install a jumper wire across terminals 30 and 87B. *See Fig. 6.* On Volvo, Mercedes-Benz, and other models so equipped, disconnect safety switch connector on air flow sensor.

Fig. 6: Jumper Wire Connection For Fuel Pump Testing

Jumper Wire
Fuel Pump Relay
Sockets for
Term. 30 & 87

Saab is shown; other models are similar.

5) Operate fuel pump on Peugeot by depressing switch on harness. On all other models, turn ignition on. Place pressure gauge as low as possible in engine compartment, then open and close valve 5 times to bleed gauge. Place valve in open position and hang in convenient location. Turn pump off.

AIR/FUEL MIXTURE CONTROL OR AIR-FLOW SENSOR

1) Remove rubber bellows to expose air-flow sensor plate. Disconnect electrical connectors on auxiliary air valve and control pressure regulator, then operate fuel pump for ten seconds to build up control pressure.

2) Using extreme care not to damage sensor plate, lift sensor plate slowly with magnet or pliers. Constant resistance due to control plunger pressure should be felt throughout range of lift. Release plate slowly, lever and control piston should follow. *See Fig. 7.*

Fig. 8: Removing Fuel Distributor Control Plunger

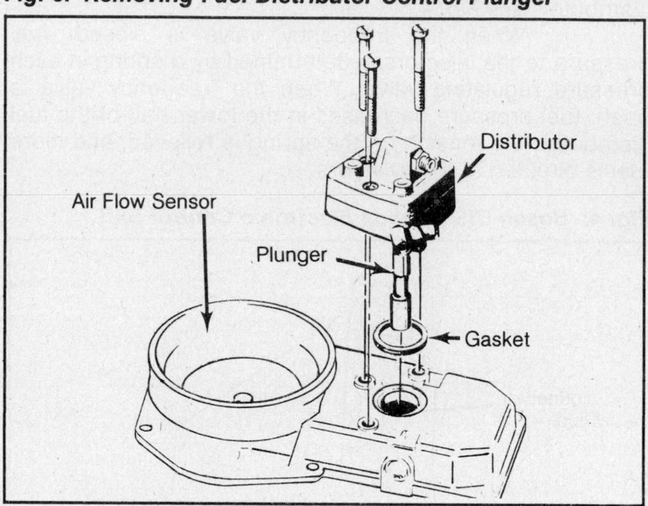
Distributor
Air Flow Sensor
Plunger
Gasket

Use care not to drop control plunger when removing fuel distributor.

Fig. 7: Checking Air Flow Sensor Operation and Alignment

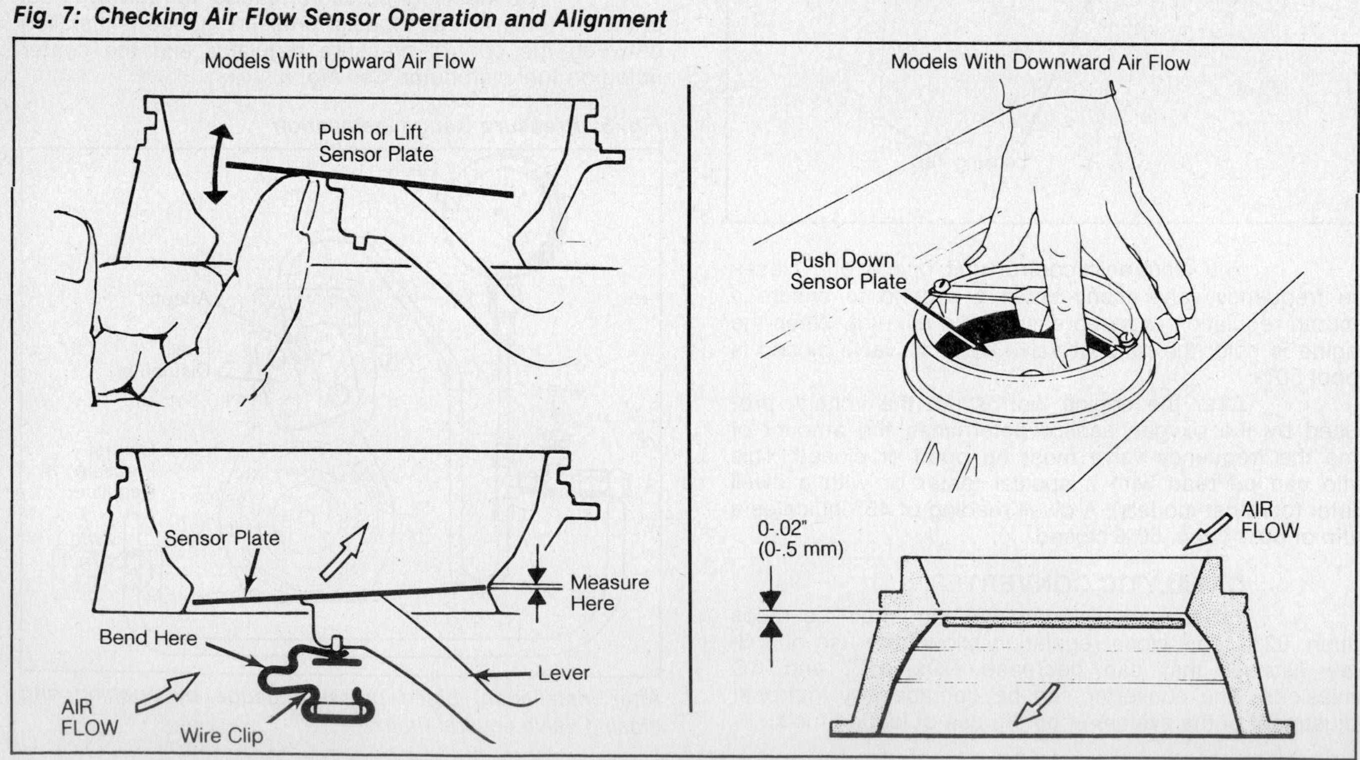
Models With Upward Air Flow
Push or Lift
Sensor Plate
Sensor Plate
Measure
Here
Bend Here
Lever
AIR
FLOW
Wire Clip
Models With Downward Air Flow
Push Down
Sensor Plate
0-.02"
(0-.5 mm)
AIR
FLOW

1983 Bosch Fuel Injection

BOSCH CIS (LAMBDA) FUEL INJECTION (Cont.)

Fig. 9: Cold Engine Control Pressure Test Graphs

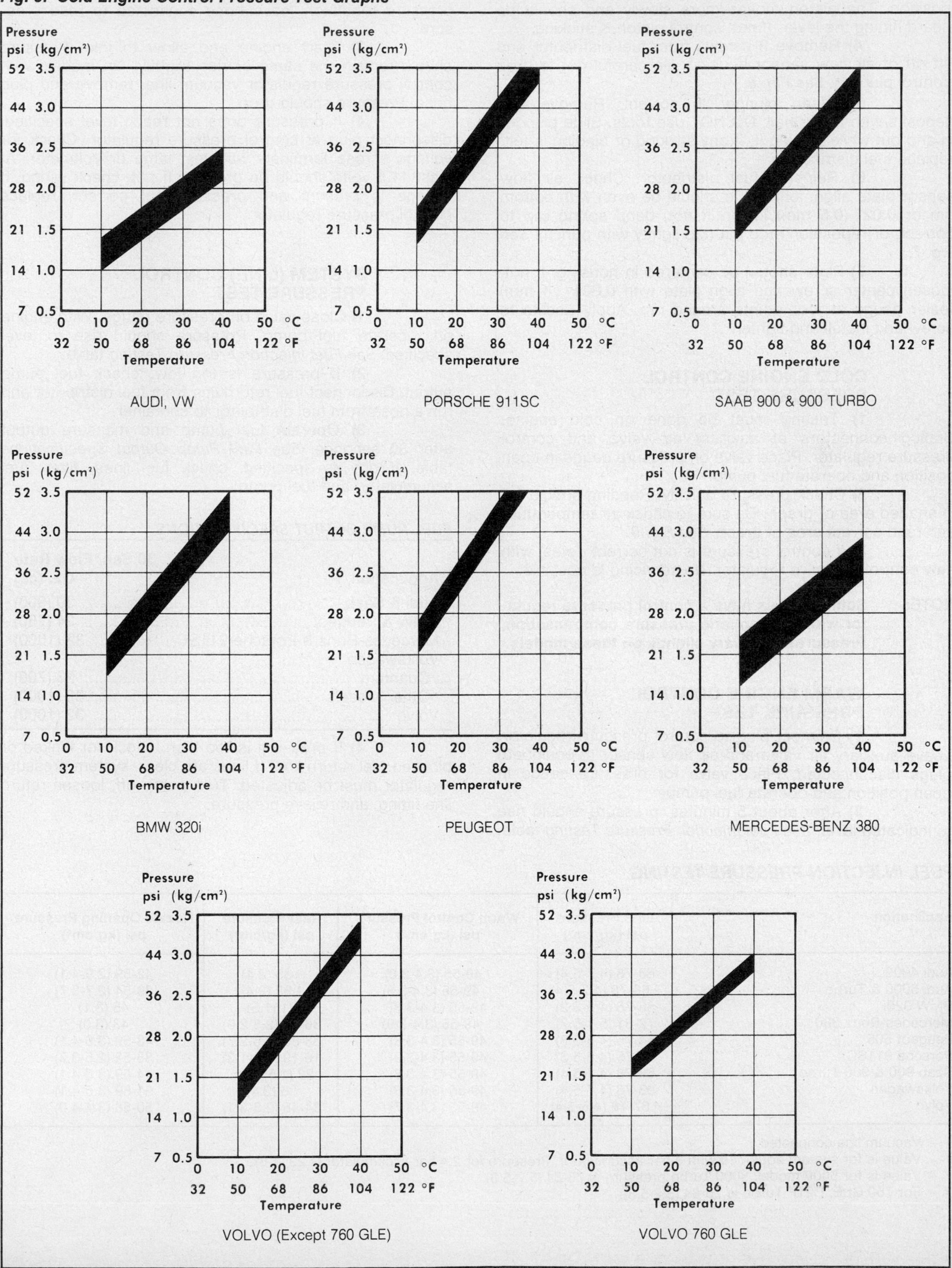
Pressure
psi (kg/cm²)
52 3.5
44 3.0
36 2.5
28 2.0
21 1.5
14 1.0
7 0.5
0 10 20 30 40 50 °C
32 50 68 86 104 122 °F
Temperature
AUDI, VW
PORSCHE 911SC
SAAB 900 & 900 TURBO
BMW 320i
PEUGEOT
MERCEDES-BENZ 380
VOLVO (Except 760 GLE)
VOLVO 760 GLE

BOSCH CIS (LAMBDA) FUEL INJECTION (Cont.)

3) Lift plate, then return it rapidly to lower position. The piston moves more slowly and should be heard hitting the lever. If not, control piston is sticking.

4) Remove 3 screws from fuel distributor and lift off of air flow sensor housing. Be careful not to drop control plunger. *See Fig. 8.*

5) Clean plunger in solvent. Remove any deposits with finger nail; DO NOT use tools. Slide plunger in and out while turning it. If any sticking or binding is felt, replace fuel distributor.

6) Reinstall fuel distributor. Check air flow sensor plate alignment. Plate should be even with bottom rim or 0.02" (0.5 mm) lower. If not, bend spring clip to correct, or reposition stop pin (tap lightly with punch). *See Fig. 7.*

7) Plate should be centered in housing. If not, loosen center screw and align plate with 0.004" (.1 mm) feeler gauge at four points around rim. Apply Loctite to screw and install and tighten.

COLD ENGINE CONTROL PRESSURE TEST

1) Testing must be done on cold engine. Unplug connectors at auxiliary air valve and control pressure regulator. Place valve on pressure gauge in open position and operate fuel pump.

2) Check pressure quickly. Reading should fall in shaded area of graph. Be sure to check air temperature and read correct area of graph. *See Fig. 9.*

3) If control pressure is not correct, retest with new control pressure regulator. No servicing is possible.

NOTE: **Some models have a control pressure regulator with atmospheric pressure compensation. Pressures may vary slightly on these models.**

WARM ENGINE CONTROL PRESSURE TEST

1) Connect plug to control pressure regulator. Leave auxiliary air valve and air flow sensor (if equipped) plugs disconnected. Place valve for pressure gauge in open position and operate fuel pump.

2) After about 5 minutes, pressure should rise to indicated level. *See Fuel Injection Pressure Testing* table. On models with vacuum hose connected to control pressure regulator, leave hose connected to read pressure.

3) Start engine and allow to idle. Pressure should remain the same or rise slightly. On models with control pressure regulator vacuum line, remove and plug hose. Pressure should drop.

4) If pressure does not reach level specified, disconnect plug at control pressure regulator. Check for voltage across terminals with test lamp or voltmeter. At least 11.5 volts should be present. If not, check wiring. If voltage is present and pressure not correct, replace control pressure regulator.

SYSTEM (LINE) CONTROL PRESSURE TEST

1) Close valve on pressure gauge. With engine off, operate fuel pump. Pressure should rise to level specified. *See Fuel Injection Pressure Testing* table.

2) If pressure is too low, check fuel pump output. Disconnect fuel return line from fuel distributor and run a hose from fuel distributor to container.

3) Operate fuel pump and measure output after 30 seconds. *See Fuel Pump Output Specifications* table. If not as specified, check fuel lines, filter, fuel accumulator, and fuel pump.

FUEL PUMP OUTPUT SPECIFICATIONS

Application	30 Sec. Flow Rate Oz. (cc)
Audi & Saab	30 (900)
BMW & Peugeot	24 (750)
Mercedes-Benz & Porsche 911SC	32 (1000)
Volkswagen	
Quantum	23 (700)
Other Models	32 (1000)
Volvo	32 (1000)

4) If pressure is too high, check for kinked or blocked fuel return line. If lines are clear, system pressure regulator must be adjusted. Turn pump off, loosen return line fitting, and relieve pressure.

FUEL INJECTION PRESSURE TESTING

Application	Line Pressure psi (kg/cm²)	Warm Control Pressure psi (kg/cm²)	Rest Pressure psi (kg/cm²)	Nozzle Opening Pressure psi (kg/cm²)
Audi 4000	68-78 (4.7-5.4)	[1] 49-55 (3.4-3.8)	[2] 35 (2.4)	42-59 (2.9-4.1)
Audi 5000 & Turbo	[3] 68-78 (4.7-5.4)	[1] 49-55 (3.4-3.8)	[2] 35 (2.4)	39-54 (2.7-3.7)
BMW 320i	65-75 (4.5-5.2)	49-55 (3.4-3.8)	21 (1.5)	45 (3.1)
Mercedes-Benz 380	72-81 (5.1-5.7)	[1] 49-55 (3.4-3.9)	36-41 (2.5-2.9)	43 (3.0)
Peugeot 505	64-75 (4.5-5.3)	49-55 (3.4-3.8)	38-39 (2.6-2.7)	43-59 (3.0-4.1)
Porsche 911SC	65-75 (4.6-5.3)	49-55 (3.4-3.9)	16-19 (1.1-1.3)	36-52 (2.5-3.7)
Saab 900 & 900 Turbo	68-78 (4.7-5.4)	49-55 (3.4-3.8)	22 (1.5) Min.	44-59 (3.0-4.1)
Volkswagen	68-78 (4.7-5.4)	49-55 (3.4-3.8)	35 (2.4)	51-59 (3.6-4.1)
Volvo	[4] 67-78 (4.6-5.4)	49-53 (3.4-3.7)	34-45 (2.3-3.1)	50-58 (3.4-4.0)

[1] – Vacuum line connected.
[2] – Value is for system equipped with 3 bar accumulator. Pressure for 2.4 bar accumulator is 23 (1.6).
[3] – Value is for 5000 model; 5000 Turbo pressure is 75-84 (5.2-5.8).
[4] – For 760 GLE; B21F Turbo is 75-84 (5.2-5.8).

BOSCH CIS (LAMBDA) FUEL INJECTION (Cont.)

5) Loosen line pressure regulator nut. Remove shims, spring(s) and plunger. Raise system pressure by adding shims; lower pressure by removing shims. Be sure "O" rings are in good condition. If piston is scored or damaged, fuel distributor must be replaced. *See Fig. 10.*

Fig. 10: Pressure Regulator in Fuel Distributor

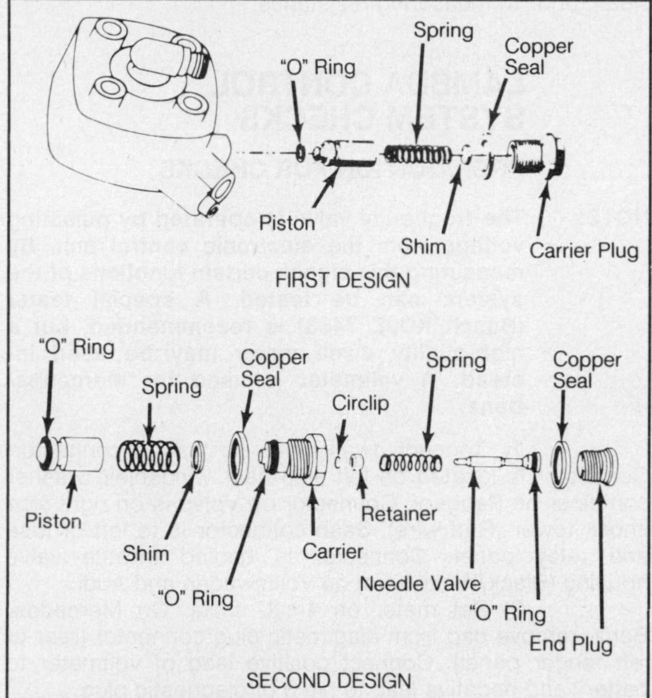

Spring
Copper Seal
"O" Ring
Piston
Shim
Carrier Plug
FIRST DESIGN
"O" Ring
Copper Seal
Spring
Copper Seal
Spring
Circlip
Piston
Retainer
Shim
Carrier
"O" Ring
Needle Valve
"O" Ring
End Plug
SECOND DESIGN

Replace fuel distributor if piston is scored or damaged.

REST PRESSURE & LEAK TEST

1) After correct warm engine control pressure has been obtained, stop fuel pump and note pressure drop. Pressure gauge valve should be in open position. Minimum pressure after 20 minutes must be as specified. *See Fuel Injection Pressure Testing* table.

2) If pressure drops too rapidly, run pump again and close valve. Stop pump and observe pressure. If values are now correct, control pressure regulator is faulty and must be replaced.

3) If pressure still drops, check all connections, fuel pump check valve, cold start valve, and fuel injectors.

COLD START VALVE, THERMO-TIME SWITCH & HOT START PULSE RELAY

1) If engine coolant is below 85°F (30°C), disconnect plug on cold start valve and connect test lamp across terminals. Remove coil high tension wire to prevent starting. Operate starter.

2) On models without hot start pulse relay, test lamp will light for several seconds, then go out. On models with relay, lamp will continue to flash off and on.

3) If lamp does not light, test thermo-time switch for continuity below opening temperature. If good, check wiring to starter terminal.

4) Remove cold start valve from manifold but leave fuel line connected. Place valve in a container. *See Fig. 11.* Connect a jumper wire from one terminal to ground, and from other terminal of cold start valve to a switch. The other side of switch should be connected to a source of battery voltage.

CAUTION: Do not connect wire directly to battery. Extreme fire danger is probable due to atomized fuel. Sparks may result if wire is touched to battery.

5) Operate fuel pump. Turn switch to "ON" position. Cold start injector should spray. Turn switch "OFF", but leave fuel pump running. Injector should not spray. Wipe off nozzle and check for leakage. With pump running, no drops should form within one minute.

Fig. 11: Testing Cold Start Injector Valve

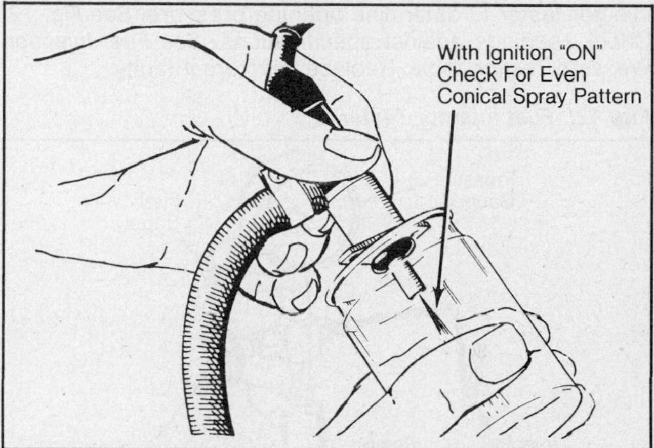

With Ignition "ON"
Check For Even
Conical Spray Pattern

After turning switch "OFF" (discontinuing electrical supply to valve), injector should cease spraying fuel.

6) Replace cold start valve if faulty. Install original valve if good, making sure that "O" ring is properly positioned.

FUEL INJECTORS

Audi & Volkswagen

1) Remove injectors but leave hoses connected. Place injectors in individual measuring containers. With sensor plate in idle position, connect jumper wire in place of fuel pump relay.

2) Disconnect fuel pump when measuring container with highest level of fuel reaches specified capacity. *See VW & Audi Fuel Injector Specifications* table.

3) Compare amounts of fuel in measuring containers. Fuel should not vary by more than specified amount. Repeat test with sensor plate in full throttle position.

VW & AUDI FUEL INJECTOR SPECIFICATIONS

Application	Fuel Capacity Oz. (cc)
Idle	.58-.78 (17-23)
Full Throttle	2.43-2.98 (72-88)

All Others

1) Remove injectors but leave hoses connected. Place injectors in individual measuring containers. Operate fuel pump to build up pressure, then turn pump off.

2) Lift air flow sensor plate half-way to operate injectors until one container has filled to 3.4 oz. (100 cc). Volume of fuel in other containers should not vary more than 10-20%. Spray pattern must be even and cone-shaped.

BOSCH CIS (LAMBDA) FUEL INJECTION (Cont.)

3) If one injector does not conform to specifications, swap hoses from it and one good injector at fuel distributor and retest. If same container is low, injector is faulty or fuel line is restricted. If other container is low, fuel distributor must be replaced.

4) Relieve system pressure and remove pressure testing gauge. Turn on pump to build up pressure. Injectors may leak slightly, but should stop leaking within 15 seconds. If drops form, check air flow sensor plate height, sticking fuel distributor plunger, or injector opening pressure.

5) Remove injectors from vehicle and use injector tester to determine opening pressure. *See Fig. 12.* Check readings against specifications. *See Fuel Injection Pressure Testing* table. Replace injectors if faulty.

Fig. 12: Fuel Injector Tester

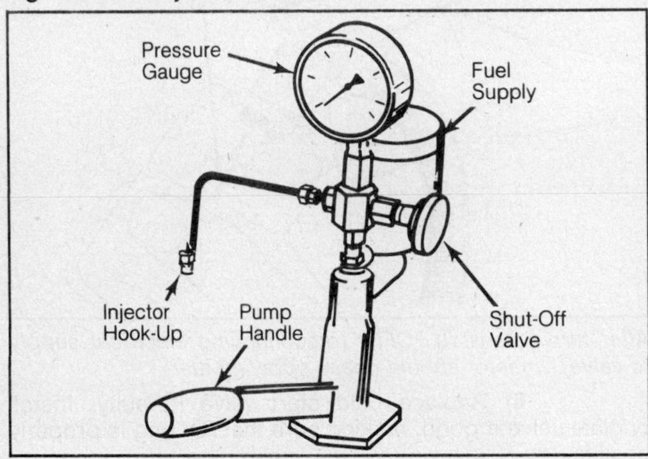
Pressure Gauge
Fuel Supply
Injector Hook-Up
Pump Handle
Shut-Off Valve

If opening pressure of injectors is not within limits, replace injectors.

AUXILIARY AIR VALVE

1) Disconnect hoses from auxiliary air valve. Use a mirror and small flashlight to inspect valve. *See Fig. 13.* At room temperature, valve should be slightly open. If equipped, disconnect wires from air flow sensor. With ignition switch "ON" valve should cover opening within 5 minutes.

Fig. 13: Checking Auxiliary Air Valve Operation

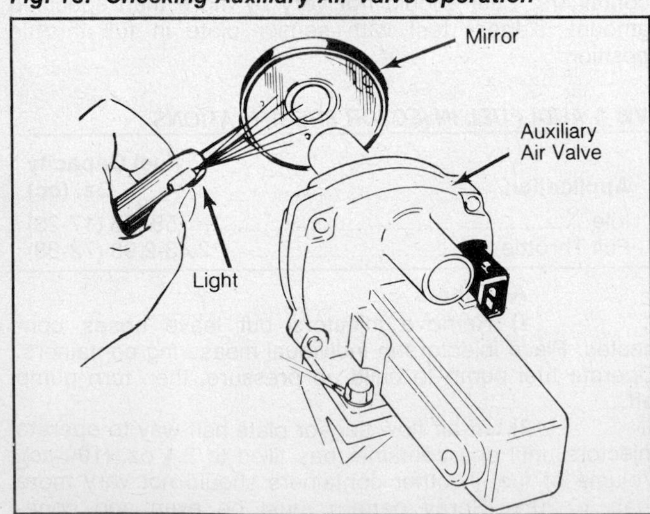
Mirror
Auxiliary Air Valve
Light

With ignition switch "ON", valve should cover opening within 5 minutes.

2) If valve does not operate properly, check for power at connector with engine running. Connect a test lamp across connector terminals. If lamp does not light, check fuse and wiring.

3) If lamp lights, check resistance of auxiliary air valve. If no resistance is measured, valve is defective. Ensure electrical connections are tight and terminals are clean, prior to measuring resistance.

LAMBDA CONTROL SYSTEM CHECKS

PREPARATION FOR CHECKS

NOTE: **The frequency valve is operated by pulsating voltage from the electronic control unit. By measuring this signal, certain functions of the system can be tested. A special tester (Bosch KDJE 7453) is recommended, but a high-quality dwell meter may be used instead. A voltmeter is used for Mercedes-Benz.**

1) Connect dwell meter to testing connector. Connector is located on left side near windshield washer container on Peugeot. Connector on Volvo is on right side shock tower (Red wire). Saab connector is to left of fuse and relay panel. Connector is behind throttle valve housing (Black/White wire) on Volkswagen and Audi.

2) Set meter on 4-cyl. scale. On Mercedes-Benz, remove cap from diagnostic plug connector (rear of left fender panel). Connect positive lead of voltmeter to battery and negative lead to pin 3 of diagnostic plug.

3) Start engine and run until warm. Disconnect oxygen sensor and observe meter needle (should not fluctuate). Place a piece of tape on meter face to indicate 50% position.

OPERATION CHECK

1) Remove fuel pump relay and connect jumper wire across sockets corresponding to terminals 30 and 87. If equipped, remove plug at air flow sensor. Turn ignition "ON".

2) Frequency valve should operate, making a buzzing noise. Dwell meter should indicate 45-65°. Disconnect wire from oxygen sensor and touch wire end to ground. Readings on dwell meter should rise. Ground one end of a 1.5 volt flashlight battery, and touch positive end to sensor wire. Readings should drop to less than 15°.

3) On models with throttle enrichment switch, operate throttle. Readings should be higher at idle or wide open throttle. *See Fig. 14.*

4) If engine is cold, enrichment switches will be closed. Disconnect lead at temperature sender. Readings should drop slightly. If engine is hot, connect temperature sender lead to ground. Reading should rise.

5) If starter enrichment relay is used, disconnect high tension lead at coil and crank engine. Readings should rise above normal level. If vacuum switches are used, apply vacuum to switch and note readings. Level should be higher with switch closed, and lower with switch open.

6) Connect oxygen sensor and start engine. With cold engine, dwell reading should be stable. When engine warms up, meter needle should fluctuate 10-20°. It

BOSCH CIS (LAMBDA) FUEL INJECTION (Cont.)

Fig. 14: Bosch CIS Lambda Electronic Control Unit Enrichment Switches (Except Quantum)

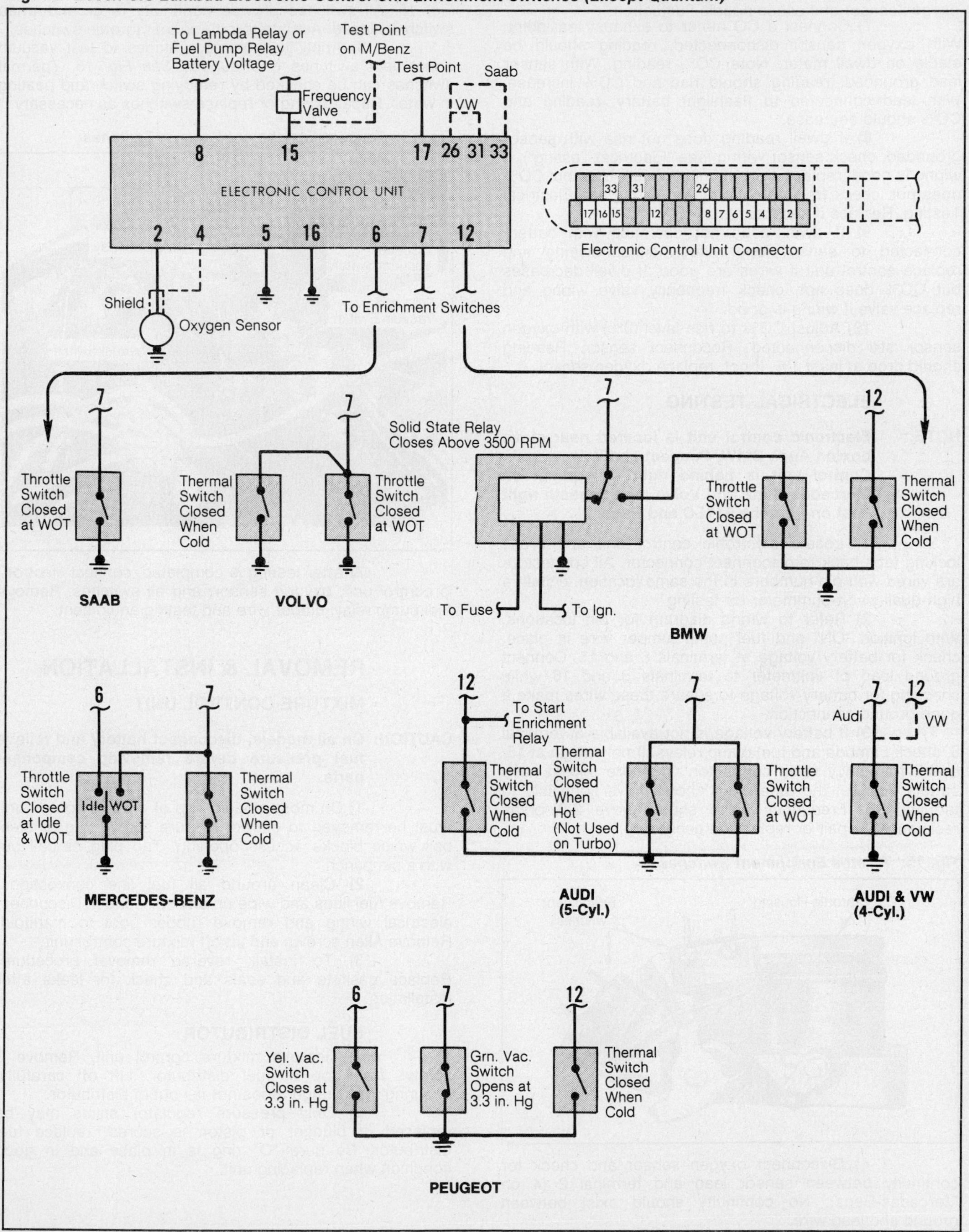
To Lambda Relay or
Fuel Pump Relay
Battery Voltage
Test Point
on M/Benz
Frequency
Valve
Test Point
Saab
VW
8
15
17 26 31 33
ELECTRONIC CONTROL UNIT
2 4 5 16 6 7 12
33 31 26
17 16 15 12 8 7 6 5 4 2
Electronic Control Unit Connector
Shield
Oxygen Sensor
To Enrichment Switches
Throttle Switch Closed at WOT
SAAB
Thermal Switch Closed When Cold
Throttle Switch Closed at WOT
VOLVO
Solid State Relay
Closes Above 3500 RPM
To Fuse
To Ign.
Throttle Switch Closed at WOT
Thermal Switch Closed When Cold
BMW
Throttle Switch Closed at Idle & WOT
Idle WOT
Thermal Switch Closed When Cold
MERCEDES-BENZ
To Start Enrichment Relay
Thermal Switch Closed When Cold
Thermal Switch Closed When Hot (Not Used on Turbo)
Throttle Switch Closed at WOT
AUDI
(5-Cyl.)
Audi
VW
Thermal Switch Closed When Cold
AUDI & VW
(4-Cyl.)
Yel. Vac. Switch Closes at 3.3 in. Hg
Grn. Vac. Switch Opens at 3.3 in. Hg
Thermal Switch Closed When Cold
PEUGEOT

BOSCH CIS (LAMBDA) FUEL INJECTION (Cont.)

may be necessary to run engine faster than idle to heat oxygen sensor and cause needle fluctuation.

7) Connect a CO meter to exhaust test point. With oxygen sensor disconnected, reading should be stable on dwell meter. Note CO% reading. With sensor lead grounded, reading should rise and CO% increase. With lead connected to flashlight battery, reading and CO% should decrease.

8) If dwell reading does not rise with sensor grounded, check sensor wiring (see "Electrical Testing"). If wiring is good, replace control unit. If dwell rises, but CO% does not, check frequency valve and wiring see Electrical Testing. Replace if necessary.

9) If dwell does not decrease with battery connected to sensor lead, check sensor wiring and replace control unit if wires are good. If dwell decreases but CO% does not, check frequency valve wiring and replace valve if wiring is good.

10) Adjust CO% to rich level (3%) with oxygen sensor still disconnected. Reconnect sensor. Reading should drop at least 1%. If not, replace oxygen sensor.

ELECTRICAL TESTING

NOTE: **Electronic control unit is located near glove box on Audi, BMW, Peugeot and Volkswagen. Control unit is behind right kick panel on Mercedes-Benz and Volvo, and beneath right seat on Porsche 911SC and Saab.**

1) Locate electronic control unit and press locking tabs back to disconnect connector. All connectors are wired with pin numbers in the same location. Obtain a high-quality volt-ohmmeter for testing.

2) Refer to wiring diagram for pin locations. With ignition "ON" and fuel pump jumper wire in place, check for battery voltage at terminals 8 and 15. Connect ground lead of voltmeter to terminals 5 and 16 while checking for battery voltage to ensure these wires make a good ground connection.

3) If battery voltage is not available at terminal 8, check Lambda and fuel pump relays. If no voltage at 15, check frequency valve connector. One wire should have battery voltage; the other wire should have continuity to terminal 15. Frequency valve should have 2-3 ohms resistance. Repair or replace as necessary.

Fig. 15: Throttle Enrichment Switches

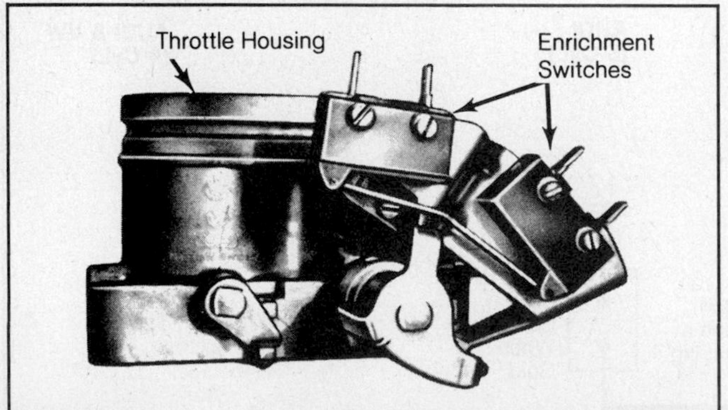
Throttle Housing
Enrichment Switches

4) Disconnect oxygen sensor and check for continuity between sensor lead and terminal 2 (4 on Mercedes-Benz). No continuity should exist between ground and lead wire.

5) All models use enrichment switches. *See Fig. 15.* All switches provide continuity to ground when switch is closed. Actuate throttle to test throttle switches.

6) Apply vacuum to switches to test vacuum enrichment switches on Peugeot. *See Fig. 16.* Thermal switches can be checked by removing switch and heating in water. Repair wiring or replace switches as necessary.

Fig. 16: Peugeot Enrichment Vacuum Switches

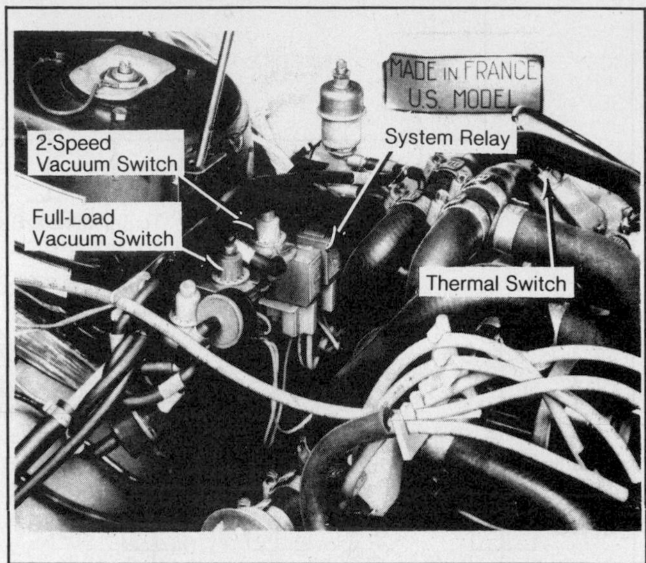
MADE IN FRANCE
U.S. MODEL
System Relay
2-Speed Vacuum Switch
Full-Load Vacuum Switch
Thermal Switch

7) After testing is completed, connect electronic control unit, oxygen sensor, and all switches. Remove fuel pump relay jumper wire and testing equipment.

REMOVAL & INSTALLATION

MIXTURE CONTROL UNIT

CAUTION: **On all models, disconnect battery and relieve fuel pressure before removing component parts.**

1) On most models, top of mixture control unit must be removed to extract mixture screw plug or steel ball which blocks access opening. Tap plug or ball out with a pin punch.

2) Clean around all fuel line connections. Remove fuel lines and wipe up any spilled fuel. Disconnect electrical wiring and remove rubber boot to manifold. Remove Allen screws and lift off mixture control unit.

3) To install, reverse removal procedure. Replace gaskets and seals and check for leaks after installation.

FUEL DISTRIBUTOR

1) Remove mixture control unit. Remove 3 screws from top of fuel distributor. Lift off carefully, ensuring that plunger does not fall out of distributor.

2) Only pressure regulator shims may be replaced. If plunger or piston is scored, replace fuel distributor. Be sure "O" ring is in place and in good condition when replacing unit.

BOSCH CIS (LAMBDA) FUEL INJECTION (Cont.)

CONTROL PRESSURE REGULATOR

Disconnect electrical plug and vacuum lines (if equipped). Remove fuel lines and wipe up any spilled fuel. Remove bolts and regulator. To install, reverse removal procedure.

AUXILIARY AIR VALVE

Remove and plug hoses. Disconnect electrical plug. Remove mounting bolts and air valve. Reverse removal procedure to install.

COLD START VALVE

Remove electrical connector and fuel line. Loosen mounting bolts and remove cold start valve. Check "O" ring and replace if necessary. Install valve.

FUEL INJECTORS

1) Clean area around valves. On BMW, remove intake cowl and pipes at number 2 and 3 cylinders. Hold valve secure and remove fuel line fitting. Do not allow valve to turn.

2) Remove retaining plate if present, and pull valves out carefully. Do not remove insulator sleeve, if possible.

3) To install, reverse removal procedure. Replace "O" rings and lubricate with a drop of oil. Place injectors in sleeve and press until seated. Tighten fuel lines and check for leaks.

THERMAL SWITCH

Drain coolant below level of switch. Be careful not to damage connectors on switch while removing. Coat threads of sensor with sealant and reinstall.

FREQUENCY VALVE

1) Disconnect electrical connector. Hold small nut at hose and loosen larger valve nut. Do not spill gasoline on rubber mounting insulator as it will cause the rubber to swell.

2) Remove return lines at fuel distributor and/or control pressure regulator. To install, reverse removal procedure, using new gaskets. Check for leaks after installation.

ELECTRONIC CONTROL UNIT

Porsche 911SC and Saab

Slide passenger seat rearward (Saab) or remove from vehicle (Porsche). Remove cover from plug and disconnect plug. Remove 3 mounting fasteners and remove control unit. Reverse removal procedure to install.

Mercedes-Benz and Volvo

Pull back carpeting or trim on right kick panel. Remove cover and disconnect plug from control unit. Remove mounting bolts and control unit. To install, reverse removal procedure.

Peugeot

Remove glove box, support, and heater hose. Disconnect plug from control unit. Remove 2 nuts from mounting studs and remove control unit. To install, reverse removal procedure.

Volkswagen

Disconnect plug from control unit beneath glove box. Remove mounting bolts and control unit. To install, reverse removal procedure.

NOTE: **Removal and installation procedures were not available for other models.**

OXYGEN SENSOR

1) Disconnect wiring from sensor. On Porsche 911SC, remove left rear wheel and protector plate. Remove shield from sensor if equipped. Remove sensor.

2) Coat threads of new sensor with anti-seize compound. Take care not to get compound into slots on end of sensor. Install sensor and tighten to 40 ft. lbs. (55 N.m) on Volvo models or to 25-30 ft. lbs. (35-41 N.m) on all other models. Refit shield and connect sensor wire.

1983 Bosch Fuel Injection

BOSCH LH JETRONIC II – VOLVO

DL & GL

DESCRIPTION

The Bosch LH-Jetronic II fuel injection system has replaced the LH-Jetronic system that was formerly used. It has integrated the fuel injection and Constant Idle Speed (CI system) functions into one system. There is only one Electronic Control Unit (ECU) to control both functions.

The LH Jetronic II fuel injection system operates with a moderate fuel pressure, held constant by a line pressure regulator. Fuel is metered into the cylinders by electrically controlled solenoid valves in the injectors. The injectors are aimed at the intake valve of each cylinder.

The duration of the injection, usually a few milliseconds, is determined by an electronic control unit. The electronic control unit receives several signals on various driving, engine and outside conditions from a set of sensors. The most important sensor in the system is the air mass meter.

The signals from the air mass meter and exhaust gas oxygen sensor provide most of the information used by the control unit to maintain proper air/fuel ratios. An idle speed adjustment screw has been provided in the throttle housing.

ELECTRONIC CONTROL UNIT

The electronic control unit is a microprocessor based computer that receives and evaluates readings from sensors located throughout the engine. The control unit then produces a control signal that is sent to the injectors so that the correct amount of fuel for any operating condition can be injected into the cylinders. Located in the right kick panel, it also controls the Constant Idle Speed system.

NOTE: For more information on the CI system, see VOLVO COMPUTERIZED ENGINE CONTROL in the COMPUTERIZED ENGINE CONTROLS Section.

FUEL SYSTEM

The fuel system consists of the fuel tank, a fuel feed pump, fuel lines, in-line fuel pump, filter, and a line pressure regulator. *See Fig. 1.*

Fuel is supplied to the injection system at a constant pressure and volume. Only the injection duration needs to be varied to meet changing engine requirements.

The fuel feed pump is an electrically operated vane pump. The pump is located near the bottom of the fuel tank. Fuel is strained through a mesh screen before entering the fuel pump. There is a check valve on the outlet side of the fuel feed pump. This prevents the fuel supply line from draining back into the tank.

The main fuel pump and filter are attached to a bracket located underneath the vehicle, under the left rear seat. The main fuel pump is an electrically operated roller pump. The pump is equipped with a check valve to prevent back flow. The pump also has an overpressure relief valve which opens if the fuel system becomes clogged and the pressure rises too high.

INJECTORS

The injectors are located in the intake manifold and point directly at the intake valve. All injectors are supplied with fuel from a common fuel manifold. The injection pulse is controlled by a needle valve assembly in the bottom of the injector. The needle valve is operated by an electric solenoid which is switched on and off by the electronic control unit. All fuel injectors inject fuel at the same time.

Fig. 1: Bosch LH Jetronic II Fuel Injection Schematic

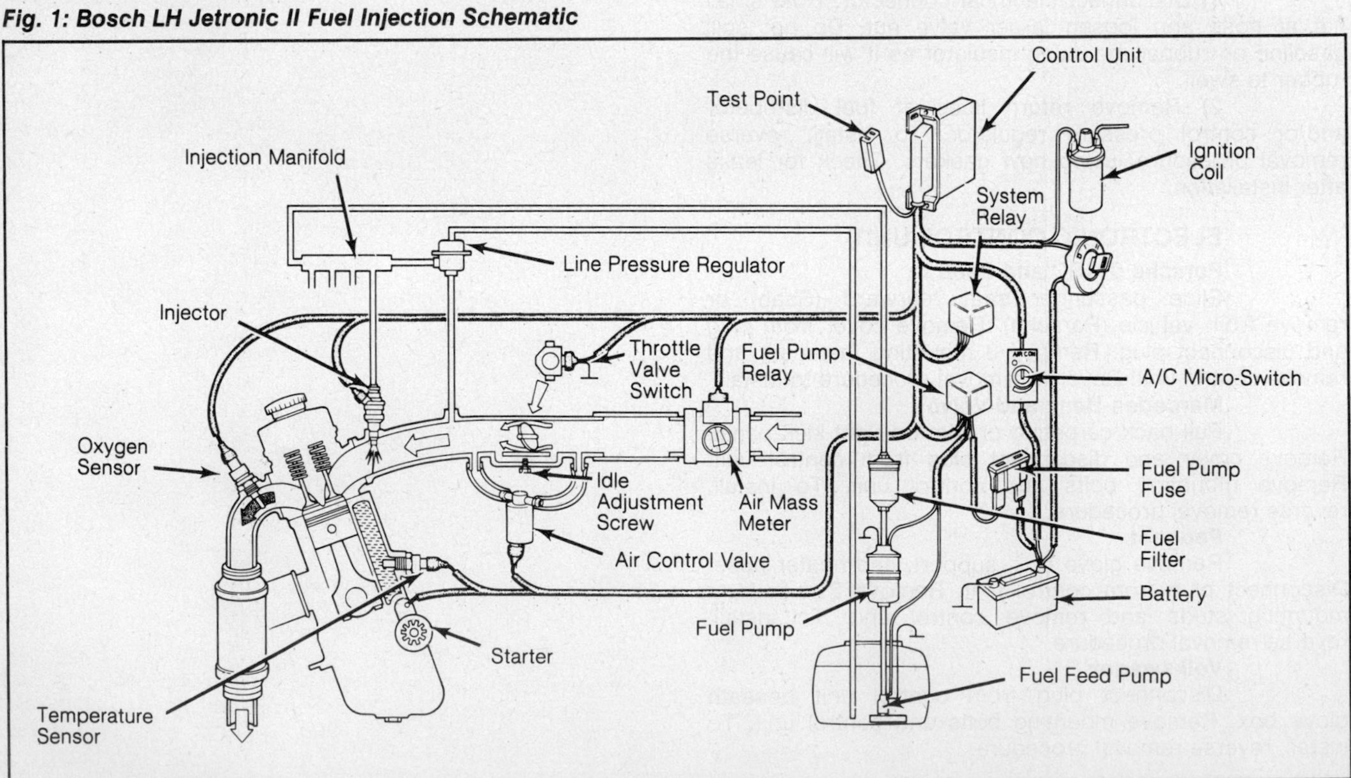
Control Unit
Test Point
Injection Manifold
Ignition Coil
System Relay
Line Pressure Regulator
Injector
Throttle Valve Switch
Fuel Pump Relay
A/C Micro-Switch
Oxygen Sensor
Idle Adjustment Screw
Air Mass Meter
Fuel Pump Fuse
Fuel Filter
Air Control Valve
Battery
Fuel Pump
Starter
Fuel Feed Pump
Temperature Sensor

BOSCH LH JETRONIC II – VOLVO (Cont.)

FUEL PUMP RELAY

The fuel pump relay is located on the firewall under the dash. This relay energizes the fuel feed pump, through a separate fuse, and the main fuel pump.

SENSORS

Air Mass Meter

This meter continually measures the amount of air entering the engine intake system. The air mass meter consists of a platinum wire filament located in the intake air stream and a circuit board with a potentiometer for CO adjustment.

The wire filament sends a temperature related signal to the circuit board for processing. Once processed, the air flow signal is sent to the electronic control unit.

When the engine stops, the filament is heated to a high temperature for less than a second. This burns off any dirt that may have collected on the wire which could result in an incorrect air flow reading.

A/C Micro Switch

The switch closes when the air conditioner is engaged. The ECU will then increase idle speed to compensate for greater engine load.

Oxygen Sensor (Lambda-Sond)

The oxygen sensor checks the exhaust gas for the presence of unburned oxygen. Unburned oxygen in the exhaust gas indicates incomplete combustion due to improper mixture, spark timing or other conditions. The oxygen sensor is located in the exhaust manifold.

Throttle Valve Switch

The throtte valve switch consists of double micro-switch. One switch is activated at idle, the other at full load conditions. The switch is located on the side of the throttle housing.

Coolant Temperature Sensor

The coolant temperature sensor is located in the cylinder head. This sensor provides the electronic control unit with an engine temperature signal. If, for example, the sensor was to read high engine temperature with the cooling system operating properly, this would indicate combustion temperature that is too high.

The likely response of the control unit would be to richen the mixture to the point allowed by the oxygen sensor and air mass meter signals. This would lower combustion and engine temperature. This sensor also operates the temperature gauge.

Engine Speed

The engine speed signal is generated by the electronic ignition distributor. The low voltage ignition primary pulses are monitored at the low tension side of the ignition coil. Injection timing is regulated by this signal.

SYSTEM RELAY

The system relay is located on the firewall under the dash, next to the fuel pump relay. This relay provides current to the electronic control unit. It is energized during filament burn off after the ignition has been switched off.

TROUBLE SHOOTING

PRELIMINARY CHECKS

The following systems and components must be in good condition and operating properly before beginning diagnosis of the fuel injection system.

- Battery connections and specific gravity.
- Ignition system.
- Emission control system.
- Air intake system leakage.
- Engine compression pressure.
- Fuel supply system pressure and flow.
- Fuel and vacuum lines.
- Injection system component and sensor electrical connections.
- Air filter.
- Vacuum line, fuel hose and pipe connections.

TROUBLE SHOOTING

Engine Difficult to Start or Will Not Start Cold

If cold engine is difficult to start, or turns over but will not fire, test the following items: Cold start injector, thermal time switch, temperature sensors, air mass meter, pump relay, and system relay.

Engine Difficult to Start or Will Not Start Hot

If hot engine is difficult to start, or cranks but will not fire, test the cylinder injectors for leakage and operation.

Poor Cold Idle

If engine runs poorly only during warm-up, test the following items: Cold start injector, blocked air control hose, cylinder injectors, thermal time switch, and air mass meter.

Poor Hot Idle

If engine runs poorly after warm-up, test the following items: Cold start injector, throttle valve, cylinder injectors, blocked air control hose, air mass meter and air temperature sensor.

CO Level Too High

If the exhaust gas CO level is too high, test the following items: Cold start injector, oxygen sensor, air mass meter, and temperature sensors.

CO Level Too Low at Idle

If the exhaust gas CO level is too low at idle speeds, adjust idle mixture setting.

Poor Engine Performance

If engine operates poorly at all speeds, test the following items: Cold start injector and throttle valve, CO adjustment incorrect, or throttle valve switch.

Excessive Fuel Consumption

If fuel consumption is noticeably high, test the following items: Cold start injector, air mass meter, and temperature sensors.

Engine "Diesels"

If engine continues to run after ignition is shut off, test the following items: Cylinder injectors, cold start injector, air mass meter, and temperature sensors.

Engine Backfires into Manifold

If engine repeatedly backfires into intake manifold, test the air mass meter.

TESTING

CAUTION: The fuel injection system maintains constant fuel pressure in the fuel lines and component parts at all times. Be sure to relieve pressure before attempting to open system at any point. Do not allow fuel to flow onto engine or electrical parts or allow an open flame in area while testing fuel system components.

BOSCH LH JETRONIC II – VOLVO (Cont.)

FUEL LINE PRESSURE

1) Connect a fuel pressure gauge between fuel line and injection manifold. Turn on ignition to activate fuel pump. Fuel pressure should be 35.5 psi (2.5 kg/cm²).

2) If pressure is too low, pinch off fuel return line and check if pressure rises. If pressure quickly rises pump and lines are functioning correctly. Replace pressure regulator and recheck pressure.

CAUTION: Do not let fuel pressure exceed 85.5 psi (6.0 kg/cm²).

3) If pressure rises slowly, fuel filters or lines are blocked. If pressure does not rise, pump is defective.

4) If fuel pressure is high, disconnect fuel return line from pressure regulator and blow in line. If line is open pressure regulator is defective and should be replaced.

5) Pressure may also be checked with engine off and fuel gauge connected. Attach a hand vacuum pump to pressure regulator. Line pressure should decrease as regulator is evacuated.

ELECTRONIC CONTROL UNIT

1) Diagnosis of the fuel injection system is accomplished by removing the connector from the control unit and checking all electric circuits ending at the connector. The tests will indicate the condition of all components and the wires leading to the tested terminal.

2) If there is a problem after all the tests are completed and no malfunction was found, the control unit is most likely at fault. Replace the control unit and recheck system to ensure that problem has been resolved.

3) Always check and repair all circuits before substituting a new control unit. If a new control unit is installed first, a faulty circuit may destroy the new control unit in the same manner as the old one. There is no testing procedure for the control unit other than substitution.

4) To gain access to the control unit and connector, remove kick panel located in front of right front door. Disconnect the wiring harness from the ECU by pressing up on the lock spring on the top end of the connector while pulling outward and down on the top of the connector. Do not pull connector straight out.

Fig. 2: Control Unit Connector Removal

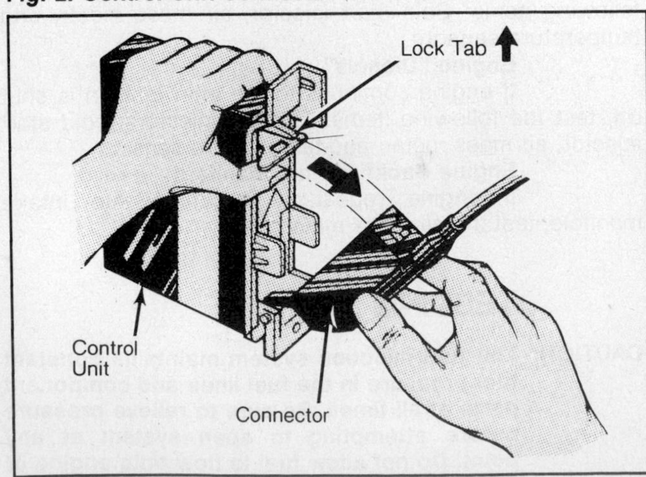
Lock Tab
Control Unit
Connector

Pull outward and down to remove connector.

5) The connector terminals are now accessible, but should not be used for testing on their front side. The front of the connector terminals can easily be damaged by test equipment.

6) To perform tests, cut boot clamp off of end of connector and slide cover off of connector. Always test from inside of connector. Terminal numbers are shown on both sides of the connector.

Fig. 3: Connector Terminal Locations

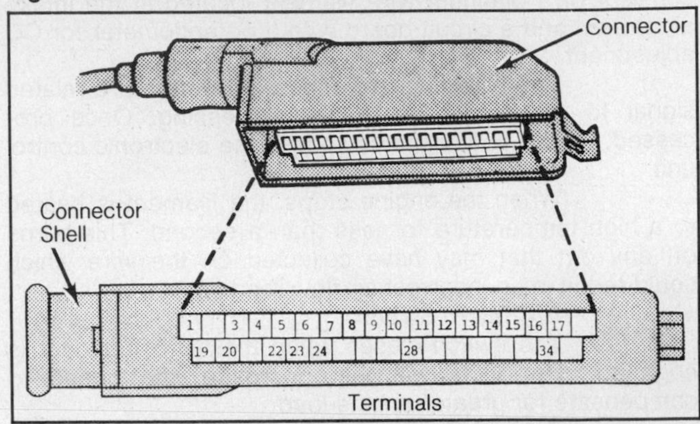
Connector
Connector Shell
1
3
4
5
6
7
8
9
10
11
12
13
14
15
16
17
19
20
22
23
24
28
34
Terminals

Always use back of terminals for test connections.

CAUTION: Do not use test connector located behind the battery. Special test equipment is required to use this connector and damage could result from using improper equipment.

IGNITION SWITCH CIRCUIT

1) Turn on ignition. Connect voltmeter to terminal 1 and ground. Voltmeter should deflect. If not, check Gray wire to ignition coil.

2) Test voltage from terminal 18 to ground. Battery voltage should be indicated. If not, check the wiring all the way back to the ignition switch. Current is supplied through fuse No. 12.

STARTER MOTOR CIRCUIT

Crank the starter motor and measure voltage at terminal 4 to ground. Battery voltage should be indicated. If not, check the wiring all the way back to the ignition switch.

SYSTEM RELAY POWER SUPPLY

Attach a jumper wire between terminal 21 and ground. Measure voltage across terminal 9 and ground. Battery voltage should be indicated. If not, check connector and wiring harness all the way back to the ignition switch. Check system relay and fuse.

FUEL PUMP CIRCUIT

1) Attach a jumper wire from terminal 17 to ground. This will enable the fuel pump relay to energize without running the starter motor. Turn the ignition switch on and listen at rear of vehicle for a buzzing sound that indicates fuel pumps are operating.

2) If pumps do not operate, check fuses 12 and 5. Fuses 12 and 5 are for the fuel pump and the fuel feed pump respectively. Fuel pump relay is protected by a blade type fuse located next to the ignition coil on the left front fender.

BOSCH LH JETRONIC II – VOLVO (Cont.)

GROUND CIRCUITS

Using an Ohmmeter

1) Turn ignition off. Connect negative lead of an ohmmeter to ground. Connect the other lead to terminals 11 and 25 in turn. Ohmmeter should indicate 0 ohms at both points.

2) If any terminal shows a high resistance or infinite resistance, the wire connected to that terminal must be traced and repaired. Wires are grounded at intake manifold.

Using a Test Light

1) Connect 1 lead of test light to the battery positive terminal or any location where full battery voltage is available. Connect the other lead of the test lamp to each ground terminal.

2) The test light should illuminate fully at each terminal. If the test light does not illuminate fully at any terminal, the wire connected to that terminal must be traced and repaired.

INJECTOR CIRCUITS

1) Turn ignition off. Connect an ohmmeter between pump relay terminal 87 and ECU terminal 13. Correct resistance should be approximately 4 ohms.

2) If meter shows approximately 5.3 ohms, either an injector or injector wire is defective. If meter reads approximately 8 ohms, 2 injectors or injector wires are defective. If meter shows 16 ohms, 3 injectors or injector wires are defective.

3) Injectors may be tested separately. Each injector should have a resistance of 16 ohms.

TEMPERATURE SENSOR CIRCUIT

1) Turn ignition off. Connect an ohmmeter between terminal 2 and ground. Resistances for various temperatures will be as follows: 290-364 ohms at 175°F (80°C), 2280-2720 at 70°F (20°C), and 8260-10,560 ohms at 15°F (-10°C).

2) If resistance is considerably higher than specified, an open circuit is indicated. If resistance is at or near 0 ohms a short circuit is indicated.

THROTTLE SWITCH

1) Turn ignition off. Connect an ohmmeter between ground and terminal 3. Depress the accelerator pedal. Meter should show 0 ohms in idle position and infinite resistance in other positions.

2) Connect ohmmeter between ground and terminal 12. Depress accelerator pedal. Meter should read 0 ohms in full throttle position and infinite resistance in other positions.

3) If any readings are incorrect, check throttle valve switch ground at intake manifold. If ground connection is correct, replace throttle valve switch.

A/C MICRO-SWITCH

Turn ignition off. Connect an ohmmeter between ground and terminal 16. Turn knob on air conditioning control panel. Resistance should decrease.

AIR MASS METER CIRCUIT

1) Turn ignition off. Connect an ohmmeter across terminals 6 and 12. Resistance should be between 0 and 1,000 ohms. If resistance does not meet specifications, CO level must be adjusted. *See appropriate Volvo article in TUNE-UP Section.*

2) If resistance is still out of specifications after adjusting CO or if CO cannot be adjusted, the circuit is defective. Turn the CO adjustment screw to the full counterclockwise position.

3) If resistance is not at or near 1000 ohms, a short circuit is indicated. Turn the CO adjustment screw to the full clockwise position. If resistance is not at or near 0 ohms, an open circuit is indicated.

SYSTEM FUNCTION CHECK

The following tests should be performed if components and circuits checked previously are found to be operating properly. If a fault is found, replace the control unit. System function is checked by measuring voltage at injectors under different operating conditions.

NOTE: **Specific meter values are not important. What is important, however, are the changes in meter deflection during different operating conditions.**

System Check

1) Peel back rubber cover from around one of the injectors. Connect the positive lead of a voltmeter to the Yellow/Red wire and the negative lead to the Green/White wire. Set meter to read 0-4 volts.

2) Remove connectors from all injectors so that engine does not start. Remove connector from temperature sensor to simulate cold start.

3) Crank engine and check meter deflection. Deflection should be large when first cranking and then decrease. Connect temperature sensor. Crank engine. Voltmeter should deflect as before but with decreased deflection. Plug in injector connectors.

4) Start engine and observe meter as engine warms up to operating temperature. If enrichment function is working properly, meter deflection should decrease slightly as engine warms up. Turn ignition off.

5) Connect a tachometer to engine. Start engine. Idle speed should be 750 RPM. Turn on air conditioning. Idle speed should increase to 900 RPM. If idle does not increase, check air control valve operation.

6) To check fast idle function, unplug temperature sensor connector while engine is idling. Engine speed should increase to 1600-2500 RPM. Connect temperature sensor, engine speed should return to normal idle.

7) Slowly increase engine speed. Voltmeter deflection should increase with engine speed. If not, check voltage signal from air mass meter.

8) Turn off ignition. Peel back rubber cover from air mass meter connector. Connect voltmeter positive lead to terminal 7 and negative lead to terminal 6. Start engine. Voltage should increase as engine speed increases. Replace and test with new control unit if air mass meter is OK.

9) With voltmeter still connected to injector, check acceleration enrichment. Quickly increase engine speed. Meter deflection should at first be large and then reduce slightly.

10) To check fuel shut-off during engine braking, increase engine speed to 2000 RPM. Quickly release throttle control. Meter deflection should go down to 0 until speed reduces to approximately 1400 RPM. At 1400 RPM, meter should show deflection again.

11) To check full throttle enrichment, unplug connector from throttle valve switch. Engine speed will increase slightly. Increase engine speed to at least 3500

BOSCH LH JETRONIC II – VOLVO (Cont.)

Fig. 4: Bosch LH Jetronic II Fuel Injection System Wiring Diagram

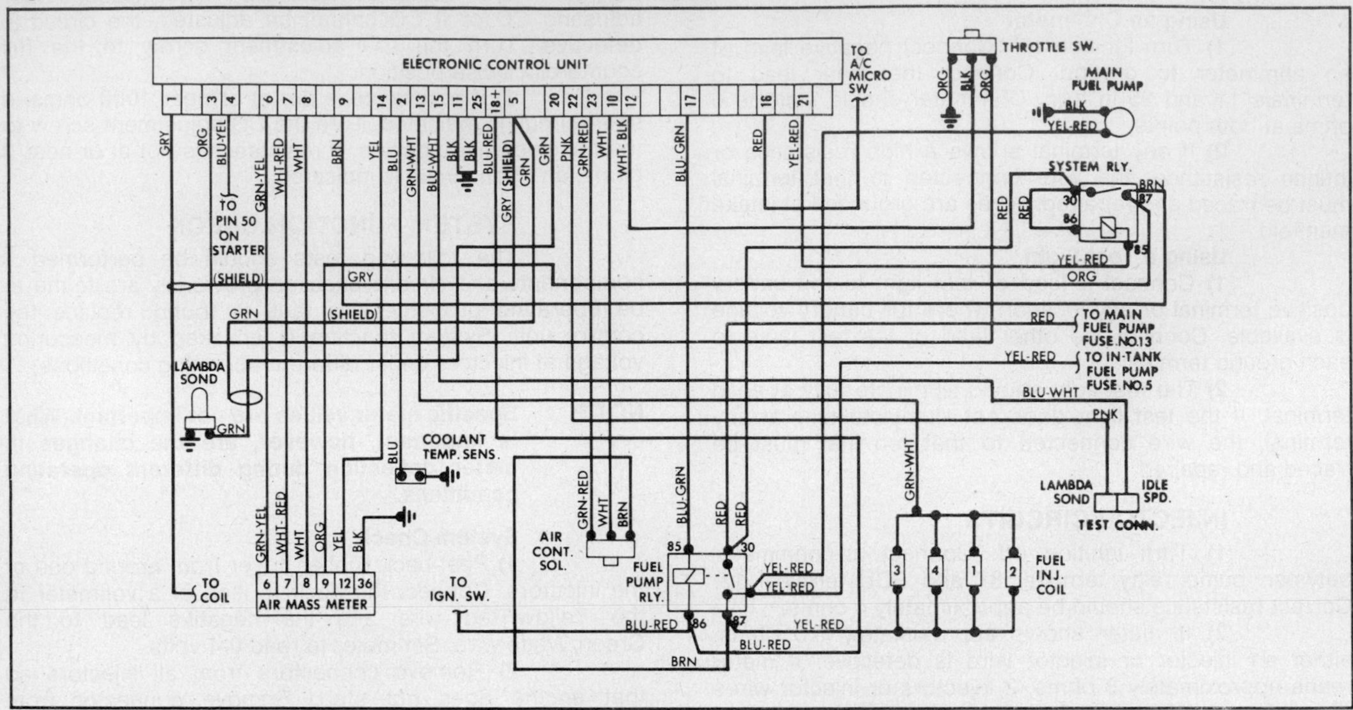
ELECTRONIC CONTROL UNIT
TO A/C MICRO SW.
THROTTLE SW.
MAIN FUEL PUMP
SYSTEM RLY.
TO PIN 50 ON STARTER
(SHIELD)
LAMBDA SOND
COOLANT TEMP. SENS.
TO MAIN FUEL PUMP FUSE NO.13
TO IN-TANK FUEL PUMP FUSE NO.5
LAMBDA SOND
IDLE SPD.
TEST CONN.
AIR CONT. SOL.
FUEL PUMP RLY.
FUEL INJ. COIL
TO COIL
AIR MASS METER
TO IGN. SW.

RPM. Connect a jumper wire between connector terminals 18 and 3. Meter deflection should increase slightly. Reconnect throttle valve switch.

12) Turn off engine. Remove voltmeter from the injector.

13) To check air mass meter measuring wire dirt burn-off, peel back boot from air mass meter connector. Connnect a voltmeter to terminals 8 and 36. Start engine and increase engine speed to over 2000 RPM. Turn off ignition. After approximately 5 seconds voltmeter should show appoximately 1 volt for 1 second.

14) Remove voltmeter. Reposition rubber boots around air mass meter and injector wiring connectors.

ADJUSTMENTS

HOT (SLOW) IDLE RPM

See the appropriate Volvo article in the TUNE-UP Section.

IDLE MIXTURE

See the appropriate Volvo article in the TUNE-UP Section.

THROTTLE VALVE

1) Loosen throttle valve switch. Turn switch clockwise. Remove link rod from throttle control pulley. Loosen throttle adjustment screw lock nut. Loosen adjustment screw until throttle valve completely closes.

2) Tighten adjustment screw until it just touches throttle valve lever. Tighten screw an additional 1/4 turn and tighten lock nut. Check throttle valve for free movement. Adjust throttle valve switch and link rod.

THROTTLE VALVE SWITCH

Loosen throttle valve switch. Turn switch counter-clockwise to stop, but not so far that throttle valve begins to move. Tighten screws. A click should be heard immediately when throttle valve moves.

THROTTLE LINK ROD

Position a .039" (1 mm) feeler gauge between throttle control pulley and idle stop. Adjust link rod so clearance between throttle valve lever and adjustment screw is .004" (.1 mm).

ISUZU I-TEC EFI SYSTEM

Impulse

DESCRIPTION

The I-TEC System is a computerized emission, ignition, and fuel control system. The I-TEC system controls engine operation and lowers exhaust emissions while maintaining good fuel economy and driveability. The Control Unit is the "brain" of the system.

The control unit monitors information from various sensors and constantly adjusts spark timing and fuel delivery. The fuel system functions governed by the control unit are fuel injection volumn and air/fuel ratio control.

The control unit governs fuel injection operation by reading data from the following sources: O_2 sensor, crank angle sensor, vehicle speed sensor, water temperature sensor, air flow sensor, and throttle valve switch.

The fuel delivery system consists of the fuel tank, fuel pump, pressure regulator, and fuel injectors. The injectors are aimed at the intake valve of each cylinder.

NOTE: **Primary sub-systems which affect fuel system operation will be covered in this article. These include the fuel supply system, fuel injectors, fuel pressure regulator, data sensors and fuel cut system. Refer to the ISUZU I-TEC CONTROL SYSTEM article in COMPUTERIZED ENGINE CONTROLS Section for more information.**

OPERATION

CONTROL UNIT

See ISUZU I-TEC CONTROL SYSTEM article in COMPUTERIZED ENGINE CONTROLS Section.

DATA SENSORS

Air Flow Sensor

The air flow sensor directly measures the amount of intake air for use by the control unit. It is located on the air cleaner housing.

Air Regulator

The air regulator operates as an air by-pass during cold, fast idle conditions. When the engine is cold, the air regulator allows an additional flow of air to enter the intake manifold.

A temperature sensive electric element closes the regulator as engine temperature increases. The air regulator is independent of the I-TEC system and is operated by the key switch through the fuel pump relay.

Vehicle Speed Sensor

The car speed sensor detects vehicle speed for the control unit. It is designed as an integeral part of the speedometer assembly.

Crank Angle Sensor

The crank angle is located on the distributor shaft below the distributor housing. It detects the engine speed and position of each piston in each cylinder.

Oxygen Sensor

The O_2 sensor monitors the density of oxygen in the exhaust gases. It is located in the exhaust manifold.

Throttle Valve Switch

An electrical switch which detects the throttle valve position at idle, intermediate and full throttle.

Water Temperature Sensor

Detects the intake manifold coolant temperature for the control unit. It is located under the intake manifold.

FUEL DELIVERY

Dropping Resistors

Dropping resistors reduce the current flow to the fuel injectors. They are in-line in the fuel injector wiring.

Fuel Injectors

Fuel is metered into the cylinders by electrically controlled solenoid valves in the injectors. Injectors are energized by the control unit.

Fuel Pressure Regulator

The pressure regulator governs the flow of fuel to the injectors. The pressure varies depending on different vehicle speed and load conditions.

Fuel Pump

The fuel pump is an electric type located in the rear of the vehicle. The pump is an integral design and must be replaced as an assembly.

FUEL CUT SYSTEM

This system shuts the flow of fuel off during vehicle deceleration to reduce exhaust emissions. Throttle valve switch position controls its operation.

The fuel cut system is activated during deceleration when vehicle speed is more than 20 mph, engine speed is more than 1850 RPM and the throttle valve is closed.

Reinjection occurs when vehicle speed is lower than 6 mph and engine RPM is lower than 1250 RPM.

VACUUM SWITCHING VALVE

Controlled by a signal from the control unit, the Vacuum Switching Valve (VSV) regulates fuel pressure. The fuel pressure varies slightly according to intake manifold vacuum.

TESTING

CAUTION: **I-TEC components and connectors are very sensitive to shock, distortion and water. Turn ignition switch to "OFF" before unplugging any electrical connectors. When testing any circuit, ALL connectors must be unplugged from Control Unit. I-TEC cables must be placed at least 4" (100 mm) away from high tension cables.**

POWER SUPPLY

1) The primary sources of current for the I-TEC system are the main relay and the No. 4 (5 amp) fuse. The No. 4 fuse is not key controlled and supplies continuous current to the control unit.

2) The main relay is activated by the key switch and is located in the relay box in the engine compartment. The fuel pump relay is also located in the

ISUZU I-TEC EFI SYSTEM (Cont.)

same box. The main ground circuits for the control unit are at terminals 31 and 32.

Fuel Injection Wiring

1) Turn ignition off and unplug harness from control unit. Turn ignition on and check if 12V is present at terminals 21 and 22 of the harness. These two wires are attached directly to the injectors. The control unit governs the injector ground circuit.

2) If battery voltage is not present, unplug the harness at the injectors and check for 12V. If voltage is not present, check the dropping resistor, main relay, and starter switch.

FUEL CUT SYSTEM

1) Warm engine to operating temperature. Turn ignition switch off. Unplug throttle valve switch harness at switch connector. Insert a fine wire into idle (I) terminal and reconnect harness with wire pulled part way out. *See Fig. 3.*

2) Start engine and run at 2500-3000 RPM. Ensure engine speed lowers to about 1250 when battery voltage is applied to the wire extending from the idle terminal. Erratic engine operation at about 1250 RPM is normal.

3) When system does not respond as noted, check the following: throttle valve switch setting and wiring. If these parts are functioning correctly, replace the control unit.

FUEL PRESSURE

CAUTION: The fuel line is under pressure. When installing an in-line fuel pressure gauge, caution must be used when disconnecting fuel lines.

1) Install fuel pressure gauge between the pressure regulator and fuel distributor pipe. Unplug the vacuum switching valve at the connector. Start engine and measure fuel pressures. *See Fuel Pressure Table.*

FUEL PRESSURE TABLE

Condition	psi (kg/cm²)
Pressure regulator vacuum hose disconnected and plugged	35.6 (2.5)
Pressure regulator vacuum hose connected (engine at 900 RPM)	28.4 (2.0)
Engine stopped and vacuum hose disconnected	28.4 (2.0)
All hoses connected and 12V applied to vacuum switching valve at 900 RPM	35.6 (2.5)

2) If fuel pressure remains unchanged during the checks, check the vacuum switching valve and restrictions in fuel hoses on the intake side of the fuel pump. The vacuum switching valve should show a resistance of about 35 ohms.

Low Fuel Pressure

Apply battery voltage directly to fuel pump. If pressure reaches normal, check the pump circuit and relay.

Loss of Pressure Immediately After Pump Stops

Check the fuel pump, pressure regulator and injectors for internal leaks and replace as necessary.

High Fuel Pressure

Check for resistrictions in the fuel circuit. High pressure may also be caused by a defective pump or pressure regulator.

COMPONENT TESTING

Air Flow Sensor & Harness

1) Partly raise the sealing gasket on the air flow sensor side of the harness connector. Using a voltmeter, check the sensor. *See Air Flow Sensor Table.*

AIR FLOW SENSOR TABLE

Wiring	Condition	Voltage
Red	Ignition On	10-14
Green	Ignition On	.2-.6
Green	Engine Running	1.0-2.0
Black	Ignition On	0

2) Check the air flow by-pass circuit for contamination and clean with carburetor cleaner as necessary. DO NOT immerse switch in carburetor cleaner.

Fig. 1: Checking Air Flow Sensor By-Pass Circuit

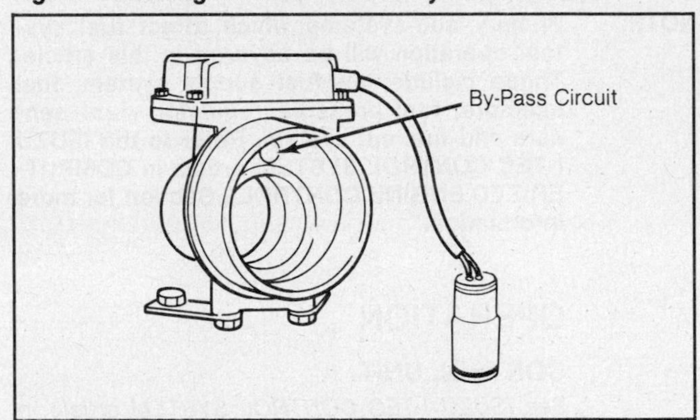
By-Pass Circuit

3) Before checking air flow wiring harness, turn ignition off and disconnect harness from sensor and control unit. Test harness with an ohmmeter.

4) All three wires must show no resistance between sensor and control unit. Also, ensure harness is not grounded.

Air Regulator

1) Warm engine to operating temperature. Disconnect throttle valve body-to-air regulator at the throttle body. Plug the hole in throttle body.

2) Start the engine. Check for variation in engine speed by closing and opening the end of the air regulator hose. The engine speed should vary less than 50 RPM. If variation is more than specified, replace the air regulator.

3) To check air regulator resistance, unplug harness at connector. The standard resistance is 38-42 ohms.

Vehicle Speed Sensor

1) Connect a circuit tester between the control unit harness connector terminal No. 5 and ground. Disconnect the speedometer cable at transmission side and turn the inner cable slowly.

2) If the tester indicates a continuity and open circuit alternately as the cable is turned, the speed sensor and circuit are operating normally.

3) To test the speed sensor, remove the meter assembly from the dash. Connect a circuit tester across

ISUZU I-TEC EFI SYSTEM (Cont.)

the terminals of the connector at the rear face of the meter assembly. *See Fig. 2.*

Fig. 2: Testing Vehicle Speed Sensor

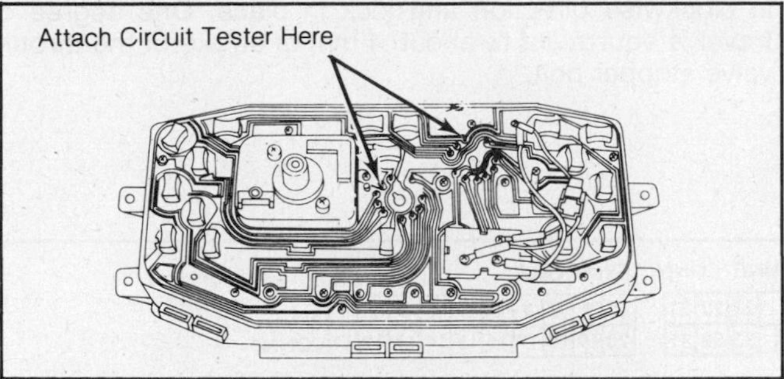
Attach Circuit Tester Here

Tester should show an alternate open/close circuit.

4) Turn the inner shaft slowly and check that the tester indicates continuity and open circuit alternately. If inoperative, speedometer must be replaced as an assembly.

Crank Angle Sensor

1) The crank angle sensor can not be tested directly. The control unit signal and wiring harness is tested. If no problems are found in the circuit, the distributor assembly must be replaced.

2) Unplug the crank angle sensor harness at the connector and control unit. There must be no resistance measured between the sensor and control unit on the White and Green wires.

3) The Black wire is the ground wire for the circuit. With key switch on, the Red wire carries battery voltage. If problem is still evident after circuit check, replace distributor assembly.

Dropping Resistors

1) Unplug the dropping resistor wiring at the connector. Measure the resistance across the center terminal of the dropping resistor side connector and other terminals.

2) The standard resistance for all terminals should be 5-7 ohms. If any of the measurements deviates from the standard value, the resistor assembly must be replaced.

Fuel Injectors

1) Unplug the fuel injector harness at the injector and measure the resistance across the terminals. All injectors must have 2-3 ohms of resistance. If not, replace injector.

2) With engine running, check fuel injector operating noise with a stethoscope. Normal operation of injectors is indicated when a regular click is heard which varies with engine speed.

3) Remove the common chamber assembly. Remove all the injectors with the fuel hoses connected. Check for fuel leakage by operating the fuel pump with battery voltage applied directly to the pump relay terminal (Black/Red wire).

4) The leakage must be less than 2 drops per minute. If leakage exceeds the limit, replace the injector.

O_2 Sensor

1) The O_2 sensor can not be tested directly but its control signal can be checked. A circuit tester having an internal resistance of approximately 20,000 ohms is necessary to test the circuit.

2) Unplug the O_2 sensor harness at connector. Insert a fine wire into the vehicle side connector and attach circuit tester. Set tester scale to 2V.

3) Start engine and check voltage when engine speed is momentarily increased. Tester needle should deflect from 0 to 8V.

Throttle Valve Switch

1) Check the operation of the accelerator and control cables for smoothness. Valve stopper must make firm contact with the throttle valve stopper screw when throttle valve is released.

2) Unplug throttle valve switch harness at connector. Make a continuity test across the terminals with the accelerator pedal depressed in steps. *See Throttle Valve Switch Table.*

THROTTLE VALVE SWITCH TABLE

Pedal Position	Terminals	Resistance (Ohms)
Idle	I & P	0
1/2 Throttle	I & P, P & F	Open Circuit
Full Throttle	P & F	0

Fig. 3: Testing Throttle Valve Switch

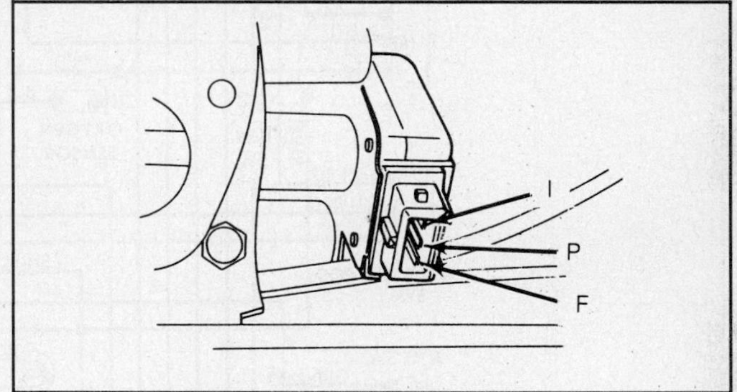
I
P
F

Check continuity between terminals.

Water Temperature Sensor

The water temperature sensor is tested by measuring the resistance across the sensor terminals. Resistance will vary with engine coolant temperature. *See Water Temperature Sensor Resistance Table.*

WATER TEMPERATURE SENSOR RESISTANCE TABLE

Coolant Temperature °F (°C)	Ohms
50 (10)	3000-5000
68 (20)	2000-3000
122 (50)	700-1000
176 (80)	200-400

REMOVAL & INSTALLATION

FUEL PUMP

Removal & Installation

Remove rear seat assembly. Unplug electrical harness at terminal located under right side part of rear seat. Disconnect hoses from fuel pump. Remove the pump guard. Remove pump from bracket. Install in reverse order of removal.

ISUZU I-TEC EFI SYSTEM (Cont.)

ADJUSTMENTS

IDLE SPEED

See appropriate article in TUNE-UP Section.

THROTTLE VALVE SWITCH

1) Throttle valve must be completely closed. Loosen throttle valve switch mounting screws slightly. Unplug connector harness at throttle valve.

2) While checking continuity between center (P) terminal and top (I) terminal, turn the switch in a clockwise direction until continuity is obtained.

3) When tester shows continuity, turn switch 1° in clockwise direction and lock in place. One degree of travel is equivalent to about .4 mm of stroke of the throttle valve stopper bolt.

Fig. 4: Isuzu I-TEC Fuel Injection Wiring Diagram

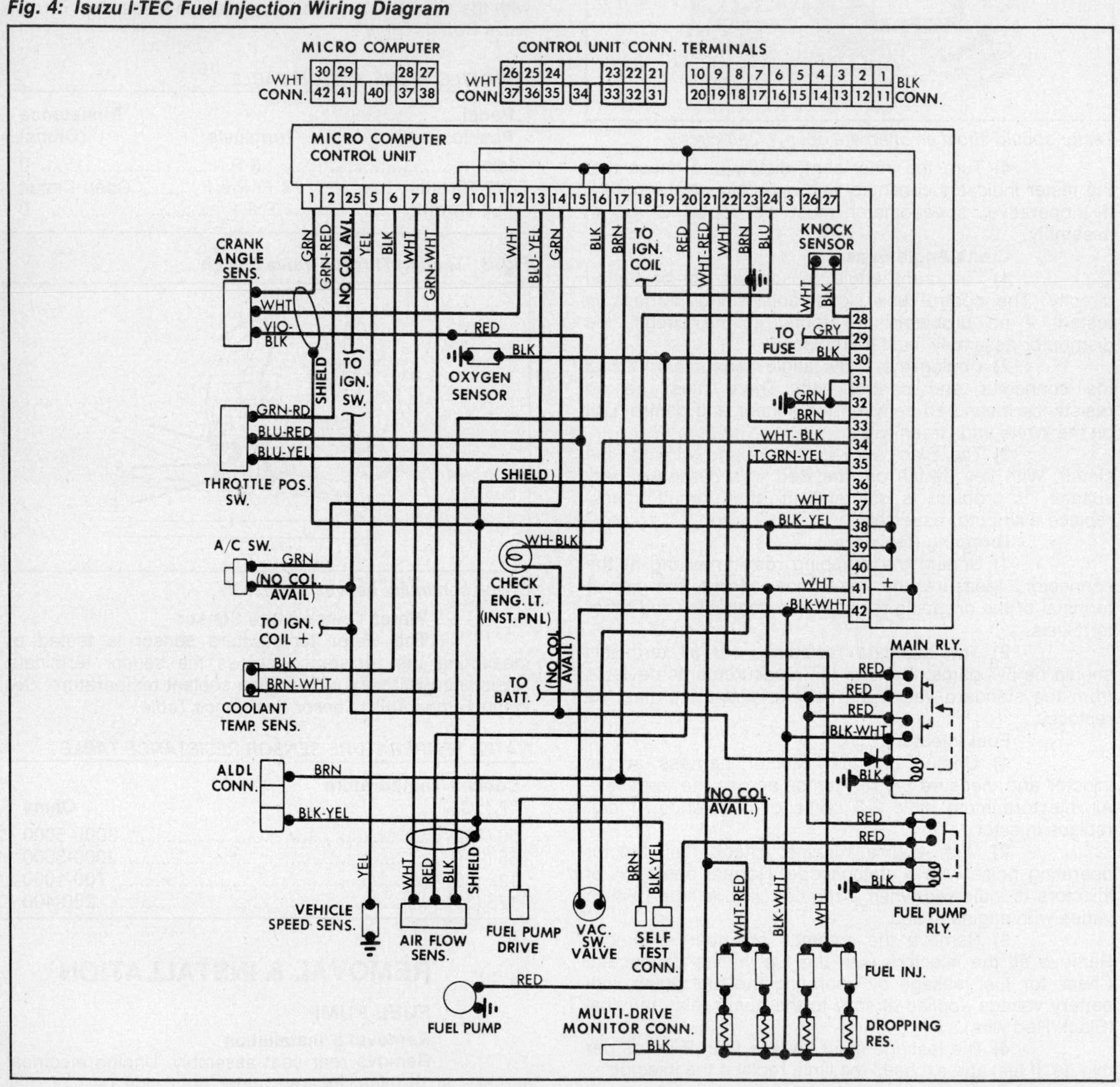
MICRO COMPUTER
CONTROL UNIT CONN. TERMINALS
WHT CONN.
WHT CONN
BLK CONN.
MICRO COMPUTER CONTROL UNIT
CRANK ANGLE SENS.
SHIELD
TO IGN. SW.
OXYGEN SENSOR
THROTTLE POS. SW.
(SHIELD)
A/C SW.
(NO COL. AVAIL)
TO IGN. COIL +
CHECK ENG. LT. (INST. PNL)
TO BATT.
COOLANT TEMP. SENS.
ALDL CONN.
KNOCK SENSOR
TO IGN. COIL
TO FUSE
MAIN RLY.
FUEL PUMP RLY.
VEHICLE SPEED SENS.
AIR FLOW SENS.
FUEL PUMP DRIVE
VAC. SW. VALVE
SELF TEST CONN.
FUEL INJ.
DROPPING RES.
FUEL PUMP
MULTI-DRIVE MONITOR CONN.

1983 Bosch Fuel Injection

LUCAS-BOSCH AFC FUEL INJECTION SYSTEM

Jaguar XJ6

DESCRIPTION

The Lucas-Bosch Air Flow Controlled (AFC) fuel injection system is an electronically controlled system operated by incoming air flow. The AFC fuel injection system also contains a feedback system which measures oxygen content of exhaust gases and maintains the air/fuel ratio at about 14.7:1.

The system consists of an electric fuel pump, fuel pressure regulator, fuel injectors, Electronic Control Unit (ECU), air flow meter, air temperature sensor, throttle switch, coolant temperature sensor, oxygen sensor, 3-way catalytic converter, and electrical relays. In addition, all models are equipped with a cold start system to aid in cold engine starts. The cold start system consists of an auxiliary air valve, cold start injector, and thermo time switch.

Air conditioned vehicles are equipped with a fuel cooler. Fuel return lines are routed through a cooler which is part of the air conditioning refrigerant system.

Fig. 1: Jaguar AFC Fuel Injection System

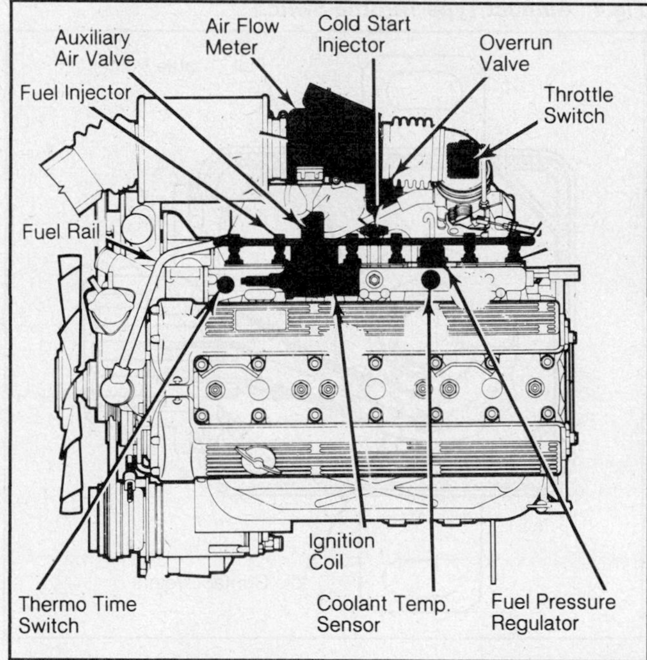
Auxiliary Air Valve
Air Flow Meter
Cold Start Injector
Overrun Valve
Fuel Injector
Throttle Switch
Fuel Rail
Ignition Coil
Thermo Time Switch
Coolant Temp. Sensor
Fuel Pressure Regulator

OPERATION

ELECTRICAL RELAYS

The main relay, diode unit, and fuel pump relay are located on the firewall next to the battery. When ignition is turned on, the main relay is activate. This connects the battery circuit to the ballast resistors and injectors. The main relay also allows current to flow to the control unit and the fuel pump switch on the air flow meter.

Relays are located in engine compartment, near battery. When engine is cranked for starting, the diode unit is activated. This energizes the auxiliary air valve, cold start system, and fuel pump.

ELECTRIC FUEL PUMP

The electric fuel pump provides fuel under pressure to the fuel pressure regulator. Power for operation during cranking mode is provided from starter relay via the diode unit. After the engine has started, control of the fuel pump is by a fuel pump circuit in the air flow meter.

The first movement of air flow meter air measuring flap (about 5°) closes the fuel pump contacts and provides power to fuel pump after engine has started. With engine stopped, no air flow is present, measuring flap closes and fuel pump contacts are opened to cut power to fuel pump. This method of circuitry reduces the risk of fire in a collision. The fuel pump is a sealed unit; no service required.

FUEL PRESSURE REGULATOR

The pressure regulator consists of a sealed, spring loaded diaphragm with a connection for intake manifold vacuum. Fuel is provided to fuel injectors under 36 psi (2.5 kg/cm²) pressure.

A connection for intake manifold vacuum provides a constant pressure differential which ensures that the amount of fuel injected is solely dependent upon injector "OPEN" time. Fuel in excess of fuel pressure or pressure differential is returned to fuel tank. No service of pressure regulator is required.

FUEL INJECTORS

A fuel rail links the fuel pressure regulator with the fuel injectors. Each cylinder is provided with a solenoid-operated injector which sprays fuel toward back of each intake valve. Each injector is energized through the ignition coil and grounded through the ECU to complete the circuit.

Each injector is linked to a resistor to reduce operating voltage to 3 volts and to protect injectors from power surges. Resistors are located in a single unit mounted on right side of firewall.

The ECU controls the length of time each injector is open. The "OPEN" time of the injector governs the amount of fuel delivered. The injectors deliver 1/2 the amount of fuel required each crankshaft revolution.

Fig. 2: Electronic Control Unit (ECU)

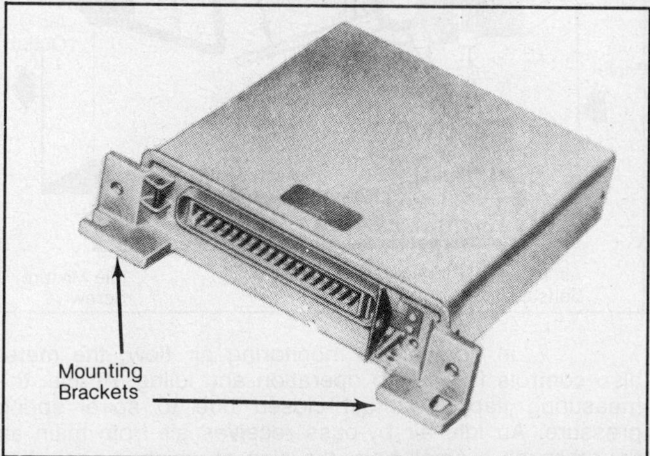
Mounting Brackets

Unit located at front of luggage compartment.

LUCAS-BOSCH AFC FUEL INJECTION SYSTEM (Cont.)

ELECTRONIC CONTROL UNIT (ECU)

All components of the control system are electrically connected to the ECU. *See Fig. 2.* The ECU is a pre-programmed computer which receives and interprets data from various sensors to calculate the amount of fuel required by the engine to maintain efficiency with minimum exhaust emissions.

Impulses from the oxygen sensor informs the ECU of oxygen content of exhaust gases and the ECU constantly adjusts the air/fuel ratio by controlling the injector "OPEN" time.

The ECU provides fuel enrichment whenever engine is cranked, regardless of engine temperature. This is activated by a direct electrical connection from the starter circuit to the ECU. The ECU is a sealed unit; no service is required. It is located in the trunk against the front bulkhead.

AIR FLOW METER

All engine air is drawn through the air flow meter. The meter is basically a tunnel with similarly shaped measuring flap and dampening flap (offset 90° on same casting).

The measuring flap swings on an axis in air stream against reverse pressure of a spiral spring and is connected to a potentiometer. The potentiometer transmits an electrical signal proportionate to the angular displacement of the measuring flap to inform the ECU of engine load. *See Fig. 3.*

Fig. 3: Lucas-Bosch AFC Air Flow Meter

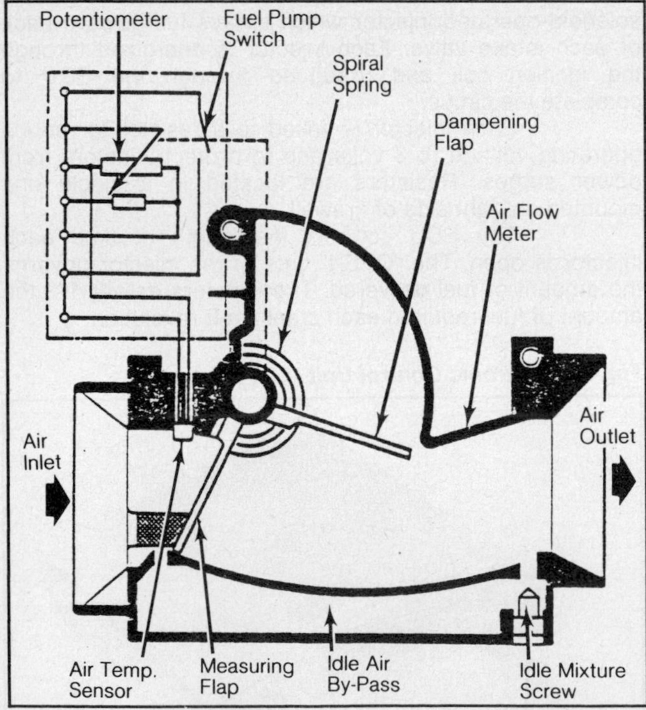
Potentiometer
Fuel Pump Switch
Spiral Spring
Dampening Flap
Air Flow Meter
Air Inlet
Air Outlet
Air Temp. Sensor
Measuring Flap
Idle Air By-Pass
Idle Mixture Screw

In addition to monitoring air flow, the meter also controls fuel pump operation and idling. At idle, the measuring flap is almost closed due to spiral spring pressure. An idle air by-pass receives air from main air flow through a small hole, the size of which is controlled by the idle mixture screw. This adjustable air by-pass influences CO levels at low engine speeds.

AIR TEMPERATURE SENSOR

The air temperature sensor is an integral component of the air flow meter which converts the temperature of incoming air into electrical signals. These electrical signals are received by the ECU and processed to adjust the amount of fuel injected by the injectors. The air temperature sensor is a non-serviceable device.

THROTTLE SWITCH

A contact type throttle switch is installed on throttle chamber. The throttle switch sends information on throttle position to ECU. On the contact switch, signals are sent when throttle is at idle or full throttle positions. *See Fig. 4.*

COOLANT TEMPERATURE SENSOR

This sensor provides ECU with temperature information relating to warm-up enrichment operation. During warm-up period after a cold engine start, additional fuel is required to maintain engine performance. As coolant temperature increases, the ECU decreases fuel enrichment until engine reaches normal operating temperature.

Fig.4: Contact Type Throttle Switch

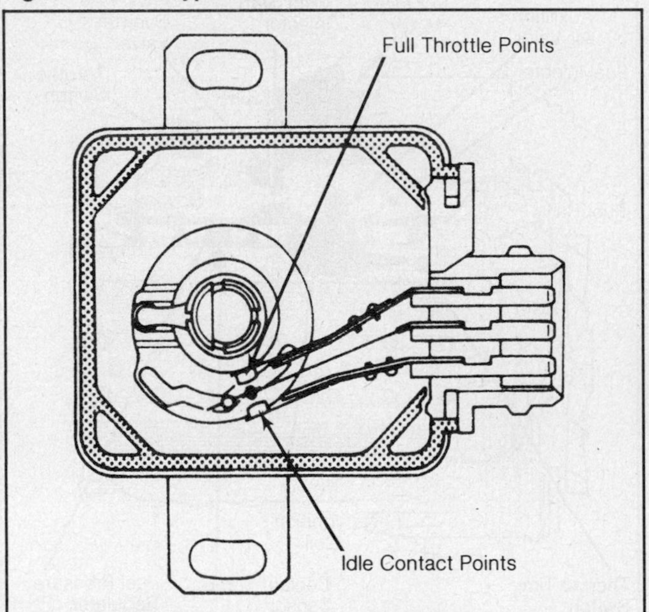
Full Throttle Points
Idle Contact Points

COLD START SYSTEM

The cold start system provides additional air and fuel during cold engine starts. The cold start system consists of an auxiliary air valve which provides additional air, cold start injector which delivers additional fuel, and a thermo time switch which controls operation of the cold start system.

The thermo time switch has a bi-metallic contact surrounded by a heating coil which is energized during engine cranking. This switch limits cold start system to 8 seconds under extreme cold engine starts in relation to engine coolant temperature. When coolant temperature is above 95°F (35°C), bi-metallic contact breaks ground circuit of cold start injector and cold start enrichment is by-passed.

LUCAS-BOSCH AFC FUEL INJECTION SYSTEM (Cont.)

Fig. 5: Auxiliary Air Valve

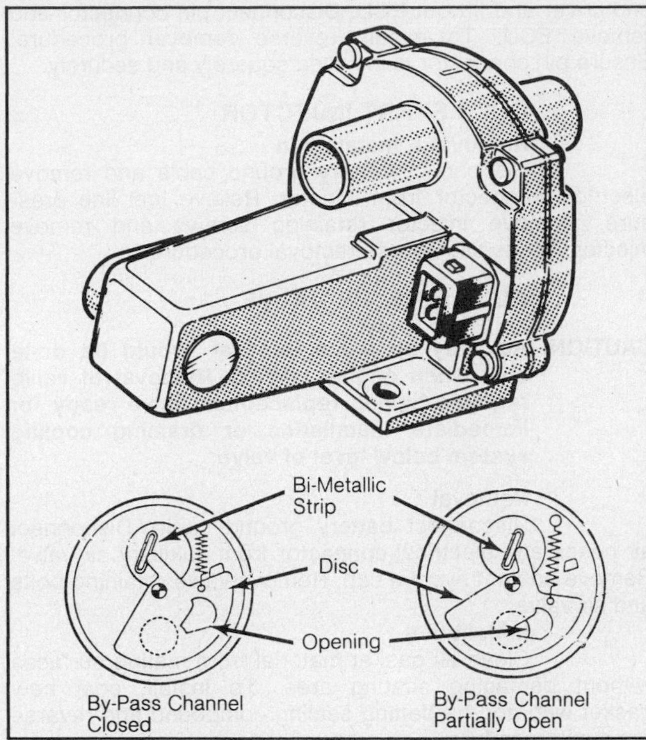
Bi-Metallic
Strip
Disc
Opening
By-Pass Channel
Closed
By-Pass Channel
Partially Open

The auxiliary air valve provides additional air during cold engine starts and warm-up period. The valve consists of an electrically heated bi-metallic strip, movable disc and air by-pass channel.

The heater coil on the bi-metallic strip is energized by the fuel pump relay. Control of the valve is based upon engine temperature. The air by-pass channel is open when engine is cold and gradually closes as temperature rises. At predetermined temperatures, air by-pass channel is blocked and additional air flow stops. *See Fig. 5.*

TESTING

NOTE: **The fuel injection system maintains constant fuel pressure in fuel lines and components. Be sure to relieve pressure before attempting to open system. Do not allow fuel to flow onto engine or electrical parts, or allow an open flame in area while testing fuel system or components.**

ELECTRONIC CONTROL UNIT (ECU)

Do not attempt to test ECU, permanent damage could result. It is possible to check plug wires for continuity. The ECU should only be judged faulty after compression is checked, ignition system has been tested and found problem-free, and all other fuel injection components have been thoroughly tested (including wiring).

FUEL PRESSURE

1) Depressurize fuel system by removing fuel pump relay and cranking engine for a few seconds. Turn ignition switch off and connect fuel pump relay.

2) Disconnect fuel rail at cold start injector and connect fuel pressure gauge. Disconnect negative lead from ignition coil and turn ignition switch on. Pressure reading should be 35.5-37 psi (2.5-2.6 kg/cm²).

3) Slow pressure drop is permissible; sudden pressure drop requires check of entire fuel system for leaks. After testing fuel pressure, depressurize fuel system, remove test equipment and reconnect fuel lines and ignition coil negative lead.

4) Operate fuel change-over switch on dash and recheck reading. Reading from both fuel tanks should agree. On all models, if pressure reading is not to specifications, replace fuel pressure regulator.

AIR TEMPERATURE SENSOR

Disconnect negative battery cable and air flow meter connector. Connect ohmmeter leads to terminals 6 and 27 on potentiometer connector. If readings are not as specified, replace air flow meter. *See Temperature/Resistance Relationship* chart.

TEMPERATURE/RESISTANCE RELATIONSHIP

Temperature °F (°C)	Ohms
32 (0)	5000
68 (20)	2500
104 (40)	1180
140 (60)	600

AUXILIARY AIR VALVE

1) Remove auxiliary air valve connector and connect an ohmmeter to both terminals. Resistance should read approximately 33 ohms. If not, continue testing as follows:

2) Remove auxiliary air valve from inlet manifold and immerse mounting plate in cold water, avoiding contact of terminals and by-pass channel with water.

3) The movable plate should fully expose by-pass channel. Gradually heat water. As temperature increases, channel should become blocked. If valve does not respond as outlined, replace auxiliary air valve.

THERMO TIME SWITCH

1) Using a thermometer, check engine coolant temperature. Compare coolant temperature with value stamped on thermo time switch body. Connect an ohmmeter between terminal "W" on switch and ground.

2) If coolant temperature is higher than switch value, a very high resistance denoting an open circuit should be obtained.

3) If coolant temperature is lower than switch value, a very low resistance denoting a closed circuit should be obtained. If switch does not respond as outlined, replace thermo time switch.

4) If switch passes resistance test, allow coolant temperature to cool below stamped value on switch. With ohmmeter connected, connect battery power via an isolating switch to terminal "G".

5) Using a stop watch, check delay time as ohmmeter changes between high and low resistance. Delay period should be as specified. *See Coolant/Delay Time Relationship* chart. If not, replace thermo time switch.

1983 Bosch Fuel Injection

LUCAS-BOSCH AFC FUEL INJECTION SYSTEM (Cont.)

COOLANT/DELAY TIME RELATIONSHIP

Temperature °F (°C)	Delay (Seconds)
32 (0)	4.5
50 (10)	3.5
95 (35)	0

COLD START INJECTOR

1) Engine must be cold to perform this test. Remove electrical connector from cold start injector and connect voltmeter across connector terminals. Crank engine. Battery voltage should be present.

2) Release fuel system pressure and remove cold start injector with fuel lines attached. Reconnect electrical connector and place injector in container.

3) As cold engine is cranked, fuel spray should be observed until thermo time switch cuts off relay. When engine is warm, no fuel spray should occur during cranking. If injector does not respond as outlined, replace cold start injector.

COOLANT TEMPERATURE SENSOR

1) Disconnect battery ground cable and electrical connector from sensor. Connect an ohmmeter between sensor terminals. Reading should be as specified. See *Temperature/Resistance Relationship* chart.

2) Disconnect ohmmeter and check resistance between each terminal and sensor body. A very high resistance denoting an open circuit should be obtained. If sensor does not respond as outlined, replace coolant temperature sensor.

TEMPERATURE/RESISTANCE RELATIONSHIP

Temperature °F (°C)	Ohms
32 (0)	5900
68 (20)	2500
104 (40)	1180
140 (60)	600
176 (80)	325

THROTTLE SWITCH

Disconnect battery ground cable and throttle switch electrical connector. Connect a powered test lamp between terminals 3 and 18 of throttle switch. Open throttle. Test lamp should glow when throttle nears wide open position. If not, replace throttle switch.

REMOVAL & INSTALLATION

AIR FLOW METER

Removal & Installation

Disconnect battery ground cable. Disconnect rubber hose from both sides of air flow meter. Remove bolts securing meter to bracket. Move air flow meter upward, unplug electrical connector and remove air flow meter. To install, reverse removal procedure.

ELECTRONIC CONTROL UNIT (ECU)

Removal & Installation

Disconnect battery ground cable. ECU is located at forward end of luggage compartment. Remove ECU cover, retaining band and cable clamp clip. Unclip end cover and lift out ECU. Disconnect pin connector and remove ECU. To install, reverse removal procedure. Ensure pin connector is installed squarely and securely.

COLD START INJECTOR

Removal & Installation

Disconnect battery ground cable and remove electrical connector from injector. Relieve fuel line pressure. Remove injector retaining screws and remove injector. To install, reverse removal procedure.

AUXILIARY AIR VALVE

CAUTION: **Auxiliary air valve removal should be done only when engine is cold. Removal of valve requires having replacement valve ready for immediate installation or draining cooling system below level of valve.**

Removal

Disconnect battery ground cable. Disconnect air hoses and electrical connector from auxiliary air valve. Remove coolant system cap. Remove valve retaining bolts and air valve.

Installation

Clean all gasket material from mating surfaces without damaging seating area. To install, coat new gasket with non-hardening sealing compound and reverse removal procedure.

COOLANT TEMPERATURE SENSOR

CAUTION: **Coolant temperature sensor removal should be done only when engine is cold. Removal of sensor requires having replacement sensor ready for immediate installation or draining cooling system below level of sensor.**

Removal & Installation

Disconnect battery ground cable. Drain coolant and unplug sensor electrical connector. Loosen and remove sensor. To install, reverse removal procedure. Use sealing compound on sensor threads. Replace sealing washers, if equipped.

THERMO TIME SWITCH

CAUTION: **Thermo time switch removal should be done only when engine is cold. Removal of switch requires having replacement switch ready for immediate installation or draining cooling system below level of switch.**

Removal & Installation

Disconnect battery ground cable. Drain coolant and disconnect switch electrical connector. Loosen and remove switch. To install, reverse removal procedure. Use sealing compound on switch threads. Replace sealing washers, if equipped.

FUEL PRESSURE REGULATOR

CAUTION: **Fuel system pressure must be relieved before removing fuel pressure regulator.**

Removal & Installation

Disconnect battery ground cable. Disconnect fuel lines and vacuum line at regulator. Remove pressure

LUCAS-BOSCH AFC FUEL INJECTION SYSTEM (Cont.)

regulator (separating from bracket, if installed). To install, reverse removal procedure.

FUEL INJECTORS

CAUTION: Fuel system pressure must be relieved before removing fuel injectors.

Removal

1) Disconnect battery ground cable. Unplug electrical connectors at injectors. Remove screws attaching fuel rail to intake manifold. Release clips holding fuel supply and return rails.

2) Remove manifold pressure pipe. Remove nuts and washers from injector clamps. Lift off fuel rail with injectors, loosen injector clamps and remove injectors from fuel rail. Remove and discard "O" rings if equipped.

Installation

To install, reverse removal procedure. Ensure electrical connectors are properly installed on injectors before installing fuel rail assembly to manifold. New "O" rings should be installed on injectors, if equipped.

ADJUSTMENTS

HOT (SLOW) IDLE RPM

See the appropriate Jaguar article in the TUNE-UP Section.

IDLE MIXTURE

See the appropriate Jaguar article in the TUNE-UP Section.

THROTTLE VALVE

1) Remove air intake hose and elbow to expose throttle valve. Loosen throttle valve lock nut on stop screw and loosen stop screw. Ensure throttle valve closes fully.

2) Insert a .002" (.05 mm) feeler gauge between throttle valve and throttle housing bore. *See Fig. 6.* With feeler gauge in position, adjust stop screw so it just touches stop arm. Tighten lock nut. Press stop arm against stop screw and remove feeler gauge.

3) Seal threads of adjusting screws and lock nuts with paint spots. Install hose and elbow. Check operation of throttle linkage and adjust if required by ensuring outer cable is secured in bracket so inner cable is under light tension, but not enough to move operating lever. Tighten lock nuts.

Fig. 6: Adjusting Jaguar Throttle Valve Clearance

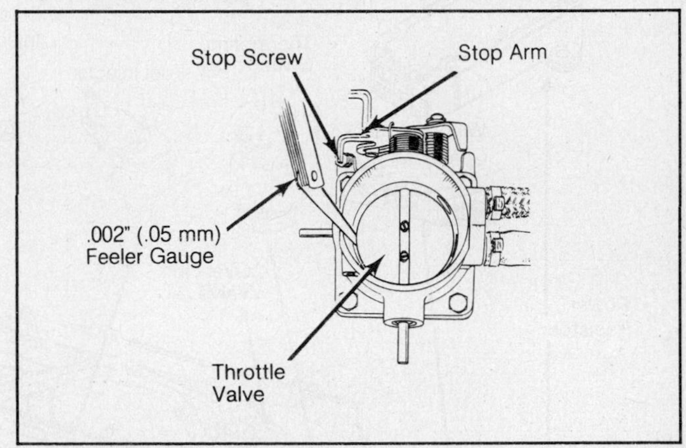
Stop Screw
Stop Arm
.002" (.05 mm)
Feeler Gauge
Throttle
Valve

Fig. 7: Jaguar XJ6 Fuel Injection Wiring Diagram

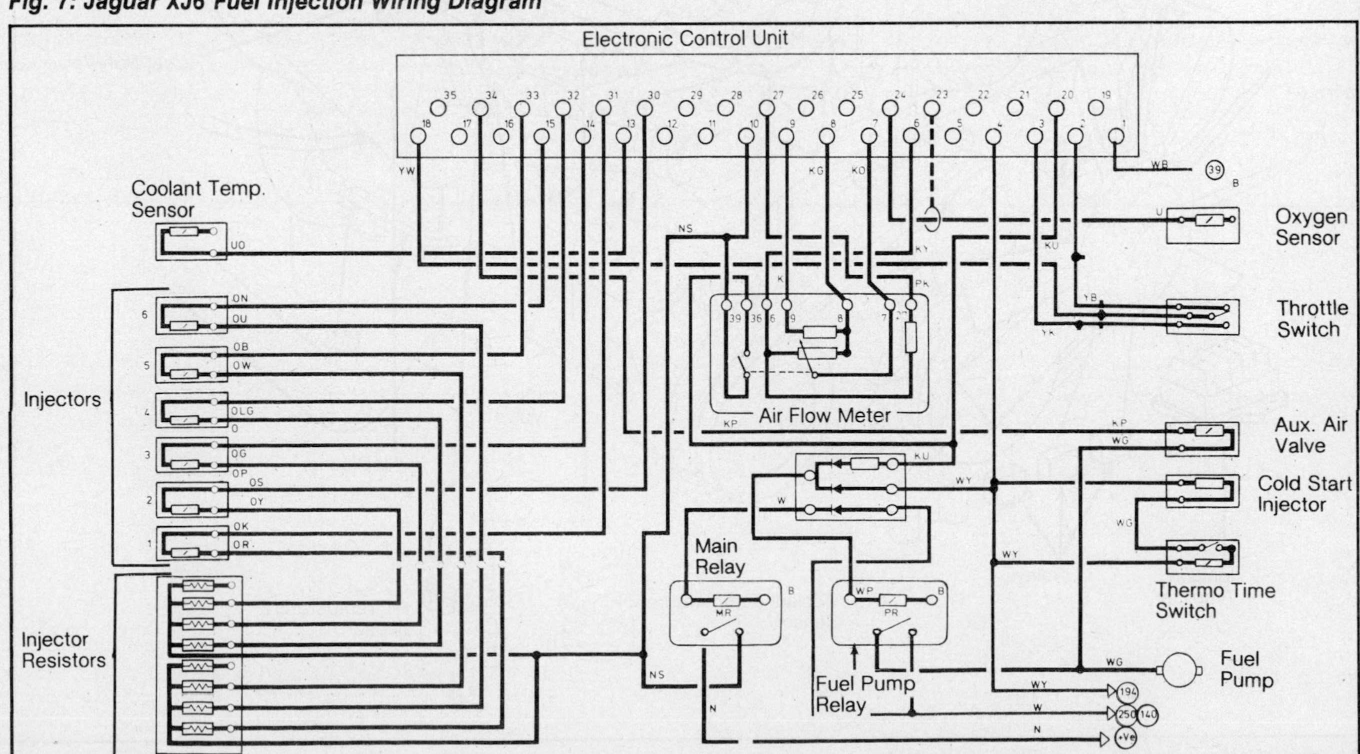
Electronic Control Unit
Coolant Temp.
Sensor
Injectors
Injector
Resistors
Air Flow Meter
Main
Relay
Fuel Pump
Relay
Oxygen
Sensor
Throttle
Switch
Aux. Air
Valve
Cold Start
Injector
Thermo Time
Switch
Fuel
Pump

1983 Fuel Injection

LUCAS-BOSCH "P" TYPE – JAGUAR

XJS

DESCRIPTION

The Lucas-Bosch "P" type fuel injection system is installed on all XJS 5.3L engines. This system relies on pressure sensing devices for incoming air flow information. The "P" type injection system consists of 2 subsystems interconnected only at the injectors. These 2 systems are the fuel system and the electronic sensing and control system.

The fuel system supplies the injectors with a constant supply of fuel at a pressure of 36 psi (2.5 kg/cm²). The electronic sensing and control system monitors engine operating conditions including load, speed, temperature, and throttle movement. The control

Fig. 1: Location of Engine Sensors & Components of "P" Type Electronic Fuel Injection System

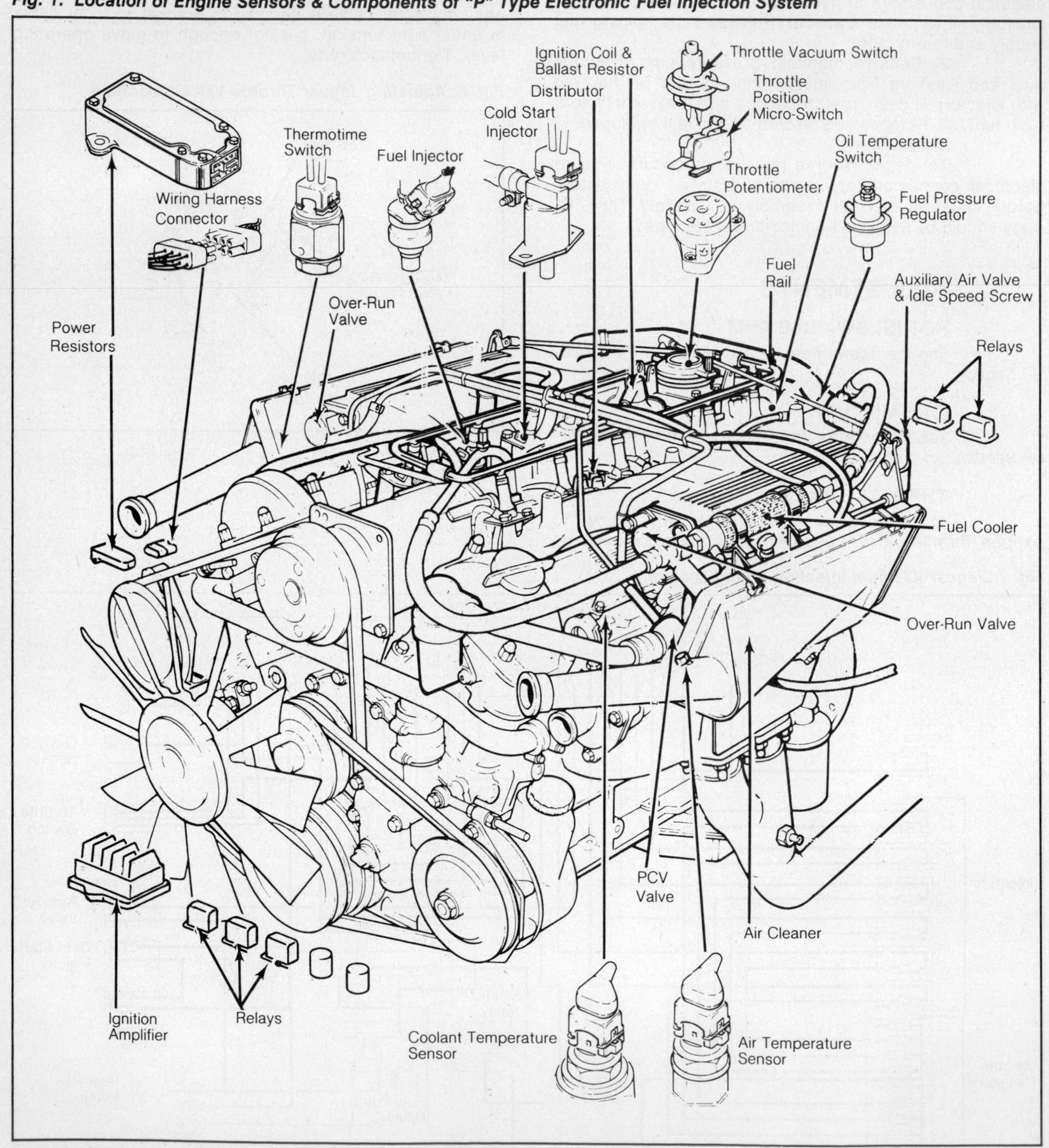
Ignition Coil &
Ballast Resistor
Throttle Vacuum Switch
Distributor
Throttle
Position
Micro-Switch
Cold Start
Injector
Thermotime
Switch
Fuel Injector
Oil Temperature
Switch
Throttle
Potentiometer
Wiring Harness
Connector
Fuel Pressure
Regulator
Fuel
Rail
Auxiliary Air Valve
& Idle Speed Screw
Over-Run
Valve
Power
Resistors
Relays
Fuel Cooler
Over-Run Valve
PCV
Valve
Air Cleaner
Ignition
Amplifier
Relays
Coolant Temperature
Sensor
Air Temperature
Sensor

Always disconnect battery ground cable before disconnecting any components of injection system.

system uses the information provided by this network of sensors to produce the proper length pulse for the injector, insuring optimum combustion for any operating conditions.

As the fuel pressure is held constant, varying the duration of the injection pulse increases or decreases the amount of fuel being injected into each cylinder. Fuel mixture is enriched for cold starting, closed throttle operation, full throttle operation, and when the throttle is rapidly opened.

The induction system consists of tuned ram pipes, air cleaners, plenum chambers and induction ports. Air is drawn through paper element air cleaners to a butterfly valve for each bank of cylinders and then to individual ports for each cylinder leading off the plenum chamber. The injectors are installed at the cylinder head end of each port with the fuel spray being aimed at the back of each intake valve.

OPERATION

ELECTRONIC CONTROL UNIT

The control unit utilizes an integrated circuit containing the digital fuel injection control chip and an analog-to-digital converter to translate information from the sensors. The fuel injection program is stored in a Read-Only-Memory (ROM) chip.

For any given manifold pressure and engine speed combination, the memory provides a fuel injection duration for optimum combustion. The electronic control unit also monitors other sensors to modify the basic speed and pressure signals so that cold starting, mixture adjustment and other areas of engine operation can be controlled

FUEL PRESSURE REGULATOR

The fuel pressure regulator maintains a constant pressure in direct proportion to intake manifold vacuum. This is accomplished by attaching a vacuum diaphragm to the regulator. This produces an injection pressure that is always a certain set amount above manifold pressure.

ENGINE LOAD SENSING

As the air flow entering the engine varies the pressure in the plenum changes. This change in pressure is monitored by the manifold pressure sensor. The manifold pressure sensor sends a signal that indicates the degree of engine load to the electronic control unit.

The manifold pressure sensor is fitted with a separate diaphragm to compensate for changes in barometric pressure. The manifold pressure sensor is located in the electronic control unit and is connected by a hose to the intake manifold balance pipe.

AIR INTAKE SYSTEM

Air is drawn from the air cleaner through the throttle plates and into the engine. A potentiometer connected to the throttle pulley converts the throttle angular position into a voltage signal that is transmitted to the electronic control unit. A vacuum operated switch and a micro-switch also provide throttle position information to the electronic control unit.

TEMPERATURE SENSORS

The temperature of the intake air and the engine coolant are constantly monitored. This information is fed directly to the electronic control unit. The air temperature sensor has very little effect on injection duration. Because of this, the air temperature sensor should be considered more as a fine-tuning device instead of as a control device.

The air temperature signal modifies the manifold pressure signal to indicate the weight (density) of the air in the intake system. This helps the control unit maintain the most efficient air/fuel ratio.

The coolant temperature sensor has greater direct control on engine operation, although its primary function is to aid in engine warm-up. This sensor combines with the cold start system and the auxiliary air valve to form the equivalent of the carburetor's automatic choke.

FLOODING PROTECTION SYSTEM

When the ignition is switched to "ON", but the engine is not cranking, the fuel pump will run for 2 seconds to raise the pressure in the fuel rail and then automatically shut off. Only after the engine has started cranking is the fuel pump turned on again.

All fuel pump switching is controlled by the electronic control unit. This system prevents flooding in case any of the injectors become faulty by remaining open when the ignition is left on.

AUXILIARY AIR VALVE

The auxiliary air valve is controlled by coolant temperature. To prevent stalling during cold start and cold idle conditions, the valve opens to allow air to by-pass the throttle plates. This increases engine speed. In addition to the main passage regulated by engine coolant, the air valve also contains a by-pass controlled by an adjusting screw.

COLD STARTING SYSTEM

During cold starting, additional fuel is injected into the intake manifolds by 2 cold start injectors. These injectors are controlled by the cold start relay and the thermotime switch.

The thermotime switch senses engine coolant temperature, and depending on temperature makes or breaks the ground circuit of the relay. When the starter circuit is activated, the cold start relay is energized with the ground circuit being completed by the thermotime switch.

The thermotime switch also limits the time that the relay is energized (12 seconds max.). The enrichment provided by the cold start system is in addition to the enrichment resulting from the coolant temperature sensors' signal to the electronic control unit.

If the temperature at the thermotime switch is above 95°F (35°C), the thermotime switch will not close and no cold start enrichment will take place.

CRANKING ENRICHMENT CIRCUIT

The electronic control unit increases the injection duration during cranking. This enrichment in addition to any enrichment that is a result of coolant temperature or cold start injection. This enrichment reduces partially after cranking stops and then falls to normal after a few seconds. This process helps keep the engine running during start-up.

OXYGEN SENSORS

The oxygen sensors measure the free oxygen concentration in the exhaust system. Too much free oxygen indicates a mixture that is too lean. Not enough free oxygen in the exhaust indicates a rich mixture. A signal is sent to the electronic control unit from the sensor to compensate for these variations in mixture. The air/fuel mixture is corrected by varying the injection duration pulse sent from the electronic control unit.

ENGINE SPEED SENSING

The engine speed signal is obtained from the distributor terminal of the coil. This signal triggers the electronic control unit to produce the time pulses to 2 groups of 6 injectors. The engine speed signal also modifies the injection duration which is already established by the manifold pressure switch signal.

FULL LOAD FUELING CIRCUIT

To obtain maximum engine power it is necessary to inhibit the closed loop control system and enrichen the fuel mixture. This is accomplished by using a vacuum operated electrical switch, sensing intake manifold vacuum, and a micro switch, operated by the throttle pulley spindle. The 2 switches are wired in parallel so that either or both can signal the need for full load fueling.

The micro switch is mounted so that its' contacts are closed when the throttle is opened beyond a certain point. As the throttle is opened beyond this point, the switch signals the electronic control unit that full load fueling is necessary. The micro switch is necessary when the vehicle is traveling at high speeds under full load conditions when intake manifold vacuum is insufficient to close the vacuum operated full load switch.

The contacts of the vacuum operated switch are actuated by a spring loaded diaphragm that senses intake manifold vacuum. When the manifold vacuum falls to low levels due to part throttle full load operation, the diaphragm closes the switch contacts. This causes the fuel system to go into an open loop mode and enriches the fuel/air mixture about 12%.

TESTING

AUXILIARY AIR VALVE TEST

1) Remove the auxiliary air valve. Fully close the adjustment screw. Immerse the air valve bulb in boiling water and observe the valve head through the side port. Valve should move smoothly to the closed position.

2) Blow through the side port, no air should pass through the valve. Allow the valve bulb to cool. The valve head should move smoothly back to open the main air passage. If the valve does not operate correctly, replacement is required. Reset the adjusting screw before reinstalling valve.

COOLANT TEMPERATURE SENSOR TEST

1) Disconnect battery ground cable. Remove connector from the temperature sensor. Connect an ohmmeter between sensor terminals. Resistance should be as specified. *See Temperature Sensor Resistance* table.

2) Check the resistance between each of the sensor terminals and the sensor case. High or infinite resistance should be present. Connect the sensor connector and the negative battery cable.

TEMPERATURE SENSOR RESISTANCE

Temperature °F (°C)	Ohms
14 (-10)	9200
32 (0)	5900
50 (10)	3700
68 (20)	2500
86 (30)	1700
104 (40)	1180
122 (50)	840
140 (60)	600
158 (70)	435
176 (80)	325
194 (90)	250
212 (100)	190

FUEL SYSTEM PRESSURE TEST

1) Depressurize the fuel system by disconnecting fuel pump relay and cranking the engine for a few seconds. Turn igntion off. Connect fuel pump relay. Disconnect cold start injector supply hose from fuel rail. Connect a pressure gauge to open port on fuel rail.

2) Remove the distributor lead from the ignition coil. Ground terminal 85 of the pump relay. Turn ignition switch "ON" and note the pressure gauge reading. Fuel pressure should be 28-30 psi (2.0-2.2 kg/cm²).

3) If either or both readings are high, check for restricted or plugged return lines. If either or both readings are low, check for blockage in the supply line or a plugged filter.

4) If no blockage is present, the pressure regulator must be adjusted. If, after adjustment, the proper pressure cannot be obtained, the regulator or fuel pump may need to be replaced.

5) Turn ignition switch "OFF" and depressurize fuel system. Remove pressure gauge and reconnect fuel line to fuel rail. Turn ignition "ON" and check the fuel system for leaks. Remove the ground connection from terminal 85 of the pump relay and reconnect the distributor lead to the ignition coil.

INJECTOR WINDING TEST

1) Using an ohmmeter, check the resistance of each injector coil. Resistance should be 2.4 ohms at room temperature.

2) Connect one ohmmeter lead to injector housing and other lead to each of the injector terminals. Ohmmeter should read infinite resistance at both terminals. If any of the injector windings are shorted or open, the injector must be replaced.

FUEL PUMP RELAY TEST

1) Turn ignition switch "ON". The fuel pump should run for 1-2 seconds and then stop. If pump does not run, or does not stop, further diagnosis is necessary.

2) Check that inertia switch cut-out button is pressed in. Remove inertia switch cover and attaching screws and check to see that the wiring harness connection is secure. Remove wiring harness connector from switch and check for continuity across switch terminals.

LUCAS-BOSCH "P" TYPE — JAGUAR (Cont.)

3) Pull button on inertia switch out and check for an open circuit across switch terminals. Reconnect wiring harness connector and replace switch cover. Reset inertia switch button.

4) If inertia switch operates to specifications, ground terminal 85 of fuel pump relay and turn ignition switch "ON". Check for battery voltage at terminal 86 of main relay. If battery voltage is not present, check battery supply from ignition switch via inertia switch.

5) Check for battery voltage at terminal 87 of main relay. If no voltage is present, check for battery voltage across terminal 85 and ground connection of main relay. If voltage is now present, replace main relay.

6) Check for battery voltage at terminal 86 of pump relay. If no voltage is present, check for an open circuit between terminal 87 of main relay and terminal 86 of pump relay and correct as necessary.

7) Check for battery voltage at terminal 87 of pump relay. If no voltage is present, check for battery voltage across terminal 85 of pump relay and ground lead. If voltage is now present, replace pump relay.

8) Check for battery voltage at terminal 30 on both relays and at fuel pump positive terminal. If no voltage exists, check for an open circuit between terminal 87 of pump relay and positive terminal of pump and correct as necessary.

9) If pump still does not operate, check ground connections or replace pump.

AIR TEMPERATURE SENSOR TEST

1) Disconnect battery terminals and air temperature sensor connector. Connect an ohmmeter between sensor terminals. Ohmmeter reading should vary with temperature. *See Air Temperature Sensor Resistance* table.

2) Check resistance between sensor body and each of the terminals. Resistance should be high or infinite. If sensor does not meet specifications, replacement is required.

AIR TEMPERATURE SENSOR RESISTANCE

Temperature °F (°C)	Ohms
14 (-10)	960
32 (0)	640
50 (10)	435
68 (20)	300
86 (30)	210
104 (40)	150
122 (50)	108
140 (60)	80

THERMOTIME SWITCH TEST

1) To test thermotime switch, it is necessary to determine temperature rating of switch. The switch is rated at 59°F (15°C) or 95°F (35°C). The rating is stamped on flat part of switch body.

2) After determining switch rating, coolant temperature must be measured. The test procedure to use depends on whether coolant temperature is above or below the rated value of switch.

Coolant Temperature Higher Than Switch Rating

1) Disconnect negative battery cable and thermotime switch connector. Connect an ohmmeter between terminal W of thermotime switch and ground.

2) Resistance should be high or infinite. Replace switch if low resistance or a short circuit reading is obtained.

Coolant Temperature Lower Than Switch Rating

1) Disconnect negative battery cable and thermotime switch connector. Connect an ohmmeter between terminal W of thermotime switch and ground.

2) A very low resistance (continuity) should be measured. Apply 12 volts to terminal G of thermotime switch.

3) Measure time delay between applying voltage and the ohmmeter reading changing from low to high resistance. Time delay should be as specified. *See Thermotime Switch Delay* table. Replace switch if it does not meet specifications.

THERMOTIME SWITCH DELAY

Coolant Temp. °F (°C)	Switch Rated 59°F (15°C)	Switch Rated 95°F (35°C)
32 (0)	3.5 Secs.	5 Secs.
50 (10)	1.2 Secs	3.5 Secs.
68 (20)	.....	2.0 Secs.
86 (30)	.....	0.5 Secs.
95 (35)	.....	0 Secs.

COLD START SYSTEM TEST

CAUTION: This test results in fuel vapor being present in engine compartment. All necessary precautions against fire or explosion should be taken.

Remove 2 setscrews and washers retaining cold start injectors in intake manifold. Remove the start injectors and place them in a container to collect sprayed fuel. Disconnect distributor lead from the coil.

Engine Temperature Below 59°F (15°C)

1) Turn ignition switch "ON" and check the cold start injectors for any leakage. Crank the engine for a few revolutions. Injectors should spray while engine cranks. Do not operate the starter any longer than necessary to complete this test.

2) If injectors do not spray, crank engine and check for battery voltage at cold start injector supply (White/Pink) cable. If voltage is present, check ground connections and wiring harness connectors at cold start injectors. Repair as necessary. If no defects are found, injectors are faulty and must be replaced.

3) Crank engine and check for battery voltage at terminal 87 of cold start relay. If voltage is present, check wiring harness between relay and cold start injectors and repair as necessary.

4) Crank engine and check for battery voltage at terminal 30 of cold start relay. If no voltage is present, check supply wire from pump relay and repair as necessary. If voltage is present, relay is not being energized or contacts are faulty.

5) Crank engine and check for battery voltage at terminal 86 of cold start relay. If voltage is present, relay is not being energized or contacts are faulty. If no voltage is present, supply wire from starter circuit is faulty and must be repaired.

6) Crank engine and check for battery voltage at terminal 85 of cold start relay. If voltage is present and relay is not energizing, there is a problem with thermotime switch circuit. Disconnect wiring harness from terminal 85 and jump terminal 85 to ground. Relay should now energize. If not, relay is faulty and must be replaced.

7) If relay energizes, check for battery voltage at terminal 87 of cold start relay. If no voltage is present at terminal 87, the contacts of relay are faulty and the relay must be replaced.

8) Reinstall cold start injectors and all cables or connectors that were removed.

Engine Temperature Above 59°F (15°C)

1) Crank engine and check voltage at terminal 87 of cold start relay. Voltage should be 0 volts. If battery voltage is present, remove wiring harness connector from terminal 85 of the cold start relay.

2) If voltage is now 0 volts, the thermotime switch is at fault and must be replaced. If battery voltage is still present at terminal 87 after disconnecting terminal 85, the cold start relay is faulty and must be replaced.

3) If cold start injectors pass fuel when no voltage is present at terminal 87, the injectors must be replaced.

OVER-RUN VALVE TEST

1) Loosen hose clamps at air filter back plates. Remove inlet hoses from back plates. Block inlet ports and start engine. If idle speed is now correct, reconnect 1 of the valves. Start engine.

2) If idle speed is not correct, connected valve is faulty and requires replacement. If idle speed is correct, reconnect second valve. If idle speed is not correct now, the second valve is faulty and must be replaced.

REMOVAL & INSTALLATION

AUXILIARY AIR VALVE

CAUTION: This procedure must not be performed on a hot engine.

Removal

1) Disconnect battery ground cable. Remove radiator cap to relieve any residual pressure left in cooling system. Reinstall radiator cap. Loosen clamps securing air hoses to auxiliary air valve and remove hoses.

2) Remove 2 screws and washers securing auxiliary air valve to coolant pipe. Remove auxiliary air valve from coolant pipe and clean off all old gasket material. Note the number of turns required to turn adjusting screw all the way in. *See Fig. 2.*

Installation

1) To install, reverse removal procedure. Set the adjusting screw on replacement valve to same number of turns noted in disassembly procedure.

2) Use non-hardening sealer on new gasket. Check coolant level and add coolant if necessary. Check and adjust idle speed if necessary.

OVER-RUN VALVE

Removal & Installation

Loosen hose clamp securing air inlet hose to over-run valve. Remove 3 screws securing over-run valve

Fig. 2: Auxiliary Air Valve Removal

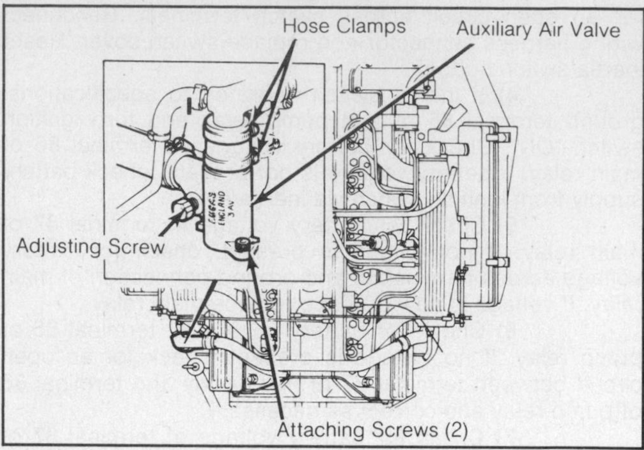
Hose Clamps
Auxiliary Air Valve
Adjusting Screw
Attaching Screws (2)

Do not remove this valve when engine is hot.

to intake manifolds. Remove over-run valves from manifold making sure to keep spacer located on right-side valve. *See Fig. 3.* To install reverse removal procedure.

Fig. 3: Over-Run Valve Removal

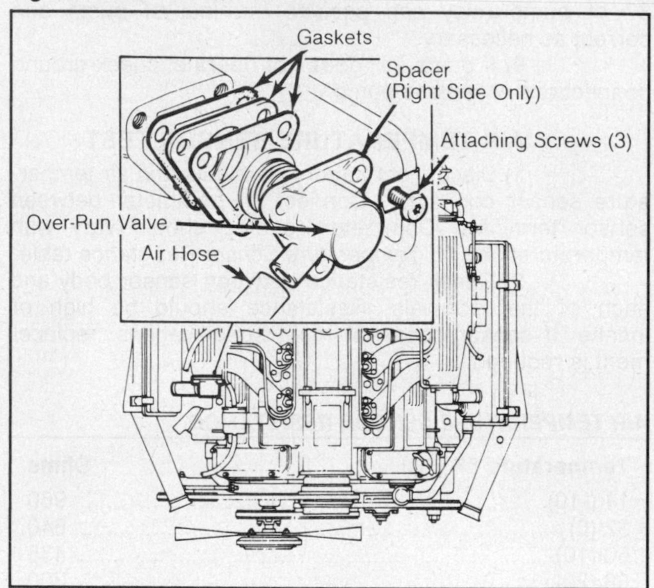
Gaskets
Spacer
(Right Side Only)
Attaching Screws (3)
Over-Run Valve
Air Hose

Do not discard spacer located on right side valve.

COOLANT TEMPERATURE SENSOR

CAUTION: This procedure must not be performed on a hot engine.

Removal & Installation

1) Disconnect battery ground cable and coolant temperature sensor connector. Remove radiator cap to release any residual pressure left in cooling system. Reinstall radiator cap.

2) Apply sealing compound to threads of new temperature sensor and install new sealing washer. Remove temperature sensor from thermostat housing and immediately install new sensor to minimize coolant loss. *See Fig. 4.* To complete installation, reverse removal procedure and check coolant level.

1983 Fuel Injection

LUCAS-BOSCH "P" TYPE — JAGUAR (Cont.)

Fig. 4: Coolant Temperature Sensor Removal

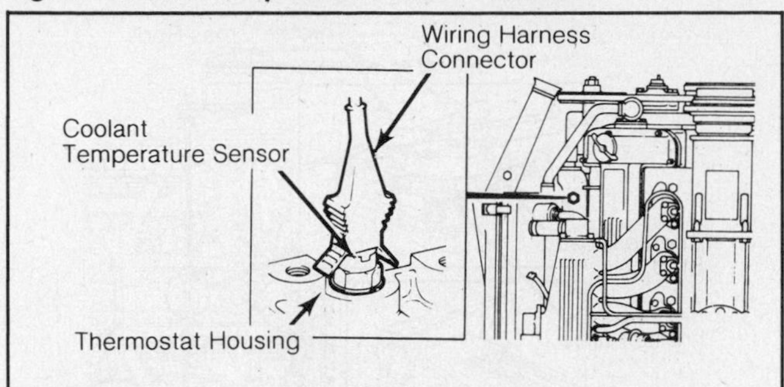
Wiring Harness
Connector
Coolant
Temperature Sensor
Thermostat Housing

Do not remove this sensor when engine is hot.

THERMOTIME SWITCH

CAUTION: This procedure must not be performed on a hot engine.

Removal & Installation

1) Disconnect battery ground cable and thermotime switch connector. Remove radiator cap to release any residual pressure left in cooling system. Reinstall radiator cap.

2) Apply sealing compound to threads of new thermotime switch and install new sealing washer. Remove thermotime switch from thermostat housing and immediately install new switch to minimize coolant loss. *See Fig. 5.* To complete installation, reverse removal procedure and check coolant level.

Fig. 5: Thermotime Switch Removal

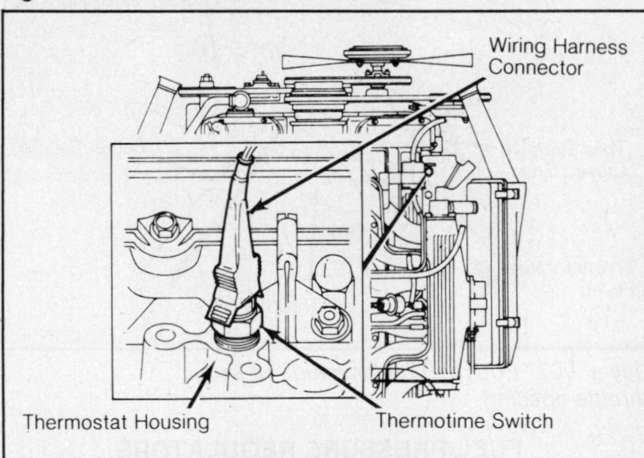
Wiring Harness
Connector
Thermostat Housing
Thermotime Switch

Do not remove this switch when engine is hot.

THROTTLE SWITCH

Removal & Installation

Disconnect battery ground cable and remove wiring harness connector from throttle switch. Remove throttle cross-rods from throttle pulley. Remove throttle pulley plate from throttle pedestal. Remove throttle switch attaching screws and lift switch clear of engine. To install, reverse removal procedure.

ELECTRONIC CONTROL UNIT

Removal & Installation

Disconnect battery ground cable. Remove control unit cover from the trunk. Remove 2 bolts securing control unit. Disconnect wiring harness plug and vacuum hose from control unit. Remove control unit from trunk. To install, reverse removal procedure.

FUEL COOLER

CAUTION: The fuel cooler/air conditioning system contains refrigerant gas under pressure. This gas can cause blindness if released improperly. It is mandatory that the air conditioning system be depressurized according to standard service procedures, prior to disconnecting the fuel cooler. All necessary precautions must be taken when depressurizing the system to prevent injury.

Removal & Installation

1) Depressurize fuel system. Depressurize air conditioning system. Disconnect refrigerant inlet and outlet hoses from fuel cooler. *See Fig. 6.* Plug refrigerant hoses immediately to prevent entry of moisture into system. Clamp off both fuel lines connected to cooler.

2) Disconnect fuel lines from cooler. Remove attaching screws and fuel cooler. To install, reverse removal procedure. Recharge the air conditioning system with refrigerant.

Fig. 6: Fuel Cooler Removal

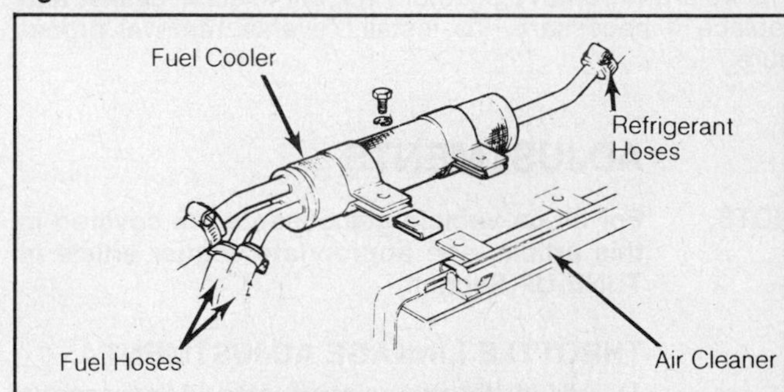
Fuel Cooler
Refrigerant
Hoses
Fuel Hoses
Air Cleaner

Depressurize A/C system before removing cooler.

FUEL PRESSURE REGULATOR

Removal & Installation

Depressurize fuel system. Remove the fuel cooler-to-pressure regulator hose from the regulator. Remove regulator securing nut. Disconnect regulator pipe from fuel rail. Move regulator upward and disconnect vacuum hose. Remove regulator-to-fuel rail hose and remove regulator. To install, reverse removal procedure.

FUEL PUMP

Removal & Installation

Disconnect battery and remove spare tire. Clamp off fuel lines connected to pump. Loosen hose clamps and remove fuel lines. Disconnect pump electrical connector. Loosen screws securing pump clamp and remove pump. To install, reverse removal procedure.

INJECTORS

Removal & Installation

Depressurize fuel system and disconnect negative battery cable. Remove the appropriate fuel rail(s). Disconnect injector wiring harness connector. Remove injector clamp nuts. Remove injector and clamp. Remove and discard injector seal. To install, reverse removal procedure and install a new injector seal.

LUCAS-BOSCH "P" TYPE — JAGUAR (Cont.)

FUEL RAIL

Removal & Installation

1) Depressurize fuel system and disconnect negative battery cable. Remove the appropriate throttle rod from throttle pedestal and swing it out of the way. Disconnect throttle cable and throttle kick-down switch from throttle pedestal.

2) Disconnect cross-pipe from intake manifold and fuel rail. Loosen regulator valve hose clamp. Disconnect cold start injector feed pipe from fuel rail. Remove Econocruise cable harness and Econocruise pipe from fuel rail.

3) Remove fuel feed and return pipes. Disconnect fuel rail halves. Loosen the fuel rail-to-injector clamps and remove fuel rail from injectors. To install, reverse removal procedure.

COLD START INJECTORS

Removal & Installation

1) Depressurize fuel system and disconnect negative battery cable. Clamp off fuel line leading to cold start injector. Remove wiring harness connector from cold start injector. Loosen hose clamp and disconnect fuel line from cold start injector.

2) Remove 2 setscrews attaching injector to manifold and remove injector. Inspect injector gasket and replace if necessary. To install, reverse removal procedure.

ADJUSTMENTS

NOTE: For all on-vehicle adjustments not covered in this article, see appropriate Jaguar article in TUNE-UP Section.

THROTTLE LINKAGE ADJUSTMENT

1) Adjust throttle closed stop if necessary. Release throttle cross-rods from throttle pulley. Loosen clamps securing levers to rear of throttle shafts.

2) With butterfly valve against closed stop, bell crank against stop, and play in coupling taken up in opening direction, tighten clamp to lock throttle lever to shaft. Repeat for other side of engine.

3) Install cross-rods onto ball connectors on throttle pulley. *See Fig. 7.* The rods must go into place without moving linkage or pulley. If adjustment is necessary, loosen lock nuts on cross-rods and adjust length of rods so that they will align with ball connectors when pulley is against closed stop.

4) Adjust fully open throttle stop so that it just touches pulley when throttle butterfly stop arms are against throttle housing. Check operation of throttle switch and kickdown switch.

THROTTLE BUTTERFLY VALVE

NOTE: Do not adjust only 1 valve. Whenever adjustments are made, always adjust both butterfly valves.

1) Remove both air cleaners. Loosen lock nut on butterfly valve stop screw. Turn stop screw all the way in. Make sure that butterfly valve closes fully.

2) Insert a 0.002" (0.05 mm) feeler gauge between top of butterfly valve and housing to hold valve open. *See Fig. 8.* Set stop screw so that it just touches

Fig. 7: Throttle Linkage Adjustment Location

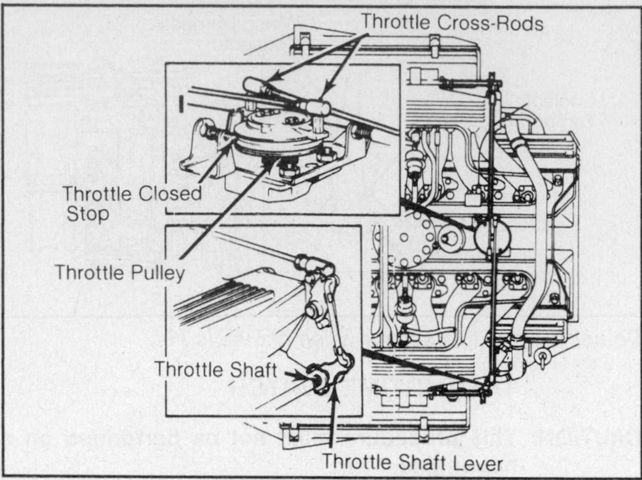
Throttle Cross-Rods
Throttle Closed Stop
Throttle Pulley
Throttle Shaft
Throttle Shaft Lever

Check throttle and kickdown switch operation after adjustment.

stop arm. Tighten lock nut. Press stop arm against stop screw and withdraw feeler gauge.

3) Repeat procedure on other side of engine. Seal threads of adjusting screws with a drop of paint. Replace air cleaners. Check throttle linkage and kickdown switch adjustment. Check operation of throttle switch.

Fig. 8: Butterfly Valve Adjustment

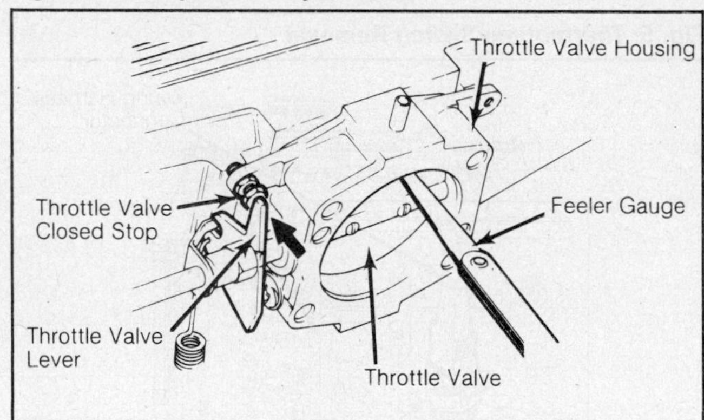
Throttle Valve Housing
Throttle Valve Closed Stop
Feeler Gauge
Throttle Valve Lever
Throttle Valve

Use a .002" (.05 mm) feeler gauge to set throttle opening.

FUEL PRESSURE REGULATORS

NOTE: Fuel pressure should only be adjusted after the complete system has been checked.

1) Depressurize fuel system. Disconnect left-side cold start injector fuel supply hose from fuel rail. Connect a pressure gauge to fuel rail. Remove screws securing both pressure regulators to intake manifolds.

2) Clamp off fuel line leading to left-bank pressure regulator inlet. Start engine. Loosen lock nuts on both pressure regulators. Turn adjuster bolt on right-bank pressure regulator until gauge reads 29.6 psi (2.1 kg/cm²).

3) Remove clamp from left-bank pressure regulator inlet and transfer it to right-bank pressure regulator inlet. Turn adjuster bolt on left-bank pressure regulator until the gauge reads 29.6 psi (2.1 kg/cm²).

1983 Fuel Injection

LUCAS-BOSCH "P" TYPE — JAGUAR (Cont.)

4) Release clamp and ensure gauge reads 28.5-30 psi (2.0-2.2 kg/cm²). Tighten lock nuts on both pressure regulators. Turn off ignition. Depressurize fuel system and remove pressure gauge. Reconnect cold start injector line and test system for leaks.

SERVICE NOTES

COLD STARTING

On low mileage vehicles exhibiting a cold starting problem, check to ensure that the cold start injectors are connected to the wiring harness. New vehicles are shipped with the harness disconnected to prevent starting problems during port and dealer handling.

ECU VACUUM SENSOR

Some models may be equipped with a vacuum reservoir located next to the ECU. This unit is connected into the vacuum sensor line and is used to prevent momentary fluctuations in vacuum from reaching the sensor.

Vehicles exhibiting a low speed engine surging condition with a slight delay in throttle response should be checked for proper routing of the vacuum hose that leads to the ECU vacuum sensor.

On some early models the routing of the hose is such that the hose can become trapped between the negative battery cable and the battery case causing a restriction. Reroute hose to correct problem.

ECU ADJUSTMENT

No attempt should be made to drill out the tamper proof plug that covers the ECU adjusting screw. Damage to the internal circuitry will result if a drill is used. Plug must be pried out using a hooked probe or stiff wire.

A special adjusting tool (60 730551) is required for making the necessary feedback adjustments after a replacing an ECU. This tool must be used to prevent damage to the internal circuitry of the ECU.

Fig. 10: Lucas-Bosch "P" Type Fuel Injection System Wiring Diagram

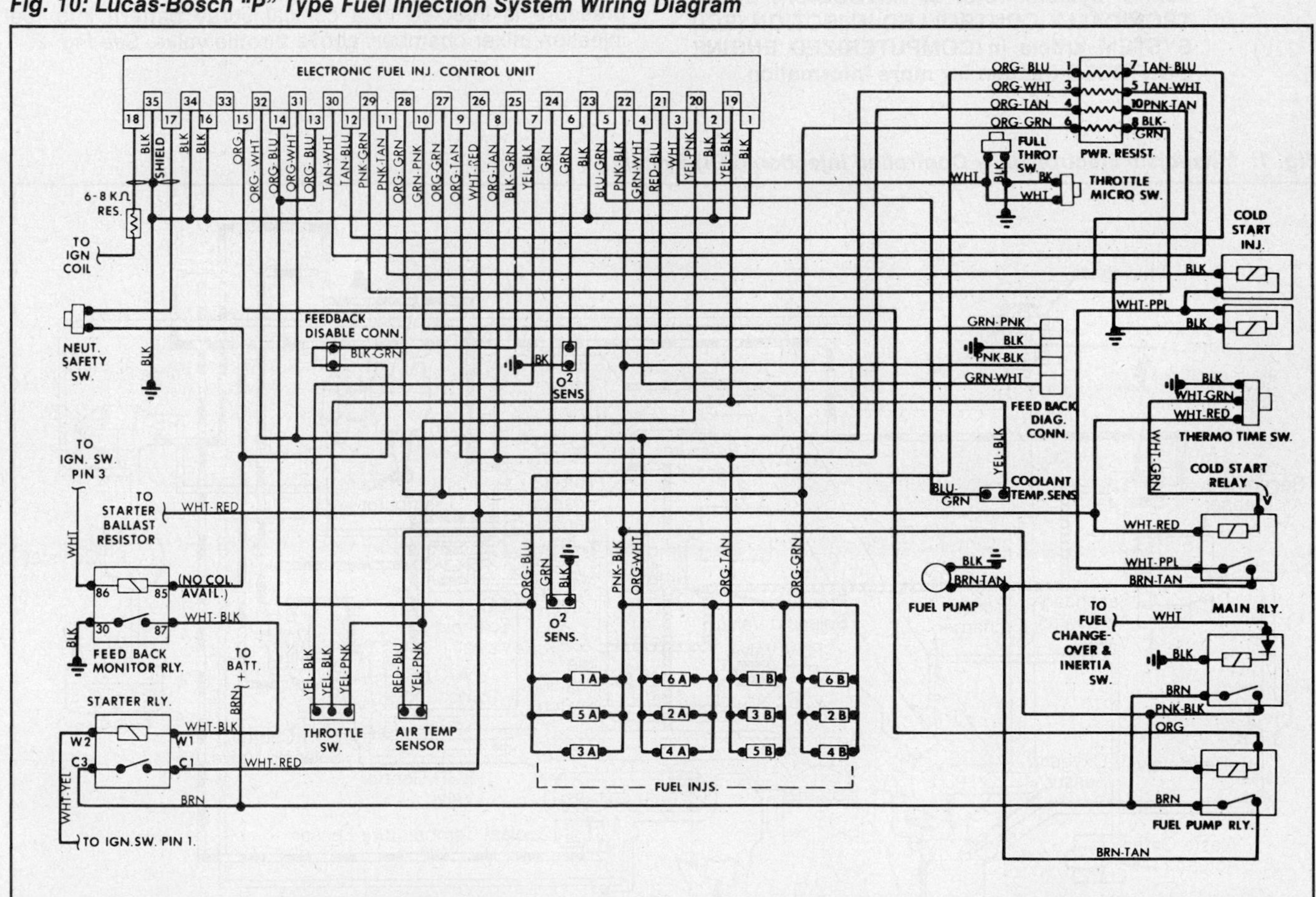
ELECTRONIC FUEL INJ. CONTROL UNIT
6-8 KΩ RES.
TO IGN COIL
NEUT. SAFETY SW.
FEEDBACK DISABLE CONN.
O^2 SENS
TO IGN. SW. PIN 3
TO STARTER BALLAST RESISTOR
(NO COL AVAIL.)
FEED BACK MONITOR RLY.
TO BATT.
STARTER RLY.
TO IGN. SW. PIN 1.
THROTTLE SW.
AIR TEMP SENSOR
FUEL INJS.
PWR. RESIST.
FULL THROT SW.
THROTTLE MICRO SW.
COLD START INJ.
FEED BACK DIAG. CONN.
THERMO TIME SW.
COLD START RELAY
COOLANT TEMP. SENS
FUEL PUMP
TO FUEL CHANGE-OVER & INERTIA SW.
MAIN RLY.
FUEL PUMP RLY.

Also see chassis wiring in WIRING DIAGRAM Section.

MITSUBISHI ECI SYSTEM

Starion Turbo

DESCRIPTION

The Electronically Controlled Injection (ECI) system is a computerized emission, ignition and fuel control system. The ECI system controls engine operation and lowers exhaust emissions while maintaining good fuel economy and driveability. The Electronic Control Unit (ECU) is the "brain" of the ECI system. The ECU controls many engine related systems to constantly adjust engine operation.

The ECI system consists of the following sub-systems: Fuel Control, Data Sensors, Electronic Control Unit (ECU), Electronic Spark Control (ESC) system, Idle Speed Control (ISC), Emission Control, Fuel Cutoff and catalytic converters.

NOTE: **Only primary fuel system components will be covered in this article: Fuel supply system, fuel injection mixer, fuel pressure regulator, ECU, data sensors, and fuel cutoff system. Because of the interrelated functions of the control system, refer to MITSUBISHI ELECTRONICALLY CONTROLLED INJECTION (ECI) SYSTEM article in COMPUTERIZED ENGINE CONTROLS Section for more information.**

OPERATION

FUEL SUPPLY

Fuel supply system consists of an electric fuel pump, control relay, fuel filter, fuel injectors, fuel pressure regulator and fuel lines. Fuel is supplied to engine through 2 electronically pulsed (timed) injector valves located in fuel injection mixer above intake manifold. The ECU controls amount of fuel metered through injectors based upon engine demand information, through data sensor signals.

FUEL INJECTION MIXER

The fuel injection mixer consists of 2 fuel injectors and a throttle valve to control air/fuel mixture flow. The mixer contains ports to generate vacuum signals for emission control systems.

Fuel is supplied to injectors by fuel supply system. From injectors fuel flows to externally mounted fuel pressure regulator. The fuel injectors are solenoid-operated devices controlled by the ECU. The injectors are alternately activated by ECU.

The ECU activates fuel injector solenoids which lift a normally closed valve off its seat. Fuel under pressure is injected in a conical spray pattern into fuel injection mixer chamber, above throttle valve. *See Fig. 2.*

Fig. 1: Mitsubishi Electronically Controlled Injection (ECI) System

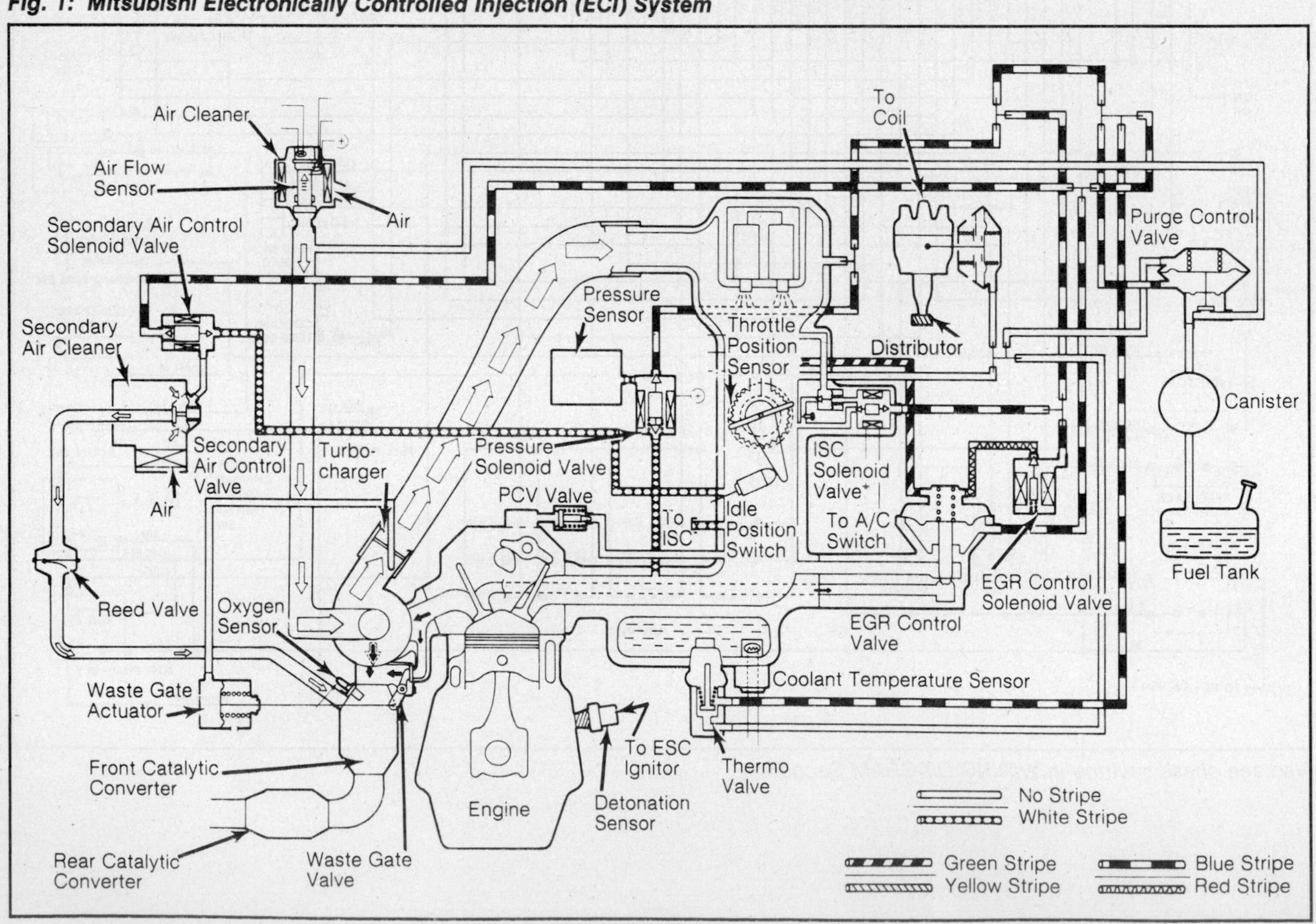

Air Cleaner
Air Flow Sensor
Air
Secondary Air Control Solenoid Valve
Secondary Air Cleaner
Secondary Air Control Valve
Air
Turbo-charger
Reed Valve
Oxygen Sensor
Waste Gate Actuator
Front Catalytic Converter
Rear Catalytic Converter
Waste Gate Valve
Engine
Pressure Sensor
Pressure Solenoid Valve
PCV Valve
To ISC
Throttle Position Sensor
Idle Position Switch
ISC Solenoid Valve*
To A/C Switch
To Coil
Distributor
Purge Control Valve
Canister
Fuel Tank
EGR Control Solenoid Valve
EGR Control Valve
Coolant Temperature Sensor
To ESC Ignitor
Detonation Sensor
Thermo Valve
No Stripe
White Stripe
Green Stripe
Yellow Stripe
Blue Stripe
Red Stripe

MITSUBISHI ECI SYSTEM (Cont.)

Turbocharged air flowing into chamber is saturated with fuel charge before passing throttle valve. The amount of fuel delivered by injectors is dependent upon the time that injector valve is held open by ECU. Fuel delivery time is modified by ECU to provide proper amount of fuel for all engine operating conditions.

Fig. 2: Sectional View of Fuel Injection Mixer

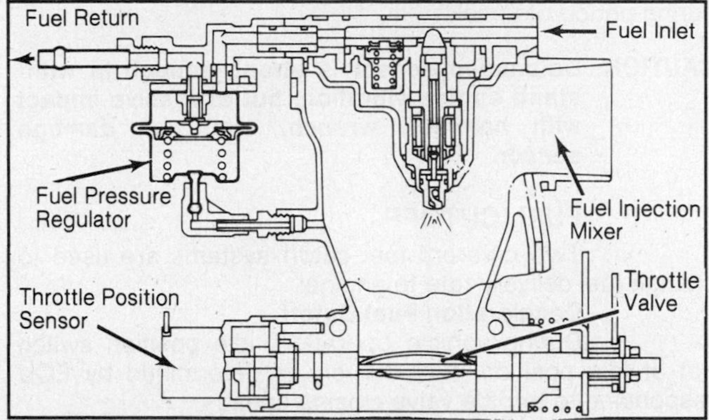
Fuel Return
Fuel Inlet
Fuel Pressure Regulator
Fuel Injection Mixer
Throttle Position Sensor
Throttle Valve

Note fuel flow through top of mixer to regulator.

FUEL PRESSURE REGULATOR

The fuel pressure regulator is externally mounted from fuel injection mixer. Fuel flows from top of fuel injectors to pressure regulator. The regulator is a diaphragm-operated relief valve with injector pressure on one side and turbocharged pressure on the other side.

The pressure regulator maintains a constant pressure drop across injectors throughout all engine operating conditions.

ELECTRONIC CONTROL UNIT (ECU)

The ECU is mounted behind passenger kick panel and controls all ECI functions. The ECU consists of a printed circuit board enclosed within a metal box. The ECU receives various signals from data sensors and switches. These signals are processed by the ECU for controlling fuel delivery.

The amount of fuel delivered is determined only by the time that injectors are open, because the fuel pressure regulator maintains a constant pressure drop across injectors. The frequency and duration of injection (fuel delivery time) is controlled by ECU.

The ECU monitors various engine and vehicle operations and computes the fuel delivery time. Fuel delivery time is modified for such operating conditions as engine cranking, cold starting, altitude, acceleration and deceleration.

When ignition switch is turned to "START" position, ECU calculates fuel delivery based primarily upon coolant temperature and throttle position. ECU sends an electrical signal to injectors to provide fuel for prescribed period of time. After ignition is released from "START" position and engine speed is above a specified RPM, ECU changes enrichment signal.

Immediately after engine starts, the ECU issues electrical signals to injectors to provide stable combustion. During engine warm-up, the ECU monitors all data sensor information and provides a richer mixture until coolant temperature reaches a preset value.

When coolant temperature exceeds preset value, ECU processes other data sensor information and issues appropriate electrical signals to injectors. This period of time is referred to as open loop mode of operation. The ECU controls fuel delivery based upon open loop programmed information until the oxygen sensor is warm enough to send modifying signals to ECU.

When the oxygen sensor is warm enough, the ECU accepts oxygen sensor information and uses it for controlling fuel delivery. When the ECU is accepting oxygen sensor information, this is referred to as closed loop mode of operation.

During closed loop operation, the ECU stores the mean values of feedback signals used to maintain 14.7:1 air fuel ratio. During open loop operation, the ECU uses these mean values to modify pre-programmed information. By doing this, the ECU can more closely control exhaust emissions even when engine is in open loop mode of operation.

DATA SENSORS

Each sensor furnishes electrical impulses to ECU. The ECU computes fuel delivery and spark timing necessary to maintain desired air/fuel mixture, thus controlling amount of fuel delivered to engine. Data sensors are interrelated to each other. Operation of each sensor is as follows:

Air Flow Sensor

This sensor is mounted in air cleaner. The sensor measures air flow rate through the air cleaner and sends a proportionate electrical signal to ECU. The ECU uses air flow sensor information for controlling fuel delivery and air injection system.

Intake Air Temperature Sensor

This sensor is mounted in air cleaner as component part of air flow sensor. The sensor measures temperature of incoming air and sends an electrical signal to ECU. The ECU uses air temperature sensor information for controlling fuel delivery.

Pressure Sensor

This sensor is mounted on firewall. An electrically controlled solenoid valve is connected to sensor. The solenoid valve has 2 hoses connected to it; 1 hose connects above throttle valve and other hose connects below throttle valve.

The solenoid valve is activated by ECU whenever ignition switch is turned to "ON" or "START" positions, for a specific period of time. When activated, the solenoid measures ambient barometric pressure from above throttle valve. Ambient barometric pressure changes due to weather and/or altitude. This information is sent to ECU for controlling fuel delivery time.

Fig. 3: Mitsubishi Pressure Sensor

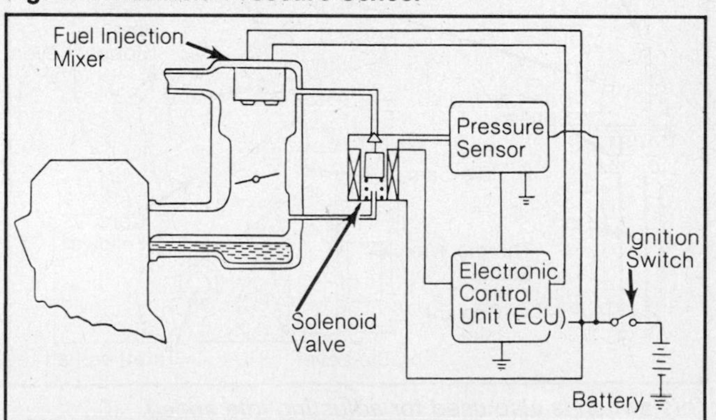
Fuel Injection Mixer
Pressure Sensor
Ignition Switch
Electronic Control Unit (ECU)
Solenoid Valve
Battery

Note solenoid valve and pressure sensor locations.

1983 Fuel Injection

MITSUBISHI ECI SYSTEM (Cont.)

After a predetermined period of time, solenoid valve is deactivated by ECU. When deactivated, the solenoid measures intake manifold pressure below throttle valve. The ECU compares barometric pressure and intake manifold pressure and an absolute value is used to determine fuel delivery and ignition timing.

The pressure sensor and solenoid valve are also used for altitude compensation. These components inform ECU of altitude. The ECU calculates air/fuel ratio necessary for engine operation in high altitude areas.

Coolant Temperature Sensor (CTS)

The coolant temperature sensor is installed in intake manifold. This sensor is a thermistor which converts temperature of engine coolant to electrical signal for use by ECU. The ECU uses coolant temperature information for controlling fuel delivery time, EGR and air injection system.

Engine Speed

Engine speed signal is received from ignition coil. Electrical signals from ignition coil are sent to ECU where time between signals is used to calculate engine speed. This information is used by ECU for controlling fuel delivery time, EGR and air injection system.

Oxygen Sensor

This sensor is mounted in exhaust system between turbocharger and front catalytic converter. Output voltage of oxygen sensor varies with oxygen content in exhaust gas stream.

When oxygen sensor signal is being interpreted by ECU, information is used to control fuel delivery time; this is called closed loop mode of operation. When oxygen sensor signals are not being interpreted by ECU, this is open loop mode of operation.

Throttle Position Sensor

This sensor is mounted on fuel injection mixer. The sensor, a rotary potentiometer, signals ECU of changes in throttle valve position. This information is used for controlling fuel delivery time.

Idle Position Switch

This switch is mounted on fuel injection mixer. When throttle valve is closed (idle position), the switch is activated. When throttle valve is at any other position, the switch is deactivated. This information is used by the ECU for controlling fuel delivery time (during deceleration) and air injection system. This switch is also used as an idle speed adjusting device.

Fig. 4: Idle Position Switch

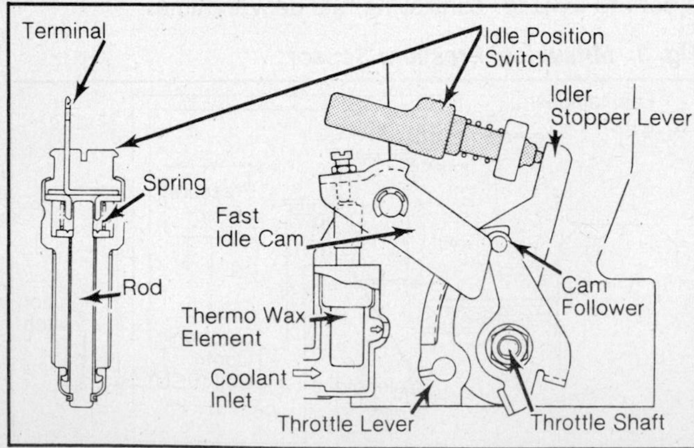

Terminal
Idle Position Switch
Idler Stopper Lever
Spring
Fast Idle Cam
Rod
Cam Follower
Thermo Wax Element
Coolant Inlet
Throttle Lever
Throttle Shaft

This switch is also used for adjusting idle speed.

Detonation Sensor

The detonation sensor (knock sensor) is located in cylinder block. This sensor converts engine vibration (knock) into an electrical signal. This signal is processed by the Electronic Spark Control (ESC) ignitor and relayed to ECU for determining amount of ignition timing retard. The ECU sends a signal to ESC ignitor to modify ignition timing. Ignition timing is retarded only during period of knock.

CAUTION: **Detonation sensor is strong enough to withstand engine vibration, but excessive impact with hammer, wrench, etc., can damage sensor.**

FUEL CUTOFF

Two different fuel cutoff systems are used to change fuel delivery rate to engine:

Deceleration Fuel Cutoff

During vehicle operation, idle position switch not at idle position, fuel delivery is determined by ECU responding to throttle valve closing speeds.

To decrease HC emissions during vehicle deceleration, fuel delivery time is decreased by ECU changing injection interval. When engine is operated under predetermined conditions, injection interval is changed from once every 3 pulses of air flow sensor to once every 6 pulses of air flow sensor.

Over Boost Fuel Cutoff

This fuel cutoff system protects the engine during turbocharger operation. When the pressure sensor detects higher manifold pressure than the predetermined value stored in ECU memory, the ECU changes fuel delivery rate. When pressure value is exceeded, the fuel injectors are energized according to ignition spark timing.

TESTING

NOTE: **Complete diagnosis requires Mitsubishi tester (MD998406). Some component checks may be made using shop test equipment. This article covers only fuel portion of system. For more information, see MITSUBISHI ELECTRONICALLY CONTROLLED INJECTION (ECI) SYSTEM article in COMPUTERIZED ENGINE CONTROLS Section.**

FUEL INJECTION MIXER & INJECTORS

1) Disconnect secondary wire from ignition coil. Disconnect vacuum hose from nipple on fuel pressure regulator. Drain radiator.

2) Remove 2 screws and 2 bolts from fuel injection mixer. Remove cover assembly from mixer. Remove and hold 1 injector in one hand. In other hand, hold cloth away from end of injector to catch fuel spray.

3) Turn ignition switch to "START" position. Injector should spray fuel in a good pattern without being injected in "streams". Perform test on other injector. DO NOT perform this test for more than 1 or 2 seconds and keep all body parts away from tip of injector.

4) Turn ignition "OFF" and check for fuel leakage at injector tip. If spray pattern is not acceptable or

MITSUBISHI ECI SYSTEM (Cont.)

fuel leakage occurs after ignition is turned off, replace injector.

5) Remove "O" ring in top of fuel injection mixer body and replace with new "O" ring. Install injectors and cover. Insert bolts and screws and tighten evenly, in steps, to specifications.

6) Reconnect vacuum hose to fuel pressure regulator. Reconnect secondary wire to ignition coil.

Fig. 5: Mitsubishi Fuel Injection Mixer

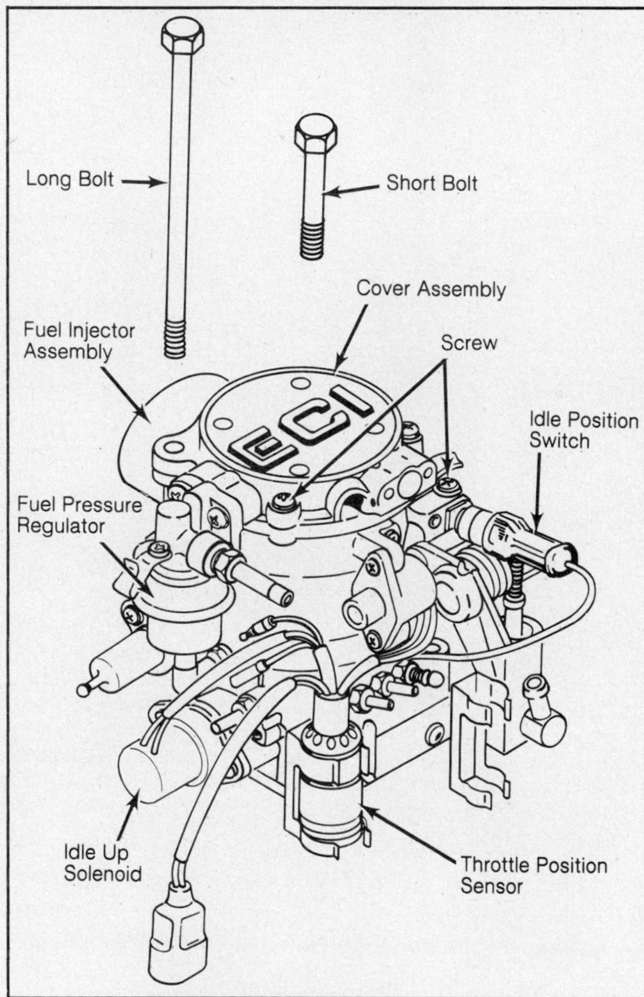

Long Bolt
Short Bolt
Cover Assembly
Fuel Injector Assembly
Screw
Idle Position Switch
Fuel Pressure Regulator
Idle Up Solenoid
Throttle Position Sensor

Note location of long and short bolts.

INJECTOR CIRCUIT

1) Unplug connector of the injector harness. Using a volt/ohmmeter, test continuity of each circuit. *See Fig. 6.*

Fig. 6: Testing Injector Circuit Continuity

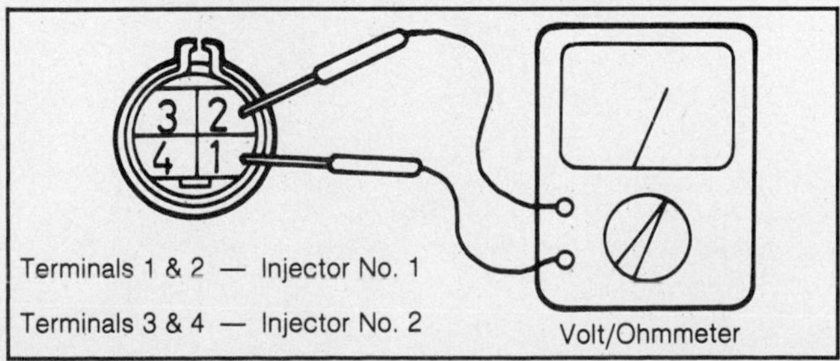

3 2
4 1
Terminals 1 & 2 — Injector No. 1
Terminals 3 & 4 — Injector No. 2
Volt/Ohmmeter

2) If continuity reading is zero or excessive, check harness for breaks or shorts. Replace harness, if required.

FUEL PUMP

1) Using a jumper wire, jumper both terminals of fuel pump "CHECK" connector. Turn ignition switch "ON" and listen for sound of fuel pump.

2) If pump is not heard running, inspect connector and wiring. If okay, disconnect electrical connector at fuel pump and apply 12 volts across terminals. If pump still does not operate, replace pump.

Fig. 7: Testing Fuel Pump

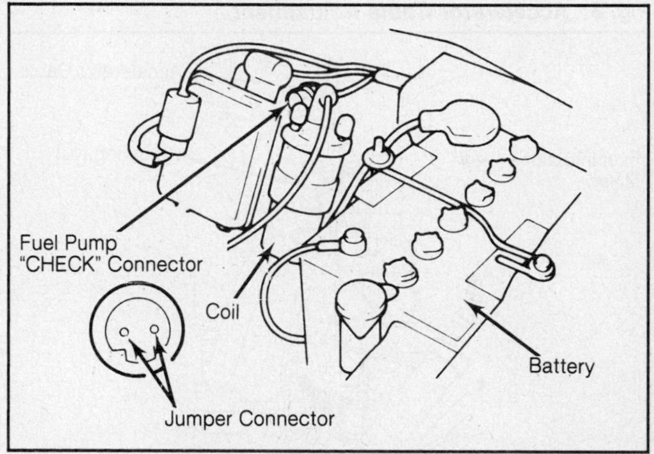

Fuel Pump "CHECK" Connector
Coil
Battery
Jumper Connector

REMOVAL & INSTALLATION

FUEL INJECTION MIXER

NOTE: Before removing any fuel line, pressure must be released from the system using the following procedure: Start engine and disconnect fuel pump connector. After engine stops, turn ignition "OFF" and disconnect battery ground cable. Reconnect fuel pump connector.

Removal

1) Disconnect battery ground cable. Remove air intake pipe and throttle cable. Drain radiator and remove water hose (between injection mixer and manifold) at injection mixer.

2) Remove vacuum hoses from injection mixer. Remove all electrical connections at mixer. Remove fuel inlet and outlet pipes at injection mixer. Remove fuel injection mixer.

Installation

1) Install injection mixer and tighten bolts and screws to specification. Coat tip of fuel pipes with gasoline and install. Use care not to damage "O" rings when installing fuel pipes to injection mixer.

2) Connect vauum hoses and electrical connectors. Install battery ground cable. Fill and purge cooling system of air. Apply grease to air intake pipe "O" ring and install air pipe.

3) Start the engine and check all hoses for fuel and water leaks.

MITSUBISHI ECI SYSTEM (Cont.)

ADJUSTMENTS

NOTE: Refer to the appropriate Mitsubishi article in TUNE-UP Section for the idle speed adjustment procedure.

ACCELERATOR CABLE

1) Start and run engine until normal operating temperature is reached. Allow engine to run at idle speed. Measure accelerator pedal free play at pedal.

2) To adjust free play, loosen cable adjusting nut at fuel injection mixer. Adjust length of cable until free play is within specifications and tighten adjusting nut.

Fig. 8: Accelerator Cable Adjustment

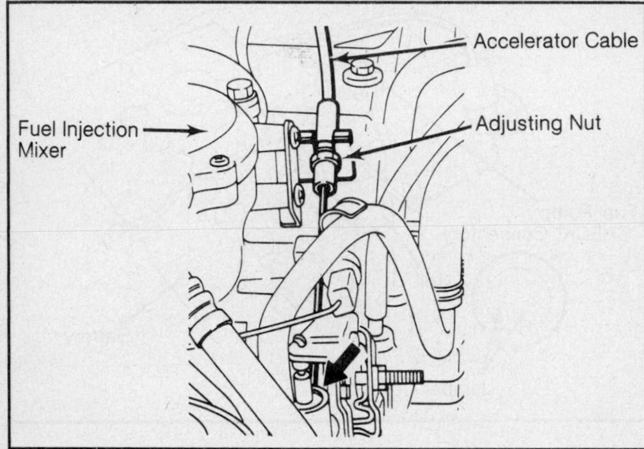
Accelerator Cable
Fuel Injection Mixer
Adjusting Nut

Measure free play at pedal. Adjust at fuel injection mixer.

ACCELERATOR CABLE FREE PLAY

Application	In. (mm)
Free Play (at Pedal)	0-.04 (0-1)

TIGHTENING SPECIFICATIONS

Application	Ft. Lbs. (N.m)
Fuel Injection Mixer	
Cover Screws	1.5-2.5 (2-3.5)
Cover Bolts	11-14 (15-19)
Fuel Injectors	1.5-2.5 (2-3.5)

AUDI & VOLKSWAGEN

Audi 4000, 5000; Volkswagen Jetta, Pickup, Quantum, Rabbit, Vanagon

DESCRIPTION

Diesel fuel injection systems consist of the fuel tank, fuel filter, distributor-type injection pump, glow plugs, throttling pintle injection nozzles, and a centrifugal governor. *See Fig. 1.*

A vane-type fuel pump, built into injection pump, supplies fuel from tank to fuel filter and then to injection pump. Injection pump supplies fuel to nozzles under high pressure, according to firing order (1-3-4-2 on 4 cylinder engines and 1-2-4-5-3 on 5 cylinder engines). Excess fuel is returned to fuel tank by return lines.

OPERATION

FUEL INJECTION PUMP

The Bosch single plunger mechanical pump consists of a low-pressure, vane-type fuel pump, a high-pressure distributor plunger injection pump, a centrifugal governor, an injection timing mechanism, an electrical fuel shut-off solenoid, and a manual injection pump shut-off valve. *See Fig. 1.*

As the vane pump rotor turns, centrifugal force holds the vanes against the walls of the pump's pressure chamber. The off-center design of the rotor and pressure chamber squeezes trapped fuel between vanes and forces it out the delivery port. Vane pressure is 42.7-99.6 psi (3-7 kg/cm²). The main pump increases this pressure to approximately 1800-2400 psi (126-168 kg/cm²). Pressures vary with model application.

The injection pump on turbo diesel models is also equipped with a boost pressure enrichment device. *See Fig. 2.* Since the turbocharger supplies more air to the engine, the boost pressure enrichment device is needed to increase the amount of fuel delivered to the engine.

At full throttle, when turbocharger boost pressure is low, no enrichment is needed. As turbocharger boost pressure increases, the pressure begins to work on the enrichment device diaphragm, forcing it down. This turns the bell crank which in turn moves the control ring further to the right. In this manner, the effective stroke of the distributor plunger is lengthened which increases the amount of fuel delivered to the injectors.

Fig. 1: Bosch Diesel Fuel Supply System

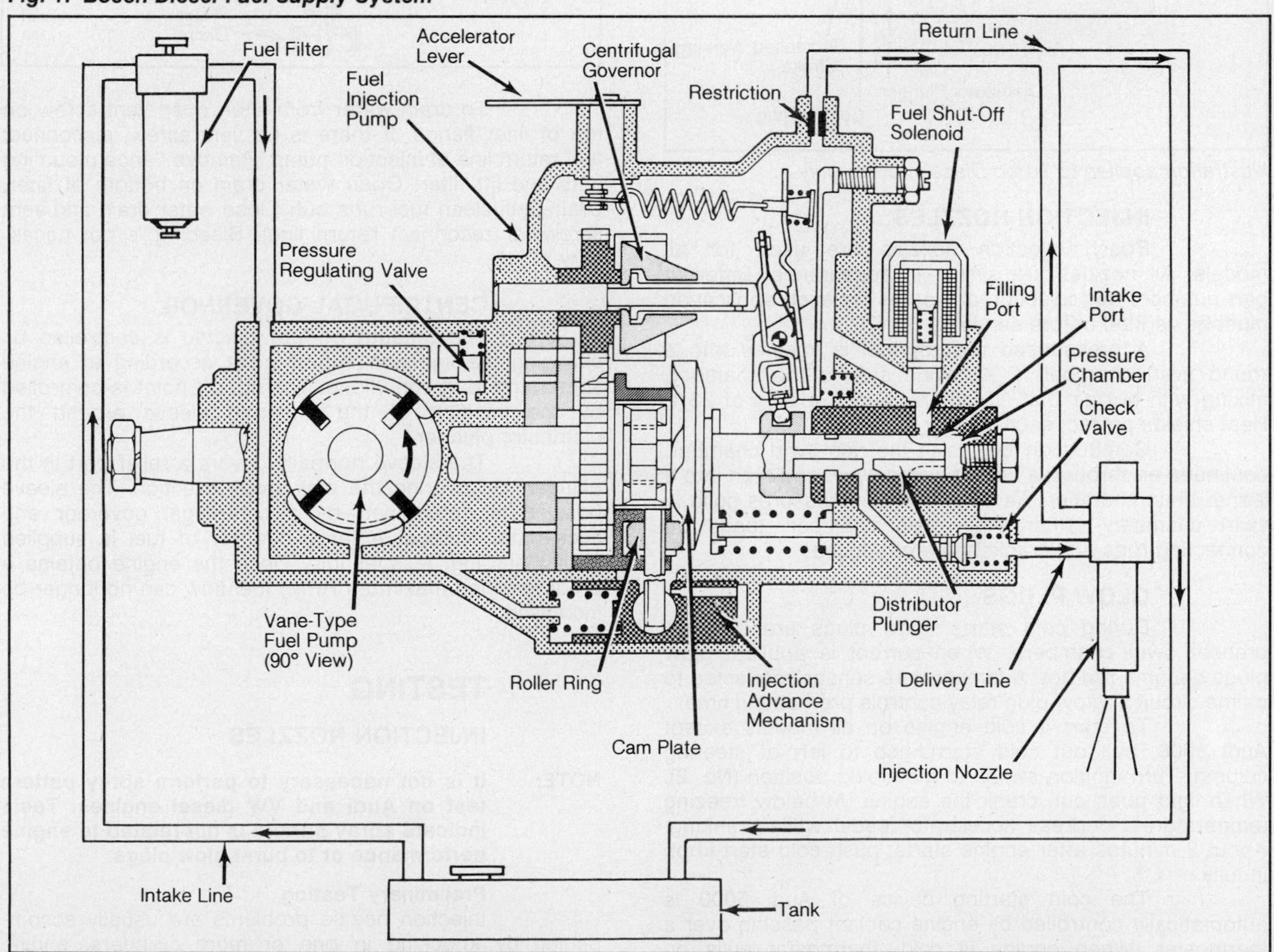
Fuel Filter
Accelerator Lever
Fuel Injection Pump
Centrifugal Governor
Return Line
Restriction
Fuel Shut-Off Solenoid
Pressure Regulating Valve
Filling Port
Intake Port
Pressure Chamber
Check Valve
Vane-Type Fuel Pump (90° View)
Roller Ring
Injection Advance Mechanism
Cam Plate
Distributor Plunger
Delivery Line
Injection Nozzle
Intake Line
Tank

Illustration applies to all models except Turbo Diesel.

AUDI & VOLKSWAGEN (Cont.)

Fig. 2: Bosch Diesel Fuel Injection Pump

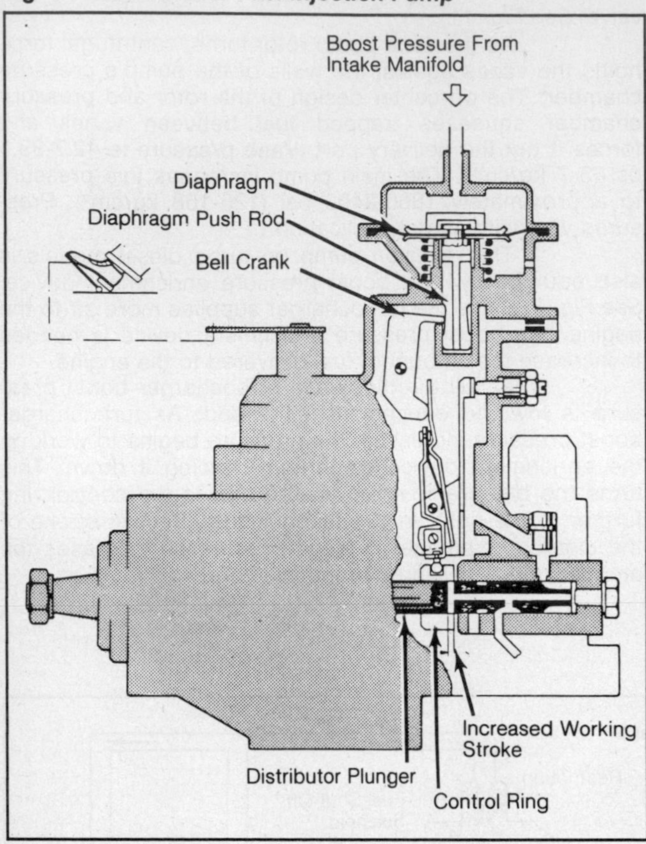
Boost Pressure From
Intake Manifold
Diaphragm
Diaphragm Push Rod
Bell Crank
Increased Working
Stroke
Distributor Plunger
Control Ring

Illustration applies to Turbo Diesel models only.

INJECTION NOZZLES

Bosch injection nozzles are used for all models. All nozzles are similar in appearance. Different part numbers and injection pressures for each application must be verified before servicing.

A pressurized mist of fuel is injected into a round swirl chamber. Fuel swirls around the chamber, mixing with hot air that is compressed to a ratio of 23:1. Heat shields protect each injector.

Combustion begins in the rich swirl chamber, continues on through a small passageway, and then into a leaner main chamber. As peak cylinder pressures build in swirl chamber, rather than main chamber, loads on connecting rods and crankshaft are reduced.

GLOW PLUGS

During cold starts, glow plugs are used to preheat swirl chambers. When current is applied, glow plugs become red hot. A temperature sensor connected to a time circuit in glow plug relay controls pre-heating time.

To start a cold engine on all models except Audi 5000, pull out cold start knob to left of steering column. Turn ignition switch to glow plug position (No. 2). When light goes out, crank the engine. At below freezing temperatures, depress accelerator pedal while cranking. About 2 minutes after engine starts, push cold start knob in fully.

The cold starting device of Audi 5000 is automatically controlled by engine coolant passing over a thermostat. When engine is cold, thermostat pulls on advance lever advancing injection timing.

FUEL FILTER

The fuel filter allows unrestricted flow of fuel from the tank to the injection pump, but stops any dirt or water. A replaceable element, similar to an oil filter cartridge, threads onto a removable flange. *See Fig. 3.*

Fig. 3: Components of Fuel Filter

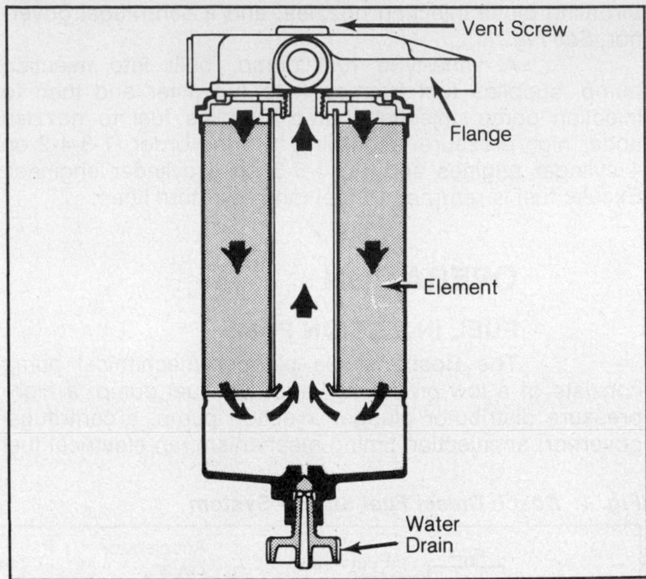
Vent Screw
Flange
Element
Water
Drain

To drain water from filter, open vent screw on top of filter flange. If there is no vent screw, disconnect fuel return line at injection pump. Remove flange mounting nuts and lift filter. Open water drain on bottom of filter. Drain until clean fuel runs out. Close water drain and vent screw (or reconnect return line). Bleeding is not necessary.

CENTRIFUGAL GOVERNOR

The amount of fuel injected is controlled by changing the injection cut-off point according to engine speed and load conditions. The cut-off point is controlled by the position of the metering sleeve around the distributor plunger.

The sleeve normally covers a relief port in the plunger. Uncovering the port stops injection. The sleeve position is determined by a centrifugal governor and accelerator linkage. A large quantity of fuel is supplied during starting, less at idle. Once the engine obtains a predetermined maximum RPM, fuel flow can no longer be increased.

TESTING

INJECTION NOZZLES

NOTE: **It is not necessary to perform spray pattern test on Audi and VW diesel engines. Tests indicate spray pattern is not related to engine performance or to burnt glow plugs.**

Preliminary Testing

Injection nozzle problems are usually accompanied by knocking in one or more cylinders, engine overheating, loss of power or performance, black exhaust smoke, and increased fuel consumption. To locate and correct faulty injectors, proceed as follows:

1) With the engine running at fast idle, loosen line unions on each injection nozzle one at a time. If engine speed remains constant with a line removed, that nozzle is defective.

2) To remove nozzle, detach injector line. Use special extra-deep socket (US 2775) to remove injection nozzles. To remove or install injector nozzles on turbo models, remachine a 1/2" (13mm) socket wrench extension to dimensions shown. *See Fig. 4.*

3) To disassemble, place upper part of nozzle in a vise and loosen lower part. Then reverse position of nozzle in vise and carefully remove internal parts from lower part of nozzle.

4) Do not interchange parts from one injector to another. When one injector is replaced, all other injectors must be tested and adjusted if necessary. Adjust injectors to 2176 psi (150 kg/cm²) for turbo models and 1885 psi (132.5 kg/cm²) for all others.

NOTE: New and rebuilt injectors have a settling effect of approximately 72.5 psi (5.1 kg/cm²). When installing new/rebuilt injectors in conjunction with used injectors, the new/rebuilt injectors must have a 72.5 psi (5.1 kg/cm²) higher opening pressure.

Fig. 4: Fuel Injector Socket Wrench Extension

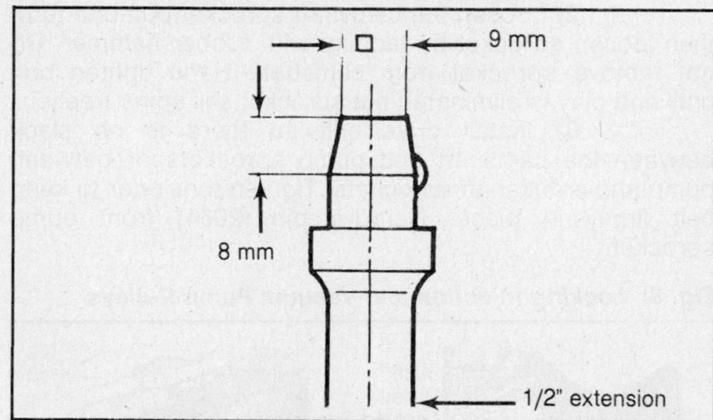
9 mm
8 mm
1/2" extension

Illustration applies to Turbo Diesel models only.

Installation

When installing injector nozzles, a new heat shield must be used. Insert heat shield with recess pointing upward. *See Fig. 5.* Tighten nozzles to specifications. Bleeding is not necessary.

Noise Test

Listen to nozzle while it is being tested on special testing gauge (US 1111). Use long, slow strokes of testing pump lever (1-2 strokes per second). If nozzle is working properly, it will "ping" as fuel emerges.

Opening Pressure Test

With testing gauge (US 1111) still connected to injector, move pump lever down slowly. Note pressure at which injection nozzle releases fuel. Nozzle working pressure must be within specifications. Adjust, if necessary, by changing shims. Thicker shims increase pressure, thinner shims decrease pressure.

Fig. 5: Exploded View of Injection Nozzle

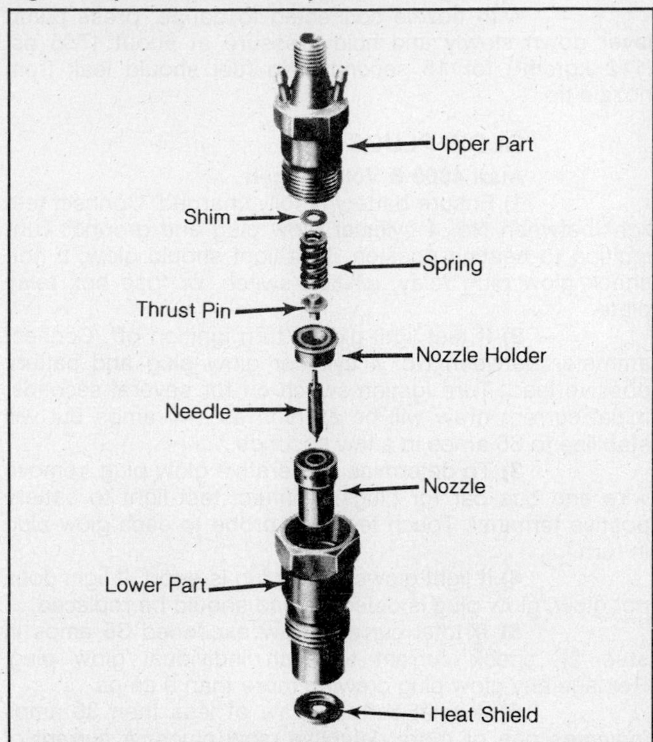
Upper Part
Shim
Spring
Thrust Pin
Nozzle Holder
Needle
Nozzle
Lower Part
Heat Shield

Heat shield must be installed as shown.

INJECTOR NOZZLE OPENING PRESSURE

Model	psi (kg/cm²)
Turbo Diesel	2248-2364 (158-166)
All Others	1740-1885 (122-132.5)

NOTE: A shim thickness increase of .0019" (0.05 mm) increases pressure by 71 psi (5.0 kg/cm²). Shims are available in thicknesses of .039-.070" (1.00-1.95 mm) in .0019" (0.05 mm) increments.

Fig. 6: Injection Nozzle Mounted on Tester

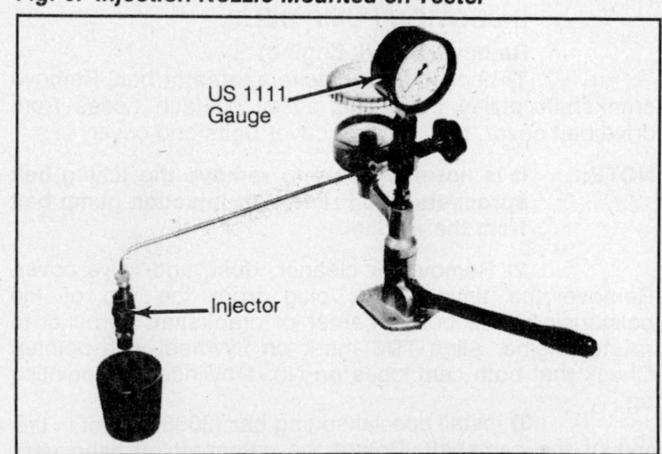
US 1111
Gauge
Injector

1983 Diesel Fuel Injection

AUDI & VOLKSWAGEN (Cont.)

Leakage Test

With nozzle connected to gauge, press pump lever down slowly and hold pressure at about 1595 psi (112 kg/cm²) for 15 seconds. No fuel should leak from nozzle tip.

GLOW PLUGS

Audi 4000 & Volkswagen

1) Ensure battery is fully charged. Connect test light between No. 4 cylinder glow plug and ground. Turn ignition to heating position. Test light should glow. If not, check glow plug relay, ignition switch, or fuse box relay plate.

2) If test light glows, turn ignition off. Connect ammeter between No. 4 cylinder glow plug and battery positive lead. Turn igntion switch on for several seconds. Initial current draw will be as high as 140 amps but will stabilize to 36 amps in a few seconds.

3) To determine inoperative glow plug, remove wire and bus bar for plugs. Connect test light to battery postive terminal. Touch test light probe to each glow plug in turn.

4) If light glows, glow plug is good. If light does not glow, glow plug is defective and should be replaced.

5) If total current draw exceeded 36 amps in step **2)**, check current to each individual glow plug. Replace any glow plug drawing more than 9 amps.

6) A total current draw of less than 36 amps indicates one or more defective glow plugs. A current of 27 amps is 1 bad glow plug, 18 amps is 2 bad glow plugs, and 9 amps is 3 bad glow plugs.

Audi 5000

1) Testing procedure for the Audi 5000 is similar to Audi 4000 and VW testing except for the following:

2) In step **1)**, connect test light to No. 5 cylinder. In step **2)**, connect ammeter between No. 5 cylinder and battery lead.

3) Each glow plug on Audi 5000 draws 12 amps. Therefore, total current draw will be 60 amps. Total current draw of less than 60 amps indicates one or more defective glow plugs.

REMOVAL & INSTALLATION

INJECTION PUMP BELT

Removal (4-Cyl. Engine)

1) Loosen and remove alternator belt. Remove crankshaft pulley bolts and pulley. Detach hoses from drive belt cover, then remove cover bolts and cover.

NOTE: **It is not necessary to remove the timing belt sprockets when removing injection pump belt from the engine.**

2) Remove air cleaner, duct, and valve cover. Remove the timing mark plug from the top of the bellhousing. Use bolt in center of crankshaft sprocket to rotate engine. Align TDC mark on flywheel with pointer. Check that both cam lobes on No. 1 cylinder are pointing up.

3) Install special setting bar (2065) in slot in the end of the camshaft. Rotate the camshaft by hand until one end of the bar touches the cylinder head. Measure the gap at the other end of the bar with a feeler gauge and divide this number by 2. Use 2 feeler gauges of this size; they will be necessary to lock camshaft on center.

Fig. 7: Installing Camshaft Locking Tool

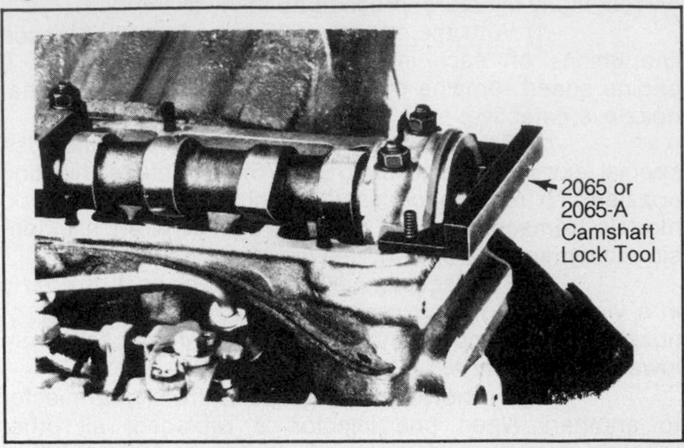
2065 or
2065-A
Camshaft
Lock Tool

4) Lock camshaft in position by inserting one feeler gauge on either side of the bar, between the bar and the cylinder head. Loosen camshaft drive belt tensioner lock nut and turn tensioner counterclockwise to remove tension from belt. Remove the belt by working it off the sprockets.

Installation

1) Ensure marks on pump sprocket, pump bracket, and pump housing are aligned. Install pump sprocket locking pin (2064). TDC mark on the flywheel should still aligned with pointer.

2) Loosen the camshaft sprocket bolt one turn, then loosen sprocket by tapping with rubber hammer. Do not remove sprocket from camshaft. Hand tighten bolt until end play is eliminated but sprocket still spins freely.

3) Install drive belt so there is no slack between the camshaft and pump sprockets or between pump and crankshaft sprockets. Tighten tensioner to keep belt firmly in place. Remove pin (2064) from pump sprocket.

Fig. 8: Locking Injection and Vacuum Pump Pulleys

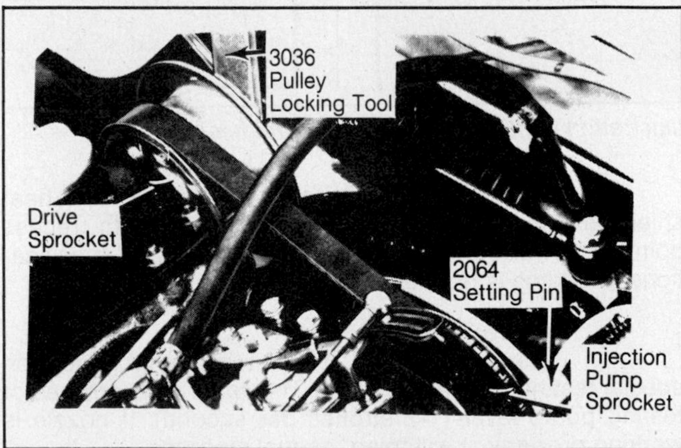
3036
Pulley
Locking Tool
Drive
Sprocket
2064
Setting Pin
Injection
Pump
Sprocket

Audi 5000 pulley identification and tool location.

4) Install belt tension tester (VW 210). Adjust belt tensioner until tension tester reads 12-13. Tighten tensioner lock nut and camshaft sprocket bolt to 33 ft. lb. (45 N.m). Remove locking tool from camshaft.

5) Turn the crankshaft 2 complete revolutions. Strike the belt with a rubber hammer between cam and pump sprockets and recheck belt tension. Readjust if necessary. Check and adjust injection pump timing.

AUDI & VOLKSWAGEN (Cont.)

Removal (5-Cyl. Engine)

1) Remove vacuum pump pulley and belt. Remove belt cover for injection pump drive belt. Set crankshaft to TDC on compression stroke of cylinder No. 1. Check timing marks to verify crankshaft position. Marks are located on flywheel/clutch housing and on injection pump sprocket mounting plate.

2) Lock injection pump sprocket in place with holding pin (2064). Hold injection pump drive sprocket with bar (3036). Remove drive sprocket retaining bolt, V-belt pulley, injection pump drive sprocket, and belt.

Installation

1) Install injection pump drive sprocket with belt. Tighten sprocket bolt until it is just possible to turn pump sprocket by hand. Check tension of belt with tool (VW 210), belt tension should be 12-13.

2) If belt tension is not within specifications, loosen mounting bolts for pump bracket and adjust position of pump. Retest for proper belt tension. Check that crankshaft position is TDC of No.1 cylinder.

3) Hold injection pump drive sprocket with tool (3036) and tighten retaining bolt to 72 ft. lb. (100 N.m). Remove locking pin from pump sprocket. Check and adjust injection pump timing. Install belt cover.

INJECTION PUMP

NOTE: **When installing pump on check runout of pump gear with a dial indicator. Maximum runout should be .008" (.2 mm). If runout is excessive, replace gear.**

Removal (4-Cyl. Engine)

1) Remove injection pump belt. Remove injection pipes and cover fuel outlets to prevent contamination. Remove solenoid wire, hoses and control cables from pump.

2) Insert pump sprocket locking tool (2064) and remove sprocket bolt. Use puller (3032 or VW 203b) to remove pump sprocket. Place puller so jaws are at a right angle to the bar and pointing in the direction of spindle rotation. Apply light tension to puller.

3) Strike puller spindle head lightly to loosen sprocket from the shaft. Do not pry on sprocket with bar or lever. Remove pump mounting bolts and remove pump from engine.

Fig. 9: Removing Fuel Injection Pump Driven Gear

3032
Puller

Audi models illustrated, Volkwagen similar.

Installation

1) Install pump on mounting plate. Leave bolts loose until timing marks are aligned. After aligning marks. Tighten mounting bolts to 18 ft. lb. (25 N.m).

2) Reconnect fuel pipes and hoses, solenoid wire and control cables. Tighten fuel pipe connections to 18 ft. lb. (25 N.m). Install sprocket on pump shaft, do not tighten nut. Turn pump sprocket by hand to align mark on sprocket with mark on mounting plate. Insert holding pin (2064) in pump sprocket. Tighten nut to 33 ft. lb. (45 N.m).

3) Make sure that crankshaft is at TDC and reinstall timing belt. Adjust belt tension and pump timing. Bleeding is not required.

Removal (5-Cyl. Engine)

1) Remove injection pump timing belt. Install sprocket locking pin (2064) in pump sprocket and loosen retaining nut 1 turn. Remove locking pin and install puller (3032) on sprocket.

2) Place puller so that jaws are at a right angle to the bar and pointing in the direction of spindle rotation. Apply light tension to puller. Tap lightly on puller spindle head to loosen sprocket from pump shaft. Remove retaining nut and sprocket from pump.

Fig. 10: Aligning Injection Pump Reference Marks

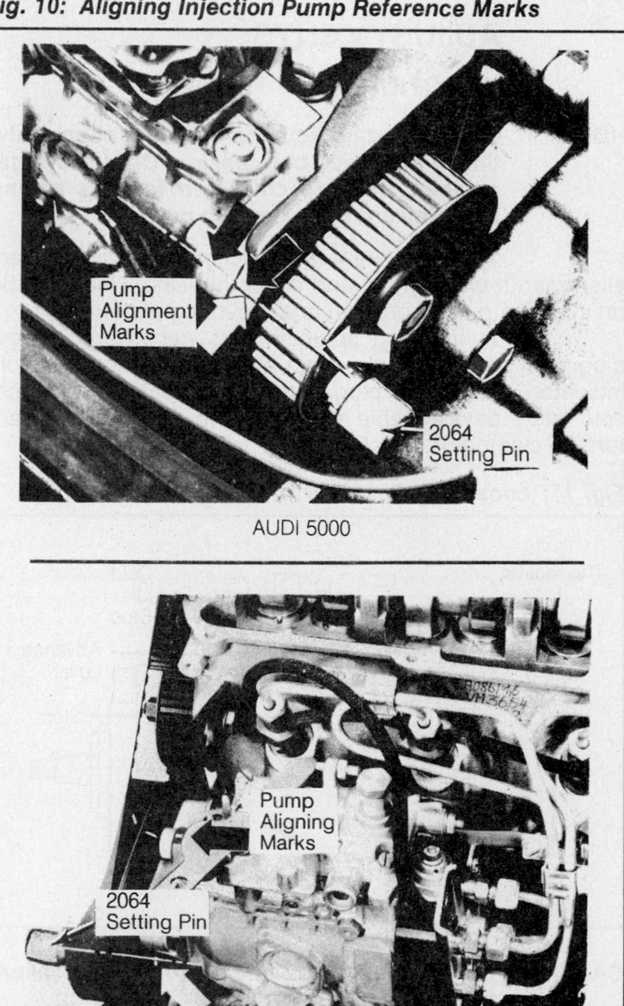
Pump
Alignment
Marks
2064
Setting Pin
AUDI 5000
Pump
Aligning
Marks
2064
Setting Pin
VOLKSWAGEN & AUDI 4000

AUDI & VOLKSWAGEN (Cont.)

3) Remove injection pipes, hoses, wire, and control cable from pump. Remove mounting bolts from pump mounting plate and bracket. Remove pump.

Installation

1) Install pump and align marks on pump and mounting plate. Install pump mounting bolts and tighten slightly. Align rear support bracket so that it contacts the pump and the cylinder block free of tension. Install bracket bolts and tighten all bolts securing pump.

2) Install injection pipes, hoses, wire and control cable. Install injection pump sprocket and holding pin (2064). Tighten sprocket retaining nut to 72 ft. lb. (100 N.m). Turn sprocket by hand until the marks on the sprocket and the mounting plate are in line.

3) Install drive belt and drive gear. Reassembly is reverse of disassembly proceedure. Check and adjust pump timing. Bleeding is not required.

FUEL FILTER

Service is limited to replacing filter at proper interval and draining water, when present. Bleeding is not required.

ADJUSTMENTS

INJECTION PUMP TIMING

NOTE: Before starting timing procedure, check valve timing and drive belt tension. On Volkswagen engines, be sure cold start lever is against stop (toward drive gear on pump).

1) Set crankshaft to TDC on No. 1 cylinder and align marks on flywheel and clutch housing. Check marks on injection pump sprocket and mounting plate.

2) If timing adjustment is necessary, remove plug from injection pump cover and install adapter and dial indicator in place of plug. On Audi models only, loosen cold start device cable by loosening screw No. 1 and turning clamp 90°. *See Fig. 11.*

Fig. 11: Loosening Cold Start Device Screw No. 1

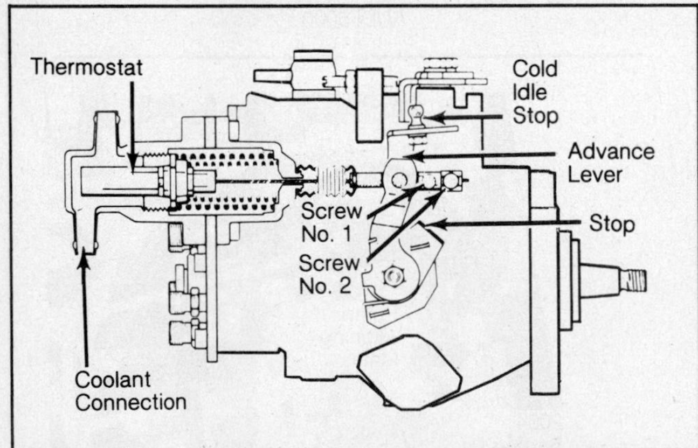
Thermostat
Cold Idle Stop
Advance Lever
Screw No. 1
Stop
Screw No. 2
Coolant Connection

CAUTION: Do not loosen screw No. 2 or pump recalibration will be necessary.

3) Preload dial indicator (2066) to .097" (2.5 mm). *See Fig. 12.* Slowly turn engine counterclockwise until dial indicator needle stops moving. Zero indicator.

Fig. 12: Adjusting Injection Pump Timing

2066 Gauge

4) Turn engine clockwise until TDC mark on flywheel lines up with reference mark. Check dial indicator reading. *See Injection Pump Timing Specifications* table.

INJECTION PUMP TIMING SPECIFICATIONS

Application	In. (mm)
Audi	
4000	
Check Specification	.035-.037 (.88-.93)
Adjusting Specification	.033-.035 (.84-.88)
5000	
Check Specification	.035-.039 (.88-.98)
Adjusting Specification	.036-.037 (.91-.95)
Volkswagen	
Turbo Diesel	
Check Specification	.035-.039 (.90-1.0)
Adjusting Specification	.039-.040 (.98-1.02)
All Others	
Check Specification	.037-.041 (.95-1.05)
Adjusting Specification	.039-.040 (.98-1.02)

5) If necessary, loosen bolts on mounting plate and support. Turn pump to adjust timing and tighten bolts. Recheck dial indicator readings. On Audi vehicles, turn clamp on cold start device back 90° to original position and tighten screw No. 1.

ACCELERATOR CABLE

CAUTION: Check and adjust idle and maximum speed before making cable adjustments.

Audi

Place accelerator pedal in full throttle position. Adjust accelerator cable by inserting clip in appropriate slot. Adjust so lever in injection pump rests against maximum speed stop but is not under tension.

Volkswagen

Place accelerator pedal in full throttle position. Adjust cable with adjusting nuts until pump lever freely contacts stop. *See Fig. 13.* Be sure ball pin on pump lever is pointing upward and touching end of elongated hole. Accelerator cable should be attached at upper hole in bracket.

AUDI & VOLKSWAGEN (Cont.)

Fig. 13: Accelerator Cable Adjusting Points

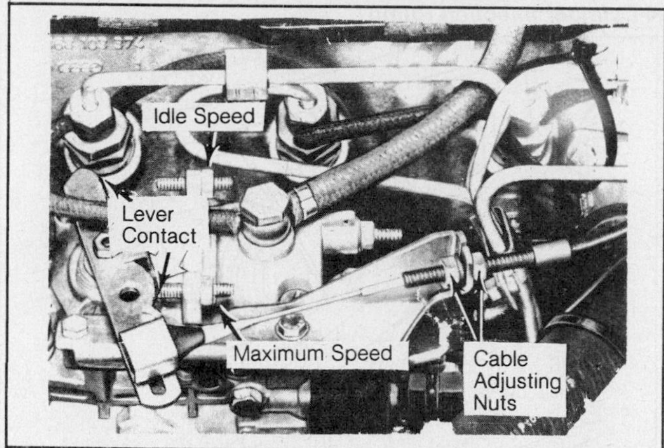
Idle Speed
Lever
Contact
Maximum Speed
Cable
Adjusting
Nuts

COLD STARTING CABLE

On Volkswagen and Audi 4000 vehicles, insert washer onto cable and install cable into bracket with rubber bushing. Insert cable into pin. Install lock washer and move lever as far as possible in direction of arrow. *See Fig. 14.* Pull cable tight and secure pin with clamping screw.

Fig. 14: Adjusting Cold Starting Cable

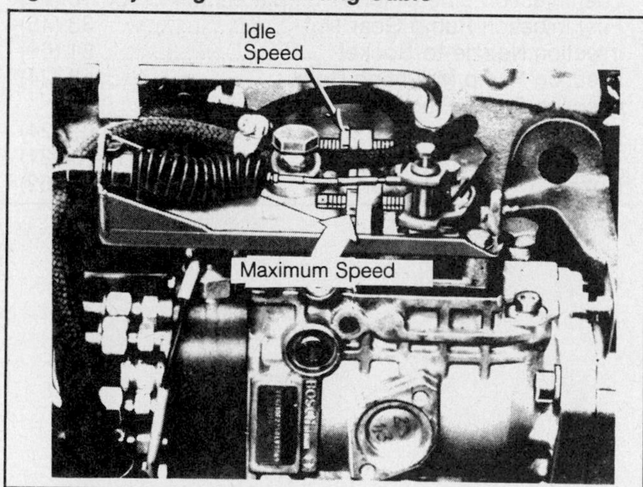
Idle
Speed
Maximum Speed

IDLE SPEED

Audi

1) Warm engine to normal operating temperature (oil temperature of 122-158°F or 50-70°C). Turn idle speed control knob on instrument panel counterclockwise to stop.

2) Connect tachometer (VW 1367 or Siemans 451) according to instructions. Loosen lock nut to adjust idle speed. Turn screw in to raise idle speed, or out to lower idle speed. Retighten lock nut. *See Fig. 15.*

Volkswagen

1) Warm engine to normal operating temperature (oil temperature of 122-158°F or 50-70°C). Connect tachometer (VW 1367 or Siemans 451) according to instructions. Adjust idle speed to specifications.

2) To adjust, loosen lock nut and turn screw in to raise idle speed, or out to lower idle speed. Retighten lock nut and seal with paint.

Fig. 15: Adjusting Audi Idle and Maximum Speed

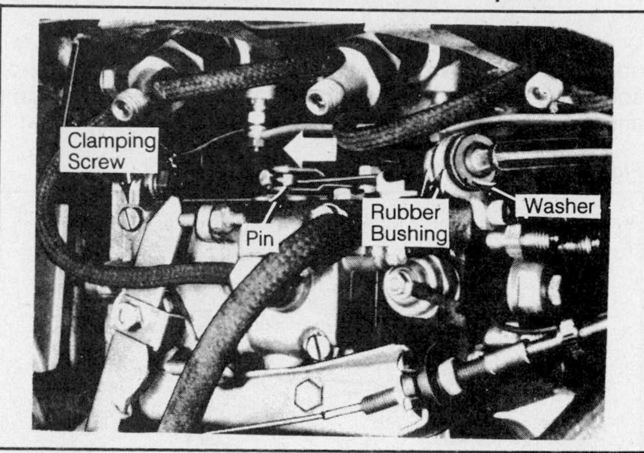
Clamping
Screw
Pin
Rubber
Bushing
Washer

IDLE SPEED

Application	RPM
Audi	
4-Cylinder	900-1000
5-Cylinder	720-780
Volkswagen	
Vanagon	800-850
All Others	810-950

MAXIMUM SPEED

Adjust idle speed to proper setting and then open throttle fully. To adjust, loosen lock nut and turn screw out to raise maximum speed, or in to lower it. Tighten lock nut when adjustment is complete. Seal lock nut and screw with paint.

MAXIMUM SPEED

Application	RPM
Vanagon	4750-4850
Turbo Diesels	5050-5150
All Others	5300-5400

STALL SPEED

Audi 5000 Auto. Trans.

1) Drive vehicle to warm up engine. Minimum oil temperature is 140° F (60° C). Turn off all electrical accessories including air conditioning. Apply hand and foot brake, engage transmission in "Drive". Ensure engine fan is not running.

2) Perform stall test at end of warm up drive, do not turn engine off. Push accelerator to floor (kick down position), stall speed must be at least 2400 RPM within 4 to 7 seconds.

CAUTION: Do not check stall speed longer than 10 seconds.

3) If stall speed is not within specifications, full load screw on injector pump must be adjusted. While holding screw with wrench, not screwdriver, loosen lock nut and turn screw clockwise 1/8 turn maximum. Tighten lock nut and recheck stall speed.

4) If stall speed is reached in less than 4 seconds, back off adjusting screw (counterclockwise) very slightly. Reseal screw with yellow paint.

AUDI & VOLKSWAGEN (Cont.)

FUEL CUT SOLENOID

All Models

If fuel cut-off solenoid valve fails, engine will not shut off with key. Before replacing fuel cut-off solenoid, it should be removed from the injection pump and cleaned. *See Fig. 16.*

Fig. 16: Injection Pump Fuel Cut Solenoid

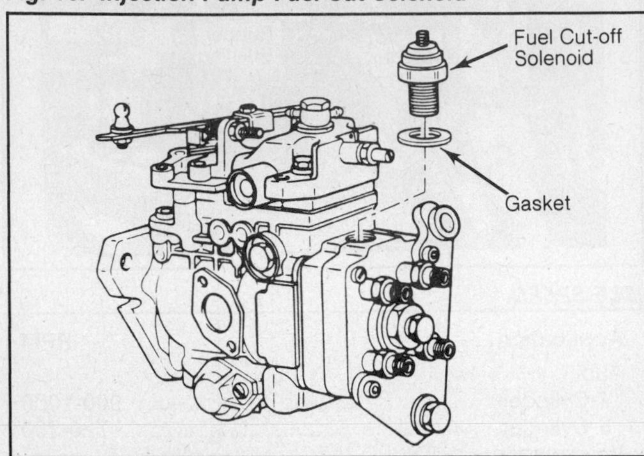
Fuel Cut-off Solenoid
Gasket

Always use new gasket.

When the solenoid and plunger are clean, the plunger must be checked for free movement in solenoid. Install solenoid in pump with a new seal. Test for proper solenoid operation by connecting to and disconnecting from battery voltage.

A manual fuel cut-off has been added to the injection pump. If the engine continues to run after key is turned off, move lever in direction of arrow. *See Fig. 17 or 18.*

Fig. 17: Manual Cut-Off Valve on 5-Cylinder Injection Pump

STOP
Manual Cut-Off Valve

Move lever in direction of arrow.

Fig. 18: Manual Cut-Off Valve on 4-Cylinder Injection Pump

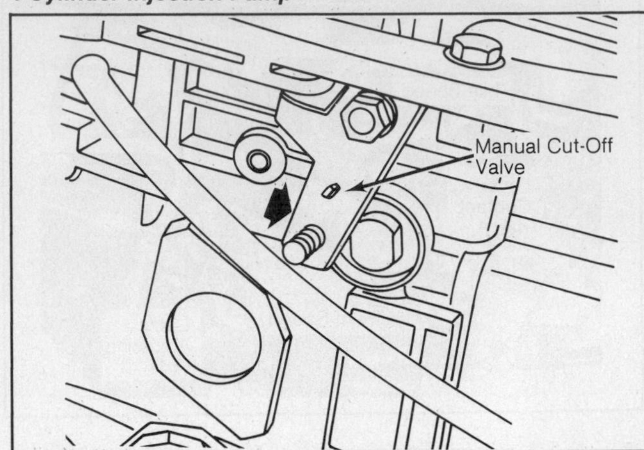
Manual Cut-Off Valve

Move lever in direction of arrow.

TIGHTENING SPECIFICATIONS

Application	Ft. Lbs. (N.m)
Camshaft Gear Bolt	33 (45)
Fuel Cut Solenoid	14 (20)
Fuel Delivery Valves	33 (45)
Fuel Injection Line Unions	18 (24)
Fuel Injection Pump Gear Nut	33 (45)
Injection Nozzle-to-Socket	51 (69)
Injection Pump Mounting Bolts	18 (24)
Injection Pump Plug	
Bronze Seal	14-18 (20-24)
Copper Seal	10-14 (14-21)
Nozzle (Upper-to-Lower Part)	51 (69)

CHRYSLER & MITSUBISHI

Chrysler Corp. Imports Colt Pickup, Ram-50 Pickup; Mitsubishi Pickup

DESCRIPTION

The Chrysler/Mitsubishi diesel fuel injection system consists of a combination injection pump and fuel distributor, four injection nozzles, a fuel tank, lines and hoses and a fuel filter assembly. The filter assembly contains a fuel filter, a fuel pre-heater, an integral priming pump and a water separator.

The injection pump is a low pressure vane type with a high pressure fuel distributor. The pump is driven from the engine timing belt. The pump has a boost compensator to supply a richer fuel mixture when the turbocharger is working; it also has an integral fuel cut-off solenoid for engine shut down.

The injectors use a needle type valve at the end of each nozzle. Injector opening pressure can be changed by adding to or subtracting from adjusting shim thickess. The adjusting shim is located just above the needle valve return spring in the injector.

Integrated into the fuel system is a "Quick Glow" glow plug system to aid in cold start operation. The glow plug system consists of a glow plug in each cylinder, two relays, a dropping resistor, a glow plug control unit and various lights and switches.

OPERATION

FUEL INJECTION PUMP

The vane pump output pressure (also referred to as the injection pump body pressure) averages between 50-100 psi depending upon the engine speed and application. The plunger type injection pump boosts this pressure to about 2000 psi.

Fig. 1: Diesel Fuel Injection Nozzle

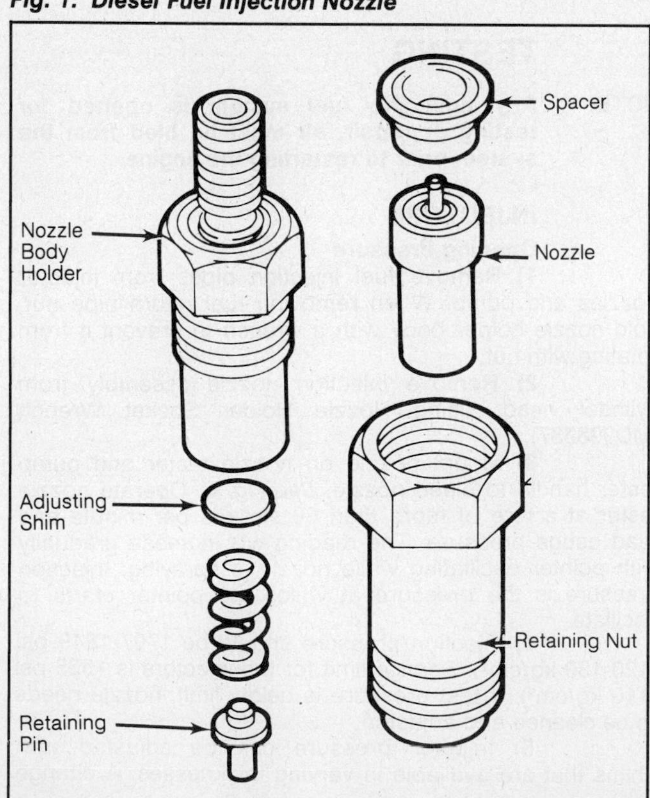
Spacer
Nozzle Body Holder
Nozzle
Adjusting Shim
Retaining Nut
Retaining Pin

INJECTORS

The injection spray nozzles spray fuel into a combustion prechamber as each compression stroke occurs. Nozzles can be disassembled, cleaned and adjusted to correct improper spray patterns.

Injector opening pressure can be adjusted with shims on top of the needle valve return spring. *See Fig. 1.* The injector receives a high pressure pulse of fuel which forces open the needle valve allowing fuel to pass into the prechamber.

GLOW PLUGS

A dropping resistor circuit has been adapted to the glow plug system. This system includes a dropping resistor and relay. In addition a new design glow plug and glow control unit are used. After system has provided an ultra-quick heating method for the glow plug, dropping resistor reduces the voltage to the plug.

The glow plug circuit has two main circuits to maintain the glow plug at constant temperature and to shorten the pre-starting time. One is the quick heat circuit which applies battery voltage directly to the glow plugs. The other is a heat stabilization circuit which decreases voltage to the glow plug by changing the power source to the dropping circuit when the glow plug reaches the design temperature.

FUEL FILTER

The fuel filter is provided to protect the fuel pump and injectors from dirt and water in the fuel. Integral heater is activated when the engine is running (9 volts or more are present at "L" terminal of alternator), and when fuel temperature is below 32-42 °F (0-6 °C). Fuel temperature sensor is in the top of the filter assembly. The

Fig. 2: Sectional View of Fuel Filter

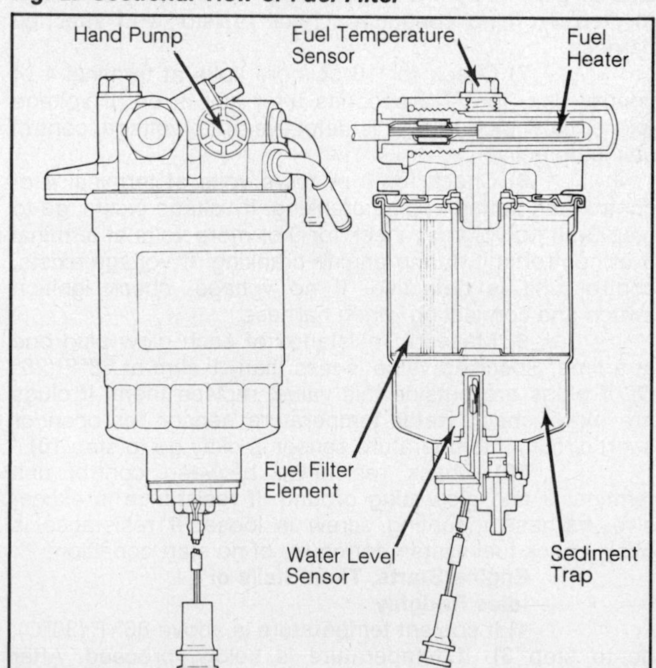
Hand Pump
Fuel Temperature Sensor
Fuel Heater
Fuel Filter Element
Water Level Sensor
Sediment Trap

hand pump is used to bleed the fuel system after servicing. *See Fig. 2.*

The lower portion of the filter assembly is a combination sediment trap and water level sensor. An accumulation of 5 cu. in. (80 cc) of water will cause the float in the water trap to rise and illuminate the water sensor warning light. The fuel filter element separates water from the fuel, then filters the fuel.

TROUBLE SHOOTING

GLOW PLUG SYSTEM

Engine Will Not Start, Engine Cold

1) Turn ignition on, and check for 10 or more volts at glow plugs for 1-6 seconds. If voltage exists go to step **5)**. If no voltage exists, check for 12 volts at battery side of glow plug relay 1. If voltage exists go to step **2)**. If no voltage exists, circuit is open in wiring harness.

2) Check for 10 or more volts at terminal 1 of control unit with ignition switch on. If voltage exists go to step **3)**. If no voltage, switch or wiring harness is defective.

3) Check continuity between glow plug side of glow plug relay 1 and plug. If continuity exists go to step **4)**. If no continuity, circuit is open in wiring harness.

4) Check for 10 or more volts, applied to terminal 2 of the control unit, approximately 1-6 seconds after ignition is on. If voltage exists, glow plug relay 1 is defective. If no voltage, check water temperature sensor and wiring harness used for detection of glow plug temperature. If both sensor and harness are okay, control unit is defective.

5) Approximately 1-6 seconds after switch is on, check for 5-8 volts at terminal 2 of control unit. Voltage lasts 6 seconds. If voltage exists, go to step **8)**. If no voltage, check for 12 volts at battery side of glow plug relay 2. If no voltage at relay, wiring harness is defective.

6) Check continuity between dropping resistor side of glow relay 2 and glow plug. If continuity exists go to step **7)**. If no continuity, check resistor and attached harness.

7) Check for 10 or more volts at terminal 4 of control unit, for 7-12 seconds after key is on. If voltage exists, glow plug relay 2 is defective. If no voltage, control unit is defective.

8) Check for 9 or more volts at terminal 4 of control unit during engine cranking. If voltage exists, go to step **9)**. If no voltage, check for 9 or more volts at terminal 3 of control unit during engine cranking. If voltage exists, control unit is defective. If no voltage, check ignition switch and connecting wiring harness.

9) Measure resistance of each glow plug one at a time. Specified value is less than .1 ohm at 68°F (20° C). If plugs are outside this value, replace them. If plugs are okay, check water temperature sensor for open or short circuit. If temperature sensor is okay go to step **10)**.

10) Check resistance between control unit terminal 9 and glow plug ground. If resistance is excessive, harness mounting screw is loose. If resistance is okay, check fuel system for cause of no start condition.

Engine Starts, Then Stalls or Idles Roughly

1) If coolant temperature is above 86° F (30°C), go to step **3)**. If temperature is below, proceed. After engine starts (charge light goes out), check for 5-8 volts supplied for 6 seconds between glow plug plate and ground.

2) If no voltage, check for 14 volts applied to terminal 12 of the control unit. If voltage exists, check operation of glow relay 2, dropping resistor for .13 ohm value, and body harness for open circuit. If no voltage, body harness is defective. If all above are okay, replace control unit.

3) If engine temperature is above 86°F (30°C), check resistance of each glow plug. Resistance should be 0.2 ohm or less at 68°F (20°C). If resistance is outside specifications, replace glow plugs. If resistance is within specifications, check fuel system or adjust idle.

Preheating Indicator Lamp (Red) Does Not Illuminate.

Check for 12 volts applied to terminal 5 of control unit when ignition switch is on. If voltage exists, replace control unit. If no voltage, check for burned out indicator lamp. Replace lamp as necessary. If lamp is okay, ignition switch or wiring harness is defective.

Preheating Indicator Lamp (Red) Remains Illuminated for More Than 3 Seconds

Check water temperature sensor. If okay replace control unit.

Start Indicator Lamp (Green) Does Not Illuminate

Check for 12 volts applied to terminal 6 of control unit when ignition switch is on. If voltage exists, replace control unit. If no voltage, check for burned out indicator lamp. Replace as necessary. If lamp is okay, ignition switch or wiring harness is defective.

Start Indicator Lamp (Green) Remains Illuminated

Check for short circuit in wiring harness. If okay, replace control unit.

TESTING

NOTE: Any time the fuel system is opened for testing or repair, air must be bled from the system prior to restarting the engine.

INJECTORS

Opening Pressure

1) Remove fuel injection pipes from injector nozzles and pump. When removing fuel return pipe nut, hold nozzle holder body with a wrench to prevent it from rotating with nut.

2) Remove injection nozzle assembly from cylinder head, using Nozzle Holder Socket Wrench (MD998387).

3) Mount nozzle on nozzle tester and pump tester handle to bleed nozzle. *See Fig. 3.* Operate nozzle tester at a rate of more than 60 strokes per minute and read gauge pressure. The reading will increase gradually with pointer oscillating while nozzle is spraying. Injection pressure is the pressure at which the pointer starts to oscillate.

4) Injection pressure should be 1707-1849 psi (120-130 kg/cm²). Service limit for the injectors is 1565 psi (110 kg/cm²). If test pressure is below limit, nozzle needs to be cleaned and adjusted.

5) Injector pressure can be adjusted with shims that are available in varying thicknesses. A change

CHRYSLER & MITSUBISHI (Cont.)

Fig. 3: Fuel Injector Pressure Testing

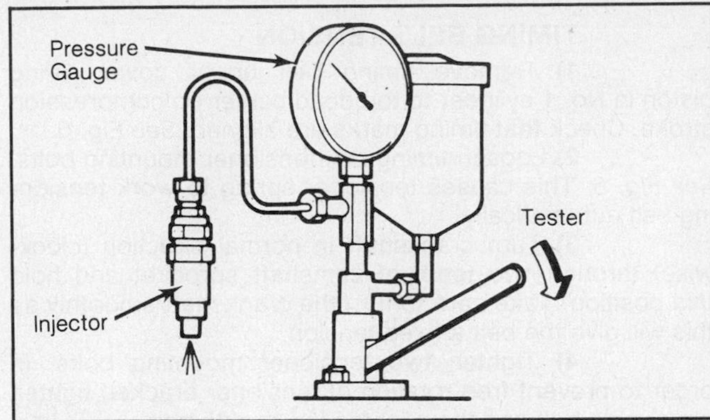
Pressure Gauge
Tester
Injector

of 0.004" (0.1 mm) will change injector pressure 142 psi (10 kg/cm²)

Spray Pattern

To test spray pattern, pump tester handle one time per second. Check spray pattern. *See Fig. 4.* If pattern is not correct, clean or replace nozzle.

Fig. 4: Injector Nozzle Spray Patterns

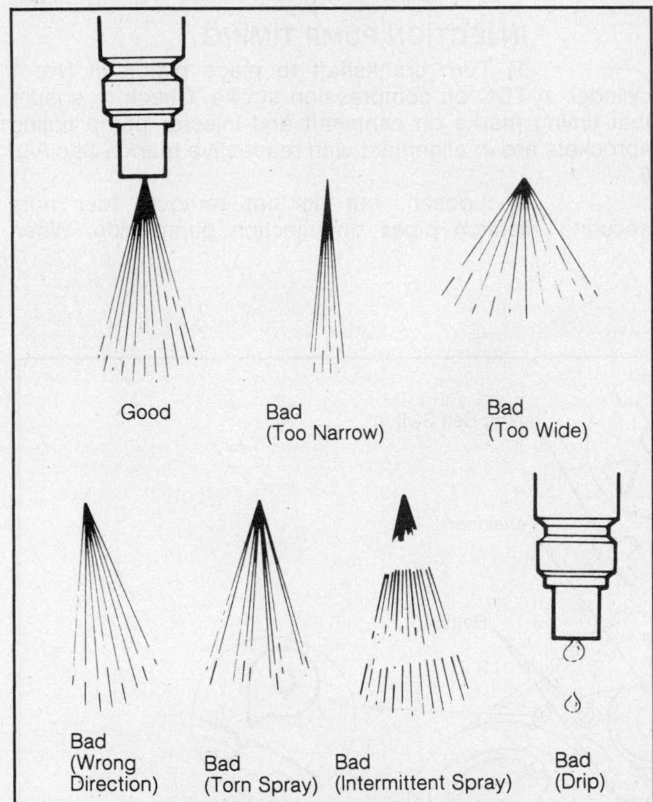
Good
Bad (Too Narrow)
Bad (Too Wide)
Bad (Wrong Direction)
Bad (Torn Spray)
Bad (Intermittent Spray)
Bad (Drip)

Nozzle Cleaning

1) Disassemble injector nozzle. If nozzle needle is damaged, fused, seized or discolored, replace entire nozzle assembly. Check all other parts for excessive wear or damage. Replace as needed.

2) Scrape off carbon deposits with a piece of wood and clean each part in cleaning solvent. After cleaning, keep parts emersed in light oil. Be sure to remove all deposits from adjusting shims, spring, push rod, spacer, nozzle body, needle and seat, and injection hole.

3) Pull needle about halfway out of body and release. Needle should slide smoothly back into place. Repeat this procedure several times, rotating needle slightly each time. If needle does not slide smoothly, replace nozzle body and needle.

4) Clean nozzle holder mounting area of cylinder head. Fit a new nozzle gasket to the nozzle before mounting in head. *See Fig. 5.*

5) Install injector nozzle to cylinder head and tighten to specified torque using Nozzle Holder Socket Wrench (MD998387).

Fig. 5: Installing Nozzle Tip Gasket

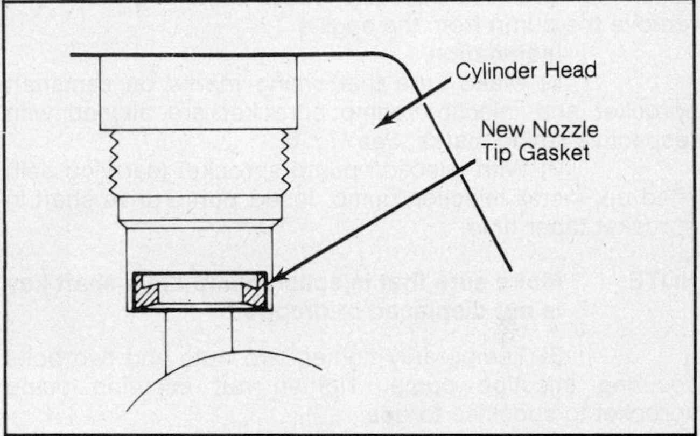
Cylinder Head
New Nozzle Tip Gasket

REMOVAL & INSTALLATION

FUEL FILTER

Removal & Installation

1) Place pan or rag under fuel filter before replacing cartridge. Disconnect water level sensor wires from sensor in bottom of fuel filter cartridge. Unscrew filter assembly from housing.

2) Move filter and sensor assembly to bench. Remove sensor and drain plug. Install sensor and plug in new filter assembly, coat gasket with fresh diesel fuel and reinstall assembly in housing. Tighten filter by hand, reconnect sensor wires and bleed filter.

Bleeding

1) Loosen the air plug on the top of the fuel filter housing. Pull out the hand pump by turning it counterclockwise. Pump the hand pump until the fuel overflowing from the vent has no air in it.

2) Close the air plug and continue to pump the hand pump until the operation of the pump feels heavy. Push the pump in and lock it by turning it clockwise.

FUEL INJECTION PUMP

Removal

1) Remove the timing belt upper cover. Remove the nut and washer securing the injection pump sprocket. Take care not to drop the nut and washer into the lower cover.

2) Turn the crankshaft to bring the No.1 piston to top dead center on the compression stroke.

3) Using a puller disengage the sprocket from the pump tapered shaft. Do not remove sprocket from engine. Set sprocket in the lower timing cover with the belt still engaged.

1983 Diesel Fuel Injection

CHRYSLER & MITSUBISHI (Cont.)

NOTE: Protect the timing belt against undue stress (twisting, bending, etc.). After belt removal, do not rotate crankshaft.

4) Remove two water hoses from the wax element and plug them to keep from losing engine coolant. Remove the boost compensator hose from the pump.

5) Remove the injection pipes from the engine. Take care to hold the delivery valve holders and the nozzles with a wrench to keep them from turning with the nut.

6) Remove the injection pump support bracket bolts. Remove the injection pump mounting nuts and remove the pump from the engine.

Installation

1) Make sure that timing marks on camshaft sprocket and injection pump sprocket are aligned with respective timing marks. *See Fig. 6.*.

2) With injection pump sprocket (carrying belt) lifted up, install injection pump. Insert pump drive shaft in sprocket taper hole.

NOTE: Make sure that injection pump drive shaft key is not displaced or dropped.

3) Temporarily tighten two nuts and two bolts securing injection pump. Tighten nut securing pump sprocket to specified torque.

4) Install injection pipes. Take care to hold delivery valve holder and nozzle with a wrench to keep them from twisting with the pipe nut.

5) Adjust timing belt tension and injector pump timing with engine stopped. Bleed fuel system before starting engine.

ADJUSTMENT

TIMING BELT TENSION

1) Remove timing belt upper cover. Bring piston in No. 1 cylinder to top dead center on compression stroke. Check that timing marks are aligned. *See Fig. 6.*

2) Loosen timing belt tensioner mounting bolts. *See Fig. 6.* This causes tensioner spring to work tensioning belt automatically.

3) Turn crankshaft in normal direction (clockwise) through two teeth of camshaft sprocket and hold this position. Take care to turn the crankshaft smoothly as this will give the belt a fixed tension.

4) Tighten two tensioner mounting bolts. In order to prevent free rotation of tensioner bracket, tighten upper side bolt and then tighten lower side bolt.

5) Turn crankshaft counterclockwise until timing marks are aligned. Check belt tension by pushing down belt with forefinger at a point halfway between cam sprocket and injection pump sprocket. Deflection should be 5/32-3/16" (4-5 mm).

6) Reset timing belt switch by depressing its knob until it is flush with base and mount timing belt upper cover. *See Fig. 6.*

INJECTION PUMP TIMING

1) Turn crankshaft to place piston in No. 1 cylinder at TDC on compression stroke. Check to ensure that timing marks on camshaft and injector pump timing sprockets are in alignment with respective marks. *See Fig. 6.*

2) Loosen, but do not remove, four nuts securing injection pipes on injection pump side. When

Fig. 6: Injection Pump Timing Marks

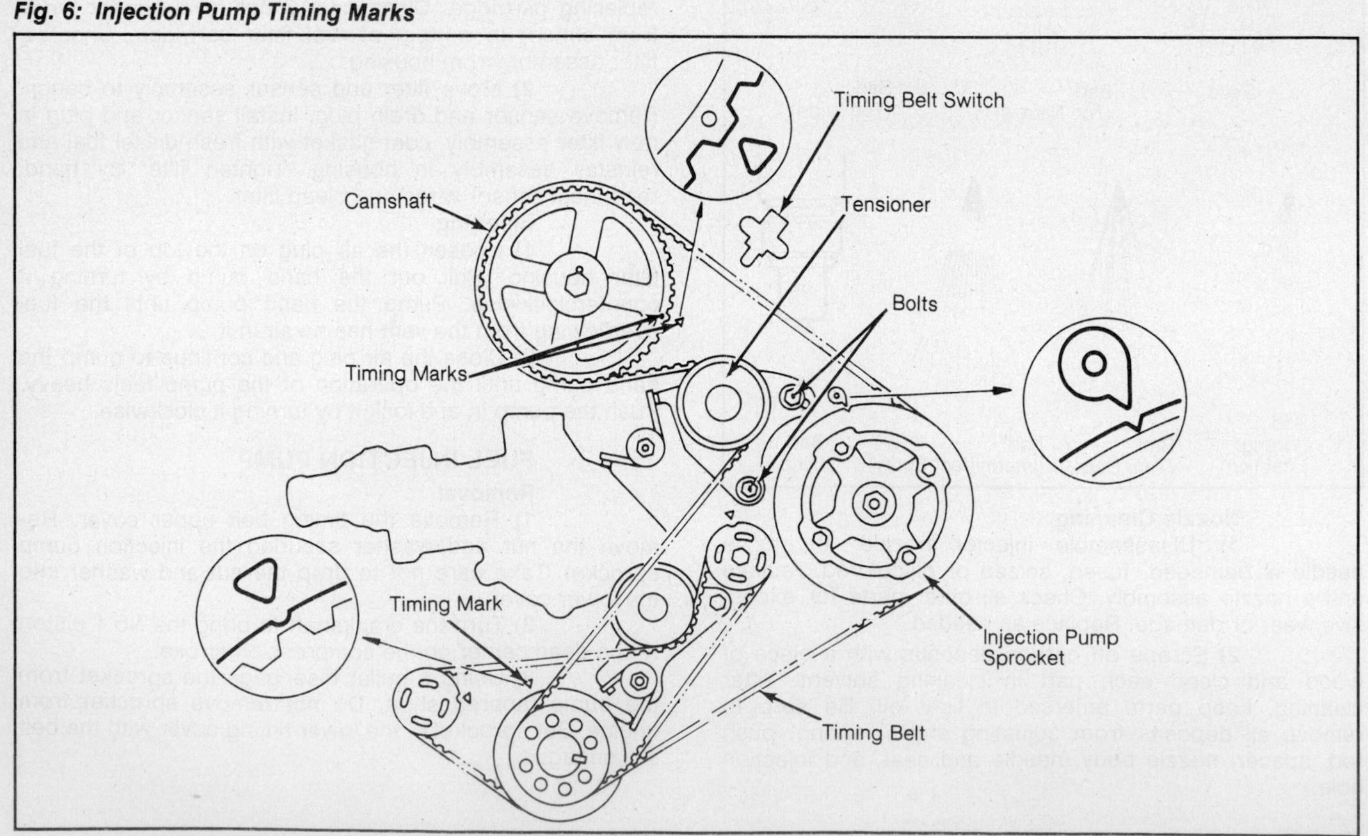
Timing Belt Switch
Camshaft
Tensioner
Bolts
Timing Marks
Timing Mark
Injection Pump
Sprocket
Timing Belt

CHRYSLER & MITSUBISHI (Cont.)

loosening nuts, hold delivery valve holder with a wrench to prevent it from rotating with nut.

3) Loosen, do not remove, two nuts and bolts holding injector pump to engine. Remove plug from rear of pump and attach Prestroke Measuring Adapter (MD998384). Before installation of adapter (MD998384) make sure that push rod is protruding .4" (10 mm). *See Fig. 7.*

4) Turn crankshaft in the direction of normal rotation until the notch on the pulley is 30° before top dead center on the compression stroke of No. 1 cylinder. Set dial indicator to zero. *See Fig 7.* Slightly turn crankshaft clockwise and counterclockwise to make sure that dial indicator does not deviate from zero. If it does, reposition crankshaft pulley to the 30° before top dead center position.

5) Turn crankshaft in direction of normal rotation to bring notch to 2° after top dead center. Check that dial indicator reads 0.0383-0.0405" (0.97-1.03 mm). If dial indicator does not read within specifications tilt injector pump body to right or left to adjust. Tighten injection pump mounting bolts and nuts to specified torque.

6) Repeat steps **4)** and **5)** to check that adjustment has been made correctly. If correct, remove prestroke measuring adapter. Reinstall plug on pump with copper gasket and tighten to specified torque. Tighten injector pipes to specified torque. Take care to hold delivery valve holder with a wrench to prevent it from turning with the nut.

Fig. 7: Adjusting Injection Pump Timing with Prestroke Measuring Adapter

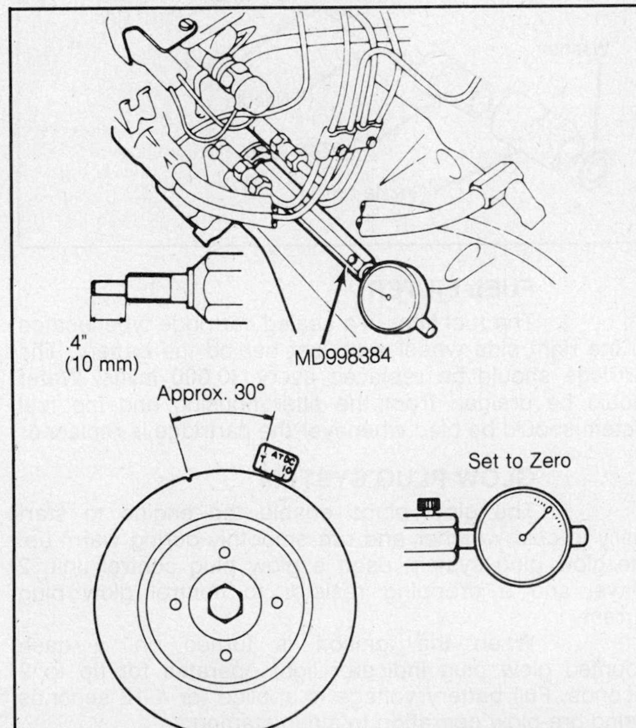
.4"
(10 mm)
MD998384
Approx. 30°
Set to Zero

THROTTLE CABLE

1) After servicing, if throttle cable needs adjustment, run engine until operating temperature is reached. Loosen adjusting nut on cable and adjust idle RPM to specifications.

2) Slide outer cable to the position where the throttle just begins to operate. Adjust the free play of the cable to .04" (1mm). Tighten lock nut.

Fig. 8: Glow Plug Control Circuit

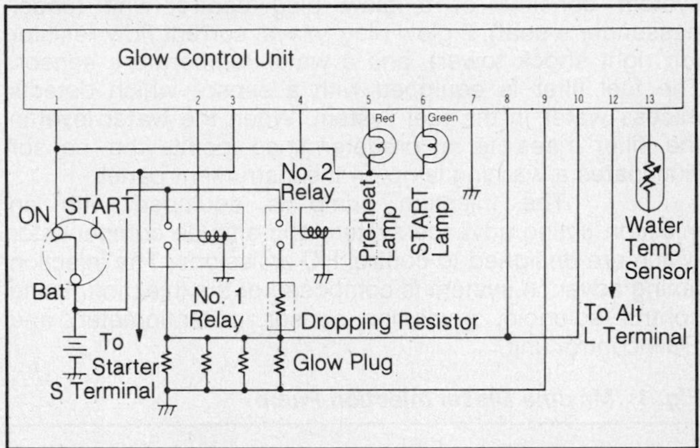
Glow Control Unit
Red
Green
No. 2
Relay
ON
START
Bat
No. 1
Relay
Pre-heat
Lamp
START
Lamp
Water
Temp
Sensor
Dropping Resistor
To Alt
L Terminal
To
Starter
S Terminal
Glow Plug

VACUUM PUMP

An auxiliary vacuum pump is used on diesel engines. This pump is driven off the alternator and supplies vacuum to run the power brake booster. To test vacuum pump on alternator, use a photoelectric tachometer and reflective tape. Connect a vacuum gauge to the hose between the vacuum pump and the brake booster. Run vacuum pump at specified RPM to obtain vacuum readings.

VACUUM PUMP SPECIFICATIONS

Alternator RPM (Engine)	Vacuum In. Hg
1500 (850)	17.3
3000 (1350)	22.8

TIGHTENING SPECIFICATIONS

Application	Ft. Lbs. (N.m)
Air Plug	6-8 (8-11)
Belt Tensioner Bolts	16-21 (22-29)
Fuel Heater	19-25 (25-34)
Fuel Return Pipe Nut	33-39 (45-53)
Fuel Temperature Sensor	15-21 (20-29)
Glow Plug	11-14 (15-19)
Hand Pump	19-25 (25-34)
Injection Pipe Nuts	17-26 (23-36)
Injection Pump Bracket Bolts	15-19 (20-26)
Injection Pump Nuts	11-15 (15-20)
Nozzle Assembly to Head	44-50 (59-68)
Water Level Sensor	9-10 (12-14)

1983 Diesel Fuel Injection

DATSUN/NISSAN – MAXIMA

DESCRIPTION

The diesel injection system includes a Bosch-Kiki VE type fuel injection pump, fuel filter, fuel lines, injector nozzles, and glow plug system. The glow plug system consists of a glow plug control unit (under passenger's seat), 2 glow plug relays, current flow resistor (on right shock tower), and a water temperature sensor. The fuel filter is equipped with a sensor which detects excess water in the fuel system. When the water level in the filter rises to a predetermined point, the sensor illuminates a warning lamp on the instrument panel.

The injection pump is equipped with an injection timing advance system and altitude compensator which are designed to control HC emissions. The injection timing advance system is composed of the injection timing control solenoid, revolution sensor, potentiometer, and EGR control unit.

Fig. 1: Maxima Diesel Injection Pump

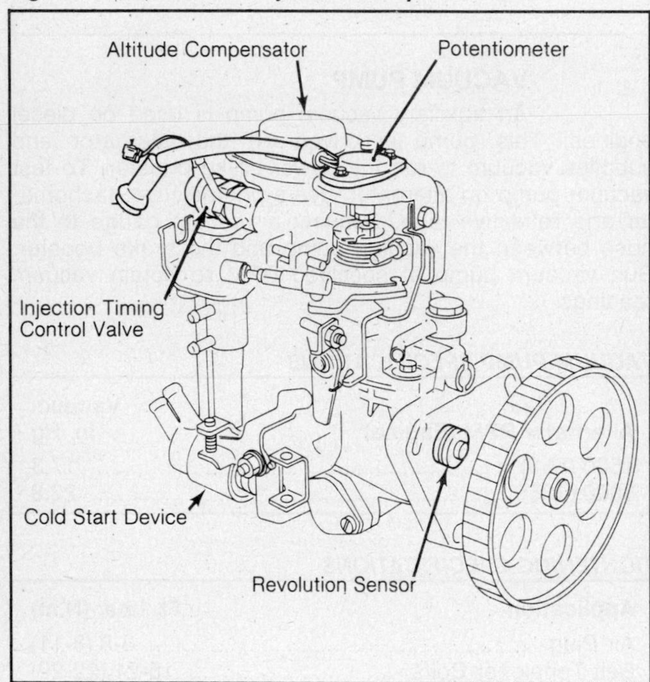
Altitude Compensator
Potentiometer
Injection Timing
Control Valve
Cold Start Device
Revolution Sensor

The solenoid valve controls the fuel by-pass passage in response to the electrical signal from the EGR control unit. The injection timing advance system is deactivated when coolant temperature is either low or extremely high.

The altitude compensator consists of an aneroid bellows and pin which is connected to the injection pump governor lever. At high altitudes, the bellows expands which causes the governor to decrease the amount of fuel delivered.

INJECTION NOZZLES

The injection nozzles spray fuel into a pre-chamber as each compression stroke occurs. Each nozzle has a fuel supply and return line. Nozzles can be disassembled, cleaned, and adjusted to correct defective spray patterns.

Shims are used to correct nozzle opening pressures, and are available in 14 sizes from .0197 to .0394" (.5-1.0 mm) in increments of .0016" (.04 mm). Changing one size nozzle shim will change injection pressure by 68 psi (4.8 kg/cm²).

Fig. 2: Exploded View of Fuel Injection Nozzle

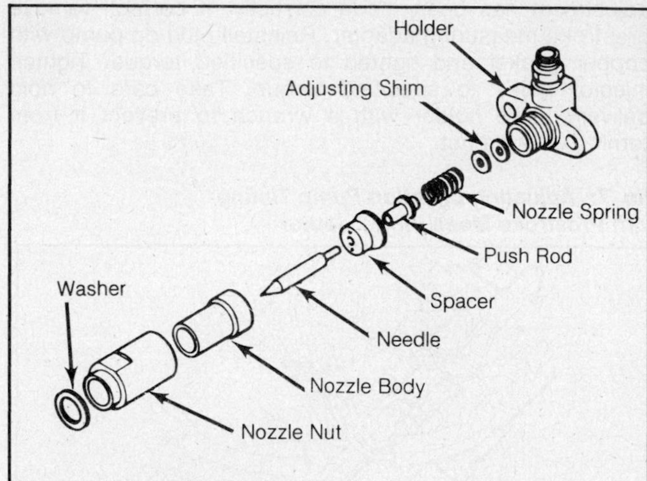
Holder
Adjusting Shim
Nozzle Spring
Push Rod
Washer
Spacer
Needle
Nozzle Body
Nozzle Nut

FUEL FILTER

The fuel filter is a sealed cartridge type located on the right side wheel well, just behind the battery. The cartridge should be replaced every 30,000 miles. Water should be drained from the filter housing and the fuel system should be bled whenever the cartridge is replaced.

GLOW PLUG SYSTEM

The glow plugs enable the engine to start easily in cold weather and run smoothly during warm-up. The glow plug system used a glow plug control unit, 2 relays, and a dropping resistor to control glow plug current.

When the ignition is turned on, a dash mounted glow plug indicator light operates for up to 9 seconds. Full battery voltage is applied for 4-12 seconds during pre-glow operation to aid in starting.

There is no pre-glow operation if coolant temperature is above 122°F (50°C). After engine has started, pre-glow relay is turned off. The after-glow circuit continues to supply reduced current to the glow plugs through the dropping resistor. During after-glow, the glow

OPERATION

FUEL INJECTION PUMP

Driven by a belt at the front of the engine, the fuel injection pump is a low pressure vane type pump with a high pressure fuel distributor. The pump draws fuel from the tank, pressurizes it, and injects a specific quantity to each cylinder at the proper time.

Excess fuel is returned to the tank through another line. In the event of pump failure, the assembly must be replaced as a complete unit. A fuel cut solenoid is used to stop fuel flow when the ignition is turned off.

The injection timing advance system controls the amount of recirculating fuel in the fuel injection pump in order to control the injection timing. The revolution sensor and potentiometer is also used by the EGR control system. When the EGR valve is actuated, the control unit activates the injection timing solenoid valve and injection timing is advanced.

DATSUN/NISSAN – MAXIMA (Cont.)

plugs operate for 5 to 32 seconds depending on engine temperature.

Glow plug relay No. 1 is used for pre-glow operation and relay No. 2 is used for after-glow operation. No. 1 relay is located on right side shock tower. No. 2 relay is on relay bracket behind battery. The temperature sensor is mounted in the thermostat housing.

TROUBLE SHOOTING

ENGINE FAILS TO START

Check for fuel delivery to injection pump and nozzles. Check fuel cut solenoid. Check for faulty injectors incorrect injection pump timing.

ROUGH IDLE

Adjust idle speed. Check for fuel or air leaks. Check valve clearance and injection pump timing. Check injection nozzles and injection pump drive belt. Check injection pump timing. Adjust or replace as needed.

LACK OF POWER

Check and adjust high idle speed screw. Check fuel filter and lines for leaks or clogs. Check throttle valve for proper operation. Bleed fuel system and drain water. Check engine compression. Check and adjust injection nozzles, injection timing, and valve clearances.

EXCESSIVE SMOKE

Check sticky throttle valve. Check clogged injection nozzles, air and fuel filters. Condition of injection pump drive belt. Check injection pump timing.

NOTE: **If the problem remains after the recommended checks, replace injection pump.**

EXCESSIVE FUEL CONSUMPTION

Fuel leakage. Check idle and high idle speed adjustments. Adjust injection timing. Check injection nozzle operation.

ENGINE WILL NOT STOP

Check fuel cut solenoid valve. Check for stuck accelerator linkage.

ENGINE NOISE WHEN WARM

Check idle speed and valve clearance. Check other engine rotating assemblies (water pump, alternator, or power steering).

GLOW PLUG SYSTEM

1) If engine fails to start or is hard to start, check if glow plug indicator lamp lights with ignition on. If not, check indicator lamp for burned out bulb.

2) If indicator lamp bulb is good, check water temperature sensor. Replace water temperature sensor if defective. If indicator lamp bulb and water temperatur sensor are good, replace glow plug control unit.

3) If glow plug indicator lamp lights with ignition on, check if charging lamp lights also. If not, check for loose terminal at alternator "L" terminal or open circuit.

4) If charging lamp does not light, check glow plugs. Replace if necessary. If glow plugs are good, check glow plug relay No. 1, No. 2, and dropping resistors. If relays and dropping resistors are good, check glow plug control unit.

TESTING

INJECTION NOZZLES

Opening Pressure

1) Blow out any dirt around injection nozzles, then remove fuel lines, nozzles, and nozzle washers. Mark nozzles for correct installation.

2) Install nozzle on pressure tester. Bleed air out, then pump at a rate of 1 stroke per second. Note pressure when nozzle opens.

3) If pressure is not within a range of 1780-1920 psi (125-135 kg/cm²), disassemble and clean nozzle. Change shims as necessary to obtain proper opening pressure.

4) Test nozzle again to ensure opening pressure is correct, then check nozzle spray pattern.

Spray Pattern

To test pattern, pump tester handle one time per second. Observe pattern. If not correct, clean or replace nozzle.

Fig. 3: Injection Nozzle Spray Patterns

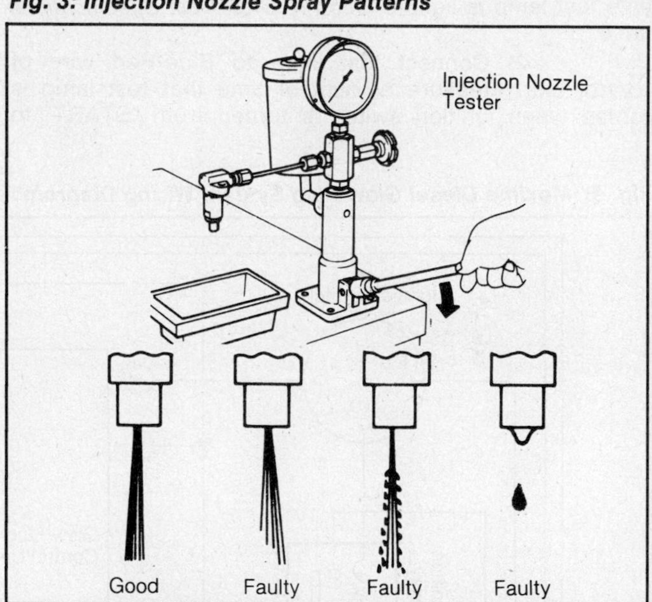
Injection Nozzle Tester
Good
Faulty
Faulty
Faulty

Nozzle Cleaning

1) Disassemble injection assembly. Thoroughly clean all parts in clean solvent. If nozzle needle is damaged or fused, seized or discolored, replace entire nozzle assembly. Check all other parts for excessive wear or damage. Replace as needed.

2) Clean nozzle assembly with a wooden stick and soft brass brush (Datsun/Nissan Nozzle Cleaning Kit IV11289004). Be sure to remove all deposits from adjusting shims, spring, push rod, spacer, nozzle body, needle and seat, and injection hole.

3) Pull needle about halfway out of body and release. Needle should slide smoothly back into place. Repeat this procedure several times, rotating needle slightly each time. If needle does not slide smoothly, replace nozzle body and needle.

1983 Diesel Fuel Injection

DATSUN/NISSAN – MAXIMA (Cont.)

GLOW PLUG SYSTEM

Indicator Lamp

Indicator lamp should light when coolant temperature is below 122°F (50°C). If not check bulb and circuit. If bulb is good, check for battery voltage at terminal 9 of glow plug control unit. If no voltage, repair wiring. If voltage present, replace control unit.

Glow Plug

Remove glow plugs. Check continuity between glow plug end terminal and body. No continuity indicates a defective glow plug.

Glow Plug Relays

Remove No. 1 and No. 2 relays. To check, apply voltage to terminal 3. Ground body on No 1 relay. Ground terminal 4 on relay No. 2. Check for continuity across terminals 1 and 2. *See Fig. 4*. Replace if defective.

Dropping Resistor

Turn ignition off. Unplug dropping resistor harness connector. Resistance should be 1/2 ohm. If not, replace unit.

Glow Plug Control Unit

1) To test pre-glow operation, connect test lamp to Blue/Yellow wire of control unit (harness connector plugged in). Turn ignition on and measure amount of time test lamp is lighted. *See Pre-Glow Test Specifications* table.

2) Connect test lamp to Blue/Red wire of control unit. Measure amount of time that test lamp is lighted when ignition switch is turned from "START" to "ON". *See After-Glow Test Specifications* table. Test lamp will be on continuously with switch in "START" position.

Fig. 4: Glow Plug Relay Test Points

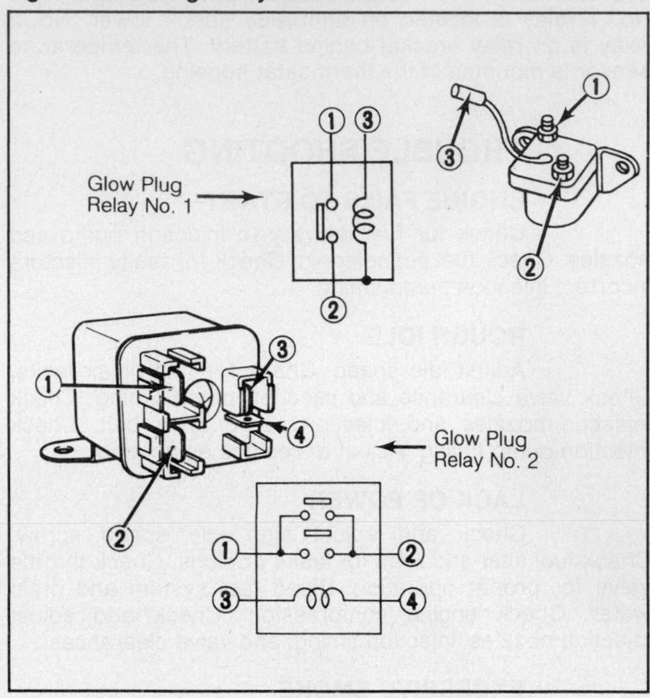
Glow Plug
Relay No. 1
Glow Plug
Relay No. 2

Fig. 5: Maxima Diesel Glow Plug System Wiring Diagram

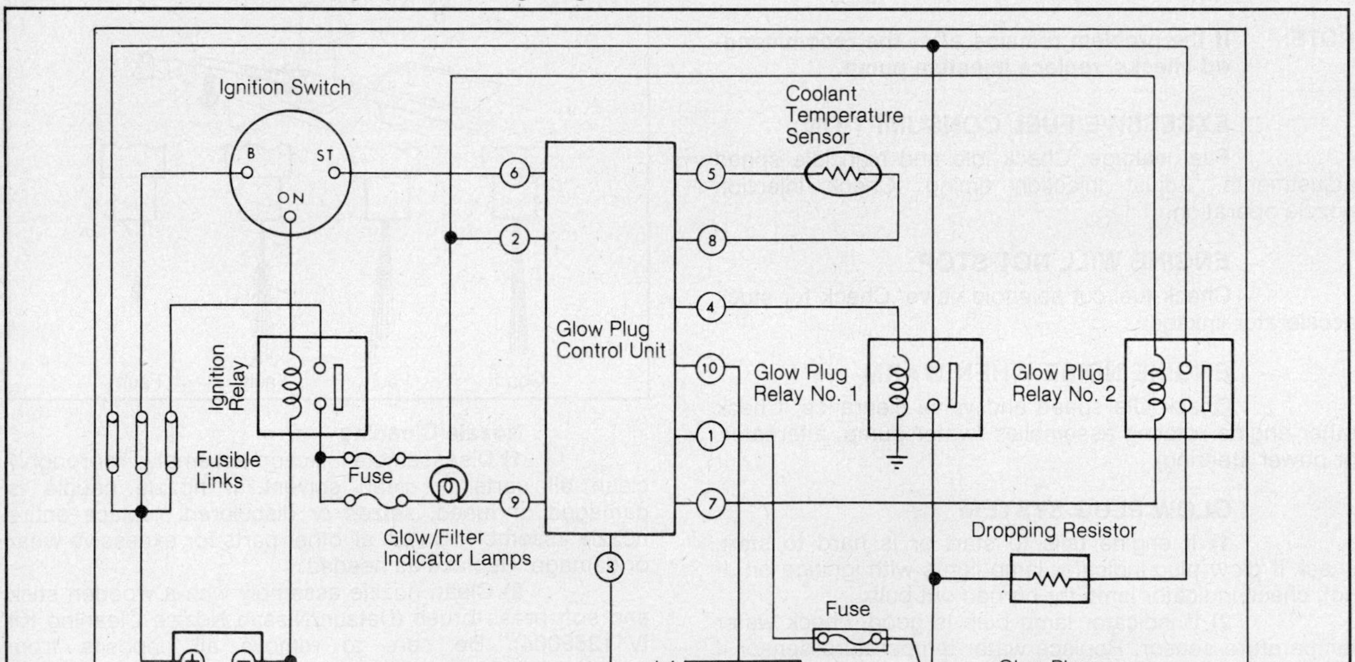

PRE-GLOW TEST SPECIFICATIONS

Coolant Temp. °F (°C)	Time in Seconds	Terminal Voltage
Below 122 (50)	13	8
	6	10.5
Above 122 (50)	0	0

AFTER-GLOW TEST SPECIFICATIONS

Coolant Temperature °F (°C)	Time in Seconds
68 (20)	17
104 (40)	9
122 (50)	0

3) Test lamp will turn off during after-glow operation when voltage reaches 7 volts. Replace glow plug control unit if defective.

COOLANT TEMPERATURE SENSOR

Coolant temperature sensor resistance varies with engine temperature. If resistance is not correct at specified temperature, replace sensor. *See Temperature Sensor Resistance Specifications* chart.

TEMPERATURE SENSOR RESISTANCE SPECIFICATIONS

Temperature °F (°C)	Ohms
50 (10)	32,500-41,500
68 (20)	22,500-27,500
122 (50)	740-940
176 (80)	290-360

FUEL CUT SOLENOID

Solenoid Check

To check the solenoid, repeatedly apply and remove battery voltage directly to the solenoid. If the solenoid is functioning properly, a distinct clicking sound should be heard. If not, the solenoid is bad and should be replaced.

INJECTION TIMING ADVANCE SYSTEM

System Check

1) Unplug solenoid valve harness connector at injection pump. Connect positive lead of voltmeter to harness connector and negative lead to solenoid body. Start engine.

2) When coolant temperature is below 86°F (30°C), ensure there is no voltage at harness connector at idle and when engine is revved up. When temperature is above 86°F (30°C), battery voltage should be present at idle. Voltage should not be present when engine is revved up.

3) If system does not respond as described, check revolution sensor, potentiometer, and wiring harness. If components are good, replace EGR control unit. Unit is located in left side kick panel.

Revolution Sensor

Unplug revolution sensor harness and connect ohmmeter to sensor leads. Ohmmeter should show resistance. If not, replace.

Potentiometer

1) Unplug potentiometer harness connector. Connect ohmmeter between Blue/Yellow and Black wires. Resistance should change as opening angle of injection pump control lever is changed.

2) Perform same test between Blue/Yellow and Blue/Red wires. Replace potentiometer if defective.

Solenoid Valve

Unplug solenoid valve connector. Apply battery voltage to solenoid and listen for a clicking sound. Replace if defective.

REMOVAL & INSTALLATION

INJECTION PUMP

Removal

1) Drain coolant and disconnect battery ground cable. Remove radiator, shroud, and hoses. Loosen pulley nuts and remove alternator, power steering, and air conditioning belts. Remove power steering pump.

NOTE: **Do not drain power steering fluid or disconnect hoses from pump during this procedure.**

2) Disconnect remaining wires and hoses from pump. Remove dust cover. Loosen spring set pin and set tensioner pulley to "free tension" position. Tighten set pin.

3) Remove injection drive belt. Loosen nut and use a gear puller to remove injection pump drive gear.

4) Disconnect injection tubes from injection nozzles. Remove injection pump nuts and bracket bolt. Remove injection pump assembly and injection tubes.

Installation

1) Set No. 1 cylinder at TDC on the compression stroke. Ensure grooves in rear plate and flywheel are aligned with each other. No. 1 cam lobe must be pointing up. *See Fig. 6.* Install injection pump.

Fig. 6: Positioning No. 1 Cam Lobe For Injection Pump Installation

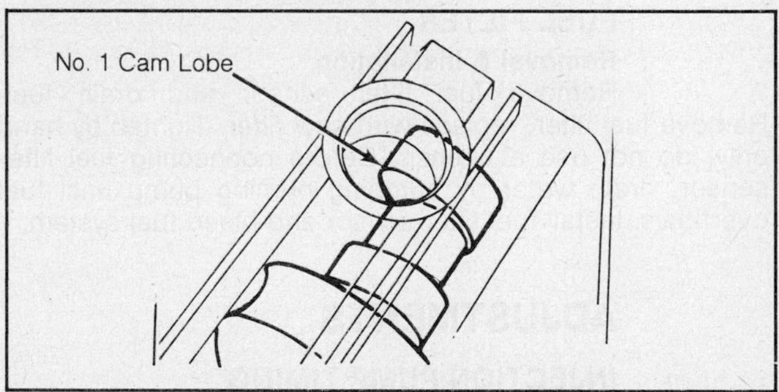

No. 1 Cam Lobe

No. 1 cylinder must be at TDC of compression stroke.

2) There are 2 keyways and 3 drive belt aligning marks on drive gear. Use keyway and aligning mark with "B" stamped next to them. Install drive gear. Tighten nut to specification.

3) With tensioner pulley in free position, install injection drive belt. Make sure that the timing marks on the belt are in alignment with the marks on the pump drive pulley and the crank damper. *See Fig. 7.*

4) If the marks on the belt are not clear, count the number of belt teeth between the timing marks on the two pulleys. There should be 20 teeth between the 2 marks.

5) Loosen the spring set pin and allow tensioner to return to "tension" position. Turn crankshaft clockwise 2 revolutions. Adjust injection timing. Tighten injection pump and connect injection tubes.

NOTE: Injection tubes should always be connected in the proper order: 4, 2, 6, 1, 5, 3 as counted from the front to the rear of the engine.

Fig. 7: Injection Pump Drive Belt Installation

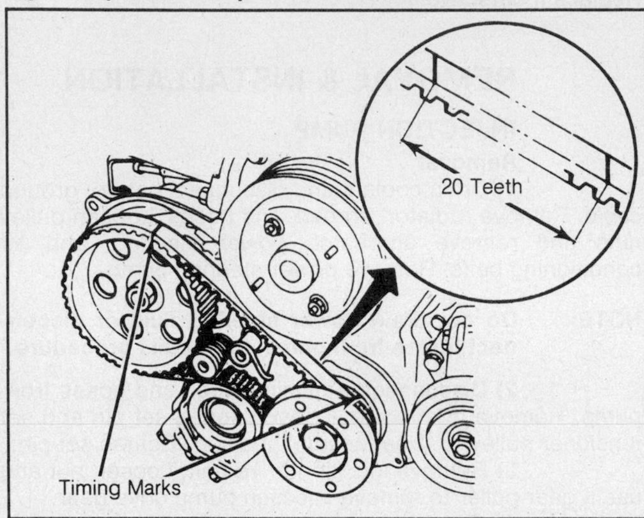
20 Teeth
Timing Marks

6) Bleed fuel system. Loosen the priming pump vent screw on the front of the fuel filter housing. Pump the filter priming pump until fuel begins to flow from the vent hole.

7) Tighten vent screw. Disconnect the fuel return hose and attach an overflow hose to the overflow connector. Place a can or other small container under the hose end and pump priming pump until fuel begins to flow from the hose. Replace overflow hose.

FUEL FILTER

Removal & Installation

Remove fuel filter sensor and drain fuel. Remove fuel filter, replace with new filter. Tighten by hand only, do not use a wrench. Before connecting fuel filter sensor, drain water by pumping priming pump until fuel overflows. Install fuel filter sensor and bleed fuel system.

ADJUSTMENTS

INJECTION PUMP TIMING

1) Drain coolant lower than cold start device. Remove cold start device water hoses. Remove power steering pump. Set No. 1 cylinder at TDC on the compression stroke. Ensure groove in rear plate and flywheel are aligned.

2) No. 1 cam lobe should be pointing up. *See Fig. 6*. Remove fuel injection tubes. Set cold start device in the free position. Turn control linkage. Place a 1/2" block between piston and linkage. *See Fig. 8*.

3) Remove plug bolt from rear of injection pump. Install special timing tool with dial indicator (Datsun/Nissan Part No. KV11229352) in bolt hole.

4) Turn crankshaft counterclockwise to 15-20° BTDC and zero dial indicator. Rotate clockwise to No. 1 cylinder TDC compression stroke. Read dial gauge. If reading is not as specified, turn injection pump body until reading is correct. *See Injection Pump Timing Specifications* table.

Fig. 8: Injection Pump Cold Start Device

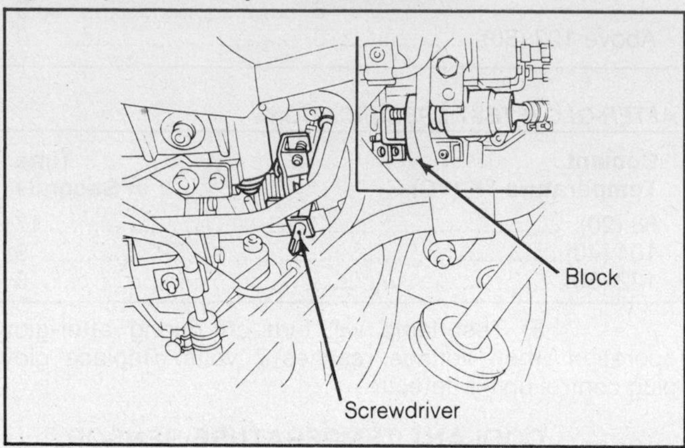
Block
Screwdriver

Fig. 9: Timing Injection Pump

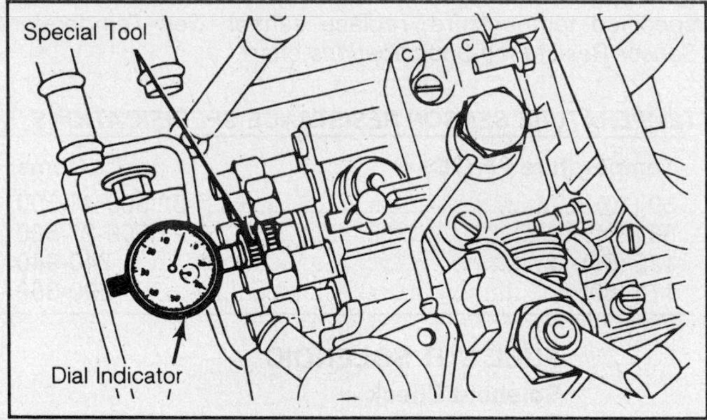
Special Tool
Dial Indicator

INJECTION PUMP TIMING SPECIFICATIONS

Application	Plunger Lift In. (mm)
Low Altitude	.0327-.0351 (.83-.89)
High Altitude	.0346-.0370 (.88-.94)

5) Tighten pump. Remove tool and replace plug bolt using new washer. Set cold start device to original position. Connect injection tubes. Install power steering pump. Connect cold start device water hoses. Refill coolant.

TIGHTENING SPECIFICATIONS

Application	Ft. Lbs. (N.m)
Injection Nozzle-to-Cylinder Head	12-15 (16-20)
Injection Nozzle-to-Tube	16-18 (22-25)
Injection Pump Plug Bolt	10-14 (14-19)
Injection Pump Drive Gear	43-51 (60-70)
Injection Pump Bracket Bolt	22-26 (31-36)
Injection Pump Mounting Nuts	12-15 (16-20)

DATSUN/NISSAN – PICKUP

DESCRIPTION

The diesel injection system includes a fuel injection pump, an injection pump controller system, governor, fuel filter, fuel lines, injector nozzles, and glow plug system. The pump controller system consists of a gearing assembly, a control unit, and a connecting rod.

The purpose of the system is to supply fuel under pressure for engine firing, and to cut the fuel supply when the ignition is turned off. The glow plug system includes a glow plug control unit, 2 glow plug relays, and a water temperature sensor.

OPERATION

FUEL INJECTION PUMP

The injection pump is a Kiki-Bosch in-line type. It is gear driven off of an idler pulley at the front of the engine. It draws fuel from the tank, pressurizes it, and injects a specific quantity to each cylinder at the proper time. Excess fuel is returned to the tank through another line. The injection pump is also equipped with an altitude compensator. In the event of pump failure, the unitmust be replaced as a complete assembly.

INJECTION PUMP CONTROLLER

The pump controller system uses a gearing assembly, and a connecting rod linking the gearing assembly to the injection pump control lever. A control unit is also used and is wired to the ignition switch.

When the ignition is in the "START" position, the gears in the assembly rotate, moving the injection pump control lever to an rich fuel condition. This aids engine starting. When the ignition is turned to "OFF", the lever is moved to a position of no fuel delivery, and the engine stops. During normal engine operation, the system maintains a normal mixture.

Fig. 1: Diesel Fuel Injection Components

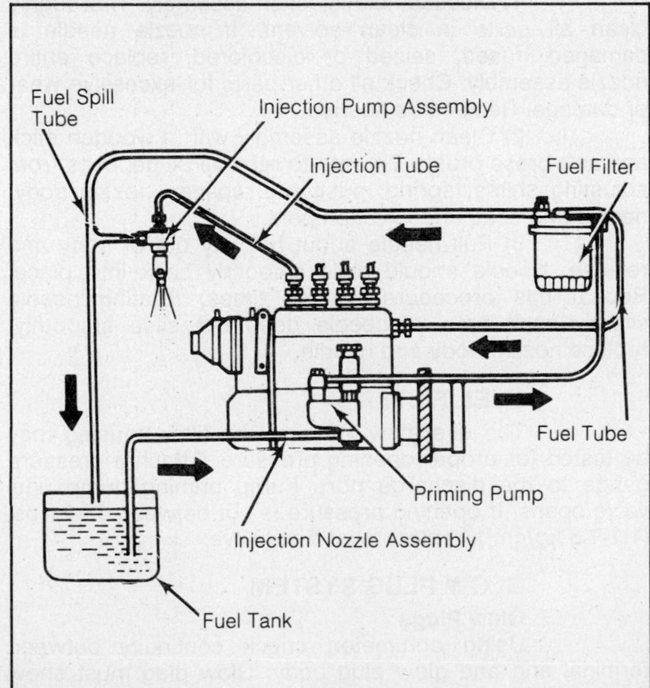
Fuel Spill Tube
Injection Pump Assembly
Injection Tube
Fuel Filter
Fuel Tube
Priming Pump
Injection Nozzle Assembly
Fuel Tank

INJECTION NOZZLES

The injection nozzles spray fuel into a swirl chamber as each compression stroke occurs. Each nozzle has a fuel supply and return line. Nozzles can be disassembled, cleaned and adjusted to correct defective spray patterns.

Shims are used to correct nozzle opening pressures. Changing shim size by .0016" (.04 mm) will change opening pressure by about 68 psi (4.8 kg/cm²).

Fig. 2: Exploded View of Fuel Injection Nozzle

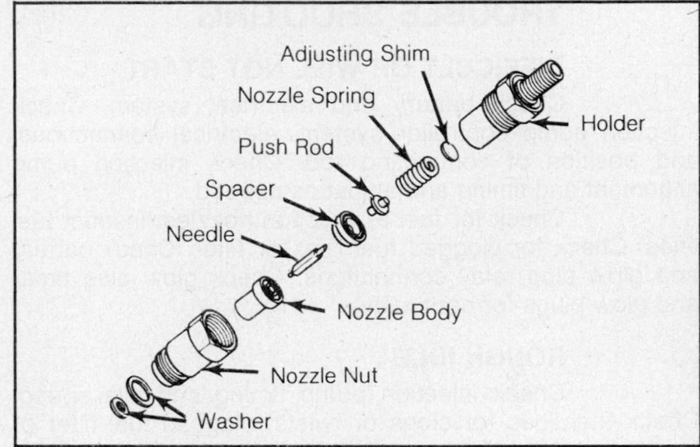
Adjusting Shim
Nozzle Spring
Holder
Push Rod
Spacer
Needle
Nozzle Body
Nozzle Nut
Washer

Fig. 3: Injection Pump Controller System

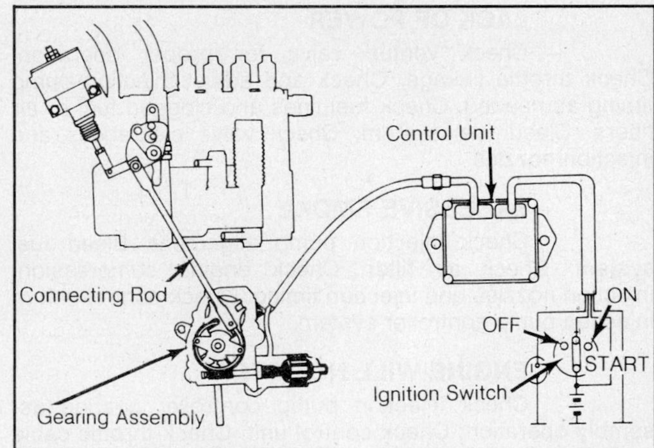
Control Unit
Connecting Rod
ON
OFF
START
Ignition Switch
Gearing Assembly

FUEL FILTER

The fuel filter is a sealed cartridge type located on the right side wheel well, just behind the windshield washer fluid reservoir. It is equipped with a water level sensor. Sensor will illuminate a warning lamp on instrument panel when the water level in the filter reaches a predetermined point. The cartridge should be replaced every 15,000 miles. Bleed fuel system whenever filter is changed.

GLOW PLUGS

The provides fast glow (pre-glow) operation before the engine starts as well as after-glow operation after the engine has started. When igntion is turned on, No. 1 relay is activated and full battery voltage is applied to the glow plugs. The glow plug indicator lamp on the instrument panel will light at this time. The No. 1 relay will automatically turn off after 6-7 seconds.

1983 Diesel Fuel Injection

DATSUN/NISSAN – PICKUP (Cont.)

When coolant temperature is lower than 122°F (50°C), No. 2 relay will be energized when the ignition switch is turned on. This activates the after-glow system. It will remain on for 20-45 seconds depending on the coolant temperature. The No. 2 relay provides the glow plugs with a reduced current flow, through the dropping resistor, after the engine has started. When coolant temperature is higher than 122°F (50°C), the after-glow system is turned on only during engine cranking.

TROUBLE SHOOTING

DIFFICULT OR WILL NOT START

Check battery and electrical system. Check injection pump controller system, electrical connections, and position of connecting rod. Check injection pump alignment and timing and adjust as needed.

Check for fuel at injection nozzles. Inspect fuel lines. Check for clogged fuel lines or filter. Check battery and glow plug relay connections. Check glow plug timer and glow plugs for continuity.

ROUGH IDLE

Check injection pump timing and idle speed. Check fuel lines for clogs or twists, clogged fuel filter or fuel leaks. Bleed fuel system. Check valve clearance and injection nozzles.

LACK OF POWER

Check venturi valve for proper operation. Check throttle linkage. Check and adjust injection pump timing as needed. Check fuel lines and clogged fuel or air filters. Bleed fuel system. Check valve clearances and injection nozzles.

EXCESSIVE SMOKE

Check injection pump alignment. Bleed fuel system. Check air filter. Check engine compression, injection nozzles and injection timing. Check control unit of injection pump controller system.

ENGINE WILL NOT STOP

Check injection pump controller gearing assembly operation. Check control unit. Check throttle cable and linkage.

NOTE: **If these checks and adjustments do not solve the problem, the fuel injection pump may be inoperative and should be repaired or replaced.**

TESTING

INJECTION NOZZLES

Opening Pressure

1) Blow out any dirt around injection nozzles, then remove fuel lines, nozzles and nozzle washers. Mark nozzles for correct installation.

2) Install nozzle on pressure tester. Bleed air out, then pump at a rate of 1 stroke per second. Note pressure when nozzle opens.

3) If pressure is not within a range of 1420-1495 psi (100-105 kg/cm²), disassemble and clean nozzle. Change shims as necessary to obtain proper opening pressure.

4) Test nozzle again to ensure opening pressure is correct. Check nozzle spray pattern.

Fig. 4: Injection Nozzle Spray Patterns

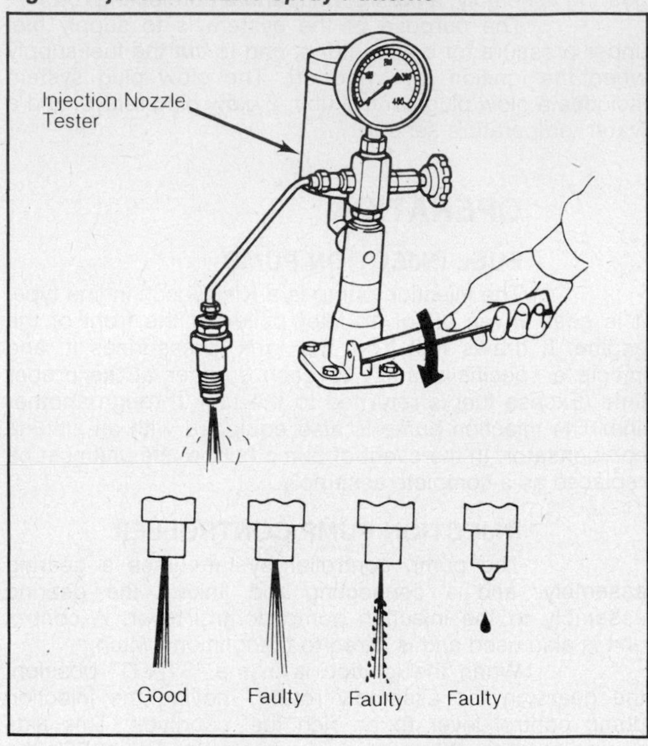
Injection Nozzle Tester
Good
Faulty
Faulty
Faulty

Spray Pattern

To test pattern, pump tester handle one time per second. Check spray pattern. If pattern is not correct, clean or replace nozzle.

Nozzle Cleaning

1) Disassemble injection assembly. Thoroughly clean all parts in clean solvent. If nozzle needle is damaged, fused, seized or discolored, replace entire nozzle assembly. Check all other parts for excessive wear or damage. Replace as needed.

2) Clean nozzle assembly with a wooden stick and soft brass brush. Be sure to remove all deposits from adjusting shims, spring, push rod, spacer, nozzle body, needle and seat, and injection hole.

3) Pull needle about halfway out of body and release. Needle should slide smoothly back into place. Repeat this procedure several times, rotating needle slightly each time. If needle does not slide smoothly, replace nozzle body and needle.

FUEL FILTER

The over-flow valve of the filter housing may be tested for proper opening pressure. Attach a pressure gauge to the discharge port. Pump priming pump until valve opens. If opening pressure is not between 16-21 psi (1.1-1.5 kg/cm²), replace over-flow valve.

GLOW PLUG SYSTEM

Glow Plugs

Using ohmmeter, check continuity between terminal end and glow plug body. Glow plug must show continuity. If not, replace.

DATSUN/NISSAN – PICKUP (Cont.)

Coolant Temperature Sensor

Coolant temperature sensor resistance varies with engine temperature. If resistance is not correct at specified temperature, replace sensor. *See Temperature Sensor Resistance Specifications* table. Sensor is located on left front side of engine.

TEMPERATURE SENSOR RESISTANCE SPECIFICATIONS

Temperature °F (°C)	Ohms
14 (-10)	7000-11,400
68 (20)	2100-2900
122 (50)	680-1000

Dropping Resistor

Turn ignition switch off. Unplug dropping resistor harness connector. Dropping resistor is located on right front fender next to battery. Resistance across terminals should be approximately 1/10 ohms. If not, replace resistor.

Glow Plug Control Unit

1) Turn off ignition switch and unplug glow plug control unit. Unit is located in right side cowl area of passenger compartment. To test control unit, wiring harness must be constructed. *See Fig. 5.*

Fig. 5: Testing Glow Plug Control Unit

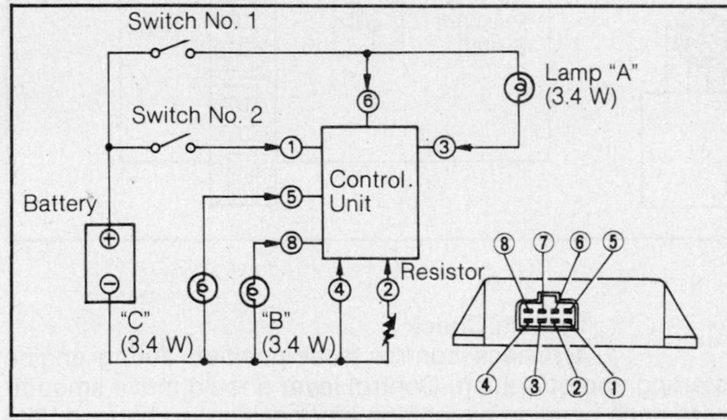

Switch No. 1
Lamp "A"
(3.4 W)
Switch No. 2
Control Unit
Battery
Resistor
"C"
(3.4 W)
"B"
(3.4 W)

Fig. 6: Glow Plug System Wiring Diagram

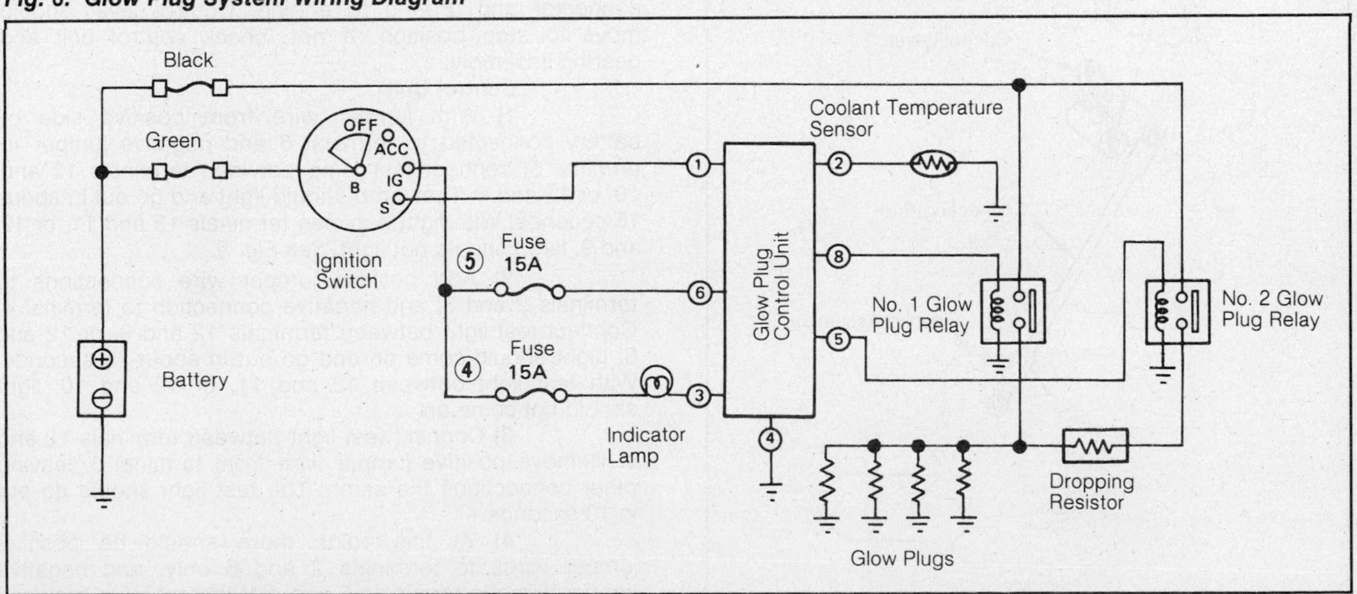

Black
Green
OFF
ACC
IG
B
S
Ignition Switch
Fuse 15A
Fuse 15A
Battery
Indicator Lamp
Glow Plug Control Unit
Coolant Temperature Sensor
No. 1 Glow Plug Relay
No. 2 Glow Plug Relay
Dropping Resistor
Glow Plugs

Also see chassis wiring in WIRING DIAGRAM Section.

2) To test indicator lamp circuit, voltage source must be 10.5 volts. Close switch No. 1 and measure the time lamp "A" is lit with various resistances. *See Indicator Lamp Circuit Test* table.

INDICATOR LAMP CIRCUIT TEST

Resistance (Ohms)	Illumination Time (Seconds)
19000	5-7
11500	4.5-6.3
5600	3.5-5.1
3700	2.9-4.3
1200	.6-1.9

3) To test pre-glow circuit, voltage source must be 10.5 volts. With switch No. 1 closed and switch No. 2 open, set resistor to 30,000 ohms. Lamp "B" should be lit for 5.3-6.7 seconds. Close switch No. 2 and set resistor to 20,000 ohms. Lamp "B" should be lit for 5.5-7.5 seconds.

4) To test after-glow system, voltage source must be 12 volts. Switch No. 1 must be closed. Close switch No. 2 and then open it. Measure time lamp "C" is lit with various resistances. *See After-Glow Circuit Test* table. Replace control unit if it fails any test.

AFTER-GLOW CIRCUIT TEST

Resistance (Ohms)	Illumination Time (Seconds)
19,000	38-55
11,500	33-49
5600	25-39
3700	20-31
1200	15-25

INJECTION PUMP CONTROLLER SYSTEM

NOTE: **It is important to follow these procedures in the order given if accurate test results are to be obtained. Failure to do so can result in damage to the system.**

1983 Diesel Fuel Injection

DATSUN/NISSAN – PICKUP (Cont.)

Fig. 7: Injection Pump Controller System Wiring Diagram

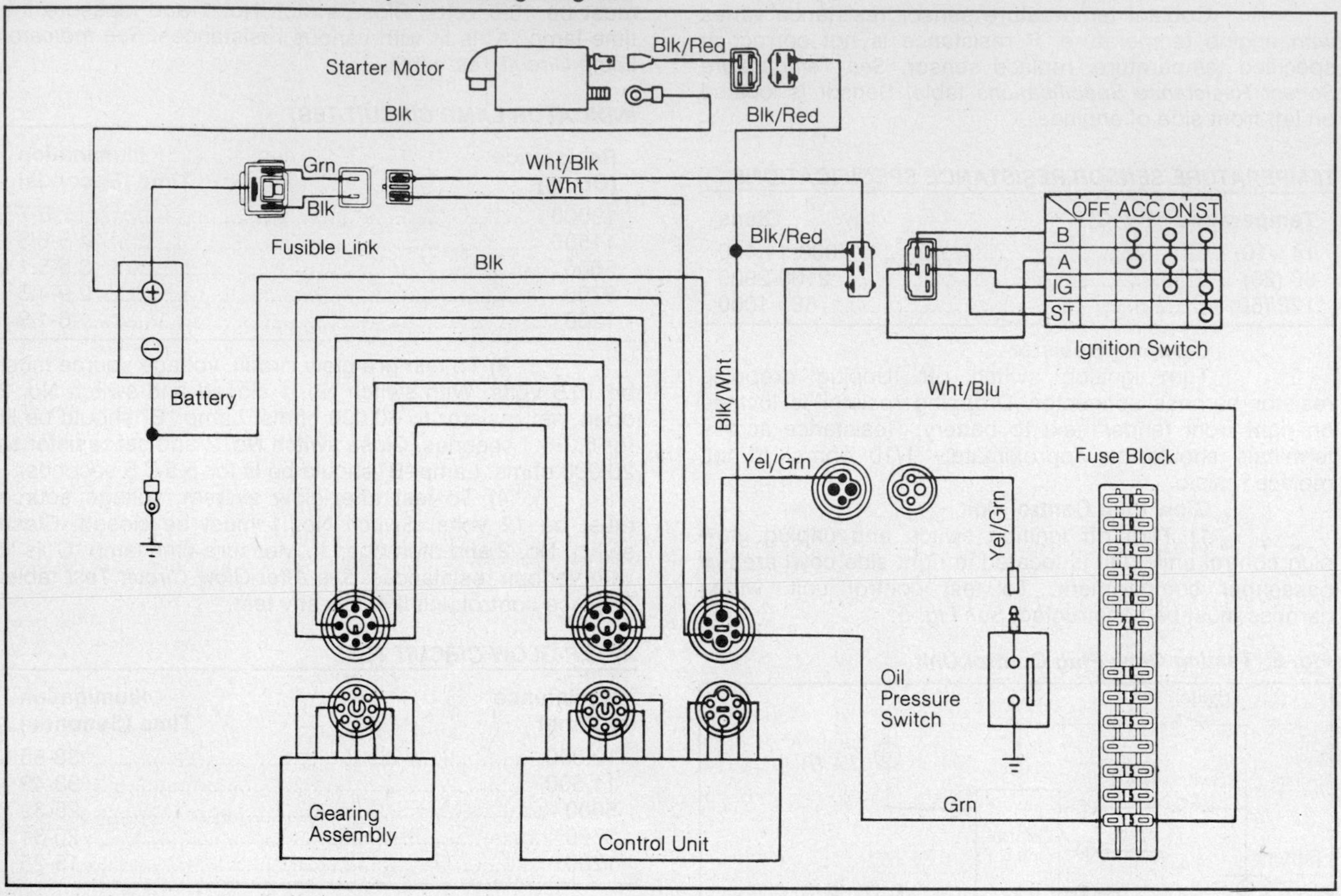

Also see chassis wiring in WIRING DIAGRAM Section.

Fig. 8: Injection Pump Control Lever Positions

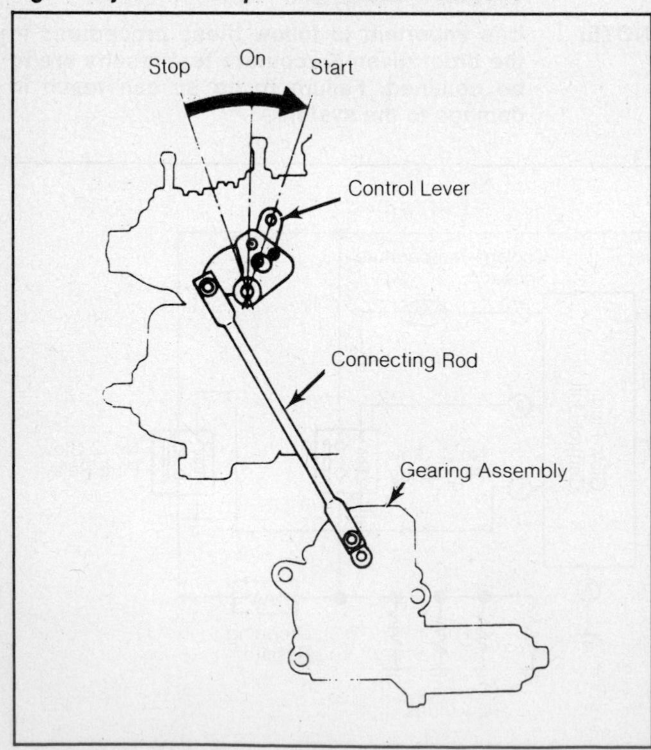
Stop
On
Start
Control Lever
Connecting Rod
Gearing Assembly

System Check

1) Check control lever position during engine starting and operation. Control lever should move smoothly to each position as ignition key position is changed. *See Fig. 8.*

2) Start engine. Unplug oil pressure switch connector and ground to engine. Control lever should move to stop position. If not, check control unit and gearing assembly.

Control Unit

1) With jumper wire from positive side of battery connected to terminal 6 and negative jumper to terminal 5, connect test lamp between terminals 12 and 10, or 12 and 8. Test lamp should light and go out in about 15 seconds. With light between terminals 12 and 11, or 12 and 9, lamp should not light. *See Fig. 9.*

2) Add positive jumper wire connections to terminals 2 and 3, and negative connection to terminal 4. Connect test light between terminals 12 and 9, or 12 and 8. Light should come on and go out in about 15 seconds. With test light between 12 and 11, or 12 and 10, light should not come on.

3) Connect test light between terminals 12 and 9. Remove positive jumper wire from terminal 3, leaving other connections the same. The test light should go out in 10 seconds.

4) At this point, there should be positive jumper wires to terminals 2 and 6 only, and negative jumper wires to terminals 5 and 4. With test lamp between

DATSUN/NISSAN – PICKUP (Cont.)

terminals 12 and 10, or 12 and 8, light should come on and go out in about 15 seconds. Lamp should not light when between 12 and 11, or 12 and 9.

5) Disconnect negative wire to terminal 4, leaving only 1 negative wire at terminal 5. With test light between terminals 12 and 11, or 12 and 8, lamp should come on and go out in about 15 seconds. With test light between 12 and 10, or 12 and 9, lamp should not come on.

Fig. 9: Testing Injection Pump Control Unit

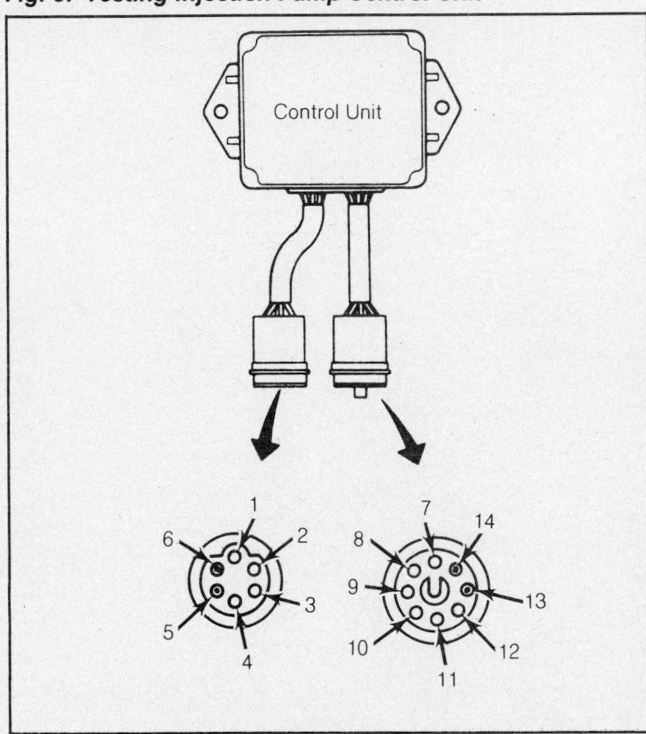
Control Unit
1
2
3
4
5
6
7
14
8
9
13
10
12
11

6) In all control unit tests, if results are as indicated the unit is good. If not, unit should be replaced.

Gearing Assembly

1) With positive battery lead connected to assembly terminal 13, and negative lead to terminal 14, the gearing assembly motor should run. *See Fig. 10.*

Fig. 10: Gearing Assembly Terminal Test Points

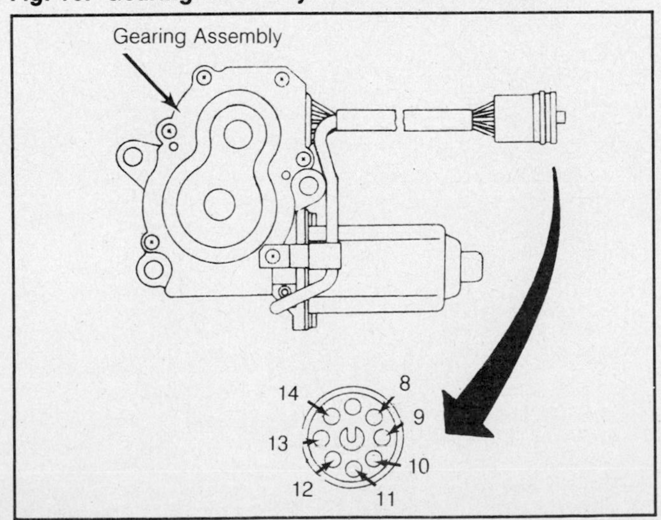
Gearing Assembly
14
8
9
13
10
12
11

2) Remove positive lead from terminal 13. With negative lead still at terminal 14, connect terminals 12 and 13 to each other with a short piece of insulated wire. Connect positive lead to terminal 8.

3) Connect a second positive lead to terminal 9 and check control lever. It should be in the start position. Move second lead to terminal 10. Lever should be in the stop position.

4) Move lead to terminal 11 and lever should move to on position. If not, assembly should be replaced.

REMOVAL & INSTALLATION

INJECTION PUMP

Removal

1) Drain coolant and disconnect battery ground cable. Remove radiator, fan and fan clutch. Remove injection tubes. Disconnect governor hose, fuel hose, injection pump controller connecting rod, and oil feed pipe bolt.

2) Remove timing gear cover. Remove timer assembly retaining nut. Using puller (ST19530000), remove timer assembly. *See Fig. 11.* Remove injection pump retaining nuts and remove pump.

Fig. 11: Removing Injection Pump

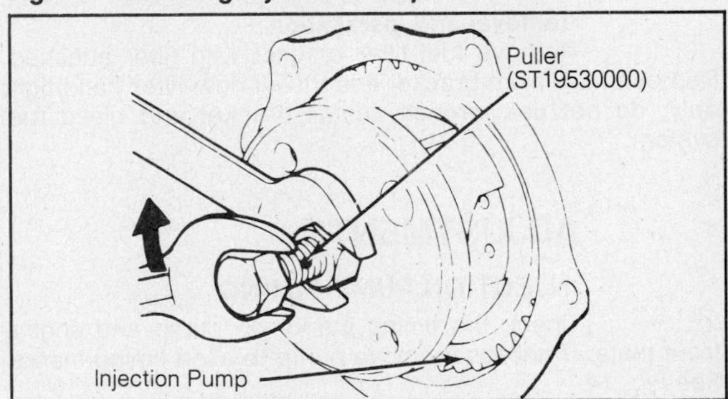
Puller
(ST19530000)
Injection Pump

Installation

1) Set No. 1 cylinder at TDC compression stroke. Hold injection pump loosely in place. Do not tighten retaining nuts. Mesh injection pump drive gear with idler gear. The "Y" marks on the gears must be aligned. *See Fig. 12.*

2) Align gear to key way of injection pump camshaft while turning crank pulley. Tighten injection pump and timer assembly retaining nuts. Adjust injection timing.

Fig. 12: Injection Pump Drive Gear Installation

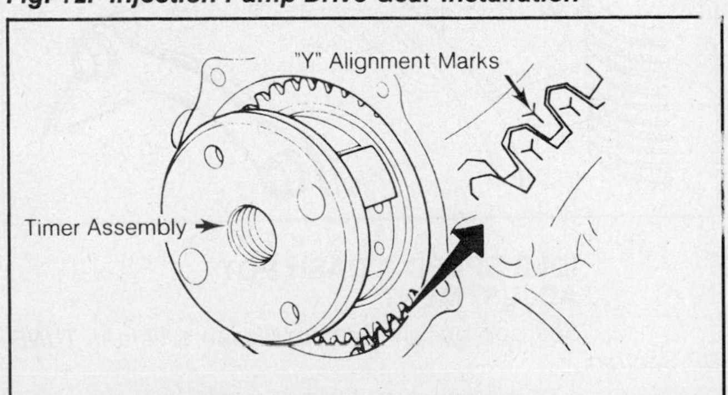
"Y" Alignment Marks
Timer Assembly

3) Bleed fuel system. Remove priming pump cap cover. Loosen air vent screws and turn priming pump counterclockwise to release.

4) Operate priming pump until all air is purged from air vents. Tighten air vent screws. Push down on pump and turn clockwise to lock. Install cap cover. *See Fig. 13.*

Fig. 13: Bleeding Fuel System

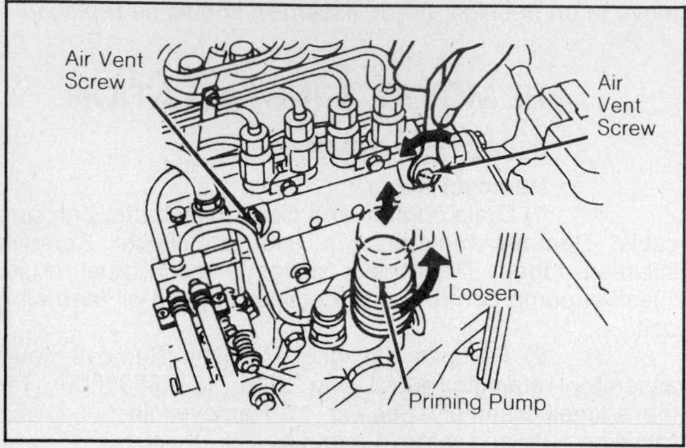
Air Vent Screw
Air Vent Screw
Loosen
Priming Pump

FUEL FILTER

Removal and Installation

Remove fuel filter bracket with filter attached. Remove filter from bracket and install new filter hand tight only, do not use wrench. Install bracket and bleed fuel system.

ADJUSTMENTS

INJECTION PUMP TIMING

Check the timing marks on pump and engine front plate. If necessary move pump to align timing marks. *See Fig. 14.*

Fig. 14: Marks for Injection Pump Timing

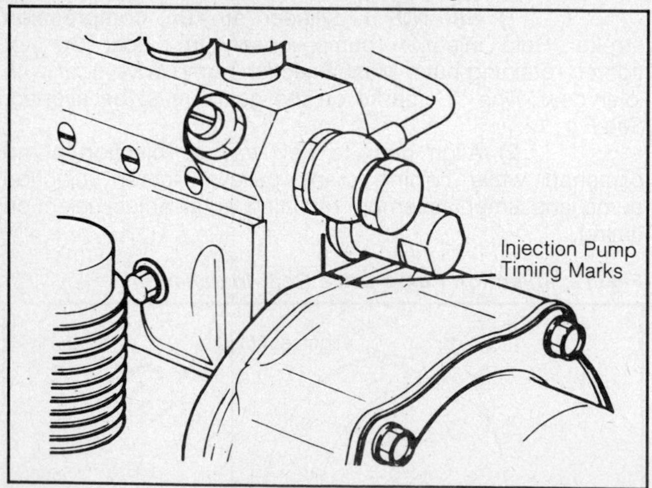
Injection Pump Timing Marks

IDLE SPEED & DASH POT ADJUSTMENT

See appropriate Datsun/Nissan article in TUNE-UP Section..

TIGHTENING SPECIFICATIONS

Application	Ft. Lbs. (N.m)
Injection Pump-to-Engine	14-18 (19-25)
Injection Nozzle-to-Engine	43-51 (60-71)
Injection Nozzle-to-Tube	22-25 (31-35)

1983 Diesel Fuel Injection

DATSUN/NISSAN – SENTRA

DESCRIPTION

The Datsun/Nissan Sentra fuel injection system consists of a combination injection pump and fuel distributor, four injection nozzles, a fuel tank, lines and hoses, and fuel filter assembly. The filter assembly contains a fuel filter, integral priming pump, and a water separator. The injectors use a needle type valve at the end of each nozzle.

Integrated into the fuel system is an glow plug system to aid in cold start operation. The glow plug system consists of a glow plug in each cylinder, two relays, a dropping resistor, a glow plug control unit and various lights and switches.

OPERATION

FUEL INJECTION PUMP

The injection pump is Bosch-Kiki VE type pump. Belt-driven from the camshaft, it is a low pressure vane type with a high pressure fuel distributor. An integral fuel cut-off solenoid for engine shut down is included. The injection pump is also equipped with an RPM sensor and a throttle position potentiometer, which are used by the EGR control system to reduce emissions.

The vane pump output pressure, also referred to as the injection pump body pressure, averages between 50-100 psi (3.5-7.0 kg/cm²) depending upon the engine speed and application. The plunger type injection pump boosts this pressure to about 2000 psi (140.6 kg/cm²).

INJECTORS

The injection spray nozzles spray fuel into a combustion prechamber as each compression stroke occurs. Nozzles can be disassembled, cleaned, and adjusted to correct improper spray patterns.

The injector receives a high pressure pulse of fuel, which forces the needle valve to open, allowing fuel to pass into the prechamber. Injector opening pressure can be adjusted with shims on top of the needle valve return spring. *See Fig. 1.*

Fig. 1: Sentra Diesel Fuel Injection Nozzle

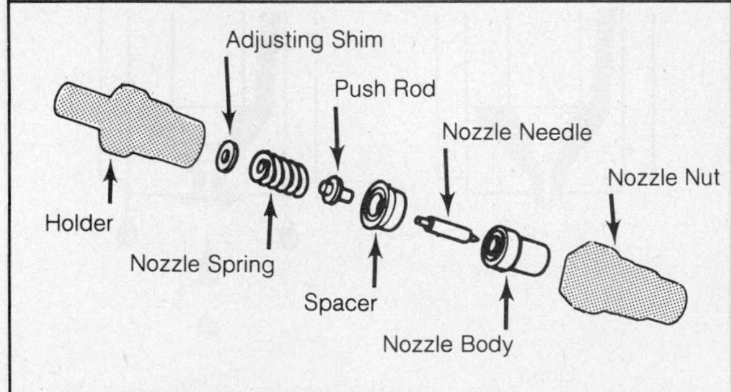
Adjusting Shim
Push Rod
Nozzle Needle
Nozzle Nut
Holder
Nozzle Spring
Spacer
Nozzle Body

GLOW PLUGS

The glow plugs enable the engine to start easily in cold weather and run smoothly during warm-up. The glow plug system uses a glow plug control unit, 2 relays, and a dropping resistor to control glow plug current.

When the ignition is turned on, a dash mounted glow plug indicator light operates for up to 9 seconds. Full battery voltage is applied for 4-12 seconds during pre-glow operation to aid in starting.

There is no pre-glow operation if coolant temperature is above 122°F (50°C). After engine has started, pre-glow relay is turned off. The after-glow circuit continues to supply reduced current to the glow plugs through the dropping resistor. During after-glow, the glow plugs operate for 5 to 32 seconds depending on engine temperature.

Glow plug relay No. 1 is used for pre-glow operation and relay No. 2 is used for after-glow operation. The No. 1 relay is located on left side shock tower, while the No. 2 relay and dropping resistor are on the firewall next to the power brake booster. The temperature sensor is mounted on the right side of engine block. The glow plug control unit is mounted behind the right side kick panel.

FUEL FILTER

The fuel filter is provided to protect the fuel pump and injectors from dirt and water in the fuel. The lower portion of the filter assembly is a combination sediment trap and water level sensor.

An accumulation of water will cause the float in the water trap to rise and illuminate the water sensor warning light. The fuel filter element separates water from the fuel, then filters the fuel. The hand pump is used to bleed the fuel system after servicing. *See Fig. 2..*

Fig. 2: Fuel Filter With Pump and Sensor

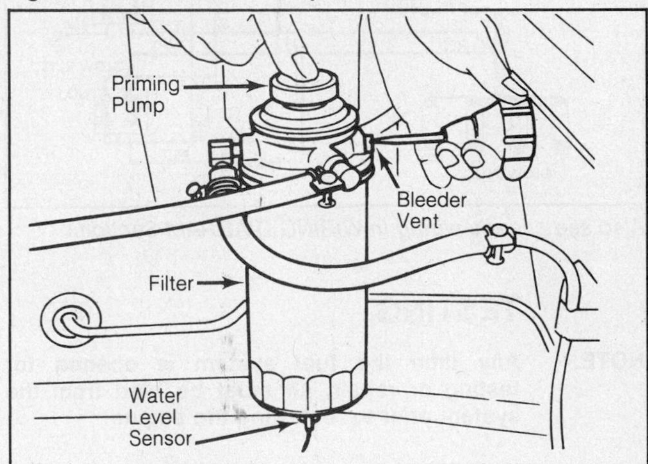
Priming Pump
Bleeder Vent
Filter
Water Level Sensor

Note bleeding operation.

TROUBLE SHOOTING

GLOW PLUGS

NOTE: **Before trouble shooting glow plug system, check the following components for proper electrical connections and operation. Battery, ignition switch and starter, ignition relay, all fuses and 4 fusible links. In addition, use ohmmeter to ensure that control unit terminal 3 is connected to ground.**

1) If engine fails to start or is hard to start, check if glow plug indicator lamp lights with ignition on. If not, check indicator lamp for burned out bulb.

1983 Diesel Fuel Injection

DATSUN/NISSAN – SENTRA (Cont.)

2) If indicator lamp bulb is good, check water temperature sensor. Replace water temperature sensor if defective. If indicator lamp bulb and water temperatur sensor are good, replace glow plug control unit.

3) If glow plug indicator lamp lights with ignition on, check if charging lamp lights also. If not, check for loose terminal at alternator "L" terminal or open circuit.

4) If charging lamp does not light, check glow plugs. Replace if necessary. If glow plugs are good, check glow plug relay No. 1, No. 2, and dropping resistors. If relays and dropping resistors are good, check glow plug control unit.

Fig. 3: Sentra Glow Plug System Wiring Diagram

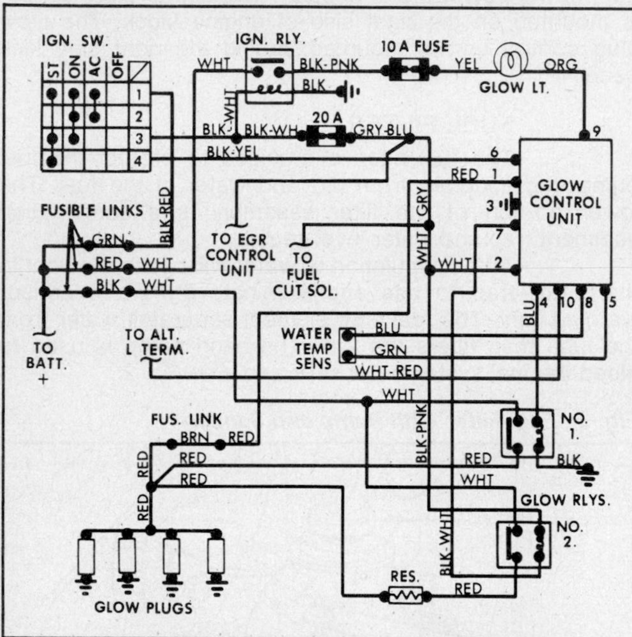
IGN. SW.
ST
ON
AC
OFF
IGN. RLY.
WHT
BLK-PNK
BLK
10 A FUSE
YEL
ORG
GLOW LT.
20 A
BLK
BLK-WH
GRY-BLU
BLK-YEL
WHT
BLK-RED
FUSIBLE LINKS
GRN
RED
WHT
BLK
TO BATT. +
TO EGR CONTROL UNIT
TO FUEL CUT SOL.
RED
GRY
GLOW CONTROL UNIT
TO ALT. L TERM.
WATER TEMP SENS
BLU
GRN
WHT-RED
FUS. LINK
BRN
NO. 1.
BLK-PNK
GLOW RLYS.
NO. 2.
BLK-WHT
RES.
GLOW PLUGS

Also see chassis wiring in WIRING DIAGRAM Section.

TESTING

NOTE: **Any time the fuel system is opened for testing or repair, air must be bled from the system prior to restarting the engine.**

INJECTORS

Opening Pressure

1) Remove fuel injection pipes from injector nozzles and pump. When removing fuel spill tube nut, hold nozzle holder body with a wrench to prevent it from rotating with nut.

2) Remove injection nozzle assembly from cylinder head. Mount nozzle on nozzle tester and pump tester handle to bleed nozzle. *See Fig. 4.*

3) Operate nozzle tester at a rate of more than 60 strokes per minute and read gauge pressure. The reading will increase gradually with pointer oscillating while nozzle is spraying. Injection pressure is the pressure at which the pointer starts to oscillate.

4) Service limit for new injectors is 1920-2033 psi (135-143 kg/cm²), used injectors 1778-1920 psi (125-135 kg/cm²). If test pressure is outside limit, nozzle needs to be cleaned and adjusted.

Fig. 4: Testing Injector Pressure

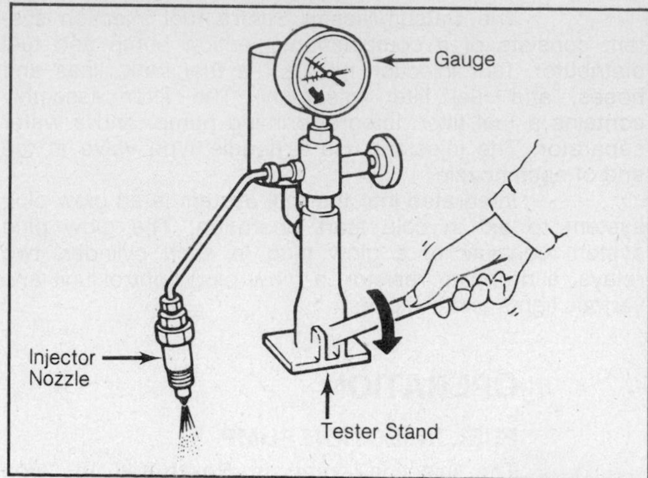
Gauge
Injector Nozzle
Tester Stand

5) Injector pressure can be adjusted with shims that are available in varying thicknesses. A change of .0016 in. (.04 mm) will change injector pressure 68 psi (4.8 kg/cm²)

Spray Pattern

1) To test spray pattern pump tester handle one time per second. Check spray pattern. *See Fig. 5.* If pattern is not correct, clean or replace nozzle.

Fig. 5: Injector Nozzle Spray Patterns

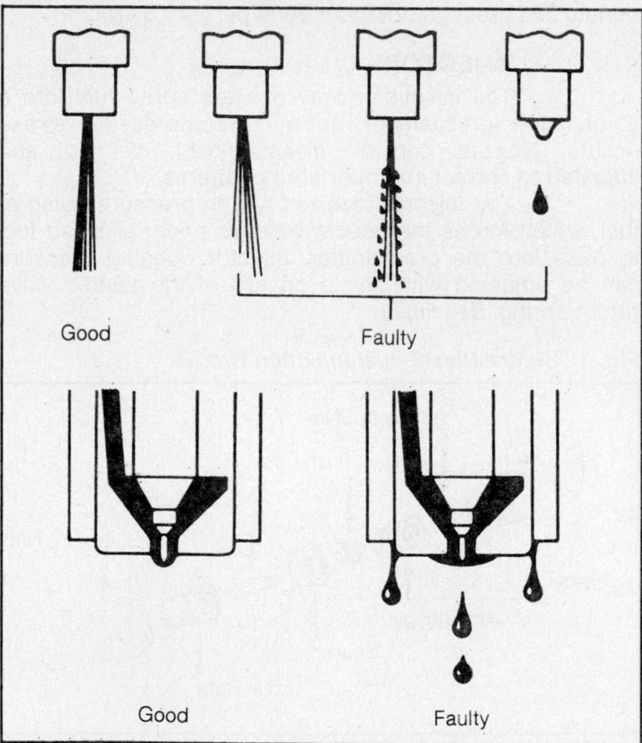
Good
Faulty
Good
Faulty

Nozzle should not drip after being tested.

2) Maintain pressure at 981-1961 psi (10-20 kg/cm²) below initial injection pressure. Check that there is no dripping from nozzle tip or around body. *See Fig. 5.* If there is leakage, overhaul or replace injector.

Nozzle Cleaning

1) Disassemble injector nozzle. If nozzle needle is damaged, fused, siezed or discolored, replace

DATSUN/NISSAN – SENTRA (Cont.)

entire nozzle assembly. Check all other parts for excessive wear or damage. Replace as needed.

2) Scrape off carbon deposits with a piece of wood and clean each part in cleaning solvent. After cleaning, keep parts emersed in light oil. Be sure to remove all deposits from adjusting shims, spring, push rod, spacer, nozzle body, needle and seat, and injection hole.

3) Pull needle about halfway out of body and release. Needle should slide smoothly back into place. Repeat this procedure several times, rotating needle slightly each time. If needle does not slide smoothly, replace nozzle body and needle.

Installation

1) Clean nozzle holder mounting area of cylinder head. Fit a new nozzle gasket to the nozzle before mounting in head. *See Fig. 6.*

2) Install injector nozzle to cylinder head and tighten to 43-51 ft.-lbs. (59-69 N.m). Reverse removal procedure for installation of injection pipes.

Fig. 6: Installing Nozzle Tip Gasket

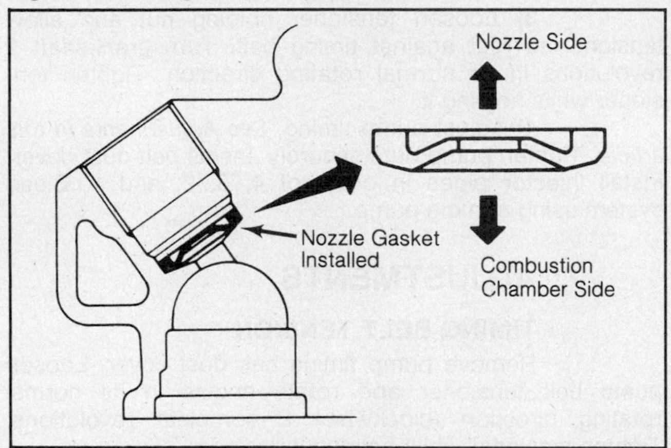
Nozzle Side
Nozzle Gasket Installed
Combustion Chamber Side

Always install a new nozzle tip gasket.

GLOW PLUG SYSTEM

Indicator Lamp

Indicator lamp should light when coolant temperature is below 122°F (50°C). If not check bulb and circuit. If bulb is good, check for battery voltage at terminal 9 of glow plug control unit. If no voltage, repair wiring. If voltage present, replace control unit.

Glow Plug

Remove glow plugs. Check continuity between glow plug end terminal and body. No continuity indicates a defective glow plug.

Fig. 7: Glow Plug Relay Test Points

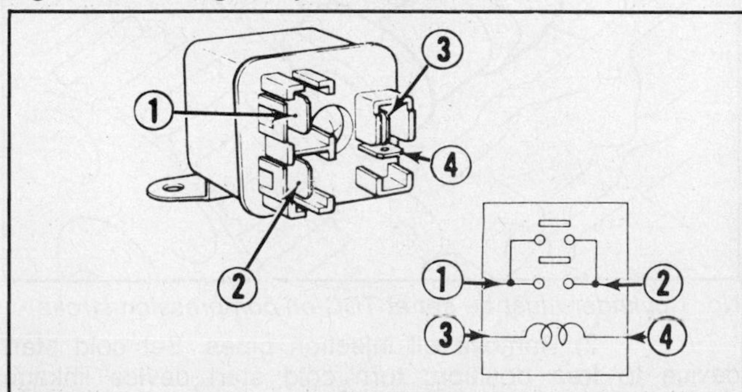
1
2
3
4
1
2
3
4

Glow Plug Relays

Remove No. 1 and No. 2 relays. To check, apply voltage to terminal 3. Ground terminal 4 on relay. Check for continuity across terminals 1 and 2. *See Fig. 7.* Replace if defective.

Dropping Resistor

Turn ignition off. Unplug dropping resistor harness connector. Resistance should be 1/10 ohm. If not, replace unit.

Glow Plug Control Unit

1) To test pre-glow operation, connect test lamp to Blue wire of control unit (harness connector plugged in). Turn ignition on and measure amount of time test lamp is lighted. *See Pre-Glow Test Specifications* table.

PRE-GLOW TEST SPECIFICATIONS

Coolant Temp. °F (°C)	Time in Seconds	Terminal Voltage
Below 122 (50)	12	8
	6	10.5
Above 122 (50)	0	0

2) Connect test lamp to Black/White wire of control unit. Measure amount of time that test lamp is lighted when ignition switch is turned from "START" to "ON". *See After-Glow Test Specifications* table. Test lamp will be on continuously with switch in "START" position.

AFTER-GLOW TEST SPECIFICATIONS

Coolant Temperature °F (°C)	Time in Seconds
Below -13 (-25)	31
68 (20)	11
104 (40)	9
122 (50)	0

3) Test lamp will turn off during after-glow operation when glow plug voltage reaches 7 volts. Replace glow plug control unit if defective.

COOLANT TEMPERATURE SENSOR

Coolant temperature sensor resistance varies with engine temperature. If resistance is not correct at specified temperature, replace sensor. *See Temperature Sensor Resistance Specifications* table.

TEMPERATURE SENSOR RESISTANCE SPECIFICATIONS

Temperature °F (°C)	Ohms
50 (10)	3700
68 (20)	2500
122 (50)	850
176 (80)	330

FUEL CUT SOLENOID

Solenoid Check

To check the solenoid, repeatedly apply and remove battery voltage directly to the solenoid. If the solenoid is functioning properly, a distinct clicking sound should be heard. If not, the solenoid is bad and should be replaced.

REMOVAL & INSTALLATION

FUEL FILTER

Removal & Installation

1) Place a pan beneath fuel filter. Remove water sensor from bottom of filter. At this point the accumulated water and fuel will drain out of the filter. If only water removal is required, replace sensor and bleed system.

2) To change filter cartridge, unscrew it from the housing. Install sensor in bottom of new filter and hand tighten filter to housing.

Bleeding

1) Loosen priming pump vent and operate hand pump until fuel overflows vent. *See Fig. 2.*

2) Disconnect fuel return hose on fuel line side. Operate priming pump until fuel flows at hose end. Connect hose. If engine will not start, loosen injection tubes at nozzle side and crank engine until fuel overflows from tubes.

FUEL INJECTION PUMP

Removal

1) Disconnect battery negative terminal and drain coolant. Disconnect accelerator cable, wires, and hoses from pump. Remove pump timing belt dust cover. Rotate engine so that No. 1 piston is TDC on compression stroke.

2) Loosen pump timing belt tensioner and remove belt. Remove injection pipes from pump and cylinder head. Holding pulley with tool (KV10109300), remove the nut and washer securing the injection pump pulley. *See Fig. 8* .

3) Using a gear puller, disengage the sprocket from the pump shaft. Remove pump-to-bracket mounting nuts and remove pump.

Fig. 8: Removing or Tightening Injector Pump Pulley Nut

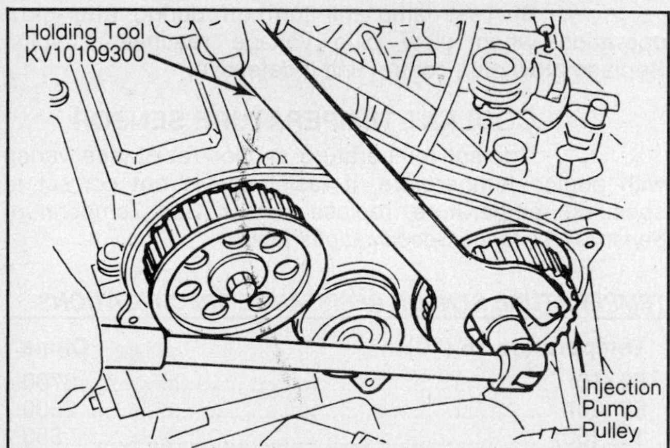
Holding Tool
KV10109300
Injection
Pump
Pulley

Use tool to keep pump sprocket from turning.

NOTE: **Protect the timing belt against undue stress (twisting and bending) and oil contamination. After belt removal do not rotate crankshaft.**

Installation

1) Locate injection pump on engine, tighten nuts temporarily. Install pump pulley on shaft. Holding pulley with tool (KV10109300), tighten nut to 43-51 ft. lbs. (59-69 N.m).

2) Ensure No. 1 cylinder is set at TDC compression stroke. Place reference mark on timing belt. Count off 23 cogs on belt and place another mark. Align reference marks with marks on camshaft pulley and injection pump pulley. *See Fig. 9.*

Fig. 9: Installing Injection Pump Timing Belt

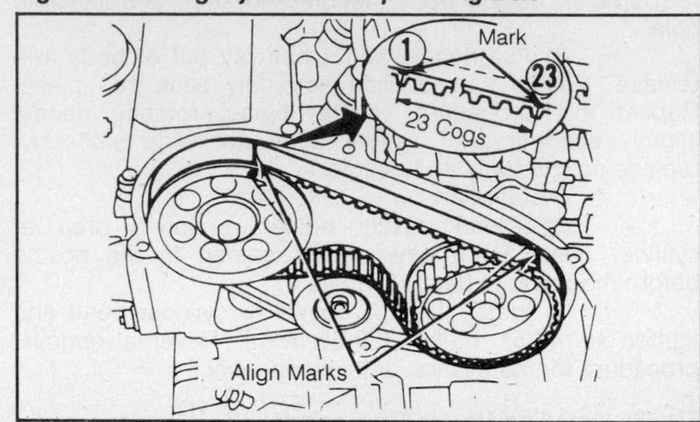
Mark
1
23
23 Cogs
Align Marks

3) Loosen tensioner holding nut and allow tensioner to rest against timing belt. Turn crankshaft 2 revolutions in its normal rotating direction. Tighten tensioner while holding it.

4) Adjust pump timing. *See Adjustments in this article*. Tighten pump nuts securely. Install belt dust cover. Install injector pipes in order of 4, 3, 2, and 1. Bleed system using priming pump.

ADJUSTMENTS

TIMING BELT TENSION

Remove pump timing belt dust cover. Loosen pump belt tensioner and rotate engine in its normal rotating direction (clockwise) 2 complete revolutions. Tighten tensioner while holding it in place.

INJECTION PUMP TIMING

1) Bring No. 1 cylinder to TDC on compression stroke. Ensure timing mark indicator and the notch in the crankshaft pulley are aligned. No. 1 cylinder camshaft lobes must be pointing up. *See Fig. 10.*

Fig. 10: Position of Cam Lobes to Set Injector Pump Timing

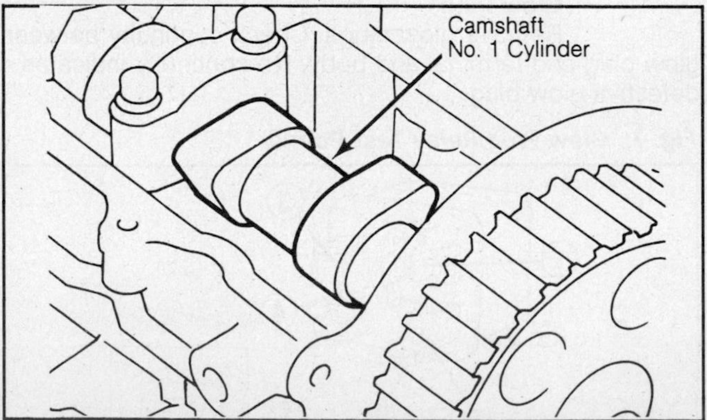
Camshaft
No. 1 Cylinder

No. 1 cylinder must be set at TDC on compression stroke.

2) Remove all injection pipes. Set cold start device to free position; turn cold start device linkage

DATSUN/NISSAN – SENTRA (Cont.)

clockwise, insert a block 0.59 " (15mm) between device and linkage.

3) Remove plug bolt from rear side of injection pump. Attach tool (KV11229352) to measure pump plunger lift. Turn crankshaft 15°-20° BTDC counterclockwise. Set dial indicator to zero. *See Fig. 11.*

Fig. 11: Measuring Injector Pump Plunger Lift

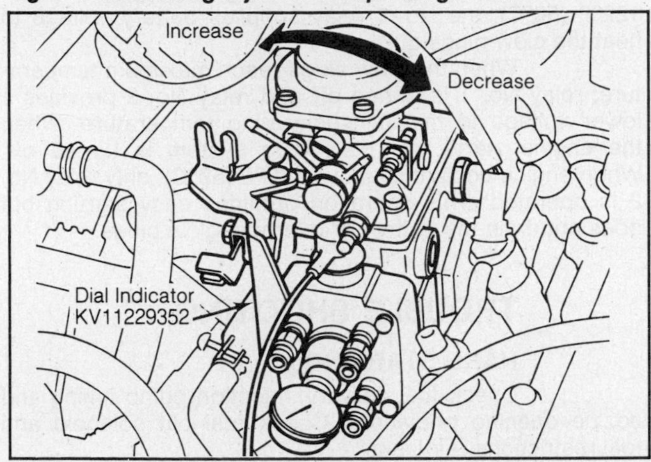
Increase
Decrease
Dial Indicator
KV11229352

Alway use new gasket when installing plug in pump.

4) Turn crankshaft clockwise until No. 1 cylinder is at TDC. Read dial gauge. Compare reading with specifications. *See Injection Pump Timing Specifications* table. If dial indicator is outside specifications, rotate pump body and retest plunger stroke lift. Repeat this operation until reading falls within specifications.

5) Remove adapter with dial indicator and replace plug bolt using new gasket. Connect fuel injection tubes in the order of 4, 3, 2 and 1. Bleed fuel system.

INJECTION PUMP TIMING SPECIFICATIONS

Application	Plunger Lift In. (mm)
High Altitude	
Man. Trans.	.0383-.0406 (.97-1.03)
Auto. Trans.	.0358-.0382 (.91-..97)
All Others	
Man. Trans.	.0358-.0382 (.91-.97)
Auto. Trans.	.0334-.0358 (.85-.91)

IDLE SPEED

See appropriate Datsun/Nissan article in TUNE-UP Section.

1983 Diesel Fuel Injection

ISUZU

I-Mark, P'UP

DESCRIPTION

The fuel injection system consists of a combination injection pump and fuel distributor, four injection nozzles, a fuel tank, lines and hoses, and fuel filter assembly. The filter assembly contains a fuel filter, integral priming pump, and a water separator. The injectors use a needle type valve at the end of each nozzle.

The glow plug system uses 4 glow plugs to assist in cold starting. The thermal glow plug system has a controller, relays, thermo switch, dropping resistor, sensing resistor, and glow plugs. Warning lights in the instrument cluster indicate when the glow plugs are operating or the fuel filter is filled with water.

OPERATION

FUEL INJECTION PUMP

The injection pump is located on the lower right side of the engine and driven by a toothed belt. It draws fuel from the tank, pressurizes it, and sends a specific quantity to each cylinder at the proper time. Excess fuel is returned from the injectors and sent back to the tank.

A fast idle system is used when coolant is below a specified temperature. A vacuum unit actuates the throttle and increases idle speed. A fuel cut solenoid is actuated by the ignition switch and stops fuel flow at the pump so the engine can be shut down. The injection pump is also equipped with an altitude compensator for proper fuel delivery at high altitudes.

INJECTION NOZZLES

The injection nozzles spray fuel into a prechamber as each compression stroke occurs. A fuel return line connects all injectors and returns excess fuel to the pump. Injectors are opened by high pressure in the fuel lines and cannot be adjusted. If spray patterns are incorrect, nozzles can be overhauled.

Injector opening pressures are adjustable. On I-Mark models, opening pressures can be adjusted by shim replacement. P'UP models use an adjustment screw in the injector nozzle.

FUEL FILTER & WATER WARNING SYSTEM

The diesel injection system uses an integral fuel filter and water separator. A water sensor is fitted into the bottom of a fuel filter cartridge and lights a warning lamp when water accumulates in the filter. A hand pump is also incorporated into the filter housing to prime the pump after filter replacement.

GLOW PLUGS

I-Mark

When the engine coolant is below 140°F (60°C), the No. 1 relay closes when the ignition switch is turned to "ON". *See Fig. 6*. This supplies battery voltage to heat the glow plugs quickly. No. 1 relay will open after about 2.5 seconds when the specified temperature of 1562°F (850°C) is reached.

The No. 2 relay should close as ignition switch is turned to "START". The No. 1 relay will remain on when the ignition switch is turned to "START" if glow plugs have not reached the specified temperature. At normal operating temperature, No. 1 relay will open when ignition turned from "START" to "ON" as long as charging relay has been activated by alternator.

P'UP

The glow plug system uses 4 glow plugs to assist in cold starting. When the engine coolant is below 122°F (50°C), the No. 1 relay supplies battery voltage to heat the glow plugs quickly.

When the glow plugs reach maximum temperature, relay No. 1 is turned off and relay No. 2 provides a lower voltage to maintain glow plug temperature. When the engine starts, the glow plug system is turned off. When engine coolant is above 122°F (50°C), only relay No. 2 is operated. This operation provides easy starting but does not drain the battery or overheat glow plugs.

TROUBLE SHOOTING

HARD STARTING

Check fuel delivery, injection pump timing and nozzle opening pressures. Check fuel cut solenoid and fuel restrictions. Air leaks.

ROUGH IDLE

Adjust idle speed. Contaminated fuel, injection timing, nozzle opening pressure, or sticking delivery valve in pump.

LACK OF POWER

Air cleaner restriction. Accelerator linkage. Exhaust restriction. Fuel contamination or restriction in lines. Injection timing.

EXHAUST SMOKE

Check for air cleaner restrictions or contaminated fuel. Injection timing or nozzle opening pressure.

GLOW PLUG INDICATOR INOPERATIVE

Check for burned out bulb. Blown fuse or fusible link. Bad connections at controller. Controller or ignition switch defective.

IMPROPER OPERATION OF GLOW PLUGS

Thermal sensor or glow plugs defective. Controller inoperative. Ignition switch "R" circuit open or intermittent.

TESTING

INJECTION NOZZLES

Spray Pattern

Remove nozzles and mount on injection nozzle tester. Pump tester lever about 4-6 times a second to observe spray pattern. *See Fig. 1*. If spray is faulty, injector must be cleaned or replaced.

1983 Diesel Fuel Injection

ISUZU (Cont.)

Fig. 1: Injection Nozzle Spray Patterns

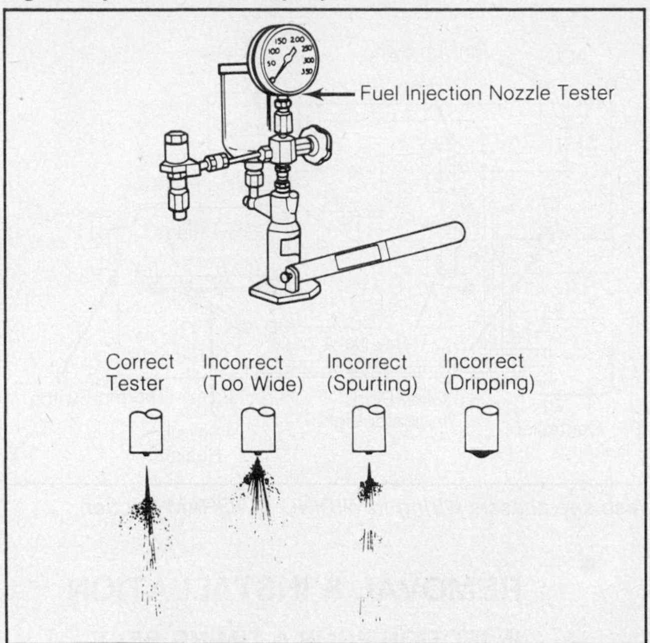
Fuel Injection Nozzle Tester
Correct Tester
Incorrect (Too Wide)
Incorrect (Spurting)
Incorrect (Dripping)

Opening Pressure

1) Pump pressure up slowly to note opening pressure. If not within 1705-1850 psi (120-130 kg/cm²) for I-Mark models or 1495-1635 psi (105-115 kg/cm²) on P'UP models, injector must be cleaned or replaced.

2) Check injector nozzles for leakage by installing in tester and maintaining a pressure of 284 psi (20 kg/cm²). If any leakage is evident, injector must be cleaned or replaced.

Nozzle Cleaning

1) Disassemble injector nozzle. If nozzle needle is damaged, fused, siezed or discolored, replace entire nozzle assembly. Check all other parts for excessive wear or damage. Replace as needed.

Fig. 2: I-Mark Injection Nozzle

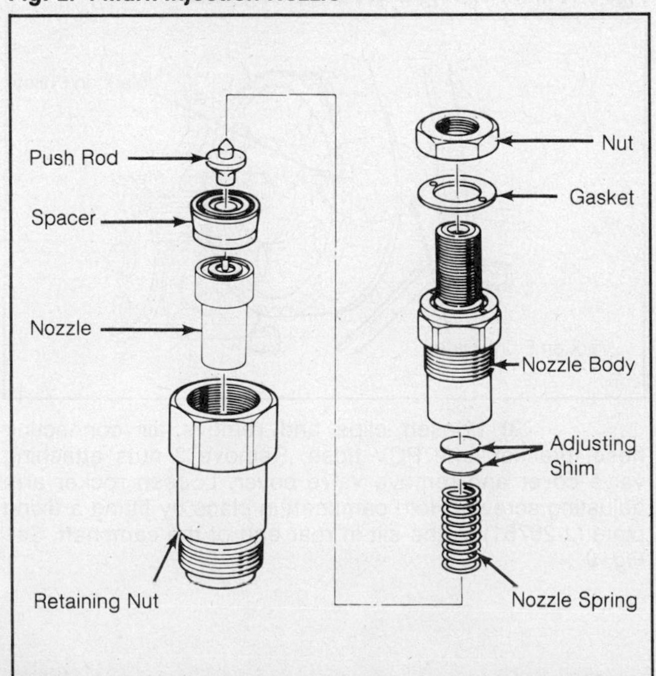
Push Rod
Spacer
Nozzle
Retaining Nut
Nut
Gasket
Nozzle Body
Adjusting Shim
Nozzle Spring

2) Scrape off carbon deposits with a piece of wood and clean each part in cleaning solvent. After cleaning, keep parts emersed in light oil. Be sure to remove all deposits from components. Nozzle must be replaced if needle seats are worn or damaged.

3) Hold nozzle vertically and insert needle. Lift needle about 1/3 way out of nozzle and release. Needle should slide smoothly back into place. Repeat this procedure several times, rotating needle slightly each time. If needle does not slide smoothly, replace nozzle body and needle.

Fig. 3: P'UP Injection Nozzle

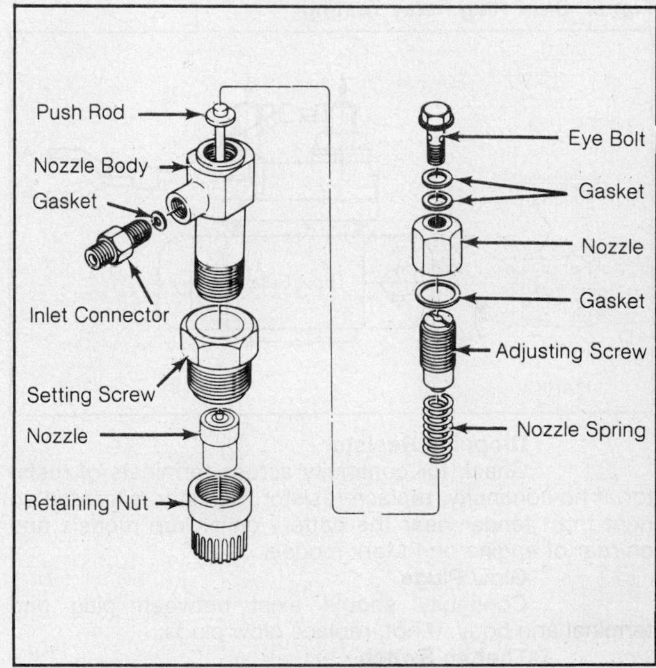
Push Rod
Nozzle Body
Gasket
Inlet Connector
Setting Screw
Nozzle
Retaining Nut
Eye Bolt
Gasket
Nozzle
Gasket
Adjusting Screw
Nozzle Spring

4) When assembling injectors, use centering tool (J-33178) to install nozzle in center of nozzle body holder. *See Fig. 4*. Tighten retaining nut to 65 ft. lbs. (88 N.m).

Fig. 4: Centering Injector Nozzle

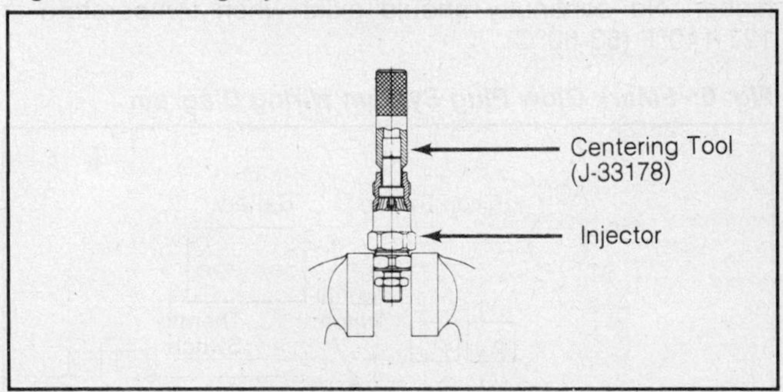
Centering Tool (J-33178)
Injector

5) After tightening retaining nut, draw out centering tool. If it can't be drawn out easily, nozzle body has not been fitted properly. Loosen retaining nut and tighten properly. Adjust nozzle opening pressure after assembly.

6) I-Mark injectors use adjustment shims to change opening pressures. Shims are available in sizes from .0197" (.5 mm) to .0394" (1 mm) in .0016" (.04 mm) increments. Every increase of .0016" (.04 mm) will increase opening pressure by 68 psi (4.8 kg/cm²).

ISUZU (Cont.)

7) In addition, .002" (.05 mm) shims are available for I-Mark models for fine tuning adjustments. Opening pressure will increase 85 psi (6 kg/cm²) for every .002" (.05 mm) shim added. Injectors on P'UP models use an adjustment screw to change opening pressure.

GLOW PLUG SYSTEM

Glow Plug Relays

No continuity should be present across terminals "C" and "D". With battery voltage applied to terminals "A" and "B", continuity should be present across "C" and "D". If not, replace relay. *See Fig. 5.*

Fig. 5: Glow Plug Relay Testing

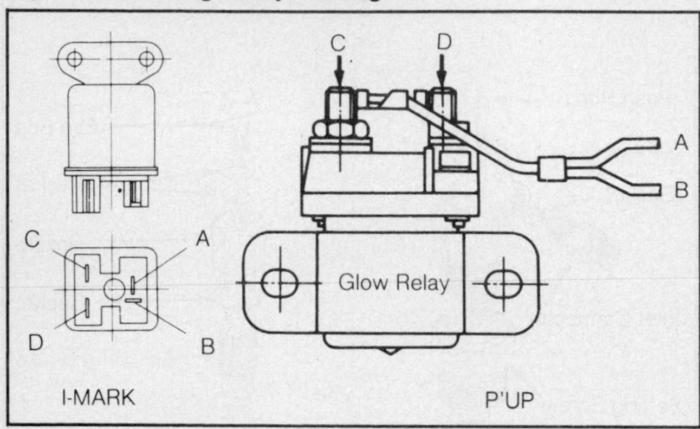
C
D
A
B
C
A
D
B
Glow Relay
I-MARK
P'UP

Dropping Resistor

Check for continuity across terminals of resistor. If no continuity, replace resistor. Resistor is located on right front fender near the battery on pickup models and on rear of engine on I-Mark models.

Glow Plugs

Continuity should exist between plug end terminal and body. If not, replace glow plugs.

Thermo Switch

1) On P'UP models, continuity should exist when switch is at a temperature lower than 109-122°F (43-50°C). No continuity should exist when above 116-127°F (47-53°C). If switch does not operate properly, replace it.

2) On I-Mark models, there should be continuity when coolant temperature is 135-145°F (57-63°C) or higher. No continuity should exist when temperature is 127-140°F (53-60°C).

Fig. 6: I-Mark Glow Plug System Wiring Diagram

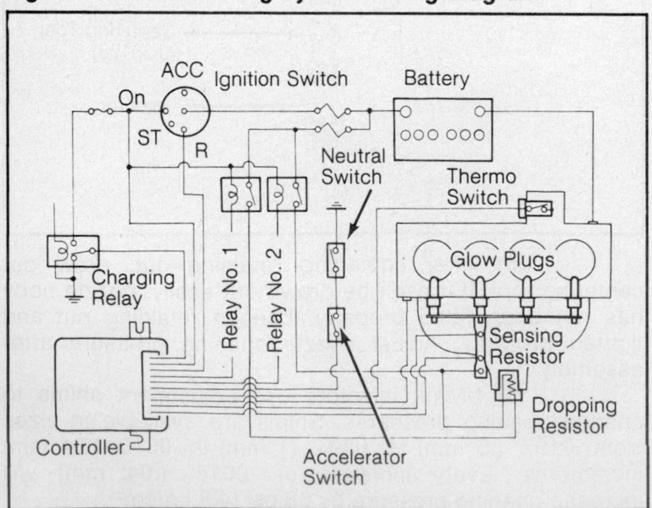
ACC
Ignition Switch
Battery
On
ST
R
Neutral Switch
Thermo Switch
Charging Relay
Relay No. 1
Relay No. 2
Glow Plugs
Sensing Resistor
Dropping Resistor
Controller
Accelerator Switch

Fig. 7: P'UP Glow Plug System Wiring Diagram

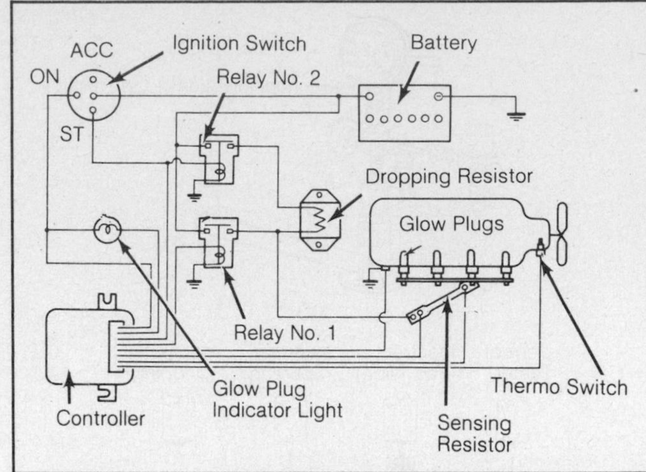
ACC
Ignition Switch
Battery
ON
Relay No. 2
ST
Dropping Resistor
Glow Plugs
Relay No. 1
Glow Plug Indicator Light
Thermo Switch
Controller
Sensing Resistor

Also see chassis wiring in WIRING DIAGRAM Section.

REMOVAL & INSTALLATION

INJECTION PUMP & TIMING BELT

NOTE: **When the timing belt is loosened or removed, it must be replaced. Do not retension or install a used timing belt.**

Removal (I-Mark)

1) Disconnect negative battery cable. Remove panel under engine, drain cooling system, and remove fan shroud. Remove fan, fan belts, and cooling fan pulley.

2) Remove 10 bolts retaining upper dust cover. Remove dust cover and by-pass hose. Set No. 1 cylinder to TDC compression stroke. Align mark on pump pulley with mark on front plate. *See Fig. 8.* Install a bolt (6mm x 1.25) through hole in injection pump pulley to hold pulley in place.

Fig. 8: I-Mark Timing Belt Pulley Alignment

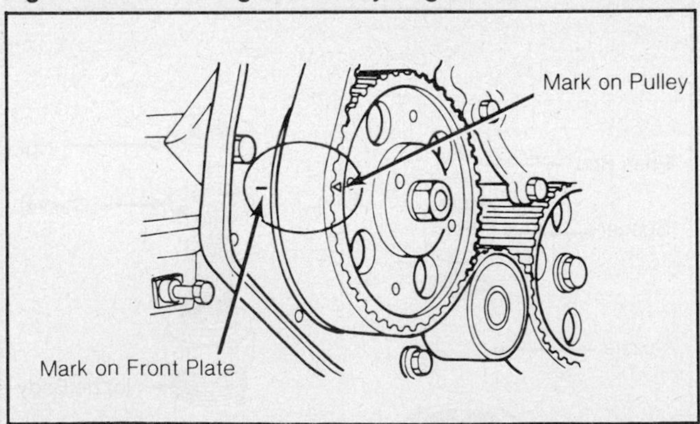
Mark on Pulley
Mark on Front Plate

3) Loosen clips and remove air connecting hose, bracket, and PCV hose. Remove 3 nuts attaching valve cover and remove valve cover. Loosen rocker arm adjusting screws. Hold camshaft in place by fitting a fixing plate (J-29761) to the slit in rear end of the camshaft. *See Fig. 9.*

ISUZU (Cont.)

Fig. 9: I-Mark Camshaft Fixing Plate Installation

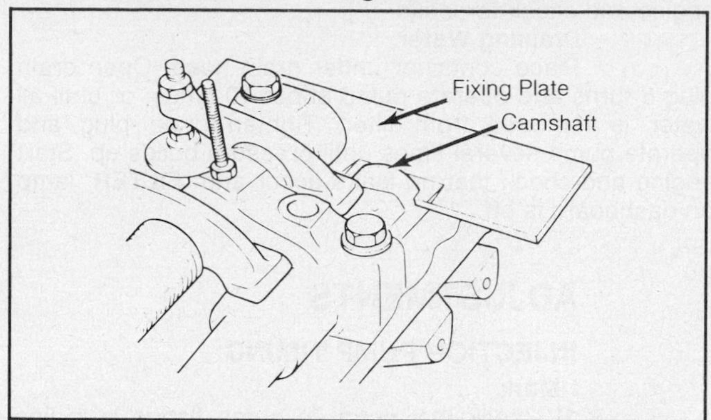
Fixing Plate
Camshaft

4) Remove damper pulley, lower dust cover, timing belt holder, and tension spring. Loosen tension pulley and plate bolts. Remove timing belt. Remove nut attaching injection pump pulley. Using gear puller, remove injection pump pulley. Remove lock bolt.

5) Disconnect wiring from fuel cut solenoid valve switch and tachometer pick-up sensor (if so equipped). Disconnect accelerator cable from pump lever. On automatic transmission models, disconnect throttle valve control cable from pump lever.

6) On all models, disconnect vacuum hose from actuator of fast idle device and fuel hoses at injection pump. Remove 6 screws attaching injection pipe clips and remove clips. Remove 8 sleeve nuts attaching injection pipe and remove pipe.

7) Remove 4 bolts attaching pump rear bracket and remove bracket. Disconnect control lever spring. Remove 2 nuts attaching injection pump flange. Remove injection pump with fast idle device.

Installation

1) Install injection pump with fast idle device by aligning notched line on flange with line on front plate. Tighten 4 bolts on rear bracket in sequence. *See Fig. 10.* Ensure that there is no clearance between rear bracket and injection pump bracket.

Fig. 10: I-Mark Injection Pump Rear Bracket Bolt Tightening Sequence

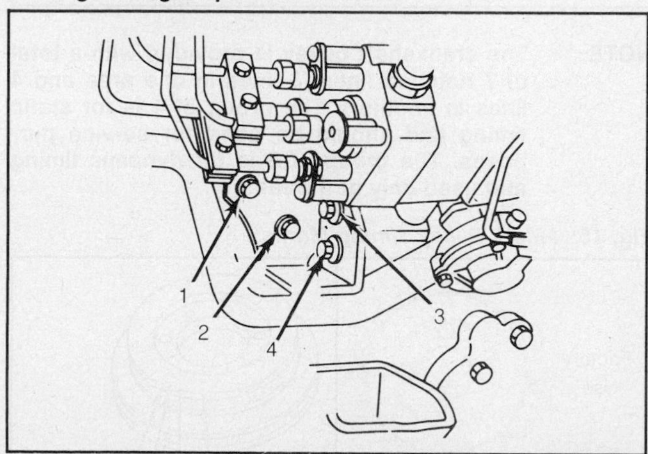
1
2
4
3

2) Install injection pump pulley by aligning it with the key groove. Align mark on pulley with mark on front plate. Tighten injection pump pulley nut to specifications using bolt to hold it in position. Remove camshaft pulley bolt.

3) Using gear puller, remove pulley from the camshaft. Install pulley on the shaft. Hand-tighten pulley bolts so pulley may be turned by hand.

4) Install timing belt counterclockwise on crankshaft pulley, idler pulley, camshaft pulley, injection pump pulley, tension pulley, and damper pulley in order. Ensure that cogs on belt and pulley engage properly.

5) Position belt so that slack is in area of tension pulley. Depress tension pulley with finger and install tension spring. Hand-tighten tension pulley plate bolts in sequence. *See Fig. 11.*

Fig. 11: I-Mark Tension Pulley Bolt Tightening Sequence

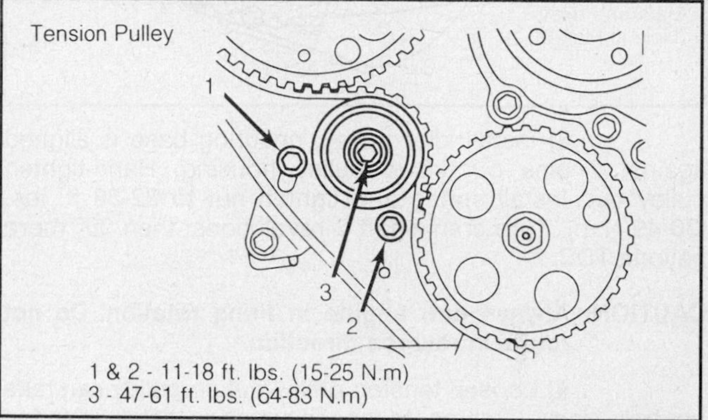
Tension Pulley
1
3
2
1 & 2 - 11-18 ft. lbs. (15-25 N.m)
3 - 47-61 ft. lbs. (64-83 N.m)

6) Tighten camshaft pulley bolts to 40-47 ft. lbs. (54-64 N.m). Remove injection pump pulley lock bolt and fixing plate on end of camshaft. Install damper pulley on hub. Ensure that No. 1 cylinder is at TDC compression stroke.

7) Tighten tensioner pulley and plate bolts in sequence. *See Fig. 11.* Belt tension between camshaft pulley and injection pump pulley should be 47-64 lbs. (21-29 kg.). Adjust valves and install valve cover. To complete installation, reverse removal procedures.

Removal (P'UP)

1) Remove battery. Remove panel under engine, drain cooling system, disconnect coolant hoses, and remove fan and shroud.

2) Remove fan belts, air conditioning compressor, and crankshaft pulley. Remove both timing belt covers, then remove tension spring and timing belt tension pulley. Remove timing belt.

3) Remove accelerator cable and wiring from injection pump. Using a back-up wrench, remove fuel lines and injection pipes from pump. Install a bolt (6mm x 1.25) through hole in injection pump pulley into threaded hole in pulley housing. Remove pulley bolts. Use a gear puller to remove injection pump pulley.

4) Check position of injection pump scribe line relative to mark on front bracket. Remove bolts and injection pump.

Installation

1) Install injection pump, aligning marks on flange and front bracket. Install injection pump pulley, using holding bolt to keep pulley from turning. Set No. 1 cyclinder at TDC compression stroke.

2) Align pulleys so marks are together. *See Fig. 12.* Install timing belt on crankshaft pulley, camshaft pulley and injection pump pulley in order. Position belt so slack is in area of idler pulley.

1983 Diesel Fuel Injection

ISUZU (Cont.)

Fig. 12: P'UP Timing Belt Pulley Alignment

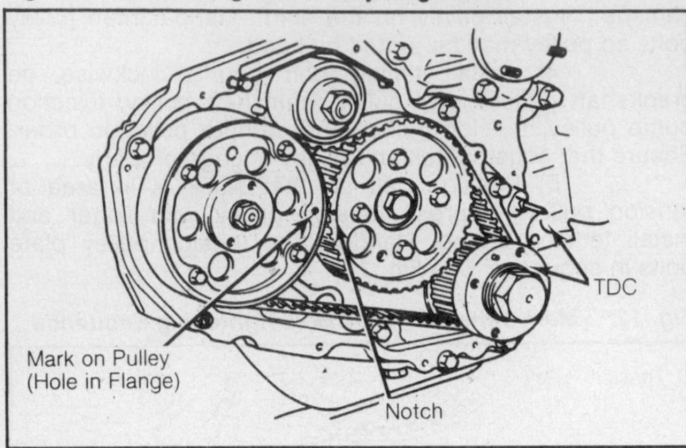
TDC
Mark on Pulley
(Hole in Flange)
Notch

3) Install idler pulley, ensuring base is aligned against 2 pins on timing pulley housing. Hand-tighten pulley nut. Install spring and tighten nut to 22-36 ft. lbs. (30-49 N.m). Turn crankshaft 2 revolutions, then 90° more beyond TDC.

CAUTION: Always turn engine in firing rotation. Do not rotate in reverse direction.

4) Loosen tension pulley nut so pulley can take up belt slack. Tighten to specifications. Install injection pump pulley flange so hole in flange is aligned with mark on camshaft pulley. Turn engine 2 revolutions and check that marks are still aligned when No. 1 cyclinder is at TDC compression stroke.

5) Belt tension between injection pump pulley and crankshaft pulley should be 33-55 lbs. (15-25 kg) when measured with tension gauge. To complete installation, reverse removal procedure. Adjust injection timing.

FUEL FILTER

Removal & Installation

1) Disconnect water sensor wiring at connector. Remove filter cartridge and pour out fuel. Remove water sensor. Install sensor on new filter cartridge.

2) Lubricate gasket with fuel, then install filter cartridge. Tighten 2/3 turn after filter contacts base. Pump hand pump 30-40 times to fill cartridge with fuel. Start engine and check for leaks.

Fig. 13: Fuel Filter and Water Separator

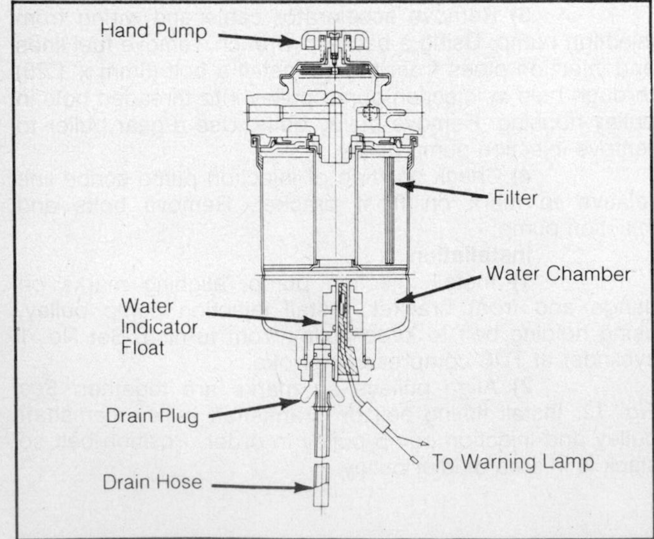
Hand Pump
Filter
Water Chamber
Water
Indicator
Float
Drain Plug
To Warning Lamp
Drain Hose

Draining Water

Place container under drain hose. Open drain plug 5 turns and operate pump about 10 times, or until all water is removed from filter. Tighten drain plug and operate pump several times until pressure builds up. Start engine and check that no leaks occur and "FILTER" lamp on dashboard is off.

ADJUSTMENTS

INJECTION PUMP TIMING

I-Mark

1) Check that notch in pump flange is in line with notched line on front plate. Set No. 1 cylinder at TDC compression stroke. Remove injection pump pulley cover (upper front cover). Ensure timing marks are aligned. *See Fig. 8.*

2) Remove valve cover and rear plug. Check that fixing plate fits smoothly into slit at rear end of the camshaft, then remove fixing plate. *See Fig. 9.* Disconnect injection pipe from pump (using back-up wrench) and remove distributor head screw.

3) Install timing gauge tool (J-28827). *See Fig. 14.* Set lift approximately .04" (1 mm) from the plunger. Turn engine until No. 1 cylinder is 45-60° BTDC, then calibrate dial indicator to zero.

Fig. 14: Adjusting I-Mark Injection Pump Timing

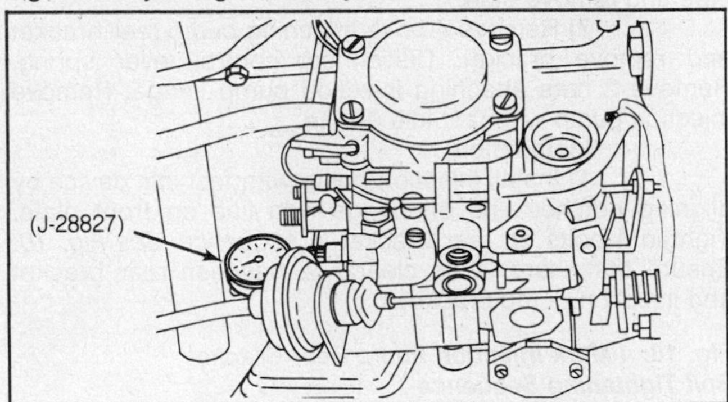
(J-28827)

NOTE: The crankshaft pulley is provided with a total of 7 notched lines (3 lines in one area and 4 lines in another). The group of 4 is for static timing and should be used for service purposes. The group of 3 is for dynamic timing and used only at the factory.

Fig. 15: I-Mark Pulley Timing Marks

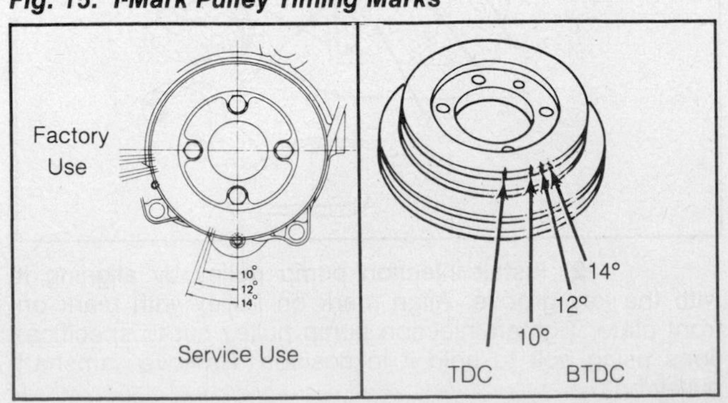
Factory
Use
Service Use
14°
12°
10°
TDC
BTDC

ISUZU (Cont.)

4) Turn crankshaft in normal direction of rotation until timing mark (12° BTDC) on crankshaft pulley is in line with indicator. *See Fig. 15.* Dial indicator should show .020" (0.5 mm). If not, loosen pump bolts and rotate pump slightly to obtain proper reading.

P'UP

1) Check that notch in pump flange is in line with notch in front bracket. Set No. 1 cylinder at TDC compression stroke. Remove injection pump pulley cover (right half of timing belt cover) to ensure timing marks are aligned. *See Fig. 12.*

2) Disconnect injection pipe from pump (using back-up wrench) and remove distributor head screw. Install timing gauge tool (J-29763 or J-28827) and set lift approximately .04" (1 mm) from the plunger.

3) Turn engine until No. 1 cylinder is 45-60° BTDC. Calibrate dial indicator to zero. Turn crankshaft pulley slightly in both directions and ensure that zero reading does not change.

4) Turn crankshaft in normal direction of rotation until timing mark (15° BTDC) on crankshaft pulley is in line with indicator. *See Fig. 16.* Dial indicator should show .020" (0.5 mm). If not, loosen pump bolts and rotate pump slightly to obtain proper timing.

Fig. 16: P'UP Timing Mark Identification

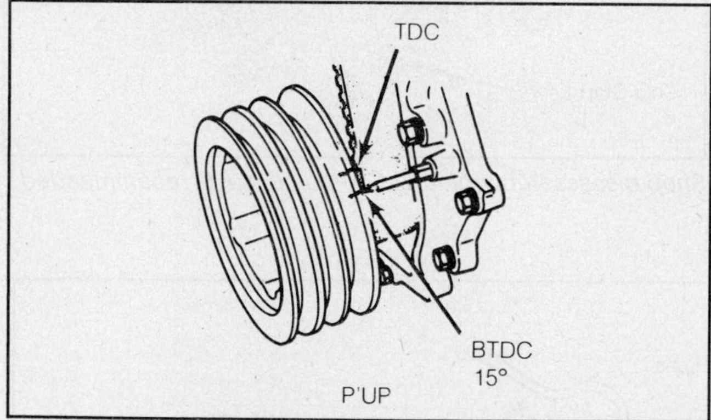

TDC
BTDC
15°
P'UP

IDLE & FAST IDLE SPEED

See the appropriate Isuzu article in TUNE-UP Section for adjustment procedures.

VACUUM PUMP

Description

An auxiliary vacuum pump is used on diesel engines. The pump is driven off of the alternator and supplies vacuum to run the power brake booster.

Testing

To test pump, use a photoelectric tachometer and reflective tape. Connect a vacuum gauge to the hose between the vacuum pump and the brake booster. Run the vacuum pump at the specified RPM to obtain vacuum readings.

VACUUM PUMP SPECIFICATIONS

Engine RPM	Vacuum (In. Hg)
850	17.3
1350	22.8

TIGHTENING SPECIFICATIONS

Application	Ft. Lbs. (N.m)
Injection Pump Pulley Nut	
I-Mark	43-50 (58-68)
P'UP	42-52 (57-71)
Timing Belt Cover Bolts	4-7 (5-10)
Injection Nozzles	51-58 (69-79)

1983 Diesel Fuel Injection

MAZDA – B2200 PICKUP

DESCRIPTION

The Mazda diesel pickup fuel injection system consists of a combination injection pump and fuel distributor, 4 fuel injection nozzles, a fuel filter with an integral priming pump, a water sedimentor, fuel lines, and the fuel tank. The engine is also equipped with a glow plug system to assist in cold starting.

The injection pump is a vane type pump and is driven by the engine timing gears. An altitude compensator and a cold start device are installed on the pump to modify injection duration as necessary. The distributor portion of the pump contains a fuel cut solenoid to stop fuel flow to the injectors after the ignition switch is turned off. *See Fig. 1.*

The injectors use a needle type valve at the end of the nozzle. Injector opening pressure can be changed by adding or subtracting adjusting shim thickness. The adjusting shim is located just above the needle valve return spring in the injector.

The glow plug system consists of a glow plug in each cylinder, 2 relays, a ballast resistor, a glow plug control unit as well as various switches and warning lights.

The sedimentor collects excess water and dirt in the fuel system. A water detected is mounted on the top of the sedimentor. The detector will turn on a warning light on the instrument panel when the water level reaches a predetermined level.

OPERATION

FUEL INJECTION PUMP

The Diesel Kiki single plunger mechanical injection pump contains a low pressure vane-type fuel pump, a high pressure distributor-type injection pump, a centrifugal governor, and an injection timing advance mechanism.

The vane pump output pressure (sometimes referred to as injection pump body pressure) averages between 50 to 100 psi depending upon engine speed and application. The plunger injection pump boosts the fuel pressure to about 2000 psi. The pump assembly is also equipped with an electric fuel shut-off valve and a cold start device for fast idle speed actuation.

Fig. 1: Diesel Kiki Diesel Fuel Injection Pump

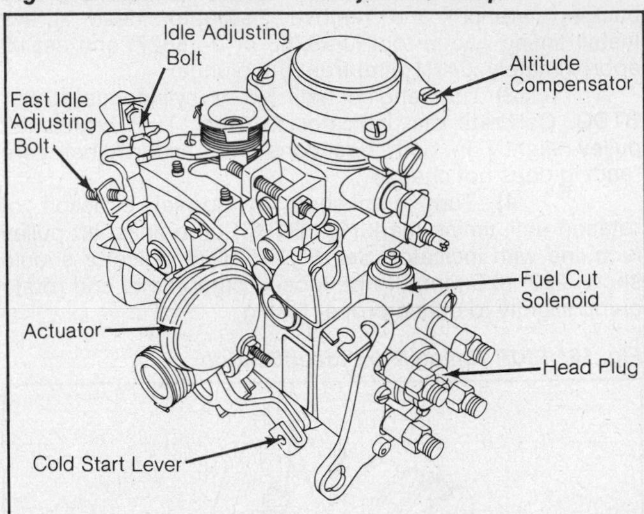
Idle Adjusting
Bolt
Altitude
Compensator
Fast Idle
Adjusting
Bolt
Fuel Cut
Solenoid
Actuator
Head Plug
Cold Start Lever

Shop dissassembly of injection pump is not recommended.

Fig. 2: Mazda B2200 Fuel System

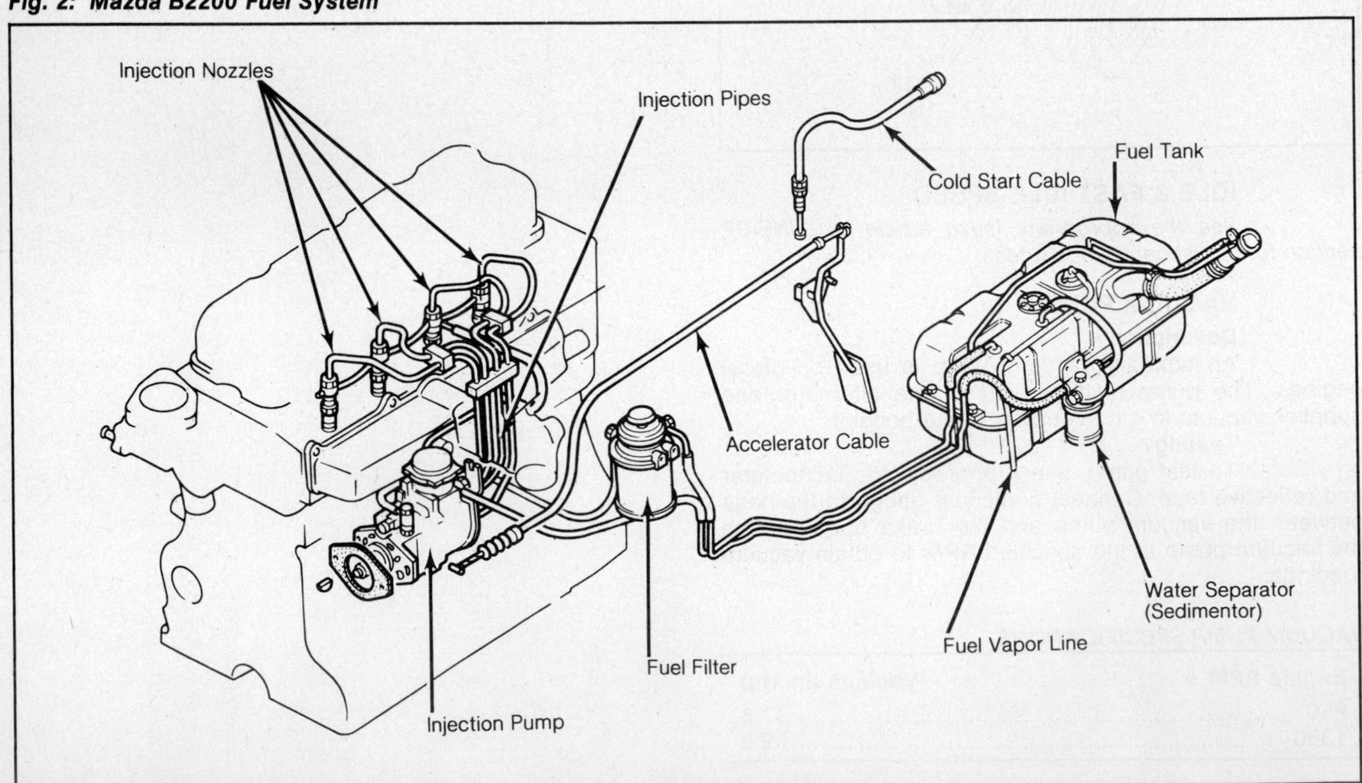
Injection Nozzles
Injection Pipes
Cold Start Cable
Fuel Tank
Accelerator Cable
Water Separator
(Sedimentor)
Fuel Vapor Line
Fuel Filter
Injection Pump

Bleed air from system whenever fuel lines are opened.

MAZDA – B2200 PICKUP (Cont.)

INJECTORS

The injection nozzles spray fuel into a pre-chamber as each compression stroke occurs. Nozzles can be disassembled, cleaned, and adjusted to correct improper spray patterns.

Injector opening pressure is adjusted with a shim on top of the needle valve return spring. *See Fig. 3.* The injector receives a high pressure pulse of fuel which forces open the needle valve allowing the fuel to pass into the prechamber.

Fig. 3: Mazda B2200 Injector

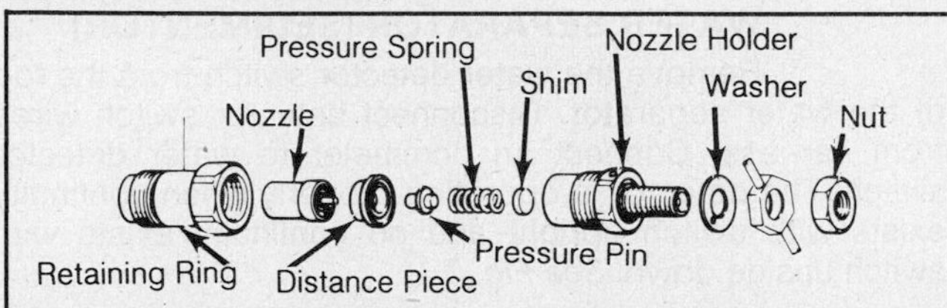
Pressure Spring
Nozzle Holder
Shim
Washer
Nozzle
Nut
Pressure Pin
Retaining Ring
Distance Piece

Injector must be free of dirt prior to reassembly.

GLOW PLUGS

The glow plug system uses 4 glow plugs (heaters) to assist in cold starting. When engine coolant is below 122°F (50°C), the No. 2 glow plug relay supplies full battery voltage to quickly heat the glow plugs.

When the glow plug reaches maximum temperature, relay No. 2 is turned off and relay No. 1 provides a reduced voltage to maintain glow plug temperature. When the engine starts, the glow plug system is turned off. *See Fig. 5.*

Fig. 4: Injector Spray Pattern

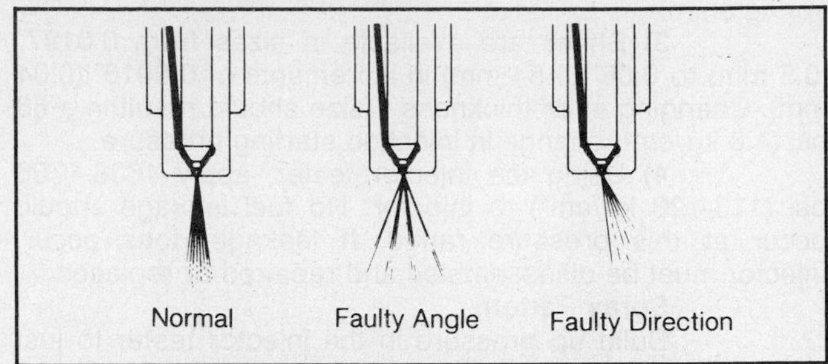
Normal
Faulty Angle
Faulty Direction

Injector must not drip when needle valve is closed.

TESTING

NOTE: Any time the fuel system is opened for testing or repair, air must be bled from the system prior to restarting the engine.

INJECTORS

Opening Pressure

1) Remove injection nozzles from engine and install each nozzle in turn on an injector tester. Test the injectors using diesel fuel at room temperature. Bleed the air out of the tester by pumping the handle several times.

2) Slowly lower tester handle and note the pressure shown on gauge when injector nozzle opens. Injection starting pressure should be 1920-1990 psi (135-140 kg/cm²). If injection starting pressure is not to

Fig. 5: Mazda B2200 Quick Start System Schematic Diagram

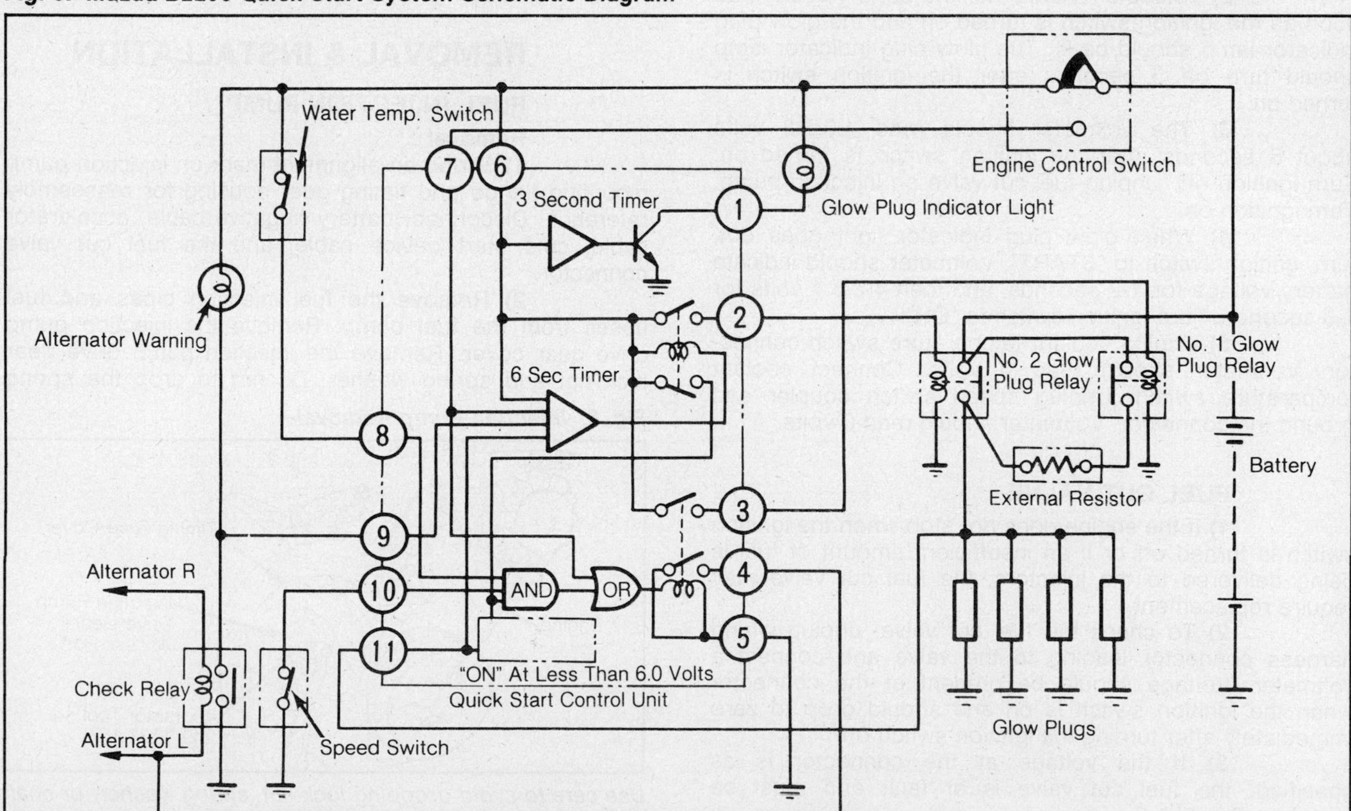
Water Temp. Switch
7
6
3 Second Timer
1
Engine Control Switch
Glow Plug Indicator Light
Alternator Warning
2
6 Sec Timer
No. 2 Glow Plug Relay
No. 1 Glow Plug Relay
8
Battery
External Resistor
3
9
Alternator R
4
10
AND
OR
11
5
Check Relay
"ON" At Less Than 6.0 Volts
Quick Start Control Unit
Alternator L
Speed Switch
Glow Plugs

Also see chassis wiring in WIRING DIAGRAM Section.

MAZDA – B2200 PICKUP (Cont.)

specifications, adjust pressure by changing the return spring shim.

3) Shims are available in sizes from 0.0197" (0.5 mm) to 0.06" (1.54 mm) in increments of 0.0016" (0.04 mm). Changing shim thickness 1 size should result in a 68 psi (4.8 kg/cm²) change in injection starting pressure.

4) Using the injector tester, apply 1636-1706 psi (115-120 kg/cm²) to injector. No fuel leakage should occur at this pressure range. If leakage does occur, injector must be disassembled and repaired or replaced.

Spray Pattern

Build up pressure in the injector tester to just below injection starting pressure. Quickly lower handle on tester and observe fuel spray pattern. Fuel should be uniformly atomized and should form a narrow cone projecting straight out of the end of the nozzle. *See Fig. 4.*

FUEL SYSTEM BLEEDING

Loosen air vent plug on top of fuel filter. Pump the head of the fuel filter until fuel flows from the air vent plug hole free of air bubbles. Depress pump handle and close vent plug. Pump handle about 15 times until resistance is felt.

GLOW PLUG SYSTEM

NOTE: Engine coolant temperature must be lower than 86°F (30°C) when checking system.

System Check

1) Connect a voltmeter between glow plug positive terminal and ground. Set the parking brake and shift the transmission out of gear. Turn the ignition switch to "ON" position and check the following:

2) Voltmeter should indicate battery voltage as soon as the ignition switch is turned on and the glow plug indicator lamp should be lit. The glow plug indicator lamp should turn off 3 seconds after the ignition switch is turned on

3) The voltmeter should read 4.3-5.2 volts about 6 seconds after the ignition switch is turned on. Turn ignition off. Unplug fuel cut valve on injection pump. Turn ignition on.

4) When glow plug indicator light goes out, turn ignition switch to "START". Voltmeter should indicate battery voltage for 1-2 seconds, and then 4.2-5.4 volts for 7-8 seconds. Turn ignition switch to "ON".

5) Unplug coolant temperature switch connector. Voltmeter should read 0 volts. Connect coolant temperature switch. Unplug speed switch coupler and ground the connector. Voltmeter should read 0 volts.

FUEL CUT VALVE

1) If the engine does not stop when the ignition switch is turned off or if an insufficient amount of fuel is being delivered to the injectors, the fuel cut valve may require replacement.

2) To check the fuel cut valve, unplug wiring harness connector leading to the valve and connect a voltmeter. Voltage should be present at the connector when the ignition switch is on and should drop to zero immediately after turning the ignition switch off.

3) If the voltage at the connector is as specified, the fuel cut valve is at fault and must be replaced. *See Fig. 6.*

Fig. 6: Fuel Cut Valve

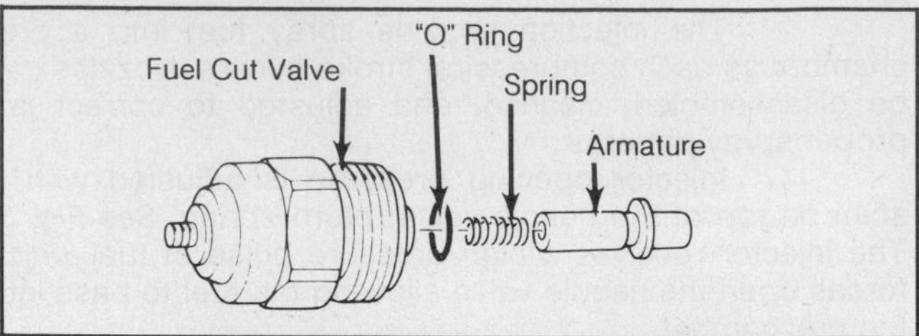
"O" Ring
Fuel Cut Valve
Spring
Armature

Armature should extend when current is turned off.

WATER SEPARATOR (SEDIMENTOR)

Remove the water detector switch from the top of the water separator. Disconnect detector switch wires from harness. Connect an ohmmeter to water detector switch. The detector is operating properly when continuity exists with switch upright and no continuity exists with switch upside down. *See Fig. 7.*

Fig. 7: Water Detector Switch Test

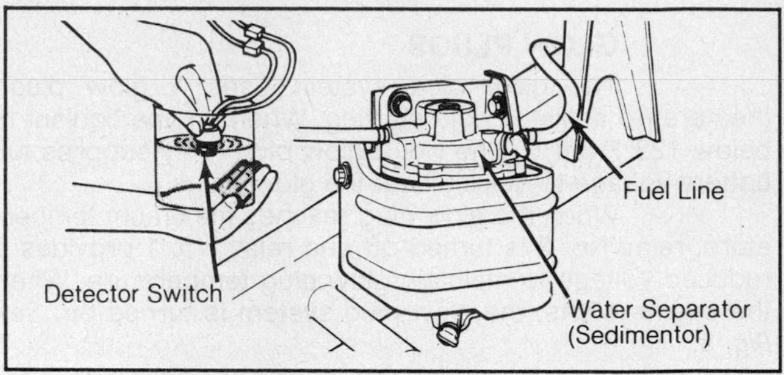
Fuel Line
Detector Switch
Water Separator
(Sedimentor)

Continuity should only exist when switch is upright.

REMOVAL & INSTALLATION

FUEL INJECTION PUMP

Removal

1) Scribe an alignment mark on injection pump mounting flange and timing gear housing for reassembly reference. Disconnect battery negative cable, accelerator cable, cold start device cable, and the fuel cut valve connector.

2) Remove the fuel injection pipes and fuel hoses from the fuel pump. Remove the injection pump drive gear cover. Remove the injection pump drive gear lock nut and spring washer. Do not to drop the spring

Fig. 8: Injection Pump Removal

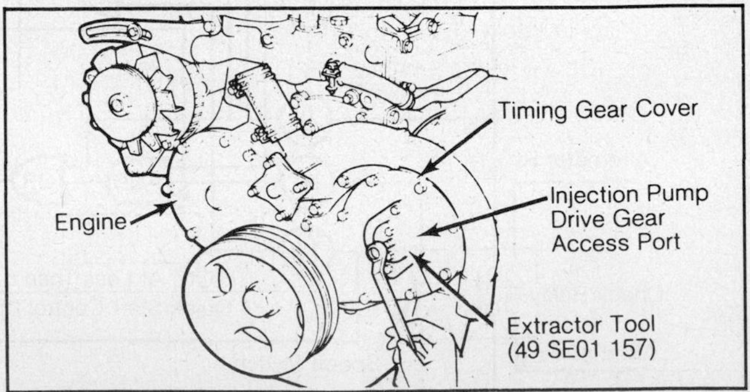
Timing Gear Cover
Injection Pump
Drive Gear
Access Port
Engine
Extractor Tool
(49 SE01 157)

Use care to avoid dropping lock nut, spring washer, or shaft key into timing gear housing.

MAZDA – B2200 PICKUP (Cont.)

washer into the timing gear case. If necessary use a steel wire to remove spring washer.

3) Remove the lock plate from the drive gear. Rotate the engine until the injection pump shaft key groove is facing up. Remove the injection pump attaching nuts and bolt.

4) Using the injection pump extractor tool (49 SE01 157) or similar tool, remove the injection pump. Take care when withdrawing the pump from the timing gear case so as not to drop the pump shaft key into the timing gear case. *See Fig. 8.*

Installation

1) To install, reverse removal procedure. Before installing the pump shaft key onto the shaft, tap the key groove in the shaft with a hammer to insure a tight fit for the key.

2) After installing the injection pump, evacuate any air present from the pump. Tighten the pump drive gear lock nut to specifications.

ADJUSTMENTS

INJECTION PUMP TIMING

1) Disconnect fuel injection pipes from fuel injection pump. Remove the hydraulic head plug from the pump. Align the timing mark (2° ATDC) on the crankshaft pulley with the indicator pin by turning the crankshaft.

2) Mount the injection timing measuring device (49 9140 076) into the hydraulic head plug hole. With the tip of the measuring tool firmly against the pump plunger, set the dial indicator to read about .08" (2 mm). *See Fig. 9.*

Fig. 9: Injection Pump Timing

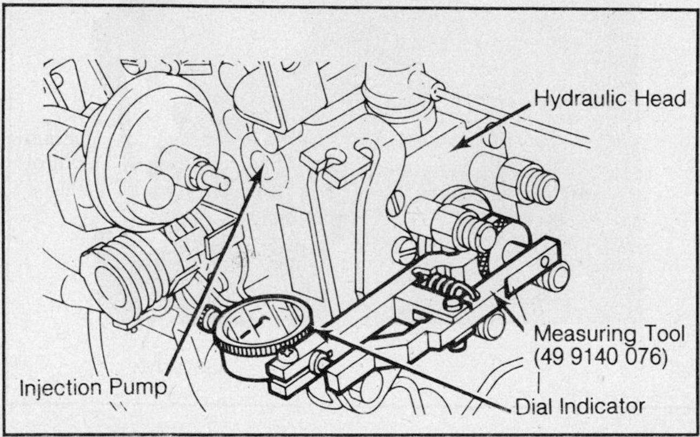
Hydraulic Head
Measuring Tool
(49 9140 076)
Injection Pump
Dial Indicator

Dial indicator should read about .04" (1 mm) when timing mark is aligned with pointer.

3) Turn the crankshaft pulley slowly counterclockwise (in reverse direction of engine rotation) about 30-50°. Make sure the dial indicator pointer stops.

4) Set the dial indicator pointer to zero. Turn the crankshaft slightly left and right to make sure that the indicator pointer does not move from zero.

5) Turn the crankshaft pulley clockwise (in direction of engine rotation) to align timing mark with indicator pin. If timing is adjusted correctly dial indicator will read .0392-.0408" (.98-1.02 mm) when the timing mark is aligned with the indicator pin.

6) If timing is not to specifications, loosen injection pump attaching nuts and bolt. Turn injection pump housing until dial indicator reading is correct.

NOTE: **Before adjusting the injection timing, turn the injection pump counterclockwise to cancel the timing gear backlash. Then turn the injector pump clockwise to adjust the injection timing.**

INTAKE SHUTTER VALVE SYSTEM

Connect a vacuum gauge to intake manifold vacuum. Start engine and run at idle. Disconnect coupler at 3-way solenoid valve. Vacuum gauge should read 17 in. Hg. If not, turn adjusting screw on intake shutter valve until vacuum reads 17 in. Hg at 700 RPM.

COLD START SYSTEM

Attach a tachometer to engine. Pull cold start knob out to the full extent of its travel. Turn the cold start lever adjusting screw (on injection pump) until engine speed is 1150-1250 RPM.

IDLE SPEED

See the appropriate Mazda article in the TUNE-UP Section.

TIGHTENING SPECIFICATIONS

Application	Ft. Lbs. (N.m)
Glow Plug	7-11 (10-15)
Injection Nozzle	43-51 (60-70)
Injection Pump Drive Gear	29-51 (40-70)

MERCEDES-BENZ

240D, 300 Series

DESCRIPTION

The fuel injection system used on Mercedes diesel models includes the following components: pre-filter, main filter, fuel injection Pump with mechanical governor, and injection nozzles. In addition, the injection pump is equipped with an altitude compensating device and a vacuum control shut-off unit. A glow plug system is used to assist in cold starting operation.

OPERATION

Fuel is pumped from fuel tank, through a pre-filter and main fuel filter into suction chamber of injection pump. Pump's camshaft operates injection pump plungers, which force fuel through delivery valves, reverse-flow dampening valves, and pressure lines to fuel injection nozzles.

FUEL INJECTION PUMP

All engines use the same type of injection pump, though 5-cylinder models have one more pump element. Turbo models have a connection from the turbocharger to the altitude compensator which allows that unit to enrich the mixture during boost operation.

The vacuum shut-off unit stops fuel delivery when the key is turned off. If it fails, a manual "STOP" lever is provided on the side of the pump. A mechanical fuel pump draws fuel from the tank and supplies it to the high pressure section of the injection pump. The pump is lubricated by engine oil.

Fig. 1: Fuel Injection Pump Components

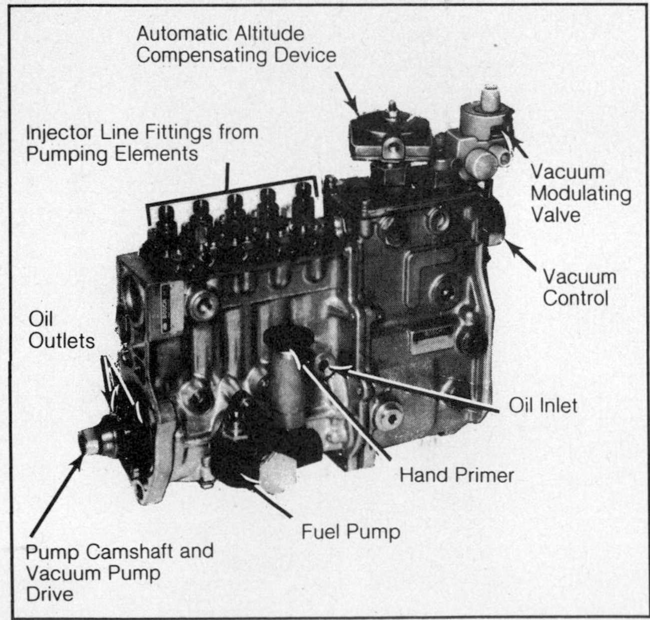
Automatic Altitude
Compensating Device
Injector Line Fittings from
Pumping Elements
Vacuum
Modulating
Valve
Vacuum
Control
Oil
Outlets
Oil Inlet
Hand Primer
Fuel Pump
Pump Camshaft and
Vacuum Pump
Drive

GOVERNOR

The governor controls idle and maximum RPM. Internal design enables the governor to have no effect on pump operation during normal operating speed range, when the accelerator is directly connected to the injection pump fuel rack. The altitude compensator does modify injection slightly during this range, compensating for air pressure variations with altitude.

Through governor action, engine RPM is held constant at idle speed, regardless of engine operating conditions (cold engine, air conditioner operation, power steering, or automatic transmission). At 5000-5100 RPM, governor limits RPM by pulling main rack back, until balance exists between engine RPM and fuel delivery.

AUTOMATIC ALTITUDE COMPENSATING DEVICE

Governor is equipped with an altitude compensating device to control emissions at various altitudes. On Turbo engines the device is connected to the intake manifold to sense boost pressure variations as well.

As altitude increases, air pressure decreases, the push rod in the compensator moves downward and pushes the main rack, slightly decreasing the amount of fuel injected (leans out the mixture).

When Turbo models are operating under boost, the rack is pushed in the other direction and more fuel is injected. Injection pump and governor operation are not affected by the compensator when the vehicle is operating near sea level (except Turbo) or idle RPM.

Fig. 2: Altitude Compensation & Vacuum Units

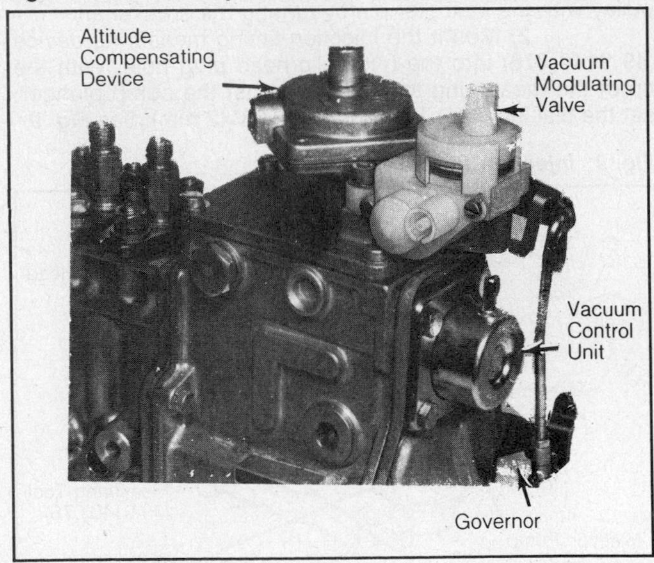
Altitude
Compensating
Device
Vacuum
Modulating
Valve
Vacuum
Control
Unit
Governor

MAIN FUEL FILTER

The main fuel filter is a disposable cartridge which is screwed onto the filter assembly. After filter is replaced, system must by bled of air.

INJECTION NOZZLES

Injection nozzles are used to spray fuel into the cylinders under the proper pressure and spray pattern for optimum combustion. Nozzles can be disassembled for cleaning and adjustment of opening pressure.

GLOW PLUG SYSTEM

All engines are equipped with pin-type glow plugs which are connected in parallel. The parallel connection allows glow plugs to operate independently of each other and provides 11 volts to each plug during the preglow process. A dual material heating element which consists of a heating coil and a control coil has allowed the heating process to be shortened to 5-7 seconds at 32°F (0°C).

Fig. 3: Cylinder Head Cross Section Showing Glow Plug

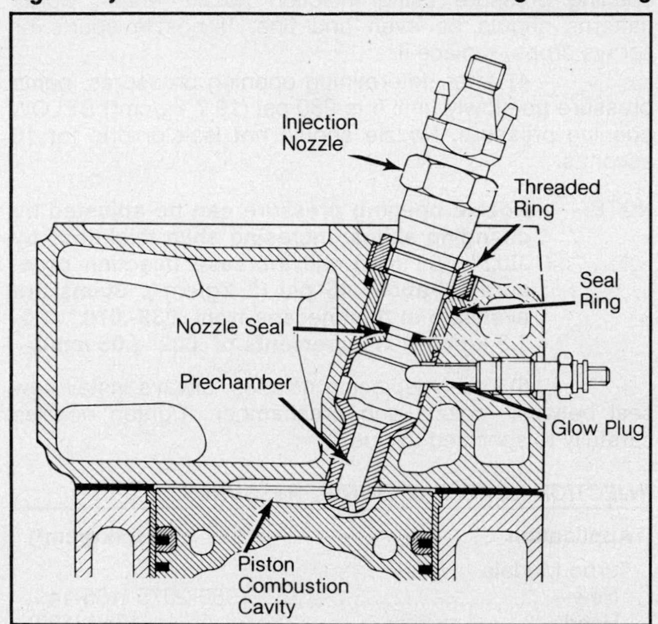

Injection Nozzle
Threaded Ring
Seal Ring
Nozzle Seal
Prechamber
Glow Plug
Piston Combustion Cavity

NOTE: This type plug is called the "Quick-Preglow" plug and is identified by a brass hexagon. It must not be interchanged with glow plugs used in previous models.

The glow plugs are grounded directly to the cylinder head through plug body. Each receives separate power directly from preglow time relay (total initial current draw is approximately 200 amperes).

The preglow time relay is located on the left inner fenderwell. The relay is protected by an 80A fusible link, mounted outside on the cover of the relay. The relay contains a temperature sensitive resistor which replaces the coolant temperature sensor used with previous relays.

A safety cutout in the relay turns off glow plug power 20-35 seconds after glow plug light goes off when no attempt has been made to start engine. This keeps battery drain to a minimum and protects glow plugs.

A switch in the relay is triggered if one or more glow plugs fail. This turns off the indicator lamp and signals a need for repair. The indicator will normally come on for at least one second even if engine is warm.

OVER-BOOST PROTECTION (TURBO MODELS ONLY)

Turbo models are equipped with an over-boost protection circuit, consisting of a pressure switch, switch-over valve and wiring. When boost pressure exceeds 16 psi (1.12 kg/cm^2), the pressure switch closes, grounding the switch-over valve.

The valve vents manifold pressure which would otherwise affect the aneroid compensator on the injection pump. This reduces the quantity of fuel injected and engine speed.

TROUBLE SHOOTING

INTERMITTENT BLACK SMOKE

Uneven nozzle operation. Opening pressures, nozzle seals and poor injection pipe sealing.

Fig. 4: Glow Plug Relay & Wiring Diagram

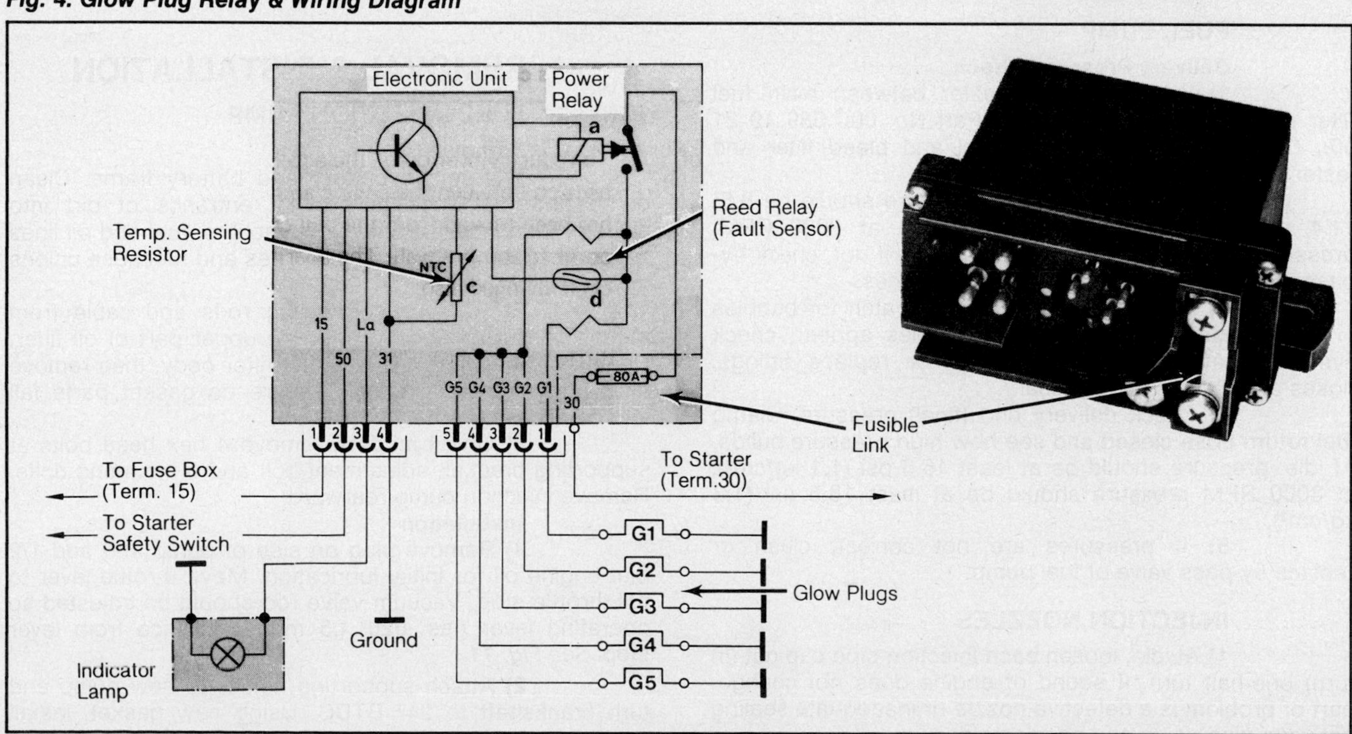

Electronic Unit
Power Relay
a
Reed Relay (Fault Sensor)
Temp. Sensing Resistor
NTC
c
d
15
La
50
31
G5 G4 G3 G2 G1
80A
30
1 2 3 4
5 4 3 2 1
Fusible Link
To Fuse Box (Term. 15)
To Starter Safety Switch
To Starter (Term.30)
G1
G2
G3
G4
G5
Glow Plugs
Ground
Indicator Lamp

1983 Diesel Fuel Injection

MERCEDES-BENZ (Cont.)

KNOCKING SOUND

Incorrect fuel. Injection pump delivery timing. Valve adjustment. Nozzle spray pattern and opening pressures. Reverse flow dampening valves. Poor compression.

ENGINE DOES NOT STOP

Defective vacuum control unit. Vacuum valve in ignition lock. Poor connections or vacuum leaks.

GLOW PLUG INDICATOR DOES NOT LIGHT, ENGINE STARTS

Burned out bulb. Broken wire to indicator.

GLOW PLUG INDICATOR DOES NOT LIGHT, ENGINE WILL NOT START

Check for possible burned out fusible link or defective preglow relay.

GLOW PLUG INDICATOR DOES NOT LIGHT, ENGINE STARTS WITH DIFFICULTY & MISSES

Glow plug in cylinder No. 1 defective or broken wire. One or more of glow plugs in cylinders 2 through 4 or 5 defective.

GLOW PLUG INDICATOR LIGHTS, ENGINE STARTS WITH DIFFICULTY & MISSES

One or more of glow plugs in cylinders 2 through 4 or 5. (Indicator may light if just 1 glow plug is defective. Disconnect 2 glow plugs and retest. If no light, preglow relay is okay).

TESTING

FUEL PUMP

Delivery Pressure Check

1) Install pressure tester between main fuel filter and injection pump (Bosch Part No. 000 589 49 21 00). Check for air bubbles in fuel and bleed filter and tester until no bubbles are present.

2) With engine idling, pressure should be 8.5-11.4 psi (0.6-0.8 kg/cm²). With engine at 3000 RPM, pressure should be 11.4 psi (0.8 kg/cm²). If not, check by-pass valve in pump or for damaged fuel lines.

3) During pressure checks, watch for bubbles in sight glass tube on tester. If bubbles appear, check system carefully for leaks. Repair or replace fittings, hoses and clamps as necessary.

4) Check delivery end (final) pressure. Clamp fuel return hose closed and see how high pressure builds. At idle, pressure should be at least 15.6 psi (1.1 kg/cm²); at 3000 RPM pressure should be at least 18.5 psi (1.3 kg/cm²).

5) If pressures are not correct, clean or replace by-pass valve of fuel pump.

INJECTION NOZZLES

1) At idle, loosen each injection pipe cap nut (in turn) one-half turn. If sound of engine does not change, part of problem is a defective nozzle or inadequate sealing between pipe union and nozzle holder.

2) Raise engine RPM above idle speed and repeat test procedure. If engine still does not run erratically with nut loosened, repair or replace that particular nozzle. If engine runs erratically when nut is loosened, nozzle is operating properly. Tighten one-half turn and check next nozzle.

3) Remove each injection nozzle and check opening pressure using injection nozzle tester. Spray patterns should be even and fine. If nozzle spurts or sprays drops, replace it.

4) After determining opening pressures, pump pressure up slowly until it is 280 psi (19.7 kg/cm²) BELOW opening pressure. Nozzle should not leak or drip for 10 seconds.

NOTE: Nozzle opening pressure can be adjusted by changing shims. Incresing shim thickness by .002" (.05 mm) will increase injection pressure by about 45 psi (3 kg/cm²). Shims are available in thicknesses from .039-.070" (1.0-1.8 kg/cm²) in increments of .002" (.05 mm).

5) When replacing nozzles, always install new seal between nozzle and prechamber. Tighten nozzles carefully to specified torque.

INJECTION NOZZLE OPENING PRESSURES

Application	[1] psi (kg/cm²)
Turbo Models	
New	1960-2075 (135-143)
Used	1740 (120)
Non-Turbo Models	
New	1670-1785 (115-123)
Used	1450 (100)

[1] – Maximum pressure variation in one engine cannot exceed 71 psi (5 kg/cm²).

REMOVAL & INSTALLATION

FUEL INJECTION PUMP

Removal

1) Remove battery and battery frame. Clean pump and fuel lines to prevent entrance of dirt into system. Disconnect all injection, vacuum, fuel and oil lines at injection pump. Plug injection lines and fuel hose unions at pump.

2) Remove connecting rods and cable from pump. On Turbo models, unscrew upper part of oil filter. Remove all engine oil lines at the filter body, then remove filter body from crankcase. Ensure no gasket parts fall into crankcase.

3) On all models, remove 4 hex head bolts at supporting bracket, adjustment bolt and 3 mounting bolts. Remove injection pump rearward.

Installation

1) Remove plug on side of pump and add 1/2 pint engine oil for initial lubrication. Move throttle lever to full throttle stop. Vacuum valve rod should be adjusted so operating lever has .020" (.5 mm) clearance from lever stop. *See Fig. 11.*

2) Attach supporting holder to new pump and turn crankshaft to 24° BTDC. Using new gasket, install pump with shaft and flange marks aligned. *See Fig. 5.*

MERCEDES-BENZ (Cont.)

Fig. 5: Injection Pump Mark Alignment

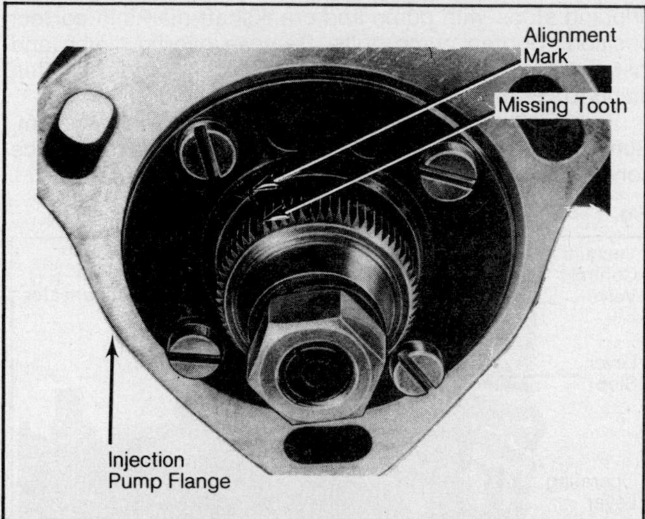
Alignment Mark
Missing Tooth
Injection Pump Flange

3) Adjust injection pump timing, then tighten mounting bolts. Install oil and fuel lines, then reinstall oil filter base and filter. Bleed fuel system.

FUEL LINE FITTINGS

Removal & Installation

1) If leakage occurs between pipe connection fitting (union) and injection pump adjusting plate, install new seals with "grooved" fittings. DO NOT loosen adjusting plate, or pump recalibration will be necessary.

2) Install new copper gasket whenever fittings are removed. Grooved end of valve carrier should be installed downward. Install other components, then oil fittings and install, tightening smoothly.

3) Install injection lines and operate primer pump until by-pass valve is heard to open. Operate engine and check for leaks.

FUEL FILTER

Removal & Installation

1) Replace filter every 30,000 miles. Loosen mounting bolt and pull downward on element and lower housing. *See Fig. 6.*

Fig. 6: Fuel Filter Replacement

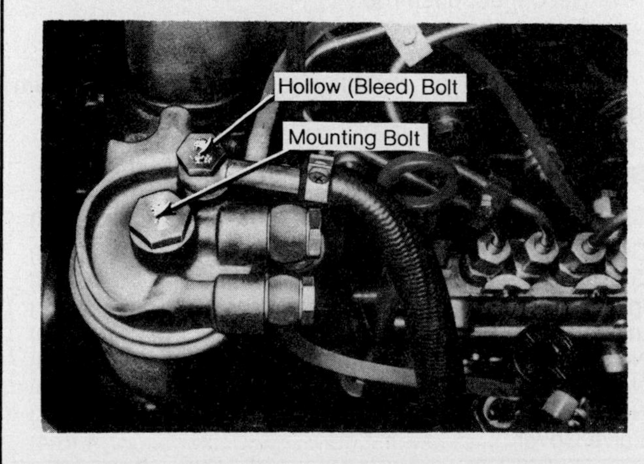
Hollow (Bleed) Bolt
Mounting Bolt

2) Install new lower housing and element. Tighten mounting bolt. Loosen hollow bolt and operate hand pump (on side of injection pump) until fuel emerges free of bubbles.

3) Retighten hollow bolt and pump until by-pass valve in injection pump opens, signalled by buzzing sound. Start engine and check for leaks.

VACUUM CONTROL UNIT

Removal

1) Unscrew lower right-hand mounting screw from vacuum control unit. *See Fig. 7.*

Fig. 7: Vacuum Control Unit Removal & Installation

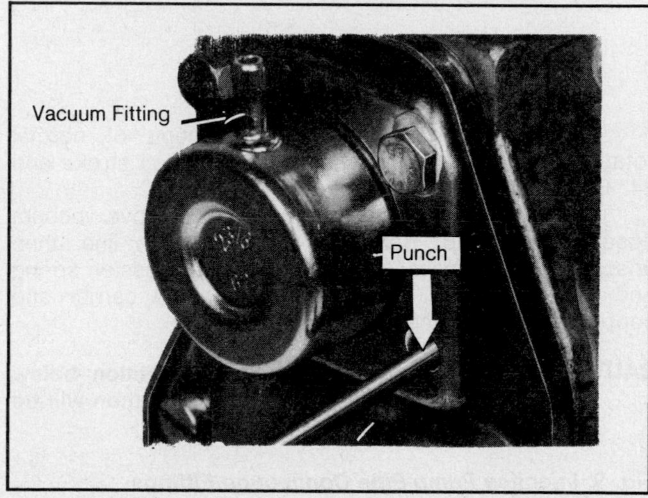
Vacuum Fitting
Punch

2) Depress "stop" lever on cylinder head cover. Measure position of main rack by inserting punch into screw bore until it touches main rack. Mark this position on punch.

3) Unscrew remaining 3 mounting screws and remove control unit.

Installation

1) Install new gasket and steel ring. Make sure tang on vacuum control unit engages in main rack. Install last 3 mounting screws removed.

2) Insert punch in lower right-hand screw bore. Check main rack position with mark on punch. When punch touches main rack, press lightly on punch and move control lever on injection pump from "stop" position to "full load" stop. Punch must follow the main rack smoothly. If correct, install remaining screw.

AUTOMATIC ALTITUDE COMPENSATING DEVICE

NOTE: **Do not attempt to remove upper cover of governor housing. Governor linkage is assembled to altitude compensating device.**

Removal

Hold altitude compensating device by small nut while turning large nut. Unscrew device and remove shims. *See Fig. 8.*

Installation

Using previously removed shims, screw compensating device into place. Be sure vent tube is positioned at lowest point to drain off any possible condensation. Hold small nut and tighten large nut.

1983 Diesel Fuel Injection

MERCEDES-BENZ (Cont.)

Fig. 8: Altitude Compensating Device Removal

Vent
Small Nut
Large Nut

ADJUSTMENTS

INJECTION PUMP TIMING

1) Turn crankshaft in direction of normal rotation until No. 1 cylinder is in compression stroke and 24° BTDC mark is aligned with pointer.

2) Clean pump connections. Remove vacuum hoses from pump. Remove No. 1 injection line, then unscrew pipe connection and remove compression spring and pressure valve. Leave pressure valve carrier and copper gasket in place. *See Fig. 9.*

CAUTION: Do not unscrew element connection below pipe connection or pump recalibration will be necessary.

Fig. 9: Injection Pump Pipe Connection Fittings

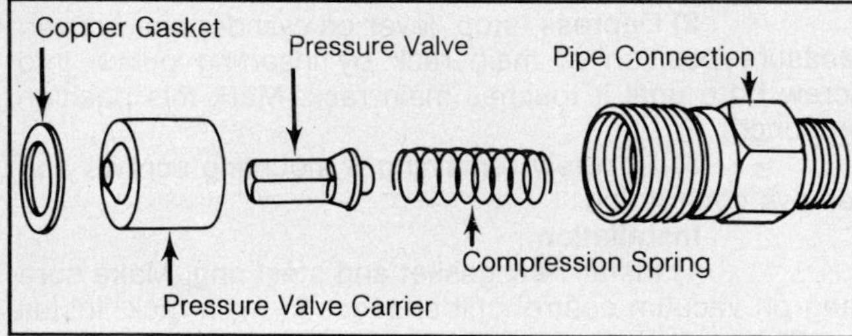
Copper Gasket
Pressure Valve
Pipe Connection
Compression Spring
Pressure Valve Carrier

Fig. 10: Checking Overflow Pipe Fuel Flow

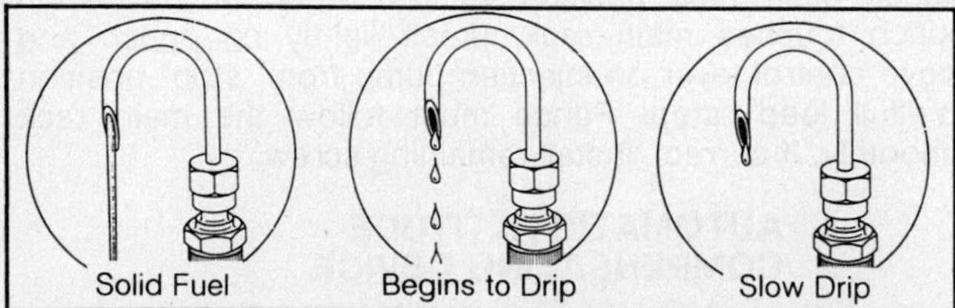
Solid Fuel
Begins to Drip
Slow Drip

3) Install pipe connection and overflow pipe. Rotate crank to 24° BTDC on compression stroke of first cylinder. Open vent or hollow screw on filter and use hand pump to pump fuel until it comes out of overflow pipe.

NOTE: Place lever at full-throttle position while adjusting timing and checking overflow.

4) Rotate crankshaft until fuel just stops dripping. One drop should fall about 3 seconds later. Note position on crankshaft pulley and adjust pump position so injection stops at 24° BTDC.

5) Turn crankshaft 2 turns to check that fuel dripping stops with pump and crankshaft marks in correct position. Tighten pump bolts. Remove overflow pipe and install pressure valve, spring and pipe connection. Tighten fitting to 29-36 ft. lbs. (39-49 N.m) in one smooth motion.

6) Install injection line and bleed fuel system. Run engine and check for leaks. If fitting leaks replace connection and gasket under pressure valve carrier.

Fig. 11: Injection Pump Adjustment Locations

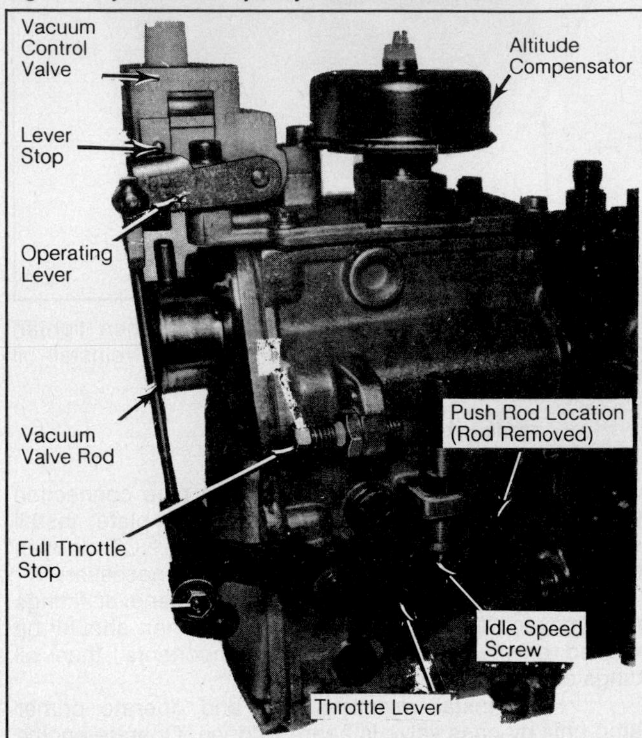
Vacuum Control Valve
Altitude Compensator
Lever Stop
Operating Lever
Push Rod Location (Rod Removed)
Vacuum Valve Rod
Full Throttle Stop
Idle Speed Screw
Throttle Lever

IDLE SPEED

1) Warm engine to normal operating temperature. Turn idle speed knob in dashboard clockwise to stop (if equipped). Disconnect push rod on throttle lever. *See Fig. 11.*

2) Adjust idle speed to 700-800 RPM using idle speed screw. Adjust push rod so no pressure is exerted against "Stop" lever and throttle lever is against idle speed screw. Reconnect push rod.

MAXIMUM SPEED

Adjust full throttle stop screw so maximum engine speed does not exceed 4900-5200 RPM.

TIGHTENING SPECIFICATIONS

Application	Ft. Lbs. (N.m)
Connecting Fitting (Union)	29-39 (39-49)
Glow Plugs	36 (49)
Injection Pipe Cap Nuts	18 (24)
Injection Pump Shaft Nut	51 (69)
Nozzle Holder-to-Head	54 (73)
Nozzle-to-Holder	54 (73)
Nozzle Holder Connector	54 (73)
Valve Cover	4 (5.4)

PEUGEOT

504, 505, 505 Turbo, 604 Turbo

DESCRIPTION

The diesel fuel injection systems consist of the fuel tank, fuel filter, distributor-type injection pump, glow plugs, throttle pintle injection nozzles and a centrifugal governor. *See Fig. 1.*

A vane type fuel pump, built into the injection pump, supplies fuel from the fuel filter to the injection pump. Injection pump supplies fuel to injection nozzles under high pressure, according to firing sequence 1-4-3-2. Excess fuel is returned to the fuel tank by return lines.

OPERATION

FUEL INJECTION PUMP

The Bosch single plunger mechanical pump consists of a low-pressure, vane-type fuel pump, a high-pressure distributor-type plunger injection pump, a centrifugal governor, and an injection timing advance mechanism. Pumps are equipped with an electrical fuel shut-off solenoid. *See Fig. 1.*

As the vane type pump rotor turns, centrifugal force holds the vanes against the walls of the pump's pressure chamber. The offset design of the rotor and pressure chamber, squeezes trapped fuel between vanes and forces it out the delivery port. Turbo models have a boost compensator to enrichen the fuel mixture under turbo boost conditions. *See. Fig. 2.*

Vane pressure of the pump is 65-73 psi (4.6-5.1 kg/cm²) at 1600 RPM or 87-94 psi (6.1-6.6 kg/cm²) at 2200 RPM. The main pump increases this pressure to approximately 1800 psi (126 kg/cm²).

NOTE: Vane pressures are given at pump speed, not engine speed.

The amount of fuel injected is controlled by changing the injection cut-off point according to engine speed and load conditions. The cut-off point is controlled by the position of the metering sleeve around the distributor plunger. The sleeve normally covers a relief port in the plunger. Uncovering the port stops injection.

The sleeve position is determined by a centrifugal governor, and accelerator linkage. A large quantity of fuel is supplied during starting, and less at idle. No fuel is allowed to pass when the engine exceeds a predetermined maximum RPM.

Fig. 1: Cutaway View of Fuel Injection Pump

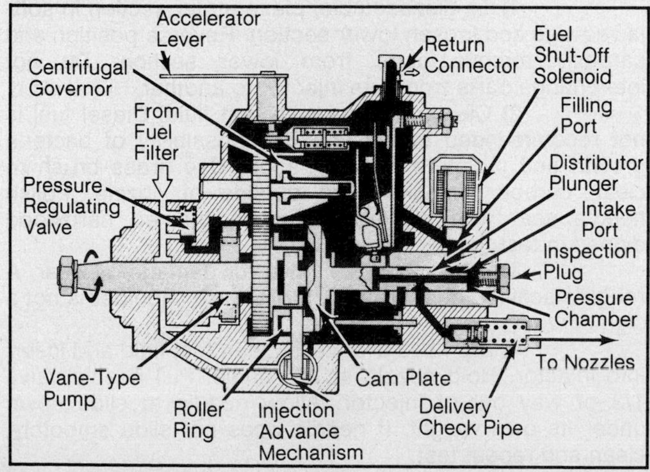

Accelerator Lever
Centrifugal Governor
Return Connector
Fuel Shut-Off Solenoid
From Fuel Filter
Filling Port
Distributor Plunger
Pressure Regulating Valve
Intake Port
Inspection Plug
Pressure Chamber
To Nozzles
Vane-Type Pump
Cam Plate
Roller Ring
Injection Advance Mechanism
Delivery Check Pipe

Fig. 2: Bosch Diesel Fuel Injection Pump

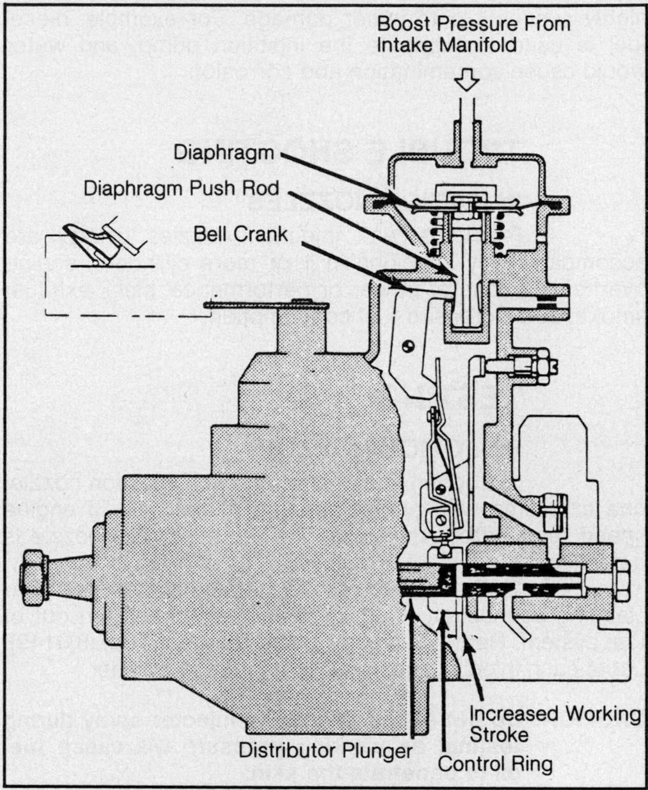

Boost Pressure From Intake Manifold
Diaphragm
Diaphragm Push Rod
Bell Crank
Increased Working Stroke
Distributor Plunger
Control Ring

Illustration applies to turbo models only.

INJECTION NOZZLES

Peugeot engines use DNO SD 1510 nozzles with KCA 17S38/4 holders. Opening pressure is 1679-1825 psi (118-128 kg/cm²) on non-turbo models or 1788-1930 (125-135 kg/cm²) on turbo models.

A pressurized mist of fuel is injected into a round swirl chamber. Combustion actually begins in rich swirl chamber and continues on through a small passageway and into leaner main chamber. As peak cylinder pressures build in swirl chamber, rather than main chamber, loads on connecting rods and crankshaft are reduced.

GLOW PLUGS

Glow plugs are used during cold starts to preheat swirl chambers. The system is switched "ON" when the key switch is turned to position "2". Preheating time depends on a coolant temperature switch connected to time circuit in the glow plug relay. Glow plugs remain on approximately 10-25 seconds after instrument panel indicator light has gone out.

Glow plugs operate when starter motor is rotating (key position "3") and cut when engine starts and start key is released back to position "2". To repeat starting attempt, key switch must first be returned to position "1". A blocking relay is incorporated in the system to interrupt electrical circuit between the control unit and glow plug relay when alternator starts charging. Automatic cold starting devices are also incorporated into the injection pump to assist starting by advancing injection timing.

1983 Diesel Fuel Injection

PEUGEOT (Cont.)

FUEL FILTER

The fuel filter is a cartridge type filter, with the housing and filter being replaced as a unit. A water separator is built into the filter, as diesel systems are highly susceptible to water damage. For example, diesel fuel is used to lubricate the injection pump, and water would cause contamination and corrosion.

TROUBLE SHOOTING

INJECTION NOZZLES

Problems with injection nozzles usually are accompanied by knocking in 1 or more cylinders, engine overheating, loss of power or performance, black exhaust smoke, and increased fuel consumption.

TESTING

INJECTION NOZZLES

1) Loosen line unions on each injection nozzle, one at a time with engine running at fast idle. If engine speed remains constant with line removed, that nozzle is defective.

2) To remove nozzle, detach injector line after cleaning connection. Plug all openings to keep dirt out of fuel system. Remove injector using Peugeot Tool (8.0149). Label each injector according to its mating cylinder.

CAUTION: Do not expose hands to injector spray during testing, as working pressure will cause fuel oil to penetrate the skin.

Spray Pattern

Injectors should not be evaluated by observing the spray pattern. Injectors which pass the opening pressure, leakage, and sound tests can be considered acceptable for service.

Fig. 3: Disassembled View of Injector Nozzle

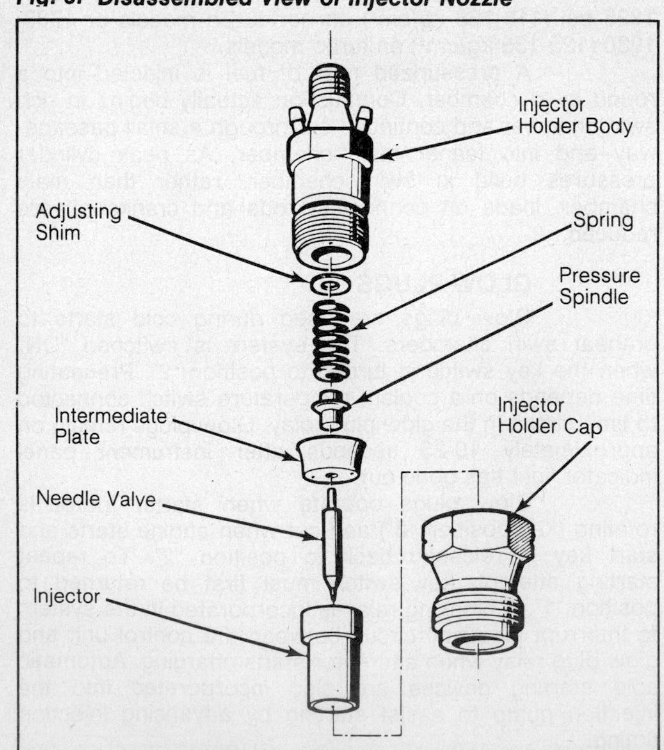
Injector
Holder Body
Adjusting
Shim
Spring
Pressure
Spindle
Intermediate
Plate
Injector
Holder Cap
Needle Valve
Injector

Opening Pressure

1) Install injector on nozzle tester. *See Fig. 4.* Engage pressure gauge. Slowly depress lever and read injector opening pressure. Nozzle should open at 1645-1788 psi (115-125 kg/cm²) on non-turbo models, 1788-1930 psi (125-135 kg/cm²) on turbo models.

Fig. 4: Testing Injection Nozzle on Test Gauge

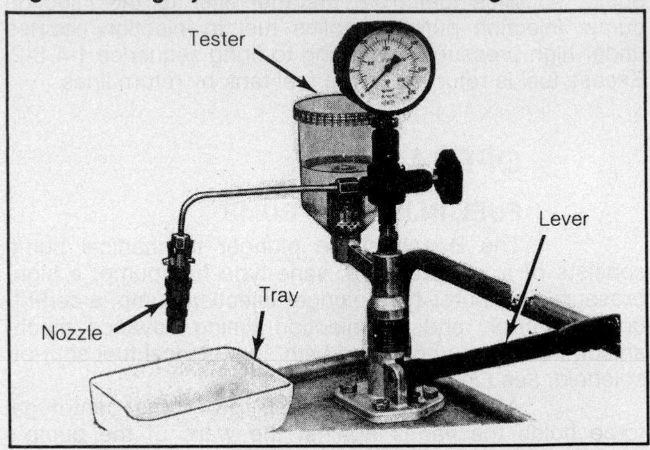
Tester
Lever
Tray
Nozzle

2) To adjust opening pressure, change shim thickness. Thicker shims will increase opening pressure; thinner shims will decrease it. Shims are available in thicknesses from .040-.077" (1.00-1.95 mm) in increments of .002" (.05 mm).

3) A .002" (.05 mm) shim will increase opening pressure by approximately 71 psi (5 kg/cm²). If opening pressure is incorrect, perform leak test before cleaning and adjusting.

Leak Test

With pressure gauge still engaged, wipe injector nozzle. Pump pressure up to 1493 psi (105 kg/cm²) on non-turbo models, 1645 (115 kg/cm²) on turbo models. Hold pressure for 10 seconds. There must be no fuel drip from injector nozzle, though a moist nozzle is acceptable.

Injection Sound Test

With gauge still disengaged, slowly depress tester lever fully (1-2 strokes per second). A good injector will emit a high pitched squeak. The sound is produced as the needle vibrates on its seat ensuring correct fuel atomization.

Nozzle Cleaning

1) To disassemble, place upper section in soft-jawed vise and loosen lower section. Reverse position and carefully remove parts from lower section. Do not interchange parts from one injector to another.

2) Clean all parts with test fluid. Diesel fuel is not recommended because of the possibility of bacteria growth and moisture contamination. Use brass brush to clean carbon deposits from outside of nozzle. Polish needle seat with a piece of close grained hardwood dipped in test fluid.

3) Inspect needle valve for damage or wear. A rough machined appearance on pressure shoulder is not a sign of wear.

4) Dip needle valve in clean test fluid and insert into injector. Hold nozzle at 45° angle. Pull needle valve 1/3 of way out of injector. Allow needle to slide down under its own weight. If needle does not slide smoothly, clean and repeat test.

PEUGEOT (Cont.)

5) Assemble all parts after cleaning. Tighten injector assembly cap to holder to specification. Install new heat shields with concave portion of shield pointing down. Use new copper gaskets. Tighten nozzles to specification.

GLOW PLUG SYSTEM

Current to glow plugs flows through starter relay to Pre-Heat Control Box (located at center of firewall). A timer in control box provides power to glow plug, depending on ambient temperature, for 10-90 seconds. The following check can be made on this system:

1) Check system ground between terminal 2 on control box and frame. Check condition of glow plug bulb and ground connection in instrument panel.

2) To locate shorted glow plugs, remove connecting straps between plugs. Connect a heavy jumper wire between terminal 5 of control box and each plug, 1 at a time.

3) Leave jumper wire connected for about 2 seconds. If glow plugs are bad, glow plug relay will cycle rapidly on and off. Replace shorted glow plugs.

REMOVAL & INSTALLATION

FUEL INJECTION PUMP

Removal

1) Remove battery. On pump, disconnect fuel supply and return lines, control cables, fuel shut-off electrovalve wire, and load sensor harness (if equipped).

2) Remove injector pipes. Remove 2 front mounting bolts, pump rear support, and pump. Cap all fuel openings.

Installation

1) Remove engine valve cover. Bring valves of No. 1 cylinder to a rocking position. Turn engine back approximately 90°. Using a valve spring compressor, compress No. 4 exhaust valve spring and move rocker arm to side.

2) Rotate engine back to rocking position of No. 1 cylinder. Remove half cones, washers, and springs from No. 4 exhaust valve. Using supports (8.0177 ZZ), install a dial indicator onto tip of No. 4 exhaust valve stem.

3) Bring engine to TDC at No. 4 cylinder. Zero the dial indicator. Rotate engine backwards to .28" (7 mm) BTDC. Clean hydraulic head on injection pump and remove inspection plug.

4) Turn pump shaft to bring double tooth of injection pump in line with double groove of engine pump hub pinion.

5) Coat a new gasket with grease and install on pump flange. Install pump on engine and install mounting bolts without tightening. Adjust injection pump timing. Tighten mounting bolts.

FUEL FILTER

1) Service is limited to draining water periodically and normal filter replacement. To drain water, loosen bleed screw on top several turns with screw driver. Loosen drain screw by hand and drain fluid until only clean fuel runs out.

2) Close drain screw and actuate manual primer pump until fuel flows without bubbles at bleed screw. Tighten bleed screw.

ADJUSTMENTS

INJECTION PUMP TIMING

1) With pump mounting bolts loose, dial indicator attached to No. 4 cylinder exhaust valve, and engine at .28" (7 mm) BTDC, rotate injection pump body away from engine (full retard). *See Fuel Injection Pump Installation.*

2) Clean the hydraulic head and remove the inspection plug. *See Fig. 1.* Using adapters (8.0117T, P, and S), install dial indicator on pump. Turn engine and locate BDC and TDC points on the pump's dial indicator. At BDC, the pump dial indicator should have some preload.

3) Zero the pump dial indicator at BDC. Bring piston No. 4 to TDC of compression stroke. Zero engine dial indicator. Turn engine 90° in reverse. Recheck pump dial indicator.

4) Turn engine in normal direction of rotation and bring No. 4 piston to .038" (1.35 mm) BTDC for non-turbo models or .016" (.40 mm) BTDC for turbo models. This corresponds to 11° BTDC for non-turbo models and 7° BTDC for turbo models.

5) Rotate pump towards the engine until pump dial indicator indicates a pump lift of .020" (.50 mm). Tighten pump mounting bolts, front and rear.

6) Check timing by rotating engine 2 turns in normal direction. Turn engine back approximately 90°.

Fig. 5: Pre-Heat Control Box Connections

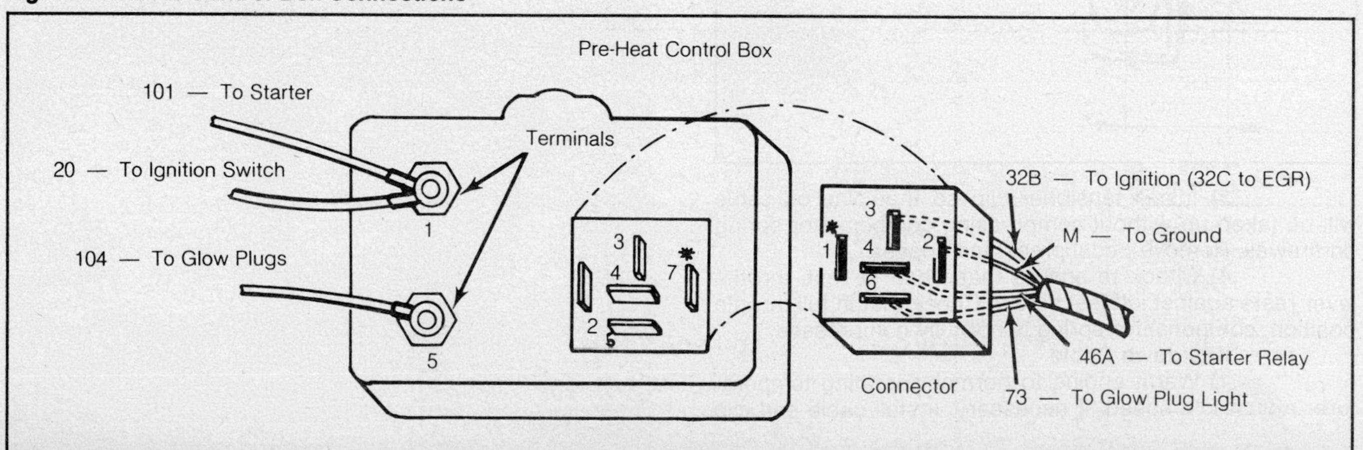
Pre-Heat Control Box
101 — To Starter
20 — To Ignition Switch
104 — To Glow Plugs
Terminals
1
5
3
4
7
2
32B — To Ignition (32C to EGR)
M — To Ground
1
2
3
4
6
46A — To Starter Relay
Connector
73 — To Glow Plug Light

1983 Diesel Fuel Injection

PEUGEOT (Cont.)

Rotate engine slowly in normal direction while watching pump dial indicator.

7) Stop turning engine when indicator shows a lift of .020" (.50 mm). No. 4 piston should then be at .038" (.97 mm) BTDC for non-turbo models, and .016" (.40 mm) BTDC for turbo models. If readjustment is necessary, rotate pump.

8) Remove dial indicators and supports. Install inspection plug with a new gasket. Install springs, washer and half cones of No. 4 exhaust valve and adjust clearance. Install pipes, hoses, and controls. Adjust cables and bleed fuel circuit.

Optimum Pump Timing

Injection pump timing may be modified if engine lacks performance or misses and is accompanied by exhaust smoke during cold start/warm-up. Only change pump timing after valve clearances, engine compression, and injector nozzles have been checked. Timing can be reset to .045" (1.15 mm) for non-turbo models or .019" (.48 mm) for turbo models.

ENGINE CONTROLS

Accelerator Cable

1) Warm engine to normal operating temperature. Adjust idle speed, if necessary. Position cable stop with elongated hole in order to obtain total cable travel of 1.77-1.93" (45-49 mm) between idle set screw and maximum RPM stop.

2) Place a .20" (5 mm) spacer between accelerator cable and its stop. Using a press (8.0204), depress accelerator pedal. Place throttle lever of pump in full throttle position.

Fig. 6: Accelerator Lever Adjustment

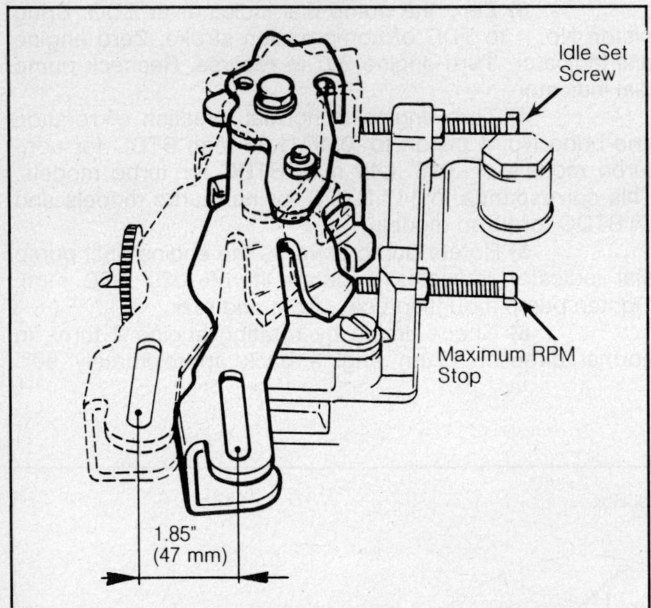
Idle Set
Screw
Maximum RPM
Stop
1.85"
(47 mm)

3) Install tensioner clip so that play on cable will be taken up without compressing compensator spring on firewall. Remove pedal press and spacer.

4) Check to ensure that when at rest, throttle lever rests against idle set screw. Check that in full throttle position, compensator spring is not fully compressed.

Kickdown Cable

1) Warm engine to normal operating temperature. Adjust idle speed, if necessary. Install cable end clip in slot which will allow for straightest routing of cable. Loosen lock nut of tensioner.

2) Adjust tensioner to obtain .004-.020" (0.1-0.5 mm) play between end clip and end of tensioner. Tighten lock nut while immobilizing tensioner.

IDLE SPEED

See the appropriate Peugeot article in the TUNE-UP Section.

TIGHTENING SPECIFICATIONS

Application	Ft. Lbs. (N.m)
Fuel Injection Line Unions	18 (25)
Glow Plugs	16 (22)
Injection Pump Mounting Bolts	15 (20)
Injector Nozzle (Upper-to-Lower Part)	45 (61)
Injector Nozzle-to-Cylinder Head	66 (90)

TOYOTA PICKUP

DESCRIPTION

The Toyota Pickup diesel injection system includes a fuel injection pump, injection nozzles, fuel filter, fuel sediment and water separator/warning device with integral priming pump, fuel lines and glow plug system. The glow plug system has a pre-heating timer (behind left kick panel), 2 glow plug relays (one on each fenderwell), a current sensor, register resistor and water temperature sensor.

OPERATION

FUEL INJECTION PUMP

The injection pump is driven by a belt at the front of the engine. If draws fuel from the tank, pressurizes it, and injects a specific quantity to each cylinder at the proper time. Excess fuel is returned to the tank through another line. The injection pump is not serviceable and should not be disassembled.

NOTE: **Air conditioned vehicles have a vacuum unit that increases idle speed when the air conditioning is on.**

INJECTION NOZZLES

The injection nozzles spray fuel into a pre-chamber as each compression stroke occurs. Each nozzle has a fuel supply and return line. Nozzles can be disassembled, cleaned and adjusted to correct defective spray patterns. Shims are used to correct nozzle opening pressures, and are available in 20 sizes from .039-.076" (1.0-1.95 mm) in increments of .002" (.05 mm). Changing one size nozzle shim will change injection pressure by 71 psi (5 kg/cm²).

Fig. 1: Toyota Diesel Fuel Injection Components

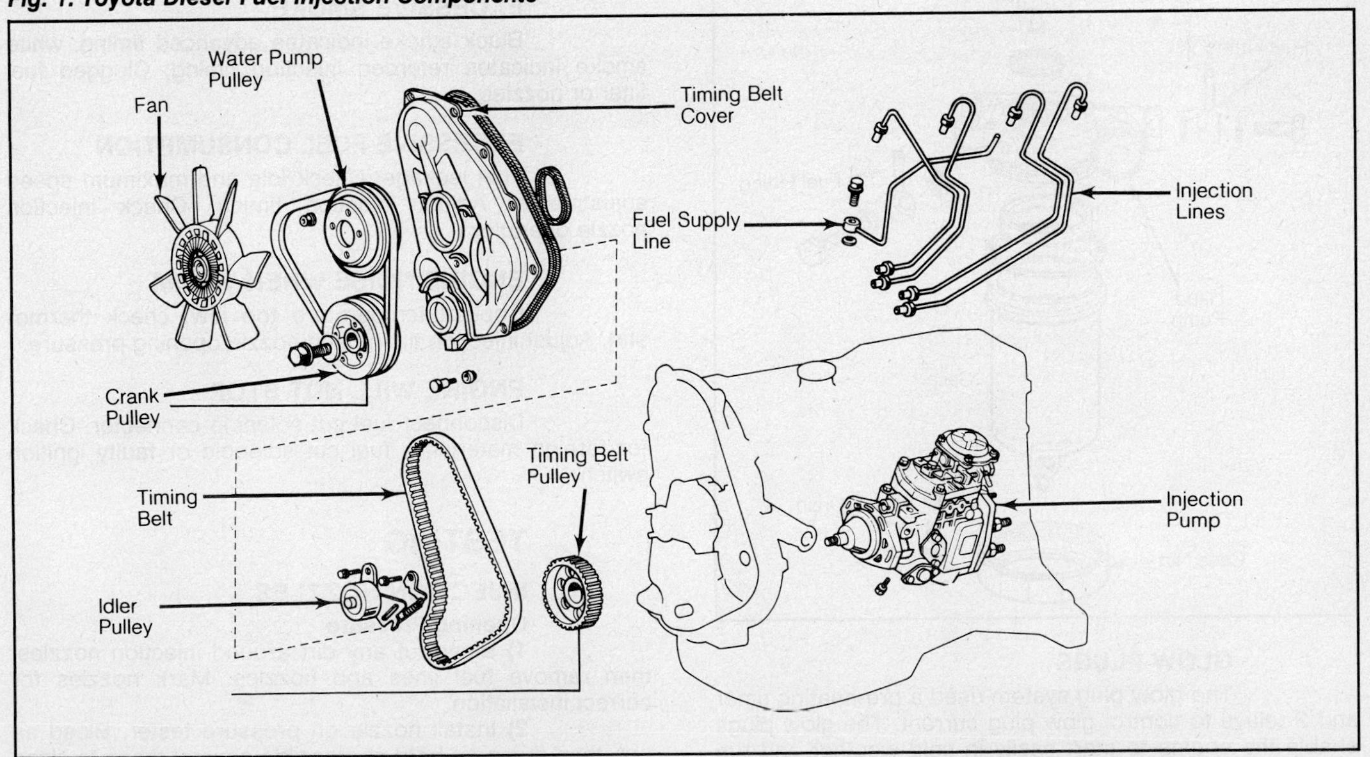
Water Pump Pulley
Fan
Timing Belt Cover
Fuel Supply Line
Injection Lines
Crank Pulley
Timing Belt
Timing Belt Pulley
Idler Pulley
Injection Pump

Fig. 2: Fuel Injection Nozzle Installation

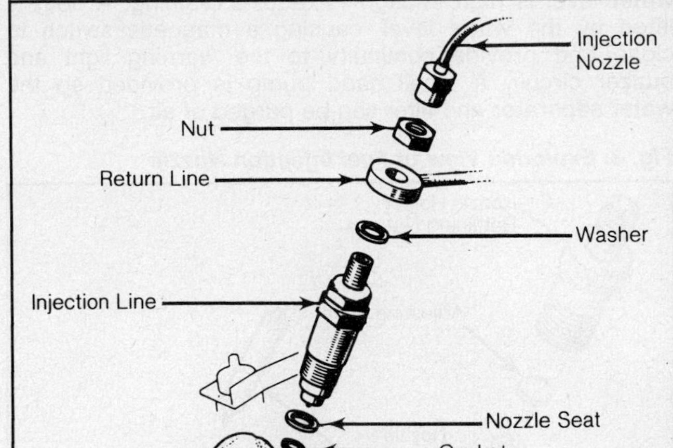
Injection Nozzle
Nut
Return Line
Washer
Injection Line
Nozzle Seat
Gasket

FUEL FILTER

The fuel filter is a sealed cartridge type, located on the firewall. The cartridge should be changed at regular intervals and when replaced, should be installed by hand, never with a wrench.

WATER-IN-FUEL WARNING SYSTEM

The fuel injection system includes a water and sediment filter in addition to the sealed cartridge filter. This unit traps water which may be present in the fuel system and holds it, preventing damage to the injection pump.

A warning light and buzzer signal when the water level is high enough to require draining. A float is lifted by the water level, causing a magnetic switch to close and provide continuity to the warning light and buzzer circuit. A small hand pump is provided so the water separator and filter can be purged of air.

Fig. 3: Exploded View of Fuel Injection Nozzle

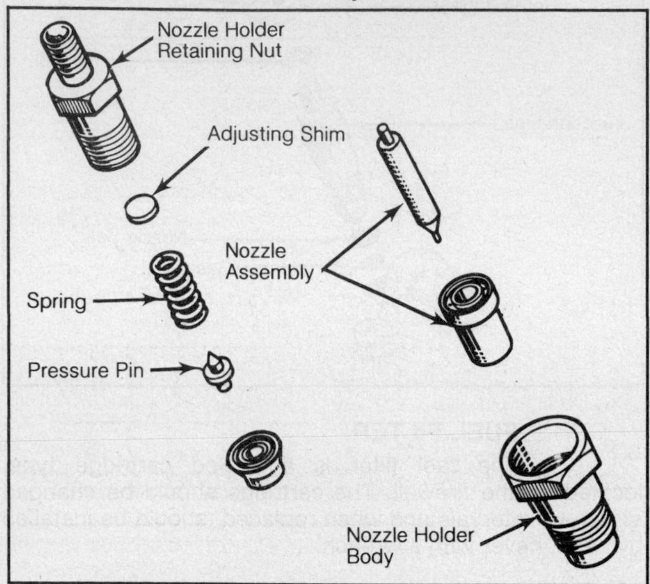
Nozzle Holder Retaining Nut
Adjusting Shim
Nozzle Assembly
Spring
Pressure Pin
Nozzle Holder Body

Fig. 4: Water-In-Fuel Warning System

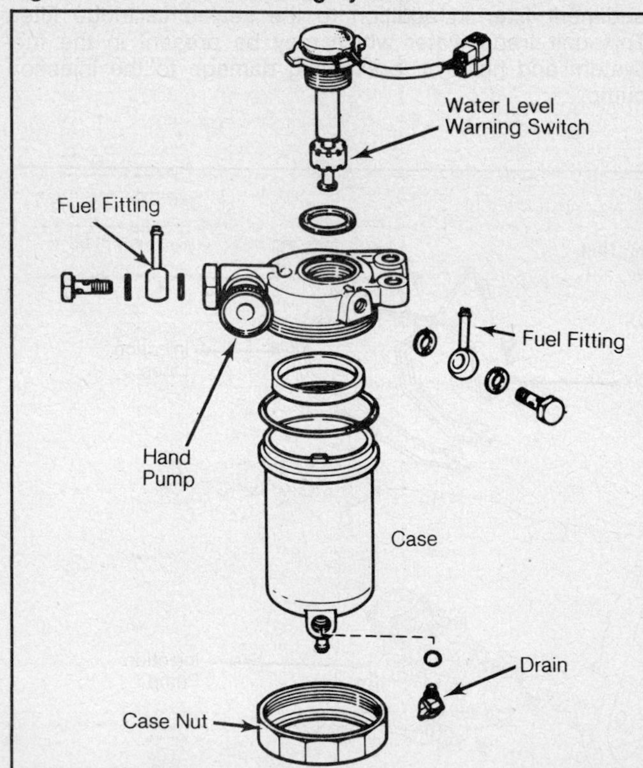
Water Level Warning Switch
Fuel Fitting
Fuel Fitting
Hand Pump
Case
Drain
Case Nut

GLOW PLUGS

The glow plug system used a pre-heating timer and 2 relays to control glow plug current. The glow plugs enable the engine to start easily in cold weather and run smoothly during warm-up. Current is applied to the glow plugs for a specific time which is determined by engine coolant temperature. When the ignition is turned on, a glow plug light operates for 4.5 seconds if coolant is below 104°F (40° C), or .5 second if coolant is above 104°F (40°C).

TIMING BELT WARNING SYSTEM

The timing belt which drives the injection pump must be replaced at 100,000 mile intervals. To ensure maintenance is done at the proper time, the vehicle is equipped with a maintenance warning system. An instrument panel lamp is controlled by a speedometer switch and lights when maintenance is due. After the timing belt is replaced, the lamp is turned off by depressing a reset button (behind grommet in speedometer bezel).

TROUBLE SHOOTING

NO FUEL AT NOZZLES

Check fuel cut solenoid. Inspect fuel lines, drain water and replace filter. Bleed fuel system. Replace injection pump.

ROUGH IDLE

Adjust accelerator cable. Adjust idle speed. Check for fuel or air leaks. Correct injection pump timing. Check injection nozzle opening pressures and adjust or clean nozzles.

LACK OF POWER

Adjust accelerator cable and stop screw. Adjust maximum RPM speed. Check fuel return line fitting on injection pump — it must be marked "OUT". Check fuel filter and injection pump timing.

EXCESSIVE SMOKE

Black smoke indicates advanced timing, white smoke indicates retarded injection timing. Clogged fuel filter or nozzles.

EXCESSIVE FUEL CONSUMPTION

Fuel leakage. Check idle and maximum speed adjustments. Adjust injection timing. Check injection nozzle operation.

ENGINE NOISE WHEN WARM

Coolant temperature too low, check thermostat. Adjust injection timing and nozzle opening pressure.

ENGINE WILL NOT STOP

Disconnect fuel cut solenoid connector. Check for foreign material in fuel cut solenoid or faulty ignition switch.

TESTING

INJECTION NOZZLES

Opening Pressure

1) Blow out any dirt around injection nozzles, then remove fuel lines and nozzles. Mark nozzles for correct installation.

2) Install nozzle on pressure tester. Bleed air out, then pump as hard as possible several times to clean

TOYOTA PICKUP (Cont.)

Fig. 5: Glow Plug System Wiring Diagram

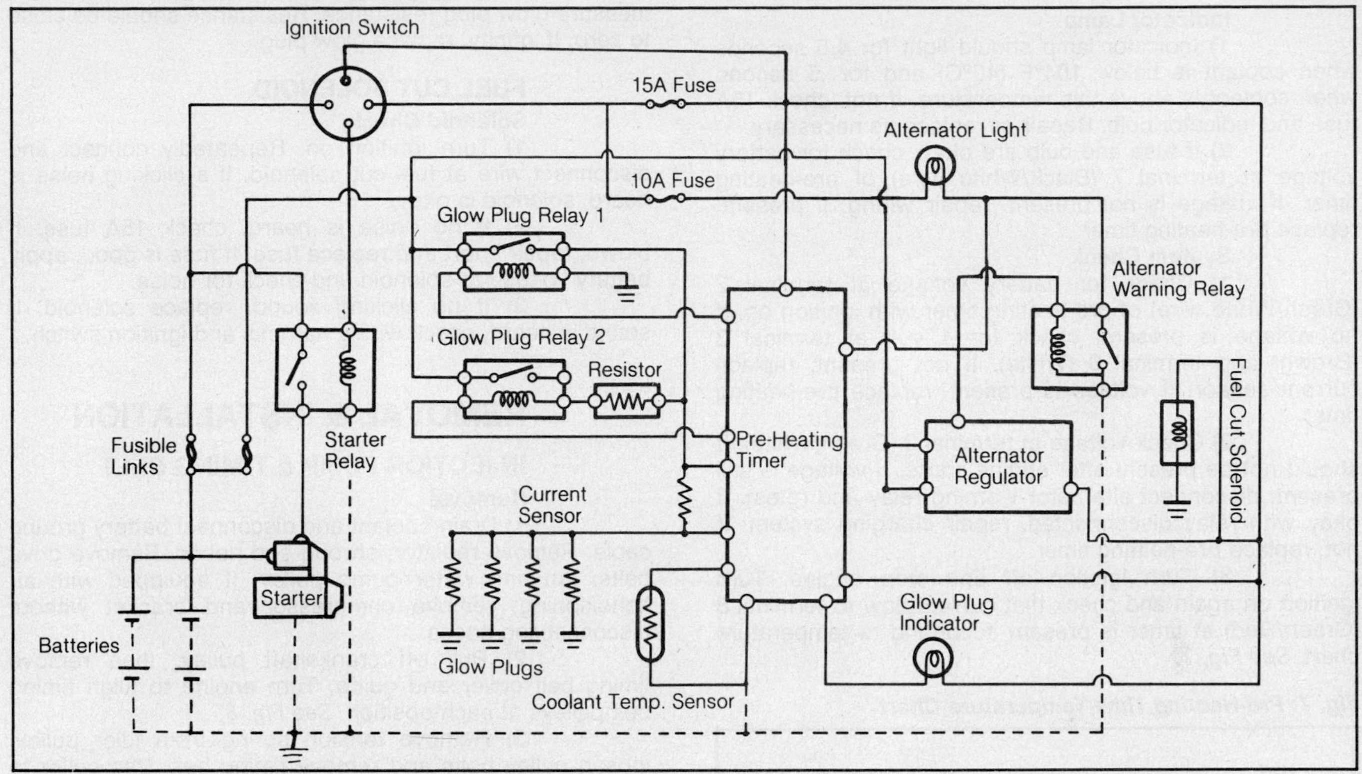
Ignition Switch
15A Fuse
Alternator Light
10A Fuse
Glow Plug Relay 1
Alternator
Warning Relay
Glow Plug Relay 2
Resistor
Fuel Cut Solenoid
Fusible
Links
Starter
Relay
Pre-Heating
Timer
Alternator
Regulator
Current
Sensor
Starter
Glow Plug
Indicator
Batteries
Glow Plugs
Coolant Temp. Sensor

Also see chassis wiring in WIRING DIAGRAM Section.

out nozzle. Pump up pressure slowly and note when nozzle opens.

3) Opening pressure should be as follows: On models prior to VIN numbers JT4LN44D5D1111497 and JT4LN44S3D1111500, pressure should be 1778-1902 psi (125-135 kg/cm²). On models after the above VIN numbers, opening pressure should be 2272 psi (160 kg/cm²).

4) If pressure is not within these specifications, disassemble and clean nozzle. Change shims as necessary to obtain proper opening pressures.

NOTE: Shims are available in 20 thicknesses in increments of .002" (.05 mm). One size change will adjust pressure 71 psi (5 kg/cm²).

5) Test nozzle again to ensure opening pressure is correct, then check for leakage.

Leakage Test

Pump pressure slowly until about 142-284 psi (10-20 kg/cm²) BELOW nozzle opening pressure. Hold pressure for at least 10 seconds; no dripping should occur. If nozzle drips, disassemble and clean, or replace. Check spray pattern.

Spray Pattern

Increase pumping speed to between 15 and 60 times per minute. At certain speeds, nozzle should "shudder" when spraying. Check spray pattern at this speed. If pattern is not correct, clean or replace nozzle. *See Fig. 6.*

Nozzle Cleaning

1) Disassemble nozzle holder. Wash parts in clean diesel fuel. Use a wooden stick to clean needle tip and soft brass brush to remove nozzle body deposits. DO NOT touch nozzle tip with fingers.

Fig. 6: Injection Nozzle Spray Patterns

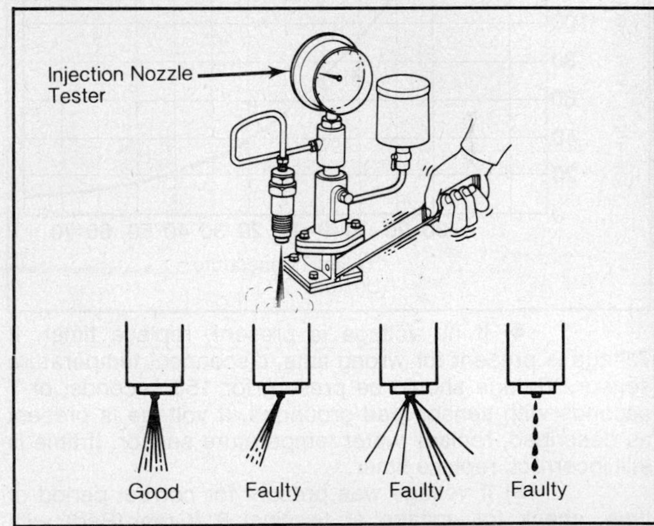
Injection Nozzle
Tester
Good
Faulty
Faulty
Faulty

Install tester as shown.

2) Inspect nozzle seat and needle tip for damage or corrosion. Replace if either is found. Hold nozzle body at about 60° to vertical and insert needle.

3) Pull needle up about one-third its length and allow to slide back down. Repeat several times, rotating needle between test. If needle does not slide down smoothly, replace nozzle.

NOTE: Injection nozzle seat gasket must be installed with concave side up when nozzle is replaced in head.

1983 Diesel Fuel Injection

TOYOTA PICKUP (Cont.)

GLOW PLUG SYSTEM

Indicator Lamp

1) Indicator lamp should light for 4.5 seconds when coolant is below 104°F (40°C) and for .5 second when coolant is above this temperature. If not, check 15A fuse and indicator bulb. Repair or replace as necessary.

2) If fuse and bulb are okay, check for battery voltage at terminal 7 (Black/White wire) of pre-heating timer. If voltage is not present, repair wiring. If present, replace pre-heating timer.

System Check

1) Check for battery voltage at terminal 2 (Green/White wire) of pre-heating timer with ignition on. If no voltage is present, check for 1 volt at terminal 3 (Brown) and terminal 9 (White). If not present, replace current sensor. If voltage is present, replace pre-heating timer.

2) Check voltage at terminal 2 (Green/White). It should not be present after engine starts. If voltage is still present, disconnect alternator warning relay and retest. If okay with relay disconnected, repair charging system. If not, replace pre-heating timer.

3) Turn ignition off and stop engine. Turn ignition on again and check that current flow to terminal 8 (Green/Red) at timer is present according to temperature chart. *See Fig. 7.*

Fig. 7: Pre-Heating Time/Temperature Chart

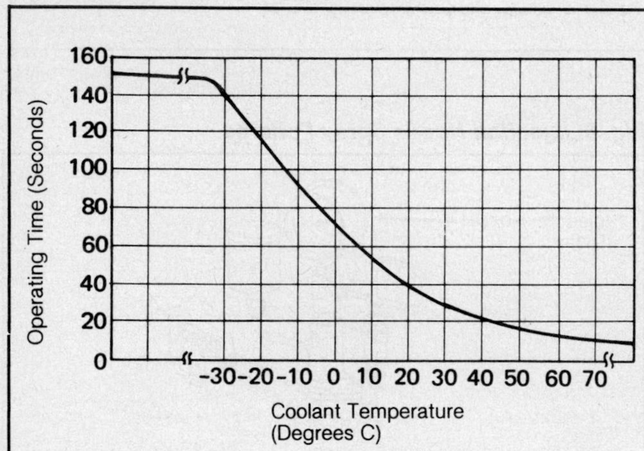
160
140
120
100
80
60
40
20
0
Operating Time (Seconds)
-30 -20 -10 0 10 20 30 40 50 60 70
Coolant Temperature
(Degrees C)

4) If no voltage is present, replace timer. If voltage is present for wrong time, disconnect temperature sensor. Voltage should be present for 150 seconds, or 7 seconds with sensor lead grounded. If voltage is present as described, replace water temperature sensor. If time is still incorrect, replace timer.

5) If voltage was present for correct period of time, check for voltage at terminal 8 (Green/Red) with ignition at "START" position. If no voltage, replace timer. If voltage is present, turn ignition off.

6) Turn ignition on again. Check for voltage at glow plugs a few seconds later. If no voltage, check for battery voltage at positive side of current sensor (above No. 3 cylinder). If present, replace sensor. If not, replace No. 1 glow plug relay.

7) Voltage at glow plugs should drop from 12 to 6 volts after a few seconds of operation. If not, check for battery voltage at positive side of ballast resistor (below intake manifold). If present, replace resistor. If not, replace No. 2 glow plug relay.

8) If all voltage measurements are correct, measure glow plug resistance. Resistance should be close to zero. If infinity, replace glow plug.

FUEL CUT SOLENOID

Solenoid Check

1) Turn ignition on. Repeatedly connect and disconnect wire at fuel cut solenoid. If a clicking noise is heard, solenoid is okay.

2) If no noise is heard, check 15A fuse. If blown, repair short and replace fuse. If fuse is good, apply battery voltage to solenoid and check for noise.

3) If no clicking sound, replace solenoid. If sound is heard, check wiring harness and ignition switch.

REMOVAL & INSTALLATION

INJECTION PUMP & TIMING BELT

Removal

1) Drain coolant and disconnect battery ground cable. Remove radiator, shroud and hoses. Remove drive belts, fan and water pump pulley. If equipped with air conditioning, remove compressor and bracket without disconnecting hoses.

2) Pull off crankshaft pulley, then remove timing belt cover and guide. Turn engine to align timing belt pulleys at each position. *See Fig. 8.*

3) Remove tension spring from idler pulley, loosen pulley bolts and remove timing belt. Use puller to remove injection pump pulley.

NOTE: **Pulley will spring off so use care to prevent damage.**

4) Check scribe marks on pump and engine to ensure correct alignment during installation. Remove injection lines, then fuel feed and return lines. Disconnect fuel cut solenoid wire and vacuum hose (if present), then remove mounting bolts and injection pump.

Installation

1) Install injection pump and connect fuel lines, wiring and vacuum hose (if equipped). Leave mounting bolts loose. Install injection pump pulley.

2) Align pulleys with marks, but place injection pump pulley mark one tooth clockwise from alignment mark. Install timing belt to camshaft gear, then injection pump gear.

Fig. 8: Injection Pump Pulley Alignment

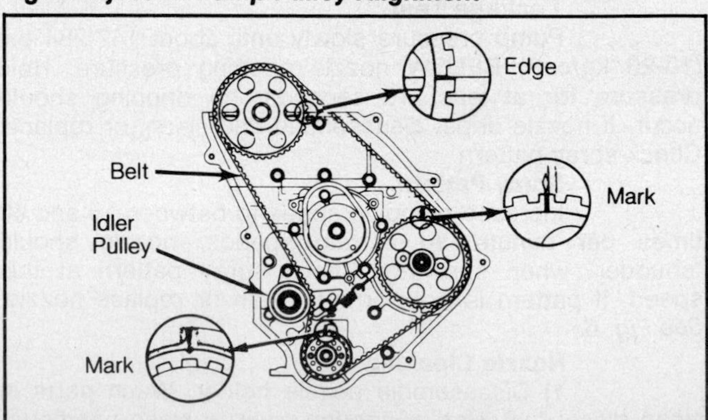
Edge
Belt
Mark
Idler
Pulley
Mark

Align marks as shown.

TOYOTA PICKUP (Cont.)

3) Install timing belt on crankshaft gear. Loosen idler pulley bolts and install spring. Temporarily install crankshaft pulley bolt and turn engine clockwise 2 revolutions to TDC.

4) Check that all alignment marks are in correct position. If not, remove belt and repeat procedure. Tighten idler pulley bolts without moving bracket. Install timing belt guide, cover and crankshaft pulley.

5) Install compressor (if equipped), pulleys, fan and drive belts. Install hoses, radiator and shroud. Connect batteries and refill cooling system, then reset maintenance switch by removing grommet in speedometer bezel and depressing switch button.

NOTE: **Switch will reset only after light has come on. If belt is replaced before light comes on, switch can be reset by removing speedometer and readjusting switch.**

6) Align injection pump with marks made before disassembly, then check injection timing.

FUEL FILTER & WATER SEPARATOR

Removal & Installation

1) Place a container under water separator drain and open drain valve 2 turns. Turn priming pump knob counterclockwise to loosen, then pump until all water is discharged. Close drain valve.

2) Remove fuel filter, using filter wrench if necessary. Apply a thin film of fuel on new filter gasket and install filter by hand.

3) Pump priming pump 30-40 times to force all air out of filter and separator. Check for fuel leaks, then turn knob clockwise to lock in position.

ADJUSTMENTS

INJECTION PUMP TIMING

1) Remove distributor head bolt on injection pump. Install special alignment tool (Toyota Part No. 09275-54010) and dial indicator to distributor head plug.

2) Set No. 1 or No. 4 cylinder to 45° BTDC on compression stroke. Set dial indicator at zero. Check to see that indicator stays at zero when crankshaft pulley is rocked slightly to left and right.

3) Turn pulley until No. 1 or No. 4 cylinder is at TDC. Injection timing should be as follows: On models prior to VIN numbers JT4LN44D5D1111497 and JT4LN44S3D1111500, plunger lift should be .046" (1.12 mm) for High Altitude models and .039" (1 mm) for all other models. On models after the above VIN numbers, plunger lift should be .046" (1.12 mm) for all models. If not, loosen injection pump bolts and all fuel connections.

4) Tilt pump body slightly and recheck injection pump stroke. When correct, tighten bolts and fuel lines. Remove tools and install distributor head bolt and washer.

Fig. 9: Injection Pump Timing

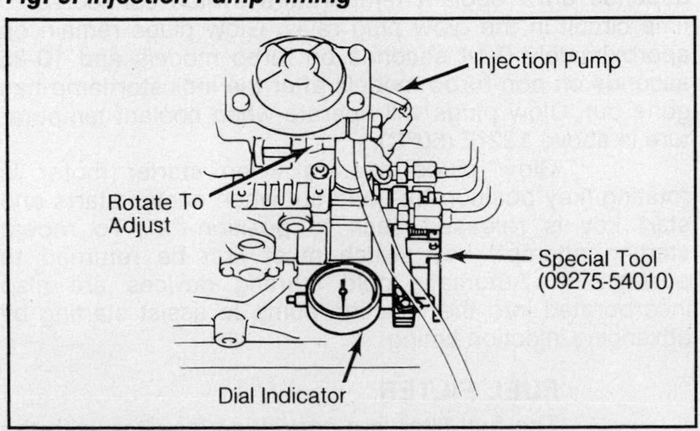
Injection Pump
Rotate To
Adjust
Special Tool
(09275-54010)
Dial Indicator

Install special tool and dial indicator as shown.

IDLE & MAXIMUM SPEED

See the appropriate Toyota article in the TUNE-UP Section.

TIGHTENING SPECIFICATIONS

Application	Ft. Lbs. (N.m)
Idler Pulley Bolts	11-15 (15-20)
Injection Nozzle-to-Cylinder Head	44-57 (60-78)
Injection Pump Bolts	11-15 (15-20)
Injection Pump Pulley Bolt	44-50 (60-68)
Nozzle Holder-to-Nozzle Body	44-57 (60-78)

1983 Diesel Fuel Injection

VOLVO

GL & 760 GLE

DESCRIPTION

The diesel fuel injection systems consist of the fuel tank, fuel filter, distributor-type injection pump, glow plug system, throttling pintle injection nozzles, and a centrifugal governor. *See Fig. 1.* Turbo diesel models have a boost compensator to enrichen fuel mixture during turbocharger operation. *See Fig. 2.*

A vane type fuel pump, built into the injection pump, supplies fuel from the fuel filter to the injection pump. Injection pump supplies fuel to injection nozzles under high pressure, according to firing sequence 1-5-3-6-2-4. Excess fuel is returned to the fuel tank by return lines. The injection pump is also equipped with a cold start device which facilitates cold weather starting and reduces exhaust smoke.

Fig. 1: Cutaway View of Bosch Fuel Injection Pump

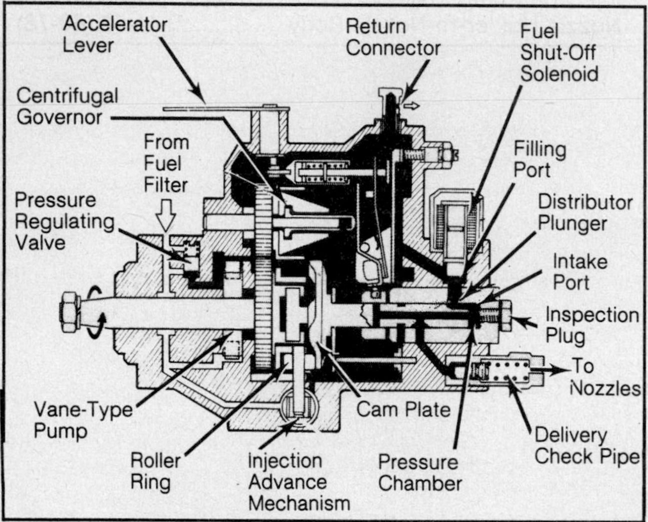
Accelerator Lever
Return Connector
Fuel Shut-Off Solenoid
Centrifugal Governor
From Fuel Filter
Filling Port
Pressure Regulating Valve
Distributor Plunger
Intake Port
Inspection Plug
To Nozzles
Vane-Type Pump
Cam Plate
Delivery Check Pipe
Roller Ring
Injection Advance Mechanism
Pressure Chamber

Fig. 2: Injection Pump With Boost Compensator

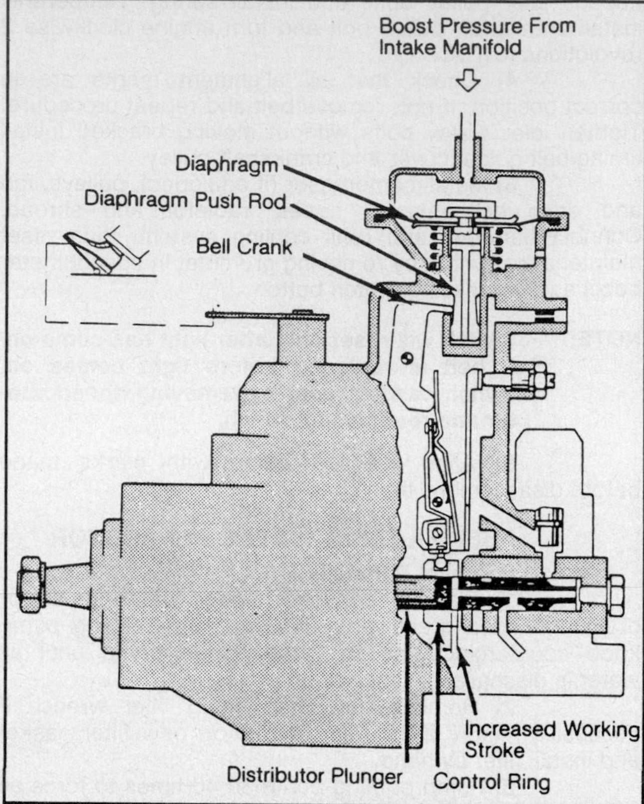
Boost Pressure From Intake Manifold
Diaphragm
Diaphragm Push Rod
Bell Crank
Increased Working Stroke
Distributor Plunger
Control Ring

Boost compensator is used on 760 GLE Turbo Diesel.

OPERATION

FUEL INJECTION PUMP

The Bosch VE type single plunger mechanical pump consists of a low-pressure, vane-type fuel pump, a high-pressure distributor-type plunger injection pump, a centrifugal governor, and an injection timing advance mechanism. Pumps are equipped with an electrical fuel shut-off solenoid. *See Fig. 1.*

As the vane type pump rotor turns, centrifugal force holds the vanes against the walls of the pump's pressure chamber. The offset design of the rotor and pressure chamber squeezes trapped fuel between vanes and forces it out the delivery port.

The amount of fuel injected is controlled by changing the injection cut-off point according to engine speed and load conditions. The cut-off point is controlled by the position of the metering sleeve around the distributor plunger. The sleeve normally covers a relief port in the plunger. Uncovering the port stops injection.

The sleeve position is determined by a centrifugal governor and the accelerator linkage. A large quantity of fuel is supplied during starting, less at idle. No fuel is allowed to pass when the engine exceeds a predetermined maximum RPM.

INJECTION NOZZLES

All engines use Bosch throttling pintle injection nozzles. These provide a pressurized mist of fuel that is injected into a round swirl chamber. Fuel swirls around the chamber mixing with hot air, compressed at 23:1 for non-turbo models or 21:1 for turbo models.

Combustion actually begins in rich swirl chamber and continues on through a small passageway and into leaner main chamber. As peak cylinder pressures build in swirl chamber, rather than main chamber, loads on connecting rods and crankshaft are reduced.

GLOW PLUGS

Glow plugs are used during cold starts to preheat swirl chambers. The system is switched on when the key switch is turned to position "II". Preheating time depends on a coolant temperature switch connected to time circuit in the glow plug relay. Glow plugs remain on approximately 0-14 seconds on turbo models and 10-25 seconds on non-turbo models after the indicator lamp has gone out. Glow plugs will operate when coolant temperature is above 122°F (50°C).

Glow plugs operate when starter motor is rotating (key position "III") and cut when engine starts and start key is released back to position "II". To repeat starting attempt, key switch must first be returned to position "I". Automatic cold starting devices are also incorporated into the injection pump to assist starting by advancing injection timing.

FUEL FILTER

The fuel filter is a cartridge type filter, with the housing and filter being replaced as a unit. A water

1983 Diesel Fuel Injection

VOLVO (Cont.)

separator is built into the filter, as diesel systems are highly susceptible to water damage due to contamination and corrosion. Fuel filter is equipped with a water drain on the bottom of the assembly.

TESTING

INJECTION NOZZLES

Problems with injection nozzles usually are accompanied by knocking in 1 or more cylinders, engine overheating, loss of power or performance, black exhaust smoke, and increased fuel consumption. To locate and correct faulty injectors, proceed as follows:

One at a time, with engine running at fast idle, loosen line unions on each injection nozzle. If engine speed remains constant with line removed that nozzle is defective.

Fig. 3: Disassembled View of Injector Nozzle

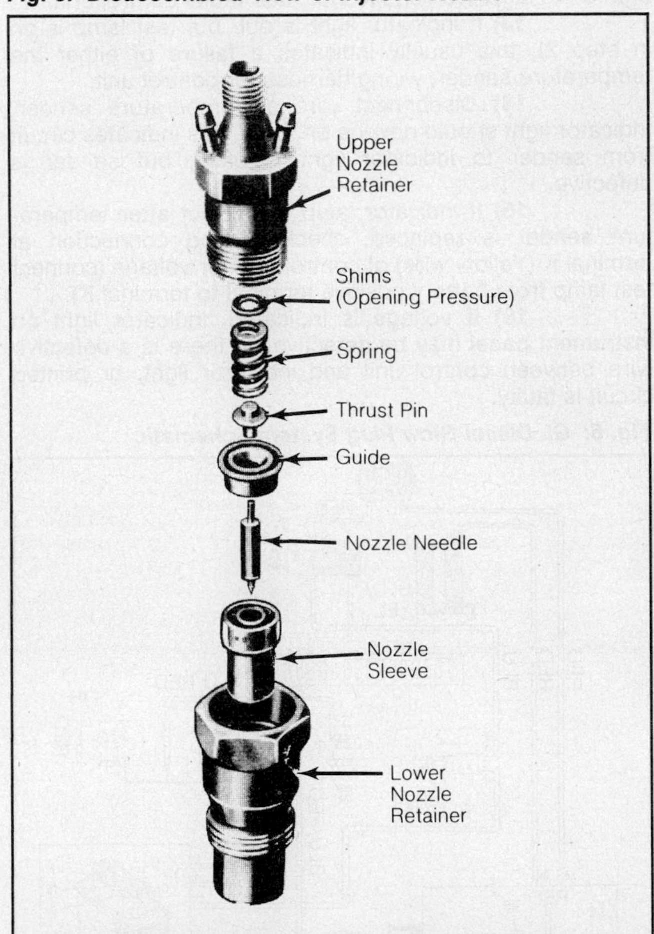
Upper
Nozzle
Retainer
Shims
(Opening Pressure)
Spring
Thrust Pin
Guide
Nozzle Needle
Nozzle
Sleeve
Lower
Nozzle
Retainer

Injector opening pressure is determined by shim thickness.

NOTE: **When one or more injectors are replaced or adjusted, all other injectors must be tested and adjusted if necessary. Failure to do so will affect engine performance.**

Spray Pattern

1) Clean all fuel connections before loosening or removing. To remove nozzle, detach injector line. Plug all openings to keep dirt out of fuel system. Seal fuel return lines with rubber plugs and hose clamps.

2) Install injector in tester. *See Fig. 4*. Bleed air from injector. Pump lever with short, quick strokes (4-6 per second). Spray jet should be compact and stop abruptly. Injector must not drip.

CAUTION: **Do not expose hands to injector spray during testing, as working pressure will cause fuel oil to penetrate the skin.**

Fig. 4: Testing Injection Nozzles

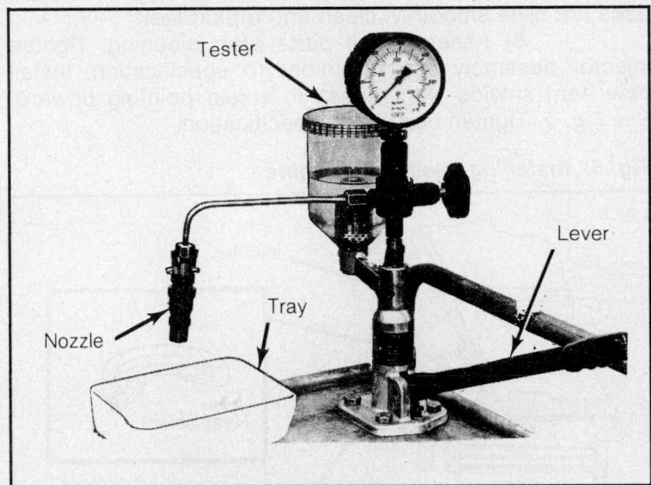
Tester
Lever
Tray
Nozzle

Bleed air from injector before testing.

Opening Pressure

Using pressure gauge, slowly depress lever and read injector opening pressure. Opening pressure is when pressure gauge starts to fluctuate. Nozzle opening pressure should be within specifications. If opening pressure is incorrect, perform leak test before adjusting.

INJECTOR NOZZLE OPENING PRESSURES

Application	psi (kg/cm^2)
Turbo	
Checking Specification	2062-2318 (145-163)
Adjusting Specification	2205-2318 (155-163)
All Others	
Checking Specification	1700-1845 (119.5-130)
Adjusting Specification	1775-1920 (125-135)

Opening Pressure Adjustment

To adjust opening pressure, change shim thickness. Thicker shims will increase opening pressure; thinner shims will decrease it. Shims are available in thicknesses from .040-.077" (1.00-1.95 mm) in increments of .002" (.05 mm). A .002" (.05 mm) shim will increase opening pressure by approximately 71 psi (5 kg/cm^2). *See Fig. 3.*

Leak Test

With nozzle installed on pressure gauge, wipe injector nozzle dry. Pump pressure up to 1560 psi (110 kg/cm^2). Hold pressure for 10 seconds. There must be no fuel drip from injector nozzle, though a moist nozzle is acceptable.

Nozzle Cleaning

1) To disassemble, place upper section of nozzle in vise, loosen lower section. Reverse position of nozzle in vice and carefully remove parts from lower section. Do not interchange parts from one injector to another.

VOLVO (Cont.)

2) Clean all parts in diesel fuel. Use brass brush to clean carbon deposits from outside of nozzle. Polish needle seat with a piece of close grained hardwood dipped in diesel fuel.

3) Inspect needle valve and nozzle sleeve for damage or wear. A rough machined appearance on pressure shoulder is not a sign of wear.

4) Dip needle valve in clean test fluid and insert into injector. Pull needle valve 1/3 of way out of injector. Allow needle to slide down under its own weight. If needle does not slide smoothly, clean and repeat test.

5) Assemble all parts after cleaning. Tighten injector assembly cap to holder to specification. Install new heat shields with recess in shield pointing upward. *See Fig. 5.* Tighten nozzles to specification.

Fig. 5: Installing Injector in Engine

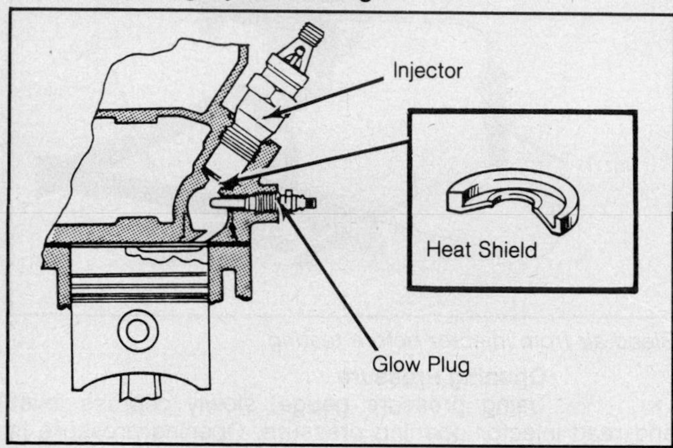
Injector
Heat Shield
Glow Plug

GLOW PLUG SYSTEM

NOTE: **Engine must be less than 100°F (40°C) when starting glow plug test.**

Non-Turbo Models

1) Connect 12-volt test lamp between glow plug terminal and ground. Turn ignition on. Check test lamp and indicator light on instrument panel. If both lights are out, control unit is defective. Go to step **9**. Control unit is under left side of instrument panel.

2) If indicator lamp is on but test lamp is out, go to step **11** and check glow plug relay. If indicator light is out, but test lamp is on, go to step **13)** and check coolant temperature sender or control unit.

3) If both indicator light and test lamp are on, check the amount of time they stay on. Indicator light time should vary from 0-45 seconds with coolant temperature.

4) Test lamp should stay on 10-25 seconds longer than indicator. If "ON" time is to short, repeat test with a new temperature sender and/or control unit.

5) Check operation with starter motor operating. Test lamp should light, indicating voltage at glow plugs. If test lamp does not light, check voltage with at terminal 50 (Blue/Yellow wire) of control unit.

6) If there is voltage, control unit is defective. If no voltage, check for open circuit between connector and control unit.

7) If test light was on during starter operation, check glow plugs individually. Place key switch in position "O". Remove bar between glow plug terminals.

8) Connect test lamp across battery positive terminal and a glow plug. If light is out at one or more glow plugs, glow plugs are faulty. If test lamp and indicator fail to light, replace control unit.

9) If indicator light and test lamp were both out in step **1)**, check terminal 15 (Blue/Red wire) of control unit for voltage (do not disconnect). If no voltage, check for open circuit between fuse box and control unit.

10) Check ground terminal 31 (Black wire) of control unit. Connect test lamp to battery positive terminal and terminal 31. If lamp does not light, check for faulty ground. If voltage, ground circuit is good but control unit is defective.

11) If indicator light is on, but test lamp is out when ignition is turned on in step **2)**, check terminal 86 (Red wire) of glow plug relay for voltage. Test lamp should light with key on.

12) Connect test lamp across battery positive terminal and relay ground (Black) wire. Voltage indicates faulty glow plug relay. No voltage indicates incorrect ground connection. Check terminal G (Blue wire) of control unit for voltage. No voltage indicates faulty control unit.

13) If indicator light is out, but test lamp is on in step **2)**, this usually indicates a failure of either the temperature sender, wiring harness, or control unit.

14) Disconnect wire at temperature sender. Indicator light should now be on. If so, this indicates circuit from sender to indicator light is okay, but sender is defective.

15) If indicator lamp is still out after temperature sender is replaced, check ground connection at terminal K (Yellow wire) of control unit for voltage (connect test lamp from battery positive terminal to terminal K).

16) If voltage is indicated, indicator light on instrument panel may be defective, or there is a defective wire between control unit and indicator light, or printed circuit is faulty.

Fig. 6: GL Diesel Glow Plug System Schematic

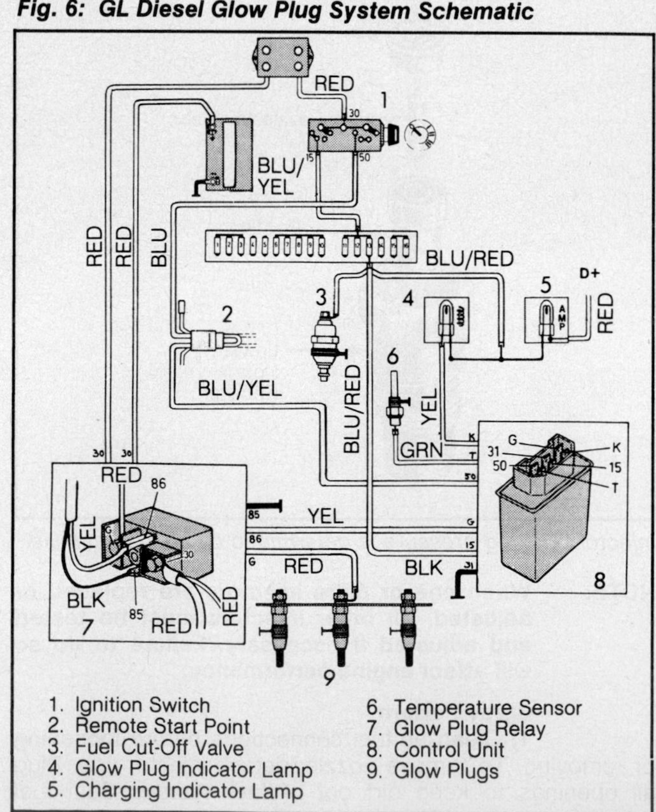
RED
1
30
15
50
BLU/
YEL
RED
RED
BLU
BLU/RED
D+
3
4
5
RED
2
6
BLU/YEL
BLU/RED
YEL
GRN
K
T
G
31
50
15
K
T
30
30
RED
86
85
YEL
86
30
G
RED
BLK
BLK
85
RED
RED
7
8
9
1. Ignition Switch
2. Remote Start Point
3. Fuel Cut-Off Valve
4. Glow Plug Indicator Lamp
5. Charging Indicator Lamp
6. Temperature Sensor
7. Glow Plug Relay
8. Control Unit
9. Glow Plugs

VOLVO (Cont.)

17) If no voltage exists, either the control unit is defective or wire between temperature sender and control unit is grounded.

18) If indicator light comes on when engine is warm, disconnect wire at temperature sender and ground it. Turn key switch to driving position "2" and check indicator light.

19) If light is on, there is an open circuit in wire between temperature sender and control unit or control unit is defective. If indicator light is out, temperature sender is faulty.

NOTE: Testing procedures for turbo diesel models are not available from manufacturer.

Fig. 7: 760 GLE Turbo Diesel Glow Plug System Schematic

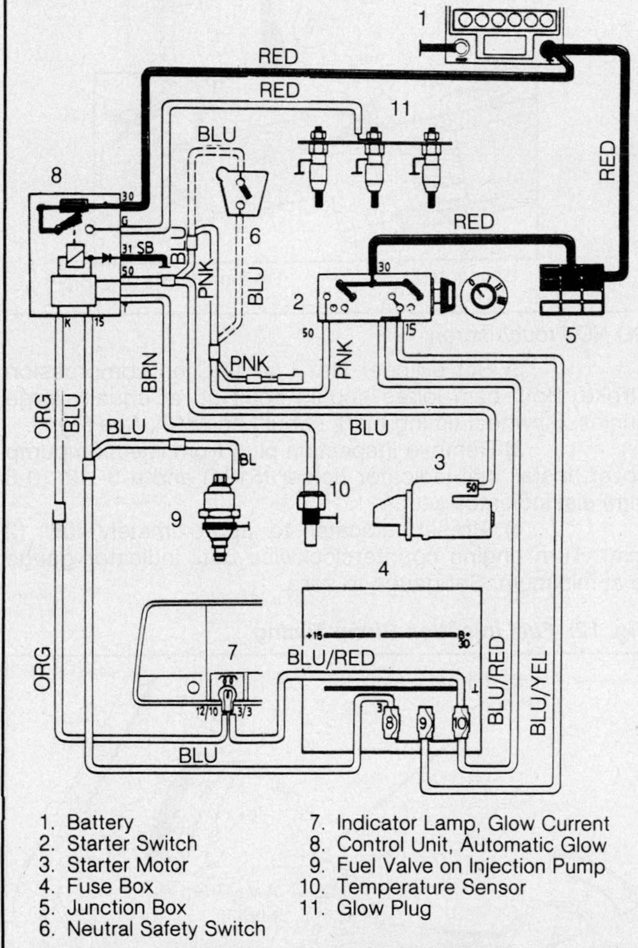
RED
RED
RED
RED
BLU
BLU
BLU
BLU
BLU
PNK
PNK
PNK
BRN
ORG
ORG
BLU/RED
BLU/RED
BLU/YEL
1. Battery
2. Starter Switch
3. Starter Motor
4. Fuse Box
5. Junction Box
6. Neutral Safety Switch
7. Indicator Lamp, Glow Current
8. Control Unit, Automatic Glow
9. Fuel Valve on Injection Pump
10. Temperature Sensor
11. Glow Plug

Also see chassis wiring in WIRING DIAGRAM Section.

COLD START DEVICE

NOTE: The cold start device can only be tested on a test bench together with the injection pump, but a simple check can be made of its operation.

1) Cold start malfunction usually is indicated by hard starting of a cold engine, failure of engine to start below 14°F (-10°C), or blue-white exhaust smoke. Check idle speed with engine cold and at normal operating temperature.

2) With cold engine, below 70°F (20°C), engine should idle at approximately 950 RPM. With engine at normal operating temperature, idle speed should be approximately 700-800 RPM.

3) The cold start lever should clear lever on injection pump. If idle speeds do not vary as specified, cold start device is defective.

Fig. 8: Cold Start Device Location

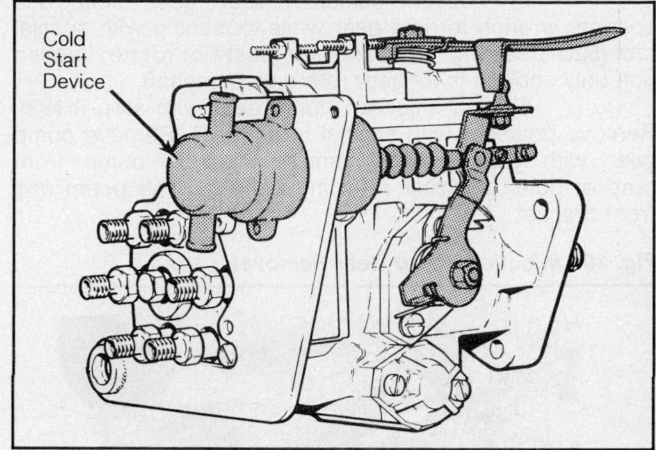
Cold
Start
Device

REMOVAL & INSTALLATION

FUEL INJECTION PUMP

NOTE: As injectors are manufactured to extremely small tolerances (pump cylinder and bore clearance is .00004-.00008" (.001-.002 mm), extreme cleanliness is a necessity. Clean all injection pump and nozzle unions before removal.

Removal

1) Use clamping pliers to pinch off coolant hoses for cold start device. Disconnect hoses at cold start device. Disconnect accelerator cable and kickdown cable (automatic transmission) from cable pulley.

2) Disconnect wire at fuel shut-off solenoid. Remove rear timing gear cover. Clean fuel line connections at injection pump. Disconnect fuel supply and return lines at pump.

Fig. 9: Injection Pump Timing Mark Alignment

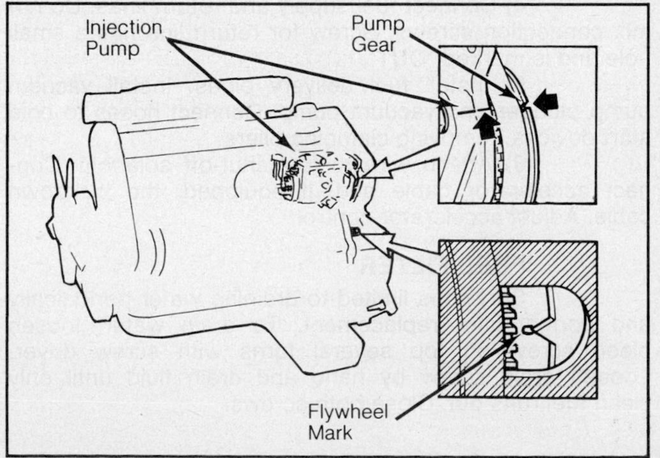
Injection
Pump
Pump
Gear
Flywheel
Mark

VOLVO (Cont.)

3) Plug open connections to prevent dirt from entering fuel system. Remove vacuum pump and pump plunger. Remove injection pump delivery pipes. Plug all openings.

4) Set cylinder No. 1 at TDC on compression stroke. Timing marks should align. Remove injection pump drive belt, after relieving tension by loosening injection pump bracket bolts. Tighten 1 bolt to retain injection pump in upper position.

5) Loosen camshaft rear gear bolt. Use spanner wrench to hold gear while loosening with special tool (5201) *See Fig. 10*. Camshaft must not rotate. Loosen bolt only enough to let gear rotate on camshaft.

6) Lock injection pump gear with stop (5193). Remove gear nut with special tool (5201). Remove pump gear with gear puller. Remove injection pump front bracket bolts and rear retaining bolts. Lift off pump and front bracket.

Fig. 10: Injection Pump Gear Removal

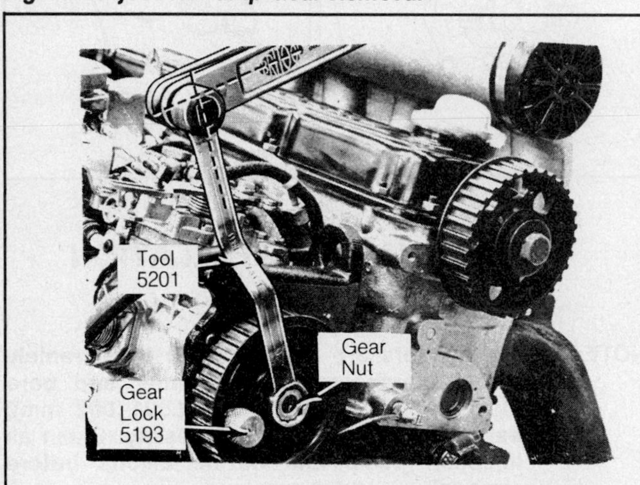
Tool
5201
Gear
Nut
Gear
Lock
5193

Installation

1) Position injection pump. Install retaining bolts finger tight, so pump position can still be adjusted. Set pump so mark on injection pump and pump bracket align. Tighten retaining bolts.

2) Make sure injection pump shaft key is correctly installed. Install gear, washer and nut. Lock gear with tool (5193) and tighten nut with tool (5201).

3) Set injection pump timing. Fill injection pump with diesel fuel if pump has been emptied or a new pump is being installed. Install rear timing gear cover.

4) Connect fuel supply and return lines. Do not mix connection screws. Screw for return line has a small hole and is marked "OUT".

5) Install fuel delivery pipes. Install vacuum pump plunger and vacuum pump. Connect hoses to cold start devices, removing clamping pliers.

6) Attach wire to fuel shut-off solenoid. Connect accelerator cable and, if equipped, the kickdown cable. Adjust accelerator control.

FUEL FILTER

Service is limited to draining water periodically and normal filter replacement. To drain water, loosen bleed screw on top several turns with screw driver. Loosen drain screw by hand and drain fluid until only clean fuel runs out. Close both screws.

ADJUSTMENTS

FUEL INJECTION PUMP TIMING

1) Remove rear timing gear cover. Disconnect cold start device by loosening screw "1", pushing lever forward and rotating it 90°. DO NOT touch screw "2". *See Fig. 11*. If it is loosened, cold start device must be reset on a test bench.

Fig. 11: Cold Start Device Connections

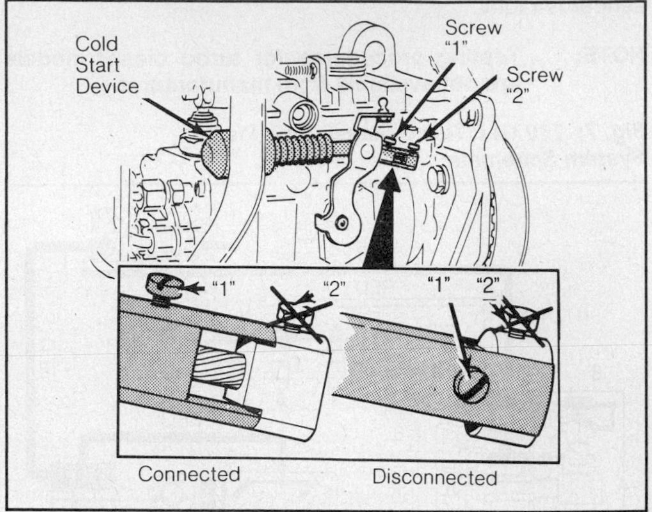
Cold
Start
Device
Screw
"1"
Screw
"2"
"1"
"2"
"1"
"2"
Connected
Disconnected

DO NOT touch screw "2".

2) Set cylinder No. 1 at TDC on compression stroke. Both cam lobes should point up at equally large angles. Flywheel timing mark should be at "0". *See Fig. 9.*

3) Remove inspection plug from injection pump cover. Install dial indicator holder (5194) and a 0-.12" (0-3 mm) dial indicator gauge.

4) Preset indicator to approximately .08" (2 mm). Turn engine counterclockwise until indicator gauge is at minimum. Set gauge to zero.

Fig. 12: Fuel Injection Pump Timing

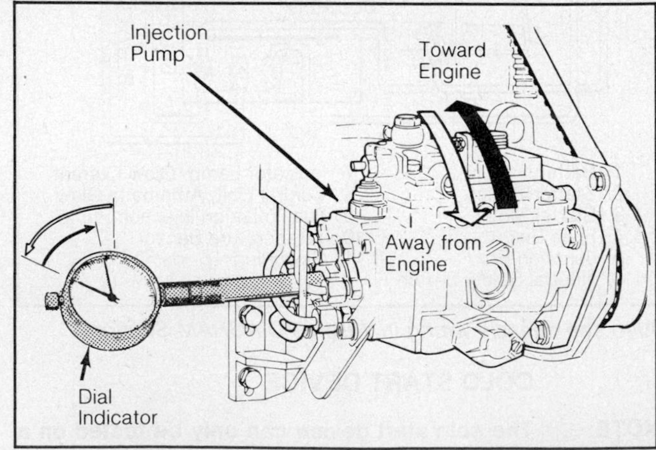
Injection
Pump
Toward
Engine
Away from
Engine
Dial
Indicator

5) Turn engine clockwise until flywheel "0" mark aligns with arrow. Indicator gauge should now read within specifications. If not, loosen injector pump bolts and rotate pump to change setting. Repeat steps **4)** and **5)**.

VOLVO (Cont.)

INJECTION PUMP PLUNGER LIFT

Application	In. (mm)
760 GLE [1]	
Checking	.0323-.0354 (.82-.90)
Adjusting	.0335 (.85)
GL	
Checking	.0323-.0354 (.82-.90)
Adjusting	.0335 (.85)

[1] - For high altitude operation, advance injection timing .0028" (.07 mm) for every 3300 ft. increase in altitude.

6) When checking pump timing, if engine is turned too far past "0" mark, it must be turned back approximately 1/4 turn and then clockwise again to "0" or settings will be incorrect.

CAUTION: If adjusting allowances are insufficient, do not tap or knock injection pump to change setting. It may be camshaft is not in proper relationship to crankshaft and/or front or rear drive belts may be improperly tensioned. Check and correct this condition and then set injection timing.

7) After adjusting injection pump setting, turn engine twice and recheck setting. Readjust as necessary. Remove dial indicator and holder. Install rear timing gear cover.

8) Connect cold start device. DO NOT turn screw "2". Push lever forward and turn sleeve 90°. Tighten screw "1".

ENGINE CONTROLS

1) Disconnect cold start device. Disconnect link rod at lever on injection pump. Adjust accelerator cable by turning sheath until cable is stretched, but does not influence pulley position. Pulley should touch idle stop.

Fig. 13: Adjusting Pump Control Cable

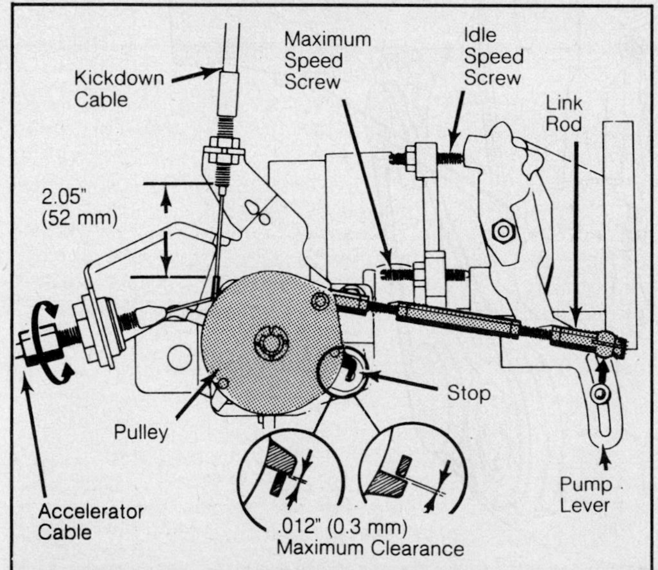

Kickdown Cable
Maximum Speed Screw
Idle Speed Screw
Link Rod
2.05" (52 mm)
Stop
Pulley
Accelerator Cable
.012" (0.3 mm) Maximum Clearance
Pump Lever

Cold start device must be disconnected before making cable adjustments.

2) Depress accelerator pedal fully. Pulley should touch full speed stop. Adjust kickdown cable on automatic transmission models. Depress accelerator pedal to floor. Kickdown cable should move approximately 2.05" (52 mm) between end positions.

3) In idle position, kickdown cable should be stretched and distance between kickdown cable clip and cable sheath should be .01-.04" (.25-1.0 mm).

4) Connect link rod to injection pump lever. Adjust link rod in maximum position by turning pulley to maximum position. Adjust link rod length so injection pump lever touches maximum speed adjusting screw.

5) Adjust link rod in idle position by returning pulley to idle stop. Move link rod ball joint in oblong hole in injection pump lever until lever touches idle adjusting screw.

6) Readjust link rod by repeating steps **4)** and **5)**. A clearance of .012" (.3 mm) is permitted between pulley and maximum speed stop. Connect cold start device.

IDLE SPEED

See the appropriate Volvo article in the TUNE-UP Section.

TIGHTENING SPECIFICATIONS

Application	Ft. Lbs. (N.m)
Fuel Injection Line Unions	18 (25)
Glow Plugs	16 (22)
Injector Nozzle (Upper-to-Lower Part)	51 (70)
Injector Nozzle-to-Cylinder Head	51 (70)
Injection Pump Gear	45 (33)
Injection Pump Mounting Bolts	15 (20)

1983 Turbocharging Systems

AUDI 4000 DIESEL & VOLKSWAGEN JETTA & QUANTUM DIESELS

DESCRIPTION

All models use a Garrett Air Research turbocharger, mounted directly to the exhaust manifold. The wastegate, which limits boost pressure, is a press fit into the turbocharger housing.

The other system components include: An intake manifold mounted blow-off valve to prevent excessive boost, a boost pressure fuel enrichment device, and an oil cooler. Engine modifications to ensure reliability include a piston cooling system (oil jet spray), and increased oil capacity.

OPERATION

At idle and light throttle, the Turbo engine operates like any other diesel engine. When more power is required, the usually wasted exhaust gases from the exhaust manifold enter the turbocharger's turbine housing and flow through the turbine blades.

Exhaust flow and turbine speed increase, as engine RPM increases. The impeller turns with the turbine and forces air into the compressor housing and intake manifold. The faster the impeller and turbine spin, the more pressurized air is provided for the engine.

If boost pressure went too high, engine damage would result. The wastegate opens when exhaust pressure exceeds a predetermined limit and allows exhaust gases to by-pass the compressor. A drain pipe is connected from the wastegate diaphragm housing to the impeller housing. This is to prevent a build up of oil or blowby from the crankcase ventilation system.

A boost pressure safety valve (blow-off valve) is used for protection in case the wastegate fails. The blow-off valve is connected to the intake manifold, and opens whenever boost pressure exceeds 11.7 psi (.8 kg/cm²). The excess boost pressure is vented to the intake pipe after the air cleaner. Some vehicles are equipped with a warning lamp which is connected to the blow-off valve. The warning lamp will light, whenever the blow-off valve operates.

Since the turbocharger supplies more air to the engine, a boost pressure enrichment device is needed to increase the amount of fuel delivered to the engine. At part throttle when boost pressure is low, no enrichment is necessary. As boost pressure increases the engines fuel requirements also increase.

TESTING

BOOST PRESSURE

1) To test the turbocharging system, use a pressure gauge (VW 1397). The gauge is equipped with a valve which locks pressure measurement when closed. Engine must be at operating temperature. Ensure there are no leaks on intake or exhaust side.

Fig. 1: Exploded View of Turbocharger System Components

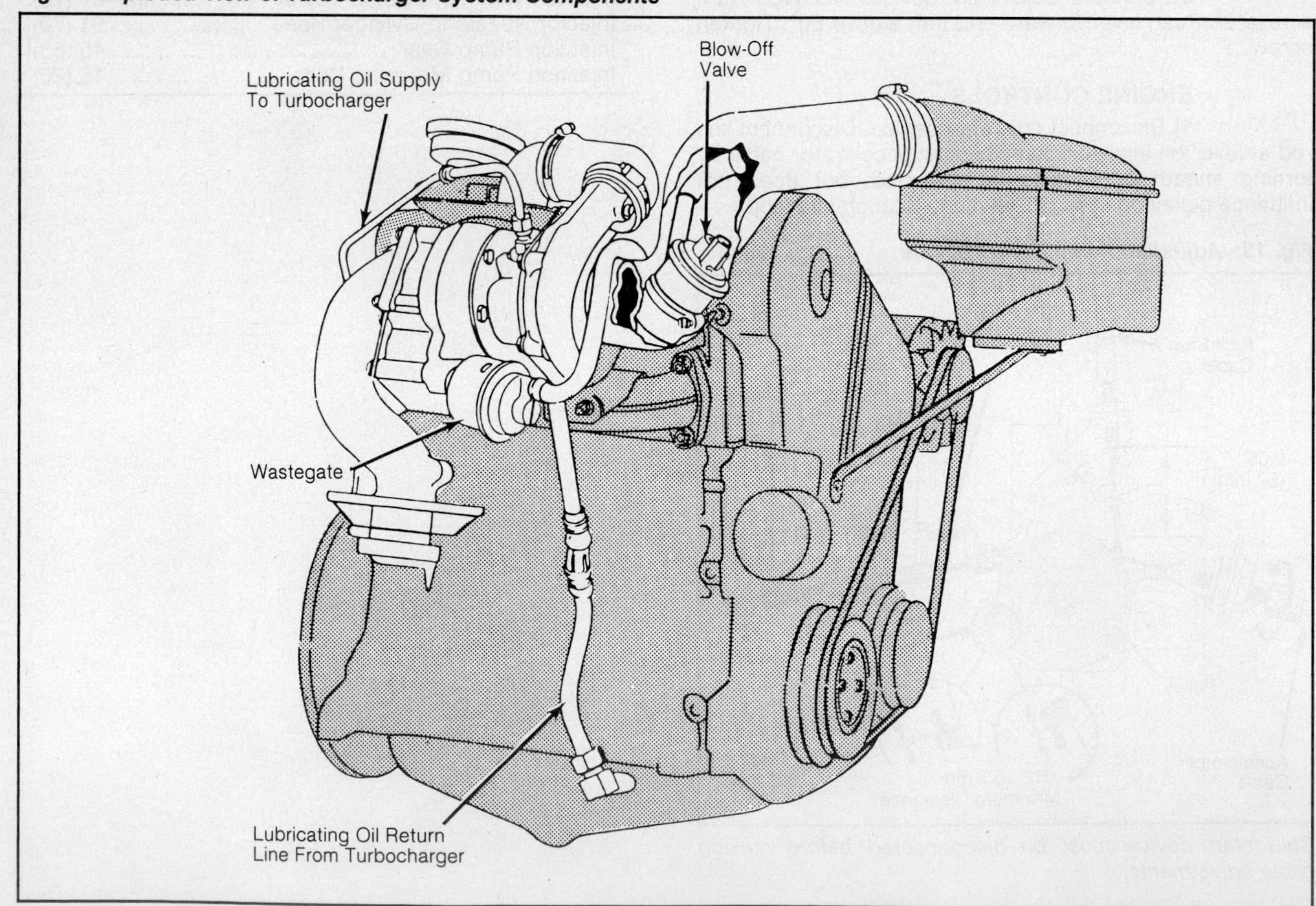
Lubricating Oil Supply
To Turbocharger
Blow-Off
Valve
Wastegate
Lubricating Oil Return
Line From Turbocharger

AUDI 4000 DIESEL & VOLKSWAGEN JETTA & QUANTUM DIESELS (Cont.)

2) Attach gauge to the boost pressure line at the fuel injection pump, using "T" fitting supplied with gauge. Use hose clamps at all connections to avoid low readings.

3) Boost pressure can only be tested on a chassis dynamometer or through road testing. Carry the gauge inside car by routing the hose out right rear corner of hood and into passenger side vent wing window. Measure boost pressure with engine at full throttle.

4) On dynamometer, check boost pressure at 4000 RPM. Place manual transmission in 3rd gear and automatic transmission in 2nd range. On road test, place manual transmission in 2nd gear and automatic transmission in 1st range. Hold road speed at 60 MPH with foot brake.

5) Boost pressure should be 9.3-10.2 psi (.65-.72 kg/cm²). If boost pressure is too high, replace turbocharger. If pressure is too low, disconnect blow-off valve hose from intake air hose.

6) Plug air hose. Repeat boost pressure test. If pressure is good, replace blow-off valve. If pressure is still not good, replace turbocharger.

REMOVAL & INSTALLATION

TURBOCHARGER

CAUTION: Always replace gaskets and seals. If turbocharger is defective, do not repair, only replace.

Removal (4000)

1) Disconnect negative battery cable. Remove engine/transmission cover plate. Loosen stabilizer bar clamps on both sides and push stabilizer bar down. Remove turbocharger heat shield nuts and oil return line.

2) Remove hoses between turbocharger and intake manifold and air cleaner. Remove oil supply line. Disconnect exhaust pipe at turcharger. Remove turbocharger-to-exhaust manifold bolts. Remove turbocharger.

Installation

To install, reverse removal procedure. Coat turbocharger-to-exhaust manifold bolts with high temperature grease (G 000 500 or equivalent). Tighten to 33 ft. lbs. (45 N.m). Tighten oil supply line bolt to 18 ft. lbs. (25 N.m).

Removal (Jetta & Rabbit)

Disconnect negative battery cable. On vehicles with automatic transmission, remove starter. Remove exhaust pipe on turbocharger. Remove oil supply line. Remove all air hoses from turbocharger. Remove oil return line. Remove turbocharger mounting bolts and turbocharger.

Installation

1) Install starter. Coat turbocharger-to-exhaust manifold bolts with high temperature grease (G 000 500 or equivalent). Attach exhaust pipe to turbocharger and tighten bolts hand tight. Attach turbocharger to exhaust manifold and tighten all 4 bolts. Tighten exhaust pipe nuts.

2) Before installing oil supply line, fill connection branch with engine oil. After installation, run engine for approximately 1 minute at idle to allow turbocharger to become properly lubricated.

AUDI 5000

DESCRIPTION

The Audi 5000 Turbo uses a KKK (Kuhnle, Kopp, Kausch) turbocharger, mounted directly to the front of the exhaust manifold. A wastegate is attached to the back of the manifold. Other system components include an additional safety switch to prevent excessive boost, oil cooler mounted behind the front spoiler, injector cooling fan, dual oil filters, and an oil thermostat.

Engine modifications include a piston cooling system (oil jet spray), low compression pistons, larger piston pins, sodium-filled exhaust valves, and increased oil capacity.

OPERATION

At idle and light throttle, the Turbo engine operates like any other engine. When more power is required, exhaust gases from the exhaust manifold enter the turbocharger's turbine housing and flow through the turbine blades.

Exhaust flow and turbine speed increase as throttle opens and RPM increase. The impeller turns with the turbine and forces air into the compressor housing and intake manifold. The faster the impeller and turbine spin, the more pressurized air is provided for the engine.

If boost pressure went too high, engine damage would result. The wastegate opens when exhaust pressure exceeds a predetermined limit and allows exhaust gases to by-pass the compressor. A boost pressure safety switch is used for protection in case the wastegate fails. This switch is connected to the intake manifold and serves as the ground for the electric fuel pump. When pressure is higher than 11.6 psi (.82 kg/cm²), the switch opens and the fuel pump stops, slowing the engine.

Fig. 1: Exploded View of Audi 5000 Turbocharger System Components

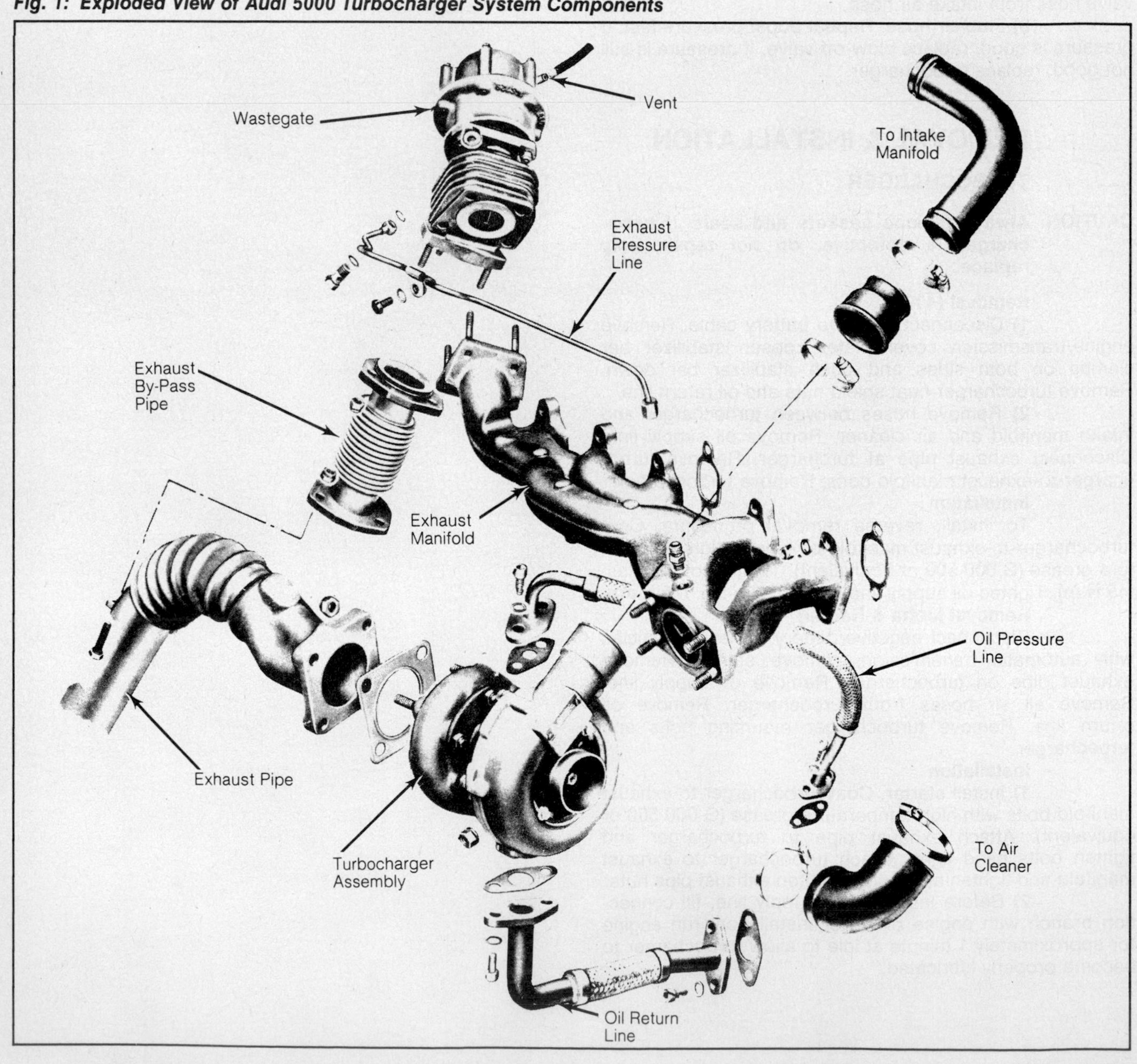
Vent
Wastegate
To Intake Manifold
Exhaust Pressure Line
Exhaust By-Pass Pipe
Exhaust Manifold
Oil Pressure Line
Exhaust Pipe
Turbocharger Assembly
To Air Cleaner
Oil Return Line

AUDI 5000 (Cont.)

An electric blower fan is used to cool the injectors and intake manifold and prevent vapor lock. A thermal switch controls fan operation and turns the fan on whenever manifold temperatures exceed 212°F (100°C).

Turbocharger operation requires a large quantity of clean oil to prevent bearing failure. Turbo models have increased oil capacity, an oil cooler, oil thermostat, and special filter. Both the turbocharger filter and the regular engine filter should be changed at regular intervals.

TESTING

BOOST PRESSURE

1) To test the turbocharging system, use a pressure gauge (VW 1397). The gauge is equipped with a valve which locks pressure measurement when closed.

2) Attach gauge to vacuum advance at distributor, using "T" fitting supplied with gauge. Be sure vacuum advance unit and charcoal canister purge valve are free of leaks. Use hose clamps at all connections to avoid low readings.

3) Boost pressure can only be tested on a chassis dynamometer or through road testing. Carry the gauge inside car by routing the hose out right rear corner of hood and into passenger side vent wing window.

4) Accelerate engine to full throttle in drive position "1". Hold vehicle speed constant with foot brake, when engine speed reaches 5500 RPM. Wait 2 seconds and close gauge valve by pulling sleeve away from dial.

NOTE: Testing should not exceed 10 seconds at full boost.

5) Boost pressure readings will vary with atmospheric pressure, temperature, and altitude. *See Boost Pressure Specifications* table. If boost pressure is too high, wastegate is defective. If boost pressure is too low, replace defective turbocharger.

BOOST PRESSURE SPECIFICATIONS

Ambient Temperature	psi (kg/cm²)
32°F (0°C)	7.3-7.9 (.50-.54)
50°F (10°C)	7.0-7.7 (.48-.52)
68°F (20°C)	6.7-7.5 (.46-.51)
77°F (25°C)	6.6-7.3 (.45-.50)
86°F (30°C)	6.4-7.1 (.44-.49)

NOTE: The boost pressure gauge in the instrument cluster is calibrated to read absolute pressure. When the engine is not running and gauge reads "1", this is normal atmospheric pressure. A reading of over "1" indicates boost pressure in the intake manifold; a reading less than "1" indicates presence of vacuum.

END PLAY & SIDE PLAY

End Play

Attach dial indicator to the turborcharger. *See Fig. 2.* Zero dial indicator, with 1 mm preload, pointing toward turbocharger shaft. Move shaft backward and forward. Maximum end play should be .008" (.2 mm).

Fig. 2: Checking Turbocharger End Play.

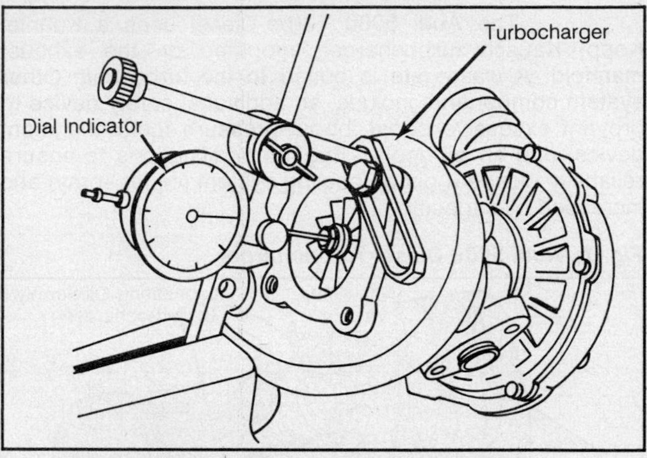
Turbocharger
Dial Indicator

Side Play

Mount dial indicator with stem on side of turbocharger shaft end nut. Zero dial indicator, with 1 mm preload, pointing toward hub of shaft. Push shaft toward dial indicator and back. Maximum side play should be .022" (.55 mm).

REMOVAL & INSTALLATION

TURBOCHARGER

Removal

1) Disconnect negative battery cable. Spray all bolts and nuts with rust solvent. Remove grille. Remove vacuum pipe between intake air boot and turbocharher. Remove intake air boot and crankcase ventilation hose.

2) Remove intake manifold-to-throttle housing hose, air filter housing cover, engine-mount heat shield, and oil supply line. Detach exhaust pipe at corrugated pipe. Loosen exhaust pipe at transmission mount and catalytic converter.

3) Remove clamp from starter housing. Remove air hose. Detach exhaust pipe from turbocharger. Remove alternator support bolt and hang alternator sideways. Remove oil return pipe. Remove turbocharger.

Installation

To install, reverse removal procedure.

AUDI 5000 DIESEL

DESCRIPTION

The Audi 5000 Turbo-Diesel uses a Kuhnle, Kopp, Kausch turbocharger, mounted on the exhaust manifold. A wastegate is bolted to the turbo unit. Other system components include, an additional safety device to prevent excessive boost, boost pressure fuel enrichment device, and an oil cooler. Engine modifications to ensure reliability incude a piston cooling system (oil jet spray) and increased oil capacity.

Fig. 1: Audi 5000 Diesel Turbocharger

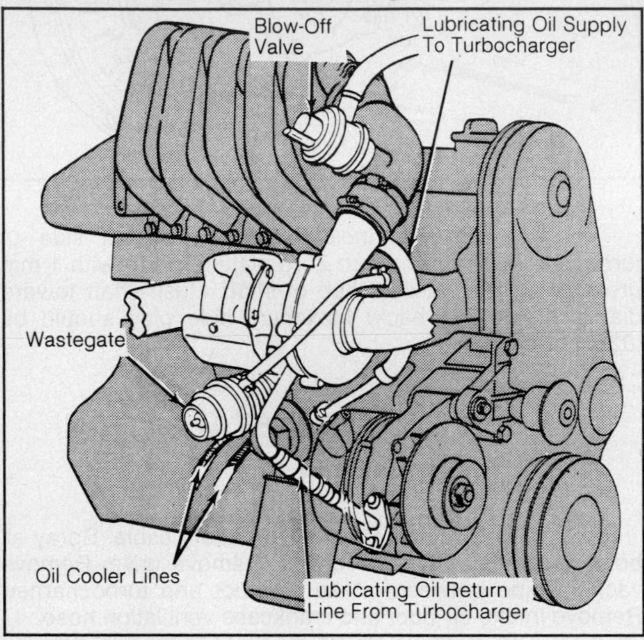
Blow-Off Valve
Lubricating Oil Supply To Turbocharger
Wastegate
Oil Cooler Lines
Lubricating Oil Return Line From Turbocharger

OPERATION

Exhaust gases from the exhaust manifold enter the turbocharger's turbine housing and flow through the turbine blades. Exhaust flow and turbine speed increase as engine RPM increases. The impeller turns with the turbine and forces air into the intake manifold. The faster the impeller and turbine spin, the more pressurized air is provided for the engine.

To prevent engine damage, the wastegate opens when exhaust pressure exceeds a safe limit and allows exhaust gases to by-pass the compressor. A blow-off valve is used for protection in case the wastegate fails.

The blow-off valve, connected to the intake manifold, opens whenever boost pressure exceeds the safe limit. Excess boost pressure is vented to the intake pipe after the air cleaner. Some vehicles are equipped with a warning lamp which will light whenever the blow-off valve operates.

A boost pressure enrichment device is used to increase the amount of fuel delivered to the engine. As boost pressure increases the engines fuel requirements also increase. The boost pressure enrichment device ensures additional fuel requirements are met.

TROUBLE SHOOTING

BOOST PRESSURE TOO HIGH

Check for defective wastegate, and/or boost pressure control line to wastegate leaking.

BOOST PRESSURE TOO LOW

Check for defective blow-off valve, wastegate or turbocharger defective, dirty air filter, and/or air leaks.

TESTING

BOOST PRESSURE

1) Ensure there is no leaks on intake or exhaust gas side. To test the turbocharging system, use a pressure gauge (VW 1397). The gauge is equipped with a valve which locks pressure measurement when closed.

CAUTION: When testing turbocharger, test time per measurement must not exceed 10 seconds.

2) Attach gauge to the boost pressure line at the fuel injection pump, using "T" fitting supplied with gauge. Use hose clamps at all connections.

3) Boost pressure can only be tested on a chassis dynamometer or through road testing. Carry the gauge inside car by routing the hose out right rear corner of hood and into passenger side vent wing window. Boost pressure to be measured with engine at full throttle during road test or on dynomometer.

4) Open gauge stop valve. On dynamometer, engine must be at 4000 RPM. Manual transmission must be in 3rd gear and automatic transmission in 2nd range. On road test, manual transmission must be in 2nd gear and automatic transmission in 1st range. Hold vehicle speed to 60 MPH using brake.

5) Boost pressure must be 9-10 psi (.6-.7 kg/cm²). If boost pressure is too high, replace wastegate.

6) If pressure is too low, disconnect and plug blow-off valve hose from intake air hose. Repeat boost pressure test.

7) If pressure is okay, replace blow-off valve. If pressure is too low, replace wastegate. Repeat pressure test. If pressure specification is not obtained, replace turbocharger.

REMOVAL & INSTALLATION

TURBOCHARGER

Removal

1) Remove air cleaner, battery, right side engine mount heat shield, engine cover plate, and alternator. Disconnect exhaust pipe from turbocharger and remove bracket from transmission.

2) Disconnect turbocharger oil supply line. Loosen lower clamp of hose to intake manifold. Remove oil return line and air tube. Remove turbocharger-to-exhaust manifold nuts. Remove turbocharger.

Installation

1) To install, reverse removal procedure. Attach turbocharger and tighten 4 nuts sufficiently that air hose on intake manifold can be attached to turbocharger. Tighten nuts fully.

2) Fill oil supply line with engine oil before installation. After turbocharger installation, run engine about 1 minute at idle to ensure oil supply of turbocharger is properly distributed.

CHRYSLER CORP. IMPORTS & MITSUBISHI TURBO DIESELS

Colt & Ram-50 Turbo Diesel Pickup
Mitsubishi Turbo Diesel Pickup

DESCRIPTION

The turbocharger is mounted on the exhaust manifold on the right side of the engine. Components of the turbocharger include turbine and compressor impellers, impeller shaft, bearings, and impeller housings *See Fig. 1*. Engine oil pressure provides constant lubrication to the impeller bearings.

Fig. 1: Cutaway View of Turbocharger Assembly

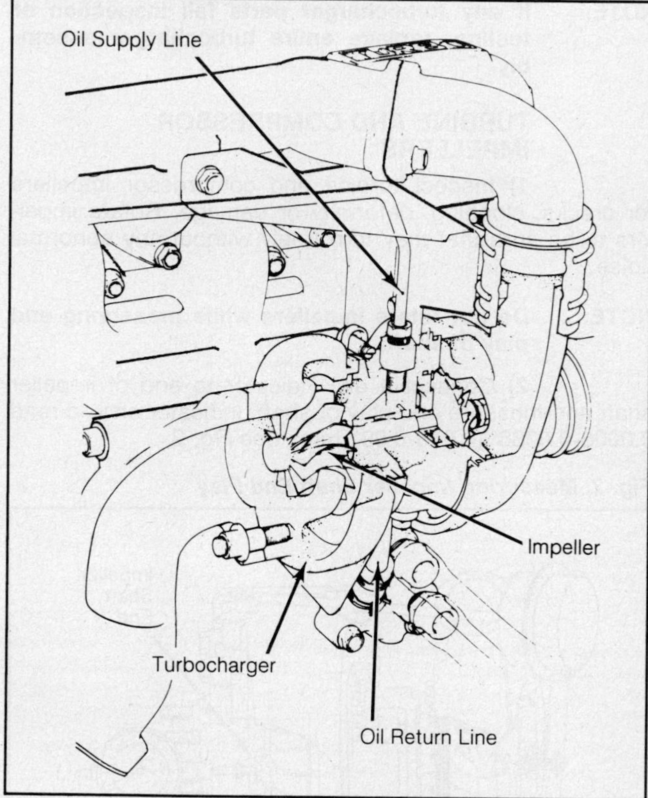
Oil Supply Line
Impeller
Turbocharger
Oil Return Line

OPERATION

The turbine impeller of the turbocharger is driven by the exhaust gases expelled from the cylinder combustion chambers. At idle speeds there is no pressurization of intake air and the engine operates like a normally aspirated engine.

With engine under partial load, the throttle valve opens and the speed and volume of exhaust gases increases which turns the turbine impeller at a faster RPM. The increased RPM of the compressor impeller boosts the pressure of the intake air.

With engine under full load, the exhaust gases are at maximum pressure and increase the RPM of the turbine and compressor impellers.

NOTE: **When engine is first started, allow it to run at idle for several minutes to ensure turbocharger has adequate oil pressure. Also, allow engine to idle for several minutes before turning engine off. This will prevent overheating of turbocharger bearings.**

TROUBLE SHOOTING

VIBRATION OR NOISE

1) Most probable causes are defective bearings and interference of moving parts with surrounding objects. Bearing failure is usually caused by poor lubrication or repeated abrupt stops and starts.

2) If lubrication to turbocharger is adequate, check for an unbalanced or bent shaft. This may be due to excessive bearing wear or entry of foreign substances that have damaged turbine or compressor wheel.

LOW BOOST PRESSURE

Check for exhaust leaks. Inspect for restricted exhaust system which would cause restrictions. Check for air leaks on compressor discharge side. Check air cleaner element for restrictions. If turbocharger shaft does not rotate smoothly when turned by hand, replace turbocharger assembly.

WHITE EXHAUST SMOKE

Inspect for oil from the turbocharger leaking into the intake or exhaust pipe. Check for clogged or deformed oil return pipe. If oil return pipe is good, oil seals in turbocharger are worn. Replace turbocharger.

REMOVAL & INSTALLATION

TURBOCHARGER

Removal

1) Disengage exhaust pipe from turbocharger. Remove turbocharger-to-intake manifold pipe. Remove heat shield. Remove oil supply pipe. Disengage oil return pipe.

2) Remove turbocharger-to-exhaust manifold nuts. Remove turbocharger. Do not allow foreign substances to enter turbocharger oil passage.

Installation

To install, reverse removal procedure. Before installing oil pipe flare nut, pour engine oil into turbocharger. Use new gaskets. Ensure all oil and air hoses are securely clamped.

1983 Turbocharging Systems

DATSUN/NISSAN 280ZX TURBO

DESCRIPTION

The Datsun 280ZX turbocharger is mounted on the exhaust manifold on the left side of the engine. Components of the turbocharger include turbine and compressor impellers (wheels), impeller shaft, bearings, impeller housings, wastegate controller and wastegate (exhaust bypass valve). *See Fig. 1.*

The pressure actuated wastegate, located at the front of the compressor housing, prevents excessive intake boost pressure. If it fails, an emergency relief valve located on the intake manifold releases any excess pressure. Engine oil pressure provides constant lubrication to the impeller bearings.

OPERATION

The turbine impeller of the turbocharger is driven by the exhaust gases expelled from the cylinder combustion chambers. At idle speeds there is no pressurization of intake air and the engine operates like a normally aspirated engine.

With engine under partial load, the throttle valve opens and more air/fuel mixture is drawn into the combustion chambers. The speed and volume of exhaust gases also increases. The increased amount of exhaust gases turns the turbine impeller at a faster RPM.

The compressor impeller turns at the same RPM as the turbine impeller because they are mounted on the same shaft. The increased RPM of the compressor impeller boosts the pressure of the intake air.

Fig. 1: Cutaway View of Datsun 280ZX Turbocharger

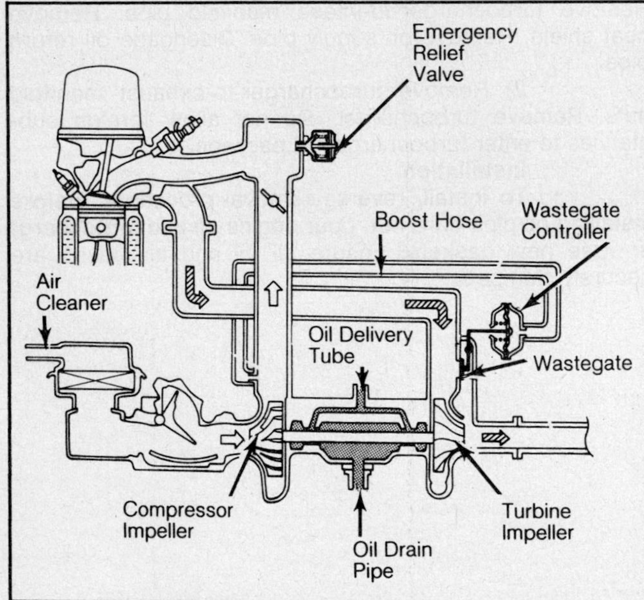
Emergency Relief Valve
Wastegate Controller
Boost Hose
Air Cleaner
Oil Delivery Tube
Wastegate
Compressor Impeller
Turbine Impeller
Oil Drain Pipe

With engine under full load, the exhaust gases are at maximum pressure and increase the RPM of the turbine and compressor impellers to an extremely high speed. The boost pressure of the intake air reaches a maximum.

When the pressure in the intake manifold reaches 6.08-6.85 psi (.43-.48 kg/cm²), the diaphragm of the wastegate controller pushes against the linkage which opens the wastegate.

Part of the exhaust gases are then routed directly into the main exhaust pipe, bypassing the turbine impeller. This maintains the boost pressure of the intake air at a constant 6.19-7.35 psi (.44-.52 kg/cm²).

If the wastegate fails to function properly, an emergency relief valve located on the intake manifold opens to atmosphere when the intake manifold pressure reaches 7.35-7.73 psi (.52-.54 kg/cm²). This prevents engine damage from excessive pressure.

TESTING

NOTE: If any turbocharger parts fail inspection or testing, replace entire turbocharger assembly.

TURBINE AND COMPRESSOR IMPELLERS

1) Inspect turbine and compressor impellers for cracks, clogging, deformity or damage. Rotate impellers to be sure that they turn freely without any abnormal noise.

NOTE: Do not rotate impellers while measuring end play of shaft.

2) Connect a dial indicator to end of impeller shaft and measure end play of shaft. Indicator should read 0.0005-0.0036" (0.013-0.091 mm). *See Fig. 2.*

Fig. 2: Measuring Impeller Shaft End Play

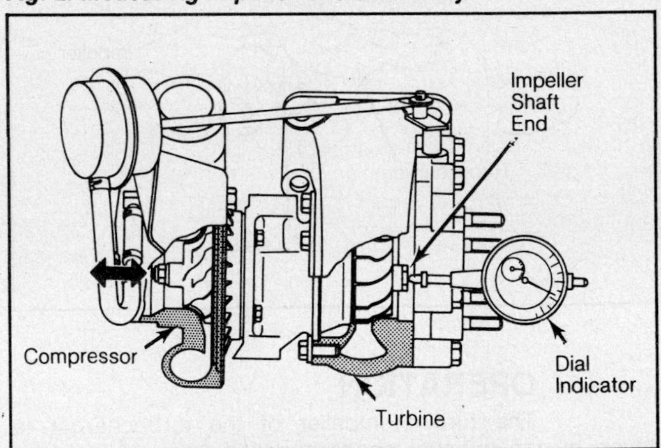
Impeller Shaft End
Compressor
Dial Indicator
Turbine

End play should be .0005-.0036" (.013-.091 mm).

WASTEGATE CONTROLLER

CAUTION: Do not apply more than 9.67 psi (.68 kg/cm²) to wastegate controller diaphragm.

1) Connect a dial indicator to end of wastegate controller pushrod. *See Fig. 3.* Disconnect boost hose at wastegate controller. Connect a pressure gauge to wastegate controller and apply 6.08-6.85 psi (.43-.48 kg/cm²). Wastegate controller pushrod should move 0.015" (0.38 mm).

2) Disconnect wastegate controller pushrod. Move wastegate lever back and forth and check for binding or sticking.

DATSUN/NISSAN 280ZX TURBO (Cont.)

Fig. 3: Testing Wastegate Controller

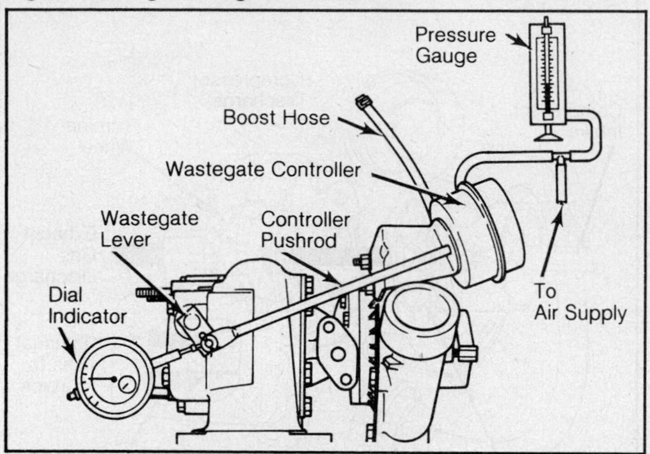
Pressure Gauge
Boost Hose
Wastegate Controller
Wastegate Lever
Controller Pushrod
Dial Indicator
To Air Supply

Pressure gauge and dial indicator required for test.

REMOVAL & INSTALLATION

TURBOCHARGER ASSEMBLY

Removal

1) Remove heat insulator, inlet tube, air duct hose and suction air pipe.

2) Disconnect exhaust gas sensor connector, front tube, oil delivery tube and oil drain pipe. *See Fig. 4.*

Fig. 4: Datsun Turbocharger Removal

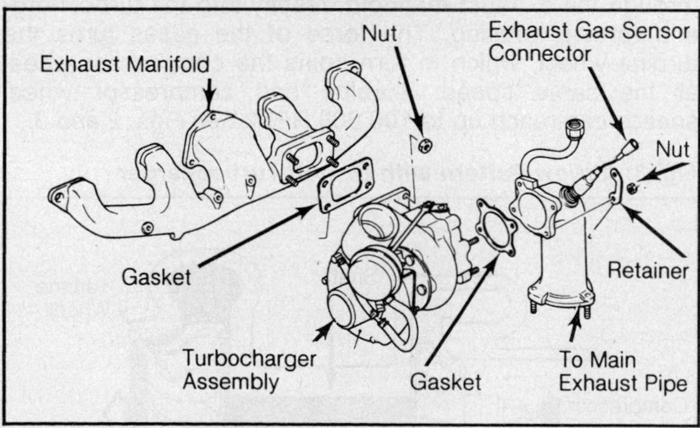
Nut
Exhaust Gas Sensor Connector
Exhaust Manifold
Nut
Gasket
Retainer
Turbocharger Assembly
Gasket
To Main Exhaust Pipe

3) Remove 4 nuts securing turbocharger to exhaust manifold. Remove turbocharger and gasket.

Installation

To install, reverse removal procedures noting the following: Replace gasket between turbocharger and exhaust manifold.

MERCEDES-BENZ TURBO DIESELS

300D, 300CD, 300SD, 300TD

DESCRIPTION

The diesel turbocharged engine (617.95) is basically the same design as the naturally aspirated diesel engine. *See Fig. 1.* Installation of the Garrett turbocharger produced an increase to 110 SAE net brake horsepower at 4200 RPM.

Fig. 1: Cutaway View of Mercedes-Benz Turbocharged Diesel Engine

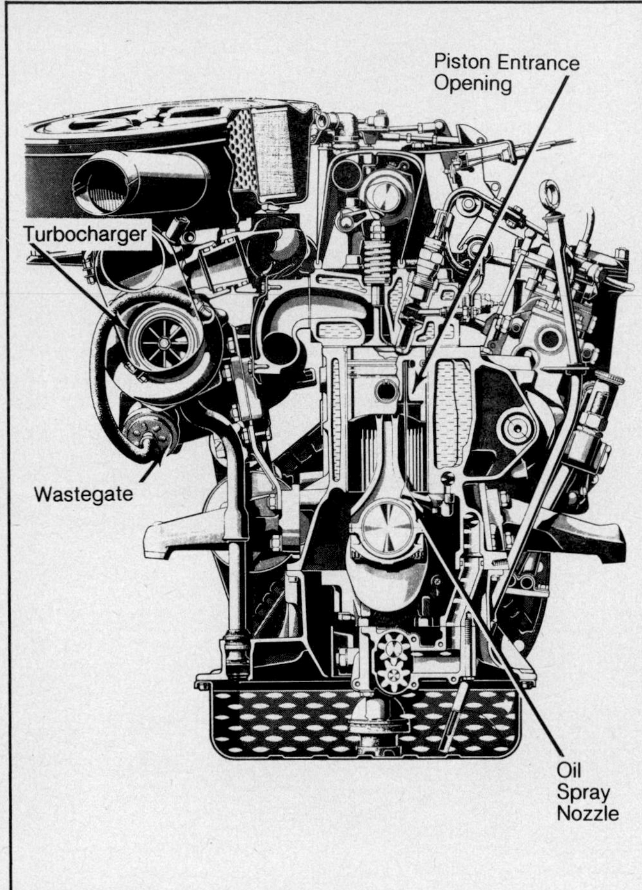
Piston Entrance Opening
Turbocharger
Wastegate
Oil Spray Nozzle

The increased power output required modifications of the crankcase, pistons, valve train, lubrication system, cooling system, and fuel injection system.

The turbocharger delivers compressed air to the engine, providing higher pressures and temperatures in the combustion chambers. The turbocharger consists of a turbine, compressor, and wastegate that prevents excessive boost pressures from damaging the engine. *See Fig. 2.*

The turbocharger's turbine wheel and compressor wheel are mounted on a common shaft and turn at the same speed. The turbocharger is mounted between the exhaust manifold and the exhaust pipe and is connected directly to the engine for lubrication and cooling. The wastegate is attached to the turbine housing. Should its boost pressure control valve malfunction, an engine overload protection system will prevent engine damage.

Fig. 2: Cutaway View of Garrett Turbocharger

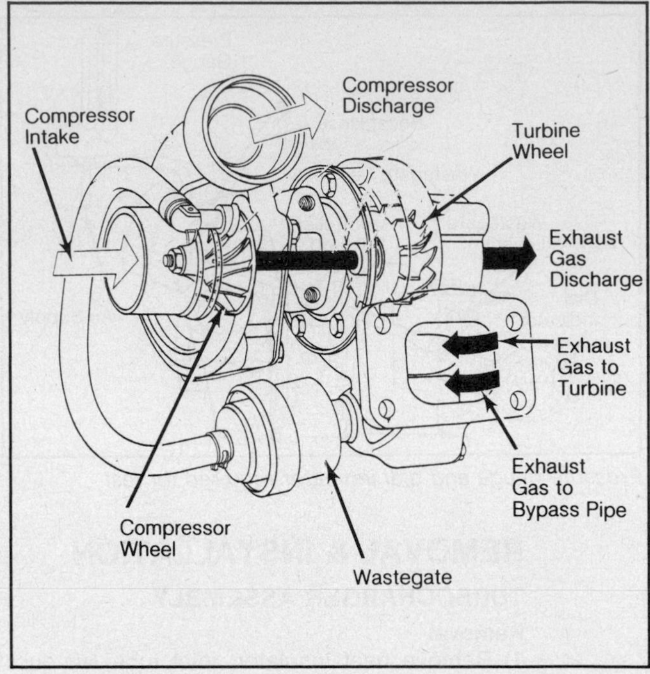
Compressor Intake
Compressor Discharge
Turbine Wheel
Exhaust Gas Discharge
Exhaust Gas to Turbine
Exhaust Gas to Bypass Pipe
Compressor Wheel
Wastegate

OPERATION

Exhaust gases leaving the cylinders flow through the exhaust manifold directly into the turbocharger's turbine housing. The force of the gases turns the turbine wheel, which in turn spins the compressor wheel at the same speed. Turbine and compressor wheel speeds can reach up to 100,000 RPM. *See Figs. 2 and 3.*

Fig. 3: Airflow Pattern with Garrett Turbocharger

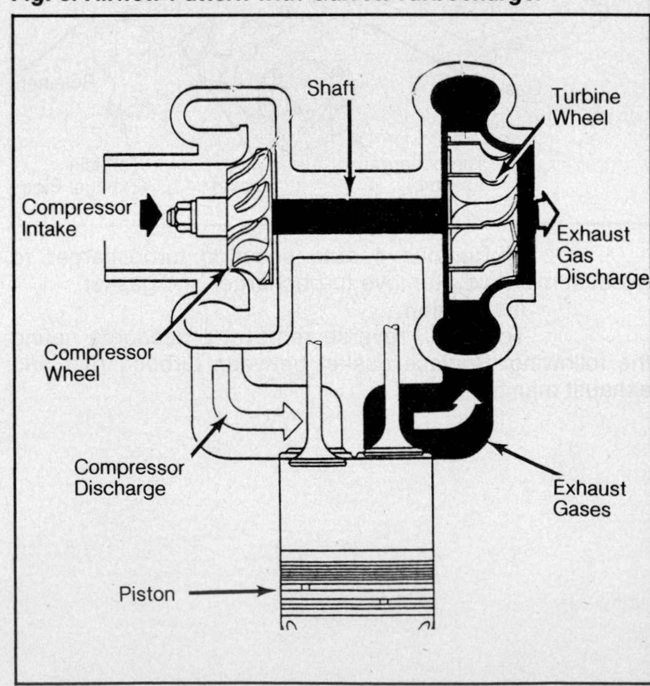
Shaft
Turbine Wheel
Compressor Intake
Exhaust Gas Discharge
Compressor Wheel
Compressor Discharge
Exhaust Gases
Piston

MERCEDES-BENZ TURBO DIESELS (Cont.)

Fresh air drawn in by the compressor wheel is compressed and delivered to the combustion chamber above the pistons. At idle, the engine operates like any other. However, with increasing load and engine speed, exhaust gases are expelled with increasing velocity. This causes the turbine wheel to turn faster, increasing boost pressure at the compressor wheel. Boost pressure is routed to the intake manifold and to individual cylinders, completing the cycle.

The aneroid compensator on top of the fuel injection pump automatically adjusts fuel quantity injected into cylinders depending on boost pressure or atmospheric pressure in intake manifold. Correct air-fuel relationship is maintained at all times.

Fig. 4: Cutaway View of Wastegate Valve

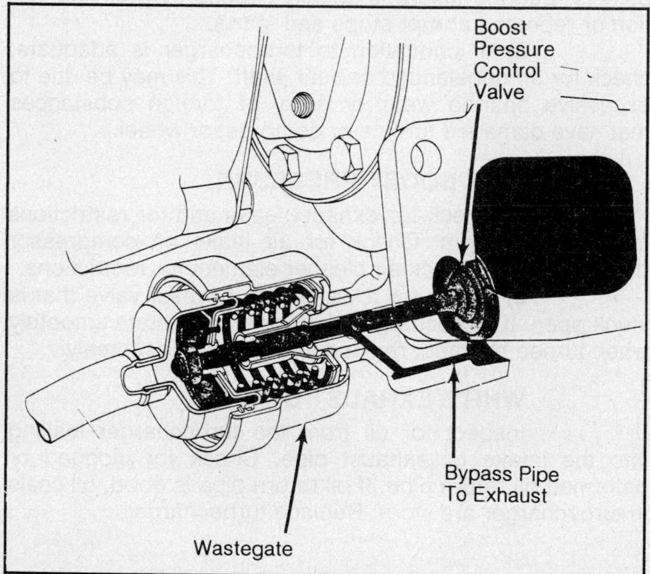
Boost
Pressure
Control
Valve
Bypass Pipe
To Exhaust
Wastegate

Should wastegate fail, a pressure switch installed in the intake manifold closes an electrical circuit, energizing a switch-over valve. This valve closes the pressure line to the intake manifold and simultaneously opens the aneroid compensator to atmosphere. This reduces the fuel quantity being injected.

The pressure switch only functions when intake manifold boost pressure reaches 16 psi (1.13 kg/cm²). When pressure drops below this figure, the pressure switch opens the electric circuit and venting of the pressure line is stopped.

LUBRICATION

Oil is supplied to the turbocharger for lubrication and cooling from the rear cover of the oil filter. The oil return line runs from the turbocharger back to the upper oil pan housing. Oil spray nozzles for cooling the pistons are connected internally to the engine lubrication system's main oil gallery. *See Fig. 1.*

TESTING

BOOST PRESSURE

1) To check turbocharger boost pressure, connect pressure gauge (617 589 02 21 00) to intake manifold after removing plug.

2) Using a dynamometer, drive vehicle in driving range "S" at full load and 4000 RPM. Boost pressure should be 10.1-11.6 psi (.71-.82 kg/cm²).

3) If boost pressure is too low, check air filter and air intake duct for obstructions. Check turbocharger for leaks between manifold and turbine housing, compressor housing discharge and intake manifold, and between intake or exhaust manifold and cylinder head.

4) Check pressure line between intake manifold and aneroid compensator and overload switch-over valve. To check valve turn ignition switch to position "2". Disconnect plug on valve and check for battery voltage at Black/Red wire.

5) If not present, check fuse number 4 or wiring. Check for ground condition of Brown/Black wire. There should be no ground connection below boost pressure of 16 psi (1.13 kg/cm²). If ground exists, check pressure switch in intake manifold or its wiring.

6) Other possible causes of low boost pressure would be a defective wastegate, requiring turbocharger replacement, or problems with the fuel injection pump, requiring removal, testing, and repair.

7) If wastegate does not open, causing boost pressure at full load operation to exceed 16 psi (1.13 kg/cm²), check hose between compressor housing and wastegate. If hose is leaking or is kinked, replace the hose. If not, replace turbocharger.

8) When dynamometer test is complete, road test vehicle with tester inside the vehicle. Drive vehicle in "L" or "S" range at 4000 RPM. Fully depress accelerator pedal. Hold engine speed at 4000 RPM with brakes (short test duration only). Boost pressure should be 10.1-11.6 psi (.71-.82 kg/cm²). If not, repeat steps **3)** through **6)**.

REMOVAL & INSTALLATION

TURBOCHARGER ASSEMBLY

Removal

1) Remove air filter. Disconnect electrical lead from coolant temperature switch. Loosen hose clamp at air intake duct. Remove vacuum line, crankcase breather pipe, air filter housing, and air intake duct. Disconnect oil supply line to turbocharger. Remove air filter mounting bracket. Disconnect exhaust flange.

2) Disconnect and remove exhaust bracket on automatic transmission. Press exhaust pipe to the rear. Remove mounting bracket for intermediate flange and 4 mounting nuts on the turbocharger.

3) Lift off turbocharger. Remove intermediate flange. Disconnect oil return pipe at turbocharger.

Installation

1) Install all parts in reverse order of removal. Before mounting the turbocharger, install intermediate flange and oil return pipe. Install flange gasket between turbocharger and exhaust manifold with reinforcing bead towards the exhaust manifold.

2) Use only heatproof nuts and bolts when installing turbocharger. Fill center turbocharger housing with approximately 4 ounces of engine oil through the engine oil supply bore, before operating turbocharger. Ensure "O" rings are mounted correctly when installing air intake duct.

MITSUBISHI STARION

DESCRIPTION

The Starion turbocharger is mounted on the exhaust manifold on the right side of the engine. Components of the turbocharger include turbine and compressor impellers, impeller shaft, bearings, impeller housings, wastegate controller, and wastegate. *See Fig. 1.* Engine oil pressure provides constant lubrication to the impeller bearings.

The pressure actuated wastegate, located at the front of the compressor housing, prevents excessive intake boost pressure. An additional safety feature is provided by the fuel injection Electronic Control Unit (ECU). The ECU will modify fuel injection pulse width when it senses intake manifold pressures that are higher than normal.

OPERATION

The turbine impeller of the turbocharger is driven by the exhaust gases expelled from the cylinder combustion chambers. At idle speeds there is no pressurization of intake air and the engine operates like a normally aspirated engine.

With engine under partial load, the throttle valve opens and more air/fuel mixture is drawn into the combustion chambers. The speed and volume of exhaust gases also increases which turns the turbine impeller at a faster RPM. The increased RPM of the compressor impeller boosts the pressure of the intake air.

With engine under full load, the exhaust gases are at maximum pressure and increase the RPM of the turbine and compressor impellers to an extremely high speed. The boost pressure of the intake air reaches a maximum.

When the pressure in the intake manifold reaches 8.4 psi (.59 kg/cm²), the diaphragm of the wastegate controller pushes against the linkage which opens the wastegate. Part of the exhaust gases are then routed directly into the main exhaust pipe, by-passing the turbine impeller. This prevents engine damage from excessive pressure.

Fig. 1: Cutaway View of Mitsubishi Starion Turbocharger

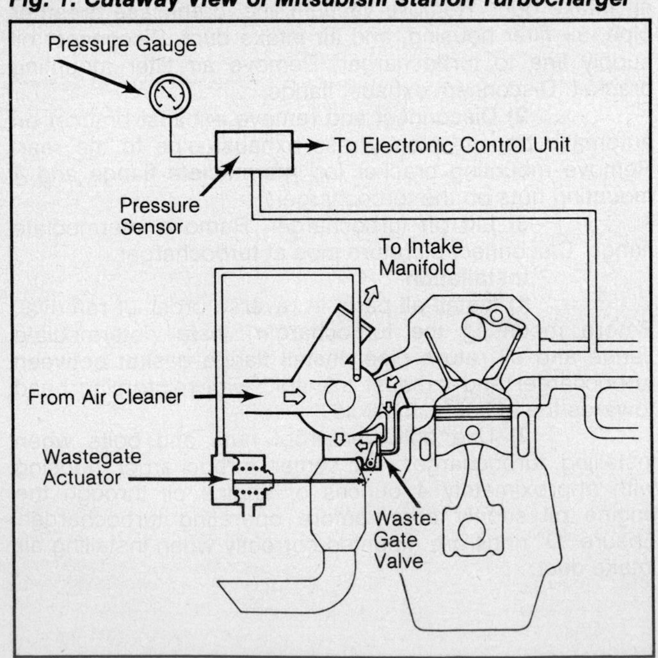
Pressure Gauge
To Electronic Control Unit
Pressure Sensor
To Intake Manifold
From Air Cleaner
Wastegate Actuator
Waste-Gate Valve

NOTE: **When engine is first started, allow it to run at idle for several minutes to ensure turbocharger has adequate oil pressure. Also, allow engine to idle for several minutes before turning engine off. This will prevent overheating of turbocharger bearings.**

TROUBLE SHOOTING

VIBRATION OR NOISE

1) Most probable causes are defective bearings and interference of moving parts with surrounding objects. Bearing failure is usually caused by poor lubrication or repeated abrupt stops and starts.

2) If lubrication to turbocharger is adaquate, check for an unbalanced or bent shaft. This may be due to excessive bearing wear or entry of foreign substances that have damaged turbine or compressor wheel.

LOW BOOST PRESSURE

1) Check for exhaust leaks and for restrictions in exhaust system. Check for air leaks on compressor discharge side. Check air cleaner element for restrictions.

2) Check for a wastegate or relief valve that is stuck open. If turbocharger shaft does not rotate smoothly when turned by hand, replace turbocharger assembly.

WHITE EXHAUST SMOKE

Inspect for oil from the turbocharger leaking into the intake or exhaust pipe. Check for clogged or deformed oil return pipe. If oil return pipe is good, oil seals in turbocharger are worn. Replace turbocharger.

REMOVAL & INSTALLATION

TURBOCHARGER

Removal

Remove air intake pipe and heat shield. Disengage exhaust pipe. Remove oil supply line. Disconnect oil return pipe. Remove turbocharger-to-intake manifold mounting nuts. Remove turbocharger. Ensure no foreign substances enter into the oil passage.

Installation

To install, reverse removal procedure. Before oil pipe flare nut is installed, pour clean engine oil into turbocharger. Use new gaskets. Tighten intake and exhaust mounting nuts to 37-50 ft. lbs. (49-68 N.m).

PEUGEOT 505 & 604 TURBO DIESELS

DESCRIPTION

The turbocharger used on turbodiesel models is mounted on the passenger side of the engine. Components include the turbine, compressor wheel, rotor shaft, bearings, and housing.

A wastegate valve prevents excessive boost pressure. Modifications made to the XD2 diesel engine to accept the turbocharger are as follows:

New intake and exhaust manifolds were designed. Cylinder heads have new valve seat material, brass valve guides, special swirl chambers and new head bolts. Oil spraying jets were added to cylinder block to help cool inner piston skirts. Crank pin diameter was increased by .19" (5 mm).

Connecting rod diameter on both ends was increased. Pistons have a new clover design in the crown and wrist pin diameter was increased by .07" (2 mm). An oil cooler and oil pump with increased output were also added.

Fig. 1: Peugeot Turbocharging System

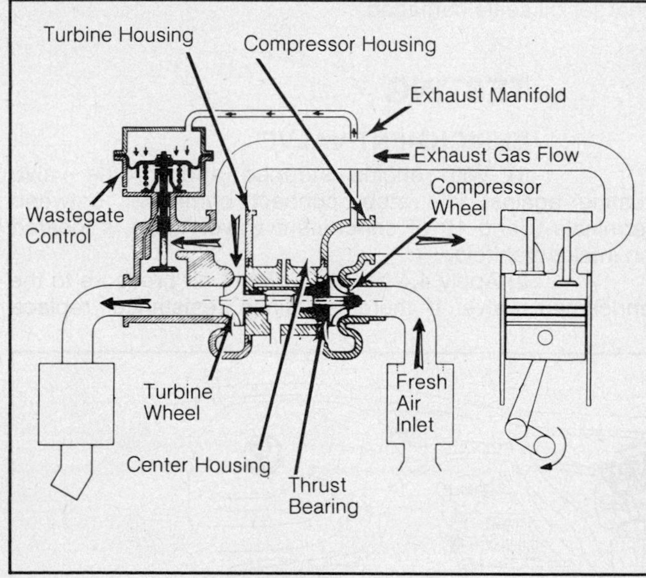
Turbine Housing
Compressor Housing
Exhaust Manifold
Exhaust Gas Flow
Compressor Wheel
Wastegate Control
Turbine Wheel
Fresh Air Inlet
Center Housing
Thrust Bearing

OPERATION

The turbocharger is driven by exhaust gases being expelled from the cylinder combustion chambers. At idle speeds there is no pressurization of incoming air and the engine operates like a normally aspirated engine. When the Peugeot diesel engine reaches approximately 1000 RPM, turbo boost begins with approximately 1.45 psi (.10 kg/cm²).

As engine RPM increases, turbo boost pressure increases, depending upon engine load. The greater the load, the higher the boost. Maximum boost pressure is approximately 8.7 psi (.61 kg/cm²). Turbine speed depends upon engine RPM and temperature. Higher temperatures create more exhaust gas pressure, resulting in higher turbine speeds.

As the cylinders receive their full capacity of incoming air, boost pressure opens the wastegate valve, diverting exhaust gases into the exhaust pipe away from the turbine. This lessens thrust on the turbine and slows it down.

TROUBLE SHOOTING

If the wastegate fails to open, it will create a high manifold pressure (up to 31 psi or 2.18 kg/cm²) at approximately 3500 RPM. This will cause the engine to misfire since compression pressure is now greater than injection pressure (22 psi or 1.55 kg/cm²).

If the wastegate valve fails to close, there will be a noticeable loss of power between 1000 and 2000 RPM, because boost pressure will not exist.

TESTING

NO LOAD PRESSURE TEST

1) Install a pressure gauge in hose between intake manifold and injector pump control unit. Accelerate engine to 3000 RPM.

2) Pressure gauge should indicate pressure just above idle speed, and read at least 5.8 psi (.40 kg/cm²) at speeds above 2000 RPM. Full load boost pressure cannot be measured in shop test without a dynamometer.

1983 Turbocharging Systems

RENAULT FUEGO TURBO

DESCRIPTION

The turbocharging system used on Renault Fuego Turbo consists of an air filter, airflow meter, turbocharger, air intake manifold chamber, air-to-air intercooler, ductwork, motor fan, and intercooler-to-throttle plate hose. A pressure gauge is located on the instrument panel. The turbocharger is fitted with a calibrated pressure check valve (wastegate) set at 13 psi (.91 kg/cm²).

The air-to-air intercooler is cooled by a fan. A saftey valve calibrated at 4.4 psi (.31 kg/cm²) controls the intercooler and is actuated by pressure from the aluminum ductwork. Pressure is delayed at the time of pressure increase and decrease by a pair of delay valves connected in series with the vacuum reservoir.

OPERATION

Air enters the air filter and proceeds through an air-flow meter. It is then compressed by an impeller and cooled by the heat exchanger before reaching the throttle body. Fuel is injected in each manifold runner and enters the air stream, just ahead of the intake valves.

The fuel-air mixture enters the cylinders through intake valves. Combustion gases leave through exhaust valves and travel through exhaust manifold to turn the impellers of the turbocharger.

The wastegate diverts the exhaust gas from the turbine directly to the exhaust system when a maximim boost of 13 psi (.91 kg/cm²) is reached. A knock sensor retards the ignition timing when the engine encounters spark knock.

TROUBLE SHOOTING

TURBO NOISE OR VIBRATION

Leaks in intake or exhaust system. Poor lubrication of turbocharger shaft. Turbocharger shaft out of balance, fins broken, penetration of foreign particles.

LACK OF ENGINE POWER

Clogged air filter. Leaks between turbocharger and cylinder head or between cylinder head and turbine. Exhaust system clogged. Pressure regulator not properly adjusted. Turbocharger shaft has tendancy to sieze.

TURBOCHARGING PRESSURE TOO HIGH

Pressure regulator feed line disconnected. Pressure regulator diaphragm ruptured. Pressure regulator valve siezed in closed position. Pressure regulator valve not properly adjusted.

BLUE SMOKE IN EXHAUST

Poor oil return flow from turbocharger. Turbocharger oil seals damaged.

TESTING

ENRICHMENT VALVE

1) With engine stopped and throttle valve resting against idle stop, connect ohmmeter between terminals 9 and 10 of enrichment valve. Valve is located on intake manifold.

2) Apply 4.4 psi (.31 kg/cm²) air pressure to the enrichment valve. If there is infinite resistance, replace

Fig. 1: Renault Fuego Turbocharging System

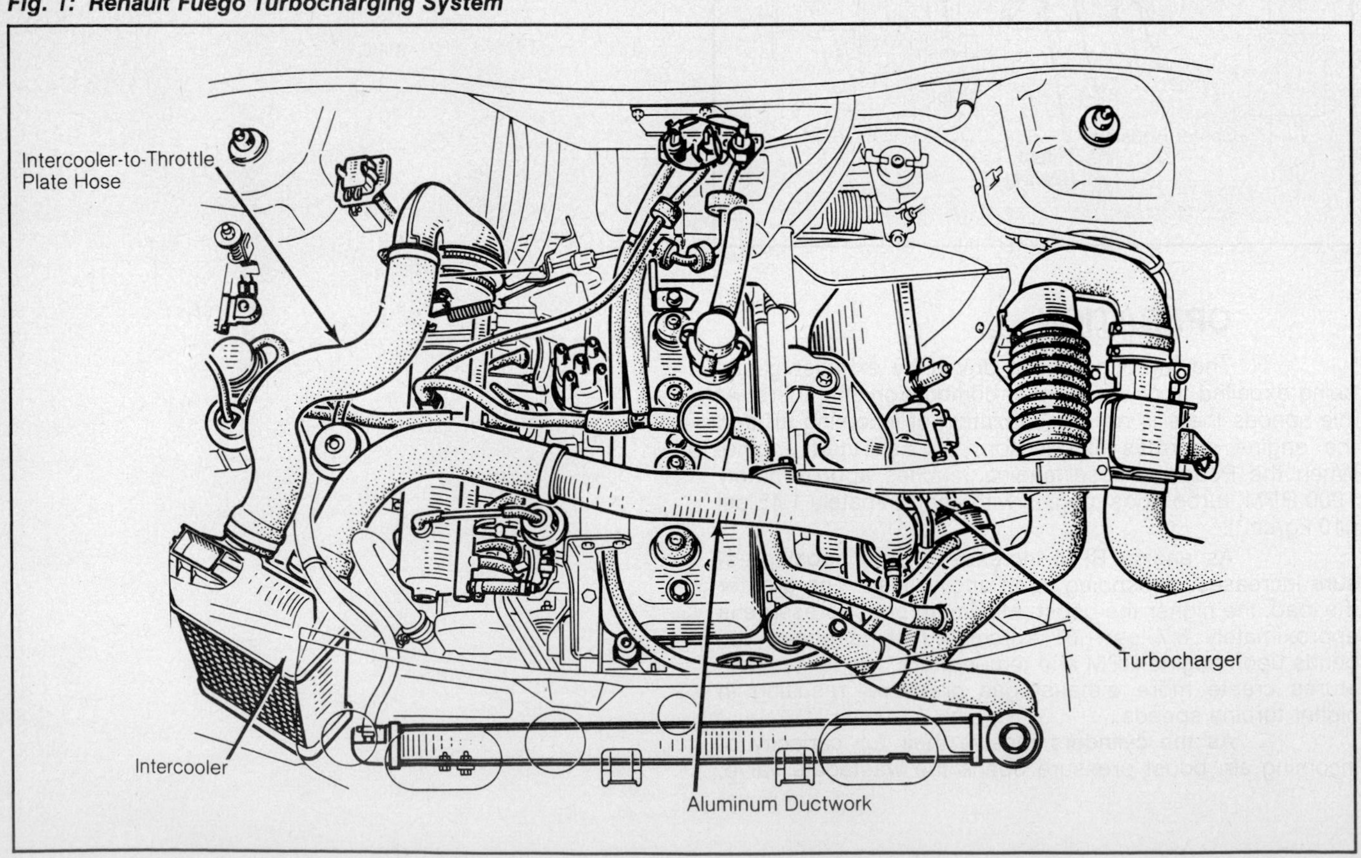
Intercooler-to-Throttle Plate Hose
Turbocharger
Intercooler
Aluminum Ductwork

RENAULT FUEGO TURBO (Cont.)

safety valve. If resistance is zero, check electrical circuit. If okay, replace enrichment valve.

DELAY VALVE

Visually inspect delay valve. It should be installed as shown in *Fig. 2.*

Fig. 2: Delay Valve Installation

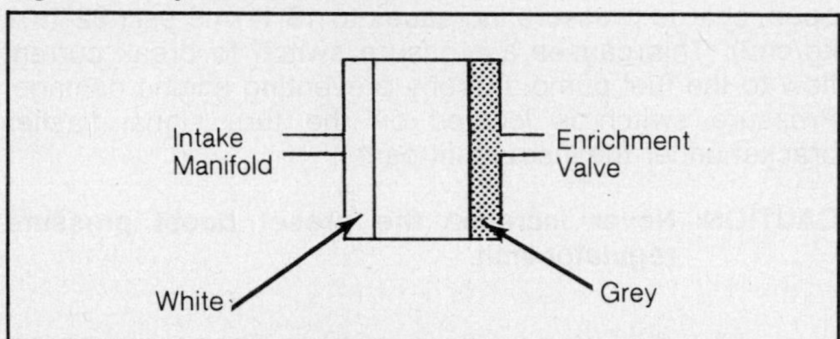

Intake
Manifold
Enrichment
Valve
White
Grey

ENRICHMENT VALVE CHECK

1) Visually inspect enrichment valve line on aluminum ductwork at turbo outlet. Line should have .012" (.30 mm) inside diameter. Apply 19 psi (1.34 kg/cm²) to enrichment valve. Accelerate engine.

2) Idle speed should drop to 2500 RPM or less. If not, apply 19 psi (1.34 kg/cm²) to enrichment valve and check resistance between enrichment valve terminals. If resistance is zero, replace enrichment valve. If resistance is infinite, check the electrical circuit for open circuit.

PRESSURE CHECK

1) Mount a magnetically supported dial indicator on the upper portion of wastegate lever arm. Connect air pump (MS 554-03) at the pressure regulator inlet and insert a manometer (0-29 psi or 0-2 kg/cm²) or special pressure gauge (Mot. 867).

Fig. 3: Installation for Pressure Check

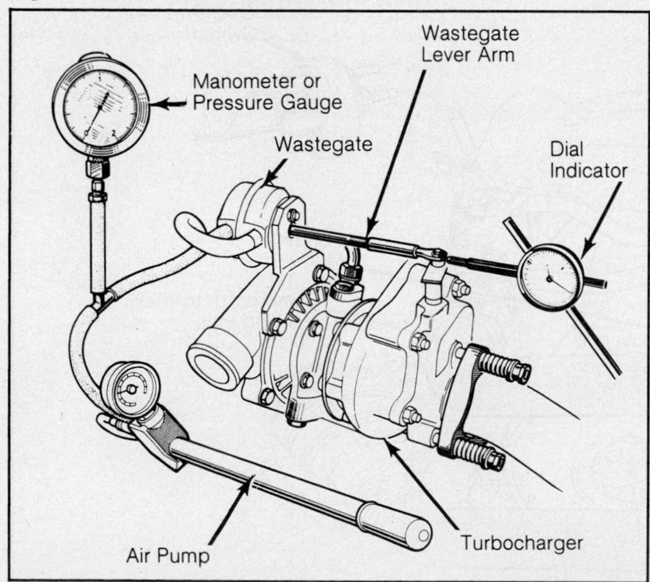

Wastegate
Lever Arm
Manometer or
Pressure Gauge
Wastegate
Dial
Indicator
Air Pump
Turbocharger

Dial indicator should read .015" (.38 mm) at 12.7 psi (.89 kg/cm²).

2) At standing position, set dial indicator at zero. Using air pump, force air into the pressure regulator until dial indicator reaches .015" (.38 mm). Manometer reading should then be 12.7 psi (.89 kg/cm²).

REMOVAL & INSTALLATION

TURBOCHARGER

Removal

1) Remove hose, aluminum ducts and heat shields from turbocharger. Free heating ducts and vacuum hose. Disconnect turbocharger from catalytic converter after removal of oxygen sensor.

2) Disconnect upper retainers from heat shield. Disconnect turbocharger oil inlet and outlet lines. Disconnect EGR hose and loosen retainers at front of the engine.

3) Disconnect turbocharger at the lower support bracket. Remove turbocharger and exhaust manifold as an assembly. Separate exhaust manifold from turbocharger.

NOTE: **Never handle or grab turbocharger at wastegate linkage. This could damage capsule diaphragm.**

Installation

1) Assemble exhaust manifold to turbocharger on the bench. Make sure all mating surfaces are clean and properly aligned. Use new self-locking screws if necessary. Replace oil inlet and outlet line gaskets.

2) Replace gasket between turbocharger and catalytic converter. Lubricate EGR line nut (MIL-A-907 B specification). To complete installation, reverse removal procedure.

3) Before attaching oil inlet line, squirt one squirt of oil into oil inlet opening. Bleed air from oil line by cranking engine while ignition is disconnected. Attach oil line to turbocharger.

NOTE: **Engine must never be cranked or allowed to run with air intake disconnected.**

AIR-TO-AIR INTERCOOLER

Removal & Installation

Remove screw securing tab. Disconnect hoses at exchanger. Unplug electrical connections between intercooler and motor fan. Pull out intercooler. To install, reverse removal procedure.

1983 Turbocharging Systems

SAAB 900 TURBO

DESCRIPTION

The Saab 900 Turbo uses the Garret Turbocharger. *See Fig. 1* Exhaust gases drive the turbine, which turns the compressor forwarding air under pressure to the throttle valve.

Excessive pressures are controlled by a boost pressure control valve or wastegate. A back-up safety device, a pressure switch, prevents engine damage in case there is failure of the wastegate. Additional engine protection is provided by the Automatic Performance Control (APC) system. The APC system senses engine knock and automatically cuts back the amount of turbo boost.

The Saab 900 Turbo is designed to operate at low engine speeds to provide increased torque at typical vehicle driving speeds. The turbine shaft is mounted in a floating, sliding-contact bearing having a high oil flow. The shaft actually floats on oil during operation.

Lubrication is supplied by the engine lubrication system. The shaft is sealed against bearing housings with sealing rings installed in shaft grooves.

OPERATION

As engine operation begins, exhaust gases flow through the turbocharger's turbine impeller, causing it to rotate. Gases are expelled through the turbine to the exhaust pipe. As the turbine spins, its shaft turns the compressor impeller, compressing the intake air.

At idle speeds the air compression has little effect upon its operation. However, as engine speed is increased (partial load), the pressurized air enters the system faster, and exhaust gases are expelled faster. The more exhaust gases passing over the turbine impeller, the faster it turns, and the more pressurized air is delivered to the engine.

At full load, the throttle valve is fully open and charge pressure increases. At 8.7-10.1 psi (.61-.71 kg/cm²), the valve in the charge pressure regulator opens permitting exhaust gases to flow directly to the exhaust pipe, bypassing the turbine impeller.

In the event the valve sticks and does not open, charge pressure increases to 13.1-14.5 psi (.92-1.02 kg/cm²). This causes a pressure switch to break current flow to the fuel pump, thereby preventing engine damage. Pressure switch is located on the turn signal flasher bracket under the instrument panel.

CAUTION: Never increase the preset boost pressure regulator limit.

TESTING

BOOST PRESSURE REGULATOR

1) Connect an air pressure gauge (83 92 813) between nipple on intake manifold and line to pressure switch. Run hose into passenger compartment and place gauge on left hand corner of instrument panel.

2) Warm up engine. On manual transmission, drive vehicle in 3rd gear at an engine speed lower than 1500 RPM. On automatic transmission, place gear selector in position "1" at engine speed lower than 1500 RPM.

3) On all models, accelerate at full throttle by pressing pedal to the floor. As engine speed approaches 3000 RPM, apply brakes while still keeping accelerator pedal pressed down.

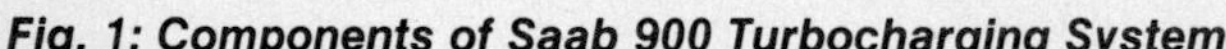

Fig. 1: Components of Saab 900 Turbocharging System

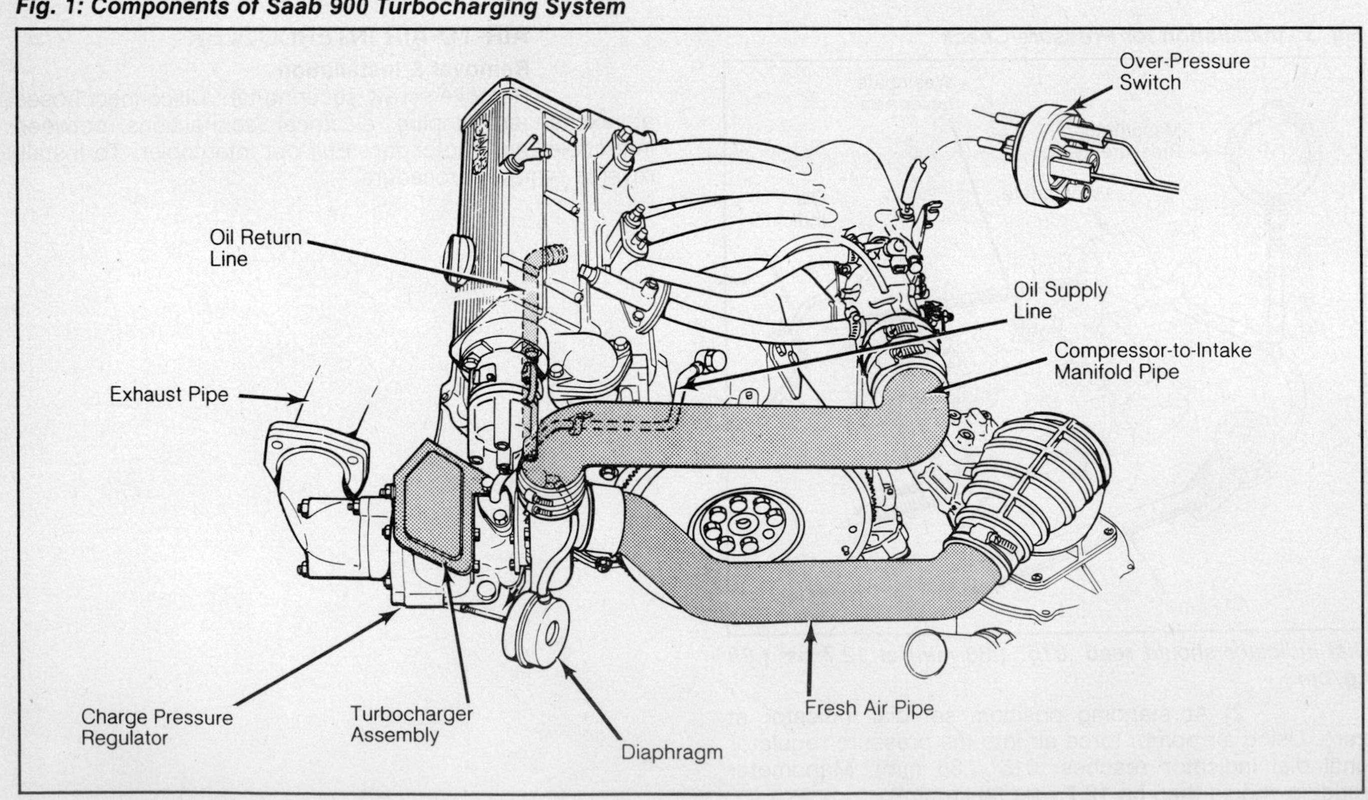
Over-Pressure Switch
Oil Return Line
Oil Supply Line
Compressor-to-Intake Manifold Pipe
Exhaust Pipe
Charge Pressure Regulator
Turbocharger Assembly
Diaphragm
Fresh Air Pipe

SAAB 900 TURBO (Cont.)

4) Note maximum pressure indicated with vehicle under full load at 3000 RPM. Charge pressure should be 6.7-7.8 psi (.46-.54 kg/cm²). Adjust boost pressure if necessary.

PRESSURE SWITCH

1) Start engine and run at idle. Disconnect hose from pressure switch at intake manifold. Connect pressure gauge and pump (cooling system tester) to pressure switch hose.

2) Increase pressure with pump and check pressure at which engine cuts out. Reading should be 13.1-14.5 psi (.92-1.02 kg/cm²). If not, replace pressure switch.

TURBO PRESSURE GAUGE

To check the pressure gauge on the instrument panel, use the same procedure as for the pressure switch. At maximum charge pressure, the needle should be within the wide Orange range. At pressure switch actuating pressure, the needle should be in front of the limit between the Orange and Red zones. If not, replace gauge.

ADJUSTMENTS

BOOST PRESSURE

To adjust boost pressure, remove wire seal and circlip from charger regulator control arm and detach diaphragm lever. Loosen lock nut on lever and rotate lever end in appropriate direction. *See Charge Pressure Adjustment* chart.

Fig. 2: Adjusting Charge Pressure Regulator

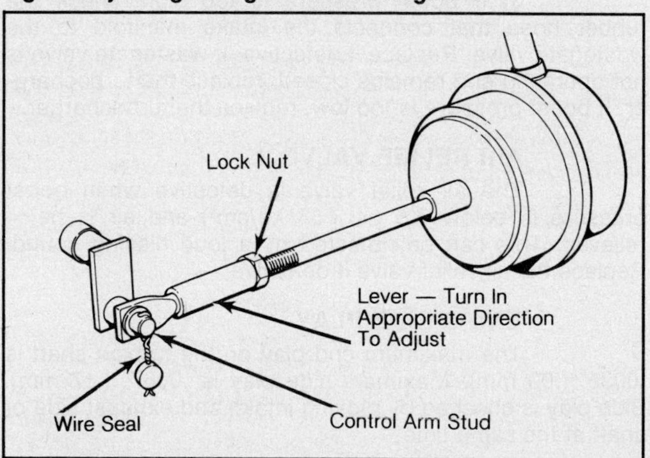
Lock Nut
Lever — Turn In Appropriate Direction To Adjust
Wire Seal
Control Arm Stud

CHARGE PRESSURE ADJUSTMENT

Gauge Reading While Driving – psi (kg/cm²)	Rotate Lever
5.51 (.38)	3 Clockwise
5.84 (.40)	2.5 Clockwise
6.13 (.42)	2 Clockwise
6.42 (.44)	1.5 Clockwise
6.72-8.03 (.46-.55)	Correct Setting
8.17 (.56)	1.5 Counterclockwise
8.47 (.58)	2 Counterclockwise
8.76 (.60)	2.5 Counterclockwise
9.05 (.62)	3 Counterclockwise

REMOVAL & INSTALLATION

TURBOCHARGER

Removal

1) Disconnect battery cables. Remove air intake and pressure connections from compressor. Loosen pre-heating hose. Remove exhaust elbow between exhaust manifold and compressor.

2) Disconnect oil supply and return lines at turbocharger. Remove bolts securing turbocharger to exhaust manifold and remove turbocharger. Plug all holes in turbocharger.

Installation

1) Attach turbocharger to intake manifold, using new gasket. Attach oil return pipe to turbocharger, using new gasket.

2) Fill oil feed channel with engine oil and attach oil pressure pipe, using new gasket. Install exhaust elbow and exhaust manifold. Install air intake and pressure connections to compressor.

CAUTION: On Hall Effect ignition systems, disconnect wiring from control unit before cranking.

3) Crank starter for approximately 30 seconds so turbocharger is primed with oil before engine operation.

1983 Turbocharging Systems

SUBARU 1800 TURBO

DESCRIPTION

The Subaru turbocharging system is designed to be effective at low engine speed with larger torque for enhancing both fuel efficiency and power output. To prevent knocking and heavier thermal loads on the engine, the turbocharger has been equipped with a wastegate which diverts exhaust gases to reduce maximum boost pressure.

An additional safety device, the air relief valve, is mounted on the intake manifold. This device will disharge excessive boost pressure to the atmosphere if the wastegate fails.

Fig. 1: Subaru Turbocharging System

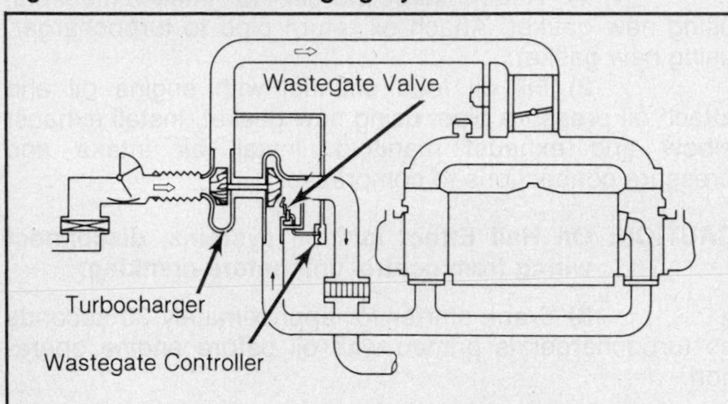
Wastegate Valve
Turbocharger
Wastegate Controller

OPERATION

The turbine impeller of the turbocharger is driven by the exhaust gases expelled from the cylinder combustion chambers. At idle speeds the engine operates like a normally aspirated engine.

As engine speed increases with opening of the throttle valve, the amount of exhaust gas increases. This leads to an increase in the rotational speed of the turbine. Turbine speed may increase to approximately 130,000 RPM.

The turbocharger is equipped with a wastegate to prevent engine damage from excessive boost pressure. Below 6.4 psi (.45 kg/cm²) the wastegate valve is closed so all exhaust gas is directed through the turbine. At the specified pressure, the wastegate diverts exhaust gases around the turbine. The wastegate valve controller diaphragm is operated by an air pressure signal from the intake manifold. The air relief valve is designed to relieve air pressure at 7.5 psi (.53 kg/cm²).

The turbocharger is lubricated by engine oil from the oil pump. Full floating type bearings are used to form desirable lubrication films on bearing surfaces during operation. Lubricating oil is also essential in cooling the turobcharger to prevent bearing failure.

No provision has been made for turbocharger disassembly or adjustment. Replace turbocharger if found to be defective.

TROUBLE SHOOTING

HIGH BOOST PRESSURE

If turbocharger fails, excessive boost pressures can cause engine knock and overheating. Also, air will intermittently be expelled from air relief valve.

LOW BOOST PRESSURE

Excessively low boost pressure can cause the following: Lack of power, poor acceleration, and increased fuel consumption. Also check for leaks in the intake and exhaust system.

OIL LEAKS

1) Worn turbocharger oil seals can cause excessive oil consumption and white smoke from the exhaust. Remove center exhaust pipe and examine the turbocharger from the exhaust side. If there is excessive carbon deposits on the turbine exhaust side, oil is leaking from the turbine.

2) The turbocharger is not necessarily leaking oil when oil is present on the blower side. Oil most likely has come from oil mists contained in blow-by gases present in the intake system.

3) Oil leaks on the intake side are accompanied by a rattle from the turbine shaft. Remove the turbocharger and check the end and side play.

TESTING

BOOST PRESSURE

1) Engine must be at normal operating temperature. Disconnect line from wastegate valve controller. Using a "T" fitting, connect an air pressure gauge. Use enough line so that gauge may be carried inside passenger compartment.

2) Boost pressure should be checked at 2400 RPM with a wide open throttle. Normal pressure is 6.4-7.5 psi (.45-.53 kg/cm²). Air relief valve should not be leaking air during test.

3) If boost pressure is too high, check the rubber hose that connects the intake manifold to the wastegate valve. Replace if defective. If wastegate valve is not operating and remains closed, replace the turbocharger. If boost pressure is too low, replace the turbocharger.

AIR RELIEF VALVE

The air relief valve is defective when boost pressure is below 7.5 psi (.53 kg/cm²) and air is being relieved. This can be detected by a loud hissing sound. Replace the air relief valve if defective.

END & SIDE PLAY

The maximum end play on the turbine shaft is .0035" (.09 mm). Maximum side play is .0067" (.17 mm). Side play is checked by moving intake and exhaust side of shaft at the same time.

VOLVO TURBO

DESCRIPTION

The Volvo Turbo uses a B21F engine equipped with an exhaust driven turbo-compressor. The turbocharger is mounted on the passenger side of the engine. Components include the turbine, compressor wheel, rotor shaft, bearings, housing, and wastegate. In addition, a pressure regulator, pressure switch, overload protection switch, and a turbo warning light on the instrument panel are connected into the system.

Engine modifications made to the B21F engine to accept the turbocharger are as follows: Pistons have increased clearance in the bore to withstand the high temperatures generated by the turbocharger. Compression ratio has been lowered to offset some of the increased charge provided by the compressor.

Exhaust valves are stellite-coated and sodium-cooled to resist high temperatures. An engine oil cooler located at the side of the radiator has an integral thermostat. The air/fuel control unit on engines equipped with the Continuous Injection System is the same as the 6-cylinder engine model, with 2 of the fuel outlets plugged.

OPERATION

The turbine wheel is driven by exhaust gases. A shaft connects the turbine wheel with the compressor wheel. As exhaust gas flow increases with engine speed, the turbine speed increases and consequently compressor discharge increases.

Turbo compressor wheels rotate at a very high speed, requiring the shaft assembly to be carefully balanced. The shaft is supported by bearings using pressurized oil for lubrication. The shaft seals are a piston ring type.

The turbocharger is connected to the standard engine oiling system. Oil supply and pressure must be sufficient to prevent shaft bearing failure. The turbo compressor is designed to provide a relatively high discharge pressure at middle range RPM. In order to prevent excessive pressure at high speeds, several controlling and regulating devices are required.

PRESSURE REGULATOR & WASTEGATE ACTUATOR

This device monitors discharge pressure from compressor. When pressure reaches 6 psi (.42 kg/cm²), regulator begins to open wastegate. As pressure increases, the regulator gradually increases wastegate opening. A control rod stroke of approximately 3/8" (10 mm) is achieved just before maximum pressure switch cuts out fuel pump relay.

ENRICHMENT PRESSURE SWITCH

A pressure switch, located on the firewall, receives compressor pressure from a fitting on intake manifold. It will close when pressure reaches 2.9 psi (.20 kg/cm²). When it closes, it grounds terminal 7 of the Lambda sond electronic control unit. This will cause Lambda system to operate on a special fixed cycle of 58.5°, allowing for fuel enrichment upon acceleration.

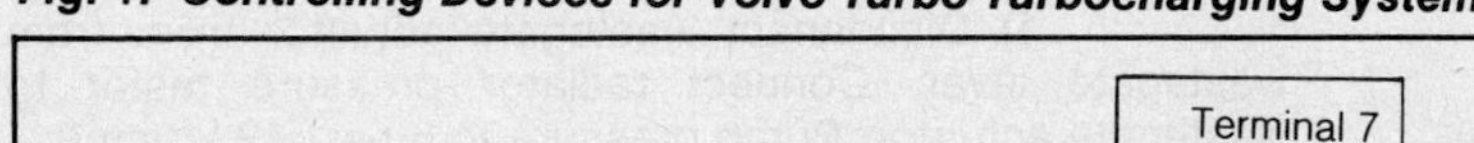
Terminal 7
Fuel Pump Relay
Turbo Pressure Warning Light
Lambda Electronic Control Unit
Overload Protection Switch
Pressure Switch For Enrichment At Acceleration
Ground
Turbo Pressure Gauge
Vacuum Pressure Unit

Fig. 1: Controlling Devices for Volvo Turbo Turbocharging System

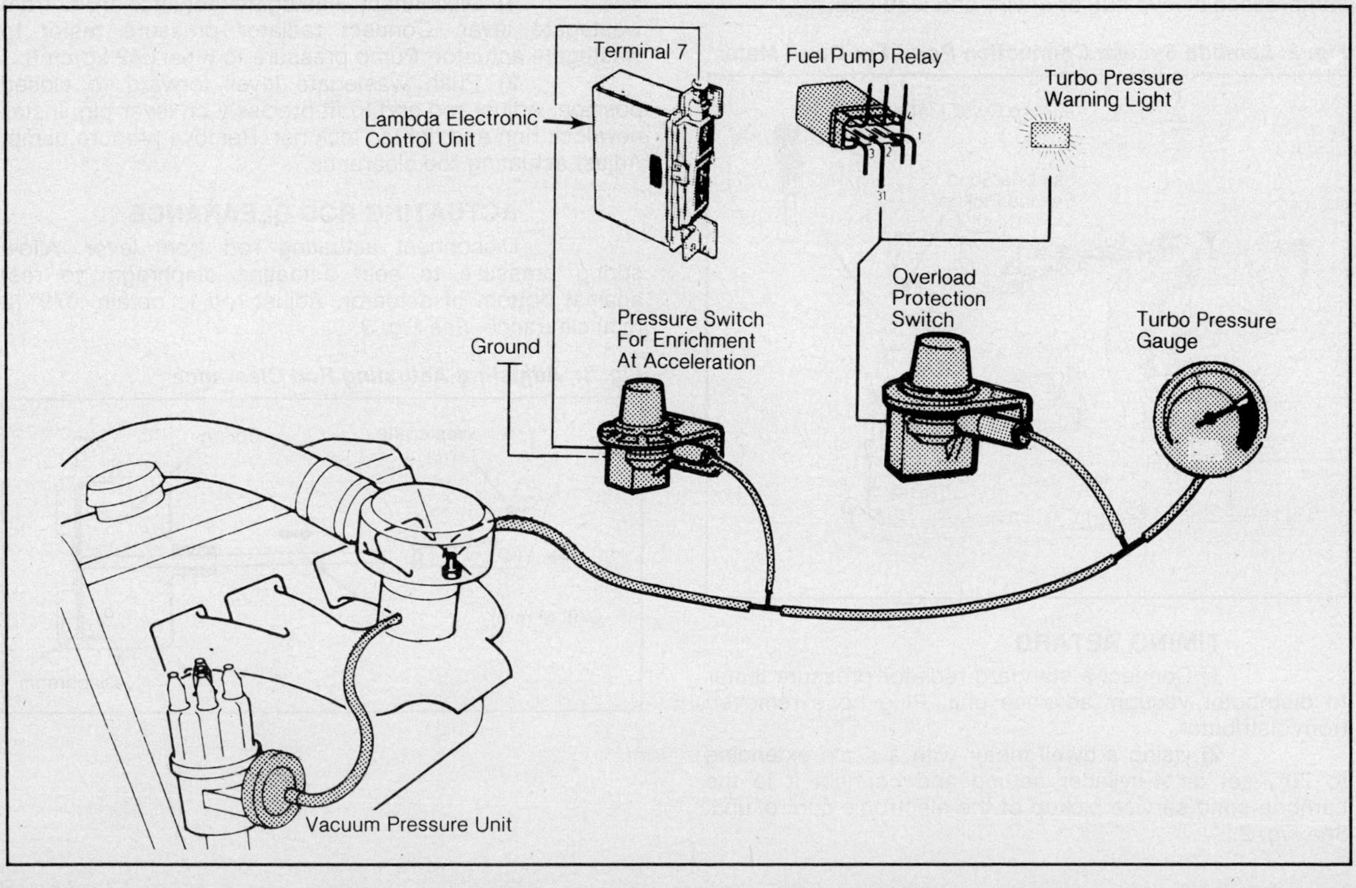

VOLVO TURBO (Cont.)

OVERLOAD PROTECTION SWITCH

Excessive compressor pressures may damage engine by inducing an overload, and are normally prevented by pressure sensor and wastegate actuator. In case of failure of that system, a second overload protection switch is activated.

The switch receives pressure input from the intake manifold. When pressure reaches 10 psi (.70 kg/cm²) the pressure switch will open a ground circuit for fuel pump relay, momentarily stopping fuel pump flow, resulting in a reduced compressor pressure.

PRESSURE CONTROL OF SPARK TIMING

The distributor centrifugal advance mechanism provides a spark timing which is too advanced when turbocharger is operating at high load. To counteract this, the distributor vacuum advance unit has a double function.

Under normal operating conditions it can advance the spark by a maximum 15°. At high pressures it retards the spark timing by a maximum 8°, when compressor pressure reaches 5 psi (.35 kg/cm²).

TESTING

COMPONENT CHECK

1) Ensure exhaust pipe-to-turbocharger nuts are properly tightened and no leaks exist between pipe and turbocharger. Nuts should be tightened to 16-18 ft. lbs. (22-25 N.m).

2) Ensure seal on control rod from pressure regulator to wastegate actuator is intact. Seal is either a compressed sleeve nut, or a wire and lead seal.

Fig. 2: Lambda System Connection Point For Dwell Meter

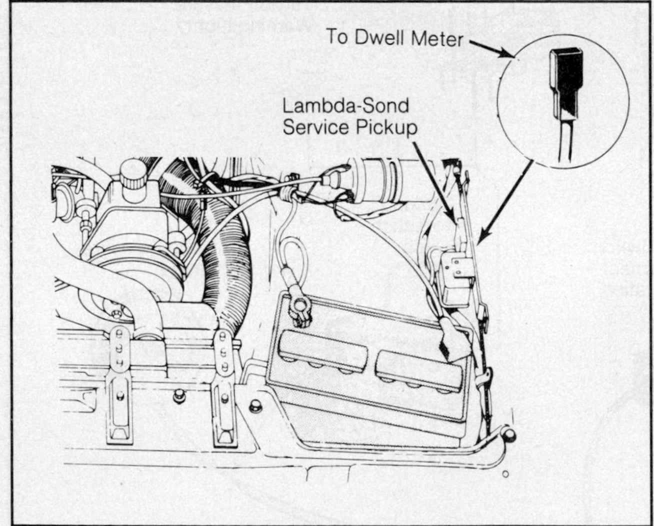

To Dwell Meter
Lambda-Sond
Service Pickup

TIMING RETARD

1) Connect a standard radiator pressure tester to distributor vacuum advance unit. Plug hose removed from distributor.

2) Using a dwell meter with a scale extending to 70°, set on 4-cylinder setting and connect it to the Lambda sond service pickup of the electronic control unit. *See Fig. 2.*

3) Start engine. Note ignition timing at idle. Pump pressure tester up to 5.1 psi (.35 kg/cm²). Ignition timing should retard 6-10°. If not, check distributor and replace vacuum advance unit, if required.

FULL LOAD ENRICHMENT SYSTEM

1) Connect standard radiator pressure tester in-line between intake manifold and pressure switch on firewall. Connect dwell meter to Lambda sond service pick-up on electronic control unit.

2) With engine running, pump up air pressure until dwell meter display reads a steady 56.0°-61.0°. Air pressure reading at this point should be 2.9 psi (.20 kg/cm²). If reading is not to specification, replace pressure switch and re-check system.

OVERLOAD PROTECTION SWITCH

With pressure tester, gauge, and dwell meter connected as in *Full Load Enrichment System* test, pump tester up until engine stalls. Air pressure reading should be 10 psi (.70 kg/cm²). At same time, air pressure indicator on instrument panel should move to red zone and red "Turbo" warning light on instrument cluster should light. If not, replace overload protection switch.

ADJUSTMENTS

BOOST PRESSURE

NOTE: **Discharge pressure and actuating rod clearance must be adjusted after replacing wastegate actuator.**

1) Disconnect wastegate actuator from from wastegate lever. Connect radiator pressure tester to wastegate actuator. Pump pressure to 6 psi (.42 kg/cm²).

2) Push wastegate lever forward to closed position. Adjust rod end to fit precisely on lever pin. Install new lock ring and tighten lock nut. Remove presure pump. Adjust actuating rod clearance.

ACTUATING ROD CLEARANCE

Disconnect actuating rod from lever. Allow spring pressure to seat actuating diaphragm to rest against bottom of actuator. Adjust rod to obtain .079" (2 mm) clearance. *See Fig. 3.*

Fig. 3: Adjusting Actuating Rod Clearance

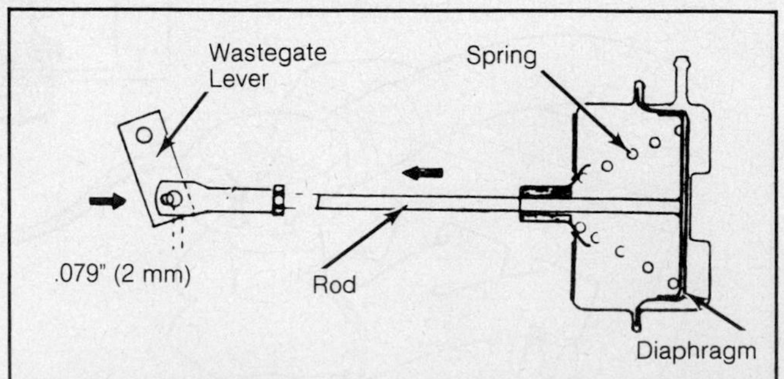

Wastegate
Lever
Spring
.079" (2 mm)
Rod
Diaphragm

VOLVO 760 GLE TURBO DIESEL

DESCRIPTION

The Volvo GLE Turbo Diesel uses a D24T engine equipped with an exhaust driven turbo-compressor. The turbocharger is mounted on the right side of the engine. Components include the turbine, compressor wheel, rotor shaft, bearings, housing, and wastegate. In addition, a blow-off valve and a turbo warning light on the instrument panel are connected into the system.

OPERATION

The turbine wheel is driven by exhaust gases. A shaft connects the turbine wheel with the compressor wheel. As exhaust gas flow increases with engine speed, the turbine speed increases and consequently compressor discharge increases.

Turbo compressor wheels rotate at a very high speed, requiring the shaft assembly to be carefully balanced. The shaft is supported by bearings using pressurized oil for lubrication. The shaft seals are a piston ring type.

The turbocharger is connected to the standard engine oiling system. Oil supply and pressure must be sufficient to prevent shaft bearing failure. The turbo compressor is designed to provide a relatively high discharge pressure at middle range RPM. To prevent excessive pressure at high speeds, several controlling and regulating devices are required.

The wastegate actuator monitors discharge pressure from compressor. When pressure reaches 10 psi (.70 kg/cm²), actuator begins to open wastegate. As pressure increases, the regulator gradually increases wastegate opening.

Excessive compressor pressures may damage engine by inducing an overload, and are normally prevented by wastegate actuator. In case of failure of that system, a blow-off valve mounted on the end of the intake manifold is activated. Blow-off valve will open when pressure reaches 11.4-12.1 psi (.80-.85 kg/cm²).

TROUBLE SHOOTING

NOTE: Replace turbocharger if it is defective.

LOW BOOST PRESSURE

1) Check for clogged air filter. Inspect for leakage between compressor housing and cylinder head or between turbine housing and cylinder head. Inspect engine for low compression, incorrect valve clearance, or not enough fuel supply.

2) Check for wastegate stuck open. Check for clogged exhaust system or faulty turbocharger.

HIGH BOOST PRESSURE

Leakage from hose between compressor housing and wastegate actuator. Wastegate actuator diaphragm damaged. Wastegate valve stuck in closed position.

ENGINE KNOCK

Cetane number of fuel too low. Incorrect injection timing. Boost pressure too high.

NOISE OR VIBRATION

Preheater plates loose or cracked. Leakage from intake or exhaust system. Poor turbocharger lubrication. Imbalance in turbocharger shaft, turbine or compressor wheel because of damage.

OIL LEAKS

Oil leakage on intake side from clogged air filter. Exhaust system loose or leaking. Excessive crankcase pressure. Oil return line blocked. Turbocharger shaft seals worn.

TESTING

PRELIMINARY CHECKS

1) Bring engine to normal operating temperature. Turn off engine. Turbocharger turbine shaft will normally stop later than engine. If not, remove intake hose from compressor housing.

2) Check compressor wheel rotates freely. Side and end play should be within specification. Ensure compressor wheel does not scrape against compressor housing when wheel is pushed radially or axially.

BOOST PRESSURE

1) Connect air pressure gauge in-line between fuel limiter and intake manifold hose. Use a "T" fitting and enough hose so gauge may be carried in passenger compartment.

2) Engine must be normal operating temperature. On manual transmission, drive in 3rd gear at approximately 1500 RPM. On automatic transmission, place selector in position "2".

3) Press accelerator pedal to floor. On automatic transmission, do not engage kickdown. Bring engine speeed to 3000 RPM with accelerator depressed. Maximum boost pressure should be 10-11 psi (.70-.77 kg/cm²).

BLOW-OFF VALVE

1) Unplug electrical connector from blow-off valve. Place jumper wire across connector terminals. Turn ignition on and check that warning lamp in instrument panel lights. If not, repair electrical circuit.

2) Plug in connector on blow-off valve. Using a pair of vise grip pliers, clamp hose between compressor housing and wastegate actuator.

CAUTION: Engine must not be raced when pliers are installed on hose. Engine damage may result.

3) On manual transmission, drive in 3rd gear. On automatic transmission, place selector in position "2". On both models, apply throttle carefully to approximately 3000 RPM while applying brakes.

4) Warning lamp should light and blow-off valve should open when pressure gauge indicates 11.4-12.1 psi (.80-.85 kg/cm²). Do not exceed this boost pressure. Remove pliers immediately after test.

END & SIDE PLAY

Maximum end and side play is .020" (.5 mm). Replace turbocharger if worn beyond limits.

VOLVO 760 GLE TURBO DIESEL (Cont.)

REMOVAL & INSTALLATION

TURBOCHARGER

Removal

1) Remove negative battery cable, intake hose from turbocharger pipe, air cleaner, and preheater hose. Remove snap ring from turbocharger intake pipe. Remove compressor intake pipe and plug hole immediately.

2) Remove hose to blow-off valve. Remove oil return pipe mounts and move pipe aside. Plug pipe opening. Remove oil supply pipe. Disengage exhaust pipe from turbocharger.

3) Raise and support vehicle. Remove exhaust pipe-to-transmission support bracket. Remove turbocharger mounting nuts and lift off turbocharger.

Installation

To install, reverse removal procedure. Use new "O" ring on compressor-to-intake manifold pipe. Use new turbocharger-to-manifold mounting nuts. Tighten to 44 ft. lbs. (60 N.m).

OVERHAUL

TURBOCHARGER

Disassembly

1) Remove turbocharger as previously described. Remove air pressure and oil by-pass hoses from compressor housing. Mark position of compressor housing relative to turbine. Separate compressor housing from turbine. DO NOT damage compressor wheel.

2) Mark position of turbine relative to turbine housing. Separate turbine from housing. Do not damage turbine wheel. Remove wastegate chamber cover. Remove gasket.

Cleaning & Inspection

1) Clean and check all parts for cracks, damage, wear, smooth mating surfaces, or blockages in oil or air channels. Ensure wastegate valve contact surfaces are not burnt. If valve is burnt, turbine housing must be replaced.

2) Check turbine wheel and bearing for damage or wear. Check end and side play. If defective, turbine assembly is replaced as an assembly.

3) Connect an air supply and air pressure gauge to the thick hose on the wastegate actuator. Plug off the thin hose. Slowly increase pressure. At 10.8-12 psi (.76-.84 kg/cm²) the valve should open .047-.051" (1.2-1.3 mm). If valve does not open as specified, replace wastegate actuator and housing.

Reassembly

1) Use new gaskets for reassembly. If installing new compressor housing, transfer nipple and plug. Coat threads with sealing compound (116 1035-9). Align identification marks made on disassembly and install turbine and compressor housing on turbine assembly.

2) Tighten turbine housing bolts to 15 ft. lbs. (20 N.m) and compressor housing bolts to 13 ft. lbs. (18 N.m). Install wastegate chamber cover with round bevel (raised portion) turned toward the valve. Use new lock washers and tighten nuts to 7 ft. lbs. (10 N.m). Install oil by-pass and pressure hoses.

BOSCH

Audi, BMW, Porsche, Renault, Saab, Volkswagen, Volvo

DESCRIPTION

Bosch electric fuel pumps are 12 volt, positive displacement roller cell type. Operating pressure is determined by one or more external fuel pressure regulators in the engine compartment. Fuel pumps include an external replaceable discharge check valve, to prevent fuel from returning to the tank when pump is turned off. Some pumps may also incorporate a damper chamber on the outlet, to prevent pulsations in the fuel lines.

Fig. 1: View of Bosch Electric Fuel Pump

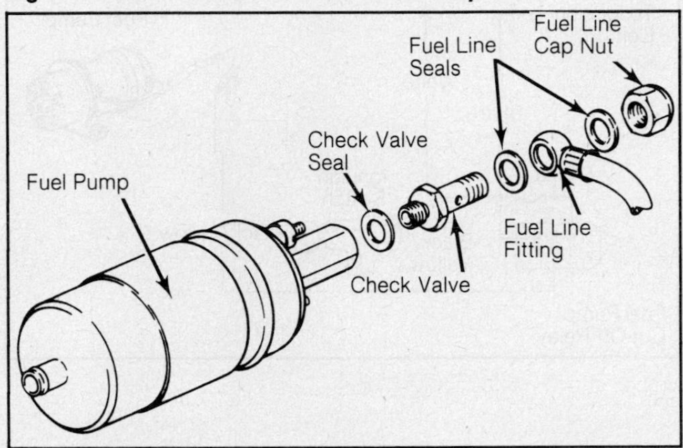
Fuel Line
Cap Nut
Fuel Line
Seals
Check Valve
Seal
Fuel Pump
Fuel Line
Fitting
Check Valve

OPERATION

Fuel pumps are actuated by relays when ignition switch is in "Start" or "Run" position, and are protected from circuit overload by fuses and/or fusible links. Fuel is circulated through pump rotor and brushes to the fuel outlet. Pumps are not serviceable and should be replaced when not operating properly. For fuel pump test procedures, see appropriate Fuel Injection article in this section.

REMOVAL & INSTALLATION

Removal

1) Fuel pressure must be relieved prior to any component removal. Carefully remove and plug fuel lines to prevent spillage. Disconnect electrical connections.

NOTE: Do not allow smoking, open flame or sparks in area while servicing fuel system components. Disconnect battery ground terminal prior to removing pump.

2) Remove mounting bolts and retain rubber insulating grommets for reinstallation. Rotate fuel pump as required to clear chassis and remove from vehicle.

Installation

1) Be sure rubber grommets and insulation are installed correctly or noise and vibration will result.

2) Hook all fuel lines and return lines to proper fittings, and be sure they are tight to avoid air and/or fuel leaks.

3) Route fuel lines so they will not vibrate or rub against other body parts. Test system for leaks with engine running.

HONDA

Accord, Civic, & Prelude

DESCRIPTION & OPERATION

A solid state relay senses negative pulsations at the ignition coil and switches the pump on when the engine is running or the starter is engaged. Relay is located under dash panel at the left side of driver's compartment. Circuit is protected by a fuse in the fuse box as well an in-line fuse.

The electric fuel pump is located at the left rear corner of vehicle on Accord models. On Civic hatchback and sedan models it is located on the left side of the fuel tank.

On Civic wagon models it is located above the right rear corner of the fuel tank. On Prelude models the fuel pump is at the left corner of fuel tank. Fuel pump is a sealed unit and is serviceable as an assembly.

TESTING

CUT-OFF RELAY

1) Remove fuse box panel mounting bolt and nut. Pull down panel and remove fuel pump cut-off relay. Turn ignition switch on. Connect positive probe of voltmeter to Black/Yellow wire terminal of fuel pump cut-off relay connector. If no voltage, check fuse and continuity of Black/Yellow wire.

2) If voltage is present, check Blue wire at cut-off relay for battery voltage. If Blue wire does not show battery voltage, check for continuity between connector and negative side of coil.

3) Turn ignition switch off. Attach jumper wire between the 2 Black/Yellow wires of connector. Turn ignition switch on.

1983 Electric Fuel Pumps

HONDA (Cont.)

4) If fuel pressure is now available and battery voltage was present at Blue wire, replace the cut-off relay. If no pressure is available, unplug fuel pump leads at pump.

5) Attach positive lead of voltmeter to Black-/Yellow wire and negative lead to Black wire. Battery voltage should be present with ignition on. If not, check continuity of Black/Yellow wire from relay and Black wire to ground.

FUEL PUMP

1) Attach jumper wire between 2 Black/Yellow wires in fuel pump cut-off relay connector. Disconnect fuel hose to carburetor and cap T-fitting. Install pressure gauge to fuel hose. Turn ignition switch on and check for normal pressure of 2-3 psi (.14-.21 kg/cm²).

2) Remove pressure gauge and hold measuring cup under fuel hose. Turn ignition switch on. Measure amount of fuel flow in 60 seconds with 10 volts minimum battery voltage. Flow should be as indicated in *Fuel Flow Specifications* chart. If not, replace fuel pump.

FUEL FLOW SPECIFICATIONS

Application	Volume oz./min. (cc/min.)
Accord	15 (450)
Civic	17 (480)
Prelude	23 (680)

REMOVAL & INSTALLATION

FUEL PUMP

Removal & Installation

1) Raise and support vehicle. On Accord and Prelude models, remove the left rear wheel. On all models, unplug electrical leads at fuel pump and clamp fuel lines between pump and tank.

2) Remove fuel pump cover bolts. Lift off cover and pump as an assembly. Disassemble pump from cover. To install, reverse removal procedure.

Fig. 1: Fuel Pump Electrical Circuit & Components

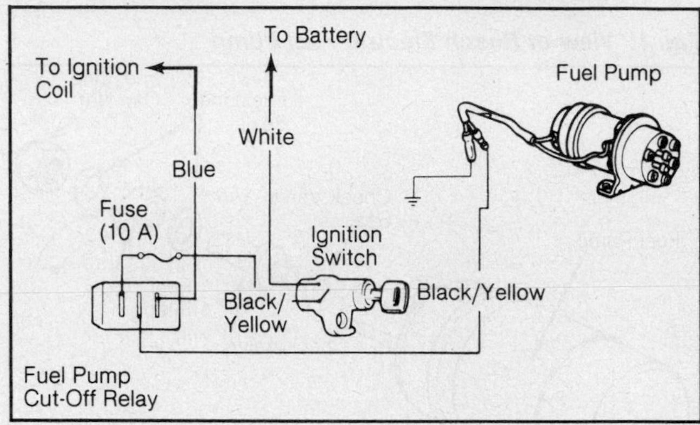
To Battery
To Ignition Coil
Fuel Pump
White
Blue
Fuse (10 A)
Ignition Switch
Black/Yellow
Black/ Yellow
Fuel Pump Cut-Off Relay

ISUZU

Impulse

DESCRIPTION

Electric fuel pump is mounted under the right rear side of vehicle near the fuel tank. No internal pump components are serviceable and entire pump should be replaced if found defective.

TESTING

PRESSURE TEST

CAUTION: The fuel line is under pressure. When installing an in-line fuel pressure gauge, caution must be used when disconnecting fuel lines.

1) Install fuel pressure gauge between the pressure regulator and fuel distributor pipe. Unplug the vacuum switching valve at the connector.

2) Vacuum switching valve is located on right side fender below ignition coil. Start engine and measure fuel pressure. Pressure should be 28.4 psi (2.0 kg/cm²).

REMOVAL & INSTALLATION

FUEL PUMP

Removal & Installation

Remove rear seat assembly. Unplug electrical harness at terminal located under right side part of rear seat. Disconnect hoses from fuel pump. Remove the pump guard. Remove pump from bracket. Install in reverse order of removal.

MAZDA

B2000 & RX7

DESCRIPTION & OPERATION

Pulsating electric fuel pump is mounted near fuel tank on frame member. Power is supplied when ignition switch is in "RUN" position. This circuit is protected by a 15 amp fuse (20 amp on RX7) at fuse panel. In-line fuel filter must be changed within recommended mileage interval before performing tests. If in doubt, install new filter.

TESTING

PRESSURE TEST

1) Remove air cleaner assembly and disconnect fuel line at carburetor. Connect pressure gauge with restrictor and a flexible hose. *See Fig. 1.* Turn ignition on and briefly vent the system into container by opening hose restrictor.

Fig. 1: Fuel Pump Pressure and Volume Test

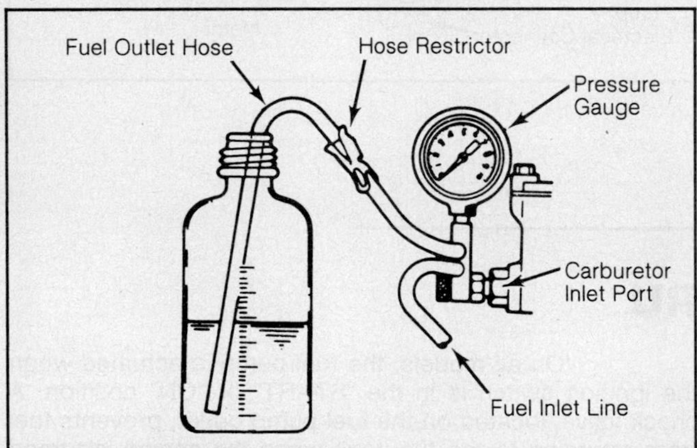
Fuel Outlet Hose
Hose Restrictor
Pressure Gauge
Carburetor Inlet Port
Fuel Inlet Line

2) Pressure should stabilize at 2.8-3.6 psi (.19-.25 kg/cm²). If not within specifications, and lines and filter are in satisfactory condition, replace pump.

VOLUME TEST

With fuel pressure within limits, open restrictor for one minute and measure fuel expelled. If not within specifications, check for restrictions in tank, line or filter. Replace pump if required.

FUEL PUMP VOLUME

Application	Volume Qt./Min. (cc/Min.)
RX7	1.5 (1400)
B2000	.8 (800)

FUEL PUMP

Removal & Installation (B2000)

Disconnect negative battery cable. Unplug connector at fuel pump. Disconnect inlet and outlet hoses at fuel pump. Remove fuel pump-to-mounting bracket nuts and remove pump. To install, reverse removal procedure.

Removal & Installation (RX7)

Remove rear floor mat and disconnect fuel pump electrical lead. Raise and support vehicle. Remove fuel pump cover. Disconnect inlet and outlet hoses from pump. Remove fuel pump. To install, reverse removal procedure.

MITSUBISHI

Datsun/Nissan Maxima, 200SX, 280ZX, 280ZX Turbo & Mitsubishi Starion

DESCRIPTION

The fuel pump is a wet type where the vane rollers are directly coupled to a motor filled with fuel. A relief valve in the pump is designed to open when pressure in the fuel system rises above a safe limit. A check valve on the fuel pump outlet prevents an abrupt drop in pressure in the fuel lines when the engine is stopped.

OPERATION

The fuel pump is actuated by a fuel pump relay when the ignition switch is in the "START" or "ON" position. As fuel goes through the pump, it is routed to a fuel damper mounted near the fuel pump. The damper reduces pulsations in the fuel lines. The fuel pump and damper are mounted in front of the fuel tank on all models.

The integral relief valve on Datsun/Nissan models is designed to relieve pressure at 43-64 psi (3.0-4.5 kg/cm²). The Mitsubishi Starion relief valve will open at 64-85 psi (4.5-5.9 kg/cm²).

TESTING

OPERATION TEST

Mitsubishi Starion

1) Connect a jumper wire across terminals of fuel pump check connector. Connector is located next to ignition coil. Turn ignition on. Listen for sound of fuel pump operating.

2) If no sound can be heard, check electrical circuit. If circuit is good, replace fuel pump.

MITSUBISHI (Cont.)

PRESSURE TEST

NOTE: **No pressure testing procedure is available from manufacturer for Mitsubishi Starion.**

Datsun/Nissan

1) Before disconnecting fuel line, relieve fuel system pressure as follows. Remove relay bracket in engine compartment. Start engine. Unplug harness connector from fuel pump relay. After engine stalls, turn ignition off and plug in connector.

2) Install fuel pressure gauge (J-25400-34) between fuel filter hose and metal pipe. Start engine and read fuel pressure. Pressure at idle should be 30 psi (2.1 kg/cm²). Pressure when accelerator is depressed should be 37 psi (2.6 kg/cm²). Replace fuel pump if fuel pressure is below specified value.

REMOVAL & INSTALLATION

FUEL PUMP

Removal & Installation

1) Disconnect negative battery cable. Relieve fuel system pressure. Raise and support the vehicle. Clamp hose between fuel tank and pump. Remove fuel hose clamps at inlet and outlet hoses at pump. Disconnect fuel hoses from fuel pump.

2) Unplug harness connector from fuel pump. Remove bolts fuel pump bracket-to-body bolts. Remove fuel pump and fuel damper from vehicle as an assembly. Separate fuel damper from fuel pump. To install, reverse removal procedures.

INSTALLATION

To install, reverse removal procedures.

Fig. 1: Sectional View of Mitsubishi Electric Fuel Pump

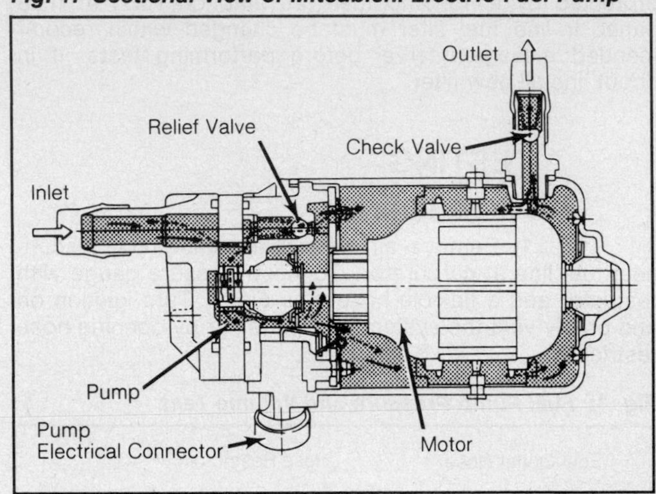
Outlet
Relief Valve
Check Valve
Inlet
Pump
Pump
Electrical Connector
Motor

SUBARU

DESCRIPTION & OPERATION

The electric fuel pump used on all models except the 1800 4WD Turbo is an electromatic plunger type pump. The fuel pump is located in the engine compartment.

The fuel pump on the 1800 4WD Turbo is a pin and roller type electric pump. The pump is equipped with an integral relief valve which is designed to relieve pressure at 61-71 psi (4.3-5.0 kg/cm²). A fuel damper is mounted on the end of the pump to reduce changes in the fuel pressure generated in the system.

Fig. 1: Sectional View of Subaru Electric Fuel Pump

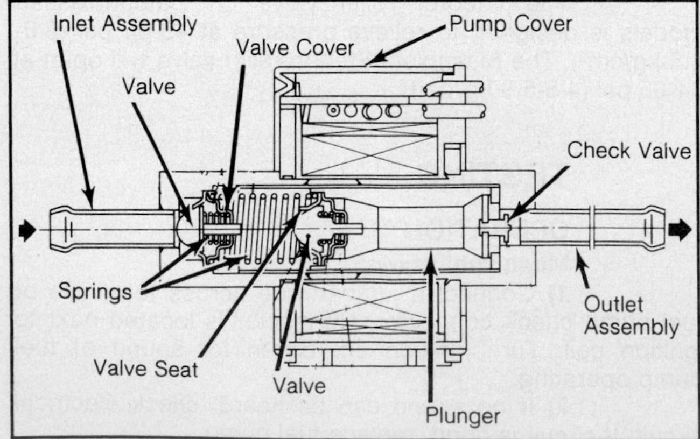
Inlet Assembly
Pump Cover
Valve Cover
Valve
Check Valve
Springs
Outlet
Assembly
Valve Seat
Valve
Plunger

Illustration does not apply to 1800 4WD Turbo.

On all models, the fuel pump is actuated when the ignition switch is in the "START" or "ON" position. A check valve, located on the fuel pump outlet, prevents fuel from returning to the fuel tank when the engine is turned off.

TESTING

Before performing the following tests, ensure hose and electrical connections are tight. Confirm fuel pump makes an operating sound when actuated.

PRESSURE TEST

All Except 1800 4WD Turbo

Disconnect fuel hose from carburetor. Connect a pressure gauge to fuel hose. Measure output pressure while operating fuel pump. Pump output pressure should be 1.3-2.0 psi (.09-.14 kg/cm²). If output pressure is not as specified, replace the fuel pump.

1800 4WD Turbo

1) Unplug the fuel pump electrical connector. Crank engine for 5 seconds to relieve fuel system pressure. Disconnect fuel hose at the fuel pressure regulator. Install a fuel pressure gauge in-line using a "T" fitting.

SUBARU (Cont.)

2) Fuel pressure at idle speed should be 26-30 psi (1.8-2.1 kg/cm²). Increase RPM and ensure fuel pressure increases correspondingly.

SUCTION TEST

Disconnect fuel hose between fuel filter and pump at the filter. Place finger over end of hose. Suction should be felt when fuel pump is actuated. If no suction is felt, replace fuel pump.

REMOVAL & INSTALLATION

FUEL PUMP

Removal & Installation

Disconnect wiring harness from fuel pump. Disconnect and plug fuel lines from pump. Remove fuel pump from bracket. To install, reverse removal procedure.

TOYOTA

Camry, Celica, Cressida, Starlet & Supra

DESCRIPTION & OPERATION

The fuel pump is a pin and roller type electric pump equipped with an integral relief valve. Internal components include a rotor, check valve, relief valve, orifice and silencer. *See Fig. 1*. On all models, pump is located in rear of vehicle in front of fuel tank. Pump is not serviceable and must be replaced as a unit if defective.

Fig. 1: Sectional View of Electric Fuel Pump

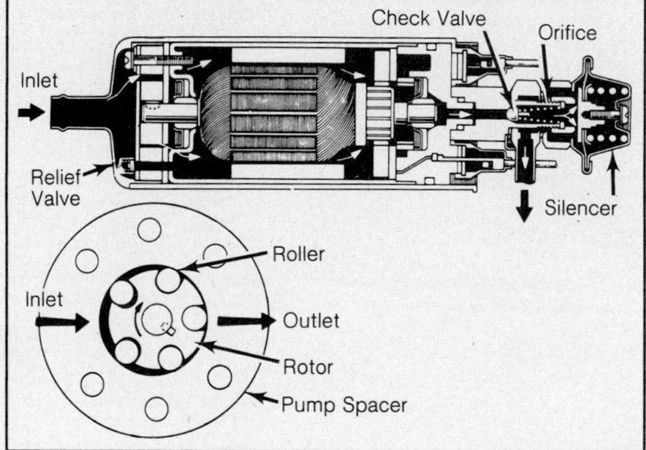
Check Valve
Orifice
Inlet
Relief Valve
Silencer
Roller
Inlet
Outlet
Rotor
Pump Spacer

TESTING

OPERATION TEST

1) Turn ignition switch on. Short both terminals of fuel pump check connector. *See Fig. 2*. Check for pressure in hose to cold start injector. Check for fuel return noise from pressure regulator.

Fig. 2: Check Connector Location

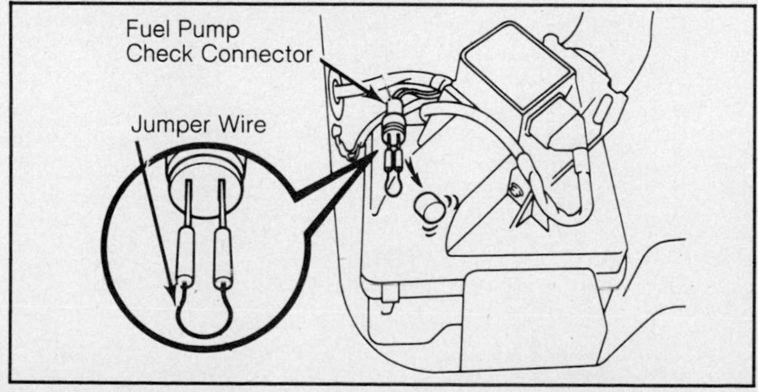
Fuel Pump
Check Connector
Jumper Wire

2) If no pressure in hose to cold start injector, check the following: Fusible link, 15 amp fuse, relay, wiring connections, and fuel pump pressure.

PRESSURE TEST

1) Disconnect negative battery cable. Unplug wiring connector from cold start injector. Loosen the union bolt of cold start injector hose on fuel delivery pipe.

2) Remove the bolt and 2 gaskets from the delivery pipe. Drain fuel in delivery pipe. Install fuel pressure gauge. *See Fig. 3*. Wipe off spilled fuel and connect battery cable. Start engine. Disconnect and plug fuel pressure regulator vacuum hose.

Fig. 3: Fuel Pressure Gauge Installation

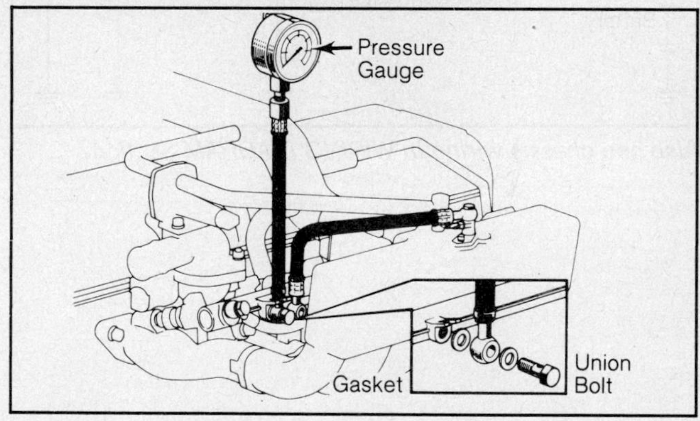
Pressure Gauge
Gasket
Union Bolt

3) With engine idling, fuel pressure should be 33-38 psi (2.3-2.7 kg/cm²). If pressure is high, replace pressure regulator. If pressure is low, check fuel system for leaks.

4) Connect pressure regulator sensing hose. With engine idling, fuel pressure should be approximately 28 psi (2.0 kg/cm²). If pressure is high, replace pressure regulator.

5) Turn ignition off. If pressure drops quickly, check fuel pump, pressure regulator, and/or injectors. Remove pressure gauge. Using new gaskets, install removed parts.

1983 Electric Fuel Pumps

TOYOTA (Cont.)

Fig. 4: Cressida & Supra Fuel Pump Wiring Diagram

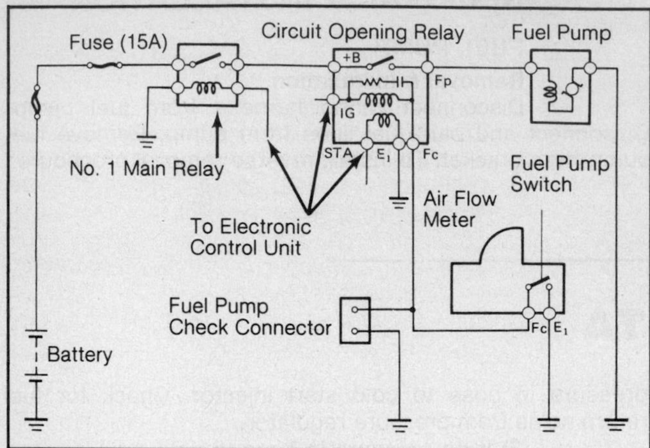
Fuse (15A)
Circuit Opening Relay
Fuel Pump
+B
Fp
IG
STA
E1
Fc
No. 1 Main Relay
Fuel Pump Switch
To Electronic Control Unit
Air Flow Meter
Fuel Pump Check Connector
Fc E1
Battery

Fig. 5: Camry, Celica & Starlet Fuel Pump Wiring Diagram

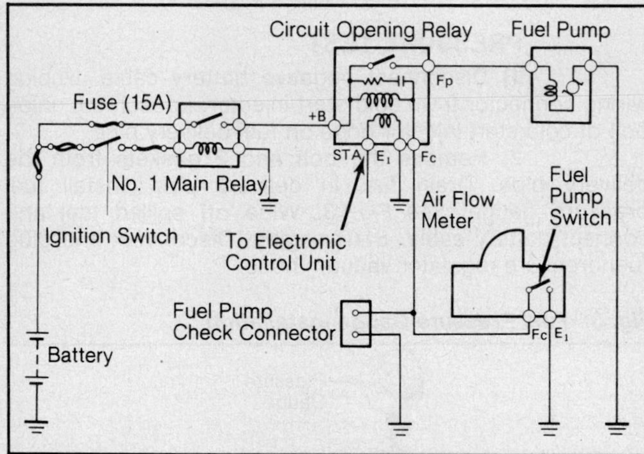
Circuit Opening Relay
Fuel Pump
Fuse (15A)
+B
Fp
STA
E1
Fc
No. 1 Main Relay
Ignition Switch
To Electronic Control Unit
Air Flow Meter
Fuel Pump Switch
Fuel Pump Check Connector
Fc E1
Battery

Also see chassis wiring in WIRING DIAGRAM Section.

SECTION 3

ELECTRICAL

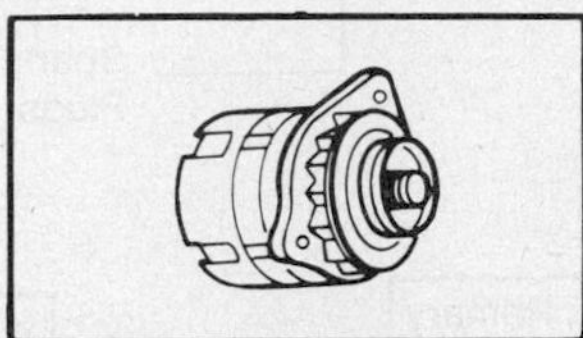

CONTENTS

TROUBLE SHOOTING

NOTE: ALSO SEE GENERAL INDEX.

Ignition Systems

TROUBLE SHOOTING

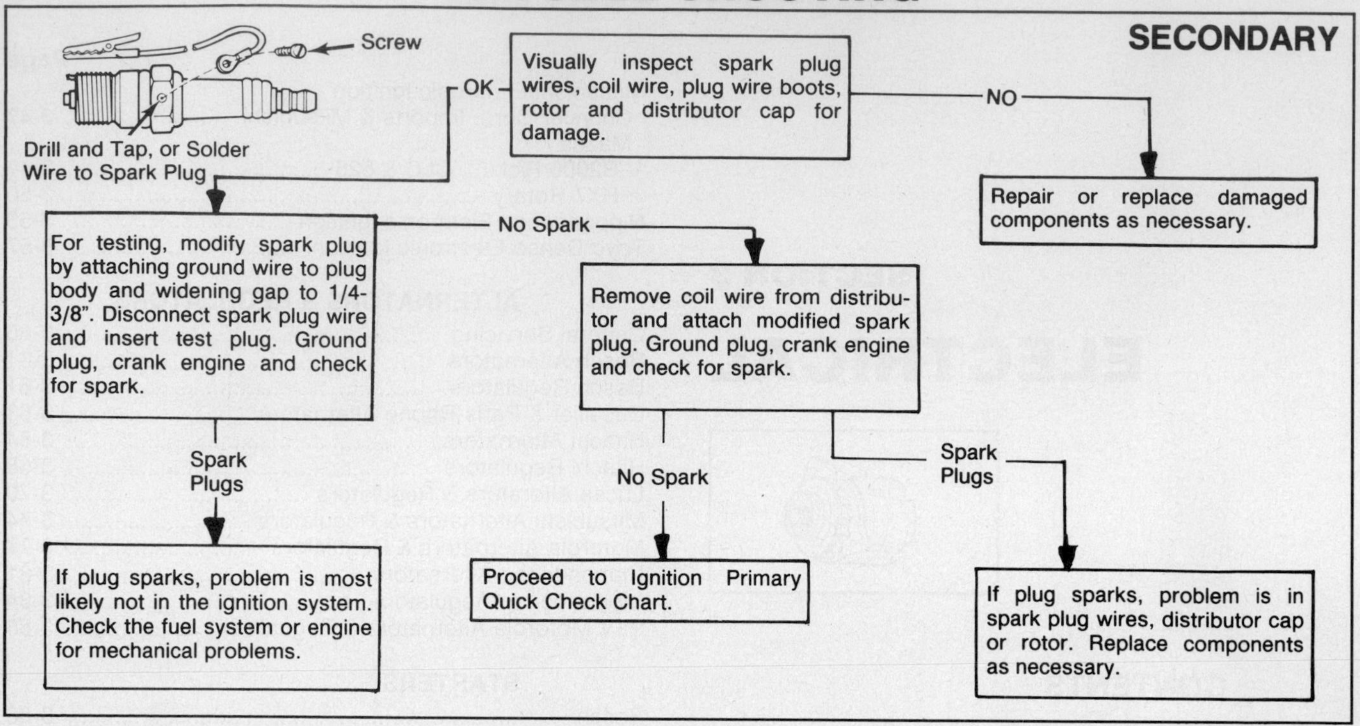
SECONDARY
Screw
Drill and Tap, or Solder
Wire to Spark Plug
OK
Visually inspect spark plug wires, coil wire, plug wire boots, rotor and distributor cap for damage.
NO
Repair or replace damaged components as necessary.
For testing, modify spark plug by attaching ground wire to plug body and widening gap to 1/4-3/8". Disconnect spark plug wire and insert test plug. Ground plug, crank engine and check for spark.
No Spark
Remove coil wire from distributor and attach modified spark plug. Ground plug, crank engine and check for spark.
Spark Plugs
If plug sparks, problem is most likely not in the ignition system. Check the fuel system or engine for mechanical problems.
No Spark
Proceed to Ignition Primary Quick Check Chart.
Spark Plugs
If plug sparks, problem is in spark plug wires, distributor cap or rotor. Replace components as necessary.

PRIMARY

Inspect all ignition secondary wiring for broken, frayed, split or cut wires. Also check for loose, corroded or disconnected connectors.

- NO → Repair or replace components as necessary.
- OK → Check battery voltage. Should be at least 11.5 volts.
  - NO → Replace or recharge battery.
  - OK → Check for battery voltage at positive terminal of coil.
    - NO → Check resistance of ballast resistor (if used) for correct value.
      - OK → Check wires from battery/ignition switch to coil. Also check coil primary and secondary resistance.
      - NO → Replace ballast resistor is value is not to specification.
    - OK → Check air gap of pick-up coil in distributor.
      - NO → Adjust or replace as necessary.
      - OK → Check pick-up coil resistance for correct value.
        - NO → Replace pick-up coil if not to specification.
        - OK → Check control module for good ground connections.
          - OK → If vehicle still fails to run, turn to appropriate article in this manual for complete primary ignition checks with specifications.

Charging Systems

TROUBLE SHOOTING

CONDITION	POSSIBLE CAUSE	CORRECTION
Vehicle Will Not Start	Dead battery	Check battery cells, alternator belt tension and alternator output
	Loose or corroded battery connections	Check all charging system connections
	Ignition circuit or switch malfunction	Check and replace as necessary
Alternator Light Stays ON With Engine Running	Loose or worn alternator drive belt	Check alternator drive belt tension and condition. See Belt Adjustment in TUNE-UP
	Loose alternator wiring connections	Check all charging system connections
	Short in alternator light wiring	See Indicator Warning Lights in SWITCHES, GAUGES & INSTRUMENT PANELS
	Defective alternator stator or diodes	See Bench Tests in ALTERNATORS & REGULATORS
	Defective regulator	See Regulator Check in ALTERNATORS & REGULATORS
Alternator Light Stays OFF With Ignition Switch ON	Blown fuse	See FUSES & CIRCUIT BREAKERS
	Defective alternator	See Testing in ALTERNATORS & REGULATORS
	Defective indicator light bulb or socket	See Indicator Warning Lights in SWITCHES, GAUGES & INSTRUMENT PANELS
Alternator Light Stays ON With Ignition Switch OFF	Short in alternator wiring	See On-Vehicle Tests in ALTERNATORS & REGULATORS
	Defective rectifier bridge	See Bench Tests in ALTERNATORS & REGULATORS
Lights or Fuses Burn Out Frequently	Defective alternator wiring	See On-Vehicle Tests in ALTERNATORS & REGULATORS
	Defective regulator	See Regulator Check in ALTERNATORS & REGULATORS
	Defective battery	Check and replace as necessary
Ammeter Gauge Shows Discharge	Loose or worn drive belt	Check alternator drive belt tension and condition See Belt Adjustment in TUNE-UP
	Defective wiring	Check all wires and wire connections
	Defective alternator or regulator	See Bench Tests and On-Vehicle Tests in ALTERNATORS & REGULATORS
	Defective ammeter, or improper ammeter wiring connections	See Testing in SWITCHES, GAUGES & INSTRUMENT PANELS
Noisy Alternator	Loose drive pulley	Tighten drive pulley attaching nut
	Loose mounting bolts	Tighten all alternator mounting bolts
	Worn or dirty bearings	See Bearing Replacement in ALTERNATORS & REGULATORS
	Defective diodes or stator	See Bench Tests in ALTERNATORS & REGULATORS
Battery Does Not Stay Charged	Loose or worn drive belt	Check alternator drive belt tension and condition. See Belt Adjustment in TUNE-UP
	Loose or corroded battery connections	Check all charging system connections
	Loose alternator connections	Check all charging system connections
	Defective alternator or battery	See On-Vehicle Tests and Bench Tests in ALTERNATORS & REGULATORS
	Defective alternator stator or diodes	See Bench Tests in ALTERNATORS & REGULATORS
	Add-on electrical accessories exceeding alternator capacity	Install larger capacity alternator
Battery Overcharged - Uses Too Much Water	Defective battery	Replace battery, check alternator output and repair as necessary
	Defective alternator	See On-Vehicle Tests and Bench Tests in ALTERNATORS & REGULATORS
	Excessive alternator voltage	Check alternator output and repair as necessary

Starting Systems

TROUBLE SHOOTING

CONDITION	POSSIBLE CAUSE	CORRECTION
Starter Fails to Operate	Dead battery or bad connections between starter and battery	Check battery charge and all wires and connections to starter
	Ignition switch faulty or misadjusted	Adjust or replace ignition switch
	Open circuit between starter switch and ignition terminal on starter relay	Check and repair wires and connections as necessary
	Starter relay or starter defective	See Testing in STARTERS
	Open solenoid pull-in wire	See Testing in STARTERS
Starter Does Not Operate and Headlights Dim	Weak battery or dead battery cell	Charge or replace battery as necessary
	Loose or corroded battery connections	Check that battery connection are clean and tight
	Internal ground in starter windings	See Testing in STARTERS
	Grounded starter fields	See Testing in STARTERS
	Armature rubbing on pole shoes	See Overhaul in STARTERS
Starter Turns but Engine Does Not Rotate	Starter clutch slipping	See Overhaul in STARTERS
	Broken clutch housing	See Overhaul in STARTERS
	Pinion shaft rusted or dry	See Overhaul in STARTERS
	Engine basic timing incorrect	See Ignition Timing in TUNE-UP
	Broken teeth on engine flywheel	Replace flywheel and check for starter pinion gear damage
Starter Will Not Crank Engine	Faulty overrunning clutch	See Overhaul in STARTERS
	Broken clutch housing	See Overhaul in STARTERS
	Broken flywheel teeth	Replace flywheel and check for starter pinion gear damage
	Armature shaft sheared or reduction gear teeth stripped	See Overhaul in STARTERS
	Weak battery	Charge or replace battery as necessary
	Faulty solenoid	See On-Vehicle Tests in STARTERS
	Poor grounds	Check all ground connections for tight and clean connections
	Ignition switch faulty or misadjusted	Adjust or replace ignition switch as necessary
Starter Cranks Engine Slowly	Battery weak or defective	Charge or replace battery as necessary
	Engine overheated	See ENGINE COOLING SYSTEMS
	Engine oil too heavy	Check that proper viscosity oil is used
	Poor battery-to-starter connections	Check that all connections between battery and starter are clean and tight
	Current draw too low or too high	See Bench Tests in STARTERS
	Bent armature, loose pole shoe screws or worn bearings	See Overhaul in STARTERS
	Burned solenoid contacts	Replace solenoid
	Faulty starter	Replace starter
Starter Engages Engine Only Momentarily	Engine timing too far advanced	See Ignition Timing In TUNE-UP
	Overrunning clutch not operating	Replace overrunning clutch. See Overhaul in STARTERS
	Broken starter clutch housing	See Overhaul in STARTERS
	Broken teeth on engine flywheel	Replace flywheel and check starter pinion gear for damage
	Weak drive assembly thrust spring	See Overhaul in STARTERS
	Weak hold-in coil	See Bench Tests in STARTERS
Starter Drive Will Not Engage	Defective point assembly	See Testing in STARTERS
	Poor point assembly ground	See Testing in STARTERS
	Defective pull-in coil	Replace starter solenoid
Starter Relay Does Not Close	Dead battery	Charge or replace battery as necessary
	Faulty wiring	Check all wiring and connections leading to relay
	Neutral safety switch faulty	Replace neutral safety switch
	Starter relay faulty	Replace starter relay

Starting Systems

TROUBLE SHOOTING (Cont.)

CONDITION	POSSIBLE CAUSE	CORRECTION
Starter Drive Will Not Disengage	Starter motor loose on mountings	Tighten starter attaching bolts
	Worn drive end bushing	See Overhaul in STARTERS
	Damaged engine flywheel teeth	Replace flywheel and check starter pinion gear for damage
	Drive yolk return spring broken or missing	Replace return spring
	Faulty ignition switch	Replace ignition switch
	Solenoid contact switch plunger stuck	Replace starter solenoid
	Faulty starter relay	Replace starter relay
	Insufficient clearance between winding leads to solenoid terminal and main contact in solenoid	Replace starter solenoid
	Starter clutch not disengaging	Replace starter clutch
	Ignition starter switch contacts sticking	Replace ignition switch
Starter Relay Operates but Solenoid Does Not	Faulty solenoid switch, switch connections or switch wiring	Check all wiring between relay and solenoid or replace relay or solenoid as necessary
	Broken lead or loose soldered connections	Repair wire or wire connections as necessary
Solenoid Plunger Vibrates When Switch is Engaged	Weak battery	Charge or replace battery as necessary
	Solenoid contacts corroded	Clean contacts or replace solenoid
	Faulty wiring	Check all wiring leading to solenoid
	Broken connections inside switch cover	Repair connections or replace solenoid
	Open hold-in wire	Replace solenoid
Low Current Draw	Worn brushes or weak brush springs	Replace brushes or brush springs as necessary
High Pitched Whine During Cranking Before Engine Fires but Engine Fires and Cranks Normally	Distance too great between starter pinion and flywheel	Align starter or check that correct starter and flywheel are being used
High Pitched Whine After Engine Fires With Key Released. Engine Fires and Cranks Normally	Distance too small between starter pinion and flywheel. Flywheel runout contributes to the intermittent nature	Align starter or check that correct starter and flywheel are being used

1983 Distributor Applications

ALL MANUFACTURERS

ALFA ROMEO

Application ¹	Federal	Calif.
Bosch		
GTV-6 2.5	0237 304 005	0237 304 005

¹ – Spider 2.0 specifications not available.

AUDI

Application	Federal	Calif.
Bosch ¹		
4000		
4-Cylinder		
Man. Trans.	049 206 B	049 206 B
Auto. Trans.	049 205 Q	049 205 Q
5-Cylinder	035 205 J	035 206 R
5000		
Man. Trans.	035 205 L	035 205 L
Auto. Trans.	035 206 A	035 206 A
5000 Turbo	035 205 H	035 205 H

¹ – Bosch basic part number is 905.

BMW

Application ¹	Federal	Calif.
Bosch		
318i	0237 002 080	0237 002 080
320i	0237 002 049	0237 002 049

¹ – 528e, 533i, 633CSi and 733i use Motronic control unit.

CHRYSLER CORP. IMPORTS

Application	Federal	Calif.
Mitsubishi		
Colt & Ram-50 Pickups		
2.0L		
Man. Trans.	MD060390 MD060264	MD060269
Auto. Trans.	MD012145	MD060269
2.6L		
Man. Trans.	MD027695	MD027697
Auto. Trans.	MD027695	MD027696
Challenger & Sapporo	MD027698	MD027699
Colt		
1.4L Man. Trans.	MD018450	MD034140
All Others	MD034140	MD034140

DATSUN/NISSAN

Application	Federal	Calif.
Hitachi		
Maxima	D6K82-01	D6K82-01
Pickup		
Exc. HD & 4WD		
2.0L	D4N82-14	.....
2.4L	D4N83-11	D4N83-14
HD	D4N82-10	D4N82-10
4WD	D4N83-13	D4N83-14

DATSUN/NISSAN (Cont.)

Application	Federal	Calif.
Hitachi		
Pulsar & Sentra		
MPG		
Man. Trans.	D4R82-12	D4RN82-12
Auto. Trans.	D4R82-13	D4R82-14
Non-MPG		
Standard	D4R81-18	.....
Optional	D4R82-25	.....
Stanza		
Man. Trans.	D4N82-01	D4N82-01
Auto. Trans.	D4N82-02	D4N81-07
200SX	D4N80-43	D4N80-43
280ZX	D6K82-01	D6K82-01
280ZX Turbo	D6P81-02	D6P81-02

HONDA

Application	Man. Trans. ¹	Auto. Trans. ¹
Accord		
Fed.	D4R80-23 TD-24C	D4R80-22 TD-14C
Calif./Hi. Alt.	D4R80-20 TD-12C	D4R80-21 TD-13C
Civic		
1300		
Fed./Hi. Alt.	D4R80-24	.....
Calif.	D4R80-26	.....
1500		
Fed./Hi. Alt.	D4R80-27	D4R80-29
Calif.	D4R80-30	D4R80-29
Prelude		
Fed./Calif.	D4R82-08 TD-03H	D4R82-09 TD-04H
High Alt.	D4R82-34 TD-08H	D4R82-09 TD-04H

¹ – Distributor numbers beginning with D4R are Hitachi distributors. Distributor numbers beginning with TD are Toyo Denso distributors.

ISUZU

Application ¹	Federal	Calif.
Nippondenso		
I-Mark	100291-0140 029100-6900	100291-0140 029100-6900
P'UP		
Man. Trans.	100291-0141	100291-0141
Auto. Trans.	100291-0160	100291-0160

¹ – Impulse uses I-TEC control unit.

JAGUAR

Application	Federal	Calif.
Lucas		
XJ6	DAC2618	DAC2618
XJS	DAC2623	DAC2623

1983 Distributor Applications

ALL MANUFACTURERS (Cont.)

MAZDA

Application	Federal	Calif.
Mitsubishi		
B2000 Pickup	8387-18-200	8387-18-200
GLC		
FWD	E563-18-200B	E563-18-200B
RWD	8325-18-200	8325-18-200
RX7	N231-18-200	N231-18-200
626		
Man. Trans.	FE01-18-200A	FE03-18-200
Auto. Trans.	FE02-18-200	FE04-18-200

MERCEDES-BENZ

Application	Federal	Calif.
Bosch [1]		
380 Series	401 010	401 010

[1] – Bosch part number prefix is 0237.

MITSUBISHI

Application	Federal	Calif.
Mitsubishi		
Cordia & Tredia		
Man. Trans.	MD060266	MD060263
Auto. Trans.	MD013880	MD013880
Montero	MD060390	MD060390
Pickup		
2.0L		
Man. Trans.		
4-Speed	MD060390	MD060269
5-Speed	MD060264	MD060269
Auto. Trans.	MD012145	MD060269
2.6L		
2WD	MD027695	MD027696
4WD	MD027695	MD027697
Starion	MD061593	MD061593

PEUGEOT

Application	Federal	Calif.
Ducellier		
505	5902.41	5902.41

PORSCHE

Application [1]	Federal	Calif.
Bosch		
911SC	0237 302 034	0237 302 034
928S	0237 401 006	0237 401 006

[1] – 944 uses DME control unit.

RENAULT

Application	Federal	Calif.
Ducellier [1]		
Fuego [2] & 18i	00 668 754	00 668 754
Le Car	00 668 068	00 668 068

[1] – Ducellier part number prefix is 77.
[2] – Fuego Turbo part number is 77 00 697 635.

SAAB

Application	Federal	Calif.
Bosch		
900	0237 021 014	0237 021 014
900 Turbo	0237 021 003	0237 021 003

SUBARU

Application	Federal	Calif.
Hitachi		
4WD Models		
Non-Turbo	D4R80-03	D4R80-03
Turbo	D4R82-03	D4R82-03
Nippondenso		
2WD Models	100291-0080	100291-0080

TOYOTA

Application [1]	Federal	Calif.
Nippondenso		
Camry	19030-74020	19030-74020
Celica		
EFI Models	19100-35120	19100-35120
Carb. Models	19100-35130	19100-35120
Corolla	19030-16010	19030-16010
Land Cruiser	19100-61102	19100-61102
Pickup	19100-35130	19100-35130
Starlet		
4-Speed	19060-13030	19060-13030
5-Speed	19100-13300	19060-13300
Tercel	19030-15020	19030-15020

[1] – Cressida & Supra use TCCS control unit.

VOLKSWAGEN

Application	Federal	Calif.
Bosch [1]		
Jetta & Scirocco		
Man. Trans.	049 206 B	049 205 B
Auto. Trans.	049 205 Q	049 205 Q
Quantum		
4-Cylinder		
Man. Trans.	049 206 B	049 206 B
Auto. Trans.	049 205 Q	049 205 Q
5-Cylinder	035 205 AG	035 205 AG
Pickup	049 205 R	049 205 R
Rabbit		
Carbureted	055 205 AA	055 205 AA
Fuel Injected	049 205 A	049 205 A
GTI	026 205 D	026 205 D
Vanagon		
1.9L	025 205 D	025 205 D
2.0L	022 205 S	039 205 S

[1] – Bosch basic part number is 905.

VOLVO

Application	Federal	Calif.
Bosch		
4-Cylinder Turbo	0237 003 024	0237 003 024
V6	0237 402 017	0237 402 017
Volvo		
4-Cylinder	1332684-8	1332684-8

1983 Distributor Specifications

ALL MANUFACTURERS (Cont.)

BOSCH DISTRIBUTOR ADVANCE SPECIFICATIONS
FOR DISTRIBUTOR RPM AND DEGREES, DIVIDE SPECIFICATIONS BY 2

Distributor Part No.[1]	Rot.[2]	AUTOMATIC ADVANCE (Engine Degrees & RPM)						VACUUM ADVANCE (Engine Deg.)			
		Deg.	RPM	Deg.	RPM	Deg.	RPM	Deg.	In. Hg	Deg.	In. Hg
022 905 205S	.....	0	1200	14	1600	25	3400	0	4	12	8
0237 002 049	CC	13	1000	24	2000	36	3500	0	3	10	11
0237 003 024	.....	0	1000	10	2100	24	5200	0	6	15	10
0237 021 003	CC	0	700	6	3000	15	5000	0	2	18	8
0237 021 014	CC	0	1200	14	3000	24	5000	0	8	15	20
0237 302 034	.....	18	1200	24	2400	28	4000	0	4.5	10	6
0237 304 005	.....	.....	.....	.....	.....	29	5000	.....	.....	.....	.....
0237 401 006	.....	0	1200	15	2400	23	6300	0	10	20	18
0237 401 010	.....	.....	.....	15	1500	26	3500	.....	.....	.....	.....
0237 402 017	.....	21	2000	25	3000	34	4000	23	6	32	9
025 905 205D	.....	0	1100	18	2400	23	3800	0	6	14	11
026 905 205D	.....	0	1300	19	2600	26	4500	0	5	14	8
035 905 205J	.....	0	1400	26	3300	30	7000	0	4.5	14	8
035 905 206R	.....	0	1400	26	3200	30	7000	0	5	14	8
039 905 205C	.....	0	1300	13	1600	25	3400	0	5	12	8
049 905 205A	.....	0	1400	18	2000	30	5200	0	10	8	12
049 905 205Q	.....	0	1400	20	2200	30	5000	0	5	12	8
049 905 206B	.....	0	1400	20	2200	30	5000	0	5	12	8
055 905 205AA	.....	0	1400	19	2100	30	5000	0	10	15	13

[1] – Specifications for all other Bosch distributors were not available from manufacturers.
[2] – C (Clockwise), CC(Counterclockwise), as viewed from rotor end.

HITACHI DISTRIBUTOR ADVANCE SPECIFICATIONS
FOR DISTRIBUTOR RPM AND DEGREES, DIVIDE SPECIFICATIONS BY 2

Distributor Part No.	Rot.[1]	AUTOMATIC ADVANCE (Engine Degrees & RPM)						VACUUM ADVANCE (Engine Deg.)			
		Deg.	RPM	Deg.	RPM	Deg.	RPM	Deg.	In. Hg	Deg.	In. Hg
42987 8110	CC	0	1000	5	1850	20	3600	0	2	24	12
D4N80-43	CC	0	1500	.....	.....	13	3200	0	3	10	8
D4N81-07	CC	0	1200	.....	.....	21	4800	0	3	25	12
D4N82-01	CC	0	1200	.....	.....	21	4800	0	3	35	9
D4N82-02	CC	0	1200	.....	.....	21	4800	0	3	35	12
D4N82-10	CC	0	1200	11	2400	19	4800	0	4	20	14
D4N82-14	CC	0	1500	.....	.....	10	4800	0	3	28	16
D4N83-11	CC	0	1200	14	2700	19	4200	0	3	25	12
D4N83-13	CC	0	1200	14	2700	19	4200	0	3	15	8
D4N83-14	CC	0	1200	14	2700	19	4200	0	3	20	10
D4R80-02	CC	0	1000	5	1850	20	3600	0	7	24	12
D4R80-20	CC	0	1000	13	2700	11.6	6000	0	6	14	12
D4R80-21	CC	0	1500	13	3000	11.8	6000	0	3	14	12
D4R80-22	CC	0	1500	13	3000	11.8	6000	0	14	7	16
D4R80-23	CC	0	1000	13	2700	11.6	6000	0	10	10	14
D4R80-24	CC	0	1000	9	2200	18	5300	0	5	20	12
D4R80-26	CC	0	1000	9	2200	18	5300	0	6	20	14
D4R80-27	CC	0	1000	12	1500	20	5500	0	5	20	14
D4R80-29	CC	0	1000	12	1500	20	5500	0	8	20	12
D4R80-30	CC	0	1000	12	1500	20	5500	0	6	20	14
D4R81-18 [2]	CC	0	1400	10	2400	25	5400	0	3	18	8.3
D4R82-08	.....	0	975	7	2500	18	6000	0	6	10	14
D4R82-09	.....	0	975	7	2500	16	6000	0	6	10	12
D4R82-12	CC	0	1400	10	2600	26	5200	0	3	20	8.3
D4R82-13	CC	0	1400	10	2600	26	5200	0	3	13	7
D4R82-14	CC	0	1400	10	2600	26	5200	0	3	14	7
D4R82-25 [3]	CC	0	1400	10	2400	24	5400	0	3	18	8.3
D4R82-34	C	0	975	7	2500	16	6000	0	6	10	14
D6K82-01	CC	0	1000	.....	.....	17	2800	0	4	30	12
D6K82-02	CC	0	1300	.....	.....	18	2700	0	3	30	11.4
D6P81-02 [4]	.....	.....	.....	.....	.....	.....	.....	.....	.....	.....	.....

[1] – C (Clockwise), CC (Counterclockwise), as viewed from rotor end.
[2] – Equipped with vacuum retard. 0°@7 in. Hg, -7°@10.2 in. Hg, -12.5@13.8 in. Hg.
[3] – Equipped with vacuum retard. 0°@3.5 in. Hg, -8°@5.9 in. Hg, -12.5@7.9 in. Hg.
[4] – No vacuum or centrifugal advance mechanisms are used.

1983 Distributor Specifications

ALL MANUFACTURERS

DUCELLIER DISTRIBUTOR ADVANCE SPECIFICATIONS
FOR DISTRIBUTOR RPM AND DEGREES, DIVIDE SPECIFICATIONS BY 2

Distributor Part No.	Rot.[1]	AUTOMATIC ADVANCE (Engine Degrees & RPM)						VACUUM ADVANCE (Engine Deg.)			
		Deg.	RPM	Deg.	RPM	Deg.	RPM	Deg.	In. Hg	Deg.	In. Hg
5209.41	C	16	1800	17	3000	32	5000	0	4	14	10
77 00 668 704	C	0	1000	14	2200	31	5000	0	3	20	13
77 00 668 754	C	0	1100	8	1500	26	4900	0	3	18	16
77 00 697 635 [2]	C	.....	.....	.....	.....	.....	.....	.....	.....	.....	.....

[1] – C (Clockwise), CC (Counterclockwise), as viewed from rotor end.
[2] – No vacuum or centrifugal advance mechanisms are used.

LUCAS DISTRIBUTOR ADVANCE SPECIFICATIONS
FOR DISTRIBUTOR RPM AND DEGREES, DIVIDE SPECIFICATIONS BY 2

Distributor Part No.	Rot.[1]	AUTOMATIC ADVANCE (Engine Degrees & RPM)						VACUUM ADVANCE (Engine Deg.)			
		Deg.	RPM	Deg.	RPM	Deg.	RPM	Deg.	In. Hg	Deg.	In. Hg
DAC2618 [2]	CC	.....	.....	.....	.....	.....	.....	.....	.....	.....	.....
DAC2623	CC	24	2000	31	4000	36	6200	0	6	4	10

[1] — C (Clockwise), CC (Counterclockwise), as viewed from rotor end.
[2] — Specifications not available from manufacturer.

MITSUBISHI DISTRIBUTOR ADVANCE SPECIFICATIONS
FOR DISTRIBUTOR RPM AND DEGREES, DIVIDE SPECIFICATIONS BY 2

Distributor Part No.	Rot.[1]	AUTOMATIC ADVANCE (Engine Degrees & RPM)						VACUUM ADVANCE (Engine Deg.)			
		Deg.	RPM	Deg.	RPM	Deg.	RPM	Deg.	In. Hg	Deg.	In. Hg
E563-18-200	C	0	1200	12	4000	16	6000	0	3	30	12
FE01-18-200A	C	0	1000	16	3100	16	5000	0	4	24	12
FE02-18-200	C	0	1000	16	3100	16	5000	0	4	20	12
FE03-18-200	C	0	1000	16	3100	16	5000	0	4	28	14
FE04-18-200	C	0	1000	16	3100	16	5000	0	4	24	12
MD013880	C	0	1000	14	2800	20	5000	0	2	26	12
MD012145	C	0	1200	12	2800	20	6000	0	3	22	11
MD018450	C	0	1000	.....	.....	20	4400	0	3	23	11
MD027695	C	0	1200	12	2800	20	6000	0	3	23	11
MD027696	C	0	1200	12	2800	20	6000	0	3	20	14
MD027697	C	0	1200	12	2800	20	6000	0	5	15	12
MD027698	C	0	1200	12	2800	20	6000	0	3	20	14
MD027699	C	0	1200	12	2800	20	6000	0	5	15	12
MD027704	C	0	1200	12	2800	20	6000	0	2	28	9
MD031650	C	0	1000	.....	.....	20	4400	0	3	25	11
MD034140	C	0	1000	.....	.....	20	4400	0	3	20	14
MD060263	C	0	1000	14	2800	20	5000	0	2	26	12
MD060264	C	0	1200	12	2800	20	6000	0	2.4	32	11
MD060266	C	0	1000	14	2800	20	5000	0	2	26	12
MD060269	C	0	1200	12	2800	20	6000	0	3	15	12
MD060390	C	0	1200	12	2800	20	6000	0	2.4	32	11
MD061593	C	0	1200	13	2300	25	5000	0	3	23	11
N201-18-200	CC	0	500	.....	.....	10	1750	0	4	11	13
N231-18-200	CC	0	1000	20	3500	20	4000	0	4	30 [2]	20
8325-18-200	C	0	1400	20	4700	20	6000	0	4	14	14
8387-18-200	C	0	1500	10	2500	17	5000	0	3	18	21

[1] – C (Clockwise), CC (Counterclockwise), as viewed from rotor end.
[2] – Leading pickup shown. Trailing pickup is 9°@16 in. Hg.

1983 Distributor Specifications

ALL MANUFACTURERS (Cont.)

NIPPONDENSO DISTRIBUTOR ADVANCE SPECIFICATIONS
FOR DISTRIBUTOR RPM AND DEGREES, DIVIDE SPECIFICATIONS BY 2

Distributor Part No.	Rot.[1]	AUTOMATIC ADVANCE (Engine Degrees & RPM)						VACUUM ADVANCE (Engine Deg.)			
		Deg.	RPM	Deg.	RPM	Deg.	RPM	Deg.	In. Hg	Deg.	In. Hg
029100-6900	CC	0	800	12	2600	18	4400	0	4	10	10
19030-15020	C	0	1100	10	2650	22	6000	0	3	26	11
19030-16010	C	0	1200	13	2800	20	6000	0	3	28	14
19030-74020	C	0	1000	14	2650	11	6000	0	2	30	15
19060-13030	C	0	1000	10	1800	16	6000	0	3	16	9
19100-13300	C	0	1000	10	3250	12	6000	0	3	16	10
19100-35120	C	0	1100	8	2000	17	5200	0	2	22	7
19100-35130	C	0	1100	8	2400	17	5200	0	2	22	7
19100-61102	C	0	1000	13	2700	16	6000	0	3	20	8
600291-0080	CC	0	1000	14	3000	19	6000	0	2	22	12

[1] – C (Clockwise); CC (Counterclockwise)

TOYO DENSO DISTRIBUTOR ADVANCE SPECIFICATIONS
FOR DISTRIBUTOR RPM AND DEGREES, DIVIDE SPECIFICATIONS BY 2

Distributor Part No.	Rot.[1]	AUTOMATIC ADVANCE (Engine Degrees & RPM)						VACUUM ADVANCE (Engine Deg.)			
		Deg.	RPM	Deg.	RPM	Deg.	RPM	Deg.	In. Hg	Deg.	In. Hg
TD-03H	CC	0	975	7	2500	18	6000	0	6	10	14
TD-04H	CC	0	975	7	2500	16	6000	0	6	10	12
TD-08H	CC	0	975	7	2500	16	6000	0	6	10	14
TD-12C	CC	0	1000	13	2700	11.6	6000	0	6	14	14
TD-13C	CC	0	1500	13	3000	11.8	6000	0	3	14	12
TD-14C	CC	0	1500	13	3000	11.8	6000	0	7	14	18
TD-24C	CC	0	1000	13	2700	11.6	6000	0	10	10	14

[1] – C (Clockwise); CC (Counterclockwise)

VOLVO DISTRIBUTOR ADVANCE SPECIFICATIONS
FOR DISTRIBUTOR RPM AND DEGREES, DIVIDE SPECIFICATIONS BY 2

Distributor Part No.	Rot.[1]	AUTOMATIC ADVANCE (Engine Degrees & RPM)						VACUUM ADVANCE (Engine Deg.)			
		Deg.	RPM	Deg.	RPM	Deg.	RPM	Deg.	In. Hg	Deg.	In. Hg
1332684-8	.....	0[2]	1700	20[2]	4000	24[2]	4500	0	8	24	21

[1] – C (Clockwise); CC (Counterclockwise)
[2] – Automatic Advance is computer controlled.

BOSCH ELECTRONIC IGNITION SYSTEM

BMW 318i & 320i; Mercedes-Benz 380 Series; Porsche 911SC & 928S; Volvo Turbo & 760 GLE

NOTE: Other BMW, Porsche and Volvo models use computer-controlled systems. See appropriate articles in the Computerized Engine Control section.

DESCRIPTION

The Bosch electronic ignition system consists of a control module, a breakerless distributor, a single or dual resistor, a high output ignition coil, an ignition switch, and battery.

Some models may use a resistor wire rather than resistors, while Mercedes-Benz models use no resistors. *See Figs. 1 and 2.* Standard centrifugal and vacuum advance/retard mechanisms are used.

The distributor contains a rotating trigger wheel and a stationary magnetic pick-up coil (unless it is repositioned by vacuum diaphragm).

OPERATION

Inside the distributor, a trigger wheel turns with the distributor shaft. The trigger wheel has one tooth or lug for each engine cylinder.

As the trigger wheel rotates past the pole of the magnetic pick-up coil, a magnetic field is created that continually builds and collapses. This produces a low voltage electrical signal.

This signal passes to the control module, which controls the dwell angle and at the same time interrupts the ignition coil's primary circuit. This induces the high secondary coil output voltage that fires the spark plugs.

SPECIFICATIONS

DWELL ANGLE

Dwell angle is controlled by the electronic control module, and is non-adjustable. Refer to table later in this article.

CENTRIFUGAL & VACUUM ADVANCE AND/OR RETARD

See the appropriate Distributor Specifications Tables in this section.

Fig. 2: Wiring Diagram of Mercedes-Benz Bosch Electronic Ignition System

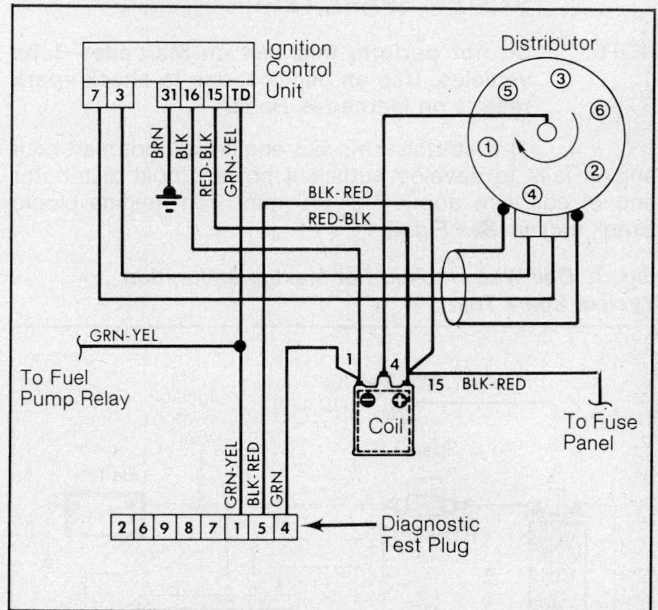

Ignition Control Unit
7 3 31 16 15 TD
BRN
BLK
RED-BLK
GRN-YEL
Distributor
BLK-RED
RED-BLK
GRN-YEL
To Fuel Pump Relay
1
4
15 BLK-RED
Coil
To Fuse Panel
GRN-YEL
BLK-RED
GRN
2 6 9 8 7 1 5 4
Diagnostic Test Plug

No resistors or resistor wires are used.

Fig. 1: Wiring Diagram of Typical Bosch Electronic Ignition System (Except Mercedes-Benz)

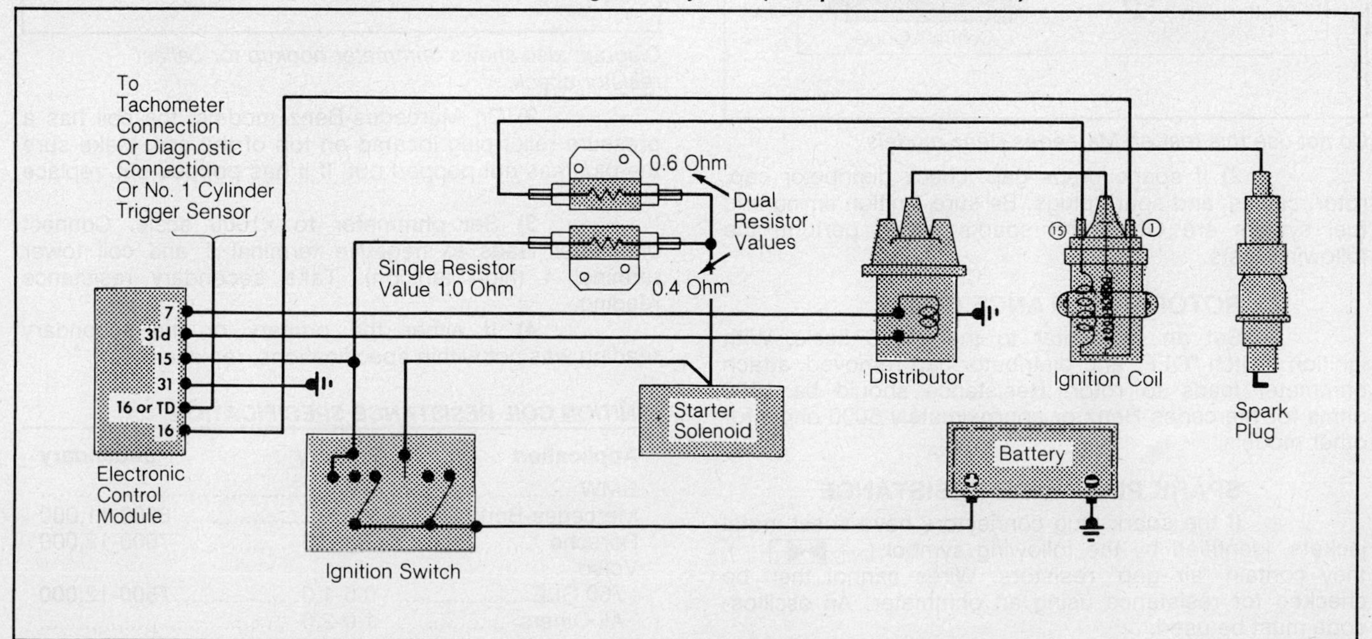

To Tachometer Connection Or Diagnostic Connection Or No. 1 Cylinder Trigger Sensor
0.6 Ohm
Dual Resistor Values
Single Resistor Value 1.0 Ohm
0.4 Ohm
7
31d
15
31
16 or TD
16
Electronic Control Module
Ignition Switch
Starter Solenoid
Distributor
Ignition Coil
Spark Plug
Battery

BOSCH ELECTRONIC IGNITION SYSTEM (Cont.)

ADJUSTMENT

No adjustment should be attempted on ignition system, except spark plug gap and ignition initial timing. Air gap is non-adjustable. However, it should be visually checked when testing. If specified clearance does not exist, replace components.

TESTING

Before testing ignition system, be sure battery is fully charged and in good condition, that all wires are sound, and connections are good. Due to high voltage, use care when working on electronic ignition system.

SYSTEM SPARK TEST

NOTE: **Do not perform this test on Mercedes-Benz vehicles. Use an oscilloscope to check spark results on Mercedes-Benz.**

1) If starter turns but engine will not start or if engine fails to develop sufficient power), hold distributor end of coil wire about 3/8" (10 mm) from engine block. Crank engine. *See Fig. 3.*

Fig. 3: Coil Wire Hookup For Making an Ignition System Spark Test

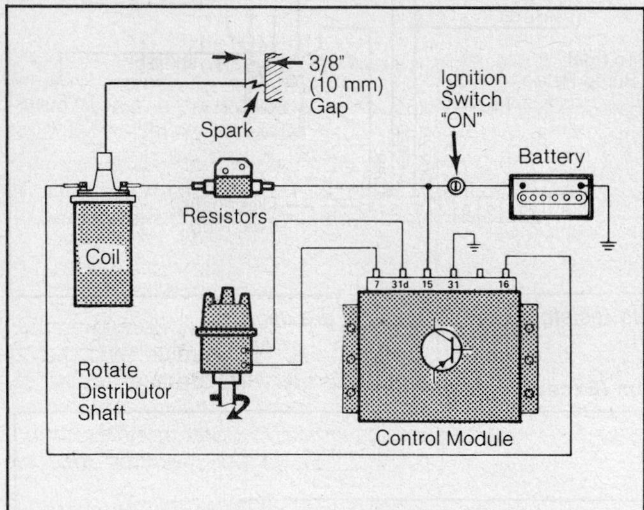

3/8"
(10 mm)
Gap
Spark
Ignition
Switch
"ON"
Battery
Resistors
Coil
7
31d
15
31
16
Rotate
Distributor
Shaft
Control Module

Do not use this test on Mercedes-Benz models.

2) If spark jumps gap, check distributor cap, rotor, cables, and spark plugs. Be sure ignition timing and fuel system are OK. If no sparks occur, perform the following tests.

ROTOR RESISTANCE CHECK

Set an ohmmeter to the x1000 scale. With ignition switch "OFF" and distributor cap removed, attach ohmmeter leads to rotor. Resistance should be 1000 ohms for Mercedes-Benz or approximately 5000 ohms for other models.

SPARK PLUG WIRE RESISTANCE

If the spark plug connectors have sheet metal jackets, identified by the following symbol (─▶◀─), they contain "air gap" resistors. Wires cannot then be checked for resistance using an ohmmeter. An oscilloscope must be used.

RESISTOR RESISTANCE CHECK

NOTE: **This test does not apply to Mercedes-Benz vehicles.**

Set an ohmmeter in the low scale. Be sure ignition switch is "OFF". Check resistance of each resistor in the primary circuit. *See Fig. 4.* Some manufacturers use resistor wires instead of ballast resistors. Most use 2 ballast resistors.

RESISTOR RESISTANCE SPECIFICATIONS

Application	Ohms
BMW	0.4 and 0.6
Porsche	0.4 and 0.6
Volvo	1.0

IGNITION COIL RESISTANCE CHECK

1) Turn ignition switch "OFF". Remove coil wires. Using an ohmmeter set at the low scale, attach leads to ignition coil primary terminals 1 and 15 (wires removed). *See Fig. 4.* Take primary resistance reading.

Fig. 4: Ohmmeter Hookup for Ignition Coil Primary and Secondary Resistance Checks

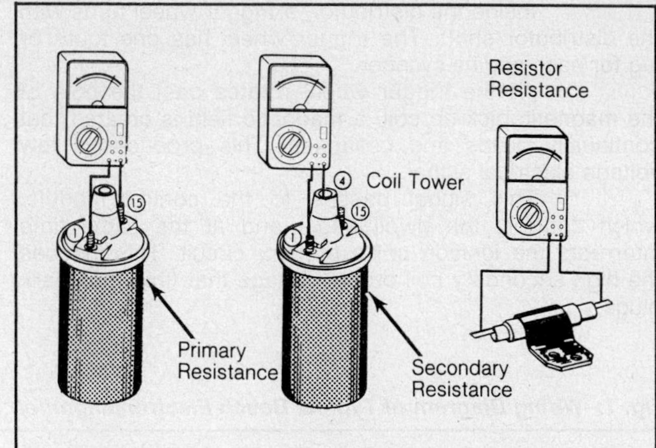

Resistor
Resistance
Coil Tower
4
15
1
Primary
Resistance
Secondary
Resistance

Diagram also shows ohmmeter hookup for ballast resistor check.

2) On Mercedes-Benz models, the coil has a pressure relief plug located on top of the coil. Make sure the plug has not popped out. If it has popped out, replace coil.

3) Set ohmmeter to x1000 scale. Connect ohmmeter leads to negative terminal 1 and coil tower terminal 4 (high tension). Take secondary resistance reading.

4) If either the primary or the secondary reading was not within specifications, replace coil.

IGNITION COIL RESISTANCE SPECIFICATION

Application	Primary	Secondary
BMW	.4	....
Mercedes-Benz	.7	8000-11,000
Porsche	.33-.46	7000-12,000
Volvo		
760 GLE	0.5-1.0	7500-12,000
All Others	1.0-2.0	....

BOSCH ELECTRONIC IGNITION SYSTEM (Cont.)

IGNITION COIL VOLTAGE CHECK

Mercedes-Benz Models

1) Connect voltmeter positive lead to diagnostic plug terminal 5 (terminal 15 on coil). Connect voltmeter negative lead to ground. Turn ignition switch "ON".

2) Voltage reading should be the same as battery voltage. If voltage reading is not correct, check voltage readings back to battery (checking through ignition switch).

3) Connect voltmeter negative lead to diagnostic plug terminal 4 (terminal 1 on coil). Voltage reading should be zero.

4) If reading is not zero, turn ignition switch "OFF" immediately. Replace electronic control unit.

All Other Models

1) Connect voltmeter negative lead to ground and positive lead to terminal 15 of coil. Turn ignition switch "ON". Voltage reading should be 4-7 volts.

2) If less than 4-7 volts, check wires, connections at ignition switch, resistors, coil, and control unit to eliminate voltage drop. If more than 4-7 volts, check for defective resistors.

3) Connect voltmeter positive lead to negative coil terminal 1. Attach negative lead to a good ground. Reading should be 0.5-2.0 volts (maximum 2.0 volts).

4) If previous tests and pick-up coil resistance, starting voltage, and control module voltage checks prove OK, substitute a known good control module. If system is now operative, install a new module.

STARTING VOLTAGE CHECK

NOTE: **This test does not apply to Mercedes-Benz vehicles.**

1) Disconnect wire leading to starter terminal 15a at the .4 ohm resistor (most models). Attach voltmeter and crank engine. Voltage should be the same as battery voltage.

2) If battery voltage is not present, check for break in electrical supply wire or contact 15a in starter relay.

PICK-UP COIL RESISTANCE CHECK

Mercedes-Benz Model

1) Make sure ignition switch is "OFF". Disconnect pick-up coil connector (Green cable) from control module. Set ohmmeter to x1000 scale. Attach ohmmeter leads to center pin (terminal 7) and to larger, outer, circular pin (terminal 3) of Green cable.

2) If resistance readings are not to specifications, remove connector from distributor, and take reading at pick-up coil pins at distributor. If readings are now correct, replace wiring harness. If readings are still not to specifications, replace pick-up coil.

All Other Models

1) Turn ignition switch "OFF", and disconnect harness connector from control module. Set ohmmeter to x100 scale. Connect ohmmeter leads to terminals 7 and 31d of harness connector. *See Fig. 5*. Measure pick-up coil resistance.

2) If resistance readings are not to specifications, remove connector from distributor, and take reading at pick-up coil pins at distributor.

3) If readings are still not to specifications, replace pick-up coil. If correct readings are obtained at distributor, but not at harness connector, replace harness.

Fig. 5: Ohmmeter Hookups for Pick-Up Coil Resistance and Short Checks

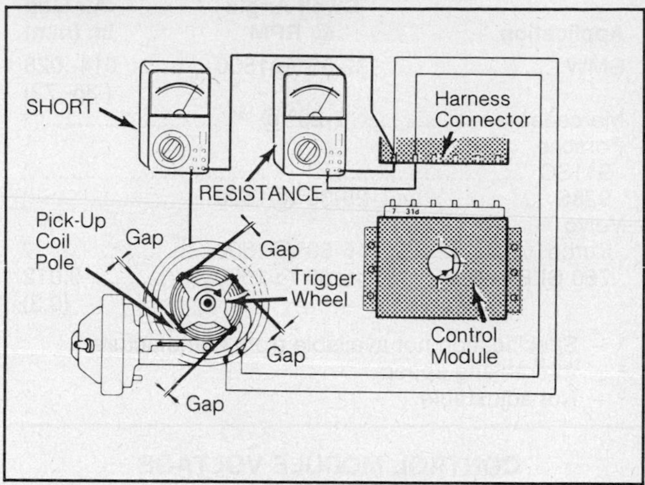
SHORT
RESISTANCE
Harness Connector
Pick-Up Coil Pole
Gap
Gap
Trigger Wheel
Gap
Gap
Control Module

PICK-UP COIL RESISTANCE SPECIFICATIONS

Application	Ohms
BMW	520-700
Mercedes-Benz	500-700
Porsche 928S	485-700
Volvo	
Turbo 4-Cylinder	950-1250
760 GLE	540-660

PICK-UP COIL SHORT CHECK

1) On Mercedes-Benz vehicles, connect one ohmmeter lead to ground. Attach other lead to control module harness terminal 3 and then to terminal 7.

2) On all other models, connect one ohmmeter lead to ground. Attach other lead to terminal 7, then to terminal 31d. Resistance reading should be greater than 200,000 ohms for Mercedes-Benz vehicles and infinity for all other models.

3) If resistance reading was not correct, disconnect harness from distributor. Connect ohmmeter leads to ground and to each pick-up coil pin in distributor. If readings are now correct, replace harness. If readings are still incorrect, replace pick-up coil.

DWELL ANGLE CHECK AND VISUAL CHECK OF PICK-UP COIL ASSEMBLY

1) Visually check trigger wheel and pick-up assembly for damage. Also check air gap between trigger wheel and pick-up coil. *See Fig. 5*.

2) If damaged or if air gap is not to specifications, replace distributor (if components cannot be replaced individually).

3) Check dwell angle, and compare it with specifications. If not within specifications, repeat Pick-Up Coil Resistance, Short, and Visual Checks. If OK, then replace control module.

BOSCH ELECTRONIC IGNITION SYSTEM (Cont.)

DWELL ANGLE & AIR GAP SPECIFICATIONS

Application	Dwell Angle @ RPM	Air Gap In. (mm)
BMW	32-53°@1500	.014-.028 (.36-.72)
Mercedes-Benz	7-25°@ [2]	[3]
Porsche		
911SC	[1]	[1]
928S	25-39°@1500	[1]
Volvo		
Turbo	45-63°@1500	[1]
760 GLE	45-60°@1500	0.012 (0.3)

[1] – Specification not available from manufacturer.
[2] – At cranking speed.
[3] – Not adjustable.

CONTROL MODULE VOLTAGE

NOTE: This test does not apply to Mercedes-Benz vehicles.

1) Disconnect connector from control module, and turn ignition switch "ON". Attach voltmeter positive lead to terminal 15 of control module harness connector. Connect negative lead to ground.

2) Battery voltage should be shown. If not, check for voltage drop in harness between ignition switch and control module.

CONTROL MODULE GROUND CHECK

NOTE: This test does not apply to Mercedes-Benz vehicles.

1) Disconnect connector at control module. Turn ignition switch "ON". Connect voltmeter positive lead to terminal 31 of control module (not harness). Connect negative lead to ground.

2) Reading should show continuity. If not, check module ground wire and repair as necessary.

FINAL CONTROL MODULE OR IGNITION COIL CHECK

NOTE: This test does not apply to Mercedes-Benz vehicles.

1) If ignition coil is suspected of being defective, substitute a known good coil, and attempt to start vehicle. If it starts, reinstall old coil and start vehicle.

2) If it then fails to start, replace with new coil. If control module is suspected, substitute a known good module, and start vehicle. If it starts, reinstall original module. If vehicle fails to start now, install new control module.

3) If system still fails to operate, disconnect tachometer connector at instrument cluster. Attempt to start engine. If engine now starts, replace tachometer.

OVERHAUL

DISASSEMBLY

1) Remove distributor cap, rotor, and dust cover. Remove vacuum unit screws and lock clasp screws. Remove screws securing electrical leads, and remove leads by carefully pulling straight out.

NOTE: Keep screws with components they attach, as screws are different lengths. Damage could result if installed in wrong location.

Fig. 6: Exploded View of Bosch Electronic Distributor

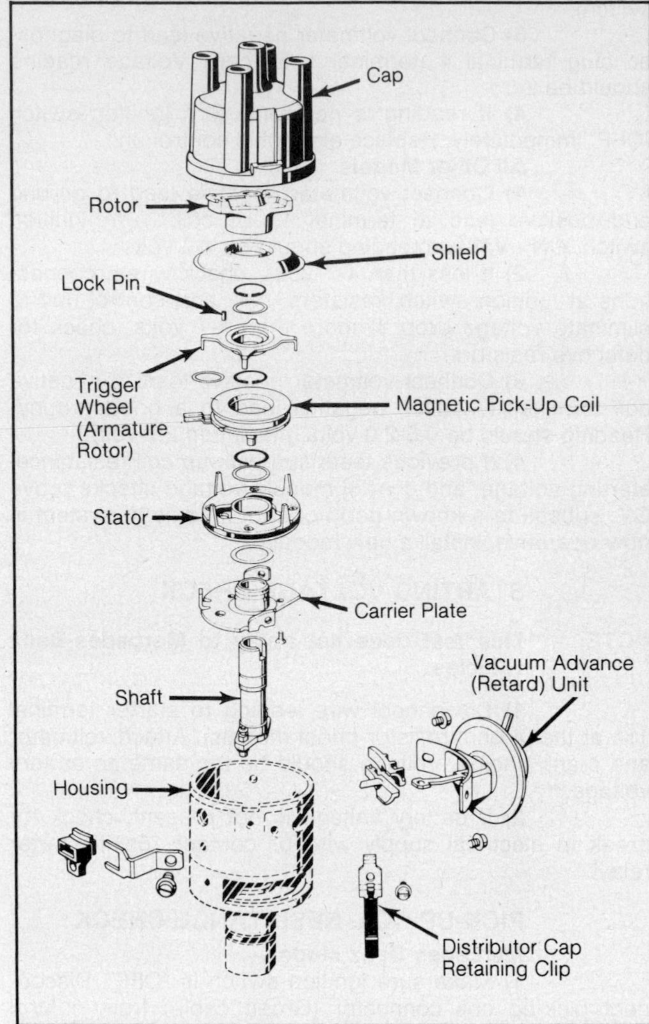
Cap
Rotor
Shield
Lock Pin
Trigger Wheel (Armature Rotor)
Magnetic Pick-Up Coil
Stator
Carrier Plate
Vacuum Advance (Retard) Unit
Shaft
Housing
Distributor Cap Retaining Clip

2) Remove trigger wheel snap ring and then shims. Using 2 screwdrivers, carefully pry upward on trigger wheel. Remove trigger wheel and lock pin. Remove screws securing pick-up coil and stator assembly carrier plate. *See Fig. 6.*

3) Remove snap ring and retaining clips. Lift carrier plate and stator straight up off shaft. Remove 3 screws to separate stator winding from carrier plate.

4) Disconnect springs to centrifugal governor. Mark drive shaft relationship to distributor shaft, and then secure drive shaft in a soft-jawed vise.

5) Carefully tap on distributor housing with a plastic mallet until circlip releases. If equipped, remove triggering contacts and attaching screws.

6) Remove resilient ring. Mark location of flange to distributor shaft. Support distributor shaft, and using a pin punch, remove pin. Remove flange and distributor shaft. Remove lock springs for centrifugal weights and then weights.

BOSCH ELECTRONIC IGNITION SYSTEM (Cont.)

Fig. 7: Removing or Installing Pick-Up Coil, Stator, and Carrier Plate

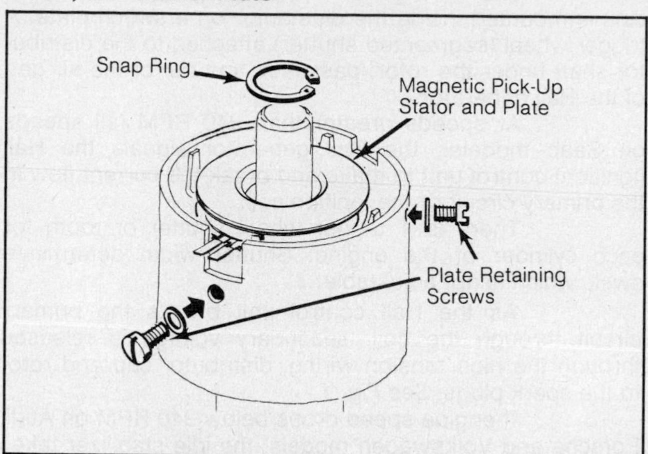
Snap Ring
Magnetic Pick-Up
Stator and Plate
Plate Retaining
Screws

INSPECTION

Check the following components, and replace any defective parts:

- Springs for weights must not be deformed or damaged in any manner.
- Holes in centrifugal governor weights must not be oval or deformed.
- Distributor shaft-to-cam clearance should not exceed .004" (.1 mm).
- Distributor shaft-to-housing clearance should not exceed .008" (.2 mm).

REASSEMBLY

1) To reassemble distributor, reverse disassembly procedure, while noting the following: Place a light coat of grease on weights and a couple of drops of oil on felt wick in center of shaft. Do not get grease or oil on pick-up coil and stator assembly.

2) When attaching stator to plate, the connector pins should be positioned opposite and above the attachment ear for carrier plate. Install lock pin with lip facing ridge on distributor shaft. Slot on trigger wheel should be aligned with groove on distributor shaft.

Fig. 8: Installing Wheel and Lock Pin

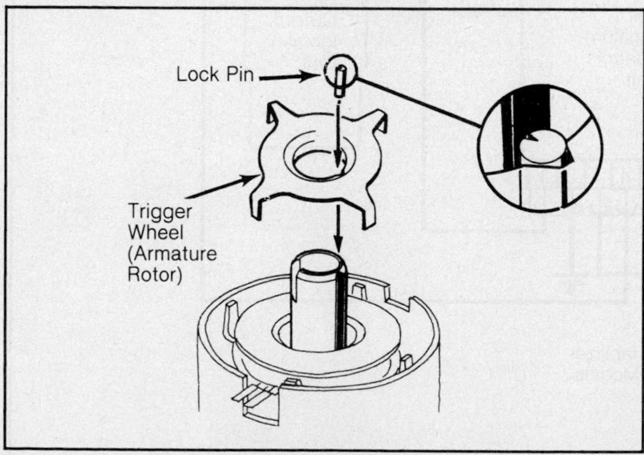
Lock Pin
Trigger
Wheel
(Armature
Rotor)

Be sure lock pin is properly installed.

BOSCH HALL EFFECT ELECTRONIC IGNITION

Audi 4000, 5000, 5000 Turbo; Saab 900, 900 Turbo; Volkswagen Models with CIS; & Calif. Vanagon

NOTE: **Federal Vanagon models use a Bosch single breaker distributor. The Audi Quattro uses the Bosch-Hitachi Digital Timing Control system. See appropriate article in the Computerized Engine Control section.**

DESCRIPTION

The Bosch Hall Effect electronic ignition system consists of a breakerless Hall Effect distributor, a Hall (ignition) control unit, ignition coil, ignition switch, and battery.

Incorporated into the ignition system on Audi, Porsche and Volkswagen models is an idle stabilizer, a solid state control unit located between the Hall (ignition) control unit and the distributor's Hall generator.

The idle stabilizer replaces the distributor in sending signals to the ignition control unit when engine speeds fall below 940 RPM.

NOTE: **Saab models do not use an idle stabilizer. On Audi 4000 (with 5-cylinder engines) and 5000 models, a gray-colored impedance transformer is installed in place of the idle stabilizer. Its purpose is to prevent interference and protect instruments from excessive voltage.**

The Hall Effect distributor has normal centrifugal and vacuum advance mechanisms. *See Fig. 10.*

OPERATION

The Hall generator (sending unit or pick-up coil) is mounted inside the distributor on a switch plate. A trigger wheel (segmented shutter) attached to the distributor shaft under the rotor, passes in and out of the air gap of the Hall generator.

At speeds greater than 940 RPM (all speeds on Saab models), the Hall generator signals the Hall (ignition) control unit to make and break the current flow in the primary circuit of the ignition coil.

There is 1 trigger wheel shutter or tooth for each cylinder of the engine. Shutter width determines dwell, which is not adjustable.

As the Hall control unit breaks the primary circuit through the coil, secondary voltage is released through the high tension wiring, distributor cap and rotor to the spark plugs. *See Fig. 1.*

If engine speed drops below 940 RPM on Audi, Porsche and Volkswagen models, the idle stabilizer takes over the duty of producing the signal to the ignition control unit (instead of the Hall generator).

The idle stabilizer is mounted on the same bracket as the Hall control unit and is wired between the distributor and the Hall control unit. It senses engine speed earlier, causing ignition timing to advance.

Advancing ignition timing causes idle speed to increase, and the Hall generator to resume its normal operation.

Fig. 1: Wiring Diagram of Bosch Hall Effect Electronic Ignition System

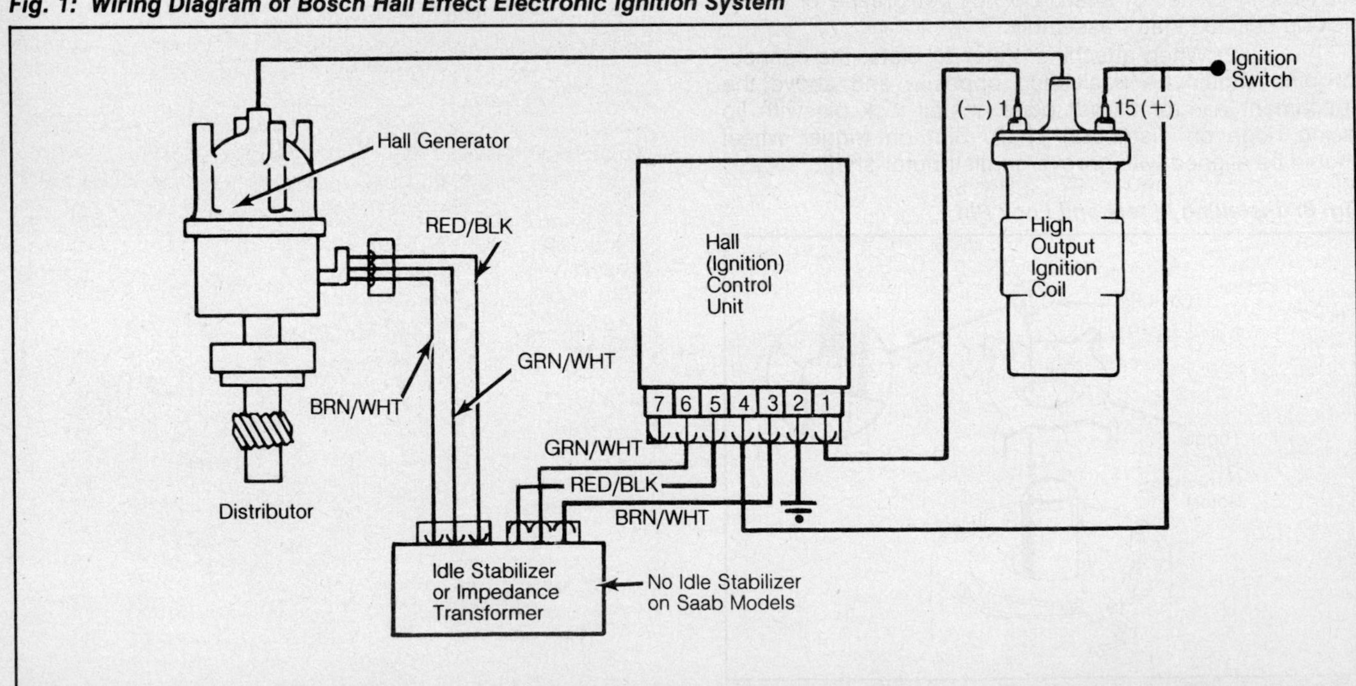
Ignition Switch
(—) 1
15 (+)
Hall Generator
RED/BLK
Hall (Ignition) Control Unit
High Output Ignition Coil
GRN/WHT
BRN/WHT
7 6 5 4 3 2 1
GRN/WHT
RED/BLK
BRN/WHT
Distributor
Idle Stabilizer or Impedance Transformer
No Idle Stabilizer on Saab Models

Saab models do not use an idle stabilizer. Control unit is connected directly to distributor. Also see chassis wiring in WIRING DIAGRAM Section.

BOSCH HALL EFFECT ELECTRONIC IGNITION (Cont.)

SPECIFICATIONS

CENTRIFUGAL & VACUUM ADVANCE

See the appropriate Distributor Specifications Table in this section.

ADJUSTMENTS

HALL EFFECT AIR GAP

Air gap is pre-set and cannot be adjusted.

TESTING - AUDI, PORSCHE & VOLKSWAGEN

PRE-TESTING PROCEDURES

Be sure battery is at full charge and in good condition before making tests. Check all wiring harnesses, ignition switch, ignition coil, spark plug cables and connectors.

CAUTION: Do not connect any 12-volt test instruments on terminal 15 of ignition coil, as this could damage electronic components. Do not connect any condenser/suppressor or powered test light to terminal 1 of ignition coil. Connect and disconnect test instruments only when ignition is turned "OFF."

On Audi 4000 (with 5-cylinder engines) and 5000 models, a gray-colored impedance transformer is installed in place of the idle stabilizer. When adjusting ignition timing, DO NOT disconnect the plugs from the impedance transformer.

However, when trouble shooting the ignition system, by-pass this unit just as you do the idle stabilizer. To do so, disconnect plugs of impedance transformer and plug them together.

CAUTION: Do not touch or remove high tension wires when engine is running or cranking. Disconnect ignition wires only when ignition is "OFF." Do not crank engine unless high tension wire is removed from distributor cap and is grounded by a jumper wire or secured as indicated under System Spark Test.

TACHOMETER ADAPTER

1) An adapter is necessary when attaching a conventional tachometer into the Hall Effect electronic ignition system. *See Fig. 2*. Tachometer Black lead is attached to engine ground. Attach adapter to tachometer Red lead.

2) Adapter is formed from 2 wires soldered together at one end. One wire (leading to coil terminal 1) must be equipped with a 1000-ohm, 1-watt resistor.

3) The second wire (leading to engine ground) must be equipped with a 12,000-ohm, 1-watt resistor. Both resistors should be soldered to attaching wires.

SYSTEM SPARK CHECK

1) If vehicle will not start or does not run properly, ensure first that starter speed is normal and that fuel system is OK. If so, check secondary voltage.

Fig. 2: Assembling and Installing Tachometer Adapter

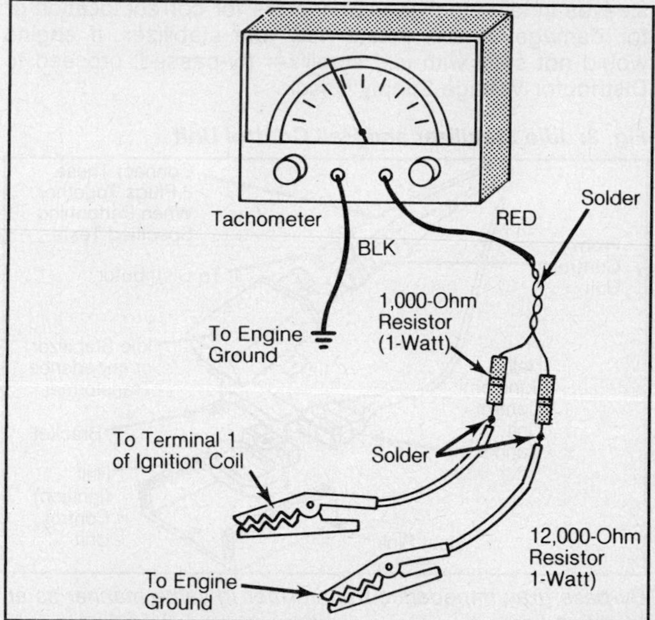
Tachometer
BLK
RED
Solder
1,000-Ohm
Resistor
(1-Watt)
To Engine
Ground
To Terminal 1
of Ignition Coil
Solder
12,000-Ohm
Resistor
1-Watt)
To Engine
Ground

Resistor connections should be soldered securely.

2) Remove coil high tension wire with suppressor from distributor cap. Hold wire approximately 3/8" from engine ground, using insulated pliers.

CAUTION: Wire must not be hand held for this test. Each end of wire should be equipped with a 1000-ohm suppressor.

3) Crank engine and check for a constant blue spark at gap to ground. If there is no spark, proceed to Idle Stabilizer Check. If there is a good spark, but engine would not start, suspect externally-damaged ignition coil.

4) Check to see if sealing compound is oozing from coil housing. If damaged, replace ignition coil and proceed to Control Unit Voltage Check.

5) If coil was not damaged, check coil high tension wire, distributor cap, rotor, spark plug wires, spark plugs, (fuel system and engine mechanical components have already been determined OK).

6) Rotor arm resistance should be 600-1400 ohms. Resistance of spark plug connectors should be 600-1400 ohms (suppressed) or 4000-6000 ohms (not suppressed). Suppressor resistance should be 600-1400 ohms. Replace defective parts if not to specifications.

7) If components in step **5)** were not defective, check for proper ignition timing, centrifugal advance, or vacuum advance. If OK, problem is not with ignition system. If ignition timing is not to specifications, adjust timing or repair ignition distributor.

IDLE STABILIZER CHECK

NOTE: On models equipped with an impedance transformer, testing procedures are the same as with an idle stabilizer.

1) If engine will not start, check idle stabilizer first. Remove both connectors from idle stabilizer, and connect them together. *See Fig. 3*. This by-passes the idle stabilizer, connecting the Hall control unit directly to the distributor's Hall generator.

BOSCH HALL EFFECT ELECTRONIC IGNITION (Cont.)

2) If engine now starts, check contacts and sleeves in idle stabilizer connectors for correct location or for damage. If OK, install new idle stabilizer. If engine would not start with idle stabilizer by-passed, proceed to Distributor Voltage Supply Check.

Fig. 3: Idle Stabilizer and Hall Control Unit

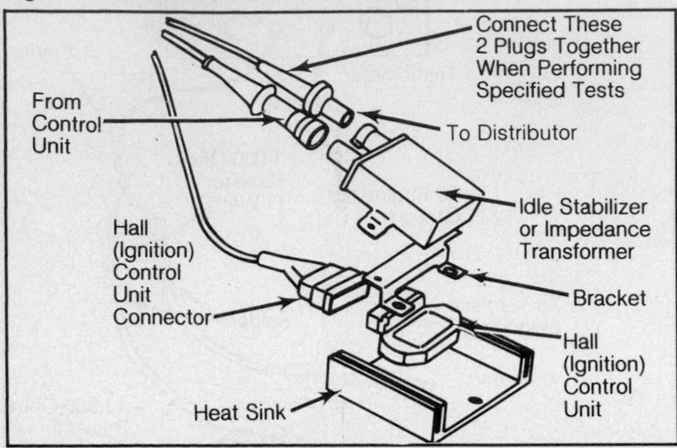
Connect These 2 Plugs Together When Performing Specified Tests
From Control Unit
To Distributor
Idle Stabilizer or Impedance Transformer
Hall (Ignition) Control Unit Connector
Bracket
Hall (Ignition) Control Unit
Heat Sink

By-pass gray impedance transformer in same manner as an idle stabilizer.

DISTRIBUTOR VOLTAGE SUPPLY CHECK

1) Remove 3-wire connector from distributor. Connect voltmeter positive lead to Red/Black wire of harness connector and negative meter lead to Brown/White wire (outside terminals of harness connector). *See Fig. 4*. Turn ignition switch "ON." Voltage reading should be at least 5 volts. Turn ignition "OFF."

2) If voltage checks OK, proceed to Hall Control Unit Check. If there is no voltage, check wiring harness from distributor to Hall control unit. Then proceed to Control Unit Voltage Check.

Fig. 4: Voltmeter Hookup for Distributor Voltage Check

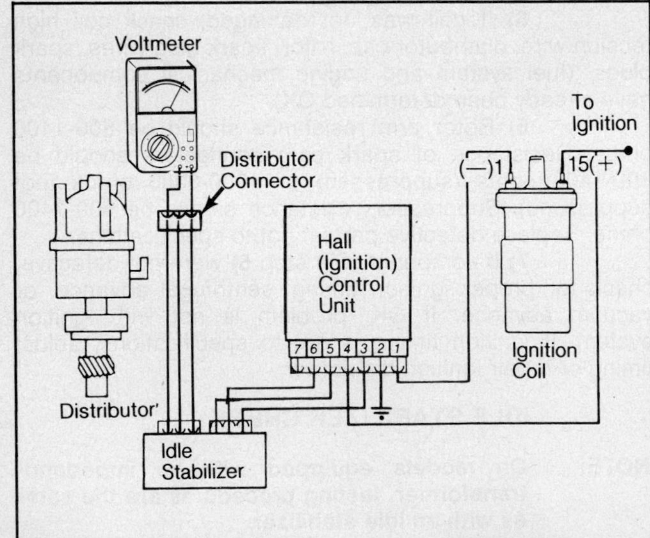
Voltmeter
To Ignition
Distributor Connector
(−)1
15(+)
Hall (Ignition) Control Unit
7 6 5 4 3 2 1
Ignition Coil
Distributor
Idle Stabilizer

Observe proper polarity when installing voltmeter.

HALL CONTROL UNIT CHECK

NOTE: For quick check procedures, see Hall Generator Check, Quick Check.

1) Be sure all connectors are securely connected. Connect voltmeter positive lead to ignition coil terminal 15. Attach negative lead to coil terminal 1. Turn ignition "ON." *See Fig. 5*.

Fig. 5: Checking Hall Control Unit

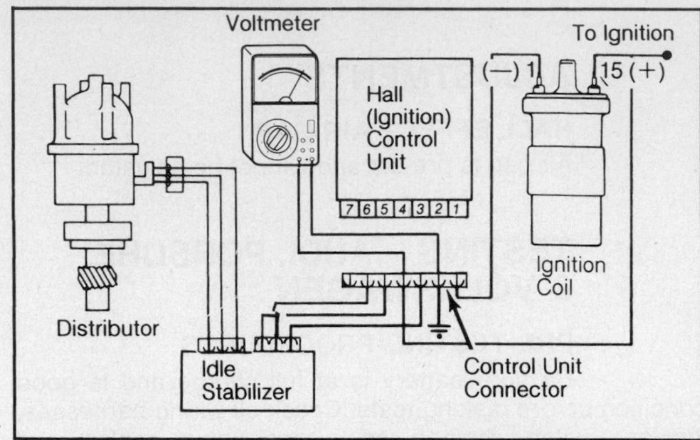
Voltmeter
To Ignition
(−) 1
15 (+)
Hall (Ignition) Control Unit
7 6 5 4 3 2 1
Ignition Coil
Distributor
Idle Stabilizer
Control Unit Connector

Check voltage at ignition coil primary terminals.

2) Reading should be 2 volts, and then fall to 0 (zero) volts after 1-2 seconds. Leave voltmeter connected, but turn ignition "OFF." If voltage reading is correct, replace Hall control unit.

3) If readings were not to specifications, disconnect 3-wire connector at distributor. Insert a metal pin in center contact of harness connector (Green/White wire). *See Fig. 6*.

4) Ground metal pin briefly. Turn ignition "ON". Voltage should increase briefly to at least 2 volts. Turn ignition "OFF". Remove pin and reconnect harness connector to distributor.

Fig. 6: Checking Hall Control Unit

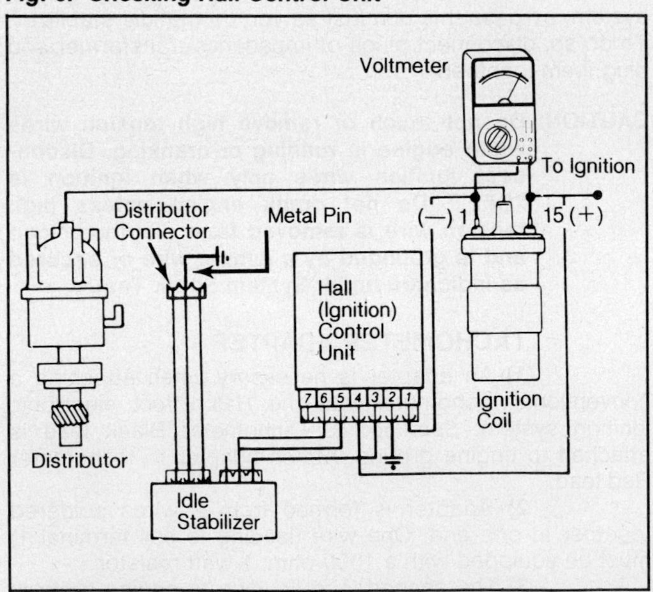
Voltmeter
To Ignition
Distributor Connector
Metal Pin
(−) 1
15 (+)
Hall (Ignition) Control Unit
7 6 5 4 3 2 1
Ignition Coil
Distributor
Idle Stabilizer

Momentarily ground pin inserted in center terminal.

5) If test results were satisfactory, proceed to Hall Generator (Sending Unit) Check. If not to specifications, check for open circuit in wiring. If none is found, replace Hall control unit.

BOSCH HALL EFFECT ELECTRONIC IGNITION (Cont.)

HALL GENERATOR CHECK

Quick Check

1) Connect a voltmeter or a test lamp between ignition coil terminal 15 and ground. Start engine and observe voltmeter or test lamp.

2) If voltmeter needle pulsates or test lamp flickers, the Hall sender and control unit are probably OK.

Thorough Check

1) Remove high tension cable from distributor cap, and ground it. Be sure control unit harness connector is attached to control unit. *See Fig. 7*.

Fig. 7: Voltmeter Hookups for Hall Generator Check

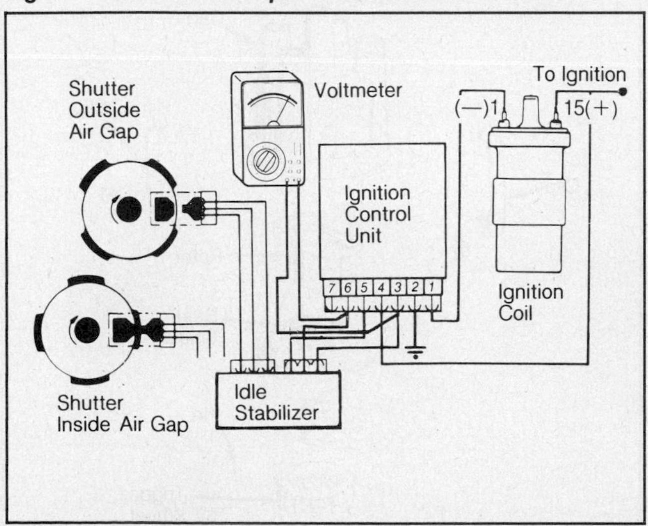
Shutter
Outside
Air Gap
Voltmeter
To Ignition
(—)1
15(+)
Ignition
Control
Unit
7 6 5 4 3 2 1
Ignition
Coil
Shutter
Inside Air Gap
Idle
Stabilizer

Harness must be connected to Hall control unit.

2) Pull back rubber boot on connector. Attach voltmeter positive lead to connector terminal 6, and negative lead to terminal 3. Be sure connector is securely plugged into control unit.

3) Turn ignition switch "ON." Turn engine over by hand, and check voltage reading. It should be 0-2 volts. Turn ignition "OFF." If not to specifications, replace Hall generator unit in distributor or replace distributor.

4) If Hall generator met specifications, test ignition coil resitance. If coil is faulty, replace coil.

IGNITION COIL RESISTANCE CHECK

Primary Resistance

Turn ignition "OFF." Remove all wires from ignition coil. Set an ohmmeter in the low scale and attach its leads to ignition coil primary terminals 1 and 15. *See Fig. 8*. Coil primary resistance should be .52-.76 ohm.

Secondary Resistance

Reset ohmmeter to x1000 scale, and connect leads to primary terminal 1 and to coil tower, terminal 4. *See Fig. 8*. Resistance should read 2400-3500 ohms.

Fig. 8: Ohmmeter Hookups for Coil Resistance Checks

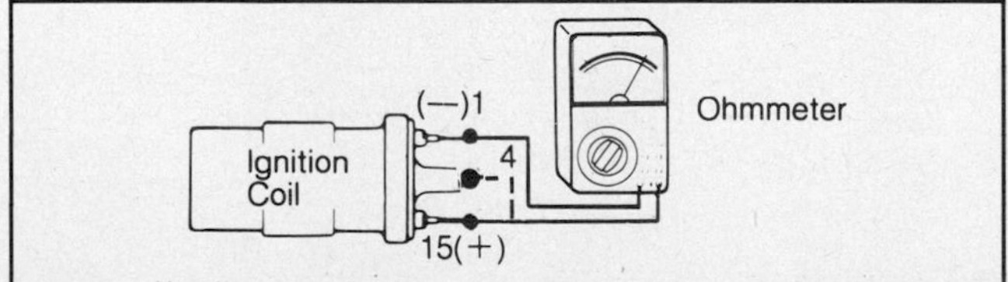
(—)1
Ohmmeter
Ignition
Coil
4
15(+)

Replace ignition coil if not to specifications.

CONTROL UNIT VOLTAGE CHECK

1) Disconnect connectors from idle stabilizer (or impedance transformer) and connect them to each other. Reconnect connector to distributor.

2) Remove connector from electronic ignition control unit. *See Fig. 9*. Connect positive voltmeter lead to terminal 4 of control unit harness connector. Attach negative lead to terminal 2 (ground).

Fig. 9: Voltmeter Hookup for Control Unit Voltage Check

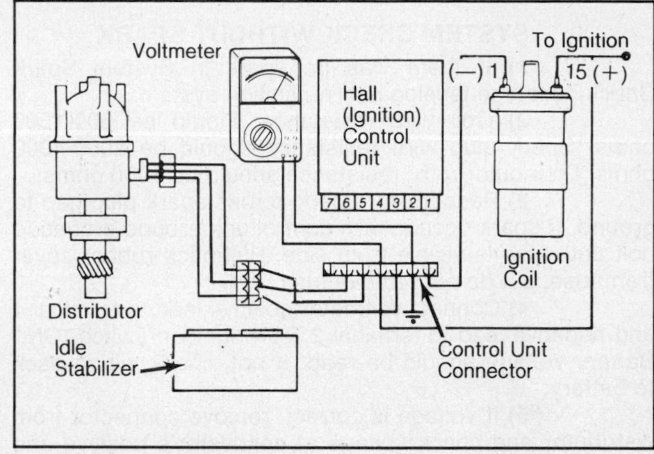
Voltmeter
To Ignition
(—)1
15(+)
Hall
(Ignition)
Control
Unit
7 6 5 4 3 2 1
Ignition
Coil
Distributor
Idle
Stabilizer
Control Unit
Connector

By-pass idle stabilizer during this test.

3) Turn ignition switch "ON." Voltmeter should register approximately battery voltage. Turn ignition "OFF." If battery voltage was not present, check and repair wiring circuit from battery to control unit.

4) If battery voltage was present, check for open circuit in wiring from Hall control unit to idle stabilizer (or impedance transformer) and on to Hall generator in distributor. Repair or replace wiring as necessary. If wiring is OK, replace Hall control unit.

5) If tests do not disclose a definite problem, substitute a new Hall control unit or Hall generator, and attempt to start engine.

TESTING – SAAB

SYSTEM SPARK CHECK

1) Check for spark by attaching plug lead to a spark plug. Make sure spark plug is grounded to engine. Crank engine, and check for spark at gap to ground.

2) If spark occurs, proceed to System Check With Spark. If none occurs, proceed to System Check Without Spark.

SYSTEM CHECK WITH SPARK

1) If spark occurred in System Spark Check, turn control unit around grounded bolt until fuse is visible from side. Pull back rubber cover from fuse, but do not remove fuse.

2) Connect voltmeter positive lead to terminal 4 and negative lead to terminal 2. Turn ignition switch "ON." Battery voltage should be read. If not, check wiring back to battery.

3) If battery voltage was present, check ignition coil primary and secondary resistance in same manner as for Audi and Volkswagen models.

BOSCH HALL EFFECT ELECTRONIC IGNITION (Cont.)

4) Primary resistance should be .52-.76 ohms. Secondary resistance should be 7,000-9,000 ohms. If not to specification, replace ignition coil.

5) If coil resistance is satisfactory, remove coil wire from distributor. Connect voltmeter positive lead to terminal 15 and negative lead to terminal 1 of ignition coil.

6) Turn ignition switch "ON." The voltmeter should drop from 6 volts to zero (0) volts within 1-2 seconds. If not, replace control unit. If so, engine should start.

SYSTEM CHECK WITHOUT SPARK

1) If there was no spark in System Spark Check, test high tension part of ignition system.

2) Coil wire resistance should be 500-1500 ohms. Spark plug wire resistance should be 2000-4000 ohms. Distributor rotor resistance should be 1000 ohms.

3) Recheck for spark across spark plug gap to ground. If spark occurs, turn control unit around grounded bolt until fuse is visible from side. Pull back rubber cover from fuse, but do not remove fuse.

4) Connect voltmeter positive lead to terminal 4 and negative lead to terminal 2. Turn ignition switch "ON." Battery voltage should be read. If not, check wiring back to battery.

5) If voltage is correct, remove connector from distributor and check voltage at connector's positive and negative terminals. Battery voltage should be read. If not, check wiring back to control unit. If satisfactory, replace control unit.

6) If battery voltage was present, connect voltmeter positive lead to control unit terminal 6 and negative lead to terminal 3. Remove distributor cap and dust cover. Turn engine over so the shutter blades are outside the Hall switch.

7) Turn ignition switch "ON." Voltage should read about .4 volt. If so, turn engine over until shutter blades enter Hall switch gap. Voltage should now read 1 volt or more. If readings are not to specifications, replace distributor.

8) If voltage in step **7)** was correct, perform steps **3)** through **6)** of System Check With Spark.

OVERHAUL

DISASSEMBLY

NOTE: The Hall Effect switch and trigger wheel (segmented shutter) cannot be removed on Saab models. If problem exists, entire distributor must be replaced.

1) Loosen ground strap and remove static shield from distributor cap. *See Fig.10*. Remove cap, rotor, carbon brush and spring. Remove dust cover.

2) Remove connector from distributor (connects Hall generator and harness leading to idle stabilizer). Remove retaining snap ring and trigger wheel (segmented shutter). Remove washers. Remove screws and lift out Hall sending unit and connecting socket.

3) Remove base plate and vacuum unit. Remove pin and distributor drive pinion and shims.

REASSEMBLY

To reassemble, reverse disassembly procedure. If a new Hall generator is to be installed, a special repair kit is available containing all necessary parts. Replace seals, and check components for cracks, corrosion and wear. Clean cap before installing.

Fig. 10: Exploded View of Bosch Hall Effect Distributor

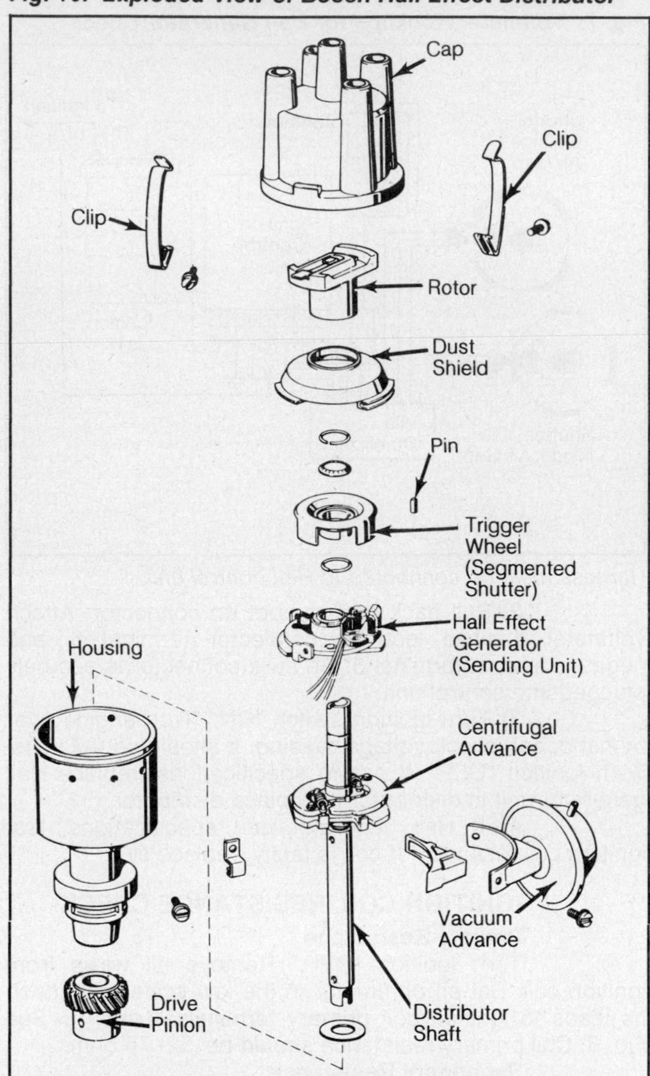
Cap
Clip
Clip
Rotor
Dust Shield
Pin
Trigger Wheel (Segmented Shutter)
Hall Effect Generator (Sending Unit)
Housing
Centrifugal Advance
Vacuum Advance
Drive Pinion
Distributor Shaft

A special kit is available for replacing Hall generator on Audi and Volkswagen models.

BOSCH SINGLE BREAKER DISTRIBUTOR

Volkswagen Vanagon (Federal)

DESCRIPTION

Vanagon Federal models are equipped with a conventional, single breaker distributor, with centrifugal advance and vacuum advance and/or retard unit.

Vacuum units may be single or dual diaphragm, and are linked to the movable portion of the breaker plate assembly to advance or retard spark.

NOTE: Some distributors may use a dual diaphragm unit to provide retard only (vacuum advance side not used).

SPECIFICATIONS

POINT GAP & CAM ANGLE

Set distributor point gap, so dwell is 44-50°. Dwell wear limit is 42-58°.

CENTRIFUGAL & VACUUM ADVANCE (OR RETARD)

See the appropriate Distributor Specifications Table in this section.

ADJUSTMENT

POINT GAP, ALIGNMENT, & DWELL

1) With rubbing block on high point of cam lobe, insert a feeler gauge blade between contacts. Check reading against specification.

2) To correct, loosen retaining screw. Place screwdriver between bosses so it engages slot. Turn it to move stationary contact point. When correct gap is obtained, then tighten screw.

3) Align points if necessary by bending stationary contact support only. Check cam angle with a dwell meter. Compare indicated reading with specification, and correct if necessary.

Fig. 1: Adjusting Contact Points

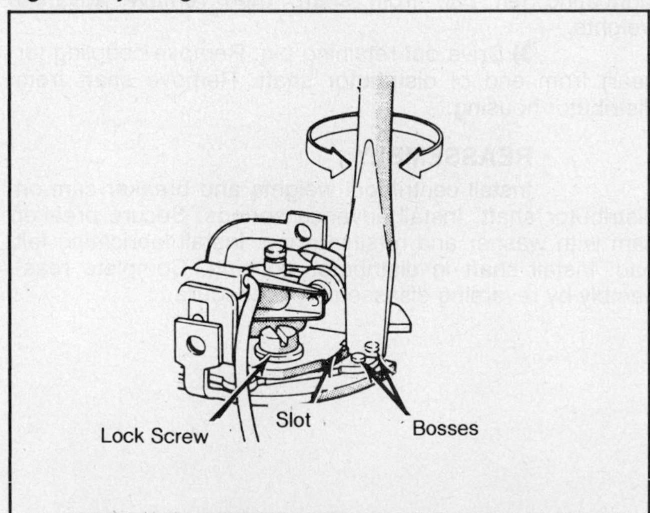
Lock Screw
Slot
Bosses

Use screwdriver to move stationary contact point.

BREAKER ARM SPRING TENSION

To check spring tension, place hook end of spring scale as close as possible to the movable breaker point. Pull scale at a right angle (90 degrees) to the movable arm, and note reading just as points begin to open.

CENTRIFUGAL ADVANCE

1) Check distributor in test stand, according to test equipment manufacturer's instructions. Operate distributor both up and down the RPM range, and check advance at all RPM settings specified. Adjust or replace springs, weights, or cam as necessary.

2) If distributor has adjustable driving collar for centrifugal advance, disassemble, and lift out shaft. *See Fig. 2.* It is not necessary to remove breaker cam assembly from shaft.

3) To adjust, loosen screws retaining driving collar. If collar is turned in direction of rotation, the advance curve rises. Turning collar in opposite direction of rotation will lower the curve.

Fig. 2: Centrifugal Advance Adjustment

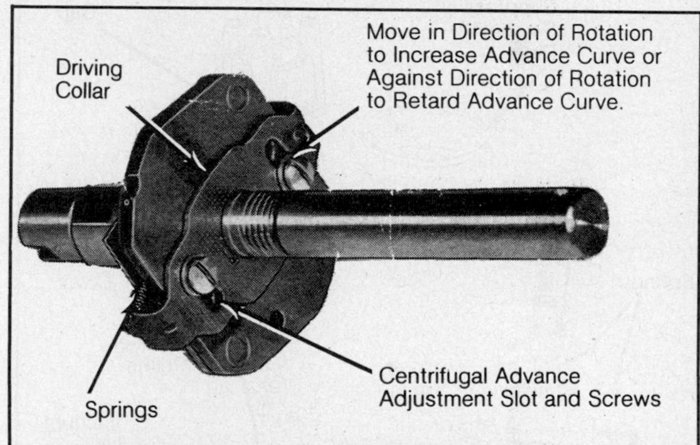
Driving Collar
Move in Direction of Rotation to Increase Advance Curve or Against Direction of Rotation to Retard Advance Curve.
Springs
Centrifugal Advance Adjustment Slot and Screws

To adjust, turn driving collar in appropriate direction.

CAUTION: Centrifugal advance curve must not be adjusted by bending spring clamps of driving collar.

Fig. 3: Centrifugal Advance Adjustment

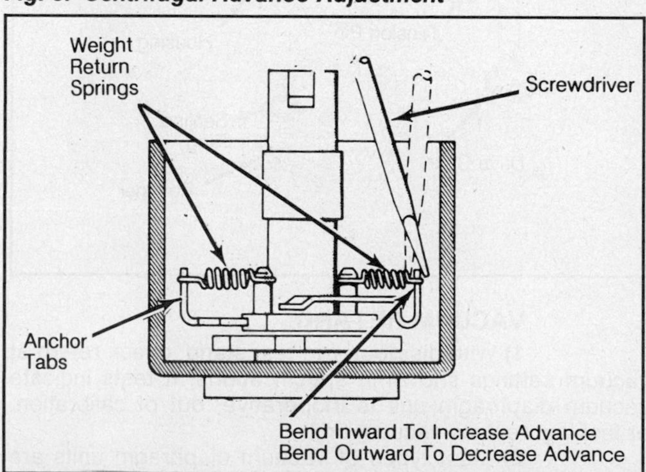
Weight Return Springs
Screwdriver
Anchor Tabs
Bend Inward To Increase Advance
Bend Outward To Decrease Advance

Modify spring tension by bending spring anchor tabs.

BOSCH SINGLE BREAKER DISTRIBUTOR (Cont.)

4) If distributor does not have adjustable driving collar, adjustment may be made by bending spring anchor tabs to modify spring tension. *See Fig. 3*.

5) To adjust for low speed operation, bend primary spring anchor tab outward to decrease advance, and inward to increase advance. For high speed operation, bend secondary spring anchor tab in or out to obtain specified settings.

VACUUM ADVANCE

1) With distributor in test stand, check advance at vacuum settings shown in specifications. If tests indicate vacuum diaphragm unit is inoperative, out of calibration, or leaking, replace vacuum unit.

2) Most types of vacuum diaphragm units are factory pre-set, and cannot be adjusted. However, on some dual diaphragm vacuum units, the vacuum advance may be increased or decreased by turning an Allen screw located in the end of diaphragm unit.

Fig. 4: Disassembled View of Bosch Distributor

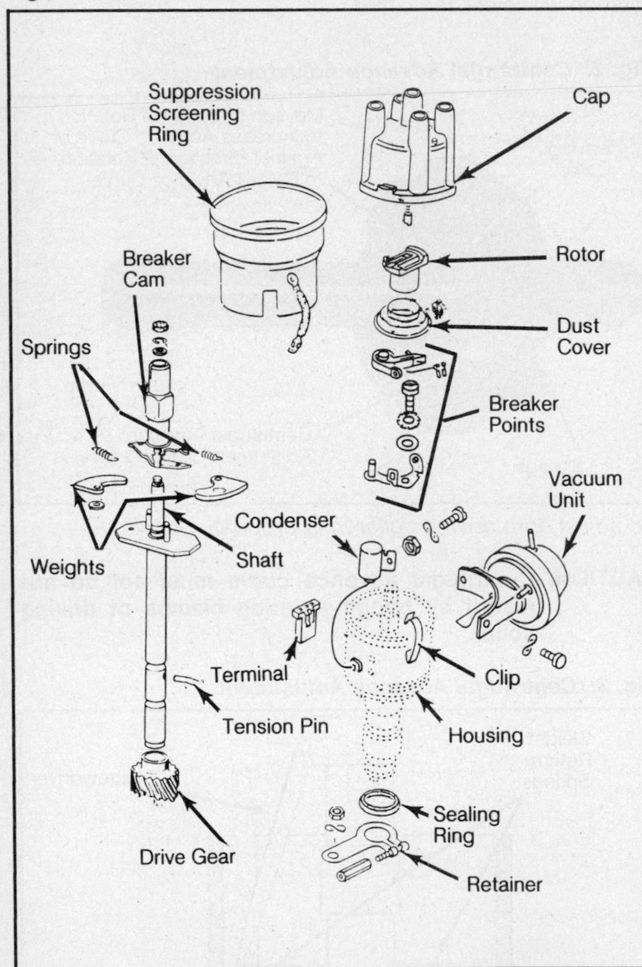
Suppression Screening Ring
Cap
Breaker Cam
Rotor
Dust Cover
Springs
Breaker Points
Vacuum Unit
Condenser
Weights
Shaft
Terminal
Clip
Tension Pin
Housing
Sealing Ring
Drive Gear
Retainer

VACUUM RETARD

1) With distributor in test stand, check retard at vacuum settings shown in specifications. If tests indicate vacuum diaphragm unit is inoperative, out of calibration, or leaking, replace vacuum unit.

2) Most types of vacuum diaphragm units are factory pre-set, and cannot be adjusted. However, on some dual diaphragm units, the maximum vacuum retard setting may be raised or lowered if necessary by turning an eccentric, located at side of vacuum unit. *See Fig. 5.*

Fig. 5: Adjusting Maximum Vacuum Retard

Turning eccentric adjusts retard setting.

OVERHAUL

NOTE: All parts should be marked or set aside separately or in groups, so that same combination can be reinstalled. Keep screws with the component that they attach, as screws are different lengths. Damage could occur if installed in wrong position.

DISASSEMBLY

1) Disconnect and remove vacuum unit. Remove breaker points and condenser. Remove breaker assembly. Note position of centrifugal advance parts, and mark them for reassembly reference. Disconnect and remove centrifugal advance springs (do not distort).

2) Using 2 screwdrivers, carefully pry upward on the lower edge of breaker cam to disengage cam retaining ring. Lift cam, washer, retaining ring and lubricating felt pad from shaft, then remove advance weights.

3) Drive out retaining pin. Remove coupling (or gear) from end of distributor shaft. Remove shaft from distributor housing.

REASSEMBLY

Install centrifugal weights and breaker cam on distributor shaft. Install advance springs. Secure breaker cam with washer and retaining ring. Install lubricating felt pad. Install shaft in distributor housing. Complete reassembly by reversing disassembly procedure.

DUCELLIER ELECTRONIC IGNITION — PEUGEOT

505

DESCRIPTION

The Ducellier electronic ignition system used by Peugeot consists of a Ducellier breakerless distributor, a Delco-Remy ignition coil and amplifier module, an ignition switch, and necessary wiring.

The distributor contains both centrifugal and vacuum advance mechanisms, a pick-up coil and a reluctor (polarity wheel). *See Fig. 1*. The ignition coil and amplifier module are mounted to a common light alloy base. The base provides both good grounding and cooling of the amplifier module.

Silicone grease, which comes with the module for application between the module and base, gives improved heat transfer. Since both units are grounded through the common base, all mounting bolts should be snug.

Fig. 1: Exploded View of Ducellier Breakerless Distributor

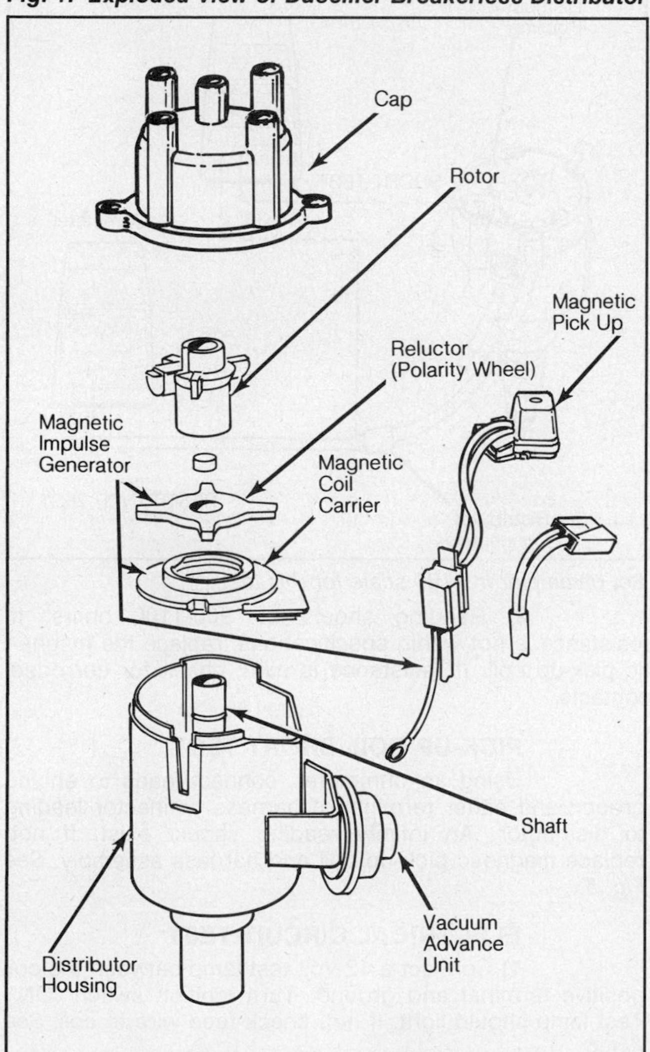
Cap
Rotor
Magnetic Pick Up
Reluctor (Polarity Wheel)
Magnetic Impulse Generator
Magnetic Coil Carrier
Shaft
Vacuum Advance Unit
Distributor Housing

The ignition coil is encased in epoxy resin instead of oil. The amplifier module receives, amplifies and sends electronic signals to provide proper spark timing.

OPERATION

The distributor contains an electronic pulse generator, consisting of a pick-up coil and a reluctor (polarity wheel). As the distributor shaft turns, the reluctor teeth approach and pass the magnetic pick-up coil. *See Fig. 2*.

As the reluctor teeth break the magnetic field around the pick-up coil, it causes signals to be transmitted to the amplifier module. The signals open and close a transistorized switch in the module.

This turns the primary circuit of the ignition coil on and off. When the primary circuit is switched off, a high voltage surge occurs in the secondary circuit, firing the spark plugs.

Fig. 2: Schematic of Ducellier Electronic Ignition System

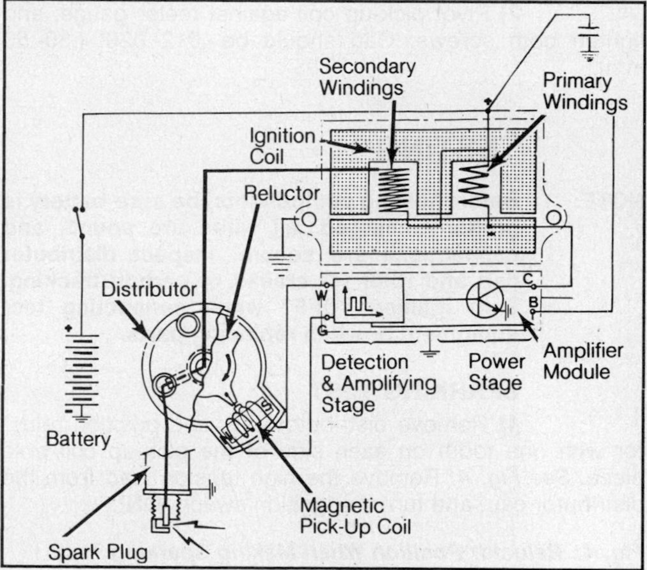
Secondary Windings
Primary Windings
Ignition Coil
Reluctor
Distributor
W
G
C
B
Detection & Amplifying Stage
Power Stage
Amplifier Module
Battery
Magnetic Pick-Up Coil
Spark Plug

Also see chassis wiring in WIRING DIAGRAM Section.

The amplifier module has 4 terminals. Terminals "W" and "G" are connected to the distributor magnetic pulse generator (pick-up coil). Terminal "B" is connected to the coil positive terminal, and terminal "C" to the coil negative terminal. *See Fig. 3*. The unit is grounded by one of its mounting bolts through the alloy base.

Fig. 3: Amplifier Module Connector Terminals

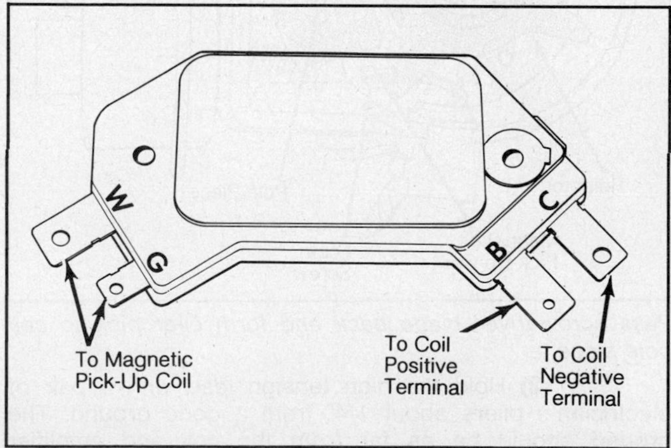
W
G
B
C
To Magnetic Pick-Up Coil
To Coil Positive Terminal
To Coil Negative Terminal

Module is grounded by mounting bolt through base.

DUCELLIER ELECTRONIC IGNITION — PEUGEOT (Cont.)

SPECIFICATIONS

CENTRIFUGAL & VACUUM ADVANCE

See the appropriate Distributor Specifications Table in this section.

ADJUSTMENTS

RELUCTOR-TO-PICK-UP COIL AIR GAP

1) Loosen both magnetic pick-up coil mounting screws. *See Fig. 4*. Position reluctor tooth in line with pick-up coil pole piece. Insert a non-magnetic feeler gauge of the proper thickness (.016" or .40 mm) between one reluctor tooth and pole piece.

2) Pivot pick-up coil against feeler gauge, and tighten both screws. Gap should be .012-.020" (.30-.50 mm).

TESTING

NOTE: Before testing components, be sure battery is properly charged, all wires are sound, and connections are secure. Inspect distributor cap and rotor for cracks or carbon tracking. Turn ignition "OFF" when connecting test equipment or when replacing parts.

SPARKING TEST

1) Remove distributor cap, and position reluctor with one tooth on each side of the pick-up coil pole piece. *See Fig. 4*. Remove the high tension lead from the distributor cap, and turn the ignition switch "ON".

Fig. 4: Reluctor Position When Making Sparking Test

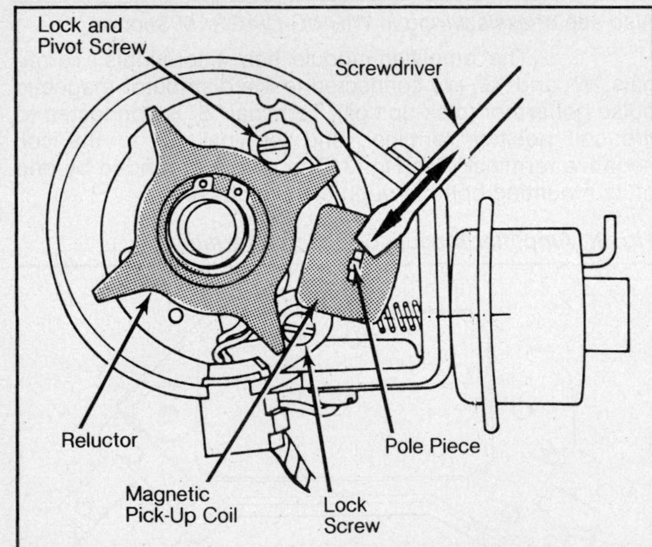
Lock and
Pivot Screw
Screwdriver
Reluctor
Pole Piece
Magnetic
Pick-Up Coil
Lock
Screw

Pass screwdriver blade back and forth over pick-up coil pole piece.

2) Hold the high tension lead with a pair of electrician's pliers about 1/4" from a good ground. The ground should be as far from the coil and amplifier assembly as possible.

3) Alternately pass the blade of a screwdriver back and forth over the pick-up coil pole piece. A spark should occur at gap each time screwdriver passes pole piece.

4) If no spark occurs, suspect the magnetic pick-up coil, ignition coil or amplifier module. If spark occurs, but engine does not perform properly, check distributor cap, rotor, high tension cables and battery condition.

PICK-UP COIL RESISTANCE TEST

1) Turn ignition switch "OFF". Disconnect connector for terminals "W" and "G" at amplifier module. Using an ohmmeter set in the x100 scale, check the resistance between terminals of harness connector leading to the distributor. *See Fig. 5*.

Fig. 5: Ohmmeter Hookup for Pick-Up Coil Resistance and Short Tests

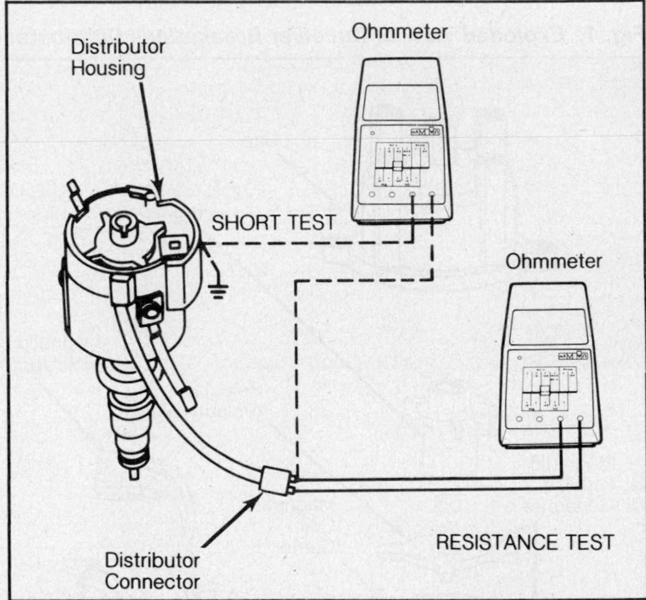
Ohmmeter
Distributor
Housing
SHORT TEST
Ohmmeter
RESISTANCE TEST
Distributor
Connector

Set ohmmeter in x100 scale for this test.

2) Reading should be 900-1100 ohms. If resistance is not within specifications, replace the magnetic pick-up coil. If resistance is high, check for corroded contacts.

PICK-UP COIL SHORT TEST

Using an ohmmeter, connect leads to engine ground and either terminal of harness connector leading to distributor. An infinity reading should exist. If not, replace magnetic pick-up coil and harness assembly. *See Fig. 5*.

ELECTRICAL CIRCUIT TEST

1) Connect a 12-volt test lamp between the coil positive terminal and ground. Turn ignition switch "ON". Test lamp should light. If not, check feed wire to coil. *See Fig. 6*.

2) Connect test lamp between the coil negative terminal and ground. Turn ignition switch "ON". Test lamp should again light. If not, check if coil primary circuit is broken or if amplifier module's power transistor is shorted.

DUCELLIER ELECTRONIC IGNITION — PEUGEOT (Cont.)

Fig. 6: Test Lamp Hookup for Electrical Circuit Test

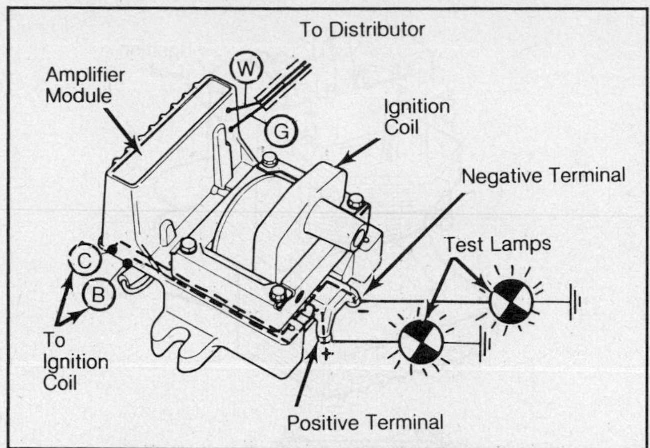
To Distributor
Amplifier Module
W
G
Ignition Coil
Negative Terminal
Test Lamps
C
B
To Ignition Coil
Positive Terminal

Lamp should light in both tests with ignition "ON".

IGNITION COIL RESISTANCE TEST

1) Using an ohmmeter set in the low scale, connect leads to coil primary (positive and negative) terminals. Resistance should be .48-.61 ohm. *See Fig. 7.*

Fig. 7: Ohmmeter Hookup for Making Ignition Coil Resistance Tests

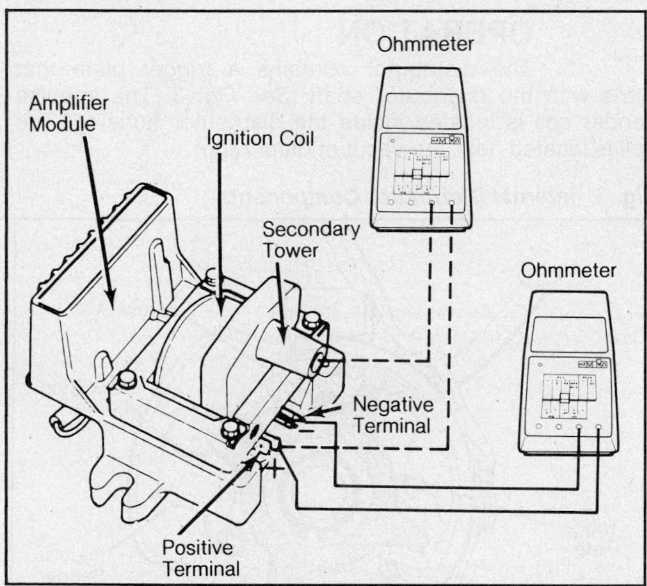
Ohmmeter
Amplifier Module
Ignition Coil
Secondary Tower
Ohmmeter
Negative Terminal
Positive Terminal

Be sure ignition is "OFF" and coil wires are disconnected before making this test.

2) Connect ohmmeter set in the x1000 scale to the coil positive terminal and its secondary tower. Reading should be 9,000-11,000 ohms. If either reading is not to specifications, replace ignition coil.

AMPLIFIER MODULE TEST

1) Disconnect distributor harness connector from amplifier module "W" and "G" terminals. Disconnect the high tension lead from distributor cap. Turn ignition switch "ON".

2) Hold high tension lead with a pair of electrician's pliers and position it 1/4" from good engine ground. The ground should be as far from the coil and amplifier module assembly as possible.

3) Use a jumper wire to feed terminal "G" of amplifier module with successive impulses from battery positive terminal. At each impulse, a spark should jump the gap to ground. If not, repeat same test with a new amplifier module. If spark now jumps gap, install new module.

OVERHAUL

DISASSEMBLY

1) Remove distributor cap, rotor, and plastic protector. Remove screw in the side of distributor. Pull upward on electrical connector to remove it from distributor housing. Remove 2 screws securing magnetic pick-up coil. *See Fig. 1.*

2) Lift out pick-up coil assembly. Remove reluctor, vacuum advance unit, magnetic coil carrier. Remove drive pinion from distributor shaft and pull shaft and centrifugal advance mechanism from housing.

REASSEMBLY

To install, reverse removal procedure.

DUCELLIER ELECTRONIC IGNITION – RENAULT

18i, Fuego & LeCar

NOTE: Fuego Turbo models use the Ducellier-Renault Computer-Controlled Electronic Ignition System. See appropriate article in this section.

DESCRIPTION

Ducellier electronic ignition system consists of a Ducellier breakerless distributor, a Delco-Remy ignition coil and electronic control unit, an ignition switch and necessary wiring.

The distributor contains both centrifugal and vacuum advance mechanisms. The distributor also contains a trigger plate (reluctor), an impulse sender (pick-up coil), seal, rotor, and cap. *See Fig. 1.*

Fig. 1: Exploded View of Renault Distributor

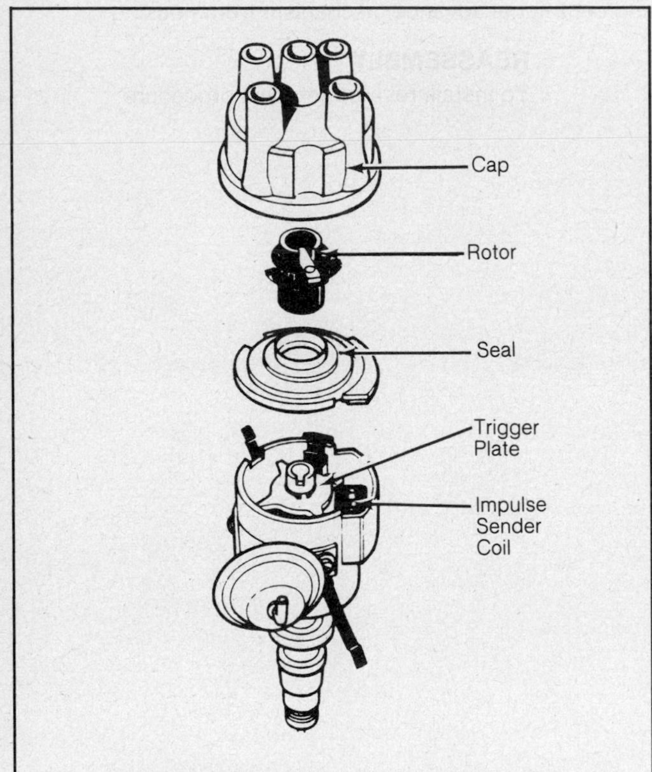
Cap
Rotor
Seal
Trigger
Plate
Impulse
Sender
Coil

Note position of impulse sender.

The ignition coil and electronic control unit are mounted to a common support, that provides both good grounding and cooling of the electronic control unit. *See Fig. 2.*

Silicone grease, which comes with each electronic control unit, is applied between the unit and support to provide improved heat transfer. Since both units are grounded through the common support base, all mounting bolts should be snug.

The ignition coil is encased in epoxy resin instead of oil. The electronic control unit receives, amplifies, and sends electronic signals to provide proper spark timing.

Fig. 2: Ignition Coil and Electronic Control Unit Assembly

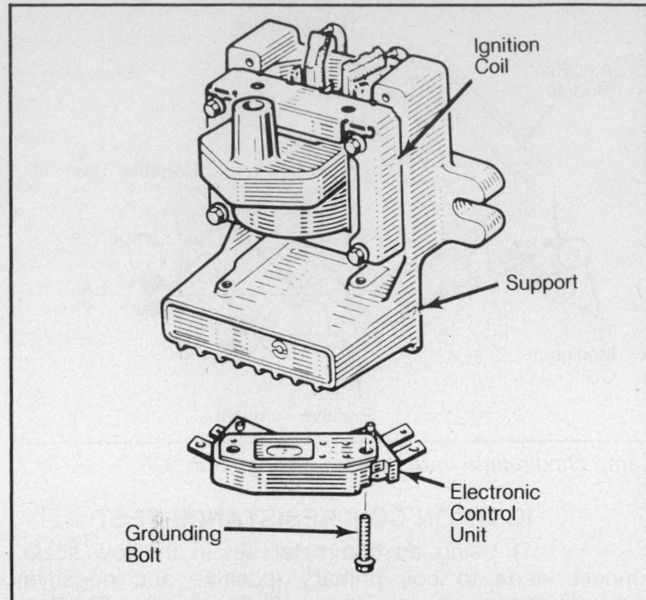
Ignition
Coil
Support
Electronic
Control
Unit
Grounding
Bolt

Components are mounted to a common support. Also see chassis wiring in WIRING DIAGRAM Section.

OPERATION

The distributor contains a trigger plate that turns with the distributor shaft. *See Fig. 3.* The impulse sender coil is located inside the distributor housing. The coil is located near the vacuum diaphragm.

Fig. 3: Internal Distributor Components

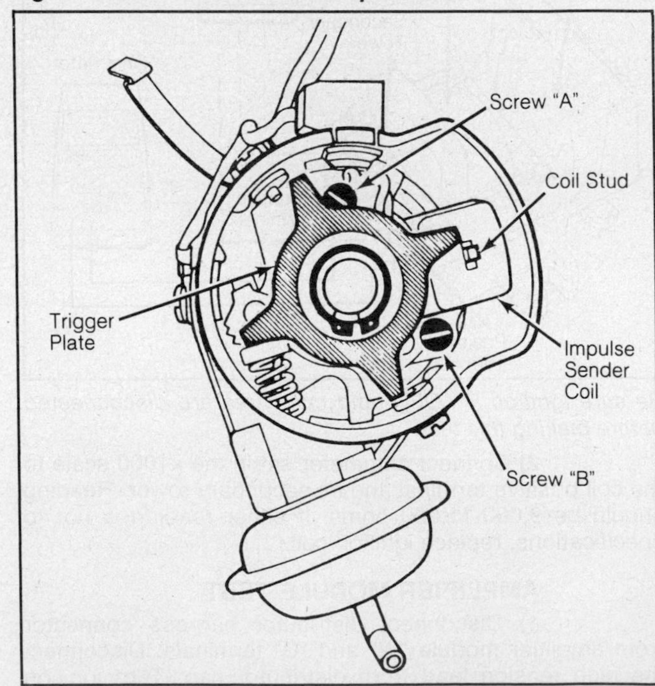
Screw "A"
Coil Stud
Trigger
Plate
Impulse
Sender
Coil
Screw "B"

To adjust gap, trigger plate arm must be aligned with stud on impulse generator.

DUCELLIER ELECTRONIC IGNITION - RENAULT (Cont.)

As the rotating trigger plate approaches and passes the impulse sender coil, a magnetic field builds and collapses, sending a signal to the electronic control unit. This signal opens and closes a transistor in the electronic control unit, turning the primary circuit in the ignition coil on and off.

When the primary coil circuit is turned off, a high voltage surge occurs in the coil secondary circuit, providing spark to the spark plugs through the distributor rotor, cap and secondary wires.

The electronic control unit has 4 terminals. *See Fig. 4*. Terminals "W" and "G" are connected to the distributor impulse sender coil.

Terminal "B" is connected to the coil positive terminal and terminal "C" to the coil negative terminal. The unit is grounded, through one of its mounting bolts, to the support shared with the ignition coil.

Fig. 4: Electronic Control Unit Terminals

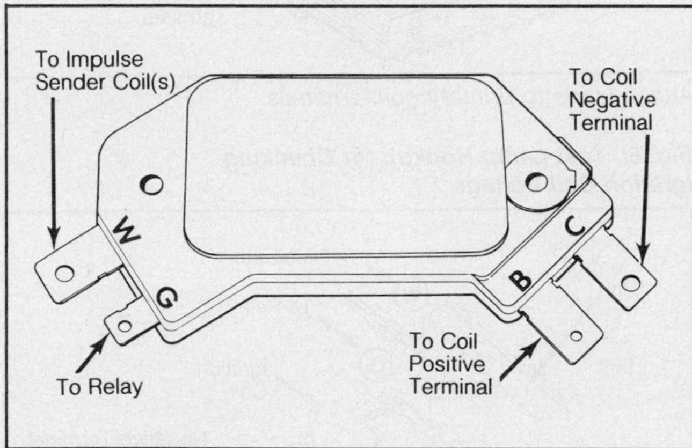
To Impulse Sender Coil(s)
To Coil Negative Terminal
W
C
B
G
To Relay
To Coil Positive Terminal

Note size of terminal "G."

SPECIFICATIONS

CENTRIFUGAL & VACUUM ADVANCE

See the appropriate Distributor Specifications Table in this section.

ADJUSTMENTS

TRIGGER PLATE-TO-IMPULSE SENDER COIL AIR GAP

1) Loosen screw "A." *See Fig. 3*. Place an .018" (.45 mm) feeler gauge between pick-up coil stud and arm of the trigger plate. *See Fig. 5*. Move slotted coil base on screw "A" side until stud on top of coil touches feeler gauge. Tighten screw "A."

2) Check air gap at all 4 arms of trigger plate. If gap is not within .012-.024" (.3-.6 mm) range for any arms of trigger plate and cannot be adjusted correctly, replace distributor.

DIAGNOSIS & TESTING

NOTE: **Before testing components, be sure battery is properly charged, all wires are sound and connections are secure. Inspect distributor cap and rotor for cracks or carbon tracking. Turn ignition "OFF" when connecting test equipment or when replacing parts.**

Fig. 5: Checking Distributor Air Gap With Feeler Gauge

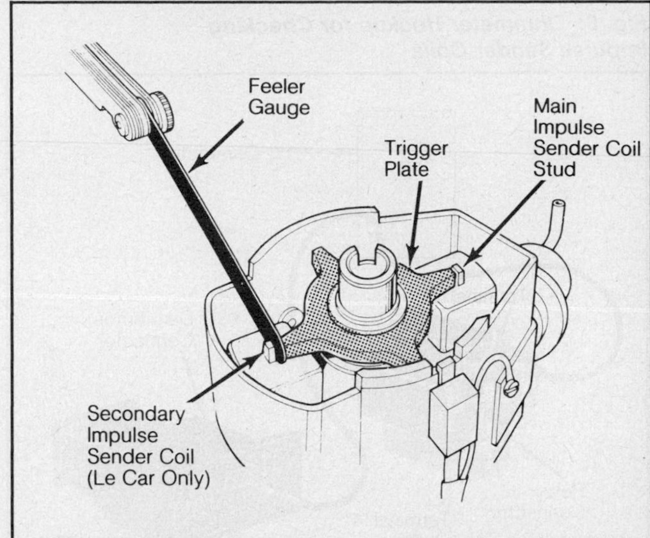
Feeler Gauge
Trigger Plate
Main Impulse Sender Coil Stud
Secondary Impulse Sender Coil (Le Car Only)

Check gap at each trigger plate tooth. Distributor with 2 impulse sender coils is used for illustration only.

IGNITION DEFECT OCCURS DURING ENGINE OPERATION

If ignition defect occurs during normal engine operation, check condition of spark plug wires, coil high tension wire and spark plugs. If engine surges or misfires due to ignition malfunction, and wires and spark plugs are not defective, replace electronic control unit.

NOTE: **Never disconnect spark plug wires when engine is running. This may cause high voltage to seek ground through distributor body, causing rotor damage or trigger plate deterioration.**

TESTING SYSTEM WHEN ENGINE WILL NOT START

In cold start situations, where the engine will not start, perform the following tests.

SPARKING TEST

1) Turn ignition switch to "ON" position. Remove distributor cap. Disconnect the high tension coil wire from distributor and hold it approximately 1/4" from a good ground. Ground should be as far away as possible from the ignition coil and electronic control unit.

2) Move a magnet in a spiral motion over impulse sender stud. A spark should jump from the gap to ground as magnet passes over coil.

3) If spark occurs but engine will not start, problem is in distributor cap, rotor, spark plug wires or fuel system. If no spark occurs, proceed with component checks.

IMPULSE SENDER COIL CHECK

NOTE: **Do not use a test light to check distributor impulse sender coil. High voltage may damage the coil.**

DUCELLIER ELECTRONIC IGNITION - RENAULT (Cont.)

1) Be sure impulse sender coil feed wires have not been cut. Disconnect the 5-wire relay connector and the 3-wire distributor connector (2 black wires, 1 gray). *See Fig. 6*.

Fig. 6: Ohmmeter Hookup for Checking Impulse Sender Coils

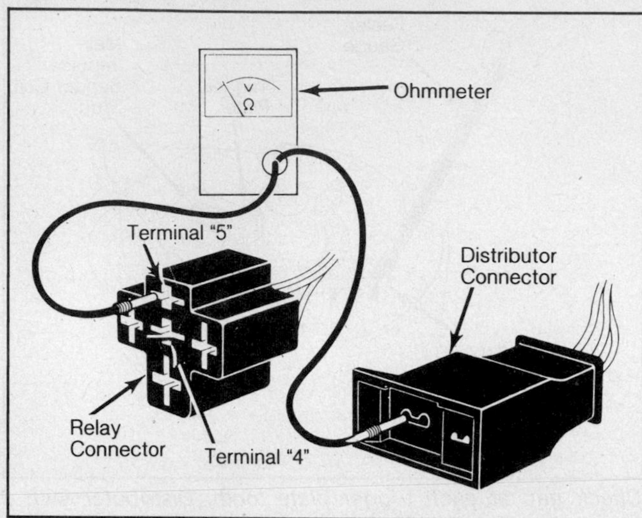
Ohmmeter
Terminal "5"
Distributor Connector
Relay Connector
Terminal "4"

Ohmmeter needle should move.

2) Connect lead of an ohmmeter to terminal 5 of the 5-wire relay harness connector. Connect the other ohmmeter lead to the double black wire terminal of distributor connector. The needle should move. If not, replace impulse sender coil.

3) To check impulse sender coil for shorts, connect ohmmeter lead to terminal 5 with second ohmmeter lead connected to distributor body. The needle should not move. If it does, replace impulse sender coil.

IGNITION COIL AND ELECTRONIC CONTROL UNIT CHECK

1) Turn the ignition switch to the "ON" position. Connect positive voltmeter lead to ignition coil positive terminal. Connect remaining lead to ignition coil negative terminal. *See Fig. 7*.

2) Quickly move a magnet back and forth over impulse sender coil. If voltmeter needle moves, but engine would not start, replace ignition coil. If needle does not move, replace ignition control unit.

NOTE: **This is only necessary when vehicle will not start, and other tests have been performed.**

ELECTRICAL CIRCUIT TEST

1) Connect a 12-volt test light between the coil positive terminal and ground. Turn ignition switch "ON". Test light should light. If not, check feed wire to coil. *See Fig. 8*.

2) Connect test light between coil negative terminal and ground. Turn ignition switch "ON". Test light should again light. If not, check if coil primary circuit is broken or if electronic control unit's power transistor is shorted.

Fig. 7: Voltmeter Hookup for Checking Ignition Coil & Electronic Control Unit

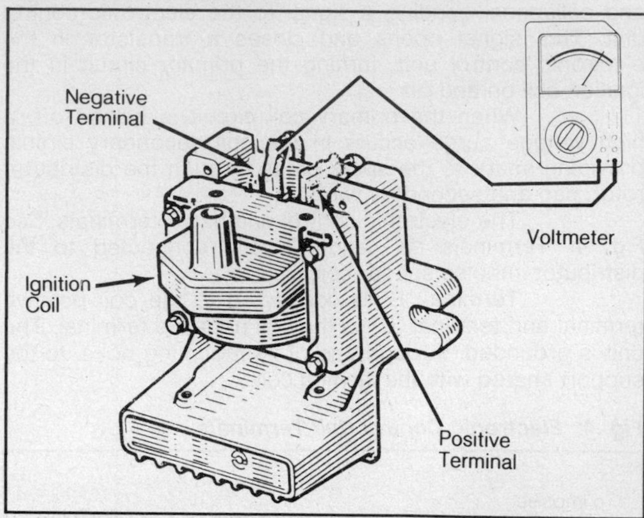
Negative Terminal
Voltmeter
Ignition Coil
Positive Terminal

Attach leads to primary coil terminals.

Fig. 8: Test Lamp Hookup for Checking Ignition Coil Voltage

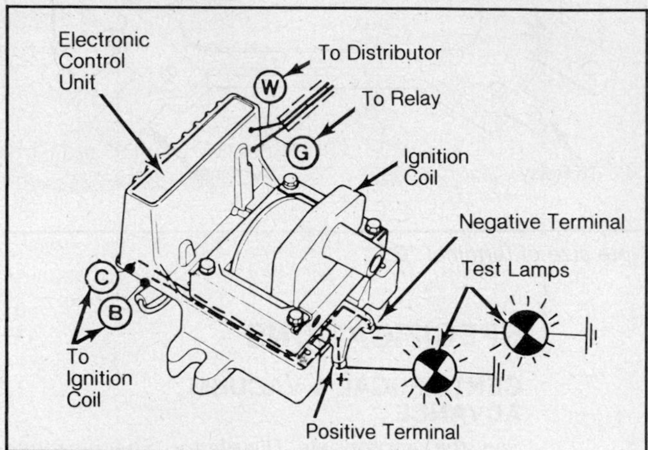
Electronic Control Unit
To Distributor
W
To Relay
G
Ignition Coil
Negative Terminal
Test Lamps
C
B
To Ignition Coil
Positive Terminal

Test light should light.

OVERHAUL

DISASSEMBLY

1) Remove distributor cap, rotor and plastic seal. Remove screws attaching impulse sender coil and remove coil and trigger plate. Remove electrical connector from distributor body.

2) Remove vacuum advance unit. Remove drive pinion from distributor shaft and remove shaft and centrifugal advance mechanism from housing.

REASSEMBLY

Reverse disassembly procedure, adjusting air gap. Adjust ignition timing at secondary coil (if equipped).

DUCELLIER ELECTRONIC IGNITION — RENAULT

Fuego Turbo

DESCRIPTION

The electronic ignition system used by Renault in the Fuego Turbo includes a computer, distributor, ignition coil, and numerous sensors. *See Fig. 1.* The ignition coil, which is part of the computer assembly, may be replaced separately if it is determined to be faulty.

Fig. 1: Wiring Diagram for Renault Fuego Turbo

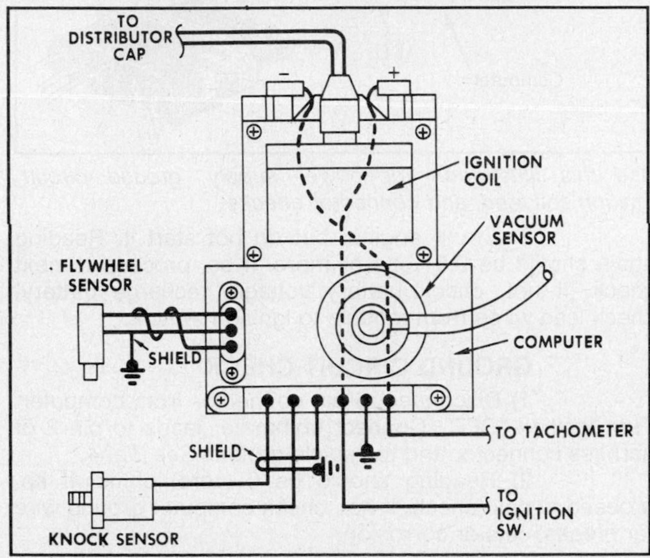
TO DISTRIBUTOR CAP
-
+
IGNITION COIL
VACUUM SENSOR
FLYWHEEL SENSOR
SHIELD
COMPUTER
TO TACHOMETER
SHIELD
TO IGNITION SW.
KNOCK SENSOR

As engine speed and crankshaft position are determined by the preset magnetic position sensor, the distributor's only function is to distribute the spark to the correct spark plug at the proper time.

The vacuum sensor, which cannot be removed from the computer housing, supplies the computer with engine load conditions. The computer also receives information from a spark knock (detonation) sensor.

The flywheel has 44 evenly spaced teeth around its circumference. Two of these have been removed 90° before top dead center and two have been removed 90° after top dead center. This is to provide precise timing marks at 90° before and after top dead center positions. Therefore there are actually only 40 flywheel teeth.

OPERATION

Engine speed and crankshaft (piston) position are determined by the non-adjustable magnetic position sensor rather than the distributor. It indicates position of top dead center and bottom dead center, as well as engine speed.

The vacuum sensor, mounted permanently on the computer housing, appears identical to vacuum diaphragms found on conventional ignition systems. However, the internal components differ greatly. Attempts to remove the vacuum sensor will break a small diameter wire leading into the computer, rendering it useless.

As the engine operates and the crankshaft flywheel turns, information is received by the computer indicating engine speed and crankshaft position. The vacuum sensor informs the computer of engine load conditions. *See Fig. 2.*

Fig. 2: Relationship of Computer and Ignition Coil

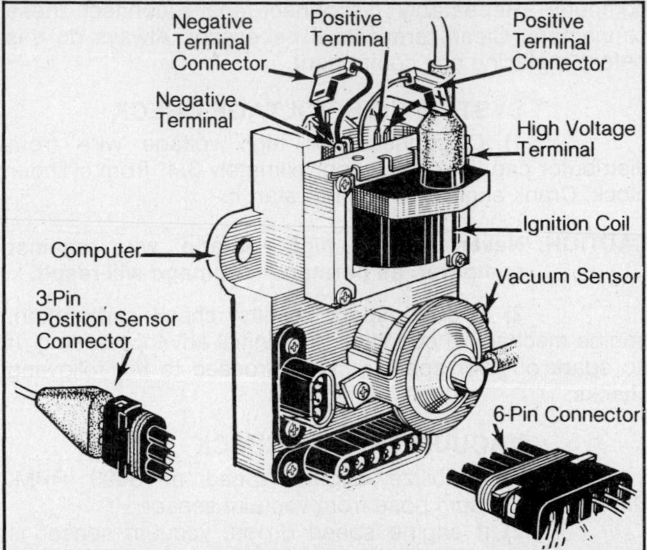
Negative Terminal Connector
Positive Terminal
Positive Terminal Connector
Negative Terminal
High Voltage Terminal
Ignition Coil
Computer
Vacuum Sensor
3-Pin Position Sensor Connector
6-Pin Connector

Vacuum sensor cannot be removed from computer.

The computer then interprets the information received, and sets the ignition advance ratio. The computer then opens and closes the primary circuit of the ignition coil, causing a build-up and collapse of the coil's magnetic field.

This in turn, causes a voltage surge in the secondary circuit of the coil. The distributor then furnishes spark to the appropriate spark plug in the correct firing order.

If the spark knock sensor detects detonation, a signal is sent to the computer. In such cases, timing will be retarded by 6°.

SPECIFICATIONS

The Fuego Turbo distributor has neither centrifugal nor vacuum advance mechanisms. Vacuum sensor is located on computer. Advance curve reference is indicated on a label attached to the computer.

ADJUSTMENT

There is no adjustment of magnetic position sensor. Distributor does not have a pick-up coil or reluctor. Ignition timing advance valve at idle speed can be checked, but cannot be adjusted. Checking for computer malfunction would be difficult, if advance were adjustable.

TESTING

CAUTION: When conducting tests, do not short out high tension current on computer housing. Do not ground ignition coil low tension or high tension windings, the primary terminals. Do not attempt to remove computer's vacuum sensor.

VISUAL SYSTEM CHECKS

Check spark plugs, spark plug wires, distributor cap and rotor, and ignition coil high tension wire. Also

DUCELLIER ELECTRONIC IGNITION — RENAULT (Cont.)

check condition of harness connectors attached to computer. Repeatedly disconnect and reconnect these connectors. Clean terminals if necessary. Always do this before replacing any component.

SYSTEM HIGH VOLTAGE CHECK

1) Disconnect coil high voltage wire from distributor cap. Hold wire approximately 3/4" from cylinder block. Crank engine, but do not start it.

CAUTION: Never ground high voltage wire against computer, as permanent damage will result.

2) If good spark results, check carburetion, engine mechanical condition, and initial advance setting. If no spark or poor spark results, proceed to the following checks.

VACUUM SENSOR CHECK

1) Stabilize engine speed at 3000 RPM. Disconnect vacuum hose from vacuum sensor.

2) If engine speed drops, vacuum sensor is operating properly. If engine speed does not drop, check condition of vacuum hose. If it is bad, replace hose and repeat check again. If hose condition was good, replace computer.

COIL VOLTAGE CHECK

1) Turn ignition "ON", but do not start engine. Connect voltmeter positive lead to coil positive terminal. *See Fig. 3*. Coil connectors should be on terminals.

Fig. 3: Checking Voltage at Positive Coil Terminal

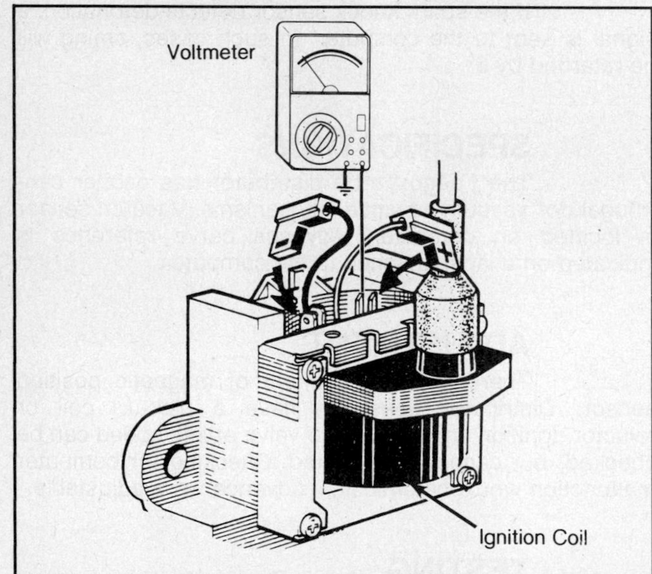
Voltmeter
Ignition Coil

Connectors need to be on terminals for test.

2) Connect negative lead to vehicle ground. Reading should be at least 9.5 volts. If good, proceed to Position Sensor Check. If less than 9.5 volts are read, proceed with next check.

POWER SUPPLY CHECK

1) Disconnect 6-pin connector from computer. Turn ignition "ON". Connect voltmeter positive lead to pin 1 of harness connector. *See Fig. 4*. Connect negative lead to vehicle ground.

Fig. 4: Computer and Harness Connector Test Terminals

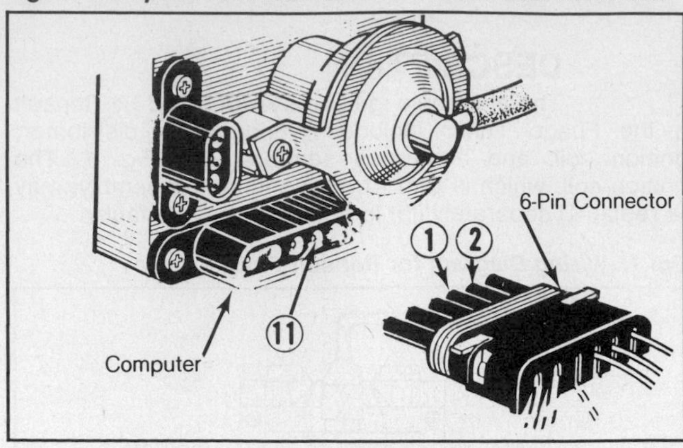
6-Pin Connector
1
2
11
Computer

Use this illustration for power supply, ground circuit, ignition coil feed, and connector checks.

2) Crank engine, but do not start it. Reading again should be 9.5 volts or more. If so, proceed to next check. If not, check battery voltage, recharge battery, check lead wires from module to ignition switch.

GROUND CIRCUIT CHECK

1) Disconnect 6-pin connector from computer. Turn ignition "OFF". Connect ohmmeter leads to pin 2 of harness connector and to vehicle ground. *See Fig. 4*.

2) Reading should be 0 (zero) ohms. If so, proceed to next check. If not, check computer ground wire for breaks, cuts or corrosion.

IGNITION COIL FEED CHECK

1) Disconnect 6-pin connector from computer. Turn ignition "OFF". Disconnect connector from positive terminal of ignition coil. Connect ohmmeter leads to cavity 11 of computer and to connector removed from positive coil terminal. *See Fig. 4*.

2) A reading of 0 (zero) ohms should be indicated. If so, proceed to next check. If not, replace computer.

6-PIN CONNECTOR CHECK

1) Connect 6-pin connector to computer. *See Fig. 4*. Turn ignition switch "ON". Disconnect connector from ignition coil positive terminal. Connect voltmeter positive lead to this connector. Attach negative lead to ground.

2) A reading of at least 9.5 volts should be indicated. If so, proceed to next check. If not, slightly shake or wiggle connector assembly. If problem continues, replace 6-pin connector.

NOTE: Testing has already established that you have power to the 6-pin connector, as well as, continuity between terminal 11 of computer and connector for ignition coil positive terminal. If there is no voltage at positive connector terminal, the 6-pin connector must be at fault.

POSITION SENSOR CHECK

1) Disconnect 3-pin connector from computer. *See Fig. 5*. Turn ignition switch "OFF". Attach ohmmeter leads to terminals 4 and 5 of 3-pin harness connector.

DUCELLIER ELECTRONIC IGNITION — RENAULT (Cont.)

Fig. 5: Connector Terminals for Magnetic Position Sensor

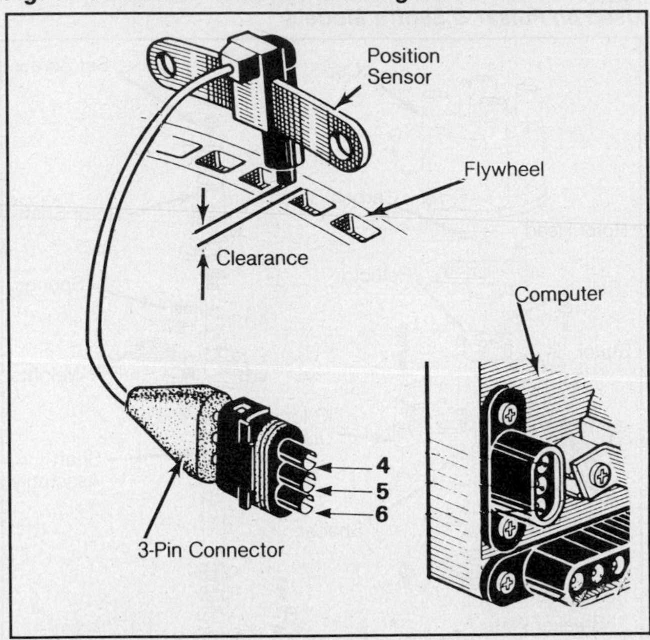
Position
Sensor
Flywheel
Clearance
Computer
4
5
6
3-Pin Connector

Use this illustration for position sensor, sensor insulation, and position sensor clearance checks

2) Resistance should read 100-200 ohms. If so, proceed to next check. If not, replace magnetic position sensor.

SENSOR INSULATION CHECK

1) Disconnect 3-pin connector. *See Fig. 5*. Turn ignition "OFF". Connect ohmmeter leads first to terminals 5 and 6 and then to terminals 4 and 6.

2) In both instances, an infinite reading should be indicated. If so, proceed to next check. If not, replace magnetic position sensor.

NOTE: **In case of infinite readings, be sure that the ohmmeter probe is properly inserted to touch bottom of terminal.**

POSITION SENSOR CLEARANCE CHECK

1) Using a plastic feeler gauge, check clearance between flywheel and magnetic position sensor. *See Fig. 5*.

2) Clearance should be .02-.06" (.5-1.5 mm). If so, proceed to next check. If not, replace sensor.

COMPUTER CHECK

1) Be sure all connectors are attached to computer. Disconnect harness connectors from coil primary terminals. Install 12-volt test lamp between 2 connectors just removed. *See Fig. 6*.

2) Crank engine. At cranking speed, lamp should flicker. If so, proceed to next check. If not, replace computer.

Fig. 6: Test Lamp Hookup for Checking Computer

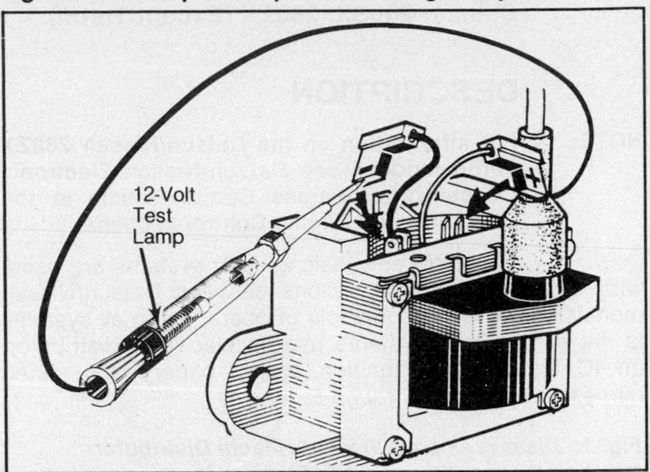
12-Volt
Test
Lamp

Attach 12-volt lamp to disconnected coil primary leads.

IGNITION COIL RESISTANCE CHECK

CAUTION: **When resistance checks are complete, be sure wires are reattached to proper terminals. Red wire goes on positive terminal. Black wire goes on negative terminal.**

Secondary Resistance

1) Disconnect harness connectors from ignition coil primary wires. Disconnect high tension wire from coil. Turn ignition "OFF". Set ohmmeter to x1000 scale. Attach ohmmeter leads to coil positive terminal and to coil high voltage terminal.

2) Ohmmeter should read 2500-5500 ohms. If so, check primary resistance. If not, replace ignition coil.

Primary Resistance

1) Remove connectors from coil primary terminals. Turn ignition "OFF". Set ohmmeter to x1 scale. Attach ohmmeter leads to coil primary terminals.

2) Reading should be .4-.8 ohm. If so, but there is no high voltage, replace computer. If resistance is not to specification, replace ignition coil.

SPARK KNOCK SENSOR CHECK

1) Attach timing light according to manufacturer's instructions. Start engine and run it at idle speed. Using a brass punch, tap lightly and repeatedly on cylinder head near spark knock detector.

2) Do not tap directly on sensor. Timing advance should drop by 6° as a result of the tapping. If not, replace sensor unit.

OVERHAUL

As the distributor has no reluctor, pick-up coil, nor centrifugal or vacuum advance, overhaul procedures are simple. Remove distributor cap and rotor. Remove pin from drive gear. Check shaft for burrs, and remove shaft from housing. Reassemble in reverse order.

HITACHI ELECTRONIC IGNITION SYSTEMS – DATSUN/NISSAN

Maxima, Pulsar, Pickup, Sentra, Stanza, 200SX, 280ZX (Except Turbo)

DESCRIPTION

NOTE: For information on the Datsun/Nissan 280ZX Turbo models, see Datsun/Nissan Electronic Concentrated Engine Control article in the Computerized Engine Control section.

Two different basic ignition systems are used, with additional minor variations between Datsun/Nissan models. However the principle of operation on all systems is the same. Both systems use an electronic distributor, an IC ignition unit, ignition coil(s), battery and wiring harness. *See Figs. 1 through 5.*

Fig. 1: Dissassembled View of Hitachi Distributor Used on Pickup, Stanza & 200SX Models

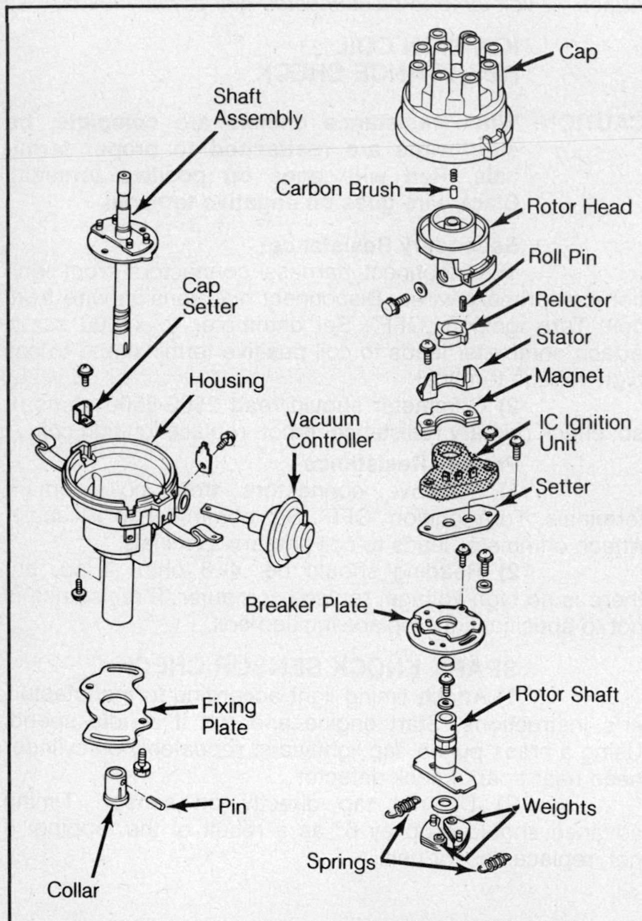
Cap
Shaft Assembly
Carbon Brush
Rotor Head
Roll Pin
Cap Setter
Reluctor
Stator
Housing
Magnet
Vacuum Controller
IC Ignition Unit
Setter
Breaker Plate
Rotor Shaft
Fixing Plate
Pin
Weights
Springs
Collar

This design is used on Pickup, Stanza, and 200SX models.

The ignition system for Maxima, Pulsar, Sentra, and 280ZX models uses one ignition coil with a single spark plug for each engine cylinder.

The ignition system used on Pickup, Stanza, and 200SX 4-cylinder models, uses 8 spark plugs. These models use special distributor caps, having 8 spark plug wire outlet terminals and 2 coil wire inlet terminals.

These models also use 2 ignition coils, one for the spark plugs on the exhaust side of the engine and one for the spark plugs on the intake side.

Fig. 2: Disassembled View of Hitachi Distributor Used on Pulsar & Sentra Models

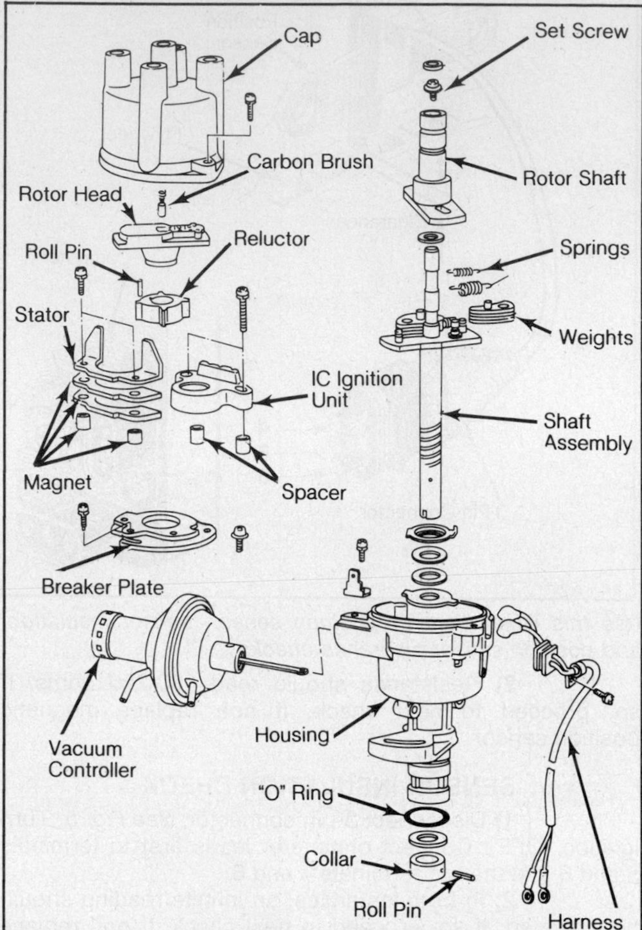
Cap
Set Screw
Carbon Brush
Rotor Shaft
Rotor Head
Reluctor
Roll Pin
Springs
Stator
Weights
IC Ignition Unit
Shaft Assembly
Magnet
Spacer
Breaker Plate
Housing
Vacuum Controller
"O" Ring
Collar
Roll Pin
Harness

This design is used on Pulsar & Sentra models.

On Pickup, Sentra, Stanza, and 200SX models, the IC ignition unit is located inside the distributor. The stator and magnet assembly also has a different shape than those of other models.

Depending upon the distributor used, the IC ignition unit may have a 2-pin connector (Maxima, Pulsar, Sentra, and 280ZX), a 3-pin connector (Pickup), or a 4-pin connector (200SX and Stanza). The IC ignition unit internal circuits also vary from model to model.

On Maxima and 280ZX models, the IC ignition unit is mounted externally on the distributor housing. The unit is connected with 2 wires to a pick-up coil located inside distributor. These models also have a fusible link between battery and ignition switch.

The Maxima and 280ZX models, which have 6-cylinder engines, feature reluctors and stators with 6 teeth. Other models have 4-cylinder engines with 4-tooth reluctors and 2-tooth stators.

OPERATION

Regardless of model, all distributors are equipped with a reluctor and stator, although the shapes may differ. The reluctor, which is mounted on the rotor shaft assembly, turns with the distributor shaft inside the stator.

HITACHI ELECTRONIC IGNITION – DATSUN/NISSAN (Cont.)

Fig. 3: Disassembled View of Hitachi Distributor Used on Maxima & 280ZX Models

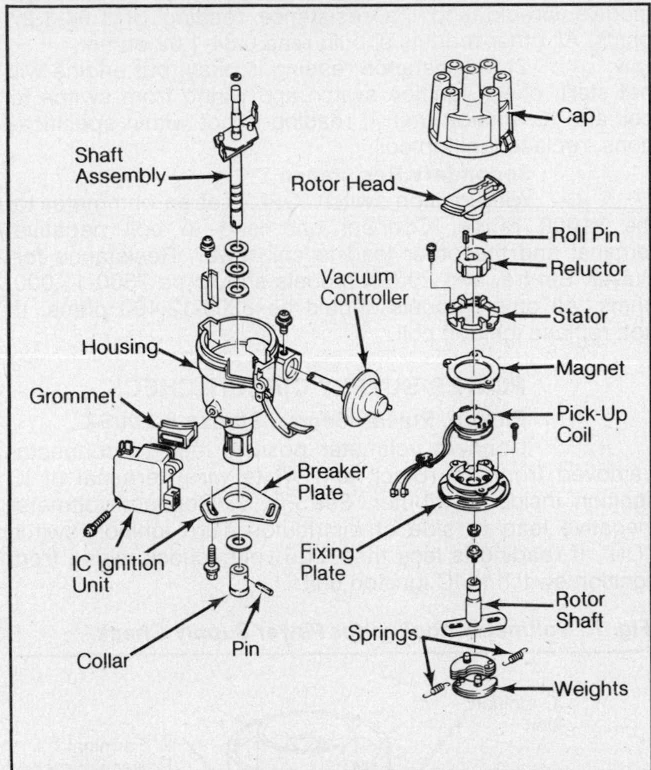
Shaft Assembly
Cap
Rotor Head
Roll Pin
Reluctor
Vacuum Controller
Stator
Housing
Magnet
Grommet
Pick-Up Coil
Breaker Plate
IC Ignition Unit
Fixing Plate
Rotor Shaft
Springs
Collar
Pin
Weights

This design is used on Maxima & 280ZX models.

As each reluctor tooth approaches and passes the stator teeth, the magnetic field changes, creating an electrical signal in the pick-up coil. The pick-up coil is combined with the IC ignition unit on Pickup, Sentra, Stanza, and 200SX models. This signal is received and processed by the IC ignition unit.

Fig. 4: IC Ignition Unit Circuit Diagram

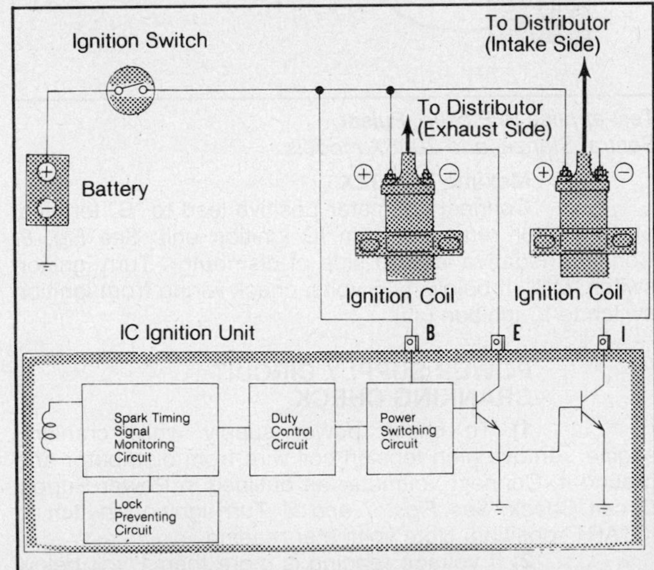
Ignition Switch
To Distributor (Intake Side)
To Distributor (Exhaust Side)
Battery
Ignition Coil
Ignition Coil
IC Ignition Unit
B
E
I
Spark Timing Signal Monitoring Circuit
Duty Control Circuit
Power Switching Circuit
Lock Preventing Circuit

This diagram is typical of 4-cylinder systems with 8 spark plugs. Also see chassis wiring in WIRING DIAGRAM Section.

The IC ignition unit turns on or cuts off current flow to the ignition coil primary circuit. When current to the primary is turned off, a high voltage surge is created in the secondary circuit, which fires the spark plug.

Ignition timing is controlled by the relationship of the reluctor to the stator. All circuits are contained in one IC ignition unit. Failure of any circuit requires replacement of entire IC ignition unit.

Fig. 5: IC Ignition Unit Circuit Diagram

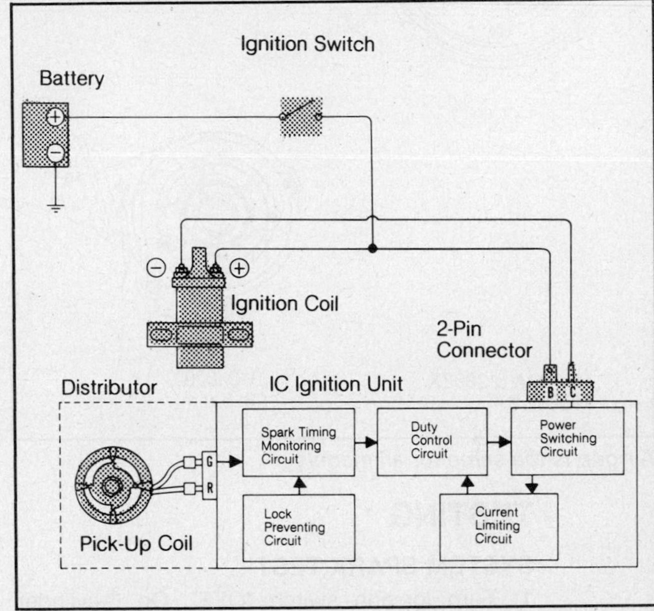
Ignition Switch
Battery
Ignition Coil
2-Pin Connector
Distributor
IC Ignition Unit
B C
Spark Timing Monitoring Circuit
Duty Control Circuit
Power Switching Circuit
G
R
Lock Preventing Circuit
Current Limiting Circuit
Pick-Up Coil

This diagram is typical of models with externally-mounted IC ignition units. Also see chassis wiring in WIRING DIAGRAM Section.

SPECIFICATIONS

CENTRIFUGAL & VACUUM ADVANCE

See the appropriate Distributor Specifications Tables in this section.

ADJUSTMENTS

AIR GAP

When installing reluctor and stator or checking air gap, loosen screws and center stator around reluctor. There should be equal air gap between each set of reluctor teeth and its matching stator teeth. *See Fig. 6.* Tighten screws securing stator. Standard air gap is .012-.020" (.3-.5 mm).

BREAKER PLATE

If breaker plate does not move smoothly in response to vacuum controller, apply grease to steel balls. If necessary, replace breaker plate assembly.

HITACHI ELECTRONIC IGNITION – DATSUN/NISSAN (Cont.)

Fig. 6: Checking Reluctor-to-Stator Air Gap

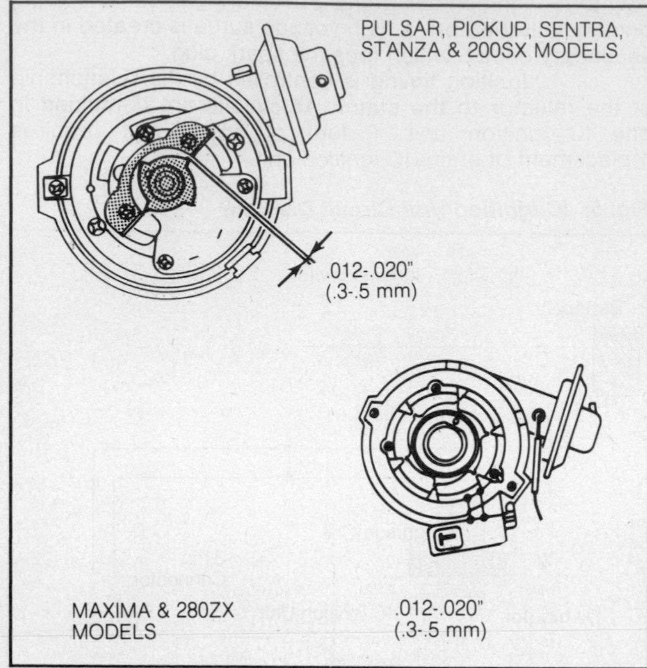
PULSAR, PICKUP, SENTRA, STANZA & 200SX MODELS
.012-.020"
(.3-.5 mm)
MAXIMA & 280ZX MODELS
.012-.020"
(.3-.5 mm)

Air gap is the same for all models

TESTING

SYSTEM SPARK TEST

1) Turn ignition switch "OFF". On 6-cylinder engines, disconnect EFI fusible link and cold start valve. On 4-cylinder engines, disconnect anti-dieseling solenoid valve connector to cut off fuel supply to engine.

2) Disconnect coil wire from distributor. Hold wire about 1/4" from engine block. Crank engine and check for sparks at wire-to-block gap.

3) If sparks occur, the IC ignition system is okay and no further ignition checks are required. If no sparks occur, proceed with tests that follow.

BATTERY VOLTAGE CHECK

1) Turn ignition switch to "OFF" position. Connect positive lead of voltmeter to battery positive terminal. Connect negative lead to battery negative terminal. Read and record battery voltage. If below 11.5 volts, battery charging or starting system is faulty.

2) With ignition switch still "OFF" and voltmeter still hooked to battery, remove coil wire from distributor, and connect it to a good ground. Crank engine and record cranking voltage registered on voltmeter. If voltage reading is less than 9.6 volts, battery charging or starting system is faulty.

SECONDARY WIRING CHECK

Connect an ohmmeter, in turn, to each spark plug wire. Attach one lead to terminal inside distributor cap and other lead to other end of wire. Resistance reading should be less than 30,000 ohms. If resistance is higher, replace high tension cables and/or distributor cap.

IGNITION COIL RESISTANCE CHECK

Primary Resistance

1) Turn ignition switch "OFF". Remove coil wires to isolate coil from system. Set ohmmeter to x1 range. Connect ohmmeter leads to the 2 primary terminals of coil. The Pickup (2.4L), Pulsar, Sentra, and 200SX models should show a resistance reading of 1.04-1.27 ohms. All other models should read 0.84-1.02 ohms.

2) If resistance reading is okay, but engine will not start, check ignition switch and wiring from switch to coil and IC ignition unit. If reading is not within specifications, replace ignition coil.

Secondary Resistance

With ignition switch "OFF", set an ohmmeter to the x1000 range. Connect one lead to coil negative terminal and the other lead to coil tower. Resistance for Pulsar, Sentra, and 200SX models should be 7300-11,000 ohms. All other models should be 8200-12,400 ohms. If not, replace ignition coil.

POWER SUPPLY CIRCUIT CHECK

Pickup, Pulsar, Sentra, Stanza & 200SX

Connect voltmeter positive lead to connector removed from "B" (Black and White wire) terminal of IC ignition inside distributor. *See Fig. 7.* Connect voltmeter negative lead to side of distributor. Turn ignition switch "ON". If reading is less than 11.5 volts, check wiring from ignition switch to IC ignition unit.

Fig. 7: Voltmeter Hookup for Power Supply Check

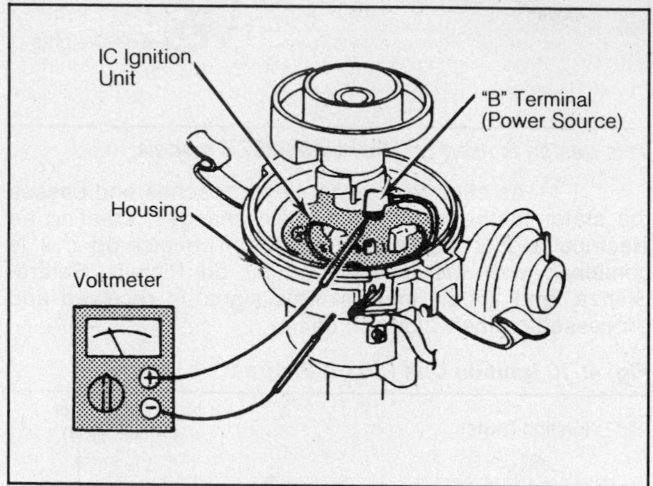
IC Ignition
Unit
"B" Terminal
(Power Source)
Housing
Voltmeter

Test applies to Pickup, Pulsar, Sentra, Stanza, and 200SX models.

Maxima & 280ZX

Connect voltmeter positive lead to "B" terminal of connector removed from IC ignition unit. *See Fig. 8.* Connect negative lead to side of distributor. Turn ignition switch "ON". If below 11.5 volts, check wiring from ignition switch to IC ignition unit.

POWER SUPPLY CIRCUIT CRANKING CHECK

1) To check power supply while cranking engine, remove high tension coil wire from distributor and ground it. Connect voltmeter as outlined in Power Supply Circuit Check. *See Figs. 7 and 8.* Turn ignition switch to "START" position. Note voltmeter reading.

2) If voltage reading is more than 1 volt below battery CRANKING voltage and/or is below 8.6 volts, check ignition switch and wiring from switch to IC ignition unit.

HITACHI ELECTRONIC IGNITION – DATSUN/NISSAN (Cont.)

Fig. 8: Voltmeter Hookup for Power Supply Check

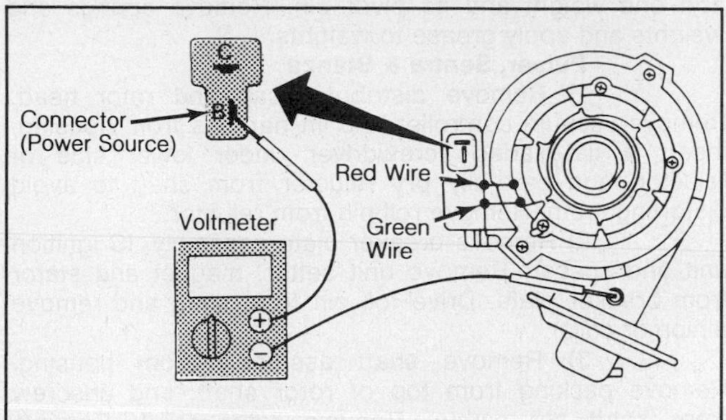
C
B
Connector
(Power Source)
Red Wire
Voltmeter
Green
Wire
T

This test applies to Maxima & 280ZX (Non-Turbo) models.

IGNITION PRIMARY CIRCUIT CHECK

Pickup, Pulsar, Sentra, Stanza & 200SX

1) Attach a voltmeter negative lead to side of distributor. On Pulsar and Sentra models connect voltmeter positive lead to Blue wire removed from IC ignition unit.

2) On Pickup, Stanza, and 200SX models, connect the voltmeter positive lead to "I" terminal of IC ignition unit connector, and then to the "E" terminal of IC ignition unit connector. *See Fig. 9.*

3) Turn ignition switch "ON" after lead has been attached to each terminal. Voltage readings should be 11.5-12.5 volts. If reading is below specifications, recheck coil primary resistance. If voltage is correct, proceed to IC Ignition Unit Ground Circuit Check.

Fig. 9: Voltmeter Hookup for Ignition Primary Circuit Check

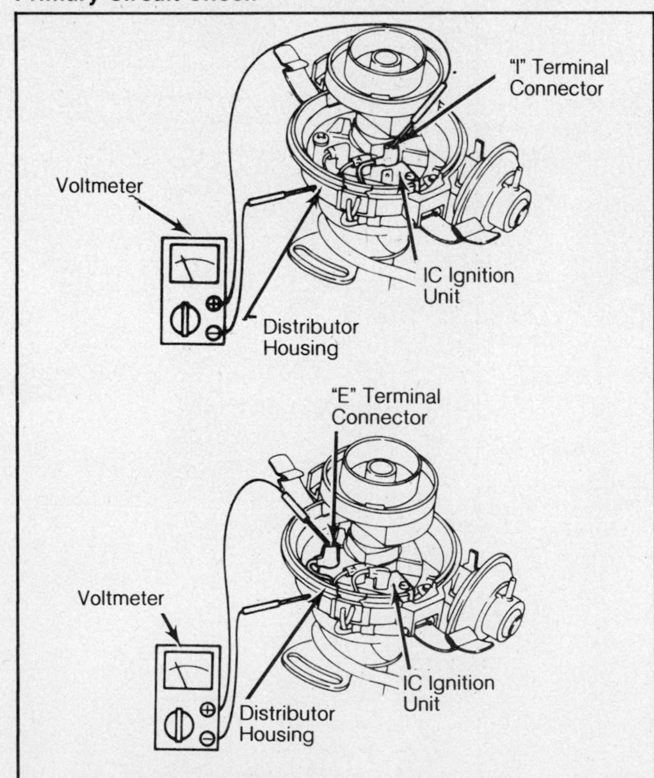
"I" Terminal
Connector
Voltmeter
IC Ignition
Unit
Distributor
Housing
"E" Terminal
Connector
Voltmeter
IC Ignition
Unit
Distributor
Housing

Hookup is for Pickup, Pulsar, Sentra, Stanza & 200SX models.

Maxima & 280ZX

1) Connect voltmeter positive lead to "C" terminal (Blue wire) of IC ignition unit connector. *See Fig. 10.* Attach negative lead to side of distributor. Turn ignition switch "ON".

Fig. 10: Voltmeter Hookup for Ignition Primary Circuit Check

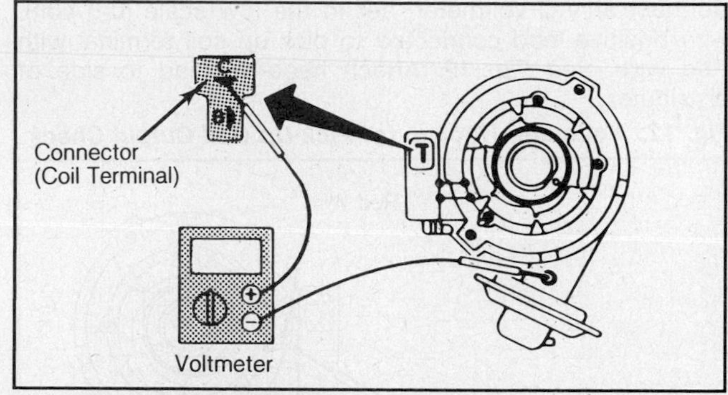
C
B
Connector
(Coil Terminal)
T
Voltmeter

Hookup is for Maxima & 280ZX models.

2) If voltage is 11.5-12.5 volts, proceed to IC Ignition Unit Ground Circuit Test. If voltage reading is below 11.5 volts, check Coil Primary Resistance, if not previously done.

IC IGNITION UNIT GROUND CIRCUIT CHECK

1) Connect voltmeter negative lead to battery negative terminal. Connect positive lead to exterior of vacuum controller. Pull high tension wire from distributor cap and ground it. Turn ignition switch to "START" position and observe voltmeter reading while cranking engine.

2) If voltage reads 0.5 volts or less, proceed to Pick-Up Coil Resistance Check. If voltage is more than 0.5 volts, check distributor ground wiring from chassis to battery, including battery connections.

PICK-UP COIL RESISTANCE CHECK

Maxima & 280ZX Only

1) For this test, engine should be at operating temperature. Turn ignition switch "OFF". Connect an ohmmeter, set to the x10 scale, to pick-up coil terminals (Green and Red wires). *See Fig. 11.*

Fig. 11: Ohmmeter Hookup for Pick-Up Coil Resistance Check

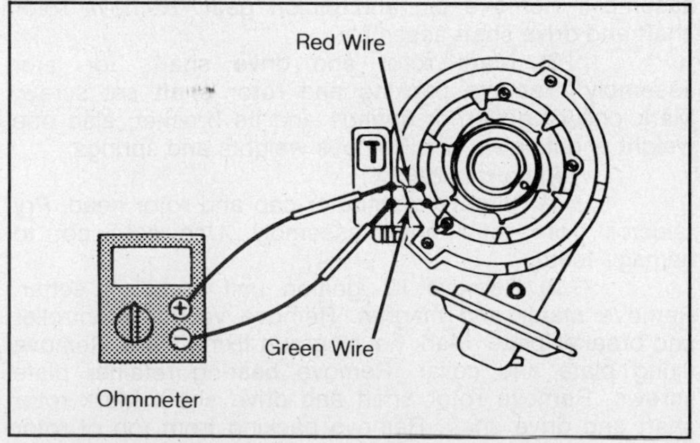
Red Wire
T
Green Wire
Ohmmeter

Check applies only to Maxima & 280ZX models.

HITACHI ELECTRONIC IGNITION – DATSUN/NISSAN (Cont.)

2) If ohmmeter reading is approximately 400 ohms, proceed to Pick-Up Coil Output Check. If ohmmeter reading varies widely from 400 ohms, check pick-up coil and wires leading to it.

PICK-UP COIL OUTPUT CHECK

Maxima & 280ZX Only

1) Engine should be at operating temperature. Connect an AC voltmeter, set to the low scale (0-5 volt), with positive lead connected to pick-up coil terminal with Red wire. *See Fig. 12.* Attach negative lead to side of distributor.

Fig. 12: Voltmeter Hookup for Pick-Up Coil Output Check

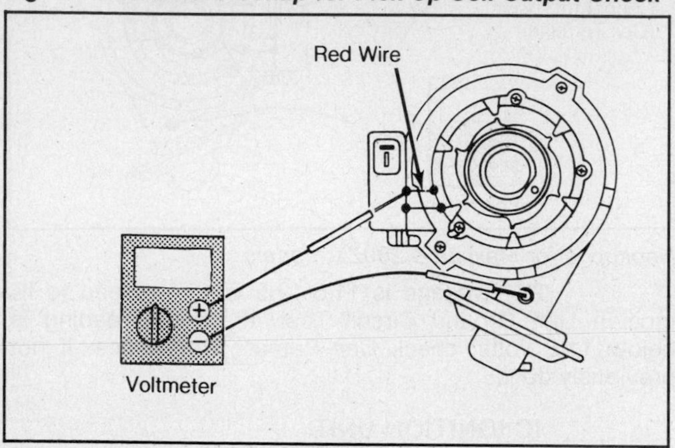
Red Wire
Voltmeter

Check can only be made on Maxima & 280ZX models.

2) Turn ignition switch to "START" position and check for movement of voltmeter needle while cranking engine. If needle wavers and the no-spark condition still exists, replace IC ignition unit.

3) If needle is steady, check physical condition of pick-up coil and reluctor. Check wiring and connector between pick-up coil and IC ignition unit.

OVERHAUL

DISASSEMBLY

Maxima & 280ZX

1) Remove distributor cap and rotor head. Remove IC ignition unit by disconnecting harness connector, removing screws and disconnecting pick-up coil wires.

2) Remove stator and magnet. Remove vacuum controller and carefully pry reluctor from shaft. Remove roll pin, pick-up coil assembly and breaker plate assembly. Remove pin and pinion gear. Remove rotor shaft and drive shaft assembly.

3) Mark rotor and drive shafts for later assembly. Remove packing and rotor shaft set screw. Mark one of governor springs and its bracket; also one weight and its pivot pin. Remove weights and springs.

Pickup & 200SX

1) Remove distributor cap and rotor head. Pry reluctor from rotor shaft assembly. Use care not to damage teeth.

2) Remove IC ignition unit and unit setter. Remove stator and magnet. Remove vacuum controller and breaker plate. Mark housing and fixing plate. Remove fixing plate and collar. Remove bearing retainer plate screws. Remove rotor shaft and drive shaft. Mark rotor shaft and drive shaft. Remove packing from top of rotor shaft and remove rotor shaft from drive shaft.

3) Mark one governor spring and its bracket and one weight and its pivot pin. Remove springs and weights and apply grease to weights.

Pulsar, Sentra & Stanza

1) Remove distributor cap and rotor head. Remove vacuum controller and lift harness from housing. Insert a flat-bladed screwdriver under lower side of reluctor, and carefully pry reluctor from shaft to avoid distorting teeth. Remove roll pin from reluctor.

2) Remove breaker plate assembly, IC ignition unit and spacer. Remove unit setter, magnet and stator from breaker plate. Drive roll pin from shaft and remove pinion or collar.

3) Remove shaft assembly from housing. Remove packing from top of rotor shaft, and unscrew rotor shaft set screw. Remove rotor shaft. Remove weights and springs from shaft assembly.

REASSEMBLY

All Models

1) To assemble, reverse disassembly procedure. Clean surfaces of IC ignition unit and distributor before assembling. Be sure pick-up coil leads (if equipped) are securely attached to IC ignition unit terminals.

2) Align match marks so parts are assembled in original positions. Be sure reluctor is centered in stator, before tightening stator screws. Drive in roll pin with its slit toward outer end of shaft. Grease top of rotor shaft. Check governor operation before installing distributor.

HITACHI ELECTRONIC IGNITION – HONDA

Accord, Civic, Prelude

DESCRIPTION

NOTE: Some Accord and Prelude models use Toyo Denso distributors. See appropriate article in this section.

Honda's Hitachi electronic distributors consist of a distributor housing, rotor and the distributor cap. The reluctor, stator, magnets, pulse generator/ignitor and breaker plate assemblies are all located inside the distributor housing.

OPERATION

The reluctor turns with the distributor shaft. It is secured to the distributor rotor shaft by a roll pin. As the reluctor turns, its 4 external teeth come in line with the 2 stator upright teeth.

As the reluctor approaches and passes the stator teeth, variations occur in the magnetic field around them. This causes the pulse generator to signal the ignitor.

Each time the reluctor teeth come in line with and then pass the stator teeth, transistors inside the ignitor are turned off and on. This results in a magnetic field building and collapsing in the primary circuit of the ignition coil. When this field collapses, a voltage surge occurs in the secondary circuit of the ignition coil.

When this occurs, a high voltage spark is fed from the coil, through the distributor rotor and cap to the secondary wiring and spark plugs.

Fig. 1: Disassembled View of Hitachi Distributor Used in Civic and Accord Models.

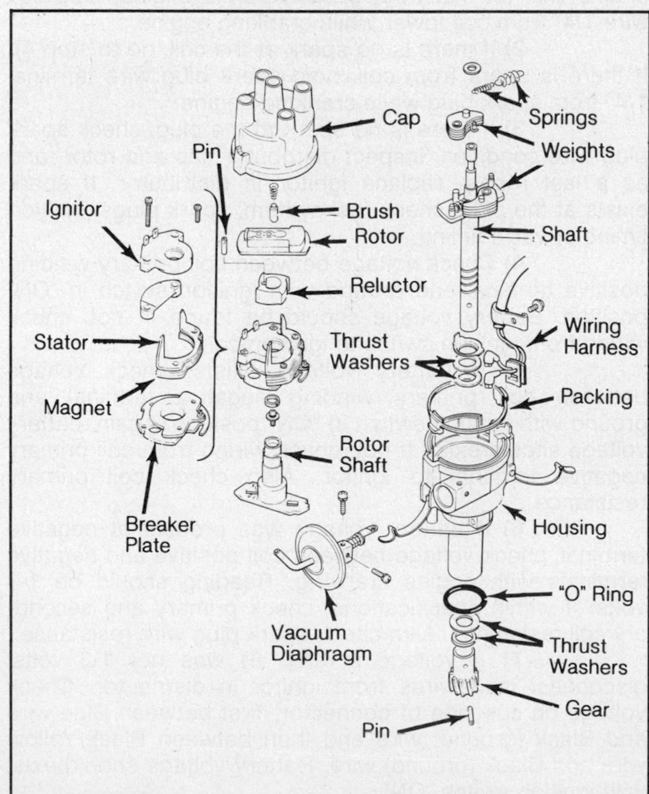
Cap
Springs
Pin
Weights
Ignitor
Brush
Rotor
Shaft
Reluctor
Stator
Wiring Harness
Thrust Washers
Magnet
Packing
Rotor Shaft
Breaker Plate
Housing
"O" Ring
Vacuum Diaphragm
Thrust Washers
Gear
Pin

Fig. 2: Disassembled View of Hitachi Distributor Used in Prelude Models.

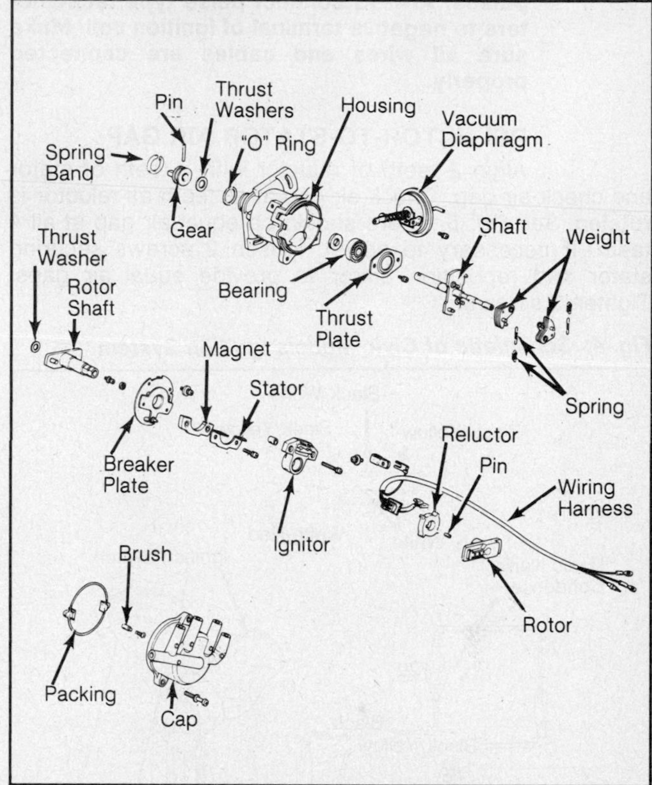
Pin
Thrust Washers
Housing
Vacuum Diaphragm
Spring Band
"O" Ring
Gear
Shaft
Weight
Thrust Washer
Rotor Shaft
Bearing
Thrust Plate
Magnet
Stator
Spring
Reluctor
Breaker Plate
Pin
Wiring Harness
Ignitor
Brush
Rotor
Packing
Cap

Fig. 3: Circuit Diagram of Accord and Prelude Models Ignition System

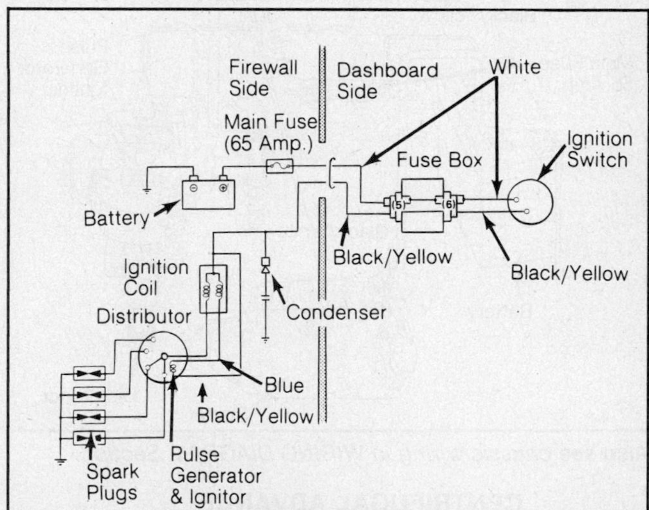
Firewall Side
Dashboard Side
White
Main Fuse (65 Amp.)
Ignition Switch
Fuse Box
Battery
Black/Yellow
Black/Yellow
Ignition Coil
Condenser
Distributor
Blue
Black/Yellow
Spark Plugs
Pulse Generator & Ignitor

Also see chassis wiring in WIRING DIAGRAM Section.

SPECIFICATIONS

CENTRIFUGAL & VACUUM ADVANCE/RETARD

See appropriate Distributor Specifications Table in this section.

ADJUSTMENTS

CAUTION: To avoid damaging the ignition system, never reverse battery polarity. Do not let pulse

HITACHI ELECTRONIC IGNITION – HONDA (Cont.)

generator wires touch ignition wires. Do not do anything that would produce abnormal pulses. Always connect pulse type tachometers to negative terminal of ignition coil. Make sure all wires and cables are connected properly.

RELUCTOR-TO-STATOR AIR GAP

Align 2 teeth of reluctor with 2 teeth of stator and check air gap. Check air gap at all teeth as reluctor is rotated. *See Fig. 5.* There should be equal air gap at all 4 teeth. If necessary to adjust, loosen 2 screws securing stator and reposition stator to provide equal air gaps. Tighten 2 screws.

Fig. 4: Schematic of Civic Models Ignition System

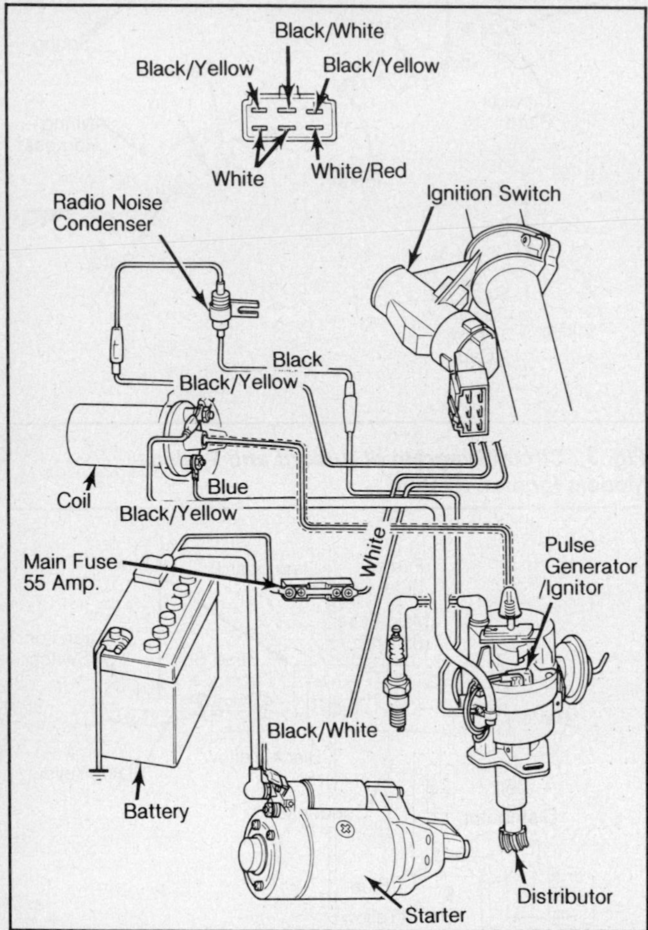
Black/White
Black/Yellow
Black/Yellow
White
White/Red
Radio Noise Condenser
Ignition Switch
Black
Black/Yellow
Coil
Blue
Black/Yellow
White
Main Fuse 55 Amp.
Pulse Generator /Ignitor
Black/White
Battery
Starter
Distributor

Also see chassis wiring in WIRING DIAGRAM Section.

CENTRIFUGAL ADVANCE

Disconnect vacuum advance hoses from distributor. Connect timing light and start engine. Increase engine speed. Timing mark (T) should appear to move past pointer toward firewall, indicating an increase in ignition advance. If not, check centrifugal advance mechanism for sticking or binding.

VACUUM ADVANCE

1) Remove distributor cap. Disconnect vacuum hoses from distributor vacuum advance or advance/retard diaphragm. Connect vacuum pump to diaphragm. Gradually draw a vacuum while watching breaker plate movement.

2) Check for smooth operation without binding. If pump indicates a loss of vacuum, replace diaphragm unit. Turn breaker plate right and left to check for free movement.

Fig. 5: Adjusting Reluctor-To-Stator Air Gap

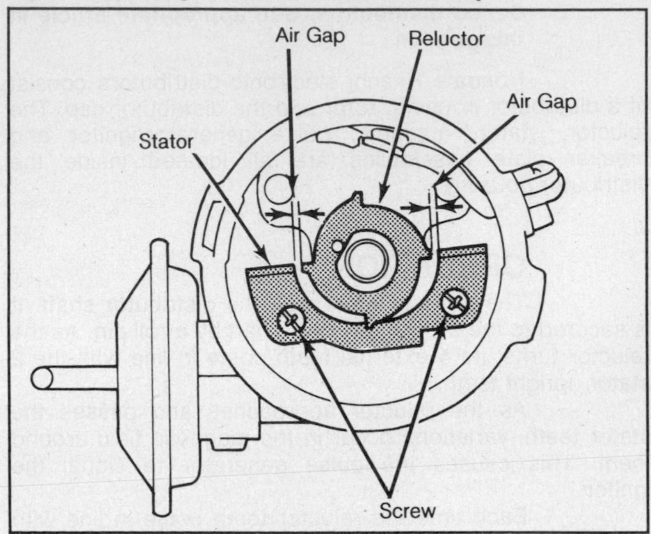
Air Gap
Reluctor
Air Gap
Stator
Screw

Air gap should be equal at all teeth.

TESTING

BASIC SYSTEM TEST

1) If engine will not start and starter will not crank engine, check battery, main fuse and electrical wiring. Check starter circuit wiring and ignition switch. If engine will not start, but starter cranks engine, hold coil wire 1/4" from coil tower while cranking engine.

2) If there is no spark at the coil, go to step **4)**. If there is spark from coil, hold spark plug wire terminal 1/4" from spark plug while cranking engine.

3) If there is no spark at the plug, check spark plug wire condition, inspect distributor cap and rotor, and as a last resort, replace ignitor in distributor. If spark exists at the plug, check fuel system, spark plugs, ignition timing or valve timing.

4) Check voltage between coil primary winding positive terminal and ground with ignition switch in "ON" position. Battery voltage should be found. If not, check wiring from ignition switch to ignition coil.

5) If battery voltage exists, check voltage between coil primary winding negative terminal and ground with ignition switch in "ON" position. Again, battery voltage should exist. If not, check wiring from coil primary negative terminal to ignitor. Also check coil primary resistance.

6) If battery voltage was present at negative terminal, check voltage between coil positive and negative terminals with engine cranking. Reading should be 1-3 volts. If within specifications, check primary and secondary coil resistance. Also check spark plug wire resistance.

7) If voltage in step **6)** was not 1-3 volts, disconnect lead wires from ignitor in distributor. Check voltage on coil side of connector, first between Blue wire and Black (ground) wire and then between Black/Yellow wire and Black (ground) wire. Battery voltage should exist with ignition switch "ON".

HITACHI ELECTRONIC IGNITION – HONDA (Cont.)

8) If not, check wiring from ignition coil to ignitor. Check continuity between ignitor terminals. *See Fig. 6.* Set ohmmeter to x100 range. Attach positive lead to terminal for Black/Yellow wire and negative lead to terminal for Blue wire. There should be continuity.

Fig. 6: Checking Continuity at Ignitor Terminals

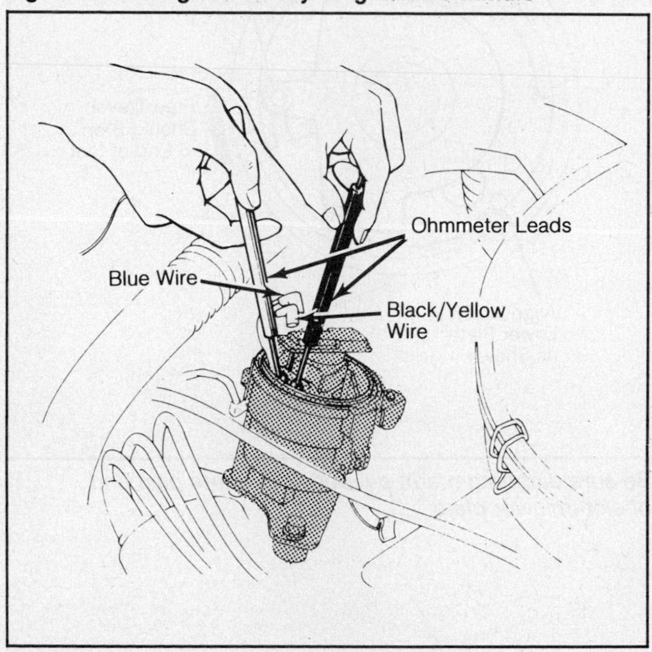
Ohmmeter Leads
Blue Wire
Black/Yellow Wire

Test as shown; then reverse probe connections.

9) Reverse ohmmeter leads (positive lead to terminal for Blue wire, negative lead to terminal for Black/Yellow wire). There should be no continuity. If incorrect results are obtained, replace ignitor and repeat test.

COMPONENT TESTS

Ignition Coil Primary Resistance

1) Turn ignition switch "OFF" and remove positive and negative wires from ignition coil terminals. Connect an ohmmeter set in the x1 range with one probe touching each primary terminal. *See Fig. 7.*

2) On Accord and Prelude models, reading should be 1.06-1.24 ohms. On Civic models, reading should be 1.0-1.3 ohms. If reading is not to specifications, replace ignition coil.

Ignition Coil Secondary Resistance

Turn ignition switch "OFF". Set ohmmeter in x1000 range. Connect ohmmeter leads to ignition coil negative terminal (wire removed) and coil tower terminal. *See Fig. 8.* On all models, secondary resistance should be 7,400-11,000 ohms. If not replace ignition coil.

Condenser Capacity

Using a condenser tester, check for 0.38-0.56 microfarads.

Ignition Wire Resistance

Carefully remove wires by pulling on their rubber boots. Do not bend wire or conductor may be broken. Check for corroded condition, cleaning if necessary. Connect ohmmeter probes (set in x1000 scale) to each end of ignition wires. Resistance reading should be less than 25,000 ohms. If not, replace wires.

Fig. 7: Checking Ignition Coil Primary Resistance

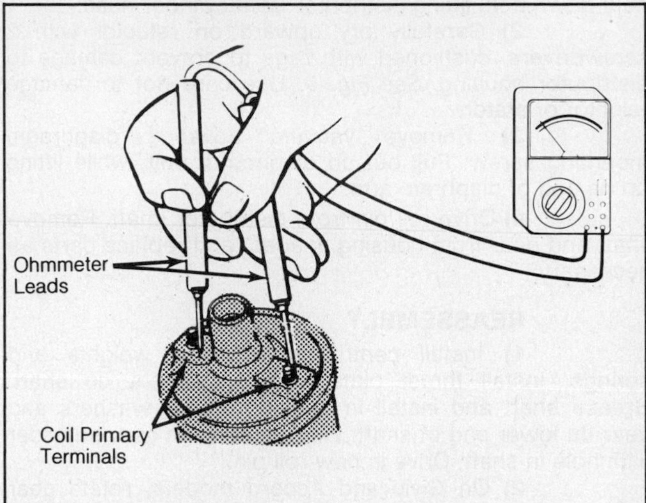
Ohmmeter Leads
Coil Primary Terminals

Attach probes to positive and negative terminals.

Fig. 8: Checking Ignition Coil Secondary Resistance

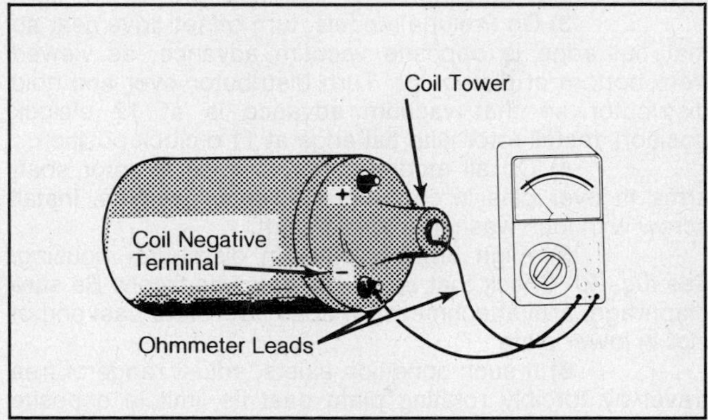
Coil Tower
Coil Negative Terminal
Ohmmeter Leads

Attach leads to negative terminal and coil tower.

Fig. 9: Removing Reluctor from Shaft

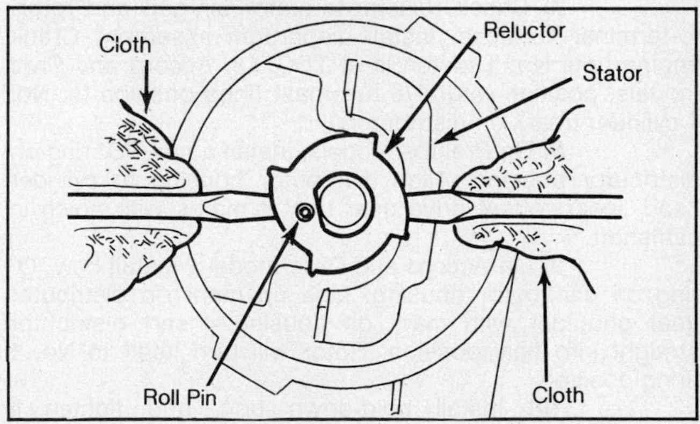
Cloth
Reluctor
Stator
Roll Pin
Cloth

Use cloths and screwdrivers to pry off reluctor.

OVERHAUL

DISASSEMBLY

1) Remove all spark plug wires and vacuum hoses from the distributor. Remove distributor cap. Remove the condenser ground wire, and disconnect pulse

HITACHI ELECTRONIC IGNITION – HONDA (Cont.)

generator/ignitor wire connector from distributor. Remove hold-down bolt, lifting distributor from cylinder head.

2) Carefully pry upward on reluctor with 2 screwdrivers, cushioned with rags to prevent damage to distributor housing. *See Fig. 9.* Use care not to damage reluctor or stator.

3) Remove vacuum advance diaphragm mounting screw. Pull out on diaphragm unit, while lifting up on end of diaphram arm.

4) Drive roll pin from distributor shaft. Remove shaft and gear from housing. Inspect and replace parts as necessary.

REASSEMBLY

1) Install centrifugal advance weights and springs. Install thrust plate and 2 washers on shaft. Grease shaft and install in housing. Put 2 washers and gear on lower end of shaft. Line up holes in gear shoulder with hole in shaft. Drive in new roll pin.

2) On Civic and Accord models, rotate gear until mark on gear shoulder lines up with mark on housing. Hold gear in line with mark and install rotor shaft on top of main shaft. Flat surface should face vacuum advance side of housing.

3) On Prelude models, turn offset drive gear so that flat edge is opposite vacuum advance, as viewed from bottom of distributor. Turn distributor over and hold distributor so that vacuum advance is at 12 o'clock position. Install rotor with flat edge at 11 o'clock position.

4) On all models, ensure holes in rotor shaft arms fit over pins in centrifugal advance weights. Install screw with lock washer in top of shaft.

5) Align breaker plate in distributor housing. *See Fig. 10.* Check that upper plate moves freely. Be sure diaphragm arm attachment pin does not rotate past end of slot in lower plate.

6) If such condition exists, adjust range of free travel by forcibly rotating plate past its limit in opposite direction. Recheck pin position. When installing reluctor, drive roll pin in place with its gap away from distributor shaft.

7) Check reluctor-to-stator air gap and rotor-to-terminal surfaces. Install diaphragm assembly. Crank engine until No. 1 piston is at TDC. On Accord and Civic models, position rotor 1/8 turn past firing position for No. 1 cylinder (mark on distributor).

8) On Prelude models, install a new "O" ring on distributor housing. Align distributor housing to cylinder head. Insert offset drive gear until it mates with notch in camshaft.

9) On Accord and Civic models, install new "O" ring on distributor housing. Line up mark on distributor gear shoulder with mark on housing. Insert distributor straight into final position. Rotor will turn itself to No. 1 firing position.

10) Install hold-down bolt, and tighten it temporarily. Set ignition timing, and tighten hold-down bolt securely. Install distributor cap, aligning mark on cap (near clamp lug) with rotor.

Fig. 10: Installation of Breaker Plate to Distributor Housing

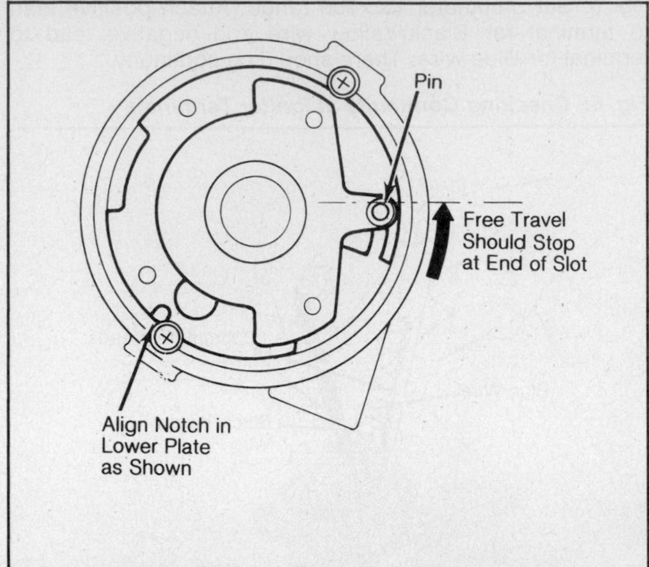
Pin
Free Travel Should Stop at End of Slot
Align Notch in Lower Plate as Shown

Be sure diaphragm arm pin does not rotate past end of slot in lower plate.

HITACHI ELECTRONIC IGNITION – SUBARU

1800, 1800 Turbo (4WD Models)

DESCRIPTION

NOTE: Subaru 2WD models use Nippondenso ignition systems.

The Hitachi electronic distributor consists of a housing, shaft assembly, rotor and distributor cap. *See Fig. 1.* A reluctor, mounted on the upper distributor shaft, combines with the stator and pick-up coil to provide ignition timing.

Fig. 1: Disassembled View of Hitachi Distributor Used on Subaru 1800 (Non-Turbo) 4WD Vehicles.

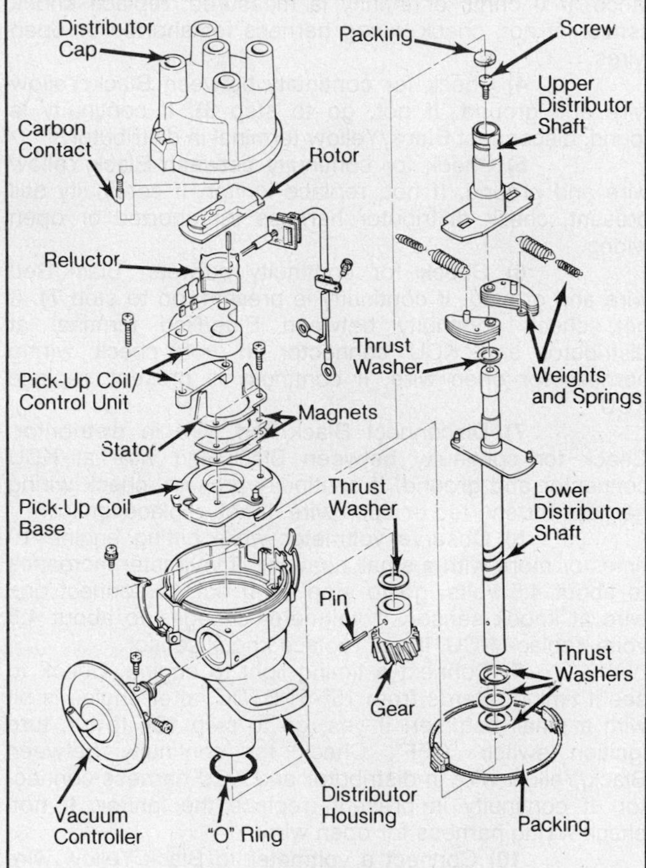
Distributor Cap
Packing
Screw
Upper Distributor Shaft
Carbon Contact
Rotor
Reluctor
Thrust Washer
Weights and Springs
Pick-Up Coil/ Control Unit
Magnets
Stator
Pick-Up Coil Base
Thrust Washer
Lower Distributor Shaft
Pin
Thrust Washers
Gear
Vacuum Controller
"O" Ring
Distributor Housing
Packing

With the ignition switch "ON", the distributor reluctor rotates past the stator. As each tooth of the reluctor approaches and passes the stator, a signal is sent to the pick-up coil/control unit. In response to the signal, the control unit then turns the primary circuit in the ignition coil on and off.

This causes a build-up and collapse of a magnetic field in the coil, resulting in a high voltage surge in the coil's secondary circuit. This fires the spark plugs. *See Fig. 2 or 3.*

SPECIFICATIONS

CENTRIFUGAL & VACUUM ADVANCE

See the appropriate Distributor Specifications Table in this section.

Fig. 2: Schematic of Subaru 1800 Non-Turbo Ignition Circuit

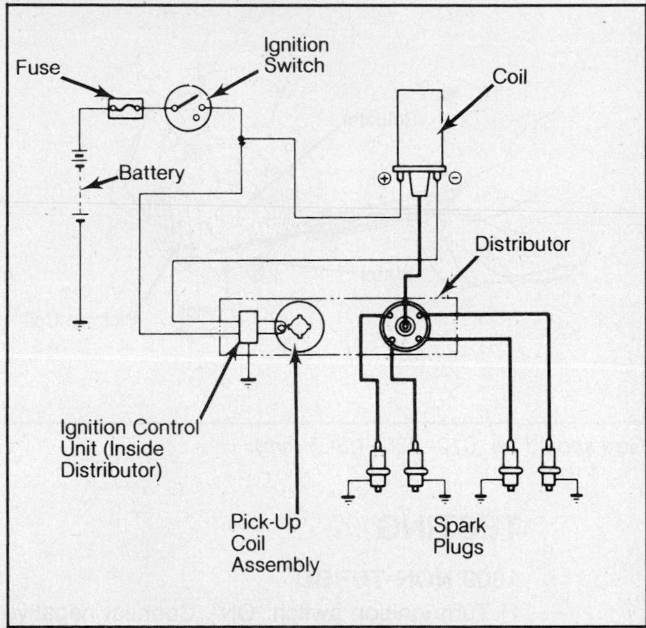
Fuse
Ignition Switch
Coil
Battery
Distributor
Ignition Control Unit (Inside Distributor)
Pick-Up Coil Assembly
Spark Plugs

Also see chassis wiring in WIRING DIAGRAM Section.

ADJUSTMENTS

AIR GAP

1) Align tooth of reluctor with upright teeth of stator. Measure gap with a feeler gauge. Air gap should be .012-.020" (.3-.5 mm).

2) If adjustment is necessary, loosen stator mounting screws. Insert a .016" (.4 mm) feeler gauge between reluctor and stator teeth. Move stator against gauge and tighten mounting screws. Recheck air gap at each reluctor tooth. *See Fig. 4.*

Fig. 3: Schematic of Subaru 1800 Turbo Ignition Circuit

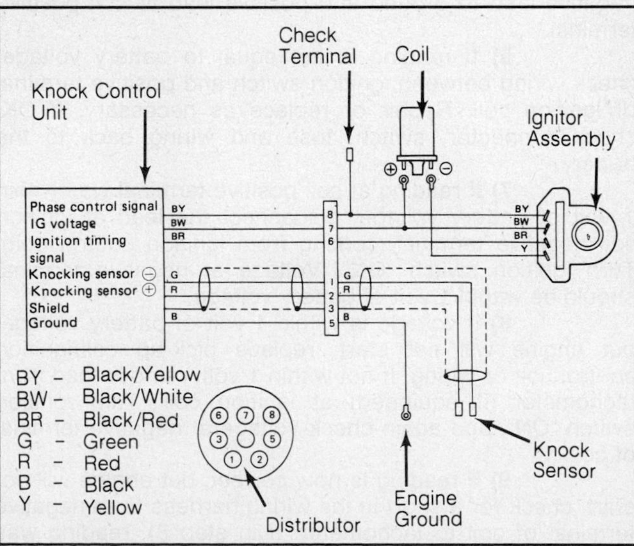
Check Terminal
Coil
Knock Control Unit
Ignitor Assembly
Phase control signal
IG voltage
Ignition timing signal
Knocking sensor ⊖
Knocking sensor ⊕
Shield
Ground
BY – Black/Yellow
BW – Black/White
BR – Black/Red
G – Green
R – Red
B – Black
Y – Yellow
Knock Sensor
Engine Ground
Distributor

Also see chassis wiring in WIRING DIAGRAM Section.

HITACHI ELECTRONIC IGNITION – SUBARU (Cont.)

Fig. 4: Adjusting Reluctor-to-Stator Air Gap

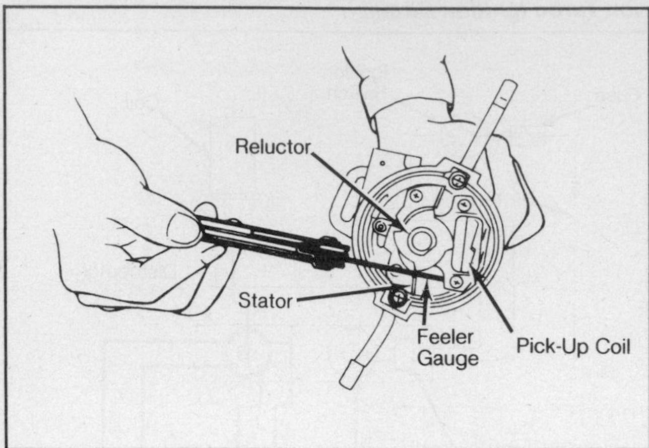

Reluctor
Stator
Feeler Gauge
Pick-Up Coil

Gap should be .012-.020" (.3-.5 mm).

TESTING

1800 NON-TURBO

1) Turn ignition switch "ON". Connect negative lead of voltmeter to ground and positive lead to negative terminal of ignition coil. Voltage should be within 1 volt of battery voltage. If not, proceed to step **5)**.

2) If reading was within 1 volt of battery voltage, turn ignition switch "OFF" and check distributor air gap. Adjust if necessary. *See Adjustments.*

3) Disconnect wires from primary terminals of ignition coil. Set ohmmeter on the x100 scale. Check coil primary resistance by attaching ohmmeter leads to positive and negative terminals. Reading should be 1.04-1.27 ohms. If not, replace ignition coil.

4) Next, check coil secondary resistance. Set ohmmeter on x1000 scale. Attach ohmmeter leads to coil negative terminal and coil tower (wire removed). Reading should be 7,360-11,040 ohms. If not, replace ignition coil.

5) If the reading in step **1)** was not within 1 volt of battery voltage, turn ignition switch "ON". Check voltage at positive terminal of ignition coil. Connect voltmeter negative lead to ground and positive lead to coil positive terminal.

6) If reading is not equal to battery voltage, check wiring between ignition switch and positive terminal of ignition coil. Repair or replace as necessary. If OK, check connector, switch, fuse and wiring back to the battery.

7) If reading at coil positive terminal was within 1 volt of battery voltage, disconnect the lead at ignition coil negative terminal (coming from ignition control unit). Turn ignition switch "ON". Voltage at negative terminal should be within 1 volt of battery voltage.

8) If voltage is within 1 volt of battery voltage, but engine will not start, replace pick-up coil/ignition control unit or wiring. If not within 1 volt, remove lead from tachometer (if equipped) at ignition coil. Turn ignition switch "ON", and again check voltage at negative terminal of coil.

9) If reading is now correct, but engine will not start, check for a short in the wiring harness from negative terminal of coil to tachometer. If in step **8)**, reading was still not within 1 volt of battery voltage, replace ignition coil.

1800 TURBO

NOTE: Use a volt-ohmmeter with a high internal impedance to check ignition system.

1) With engine at idle speed, check voltage at Black/Yellow wire (check terminal) of Knock Control Unit (KCU). If about 1.7 volts are present, go to step **8)**. If not, turn ignition switch "OFF".

2) Disconnect the KCU to distributor harness connector. Check for continuity between Black wire and ground. If no continuity is found, check for bad ground or wiring harness.

3) Measure resistance between Green and Red wires (knock sensor). If either 0 ohms or infinity is measured, disconnect knock sensor and measure resistance. If 0 ohms or infinity is measured, replace knock sensor. If not, check wiring harness for shorted or open wires.

4) Check for continuity between Black/Yellow wire and ground. If not, go to step **6)**. If continuity is found, disconnect Black/Yellow terminal in distributor.

5) Check for continuity between Black/Yellow wire and ground. If not, replace ignitor. If continuity still present, check distributor harness for shorted or open wiring.

6) Check for continuity between Black/Red wire and ground. If continuity is present, go to step **7)**. If not, check continuity between Blue/Red terminal at distributor and KCU connector. If not, check wiring harness for open wire. If continuity is present, replace KCU.

7) Disconnect Black/Red wire in distributor. Check for continuity between Black/Red wire at KCU connector and ground. If continuity present, check wiring harness for shorted or open wire. If not, replace ignitor.

8) Observe voltmeter while hitting engine 10 times or more with a small hammer. If voltmeter increases to about 4.5 volts, go to step **9)**. If not, disconnect one wire at knock sensor. If voltmeter changes to about 4.5 volts, replace KCU. If not, replace knock sensor.

9) Connect a timing light to engine. Check to see if timing retards from 15°-5° BTDC, after engine is hit with a small hammer. If yes, go to step **10)**. If not, turn ignition switch "OFF". Check for continuity between Black/Yellow wire in distributor and KCU harness connector. If continuity is present, replace the ignitor. If not, check wiring harness for open wire.

10) Connect a voltmeter to Black/Yellow wire (check terminal). Observe voltmeter while hitting engine with small hammer. When voltmeter reads about 4.5 volts, increase engine speed. Voltmeter should drop to about 1.7 volts when engine is over 4850 RPM. If so, knock sensor system is okay. If not, turn ignition switch "OFF".

11) Disconnect the KCU wiring harness. Start engine. With engine at idle speed, measure voltage between the Black/Red wire from the distributor and ground. If about .5 volts are present, replace the KCU. If 0 volts are present, turn ignition switch "OFF".

12) Check continuity between the Black/Yellow wire from the distributor and ground. If continuity is present, go to step **7)**. If not, check continuity between Black/Red terminal in distributor and KCU connector terminal. If no continuity, check wiring harness for open wire. If continuity is present, replace ignitor.

HITACHI ELECTRONIC IGNITION – SUBARU (Cont.)

OVERHAUL

DISASSEMBLY

1) Remove distributor cap and rotor. Remove vacuum controller by loosening screws, and pulling vacuum controller out of distributor housing. Disconnect electrical wires from pick-up coil/control unit. Remove unit, wires and rubber seal from distributor housing.

2) Remove gear from distributor shaft by driving out pin. Remove thrust washers with gear. Remove screws attaching pick-up coil base to distributor housing. Pull pick-up coil base, distributor shaft, and governor assembly from housing.

3) Remove dust-proof packing from top of distributor shaft. Remove screw from top of shaft. Separate upper and lower distributor shaft assemblies. Remove centrifugal weights and springs from lower distributor shaft.

REASSEMBLY

Reassemble in reverse order of disassembly, noting the following:

- When installing rotor assembly, match pick-up coil pole piece with notch in rotor. *See Fig. 5.*

Fig. 5: Installing Distributor Rotor Assembly

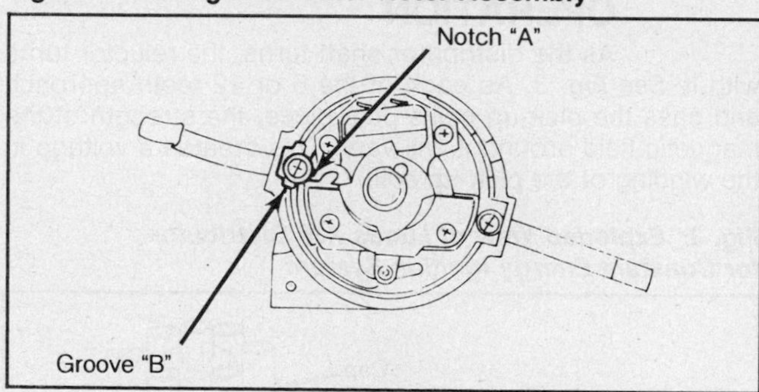
Notch "A"
Groove "B"

Match notch in rotor and pick-up coil pole piece.

- When installing vacuum controller, tighten only the screw holding the controller to the housing. Tighten screw between lever and pick-up coil base when installing pick-up coil.
- When installing pick-up coil, adjust air gap to specifications.
- Align match mark "A" on pinion gear with right side of notch "B" on lower end of housing. *See Fig. 6.*
- After assembly, check centrifugal advance by using a distributor tester.

Fig. 6: Aligning Pinion Gear With Housing

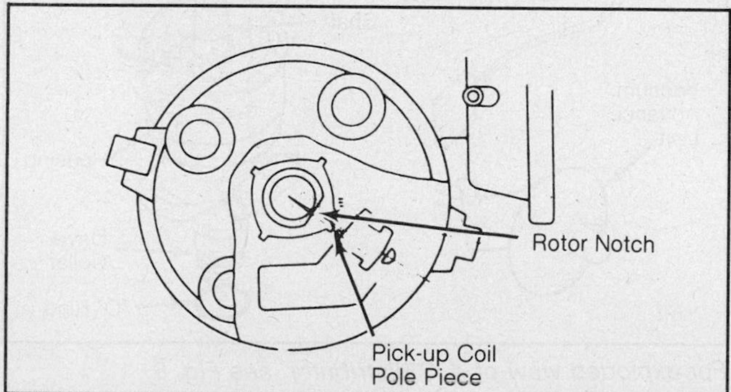
Rotor Notch
Pick-up Coil
Pole Piece

Mark "A" should align with right side of notch "B".

LUCAS CONSTANT ENERGY IGNITION

Jaguar XJ6, XJS

DESCRIPTION

The Lucas Constant Energy Ignition System maintains energy stored in the ignition coil at a constant level, allowing the output voltage to remain constant over a wide range of engine speeds.

Fig. 1: Wiring Schematic for Lucas Constant Energy Ignition System for XJ6 Models

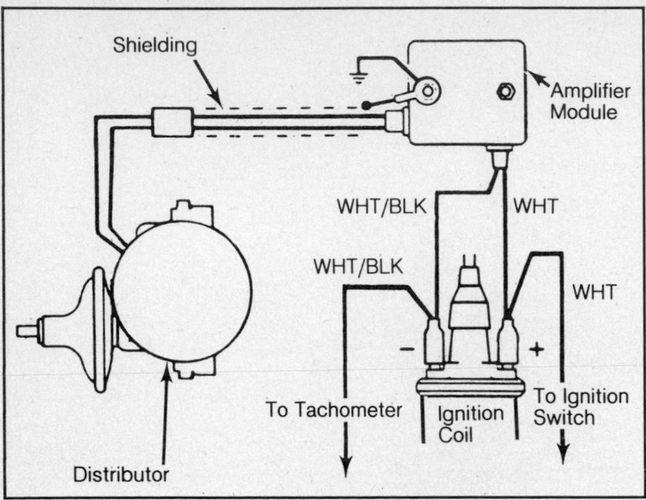
Shielding
Amplifier Module
WHT/BLK
WHT
WHT/BLK
WHT
−
+
To Tachometer
Ignition Coil
To Ignition Switch
Distributor

Also see chassis wiring in WIRING DIAGRAM Section.

The system also provides for a variable dwell for more optimum performance. A long dwell is provided at high speeds for adequate energy storage in the coil. A dwell is provided at lower speeds for minimum power loss.

Fig. 2: Wiring Schematic for Lucas Constant Energy Ignition System for XJS Models

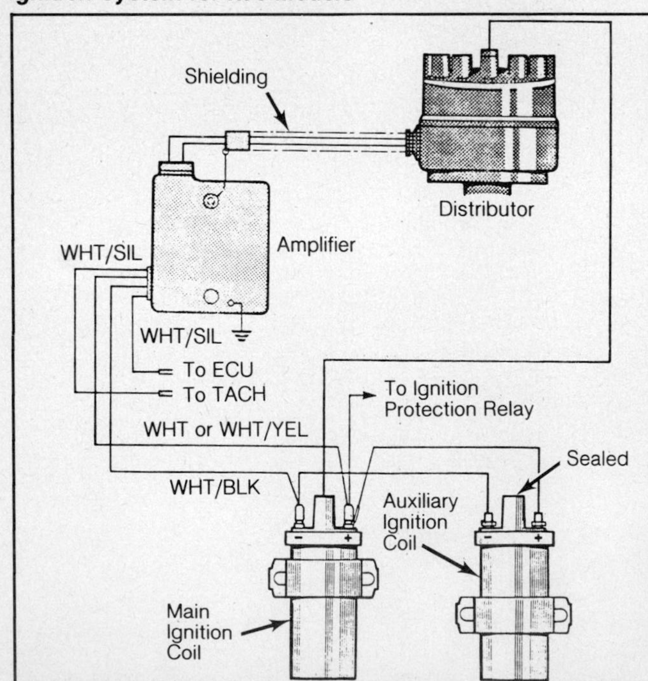
Shielding
Distributor
Amplifier
WHT/SIL
WHT/SIL
To ECU
To TACH
To Ignition Protection Relay
WHT or WHT/YEL
Sealed
WHT/BLK
Auxiliary Ignition Coil
Main Ignition Coil

Also see chassis wiring in WIRING DIAGRAM Section.

The power lost in both the coil and amplifier module is greatly reduced, compared to equivalent constant dwell systems. The system includes a breakerless distributor, amplifier module, an ignition coil, ignition switch, and battery. *See Fig. 1*. No ballast resistor is required.

The distributor has conventional centrifugal and vacuum advance systems, an anti-flash shield, rotor, reluctor, and pick-up coil. *See Fig. 2*. The reluctor is a gear-shaped component with 6 or 12 teeth, one for each cylinder of the engine. It is mounted on the distributor shaft.

The pick-up coil includes a winding, pole piece and a permanent magnet. A 2-wire shielded harness connects it directly to the amplifier module. The amplifier module, housed in an aluminum case, is located near the distributor.It has a 2-wire harness, which connects to the coil primary terminals.

On XJS models, 2 ignition coils are used. *See Fig. 2*. The main coil is connected in parallel with the primary windings of the auxiliary coil. The secondary circuit of the auxiliary coil is not used and the coil tower is sealed. Amplifier modules are not interchangeable between models.

OPERATION

As the distributor shaft turns, the reluctor turns with it. *See Fig. 3*. As each of the 6 or 12 teeth approach and pass the pick-up coil's pole piece, the strength of the magnetic field around it will vary. This creates a voltage in the winding of the pick-up coil.

Fig. 3: Exploded View of Lucas XJ6 Distributor for Constant Energy Ignition System

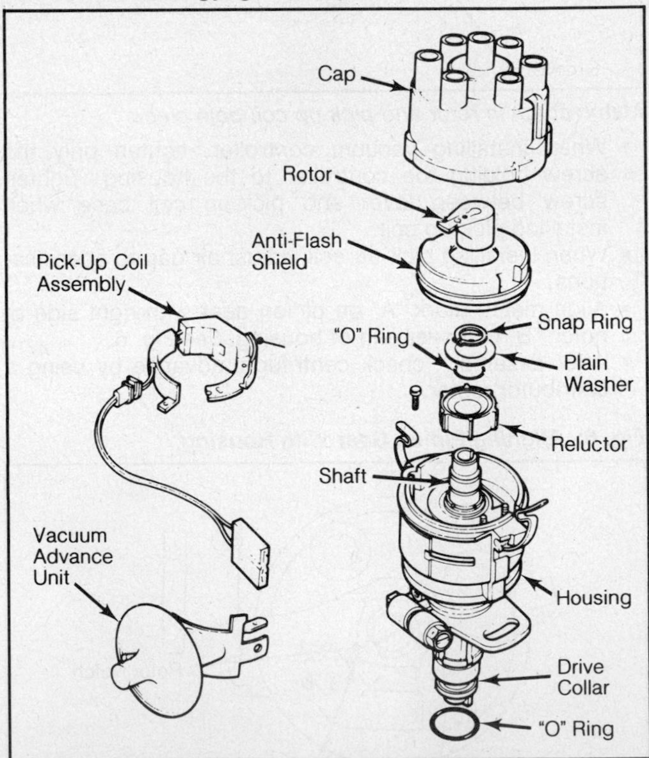
Cap
Rotor
Anti-Flash Shield
Pick-Up Coil Assembly
Snap Ring
"O" Ring
Plain Washer
Reluctor
Shaft
Vacuum Advance Unit
Housing
Drive Collar
"O" Ring

For exploded view of XJS distributor, see Fig. 8.

LUCAS CONSTANT ENERGY IGNITION (Cont.)

The rise and fall of this voltage is sensed by the amplifier module, which then sends a signal, cutting off voltage to the primary circuit of the ignition coil. This causes a voltage surge in the secondary, firing the spark plugs at the proper time.

SPECIFICATIONS

CENTRIFUGAL & VACUUM ADVANCE

See the appropriate Distributor Specifications Table in this section.

ADJUSTMENT

RELUCTOR-TO-PICK-UP COIL AIR GAP

1) Normally air gap will not need resetting unless it has been tampered with. Always use a plastic feeler gauge when checking or setting air gap. *See Fig. 4*. Gap must be checked at each reluctor tooth.

Fig. 4: Adjusting Reluctor-to-Pick-Up Coil Air Gap

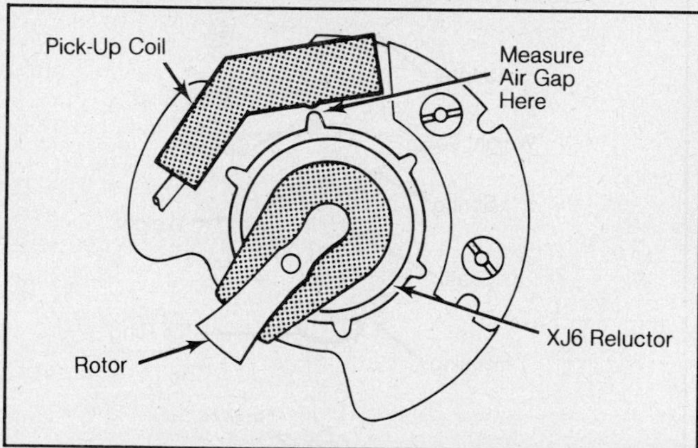

Pick-Up Coil
Measure
Air Gap
Here
XJ6 Reluctor
Rotor

Although XJ6 model is shown, procedure is same for XJS.

2) To check air gap, align reluctor tooth with pole piece of pick-up coil. Insert proper plastic feeler gauge. Original factory-set air gap is .006-.008" (.15-.20 mm). Set air gap during service at .008-.014" (.20-.35 mm). Check gap at each of the other reluctor teeth.

3) To adjust air gap, loosen pick-up coil mounting screws. Align reluctor tooth with pole piece of pick-up coil. Insert proper feeler gauge and move pick-up coil against gauge. Tighten mounting screws.

TESTING

BATTERY VOLTAGE CHECK

1) Check battery condition and specific gravity. Connect voltmeter positive lead to battery positive post. Connect negative lead to battery negative post.

2) Reading should be at least 12 volts. If not, charge battery.

SYSTEM SPARKING CHECK

1) Disconnect high tension wire from center of distributor cap. Hold wire 1/4" from good engine ground.

2) Crank engine. If a good spark is obtained, check spark plug wires, spark plugs, distributor cap and rotor. If no spark or poor spark is obtained, conduct the following component checks.

COIL VOLTAGE CHECKS

Positive Terminal

1) Turn ignition switch "ON". Connect voltmeter positive lead to ignition coil positive terminal. Connect negative lead to ground. *See Fig. 5*.

Fig. 5: Checking Ignition Coil Voltage

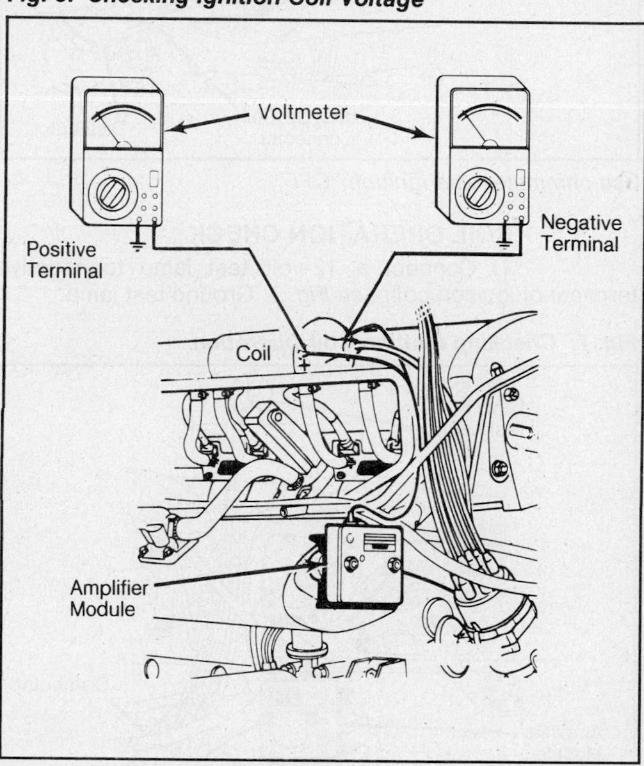

Voltmeter
Negative
Terminal
Positive
Terminal
Coil
Amplifier
Module

Check voltage at both positive and negative terminals.

2) Reading should be 12 volts. If voltage is less than 11 volts, check wiring back to ignition switch and battery.

Negative Terminal

1) With ignition switch still "ON" and negative voltmeter lead attached to ground, move the positive voltmeter lead to ignition coil negative terminal. *See Fig. 5*. Reading again should be 12 volts.

2) If a 0 (zero) reading is obtained, disconnect amplifier module lead from coil negative terminal. If voltage is still zero, a faulty ignition coil is indicated.

3) If a 0 (zero) reading was obtained in step **1)**, but a 12-volt reading was obtained after disconnecting amplifier module lead from coil negative terminal, suspect a faulty amplifier module.

PICK-UP COIL RESISTANCE CHECK

1) Disconnect pick-up coil connector from amplifier module. *See Fig. 6*. Be sure ignition is "OFF". Set ohmmeter in x100 scale. Insert ohmmeter leads into 2 pick-up coil harness terminals.

2) Resistance reading should be 2000-5000 ohms. If not, replace pick-up coil and harness assembly.

LUCAS CONSTANT ENERGY IGNITION (Cont.)

Fig. 6: Checking Pick-Up Coil Resistance

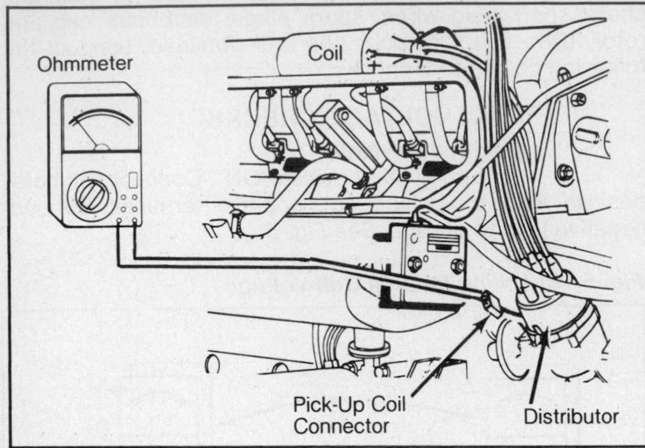
Ohmmeter
Coil
Pick-Up Coil
Connector
Distributor

Use ohmmeter with ignition "OFF".

COIL OPERATION CHECK

1) Connect a 12-volt test lamp to negative terminal of ignition coil. *See Fig. 7.* Ground test lamp.

Fig. 7: Checking Ignition Coil Operation

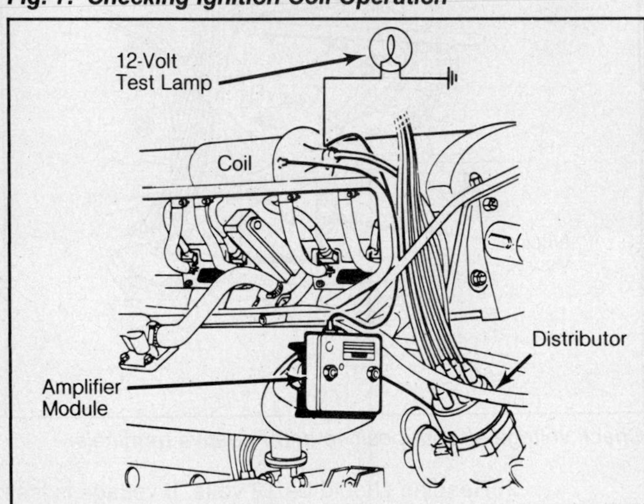
12-Volt
Test Lamp
Coil
Distributor
Amplifier
Module

Use 12-volt lamp with ignition turned "ON".

2) Crank the engine, but do not start it. Test lamp should flicker slightly.

AMPLIFIER LEAD TEST

Tachometer Lead

Connect ohmmeter leads to tachometer lead and to coil negative terminal. Reading should be 8,000-12,000 ohms. If not, replace amplifier.

ECU (Fuel-Injection) Lead

Connect ohmmeter leads to ECU connector and coil negative terminal. Reading should be 5,450-8,160 ohms. If not, replace amplifier.

OVERHAUL

DISTRIBUTOR

Disassembly

1) Disconnect negative battery cable, and remove distributor from vehicle. Remove distributor cap by releasing spring clips. Pull off rotor from keyed shaft. Remove anti-flash shield. Remove snap ring holding reluctor to distributor shaft. Remove plain washer, "O" ring, and felt pad..

Fig. 8: Exploded View of Lucas XJS Distributor

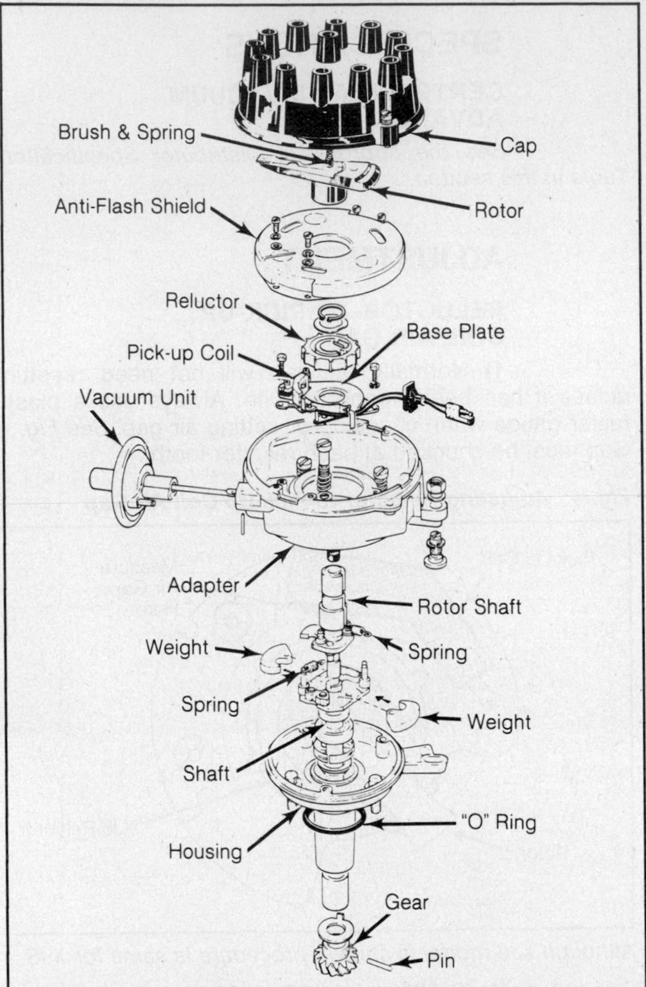
Brush & Spring
Cap
Rotor
Anti-Flash Shield
Reluctor
Base Plate
Pick-up Coil
Vacuum Unit
Adapter
Rotor Shaft
Weight
Spring
Spring
Weight
Shaft
"O" Ring
Housing
Gear
Pin

See Fig. 3 for exploded view of XJ6 distributor.

2) Remove U-shaped key, and lift reluctor from distributor shaft. Remove attaching screws or roll pin, and lift vacuum advance unit from base plate peg. Do not loosen 2 barrel nuts, securing pick-up coil. However, loosen mounting screws to remove pick-up coil and base plate assembly.

3) Drive pin from drive gear collar. Check shaft for burrs, and remove distributor shaft from housing. Disassemble auto-advance mechanism as necessary.

Reassembly

1) To assemble distributor, reverse disassembly procedure. Check parts for wear, and lubricate weight assembly, felt pad, shaft and moving plate with Rocol "Moly Pad" or equivalent. Be sure all parts are properly assembled and that they move freely.

2) Install distributor in vehicle, and reconnect negative battery cable. Adjust air gap and ignition timing, if necessary.

MITSUBISHI ELECTRONIC IGNITION

Chrysler Corp. Imports Colt, Colt Pickup, Challenger, Ram-50 Pickup, Sapporo; Mazda B2000 Pickup, GLC, 626 and Mitsubishi Cordia, Montero, Pickup, Starion, Tredia

DESCRIPTION

Mitsubishi breakerless ignition consists of an electronic control module (ignitor), ignition coil, pick-up coil, and distributor. The control module is mounted inside the distributor with the pick-up coil assembly.

Mitsubishi Starion models are equipped with Electronically Controlled Injection System, which controls fuel injection and ignition timing retard.

Mazda B2000 Pickups models with Calif. and High Alt. emissions, use a vacuum delay valve during acceleration. Calif. B2000 Pickups also use a water thermo valve to cut advance during cold operation.

OPERATION

Whenever the ignition switch is "ON", the primary circuit of the ignition coil is energized. As the distributor shaft rotates, the armature (reluctor) rotates inside the magnetic pick-up coil (stator) assembly.

As the teeth of the armature pass the pegs of the pick-up coil, a signal is sent to the control module (ignitor). The module then breaks the primary circuit in the coil. This causes a high voltage surge in the coil secondary circuit. This high voltage is required to fire the spark plugs.

SPECIFICATIONS

CENTRIFUGAL & VACUUM ADVANCE

See the appropriate Distributor Specifications Tables in this section.

Fig. 1: Wiring Schematic of Mitsubishi Electronic Ignition System With Internal Control Module

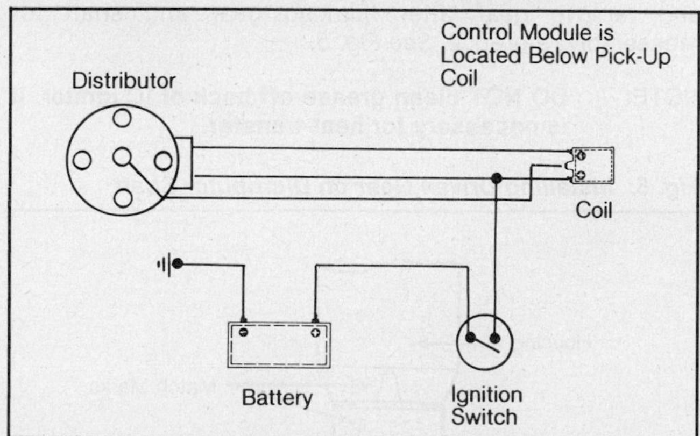
Control Module is Located Below Pick-Up Coil
Distributor
Coil
Battery
Ignition Switch

Also see chassis wiring in WIRING DIAGRAM Section.

ADJUSTMENTS

NOTE: **Air gap is not adjustable if model is not listed in table.**

Fig. 2: Wiring Schematic of Starion With Electronically Controlled Injection System

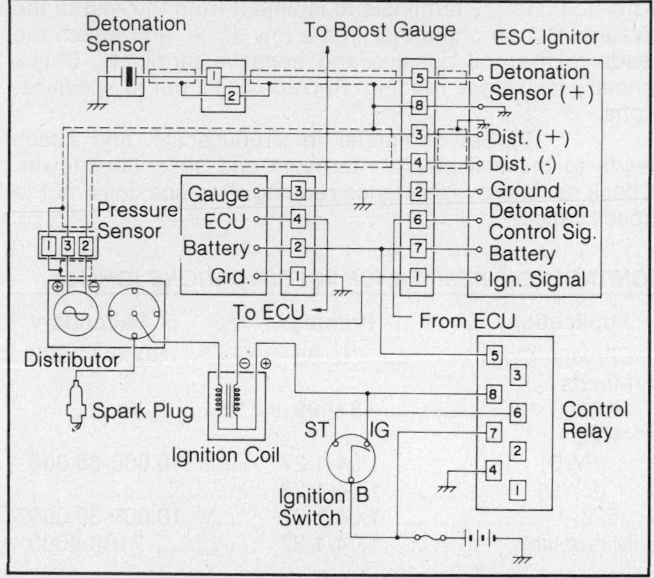
Detonation Sensor
To Boost Gauge
ESC Ignitor
Detonation Sensor (+)
Dist. (+)
Dist. (-)
Ground
Detonation Control Sig.
Battery
Ign. Signal
Pressure Sensor
Gauge
ECU
Battery
Grd.
To ECU
From ECU
Distributor
Spark Plug
Ignition Coil
ST
IG
Ignition Switch
B
Control Relay

Also see chassis wiring in WIRING DIAGRAM Section.

RELUCTOR-TO-PICK-UP COIL AIR GAP

Align teeth of reluctor with pegs of pick-up coil and breaker plate assembly. Using a feeler gauge, check for correct air gap. To adjust, loosen set screws, and move pick-up coil on GLC (RWD).

PICK-UP COIL AIR GAP

Application	In. (mm)
GLC (RWD)	.012-.018 (.30-.45)

NOTE: **No adjustments should be attempted on the ignition system except pick-up coil air gap, spark plug gap, and initial ignition timing.**

TESTING

NOTE: **Be sure battery is at full charge and in good condition before making any tests. Check all wiring harnesses, ignition switch, coil and spark plug cables and connectors.**

HIGH VOLTAGE TEST

Connect a remote starter switch in the starting circuit. Remove coil wire from distributor cap. Turn ignition switch "ON" and hold coil wire 1/4" from cylinder block. Crank engine. If no spark or only a weak spark results, perform the following tests.

SECONDARY WIRE RESISTANCE TEST

1) Test coil and spark plug cables with an ohmmeter. Do not puncture secondary wires when making the resistance check. Connect leads to each end of the cable.

2) Resistance for Mazda and Mitsubishi vehicles should not exceed 16,000 ohms for each 39" (1 m). For Chrysler Corp. vehicles, resistance should not exceed 22,000 ohms per cable.

MITSUBISHI ELECTRONIC IGNITION (Cont.)

IGNITION COIL RESISTANCE TEST

1) Turn ignition switch "OFF". Remove wires from coil primary terminals to isolate it from the rest of the system. Set an ohmmeter in the low scale, and attach the leads to the coil positive and negative terminals. Check primary resistance reading. Replace coil if not to specifications.

2) Set ohmmeter in x1000 scale, and attach leads to the coil positive terminal and secondary tower. Check secondary resistance reading. Replace coil if not to specifications.

IGNITION COIL RESISTANCE SPECIFICATIONS (OHMS)

Application	Primary	Secondary
Chrysler Corp.	.70-.85	9000-11,000
Mazda		
B2000 [1]	.81-.99	....
GLC		
(FWD) [1]	1.04-1.27	10,000-30,000
(RWD) [1]	1.04-1.27	....
626 [1]	1.04-1.27	10,000-30,000
Mitsubishi	1.04-1.27	7100-9600

[1] – With coil at normal operating temperature.

MAGNETIC PICK-UP COIL RESISTANCE TEST

1) Turn ignition switch "OFF". Set an ohmmeter in the x100 scale. Attach leads to pick-up coil's distributor connector terminals. *See Fig. 3.*

Fig. 3: Checking Pick-Up Coil Resistance

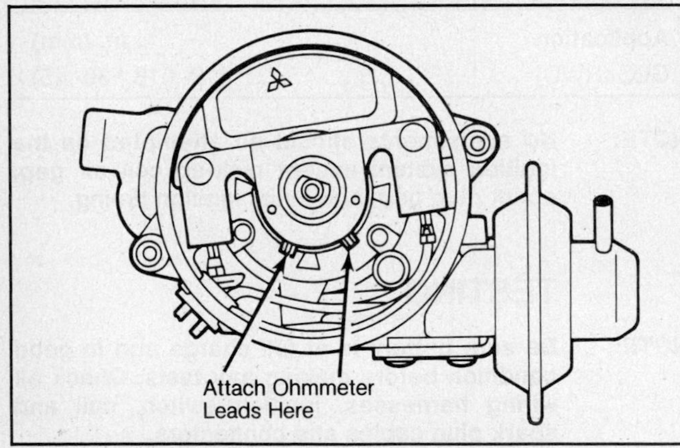
Attach Ohmmeter
Leads Here

Attach ohmmeter leads to points shown.

2) Compare resistance readings obtained with table. *See Pick-up Coil Resistance Table.*

PICK-UP COIL RESISTANCE

Application	Ohms
Chrysler Corp.	920-1120
Mazda 626 and B2000 [1]	945-1155
Mitsubishi	920-1120

[1] – Measure resistance at 68°F (20°C).

IGNITION MODULE TEST

Chrysler Corp. & Mitsubishi

Connect the ignitor, lamp, and battery. *See Fig. 4.* Using a dry cell battery or continuity tester, apply voltage to the signal input terminal of the ignitor unit. Lamp should light when voltage is applied, and go out when voltage is removed. If not, ignitor is bad.

NOTE: **This test can only determine when ignitor is bad. Even if ignitor tests out as good, it could still be defective.**

Fig. 4: Checking Ignitor With Battery and Test Lamp

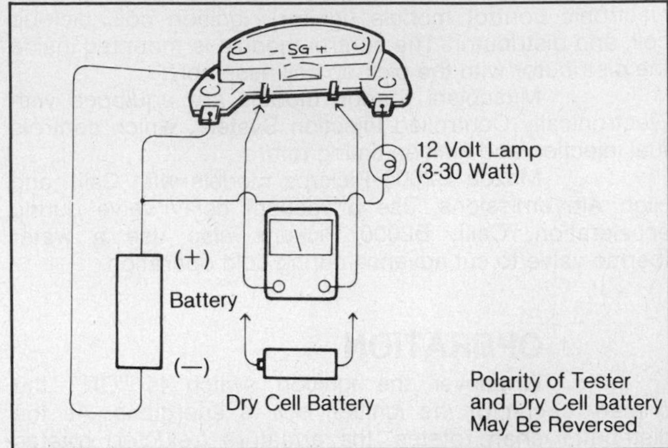
- SG +
12 Volt Lamp
(3-30 Watt)
(+)
Battery
(–)
Dry Cell Battery
Polarity of Tester
and Dry Cell Battery
May Be Reversed

Use low-voltage dry cell battery or ohmmeter.

OVERHAUL

DISASSEMBLY

1) Remove distributor cap. Remove rotor. Remove governor assembly. Note location of 2 different governor springs, for reassembly in original location. Remove attaching screws. Remove pick-up coil and IC ignitor assembly.

NOTE: **Governor assembly locking bolt is very tight. Use either a box wrench or socket wrench.**

2) Pull out the ignitor carefully from pick-up coil (if applicable). Remove the vacuum control unit. Remove the breaker assembly. Remove pin holding gear to shaft and remove gear after marking gear and shaft for reassembly reference. *See Fig. 5.*

NOTE: **DO NOT clean grease off back of IC ignitor. It is necessary for heat transfer.**

Fig. 5: Installing Driven Gear on Distributor Shaft

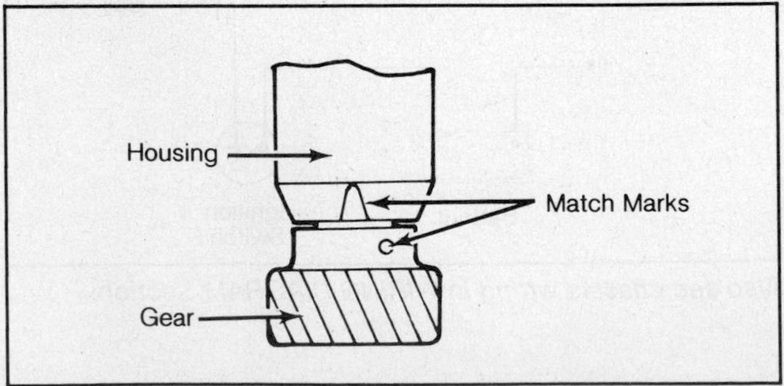
Housing
Match Marks
Gear

Align match marks and install pin.

MITSUBISHI ELECTRONIC IGNITION (Cont.)

Fig. 6: Exploded View of Mazda GLC Distributor

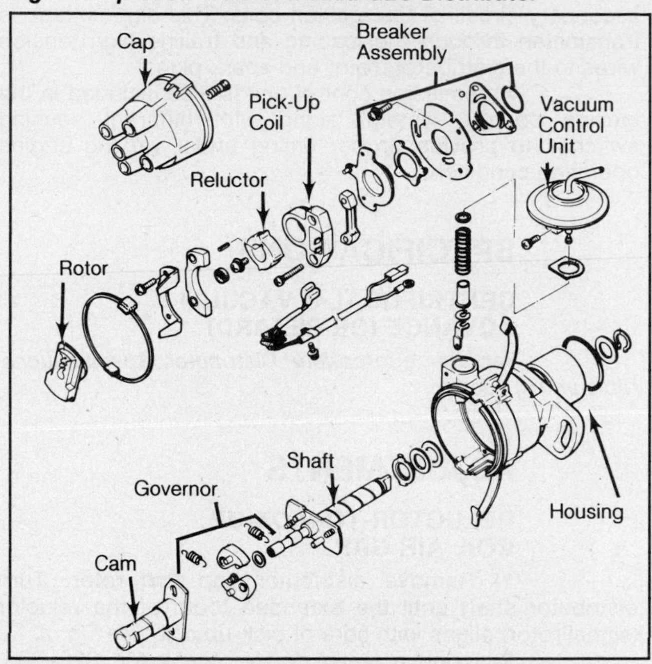
Cap
Breaker Assembly
Pick-Up Coil
Vacuum Control Unit
Reluctor
Rotor
Shaft
Governor
Housing
Cam

Note location of governor springs for reassembly.

REASSEMBLY

Reverse removal procedure. Inspect cap and rotor for cracks and deposits on inside surfaces. Be sure no metallic dust or filings adhere to breaker assembly, and is clean prior to reassembly.

Fig. 7: Exploded View of Chrysler Corp., Mazda B2000, 626 & Mitsubishi Distributor

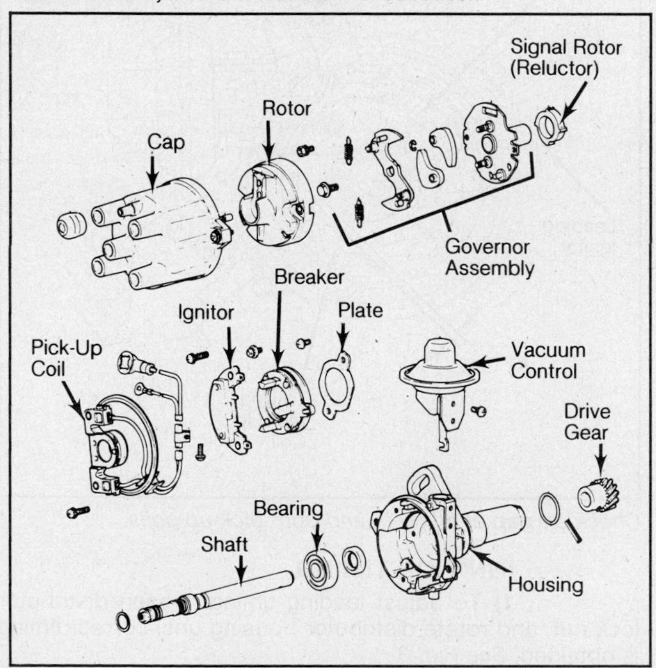
Signal Rotor (Reluctor)
Rotor
Cap
Governor Assembly
Breaker
Ignitor
Plate
Pick-Up Coil
Vacuum Control
Drive Gear
Bearing
Shaft
Housing

Note location of governor springs for reassembly.

MITSUBISHI ELECTRONIC IGNITION MAZDA ROTARY ENGINE

Mazda RX7

DESCRIPTION

The Mitsubishi electronic ignition system, used on the Mazda RX7 rotary engine, is unique in that it has 2 sets of spark plugs (leading and trailing). There is one set in the front rotor housing and one in the rear rotor housing. *See Fig. 1.* There are also 2 ignition coils, 2 pick-up coils located in the distributor, and 2 coil-to-distributor high tension wires.

Fig. 1: Schematic of RX7 Ignition System

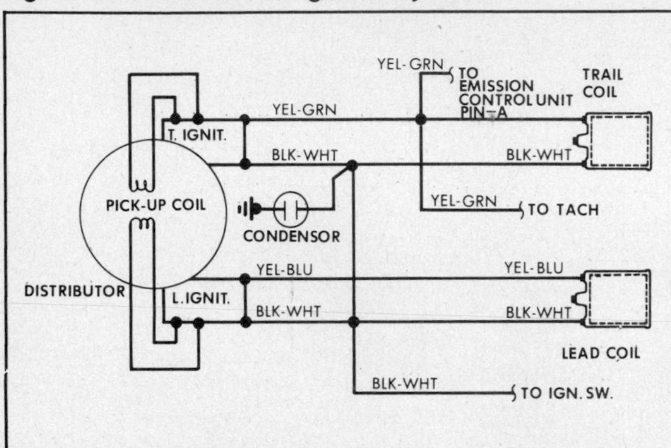
YEL-GRN
TO EMISSION CONTROL UNIT PIN-A
TRAIL COIL
YEL-GRN
T. IGNIT.
BLK-WHT
BLK-WHT
PICK-UP COIL
CONDENSOR
YEL-GRN
TO TACH
YEL-BLU
YEL-BLU
DISTRIBUTOR
L.IGNIT.
BLK-WHT
BLK-WHT
LEAD COIL
BLK-WHT
TO IGN. SW.

Also see chassis wiring in WIRING DIAGRAM Section.

There are 2 separate ignitors, mounted externally on the distributor housing. One is for the leading side and the other for the trailing side. Other system components include a battery, ignition switch, ignition control switches, (water temperature, altitude, etc.), and various relays.

All models are equipped with an ignition control system and centrifugal advance mechanisms. All models have vacuum control units for both leading and trailing sides.

OPERATION

A reluctor (signal rotor) is mounted on the reluctor (rotor) shaft. It turns inside 2 magnetic pick-up coils, one for the leading side and one for the trailing side. *See Fig. 2.*

As each tooth of the reluctor approaches and then passes the leading pick-up coil, a signal is generated. It is sent to the leading ignitor, which breaks the primary circuit in the leading ignition coil.

As each tooth passes the leading pick-up coil, the previous passing tooth approaches and becomes aligned with the trailing pick-up coil. This triggers a signal to the trailing ignitor, which breaks the primary circuit in the trailing ignition coil.

Therefore, immediately after the leading spark plug fires, the trailing spark plug also fires, providing more complete and efficient combustion while reducing HC and CO emissions.

As the primary circuit is broken in the leading and trailing ignition coils, a voltage surge occurs in the secondary circuit of the ignition coils. This high voltage is transmitted through the leading and trailing high tension wires to the distributor, rotor and spark plugs.

An emission control unit is also included in the ignition control system, along with different sensing switches to provide proper timing under varying engine operating conditions.

SPECIFICATIONS

CENTRIFUGAL & VACUUM ADVANCE (OR RETARD)

See the appropriate Distributor Specifications Table in this section.

ADJUSTMENTS

RELUCTOR-TO-PICK-UP COIL AIR GAP

1) Remove distributor cap and rotor. Turn distributor shaft until the extended tooth of the reluctor (signal rotor) aligns with core of pick-up coil. *See Fig. 2.*

2) Using a feeler gauge, check for .020-.035" (.5-.9 mm) air gap. If gap is incorrect, replace pick-up coil and bearing assembly or distributor drive shaft, if necessary.

Fig. 2: Adjusting Distributor Air Gap

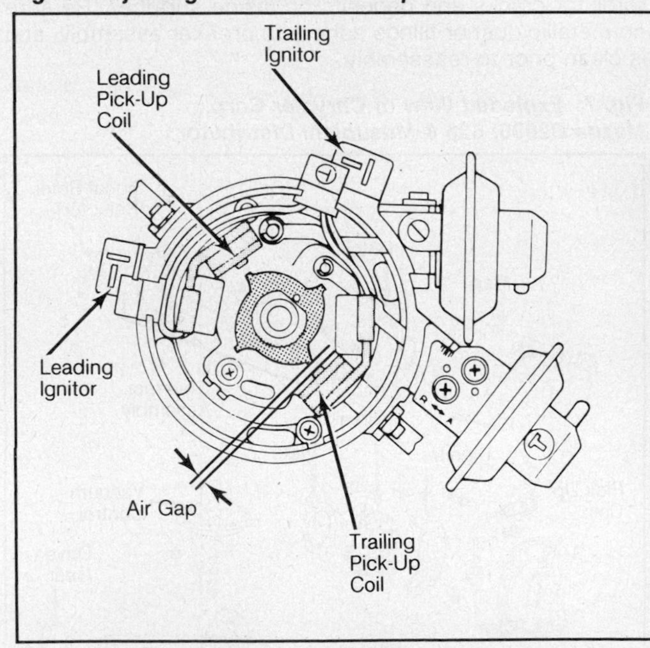
Trailing Ignitor
Leading Pick-Up Coil
Leading Ignitor
Air Gap
Trailing Pick-Up Coil

Check air gap at all teeth and both pick-up coils.

IGNITION TIMING

1) To adjust leading timing, loosen distributor lock nut, and rotate distributor housing until correct timing is obtained. *See Fig. 3.*

2) To adjust trailing timing, loosen the screws securing the trailing vacuum unit. Move the vacuum unit outward (to advance) or inward (to retard). Retighten screws when correct timing is obtained.

MITSUBISHI ELECTRONIC IGNITION MAZDA ROTARY ENGINE (Cont.)

Fig. 3: Adjusting Ignition Timing

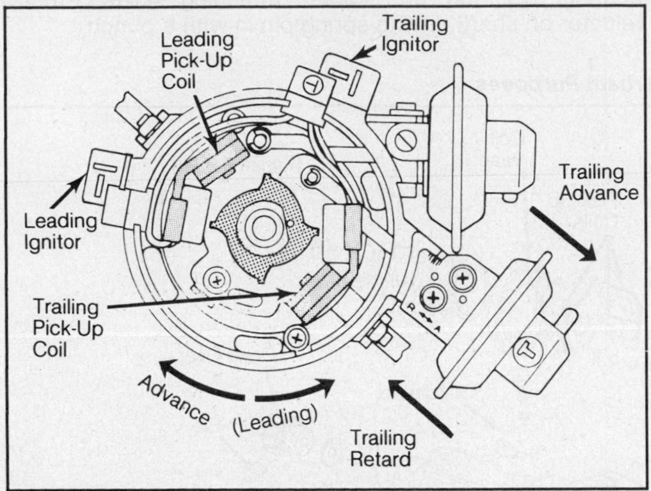
Leading Pick-Up Coil
Trailing Ignitor
Trailing Advance
Leading Ignitor
Trailing Pick-Up Coil
Advance
(Leading)
Trailing Retard

Distributor position determines leading time, while vacuum unit position adjusts trailing timing.

TESTING

HIGH TENSION WIRE RESISTANCE CHECK

Turn ignition switch "OFF". Connect ohmmeter leads to each end of coil-to-distributor high tension wire. Resistance should not exceed 16,000 ohms (±6,400 ohms) per 39.37" (1 m).

IGNITION COIL RESISTANCE CHECK

Set an ohmmeter in the low scale. With ignition switch turned "OFF", and coil wires disconnected, attach ohmmeter leads to primary terminals of leading coil and then trailing coil. Primary resistance should be 1.22-1.48 ohms for each ignition coil.

PICK-UP COIL RESISTANCE CHECK

1) Set an ohmmeter in the x100 scale. Turn ignition switch "OFF". Disconnect connector between ignitor and distributor. *See Fig. 4.*

Fig. 4: Ohmmeter Hookup for Pick-Up Coil Resistance Check

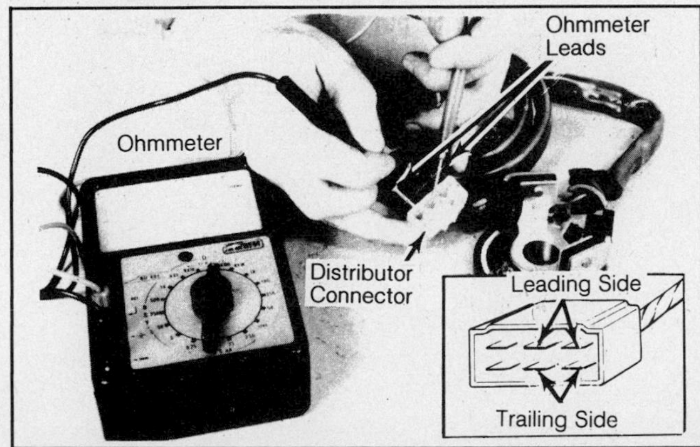
Ohmmeter Leads
Ohmmeter
Distributor Connector
Leading Side
Trailing Side

Replace pick-up coil and bearing plate assembly if reading is not 600-700 ohms.

2) Connect ohmmeter leads to leading terminals and then to trailing terminals. Resistance should be 600-700 ohms at 68° F (20° C) for each set of pick-up coils. If not, replace pick-up coil and bearing assembly.

PICK-UP COIL OPERATION CHECK

1) With distributor connector still disconnected, touch ammeter leads to leading terminals and then to trailing terminals.

2) Place a screwdriver against core of pick-up coil being tested. Indicator of meter should move each time screwdriver is taken quickly away from core. If not, replace pick-up coil and bearing assembly.

IGNITOR CHECK

1) Remove ignitor from distributor base. Make a circuit as shown in *Fig. 5* using wire and a test bulb. Use a 12 volt bulb of less than 10 watts.

Fig. 5: Test Lamp Hookup for Checking Ignitor Operation

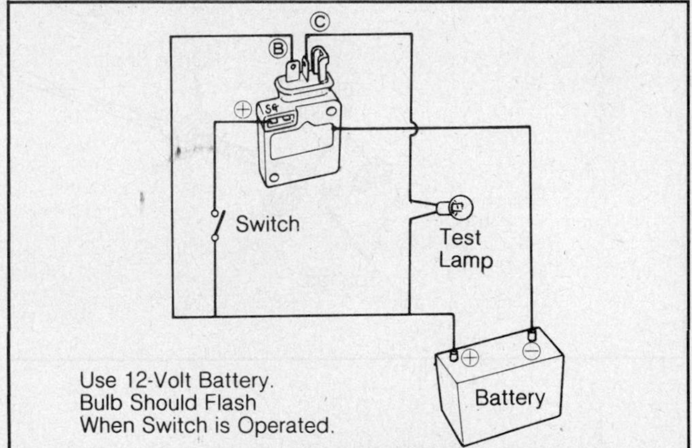
C
B
⊕
Switch
E
Test Lamp
Use 12-Volt Battery.
Bulb Should Flash
When Switch is Operated.
⊕
⊖
Battery

Bulbs should flash when switch is operated.

2) Quickly operate switch "ON " and "OFF", and make sure test lamp flashes. If not, replace ignitor.

OVERHAUL

DISASSEMBLY

1) Remove distributor cap, rotor and seal cover. *See Fig. 6.* Remove ignitors and attaching screws from distributor housing. Remove clips holding vacuum diaphragm links. Remove attaching screws and vacuum control units from distributor housing. Remove condenser.

2) Remove reluctor shaft attaching screw from end of shaft. Remove pick-up coil base bearing attaching screws. Remove reluctor, reluctor shaft, pick-up coils and coil base bearing assembly from top of distributor drive shaft.

3) Remove reluctor from reluctor shaft, using puller. Remove spring pin. Remove governors by removing springs. Drive lock pin out of drive gear, using a small drift. Remove gear and washers. Remove drive shaft through top of distributor housing.

REASSEMBLY

1) Inspect distributor cap and rotor for cracks, carbon tracks, and burned or corroded terminals.

MITSUBISHI ELECTRONIC IGNITION MAZDA ROTARY ENGINE (Cont.)

2) Assemble distributor in reverse order of disassembly, noting the following: Install reluctor shaft onto distributor drive shaft, engaging slots of reluctor shaft and governor pins. Install pick-up coil and coil base bearing assembly and tighten attaching screws. Install reluctor on shaft, driving spring pin in with a punch.

Fig. 6: Disassembled View of RX7 Mitsubishi Distributor for Overhaul Purposes

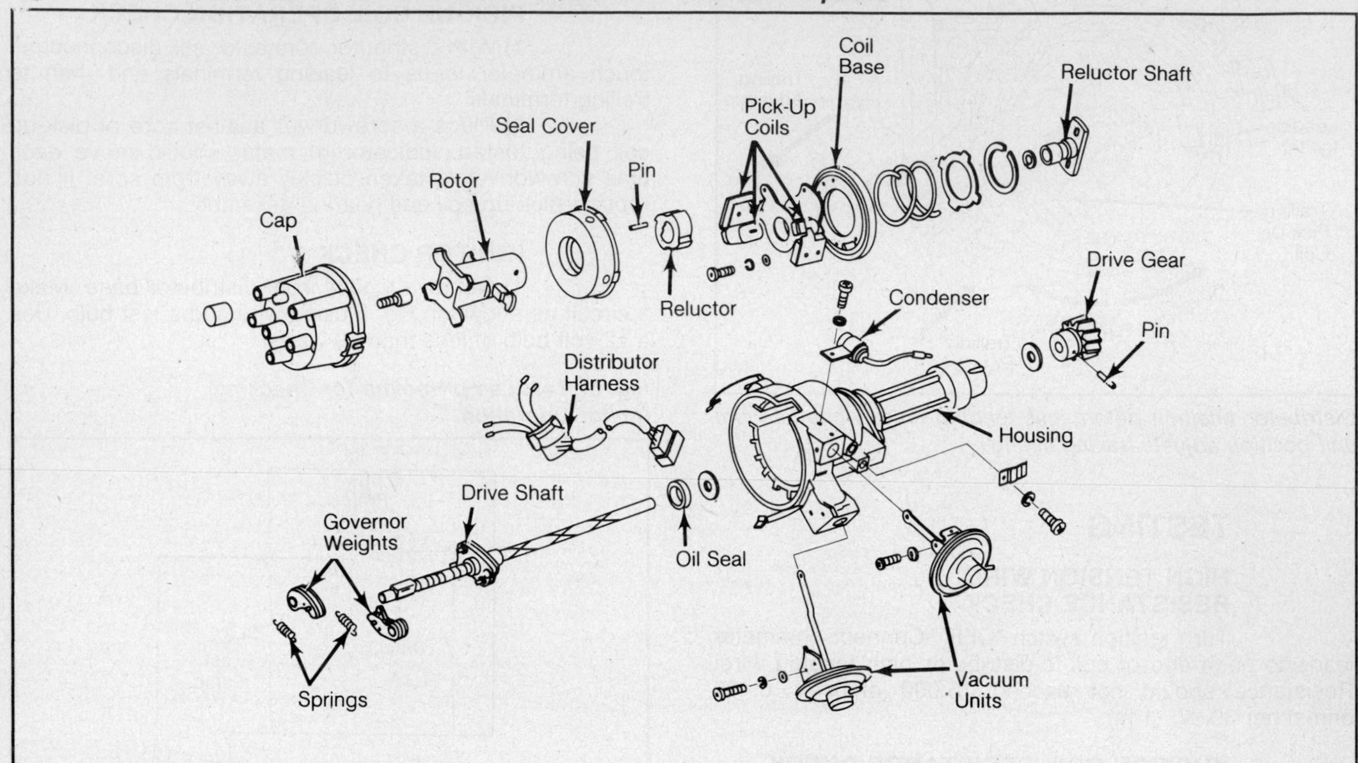
Coil Base
Reluctor Shaft
Pick-Up Coils
Seal Cover
Pin
Rotor
Cap
Reluctor
Drive Gear
Condenser
Pin
Distributor Harness
Housing
Drive Shaft
Governor Weights
Oil Seal
Springs
Vacuum Units

NIPPONDENSO ELECTRONIC IGNITION

Isuzu I-Mark, Impulse, P'UP; Subaru 1600 (2WD), 1800 (2WD); Toyota Camry, Celica, Corolla, Cressida, Land Cruiser, Pickup, Starlet, Supra & Tercel

DESCRIPTION

The Nippondenso electronic ignition system includes a breakerless distributor, an ignitor (ignition control unit), a special ignition coil, and ignition switch. The distributor consists of a housing, rotor, and cap. It contains a signal rotor (timing rotor or reluctor), magnet, and a magnetic pick-up coil assembly. *See Fig. 1.*

On Subaru models, the ignitor is mounted inside the distributor. On Toyota Camry, Corolla and Tercel models, the ignitor and ignition coil are inside the distributor. On other models, the transistorized ignitor is mounted on the ignition coil housing.

Toyota Cressida and Supra models use Electronic Spark Advance (ESA), and Isuzu Impulse use I-TEC ignition systems. Both systems use a computer to control spark advance. All other distributor models contain conventional centrifugal and vacuum advance mechanisms.

Fig. 1: Exploded View of Typical Nippondenso Distributor

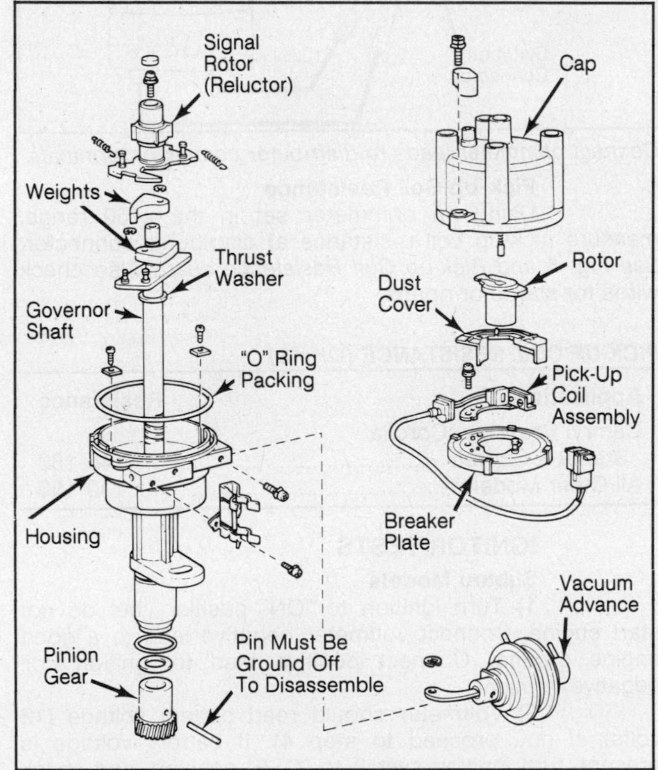
Signal
Rotor
(Reluctor)
Cap
Weights
Thrust
Washer
Rotor
Dust
Cover
Governor
Shaft
"O" Ring
Packing
Pick-Up
Coil
Assembly
Housing
Breaker
Plate
Vacuum
Advance
Pinion
Gear
Pin Must Be
Ground Off
To Disassemble

Toyota distributor is shown. Some distributors contain an integral ignitor.

OPERATION

EXCEPT ESA & I-TEC

As the signal rotor turns with the distributor shaft, its teeth (one for each engine cylinder) pass the magnetic pick-up coil assembly. *See Fig. 2.*

As the air gap changes with the approach and passing of each tooth, the magnetic field varies. This creates a signal in the pick-up coil assembly. The ignitor senses this signal, and turns the ignition coil primary circuit on and off.

Fig. 2: Schematic of Nippondenso Electronic Ignition Circuit

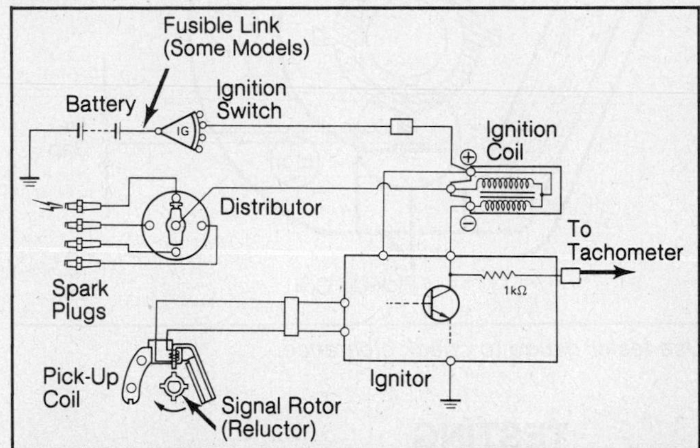
Fusible Link
(Some Models)
Battery
Ignition
Switch
IG
Ignition
Coil
Distributor
To
Tachometer
1kΩ
Spark
Plugs
Pick-Up
Coil
Ignitor
Signal Rotor
(Reluctor)

Some models have EFI relays or other minor variations.

This causes the magnetic field in coil primary circuit to build and collapse, resulting in a voltage surge in the secondary, which fires the spark plugs.

Fig. 3: Schematic of Toyota ESA Ignition System Circuit

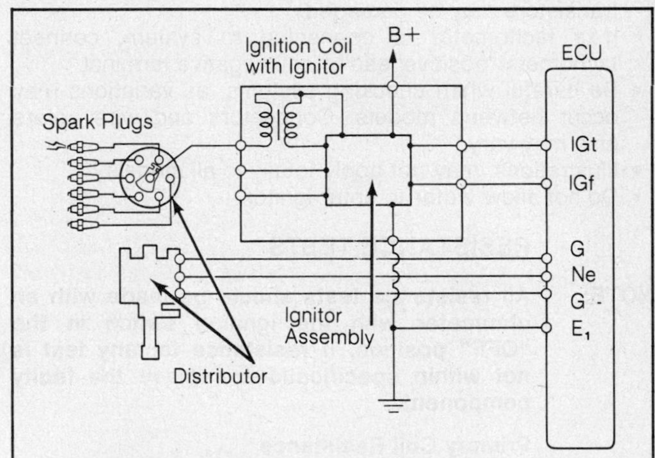
B+
Ignition Coil
with Ignitor
ECU
Spark Plugs
IGt
IGf
G
Ne
G-
E1
Ignitor
Assembly
Distributor

Ignition spark advance is computer controlled.

SPECIFICATIONS

CENTRIFUGAL & VACUUM ADVANCE

See the appropriate Distributor Specifications Table in this section.

ADJUSTMENTS

PICK-UP COIL-TO-SIGNAL ROTOR (RELUCTOR) AIR GAP

1) Using a flat feeler gauge, check air gap between pick-up coil pole piece and each reluctor tooth. Gaps should be equal and .008-.016" (0.2-0.4mm).

2) If not, loosen screws, and move pick-up coil against feeler gauge of proper thickness. Tighten screws, and recheck air gap. *See Fig. 4.*

NIPPONDENSO ELECTRONIC IGNITION (Cont.)

Fig. 4: Checking Signal Rotor-to-Pick-Up Coil Air Gap

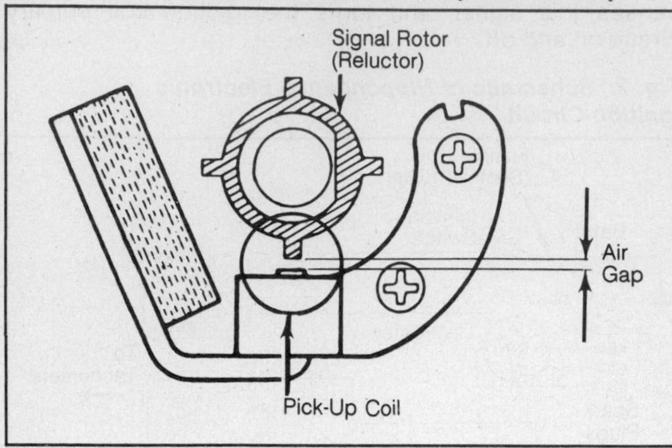
Signal Rotor
(Reluctor)
Air
Gap
Pick-Up Coil

Use feeler gauge to check clearance.

TESTING

CAUTION: The following precautions should be observed while servicing or testing a Nippondenso ignition system.

- Ensure all connections are correct, reverse battery polarity may damage ignitor (ignition control unit).
- Do not disconnect battery while engine is running or transistors may be damaged.
- If a tachometer is connected to system, connect tachometer positive lead to coil negative terminal.
- Be careful when checking systems, as variations may occur between models. Connectors and wire colors also may vary.
- Illustrations, may not apply totally to all models.
- Do not allow water to enter ignitor.

RESISTANCE TESTS

NOTE: All resistance tests should be made with an ohmmeter with the ignition switch in the "OFF" position. If resistance for any test is not within specifications, replace the faulty component.

Primary Coil Resistance

Isolate coil from remainder of system. Connect an ohmmeter, set in x1 range, so leads touch coil positive and negative primary terminals. *See Ignition Coil Resistance table*.

IGNITION COIL RESISTANCE (OHMS)

Application	Primary Resistance	Secondary Resistance
Isuzu	1.1-1.5	10,200-13,800
Subaru	1.1-1.4	10,800-14,600
Toyota		
Celica & Pickup (Type IV)	0.8-1.1	10,700-14,500
Camry, Corolla Tercel	0.4-0.5	7700-10,400
Land Cruiser	0.5-0.7	11,500-15,500
Cressida, Pickup (Type III), Supra	0.4-0.5	8500-11,500
Starlet	1.3-1.7	10,700-14,500

Secondary Coil Resistance

With coil still isolated from rest of system, set an ohmmeter in the x100 range. Connect leads to coil positive terminal and to coil tower (high tension terminal). *See Ignition Coil Resistance table*.

Insulation Resistance

Connect 1 ohmmeter lead to the coil positive terminal and the other to the coil mounting bracket. Reading on all models should exceed 10 megohms (infinity).

High Tension Wire Resistance

1) Set ohmmeter to x1000 scale and attach leads to each end of high tension wire. On Isuzu I'Mark and P'UP, resistance should not exceed 73,500 ohms per foot.

2) On all other models, resistance should not exceed 25,000 ohms. If it does, replace wires.

Fig. 5: Checking Pick-Up Coil Resistance

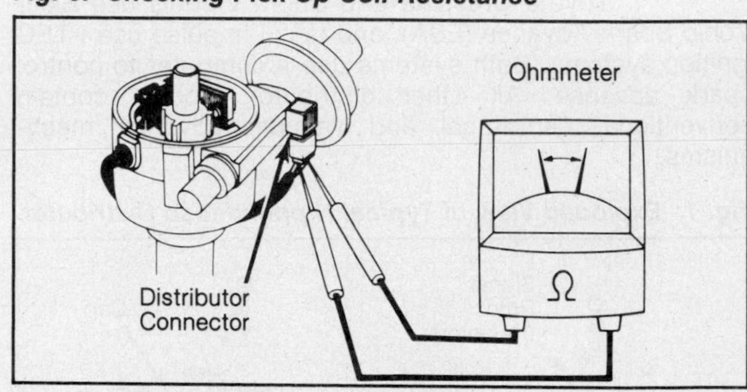
Ohmmeter
Distributor
Connector
Ω

Connect ohmmeter leads to distributor connector terminals.

Pick-Up Coil Resistance

Using an ohmmeter set in the x100 range, measure pick-up coil resistance at distributor connector. *See Fig. 5 and Pick-up Coil Resistance chart*. Also check wires for shorts or opens.

PICK-UP COIL RESISTANCE (OHMS)

Application	Resistance
Camry, Cressida, Corolla Starlet & Supra	140-180
All Other Models	130-190

IGNITOR TESTS

Subaru Models

1) Turn ignition to "ON" position, but do not start engine. Connect voltmeter negative lead to a good engine ground. Connect positive lead to ignition coil negative terminal.

2) Voltmeter should read battery voltage (12 volts). If not, proceed to step **4)**. If battery voltage is present, turn ignition switch to "OFF" position, and check air gap at distributor pick-up coil.

3) If not to specifications, adjust air gap. If okay, disconnect all wires from ignition coil primary terminals, and check both primary and secondary coil resistance. If not to specifications, replace ignition coil. If okay, proceed to step **9)**.

4) Connect voltmeter negative lead to a good engine ground. Connect positive lead to ignition coil positive terminal. Turn ignition switch to "ON" position. Voltmeter should again read battery voltage.

NIPPONDENSO ELECTRONIC IGNITION (Cont.)

5) If not, check the power supply harness, ignition switch, fuse, and noise suppressor condenser. Repair or replace components, as necessary.

6) If battery voltage was present in step **4)**, turn ignition switch to "OFF" position. Disconnect the distributor wire from the ignition coil negative terminal. Turn ignition switch to "ON" position.

7) Voltmeter should read battery voltage. If so, proceed to step **9)**. If not, turn ignition switch to "OFF" position, and disconnect tachometer wire from ignition coil negative terminal. Turn ignition switch back to "ON" position.

8) If battery voltage is not present now, replace ignition coil. If voltmeter indicated battery voltage in step **7)** with tachometer disconnected, check tachometer system for short circuit. Repair or replace, as necessary.

Fig. 6: Checking Toyota with Internal Coil & Ignitor

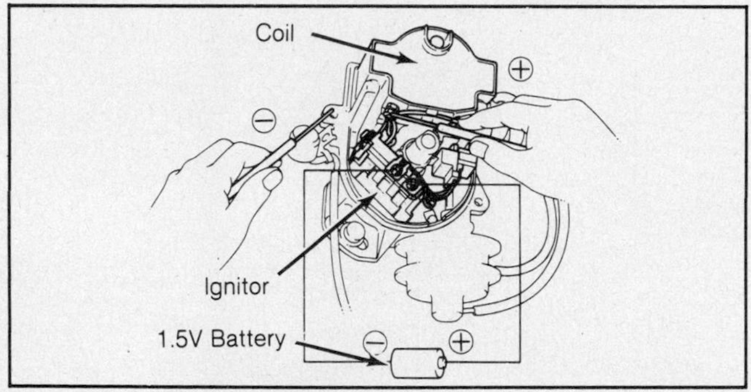

Coil
Ignitor
1.5V Battery

9) If ignition coil resistance was okay in step **3)** or if battery voltage at negative coil terminal was present in step **7)**, check for short circuit or open circuit between ignitor and both the ignition coil and distributor pick-up coil

10) If wiring from ignitor is okay, replace pick-up coil and ignitor.

Fig. 7: Checking Isuzu & Toyota with Coil-Mounted Ignitor

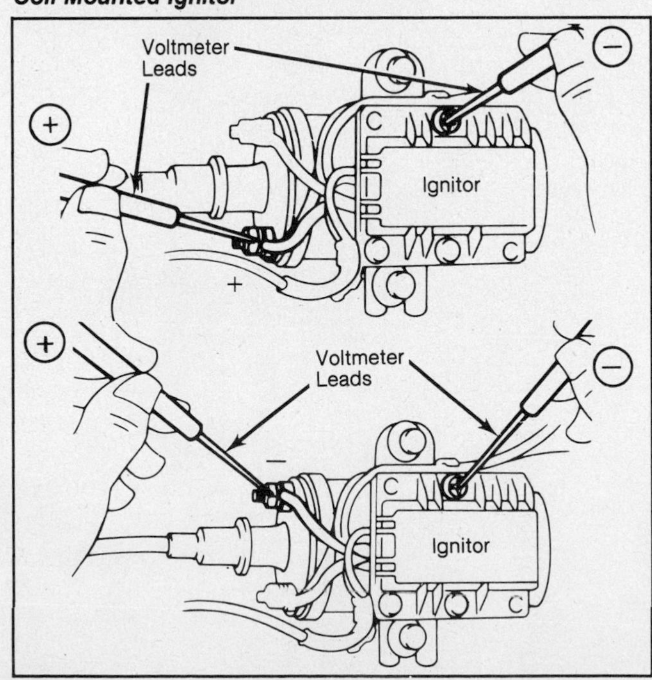

Voltmeter Leads
Ignitor
Voltmeter Leads
Ignitor

Check voltage at both positive and negative coil terminals.

Isuzu (Except Impulse) & Toyota (Except Cressida & Supra) Models

1) Turn ignition switch to "ON" position. Connect negative voltmeter lead-to-ground and positive lead-to-ignition coil positive terminal. *See Fig. 6 or 7.* Voltage reading should be 12 volts.

2) With negative lead still attached to ground, connect voltmeter positive lead-to-ignition coil negative terminal. *See Fig. 6 or 7.* Voltage should read 12 volts. Unplug wiring harness connector from distributor.

CAUTION: In step 3) below, do not apply voltage for more than 5 seconds.

3) Using a 1.5-volt dry cell battery (no more than 3-volt battery), connect battery positive pole-to-Pink wire terminal. *See Fig. 6 or 8.* Connect negative pole-to-White wire terminal.

Fig. 8: Checking Ignitor Operation with 1.5 Volt Battery

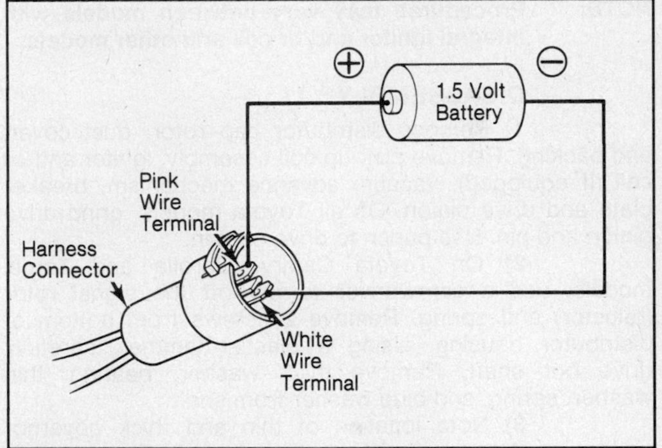

1.5 Volt Battery
Pink Wire Terminal
Harness Connector
White Wire Terminal

Apply voltage less than 5 seconds.

4) Voltage at negative terminal of coil should be as indicated in *Ignitor Test Voltage Specifications table.*

IGNITOR TEST VOLTAGE SPECIFICATIONS

Application	Volts
Isuzu	5
Toyota	
Camry, Celica, Pickup (Type III)	8-10
Corolla, Tercel	5-10
Land Cruiser, Pickup (Type IV)	5-8
Starlet	3

Toyota Cressida & Supra Models

1) Turn ignition switch to "ON" position. Disconnect Brown and Yellow wire connector. Use a voltmeter to check for 12 volts. If not check wiring or fuse. Reconnect the Brown wire.

2) Disconnect the coil wire at the distributor. Place coil wire about 1/4" from a good ground. Disconnect the Pink and White wiring connector.

3) Using a 3-volt dry cell battery (no more than 5-volt battery), connect battery positive pole-to-Pink wire terminal. *See Fig. 9.* Connect negative pole-to-coil ground.

4) Check for spark from coil wire after 1 second delay. If no spark occurs, replace ignitor.

NIPPONDENSO ELECTRONIC IGNITION (Cont.)

Fig. 9: Checking Ignitor Operation with 3-Volt Battery

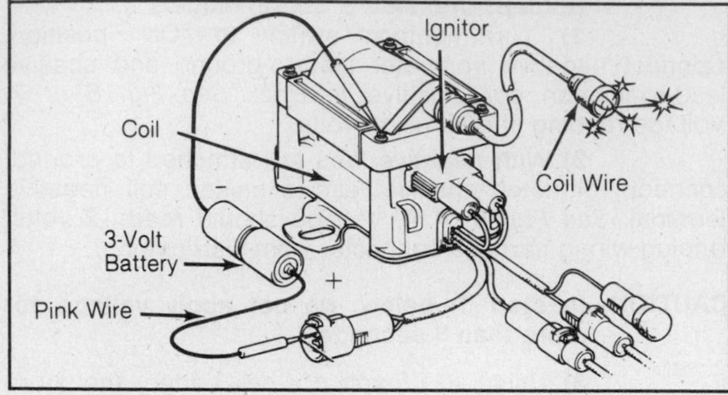
Ignitor
Coil
Coil Wire
–
3-Volt
Battery
+
Pink Wire

Do not use more than 5-volt battery.

OVERHAUL

NOTE: Procedures may vary between models with integral ignitor and/or coil and other models.

DISASSEMBLY

1) Remove distributor cap rotor, dust cover, and packing. Remove pick-up coil assembly, ignitor and/or coil (if equipped), vacuum advance mechanism, breaker plate and drive pinion. On all Toyota models, grind drive pinion and pin. Use punch to drive out pin.

2) On Toyota Camry, Corolla and Tercel models, use a screwdriver to pry off the signal rotor (reluctor) and spring. Remove 2 screws from bottom of distributor housing. Using a plastic hammer, carefully drive out shaft. Remove thick washer, bearing, thin washer, spring, and blue washer from shaft.

3) Note location of thin and thick governor springs, and remove springs (if equipped). Remove cam cap, signal rotor (reluctor), weight snap ring and weights.

REASSEMBLY

1) Assemble in reverse order of disassembly. Lightly grease signal rotor (reluctor) inner surface.

2) Install on shaft aligning proper mark on stopper plate ("10.5" on Isuzu and Land Cruiser; "11" on Subaru; "10.5" on Celica, Pickup; and "8.5" on Starlet.) On all other Toyota models, align drill mark on drive pinion with punch mark on distributor housing.

NOTE: On Toyota models, install new drive pinion and pin.

3) When installing breaker plate, align 4 clips of plate with 4 grooves in housing.

4) When replacing pinion, replace pin and drive pinion as a set. Adjust air gap between signal rotor and pick-up coil.

TOYO DENSO ELECTRONIC IGNITION – HONDA

Accord, Prelude

DESCRIPTION

NOTE: Some Honda models use Hitachi distributors. See appropriate article in this section.

Honda's Toyo Denso electronic distributors consist of a distributor housing, rotor and the distributor cap. The reluctor, stator, magnets, pick-up coil and breaker plate assemblies are all located inside the distributor housing.

Fig. 1: Disassembled View of Toyo Denso Distributor Used On Accord Models.

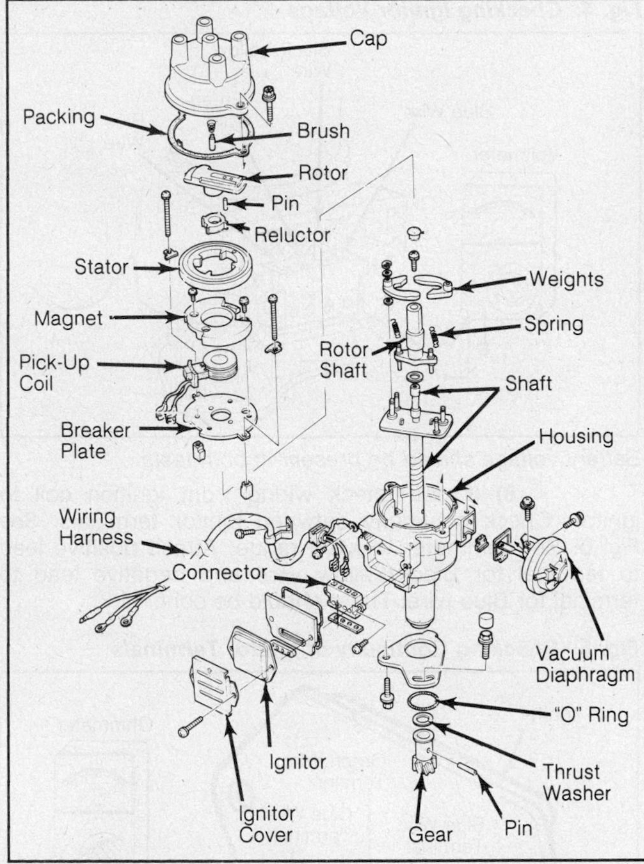
Cap
Packing
Brush
Rotor
Pin
Reluctor
Stator
Weights
Magnet
Spring
Rotor Shaft
Pick-Up Coil
Shaft
Breaker Plate
Housing
Wiring Harness
Connector
Vacuum Diaphragm
"O" Ring
Ignitor
Thrust Washer
Ignitor Cover
Gear
Pin

The ignitor on Toyo Denso distributors is mounted externally on the distributor housing. All models use a centrifugal and vacuum advance system.

OPERATION

The reluctor, secured to the distributor rotor shaft by a roll pin, turns with the distributor shaft. As it turns, its 4 external teeth come in line with the 4 teeth of the ring-shaped stator.

As the reluctor approaches and passes the stator teeth, variations occur in the magnetic field around them. This causes the pick-up coil to signal the ignitor.

As these signals are received, transistors inside the ignitor are turned off and on. This results in a magnetic field building and collapsing in the primary circuit of the ignition coil. When this field collapses, a voltage surge occurs in the secondary circuit of the ignition coil.

When this occurs, a high voltage spark is fed from the coil, through the distributor rotor and cap to the secondary wiring and spark plugs.

Fig. 2: Disassembled View of Toyo Denso Distributor Used On Prelude Models

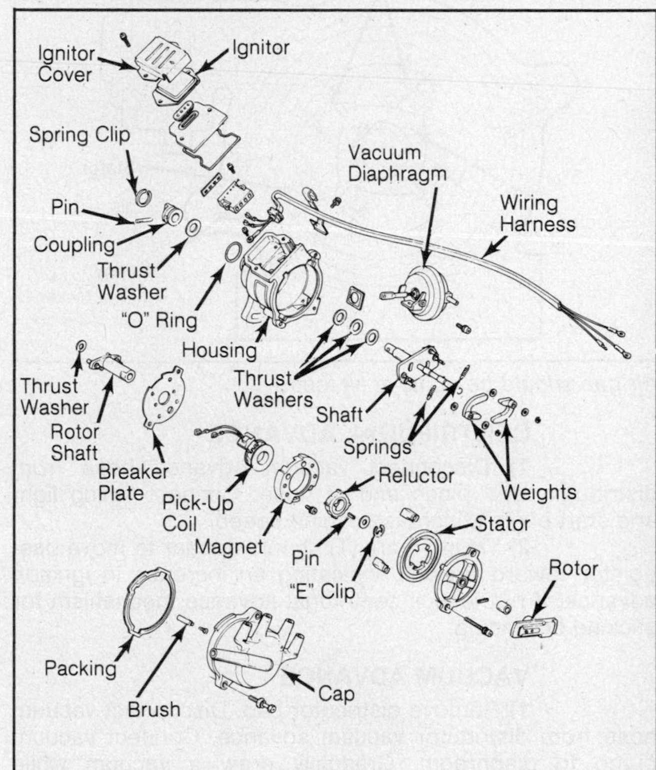
Ignitor Cover
Ignitor
Spring Clip
Vacuum Diaphragm
Pin
Wiring Harness
Coupling
Thrust Washer
"O" Ring
Housing
Thrust Washer
Thrust Washers
Shaft
Rotor Shaft
Springs
Breaker Plate
Reluctor
Weights
Pick-Up Coil
Stator
Magnet
Pin
Rotor
"E" Clip
Packing
Cap
Brush

SPECIFICATIONS

CENTRIFUGAL & VACUUM ADVANCE

See appropriate Distributor Specifications Table in this section.

ADJUSTMENT

CAUTION: To avoid damaging the ignition system, never reverse battery polarity. Do not let pick-up coil wires touch ignition wires. Do not do anything that would produce abnormal pulses. Always connect pulse type tachometers to negative terminal of ignition coil. Make sure all wires and cables are connected properly.

RELUCTOR-TO-STATOR AIR GAP

1) Align 4 teeth of reluctor with 4 teeth of stator, and check air gap. Check air gap at all teeth as reluctor is rotated. *See Fig. 3.* There should be equal air gap at all 4 teeth. If not, check for damage to stator or reluctor.

2) If necessary to adjust, loosen 2 screws securing stator, and reposition stator to provide equal air gaps. Tighten 2 screws.

TOYO DENSO ELECTRONIC IGNITION SYSTEMS – HONDA (Cont.)

Fig. 3: Adjusting Reluctor-To-Stator Air Gap

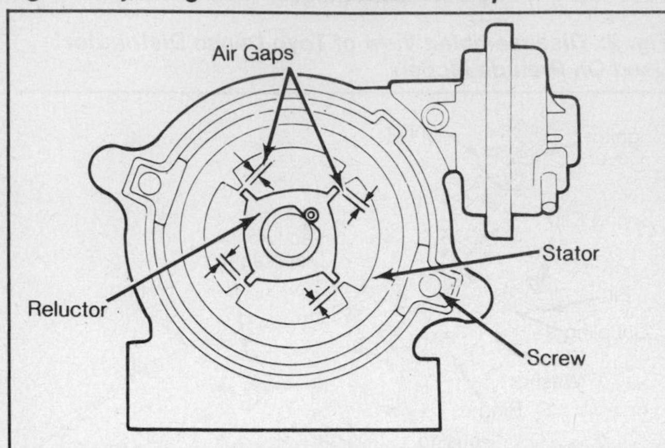
Air Gaps
Stator
Reluctor
Screw

Air gap should be equal at all teeth.

CENTRIFUGAL ADVANCE

1) Disconnect vacuum advance hose from distributor, and pinch end of hose. Connect timing light and start engine. Increase engine speed.

2) Timing mark (T) should appear to move past pointer toward firewall, indicating an increase in ignition advance. If not, check centrifugal advance mechanism for sticking or binding.

VACUUM ADVANCE

1) Remove distributor cap. Disconnect vacuum hose from distributor vacuum advance. Connect vacuum pump to diaphragm. Gradually draw a vacuum while watching breaker plate movement.

2) Check for smooth operation without binding. If pump indicates a loss of vacuum, replace diaphragm unit. Turn breaker plate right and left to check for free movement.

TESTING

BASIC SYSTEM TEST

1) If engine will not start and starter will not crank engine, check battery, main fuse and electrical wiring. Check starter circuit wiring and ignition switch. If engine will not start, but starter cranks engine, hold coil wire 1/4" from coil tower while cranking engine.

2) If there is no spark, go to step **4)**. If there is spark from coil, hold spark plug wire terminal 1/4" from spark plug while cranking engine.

3) If there is no spark at the plug, check spark plug wire condition, inspect distributor cap and rotor, and as a last resort, replace ignitor on distributor housing. If spark exists at the plug, check fuel system, spark plugs, ignition timing or valve timing.

4) Turn ignition switch to "ON" position. Check voltage between coil primary winding positive terminal and ground. Battery voltage should be found. If not, check wiring from ignition switch to ignition coil.

5) If battery voltage exists, be sure ignition switch is still in the "ON" position. Check voltage between coil primary winding negative terminal and ground. Again, battery voltage should exist. If not, check wiring from coil primary negative terminal to ignitor. Also check coil primary resistance.

6) If battery voltage was present at negative terminal, check voltage between coil positive and negative terminals with engine cranking. Reading should be 1-3 volts. If within specifications, check primary and secondary coil resistance. Also check spark plug wire resistance.

7) If voltage in step **6)** was not 1-3 volts, disconnect lead wires from ignitor. Check voltage on coil side of connector, first between Blue wire and Black (ground) wire and then between Black/Yellow wire and Black (ground) wire. *See Fig. 4.* Battery voltage should exist with ignition switch "ON".

Fig. 4: Checking Ignitor Voltage

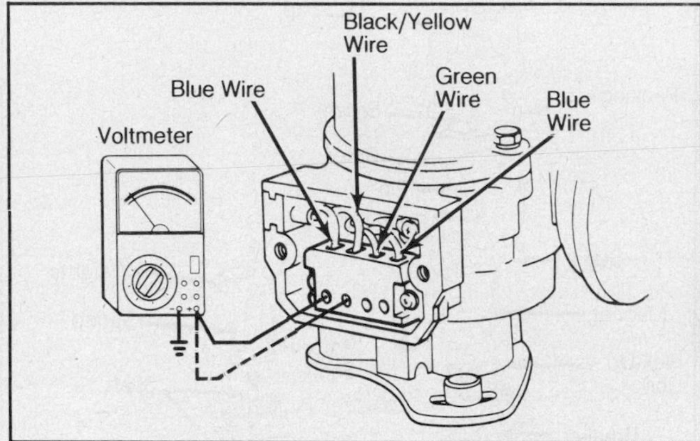
Black/Yellow
Wire
Blue Wire
Green
Wire
Blue
Wire
Voltmeter

Battery voltage should be present in both tests.

8) If not, check wiring from ignition coil to ignitor. Check continuity between ignitor terminals. *See Fig. 5.* Set ohmmeter to x100 range. Attach positive lead to terminal for Black/Yellow wire and negative lead to terminal for Blue wire. There should be continuity.

Fig. 5: Checking Continuity at Ignitor Terminals

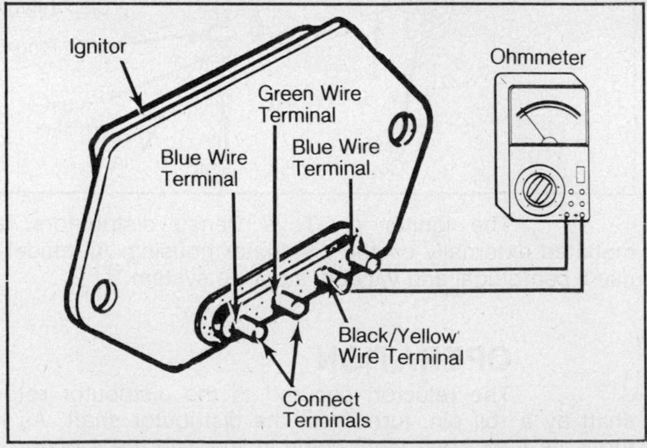
Ignitor
Ohmmeter
Green Wire
Terminal
Blue Wire
Terminal
Blue Wire
Terminal
Black/Yellow
Wire Terminal
Connect
Terminals

Test as shown and then reverse ohmmeter connections.

9) Reverse ohmmeter leads (positive lead to terminal for Blue wire, negative lead to terminal for Black/Yellow wire). There should be no continuity. If incorrect results are obtained, replace ignitor and repeat test.

TOYO DENSO ELECTRONIC IGNITION SYSTEMS – HONDA (Cont.)

COMPONENT TESTS

Ignition Coil Primary Resistance

1) Turn ignition switch "OFF" and remove positive and negative wires from ignition coil terminals. Connect an ohmmeter set in the x1 range with one probe touching each primary terminal.

2) Reading should be 1.06-1.24 ohms. If reading is not to specifications, replace ignition coil.

Ignition Coil Secondary Resistance

1) Turn ignition switch "OFF". Set ohmmeter in x1000 range. Connect ohmmeter leads to ignition coil negative terminal (wire removed) and coil tower terminal.

2) Resistance should be 7,400-11,000 ohms. If not replace ignition coil.

Condenser Capacity

Using a condenser tester, check for 0.38-0.56 microfarads.

Ignition Wire Resistance

1) Carefully remove wires by pulling on their rubber boots. Do not bend wire or conductor may be broken. Check for corroded condition, cleaning if necessary. Connect ohmmeter probes (set in x1000 scale) to each end of ignition wires.

2) Resistance reading should be 25,000 ohms or less per wire. If not, replace wires.

OVERHAUL

DISASSEMBLY

1) Remove spark plug wires and vacuum hoses from distributor. Remove distributor cap. Remove condenser ground wire and disconnect pick-up coil wire connector from distributor. Remove hold-down bolt, lifting distributor from cylinder head.

2) Carefully pry upward on reluctor with 2 screwdrivers, cushioned with rags to prevent damage to distributor housing. Use care not to damage reluctor or stator.

3) Remove advance diaphragm mounting screw. Pull out on diaphragm unit, while pushing down on end of diaphram arm.

4) Drive roll pin from distributor shaft. Remove shaft and gear from housing. Inspect and replace parts as necessary.

REASSEMBLY

Accord

1) Grease the distributor shaft and rotor shaft. Assemble shafts and secure with screw and rubber plug. Install centrifugal advance weights and springs. Install shaft assembly into distributor housing, with flat surface of rotor shaft facing the ignitor. *See Fig. 6.*

2) With flat surface still facing ignitor, install washer and gear. Marks on housing and gear should align. Drive in new roll pin.

3) Align pin on stator with hole in advance diaphragm arm. *See Fig. 6.* Drop arm into place over pin. Install and tighten hold-down screws. Install reluctor, and check air gap. Gap should be equal at each tooth. If not, check for damage to stator or reluctor.

4) Inspect rotor and cap for roughness or pitting. Scrape or file off carbon deposits with an oil stone or No. 600 sandpaper. Apply a thin coat of silicone grease to rotor tip.

Fig. 6: Installing Accord Models Rotor Shaft and Advance Unit

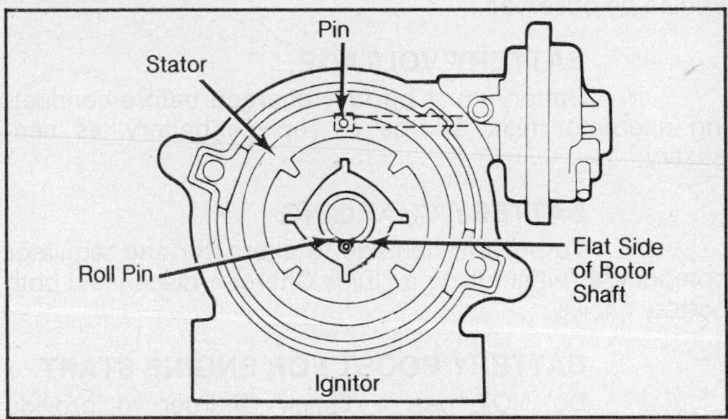
Pin
Stator
Roll Pin
Flat Side of Rotor Shaft
Ignitor

Flat side of rotor shaft should be toward ignitor.

5) Crank engine until No. 1 piston is at TDC. Install new "O" ring on distributor housing. Position rotor 1/8 turn past firing position for No. 1 cylinder on distributor).

6) Install distributor. Insert distributor straight into final position. Rotor will turn itself to No. 1 firing position. Mounting bracket should be centered over its bolt hole.

7) Install hold-down bolt and tighten it temporarily. Set ignition timing, and tighten hold-down bolt securely. Install distributor cap, aligning mark on cap with rotor.

Prelude

1) Install centrifugal advance weights and springs. Install thrust plate and ball bearing on shaft. Grease shaft and install in housing. Put washer and gear on lower end of shaft. Line up holes in gear shoulder with hole in shaft. Drive in new roll pin.

2) Turn offset drive gear so that index mark on coupling is aligned with tab on mounting flange, as viewed from bottom of distributor. *See Fig. 7.* Turn distributor over and install rotor shaft to the main shaft so that the ignition rotor points to cylinder 1 terminal on distributor cap.

Fig. 7: Aligning Prelude Models Offset Drive Gear to Main Shaft

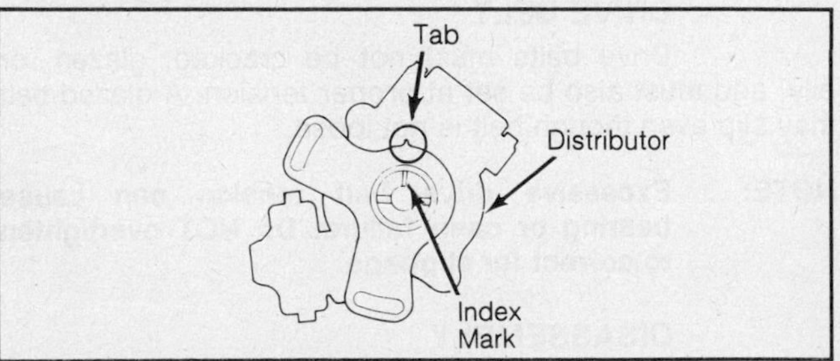
Tab
Distributor
Index Mark

View is from bottom of distributor.

3) Ensure holes in rotor shaft arms fit over pins in centrifugal advance weights. Install screw with lock washer in top of shaft. Install breaker plate in distributor housing. Install reluctor. Drive roll pin in place with its gap away from distributor shaft.

4) Check reluctor-to-stator air gap and rotor-to-terminal surfaces. Install diaphragm assembly. Crank engine until No. 1 piston is at TDC. Install new "O" ring housing and insert coupling until it mates with notch in camshaft.

Alternators & Regulators

GENERAL SERVICING

TESTING

In order to properly diagnose charging system performance, the following conditions and precautions should be observed.

BATTERY VOLTAGE

Battery must be fully charged before conducting alternator test. Charge or replace battery, as necessary.

BATTERY CHARGING

To prevent damage to alternator and regulator components when using a Quick Charger, disconnect both battery cables.

BATTERY BOOST FOR ENGINE START

Do NOT use a Quick Charger to provide starting voltage. Connect booster battery's negative lead to negative terminal of vehicle battery; its positive lead to positive terminal of battery.

ON-VEHICLE TESTING

Perform tests at normal operating temperatures. Accelerate engine gradually to desired testing RPM, and return it to lower RPM as soon as possible. Do NOT race engine.

CAUTION: Never disconnect battery or alternator leads while alternator is running. Reverse polarity or excessive voltage will severely damage the charging system.

ELECTRICAL CONNECTIONS

All electrical connections must be clean and snug for proper system operation. It is recommended that battery cables be disconnected, cleaned, and tightened whenever performing charging system maintenance. Regulator must also be properly grounded.

COMPONENT REPLACEMENT

In order to prevent stray voltage or shorts, always disconnect battery prior to alternator or regulator removal.

DRIVE BELT

Drive belts must not be cracked, glazed, or oily, and must also be set at proper tension. A glazed belt may slip even though belt is not loose.

NOTE: Excessive drive belt tension can cause bearing or case failure. Do NOT overtighten to correct for slippage.

DISASSEMBLY

For proper orientation when reassembling, case halves and stator should be scribed prior to separation.

DIODE TEST & REPLACEMENT

Never use a high voltage source to test diodes. Use a low voltage source to check for one-way current flow. If replacement is required, soldering operations must be performed quickly to prevent diode damage. Diode lead should be pinched with pliers to prevent heat transfer to diode.

ROTOR & STATOR TESTING

Continuity with minimum resistance should be noted between slip rings. *See Fig. 1*. No continuity should exist between either slip ring and rotor core or shaft. *See Fig. 2*. Stator conduction is normal when there is continuity between leads of stator coil. *See Fig. 3*. Stator conduction is NOT normal between stator coil leads and stator core. *See Fig. 4*.

Fig. 1: Rotor Coil Continuity Test

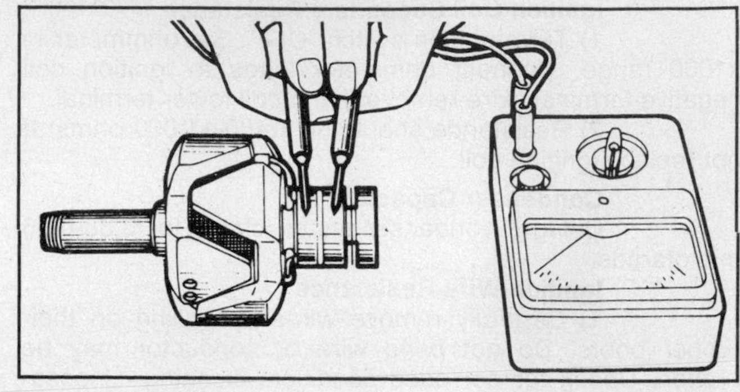

Fig. 2: Rotor Coil Ground Test

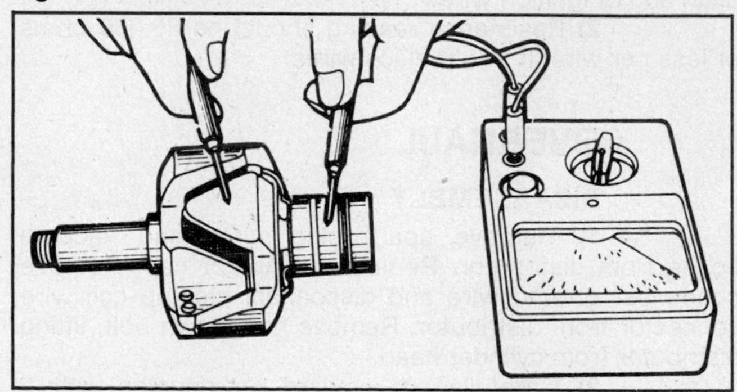

Fig. 3: Stator Coil Continuity Test

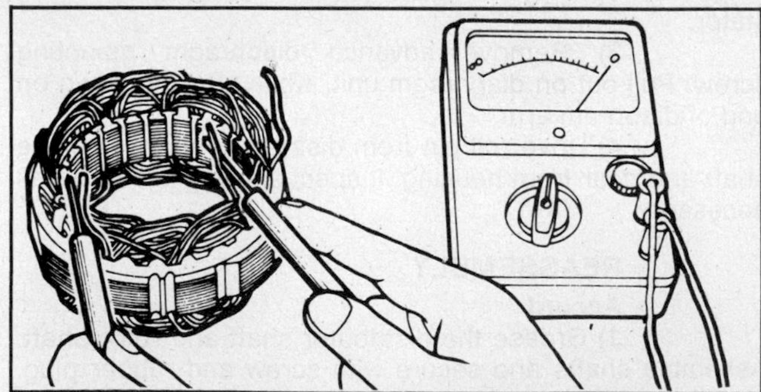

Fig. 4: Stator Coil Ground Test

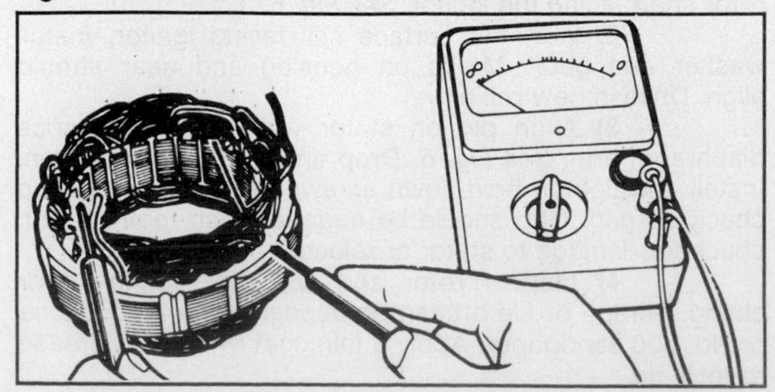

BOSCH ALTERNATORS WITH INTEGRAL REGULATORS

Alfa Romeo, Audi, BMW, Mercedes-Benz, Porsche, Saab, Volkswagen, Volvo

DESCRIPTION

Bosch alternators are conventional 3-phase, self-rectifying type alternators. Nine rectifier diodes are connected to stator windings (3 to each phase lead). Diodes change alternator A.C. voltage to D.C. voltage coming out "B+" and "D+" terminals of the alternator. Bosch regulators are transistorized solid state and integral with alternator.

ON-VEHICLE TESTING

NOTE: **Off-vehicle testing is included in OVERHAUL procedures in this article.**

WIRING CONTINUITY TEST

1) Disconnect terminal plug from rear of alternator and connect a voltmeter negative terminal to ground. Turn ignition "ON", connect positive lead to each of the connector wires in turn.

2) Voltmeter should read battery voltage as each positive connection is made. If not, trace each wire to find fault.

VOLTAGE DROP TEST – GROUND SIDE

Connect voltmeter between negative terminal of battery and alternator housing. Start engine and run at approximately 3000 RPM. If voltmeter reading exceeds .25 volt, a high resistance in negative side of charging circuit is indicated. If so, check for loose, dirty or corroded connections.

OUTPUT TEST

1) Disconnect terminal plug from rear of alternator and connect ammeter in series between alternator center terminal and corresponding socket in terminal plug. Connect a jumper lead between the "D+" terminal and its corresponding socket in terminal plug.

2) Start engine and run at approximately 3000 RPM. Turn on headlights and leave on for 5 minutes. Ammeter should read maximum alternator amperage at normal operating temperature.

REGULATOR CONTROL VOLTAGE TEST

1) All applicable regulators are designed to maintain from 13.7 to 14.5 volts at a load current of 5 to 7 amps. Alternator should be driven at 4000 RPM and load current set at load current rating.

2) Resistance and speed of alternator may be readjusted if necessary. Read voltage within 1 minute. If not within specifications, regulator requires replacement.

NOTE: **Test cables should not be removed or load excessively reduced during testing procedure. Considerable load variations may damage the diodes.**

ADJUSTMENT

If regulator fails to keep voltage within specified limits, it must be replaced. No adjusting procedures are recommended.

APPLICATION

Model	Volts/Amps	[1] Bosch Part No.
Alfa Romeo		
All Models	14/55	489 715-6
Audi		
4000		
4-Cylinder		
Gasoline	14/55	[2] 175 903 023T
Turbo Diesel		
Without A/C	14/55	[2] 068 903 017C
With A/C	14/75	[2] 068 903 017D
5-Cylinder		
Without A/C	14/75	[2] 068 903 017D
With A/C	14/90	[2] 068 903 017E
5000, 5000 Turbo		
Without A/C	14/75	[2] 068 903 017D
With A/C	14/90	[2] 068 903 017E
BMW		
318i	14/65	489 191
320i	14/65	489 718
All Others	14/65	489 030
Mercedes-Benz		
240D	14/55	489 933
300 D, CD	14/55	489 933
300 SD, TD	14/55	489 932
380 Series	14/70	489 930
Porsche		
944	14/90	[2] 944 603 108 01
911SC	14/90	[2] 911 603 120 04
928	[3]	[3]
Saab		
900, 900 Turbo	14/70	489 735
Volkswagen		
Jetta, Rabbit, Scirocco	14/55	[2] 175 903 023T
Quantum		
Without A/C	14/55	[2] 175 903 023T
With A/C	14/90	[2] 175 903 017E
Vanagon		
Gasoline		
Air-Cooled	14/65	[2] 070 903 017
Water-Cooled	14/65	[2] 035 903 017A
Diesel	14/65	[2] 068 903 017F
Volvo		
DL, GL, GLT		
Gasoline	14/70	469 568
Diesel	14/55	489 070
760 GLE		
Gasoline	14/70	[2] 1323351-5
Heavy Duty	14/90	[2] 1324142-7
Diesel	14/55	[2] 1323488-5

[1] – Bosch part numbers are preceded by 0 120 for alternators. Integral regulator models are numbered 469 and 489.

[2] – Vehicle manufacturer's part number.

[3] – Information not available from manufacturer.

BOSCH ALTERNATORS WITH INTEGRAL REGULATOR (Cont.)

Fig. 1: Cutaway View of Bosch Alternator

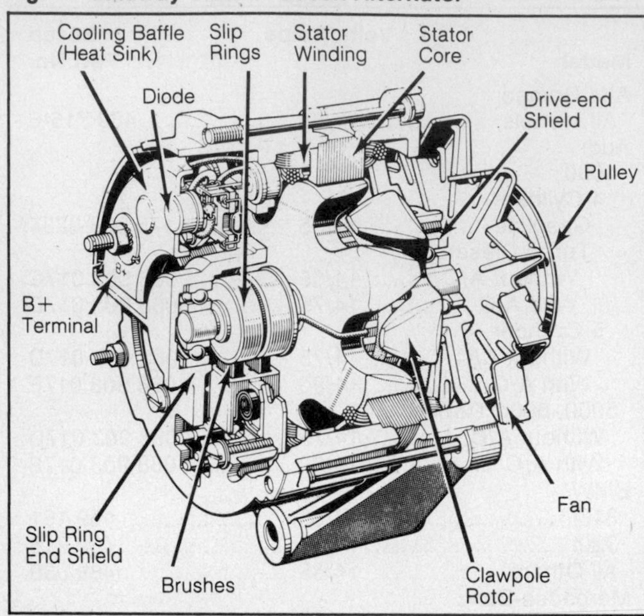
Cooling Baffle (Heat Sink)
Slip Rings
Stator Winding
Stator Core
Diode
Drive-end Shield
Pulley
B+ Terminal
Fan
Slip Ring End Shield
Brushes
Clawpole Rotor

OVERHAUL

DISASSEMBLY

1) Scribe mark for alignment on front and rear alternator housing. Remove nut, pulley, fan and key. Unscrew brush plate assembly and remove from alternator. Remove frame bolts and separate rear frame from front frame with rotor.

2) Press rotor from frame and bearing from rotor. Remove insulation from wires and cut wires as close to soldered joints as possible. Diodes may be tested at this point without further disassembly.

3) Use care with insulating bushings under positive diode carrier. To remove negative carrier, extract threaded studs. When one diode has been damaged due to short circuiting, the 3 complementing diodes must also be replaced. Loosen nuts on both "B+" terminal bolts and lift positive carrier (heat sink) up and back.

TESTING AND REPAIRING

Diode Assemblies

1) Test diodes with tester before dismantling slip ring and end frame. DO NOT lay positive diode carrier on housing or a false reading will be obtained. Disconnect conductor from "D+" to exciter diodes at heat sink.

2) Unscrew spring and brush holder and remove from alternator. Unsolder stator lead and negative diode connections. Unscrew exciter diodes heat sink and remove together with positive diodes heat sink. Clean all components with a non-residue solvent prior to further testing.

Stator

Test stator for short circuits to ground. Tester voltage should be 40V AC. Measure resistance of stator windings between phase connections. Resistance should be .10 to .14 ohms on Saab models or .20 to .22 ohms on all other models.

Rotor

1) Test claw pole rotor for short circuits to ground using 40V AC tester. Measure resistance of exciter (field coil) in rotor with ohmmeter across slip rings. Resistance should be 4.0-4.4 ohms.

2) If necessary, turn slip rings in a lathe, noting maximum runout of .001" (.03 mm) and minimum diameter of 1.25" (31.5 mm). Maximum pole wheel runout should not exceed .002" (.05 mm).

Diode Replacement

If diodes are found to be defective, entire diode plate assembly should be replaced. Care must be exercised in soldering near diodes due to possible damage from excess heat. Use flat-jawed pliers as heat sink applied to leads when soldering diode connections.

Drive End Frame

Check ball bearings for wear and replace as necessary. Lubricate ball bearings on one side. Press ball bearing into drive end frame with shielded side downward. Install retainer plate. Press ball bearing on slip ring end of rotor and press drive end frame onto drive end of rotor.

Carbon Brushes

Minimum brush length is .2" (5 mm). If replacement is required, grip brush with flat-jawed pliers and unsolder brushes. Do not allow solder to run into strands of brush leads. Brush must be free to slide in holder with normal spring tension of 10-14 ozs. (283-397 g).

REASSEMBLY

1) Solder stator and diode connections using caution not to overheat diodes. Place stator and diode assembly in rear housing and secure with screws.

2) Lubricate new rear bearing and press onto rotor shaft, ensure shielded side of bearing faces slip rings. Place front bearing in housing with shielded side rearward. Install retainer plate.

3) Place spacer ring on rotor shaft and install rotor assembly into front housing. Press front bearing retaining ring over shaft and into front housing with a socket.

4) Coat bearing bore of rear housing with grease and install spring washer. Assemble front housing with rotor to rear housing, using a turning or twisting motion to seat rear bearing. Line up scribed alignment marks and install screws through housing.

5) Install shaft key, washer, fan, spacer, pulley, lock washer and nut. Install brush and connector plug assembly and retain with screws.

DUCELLIER & PARIS-RHONE ALTERNATORS

Renault Fuego & LeCar

DESCRIPTION

Alternator is a conventional 3-phase, self-rectifying type. Six silicon rectifier diodes are connected to form a full-wave, 3-phase rectifying bridge. Three exciter diodes are connected to stator windings.

ALTERNATOR APPLICATION

Model	Rating	Part No.
Fuego		
Ducellier	50	516 020
Paris-Rhone	75	A14N51
LeCar		
Paris-Rhone	50	A13R243

TESTING

ON-VEHICLE TESTING

Load Test

1) Connect a voltmeter to battery. Start engine and raise engine speed until voltmeter stabilizes. Voltmeter should read 13.5-15 volts.

2) Turn on all electrical accessories. Voltmeter must read 13.5-15 volts. If not, check for shorted diode, open stator winding, worn brushes or replace regulator.

OVERHAUL

DISASSEMBLY

1) Remove brush holder and regulator retaining screws and carefully remove. Scribe a mark on end frames for reassembly reference.

2) Remove through bolts. Separate end frames by inserting 2 screwdrivers into notches on sides of alternator.

CAUTION: Do not insert screwdrivers deeper than .08" (2 mm) or damage may occur to stator windings.

3) Remove nuts and washers for positive and negative diode holders from end frame. Carefully remove stator from end frame.

4) Hold rotor in a vise using special wood blocks to prevent damage to rotor. Remove nut, washer, pulley, fan, key and spacer.

5) Remove retaining screws from bearing cap. Push rotor shaft from end frame. Press bearing from end frame. Use a puller to remove bearing from slip ring end of rotor.

BENCH TESTING

Rotor

Use 40V AC for testing rotor. Check rotor winding resistance across slip rings with ohmmeter and insulation between slip rings and rotor with test lamp. Replace rotor if grounded or if resistance is greater than 4.4 ohms on LeCar models, or 3.6 ohms on Fuego models.

Stator

Use 40V AC for testing stator. Check stator coils for resistance with leads disconnected using an ohmmeter. Check for shorts between core and leads with test lamp. Replace stator if grounded or shorted.

Diodes

Use ohmmeter to perform conduction test on diodes. Observe current flow in one direction only from terminal-to-plate for positive diodes and from plate-to-terminal for negative diodes. If open or shorted, replace entire diode assembly.

NOTE: Diode terminals must be disconnected during testing.

REASSEMBLY

To reassemble, reverse removal procedure.

Fig. 1: Exploded View of Renault Alternator

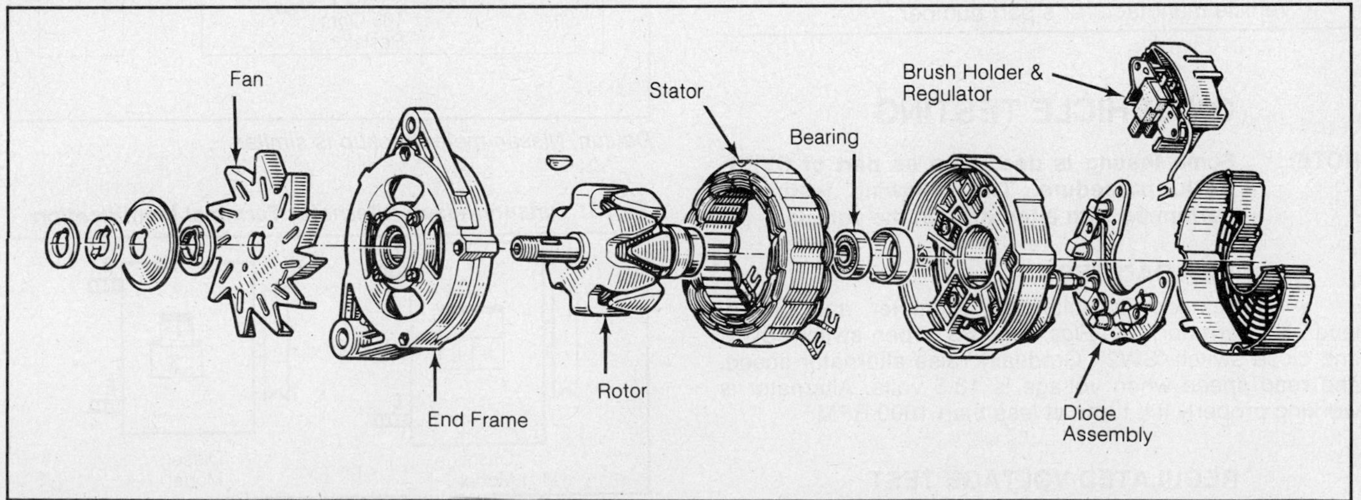
Fan
Stator
Bearing
Brush Holder &
Regulator
End Frame
Rotor
Diode
Assembly

Paris-Rhone alternator is shown; Ducellier type is similar.

HITACHI ALTERNATORS

Datsun/Nissan, Isuzu, Subaru

DESCRIPTION

Hitachi alternators are conventional 3-phase, self-rectifying type alternators. Six diodes (3 positive and 3 negative) are used to rectify current.

All models are equipped with integral-type IC regulators, except Isuzu models equipped with gasoline engines. Isuzu models with diesel engines have IC regulators.

APPLICATION

Model	Hitachi No.
Datsun/Nissan	
Maxima	
Gasoline	LR160-82B
Diesel	LR160-97C
Pickup	
Gasoline	
Standard	LR150-98B
Heavy Duty	LR160-78, LR160-78B
Diesel	LR160-97B, LR150-133E
Pulsar	LR150-125B
Sentra	LR150-125B
Stanza	LR160-104
200SX	LR160-109B
280ZX	
Non Turbo	LR160-82B
Turbo	LR170-028
Isuzu	
I'Mark	
Gasoline	LT150-144
Diesel	LR150-78
Impulse	[1] 8-94231-307-2
P'UP	
Gasoline	
2-WD	LT150-144
4-WD	LT150-131B
Diesel	LR150-78
Subaru	
Non Turbo	LR155-15C
Turbo	LR155-18

[1] – Vehicle manufacturer's part number.

ON-VEHICLE TESTING

NOTE: **Some testing is described as part of OVERHAUL procedure. The following testing is performed with alternator on the vehicle.**

NO LOAD TEST

Connect a voltmeter, ammeter and battery leads-to-alternator. *See Figs. 2 and 3.* Open switch "SW1" and close switch "SW2". Gradually raise alternator speed, and read speed when voltage is 13.5 volts. Alternator is working properly if it turns at less than 1000 RPM.

REGULATED VOLTAGE TEST

Open switch "SW1" and close "SW2". *See Fig. 2.* Turn alternator at 5000 RPM. The IC regulator is normal if voltage is within range. *See Regulator Voltage Specifications table.*

Fig. 1: Disassembled View of Typical Hitachi Alternator

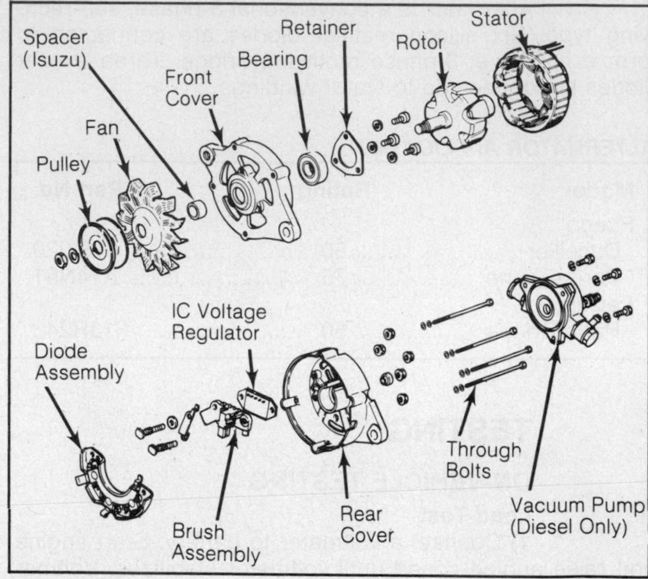
Spacer
(Isuzu)
Retainer
Stator
Rotor
Bearing
Front
Cover
Fan
Pulley
IC Voltage
Regulator
Diode
Assembly
Through
Bolts
Rear
Cover
Vacuum Pump
(Diesel Only)
Brush
Assembly

Datsun/Nissan Pickup alternator is illustrated.

Fig. 2: Subaru Alternator Test Connections

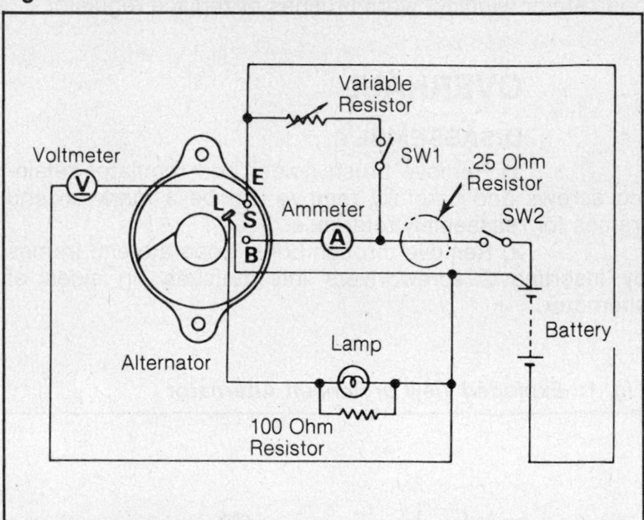
Variable
Resistor
Voltmeter
V
SW1
.25 Ohm
Resistor
E
L
S
Ammeter
A
SW2
B
Battery
Lamp
Alternator
100 Ohm
Resistor

Datsun/Nissan meter hookup is similar.

Fig. 3: Datsun/Nissan Alternator Terminal Identification

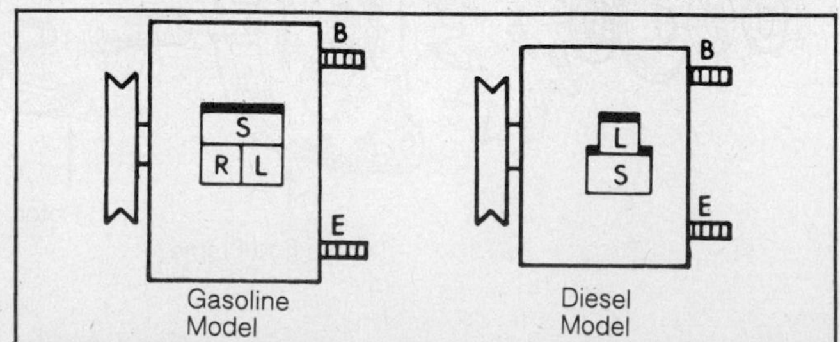
B
S
R
L
E
Gasoline
Model
B
L
S
E
Diesel
Model

Terminals "S", "L", "BAT" and "E" are marked on rear cover.

HITACHI ALTERNATORS (Cont.)

REGULATED VOLTAGE SPECIFICATIONS [1]

Application	[2] Volts
Datsun/Nissan	14.4-15.0
Isuzu	
Gasoline Models	13.8-14.8
Diesel Models	14.0-14.6
Subaru	14.2-14.8

[1] – At 68°F (20°C).
[2] – With fully-charged battery.

OUTPUT TEST

1) Set variable resistor to minimum resistance position. *See Fig. 2.* Close switches "SW1" and "SW2".

2) Keep voltage constant while raising alternator speed by adjusting variable resistor. Measure alternator output current at 2500 and 5000 alternator RPM. *See Output Specifications table.*

ALTERNATOR OUTPUT SPECIFICATIONS

Alternator	[1] Amps@ 2500 RPM	[1] Amps@ 5000 RPM
LR150-78	40	50
LR150-98B	40	50
LR150-99	40	50
LR150-125B	42	50
LR155-15	50	55
LR160-78	50	60
LR160-82B	50	60
LR160-97C	52	60
LR160-104	50	60
LR160-109	50	70
LR170-028	50	70
LT150-131B	40	50
LT150-144	40	50
8-94231-307-2 [2]	50	60

[1] – Alternator RPM.
[2] – Isuzu part number for Impulse.

DATSUN/NISSAN ALTERNATOR OPERATING TEST

Ensure battery is fully charged. Connect a 30-volt voltmeter. *See Fig. 4.* Turn ignition switch to "ON" position and test as follows.

Fig. 4: Datsun/Nissan Alternator Operating Test Connections

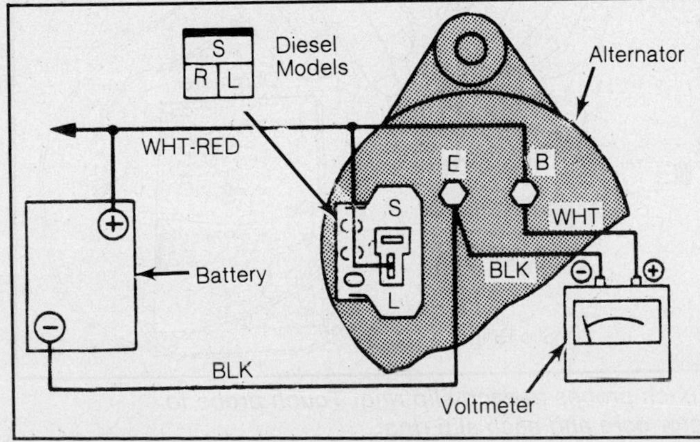
S
R L
Diesel
Models
Alternator
WHT-RED
E
B
S
WHT
Battery
BLK
L
BLK
Voltmeter

Diesel alternator terminals vary slightly.

1) If charge light remains off, disconnect connector from rear of alternator and ground "L" lead wire.

NOTE: With alternator side "L" terminal grounded, internal short occurs when positive diode is short-circuited.

2) If light remains off, replace indicator bulb and retest. If light is on, reconnect connector. On gasoline models, ground "F" terminal by touching brush with grounded wire. On diesel models, use a screwdriver to ground brush to alternator body. If light stays on, replace IC regulator. If light goes out, repair alternator.

3) If light came on when ignition was turned to "ON" position, start and idle engine. If light is dim, flickers or remains bright, remove and repair alternator. If light went off at idle, run engine at 1500 RPM, and turn headlights on high beam.

4) If charge light is on dim, idle engine, and measure voltage between terminals "B" and "L". If less than .5 volt, alternator is OK. If more than .5 volt, remove and repair alternator.

NOTE: Terminals "S", "L", "BAT" and "E" are marked on rear cover of alternator.

5) If charge light went off at 1500 RPM with lights on high beam, measure "B" voltage. If more than 15.5 volts, replace IC regulator. If 13-15 volts, idle engine and check indicator light. If off, system is OK. If on, repair alternator.

RESISTANCE & CONTINUITY TEST

All Models

1) Measure rotor coil resistance, using an ohmmeter, across "E" and "L" terminals on Datsun/Nissan models, or "F" and "E" terminals on all other models. Rotor coil circuit is normal if resistance is 4-5 ohms.

2) If resistance is high, there is poor contact between brushes and commutator. If no continuity exists between "E" and "L" terminals on Datsun/Nissan models or "F" and "E" terminals on all other models, there may be an open rotor coil circuit, brush sticking or a broken lead wire.

3) If resistance is low, it indicates a rotor coil layer short or grounded circuit.

NOTE: The following test will not indicate an open state of the diodes. Tester will indicate continuity regardless of diode conditions, if tester leads are connected to the terminals with polarity reversed.

4) Connect positive lead of tester-to-alternator "N" terminal, and tester negative lead-to-alternator "A" terminal. If tester shows continuity, one or more positive diodes are shorted.

5) Connect positive lead of tester-to-alternator "E" terminal, and tester negative lead-to-alternator "N" terminal. If continuity is indicated, one or more of the negative diodes are shorted.

INTEGRATED CIRCUIT (IC) REGULATOR TEST

An integrated circuit regulator is used on all models, except Isuzu models equipped with gasoline engines. The IC voltage regulator is soldered to the brush

HITACHI ALTERNATORS (Cont.)

assembly and mounted inside the alternator. To test regulator, proceed as follows.

1) Secure a 10-ohm 3-watt resistor, a 0-to-300-ohm 3-watt variable resistor, two 12-volt batteries and a DC voltmeter. Connect equipment to vehicle. *See Fig. 5*.

NOTE: Isuzu diesel models may use a terminal "B", Datsun/Nissan and Subaru models use a terminal "L".

Fig. 5: IC Regulator Testing Hookup

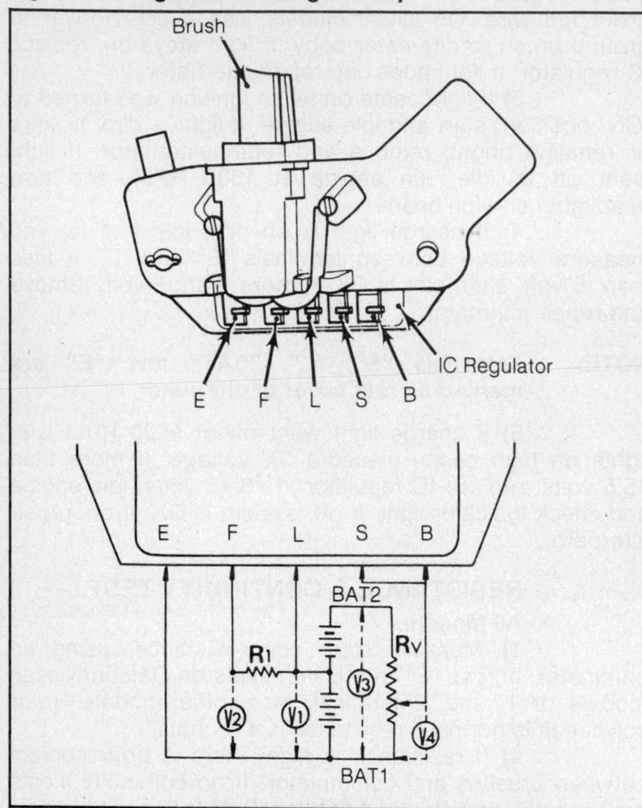
Brush
IC Regulator
E F L S B
E F L S B
BAT2
R1
Rv
V3
V2
V1
V4
BAT1

Terminal letters may be different for Isuzu diesel models.

2) Check voltage at "BAT1" (V1 voltage). If V1 voltage is not 10-13 volts, charge or replace battery as necessary.

3) Disconnect lead at terminal "S", and check voltage between terminals "F" and "E" (V2). If less than 2.0 volts, regulator is functioning properly. If higher, replace regulator.

4) Measure total voltage of batteries 1 and 2 (V3). If not 20-26 volts, recharge or replace batteries.

5) Gradually increase variable resistance (Rv) from 0 ohms and check voltage (V2) between terminals "F" and "E". At some point, voltage reading (V2) should increase to 10-13 volts to equal V1 reading, measured in step **2)**.

6) If variation does not occur in V2 voltage reading, as described, regulator is defective.

7) Measure voltage (V4) between center tap of variable resistor (Rv) and terminal "E". With resistance set as in previous step, voltage should be as shown in *Regulator Voltage Specifications* table in this article.

8) Remove test lead from terminal "S" and connect to terminal "B". Measure voltage between terminals "B" and "E", as you gradually increase voltage with variable resistor (Rv).

9) Voltage should increase from below 2 volts to 10-13 volts. If voltage does not vary, the regulator is defective and should be replaced.

10) Measure voltage (V4) between center tap of variable resistor (Rv) and terminal "E", without actuating variable resistor. Voltage should now be 0.5-2.0 volts higher than *Regulator Voltage Specifications* table indicates. If voltage does not meet specifications, replace regulator.

OVERHAUL

DISASSEMBLY

NOTE: Alternators for vehicles with diesel engines may vary slightly, due to vacuum pump mounted on alternator.

1) Remove through bolts. Separate front cover with rotor from rear cover with stator by lightly tapping on front cover with plastic hammer.

2) Place front cover and rotor assembly in protected vise with pulley nut up. Use aluminum plates if necessary to prevent vise surfaces from damaging rotor.

3) Remove pulley nut. Take off pulley, fan and washers. Pull out spacer. Remove rotor. Remove screws from front cover. Lift out bearing retainer and bearing.

4) Remove attaching nuts. Lift stator, diode assembly and brush assembly from rear cover. Using a soldering iron, disconnect diode assembly, brush assembly and IC regulator together from stator leads.

NOTE: Melting of solder should be done as rapidly as possible to prevent damage to diodes and IC regulator.

5) To disconnect diode assembly, remove 1/8" rivet and melt solder on terminal "L".

6) To replace IC regulator, unsolder regulator terminals. Remove 2 bolts. Do not remove these bolts unless regulator is to be replaced.

INSPECTION & REPAIR

BENCH TESTS

Rotor

1) Apply tester to slip rings of rotor. If ohm reading is within 4-5 ohms, rotor continuity is satisfactory. If not, an open connection to the field coil may exist.

Fig. 6: Rotor Field Coil Conduction Test

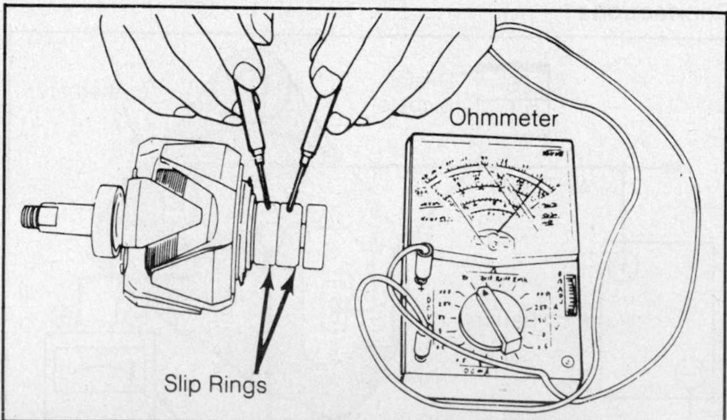
Ohmmeter
Slip Rings

Touch probes to each slip ring. Touch probe to rotor core and each slip ring.

HITACHI ALTERNATORS (Cont.)

2) Apply test probes to slip ring and rotor core to check for ground. If continuity exists, replace rotor assembly.

Stator

1) The stator is normal when there is continuity between individual stator core terminals. When there is no continuity between terminals, replace stator.

2) Touch ohmmeter leads to stator core and to each stator coil lead wire (including neutral wire). If there is no continuity, stator condition is satisfactory. If continuity exists, stator is grounded and must be replaced.

Diodes

1) Perform a continuity test on all diodes in both directions using an ohmmeter. Test the continuity between each terminal and plate. Diode installed on a "+" plate is a positive diode, which allows current to flow from terminal to "+" plate only. Current does NOT flow from "+" plate to the terminal.

2) A diode installed on the "–" plate is a negative diode, and allows current to flow from the "–" plate to the terminal only. Current does NOT flow from the terminal to the "–" plate.

3) If current flows in both directions, the diode is shorted. If current does not flow in either direction, the diode is open. If any diode is defective, replace the entire diode assembly (individual diodes are not serviceable).

Brushes & Brush Springs

1) Inspect brushes for freedom of movement in holder. Clean brush holder if necessary. Check brushes for cracks and wear. Replace if beyond wear limit lines.

2) Brush wear limit is .22" (5.5 mm) on Isuzu gasoline models; .24" (6 mm) on Datsun/Nissan Maxima & Pickup diesel models; .55" (14 mm) on Isuzu diesel models; and .28" (7 mm) on all other models.

3) Check brush springs for corrosion, damage and proper tension. Tension should be 9-12.2 oz. (2.5-3.4 N) on all gasoline and Datsun/Nissan diesel models; 11-15 oz. (3.0-4.1 N) on all other diesel models with .08" (2 mm) protrusion from holder.

4) Test brush holder to ensure no continuity exists between holder and brush. Replace if required.

REASSEMBLY

1) Reinstall diode assembly and stator-to-rear cover. Solder stator coil lead wires-to-terminals of diode assembly, as quickly as possible. Reinstall diode cover.

NOTE: **Soldering must be done quickly to avoid damage to diodes.**

2) Assemble brushes-to-brush holder, with approximately .43" (11 mm) protruding. Insert holder into alternator. Reinstall rotor-to-front cover.

3) Place assembly in vise and replace pulley and components. Tighten pulley nut to 29-43 ft. lbs. (39-59 N.m). Insert and tighten housing through bolts to 27-35 INCH lbs. (3-4 N.m).

HITACHI REGULATORS

Isuzu (Gasoline Models Only)

DESCRIPTION

Regulator system consists of a voltage regulator and a charge relay. The voltage regulator has 2 sets of contact points to control alternator voltage. An armature plate, placed between the 2 sets of contacts, moves upward, downward, or vibrates.

The lower contacts, when closed, complete the field circuit direct to ground. The upper contacts complete the field circuit to ground when closed, through a resistance (field coil), causing the alternator to charge.

The charge relay is similar in construction to the voltage regulator. When upper contacts are closed, the ignition warning light goes on.

APPLICATION

Model	Hitachi No.
I-Mark	[1]
P'UP	TLIZ-87

[1] – Isuzu part number is 8-94208-462-0.

TESTING

VOLTAGE REGULATOR

I-Mark

1) Connect a voltmeter between condenser lead and ground. Turn all electrical loads off including blower relay connector. *See Fig. 1.* The voltage relay is working properly when lower side points are closed when engine is off and when upper points are closed when engine is running at idle.

Fig. 1: Regulator Test Connection for Isuzu I-Mark

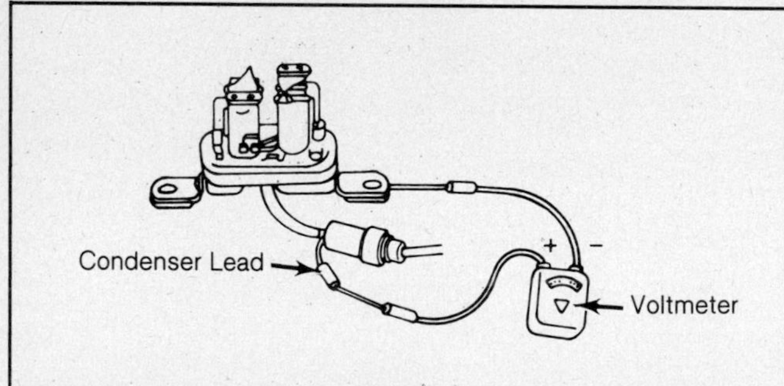
Condenser Lead
Voltmeter

Connect voltmeter between condenser lead and voltage regulator mounting bracket.

2) If points are not working properly, check coil resistance. If normal, adjust relay. Start engine and increase speed gradually. Voltage should increase with engine speed up to 1400-1850 RPM. Normal condition of regulator is indicated when voltage is 13.8-14.8 volts.

P'UP

1) Connect voltmeter and ammeter to vehicle. *See Fig. 2.* Start engine and maintain speed at 2500 RPM for a few minutes. Check that ammeter reading is 5 amps. or less.

Fig. 2: Regulator Test Connections for Isuzu P'UP

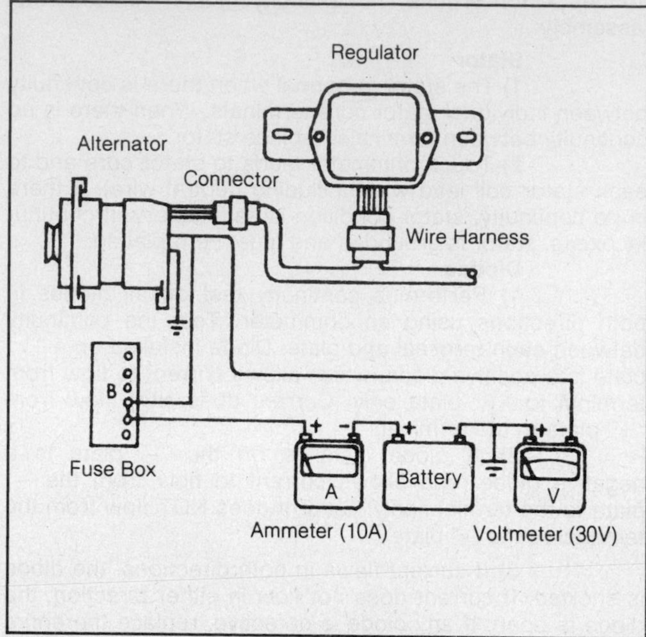
Regulator
Alternator
Connector
Wire Harness
B
Fuse Box
A
Battery
V
Ammeter (10A)
Voltmeter (30V)

Connect voltmeter and ammeter as shown.

2) If reading remains higher than 5 amps., remove battery and substitute with battery known to be fully charged. Recheck to ensure ammeter reading is less than 5 amps.

3) Lower engine speed to idle and again increase it gradually to 2500 RPM. Note voltmeter reading. Function of regulator is normal if measured value is 13.8-14.8 volts.

4) If voltmeter reading is not within specified range, regulator is in need of adjustment.

VOLTAGE RELAY

I-Mark Only

Connect voltmeter between negative terminal and ground. Increase engine speed gradually. Voltmeter reading should be 4.0-5.8 volts when indicator light goes out. If not voltage relay needs adjustment.

ADJUSTMENT

VOLTAGE RELAY

I-Mark Only

1) If cut-in voltage is too high, bend coil arm "A" down. Bend up if voltage is too low. *See Fig. 3.*

2) If adjustment of core arm does not correct cut-in voltage, adjust point gap. To adjust point gap. Disconnect battery. Check armature core gap with armature depressed until moving point is in contact with "B" side point.

3) Adjust core gap to .012" (.30 mm) by bending point arm "B". Release armature and adjust point gap between "B" side point and moving point to .016-.047" (.40-1.2 mm) by bending point arm "C".

HITACHI REGULATORS (Cont.)

Fig. 3: Voltage Relay Adjustment for Isuzu I-Mark

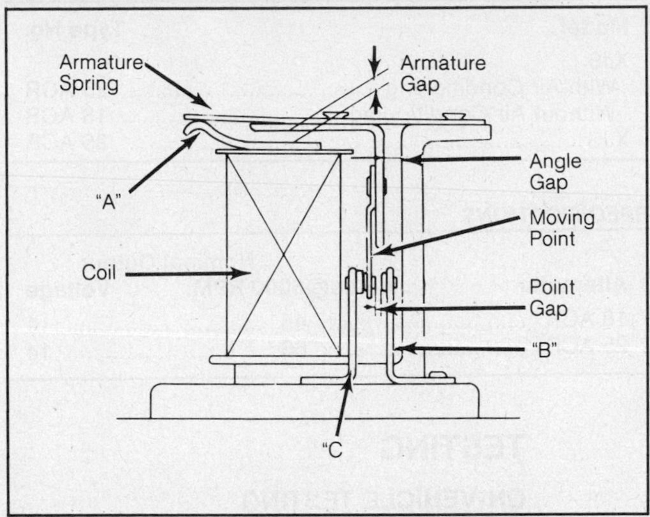
Armature Spring
Armature Gap
Angle Gap
"A"
Moving Point
Coil
Point Gap
"B"
"C"

4) After point adjustment, recheck cut-in voltage. If not within 4.0-5.8 volts, repeat cut-in voltage adjustment.

NOTE: Voltage regulators and charge relays on P'UP models are adjusted in the same manner.

P'UP Only

1) Disconnect and remove voltage regulator from vehicle. If contact points are roughened, smooth with fine sandpaper. Check and adjust core gap first, then point gap. Yoke gap adjustment is not necessary.

2) Adjust core gap by loosening screws attaching contact set to yoke. Move contact set upward or downward as required. Adjust point gap by loosening screw attaching upper contact. Move upper contact up or down as required.

3) After core and point gaps have been adjusted, adjust regulated voltage by means of adjusting screw. Turn screw in to increase regulated voltage or out to decrease voltage.

4) When correct voltage adjustment is obtained, secure with lock nut. When adjustment procedure is complete, reinstall regulator and perform on car check.

Fig. 4: Schematic of Regulator for Isuzu P'UP

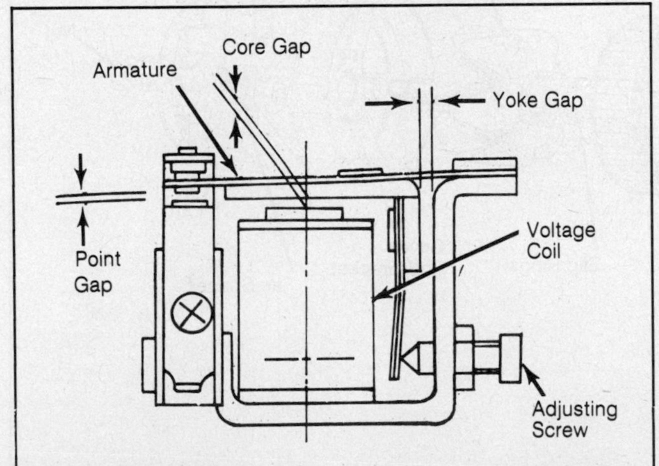
Core Gap
Armature
Yoke Gap
Point Gap
Voltage Coil
Adjusting Screw

Charge relay is similar.

VOLTAGE REGULATOR SPECIFICATIONS

Application	Specification
Battery Voltage	12 Volts
Regulated Voltage	13.8-14.8 Volts
Voltage Coil Resistance	[1] 10.3 Ohms
Yoke Gap	[2]
Core Gap	.024-.039" (.6-1.0 mm)
Point Gap	.012-.016" (.3-.4 mm)

1 – I-Mark resistance is 102 ohms.
2 – No yoke adjustment is required.

VOLTAGE RELAY SPECIFICATIONS

Application	Specification
Released Voltage	[1] 5 Volts
Voltage Coil Resistance	[2] 31.9 Ohms
Yoke Gap	[3]
Core Gap	.032-.039" (.8-1.0 mm)
Point Gap	.016-.024" (.4-.6 mm)

1 – Measured at "A" terminal.
2 – I-Mark resistance is 24 ohms.
3 – No yoke adjustment is required.

LUCAS ALTERNATORS WITH INTEGRAL REGULATORS

Jaguar XJ6, XJS

NOTE: Some Jaguar models may be equipped with Motorola alternators. See appropriate article in this section.

DESCRIPTION

Lucas ACR model alternators have an integral, non-adjustable voltage regulator, mounted in the slip ring end bracket. Individual connectors are used to connect external wiring to the alternator.

The rotor, which turns inside the stator, has its field windings connected to 2 face-type slip rings. It is supported in the drive-end bracket by ball bearings and in the end cover by needle roller bearings.

One positive and 1 negative carbon brush ride against concentric brass slip rings attached to rotor. The heat sink, rectifier, and terminal block assembly incorporates 6 silicon diodes, forming a full-wave rectifier bridge circuit, and 3 diodes which supply current to the rotor windings.

Individual diodes cannot be removed from the heat sink assemblies. A surge protection diode, in the outer face of the slip ring end bracket, protects the diode pack from high transient voltages resulting from faulty cable connections.

NOTE: Precautions should be taken while attaching and detaching cables, as surge protection is limited. Observe polarity and never connect or disconnect wires while engine is running.

APPLICATION

Model	Type No.
XJ6	
With Air Conditioning	25 ACR
Without Air Conditioning	18 ACR
XJS	25 ACR

SPECIFICATIONS

Alternator	Nominal Output Amps@6000 RPM	Voltage
18 ACR	45	14
25 ACR	66	14

TESTING

ON-VEHICLE TESTING

Preliminary Checks

1) Alternator drive belt must be properly adjusted. Battery and connections must be in good condition. Charge warning bulb and circuits continuous in order to properly test charging system.

2) Polarity of alternator and battery terminals MUST be observed to prevent system damage. Warm engine 3-4 minutes before testing. Battery ground cable should be disconnected when attaching jumper wires to alternator and regulator.

Fig. 1: Exploded View of Lucas 25 ACR Alternator with Integral Regulator

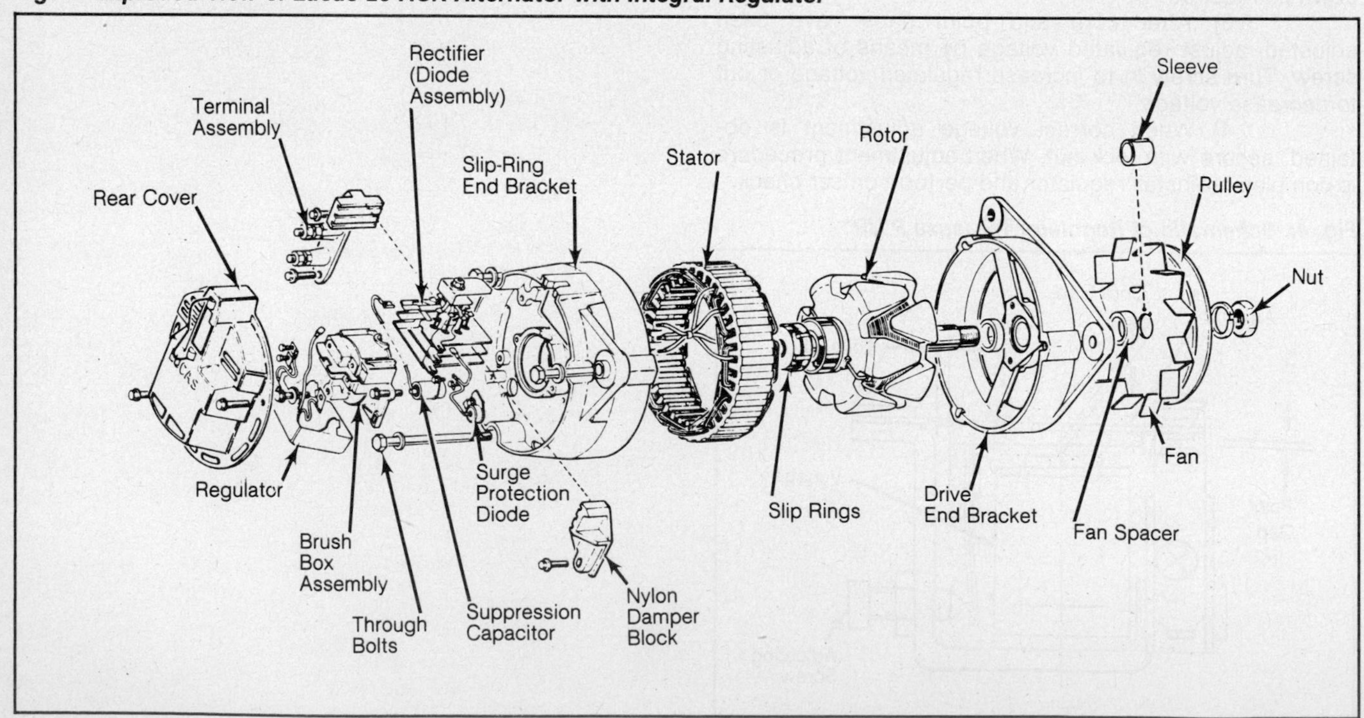
Rectifier (Diode Assembly)
Terminal Assembly
Sleeve
Rotor
Slip-Ring End Bracket
Stator
Pulley
Rear Cover
Nut
Fan
Regulator
Surge Protection Diode
Slip Rings
Drive End Bracket
Fan Spacer
Brush Box Assembly
Nylon Damper Block
Through Bolts
Suppression Capacitor

LUCAS ALTERNATORS WITH INTEGRAL REGULATORS (Cont.)

Alternator Tests

1) Remove individual connectors from alternator. Turn ignition switch to "ON" position. Connect negative voltmeter lead to ground. Attach positive lead, in turn, to each disconnected lead. Voltmeter should indicate battery voltage at each lead.

2) If reading is zero (0) at main output lead, check wiring to starter solenoid and battery. If zero (0) when connected to "IND" lead, check for ground or open circuit between warning light and alternator connector.

3) If reading is zero (0) when connected to "S" lead, check wiring back to starter solenoid and battery. A break in the sensing lead will result in alternator not charging and warning light not working.

4) Attach connectors to alternator. Turn ignition switch to "ON" position. With negative lead of voltmeter still attached to ground, connect positive lead to "IND" terminal. *See Fig. 2.* Voltmeter should indicate approximately 2 volts.

Fig. 2: Test Voltage at "IND" Terminal

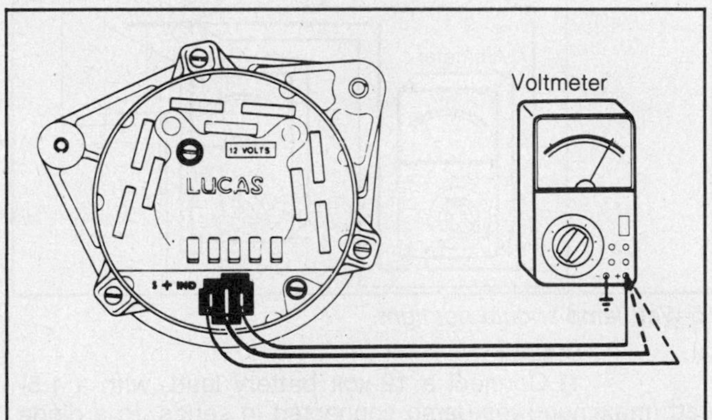

Voltmeter
12 VOLTS
LUCAS
S + IND

Alternator connectors should be in place.

5) If reading is zero (0), suspect surge protection diode. If voltmeter indicates battery voltage, suspect brushes, rotor, or regulator.

6) With voltmeter negative lead attached to ground, attach positive lead to metal link on regulator. *See Fig. 3.* Turn ignition switch to "ON" position. Voltmeter should indicate approximately 0.5 volt. If 12 volts are indicated, regulator is faulty.

Fig. 3: Test Voltage at Regulator Metal Link

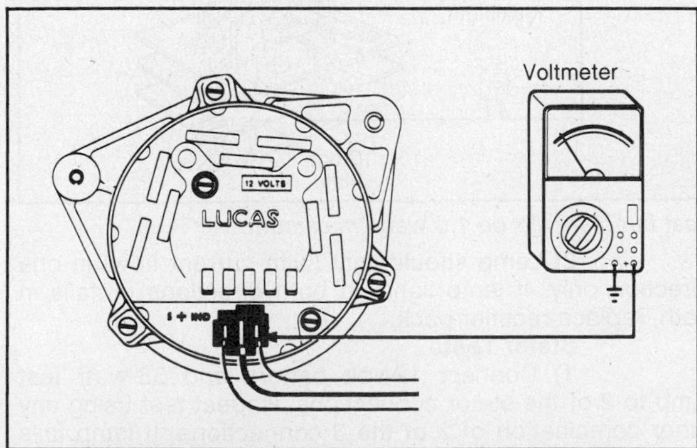

Voltmeter
12 VOLTS
LUCAS
S + IND

If 12 volts are indicated, regulator is faulty.

7) If reading is now 0.5 volts, but 12 volts was registered in step **5)**, check brushes, rotor, and slip rings.

NOTE: **If warning light operates with ignition in "OFF" position, but goes out when switch is in "ON" position, check voltage at "IND" terminal with switch in "OFF" position. If battery voltage is indicated, diode pack is faulty.**

8) Start engine, and run it at a constant 2500 RPM. With voltmeter negative lead attached to ground, attach positive lead to "IND" terminal. *See Fig. 4.* Note voltage. Connect positive lead to alternator's main output terminal. Voltage readings should be the same. If a difference of more than 0.5 volt exists, suspect diodes.

Fig. 4: Test Voltage at "IND" and Main Output Terminals

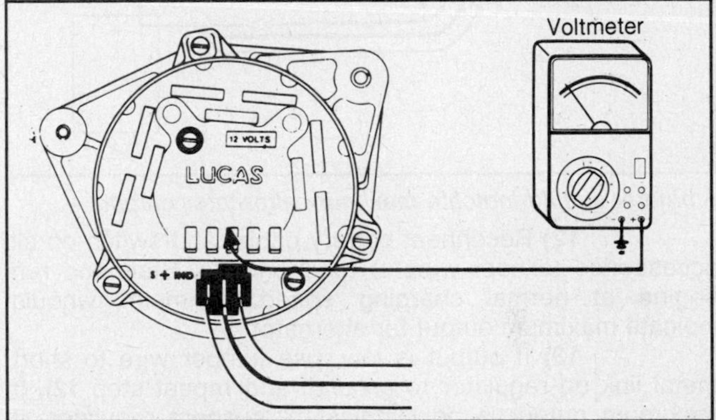

Voltmeter
12 VOLTS
LUCAS
S + IND

Readings should be same with engine at 2500 RPM.

9) Connect voltmeter between battery insulated terminal and alternator's main output terminal. *See Fig. 5.* Start and run engine at approximately 2500 RPM. Voltmeter should not exceed 0.5 volt.

10) If higher reading exists, check wiring from alternator to battery for loose or dirty connections.

NOTE: **If warning light glows while engine is running at normal charging speeds, problem may be a faulty diode pack or dirty or loose connections in battery-to-alternator wiring.**

Fig. 5: Test Voltage at Main Output and Battery Insulated Terminals

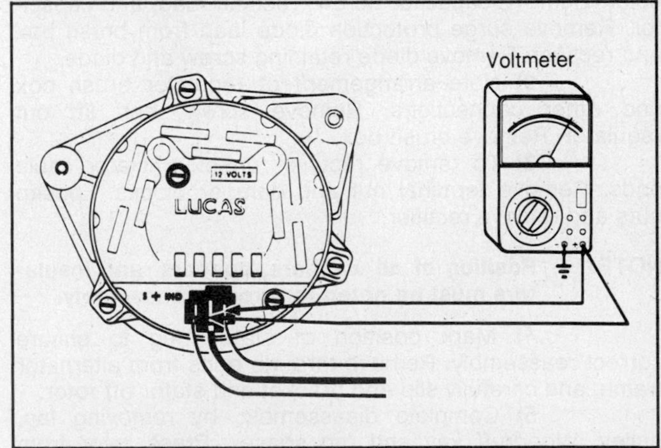

Voltmeter
12 VOLTS
LUCAS
S + IND

If more than 0.5 volt, check battery-to-alternator circuit.

11) Disconnect battery ground cable. Disconnect alternator. Connect an ammeter between main

LUCAS ALTERNATORS WITH INTEGRAL REGULATORS

terminal and disconnected main lead. *See Fig. 6*. Connect a jumper wire between "IND" terminal and "IND" lead.

Fig. 6: Test Voltage Under Accessory Load

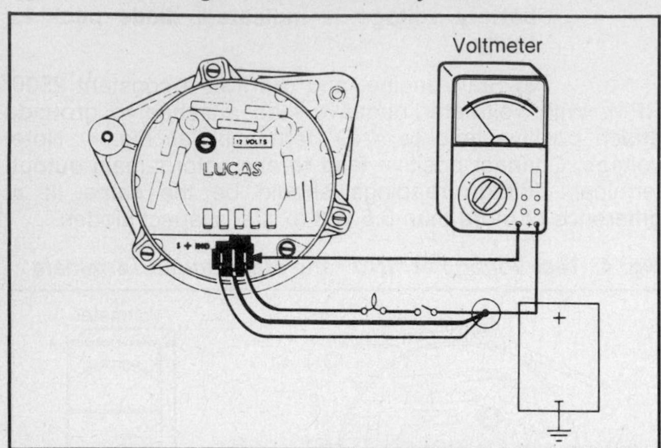
Voltmeter
12 VOLTS
LUCAS

Ammeter should indicate maximum alternator output.

12) Reconnect battery cable, and switch on all accessories (except wipers) for 1 minute. Start and run engine at normal charging speed. Ammeter whould indicate maximum output for alternator.

13) If output is low, use jumper wire to short metal link on regulator to ground, and repeat step **12)**. If maximum output is now indicated, suspect regulator. If output is still low, suspect stator windings.

14) Disconnect battery ground cable. Connect ammeter in series with alternator main output cable and starter solenoid. Reconnect battery cable. Connect voltmeter across battery terminals.

15) Start and run engine at 1500 RPM, until ammeter reads less than 10 amps. Voltmeter should read 13.6-14.4 volts. An incorrect reading indicates faulty regulator.

OVERHAUL

DISASSEMBLY

1) Remove end cover. Note wire positions and color. Remove capacitor screw, rectifier lead, and capacitor. Remove surge protection diode lead from brush box and rectifier. Remove diode retaining screw and diode.

2) Note arrangement of regulator brush box and other connections. Remove screw, and lift out regulator. Remove brush box.

3) To remove rectifier, unsolder stator cable ends. Remove terminal nut and damper blocks. Loosen nuts and remove rectifier.

NOTE: **Position of all washers, spacers, and insulators must be noted for proper reassembly.**

4) Mark position of stator ring to ensure correct reassembly. Remove through bolts from alternator frame, and carefully slip end bracket and stator off rotor.

5) Complete disassembly, by removing fan, pulley, Woodruff key and fan spacer. Press rotor from drive end bracket and remove bearing from bracket. Replace as necessary.

BENCH TESTING

Rotor Test

1) Connect ohmmeter leads to each slip ring. Resistance should be 3.2-3.6 ohms.

2) Using a 110-volt A.C. supply and a 15-watt test lamp, check for insulation between one of the slip rings and rotor frame. *See Fig. 7*. If lamp lights, rotor is shorted.

Fig. 7: Checking Insulation with a 110-Volt Test Lamp

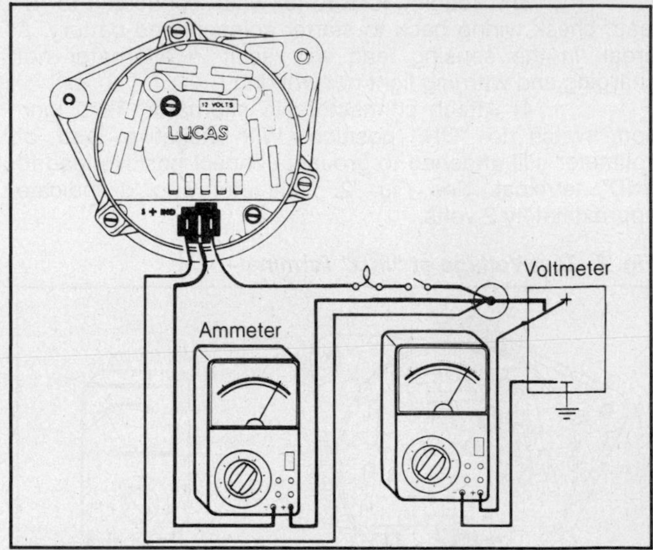
12 VOLTS
LUCAS
Voltmeter
Ammeter

15-Watt lamp should not light.

Diodes

1) Connect a 12-volt battery lead, with a 1.5-watt (maximum) test lamp connected in series, to a diode plate. Connect other battery lead, in turn, to each diode pin. *See Fig. 8*. Then reverse the connections.

Fig. 8: Testing Diodes in Rectifier Assembly

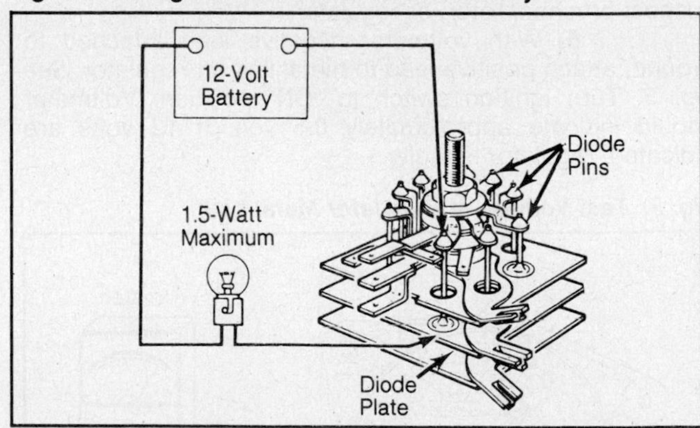
12-Volt
Battery
Diode
Pins
1.5-Watt
Maximum
Diode
Plate

Test lamp should be 1.5 watts maximum.

2) Lamp should light (with current flow) in one direction only. If lamp lights in both directions or fails in both, replace rectifier pack.

Stator Tests

1) Connect 12-volt battery and 36-watt test lamp to 2 of the stator connections. Repeat test using any other combination of 2 of the 3 connections. If lamp fails to light in either test, stator has an open coil.

LUCAS ALTERNATORS WITH INTEGRAL REGULATORS (Cont.)

2) Use 110-volt 15-watt test lamp, check insulation between any one of the 3 stator connections and laminations. *See Fig. 9*. If lamp lights, replace stator.

Fig. 9: Testing Stator Assembly Insulation

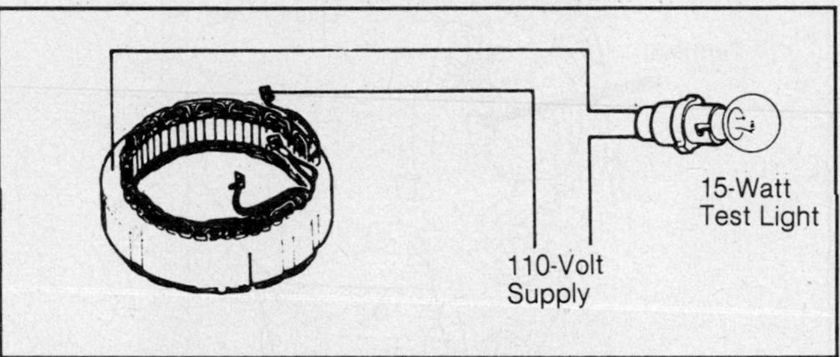
15-Watt
Test Light
110-Volt
Supply

Wires at each connection should be soldered.

COMPONENT REPLACEMENT

Regulator

Aluminum casing of control unit must not make contact with alternator body when installed. (Shorted field circuit could result in maximum alternator output at all times regardless of battery condition.)

Brushes

Installed brushes must extend at least .2" (5 mm) from housing and springs should indicate 9-13 oz. (255-368 g) tension when brush is pushed back flush with housing. If beyond limits, replace brush assembly.

REASSEMBLY

1) Reverse disassembly procedure, and note the following. Intall slip ring end bearing, ensure open side faces rotor and seat fully.

2) To replace rotor-to-drive end bracket, support inner track of bearing with piece of tubing. DO NOT use drive end bracket as the only support for the bearing when fitting rotor.

3) Resolder stator connections. Reconnect regulator leads, ensure correct arrangement.

MITSUBISHI ALTERNATORS WITH INTEGRAL REGULATORS

Chrysler Corp. Imports, Mazda & Mitsubishi

DESCRIPTION

Mitsubishi alternators are conventional 3-phase, self-rectifying type units containing 6 diodes (3 positive and 3 negative) which are used to rectify current. A case-mounted Integrated Circuit (IC) regulator is used on all models.

APPLICATION

Model	Volt/Amps	Part No.
Chrysler Corp. Imports		
Challenger, Sapporo	12/50	AQ2250G
Colt	12/45	A2T16371
Colt & Ram-50		
Pickups		
2.0L Engine	12/45	[1] MD063781
2.6L Engine	12/45	[1] MD064066
Diesel	12/50	[1] MD013740
Mazda		
B2000	13.5/50	A00IT23370
B2200	13.5/40	A00IT23479
GLC		
FWD	12/50	[1] E56318300A
RWD	14/30	[1] D50116300R
RX7	12/50	[1] N22118300
626	12/60	[1] FE0118300R
Mitsubishi		
Cordia	12/65	A3T32877
Montero	12/45	[1] MD064068
Pickup		
2.0L Engine	12/45	[1] MD025679
2.6L Engine	12/45	[1] MD064066
Diesel	12/45	[1] MD072582
Starion Turbo	12/65	[1] MD02677
Tredia	12/65	A3T32877

[1] – Vehicle manufacturer's part number.

TESTING

ON-VEHICLE TEST

CAUTION: DO NOT short across any alternator terminals or run vehicle with any wires disconnected. Battery must be fully charged for tests to be accurate.

Output Test

1) With ignition switch off, check voltage at "R" terminal and "L" terminal. Reading at both terminals should be 0 volts. If not 0 volts, alternator is defective.

2) Turn ignition switch on but do not start engine. Voltage at "L" should be 1-3 volts. If voltage is 0, alternator and regulator are defective.

3) If voltage at "L" is close to battery voltage with ignition on, short circuit the "F" terminal to rear alternator housing. *See Fig. 1.*

4) Read the voltage at "L" with "F" terminal shorted. If voltage is lower than battery voltage, regulator is defective. If voltage is close to battery voltage, alternator is defective.

5) With ignition switch off and battery ground cable disconnected, connect ammeter between alternator terminal "B" and cable. Connect voltmeter between "B" (+) terminal and ground. *See Fig. 2.*

Fig. 1: Alternator "F" Terminal Location

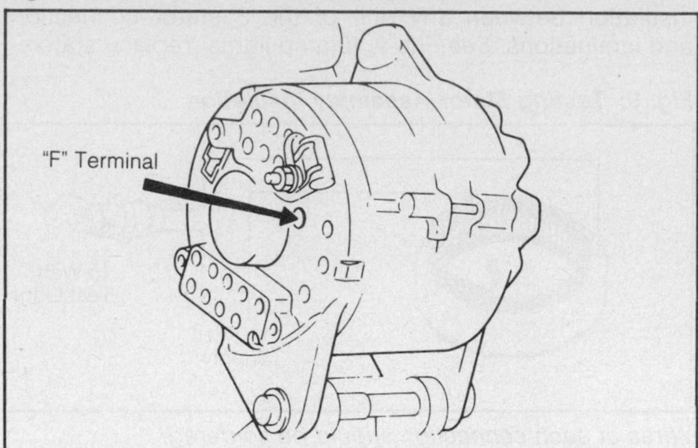
"F" Terminal

Terminal is located .8" (20 mm) below the hole.

Fig. 2: Alternator Output Test Arrangement

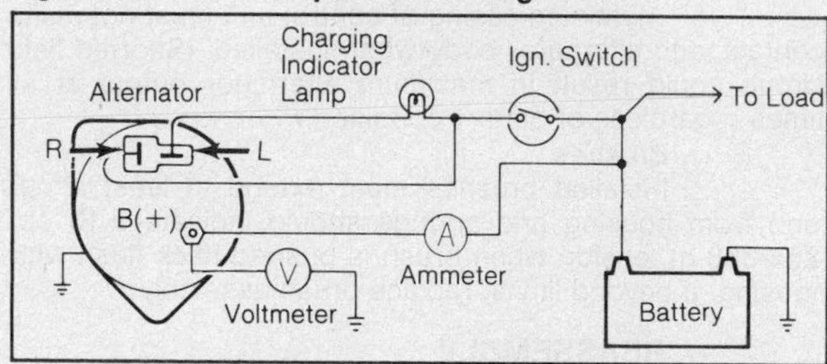
Alternator
Charging
Indicator
Lamp
Ign. Switch
To Load
R
L
B(+)
A
Ammeter
V
Voltmeter
Battery

6) Start engine and accelerate to 2000-3000 RPM. Turn on all lights and check ammeter for output.

OVERHAUL

DISASSEMBLY

1) After removing through bolts, insert screwdriver between front housing and stator to separate.

2) Hold the rotor in a soft jawed vice. Remove pulley nut, pulley, fan, and spacer. Remove rotor drive end housing by lightly tapping end housing with a soft mallet.

3) To separate stator from diode end housing, unsolder three negative diode leads and connections between diodes. Hold the stator lead with a needle nose plier to prevent rectifier from overheating.

4) Remove condenser from the "B" terminal. Unsolder the "L" and "B" terminal from the rectifier assembly. Lift out rectifier assembly and brush holder.

TESTING

Diode Assemblies

1) Check each diode with ohmmeter in forward and reverse direction. If the diode shows large resistance in one direction and small resistance in other direction, diode is normal.

2) If diode shows small resistance in both directions, it is shorted. If large resistance is shown in both directions, diode is open. Heat sink and diodes are replaced as an assembly.

Integral Regulator (Colt & Ram-50 Pickup & Mitsubishi Pickup Only)

1) Secure a 10-ohm 20-watt resistor, a 0-to-300-ohm 20-watt variable resistor, two 12-volt batteries

MITSUBISHI ALTERNATORS WITH INTEGRAL REGULATORS (Cont.)

and a DC voltmeter. Connect test equipment to vehicle. Set variable resistor to middle of resistance range. *See Fig. 3*. Observe voltage at (V_1) voltmeter.

Fig. 3: Testing Mitsubishi Integral Regulator

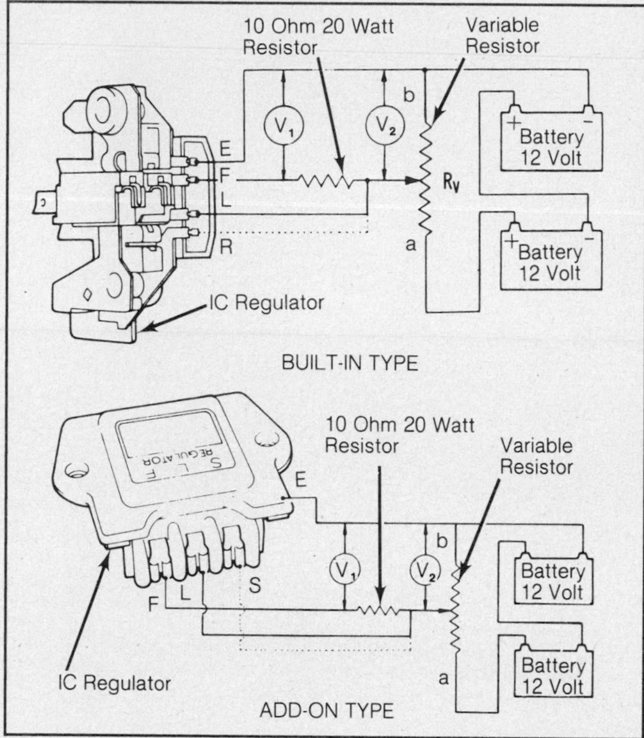

10 Ohm 20 Watt Resistor
Variable Resistor
E
F
L
R
b
a
V_1
V_2
R_V
Battery 12 Volt
Battery 12 Volt
IC Regulator
BUILT-IN TYPE
10 Ohm 20 Watt Resistor
Variable Resistor
E
F
L
S
b
a
Battery 12 Volt
Battery 12 Volt
IC Regulator
ADD-ON TYPE

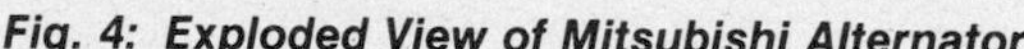

2) If voltage is less than 2 volts, move variable resistor toward "a". Observe voltage at (V_1) voltmeter. Stop moving variable resistor when (V_1) voltmeter makes a sudden increase. Do not exceed 15.5 volts. Regulator is good if (V_2) voltmeter is between 14-15 volts at 68°F (20°C). If not, replace regulator.

3) If voltage is more than 10 volts, move variable resistor toward "b". Observe voltage at (V_1) voltmeter. Stop moving variable resistor when (V_1) makes a sudden decrease. Regulator is good if (V_2) voltmeter is between 14-15 volts at 68°F (20°C). If not, replace regulator.

Rotor Field Continuity

Check continuity across field coil slip rings. A reading of 3-4 ohms must be obtained. No continuity, replace rotor.

Rotor Field Coil Ground

Check continuity between individual slip rings and rotor core/shaft. If there is continuity, coil or slip ring is grounded, replace rotor.

Stator Coil Ground

Ensure no continuity exists between stator coil leads and stator core.

Stator Coil Continuity

Check continuity between leads of stator coil. If there is no continuity, replace stator.

Brush Wear Limit

Brushes must be replaced when worn to 1/3 of original length. This limit is indicated by a wear limit line on the side of each brush.

Brush Spring Pressure

Standard tension should be 12-16 oz. (340-453 g). Replace if less than 7 oz. (198 g) or if springs are corroded.

Fig. 4: Exploded View of Mitsubishi Alternator

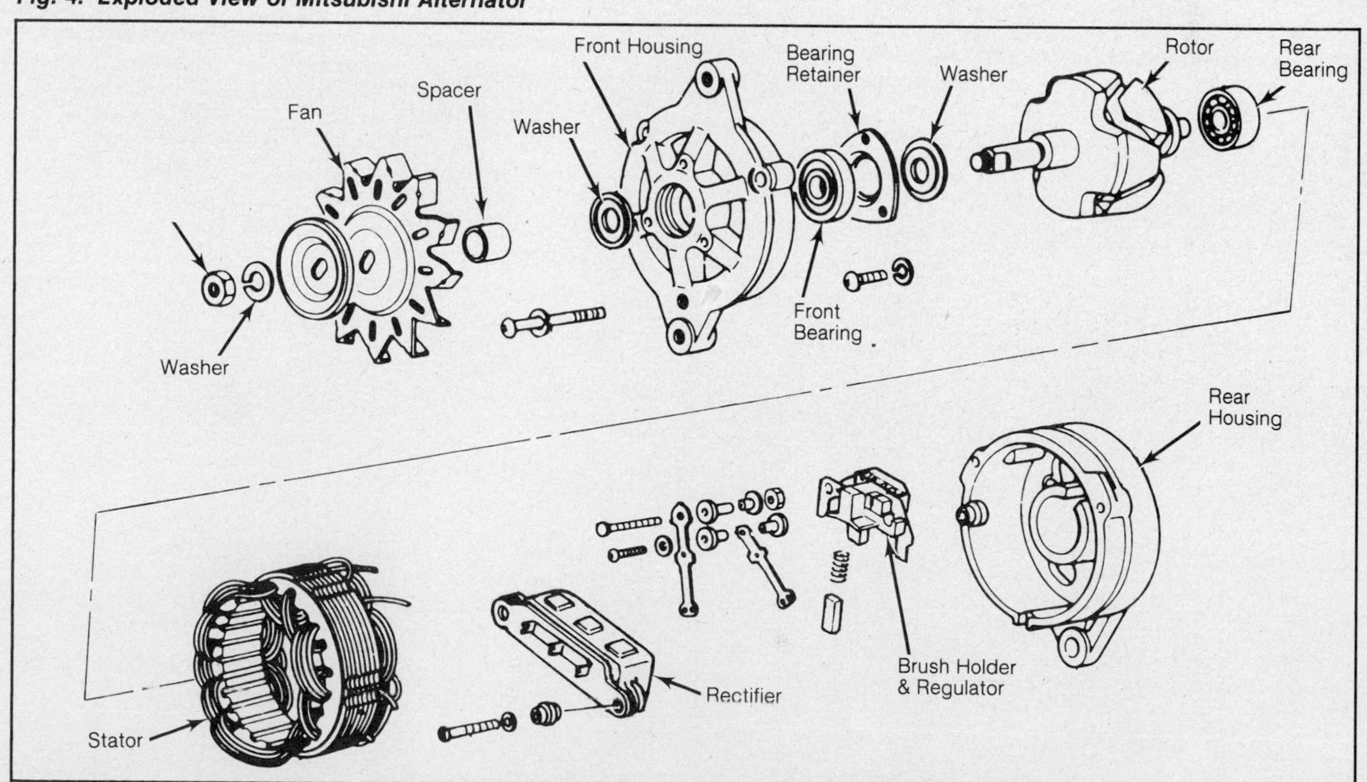

Front Housing
Bearing Retainer
Washer
Rotor
Rear Bearing
Spacer
Fan
Washer
Washer
Front Bearing
Rear Housing
Brush Holder & Regulator
Rectifier
Stator

Alternators & Regulators

MITSUBISHI ALTERNATORS WITH INTEGRAL REGULATORS (Cont.)

COMPONENT REPLACEMENT

Brushes

To remove brushes from holder, unsolder pigtail from terminal. To replace, solder pigtail to terminal ensure that 1/4" of brush will be located in brush holder.

Diodes

The diodes and rectifier are serviced as an assembly. If any diodes are defective, replace rectifier assembly.

Drive End Bearing

Remove bearing retainer set screws. Press bearing out of front housing.

Rear Bearing

Remove rear bearing from housing assembly using a press or bearing puller.

Voltage Regulator

The voltage regulator and brush holder are combined in one unit. If regulator is found to be defective, replace as an assembly.

REASSEMBLY

Reassemble by reversing disassembly procedures. Soldering of rectifier leads should be done in less than 5 seconds to prevent damage to diodes. When installing the rotor assembly in the rear housing, hold the brushes in position by inserting a stiff piece of wire into the access hole in rear housing.

MOTOROLA ALTERNATORS WITH INTEGRAL REGULATORS

Jaguar XJ6, XJS

NOTE: **Some XJ6 and XJS models use Lucas alternators. See appropriate article in this section.**

DESCRIPTION

Motorola alternators are conventional 3-phase, self-rectifying type alternators. Six silicon diodes, 3 positive and 3 negative, are used to rectify AC current.

APPLICATION

Model	Type
XJ6 With Air Conditioning	9AR 2512P
XJS	9AR 2533P

SPECIFICATIONS

Application	Amps@RPM	Voltage
XJ6	70@1050	14
XJS	70@1100	14

TESTING

ON-VEHICLE TESTING

Preliminary Checks

1) Ensure battery is fully charged and alternator drive belt is properly adjusted. Never disconnect battery, alternator or regulator with engine running.

2) Do not ground field winding (terminal EX), connected to regulator by Green wire. Always disconnect battery, if alternator is to be removed or installed.

Stator Winding Test

1) Turn ignition switch to "OFF" position. Using a voltmeter, check voltage on any of the 3 phases of stator windings, accessible through ventilation holes.

2) Connect voltmeter negative lead to ground and positive lead to phase winding. *See Fig. 2*. Voltmeter should indicate zero (0) volts.

Fig. 2: Checking Voltage Between Stator Windings and Ground

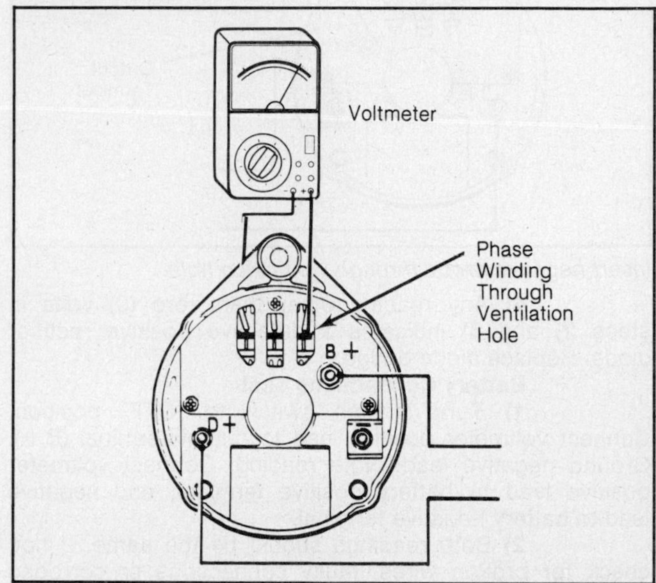
Voltmeter
Phase Winding Through Ventilation Hole
B +
D +

Insert voltmeter positive probe through ventilation hole.

3) Connect negative lead to phase winding, and positive lead to output terminal (B+). *See Fig. 3*. Voltmeter should read zero (0) volts.

Fig. 1: Exploded View of Motorola Alternator Used by Jaguar

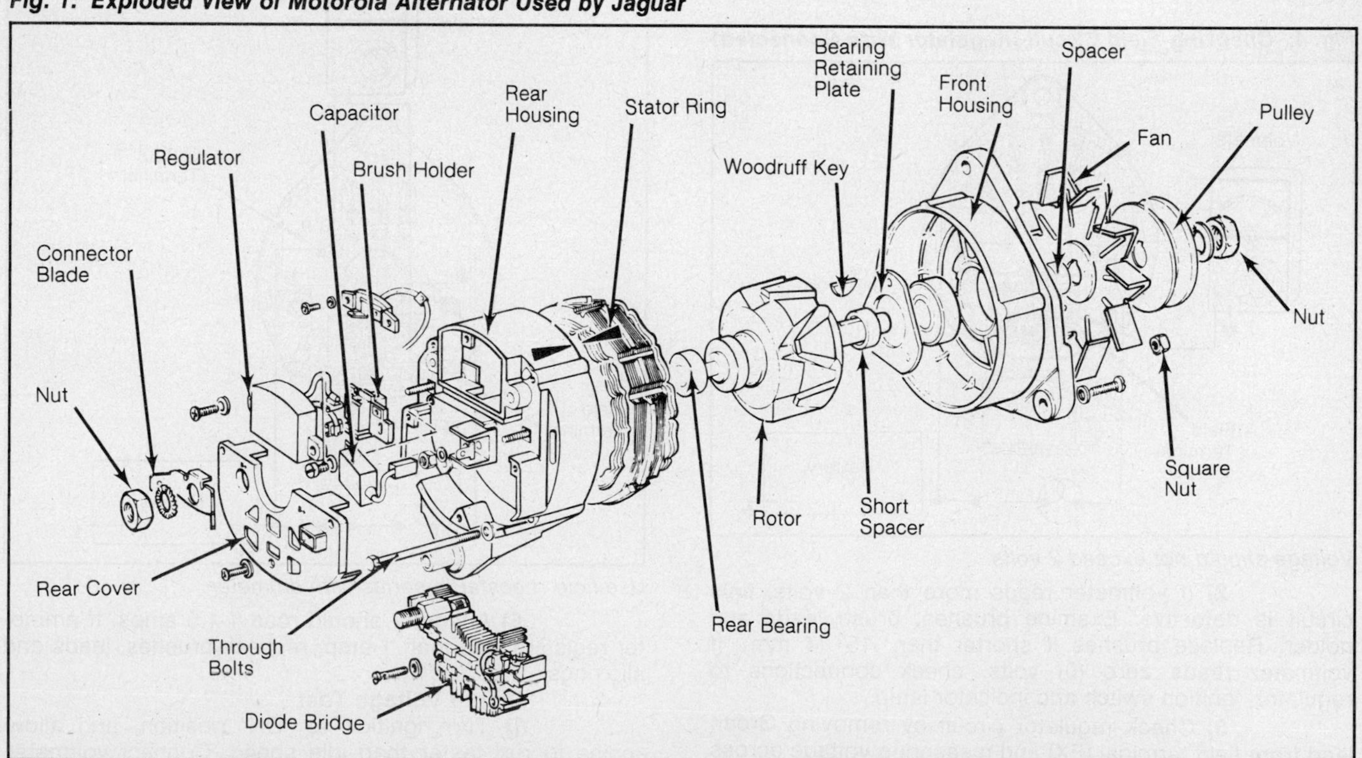
Bearing Retaining Plate
Spacer
Rear Housing
Front Housing
Capacitor
Stator Ring
Pulley
Fan
Regulator
Brush Holder
Woodruff Key
Connector Blade
Nut
Nut
Square Nut
Rotor
Short Spacer
Rear Cover
Rear Bearing
Through Bolts
Diode Bridge

MOTOROLA ALTERNATORS WITH INTEGRAL REGULATORS (Cont.)

Fig. 3: Checking Voltage Between Stator Windings and Alternator Positive Terminal

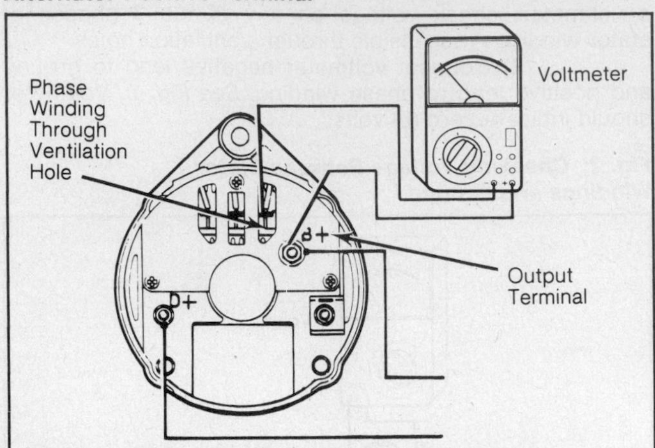
Phase
Winding
Through
Ventilation
Hole
Voltmeter
B+
Output
Terminal
D+

Insert negative probe through ventilation hole.

4) Any reading other than zero (0) volts in steps **2)** and **3)** indicates a defective positive rectifier diode. Replace diode bridge.

Battery Connections Test

1) Turn ignition switch to "OFF" position. Connect voltmeter positive lead to output terminal (B+). Ground negative lead. Note reading. Connect voltmeter positive lead to battery positive terminal, and negative lead to battery negative terminal.

2) Both readings should be the same. If not, check for broken wires, faulty connections or corroded terminals.

Field Circuit Test

1) Turn ignition to "ON" position, but do not start engine. Check voltage at slip ring by touching positive probe of voltmeter to field terminal (EX) with regulator attaching screws removed. *See Fig. 4.*

Fig. 4: Checking Field Circuit (Regulator Wire Connected)

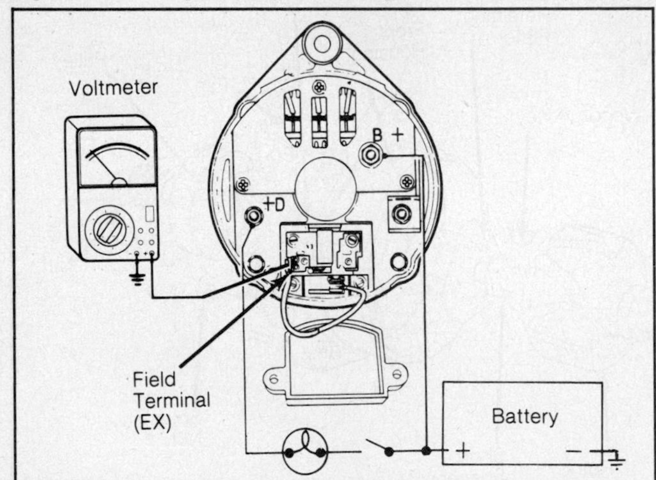
Voltmeter
B +
+D
Field
Terminal
(EX)
Battery
+

Voltage should not exceed 2 volts.

2) If voltmeter reads more than 2 volts, field circuit is defective. Examine brushes, brush leads and holder. Replace brushes if shorter than .15" (4 mm). If voltmeter reads zero (0) volts, check connections to regulator, ignition switch and indicator lamp.

3) Check regulator circuit by removing Green lead from field terminal (EX) and measuring voltage across field windings. *See Fig. 5.* Voltage should not exceed 2 volts. If voltage is correct, proceed to *Output Voltage Test.* If 8-12 volts is indicated, alternator is defective.

Fig. 5: Checking Regulator Circuit with Voltmeter

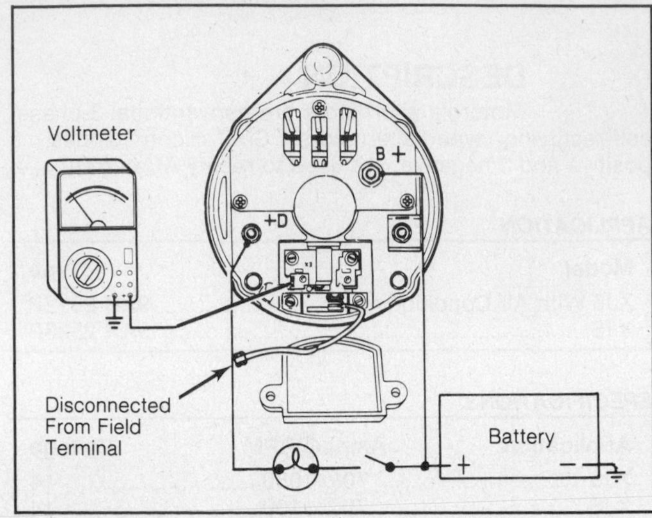
Voltmeter
B +
+D
Disconnected
From Field
Terminal
Battery
+

Green wire must be removed from field terminal.

4) Turn ignition switch to "ON" position, and run engine faster than idle speed. If incorrect readings were experienced in previous test, retest field circuit by disconnecting regulator from field terminal (EX).

5) Connect an ammeter between field (EX) terminal and output terminal (B+). Use a field rheostat in series with ammeter. This will prevent damage to ammeter from excessive current flow if field is shorted. *See Fig. 6.*

Fig. 6: Checking Field Circuit with an Ammeter

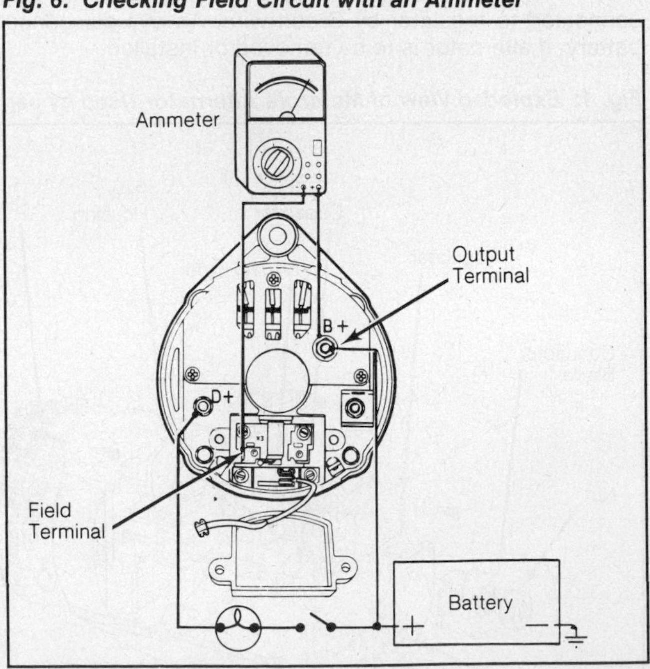
Ammeter
Output
Terminal
B+
D+
Field
Terminal
Battery
+

Use field rheostat in series with ammeter.

6) Ammeter should read 1-1.5 amps. If ammeter registers less than 1 amp, recheck brushes, leads and slip rings.

Output Voltage Test

1) Turn ignition to "ON" position, and allow engine to run faster than idle speed. Connect voltmeter

MOTOROLA ALTERNATORS WITH INTEGRAL REGULATORS (Cont.)

negative lead to ground and positive lead to output terminal (B+). *See Fig. 7*.

Fig. 7: Checking Alternator Output Voltage

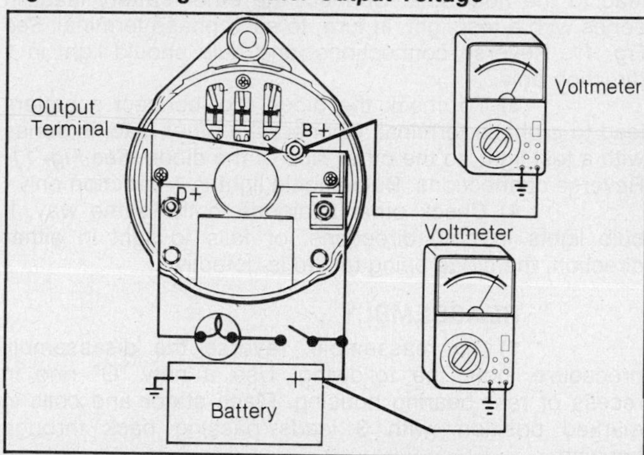
Voltmeter
Output Terminal
B+
D+
Voltmeter
Battery

Voltage should equal battery voltage.

2) Check voltage across battery terminals. Both voltage readings should be 13.7-14.7 volts. If voltage differs more than .3 volt between battery and output terminals, check wiring and terminals for corrosion or breaks.

Voltage Comparison Test

1) Turn ignition switch to "ON" position, and run engine faster than idle speed. Attach voltmeter negative lead to ground. In turn, touch positive lead to output terminal (B+) and to D+ terminal.

2) Voltage readings should be the same at both points. If voltage varies more than .5 volt, a faulty diode exists.

Regulator and Diode Test

1) Disconnect regulator field lead (EX). Attach jumper wire from field terminal (EX) to output terminal (B+). *See Fig. 8*. Turn ignition to "ON" position. Run engine at fast idle speed.

Fig. 8: Checking Regulator and Diodes

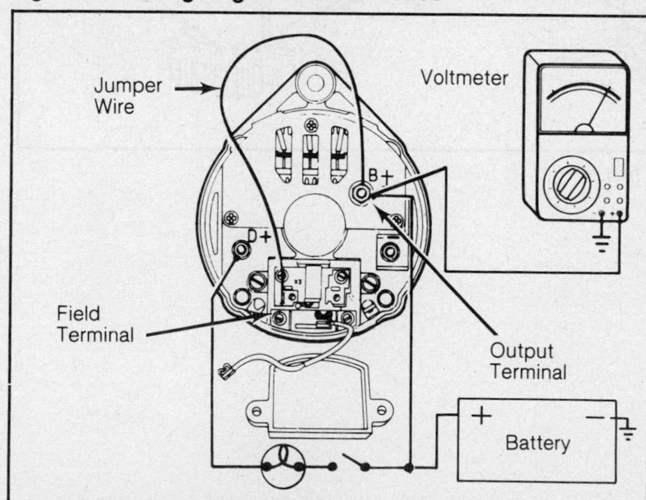
Jumper Wire
Voltmeter
B+
D+
Field Terminal
Output Terminal
Battery

Attach jumper wire to field and output terminals.

2) Connect negative lead of voltmeter to ground and positive lead to output terminal (B+). If voltage rises to 14-16 volts, but did not reach 14 volts in *Output Voltage Test,* regulator is defective.

3) If output voltage does not rise, and field current tested as good in *Field Circuit Test,* either alternator stator or rectifier diodes are defective.

OVERHAUL

DISASSEMBLY

1) Remove nut, lock washer, and connector blade from output terminal (B+). Remove set screw and washer, securing capacitor to housing. Separate connector blade and remove capacitor.

2) Remove rear cover. Identify wiring colors. Remove regulator. Remove brush holder. Clamp pulley, and remove pulley nut. Remove small washer, fan and large washer from spindle. Remove Woodruff key and spacer.

3) Remove 4 through bolts, washers and square nuts. Separate front and rear housings. If separation is difficult, place spindle in protected jaws of vise. Using care not to damage stator and windings, remove rear housing, stator and diode bridge. Rear bearing will remain with spindle.

4) Remove spindle from vise. Remove front housing and spacer. Remove bearings, if necessary. Mark position of stator ring in rear housing to ensure proper reassembly.

5) To avoid overheating diodes, rapidly unsolder leads of 3-phase windings and Red D+ lead from diode bridge. Use long-nosed pliers to grip each terminal as wire is unsoldered.

6) Remove diode bridge and washers. Lift housing from stator, detach 2 terminals from housing, and remove D+ lead.

BENCH TESTING

Brush Assembly Test

1) Using a test light, touch probes to each brush. Bulb should not light. *See Fig. 9*.

Fig. 9: Checking Brush Assembly with a Test Light

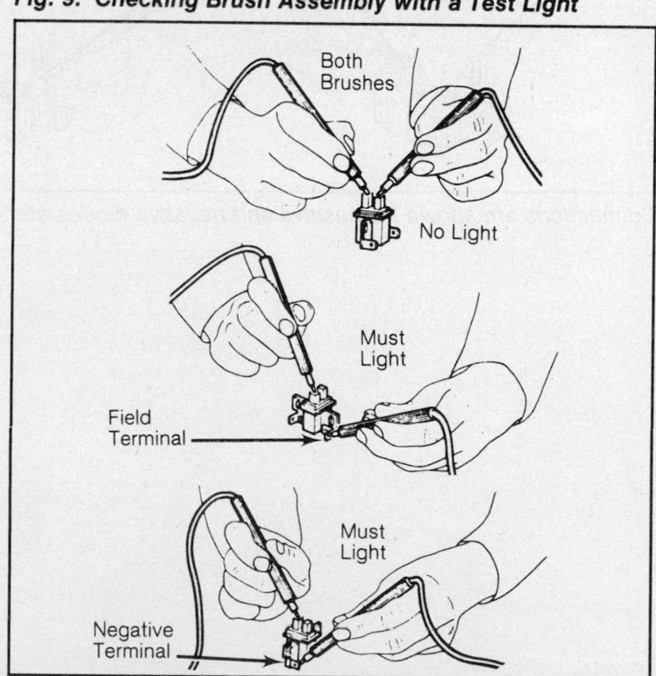
Both Brushes
No Light
Must Light
Field Terminal
Must Light
Negative Terminal

Bulb should not light when both brushes are touched.

MOTOROLA ALTERNATORS WITH INTEGRAL REGULATORS (Cont.)

2) Connect test leads to field terminal and its corresponding brush. Bulb must light, even when brush is moved in its holder. Test negative terminal and corresponding brush in similiar manner. Bulb must again light even if brush is moved in its holder.

Rotor Test

Connect ohmmeter leads to each slip ring. *See Fig. 10*. Resistance should be between 3.8 and 5.2 ohms. With ohmmeter connected between a slip ring and alternator housing, reading should be infinity.

Fig. 10: Checking Rotor Resistance with an Ohmmeter

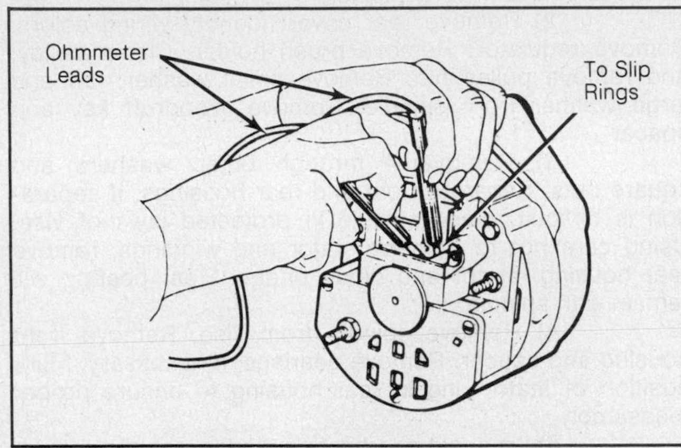
Ohmmeter
Leads
To Slip
Rings

Leads should touch each slip ring.

Diode Test

1) To check positive diode, connect a battery lead in series with a test light to B+ terminal. Connect other lead, in turn, to each phase terminal. *See Fig. 11*. Reverse connections. Bulb should light in 1 direction only.

2) To check negative diode, connect a battery lead to the heat sink. Connect the other battery lead, in series with a test light, in turn, to each phase terminal. *See Fig. 11*. Reverse connections, and bulb should light in 1 direction only.

3) To check the diode trio, connect a battery lead to a phase terminal. Connect the other lead, in series with a test light, to the other side of the diode. *See Fig. 11*. Reverse connections. Bulb should light in 1 direction only.

4) Check other 2 diodes in the same way. If bulb lights in both directions, or fails to light in either direction, the diode being tested is defective.

REASSEMBLY

1) To reassemble, reverse the disassembly procedure, note the following. Use a new "O" ring in recess of rear bearing housing. Place stator and coils in marked position, with 3 leads passing back through housing.

2) When soldering leads, use long-nose pliers as a heat sink to protect diode assembly from exessive heat. Use new bearings, as required. Larger inside diameter of short spacer (on front end of spindle) should be next to rotor.

3) If front bearing was removed, use Loctite sealing compound on screw threads and capped holes in retainer plate. Use Loctite on through bolt and nut threads.

Fig. 11: Checking Diodes with a 12-Volt Test Light

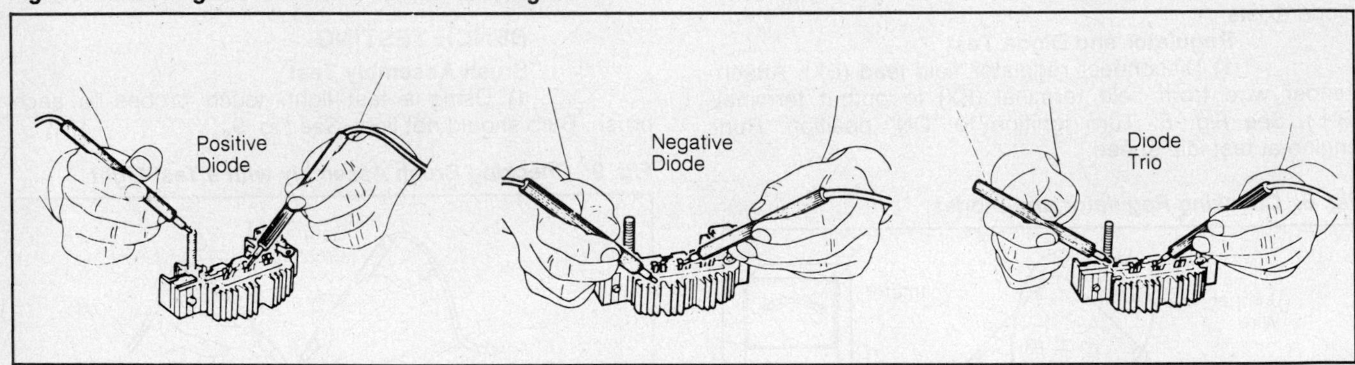
Positive
Diode
Negative
Diode
Diode
Trio

Connections are shown for positive and negative diodes and diode trio.

NIPPONDENSO ALTERNATORS

Honda Accord, Civic, Prelude; Toyota Camry, Celica, Corolla, Cressida, Land Cruiser, Pickup, Starlet, Supra, Tercel

DESCRIPTION

Nippondenso alternators are conventional 3-phase alternators utilizing 6 diodes (3 positive and 3 negative) to rectify current. Charge control may be by either internal Integrated Circuit (IC), or external IC or contact point type regulators.

TESTING

NOTE: Also see NIPPONDENSO REGULATORS in this section.

TOYOTA ON-VEHICLE TESTS

Preliminary Inspection

Check alternator mounting and drive belt tension. Inspect turn signal and gauge fuses. Check alternator and regulator wire connections for tightness. Battery must be fully charged prior to beginning test.

No Load Test

1) Connect a voltmeter and ammeter to charging circuit. *See Fig. 2*. Check amperage and voltage with engine running at 2000 RPM. On models with external contact point voltage regulators, voltage should be 13.8-14.8 volts.

NIPPONDENSO ALTERNATOR APPLICATION

Model	Amps.	[1] Part No.
Honda		
Accord	60	31100-PC1-004
Civic	45	31100-PA6-014
Prelude	60	31100-PC6-004
Toyota		
Camry	70	27060-63020
Celica	55	27060-35040
	60	27020-35020
Corolla	50	27020-15110
	55	27060-15030
Cressida	65	27060-43030-84
Land Cruiser	40	27020-61100
	55	27020-61071
Pickup		
Diesel	55	27020-54080
Gas	40	27020-35050
Starlet	55	27060-13020
Supra	65	27060-43030-84
Tercel		
Conventional	50	27020-15120
IC Type	55	27060-15020

[1] – Vehicle manufacturer's part number.

2) On models with external IC type voltage regulators, voltage should be 14.0-14.7 volts on Land Cruiser and Pickups with gasoline engines. On all other Toyota models, voltage should be 13.8-14.4 volts. On all models, current draw should be less than 10 amps.

Fig. 1: Exploded View of Nippondenso Alternator for Toyota Pickup

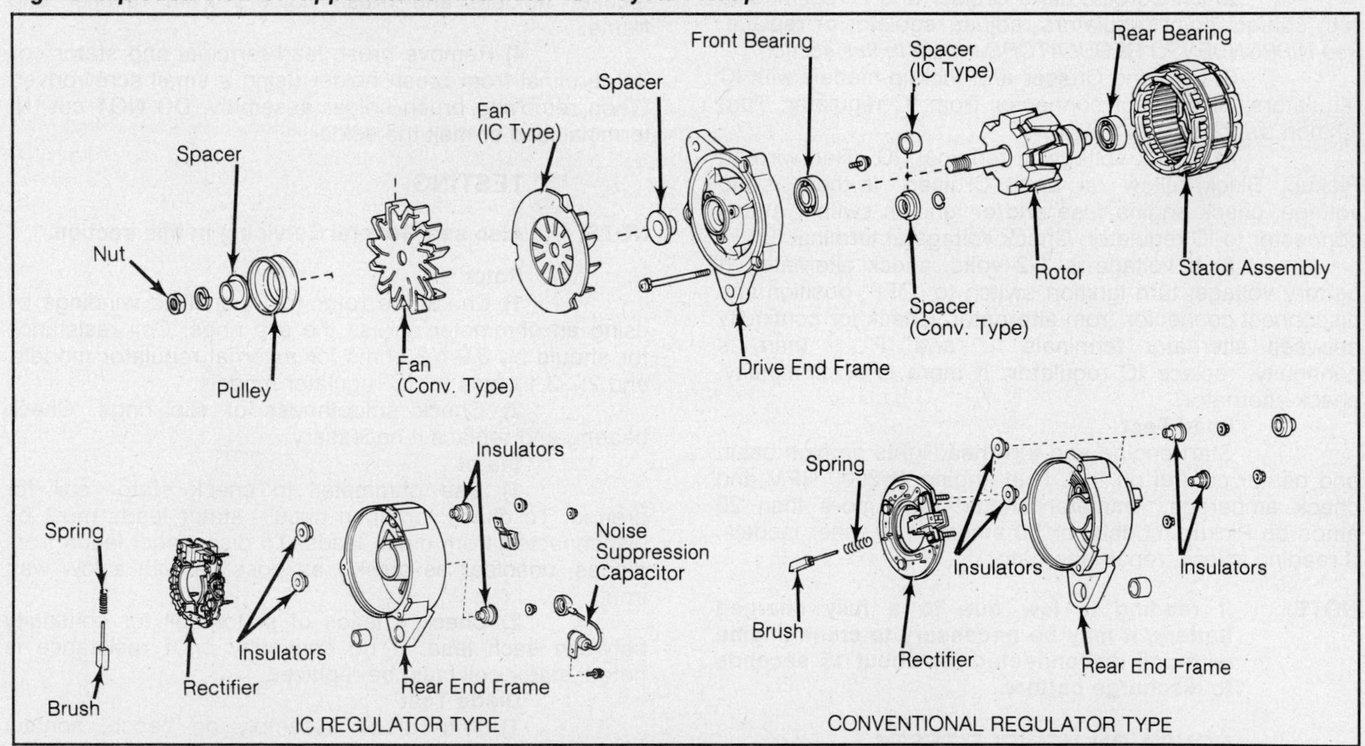
Front Bearing
Spacer
(IC Type)
Rear Bearing
Spacer
Fan
(IC Type)
Spacer
Nut
Rotor
Stator Assembly
Spacer
(Conv. Type)
Drive End Frame
Fan
(Conv. Type)
Pulley
Insulators
Spring
Noise
Suppression
Capacitor
Spring
Insulators
Insulators
Insulators
Brush
Rectifier
Rear End Frame
Brush
Rectifier
Rear End Frame
IC REGULATOR TYPE
CONVENTIONAL REGULATOR TYPE

Honda and Toyota alternators are similar. Some have integral IC regulators, others have external regulators.

NIPPONDENSO ALTERNATORS (Cont.)

Fig. 2: Meter Hookups for Toyota No Load Test

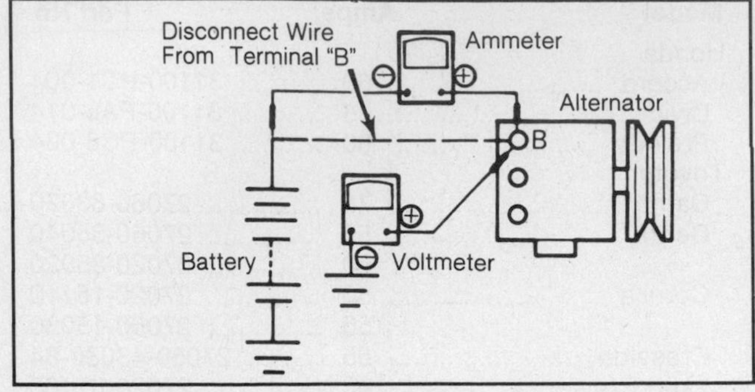
Disconnect Wire
From Terminal "B"
Ammeter
Alternator
B
Battery
Voltmeter

Do not cause a short condition when making connections.

3) For further testing procedures for Toyota models with internal IC regulators, proceed to step **4)**. To further test Toyota models with external IC or contact point type regulators, proceed to *Terminal "F" Voltage Test*.

4) If voltage reading in step **2)** was above the specified range, replace IC regulator. If voltage reading was less than specified range, run engine at idle. Connect terminal "F" (located inside rear of alternator housing) to ground.

5) If voltage reading now climbs to within specified range, replace IC regulator. If reading remains below specified range, replace alternator.

Terminal "F" Voltage Test

1) If voltage reading was above specified range in step **2)** of *No Load Test*, replace IC regulator. If voltage reading is less than specified range, turn off engine.

2) On Corolla, Land Cruiser and Tercel models with contact point regulators, adjust regulator or replace. *See NIPPONDENSO REGULATORS article in this section.*

3) On Land Cruiser and Pickup models with IC regulators, disconnect connector from IC regulator. Turn ignition switch to "ON" position.

4) Check voltage at terminal "IG" (Red wire on Pickup, Black/Yellow on Land Cruiser). If there is no voltage, check engine fuse and/or ignition switch. Attach connector to IC regulator. Check voltage at terminal "L".

5) If voltage is 1-2 volts, check alternator. If battery voltage, turn ignition switch to "OFF" position and disconnect connector from alternator. Check for continuity between alternator terminals "L" and "F". If there is continuity, replace IC regulator. If there is no continuity, check alternator.

Load Test

Start engine and turn headlights on high beam and heater control on "HI". Run engine at 2000 RPM and check amperage. Ammeter should read more than 20 amps on Pickup models, or 30 amps on all other models. If reading is less, repair alternator.

NOTE: **If reading is low due to a fully charged battery, it may be necessary to crank engine with coil disconnected for about 15 seconds to discharge battery.**

HONDA ON-VEHICLE TESTS

Preliminary Inspection

Check alternator mounting and drive belt tension. Inspect turn signal and gauge fuses. Check alternator and regulator wire connections for tightness. Battery must be fully charged prior to beginning test.

Alternator Output Test

1) With engine off, disconnect wire from alternator terminal "B". *See Fig. 2.* Connect ammeter positive lead to terminal "B", and negative lead to wire just removed.

NOTE: **On Civic models, by-pass voltage regulator by disconnecting its connector. Connect jumper wire from battery positive terminal to Red/White wire at connector.**

2) Start engine. Turn on bright beam of headlights, rear window defroster, and turn heater fan switch to highest setting. Run engine at 2000 RPM.

3) Check alternator output. Ammeter should show approximately 60 amps for Accord and Prelude, or 45 amps for Civic. Check alternator if not to specifications.

OVERHAUL

DISASSEMBLY

1) Remove retaining screws and pry drive end frame from stator with screwdriver. If necessary, tap lightly on drive end frame with mallet.

2) Secure rotor core in padded vise, and remove pulley attaching nut. Remove pulley, fan and spacer. Press rotor from drive end frame. Remove bearing retainer from end frame. Remove bearing, felt cover and felt ring.

3) Remove rectifier holder securing nuts and brush holder attaching screws. Separate stator with rectifier holders and brush holders from rectifier end frame.

4) Remove brush lead terminal and stator coil "N" terminal from brush holder using a small screwdriver. When removing brush holder assembly, DO NOT cut "N" terminal lead or melt the solder.

TESTING

NOTE: **Also see General Servicing in this section.**

Rotor

1) Check the rotor for open field windings by using an ohmmeter across the slip rings. Coil resistance for should be 3.9-4.2 ohms for external regulator models, and 2.7-3.1 ohms for IC regulator models.

2) Check smoothness of slip rings. Check bearing and replace if necessary.

Stator

1) Use ohmmeter to check stator coil for ground. To check for open circuit, stator leads must be disconnected from diode leads. To disconnect leads from diodes, unsolder as quickly as possible with a low watt iron.

2) Check 4 leads of stator coil for continuity between each lead. If no continuity or if resistance is noted, stator coil must be replaced.

Diode Test

1) With diode assembly on bench, contact diode plate with one probe and each of 3 diode leads with other probe. Note ohmmeter reading. Reverse probes and repeat test. Check all diodes in this manner.

NIPPONDENSO ALTERNATORS (Cont.)

2) All diodes should show a low reading in one direction and NO reading in the opposite direction. If any rectifier (diode) is defective, replace holder assembly.

COMPONENT REPLACEMENT

Brushes

1) Check for cracks and minimum length of .22" (5.5 mm). If damaged or worn beyond limit, replace brushes. Brushes should slide smoothly in holders. Install new springs when replacing brushes. Solder brush wire.

2) New brush protrusion should be .413" (10.5 mm) for Camry models, .610" (15.5 mm) for Honda models, and .492" (12.5 mm) for all other models.

REASSEMBLY

1) Press brushes into holder against spring tension. To prevent brushes from falling, insert a stiff wire through hole in rectifier, frame and brush holder.

2) Pack multipurpose grease into rear bearing. Press bearing onto rotor shaft. Pack drive end bearing with grease, and install. Install felt ring, cover and bearing retainer.

3) Ensure drive end frame and rectifier end frame with stator are assembled in original alignment. Tighten body screws and remove brush retaining wire.

NIPPONDENSO REGULATORS

Honda Accord, Civic, Prelude; Toyota Camry, Celica, Corolla, Cressida, Pickup, Land Cruiser, Starlet, Supra, Tercel

DESCRIPTION

External Nippondenso regulators may be either dual contact point or Integrated Circuit (IC) type. Dual contact point type are adjustable. IC type are not adjustable. IC type must be replaced if found defective.

APPLICATION

Model	[1] Part No.
Honda	
Accord & Prelude	31400-SA5-004
Civic	31400-SA0-672
Toyota	
Camry	27700-63020
Celica, Cressida & Supra	27700-43010
Corolla, Tercel	
Standard Type	27700-13090
IC Type	27700-43010
Land Cruiser	
Standard Type	27700-13060
IC Type	27700-38100
Pickup	
Diesel	27700-57060
Gas	27700-38113
Starlet	27700-13070

[1] – Vehicle manufacturer's part number. Some regulators are integrated circuit (IC) type. Part number furnished for information only.

TESTING

VOLTAGE REGULATOR

NOTE: Substitution of a known good regulator for one suspected of malfunctioning will frequently save time during testing.

Toyota No Load Test

1) Disconnect wire from "B" terminal of alternator, and connect to ammeter negative lead. Connect ammeter positive lead to "B" terminal of alternator.

2) With engine running at varying speeds from idle to 2000 RPM, voltage should be 14.0-14.7 volts on Land Cruiser and Pickups with gasoline engines or 13.8-14.8 volts on all other models. Amperage should be less than 10 amps. If not within specifications, adjust or replace regulator as required. *See ADJUSTMENT in this article.*

Toyota Regulator Circuit Resistance Test (Contact Point Type Only)

1) Disconnect regulator connector. Using an ohmmeter, check resistance between regulator terminals "IG" and "F". *See Fig. 1.* Resistance should be zero (0) when at rest, and approximately 11 ohms when pulled in.

2) Measure resistance between terminals "L" and "E". Reading should zero (0) ohms at rest, and approximately 100 ohms when pulled in.

3) Measure resistance between terminals "B" and "E". Reading should be infinity at rest, and approximately 100 ohms when pulled in.

Fig. 1: Identification of Toyota Regulator Connector Terminals

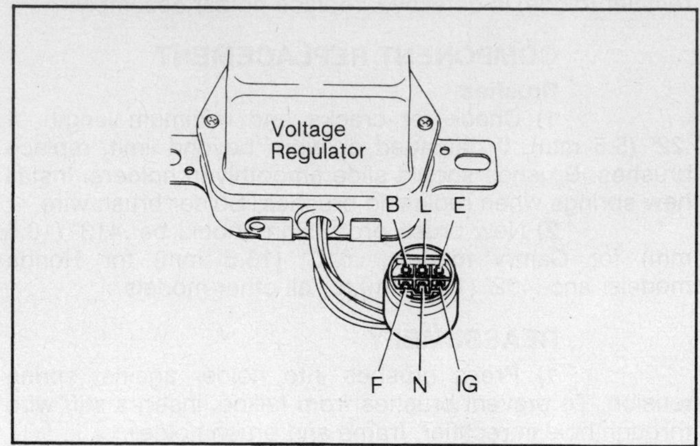
Voltage
Regulator
B L E
F N IG

Check regulator resistance as indicated.

4) Measure resistance between terminals "B" and "L". Reading should be infinity at rest, and zero (0) ohms when pulled in.

5) Measure resistance between terminals "N" and "E". Reading should be approximately 23 ohms.

6) If any of the above checks are not to specifications, replace regulator.

Honda Voltage Regulator No Load Test (Contact Point Type)

1) Turn all lights and accessories off. Check all fuses. With engine idling, remove negative cable from battery. Connect voltmeter negative lead to disconnected negative cable. *See Fig. 2.* Connect voltmeter positive lead to battery positive cable.

Fig. 2: Voltmeter/Ammeter Hookup for Honda No Load Test

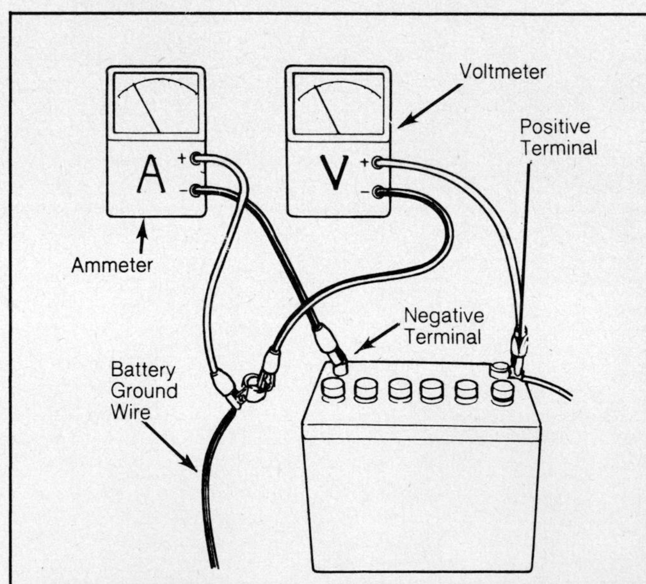
Voltmeter
Positive
Terminal
A
V
Ammeter
Negative
Terminal
Battery
Ground
Wire

Observe polarity to prevent shorts.

2) If engine continues to run, proceed to step **5)**. If engine immediately stops when negative cable is disconnected, reconnect cable and start car. Check voltage at Black/Yellow wire at regulator connector.

3) If there is no voltage, check for continuity between 10 amp regulator/fuel pump fuse and connector

NIPPONDENSO REGULATORS (Cont.)

J27. Repair or replace parts as necessary. If voltage was present, check White/Red wire for system voltage at all connectors between regulator and alternator.

4) If voltage is available at alternator, check alternator output. If no voltage in White/Red wire at regulator, replace regulator.

5) Operate engine speed from 2000-4000 RPM, and note voltage reading. Reading should be 13.5-14.5 volts. If not within specifications, adjust voltage relay.

Honda Voltage Regulator No Load Test (IC Regulator Type)

1) Check voltage at regulator terminal "F" (White/Red wire). Turn ignition to "ON" position. Voltmeter should read 9-11 volts. Start engine and operate at idle speed. Voltmeter should read 5-7.5 volts.

2) Increase engine speed to 3000 RPM. Voltmeter should increase as engine RPM increases to around 12 volts. If not, replace regulator.

3) Repeat steps **1)** and **2)**, with voltmeter attached to regulator terminal "B" (White wire). Operate engine speed between idle and 3000 RPM. Voltmeter should read 14.5-15.5 volts. If not, replace regulator.

ADJUSTMENT

NOTE: Adjustments are not applicable to sealed units. If points are slightly oxidized or pitted, dress contacts with sandpaper (400 grit or finer). If points are oxidized or pitted excessively, replace regulator assembly.

Voltage Regulator & Relay

1) For relay, connect voltmeter between "N" terminal (White wire) and ground. Gradually increase engine speed. Voltmeter reading should be 4.0-5.8 volts when indicator light goes out. *See Fig. 3*. For regulator, connect voltmeter as described under testing. Adjust regulator and relay by bending adjusting arm as follows.

Fig. 3: Adjustments for Voltage Relay

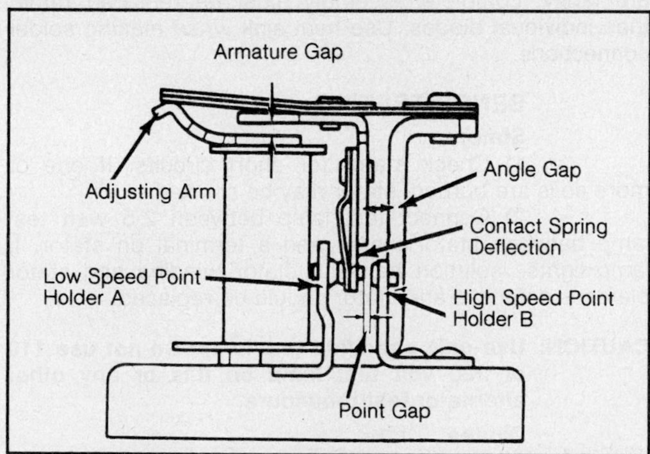
Armature Gap
Angle Gap
Adjusting Arm
Contact Spring
Deflection
Low Speed Point
Holder A
High Speed Point
Holder B
Point Gap

Voltage regulator adjustment is similar.

2) If cut-in or regulated voltage is too high, adjust by bending core adjusting arm down. Bend arm up if voltage is too low. If adjustment of core arm does not correct voltage, proceed with point gap adjustment. Disconnect negative cable from battery.

3) On Honda Civic, check armature core gap with armature depressed until moving point is in contact with "B" side point. Armature core gap should be .02" (.5 mm) or less. If not, replace regulator. Release the armature and adjust the point gap between the "B" side point and the moving point by bending point arm "A".

4) On Toyota models, point gap should be .016-.047" (0.4-1.2 mm). Angle gap should be .02" (.5 mm) or less when armature is pressed to coil. After adjustment, recheck cut-in or regulated voltage. If not within specifications, repeat voltage adjustment.

NOTE: Regulator cover must be installed after adjustments prior to further testing.

SEV MOTOROLA ALTERNATORS WITH IC REGULATORS

DESCRIPTION

SEV Motorola alternators are conventional 3-phase, self-rectifying type alternators. Six silicon diodes (3 positive and 3 negative) are used to rectify AC current.

NOTE: **Either SEV Motorola or Bosch alternators may be used on all models listed. Due to the wide variance in application and output for the various models, not all individual part numbers and ratings may be shown. Always check identification plate attached to housing.**

ALTERNATOR APPLICATION

Model	Amp Rating	[1] Part No.
BMW	65	9GD2NA2A25
Peugeot	72	9AR26072P
	70	9AR2990P
Renault	50	9AR2659K
Saab	70	9AR2638P
Volkswagen	55	8AR2064K
	55	9JG2KA2F56
	55	9LG2KB2F51
	65	9JG2NA2F52
	65	9JG2NA2F53
	65	9JG2NA2F54
	65	9JG2NF2F58
	65	9LG2NB2F55

[1] – Motorola part numbers.

TESTING

NOTE: **Some testing is described as part of OVERHAUL procedure in this article. The following testing is performed with alternator installed on vehicle.**

ON-VEHICLE TEST

1) Disconnect battery cables and install cutout switch, variable resistance, ammeter and voltmeter. *See Fig. 1.* Connect ground cable and check that cutout switch is in closed position.

Fig. 1: Alternator Testing Set-Up

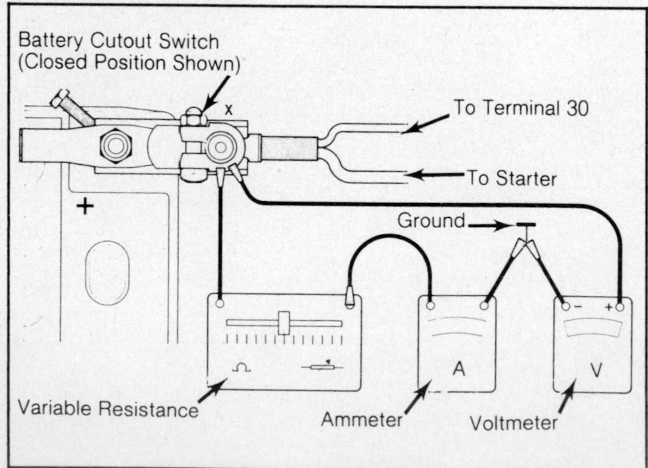
Battery Cutout Switch
(Closed Position Shown)
X
To Terminal 30
To Starter
+
Ground
A
V
Variable Resistance
Ammeter
Voltmeter

2) Start engine and run at 3000-4000 RPM (do not exceed manufacturer's RPM limits). Adjust variable resistance to give the following amperage readings: Models with 65 amp alternators – 45 amps, with 55 amp alternators – 25 amps.

3) Open battery cutout switch to separate battery from test circuit. Load current is now determined by variable resistance. Readjust variable resistance to provide Test Output Amperage. Voltage should be between 13.1-14.4 volts. If not, replace regulator.

CAUTION: **Never run alternator without battery connected unless variable resistor is installed to provide load. Alternator or regulator or both could be severely damaged without providing current load.**

OVERHAUL

NOTE: **Since battery current reaches the alternator when the ignition is not on, battery ground strap should be disconnected when removing or installing alternator.**

DISASSEMBLY

1) Remove drive pulley and cooling fan. Remove regulator and brush assembly. Mark alternator assembly for proper orientation during reassembly.

2) Remove through bolts and carefully separate front housing with rotor from rear housing with stator. Rotor may be removed from housing after bearing retaining plate screws have been removed.

NOTE: **Bearings must be removed and installed using press with adaptors. Never reinstall used bearings.**

3) Remove nuts holding diode assembly to rear housing and separate housing and stator. If diodes are faulty, complete assembly must be replaced rather than individual diodes. Use heat sink when making solder connections.

BENCH TESTING

Stator

1) Check stator for short circuits. If one or more coils are burned, stator may be shorted.

2) Connect test lamp between 2-5 watt test lamp between stator plates and a terminal on stator. If lamp lights, isolation between stator winding and stator plates is defective and stator should be replaced.

CAUTION: **Use only specified test lamp. Do not use 110 or 220 volt test lamp on this or any other alternator test procedure.**

Diodes

1) Check diodes with a diode tester for shorts or open circuits. If any diode is defective, entire diode assembly must be replaced.

2) If diode tester is not available, diode leads should be quickly and carefully unsoldered and tested with an ohmmeter.

3) Diodes should show low resistance in flow direction and high resistance in reverse direction.

SEV MOTOROLA ALTERNATORS WITH IC REGULATORS (Cont.)

Fig. 2: Checking Stator For Shorts

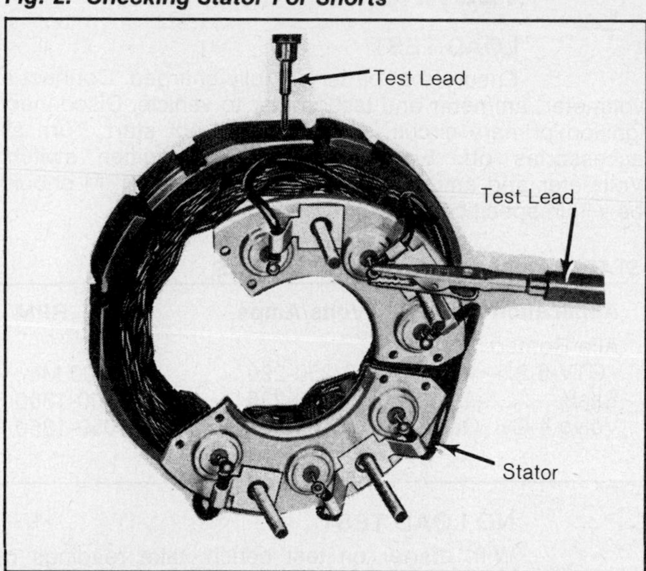
Test Lead
Test Lead
Stator

Rotor

1) Check that slip rings are not dirty or burned. Check winding for breakage or damaged isolation. Measure resistance between slip rings.

2) Normal resistance should be approximately 4.5 ohms. If winding is faulty, rotor must be replaced.

NOTE: It is recommended that bearings be replaced whenever alternator is disassembled.

Brush Holder

1) Connect 12 volt test lamp between brushes. Lamp should not light. Connect test lamp between "DF" terminal and "+" brush. Lamp should give steady light even if brush and/or terminal cable is moved.

2) Connect 12 volt test lamp between brush holder frame and "–" brush. Lamp should give steady light. If test results are not satisfactory or brush length is less than 3/16", replace brush holder.

PARTS REPLACEMENT

Diodes

1) Mark leads connecting stator to diodes, quickly and carefully unsolder leads. Place new diode holder in exact position of holder being replaced.

2) Solder new leads while holding with pliers acting as a heat sink. Use minimum 100-watt, well-heated soldering iron. Never change places of diode holders.

3) Positive holder is isolated from frame by means of isolation washers and sleeves, and its diodes are marked in Red. Negative holder is not isolated and its diodes are marked in Black.

CAUTION: Heat sink must be used during soldering to avoid damage to diodes from overheating.

REASSEMBLY

1) Alternator is assembled by reversing disassembly procedures. Rotor must be pressed into drive end shield. Connect test lamp between "B+" terminal and alternator frame, reverse connections.

2) Lamp should light only in one direction. After completion of assembly, test run alternator on bench using same procedure as described under *ON-VEHICLE TEST*.

Fig. 3: Checking Brush Holder

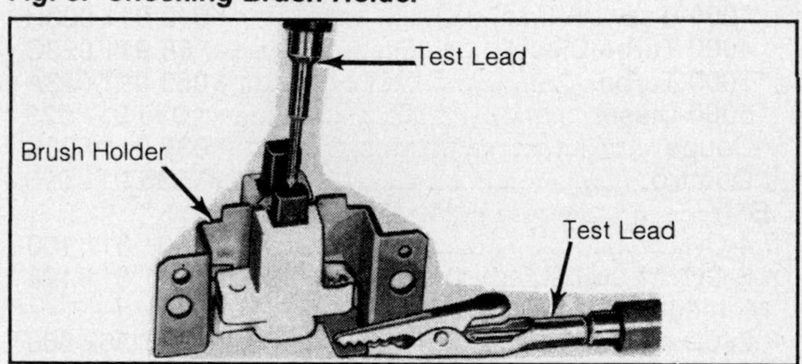
Test Lead
Brush Holder
Test Lead

NOTE: Brush length is measured between brush contact surface and holder, with brush resting against spring.

Fig. 4: Exploded View of SEV Motorola Alternator

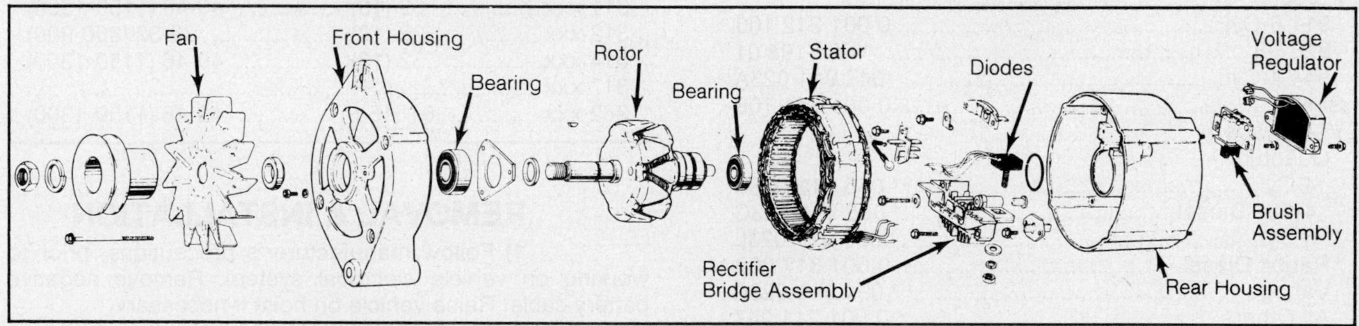
Fan
Front Housing
Bearing
Rotor
Bearing
Stator
Diodes
Voltage Regulator
Brush Assembly
Rectifier Bridge Assembly
Rear Housing

Volkswagen shown; all other models similar.

Starters

BOSCH

Alfa Romeo, Audi, BMW, Mercedes-Benz, Peugeot, Porsche, Saab, Volkswagen & Volvo

NOTE: Some Audi 4000 and Volkswagen Quantum models with diesel engines may use Mitsubishi starters. See appropriate article in this section.

DESCRIPTION

Starter is a brush type, series wound electric motor equipped with an overrunning clutch. Integral solenoid mounted on the starter engages starter pinion gear with flywheel ring gear when starter is engaged.

Field frame is enclosed by commutator end frame and drive bushing and carries pole shoes and field coils. A spline on the drive end of the armature shaft carries drive assembly. Armature shaft is supported at both end by sintered bronze bushings.

BOSCH STARTER APPLICATION

Model	Type or Part No.
Alfa Romeo	
Spider 2.0	[1] 105 12 05030 03
GTV-6 2.5	0 001 311 139
Audi	
4000 Gas	[1] 049 911 023H
4000 Turbo Diesel	[1] 68 911 023C
5000 Turbo	[1] 069 911 023A
5000 Diesel	[1] 035 911 023
Coupe	[1] 035 911 023K
Quattro	[1] 035 911 023
BMW	
4-Cyl.	0 001 311 100
6-Cyl.	0 001 311 125
Mercedes-Benz	
240D 4-Cyl.	0 001 362 600
300 Series	0 001 362 600
380 Series	0 001 314 018
Peugeot	
505 Gas	0 001 208 507
All Others	0 001 362 081
Porsche	
911 6-Cyl.	0 001 312 100
928 V8	[1] 604 103 01
944 4-Cyl.	[1] 047 911 023A
Saab	0 001 311 108
Volkswagen	
Quantum	
4-Cyl.	[1 2] 056 911 023B
4-Cyl. Diesel	[1] 068 911 023C
5-Cyl.	[1] 035 911 023L
Rabbit Diesel	0 001 317 009
Vanagon	[1 3] 091 911 023B
All Others	[4] 0 001 211 247
Volvo	
DL, GL, GLT 4-Cyl.	0 001 311 103
GL Diesel	0 001 362 069
760 GLE 6-Cyl.	0 001 311 106
760 GLE Diesel	0 001 362 .....

[1] – Manufacturer's part number.
[2] – Man. trans. shown; auto. trans. is 049 811 023G.
[3] – Man. trans. shown; auto. trans. is 033 911 023D.
[4] – Man. trans. shown; auto. trans. is 0 001 212 206.

TESTING

LOAD TEST

Ensure that battery is fully charged. Connect a voltmeter, ammeter and tachometer to vehicle. Disconnect ignition primary circuit, so engine will not start. Turn all accessories off. Engage starter with ignition switch. Voltmeter and ammeter reading, and starter RPM should be within specifications.

STARTER LOAD TEST SPECIFICATIONS

Application	Volts/Amps	RPM
Alfa Romeo		
GTV-6 2.5	9/250-290	1200 Min.
Saab	9/205-235	1000-1300
Volvo 4-Cyl. Gas	9/185-220	1050-1350

NO LOAD TEST

With starter on test bench, take readings of starter current, voltage and RPM. Readings should be within specifications.

STARTER NO LOAD TEST SPECIFICATIONS

Model	Volts/Amps.	RPM
208 xxx	11.5/35-55	6000-8000
211 xxx	11.5/30-50	6000-9000
212 xxx	11.5/35-55	6000-8000
311 xxx	11.5/30-50	5500-7500
312 xxx	11/55-85	8500-10,500
317 xxx	....	....
362 xxx	11.5/65-95	6500-8500

BRUSH LENGTH & SPRING TENSION SPECIFICATIONS

Application	In. (mm)	Ozs. (g)
208 xxx	.52 (13)	40-50 (1150-1350)
211 xxx	.52 (13)	40-46 (1150-1300)
212 xxx	.....	.....
311 xxx	.52 (13)	40-46 (1150-1300)
312 xxx	.39 (10)	29-32 (800-900)
314 xxx	.52 (13)	40-46 (1150-1300)
317 xxx	.....	.....
362 xxx	.61 (15.5)	40-46 (1150-1300)

REMOVAL & INSTALLATION

1) Follow manufacturer's precautions, prior to working on vehicle electrical system. Remove negative battery cable. Raise vehicle on hoist if necessary.

2) On Audi 4000, and Volkswagen Jetta and Quantum models with diesel engine, install engine support. Remove right side engine mount and support. Mark starter wiring and remove.

3) On Saab models, remove flywheel cover and starter heat shield. Remove gear box dipstick on models with manual transmission. On Saab Turbo models, remove turbocharger support. Loosen oil return pipe at turbocharger. On all Saab models, remove front and rear starter mounts. Remove starter through front panel opening.

BOSCH (Cont.)

Fig. 1: Exploded View of Typical Bosch Starter

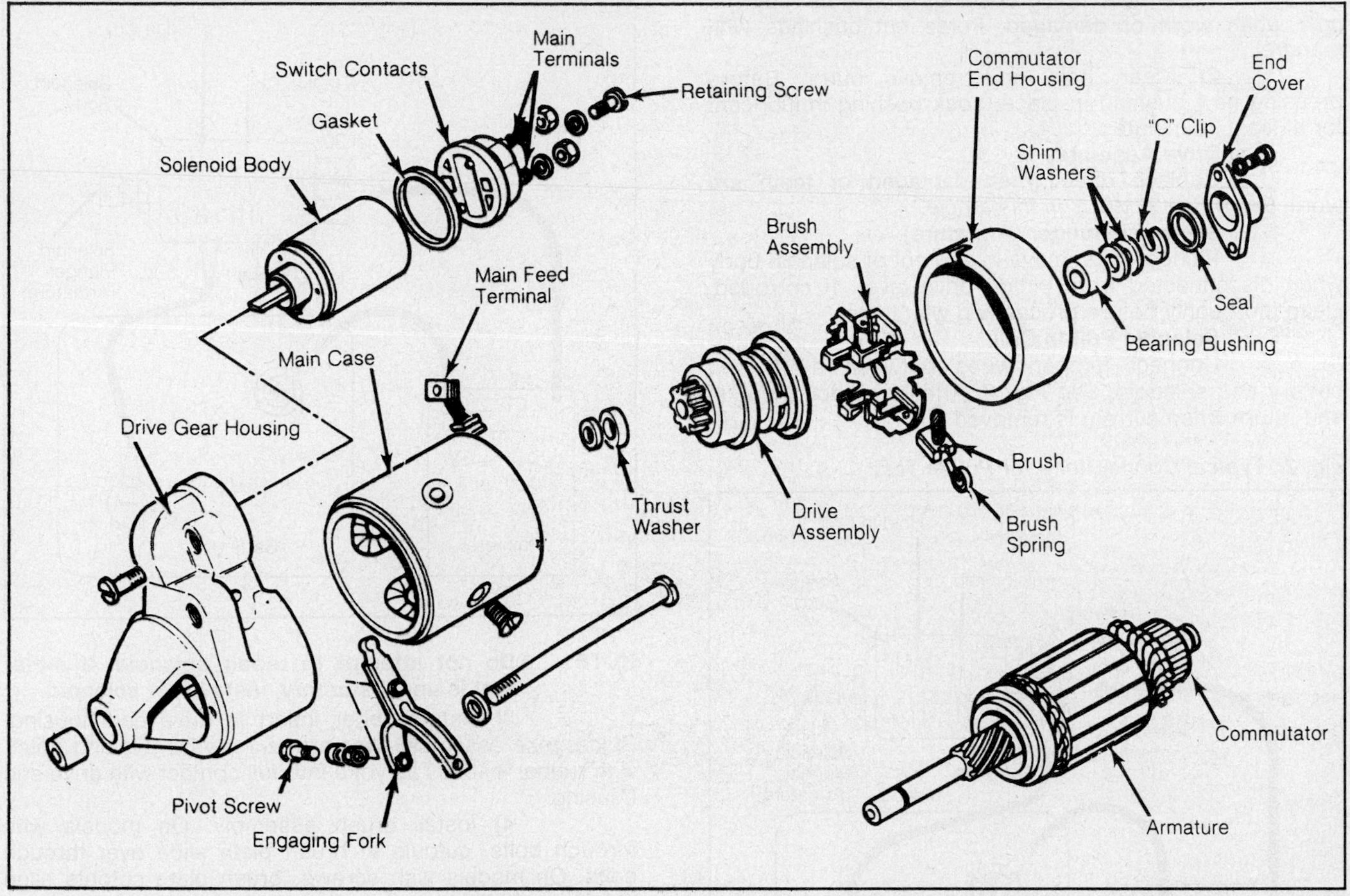
Main Terminals
Switch Contacts
Retaining Screw
Gasket
Solenoid Body
Commutator End Housing
End Cover
"C" Clip
Shim Washers
Brush Assembly
Seal
Bearing Bushing
Main Feed Terminal
Main Case
Drive Gear Housing
Thrust Washer
Drive Assembly
Brush
Brush Spring
Commutator
Armature
Pivot Screw
Engaging Fork

4) On all other models, mark starter wiring for reassembly. Support starter and remove starter mounting bolts. Remove starter from vehicle. To install, reverse removal procedure.

OVERHAUL

DISASSEMBLY

1) Clamp starter in vise. Remove nut and washer from solenoid main terminal connection. Remove solenoid retaining screws and unhook solenoid plunger.

2) Remove screws and end cap with rubber seal from commutator end housing. Wipe grease from armature shaft and remove "C" clip with shims.

3) Remove bolts or nuts from studs and lift off commutator end housing. Lift springs clear of brushes and slide brushes from holders. Remove brush plate from housing.

4) Separate drive end housing and armature assembly from yoke by tapping apart. Remove armature assembly from drive end housing while at the same time uncoupling actuating arm.

5) To remove actuating arm, remove rubber insert from drive end housing. Remove pivot arm screw and nut and extract actuating arm.

6) To remove drive pinion assembly from armature shaft, separate thrust collar from over "C" clip. Remove "C" clip from its groove and drive pinion assembly off armature shaft.

CLEANING & INSPECTING

Clean all parts with cleaning agent. Inspect for wear or damage, apply thin coat of oil to running surfaces.

PARTS REPLACEMENT & TESTING

Brushes & Springs

1) Check brush spring pressure with spring scale. Check brushes for minimum length and freedom of movement in holders.

2) If necessary, replace brushes by cutting old brush leads midway between connection and old brush. Solder new brushes to original leads.

Armature

1) Check commutator-to-shaft (or core) for short circuit with 110 volt AC test lamp. Test lamp should not light (a slight glowing is okay).

2) Using an armature growler, check armature coils for short circuit between windings. Check commutator for pits, burns or rough surface.

3) If out of round exceeds .002" (.05 mm), or grooves or burned spots cannot be removed with fine crocus cloth, turn commutator. Undercut insulation between commutator bars to a maximum depth of .024" (.6 mm).

NOTE: **Never use emery cloth or a file on commutator; turn on a lathe only.**

Starters

BOSCH (Cont.)

Bushings

1) Self-lubricating bushings should be replaced only when worn or damaged. Force out bushings with mandrel.

2) Clean hole and remove burrs. Before pressing new bushing in place, soak bushing in lubricant for at least 30 minutes.

Drive Assembly

Replace drive when damaged or teeth are worn. *See DISASSEMBLY in this article.*

Solenoid Plunger (Armature)

Plunger must move in and out of solenoid body when disconnected from pinion drive lever. If corroded, clean thoroughly before proceeding with tests.

Solenoid Pull-In Coil

Connect jumper wires between a 12 volt battery and solenoid. *See Fig. 2.* Armature should pull in and return when current is removed.

Fig. 2: Typical Connections for Pull-In Test

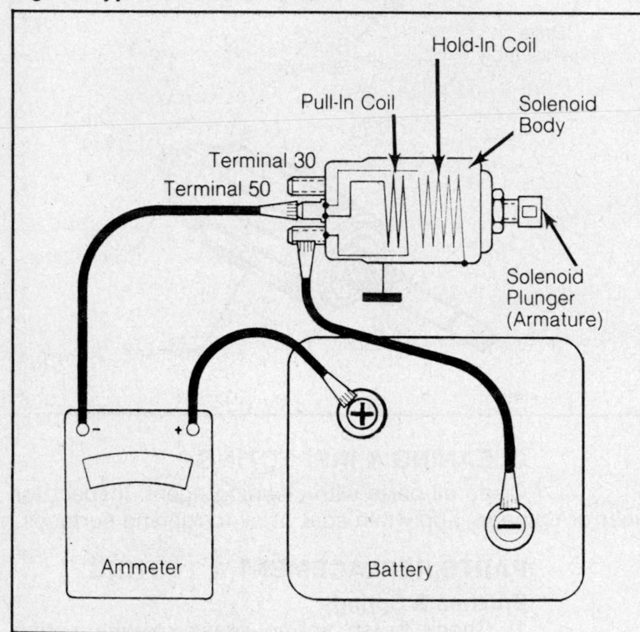
Hold-In Coil
Pull-In Coil
Solenoid Body
Terminal 30
Terminal 50
Solenoid Plunger (Armature)
Ammeter
Battery

Hold-In Coil

Connect jumper wires between a 12 volt battery and solenoid, while pressing armature into solenoid by hand. *See Fig. 3.* Armature should remain held in. Disconnect jumper terminal 50 and armature should immediately return to its outer position.

REASSEMBLY

1) Slide drive pinion assembly and thrust washer onto armature shaft. Install "C" clip into groove in armature shaft and pull thrust washer up over clip.

2) Align fork in drive end housing and insert pivot pin. Slide armature assembly into drive end housing, coupling the shift fork onto the drive pinion flange.

Fig. 3: Typical Connections for Hold-In Test

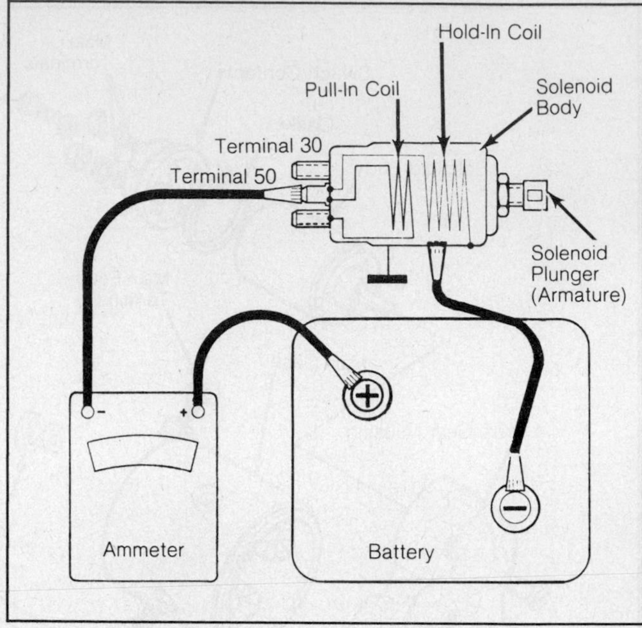
Hold-In Coil
Pull-In Coil
Solenoid Body
Terminal 30
Terminal 50
Solenoid Plunger (Armature)
Ammeter
Battery

NOTE: **Do not attempt to repair solenoid. If either test is unsatisfactory, install new solenoid.**

3) Install rubber insert in drive end housing. Guide yoke assembly over armature while aligning notch with rubber insert. Tap yoke into full contact with drive end housing.

4) Install brush assembly. On models with through bolts, cutouts in brush plate slide over through bolts. On models with screws, brush plate cutouts align with loops in field windings.

5) Plates are properly positioned when screws are installed in commutator end housing. Install brushes and springs. Ensure field winding brush leads do not contact yoke.

6) Slide commutator end housing into position and secure with nuts and washers or screws, as necessary. Install drive end housing. Install shims onto armature shaft at commutator end to eliminate end play and install "C" clip in groove.

7) Install bearing cap seal on commutator end housing. Lubricate end of armature shaft with lithium-based grease and install bearing cap. Lubricate plunger hook and place in position over shift fork in drive end housing.

8) Install solenoid body with return spring properly positioned. Tighten retaining screws and field connections.

DUCELLIER & PARIS-RHONE

All Peugeot & Renault Models

DESCRIPTION

Starter is a conventional, 12-volt, 4-pole unit with a solenoid assembly mounted on the starter case. Starter has an overrunning clutch, connected by a shift lever to the solenoid plunger.

APPLICATION

Model	[1] Part No.
Peugeot	
504, 505 & 604 Diesels	D11 E191
505 Gas	
Ducellier	533002A
Paris-Rhone	D9 E54
Renault	
Fuego & Fuego Turbo	D10 E79
LeCar	
Ducellier	534047
Paris-Rhone	D9 E79
18i	D10 E63, D10 E76, D10 E79, D10 E80

[1] – Unless specified, all models are manufactured by Paris-Rhone.

TESTING

LOCK TEST

LeCar

Follow instructions and procedures outlined in manual furnished with tester. Use a fully-charged battery to perform test at a temperature of 77° F (25° C). Starter torque should be 9 ft. lbs. (12 N.m) at 400 amps.

Fuego & Fuego Turbo

Follow instructions and procedures outlined in manual furnished with tester. Use a fully-charged battery to perform test at a temperature of 77° F (25° C). Starter torque should be 14 ft lbs. (19 N.m) at 600 amps.

OPERATIONAL TEST

Peugeot

1) Disconnect coil high tension wire (except diesel). Connect tachometer to engine. Connect ammeter between battery and starter. Energize starter for maximum of 15 seconds.

2) Gasoline engine should turn at 120 RPM with a maximum draw of 250 amps. Diesel engine should turn at 120 RPM with a maximum draw of 350 amps.

NOTE: **Further test procedures are not furnished by manufacturers.**

OVERHAUL

DISASSEMBLY

1) Disconnect wire between starter motor and solenoid. Remove nuts on through bolts, and remove rear shield and back plate. Carefully lift out brushes. Remove circlip on end of armature, if equipped.

2) Remove rear bearing on armature shaft. Remove armature housing. Remove connecting fork retaining pin (between starter and solenoid). Remove nuts securing solenoid. Remove solenoid and armature.

PARTS REPLACEMENT & TESTING

Brushes

Inspect brushes. If damaged or less than 5/16" (8 mm) long, install new brushes. Unsolder brushes to be replaced. Solder on new brushes. Check armature and reassemble.

Commutator

Check commutator surface for burns, pits, gouges, scoring or out-of-round. Dress with a lathe if required and polish with fine sandpaper. Check that segment insulators undercut to depth of .020" (.5 mm).

Fig. 1: Disassembled View of Paris-Rhone D10 E79 Starter

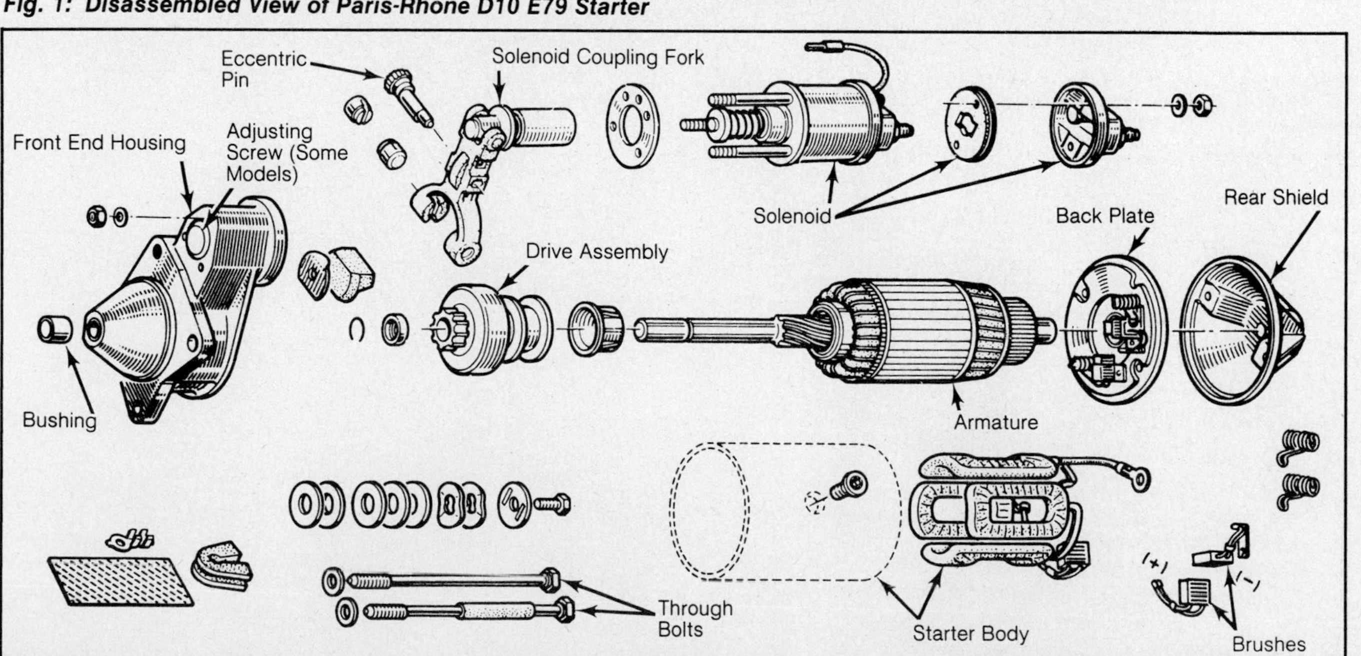
Eccentric Pin
Solenoid Coupling Fork
Front End Housing
Adjusting Screw (Some Models)
Solenoid
Rear Shield
Back Plate
Drive Assembly
Bushing
Armature
(+)
(–)
Through Bolts
Starter Body
Brushes

DUCELLIER & PARIS-RHONE (Cont.)

Drive Pinion

To remove drive pinion from armature, tap stop collar with a drift. This will expose circlip holding drive pinion. Remove circlip. To install, position circlip on shaft and push stop collar over it.

Armature

Check armature for open, shorted or grounded circuits. Inspect armature shaft for bend and core for scoring or loose windings.

NOTE: **Do not attempt to straighten a bent shaft. Replace armature if shaft is bent or if core is damaged.**

Bearings

Inspect front and rear bearings for wear and excessive clearance with armature shaft. Replace if damaged or in case of excessive clearance.

REASSEMBLY

1) Clean all parts and coat sliding surfaces with multi-purpose grease. Assemble in reverse order of disassembly and check pinion clearance.

2) Disconnect starter field terminal from solenoid and energize solenoid with 12 volt battery. Measure clearance of pinion gear to stop collar.

3) Clearance should be .06" (1.5 mm). Adjust to proper clearance by turning eccentric pin in solenoid fork or turning adjusting screw in front of solenoid in or out.

HITACHI & MITSUBISHI

Audi 4000 Diesel, Calif. Honda Civic, All Chrysler Corp. Imports, Datsun/Nissan, Isuzu, Mazda, Mitsubishi & Volkwagen Quantum Diesel Models

NOTE: Some Audi 4000 Diesel and Volkwagen Quantum Diesel models use Bosch starters. Some Calif. Honda Civic models use Nippondenso starters. See appropriate article in this section.

DESCRIPTION

Starter is a conventional 12-volt, 4-pole brush-type motor, with either direct or reduction gear drive. The starter-mounted solenoid shifts overrunning clutch and pinion into flywheel when starter is energized.

HITACHI STARTER APPLICATION

Model	Type or Part No.
Datsun/Nissan	
Maxima	
Gasoline	S114-254D
Diesel	S13-65
Pickup	
Gasoline	
Man. Trans.	S114-348
Auto. Trans.	S114-295
Diesel	S13-45B
Pulsar	
Man. Trans.	S114-315
Auto. Trans.	S114-317
Sentra	
Gasoline	
Man. Trans.	S114-315
Auto. Trans.	S114-317
Diesel	S114-357
Stanza	S114-320A
200SX	
Man. Trans	S114-348
Auto. Trans.	S114-295
280ZX	S114-254D
Honda Civic (Calif.) [1]	31200 PA6-005
Isuzu	
I-Mark	
Gasoline	[2] 8-94222-688-0
Diesel	[2] 8-94115-567-0
Impulse	[2] 8-94130-560-0
P'UP	
Gasoline	[2] 8-94234-065-0
Diesel	[2] 5-81100-183-0

[1] – Some Calif. models use Nippondenso starters.
[2] – Vehicle manufacturer's part number.

TESTING

STARTER PERFORMANCE TESTS

No Load Tests

Connect starter in series with a 12-volt battery, a voltmeter and a 1000 amp ammeter. *Compare readings with Starter No Load Specifications.*

MITSUBISHI STARTER APPLICATION

Model	Type or Part No.
Audi 4000 Diesel [1]	[2] 035 911 023D
Chrysler Corp. Imports	
Colt	
Man. Trans.	MD027120
Auto. Trans.	MD027400
Challenger & Sapporo	
Man. Trans.	MD027400
Auto. Trans.	MD027382
Colt & Ram-50 Pickups	
Gasoline	
Man. Trans.	MD027401
Auto. Trans	MD027382
Diesel	MD050205
Mazda	
B2000 Pickup Gasoline	
Man. Trans.	[2] HE19-18-400A
Auto. Trans.	[2] HE20-18-400
B2200 Pickup Diesel	[2] S211-18-400
GLC	
FWD Sedan	[2] E301-18-400
RWD Wagon	
Man. Trans.	[2] D501-18-400
Auto. Trans.	[2] D502-18-400
RX7	
Man. Trans.	[2] N221-18-400
Auto. Trans.	[2] N202-18-400A
626	[2] FE05-18-400
Mitsubishi	
Cordia & Tredia	
Man. Trans.	MD001333
Auto. Trans.	MD021674
Montero & Starion Turbo	MD027401
Pickup	
Gasoline	
Man. Trans.	MD027401
Auto. Trans	MD027382
Diesel	MD050205
Volkswagen Quantum Diesel [1]	[2] 035 911-023D

[1] – Some models use Bosch starters.
[2] – Vehicle manufacturer's part number.

HITACHI STARTER NO LOAD TEST SPECIFICATIONS [1]

Application	Max. Amps	Min. RPM
Datsun/Nissan		
Maxima Gasoline	100	3900
Maxima Diesel	150	3900
Pickup, Pulsar, Sentra & Stanza Gasoline	60	7000
Pickup Diesel	150	3500
Sentra Diesel	100	3900
200SX		
Gasoline	60	6000
Diesel	60	7000
280ZX	100	3900
Honda Civic (Calif.)	70	6000
Isuzu Impulse	60	6000
P'UP		
Gasoline	70	6000
Diesel	120	4000

[1] – Applied voltage of 11.5-12 volts.

HITACHI & MITSUBISHI (Cont.)

MITSUBISHI STARTER NO LOAD SPECIFICATIONS [1]

Application	Max. Amps	Min. RPM
Chrysler Corp. Imports		
Colt & Ram-50		
Pickups		
Gasoline		
Man. Trans.	60	6500
Auto. Trans.	100	3000
Diesel	130	4000
Challenger, Colt & Sapporo		
Man. Trans.	60	6600
Auto. Trans.	90	3300
Mazda		
B2000 Pickup	53	6800
B2200 Pickup	180	3800
GLC		
FWD Sedan	53	6800
RWD Wagon	53	6800
RX7		
Man. Trans.	60	6500
Auto. Trans.	100	3500
626		
Man. Trans.	60	6500
Auto. Trans.	60	6600
Mitsubishi		
Cordia & Tredia	60	6500
Montero	60	6500
Pickup		
Gasoline		
Man. Trans.	60	6500
Auto. Trans.	100	3000
Diesel	130	4000
Starion Turbo		
Man. Trans.	60	6500
Auto. Trans.	100	3000

[1] – Applied voltage of 11.5-12 volts.

Load (Lock Torque) Test

Mount starter in a test stand to perform torque measurement test. Follow manufacturer's instructions for test stand operation. With voltage adjusted, ammeter reading and torque should be within specifications.

Fig. 1: Connections for Conducting Solenoid Pull-In Test

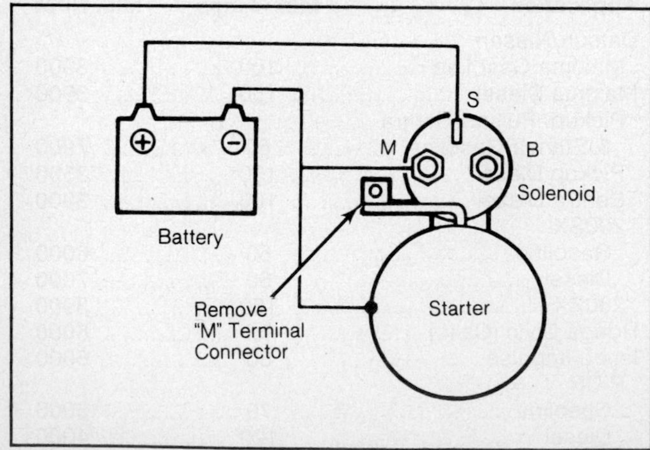
S
M
B
Solenoid
Battery
Remove
"M" Terminal
Connector
Starter

Remove solenoid-to-starter lead before testing.

HITACHI STARTER LOAD TEST SPECIFICATIONS [1]

Application	Max. Amps	Volts	Torque Ft. Lbs. (N.m)
Honda			
Civic (Calif.)	200	8	3.3 (4.5)
Isuzu			
Impulse	200	9.1	3.4 (4.6)
P'UP			
Gasoline	200	7.4	3.6 (4.9)
Diesel	[2]	[2]	[2]

[1] – At minimum turning speed of 1100-1200 RPM.
[2] – Information not available from manufacturer.

MITSUBISHI STARTER LOAD TEST SPECIFICATIONS [1]

Application	Max. Amps	Volts	Torque Ft. Lbs. (N.m)
Mazda			
B2000 Pickup	310	5	5.4 (7.5)
B2200 Pickup	1050	2	21.7 (30)
GLC			
FWD	310	5	5.4 (7.5)
Wagon	310	5	5.4 (7.5)
RX7			
Man. Trans.	600	5	6.9 (9.6)
Auto. Trans.	1100	4	22.4 (31)
626	310	5	5.4 (7.5)

[1] – Turning speed not specified by manufacturer.

SOLENOID TESTS

NOTE: **Make tests with solenoid removed from starter or remove solenoid lead to starter before testing. Ensure solenoid plunger and sleeve are clean and dry before performing tests. Make tests in less than 10 seconds to prevent coil damage.**

Pull-In Coil Test

1) Connect jumper between positive post of 12-volt battery and "S" terminal. Connect a second jumper to negative battery terminal and touch "M" (MT) terminal (and between terminal "S" and switch body). *See Fig. 1.*

2) If pinion moves outward (or plunger is pulled-in), pull-in coil is good. If not, replace magnetic switch.

Hold-In Coil Test

1) Connect a jumper wire between the "M" (MT) terminal and solenoid case. Apply 8 volts to "S" terminal to pull in the plunger. *See Fig. 2.* Disconnect lead to "M" (MT) terminal.

2) If pinion remains out (plunger is pulled-in), hold-in coil is good. If not, replace magnetic switch.

Return Test

1) Apply 12 volts between "M" (MT) terminal and the solenoid case. Pull pinion out and release it (push plunger into solenoid body by hand). *See Fig. 3.*

2) If the case is short-circuited, the pinion will remain out (plunger will be attracted). If nothing happens, solenoid is good.

HITACHI & MITSUBISHI (Cont.)

Fig. 2: Connections for Conducting Solenoid Hold-In Test

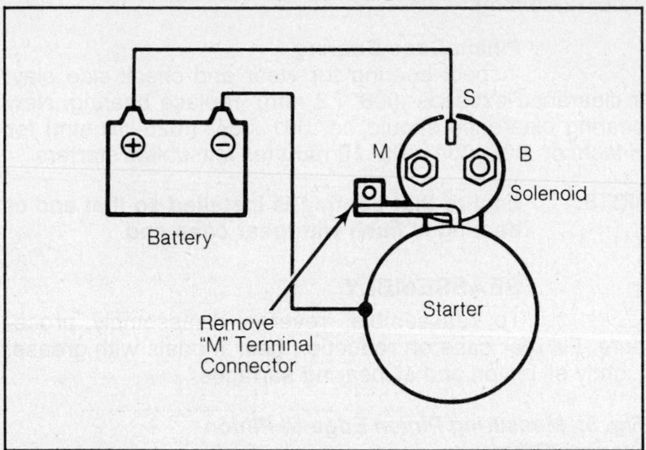
S
M
B
Solenoid
Battery
Remove
"M" Terminal
Connector
Starter

Make tests in less than 10 seconds to avoid solenoid damage.

Fig. 3: Connections for Conducting Return Test

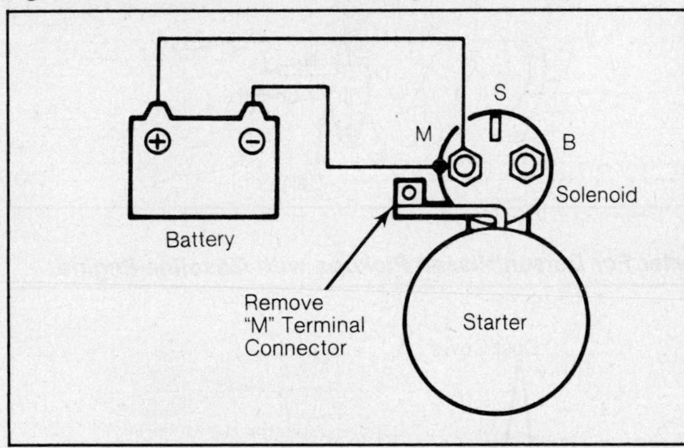
S
M
B
Solenoid
Battery
Remove
"M" Terminal
Connector
Starter

Connect battery to "M" terminal and solenoid case.

REMOVAL & INSTALLATION

1) On all models, remove negative battery cable. If necessary raise vehice on hoist. Remove starter mounting bolts. Remove starter from vehicle.

2) On Isuzu I-Mark models, remove EGR pipe. Remove starter bolts. Remove starter from under intake manifold. To install, reverse removal procedure.

OVERHAUL

DISASSEMBLY

NOTE: Procedures may vary slightly between conventional and reduction gear starters.

1) Loosen nut securing connecting plate-to-magnetic switch "M" terminal. Remove screws securing magnetic switch and remove switch (solenoid) assembly. Remove through bolts and brush cover assembly. Tap yoke assembly loose with wooden mallet. Remove yoke, armature assembly and pinion shift lever.

2) Remove pinion stop ring from end of armature shaft by pushing stop ring to clutch side. Remove snap ring and overrunning clutch assembly from armature shaft.

CLEANING & INSPECTION

Clean all parts. Do not use grease dissolving solvent on overrunning clutch, armature assembly, solenoid assembly or field coils due to possible damage. Inspect all parts for damage or wear and replace as required.

BENCH TESTS

Brushes & Springs

Check brush spring tension using a spring scale. Check brush contact surface condition and brush length. Check lead clip and wire connections and condition of brush holders. Replace as required. *See Brush Spring Tension and Minumum Brush Length Charts.*

BRUSH SPRING TENSION

Application	Ozs. (g)
Chrysler Corp. Imports	46-59 (1302-1670)
Datsun/Nissan	
Pickup	
Gasoline	50-66 (1415-1868)
Diesel	109-144 (3085-4075)
Pulsar, Sentra Gasoline & Stanza	64-78 (1811-2207)
Maxima Diesel	96-106 (2717-3000)
200SX	64-78 (1811-2207)
280ZX & Maxima Gasoline & Sentra Diesel	56-70 (1585-1981)
Honda Civic (Calif.)	51-59 (1443-1670)
Isuzu	
I-Mark Diesel	96-106 (2717-3000)
All Others	56 (1585)
Mazda	
B2000 & B2200 Pickups	50-62 (1415-1766)
RX7	50-92 (1415-2604)
All Other Models	46-60 (1302-1700)
Mitsubishi	46-59 (1302-1670)

Armature

Check external condition of armature for scoring or other damage. Measure shaft distortion with dial indicator. Replace armature if shaft distortion exceeds .003" (.08 mm) on Datsun/Nissan and I-Mark (Diesel) models, or .004" (.10 mm) on all other models.

MINIMUM BRUSH LENGTH

Application	In. (mm)
Chrysler Corp. Imports	.45 (11.5)
Datsun/Nissan	
Maxima Diesel	.35 (9)
Pickup Diesel	.28 (7)
Pickup Gasolline & 200SX	.47 (12)
Pulsar, Sentra, Stanza, Maxima Gasoline & 280ZX	.43 (11)
Honda Civic (Calif.)	.47 (12)
Isuzu	
I-Mark	.37 (9.5)
Pickup	
Gasoline	.47 (12)
Diesel	.35-.37 (9-9.5)
Mazda	.45 (11.5)
Mitsubishi	.45 (11.5)

HITACHI & MITSUBISHI (Cont.)

Commutator

1) Inspect commutator for roughness, grooves, burns or pitting. Sand lightly with 500 grit sandpaper if necessary. Check commutator for out-of-round and mica insulators undercut to a depth of .020-.031" (.5-.8 mm).

2) If necessary, commutator may be turned less than .04" (1 mm) from original size and mica undercut. Replace if excessively worn.

Field Coil

1) Check field coil continuity by connecting test probe of circuit tester or an ohmmeter to the field coil positive terminal and brush holder. If circuit is open, replace field coil.

2) Check for grounding of field coils by placing one probe of circuit tester on starter housing and other probe to field coil positive terminal. If little or no resistance, field coil is grounded and must be replaced.

Overrunning Clutch Assembly

1) Inspect pinion assembly and sleeve. Sleeve should slide freely on armature shaft and spline. If damage or resistance is noted, replace assembly.

2) Check pinion and flywheel teeth for excessive rubbing or damaged teeth. Replace as required.

Pinion Gear Clearance

1) The clearance between the pinion gear and pinion stopper collar should be .012-.098" (.3-2.5 mm) on Hitachi starters, or .02-.08" (.51-2.03 mm) on Mitsubishi starters, when solenoid is engaged. Adjust as necessary by changing shims between solenoid and starter yoke.

2) On Mazda B2200 models, projection distance (starter housing-to-front face of gear) should be .67" (17 mm). On Mazda RX-7 models, projection should be 1.06" (27.5 mm).

Pinion Case Bearing

Inspect bearing for wear and check side play. If clearance exceeds .008" (.2 mm), replace bearing. New bearing clearance should be .001-.004" (.025-.10 mm) for Hitachi or .002-.004" (.05-.10 mm) for Mitsubishi starters.

NOTE: Ensure that bearing is installed so that end of bearing is flush with gear case end.

REASSEMBLY

To reassemble, reverse disassembly procedure. Fill rear case on reduction gear models with grease. Lightly oil pinion and all bearing surfaces.

Fig. 5: Measuring Pinion Edge-to-Pinion Stopper Clearance

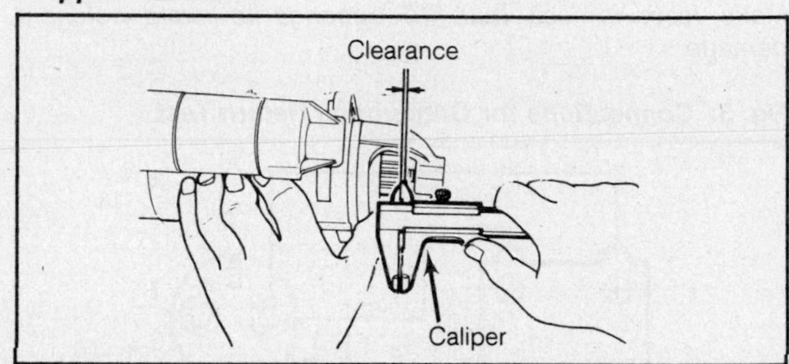
Clearance
Caliper

Fig. 4: Disassembled View of a Typical Hitachi Conventional Starter For Datsun/Nissan Pickups with Gasoline Engine

Dust Cover
"E" Ring
Thrust Washers
Magnetic Switch Assy.
Dust Cover
Brush Spring
Torsion Spring
Shift Lever Assembly
Through Bolt
Rear Cover
Brush Holder
Brush
Yoke
Field Coil
Armature
Rear Cover Metal
Center Bracket
Pinion Assembly
Pinion Stopper
Stopper Clip
Gear Case
Gear Case Metal

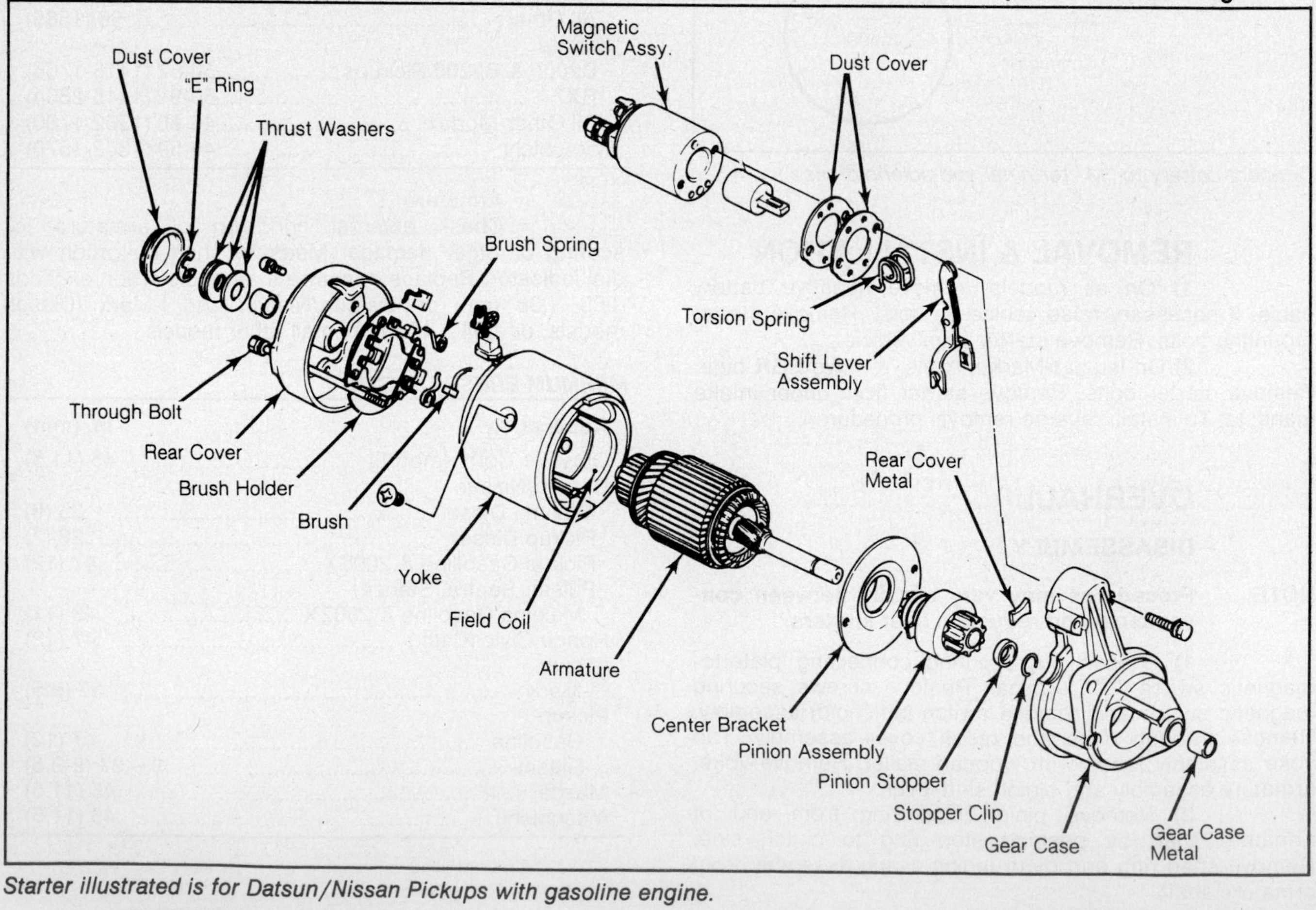

Starter illustrated is for Datsun/Nissan Pickups with gasoline engine.

HITACHI & MITSUBISHI (Cont.)

Fig. 5: Disassembled View of Typical Hitachi Reduction Gear Starter For Datsun/Nissan Maxima with Gasoline Engine and Isuzu I-Mark With Diesel Engine

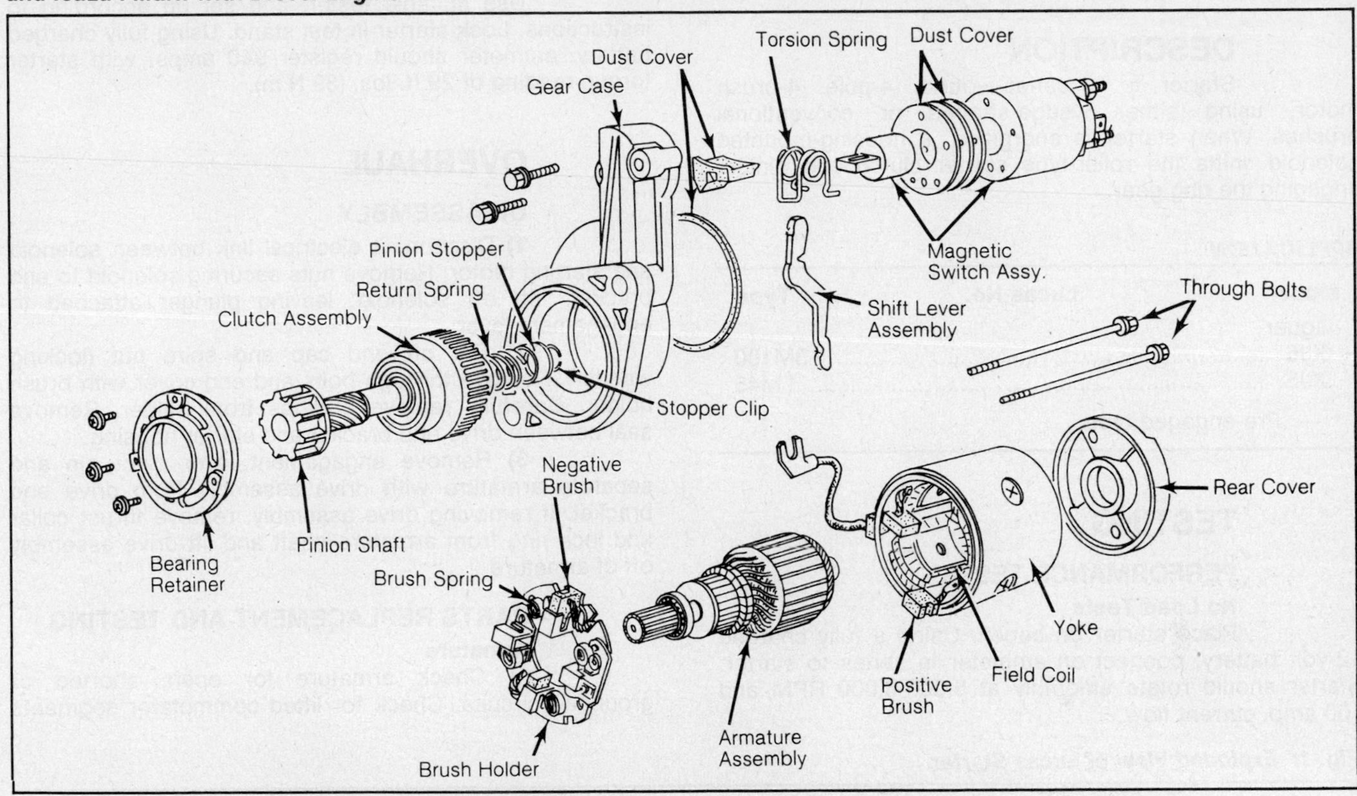
Torsion Spring
Dust Cover
Dust Cover
Gear Case
Magnetic Switch Assy.
Pinion Stopper
Return Spring
Clutch Assembly
Shift Lever Assembly
Through Bolts
Stopper Clip
Negative Brush
Rear Cover
Bearing Retainer
Pinion Shaft
Brush Spring
Yoke
Field Coil
Positive Brush
Armature Assembly
Brush Holder

Fig. 6: Disassembled View of Typical Mitsubishi Conventional Starter For Mazda B2200 Diesel Pickup

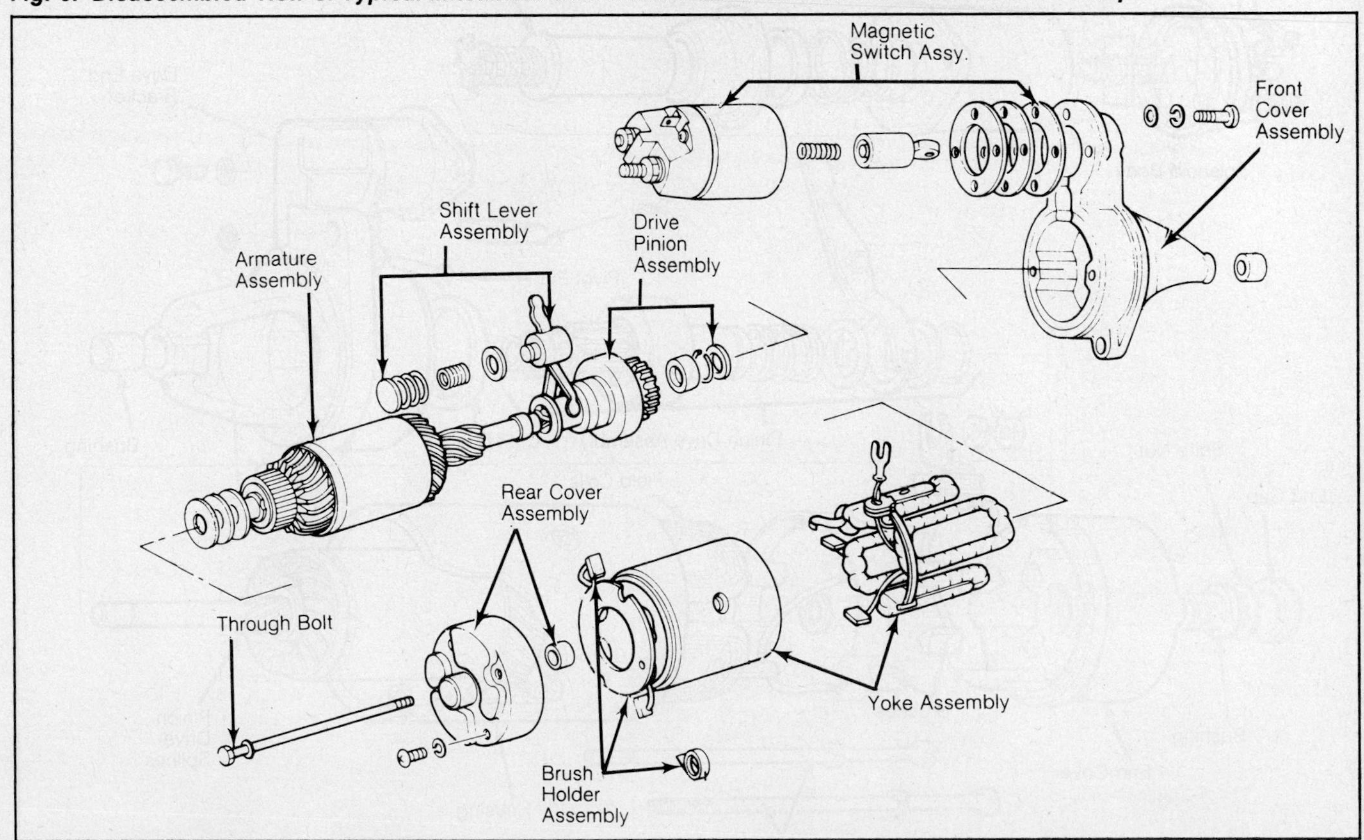
Magnetic Switch Assy.
Front Cover Assembly
Shift Lever Assembly
Drive Pinion Assembly
Armature Assembly
Rear Cover Assembly
Through Bolt
Yoke Assembly
Brush Holder Assembly

Starters

LUCAS

Jaguar XJ6, XJS

DESCRIPTION

Starter is a series-wound, 4-pole, 4-brush motor, using either wedge-shaped or conventional brushes. When starter is energized, a housing-mounted solenoid shifts the roller-type starter clutch and pinion, engaging the ring gear.

APPLICATION

Model	Lucas No.	Type
Jaguar		
XJ6	....	[1] 3M100
XJS	....	[1] M45

[1] — Pre-engaged type.

TESTING

PERFORMANCE TESTS

No Load Tests

Place starter on bench. Using a fully charged 12-volt battery, connect an ammeter in series to starter. Starter should rotate smoothly at 5,000-6,000 RPM and 100 amp. current flow.

Lock Test

Use suitable tester, and set up according to instructions. Lock starter in test stand. Using fully charged battery, ammeter should register 940 amps. with starter torque reading of 29 ft. lbs. (39 N.m).

OVERHAUL

DISASSEMBLY

1) Disconnect electrical link between solenoid and starting motor. Remove nuts securing solenoid to end bracket. Lift off solenoid, leaving plunger attached to engagement lever.

2) Pry off end cap and spire nut (locking washer). Remove through bolts and end cover with brush holder. Carefully remove brushes from holder. Remove seal between drive end bracket and starter housing.

3) Remove engagement lever pivot pin and separate armature with drive assembly from drive end bracket. If removing drive assembly, remove thrust collar and lock ring from armature shaft and lift drive assembly off of armature.

PARTS REPLACEMENT AND TESTING

Armature

1) Check armature for open, shorted or grounded circuits. Check for lifted commutator segments

Fig. 1: Exploded View of Lucas Starter

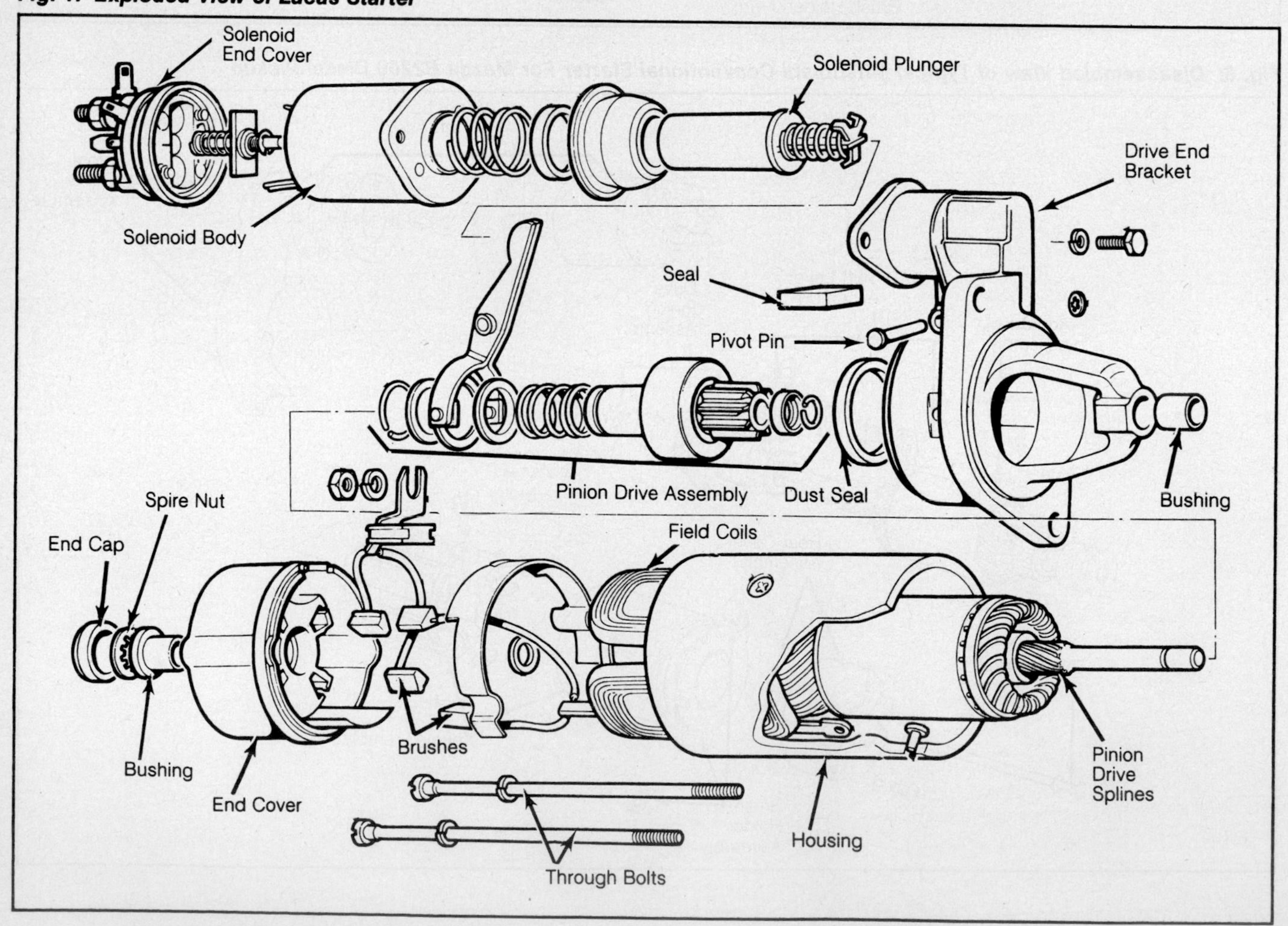
Solenoid End Cover
Solenoid Plunger
Drive End Bracket
Solenoid Body
Seal
Pivot Pin
Pinion Drive Assembly
Dust Seal
Bushing
Spire Nut
End Cap
Field Coils
Brushes
Bushing
End Cover
Pinion Drive Splines
Housing
Through Bolts

LUCAS (Cont.)

and loose turns in armature winding. Check armature for scoring.

2) A scored armature could indicate a loose pole shoe or a bent armature shaft. Do not attempt to true a distorted shaft or machine the armature core. Replace it, if damaged.

Commutator

1) Clean commutator with cloth moistened in suitable solvent. If necessary, use fine sandpaper.

2) If further clean up is necessary, turn down in lathe, removing only as much metal as is absolutely necessary. Do not undercut insulators between commutator segments.

Brushes & Springs

1) Check that brushes move freely in holders. Hold back brush springs, and pull gently on connecting wires. If movement is sluggish, remove brush from holder and clean with solvent moistened cloth.

2) Replace brushes if less than 3/8" (9.5 mm) long. Replace springs if tension is less than 36 ozs. (800 g).

Field Coils

1) Using a test lamp or voltemeter with a battery connected in series, check for open or grounded coils. If any coil is defective, replace all coils. Mark housing and pole shoes for installation in original position.

2) Remove pole piece screws, and pry pole shoes, coils, and insulation pieces from housing. To install, reverse removal procedure.

Bushings

1) In event of excessive wear or damage, remove old bushings with suitable mandrel or extractor.

CAUTION: New porous bronze bushings must be soaked in light engine oil for at least 24 hours before installation.

2) Press bushings into position. Fit new bushing, using highly polished mandrel .0005" (.013 mm) larger than diameter of shaft.

NOTE: To prevent loss of porosity, do not ream bushing after its installation.

Starter Solenoid

1) Disconnect all cables and connectors from solenoid. Connect a 12-volt power supply between starter terminal and small unmarked solenoid terminal.

2) Connect a test lamp across main terminals. Test lamp should light, indicating contacts are closed. Disconnect power from small solenoid terminal, and lamp should go out, indicating contacts have been opened.

3) To check winding continuity, connect ohmmeter between starter terminal and ground on solenoid body. Resistance should be 1.01-1.07 ohms.

4) To check pull-in winding, check across small unmarked terminal and starter terminal. Resistance should be .36-.42 ohm.

5) To check hold-in winding, connect ohmmeter between ground on solenoid body and unmarked terinal. Resistance should be 1.49-1.71 ohm.

REASSEMBLY

1) Be sure that all parts are clean. Reverse disassembly procedure, using a new lock ring and splre nut. Lightly lubricate bearing surfaces and pivot pin.

2) Armature end play should be adjusted to maximum end play of .010" (.25 mm) by driving retaining ring (spire nut) to proper position.

Fig. 2: Cutaway View of Lucas Starter Solenoid

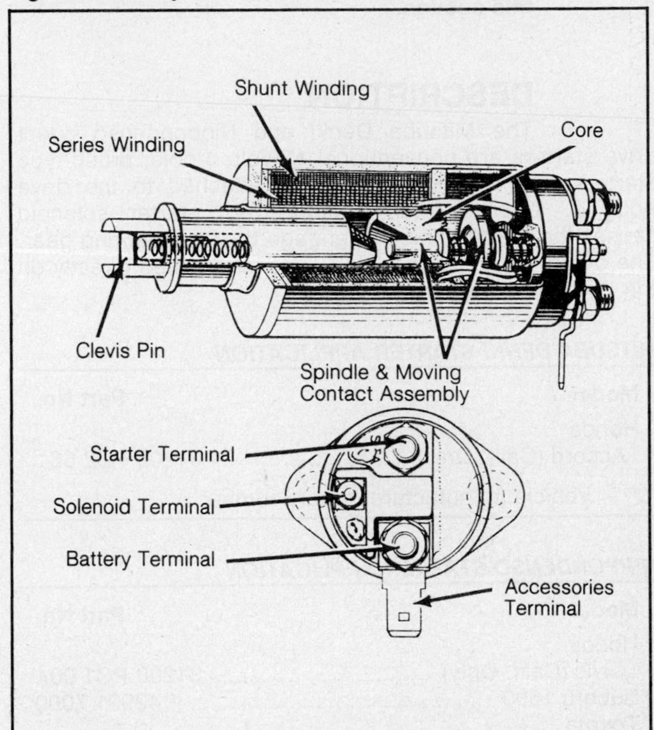
Shunt Winding
Core
Series Winding
Clevis Pin
Spindle & Moving Contact Assembly
Starter Terminal
Solenoid Terminal
Battery Terminal
Accessories Terminal

MITSUBA DENKI & NIPPONDENSO DIRECT DRIVE

Honda Accord, Civic (Calif.); Subaru 1600; Toyota Tercel

NOTE: **Some Calif. Honda Civics are equipped with Hitachi starters. See appropriate article in this section.**

DESCRIPTION

The Mitsuba Denki and Nippondenso direct drive starters are conventional 12-volt, 4-pole, brush-type starters. The integral solenoid is attached to the drive housing. When starter is energized, starter solenoid causes the starter pinion to engage the flywheel ring gear. The overrunning clutch pinion drive is mounted directly on the drive end of armature shaft.

MITSUBA DENKI STARTER APPLICATION

Model	[1] Part No.
Honda	
Accord (Calif. Only)	31200 PC2 681

[1] – Vehicle manufacturer's part number.

NIPPONDENSO STARTER APPLICATION

Model	[1] Part No.
Honda	
Civic (Calif. Only)	31200 PC1 004
Subaru 1600	[2] 42991 7000
Toyota	
Tercel	28100 15011

[1] – Vehicle manufacturer's part number.
[2] – Nippondenso model number is 028000-6520.

TESTING

PERFORMANCE TESTS

No Load Test

Place starter on bench. Connect a fully-charged 12-volt battery to starter. *See Fig. 1*. Starter should rotate smoothly. Observe starter amp draw and RPM. *See Starter No Load Test Chart.*

Fig. 1: Connect Circuits for No Load Test

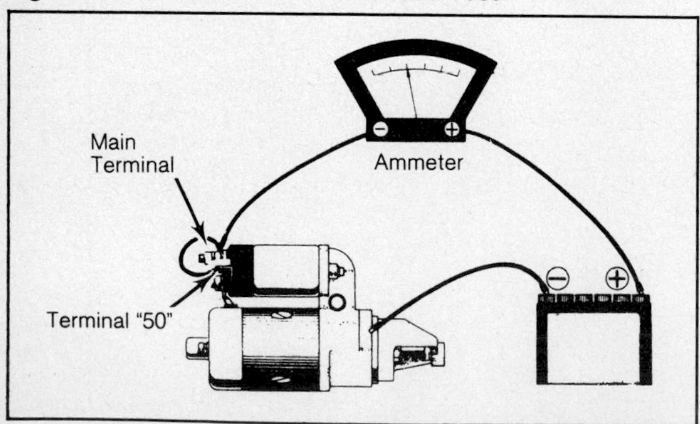

Main Terminal
Ammeter
Terminal "50"

STARTER NO LOAD TEST

Application	Volts/Max. Amps	Min. RPM
Honda Accord	11.5/90	3500
All Others	11/50	5000

Lock Test

To perform lock test, follow procedures outlined in tester instruction manual. With starter locked in test stand. Adjust voltage to specification. Observe starter amp draw and torque output. *See Starter Lock Test Chart.*

STARTER LOCK TEST

Application	Volts/Max. Amps	Torque Ft. Lbs. (N.m)
Honda Accord	2.4/450	8 (11)
All Others	7.7/600	9 (12)

Cranking Test (Calif. Honda Accord & Civic)

1) Hook up voltmeter and ammeter. *See Fig. 2.* Disconnect ignition coil secondary wire from distributor and ground it. Turn ignition switch to start.

2) Check cranking voltage and current draw. Voltage should be no less than 8.0 volts. Current draw should be less than 200 amps. Cranking speed should be approximately 300 RPM.

Fig. 2: Cranking Test Hookup for Honda

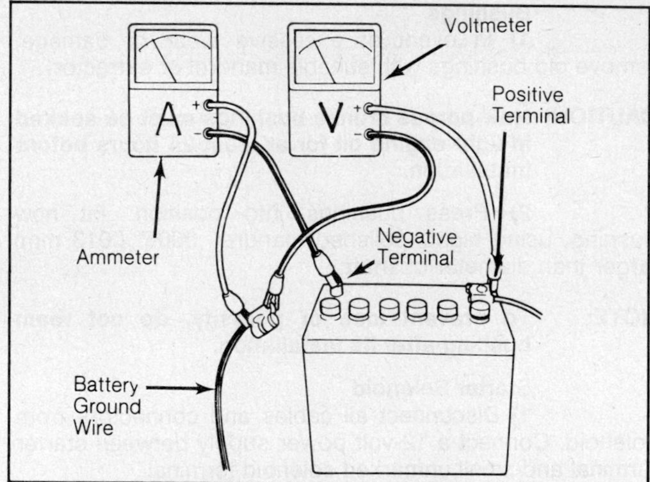

Voltmeter
Positive Terminal
A
V
Ammeter
Negative Terminal
Battery Ground Wire

Ensure voltmeter and ammeter connections are correct.

SOLENOID TESTS

NOTE: **Tests must be performed with starter assembled and "M" (field) lead from starter disconnected at the solenoid.**

Pull-In Test

Connect test equipment to starter. *See Fig. 3.* Connect battery negative cable to starter body and "C" terminal ("M" on Subaru). Battery positive is connected to terminal "50" ("S" terminal on Subaru). If starter plunger jumps out, pull-in coil is satisfactory.

MITSUBA DENKI & NIPPONDENSO DIRECT DRIVE (Cont.)

Hold-In Test

Connect test equipment to starter. *See Fig. 3*. Disconnect "C" terminal ("M" terminal on Subaru). The starter pinion should remain projected. If not, replace hold-in coil.

Fig. 3: Solenoid Test Hookup

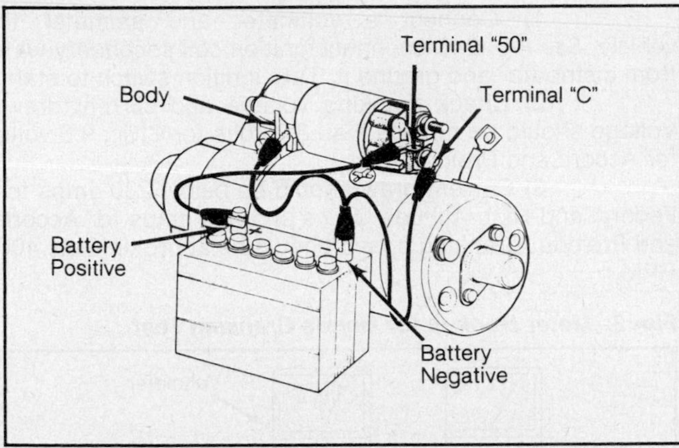
Terminal "50"
Body
Terminal "C"
Battery Positive
Battery Negative

"M" (field) lead should be disconnected at solenoid.

Plunger Return Test

Connect test equipment to starter. *See Fig. 3*. Disconnect switch body lead. Starter pinion should return quickly.

REMOVAL & INSTALLATION

Disconnect negative battery cable. If necessary, raise vehicle on hoist. Remove starter wiring and mounting bolts. Remove starter from vehicle. To install, reverse removal procedure.

OVERHAUL

DISASSEMBLY

1) Disconnect field coil wire from starter solenoid main terminal and remove solenoid attaching bolts. Unhook solenoid unit from pinion lever.

2) Remove bearing cover, armature shaft lock plate, washer, seal and spring. Remove through bolts, commutator end frame, brush holder and yoke.

3) Remove pinion lever set bolt, rubber piece, plate, armature and pinion lever from housing. Remove pinion stop collar from armature shaft end and remove starter clutch.

BENCH TESTS

Armature

Check armature with a growler. Check if armature shaft is bent. Inspect bushings for condition and maximum clearance of .008" (.20 mm). Replace if required.

Commutator

1) Clean surface and polish with No. 400 sandpaper if required. If surface is scored, burned, out of round or pitted. *See Commutator Concentric Specification Table*. Dress in a lathe only enough to restore smooth concentric surface.

2) Mica depth should be .016-.031" (.40-.80 mm) standard with a limit of .008" (.20 mm). If beyond limit, undercut with a hacksaw blade to standard depth.

COMMUTATOR CONCENTRIC SPECIFICATION

Application	Max. Out-of-Round
Honda	.002" (.05 mm)
Subaru	.016" (.4 mm)
Toyota Tercel	.016" (.4 mm)
All Others	.012 (.3 mm)

Brushes & Springs

1) Check brush holder insulation. Connect one lead of ammeter to brush holder positive side and other lead to negative side. If test needle moves, brush holder is shorted and must be replaced.

2) Check brush length. Minimum length is .47 (12 mm) on Honda models, .43" (11 mm) on Subaru models, .39" (10 mm) on all other models. If less, replace brushes.

3) Check spring tension. Spring tension should be 37-48 ounces (1050-1350 g). Brushes must move freely in holders.

Field Coils

1) Connect a circuit tester lead to field coil. Connect other lead to soldered portion of brush lead. If meter does not register, repair or replace field coil.

2) Check field coil for ground by connecting a test lead to field coil lead. Connect other lead to starter housing. If meter registers, repair or replace coil.

REASSEMBLY

1) Clean all parts. Apply coat of multipurpose grease to sliding surface of armature shaft splines, starter clutch bushing, pinion lever and moving stud.

2) Reassemble in reverse order of disassembly. After completing reassembly, if clearance between pinion gear and stop collar is not .004-.160" (.10-4.0 mm), adjust by lengthening or shortening plunger shaft.

Fig. 4: Exploded View of Typical Nippondenso Direct Drive Starter Motor

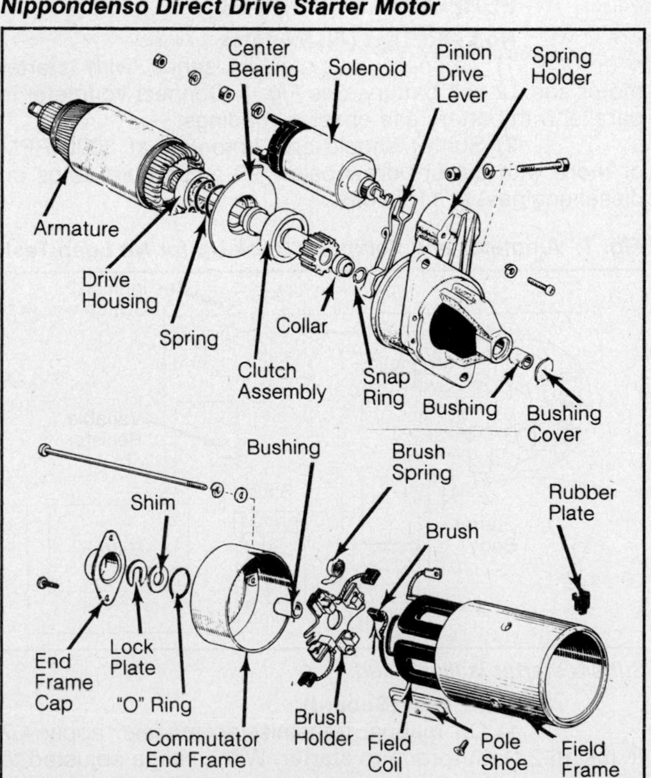
Center Bearing
Solenoid
Pinion Drive Lever
Spring Holder
Armature
Drive Housing
Spring
Collar
Clutch Assembly
Snap Ring
Bushing
Bushing Cover
Bushing
Brush Spring
Rubber Plate
Shim
Brush
End Frame Cap
Lock Plate
"O" Ring
Commutator End Frame
Brush Holder
Field Coil
Pole Shoe
Field Frame

NIPPONDENSO REDUCTION GEAR

Honda Accord, Civic, Prelude; Subaru 1800; Toyota Camry, Celica, Cressida, Land Cruiser, Pickup, Starlet, Supra

DESCRIPTION

The starter is a 12-volt, 4-brush, solenoid-actuated, gear reduction type motor, equipped with an overrunning clutch. The brush holder assembly retains brushes and springs in the starter housing.

APPLICATION

Model	[1] Part No.
Honda	
Accord	31200 PC2 662
Civic (Federal & Hi. Alt.)	31200 PC0 891
Prelude	31200 PC2 661
Subaru	
1800	
Man. Trans.	028000-8580
Auto. Trans. & Turbo	028000-8570
Toyota	
Camry	28100 63020
Celica	28100 34080
Corolla	28100 15040
Cressida & Supra	28100 45033
Land Cruiser	28100 60070
Pickup (Gas)	28100 34080
Pickup (Diesel)	28100 54090
Starlet	28100 13010

[1] – Vehicle manufacturer's part number.

TESTING

PERFORMANCE TESTS

No Load Test (All Models)

1) Connect ammeter in series with starter motor and 12-volt battery. *See Fig. 1.* Connect voltmeter in parallel with battery and observe readings.

2) Starter should spin smoothly at 3000 RPM or more with current draw below 90 amps (180 amps on diesel engines) at 11.5 volts.

Fig. 1: Ammeter and Voltmeter Hook-Up for No Load Test

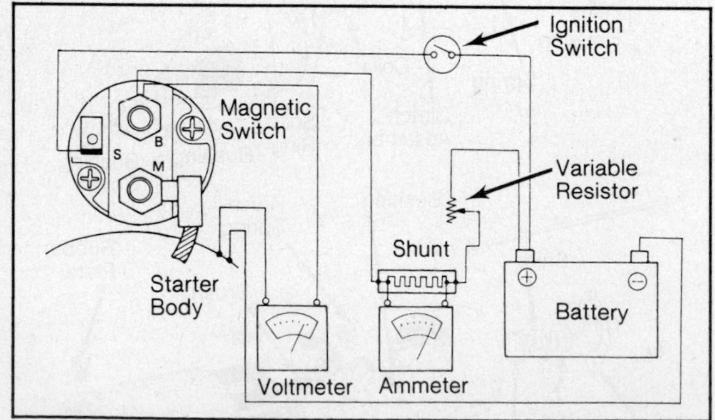
Ignition Switch
Magnetic Switch
B
S
M
Variable Resistor
Shunt
Starter Body
Battery
Voltmeter
Ammeter

Subaru starter is illustrated.

Load Test (Subaru)

1) On manual transmission models, apply 4.7 ft. lbs. (6.2 N.m) torque to starter. With voltage adjusted to 8.5 volts, starter should rotate at 1180 RPM with current draw below 230 amps.

2) On automatic transmission and turbo models, apply 9.4 ft. lbs. (12.5 N.m) torque to starter. With voltage adjusted to 9 volts, starter should rotate at 1000 RPM with current draw below 350 amps.

Cranking Test (Honda)

1) Connect a voltmeter and ammeter to vehicle. *See Fig. 2.* Disconnect ignition coil secondary wire from distributor and ground it. Turn ignition switch to start.

2) Check cranking voltage and current draw. Voltage should be no less than 8.0 volts for Civic, 9.6 volts for Accord and Prelude.

3) Current draw should be below 230 amps for Federal and High Altitude Civics and 350 amps for Accord and Prelude. Cranking speed should be approximately 400 RPM.

Fig. 2: Meter Hookup for Honda Cranking Test

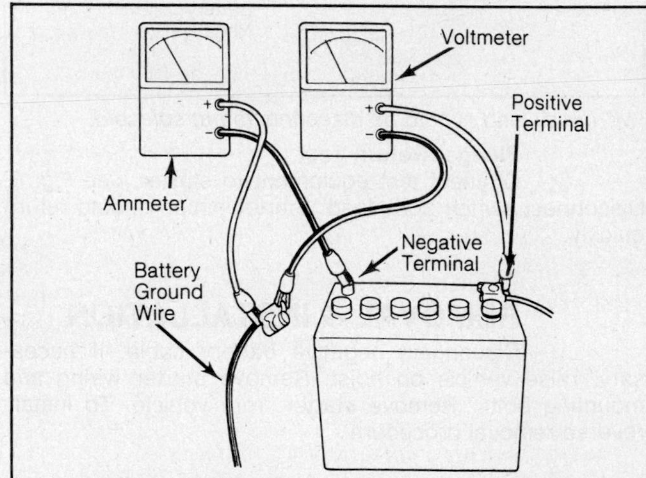
Voltmeter
Positive Terminal
Ammeter
Negative Terminal
Battery Ground Wire

Be sure voltmeter and ammeter connections are correct.

REMOVAL & INSTALLATION

Disconnect negative battery cable. If necessary, raise vehicle on hoist. Remove wiring and starter mounting bolts. Remove starter from vehicle. To install, reverse removal procedure.

OVERHAUL

DISASSEMBLY

1) Disconnect wire(s) to solenoid switch. Remove bolts and remove field frame with armature from solenoid switch. Remove "O" ring and felt seal.

2) Remove starter gear housing screws from solenoid switch. Pull out clutch assembly and gears. Remove ball from clutch shaft hole or from magnetic switch. Remove brushes from brush holder. Pull armature out of field frame.

3) Clean parts with air pressure. DO NOT clean starter and/or components in solvent. Check all parts for wear or damage.

NIPPONDENSO REDUCTION GEAR (Cont.)

PARTS REPLACEMENT & TESTING

Brushes & Springs

1) Check brush length. If less than specification, replace brushes. *See Brush Length Specification Chart.*

BRUSH LENGTH SPECIFICATIONS

Application	In. (mm)
Camry, Celica & Subaru Auto. Trans.	.33 (8.5)
Honda, Starlet & Subaru (Man. Trans.)	.35 (9)
Toyota Diesel Engine	.47 (12)
All Others	.39 (10)

2) Check condition of brush holders, springs, spring clip and insulation between positive and negative holders and repair or replace as needed.

Commutator

1) Inspect commutator for roughness. If surface is pitted, stepped or grooved, it should be lightly sanded with No. 400 sandpaper. Check commutator for out-of-round.

2) If out-of-round is more than .002" (.05 mm) on Subaru and Toyota, or .001" (.03 mm) on Honda, turn commutator on lathe until out-of-round is within specification.

3) Wear or cutting limit of commutator is 1.22" (31 mm) for Cressida and Supra, 1.26" (26 mm) for Civic, or 1.14" (29 mm) for all others.

4) If worn less than .008" (.20 mm), insulating mica should be undercut to a depth of approximately .028-.035" (.71-.89 mm) on Toyota diesel models, or .015-.031" (.40-.80 mm) on all other models..

Armature Coil

1) Check commutator and armature coil core for continuity, if continuity exists, replace armature. Check armature with a growler for shorts. Replace if shorted.

2) Check for continuity between segments on commutator. If no continuity exists, replace armature.

Field Coil

Check field coil for open circuits. There should be continuity between lead wire and field coil brush lead. If not, replace field coil. Check for continuity between field coils and end frame. If continuity exists, replace field coil.

Solenoid Pull-In Coil Test

Connect 2 battery negative leads to main terminal ("C" terminal on Subaru and Toyota) and ground. Connect a 12-volt battery positive lead to solenoid "ST" terminal (terminal "50" on Subaru and Toyota). *See Fig. 3.* Plunger should extend firmly. If not, replace solenoid.

Fig. 3: Solenoid Pull-In Coil Test

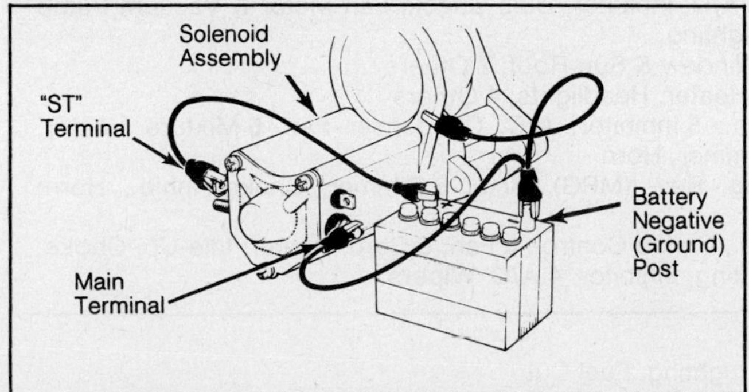
Solenoid Assembly
"ST" Terminal
Battery Negative (Ground) Post
Main Terminal

Connect battery positive to "ST" terminal (terminal "50" on Subaru and Toyota).

Solenoid Hold-In Coil Test

After pull-in testing, disconnect battery negative lead from main terminal ("C" terminal on Subaru and Toyota). Plunger should remain extended. If not, replace solenoid. *See Fig. 3.*

REASSEMBLY

To reassemble, reverse disassembly procedure and note the following: Coat all sliding or moving surfaces of shaft splines, bushings and solenoid with multi-purpose grease. Apply molybdenum disulfide grease to clutch assembly cavity to retain steel ball.

Fig. 5: View of Nippondenso Reduction Gear Starter

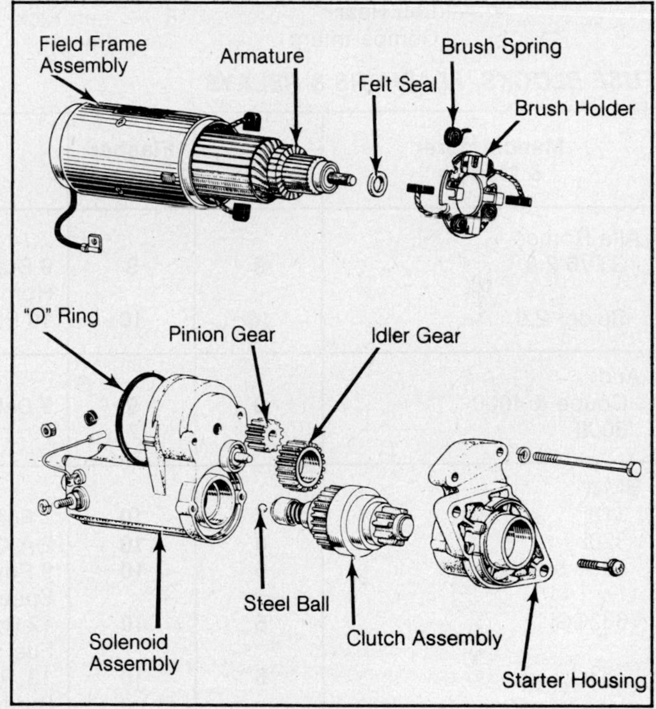
Field Frame Assembly
Armature
Brush Spring
Felt Seal
Brush Holder
"O" Ring
Pinion Gear
Idler Gear
Steel Ball
Solenoid Assembly
Clutch Assembly
Starter Housing

ALFA ROMEO – HONDA

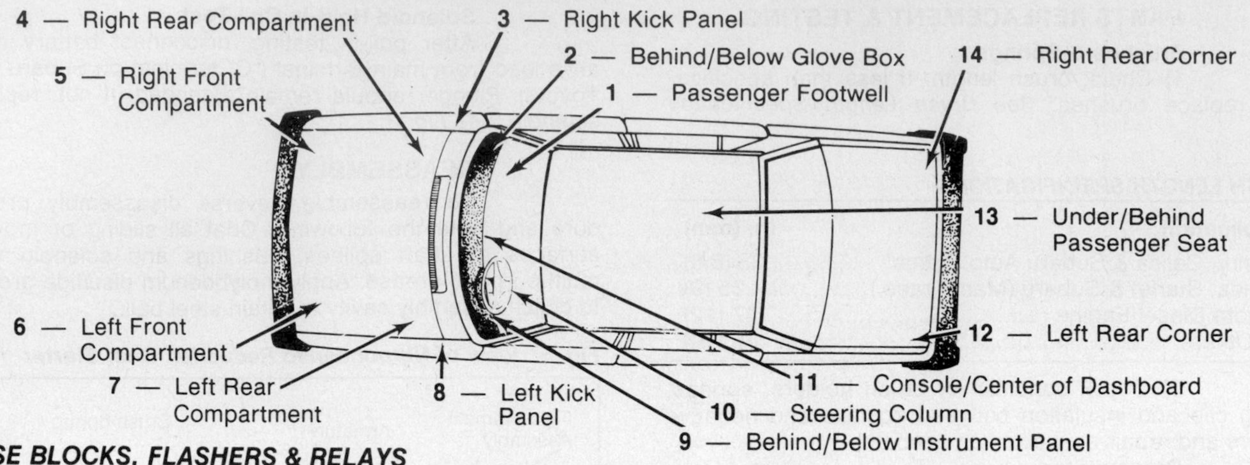
4 — Right Rear Compartment
5 — Right Front Compartment
3 — Right Kick Panel
2 — Behind/Below Glove Box
1 — Passenger Footwell
14 — Right Rear Corner
13 — Under/Behind Passenger Seat
12 — Left Rear Corner
6 — Left Front Compartment
7 — Left Rear Compartment
8 — Left Kick Panel
11 — Console/Center of Dashboard
10 — Steering Column
9 — Behind/Below Instrument Panel

FUSE BLOCKS, FLASHERS & RELAYS

Manufacturer & Models	Fuse Locations	Flasher Locations	Relay Locations
Alfa Romeo			
GTV6 2.5	9	9	**9** Brake Fluid Warning, Power Windows, Defogger, Engine Fan, Horn, A/C
Spider 2.0	10	10	**10** Power Windows, Horn, Ignition Switch Light Timer, A/C
Audi			
Coupe & 4000	9	9	**9** Defogger, Fuel Pump, Load Reduction, Wiper; **2** Others
5000	7	7	**7**
BMW			
318i	7	10	**7** Fuel Pump, Fuel Shut-Off; **8** Start; **11** Fresh/Recirc. Air
320i	6	10	**2** A/C; **7** Speed; **6** Others
528e & 533i	6	10	**9** Power Windows; **6** Low Beam Check, Fan High & Normal Speed, Fuel Pump, Purge Valve
633CSi	6	10	**12** Rear Lights Check; **11** Heat/Cool; **9** Starter; **6** Fuel Control, Fuel Pump, Purge Valve
733i	6	10	**13** Rear Lights Check; **9** power Windows, Starter; **6** Fuel Pump, Purge Valve; **4** Main; **6**
Chrysler Imports			
Challenger	9	7	**11** Door Chime; **5** Wipers; **8** ESS; **7** Others
Colt	9	9	**9** Coolant Fan; **8** ESS
Colt & Ram-50 Pickups	8	9	**9**
Sapporo	9	7	**11** Door Chime; **5** Wipers; **8** ESS; **7** Others
Datsun/Nissan			
200SX	9	9	**3** Ign.; **4** A/C; **5** Others
280ZX & 280ZX Turbo	3	9	**1** Ign., Acc., Cruise Control, Fuel Pump; **4** Horn & EFI; **12** Cruise Control; **5** A/C, Inhibitor, Bulb Check, Fan Motor & Vacuum Pump (Turbo), Lighting
Maxima	2	9	**8** Power Window & Sun Roof; **7** Others
Pickup	8	7	**7** Horn; **8** Heater, Headlights; **4** Others
Pulsar	8	9	**8** Acc., Ign.; **5** Inhibitor, A/C, Condenser Fan; **6** Mixture Heater, Choke, Dimmer, Horn
Sentra	9	9	**9** Ign., Eng. Rev. (MPG), Acc.; **6** Dimmer, Choke, Inhib., Horn; **5** Others
Stanza	2	9	**2** Ign., Acc., Cruise Control; **6** Fan; **5** Carb. Heater; Idle-Up, Choke, Horn, Lighting, Inhibitor, **4** A/C, Wipers
Honda			
Accord	9	9	**9** Wipers, Lighting, Fuel Cut
Civic	9	9	**5** A/C, Cooling Fans; **9** Brake Warning Light, Wipers, Hazard
Prelude	9	9	**7** Heater Fan, Fuel Cut-Off Solenoid

ISUZU – SAAB

FUSE BLOCKS, FLASHERS & RELAYS

Manufacturer & Models	Fuse Locations	Flasher Locations	Relay Locations
Isuzu			
I-Mark	8	9	**9** Heater; **6** Others
Impulse	5, 9	9	**5** Lighting, Dimmer, Tail lights, Headlight Cover, **7** Wiper Motor
Pickups	7	9	**4** Glow Plugs; **9** Heater; **7** Fuel Pump; **6** Others
Jaguar			
XJ6	9, 2, 6	2	**9** A/C, Heater; **5** Horn; **2** Back-Up Light, Fuel Pump Protection, Ignition Load, Starter; **6** Dimmer, Cold Start, Fuel Pump
XJS	9	2	**12** Antenna; **6** Cooling Fan, Dimmer, Horn; **14** Fuel Pump; **4** Starter Injector, Starter; **2** Others
Mazda			
B2000 & B2200 Pickups	7	9	**4** Check & Choke; **7** Glow Plug; **6** Horn, A/C; **9** Wipers
GLC Hatchback	9	9	**6** Choke, A/C; Horn; **9** Wipers, Others
GLC Wagon	9	9	**6** Check; **5** Horn; **9** Wipers
RX7	9	8	**7** Check & Choke, Hot Start, A/C; **9** Horn, Antenna
626	9	9	**9** Wipers, Horn
Mercedes-Benz			
240D	7	11	**12** Antenna; **9** Windows, Defogger; **6** Others
300D, CD & TD	7	11	**12** Antenna; **9** Power Windows; **6** Others
300SD	7	11	**6** Glow Plug, Antenna; **7** Others
380SL	1	11	**12** Antenna; **2** Fuel Pump; **8** Others
380 SEC & SEL	1	9	**8** Seat Belt; **12** Antenna; **7** Others
Mitsubishi			
Cordia & Tredia	10	8	**3** Heater; **5** Intermittent Wiper, Headlight, Engine Fan, Dimmer, Tail Light, Power Steering; **8** Select Control, E.S.S., Alarm, Stop Light Failure Indicator, Hazard Flasher, Seat Belt, Defogger, Speed Control; **11** Door Lock Control, Door Lock Power; **Drivers Door** Power Window
Montero	8	8	**2** Heater; **3** Seat Belt Timer; **4** Light Control; **8** Headlight Washer, Hazard Flasher, Intermittent Wiper, E.S.S. Control
Pickup	8	9	**6** Lighting, Starter, GLow Plug; **7** Intermittent Wiper; **9** Seat Belt Hazard Flasher
Starion Turbo	9	8	**4** Speed Control Vacuum Pump; **6** Headlight Doors, Lighting, Wiper, Power Window, Rear Defogger; **8** Hazard Flasher; **11** Passing Control
Peugeot			
504	9	9	**7** Starter; **9** Others
505	7	11	**6** Cooling Fan, Starter; **9** Cruise Control, Fuel Pump; **5** Others
604	9	11	**5** Fan, Coil; **9** Others
Porsche			
911SC	6, 12	9	**6**
928S	1	3	**11** Seat Belt; **12** Rear Wiper; **13** Seat Release; **3** Others
944	9	9	**9** Fan, Fuel Pump, A/C, Headlight Washer, Defogger, Horn, Wipers, Turn Signals
Renault			
Fuego & Fuego Turbo	9	7	**13** Injector; **7** Others
Le Car	11	10	**10** Seat Belt
18i	9	9	**7**
Saab			
900 & 900 Turbo	7	9	**9** Wiper, ECU; **7** Horn, A/C Fan, Hot Start, Fuel Pump, Radiator Fan, Defogger, Lights

Fuse Blocks, Flashers & Relays

SUBARU-VOLVO

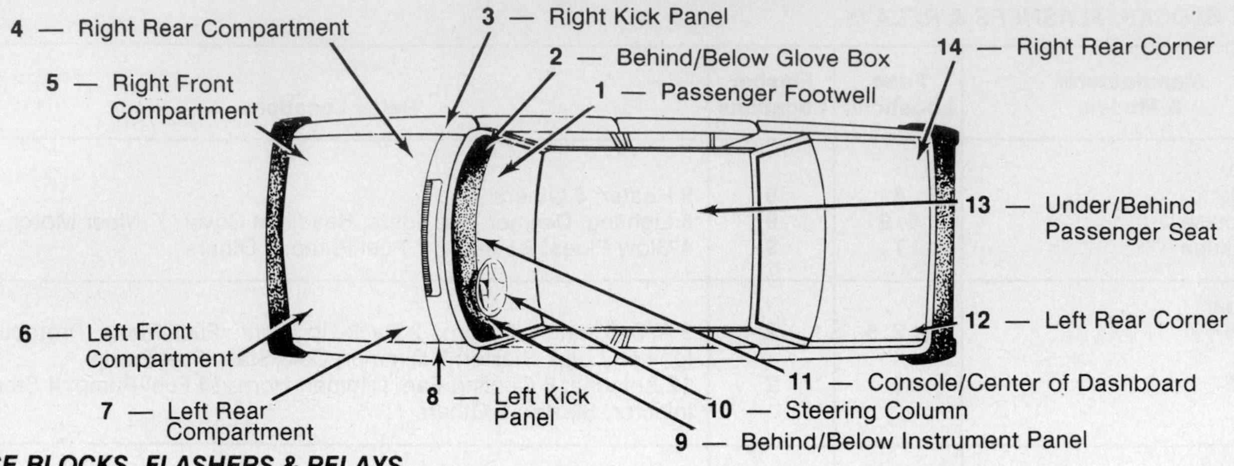

4 — Right Rear Compartment
3 — Right Kick Panel
2 — Behind/Below Glove Box
14 — Right Rear Corner
5 — Right Front Compartment
1 — Passenger Footwell
13 — Under/Behind Passenger Seat
12 — Left Rear Corner
6 — Left Front Compartment
11 — Console/Center of Dashboard
8 — Left Kick Panel
10 — Steering Column
7 — Left Rear Compartment
9 — Behind/Below Instrument Panel

FUSE BLOCKS, FLASHERS & RELAYS

Manufacturer & Models	Fuse Locations	Flasher Locations	Relay Locations
Subaru			
All Models	**9**	**9**	**13** Ignition; **9** A/C, Lighting, Choke, Kick-Down
Toyota			
Camry	**3, 6, 8**	**9**	**2** Heater, Circuit Opener, Seat Belt Warning; **6** A/C Fan, Radiator Fan, EFI Main, Engine Main, Headlight; **7** Antenna; **8** Tail Light, Defogger
Celica	**5, 8**	**9**	**5** Headlight Retract, EFI, Chime, Dimmer, Headlight, Tail Light, Ign. Main; **8** Defogger, Ign. Key Light, Charge Light; **2** Blower, Wiper; **11** Headlight Retract Control; **9** Overdrive, Seatbelt, Door Lock
Corolla	**3, 6, 8**	**9**	**6** Chime; **2** Heater, Charge Lamp; **8** Tail Light; **9** Seatbelt, Overdrive; **6** Headlight, Ignition
Cressida	**3, 6, 8**	**9**	**2** Defogger Timer, Circuit Opening, Heater, A/C-Cut; **6** EFI, Ign. Main, Headlight, Tail Light; **8** Tail Light Failure, Brake Light Failure, Charge Light, Ign. Key Light, Main Power Window, Door Lock Control; **9** Door Lock, Power Window; **11** Warm-Up, Wiper Control
Land Cruiser	**9, 4**	**9**	**7** Starter; **3** Charge; **9** Others
Pickup	**9**	**11**	**3** Clock, Wiper; **8** Discharge Light; **2** Seatbelt
Starlet	**9**	**9**	**3** Seatbelt Warning; **8** Headlight Cleaner; **9** Others
Supra	**9, 6**	**9**	**6** Dimmer, Headlight, Tail Light, Ign. Main, EFI; **9** Door Lock; **8** Power Window Main, Fog Light, Circuit Opener, Charge Light, Defogger, Ignition Key Light; **11** Warm-Up, High-Speed; **2** A/C-Cut, Wipers, Heater
Tercel	**8, 2, 6**	**9**	**5** Chime; **2** Seat Belt Warning; **3** Sun Roof, Heater, Defogger, Charge Light; **6** Dimmer, A/C, Ign. Main, Radiator Fan, Headlight; **8** Wiper, Tail Light
Volkswagen			
Jetta	**9**	**9**	**9**
Quantum	**9**	**9**	**9** Fuel Pump, Seat Belt Warning, Up-Shift Indicator, A/C, Dual Horn, Wipers, Oxygen Sensor, Power Windows, Hot-Start, Cat. Converter
Rabbit	**9**	**9**	**9**
Rabbit Pickup	**9**	**9**	**9**
Scirocco	**9**	**9**	**9**
Vanagon	**9**	**9**	**2** Aux. Heater; **9** Others
Volvo			
760 GLE	**11**	**11**	**11** Bulb Warning, Chime, Fuel Injection, Temperature Warning, Auto. Headlights, Overdrive, Windows & Fan, Central Lock, Lights, Oxygen Sensor, Ignition Advance
DL, GL, Turbo	**8**	**11**	**7** Cooling Fan, Glow Plug; **9** Delay Interval Light; **8** Fuel Pump, Wiper; **10** Seat Belt; **6** Headlight; **11** Others

ALFA ROMEO

GTV-6 2.5

Fuse Block

Fuse block is located under ventilator duct on the left side of steering column. Circuits protected include:

1 – 16 Amp Defogger
2 – 16 Amp Spare Fuse
3 – 16 Amp A/C Fan & Electromagnetic Clutch
4 – 8 Amp Door Mirrors, Courtesy Light, Brake Lights, Clock, Ignition Switch Seat Light, Audio, Door Reminder, Buzzer, Hazard Flashers, Fuse Block Light
5 – 8 Amp Fuel Injection
6 – 8 Amp Wipers, Cigar Lighter, Glove Box Light
7 – 8 Amp Ignition Switch Wired Items, Back-Up Lights, Defogger, A/C, Pulse Generator, Rev Counter, Speedometer, Power Windows
8 – 8 Amp Electronic Injection Feeding
9 – 8 Amp Right Front & Left Rear Parking Lights, Right Front Side Marker, Right License Light, Left Rear Side Marker Light
10 – 8 Amp Left Front & Right Rear Parking Lights, Left Front Side Marker, Engine Compartment Light, Instrument Cluster Light, Parking Lights Warning Light, Cigar Lighter Light, Ashtray Light, Left License Light, Right Rear Side Marker Light
11 – 8 Amp Left Low Beam
12 – 8 Amp Right Low Beam
13 – 8 Amp Left High Beam & Warning Light
14 – 8 Amp Right High Beam

SPIDER 2.0

Fuse block is located under instrument panel. Protected circuits include:

1 – 16 Amp Power Windows
2 – 16 Amp Spare Fuse
3 – 16 Amp Spare Fuse
4 – 8 Amp Digital Clock
5 – 8 Amp Fuse Block Illumination, Door Buzzer, Radio
6 – 8 Amp Wiper/Washer
7 – 8 Amp Back-Up Lights, Instrument Panel Lights
8 – 8 Amp Power Window Relay
9 – 8 Amp Speedometer & Tachometer Illumination, Left Front & Right Rear Parking Lights, Left License Light
10 – 8 Amp Right Front & Left Rear Parking Lights, Right License Light
11 – 8 Amp Left Low Beam
12 – 8 Amp Right Low Beam
13 – 8 Amp Left High Beam
14 – 8 Amp Right High Beam

AUDI

COUPE

Fuse Block

Fuse block is located at left side of engine compartment. It contains 22 numbered fuses. Circuits protected are as follows:

1 – 15 Amp Fog Lights
2 – 15 Amp Emergency Flasher
3 – 25 Amp Horn, Cigar Lighter, Clock, Reading Lights, Footwell Light
4 – 15 Amp Brake Lights, Luggage Compartment Light, Interior Light, Vanity Mirror
5 – Not Used
6 – 5 Amp Right Side Marker Light
7 – 5 Amp Left Side Marker Light
8 – 10 Amp Right High Beam
9 – 10 Amp Left High Beam
10 – 10 Amp Right Low Beam
11 – 10 Amp Left Low Beam
12 – 15 Amp Instrument Lights, Back-Up Light
13 – 15 Amp Fuel Pump
14 – 15 Amp License Plate Light
15 – 15 Amp Windshield Wipers, Turn Signals
16 – 30 Amp Rear Window Defogger
17 – 30 Amp Heater Control Light, A/C, Glove Box Light
18 – 25 Amp Rear Window Wiper
19 – 10 Amp Central Locking System, Electric Mirrors
20 – 20 Amp Seat Heating
21 – 25 Amp Rear Cigar Lighter
22 – Not Used

4000

Fuse Block

Fuse block is located at left side of engine compartment. It contains 22 numbered fuses. Circuits protected are as follows:

1 – 15 Amp Fog Lights
2 – 15 Amp Emergency Flasher
3 – 25 Amp Horn, Cigar Lighter, Clock, Reading Lights, Footwell Light
4 – 15 Amp Brake Lights, Luggage Compartment Light, Interior Light, Vanity Mirror
5 – Not Used
6 – 5 Amp Right Side Marker Light
7 – 5 Amp Left Side Marker Light
8 – 10 Amp Right High Beam
9 – 10 Amp Left High Beam
10 – 10 Amp Right Low Beam
11 – 10 Amp Left Low Beam
12 – 15 Amp Instrument Lights, Back-Up Light
13 – 15 Amp Fuel Pump
14 – 15 Amp License Plate Light
15 – 15 Amp Windshield Wipers, Turn Signals
16 – 30 Amp Rear Window Defogger
17 – 30 Amp Heater Control Light, A/C, Glove Box Light
18 – 25 Amp Sun Roof
19 – 10 Amp Central Locking System, Electric Mirrors
20 – 20 Amp Seat Heating
21 – 25 Amp A/C Compressor (Diesel Models)
22 – 80 Amp Glow Plugs (Diesel Models)

AUDI (Cont.)

5000

Fuse Block

Fuse block is located in engine compartment left rear corner. Fuses are numbered from 1 to 17, with 17 closest to the front of the car and 1 nearest the rear. Circuits protected are:

1 – 25 Amp A/C-Heater Fan, Tachometer
2 – Not Used
3 – 8 Amp Left High Beam
4 – 8 Amp Right High Beam
5 – 16 Amp Fuel Pump
6 – 8 Amp Right Side Marker Light, Right Tail Light
7 – 8 Amp Left Marker Light, Left Tail Light, Engine Compartment Light
8 – 8 Amp Instrument Panel, Glove Compartment & License Plate Lights
9 – 16 Amp Gauges, Power Windows, Cruise Control, Sunroof, Audio
10 – 25 Amp Engine Fan
11 – 16 Amp Brake Lights
12 – 16 Amp Cigar Lighter, Audio, Antenna, Clock, Mirrors
13 – 8 Amp Right Low Beam
14 – 8 Amp Left Low Beam
15 – 16 Amp Back-Up Lights, Wiper/Washer Motor
16 – 25 Amp Defogger
17 – 8 Amp Flashers, Turn Signals

The following fuses are in addition to numbered fuses.

18 – 25 Amp Power Windows
19 – 16 Amp Rear Cigar Lighters
20 – 8 Amp Central Locking System

BMW

318i

Fuse Block

Fuse block is located at left front corner of engine compartment. Fuses are arranged in 2 rows of 15. Protected circuits are:

1 – 8 Amp Left High Beam
2 – 8 Amp Right High Beam
3 – 15 Amp 196°F (91°C) Auxiliary Fan
4 – 15 Amp Turn Signal, Clock Light
5 – 30 Amp Wiper/Washer Motor
6 – 8 Amp Brake Lights, Cruise Control
7 – 15 Amp Horn
8 – 30 Amp Defogger, Oxygen Sensor Light
9 – 15 Amp Engine Electrics
10 – 8 Amp Instrument Lights, Seat Belt Warning Light & Buzzer, Back-Up Light, Check Control
11 – 15 Amp Main & Auxiliary Fuel Pumps
12 – 8 Amp Audio, Instruments
13 – 8 Amp Left Low Beam
14 – 8 Amp Right Low Beam
15 – Not Connected
16 – Not Connected
17 – 30 Amp Sun Roof
18 – 30 Amp 210°F (99°C) Auxiliary Fan
19 – 8 Amp Power Mirrors, Mirror Heating
20 – 30 Amp Heater Blower, A/C
21 – 8 Amp Interior Lights, Radio Memory, Instrument Panel Lights, Glove Box Light, Flashlight, Clock, Luggage Compartment Light, Warning Gongs
22 – 8 Amp Left Rear Light, Left Front Position Light, Left Side Marker Light
23 – 8 Amp Right Rear Light, Right Front Position Light, Right Side Marker Light, License Light
24 – 15 Amp Hazard Flasher Lights
25 – Not Used
26 – Not Used
27 – 30 Amp Central Locking System, Door Lock Heating, Anit-Theft Protection, On-Board Heater
28 – 30 Amp Cigar Lighter, Power Antenna
29 – 8 Amp Left Fog Light
30 – 8 Amp Right Fog Light

320i

Fuse Block

Fuse block is located at left front corner of engine compartment. Fuses are arranged in 6 rows of 3, with first row toward battery. Number 1 fuse is next to front relay. Protected circuits are:

1 – 8 Amp Right Fog Light
2 – 8 Amp Left Fog Light
3 – 16 Amp Fuel Pump
4 – 8 Amp Right Low Beam
5 – 8 Amp Left Low Beam
6 – 8 Amp Dash, Tail, Hood & Right Park Lights
7 – 16 Amp High Beam
8 – 16 Amp High Beam
9 – 8 Amp Left Park & Tail Lights
10 – 16 Amp Defogger
11 – 25 Amp Heater Fan, A/C Fan
12 – 8 Amp Brake Lights, Audio, Tachometer
13 – 25 Amp Auxiliary Fan
14 – 16 Amp Back-Up Lights, Gauges, Warning Lights
15 – 16 Amp Horn, Wiper/Washer, Power Mirror
16 – 16 Amp Cigar Lighter
17 – 8 Amp Turn Signals, Clock, Buzzers, Flashers
18 – Not Used

528e & 533i

Fuse Block

All models have fuse block at left front corner of engine compartment. Fuses are numbered with details of equipment connected and ampere rarting. Fuses protect the following circuits:

1 – 8 Amp Fuel Pump
2 – 8 Amp Right Low Beam
3 – 8 Amp Left Low Beam
4 – 16 Amp Cigar Lighter, Power Antenna, Heating Adjustment, Seat Heating, Programmable Seat Adjustment, Parking Lights

BMW (Cont.)

5 – 8 Amp Hazard Warning System, Interior Light, Luggage Light, Reading Light, Clock, Central Locking System, Computer, Theft Warning System, Service Indicator, Door Lock Heating, Check Control
6 – 8 Amp Warning Lights, Tachometer, Mirror, On-Board Computer, Central Warning Light, Fuel Consumption, Service Indicator, Check Control, Window Regulator, Vehicle Light Adjustment, Reversing, Cruise Control, Back-Up Light
7 – 8 Amp Right High Beam
8 – 8 Amp Left High Beam
9 – 8 Amp Right Parking & Tail Lights, Engine Compartment Light, Rear Fog Light, Instrument Panel & License Plate Lights
10 – 8 Amp Left Parking & Tail Lights
11 – 16 Amp Turn Signals, Windshield Wiper/Washer, Horn Relay, Headlight, Headlight Cleaner System
12 – 8 Amp Audio, Brake Lights
13 – 16 Amp Defogger, Sun Roof
14 – 25 Amp A/C-Heater Fan
15 – 8 Amp Right Fog Light
16 – 8 Amp Left Fog Light
17 – 25 Amp Auxiliary Fan

633CSi & 733i

Fuse Block

Fuse block is located at left front corner of engine compartment. Fuses are arranged in 2 rows of 15. Protected circuits are:

1 – 15 Amp Left High Beam
2 – 15 Amp Right High Beam
3 – 15 Amp 196°F (91°C) Auxiliary Fan
4 – 15 Amp Turn Signal
5 – 25 Amp Wiper/Washer Motor, Intensive-Cleaner
6 – 8 Amp Brake Lights, Cruise Control
7 – 15 Amp Horn
8 – Not Connected
9 – 15 Amp Engine Electrics
10 – 8 Amp Instruments, On-Board Computer
11 – 15 Amp Main & Auxiliary Fuel Pumps
12 – 8 Amp Audio, Instruments
13 – 8 Amp Left Low Beam
14 – 8 Amp Right Low Beam
15 – Not Connected
16 – 30 Amp Heater Blower
17 – 8 Amp Back-Up Lights, Power Mirror, Mirror Heating, A/C, Seatbelt Warning Light
18 – 30 Amp 210°F (99°C) Auxiliary Fan
19 – 25 Amp Sunroof, Heated Seat
20 – 25 Amp Defogger
21 – 8 Amp Interior Lights, Radio, Glove Box Light, Flashlight, Seat Belt Buzzer
22 – 8 Amp Left Parking Light
23 – 8 Amp Right Parking Light, Engine Compartment Light, License Light, Instrument Panel Lights, Make-Up Mirror Light
24 – 15 Amp Hazard Flasher Lights
25 – Not Used
26 – 30 Amp Power Windows
27 – 25 Amp Central Locking, Door Lock Heating, Anti-Theft Protection, On-Board Computer
28 – 25 Amp Cigar Lighter, Power Antenna, Parked Car Heater
29 – 8 Amp Left Fog Light
30 – 8 Amp Right Fog Light

CHRYSLER CORP. IMPORTS

COLT PICKUP & RAM-50 PICKUP

Fuse Block

Fuse block is located beneath instrument panel on left side. Fuses are numbered with first fuse at top left and last fuse at bottom right. Protected circuits are as follows:

1 – 10 Amp Dome Light
2 – 10 Amp Hazard Lights
3 – 10 Amp Brake Lights
4 – 15 Amp Turn Signals

Next Row:

5 – 15 Amp Radio, Wipers
6 – 15 Amp Heater
7 – 10 Amp Horn
8 – 10 Amp Tail Lights

CHALLENGER & SAPPORO

Fuse Block

Main fuse block is on left kick panel. Two 5 amp fuses are at battery and headlight fuses are in-line nearby. The fuse block fuses are numbered from front of vehicle toward rear and protect the following circuits:

1 – 10 Amp Clock, Dome Light
2 – 10 Amp Flashers
3 – 15 Amp Brake Lights
4 – 20 Amp Defogger
5 – 20 Amp Heater
6 – 10 Amp Tail Lights, Parking Lights
7 – 15 Amp Wiper/Washer
8 – 15 Amp Audio, Cigar Lighter, Horn
9 – 10 Amp Turn Signals, Gauges
10 – 10 Amp Back-Up Lights, Voltage Regulator, Remote Control Mirror
11 – 1.4 Watt Check Light

COLT

Fuse Block

Fuse block is located beneath instrument panel on left side. Fuses are numbered from left to right and protect these circuits:

1 – 15 Amp High Beam & High Beam Indicator
2 – 15 Amp Low Beam
3 – 15 Amp Tail Lights, Parking Light, Side Marker Lights, License Light, Gauge Lights, Switch Lights, Ashtray Light, Instrument Panel Lights, Clock Light
4 – 15 Amp Brake Lights, Seat Belt Indicator & Buzzer
5 – 15 Amp Flashers, Dome Light, Luggage Compartment Light, Door Indicator, Digital Clock Display
6 – 15 Amp Heater, Horn, Clock Power
7 – 15 Amp Cigar Lighter, Audio, Power Mirror

CHRYSLER CORP. IMPORTS (Cont.)

8 – 15 Amp Turn Signals, Indicator, Gauges, Rear Wiper/Washer, Oil Pressure Gaugem, Warning Indicators
9 – 15 Amp Wiper/Washer
10 – 15 Amp Back-Up Lights, Defogger, Defogger Indicator

DATSUN/NISSAN

200SX

Fuse Block

Fuse block is below glove box on right side of dashboard. The fuses and circuits protected are:

1 – 15 Amp Right Headlight
2 – 15 Amp Left Headlight
3 – 10 Amp Brake Lights, Horn
4 – 10 Amp Hazard Flasher
5 – 10 Amp Courtesy Lights, Clock
6 – 15 Amp Tail Light
7 – 10 Amp Mirror Control, Cigar Lighter
8 – 20 Amp Heater, A/C
9 – 15 Amp Heater, A/C
10 – 10 Amp Wiper, Washer
11 – Audio
12 – Defogger
13 – Engine Control
14 – 10 Amp Turn Signals, Gauge Lights
15 – 15 Amp Ignition Coil

280ZX & 280ZX TURBO

Fuse Block

Fuse block is located in right kick panel and contains 12 fuses which protect the following circuits:

1 – 10 Amp Right Headlight
2 – 10 Amp Left Headlight, High Beam Indicator
3 – 15 Amp Horn, Power Door Lock
4 – 15 Amp Brake Lights
5 – 10 Amp Clearance, Tail Lights
6 – 10 Amp Interior, Clock
7 – 10 Amp Hazard Flasher
8 – 20 Amp Heater, A/C
9 – 10 Amp Audio
10 – 10 Amp Rear Wiper/Washer
11 – 15 Amp Front Wiper/Washer, Headlight Cleaner
12 – 10 Amp Flasher, Reverse, Cruise Control
13 – 10 Amp Meter, Gauge
14 – 20 Amp Rear Defroster
15 – 15 Amp Cigar Lighter
16 – 15 Amp Radiator Fan Motor

MAXIMA

Fuse Block

Fuse block is under glove compartment on right side of dashboard. A switch turns off the clock, timer and voice warning system so battery will not discharge during long storage. Fuses are numbered from left to right and protect circuits as follows:

1 – 10 Amp Bulb Check Relay, Back-Up Light Switch, Inhibitor Switch, Fuel Filter Amp, EGR Control Unit, Fast Glow Control Unit, Glow Plug Relay
2 – 20 Amp Defogger
3 – 10 Amp Warning Lights, Gauges, Voice Warning System, Power Antenna Timer, Tachometer, Time Control Unit, Speed Control
4 – 20 Amp Power Antenna, Rear Wiper/Washer Motor
5 – 20 Amp Wiper Motor, Wiper Relay, Washer Motor, Mirror Switch, Heater Unit, Time Control Unit
6 & 7 – 15 Amp Heater Motor
8 – 10 Amp Cassette Deck, Clock
9 – 10 Amp Flasher Relay, Hazard Switch, Room Light, Step Light, Key Warning Switch, Steering Lock Switch
10 – 10 Amp Horn Relay
11 – 10 Amp Extended Storage Switch
12 – 15 Amp Lighting Switch
13 – 10 Amp Brake Light Switch
14 – 10 Amp Left Headlight
15 – 10 Amp Right Headlight

PICKUP

Fuse Block

Main fuse block is located on left kick panel. Fuses are numbered and protect the following circuits:

1 – 10 Amp Coil No. 2 (Not Used on Diesel)
2 – 15 Amp Coil No. 1, Fuel Pump, Emissions, Glow Plugs (Diesel)
3 – 15 Amp Rear Defogger
4 – 15 Amp Gauges, Back-Up Lights
5 – Not Used
6 – 15 Amp Wiper/Washer, A/C
7 – 15 Amp Audio, Cigar Lighter
8 – 10 Amp Clock
9 – Not Used
10 – 20 Amp Blower Motor
11 – 10 Amp Horn
12 – 15 Amp Brake Lights, Flashers
13 – 15 Amp Marker Lights, Tail Lights
14 – 10 Amp Left Headlight
15 – 10 Amp Right Headlight

PULSAR

Fuse Block

Fuse block is located under dash by driver's door. Fuses are numbered and protect the following circuits:

1 – 10 Amp Right Headlight
2 – 10 Amp Left Headlight
3 – 10 Amp Brake Lights
4 – 10 Amp Tail Lights, Illumination Lights
5 – 10 Amp Clock, Illumination Light
6 – 10 Amp Horn, Hazard Lights
7 – 10 Amp Audio, Rear Wiper
8 – 20 Amp Front Wiper
9 – 20 Amp Heater, A/C
10 – 10 Amp Cigar Lighter
11 – 10 Amp Flasher, Gauge Lights
12 & 13 – 20 Amp Defogger
14 – 20 Amp Engine Control
15 & 16 – 20 Amp Fan Motor
17 – 10 Amp Fuel Pump

DATSUN/NISSAN (Cont.)

SENTRA

Fuse Block

Fuse block is located under dash by driver's door. Fuses are numbered and protect the following circuits:

1 – 10 Amp Right Headlight
2 – 10 Amp Left Headlight
3 – 10 Amp Brake Lights
4 – 10 Amp Tail Lights, Illumination Lights
5 – 10 Amp Clock, Dome Light
6 – 10 Amp Horn, Hazard Light
7 – 10 Amp Audio, Rear Wiper
8 – 20 Amp Front Wiper
9 – 20 Amp Heater
10 – 20 Amp A/C
11 – 10 Amp Cigar Lighter
12 – 10 Amp Flasher, Gauges
13 – 20 Amp Defogger
14 – 20 Amp Engine Control
15 – 10 Amp Fan Motor

STANZA

Fuse Block

Fuse block is located below glove compartment. There are 15 fuses arranged in a single row to protect the following circuits:

1 – 20 Amp Radiator Fan
2 – 20 Amp Rear Window Defogger
3 – 10 Amp Flasher, Meters and Gauges, Horn, Back-Up Lights
4 – 10 Amp Coil Switch Module, Auto-Choke, Engine Revolution Switch
5 – Blower Motor
6 – Windshield Wiper/Washer, Cigar Lighter
7 – Audio
8 – Rear Wiper/Washer
9 – A/C
10 – Brake Lights, Trunk Light, Step Light, Cruise Control
11 – Interior Light, Clock
12 – Clearance Light, Meter Illumination, License Light, Side Marker Lights
13 – Hazard Flasher, Horn
14 – Left Headlight
15 – Right Headlight

ALL MODELS

Fusible Link

Fusible link is located in wire between battery and alternator near the battery. Its purpose is to protect the alternator and related circuits.

HONDA

ACCORD

Fuse Block

Fuse block is located in a swing-down panel to left of steering column. Moving from left to right, protected circuits are:

1 – 15 Amp Right High Beam, High Beam Indicator
2 – 15 Amp Left High Beam
3 – 10 Amp Left Low Beam
4 – 10 Amp Right Low Beam
5 – 10 Amp Blower Motor, A/C, Recirculation Solenoid, Flow Solenoid, Defogger Relay, Ignition Switch
6 – 20 Amp Turn Signals, Back-Up Lights, Fuel Gauge, Temperature Gauge, Brake Warning Light, Oil Pressure Light, Low Fuel Light
7 – 15 Amp Defogger
8 – 20 Amp Cooling Fan, A/C
9 – 10 Amp Tachometer, Clock, Cruise Control, Safety Light, Warning Lights and Meters
10 – 10 Amp Front and Rear Wiper/Washer
11 – 10 Amp Regulator, Fuel Pump, Solenoid Valves, Speed Sensor, Vacuum Switch, Charge Pilot
12 – 15 Amp Tail Lights, Side Marker Lights, License Light, Dash Illumination and Dimmer, Glove Box Light, Ashtray Light, Cigar Lighter Illumination, Gauge Lights, Heater Control Illumination, Clock, License Light
13 – 10 Amp Brake Light, Horn, Hazard Light
14 – 15 Amp Interior Light, Tail Gate Light, Cigar Lighter, Clock, Auto Clock, Fuse Maintenance Switch Light, Seat Belt Buzzer

CIVIC

Fuse Block

Fuse block is located in panel to left of steering column. Circuits protected, from right to left, are:

1 – 10 Amp Right Low Beam
2 – 10 Amp Left Low Beam
3 – 10 Amp Right High Beam
4 – 10 Amp Left High Beam
5 – 10 Amp Regulator, Fuel Pump Relay, Solenoid Valves, Speed Sensor, Idle Compensation Unit
6 – 15 Amp Washer/Wiper Motors
7 – 10 Amp Brake Lights, Turn Signals, Back-Up Lights, Gauges, Warning Lights
8 – 10 Amp Interior Light, Trunk Light, Cigar Lighter, Clock, Buzzer
9 – 15 Amp Brake Lights, Horn, Hazard Lights
10 – 15 Amp Tail Lights, Marker Lights, Parking Lights, License Lights, Gauge Lights, Ignition Switch Light, Heater Panel Light, A/T Console Light
11 – 15 Amp Defogger
12 – 15 Amp Heater Motor
13 – 15 Amp Cooling Fan Motor
14 – 10 Amp Audio

Relays

Relays located on the panel are identified from right to left as: Intermittent Wipers, Hazard Flashers, Turn Signals, Fuel Pump Cut-Off. The 2 relays above the panel are the Seat Belt Buzzer and the Brake Warning Light Relay.

Fuses & Circuit Breakers

HONDA (Cont.)

PRELUDE

Fuse Block

Fuse block is located in swing-down panel to left of steering column. Fuses are arranged in 2 rows. Moving from right to left, short row first, protected circuits are:

1 – 20 Amp Defogger
2 – 15 Amp Interior Light, Trunk Light, Cigar Lighter, Fuse Block Light, Digital Clock
3 – 15 Amp Tail Lights, Side Marker Lights, License Plate Light, Parking Lights, Gauge Lights, Interior Lights
4 – 10 Amp Hazard/Turn Signal Flasher, Radio Memory
5 – 10 Amp Turn Signals, Back-Up Lights, Tachometer, Speedometer, Gauges, Safety Indicator, Warning Lights, Digital Clock, Beepers and Timers
6 – 20 Amp Wiper/Washer, Sun Roof Relay
7 – Not Used
8 – 10 Amp Cooling Fan Relay
9 – 10 Amp Defroster Relay
10 – 20 Amp Blower Motor, Heater Controls, A/C
11 – 10 Amp Audio

In-Line Fuses

One or 2 main fuses are installed near the battery to protect entire electrical system. A spare fuse is provided inside fuse block cover.

ISUZU

ISUZU I-MARK

Fuse Block

Fuse block is located in left kick panel. Fuses are numbered. Circuits protected are as follows:

1 – 10 Amp Brake Lights
2 – 10 Amp Horn
3 – 10 Amp Clock, Hazard Lights, Interior Lights
4 – 15 Amp Cigar Lighter, Audio
5 – 15 Amp Meter
6 – 10 Amp Turn Signal, Back-Up Light
7 – 10 Amp Wiper/Washer
8 – 10 Amp Rear Wiper/Washer
9 – 10 Amp A/C
10 – 15 Amp Heater

IMPULSE

Fuse Block

Main fuse block is located under left side of instrument panel. Auxiliary fuse block is inside engine compartment. Fuses are numbered. Protected circuits include:

Main Fuse Block
1 – 10 Amp Brake Lights, Cuise Control
2 – 15 Amp Hazard Lights, Digital Clock
3 – 10 Amp Interior Lights, Clock
4 – 5 Amp Electronic Memory
5 – 15 Amp Defogger
6 – 10 Amp A/C
7 – Not Used
8 – 20 Amp Cigar Lighter, Audio
9 – 15 Amp Front Wipers
10 – 20 Amp Rear Wipers
11 – 20 Amp Left Power Window
12 – 20 Amp Right Power Window
13 – 15 Amp Back-Up Lights, Turn Signals
14 – 15 Amp Instruments and Gauges

Auxiliary Fuse Block
1 – 15 Amp Spare Fuse
2 – 20 Amp Spare Fuse
3 – 15 Amp Tail Lights
4 – 15 Amp Low Beams
5 – 15 Amp High Beams
6 – 15 Amp Headlight Covers

P'UP

Fuse Block

Fuse block is located in engine compartment on left fenderwell. Fuses are numbered and protect the following circuits:

1 – 15 Amp Tail Lights, Instrument Panel Lights
2 – 20 Amp A/C System, Heater
3 – 15 Amp Horn, Brake Lights
4 – 15 Amp Back-Up Lights, Turn Signals
5 – 15 Amp Regulator
6 – 15 Amp Wiper/Washer, Audio, Cigar Lighter

JAGUAR

XJ6

Fuse Block

Main fuse block is located behind instrument panel. Access to fuses is obtained by turning access panel retaining pin counterclockwise until it unlocks. Panel will then drop slightly and bottom edge may be lifted clear of opening. Auxiliary fuse block is similarly located below glove box. Headlight fuse box is located on left fender in engine compartment. Circuits protected are as follows:

Main Fuse Block
1 – 20 Amp Fog Lights
2 – 15 Amp Hazard Warning System, Seat Belts, Logic Unit
3 – 15 Amp Map and Interior Lights, Clock, Power Antenna
4 – 15 Amp Back-Up Lights, Gauges, Warning Indicators
5 – 35 Amp Defogger
6 – 35 Amp Windshield Wipers
7 – 2 Amp Trip Computer
8 – 15 Amp Instrument Panel Lights, Cigar Lighter, Glove Box Light
9 – Not Used

JAGUAR (Cont.)

10 – 15 Amp Turn Signals
11 – 35 Amp Horn Relay, Radiator Auxiliary Fan, Wipers, Brake Lights, Service Interval Counter, Auto. Trans. Kickdown Solenoid
12 – 2 Amp Cruise Control

Auxiliary Fuse Block
13 – 15 Amp A/C Relay & Clutch
14 & 15 – 3 Amp Front Parking Lights
16 – 50 Amp A/C or Heater Motor
17 – 3 Amp Door Lock Relay, Mirrors, Door Lights

Headlight Fuse Block
1 – 15 Amp Radiator Cooling Fan
2 – 20 Amp Right Low Beam
3 – 35 Amp Right High Beam
4 – 20 Amp Left Low Beam
5 – 35 Amp Left High Beam

XJS

Fuse block is located behind instrument panel on driver's side. Auxiliary fuse block is located below glove box. Headlight fuse box is located on left fender in engine compartment. Circuits protected are as follows:

Main Fuse Block
1 – 20 Amp Fog Lights
2 – 15 Amp Hazard Lights, Seat Belt Logic Unit
3 – 35 Amp Trunk Light, Cigar Lighter, Power Antenna, Clock
4 – 10 Amp Panel Instruments, Back-Up Lights
5 – 15 Amp Turn Signals, Brake Lights, Auto Kick-Down Solenoid
6 – 10 Amp Rear Fog Lights
7 – 10 Amp Panel Lights, Cigar Lighter, Selector Illumination
8 – 3 Amp Door Locks, Electric Mirror
9 – 35 Amp Wipers
10 – 50 Amp A/C Motors
11 – 35 Amp A/C Controls, Horn, Washers, Radiator Cooling Fan
12 – 35 Amp Defogger, Heated Mirrors

Auxiliary Fuse Block
13 – 10 Amp Interior and Map Lights
14 – 3 Amp Left Side Marker Lights
15 – 3 Amp Right Side Marker Lights
16 – 20 Amp Cigar Lighter
17 – 3 Amp Cruise Control

Headlight Fuse Block
1 – 25 Amp Cooling Fan
2 – 25 Amp Left High Beam
3 – 10 Amp Left Low Beam
4 – 25 Amp Right High Beam
5 – 10 Amp Right Low Beam

MAZDA

626

Fuse Block

Fuse block is located beneath instrument panel to left of steering column. Capacities and circuits covered are listed on the fuse block cover. Fuses are arranged in 3 rows. Going from top to bottom, left row to right row, circuit information is as follows:

Left Row
1 – 15 Amp Brake Lights, Horn
2 – 30 Amp Power Door Locks
3 – Not Used
4 – 20 Amp Headlight Cleaner
5 – 15 Amp Engine Power
6 – Not Used
7 – 20 Amp Cooling Fan

Middle Row:
8 – 20 Amp Cooling Fan
9 – 15 Amp Interior Lights
10 – 10 Amp Tail Lights
11 – 10 Amp Gauges
12 – 15 Amp Sun Roof
13 – 15 Amp Wipers
14 – 15 Amp Audio

Right Row
15 – 30 Amp Spare Fuse
16 – 15 Amp Spare Fuse
17 – 15 Amp Spare Fuse
18 – 30 Amp Power Windows
19 – 20 Amp Defogger
20 – 15 Rear Wiper

GLC WAGON

Fuse Block

The fuse block is located under the instrument panel and contains 10 fuses. Circuits protected are as follows, counting from top to bottom, left to right:

1 – 10 Amp Defogger, Audio
2 – 15 Amp Wiper/Washer
3 – 15 Amp Rear Wiper/Washer, Heater
4 – 10 Amp Cigar Lighter
5 – Not Used

Next Row
6 – 10 Amp Emission Control
7 – 10 Amp Kick Down, Meters & Warning Lights, Back-Up Lights, Seat Belt Warning Light & Buzzer
8 – Not Used
9 – 15 Amp Brake Lights, Horn
10 – 15 Amp Back Door Release, Key Reminder, Interior Light, Clock
11 – Illumination Lights, License Light, Tail & Front Parking Lights
12 – 10 Amp Turn Signals, Flasher
13 – Not Used

GLC HATCHBACK

Fuse Block

Fuse block is located at the left side of steering column. Fuses are arranged in 3 rows. Fuses and the circuits protected are:

1 – 15 Amp Side Marker Lights, Parking Lights, Tail Lights, Illmination Lights, Cruise Control

MAZDA (Cont.)

2 – Not Used
3 – 15 Amp Headlights

Next Row:

4 – 15 Amp Clock, Tail, Parking, License, Panel, Illumination & Marker Lights
5 – 15 Amp Cigar Lighter, Audio
6 – 20 Amp Front Wiper/Washer
7 – 20 Amp Cooling Fan, A/C
8 – 15 Amp Heater Blower
9 – 15 Amp Rear Wiper/Washer

Next Row:

10 – 15 Amp Defogger
11 – 10 Amp Regulator, Emission Control
12 – 10 Amp Gauges, Optional Clock, Brake Lights, Seat Belt Warning, Cooling Fan, Kickdown, Back-Up Lights
13 – 30 Amp Power Door Lock
14 – 15 Amp Brake Lights, Horn
15 – 10 Amp Turn Signals, Flashers, Courtesy Lights, Buzzers

RX7

Fuse Block

Fuse block is located to left side of steering column. Fuses protect, from top to bottom and left to right, the following circuits:

1 – 20 Amp Heater & A/C, Glove Box Light
2 – 15 Amp Defogger
3 – 20 Amp Audio, Power Antenna
4 – 10 Amp Wiper/Washer
5 – 10 Amp Wiper/Washer
6 – 30 Amp Power Windows
7 – 10 Amp Cruise Control

Next Row:

8 – 20 Amp Gas Filler Door, Rear Hatch Release
9 – 15 Amp Brake Lights, Horn
10 – 15 Amp Auto Clock, Courtesy Lights, Chime, Cigar Lighter, Buzzer
11 – 10 Amp Mirrors, A/C, Turn Signals, Flashers, Headlights
12 – 10 Amp Panel Lights, Headlight Motors, Headlight Washers
13 – 10 Amp Gauges, Back-Up Lights, Clock, Timer Unit
14 – 15 Amp Kickdown Solenoid, Charging System, Emissions

B2000 & B2200 PICKUPS

Fuse Block

Fuse block is located in left rear corner of engine compartment and contains 2 rows of fuses. Protected circuits include:

1 – 15 Amp Turn Signals, Brake Lights, Horn
2 – 10 Amp Headlights
3 – 10 Amp Back-Up Lights, Gauges, Clock, Warning System
4 – 15 Amp Alternator, Emissions, Solenoids
5 – Not Used

Next Row

6 – 10 Amp Interior Light, Clock
7 – 15 Amp Heater, Audio
8 – 10 Amp Wiper/Washer
9 – 10 Amp Cigar Lighter
10 – Not Used

In-Line Fuses

A fuse block containing large in-line fuses is installed in engine compartment near battery. Fuse amperage and circuits protected is printed on fuse block cover.

MERCEDES-BENZ

380SL

Fuse Block

Main fuse block is located on right kick panel. Fuse capacities and the circuits protected are listed on fuse block cover.

ALL OTHER MODELS

Fuse Block

Fuse block is located at left rear corner of engine compartment. Fuse capacities and circuits protected are listed on the fuse block cover.

In-Line Fuses

Additional fuses for optional equipment and/or standard extras such as sliding sun roof, heated rear window, radio, automatic antenna, electric windows and air conditioning are located in engine compartment.

MITSUBISHI

NOTE: **Refer to Latest Changes & Corrections for Starion information.**

CORDIA

Fuse Block

The fuse block is located beneath the instrument cluster in front of the driver's seat. They are arranged in 3 rows, with numbers starting at the top left. Protected circuits include:

1 – 10 Amp Dome Light
2 – 10 Amp Brake Lights
3 – 10 Amp Hazard Lights
4 – 20 Amp Defogger
5 – Not Used

Next Row:

6 – 20 Amp Heater
7 – 10 Amp Horn
8 – 15 Amp Wiper
9 – 15 Amp Radio
10 – Not Used

MITSUBISHI (Cont.)

Next Row
- 11 – 10 Amp Turn Signals
- 12 – 10 Amp Back-Up Lights
- 13 – 10 Amp Tail Lights
- 14 – Not Used
- 15 – Not Used

MONTERO

Fuse Block

Fuse block is located beneath instrument panel on left side. Fuses are numbered with first fuse at top left and last fuse at bottom right. Protected circuits are as follows:

- 1 – 20 Amp Dome Light, Hazard Lights, Clock
- 2 – 10 Amp Tail Lights
- 3 – 10 Amp Turn Signals
- 4 – 15 Amp Backup Lights, Gauges
- 5 – 15 Amp Defogger
- 6 – 20 Amp Heater
- 7 – 15 Amp Brake Lights
- 8 – 10 Amp Horn, Front Wiper/Washer
- 9 – 10 Amp Rear Wiper/Washer
- 10 – 15 Amp Cigar Lighter, Radio

PICKUP

Fuse Block

Fuse block is located beneath instrument panel on left side. Fuses are numbered with first fuse at top left and last fuse at bottom right. Protected circuits are as follows:

- 1 – 10 Amp Dome Light
- 2 – 10 Amp Hazard Lights
- 3 – 10 Amp Brake Lights
- 4 – 15 Amp Turn Signals

Next Row:
- 5 – 15 Amp Radio, Wipers
- 6 – 15 Amp Heater
- 7 – 10 Amp Horn
- 8 – 10 Amp Tail Lights

TREDIA

Fuse Block

Fuse block is located behind oddment box in left side of steering column. Fuses are arranged in 3 rows, with numbers starting from left to rignt and starting with the bottom row. Protected circuits include:

- 1 – 10 Amp Dome Light
- 2 – 10 Amp Brake Light
- 3 – 10 Amp Hazard Light
- 4 – 20 Amp Defogger
- 5 – 20 Amp Heater
- 6 – 10 Amp Horn
- 7 – 15 Amp Wipers
- 8 – 15 Amp Radio
- 9 – 10 Amp Turn Signals
- 10 – 10 Amp Backup Lights
- 11 – 10 Amp Tail Lights

PEUGEOT

504

Fuse Block

Fuse block is located behind lower left corner of instrument panel. Fuses are arranged in a single row and numbered from left to right. Circuits protected are:

- 1 – 5 Amp Parking, Side Marker, License & Dashboard Lights
- 2 – 10 Amp Clock, Courtesy Lights, Trunk Light, Horn, Cigar Lighter, Hazard Lights, Ignition Buzzer
- 3 – 10 Amp Back-Up, Brake Lights, Low Fuel Light, Preheat Relay, Preheat Indicator Light, Temperature Indicator, Engine Fan, Seat Belt Buzzer & Light
- 4 – 16 Amp Defogger, Wiper Switch, Wiper Motor & Relay, Washer Pump
- 5 – 10 Amp Warning Indicators, Turn Signals, Gauges, Heater Blower Motor, Audio

505

Fuse Block

Fuse block is located on top of left front fenderwell. Fuses are arranged in 2 rows, and numbered from front to back, starting with row closest to engine.

- 1 – 8 Amp Fog Lights
- 2 – 25 Amp Power Windows, Sun Roof
- 3 – 20 Amp Wiper/Washer, Turn Signals, Instrument Cluster Lights, Indicatator & Warning Lights, Defogger Control Switch
- 4 – 15 Amp Glove Box Light, Cigar Lighter, Radio Memory, Door & Fuel Filler Door Locks
- 5 – 20 Amp Horn, Hazard Lights, Clock, Antenna
- 6 – 25 Amp Fuel Pump
- 7 – 15 Amp Key Chime, Interior Lights, Trunk Light
- 8 – 15 Amp Back-Up Lights, Declutchable Fan, Twin Speed Relays, Tachometer, Brake Lights
- 9 – 25 Amp Rear Defogger Relay
- 10 – 25 Amp Heater & A/C Blower
- 11 – 15 Amp Extra Fuse
- 12 – 15 Amp Front Parking Lights, Instruments, Console and Courtesy Mirror Illumination
- 13 – 8 Amp Tail Lights, License Plate Light
- 14 – 8 Amp Audio, Antenna Up Mode

In-Line Fuse

Located under dash, to the left of steering column, is a 5 amp in-line fuse for the cruise control circuit.

604

Fuse Block

Fuse block is located behind cover on left end of instrument panel. Fuses are arranged in 2 rows and numbered from left to right, top row first. Protected circuits are:

- 1 – 10 Amp Cigar Lighter, Radio Memory, Glove Compartment Light, Map light, Horn, Hazzard Warning Lights, Interior Lights, Trunk Light, Ignition Key Illumination

PEUGEOT (Cont.)

2 – 10 Amp Brake Light Test, A/C Microswitch & Thermostat, Disengaging Fan Relay, Seat Belt Timer, Brake Lights, Fan Thermocontact, Auxiliary Fan Relay, Back-up Lights, Preheat Control Box, Low Fuel Warning Light, Overheat Warning light, Low Water Level Warning Light
3 – 5 Amp Spare Fuse
4 – 15 Amp Radio & Antenna
5 – 15 Amp Fuel Gauge, Water Temperature Gauge, Brake Warning Light, Oil Pressure/Filter Clog Warning Light, Charge Indicator, Heater & A/C Blower, Heated Driver's Seat
6 – 10 Amp Parking Lights, Tail Lights, Side Marker Lights, Console Illumination, Illumination of Switches & Ashtray
7 – 25 Amp Auxiliary Fan Relay
8 – 15 Amp Extra Fuse
9 – 15 Amp Defogger, Sun Roof, Rear Window Switches
10 – 15 Amp Front Window Switches
11 – 5 Amp Cruise Control
12 – 15 Amp Front Window Relay
13 – 15 Amp Rear Window Relay
14 – 15 Amp Sun Roof Relay, Window & Sun Roof Control Circuit

PORSCHE

911SC

Fuse Block

Fuse block is located inside luggage compartment on left side and contains 21 fuses. An additional fuse block is located in engine compartment on left side under regulator cover. Secondary fuse block protects Heater Fan Relay (5 amp), Heater Fan (25 amp) and Rear Window Defogger and Wiper Return (25 amp). Main fuses, numbered from front of vehicle to rear, protect the following circuits:

1 – 25 Amp Fog Lights
2 – 5 Amp License Plate Lights
3 – 5 Amp Right Front & Rear Parking Lights
4 – 5 Amp Left Front & Rear Parking Lights, Engine Compartment Light
5 – 8 Amp Right Low Beam
6 – 8 Amp Left Low Beam
7 – 8 Amp Right High Beam
8 – 8 Amp Left High Beam & Indicator
9 – 5 Amp Right Turn Signal
10 – 5 Amp Left Turn Signal
11 – 16 Amp Turn Signal Relay, Brake Lights, Back-Up Lights
12 – 25 Amp Rear Defogger, Fresh Air Blower, Control Light Auto A/C Control
13 – 25 Amp Front Wiper/Washer, Cigar Lighter
14 – 25 Amp Sunroof, Mirrors, Rear Wiper/Washer
15 – 8 Amp Brake Lights, Cruise Control
16 – 25 Amp Fuel Pump
17 – 16 Amp Hazard Flasher, Front Defogger
18 – 5 Amp Courtesy Lights, Clock, Trunk Light, Oxygen Sensor
19 – 25 Amp Headlight Washer
20 – 25 Amp A/C Blower Motor
21 – 25 Amp Power Windows

928S

Fuse Block

Fuse block is located in passenger footwell. It contains 34 fuses and 22 relays. Two 400mA in-line fuses are located above the fuse panel and protect the security system. Circuits protected by fuses are as follows, from left to right:

1 – 16 Amp Fog Lights
2 – Not Connected
3 – 8 Amp License Light, Engine Compartment Light
4 – 8 Amp Switch Illumination Light
5 – 16 Amp Cigar Lighter
6 – 16 Amp Windshield Wipers
7 – Not Used
8 – 16 Amp Sunroof
9 – 8 Amp Back-Up Lights, Mirror, Rear Wiper, A/C
10 – 8 Amp Brake Lights, Automatic Speed Control
11 – 8 Amp Instrument Panel Lights
12 – 8 Amp Instrument Warning Lights
13 – Not Connected
14 – 25 Amp Power Seats
15 – 16 Amp Power Antenna, Horn, Rear Wiper
16 – 25 Amp Electric Radiator Fan
17 – 25 Amp Heater, Air Conditioning Blower
18 – 25 Amp Rear Window Defogger
19 – 16 Amp Headlight Motor
20 – 16 Amp Headlight Washer
21 – 25 Amp Power Windows
22 – 16 Amp Fuel Pump
23 – 8 Amp Interior Lights, Clock
24 – 8 Amp Left High Beam
25 – 8 Amp Right High Beam
26 – 8 Amp Left Low Beam
27 – 8 Amp Right Low Beam
28 – 8 Amp Left Side Markers
29 – 8 Amp Right Side Markers
30 – 8 Amp Front Left Turn Signal
31 – 8 Amp Rear Left Turn Signal
32 – 8 Amp Front Right Turn Signal
33 – 8 Amp Rear Right Turn Signal
34 – Not Connected

Fig. 1: Porsche 928S Fuse and Relay Block

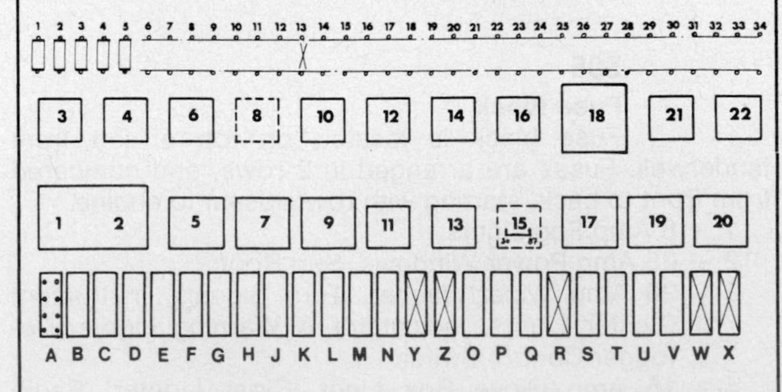
1 2 3 4 5 6 7 8 9 10 11 12 13 14 15 16 17 18 19 20 21 22 23 24 25 26 27 28 29 30 31 32 33 34
3 4 6 8 10 12 14 16 18 21 22
1 2 5 7 9 11 13 15 17 19 20
A B C D E F G H J K L M N Y Z O P Q R S T U V W X

PORSCHE (Cont.)

Relay Block

Relay circuits are below the fuses in the main electrical panel. Other relays include the seat return relay (below seat), the rear wiper relay (at left rear corner behind tool kit tray) and the seat belt relay (behind radio).

1 & 2 – Defogger
3 – Not Used
4 – Not Used
5 – Hazard Flasher Unit
6 – Window Controls
7 – Headlight Washer Pump
8 – Not Used
9 – Not Used
10 – Horns
11 – Not Used
12 – Fog Lights
13 – Intermittent Wiper Speed Control
14 – Starter Relay Bridge
15 – Washer Pump
16 – EFI Control Unit
17 – Fuel Pump
18 – Extra Cooling Fan for A/C
19 & 20 – Retractable Headlight Relay
21 – Fresh Air Fan
22 – Defroster

944

Fuse Block

Main fuse block is located under the instrument panel on the left side of steering column. An additional block is located above main block. The numbering of fuses begins on the left side of the panel. Circuits protected are as follows.

1 – 8 Amp Left Low Beam
2 – 8 Amp Right Low Beam
3 – 8 Amp Left High Beam
4 – 8 Amp Right High Beam
5 – Not Used
6 – 8 Amp Brake Lights, Flasher
7 – 8 Amp Clock, Interior Light, Radio, Cigar Lighter
8 – 8 Amp Turn Signal Indicators
9 – 8 Amp Back-Up Lights, Rear Wiper, Outside Mirrors
10 – 16 Amp Fresh Air Fan
11 – 8 Amp Front Wipers
12 – 8 Amp Panel Illumination, Luggage & Ashtray Lights, License Light
13 – 8 Amp Right Marker Light
14 – 8 Amp Left Marker Light, Engine Compartment Light
15 – 16 Amp Fog Lights

Auxiliary Block

1 – 8 Amp Retractable Headlights
2 – 16 Amp Fuel Pump
3 – 16 Amp Radiator Fan, Antenna
4 – 25 Amp Defogger
5 – 16 Amp A/C Fan, Condensor Fan
6 – 25 Amp A/C Compressor, Fresh Air Fan
7 – Not Used
8 – 25 Amp Power Windows
9 – Not Connected

RENAULT

FUEGO & FUEGO TURBO

Fuse Block

Fuse block is located underneath dashboard on left side of steering column. Fuses are numbered in vertical rows from right to left, bottom to top.

1 – 8 Amp Turn Signal & Flasher
2 – Not Used
3 – 5 Amp Brake Lights
4 – 5 Amp Wiper Park Motor
5 – 5 Amp Audio, Wiper/Washer
6 – 8 Amp Interior Lights, Cigar Lighter, Buzzer, Luggage Compartment Light
7 – Not Used
8 – Not Used
9 – 16 Amp Defogger
10 – 5 Amp Left Parking Lights
11 – 16 Amp Left Power Window
12 – 5 Amp Right Parking Lights
13 – 16 Amp Right Power Window
14 – 5 Amp Instrument Cluster Feed
15 – 5 Amp Back-Up Lights, Intermittent Wipers
16 – 1.5 Amp Auto. Transmission Control
17 – Not Used
18 – Not Used
19 – 16 Amp A/C-Heater Fan, Sun Roof, Rear Wiper

LE CAR

Fuse Block

Fuse block is located underneath dashboard on right side of steering column. Fuses are numbered from left to right and protect these circuits:

1 – 5 Amp A/C Relay Feed
2 – 5 Amp Wiper Motor
3 – 5 Amp Left Parking Lights, Dash Lights
4 – 5 Amp Right Parking Lights, Cigar Lighter Light
5 – 8 Amp Wiper/Washer and Wiper Motor
6 – 5 Amp Cigar Lighter, Courtesy Light
7 – 8 Amp Heater Motor, Audio
8 – 5 Amp Turn Signals
9 – Not Used
10 – 16 Amp Back-Up Lights, Defogger, Brake Lights, Rear Wiper, A/C Relay, Seat Belt Buzzer

18i

Fuse Block

Fuse panel is located to left of steering column under edge of dashboard. Fuses are numbered from right to left, with even-numbered fuses in top row, and odd-numbered fuses in bottom row. The circuits protected are:

1 – 8 Amp Turn Signals, Flashers

RENAULT (Cont.)

2 – 5 Amp Wiper Park Circuit
3 – Not Used
4 – Not Used
5 – Not Used
6 – 8 Amp Cigar Lighter, Courtesy Lights
7 – Not Used
8 – 16 Amp Wiper/Washer
9 – Not Used
10 – 5 Amp Left Parking Lights, Instrument Panel Lights
11 – 10 Amp Left Power Window
12 – 5 Amp Right Parking Lights, Switch Lights
13 – 10 Amp Right Power Window
14 – 5 Amp Gauges
15 – 1.5 Amp Back-Up Lights, Intermittent Wiper Relay
16 – 1.5 Amp Auto. Trans.
17 – 16 Amp Heater & A/C Fan
18 – 16 Amp Defogger

SAAB

900

Fuse Block

Fuse block is located in engine compartment near left rear corner. Fuse capacities and circuits protected are as follows:

1 – 8 Amp Right High Beam
2 – 8 Amp Left High Beam
3 – 8 Amp Right Low Beam
4 – 8 Amp Left Low Beam
5 – 25 Amp Engine Fan
6 – 16 Amp Defogger
7 – 5 Amp Interior Lights
8 – 16 Amp Fuel Pump
9 – 8 Amp Hazard Flashers
10 – 8 Amp Brake Lights
11 – 8 Amp Rear Fog Lights
12 – 5 Amp Right Parking Lights
13 – 5 Amp Left Parking Lights
14 – 16 Amp Horn, Power Windows
15 – 8 Amp Headlight Wipers
16 – 16 Amp Heated Driver's Seat, Sun Roof
17 – 25 Amp Ventilation Fan
18 – 16 Amp A/C
19 – 8 Amp Instrument Panel Illumination
20 – 8 Amp Turn Signals
21 – 8 Amp Wiper/Washer
22 – 16 Amp Cornering Lights

SUBARU

ALL MODELS

Fuse Block

The fuse block is located underneath dashboard on left side. Fuses are arranged in 2 horizontal rows and are numbered from left to right starting on top row. Circuits protected are as follows:

1 – 10 Amp Clock, Brake Lights
2 – 10 Amp Horn Switch, Hazard Switch
3 – 10 Amp ECM (Non-Turbo Charged Models)
4 – 10 Amp Charge Indicator Light
5 – 15 Amp Cooling Fan, Audio
6 – 15 Amp Cigar Lighter, Remote Controlled Rearview Mirror Switch
7 – 20 Amp Wiper Switch
8 – 20 Amp Heater Blower Motor
9 – 10 Amp Right Headlight
10 – 10 Amp Left Headlight
11 – 15 Amp License Light, Tail Light
12 – 15 Amp Ignition Coil
13 – 15 Amp Cruise Control
14 – 15 Amp Kick-Down Relay
15 – 15 Amp Defogger
16 – 15 Amp Back-Up Light, Turn Signal Switch, Power Window Relay

TOYOTA

CAMRY

Fuse Block

Three fuse blocks are used. The main fuse block is located on driver's side kick panel behind a cover. The others are located in engine compartment on left side and on passenger's side kick panel. Fuses are arranged in 3 rows. Fuses are numbered from left to right and top to bottom. They protect circuits as follows:

Main Block
1 – 15 Amp Power Antenna
2 – 15 Amp Cruise Control System
3 – 7.5 Amp Discharge Warning Light, Ignition Main, Engine Cooling Fan Relay
4 – 20 Amp Windshield Wipers & Washers (Front & Rear)
5 – 15 Amp Stop Lights
6 – 7.5 Amp Turn Signals and Indicator Lights
7 – 7.5 Amp Back-Up Lights, Engine Temp. Gauge, Fuel Gauge, Low Level Light (Fuel & Oil Pressure), Window Defogger Relay, Brake System Warning Light, Door Main Relay, Tachometer
8 – 15 Amp Instrument Panel Lights, License Plate Lights, Tail Lights, Parking Lights
9 – 7.5 Amp Audio
10 – 7.5 Amp Clock, Interior Lights, Iluminated Start-Up System, Trunk Light, Personal Lights, Open Door Warning Light
11 – 15 Amp Cigar Lighter, Clock (Digital Type), Remote Controlled Rear View Mirror
12 – 10 Amp A/C

Engine Fuse Block
13 – 7.5 Amp Carb. Choke Heater, Discharge Warning Light Relay

TOYOTA (Cont.)

14 – 15 Amp Left Headlights & High Beam Indicator
15 – 15 Amp Emergency Flasher & Indicator Light
16 – 15 Amp EFI System
17 – 15 Amp Right Headlights & High Beam Indicator
18 – 15 Amp Emission Control System, Alternator Voltage Regulator (IG Terminal), Fuel Cut Solenoid
19 – 15 Amp Radio

CELICA

Fuse Block

Three fuse blocks are used. The main fuse block is located on driver's side kick panel behind a cover. The others are located in engine compartment on left side and on the passenger's side kick panel. Fuses are arranged in 2 rows. Fuses are numbered from top to bottom and left to right. They protect circuits as follows:

Main Block
1 – 7.5 Amp Gauges & Warning Lights, Overdrive Solenoid, Back-Up Lights, Heater Main Relay Coil, Defogger Light, Oil Pressure Gauge, Voltmeter
2 – 7.5 Amp Interior Light, Key Reminder Buzzer, Luggage Light, Open Door Light, Personal Lights, Illuminated Start-Up Lights, Door Courtesy Lights
3 – 7.5 Amp Audio
4 – 15 Amp Cigar Lighter, Clock, Mirror
5 – 15 Amp Cruise Control
6 – 7.5 Amp Retractable Headlight System
7 – 7.5 Amp Turn Signals
8 – 7.5 Amp Discharge Warning Light & Ignition Main Relay Coil

Engine Fuse Block
9 – 7.5 Amp Discharge Warning Light Relay Coil
10 – 15 Amp Alternator With IC Regulator & Emission Control System
11 – 20 Amp Windshield Wipers & Washers (Front & Rear)
12 – 15 Amp Emergency Flashers and Indicator Lights, Horns, Audio
13 – 15 Amp Stop Lights
14 – 15 Amp Auto. Trans. Shift Position Indicator Light, Digital Clock, Side Marker Lights, Instrument Lights, Parking Lights, License Plate Lights, Tail Lights
15 – 15 Amp Right High Beam & High Beam Indicator Light
16 – 15 Amp Right Low Beam
17 – 15 Amp Left High Beam
18 – 15 Amp Left Low Beam

Passenger's Side Fuse Block
19 – 10 Amp Air Conditioner Main Relay Coil

Circuit Breakers

The sun roof and rear window defogger are protected by circuit breakers located on the driver's side fuse block. The heater blower motor is protected by a circuit breaker located on the passenger's fuse block.

COROLLA

Fuse Block

Three fuse blocks are used. One is in the engine compartment on left side. The others are under the left side of instrument panel and on the left kick panel. Starting from top to bottom and from left to right, protected circuits are:

Instrument Panel Fuse Block
1 – 20 Amp Heater Main Relay, Windshield Wipers & Washers (Front & Rear)
2 – 7.5 Amp Audio
3 – 7.5 Amp Spare Fuse
4 – 7.5 Amp Auto. Trans. Overdrive solenoid, Back-Up Lights, Brake System Warning Lights, Engine Temp. Gauge, Fuel Gauge Oil Pressure Light & Gauge, Seat Belt Reminder, Voltmeter
5 – 15 Amp Cigar Lighter & Digital Clock
6 – 7.5 Amp Turn Signal Lights & Indicator
7 – 7.5 Amp Discharge Light & Ignition Main Relay

Kick Panel Fuse Block
8 – 15 Amp Rear Window Defogger & Indicator Light
9 – 15 Amp License Plate Lights, Instrument Panel Lights, Parking Lights, Rear Side Marker Lights, Tail Lights, Auto. Trans. Shift Indicator Light
10 – 7.5 Amp Clock, Interior Light, Luggage Light, Open Door Warning Light, Key Reminder Buzzer
11 – 15 Amp Stop Lights

Engine Compartment Fuse Block
12 – 15 Amp Left Headlights
13 – 15 Amp Right Headlights
14 – 15 Amp Flashers, Horn, Radio
15 – 7.5 Amp Carburetor Choke Heater
16 – 15 Amp A/C & Heater Fan
17 – 15 Amp Voltage Regulator, Charge Relay, Emission Control System, Fuel Cut Solenoid

CRESSIDA

Fuse Block

Three fuse blocks are used. The main fuse block is in the Driver's kick panel. The others are located in the engine compartment and in the passenger's side kick panel. Fuses are numbered from left to right, and top to bottom. They protect the following circuits:

Main Fuse Block
1 – 7.5 Amp Turn Signals & Indicator Lights
2 – 15 Amp Cruise Control, Rear Wiper/Washer, Overdrive Solenoid, Power Antenna
3 – 7.5 Amp Gauges, Warning Lights, Heater, Air Conditioner Main Relay Coil, Back-Up Lights, Shoulder Belt Control
4 – 5 Amp Interior Lights, Clock, Luggage Compartment Light, Personal Lights, Power Antenna
5 – 7.5 Amp Fuel Inj. Control System, Discharge Light
6 – 7.5 Amp Audio, Clock
7 – 15 Amp Cigar Lighter, Power Antenna

Passenger's Side Fuse Block
8 – 10 Amp A/C

Engine Fuse Panel
9 – 7.5 Amp Alternator (L Terminal)
10 – 15 Amp Alternator (G Terminal)
11 – 15 Amp Horn, Radio, Emergency Flashers & Indicator
12 – 15 Amp Parking Lights, Glove Box Light, Shift Position Light, Rear Side Markers, Tail Lights, Instrument Panel Lights, License Plate Light
13 – 15 Amp Right Headlight, High Beam Indicator
14 – 15 Amp Left Headlight, High Beam Indicator

Fuses & Circuit Breakers

TOYOTA (Cont.)

15 – 15 Amp EFI Control System
16 – 20 Amp Windshield Wipers & Washer
17 – 15 Amp Brake Lights

Circuit Breakers

The rear defogger circuit breaker is on the main panel. It is reset by inserting a pin into the small hole on top. The power windows, door locks and sun roof are protected by one large circuit breaker. Press the button to reset this breaker.

LAND CRUISER (FJ40)

Fuse Block

Main fuse block is under the left side of instrument panel. They are numbered from top to bottom in a single row. The Ammeter fuses are near the battery, a 15 amp A/C fuse is near heater fan motor, and the 5 amp Engine Fan fuse is behind instrument panel. Fuses in the main block protect the following circuits:

1 – 15 Amp Tail, Parking, Side Marker, License, Dome & Instrument Panel Lights
2 – 15 Amp Horn, Brake Lights, Hazard Flashers, Engine Fan
3 – 15 Amp Headlights & High Beam Indicator
4 – 5 Amp Audio
5 – 15 Amp Cigar Lighter
6 – 15 Amp Engine Controls
7 – 20 Amp Heater Fan (Front & Rear)
8 – 20 Amp Turn Signals & Indicators, Back-Up Lights, Wiper/Washer

LAND CRUISER (FJ60 STATION WAGON)

Fuse Block

Main fuse block is located at left side of instrument panel. There are four rows of fuses, starting from top to bottom and from left to right. The circuits protected are:

1 – 10 Amp Right High Beam & High Beam Indicator
2 – 10 Amp Left High Beam & High Beam Indicator
3 – 15 Amp Cigar & Power Antenna
4 – 7.5 Amp Audio
5 – 15 Amp Parking, Side Marker, Instrument Panel, Glove Box, License & Tail Lights
6 – 15 Amp Brake Lights
7 – 15 Amp Horn, Hazard Flashers & Indicators
8 – (Gasoline Engine) 10 Amp Emission Control System, Electric Fan Relay, Fuel Cut Solenoid, Outer Vent Control Valve
(Diesel Engine) 15 Amp Brake Warning Light, Alternator, Temperature Gauge, Fuel Control Relay & Gauge, Heater Relay Coil, Oil Pressure Gauge, 4WD Light
9 – 7.5 Amp Turn Signal & Indicator Lights
10 – 20 Amp Wiper/Washer (Front & Rear), Back-Up Lights, Winch Control Switch
11 – 10 Amp A/C
12 – 7.5 Amp Glow Plug Timer, Relay Coil & Indicator
13 – 7.5 Amp Interior & Trunk Light, Electric Fan Relay
14 – 7.5 Amp Discharge Warning Light
15 – (Gasoline Engine) 7.5 Amp Brake Warning Light, Discharge Warning Light, Temp. Gauge, Fuel Gauge, Heater Main Relay Coil, Ignition Main Realay Coil, Oil Pressure Gauge, 4WD Indicator Light
(Diesel Engine) 7.5 Amp Fuel Control Relay, Glow Plug Relay Coil & Starter Relay Coil
16 – 7.5 Amp Spare Fuse
17 – 15 Amp Spare Fuse

Circuit Breakers

The defogger and heater blower are protected by two circuit breakers located in the fuse block. It is reset by inserting a pin into the small hole on top.

PICKUP

Fuse Block

Fuse block is located on left side of instrument panel. Fuses are numbered from left to right and top to bottom. Circuits protected are:

1 – 15 Amp Brake Lights
2 – 15 Amp Marker Lights, Instrument Panel Lights, License Light, Parking Lights, Tail Lights
3 – 15 Amp Horn, Emergency Flashers
4 – 15 Amp Cigar Lighter
5 – 7.5 Amp Audio
6 – 7.5 Amp Overdrive Solenoid, Cruise Control, Warning Lights & Buzzers, Gauges, Heater Main Relay Coil
7 – 7.5 Amp Turn Signals
8 – 7.5 Interior Light
9 – 10 Amp A/C
10 – 15 Amp High Beam Indicator, Left Headlight
11 – 15 Amp High Beam Indicator, Right Headlight
12 – 15 Amp Voltage Regulator, Alternator, Emission Control System, Glow Plug Timer
13 – 20 Amp Windshield Wiper & Washer
14 – 20 Amp Spare Fuse
15 – 15 Amp Spare Fuse

Circuit Breakers

Heater is protected by a 20 amp circuit breaker located in fuse block.

STARLET

Fuse Block

Fuse block is located at left side of instrument panel. Fuses are arranged top to bottom and left to right. Circuits protected are as follows:

1 – 10 Amp Right Headlight & Indicator Light
2 – 10 Amp Left Headlight & Indicator Light
3 – 15 Amp Rear Defogger, Side Marker, Parking, License, Instrument Panel & Tail Lights
4 – 10 Amp Brake Lights
5 – 10 Amp Cigar Lighter
6 – 5 Amp Audio
7 – 15 Amp Emergency Flashers & Indicator, Horn
8 – 10 Amp A/C
9 – 7.5 Amp Turn Signal & Indicator Lights
10 – 7.5 Amp Back-Up Lights, Temp. Gauge, Fuel Gauge, Oil Pressure Light, Parking Light
11 – 5 Amp Interior Light & Clock
12 – 10 Amp EFI Main Relay, Alternator, Discharge Warning Light
13 – 15 Amp Wipers and Washers (Front & Rear)
14 – 15 Amp Rear Window Defogger
15 – 5 Amp Discharge Warning Light
16 – 20 Amp A/C or Heater Main Relay
17 – 10 Amp Spare Fuse

TOYOTA (Cont.)

SUPRA

Fuse Block

Three fuse blocks are used. The main fuse block is located in left kick panel. The others are located on right side of engine compartment and in the right kick panel. Starting from left to right and from top to bottom, circuits protected are as follows:

Main Fuse Block

1 – 7.5 Amp Overdrive Solenoid, Back-Up Lights, Gauges, Warning & Indicator Lights, Power Window Relay Coil, Defogger & Indicator Light, Speedometer, Heater Main Relay Coil
2 – 7.5 Amp Interior Light, Buzzer, Courtesy Lights
3 – 7.5 Amp Audio
4 – 15 Amp Cigar Lighter, Clock (Digital Type), Power Mirror, Trip Computer
5 – 15 Amp Trip Computer
6 – 15 Amp Cruise Control
7 – 7.5 Amp Retractable Headlights
8 – 7.5 Amp Turn Signal & Indicator Lights
9 – 7.5 Amp Discharge Warning Light, Ignition Main Relay Coil, EFI Main Relay No. 1 & No. 2.
10 – 15 Amp Fog Lights

Engine Fuse Block

11 – 7.5 Amp Discharge Warning Light Relay
12 – 15 Amp Fuel Inj. Control System, Discharge Warning Light Relay Coil, Trip Computer
13 – 15 Amp Alternator
14 – 20 Amp Wiper & Washer (Front & Rear)
15 – 15 Amp Emergency Flashers, Horns, Audio
16 – 15 Amp Cruise Control, Brake Lights
17 – 15 Amp Shift Position Light, Clock, Marker Lights, Panel Lights, Interior Lights, License Light, Parking Lights, Tail Lights, Fog Light Relay
18 – 15 Amp Right High Beam & Indicator
19 – 15 Amp Right Low Beam
20 – 15 Amp Left High Beam
21 – 15 Amp Left Low Beam

Right Kick Panel

22 – 10 Amp A/C

Circuit Breakers

The heater blower/air conditioner motor is protected by a 30 amp circuit breaker located in the passenger's side kick panel. In the main fuse panel, the sun roof, magnetic door lock control and power windows are protected by a 30 amp circuit breaker. Located in the same panel is a 30 amp circuit breaker which protects the rear window defogger.

TERCEL

Fuse Block

Three fuse blocks are used. The main fuse block is located in left kick panel. The others are located in the engine compartment and in behind the passenger's side speaker housing. Fuses in main block are numbered starting with the vertical fuse at left, then from top to bottom. Engine compartment fuses are also numbered starting with forward fuse closest to engine.

Main Fuse Block

1 – 7.5 Amp Spare Fuse
2 – 15 Amp Spare Fuse
3 – 7.5 Amp Turn Signal & Indicator Lights
4 – 7.5 Amp Discharge Warning Light, Ignition Main Relay, Engine Fan
5 – 7.5 Amp Audio
6 – 15 Amp Cigar Lighter, Digital Clock
7 – 7.5 Amp Clock, Convenience Lights
8 – 15 Amp Brake Lights
9 – 15 Amp Shift Position Light, Instrument Panel, License Plate, Parking Tail Lights
10 – 7.5 Amp Temp. Gauge, Fuel Gauge, Oil Pressure Light, Back-Up Lights, Heater Main Relay, Sun Roof Relay
11 – 20 Amp Wipers & Washers (Front & Rear)

Engine Fuse Block

12 – 15 Amp Alternator, Fuel Cut Solenoid
13 – 15 Amp No Circuit
14 – 15 Amp Right Headlights & Indicator
15 – 15 Amp Left Headlights & Indicator
16 – 7.5 Amp Emission Control System, Carb. Choke Heater Coil, Discharge Warning System, Alternator Voltage Regulator
17 – 15 Amp Emergency Flashers, Horn

Passenger's Side Fuse Block

18 – 10 Amp Air Conditioner

Circuit Breakers

The defogger and sun roof are protected by circuit breakers behind the left kick panel. Push a pin into the hole in the circuit breaker to reset it. The heater, air conditioner and boost ventilator are protected by a circuit breaker behind the passenger's side kick panel and are reset the same way.

FUSIBLE LINKS

All Models

A fusible link is located in main battery feed wire near the battery. Link protects all circuits except for starter motor.

VOLKSWAGEN

JETTA, QUANTUM, RABBIT CONVERTIBLE & SCIROCCO

Fuse Block

Fuse block is located under dashboard on left side. Additional in-line fuses above the block protect Rear Wipers (8 amp), Fuel Pump (16 amp), and A/C (25 amp). Circuits protected are as follows:

1 – 30 Amp Radiator Fan
2 – 10 Amp Brake Lights
3 – 10 Amp Cigar Lighter, Radio, Clock, Interior Lights, Central Locking System
4 – 15 Amp Hazard Lights
5 – 15 Amp Electric Fuel Pump
6 – Not Used
7 – 10 Amp Left Tail Lights, Parking Lights, Side Marker Lights
8 – 10 Amp Right Tail Lights, Parking Lights, Side Marker Lights
9 – 10 Amp Right High Beam, High Beam Indicator
10 – 10 Amp Left High Beam
11 – 15 Amp Wiper/Washer
12 – 15 Amp Rear Wiper/Washer, Coolant Level Checking Device, Outside Rearview Mirror Adjuster

VOLKSWAGEN (Cont.)

13 – 15 Amp Defogger
14 – 15 Amp Fresh Air Fan
15 – 10 Amp Back-Up Lights, Shift Console Lights
16 – 10 Amp Horn
17 – Not Used
18 – 10 Amp Throttle Switch
19 – 10 Amp Turn Signals
20 – 10 Amp License Lights, Glove Compartment Light
21 – 10 Amp Left Low Beam
22 – 10 Amp Right Low Beam

RABBIT

Fuse Block

Fuse block is located at left side of instrument panel under a cover. The fuses are numbered. Starting at top right corner coming toward front, then from right to left, circuits are:

1 – 30 Amp Radiator Fan
2 – 15 Amp Parking Lights
3 – 20 Amp Horn
4 – 4 Amp Panel Lights
5 – 30 Amp Fuel Pump
6 – 10 Amp Rear Wiper
7 – 15 Amp Turn Signals
8 – 5 Amp Audio
9 – 10 Amp Back-Up Lights
10 – 25 Amp A/C-Heater Motor
11 – 25 Amp Defogger
12 – 20 Amp Front Wiper/Washer
13 – 15 Amp Brake Lights, Hazard Lights
14 – 15 Amp Courtesy Lights
15 – 10 Amp Cigar Lighter
16 – 4 Amp Horn Relay

RABBIT PICKUP

Fuse Block

Fuse block is located at left side of instrument panel under a cover. The fuses are numbered. Starting at top right corner coming toward front, then from right to left, circuits are:

1 – 30 Amp Radiator Fan
2 – 15 Amp Parking Lights
3 – 20 Amp Horn
4 – 4 Amp Panel Lights
5 – 30 Amp Fuel Pump Relay
6 – 15 Amp Turn Signals
7 – 5 Amp Audio
8 – 10 Amp Back-Up Lights
9 – 25 Amp A/C-Heater Motor
10 – 25 Amp Defogger
11 – 20 Amp Front Wiper/Washer
12 – 15 Amp Brake Lights, Hazard Lights
13 – 15 Amp Courtesy Lights
14 – 10 Amp Cigar Lighter
15 – 4 Amp Horn Relay

VANAGON

Fuse Block

Fuse block is located under dashboard on left side of steering column. Fuse block contains 12 circuits. In addition, a 16 amp fuse is located at right side of fuse panel to protect blower fan. Circuits protected in main fuse block are as follows:

1 – 8 Amp Left Tail, Parking & Marker Lights
2 – 8 Amp Right Tail, Parking, Marker & License Lights
3 – 8 Amp Left Low Beam
4 – 8 Amp Right Low Beam
5 – 8 Amp Left High Beam & Indicator
6 – 8 Amp Right High Beam
7 – 8 Amp Accessories, Radiator Fan (Diesel)
8 – 8 Amp Cigar Lighter, Brake Lights, Interior Lights
9 – 16 Amp Hazard Warning Lights
10 – 16 Amp Windshield Wiper/Washer, Defogger
11 – 8 Amp Turn Signals
12 – 8 Amp Horn, Back-Up Lights

Relays

Relays are arranged from left to right in the fuse block: Flasher, Blank, Load Reduction, Key Buzzer, Wipers.

VOLVO

760 GLE

Fuse Block

The fuse block is located behind a cover in front of the shift lever on center console. There are 22 fuses in 2 rows. Fuses are numbered from left to right, starting with top row. Circuits protected are as follows:

1 – 25 Amp Fuel Pump
2 – 25 Amp Central Locking System, Hazard Lights
3 – 15 Amp Fog Lights
4 – 15 Amp Brake Lights
5 – 15 Amp Glove Box Light, Clock, Radio, Engine Compartment Light, Interior Light, Trunk Light, Antenna, Door Open Warning
6 – 25 Amp Cooling Fan
7 – 30 Amp Power Windows
8 – 15 Amp Turn Signals
9 – 30 Amp Defogger, Sun Roof
10 – 25 Amp Heated Front Seat
11 – 25 Amp Heater Fan, A/C, Climate Control Unit, Cruise Control
12 – 15 Amp Cigar Lighter, Rear View Mirrors, Audio
13 – 25 Amp Horn, Washer/Wiper, Heater Fan
14 – 30 Amp Heater Fan
15 – 15 Amp Tank Pump
16 – 15 Amp Rear Fog Lamps
17 – 15 Amp Left High Beam
18 – 15 Amp Right High Beam
19 – 15 Amp Left Low Beam
20 – 15 Amp Right Low Beam
21 – 15 Amp Ashtray Light, Instrument & Control Lights, Left Position Lights, License Plate Lights
22 – 15 Amp Seat Belt Light, Right Position Lights, Fog Lights

VOLVO (Cont.)

DL, GL & TURBO

Fuse Block

Fuse block is located in left kick panel behind cover. Fuses are numbered from top to bottom and space is provided for spare fuses at bottom of block. Circuits protected are as follows:

1 – 8 Amp Cigar Lighter, Rear Wipers, Audio, Mirrors, Power Antenna, Cruise Control
2 – 16 Amp Horn, Wiper/Washer
3 – 25 Amp Heater Fan
4 – 8 Amp Warning Buzzers
5 – 8 Amp Fuel Pump (Feed Pump)
6 – 8 Amp Brake Lights, Courtesy Light Relay
7 – 16 Amp Main Fuel Pump, Oxygen Sensor
8 – 8 Amp Courtesy Lights, Locking System
9 – 8 Amp Hazard Flashers
10 – 16 Amp Power Windows
11 – 16 Amp Overdrive, Defogger
12 – 8 Amp Back-Up Lights, Power Window Relay, Heated Driver's Seat, A/C
13 – 8 Amp Gauges, Turn Signals, Belt Warning, Fuel Injection Relay, Diesel Control Unit
14 – Spare
15 – 8 Amp Left Parking & Marker Lights, License Light
16 – 8 Amp Right Parking & Marker Lights, Headlight Buzzer, Instrument Panel Lights

SECTION 4

WIRING DIAGRAMS

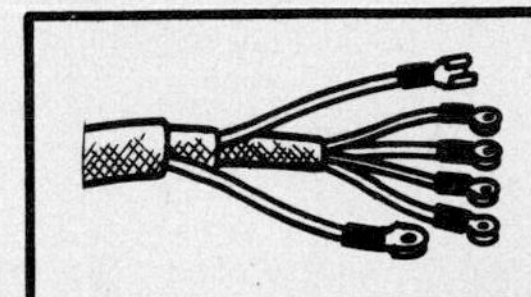

ARRANGEMENT OF DATA

The Wiring Diagram Section contains Chassis Wiring Diagrams spread across several pages for more efficient reading.

CONTENTS

⋆ – Indicates new style wiring diagrams.

NOTE: ALSO SEE GENERAL INDEX.

MITCHELL'S WIRING DIAGRAMS

Mitchell obtains diagrams and wiring change bulletins from all the import manufacturers. These are all checked and redrawn in a consistent style for easy use. All diagrams are arranged with the front of the vehicle at the left side of the first page, and the taillights at the right edge of the last page. Accessories are shown near the end of the diagram. Components are shown in their approximate location in the vehicle, though due to crowded pages, it is not possible to shown exact positioning .

Several diagrams in this manual have been drawn in a new style. The improved layout allows space for internal switch details and connector shapes. Removing some of the wiring maze reduces eyestrain and wasted time from searching across several pages. Any wires that don't connect directly to their components are labeled so you know where they go. There is a component list at the front of the diagrams. It refers you to components, using grid numbers at the top and bottom of the pages.

HOW TO USE THE NEW DIAGRAMS

1) The front part of the diagram contains a reference list of the major electrical components. Find the component or system you wish to trace.

2) Use the grid numbers to find the component on the wiring diagram pages.

3) The vehicle locations shown at the bottom of the page will help you to find the approximate location of the component on the actual vehicle.

4) Find the circuit you need to service. The internals are shown for switches and relays so you can understand how the circuit operates.

5) If the wires are not drawn all the way to another component, a reference will tell you their destination.

6) Use the reference list and grid to find the other component rather than tracing a wire through several pages.

WIRING SYMBOLS

Standard wiring symbols are used on our diagrams. The list below will help clarify any symbols that are not easily understood at a glance. Most components are labeled "Motor", "Switch" or "Relay" in addition to being drawn with the standard symbol.

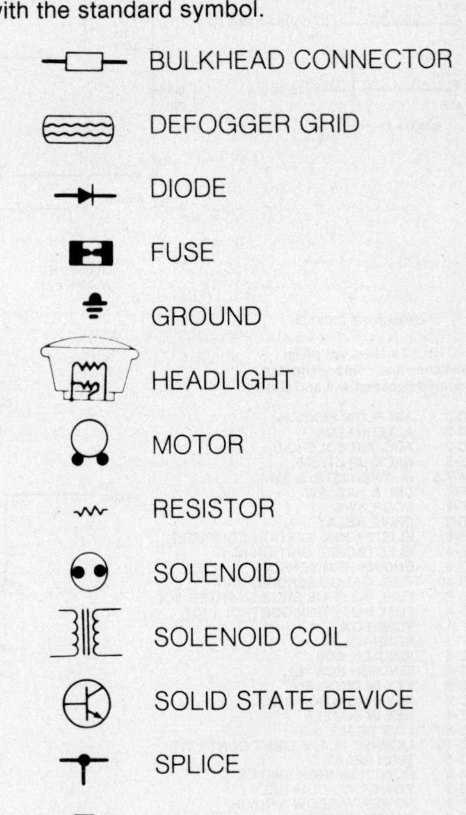
BULKHEAD CONNECTOR
DEFOGGER GRID
DIODE
FUSE
GROUND
HEADLIGHT
MOTOR
RESISTOR
SOLENOID
SOLENOID COIL
SOLID STATE DEVICE
SPLICE
SWITCH
TAIL OR DIRECTIONAL LIGHT

1983 Alfa Romeo

SPIDER 2.0

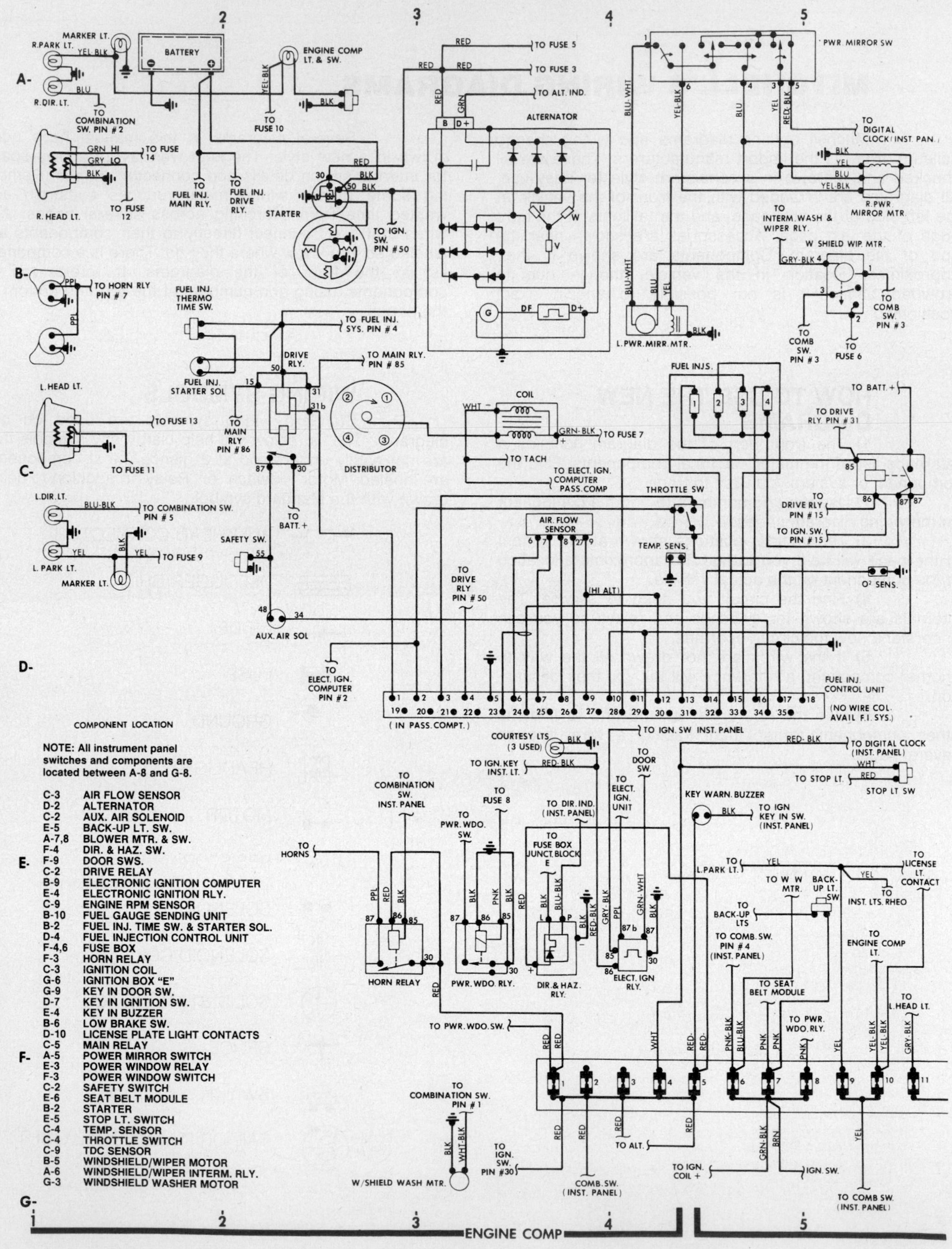

COMPONENT LOCATION
NOTE: All instrument panel switches and components are located between A-8 and G-8.
C-3 AIR FLOW SENSOR
D-2 ALTERNATOR
C-2 AUX. AIR SOLENOID
E-5 BACK-UP LT. SW.
A-7,8 BLOWER MTR. & SW.
F-4 DIR. & HAZ. SW.
F-9 DOOR SWS.
C-2 DRIVE RELAY
B-9 ELECTRONIC IGNITION COMPUTER
E-4 ELECTRONIC IGNITION RLY.
C-9 ENGINE RPM SENSOR
B-10 FUEL GAUGE SENDING UNIT
B-2 FUEL INJ. TIME SW. & STARTER SOL.
D-4 FUEL INJECTION CONTROL UNIT
F-4,6 FUSE BOX
F-3 HORN RELAY
C-3 IGNITION COIL
G-6 IGNITION BOX "E"
G-9 KEY IN DOOR SW.
D-7 KEY IN IGNITION SW.
E-4 KEY IN BUZZER
B-6 LOW BRAKE SW.
D-10 LICENSE PLATE LIGHT CONTACTS
C-5 MAIN RELAY
A-5 POWER MIRROR SWITCH
E-3 POWER WINDOW RELAY
F-3 POWER WINDOW SWITCH
C-2 SAFETY SWITCH
E-6 SEAT BELT MODULE
B-2 STARTER
E-5 STOP LT. SWITCH
C-4 TEMP. SENSOR
C-4 THROTTLE SWITCH
C-9 TDC SENSOR
B-5 WINDSHIELD/WIPER MOTOR
A-6 WINDSHIELD/WIPER INTERM. RLY.
G-3 WINDSHIELD WASHER MOTOR
MARKER LT.
R.PARK LT.
R.DIR. LT.
BATTERY
ENGINE COMP LT. & SW.
TO FUSE 10
TO COMBINATION SW. PIN # 2
TO FUSE 5
TO FUSE 3
TO ALT. IND.
ALTERNATOR
PWR. MIRROR SW
TO DIGITAL CLOCK/INST. PAN.
R. PWR MIRROR MTR.
TO INTERM. WASH & WIPER RLY.
W SHIELD WIP MTR.
TO COMB SW. PIN # 3
TO FUSE 6
L. PWR. MIRR. MTR.
R. HEAD LT.
TO FUSE 14
TO FUSE 12
TO FUEL INJ. MAIN RLY.
TO FUEL INJ. DRIVE RLY.
STARTER
TO IGN. SW. PIN # 50
TO HORN RLY PIN # 7
FUEL INJ. THERMO TIME SW.
TO FUEL INJ. SYS. PIN # 4
FUEL INJ. STARTER SOL
DRIVE RLY.
TO MAIN RLY. PIN # 85
TO MAIN RLY PIN # 86
DISTRIBUTOR
L. HEAD LT.
TO FUSE 13
TO FUSE 11
L. DIR. LT.
TO COMBINATION SW. PIN # 5
TO FUSE 9
L. PARK LT.
MARKER LT.
TO BATT. +
SAFETY SW.
AUX. AIR SOL
TO DRIVE RLY PIN # 50
TO ELECT. IGN. COMPUTER PIN # 2
COIL
TO FUSE 7
TO TACH
TO ELECT. IGN. COMPUTER PASS. COMP
AIR FLOW SENSOR
FUEL INJS.
TO BATT. +
TO DRIVE RLY. PIN # 31
THROTTLE SW
TO DRIVE RLY PIN # 15
TO IGN. SW. PIN # 15
TEMP. SENS.
O2 SENS.
(HI ALT)
FUEL INJ. CONTROL UNIT
(NO WIRE COL. AVAIL F.I. SYS.)
(IN PASS. COMPT.)
COURTESY LTS (3 USED)
TO IGN. SW INST. PANEL
TO IGN. KEY INST. LT.
TO DOOR SW.
TO DIGITAL CLOCK (INST. PANEL)
TO STOP LT.
STOP LT SW
TO COMBINATION SW. INST. PANEL
TO FUSE 8
TO PWR. WDO. SW.
TO DIR. IND. (INST. PANEL)
TO ELECT. IGN. UNIT
TO FUSE BOX JUNCT. BLOCK E
KEY WARN. BUZZER
TO IGN KEY IN SW. (INST. PANEL)
TO HORNS
TO L. PARK LT.
TO W W MTR.
BACK-UP LT. SW
TO LICENSE LT. CONTACT
TO INST. LTS. RHEO
TO BACK-UP LTS
TO COMB. SW. PIN # 4 (INST. PANEL)
TO ENGINE COMP LT.
HORN RELAY
PWR. WDO. RLY.
DIR. & HAZ. RLY.
ELECT. IGN RLY.
TO SEAT BELT MODULE
TO PWR. WDO. RLY.
TO L. HEAD LT.
TO PWR. WDO. SW.
TO COMBINATION SW. PIN # 1
TO IGN. SW. PIN # 30
W/SHIELD WASH MTR.
COMB. SW. (INST. PANEL)
TO ALT.
TO IGN. COIL +
IGN. SW.
TO COMB SW. (INST. PANEL)
ENGINE COMP

1983 Alfa Romeo

SPIDER 2.0 (Cont.)

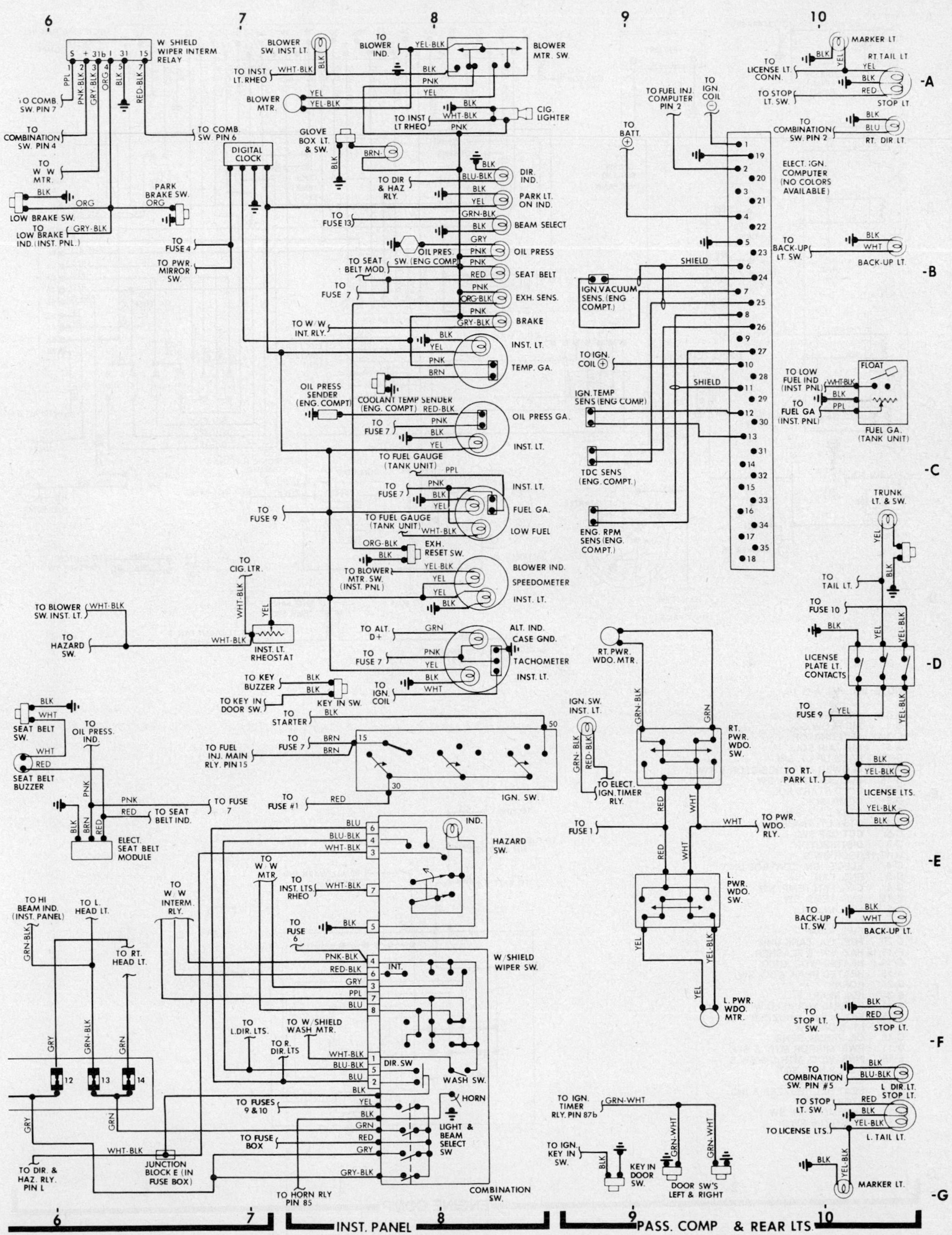

6
7
8
9
10
W. SHIELD WIPER INTERM RELAY
TO COMB. SW. PIN 7
TO COMBINATION SW. PIN 4
TO W W MTR.
TO COMB. SW. PIN 6
PARK BRAKE SW.
LOW BRAKE SW.
TO LOW BRAKE IND. (INST. PNL.)
TO FUSE 4
TO PWR. MIRROR SW.
DIGITAL CLOCK
BLOWER SW. INST LT.
TO INST LT. RHEO
BLOWER MTR.
TO BLOWER IND.
BLOWER MTR. SW.
TO INST LT RHEO
CIG. LIGHTER
GLOVE BOX LT. & SW.
TO DIR & HAZ RLY.
DIR. IND.
PARK LT. ON IND.
TO FUSE 13
BEAM SELECT
OIL PRES. SW. (ENG COMP)
OIL PRESS
TO SEAT BELT MOD.
SEAT BELT
TO FUSE 7
EXH. SENS.
BRAKE
TO W/W INT. RLY.
INST. LT.
TEMP. GA.
OIL PRESS SENDER (ENG. COMPT)
COOLANT TEMP SENDER (ENG. COMPT)
OIL PRESS GA.
TO FUSE 7
INST. LT.
TO FUEL GAUGE (TANK UNIT)
INST. LT.
TO FUSE 7
FUEL GA.
TO FUSE 9
TO FUEL GAUGE (TANK UNIT)
LOW FUEL
EXH. RESET SW.
TO BLOWER MTR. SW. (INST. PNL)
BLOWER IND.
SPEEDOMETER
INST. LT.
TO CIG. LTR.
TO BLOWER SW. INST. LT.
TO HAZARD SW.
INST. LT. RHEOSTAT
TO ALT. D+
ALT. IND.
CASE GND.
TO FUSE 7
TACHOMETER
INST. LT.
TO IGN. COIL
TO KEY BUZZER
TO KEY IN DOOR SW.
KEY IN SW.
TO STARTER
TO FUEL INJ. MAIN RLY. PIN 15
TO FUSE 7
IGN. SW.
TO FUSE #1
SEAT BELT SW.
TO OIL PRESS. IND.
SEAT BELT BUZZER
TO SEAT BELT IND.
TO FUSE 7
ELECT. SEAT BELT MODULE
HAZARD SW.
IND.
TO W W MTR
TO INST. LTS RHEO
TO FUSE 6
W/SHIELD WIPER SW.
INT.
TO HI BEAM IND. (INST. PANEL)
TO L. HEAD LT.
TO RT. HEAD LT.
TO W W INTERM. RLY.
TO L.DIR. LTS.
TO W/SHIELD WASH MTR.
TO R. DIR. LTS
DIR. SW
WASH SW.
HORN
TO FUSES 9 & 10
TO FUSE BOX
LIGHT & BEAM SELECT SW
TO DIR. & HAZ. RLY. PIN L
JUNCTION BLOCK E (IN FUSE BOX)
TO HORN RLY PIN 85
COMBINATION SW.
TO FUEL INJ. COMPUTER PIN 2
TO IGN COIL
TO BATT.
ELECT. IGN. COMPUTER (NO COLORS AVAILABLE)
SHIELD
IGN. VACUUM SENS. (ENG COMPT.)
TO IGN. COIL
IGN. TEMP SENS (ENG COMP)
TDC SENS (ENG. COMPT.)
ENG. RPM SENS (ENG. COMPT.)
RT. PWR. WDO. MTR.
IGN. SW. INST. LT.
RT. PWR. WDO. SW.
TO ELECT. IGN. TIMER RLY.
TO FUSE 1
TO PWR. WDO. RLY.
L. PWR. WDO. SW.
L. PWR. WDO. MTR.
TO IGN. TIMER RLY. PIN 87b
TO IGN. KEY IN SW.
KEY IN DOOR SW.
DOOR SW'S LEFT & RIGHT
MARKER LT
RT. TAIL LT
TO LICENSE LT. CONN.
TO STOP LT. SW.
STOP LT.
TO COMBINATION SW. PIN 2
RT. DIR. LT.
TO BACK-UP LT. SW.
BACK-UP LT.
TO LOW FUEL IND (INST PNL)
FLOAT
TO FUEL GA (INST. PNL)
FUEL GA. (TANK UNIT)
TRUNK LT. & SW.
TO TAIL LT.
TO FUSE 10
LICENSE PLATE LT. CONTACTS
TO FUSE 9
TO RT. PARK LT.
LICENSE LTS.
TO BACK-UP LT. SW.
BACK-UP LT.
TO STOP LT. SW.
STOP LT.
TO COMBINATION SW. PIN #5
L. DIR. LT.
STOP LT.
TO STOP LT. SW.
TO LICENSE LTS.
L. TAIL LT.
MARKER LT.
-A
-B
-C
-D
-E
-F
-G
INST. PANEL
PASS. COMP & REAR LTS

1983 Alfa Romeo

GTV-6 2.5

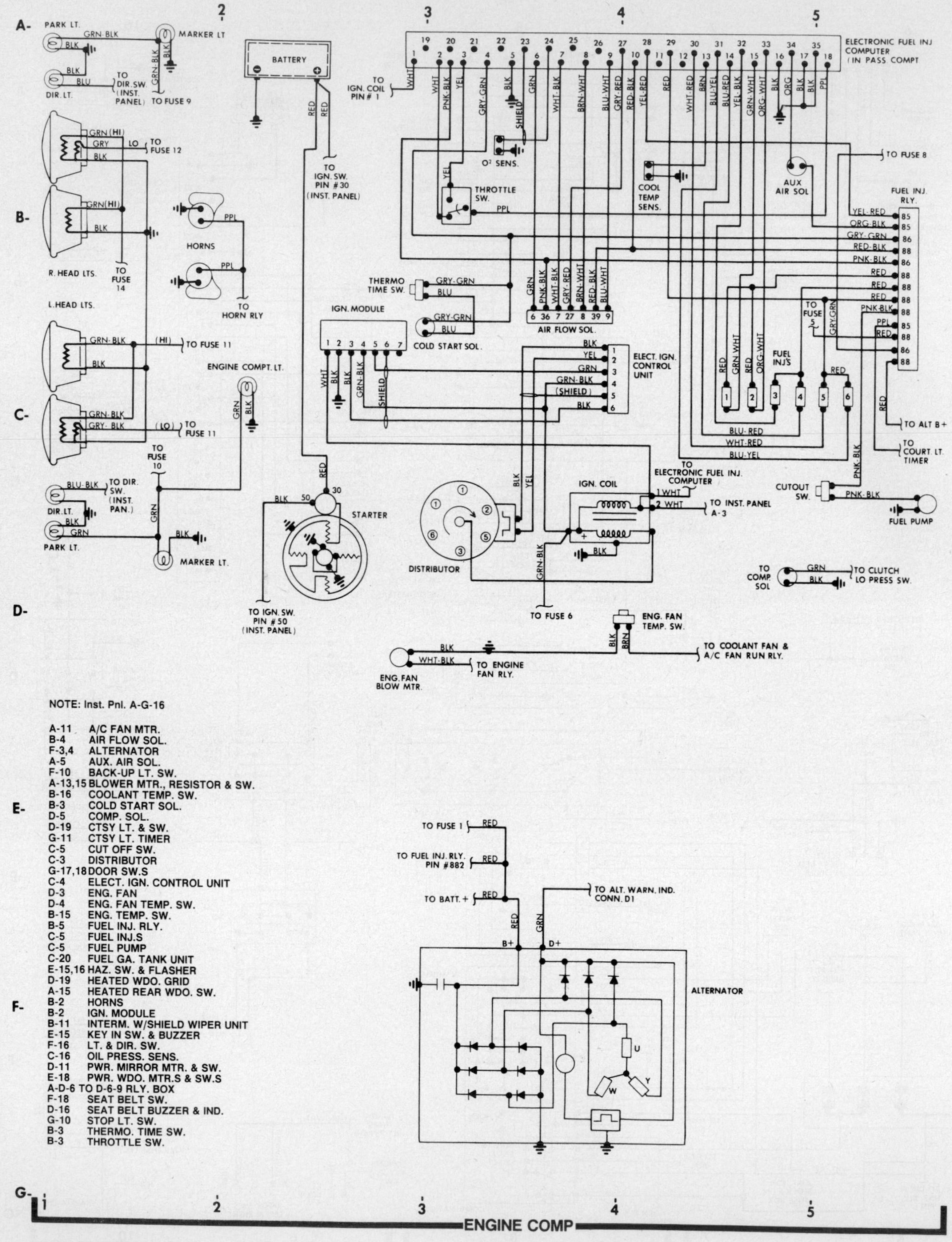
PARK LT.
MARKER LT
DIR. LT.
TO DIR. SW. (INST. PANEL)
TO FUSE 9
BATTERY
TO IGN. SW. PIN #30 (INST. PANEL)
TO IGN. COIL PIN # 1
ELECTRONIC FUEL INJ COMPUTER (IN PASS COMPT
TO FUSE 12
R. HEAD LTS.
TO FUSE 14
HORNS
TO HORN RLY
L. HEAD LTS.
TO FUSE 11
ENGINE COMPT. LT.
O² SENS.
THROTTLE SW.
COOL TEMP SENS.
AUX AIR SOL
TO FUSE 8
FUEL INJ. RLY.
THERMO TIME SW.
IGN. MODULE
COLD START SOL.
AIR FLOW SOL.
ELECT. IGN. CONTROL UNIT
FUEL INJ'S
TO ALT B+
TO COURT. LT. TIMER
TO FUSE 10
TO DIR. SW. (INST. PAN.)
STARTER
DISTRIBUTOR
IGN. COIL
TO ELECTRONIC FUEL INJ. COMPUTER
TO INST. PANEL A-3
CUTOUT SW.
FUEL PUMP
TO IGN. SW. PIN #50 (INST. PANEL)
TO FUSE 6
TO COMP. SOL
TO CLUTCH LO PRESS SW.
ENG. FAN TEMP. SW.
TO COOLANT FAN & A/C FAN RUN RLY.
TO ENGINE FAN RLY.
ENG. FAN BLOW MTR.
NOTE: Inst. Pnl. A-G-16
A-11 A/C FAN MTR.
B-4 AIR FLOW SOL.
F-3,4 ALTERNATOR
A-5 AUX. AIR SOL.
F-10 BACK-UP LT. SW.
A-13,15 BLOWER MTR., RESISTOR & SW.
B-16 COOLANT TEMP. SW.
B-3 COLD START SOL.
D-5 COMP. SOL.
D-19 CTSY LT. & SW.
G-11 CTSY LT. TIMER
C-5 CUT OFF SW.
C-3 DISTRIBUTOR
G-17,18 DOOR SW.S
C-4 ELECT. IGN. CONTROL UNIT
D-3 ENG. FAN
D-4 ENG. FAN TEMP. SW.
B-15 ENG. TEMP. SW.
B-5 FUEL INJ. RLY.
C-5 FUEL INJ.S
C-5 FUEL PUMP
C-20 FUEL GA. TANK UNIT
E-15,16 HAZ. SW. & FLASHER
D-19 HEATED WDO. GRID
A-15 HEATED REAR WDO. SW.
B-2 HORNS
B-2 IGN. MODULE
B-11 INTERM. W/SHIELD WIPER UNIT
E-15 KEY IN SW. & BUZZER
F-16 LT. & DIR. SW.
C-16 OIL PRESS. SENS.
D-11 PWR. MIRROR MTR. & SW.
E-18 PWR. WDO. MTR.S & SW.S
A-D-6 TO D-6-9 RLY. BOX
F-18 SEAT BELT SW.
D-16 SEAT BELT BUZZER & IND.
G-10 STOP LT. SW.
B-3 THERMO. TIME SW.
B-3 THROTTLE SW.
TO FUSE 1
TO FUEL INJ. RLY. PIN #882
TO BATT. +
TO ALT. WARN. IND. CONN. D1
ALTERNATOR
ENGINE COMP

1983 Alfa Romeo

GTV-6 2.5 (Cont.)

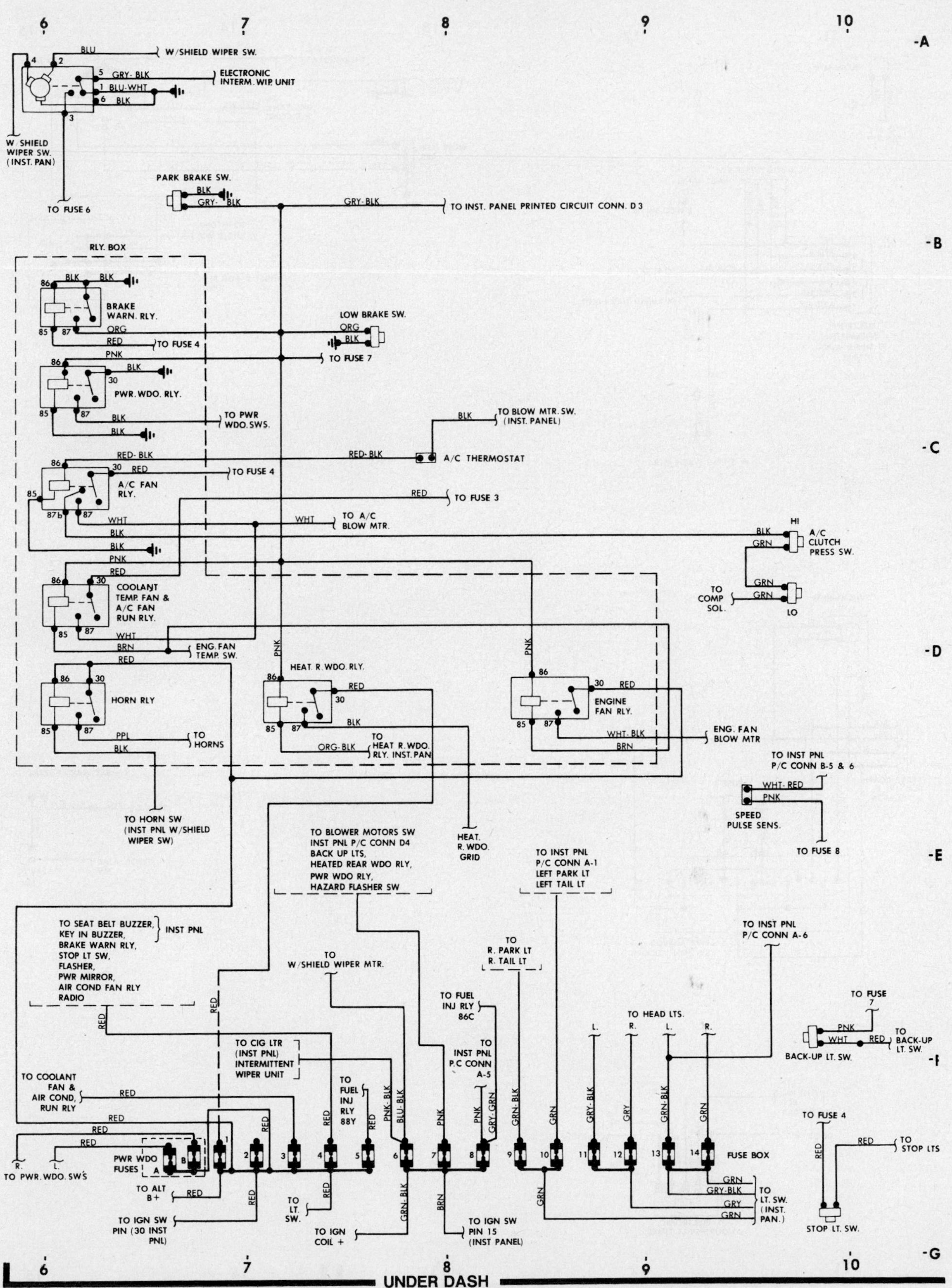

W/SHIELD WIPER SW.
ELECTRONIC INTERM. WIP. UNIT
W SHIELD WIPER SW. (INST. PAN)
TO FUSE 6
PARK BRAKE SW.
TO INST. PANEL PRINTED CIRCUIT CONN. D3
RLY. BOX
BRAKE WARN. RLY.
LOW BRAKE SW.
TO FUSE 4
TO FUSE 7
PWR. WDO. RLY.
TO PWR WDO. SWS.
TO BLOW MTR. SW. (INST. PANEL)
A/C THERMOSTAT
A/C FAN RLY.
TO FUSE 4
TO FUSE 3
TO A/C BLOW MTR.
A/C CLUTCH PRESS SW.
COOLANT TEMP. FAN & A/C FAN RUN RLY.
TO COMP SOL.
ENG. FAN TEMP. SW.
HEAT. R. WDO. RLY.
HORN RLY
ENGINE FAN RLY.
TO HORNS
TO HEAT R. WDO. RLY. INST. PAN
ENG. FAN BLOW MTR
TO INST PNL P/C CONN B-5 & 6
SPEED PULSE SENS.
TO FUSE 8
TO HORN SW (INST PNL W/SHIELD WIPER SW)
HEAT. R. WDO. GRID
TO BLOWER MOTORS SW INST PNL P/C CONN D4 BACK UP LTS, HEATED REAR WDO RLY, PWR WDO RLY, HAZARD FLASHER SW
TO INST PNL P/C CONN A-1 LEFT PARK LT LEFT TAIL LT
TO SEAT BELT BUZZER, KEY IN BUZZER, BRAKE WARN RLY, STOP LT SW, FLASHER, PWR MIRROR, AIR COND FAN RLY RADIO
INST PNL
TO W/SHIELD WIPER MTR.
TO R. PARK LT R. TAIL LT
TO INST PNL P/C CONN A-6
TO FUEL INJ RLY 86C
TO HEAD LTS.
TO FUSE 7
TO BACK-UP LT. SW.
BACK-UP LT. SW.
TO CIG LTR (INST PNL) INTERMITTENT WIPER UNIT
TO INST PNL P.C CONN A-5
TO FUEL INJ RLY 88Y
TO COOLANT FAN & AIR COND. RUN RLY
TO FUSE 4
TO STOP LTS
PWR WDO FUSES
FUSE BOX
TO PWR. WDO. SW'S
TO ALT B+
TO LT. SW.
TO LT. SW. (INST. PAN.)
STOP LT. SW.
TO IGN SW PIN (30 INST PNL)
TO IGN COIL +
TO IGN SW PIN 15 (INST PANEL)

1983 Alfa Romeo

GTV-6 2.5 (Cont.)

A- 11 12 13 14 15

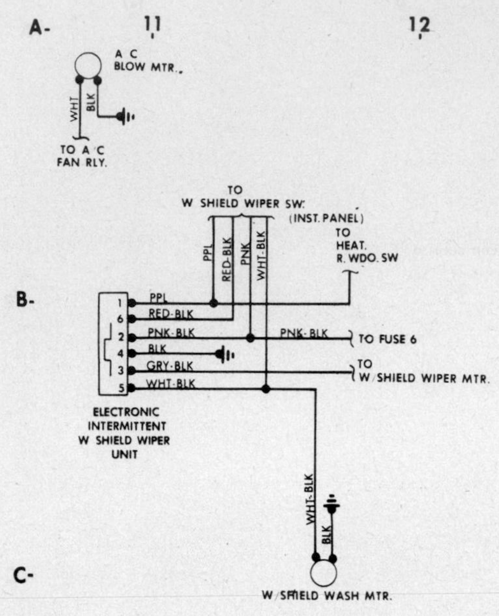
A/C BLOW MTR.
WHT
BLK
TO A/C FAN RLY.
TO W SHIELD WIPER SW. (INST. PANEL)
PPL
RED-BLK
PNK
WHT-BLK
TO HEAT. R. WDO. SW
PPL
RED-BLK
PNK-BLK
BLK
GRY-BLK
WHT-BLK
PNK-BLK
TO FUSE 6
TO W/SHIELD WIPER MTR.
ELECTRONIC INTERMITTENT W SHIELD WIPER UNIT
WHT-BLK
BLK
W/SHIELD WASH MTR.

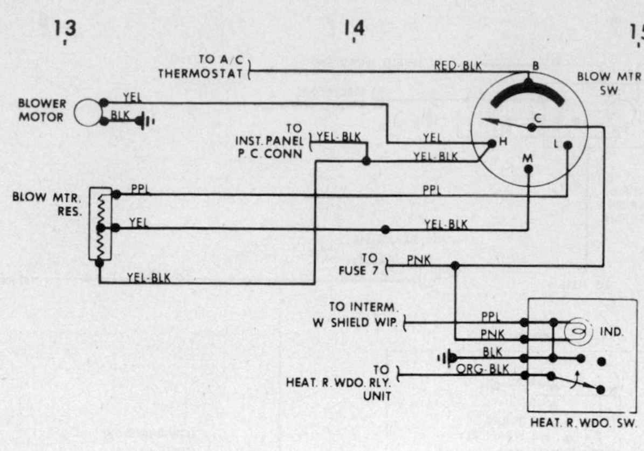
TO A/C THERMOSTAT
RED-BLK
BLOW MTR SW.
BLOWER MOTOR
YEL
BLK
TO INST. PANEL P C CONN
YEL-BLK
YEL
YEL-BLK
BLOW MTR. RES.
PPL
YEL
YEL-BLK
TO FUSE 7
PNK
TO INTERM. W SHIELD WIP.
PPL
PNK
BLK
ORG-BLK
IND.
TO HEAT. R. WDO. RLY. UNIT
HEAT. R. WDO. SW.

B-

C-

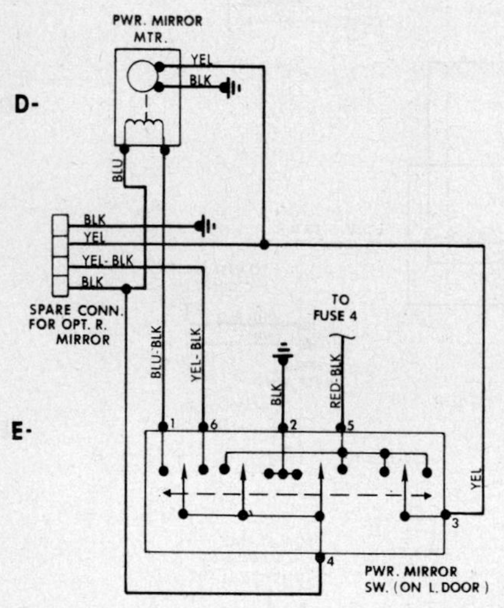
PWR. MIRROR MTR.
YEL
BLK
BLU
BLK
YEL
YEL-BLK
BLK
SPARE CONN. FOR OPT. R. MIRROR
BLU-BLK
YEL-BLK
BLK
TO FUSE 4
RED-BLK
YEL
PWR. MIRROR SW. (ON L. DOOR)

D-

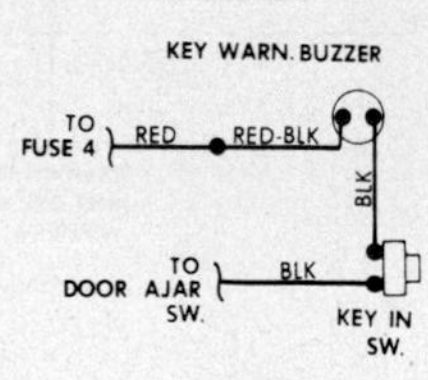
KEY WARN. BUZZER
TO FUSE 4
RED
RED-BLK
BLK
TO DOOR AJAR SW.
BLK
KEY IN SW.

E-

F-

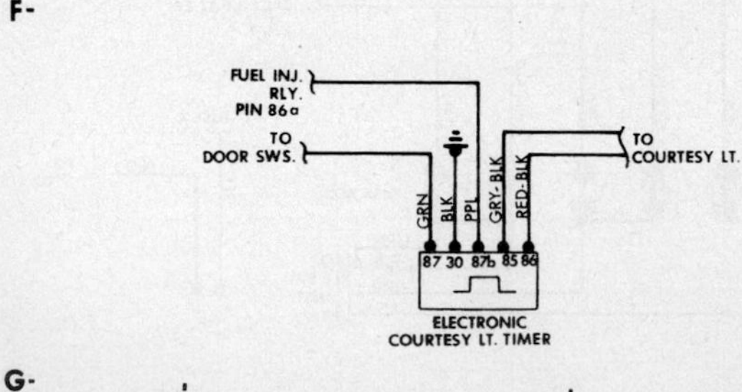
FUEL INJ. RLY. PIN 86a
TO DOOR SWS.
TO COURTESY LT.
GRN
BLK
PPL
GRY-BLK
RED-BLK
87 30 87b 85 86
ELECTRONIC COURTESY LT. TIMER

G- 11 12 13 14 15

1983 Alfa Romeo

GTV-6 2.5 (Cont.)

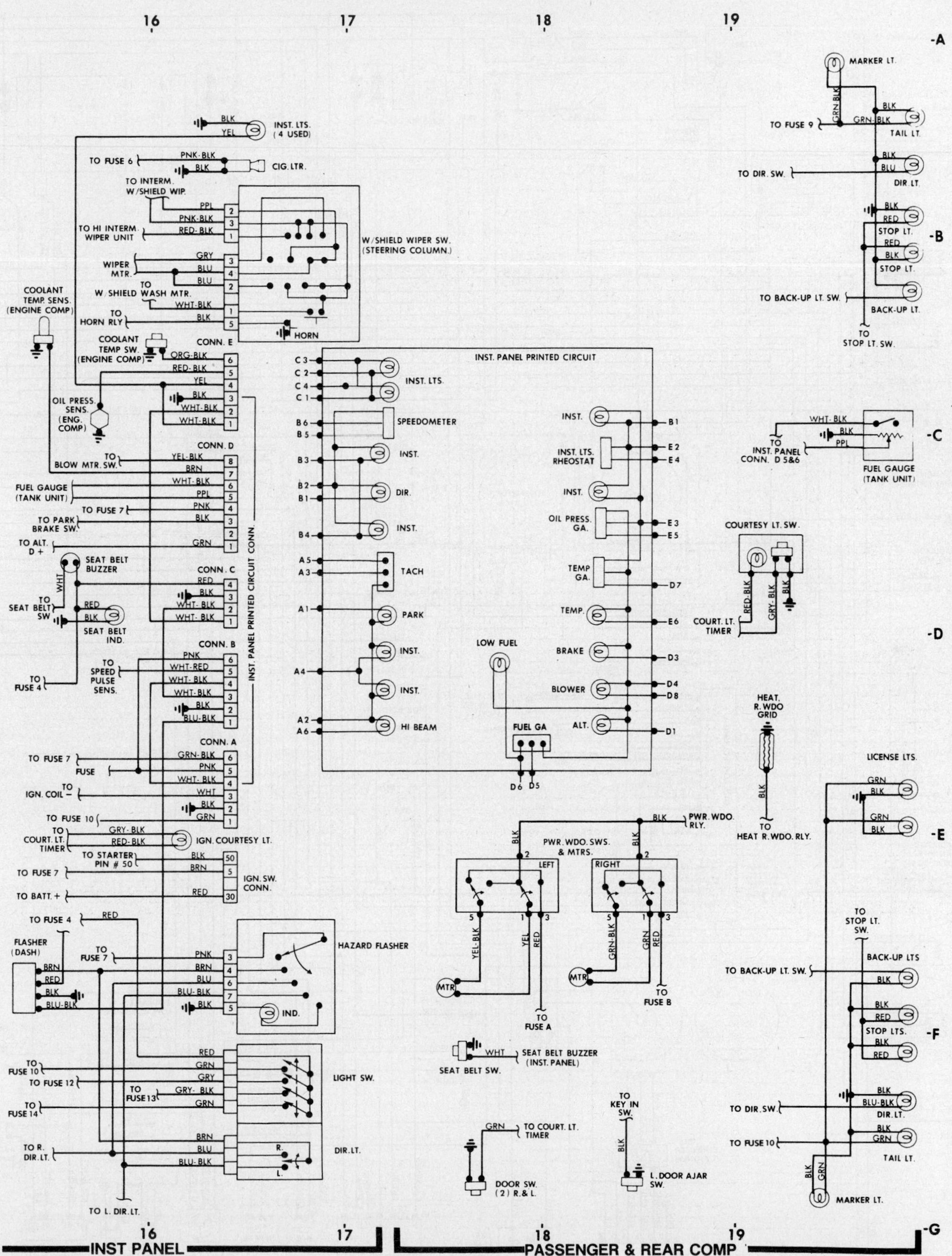

INST. LTS. (4 USED)
TO FUSE 6
CIG. LTR.
TO INTERM. W/SHIELD WIP.
TO HI INTERM. WIPER UNIT
W/SHIELD WIPER SW. (STEERING COLUMN)
WIPER MTR.
TO W/SHIELD WASH MTR.
TO HORN RLY
HORN
COOLANT TEMP. SENS. (ENGINE COMP)
COOLANT TEMP SW. (ENGINE COMP)
CONN. E
OIL PRESS. SENS. (ENG. COMP)
CONN. D
TO BLOW MTR. SW.
FUEL GAUGE (TANK UNIT)
TO FUSE 7
TO PARK BRAKE SW.
TO ALT. D +
SEAT BELT BUZZER
CONN. C
TO SEAT BELT SW
SEAT BELT IND.
CONN. B
TO SPEED PULSE SENS.
TO FUSE 4
INST. PANEL PRINTED CIRCUIT CONN.
CONN. A
FUSE
TO IGN. COIL −
TO FUSE 10
TO COURT. LT. TIMER
IGN. COURTESY LT.
TO STARTER PIN # 50
TO BATT. +
IGN. SW. CONN.
FLASHER (DASH)
HAZARD FLASHER
IND.
LIGHT SW.
TO FUSE 12
TO FUSE 13
TO FUSE 14
TO R. DIR. LT.
DIR. LT.
TO L. DIR. LT.
INST. PANEL PRINTED CIRCUIT
INST. LTS.
SPEEDOMETER
INST.
DIR.
TACH
PARK
HI BEAM
LOW FUEL
FUEL GA
INST. LTS. RHEOSTAT
OIL PRESS. GA.
TEMP GA.
TEMP.
BRAKE
BLOWER
ALT.
PWR. WDO. SWS. & MTRS.
LEFT
RIGHT
PWR. WDO. RLY.
MTR
TO FUSE A
TO FUSE B
SEAT BELT SW.
SEAT BELT BUZZER (INST. PANEL)
TO COURT. LT. TIMER
DOOR SW. (2) R. & L.
TO KEY IN SW.
L. DOOR AJAR SW.
MARKER LT.
TO FUSE 9
TAIL LT.
TO DIR. SW.
DIR. LT.
STOP LT.
TO BACK-UP LT. SW.
BACK-UP LT.
TO STOP LT. SW.
TO INST. PANEL CONN. D 5&6
FUEL GAUGE (TANK UNIT)
COURTESY LT. SW.
COURT. LT. TIMER
HEAT. R. WDO GRID
TO HEAT R. WDO. RLY.
LICENSE LTS.
TO STOP LT. SW.
BACK-UP LTS
STOP LTS.
INST PANEL
PASSENGER & REAR COMP

1983 Audi

4000 & COUPE 4- & 5-CYLINDER

ENGINE COMPARTMENT & FUSE BLOCK

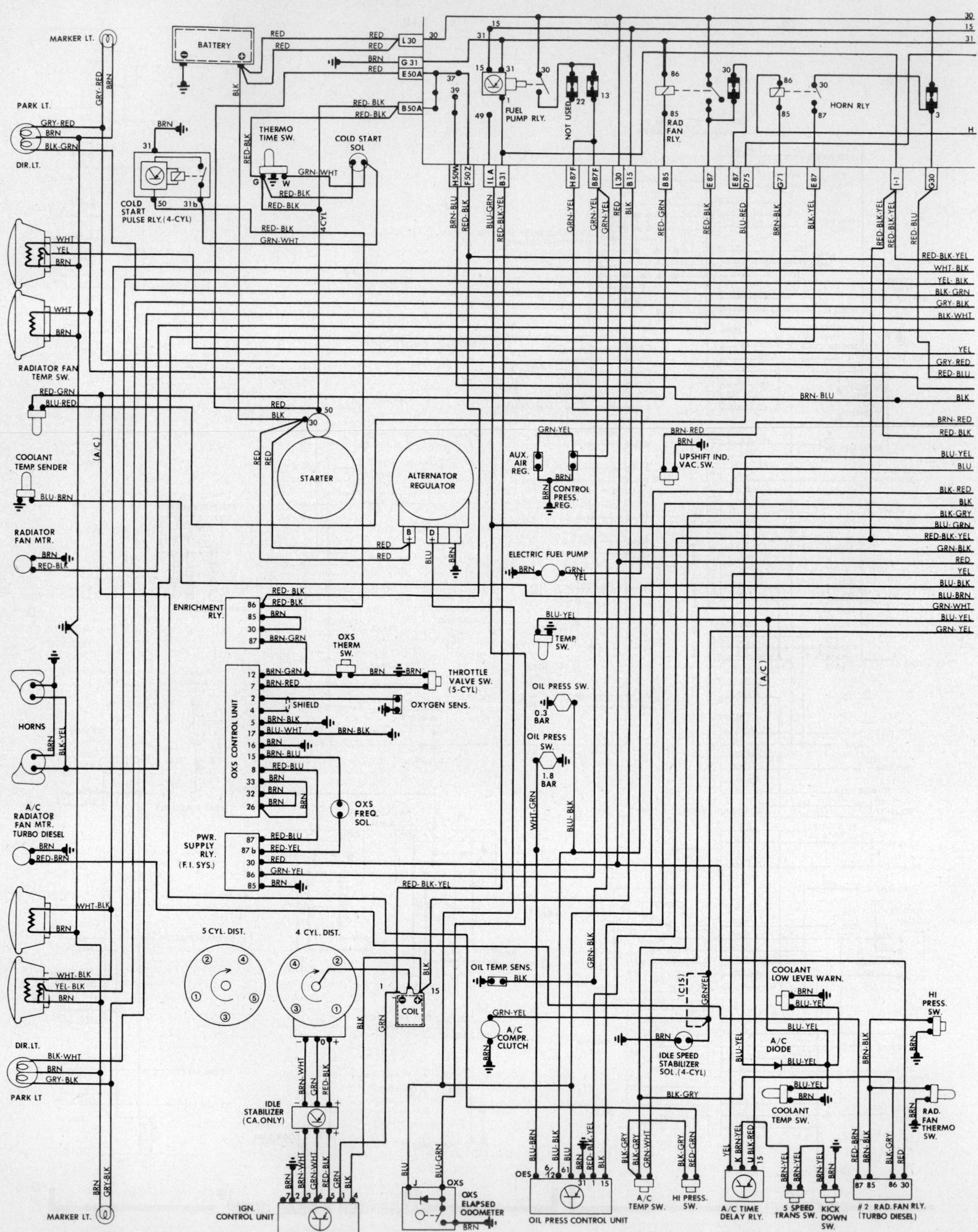
MARKER LT.
BATTERY
PARK LT.
DIR. LT.
THERMO TIME SW.
COLD START SOL
COLD START PULSE RLY. (4-CYL)
FUEL PUMP RLY.
NOT USED
RAD FAN RLY.
HORN RLY
RADIATOR FAN TEMP. SW.
COOLANT TEMP. SENDER
RADIATOR FAN MTR.
STARTER
ALTERNATOR REGULATOR
AUX. AIR REG.
CONTROL PRESS. REG.
UPSHIFT IND. VAC. SW.
ELECTRIC FUEL PUMP
ENRICHMENT RLY.
OXS THERM SW.
THROTTLE VALVE SW. (5-CYL)
OXYGEN SENS.
SHIELD
OXS CONTROL UNIT
TEMP SW.
OIL PRESS SW. 0.3 BAR
OIL PRESS SW. 1.8 BAR
HORNS
OXS FREQ. SOL.
A/C RADIATOR FAN MTR. TURBO DIESEL
PWR. SUPPLY RLY. (F.I. SYS.)
5 CYL. DIST.
4 CYL. DIST.
COIL
OIL TEMP. SENS.
A/C COMPR. CLUTCH
IDLE SPEED STABILIZER SOL. (4-CYL)
COOLANT LOW LEVEL WARN.
HI PRESS. SW.
A/C DIODE
COOLANT TEMP SW.
RAD. FAN THERMO SW.
IDLE STABILIZER (CA. ONLY)
IGN. CONTROL UNIT
OXS ELAPSED ODOMETER
OIL PRESS CONTROL UNIT
A/C TEMP SW.
HI PRESS. SW.
A/C TIME DELAY RLY.
5 SPEED TRANS SW.
KICK DOWN SW.
2 RAD. FAN RLY. (TURBO DIESEL)
PARK LT
MARKER LT.

4000 & COUPE 4- & 5-CYLINDER (Cont.)

FUSE BLOCK & UNDERDASH

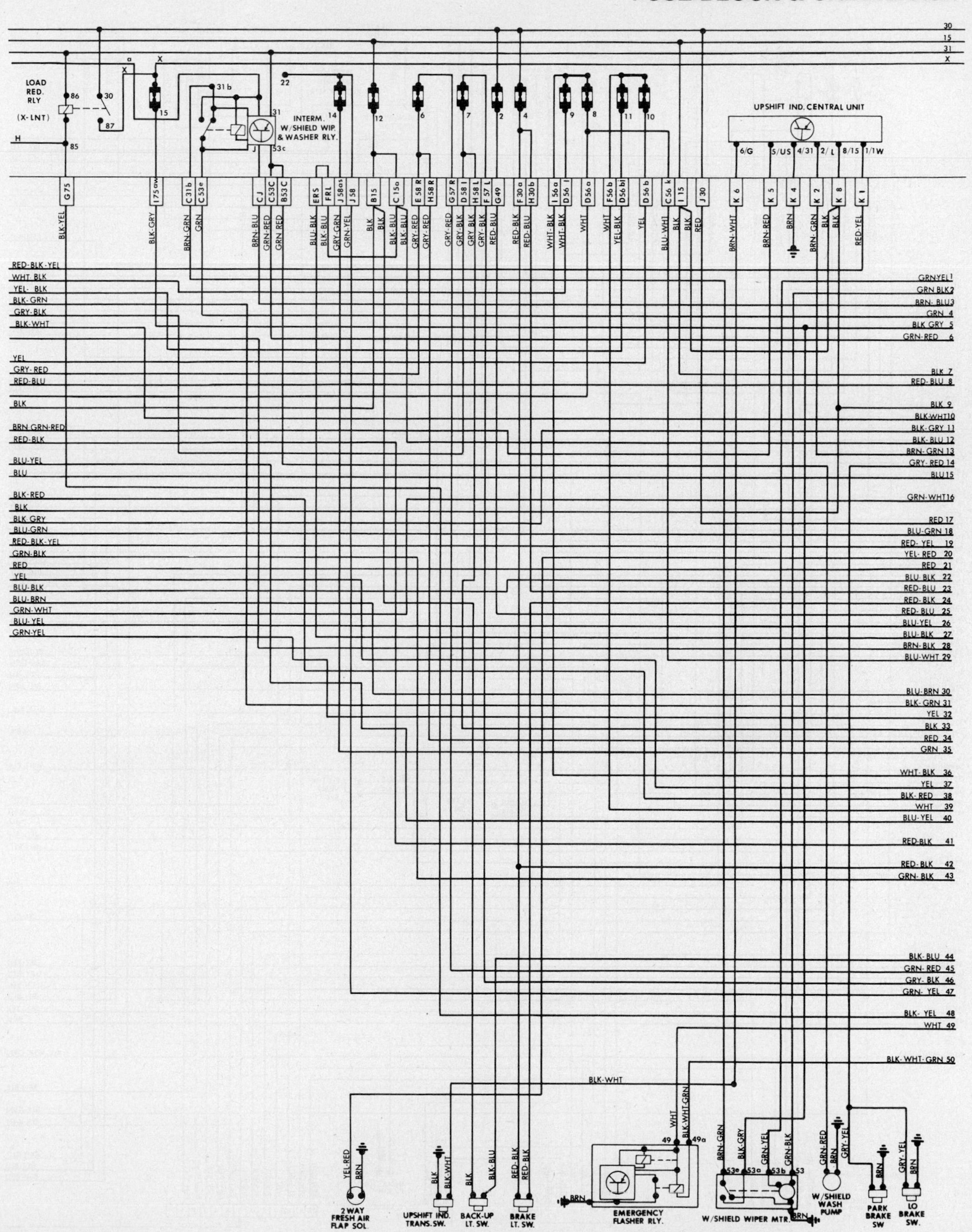

1983 Audi

4000 & COUPE 4- & 5-CYLINDER (Cont.)

FUSE BLOCK & UNDERDASH

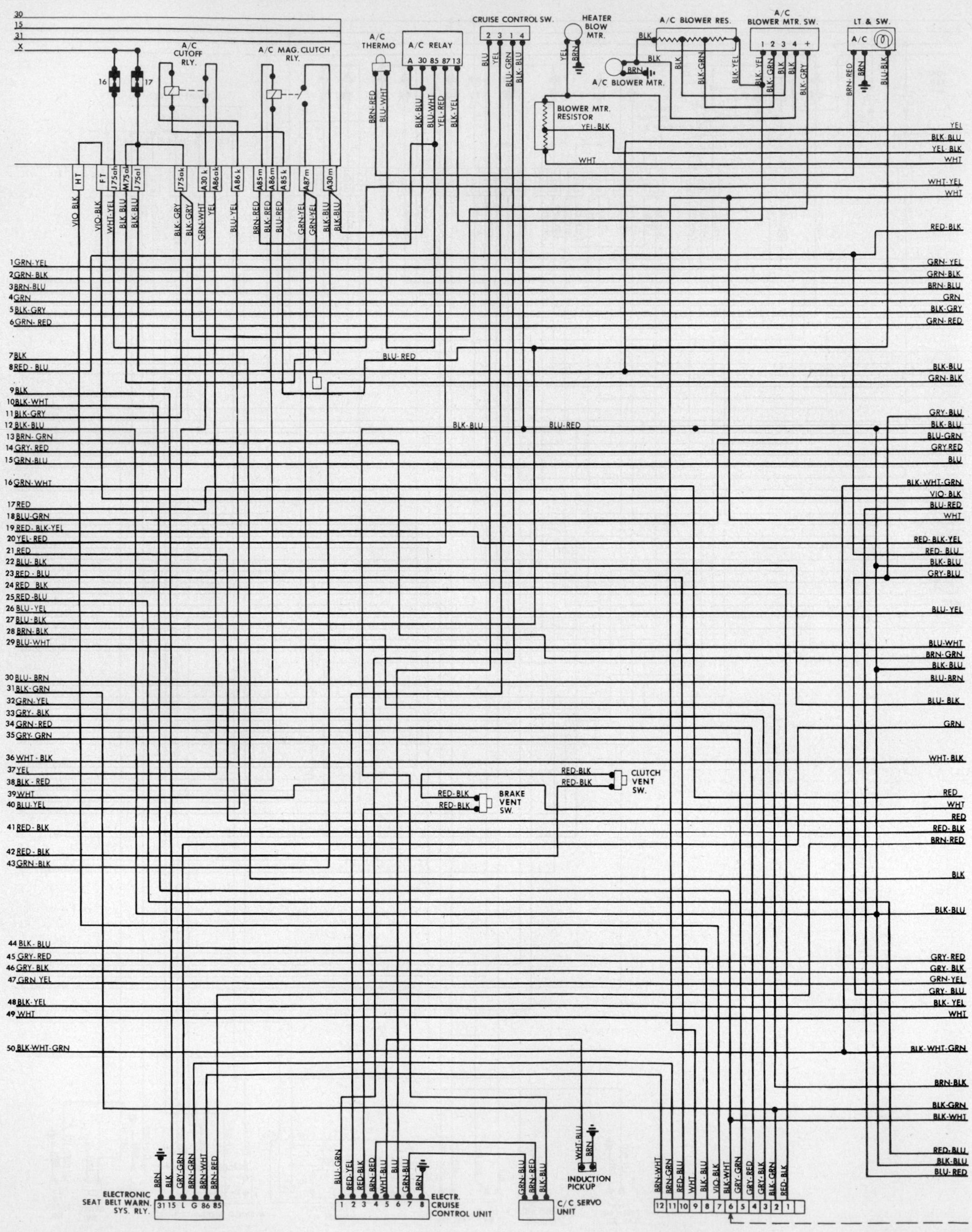

30
15
31
X
16
17
A/C CUTOFF RLY.
A/C MAG. CLUTCH RLY.
A/C THERMO
A/C RELAY
A 30 85 87 13
CRUISE CONTROL SW.
2 3 1 4
HEATER BLOW MTR.
A/C BLOWER RES.
A/C BLOWER MTR. SW.
1 2 3 4 +
LT & SW.
A/C
A/C BLOWER MTR.
BLOWER MTR. RESISTOR
YEL-BLK
WHT
HT
FT
J75ah
M75al
J75al
J75ak
A30 k
A86ak
A86 k
A85m
A86m
A85 k
A87m
A30m
VIO-BLK
VIO-BLK
WHT-YEL
BLK-BLU
BLK-BLU
BLK-GRY
BLK-GRY
GRN-WHT
YEL
BLU-YEL
BRN-RED
BLK-RED
BLU-RED
GRN-YEL
BLK-BLU
BLK-BLU
BRN-RED
BLU-WHT
BLK-BLU
BLU-WHT
YEL-RED
BLK-YEL
BLU
YEL
BLU-GRN
BLK-BLU
YEL
BRN
BLK
BLK
BRN
BLK
BLK-GRN
BLK-YEL
BLK-YEL
BLK-GRN
BLK
BLK
BLK-GRY
BRN-RED
BRN
BLU-BLK
1 GRN-YEL
2 GRN-BLK
3 BRN-BLU
4 GRN
5 BLK-GRY
6 GRN-RED
7 BLK
8 RED-BLU
9 BLK
10 BLK-WHT
11 BLK-GRY
12 BLK-BLU
13 BRN-GRN
14 GRY-RED
15 GRN-BLU
16 GRN-WHT
17 RED
18 BLU-GRN
19 RED-BLK-YEL
20 YEL-RED
21 RED
22 BLU-BLK
23 RED-BLU
24 RED-BLK
25 RED-BLU
26 BLU-YEL
27 BLU-BLK
28 BRN-BLK
29 BLU-WHT
30 BLU-BRN
31 BLK-GRN
32 GRN-YEL
33 GRY-BLK
34 GRN-RED
35 GRY-GRN
36 WHT-BLK
37 YEL
38 BLK-RED
39 WHT
40 BLU-YEL
41 RED-BLK
42 RED-BLK
43 GRN-BLK
44 BLK-BLU
45 GRY-RED
46 GRY-BLK
47 GRN-YEL
48 BLK-YEL
49 WHT
50 BLK-WHT-GRN
BLU-RED
BLK-BLU
BLU-RED
RED-BLK
RED-BLK
BRAKE VENT SW.
RED-BLK
RED-BLK
CLUTCH VENT SW.
YEL
BLK-BLU
YEL-BLK
WHT
WHT-YEL
WHT
RED-BLK
GRN-YEL
GRN-BLK
BRN-BLU
GRN
BLK-GRY
GRN-RED
BLK-BLU
GRN-BLK
GRY-BLU
BLK-BLU
BLU-GRN
GRY-RED
BLU
BLK-WHT-GRN
VIO-BLK
BLU-RED
WHT
RED-BLK-YEL
RED-BLU
BLK-BLU
GRY-BLU
BLU-YEL
BLU-WHT
BRN-GRN
BLK-BLU
BLU-BRN
BLU-BLK
GRN
WHT-BLK
RED
WHT
RED
RED-BLK
BRN-RED
BLK
BLK-BLU
GRY-RED
GRY-BLK
GRN-YEL
GRY-BLU
BLK-YEL
WHT
BLK-WHT-GRN
BRN-BLK
BLK-GRN
BLK-WHT
RED-BLU
BLK-BLU
BLU-RED
BRN
BLK
GRY-GRN
BRN-GRN
BRN-WHT
BRN-RED
ELECTRONIC SEAT BELT WARN. SYS. RLY.
31 15 L G 86 85
BLU-GRN
RED-YEL
RED-BLK
BRN-RED
WHT-BLU
BLU
GRN-BLU
BRN
1 2 3 4 5 6 7 8
ELECTR. CRUISE CONTROL UNIT
GRN-BLU
BRN-RED
BLK-BLU
C/C SERVO UNIT
WHT-BLU
BRN
INDUCTION PICKUP
BRN-WHT
BRN-GRN
RED-BLU
WHT
BLK-BLU
VIO-BLK
BLK-WHT
GRY-GRN
GRY-RED
BLK-GRN
RED-BLK
12 11 10 9 8 7 6 5 4 3 2 1

1983 Audi

4000 & COUPE 4- & 5-CYLINDER (Cont.)

INSTRUMENT PANEL & REAR COMPARTMENT

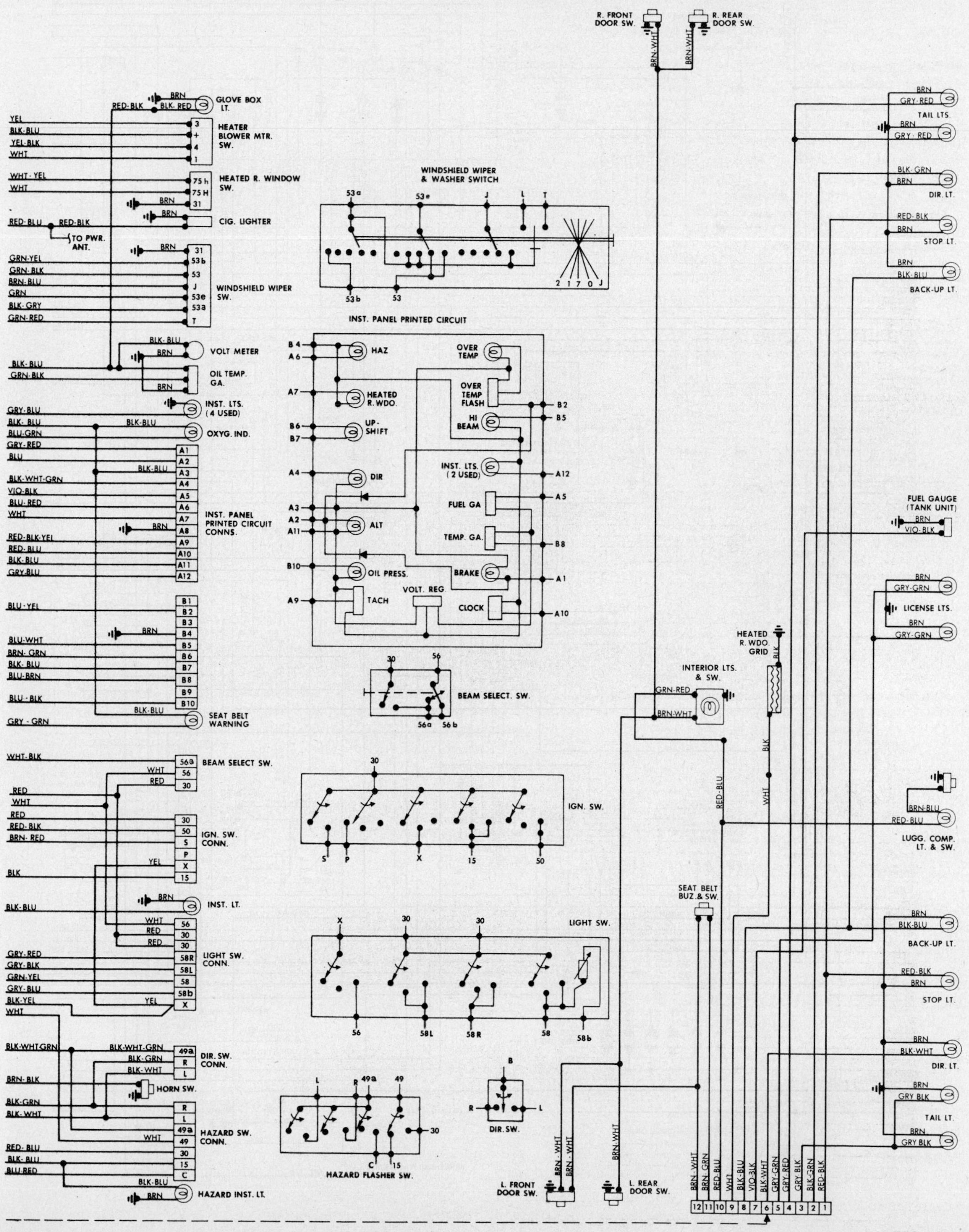

1983 Audi

5000 5-CYLINDER & DIESEL

ENGINE COMPARTMENT & FUSE BLOCK

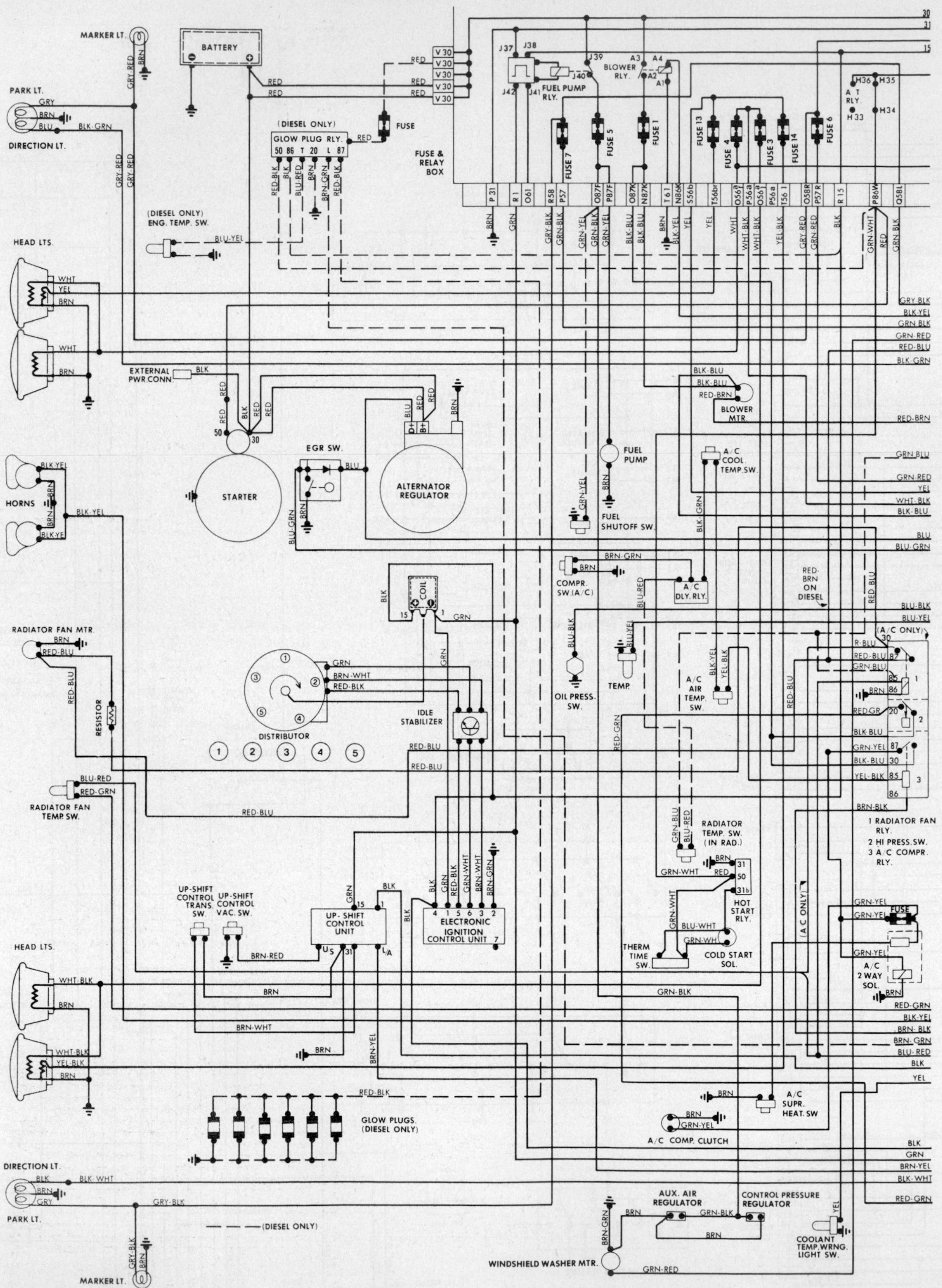
MARKER LT.
BATTERY
PARK LT.
DIRECTION LT.
(DIESEL ONLY)
GLOW PLUG RLY.
FUSE
FUSE & RELAY BOX
FUEL PUMP RLY.
BLOWER RLY.
A T RLY.
FUSE 7
FUSE 5
FUSE 1
FUSE 13
FUSE 4
FUSE 3
FUSE 14
FUSE 6
(DIESEL ONLY) ENG. TEMP. SW.
HEAD LTS.
EXTERNAL PWR.CONN
BLOWER MTR.
FUEL PUMP
A/C COOL. TEMP. SW.
HORNS
STARTER
EGR SW.
ALTERNATOR REGULATOR
FUEL SHUTOFF SW.
COMPR. SW.(A/C)
A/C DLY. RLY.
RED-BRN ON DIESEL
(A/C ONLY)
RADIATOR FAN MTR.
COIL
OIL PRESS. SW.
TEMP.
A/C AIR TEMP. SW.
DISTRIBUTOR
IDLE STABILIZER
RESISTOR
RADIATOR FAN TEMP. SW.
1 RADIATOR FAN RLY.
2 HI PRESS. SW.
3 A/C COMPR. RLY.
RADIATOR TEMP. SW. (IN RAD.)
HOT START RLY.
UP-SHIFT CONTROL TRANS SW.
UP-SHIFT CONTROL VAC. SW.
UP-SHIFT CONTROL UNIT
ELECTRONIC IGNITION CONTROL UNIT
THERM TIME SW.
COLD START SOL.
(A/C ONLY)
A/C 2 WAY SOL.
A/C SUPR. HEAT. SW
A/C COMP. CLUTCH
GLOW PLUGS (DIESEL ONLY)
AUX. AIR REGULATOR
CONTROL PRESSURE REGULATOR
COOLANT TEMP. WRNG. LIGHT SW.
WINDSHIELD WASHER MTR.
(DIESEL ONLY)

5000 5-CYLINDER & DIESEL (Cont.)

FUSE BLOCK & UNDERDASH

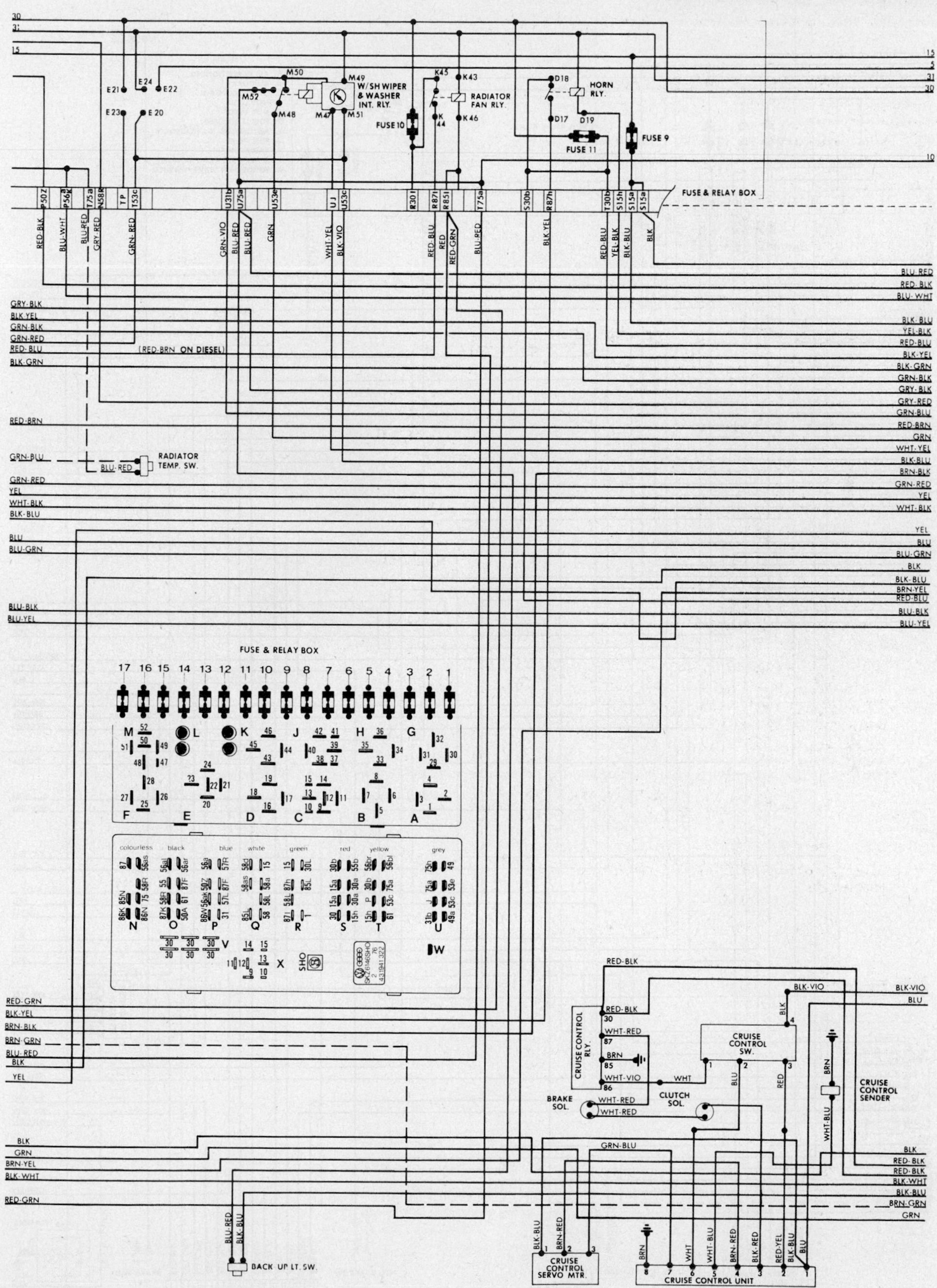

FUSE 10
FUSE 11
FUSE 9
W/SH WIPER & WASHER INT. RLY.
RADIATOR FAN RLY.
HORN RLY.
FUSE & RELAY BOX
(RED-BRN ON DIESEL)
RADIATOR TEMP. SW.
CRUISE CONTROL RLY.
CRUISE CONTROL SW.
CRUISE CONTROL SENDER
BRAKE SOL.
CLUTCH SOL.
BACK UP LT. SW.
CRUISE CONTROL SERVO MTR.
CRUISE CONTROL UNIT

1983 Audi

5000 5-CYLINDER & DIESEL (Cont.)

FUSE BLOCK & UNDERDASH

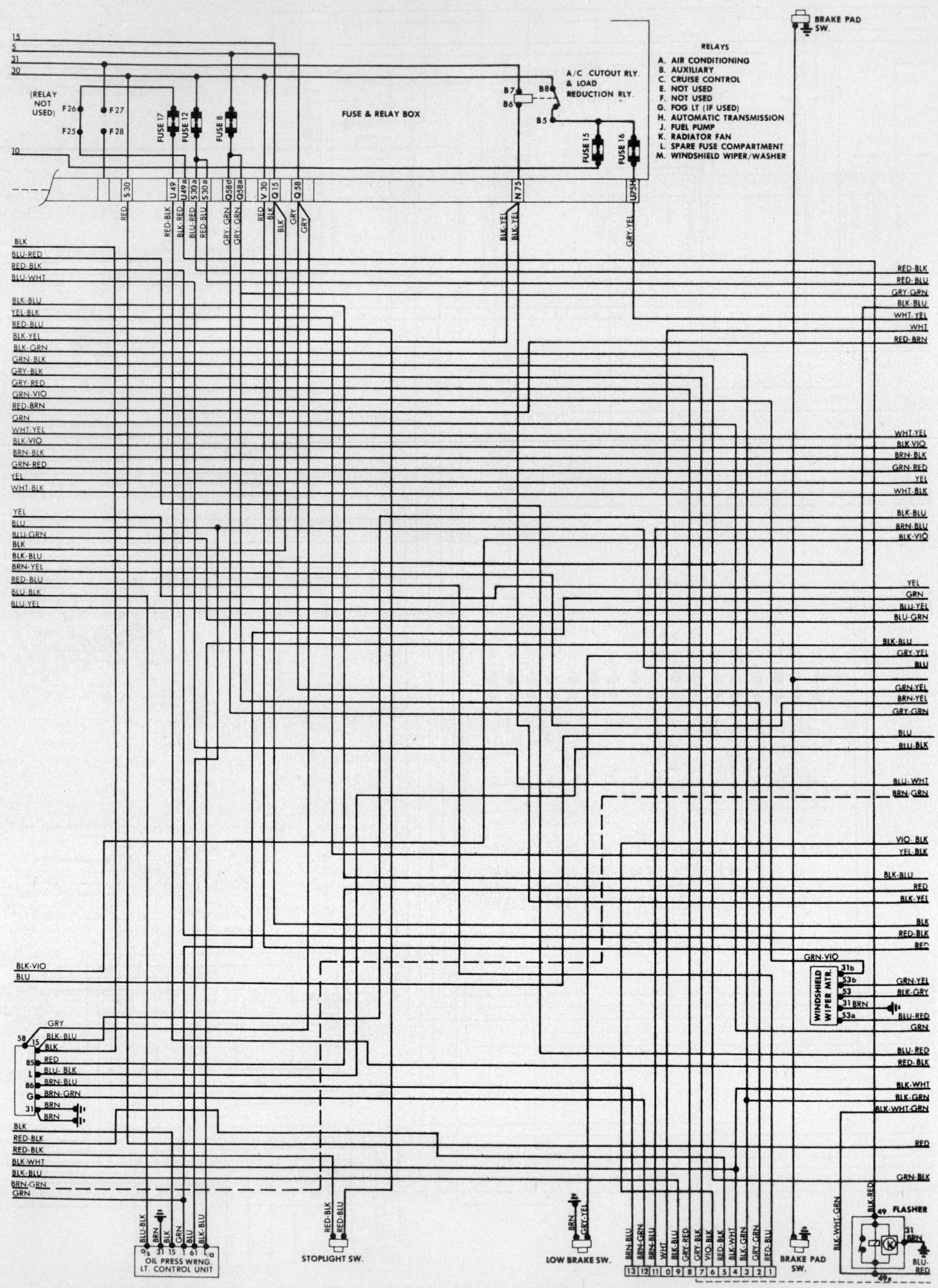
BRAKE PAD SW.
RELAYS
A. AIR CONDITIONING
B. AUXILIARY
C. CRUISE CONTROL
E. NOT USED
F. NOT USED
G. FOG LT (IF USED)
H. AUTOMATIC TRANSMISSION
J. FUEL PUMP
K. RADIATOR FAN
L. SPARE FUSE COMPARTMENT
M. WINDSHIELD WIPER/WASHER
A/C CUTOUT RLY. & LOAD REDUCTION RLY.
FUSE & RELAY BOX
(RELAY NOT USED)
FUSE 17
FUSE 12
FUSE 8
FUSE 15
FUSE 16
WINDSHIELD WIPER MTR.
OIL PRESS WRNG. LT. CONTROL UNIT
STOPLIGHT SW.
LOW BRAKE SW.
BRAKE PAD SW.
FLASHER

1983 Audi

5000 5-CYLINDER & DIESEL (Cont.)

INSTRUMENT PANEL & REAR COMPARTMENT

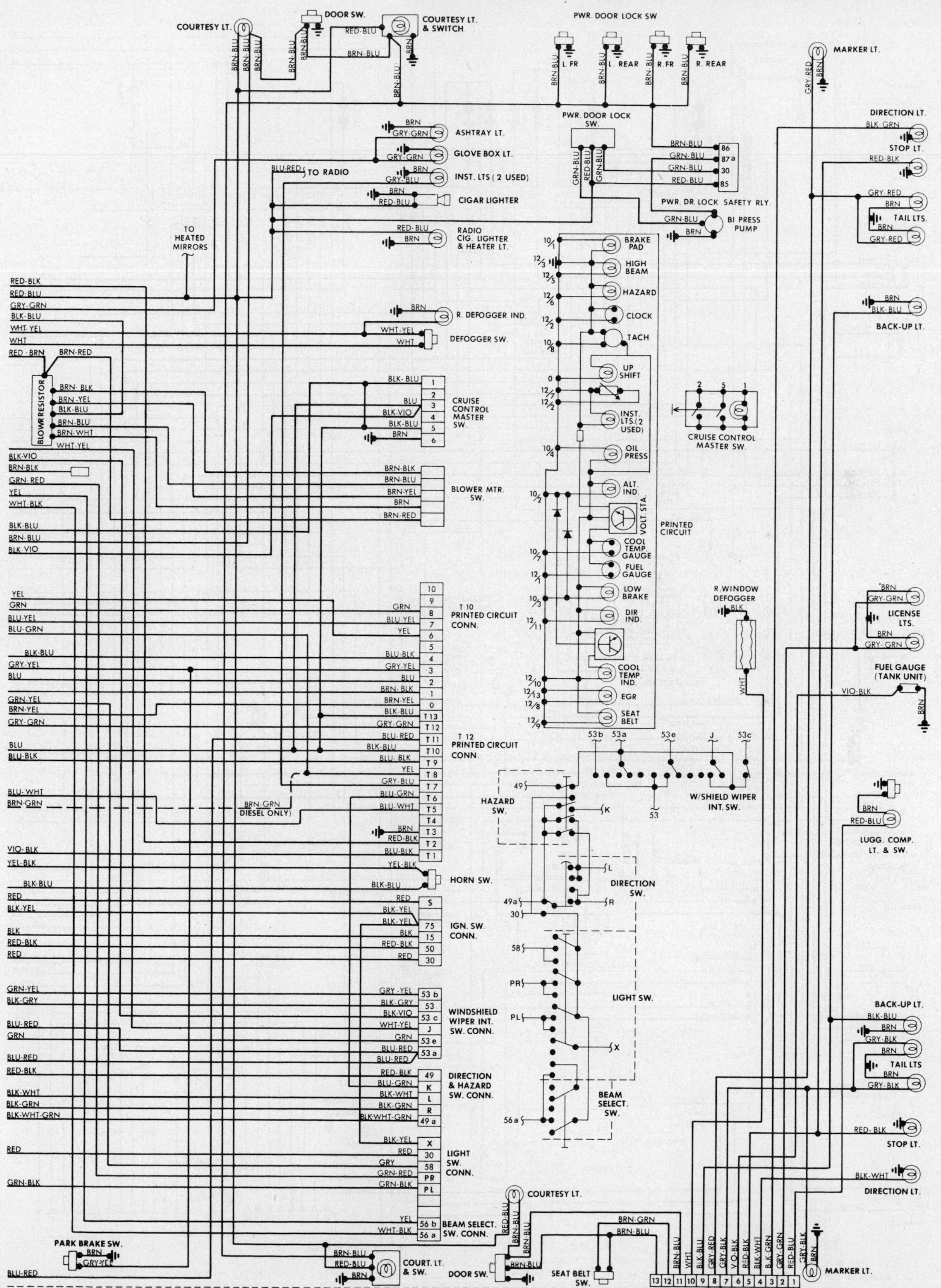

1983 Audi

QUATTRO

ENGINE COMPARTMENT & FUSE BLOCK

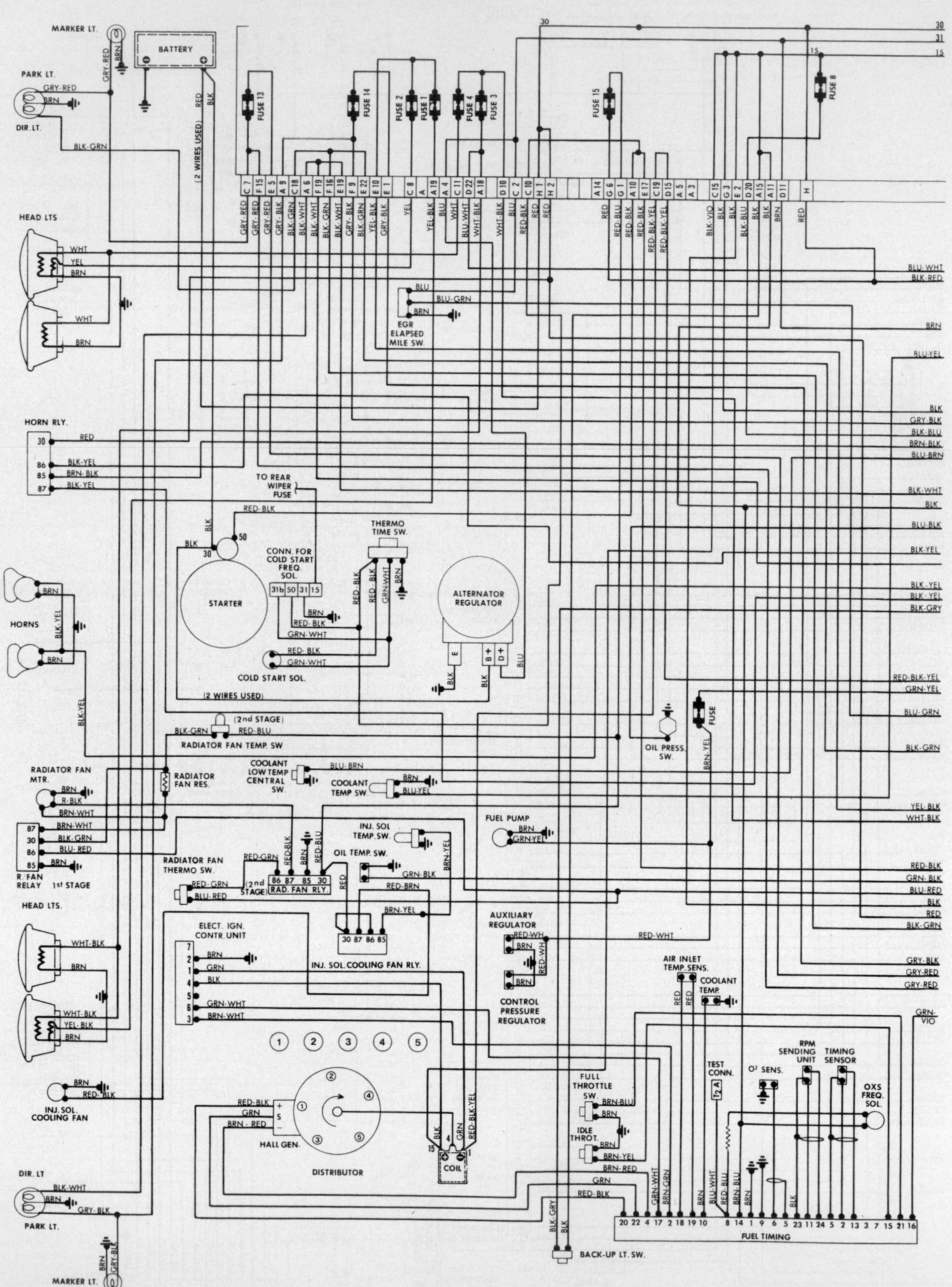
MARKER LT.
BATTERY
PARK LT.
DIR. LT.
HEAD LTS
HORN RLY.
TO REAR WIPER FUSE
THERMO TIME SW.
CONN. FOR COLD START FREQ. SOL.
STARTER
ALTERNATOR REGULATOR
COLD START SOL.
(2 WIRES USED)
HORNS
EGR ELAPSED MILE SW.
RADIATOR FAN TEMP. SW
RADIATOR FAN MTR.
RADIATOR FAN RES.
COOLANT LOW TEMP CENTRAL SW.
COOLANT TEMP SW.
R/FAN RELAY 1st STAGE
RADIATOR FAN THERMO SW.
RAD. FAN RLY.
INJ. SOL TEMP. SW.
OIL TEMP. SW.
FUEL PUMP
OIL PRESS. SW.
AUXILIARY REGULATOR
CONTROL PRESSURE REGULATOR
ELECT. IGN. CONTR. UNIT
INJ. SOL. COOLING FAN RLY.
AIR INLET TEMP. SENS.
COOLANT TEMP.
INJ. SOL. COOLING FAN
HALL GEN.
DISTRIBUTOR
COIL
FULL THROTTLE SW.
IDLE THROT.
TEST CONN.
O² SENS.
RPM SENDING UNIT
TIMING SENSOR
OXS FREQ. SOL.
FUEL TIMING
BACK-UP LT. SW.

1983 Audi

QUATTRO (Cont.)

FUSE BLOCK & UNDERDASH

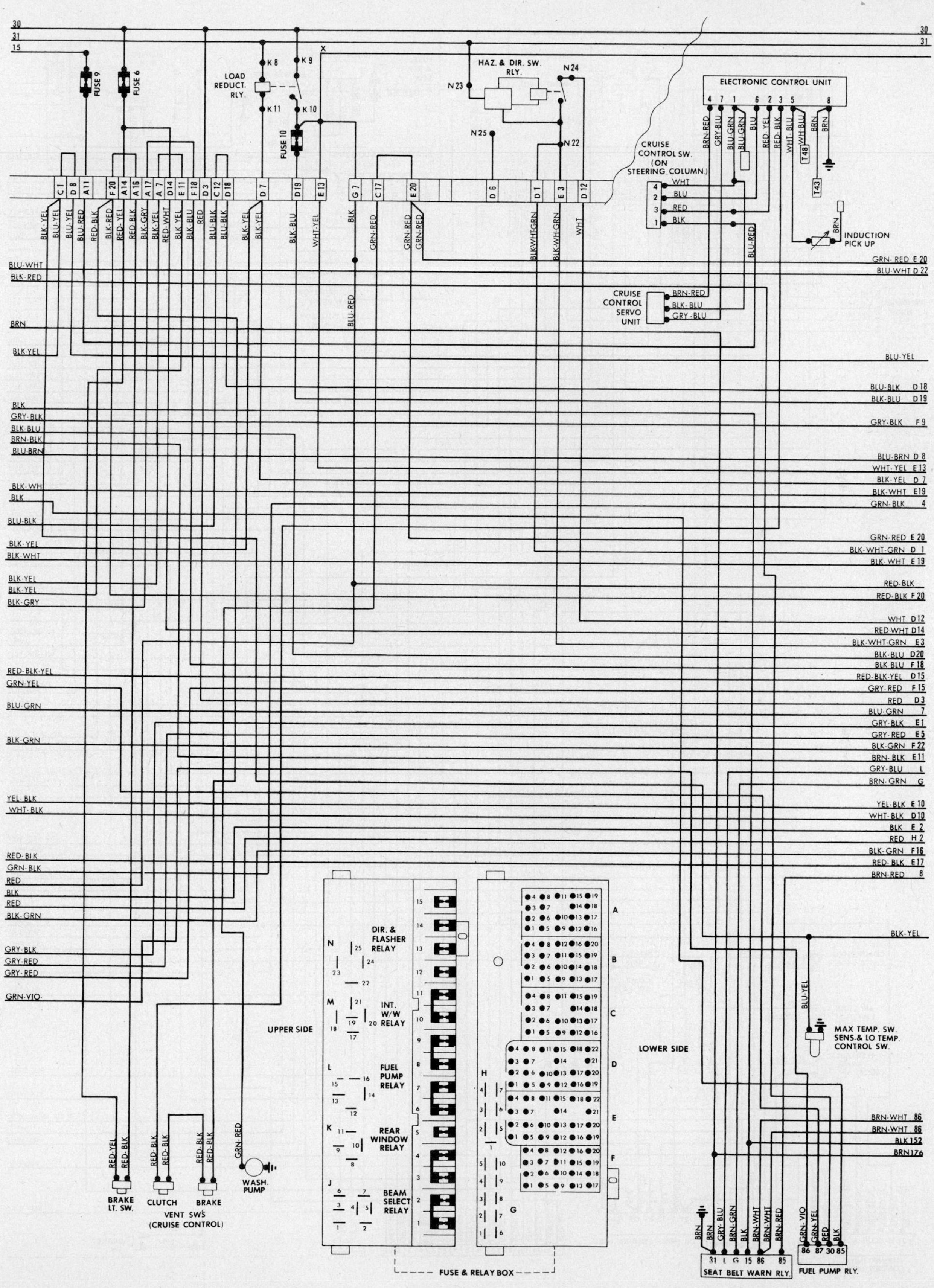

1983 Audi

QUATTRO (Cont.)

FUSE BLOCK & UNDERDASH

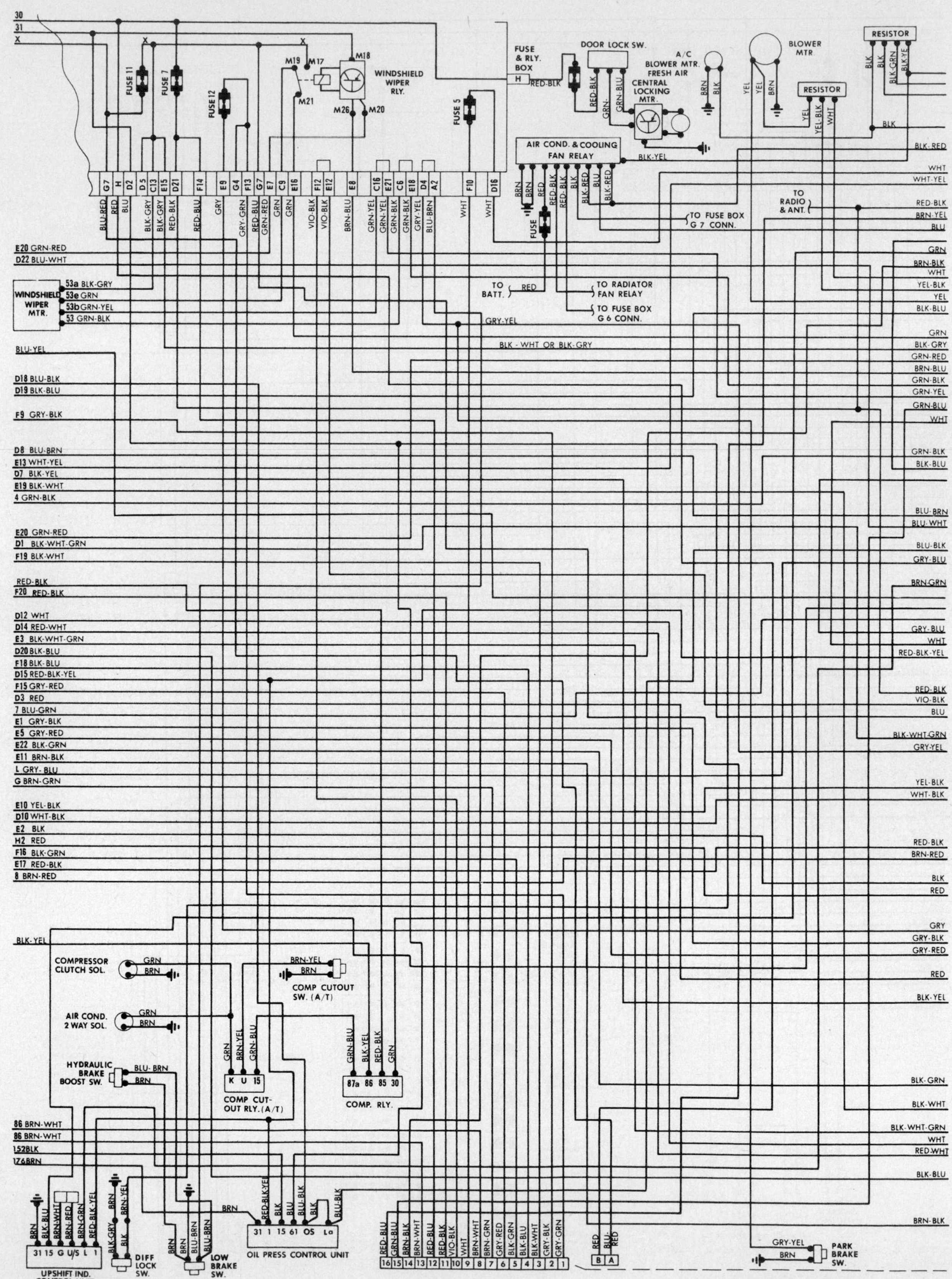
30
31
X
FUSE 11
FUSE 7
FUSE 12
M19
M17
M18
WINDSHIELD WIPER RLY.
M21
M26
M20
FUSE 5
FUSE & RLY. BOX
H
RED-BLK
DOOR LOCK SW.
A/C BLOWER MTR. FRESH AIR
CENTRAL LOCKING MTR.
BLOWER MTR
RESISTOR
RESISTOR
AIR COND. & COOLING FAN RELAY
BLK-YEL
TO RADIO & ANT.
TO FUSE BOX G 7 CONN.
TO BATT.
RED
TO RADIATOR FAN RELAY
TO FUSE BOX G 6 CONN.
GRY-YEL
BLK - WHT OR BLK-GRY
E20 GRN-RED
D22 BLU-WHT
WINDSHIELD WIPER MTR.
53a BLK-GRY
53e GRN
53b GRN-YEL
53 GRN-BLK
BLU-YEL
D18 BLU-BLK
D19 BLK-BLU
F9 GRY-BLK
D8 BLU-BRN
E13 WHT-YEL
D7 BLK-YEL
E19 BLK-WHT
4 GRN-BLK
E20 GRN-RED
D1 BLK-WHT-GRN
F19 BLK-WHT
RED-BLK
F20 RED-BLK
D12 WHT
D14 RED-WHT
E3 BLK-WHT-GRN
D20 BLK-BLU
F18 BLK-BLU
D15 RED-BLK-YEL
F15 GRY-RED
D3 RED
7 BLU-GRN
E1 GRY-BLK
E5 GRY-RED
E22 BLK-GRN
E11 BRN-BLK
L GRY-BLU
G BRN-GRN
E10 YEL-BLK
D10 WHT-BLK
E2 BLK
H2 RED
F16 BLK-GRN
E17 RED-BLK
8 BRN-RED
BLK-YEL
COMPRESSOR CLUTCH SOL.
COMP CUTOUT SW. (A/T)
AIR COND. 2 WAY SOL.
HYDRAULIC BRAKE BOOST SW.
COMP CUT-OUT RLY. (A/T)
COMP. RLY.
86 BRN-WHT
86 BRN-WHT
152BLK
176BRN
UPSHIFT IND. CONTROL UNIT
DIFF LOCK SW.
LOW BRAKE SW.
OIL PRESS CONTROL UNIT
PARK BRAKE SW.
GRY-YEL
BRN

1983 Audi

QUATTRO (Cont.)

INSTRUMENT PANEL & REAR COMPARTMENT

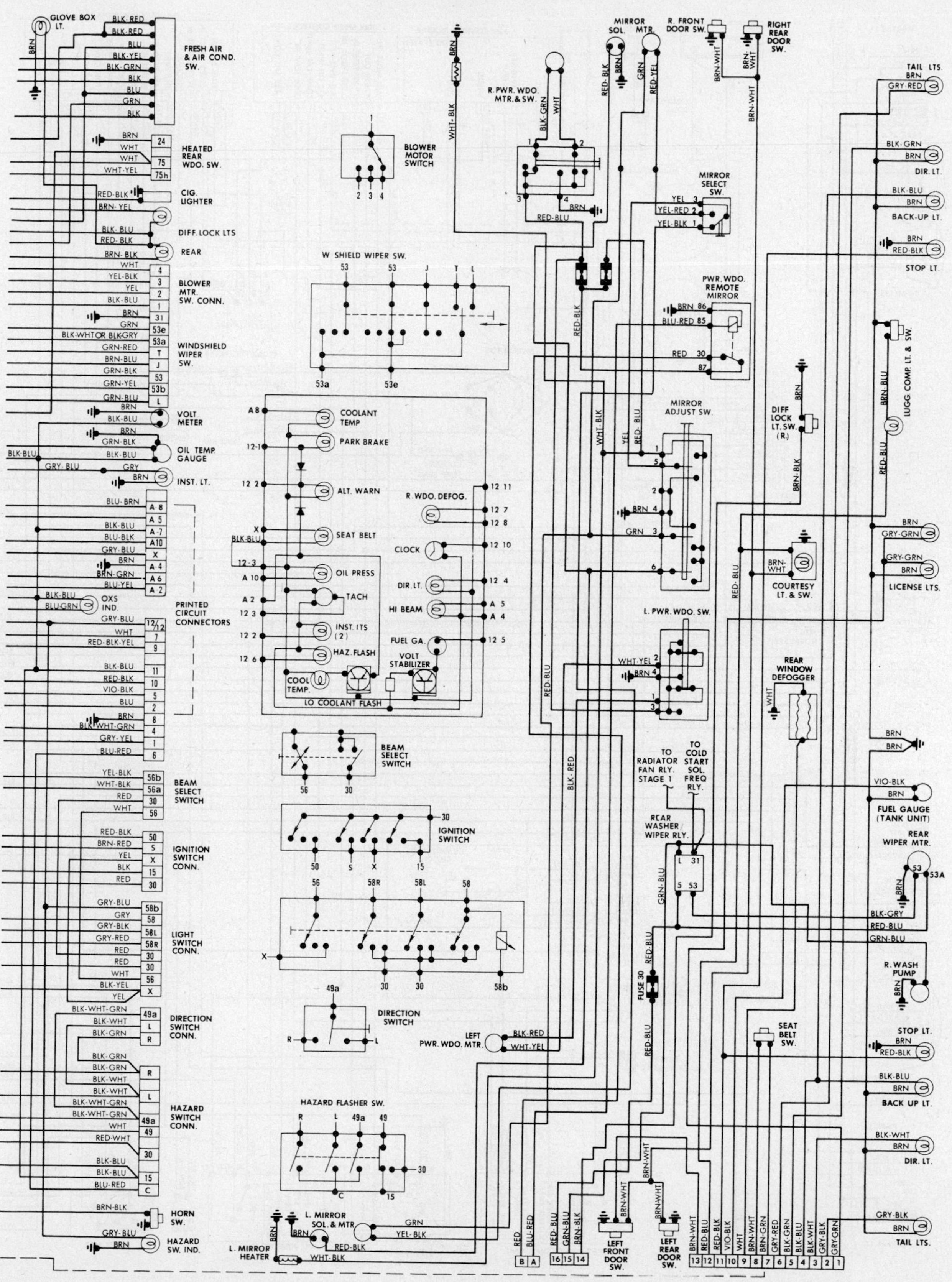

1983 BMW

318i

ENGINE COMPARTMENT

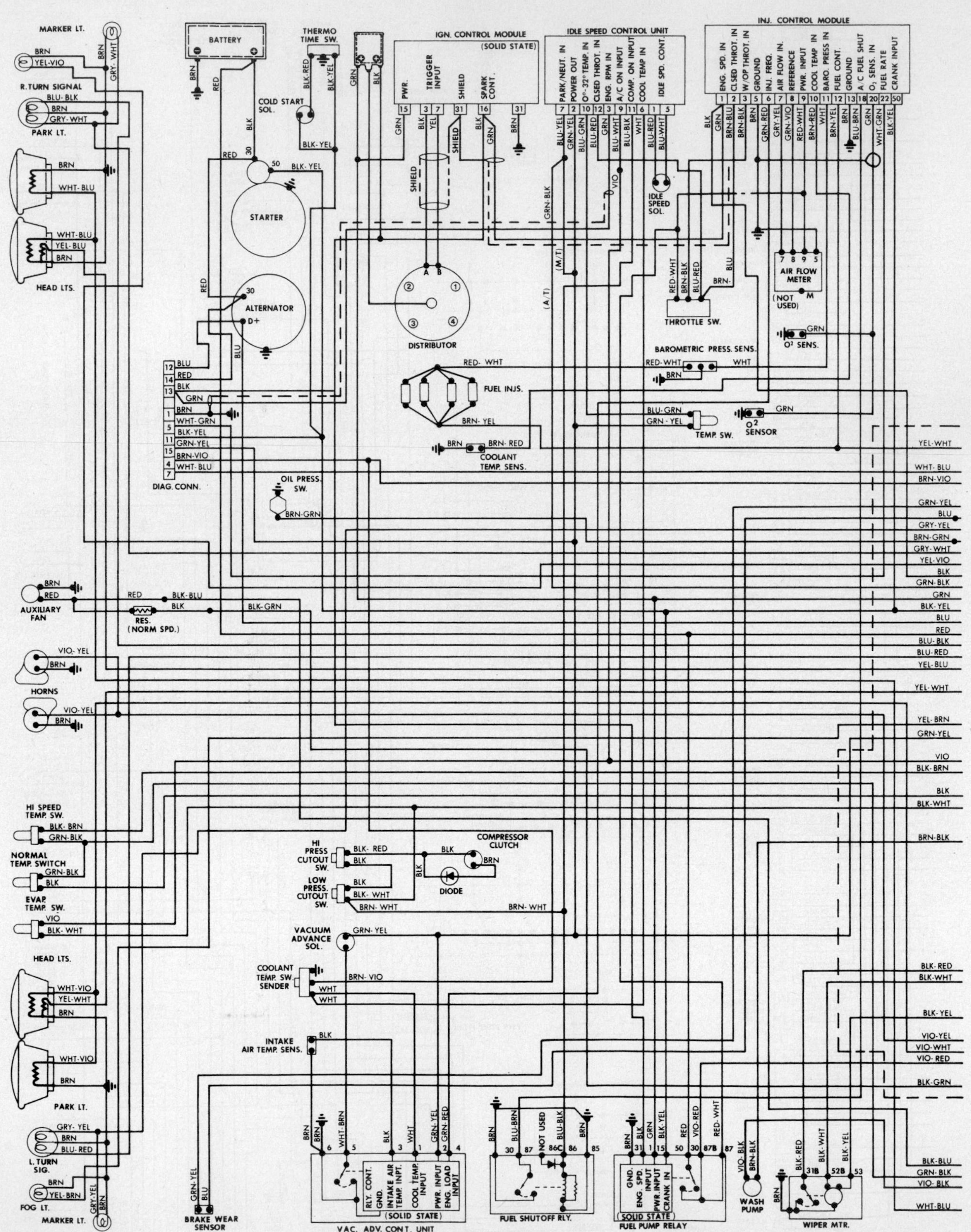
MARKER LT.
R. TURN SIGNAL
PARK LT.
HEAD LTS.
BATTERY
STARTER
ALTERNATOR
DIAG. CONN.
THERMO TIME SW.
COLD START SOL.
IGN. CONTROL MODULE
(SOLID STATE)
PWR.
TRIGGER INPUT
SHIELD
SPARK CONT.
DISTRIBUTOR
IDLE SPEED CONTROL UNIT
PARK/NEUT. IN
POWER OUT
O°-32° TEMP. IN
CLSED THROT. IN
ENG. RPM IN
A/C ON INPUT
COMP. ON INPUT
COOL TEMP IN
IDLE SPD. CONT.
IDLE SPEED SOL.
INJ. CONTROL MODULE
ENG. SPD. IN
CLSED THROT. IN
W/OP THROT. IN
GROUND
INJ. FREQ.
AIR FLOW IN.
REFERENCE
PWR. INPUT
COOL TEMP IN
BARO. PRESS IN
FUEL CONT.
GROUND
A/C FUEL SHUT
O₂ SENS. IN
FUEL RATE
CRANK INPUT
THROTTLE SW.
AIR FLOW METER
(NOT USED)
O² SENS.
BAROMETRIC PRESS. SENS.
FUEL INJS.
TEMP. SW.
O² SENSOR
COOLANT TEMP. SENS.
OIL PRESS. SW.
AUXILIARY FAN
RES. (NORM SPD.)
HORNS
HI SPEED TEMP. SW.
NORMAL TEMP. SWITCH
EVAP. TEMP. SW.
HI PRESS CUTOUT SW.
LOW PRESS. CUTOUT SW.
COMPRESSOR CLUTCH
DIODE
VACUUM ADVANCE SOL.
COOLANT TEMP. SW. SENDER
INTAKE AIR TEMP. SENS.
L. TURN SIG.
FOG LT.
BRAKE WEAR SENSOR
RLY. CONT.
GND.
INTAKE AIR TEMP. INPT.
COOL TEMP. INPUT
PWR. INPUT
ENG. LOAD INPUT
(SOLID STATE)
VAC. ADV. CONT. UNIT
NOT USED
FUEL SHUTOFF RLY.
GND.
ENG. SPD. INPUT
PWR INPUT
CRANK IN
SOLID STATE
FUEL PUMP RELAY
WASH PUMP
WIPER MTR.

318i (Cont.)

FUSE BLOCK & UNDERDASH

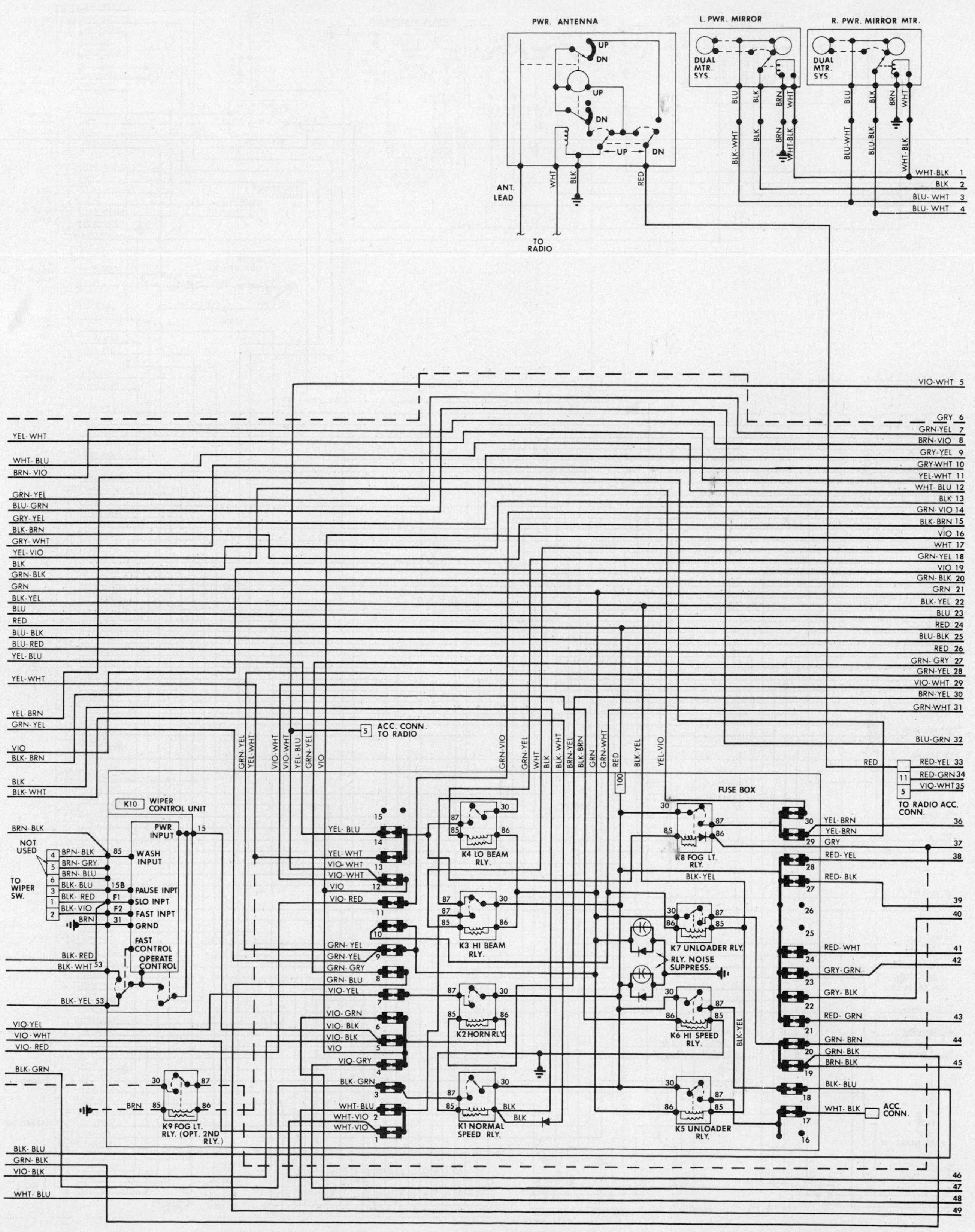
PWR. ANTENNA
L. PWR. MIRROR
R. PWR. MIRROR MTR.
DUAL MTR. SYS.
ANT. LEAD
TO RADIO
ACC. CONN. TO RADIO
K10 WIPER CONTROL UNIT
TO WIPER SW.
NOT USED
K4 LO BEAM RLY.
K3 HI BEAM RLY.
K2 HORN RLY.
K1 NORMAL SPEED RLY.
K9 FOG LT. RLY. (OPT. 2ND RLY.)
FUSE BOX
K8 FOG LT. RLY.
K7 UNLOADER RLY.
RLY. NOISE SUPPRESS.
K6 HI SPEED RLY.
K5 UNLOADER RLY.
TO RADIO ACC. CONN.
ACC. CONN.

1983 BMW

318i (Cont.)

UNDERDASH & INSTRUMENT PANEL

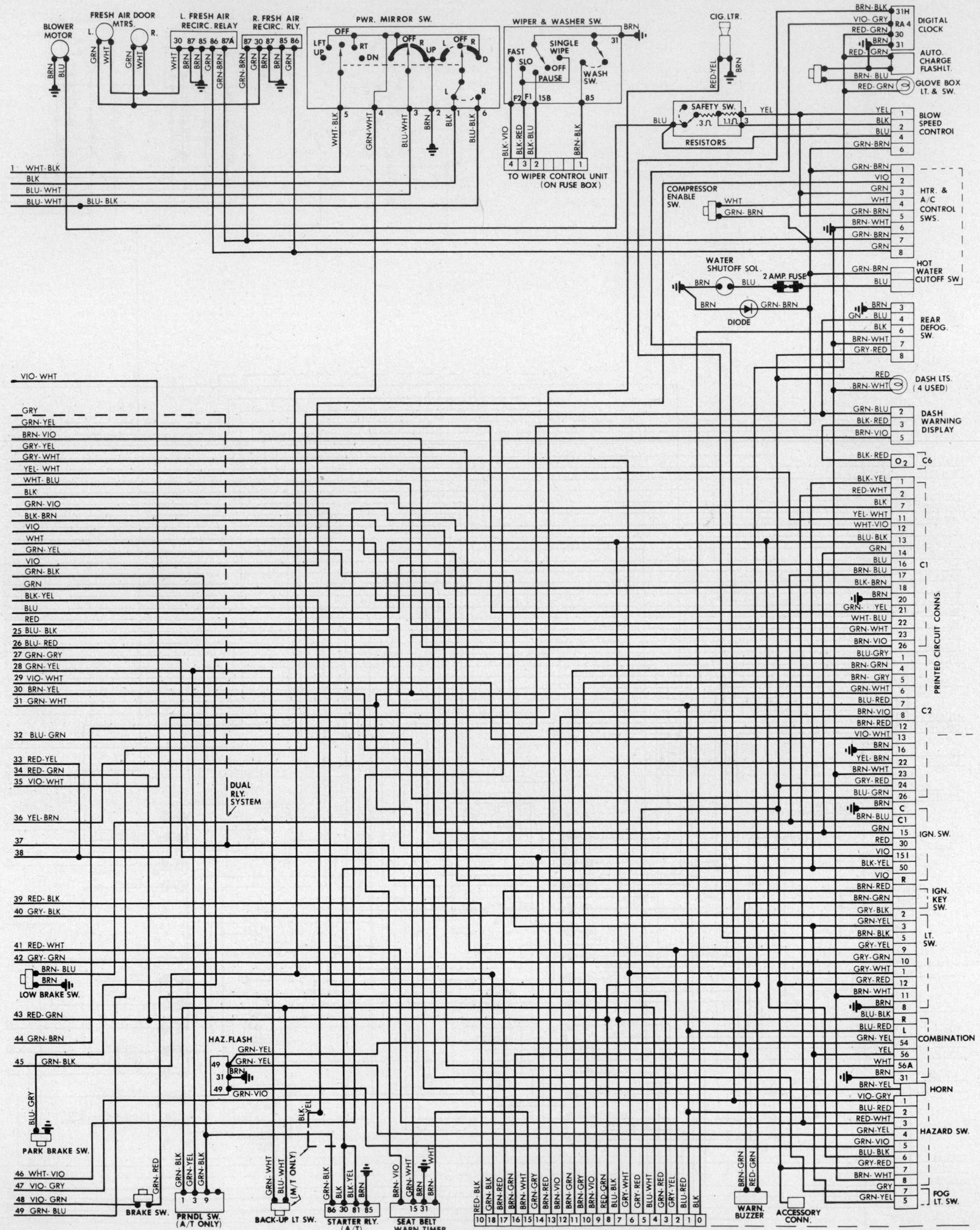
BLOWER MOTOR
FRESH AIR DOOR MTRS.
L. FRESH AIR RECIRC. RELAY
R. FRSH AIR RECIRC. RLY.
PWR. MIRROR SW.
WIPER & WASHER SW.
FAST
SLO
SINGLE WIPE
OFF
PAUSE
WASH SW.
TO WIPER CONTROL UNIT (ON FUSE BOX)
CIG. LTR.
DIGITAL CLOCK
AUTO. CHARGE FLASH LT.
GLOVE BOX LT. & SW.
SAFETY SW.
RESISTORS
BLOW SPEED CONTROL
COMPRESSOR ENABLE SW.
HTR. & A/C CONTROL SWS.
WATER SHUTOFF SOL.
2 AMP. FUSE
DIODE
HOT WATER CUTOFF SW.
REAR DEFOG. SW.
DASH LTS. (4 USED)
DASH WARNING DISPLAY
PRINTED CIRCUIT CONNS.
IGN. SW.
IGN. KEY SW.
LT. SW.
COMBINATION
HORN
HAZARD SW.
FOG LT. SW.
DUAL RLY. SYSTEM
LOW BRAKE SW.
HAZ. FLASH
PARK BRAKE SW.
BRAKE SW.
PRNDL SW. (A/T ONLY)
BACK-UP LT SW.
(M/T ONLY)
STARTER RLY. (A/T)
SEAT BELT WARN. TIMER
WARN. BUZZER
ACCESSORY CONN.

318i (Cont.)

INSTRUMENT PANEL, REAR COMPARTMENT & ACCESSORIES

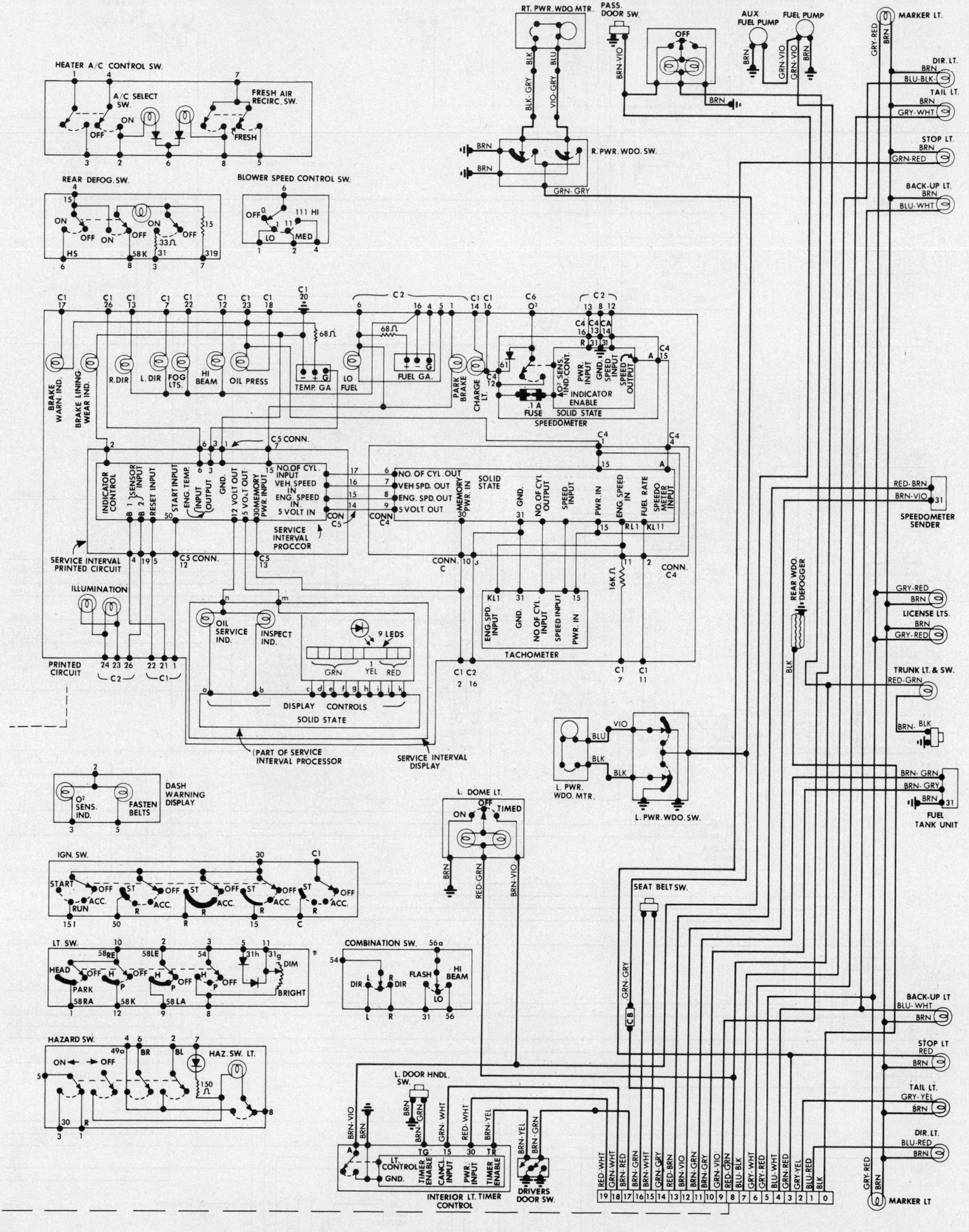
HEATER A/C CONTROL SW.
A/C SELECT SW.
FRESH AIR RECIRC. SW.
REAR DEFOG. SW.
BLOWER SPEED CONTROL SW.
RT. PWR. WDO MTR.
PASS. DOOR SW.
AUX FUEL PUMP
FUEL PUMP
MARKER LT.
DIR. LT.
TAIL LT.
STOP LT.
BACK-UP LT.
R. PWR. WDO. SW.
BRAKE WARN. IND.
BRAKE LINING WEAR IND.
R. DIR
L. DIR
FOG LTS.
HI BEAM
OIL PRESS
TEMP. GA
LO FUEL
FUEL GA.
PARK BRAKE
CHARGE LT.
INDICATOR ENABLE
SOLID STATE
SPEEDOMETER
C5 CONN.
SERVICE INTERVAL PROCCOR
SERVICE INTERVAL PRINTED CIRCUIT
ILLUMINATION
TACHOMETER
SPEEDOMETER SENDER
REAR WDO. DEFOGGER
LICENSE LTS.
TRUNK LT. & SW.
PRINTED CIRCUIT
OIL SERVICE IND.
INSPECT IND.
9 LEDS
DISPLAY CONTROLS
SOLID STATE
(PART OF SERVICE INTERVAL PROCESSOR
SERVICE INTERVAL DISPLAY
L. PWR. WDO. MTR.
L. PWR. WDO. SW.
FUEL TANK UNIT
DASH WARNING DISPLAY
O² SENS. IND.
FASTEN BELTS
L. DOME LT.
IGN. SW.
SEAT BELT SW.
LT. SW.
COMBINATION SW.
HAZARD SW.
HAZ. SW. LT.
L. DOOR HNDL. SW.
INTERIOR LT. TIMER CONTROL
DRIVERS DOOR SW.
MARKER LT

1983 BMW

320i

ENGINE COMPARTMENT

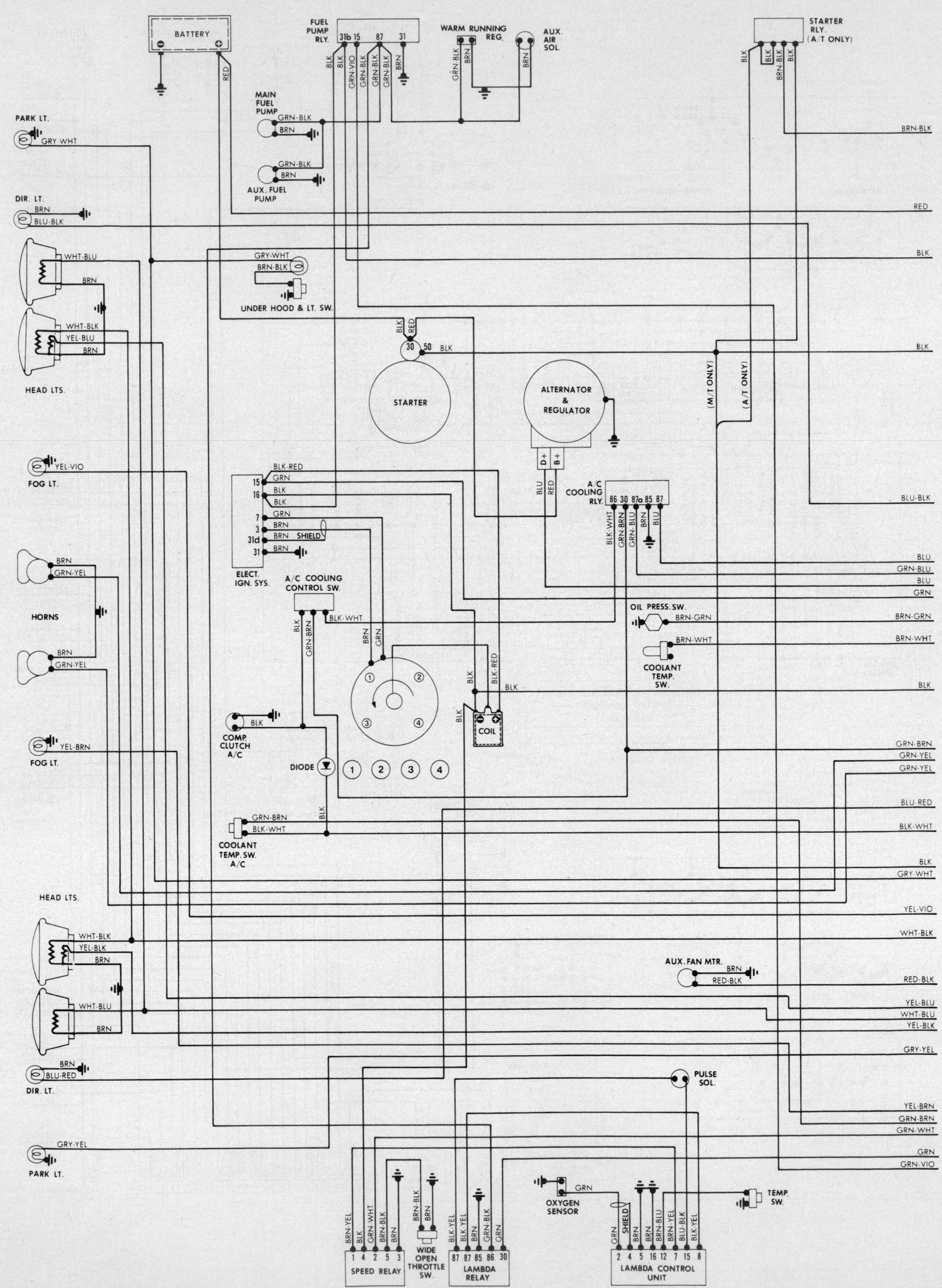

BATTERY
FUEL PUMP RLY.
31b 15 87 31
WARM RUNNING REG.
AUX. AIR SOL.
STARTER RLY. (A/T ONLY)
MAIN FUEL PUMP
AUX. FUEL PUMP
PARK LT.
DIR. LT.
HEAD LTS.
UNDER HOOD & LT. SW.
STARTER
ALTERNATOR & REGULATOR
(M/T ONLY)
(A/T ONLY)
FOG LT.
ELECT. IGN. SYS.
A/C COOLING RLY.
A/C COOLING CONTROL SW.
OIL PRESS. SW.
COOLANT TEMP. SW.
HORNS
COIL
COMP. CLUTCH A/C
DIODE
COOLANT TEMP. SW. A/C
AUX. FAN MTR.
PULSE SOL.
OXYGEN SENSOR
TEMP. SW.
SPEED RELAY
WIDE OPEN THROTTLE SW.
LAMBDA RELAY
LAMBDA CONTROL UNIT

320i (Cont.)

FUSE BLOCK & UNDERDASH

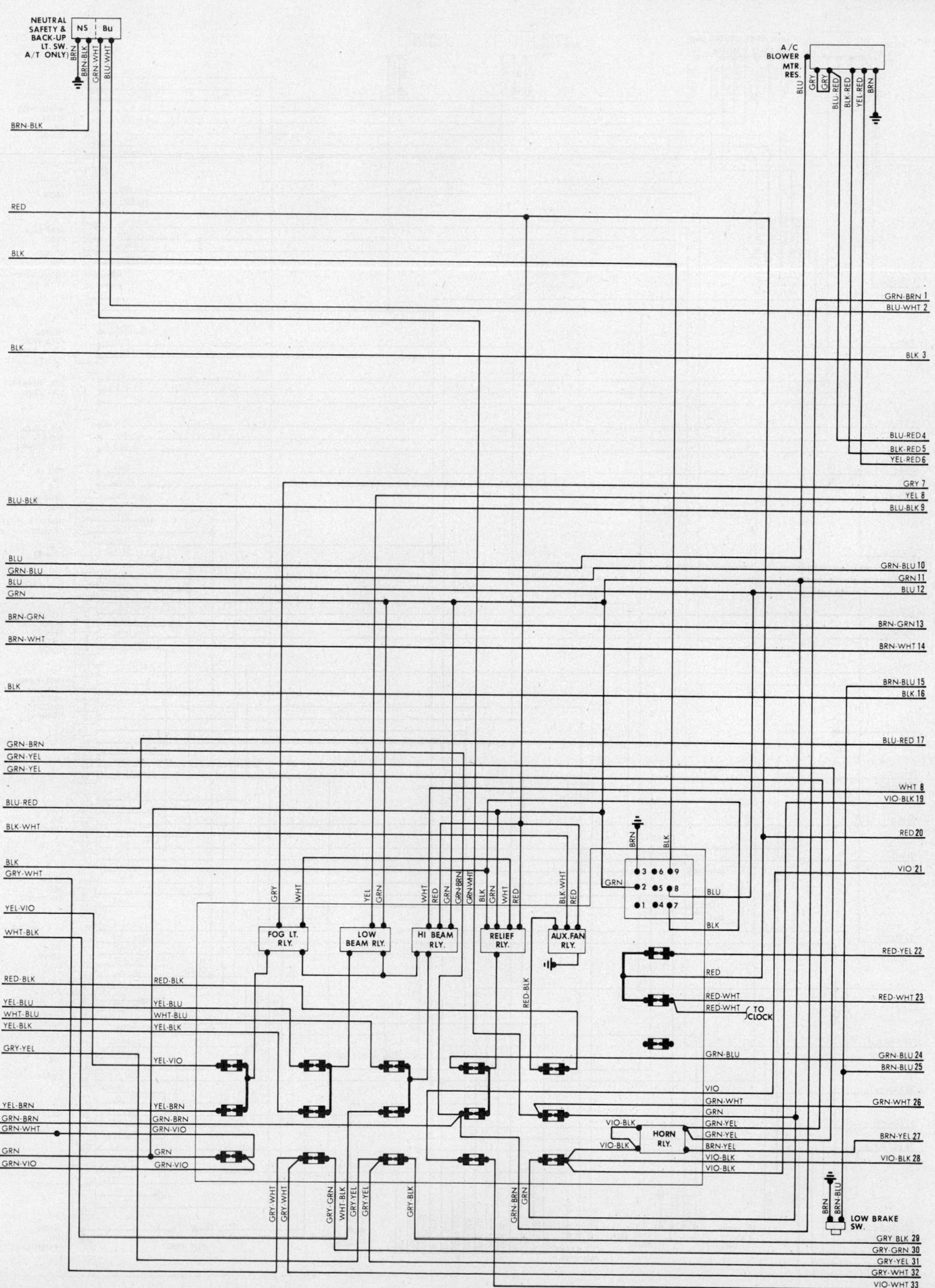

NEUTRAL SAFETY & BACK-UP LT. SW. A/T ONLY)
NS
Bu
A/C BLOWER MTR. RES.
GRN-BRN 1
BLU-WHT 2
BLK 3
BLU-RED 4
BLK-RED 5
YEL-RED 6
GRY 7
YEL 8
BLU-BLK 9
GRN-BLU 10
GRN 11
BLU 12
BRN-GRN 13
BRN-WHT 14
BRN-BLU 15
BLK 16
BLU-RED 17
WHT 8
VIO-BLK 19
RED 20
VIO 21
RED-YEL 22
RED-WHT 23
GRN-BLU 24
BRN-BLU 25
GRN-WHT 26
BRN-YEL 27
VIO-BLK 28
GRY-BLK 29
GRY-GRN 30
GRY-YEL 31
GRY-WHT 32
VIO-WHT 33
FOG LT. RLY.
LOW BEAM RLY.
HI BEAM RLY.
RELIEF RLY.
AUX. FAN RLY.
HORN RLY.
TO CLOCK
LOW BRAKE SW.

1983 BMW

320i (Cont.)

UNDERDASH & INSTRUMENT PANEL

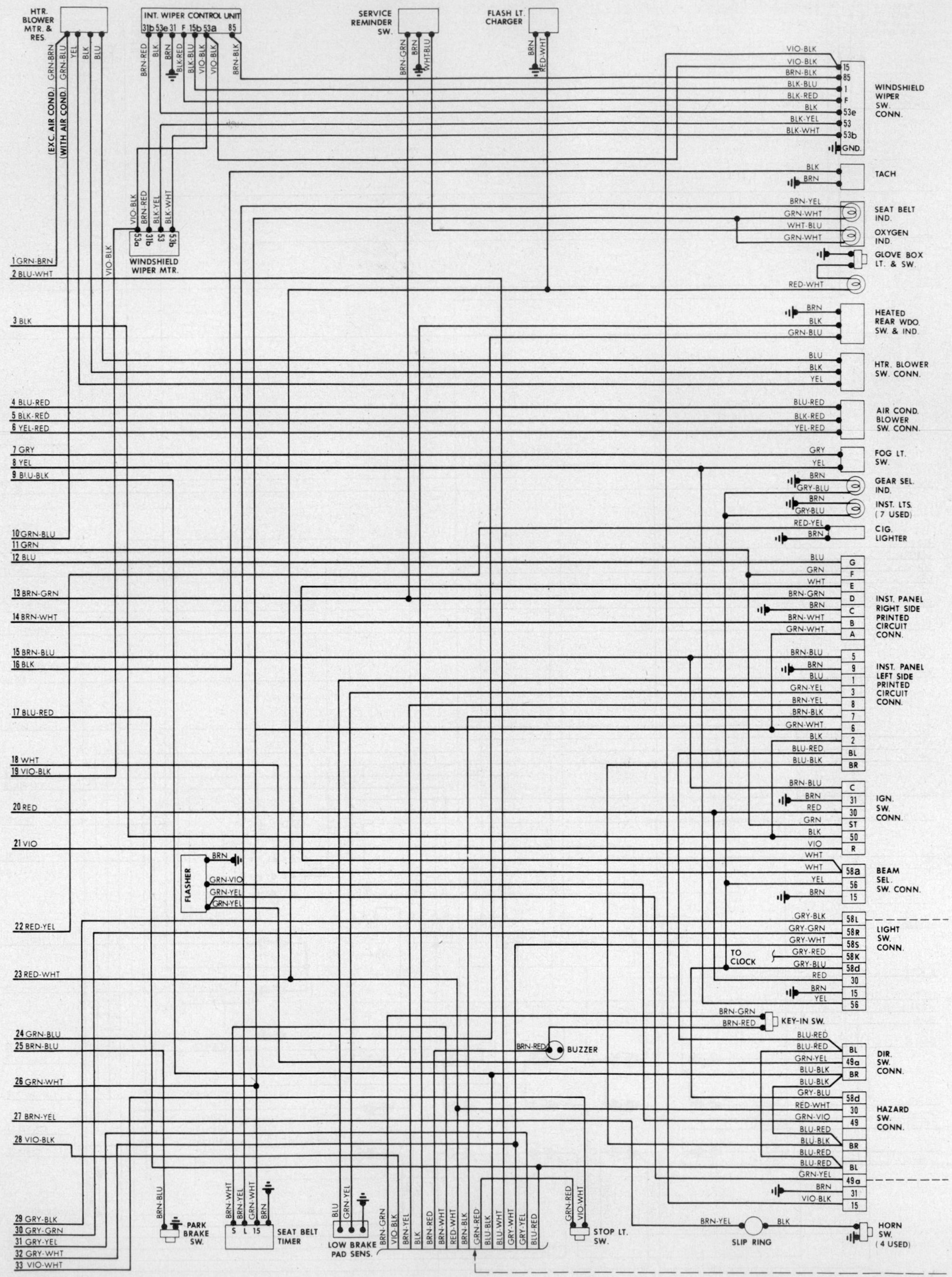

HTR. BLOWER MTR. & RES.
INT. WIPER CONTROL UNIT
SERVICE REMINDER SW.
FLASH LT. CHARGER
WINDSHIELD WIPER SW. CONN.
TACH
SEAT BELT IND.
OXYGEN IND.
GLOVE BOX LT. & SW.
WINDSHIELD WIPER MTR.
HEATED REAR WDO. SW. & IND.
HTR. BLOWER SW. CONN.
AIR COND. BLOWER SW. CONN.
FOG LT. SW.
GEAR SEL. IND.
INST. LTS. (7 USED)
CIG. LIGHTER
INST. PANEL RIGHT SIDE PRINTED CIRCUIT CONN.
INST. PANEL LEFT SIDE PRINTED CIRCUIT CONN.
IGN. SW. CONN.
BEAM SEL. SW. CONN.
LIGHT SW. CONN.
TO CLOCK
KEY-IN SW.
BUZZER
FLASHER
DIR. SW. CONN.
HAZARD SW. CONN.
PARK BRAKE SW.
SEAT BELT TIMER
LOW BRAKE PAD SENS.
STOP LT. SW.
SLIP RING
HORN SW. (4 USED)
(EXC. AIR COND.)
(WITH AIR COND.)
1 GRN-BRN
2 BLU-WHT
3 BLK
4 BLU-RED
5 BLK-RED
6 YEL-RED
7 GRY
8 YEL
9 BLU-BLK
10 GRN-BLU
11 GRN
12 BLU
13 BRN-GRN
14 BRN-WHT
15 BRN-BLU
16 BLK
17 BLU-RED
18 WHT
19 VIO-BLK
20 RED
21 VIO
22 RED-YEL
23 RED-WHT
24 GRN-BLU
25 BRN-BLU
26 GRN-WHT
27 BRN-YEL
28 VIO-BLK
29 GRY-BLK
30 GRY-GRN
31 GRY-YEL
32 GRY-WHT
33 VIO-WHT

320i (Cont.)

INSTRUMENT PANEL & REAR COMPARTMENT

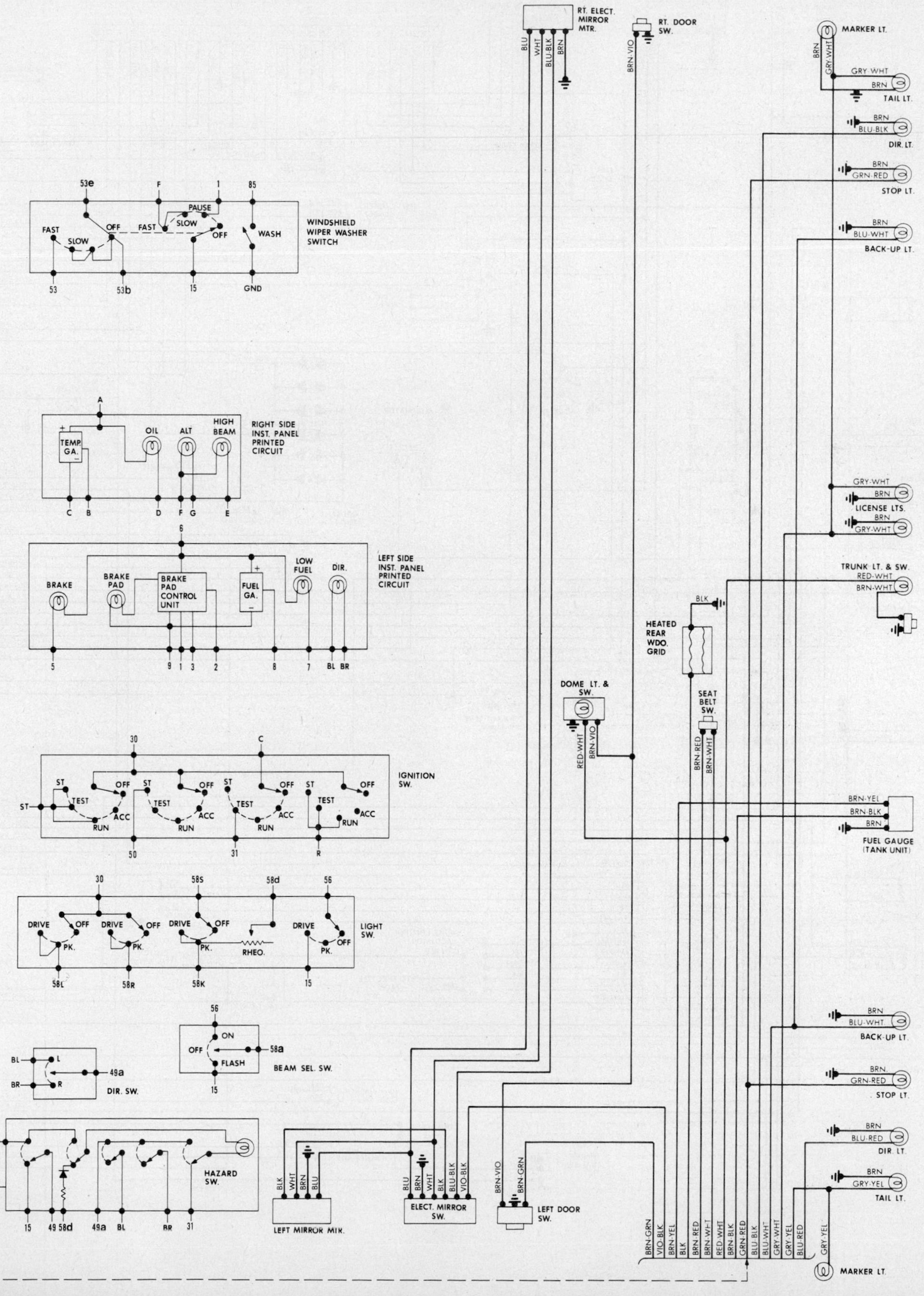
RT. ELECT. MIRROR MTR.
BLU
WHT
BLU-BLK
BRN
RT. DOOR SW.
BRN-VIO
MARKER LT.
BRN
GRY-WHT
TAIL LT.
BLU-BLK
DIR. LT.
GRN-RED
STOP LT.
BLU-WHT
BACK-UP LT.
53e
F
1
85
PAUSE
FAST
SLOW
OFF
WASH
WINDSHIELD WIPER WASHER SWITCH
53
53b
15
GND
A
TEMP. GA.
OIL
ALT
HIGH BEAM
RIGHT SIDE INST. PANEL PRINTED CIRCUIT
C
B
D
F
G
E
6
BRAKE
BRAKE PAD
BRAKE PAD CONTROL UNIT
FUEL GA.
LOW FUEL
DIR.
LEFT SIDE INST. PANEL PRINTED CIRCUIT
5
9
1
3
2
8
7
BL
BR
LICENSE LTS.
TRUNK LT. & SW.
RED-WHT
BRN-WHT
BLK
HEATED REAR WDO. GRID
DOME LT. & SW.
RED-WHT
SEAT BELT SW.
BRN-RED
BRN-WHT
30
C
ST
TEST
OFF
ACC
RUN
IGNITION SW.
50
31
R
BRN-YEL
BRN-BLK
FUEL GAUGE (TANK UNIT)
30
58S
58d
56
DRIVE
PK.
RHEO.
LIGHT SW.
58L
58R
58K
15
56
ON
OFF
FLASH
58a
BEAM SEL. SW.
15
BL
L
R
BR
49a
DIR. SW.
HAZARD SW.
15
49
58d
49a
BL
BR
31
BLK
LEFT MIRROR MTR.
ELECT. MIRROR SW.
VIO-BLK
BRN-GRN
LEFT DOOR SW.
BRN-GRN
VIO-BLK
BRN-YEL
BLK
BRN-RED
BRN-WHT
RED-WHT
BRN-BLK
GRN-RED
BLU-BLK
BLU-WHT
GRY-WHT
GRY-YEL
BLU-RED
BACK-UP LT.
STOP LT.
DIR. LT.
TAIL LT.
MARKER LT.

1983 BMW

528e & 533i

ENGINE COMPARTMENT

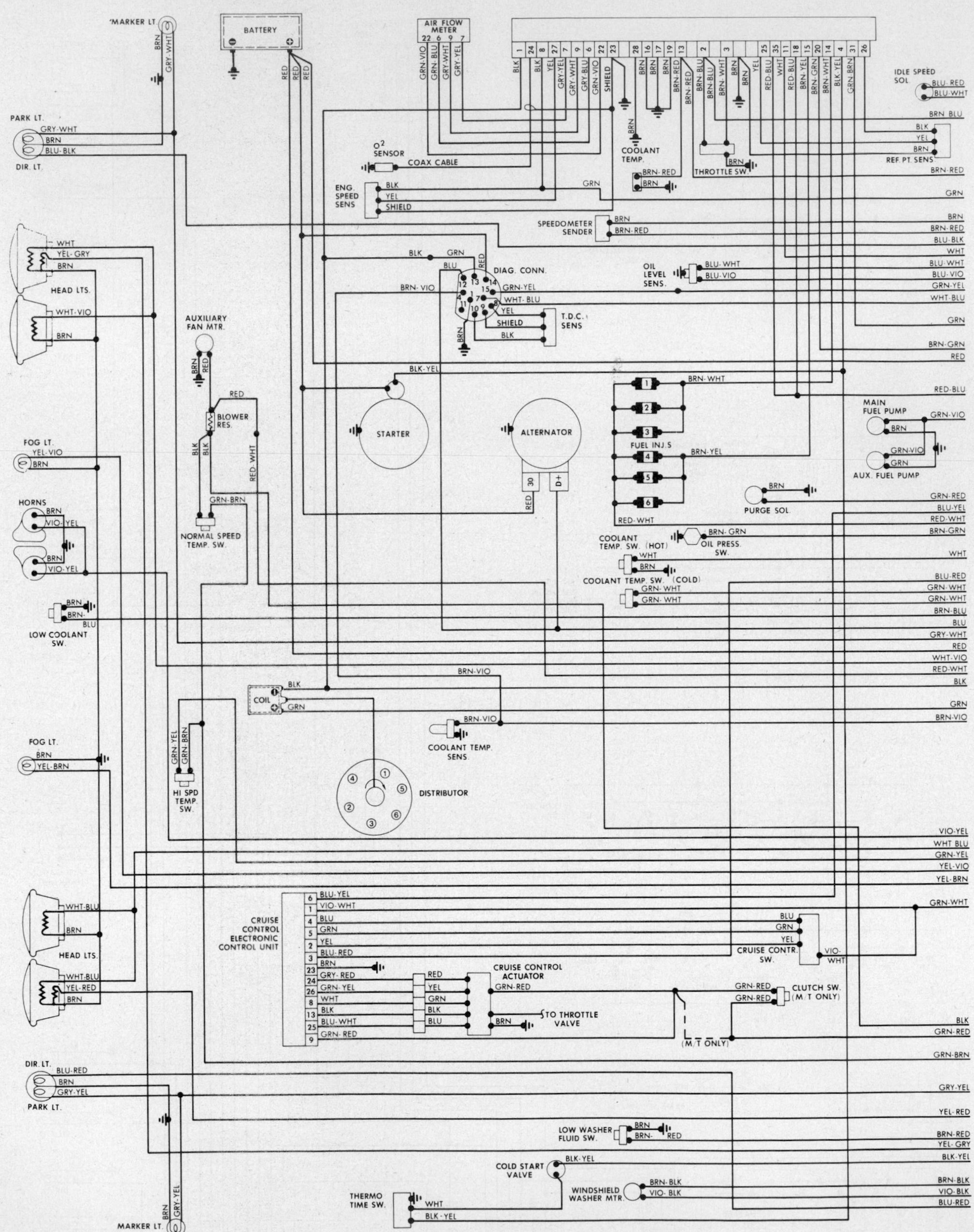
MARKER LT.
BATTERY
AIR FLOW METER
PARK LT.
DIR. LT.
O2 SENSOR
COAX CABLE
ENG. SPEED SENS
COOLANT TEMP.
THROTTLE SW.
IDLE SPEED SOL.
REF. PT. SENS
SPEEDOMETER SENDER
HEAD LTS.
DIAG. CONN.
OIL LEVEL SENS.
T.D.C. SENS
AUXILIARY FAN MTR.
BLOWER RES.
STARTER
ALTERNATOR
FUEL INJ.S
MAIN FUEL PUMP
AUX. FUEL PUMP
PURGE SOL.
FOG LT.
HORNS
NORMAL SPEED TEMP. SW.
COOLANT TEMP. SW. (HOT)
OIL PRESS. SW.
COOLANT TEMP. SW. (COLD)
LOW COOLANT SW.
COIL
COOLANT TEMP. SENS.
HI SPD TEMP. SW.
DISTRIBUTOR
CRUISE CONTROL ELECTRONIC CONTROL UNIT
CRUISE CONTROL ACTUATOR
TO THROTTLE VALVE
CRUISE CONTR. SW.
CLUTCH SW. (M/T ONLY)
(M/T ONLY)
LOW WASHER FLUID SW.
COLD START VALVE
WINDSHIELD WASHER MTR.
THERMO TIME SW.

528e & 533i (Cont.)

FUSE BLOCK & UNDERDASH

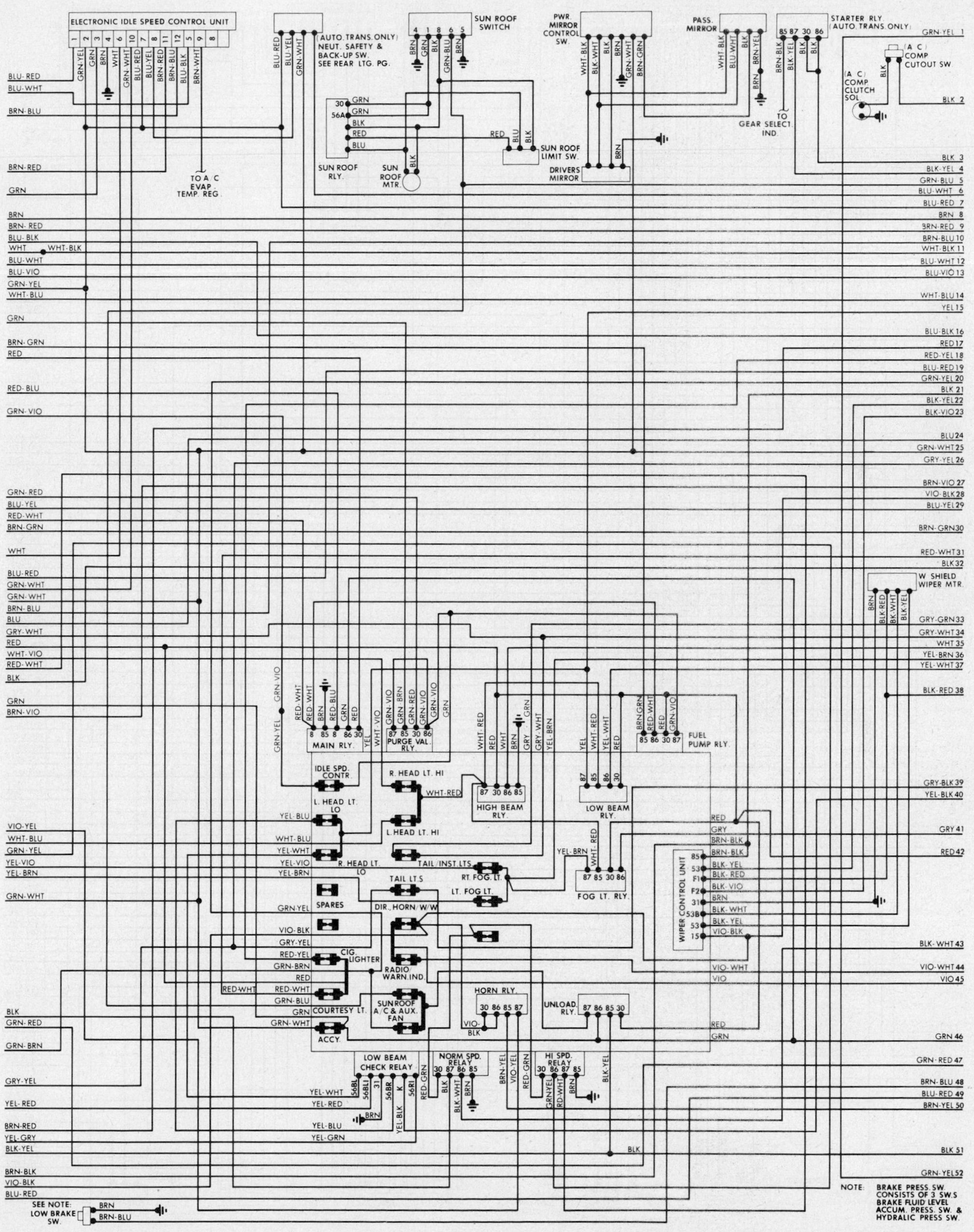
ELECTRONIC IDLE SPEED CONTROL UNIT
(AUTO. TRANS. ONLY) NEUT. SAFETY & BACK-UP SW. SEE REAR LTG. PG.
SUN ROOF SWITCH
PWR. MIRROR CONTROL SW.
PASS. MIRROR
STARTER RLY (AUTO. TRANS. ONLY)
(A/C) COMP CUTOUT SW
(A/C) COMP CLUTCH SOL.
TO GEAR SELECT. IND.
SUN ROOF LIMIT SW.
DRIVERS MIRROR
SUN ROOF RLY.
SUN ROOF MTR.
TO A/C EVAP. TEMP. REG.
W. SHIELD WIPER MTR.
MAIN RLY.
PURGE VAL. RLY.
IDLE SPD. CONTR.
R. HEAD LT. HI
L. HEAD LT. LO
L. HEAD LT. HI
R. HEAD LT. LO
HIGH BEAM RLY.
LOW BEAM RLY.
FUEL PUMP RLY.
TAIL/INST. LTS.
TAIL LTS
RT. FOG. LT.
LT. FOG LT.
FOG LT. RLY.
WIPER CONTROL UNIT
SPARES
DIR., HORN W/W
CIG. LIGHTER
RADIO/WARN. IND.
SUNROOF A/C & AUX. FAN
COURTESY LT.
ACCY.
HORN RLY.
UNLOAD. RLY.
LOW BEAM CHECK RELAY
NORM SPD. RELAY
HI SPD. RELAY
SEE NOTE: LOW BRAKE SW.
GRN-YEL 1
BLK 2
BLK 3
BLK-YEL 4
GRN-BLU 5
BLU-WHT 6
BLU-RED 7
BRN 8
BRN-RED 9
BRN-BLU 10
WHT-BLK 11
BLU-WHT 12
BLU-VIO 13
WHT-BLU 14
YEL 15
BLU-BLK 16
RED 17
RED-YEL 18
BLU-RED 19
GRN-YEL 20
BLK 21
BLK-YEL 22
BLK-VIO 23
BLU 24
GRN-WHT 25
GRY-YEL 26
BRN-VIO 27
VIO-BLK 28
BLU-YEL 29
BRN-GRN 30
RED-WHT 31
BLK 32
GRY-GRN 33
GRY-WHT 34
WHT 35
YEL-BRN 36
YEL-WHT 37
BLK-RED 38
GRY-BLK 39
YEL-BLK 40
GRY 41
RED 42
BLK-WHT 43
VIO-WHT 44
VIO 45
GRN 46
GRN-RED 47
BRN-BLU 48
BLU-RED 49
BRN-YEL 50
BLK 51
GRN-YEL 52
NOTE: BRAKE PRESS. SW. CONSISTS OF 3 SW.S BRAKE FLUID LEVEL ACCUM. PRESS. SW. & HYDRALIC PRESS SW.

1983 BMW

528e & 533i (Cont.)

UNDERDASH

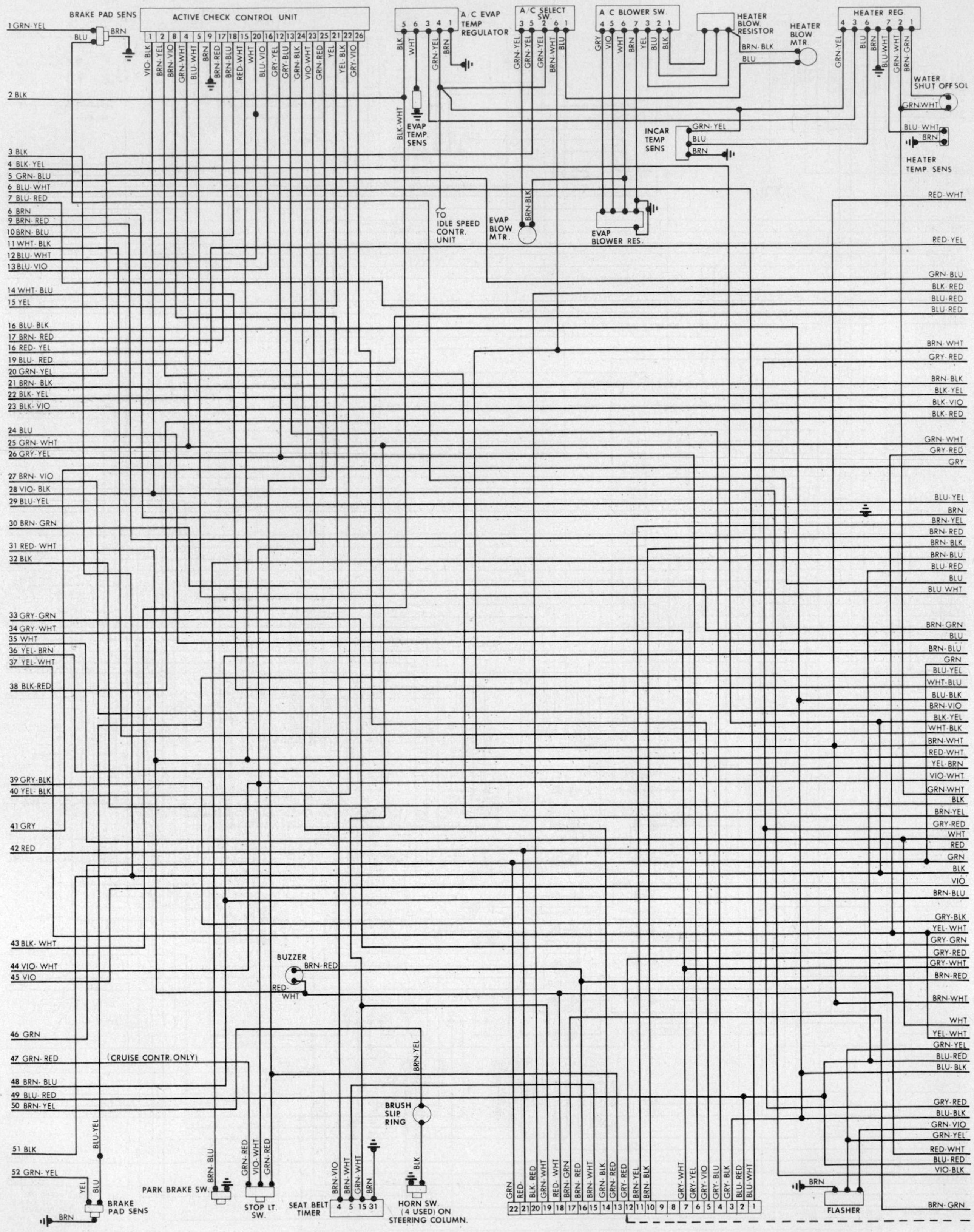
BRAKE PAD SENS
ACTIVE CHECK CONTROL UNIT
1 2 8 4 5 9 17 18 15 20 16 12 13 24 23 25 21 22 26
A/C EVAP TEMP REGULATOR
5 6 3 4 1
A/C SELECT SW.
3 5 2 6 1
A/C BLOWER SW.
4 5 6 7 3 2 1
HEATER BLOW. RESISTOR
HEATER BLOW MTR
HEATER REG.
4 3 6 7 2 1
WATER SHUT OFF SOL
INCAR TEMP SENS
HEATER TEMP. SENS
EVAP TEMP. SENS
TO IDLE SPEED CONTR. UNIT
EVAP BLOW MTR.
EVAP BLOWER RES.
1 GRN-YEL
2 BLK
3 BLK
4 BLK-YEL
5 GRN-BLU
6 BLU-WHT
7 BLU-RED
8 BRN
9 BRN-RED
10 BRN-BLU
11 WHT-BLK
12 BLU-WHT
13 BLU-VIO
14 WHT-BLU
15 YEL
16 BLU-BLK
17 BRN-RED
18 RED-YEL
19 BLU-RED
20 GRN-YEL
21 BRN-BLK
22 BLK-YEL
23 BLK-VIO
24 BLU
25 GRN-WHT
26 GRY-YEL
27 BRN-VIO
28 VIO-BLK
29 BLU-YEL
30 BRN-GRN
31 RED-WHT
32 BLK
33 GRY-GRN
34 GRY-WHT
35 WHT
36 YEL-BRN
37 YEL-WHT
38 BLK-RED
39 GRY-BLK
40 YEL-BLK
41 GRY
42 RED
43 BLK-WHT
44 VIO-WHT
45 VIO
46 GRN
47 GRN-RED
48 BRN-BLU
49 BLU-RED
50 BRN-YEL
51 BLK
52 GRN-YEL
(CRUISE CONTR. ONLY)
BUZZER
BRUSH SLIP RING
BRAKE PAD SENS
PARK BRAKE SW.
STOP LT. SW.
SEAT BELT TIMER
4 5 15 31
HORN SW. (4 USED) ON STEERING COLUMN.
22 21 20 19 18 17 16 15 14 13 12 11 10 9 8 7 6 5 4 3 2 1
FLASHER

528e & 533i (Cont.)

INSTRUMENT PANEL, REAR COMPARTMENT & ACCESSORIES

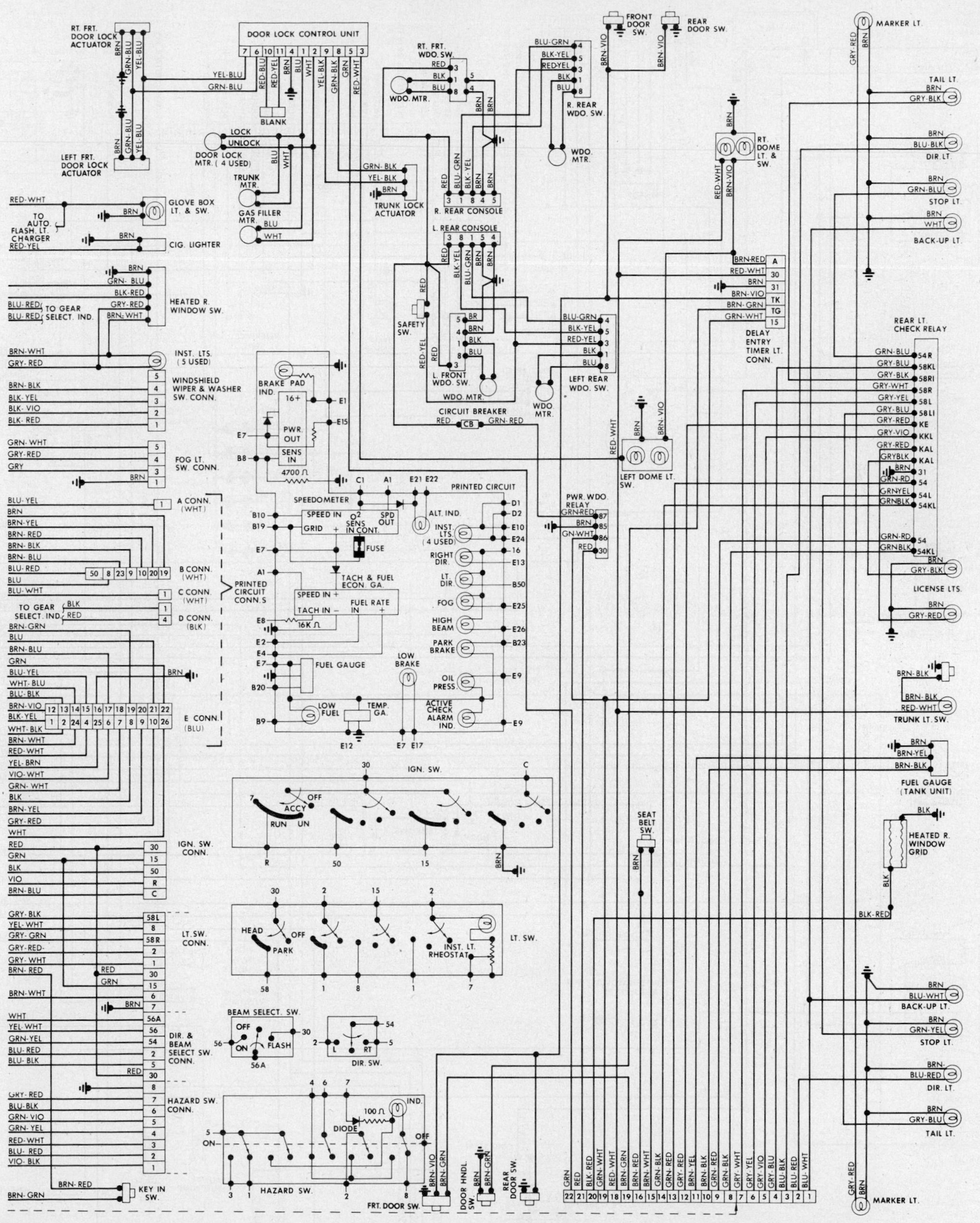
RT. FRT. DOOR LOCK ACTUATOR
DOOR LOCK CONTROL UNIT
BLANK
LOCK
UNLOCK
DOOR LOCK MTR. (4 USED)
TRUNK MTR.
GAS FILLER MTR.
LEFT FRT. DOOR LOCK ACTUATOR
RT. FRT. WDO. SW.
WDO. MTR.
TRUNK LOCK ACTUATOR
R. REAR CONSOLE
L. REAR CONSOLE
R. REAR WDO. SW.
FRONT DOOR SW.
REAR DOOR SW.
MARKER LT.
TAIL LT.
DIR. LT.
STOP LT.
BACK-UP LT.
RT. DOME LT. & SW.
GLOVE BOX LT. & SW.
TO AUTO. FLASH. LT. CHARGER
CIG. LIGHTER
HEATED R. WINDOW SW.
TO GEAR SELECT. IND.
INST. LTS. (5 USED)
WINDSHIELD WIPER & WASHER SW. CONN.
FOG LT. SW. CONN.
BRAKE PAD IND.
SAFETY SW.
L. FRONT WDO. SW.
LEFT REAR WDO. SW.
CIRCUIT BREAKER
DELAY ENTRY TIMER LT. CONN.
REAR LT. CHECK RELAY
LEFT DOME LT. SW.
PWR. WDO. RELAY
PRINTED CIRCUIT
SPEEDOMETER
ALT. IND.
INST. LTS. (4 USED)
RIGHT DIR.
LT. DIR.
FOG
HIGH BEAM
PARK BRAKE
OIL PRESS.
ACTIVE CHECK ALARM IND.
LOW BRAKE
FUEL GAUGE
LOW FUEL
TEMP. GA.
TACH & FUEL ECON. GA.
FUSE
A CONN. (WHT)
B CONN. (WHT)
C CONN. (WHT)
D CONN. (BLK)
E CONN. (BLU)
PRINTED CIRCUIT CONN.S
LICENSE LTS.
TRUNK LT. SW.
FUEL GAUGE (TANK UNIT)
HEATED R. WINDOW GRID
IGN. SW.
IGN. SW. CONN.
SEAT BELT SW.
LT. SW.
LT. SW. CONN.
INST. LT. RHEOSTAT
BEAM SELECT. SW.
DIR. SW.
DIR. & BEAM SELECT SW. CONN.
HAZARD SW. CONN.
HAZARD SW.
DIODE
KEY IN SW.
FRT. DOOR SW.
DOOR HNDL. SW.
REAR DOOR SW.

1983 BMW

633CSi & 733i

ENGINE COMPARTMENT

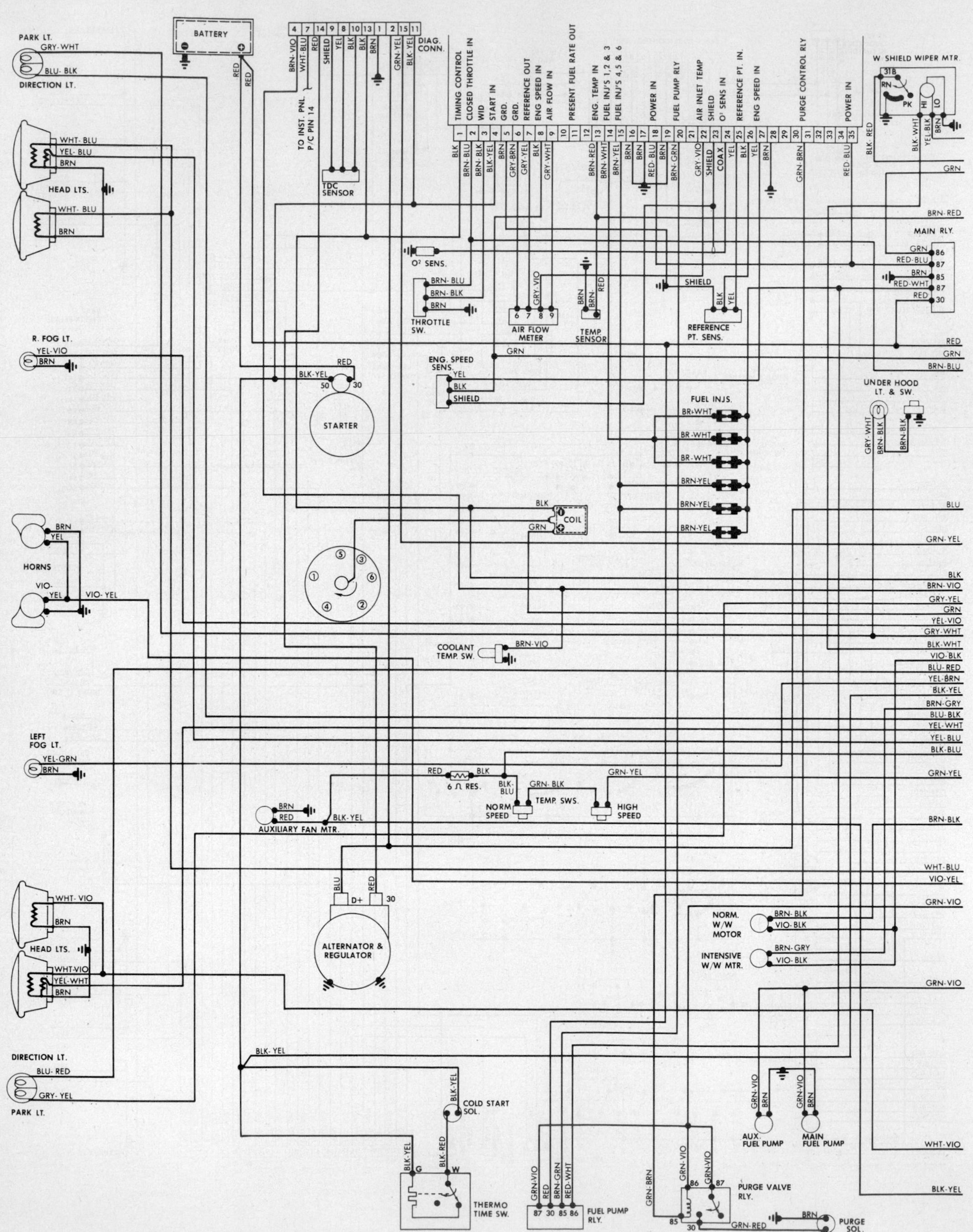
PARK LT.
GRY-WHT
BLU-BLK
DIRECTION LT.
BATTERY
RED
DIAG. CONN.
4 7 14 9 8 10 13 1 2 15 11
BRN-VIO
WHT-BLU
RED
SHIELD
YEL
BLK
BLK
BRN
GRN-YEL
BLK-YEL
TO INST. PNL. P/C PIN 14
TDC SENSOR
TIMING CONTROL
CLOSED THROTTLE IN
WID
START IN
GRD.
GRD.
REFERENCE OUT
ENG SPEED IN
AIR FLOW IN
PRESENT FUEL RATE OUT
ENG. TEMP IN
FUEL INJ'S 1, 2 & 3
FUEL INJ'S 4, 5 & 6
POWER IN
FUEL PUMP RLY
AIR INLET TEMP
SHIELD
O² SENS IN
REFERENCE PT. IN.
ENG SPEED IN
PURGE CONTROL RLY
POWER IN
1 2 3 4 5 6 7 8 9 10 11 12 13 14 15 16 17 18 19 20 21 22 23 24 25 26 27 28 29 30 31 32 33 34 35
W SHIELD WIPER MTR.
31B
RN
PK
HI
LO
BLK-WHT
YEL-BLK
BRN
WHT-BLU
YEL-BLU
BRN
HEAD LTS.
WHT-BLU
BRN
O² SENS.
BRN-BLU
BRN-BLK
BRN
THROTTLE SW.
GRY-VIO
6 7 8 9
AIR FLOW METER
BRN
BRN
RED
TEMP SENSOR
SHIELD
BLK
YEL
REFERENCE PT. SENS.
MAIN RLY.
GRN 86
RED-BLU 87
BRN 85
RED-WHT 87
RED 30
GRN
BRN-RED
RED
GRN
BRN-BLU
R. FOG LT.
YEL-VIO
BRN
BLK-YEL
RED
50
30
STARTER
ENG. SPEED SENS.
YEL
BLK
SHIELD
GRN
FUEL INJS.
BR-WHT
BR-WHT
BR-WHT
BRN-YEL
BRN-YEL
BRN-YEL
UNDER HOOD LT. & SW.
GRY-WHT
BRN-BLK
BRN-BLK
BLU
BLK
COIL
GRN
GRN-YEL
BRN
YEL
HORNS
VIO-YEL
VIO-YEL
BLK
BRN-VIO
GRY-YEL
GRN
YEL-VIO
GRY-WHT
BLK-WHT
VIO-BLK
BLU-RED
YEL-BRN
BLK-YEL
BRN-GRY
BLU-BLK
YEL-WHT
YEL-BLU
BLK-BLU
COOLANT TEMP. SW.
BRN-VIO
LEFT FOG LT.
YEL-GRN
BRN
RED
6 Ω RES.
BLK
BLK-BLU
GRN-BLK
TEMP. SWS.
GRN-YEL
NORM SPEED
HIGH SPEED
GRN-YEL
BRN
RED
BLK-YEL
AUXILIARY FAN MTR.
BRN-BLK
WHT-BLU
VIO-YEL
BLU
RED
D+
30
ALTERNATOR & REGULATOR
WHT-VIO
BRN
HEAD LTS.
WHT-VIO
YEL-WHT
BRN
GRN-VIO
NORM. W/W MOTOR
BRN-BLK
VIO-BLK
INTENSIVE W/W MTR.
BRN-GRY
VIO-BLK
GRN-VIO
DIRECTION LT.
BLU-RED
GRY-YEL
PARK LT.
BLK-YEL
BLK-YEL
COLD START SOL.
BLK-YEL
BLK-RED
G
W
THERMO TIME SW.
GRN-VIO
RED
BRN-GRN
RED-WHT
87 30 85 86
FUEL PUMP RLY.
GRN-BRN
GRN-VIO
GRN-VIO
86
87
85
30
PURGE VALVE RLY.
GRN-RED
BRN
PURGE SOL.
GRN-VIO
BRN
GRN-VIO
BRN
AUX. FUEL PUMP
MAIN FUEL PUMP
WHT-VIO
BLK-YEL

1983 BMW

633CSi & 733i (Cont.)

FUSE BLOCK & UNDERDASH

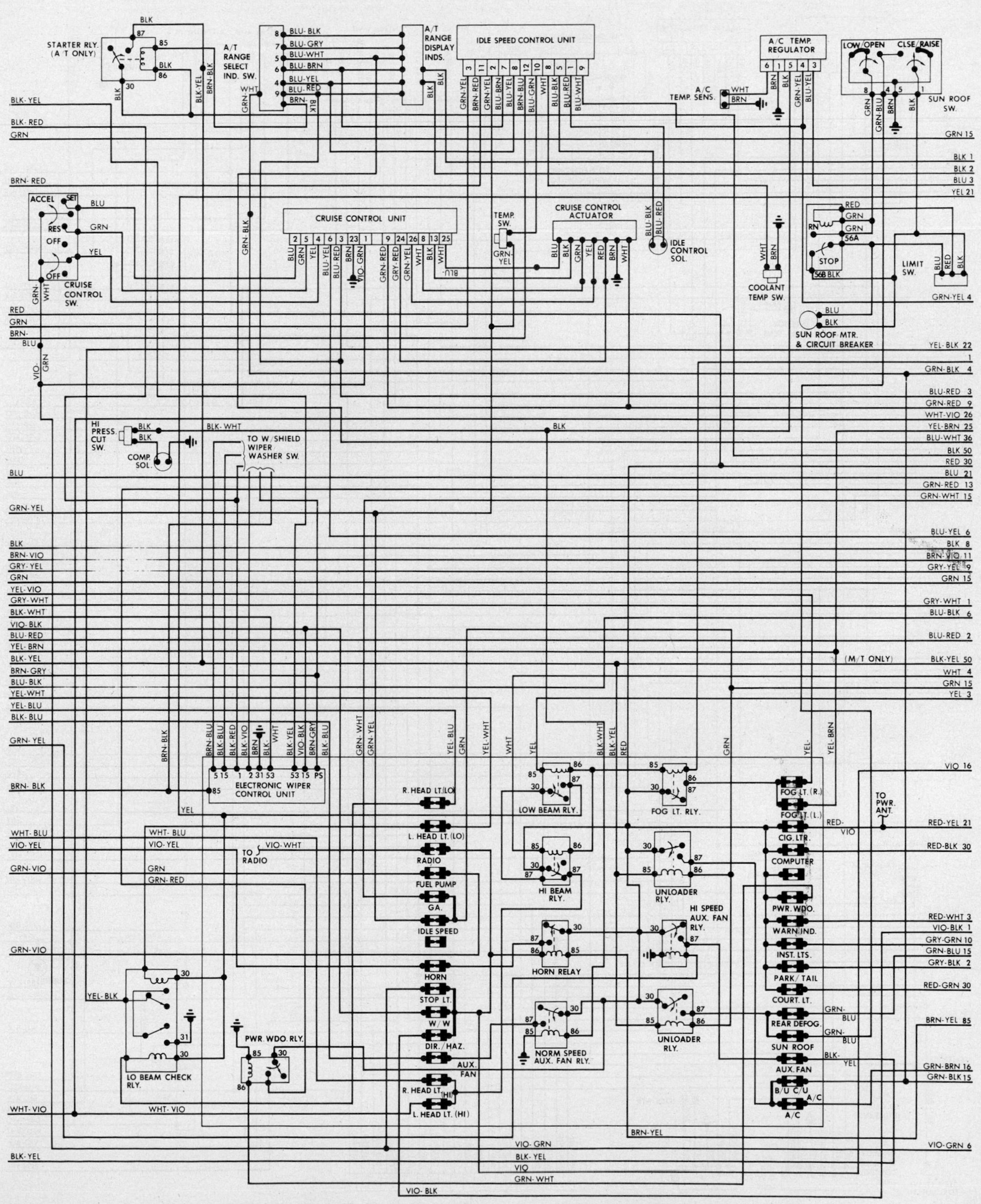

STARTER RLY. (A/T ONLY)
A/T RANGE SELECT IND. SW.
A/T RANGE DISPLAY INDS.
IDLE SPEED CONTROL UNIT
A/C TEMP. REGULATOR
A/C TEMP. SENS.
LOW/OPEN
CLSE/RAISE
SUN ROOF SW.
ACCEL
SET
RES
OFF
CRUISE CONTROL SW.
CRUISE CONTROL UNIT
TEMP. SW.
CRUISE CONTROL ACTUATOR
IDLE CONTROL SOL.
COOLANT TEMP SW.
STOP
LIMIT SW.
SUN ROOF MTR. & CIRCUIT BREAKER
HI PRESS. CUT SW.
COMP. SOL.
TO W/SHIELD WIPER WASHER SW.
(M/T ONLY)
ELECTRONIC WIPER CONTROL UNIT
TO RADIO
TO PWR. ANT.
R. HEAD LT. (LO)
L. HEAD LT. (LO)
RADIO
FUEL PUMP
GA.
IDLE SPEED
HORN
STOP LT.
W/W
DIR./HAZ.
AUX. FAN
R. HEAD LT. (HI)
L. HEAD LT. (HI)
LOW BEAM RLY.
HI BEAM RLY.
HORN RELAY
NORM SPEED AUX. FAN RLY.
FOG LT. RLY.
UNLOADER RLY.
HI SPEED AUX. FAN RLY.
FOG LT. (R.)
FOG LT. (L.)
CIG. LTR.
COMPUTER
PWR. WDO.
WARN. IND.
INST. LTS.
PARK/TAIL
COURT. LT.
REAR DEFOG.
SUN ROOF
AUX. FAN
B/U C/U
A/C
LO BEAM CHECK RLY.
PWR. WDO. RLY.
BLK-YEL
BLK-RED
GRN
BRN-RED
RED
BLU
GRN-YEL
BLK
BRN-VIO
GRY-YEL
YEL-VIO
GRY-WHT
BLK-WHT
VIO-BLK
BLU-RED
YEL-BRN
BRN-GRY
BLU-BLK
YEL-WHT
YEL-BLU
BLK-BLU
BRN-BLK
WHT-BLU
VIO-YEL
GRN-VIO
WHT-VIO
VIO-GRN
VIO
GRN-WHT
VIO-BLK
BRN-YEL
GRN 15
BLK 1
BLK 2
BLU 3
YEL 21
GRN-YEL 4
YEL-BLK 22
GRN-BLK 4
BLU-RED 3
GRN-RED 9
WHT-VIO 26
YEL-BRN 25
BLU-WHT 36
BLK 50
RED 30
BLU 21
GRN-RED 13
GRN-WHT 15
BLU-YEL 6
BLK 8
BRN-VIO 11
GRY-YEL 9
GRN 15
GRY-WHT 1
BLU-BLK 6
BLU-RED 2
BLK-YEL 50
WHT 4
GRN 15
YEL 3
VIO 16
RED-YEL 21
RED-BLK 30
RED-WHT 3
VIO-BLK 1
GRY-GRN 10
GRN-BLU 15
GRY-BLK 2
RED-GRN 30
BRN-YEL 85
GRN-BRN 16
GRN-BLK 15
VIO-GRN 6

1983 BMW

633CSi & 733i (Cont.)

UNDERDASH

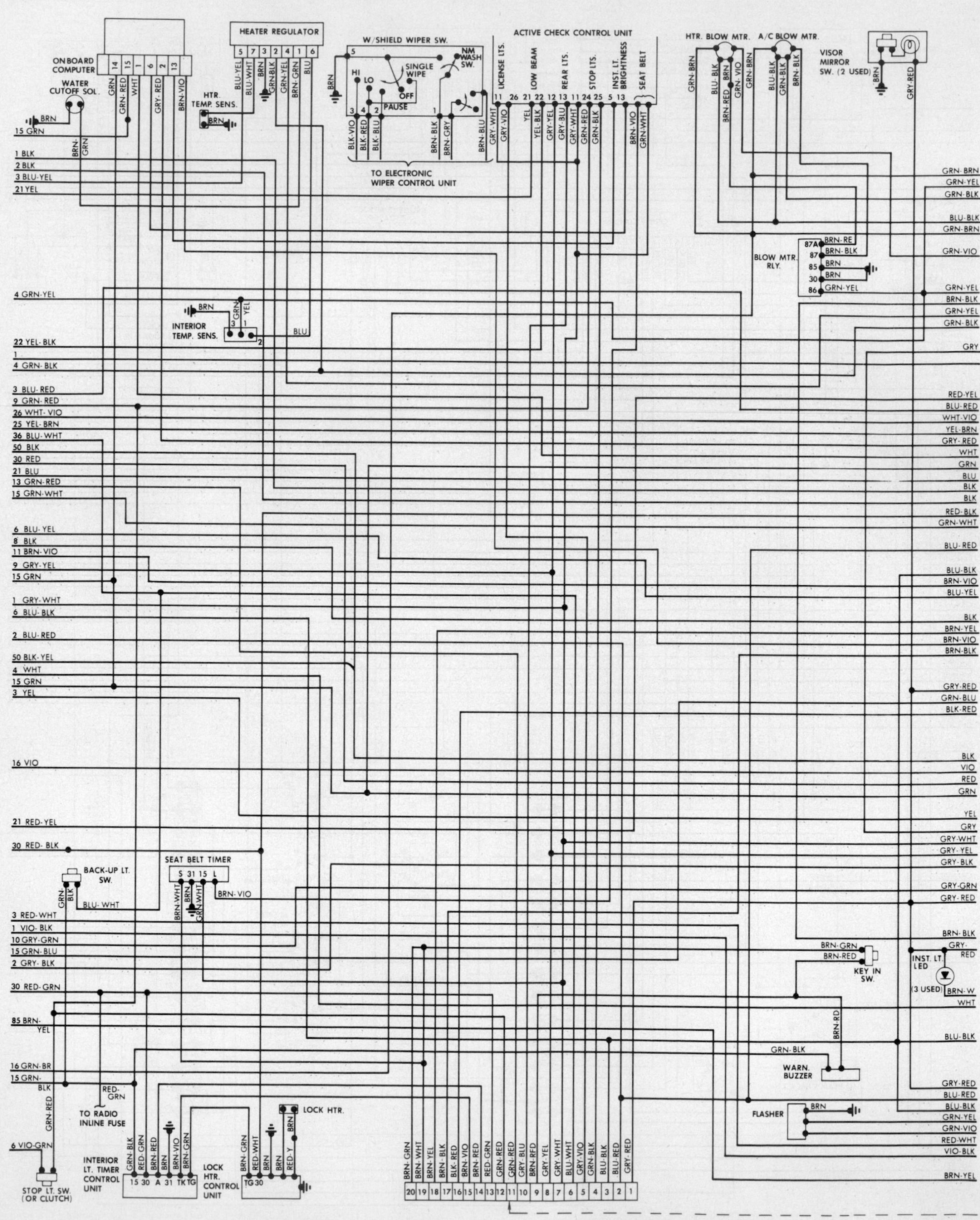

ONBOARD COMPUTER
WATER CUTOFF SOL.
HEATER REGULATOR
HTR. TEMP. SENS.
W/SHIELD WIPER SW.
HI
LO
SINGLE WIPE
OFF
PAUSE
NM WASH SW.
TO ELECTRONIC WIPER CONTROL UNIT
ACTIVE CHECK CONTROL UNIT
LICENSE LTS.
LOW BEAM
REAR LTS.
STOP LTS.
INST. LT. BRIGHTNESS
SEAT BELT
HTR. BLOW MTR.
A/C BLOW MTR.
VISOR MIRROR SW. (2 USED)
BLOW MTR. RLY.
INTERIOR TEMP. SENS.
SEAT BELT TIMER
BACK-UP LT. SW.
TO RADIO INLINE FUSE
STOP LT. SW. (OR CLUTCH)
INTERIOR LT. TIMER CONTROL UNIT
LOCK HTR. CONTROL UNIT
LOCK HTR.
KEY IN SW.
INST. LT. LED
(3 USED)
WARN. BUZZER
FLASHER

633CSi & 733i (Cont.)

INSTRUMENT PANEL, REAR COMPARTMENT & ACCESSORIES

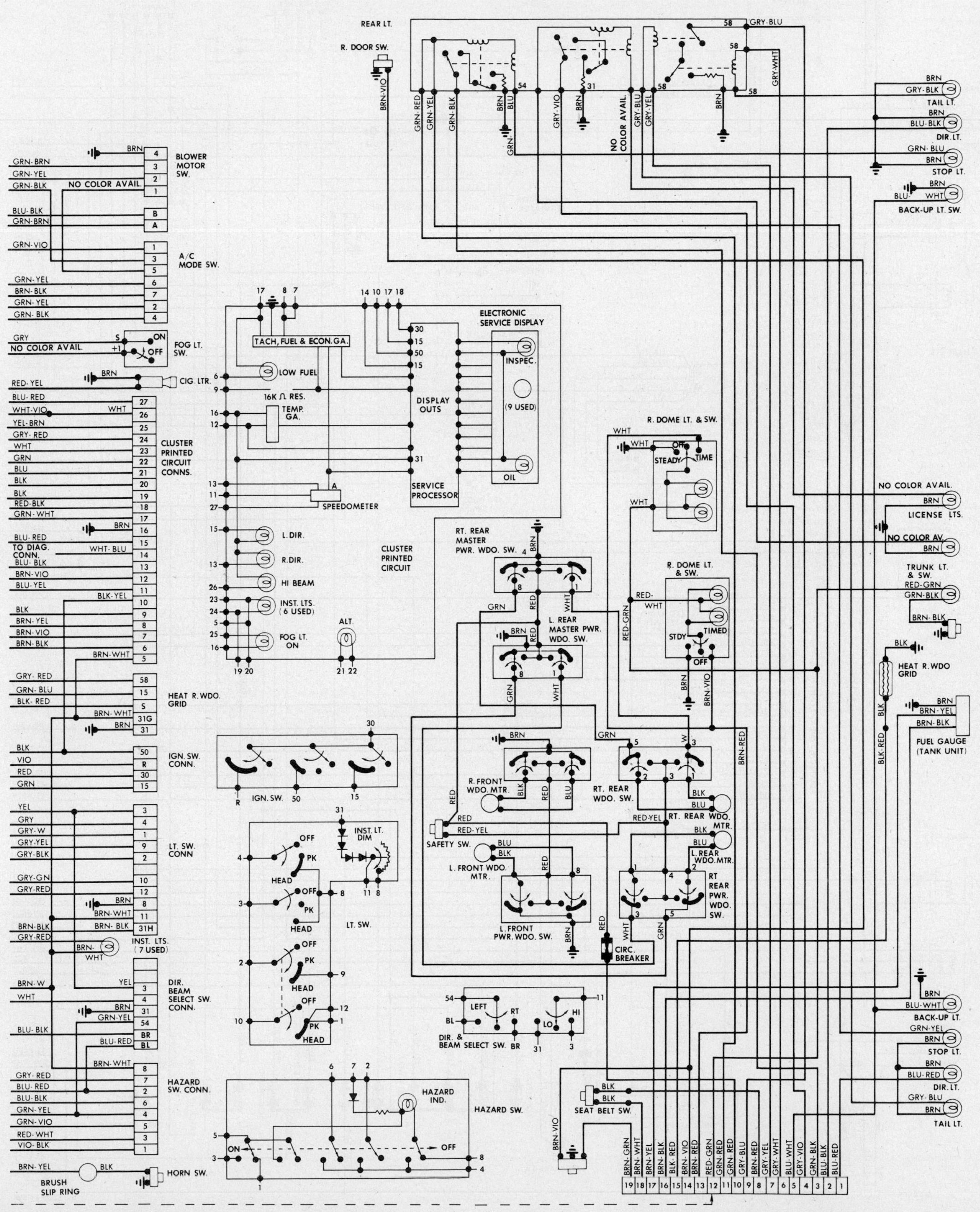
REAR LT.
R. DOOR SW.
TAIL LT.
DIR. LT.
STOP LT.
BACK-UP LT. SW.
BLOWER MOTOR SW.
NO COLOR AVAIL.
A/C MODE SW.
FOG LT. SW.
CIG. LTR.
CLUSTER PRINTED CIRCUIT CONNS.
TACH, FUEL & ECON. GA.
LOW FUEL
16K Ω RES.
TEMP. GA.
ELECTRONIC SERVICE DISPLAY
INSPEC.
(9 USED)
DISPLAY OUTS
OIL
SERVICE PROCESSOR
SPEEDOMETER
L. DIR.
R. DIR.
HI BEAM
INST. LTS. (6 USED)
FOG LT. ON
ALT.
CLUSTER PRINTED CIRCUIT
R. DOME LT. & SW.
STEADY
TIME
RT. REAR MASTER PWR. WDO. SW.
L. REAR MASTER PWR. WDO. SW.
R. DOME LT. & SW.
STDY
TIMED
OFF
NO COLOR AVAIL.
LICENSE LTS.
NO COLOR AV.
TRUNK LT. & SW.
HEAT R. WDO GRID
FUEL GAUGE (TANK UNIT)
HEAT R. WDO. GRID
IGN. SW. CONN.
IGN. SW.
LT. SW. CONN
INST. LT. DIM
HEAD
LT. SW.
INST. LTS. (7 USED)
DIR. BEAM SELECT SW. CONN.
HAZARD SW. CONN.
BRUSH SLIP RING
HORN SW.
R. FRONT WDO. MTR.
SAFETY SW.
L. FRONT WDO. MTR.
L. FRONT PWR. WDO. SW.
RT. REAR WDO. SW.
RT. REAR WDO. MTR.
L. REAR WDO. MTR.
RT REAR PWR. WDO. SW.
CIRC. BREAKER
DIR. & BEAM SELECT SW.
LEFT
RT
LO
HI
HAZARD IND.
HAZARD SW.
ON
OFF
SEAT BELT SW.
BACK-UP LT.
STOP LT.
DIR. LT.
TAIL LT.

1983 Chrysler Corp. Imports

CHALLENGER & SAPPORO

ENGINE COMPARTMENT & FUSE BLOCK

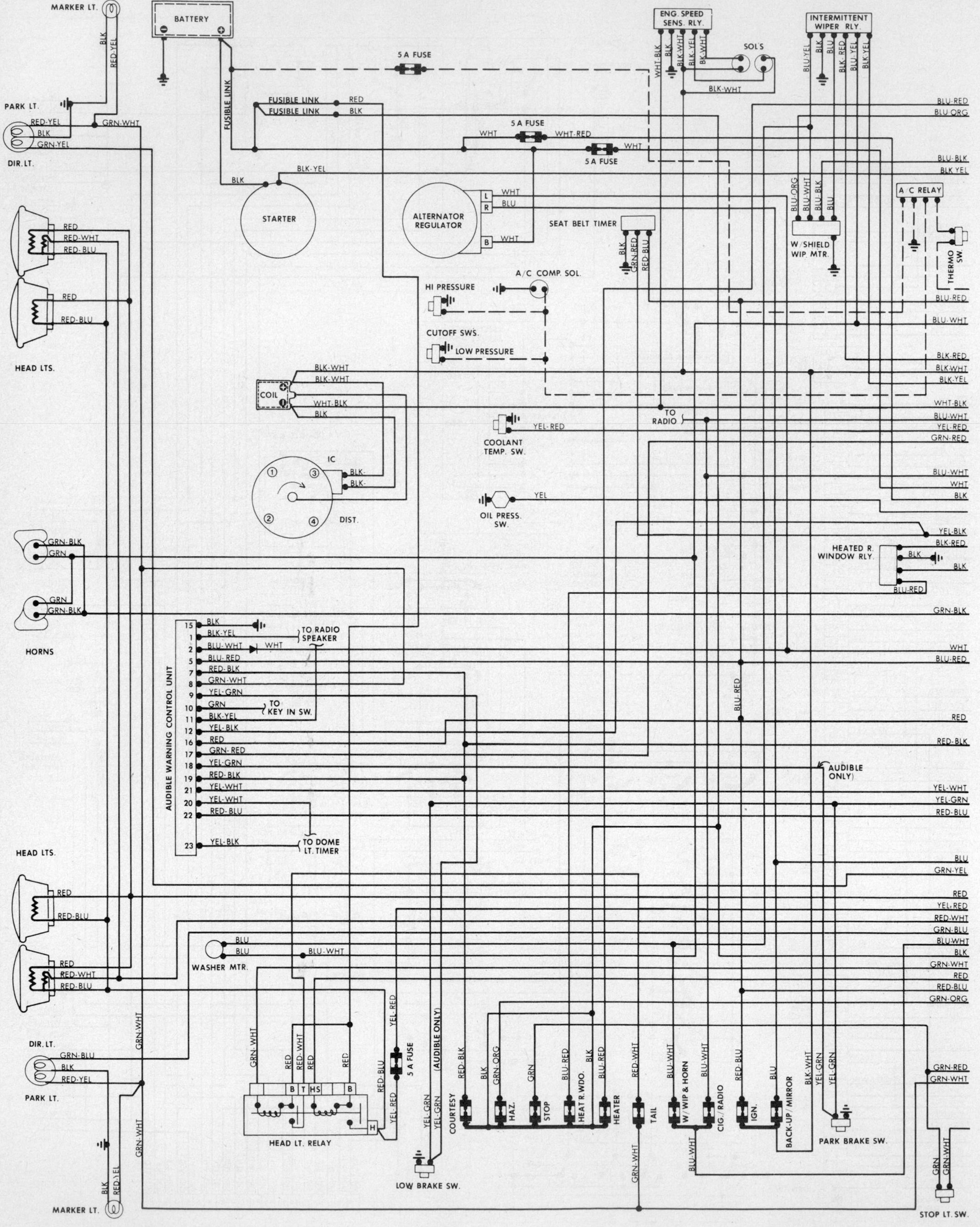
MARKER LT.
BATTERY
5 A FUSE
ENG. SPEED SENS. RLY.
SOL'S
INTERMITTENT WIPER RLY.
PARK LT.
DIR. LT.
FUSIBLE LINK
FUSIBLE LINK
FUSIBLE LINK
STARTER
ALTERNATOR REGULATOR
SEAT BELT TIMER
A/C RELAY
W/SHIELD WIP. MTR.
THERMO SW.
A/C COMP. SOL.
HI PRESSURE
CUTOFF SWS.
LOW PRESSURE
HEAD LTS.
COIL
TO RADIO
COOLANT TEMP. SW.
IC
DIST.
OIL PRESS. SW.
HEATED R. WINDOW RLY.
HORNS
AUDIBLE WARNING CONTROL UNIT
TO RADIO SPEAKER
TO KEY IN SW.
TO DOME LT. TIMER
AUDIBLE ONLY)
HEAD LTS.
WASHER MTR.
DIR. LT.
PARK LT.
HEAD LT. RELAY
5 A FUSE
(AUDIBLE ONLY)
COURTESY
HAZ.
STOP
HEAT R. WDO.
HEATER
TAIL
W/WIP & HORN
CIG./RADIO
IGN.
BACK-UP/MIRROR
PARK BRAKE SW.
LOW BRAKE SW.
MARKER LT.
STOP LT. SW.

CHALLENGER & SAPPORO (Cont.)

INSTRUMENT PANEL & REAR COMPARTMENT

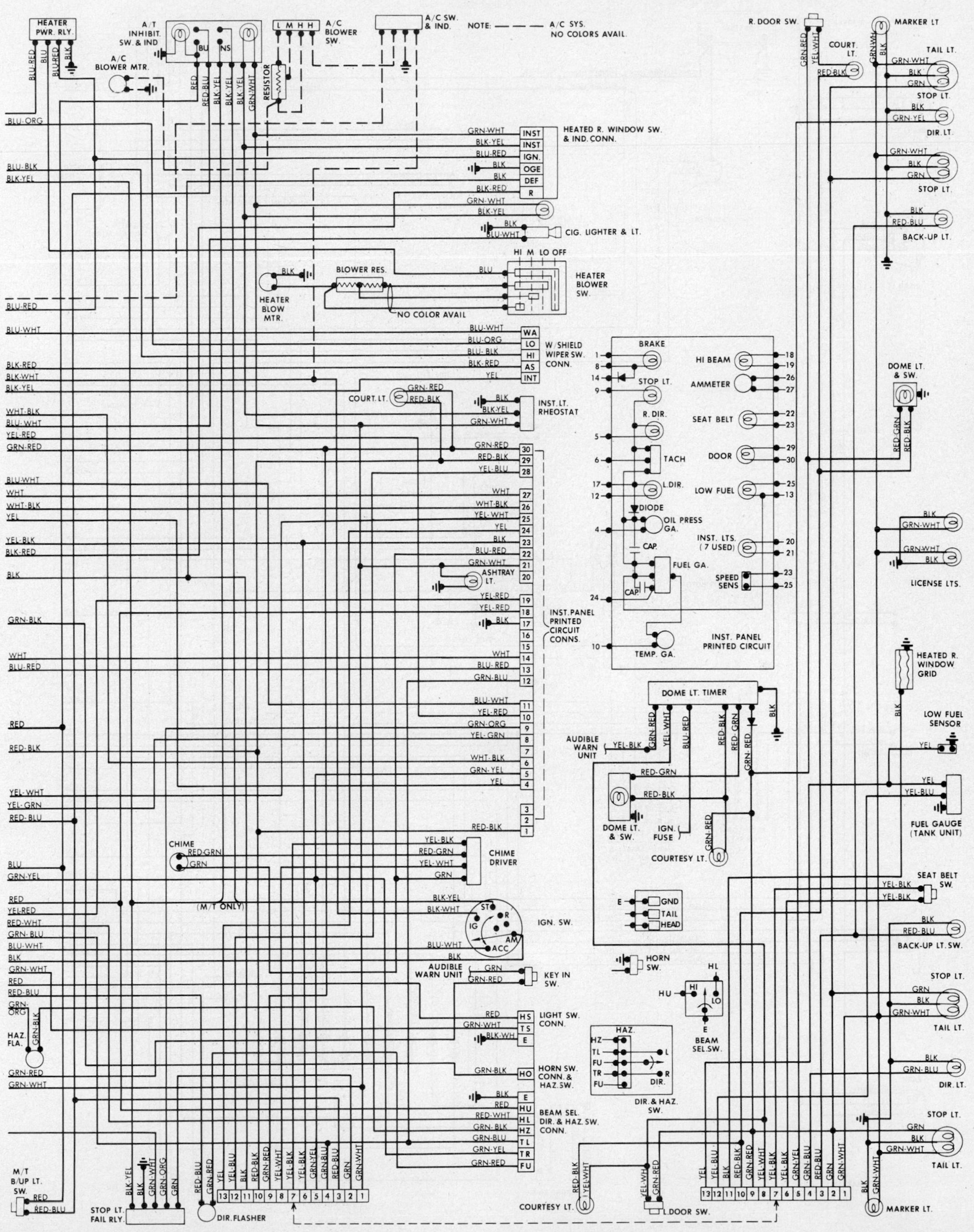
HEATER PWR. RLY.
A/T INHIBIT. SW. & IND
A/C BLOWER SW.
A/C SW. & IND.
NOTE: A/C SYS. NO COLORS AVAIL.
A/C BLOWER MTR.
RESISTOR
HEATED R. WINDOW SW. & IND. CONN.
CIG. LIGHTER & LT.
BLOWER RES.
HEATER BLOW MTR.
NO COLOR AVAIL
HEATER BLOWER SW.
W/SHIELD WIPER SW. CONN.
COURT. LT.
INST. LT. RHEOSTAT
ASHTRAY LT.
INST. PANEL PRINTED CIRCUIT CONNS.
CHIME
CHIME DRIVER
(M/T ONLY)
IGN. SW.
AUDIBLE WARN UNIT
KEY IN SW.
LIGHT SW. CONN.
HAZ. FLA.
HORN SW. CONN. & HAZ. SW.
BEAM SEL. DIR. & HAZ. SW. CONN.
M/T B/UP LT. SW.
STOP LT. FAIL RLY.
DIR. FLASHER
BRAKE
STOP LT.
R. DIR.
TACH
L. DIR.
DIODE
OIL PRESS GA.
CAP.
FUEL GA.
TEMP. GA.
HI BEAM
AMMETER
SEAT BELT
DOOR
LOW FUEL
INST. LTS. (7 USED)
SPEED SENS
INST. PANEL PRINTED CIRCUIT
DOME LT. TIMER
AUDIBLE WARN UNIT
DOME LT. & SW.
IGN. FUSE
COURTESY LT.
HORN SW.
BEAM SEL. SW.
DIR. & HAZ. SW.
R. DOOR SW.
COURT. LT.
MARKER LT
TAIL LT.
STOP LT.
DIR. LT.
BACK-UP LT.
DOME LT. & SW.
LICENSE LTS.
HEATED R. WINDOW GRID
LOW FUEL SENSOR
FUEL GAUGE (TANK UNIT)
SEAT BELT SW.
BACK-UP LT. SW.
L. DOOR SW.
MARKER LT.

1983 Chrysler Corp. Imports

COLT

ENGINE COMPARTMENT & FUSE BLOCK

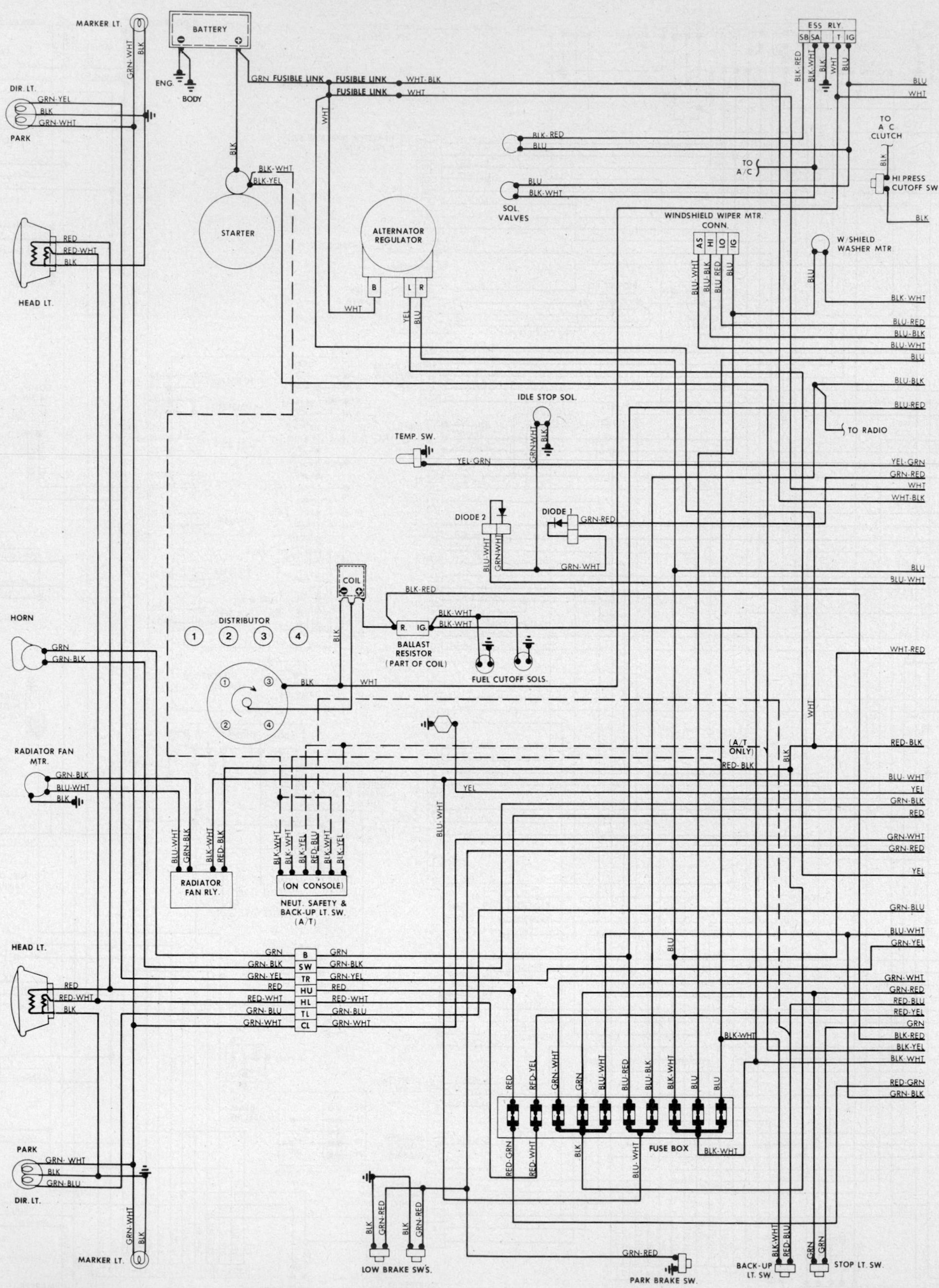

MARKER LT.
BATTERY
ENG.
BODY
FUSIBLE LINK
DIR. LT.
PARK
STARTER
ALTERNATOR REGULATOR
HEAD LT.
ESS RLY.
SB SA T IG
TO A/C CLUTCH
TO A/C
HI PRESS CUTOFF SW.
SOL. VALVES
WINDSHIELD WIPER MTR. CONN.
AS HI LO IG
W/SHIELD WASHER MTR
IDLE STOP SOL.
TEMP. SW.
TO RADIO
DIODE 2
DIODE 1
COIL
BALLAST RESISTOR (PART OF COIL)
FUEL CUTOFF SOLS.
HORN
DISTRIBUTOR
RADIATOR FAN MTR.
(A/T ONLY)
RADIATOR FAN RLY.
(ON CONSOLE)
NEUT. SAFETY & BACK-UP LT. SW. (A/T)
B
SW
TR
HU
HL
TL
CL
FUSE BOX
LOW BRAKE SW'S.
PARK BRAKE SW.
BACK-UP LT. SW.
STOP LT. SW.

1983 Chrysler Corp. Imports

COLT (Cont.)

INSTRUMENT PANEL, UNDERDASH & REAR COMPARTMENT

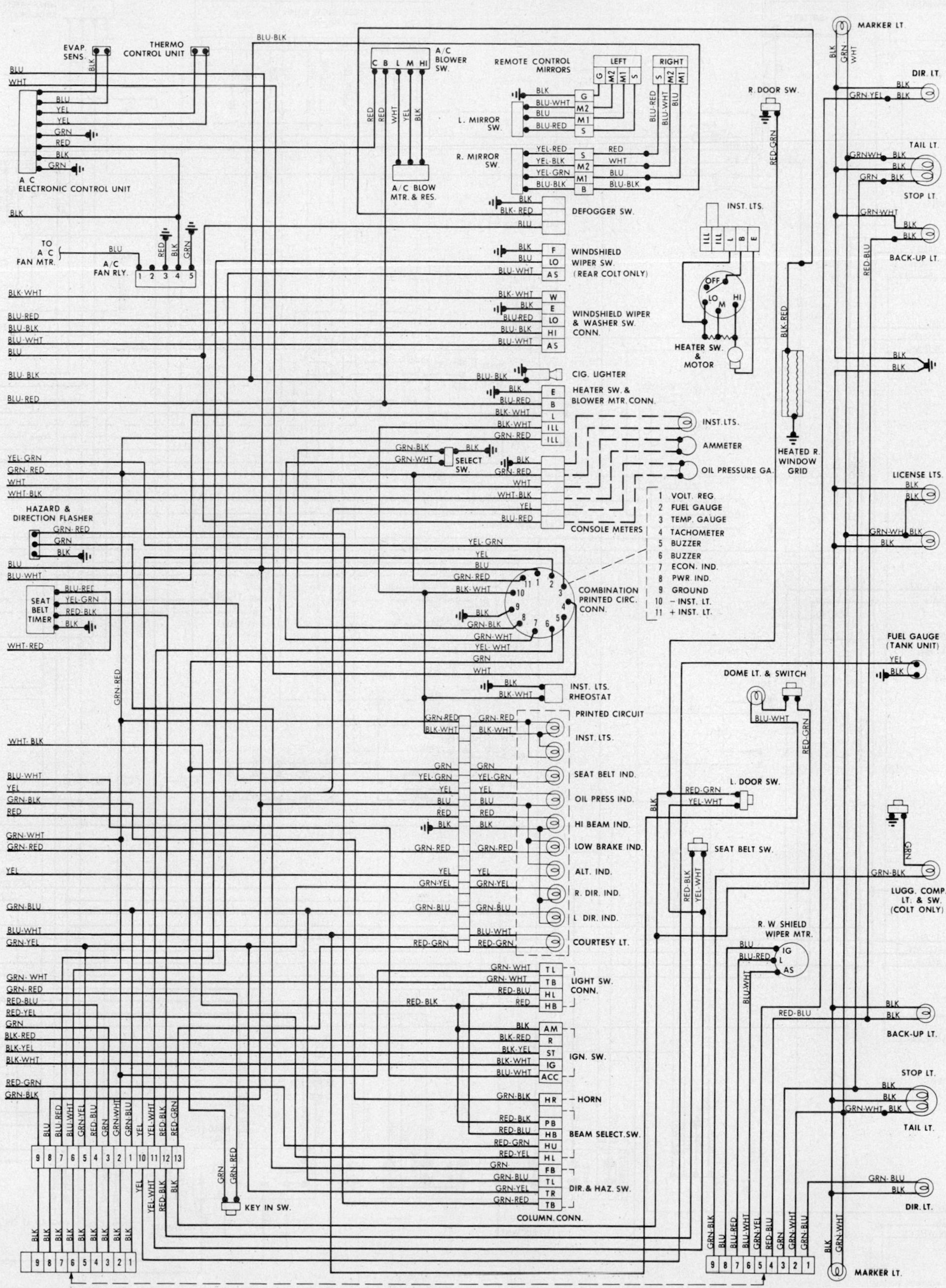

EVAP SENS.
THERMO CONTROL UNIT
A/C ELECTRONIC CONTROL UNIT
TO A/C FAN MTR.
A/C FAN RLY.
A/C BLOWER SW.
A/C BLOW MTR. & RES.
REMOTE CONTROL MIRRORS
LEFT
RIGHT
L. MIRROR SW.
R. MIRROR SW.
DEFOGGER SW.
WINDSHIELD WIPER SW. (REAR COLT ONLY)
WINDSHIELD WIPER & WASHER SW. CONN.
CIG. LIGHTER
HEATER SW. & BLOWER MTR. CONN.
INST. LTS.
AMMETER
OIL PRESSURE GA.
SELECT SW.
CONSOLE METERS
1 VOLT. REG.
2 FUEL GAUGE
3 TEMP. GAUGE
4 TACHOMETER
5 BUZZER
6 BUZZER
7 ECON. IND.
8 PWR. IND.
9 GROUND
10 − INST. LT.
11 + INST. LT.
COMBINATION PRINTED CIRC. CONN.
HAZARD & DIRECTION FLASHER
SEAT BELT TIMER
INST. LTS. RHEOSTAT
PRINTED CIRCUIT
INST. LTS.
SEAT BELT IND.
OIL PRESS IND.
HI BEAM IND.
LOW BRAKE IND.
ALT. IND.
R. DIR. IND.
L DIR. IND.
COURTESY LT.
LIGHT SW. CONN.
IGN. SW.
HORN
BEAM SELECT SW.
DIR. & HAZ. SW.
COLUMN CONN.
KEY IN SW.
R. DOOR SW.
INST. LTS.
HEATER SW. & MOTOR
OFF
LO
M
HI
HEATED R. WINDOW GRID
DOME LT. & SWITCH
L. DOOR SW.
SEAT BELT SW.
R. W SHIELD WIPER MTR.
MARKER LT.
DIR. LT.
TAIL LT.
STOP LT.
BACK-UP LT.
LICENSE LTS.
FUEL GAUGE (TANK UNIT)
LUGG. COMP. LT. & SW. (COLT ONLY)
BACK-UP LT.
STOP LT.
TAIL LT.
DIR. LT.
MARKER LT.

1983 Chrysler Corp. Imports

COLT & RAM-50 PICKUPS

ENGINE COMPARTMENT & FUSE BLOCK

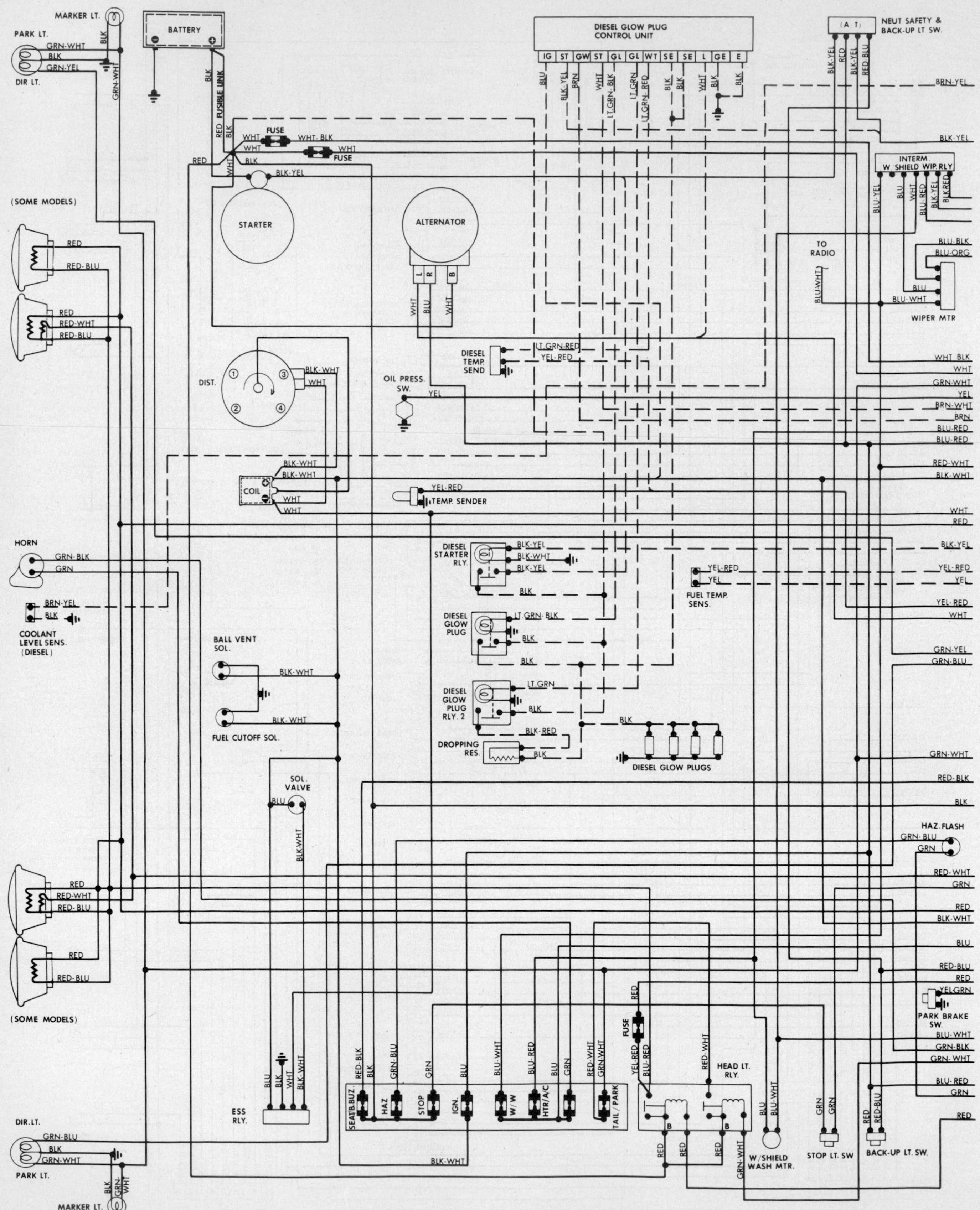
MARKER LT.
PARK LT.
DIR LT.
BATTERY
FUSIBLE LINK
FUSE
STARTER
ALTERNATOR
DIESEL GLOW PLUG CONTROL UNIT
IG ST GW ST GL GL WT SE SE L GE E
NEUT SAFETY & BACK-UP LT SW.
INTERM W SHIELD WIP RLY
TO RADIO
WIPER MTR
(SOME MODELS)
DIESEL TEMP. SEND
DIST.
OIL PRESS. SW.
COIL
TEMP. SENDER
HORN
DIESEL STARTER RLY.
FUEL TEMP. SENS.
COOLANT LEVEL SENS. (DIESEL)
DIESEL GLOW PLUG
BALL VENT SOL.
FUEL CUTOFF SOL.
DIESEL GLOW PLUG RLY. 2
DROPPING RES.
DIESEL GLOW PLUGS
SOL. VALVE
HAZ. FLASH
PARK BRAKE SW.
(SOME MODELS)
ESS RLY.
SEAT B.BUZ.
HAZ
STOP
IGN.
W/W
HTR/A/C
TAIL/PARK
HEAD LT. RLY.
W/SHIELD WASH MTR.
STOP LT. SW
BACK-UP LT. SW.
DIR. LT.
PARK LT.
MARKER LT.

COLT & RAM-50 PICKUPS (Cont.)

INSTRUMENT PANEL & REAR COMPARTMENT

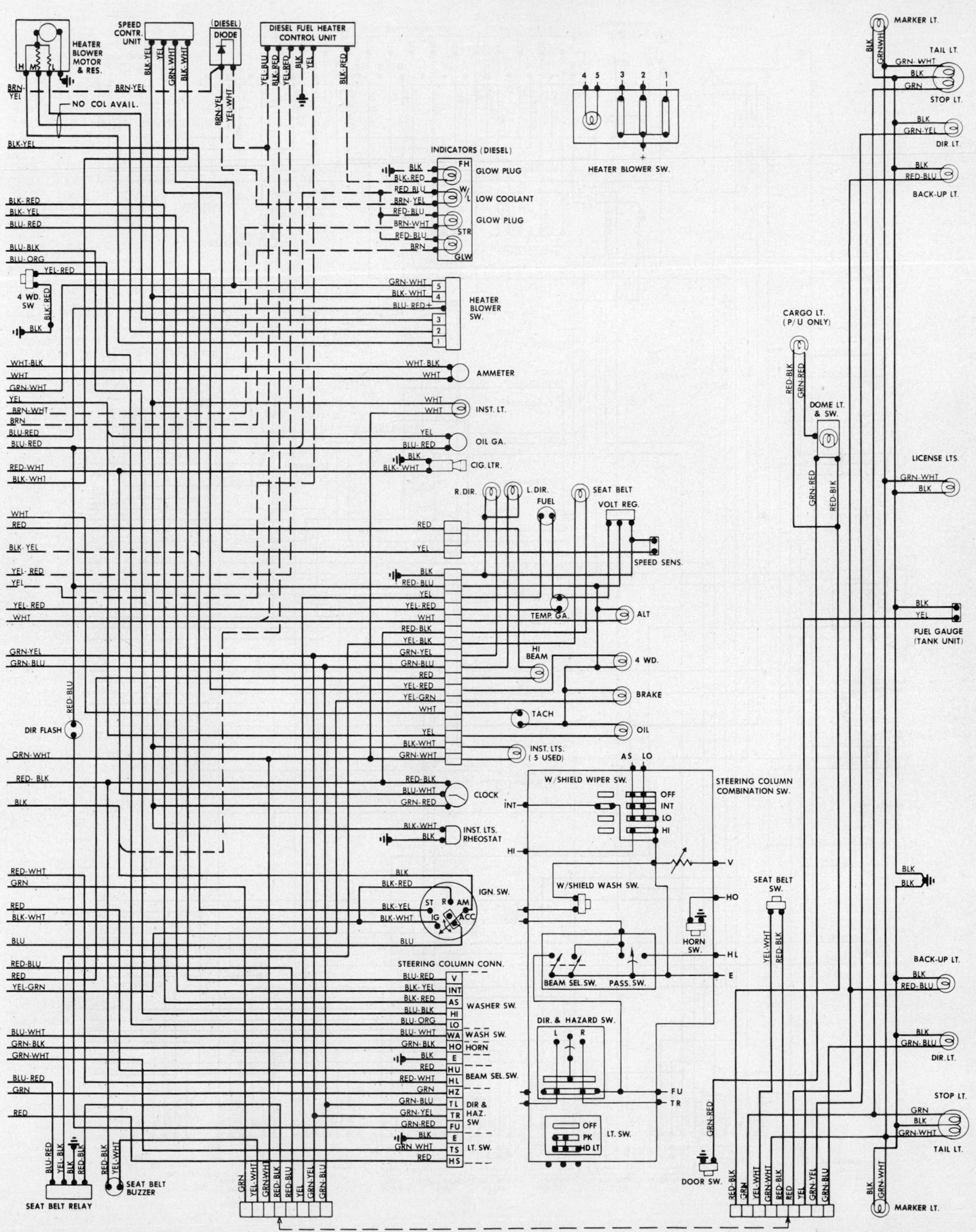
HEATER BLOWER MOTOR & RES.
SPEED CONTR. UNIT
(DIESEL) DIODE
DIESEL FUEL HEATER CONTROL UNIT
NO COL AVAIL.
INDICATORS (DIESEL)
GLOW PLUG
LOW COOLANT
GLOW PLUG
HEATER BLOWER SW.
4 WD. SW
AMMETER
INST. LT.
OIL GA.
CIG. LTR.
R. DIR.
L. DIR.
FUEL
SEAT BELT
VOLT REG.
SPEED SENS.
TEMP. GA.
ALT
HI BEAM
4 WD.
BRAKE
TACH
OIL
INST. LTS. (5 USED)
DIR FLASH
CLOCK
INST. LTS. RHEOSTAT
IGN. SW.
STEERING COLUMN CONN.
WASHER SW.
WASH SW.
HORN
BEAM SEL. SW.
DIR & HAZ. SW
LT. SW.
W/SHIELD WIPER SW.
STEERING COLUMN COMBINATION SW.
W/SHIELD WASH SW.
HORN SW.
BEAM SEL. SW.
PASS. SW.
DIR. & HAZARD SW.
SEAT BELT SW.
DOOR SW.
SEAT BELT RELAY
SEAT BELT BUZZER
MARKER LT.
TAIL LT.
STOP LT.
DIR LT.
BACK-UP LT.
CARGO LT. (P/U ONLY)
DOME LT. & SW.
LICENSE LTS.
FUEL GAUGE (TANK UNIT)

1983 Datsun/Nissan

200SX

ENGINE COMPARTMENT

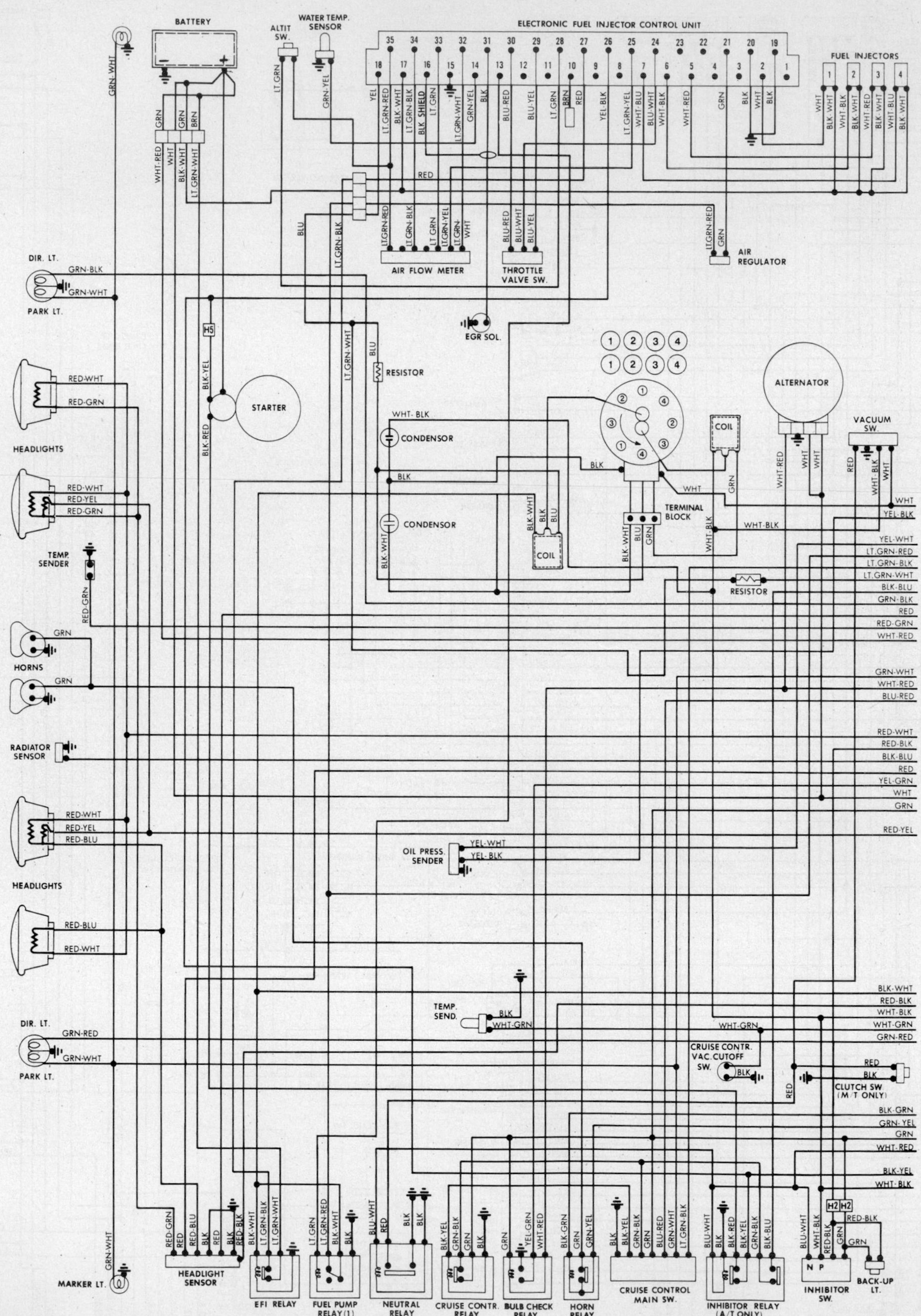
BATTERY
ALTIT SW.
WATER TEMP. SENSOR
ELECTRONIC FUEL INJECTOR CONTROL UNIT
FUEL INJECTORS
DIR. LT.
PARK LT.
AIR FLOW METER
THROTTLE VALVE SW.
AIR REGULATOR
EGR SOL.
RESISTOR
STARTER
HEADLIGHTS
CONDENSOR
COIL
ALTERNATOR
VACUUM SW.
TERMINAL BLOCK
TEMP. SENDER
HORNS
RADIATOR SENSOR
OIL PRESS. SENDER
TEMP. SEND.
CRUISE CONTR. VAC. CUTOFF SW.
CLUTCH SW (M/T ONLY)
MARKER LT.
HEADLIGHT SENSOR
EFI RELAY
FUEL PUMP RELAY (1)
NEUTRAL RELAY
CRUISE CONTR. RELAY
BULB CHECK RELAY
HORN RELAY
CRUISE CONTROL MAIN SW.
INHIBITOR RELAY (A/T ONLY)
INHIBITOR SW.
BACK-UP LT.

1983 Datsun/Nissan

200SX (Cont.)

FUSE BLOCK & UNDERDASH

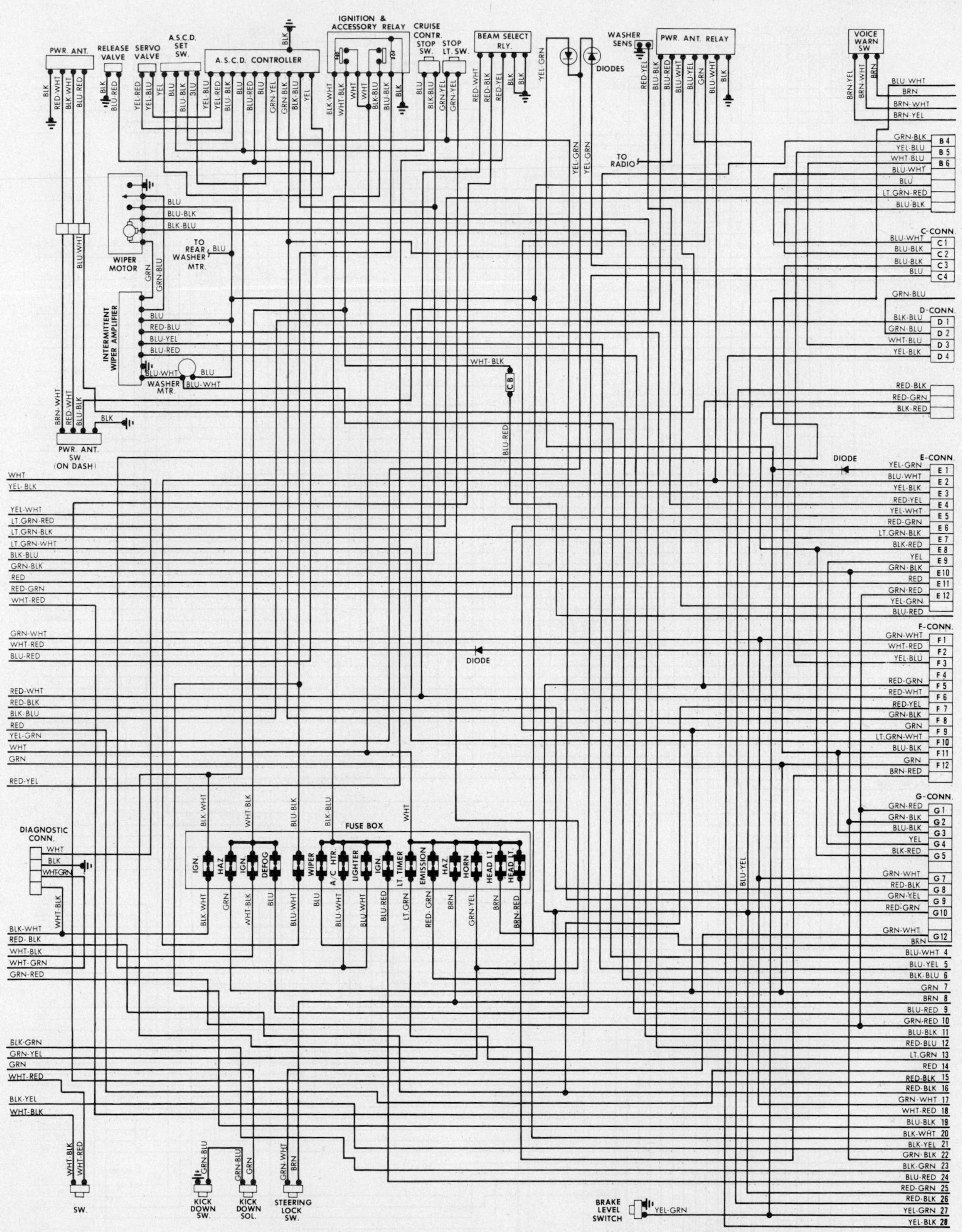

1983 Datsun/Nissan

200SX (Cont.)

UNDERDASH

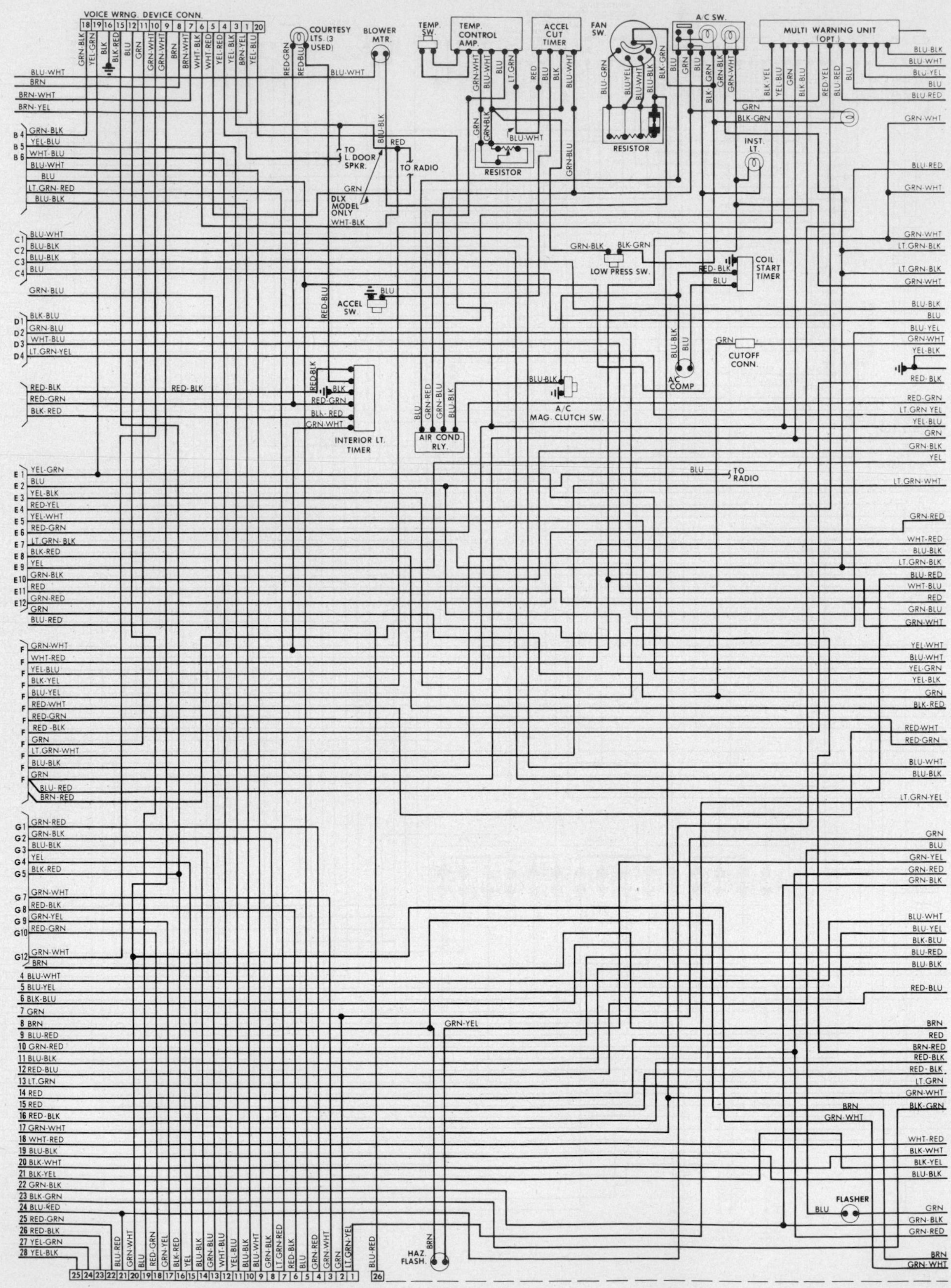

200SX (Cont.)

INSTRUMENT PANEL, REAR COMPARTMENT & ACCESSORIES

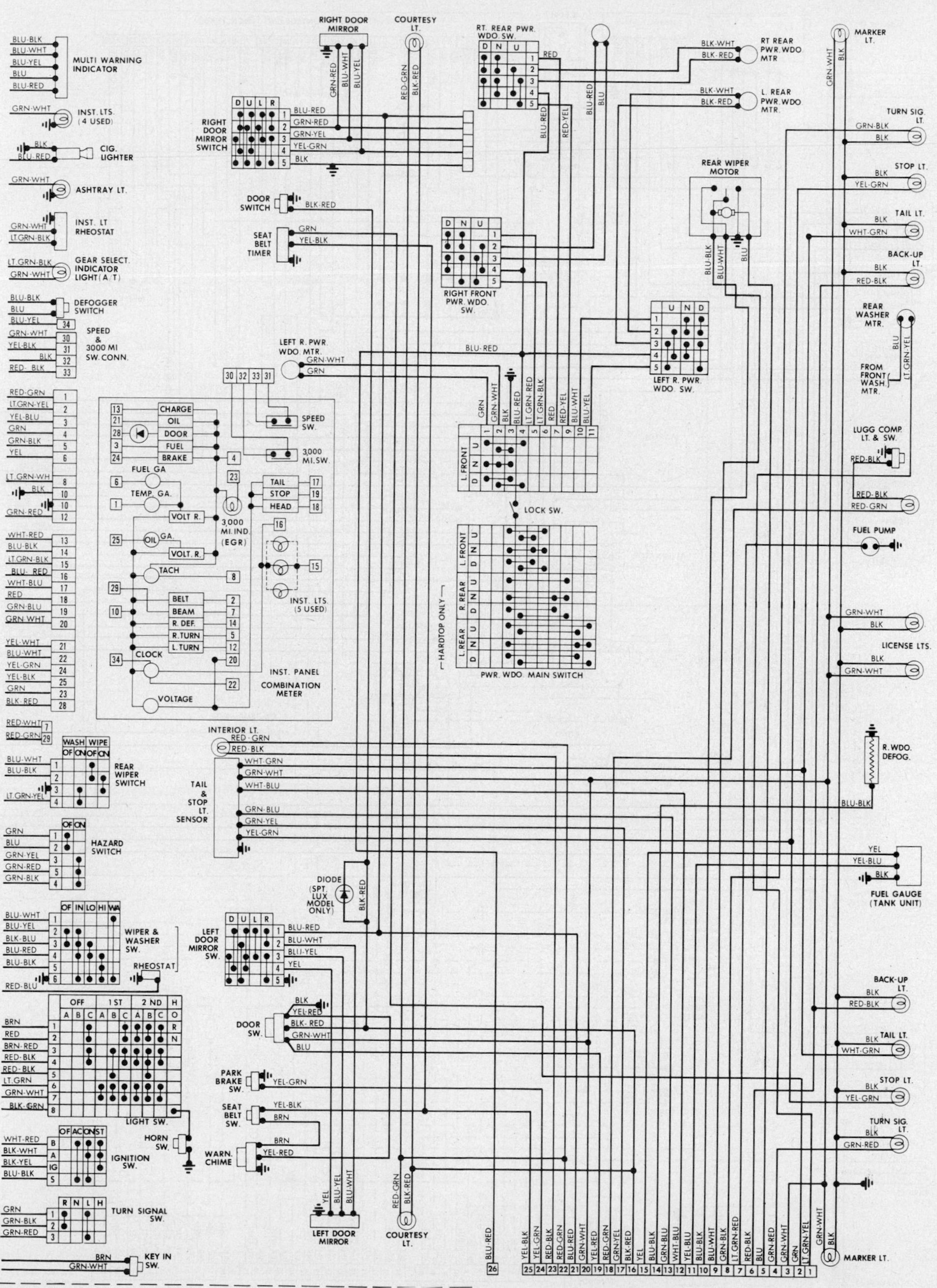
MULTI WARNING INDICATOR
INST. LTS. (4 USED)
CIG. LIGHTER
ASHTRAY LT.
INST. LT RHEOSTAT
GEAR SELECT. INDICATOR LIGHT (A/T)
DEFOGGER SWITCH
SPEED & 3000 MI SW. CONN.
RIGHT DOOR MIRROR
COURTESY LT.
RT. REAR PWR. WDO. SW.
RT REAR PWR. WDO MTR
L. REAR PWR. WDO MTR.
MARKER LT.
TURN SIG. LT.
STOP LT.
TAIL LT.
BACK-UP LT.
REAR WIPER MOTOR
RIGHT DOOR MIRROR SWITCH
DOOR SWITCH
SEAT BELT TIMER
RIGHT FRONT PWR. WDO. SW.
LEFT R. PWR. WDO. MTR.
LEFT R. PWR. WDO. SW.
REAR WASHER MTR.
FROM FRONT WASH. MTR.
LUGG COMP. LT. & SW.
SPEED SW.
3,000 MI. SW.
CHARGE
OIL
DOOR
FUEL
BRAKE
FUEL GA
TEMP. GA.
VOLT. R.
3,000 MI. IND. (EGR)
TAIL
STOP
HEAD
OIL GA.
TACH
INST. LTS. (5 USED)
BELT
BEAM
R. DEF.
R. TURN
L. TURN
CLOCK
VOLTAGE
INST. PANEL COMBINATION METER
LOCK SW.
FUEL PUMP
HARDTOP ONLY
PWR. WDO. MAIN SWITCH
LICENSE LTS.
INTERIOR LT.
TAIL & STOP LT. SENSOR
R. WDO. DEFOG.
REAR WIPER SWITCH
HAZARD SWITCH
FUEL GAUGE (TANK UNIT)
DIODE (SPT LUX MODEL ONLY)
WIPER & WASHER SW.
RHEOSTAT
LEFT DOOR MIRROR SW.
DOOR SW.
PARK BRAKE SW.
SEAT BELT SW.
WARN. CHIME
LIGHT SW.
HORN SW.
IGNITION SW.
TURN SIGNAL SW.
KEY IN SW.
LEFT DOOR MIRROR
COURTESY LT.
MARKER LT.

1983 Datsun/Nissan

280ZX & 280ZX TURBO

ENGINE COMPARTMENT

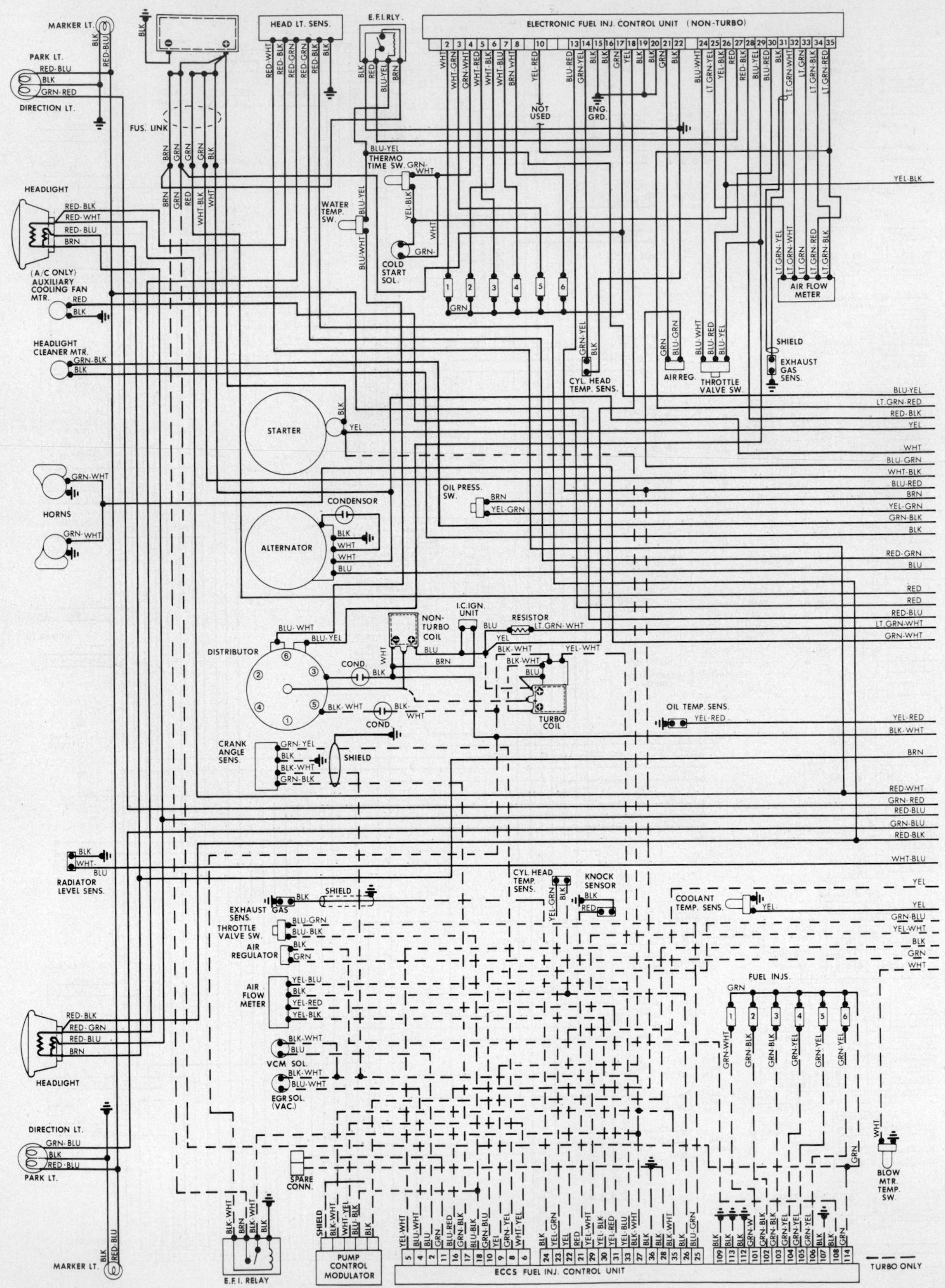
MARKER LT.
PARK LT.
DIRECTION LT.
HEAD LT. SENS.
E.F.I. RLY.
ELECTRONIC FUEL INJ. CONTROL UNIT (NON-TURBO)
NOT USED
ENG. GRD.
FUS. LINK
HEADLIGHT
THERMO TIME SW.
WATER TEMP. SW.
COLD START SOL.
AIR FLOW METER
(A/C ONLY) AUXILIARY COOLING FAN MTR.
HEADLIGHT CLEANER MTR.
SHIELD
EXHAUST GAS SENS.
CYL. HEAD TEMP. SENS.
AIR REG.
THROTTLE VALVE SW.
STARTER
HORNS
OIL PRESS. SW.
CONDENSOR
ALTERNATOR
I.C. IGN. UNIT
RESISTOR
NON-TURBO COIL
DISTRIBUTOR
COND.
TURBO COIL
OIL TEMP. SENS.
CRANK ANGLE SENS.
RADIATOR LEVEL SENS.
CYL. HEAD TEMP. SENS.
KNOCK SENSOR
COOLANT TEMP. SENS.
EXHAUST GAS SENS.
THROTTLE VALVE SW.
AIR REGULATOR
AIR FLOW METER
FUEL INJS.
VCM SOL.
EGR SOL. (VAC.)
SPARE CONN.
BLOW MTR. TEMP. SW.
E.F.I. RELAY
PUMP CONTROL MODULATOR
ECCS FUEL INJ. CONTROL UNIT
TURBO ONLY

1983 Datsun/Nissan

280ZX & 280ZX TURBO

UNDERDASH

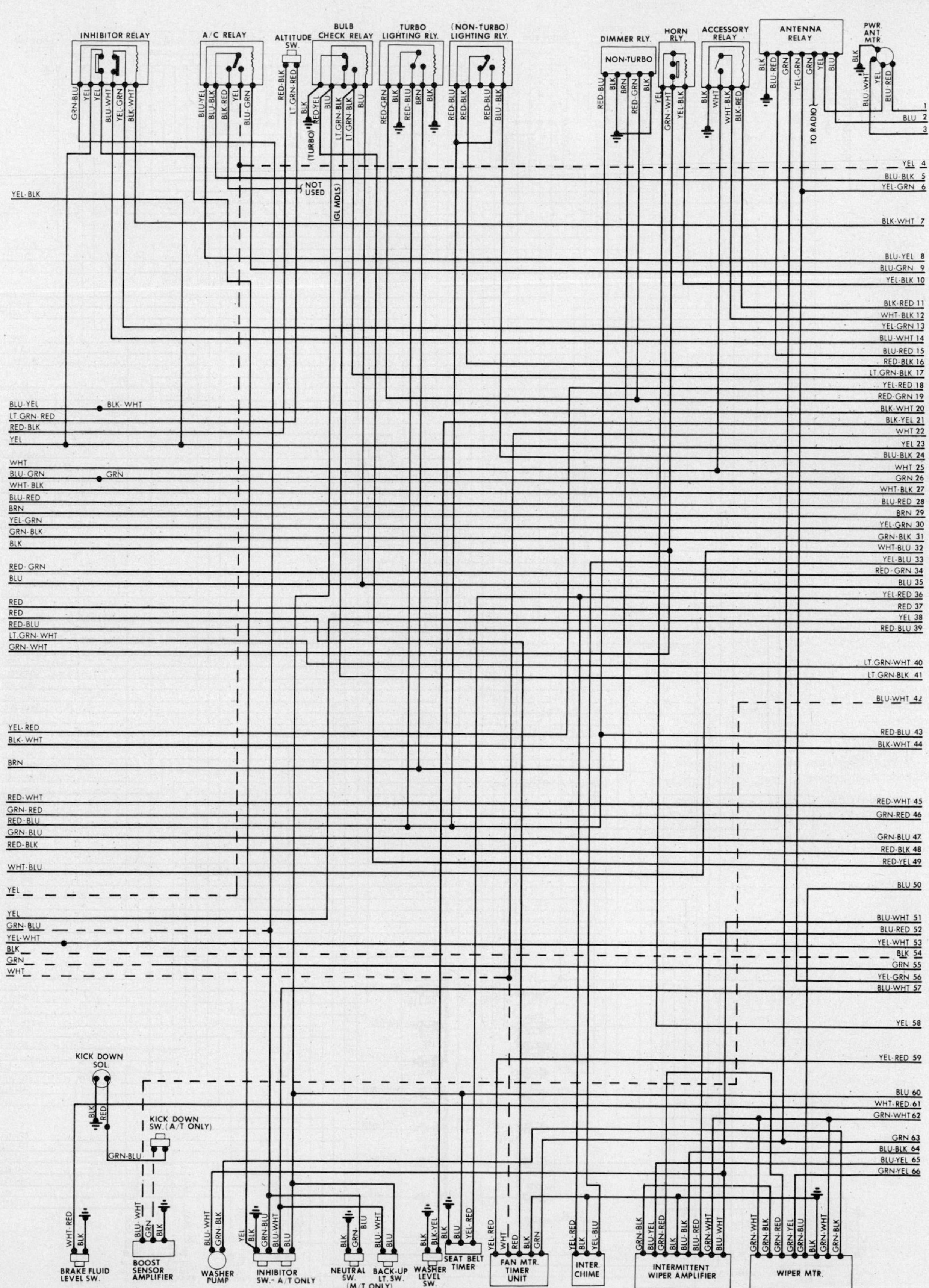
INHIBITOR RELAY
A/C RELAY
ALTITUDE SW.
BULB CHECK RELAY
TURBO LIGHTING RLY.
(NON-TURBO) LIGHTING RLY.
DIMMER RLY.
NON-TURBO
HORN RLY.
ACCESSORY RELAY
ANTENNA RELAY
PWR. ANT. MTR.
TO RADIO
NOT USED
(TURBO)
(GL MDLS)
YEL 4
BLU-BLK 5
YEL-GRN 6
BLK-WHT 7
BLU-YEL 8
BLU-GRN 9
YEL-BLK 10
BLK-RED 11
WHT-BLK 12
YEL-GRN 13
BLU-WHT 14
BLU-RED 15
RED-BLK 16
LT.GRN-BLK 17
YEL-RED 18
RED-GRN 19
BLK-WHT 20
BLK-YEL 21
WHT 22
YEL 23
BLU-BLK 24
WHT 25
GRN 26
WHT-BLK 27
BLU-RED 28
BRN 29
YEL-GRN 30
GRN-BLK 31
WHT-BLU 32
YEL-BLU 33
RED-GRN 34
BLU 35
YEL-RED 36
RED 37
YEL 38
RED-BLU 39
LT.GRN-WHT 40
LT.GRN-BLK 41
BLU-WHT 42
RED-BLU 43
BLK-WHT 44
RED-WHT 45
GRN-RED 46
GRN-BLU 47
RED-BLK 48
RED-YEL 49
BLU 50
BLU-WHT 51
BLU-RED 52
YEL-WHT 53
BLK 54
GRN 55
YEL-GRN 56
BLU-WHT 57
YEL 58
YEL-RED 59
BLU 60
WHT-RED 61
GRN-WHT 62
GRN 63
BLU-BLK 64
BLU-YEL 65
GRN-YEL 66
KICK DOWN SOL.
KICK DOWN SW. (A/T ONLY)
BRAKE FLUID LEVEL SW.
BOOST SENSOR AMPLIFIER
WASHER PUMP
INHIBITOR SW.- A/T ONLY
NEUTRAL SW. (M/T ONLY)
BACK-UP LT. SW.
WASHER LEVEL SW.
SEAT BELT TIMER
FAN MTR. TIMER UNIT
INTER. CHIME
INTERMITTENT WIPER AMPLIFIER
WIPER MTR.

1983 Datsun/Nissan

280ZX & 280ZX TURBO

FUSE BLOCK & UNDERDASH

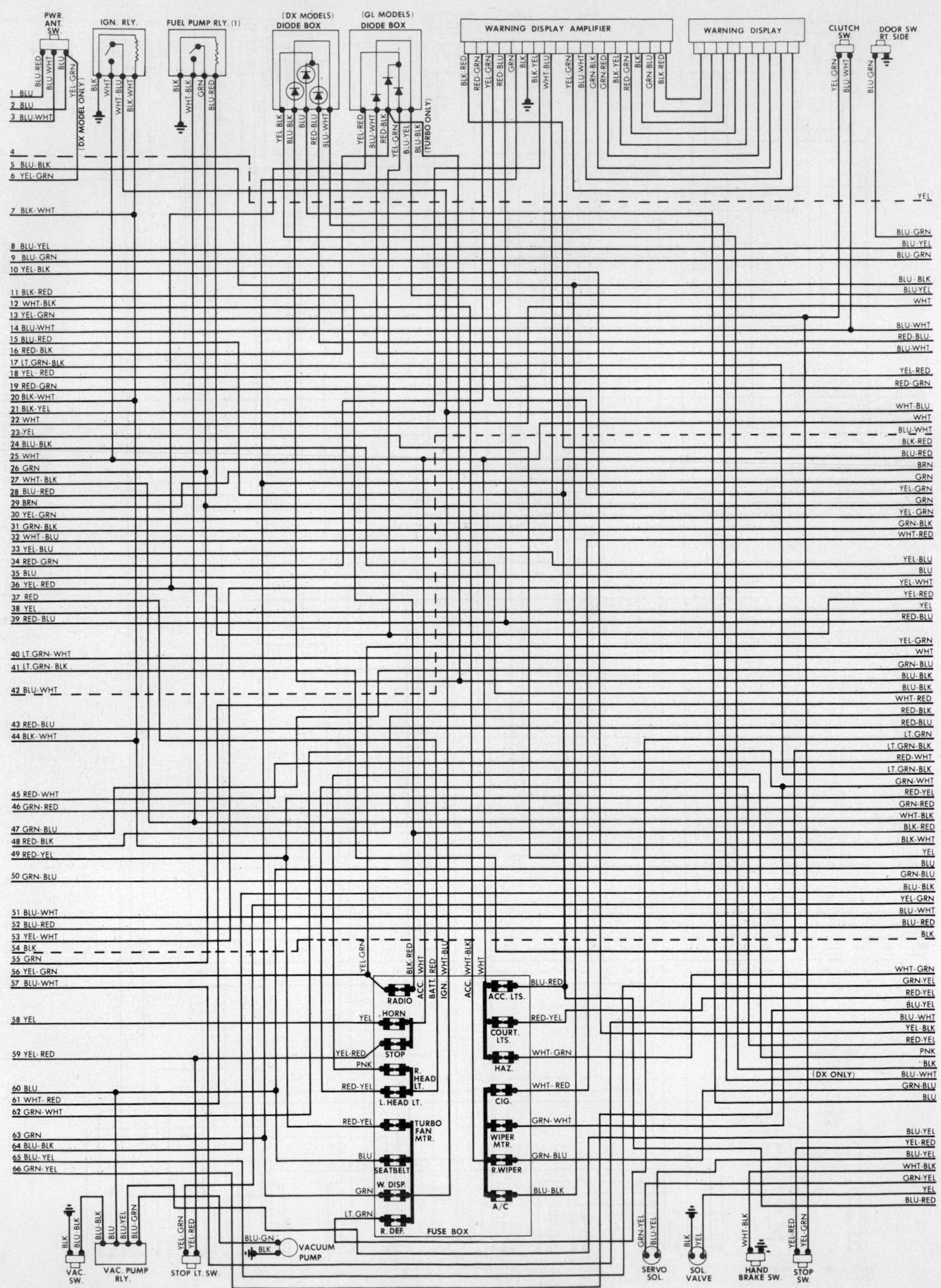

1983 Datsun/Nissan

280ZX & 280ZX TURBO

UNDERDASH

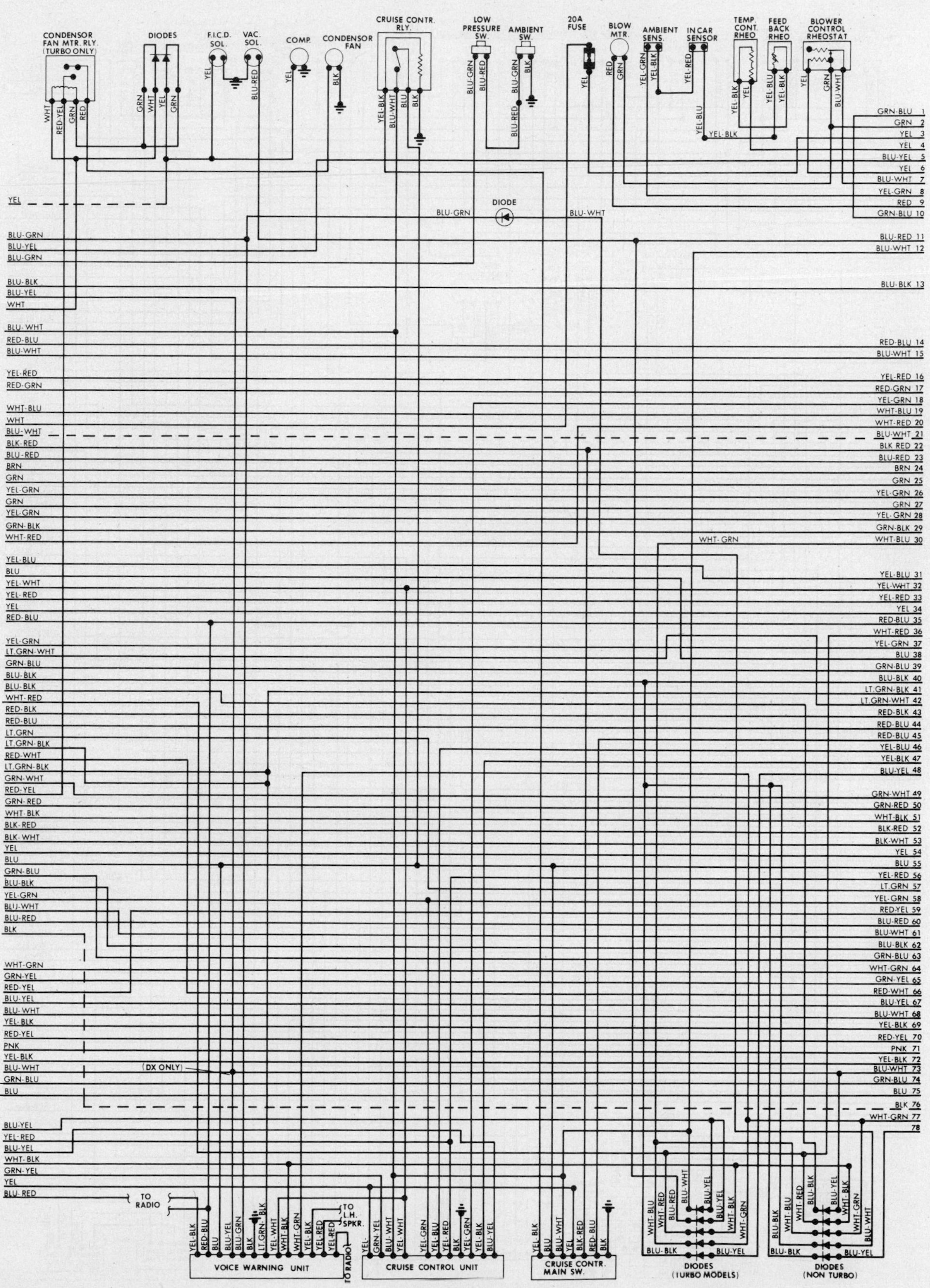
CONDENSOR FAN MTR. RLY. (TURBO ONLY)
DIODES
F.I.C.D. SOL.
VAC. SOL.
COMP.
CONDENSOR FAN
CRUISE CONTR. RLY.
LOW PRESSURE SW.
AMBIENT SW.
20A FUSE
BLOW MTR.
AMBIENT SENS.
IN CAR SENSOR
TEMP. CONT. RHEO
FEED BACK RHEO
BLOWER CONTROL RHEOSTAT
DIODE
GRN-BLU 1
GRN 2
YEL 3
YEL 4
BLU-YEL 5
YEL 6
BLU-WHT 7
YEL-GRN 8
RED 9
GRN-BLU 10
BLU-RED 11
BLU-WHT 12
BLU-BLK 13
RED-BLU 14
BLU-WHT 15
YEL-RED 16
RED-GRN 17
YEL-GRN 18
WHT-BLU 19
WHT-RED 20
BLU-WHT 21
BLK-RED 22
BLU-RED 23
BRN 24
GRN 25
YEL-GRN 26
GRN 27
YEL-GRN 28
GRN-BLK 29
WHT-BLU 30
YEL-BLU 31
YEL-WHT 32
YEL-RED 33
YEL 34
RED-BLU 35
WHT-RED 36
YEL-GRN 37
BLU 38
GRN-BLU 39
BLU-BLK 40
LT.GRN-BLK 41
LT.GRN-WHT 42
RED-BLK 43
RED-BLU 44
RED-BLU 45
YEL-BLU 46
YEL-BLK 47
BLU-YEL 48
GRN-WHT 49
GRN-RED 50
WHT-BLK 51
BLK-RED 52
BLK-WHT 53
YEL 54
BLU 55
YEL-RED 56
LT.GRN 57
YEL-GRN 58
RED-YEL 59
BLU-RED 60
BLU-WHT 61
BLU-BLK 62
GRN-BLU 63
WHT-GRN 64
GRN-YEL 65
RED-WHT 66
BLU-YEL 67
BLU-WHT 68
YEL-BLK 69
RED-YEL 70
PNK 71
YEL-BLK 72
BLU-WHT 73
GRN-BLU 74
BLU 75
BLK 76
WHT-GRN 77
78
(DX ONLY)
TO RADIO
TO L.H. SPKR.
TO RADIO
VOICE WARNING UNIT
CRUISE CONTROL UNIT
CRUISE CONTR. MAIN SW.
DIODES (TURBO MODELS)
DIODES (NON TURBO)

1983 Datsun/Nissan

280ZX & 280ZX TURBO

UNDERDASH & INSTRUMENT PANEL

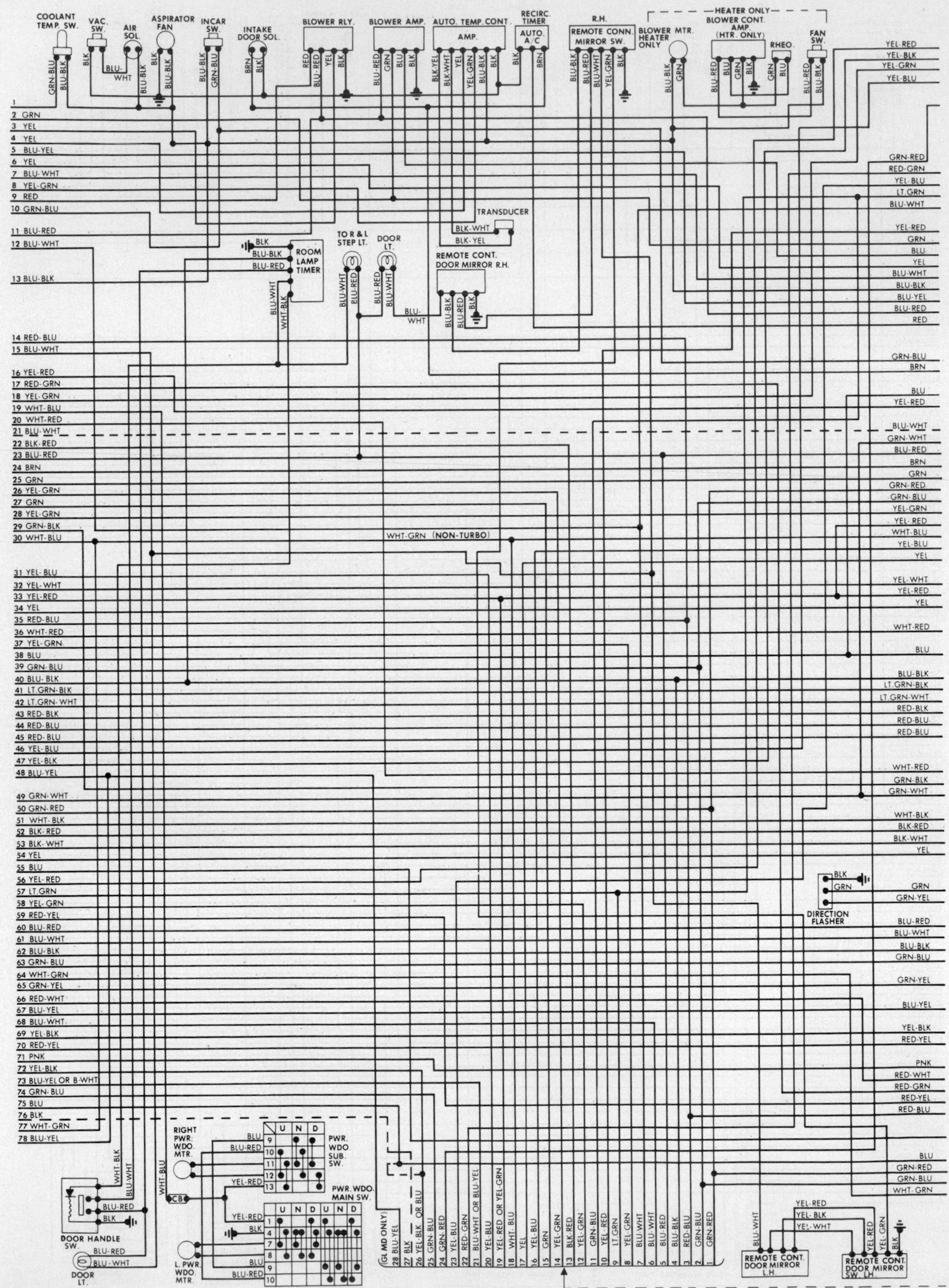

280ZX & 280ZX TURBO

INSTRUMENT PANEL & REAR COMPARTMENT

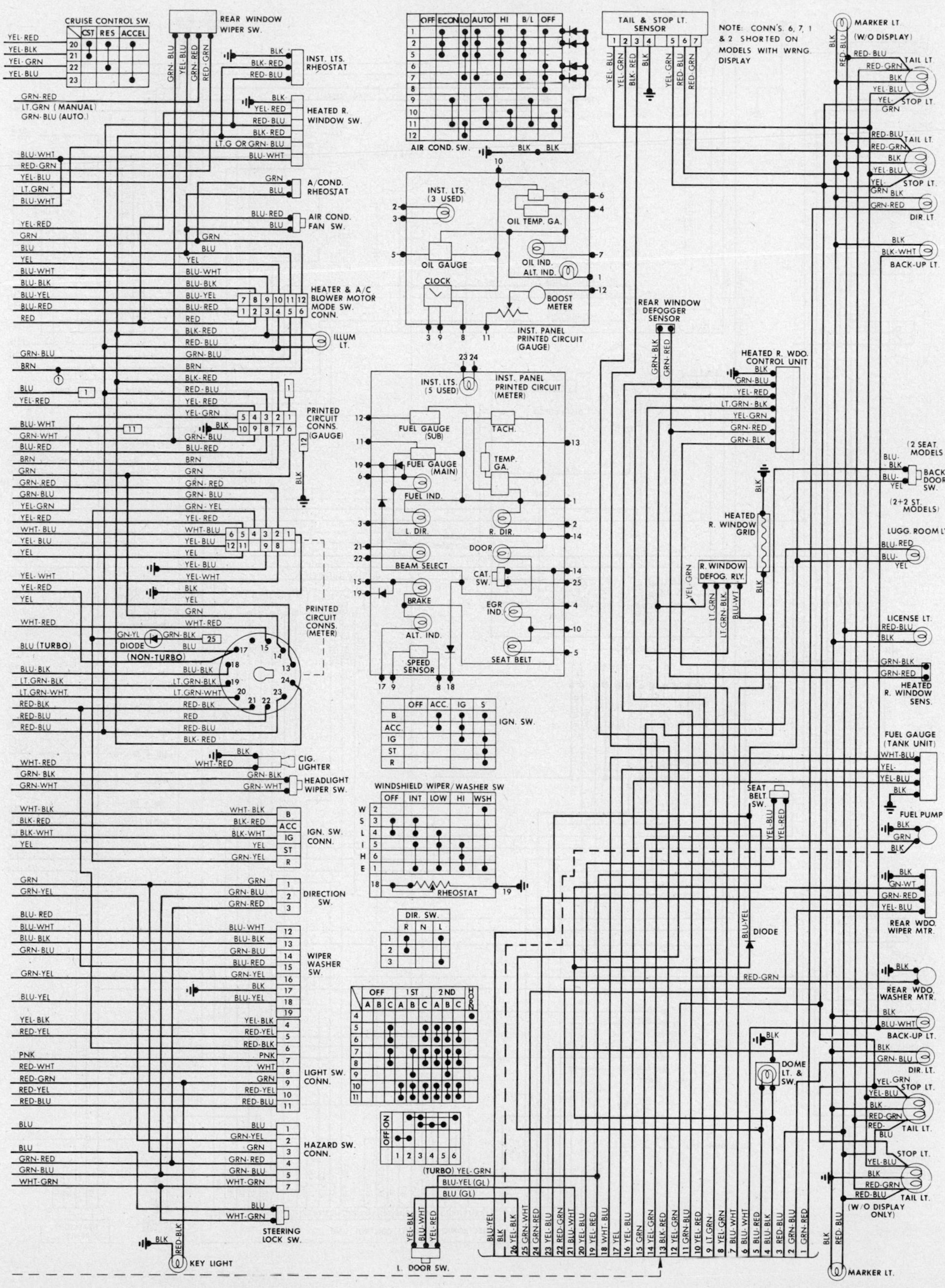
CRUISE CONTROL SW.
CST RES ACCEL
REAR WINDOW WIPER SW.
INST. LTS. RHEOSTAT
HEATED R. WINDOW SW.
AIR COND. SW.
OFF ECON LO AUTO HI B/L OFF
TAIL & STOP LT. SENSOR
NOTE: CONN'S. 6, 7, 1 & 2 SHORTED ON MODELS WITH WRNG. DISPLAY
MARKER LT. (W/O DISPLAY)
TAIL LT.
STOP LT.
DIR. LT.
BACK-UP LT.
A/COND. RHEOSTAT
AIR COND. FAN SW.
INST. LTS. (3 USED)
OIL TEMP. GA.
OIL GAUGE
OIL IND.
ALT. IND.
CLOCK
BOOST METER
INST. PANEL PRINTED CIRCUIT (GAUGE)
HEATER & A/C BLOWER MOTOR MODE SW. CONN.
ILLUM LT.
REAR WINDOW DEFOGGER SENSOR
HEATED R. WDO. CONTROL UNIT
PRINTED CIRCUIT CONNS. (GAUGE)
INST. LTS. (5 USED)
INST. PANEL PRINTED CIRCUIT (METER)
FUEL GAUGE (SUB)
TACH.
FUEL GAUGE (MAIN)
TEMP. GA.
FUEL IND.
L. DIR.
R. DIR.
DOOR
BEAM SELECT
CAT SW.
BRAKE
EGR IND.
ALT. IND.
SPEED SENSOR
SEAT BELT
(2 SEAT MODELS)
BACK DOOR SW.
(2+2 ST. MODELS)
HEATED R. WINDOW GRID
LUGG. ROOM LT.
R. WINDOW DEFOG. RLY.
PRINTED CIRCUIT CONNS. (METER)
DIODE
(NON-TURBO)
BLU (TURBO)
LICENSE LT.
HEATED R. WINDOW SENS.
IGN. SW.
OFF ACC. IG S
CIG. LIGHTER
HEADLIGHT WIPER SW.
FUEL GAUGE (TANK UNIT)
WINDSHIELD WIPER/WASHER SW
OFF INT LOW HI WSH
RHEOSTAT
SEAT BELT SW.
FUEL PUMP
IGN. SW. CONN.
DIRECTION SW.
DIR. SW.
R N L
REAR WDO. WIPER MTR.
WIPER WASHER SW.
DIODE
REAR WDO. WASHER MTR.
OFF 1ST 2ND HORN
LIGHT SW. CONN.
DOME LT. & SW.
HAZARD SW. CONN.
(TURBO) YEL-GRN
BLU-YEL (GL)
BLU (GL)
STEERING LOCK SW.
KEY LIGHT
L. DOOR SW.
MARKER LT.
(W/O DISPLAY ONLY)

1983 Datsun/Nissan

MAXIMA & MAXIMA DIESEL

ENGINE COMPARTMENT

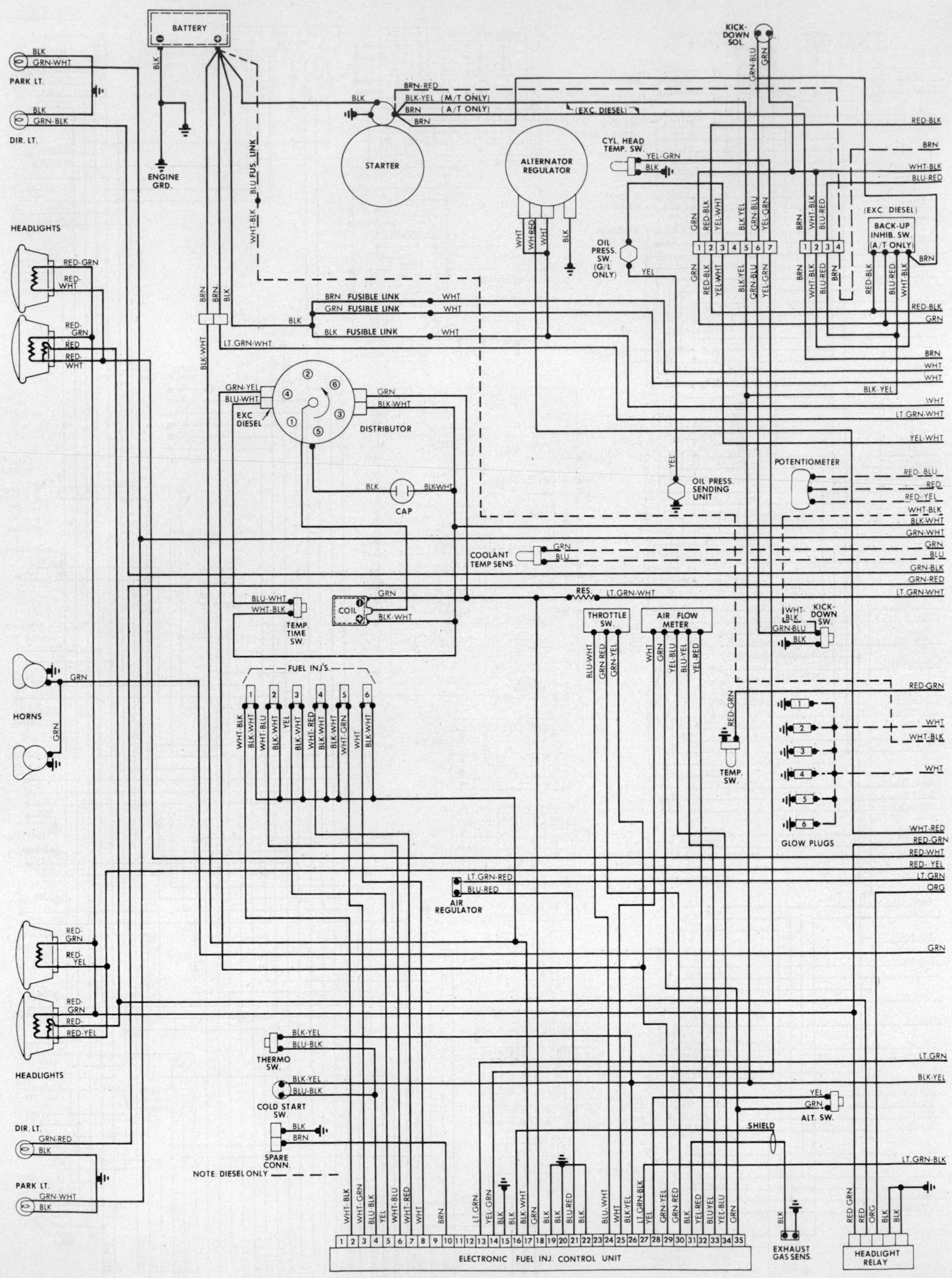
BATTERY
PARK LT.
DIR. LT.
ENGINE GRD.
HEADLIGHTS
STARTER
ALTERNATOR REGULATOR
KICK-DOWN SOL.
CYL. HEAD TEMP. SW.
OIL PRESS. SW. (G/L ONLY)
(EXC. DIESEL)
BACK-UP INHIB. SW. (A/T ONLY)
FUSIBLE LINK
DISTRIBUTOR
EXC DIESEL
CAP
OIL PRESS. SENDING UNIT
POTENTIOMETER
COOLANT TEMP SENS
RES.
COIL
TEMP. TIME SW.
THROTTLE SW.
AIR FLOW METER
KICK-DOWN SW.
FUEL INJ'S.
HORNS
TEMP. SW.
GLOW PLUGS
AIR REGULATOR
THERMO SW.
COLD START SW.
SPARE CONN.
NOTE: DIESEL ONLY
ALT. SW.
SHIELD
ELECTRONIC FUEL INJ. CONTROL UNIT
EXHAUST GAS SENS.
HEADLIGHT RELAY

1983 Datsun/Nissan

MAXIMA & MAXIMA DIESEL (Cont.)

ENGINE COMPARTMENT & UNDERDASH

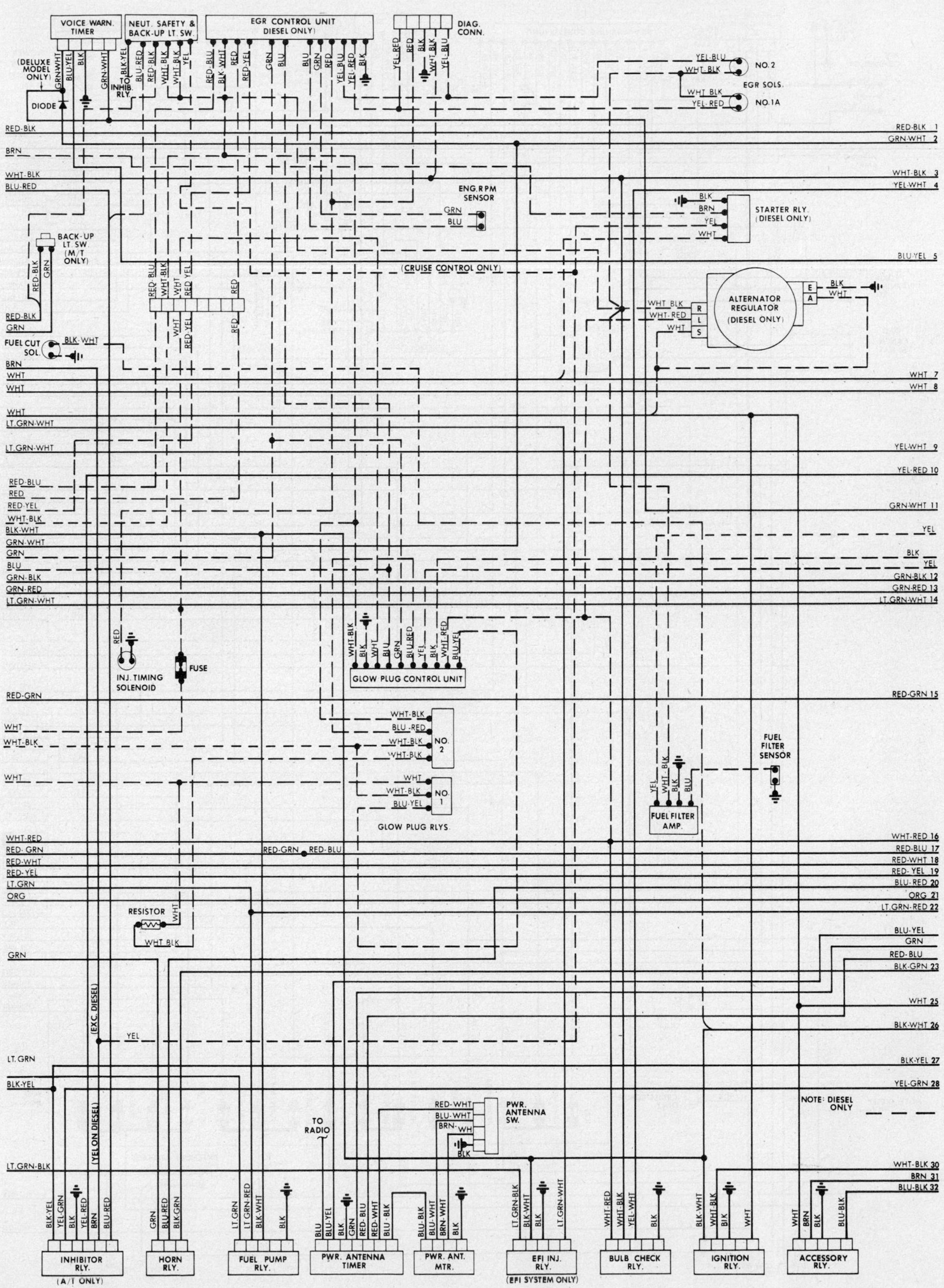
VOICE WARN. TIMER
NEUT. SAFETY & BACK-UP LT. SW.
EGR CONTROL UNIT (DIESEL ONLY)
DIAG. CONN.
(DELUXE MODEL ONLY)
DIODE
TO INHIB. RLY.
NO. 2
EGR SOLS.
NO. 1A
ENG. RPM SENSOR
STARTER RLY. (DIESEL ONLY)
BACK-UP LT. SW (M/T ONLY)
(CRUISE CONTROL ONLY)
ALTERNATOR REGULATOR (DIESEL ONLY)
FUEL CUT SOL.
INJ. TIMING SOLENOID
FUSE
GLOW PLUG CONTROL UNIT
GLOW PLUG RLYS.
FUEL FILTER SENSOR
FUEL FILTER AMP.
RESISTOR
(EXC. DIESEL)
(YEL ON DIESEL)
PWR. ANTENNA SW.
TO RADIO
NOTE: DIESEL ONLY
INHIBITOR RLY. (A/T ONLY)
HORN RLY.
FUEL PUMP RLY.
PWR. ANTENNA TIMER
PWR. ANT. MTR.
EFI INJ. RLY. (EFI SYSTEM ONLY)
BULB CHECK RLY.
IGNITION RLY.
ACCESSORY RLY.
RED-BLK 1
GRN-WHT 2
WHT-BLK 3
YEL-WHT 4
BLU-YEL 5
WHT 7
WHT 8
YEL-WHT 9
YEL-RED 10
GRN-WHT 11
GRN-BLK 12
GRN-RED 13
LT. GRN-WHT 14
RED-GRN 15
WHT-RED 16
RED-BLU 17
RED-WHT 18
RED-YEL 19
BLU-RED 20
ORG 21
LT. GRN-RED 22
BLK-GRN 23
WHT 25
BLK-WHT 26
BLK-YEL 27
YEL-GRN 28
WHT-BLK 30
BRN 31
BLU-BLK 32

1983 Datsun/Nissan

MAXIMA & MAXIMA DIESEL (Cont.)

FUSE BLOCK & UNDERDASH

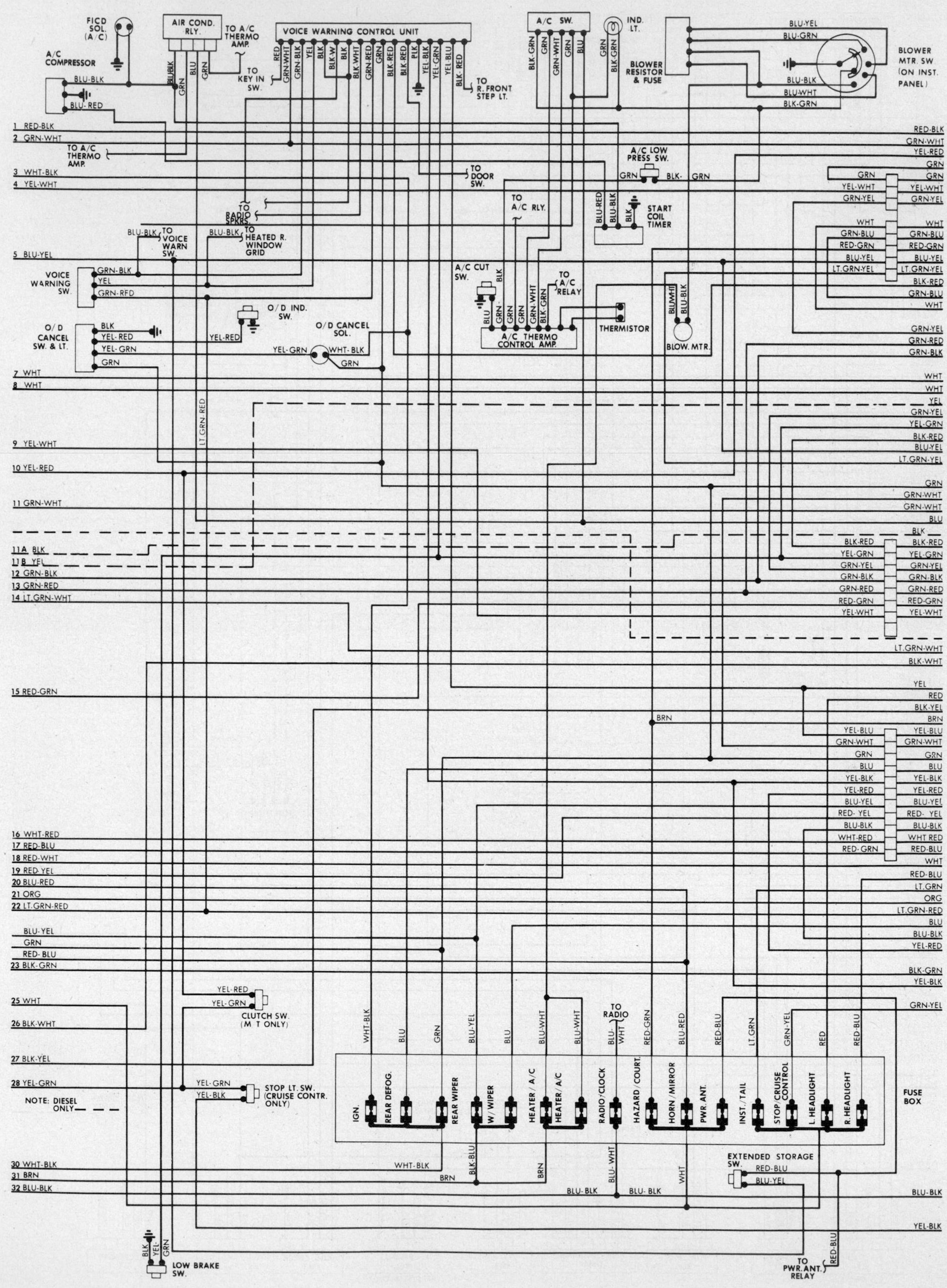
FICD SOL. (A/C)
AIR COND. RLY.
TO A/C THERMO AMP.
VOICE WARNING CONTROL UNIT
A/C COMPRESSOR
TO KEY IN SW.
TO R. FRONT STEP LT.
A/C SW.
IND. LT.
BLOWER RESISTOR & FUSE
BLOWER MTR. SW (ON INST. PANEL)
A/C LOW PRESS SW.
TO DOOR SW.
TO A/C RLY.
START COIL TIMER
TO RADIO SPKRS.
TO VOICE WARN SW.
TO HEATED R. WINDOW GRID
VOICE WARNING SW.
A/C CUT SW.
TO A/C RELAY
O/D IND. SW.
O/D CANCEL SW. & LT.
O/D CANCEL SOL.
A/C THERMO CONTROL AMP.
THERMISTOR
BLOW. MTR.
CLUTCH SW. (M T ONLY)
STOP LT. SW. (CRUISE CONTR. ONLY)
NOTE: DIESEL ONLY
TO RADIO
IGN.
REAR DEFOG.
REAR WIPER
W/ WIPER
HEATER / A/C
HEATER / A/C
RADIO/CLOCK
HAZARD/COURT.
HORN / MIRROR
PWR. ANT.
INST./TAIL
STOP CRUISE CONTROL
L. HEADLIGHT
R. HEADLIGHT
FUSE BOX
EXTENDED STORAGE SW.
LOW BRAKE SW.
TO PWR. ANT. RELAY

1983 Datsun/Nissan

MAXIMA & MAXIMA DIESEL (Cont.)

UNDERDASH

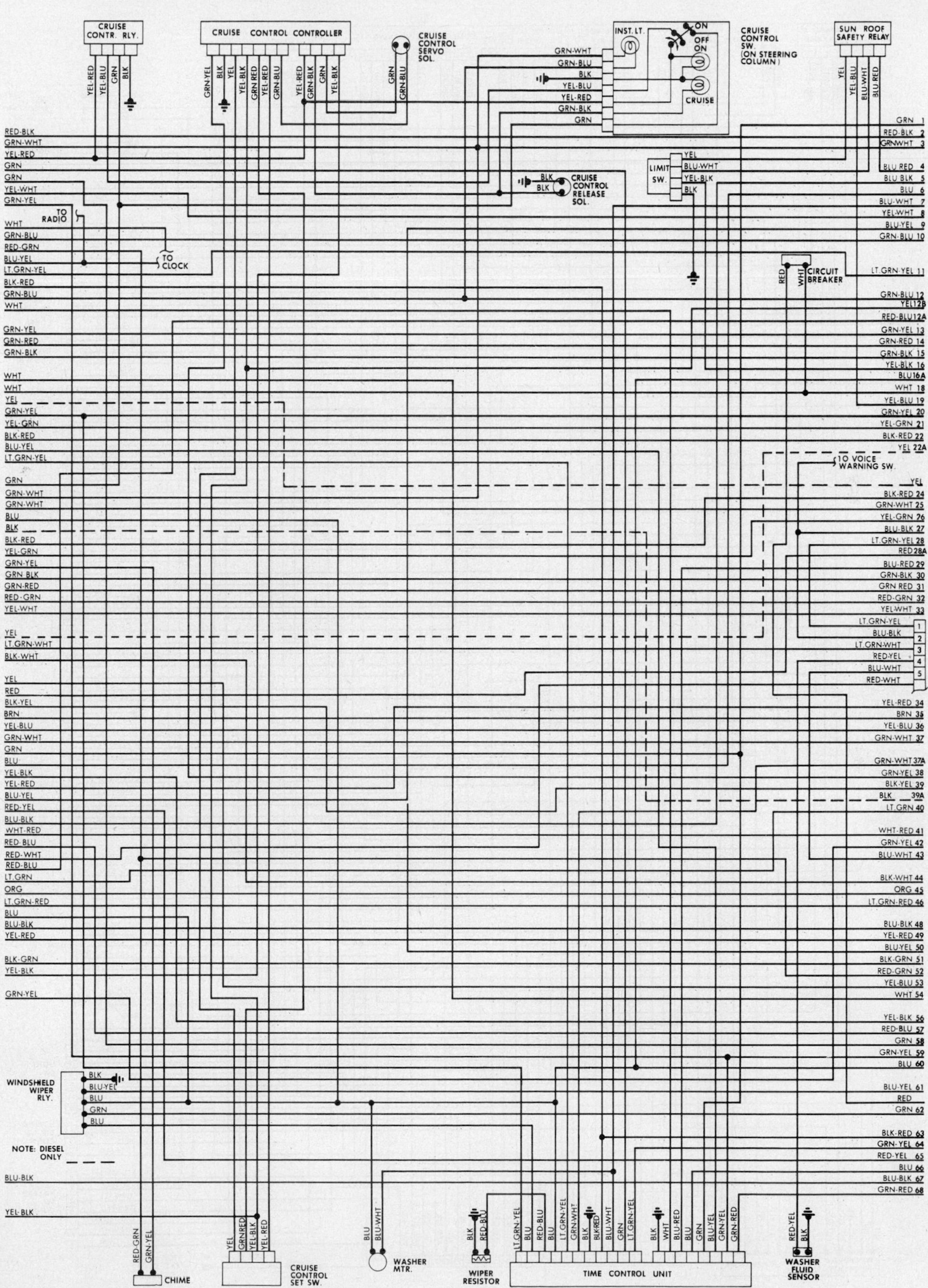
CRUISE CONTR. RLY.
CRUISE CONTROL CONTROLLER
CRUISE CONTROL SERVO SOL.
INST. LT.
ON
OFF
ON
CRUISE
CRUISE CONTROL SW. (ON STEERING COLUMN)
SUN ROOF SAFETY RELAY
TO RADIO
TO CLOCK
CRUISE CONTROL RELEASE SOL.
LIMIT SW.
CIRCUIT BREAKER
TO VOICE WARNING SW.
WINDSHIELD WIPER RLY.
NOTE: DIESEL ONLY
CHIME
CRUISE CONTROL SET SW.
WASHER MTR.
WIPER RESISTOR
TIME CONTROL UNIT
WASHER FLUID SENSOR

1983 Datsun/Nissan

MAXIMA & MAXIMA DIESEL (Cont.)

INSTRUMENT PANEL & UNDERDASH

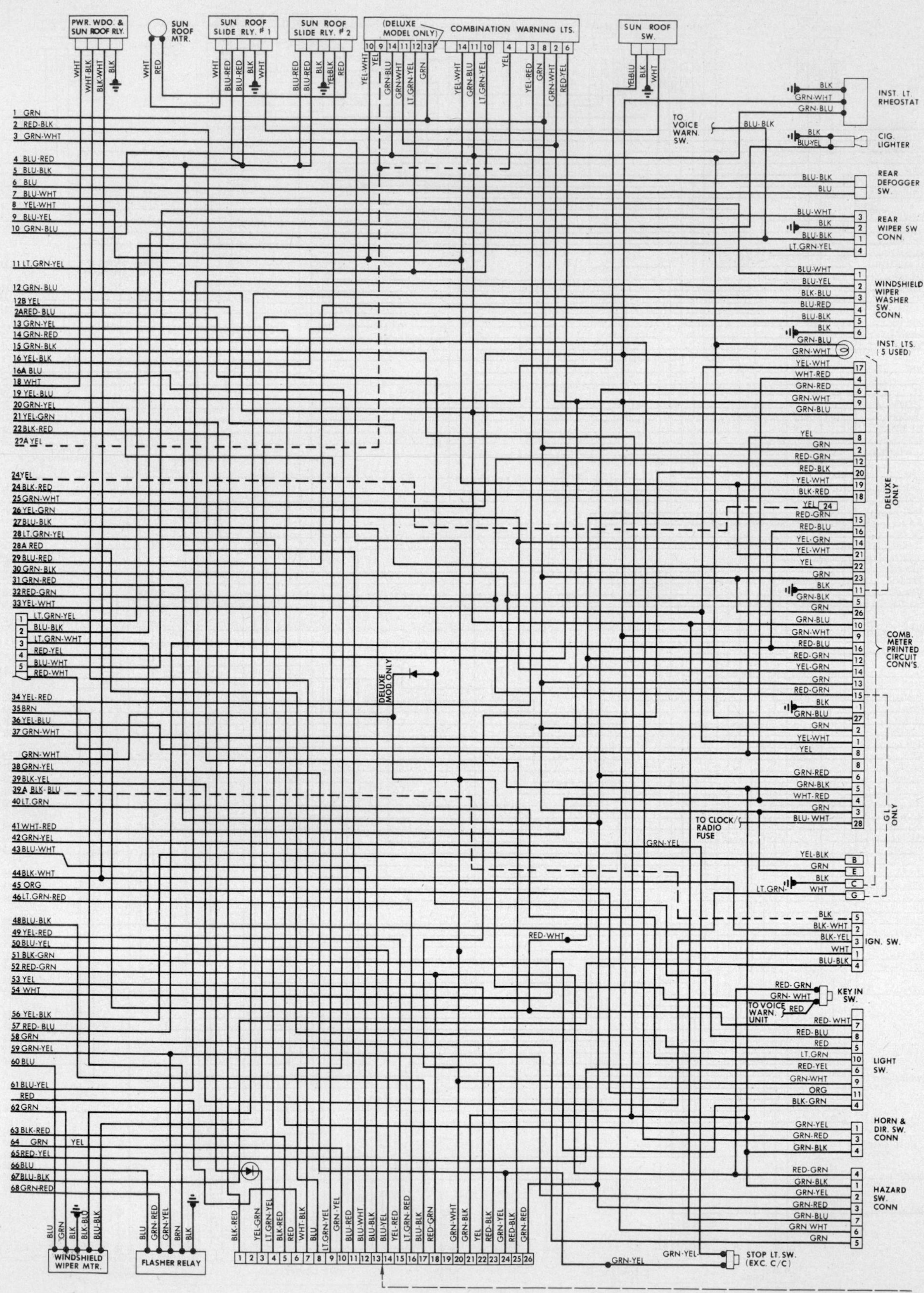

MAXIMA & MAXIMA DIESEL (Cont.)

INSTRUMENT PANEL, REAR COMPARTMENT & ACCESSORIES

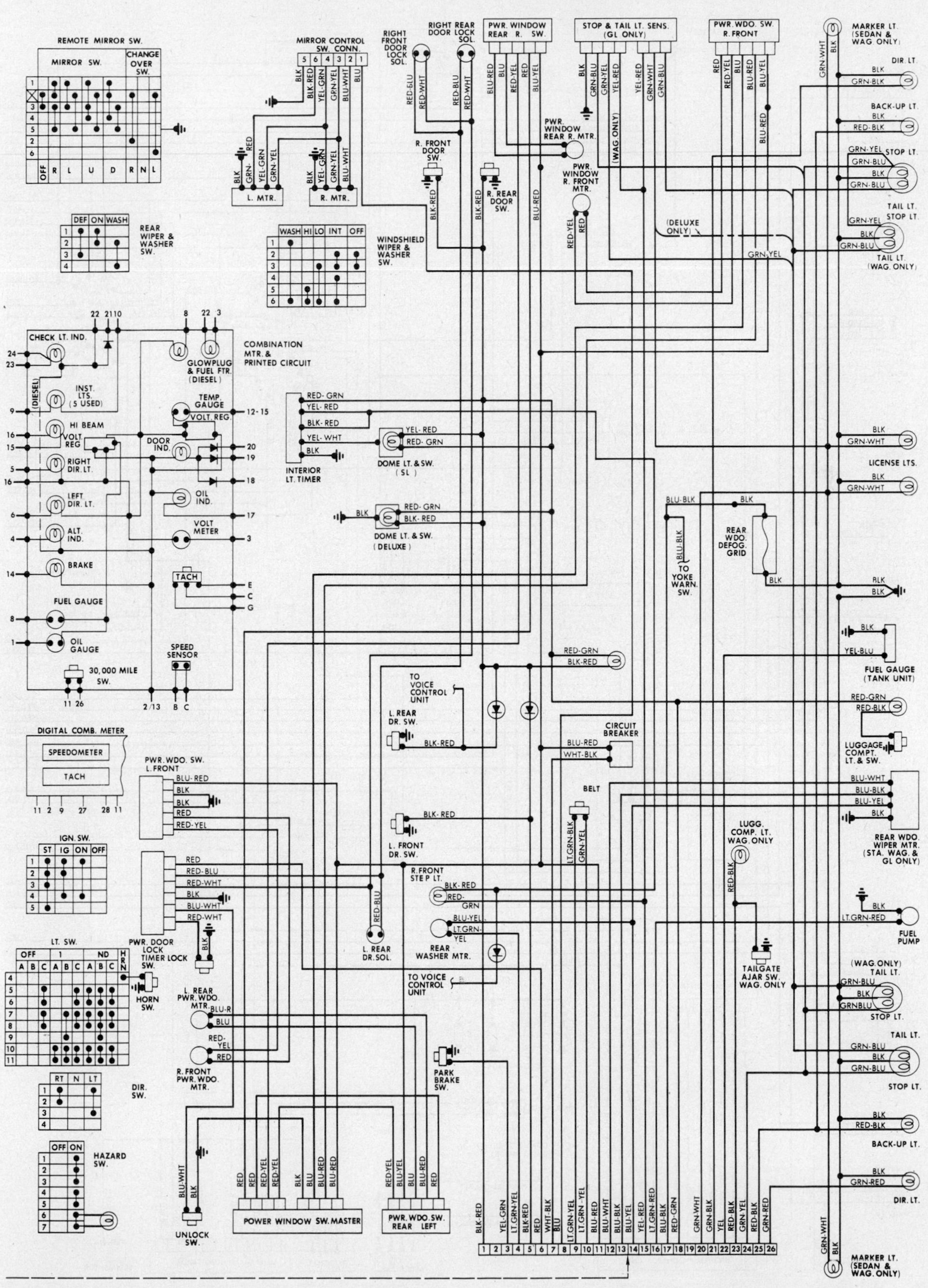
REMOTE MIRROR SW.
MIRROR SW.
CHANGE OVER SW.
MIRROR CONTROL SW. CONN.
L. MTR.
R. MTR.
RIGHT FRONT DOOR LOCK SOL.
RIGHT REAR DOOR LOCK SOL.
R. FRONT DOOR SW.
R. REAR DOOR SW.
PWR. WINDOW REAR R. SW.
PWR. WINDOW REAR R. MTR.
PWR. WINDOW R. FRONT MTR.
STOP & TAIL LT. SENS. (GL ONLY)
PWR. WDO. SW. R. FRONT
MARKER LT. (SEDAN & WAG. ONLY)
DIR. LT.
BACK-UP LT.
STOP LT.
TAIL LT.
TAIL LT. (WAG. ONLY)
REAR WIPER & WASHER SW.
WINDSHIELD WIPER & WASHER SW.
CHECK LT. IND.
COMBINATION MTR. & PRINTED CIRCUIT
GLOWPLUG & FUEL FTR. (DIESEL)
INST. LTS. (5 USED)
TEMP. GAUGE
VOLT. REG
HI BEAM
DOOR IND.
RIGHT DIR. LT.
LEFT DIR. LT.
OIL IND.
ALT. IND.
VOLT METER
BRAKE
TACH
FUEL GAUGE
OIL GAUGE
30,000 MILE SW.
SPEED SENSOR
INTERIOR LT. TIMER
DOME LT. & SW. (SL)
DOME LT. & SW. (DELUXE)
LICENSE LTS.
REAR WDO. DEFOG. GRID
TO YOKE WARN. SW.
FUEL GAUGE (TANK UNIT)
TO VOICE CONTROL UNIT
L. REAR DR. SW.
CIRCUIT BREAKER
LUGGAGE COMPT. LT. & SW.
DIGITAL COMB. METER
SPEEDOMETER
TACH
PWR. WDO. SW. L. FRONT
BELT
REAR WDO. WIPER MTR. (STA. WAG. & GL ONLY)
L. FRONT DR. SW.
IGN. SW.
LUGG. COMP. LT. WAG. ONLY
R. FRONT STEP LT.
FUEL PUMP
REAR WASHER MTR.
L. REAR DR. SOL.
LT. SW.
PWR. DOOR LOCK TIMER LOCK SW.
HORN SW.
TAILGATE AJAR SW. WAG. ONLY
L. REAR PWR. WDO. MTR.
R. FRONT PWR. WDO. MTR.
PARK BRAKE SW.
DIR. SW.
HAZARD SW.
UNLOCK SW.
POWER WINDOW SW. MASTER
PWR. WDO. SW. REAR LEFT

1983 Datsun/Nissan

PICKUP & PICKUP DIESEL

ENGINE COMPARTMENT

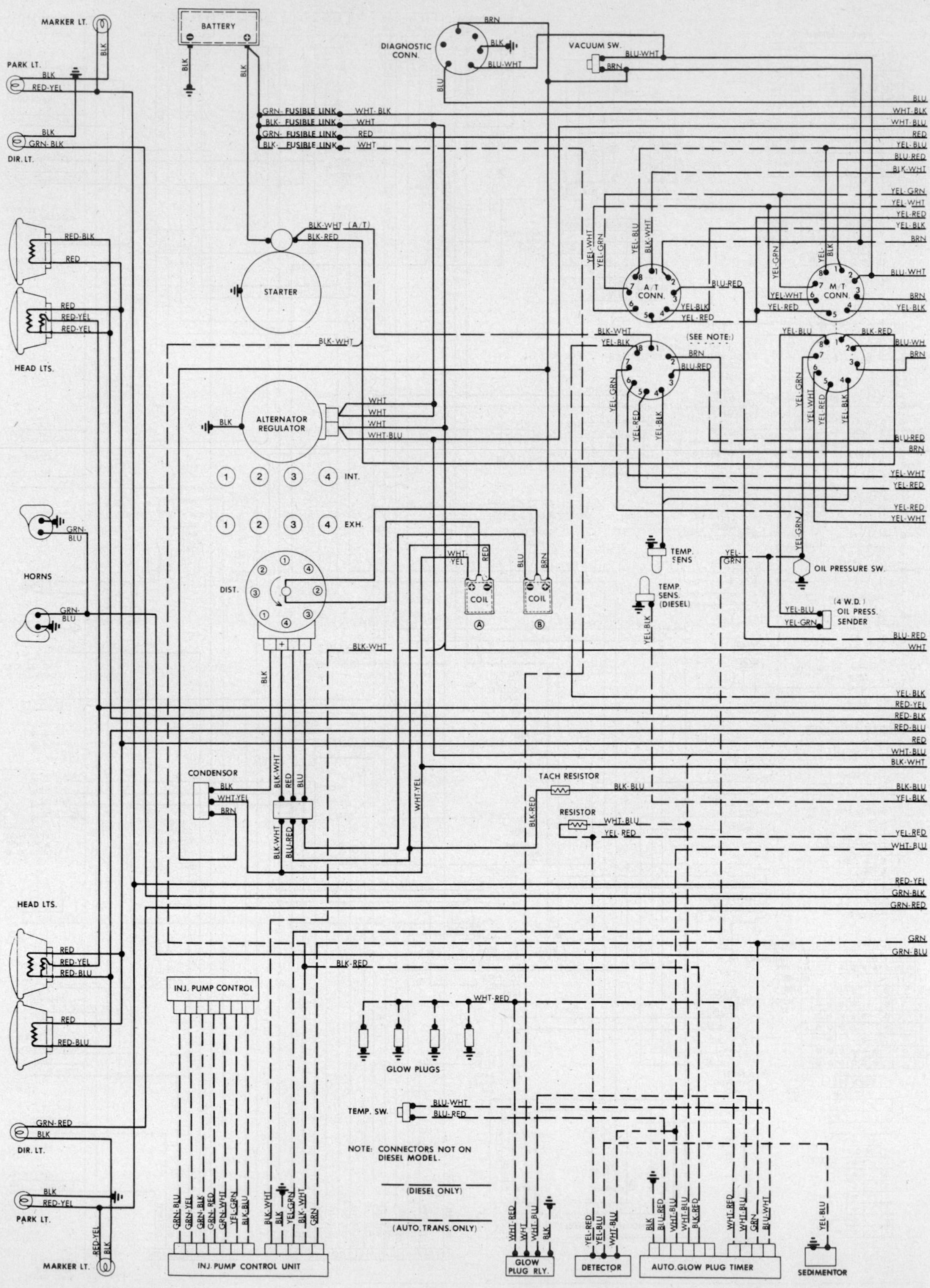

MARKER LT.
PARK LT.
DIR. LT.
HEAD LTS.
HORNS
BATTERY
GRN- FUSIBLE LINK
BLK- FUSIBLE LINK
GRN- FUSIBLE LINK
BLK- FUSIBLE LINK
STARTER
ALTERNATOR REGULATOR
DIAGNOSTIC CONN.
VACUUM SW.
A/T CONN.
M/T CONN.
(SEE NOTE:)
1 2 3 4 INT.
1 2 3 4 EXH.
DIST.
COIL A
COIL B
TEMP. SENS
TEMP. SENS. (DIESEL)
OIL PRESSURE SW.
(4 W.D.) OIL PRESS. SENDER
CONDENSOR
TACH RESISTOR
RESISTOR
INJ. PUMP CONTROL
GLOW PLUGS
TEMP. SW.
NOTE: CONNECTORS NOT ON DIESEL MODEL.
(DIESEL ONLY)
(AUTO. TRANS. ONLY)
INJ. PUMP CONTROL UNIT
GLOW PLUG RLY.
DETECTOR
AUTO. GLOW PLUG TIMER
SEDIMENTOR

1983 Datsun/Nissan

PICKUP & PICKUP DIESEL (Cont.)

FUSE BLOCK & UNDERDASH

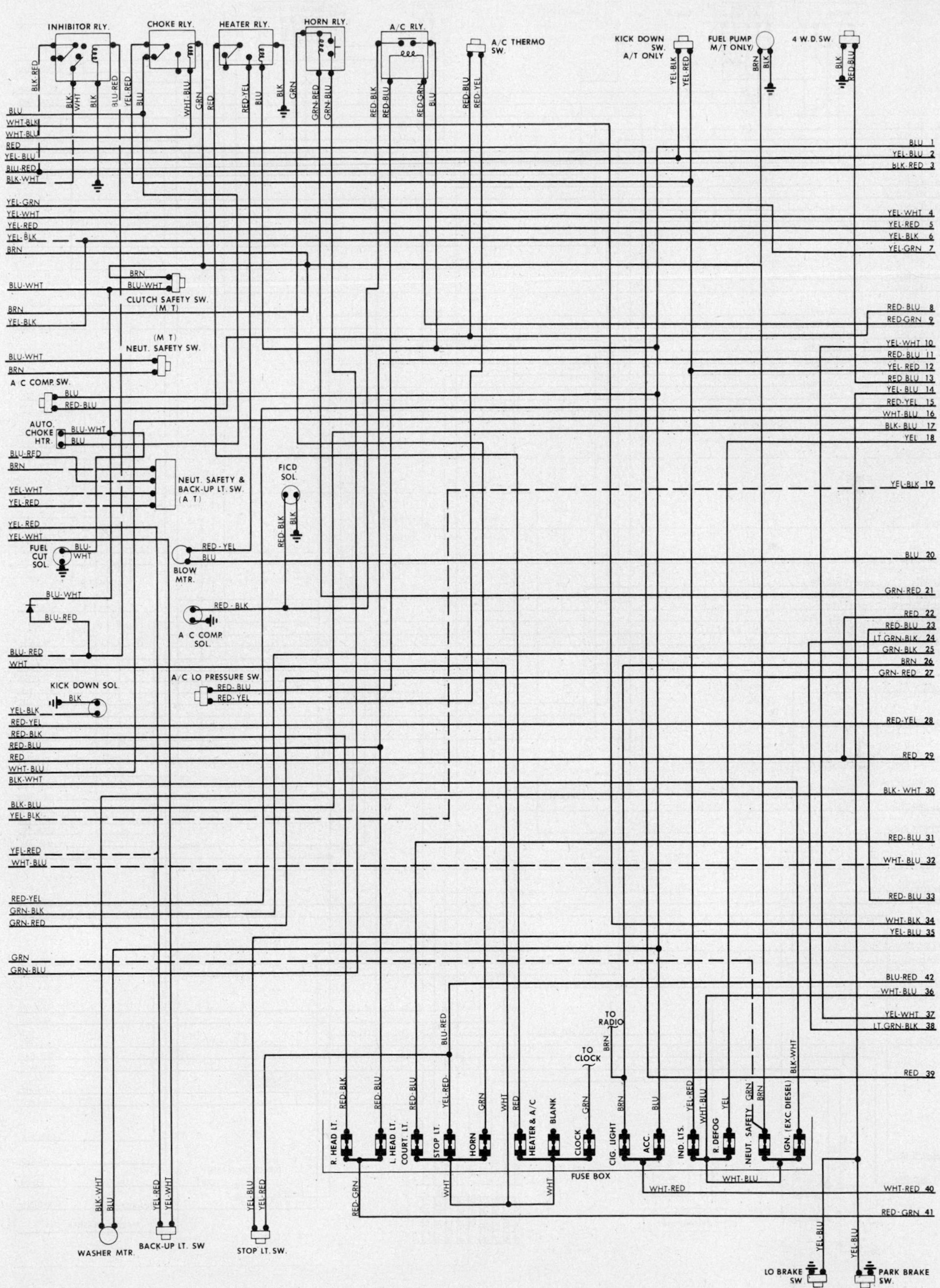
INHIBITOR RLY.
CHOKE RLY.
HEATER RLY.
HORN RLY.
A/C RLY.
A/C THERMO SW.
KICK DOWN SW. A/T ONLY
FUEL PUMP M/T ONLY
4 W.D. SW.
CLUTCH SAFETY SW. (M T)
(M T) NEUT. SAFETY SW.
A C COMP. SW.
AUTO. CHOKE HTR.
NEUT. SAFETY & BACK-UP LT. SW. (A T)
FICD SOL.
FUEL CUT SOL.
BLOW MTR.
A C COMP. SOL.
A/C LO PRESSURE SW.
KICK DOWN SOL.
TO RADIO
TO CLOCK
R. HEAD LT.
L. HEAD LT.
COURT. LT.
STOP LT.
HORN
HEATER & A/C
BLANK
CLOCK
CIG. LIGHT
ACC.
IND. LTS.
R. DEFOG
NEUT. SAFETY
IGN. (EXC DIESEL)
FUSE BOX
WASHER MTR.
BACK-UP LT. SW
STOP LT. SW.
LO BRAKE SW
PARK BRAKE SW.
BLU 1
YEL-BLU 2
BLK-RED 3
YEL-WHT 4
YEL-RED 5
YEL-BLK 6
YEL-GRN 7
RED-BLU 8
RED-GRN 9
YEL-WHT 10
RED-BLU 11
YEL-RED 12
RED-BLU 13
YEL-BLU 14
RED-YEL 15
WHT-BLU 16
BLK-BLU 17
YEL 18
YEL-BLK 19
BLU 20
GRN-RED 21
RED 22
RED-BLU 23
LT GRN-BLK 24
GRN-BLK 25
BRN 26
GRN-RED 27
RED-YEL 28
RED 29
BLK-WHT 30
RED-BLU 31
WHT-BLU 32
RED-BLU 33
WHT-BLK 34
YEL-BLU 35
BLU-RED 42
WHT-BLU 36
YEL-WHT 37
LT GRN-BLK 38
RED 39
WHT-RED 40
RED-GRN 41

1983 Datsun/Nissan

PICKUP & PICKUP DIESEL (Cont.)

UNDERDASH

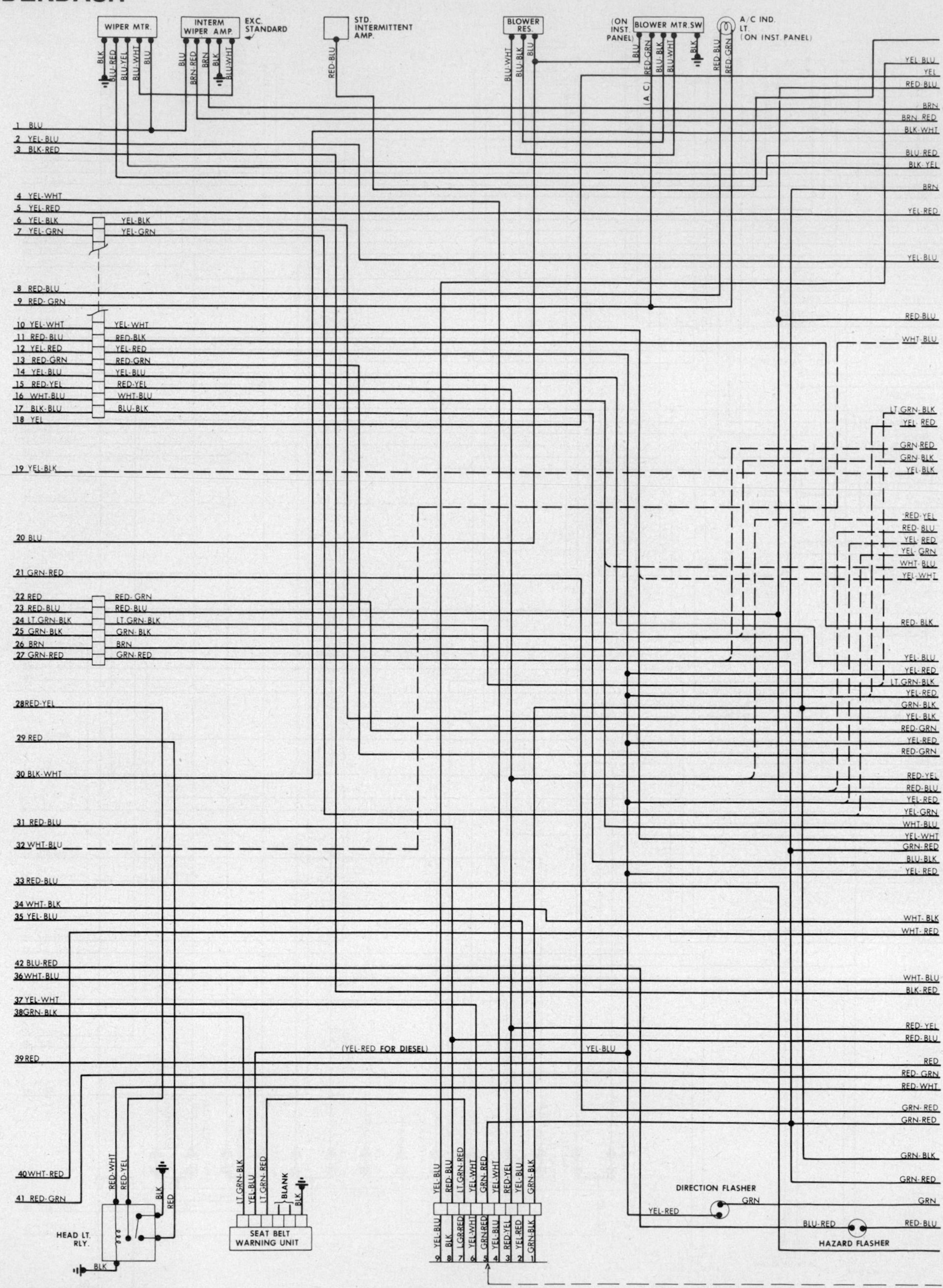

PICKUP & PICKUP DIESEL (Cont.)

INSTRUMENT PANEL & REAR COMPARTMENT

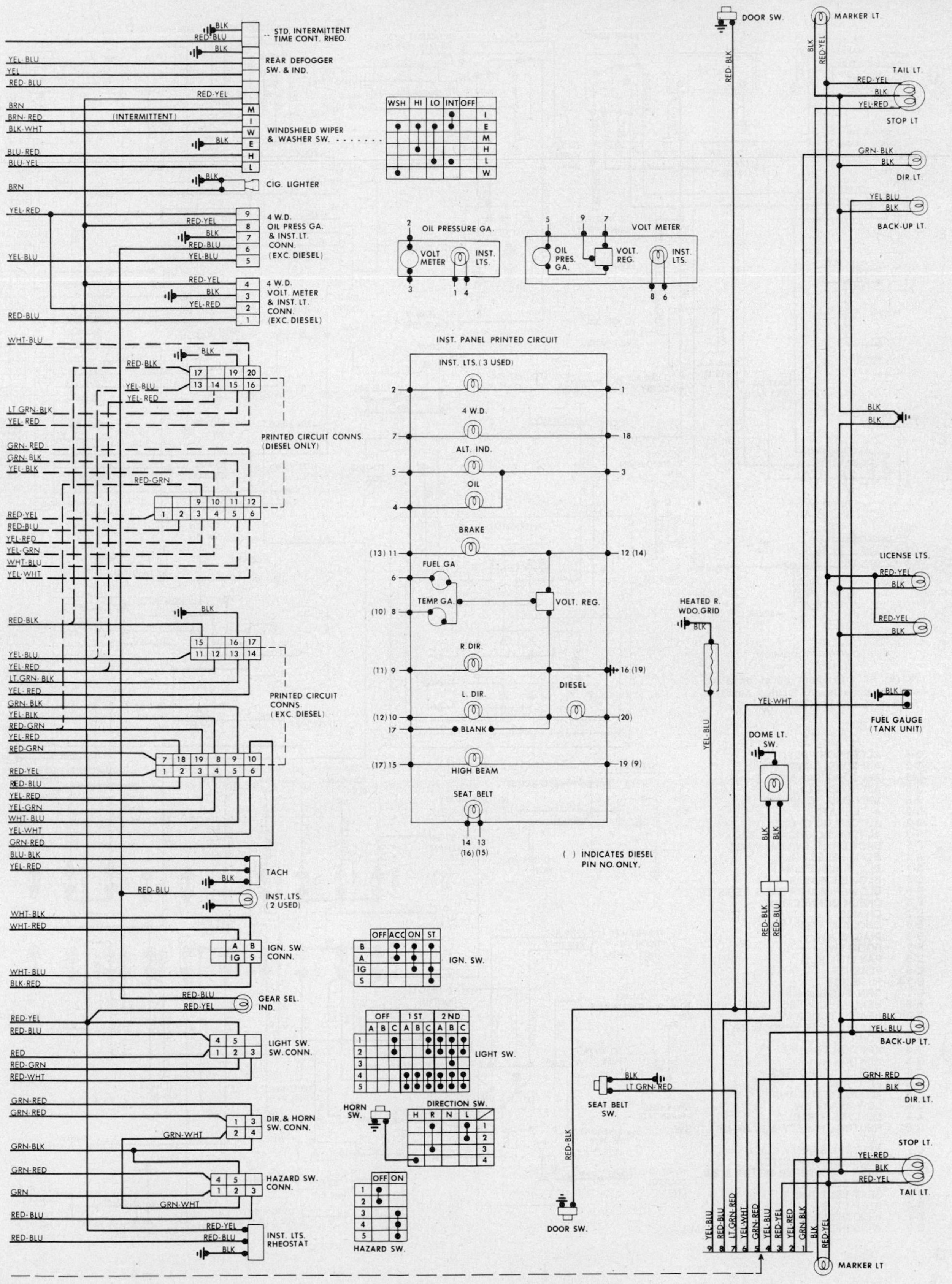
STD. INTERMITTENT TIME CONT. RHEO.
REAR DEFOGGER SW. & IND.
WINDSHIELD WIPER & WASHER SW.
CIG. LIGHTER
4 W.D. OIL PRESS GA. & INST. LT. CONN. (EXC. DIESEL)
4 W.D. VOLT. METER & INST. LT. CONN. (EXC. DIESEL)
PRINTED CIRCUIT CONNS. (DIESEL ONLY)
PRINTED CIRCUIT CONNS. (EXC. DIESEL)
TACH
INST. LTS. (2 USED)
IGN. SW. CONN.
GEAR SEL. IND.
LIGHT SW. SW. CONN.
DIR. & HORN SW. CONN.
HAZARD SW. CONN.
INST. LTS. RHEOSTAT
OIL PRESSURE GA.
VOLT METER
INST. PANEL PRINTED CIRCUIT
INST. LTS. (3 USED)
4 W.D.
ALT. IND.
OIL
BRAKE
FUEL GA
TEMP. GA.
VOLT. REG.
R. DIR.
L. DIR.
DIESEL
BLANK
HIGH BEAM
SEAT BELT
( ) INDICATES DIESEL PIN NO. ONLY.
IGN. SW.
LIGHT SW.
HORN SW.
DIRECTION SW.
HAZARD SW.
SEAT BELT SW.
DOOR SW.
HEATED R. WDO. GRID
DOME LT. SW.
MARKER LT.
TAIL LT.
STOP LT
DIR. LT.
BACK-UP LT.
LICENSE LTS.
FUEL GAUGE (TANK UNIT)
BACK-UP LT.
DIR. LT.
STOP LT.
TAIL LT.
MARKER LT

1983 Datsun/Nissan

PULSAR

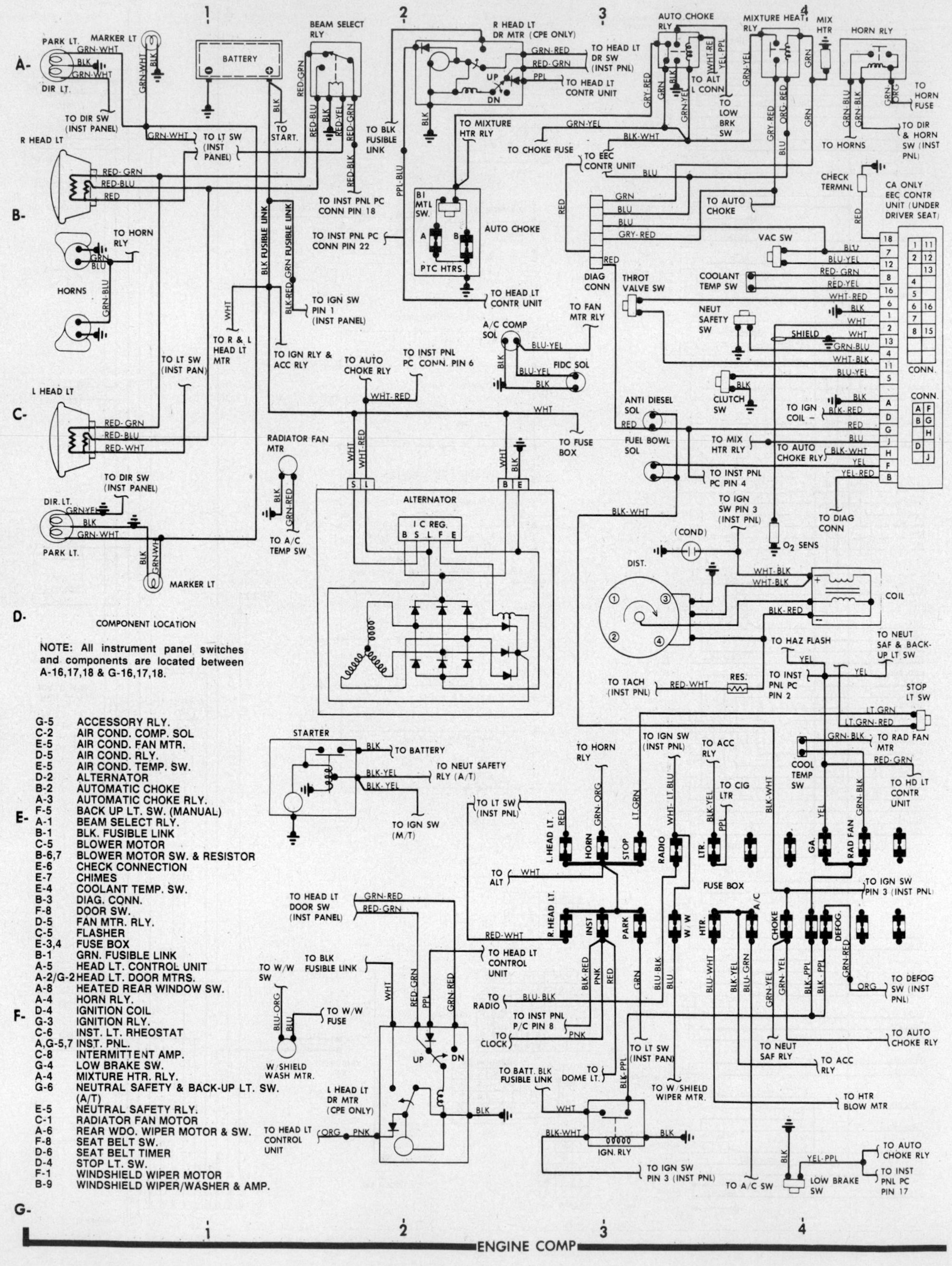
COMPONENT LOCATION
NOTE: All instrument panel switches and components are located between A-16,17,18 & G-16,17,18.
G-5 ACCESSORY RLY.
C-2 AIR COND. COMP. SOL
E-5 AIR COND. FAN MTR.
D-5 AIR COND. RLY.
E-5 AIR COND. TEMP. SW.
D-2 ALTERNATOR
B-2 AUTOMATIC CHOKE
A-3 AUTOMATIC CHOKE RLY.
F-5 BACK UP LT. SW. (MANUAL)
A-1 BEAM SELECT RLY.
B-1 BLK. FUSIBLE LINK
C-5 BLOWER MOTOR
B-6,7 BLOWER MOTOR SW. & RESISTOR
E-6 CHECK CONNECTION
E-7 CHIMES
E-4 COOLANT TEMP. SW.
B-3 DIAG. CONN.
F-8 DOOR SW.
D-5 FAN MTR. RLY.
C-5 FLASHER
E-3,4 FUSE BOX
B-1 GRN. FUSIBLE LINK
A-5 HEAD LT. CONTROL UNIT
A-2/G-2 HEAD LT. DOOR MTRS.
A-8 HEATED REAR WINDOW SW.
A-4 HORN RLY.
D-4 IGNITION COIL
G-3 IGNITION RLY.
C-6 INST. LT. RHEOSTAT
A,G-5,7 INST. PNL.
C-8 INTERMITTENT AMP.
G-4 LOW BRAKE SW.
A-4 MIXTURE HTR. RLY.
G-6 NEUTRAL SAFETY & BACK-UP LT. SW. (A/T)
E-5 NEUTRAL SAFETY RLY.
C-1 RADIATOR FAN MOTOR
A-6 REAR WDO. WIPER MOTOR & SW.
F-8 SEAT BELT SW.
D-6 SEAT BELT TIMER
D-4 STOP LT. SW.
F-1 WINDSHIELD WIPER MOTOR
B-9 WINDSHIELD WIPER/WASHER & AMP.
ENGINE COMP

PULSAR (Cont.)

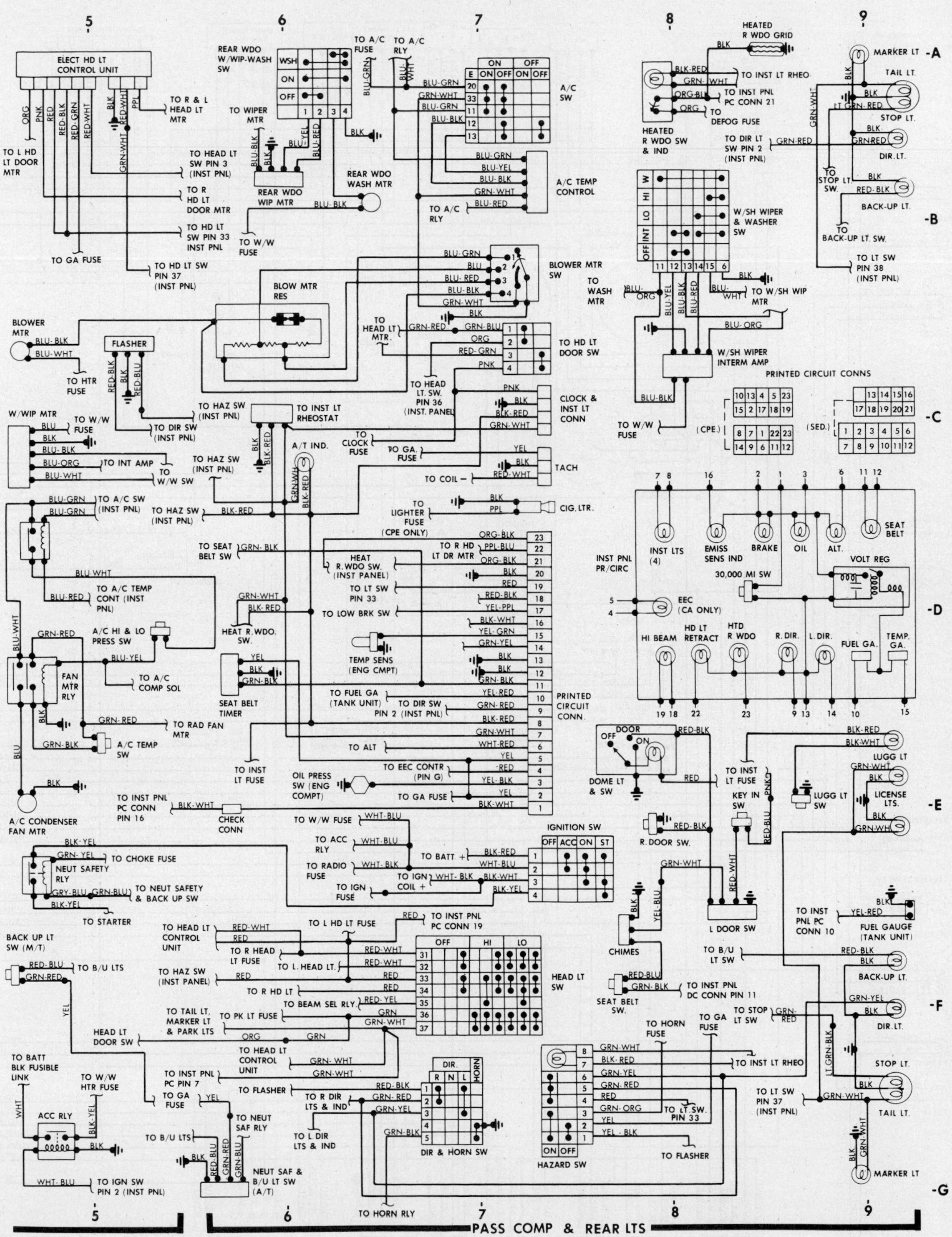
ELECT HD LT CONTROL UNIT
TO R & L HEAD LT MTR
TO L HD LT DOOR MTR
TO HEAD LT SW PIN 3 (INST PNL)
TO R HD LT DOOR MTR
TO HD LT SW PIN 33 INST PNL
TO GA FUSE
TO HD LT SW PIN 37 (INST PNL)
REAR WDO W/WIP-WASH SW
TO WIPER MTR
REAR WDO WIP MTR
REAR WDO WASH MTR
TO W/W FUSE
TO A/C FUSE
TO A/C RLY
A/C SW
A/C TEMP CONTROL
BLOWER MTR SW
BLOW MTR RES
BLOWER MTR
FLASHER
TO HTR FUSE
TO HEAD LT MTR.
TO HD LT DOOR SW
TO HEAD LT. SW. PIN 36 (INST. PANEL)
CLOCK & INST LT CONN
TACH
TO COIL
CIG. LTR.
TO LIGHTER FUSE (CPE ONLY)
W/WIP MTR
TO W/W FUSE
TO INT AMP
TO W/W SW
TO HAZ SW (INST PNL)
TO DIR SW (INST PNL)
TO INST LT RHEOSTAT
A/T IND.
TO CLOCK FUSE
TO GA. FUSE
TO A/C SW (INST PNL)
TO A/C TEMP CONT (INST PNL)
A/C HI & LO PRESS SW
FAN MTR RLY
TO A/C COMP SOL
TO RAD FAN MTR
A/C TEMP SW
A/C CONDENSER FAN MTR
TO SEAT BELT SW
HEAT R.WDO SW. (INST PANEL)
TO R HD LT DR MTR
TO LT SW PIN 33
TO LOW BRK SW
HEAT R.WDO. SW.
TEMP SENS (ENG CMPT)
SEAT BELT TIMER
TO FUEL GA (TANK UNIT)
TO DIR SW PIN 2 (INST PNL)
PRINTED CIRCUIT CONN.
TO ALT
TO INST LT FUSE
OIL PRESS SW (ENG COMPT)
TO EEC CONTR (PIN G)
TO GA FUSE
TO INST PNL PC CONN PIN 16
CHECK CONN
TO W/W FUSE
TO ACC RLY
TO RADIO FUSE
TO IGN FUSE
TO BATT +
TO IGN COIL +
IGNITION SW
OFF ACC ON ST
TO CHOKE FUSE
NEUT SAFETY RLY
TO NEUT SAFETY & BACK UP SW
TO STARTER
BACK UP LT SW (M/T)
TO B/U LTS
TO HEAD LT CONTROL UNIT
TO R HEAD LT FUSE
TO L HD LT FUSE
TO L. HEAD LT.
TO INST PNL PC CONN 19
TO HAZ SW (INST PANEL)
TO R HD LT
TO BEAM SEL RLY
TO TAIL LT, MARKER LT & PARK LTS
TO PK LT FUSE
HEAD LT DOOR SW
HEAD LT SW
OFF HI LO
TO HEAD LT CONTROL UNIT
TO INST PNL PC PIN 7
TO GA FUSE
TO FLASHER
TO R DIR LTS & IND
TO L DIR LTS & IND
TO NEUT SAF RLY
TO B/U LTS
TO BATT BLK FUSIBLE LINK
TO W/W HTR FUSE
ACC RLY
TO IGN SW PIN 2 (INST PNL)
NEUT SAF & B/U LT SW (A/T)
DIR. R N L HORN
DIR & HORN SW
TO HORN RLY
HAZARD SW
ON OFF
TO HORN FUSE
TO GA FUSE
TO INST LT RHEO
TO LT SW. PIN 33
TO FLASHER
HEATED R WDO GRID
HEATED R WDO SW & IND
TO INST LT RHEO
TO INST PNL PC CONN 21
TO DEFOG FUSE
TO DIR LT SW PIN 2 (INST PNL)
W/SH WIPER & WASHER SW
OFF INT LO HI W
TO WASH MTR
TO W/SH WIP MTR
W/SH WIPER INTERM AMP
TO W/W FUSE
PRINTED CIRCUIT CONNS
(CPE.)
(SED.)
INST LTS (4)
EMISS SENS IND
BRAKE
OIL
ALT.
SEAT BELT
VOLT REG
INST PNL PR/CIRC
30,000 MI SW
EEC (CA ONLY)
HI BEAM
HD LT RETRACT
HTD R WDO
R. DIR.
L. DIR.
FUEL GA.
TEMP. GA.
DOOR OFF ON
DOME LT & SW
TO INST LT FUSE
KEY IN SW
R. DOOR SW.
L DOOR SW
CHIMES
SEAT BELT SW.
TO INST PNL DC CONN PIN 11
TO B/U LT SW
TO STOP LT SW
MARKER LT
TAIL LT.
STOP LT.
DIR. LT.
TO STOP LT. SW.
BACK-UP LT.
TO BACK-UP LT. SW.
TO LT SW PIN 38 (INST PNL)
LUGG LT
LUGG LT SW
LICENSE LTS.
TO INST PNL PC CONN 10
FUEL GAUGE (TANK UNIT)
BACK-UP LT.
DIR. LT.
STOP LT.
TO LT SW PIN 37 (INST PNL)
TAIL LT.
MARKER LT
PASS COMP & REAR LTS

1983 Datsun/Nissan

SENTRA GAS – EXCEPT MPG

ENGINE COMPARTMENT

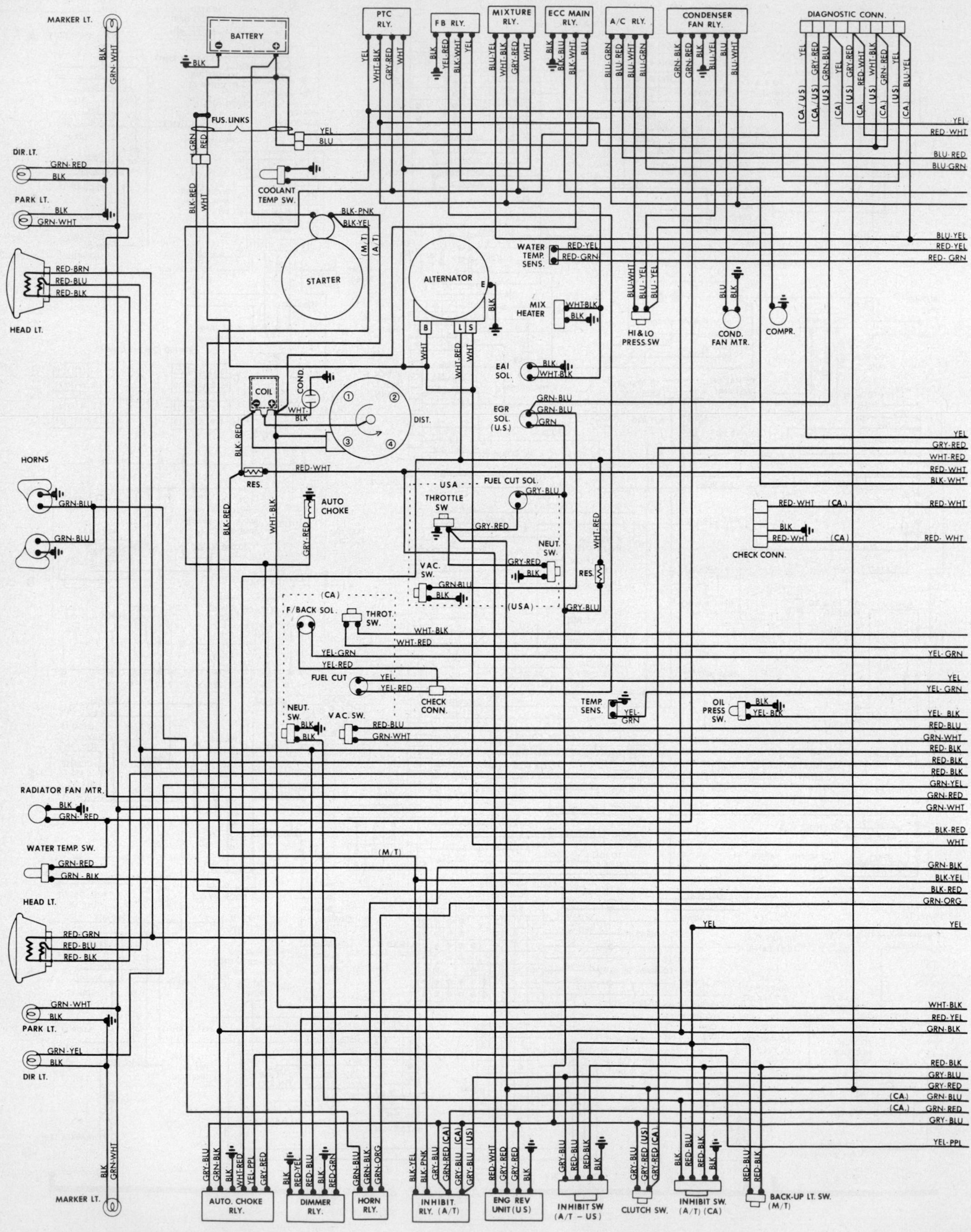
MARKER LT.
BATTERY
FUS. LINKS
PTC RLY.
FB RLY.
MIXTURE RLY.
ECC MAIN RLY.
A/C RLY.
CONDENSER FAN RLY.
DIAGNOSTIC CONN.
DIR. LT.
PARK LT.
COOLANT TEMP SW.
HEAD LT.
STARTER
ALTERNATOR
WATER TEMP. SENS.
MIX HEATER
HI & LO PRESS. SW
COND. FAN MTR.
COMPR.
EAI SOL.
COIL
COND.
DIST.
EGR SOL. (U.S.)
HORNS
RES.
AUTO CHOKE
FUEL CUT SOL.
THROTTLE SW
VAC. SW.
NEUT. SW.
CHECK CONN.
F/BACK SOL.
THROT. SW.
FUEL CUT
TEMP. SENS.
OIL PRESS SW.
RADIATOR FAN MTR.
WATER TEMP. SW.
AUTO. CHOKE RLY.
DIMMER RLY.
HORN RLY.
INHIBIT. RLY. (A/T)
ENG REV UNIT (US)
INHIBIT SW (A/T – US)
CLUTCH SW.
INHIBIT SW. (A/T) (CA)
BACK-UP LT. SW. (M/T)

1983 Datsun/Nissan

SENTRA GAS – EXCEPT MPG (Cont.)

FUSE BLOCK & UNDERDASH

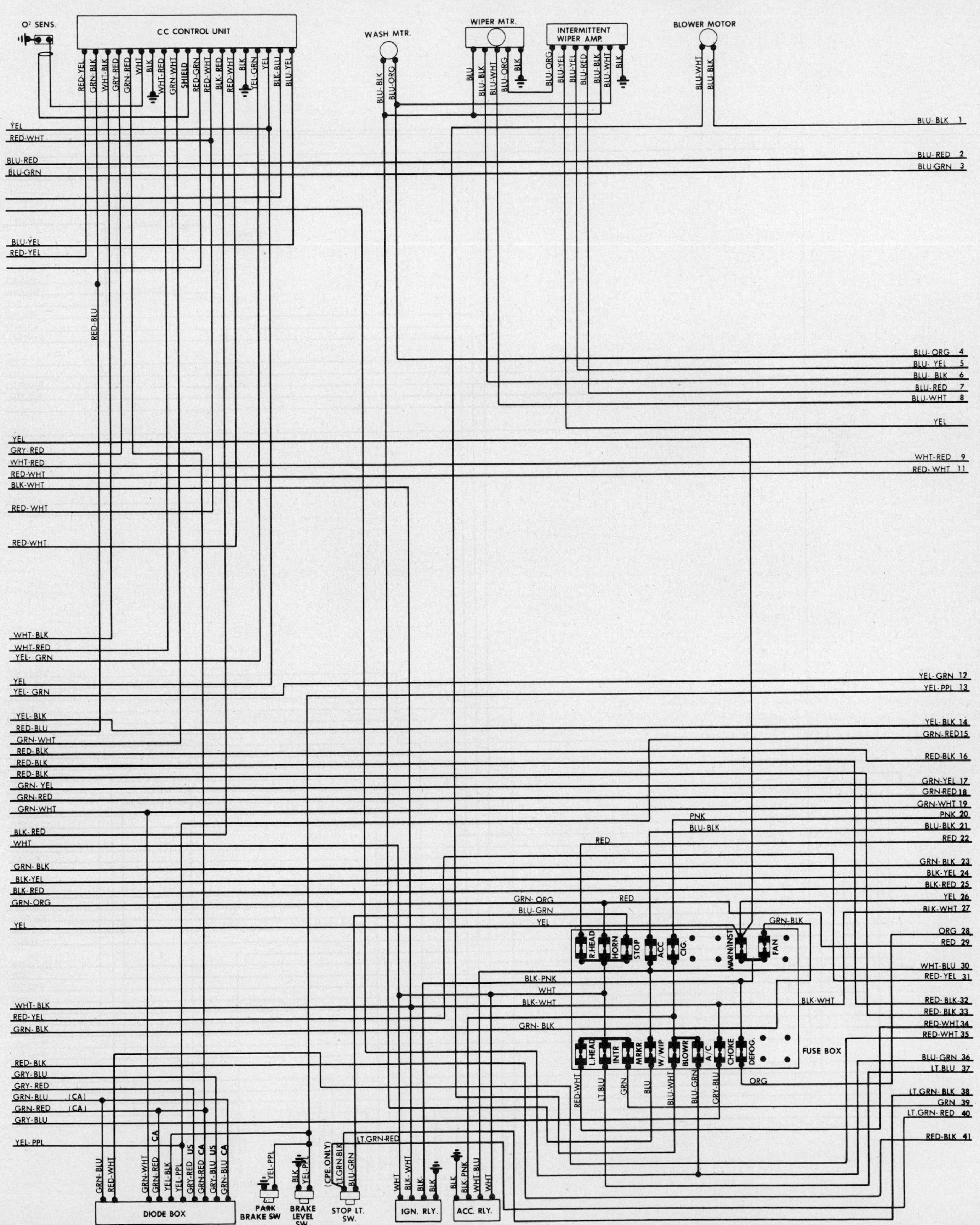

O² SENS.
CC CONTROL UNIT
RED-YEL
GRN-BLK
WHT-BLK
GRY-RED
GRN-RED
WHT
BLK
WHT-RED
GRN-WHT
SHIELD
RED-GRN
RED-WHT
BLK-RED
RED-WHT
BLK
YEL GRN
YEL
BLK-BLU
BLU-YEL
WASH MTR.
BLU-BLK
BLU-ORG
WIPER MTR.
BLU
BLU-BLK
BLU-WHT
BLU-ORG
BLK
INTERMITTENT WIPER AMP.
BLU-ORG
BLU-YEL
BLU-YEL
BLU-RED
BLU-BLK
BLU-WHT
BLK
BLOWER MOTOR
BLU-WHT
BLU-BLK
BLU-BLK 1
BLU-RED 2
BLU-GRN 3
BLU-ORG 4
BLU-YEL 5
BLU-BLK 6
BLU-RED 7
BLU-WHT 8
YEL
WHT-RED 9
RED-WHT 11
YEL-GRN 12
YEL-PPL 13
YEL-BLK 14
GRN-RED 15
RED-BLK 16
GRN-YEL 17
GRN-RED 18
GRN-WHT 19
PNK 20
BLU-BLK 21
RED 22
GRN-BLK 23
BLK-YEL 24
BLK-RED 25
YEL 26
BLK-WHT 27
ORG 28
RED 29
WHT-BLU 30
RED-YEL 31
RED-BLK 32
RED-BLK 33
RED-WHT 34
RED-WHT 35
BLU-GRN 36
LT.BLU 37
LT.GRN-BLK 38
GRN 39
LT.GRN-RED 40
RED-BLK 41
YEL
RED-WHT
BLU-RED
BLU-GRN
BLU-YEL
RED-YEL
RED-BLU
YEL
GRY-RED
WHT-RED
RED-WHT
BLK-WHT
RED-WHT
RED-WHT
WHT-BLK
WHT-RED
YEL-GRN
YEL
YEL-GRN
YEL-BLK
RED-BLU
GRN-WHT
RED-BLK
RED-BLK
RED-BLK
GRN-YEL
GRN-RED
GRN-WHT
BLK-RED
WHT
GRN-BLK
BLK-YEL
BLK-RED
GRN-ORG
YEL
WHT-BLK
RED-YEL
GRN-BLK
RED-BLK
GRY-BLU
GRY-RED
GRN-BLU (CA)
GRN-RED (CA)
GRY-BLU
YEL-PPL
PNK
BLU-BLK
RED
GRN-ORG
BLU-GRN
YEL
RED
GRN-BLK
R.HEAD
HORN
STOP
ACC
CIG.
WARN/INST
FAN
BLK-PNK
WHT
BLK-WHT
GRN-BLK
BLK-WHT
L.HEAD
INTR
MRKR
W/WIP
BLOWR
A/C
CHOKE
DEFOG.
FUSE BOX
ORG
RED-WHT
LT.BLU
GRN
BLU
BLU-WHT
BLU-GRN
GRY-BLU
LT.GRN-RED
GRN-BLU
RED-WHT
GRN-WHT
GRN-RED
YEL-BLK
YEL-PPL
GRY-RED US
GRN-RED CA
GRY-BLU US
GRN-BLU CA
CA
DIODE BOX
YEL-PPL
PARK BRAKE SW
BLK
YEL-PPL
BRAKE LEVEL SW.
(CPE ONLY)
LT.GRN-BLK
BLU-GRN
STOP LT. SW.
WHT
BLK-WHT
BLK
IGN. RLY.
BLK
BLK-PNK
WHT-BLU
WHT
ACC. RLY.

1983 Datsun/Nissan

SENTRA GAS – EXCEPT MPG (Cont.)

UNDERDASH

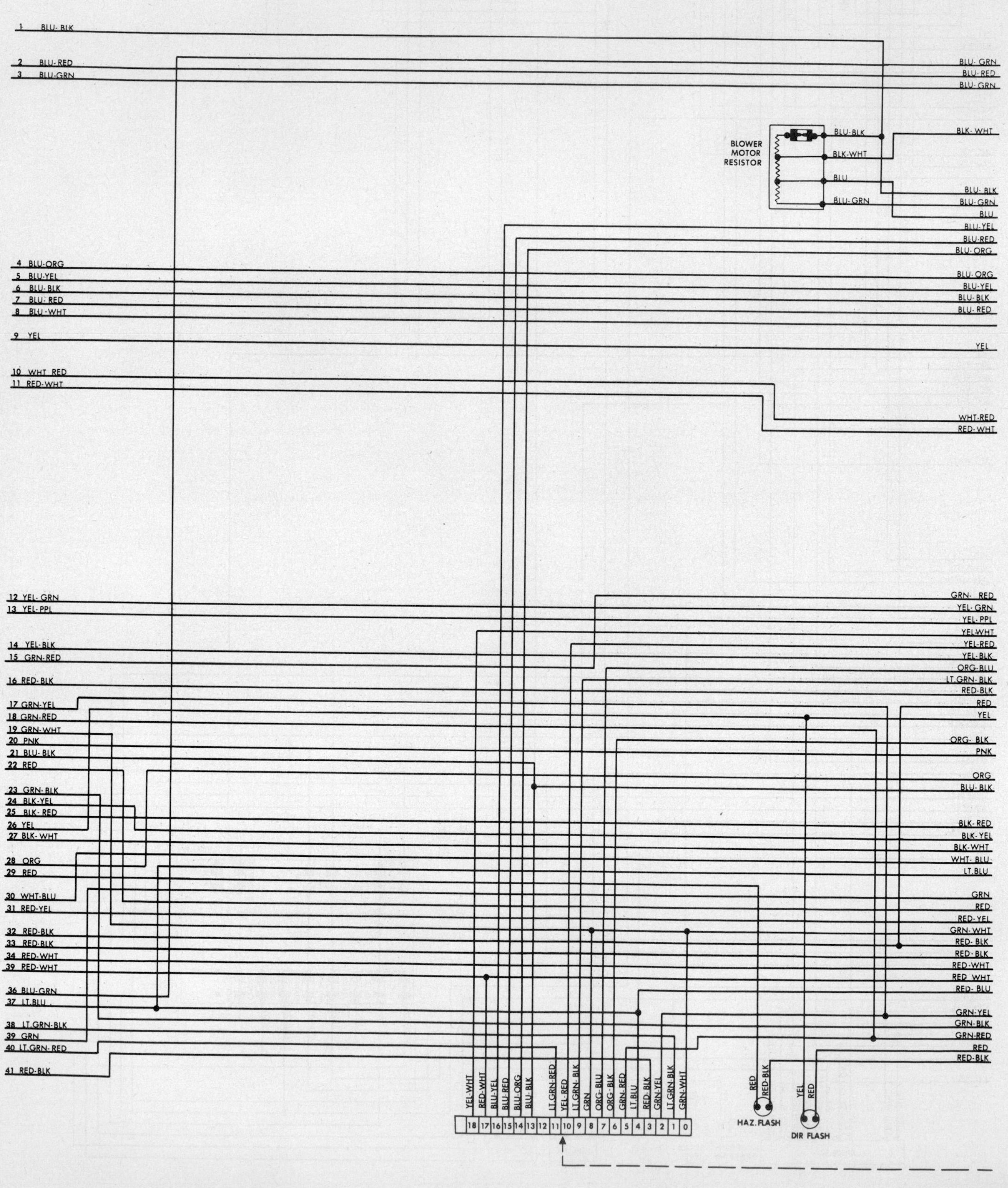
1 BLU-BLK
2 BLU-RED
3 BLU-GRN
BLU-GRN
BLU-RED
BLU-GRN
BLOWER MOTOR RESISTOR
BLU-BLK
BLK-WHT
BLU
BLU-GRN
BLK-WHT
BLU-BLK
BLU-GRN
BLU
BLU-YEL
BLU-RED
BLU-ORG
4 BLU-ORG
5 BLU-YEL
6 BLU-BLK
7 BLU-RED
8 BLU-WHT
BLU-ORG
BLU-YEL
BLU-BLK
BLU-RED
9 YEL
YEL
10 WHT RED
11 RED-WHT
WHT-RED
RED-WHT
12 YEL-GRN
13 YEL-PPL
14 YEL-BLK
15 GRN-RED
16 RED-BLK
17 GRN-YEL
18 GRN-RED
19 GRN-WHT
20 PNK
21 BLU-BLK
22 RED
23 GRN-BLK
24 BLK-YEL
25 BLK-RED
26 YEL
27 BLK-WHT
28 ORG
29 RED
30 WHT-BLU
31 RED-YEL
32 RED-BLK
33 RED-BLK
34 RED-WHT
39 RED-WHT
36 BLU-GRN
37 LT.BLU
38 LT.GRN-BLK
39 GRN
40 LT.GRN-RED
41 RED-BLK
GRN-RED
YEL-GRN
YEL-PPL
YEL-WHT
YEL-RED
YEL-BLK
ORG-BLU
LT.GRN-BLK
RED-BLK
RED
YEL
ORG-BLK
PNK
ORG
BLU-BLK
BLK-RED
BLK-YEL
BLK-WHT
WHT-BLU
LT.BLU
GRN
RED
RED-YEL
GRN-WHT
RED-BLK
RED-BLK
RED-WHT
RED WHT
RED-BLU
GRN-YEL
GRN-BLK
GRN-RED
RED
RED-BLK
YEL-WHT
RED-WHT
BLU-YEL
BLU-RED
BLU-ORG
BLU-BLK
LT.GRN-RED
YEL-RED
LT.GRN-BLK
GRN
ORG-BLU
ORG-BLK
GRN-RED
LT.BLU
RED-BLK
GRN-YEL
LT.GRN-BLK
GRN-WHT
18 17 16 15 14 13 12 11 10 9 8 7 6 5 4 3 2 1 0
RED
RED-BLK
HAZ.FLASH
YEL
RED
DIR FLASH

1983 Datsun/Nissan

SENTRA GAS – EXCEPT MPG (Cont.)

INSTRUMENT PANEL & REAR COMPARTMENT

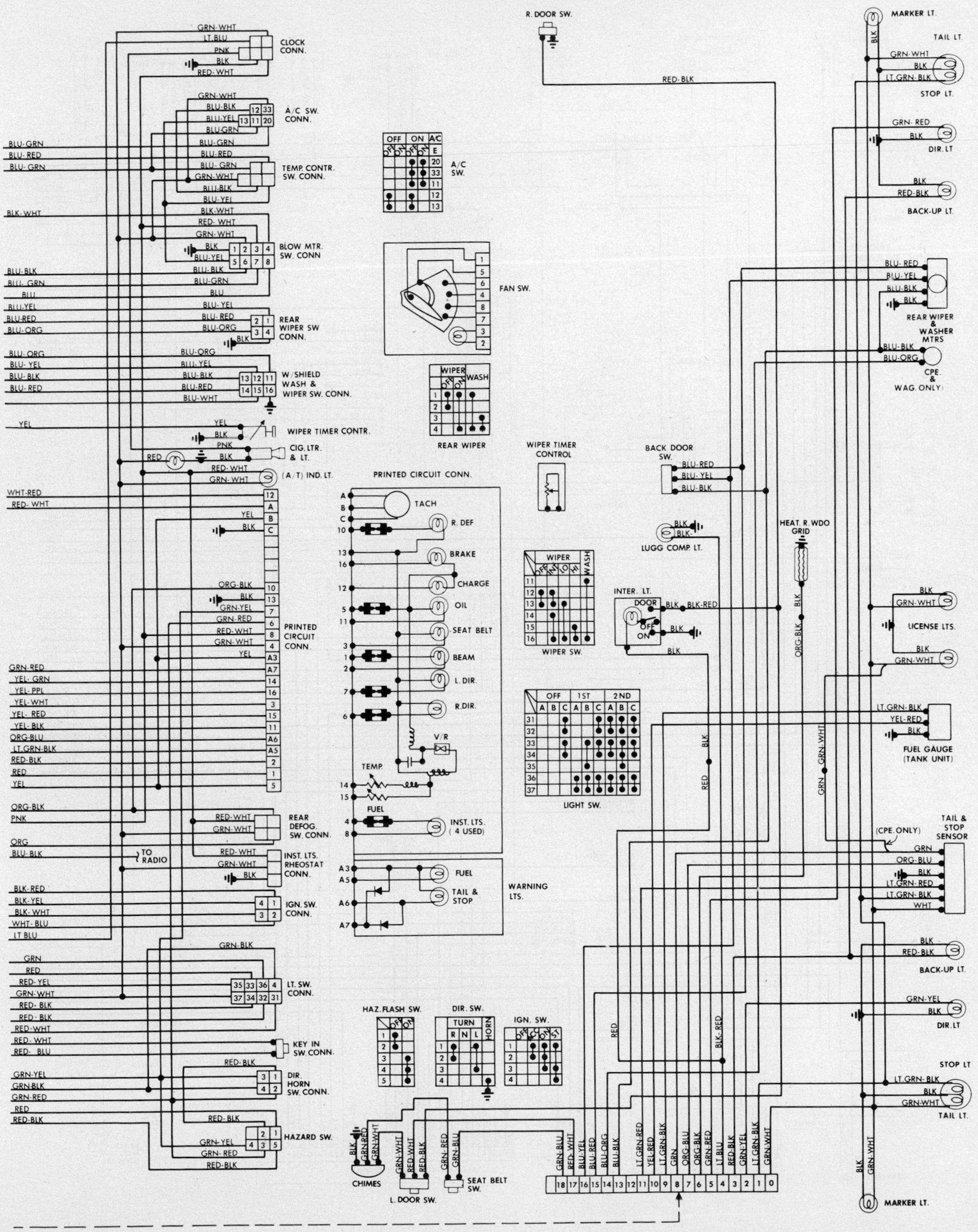

CLOCK CONN.
A/C SW. CONN.
TEMP. CONTR. SW. CONN.
BLOW MTR. SW. CONN
REAR WIPER SW CONN.
W/SHIELD WASH & WIPER SW. CONN.
WIPER TIMER CONTR.
CIG. LTR. & LT.
(A/T) IND. LT.
PRINTED CIRCUIT CONN.
REAR DEFOG. SW. CONN.
TO RADIO
INST. LTS. RHEOSTAT CONN.
IGN. SW. CONN.
LT. SW. CONN.
KEY IN SW. CONN.
DIR. HORN SW. CONN.
HAZARD SW.
A/C SW.
FAN SW.
REAR WIPER
WIPER TIMER CONTROL
TACH
R. DEF
BRAKE
CHARGE
OIL
SEAT BELT
BEAM
L. DIR.
R. DIR.
V/R
TEMP.
FUEL
INST. LTS. (4 USED)
TAIL & STOP
WARNING LTS.
WIPER SW.
LIGHT SW.
HAZ. FLASH SW.
DIR. SW.
IGN. SW.
CHIMES
L. DOOR SW.
SEAT BELT SW.
R. DOOR SW.
BACK DOOR SW.
LUGG COMP. LT.
INTER. LT.
HEAT. R. WDO GRID
MARKER LT.
TAIL LT.
STOP LT.
DIR. LT
BACK-UP LT.
REAR WIPER & WASHER MTRS
CPE. & WAG. ONLY
LICENSE LTS.
FUEL GAUGE (TANK UNIT)
TAIL & STOP SENSOR
(CPE. ONLY)

1983 Datsun/Nissan

SENTRA MPG & DIESEL

ENGINE COMPARTMENT

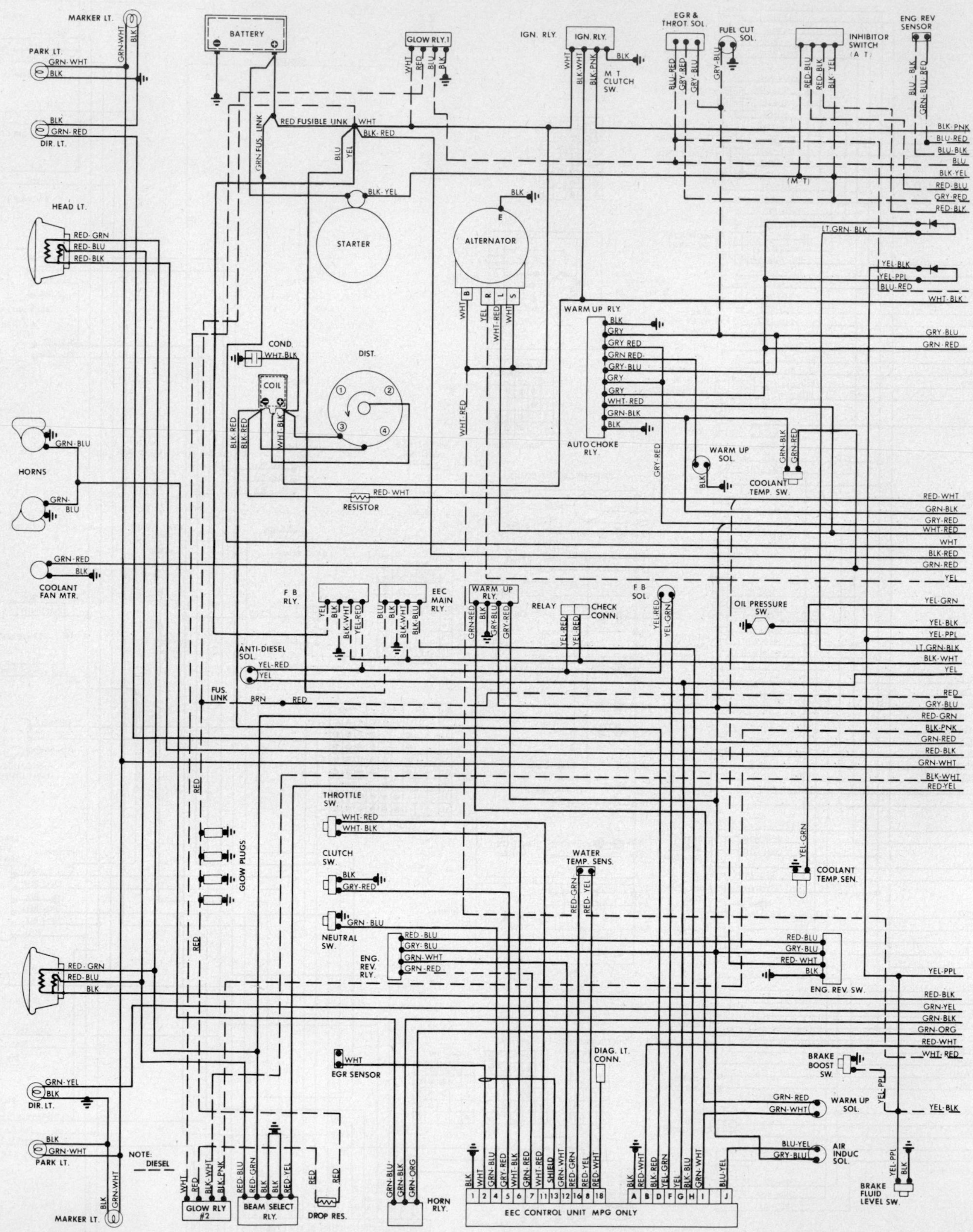
MARKER LT.
PARK LT.
DIR. LT.
HEAD LT.
HORNS
COOLANT FAN MTR.
BATTERY
GLOW RLY.1
RED FUSIBLE LINK
GRN FUS. LINK
STARTER
ALTERNATOR
IGN. RLY.
M.T. CLUTCH SW.
EGR & THROT. SOL.
FUEL CUT SOL.
INHIBITOR SWITCH (A.T.)
ENG. REV SENSOR
COND.
COIL
DIST.
RESISTOR
WARM UP RLY.
AUTO CHOKE RLY.
WARM UP SOL.
COOLANT TEMP. SW.
F.B. RLY.
EEC MAIN RLY.
RELAY
CHECK CONN.
F.B. SOL.
OIL PRESSURE SW.
ANTI-DIESEL SOL.
FUS. LINK
THROTTLE SW.
CLUTCH SW.
NEUTRAL SW.
ENG. REV. RLY.
GLOW PLUGS
WATER TEMP. SENS.
COOLANT TEMP. SEN.
ENG. REV. SW.
EGR SENSOR
DIAG. LT. CONN.
BRAKE BOOST SW.
WARM UP SOL.
AIR INDUC SOL.
BRAKE FLUID LEVEL SW.
NOTE: DIESEL
GLOW RLY #2
BEAM SELECT RLY.
DROP RES.
HORN RLY.
EEC CONTROL UNIT MPG ONLY

SENTRA MPG & DIESEL (Cont.)

FUSE BLOCK & UNDERDASH

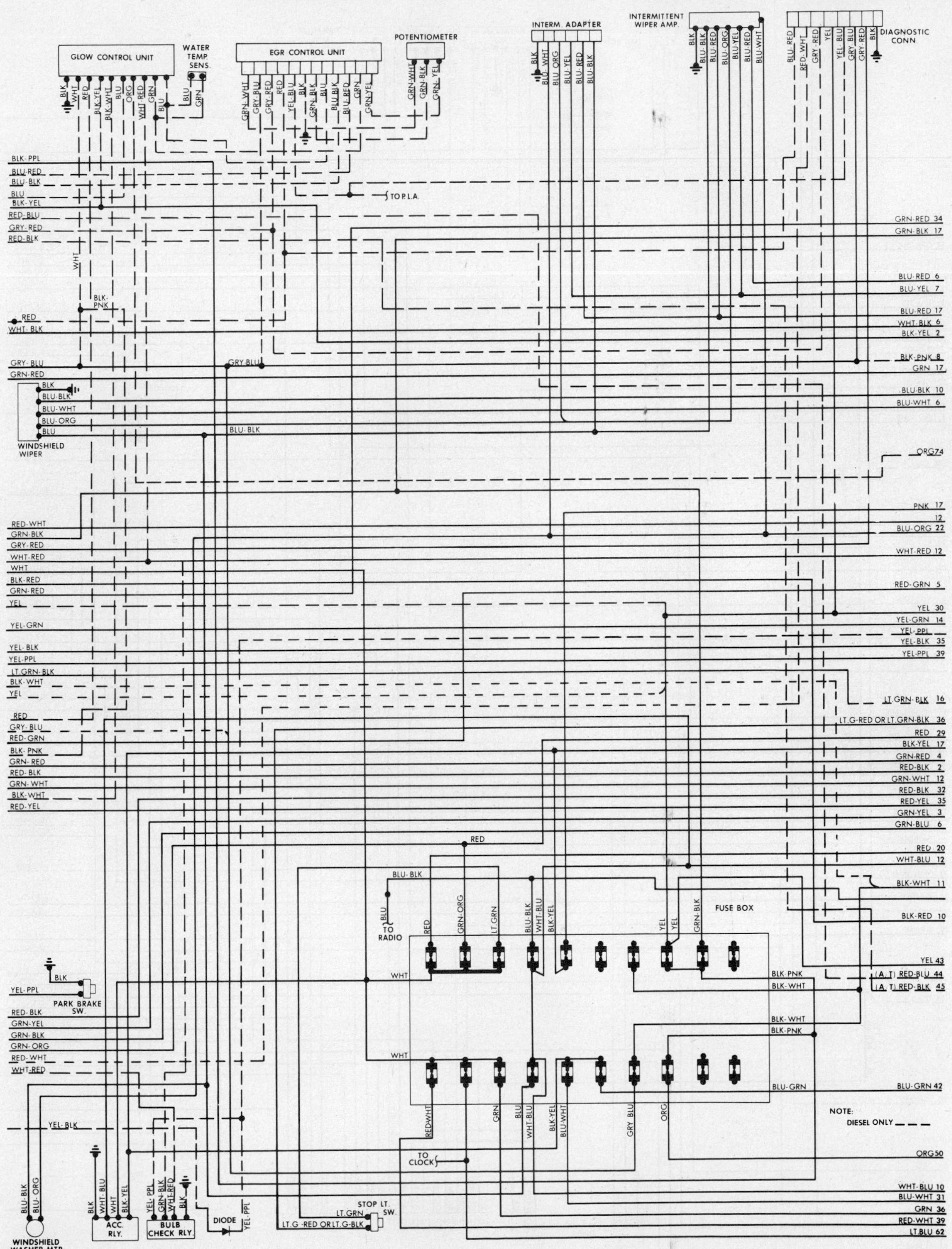

1983 Datsun/Nissan

SENTRA MPG & DIESEL (Cont.)

UNDERDASH

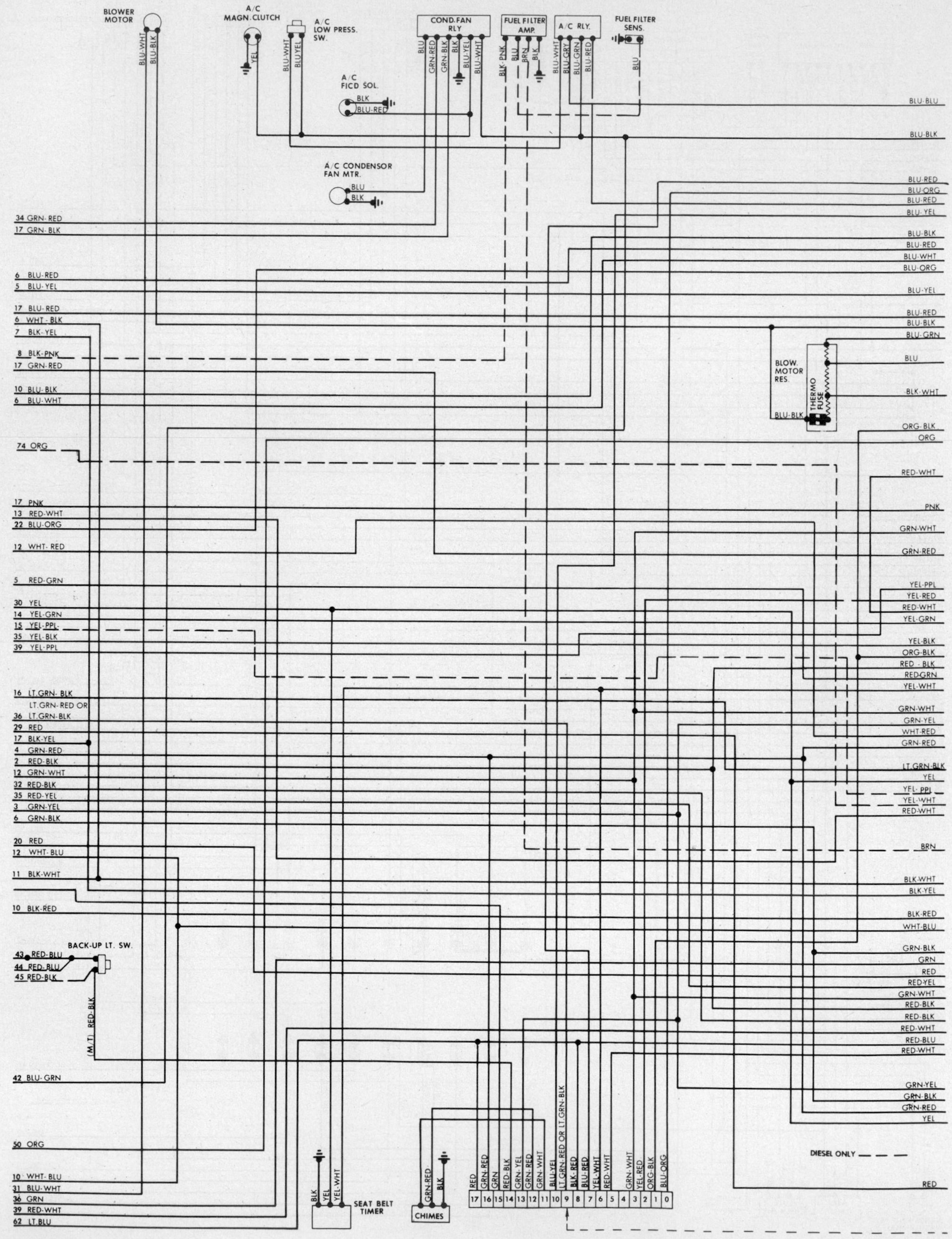
BLOWER MOTOR
A/C MAGN. CLUTCH
A/C LOW PRESS. SW.
COND. FAN RLY
FUEL FILTER AMP.
A/C RLY.
FUEL FILTER SENS.
A/C FICD SOL.
A/C CONDENSOR FAN MTR.
BLOW. MOTOR RES.
THERMO FUSE
BACK-UP LT. SW.
SEAT BELT TIMER
CHIMES
DIESEL ONLY

SENTRA MPG & DIESEL (Cont.)

INSTRUMENT PANEL & REAR COMPARTMENT

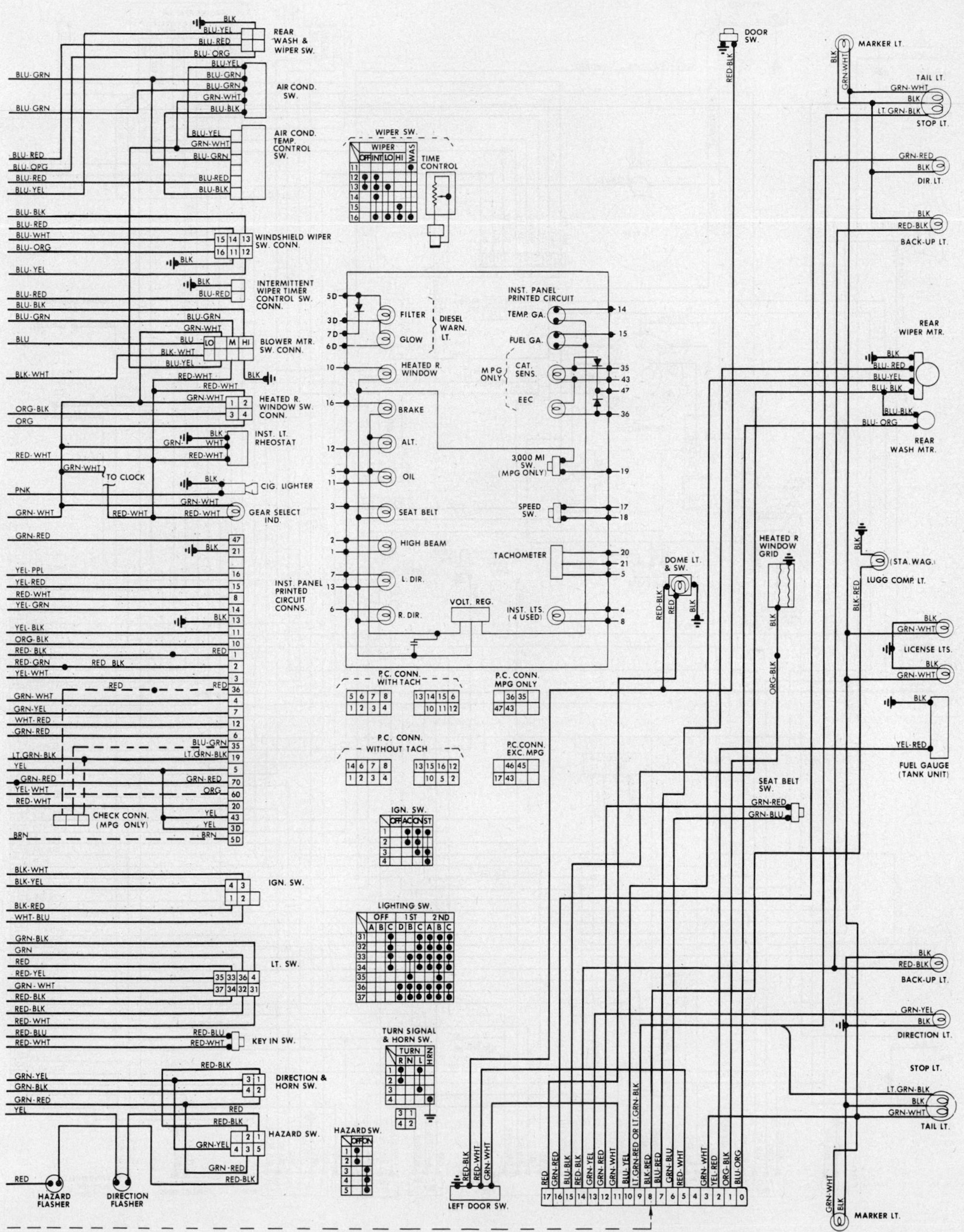
REAR WASH & WIPER SW.
AIR COND. SW.
AIR COND. TEMP. CONTROL SW.
WIPER SW.
TIME CONTROL
WINDSHIELD WIPER SW. CONN.
INTERMITTENT WIPER TIMER CONTROL SW. CONN.
BLOWER MTR. SW. CONN.
HEATED R. WINDOW SW. CONN.
INST. LT. RHEOSTAT
TO CLOCK
CIG. LIGHTER
GEAR SELECT IND.
INST. PANEL PRINTED CIRCUIT CONNS.
CHECK CONN. (MPG ONLY)
IGN. SW.
LT. SW.
KEY IN SW.
DIRECTION & HORN SW.
HAZARD SW.
HAZARD FLASHER
DIRECTION FLASHER
FILTER
GLOW
DIESEL WARN. LT.
HEATED R. WINDOW
BRAKE
ALT.
OIL
SEAT BELT
HIGH BEAM
L. DIR.
R. DIR.
VOLT. REG.
INST. PANEL PRINTED CIRCUIT
TEMP. GA.
FUEL GA.
MPG ONLY
CAT. SENS.
EEC
3,000 MI SW. (MPG ONLY)
SPEED SW.
TACHOMETER
INST. LTS. (4 USED)
P.C. CONN. WITH TACH
P.C. CONN. MPG ONLY
P.C. CONN. WITHOUT TACH
P.C. CONN. EXC. MPG
IGN. SW.
LIGHTING SW.
TURN SIGNAL & HORN SW.
HAZARD SW.
LEFT DOOR SW.
DOOR SW.
DOME LT. & SW.
HEATED R WINDOW GRID
SEAT BELT SW.
MARKER LT.
TAIL LT.
STOP LT.
DIR. LT.
BACK-UP LT.
REAR WIPER MTR.
REAR WASH MTR.
(STA. WAG.)
LUGG COMP. LT.
LICENSE LTS.
FUEL GAUGE (TANK UNIT)
BACK-UP LT.
DIRECTION LT.
STOP LT.
TAIL LT.
MARKER LT.

1983 Datsun/Nissan

STANZA

ENGINE COMPARTMENT

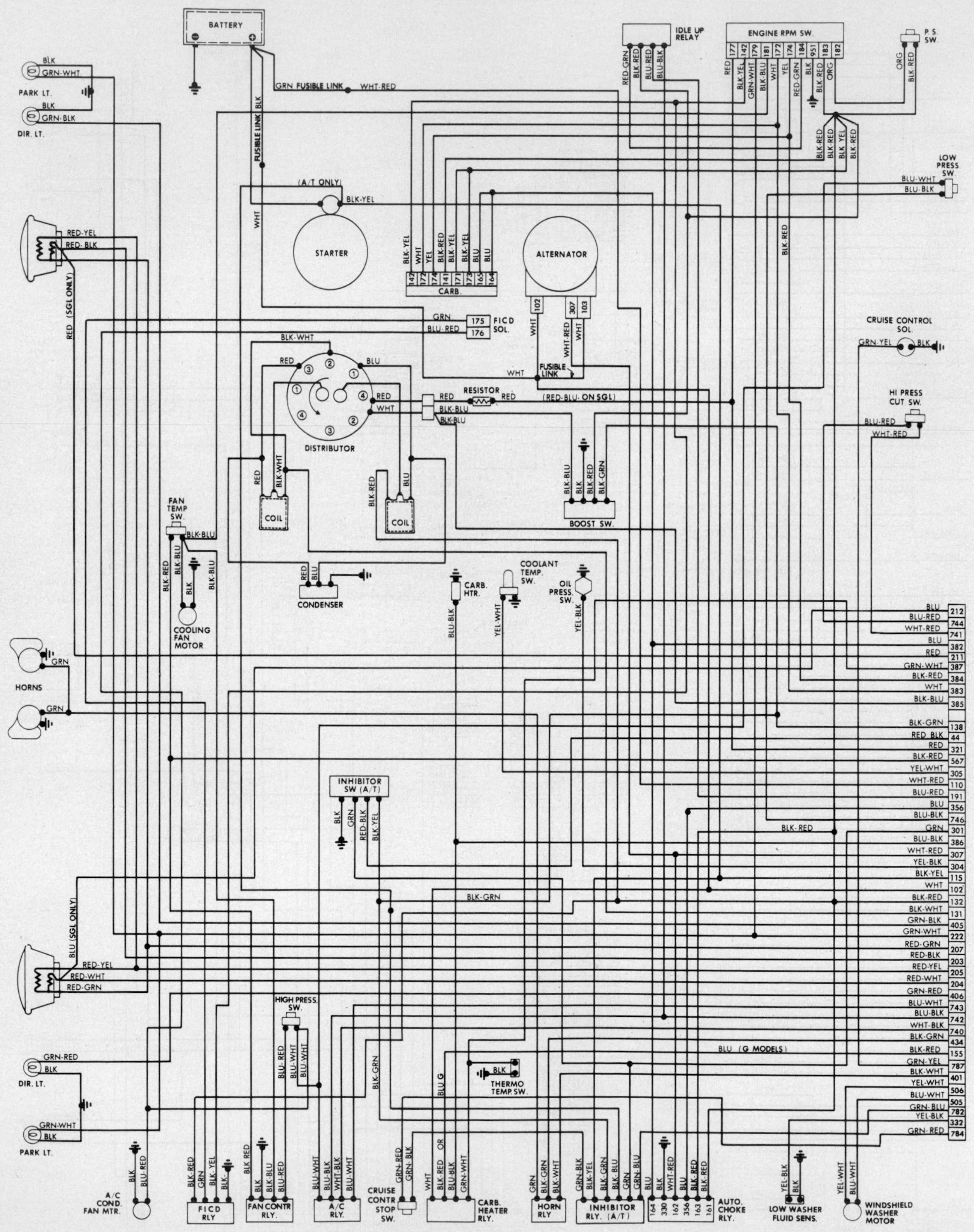
BATTERY
PARK LT.
DIR. LT.
STARTER
ALTERNATOR
CARB.
FICD SOL.
DISTRIBUTOR
RESISTOR
COIL
CONDENSER
BOOST SW.
FAN TEMP SW.
COOLING FAN MOTOR
HORNS
CARB. HTR.
COOLANT TEMP. SW.
OIL PRESS. SW.
IDLE UP RELAY
ENGINE RPM SW.
P.S. SW.
LOW PRESS SW.
CRUISE CONTROL SOL.
HI PRESS CUT SW.
INHIBITOR SW (A/T)
HIGH PRESS. SW.
THERMO TEMP SW.
A/C COND. FAN MTR.
FICD RLY
FAN CONTR RLY.
A/C RLY.
CRUISE CONTR STOP SW.
CARB. HEATER RLY.
HORN RLY
INHIBITOR RLY. (A/T)
AUTO. CHOKE RLY.
LOW WASHER FLUID SENS.
WINDSHIELD WASHER MOTOR

STANZA (Cont.)

FUSE BLOCK & UNDERDASH

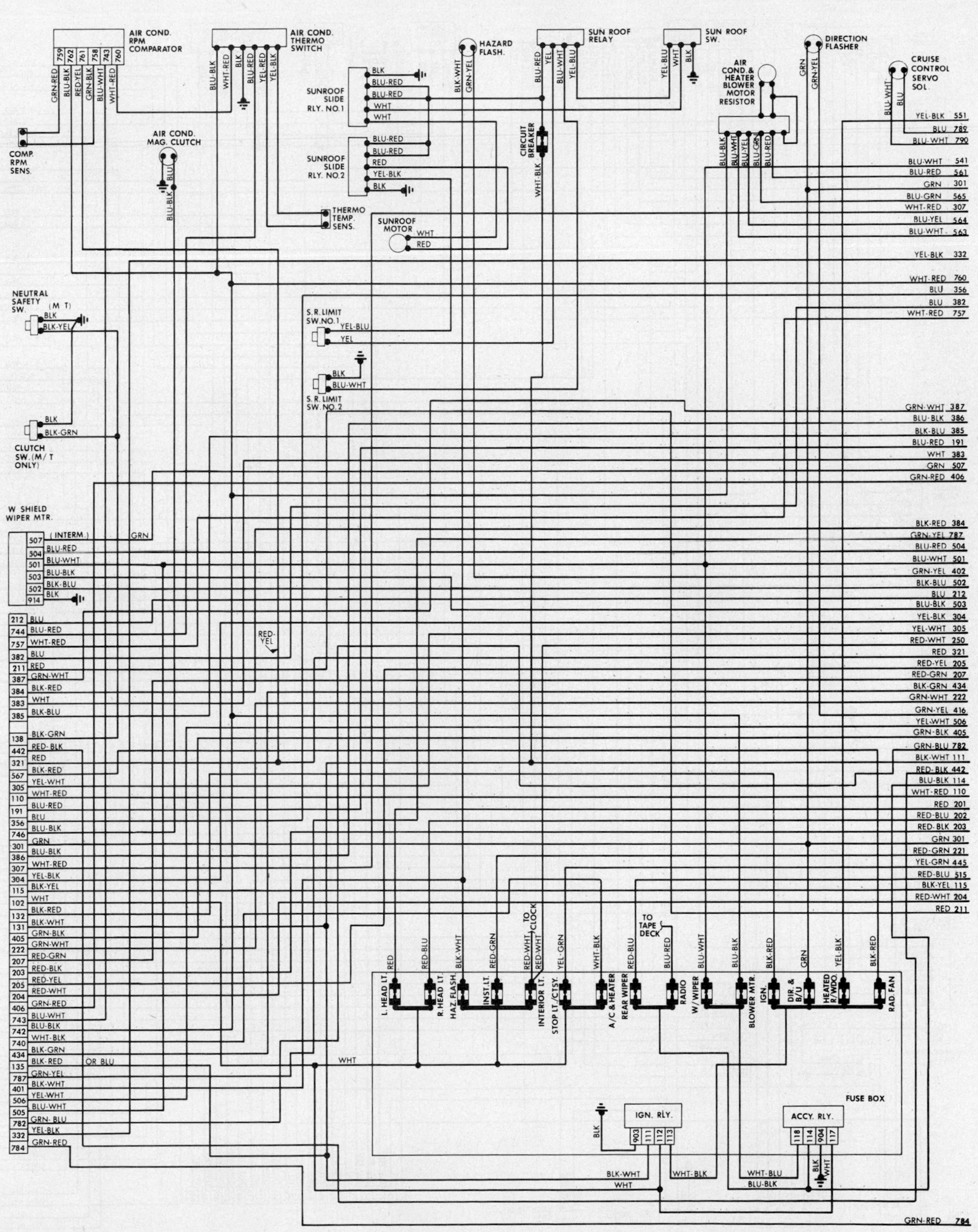

1983 Datsun/Nissan

STANZA (Cont.)

UNDERDASH

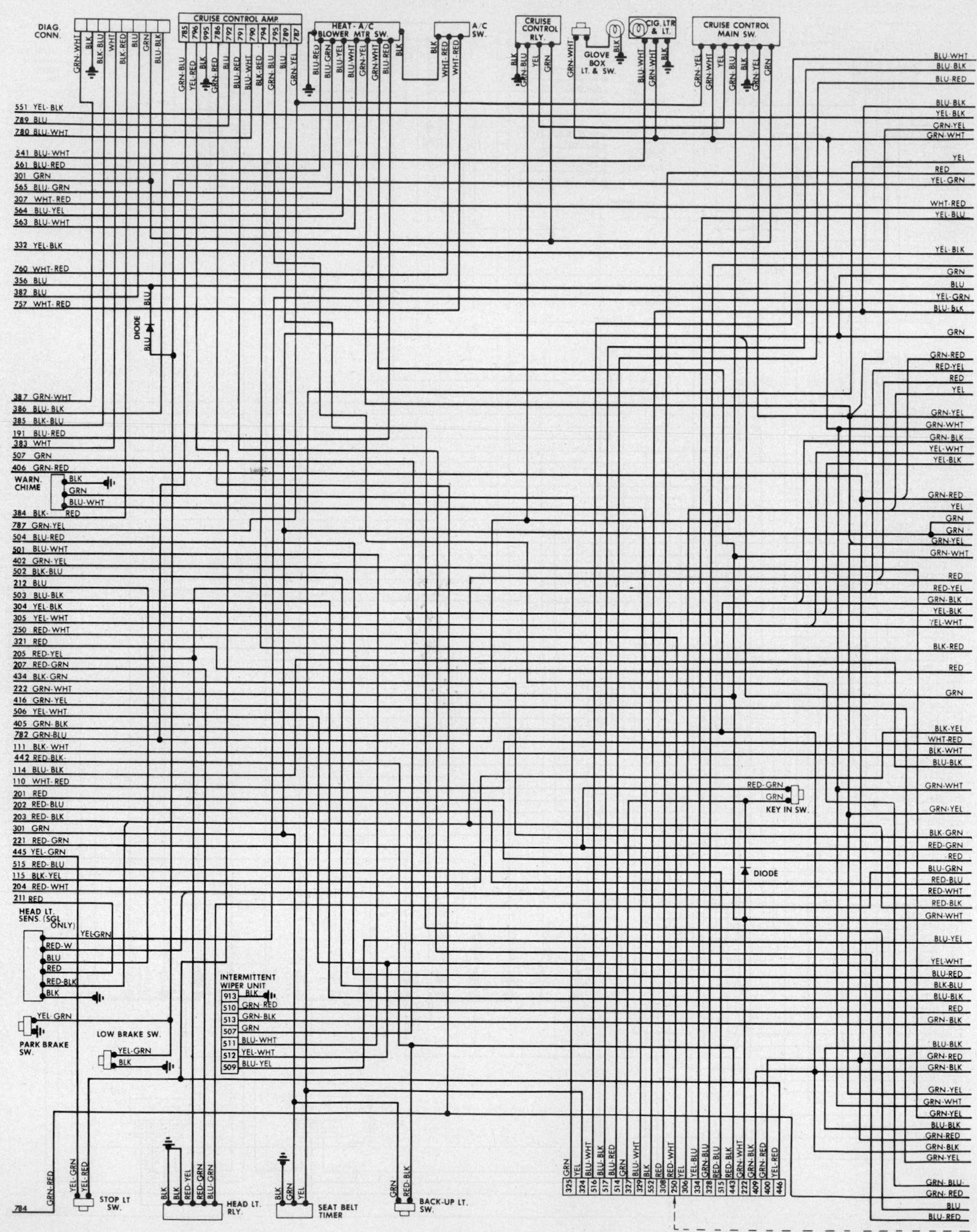

1983 Datsun/Nissan

STANZA (Cont.)

INSTRUMENT PANEL, UNDERDASH & REAR COMPARTMENT

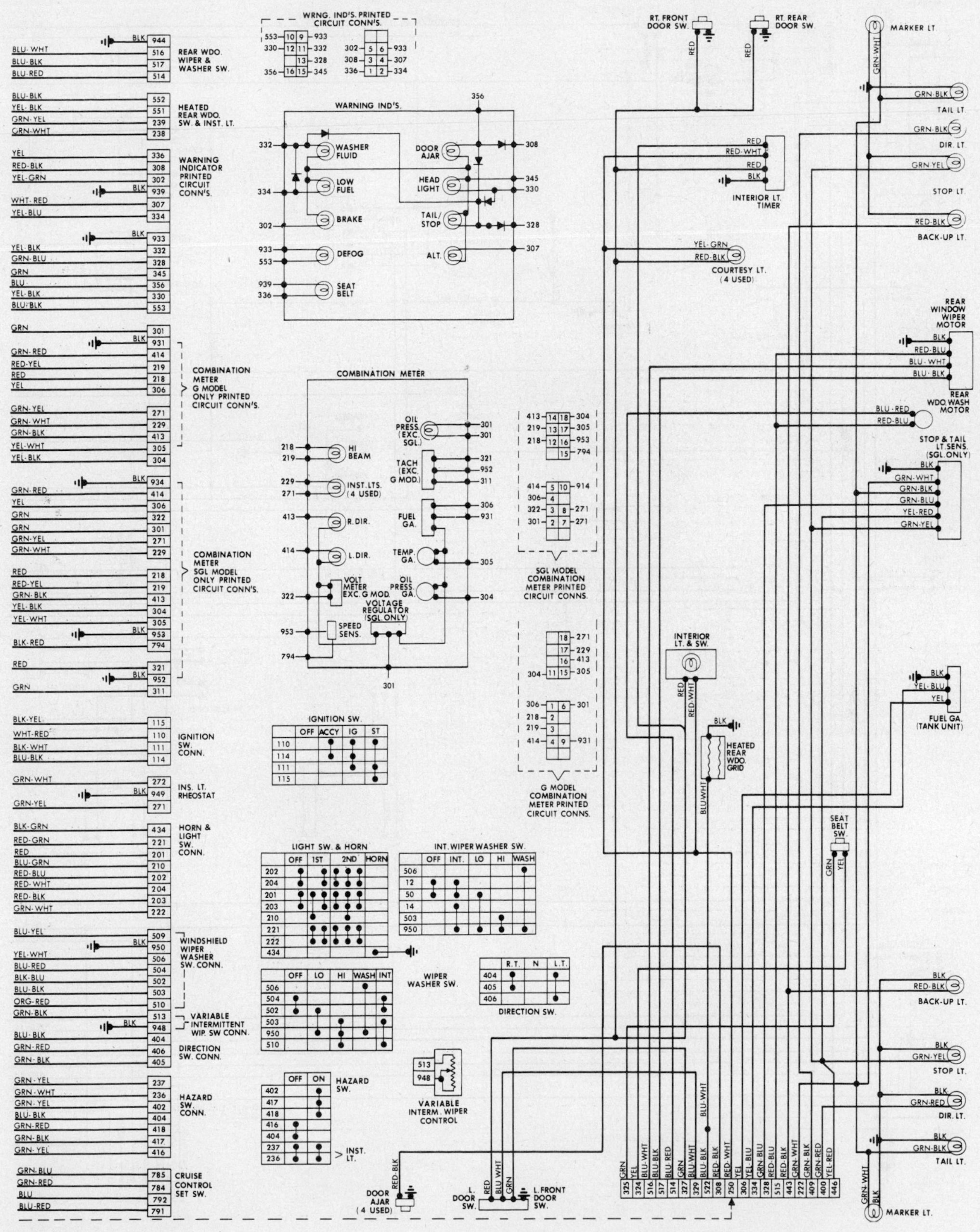

REAR WDO. WIPER & WASHER SW.
HEATED REAR WDO. SW. & INST. LT.
WARNING INDICATOR PRINTED CIRCUIT CONN'S.
COMBINATION METER G MODEL ONLY PRINTED CIRCUIT CONN'S.
COMBINATION METER SGL MODEL ONLY PRINTED CIRCUIT CONN'S.
IGNITION SW. CONN.
INS. LT. RHEOSTAT
HORN & LIGHT SW. CONN.
WINDSHIELD WIPER WASHER SW. CONN.
VARIABLE INTERMITTENT WIP. SW CONN.
DIRECTION SW. CONN.
HAZARD SW. CONN.
CRUISE CONTROL SET SW.
WRNG. IND'S. PRINTED CIRCUIT CONN'S.
WARNING IND'S.
WASHER FLUID
LOW FUEL
BRAKE
DEFOG
SEAT BELT
DOOR AJAR
HEAD LIGHT
TAIL/STOP
ALT.
COMBINATION METER
OIL PRESS. (EXC. SGL.)
HI BEAM
TACH (EXC. G MOD.)
INST. LTS. (4 USED)
FUEL GA.
R. DIR.
L. DIR.
TEMP. GA.
VOLT METER EXC. G MOD.
OIL PRESS. GA.
VOLTAGE REGULATOR (SGL ONLY)
SPEED SENS.
SGL MODEL COMBINATION METER PRINTED CIRCUIT CONNS.
G MODEL COMBINATION METER PRINTED CIRCUIT CONNS.
IGNITION SW.
OFF ACCY IG ST
LIGHT SW. & HORN
OFF 1ST 2ND HORN
INT. WIPER WASHER SW.
OFF INT. LO HI WASH
WIPER WASHER SW.
OFF LO HI WASH INT
DIRECTION SW.
R.T. N L.T.
HAZARD SW.
OFF ON
INST. LT.
VARIABLE INTERM. WIPER CONTROL
DOOR AJAR (4 USED)
L. DOOR SW.
L. FRONT DOOR SW.
RT. FRONT DOOR SW.
RT. REAR DOOR SW.
INTERIOR LT. TIMER
COURTESY LT. (4 USED)
INTERIOR LT. & SW.
HEATED REAR WDO. GRID
SEAT BELT SW.
MARKER LT.
TAIL LT.
DIR. LT.
STOP LT.
BACK-UP LT.
REAR WINDOW WIPER MOTOR
REAR WDO. WASH MOTOR
STOP & TAIL LT. SENS. (SGL. ONLY)
FUEL GA. (TANK UNIT)

1983 Honda

ACCORD

ENGINE COMPARTMENT

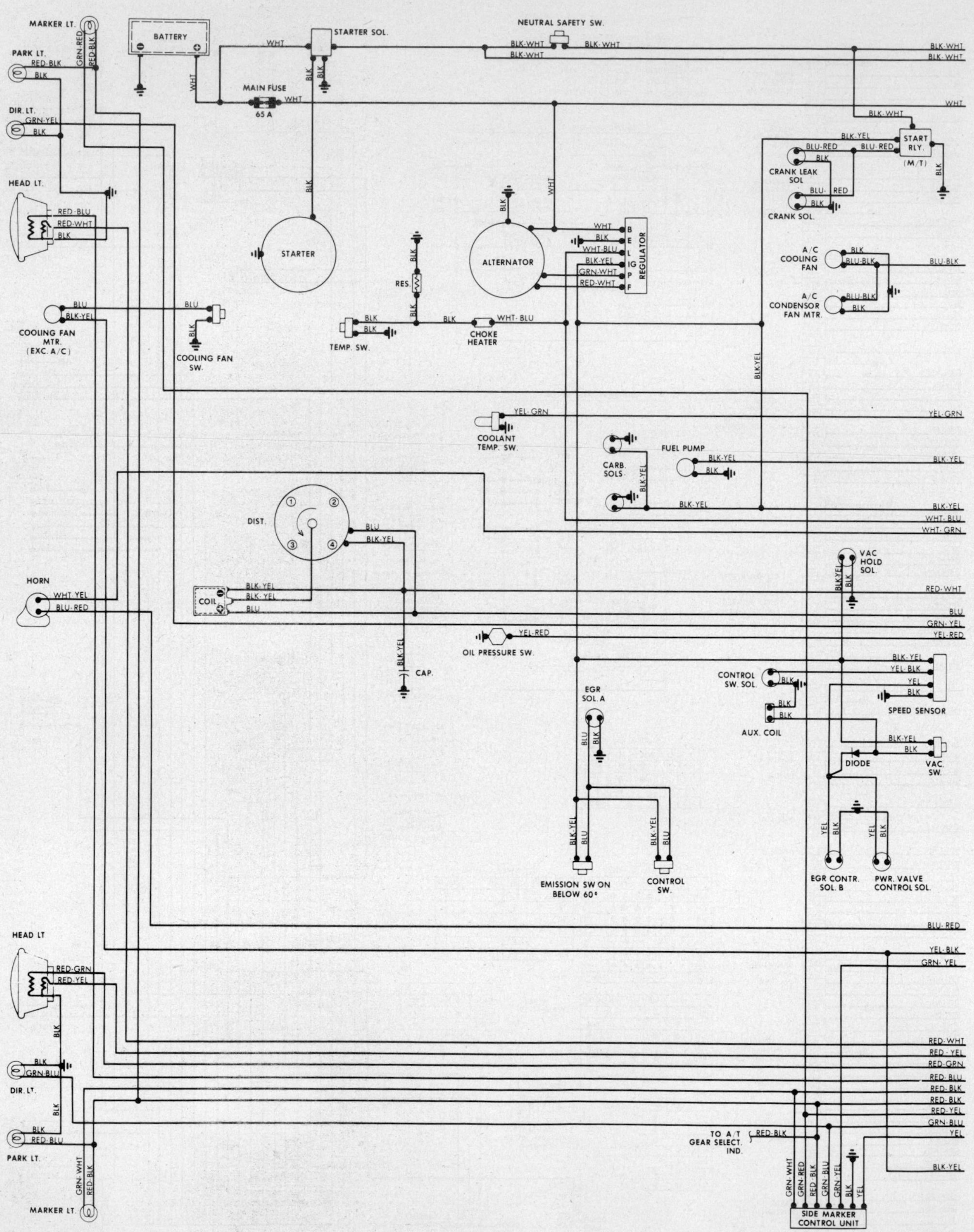

MARKER LT.
PARK LT.
DIR. LT.
HEAD LT.
BATTERY
STARTER SOL.
MAIN FUSE
65 A
NEUTRAL SAFETY SW.
START RLY.
(M/T)
CRANK LEAK SOL
CRANK SOL.
STARTER
ALTERNATOR
REGULATOR
RES.
A/C COOLING FAN
A/C CONDENSOR FAN MTR.
COOLING FAN MTR. (EXC. A/C)
COOLING FAN SW.
TEMP. SW.
CHOKE HEATER
COOLANT TEMP. SW.
CARB. SOLS
FUEL PUMP
DIST.
HORN
COIL
CAP.
OIL PRESSURE SW.
VAC HOLD SOL.
CONTROL SW. SOL.
AUX. COIL
SPEED SENSOR
EGR SOL. A
DIODE
VAC. SW.
EMISSION SW ON BELOW 60°
CONTROL SW.
EGR CONTR. SOL. B
PWR. VALVE CONTROL SOL.
HEAD LT
DIR. LT.
PARK LT.
MARKER LT.
TO A/T GEAR SELECT. IND.
SIDE MARKER CONTROL UNIT

1983 Honda

ACCORD (Cont.)

FUSE BLOCK & UNDERDASH

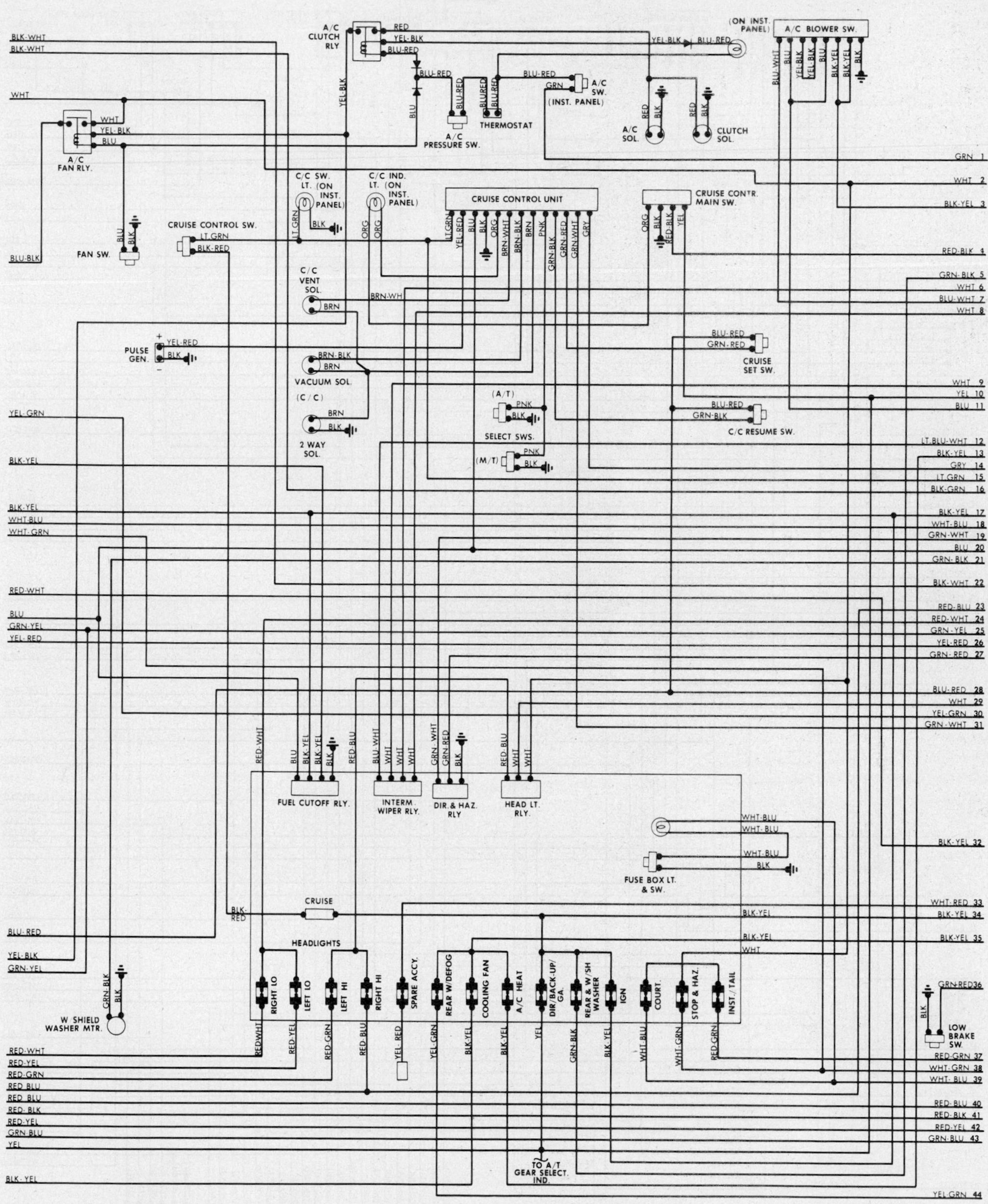
A/C CLUTCH RLY
A/C FAN RLY.
FAN SW.
CRUISE CONTROL SW.
C/C SW. LT. (ON INST. PANEL)
C/C IND. LT. (ON INST. PANEL)
A/C PRESSURE SW.
THERMOSTAT
A/C SW. (INST. PANEL)
(ON INST. PANEL) A/C BLOWER SW.
A/C SOL.
CLUTCH SOL.
CRUISE CONTROL UNIT
CRUISE CONTR. MAIN SW.
C/C VENT SOL.
PULSE GEN.
VACUUM SOL.
(C/C)
2 WAY SOL.
CRUISE SET SW.
(A/T)
SELECT SWS.
(M/T)
C/C RESUME SW.
FUEL CUTOFF RLY.
INTERM. WIPER RLY.
DIR. & HAZ. RLY
HEAD LT. RLY.
FUSE BOX LT. & SW.
CRUISE
HEADLIGHTS
RIGHT LO
LEFT LO
LEFT HI
RIGHT HI
SPARE ACCY.
REAR W/DEFOG
COOLING FAN
A/C HEAT
DIR/BACK-UP/GA.
REAR & W/SH WASHER
IGN
COURT.
STOP & HAZ.
INST./TAIL
W SHIELD WASHER MTR.
LOW BRAKE SW.
TO A/T GEAR SELECT. IND.
GRN 1
WHT 2
BLK-YEL 3
RED-BLK 4
GRN-BLK 5
WHT 6
BLU-WHT 7
WHT 8
WHT 9
YEL 10
BLU 11
LT.BLU-WHT 12
BLK-YEL 13
GRY 14
LT.GRN 15
BLK-GRN 16
BLK-YEL 17
WHT-BLU 18
GRN-WHT 19
BLU 20
GRN-BLK 21
BLK-WHT 22
RED-BLU 23
RED-WHT 24
GRN-YEL 25
YEL-RED 26
GRN-RED 27
BLU-RED 28
WHT 29
YEL-GRN 30
GRN-WHT 31
BLK-YEL 32
WHT-RED 33
BLK-YEL 34
BLK-YEL 35
GRN-RED 36
RED-GRN 37
WHT-GRN 38
WHT-BLU 39
RED-BLU 40
RED-BLK 41
RED-YEL 42
GRN-BLU 43
YEL-GRN 44

1983 Honda

ACCORD (Cont.)

UNDERDASH

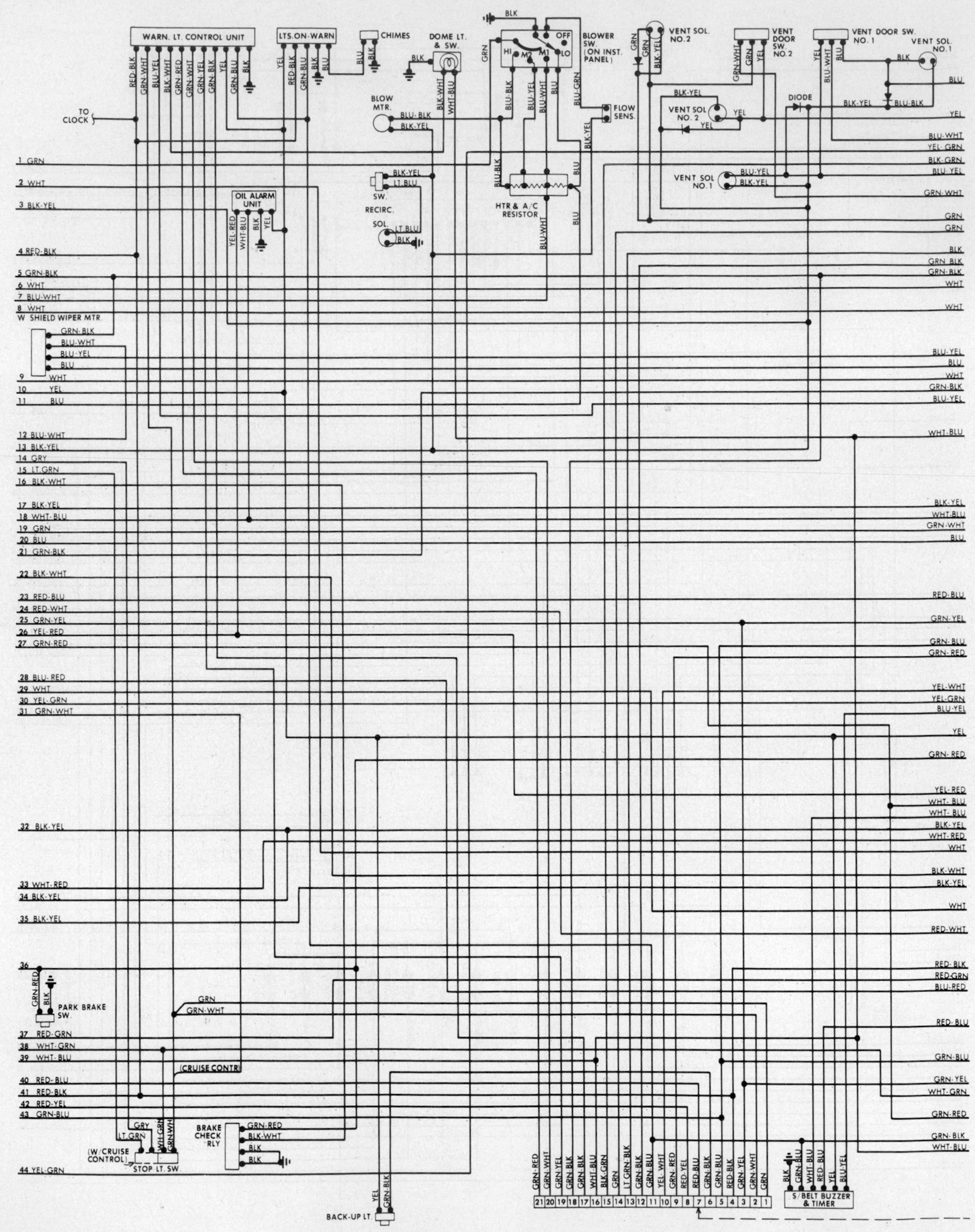

WARN. LT. CONTROL UNIT
LTS.ON-WARN
CHIMES
DOME LT. & SW.
BLOWER SW. (ON INST. PANEL)
VENT SOL. NO. 2
VENT DOOR SW. NO. 2
VENT DOOR SW. NO. 1
VENT SOL. NO. 1
TO CLOCK
BLOW MTR.
FLOW SENS.
DIODE
SW.
RECIRC. SOL.
OIL ALARM UNIT
HTR & A/C RESISTOR
W SHIELD WIPER MTR.
PARK BRAKE SW.
(CRUISE CONTR)
(W/CRUISE CONTROL)
STOP LT. SW.
BRAKE CHECK RLY
BACK-UP LT.
S/BELT BUZZER & TIMER

ACCORD (Cont.)

INSTRUMENT PANEL & REAR COMPARTMENT

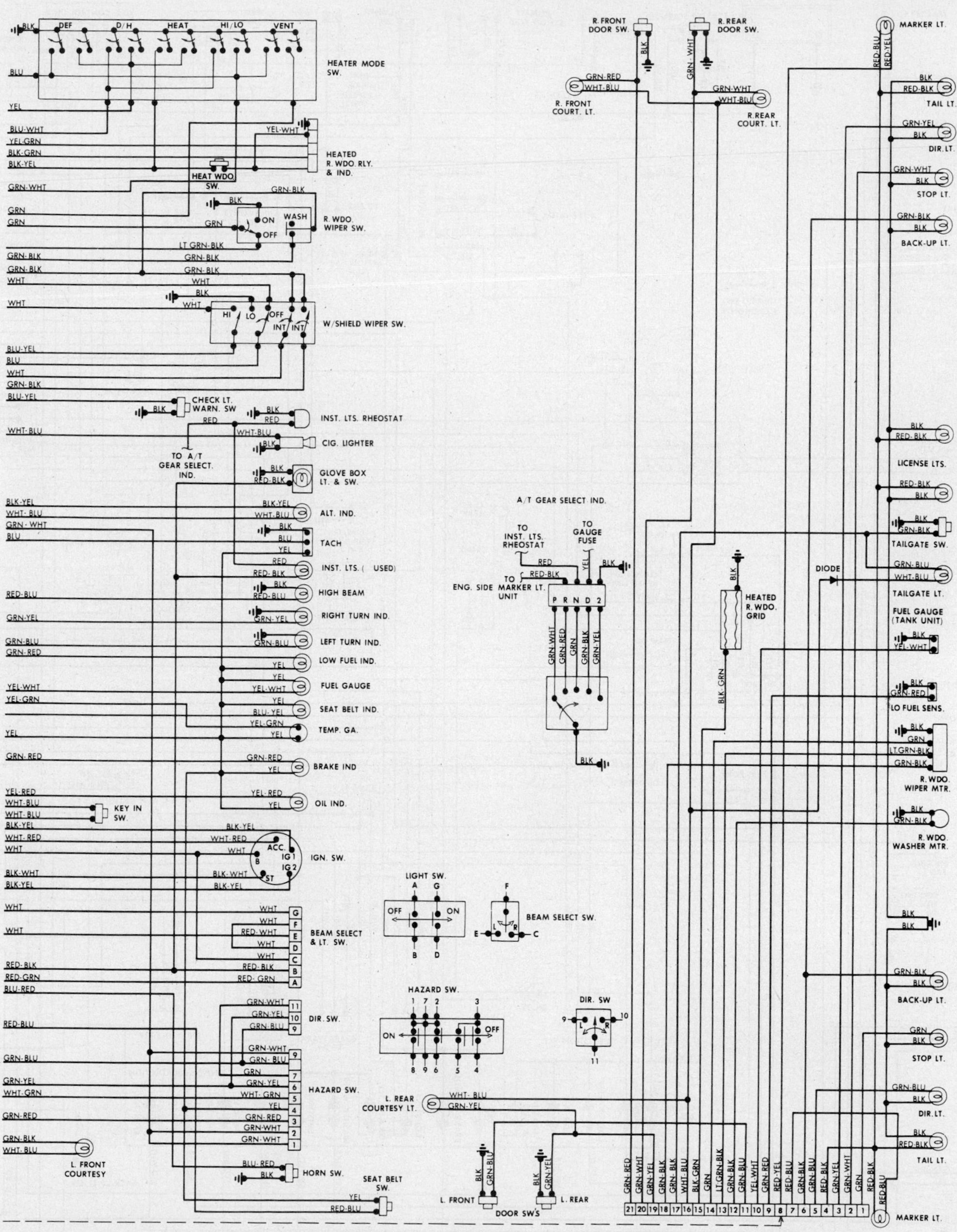

HEATER MODE SW.
DEF
D/H
HEAT
HI/LO
VENT
HEATED R. WDO. RLY. & IND.
HEAT WDO. SW.
R. WDO. WIPER SW.
WASH
ON
OFF
W/SHIELD WIPER SW.
HI
LO
INT
CHECK LT. WARN. SW
INST. LTS. RHEOSTAT
CIG. LIGHTER
TO A/T GEAR SELECT. IND.
GLOVE BOX LT. & SW.
ALT. IND.
TACH
INST. LTS. (USED)
HIGH BEAM
RIGHT TURN IND.
LEFT TURN IND.
LOW FUEL IND.
FUEL GAUGE
SEAT BELT IND.
TEMP. GA.
BRAKE IND
OIL IND.
KEY IN SW.
IGN. SW.
ACC.
IG1
IG2
ST
BEAM SELECT & LT. SW.
DIR. SW.
HAZARD SW.
L. FRONT COURTESY
HORN SW.
SEAT BELT SW.
LIGHT SW.
BEAM SELECT SW.
HAZARD SW.
DIR. SW.
L. REAR COURTESY LT.
L. FRONT
L. REAR
DOOR SW'S
A/T GEAR SELECT IND.
TO INST. LTS. RHEOSTAT
TO GAUGE FUSE
TO ENG. SIDE MARKER LT. UNIT
P R N D 2
HEATED R. WDO. GRID
DIODE
R. FRONT DOOR SW.
R. REAR DOOR SW.
R. FRONT COURT. LT.
R. REAR COURT. LT.
MARKER LT.
TAIL LT.
DIR. LT.
STOP LT.
BACK-UP LT.
LICENSE LTS.
TAILGATE SW.
TAILGATE LT.
FUEL GAUGE (TANK UNIT)
LO FUEL SENS.
R. WDO. WIPER MTR.
R. WDO. WASHER MTR.
BACK-UP LT.
STOP LT.
DIR. LT.
TAIL LT.
MARKER LT.

1983 Honda

CIVIC

ENGINE COMPARTMENT & FUSE BLOCK

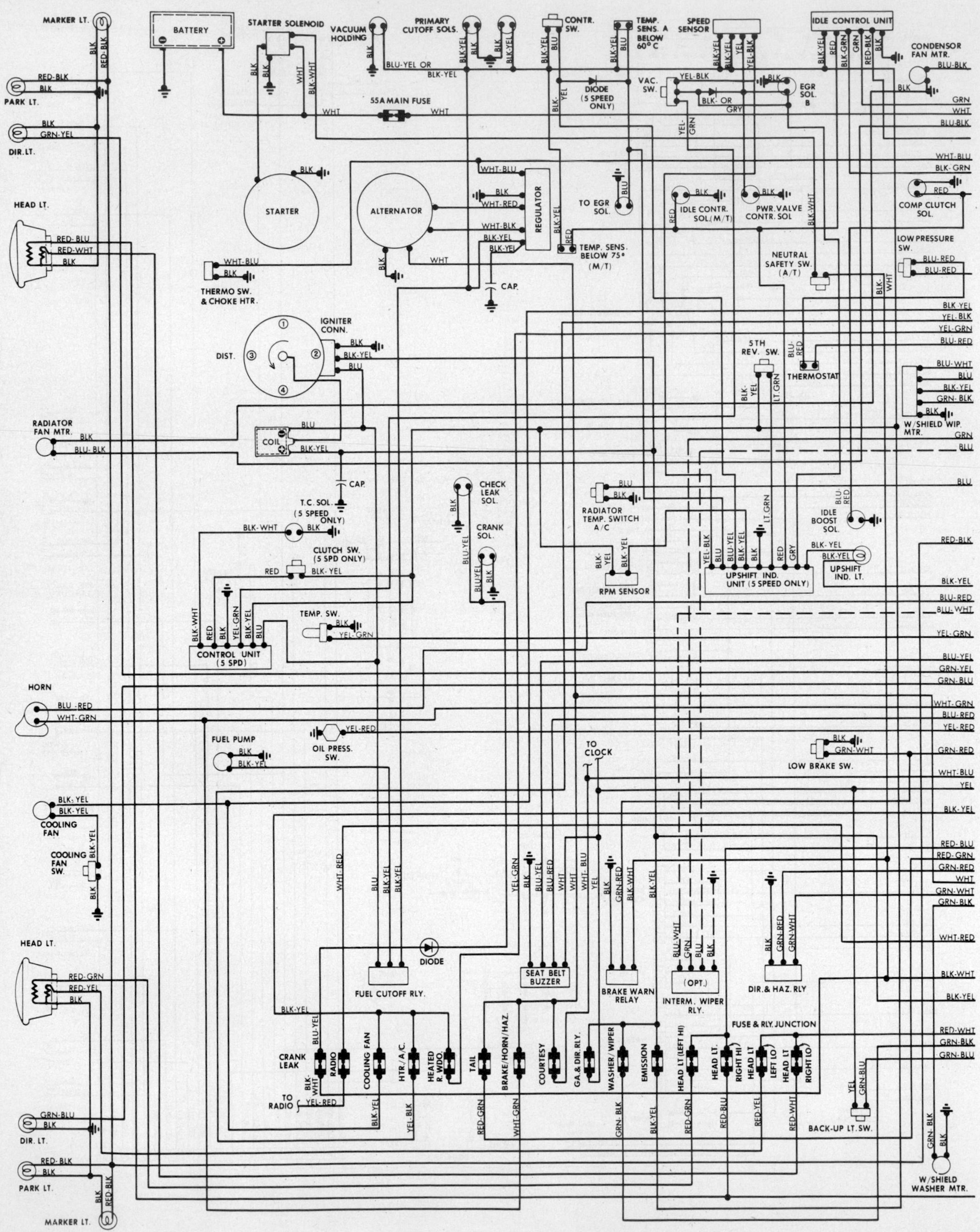
MARKER LT.
BATTERY
STARTER SOLENOID
VACUUM HOLDING
PRIMARY CUTOFF SOLS.
CONTR. SW.
TEMP. SENS. A BELOW 60° C
SPEED SENSOR
IDLE CONTROL UNIT
CONDENSOR FAN MTR.
PARK LT.
DIR. LT.
55A MAIN FUSE
DIODE (5 SPEED ONLY)
VAC. SW.
EGR SOL. B
HEAD LT.
STARTER
ALTERNATOR
REGULATOR
TO EGR SOL.
IDLE CONTR. SOL.(M/T)
PWR. VALVE CONTR. SOL
COMP CLUTCH SOL.
TEMP. SENS. BELOW 75° (M/T)
LOW PRESSURE SW.
NEUTRAL SAFETY SW. (A/T)
THERMO SW. & CHOKE HTR.
CAP.
IGNITER CONN.
DIST.
5TH REV. SW.
THERMOSTAT
W/SHIELD WIP. MTR.
RADIATOR FAN MTR.
COIL
CAP.
T.C. SOL. (5 SPEED ONLY)
CHECK LEAK SOL.
RADIATOR TEMP. SWITCH A/C
IDLE BOOST SOL.
CRANK SOL.
CLUTCH SW. (5 SPD ONLY)
UPSHIFT IND. UNIT (5 SPEED ONLY)
UPSHIFT IND. LT.
RPM SENSOR
TEMP. SW.
CONTROL UNIT (5 SPD)
HORN
FUEL PUMP
OIL PRESS. SW.
TO CLOCK
LOW BRAKE SW.
COOLING FAN
COOLING FAN SW.
DIODE
FUEL CUTOFF RLY.
SEAT BELT BUZZER
BRAKE WARN RELAY
(OPT.)
INTERM. WIPER RLY.
DIR. & HAZ. RLY
FUSE & RLY. JUNCTION
CRANK LEAK
RADIO
COOLING FAN
HTR/A/C
HEATED R. WDO.
TAIL
BRAKE/HORN/HAZ.
COURTESY
GA. & DIR. RLY.
WASHER/WIPER
EMISSION
HEAD LT (LEFT HI)
HEAD LT. RIGHT HI
HEAD LT LEFT LO
HEAD LT RIGHT LO
TO RADIO
BACK-UP LT. SW.
W/SHIELD WASHER MTR.

1983 Honda

CIVIC (Cont.)

INSTRUMENT PANEL, UNDERDASH & REAR COMPARTMENT

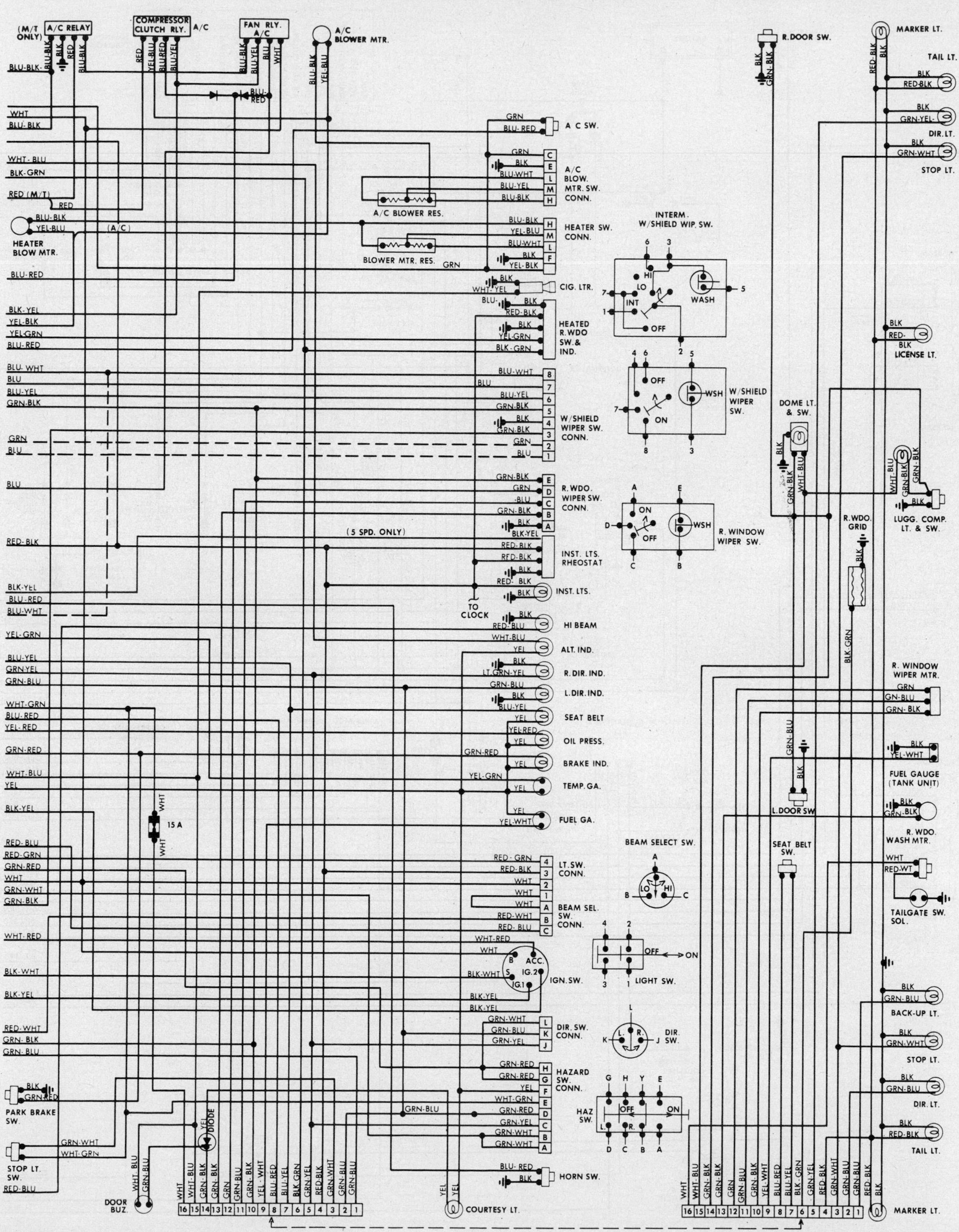
(M/T ONLY)
A/C RELAY
COMPRESSOR CLUTCH RLY.
A/C
FAN RLY. A/C
A/C BLOWER MTR.
A C SW.
A/C BLOW. MTR. SW. CONN.
A/C BLOWER RES.
HEATER BLOW MTR.
HEATER SW. CONN.
BLOWER MTR. RES.
CIG. LTR.
HEATED R.WDO SW. & IND.
W/SHIELD WIPER SW. CONN.
R. WDO. WIPER SW. CONN.
(5 SPD. ONLY)
INST. LTS. RHEOSTAT
INST. LTS.
TO CLOCK
HI BEAM
ALT. IND.
R. DIR. IND.
L. DIR. IND.
SEAT BELT
OIL PRESS.
BRAKE IND.
TEMP. GA.
FUEL GA.
15 A
LT. SW. CONN.
BEAM SEL. SW. CONN.
IGN. SW.
DIR. SW. CONN.
HAZARD SW. CONN.
HORN SW.
PARK BRAKE SW.
STOP LT. SW.
DOOR BUZ.
YEL DIODE
COURTESY LT.
INTERM. W/SHIELD WIP. SW.
WASH
W/SHIELD WIPER SW.
R. WINDOW WIPER SW.
BEAM SELECT SW.
LIGHT SW.
DIR. SW.
HAZ SW.
R. DOOR SW.
MARKER LT.
TAIL LT.
DIR. LT.
STOP LT.
LICENSE LT.
DOME LT. & SW.
LUGG. COMP. LT. & SW.
R. WDO. GRID
R. WINDOW WIPER MTR.
FUEL GAUGE (TANK UNIT)
L. DOOR SW.
R. WDO. WASH MTR.
SEAT BELT SW.
TAILGATE SW. SOL.
BACK-UP LT.
STOP LT.
DIR. LT.
TAIL LT.
MARKER LT.

1983 Honda

PRELUDE

ENGINE COMPARTMENT & FUSE BLOCK

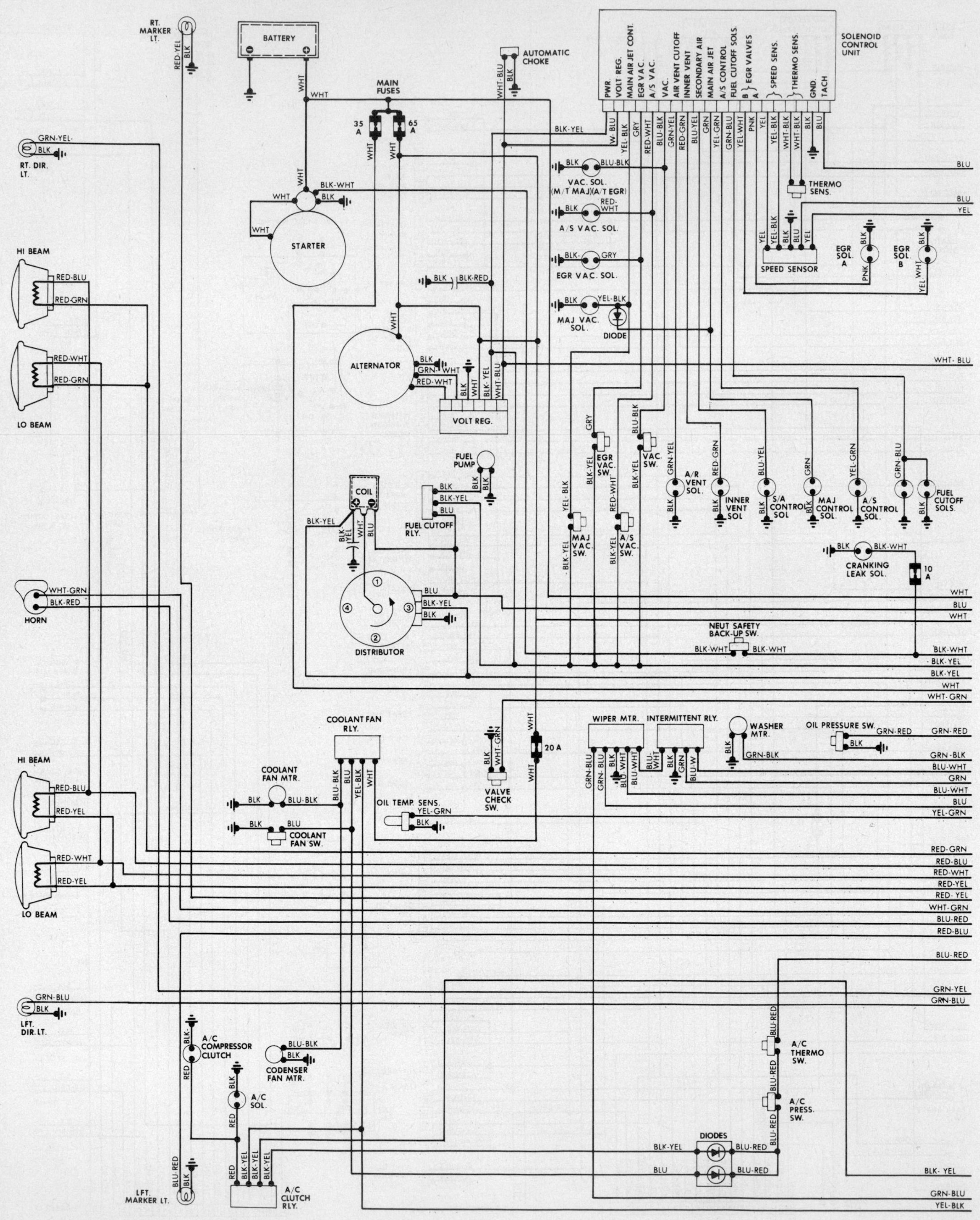
RT. MARKER LT.
BATTERY
AUTOMATIC CHOKE
MAIN FUSES
35 A
65 A
SOLENOID CONTROL UNIT
PWR.
VOLT REG.
MAIN AIR JET CONT.
EGR VAC.
A/S VAC.
VAC.
AIR VENT CUTOFF
INNER VENT
SECONDARY AIR
MAIN AIR JET
A/S CONTROL
FUEL CUTOFF SOLS.
EGR VALVES
SPEED SENS.
THERMO SENS.
GND.
TACH
RT. DIR. LT.
STARTER
VAC. SOL. (M/T MAJ)(A/T EGR)
A/S VAC. SOL.
EGR VAC. SOL.
MAJ VAC. SOL.
DIODE
THERMO SENS.
SPEED SENSOR
EGR SOL. A
EGR SOL. B
HI BEAM
LO BEAM
ALTERNATOR
VOLT REG.
FUEL PUMP
COIL
FUEL CUTOFF RLY.
EGR VAC. SW.
VAC. SW.
A/R VENT SOL.
INNER VENT SOL
S/A CONTROL SOL
MAJ CONTROL SOL.
A/S CONTROL SOL.
FUEL CUTOFF SOLS.
MAJ VAC. SW.
A/S VAC. SW.
CRANKING LEAK SOL.
10 A
HORN
DISTRIBUTOR
NEUT SAFETY BACK-UP SW.
COOLANT FAN RLY.
COOLANT FAN MTR.
COOLANT FAN SW.
OIL TEMP. SENS.
VALVE CHECK SW.
20 A
WIPER MTR.
INTERMITTENT RLY.
WASHER MTR.
OIL PRESSURE SW.
HI BEAM
LO BEAM
LFT. DIR. LT.
A/C COMPRESSOR CLUTCH
CODENSER FAN MTR.
A/C SOL.
A/C THERMO SW.
A/C PRESS. SW.
DIODES
LFT. MARKER LT.
A/C CLUTCH RLY.

1983 Honda

PRELUDE (Cont.)

FUSE BLOCK & ACCESSORIES

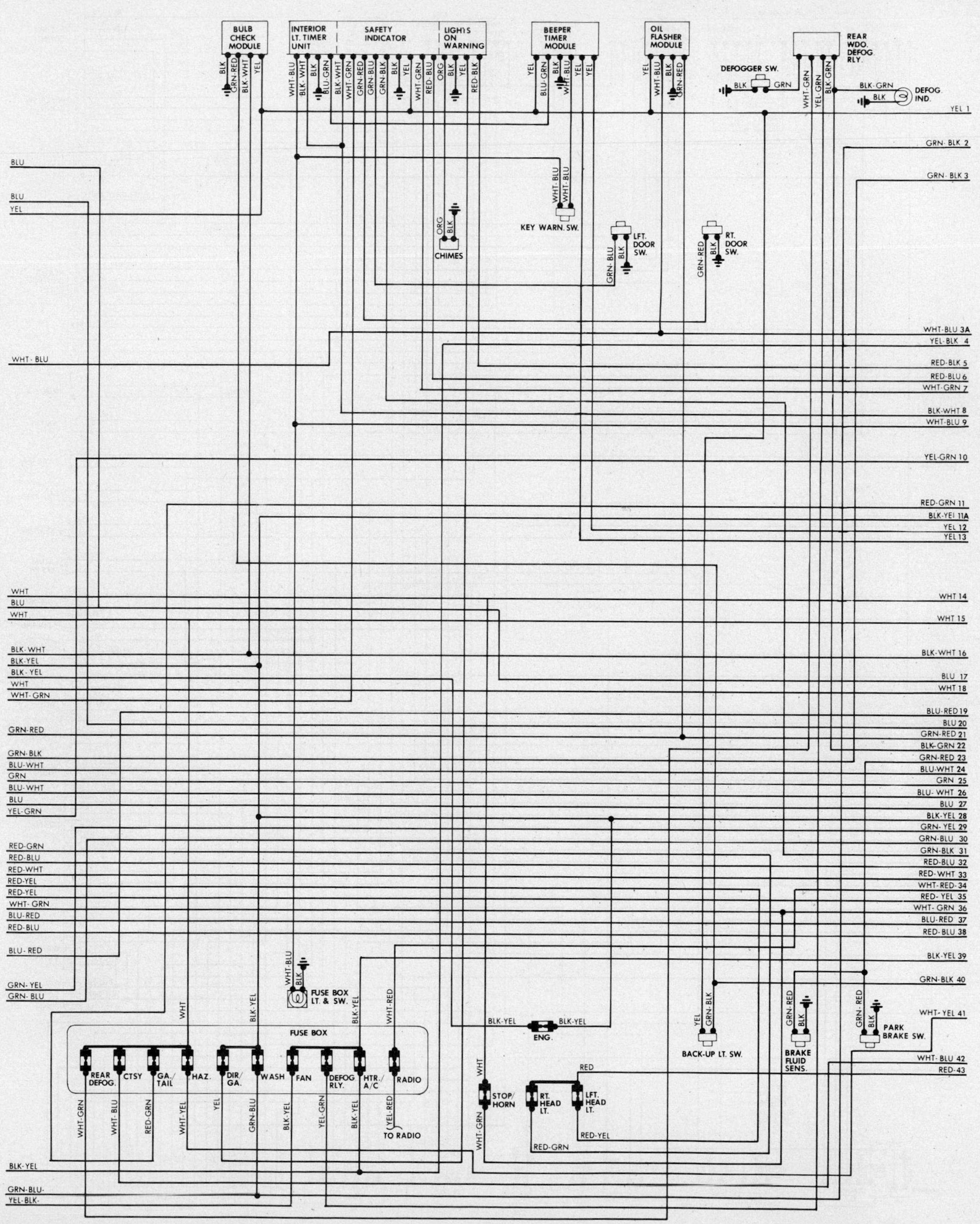

BULB CHECK MODULE
INTERIOR LT. TIMER UNIT
SAFETY INDICATOR
LIGHTS ON WARNING
BEEPER TIMER MODULE
OIL FLASHER MODULE
REAR WDO. DEFOG. RLY.
DEFOGGER SW.
DEFOG. IND.
KEY WARN. SW.
CHIMES
LFT. DOOR SW.
RT. DOOR SW.
FUSE BOX LT. & SW.
FUSE BOX
REAR DEFOG.
CTSY
GA./TAIL
HAZ.
DIR/GA.
WASH
FAN
DEFOG RLY.
HTR./A/C
RADIO
TO RADIO
ENG.
STOP/HORN
RT. HEAD LT.
LFT. HEAD LT.
BACK-UP LT. SW.
BRAKE FLUID SENS.
PARK BRAKE SW.
YEL 1
GRN-BLK 2
GRN-BLK 3
WHT-BLU 3A
YEL-BLK 4
RED-BLK 5
RED-BLU 6
WHT-GRN 7
BLK-WHT 8
WHT-BLU 9
YEL-GRN 10
RED-GRN 11
BLK-YEL 11A
YEL 12
YEL 13
WHT 14
WHT 15
BLK-WHT 16
BLU 17
WHT 18
BLU-RED 19
BLU 20
GRN-RED 21
BLK-GRN 22
GRN-RED 23
BLU-WHT 24
GRN 25
BLU-WHT 26
BLU 27
BLK-YEL 28
GRN-YEL 29
GRN-BLU 30
GRN-BLK 31
RED-BLU 32
RED-WHT 33
WHT-RED 34
RED-YEL 35
WHT-GRN 36
BLU-RED 37
RED-BLU 38
BLK-YEL 39
GRN-BLK 40
WHT-YEL 41
WHT-BLU 42
RED 43

1983 Honda

PRELUDE (Cont.)

INSTRUMENT PANEL, UNDERDASH & ACCESSORIES

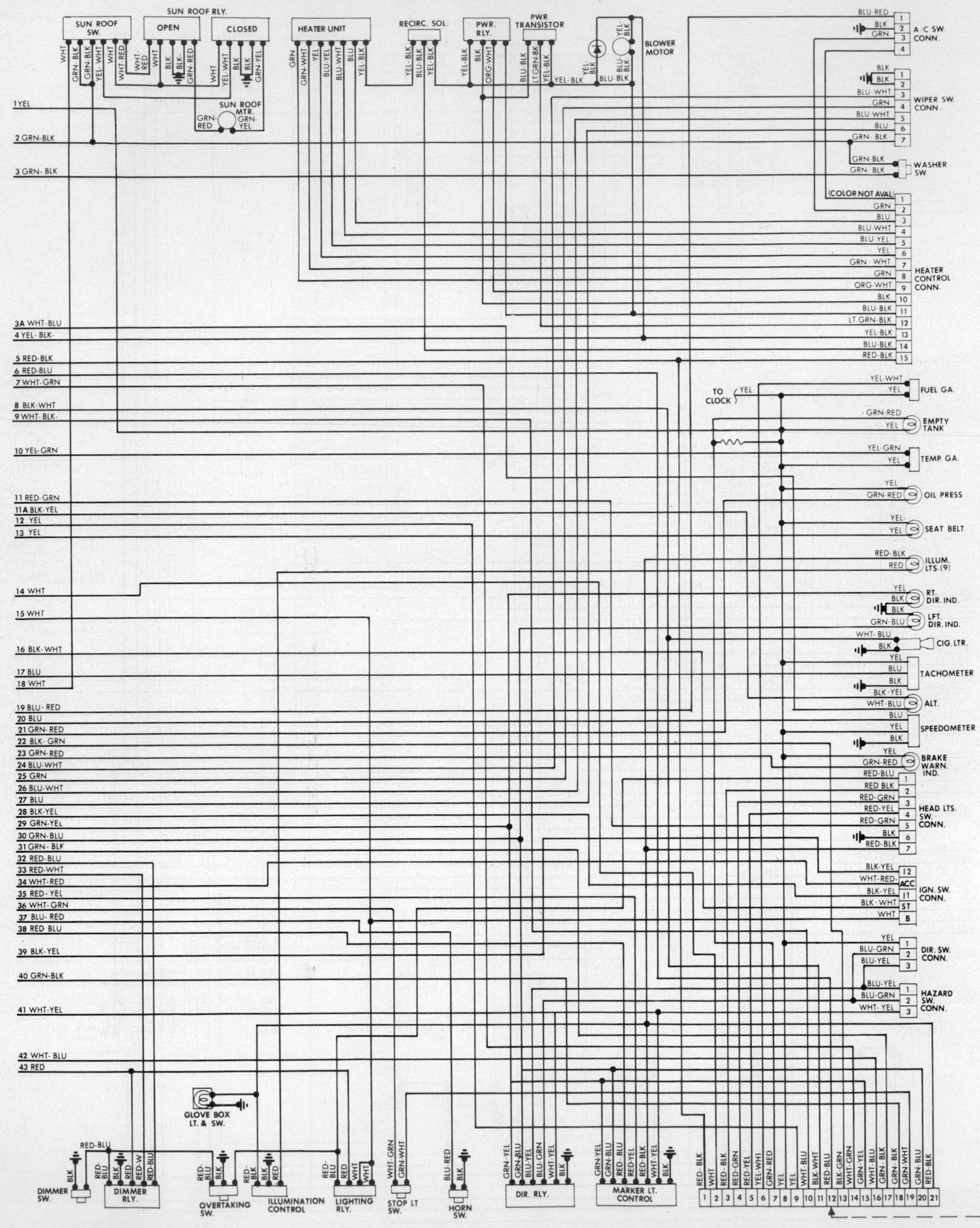
SUN ROOF RLY.
SUN ROOF SW.
OPEN
CLOSED
HEATER UNIT
RECIRC. SOL.
PWR. RLY.
PWR. TRANSISTOR
BLOWER MOTOR
SUN ROOF MTR.
A/C SW. CONN.
WIPER SW. CONN.
WASHER SW.
HEATER CONTROL CONN.
FUEL GA.
TO CLOCK
EMPTY TANK
TEMP. GA.
OIL PRESS
SEAT BELT
ILLUM. LTS.(9)
RT. DIR. IND.
LFT. DIR. IND.
CIG. LTR.
TACHOMETER
ALT.
SPEEDOMETER
BRAKE WARN. IND.
HEAD LTS. SW. CONN.
IGN. SW. CONN.
DIR. SW. CONN.
HAZARD SW. CONN.
GLOVE BOX LT. & SW.
DIMMER SW.
DIMMER RLY.
OVERTAKING SW.
ILLUMINATION CONTROL
LIGHTING RLY.
STOP LT SW.
HORN SW.
DIR. RLY.
MARKER LT. CONTROL

1983 Honda

PRELUDE (Cont.)

REAR COMPARTMENT & ACCESSORIES

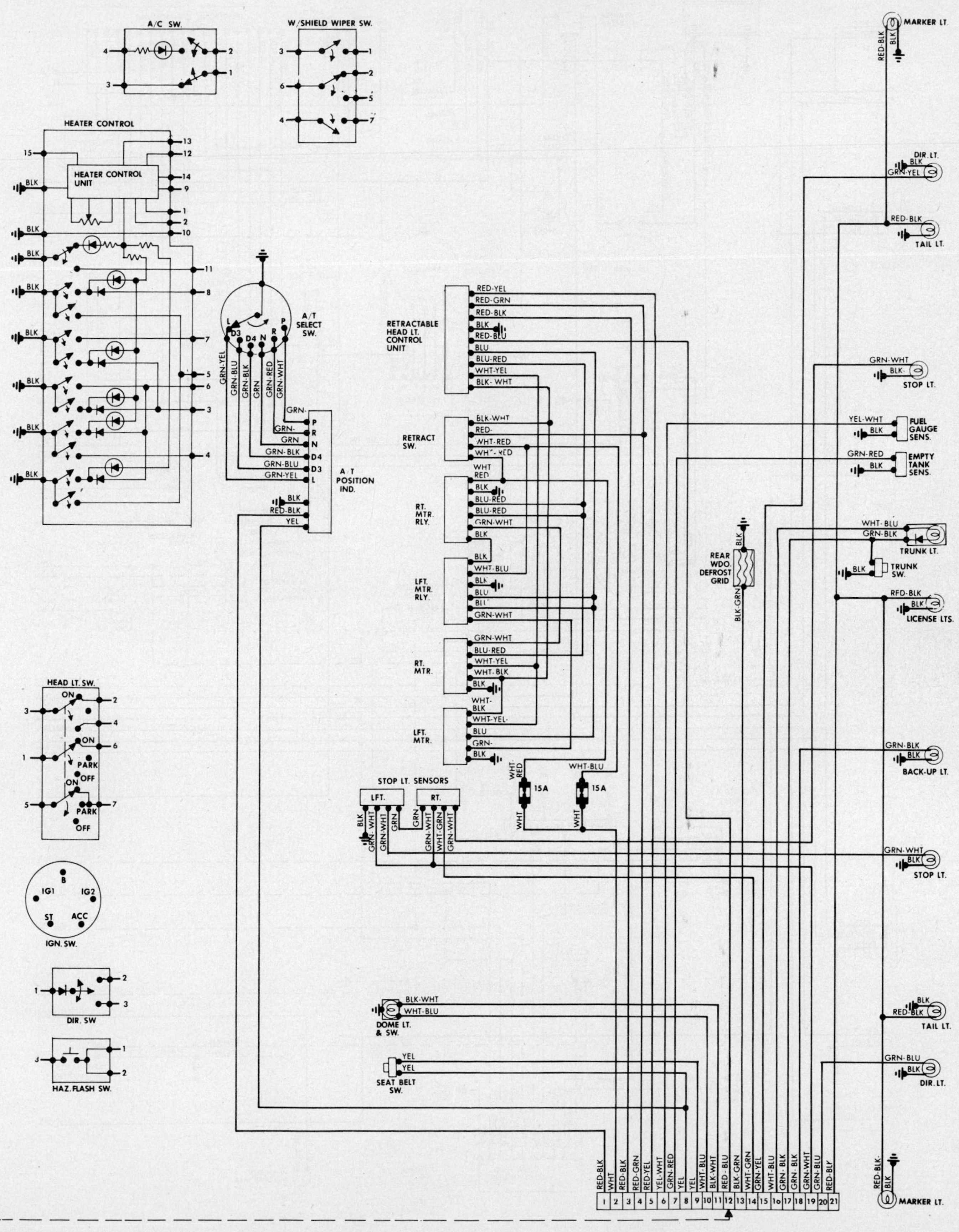

A/C SW.
W/SHIELD WIPER SW.
HEATER CONTROL
HEATER CONTROL UNIT
A/T SELECT SW.
A/T POSITION IND.
RETRACTABLE HEAD LT. CONTROL UNIT
RETRACT SW.
RT. MTR. RLY.
LFT. MTR. RLY.
RT. MTR.
LFT. MTR.
HEAD LT. SW.
IGN. SW.
DIR. SW
HAZ. FLASH SW.
STOP LT. SENSORS
LFT.
RT.
15A
DOME LT. & SW.
SEAT BELT SW.
MARKER LT.
DIR. LT.
TAIL LT.
STOP LT.
FUEL GAUGE SENS.
EMPTY TANK SENS.
TRUNK LT.
TRUNK SW.
REAR WDO. DEFROST GRID
LICENSE LTS.
BACK-UP LT.

1983 Isuzu

I-MARK & I-MARK DIESEL

ENGINE COMPARTMENT

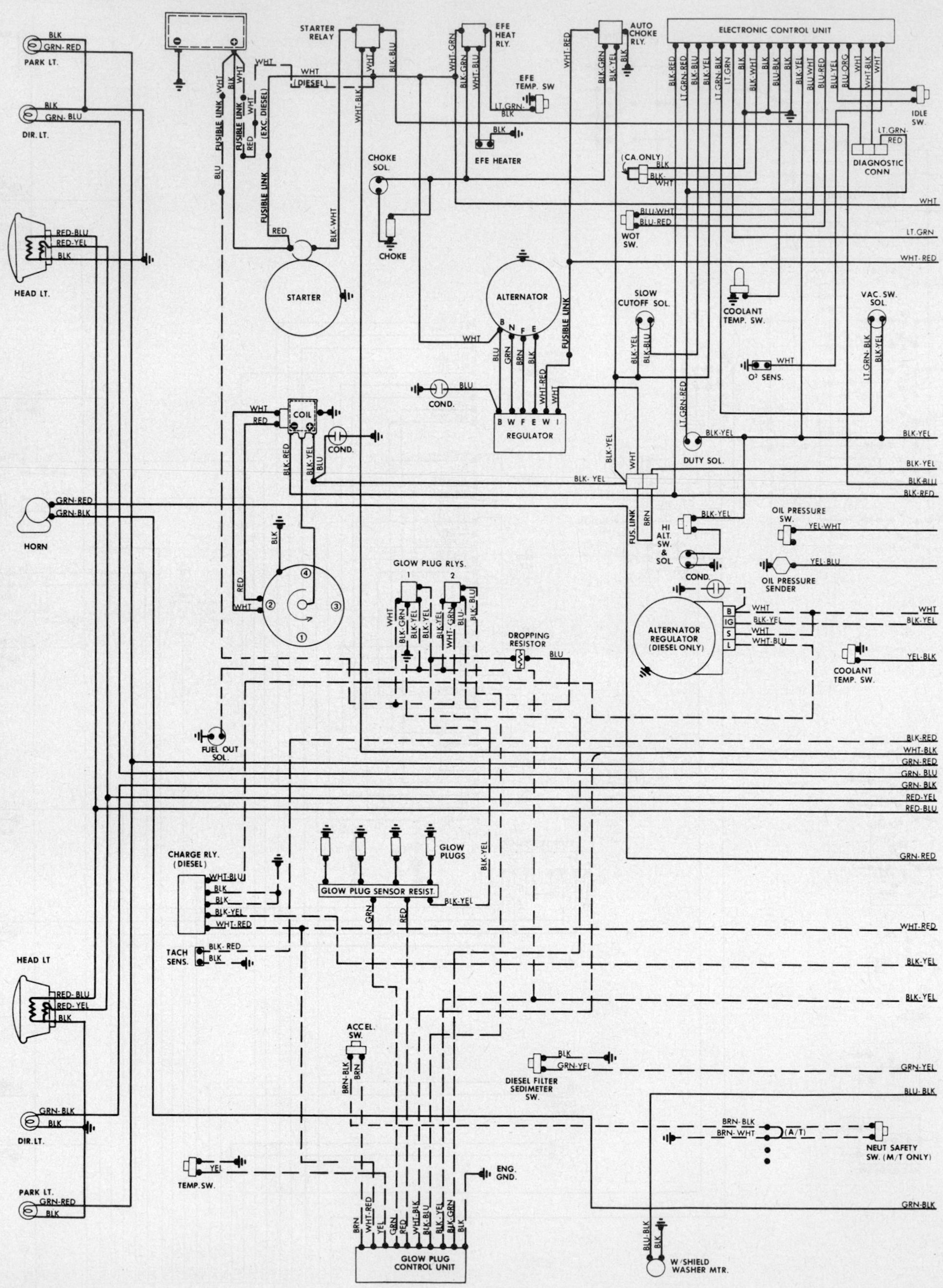
PARK LT.
DIR. LT.
HEAD LT.
HORN
STARTER RELAY
EFE HEAT RLY.
AUTO CHOKE RLY.
ELECTRONIC CONTROL UNIT
EFE TEMP. SW
EFE HEATER
IDLE SW.
DIAGNOSTIC CONN
(CA. ONLY)
CHOKE SOL.
CHOKE
FUSIBLE LINK
(DIESEL)
(EXC. DIESEL)
STARTER
ALTERNATOR
WOT SW.
SLOW CUTOFF SOL.
COOLANT TEMP. SW.
VAC. SW. SOL.
O² SENS.
COND.
REGULATOR
COIL
DUTY SOL.
FUS. LINK
HI ALT. SW. & SOL.
OIL PRESSURE SW.
OIL PRESSURE SENDER
GLOW PLUG RLYS.
DROPPING RESISTOR
ALTERNATOR REGULATOR (DIESEL ONLY)
FUEL OUT SOL.
GLOW PLUGS
GLOW PLUG SENSOR RESIST.
CHARGE RLY. (DIESEL)
TACH SENS.
HEAD LT
ACCEL. SW.
DIESEL FILTER SEDIMETER SW.
(A/T)
NEUT SAFETY SW. (M/T ONLY)
DIR. LT.
TEMP. SW.
ENG. GND.
PARK LT.
GLOW PLUG CONTROL UNIT
W/SHIELD WASHER MTR.

I-MARK & I-MARK DIESEL (Cont.)

FUSE BLOCK & UNDERDASH

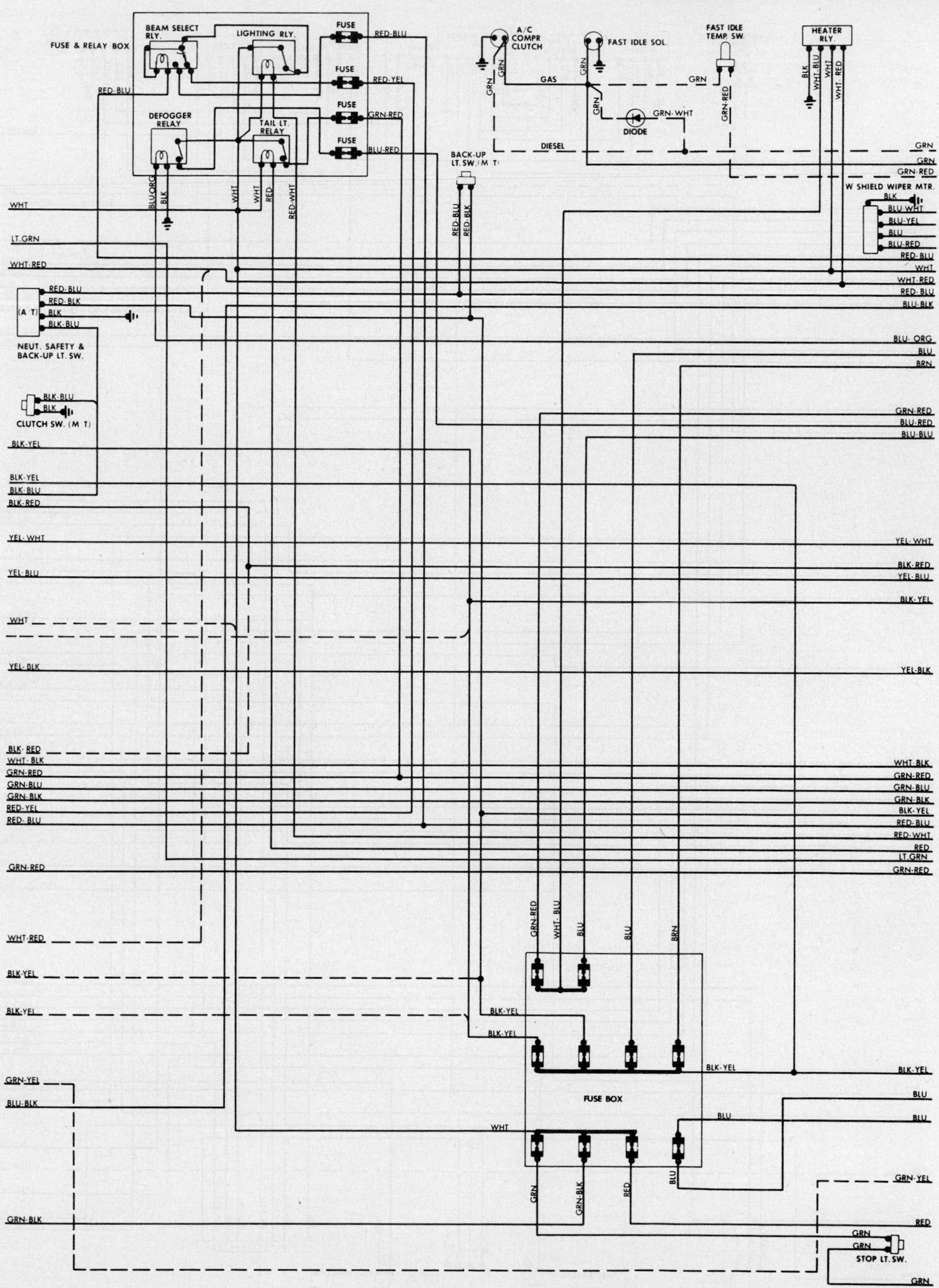
FUSE & RELAY BOX
BEAM SELECT RLY.
LIGHTING RLY.
FUSE
RED-BLU
RED-YEL
GRN-RED
BLU-RED
DEFOGGER RELAY
TAIL LT. RELAY
A/C COMPR CLUTCH
FAST IDLE SOL.
FAST IDLE TEMP. SW.
HEATER RLY.
GAS
DIESEL
DIODE
GRN-WHT
BACK-UP LT. SW. (M T)
W SHIELD WIPER MTR.
NEUT. SAFETY & BACK-UP LT. SW.
CLUTCH SW. (M T)
FUSE BOX
STOP LT. SW.
WHT
LT. GRN
WHT-RED
RED-BLK
BLK
BLK-BLU
BLK-YEL
BLK-RED
YEL-WHT
YEL-BLU
YEL-BLK
WHT-BLK
GRN-BLU
GRN-BLK
RED-WHT
GRN-YEL
BLU-BLK
GRN
BLU-WHT
BLU-YEL
BLU
BLU-ORG
BRN
WHT-BLU
RED

1983 Isuzu

I-MARK & I-MARK DIESEL (Cont.)

UNDERDASH & INSTRUMENT PANEL

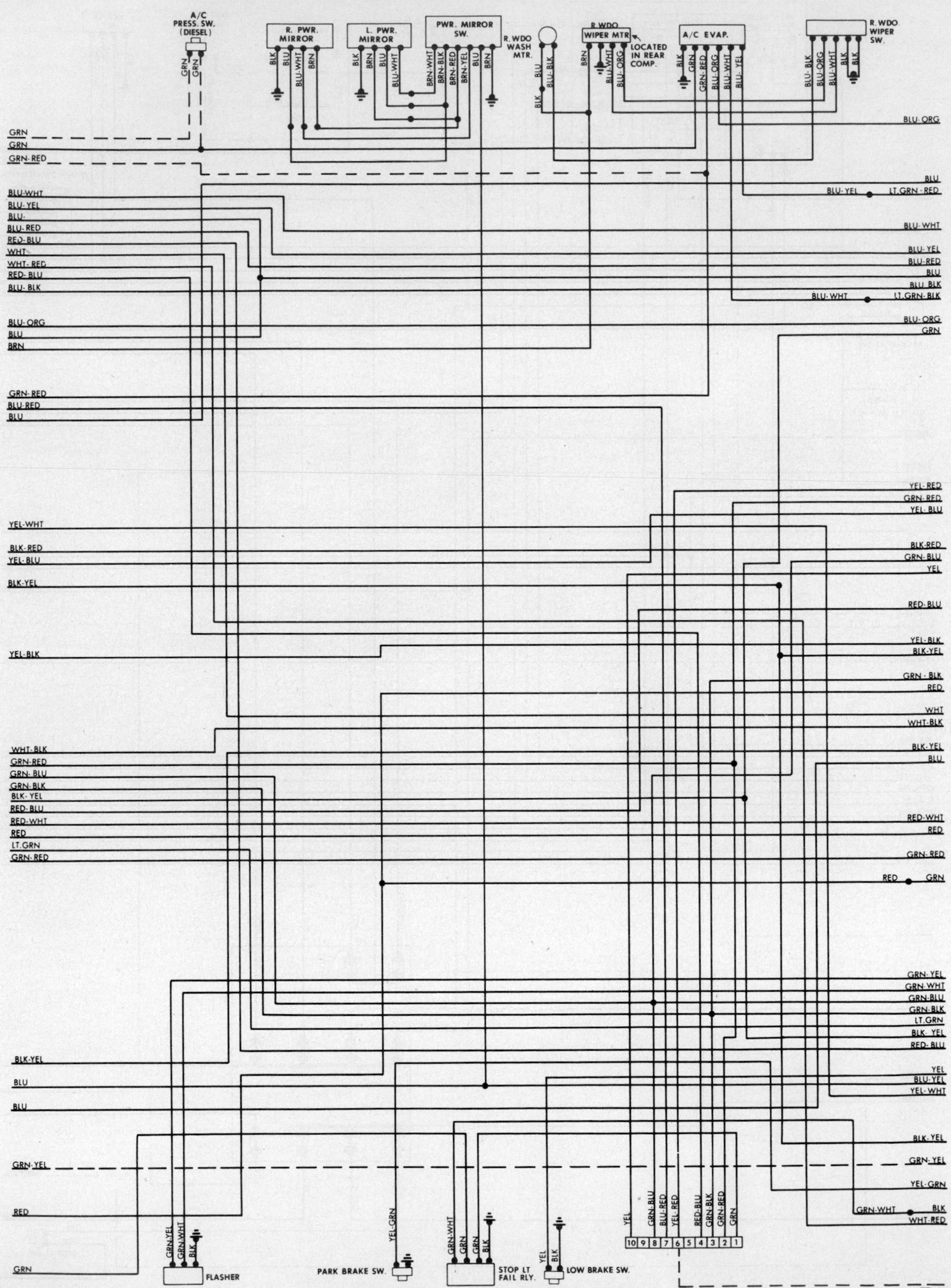
A/C PRESS. SW. (DIESEL)
R. PWR. MIRROR
L. PWR. MIRROR
PWR. MIRROR SW.
R. WDO WASH MTR.
R. WDO WIPER MTR
LOCATED IN REAR COMP.
A/C EVAP.
R. WDO WIPER SW.
FLASHER
PARK BRAKE SW.
STOP LT FAIL RLY.
LOW BRAKE SW.
10 9 8 7 6 5 4 3 2 1
GRN
GRN
GRN-RED
BLU-WHT
BLU-YEL
BLU
BLU-RED
RED-BLU
WHT
WHT-RED
RED-BLU
BLU-BLK
BLU-ORG
BLU
BRN
GRN-RED
BLU-RED
BLU
YEL-WHT
BLK-RED
YEL-BLU
BLK-YEL
YEL-BLK
WHT-BLK
GRN-RED
GRN-BLU
GRN-BLK
BLK-YEL
RED-BLU
RED-WHT
RED
LT.GRN
GRN-RED
BLK-YEL
BLU
BLU
GRN-YEL
RED
GRN
BLU-ORG
BLU
BLU-YEL
LT.GRN-RED
BLU-WHT
BLU-YEL
BLU-RED
BLU
BLU-BLK
BLU-WHT
LT.GRN-BLK
BLU-ORG
GRN
YEL-RED
GRN-RED
YEL-BLU
BLK-RED
GRN-BLU
YEL
RED-BLU
YEL-BLK
BLK-YEL
GRN-BLK
RED
WHT
WHT-BLK
BLK-YEL
BLU
RED-WHT
RED
GRN-RED
RED
GRN
GRN-YEL
GRN-WHT
GRN-BLU
GRN-BLK
LT.GRN
BLK-YEL
RED-BLU
YEL
BLU-YEL
YEL-WHT
BLK-YEL
GRN-YEL
YEL-GRN
GRN-WHT
BLK
WHT-RED

1983 Isuzu

I-MARK & I-MARK DIESEL (Cont.)

INSTRUMENT PANEL, REAR COMPARTMENT & ACCESSORIES

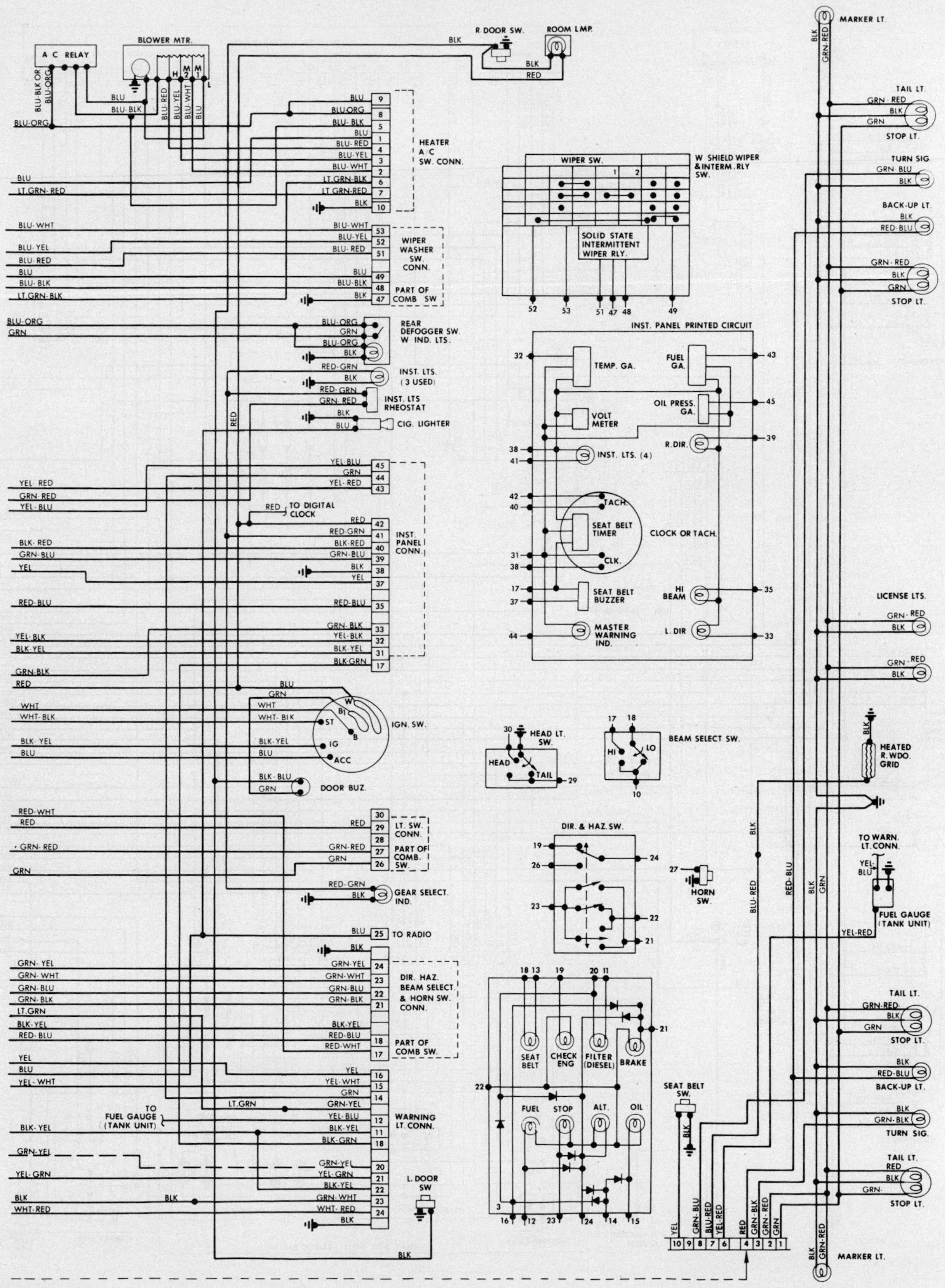

A C RELAY
BLOWER MTR.
R. DOOR SW.
ROOM LMP.
MARKER LT.
TAIL LT.
STOP LT.
TURN SIG.
BACK-UP LT.
HEATER A/C SW. CONN.
WIPER SW.
W SHIELD WIPER & INTERM. RLY SW.
SOLID STATE INTERMITTENT WIPER RLY.
WIPER WASHER SW. CONN.
PART OF COMB SW
REAR DEFOGGER SW. W IND. LTS.
INST. LTS. (3 USED)
INST. LTS RHEOSTAT
CIG. LIGHTER
INST. PANEL PRINTED CIRCUIT
TEMP. GA.
FUEL GA.
OIL PRESS. GA.
VOLT METER
R. DIR.
INST. LTS. (4)
TO DIGITAL CLOCK
INST. PANEL CONN.
TACH.
SEAT BELT TIMER
CLOCK OR TACH.
CLK.
SEAT BELT BUZZER
HI BEAM
MASTER WARNING IND.
L. DIR
LICENSE LTS.
IGN. SW.
DOOR BUZ.
HEAD LT. SW.
HEAD
TAIL
BEAM SELECT SW.
HEATED R. WDO. GRID
LT. SW. CONN.
PART OF COMB. SW.
DIR. & HAZ. SW.
HORN SW.
TO WARN. LT. CONN.
GEAR SELECT. IND.
FUEL GAUGE (TANK UNIT)
TO RADIO
DIR. HAZ. BEAM SELECT. & HORN SW. CONN.
PART OF COMB SW.
SEAT BELT
CHECK ENG
FILTER (DIESEL)
BRAKE
FUEL
STOP
ALT.
OIL
SEAT BELT SW.
TO FUEL GAUGE (TANK UNIT)
WARNING LT. CONN.
L. DOOR SW

1983 Isuzu

IMPULSE

ENGINE COMPARTMENT

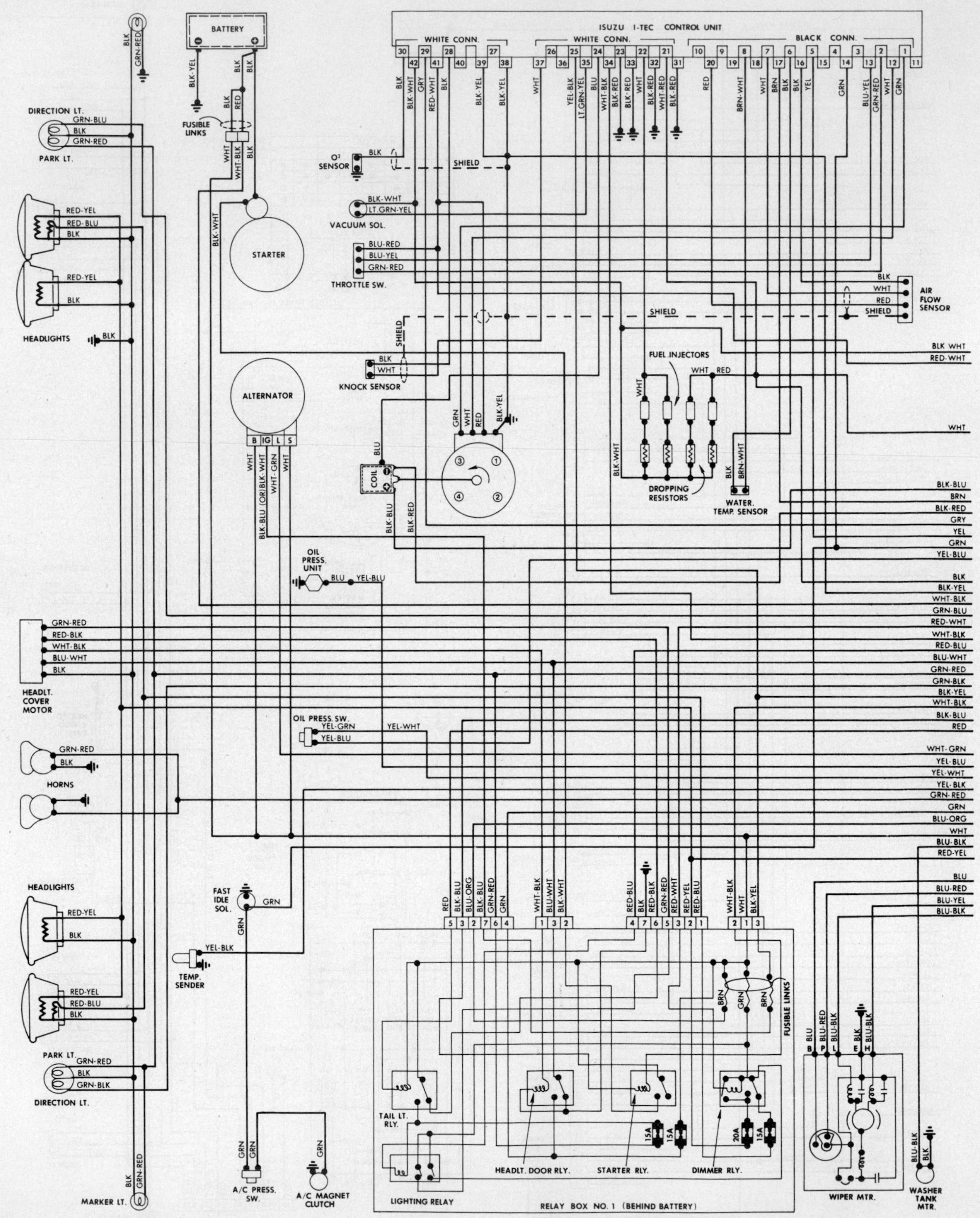
BATTERY
ISUZU I-TEC CONTROL UNIT
WHITE CONN.
WHITE CONN.
BLACK CONN.
DIRECTION LT.
PARK LT.
FUSIBLE LINKS
O² SENSOR
SHIELD
VACUUM SOL.
STARTER
THROTTLE SW.
AIR FLOW SENSOR
HEADLIGHTS
KNOCK SENSOR
FUEL INJECTORS
ALTERNATOR
COIL
DROPPING RESISTORS
WATER TEMP. SENSOR
OIL PRESS. UNIT
HEADLT. COVER MOTOR
OIL PRESS. SW.
HORNS
HEADLIGHTS
FAST IDLE SOL.
TEMP. SENDER
PARK LT.
DIRECTION LT.
MARKER LT.
A/C PRESS. SW.
A/C MAGNET CLUTCH
TAIL LT. RLY.
LIGHTING RELAY
HEADLT. DOOR RLY.
STARTER RLY.
DIMMER RLY.
RELAY BOX NO. 1 (BEHIND BATTERY)
FUSIBLE LINKS
WIPER MTR.
WASHER TANK MTR.

1983 Isuzu

IMPULSE (Cont.)

UNDERDASH

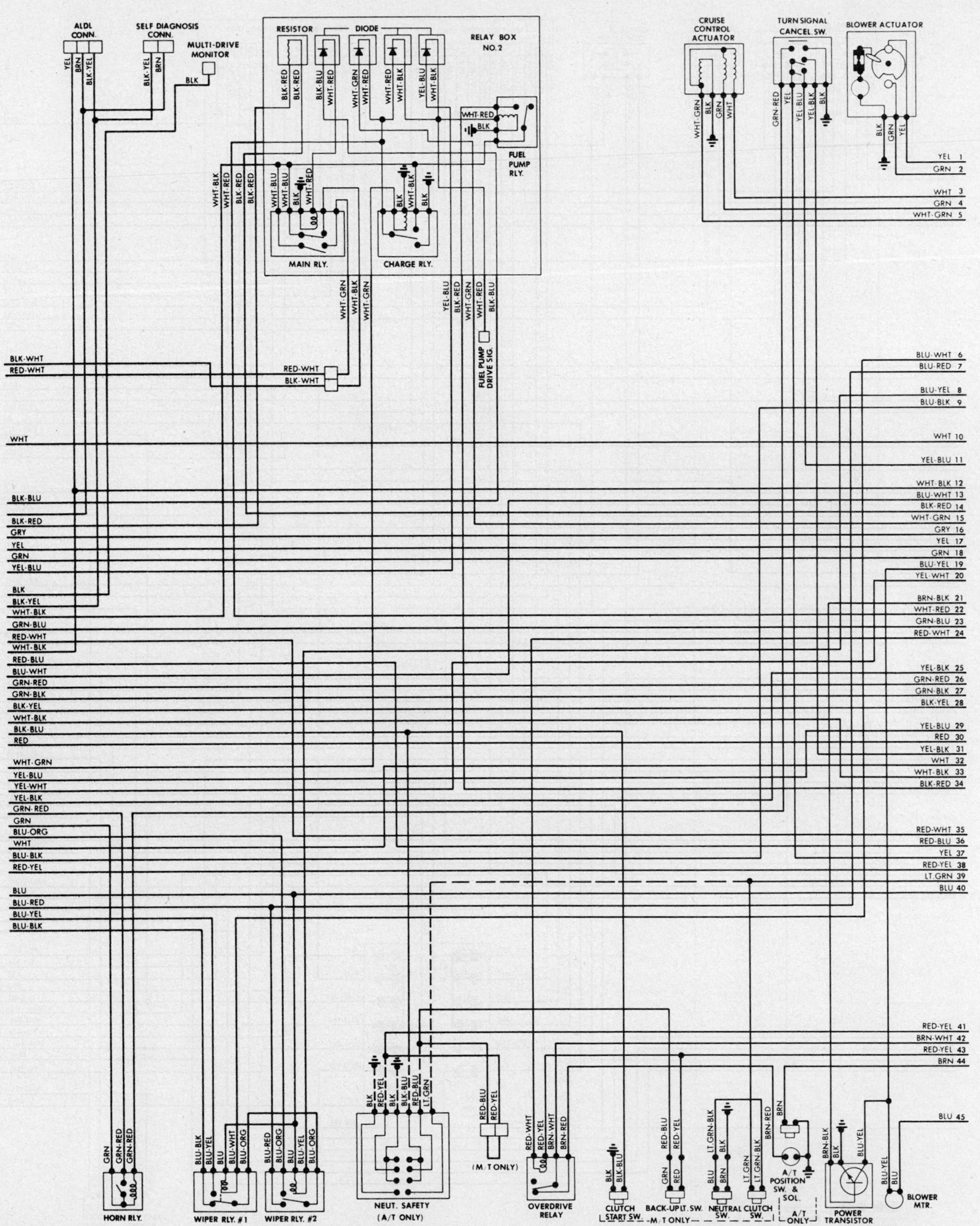

ALDL CONN.
SELF DIAGNOSIS CONN.
MULTI-DRIVE MONITOR
RESISTOR
DIODE
RELAY BOX NO. 2
FUEL PUMP RLY.
MAIN RLY.
CHARGE RLY.
FUEL PUMP DRIVE SIG.
CRUISE CONTROL ACTUATOR
TURN SIGNAL CANCEL SW.
BLOWER ACTUATOR
HORN RLY.
WIPER RLY. #1
WIPER RLY. #2
NEUT. SAFETY (A/T ONLY)
(M/T ONLY)
OVERDRIVE RELAY
CLUTCH START SW.
BACK-UP LT. SW.
M/T ONLY
NEUTRAL SW.
CLUTCH SW.
A/T POSITION SW. & SOL.
A/T ONLY
POWER TRANSISTOR
BLOWER MTR.

1983 Isuzu

IMPULSE (Cont.)

FUSE BLOCK & UNDERDASH

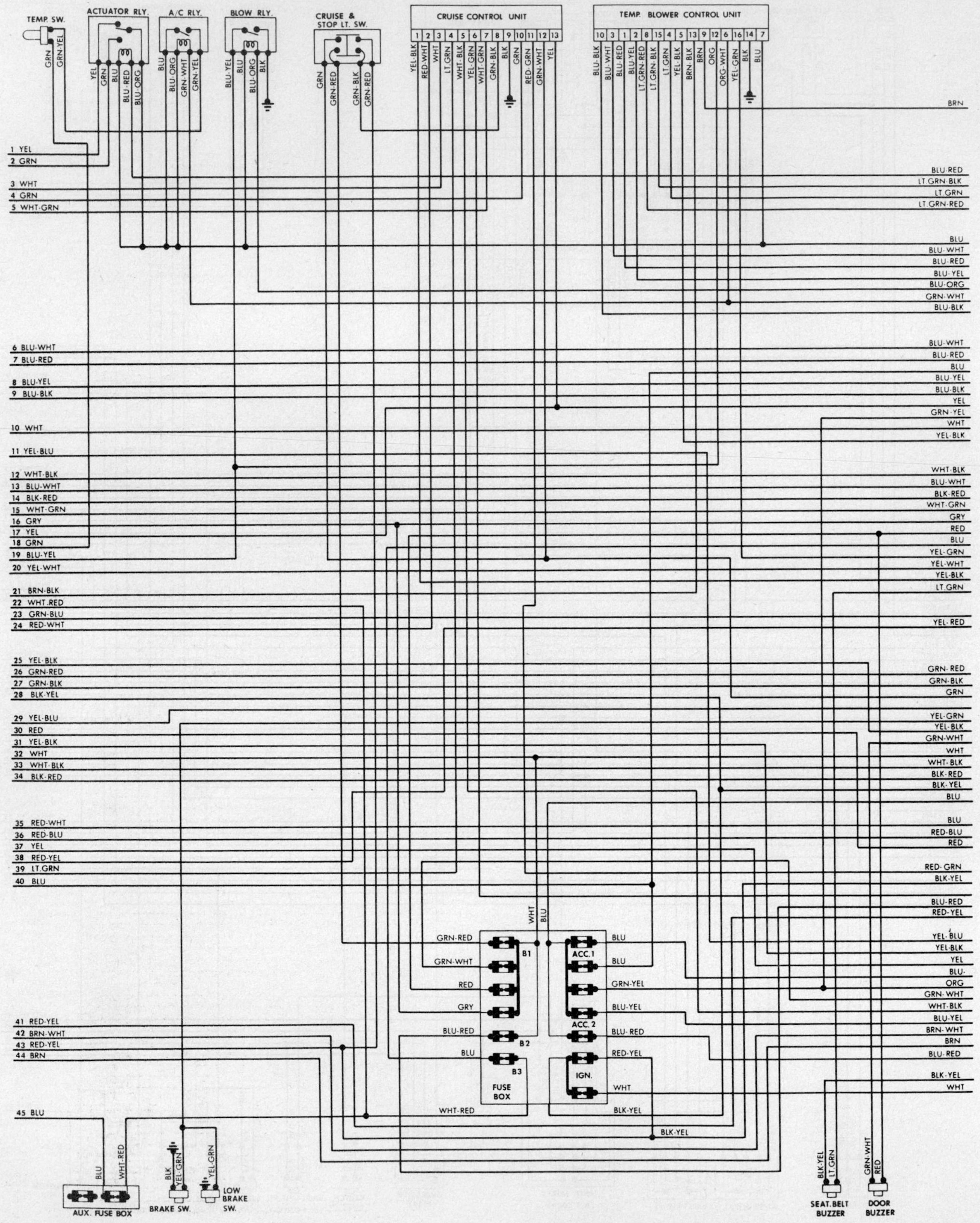

IMPULSE (Cont.)

INSTRUMENT PANEL & UNDERDASH

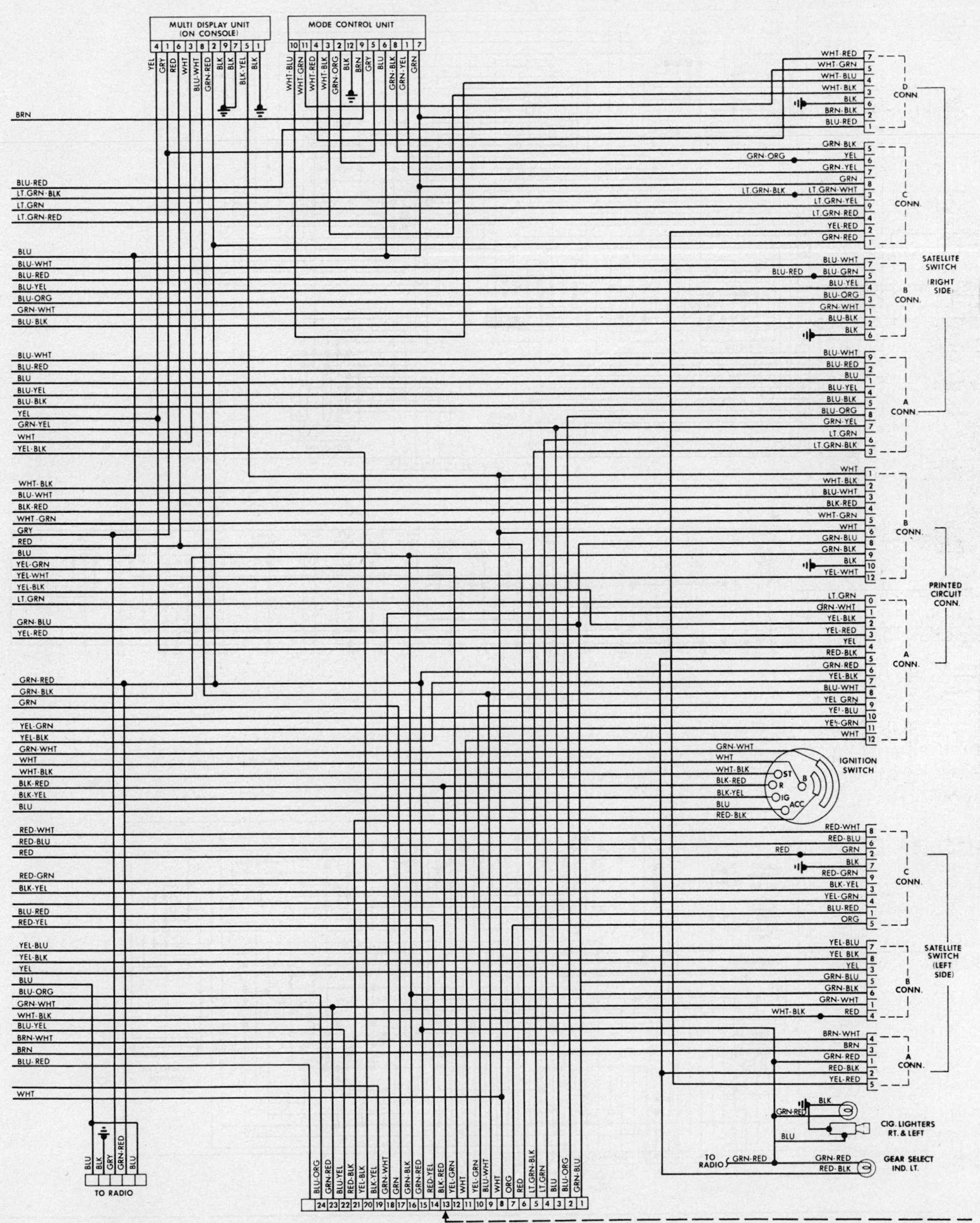

1983 Isuzu

IMPULSE (Cont.)

INSTRUMENT PANEL

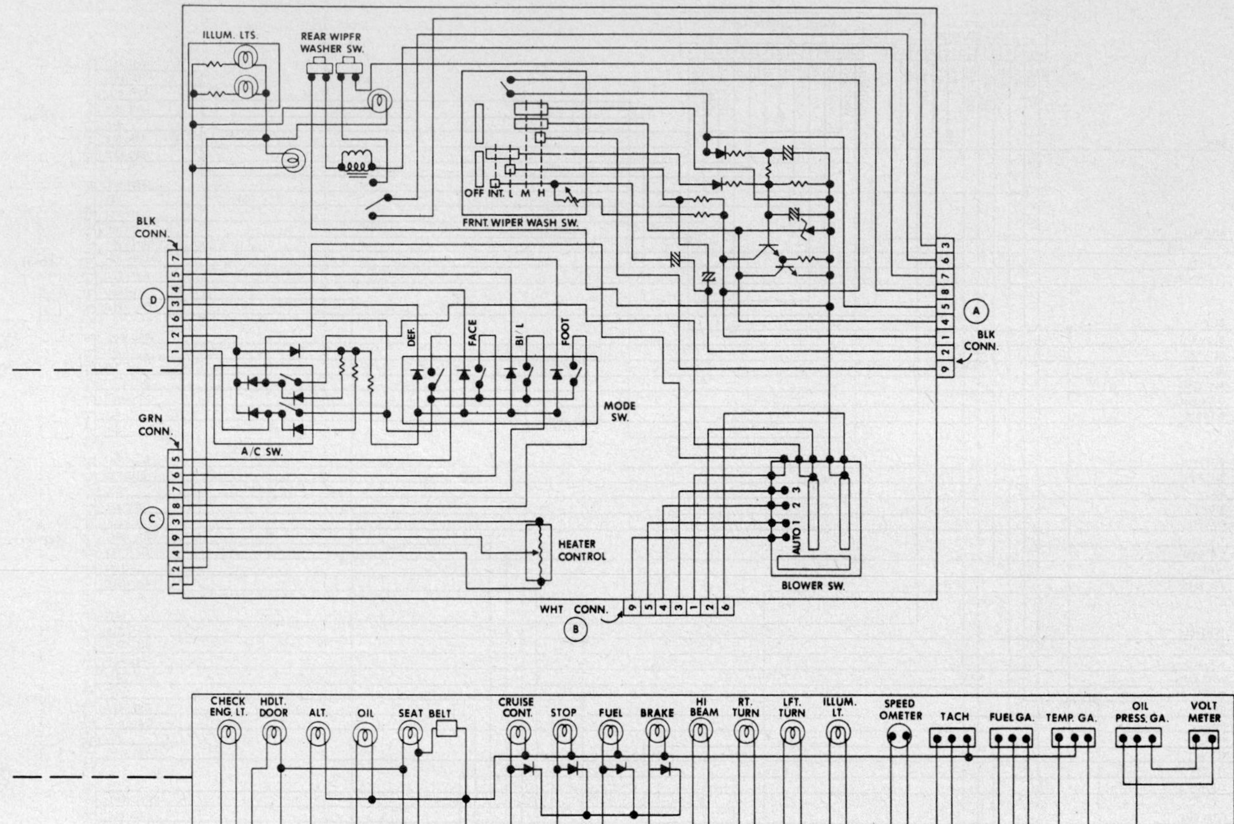
ILLUM. LTS.
REAR WIPER WASHER SW.
OFF INT. L M H
FRNT. WIPER WASH SW.
BLK CONN.
D
A
BLK CONN.
DEF.
FACE
BI/L
FOOT
MODE SW.
GRN CONN.
A/C SW.
C
HEATER CONTROL
AUTO 1 2 3
BLOWER SW.
WHT CONN.
B
CHECK ENG. LT.
HDLT. DOOR
ALT.
OIL
SEAT BELT
CRUISE CONT.
STOP
FUEL
BRAKE
HI BEAM
RT. TURN
LFT. TURN
ILLUM. LT.
SPEED OMETER
TACH
FUEL GA.
TEMP. GA.
OIL PRESS. GA.
VOLT METER
B1 B2 B3 B10 B5 B12 A0 BG A2 A1 A12 A11 A3 B8 B9 A6 A5 A4 B4 A8 A9 A7 A10

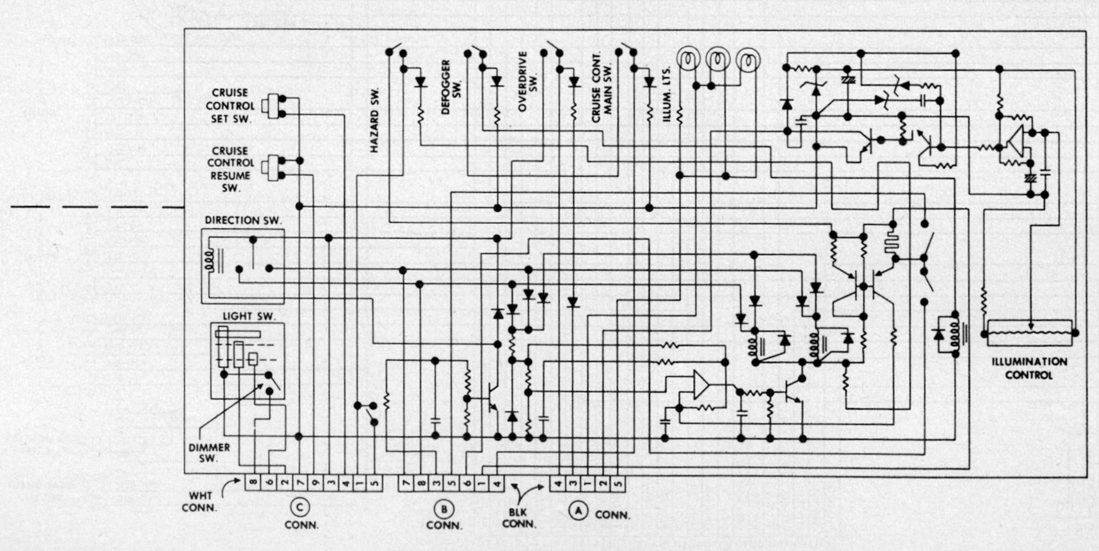
CRUISE CONTROL SET SW.
CRUISE CONTROL RESUME SW.
HAZARD SW.
DEFOGGER SW.
OVERDRIVE SW.
CRUISE CONT. MAIN SW.
ILLUM. LTS.
DIRECTION SW.
LIGHT SW.
DIMMER SW.
ILLUMINATION CONTROL
WHT CONN.
C CONN.
B CONN.
BLK CONN.
A CONN.

IMPULSE (Cont.)

REAR COMPARTMENT & ACCESSORIES

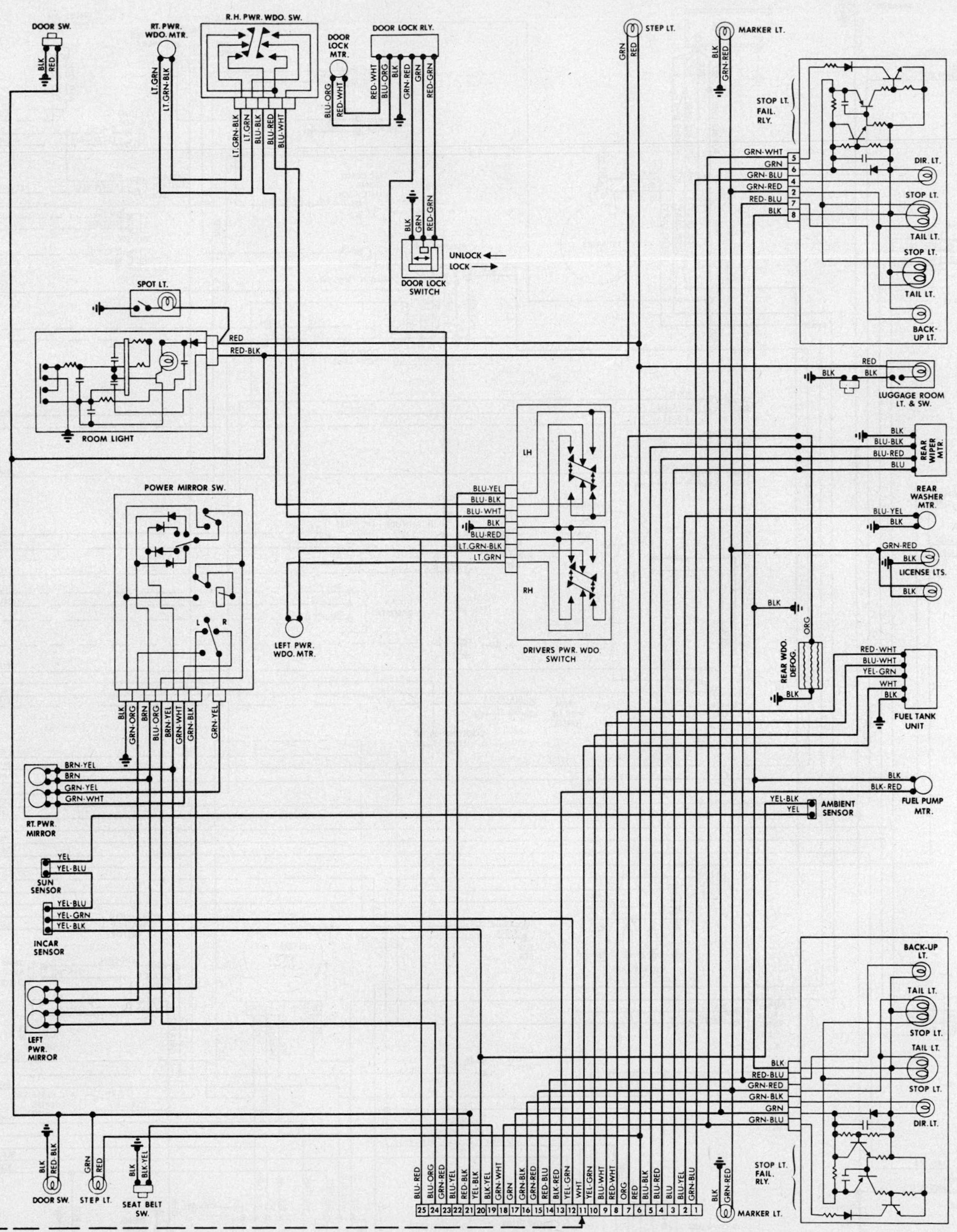

1983 Isuzu

P'UP & P'UP DIESEL

ENGINE COMPARTMENT

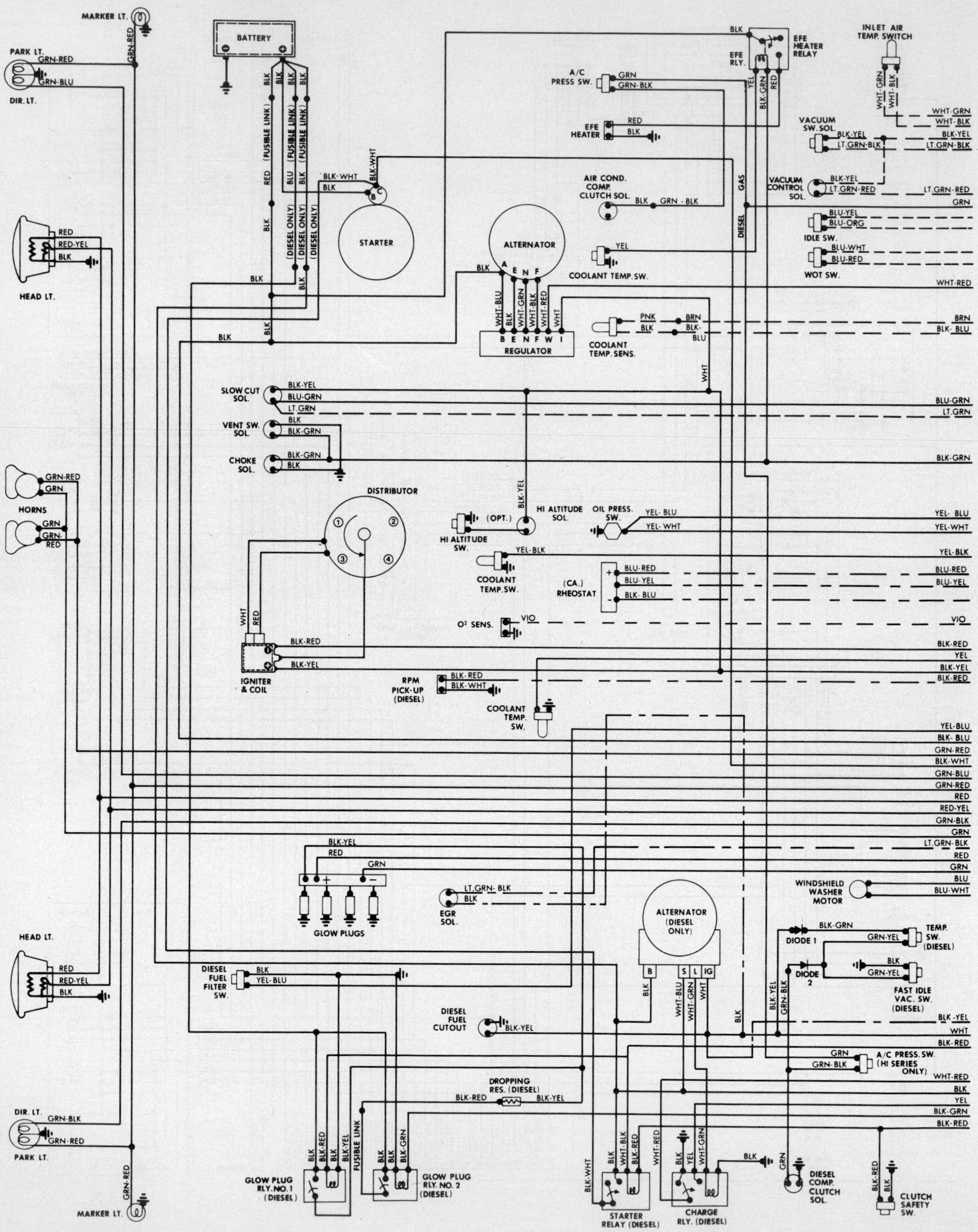
MARKER LT.
PARK LT.
DIR. LT.
BATTERY
(FUSIBLE LINK)
(DIESEL ONLY)
STARTER
ALTERNATOR
REGULATOR
EFE HEATER RELAY
EFE RLY.
INLET AIR TEMP. SWITCH
A/C PRESS SW.
EFE HEATER
AIR COND. COMP. CLUTCH SOL.
VACUUM SW. SOL.
VACUUM CONTROL SOL.
IDLE SW.
WOT SW.
COOLANT TEMP. SW.
COOLANT TEMP. SENS.
HEAD LT.
SLOW CUT SOL.
VENT SW. SOL.
CHOKE SOL.
HORNS
DISTRIBUTOR
HI ALTITUDE SW.
(OPT.)
HI ALTITUDE SOL.
OIL PRESS. SW.
COOLANT TEMP. SW.
(CA.) RHEOSTAT
O2 SENS.
IGNITER & COIL
RPM PICK-UP (DIESEL)
COOLANT TEMP. SW.
GLOW PLUGS
EGR SOL.
WINDSHIELD WASHER MOTOR
ALTERNATOR (DIESEL ONLY)
DIODE 1
DIODE 2
TEMP. SW. (DIESEL)
FAST IDLE VAC. SW. (DIESEL)
DIESEL FUEL FILTER SW.
DIESEL FUEL CUTOUT
A/C PRESS. SW. (HI SERIES ONLY)
DROPPING RES. (DIESEL)
GLOW PLUG RLY. NO. 1 (DIESEL)
GLOW PLUG RLY. NO. 2 (DIESEL)
FUSIBLE LINK
STARTER RELAY (DIESEL)
CHARGE RLY. (DIESEL)
DIESEL COMP. CLUTCH SOL.
CLUTCH SAFETY SW.
GAS
DIESEL

P'UP & P'UP DIESEL (Cont.)

FUSE BLOCK & UNDERDASH

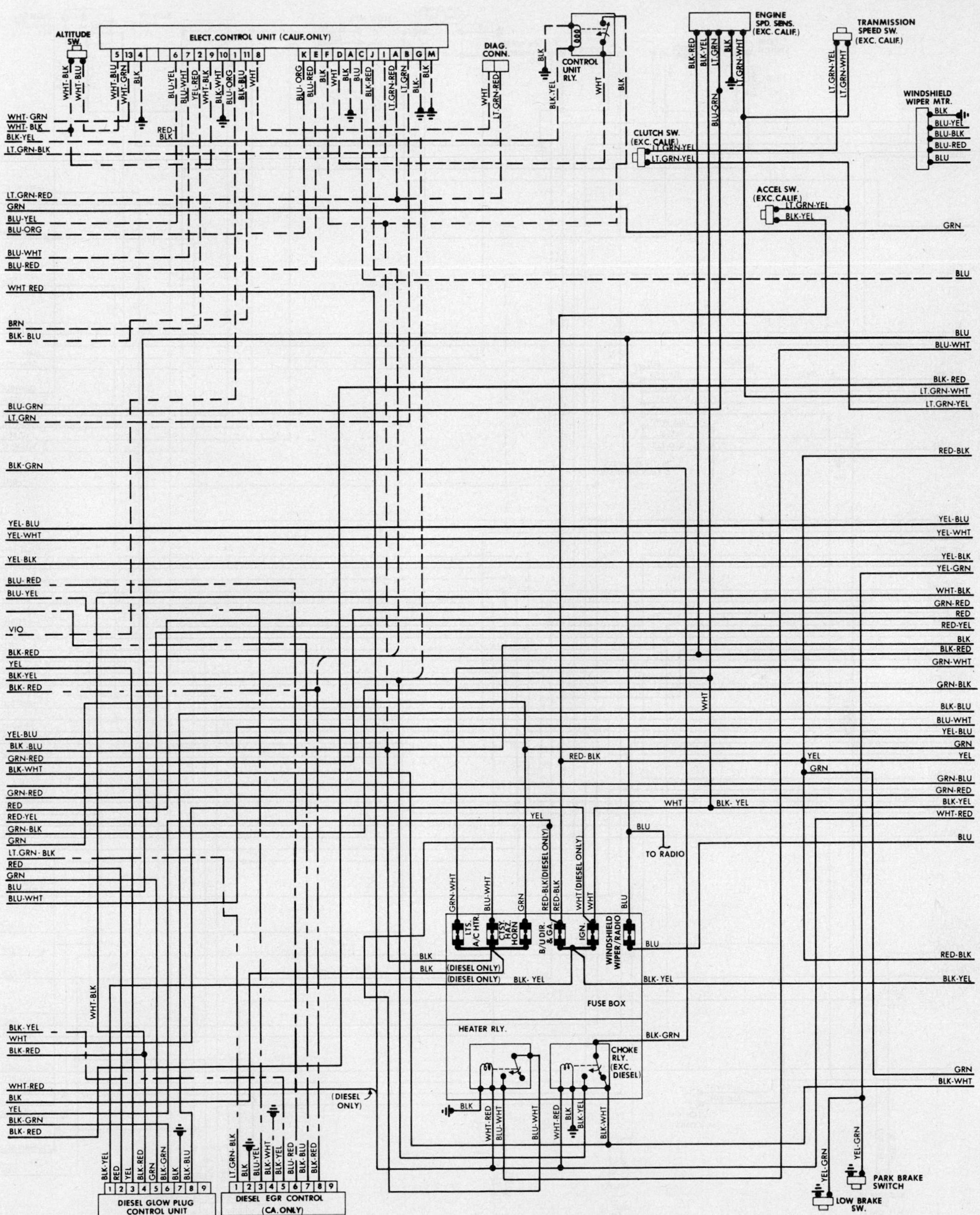
ALTITUDE SW.
ELECT. CONTROL UNIT (CALIF. ONLY)
DIAG. CONN.
CONTROL UNIT RLY.
ENGINE SPD. SENS. (EXC. CALIF.)
TRANMISSION SPEED SW. (EXC. CALIF.)
WINDSHIELD WIPER MTR.
CLUTCH SW. (EXC. CALIF.)
ACCEL SW. (EXC. CALIF.)
TO RADIO
LTS. A/C HTR.
CTSY. HAZ. HORN
B/U DIR. & GA.
IGN.
WINDSHIELD WIPER/RADIO
(DIESEL ONLY)
FUSE BOX
HEATER RLY.
CHOKE RLY. (EXC. DIESEL)
(DIESEL ONLY)
DIESEL GLOW PLUG CONTROL UNIT
DIESEL EGR CONTROL (CA. ONLY)
PARK BRAKE SWITCH
LOW BRAKE SW.

1983 Isuzu

P'UP & P'UP DIESEL (Cont.)

UNDERDASH

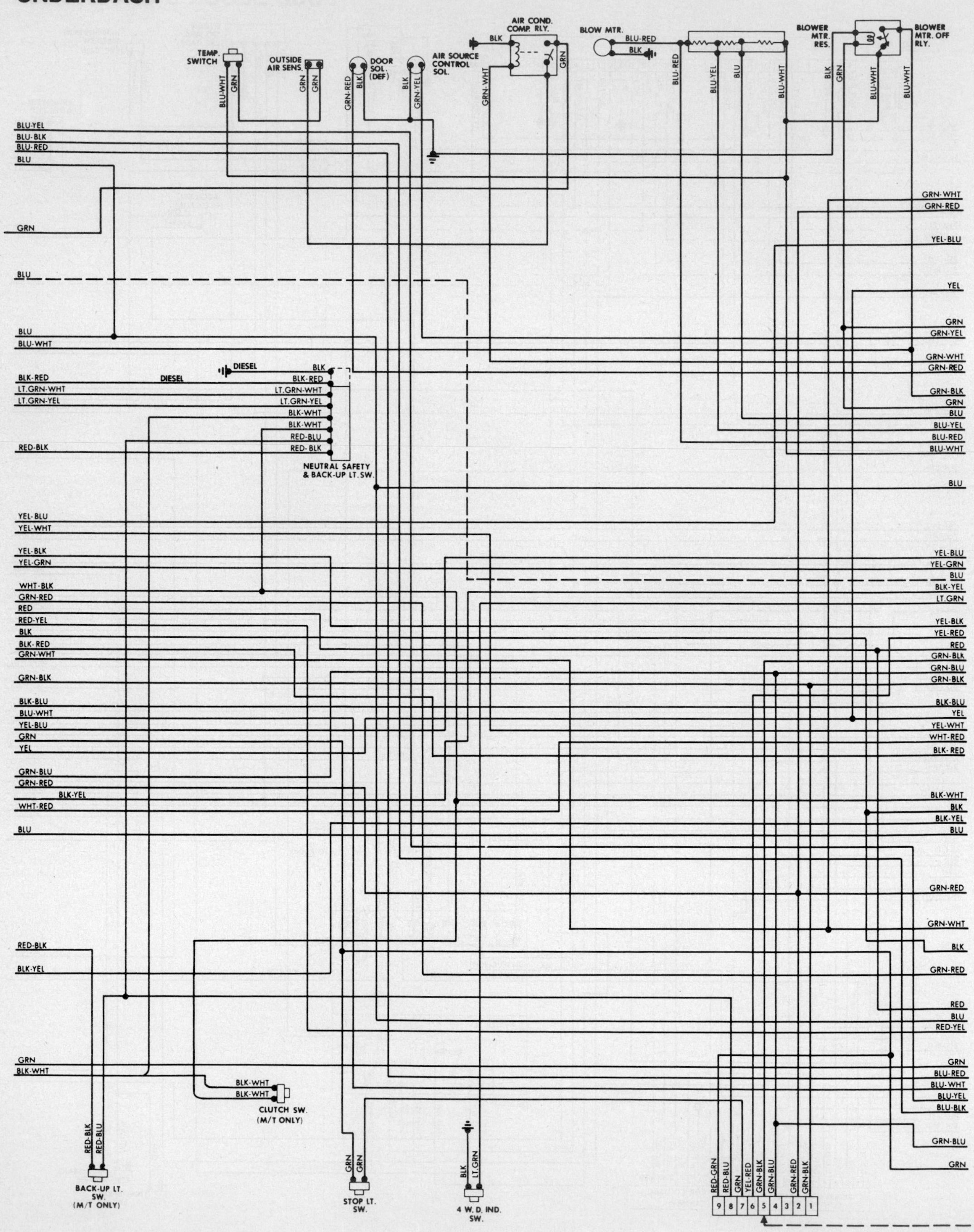

TEMP. SWITCH
OUTSIDE AIR SENS.
DOOR SOL. (DEF)
AIR SOURCE CONTROL SOL.
AIR COND. COMP. RLY.
BLOW MTR.
BLOWER MTR. RES.
BLOWER MTR. OFF RLY.
BLU-WHT
GRN
GRN-RED
BLK
GRN-YEL
GRN-WHT
BLU-RED
BLU-YEL
BLU
BLU-YEL
BLU-BLK
BLU-RED
BLU
GRN
BLU
BLU
BLU-WHT
DIESEL
BLK-RED
LT.GRN-WHT
LT.GRN-YEL
BLK-WHT
RED-BLU
RED-BLK
NEUTRAL SAFETY & BACK-UP LT. SW.
YEL-BLU
YEL-WHT
YEL-BLK
YEL-GRN
WHT-BLK
GRN-RED
RED
RED-YEL
BLK
BLK-RED
GRN-WHT
GRN-BLK
BLK-BLU
BLU-WHT
YEL-BLU
GRN
YEL
GRN-BLU
GRN-RED
BLK-YEL
WHT-RED
BLU
RED-BLK
BLK-YEL
GRN
BLK-WHT
BACK-UP LT. SW. (M/T ONLY)
CLUTCH SW. (M/T ONLY)
STOP LT. SW.
LT.GRN
4 W.D. IND. SW.
GRN-WHT
GRN-RED
YEL-BLU
YEL
GRN
GRN-YEL
GRN-WHT
GRN-RED
GRN-BLK
GRN
BLU
BLU-YEL
BLU-RED
BLU-WHT
BLU
YEL-BLU
YEL-GRN
BLU
BLK-YEL
LT.GRN
YEL-BLK
YEL-RED
RED
GRN-BLK
GRN-BLU
GRN-BLK
BLK-BLU
YEL
YEL-WHT
WHT-RED
BLK-RED
BLK-WHT
BLK
BLK-YEL
BLU
GRN-RED
GRN-WHT
BLK
GRN-RED
RED
BLU
RED-YEL
GRN
BLU-RED
BLU-WHT
BLU-YEL
BLU-BLK
GRN-BLU
GRN
RED-GRN
RED-BLU
GRN
YEL-RED
GRN-BLK
GRN-BLU
GRN-RED
GRN-BLK
9 8 7 6 5 4 3 2 1

P'UP & P'UP DIESEL (Cont.)

INSTRUMENT PANEL & REAR COMPARTMENT

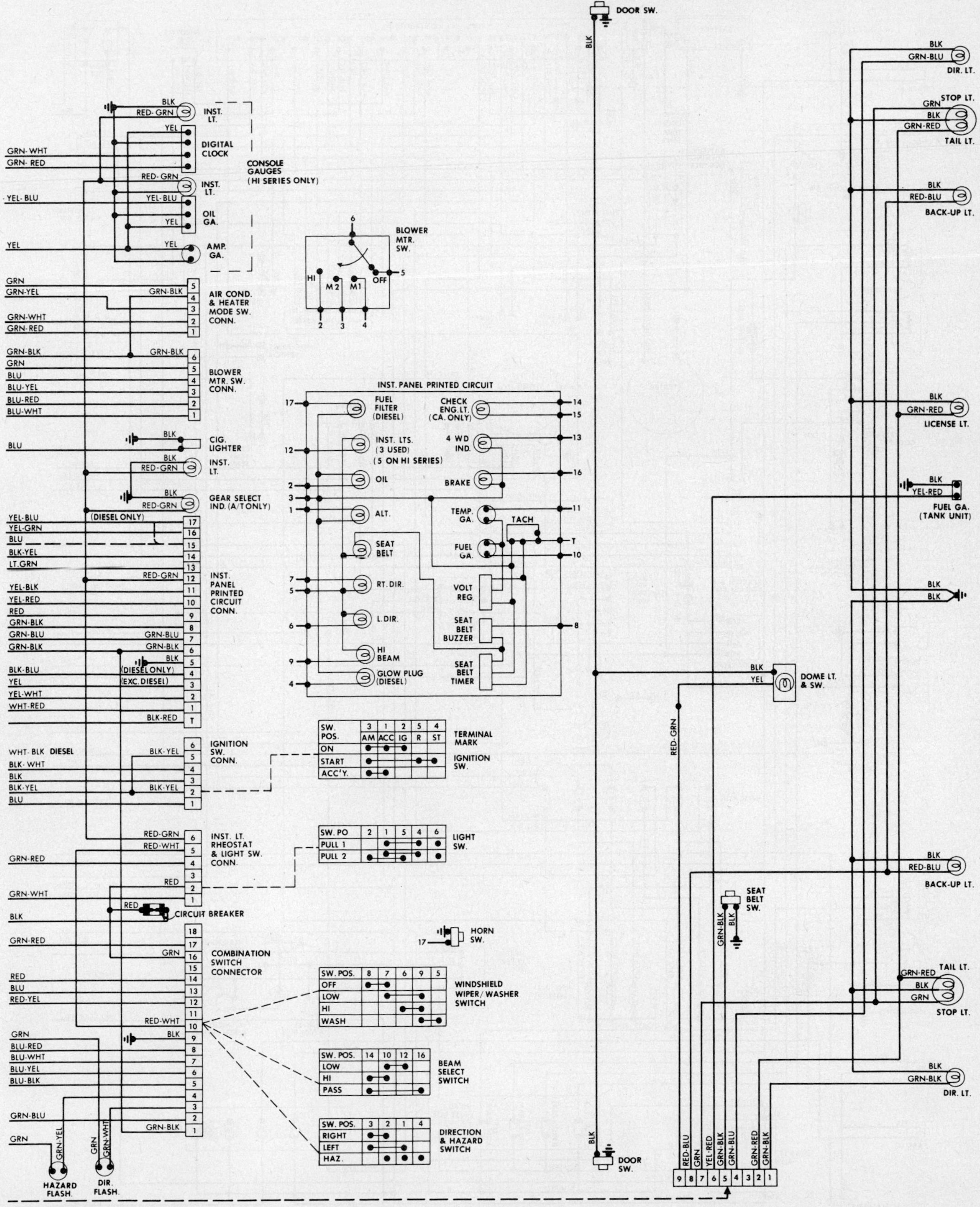
DOOR SW.
INST. LT.
DIGITAL CLOCK
CONSOLE GAUGES (HI SERIES ONLY)
OIL GA.
AMP. GA.
BLOWER MTR. SW.
HI
M2
M1
OFF
AIR COND. & HEATER MODE SW. CONN.
BLOWER MTR. SW. CONN.
CIG. LIGHTER
GEAR SELECT IND. (A/T ONLY)
(DIESEL ONLY)
INST. PANEL PRINTED CIRCUIT CONN.
(EXC. DIESEL)
IGNITION SW. CONN.
INST. LT. RHEOSTAT & LIGHT SW. CONN.
CIRCUIT BREAKER
COMBINATION SWITCH CONNECTOR
HAZARD FLASH.
DIR. FLASH.
INST. PANEL PRINTED CIRCUIT
FUEL FILTER (DIESEL)
CHECK ENG. LT. (CA. ONLY)
INST. LTS. (3 USED) (5 ON HI SERIES)
4 WD IND.
OIL
BRAKE
ALT.
TEMP. GA.
TACH
SEAT BELT
FUEL GA.
RT. DIR.
VOLT REG.
L. DIR.
SEAT BELT BUZZER
HI BEAM
GLOW PLUG (DIESEL)
SEAT BELT TIMER
TERMINAL MARK
IGNITION SW.
SW. POS.
AM ACC IG R ST
ON
START
ACC'Y.
LIGHT SW.
SW. PO
PULL 1
PULL 2
HORN SW.
WINDSHIELD WIPER/WASHER SWITCH
OFF
LOW
HI
WASH
BEAM SELECT SWITCH
PASS
DIRECTION & HAZARD SWITCH
RIGHT
LEFT
HAZ.
DIR. LT.
STOP LT.
TAIL LT.
BACK-UP LT.
LICENSE LT.
FUEL GA. (TANK UNIT)
DOME LT. & SW.
SEAT BELT SW.
GRN-WHT
GRN-RED
YEL-BLU
YEL
RED-GRN
BLK
GRN
GRN-YEL
GRN-BLK
BLU
BLU-YEL
BLU-RED
BLU-WHT
YEL-GRN
BLK-YEL
LT.GRN
YEL-BLK
YEL-RED
RED
GRN-BLU
BLK-BLU
YEL-WHT
WHT-RED
BLK-RED
WHT-BLK DIESEL
BLK-WHT
RED-WHT
RED-YEL
BLU-BLK
RED-BLU
YEL-RED

1983 Jaguar

XJ6

ENGINE COMPARTMENT & FUSE BLOCK

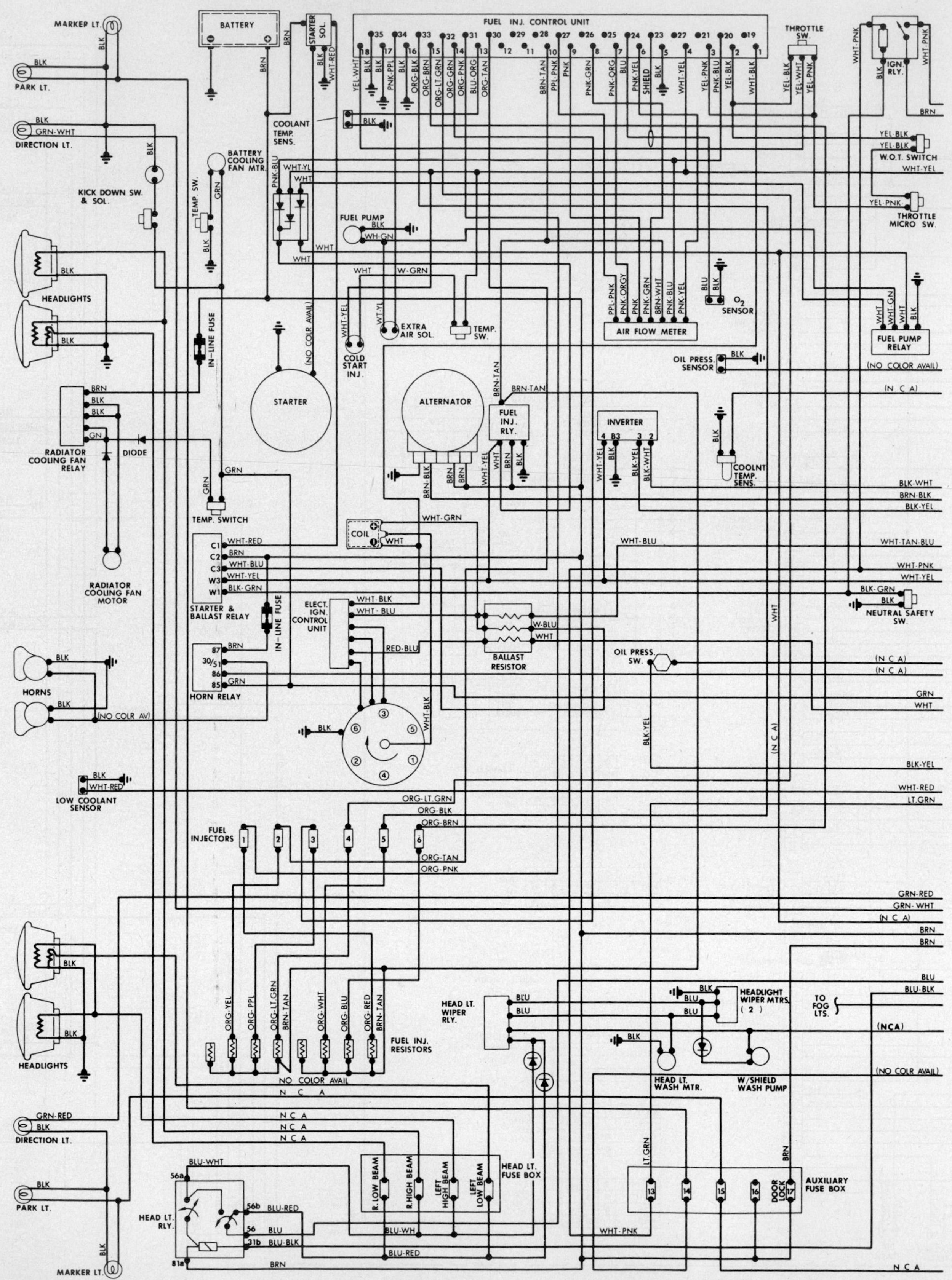
MARKER LT.
PARK LT.
DIRECTION LT.
KICK DOWN SW. & SOL.
HEADLIGHTS
BATTERY
STARTER SOL.
FUEL INJ. CONTROL UNIT
THROTTLE SW.
IGN. RLY.
COOLANT TEMP. SENS.
BATTERY COOLING FAN MTR.
TEMP. SW.
FUEL PUMP
W.O.T. SWITCH
THROTTLE MICRO SW.
EXTRA AIR SOL.
TEMP. SW.
COLD START INJ.
AIR FLOW METER
O_2 SENSOR
FUEL PUMP RELAY
OIL PRESS. SENSOR
IN-LINE FUSE
STARTER
ALTERNATOR
FUEL INJ. RLY.
INVERTER
COOLNT TEMP. SENS.
RADIATOR COOLING FAN RELAY
DIODE
TEMP. SWITCH
COIL
RADIATOR COOLING FAN MOTOR
STARTER & BALLAST RELAY
ELECT. IGN. CONTROL UNIT
BALLAST RESISTOR
NEUTRAL SAFETY SW.
OIL PRESS. SW.
HORNS
HORN RELAY
LOW COOLANT SENSOR
FUEL INJECTORS
HEAD LT. WIPER RLY.
HEADLIGHT WIPER MTRS. (2)
TO FOG LTS.
FUEL INJ. RESISTORS
HEAD LT. WASH MTR.
W/SHIELD WASH PUMP
HEAD LT. RLY.
R. LOW BEAM
R. HIGH BEAM
LEFT HIGH BEAM
LEFT LOW BEAM
HEAD LT. FUSE BOX
DOOR LOCK
AUXILIARY FUSE BOX

XJ6 (Cont.)

UNDERDASH & FUSE BLOCK

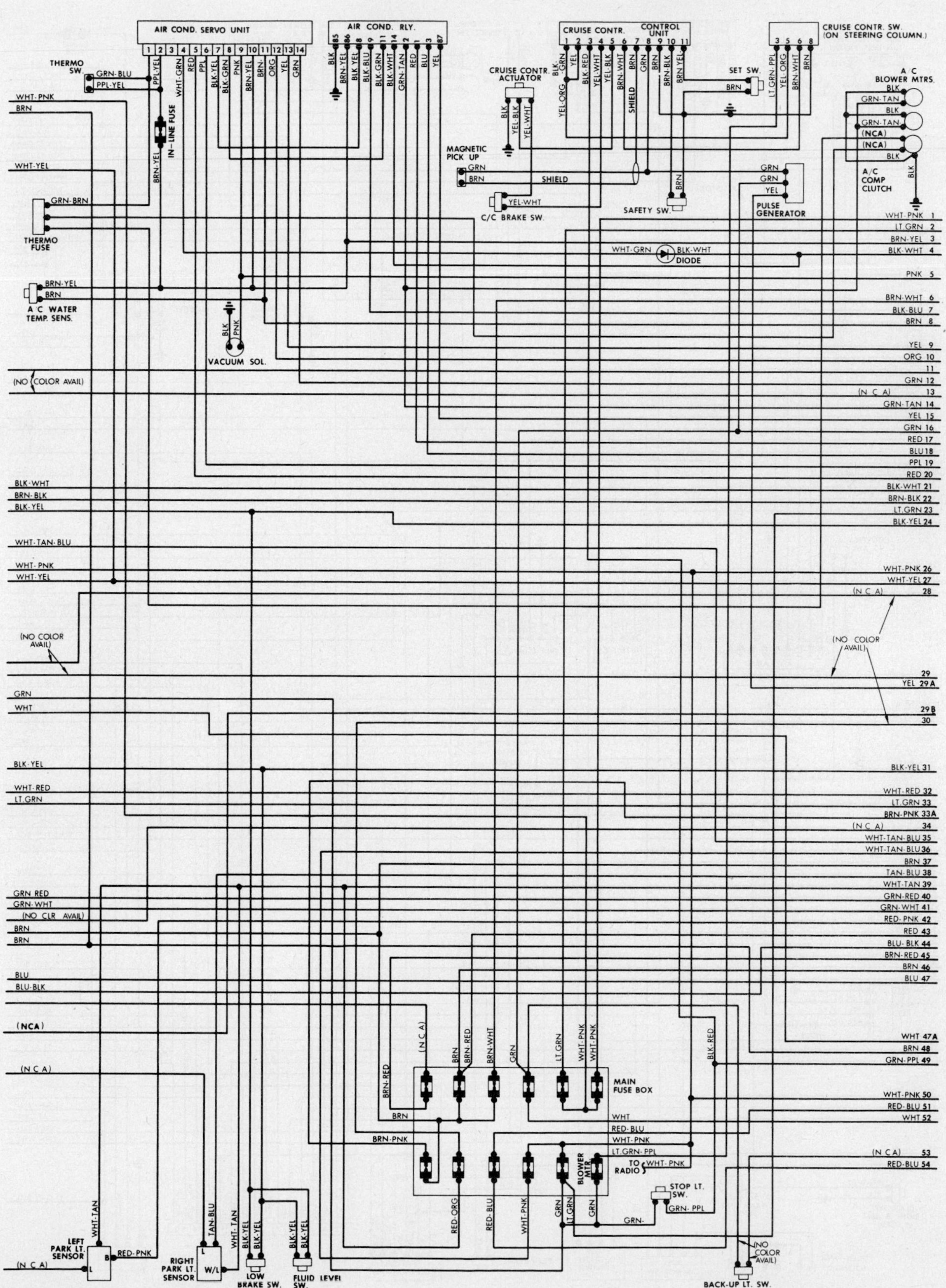

1983 Jaguar

XJ6 (Cont.)

UNDERDASH

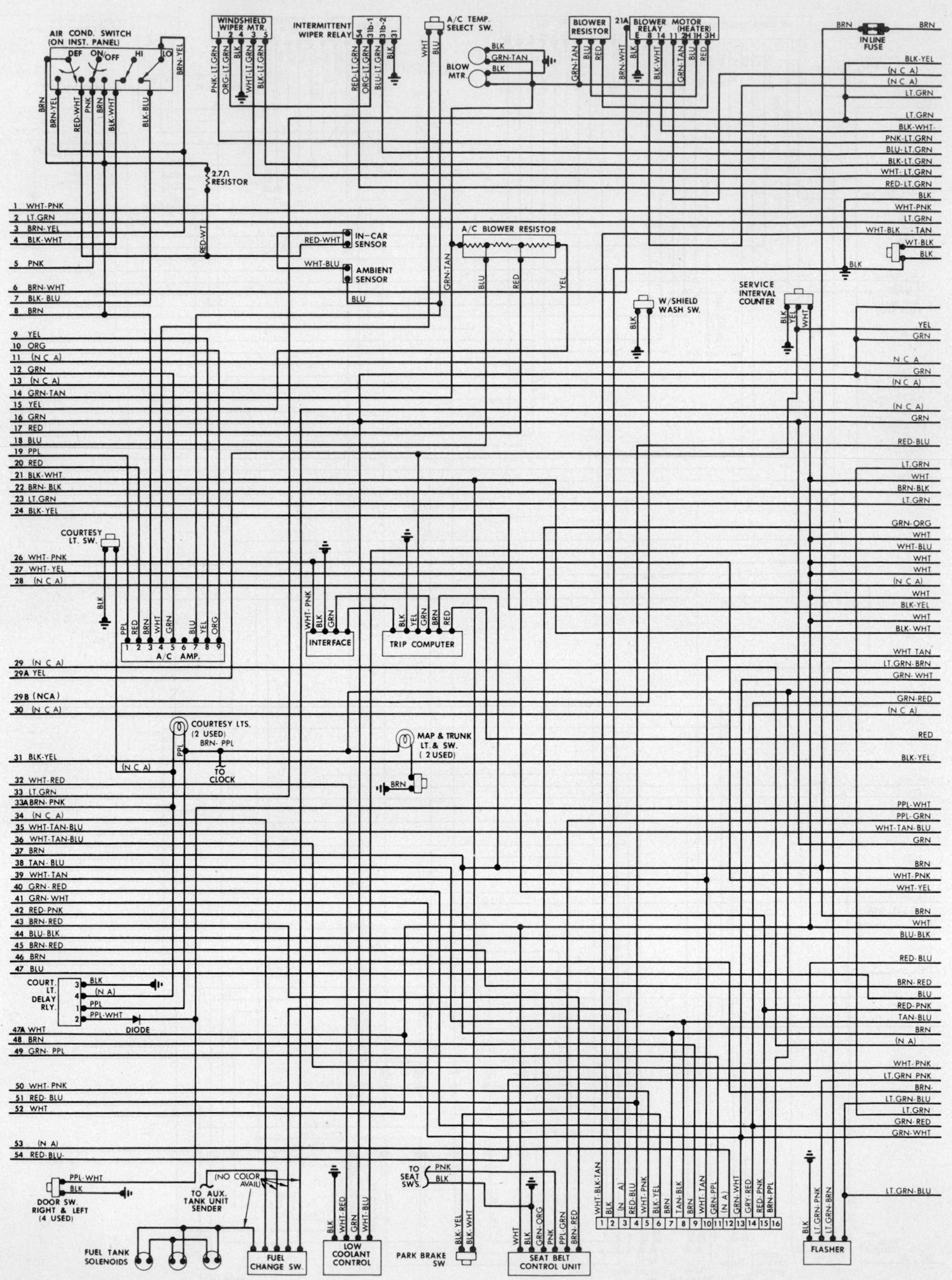

1983 Jaguar

XJ6 (Cont.)

INSTRUMENT PANEL, REAR COMPARTMENT & ACCESSORIES

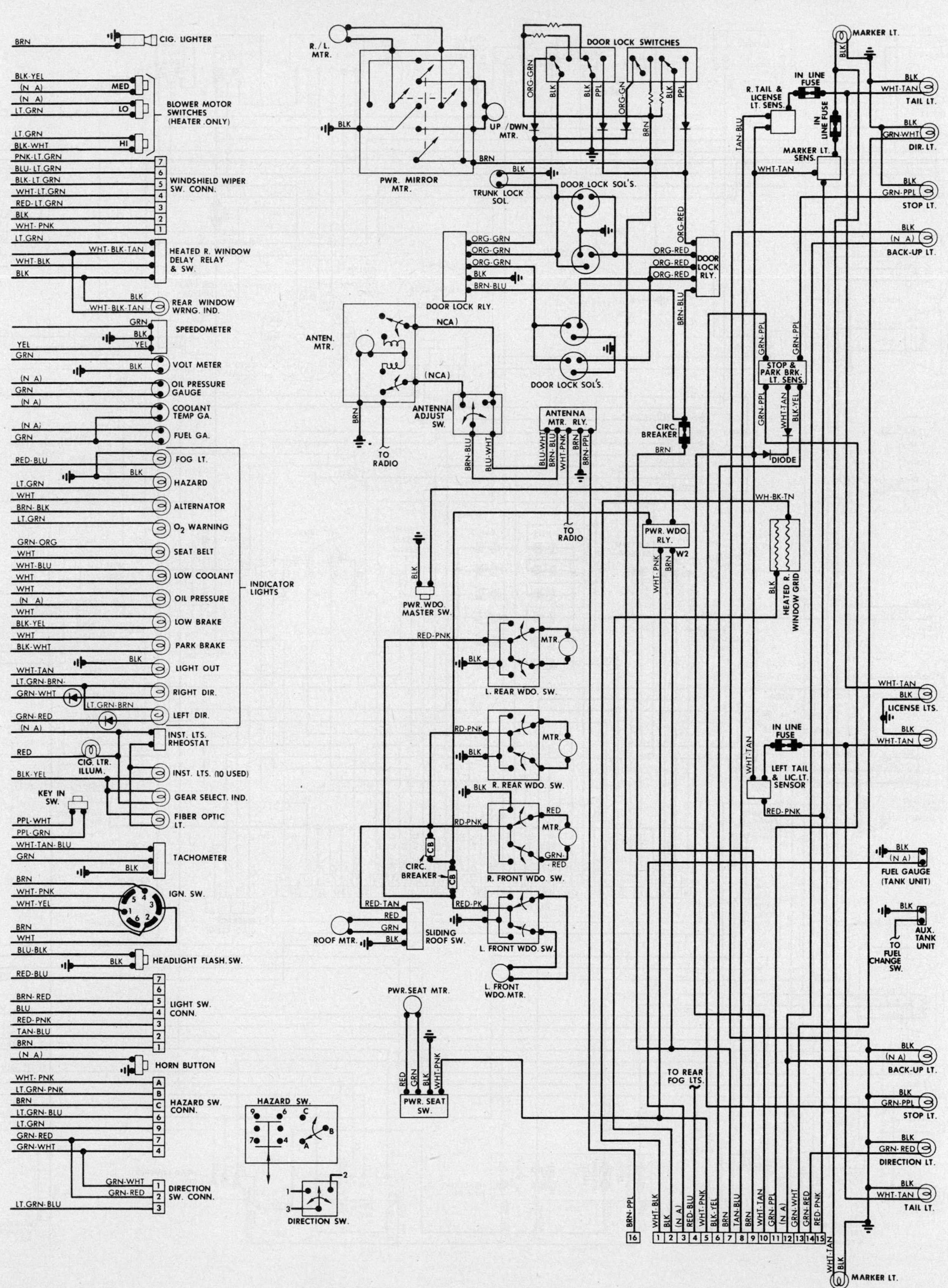

1983 Jaguar

XJS

ENGINE COMPARTMENT & FUSE BLOCK

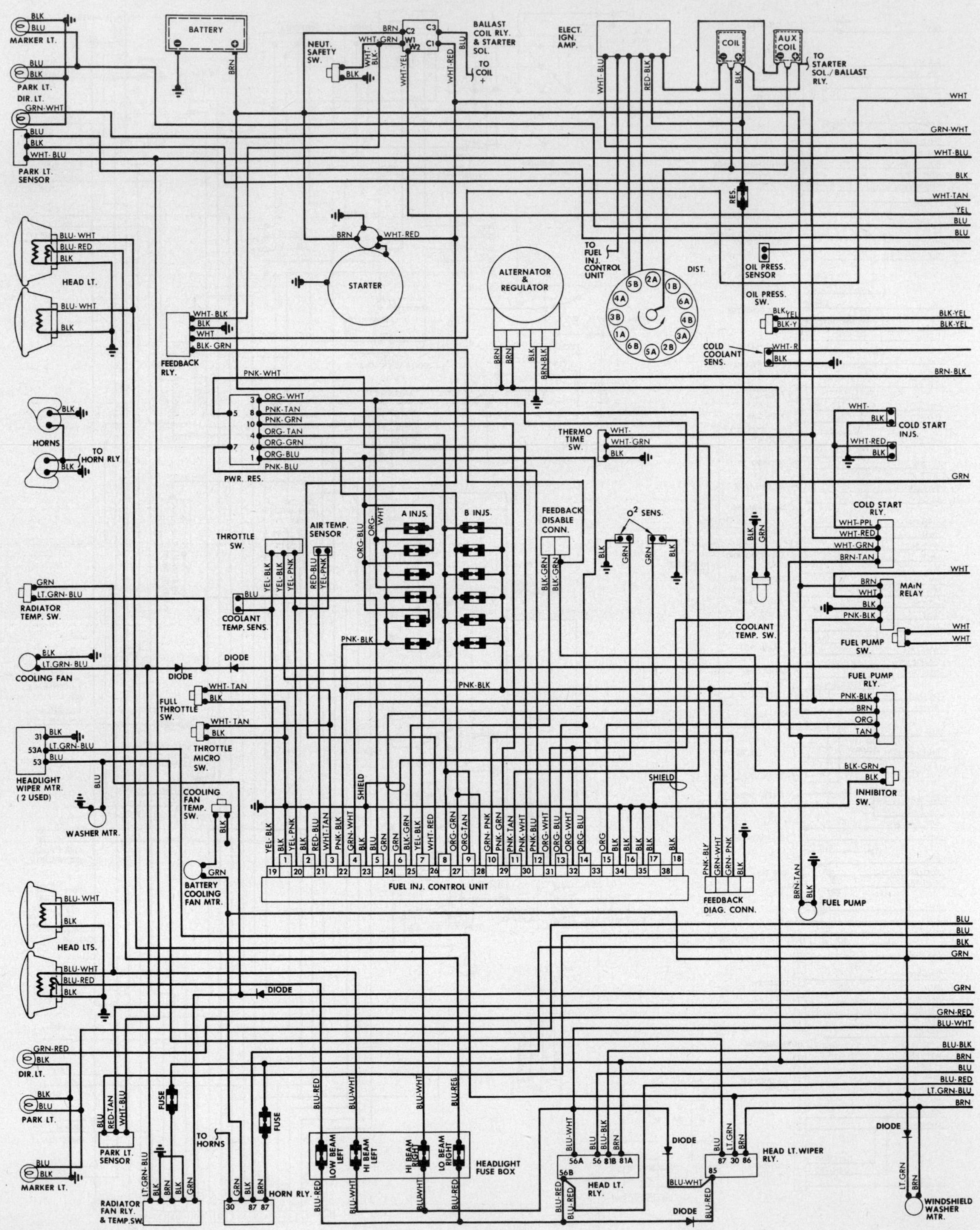
MARKER LT.
PARK LT.
DIR. LT.
PARK LT. SENSOR
BATTERY
NEUT. SAFETY SW.
BALLAST COIL RLY. & STARTER SOL.
TO COIL
ELECT. IGN. AMP.
COIL
AUX COIL
TO STARTER SOL./ BALLAST RLY.
RES.
HEAD LT.
STARTER
ALTERNATOR & REGULATOR
TO FUEL INJ. CONTROL UNIT
DIST.
OIL PRESS. SENSOR
OIL PRESS. SW.
COLD COOLANT SENS.
FEEDBACK RLY.
HORNS
TO HORN RLY
PWR. RES.
THERMO TIME SW.
COLD START INJS.
A INJS.
B INJS.
FEEDBACK DISABLE CONN.
O² SENS.
THROTTLE SW.
AIR TEMP. SENSOR
COLD START RLY.
MAIN RELAY
RADIATOR TEMP. SW.
COOLANT TEMP. SENS.
COOLANT TEMP. SW.
FUEL PUMP SW.
COOLING FAN
DIODE
FULL THROTTLE SW.
FUEL PUMP RLY.
THROTTLE MICRO SW.
HEADLIGHT WIPER MTR. (2 USED)
SHIELD
INHIBITOR SW.
WASHER MTR.
COOLING FAN TEMP. SW.
BATTERY COOLING FAN MTR.
FUEL INJ. CONTROL UNIT
FEEDBACK DIAG. CONN.
FUEL PUMP
HEAD LTS.
DIR. LT.
PARK LT.
MARKER LT.
FUSE
TO HORNS
PARK LT. SENSOR
RADIATOR FAN RLY. & TEMP. SW.
HORN RLY.
LOW BEAM LEFT
HI BEAM LEFT
HI BEAM RIGHT
LO BEAM RIGHT
HEADLIGHT FUSE BOX
HEAD LT. RLY.
HEAD LT. WIPER RLY.
WINDSHIELD WASHER MTR.

XJS (Cont.)

UNDERDASH & FUSE BLOCK

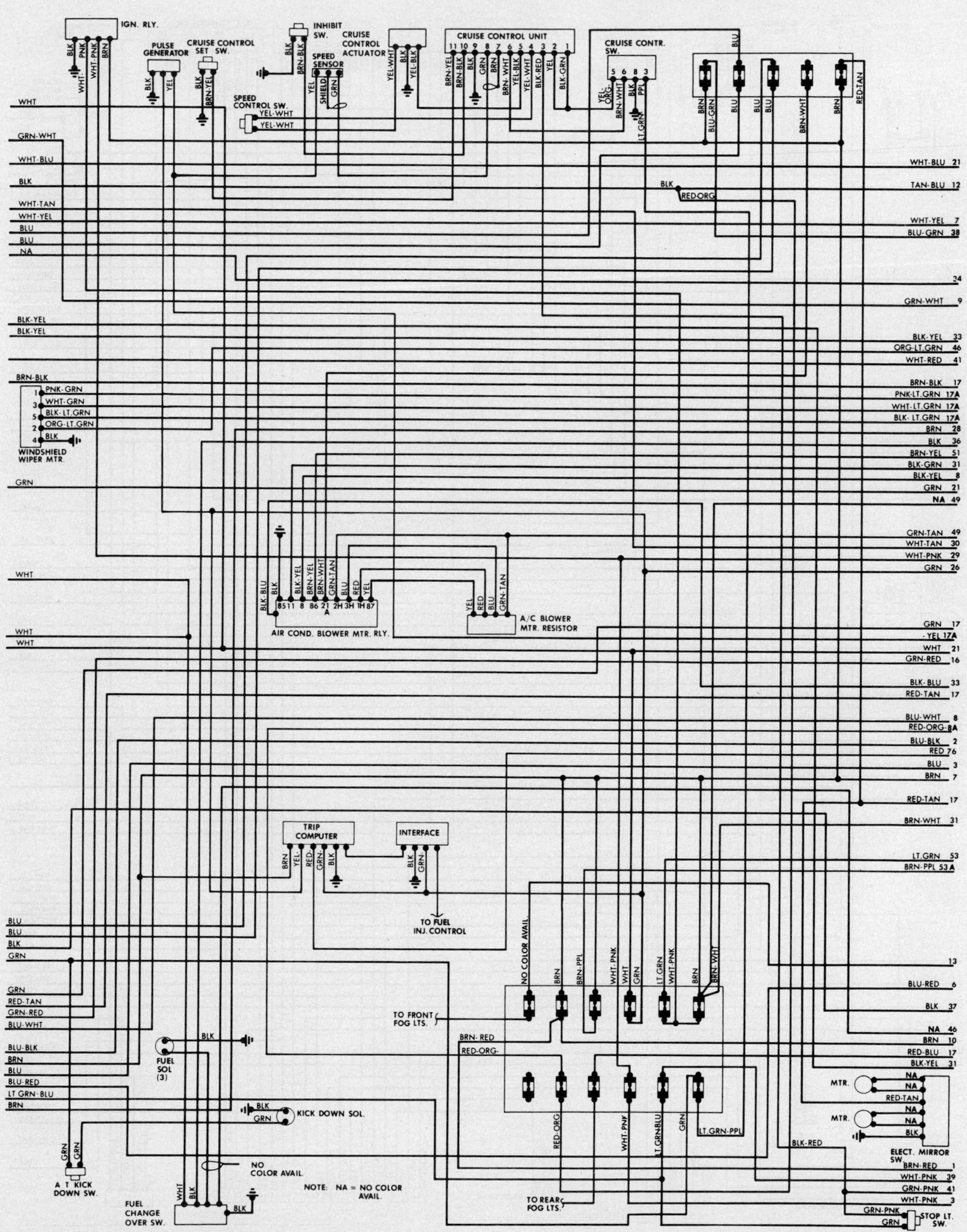

1983 Jaguar

XJS (Cont.)

UNDERDASH

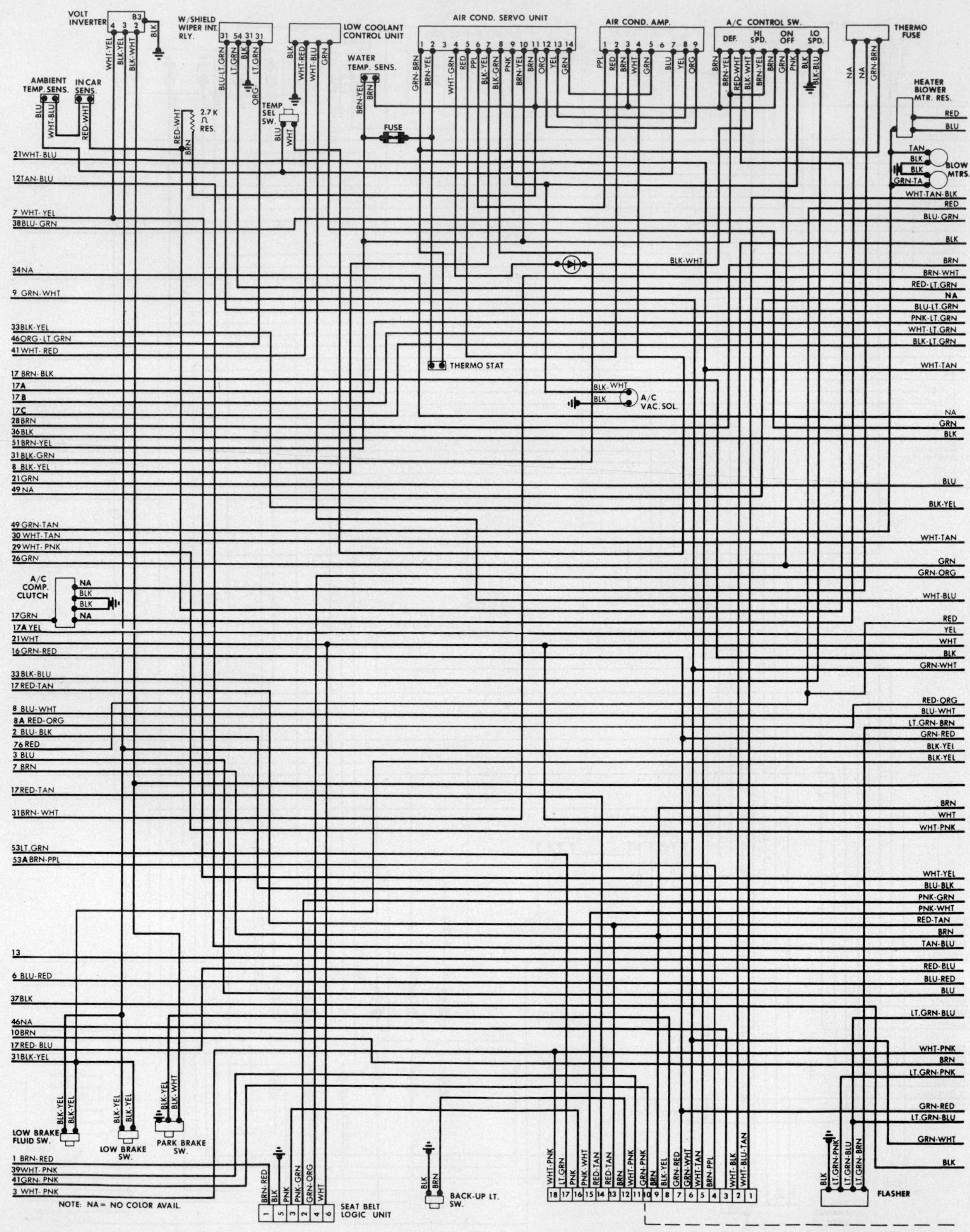

NOTE: NA = NO COLOR AVAIL.

XJS (Cont.)

INSTRUMENT PANEL & REAR COMPARTMENT

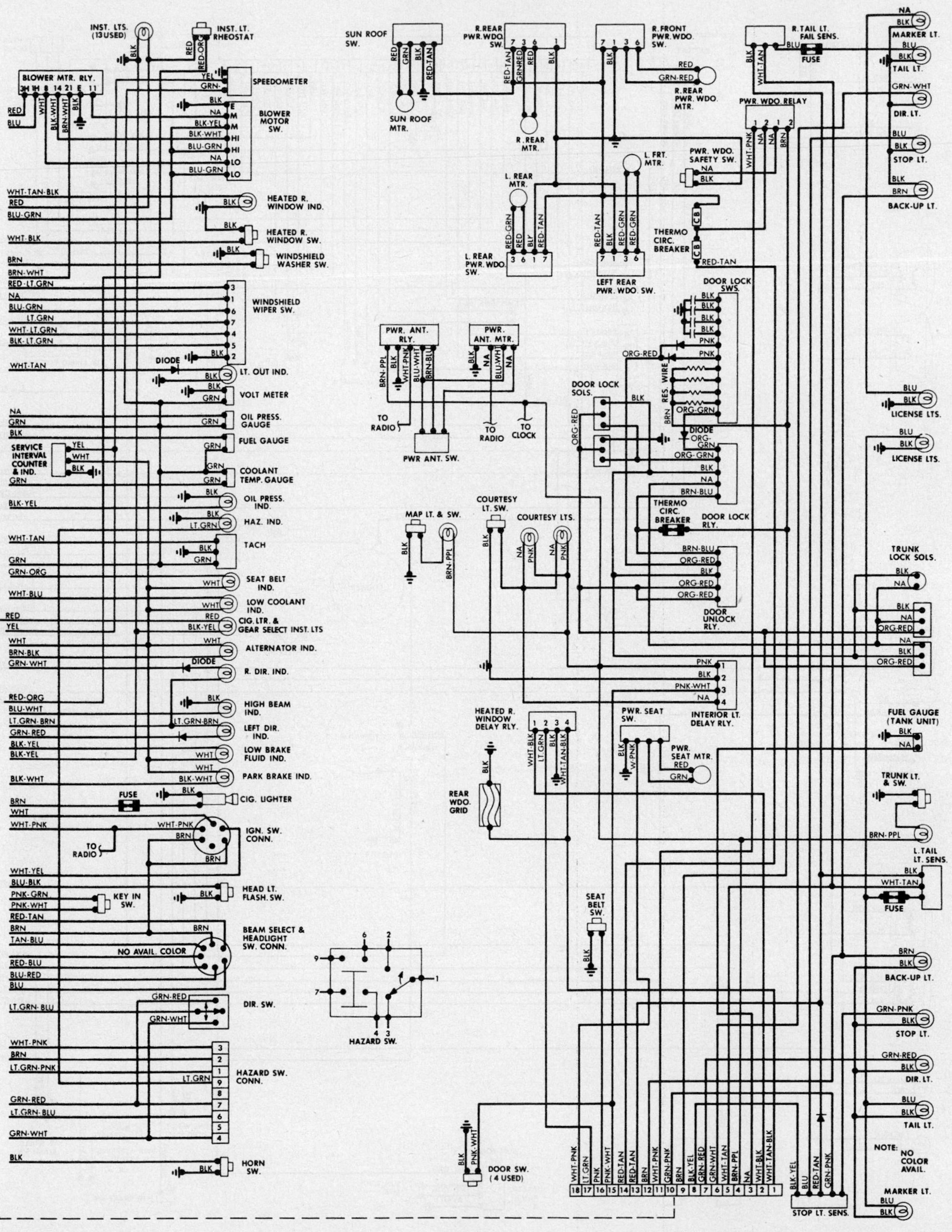
INST. LTS. (13 USED)
INST. LT. RHEOSTAT
BLOWER MTR. RLY.
SPEEDOMETER
BLOWER MOTOR SW.
HEATED R. WINDOW IND.
HEATED R. WINDOW SW.
WINDSHIELD WASHER SW.
WINDSHIELD WIPER SW.
DIODE
LT. OUT IND.
VOLT METER
OIL PRESS. GAUGE
FUEL GAUGE
SERVICE INTERVAL COUNTER & IND.
COOLANT TEMP. GAUGE
OIL PRESS. IND.
HAZ. IND.
TACH
SEAT BELT IND.
LOW COOLANT IND.
CIG. LTR. & GEAR SELECT INST. LTS
ALTERNATOR IND.
R. DIR. IND.
HIGH BEAM IND.
LEFT DIR. IND.
LOW BRAKE FLUID IND.
PARK BRAKE IND.
FUSE
CIG. LIGHTER
IGN. SW. CONN.
TO RADIO
KEY IN SW.
HEAD LT. FLASH. SW.
BEAM SELECT & HEADLIGHT SW. CONN.
NO AVAIL. COLOR
DIR. SW.
HAZARD SW. CONN.
HORN SW.
HAZARD SW.
SUN ROOF SW.
SUN ROOF MTR.
R. REAR PWR. WDO. SW.
R. REAR MTR.
R. FRONT PWR. WDO. SW.
R. REAR PWR. WDO. MTR.
L. FRT. MTR.
L. REAR MTR.
PWR. WDO. SAFETY SW.
THERMO CIRC. BREAKER
L. REAR PWR. WDO. SW.
LEFT REAR PWR. WDO. SW.
R. TAIL LT. FAIL SENS.
PWR. WDO. RELAY
PWR. ANT. RLY.
PWR. ANT. MTR.
TO RADIO
TO CLOCK
PWR ANT. SW.
DOOR LOCK SWS.
RES. WIRE
DOOR LOCK SOLS.
THERMO CIRC. BREAKER
DOOR LOCK RLY.
DOOR UNLOCK RLY.
MAP LT. & SW.
COURTESY LT. SW.
COURTESY LTS.
INTERIOR LT. DELAY RLY.
HEATED R. WINDOW DELAY RLY.
PWR. SEAT SW.
PWR. SEAT MTR.
REAR WDO. GRID
SEAT BELT SW.
DOOR SW. (4 USED)
STOP LT. SENS.
MARKER LT.
TAIL LT.
DIR. LT.
STOP LT.
BACK-UP LT.
LICENSE LTS.
TRUNK LOCK SOLS.
FUEL GAUGE (TANK UNIT)
TRUNK LT. & SW.
L. TAIL LT. SENS.
NOTE: NO COLOR AVAIL.

1983 Mazda

626

ENGINE COMPARTMENT

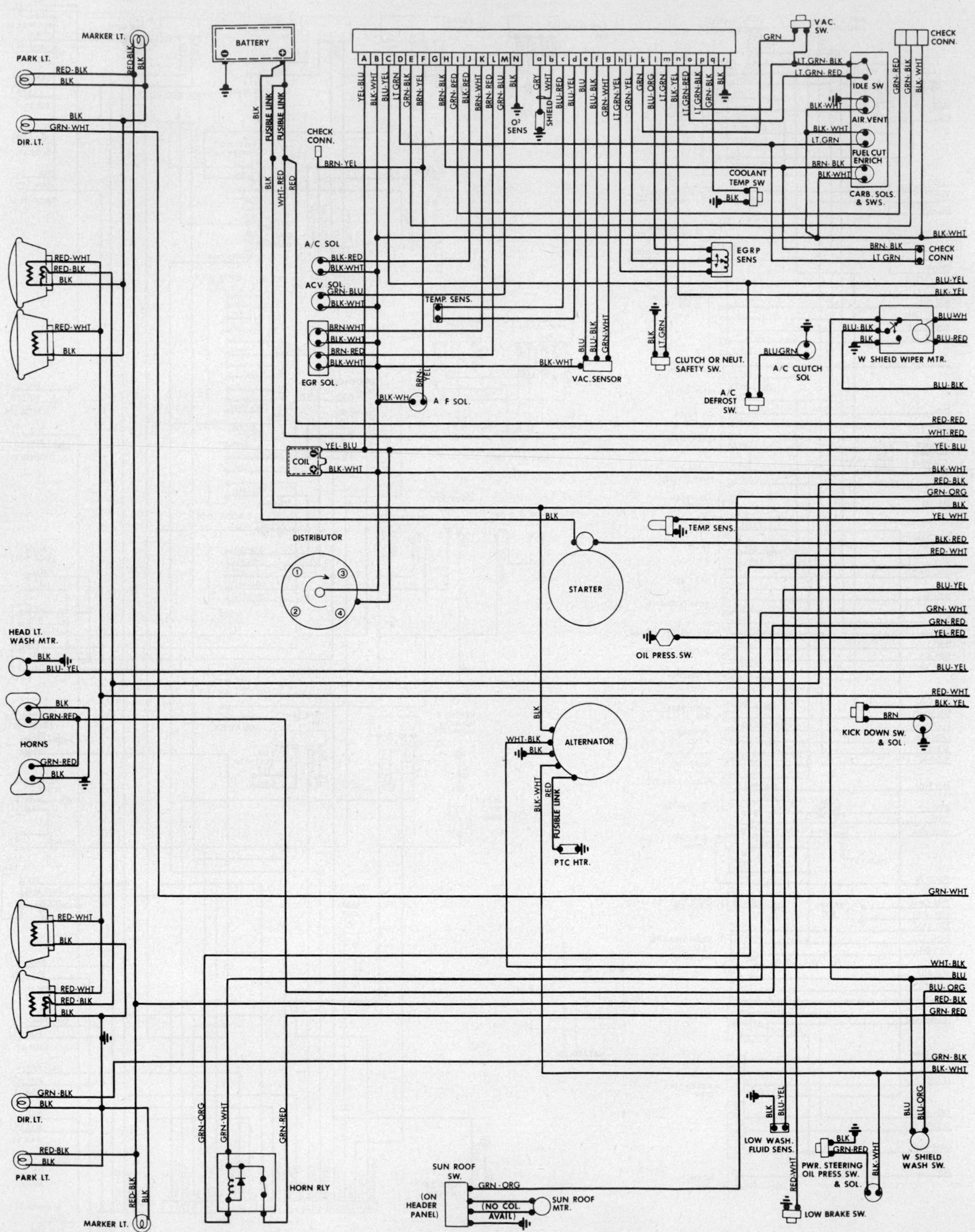

MARKER LT.
PARK LT.
DIR. LT.
BATTERY
FUSIBLE LINK
CHECK CONN.
A/C SOL
ACV SOL.
TEMP. SENS.
EGR SOL.
A F SOL.
COIL
DISTRIBUTOR
STARTER
ALTERNATOR
PTC HTR.
O² SENS
VAC. SW.
CHECK CONN.
IDLE SW
AIR VENT
FUEL CUT ENRICH
CARB. SOLS. & SWS.
COOLANT TEMP SW
EGRP SENS
VAC. SENSOR
CLUTCH OR NEUT. SAFETY SW.
A/C CLUTCH SOL
A/C DEFROST SW.
W SHIELD WIPER MTR.
TEMP. SENS.
OIL PRESS. SW.
KICK DOWN SW. & SOL.
HEAD LT. WASH MTR.
HORNS
HORN RLY
SUN ROOF SW.
(ON HEADER PANEL)
(NO COL. AVAIL)
SUN ROOF MTR.
LOW WASH. FLUID SENS.
PWR. STEERING OIL PRESS SW. & SOL.
LOW BRAKE SW.
W SHIELD WASH SW.

626 (Cont.)

FUSE BLOCK & UNDERDASH

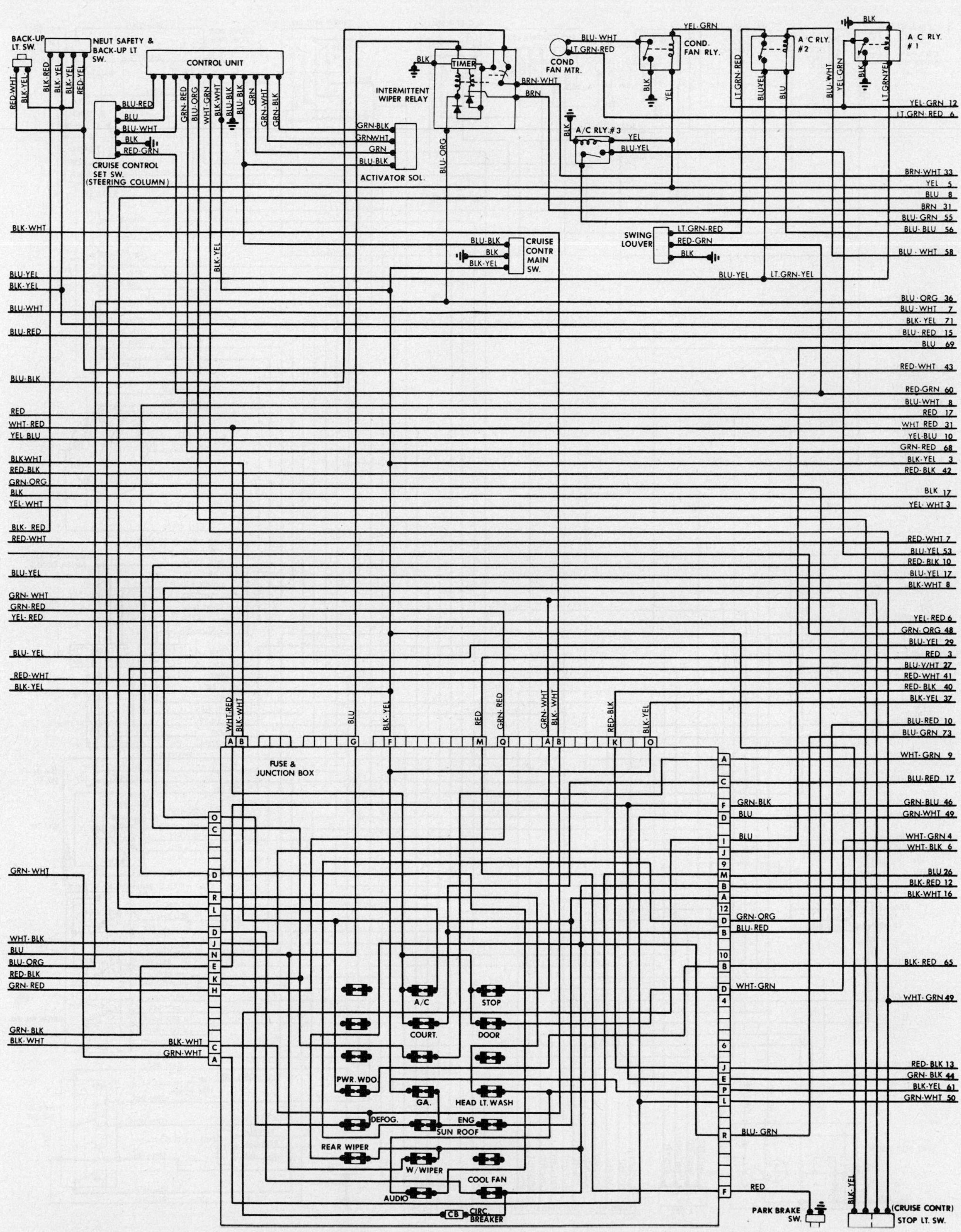

BACK-UP LT. SW.
NEUT SAFETY & BACK-UP LT SW.
CONTROL UNIT
RED-WHT
BLK-YEL
BLK-RED
BLK-YEL
BLK-YEL
RED-YEL
BLU-RED
BLU
BLU-WHT
BLK
RED-GRN
CRUISE CONTROL SET SW. (STEERING COLUMN)
GRN-RED
BLU-ORG
WHT-GRN
BLK-WHT
BLU-BLK
BLU-BLK
GRN
GRN-WHT
GRN-BLK
INTERMITTENT WIPER RELAY
TIMER
BLK
BRN-WHT
BRN
GRN-BLK
GRN-WHT
GRN
BLU-BLK
ACTIVATOR SOL.
BLU-ORG
COND FAN MTR.
BLU-WHT
LT.GRN-RED
YEL-GRN
COND. FAN RLY.
A/C RLY. #2
A/C RLY. #1
A/C RLY. #3
YEL
BLU-YEL
LT.GRN-RED
BLU-YEL
BLU
BLU-WHT
YEL-GRN
LT.GRN-YEL
SWING LOUVER
LT.GRN-RED
RED-GRN
BLK
BLU-BLK
BLK
BLK-YEL
CRUISE CONTR MAIN SW.
BLU-YEL
LT.GRN-YEL
YEL-GRN 12
LT.GRN-RED 6
BRN-WHT 33
YEL 5
BLU 8
BRN 31
BLU-GRN 55
BLU-BLU 56
BLU-WHT 58
BLU-ORG 36
BLU-WHT 7
BLK-YEL 71
BLU-RED 15
BLU 69
RED-WHT 43
RED-GRN 60
BLU-WHT 8
RED 17
WHT-RED 31
YEL-BLU 10
GRN-RED 68
BLK-YEL 3
RED-BLK 42
BLK 17
YEL-WHT 3
RED-WHT 7
BLU-YEL 53
RED-BLK 10
BLU-YEL 17
BLK-WHT 8
YEL-RED 6
GRN-ORG 48
BLU-YEL 29
RED 3
BLU-WHT 27
RED-WHT 41
RED-BLK 40
BLK-YEL 37
BLU-RED 10
BLU-GRN 73
WHT-GRN 9
BLU-RED 17
GRN-BLU 46
GRN-WHT 49
WHT-GRN 4
WHT-BLK 6
BLU 26
BLK-RED 12
BLK-WHT 16
BLK-RED 65
WHT-GRN 49
RED-BLK 13
GRN-BLK 44
BLK-YEL 61
GRN-WHT 50
BLK-WHT
BLU-YEL
BLK-YEL
BLU-WHT
BLU-RED
BLU-BLK
RED
WHT-RED
YEL-BLU
BLK-WHT
RED-BLK
GRN-ORG
BLK
YEL-WHT
BLK-RED
RED-WHT
BLU-YEL
GRN-WHT
GRN-RED
YEL-RED
BLU-YEL
RED-WHT
BLK-YEL
GRN-WHT
WHT-BLK
BLU
BLU-ORG
RED-BLK
GRN-RED
GRN-BLK
BLK-WHT
BLK-WHT
GRN-WHT
WHT-RED
BLK-WHT
BLU
BLK-YEL
RED
GRN-RED
GRN-WHT
BLK-WHT
RED-BLK
BLK-YEL
FUSE & JUNCTION BOX
GRN-BLK
BLU
BLU
GRN-ORG
BLU-RED
WHT-GRN
BLU-GRN
RED
A/C
STOP
COURT.
DOOR
PWR. WDO.
GA.
HEAD LT. WASH
DEFOG.
ENG
SUN ROOF
REAR WIPER
W/WIPER
COOL FAN
AUDIO
CB
CIRC BREAKER
PARK BRAKE SW.
BLK-YEL
(CRUISE CONTR) STOP LT. SW.

1983 Mazda

626 (Cont.)

INSTRUMENT PANEL & UNDERDASH

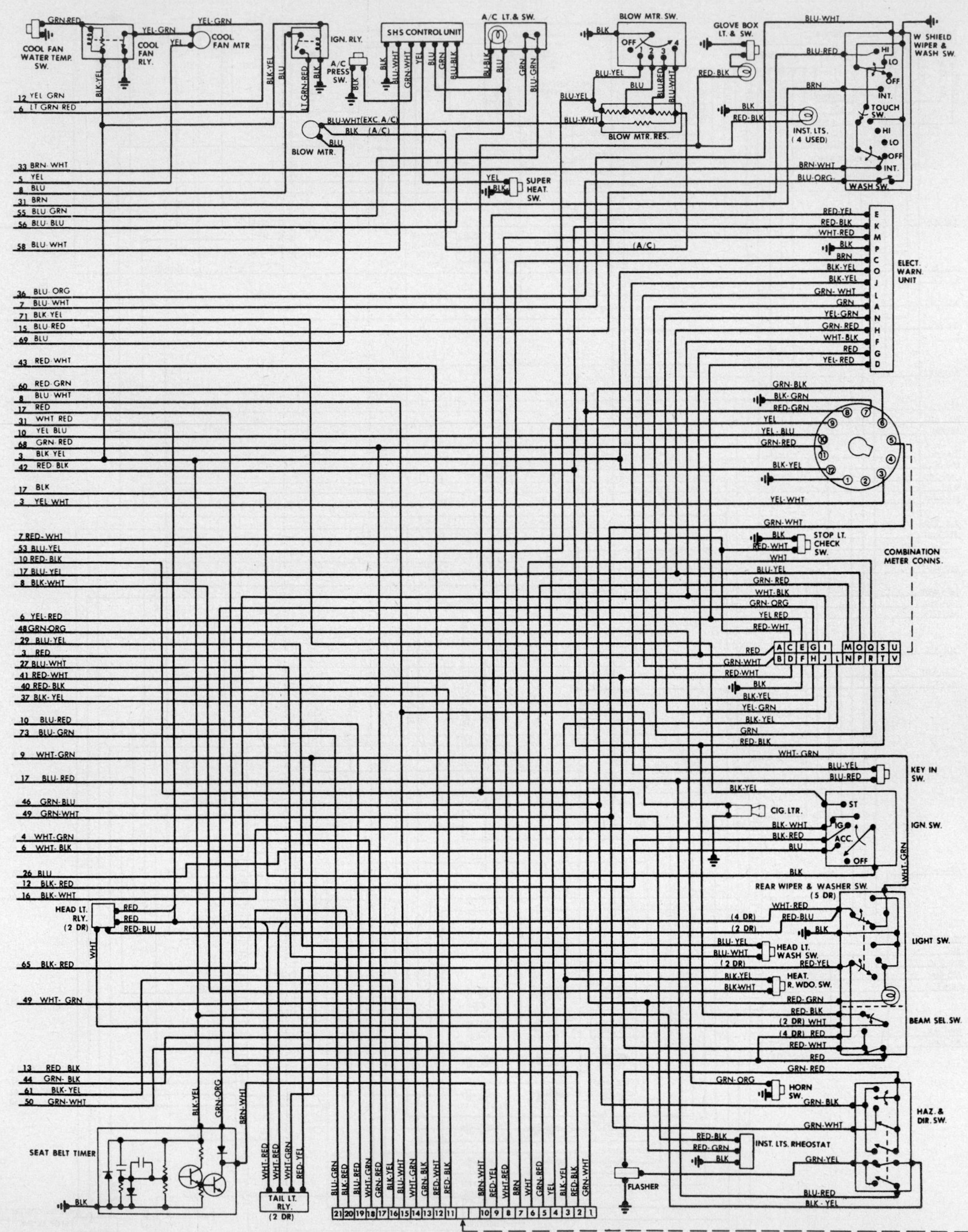

COOL FAN WATER TEMP. SW.
COOL FAN RLY.
COOL FAN MTR
IGN. RLY.
A/C PRESS SW.
SHS CONTROL UNIT
A/C LT. & SW.
BLOW MTR. SW.
GLOVE BOX LT. & SW.
W SHIELD WIPER & WASH SW.
BLOW MTR.
BLOW MTR. RES.
INST. LTS. (4 USED)
SUPER HEAT. SW.
TOUCH SW.
WASH SW.
ELECT. WARN. UNIT
STOP LT. CHECK SW.
COMBINATION METER CONNS.
KEY IN SW.
CIG. LTR.
IGN. SW.
REAR WIPER & WASHER SW. (5 DR)
HEAD LT. RLY. (2 DR)
HEAD LT. WASH SW. (2 DR)
HEAT. R. WDO. SW.
LIGHT SW.
BEAM SEL. SW.
HORN SW.
HAZ. & DIR. SW.
INST. LTS. RHEOSTAT
FLASHER
SEAT BELT TIMER
TAIL LT. RLY. (2 DR)

1983 Mazda

626 (Cont.)

INSTRUMENT PANEL, REAR COMPARTMENT & ACCESSORIES

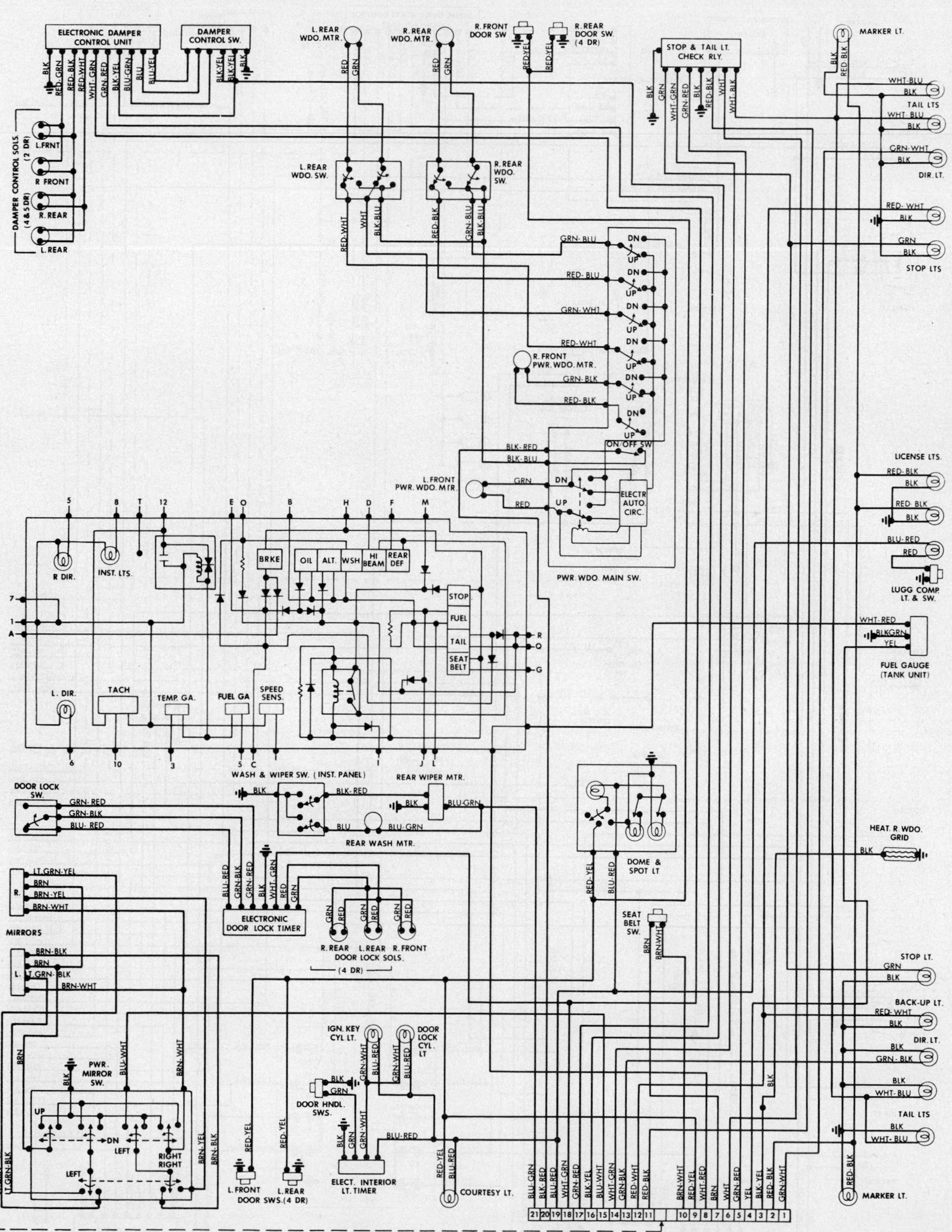

ELECTRONIC DAMPER CONTROL UNIT
DAMPER CONTROL SW.
L. REAR WDO. MTR.
R. REAR WDO. MTR.
R. FRONT DOOR SW
R. REAR DOOR SW. (4 DR)
STOP & TAIL LT. CHECK RLY.
MARKER LT.
TAIL LTS
DIR. LT.
STOP LTS
DAMPER CONTROL SOLS.
L. FRNT
R FRONT
R. REAR
L. REAR
L. REAR WDO. SW.
R. REAR WDO. SW.
R. FRONT PWR. WDO. MTR.
ON-OFF SW
L. FRONT PWR. WDO. MTR.
ELECTR AUTO CIRC.
PWR. WDO. MAIN SW.
LICENSE LTS.
LUGG COMP. LT. & SW.
FUEL GAUGE (TANK UNIT)
R DIR.
INST. LTS.
BRKE
OIL
ALT.
WSH
HI BEAM
REAR DEF
STOP
FUEL
TAIL
SEAT BELT
L. DIR.
TACH
TEMP. GA.
FUEL GA
SPEED SENS.
WASH & WIPER SW. (INST. PANEL)
REAR WIPER MTR.
REAR WASH MTR.
DOOR LOCK SW.
DOME & SPOT LT
HEAT. R. WDO. GRID
ELECTRONIC DOOR LOCK TIMER
R. REAR
L. REAR
R. FRONT
DOOR LOCK SOLS.
(4 DR)
MIRRORS
SEAT BELT SW.
STOP LT.
BACK-UP LT.
IGN. KEY CYL LT.
DOOR LOCK CYL. LT
PWR. MIRROR SW.
UP
DN
LEFT
RIGHT
DOOR HNDL. SWS.
ELECT. INTERIOR LT. TIMER
L. FRONT DOOR SWS.
L. REAR (4 DR)
COURTESY LT.

1983 Mazda

B2000 PICKUP & B2200 DIESEL PICKUP

ENGINE COMPARTMENT & FUSE BLOCK

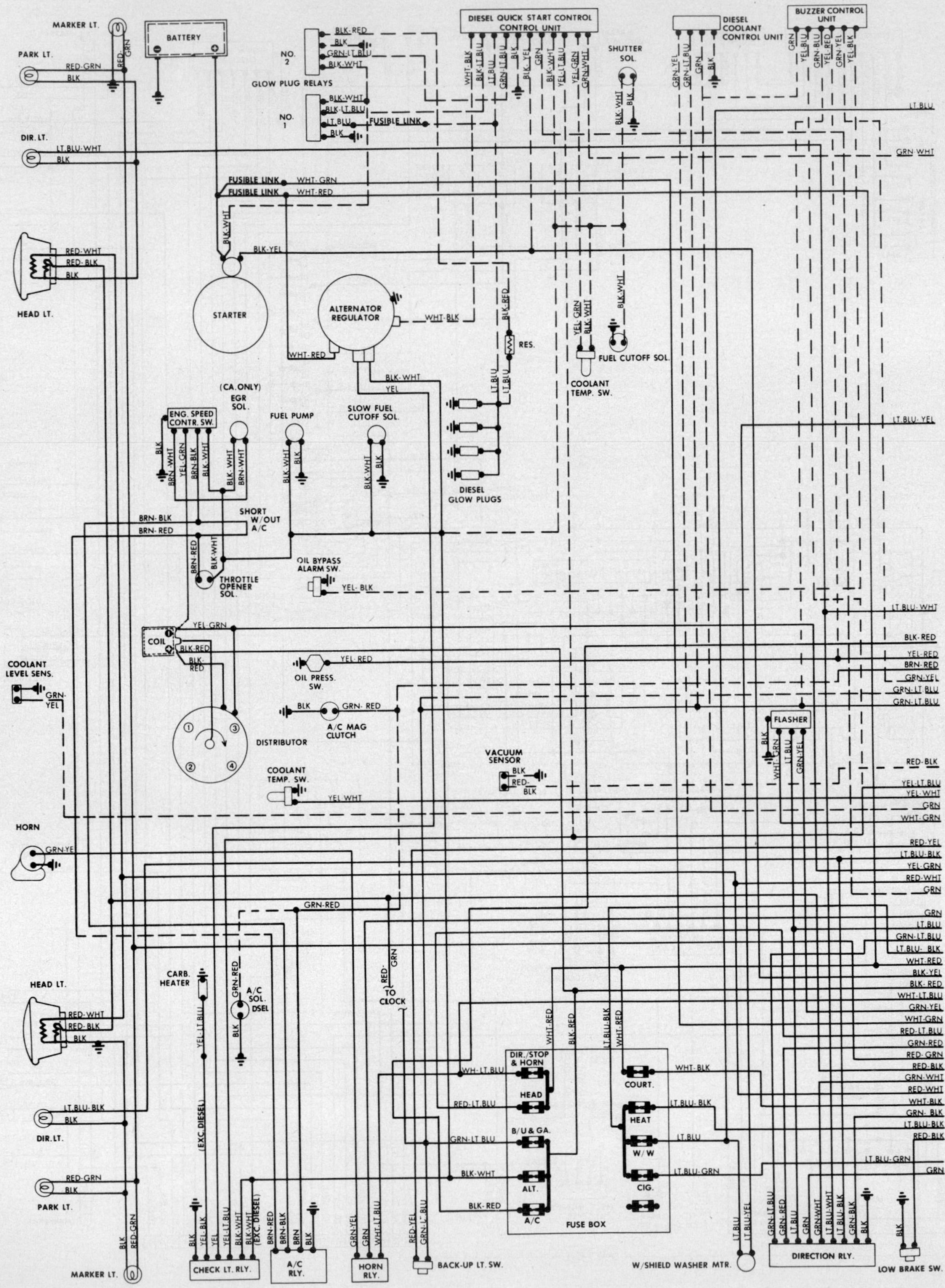

MARKER LT.
PARK LT.
BATTERY
GLOW PLUG RELAYS
DIESEL QUICK START CONTROL CONTROL UNIT
DIESEL COOLANT CONTROL UNIT
BUZZER CONTROL UNIT
SHUTTER SOL.
DIR. LT.
FUSIBLE LINK
HEAD LT.
STARTER
ALTERNATOR REGULATOR
RES.
FUEL CUTOFF SOL.
COOLANT TEMP. SW.
(CA. ONLY)
EGR SOL.
ENG. SPEED CONTR. SW.
FUEL PUMP
SLOW FUEL CUTOFF SOL.
DIESEL GLOW PLUGS
SHORT W/OUT A/C
THROTTLE OPENER SOL.
OIL BYPASS ALARM SW.
COIL
COOLANT LEVEL SENS.
OIL PRESS. SW.
A/C MAG CLUTCH
DISTRIBUTOR
VACUUM SENSOR
FLASHER
HORN
CARB. HEATER
A/C SOL. DSEL
TO CLOCK
DIR./STOP & HORN
HEAD
B/U & GA.
ALT.
A/C
COURT.
HEAT
W/W
CIG.
FUSE BOX
(EXC. DIESEL)
CHECK LT. RLY.
A/C RLY.
HORN RLY.
BACK-UP LT. SW.
W/SHIELD WASHER MTR.
DIRECTION RLY.
LOW BRAKE SW.

1983 Mazda

B2000 PICKUP & B2200 DIESEL PICKUP (Cont.)

INSTRUMENT PANEL, UNDERDASH & REAR COMPARTMENT

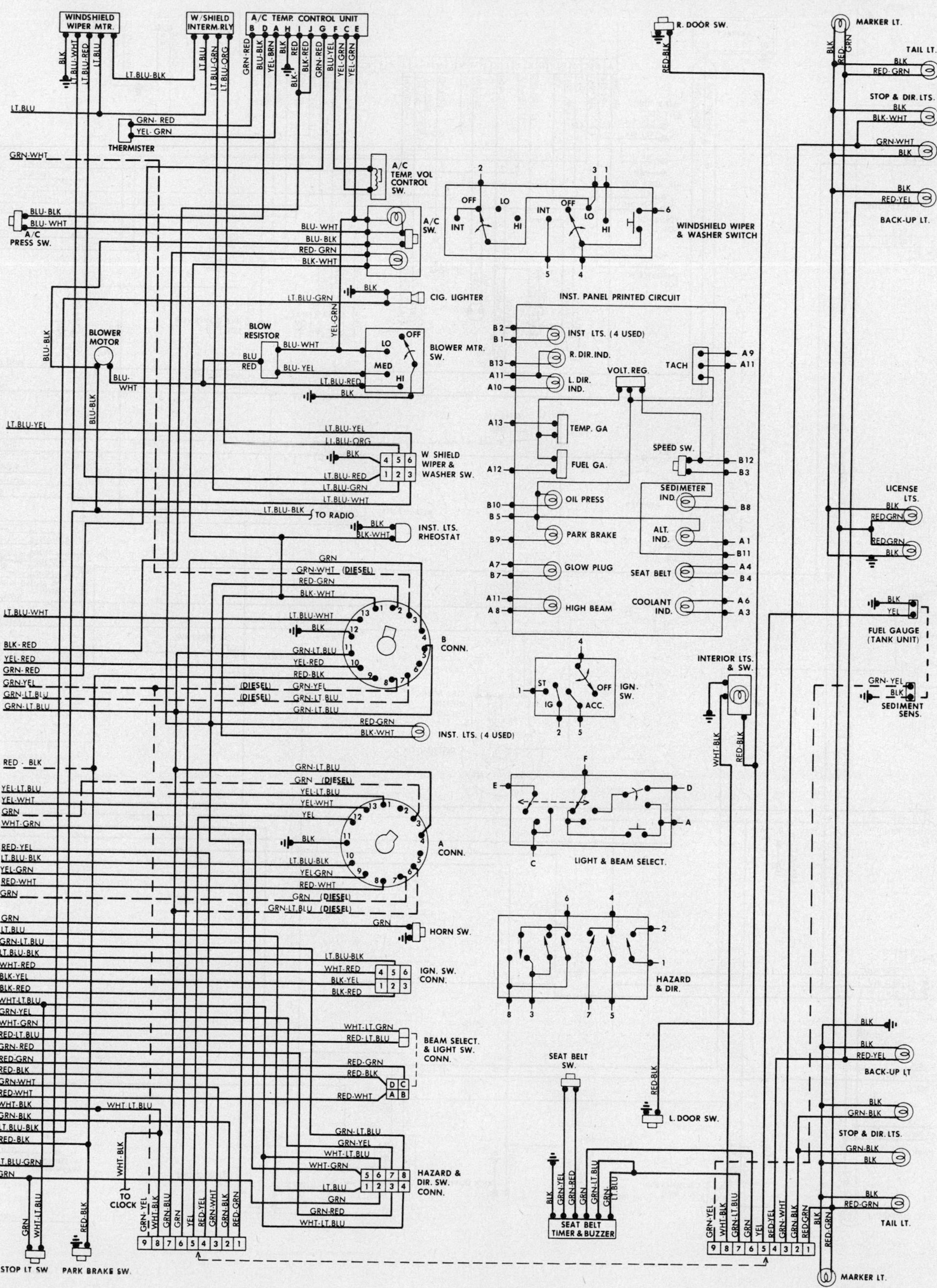

WINDSHIELD WIPER MTR.
W/SHIELD INTERM. RLY
A/C TEMP. CONTROL UNIT
THERMISTER
A/C TEMP. VOL CONTROL SW.
A/C PRESS SW.
A/C SW.
CIG. LIGHTER
BLOWER MOTOR
BLOW RESISTOR
BLOWER MTR. SW.
W SHIELD WIPER & WASHER SW.
TO RADIO
INST. LTS. RHEOSTAT
B CONN.
INST. LTS. (4 USED)
A CONN.
HORN SW.
IGN. SW. CONN.
BEAM SELECT. & LIGHT SW. CONN.
HAZARD & DIR. SW. CONN.
TO CLOCK
STOP LT SW
PARK BRAKE SW.
WINDSHIELD WIPER & WASHER SWITCH
INST. PANEL PRINTED CIRCUIT
INST LTS. (4 USED)
R. DIR. IND.
L. DIR. IND.
VOLT. REG.
TACH
TEMP. GA
FUEL GA.
SPEED SW.
OIL PRESS
SEDIMETER IND.
PARK BRAKE
ALT. IND.
GLOW PLUG
SEAT BELT
HIGH BEAM
COOLANT IND.
IGN. SW.
LIGHT & BEAM SELECT.
HAZARD & DIR.
SEAT BELT SW.
SEAT BELT TIMER & BUZZER
L. DOOR SW.
R. DOOR SW.
INTERIOR LTS. & SW.
MARKER LT.
TAIL LT.
STOP & DIR. LTS.
BACK-UP LT.
LICENSE LTS.
FUEL GAUGE (TANK UNIT)
SEDIMENT SENS.

1983 Mazda

GLC – EXCEPT WAGON

ENGINE COMPARTMENT

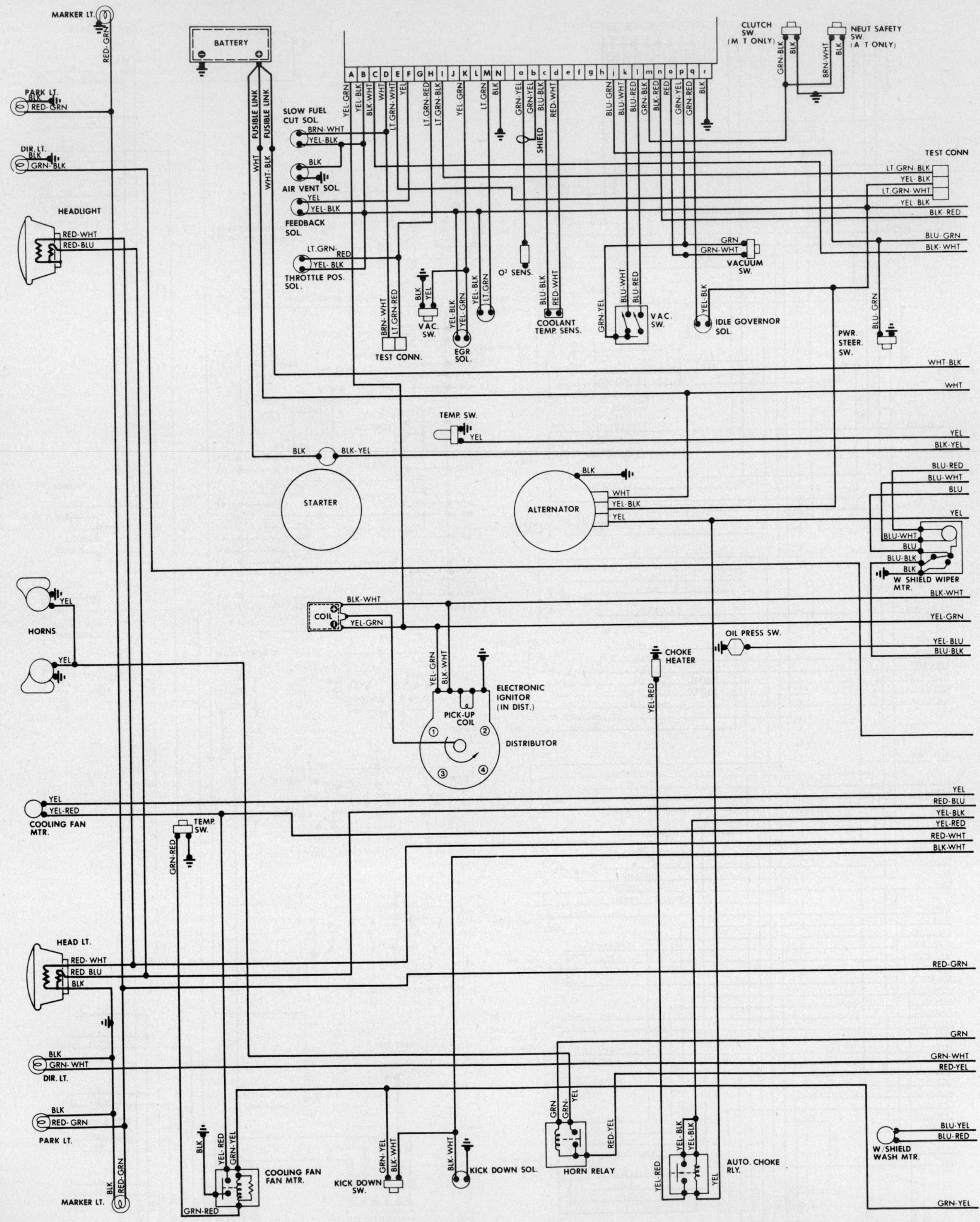

MARKER LT.
BATTERY
PARK LT.
DIR. LT.
HEADLIGHT
SLOW FUEL CUT SOL.
AIR VENT SOL.
FEEDBACK SOL.
THROTTLE POS. SOL.
FUSIBLE LINK
TEST CONN.
VAC. SW.
EGR SOL.
O² SENS.
COOLANT TEMP. SENS.
VAC. SW.
VACUUM SW.
IDLE GOVERNOR SOL.
CLUTCH SW. (M T ONLY)
NEUT SAFETY SW. (A T ONLY)
TEST CONN
PWR. STEER. SW.
TEMP. SW.
STARTER
ALTERNATOR
W SHIELD WIPER MTR.
HORNS
COIL
ELECTRONIC IGNITOR (IN DIST.)
PICK-UP COIL
DISTRIBUTOR
OIL PRESS SW.
CHOKE HEATER
COOLING FAN MTR.
TEMP. SW.
HEAD LT.
DIR. LT.
PARK LT.
MARKER LT.
COOLING FAN FAN MTR.
KICK DOWN SW.
KICK DOWN SOL.
HORN RELAY
AUTO. CHOKE RLY.
W/SHIELD WASH MTR.

1983 Mazda

GLC – EXCEPT WAGON (Cont.)

FUSE BLOCK & UNDERDASH

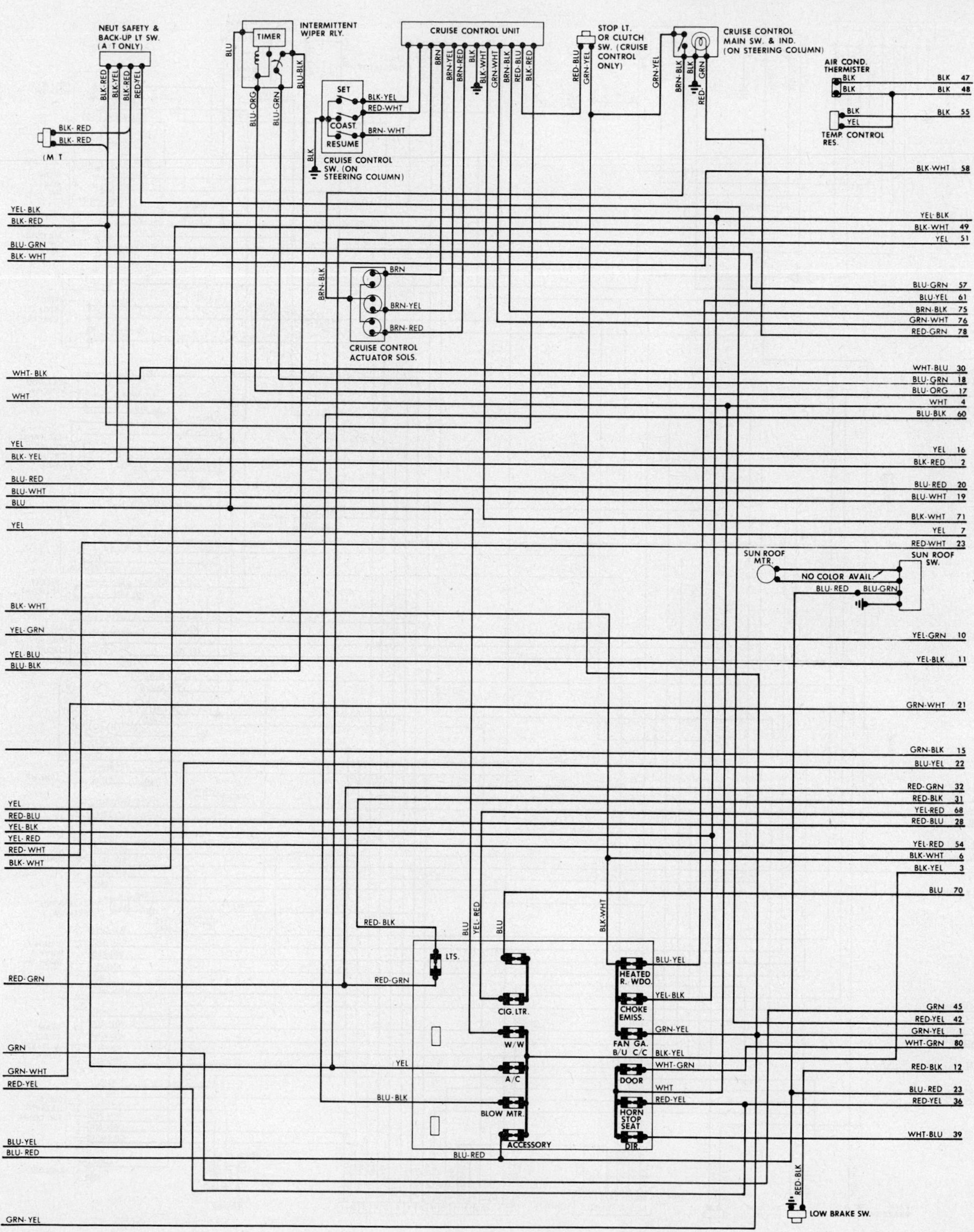

NEUT SAFETY & BACK-UP LT SW. (A T ONLY)
INTERMITTENT WIPER RLY.
TIMER
CRUISE CONTROL UNIT
STOP LT. OR CLUTCH SW. (CRUISE CONTROL ONLY)
CRUISE CONTROL MAIN SW. & IND. (ON STEERING COLUMN)
AIR COND. THERMISTER
TEMP. CONTROL RES.
SET
COAST
RESUME
CRUISE CONTROL SW. (ON STEERING COLUMN)
CRUISE CONTROL ACTUATOR SOLS.
SUN ROOF MTR.
SUN ROOF SW.
NO COLOR AVAIL.
LTS.
CIG. LTR.
W/W
A/C
BLOW MTR.
ACCESSORY
HEATED R. WDO.
CHOKE EMISS.
FAN GA. B/U C/C
DOOR
HORN STOP SEAT
DIR.
LOW BRAKE SW.
BLK 47
BLK 48
BLK 55
BLK-WHT 58
YEL-BLK
BLK-WHT 49
YEL 51
BLU-GRN 57
BLU-YEL 61
BRN-BLK 75
GRN-WHT 76
RED-GRN 78
WHT-BLU 30
BLU-GRN 18
BLU-ORG 17
WHT 4
BLU-BLK 60
YEL 16
BLK-RED 2
BLU-RED 20
BLU-WHT 19
BLK-WHT 71
YEL 7
RED-WHT 23
YEL-GRN 10
YEL-BLK 11
GRN-WHT 21
GRN-BLK 15
BLU-YEL 22
RED-GRN 32
RED-BLK 31
YEL-RED 68
RED-BLU 28
YEL-RED 54
BLK-WHT 6
BLK-YEL 3
BLU 70
GRN 45
RED-YEL 42
GRN-YEL 1
WHT-GRN 80
RED-BLK 12
BLU-RED 23
RED-YEL 36
WHT-BLU 39

1983 Mazda

GLC – EXCEPT WAGON (Cont.)

UNDERDASH, FUSE BLOCK & INSTRUMENT PANEL

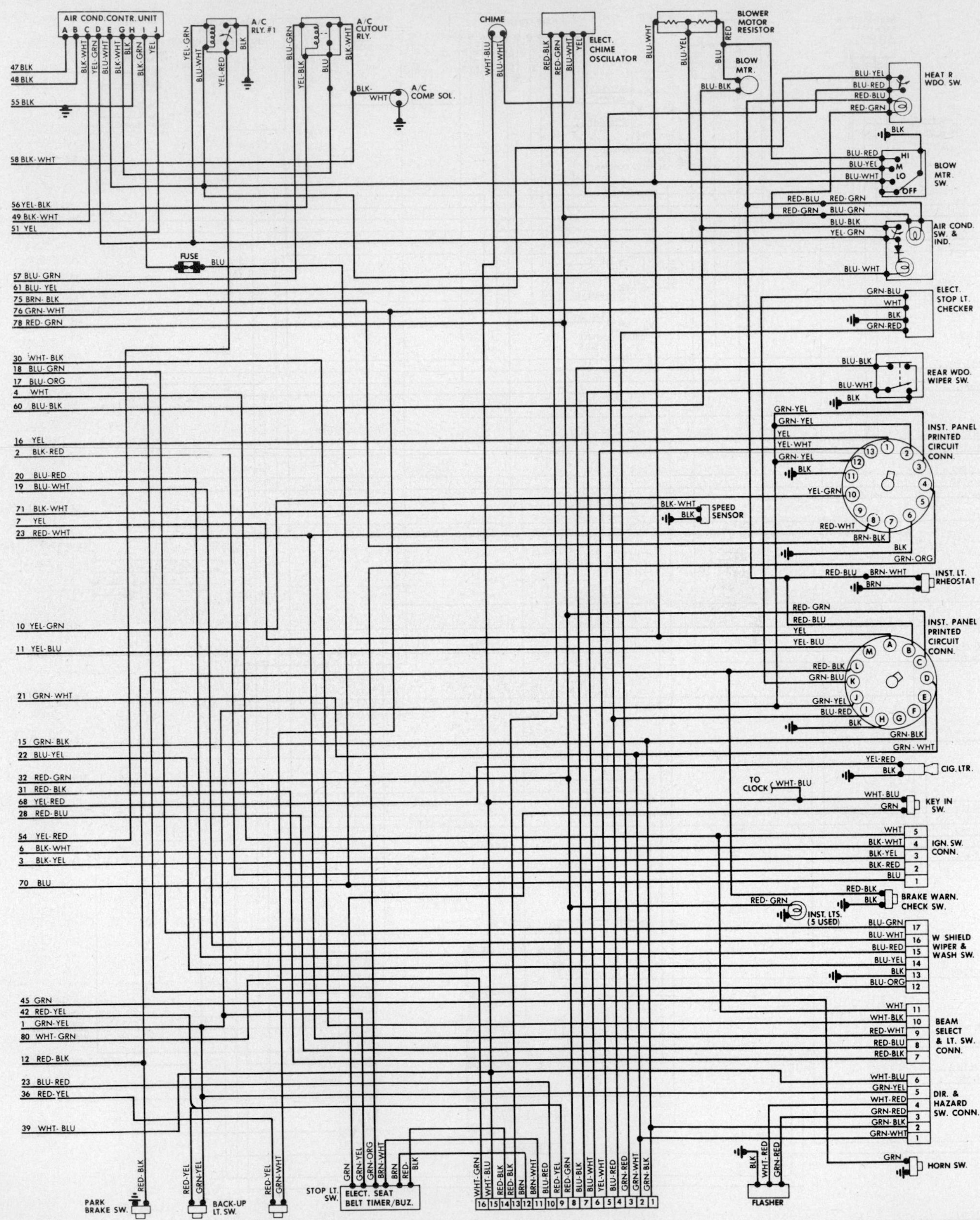

AIR COND. CONTR. UNIT
A/C RLY. #1
A/C CUTOUT RLY.
A/C COMP. SOL.
CHIME
ELECT. CHIME OSCILLATOR
BLOWER MOTOR RESISTOR
BLOW MTR.
HEAT R WDO SW.
BLOW MTR. SW.
AIR COND. SW. & IND.
ELECT. STOP LT. CHECKER
REAR WDO. WIPER SW.
INST. PANEL PRINTED CIRCUIT CONN.
SPEED SENSOR
INST. LT. RHEOSTAT
FUSE
CIG. LTR.
TO CLOCK
KEY IN SW.
IGN. SW. CONN.
BRAKE WARN. CHECK SW.
INST. LTS. (5 USED)
W SHIELD WIPER & WASH SW.
BEAM SELECT & LT. SW. CONN.
DIR. & HAZARD SW. CONN.
HORN SW.
FLASHER
PARK BRAKE SW.
BACK-UP LT. SW.
STOP LT. SW.
ELECT. SEAT BELT TIMER/BUZ.

GLC – EXCEPT WAGON (Cont.)

REAR COMPARTMENT & ACCESSORIES

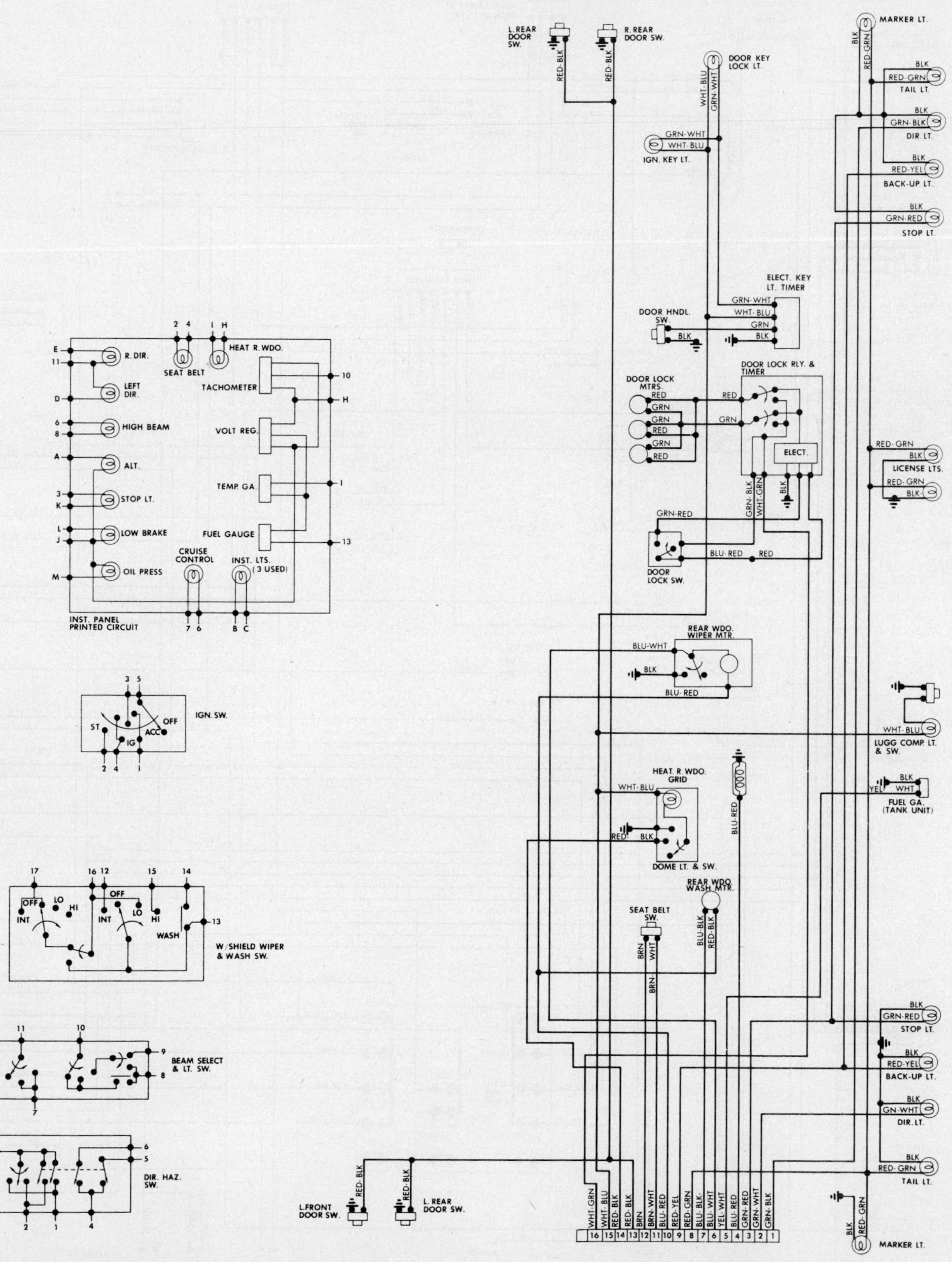
L. REAR DOOR SW.
R. REAR DOOR SW.
DOOR KEY LOCK LT.
IGN. KEY LT.
MARKER LT.
TAIL LT.
DIR. LT.
BACK-UP LT.
STOP LT.
ELECT. KEY LT. TIMER
DOOR HNDL. SW.
DOOR LOCK MTRS.
DOOR LOCK RLY. & TIMER
ELECT.
LICENSE LTS.
DOOR LOCK SW.
REAR WDO. WIPER MTR.
LUGG COMP. LT. & SW.
FUEL GA. (TANK UNIT)
HEAT. R. WDO. GRID
DOME LT. & SW.
REAR WDO. WASH MTR.
SEAT BELT SW.
L. FRONT DOOR SW.
R. DIR.
LEFT DIR.
HIGH BEAM
ALT.
STOP LT.
LOW BRAKE
OIL PRESS
SEAT BELT
HEAT R. WDO.
TACHOMETER
VOLT REG.
TEMP. GA.
FUEL GAUGE
CRUISE CONTROL
INST. LTS. (3 USED)
INST. PANEL PRINTED CIRCUIT
IGN. SW.
W/SHIELD WIPER & WASH SW.
BEAM SELECT & LT. SW.
DIR. HAZ. SW.

1983 Mazda

GLC WAGON

ENGINE COMPARTMENT & FUSE BLOCK

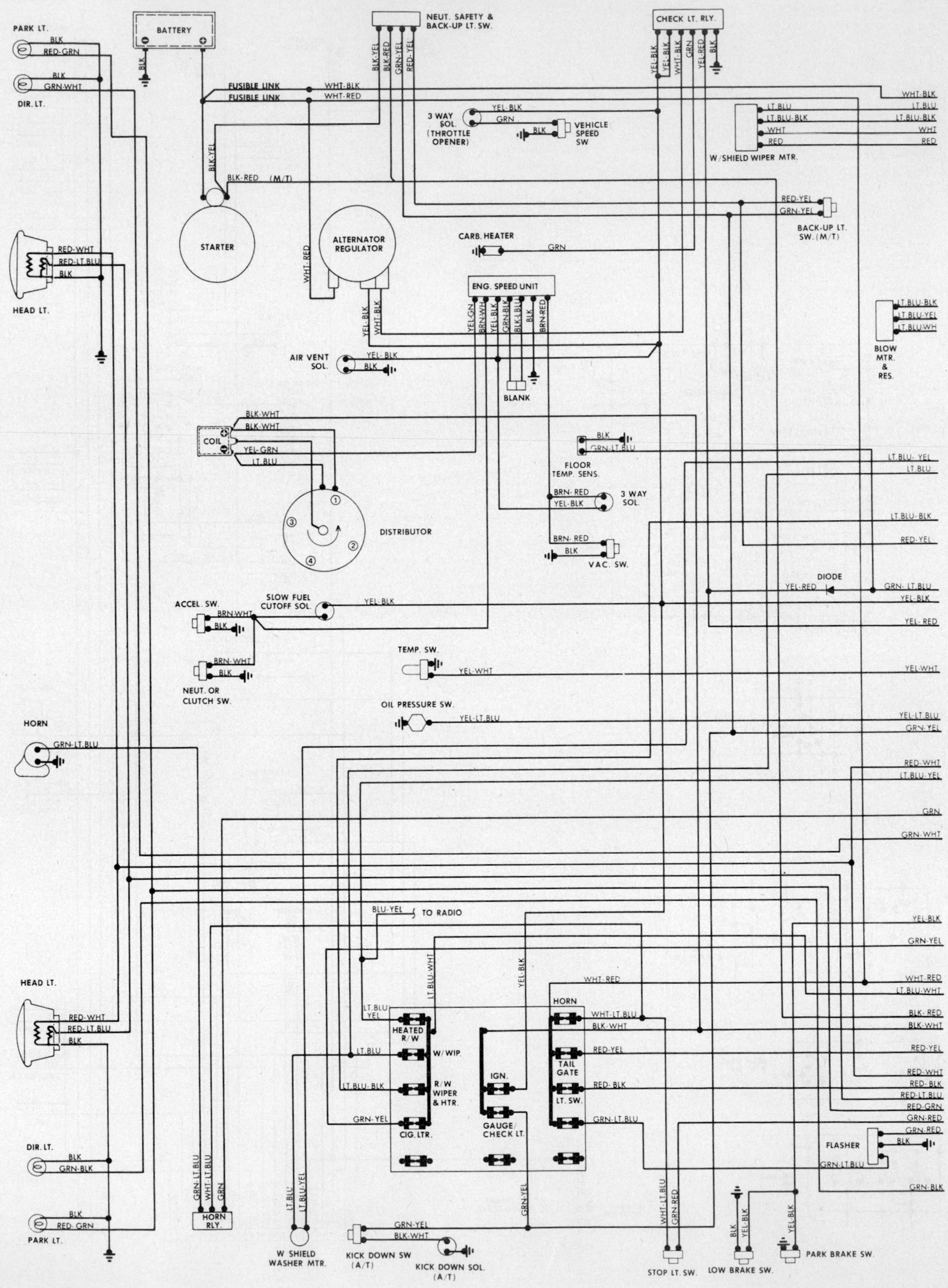
PARK LT.
BATTERY
NEUT. SAFETY & BACK-UP LT. SW.
CHECK LT. RLY.
DIR. LT.
FUSIBLE LINK
FUSIBLE LINK
3 WAY SOL. (THROTTLE OPENER)
VEHICLE SPEED SW
W/SHIELD WIPER MTR.
STARTER
ALTERNATOR REGULATOR
BACK-UP LT. SW. (M/T)
CARB. HEATER
HEAD LT.
ENG. SPEED UNIT
AIR VENT SOL.
BLANK
BLOW MTR. & RES.
COIL
FLOOR TEMP. SENS.
3 WAY SOL.
DISTRIBUTOR
VAC. SW.
DIODE
ACCEL. SW.
SLOW FUEL CUTOFF SOL.
TEMP. SW.
NEUT. OR CLUTCH SW.
OIL PRESSURE SW.
HORN
TO RADIO
HEAD LT.
HEATED R/W
W/WIP.
R/W WIPER & HTR.
CIG. LTR.
IGN.
GAUGE/ CHECK LT.
HORN
TAIL GATE
LT. SW.
FLASHER
DIR. LT.
PARK LT.
HORN RLY.
W SHIELD WASHER MTR.
KICK DOWN SW (A/T)
KICK DOWN SOL. (A/T)
STOP LT. SW.
LOW BRAKE SW.
PARK BRAKE SW.

1983 Mazda

GLC WAGON (Cont.)

UNDERDASH, INSTRUMENT PANEL & REAR COMPARTMENT

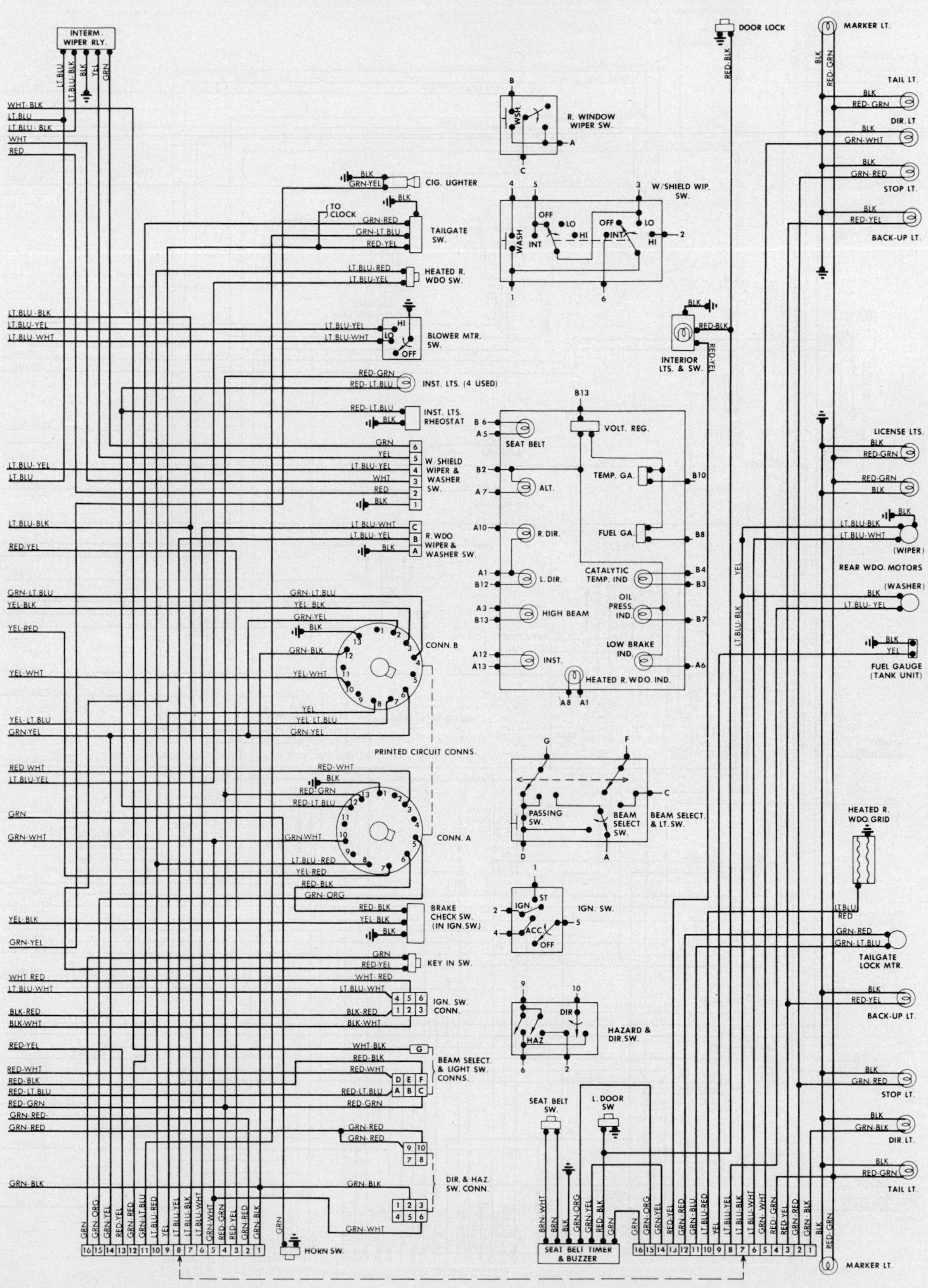
INTERM. WIPER RLY.
DOOR LOCK
MARKER LT.
TAIL LT.
DIR. LT
STOP LT.
BACK-UP LT.
R. WINDOW WIPER SW.
W/SHIELD WIP. SW.
CIG. LIGHTER
TO CLOCK
TAILGATE SW.
HEATED R. WDO SW.
BLOWER MTR. SW.
INTERIOR LTS. & SW.
INST. LTS. (4 USED)
INST. LTS. RHEOSTAT
VOLT. REG.
SEAT BELT
W. SHIELD WIPER & WASHER SW.
TEMP. GA.
ALT.
LICENSE LTS.
R. WDO. WIPER & WASHER SW.
R. DIR.
FUEL GA.
(WIPER)
REAR WDO. MOTORS
(WASHER)
L. DIR.
CATALYTIC TEMP. IND
OIL PRESS. IND.
HIGH BEAM
LOW BRAKE IND.
INST.
HEATED R. WDO. IND.
CONN. B
FUEL GAUGE (TANK UNIT)
PRINTED CIRCUIT CONNS.
PASSING SW.
BEAM SELECT SW.
BEAM SELECT. & LT. SW.
CONN. A
HEATED R. WDO. GRID
BRAKE CHECK SW. (IN IGN. SW.)
IGN. SW.
TAILGATE LOCK MTR.
KEY IN SW.
IGN. SW. CONN.
HAZARD & DIR. SW.
BEAM SELECT. & LIGHT SW. CONNS.
SEAT BELT SW.
L. DOOR SW
DIR. & HAZ. SW. CONN.
HORN SW.
SEAT BELT TIMER & BUZZER

1983 Mazda

RX7

ENGINE COMPARTMENT

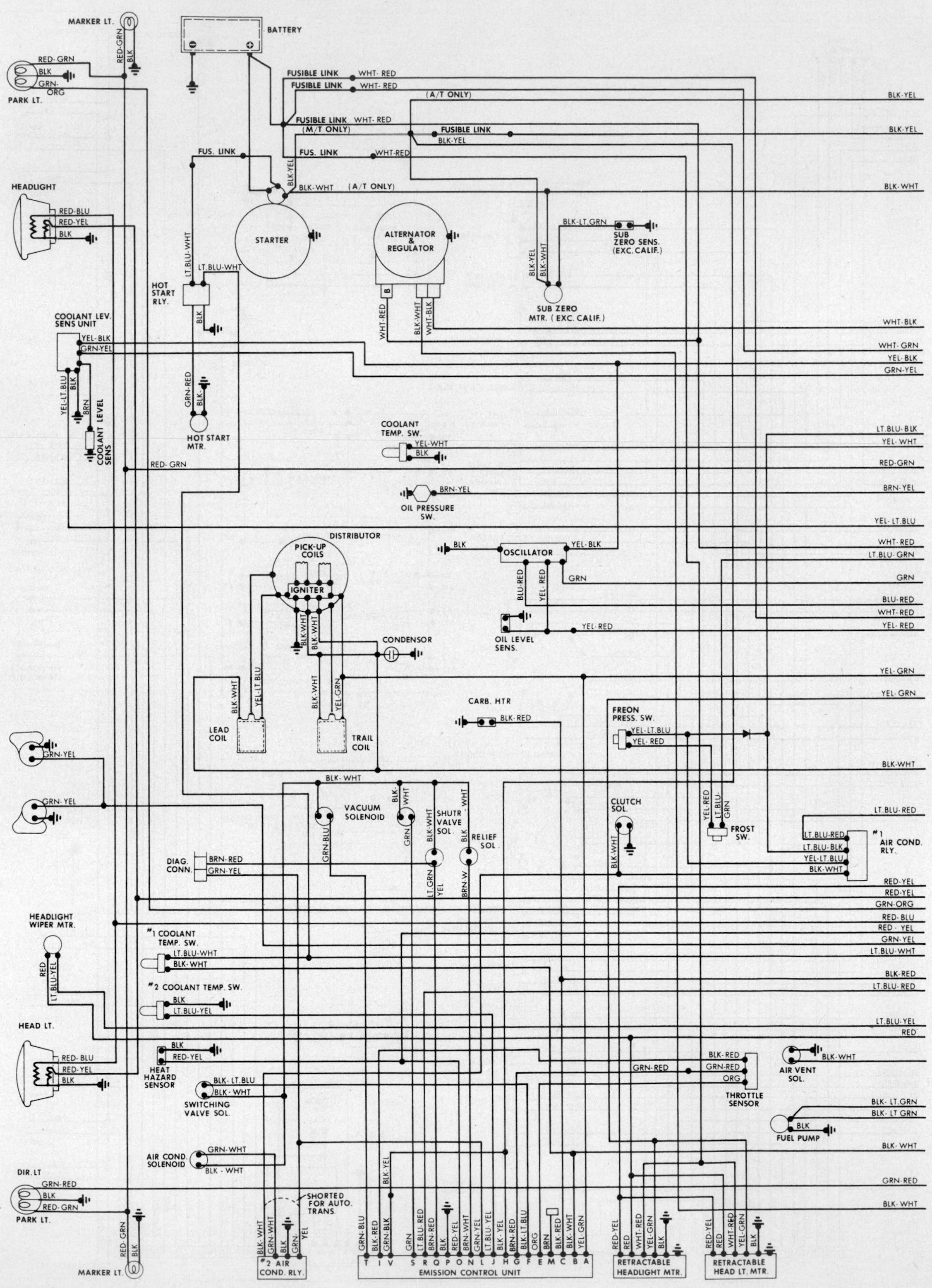

MARKER LT.
RED-GRN
BLK
BATTERY
PARK LT.
GRN-ORG
FUSIBLE LINK
WHT-RED
(A/T ONLY)
BLK-YEL
(M/T ONLY)
FUS. LINK
BLK-WHT
HEADLIGHT
RED-BLU
RED-YEL
STARTER
ALTERNATOR & REGULATOR
BLK-LT.GRN
SUB ZERO SENS. (EXC. CALIF.)
SUB ZERO MTR. (EXC. CALIF.)
LT.BLU-WHT
HOT START RLY.
COOLANT LEV. SENS UNIT
YEL-BLK
GRN-YEL
YEL-LT.BLU
BRN
COOLANT LEVEL SENS
WHT-BLK
WHT-GRN
GRN-RED
HOT START MTR.
COOLANT TEMP. SW.
YEL-WHT
LT.BLU-BLK
OIL PRESSURE SW.
BRN-YEL
YEL-LT.BLU
DISTRIBUTOR
PICK-UP COILS
IGNITER
OSCILLATOR
WHT-RED
LT.BLU-GRN
GRN
BLU-RED
YEL-RED
OIL LEVEL SENS.
CONDENSOR
YEL-GRN
LEAD COIL
TRAIL COIL
CARB. HTR
BLK-RED
FREON PRESS. SW.
YEL-LT.BLU
YEL-RED
VACUUM SOLENOID
SHUTR VALVE SOL.
RELIEF SOL.
GRN-BLU
CLUTCH SOL.
FROST SW.
LT.BLU-RED
LT.BLU-BLK
YEL-LT.BLU
#1 AIR COND. RLY.
DIAG. CONN.
BRN-RED
RED-YEL
GRN-ORG
RED-BLU
LT.BLU-WHT
HEADLIGHT WIPER MTR.
#1 COOLANT TEMP. SW.
#2 COOLANT TEMP. SW.
LT.BLU-YEL
RED
HEAD LT.
HEAT HAZARD SENSOR
BLK-LT.BLU
SWITCHING VALVE SOL.
BLK-RED
ORG
THROTTLE SENSOR
AIR VENT SOL.
BLK-LT.GRN
FUEL PUMP
AIR COND. SOLENOID
GRN-WHT
DIR. LT
SHORTED FOR AUTO. TRANS
#2 AIR COND. RLY.
EMISSION CONTROL UNIT
T I V S R Q P O N L J H G F E M C B A
RETRACTABLE HEADLIGHT MTR.
RETRACTABLE HEAD LT. MTR.

RX7 (Cont.)

FUSE BLOCK & UNDERDASH

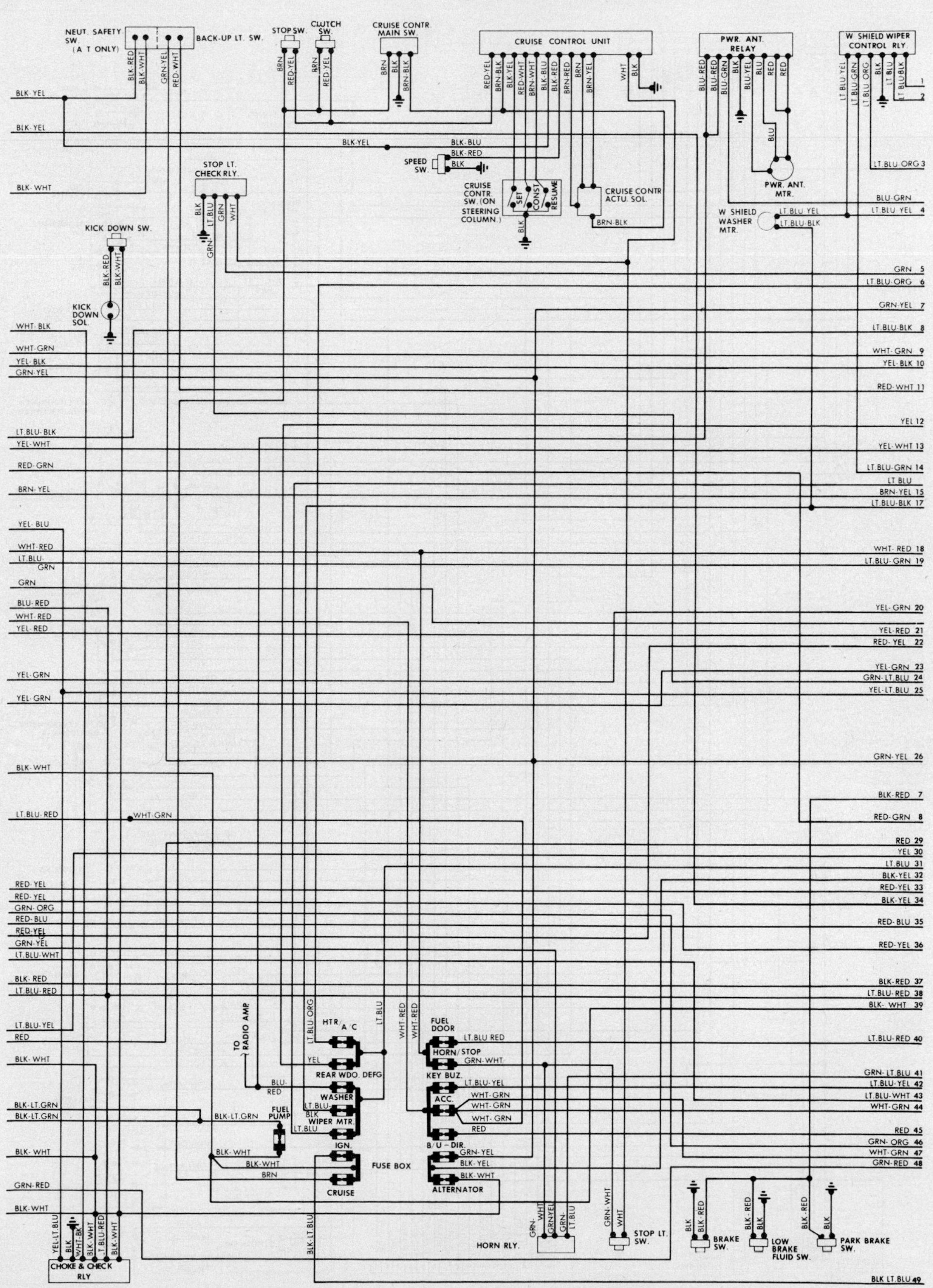
NEUT. SAFETY SW. (A T ONLY)
BACK-UP LT. SW.
STOP SW.
CLUTCH SW.
CRUISE CONTR. MAIN SW.
CRUISE CONTROL UNIT
PWR. ANT. RELAY
W. SHIELD WIPER CONTROL RLY.
STOP LT. CHECK RLY.
SPEED SW.
CRUISE CONTR. SW. (ON STEERING COLUMN.)
SET
CONST
RESUME
CRUISE CONTR ACTU. SOL.
PWR. ANT. MTR.
W SHIELD WASHER MTR.
KICK DOWN SW.
KICK DOWN SOL.
TO RADIO AMP
FUEL PUMP
HTR/A/C
REAR WDO. DEFG
WASHER
WIPER MTR.
IGN.
CRUISE
FUSE BOX
FUEL DOOR
HORN/STOP
KEY BUZ.
ACC.
B/U - DIR.
ALTERNATOR
HORN RLY.
STOP LT. SW.
BRAKE SW.
LOW BRAKE FLUID SW.
PARK BRAKE SW.
CHOKE & CHECK RLY

1983 Mazda

RX7 (Cont.)

INSTRUMENT PANEL & UNDERDASH

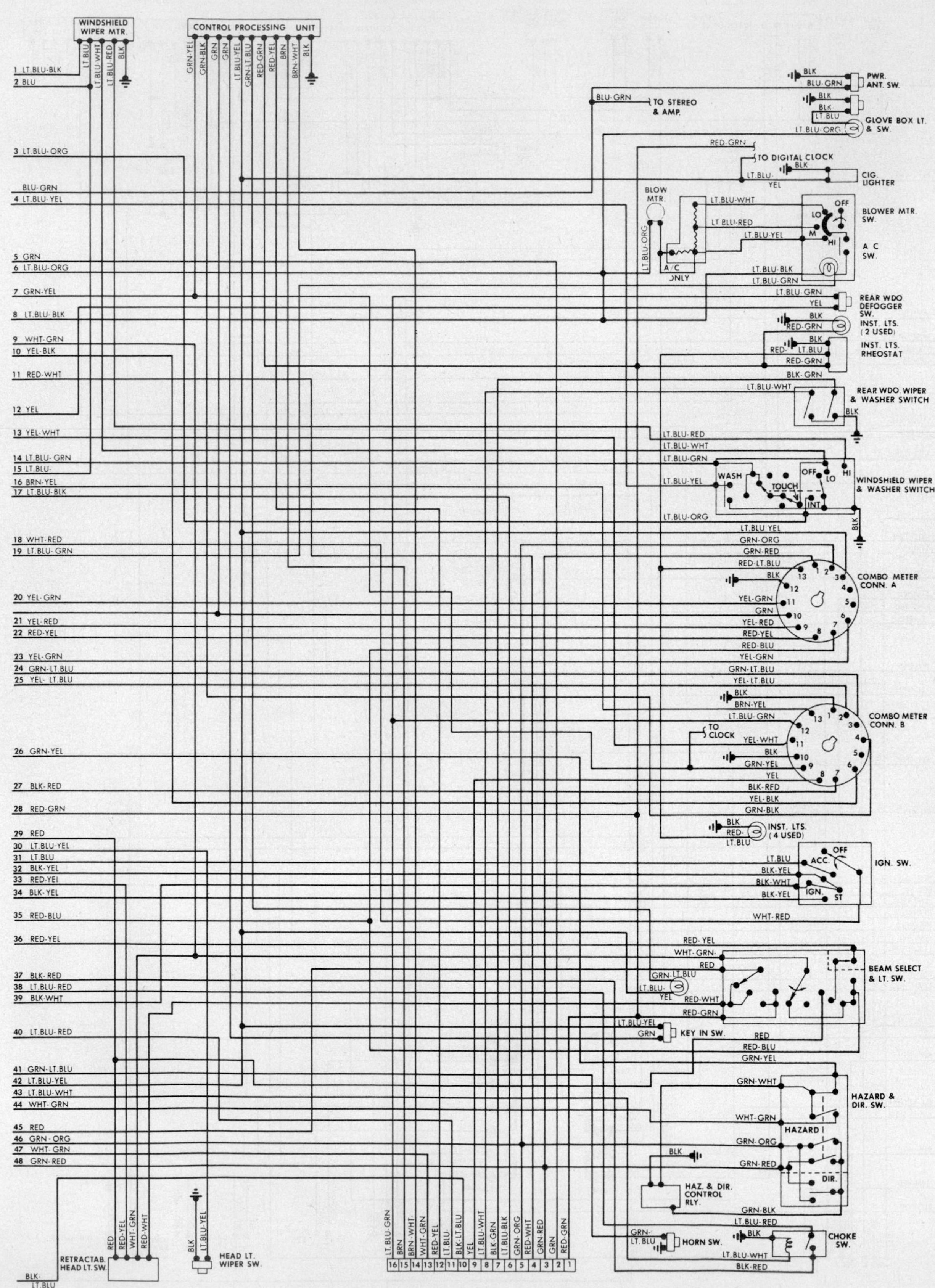
WINDSHIELD WIPER MTR.
LT.BLU
LT.BLU-WHT
LT.BLU-RED
BLK
CONTROL PROCESSING UNIT
GRN-YEL
GRN-BLK
GRN
GRN
LT.BLU-YEL
GRN-LT.BLU
RED-GRN
RED-YEL
BRN
BRN-WHT
BLK
1 LT.BLU-BLK
2 BLU
3 LT.BLU-ORG
BLU-GRN
4 LT.BLU-YEL
5 GRN
6 LT.BLU-ORG
7 GRN-YEL
8 LT.BLU-BLK
9 WHT-GRN
10 YEL-BLK
11 RED-WHT
12 YEL
13 YEL-WHT
14 LT.BLU-GRN
15 LT.BLU-
16 BRN-YEL
17 LT.BLU-BLK
18 WHT-RED
19 LT.BLU-GRN
20 YEL-GRN
21 YEL-RED
22 RED-YEL
23 YEL-GRN
24 GRN-LT.BLU
25 YEL- LT.BLU
26 GRN-YEL
27 BLK-RED
28 RED-GRN
29 RED
30 LT.BLU-YEL
31 LT.BLU
32 BLK-YEL
33 RED-YEL
34 BLK-YEL
35 RED-BLU
36 RED-YEL
37 BLK-RED
38 LT.BLU-RED
39 BLK-WHT
40 LT.BLU-RED
41 GRN-LT.BLU
42 LT.BLU-YEL
43 LT.BLU-WHT
44 WHT-GRN
45 RED
46 GRN-ORG
47 WHT-GRN
48 GRN-RED
BLU-GRN
TO STEREO & AMP.
BLK
BLU-GRN
PWR. ANT. SW.
BLK
BLK
LT.BLU
LT.BLU-ORG
GLOVE BOX LT. & SW.
RED-GRN
TO DIGITAL CLOCK
LT.BLU-YEL
BLK
CIG. LIGHTER
BLOW MTR.
LT.BLU-ORG
LT.BLU-WHT
LT.BLU-RED
LT.BLU-YEL
A/C ONLY
OFF
LO
M
HI
BLOWER MTR. SW.
A/C SW.
LT.BLU-BLK
LT.BLU-GRN
LT.BLU-GRN
YEL
REAR WDO DEFOGGER SW.
BLK
RED-GRN
INST. LTS. (2 USED)
BLK
RED-
LT.BLU
RED-GRN
INST. LTS. RHEOSTAT
BLK-GRN
LT.BLU-WHT
REAR WDO WIPER & WASHER SWITCH
BLK
LT.BLU-RED
LT.BLU-WHT
LT.BLU-GRN
LT.BLU-YEL
WASH
TOUCH
OFF
LO
HI
INT
WINDSHIELD WIPER & WASHER SWITCH
LT.BLU-ORG
BLK
LT.BLU YEL
GRN-ORG
GRN-RED
RED-LT.BLU
BLK
YEL-GRN
GRN
YEL-RED
RED-YEL
RED-BLU
YEL-GRN
GRN-LT.BLU
YEL-LT.BLU
COMBO METER CONN. A
BLK
BRN-YEL
LT.BLU-GRN
TO CLOCK
YEL-WHT
BLK
GRN-YEL
YEL
BLK-RED
YEL-BLK
GRN-BLK
COMBO METER CONN. B
BLK
RED-
LT.BLU
INST. LTS. (4 USED)
LT.BLU
BLK-YEL
BLK-WHT
BLK-YEL
ACC.
OFF
IGN.
ST
IGN. SW.
WHT-RED
RED-YEL
WHT-GRN
RED
GRN-LT.BLU
LT.BLU-YEL
RED-WHT
RED-GRN
BEAM SELECT & LT. SW.
LT.BLU-YEL
GRN
KEY IN SW.
RED
RED-BLU
GRN-YEL
GRN-WHT
WHT-GRN
HAZARD
GRN-ORG
GRN-RED
DIR.
HAZARD & DIR. SW.
BLK
HAZ. & DIR. CONTROL RLY.
GRN-BLK
LT.BLU-RED
GRN-LT.BLU
HORN SW.
BLK
LT.BLU-WHT
BLK-RED
CHOKE SW.
RED
RED-YEL
WHT-GRN
RED-WHT
RETRACTAB. HEAD LT. SW.
BLK-LT.BLU
BLK
LT.BLU-YEL
HEAD LT. WIPER SW.
LT.BLU-GRN
BRN
BRN-WHT
WHT-GRN
RED-YEL
LT.BLU-
BLK-LT.BLU
YEL
LT.BLU-WHT
BLK-GRN
LT.BLU-BLK
GRN-ORG
RED-WHT
GRN-RED
GRN
RED-GRN
16 15 14 13 12 11 10 9 8 7 6 5 4 3 2 1

RX7 (Cont.)

REAR COMPARTMENT & ACCESSORIES

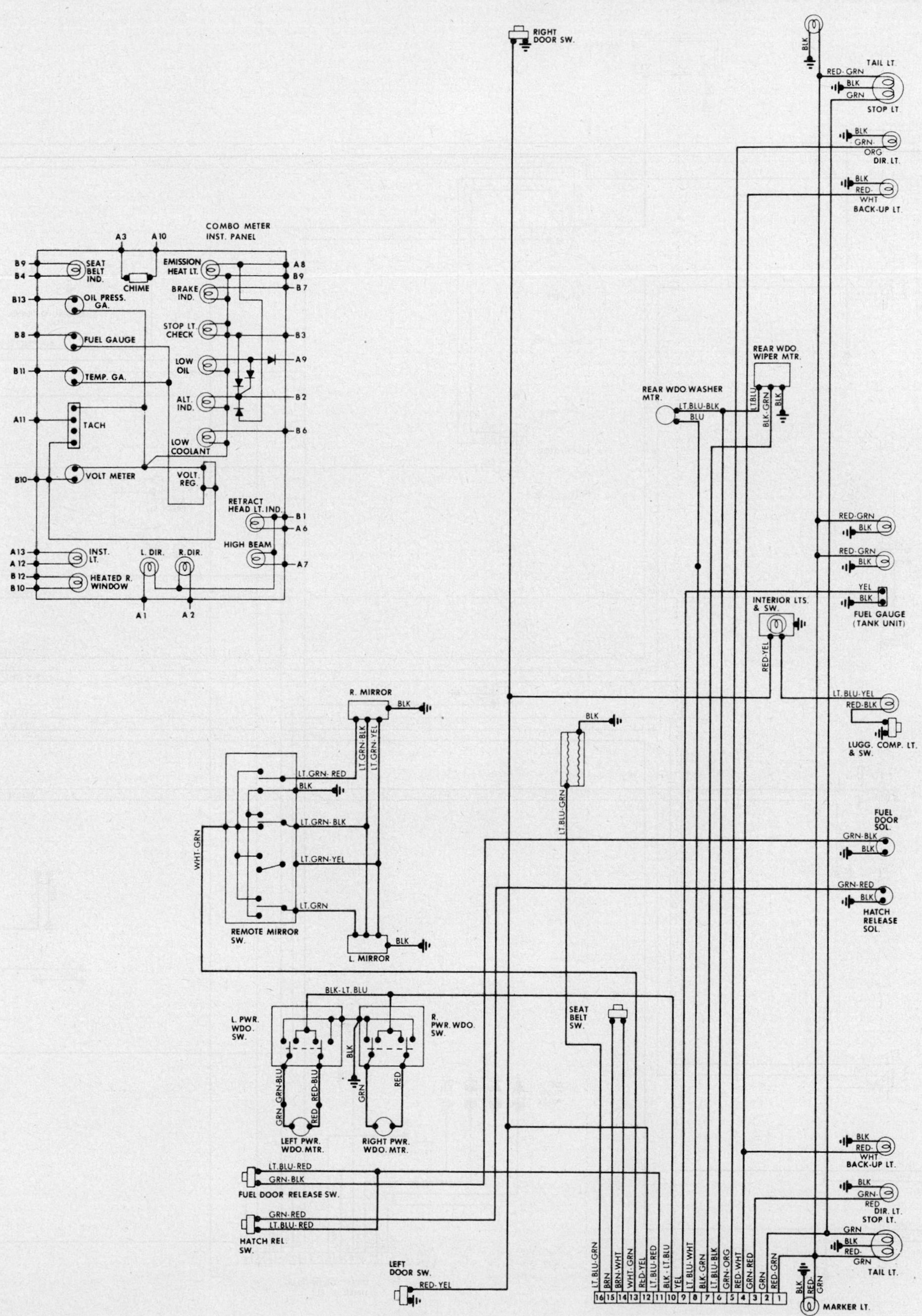
RIGHT DOOR SW.
TAIL LT.
RED-GRN
BLK
GRN
STOP LT.
BLK
GRN-ORG
DIR. LT.
BLK
RED-WHT
BACK-UP LT.
COMBO METER INST. PANEL
A3
A10
B9
B4
SEAT BELT IND.
CHIME
EMISSION HEAT LT.
A8
B9
B7
B13
OIL PRESS. GA.
BRAKE IND.
B8
FUEL GAUGE
STOP LT. CHECK
B3
LOW OIL
A9
B11
TEMP. GA.
ALT. IND.
B2
A11
TACH
B6
LOW COOLANT
B10
VOLT METER
VOLT. REG.
RETRACT HEAD LT. IND.
B1
A6
HIGH BEAM
A7
A13
A12
INST. LT.
L. DIR.
R. DIR.
B12
B10
HEATED R. WINDOW
A1
A2
REAR WDO WIPER MTR.
REAR WDO WASHER MTR.
LT.BLU-BLK
BLU
LT.BLU
BLK-GRN
BLK
RED-GRN
BLK
RED-GRN
BLK
YEL
BLK
FUEL GAUGE (TANK UNIT)
INTERIOR LTS. & SW.
RED-YEL
LT.BLU-YEL
RED-BLK
LUGG. COMP. LT. & SW.
R. MIRROR
BLK
LT.GRN-BLK
LT.GRN-YEL
LT.GRN-RED
BLK
LT.GRN-BLK
LT.GRN-YEL
LT.GRN
WHT-GRN
REMOTE MIRROR SW.
L. MIRROR
BLK
BLK
LT.BLU-GRN
FUEL DOOR SOL.
GRN-BLK
BLK
GRN-RED
BLK
HATCH RELEASE SOL.
BLK-LT.BLU
L. PWR. WDO. SW.
R. PWR. WDO. SW.
SEAT BELT SW.
BLK
GRN
RED
GRN-BLU
RED-BLU
GRN
RED
LEFT PWR. WDO. MTR.
RIGHT PWR. WDO. MTR.
LT.BLU-RED
GRN-BLK
FUEL DOOR RELEASE SW.
GRN-RED
LT.BLU-RED
HATCH REL SW.
LEFT DOOR SW.
RED-YEL
LT.BLU-GRN
BRN
BRN-WHT
WHT-GRN
RED-YEL
LT.BLU-RED
BLK-LT.BLU
YEL
LT.BLU-WHT
BLK-GRN
LT.BLU-BLK
GRN-ORG
RED-WHT
GRN-RED
GRN
RED-GRN
16 15 14 13 12 11 10 9 8 7 6 5 4 3 2 1
BLK
RED-WHT
BACK-UP LT.
BLK
GRN-RED
DIR. LT. STOP LT.
GRN
BLK
RED-GRN
TAIL LT.
BLK
RED-GRN
MARKER LT.

1983 Mercedes-Benz

240D DIESEL & 300D, 300CD & 300TD TURBO DIESELS

ENGINE COMPARTMENT

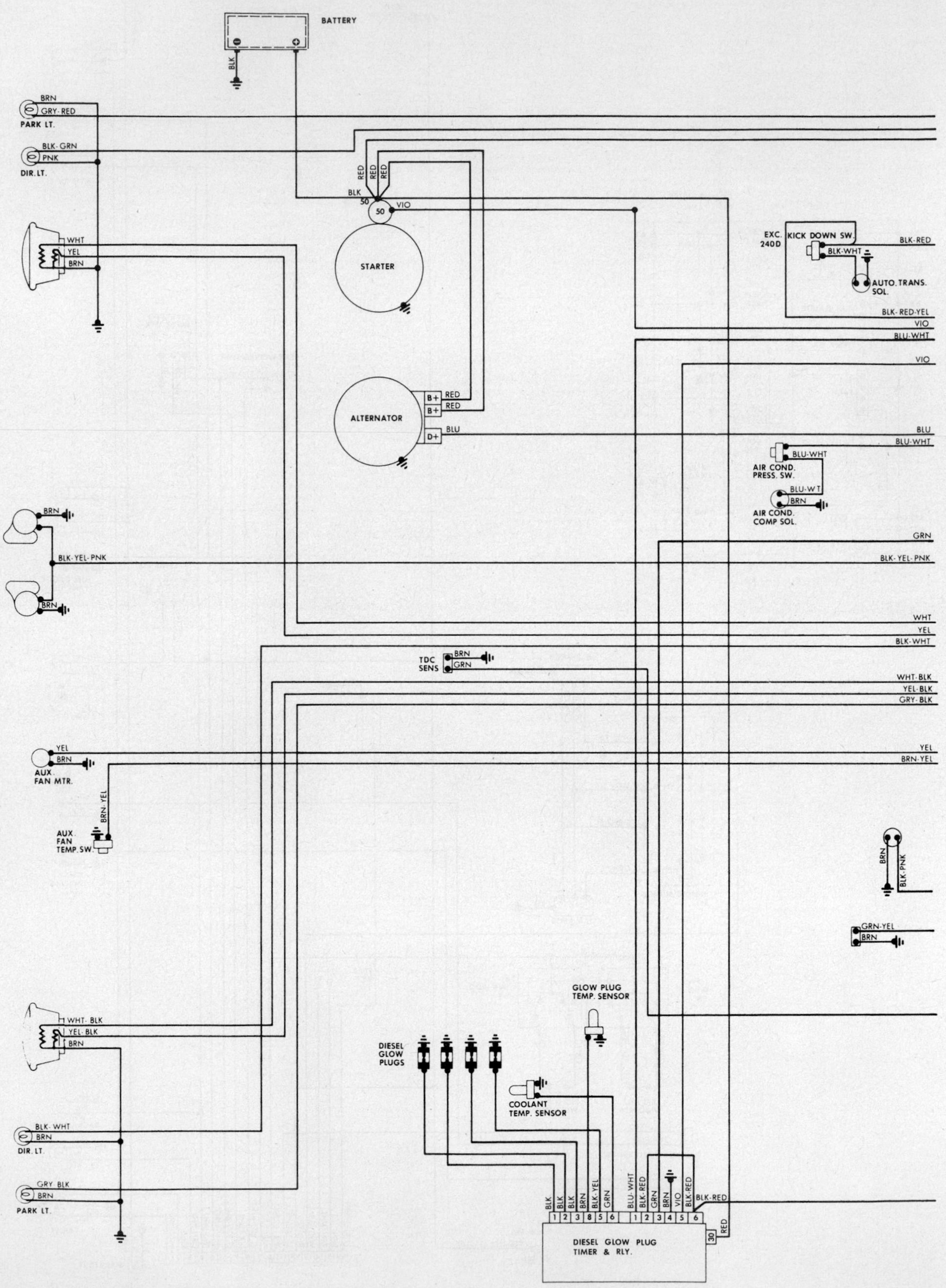

BATTERY
BLK
BRN
GRY-RED
PARK LT.
BLK-GRN
PNK
DIR. LT.
WHT
YEL
BRN
RED
RED
RED
BLK
50
50
VIO
STARTER
EXC. 240D
KICK DOWN SW.
BLK-WHT
BLK-RED
AUTO. TRANS. SOL.
BLK-RED-YEL
VIO
BLU-WHT
VIO
ALTERNATOR
B+
B+
D+
RED
RED
BLU
BLU
BLU-WHT
BLU-WHT
AIR COND. PRESS. SW.
BLU-WHT
BRN
AIR COND. COMP SOL.
BRN
BLK-YEL-PNK
BRN
GRN
BLK-YEL-PNK
WHT
YEL
BLK-WHT
TDC SENS
BRN
GRN
WHT-BLK
YEL-BLK
GRY-BLK
YEL
BRN
AUX FAN MTR.
YEL
BRN-YEL
BRN-YEL
AUX FAN TEMP. SW.
BRN
BLK-PNK
GRN-YEL
BRN
GLOW PLUG TEMP. SENSOR
DIESEL GLOW PLUGS
COOLANT TEMP. SENSOR
WHT-BLK
YEL-BLK
BRN
BLK-WHT
BRN
DIR. LT.
GRY BLK
BRN
PARK LT.
BLK
BLK
BLK
BRN
BLK-YEL
GRN
BLU-WHT
BLK-RED
GRN
BRN
VIO
BLK-RED
BLK-RED
1 2 3 8 5 6 1 2 3 4 5 6
30
RED
DIESEL GLOW PLUG TIMER & RLY.

1983 Mercedes-Benz

240D DIESEL & 300D, 300CD & 300TD TURBO DIESELS (Cont.)

UNDERDASH & FUSE BLOCK

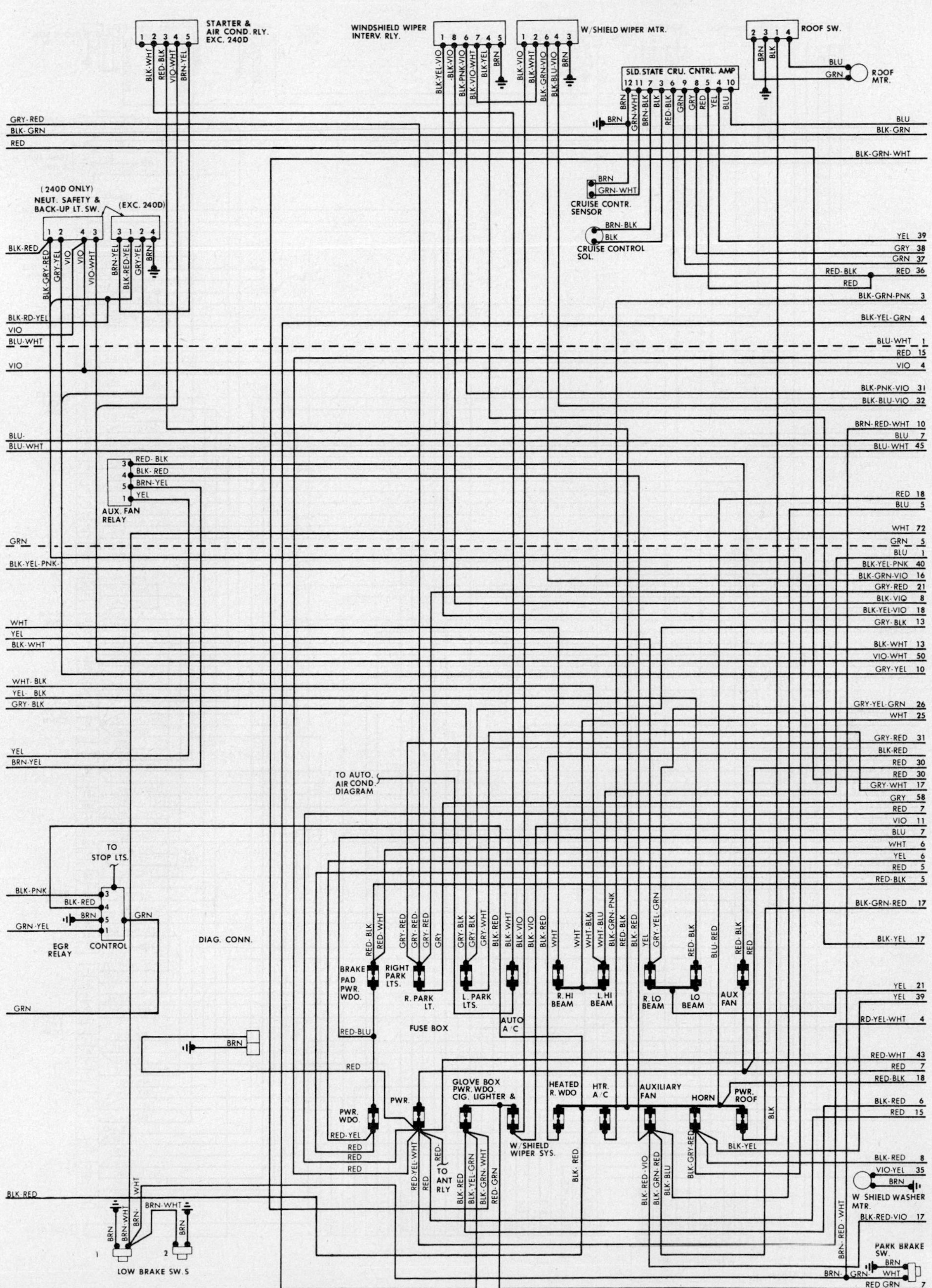
STARTER & AIR COND. RLY. EXC. 240D
WINDSHIELD WIPER INTERV. RLY.
W/SHIELD WIPER MTR.
ROOF SW.
ROOF MTR.
SLD. STATE CRU. CNTRL. AMP
CRUISE CONTR. SENSOR
CRUISE CONTROL SOL.
(240D ONLY) NEUT. SAFETY & BACK-UP LT. SW.
(EXC. 240D)
AUX. FAN RELAY
TO AUTO. AIR COND. DIAGRAM
TO STOP LTS.
EGR RELAY
CONTROL
DIAG. CONN.
BRAKE PAD PWR. WDO.
RIGHT PARK LTS.
R. PARK LT.
L. PARK LTS.
R. HI BEAM
L. HI BEAM
R. LO BEAM
LO BEAM
AUX FAN
FUSE BOX
AUTO A/C
GLOVE BOX PWR. WDO. CIG. LIGHTER &
HEATED R. WDO
HTR. A/C
AUXILIARY FAN
HORN
PWR. ROOF
PWR. WDO.
PWR.
W/SHIELD WIPER SYS.
TO ANT RLY
W. SHIELD WASHER MTR.
PARK BRAKE SW.
LOW BRAKE SW.S

1983 Mercedes-Benz

240D DIESEL & 300D, 300CD & 300TD TURBO DIESELS (Cont.)

INSTRUMENT PANEL & UNDERDASH

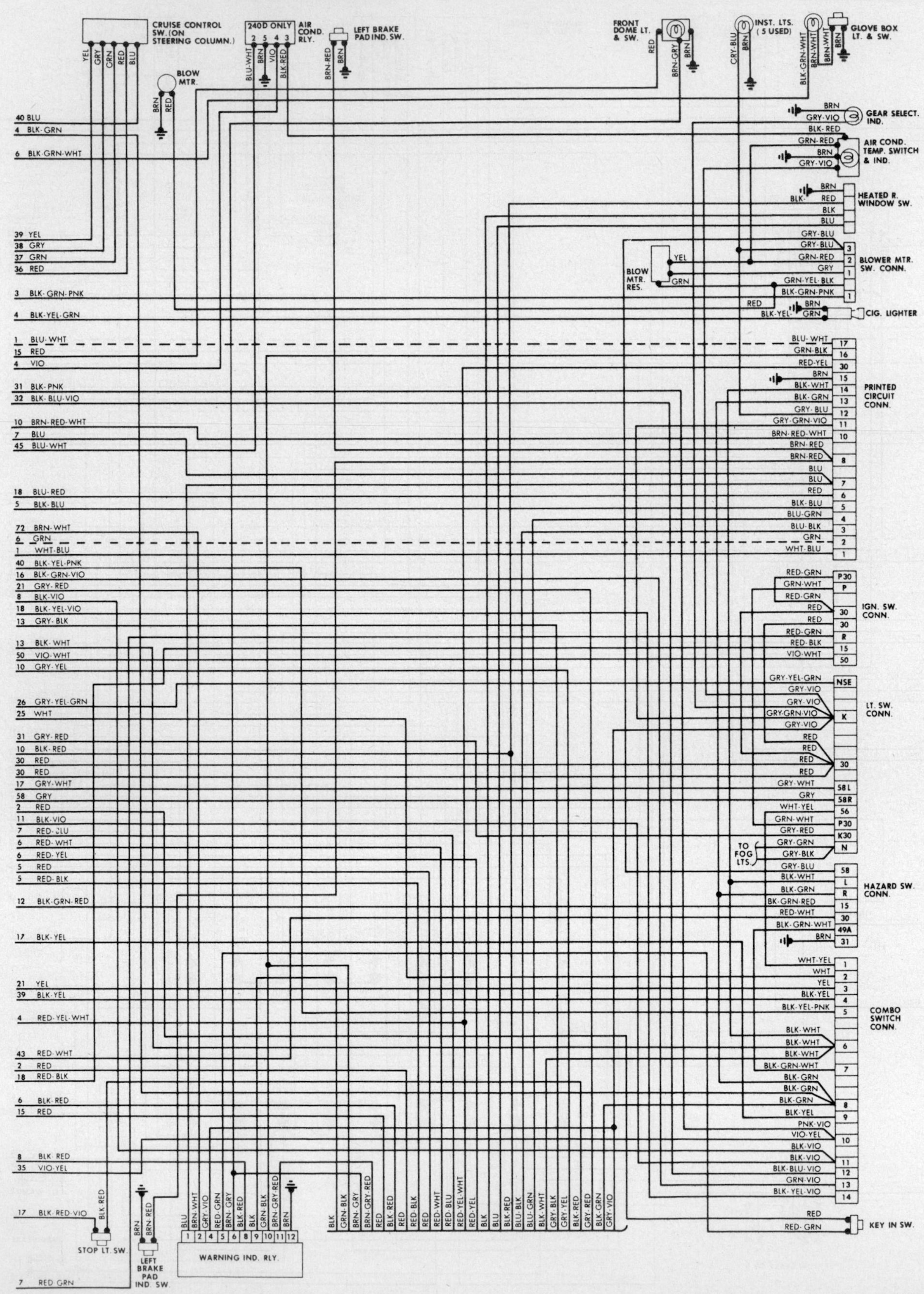

1983 Mercedes-Benz

240D DIESEL & 300D, 300CD & 300TD TURBO DIESELS (Cont.)

REAR COMPARTMENT & ACCESSORIES

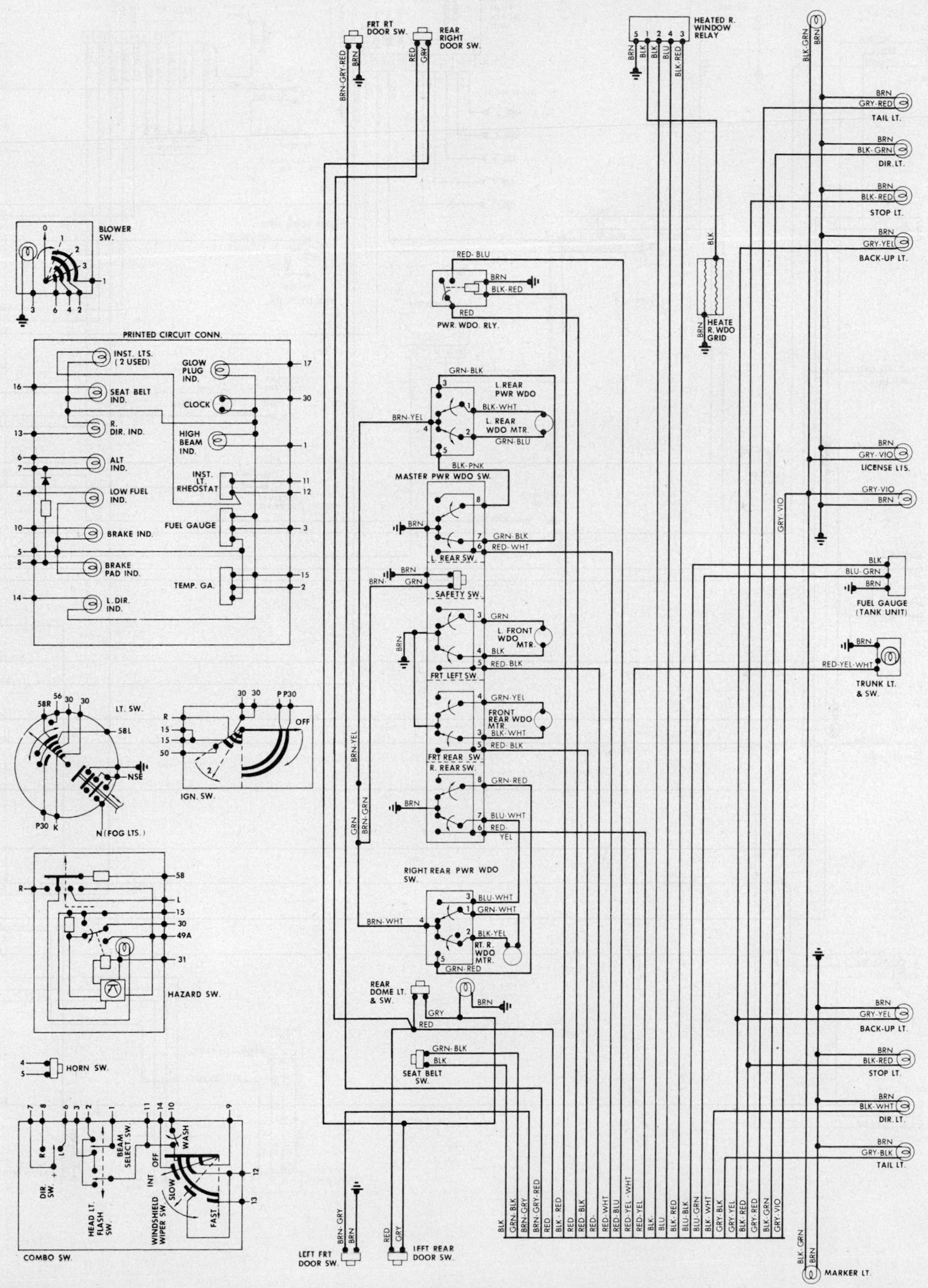

FRT RT DOOR SW.
REAR RIGHT DOOR SW.
HEATED R. WINDOW RELAY
BLOWER SW.
PRINTED CIRCUIT CONN.
INST. LTS. (2 USED)
SEAT BELT IND.
R. DIR. IND.
ALT IND.
LOW FUEL IND.
BRAKE IND.
BRAKE PAD IND.
L. DIR. IND.
GLOW PLUG IND.
CLOCK
HIGH BEAM IND.
INST. LT. RHEOSTAT
FUEL GAUGE
TEMP. GA.
LT. SW.
N (FOG LTS.)
IGN. SW.
HAZARD SW.
HORN SW.
COMBO SW.
DIR SW.
HEAD LT. FLASH SW.
BEAM SELECT SW.
WINDSHIELD WIPER SW.
PWR. WDO. RLY.
L. REAR PWR WDO
L. REAR WDO MTR.
MASTER PWR WDO SW.
L. REAR SW.
SAFETY SW.
L. FRONT WDO MTR.
FRT LEFT SW.
FRONT REAR WDO MTR.
FRT REAR SW.
R. REAR SW.
RIGHT REAR PWR WDO SW.
RT. R. WDO MTR.
REAR DOME LT. & SW.
SEAT BELT SW.
LEFT FRT DOOR SW.
LEFT REAR DOOR SW.
HEATE R. WDO GRID
TAIL LT.
DIR. LT.
STOP LT.
BACK-UP LT.
LICENSE LTS.
FUEL GAUGE (TANK UNIT)
TRUNK LT. & SW.
MARKER LT.

1983 Mercedes-Benz

300SD TURBO DIESEL

ENGINE COMPARTMENT

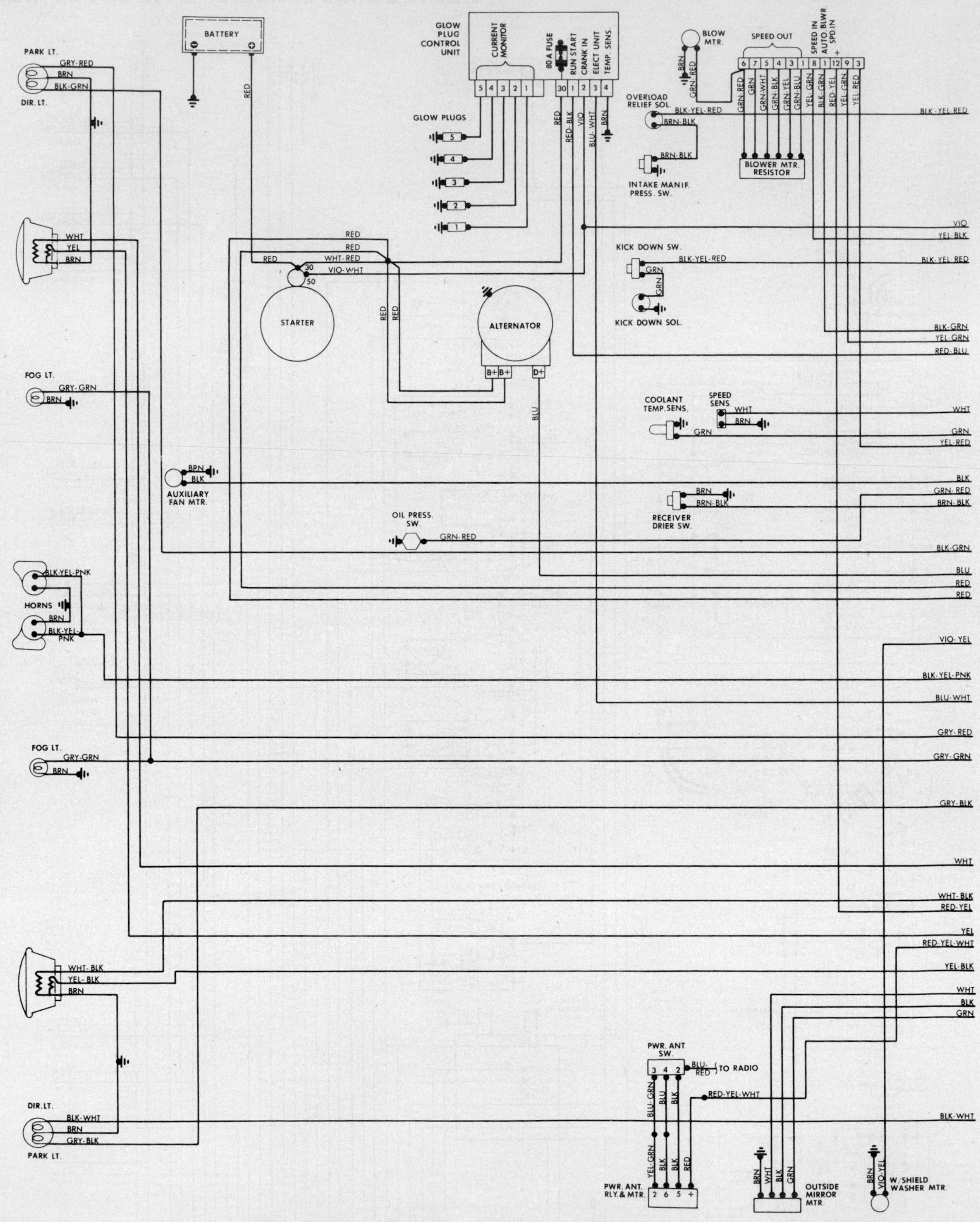
BATTERY
PARK LT.
DIR. LT.
GRY-RED
BRN
BLK-GRN
RED
GLOW PLUG CONTROL UNIT
CURRENT MONITOR
80 A FUSE
RUN START
CRANK IN
ELECT UNIT
TEMP. SENS.
GLOW PLUGS
BLOW MTR.
SPEED OUT
SPEED IN
AUTO BLWR. SPD IN
OVERLOAD RELIEF SOL.
INTAKE MANIF. PRESS. SW.
BLOWER MTR. RESISTOR
BLK-YEL-RED
BRN-BLK
WHT
YEL
STARTER
ALTERNATOR
WHT-RED
VIO-WHT
KICK DOWN SW.
KICK DOWN SOL.
VIO
YEL-BLK
BLK-GRN
YEL-GRN
RED-BLU
FOG LT.
GRY-GRN
COOLANT TEMP. SENS.
SPEED SENS.
GRN
YEL-RED
AUXILIARY FAN MTR.
BLK
GRN-RED
RECEIVER DRIER SW.
OIL PRESS. SW.
BLU
HORNS
BLK-YEL-PNK
VIO-YEL
BLU-WHT
GRY-BLK
WHT-BLK
RED-YEL
RED-YEL-WHT
YEL-BLK
PWR. ANT SW.
TO RADIO
BLU-GRN
PWR. ANT. RLY. & MTR.
YEL-GRN
OUTSIDE MIRROR MTR.
W/SHIELD WASHER MTR.
BLK-WHT
GRY-BLK

300SD TURBO DIESEL (Cont.)

FUSE BLOCK & UNDERDASH

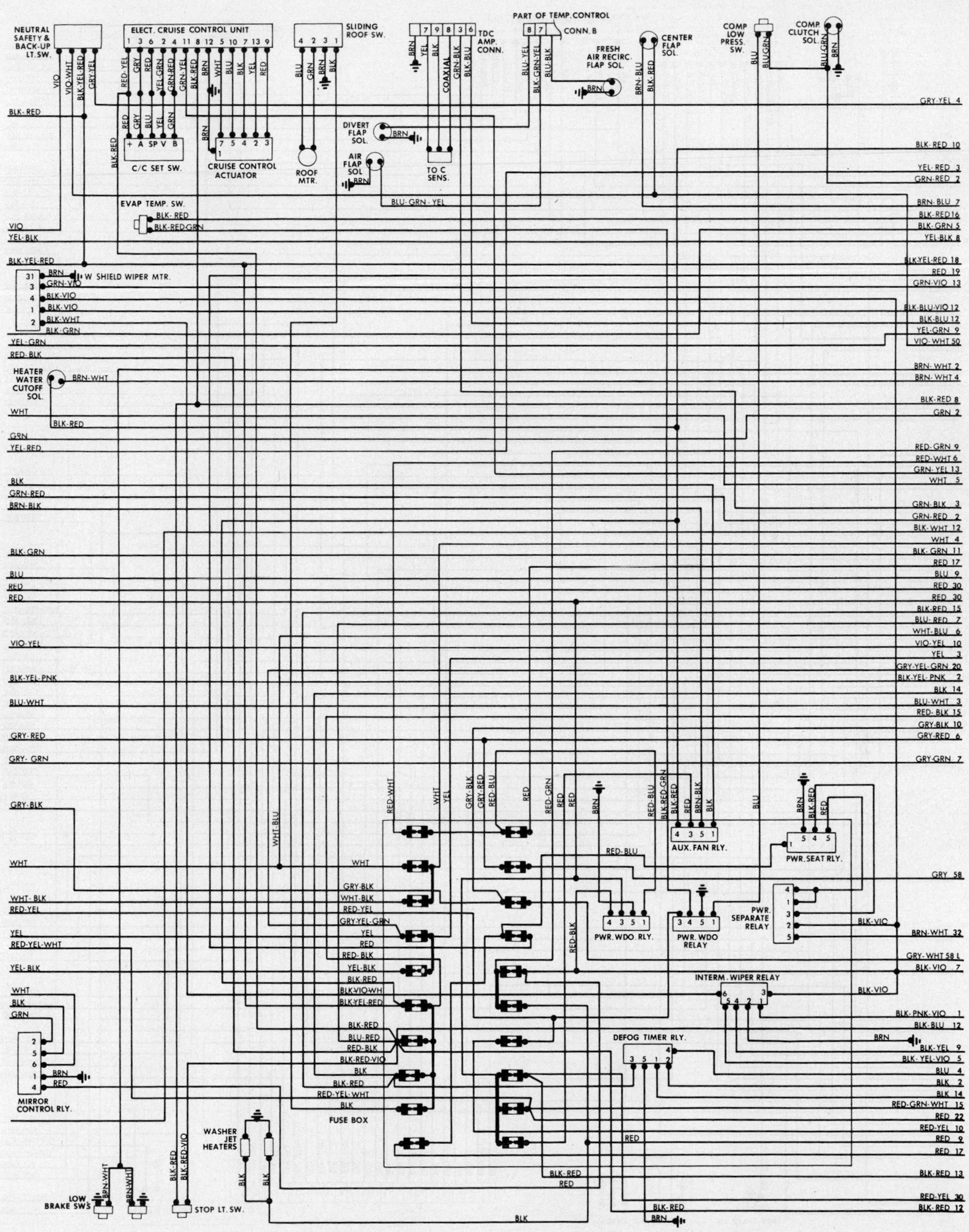
NEUTRAL SAFETY & BACK-UP LT. SW.
ELECT. CRUISE CONTROL UNIT
SLIDING ROOF SW.
TDC AMP. CONN.
PART OF TEMP. CONTROL
CONN. B
FRESH AIR RECIRC. FLAP SOL.
CENTER FLAP SOL.
COMP LOW PRESS. SW.
COMP. CLUTCH SOL.
C/C SET SW.
CRUISE CONTROL ACTUATOR
ROOF MTR.
DIVERT FLAP SOL.
AIR FLAP SOL
TO C SENS.
COAXIAL
EVAP TEMP. SW.
W SHIELD WIPER MTR.
HEATER WATER CUTOFF SOL.
AUX. FAN RLY.
PWR. SEAT RLY.
PWR. WDO. RLY.
PWR. WDO RELAY
PWR. SEPARATE RELAY
INTERM. WIPER RELAY
DEFOG TIMER RLY.
MIRROR CONTROL RLY.
FUSE BOX
WASHER JET HEATERS
LOW BRAKE SWS
STOP LT. SW.

1983 Mercedes-Benz

300SD TURBO DIESEL (Cont.)

UNDERDASH

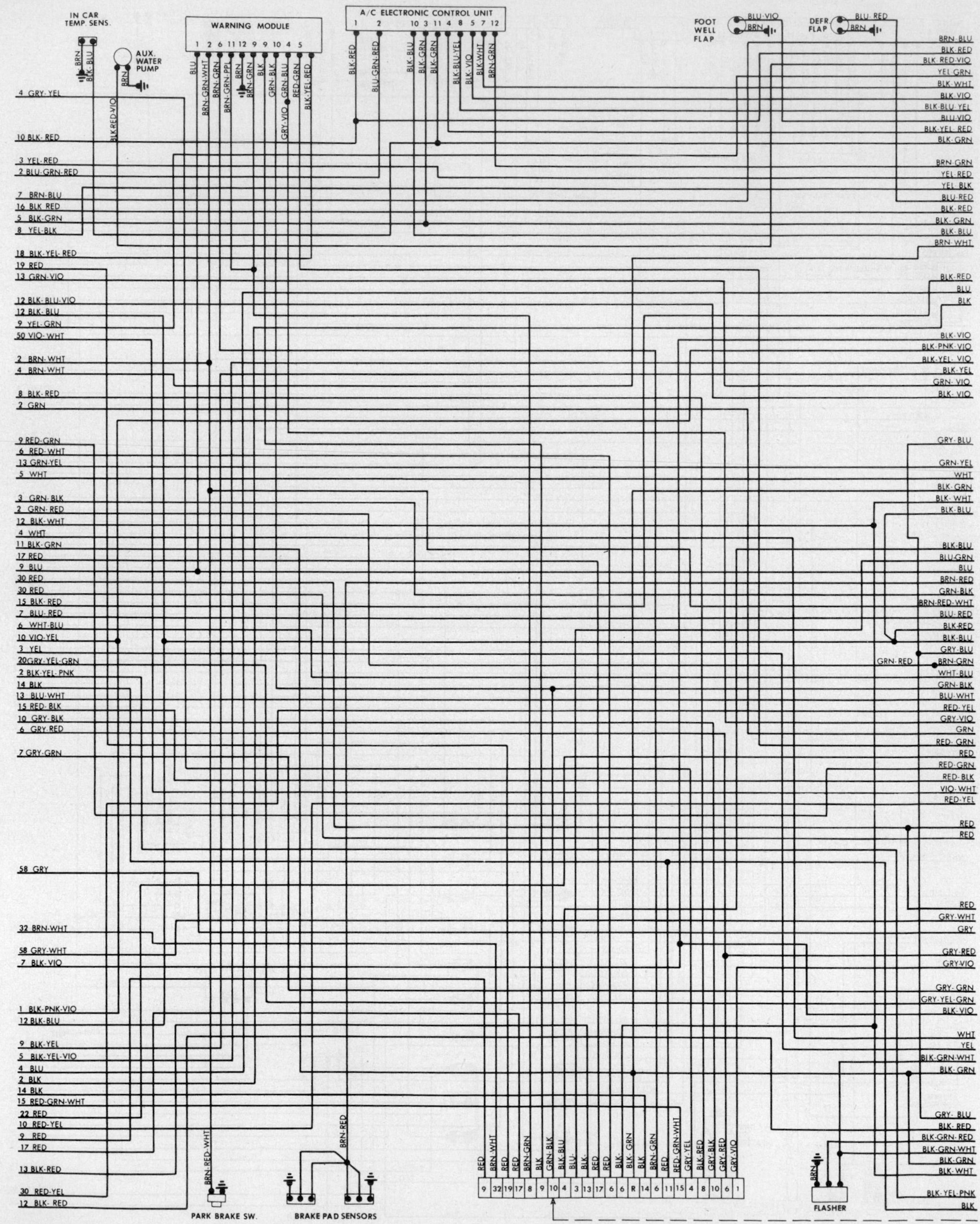

300SD TURBO DIESEL (Cont.)

INSTRUMENT PANEL, REAR COMPARTMENT & ACCESSORIES

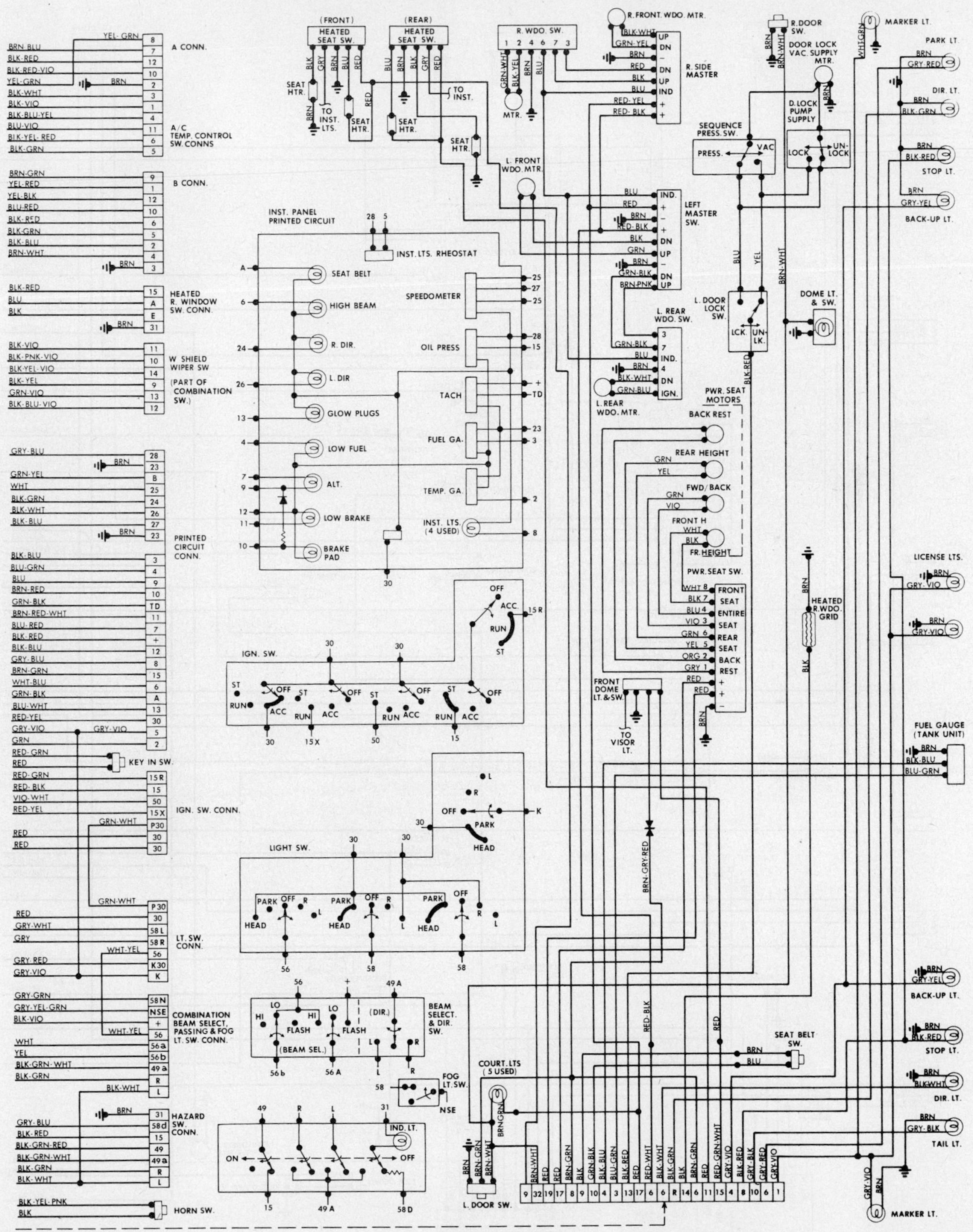

A CONN.
A/C TEMP. CONTROL SW. CONNS
B CONN.
HEATED R. WINDOW SW. CONN.
W SHIELD WIPER SW (PART OF COMBINATION SW.)
PRINTED CIRCUIT CONN.
KEY IN SW.
IGN. SW. CONN.
LT. SW. CONN.
COMBINATION BEAM SELECT, PASSING & FOG LT. SW. CONN.
HAZARD SW. CONN.
HORN SW.
(FRONT) HEATED SEAT SW.
(REAR) HEATED SEAT SW.
SEAT HTR.
TO INST. LTS.
TO INST.
R. WDO. SW.
R. FRONT WDO. MTR.
R. SIDE MASTER
L. FRONT WDO. MTR.
LEFT MASTER SW.
L. REAR WDO. SW.
L. REAR WDO. MTR.
INST. PANEL PRINTED CIRCUIT
INST. LTS. RHEOSTAT
SEAT BELT
HIGH BEAM
R. DIR.
L. DIR
GLOW PLUGS
LOW FUEL
ALT.
LOW BRAKE
BRAKE PAD
SPEEDOMETER
OIL PRESS
TACH
FUEL GA.
TEMP. GA.
INST. LTS. (4 USED)
IGN. SW.
LIGHT SW.
BEAM SELECT. & DIR. SW.
FOG LT. SW.
IND. LT.
R. DOOR SW.
DOOR LOCK VAC. SUPPLY MTR.
SEQUENCE PRESS. SW.
D. LOCK PUMP SUPPLY
L. DOOR LOCK SW.
DOME LT. & SW.
PWR. SEAT MOTORS
BACK REST
REAR HEIGHT
FWD/BACK
FRONT H
FR. HEIGHT
PWR. SEAT SW.
FRONT DOME LT. & SW.
TO VISOR LT.
HEATED R. WDO. GRID
SEAT BELT SW.
COURT. LTS (5 USED)
L. DOOR SW.
MARKER LT.
PARK LT.
DIR. LT.
STOP LT.
BACK-UP LT.
LICENSE LTS.
FUEL GAUGE (TANK UNIT)
TAIL LT.

1983 Mercedes-Benz

380SEC & 380SEL

ENGINE COMPARTMENT

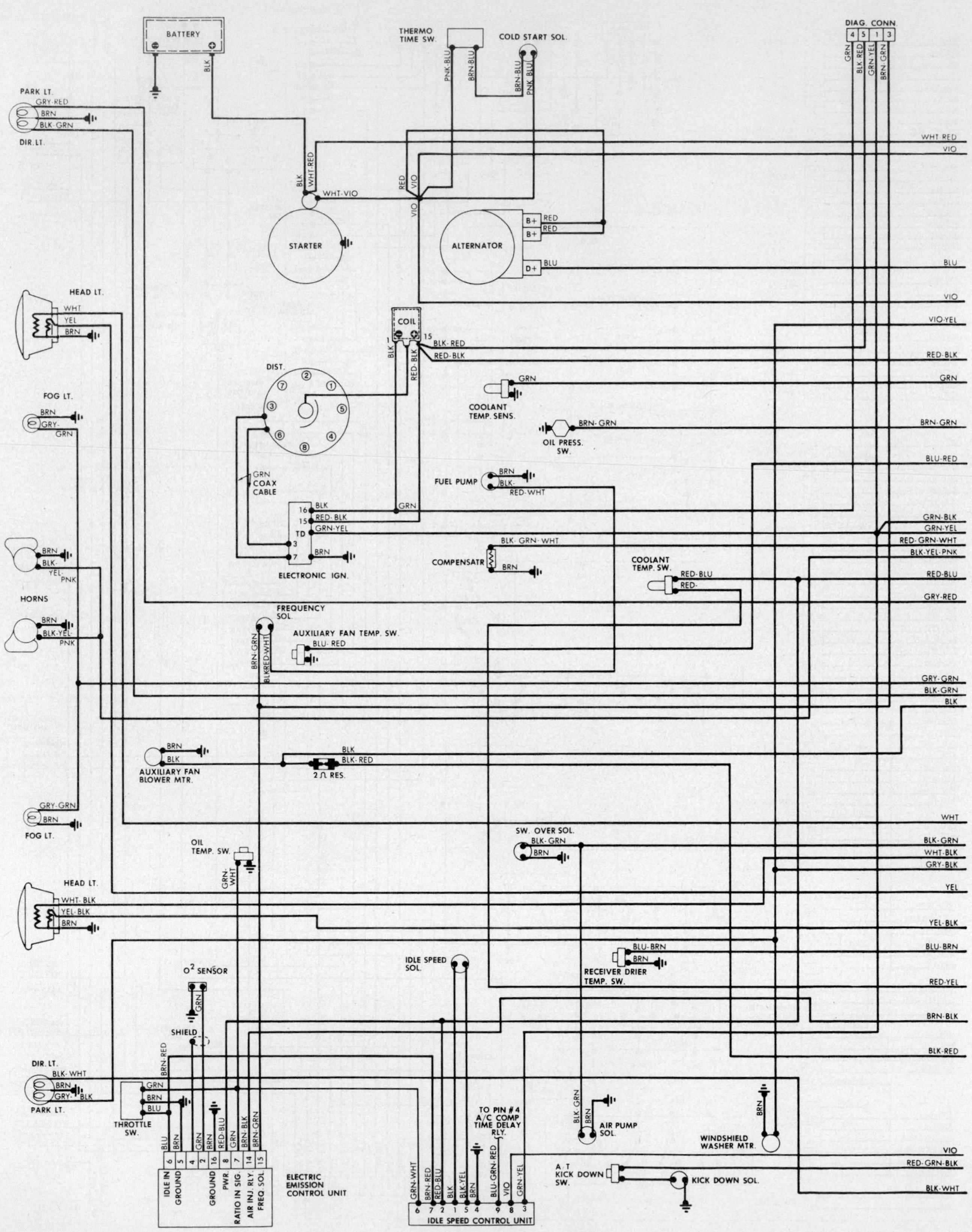
BATTERY
THERMO TIME SW.
COLD START SOL.
DIAG. CONN
PARK LT.
DIR. LT.
STARTER
ALTERNATOR
HEAD LT.
COIL
DIST.
FOG LT.
COOLANT TEMP. SENS.
OIL PRESS. SW.
FUEL PUMP
GRN COAX CABLE
ELECTRONIC IGN.
COMPENSATR
COOLANT TEMP. SW.
HORNS
FREQUENCY SOL.
AUXILIARY FAN TEMP. SW.
AUXILIARY FAN BLOWER MTR.
2 Ω RES.
OIL TEMP. SW.
SW. OVER SOL.
IDLE SPEED SOL.
RECEIVER DRIER TEMP. SW.
O2 SENSOR
SHIELD
THROTTLE SW.
TO PIN #4 A/C COMP TIME DELAY RLY.
AIR PUMP SOL.
WINDSHIELD WASHER MTR.
A/T KICK DOWN SW.
KICK DOWN SOL.
IDLE IN
GROUND
PWR.
RATIO IN SIG.
AIR INJ. RLY.
FREQ. SOL.
ELECTRIC EMISSION CONTROL UNIT
IDLE SPEED CONTROL UNIT
WHT-RED
VIO
BLU
VIO-YEL
RED-BLK
GRN
BRN-GRN
BLU-RED
GRN-BLK
GRN-YEL
RED-GRN-WHT
BLK-YEL-PNK
RED-BLU
GRY-RED
GRY-GRN
BLK-GRN
BLK
WHT
WHT-BLK
GRY-BLK
YEL
YEL-BLK
BLU-BRN
RED-YEL
BRN-BLK
BLK-RED
RED-GRN-BLK
BLK-WHT

1983 Mercedes-Benz

380SEC & 380SEL (Cont.)

FUSE BLOCK & UNDERDASH

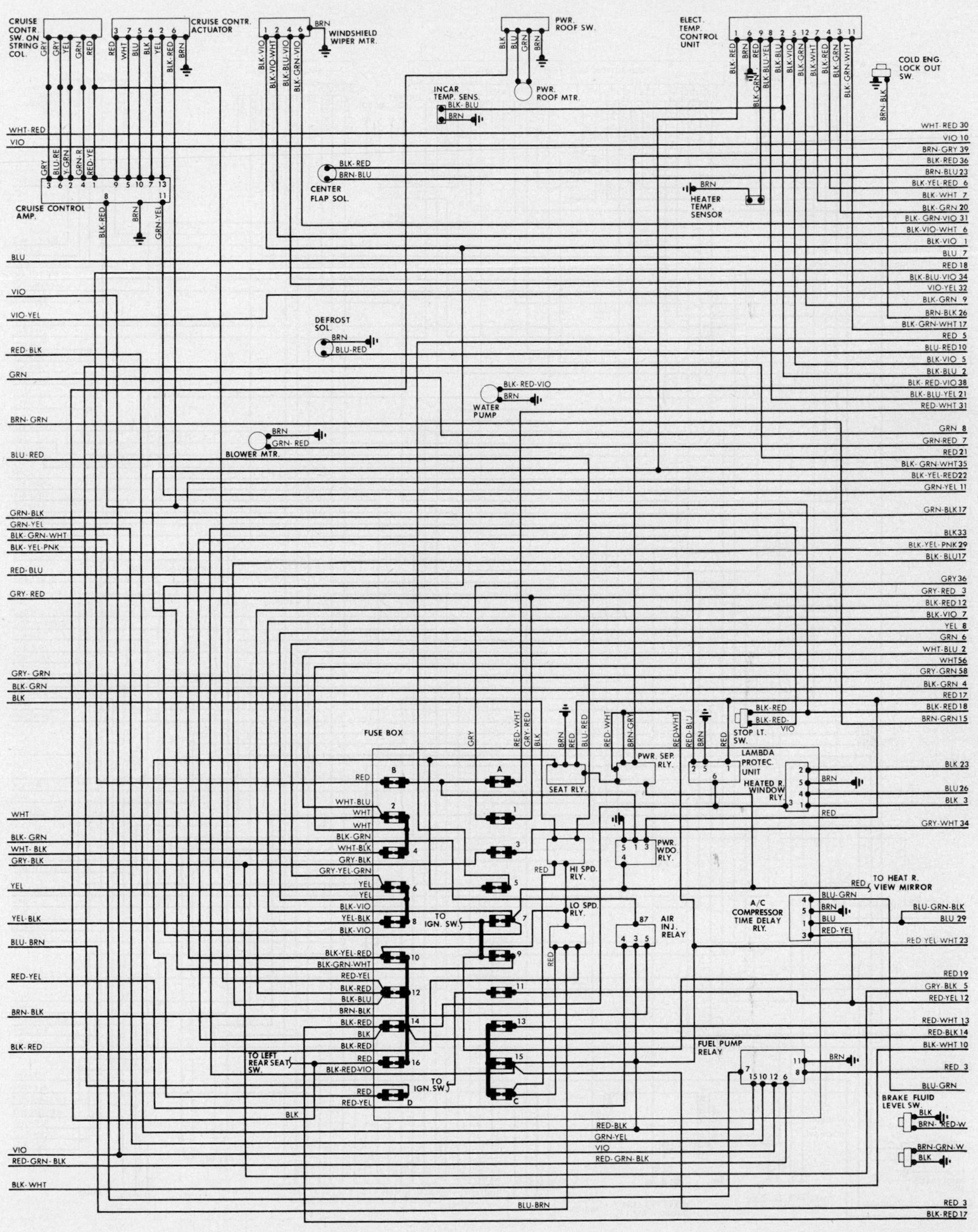

CRUISE CONTR. SW. ON STRING COL.
CRUISE CONTR. ACTUATOR
WINDSHIELD WIPER MTR.
PWR. ROOF SW.
PWR. ROOF MTR.
ELECT. TEMP. CONTROL UNIT
COLD ENG. LOCK OUT SW.
INCAR TEMP. SENS.
CRUISE CONTROL AMP.
CENTER FLAP SOL.
HEATER TEMP. SENSOR
DEFROST SOL.
WATER PUMP
BLOWER MTR.
FUSE BOX
SEAT RLY.
PWR. SEP. RLY.
STOP LT. SW.
LAMBDA PROTEC. UNIT
HEATED R. WINDOW RLY.
HI SPD. RLY.
PWR. WDO. RLY.
LO SPD. RLY.
AIR INJ. RELAY
A/C COMPRESSOR TIME DELAY RLY.
TO HEAT R. VIEW MIRROR
TO IGN. SW.
TO LEFT REAR SEAT SW.
FUEL PUMP RELAY
BRAKE FLUID LEVEL SW.
WHT-RED 30
VIO 10
BRN-GRY 39
BLK-RED 36
BRN-BLU 23
BLK-YEL-RED 6
BLK-WHT 7
BLK-GRN 20
BLK-GRN-VIO 31
BLK-VIO-WHT 6
BLK-VIO 1
BLU 7
RED 18
BLK-BLU-VIO 34
VIO-YEL 32
BLK-GRN 9
BRN-BLK 26
BLK-GRN-WHT 17
RED 5
BLU-RED 10
BLK-VIO 5
BLK-BLU 2
BLK-RED-VIO 38
BLK-BLU-YEL 21
RED-WHT 31
GRN 8
GRN-RED 7
RED 21
BLK-GRN-WHT 35
BLK-YEL-RED 22
GRN-YEL 11
GRN-BLK 17
BLK 33
BLK-YEL-PNK 29
BLK-BLU 17
GRY 36
GRY-RED 3
BLK-RED 12
BLK-VIO 7
YEL 8
GRN 6
WHT-BLU 2
WHT 56
GRY-GRN 58
BLK-GRN 4
RED 17
BLK-RED 18
BRN-GRN 15
BLK 23
BLU 26
BLK 3
GRY-WHT 34
BLU-GRN-BLK
BLU 29
RED-YEL-WHT 23
RED 19
GRY-BLK 5
RED-YEL 12
RED-WHT 13
RED-BLK 14
BLK-WHT 10
RED 3
BLU-GRN
RED 3
BLK-RED 17
WHT-RED
VIO
BLU
VIO-YEL
RED-BLK
GRN
BRN-GRN
BLU-RED
GRN-BLK
GRN-YEL
BLK-GRN-WHT
BLK-YEL-PNK
RED-BLU
GRY-RED
GRY-GRN
BLK-GRN
BLK
WHT
WHT-BLK
GRY-BLK
YEL
YEL-BLK
BLU-BRN
RED-YEL
BRN-BLK
BLK-RED
RED-GRN-BLK
BLK-WHT
RED-BLK
GRN-YEL
BLU-BRN

1983 Mercedes-Benz

380SEC & 380SEL (Cont.)

UNDERDASH & INSTRUMENT PANEL

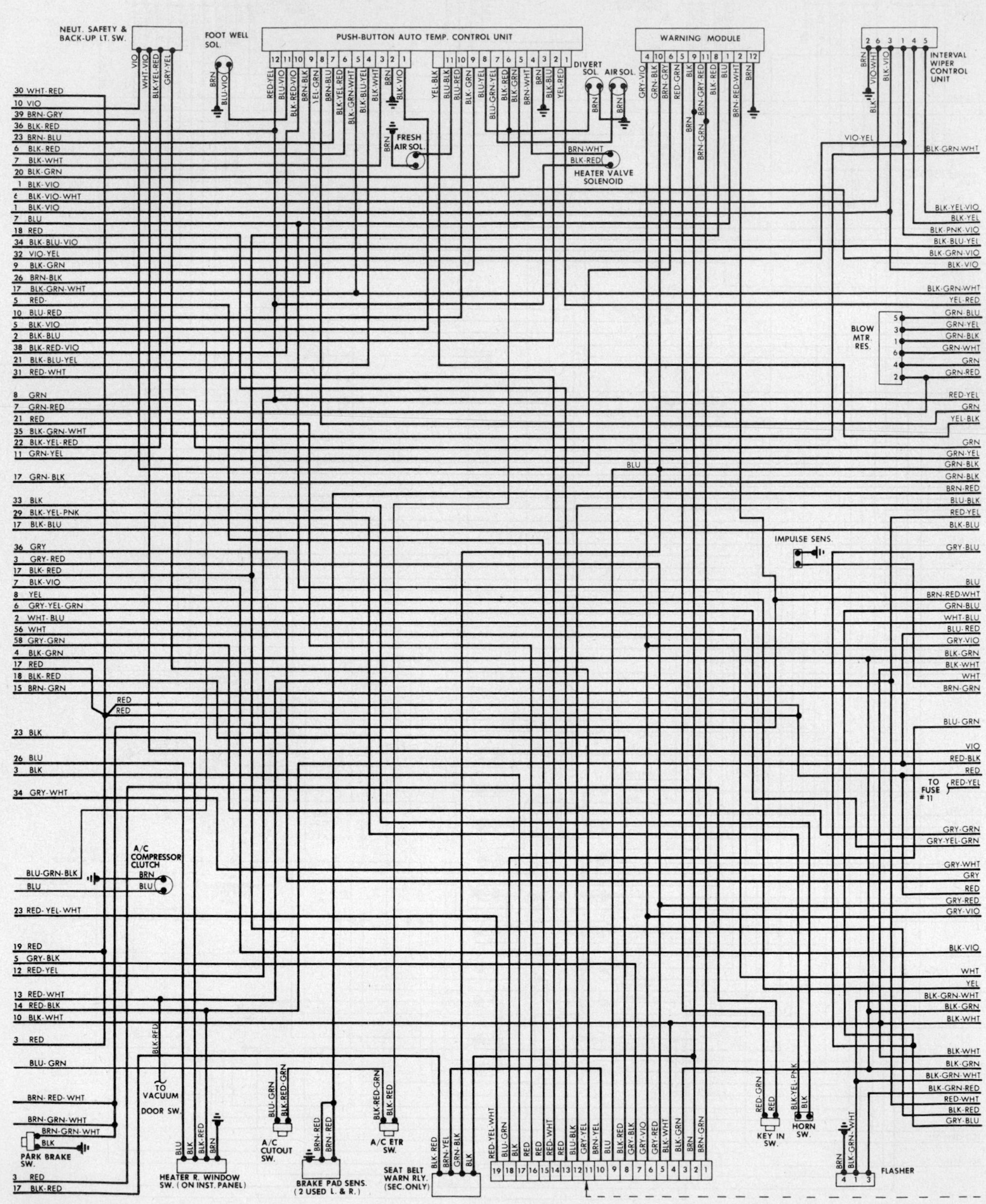
NEUT. SAFETY & BACK-UP LT. SW.
FOOT WELL SOL.
PUSH-BUTTON AUTO TEMP. CONTROL UNIT
DIVERT SOL.
AIR SOL.
FRESH AIR SOL.
HEATER VALVE SOLENOID
WARNING MODULE
INTERVAL WIPER CONTROL UNIT
BLOW MTR. RES.
IMPULSE SENS.
TO FUSE #11
A/C COMPRESSOR CLUTCH
TO VACUUM DOOR SW.
PARK BRAKE SW.
HEATER R. WINDOW SW. (ON INST. PANEL)
A/C CUTOUT SW.
BRAKE PAD SENS. (2 USED L. & R.)
A/C ETR SW.
SEAT BELT WARN RLY. (SEC. ONLY)
KEY IN SW.
HORN SW.
FLASHER

380SEC & 380SEL (Cont.)

INSTRUMENT PANEL, REAR COMPARTMENT & ACCESSORIES

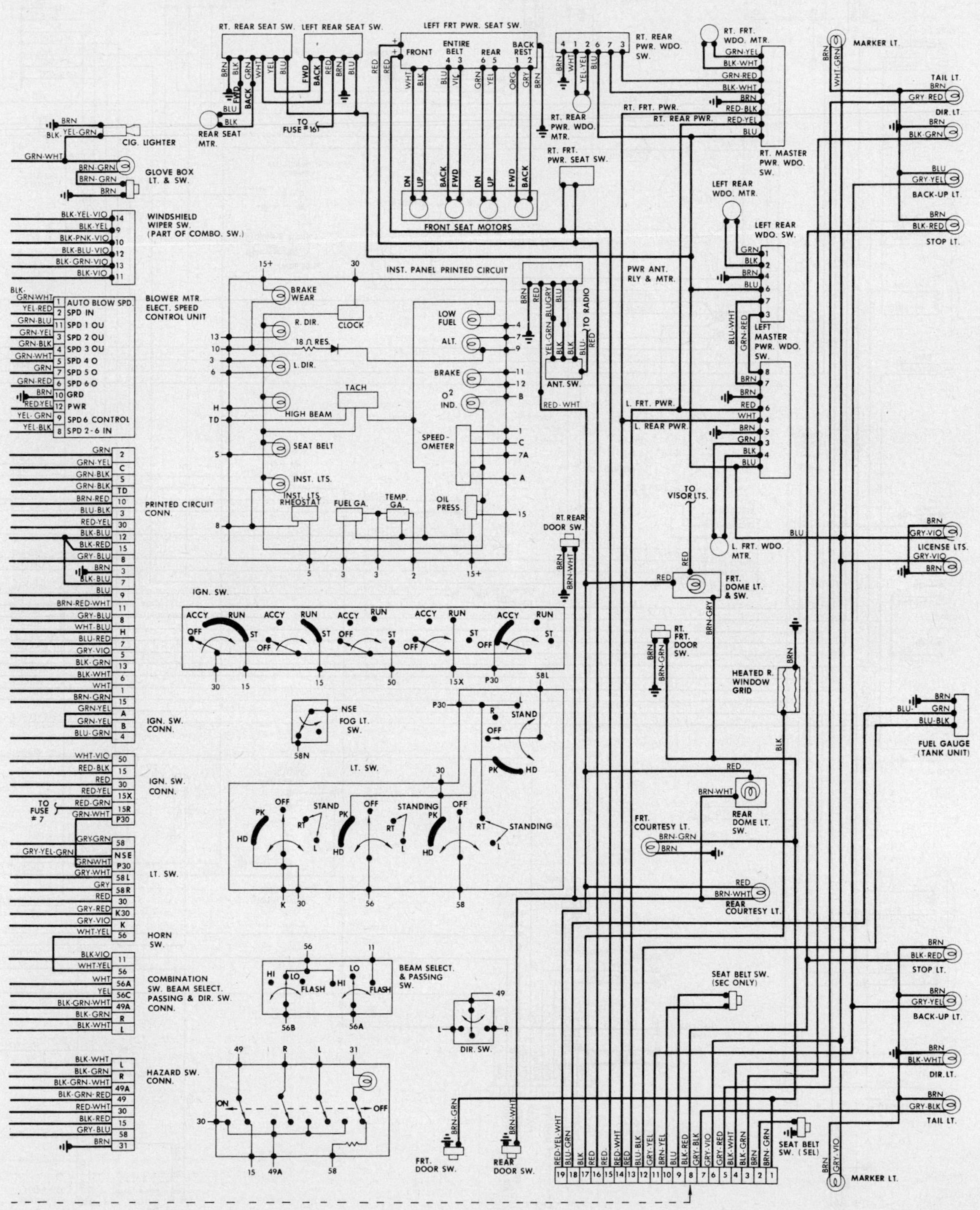
RT. REAR SEAT SW.
LEFT REAR SEAT SW.
LEFT FRT PWR. SEAT SW.
RT. REAR PWR. WDO. SW.
RT. FRT. WDO. MTR.
MARKER LT.
TAIL LT.
DIR. LT.
BACK-UP LT.
STOP LT.
CIG. LIGHTER
GLOVE BOX LT. & SW.
REAR SEAT MTR.
TO FUSE #16
RT. REAR PWR. WDO. MTR.
RT. FRT. PWR. SEAT SW.
RT. MASTER PWR. WDO. SW.
LEFT REAR WDO. MTR.
LEFT REAR WDO. SW.
FRONT SEAT MOTORS
WINDSHIELD WIPER SW. (PART OF COMBO. SW.)
BLOWER MTR. ELECT. SPEED CONTROL UNIT
INST. PANEL PRINTED CIRCUIT
PWR ANT. RLY & MTR.
LEFT MASTER PWR. WDO. SW.
ANT. SW.
TO RADIO
PRINTED CIRCUIT CONN.
TO VISOR LTS.
RT. REAR DOOR SW.
L. FRT. WDO. MTR.
LICENSE LTS.
FRT. DOME LT. & SW.
RT. FRT. DOOR SW.
HEATED R. WINDOW GRID
FUEL GAUGE (TANK UNIT)
IGN. SW.
IGN. SW. CONN.
NSE FOG LT. SW.
LT. SW.
REAR DOME LT. SW.
FRT. COURTESY LT.
REAR COURTESY LT.
HORN SW.
COMBINATION SW. BEAM SELECT. PASSING & DIR. SW. CONN.
BEAM SELECT. & PASSING SW.
SEAT BELT SW. (SEC ONLY)
DIR. SW.
HAZARD SW. CONN.
FRT. DOOR SW.
REAR DOOR SW.
SEAT BELT SW. (SEL)

1983 Mercedes-Benz

380SL

ENGINE COMPARTMENT

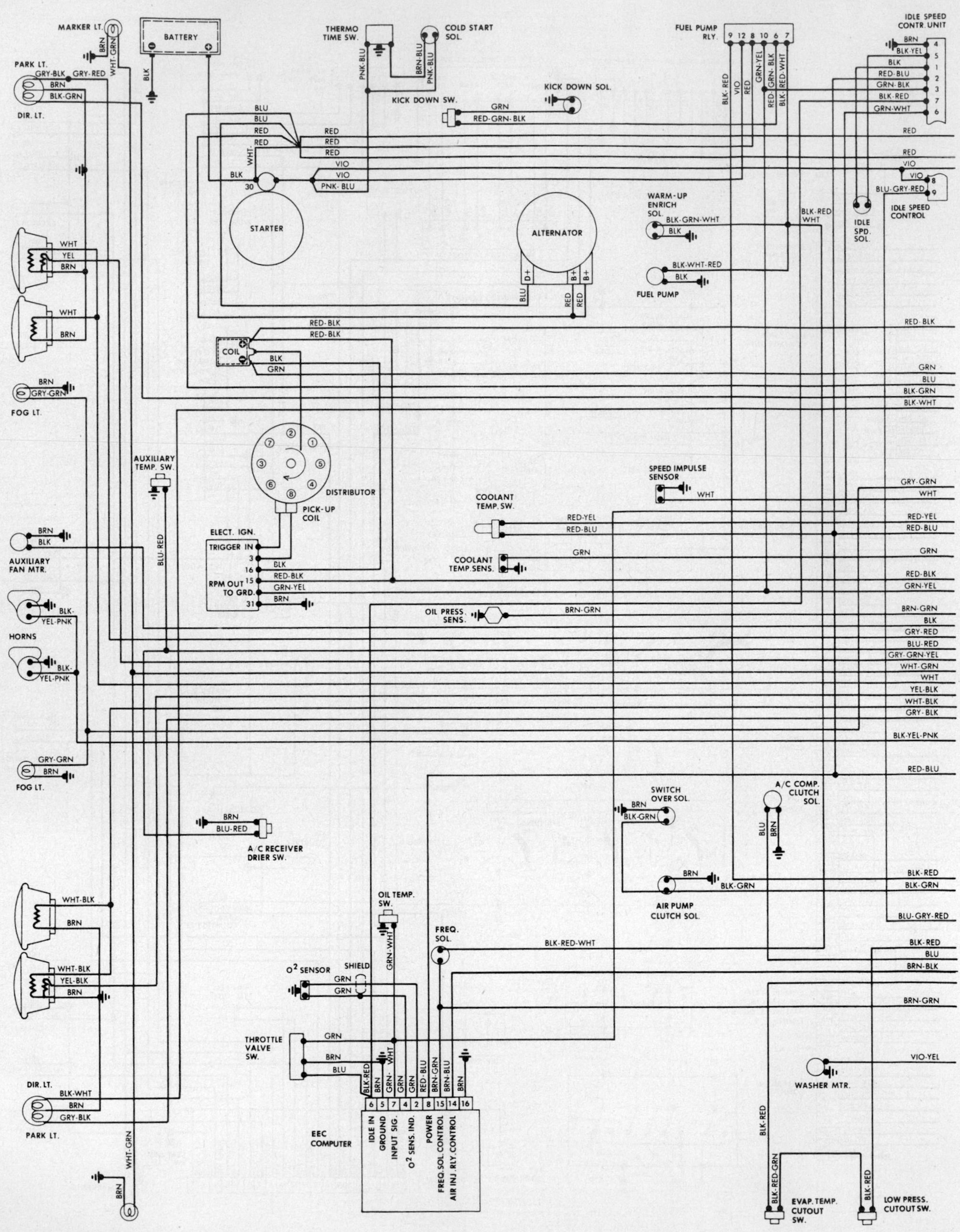

MARKER LT.
BATTERY
PARK LT.
DIR. LT.
THERMO TIME SW.
COLD START SOL.
KICK DOWN SW.
KICK DOWN SOL.
FUEL PUMP RLY.
IDLE SPEED CONTR. UNIT
STARTER
ALTERNATOR
WARM-UP ENRICH SOL.
FUEL PUMP
IDLE SPD. SOL.
IDLE SPEED CONTROL
COIL
FOG LT.
AUXILIARY TEMP. SW.
DISTRIBUTOR
PICK-UP COIL
ELECT. IGN.
TRIGGER IN
RPM OUT TO GRD.
SPEED IMPULSE SENSOR
COOLANT TEMP. SW.
COOLANT TEMP. SENS.
OIL PRESS. SENS.
AUXILIARY FAN MTR.
HORNS
A/C RECEIVER DRIER SW.
SWITCH OVER SOL.
A/C COMP. CLUTCH SOL.
AIR PUMP CLUTCH SOL.
OIL TEMP. SW.
FREQ. SOL.
O2 SENSOR
SHIELD
THROTTLE VALVE SW.
EEC COMPUTER
IDLE IN
GROUND
INPUT SIG.
O2 SENS. IND.
POWER
FREQ. SOL. CONTROL
AIR INJ. RLY. CONTROL
WASHER MTR.
EVAP. TEMP. CUTOUT SW.
LOW PRESS. CUTOUT SW.

1983 Mercedes-Benz

380SL (Cont.)

FUSE BLOCK & UNDERDASH

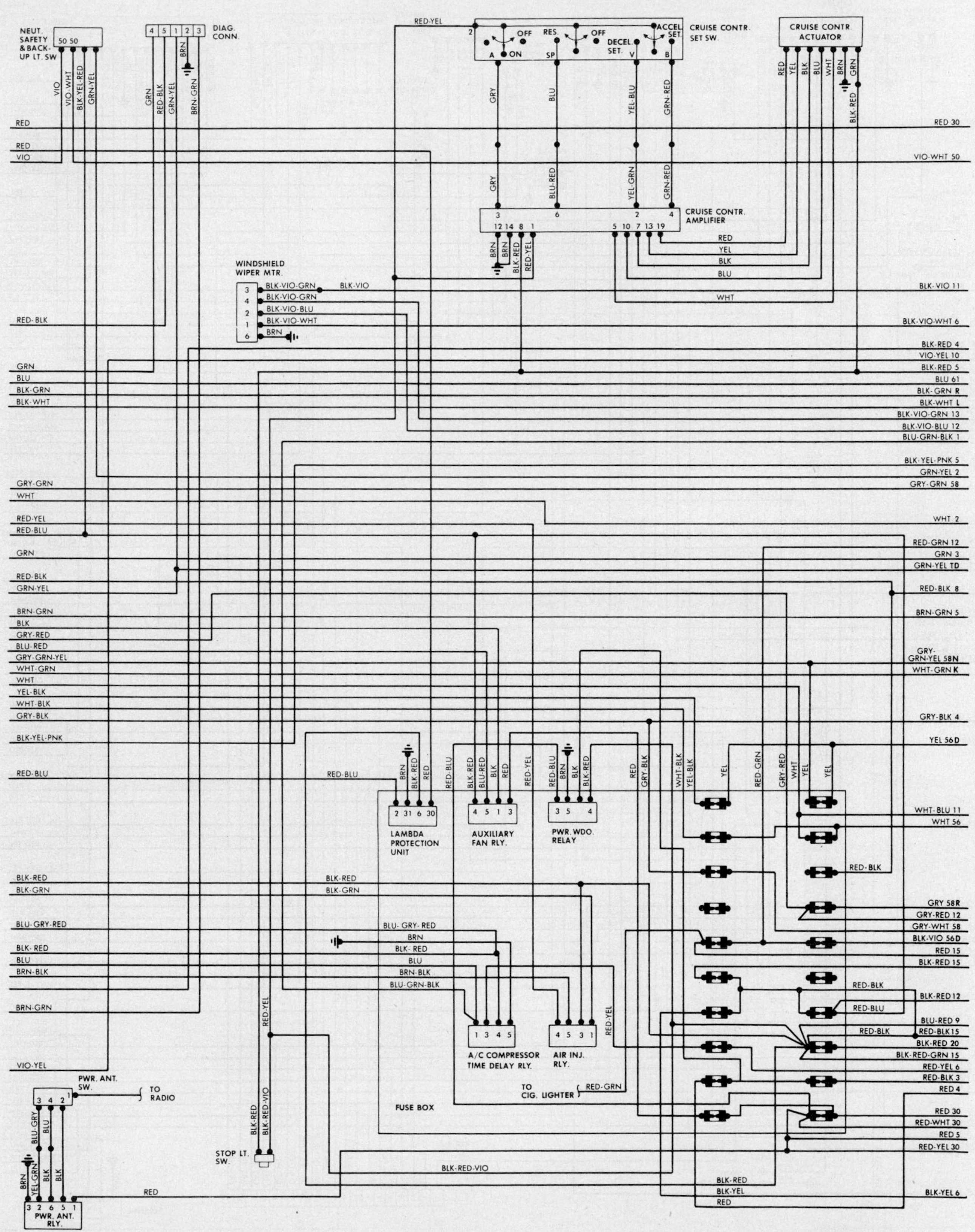
NEUT. SAFETY & BACK-UP LT. SW
DIAG. CONN.
CRUISE CONTR. SET SW.
CRUISE CONTR. ACTUATOR
CRUISE CONTR. AMPLIFIER
WINDSHIELD WIPER MTR.
LAMBDA PROTECTION UNIT
AUXILIARY FAN RLY.
PWR. WDO. RELAY
A/C COMPRESSOR TIME DELAY RLY.
AIR INJ. RLY.
TO CIG. LIGHTER
FUSE BOX
PWR. ANT. SW.
TO RADIO
STOP LT. SW.
PWR. ANT. RLY.
RED 30
VIO-WHT 50
BLK-VIO 11
BLK-VIO-WHT 6
BLK-RED 4
VIO-YEL 10
BLK-RED 5
BLU 61
BLK-GRN R
BLK-WHT L
BLK-VIO-GRN 13
BLK-VIO-BLU 12
BLU-GRN-BLK 1
BLK-YEL-PNK 5
GRN-YEL 2
GRY-GRN 58
WHT 2
RED-GRN 12
GRN 3
GRN-YEL TD
RED-BLK 8
BRN-GRN 5
GRY-GRN-YEL 58N
WHT-GRN K
GRY-BLK 4
YEL 56D
WHT-BLU 11
WHT 56
GRY 58R
GRY-RED 12
GRY-WHT 58
BLK-VIO 56D
RED 15
BLK-RED 15
BLK-RED 12
BLU-RED 9
RED-BLK 15
BLK-RED 20
BLK-RED-GRN 15
RED-YEL 6
RED-BLK 3
RED 4
RED 30
RED-WHT 30
RED 5
RED-YEL 30
BLK-YEL 6

1983 Mercedes-Benz

380SL (Cont.)

UNDERDASH

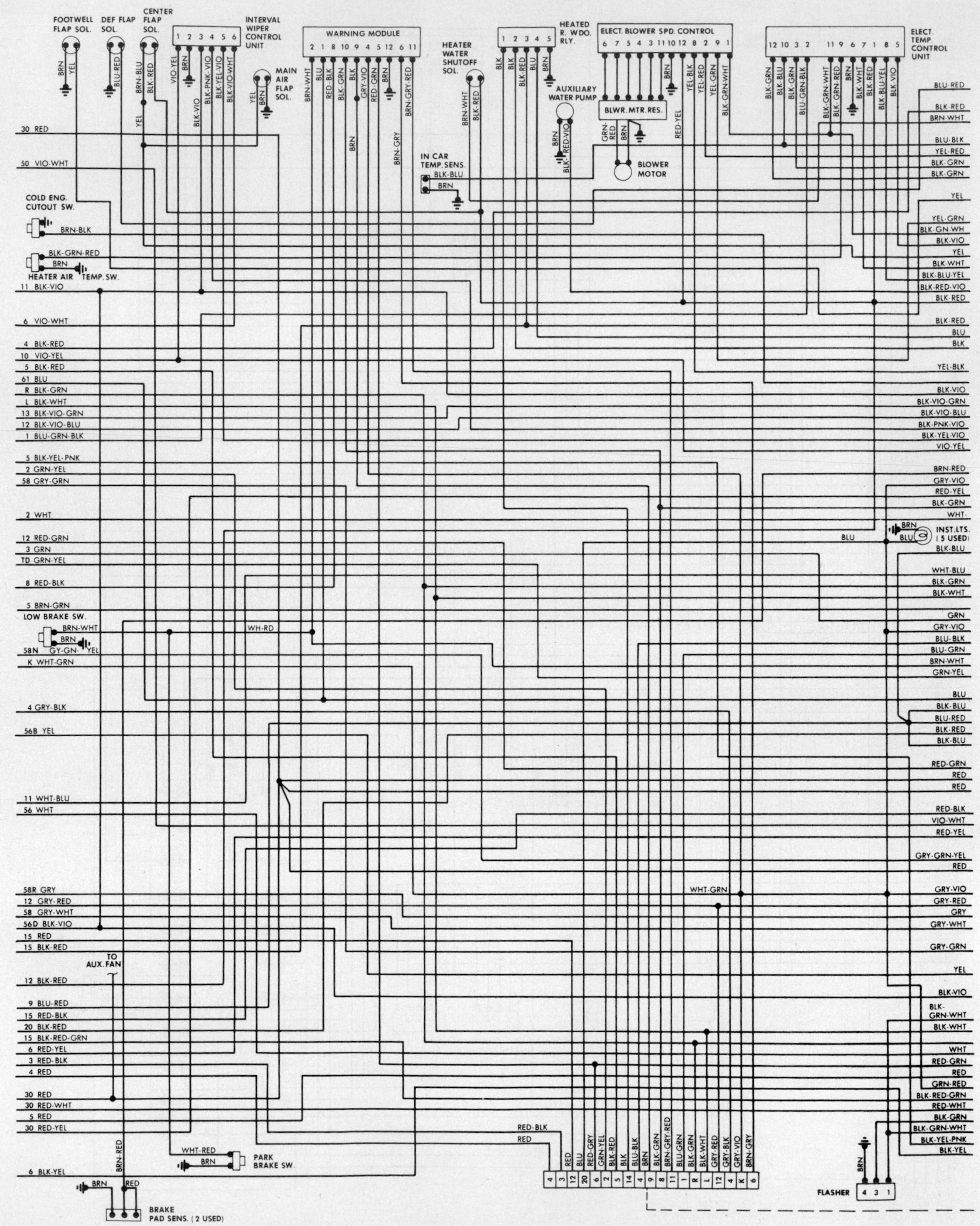
FOOTWELL FLAP SOL.
DEF FLAP SOL.
CENTER FLAP SOL.
INTERVAL WIPER CONTROL UNIT
WARNING MODULE
HEATER WATER SHUTOFF SOL.
HEATED R. WDO. RLY.
ELECT. BLOWER SPD. CONTROL
ELECT. TEMP CONTROL UNIT
MAIN AIR FLAP SOL.
AUXILIARY WATER PUMP
BLWR. MTR. RES.
BLOWER MOTOR
IN CAR TEMP. SENS.
COLD ENG. CUTOUT SW.
HEATER AIR TEMP. SW.
LOW BRAKE SW.
INST. LTS. (5 USED)
TO AUX. FAN
PARK BRAKE SW.
BRAKE PAD SENS. (2 USED)
FLASHER

380SL (Cont.)

INSTRUMENT PANEL, REAR COMPARTMENT & ACCESSORIES

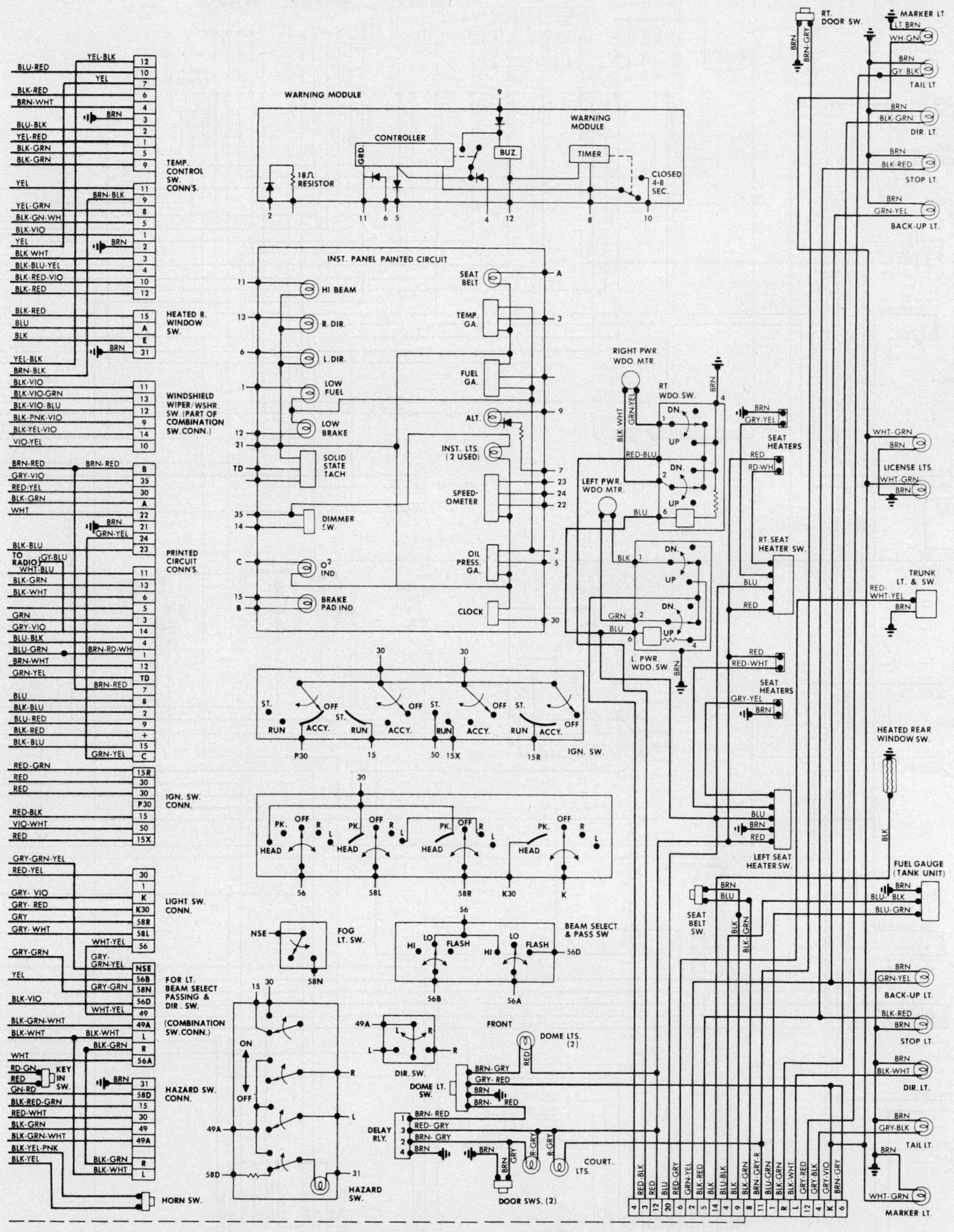
WARNING MODULE
CONTROLLER
18Ω RESISTOR
BUZ.
TIMER
CLOSED 4-8 SEC.
INST. PANEL PAINTED CIRCUIT
HI BEAM
R. DIR.
L. DIR.
LOW FUEL
LOW BRAKE
SOLID STATE TACH
DIMMER SW.
O2 IND.
BRAKE PAD IND.
SEAT BELT
TEMP. GA.
FUEL GA.
ALT.
INST. LTS. (2 USED)
SPEEDOMETER
OIL PRESS. GA.
CLOCK
TEMP. CONTROL SW. CONN'S.
HEATED R. WINDOW SW.
WINDSHIELD WIPER/WSHR. SW. (PART OF COMBINATION SW.CONN.)
PRINTED CIRCUIT CONN'S.
IGN. SW. CONN.
LIGHT SW. CONN.
FOR LT. BEAM SELECT PASSING & DIR. SW.
(COMBINATION SW.CONN.)
HAZARD SW. CONN.
KEY IN SW.
HORN SW.
IGN. SW.
FOG LT. SW.
BEAM SELECT & PASS SW
HI
LO
FLASH
DIR. SW.
HAZARD SW.
DELAY RLY.
DOME LT. SW.
DOME LTS. (2)
FRONT
DOOR SWS. (2)
COURT. LTS.
RIGHT PWR. WDO. MTR.
RT WDO. SW.
LEFT PWR. WDO MTR.
L. PWR. WDO. SW.
SEAT HEATERS
RT. SEAT HEATER SW.
LEFT SEAT HEATER SW.
SEAT BELT SW.
RT. DOOR SW.
MARKER LT.
TAIL LT.
DIR. LT.
STOP LT.
BACK-UP LT.
LICENSE LTS.
TRUNK LT. & SW.
HEATED REAR WINDOW SW.
FUEL GAUGE (TANK UNIT)
BACK-UP LT.
STOP LT.
DIR. LT.
TAIL LT.
MARKER LT.

1983 Mitsubishi

CORDIA & TREDIA

ENGINE COMPARTMENT

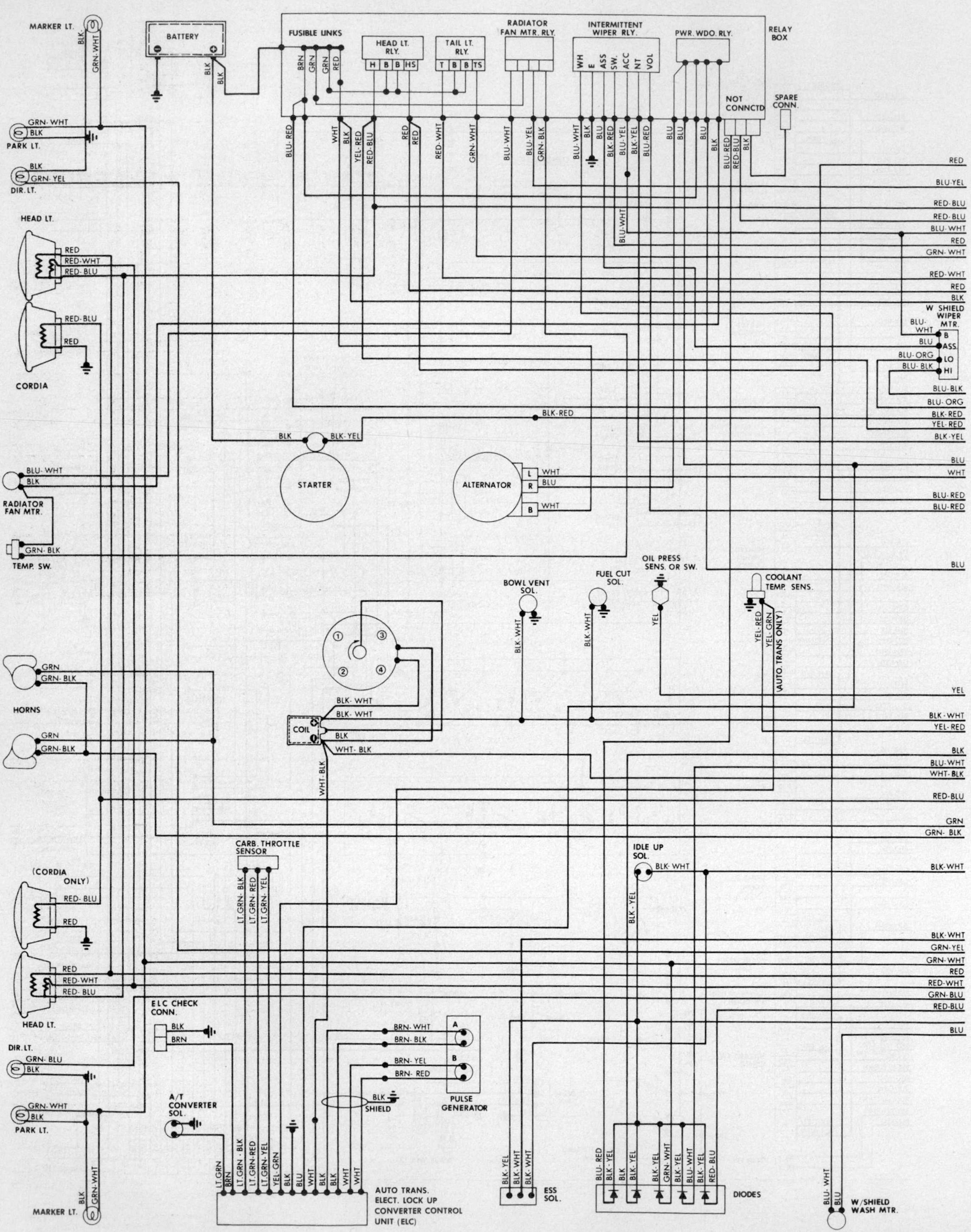
MARKER LT.
BATTERY
FUSIBLE LINKS
HEAD LT. RLY.
TAIL LT. RLY.
RADIATOR FAN MTR. RLY.
INTERMITTENT WIPER RLY.
PWR. WDO. RLY.
RELAY BOX
NOT CONNCTD
SPARE CONN.
PARK LT.
DIR. LT.
HEAD LT.
CORDIA
W SHIELD WIPER MTR.
STARTER
ALTERNATOR
RADIATOR FAN MTR.
TEMP. SW.
BOWL VENT SOL.
FUEL CUT SOL.
OIL PRESS SENS. OR SW.
COOLANT TEMP. SENS.
(AUTO. TRANS ONLY)
HORNS
COIL
CARB. THROTTLE SENSOR
IDLE UP SOL.
(CORDIA ONLY)
ELC CHECK CONN.
PULSE GENERATOR
SHIELD
A/T CONVERTER SOL.
AUTO TRANS. ELECT. LOCK UP CONVERTER CONTROL UNIT (ELC)
ESS SOL.
DIODES
W/SHIELD WASH MTR.

CORDIA & TREDIA (Cont.)

FUSE BLOCK & UNDERDASH

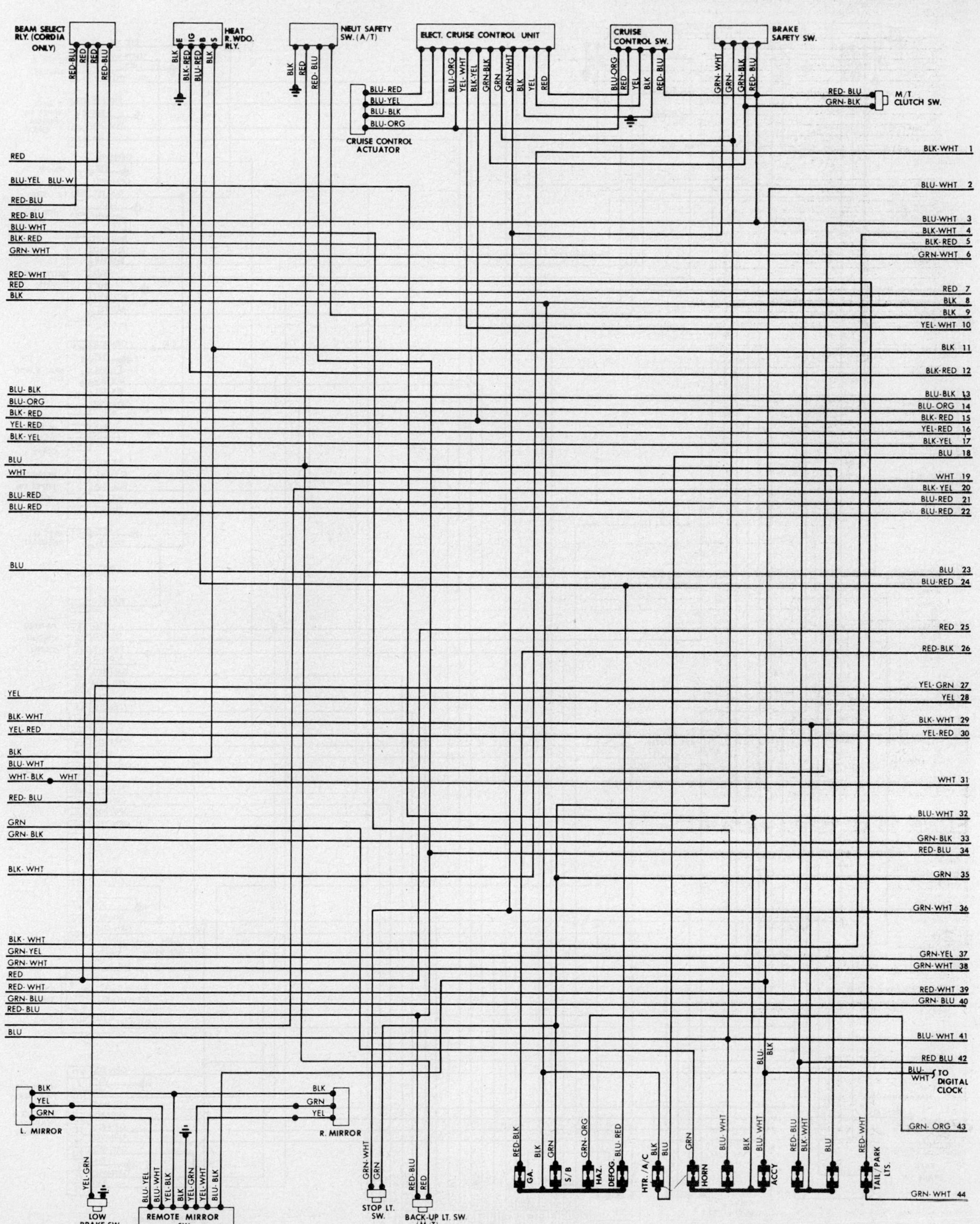
BEAM SELECT RLY. (CORDIA ONLY)
HEAT R. WDO. RLY.
NEUT SAFETY SW. (A/T)
ELECT. CRUISE CONTROL UNIT
CRUISE CONTROL SW.
BRAKE SAFETY SW.
M/T CLUTCH SW.
CRUISE CONTROL ACTUATOR
BLU-RED
BLU-YEL
BLU-BLK
BLU-ORG
RED-BLU
GRN-BLK
BLK-WHT 1
BLU-WHT 2
BLU-WHT 3
BLK-WHT 4
BLK-RED 5
GRN-WHT 6
RED 7
BLK 8
BLK 9
YEL-WHT 10
BLK 11
BLK-RED 12
BLU-BLK 13
BLU-ORG 14
BLK-RED 15
YEL-RED 16
BLK-YEL 17
BLU 18
WHT 19
BLK-YEL 20
BLU-RED 21
BLU-RED 22
BLU 23
BLU-RED 24
RED 25
RED-BLK 26
YEL-GRN 27
YEL 28
BLK-WHT 29
YEL-RED 30
WHT 31
BLU-WHT 32
GRN-BLK 33
RED-BLU 34
GRN 35
GRN-WHT 36
GRN-YEL 37
GRN-WHT 38
RED-WHT 39
GRN-BLU 40
BLU-WHT 41
RED BLU 42
TO DIGITAL CLOCK
GRN-ORG 43
GRN-WHT 44
L. MIRROR
R. MIRROR
LOW BRAKE SW.
REMOTE MIRROR SW.
STOP LT. SW.
BACK-UP LT. SW. (M/T)
GA.
S/B
HAZ.
DEFOG.
HTR./A/C
HORN
ACCY
TAIL/PARK LTS.

1983 Mitsubishi

CORDIA & TREDIA (Cont.)

INSTRUMENT PANEL & UNDERDASH

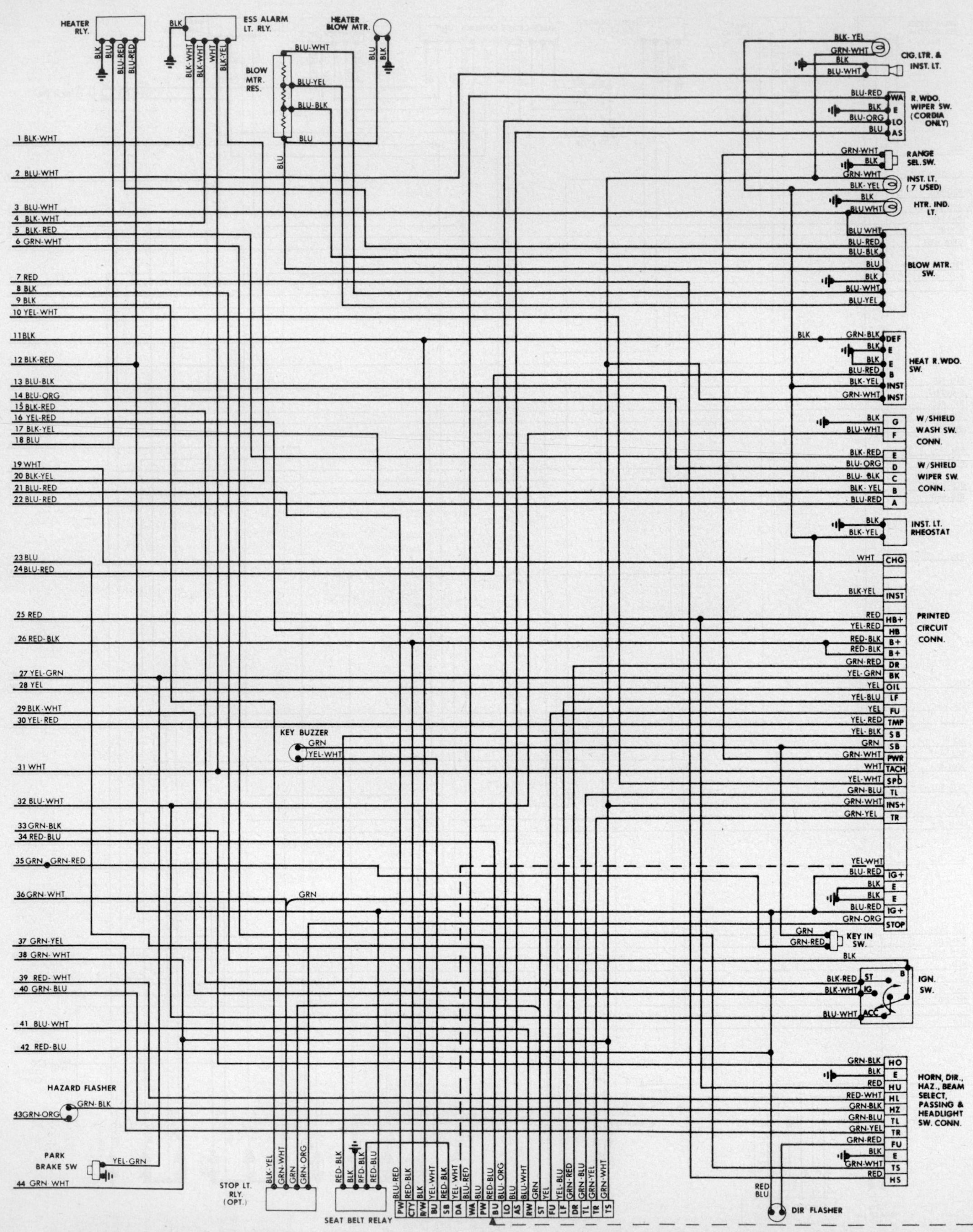
HEATER RLY.
ESS ALARM LT. RLY.
HEATER BLOW MTR.
BLOW MTR. RES.
BLK
BLU
BLU-RED
BLK-WHT
WHT
BLK-YEL
BLU-WHT
BLU-YEL
BLU-BLK
1 BLK-WHT
2 BLU-WHT
3 BLU-WHT
4 BLK-WHT
5 BLK-RED
6 GRN-WHT
7 RED
8 BLK
9 BLK
10 YEL-WHT
11 BLK
12 BLK-RED
13 BLU-BLK
14 BLU-ORG
15 BLK-RED
16 YEL-RED
17 BLK-YEL
18 BLU
19 WHT
20 BLK-YEL
21 BLU-RED
22 BLU-RED
23 BLU
24 BLU-RED
25 RED
26 RED-BLK
27 YEL-GRN
28 YEL
29 BLK-WHT
30 YEL-RED
31 WHT
32 BLU-WHT
33 GRN-BLK
34 RED-BLU
35 GRN GRN-RED
36 GRN-WHT
37 GRN-YEL
38 GRN-WHT
39 RED-WHT
40 GRN-BLU
41 BLU-WHT
42 RED-BLU
HAZARD FLASHER
43 GRN-ORG
GRN-BLK
PARK BRAKE SW
YEL-GRN
44 GRN-WHT
KEY BUZZER
GRN
YEL-WHT
STOP LT. RLY. (OPT.)
SEAT BELT RELAY
BLK-YEL
GRN-WHT
GRN-ORG
RED-BLK
RED-BLU
PW CTY R/W BU SB DA WA BU PW BU LO AS RW ST FU LF DR TL TR TS
CIG. LTR. & INST. LT.
R. WDO. WIPER SW. (CORDIA ONLY)
WA E LO AS
RANGE SEL. SW.
INST. LT. (7 USED)
HTR. IND. LT.
BLOW MTR. SW.
HEAT R. WDO. SW.
DEF E E B INST INST
W/SHIELD WASH SW. CONN.
G F
W/SHIELD WIPER SW. CONN.
E D C B A
INST. LT. RHEOSTAT
PRINTED CIRCUIT CONN.
CHG INST HB+ HB B+ B+ DR BK OIL LF FU TMP SB SB PWR TACH SPD TL INS+ TR
IG+ E E IG+ STOP
KEY IN SW.
IGN. SW.
ST IG ACC B
HORN, DIR., HAZ., BEAM SELECT, PASSING & HEADLIGHT SW. CONN.
HO E HU HL HZ TL TR FU E TS HS
DIR FLASHER
RED BLU

CORDIA & TREDIA (Cont.)

REAR COMPARTMENT & ACCESSORIES

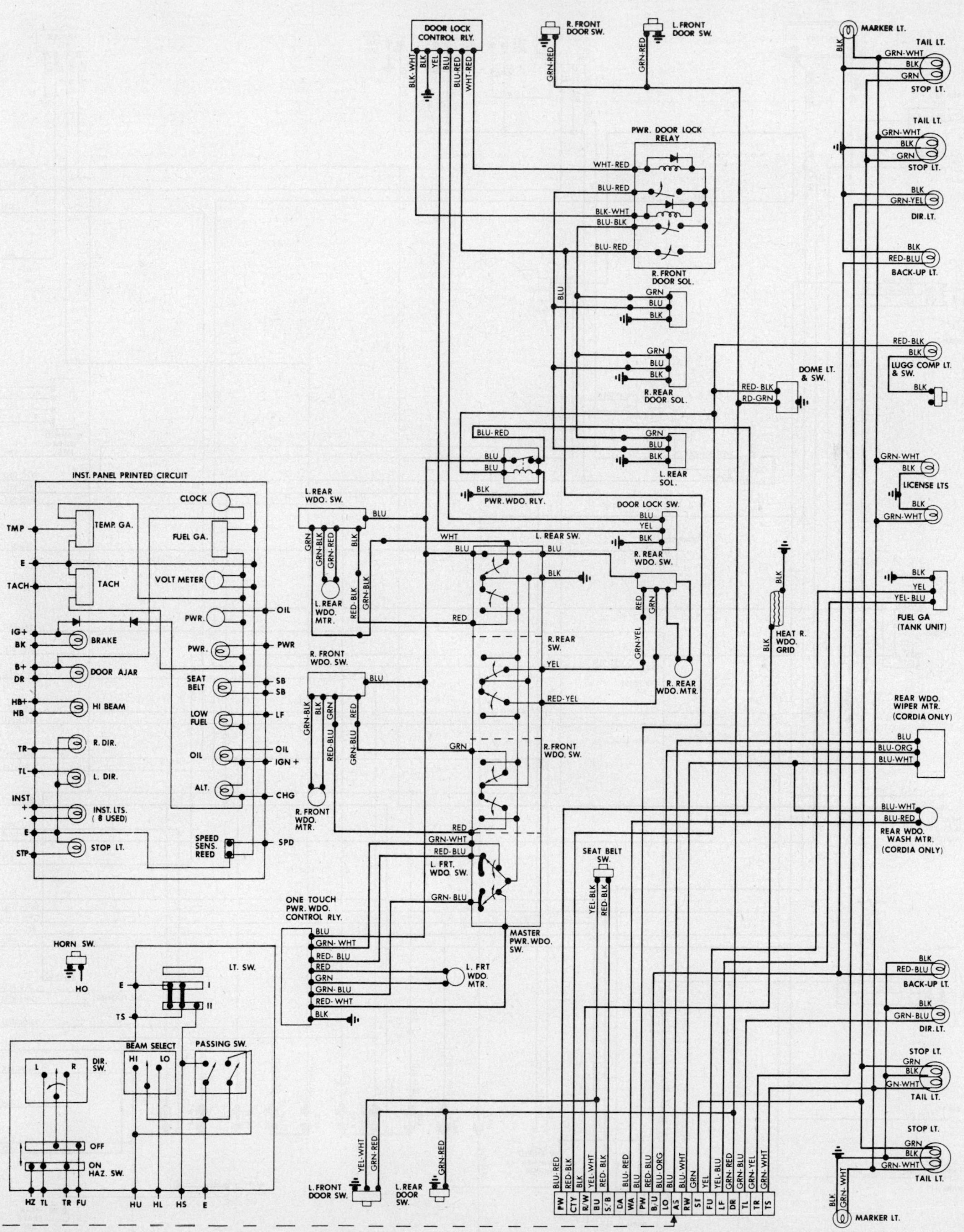
DOOR LOCK CONTROL RLY.
R. FRONT DOOR SW.
L. FRONT DOOR SW.
MARKER LT.
TAIL LT.
STOP LT.
PWR. DOOR LOCK RELAY
DIR. LT.
BACK-UP LT.
R. FRONT DOOR SOL.
LUGG COMP LT. & SW.
DOME LT. & SW.
R. REAR DOOR SOL.
L. REAR SOL.
PWR. WDO. RLY.
LICENSE LTS
INST. PANEL PRINTED CIRCUIT
L. REAR WDO. SW.
DOOR LOCK SW.
L. REAR SW.
R. REAR WDO. SW.
CLOCK
TEMP. GA.
FUEL GA.
TACH
VOLT METER
L. REAR WDO. MTR.
HEAT R. WDO. GRID
FUEL GA (TANK UNIT)
BRAKE
DOOR AJAR
HI BEAM
SEAT BELT
LOW FUEL
R. DIR.
L. DIR.
OIL
ALT.
INST. LTS. (8 USED)
STOP LT.
SPEED SENS. REED
R. FRONT WDO. SW.
R. REAR SW.
R. REAR WDO. MTR.
R. FRONT WDO. MTR.
REAR WDO. WIPER MTR. (CORDIA ONLY)
REAR WDO. WASH MTR. (CORDIA ONLY)
L. FRT. WDO. SW.
ONE TOUCH PWR. WDO. CONTROL RLY.
MASTER PWR. WDO. SW.
L. FRT WDO. MTR.
SEAT BELT SW.
HORN SW.
LT. SW.
BEAM SELECT
PASSING SW.
DIR. SW.
OFF
ON HAZ. SW.
L. FRONT DOOR SW.
L. REAR DOOR SW.
PW CTY R/W SB S/B DA WA PW B/U LO AS RW ST FU LF DR TL TR TS
HZ TL TR FU HU HL HS E

1983 Mitsubishi

MONTERO

ENGINE COMPARTMENT & FUSE BLOCK

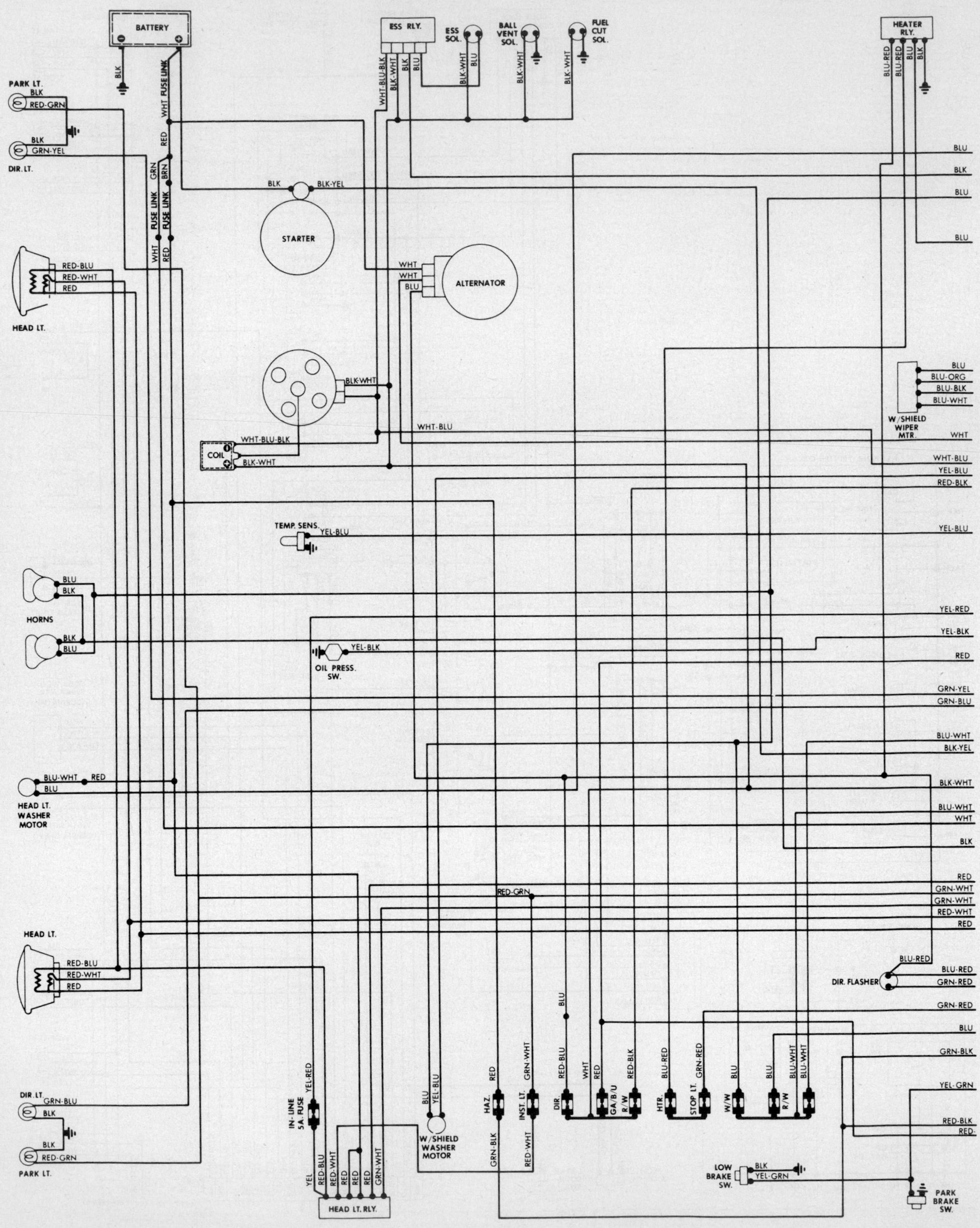

BATTERY
PARK LT.
DIR. LT.
HEAD LT.
HORNS
HEAD LT. WASHER MOTOR
HEAD LT.
DIR. LT
PARK LT.
FUSE LINK
ESS RLY.
ESS SOL.
BALL VENT SOL.
FUEL CUT SOL.
STARTER
ALTERNATOR
COIL
TEMP. SENS.
OIL PRESS. SW.
HEATER RLY.
W/SHIELD WIPER MTR.
DIR. FLASHER
IN-LINE 5A. FUSE
HEAD LT. RLY.
W/SHIELD WASHER MOTOR
HAZ.
INST. LT.
DIR.
GA/B/U
R/W
HTR.
STOP LT.
W/W
LOW BRAKE SW.
PARK BRAKE SW.
BLK
RED-GRN
GRN-YEL
WHT
RED
GRN
BRN
RED-BLU
RED-WHT
BLU
BLU-WHT
GRN-BLU
BLK-YEL
WHT-BLU-BLK
BLK-WHT
WHT-BLU
YEL-BLU
YEL-BLK
BLU-RED
BLU-ORG
BLU-BLK
RED-BLK
YEL-RED
BLK-YEL
GRN-WHT
GRN-RED
GRN-BLK
YEL-GRN
YEL

1983 Mitsubishi

MONTERO (Cont.)

INSTRUMENT PANEL & REAR COMPARTMENT

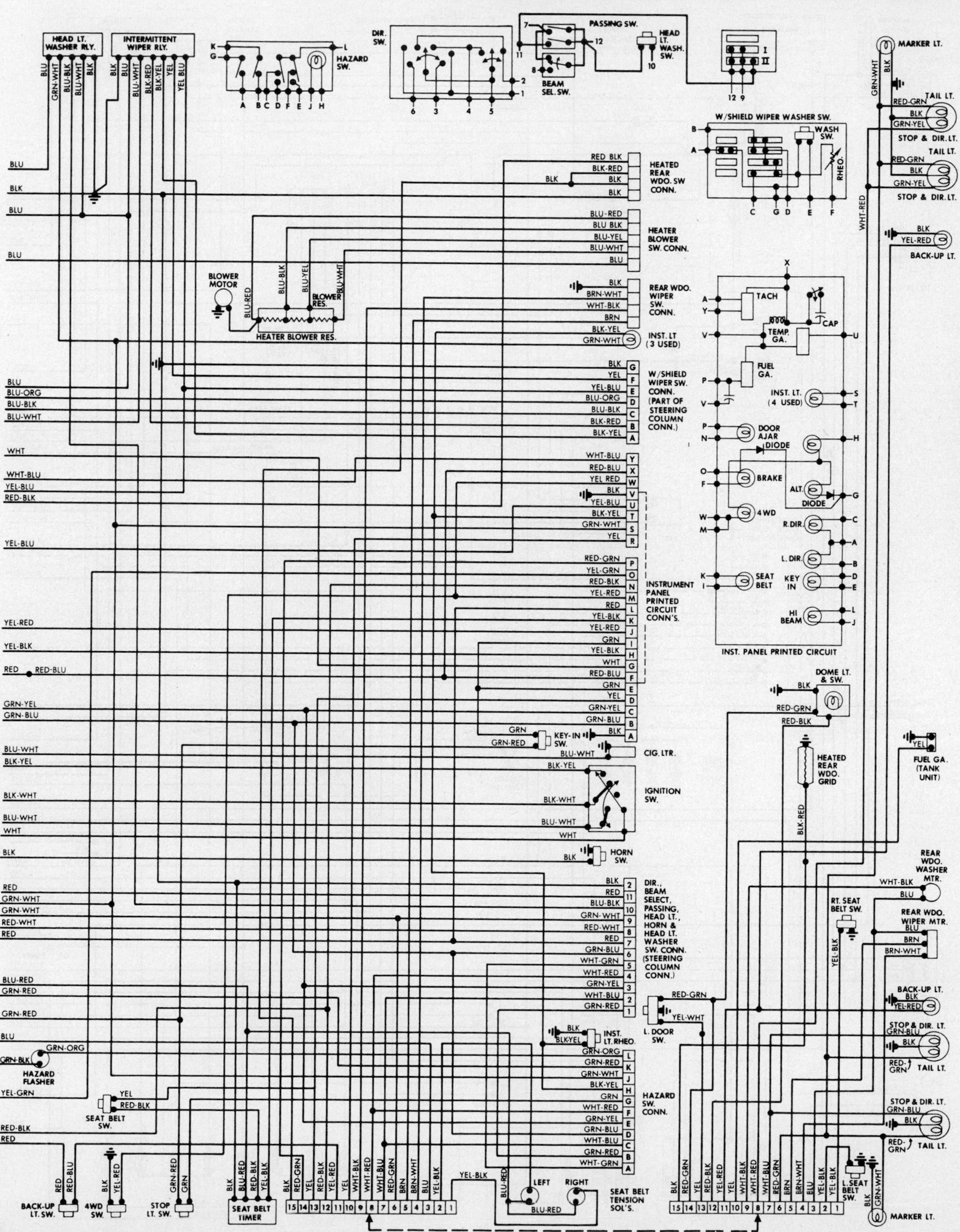

HEAD LT. WASHER RLY.
INTERMITTENT WIPER RLY.
HAZARD SW.
DIR. SW.
PASSING SW.
HEAD LT. WASH. SW.
BEAM SEL. SW.
MARKER LT.
TAIL LT.
STOP & DIR. LT.
W/SHIELD WIPER WASHER SW.
WASH SW.
RHEO.
HEATED REAR WDO. SW CONN.
HEATER BLOWER SW. CONN.
BLOWER MOTOR
BLOWER RES.
HEATER BLOWER RES.
REAR WDO. WIPER SW. CONN.
INST. LT (3 USED)
BACK-UP LT.
TACH
CAP
TEMP. GA.
FUEL GA.
INST. LT. (4 USED)
W/SHIELD WIPER SW. CONN. (PART OF STEERING COLUMN CONN.)
DOOR AJAR
DIODE
BRAKE
ALT.
4WD
R. DIR.
L. DIR.
SEAT BELT
KEY IN
HI BEAM
INSTRUMENT PANEL PRINTED CIRCUIT CONN'S.
INST. PANEL PRINTED CIRCUIT
DOME LT. & SW.
KEY-IN SW.
CIG. LTR.
FUEL GA. (TANK UNIT)
HEATED REAR WDO. GRID
IGNITION SW.
HORN SW.
REAR WDO. WASHER MTR.
DIR., BEAM SELECT, PASSING, HEAD LT., HORN & HEAD LT. WASHER SW. CONN. (STEERING COLUMN CONN.)
RT. SEAT BELT SW.
REAR WDO. WIPER MTR.
L. DOOR SW.
INST. LT. RHEO.
HAZARD FLASHER
HAZARD SW. CONN.
SEAT BELT SW.
BACK-UP LT. SW.
4WD SW.
STOP LT. SW.
SEAT BELT TIMER
LEFT
RIGHT
SEAT BELT TENSION SOL'S.
L. SEAT BELT SW.
MARKER LT.

1983 Mitsubishi

PICKUP

ENGINE COMPARTMENT & FUSE BLOCK

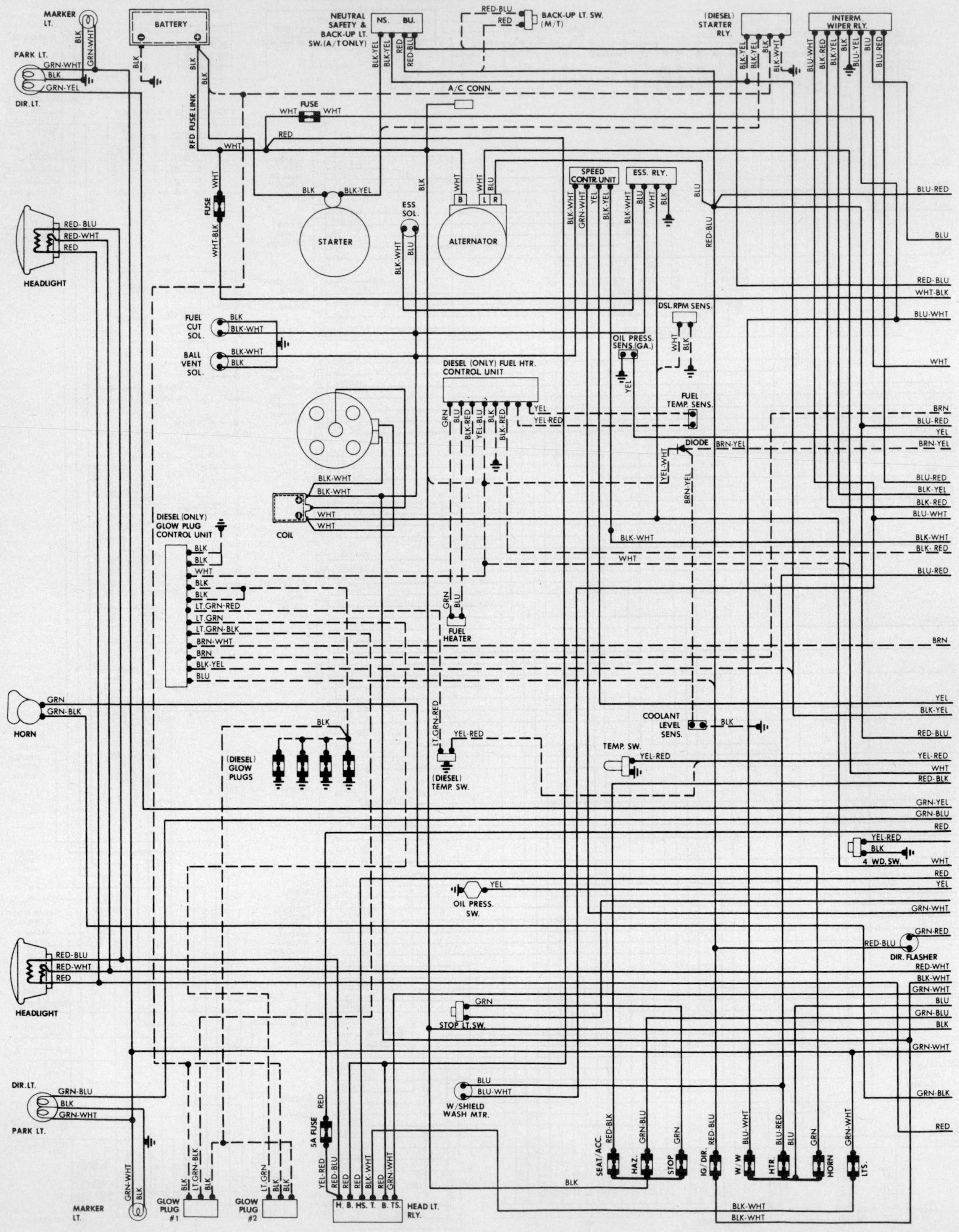

MARKER LT.
PARK LT.
DIR. LT.
BATTERY
NEUTRAL SAFETY & BACK-UP LT. SW. (A/T ONLY)
NS.
BU.
BACK-UP LT. SW. (M/T)
(DIESEL) STARTER RLY.
INTERM. WIPER RLY.
A/C CONN.
FUSE
RED FUSE LINK
STARTER
ESS SOL.
ALTERNATOR
SPEED CONTR. UNIT
ESS. RLY.
HEADLIGHT
FUEL CUT SOL.
BALL VENT SOL.
DSL. RPM SENS.
OIL PRESS. SENS. (GA.)
DIESEL (ONLY) FUEL HTR. CONTROL UNIT
FUEL TEMP. SENS.
DIODE
COIL
DIESEL (ONLY) GLOW PLUG CONTROL UNIT
FUEL HEATER
HORN
COOLANT LEVEL SENS.
TEMP. SW.
(DIESEL) GLOW PLUGS
(DIESEL) TEMP. SW.
4 WD. SW.
OIL PRESS. SW.
DIR. FLASHER
STOP LT. SW.
W/SHIELD WASH MTR.
5A FUSE
GLOW PLUG #1
GLOW PLUG #2
HEAD LT. RLY.
H. B. HS. T. B. TS.
SEAT/ACC.
HAZ.
STOP
IG/DIR.
W/W
HTR.
HORN
LTS.

PICKUP (Cont.)

INSTRUMENT PANEL & REAR COMPARTMENT

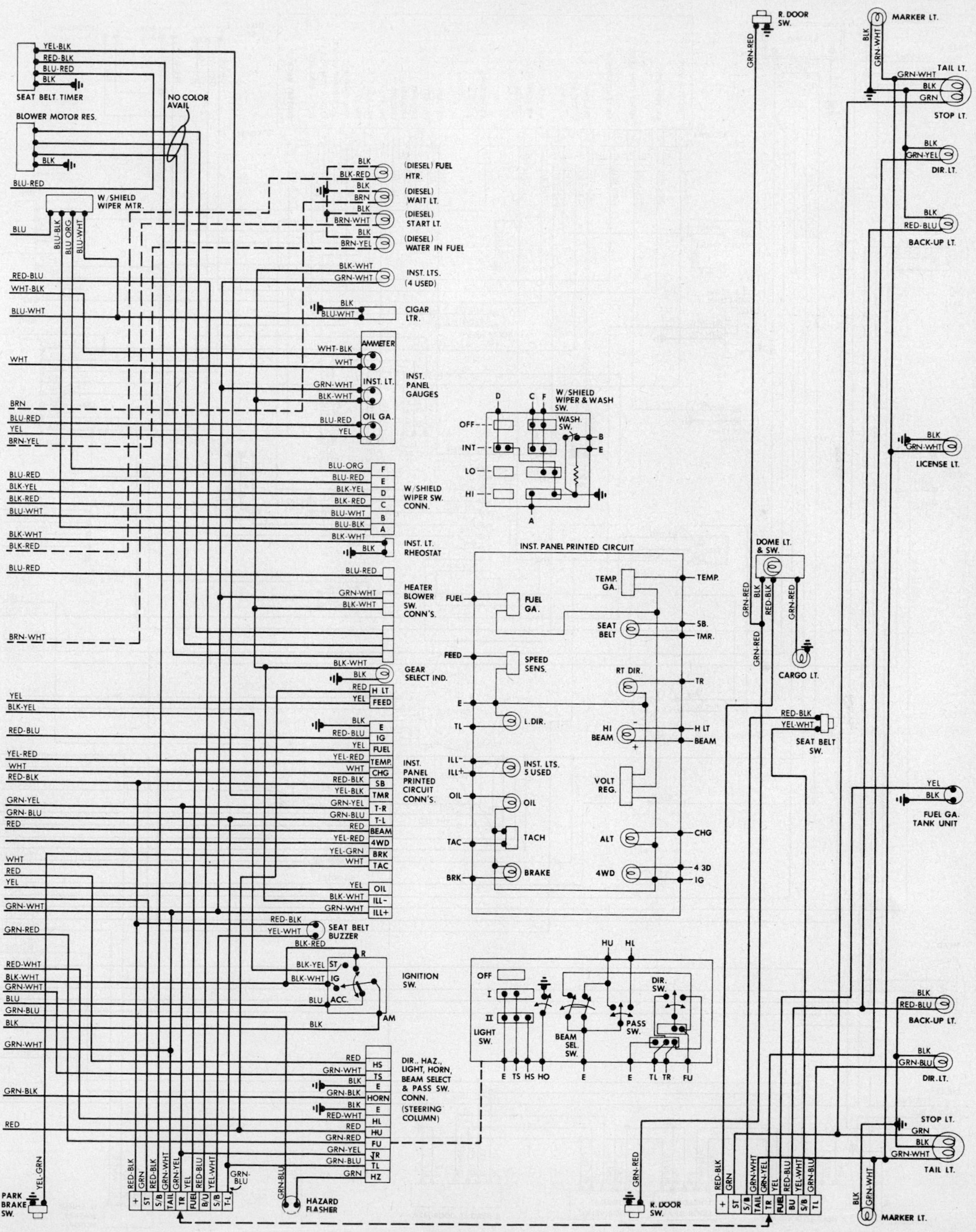

SEAT BELT TIMER
BLOWER MOTOR RES.
NO COLOR AVAIL
W/SHIELD WIPER MTR.
(DIESEL) FUEL HTR.
(DIESEL) WAIT LT.
(DIESEL) START LT.
(DIESEL) WATER IN FUEL
INST. LTS. (4 USED)
CIGAR LTR.
AMMETER
INST. LT.
OIL GA.
INST. PANEL GAUGES
W/SHIELD WIPER & WASH SW.
WASH. SW.
OFF
INT
LO
HI
W/SHIELD WIPER SW. CONN.
INST. LT. RHEOSTAT
HEATER BLOWER SW. CONN'S.
GEAR SELECT IND.
INST. PANEL PRINTED CIRCUIT
INST. PANEL PRINTED CIRCUIT CONN'S.
TEMP. GA.
FUEL GA.
SEAT BELT
SPEED SENS.
RT DIR.
L. DIR.
HI BEAM
INST. LTS. 5 USED
OIL
VOLT REG.
TACH
ALT
BRAKE
4WD
SEAT BELT BUZZER
IGNITION SW.
LIGHT SW.
BEAM SEL. SW.
DIR. SW.
PASS SW.
DIR., HAZ., LIGHT, HORN, BEAM SELECT & PASS SW. CONN. (STEERING COLUMN)
PARK BRAKE SW.
HAZARD FLASHER
R. DOOR SW.
MARKER LT.
TAIL LT.
STOP LT.
DIR. LT.
BACK-UP LT.
LICENSE LT.
DOME LT. & SW.
CARGO LT.
SEAT BELT SW.
FUEL GA. TANK UNIT

1983 Mitsubishi

STARION

ENGINE COMPARTMENT

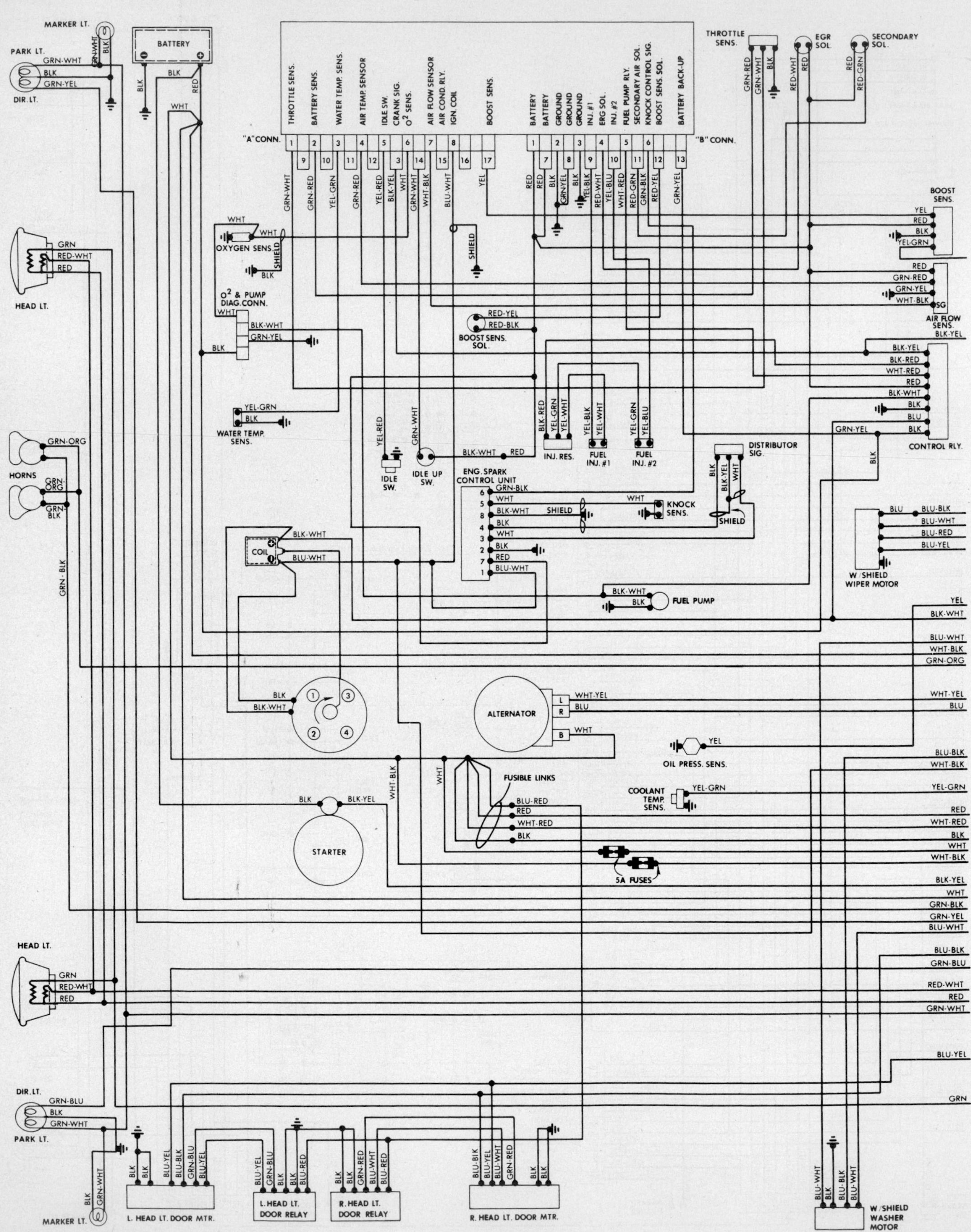
MARKER LT.
PARK LT.
DIR. LT.
BATTERY
THROTTLE SENS.
BATTERY SENS.
WATER TEMP. SENS.
AIR TEMP SENSOR
IDLE SW.
CRANK SIG.
O² SENS.
AIR FLOW SENSOR
AIR COND. RLY.
IGN. COIL
BOOST SENS.
BATTERY
BATTERY
GROUND
GROUND
GROUND
INJ. #1
EGR SOL.
INJ. #2
FUEL PUMP RLY.
SECONDARY AIR SOL.
KNOCK CONTROL SIG.
BOOST SENS. SOL.
BATTERY BACK-UP
"A" CONN.
"B" CONN.
THROTTLE SENS.
EGR SOL.
SECONDARY SOL.
BOOST SENS.
OXYGEN SENS.
SHIELD
HEAD LT.
O² & PUMP DIAG. CONN.
BOOST SENS. SOL.
AIR FLOW SENS.
WATER TEMP. SENS.
INJ. RES.
FUEL INJ. #1
FUEL INJ. #2
DISTRIBUTOR SIG.
CONTROL RLY.
HORNS
IDLE SW.
IDLE UP SW.
ENG. SPARK CONTROL UNIT
KNOCK SENS.
COIL
FUEL PUMP
W/SHIELD WIPER MOTOR
ALTERNATOR
OIL PRESS. SENS.
FUSIBLE LINKS
COOLANT TEMP. SENS.
STARTER
5A FUSES
HEAD LT.
DIR. LT.
PARK LT.
MARKER LT.
L. HEAD LT. DOOR MTR.
L. HEAD LT. DOOR RELAY
R. HEAD LT. DOOR RELAY
R. HEAD LT. DOOR MTR.
W/SHIELD WASHER MOTOR

STARION (Cont.)

FUSE BLOCK & UNDERDASH

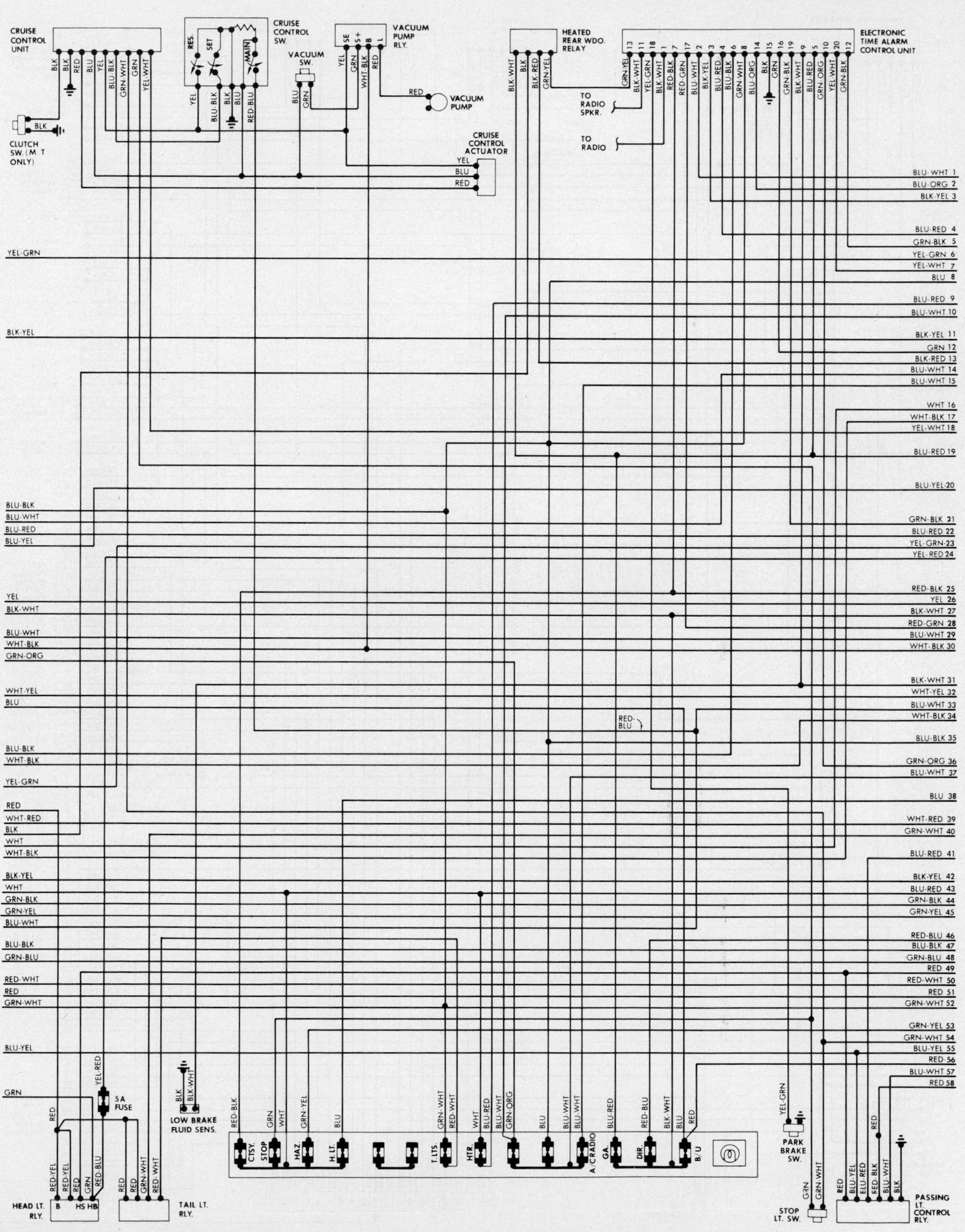

1983 Mitsubishi

STARION (Cont.)

INSTRUMENT PANEL & UNDERDASH

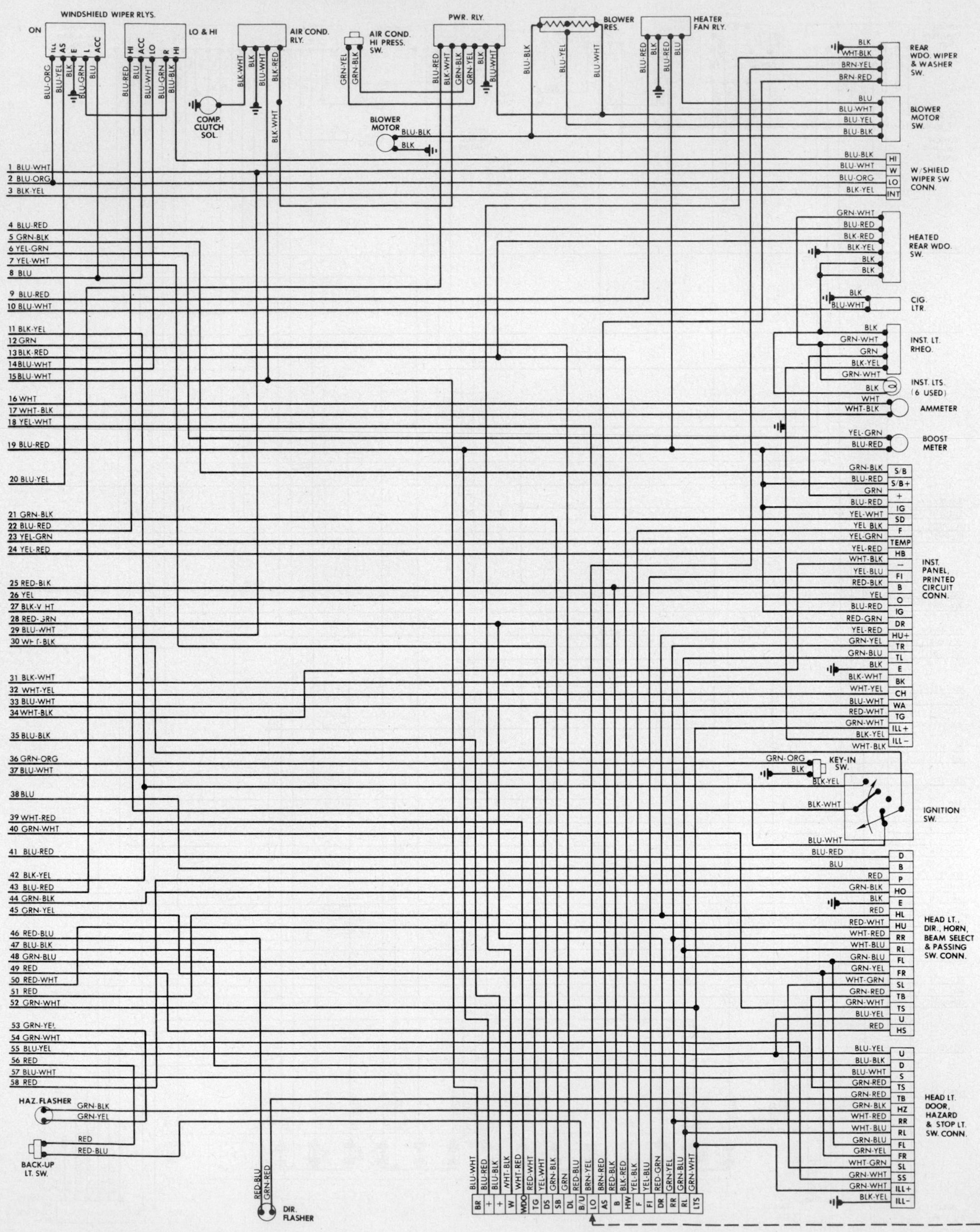
WINDSHIELD WIPER RLYS.
ON
LO & HI
AIR COND. RLY.
AIR COND. HI PRESS. SW.
PWR. RLY.
BLOWER RES.
HEATER FAN RLY.
COMP. CLUTCH SOL.
BLOWER MOTOR
REAR WDO. WIPER & WASHER SW.
BLOWER MOTOR SW.
W/SHIELD WIPER SW CONN.
HEATED REAR WDO. SW.
CIG. LTR.
INST. LT. RHEO.
INST. LTS. (6 USED)
AMMETER
BOOST METER
INST. PANEL, PRINTED CIRCUIT CONN.
KEY-IN SW.
IGNITION SW.
HEAD LT., DIR., HORN, BEAM SELECT & PASSING SW. CONN.
HEAD LT. DOOR, HAZARD & STOP LT. SW. CONN.
HAZ. FLASHER
BACK-UP LT. SW.
DIR. FLASHER

STARION (Cont.)

REAR COMPARTMENT & ACCESSORIES

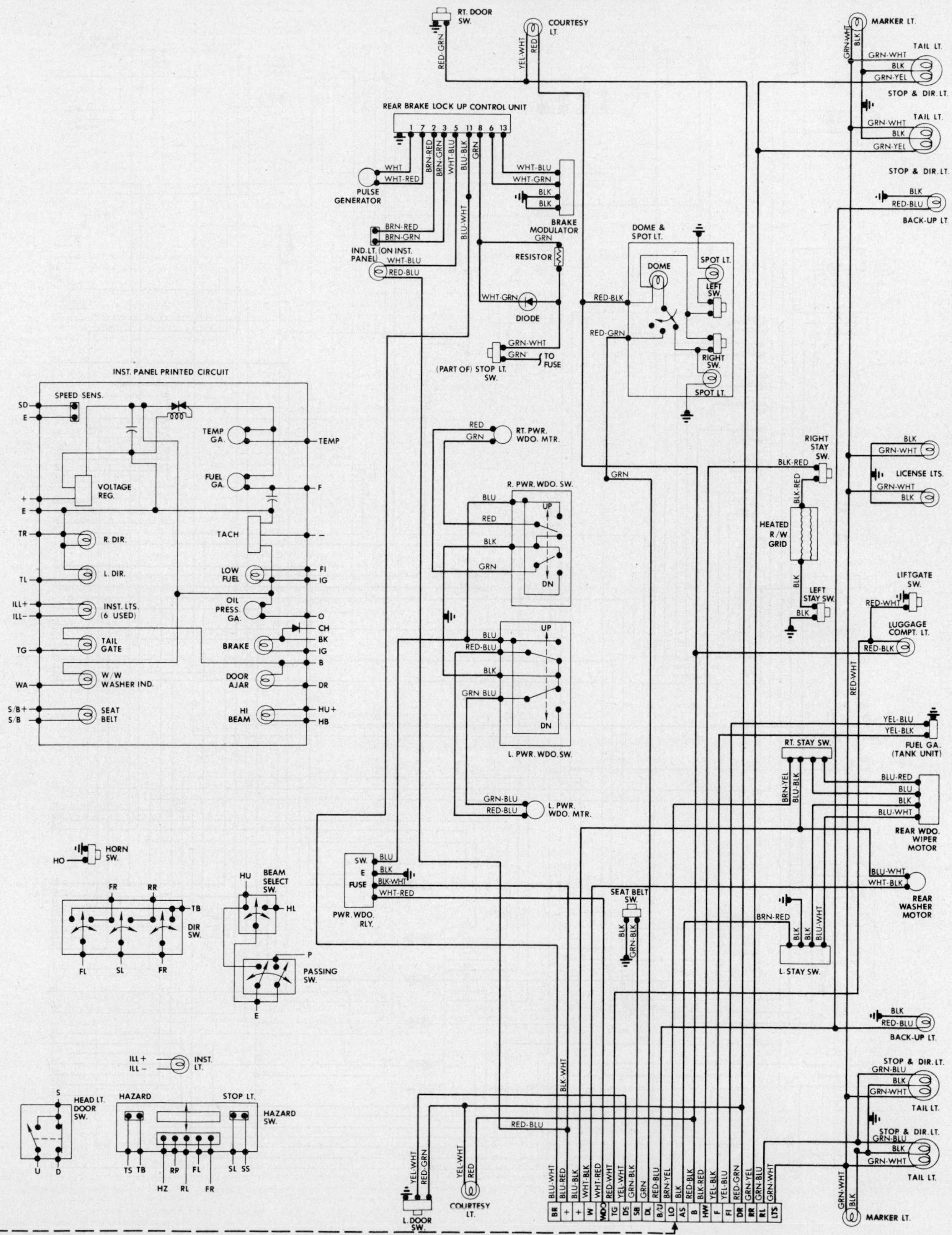

1983 Peugeot

504 DIESEL

ENGINE COMPARTMENT & FUSE BLOCK

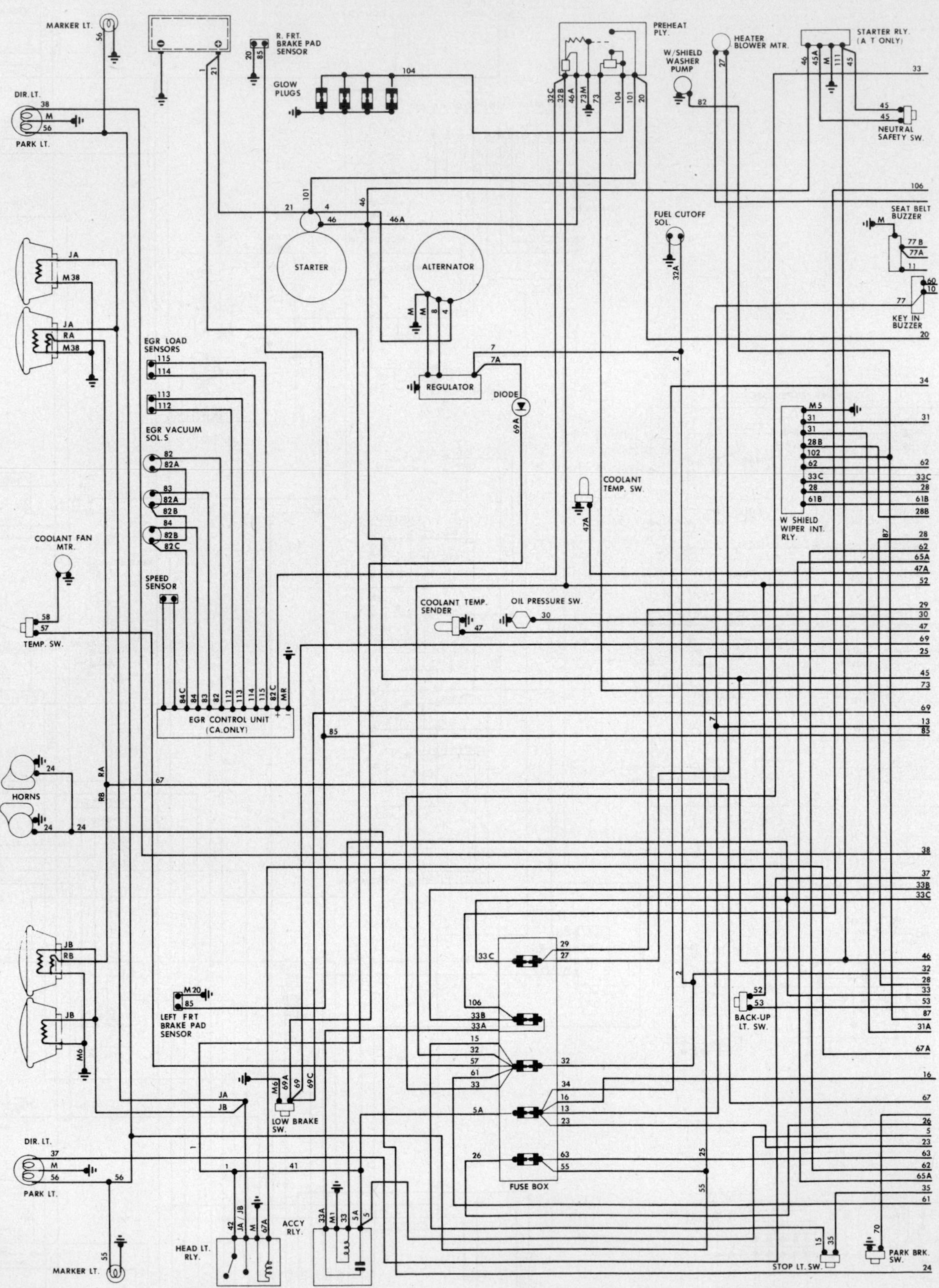
MARKER LT.
R. FRT. BRAKE PAD SENSOR
GLOW PLUGS
PREHEAT RLY.
W/SHIELD WASHER PUMP
HEATER BLOWER MTR.
STARTER RLY. (A T ONLY)
NEUTRAL SAFETY SW.
DIR. LT.
PARK LT.
STARTER
ALTERNATOR
FUEL CUTOFF SOL.
SEAT BELT BUZZER
KEY IN BUZZER
EGR LOAD SENSORS
REGULATOR
DIODE
EGR VACUUM SOL.S
W SHIELD WIPER INT. RLY.
COOLANT TEMP. SW.
COOLANT FAN MTR.
SPEED SENSOR
COOLANT TEMP. SENDER
OIL PRESSURE SW.
TEMP. SW.
EGR CONTROL UNIT (CA. ONLY)
HORNS
LEFT FRT BRAKE PAD SENSOR
BACK-UP LT. SW.
LOW BRAKE SW.
FUSE BOX
DIR. LT.
PARK LT.
MARKER LT.
HEAD LT. RLY.
ACCY RLY.
STOP LT. SW.
PARK BRK. SW.

1983 Peugeot

504 DIESEL (Cont.)

INSTRUMENT PANEL & REAR COMPARTMENT

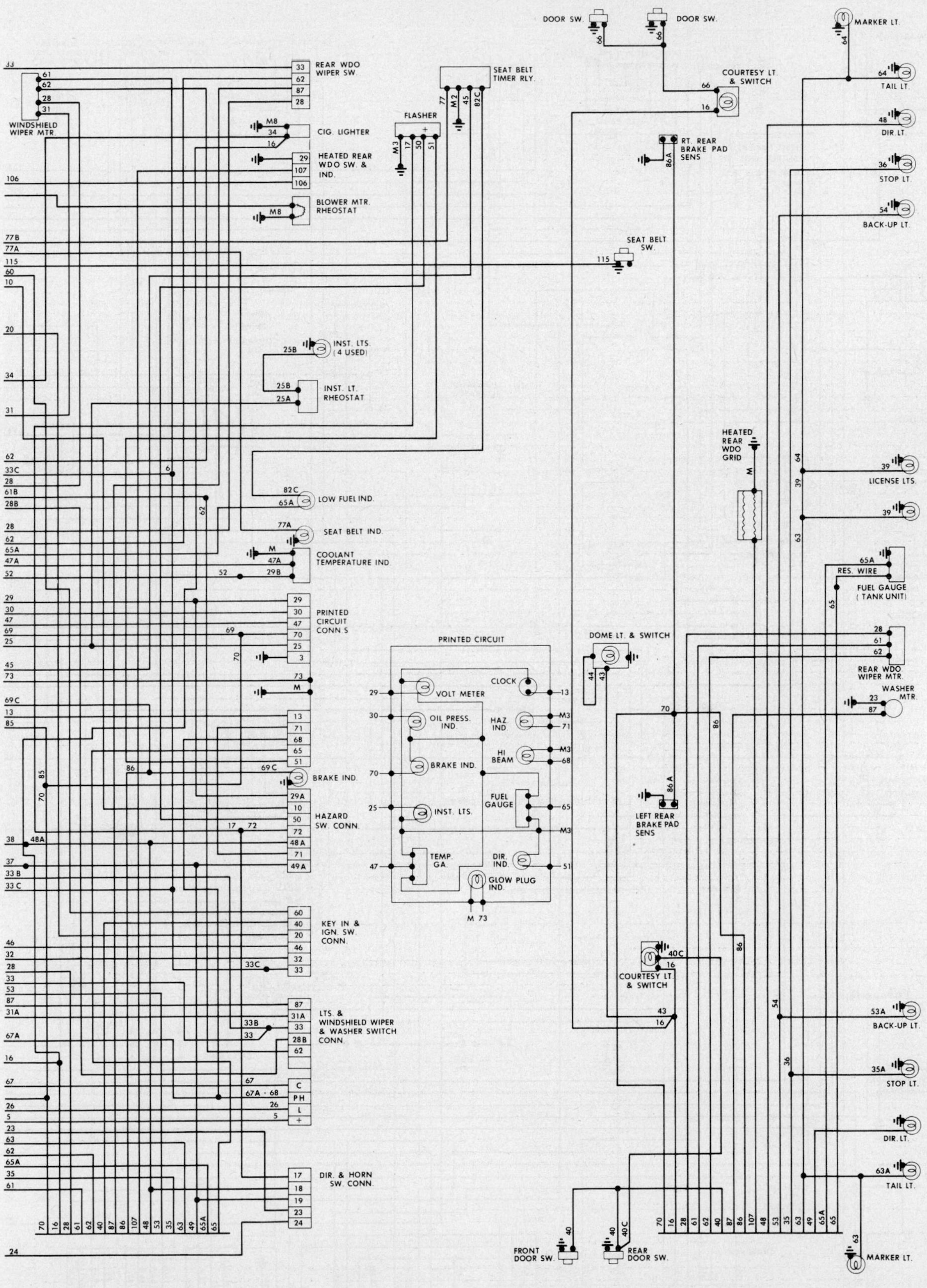

DOOR SW.
DOOR SW.
MARKER LT.
REAR WDO WIPER SW.
SEAT BELT TIMER RLY.
COURTESY LT & SWITCH
TAIL LT.
WINDSHIELD WIPER MTR.
FLASHER
CIG. LIGHTER
DIR. LT.
RT. REAR BRAKE PAD SENS
HEATED REAR WDO SW. & IND.
STOP LT.
BLOWER MTR. RHEOSTAT
BACK-UP LT.
SEAT BELT SW.
INST. LTS. (4 USED)
INST. LT. RHEOSTAT
HEATED REAR WDO GRID
LICENSE LTS.
LOW FUEL IND.
SEAT BELT IND.
COOLANT TEMPERATURE IND.
RES. WIRE
FUEL GAUGE (TANK UNIT)
PRINTED CIRCUIT CONN.S
PRINTED CIRCUIT
DOME LT. & SWITCH
REAR WDO WIPER MTR.
CLOCK
VOLT METER
WASHER MTR.
OIL PRESS. IND.
HAZ IND
HI BEAM
BRAKE IND.
BRAKE IND.
FUEL GAUGE
LEFT REAR BRAKE PAD SENS
HAZARD SW. CONN.
INST. LTS.
TEMP. GA.
DIR. IND.
GLOW PLUG IND.
KEY IN & IGN. SW. CONN.
COURTESY LT. & SWITCH
LTS. & WINDSHIELD WIPER & WASHER SWITCH CONN.
BACK-UP LT.
STOP LT.
DIR. LT.
DIR. & HORN SW. CONN.
TAIL LT.
FRONT DOOR SW.
REAR DOOR SW.
MARKER LT.

1983 Peugeot

505 & 505 TURBO DIESEL

ENGINE COMPARTMENT

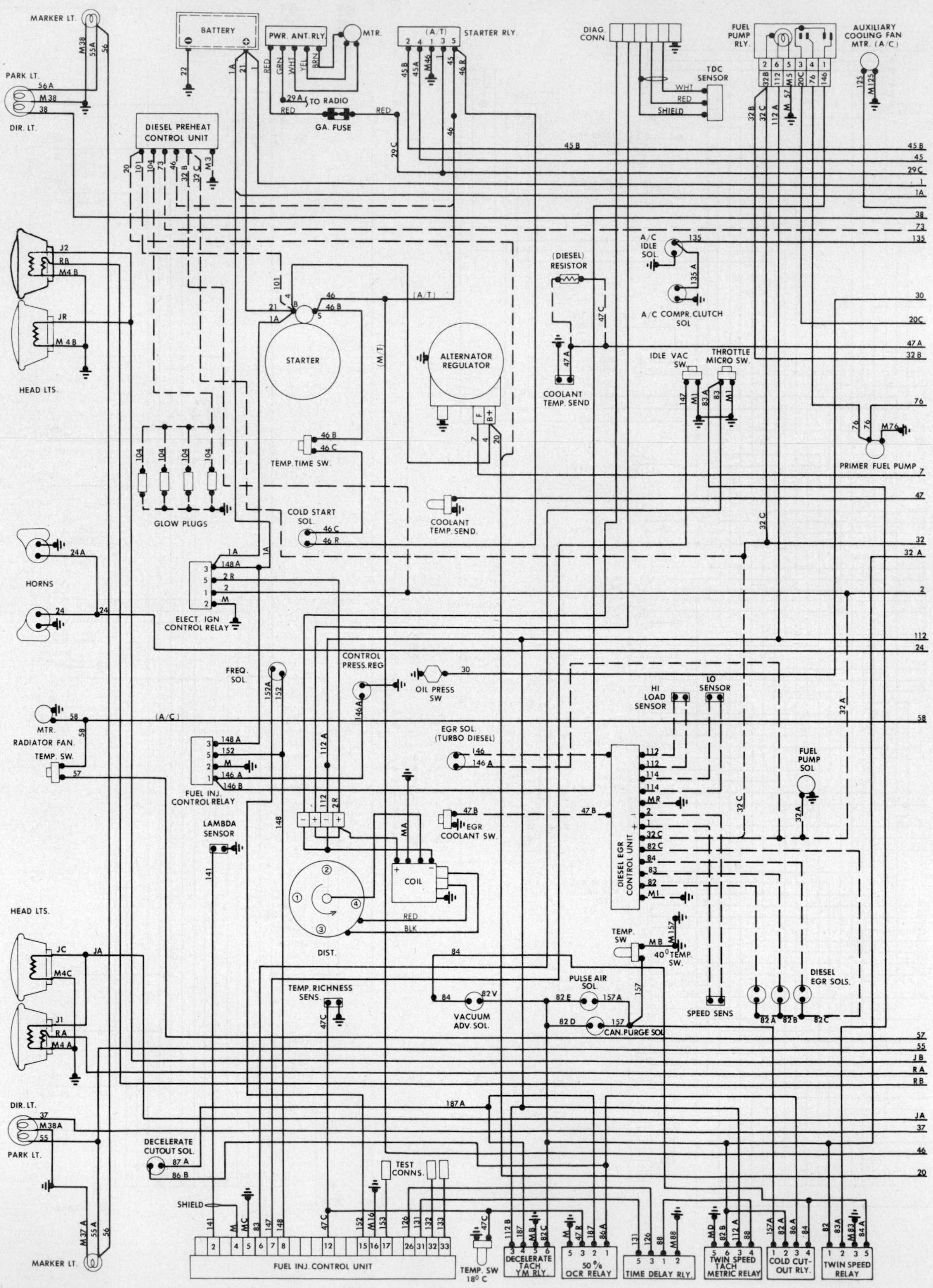
MARKER LT.
PARK LT.
DIR. LT.
BATTERY
PWR. ANT. RLY.
MTR.
TO RADIO
GA. FUSE
STARTER RLY.
DIAG. CONN
TDC SENSOR
FUEL PUMP RLY.
AUXILIARY COOLING FAN MTR. (A/C)
DIESEL PREHEAT CONTROL UNIT
HEAD LTS.
A/C IDLE SOL.
(DIESEL) RESISTOR
A/C COMPR. CLUTCH SOL
STARTER
ALTERNATOR REGULATOR
COOLANT TEMP. SEND
IDLE VAC SW.
THROTTLE MICRO SW.
PRIMER FUEL PUMP
TEMP. TIME SW.
GLOW PLUGS
COLD START SOL.
COOLANT TEMP. SEND.
HORNS
ELECT. IGN CONTROL RELAY
FREQ. SOL.
CONTROL PRESS. REG
OIL PRESS SW
HI LOAD SENSOR
LO SENSOR
MTR. RADIATOR FAN.
TEMP. SW.
FUEL INJ. CONTROL RELAY
EGR SOL. (TURBO DIESEL)
FUEL PUMP SOL
LAMBDA SENSOR
EGR COOLANT SW.
DIESEL EGR CONTROL UNIT
COIL
DIST.
TEMP. SW
40° TEMP. SW.
DIESEL EGR SOLS.
TEMP. RICHNESS SENS.
PULSE AIR SOL.
VACUUM ADV. SOL.
CAN. PURGE SOL
SPEED SENS
DECELERATE CUTOUT SOL.
TEST CONNS.
SHIELD
FUEL INJ. CONTROL UNIT
TEMP. SW 18° C
DECELERATE TACH YM RLY.
50% OCR RELAY
TIME DELAY RLY.
TWIN SPEED TACH METRIC RELAY
COLD CUT-OUT RLY.
TWIN SPEED RELAY

1983 Peugeot

505 & 505 TURBO DIESEL (Cont.)

FUSE BLOCK & UNDERDASH

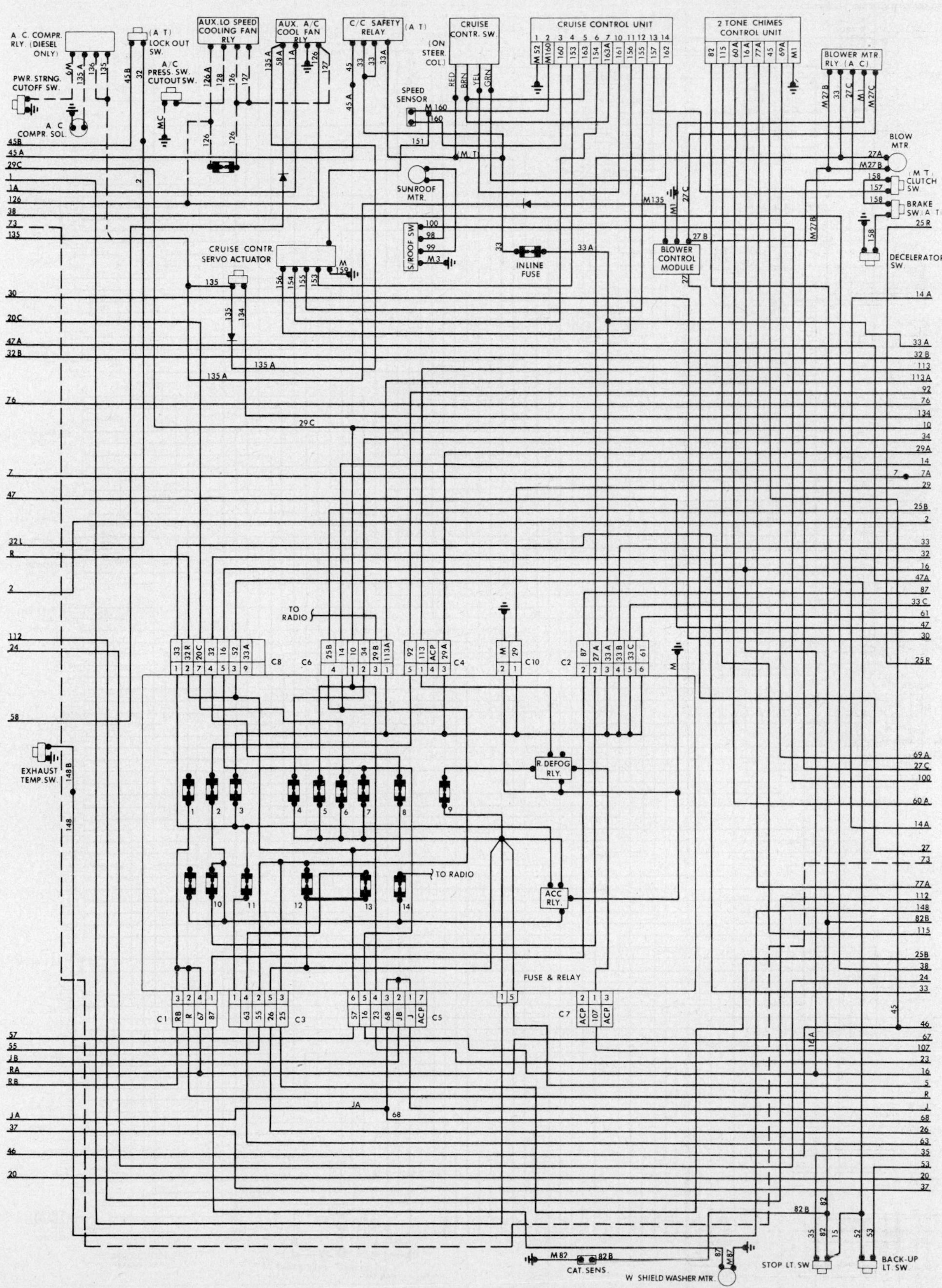
A.C. COMPR. RLY. (DIESEL ONLY)
(A T) LOCK OUT SW.
AUX. LO SPEED COOLING FAN RLY
AUX. A/C COOL FAN RLY
C/C SAFETY RELAY (A T)
CRUISE CONTR. SW. (ON STEER. COL.)
CRUISE CONTROL UNIT
2 TONE CHIMES CONTROL UNIT
BLOWER MTR RLY (A C)
PWR. STRNG. CUTOFF SW.
A/C PRESS. SW. CUTOUT SW.
A.C COMPR. SOL.
SPEED SENSOR
SUNROOF MTR.
S/ROOF SW
CRUISE CONTR. SERVO ACTUATOR
INLINE FUSE
BLOWER CONTROL MODULE
BLOW MTR
(M T) CLUTCH SW
BRAKE SW (A T)
DECELERATOR SW.
TO RADIO
R. DEFOG RLY.
ACC RLY.
EXHAUST TEMP. SW.
FUSE & RELAY
CAT. SENS.
W. SHIELD WASHER MTR.
STOP LT. SW
BACK-UP LT. SW.

1983 Peugeot

505 & 505 TURBO DIESEL (Cont.)

UNDERDASH & INSTRUMENT PANEL

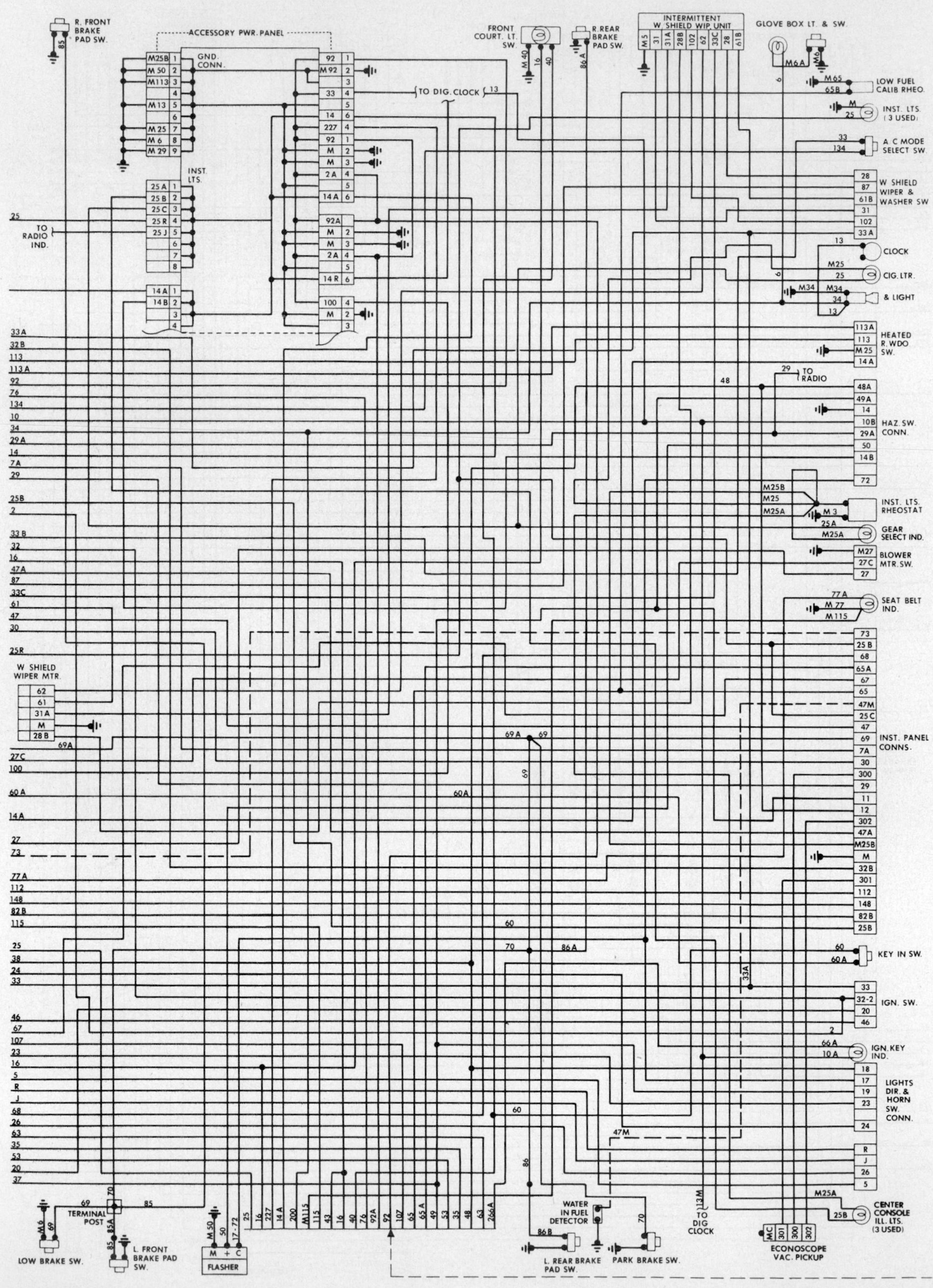

1983 Peugeot

505 & 505 TURBO DIESEL (Cont.)

REAR COMPARTMENT & ACCESSORIES

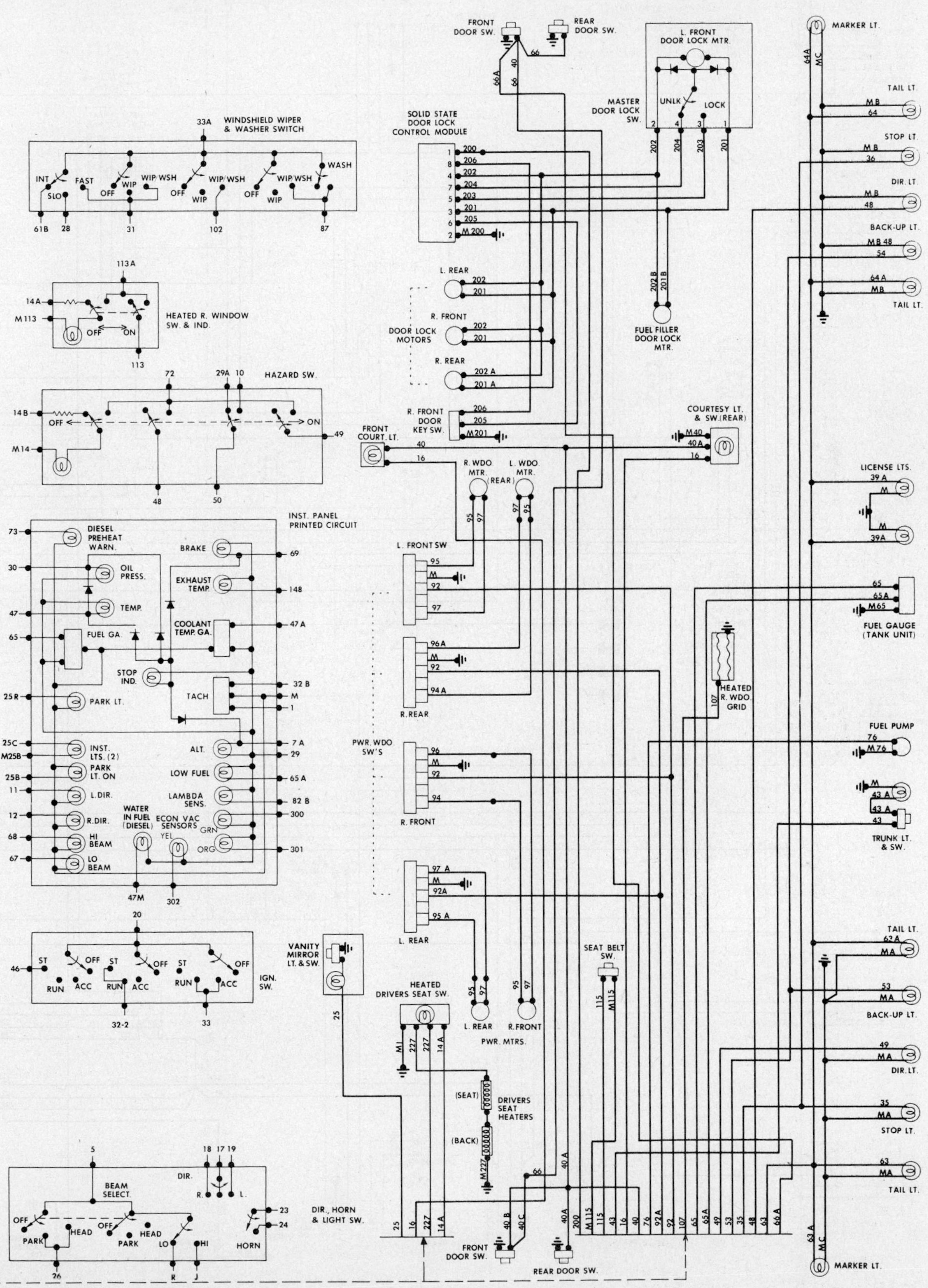
FRONT DOOR SW.
REAR DOOR SW.
L. FRONT DOOR LOCK MTR.
MASTER DOOR LOCK SW.
UNLK
LOCK
MARKER LT.
TAIL LT.
STOP LT.
DIR. LT.
BACK-UP LT.
WINDSHIELD WIPER & WASHER SWITCH
SOLID STATE DOOR LOCK CONTROL MODULE
L. REAR
R. FRONT
DOOR LOCK MOTORS
R. REAR
FUEL FILLER DOOR LOCK MTR.
HEATED R. WINDOW SW. & IND.
HAZARD SW.
R. FRONT DOOR KEY SW.
FRONT COURT. LT.
COURTESY LT. & SW.(REAR)
R. WDO MTR.
L. WDO. MTR.
(REAR)
LICENSE LTS.
INST. PANEL PRINTED CIRCUIT
DIESEL PREHEAT WARN.
OIL PRESS.
TEMP.
FUEL GA.
BRAKE
EXHAUST TEMP.
COOLANT TEMP. GA.
STOP IND.
TACH
PARK LT.
INST. LTS. (2)
PARK LT. ON
L. DIR.
R. DIR.
HI BEAM
LO BEAM
ALT.
LOW FUEL
LAMBDA SENS.
WATER IN FUEL (DIESEL)
ECON VAC SENSORS
YEL
GRN
ORG
L. FRONT SW
R. REAR
PWR. WDO SW'S
R. FRONT
L. REAR
FUEL GAUGE (TANK UNIT)
HEATED R. WDO. GRID
FUEL PUMP
TRUNK LT. & SW.
IGN. SW.
VANITY MIRROR LT. & SW.
HEATED DRIVERS SEAT SW.
SEAT BELT SW.
L. REAR
R. FRONT
PWR. MTRS.
(SEAT)
DRIVERS SEAT HEATERS
(BACK)
BEAM SELECT.
DIR.
DIR., HORN & LIGHT SW.
HORN
FRONT DOOR SW.
REAR DOOR SW.

1983 Peugeot

604 TURBO DIESEL

ENGINE COMPARTMENT

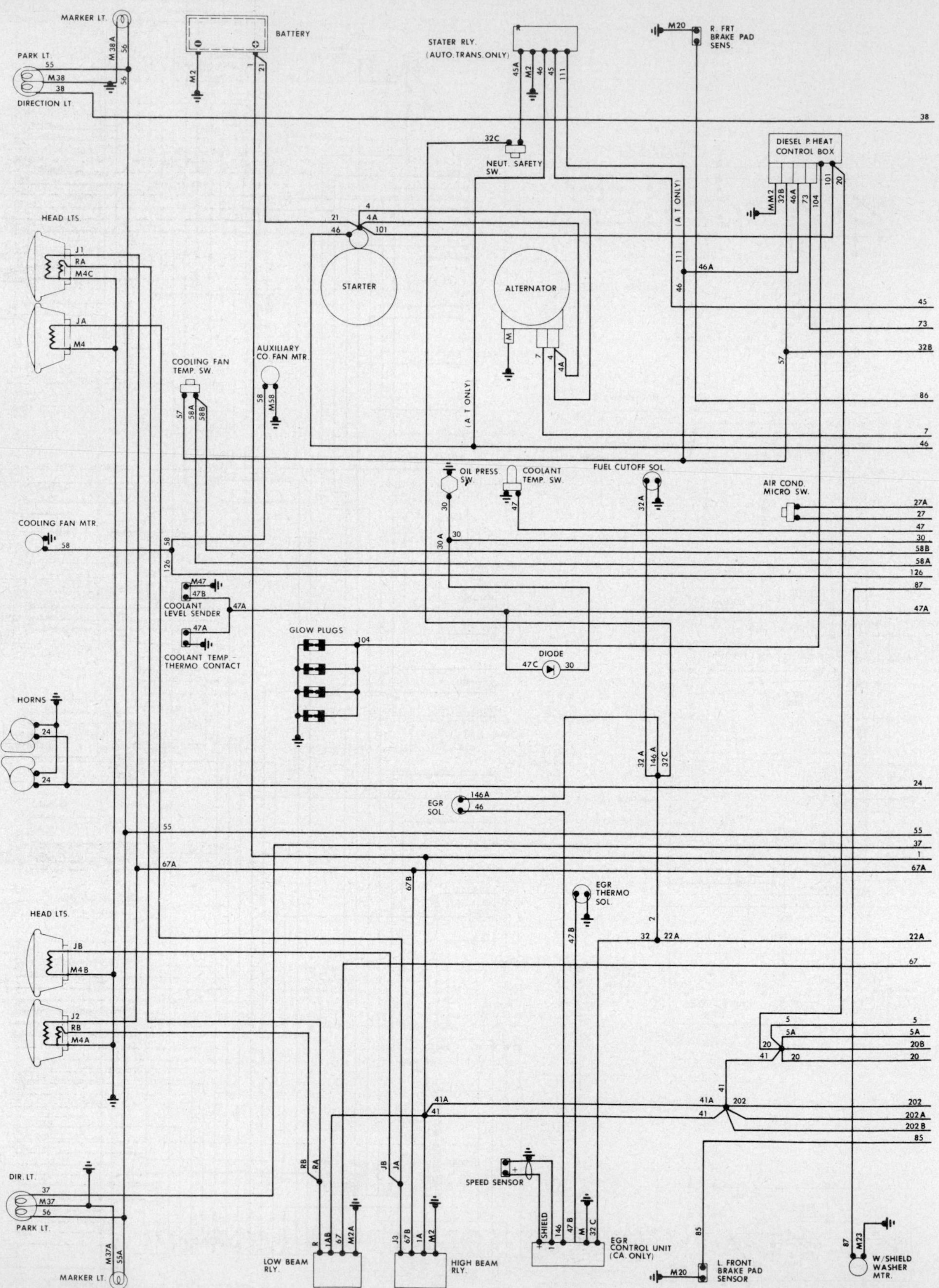

MARKER LT.
PARK LT.
DIRECTION LT.
BATTERY
STATER RLY.
(AUTO TRANS ONLY)
R. FRT
BRAKE PAD
SENS.
DIESEL P. HEAT
CONTROL BOX
NEUT. SAFETY
SW.
HEAD LTS.
STARTER
ALTERNATOR
(A T ONLY)
COOLING FAN
TEMP. SW.
AUXILIARY
CO. FAN MTR.
OIL PRESS.
SW.
COOLANT
TEMP. SW.
FUEL CUTOFF SOL.
AIR COND.
MICRO SW.
COOLING FAN MTR.
COOLANT
LEVEL SENDER
COOLANT TEMP.
THERMO CONTACT
GLOW PLUGS
DIODE
HORNS
EGR
SOL.
EGR
THERMO
SOL.
HEAD LTS.
DIR. LT.
PARK LT.
MARKER LT.
SPEED SENSOR
SHIELD
LOW BEAM
RLY.
HIGH BEAM
RLY.
EGR
CONTROL UNIT
(CA. ONLY)
L. FRONT
BRAKE PAD
SENSOR
W/SHIELD
WASHER
MTR.

604 TURBO DIESEL (Cont.)

FUSE BLOCK & UNDERDASH

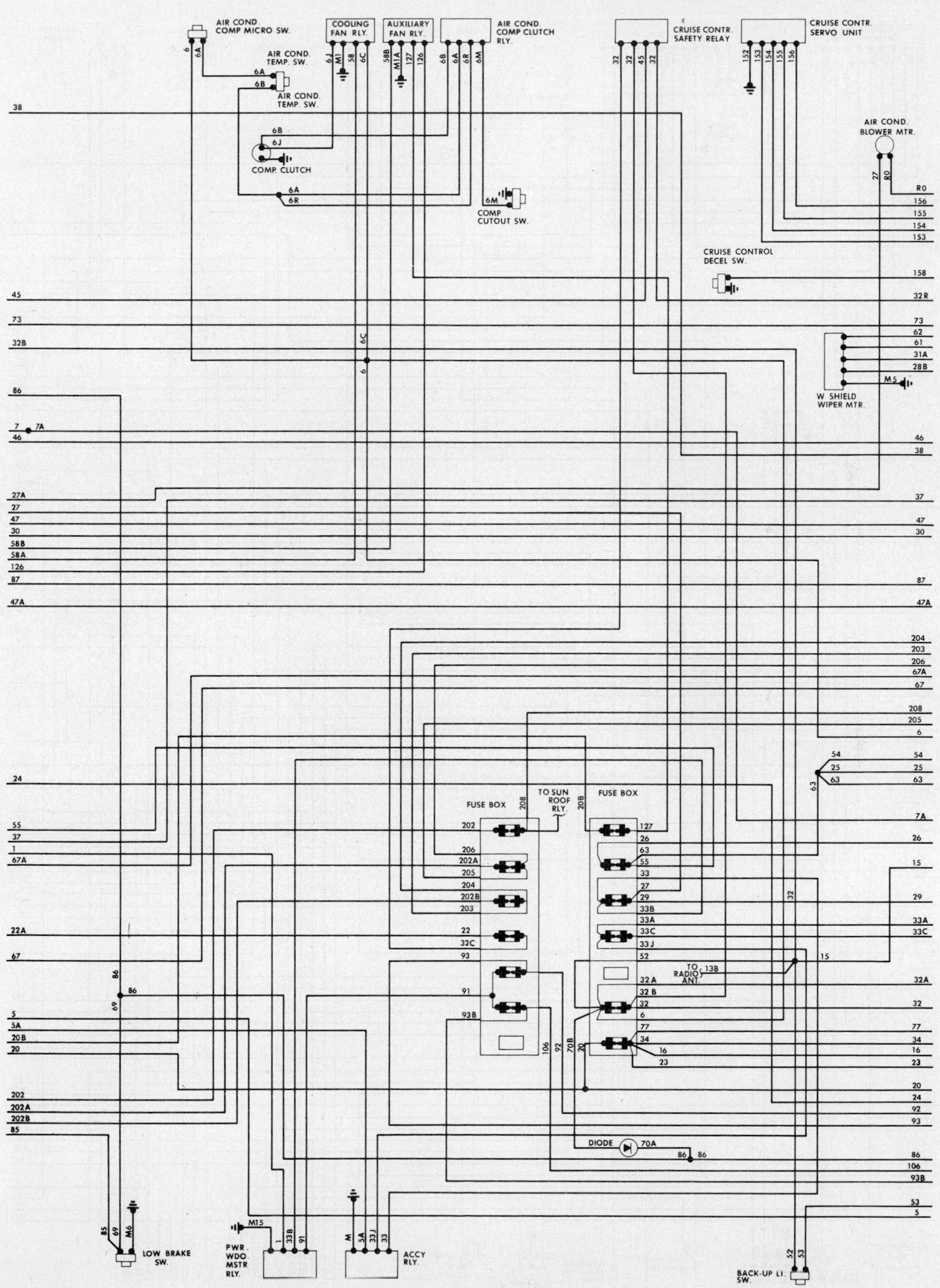

1983 Peugeot

604 TURBO DIESEL (Cont.)

UNDERDASH

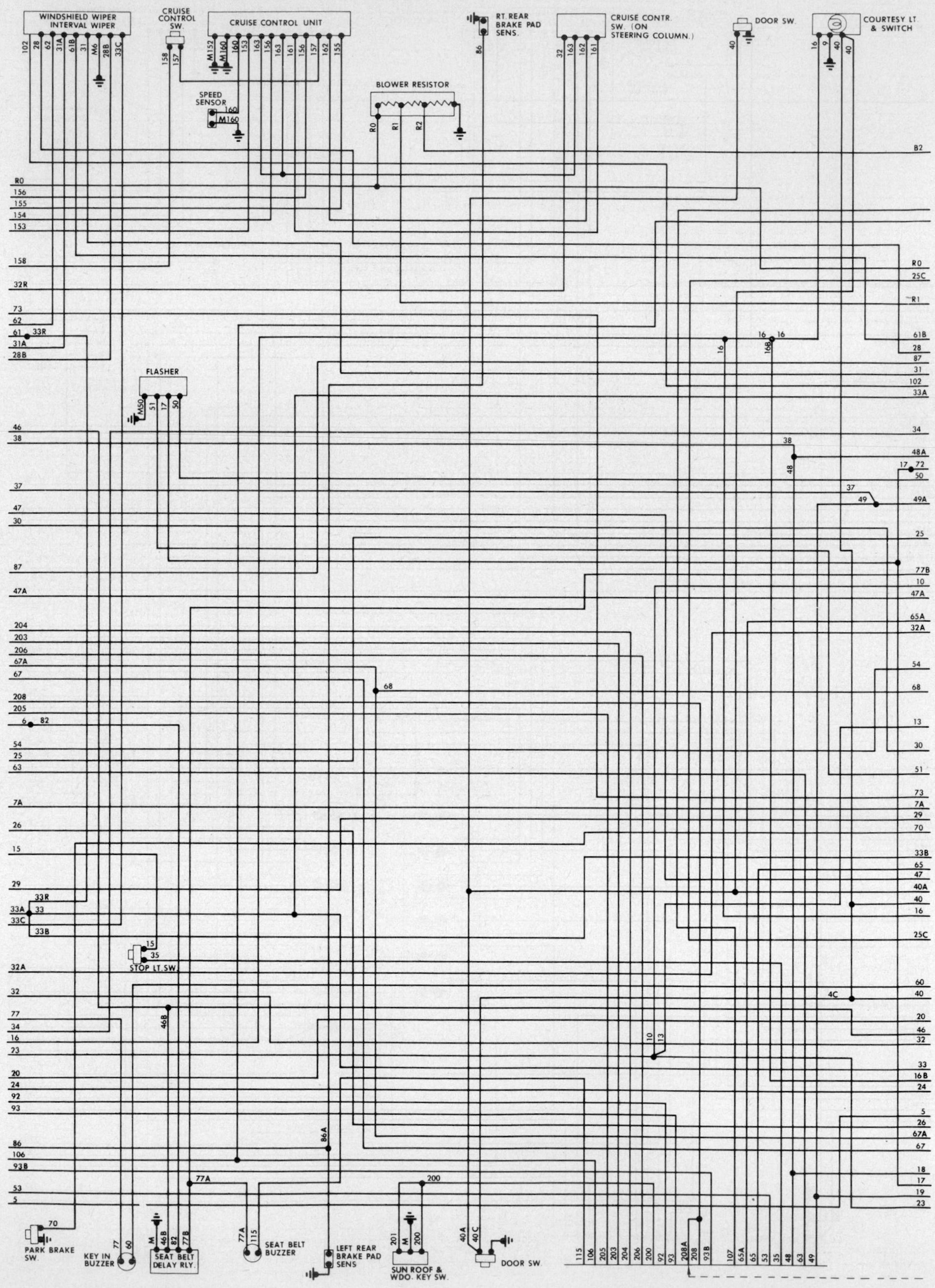
WINDSHIELD WIPER INTERVAL WIPER
CRUISE CONTROL SW.
CRUISE CONTROL UNIT
SPEED SENSOR
BLOWER RESISTOR
RT REAR BRAKE PAD SENS.
CRUISE CONTR. SW. (ON STEERING COLUMN.)
DOOR SW.
COURTESY LT. & SWITCH
FLASHER
STOP LT. SW.
PARK BRAKE SW.
KEY IN BUZZER
SEAT BELT DELAY RLY.
SEAT BELT BUZZER
LEFT REAR BRAKE PAD SENS
SUN ROOF & WDO. KEY SW.
DOOR SW.

604 TURBO DIESEL (Cont.)

INSTRUMENT PANEL, REAR COMPARTMENT & ACCESSORIES

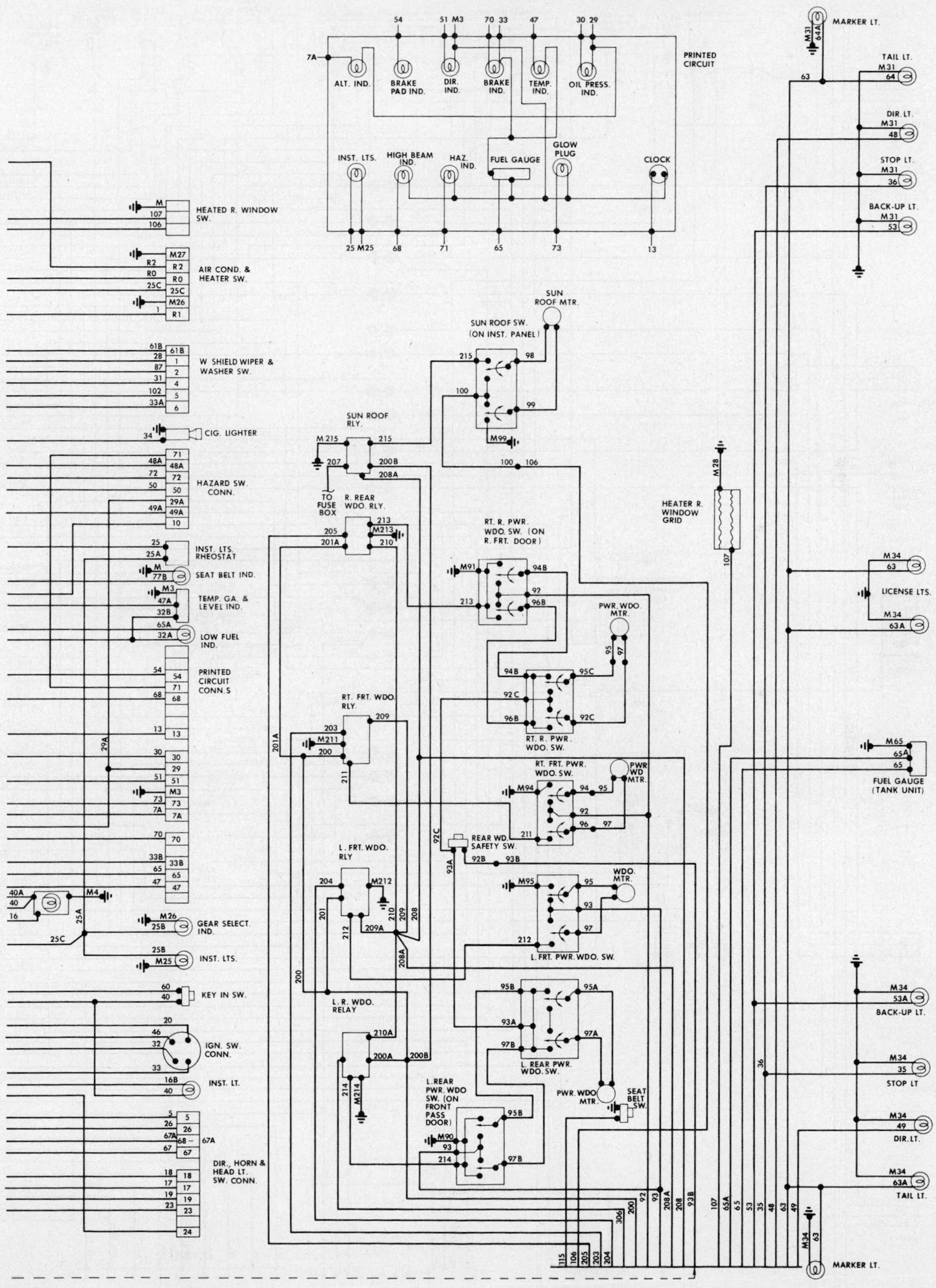

PRINTED CIRCUIT
ALT. IND.
BRAKE PAD IND.
DIR. IND.
BRAKE IND.
TEMP. IND.
OIL PRESS. IND.
INST. LTS.
HIGH BEAM IND.
HAZ. IND.
FUEL GAUGE
GLOW PLUG
CLOCK
MARKER LT.
TAIL LT.
DIR. LT.
STOP LT.
BACK-UP LT.
HEATED R. WINDOW SW.
AIR COND. & HEATER SW.
W. SHIELD WIPER & WASHER SW.
CIG. LIGHTER
HAZARD SW. CONN.
INST. LTS. RHEOSTAT
SEAT BELT IND.
TEMP. GA. & LEVEL IND.
LOW FUEL IND.
PRINTED CIRCUIT CONN.S
GEAR SELECT. IND.
INST. LTS.
KEY IN SW.
IGN. SW. CONN.
INST. LT.
DIR., HORN & HEAD LT. SW. CONN.
SUN ROOF MTR.
SUN ROOF SW. (ON INST. PANEL)
SUN ROOF RLY.
TO FUSE BOX
R. REAR WDO. RLY.
RT. R. PWR. WDO. SW. (ON R. FRT. DOOR)
HEATER R. WINDOW GRID
PWR. WDO MTR.
RT. R. PWR. WDO. SW.
RT. FRT. WDO RLY.
RT. FRT. PWR. WDO. SW.
PWR WD MTR.
REAR WD. SAFETY SW.
L. FRT. WDO. RLY
WDO. MTR.
L. FRT. PWR. WDO. SW.
L. R. WDO. RELAY
L. REAR PWR. WDO. SW.
PWR. WDO MTR.
SEAT BELT SW.
L.REAR PWR. WDO SW. (ON FRONT PASS DOOR)
LICENSE LTS.
FUEL GAUGE (TANK UNIT)
BACK-UP LT.
STOP LT
DIR. LT.
TAIL LT.
MARKER LT.

1983 Porsche

911SC

FRONT COMPARTMENT, FUSE BLOCK & UNDERDASH

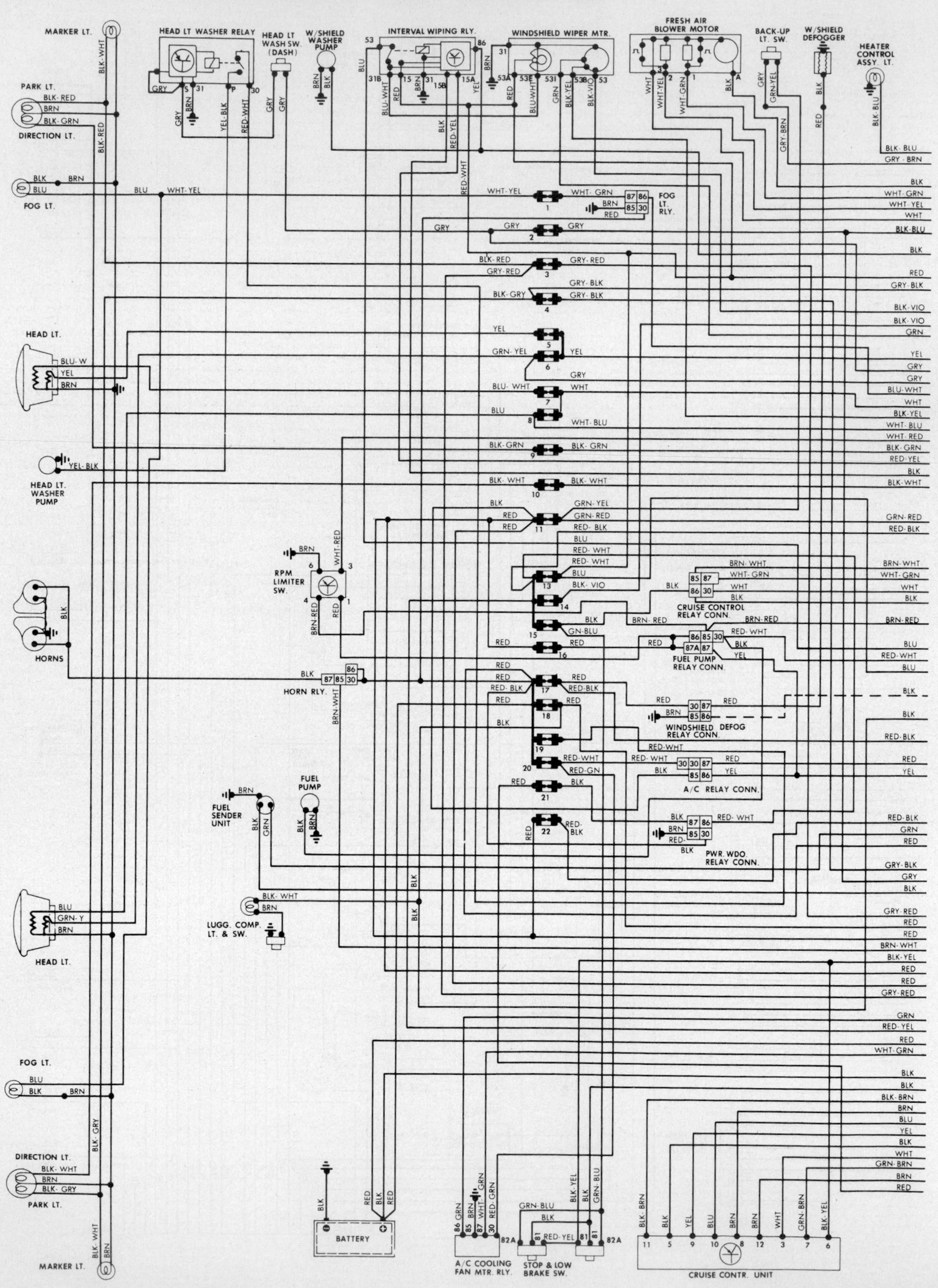

MARKER LT.
PARK LT.
DIRECTION LT.
FOG LT.
HEAD LT.
HEAD LT. WASHER PUMP
HORNS
HEAD LT WASHER RELAY
HEAD LT WASH SW. (DASH)
W/SHIELD WASHER PUMP
INTERVAL WIPING RLY.
WINDSHIELD WIPER MTR.
FRESH AIR BLOWER MOTOR
BACK-UP LT. SW.
W/SHIELD DEFOGGER
HEATER CONTROL ASSY. LT.
FOG LT. RLY.
RPM LIMITER SW.
HORN RLY.
CRUISE CONTROL RELAY CONN.
FUEL PUMP RELAY CONN.
WINDSHIELD DEFOG RELAY CONN.
A/C RELAY CONN.
PWR. WDO RELAY CONN.
FUEL SENDER UNIT
FUEL PUMP
LUGG. COMP. LT. & SW.
BATTERY
A/C COOLING FAN MTR. RLY.
STOP & LOW BRAKE SW.
CRUISE CONTR. UNIT

1983 Porsche

911SC (Cont.)

UNDERDASH & INSTRUMENT PANEL

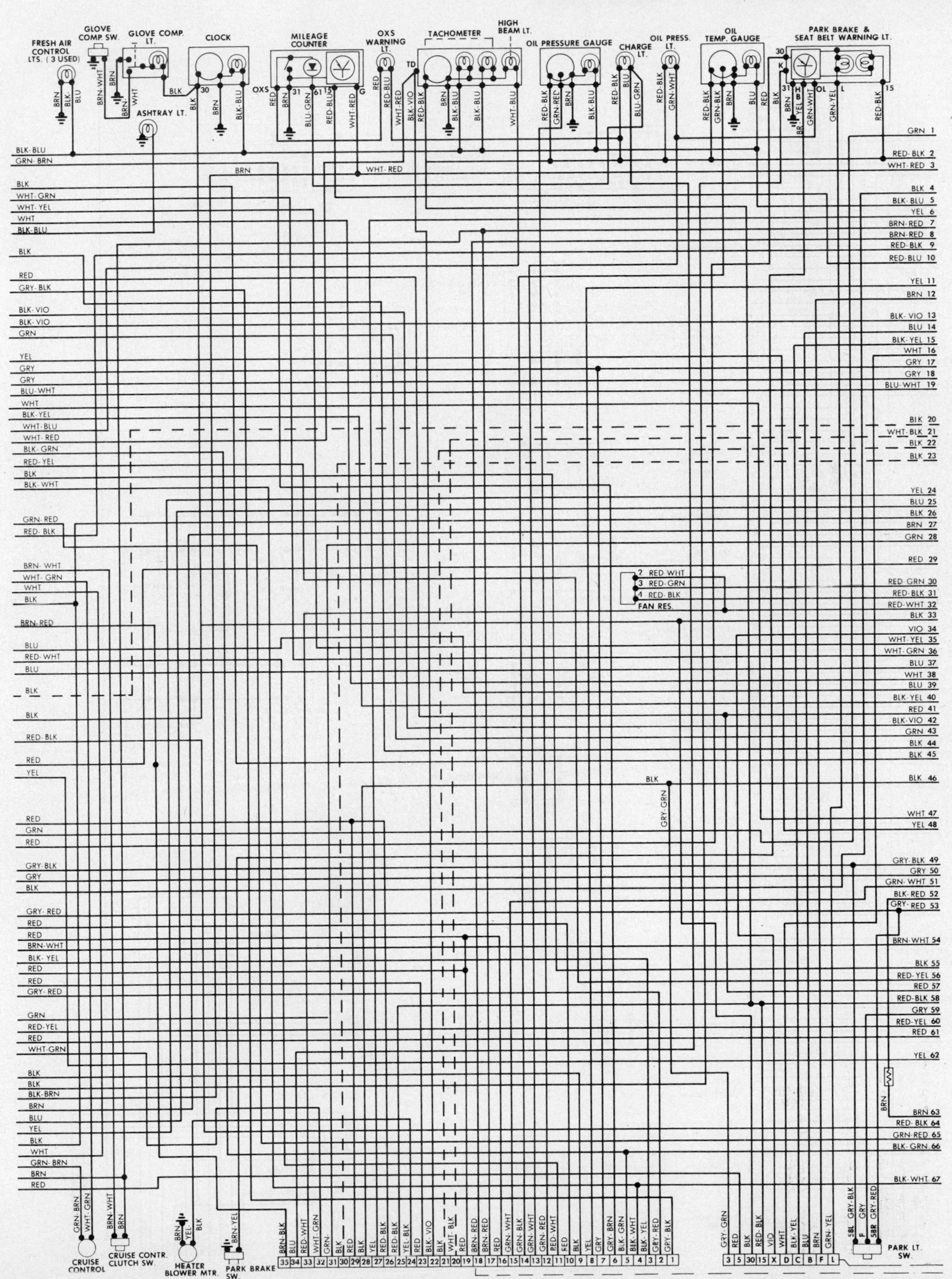

FRESH AIR CONTROL LTS. (3 USED)
GLOVE COMP. SW.
GLOVE COMP. LT.
CLOCK
ASHTRAY LT.
MILEAGE COUNTER
OXS WARNING LT.
TACHOMETER
HIGH BEAM LT.
OIL PRESSURE GAUGE
CHARGE LT.
OIL PRESS. LT.
OIL TEMP. GAUGE
PARK BRAKE & SEAT BELT WARNING LT.
FAN RES.
CRUISE CONTROL
CRUISE CONTR. CLUTCH SW.
HEATER BLOWER MTR.
PARK BRAKE SW.
PARK LT. SW.

1983 Porsche

911SC (Cont.)

INSTRUMENT PANEL

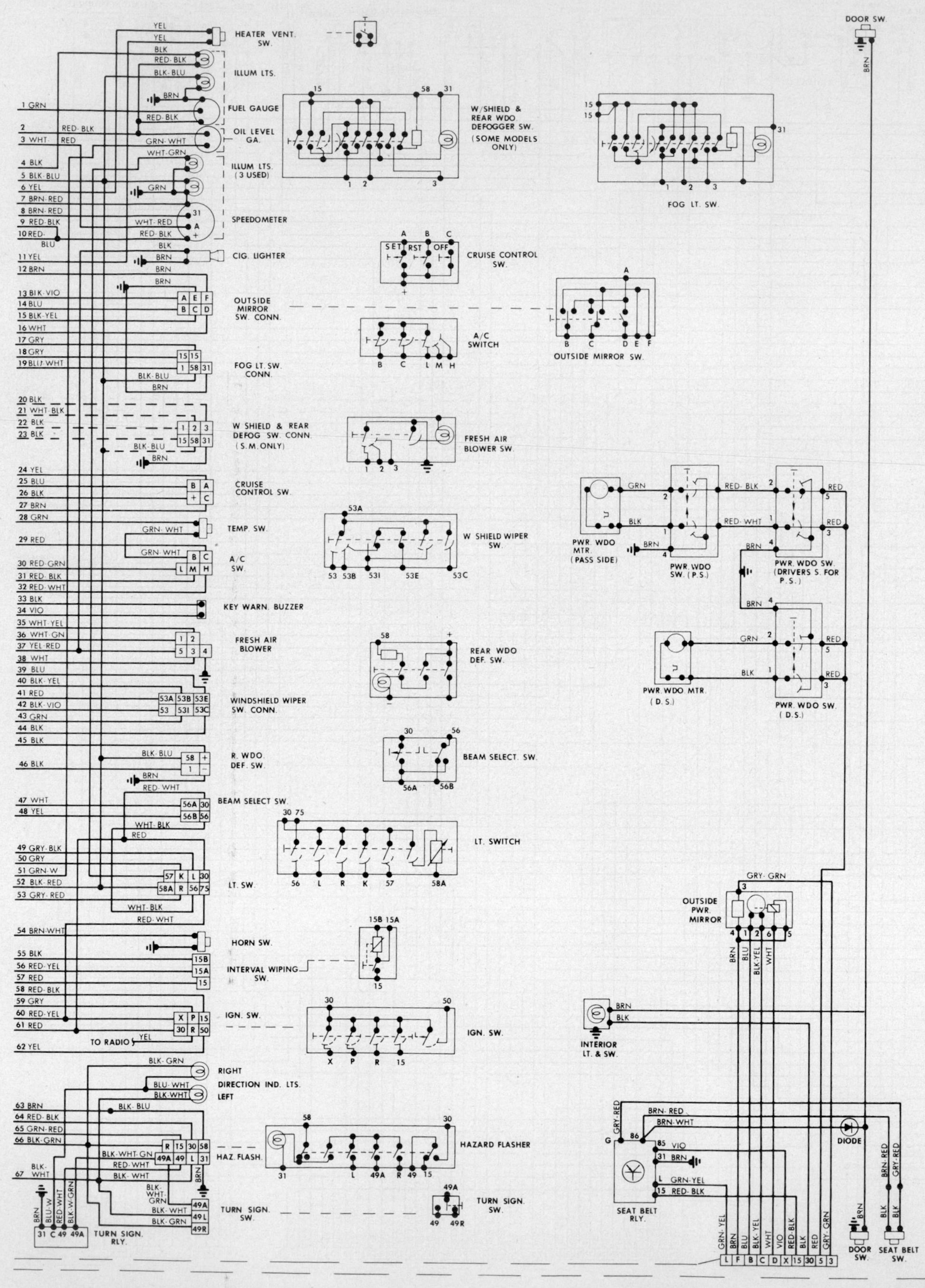

HEATER VENT. SW.
ILLUM LTS.
FUEL GAUGE
OIL LEVEL GA.
ILLUM LTS. (3 USED)
SPEEDOMETER
CIG. LIGHTER
OUTSIDE MIRROR SW. CONN.
FOG LT. SW. CONN.
W SHIELD & REAR DEFOG SW. CONN. (S.M. ONLY)
CRUISE CONTROL SW.
TEMP. SW.
A/C SW.
KEY WARN. BUZZER
FRESH AIR BLOWER
WINDSHIELD WIPER SW. CONN.
R. WDO. DEF. SW.
BEAM SELECT SW.
LT. SW.
HORN SW.
INTERVAL WIPING SW.
IGN. SW.
TO RADIO
RIGHT
DIRECTION IND. LTS.
LEFT
HAZ. FLASH.
TURN SIGN. SW.
TURN SIGN. RLY.
W/SHIELD & REAR WDO DEFOGGER SW. (SOME MODELS ONLY)
CRUISE CONTROL SW.
A/C SWITCH
FRESH AIR BLOWER SW.
W. SHIELD WIPER SW.
REAR WDO DEF. SW.
BEAM SELECT SW.
LT. SWITCH
IGN. SW.
HAZARD FLASHER
TURN SIGN. SW.
FOG LT. SW.
OUTSIDE MIRROR SW.
PWR. WDO MTR. (PASS SIDE)
PWR. WDO SW. (P.S.)
PWR. WDO SW. (DRIVERS S. FOR P.S.)
PWR. WDO MTR. (D.S.)
PWR. WDO SW. (D.S.)
OUTSIDE PWR. MIRROR
INTERIOR LT. & SW.
SEAT BELT RLY.
DIODE
DOOR SW.
SEAT BELT SW.

911SC (Cont.)

ENGINE COMPARTMENT & REAR COMPARTMENT

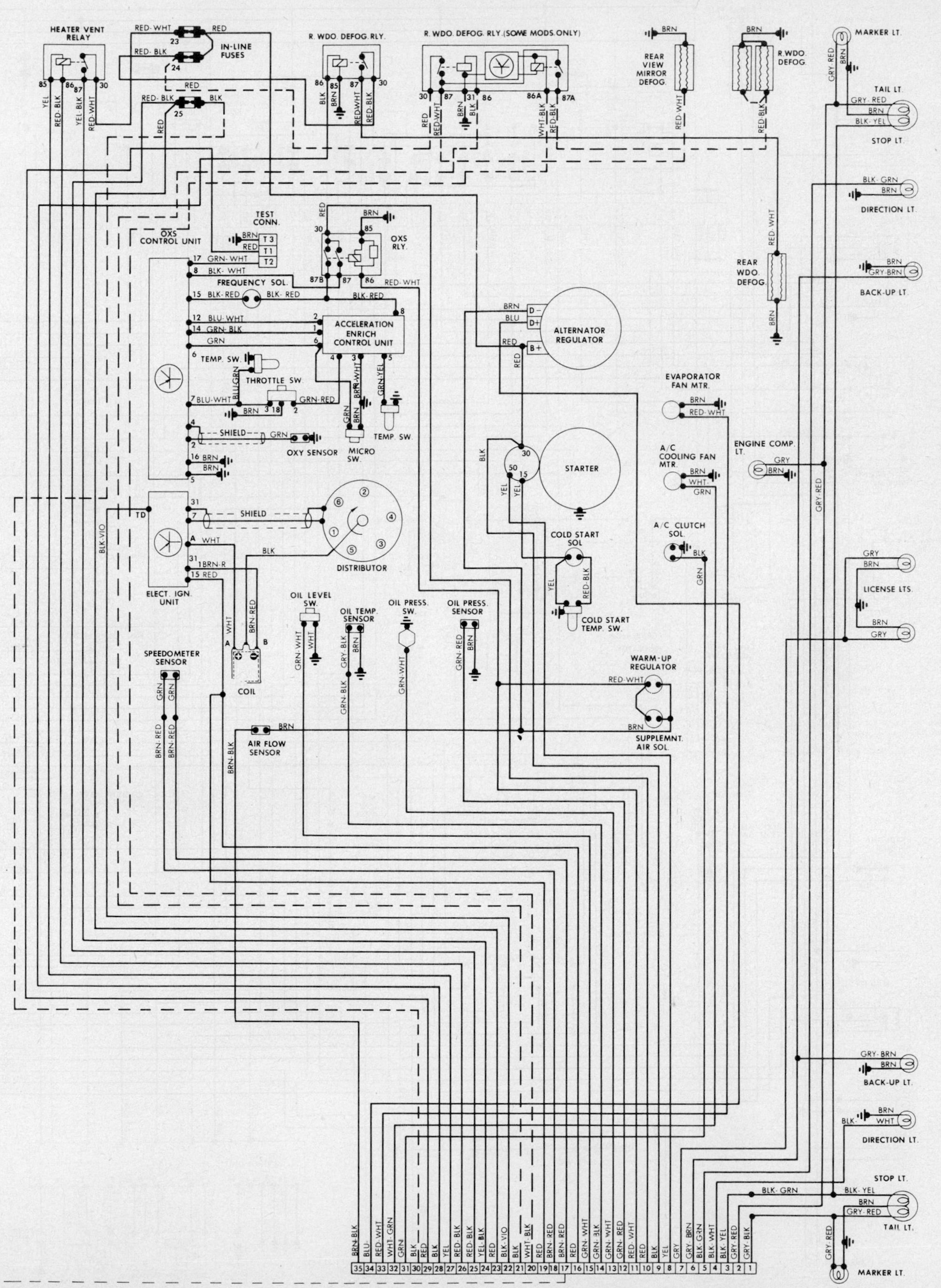
HEATER VENT RELAY
IN-LINE FUSES
R. WDO. DEFOG. RLY.
R. WDO. DEFOG. RLY. (SOME MODS. ONLY)
REAR VIEW MIRROR DEFOG.
R. WDO. DEFOG.
MARKER LT.
TAIL LT.
STOP LT.
DIRECTION LT.
BACK-UP LT.
REAR WDO. DEFOG.
TEST CONN.
OXS RLY.
OXS CONTROL UNIT
FREQUENCY SOL.
ACCELERATION ENRICH CONTROL UNIT
TEMP. SW.
THROTTLE SW.
SHIELD
OXY SENSOR
MICRO SW.
ALTERNATOR REGULATOR
EVAPORATOR FAN MTR.
STARTER
A/C COOLING FAN MTR.
ENGINE COMP. LT.
A/C CLUTCH SOL.
COLD START SOL.
COLD START TEMP. SW.
LICENSE LTS.
DISTRIBUTOR
ELECT. IGN. UNIT
OIL LEVEL SW.
OIL TEMP. SENSOR
OIL PRESS. SW.
OIL PRESS. SENSOR
SPEEDOMETER SENSOR
COIL
AIR FLOW SENSOR
WARM-UP REGULATOR
SUPPLEMNT. AIR SOL.
35 34 33 32 31 30 29 28 27 26 25 24 23 22 21 20 19 18 17 16 15 14 13 12 11 10 9 8 7 6 5 4 3 2 1

1983 Porsche

928S

ENGINE COMPARTMENT & FUSE BLOCK

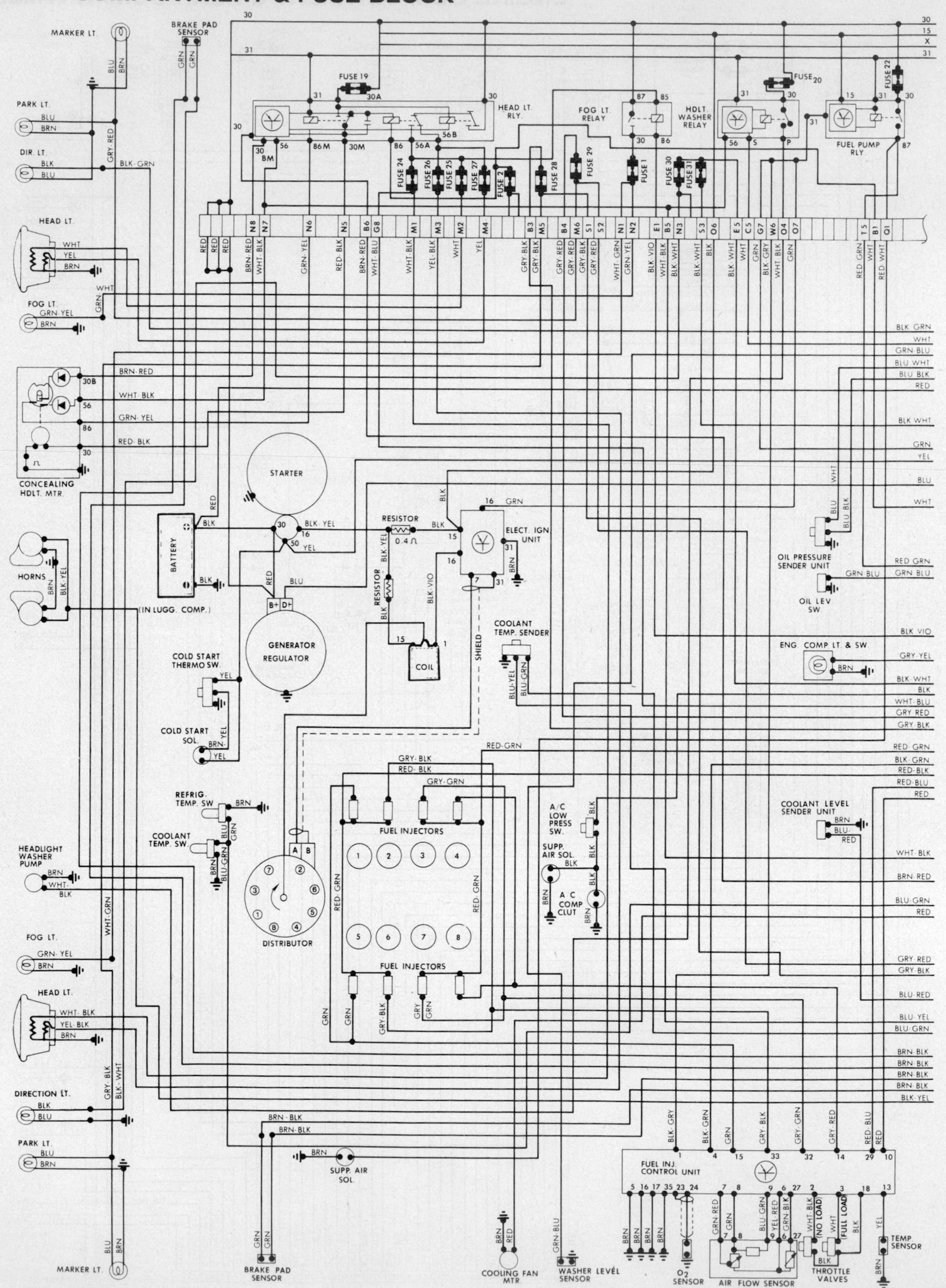

MARKER LT.
BRAKE PAD SENSOR
PARK LT.
DIR. LT.
HEAD LT.
FOG LT.
CONCEALING HDLT. MTR.
HORNS
BATTERY
(IN LUGG. COMP.)
STARTER
RESISTOR
0.4 Ω
ELECT. IGN UNIT
GENERATOR REGULATOR
COIL
SHIELD
COLD START THERMO SW.
COLD START SOL.
REFRIG. TEMP. SW
COOLANT TEMP. SW.
HEADLIGHT WASHER PUMP
DISTRIBUTOR
FUEL INJECTORS
COOLANT TEMP. SENDER
A/C LOW PRESS SW.
SUPP. AIR SOL.
A/C COMP CLUT
HEAD LT. RLY.
FOG LT. RELAY
HDLT. WASHER RELAY
FUEL PUMP RLY.
OIL PRESSURE SENDER UNIT
OIL LEV SW.
ENG. COMP. LT. & SW.
COOLANT LEVEL SENDER UNIT
DIRECTION LT.
SUPP. AIR SOL.
FUEL INJ. CONTROL UNIT
COOLING FAN MTR.
WASHER LEVEL SENSOR
O2 SENSOR
AIR FLOW SENSOR
THROTTLE VALVES
TEMP SENSOR
(NO LOAD)
(FULL LOAD)

928S (Cont.)

FUSE BLOCK & UNDERDASH

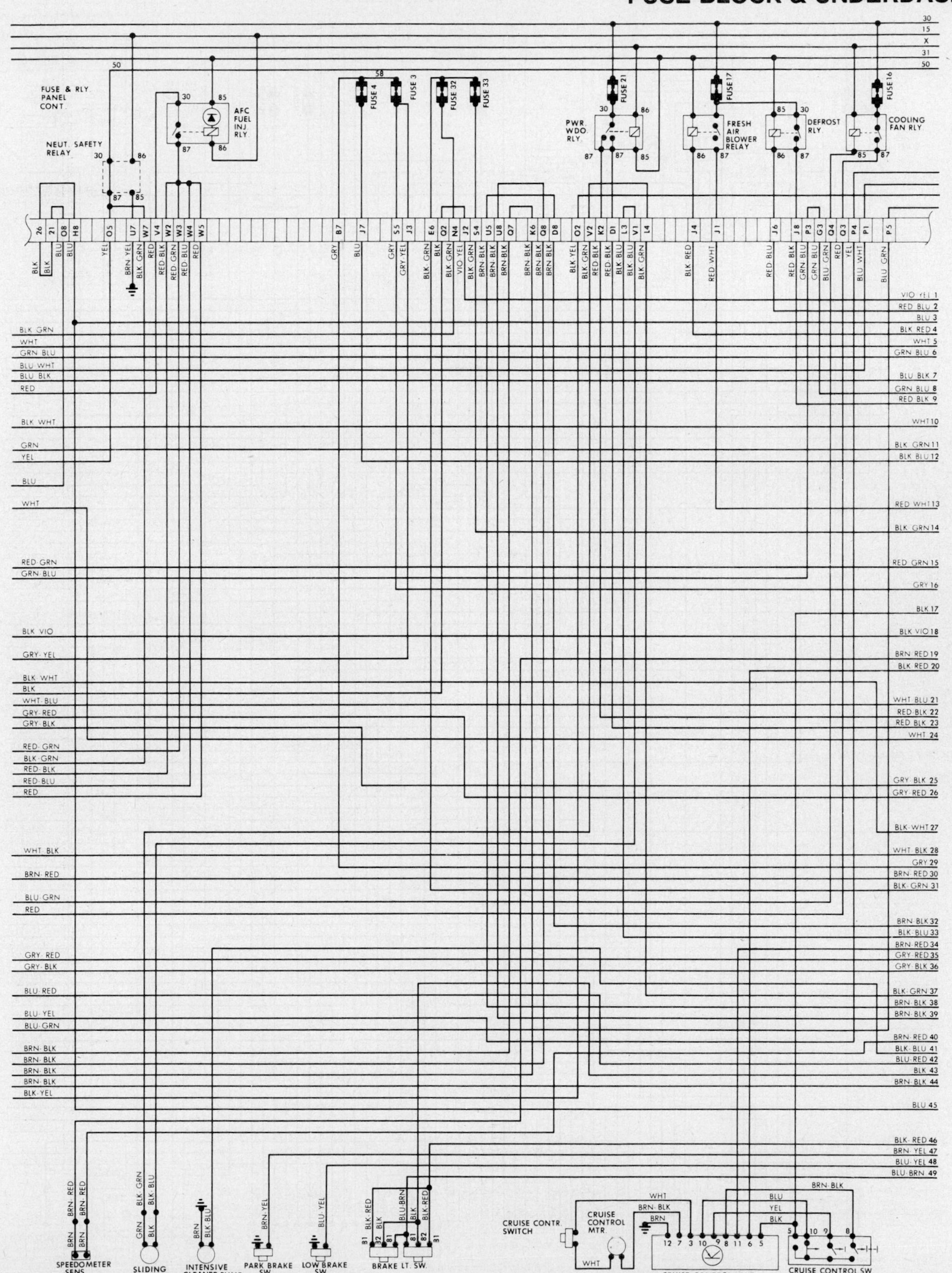

1983 Porsche

928S (Cont.)

FUSE BLOCK & UNDERDASH

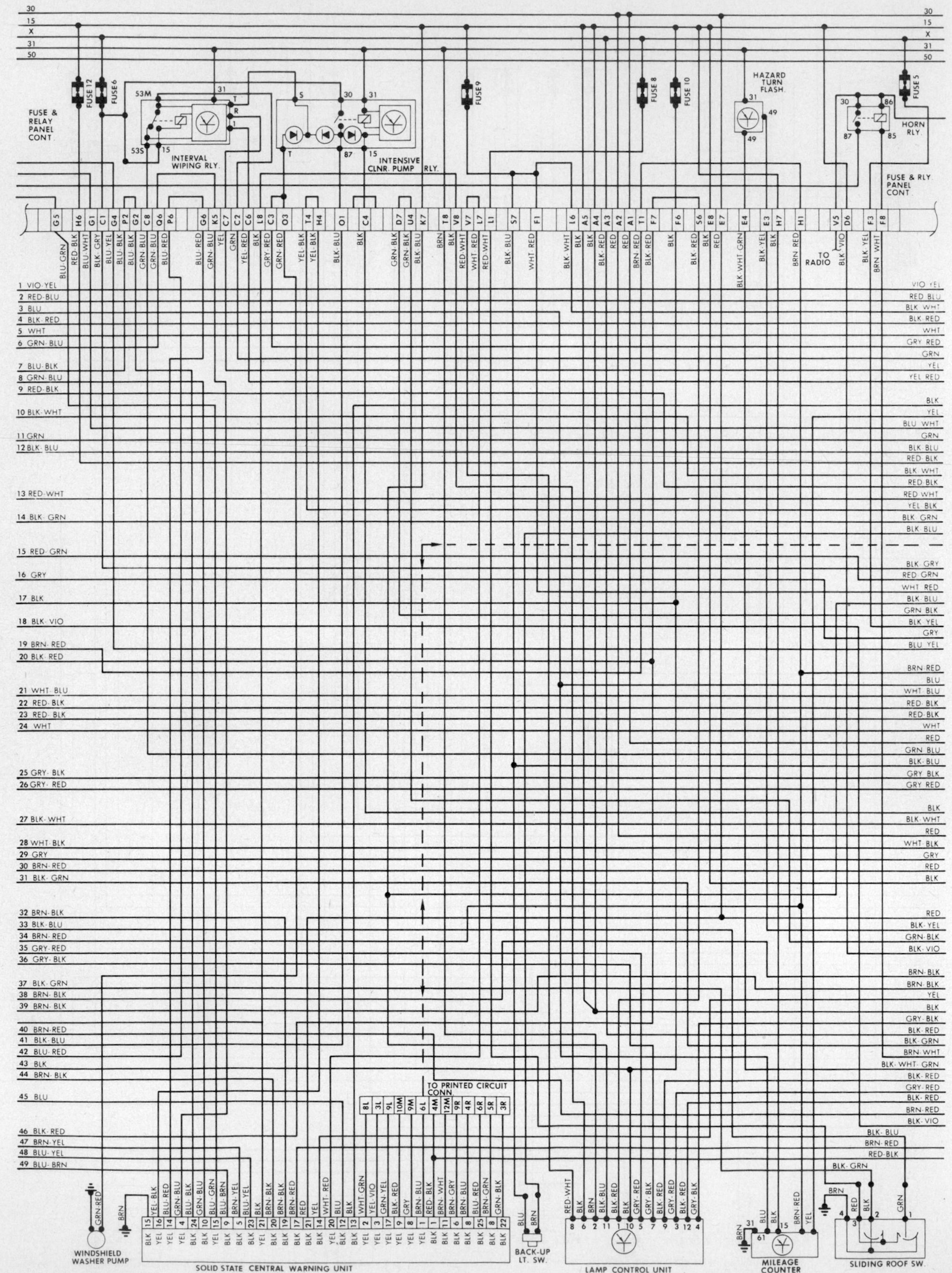

1983 Porsche

928S (Cont.)

FUSE BLOCK & UNDERDASH

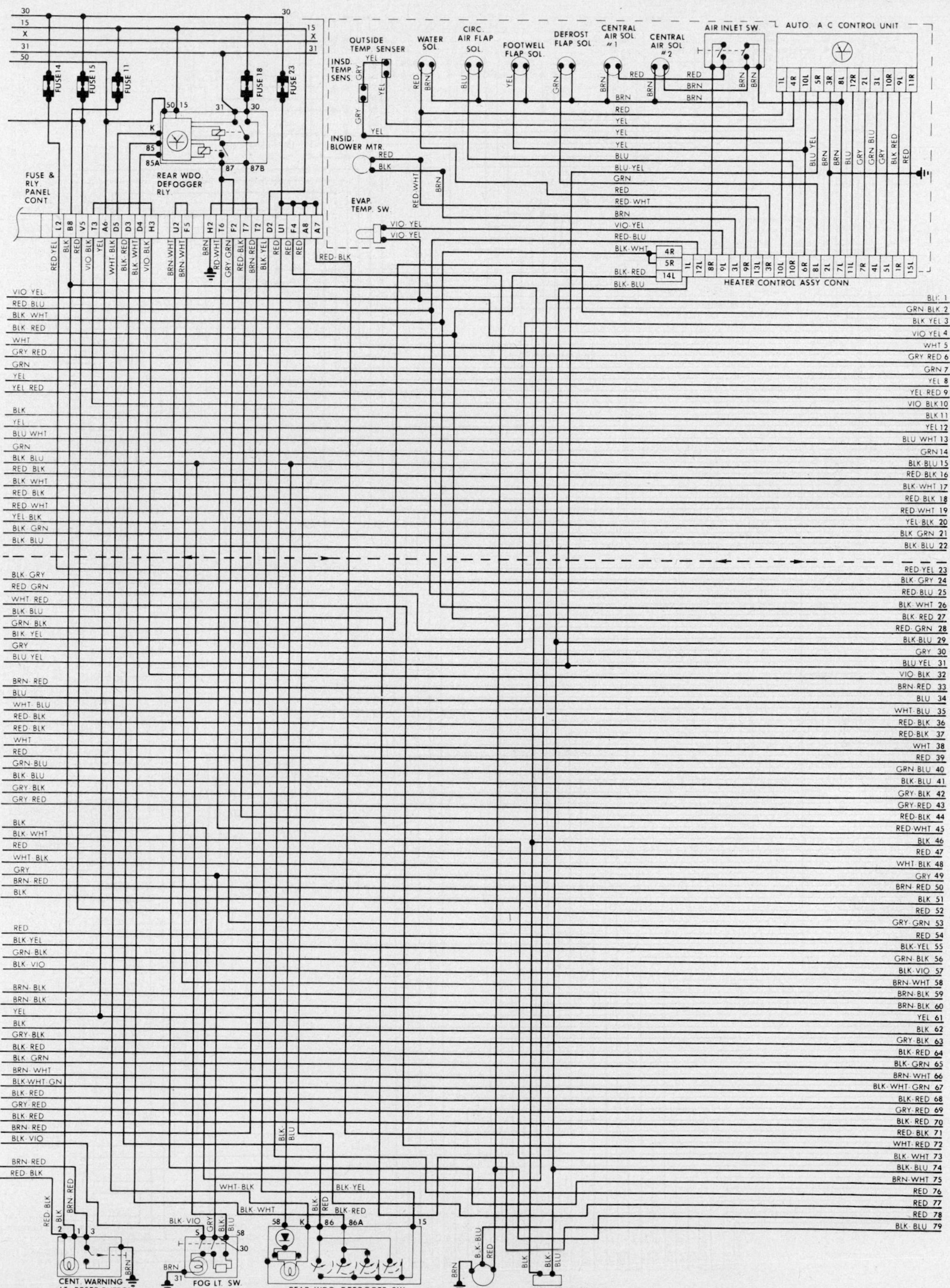

1983 Porsche

928S (Cont.)

INSTRUMENT PANEL

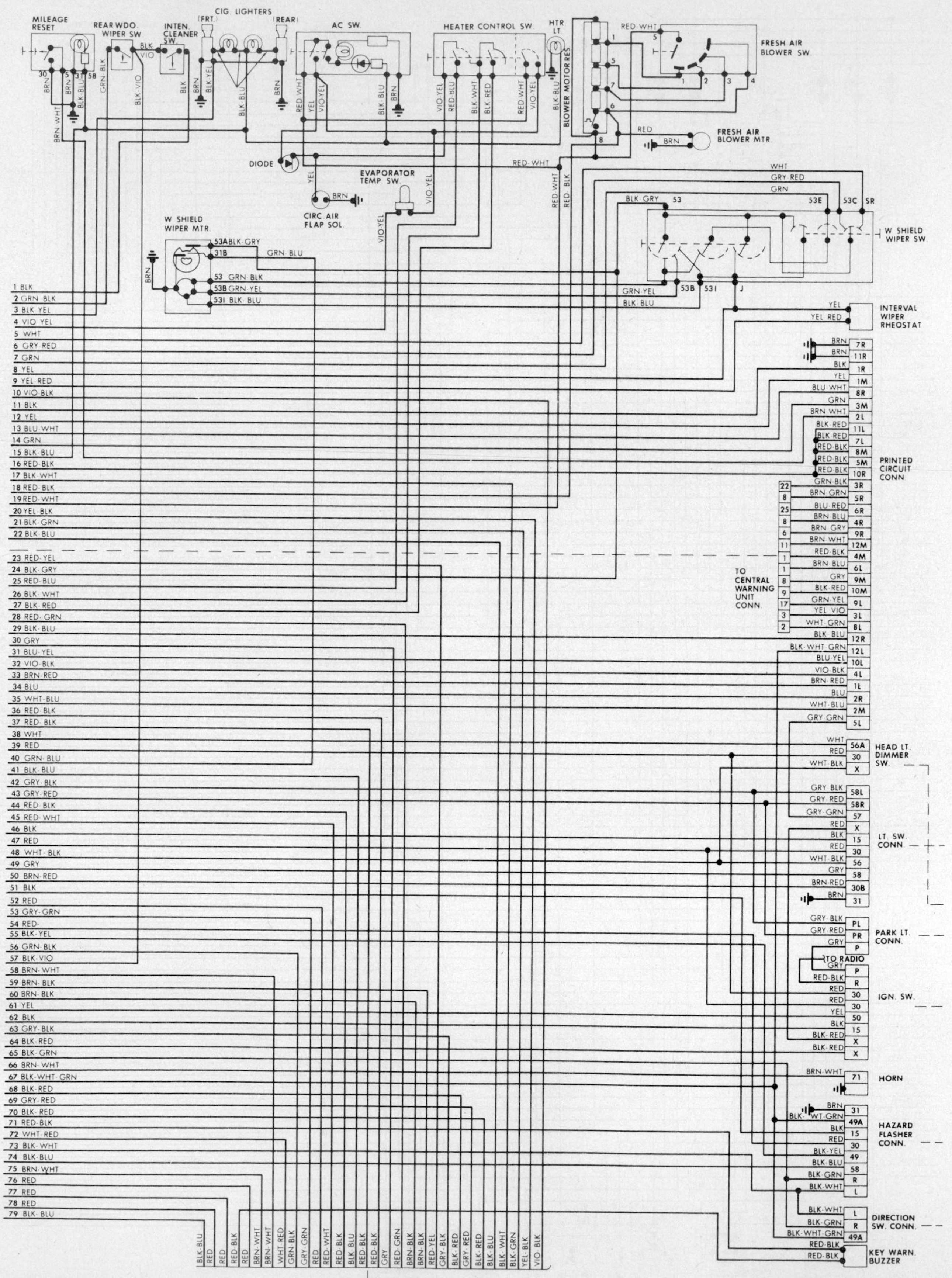

MILEAGE RESET
REAR WDO. WIPER SW
INTEN. CLEANER SW
CIG. LIGHTERS (FRT) (REAR)
AC SW.
HEATER CONTROL SW.
HTR LT
BLOWER MOTOR RES
FRESH AIR BLOWER SW.
FRESH AIR BLOWER MTR.
DIODE
EVAPORATOR TEMP. SW.
CIRC AIR FLAP SOL.
W SHIELD WIPER MTR.
W SHIELD WIPER SW.
INTERVAL WIPER RHEOSTAT
PRINTED CIRCUIT CONN
TO CENTRAL WARNING UNIT CONN.
HEAD LT. DIMMER SW.
LT. SW. CONN.
PARK LT. CONN.
TO RADIO
IGN. SW.
HORN
HAZARD FLASHER CONN.
DIRECTION SW. CONN.
KEY WARN. BUZZER

928S (Cont.)

INSTRUMENT PANEL & REAR COMPARTMENT

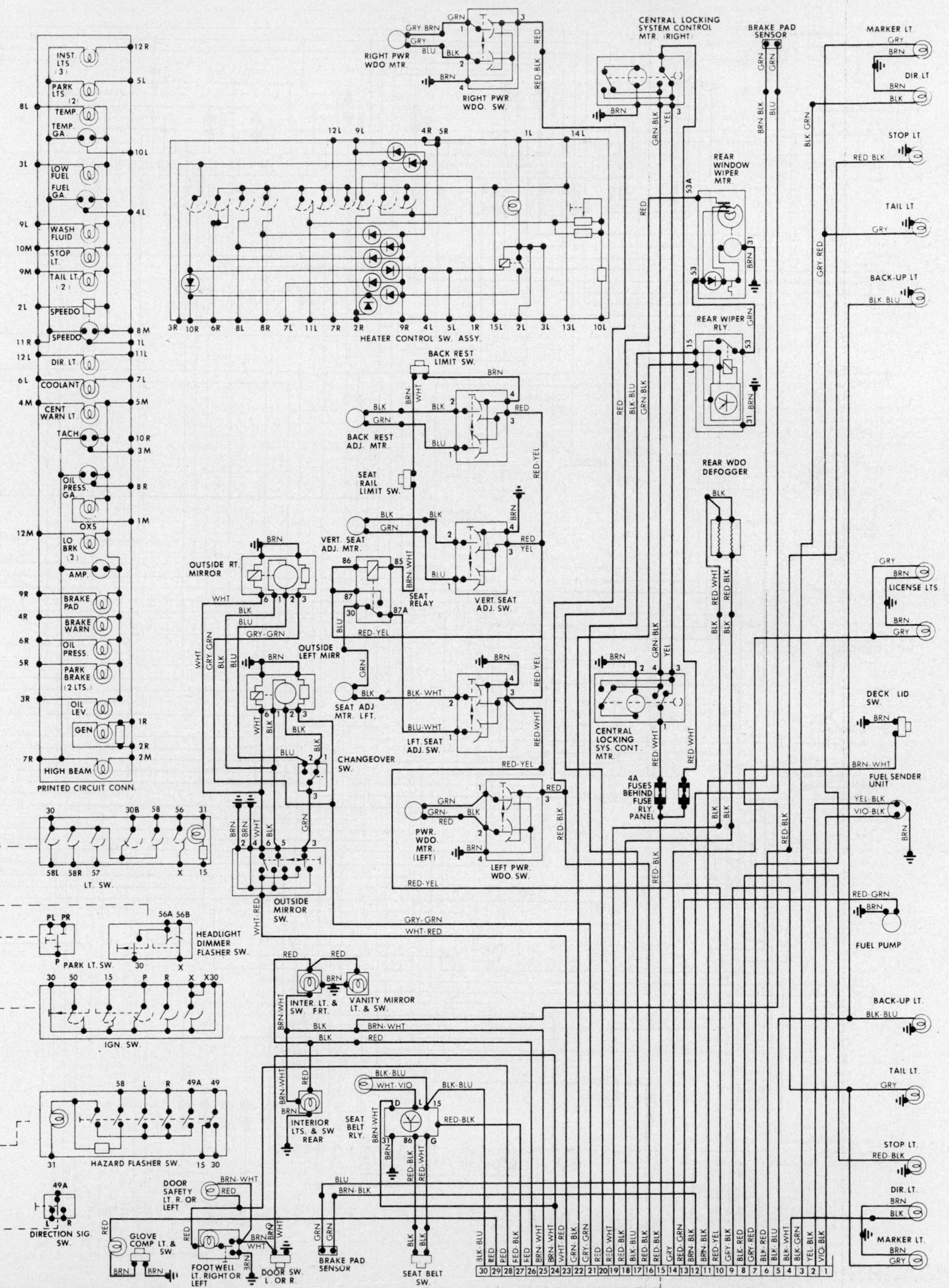
RIGHT PWR WDO MTR.
RIGHT PWR. WDO. SW.
CENTRAL LOCKING SYSTEM CONTROL MTR. (RIGHT)
BRAKE PAD SENSOR
MARKER LT.
DIR. LT.
STOP LT.
TAIL LT.
BACK-UP LT.
REAR WINDOW WIPER MTR.
REAR WIPER RLY.
HEATER CONTROL SW. ASSY.
INST. LTS. (3)
PARK LTS. (2)
TEMP.
TEMP. GA.
LOW FUEL
FUEL GA.
WASH FLUID
STOP LT.
TAIL LT. (2)
SPEEDO
DIR. LT.
COOLANT
CENT. WARN LT.
TACH
OIL PRESS. GA.
OXS
LO BRK (2)
AMP.
BRAKE PAD
BRAKE WARN
OIL PRESS.
PARK BRAKE (2 LTS.)
OIL LEV.
GEN
HIGH BEAM
PRINTED CIRCUIT CONN.
BACK REST LIMIT SW.
BACK REST ADJ. MTR.
SEAT RAIL LIMIT SW.
VERT. SEAT ADJ. MTR.
VERT. SEAT ADJ. SW.
SEAT RELAY
OUTSIDE RT. MIRROR
OUTSIDE LEFT MIRR
SEAT ADJ MTR. LFT.
LFT. SEAT ADJ. SW.
CHANGEOVER SW.
REAR WDO DEFOGGER
LICENSE LTS.
DECK LID SW.
FUEL SENDER UNIT
CENTRAL LOCKING SYS. CONT. MTR.
4A FUSES BEHIND FUSE RLY. PANEL
PWR. WDO. MTR. (LEFT)
LEFT PWR. WDO. SW.
LT. SW.
OUTSIDE MIRROR SW.
FUEL PUMP
PARK LT. SW.
HEADLIGHT DIMMER FLASHER SW.
INTER. LT. & SW. FRT.
VANITY MIRROR LT. & SW.
IGN. SW.
HAZARD FLASHER SW.
INTERIOR LTS. & SW REAR
SEAT BELT RLY.
DIRECTION SIG. SW.
DOOR SAFETY LT. R. OR LEFT
GLOVE COMP LT. & SW.
FOOTWELL LT. RIGHT OR LEFT
DOOR SW. L OR R.
BRAKE PAD SENSOR
SEAT BELT SW.

1983 Porsche

944

ENGINE COMPARTMENT & FUSE BLOCK

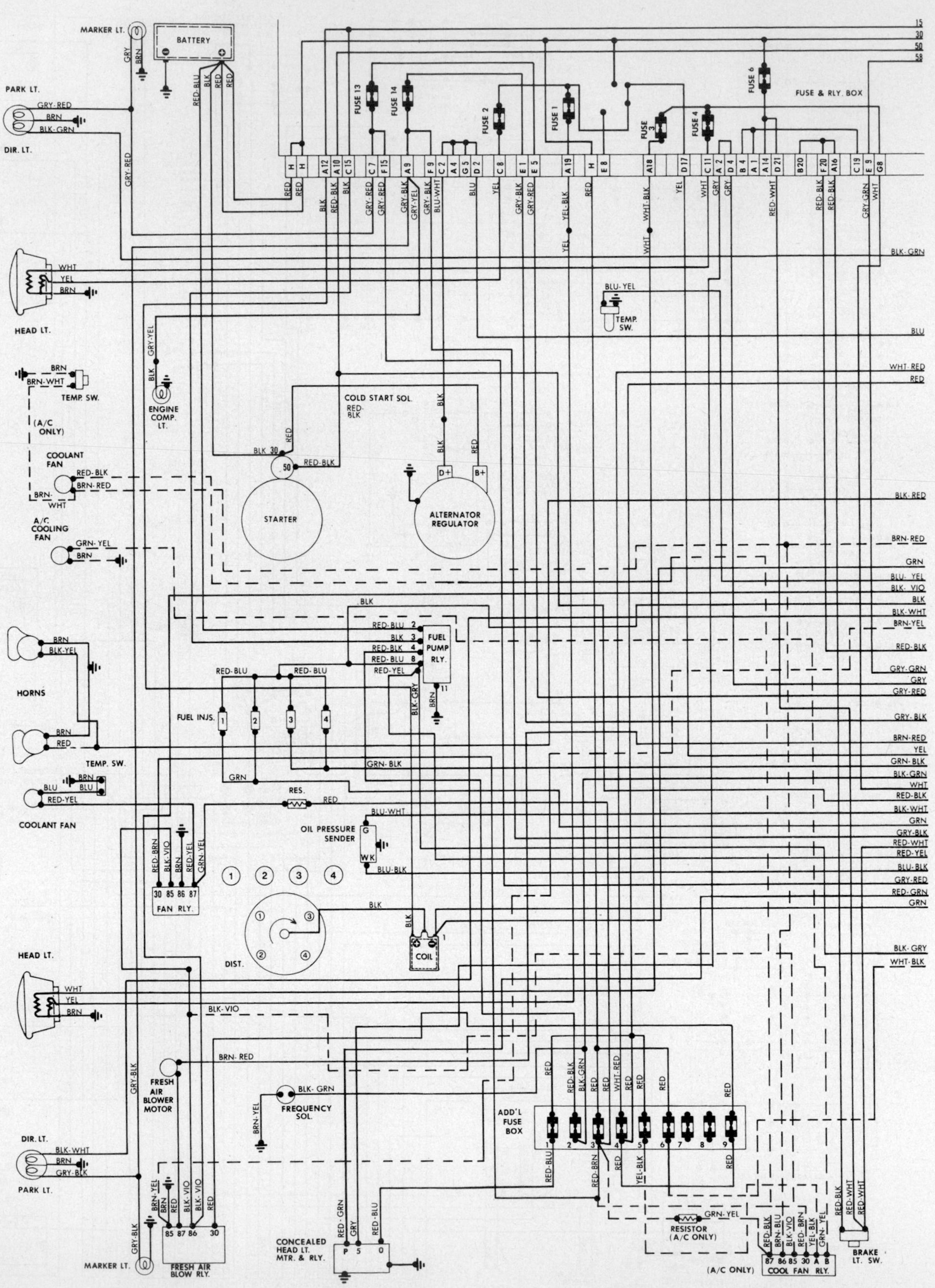

MARKER LT.
BATTERY
PARK LT.
DIR. LT.
HEAD LT.
TEMP. SW.
(A/C ONLY)
COOLANT FAN
A/C COOLING FAN
ENGINE COMP. LT.
COLD START SOL.
STARTER
ALTERNATOR REGULATOR
FUSE & RLY. BOX
FUSE 13
FUSE 14
FUSE 2
FUSE 1
FUSE 3
FUSE 4
FUSE 6
HORNS
FUEL INJS.
FUEL PUMP RLY.
RES.
OIL PRESSURE SENDER
FAN RLY.
DIST.
COIL
FRESH AIR BLOWER MOTOR
FREQUENCY SOL.
ADD'L FUSE BOX
RESISTOR (A/C ONLY)
(A/C ONLY)
COOL FAN RLY.
BRAKE LT. SW.
CONCEALED HEAD LT. MTR. & RLY.
FRESH AIR BLOW RLY.

1983 Porsche

944 (Cont.)

UNDERDASH & FUSE BLOCK

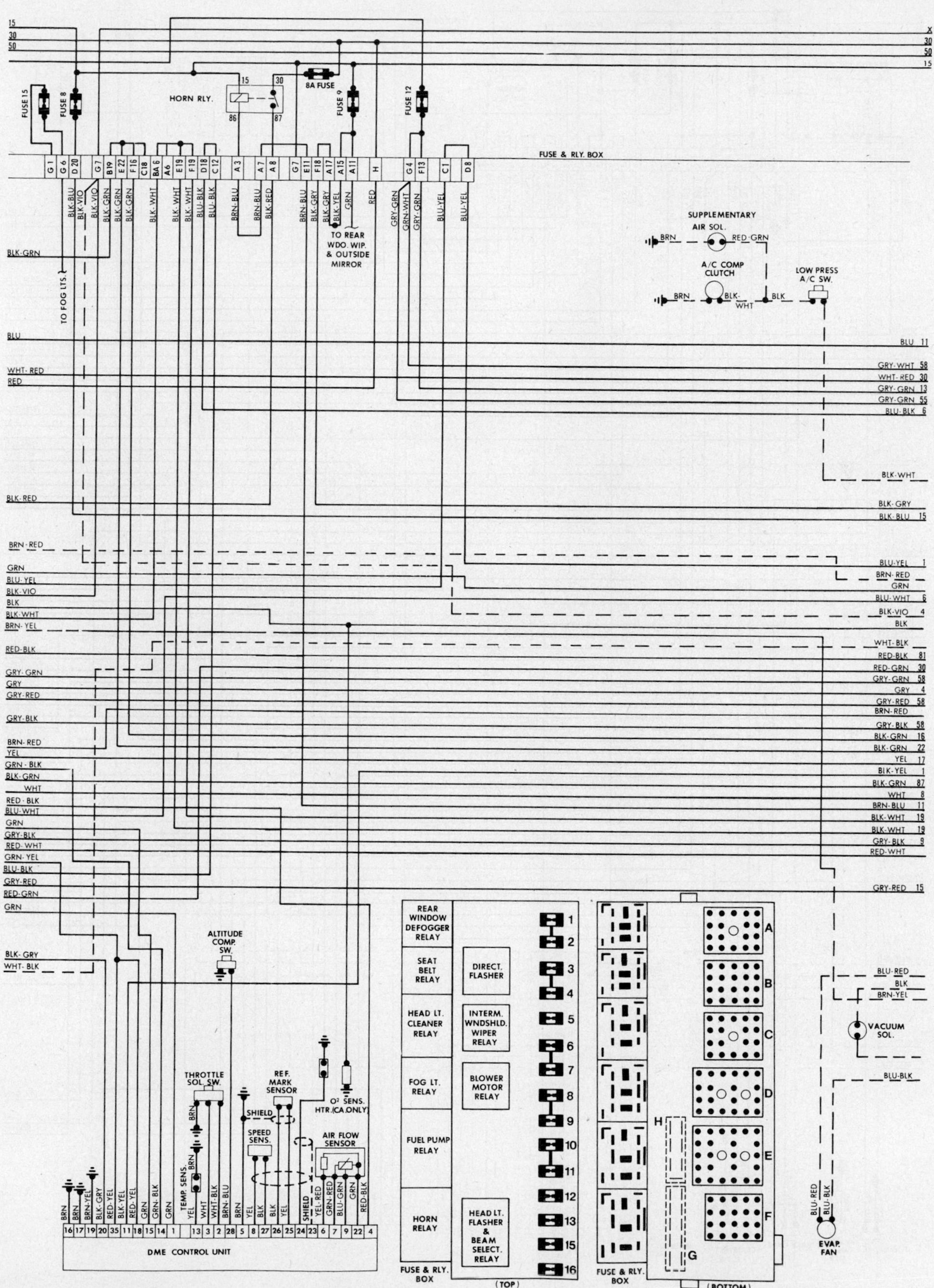

1983 Porsche

944 (Cont.)

UNDERDASH & FUSE BLOCK

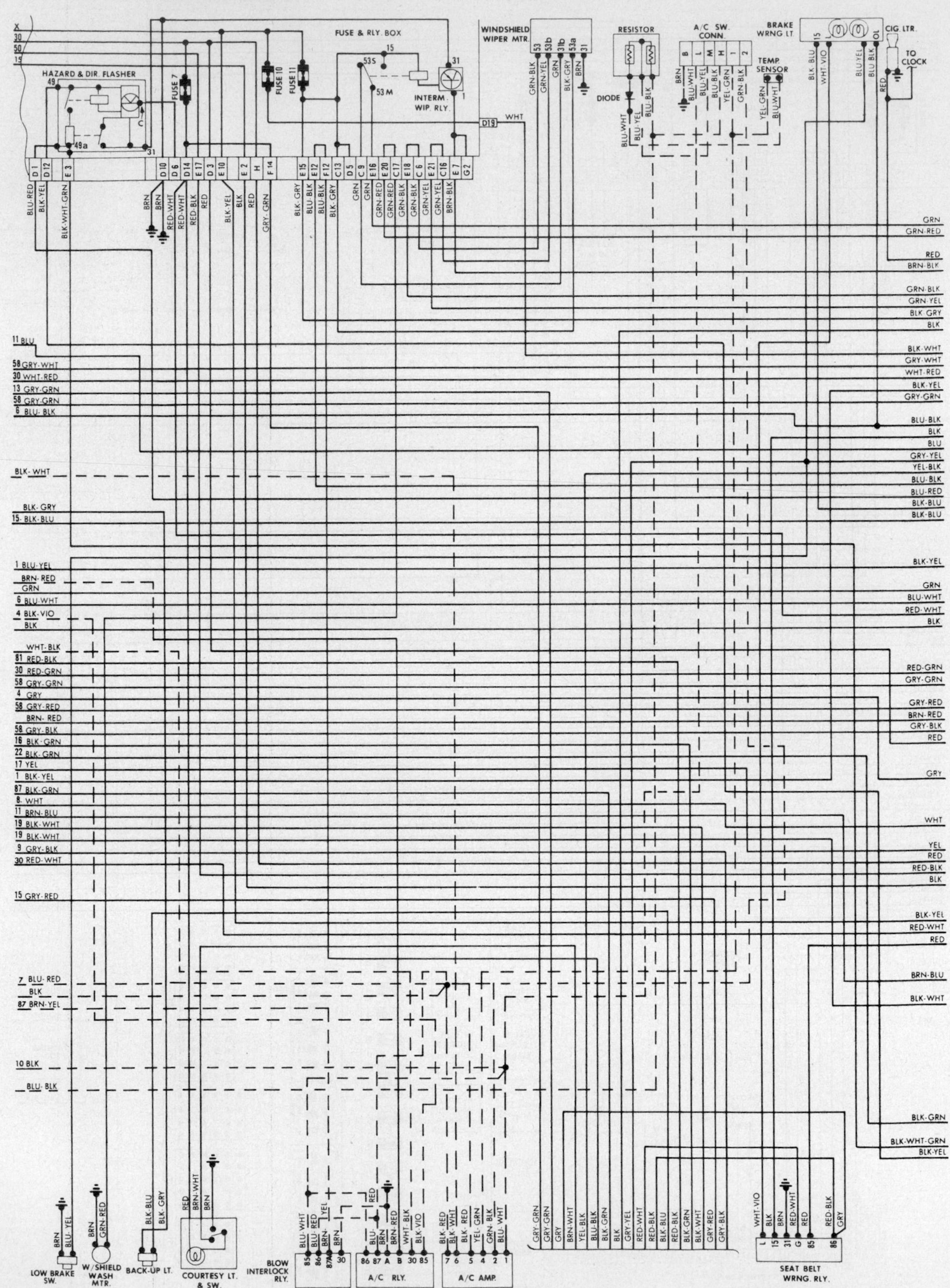

HAZARD & DIR. FLASHER
FUSE 7
FUSE & RLY. BOX
FUSE 10
FUSE 11
INTERM. WIP. RLY.
WINDSHIELD WIPER MTR.
RESISTOR
DIODE
A/C SW. CONN.
TEMP. SENSOR
BRAKE WRNG. LT.
CIG. LTR.
TO CLOCK
LOW BRAKE SW.
W/SHIELD WASH MTR.
BACK-UP LT.
COURTESY LT. & SW.
BLOW INTERLOCK RLY.
A/C RLY.
A/C AMP.
SEAT BELT WRNG. RLY.

944 (Cont.)

INSTRUMENT PANEL & REAR COMPARTMENT

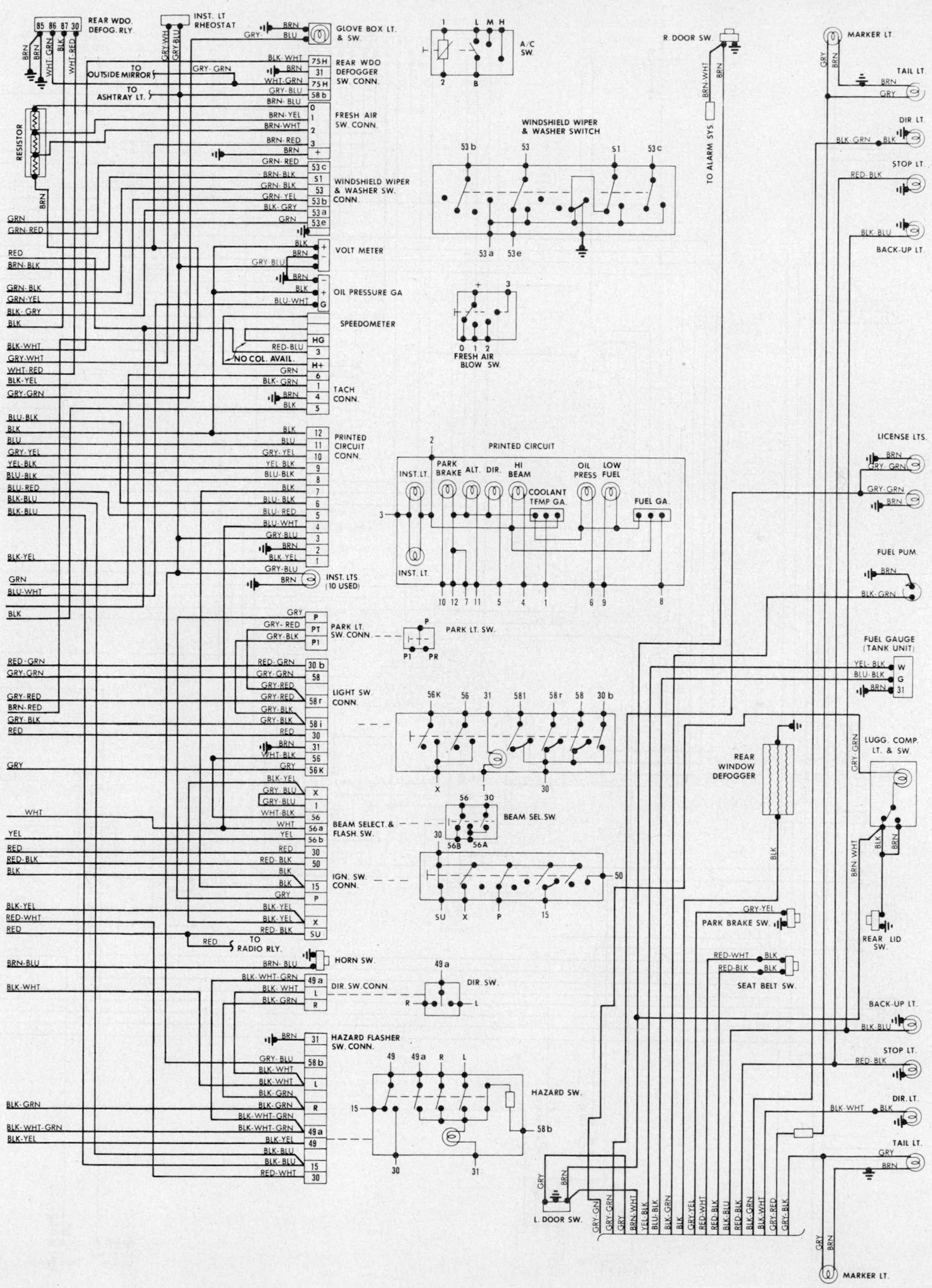

REAR WDO. DEFOG. RLY.
INST. LT RHEOSTAT
GLOVE BOX LT. & SW.
A/C SW.
R. DOOR SW.
MARKER LT.
TAIL LT.
DIR LT.
STOP LT.
BACK-UP LT.
TO OUTSIDE MIRROR
TO ASHTRAY LT.
REAR WDO DEFOGGER SW. CONN.
RESISTOR
FRESH AIR SW. CONN.
WINDSHIELD WIPER & WASHER SWITCH
WINDSHIELD WIPER & WASHER SW. CONN.
TO ALARM SYS
VOLT METER
OIL PRESSURE GA
FRESH AIR BLOW SW.
SPEEDOMETER
NO COL. AVAIL.
TACH CONN.
PRINTED CIRCUIT CONN.
PRINTED CIRCUIT
INST. LT.
PARK BRAKE
ALT.
DIR.
HI BEAM
COOLANT TEMP GA.
OIL PRESS
LOW FUEL
FUEL GA.
LICENSE LTS.
FUEL PUM
INST. LTS (10 USED)
PARK LT. SW. CONN.
PARK LT. SW.
FUEL GAUGE (TANK UNIT)
LIGHT SW. CONN.
LUGG. COMP. LT. & SW.
REAR WINDOW DEFOGGER
BEAM SELECT.& FLASH. SW.
BEAM SEL.SW.
IGN. SW. CONN.
TO RADIO RLY.
PARK BRAKE SW.
REAR LID SW.
HORN SW.
SEAT BELT SW.
DIR. SW.CONN
DIR. SW.
HAZARD FLASHER SW. CONN.
HAZARD SW.
L. DOOR SW.

1983 Renault

18i

ENGINE COMPARTMENT

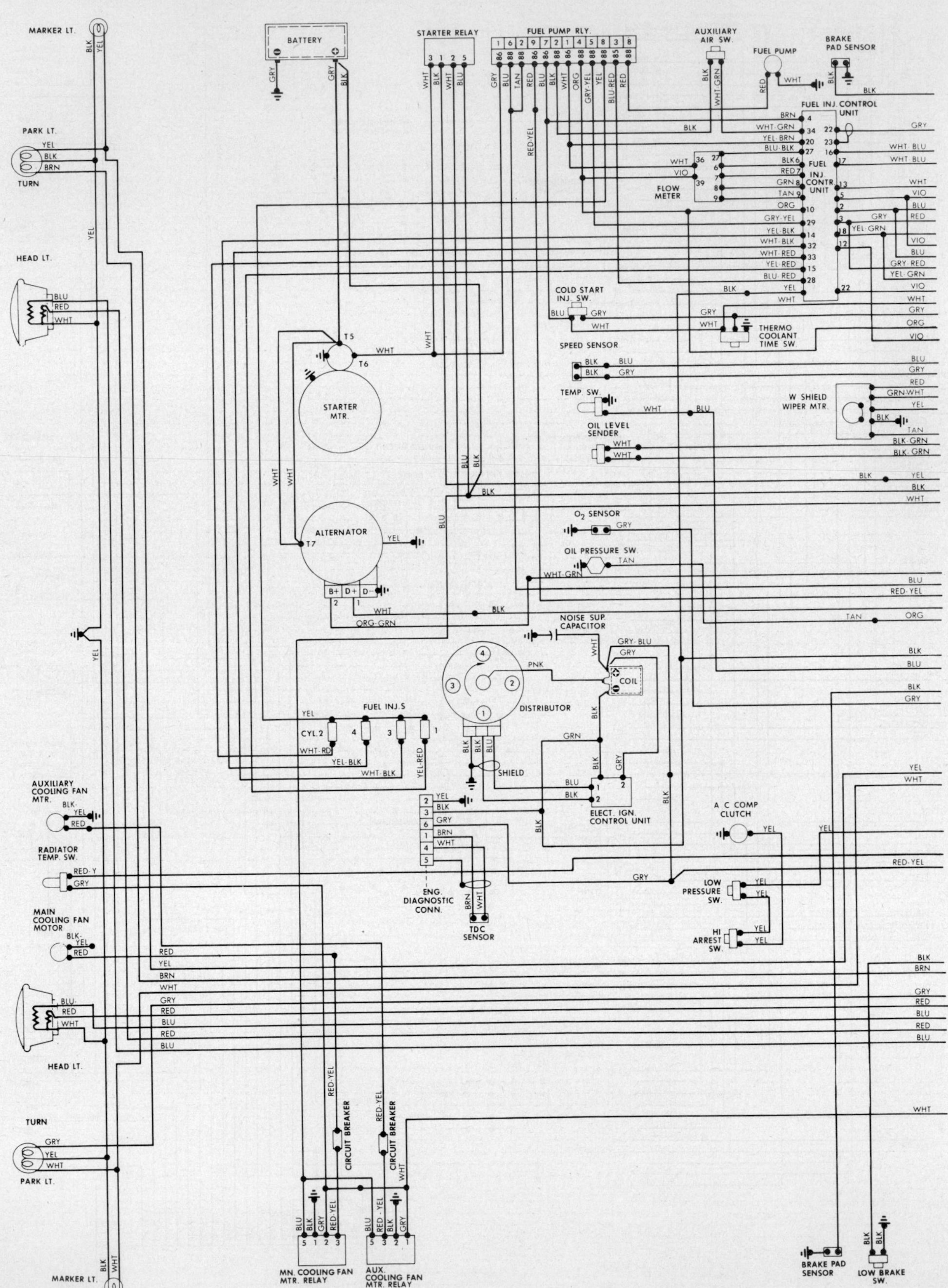

MARKER LT.
BATTERY
STARTER RELAY
FUEL PUMP RLY.
AUXILIARY AIR SW.
FUEL PUMP
BRAKE PAD SENSOR
FUEL INJ. CONTROL UNIT
PARK LT.
TURN
FLOW METER
FUEL INJ CONTR UNIT
HEAD LT.
COLD START INJ. SW.
THERMO COOLANT TIME SW.
SPEED SENSOR
STARTER MTR.
TEMP. SW.
W SHIELD WIPER MTR.
OIL LEVEL SENDER
ALTERNATOR
O2 SENSOR
OIL PRESSURE SW.
NOISE SUP. CAPACITOR
COIL
DISTRIBUTOR
FUEL INJ.S
CYL.2
SHIELD
AUXILIARY COOLING FAN MTR.
ELECT. IGN. CONTROL UNIT
A C COMP CLUTCH
RADIATOR TEMP. SW.
ENG. DIAGNOSTIC CONN.
LOW PRESSURE SW.
MAIN COOLING FAN MOTOR
TDC SENSOR
HI ARREST SW.
HEAD LT.
TURN
CIRCUIT BREAKER
CIRCUIT BREAKER
PARK LT.
MARKER LT.
MN. COOLING FAN MTR. RELAY
AUX. COOLING FAN MTR. RELAY
BRAKE PAD SENSOR
LOW BRAKE SW.

1983 Renault

18i (Cont.)

FUSE BLOCK & UNDERDASH

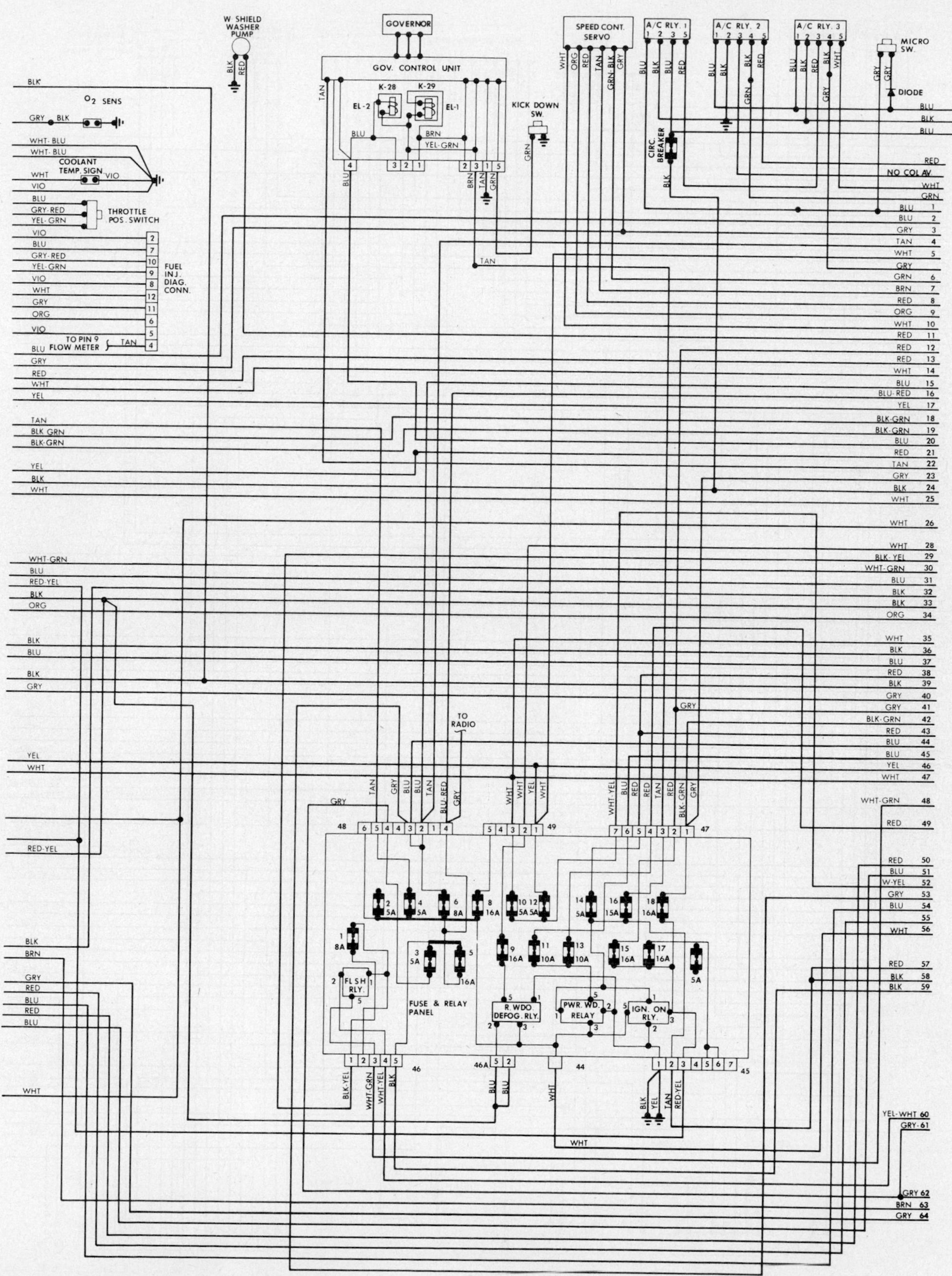
W SHIELD WASHER PUMP
GOVERNOR
GOV. CONTROL UNIT
K-28
K-29
EL-2
EL-1
KICK DOWN SW.
SPEED CONT. SERVO
A/C RLY. 1
A/C RLY. 2
A/C RLY. 3
MICRO SW.
DIODE
CIRC. BREAKER
NO COL AV.
O2 SENS
COOLANT TEMP. SIGN.
THROTTLE POS. SWITCH
FUEL INJ. DIAG. CONN.
TO PIN 9 FLOW METER
TO RADIO
FL SH RLY.
FUSE & RELAY PANEL
R. WDO DEFOG. RLY.
PWR. WD. RELAY
IGN. ON RLY.
BLU 1
BLU 2
GRY 3
TAN 4
WHT 5
GRN 6
BRN 7
RED 8
ORG 9
WHT 10
RED 11
RED 12
RED 13
WHT 14
BLU 15
BLU-RED 16
YEL 17
BLK-GRN 18
BLK-GRN 19
BLU 20
RED 21
TAN 22
GRY 23
BLK 24
WHT 25
WHT 26
WHT 28
BLK-YEL 29
WHT-GRN 30
BLU 31
BLK 32
BLK 33
ORG 34
WHT 35
BLK 36
BLU 37
RED 38
BLK 39
GRY 40
GRY 41
BLK-GRN 42
RED 43
BLU 44
BLU 45
YEL 46
WHT 47
WHT-GRN 48
RED 49
RED 50
BLU 51
W-YEL 52
GRY 53
BLU 54
55
WHT 56
RED 57
BLK 58
BLK 59
YEL-WHT 60
GRY 61
GRY 62
BRN 63
GRY 64

1983 Renault

18i (Cont.)

UNDERDASH

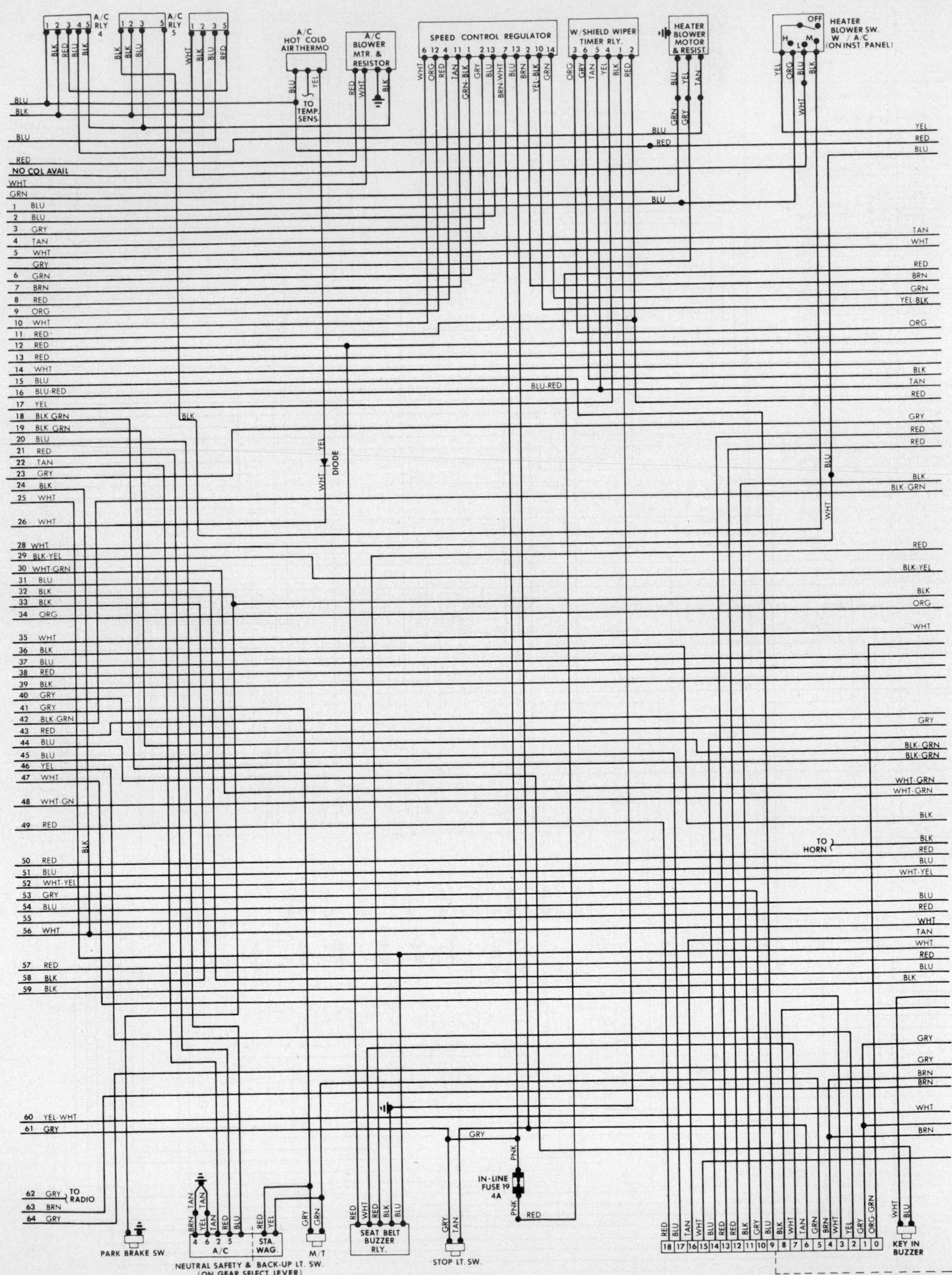

1983 Renault

18i (Cont.)

INSTRUMENT PANEL, REAR COMPARTMENT & ACCESSORIES

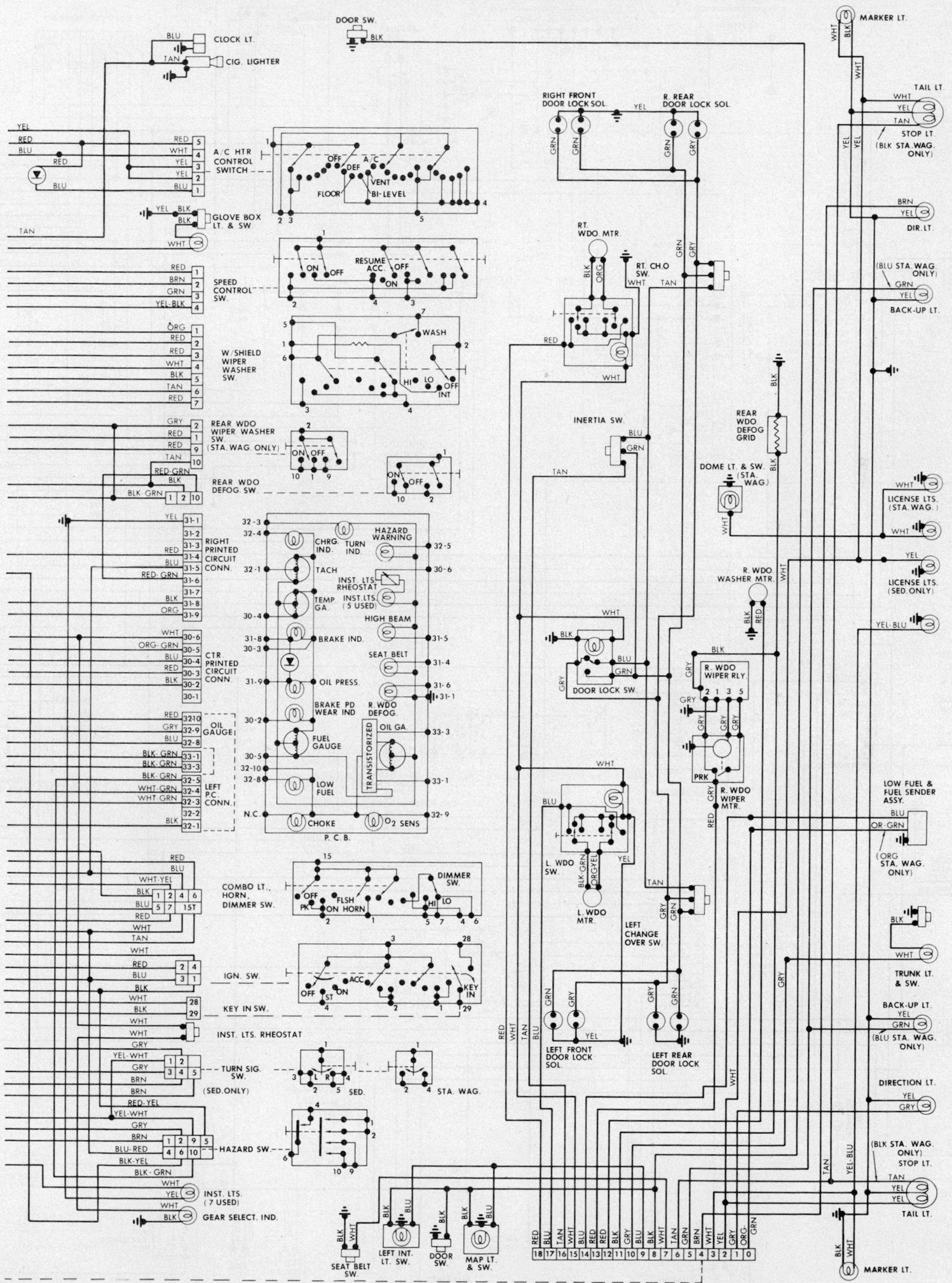

1983 Renault

FUEGO & FUEGO TURBO

ENGINE COMPARTMENT

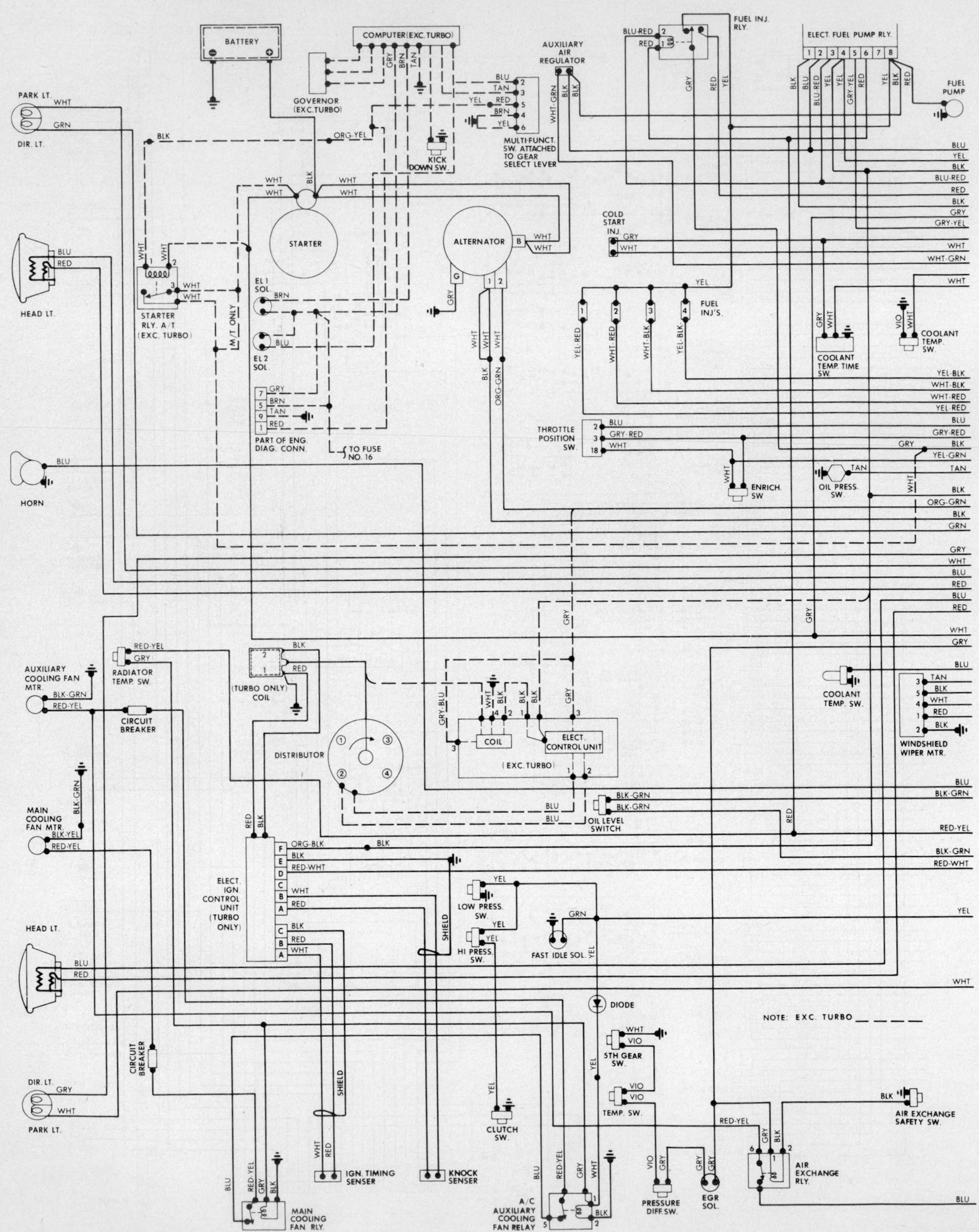

BATTERY
COMPUTER (EXC. TURBO)
GOVERNOR (EXC. TURBO)
KICK DOWN SW.
MULTI-FUNCT. SW. ATTACHED TO GEAR SELECT LEVER
AUXILIARY AIR REGULATOR
FUEL INJ. RLY.
ELECT. FUEL PUMP RLY.
FUEL PUMP
PARK LT.
DIR. LT.
HEAD LT.
STARTER RLY. A/T (EXC. TURBO)
STARTER
ALTERNATOR
COLD START INJ.
FUEL INJ'S.
EL 1 SOL.
EL 2 SOL.
M/T ONLY
PART OF ENG. DIAG. CONN.
TO FUSE NO. 16
COOLANT TEMP. TIME SW.
COOLANT TEMP. SW.
THROTTLE POSITION SW.
ENRICH. SW
OIL PRESS. SW.
HORN
AUXILIARY COOLING FAN MTR.
RADIATOR TEMP. SW.
CIRCUIT BREAKER
(TURBO ONLY) COIL
DISTRIBUTOR
COIL
ELECT. CONTROL UNIT
(EXC. TURBO)
OIL LEVEL SWITCH
WINDSHIELD WIPER MTR.
MAIN COOLING FAN MTR.
ELECT. IGN CONTROL UNIT (TURBO ONLY)
LOW PRESS. SW.
HI PRESS. SW.
SHIELD
FAST IDLE SOL.
DIODE
NOTE: EXC. TURBO — — —
5TH GEAR SW.
TEMP. SW.
CLUTCH SW.
AIR EXCHANGE SAFETY SW.
AIR EXCHANGE RLY.
IGN. TIMING SENSER
KNOCK SENSER
MAIN COOLING FAN RLY.
A/C AUXILIARY COOLING FAN RELAY
PRESSURE DIFF. SW.
EGR SOL.

1983 Renault

FUEGO & FUEGO TURBO (Cont.)

FUSE BLOCK & UNDERDASH

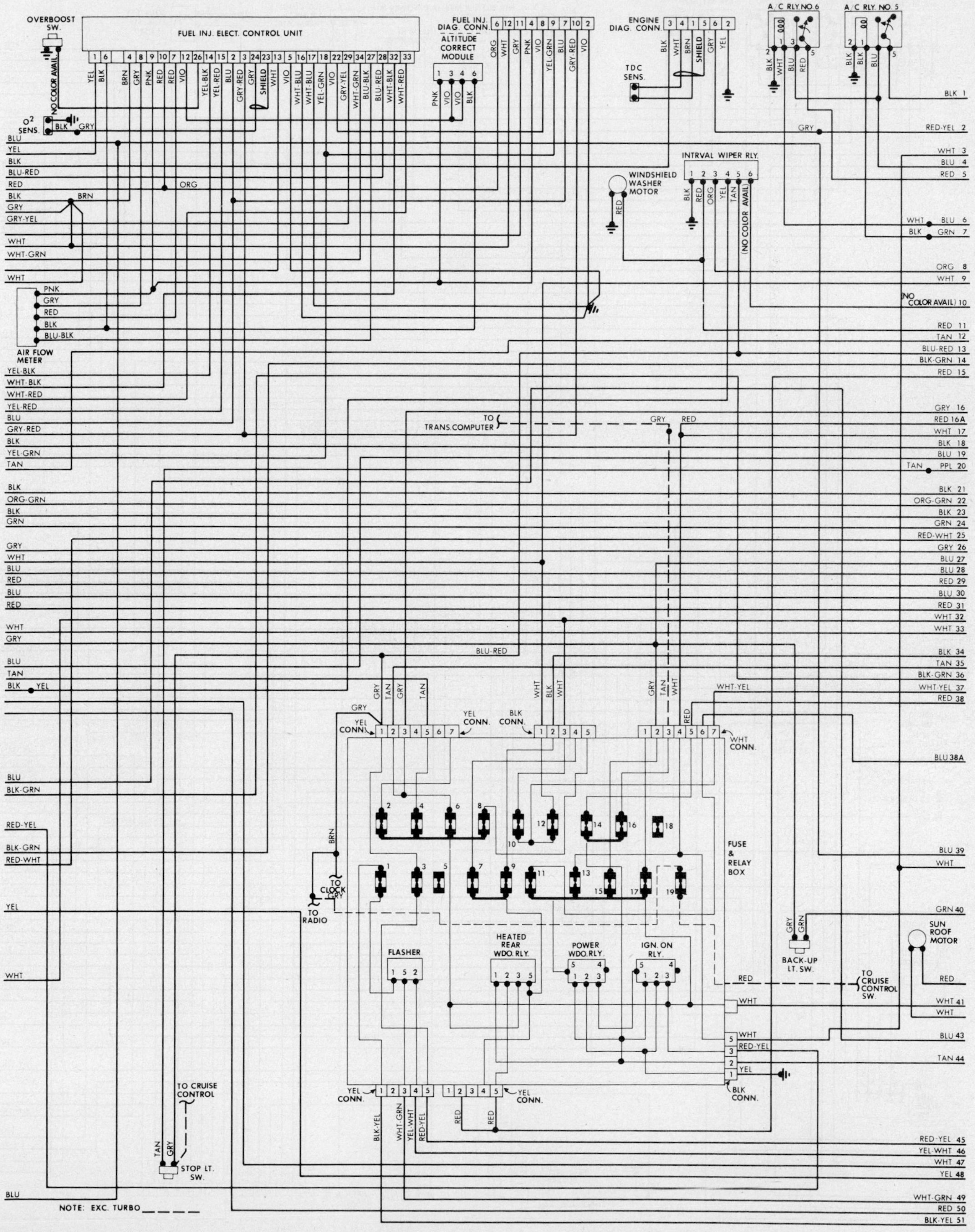
OVERBOOST SW.
FUEL INJ. ELECT. CONTROL UNIT
FUEL INJ. DIAG. CONN.
ALTITUDE CORRECT MODULE
ENGINE DIAG. CONN.
TDC SENS.
A/C RLY. NO. 6
A/C RLY. NO. 5
INTRVAL WIPER RLY.
WINDSHIELD WASHER MOTOR
O2 SENS.
AIR FLOW METER
TO TRANS. COMPUTER
YEL CONN.
BLK CONN.
WHT CONN.
FUSE & RELAY BOX
TO CLOCK
TO RADIO
FLASHER
HEATED REAR WDO. RLY.
POWER WDO. RLY.
IGN. ON RLY.
BACK-UP LT. SW.
SUN ROOF MOTOR
TO CRUISE CONTROL SW.
TO CRUISE CONTROL
STOP LT. SW.
NOTE: EXC. TURBO

1983 Renault

FUEGO & FUEGO TURBO (Cont.)

UNDERDASH

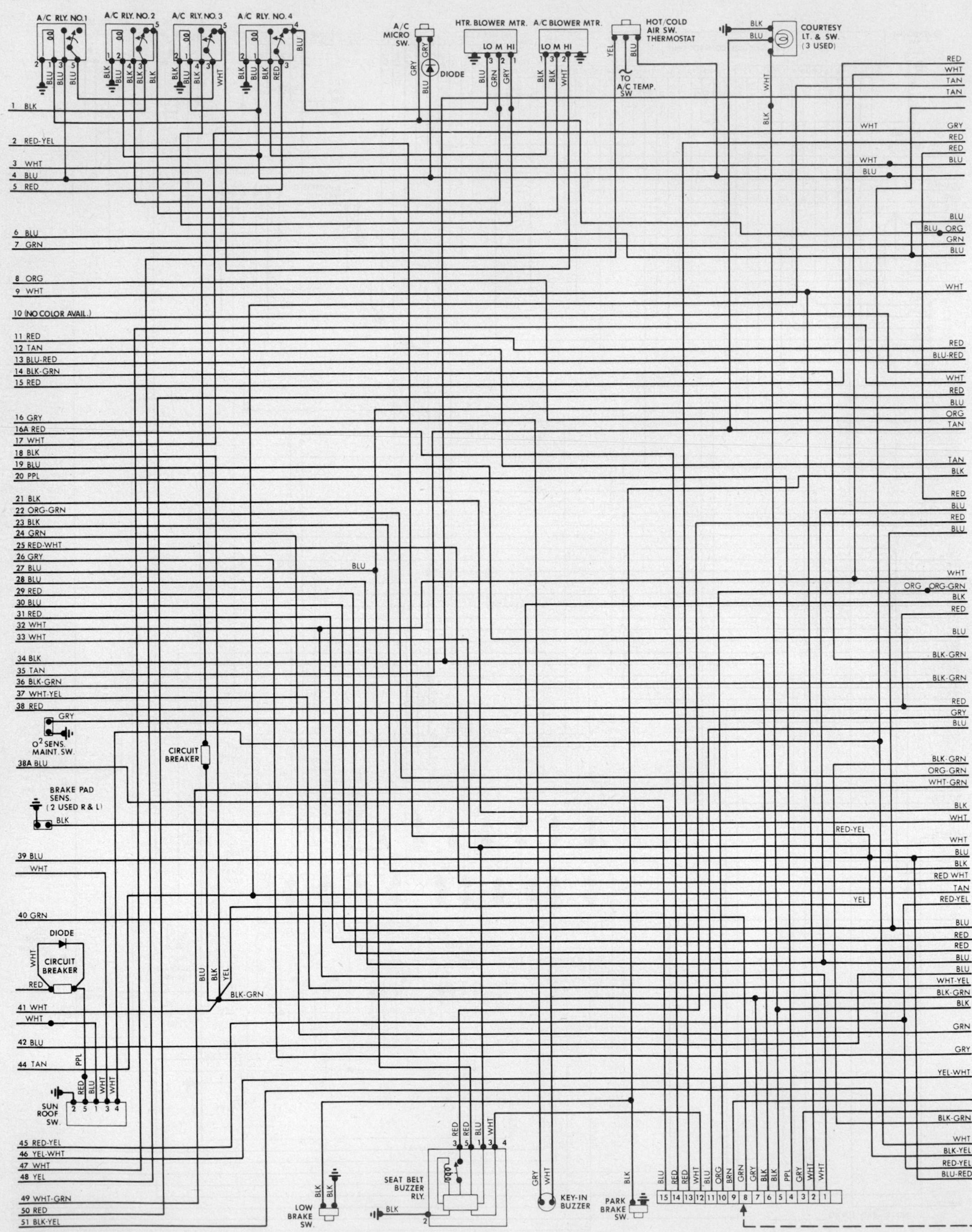
A/C RLY. NO. 1
A/C RLY. NO. 2
A/C RLY. NO. 3
A/C RLY. NO. 4
A/C MICRO SW.
DIODE
HTR. BLOWER MTR.
A/C BLOWER MTR.
LO M HI
HOT/COLD AIR SW. THERMOSTAT
TO A/C TEMP. SW
COURTESY LT. & SW. (3 USED)
1 BLK
2 RED-YEL
3 WHT
4 BLU
5 RED
6 BLU
7 GRN
8 ORG
9 WHT
10 (NO COLOR AVAIL.)
11 RED
12 TAN
13 BLU-RED
14 BLK-GRN
15 RED
16 GRY
16A RED
17 WHT
18 BLK
19 BLU
20 PPL
21 BLK
22 ORG-GRN
23 BLK
24 GRN
25 RED-WHT
26 GRY
27 BLU
28 BLU
29 RED
30 BLU
31 RED
32 WHT
33 WHT
34 BLK
35 TAN
36 BLK-GRN
37 WHT-YEL
38 RED
O2 SENS. MAINT. SW.
38A BLU
CIRCUIT BREAKER
BRAKE PAD SENS. (2 USED R & L)
39 BLU
40 GRN
DIODE
CIRCUIT BREAKER
41 WHT
42 BLU
44 TAN
SUN ROOF SW.
45 RED-YEL
46 YEL-WHT
47 WHT
48 YEL
49 WHT-GRN
50 RED
51 BLK-YEL
LOW BRAKE SW.
SEAT BELT BUZZER RLY.
KEY-IN BUZZER
PARK BRAKE SW.
15 14 13 12 11 10 9 8 7 6 5 4 3 2 1

FUEGO & FUEGO TURBO (Cont.)

INSTRUMENT PANEL, REAR COMPARTMENT & ACCESSORIES

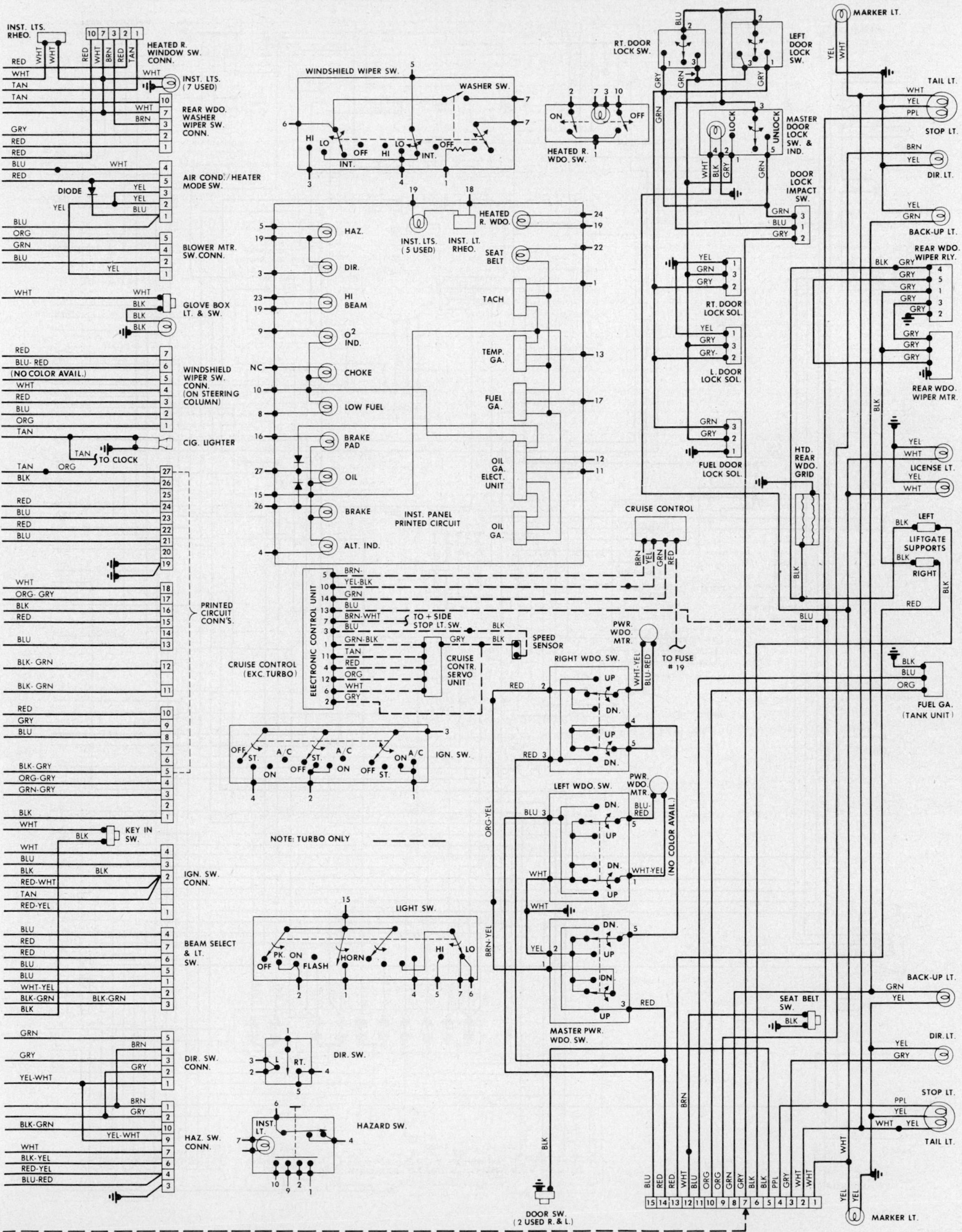
INST. LTS. RHEO.
HEATED R. WINDOW SW. CONN.
INST. LTS. (7 USED)
REAR WDO. WASHER WIPER SW. CONN.
AIR COND./HEATER MODE SW.
DIODE
BLOWER MTR. SW. CONN.
GLOVE BOX LT. & SW.
WINDSHIELD WIPER SW. CONN. (ON STEERING COLUMN)
(NO COLOR AVAIL.)
CIG. LIGHTER
TO CLOCK
PRINTED CIRCUIT CONN'S.
KEY IN SW.
IGN. SW. CONN.
BEAM SELECT & LT. SW.
DIR. SW. CONN.
HAZ. SW. CONN.
WINDSHIELD WIPER SW.
WASHER SW.
HI LO INT. OFF
HEATED R. WDO. SW.
HAZ.
DIR.
HI BEAM
O2 IND.
CHOKE
LOW FUEL
BRAKE PAD
OIL
BRAKE
ALT. IND.
INST. LTS. (5 USED)
INST. LT. RHEO.
HEATED R. WDO.
SEAT BELT
TACH
TEMP. GA.
FUEL GA.
OIL GA. ELECT. UNIT
OIL GA.
INST. PANEL PRINTED CIRCUIT
ELECTRONIC CONTROL UNIT
TO + SIDE STOP LT. SW.
CRUISE CONTR. SERVO UNIT
SPEED SENSOR
CRUISE CONTROL (EXC. TURBO)
CRUISE CONTROL
TO FUSE #19
PWR. WDO. MTR.
RIGHT WDO. SW.
IGN. SW.
OFF ST. A/C ON
LEFT WDO. SW.
NOTE: TURBO ONLY
LIGHT SW.
PK. ON OFF FLASH HORN HI LO
MASTER PWR. WDO. SW.
DIR. SW.
HAZARD SW.
INST. LT.
DOOR SW. (2 USED R. & L.)
RT. DOOR LOCK SW.
LEFT DOOR LOCK SW.
MASTER DOOR LOCK SW. & IND.
LOCK UNLOCK
DOOR LOCK IMPACT SW.
RT. DOOR LOCK SOL.
L. DOOR LOCK SOL.
FUEL DOOR LOCK SOL.
HTD. REAR WDO. GRID
MARKER LT.
TAIL LT.
STOP LT.
DIR. LT.
BACK-UP LT.
REAR WDO. WIPER RLY.
REAR WDO. WIPER MTR.
LICENSE LT.
LEFT LIFTGATE SUPPORTS RIGHT
FUEL GA. (TANK UNIT)
SEAT BELT SW.

1983 Renault

LE CAR

ENGINE COMPARTMENT & FUSE BLOCK

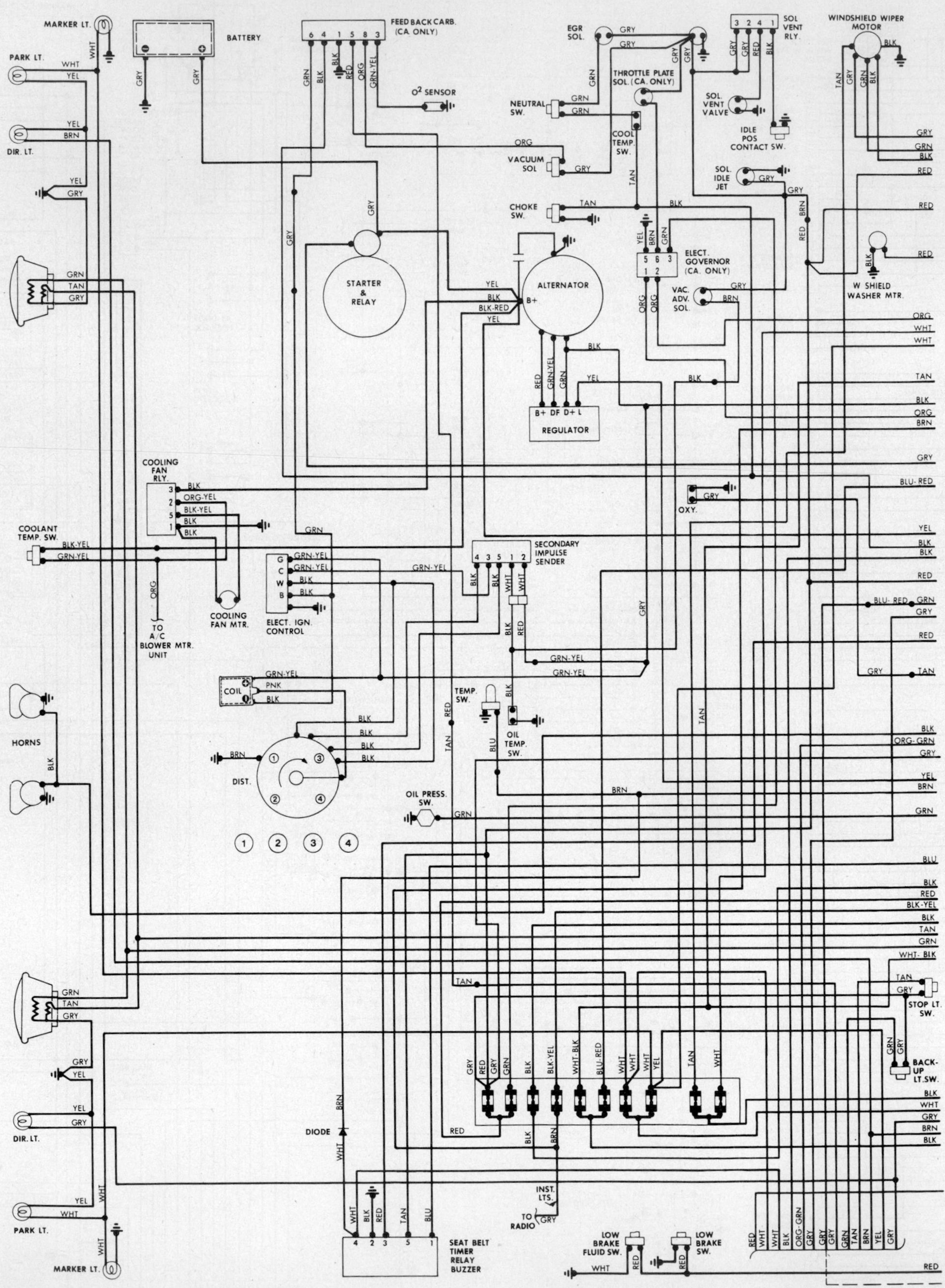

MARKER LT.
PARK LT.
BATTERY
FEED BACK CARB. (CA. ONLY)
O2 SENSOR
EGR SOL.
THROTTLE PLATE SOL. (CA. ONLY)
SOL VENT RLY.
WINDSHIELD WIPER MOTOR
DIR. LT.
NEUTRAL SW.
COOL TEMP. SW.
VACUUM SOL
SOL. VENT VALVE
IDLE POS CONTACT SW.
SOL. IDLE JET
CHOKE SW.
STARTER & RELAY
ALTERNATOR
ELECT. GOVERNOR (CA. ONLY)
VAC. ADV. SOL.
W SHIELD WASHER MTR.
REGULATOR
COOLING FAN RLY.
OXY.
COOLANT TEMP. SW.
SECONDARY IMPULSE SENDER
TO A/C BLOWER MTR. UNIT
COOLING FAN MTR.
ELECT. IGN. CONTROL
COIL
TEMP. SW.
OIL TEMP. SW.
HORNS
DIST.
OIL PRESS. SW.
STOP LT. SW.
BACK-UP LT. SW.
DIODE
INST. LTS.
TO RADIO
SEAT BELT TIMER RELAY BUZZER
LOW BRAKE FLUID SW.
LOW BRAKE SW.

1983 Renault

LE CAR (Cont.)

INSTRUMENT PANEL & REAR COMPARTMENT

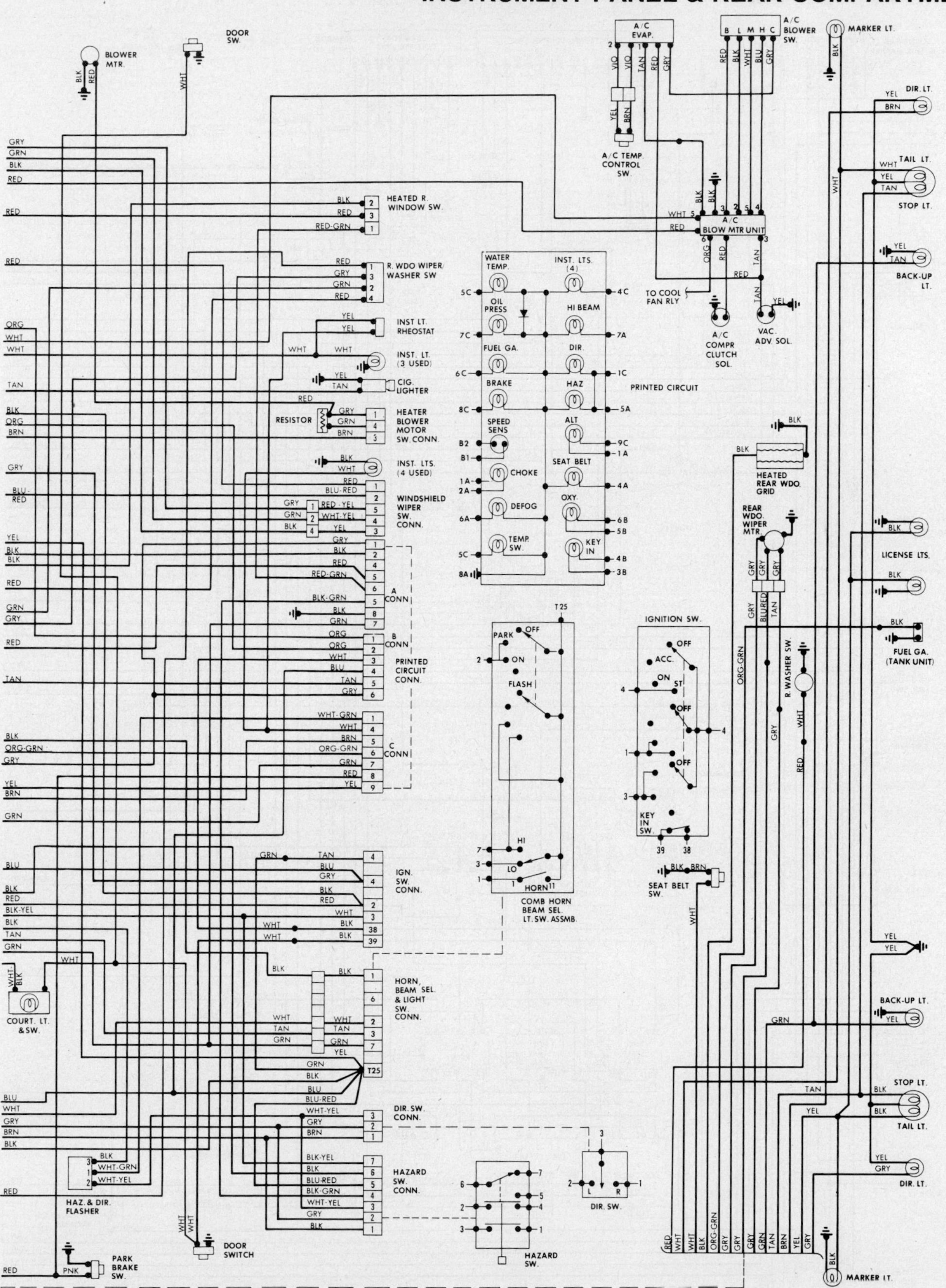
BLOWER MTR.
DOOR SW.
A/C EVAP.
A/C BLOWER SW.
MARKER LT.
DIR. LT.
TAIL LT.
STOP LT.
A/C TEMP. CONTROL SW.
HEATED R. WINDOW SW.
A/C BLOW MTR UNIT
R. WDO WIPER/ WASHER SW
BACK-UP LT.
WATER TEMP.
INST. LTS. (4)
OIL PRESS
HI BEAM
FUEL GA.
DIR.
BRAKE
HAZ
SPEED SENS
ALT
CHOKE
SEAT BELT
DEFOG
OXY.
TEMP. SW.
KEY IN
TO COOL FAN RLY
A/C COMPR CLUTCH SOL.
VAC. ADV. SOL.
PRINTED CIRCUIT
INST LT. RHEOSTAT
INST. LT. (3 USED)
CIG. LIGHTER
RESISTOR
HEATER BLOWER MOTOR SW. CONN.
INST. LTS. (4 USED)
WINDSHIELD WIPER SW. CONN.
HEATED REAR WDO. GRID
REAR WDO. WIPER MTR.
LICENSE LTS.
FUEL GA. (TANK UNIT)
A CONN
B CONN
PRINTED CIRCUIT CONN.
C CONN
PARK
OFF
ON
FLASH
IGNITION SW.
ACC.
ST
KEY IN SW.
R. WASHER SW.
HI
LO
HORN
COMB HORN BEAM SEL. LT. SW. ASSMB.
SEAT BELT SW.
IGN. SW. CONN.
HORN, BEAM SEL. & LIGHT SW. CONN.
COURT. LT. & SW.
DIR. SW. CONN.
HAZ. & DIR. FLASHER
HAZARD SW. CONN.
DIR. SW.
HAZARD SW.
DOOR SWITCH
PARK BRAKE SW.

1983 Saab

900 & 900 TURBO

ENGINE COMPARTMENT

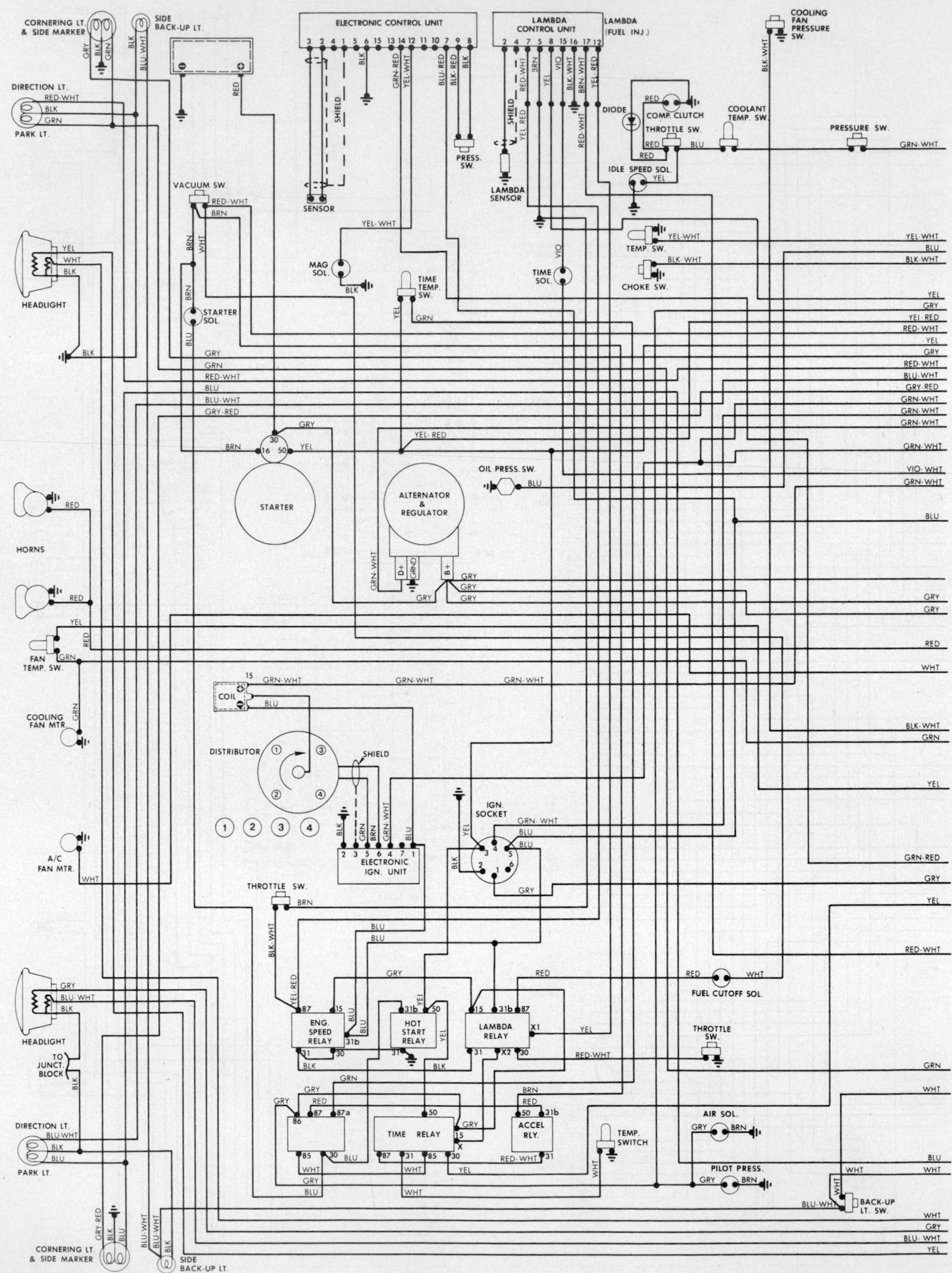
CORNERING LT. & SIDE MARKER
SIDE BACK-UP LT.
ELECTRONIC CONTROL UNIT
LAMBDA CONTROL UNIT
LAMBDA (FUEL INJ.)
COOLING FAN PRESSURE SW.
DIRECTION LT.
PARK LT.
SHIELD
PRESS. SW.
LAMBDA SENSOR
DIODE
COMP. CLUTCH
THROTTLE SW.
COOLANT TEMP. SW.
PRESSURE SW.
IDLE SPEED SOL.
SENSOR
VACUUM SW.
MAG SOL.
TIME TEMP. SW.
TIME SOL.
TEMP. SW.
CHOKE SW.
HEADLIGHT
STARTER SOL.
STARTER
ALTERNATOR & REGULATOR
OIL PRESS. SW.
HORNS
FAN TEMP. SW.
COIL
COOLING FAN MTR.
DISTRIBUTOR
ELECTRONIC IGN. UNIT
IGN. SOCKET
A/C FAN MTR.
THROTTLE SW.
FUEL CUTOFF SOL.
ENG. SPEED RELAY
HOT START RELAY
LAMBDA RELAY
HEADLIGHT
TO JUNCT. BLOCK
TIME RELAY
ACCEL RLY.
TEMP. SWITCH
AIR SOL.
PILOT PRESS.
BACK-UP LT. SW.
DIRECTION LT.
PARK LT.
CORNERING LT. & SIDE MARKER
SIDE BACK-UP LT.

1983 Saab

900 & 900 TURBO (Cont.)

FUSE BLOCK & UNDERDASH

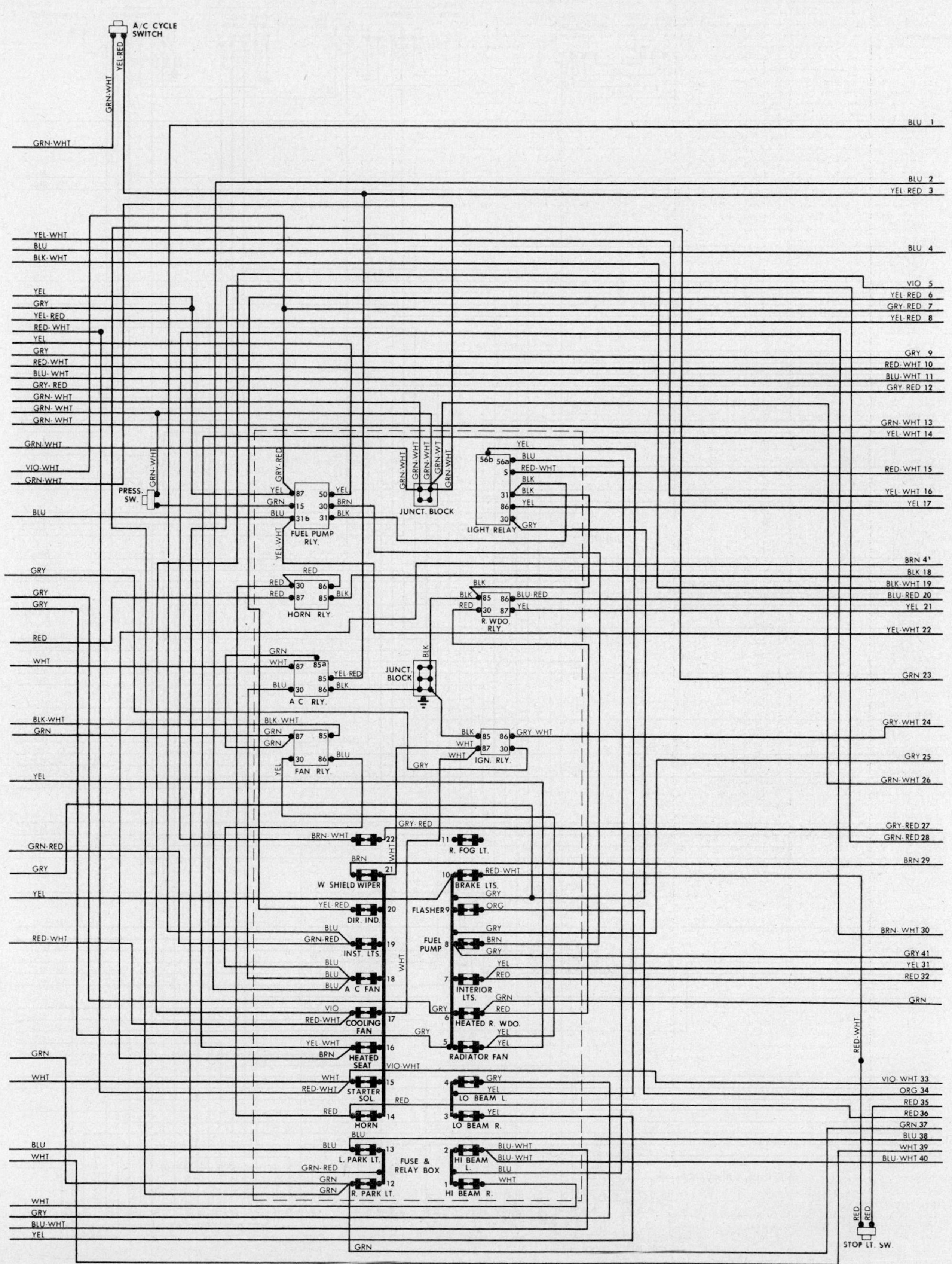
A/C CYCLE SWITCH
PRESS. SW.
FUEL PUMP RLY.
JUNCT. BLOCK
LIGHT RELAY
HORN RLY.
R. WDO. RLY.
A C RLY.
JUNCT. BLOCK
FAN RLY.
IGN. RLY.
R. FOG LT.
W. SHIELD WIPER
BRAKE LTS.
DIR. IND.
FLASHER
INST. LTS.
FUEL PUMP
A C FAN
INTERIOR LTS.
COOLING FAN
HEATED R. WDO.
HEATED SEAT
RADIATOR FAN
STARTER SOL.
LO BEAM L.
HORN
LO BEAM R.
L. PARK LT.
FUSE & RELAY BOX
HI BEAM L.
R. PARK LT.
HI BEAM R.
STOP LT. SW.
BLU 1
BLU 2
YEL-RED 3
BLU 4
VIO 5
YEL-RED 6
GRY-RED 7
YEL-RED 8
GRY 9
RED-WHT 10
BLU-WHT 11
GRY-RED 12
GRN-WHT 13
YEL-WHT 14
RED-WHT 15
YEL-WHT 16
YEL 17
BRN 4'
BLK 18
BLK-WHT 19
BLU-RED 20
YEL 21
YEL-WHT 22
GRN 23
GRY-WHT 24
GRY 25
GRN-WHT 26
GRY-RED 27
GRN-RED 28
BRN 29
BRN-WHT 30
GRY 41
YEL 31
RED 32
GRN
VIO-WHT 33
ORG 34
RED 35
RED 36
GRN 37
BLU 38
WHT 39
BLU-WHT 40

1983 Saab

900 & 900 TURBO (Cont.)

UNDERDASH

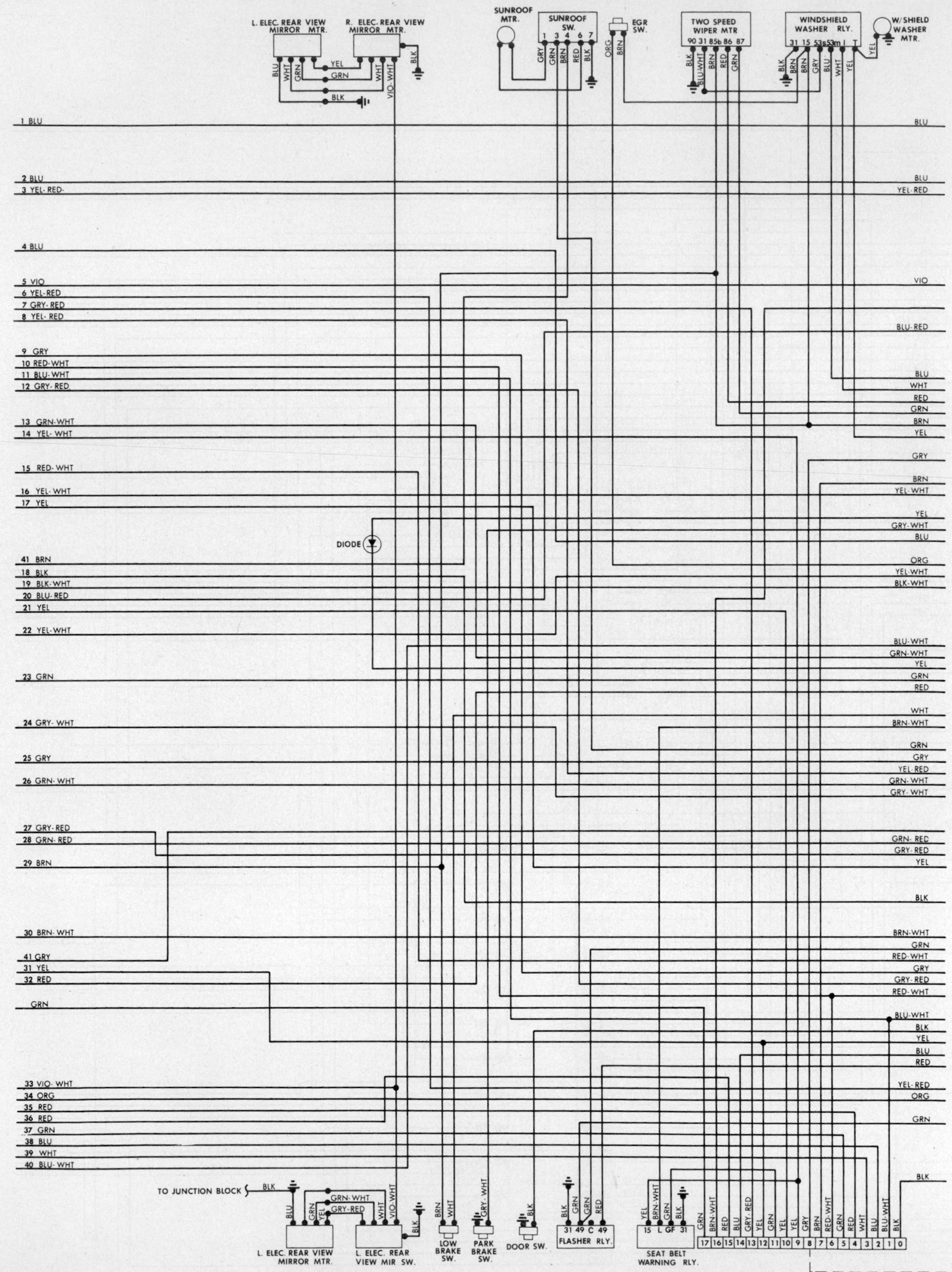
L. ELEC. REAR VIEW MIRROR MTR.
R. ELEC. REAR VIEW MIRROR MTR.
SUNROOF MTR.
SUNROOF SW.
EGR SW.
TWO SPEED WIPER MTR
WINDSHIELD WASHER RLY.
W/SHIELD WASHER MTR.
DIODE
TO JUNCTION BLOCK
L. ELEC. REAR VIEW MIRROR MTR.
L. ELEC. REAR VIEW MIR SW.
LOW BRAKE SW.
PARK BRAKE SW.
DOOR SW.
FLASHER RLY.
SEAT BELT WARNING RLY.

1983 Saab

900 & 900 TURBO (Cont.)

INSTRUMENT PANEL, REAR COMPARTMENT & ACCESSORIES

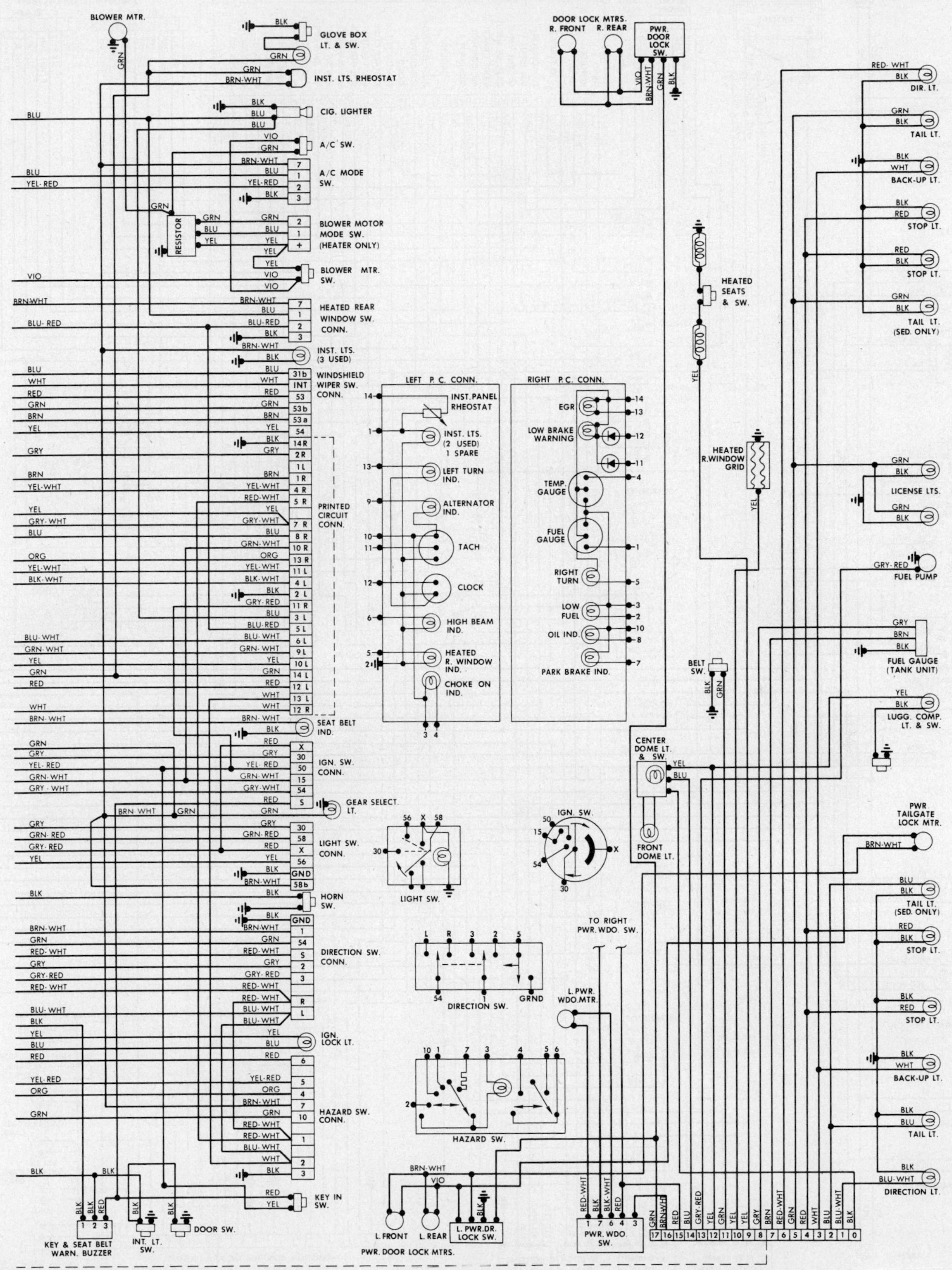

1983 Subaru

1600, 1800 & 1800 TURBO

ENGINE COMPARTMENT

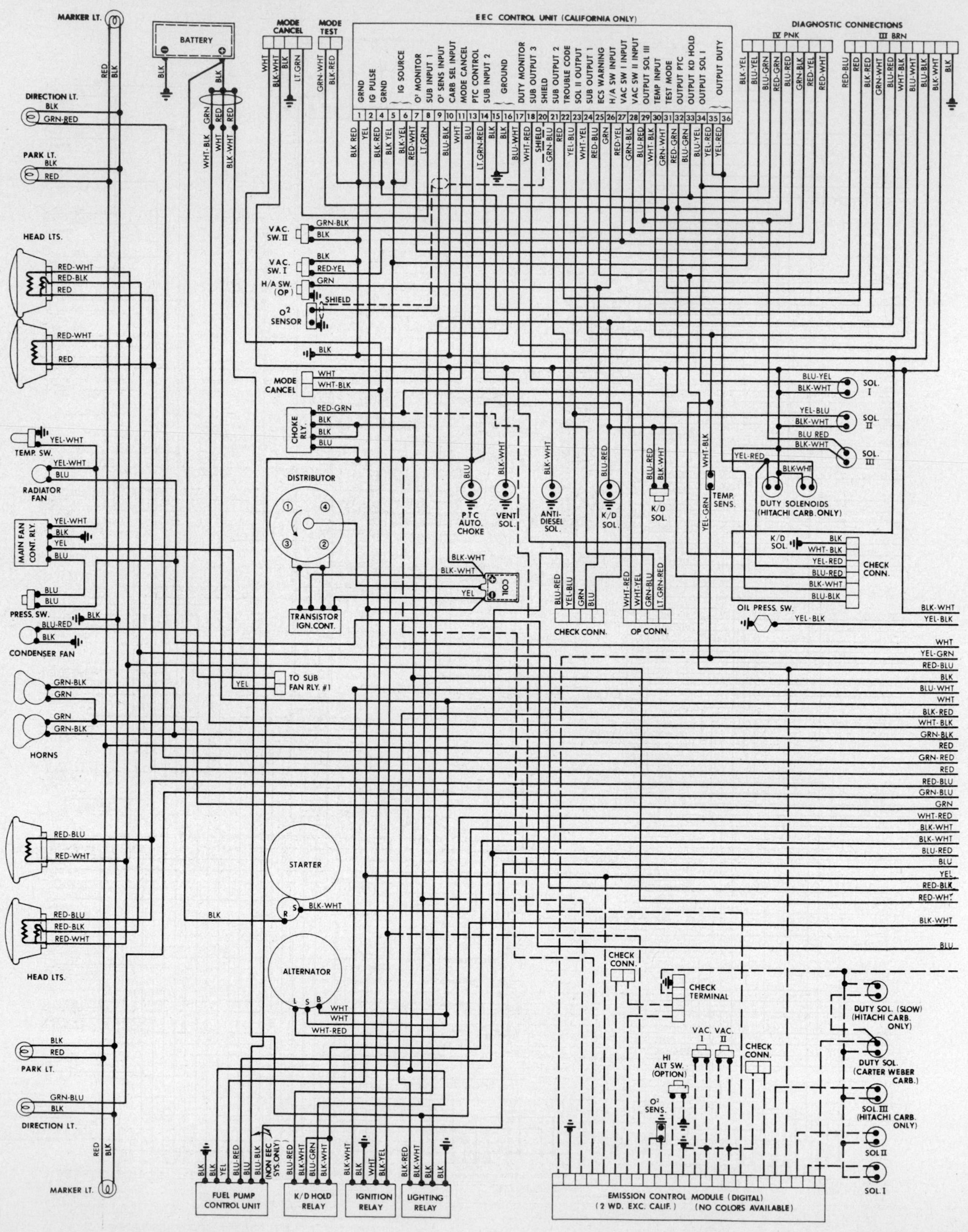
MARKER LT.
BATTERY
MODE CANCEL
MODE TEST
EEC CONTROL UNIT (CALIFORNIA ONLY)
GRND
IG PULSE
GRND
IG SOURCE
O² MONITOR
SUB INPUT 1
O² SENS INPUT
CARB SEL INPUT
MODE CANCEL
PTC CONTROL
SUB INPUT 2
GROUND
DUTY MONITOR
SUB OUTPUT 3
SHIELD
SUB OUTPUT 2
TROUBLE CODE
SOL II OUTPUT
SUB OUTPUT 1
ECS WARNING
H/A SW INPUT
VAC SW I INPUT
VAC SW II INPUT
OUTPUT SOL III
TEMP INPUT
TEST MODE
OUTPUT PTC
OUTPUT KD HOLD
OUTPUT SOL I
OUTPUT DUTY
DIAGNOSTIC CONNECTIONS
IV PNK
III BRN
DIRECTION LT.
PARK LT.
HEAD LTS.
VAC. SW. II
VAC. SW. I
H/A SW. (OP)
O² SENSOR
SHIELD
MODE CANCEL
CHOKE RLY.
SOL. I
SOL. II
SOL. III
TEMP. SW.
RADIATOR FAN
DISTRIBUTOR
PTC AUTO. CHOKE
VENT SOL.
ANTI-DIESEL SOL.
K/D SOL.
K/D SOL.
TEMP. SENS.
DUTY SOLENOIDS (HITACHI CARB. ONLY)
MAIN FAN CONT. RLY.
K/D SOL.
CHECK CONN.
COIL
TRANSISTOR IGN. CONT.
CHECK CONN.
OP CONN.
OIL PRESS. SW.
PRESS. SW.
CONDENSER FAN
TO SUB FAN RLY. #1
HORNS
STARTER
ALTERNATOR
HEAD LTS.
CHECK CONN.
CHECK TERMINAL
DUTY SOL. (SLOW) (HITACHI CARB. ONLY)
VAC. I
VAC. II
CHECK CONN.
HI ALT SW. (OPTION)
DUTY SOL. (CARTER WEBER CARB.)
O² SENS.
SOL. III (HITACHI CARB. ONLY)
SOL II
SOL I
PARK LT.
DIRECTION LT.
MARKER LT.
(NON EEC SYS. ONLY)
FUEL PUMP CONTROL UNIT
K/D HOLD RELAY
IGNITION RELAY
LIGHTING RELAY
EMISSION CONTROL MODULE (DIGITAL)
(2 WD. EXC. CALIF.) (NO COLORS AVAILABLE)

1983 Subaru

1600, 1800 & 1800 TURBO (Cont.)

FUSE BLOCK & UNDERDASH

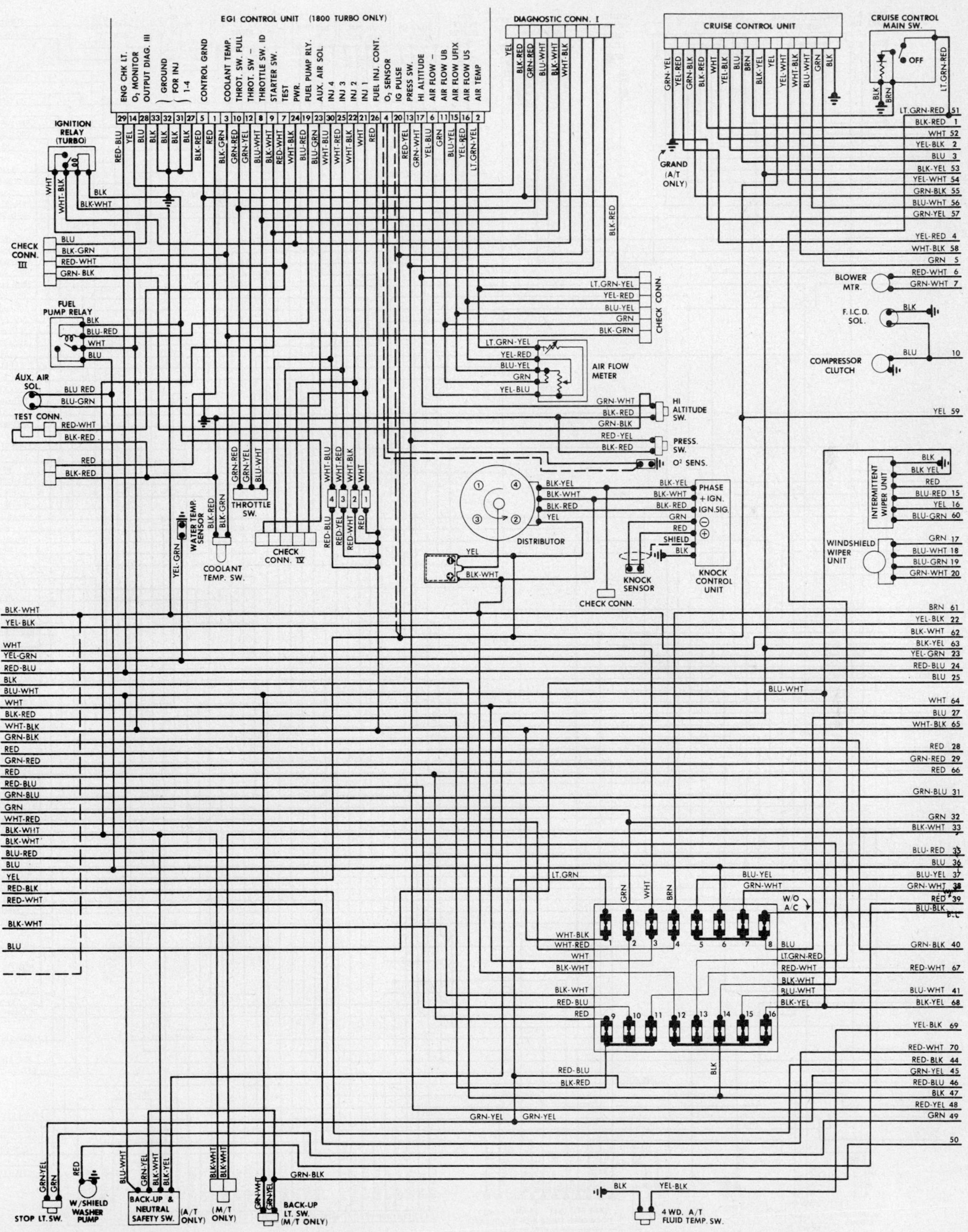
EGI CONTROL UNIT (1800 TURBO ONLY)
DIAGNOSTIC CONN. I
CRUISE CONTROL UNIT
CRUISE CONTROL MAIN SW.
IGNITION RELAY (TURBO)
CHECK CONN. III
FUEL PUMP RELAY
AUX. AIR SOL.
TEST CONN.
CHECK CONN.
AIR FLOW METER
HI ALTITUDE SW.
PRESS. SW.
O2 SENS.
DISTRIBUTOR
KNOCK SENSOR
KNOCK CONTROL UNIT
THROTTLE SW.
WATER TEMP. SENSOR
COOLANT TEMP. SW.
CHECK CONN. IV
BLOWER MTR.
F.I.C.D. SOL.
COMPRESSOR CLUTCH
INTERMITTENT WIPER UNIT
WINDSHIELD WIPER UNIT
GRAND (A/T ONLY)
W/O A/C
STOP LT. SW.
W/SHIELD WASHER PUMP
BACK-UP & NEUTRAL SAFETY SW. (A/T ONLY)
(M/T ONLY)
BACK-UP LT. SW. (M/T ONLY)
4 WD. A/T FLUID TEMP. SW.

1983 Subaru

1600, 1800 & 1800 TURBO (Cont.)

UNDERDASH

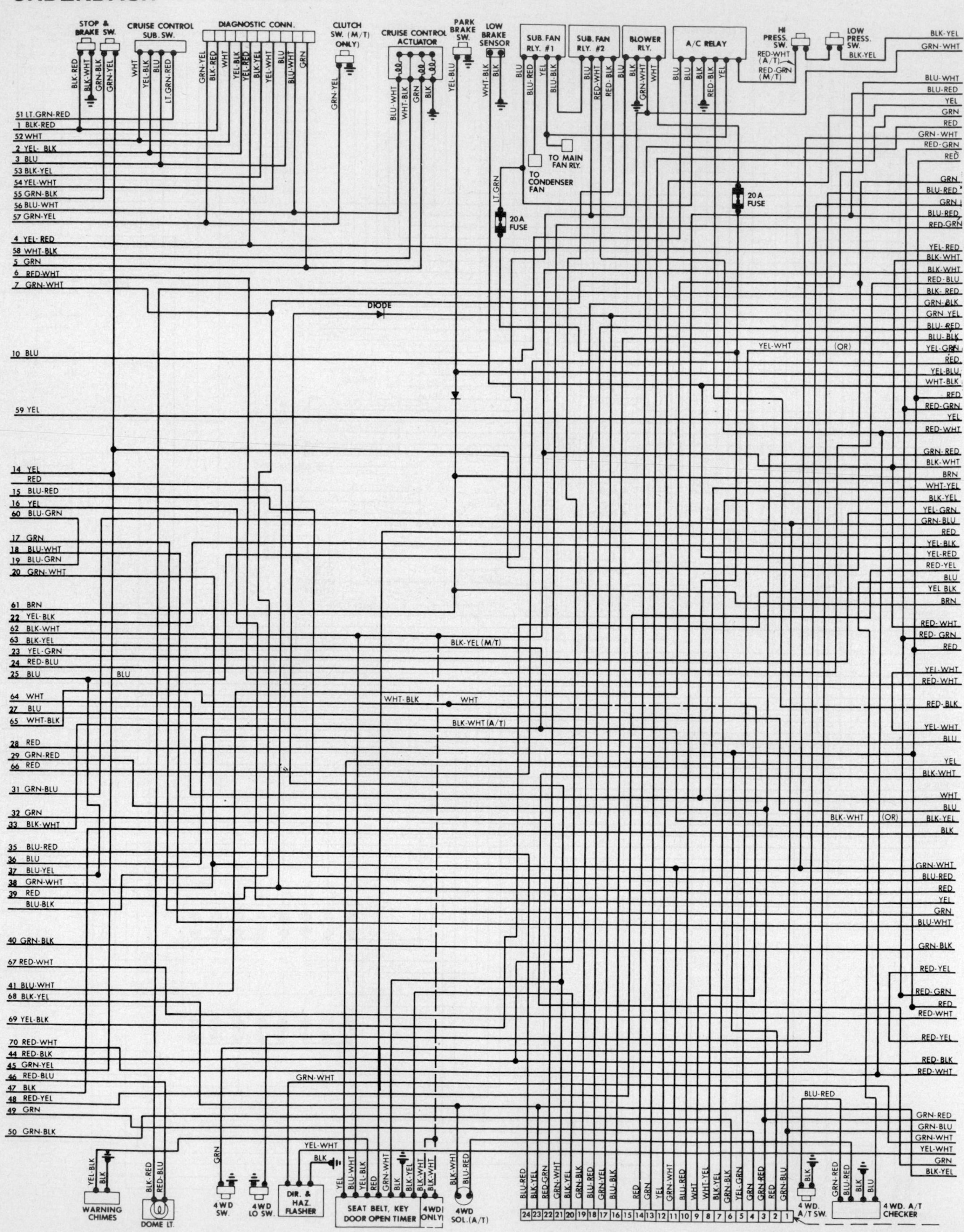

STOP & BRAKE SW.
CRUISE CONTROL SUB. SW.
DIAGNOSTIC CONN.
CLUTCH SW. (M/T) ONLY)
CRUISE CONTROL ACTUATOR
PARK BRAKE SW.
LOW BRAKE SENSOR
SUB. FAN RLY. #1
SUB. FAN RLY. #2
BLOWER RLY.
A/C RELAY
HI PRESS. SW.
LOW PRESS. SW.
TO MAIN FAN RLY.
TO CONDENSER FAN
20 A FUSE
20 A FUSE
DIODE
WARNING CHIMES
DOME LT.
4 WD SW.
4 WD LO SW.
DIR. & HAZ. FLASHER
SEAT BELT, KEY DOOR OPEN TIMER
4WD ONLY
4WD SOL. (A/T)
4 WD. A/T SW.
4 WD. A/T CHECKER

1983 Subaru

1600, 1800 & 1800 TURBO (Cont.)

INSTRUMENT PANEL, REAR COMPARTMENT & ACCESSORIES

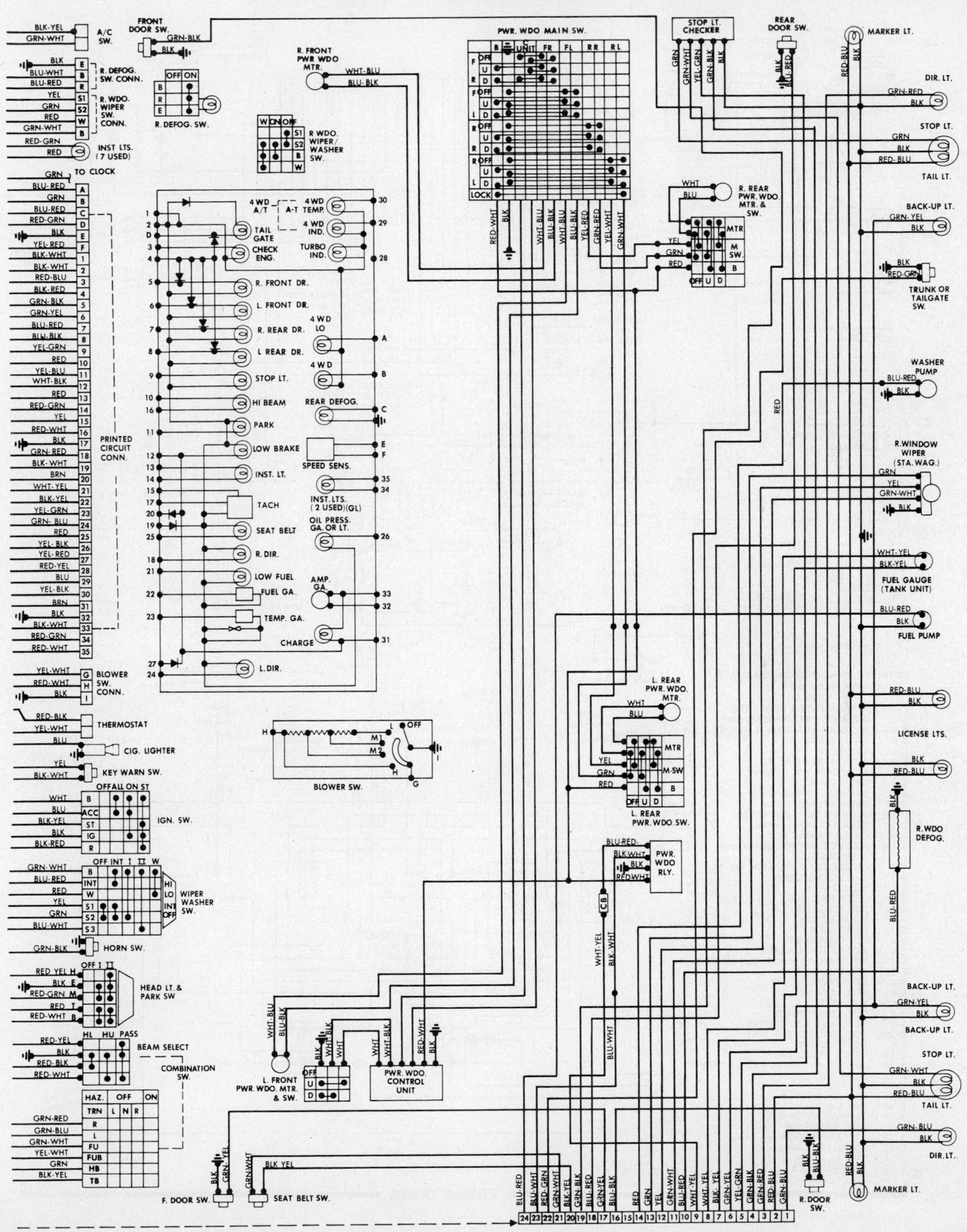

A/C SW.
FRONT DOOR SW.
PWR. WDO MAIN SW.
STOP LT. CHECKER
REAR DOOR SW.
MARKER LT.
R. DEFOG. SW. CONN.
R. WDO. WIPER SW. CONN.
R. DEFOG. SW.
R. FRONT PWR WDO MTR.
DIR. LT.
STOP LT.
TAIL LT.
R WDO. WIPER/WASHER SW.
INST LTS. (7 USED)
TO CLOCK
R. REAR PWR. WDO. MTR. & SW.
BACK-UP LT.
TRUNK OR TAILGATE SW.
4 WD A/T
A-T TEMP.
4 WD IND.
TURBO IND.
TAIL GATE
CHECK ENG.
R. FRONT DR.
L. FRONT DR.
R. REAR DR.
L REAR DR.
4 WD LO
4 WD
STOP LT.
HI BEAM
REAR DEFOG.
PARK
LOW BRAKE
SPEED SENS.
INST. LT.
INST. LTS. (2 USED)(GL)
TACH
SEAT BELT
OIL PRESS. GA. OR LT.
R. DIR.
LOW FUEL
AMP. GA.
FUEL GA.
TEMP. GA.
CHARGE
L. DIR.
PRINTED CIRCUIT CONN.
WASHER PUMP
R.WINDOW WIPER (STA. WAG.)
FUEL GAUGE (TANK UNIT)
FUEL PUMP
BLOWER SW. CONN.
THERMOSTAT
CIG. LIGHTER
KEY WARN SW.
BLOWER SW.
L. REAR PWR. WDO. MTR.
L. REAR PWR. WDO. SW.
LICENSE LTS.
IGN. SW.
R.WDO DEFOG.
WIPER WASHER SW.
PWR. WDO RLY.
HORN SW.
HEAD LT. & PARK SW
BEAM SELECT
COMBINATION SW.
L. FRONT PWR. WDO. MTR. & SW.
PWR. WDO. CONTROL UNIT
BACK-UP LT.
STOP LT.
TAIL LT.
DIR. LT.
MARKER LT.
F. DOOR SW.
SEAT BELT SW.
R. DOOR SW.

1983 Toyota

CAMRY

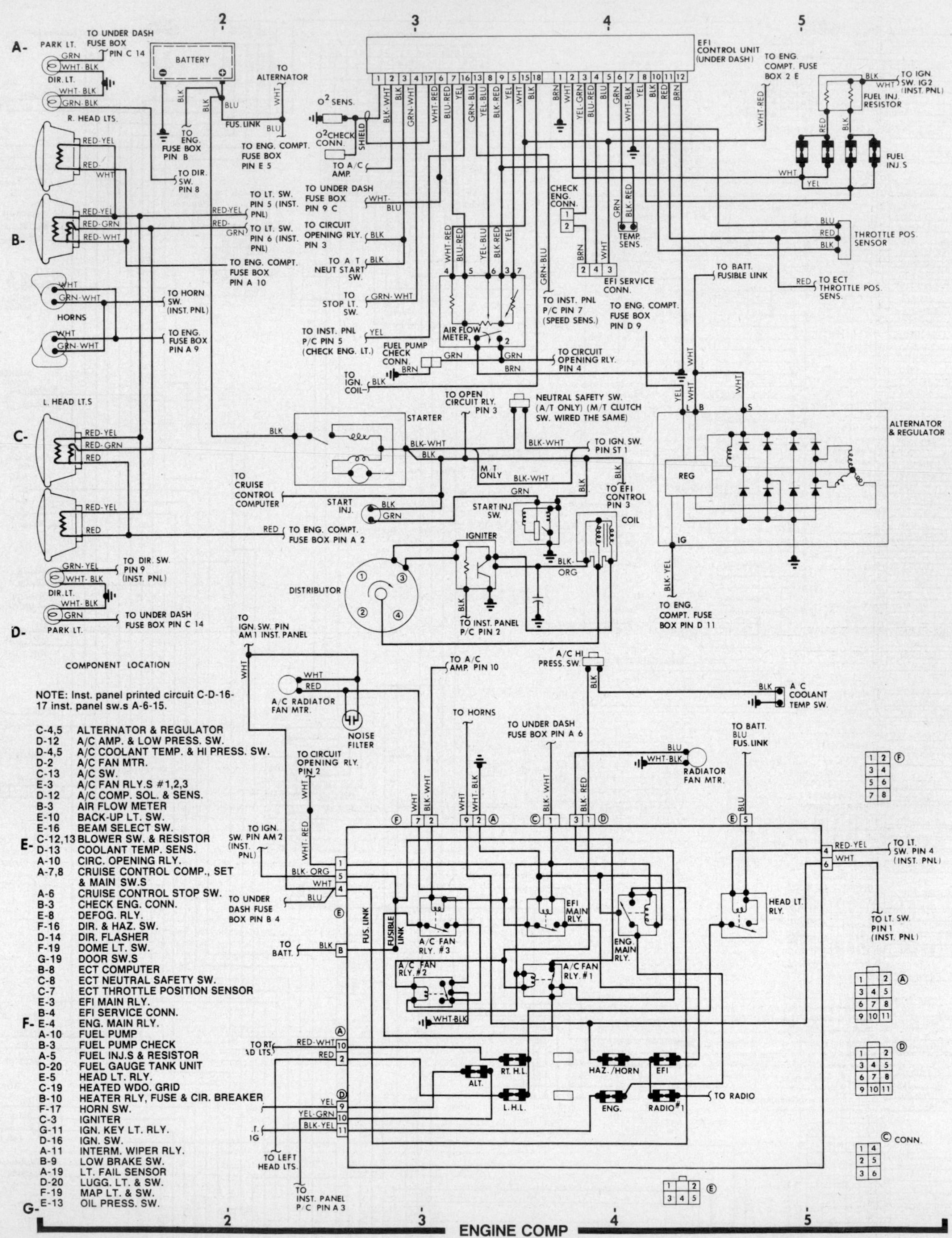
COMPONENT LOCATION
NOTE: Inst. panel printed circuit C-D-16-17 inst. panel sw.s A-6-15.
C-4,5 ALTERNATOR & REGULATOR
D-12 A/C AMP. & LOW PRESS. SW.
D-4,5 A/C COOLANT TEMP. & HI PRESS. SW.
D-2 A/C FAN MTR.
C-13 A/C SW.
E-3 A/C FAN RLY.S #1,2,3
D-12 A/C COMP. SOL. & SENS.
B-3 AIR FLOW METER
E-10 BACK-UP LT. SW.
E-16 BEAM SELECT SW.
C-12,13 BLOWER SW. & RESISTOR
D-13 COOLANT TEMP. SENS.
A-10 CIRC. OPENING RLY.
A-7,8 CRUISE CONTROL COMP., SET & MAIN SW.S
A-6 CRUISE CONTROL STOP SW.
B-3 CHECK ENG. CONN.
E-8 DEFOG. RLY.
F-16 DIR. & HAZ. SW.
D-14 DIR. FLASHER
F-19 DOME LT. SW.
G-19 DOOR SW.S
B-8 ECT COMPUTER
C-8 ECT NEUTRAL SAFETY SW.
C-7 ECT THROTTLE POSITION SENSOR
E-3 EFI MAIN RLY.
B-4 EFI SERVICE CONN.
E-4 ENG. MAIN RLY.
A-10 FUEL PUMP
B-3 FUEL PUMP CHECK
A-5 FUEL INJ.S & RESISTOR
D-20 FUEL GAUGE TANK UNIT
E-5 HEAD LT. RLY.
C-19 HEATED WDO. GRID
B-10 HEATER RLY, FUSE & CIR. BREAKER
F-17 HORN SW.
C-3 IGNITER
G-11 IGN. KEY LT. RLY.
D-16 IGN. SW.
A-11 INTERM. WIPER RLY.
B-9 LOW BRAKE SW.
A-19 LT. FAIL SENSOR
D-20 LUGG. LT. & SW.
F-19 MAP LT. & SW.
E-13 OIL PRESS. SW.

1983 Toyota

CAMRY (Cont.)

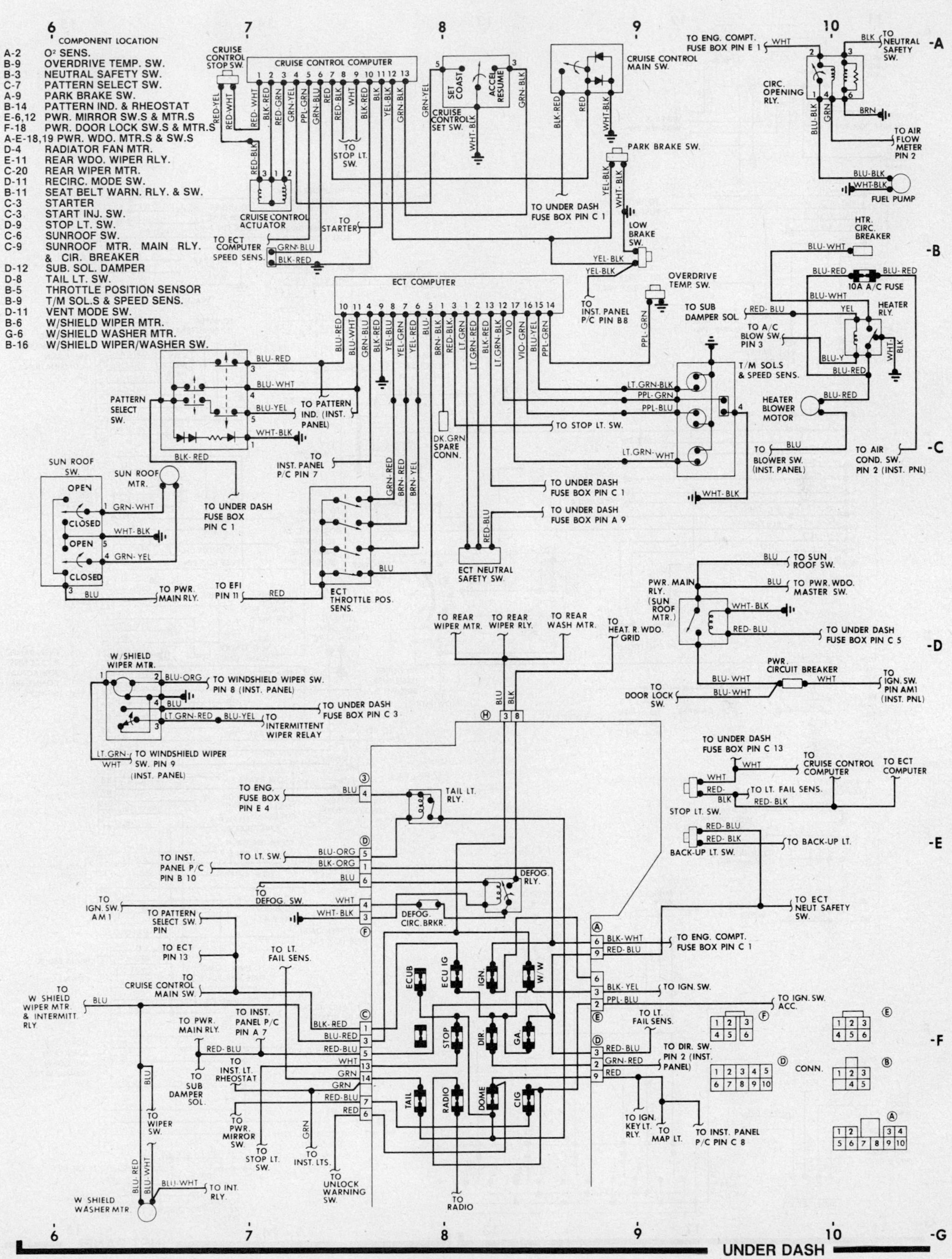
COMPONENT LOCATION
A-2 O² SENS.
B-9 OVERDRIVE TEMP. SW.
B-3 NEUTRAL SAFETY SW.
C-7 PATTERN SELECT SW.
A-9 PARK BRAKE SW.
B-14 PATTERN IND. & RHEOSTAT
E-6,12 PWR. MIRROR SW.S & MTR.S
F-18 PWR. DOOR LOCK SW.S & MTR.S
A-E-18,19 PWR. WDO. MTR.S & SW.S
D-4 RADIATOR FAN MTR.
E-11 REAR WDO. WIPER RLY.
C-20 REAR WIPER MTR.
D-11 RECIRC. MODE SW.
B-11 SEAT BELT WARN. RLY. & SW.
C-3 STARTER
C-3 START INJ. SW.
D-9 STOP LT. SW.
C-6 SUNROOF SW.
C-9 SUNROOF MTR. MAIN RLY. & CIR. BREAKER
D-12 SUB. SOL. DAMPER
D-8 TAIL LT. SW.
B-5 THROTTLE POSITION SENSOR
B-9 T/M SOL.S & SPEED SENS.
D-11 VENT MODE SW.
B-6 W/SHIELD WIPER MTR.
G-6 W/SHIELD WASHER MTR.
B-16 W/SHIELD WIPER/WASHER SW.
CRUISE CONTROL STOP SW.
CRUISE CONTROL COMPUTER
CRUISE CONTROL SET SW.
SET COAST
ACCEL RESUME
CRUISE CONTROL MAIN SW.
PARK BRAKE SW.
CIRC. OPENING RLY.
TO NEUTRAL SAFETY SW.
TO AIR FLOW METER PIN 2
FUEL PUMP
CRUISE CONTROL ACTUATOR
TO STARTER
TO ECT COMPUTER SPEED SENS.
TO UNDER DASH FUSE BOX PIN C 1
LOW BRAKE SW.
HTR. CIRC. BREAKER
10A A/C FUSE
HEATER RLY.
ECT COMPUTER
OVERDRIVE TEMP. SW.
TO SUB DAMPER SOL.
TO A/C BLOW SW. PIN 3
T/M SOLS & SPEED SENS.
HEATER BLOWER MOTOR
PATTERN SELECT SW.
TO PATTERN IND. (INST. PANEL)
TO STOP LT. SW.
TO BLOWER SW. (INST. PANEL)
TO AIR COND. SW. PIN 2 (INST. PNL)
DK.GRN SPARE CONN.
SUN ROOF SW.
SUN ROOF MTR.
OPEN
CLOSED
TO INST. PANEL P/C PIN 7
TO UNDER DASH FUSE BOX PIN C 1
TO UNDER DASH FUSE BOX PIN A 9
ECT NEUTRAL SAFETY SW.
TO PWR. MAIN RLY.
TO EFI PIN 11
ECT THROTTLE POS. SENS.
TO SUN ROOF SW.
PWR. MAIN RLY. (SUN ROOF MTR.)
TO PWR. WDO. MASTER SW.
TO UNDER DASH FUSE BOX PIN C 5
TO REAR WIPER MTR.
TO REAR WIPER RLY.
TO REAR WASH MTR.
TO HEAT. R. WDO. GRID
PWR. CIRCUIT BREAKER
TO DOOR LOCK SW.
TO IGN. SW. PIN AM1 (INST. PNL)
W/SHIELD WIPER MTR.
TO WINDSHIELD WIPER SW. PIN 8 (INST. PANEL)
TO UNDER DASH FUSE BOX PIN C 3
TO INTERMITTENT WIPER RELAY
TO WINDSHIELD WIPER SW. PIN 9 (INST. PANEL)
TO UNDER DASH FUSE BOX PIN C 13
TO CRUISE CONTROL COMPUTER
TO ECT COMPUTER
TO LT. FAIL SENS.
STOP LT. SW.
TO ENG. FUSE BOX PIN E 4
TAIL LT. RLY.
TO BACK-UP LT.
BACK-UP LT. SW.
TO INST. PANEL P/C PIN B 10
TO LT. SW.
DEFOG. RLY.
TO DEFOG. SW.
TO IGN. SW. AM1
TO PATTERN SELECT SW. PIN
DEFOG. CIRC. BRKR.
TO ECT NEUT SAFETY SW.
TO ECT PIN 13
TO LT. FAIL SENS.
TO ENG. COMPT. FUSE BOX PIN C 1
TO CRUISE CONTROL MAIN SW.
TO IGN. SW.
TO IGN. SW. ACC.
TO W SHIELD WIPER MTR. & INTERMITT. RLY
TO PWR. MAIN RLY.
TO INST. PANEL P/C PIN A 7
TO SUB DAMPER SOL.
TO INST. LT. RHEOSTAT
TO DIR. SW. PIN 2 (INST. PANEL)
ECUB
ECU IG
IGN.
W/W
STOP
DIR.
GA.
TAIL
RADIO
DOME
CIG
CONN.
TO WIPER SW.
TO PWR. MIRROR SW.
TO STOP LT. SW.
TO INST. LTS.
TO UNLOCK WARNING SW.
TO RADIO
TO IGN. KEY LT. RLY.
TO MAP LT.
TO INST. PANEL P/C PIN C 8
W SHIELD WASHER MTR.
TO INT. RLY.
UNDER DASH

1983 Toyota

CAMRY (Cont.)

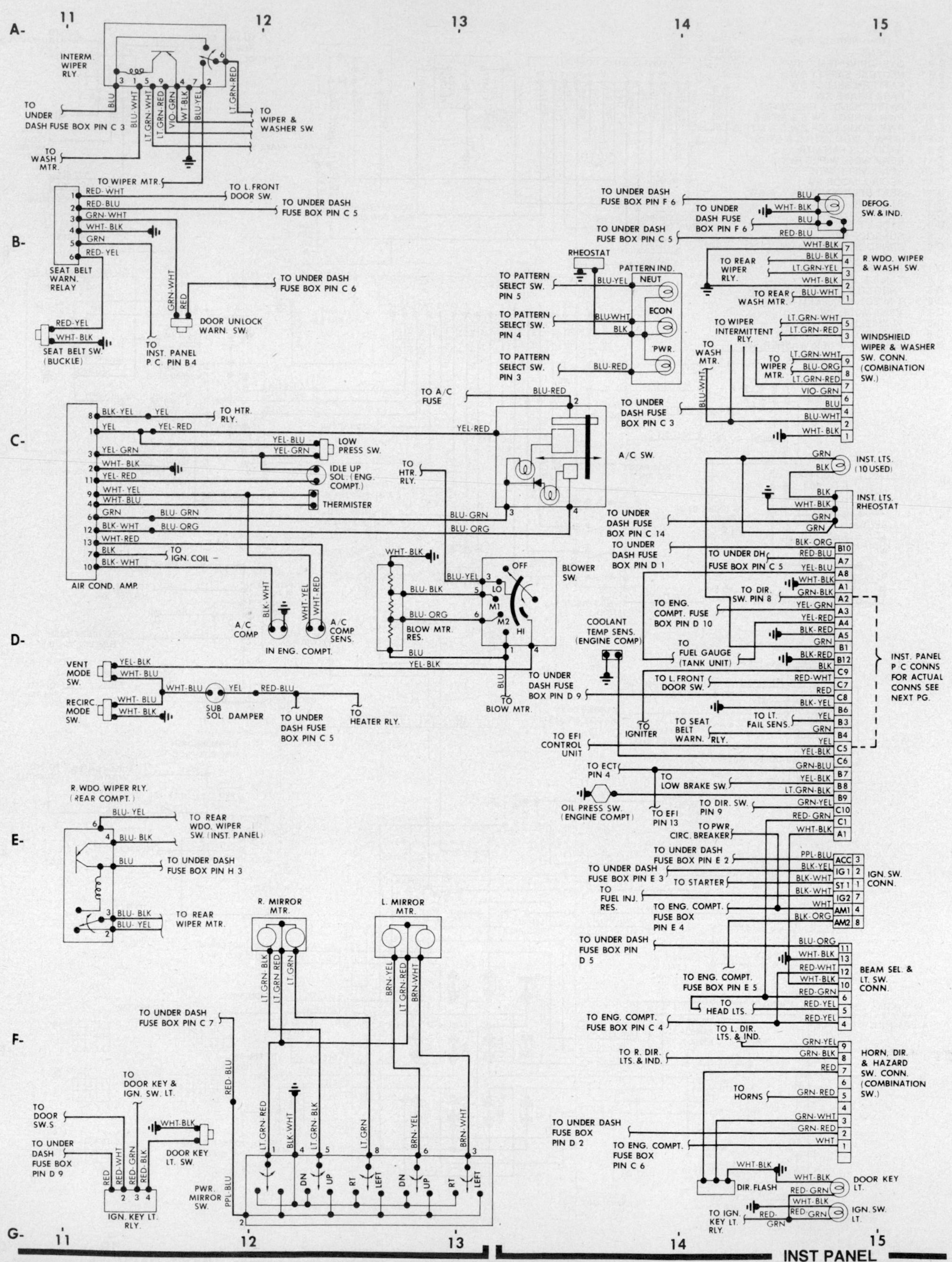

INTERM WIPER RLY
TO UNDER DASH FUSE BOX PIN C 3
TO WASH MTR.
TO WIPER & WASHER SW.
TO WIPER MTR
TO L. FRONT DOOR SW.
TO UNDER DASH FUSE BOX PIN C 5
SEAT BELT WARN. RELAY
TO UNDER DASH FUSE BOX PIN C 6
DOOR UNLOCK WARN. SW.
SEAT BELT SW. (BUCKLE)
TO INST. PANEL P. C. PIN B4
TO HTR. RLY.
LOW PRESS SW.
IDLE UP SOL. (ENG. COMPT.)
THERMISTER
TO IGN. COIL –
AIR COND. AMP.
A/C COMP
A/C COMP SENS.
IN ENG. COMPT.
VENT MODE SW.
RECIRC. MODE SW.
SUB SOL. DAMPER
TO UNDER DASH FUSE BOX PIN C 5
TO HEATER RLY.
R. WDO. WIPER RLY. (REAR COMPT.)
TO REAR WDO. WIPER SW. (INST. PANEL)
TO UNDER DASH FUSE BOX PIN H 3
TO REAR WIPER MTR.
R. MIRROR MTR.
L. MIRROR MTR.
TO UNDER DASH FUSE BOX PIN C 7
TO DOOR KEY & IGN. SW. LT.
TO DOOR SW.S
TO UNDER DASH FUSE BOX PIN D 9
DOOR KEY LT. SW.
IGN. KEY LT. RLY.
PWR. MIRROR SW.
DN UP RT LEFT DN UP RT LEFT
TO A/C FUSE
A/C SW.
TO HTR. RLY.
BLOWER SW.
OFF LO M1 M2 HI
BLOW MTR. RES.
TO UNDER DASH FUSE BOX PIN D 9
TO BLOW MTR.
RHEOSTAT
PATTERN IND.
NEUT ECON PWR.
TO PATTERN SELECT SW. PIN 5
TO PATTERN SELECT SW. PIN 4
TO PATTERN SELECT SW. PIN 3
TO UNDER DASH FUSE BOX PIN F 6
TO UNDER DASH FUSE BOX PIN F 6
TO UNDER DASH FUSE BOX PIN C 5
DEFOG. SW. & IND.
TO REAR WIPER RLY.
TO REAR WASH MTR.
R WDO. WIPER & WASH SW.
TO WIPER INTERMITTENT RLY.
TO WASH MTR.
TO WIPER MTR.
WINDSHIELD WIPER & WASHER SW. CONN. (COMBINATION SW.)
TO UNDER DASH FUSE BOX PIN C 3
INST. LTS. (10 USED)
INST. LTS. RHEOSTAT
TO UNDER DASH FUSE BOX PIN C 14
TO UNDER DASH FUSE BOX PIN D 1
TO UNDER DH FUSE BOX PIN C 5
TO DIR. SW. PIN 8
TO ENG. COMPT. FUSE BOX PIN D 10
COOLANT TEMP SENS. (ENGINE COMP)
TO FUEL GAUGE (TANK UNIT)
TO L. FRONT DOOR SW.
TO LT. FAIL SENS.
TO SEAT BELT WARN. RLY.
TO IGNITER
TO EFI CONTROL UNIT
TO ECT PIN 4
TO LOW BRAKE SW.
OIL PRESS SW. (ENGINE COMPT)
TO EFI PIN 13
TO DIR. SW. PIN 9
TO PWR. CIRC. BREAKER
INST. PANEL P C CONNS FOR ACTUAL CONNS SEE NEXT PG.
TO UNDER DASH FUSE BOX PIN E 2
TO UNDER DASH FUSE BOX PIN E 3
TO STARTER
TO FUEL INJ. RES.
TO ENG. COMPT. FUSE BOX PIN E 4
IGN. SW. CONN.
ACC IG1 ST1 IG2 AM1 AM2
TO UNDER DASH FUSE BOX PIN D 5
TO ENG. COMPT. FUSE BOX PIN E 5
TO HEAD LTS.
BEAM SEL. & LT. SW. CONN.
TO ENG. COMPT. FUSE BOX PIN C 4
TO L. DIR. LTS. & IND.
TO R. DIR. LTS. & IND.
HORN, DIR. & HAZARD SW. CONN. (COMBINATION SW.)
TO HORNS
TO UNDER DASH FUSE BOX PIN D 2
TO ENG. COMPT. FUSE BOX PIN C 6
DIR. FLASH
DOOR KEY LT.
IGN. SW. LT.
TO IGN. KEY LT. RLY.
INST PANEL

1983 Toyota

CAMRY (Cont.)

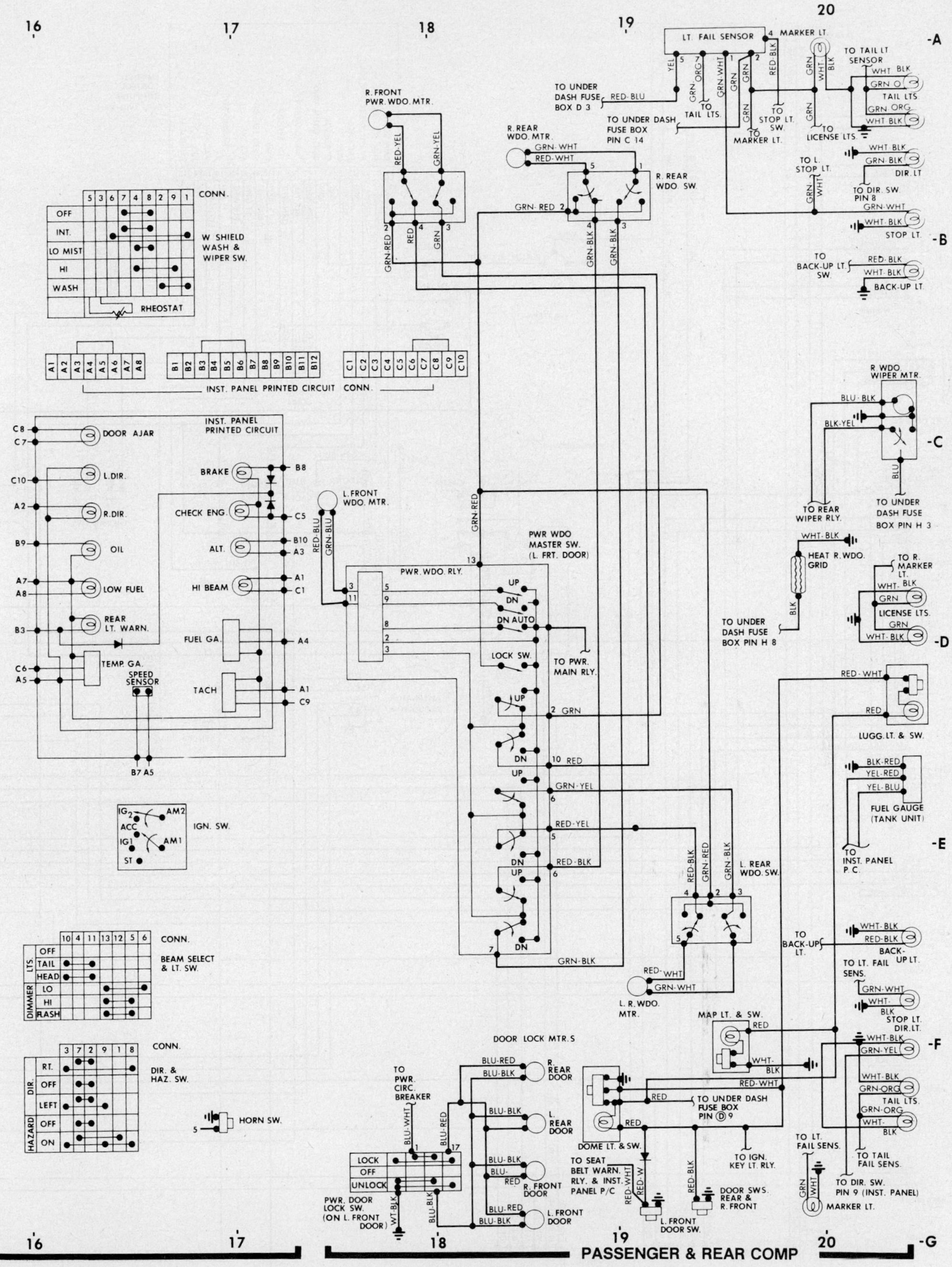

LT. FAIL SENSOR
MARKER LT.
TO TAIL LT SENSOR
TAIL LTS.
TO UNDER DASH FUSE BOX D 3
TO UNDER DASH FUSE BOX PIN C 14
TO TAIL LTS.
TO STOP LT. SW.
TO MARKER LT.
TO LICENSE LTS.
DIR. LT
TO DIR. SW. PIN 8
STOP LT.
TO BACK-UP LT. SW.
BACK-UP LT.
R. FRONT PWR. WDO. MTR.
R. REAR WDO. MTR.
R. REAR WDO. SW.
CONN.
W SHIELD WASH & WIPER SW.
OFF
INT.
LO MIST
HI
WASH
RHEOSTAT
INST. PANEL PRINTED CIRCUIT CONN.
R. WDO WIPER MTR.
TO REAR WIPER RLY.
TO UNDER DASH FUSE BOX PIN H 3
HEAT R. WDO. GRID
TO R. MARKER LT.
LICENSE LTS.
TO UNDER DASH FUSE BOX PIN H 8
DOOR AJAR
INST. PANEL PRINTED CIRCUIT
BRAKE
L. DIR.
R. DIR.
CHECK ENG.
OIL
ALT.
LOW FUEL
HI BEAM
REAR LT. WARN.
FUEL GA.
TEMP. GA.
SPEED SENSOR
TACH
L. FRONT WDO. MTR.
PWR WDO MASTER SW. (L. FRT. DOOR)
PWR. WDO. RLY.
UP
DN
DN AUTO
LOCK SW.
TO PWR. MAIN RLY.
LUGG. LT. & SW.
FUEL GAUGE (TANK UNIT)
TO INST. PANEL P.C.
IGN. SW.
L. REAR WDO. SW.
L. R. WDO. MTR.
TO BACK-UP LT.
BACK-UP LT.
TO LT. FAIL SENS.
STOP LT. DIR. LT.
CONN.
BEAM SELECT & LT. SW.
OFF
TAIL
HEAD
LO
HI
FLASH
DIMMER
LTS.
MAP LT. & SW.
DOOR LOCK MTR.S
CONN.
DIR. & HAZ. SW.
RT.
OFF
LEFT
ON
DIR.
HAZARD
HORN SW.
TO PWR. CIRC. BREAKER
R. REAR DOOR
L. REAR DOOR
R. FRONT DOOR
L. FRONT DOOR
LOCK
UNLOCK
PWR. DOOR LOCK SW. (ON L. FRONT DOOR)
DOME LT. & SW.
TO UNDER DASH FUSE BOX PIN D 9
TO SEAT BELT WARN. RLY. & INST. PANEL P/C
L. FRONT DOOR SW.
DOOR SWS. REAR & R. FRONT
TO IGN. KEY LT. RLY.
TO LT. FAIL SENS.
TO TAIL FAIL SENS.
TO DIR. SW. PIN 9 (INST. PANEL)
MARKER LT.
PASSENGER & REAR COMP

1983 Toyota

CELICA

ENGINE COMPARTMENT

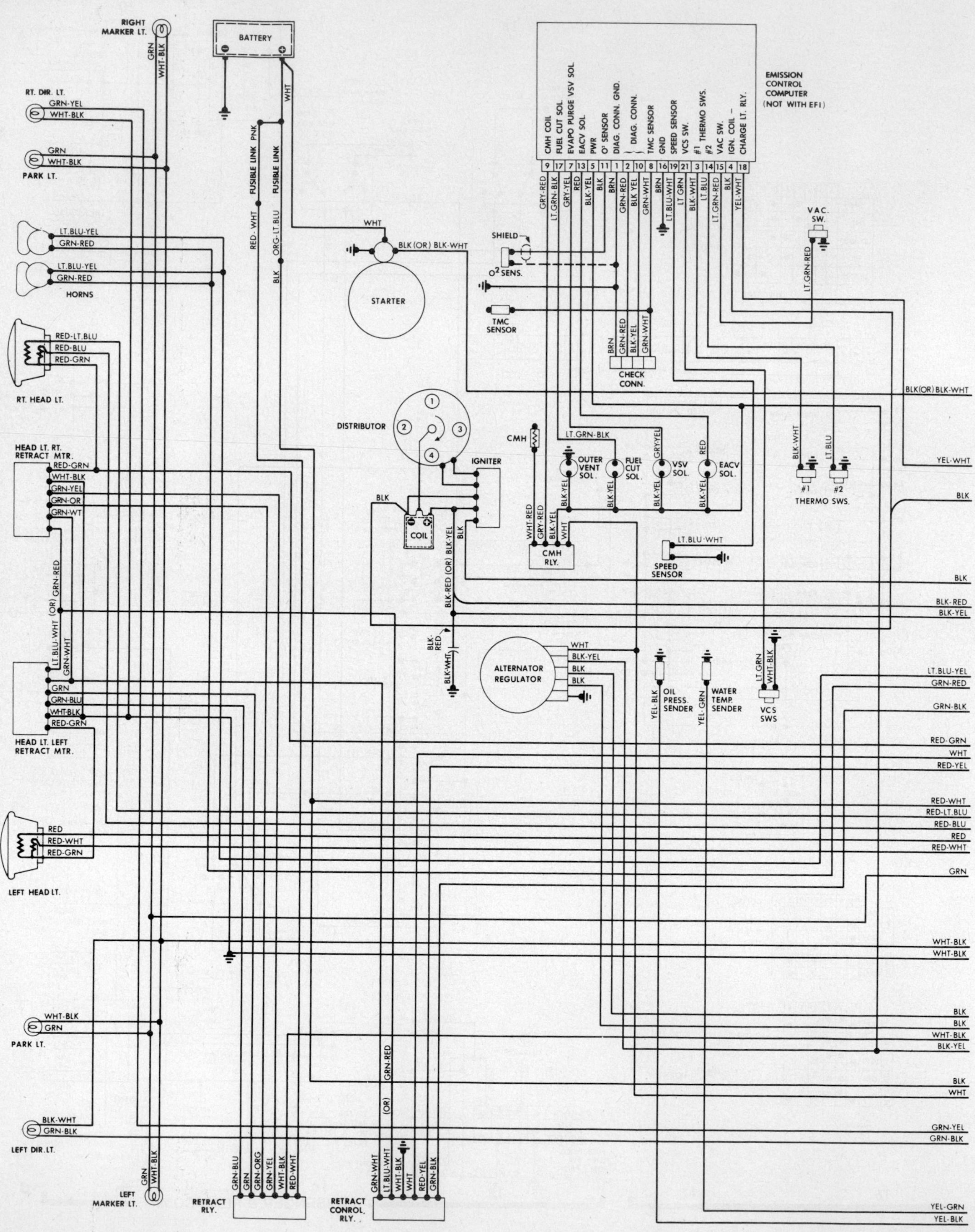

RIGHT MARKER LT.
BATTERY
EMISSION CONTROL COMPUTER (NOT WITH EFI)
CMH COIL
FUEL CUT SOL.
EVAPO PURGE VSV SOL.
EACV SOL.
PWR
O² SENSOR
DIAG. CONN. GND.
DIAG. CONN.
TMC SENSOR
GND
SPEED SENSOR
VCS SW.
#1 THERMO SWS.
#2
VAC SW.
IGN. COIL –
CHARGE LT. RLY.
RT. DIR. LT.
PARK LT.
HORNS
RT. HEAD LT.
FUSIBLE LINK PNK
FUSIBLE LINK
STARTER
SHIELD
O² SENS.
TMC SENSOR
CHECK CONN.
VAC. SW.
DISTRIBUTOR
IGNITER
COIL
CMH
OUTER VENT SOL.
FUEL CUT SOL.
VSV SOL.
EACV SOL.
THERMO SWS.
CMH RLY.
SPEED SENSOR
HEAD LT. RT. RETRACT MTR.
HEAD LT. LEFT RETRACT MTR.
ALTERNATOR REGULATOR
OIL PRESS. SENDER
WATER TEMP. SENDER
VCS SWS
LEFT HEAD LT.
PARK LT.
LEFT DIR. LT.
LEFT MARKER LT.
RETRACT RLY.
RETRACT CONROL RLY.

1983 Toyota

CELICA (Cont.)

ENGINE COMPARTMENT & FUSE BLOCK

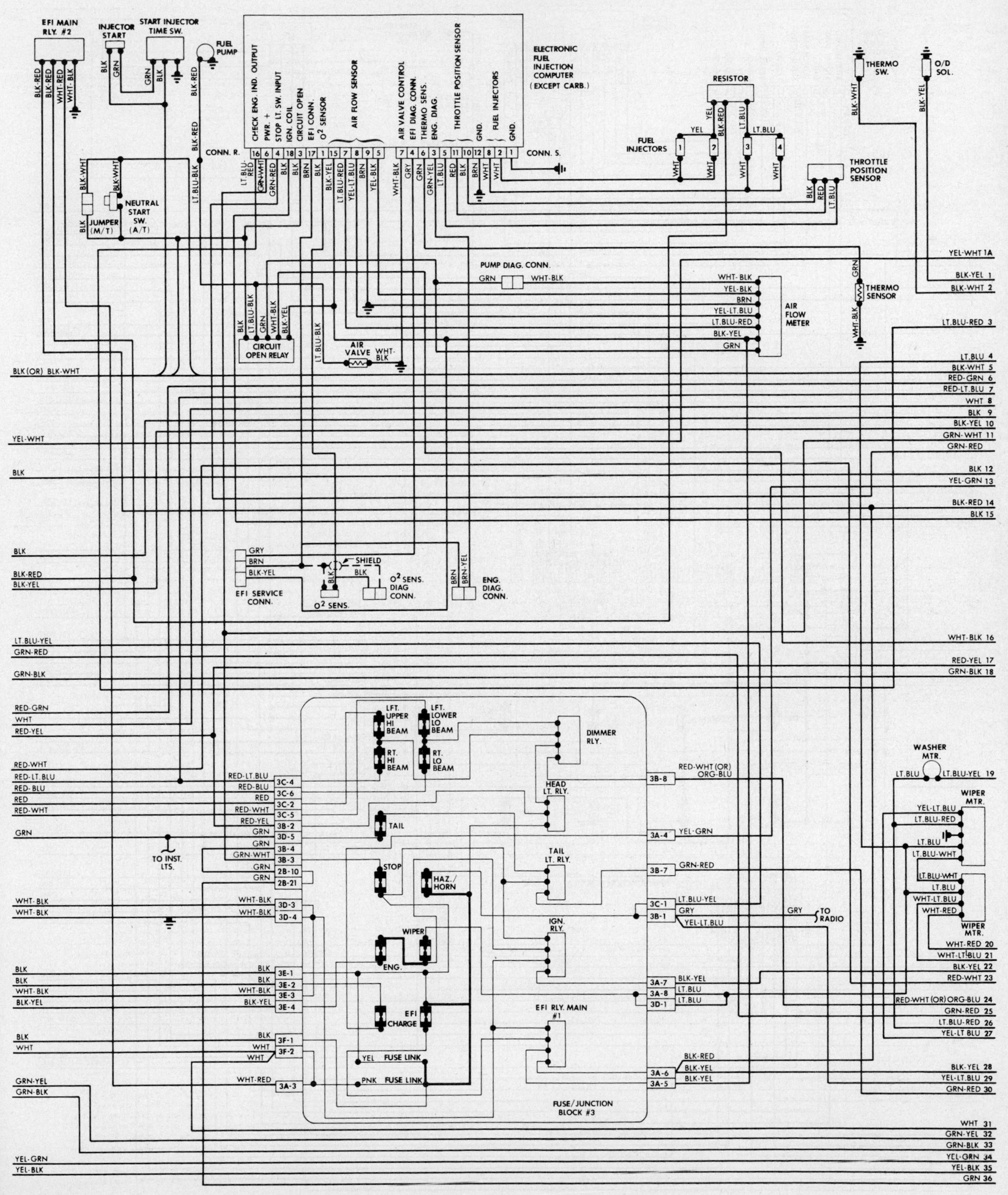
EFI MAIN RLY. #2
INJECTOR START
START INJECTOR TIME SW.
FUEL PUMP
ELECTRONIC FUEL INJECTION COMPUTER (EXCEPT CARB.)
CHECK ENG. IND. OUTPUT
PWR. +
STOP LT. SW. INPUT
IGN. COIL
CIRCUIT OPEN
EFI CONN.
O² SENSOR
AIR FLOW SENSOR
AIR VALVE CONTROL
EFI DIAG. CONN.
THERMO SENS.
ENG. DIAG.
THROTTLE POSITION SENSOR
GND.
FUEL INJECTORS
CONN. R.
CONN. S.
RESISTOR
FUEL INJECTORS
THERMO SW.
O/D SOL.
THROTTLE POSITION SENSOR
NEUTRAL START SW. (A/T)
JUMPER (M/T)
PUMP DIAG. CONN.
THERMO SENSOR
AIR FLOW METER
CIRCUIT OPEN RELAY
AIR VALVE
EFI SERVICE CONN.
SHIELD
O² SENS.
O² SENS. DIAG CONN.
ENG. DIAG. CONN.
LFT. UPPER HI BEAM
LFT. LOWER LO BEAM
RT. HI BEAM
RT. LO BEAM
DIMMER RLY.
HEAD LT. RLY.
TAIL
TAIL LT. RLY.
STOP
HAZ./HORN
IGN. RLY.
WIPER
ENG.
EFI CHARGE
EFI RLY. MAIN #1
FUSE LINK
FUSE/JUNCTION BLOCK #3
TO INST. LTS.
TO RADIO
WASHER MTR.
WIPER MTR.
YEL-WHT 1A
BLK-YEL 1
BLK-WHT 2
LT.BLU-RED 3
LT.BLU 4
BLK-WHT 5
RED-GRN 6
RED-LT.BLU 7
WHT 8
BLK 9
BLK-YEL 10
GRN-WHT 11
GRN-RED
BLK 12
YEL-GRN 13
BLK-RED 14
BLK 15
WHT-BLK 16
RED-YEL 17
GRN-BLK 18
LT.BLU-YEL 19
WHT-RED 20
WHT-LT.BLU 21
BLK-YEL 22
RED-WHT 23
RED-WHT (OR) ORG-BLU 24
GRN-RED 25
LT.BLU-RED 26
YEL-LT BLU 27
BLK-YEL 28
YEL-LT.BLU 29
GRN-RED 30
WHT 31
GRN-YEL 32
GRN-BLK 33
YEL-GRN 34
YEL-BLK 35
GRN 36
BLK (OR) BLK-WHT
YEL-WHT
BLK
BLK-RED
BLK-YEL
LT.BLU-YEL
GRN-RED
GRN-BLK
RED-GRN
WHT
RED-YEL
RED-WHT
RED-LT.BLU
RED-BLU
RED
GRN
WHT-BLK
BLK-YEL
GRN-YEL
YEL-GRN
YEL-BLK
3C-4
3C-6
3C-2
3C-5
3B-2
3D-5
3B-4
3B-3
2B-10
2B-21
3D-3
3D-4
3E-1
3E-2
3E-3
3E-4
3F-1
3F-2
3A-3
3B-8
3A-4
3B-7
3C-1
3B-1
3A-7
3A-8
3D-1
3A-6
3A-5

1983 Toyota

CELICA (Cont.)

FUSE BLOCK & UNDERDASH

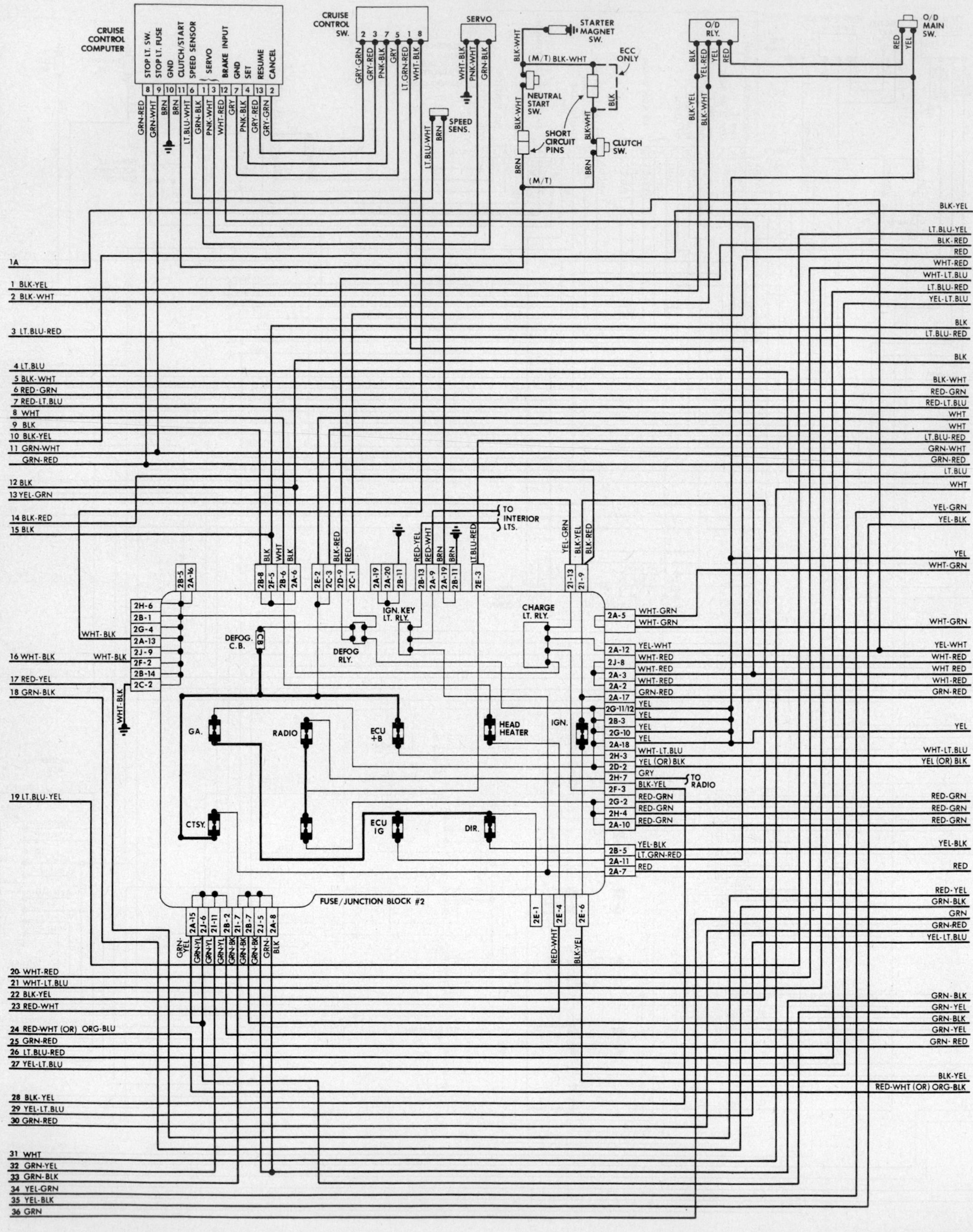

CRUISE CONTROL COMPUTER
STOP LT. SW.
STOP LT. FUSE
GND
CLUTCH/START
SPEED SENSOR
SERVO
BRAKE INPUT
GND
SET
RESUME
CANCEL
CRUISE CONTROL SW.
SERVO
STARTER MAGNET SW.
(M/T) BLK-WHT
ECC ONLY
NEUTRAL START SW.
SHORT CIRCUIT PINS
CLUTCH SW.
(M/T)
SPEED SENS.
O/D RLY.
O/D MAIN SW.
1A
1 BLK-YEL
2 BLK-WHT
3 LT.BLU-RED
4 LT.BLU
5 BLK-WHT
6 RED-GRN
7 RED-LT.BLU
8 WHT
9 BLK
10 BLK-YEL
11 GRN-WHT
GRN-RED
12 BLK
13 YEL-GRN
14 BLK-RED
15 BLK
16 WHT-BLK
17 RED-YEL
18 GRN-BLK
19 LT.BLU-YEL
20 WHT-RED
21 WHT-LT.BLU
22 BLK-YEL
23 RED-WHT
24 RED-WHT (OR) ORG-BLU
25 GRN-RED
26 LT.BLU-RED
27 YEL-LT.BLU
28 BLK-YEL
29 YEL-LT.BLU
30 GRN-RED
31 WHT
32 GRN-YEL
33 GRN-BLK
34 YEL-GRN
35 YEL-BLK
36 GRN
TO INTERIOR LTS.
DEFOG. C.B.
DEFOG RLY.
IGN. KEY LT. RLY.
CHARGE LT. RLY.
GA.
RADIO
ECU +B
HEAD HEATER
IGN.
CTSY.
ECU IG
DIR.
TO RADIO
FUSE/JUNCTION BLOCK #2
BLK-YEL
LT.BLU-YEL
BLK-RED
RED
WHT-RED
WHT-LT.BLU
LT.BLU-RED
YEL-LT.BLU
BLK
LT.BLU-RED
BLK
BLK-WHT
RED-GRN
RED-LT.BLU
WHT
WHT
LT.BLU-RED
GRN-WHT
GRN-RED
LT.BLU
WHT
YEL-GRN
YEL-BLK
YEL
WHT-GRN
WHT-GRN
YEL-WHT
WHT-RED
WHT-RED
WHT-RED
GRN-RED
YEL
WHT-LT.BLU
YEL (OR) BLK
RED-GRN
RED-GRN
RED-GRN
YEL-BLK
RED
RED-YEL
GRN-BLK
GRN
GRN-RED
YEL-LT.BLU
GRN-BLK
GRN-YEL
GRN-BLK
GRN-YEL
GRN-RED
BLK-YEL
RED-WHT (OR) ORG-BLK

1983 Toyota

CELICA (Cont.)

UNDERDASH

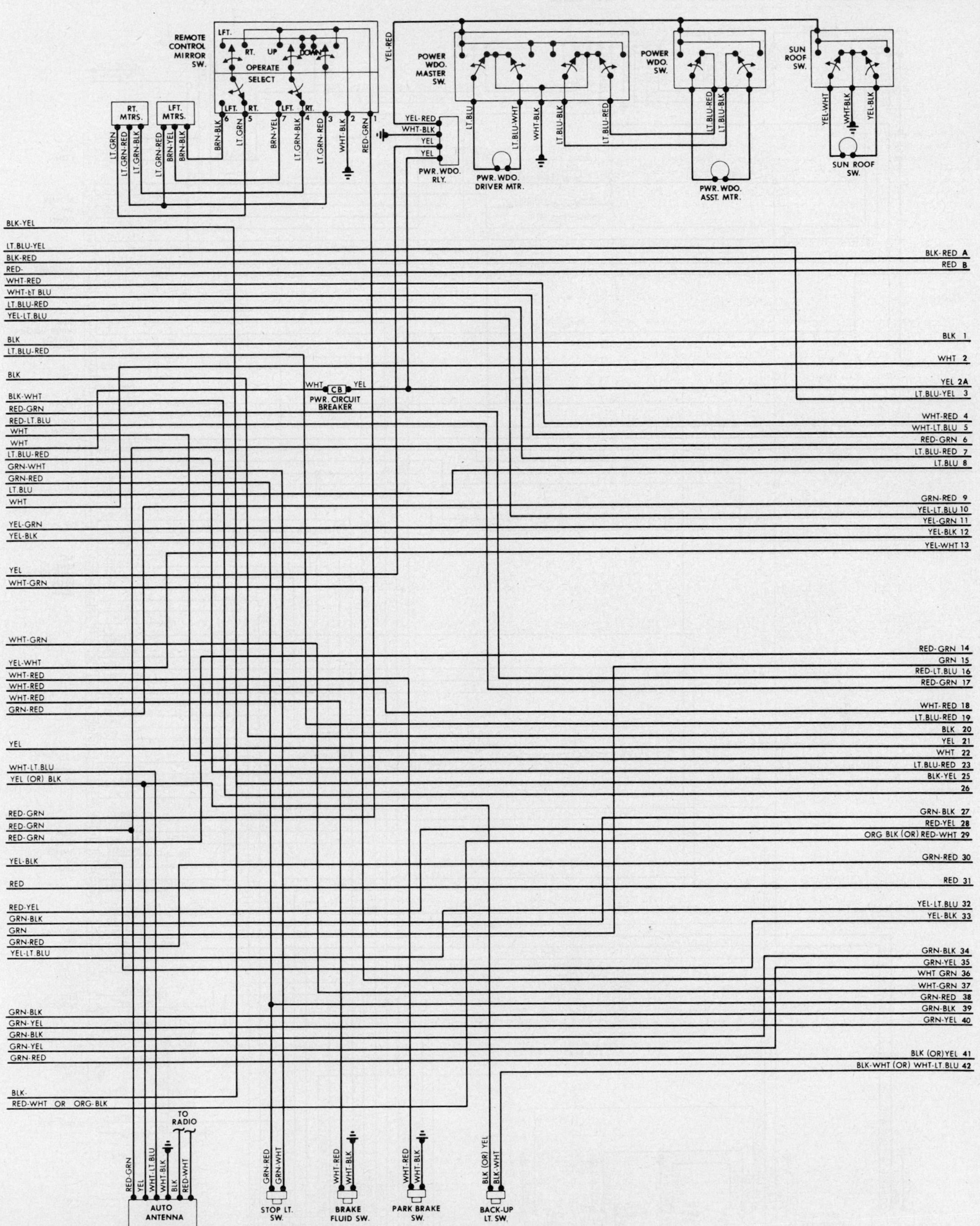
REMOTE CONTROL MIRROR SW.
LFT.
RT.
UP
DOWN
OPERATE
SELECT
RT. MTRS.
LFT. MTRS.
POWER WDO. MASTER SW.
POWER WDO. SW.
SUN ROOF SW.
PWR. WDO. RLY.
PWR. WDO. DRIVER MTR.
PWR. WDO. ASST. MTR.
SUN ROOF SW.
PWR. CIRCUIT BREAKER
CB
BLK-RED A
RED B
BLK 1
WHT 2
YEL 2A
LT.BLU-YEL 3
WHT-RED 4
WHT-LT.BLU 5
RED-GRN 6
LT.BLU-RED 7
LT.BLU 8
GRN-RED 9
YEL-LT.BLU 10
YEL-GRN 11
YEL-BLK 12
YEL-WHT 13
RED-GRN 14
GRN 15
RED-LT.BLU 16
RED-GRN 17
WHT-RED 18
LT.BLU-RED 19
BLK 20
YEL 21
WHT 22
LT.BLU-RED 23
BLK-YEL 25
26
GRN-BLK 27
RED-YEL 28
ORG BLK (OR) RED-WHT 29
GRN-RED 30
RED 31
YEL-LT.BLU 32
YEL-BLK 33
GRN-BLK 34
GRN-YEL 35
WHT GRN 36
WHT-GRN 37
GRN-RED 38
GRN-BLK 39
GRN-YEL 40
BLK (OR) YEL 41
BLK-WHT (OR) WHT-LT.BLU 42
TO RADIO
AUTO ANTENNA
STOP LT. SW.
BRAKE FLUID SW.
PARK BRAKE SW.
BACK-UP LT. SW.

1983 Toyota

CELICA (Cont.)

UNDERDASH & INSTRUMENT PANEL

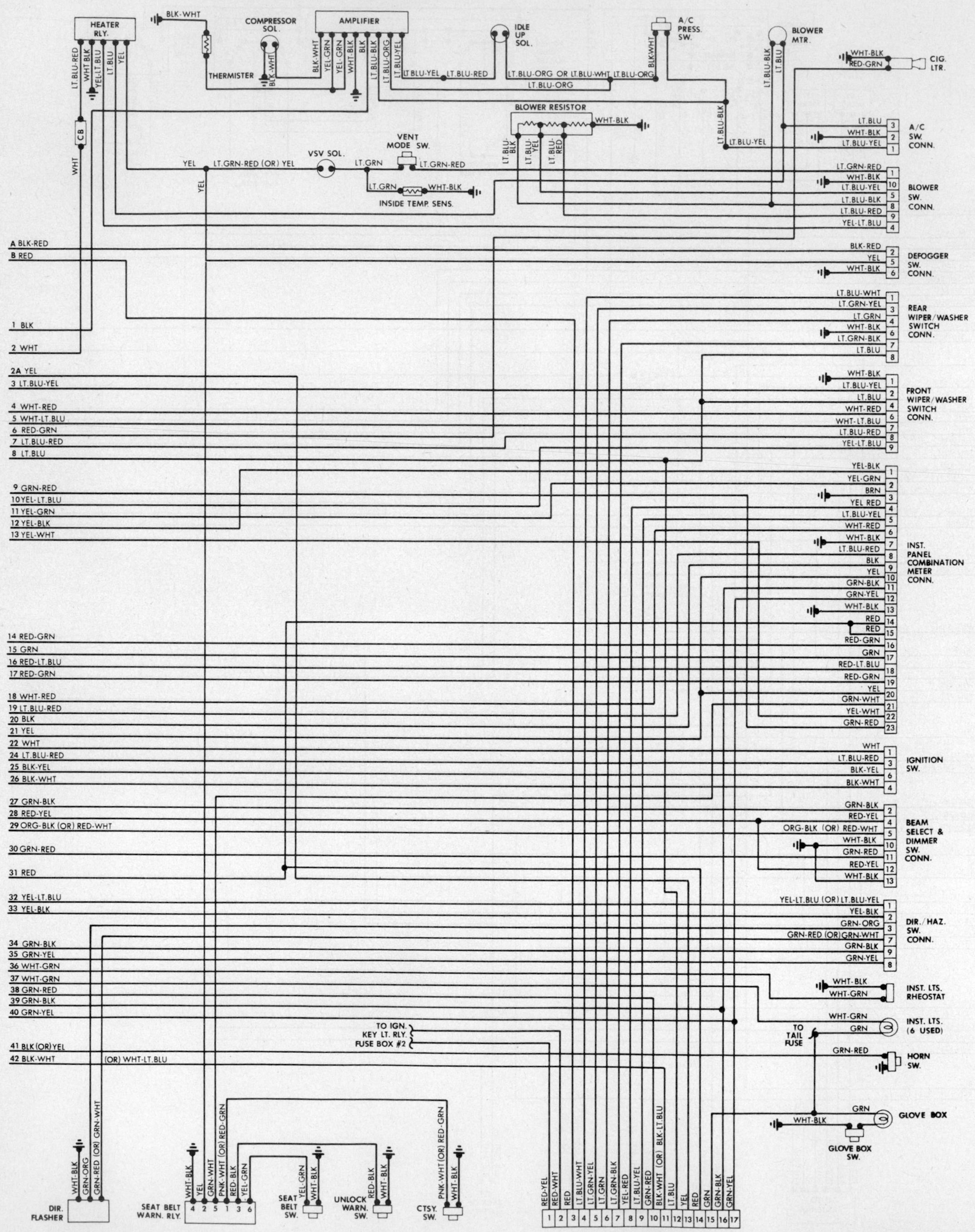
HEATER RLY.
COMPRESSOR SOL.
AMPLIFIER
IDLE UP SOL.
A/C PRESS. SW.
BLOWER MTR.
CIG. LTR.
THERMISTER
BLOWER RESISTOR
VENT MODE SW.
VSV SOL.
INSIDE TEMP SENS.
A/C SW. CONN.
BLOWER SW. CONN.
DEFOGGER SW. CONN.
REAR WIPER/WASHER SWITCH CONN.
FRONT WIPER/WASHER SWITCH CONN.
INST. PANEL COMBINATION METER CONN.
IGNITION SW.
BEAM SELECT & DIMMER SW. CONN.
DIR./HAZ. SW. CONN.
INST. LTS. RHEOSTAT
INST. LTS. (6 USED)
TO TAIL FUSE
HORN SW.
GLOVE BOX
GLOVE BOX SW.
TO IGN. KEY LT. RLY. FUSE BOX #2
DIR. FLASHER
SEAT BELT WARN. RLY.
SEAT BELT SW.
UNLOCK WARN. SW.
CTSY. SW.
A BLK-RED
B RED
1 BLK
2 WHT
2A YEL
3 LT.BLU-YEL
4 WHT-RED
5 WHT-LT.BLU
6 RED-GRN
7 LT.BLU-RED
8 LT.BLU
9 GRN-RED
10 YEL-LT.BLU
11 YEL-GRN
12 YEL-BLK
13 YEL-WHT
14 RED-GRN
15 GRN
16 RED-LT.BLU
17 RED-GRN
18 WHT-RED
19 LT.BLU-RED
20 BLK
21 YEL
22 WHT
24 LT.BLU-RED
25 BLK-YEL
26 BLK-WHT
27 GRN-BLK
28 RED-YEL
29 ORG-BLK (OR) RED-WHT
30 GRN-RED
31 RED
32 YEL-LT.BLU
33 YEL-BLK
34 GRN-BLK
35 GRN-YEL
36 WHT-GRN
37 WHT-GRN
38 GRN-RED
39 GRN-BLK
40 GRN-YEL
41 BLK (OR) YEL
42 BLK-WHT
(OR) WHT-LT.BLU

1983 Toyota

CELICA (Cont.)

REAR COMPARTMENT & ACCESSORIES

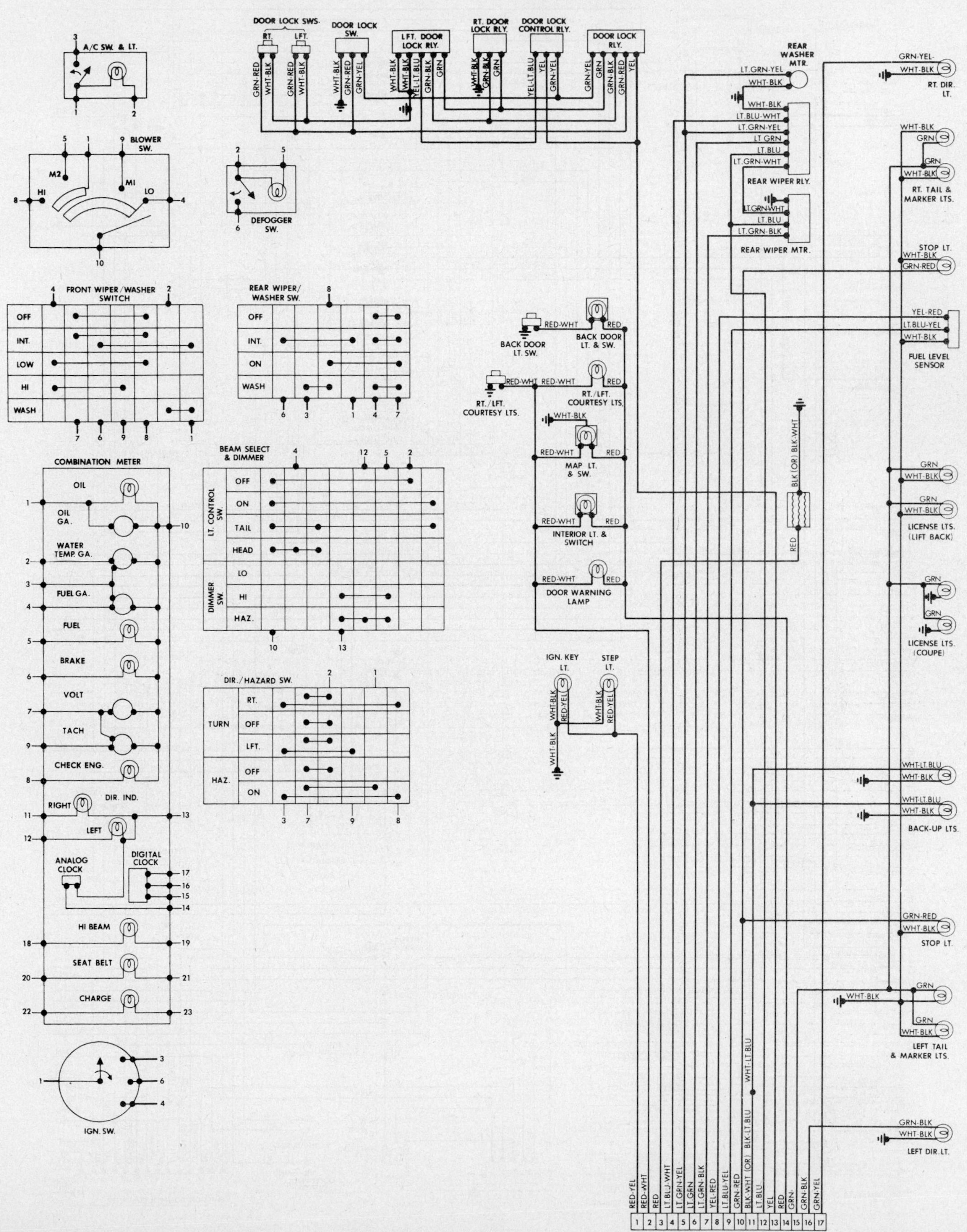

A/C SW. & LT.
BLOWER SW.
DEFOGGER SW.
DOOR LOCK SWS.
RT.
LFT.
DOOR LOCK SW.
LFT. DOOR LOCK RLY.
RT. DOOR LOCK RLY.
DOOR LOCK CONTROL RLY.
DOOR LOCK RLY.
REAR WASHER MTR.
RT. DIR. LT.
REAR WIPER RLY.
REAR WIPER MTR.
RT. TAIL & MARKER LTS.
STOP LT.
FRONT WIPER/WASHER SWITCH
REAR WIPER/WASHER SW.
OFF
INT.
LOW
HI
WASH
ON
BACK DOOR LT. SW.
BACK DOOR LT. & SW.
RT./LFT. COURTESY LTS.
MAP LT. & SW.
INTERIOR LT. & SWITCH
DOOR WARNING LAMP
FUEL LEVEL SENSOR
LICENSE LTS. (LIFT BACK)
LICENSE LTS. (COUPE)
COMBINATION METER
OIL
OIL GA.
WATER TEMP. GA.
FUEL GA.
FUEL
BRAKE
VOLT
TACH
CHECK ENG.
RIGHT
LEFT
DIR. IND.
ANALOG CLOCK
DIGITAL CLOCK
HI BEAM
SEAT BELT
CHARGE
IGN. SW.
BEAM SELECT & DIMMER
LT. CONTROL SW.
TAIL
HEAD
LO
DIMMER SW.
HAZ.
DIR./HAZARD SW.
RT.
TURN
LFT.
IGN. KEY LT.
STEP LT.
BACK-UP LTS.
STOP LT.
LEFT TAIL & MARKER LTS.
LEFT DIR. LT.

1983 Toyota

COROLLA – EXCEPT TERCEL

ENGINE COMPARTMENT & FUSE BLOCK

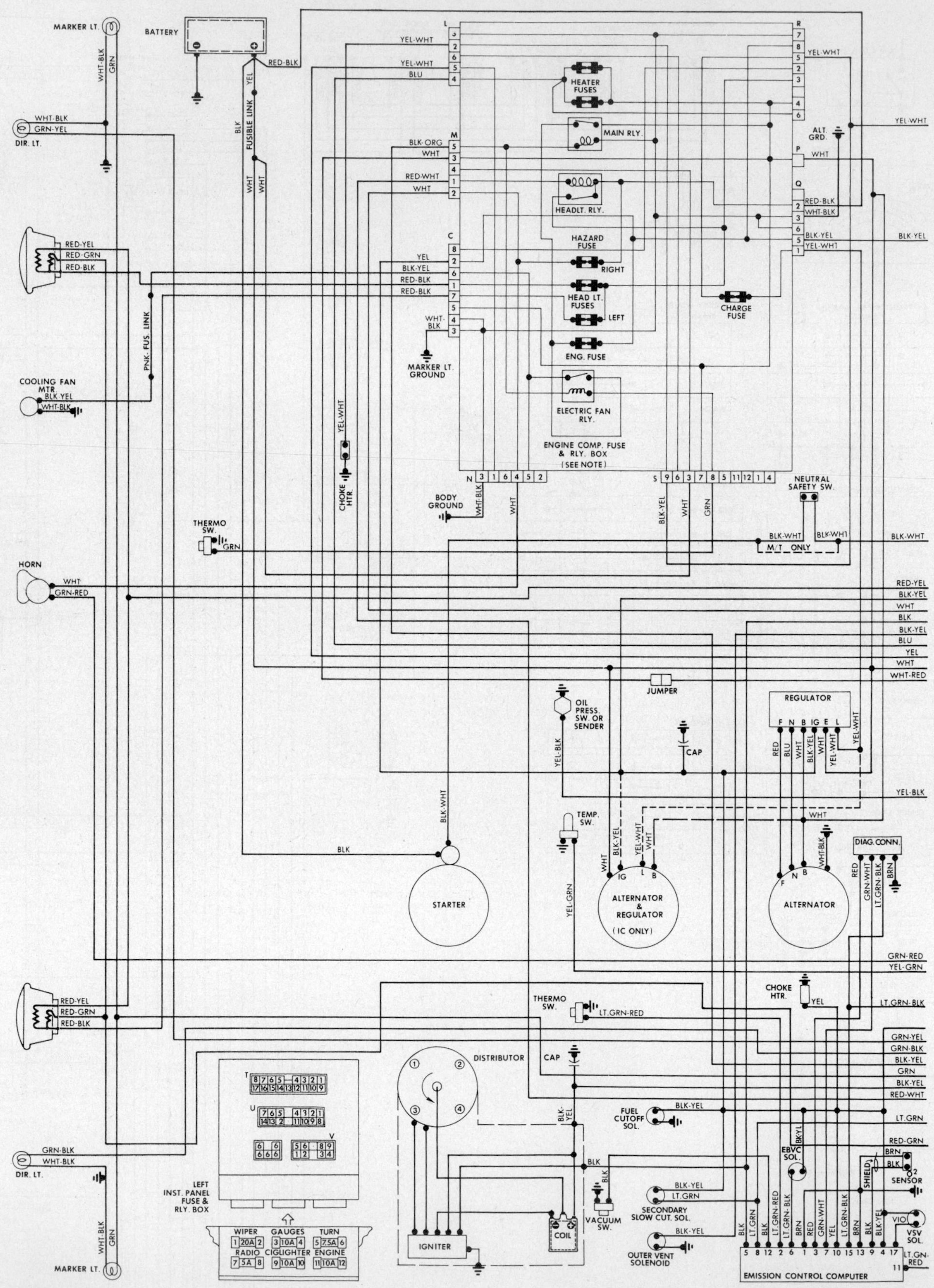
MARKER LT.
BATTERY
DIR. LT.
FUSIBLE LINK
PNK. FUS. LINK
COOLING FAN MTR
HEATER FUSES
MAIN RLY.
HEADLT. RLY.
HAZARD FUSE
RIGHT
HEAD LT. FUSES
LEFT
ENG. FUSE
CHARGE FUSE
ALT. GRD.
MARKER LT. GROUND
ELECTRIC FAN RLY.
ENGINE COMP. FUSE & RLY. BOX (SEE NOTE)
CHOKE HTR.
BODY GROUND
NEUTRAL SAFETY SW.
M/T ONLY
THERMO SW.
HORN
JUMPER
OIL PRESS. SW. OR SENDER
CAP
REGULATOR
TEMP. SW.
STARTER
ALTERNATOR & REGULATOR (IC ONLY)
ALTERNATOR
DIAG. CONN.
DISTRIBUTOR
FUEL CUTOFF SOL.
EBVC SOL.
O2 SENSOR
SHIELD
SECONDARY SLOW CUT. SOL.
VACUUM SW.
COIL
IGNITER
OUTER VENT SOLENOID
VSV SOL.
EMISSION CONTROL COMPUTER
LEFT INST. PANEL FUSE & RLY. BOX
WIPER
GAUGES
TURN
RADIO
CIG. LIGHTER
ENGINE
20A
10A
7.5A

1983 Toyota

COROLLA – EXCEPT TERCEL (Cont.)

FUSE BLOCK & UNDERDASH

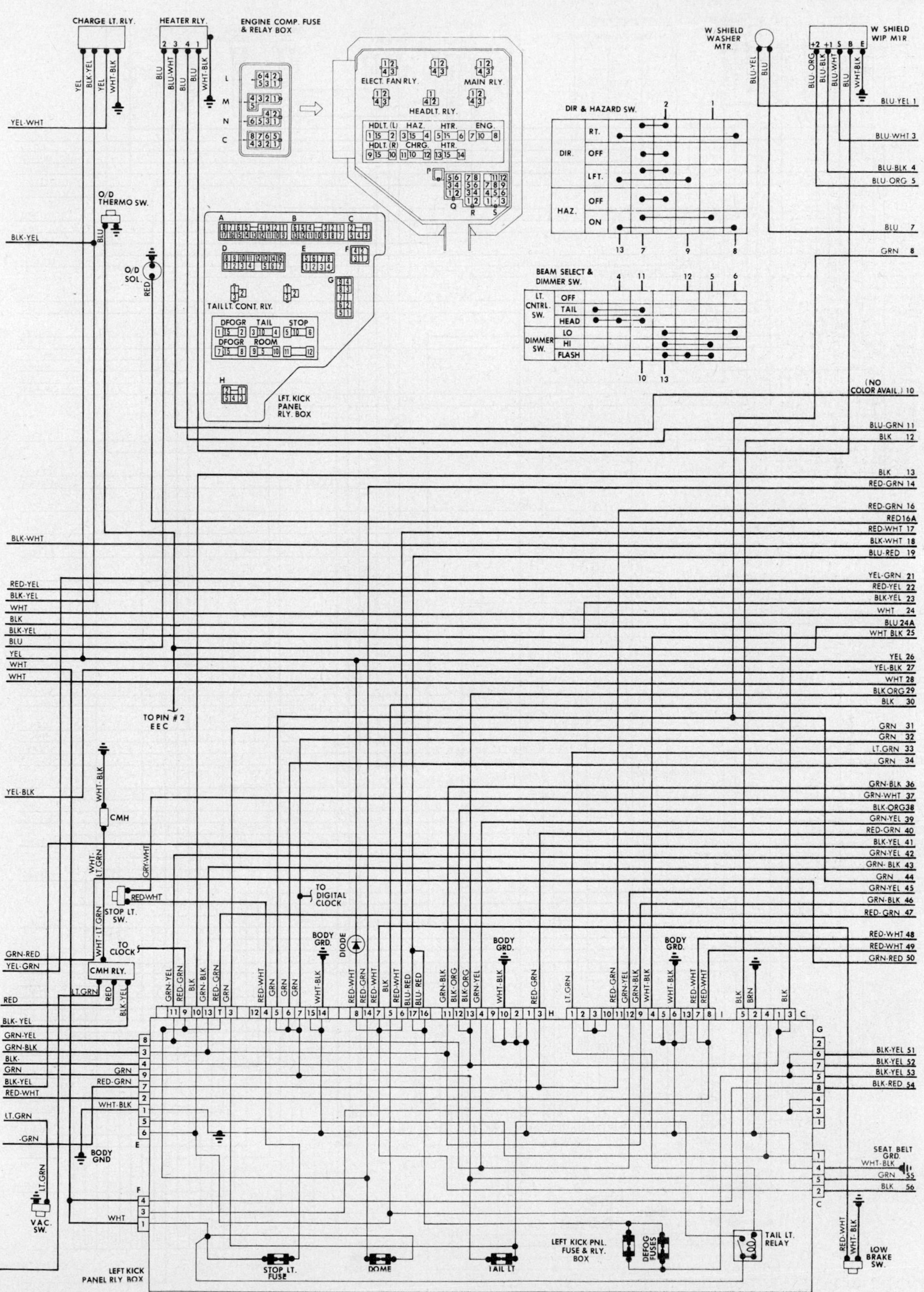
CHARGE LT. RLY.
HEATER RLY.
ENGINE COMP. FUSE & RELAY BOX
ELECT. FAN RLY.
MAIN RLY.
HEADLT. RLY.
W. SHIELD WASHER MTR.
W. SHIELD WIP MTR
DIR & HAZARD SW.
BEAM SELECT & DIMMER SW.
O/D THERMO SW.
O/D SOL
TAIL LT. CONT. RLY.
LFT. KICK PANEL RLY. BOX
TO PIN #2 EEC
CMH
STOP LT. SW.
TO CLOCK
CMH RLY.
TO DIGITAL CLOCK
BODY GRD.
DIODE
BODY GND
VAC. SW.
LEFT KICK PANEL RLY BOX
STOP LT. FUSE
DOME
TAIL LT
LEFT KICK PNL. FUSE & RLY. BOX
DEFOG FUSES
TAIL LT. RELAY
SEAT BELT GRD.
LOW BRAKE SW.

1983 Toyota

COROLLA – EXCEPT TERCEL (Cont.)

FUSE BLOCK & UNDERDASH

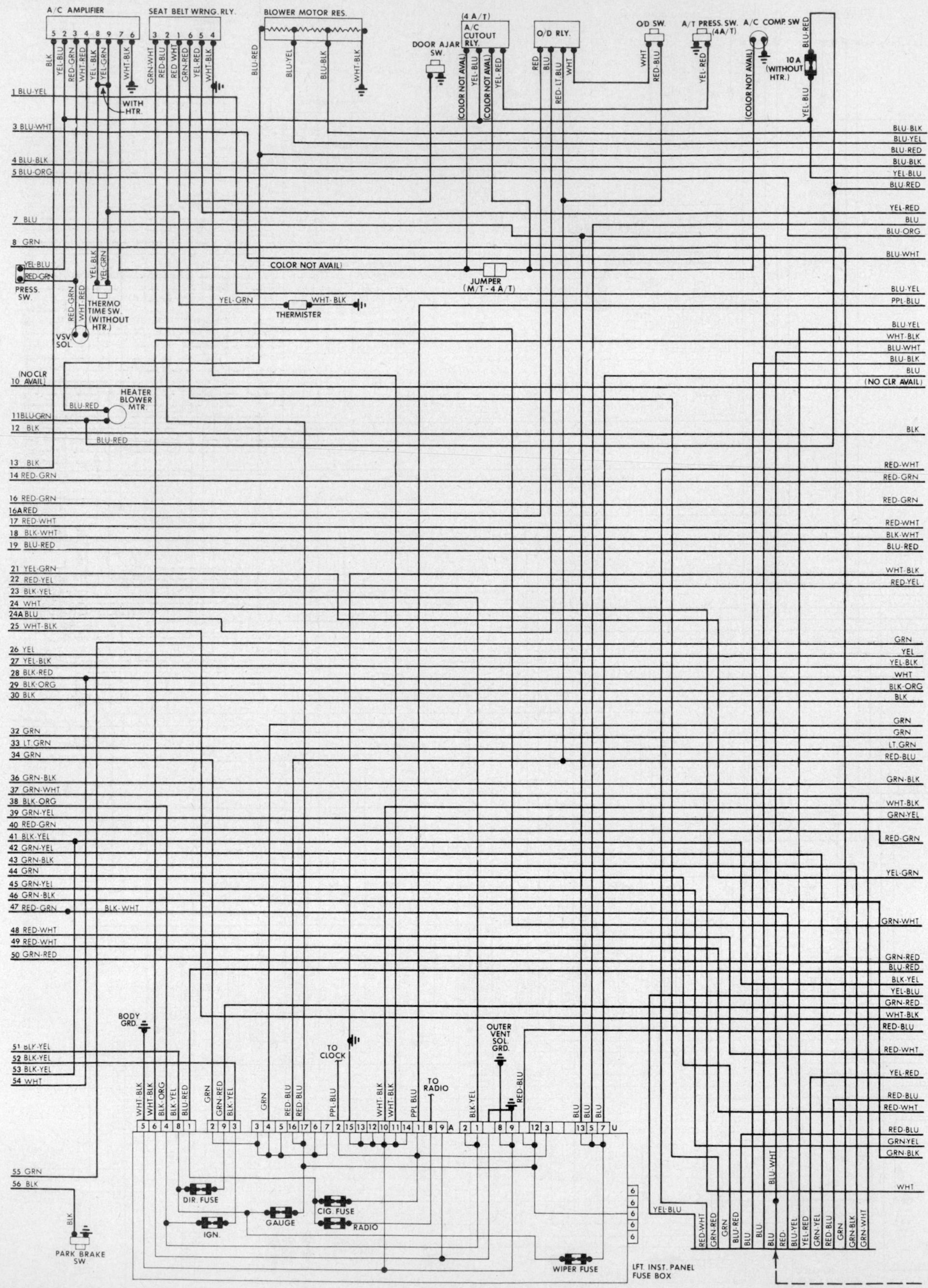

A/C AMPLIFIER
SEAT BELT WRNG. RLY.
BLOWER MOTOR RES.
DOOR AJAR SW.
A/C CUTOUT RLY.
O/D RLY.
O/D SW.
A/T PRESS. SW.
A/C COMP. SW
10 A (WITHOUT HTR.)
WITH HTR.
PRESS. SW.
THERMO TIME SW. (WITHOUT HTR.)
VSV SOL
COLOR NOT AVAIL
JUMPER (M/T - 4 A/T)
THERMISTER
HEATER BLOWER MTR
BODY GRD.
TO CLOCK
TO RADIO
OUTER VENT SOL. GRD.
DIR. FUSE
IGN.
GAUGE
CIG. FUSE
RADIO
WIPER FUSE
LFT. INST. PANEL FUSE BOX
PARK BRAKE SW

1983 Toyota

COROLLA – EXCEPT TERCEL (Cont.)

INSTRUMENT PANEL & REAR COMPARTMENT

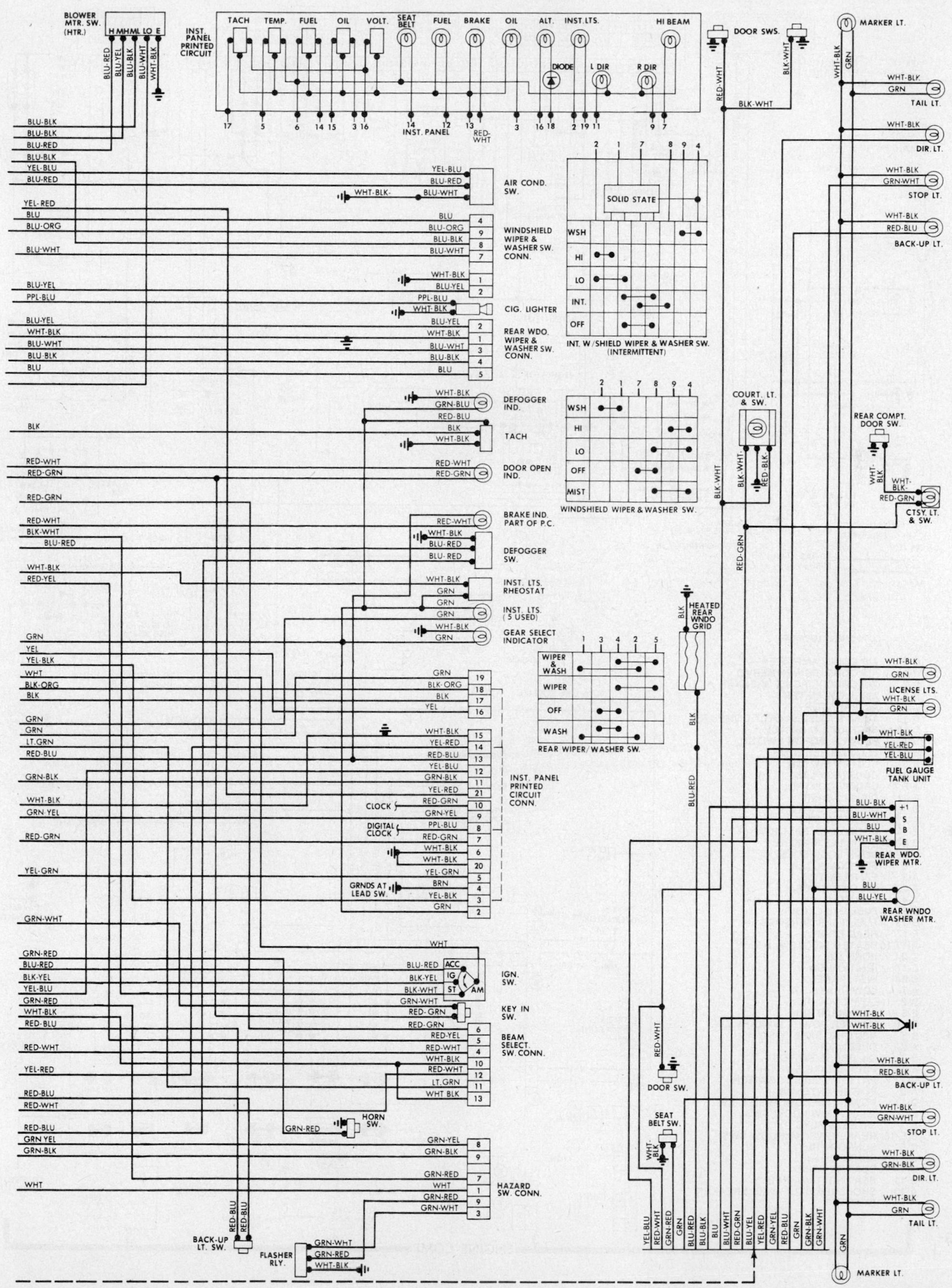

BLOWER MTR. SW. (HTR.)
INST. PANEL PRINTED CIRCUIT
TACH
TEMP.
FUEL
OIL
VOLT.
SEAT BELT
BRAKE
ALT.
INST. LTS.
HI BEAM
DIODE
L DIR
R DIR
DOOR SWS.
MARKER LT.
TAIL LT.
DIR. LT.
STOP LT.
BACK-UP LT.
AIR COND. SW.
WINDSHIELD WIPER & WASHER SW. CONN.
SOLID STATE
INT. W/SHIELD WIPER & WASHER SW. (INTERMITTENT)
CIG. LIGHTER
REAR WDO. WIPER & WASHER SW. CONN.
DEFOGGER IND.
COURT. LT. & SW.
REAR COMPT. DOOR SW.
WINDSHIELD WIPER & WASHER SW.
DOOR OPEN IND.
CTSY. LT. & SW.
BRAKE IND. PART OF P.C.
DEFOGGER SW.
INST. LTS. RHEOSTAT
INST. LTS. (5 USED)
GEAR SELECT INDICATOR
HEATED REAR WNDO GRID
REAR WIPER/WASHER SW.
LICENSE LTS.
FUEL GAUGE TANK UNIT
INST. PANEL PRINTED CIRCUIT CONN.
CLOCK
DIGITAL CLOCK
REAR WDO. WIPER MTR.
GRNDS AT LEAD SW.
REAR WNDO WASHER MTR.
IGN. SW.
KEY IN SW.
BEAM SELECT. SW. CONN.
DOOR SW.
HORN SW.
SEAT BELT SW.
HAZARD SW. CONN.
BACK-UP LT. SW.
FLASHER RLY.

1983 Toyota

CRESSIDA

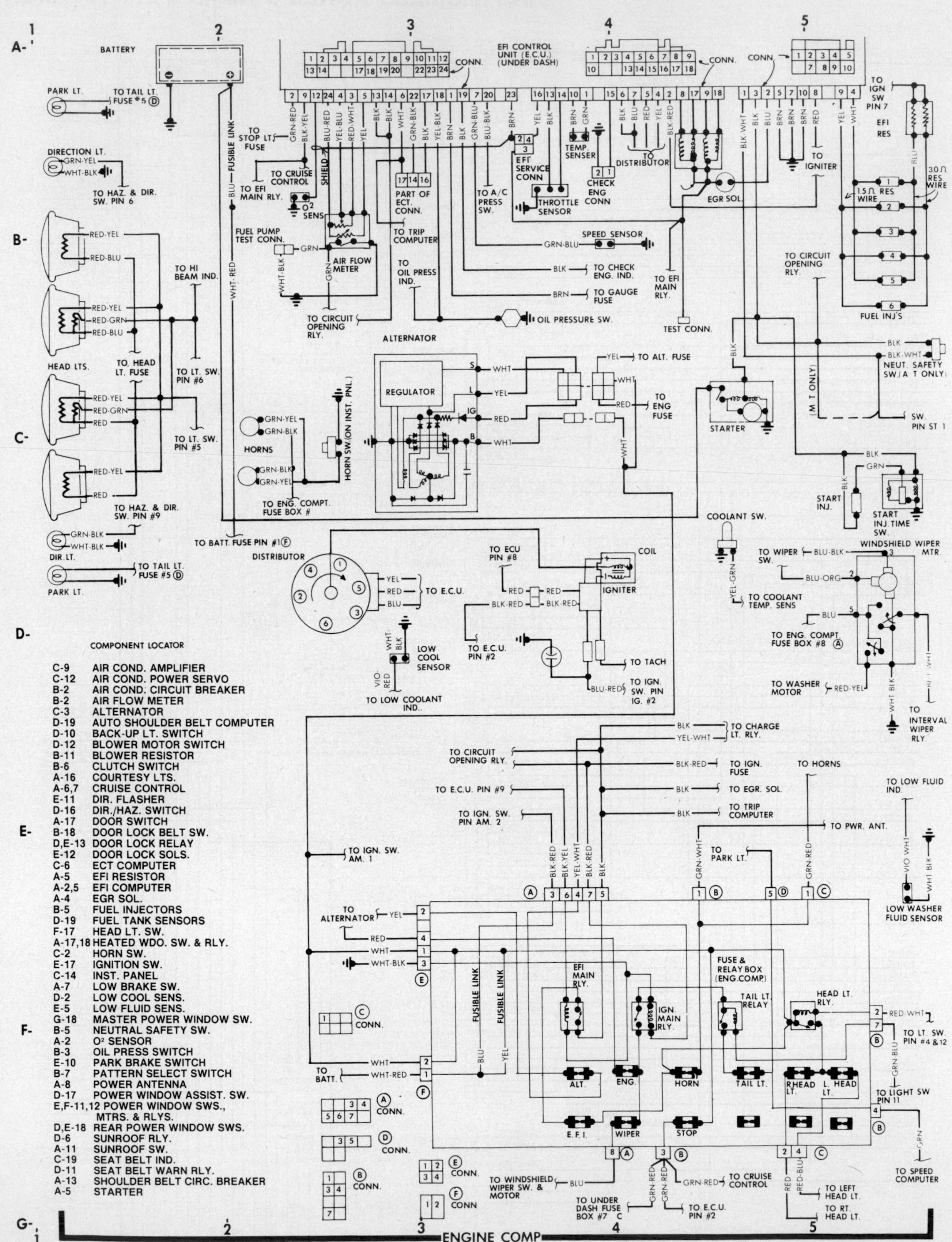
BATTERY
EFI CONTROL UNIT (E.C.U.) (UNDER DASH)
PARK LT.
DIRECTION LT.
HEAD LTS.
DIR. LT.
HORNS
ALTERNATOR
REGULATOR
STARTER
DISTRIBUTOR
COIL
IGNITER
AIR FLOW METER
THROTTLE SENSOR
SPEED SENSOR
OIL PRESSURE SW.
COOLANT SW.
LOW COOL SENSOR
EGR SOL.
FUEL INJ'S
EFI RES
NEUT. SAFETY SW. (A T ONLY)
START INJ.
START INJ. TIME SW.
WINDSHIELD WIPER MTR.
LOW WASHER FLUID SENSOR
FUSE & RELAY BOX (ENG. COMP.)
EFI MAIN RLY.
IGN. MAIN RLY.
TAIL LT. RELAY
HEAD LT. RLY.
ALT.
ENG.
HORN
TAIL LT.
R HEAD LT.
L. HEAD LT.
E.F.I.
WIPER
STOP
COMPONENT LOCATOR
C-9 AIR COND. AMPLIFIER
C-12 AIR COND. POWER SERVO
B-2 AIR COND. CIRCUIT BREAKER
B-2 AIR FLOW METER
C-3 ALTERNATOR
D-19 AUTO SHOULDER BELT COMPUTER
D-10 BACK-UP LT. SWITCH
D-12 BLOWER MOTOR SWITCH
B-11 BLOWER RESISTOR
B-6 CLUTCH SWITCH
A-16 COURTESY LTS.
A-6,7 CRUISE CONTROL
E-11 DIR. FLASHER
D-16 DIR./HAZ. SWITCH
A-17 DOOR SWITCH
B-18 DOOR LOCK BELT SW.
D,E-13 DOOR LOCK RELAY
E-12 DOOR LOCK SOLS.
C-6 ECT COMPUTER
A-5 EFI RESISTOR
A-2,5 EFI COMPUTER
A-4 EGR SOL.
B-5 FUEL INJECTORS
D-19 FUEL TANK SENSORS
F-17 HEAD LT. SW.
A-17,18 HEATED WDO. SW. & RLY.
C-2 HORN SW.
E-17 IGNITION SW.
C-14 INST. PANEL
A-7 LOW BRAKE SW.
D-2 LOW COOL SENS.
E-5 LOW FLUID SENS.
G-18 MASTER POWER WINDOW SW.
B-5 NEUTRAL SAFETY SW.
A-2 O² SENSOR
B-3 OIL PRESS SWITCH
E-10 PARK BRAKE SWITCH
B-7 PATTERN SELECT SWITCH
A-8 POWER ANTENNA
D-17 POWER WINDOW ASSIST. SW.
E,F-11,12 POWER WINDOW SWS., MTRS. & RLYS.
D,E-18 REAR POWER WINDOW SWS.
D-6 SUNROOF RLY.
A-11 SUNROOF SW.
C-19 SEAT BELT IND.
D-11 SEAT BELT WARN RLY.
A-13 SHOULDER BELT CIRC. BREAKER
A-5 STARTER
ENGINE COMP

1983 Toyota

CRESSIDA (Cont.)

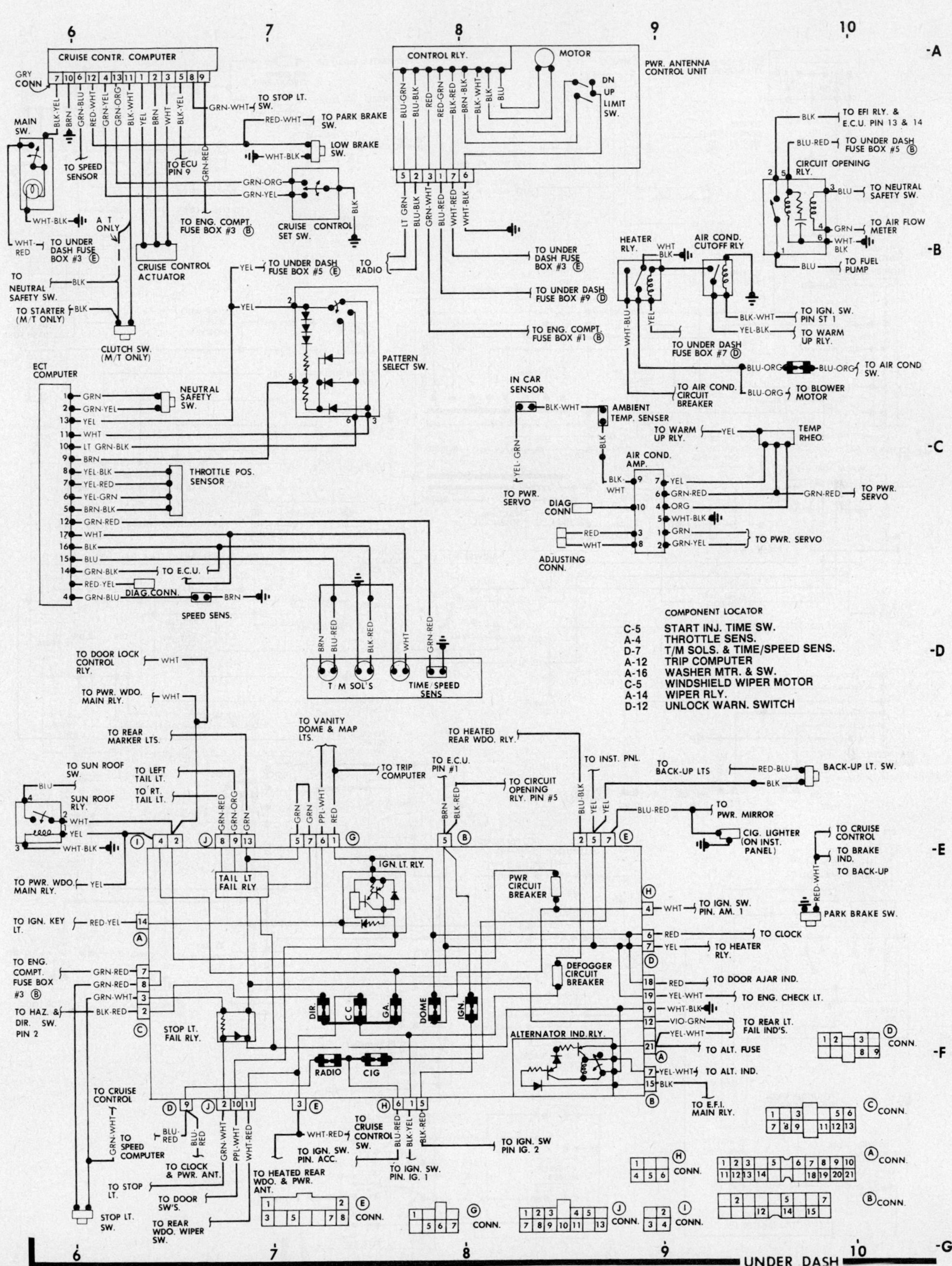

CRUISE CONTR. COMPUTER
GRY CONN
MAIN SW.
TO SPEED SENSOR
TO ECU PIN 9
TO STOP LT. SW.
TO PARK BRAKE SW.
LOW BRAKE SW.
CRUISE CONTROL SET SW.
TO ENG. COMPT. FUSE BOX #3 B
A T ONLY
TO UNDER DASH FUSE BOX #3 E
CRUISE CONTROL ACTUATOR
TO NEUTRAL SAFETY SW.
TO STARTER (M/T ONLY)
CLUTCH SW. (M/T ONLY)
CONTROL RLY.
MOTOR
PWR. ANTENNA CONTROL UNIT
DN
UP
LIMIT SW.
TO RADIO
TO UNDER DASH FUSE BOX #3 E
TO UNDER DASH FUSE BOX #9 D
TO ENG. COMPT. FUSE BOX #1 B
TO UNDER DASH FUSE BOX #5 E
PATTERN SELECT SW.
ECT COMPUTER
NEUTRAL SAFETY SW.
THROTTLE POS. SENSOR
TO E.C.U.
DIAG.CONN.
SPEED SENS.
T M SOL'S
TIME/SPEED SENS
TO EFI RLY. & E.C.U. PIN 13 & 14
TO UNDER DASH FUSE BOX #5 B
CIRCUIT OPENING RLY.
TO NEUTRAL SAFETY SW.
TO AIR FLOW METER
TO FUEL PUMP
HEATER RLY.
AIR COND. CUTOFF RLY
TO IGN. SW. PIN ST 1
TO WARM UP RLY.
TO UNDER DASH FUSE BOX #7 D
TO AIR COND SW.
TO AIR COND. CIRCUIT BREAKER
TO BLOWER MOTOR
IN CAR SENSOR
AMBIENT TEMP. SENSER
TO WARM UP RLY.
TEMP RHEO.
AIR COND. AMP.
TO PWR. SERVO
DIAG CONN
TO PWR. SERVO
ADJUSTING CONN.
COMPONENT LOCATOR
C-5 START INJ. TIME SW.
A-4 THROTTLE SENS.
D-7 T/M SOLS. & TIME/SPEED SENS.
A-12 TRIP COMPUTER
A-16 WASHER MTR. & SW.
C-5 WINDSHIELD WIPER MOTOR
A-14 WIPER RLY.
D-12 UNLOCK WARN. SWITCH
TO DOOR LOCK CONTROL RLY.
TO PWR. WDO. MAIN RLY.
TO REAR MARKER LTS.
TO VANITY DOME & MAP LTS.
TO HEATED REAR WDO. RLY.
TO SUN ROOF SW.
TO LEFT TAIL LT.
TO RT. TAIL LT.
SUN ROOF RLY.
TO TRIP COMPUTER
TO E.C.U. PIN #1
TO CIRCUIT OPENING RLY. PIN #5
TO INST. PNL.
TO BACK-UP LTS
BACK-UP LT. SW.
TO PWR. MIRROR
CIG. LIGHTER (ON INST. PANEL)
TO CRUISE CONTROL
TO BRAKE IND.
TO BACK-UP
PARK BRAKE SW.
TO PWR. WDO. MAIN RLY.
TAIL LT FAIL RLY
IGN. LT. RLY.
PWR CIRCUIT BREAKER
TO IGN. SW. PIN. AM. 1
TO IGN. KEY LT.
TO CLOCK
TO HEATER RLY.
TO ENG. COMPT. FUSE BOX #3 B
DEFOGGER CIRCUIT BREAKER
TO DOOR AJAR IND.
TO ENG. CHECK LT.
TO HAZ. & DIR. SW. PIN 2
STOP LT. FAIL RLY.
DIR.
CC
GA
DOME
IGN
ALTERNATOR IND. RLY.
TO REAR LT. FAIL IND'S.
TO ALT. FUSE
RADIO
CIG
TO ALT. IND.
TO E.F.I. MAIN RLY.
TO CRUISE CONTROL
TO SPEED COMPUTER
TO CLOCK & PWR. ANT.
TO STOP LT.
TO DOOR SW'S.
TO REAR WDO. WIPER SW.
STOP LT. SW.
TO HEATED REAR WDO. & PWR. ANT.
TO IGN. SW. PIN. ACC.
TO CRUISE CONTROL SW.
TO IGN. SW. PIN. IG. 1
TO IGN. SW PIN IG. 2
E CONN.
G CONN.
J CONN.
I CONN.
H CONN.
D CONN.
C CONN.
A CONN.
B CONN.
UNDER DASH

1983 Toyota

CRESSIDA (Cont.)

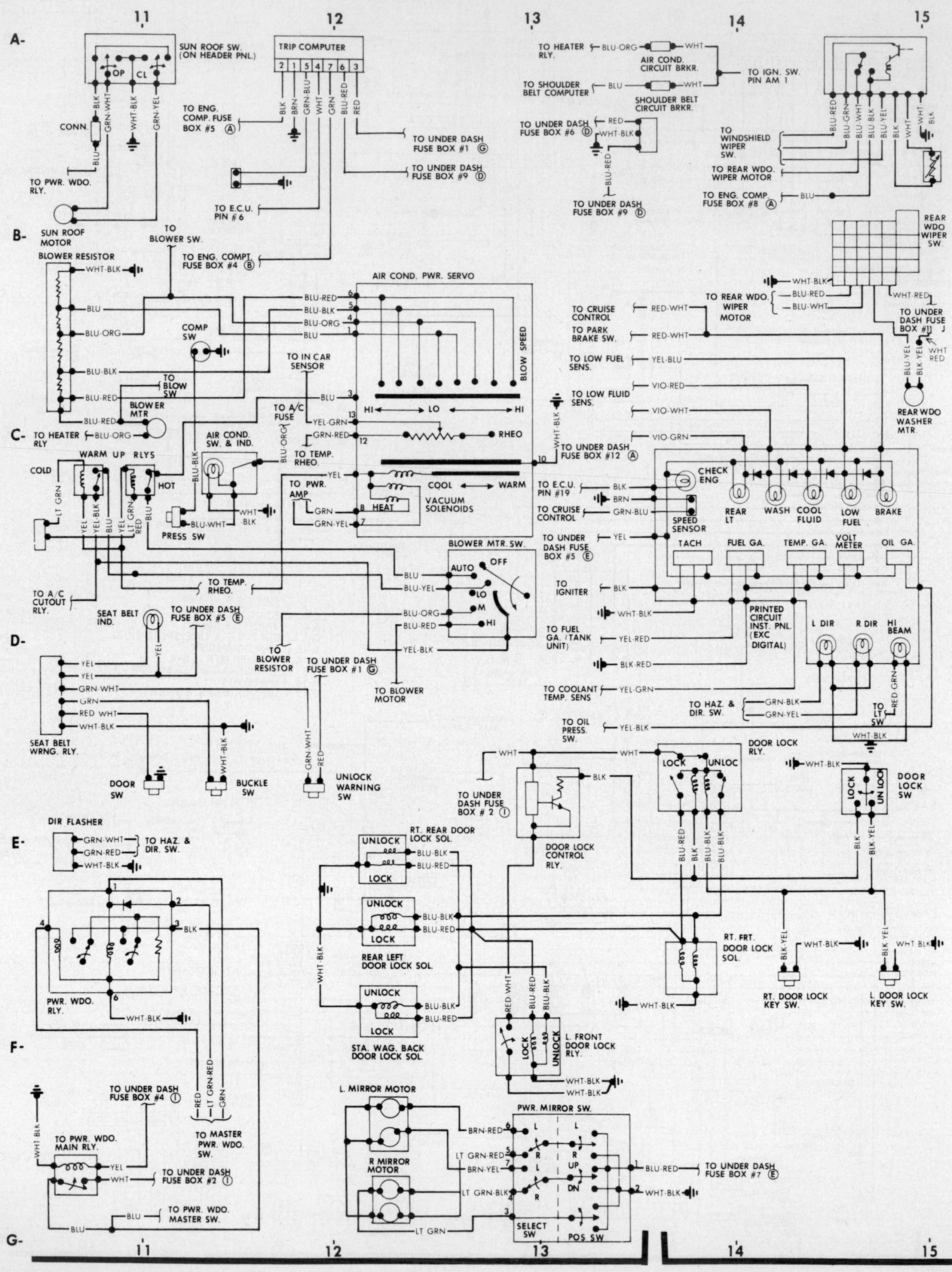
SUN ROOF SW. (ON HEADER PNL.)
TRIP COMPUTER
TO ENG. COMP. FUSE BOX #5
TO UNDER DASH FUSE BOX #1
TO UNDER DASH FUSE BOX #9
TO E.C.U. PIN #6
TO PWR. WDO. RLY.
SUN ROOF MOTOR
TO HEATER RLY.
AIR COND. CIRCUIT BRKR.
TO IGN. SW. PIN AM 1
TO SHOULDER BELT COMPUTER
SHOULDER BELT CIRCUIT BRKR.
TO UNDER DASH FUSE BOX #6
TO WINDSHIELD WIPER SW.
TO REAR WDO. WIPER MOTOR
TO ENG. COMP. FUSE BOX #8
REAR WDO WIPER SW.
BLOWER RESISTOR
TO BLOWER SW.
TO ENG. COMPT. FUSE BOX #4
AIR COND. PWR. SERVO
COMP SW
TO IN CAR SENSOR
BLOWER MTR
TO A/C FUSE
AIR COND. SW. & IND.
TO TEMP. RHEO.
WARM UP RLYS
COLD
HOT
TO PWR. AMP
PRESS SW
HEAT
COOL
WARM
VACUUM SOLENOIDS
BLOW SPEED
RHEO
TO CRUISE CONTROL
TO PARK BRAKE SW.
TO LOW FUEL SENS.
TO LOW FLUID SENS.
TO UNDER DASH FUSE BOX #12
TO REAR WDO. WIPER MOTOR
TO UNDER DASH FUSE BOX #11
REAR WDO WASHER MTR.
CHECK ENG
TO E.C.U. PIN #19
SPEED SENSOR
REAR LT
WASH
COOL FLUID
LOW FUEL
BRAKE
TACH
FUEL GA.
TEMP. GA.
VOLT METER
OIL GA.
TO UNDER DASH FUSE BOX #5
BLOWER MTR. SW.
AUTO
OFF
LO
M
HI
TO IGNITER
PRINTED CIRCUIT INST. PNL. (EXC DIGITAL)
L DIR
R DIR
HI BEAM
TO FUEL GA. (TANK UNIT)
TO COOLANT TEMP. SENS
TO HAZ. & DIR. SW.
TO LT SW
TO OIL PRESS. SW.
TO A/C CUTOUT RLY.
SEAT BELT IND.
TO BLOWER RESISTOR
TO UNDER DASH FUSE BOX #1
TO BLOWER MOTOR
SEAT BELT WRNG. RLY.
DOOR SW
BUCKLE SW
UNLOCK WARNING SW
DOOR LOCK RLY.
LOCK
UNLOC
DOOR LOCK SW
TO UNDER DASH FUSE BOX #2
DOOR LOCK CONTROL RLY.
DIR FLASHER
RT. REAR DOOR LOCK SOL.
UNLOCK
REAR LEFT DOOR LOCK SOL.
STA. WAG. BACK DOOR LOCK SOL.
RT. FRT. DOOR LOCK SOL.
RT. DOOR LOCK KEY SW.
L. DOOR LOCK KEY SW.
PWR. WDO. RLY.
L. FRONT DOOR LOCK RLY.
TO UNDER DASH FUSE BOX #4
TO MASTER PWR. WDO. SW.
L. MIRROR MOTOR
R MIRROR MOTOR
PWR. MIRROR SW.
UP
DN
SELECT SW
POS SW
TO UNDER DASH FUSE BOX #7
TO PWR. WDO. MAIN RLY.
TO UNDER DASH FUSE BOX #2
TO PWR. WDO. MASTER SW.

1983 Toyota

CRESSIDA (Cont.)

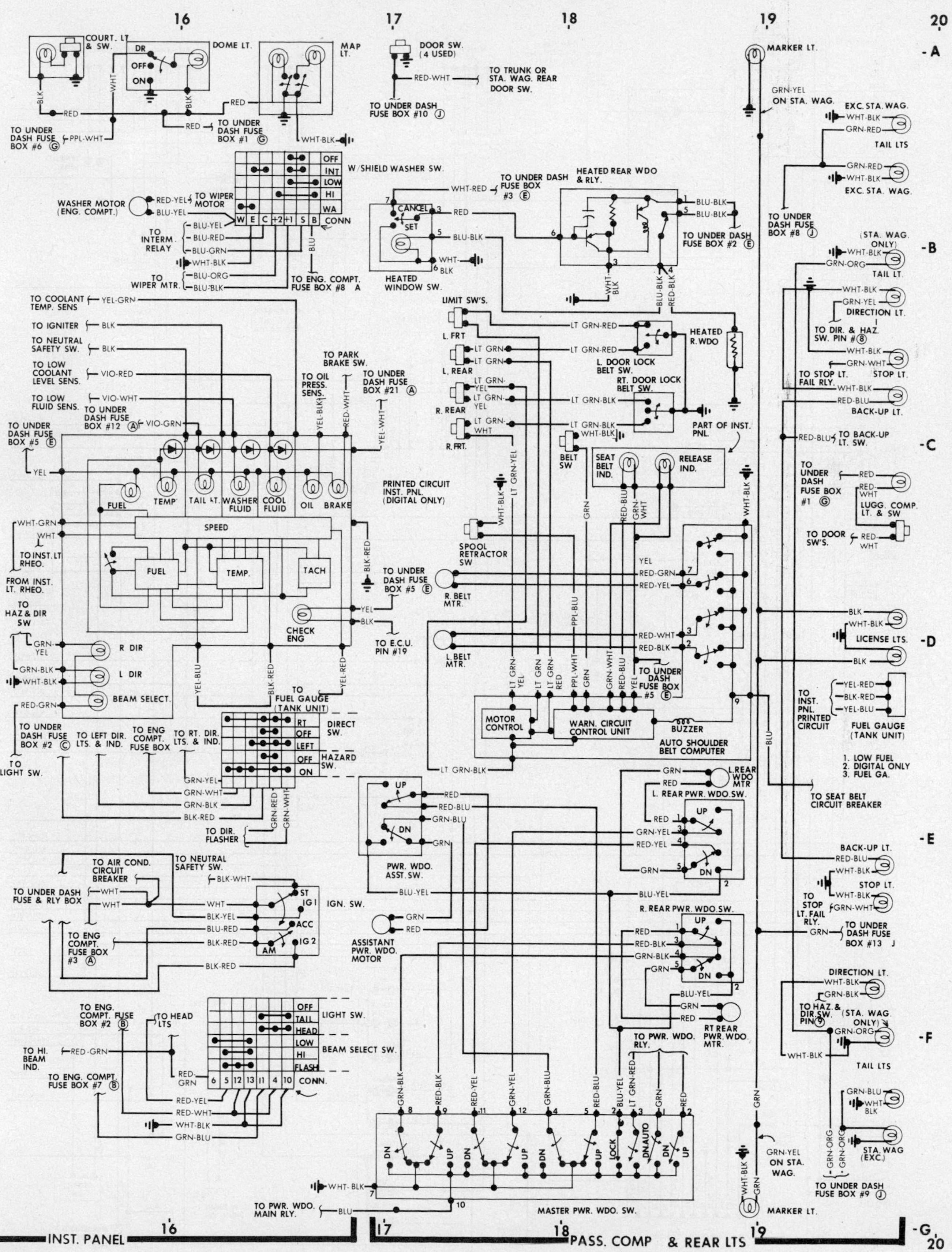
16
17
18
19
20
COURT. LT & SW.
DOME LT.
DR
OFF
ON
MAP LT.
DOOR SW. (4 USED)
TO TRUNK OR STA. WAG. REAR DOOR SW.
TO UNDER DASH FUSE BOX #10 J
MARKER LT.
GRN-YEL ON STA. WAG.
EXC. STA. WAG.
TAIL LTS
TO UNDER DASH FUSE BOX #6 G
TO UNDER DASH FUSE BOX #1 G
W/SHIELD WASHER SW.
OFF
INT
LOW
HI
WA
CONN
WASHER MOTOR (ENG. COMPT.)
TO WIPER MOTOR
TO INTERM. RELAY
TO WIPER MTR.
TO ENG. COMPT. FUSE BOX #8 A
TO UNDER DASH FUSE BOX #3 E
HEATED REAR WDO & RLY.
CANCEL
SET
HEATED WINDOW SW.
TO UNDER DASH FUSE BOX #2 E
TO UNDER DASH FUSE BOX #8 J
(STA. WAG. ONLY)
TAIL LT.
DIRECTION LT.
TO DIR. & HAZ. SW. PIN #8
STOP LT.
TO STOP LT. FAIL RLY.
BACK-UP LT.
TO BACK-UP LT. SW.
TO COOLANT TEMP. SENS
TO IGNITER
TO NEUTRAL SAFETY SW.
TO LOW COOLANT LEVEL SENS.
TO LOW FLUID SENS.
TO UNDER DASH FUSE BOX #12 A
TO UNDER DASH FUSE BOX #5 E
TO PARK BRAKE SW.
TO OIL PRESS. SENS.
TO UNDER DASH FUSE BOX #21 A
LIMIT SW'S.
L. FRT
L. REAR
R. REAR
R. FRT.
HEATED R. WDO
L. DOOR LOCK BELT SW.
RT. DOOR LOCK BELT SW.
PART OF INST. PNL.
TEMP
TAIL LT.
WASHER FLUID
COOL FLUID
OIL
BRAKE
FUEL
PRINTED CIRCUIT INST. PNL. (DIGITAL ONLY)
BELT SW
SEAT BELT IND.
RELEASE IND.
SPEED
TEMP.
TACH
TO INST. LT RHEO.
FROM INST. LT. RHEO.
SPOOL RETRACTOR SW
TO UNDER DASH FUSE BOX #5 E
R. BELT MTR.
L. BELT MTR.
TO UNDER DASH FUSE BOX #1 G
LUGG. COMP. LT. & SW
TO DOOR SW'S.
LICENSE LTS.
CHECK ENG
TO E.C.U. PIN #19
TO HAZ & DIR SW
R DIR
L DIR
BEAM SELECT.
TO FUEL GAUGE (TANK UNIT)
TO UNDER DASH FUSE BOX #5 E
MOTOR CONTROL
WARN. CIRCUIT CONTROL UNIT
BUZZER
AUTO SHOULDER BELT COMPUTER
TO INST. PNL. PRINTED CIRCUIT
FUEL GAUGE (TANK UNIT)
1. LOW FUEL
2. DIGITAL ONLY
3. FUEL GA.
TO UNDER DASH FUSE BOX #2 C
TO LEFT DIR. LTS. & IND.
TO ENG COMPT. FUSE BOX
TO RT. DIR. LTS. & IND.
TO LIGHT SW.
RT
OFF
LEFT
OFF
ON
DIRECT SW.
HAZARD SW.
TO DIR. FLASHER
L. REAR WDO MTR
L. REAR PWR. WDO. SW.
UP
DN
TO SEAT BELT CIRCUIT BREAKER
PWR. WDO. ASST. SW.
TO AIR COND. CIRCUIT BREAKER
TO NEUTRAL SAFETY SW.
TO UNDER DASH FUSE & RLY BOX
ST
IG1
ACC
AM
IG2
IGN. SW.
TO ENG COMPT. FUSE BOX #3 A
ASSISTANT PWR. WDO. MOTOR
R. REAR PWR. WDO. SW.
TO STOP LT. FAIL RLY.
TO UNDER DASH FUSE BOX #13 J
RT REAR PWR. WDO. MTR.
TO ENG. COMPT. FUSE BOX #2 B
TO HEAD LTS
OFF
TAIL
HEAD
LOW
HI
FLASH
LIGHT SW.
BEAM SELECT SW.
TO HI. BEAM IND.
TO ENG. COMPT. FUSE BOX #7 B
CONN.
TO PWR. WDO. RLY.
TO HAZ. & DIR. SW. PIN 9
(STA. WAG. ONLY)
STA. WAG (EXC.)
LOCK
AUTO
GRN-YEL ON STA. WAG.
TO UNDER DASH FUSE BOX #9 J
TO PWR. WDO. MAIN RLY.
MASTER PWR. WDO. SW.
MARKER LT.
INST. PANEL
PASS. COMP & REAR LTS
-A
-B
-C
-D
-E
-F
-G

1983 Toyota

LAND CRUISER

ENGINE COMPARTMENT, FUSE BLOCK & UNDERDASH

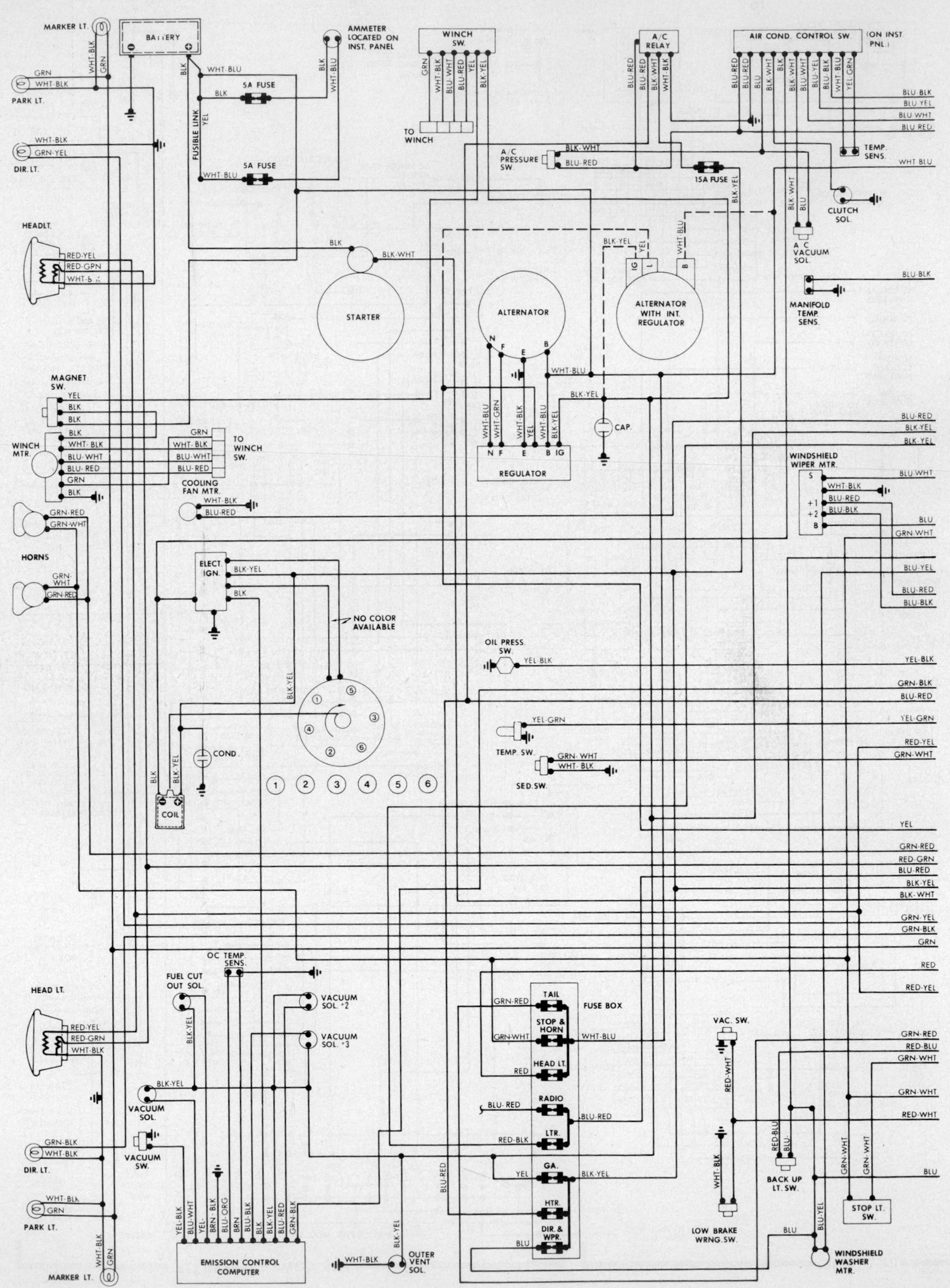
MARKER LT.
BATTERY
AMMETER LOCATED ON INST. PANEL
WINCH SW.
A/C RELAY
AIR COND. CONTROL SW. (ON INST. PNL.)
PARK LT.
DIR. LT.
5A FUSE
FUSIBLE LINK
TO WINCH
A/C PRESSURE SW.
15A FUSE
TEMP. SENS.
CLUTCH SOL.
HEADLT.
A/C VACUUM SOL.
STARTER
ALTERNATOR
ALTERNATOR WITH INT. REGULATOR
MANIFOLD TEMP. SENS.
MAGNET SW.
CAP.
REGULATOR
WINCH MTR.
TO WINCH SW.
COOLING FAN MTR.
WINDSHIELD WIPER MTR.
HORNS
ELECT. IGN.
NO COLOR AVAILABLE
OIL PRESS. SW.
TEMP. SW.
SED. SW.
COND.
COIL
OC TEMP. SENS.
FUEL CUT OUT SOL.
VACUUM SOL. *2
VACUUM SOL. *3
HEAD LT.
FUSE BOX
TAIL
STOP & HORN
HEAD LT.
RADIO
LTR.
GA.
HTR.
DIR. & WPR.
VAC. SW.
VACUUM SOL.
VACUUM SW.
BACK UP LT. SW.
STOP LT. SW.
LOW BRAKE WRNG. SW.
WINDSHIELD WASHER MTR.
EMISSION CONTROL COMPUTER
OUTER VENT SOL.
DIR. LT.
PARK LT.
MARKER LT.

1983 Toyota

LAND CRUISER (Cont.)

INSTRUMENT PANEL, UNDERDASH & REAR COMPARTMENT

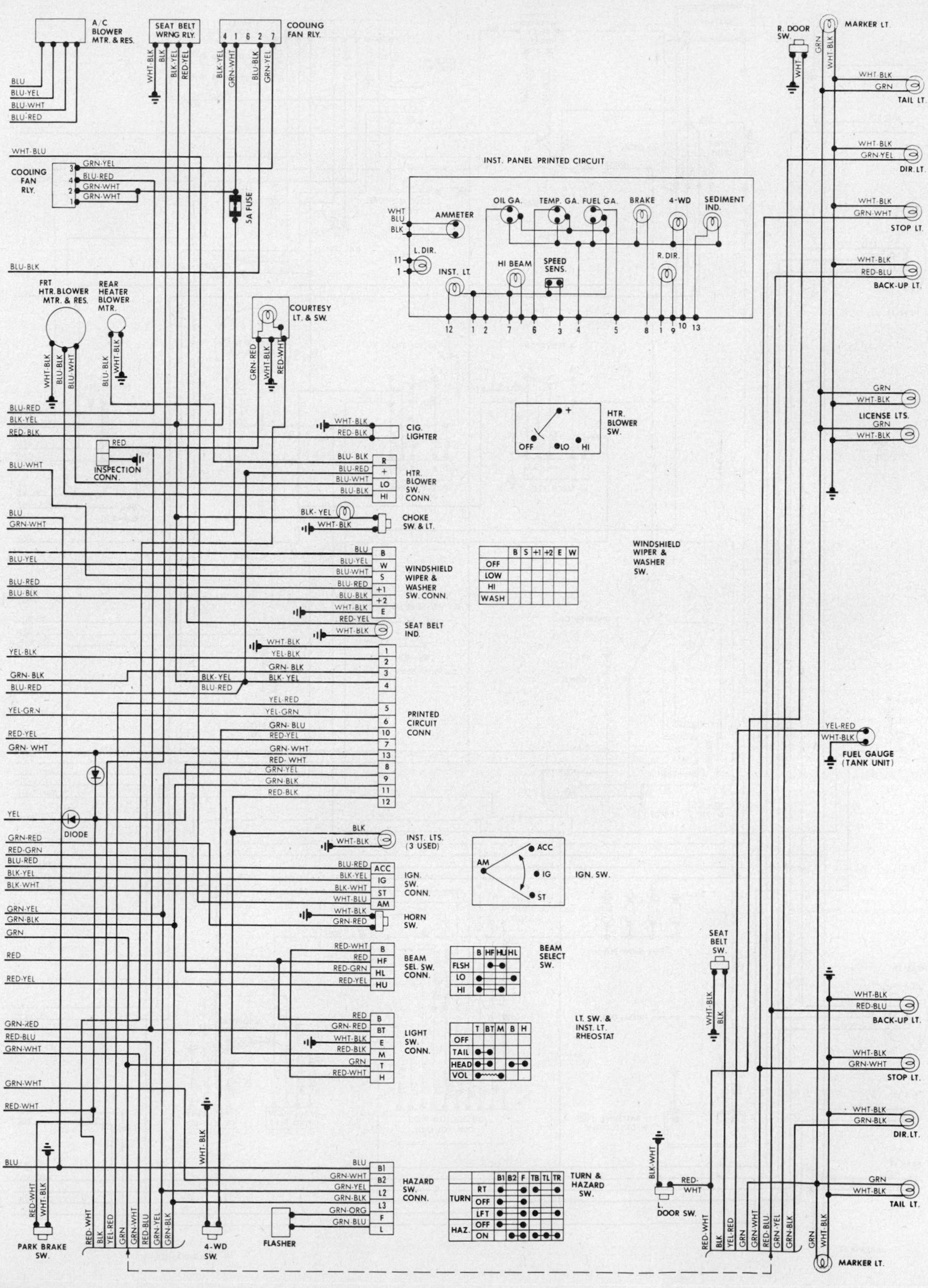

A/C BLOWER MTR. & RES.
SEAT BELT WRNG RLY.
COOLING FAN RLY.
R. DOOR SW.
MARKER LT.
TAIL LT.
COOLING FAN RLY.
5A FUSE
INST. PANEL PRINTED CIRCUIT
AMMETER
OIL GA.
TEMP. GA.
FUEL GA.
BRAKE
4-WD
SEDIMENT IND.
L. DIR.
INST. LT.
HI BEAM
SPEED SENS.
R. DIR.
DIR. LT.
STOP LT.
BACK-UP LT.
FRT HTR. BLOWER MTR. & RES.
REAR HEATER BLOWER MTR.
COURTESY LT. & SW.
LICENSE LTS.
CIG. LIGHTER
HTR. BLOWER SW.
OFF
LO
HI
INSPECTION CONN.
HTR. BLOWER SW. CONN.
CHOKE SW. & LT.
WINDSHIELD WIPER & WASHER SW. CONN.
WINDSHIELD WIPER & WASHER SW.
OFF
LOW
HI
WASH
SEAT BELT IND.
PRINTED CIRCUIT CONN
FUEL GAUGE (TANK UNIT)
DIODE
INST. LTS. (3 USED)
IGN. SW. CONN.
ACC
IG
ST
AM
IGN. SW.
HORN SW.
BEAM SEL. SW. CONN.
BEAM SELECT SW.
FLSH
LO
HI
SEAT BELT SW.
LIGHT SW. CONN.
LT. SW. & INST. LT. RHEOSTAT
OFF
TAIL
HEAD
VOL
HAZARD SW. CONN.
TURN & HAZARD SW.
TURN
RT
OFF
LFT
HAZ.
ON
L. DOOR SW.
PARK BRAKE SW.
4-WD SW.
FLASHER

1983 Toyota

PICKUP & DIESEL PICKUP

ENGINE COMPARTMENT

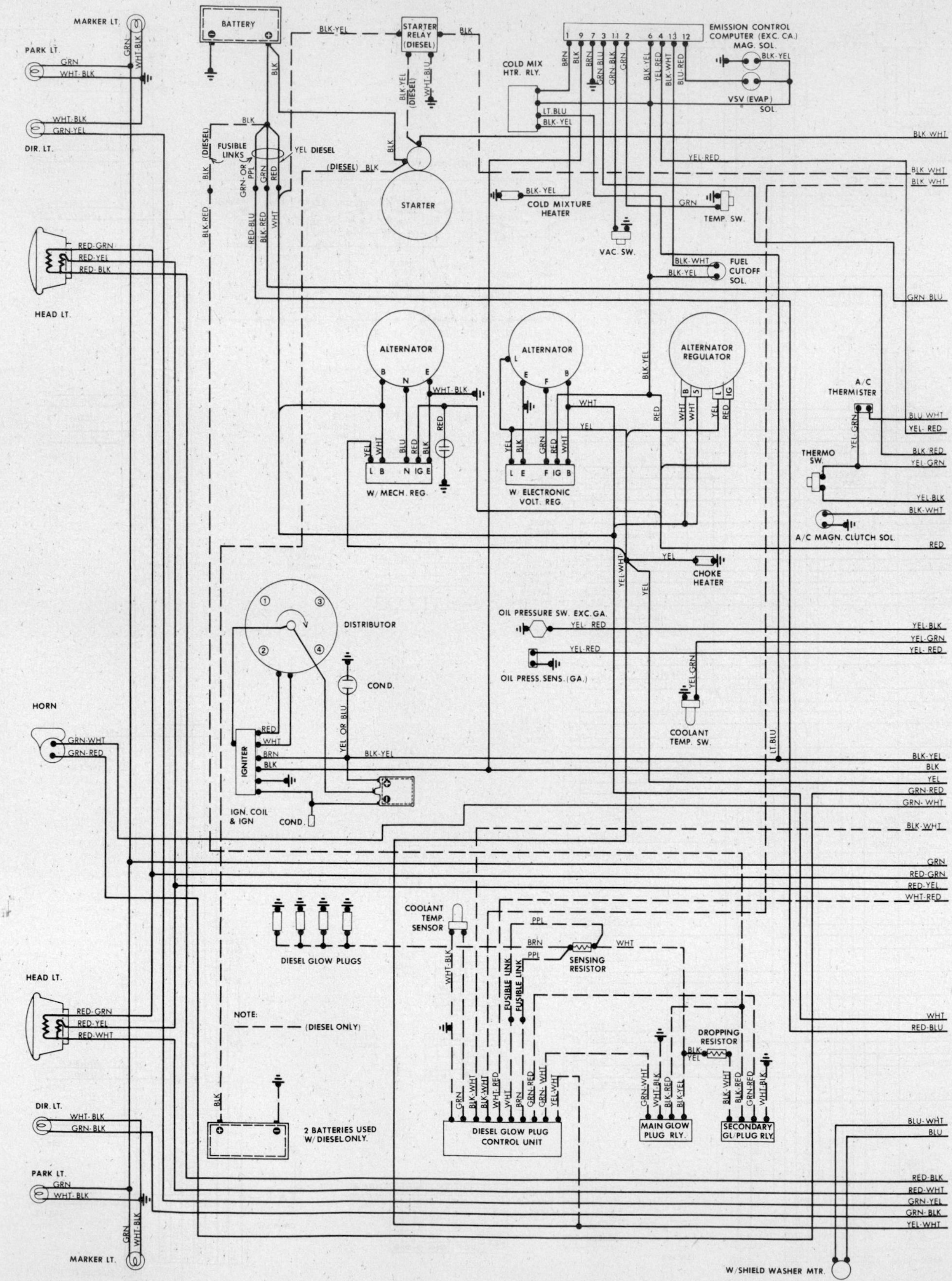

MARKER LT.
PARK LT.
DIR. LT.
HEAD LT.
BATTERY
STARTER RELAY (DIESEL)
FUSIBLE LINKS
YEL DIESEL
STARTER
COLD MIX HTR. RLY.
EMISSION CONTROL COMPUTER (EXC. CA.)
MAG. SOL.
VSV (EVAP) SOL.
COLD MIXTURE HEATER
TEMP. SW.
VAC. SW.
FUEL CUTOFF SOL.
ALTERNATOR
ALTERNATOR
ALTERNATOR REGULATOR
W/ MECH. REG.
W/ ELECTRONIC VOLT. REG.
A/C THERMISTER
THERMO SW.
A/C MAGN. CLUTCH SOL.
CHOKE HEATER
DISTRIBUTOR
COND.
OIL PRESSURE SW. EXC. GA.
OIL PRESS. SENS. (GA.)
COOLANT TEMP. SW.
HORN
IGNITER
IGN. COIL & IGN
COND.
DIESEL GLOW PLUGS
COOLANT TEMP. SENSOR
SENSING RESISTOR
FUSIBLE LINK
FUSIBLE LINK
NOTE:
(DIESEL ONLY)
DROPPING RESISTOR
2 BATTERIES USED W/ DIESEL ONLY.
DIESEL GLOW PLUG CONTROL UNIT
MAIN GLOW PLUG RLY.
SECONDARY GL/PLUG RLY.
HEAD LT.
DIR. LT.
PARK LT.
MARKER LT.
W/SHIELD WASHER MTR.

1983 Toyota

PICKUP & DIESEL PICKUP (Cont.)

FUSE BLOCK & UNDERDASH

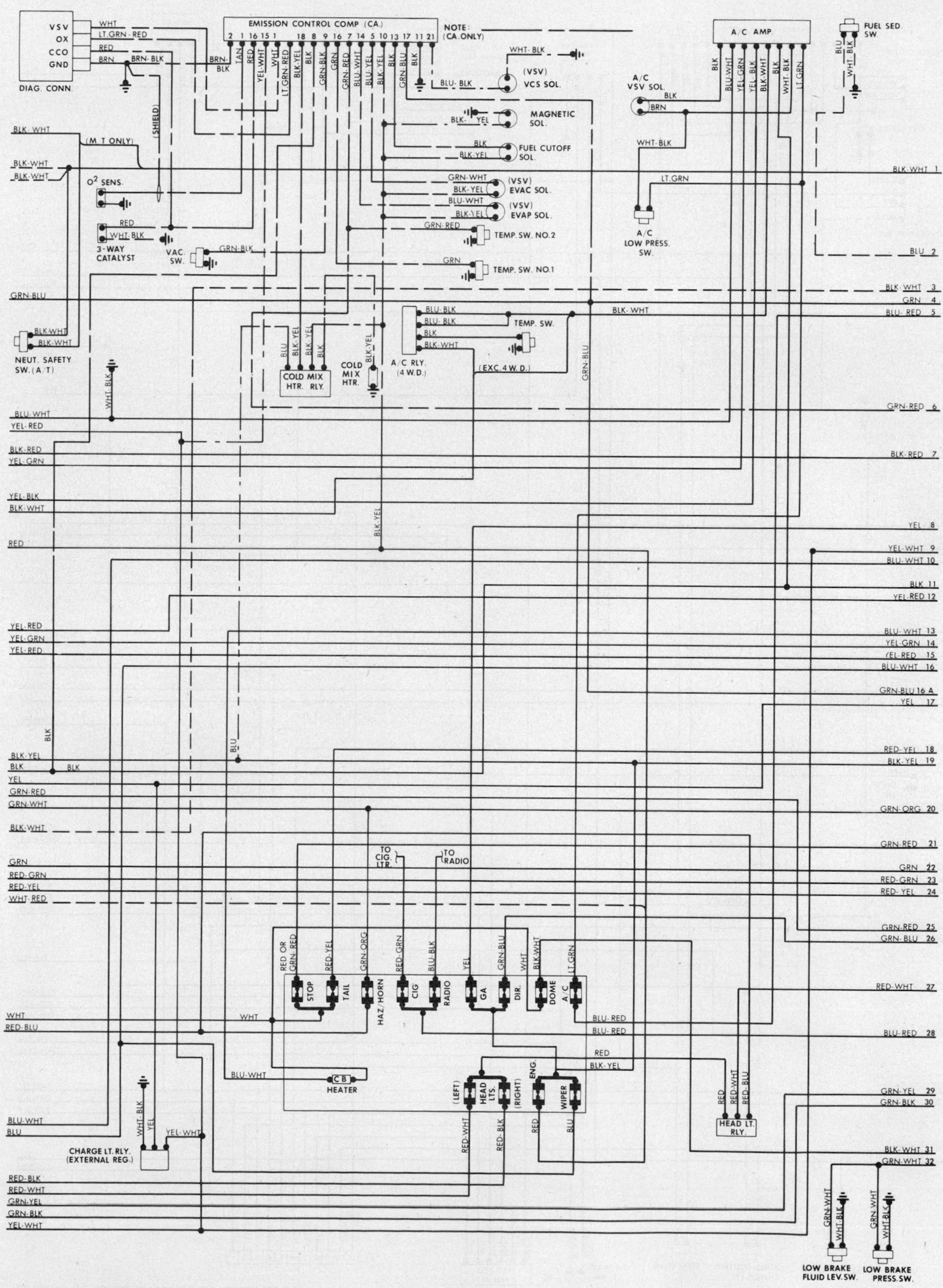

1983 Toyota

PICKUP & DIESEL PICKUP (Cont.)

UNDERDASH

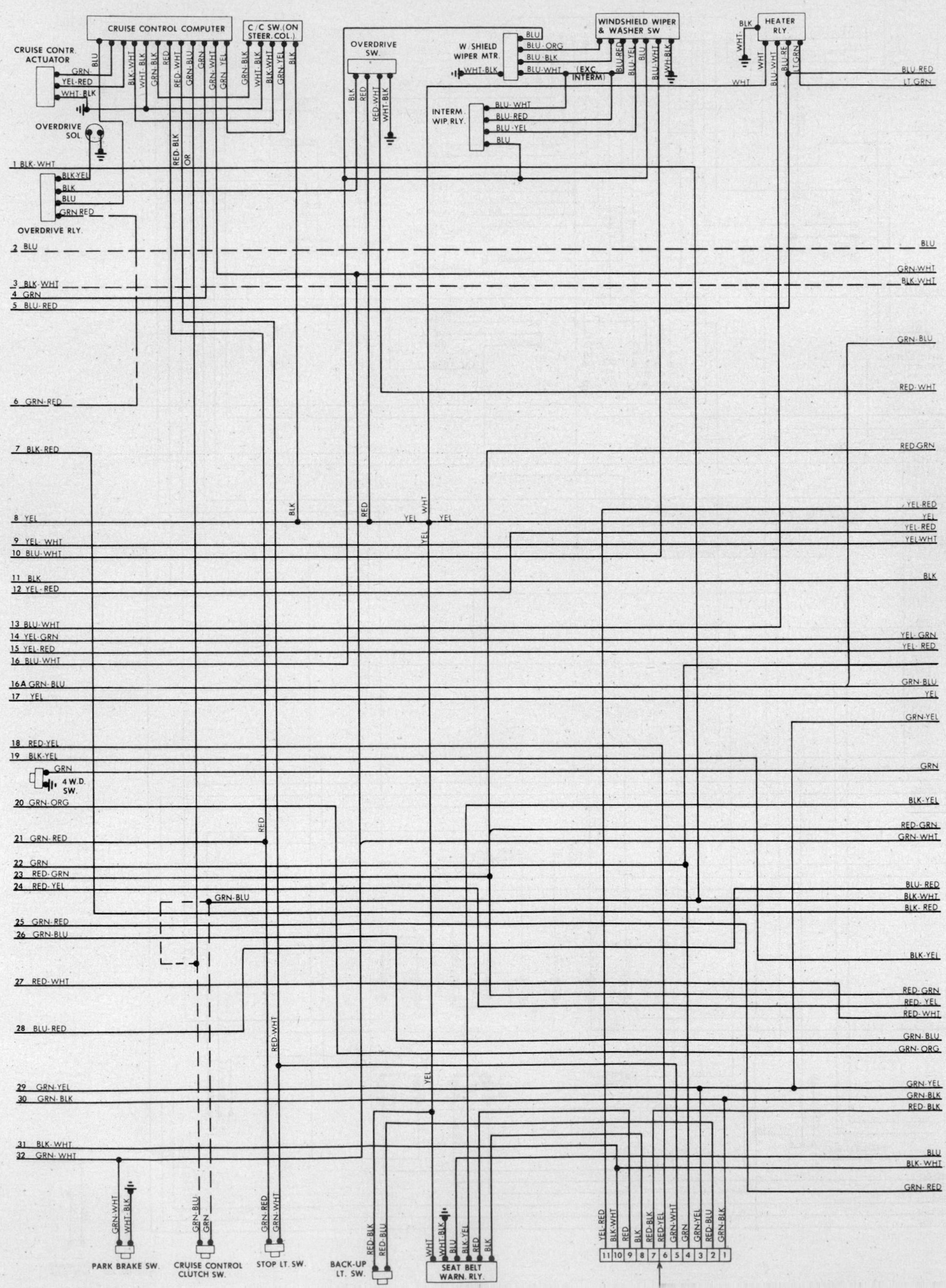
CRUISE CONTROL COMPUTER
C/C SW. (ON STEER. COL.)
OVERDRIVE SW.
W. SHIELD WIPER MTR.
WINDSHIELD WIPER & WASHER SW
HEATER RLY.
CRUISE CONTR. ACTUATOR
OVERDRIVE SOL
INTERM. WIP. RLY.
OVERDRIVE RLY.
(EXC INTERM)
4 W.D. SW.
PARK BRAKE SW.
CRUISE CONTROL CLUTCH SW.
STOP LT. SW.
BACK-UP LT. SW.
SEAT BELT WARN. RLY.
1 BLK-WHT
2 BLU
3 BLK-WHT
4 GRN
5 BLU-RED
6 GRN-RED
7 BLK-RED
8 YEL
9 YEL-WHT
10 BLU-WHT
11 BLK
12 YEL-RED
13 BLU-WHT
14 YEL-GRN
15 YEL-RED
16 BLU-WHT
16A GRN-BLU
17 YEL
18 RED-YEL
19 BLK-YEL
20 GRN-ORG
21 GRN-RED
22 GRN
23 RED-GRN
24 RED-YEL
25 GRN-RED
26 GRN-BLU
27 RED-WHT
28 BLU-RED
29 GRN-YEL
30 GRN-BLK
31 BLK-WHT
32 GRN-WHT

PICKUP & DIESEL PICKUP (Cont.)

INSTRUMENT PANEL & REAR COMPARTMENT

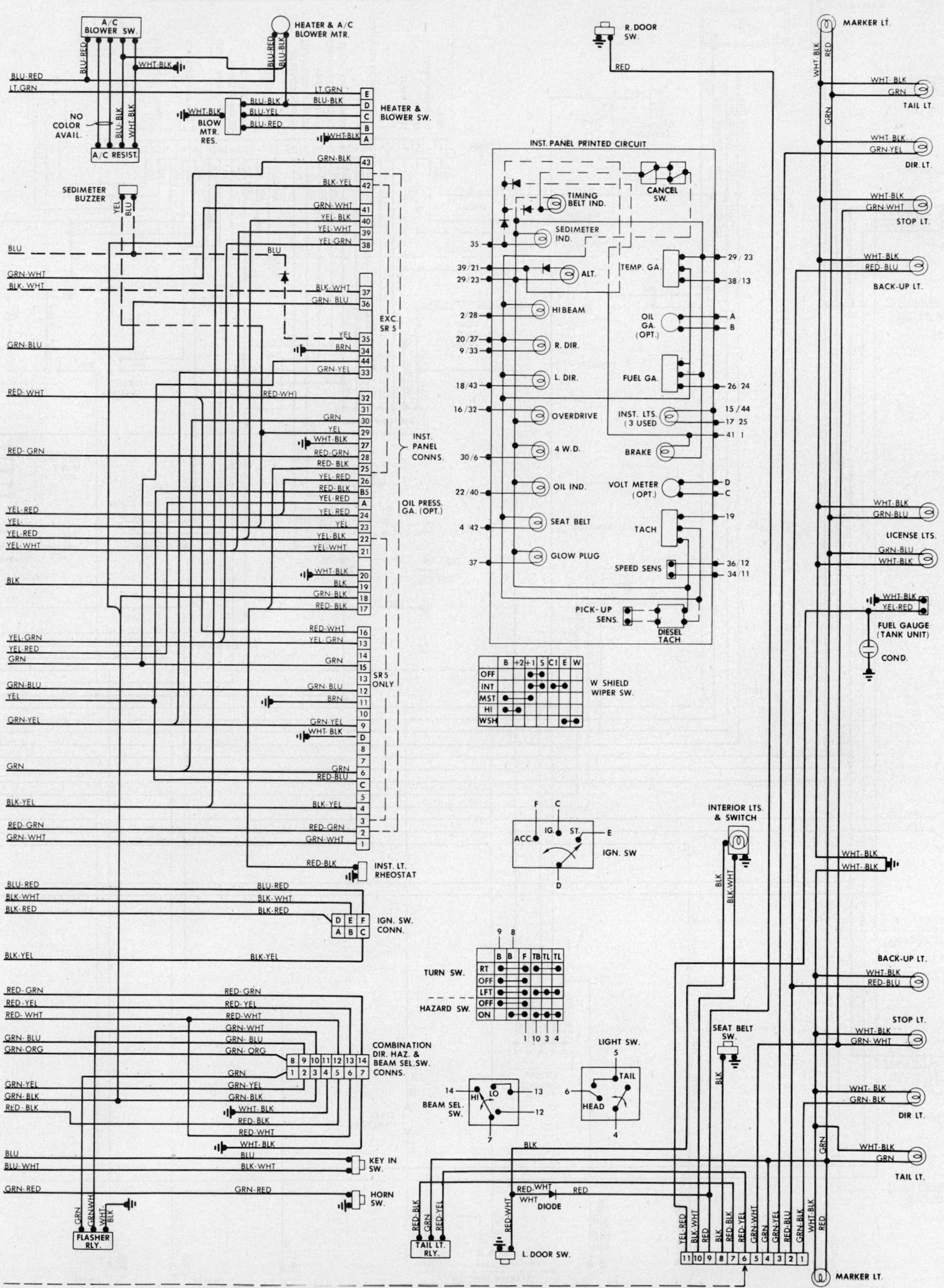
A/C BLOWER SW.
HEATER & A/C BLOWER MTR.
NO COLOR AVAIL.
A/C RESIST.
BLOW MTR. RES.
HEATER & BLOWER SW.
SEDIMETER BUZZER
EXC. SR 5
INST. PANEL CONNS.
OIL PRESS. GA. (OPT.)
SR5 ONLY
INST. LT. RHEOSTAT
IGN. SW. CONN.
COMBINATION DIR. HAZ. & BEAM SEL. SW. CONNS.
KEY IN SW.
HORN SW.
FLASHER RLY.
INST. PANEL PRINTED CIRCUIT
TIMING BELT IND.
CANCEL SW.
SEDIMETER IND.
ALT.
TEMP. GA.
HI BEAM
OIL GA. (OPT.)
R. DIR.
L. DIR.
FUEL GA.
OVERDRIVE
INST. LTS. (3 USED)
4 W.D.
BRAKE
OIL IND.
VOLT METER (OPT.)
SEAT BELT
TACH
GLOW PLUG
SPEED SENS
PICK-UP SENS.
DIESEL TACH
W SHIELD WIPER SW.
IGN. SW
TURN SW.
HAZARD SW.
BEAM SEL. SW.
LIGHT SW.
HEAD
TAIL
TAIL LT. RLY.
DIODE
L. DOOR SW.
R. DOOR SW.
INTERIOR LTS. & SWITCH
SEAT BELT SW.
MARKER LT.
TAIL LT.
DIR. LT.
STOP LT.
BACK-UP LT.
LICENSE LTS.
FUEL GAUGE (TANK UNIT)
COND.

1983 Toyota

STARLET

ENGINE COMPARTMENT

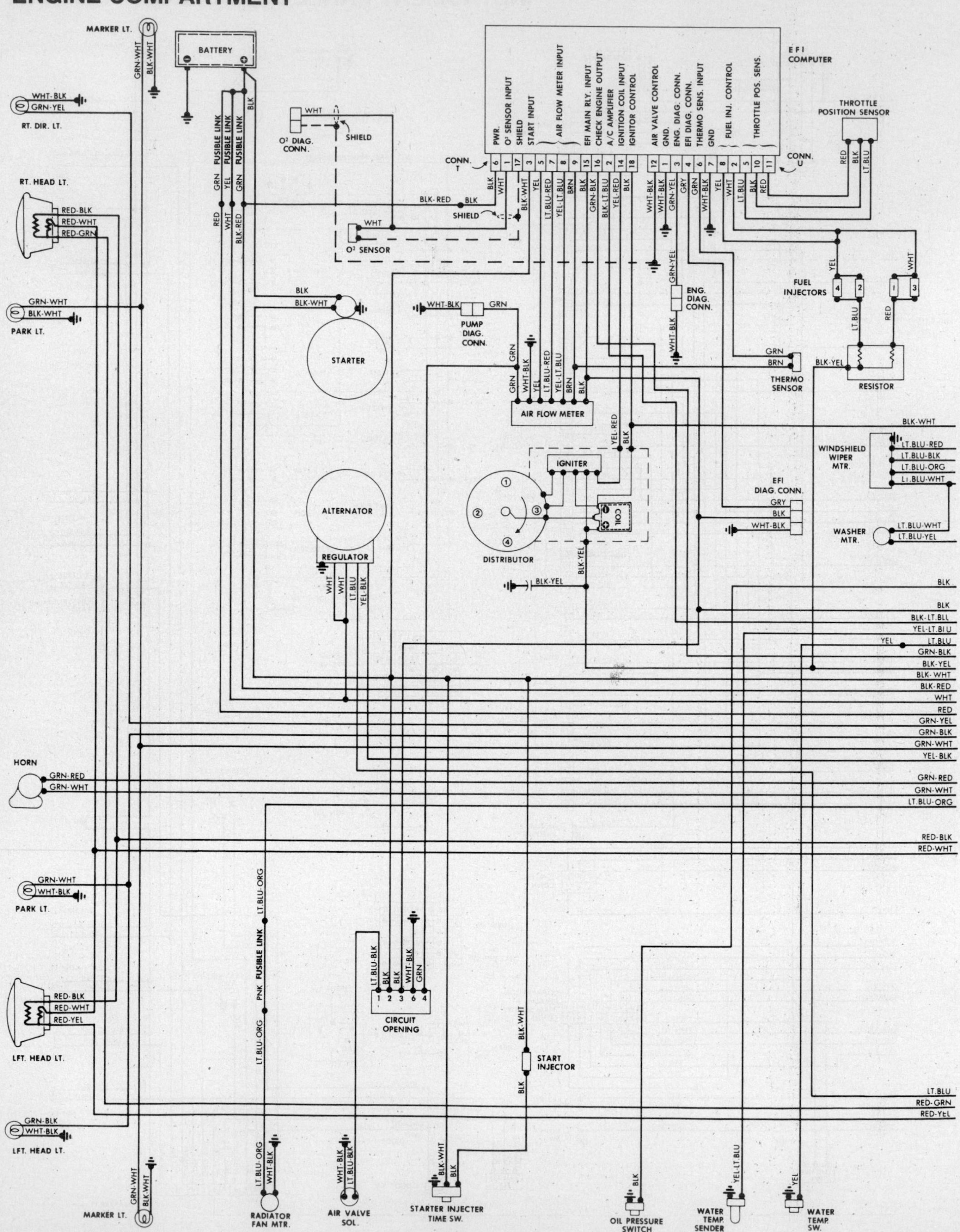

MARKER LT.
BATTERY
RT. DIR. LT.
RT. HEAD LT.
PARK LT.
HORN
LFT. HEAD LT.
FUSIBLE LINK
O² DIAG. CONN.
SHIELD
O² SENSOR
STARTER
ALTERNATOR
REGULATOR
EFI COMPUTER
CONN. T
CONN. U
PWR.
O² SENSOR INPUT
SHIELD
START INPUT
AIR FLOW METER INPUT
EFI MAIN RLY. INPUT
CHECK ENGINE OUTPUT
A/C AMPLIFIER
IGNITION COIL INPUT
IGNITOR CONTROL
AIR VALVE CONTROL
GND.
ENG. DIAG. CONN.
EFI DIAG. CONN.
THERMO SENS. INPUT
GND
FUEL INJ. CONTROL
THROTTLE POS. SENS.
THROTTLE POSITION SENSOR
FUEL INJECTORS
RESISTOR
ENG. DIAG. CONN.
PUMP DIAG. CONN.
AIR FLOW METER
THERMO SENSOR
IGNITER
COIL
DISTRIBUTOR
WINDSHIELD WIPER MTR.
EFI DIAG. CONN.
WASHER MTR.
CIRCUIT OPENING
START INJECTOR
RADIATOR FAN MTR.
AIR VALVE SOL.
STARTER INJECTER TIME SW.
OIL PRESSURE SWITCH
WATER TEMP. SENDER
WATER TEMP. SW.

1983 Toyota

STARLET (Cont.)

FUSE BLOCK & UNDERDASH

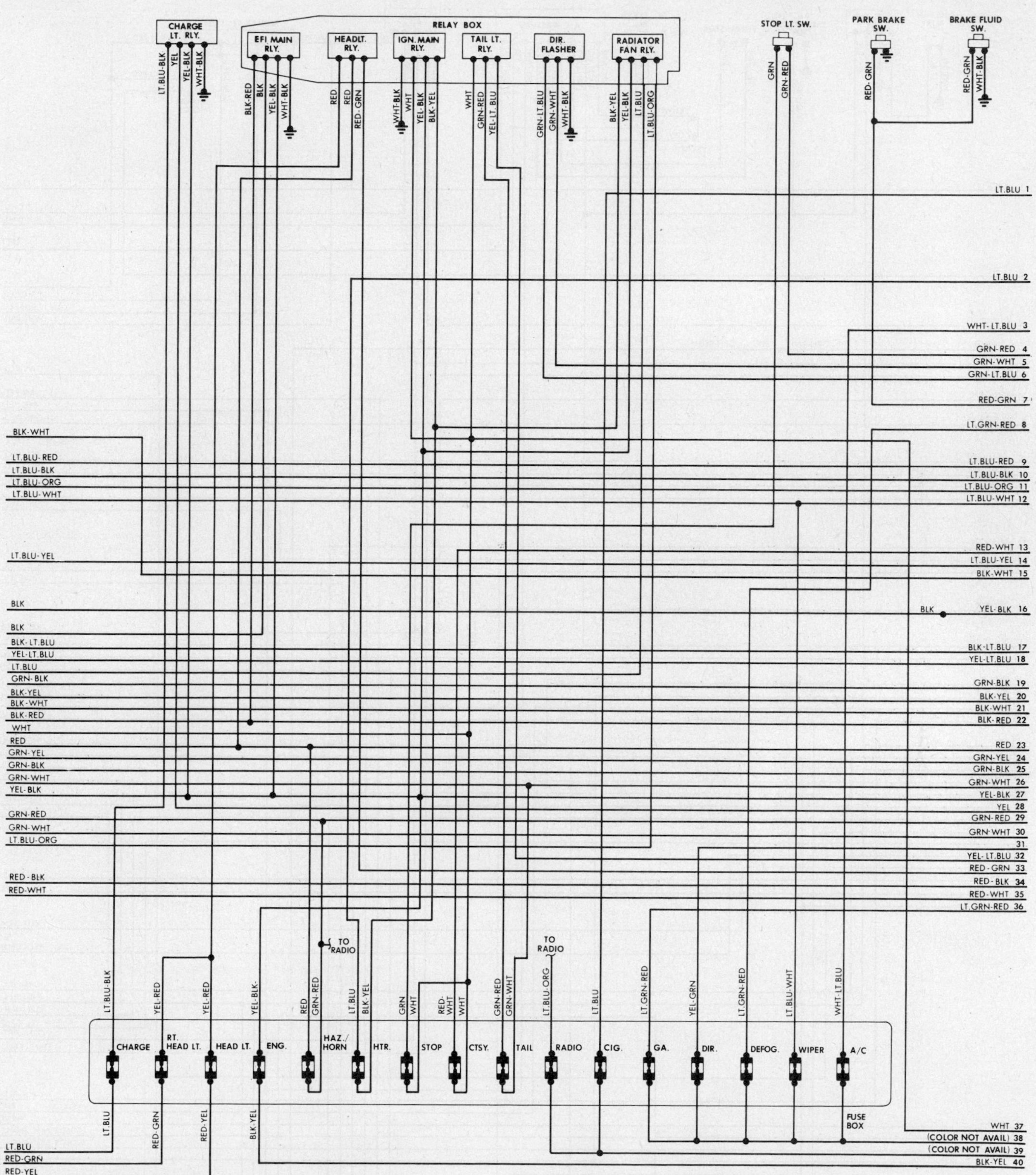

CHARGE LT. RLY.
RELAY BOX
EFI MAIN RLY.
HEADLT. RLY.
IGN. MAIN RLY.
TAIL LT. RLY.
DIR. FLASHER
RADIATOR FAN RLY.
STOP LT. SW.
PARK BRAKE SW.
BRAKE FLUID SW.
LT.BLU 1
LT.BLU 2
WHT-LT.BLU 3
GRN-RED 4
GRN-WHT 5
GRN-LT.BLU 6
RED-GRN 7
LT.GRN-RED 8
LT.BLU-RED 9
LT.BLU-BLK 10
LT.BLU-ORG 11
LT.BLU-WHT 12
RED-WHT 13
LT.BLU-YEL 14
BLK-WHT 15
YEL-BLK 16
BLK-LT.BLU 17
YEL-LT.BLU 18
GRN-BLK 19
BLK-YEL 20
BLK-WHT 21
BLK-RED 22
RED 23
GRN-YEL 24
GRN-BLK 25
GRN-WHT 26
YEL-BLK 27
YEL 28
GRN-RED 29
GRN-WHT 30
31
YEL-LT.BLU 32
RED-GRN 33
RED-BLK 34
RED-WHT 35
LT.GRN-RED 36
WHT 37
(COLOR NOT AVAIL) 38
(COLOR NOT AVAIL) 39
BLK-YEL 40
TO RADIO
CHARGE
RT. HEAD LT.
HEAD LT.
ENG.
HAZ./HORN
HTR.
STOP
CTSY.
TAIL
RADIO
CIG.
GA.
DIR.
DEFOG.
WIPER
A/C
FUSE BOX

1983 Toyota

STARLET (Cont.)

UNDERDASH

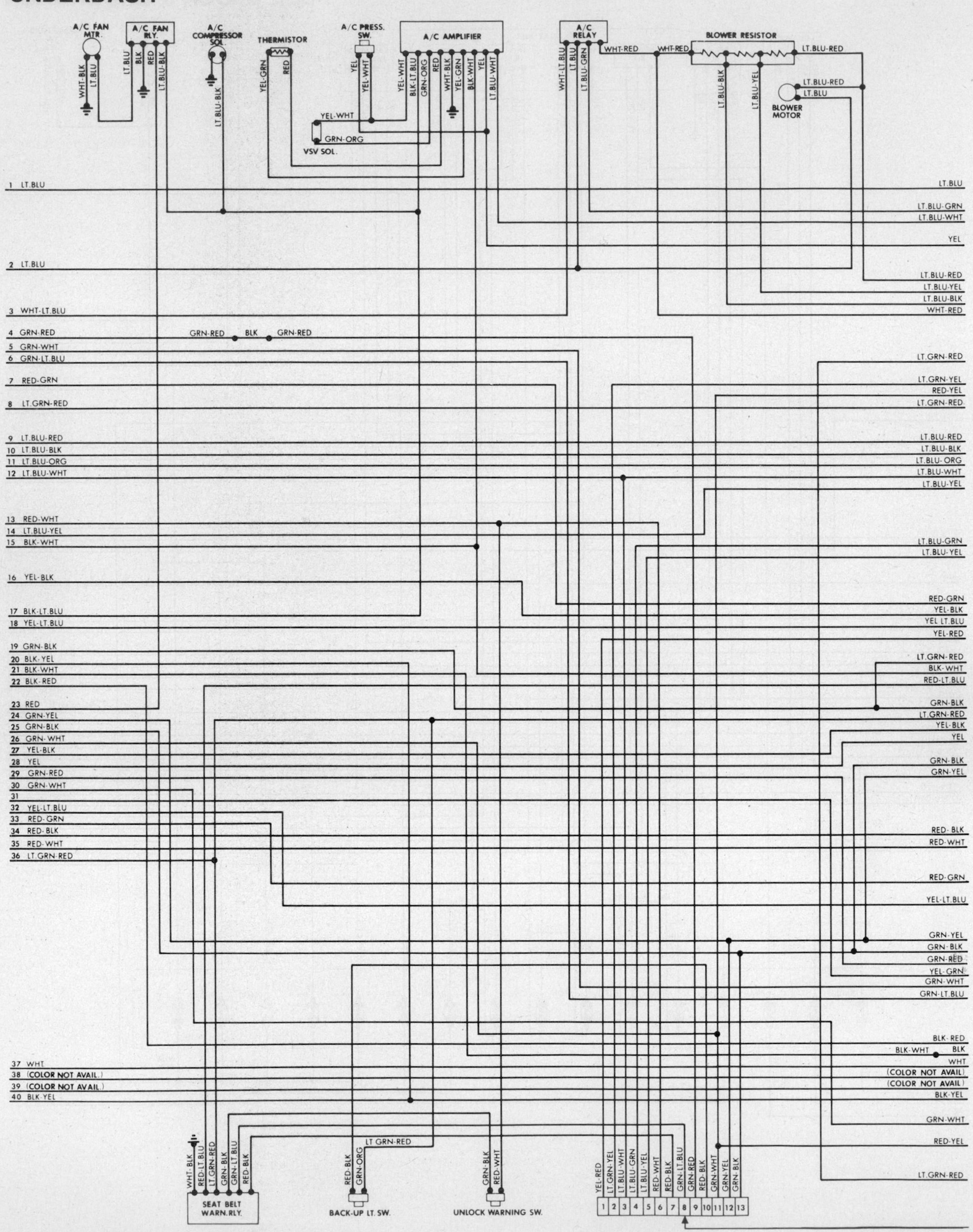
A/C FAN MTR.
A/C FAN RLY.
A/C COMPRESSOR SOL.
THERMISTOR
A/C PRESS. SW.
A/C AMPLIFIER
A/C RELAY
BLOWER RESISTOR
BLOWER MOTOR
VSV SOL.
1 LT.BLU
2 LT.BLU
3 WHT-LT.BLU
4 GRN-RED
5 GRN-WHT
6 GRN-LT.BLU
7 RED-GRN
8 LT.GRN-RED
9 LT.BLU-RED
10 LT.BLU-BLK
11 LT.BLU-ORG
12 LT.BLU-WHT
13 RED-WHT
14 LT.BLU-YEL
15 BLK-WHT
16 YEL-BLK
17 BLK-LT.BLU
18 YEL-LT.BLU
19 GRN-BLK
20 BLK-YEL
21 BLK-WHT
22 BLK-RED
23 RED
24 GRN-YEL
25 GRN-BLK
26 GRN-WHT
27 YEL-BLK
28 YEL
29 GRN-RED
30 GRN-WHT
31
32 YEL-LT.BLU
33 RED-GRN
34 RED-BLK
35 RED-WHT
36 LT.GRN-RED
37 WHT
38 (COLOR NOT AVAIL.)
39 (COLOR NOT AVAIL.)
40 BLK-YEL
SEAT BELT WARN. RLY.
BACK-UP LT. SW.
UNLOCK WARNING SW.

STARLET (Cont.)

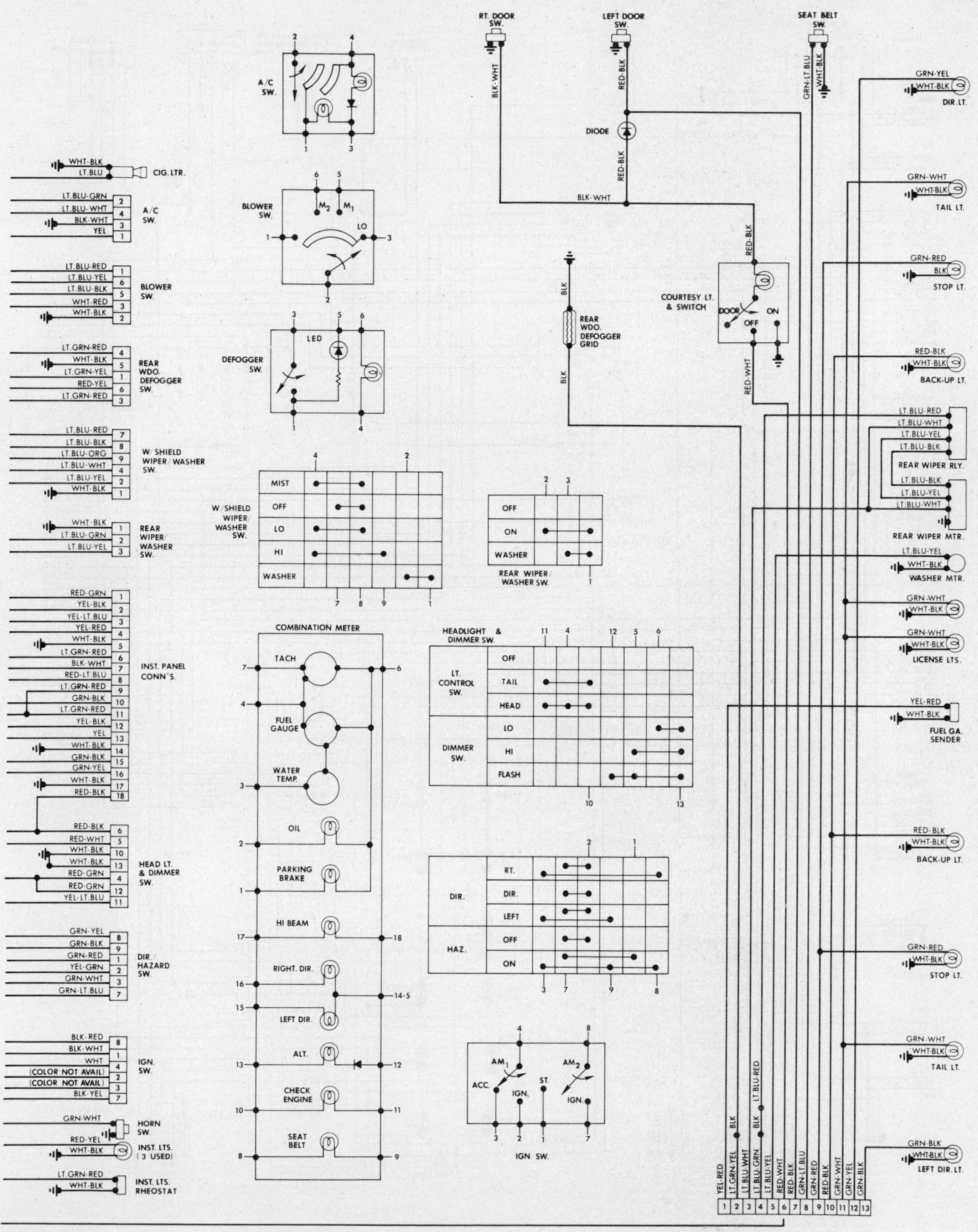

REAR COMPARTMENT
RT. DOOR SW.
LEFT DOOR SW.
SEAT BELT SW.
A/C SW.
CIG. LTR.
BLOWER SW.
DIODE
COURTESY LT. & SWITCH
DEFOGGER SW.
REAR WDO. DEFOGGER GRID
REAR WDO. DEFOGGER SW.
W/SHIELD WIPER/WASHER SW.
REAR WIPER/WASHER SW.
INST. PANEL CONN'S.
COMBINATION METER
TACH
FUEL GAUGE
WATER TEMP.
OIL
PARKING BRAKE
HI BEAM
RIGHT. DIR.
LEFT DIR.
ALT.
CHECK ENGINE
SEAT BELT
HEADLIGHT & DIMMER SW.
LT. CONTROL SW.
DIMMER SW.
HEAD LT. & DIMMER SW.
DIR./HAZARD SW.
IGN. SW.
HORN SW.
INST. LTS. (3 USED)
INST. LTS. RHEOSTAT
DIR. LT.
TAIL LT.
STOP LT.
BACK-UP LT.
REAR WIPER RLY.
REAR WIPER MTR.
WASHER MTR.
LICENSE LTS.
FUEL GA. SENDER
LEFT DIR. LT.

1983 Toyota

SUPRA

ENGINE COMPARTMENT & FUSE BLOCK

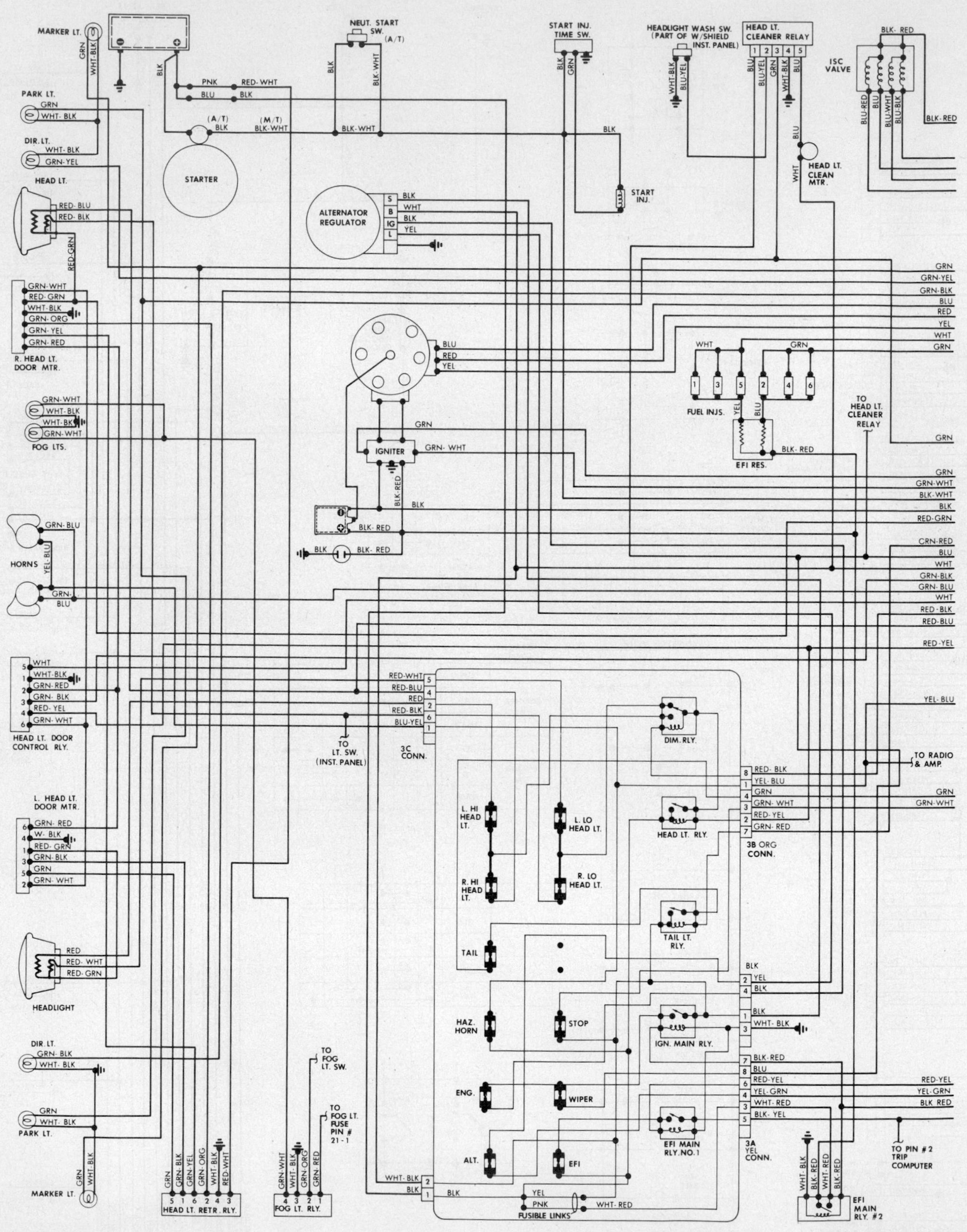

MARKER LT.
PARK LT.
DIR. LT.
HEAD LT.
R. HEAD LT. DOOR MTR.
FOG LTS.
HORNS
HEAD LT. DOOR CONTROL RLY.
L. HEAD LT. DOOR MTR.
HEADLIGHT
DIR. LT.
PARK LT.
MARKER LT.
HEAD LT. RETR. RLY.
FOG LT. RLY.
TO FOG LT. SW.
TO FOG LT. FUSE PIN # 21-1
STARTER
NEUT. START SW. (A/T)
ALTERNATOR REGULATOR
IGNITER
TO LT. SW. (INST. PANEL)
3C CONN.
START INJ. TIME SW.
START INJ.
HEADLIGHT WASH SW. (PART OF W/SHIELD INST. PANEL)
HEAD LT. CLEANER RELAY
HEAD LT. CLEAN MTR.
ISC VALVE
FUEL INJS.
EFI RES.
TO HEAD LT. CLEANER RELAY
DIM. RLY.
L. HI HEAD LT.
L. LO HEAD LT.
R. HI HEAD LT.
R. LO HEAD LT.
HEAD LT. RLY.
3B ORG CONN.
TO RADIO & AMP.
TAIL
TAIL LT. RLY.
HAZ. HORN
STOP
IGN. MAIN RLY.
ENG.
WIPER
ALT.
EFI
EFI MAIN RLY. NO. 1
3A YEL CONN.
FUSIBLE LINKS
TO PIN # 2 TRIP COMPUTER
EFI MAIN RLY. # 2

UNDERDASH

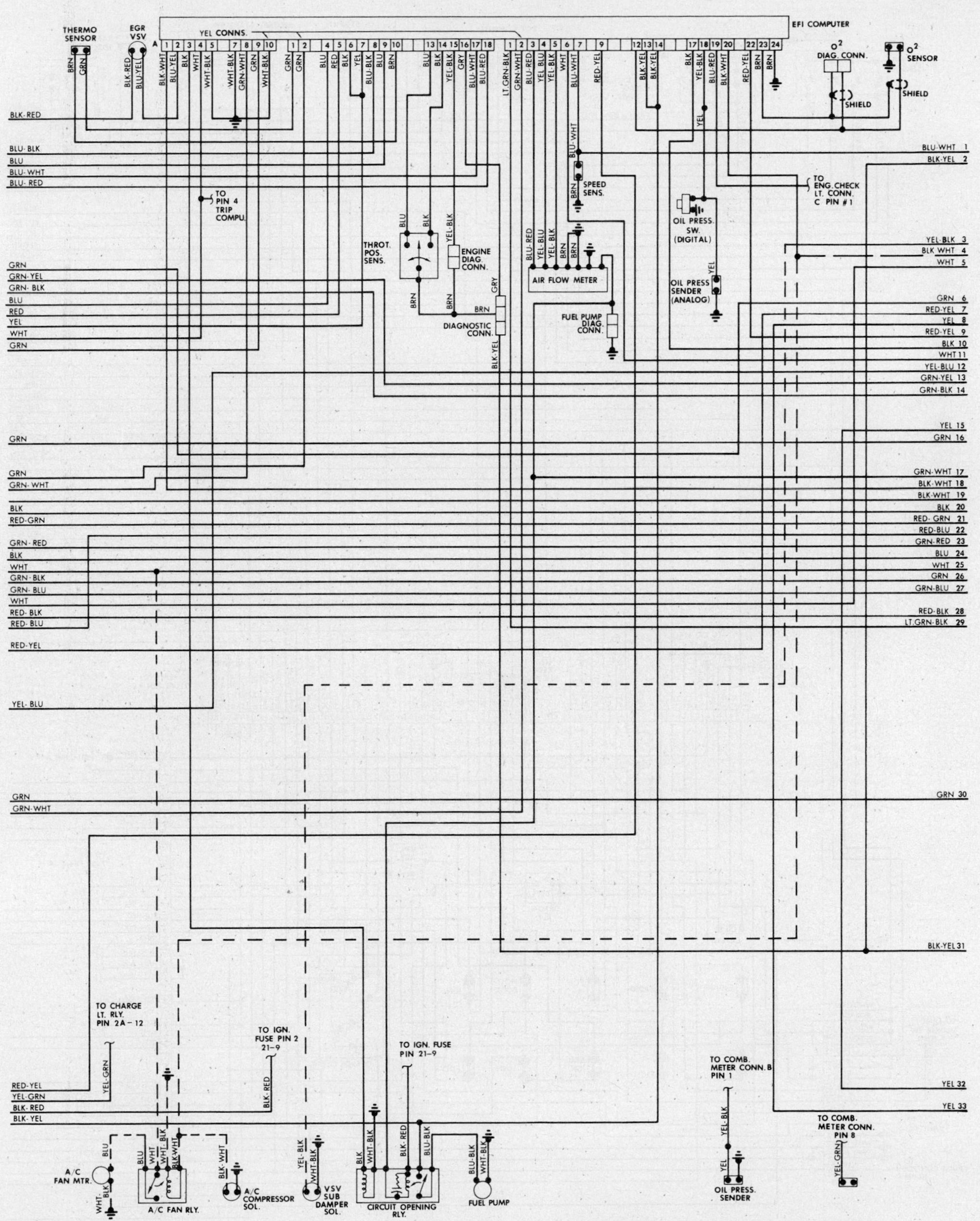
EFI COMPUTER
YEL CONNS.
THERMO SENSOR
EGR VSV
THROT. POS. SENS.
ENGINE DIAG. CONN.
DIAGNOSTIC CONN.
SPEED SENS.
AIR FLOW METER
FUEL PUMP DIAG. CONN.
OIL PRESS. SW. (DIGITAL)
OIL PRESS SENDER (ANALOG)
O2 DIAG. CONN.
O2 SENSOR
SHIELD
TO PIN 4 TRIP COMPU.
TO ENG. CHECK LT. CONN. C PIN # 1
TO CHARGE LT. RLY. PIN 2A-12
TO IGN. FUSE PIN 2 21-9
TO IGN. FUSE PIN 21-9
TO COMB. METER CONN. B PIN 1
TO COMB. METER CONN. PIN 8
A/C FAN MTR.
A/C FAN RLY.
A/C COMPRESSOR SOL.
VSV SUB DAMPER SOL.
CIRCUIT OPENING RLY.
FUEL PUMP
OIL PRESS. SENDER

1983 Toyota

SUPRA (Cont.)

FUSE BLOCK & UNDERDASH

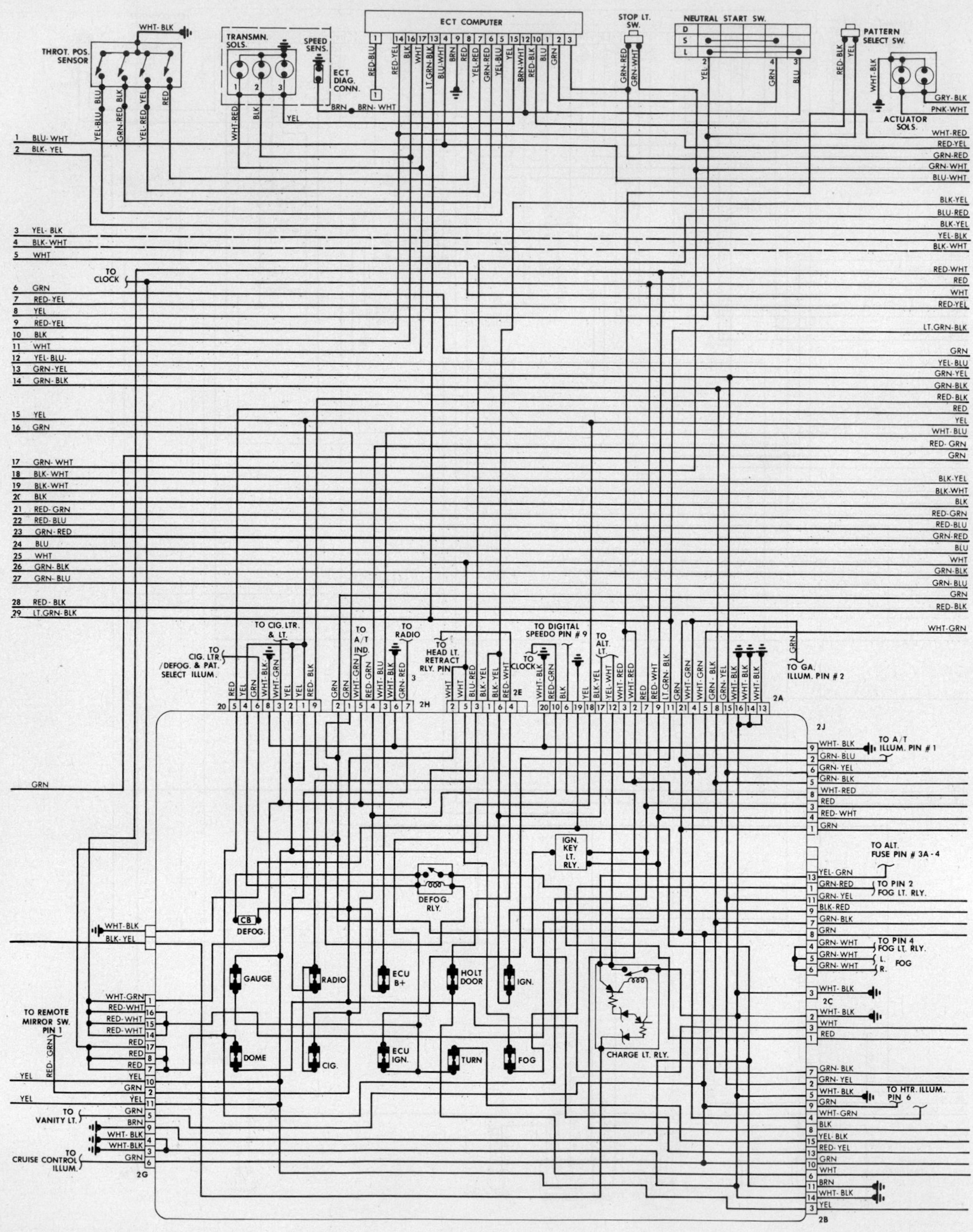

1983 Toyota

SUPRA (Cont.)

UNDERDASH

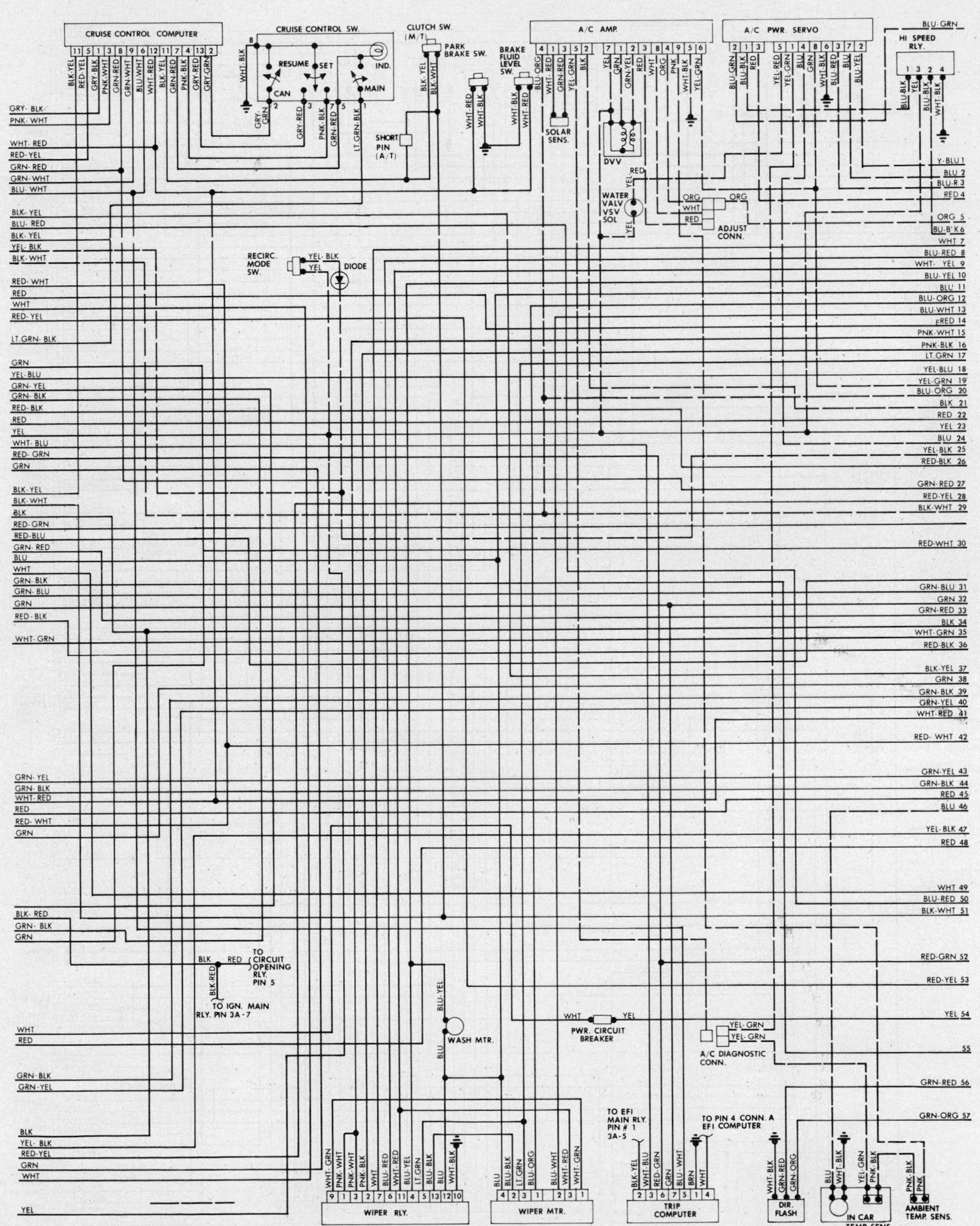

CRUISE CONTROL COMPUTER
CRUISE CONTROL SW.
CLUTCH SW. (M/T)
PARK BRAKE SW.
BRAKE FLUID LEVEL SW.
A/C AMP.
A/C PWR. SERVO
HI SPEED RLY.
RESUME
SET
CAN
IND.
MAIN
SHORT PIN (A/T)
SOLAR SENS.
DVV
WATER VALV VSV SOL
ADJUST CONN.
RECIRC. MODE SW.
DIODE
TO CIRCUIT OPENING RLY. PIN 5
TO IGN. MAIN RLY. PIN 3A-7
WASH MTR.
PWR. CIRCUIT BREAKER
A/C DIAGNOSTIC CONN.
TO EFI MAIN RLY. PIN # 1 3A-5
TO PIN 4 CONN. A EFI COMPUTER
WIPER RLY.
WIPER MTR.
TRIP COMPUTER
DIR. FLASH
IN CAR TEMP. SENS.
AMBIENT TEMP. SENS.

1983 Toyota

SUPRA (Cont.)

INSTRUMENT PANEL & UNDERDASH

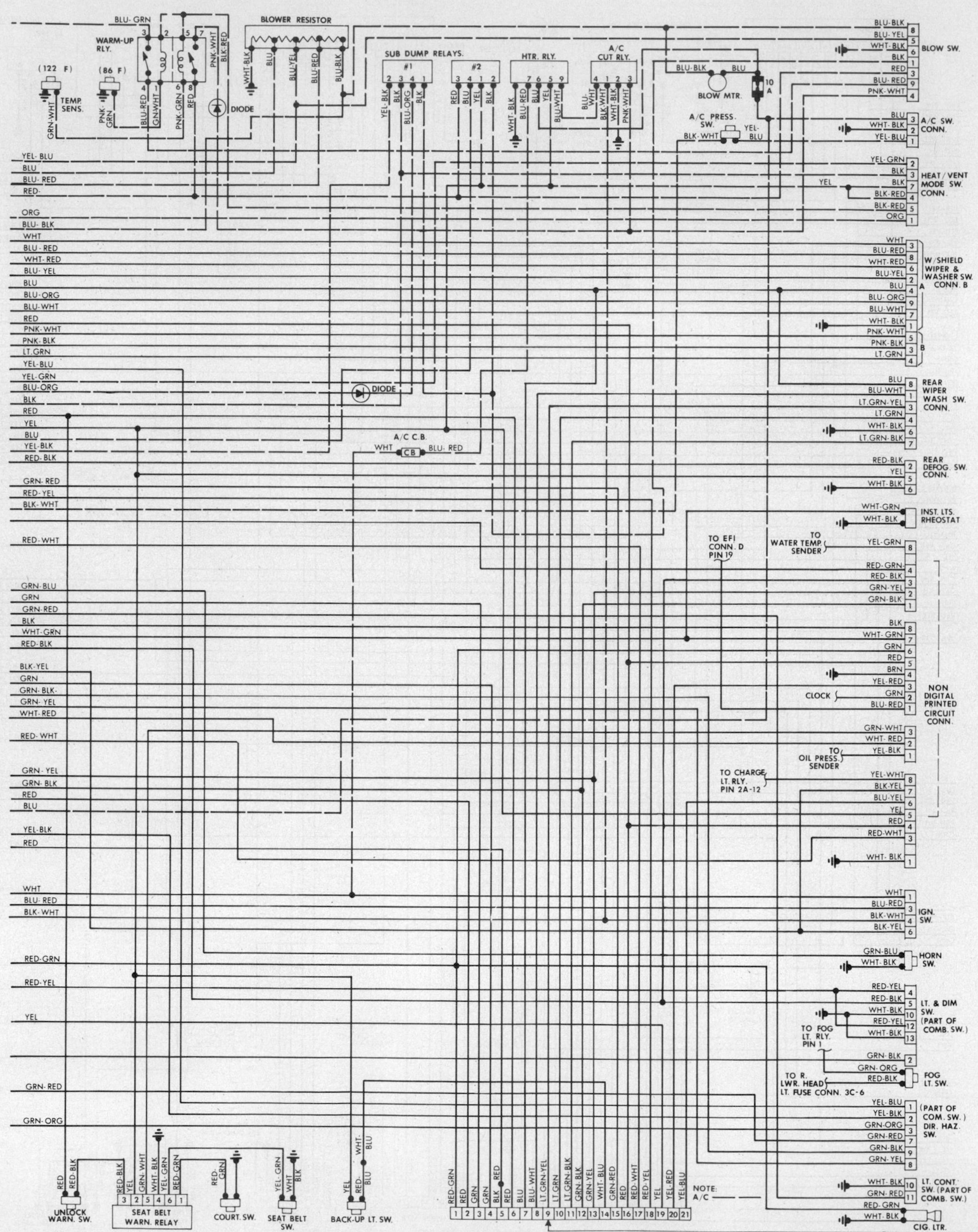

BLOWER RESISTOR
WARM-UP RLY.
(122 F)
(86 F)
TEMP. SENS.
DIODE
SUB DUMP RELAYS.
#1
#2
HTR. RLY.
A/C CUT RLY.
BLOW MTR.
10 A
A/C PRESS. SW.
BLOW SW.
A/C SW. CONN.
HEAT/VENT MODE SW. CONN.
W/SHIELD WIPER & WASHER SW. CONN. B
REAR WIPER WASH SW. CONN.
A/C C.B.
REAR DEFOG. SW. CONN.
INST. LTS. RHEOSTAT
TO WATER TEMP. SENDER
TO EFI CONN. D PIN 19
CLOCK
NON DIGITAL PRINTED CIRCUIT CONN.
TO OIL PRESS. SENDER
TO CHARGE LT. RLY. PIN 2A-12
IGN. SW.
HORN SW.
LT. & DIM SW. (PART OF COMB. SW.)
TO FOG LT. RLY. PIN 1
FOG LT. SW.
TO R. LWR. HEAD LT. FUSE CONN. 3C-6
(PART OF COM. SW.) DIR. HAZ. SW.
LT. CONT. SW. (PART OF COMB. SW.)
CIG. LTR.
UNLOCK WARN. SW.
SEAT BELT WARN. RELAY
COURT. SW.
SEAT BELT SW.
BACK-UP LT. SW.
NOTE: A/C

1983 Toyota

SUPRA (Cont.)

REAR COMPARTMENT & ACCESSORIES

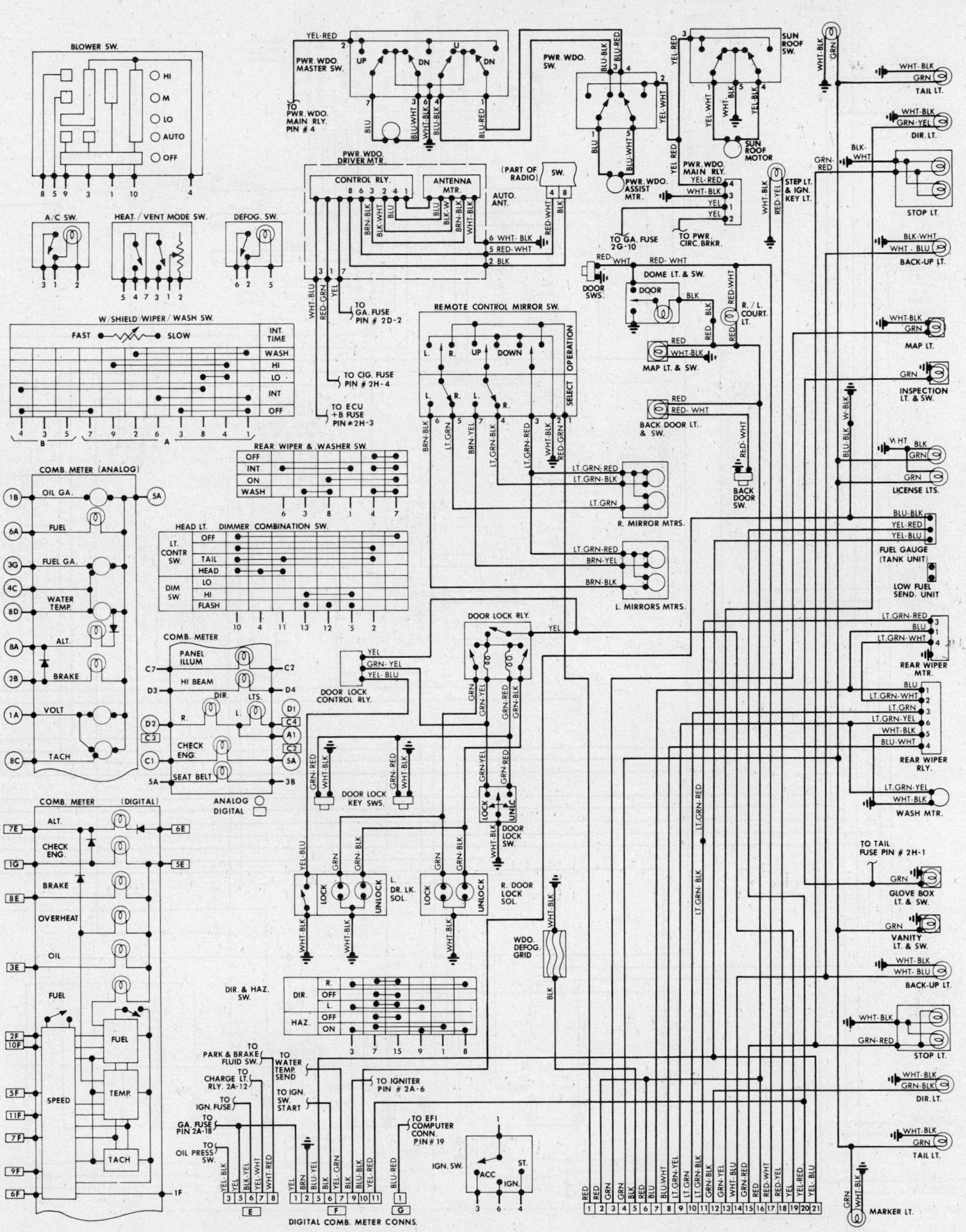

BLOWER SW.
HI
M
LO
AUTO
OFF
A/C SW.
HEAT./VENT MODE SW.
DEFOG. SW.
W/SHIELD/WIPER/WASH SW.
FAST
SLOW
INT. TIME
WASH
HI
LO
INT
OFF
COMB. METER (ANALOG)
OIL GA.
FUEL
FUEL GA.
WATER TEMP.
ALT.
BRAKE
VOLT
TACH
COMB. METER (DIGITAL)
CHECK ENG.
OVERHEAT
OIL
SPEED
TEMP.
REAR WIPER & WASHER SW.
HEAD LT. DIMMER COMBINATION SW.
COMB. METER
PANEL ILLUM
HI BEAM
DIR.
LTS.
SEAT BELT
ANALOG
DIGITAL
PWR. WDO. MASTER SW.
UP
DN
TO PWR. WDO. MAIN RLY. PIN # 4
PWR. WDO. DRIVER MTR.
CONTROL RLY.
ANTENNA MTR.
AUTO. ANT.
(PART OF RADIO)
TO GA. FUSE PIN # 2D-2
TO CIG. FUSE PIN # 2H-4
TO ECU +B FUSE PIN # 2H-3
REMOTE CONTROL MIRROR SW.
OPERATION
SELECT
R. MIRROR MTRS.
L. MIRRORS MTRS.
DOOR LOCK RLY.
DOOR LOCK CONTROL RLY.
DOOR LOCK KEY SWS.
DOOR LOCK SW.
L. DR. LK. SOL.
R. DOOR LOCK SOL.
LOCK
UNLOCK
WDO. DEFOG. GRID
DIR. & HAZ. SW.
TO PARK & BRAKE FLUID SW.
TO WATER TEMP. SEND
TO CHARGE LT. RLY. 2A-12
TO IGN. FUSE
TO GA. FUSE PIN 2A-18
TO OIL PRESS SW.
TO IGN. SW. START
TO IGNITER PIN # 2A-6
TO EFI COMPUTER CONN. PIN # 19
IGN. SW.
ACC
IGN.
ST.
DIGITAL COMB. METER CONNS.
PWR. WDO. SW.
PWR. WDO. ASSIST MTR.
PWR. WDO. MAIN RLY.
TO GA. FUSE 2G-10
TO PWR. CIRC. BRKR.
SUN ROOF SW.
SUN ROOF MOTOR
STEP LT. & IGN. KEY LT.
DOOR SWS.
DOME LT. & SW.
DOOR
R./L. COURT. LT.
MAP LT. & SW.
BACK DOOR LT. & SW.
BACK DOOR SW.
TAIL LT.
DIR. LT.
STOP LT.
BACK-UP LT.
MAP LT.
INSPECTION LT. & SW.
LICENSE LTS.
FUEL GAUGE (TANK UNIT)
LOW FUEL SEND. UNIT
REAR WIPER MTR.
REAR WIPER RLY.
WASH MTR.
TO TAIL FUSE PIN # 2H-1
GLOVE BOX LT. & SW.
VANITY LT. & SW.
MARKER LT.

1983 Toyota

TERCEL

ENGINE COMPARTMENT & FUSE BLOCK

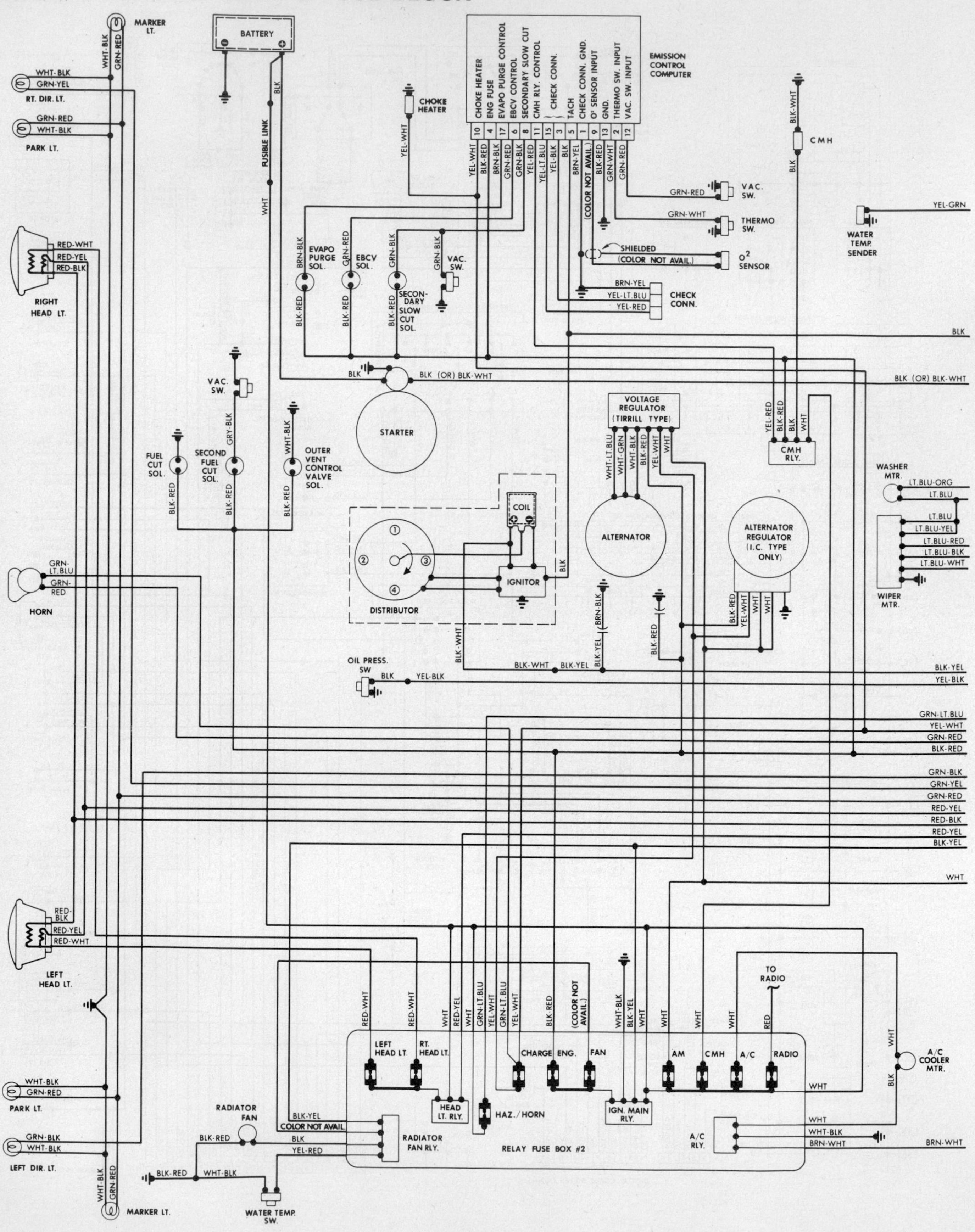

MARKER LT.
BATTERY
WHT-BLK
GRN-RED
GRN-YEL
RT. DIR. LT.
PARK LT.
BLK
FUSIBLE LINK
WHT
CHOKE HEATER
YEL-WHT
CHOKE HEATER
ENG FUSE
EVAPO PURGE CONTROL
EBCV CONTROL
SECONDARY SLOW CUT
CMH RLY. CONTROL
CHECK CONN.
TACH
CHECK CONN. GND.
O² SENSOR INPUT
GND.
THERMO SW. INPUT
VAC. SW. INPUT
EMISSION CONTROL COMPUTER
10 4 17 6 8 11 15 3 5 1 9 13 2 12
YEL-WHT
BLK-RED
BRN-BLK
GRN-RED
GRN-BLK
YEL-RED
YEL-LT.BLU
YEL-BLK
BRN-YEL
(COLOR NOT AVAIL.)
GRN-WHT
VAC. SW.
THERMO SW.
SHIELDED
O² SENSOR
CHECK CONN.
YEL-LT.BLU
YEL-RED
BLK-WHT
CMH
WATER TEMP. SENDER
YEL-GRN
RED-WHT
RED-YEL
RED-BLK
RIGHT HEAD LT.
EVAPO PURGE SOL.
EBCV SOL.
SECON-DARY SLOW CUT SOL.
VAC. SW.
BLK (OR) BLK-WHT
VAC. SW.
STARTER
FUEL CUT SOL.
SECOND FUEL CUT SOL.
GRY-BLK
OUTER VENT CONTROL VALVE SOL.
WHT-BLK
VOLTAGE REGULATOR (TIRRILL TYPE)
WHT-LT.BLU
WHT-GRN
WHT-BLK
BLK-RED
YEL-WHT
YEL-RED
CMH RLY.
WASHER MTR.
LT.BLU-ORG
LT.BLU
LT.BLU-YEL
LT.BLU-RED
LT.BLU-BLK
LT.BLU-WHT
WIPER MTR.
GRN-LT.BLU
HORN
COIL
DISTRIBUTOR
IGNITOR
ALTERNATOR
ALTERNATOR REGULATOR (I.C. TYPE ONLY)
BRN-BLK
BLK-YEL
OIL PRESS. SW
YEL-BLK
GRN-LT.BLU
YEL-WHT
GRN-RED
BLK-RED
GRN-BLK
GRN-YEL
GRN-RED
RED-YEL
RED-BLK
RED-YEL
BLK-YEL
WHT
LEFT HEAD LT.
TO RADIO
RED
LEFT HEAD LT.
RT. HEAD LT.
CHARGE
ENG.
FAN
AM
CMH
A/C
RADIO
A/C COOLER MTR.
HEAD LT. RLY.
HAZ./HORN
IGN. MAIN RLY.
WHT-BLK
BRN-WHT
A/C RLY.
RELAY FUSE BOX #2
PARK LT.
LEFT DIR. LT.
RADIATOR FAN
COLOR NOT AVAIL.
RADIATOR FAN RLY.
WATER TEMP. SW.
MARKER LT.

1983 Toyota

TERCEL (Cont.)

UNDERDASH & FUSE BLOCK

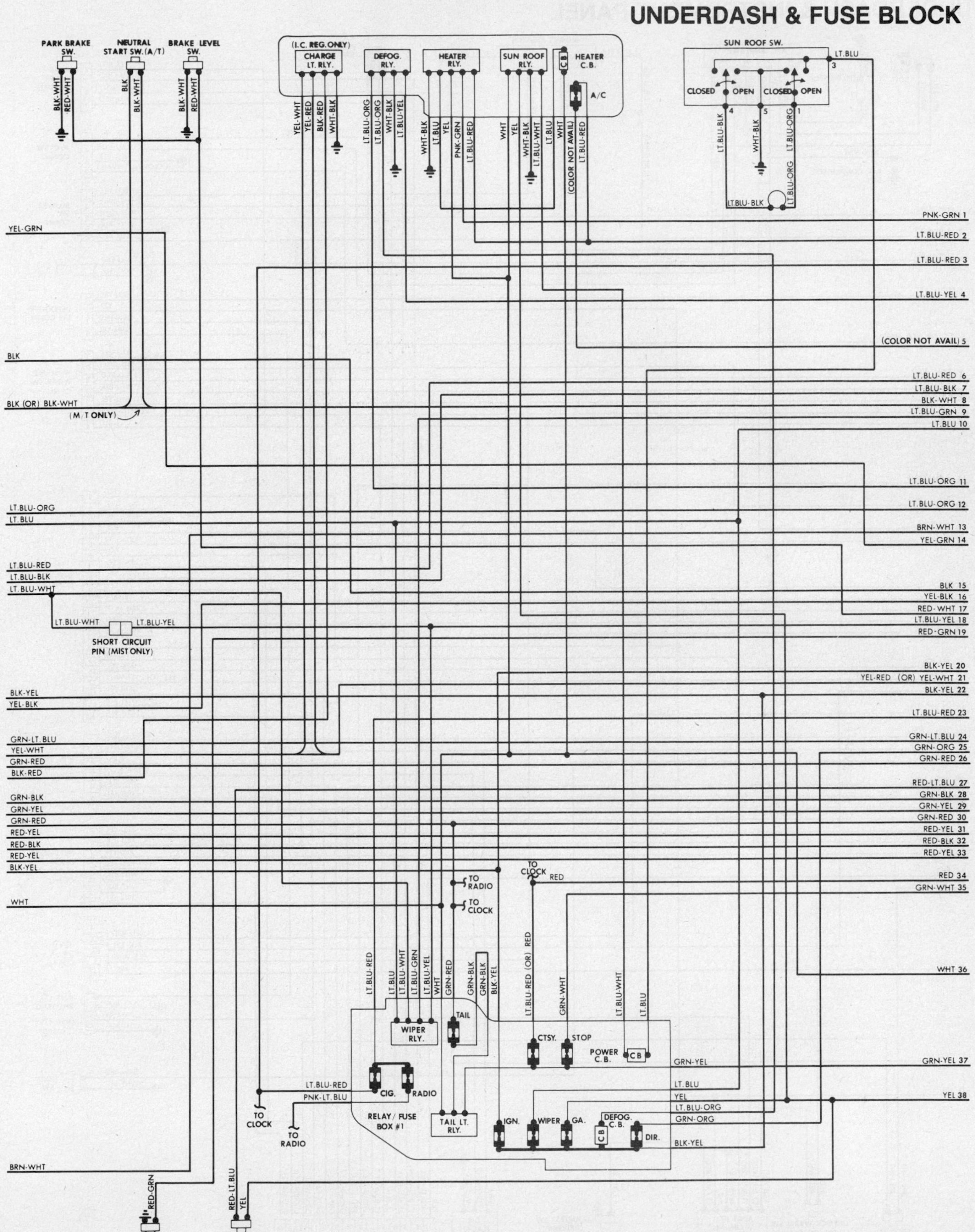
PARK BRAKE SW.
NEUTRAL START SW. (A/T)
BRAKE LEVEL SW.
BLK-WHT
RED-WHT
BLK
BLK-WHT
(I.C. REG. ONLY)
CHARGE LT. RLY.
DEFOG. RLY.
HEATER RLY.
SUN ROOF RLY.
HEATER C.B.
A/C
YEL-WHT
YEL-RED
BLK-RED
WHT-BLK
LT.BLU-ORG
WHT-BLK
LT.BLU-YEL
LT.BLU
YEL
PNK-GRN
LT.BLU-RED
WHT
LT.BLU-WHT
(COLOR NOT AVAIL.)
SUN ROOF SW.
CLOSED
OPEN
LT.BLU-BLK
LT.BLU-ORG
YEL-GRN
BLK
BLK (OR) BLK-WHT
(M/T ONLY)
LT.BLU-ORG
LT.BLU
LT.BLU-RED
LT.BLU-BLK
LT.BLU-WHT
LT.BLU-YEL
SHORT CIRCUIT PIN (MIST ONLY)
BLK-YEL
YEL-BLK
GRN-LT.BLU
YEL-WHT
GRN-RED
BLK-RED
GRN-BLK
GRN-YEL
RED-YEL
RED-BLK
WHT
BRN-WHT
PNK-GRN 1
LT.BLU-RED 2
LT.BLU-RED 3
LT.BLU-YEL 4
(COLOR NOT AVAIL) 5
LT.BLU-RED 6
LT.BLU-BLK 7
BLK-WHT 8
LT.BLU-GRN 9
LT.BLU 10
LT.BLU-ORG 11
LT.BLU-ORG 12
BRN-WHT 13
YEL-GRN 14
BLK 15
YEL-BLK 16
RED-WHT 17
LT.BLU-YEL 18
RED-GRN 19
BLK-YEL 20
YEL-RED (OR) YEL-WHT 21
BLK-YEL 22
LT.BLU-RED 23
GRN-LT.BLU 24
GRN-ORG 25
GRN-RED 26
RED-LT.BLU 27
GRN-BLK 28
GRN-YEL 29
GRN-RED 30
RED-YEL 31
RED-BLK 32
RED-YEL 33
RED 34
GRN-WHT 35
WHT 36
GRN-YEL 37
YEL 38
TO RADIO
TO CLOCK
RED
LT.BLU-GRN
GRN-RED
GRN-BLK
BLK-YEL
LT.BLU-RED (OR) RED
GRN-WHT
WIPER RLY.
TAIL
CTSY.
STOP
POWER C.B.
CB
CIG.
RADIO
PNK-LT.BLU
RELAY / FUSE BOX #1
TAIL LT. RLY.
IGN.
WIPER
GA.
DEFOG. C.B.
DIR.
GRN-ORG
RED-GRN
4 WD IND. SW.
RED-LT.BLU
BACK-UP LT. SW.

1983 Toyota

TERCEL (Cont.)

UNDERDASH & INSTRUMENT PANEL

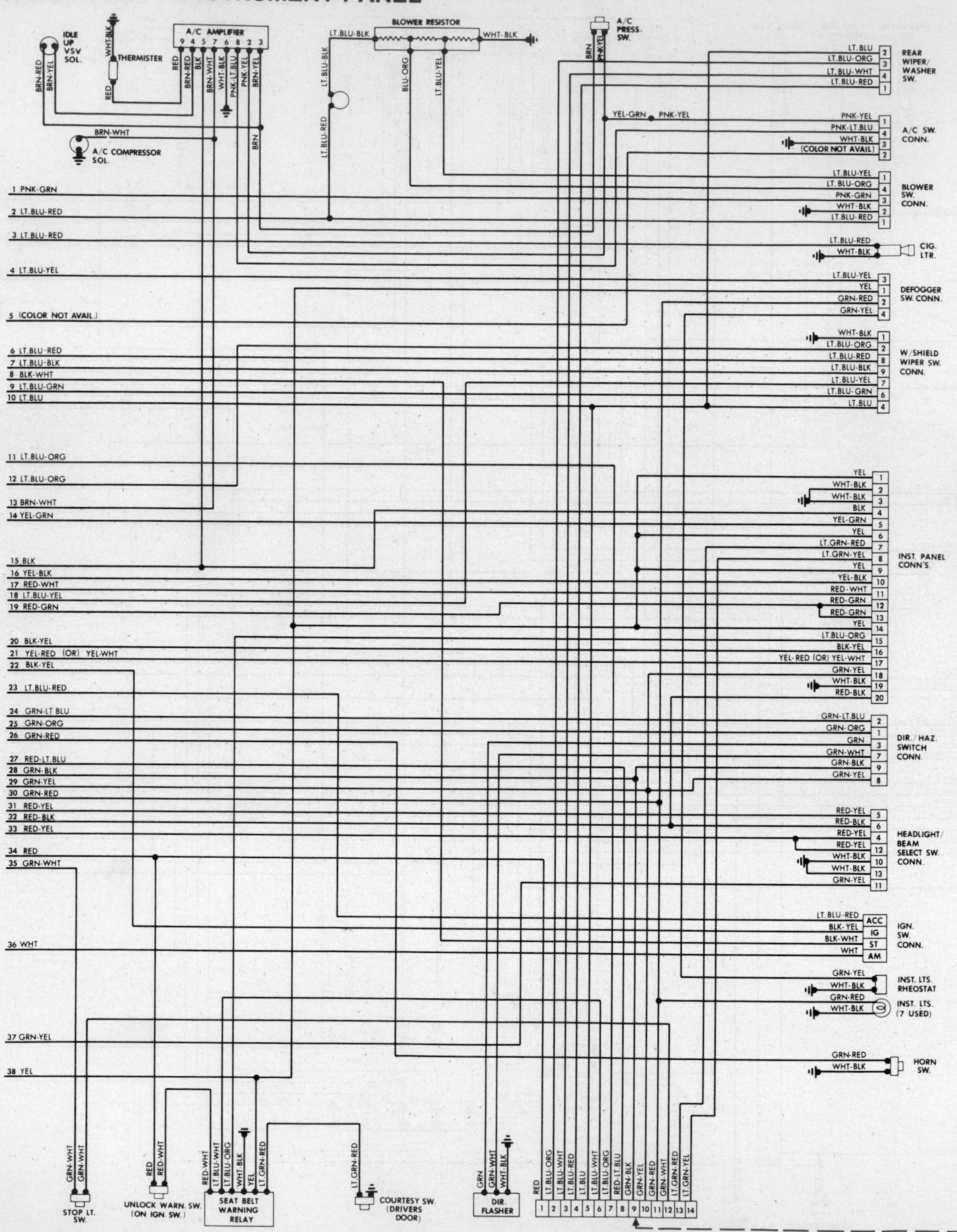

IDLE UP VSV SOL.
THERMISTER
A/C AMPLIFIER
BLOWER RESISTOR
A/C PRESS. SW.
A/C COMPRESSOR SOL.
1 PNK-GRN
2 LT.BLU-RED
3 LT.BLU-RED
4 LT.BLU-YEL
5 (COLOR NOT AVAIL.)
6 LT.BLU-RED
7 LT.BLU-BLK
8 BLK-WHT
9 LT.BLU-GRN
10 LT.BLU
11 LT.BLU-ORG
12 LT.BLU-ORG
13 BRN-WHT
14 YEL-GRN
15 BLK
16 YEL-BLK
17 RED-WHT
18 LT.BLU-YEL
19 RED-GRN
20 BLK-YEL
21 YEL-RED (OR) YEL-WHT
22 BLK-YEL
23 LT.BLU-RED
24 GRN-LT BLU
25 GRN-ORG
26 GRN-RED
27 RED-LT.BLU
28 GRN-BLK
29 GRN-YEL
30 GRN-RED
31 RED-YEL
32 RED-BLK
33 RED-YEL
34 RED
35 GRN-WHT
36 WHT
37 GRN-YEL
38 YEL
REAR WIPER/ WASHER SW.
A/C SW. CONN.
(COLOR NOT AVAIL)
BLOWER SW. CONN.
CIG. LTR.
DEFOGGER SW. CONN.
W/SHIELD WIPER SW. CONN.
INST. PANEL CONN'S.
DIR./HAZ. SWITCH CONN.
HEADLIGHT/ BEAM SELECT SW. CONN.
IGN. SW. CONN.
ACC
IG
ST
AM
INST. LTS. RHEOSTAT
INST. LTS. (7 USED)
HORN SW.
STOP LT. SW.
UNLOCK WARN. SW. (ON IGN. SW.)
SEAT BELT WARNING RELAY
COURTESY SW. (DRIVERS DOOR)
DIR. FLASHER

1983 Toyota

TERCEL (Cont.)

REAR COMPARTMENT & ACCESSORIES

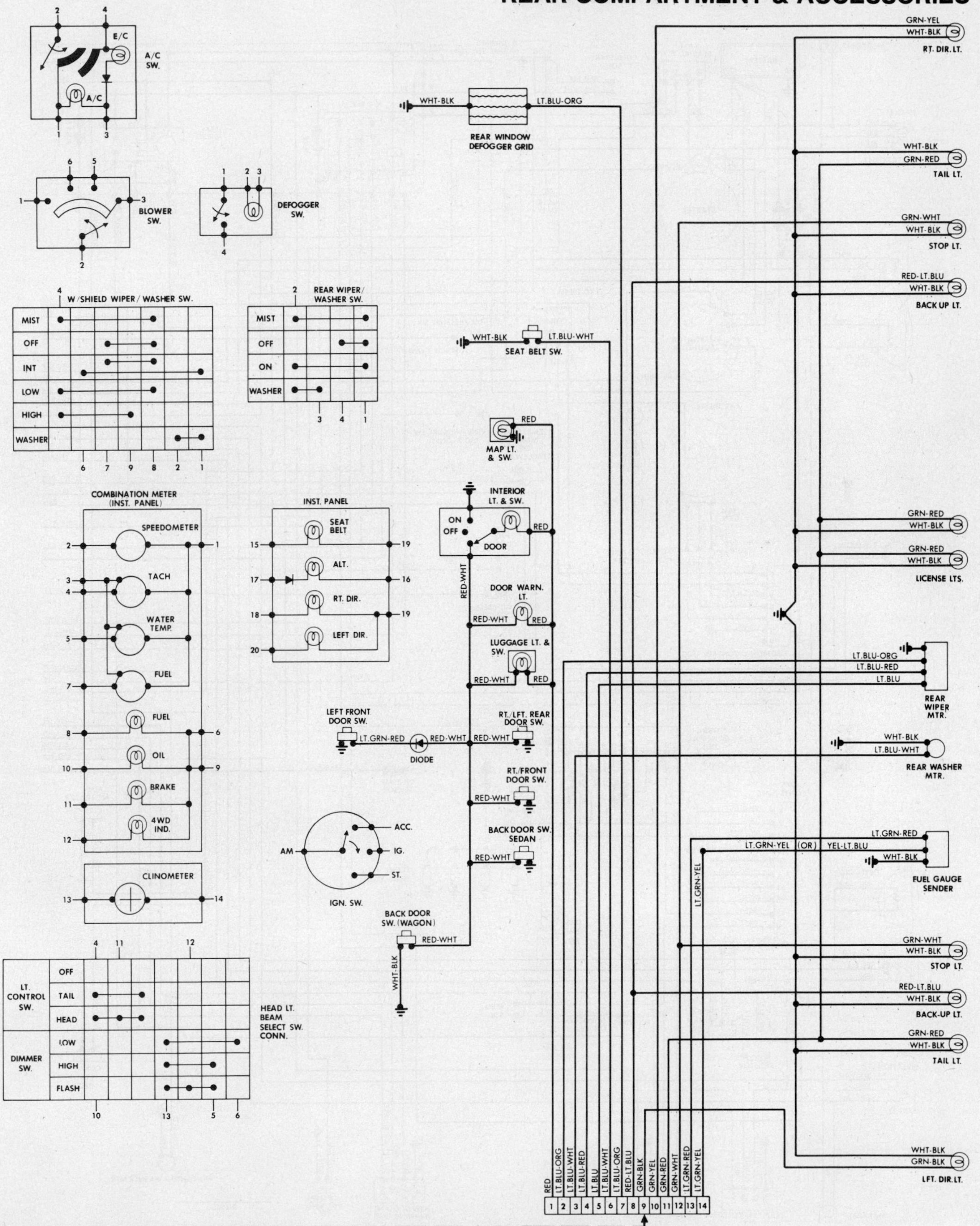
A/C SW.
E/C
A/C
BLOWER SW.
DEFOGGER SW.
W/SHIELD WIPER/WASHER SW.
MIST
OFF
INT
LOW
HIGH
WASHER
REAR WIPER/WASHER SW.
ON
COMBINATION METER (INST. PANEL)
SPEEDOMETER
TACH
WATER TEMP.
FUEL
OIL
BRAKE
4WD IND.
CLINOMETER
INST. PANEL
SEAT BELT
ALT.
RT. DIR.
LEFT DIR.
AM
ACC.
IG.
ST.
IGN. SW.
LT. CONTROL SW.
TAIL
HEAD
DIMMER SW.
FLASH
HEAD LT. BEAM SELECT SW. CONN.
REAR WINDOW DEFOGGER GRID
SEAT BELT SW.
MAP LT. & SW.
INTERIOR LT. & SW.
DOOR
DOOR WARN. LT.
LUGGAGE LT. & SW.
LEFT FRONT DOOR SW.
DIODE
RT./LFT. REAR DOOR SW.
RT./FRONT DOOR SW.
BACK DOOR SW. SEDAN
BACK DOOR SW. (WAGON)
RT. DIR. LT.
TAIL LT.
STOP LT.
BACK UP LT.
LICENSE LTS.
REAR WIPER MTR.
REAR WASHER MTR.
LT.GRN-YEL (OR) YEL-LT.BLU
FUEL GAUGE SENDER
BACK-UP LT.
LFT. DIR. LT.
WHT-BLK
LT.BLU-ORG
LT.BLU-WHT
LT.BLU-RED
LT.BLU
RED
RED-WHT
LT.GRN-RED
LT.GRN-YEL
GRN-YEL
GRN-RED
GRN-WHT
GRN-BLK
RED-LT.BLU

1983 Volkswagen

JETTA, RABBIT CONVERTIBLE & SCIROCCO

ENGINE COMPARTMENT & FUSE BLOCK

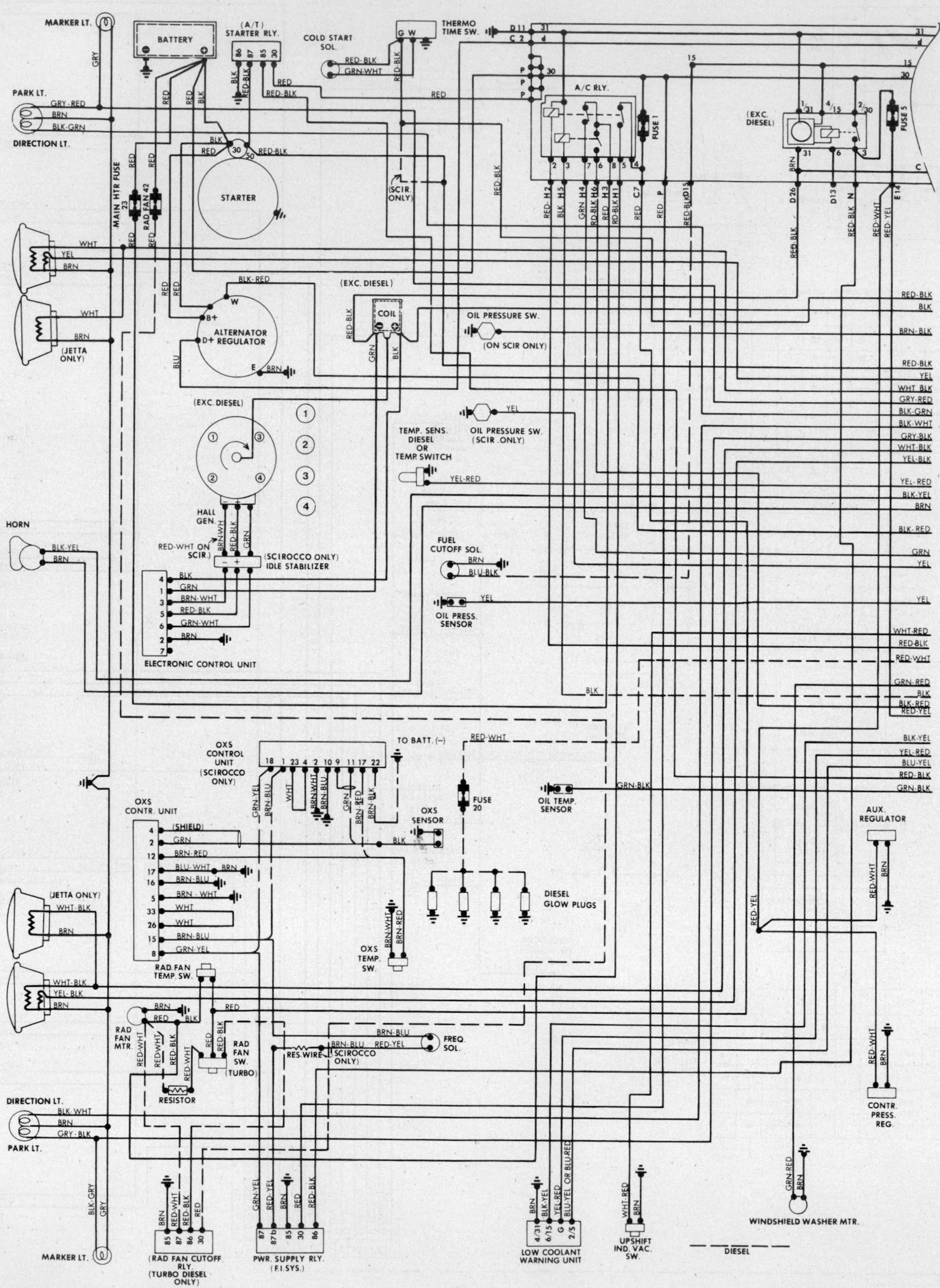
MARKER LT.
BATTERY
(A/T) STARTER RLY.
COLD START SOL.
THERMO TIME SW.
PARK LT.
DIRECTION LT.
STARTER
A/C RLY.
FUSE 1
(EXC. DIESEL)
FUSE 5
MAIN HTR FUSE 23
RAD FAN 42
(SCIR. ONLY)
(JETTA ONLY)
ALTERNATOR REGULATOR
(EXC. DIESEL)
COIL
OIL PRESSURE SW.
(ON SCIR ONLY)
OIL PRESSURE SW. (SCIR. ONLY)
TEMP. SENS. DIESEL OR TEMP. SWITCH
HORN
HALL GEN.
RED-WHT ON SCIR.
(SCIROCCO ONLY) IDLE STABILIZER
ELECTRONIC CONTROL UNIT
FUEL CUTOFF SOL.
OIL PRESS. SENSOR
OXS CONTROL UNIT (SCIROCCO ONLY)
TO BATT. (−)
OXS CONTR. UNIT
OXS SENSOR
FUSE 20
OIL TEMP. SENSOR
AUX. REGULATOR
DIESEL GLOW PLUGS
OXS TEMP. SW.
RAD. FAN TEMP. SW.
RAD FAN MTR.
RAD FAN SW. (TURBO)
RES. WIRE
(SCIROCCO ONLY)
FREQ. SOL.
RESISTOR
CONTR. PRESS. REG.
LOW COOLANT WARNING UNIT
UPSHIFT IND. VAC. SW.
WINDSHIELD WASHER MTR.
DIESEL
(RAD FAN CUTOFF RLY (TURBO DIESEL ONLY)
PWR. SUPPLY RLY. (F.I. SYS.)

1983 Volkswagen

JETTA, RABBIT CONVERTIBLE & SCIROCCO (Cont.)

FUSE BLOCK & UNDERDASH

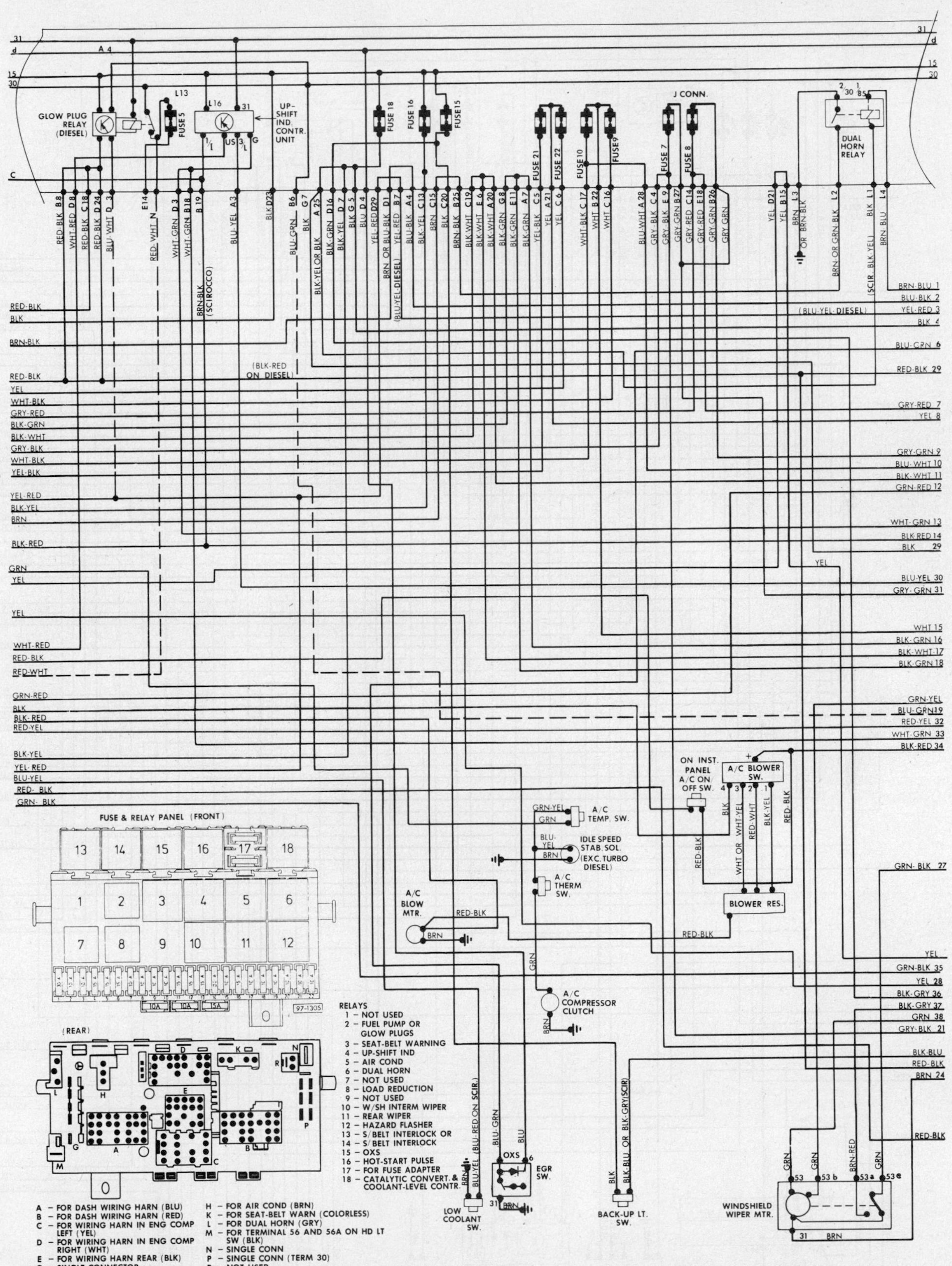
GLOW PLUG RELAY (DIESEL)
UP-SHIFT IND. CONTR. UNIT
J CONN.
DUAL HORN RELAY
ON INST. PANEL A/C ON/OFF SW.
A/C BLOWER SW.
A/C TEMP. SW.
IDLE SPEED STAB. SOL. (EXC. TURBO DIESEL)
A/C THERM SW.
A/C BLOW MTR.
BLOWER RES.
A/C COMPRESSOR CLUTCH
LOW COOLANT SW.
OXS
EGR SW.
BACK-UP LT. SW.
WINDSHIELD WIPER MTR.
FUSE & RELAY PANEL (FRONT)
(REAR)
RELAYS
1 - NOT USED
2 - FUEL PUMP OR GLOW PLUGS
3 - SEAT-BELT WARNING
4 - UP-SHIFT IND
5 - AIR COND
6 - DUAL HORN
7 - NOT USED
8 - LOAD REDUCTION
9 - NOT USED
10 - W/SH INTERM WIPER
11 - REAR WIPER
12 - HAZARD FLASHER
13 - S/BELT INTERLOCK OR
14 - S/BELT INTERLOCK
15 - OXS
16 - HOT-START PULSE
17 - FOR FUSE ADAPTER
18 - CATALYTIC CONVERT. & COOLANT-LEVEL CONTR.
A - FOR DASH WIRING HARN (BLU)
B - FOR DASH WIRING HARN (RED)
C - FOR WIRING HARN IN ENG COMP LEFT (YEL)
D - FOR WIRING HARN IN ENG COMP RIGHT (WHT)
E - FOR WIRING HARN REAR (BLK)
G - SINGLE CONNECTOR
H - FOR AIR COND (BRN)
K - FOR SEAT-BELT WARN (COLORLESS)
L - FOR DUAL HORN (GRY)
M - FOR TERMINAL 56 AND 56A ON HD LT SW (BLK)
N - SINGLE CONN
P - SINGLE CONN (TERM 30)
R - NOT USED
97-1305

1983 Volkswagen

JETTA, RABBIT CONVERTIBLE & SCIROCCO (Cont.)

FUSE BLOCK & UNDERDASH

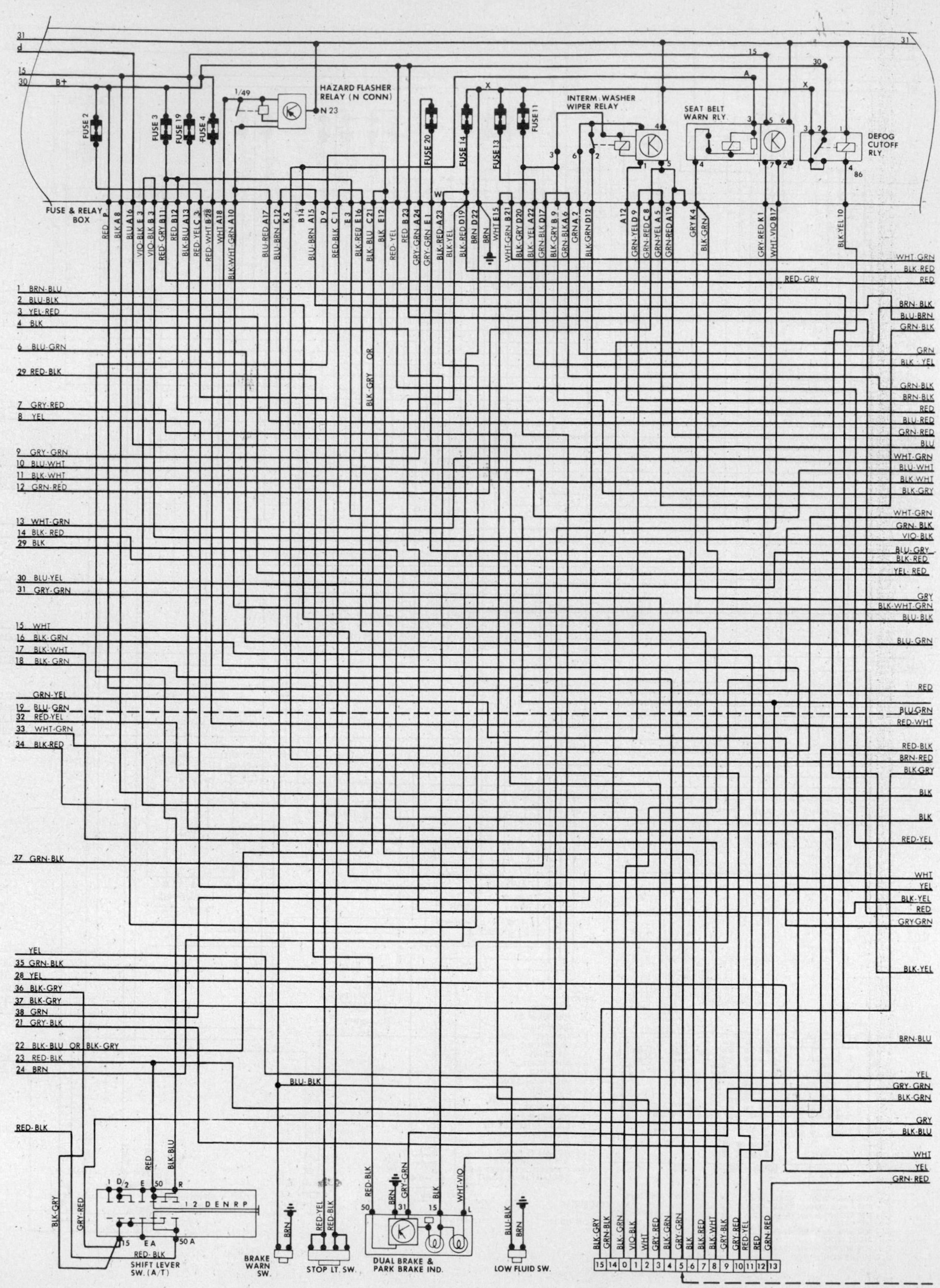

HAZARD FLASHER RELAY (N CONN)
INTERM. WASHER WIPER RELAY
SEAT BELT WARN RLY
DEFOG CUTOFF RLY
FUSE & RELAY BOX
SHIFT LEVER SW. (A/T)
BRAKE WARN SW.
STOP LT. SW.
DUAL BRAKE & PARK BRAKE IND.
LOW FLUID SW.

1983 Volkswagen

JETTA, RABBIT CONVERTIBLE & SCIROCCO (Cont.)

INSTRUMENT PANEL & REAR COMPARTMENT

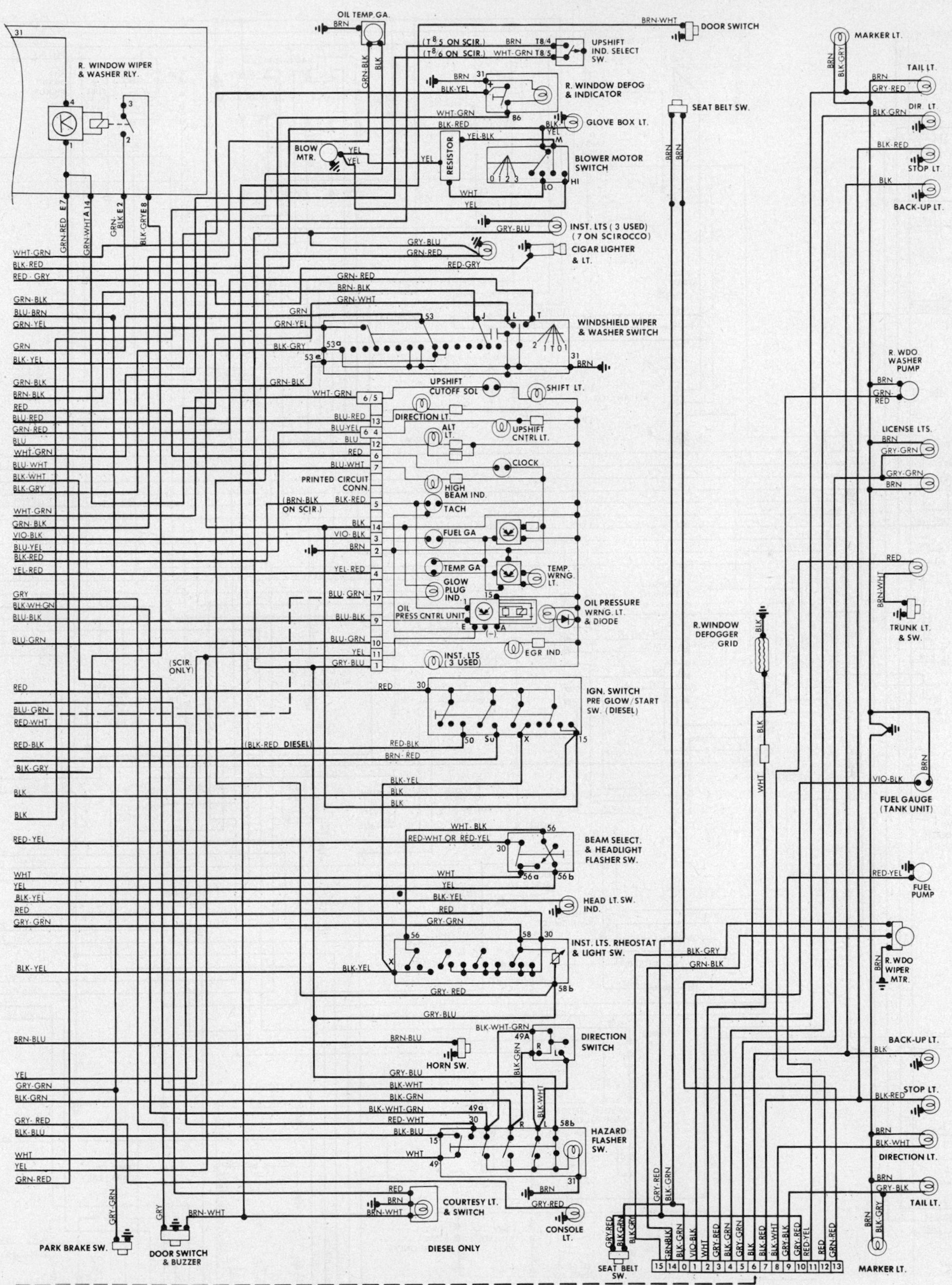

R. WINDOW WIPER & WASHER RLY.
OIL TEMP. GA.
DOOR SWITCH
UPSHIFT IND. SELECT SW.
R. WINDOW DEFOG & INDICATOR
GLOVE BOX LT.
BLOW MTR.
RESISTOR
BLOWER MOTOR SWITCH
SEAT BELT SW.
MARKER LT.
TAIL LT.
DIR. LT.
STOP LT.
BACK-UP LT.
INST. LTS (3 USED) (7 ON SCIROCCO)
CIGAR LIGHTER & LT.
WINDSHIELD WIPER & WASHER SWITCH
UPSHIFT CUTOFF SOL.
SHIFT LT.
R. WDO. WASHER PUMP
DIRECTION LT.
ALT LT.
UPSHIFT CNTRL LT.
CLOCK
LICENSE LTS.
PRINTED CIRCUIT CONN.
HIGH BEAM IND.
TACH
FUEL GA.
TEMP. GA.
TEMP. WRNG. LT.
GLOW PLUG IND.
OIL PRESS CNTRL UNIT
OIL PRESSURE WRNG. LT. & DIODE
TRUNK LT. & SW.
R. WINDOW DEFOGGER GRID
EGR IND.
INST. LTS (3 USED)
IGN. SWITCH PRE GLOW/START SW. (DIESEL)
FUEL GAUGE (TANK UNIT)
BEAM SELECT. & HEADLIGHT FLASHER SW.
FUEL PUMP
HEAD LT. SW. IND.
INST. LTS. RHEOSTAT & LIGHT SW.
R. WDO WIPER MTR.
DIRECTION SWITCH
HORN SW.
BACK-UP LT.
STOP LT.
HAZARD FLASHER SW.
DIRECTION LT.
TAIL LT.
COURTESY LT. & SWITCH
CONSOLE LT.
PARK BRAKE SW.
DOOR SWITCH & BUZZER
DIESEL ONLY
SEAT BELT SW.
MARKER LT.

1983 Volkswagen

RABBIT & RABBIT PICKUP INCLUDING DIESELS

ENGINE COMPARTMENT & FUSE BLOCK

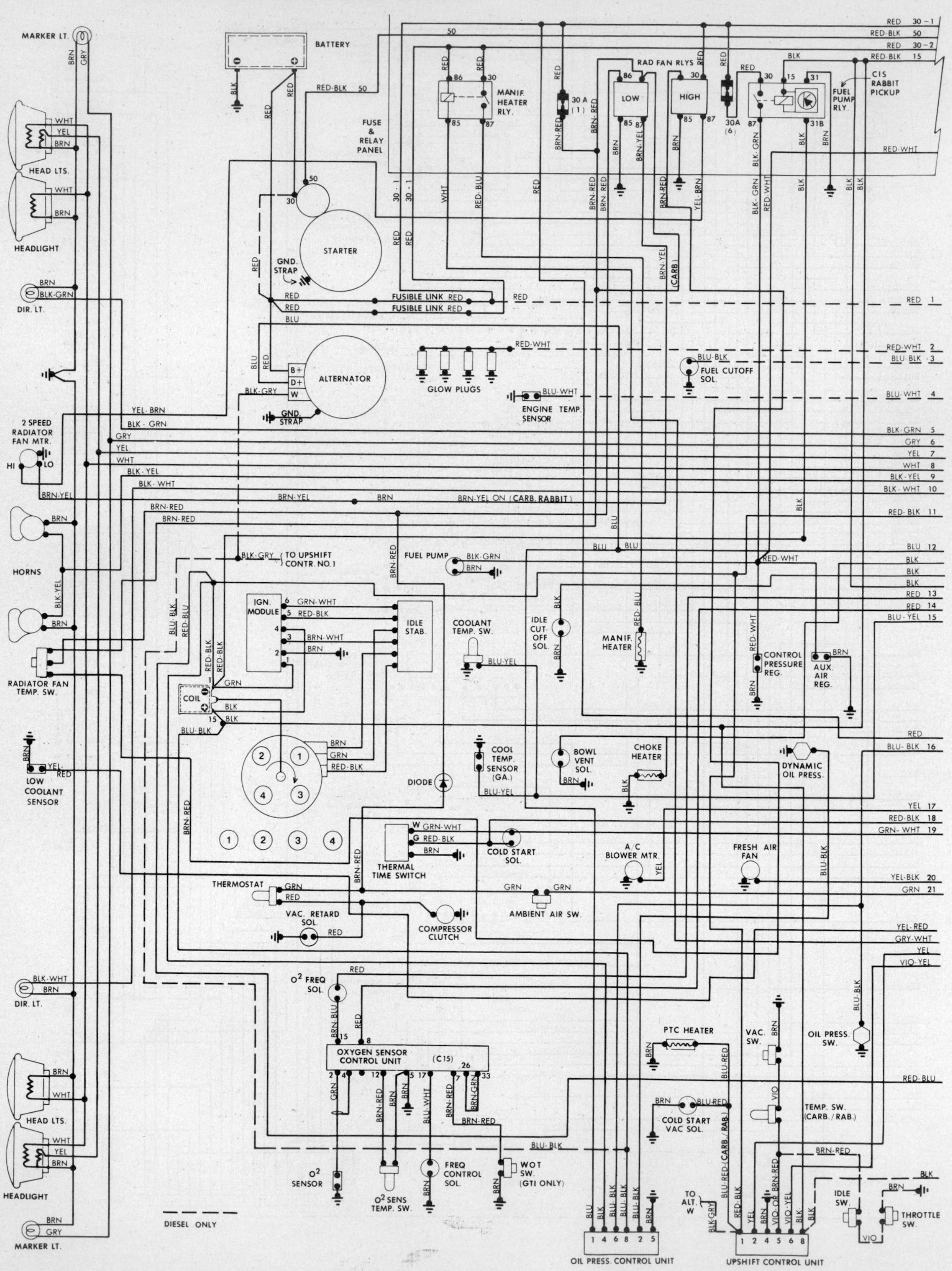

MARKER LT.
BATTERY
FUSE & RELAY PANEL
MANIF. HEATER RLY.
RAD FAN RLYS
LOW
HIGH
FUEL PUMP RLY.
CIS RABBIT PICKUP
HEAD LTS.
HEADLIGHT
STARTER
GND. STRAP
DIR. LT.
FUSIBLE LINK
ALTERNATOR
GLOW PLUGS
FUEL CUTOFF SOL.
ENGINE TEMP. SENSOR
2 SPEED RADIATOR FAN MTR.
HORNS
TO UPSHIFT CONTR. NO. 1
FUEL PUMP
IGN. MODULE
IDLE STAB.
COOLANT TEMP. SW.
IDLE CUT-OFF SOL.
MANIF. HEATER
CONTROL PRESSURE REG.
AUX. AIR REG.
RADIATOR FAN TEMP. SW.
COIL
COOL TEMP. SENSOR (GA.)
BOWL VENT SOL.
CHOKE HEATER
DYNAMIC OIL PRESS.
LOW COOLANT SENSOR
DIODE
THERMAL TIME SWITCH
COLD START SOL.
A/C BLOWER MTR.
FRESH AIR FAN
THERMOSTAT
VAC. RETARD SOL.
COMPRESSOR CLUTCH
AMBIENT AIR SW.
O2 FREQ SOL.
OXYGEN SENSOR CONTROL UNIT (C15)
PTC HEATER
VAC. SW.
OIL PRESS. SW.
COLD START VAC SOL.
TEMP. SW. (CARB. / RAB.)
O2 SENSOR
O2 SENS TEMP. SW.
FREQ CONTROL SOL.
WOT SW. (GTI ONLY)
TO ALT. W
IDLE SW.
THROTTLE SW.
DIESEL ONLY
OIL PRESS. CONTROL UNIT
UPSHIFT CONTROL UNIT

RABBIT & RABBIT PICKUP INCLUDING DIESELS (Cont.)

ENGINE COMPARTMENT & FUSE BLOCK

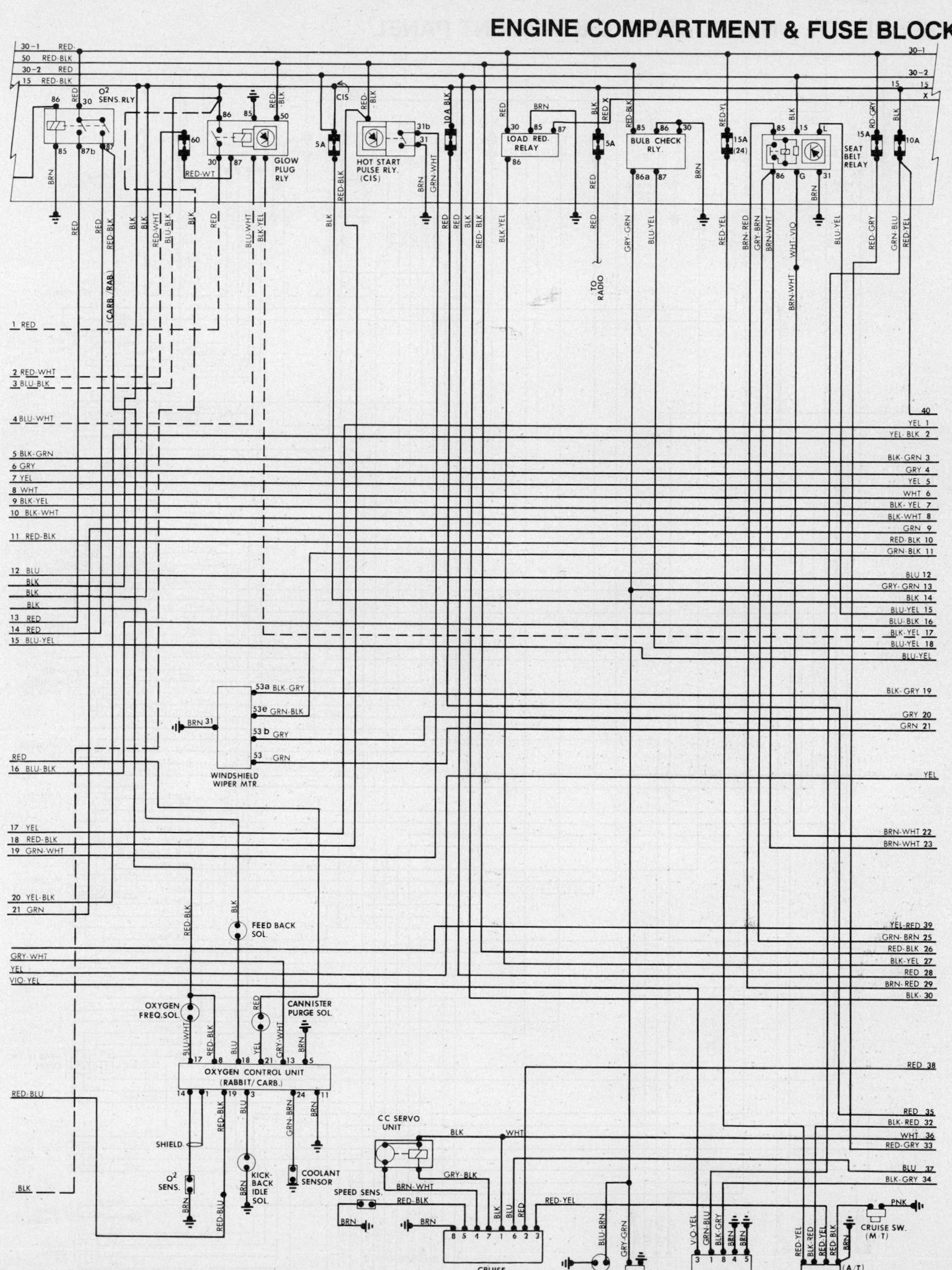
O2 SENS. RLY
GLOW PLUG RLY
HOT START PULSE RLY. (CIS)
LOAD RED. RELAY
BULB CHECK RLY.
SEAT BELT RELAY
TO RADIO
(CARB./RAB.)
WINDSHIELD WIPER MTR.
FEED BACK SOL.
OXYGEN FREQ. SOL.
CANNISTER PURGE SOL.
OXYGEN CONTROL UNIT (RABBIT/CARB.)
SHIELD
O2 SENS.
KICK-BACK IDLE SOL.
COOLANT SENSOR
CC SERVO UNIT
SPEED SENS.
CRUISE CONTROL UNIT
BRAKE PROP SOLENOID
PARK BRAKE IND. LT SW.
TRANS. SW.
BRAKE & STOP LT. SW.
CRUISE SW. (M T)
(A/T)

1983 Volkswagen

RABBIT & RABBIT PICKUP INCLUDING DIESELS (Cont.)

FUSE BLOCK, UNDERDASH & INSTRUMENT PANEL

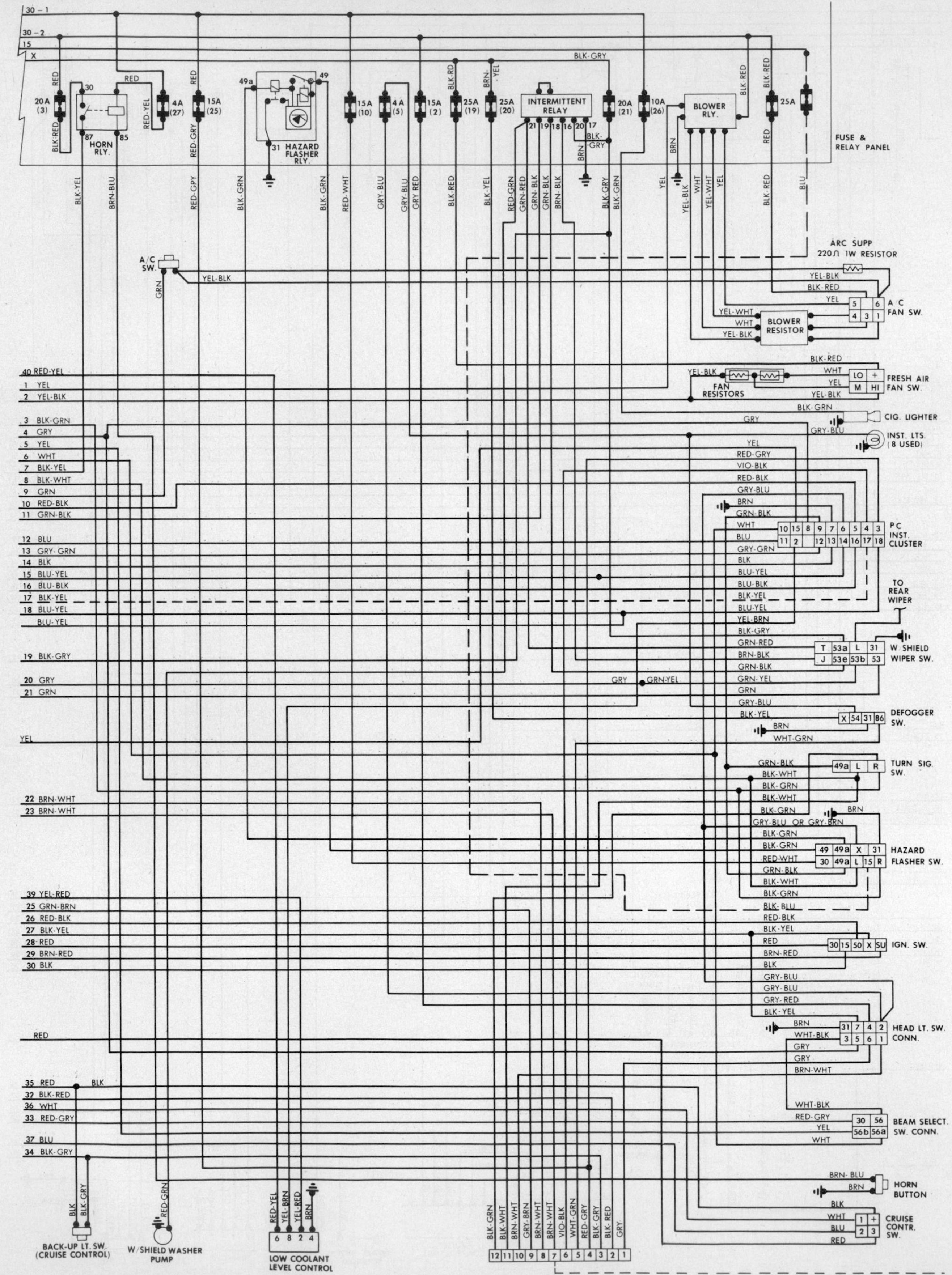
HORN RLY.
HAZARD FLASHER RLY.
INTERMITTENT RELAY
BLOWER RLY.
FUSE & RELAY PANEL
A/C SW.
ARC SUPP 220Ω 1W RESISTOR
A/C FAN SW.
BLOWER RESISTOR
FAN RESISTORS
FRESH AIR FAN SW.
CIG. LIGHTER
INST. LTS. (8 USED)
PC INST. CLUSTER
TO REAR WIPER
W SHIELD WIPER SW.
DEFOGGER SW.
TURN SIG. SW.
HAZARD FLASHER SW.
IGN. SW.
HEAD LT. SW. CONN.
BEAM SELECT. SW. CONN.
HORN BUTTON
CRUISE CONTR. SW.
BACK-UP LT. SW. (CRUISE CONTROL)
W/SHIELD WASHER PUMP
LOW COOLANT LEVEL CONTROL

RABBIT & RABBIT PICKUP INCLUDING DIESELS (Cont.)

FUSE BLOCK & REAR COMPARTMENT

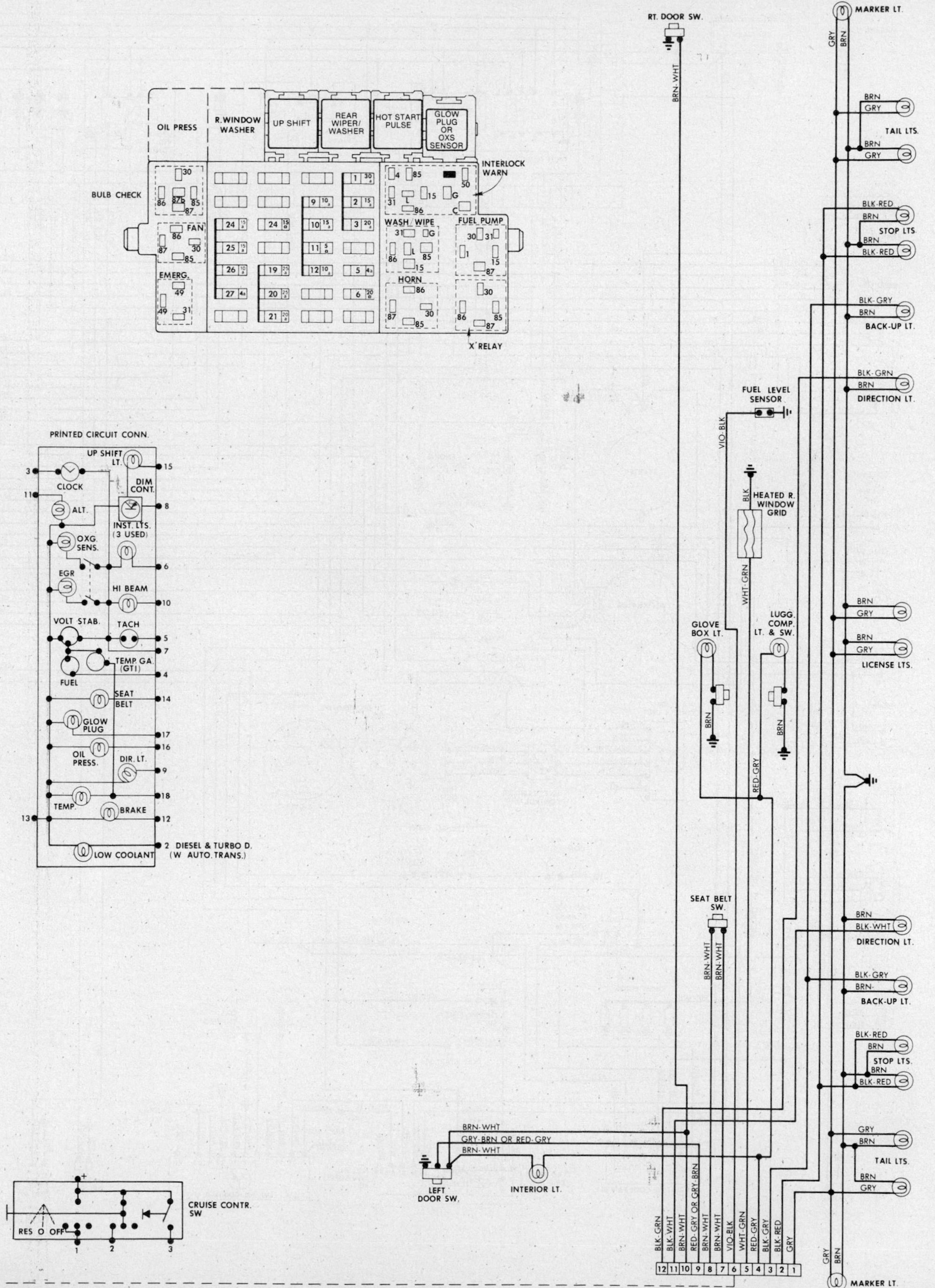

RT. DOOR SW.
MARKER LT.
TAIL LTS.
STOP LTS.
BACK-UP LT.
DIRECTION LT.
FUEL LEVEL SENSOR
HEATED R. WINDOW GRID
GLOVE BOX LT.
LUGG. COMP. LT. & SW.
LICENSE LTS.
SEAT BELT SW.
LEFT DOOR SW.
INTERIOR LT.
OIL PRESS
R. WINDOW WASHER
UP SHIFT
REAR WIPER/WASHER
HOT START PULSE
GLOW PLUG OR OXS SENSOR
BULB CHECK
FAN
EMERG.
INTERLOCK WARN
WASH/WIPE
FUEL PUMP
HORN
X RELAY
PRINTED CIRCUIT CONN.
UP SHIFT LT.
CLOCK
DIM CONT.
ALT.
INST. LTS. (3 USED)
OXG. SENS.
EGR
HI BEAM
VOLT STAB.
TACH
TEMP. GA. (GTI)
FUEL
SEAT BELT
GLOW PLUG
OIL PRESS.
DIR. LT.
TEMP.
BRAKE
LOW COOLANT
2 DIESEL & TURBO D. (W AUTO. TRANS.)
CRUISE CONTR. SW
RES O OFF

1983 Volkswagen

QUANTUM & QUANTUM DIESEL

ENGINE COMPARTMENT & FUSE BLOCK

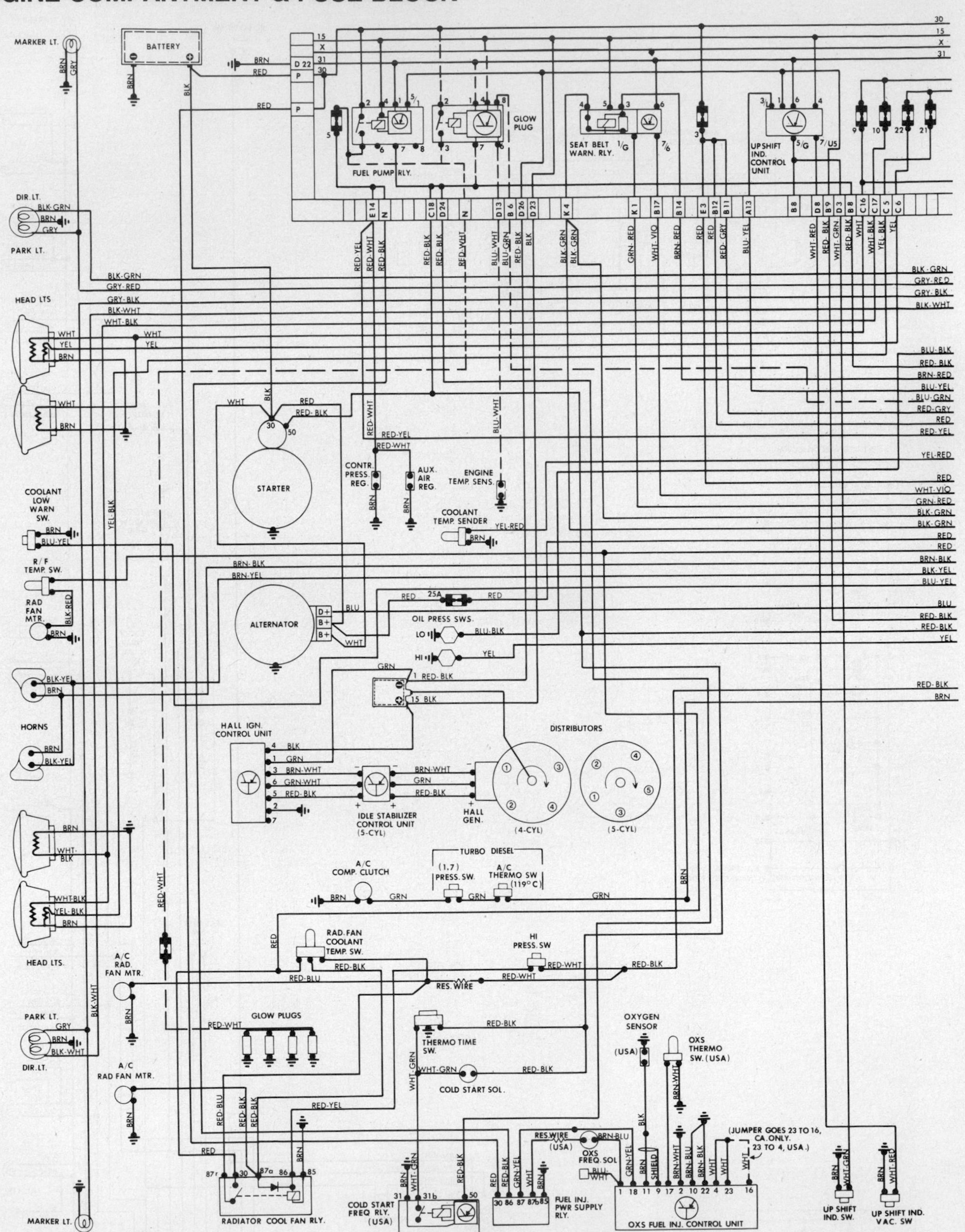
MARKER LT.
BATTERY
GLOW PLUG
FUEL PUMP RLY.
SEAT BELT WARN. RLY.
UPSHIFT IND. CONTROL UNIT
DIR. LT.
PARK LT.
HEAD LTS
STARTER
CONTR. PRESS. REG.
AUX. AIR REG.
ENGINE TEMP. SENS.
COOLANT TEMP. SENDER
COOLANT LOW WARN SW.
R/F TEMP. SW.
RAD FAN MTR.
ALTERNATOR
OIL PRESS SWS.
HORNS
HALL IGN. CONTROL UNIT
IDLE STABILIZER CONTROL UNIT (5-CYL)
HALL GEN.
DISTRIBUTORS
(4-CYL)
(5-CYL)
TURBO DIESEL
A/C COMP. CLUTCH
(1.7) PRESS. SW.
A/C THERMO SW (119°C)
RAD. FAN COOLANT TEMP. SW.
HI PRESS. SW
HEAD LTS.
A/C RAD. FAN MTR.
RES. WIRE
GLOW PLUGS
THERMO TIME SW.
COLD START SOL.
OXYGEN SENSOR (USA)
OXS THERMO SW. (USA)
A/C RAD FAN MTR.
(JUMPER GOES 23 TO 16, CA. ONLY. 23 TO 4, USA.)
RES. WIRE (USA)
OXS FREQ. SOL
RADIATOR COOL FAN RLY.
COLD START FREQ RLY. (USA)
FUEL INJ. PWR SUPPLY RLY.
OXS FUEL INJ. CONTROL UNIT
UP SHIFT IND. SW.
UP SHIFT IND. VAC. SW

QUANTUM & QUANTUM DIESEL (Cont.)

FUSE BLOCK & UNDERDASH

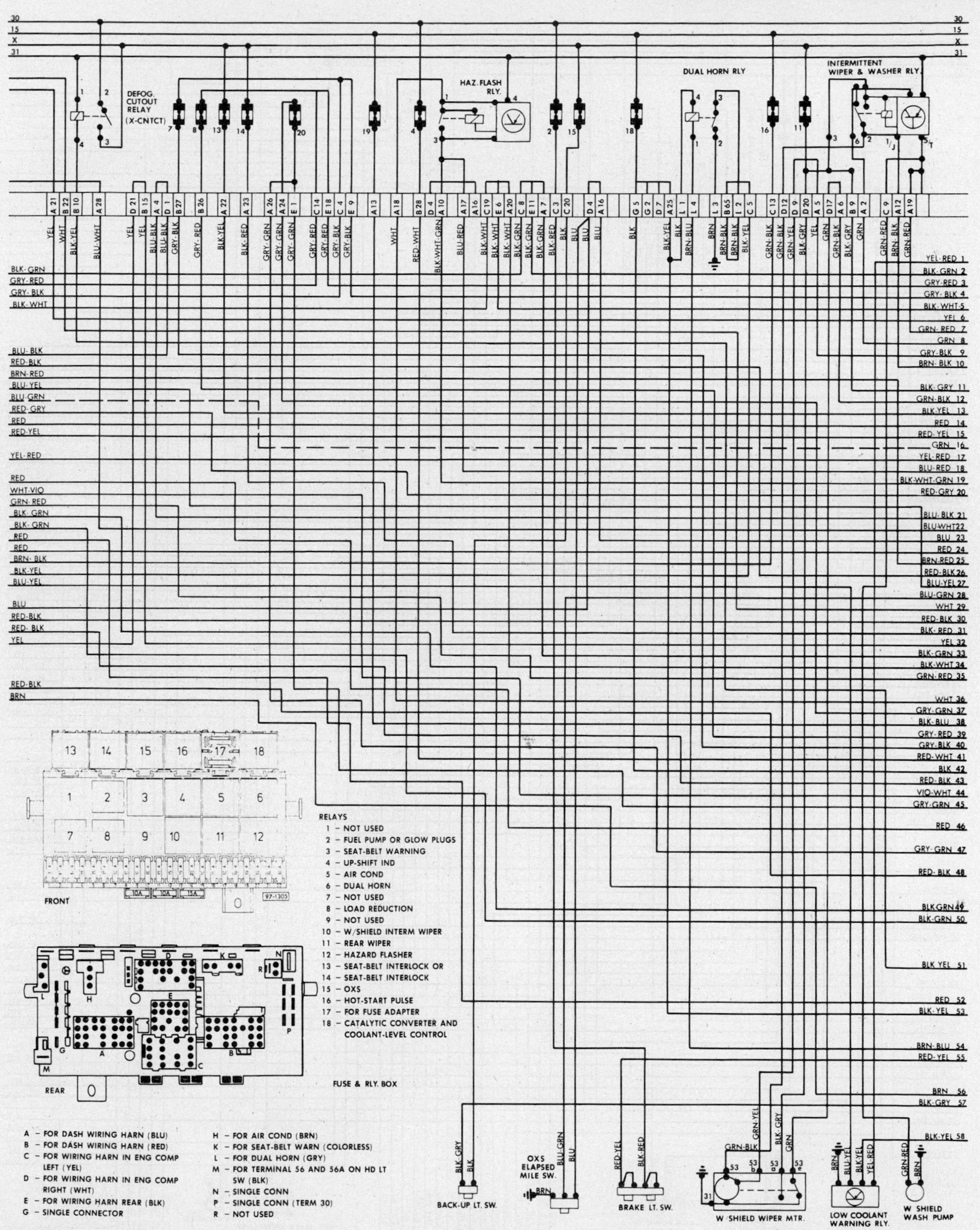
DEFOG. CUTOUT RELAY (X-CNTCT)
HAZ. FLASH RLY.
DUAL HORN RLY
INTERMITTENT WIPER & WASHER RLY.
FRONT
REAR
FUSE & RLY. BOX
RELAYS
1 – NOT USED
2 – FUEL PUMP OR GLOW PLUGS
3 – SEAT-BELT WARNING
4 – UP-SHIFT IND
5 – AIR COND
6 – DUAL HORN
7 – NOT USED
8 – LOAD REDUCTION
9 – NOT USED
10 – W/SHIELD INTERM WIPER
11 – REAR WIPER
12 – HAZARD FLASHER
13 – SEAT-BELT INTERLOCK OR
14 – SEAT-BELT INTERLOCK
15 – OXS
16 – HOT-START PULSE
17 – FOR FUSE ADAPTER
18 – CATALYTIC CONVERTER AND COOLANT-LEVEL CONTROL
A – FOR DASH WIRING HARN (BLU)
B – FOR DASH WIRING HARN (RED)
C – FOR WIRING HARN IN ENG COMP LEFT (YEL)
D – FOR WIRING HARN IN ENG COMP RIGHT (WHT)
E – FOR WIRING HARN REAR (BLK)
G – SINGLE CONNECTOR
H – FOR AIR COND (BRN)
K – FOR SEAT-BELT WARN (COLORLESS)
L – FOR DUAL HORN (GRY)
M – FOR TERMINAL 56 AND 56A ON HD LT SW (BLK)
N – SINGLE CONN
P – SINGLE CONN (TERM 30)
R – NOT USED
BACK-UP LT. SW.
OXS ELAPSED MILE SW.
BRAKE LT. SW.
W/SHIELD WIPER MTR.
LOW COOLANT WARNING RLY.
W/SHIELD WASH PUMP

1983 Volkswagen

QUANTUM & QUANTUM DIESEL (Cont.)

FUSE BLOCK & UNDERDASH

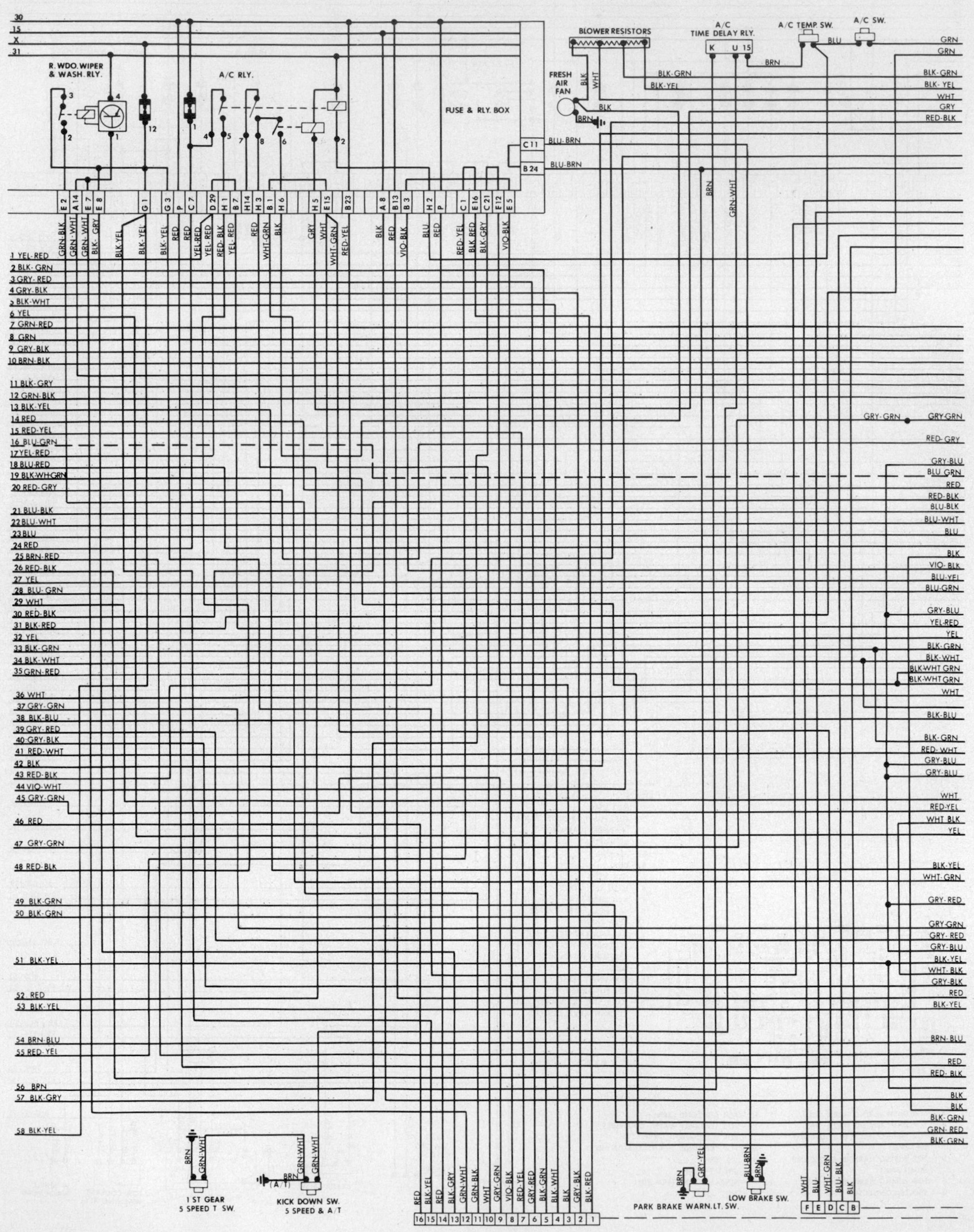
30
15
X
31
R. WDO. WIPER & WASH. RLY.
A/C RLY.
FUSE & RLY. BOX
BLOWER RESISTORS
A/C TIME DELAY RLY.
A/C TEMP. SW.
A/C SW.
FRESH AIR FAN
C 11
B 24
BLU-BRN
1 YEL-RED
2 BLK-GRN
3 GRY-RED
4 GRY-BLK
5 BLK-WHT
6 YEL
7 GRN-RED
8 GRN
9 GRY-BLK
10 BRN-BLK
11 BLK-GRY
12 GRN-BLK
13 BLK-YEL
14 RED
15 RED-YEL
16 BLU-GRN
17 YEL-RED
18 BLU-RED
19 BLK-WH-GRN
20 RED-GRY
21 BLU-BLK
22 BLU-WHT
23 BLU
24 RED
25 BRN-RED
26 RED-BLK
27 YEL
28 BLU-GRN
29 WHT
30 RED-BLK
31 BLK-RED
32 YEL
33 BLK-GRN
34 BLK-WHT
35 GRN-RED
36 WHT
37 GRY-GRN
38 BLK-BLU
39 GRY-RED
40 GRY-BLK
41 RED-WHT
42 BLK
43 RED-BLK
44 VIO-WHT
45 GRY-GRN
46 RED
47 GRY-GRN
48 RED-BLK
49 BLK-GRN
50 BLK-GRN
51 BLK-YEL
52 RED
53 BLK-YEL
54 BRN-BLU
55 RED-YEL
56 BRN
57 BLK-GRY
58 BLK-YEL
1 ST GEAR 5 SPEED T SW.
KICK DOWN SW. 5 SPEED & A/T
PARK BRAKE WARN. LT. SW.
LOW BRAKE SW.

1983 Volkswagen

QUANTUM & QUANTUM DIESEL (Cont.)

INSTRUMENT PANEL & REAR COMPARTMENT

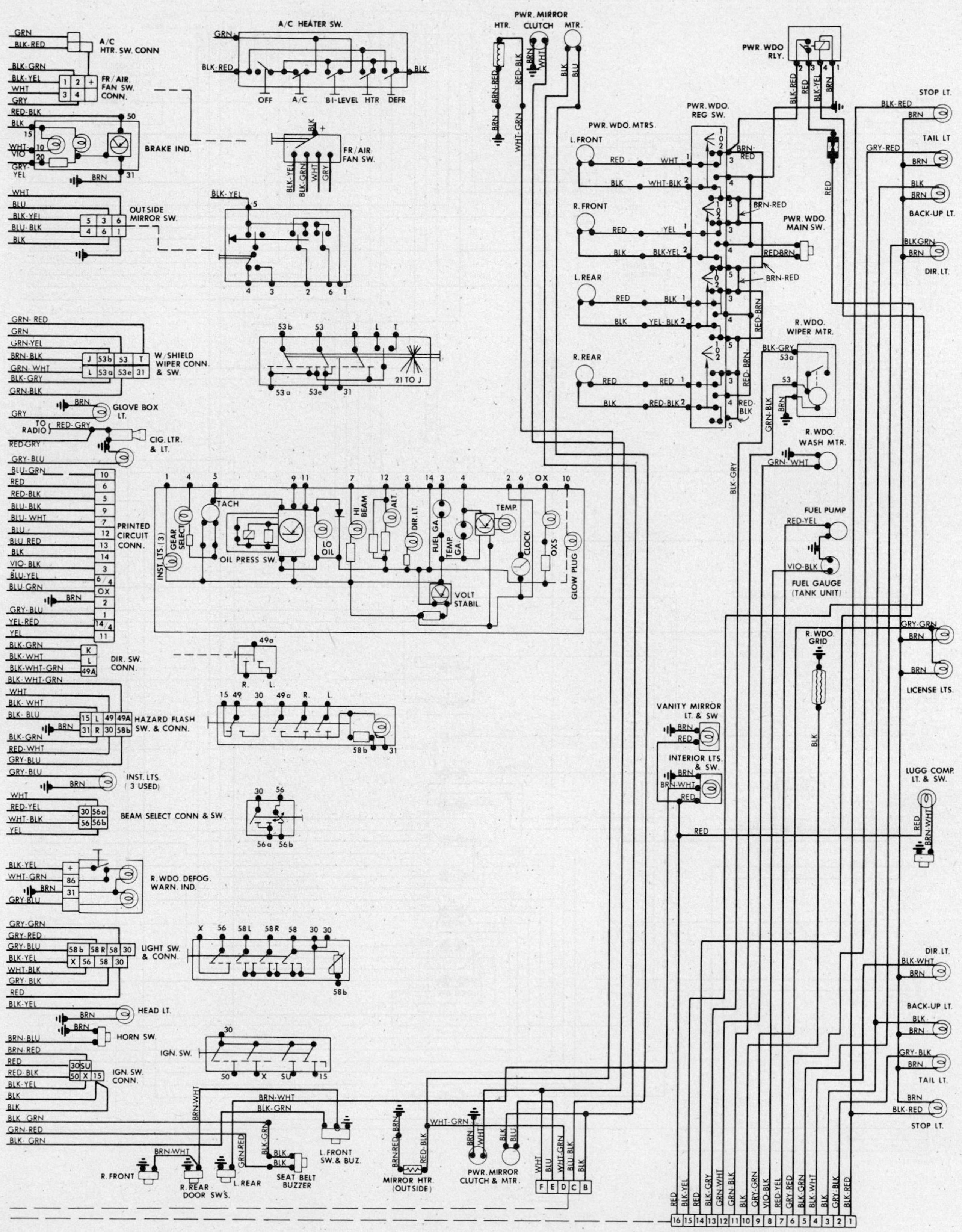

A/C HTR. SW. CONN
A/C HEATER SW.
FR/AIR FAN SW. CONN.
BRAKE IND.
FR/AIR FAN SW.
OUTSIDE MIRROR SW.
W/SHIELD WIPER CONN. & SW.
GLOVE BOX LT.
CIG. LTR. & LT.
PRINTED CIRCUIT CONN.
TACH
OIL PRESS SW.
LO OIL
HI BEAM
ALT.
DIR. LT.
FUEL GA.
TEMP GA.
TEMP.
CLOCK
OXS
GLOW PLUG
VOLT STABIL.
DIR. SW. CONN.
HAZARD FLASH SW. & CONN.
INST. LTS. (3 USED)
BEAM SELECT CONN & SW.
R. WDO. DEFOG. WARN. IND.
LIGHT SW. & CONN.
HEAD LT.
HORN SW.
IGN. SW.
IGN SW. CONN.
R. FRONT
R. REAR DOOR SW'S.
L. REAR
SEAT BELT BUZZER
L. FRONT SW. & BUZ.
MIRROR HTR. (OUTSIDE)
PWR. MIRROR CLUTCH & MTR.
PWR. MIRROR
HTR.
CLUTCH
MTR.
PWR. WDO. MTRS.
L. FRONT
R. FRONT
L. REAR
R. REAR
PWR. WDO. REG SW.
PWR. WDO RLY.
PWR. WDO. MAIN SW.
R. WDO. WIPER MTR.
R. WDO. WASH MTR.
FUEL PUMP
FUEL GAUGE (TANK UNIT)
R. WDO. GRID
VANITY MIRROR LT. & SW
INTERIOR LTS. & SW.
STOP LT.
TAIL LT.
BACK-UP LT.
DIR. LT.
LICENSE LTS.
LUGG COMP. LT. & SW.

1983 Volkswagen

VANAGON & VANAGON DIESEL

FRONT COMPARTMENT & FUSE BLOCK

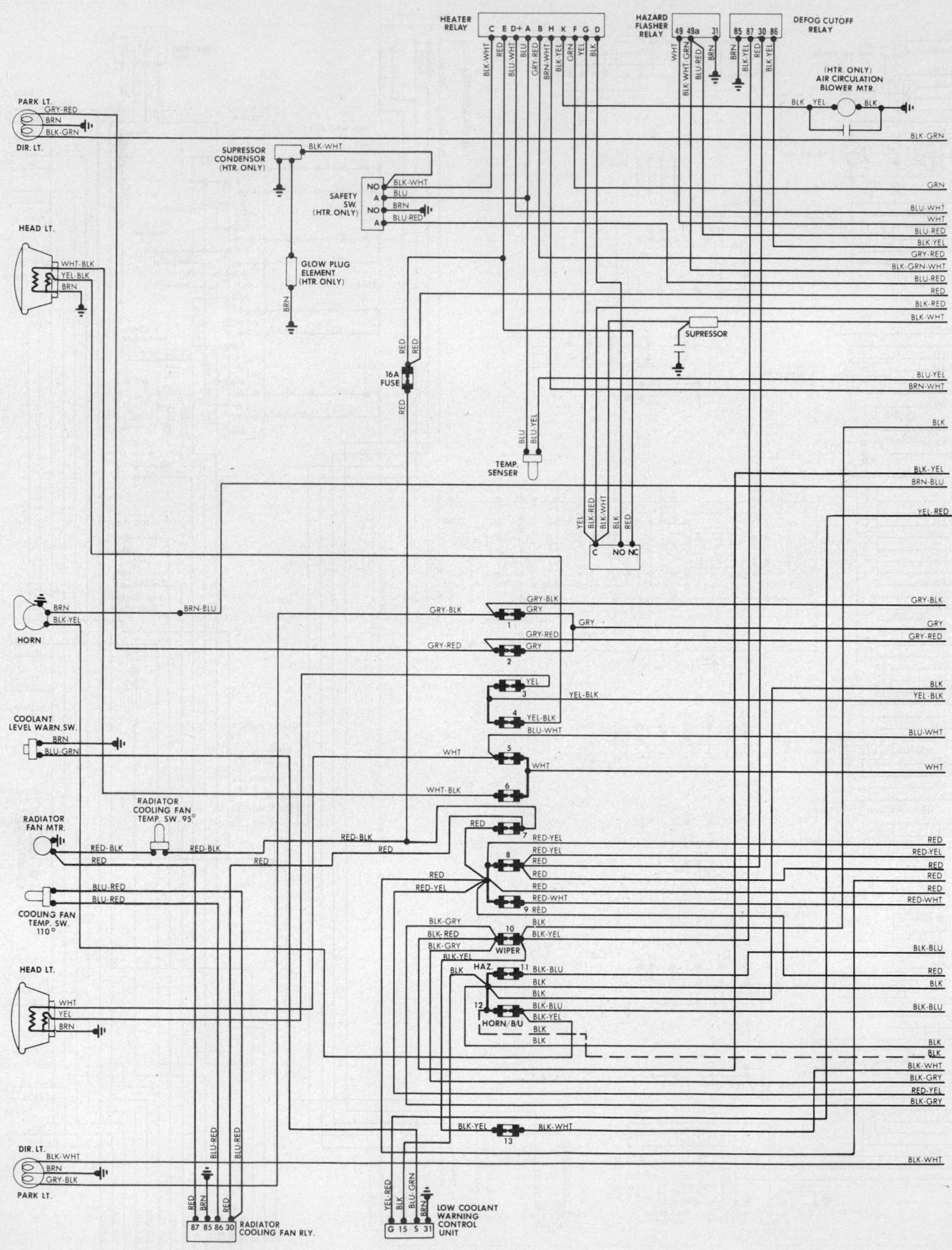
HEATER RELAY
HAZARD FLASHER RELAY
DEFOG CUTOFF RELAY
(HTR. ONLY) AIR CIRCULATION BLOWER MTR.
PARK LT.
DIR. LT.
SUPRESSOR CONDENSOR (HTR. ONLY)
SAFETY SW. (HTR. ONLY)
HEAD LT.
GLOW PLUG ELEMENT (HTR. ONLY)
SUPRESSOR
16A FUSE
TEMP. SENSER
HORN
COOLANT LEVEL WARN. SW.
RADIATOR COOLING FAN TEMP. SW. 95°
RADIATOR FAN MTR.
COOLING FAN TEMP. SW. 110°
WIPER
HAZ.
HORN/B/U
RADIATOR COOLING FAN RLY.
LOW COOLANT WARNING CONTROL UNIT

1983 Volkswagen

VANAGON & VANAGON DIESEL (Cont.)

FRONT COMPARTMENT & UNDERDASH

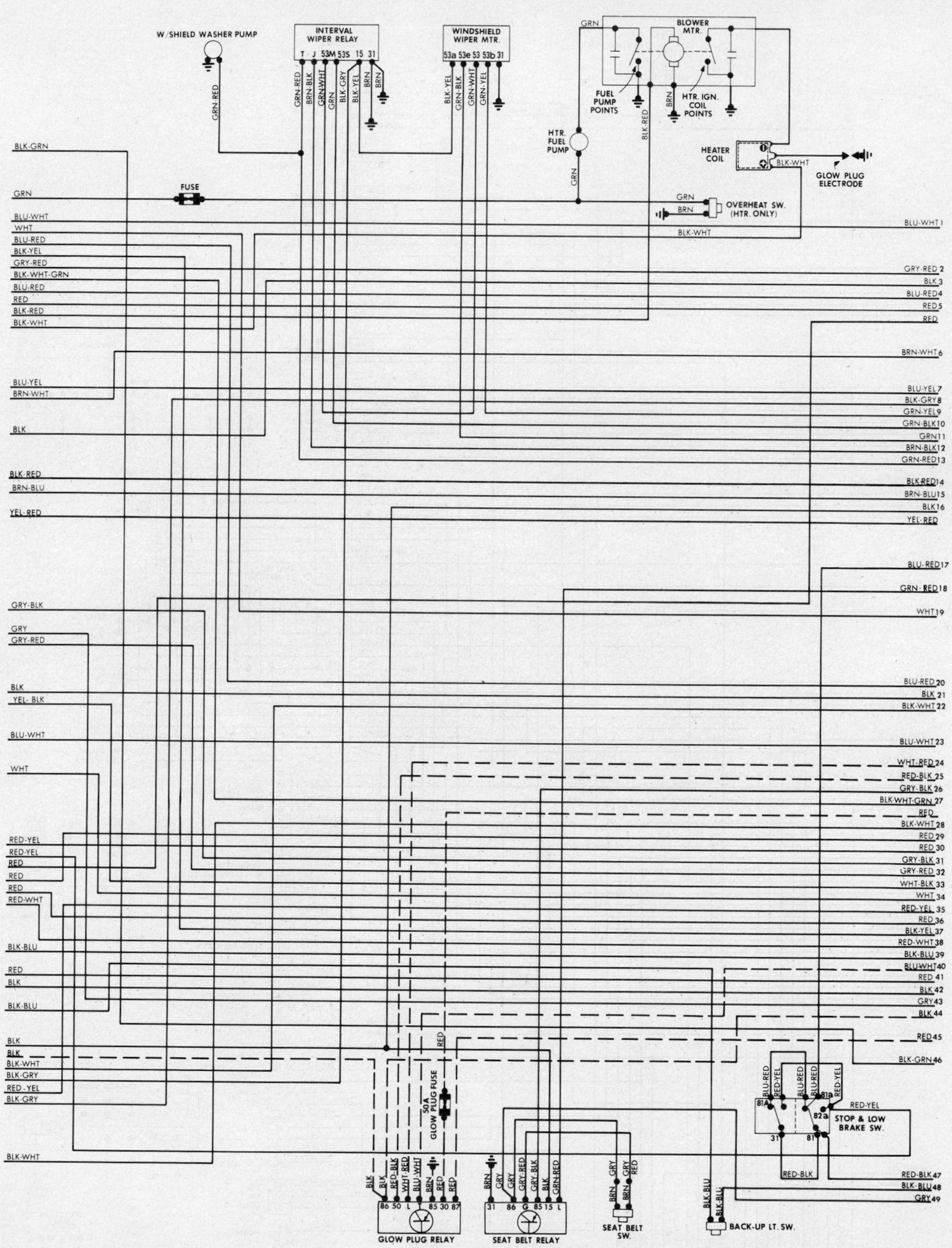

W/SHIELD WASHER PUMP
INTERVAL WIPER RELAY
T J 53M 53S 15 31
WINDSHIELD WIPER MTR.
53a 53e 53 53b 31
BLOWER MTR.
FUEL PUMP POINTS
HTR. IGN. COIL POINTS
HTR. FUEL PUMP
HEATER COIL
GLOW PLUG ELECTRODE
FUSE
OVERHEAT SW. (HTR. ONLY)
BLU-WHT 1
GRY-RED 2
BLK 3
BLU-RED 4
RED 5
BRN-WHT 6
BLU-YEL 7
BLK-GRY 8
GRN-YEL 9
GRN-BLK 10
GRN 11
BRN-BLK 12
GRN-RED 13
BLK-RED 14
BRN-BLU 15
BLK 16
BLU-RED 17
GRN-RED 18
WHT 19
BLU-RED 20
BLK 21
BLK-WHT 22
BLU-WHT 23
WHT-RED 24
RED-BLK 25
GRY-BLK 26
BLK-WHT-GRN 27
BLK-WHT 28
RED 29
RED 30
GRY-BLK 31
GRY-RED 32
WHT-BLK 33
WHT 34
RED-YEL 35
RED 36
BLK-YEL 37
RED-WHT 38
BLK-BLU 39
BLU-WHT 40
RED 41
BLK 42
GRY 43
BLK 44
RED 45
BLK-GRN 46
RED-BLK 47
BLK-BLU 48
GRY 49
50A GLOW PLUG FUSE
86 50 L 85 30 87
GLOW PLUG RELAY
31 86 G 85 15 L
SEAT BELT RELAY
SEAT BELT SW.
BACK-UP LT. SW.
81A 81 81a 82a 31
STOP & LOW BRAKE SW.

1983 Volkswagen

VANAGON & VANAGON DIESEL (Cont.)

UNDERDASH & INSTRUMENT PANEL

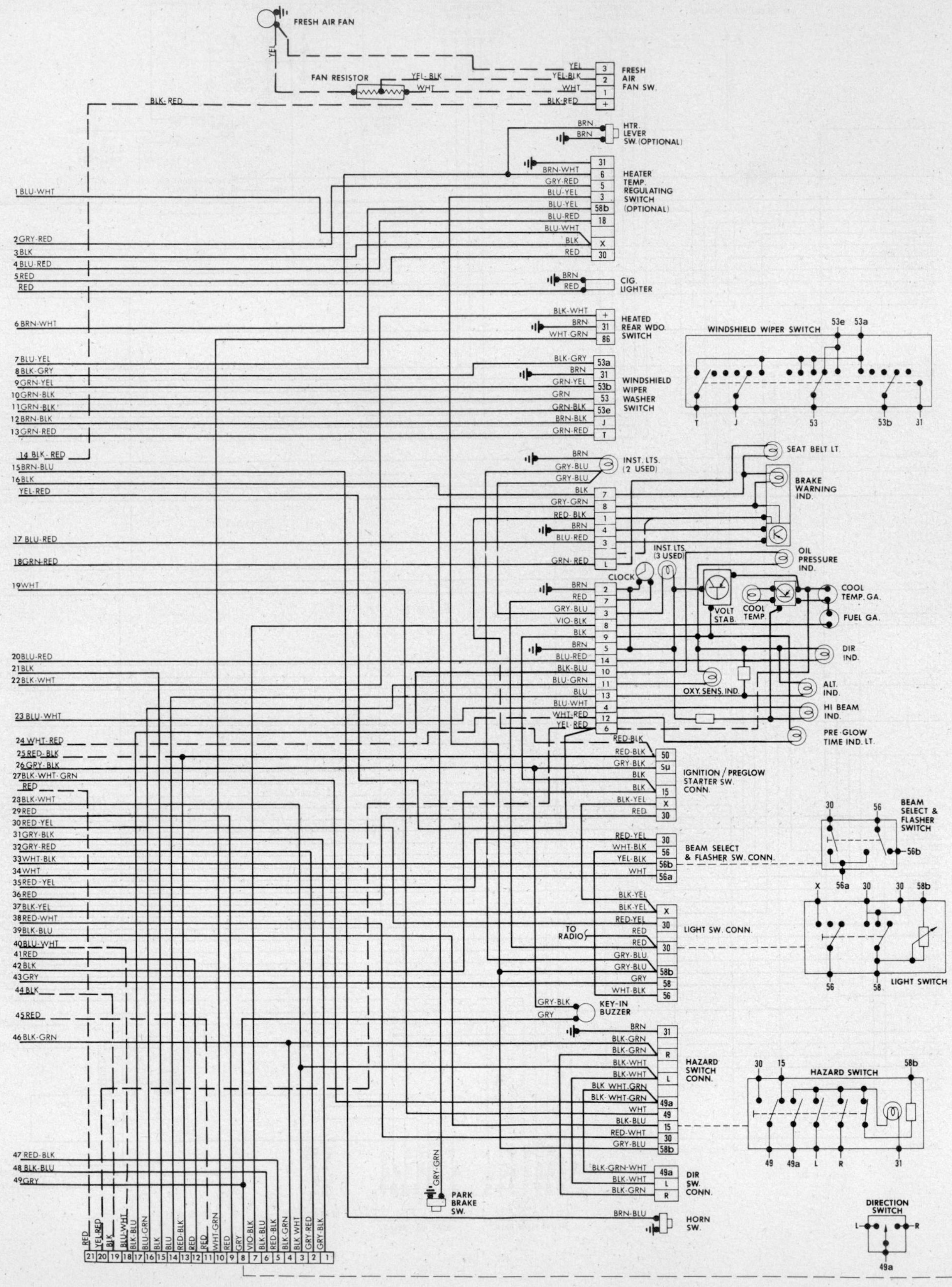

1983 Volkswagen

VANAGON & VANAGON DIESEL (Cont.)

ENGINE COMPARTMENT & REAR COMPARTMENT

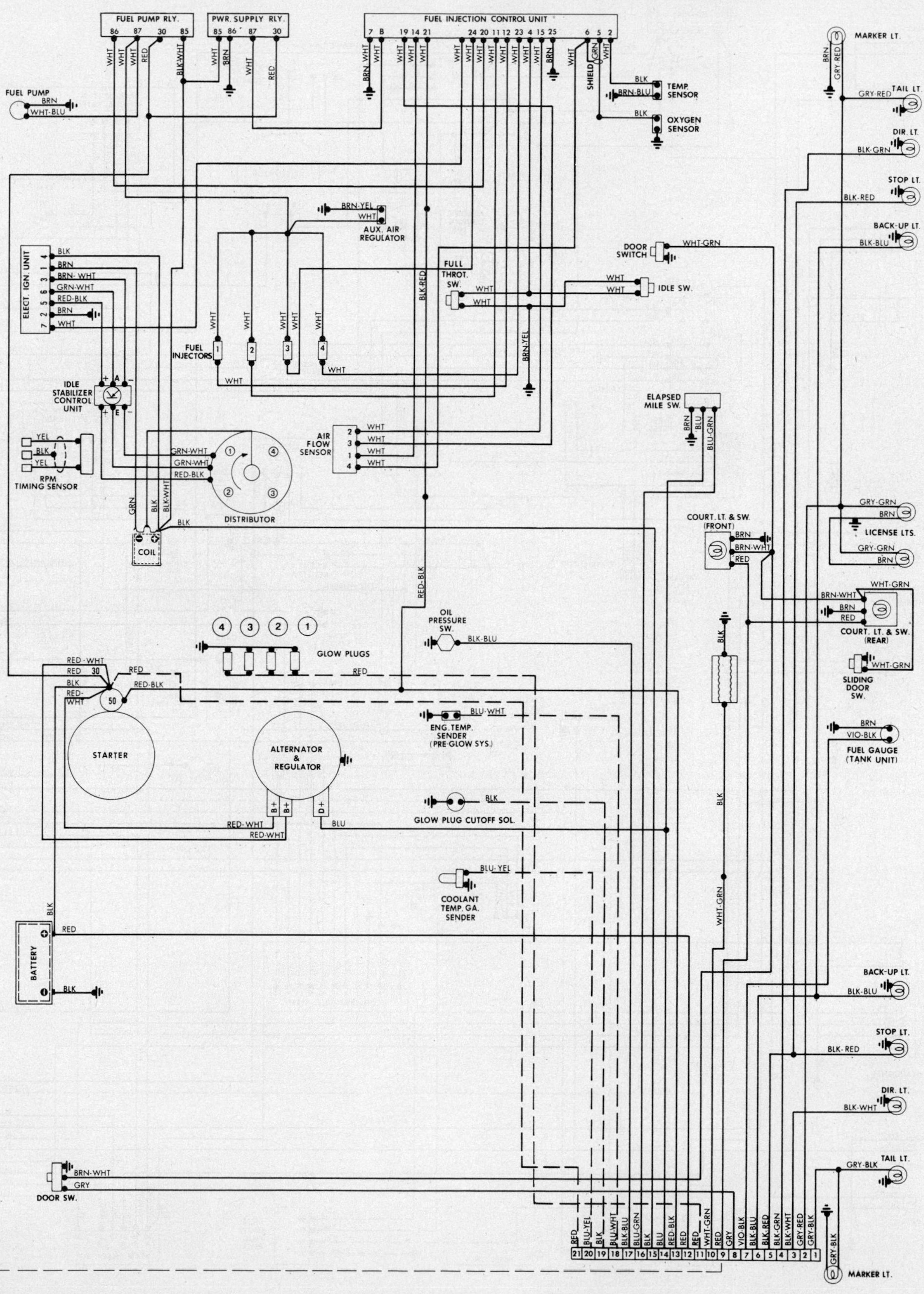
FUEL PUMP RLY.
PWR. SUPPLY RLY.
FUEL INJECTION CONTROL UNIT
FUEL PUMP
TEMP. SENSOR
OXYGEN SENSOR
MARKER LT.
TAIL LT.
DIR. LT.
STOP LT.
BACK-UP LT.
AUX. AIR REGULATOR
DOOR SWITCH
ELECT. IGN. UNIT
FULL THROT. SW.
IDLE SW.
FUEL INJECTORS
IDLE STABILIZER CONTROL UNIT
ELAPSED MILE SW.
AIR FLOW SENSOR
RPM TIMING SENSOR
DISTRIBUTOR
COIL
COURT. LT. & SW. (FRONT)
LICENSE LTS.
COURT. LT. & SW. (REAR)
OIL PRESSURE SW.
GLOW PLUGS
SLIDING DOOR SW.
STARTER
ALTERNATOR & REGULATOR
ENG. TEMP. SENDER (PRE-GLOW SYS.)
FUEL GAUGE (TANK UNIT)
GLOW PLUG CUTOFF SOL.
COOLANT TEMP. GA. SENDER
BATTERY
DOOR SW.

1983 Volvo

DL, GL, TURBO, & DL DIESEL

ENGINE COMPARTMENT

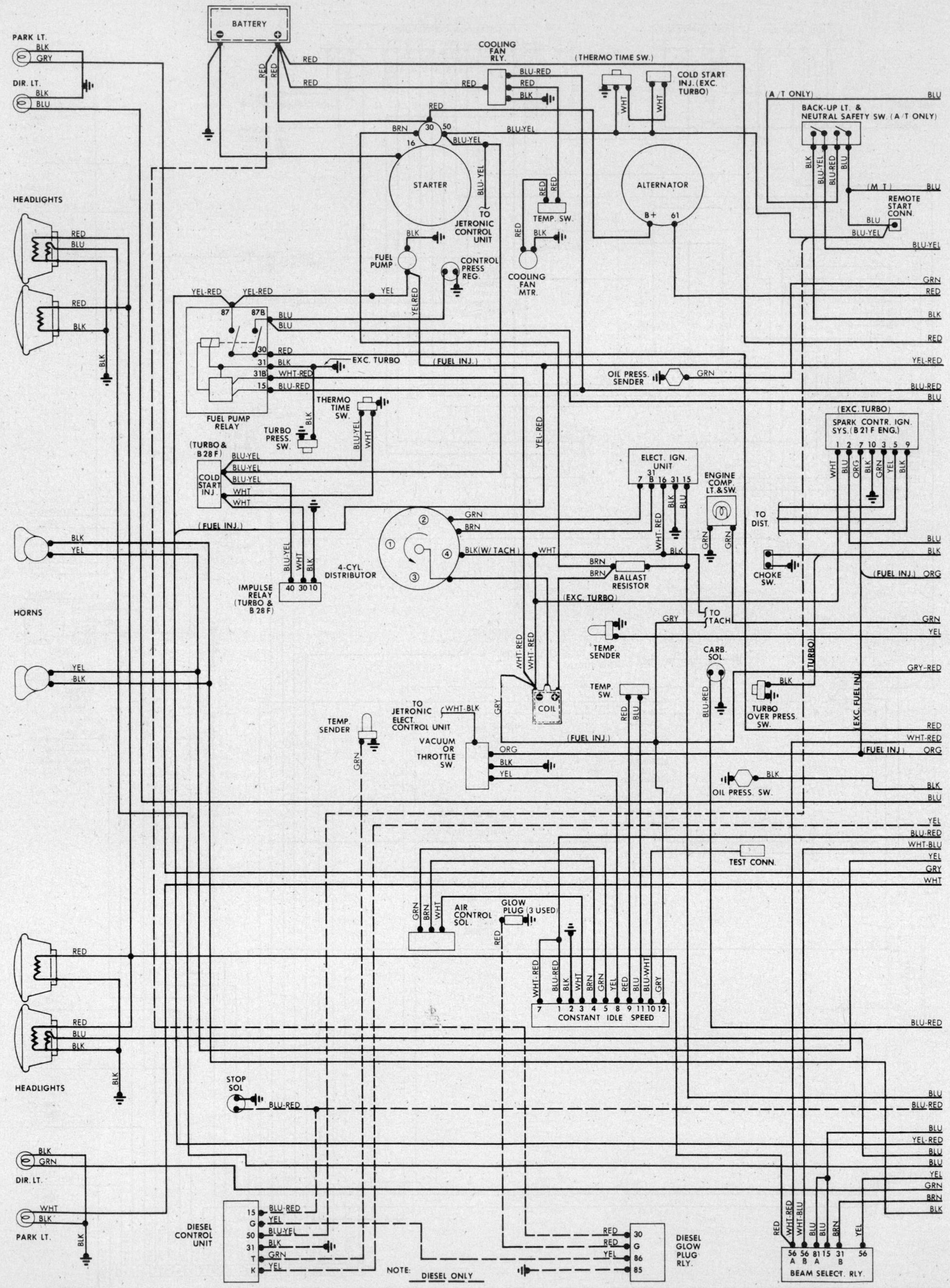
BATTERY
PARK LT.
DIR. LT.
HEADLIGHTS
HORNS
COOLING FAN RLY.
(THERMO TIME SW.)
COLD START INJ. (EXC. TURBO)
(A/T ONLY)
BACK-UP LT. & NEUTRAL SAFETY SW. (A/T ONLY)
STARTER
TO JETRONIC CONTROL UNIT
TEMP. SW.
ALTERNATOR
(M/T)
REMOTE START CONN.
FUEL PUMP
CONTROL PRESS REG.
COOLING FAN MTR.
FUEL PUMP RELAY
EXC. TURBO
(FUEL INJ.)
OIL PRESS. SENDER
THERMO TIME SW.
TURBO PRESS. SW.
(TURBO & B28F)
COLD START INJ.
(EXC. TURBO)
SPARK CONTR. IGN. SYS. (B21F ENG.)
ELECT. IGN. UNIT
ENGINE COMP. LT. & SW.
TO DIST.
4-CYL. DISTRIBUTOR
IMPULSE RELAY (TURBO & B28F)
BALLAST RESISTOR
CHOKE SW.
TO TACH
TEMP. SENDER
CARB. SOL.
(TURBO)
TEMP. SW.
COIL
TURBO OVER PRESS. SW.
(EXC. FUEL INJ.)
TO JETRONIC ELECT. CONTROL UNIT
VACUUM OR THROTTLE SW.
OIL PRESS. SW.
TEST CONN.
AIR CONTROL SOL.
GLOW PLUG (3 USED)
CONSTANT IDLE SPEED
STOP SOL
DIESEL CONTROL UNIT
DIESEL GLOW PLUG RLY.
NOTE: DIESEL ONLY
BEAM SELECT. RLY.

1983 Volvo

DL, GL, TURBO, & DL DIESEL (Cont.)

FUSE BLOCK & UNDERDASH

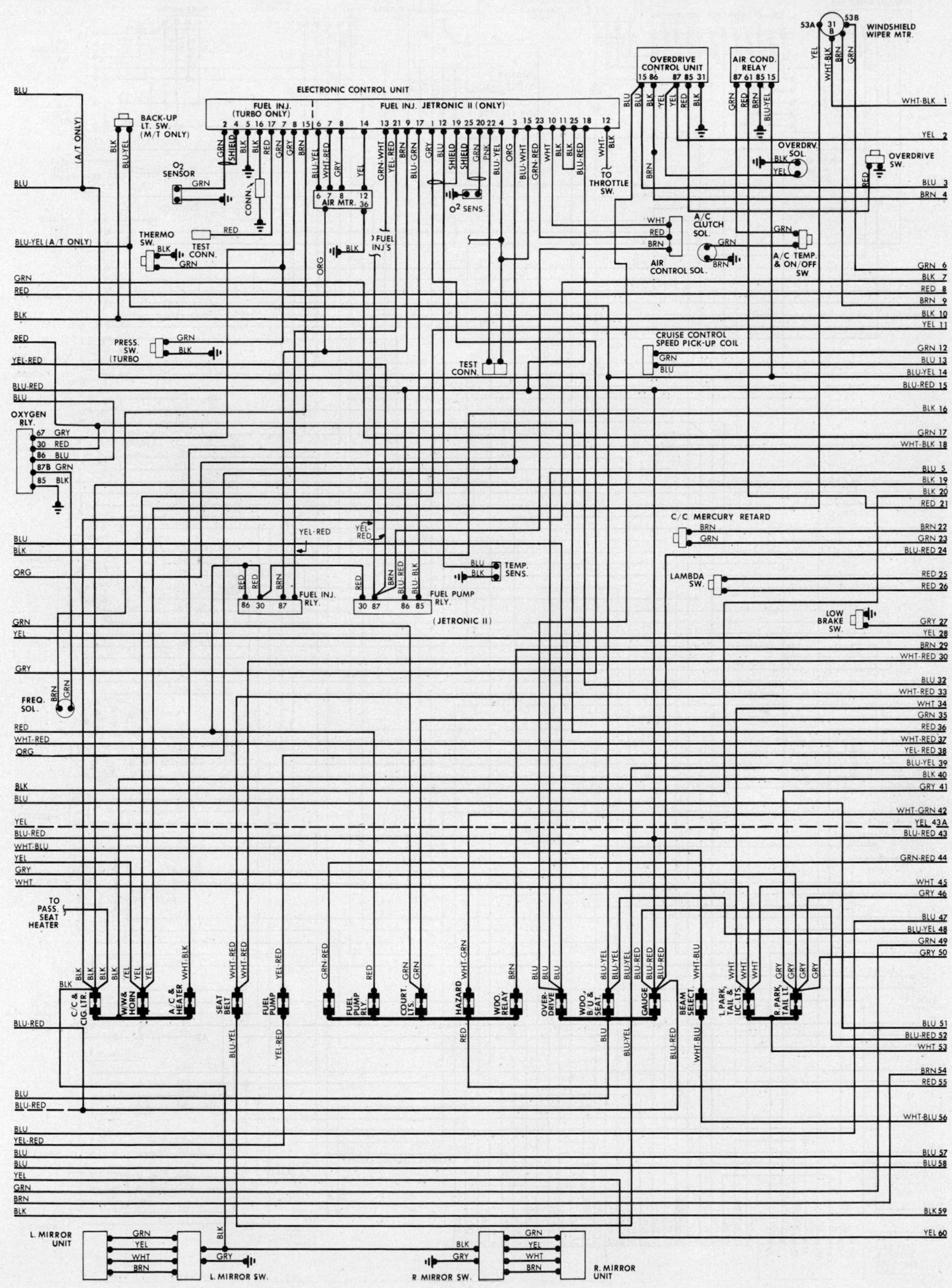

ELECTRONIC CONTROL UNIT
FUEL INJ. (TURBO ONLY)
FUEL INJ. JETRONIC II (ONLY)
OVERDRIVE CONTROL UNIT
AIR COND. RELAY
WINDSHIELD WIPER MTR.
BACK-UP LT. SW. (M/T ONLY)
O2 SENSOR
THERMO SW.
TEST CONN.
AIR MTR.
FUEL INJ'S
O2 SENS.
TO THROTTLE SW.
OVERDRV. SOL.
OVERDRIVE SW.
A/C CLUTCH SOL.
AIR CONTROL SOL.
A/C TEMP. & ON/OFF SW
PRESS. SW. (TURBO)
CRUISE CONTROL SPEED PICK-UP COIL
OXYGEN RLY.
C/C MERCURY RETARD
TEMP. SENS.
FUEL INJ. RLY.
FUEL PUMP RLY.
(JETRONIC II)
LAMBDA SW.
LOW BRAKE SW.
FREQ. SOL.
TO PASS. SEAT HEATER
C/C & CIG. LTR.
W/W & HORN
A/C & HEATER
SEAT BELT
FUEL PUMP
FUEL PUMP RLY.
COURT. LTS.
HAZARD
WDO. RELAY
OVER-DRIVE
WDO. B/U & SEAT
GAUGE
BEAM SELECT
L. PARK, TAIL & LIC. LTS.
R. PARK, TAIL LT.
L. MIRROR UNIT
L. MIRROR SW.
R MIRROR SW.
R. MIRROR UNIT

1983 Volvo

DL, GL, TURBO, & DL DIESEL (Cont.)

INSTRUMENT PANEL & UNDERDASH

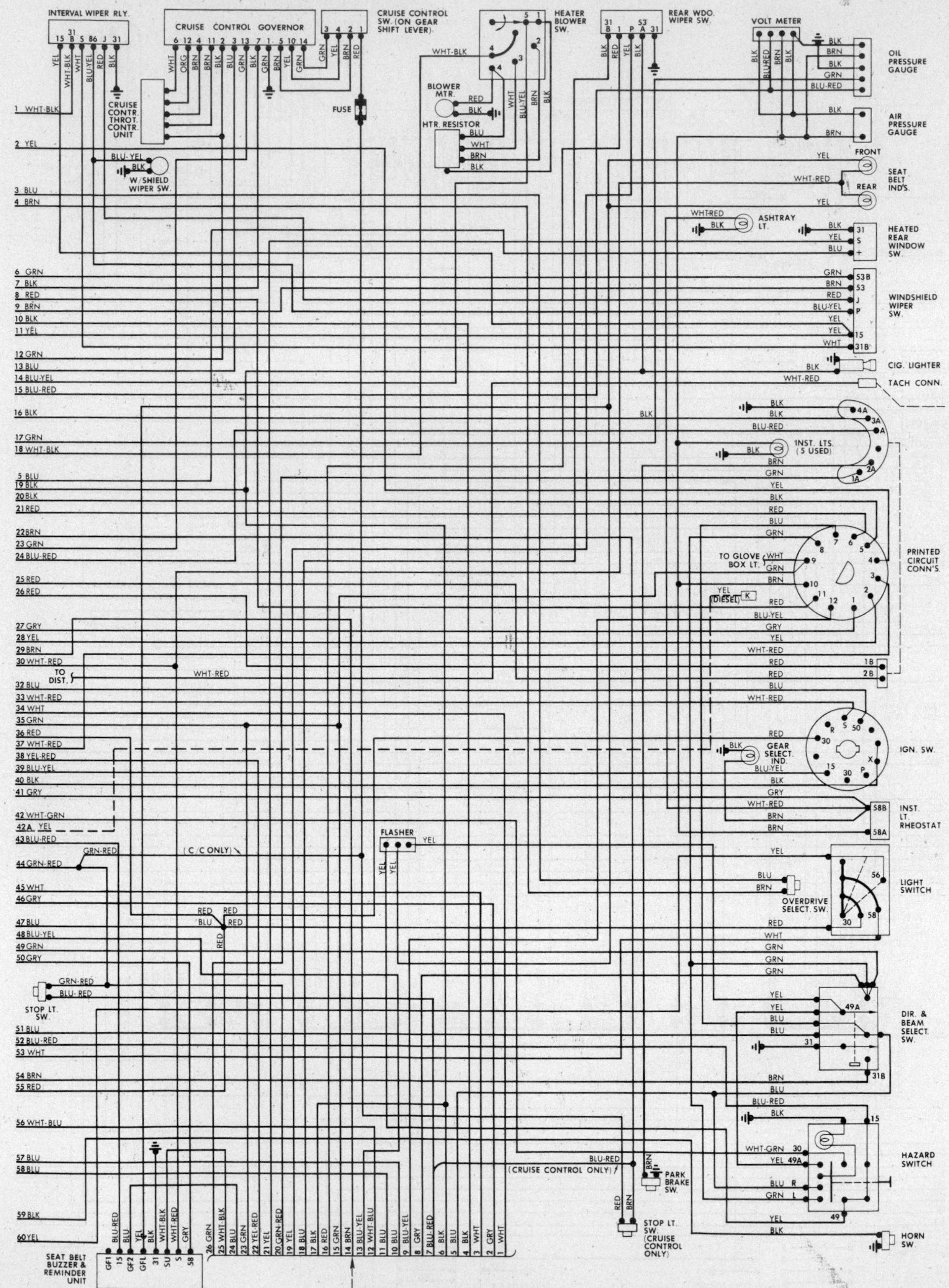

INTERVAL WIPER RLY.
CRUISE CONTROL GOVERNOR
CRUISE CONTROL SW. (ON GEAR SHIFT LEVER)
HEATER BLOWER SW.
REAR WDO. WIPER SW.
VOLT METER
OIL PRESSURE GAUGE
AIR PRESSURE GAUGE
CRUISE CONTR. THROT. CONTR. UNIT
FUSE
BLOWER MTR.
HTR. RESISTOR
W/SHIELD WIPER SW.
SEAT BELT IND'S.
FRONT
REAR
ASHTRAY LT.
HEATED REAR WINDOW SW.
WINDSHIELD WIPER SW.
CIG. LIGHTER
TACH CONN.
INST. LTS. (5 USED)
TO GLOVE BOX LT.
PRINTED CIRCUIT CONN'S.
TO DIST.
GEAR SELECT. IND.
IGN. SW.
INST. LT. RHEOSTAT
FLASHER
(C/C ONLY)
OVERDRIVE SELECT. SW.
LIGHT SWITCH
STOP LT. SW.
DIR. & BEAM SELECT. SW.
HAZARD SWITCH
(CRUISE CONTROL ONLY)
PARK BRAKE SW.
STOP LT. SW. (CRUISE CONTROL ONLY)
HORN SW.
SEAT BELT BUZZER & REMINDER UNIT

1983 Volvo

DL, GL, TURBO, & DL DIESEL (Cont.)

REAR COMPARTMENT & ACCESSORIES

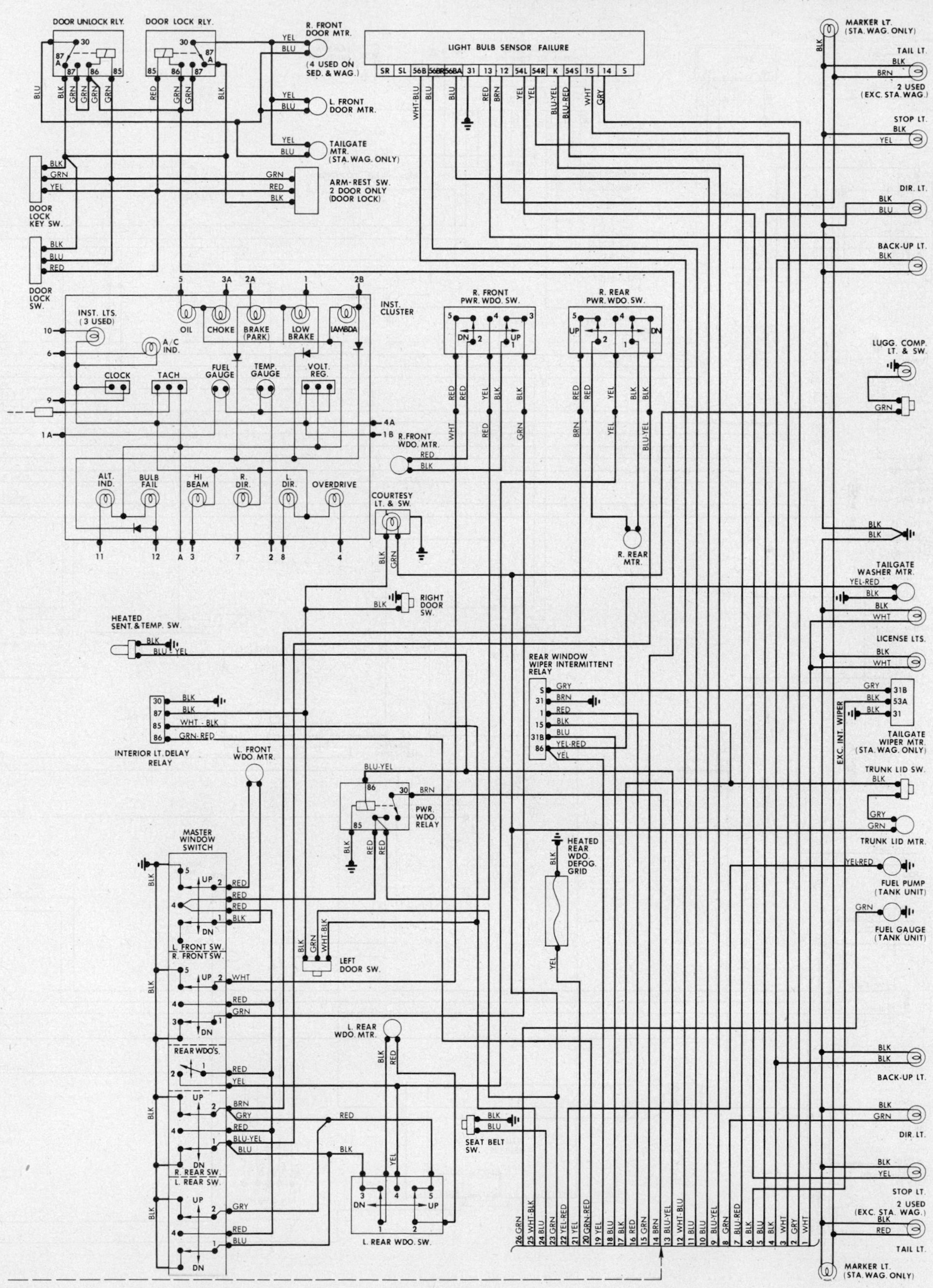

DOOR UNLOCK RLY.
DOOR LOCK RLY.
R. FRONT DOOR MTR.
(4 USED ON SED. & WAG.)
L. FRONT DOOR MTR.
TAILGATE MTR. (STA. WAG. ONLY)
ARM-REST SW. 2 DOOR ONLY (DOOR LOCK)
DOOR LOCK KEY SW.
DOOR LOCK SW.
LIGHT BULB SENSOR FAILURE
INST. CLUSTER
INST. LTS. (3 USED)
A/C IND.
OIL
CHOKE
BRAKE (PARK)
LOW BRAKE
LAMBDA
FUEL GAUGE
TEMP GAUGE
VOLT. REG.
CLOCK
TACH
ALT. IND.
BULB FAIL
HI BEAM
R. DIR.
L. DIR.
OVERDRIVE
R. FRONT PWR. WDO. SW.
R. REAR PWR. WDO. SW.
R. FRONT WDO. MTR.
COURTESY LT. & SW.
R. REAR MTR.
RIGHT DOOR SW.
HEATED SENT. & TEMP. SW.
INTERIOR LT. DELAY RELAY
L. FRONT WDO. MTR.
PWR. WDO RELAY
REAR WINDOW WIPER INTERMITTENT RELAY
HEATED REAR WDO DEFOG. GRID
MASTER WINDOW SWITCH
L. FRONT SW.
R. FRONT SW.
REAR WDO'S.
R. REAR SW.
L. REAR SW.
LEFT DOOR SW.
L. REAR WDO. MTR.
L. REAR WDO. SW.
SEAT BELT SW.
MARKER LT. (STA. WAG. ONLY)
TAIL LT.
2 USED (EXC. STA. WAG.)
STOP LT.
DIR. LT.
BACK-UP LT.
LUGG. COMP. LT. & SW.
TAILGATE WASHER MTR.
LICENSE LTS.
EXC. INT. WIPER
TAILGATE WIPER MTR. (STA. WAG. ONLY)
TRUNK LID SW.
TRUNK LID MTR.
FUEL PUMP (TANK UNIT)
FUEL GAUGE (TANK UNIT)
26 GRN
25 WHT-BLK
24 BLU
23 GRN
22 YEL-RED
21 YEL
20 GRN-RED
19 YEL
18 BLU
17 BLK
16 RED
15 GRN
14 BRN
13 BLU-YEL
12 WHT-BLU
11 BLU
10 BLU-YEL
9 BLK
8 GRN
7 BLU-RED
6 BLK
5 BLU
4 BLK
3 WHT
2 GRY
1 WHT

1983 Volvo

760 GLE & 760 GLE TURBO DIESEL

ENGINE COMPARTMENT

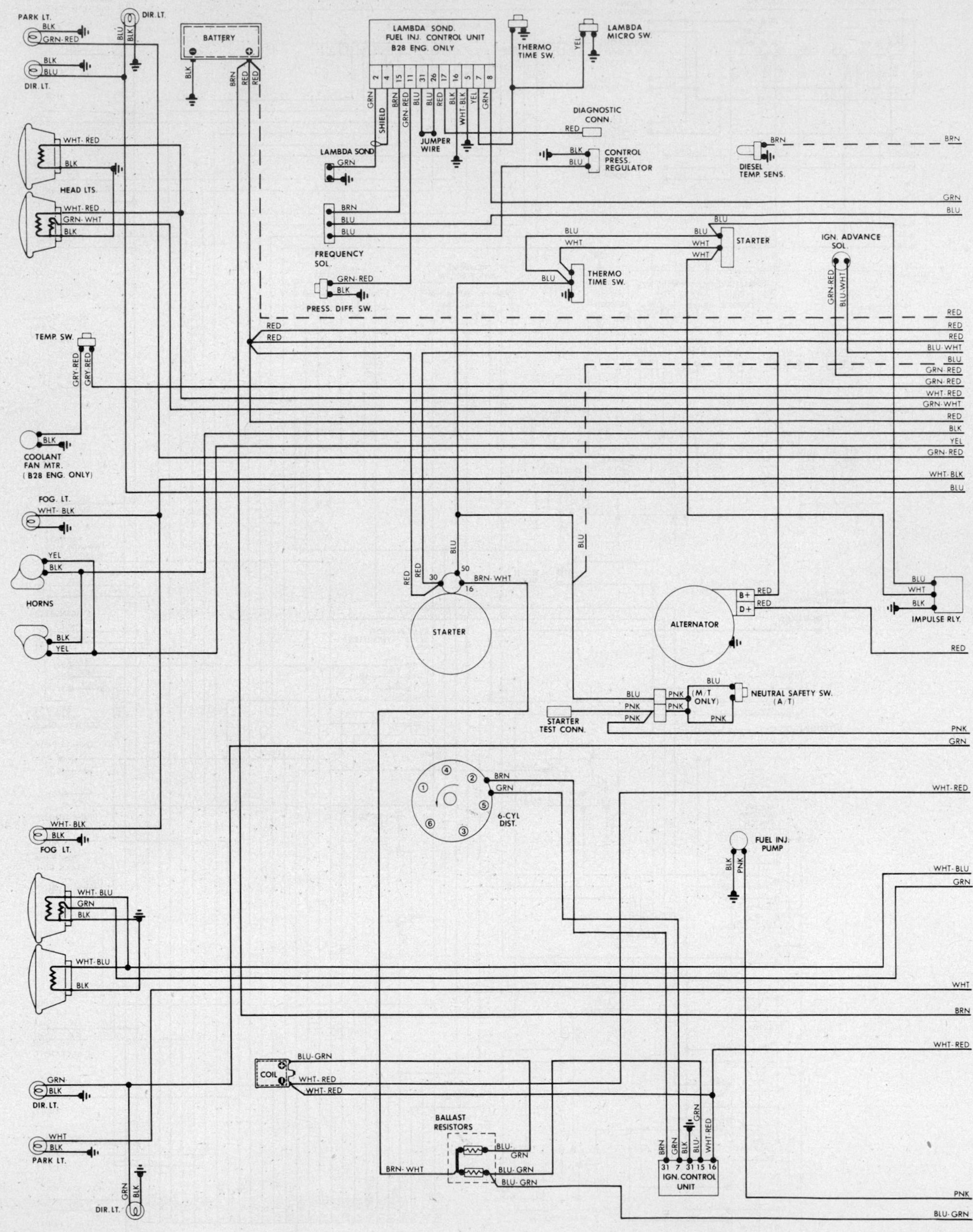
PARK LT.
DIR. LT.
BATTERY
LAMBDA SOND.
FUEL INJ. CONTROL UNIT
B28 ENG. ONLY
THERMO
TIME SW.
LAMBDA
MICRO SW.
DIAGNOSTIC
CONN.
JUMPER
WIRE
LAMBDA SOND
SHIELD
CONTROL
PRESS.
REGULATOR
DIESEL
TEMP. SENS.
HEAD LTS.
FREQUENCY
SOL.
STARTER
IGN. ADVANCE
SOL.
THERMO
TIME SW.
PRESS. DIFF. SW.
TEMP. SW.
COOLANT
FAN MTR.
(B28 ENG. ONLY)
FOG. LT.
HORNS
STARTER
ALTERNATOR
IMPULSE RLY.
STARTER
TEST CONN.
(M/T
ONLY)
NEUTRAL SAFETY SW.
(A/T)
6-CYL
DIST.
FUEL INJ.
PUMP
FOG LT.
COIL
BALLAST
RESISTORS
IGN. CONTROL
UNIT
DIR. LT.
PARK LT.
DIR. LT.

1983 Volvo

760 GLE & 760 GLE TURBO DIESEL (Cont.)

ENGINE COMPARTMENT

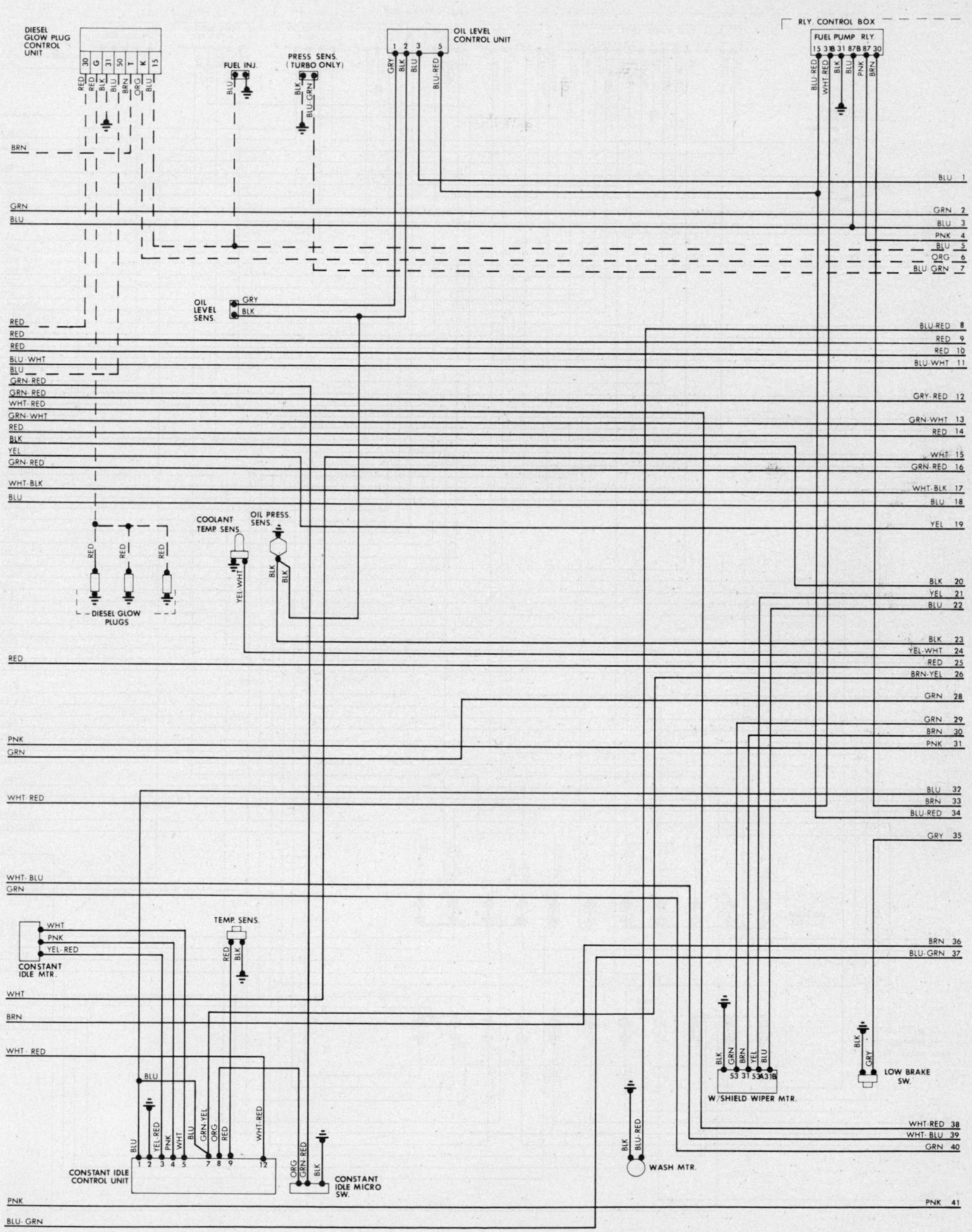
DIESEL GLOW PLUG CONTROL UNIT
FUEL INJ.
PRESS SENS. (TURBO ONLY)
OIL LEVEL CONTROL UNIT
RLY. CONTROL BOX
FUEL PUMP RLY.
OIL LEVEL SENS.
COOLANT TEMP SENS.
OIL PRESS. SENS.
DIESEL GLOW PLUGS
CONSTANT IDLE MTR.
TEMP. SENS.
CONSTANT IDLE CONTROL UNIT
CONSTANT IDLE MICRO SW.
WASH MTR.
W/SHIELD WIPER MTR.
LOW BRAKE SW.

1983 Volvo

760 GLE & 760 GLE TURBO DIESEL (Cont.)

FUSE BLOCK & UNDERDASH

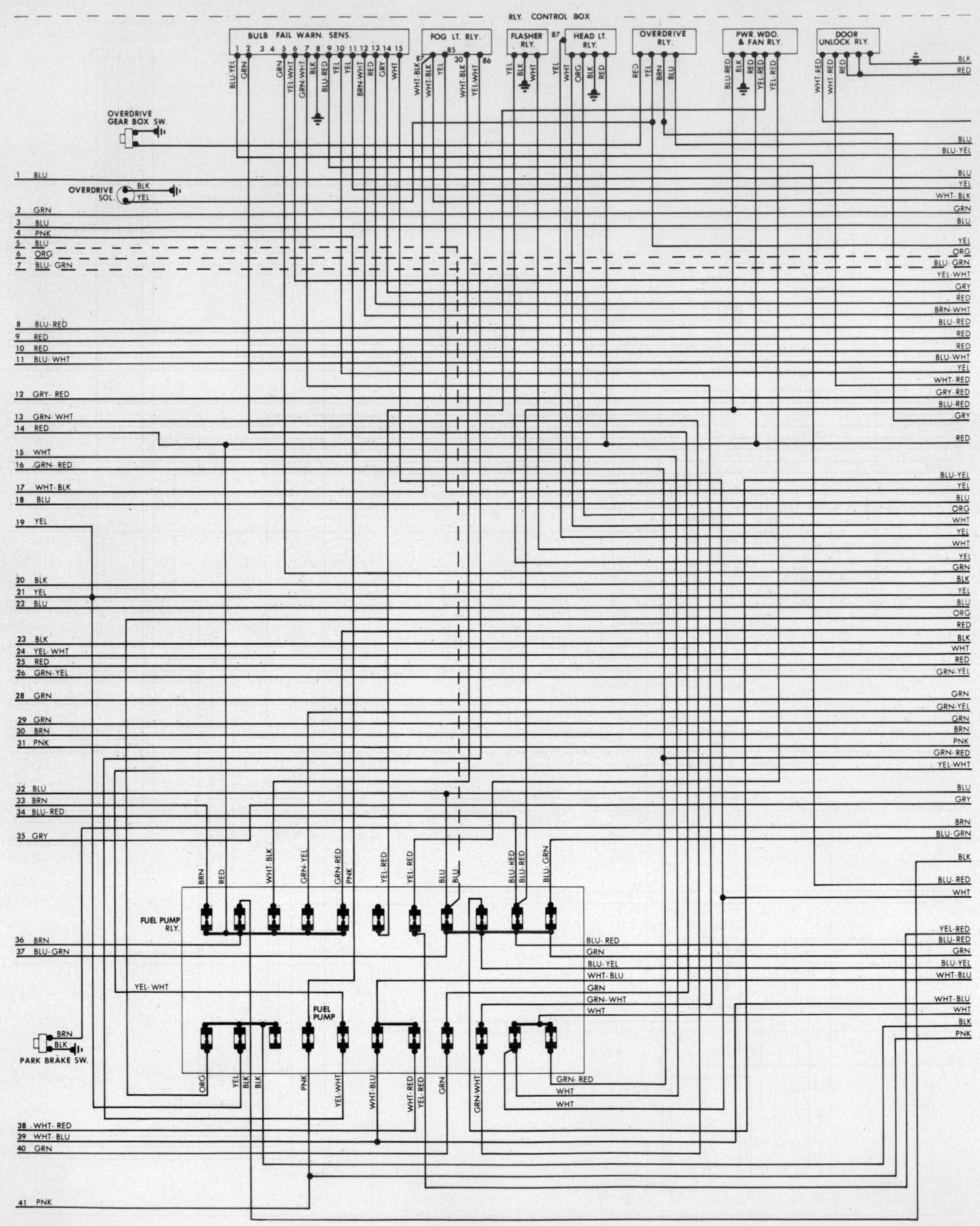

RLY. CONTROL BOX
BULB FAIL WARN. SENS.
FOG LT. RLY.
FLASHER RLY.
HEAD LT. RLY.
OVERDRIVE RLY.
PWR. WDO. & FAN RLY.
DOOR UNLOCK RLY.
OVERDRIVE GEAR BOX SW.
OVERDRIVE SOL.
FUEL PUMP RLY.
FUEL PUMP
PARK BRAKE SW.
1 BLU
2 GRN
3 BLU
4 PNK
5 BLU
6 ORG
7 BLU-GRN
8 BLU-RED
9 RED
10 RED
11 BLU-WHT
12 GRY-RED
13 GRN-WHT
14 RED
15 WHT
16 GRN-RED
17 WHT-BLK
18 BLU
19 YEL
20 BLK
21 YEL
22 BLU
23 BLK
24 YEL-WHT
25 RED
26 GRN-YEL
28 GRN
29 GRN
30 BRN
31 PNK
32 BLU
33 BRN
34 BLU-RED
35 GRY
36 BRN
37 BLU-GRN
38 WHT-RED
39 WHT-BLU
40 GRN
41 PNK

760 GLE & 760 GLE TURBO DIESEL (Cont.)

UNDERDASH

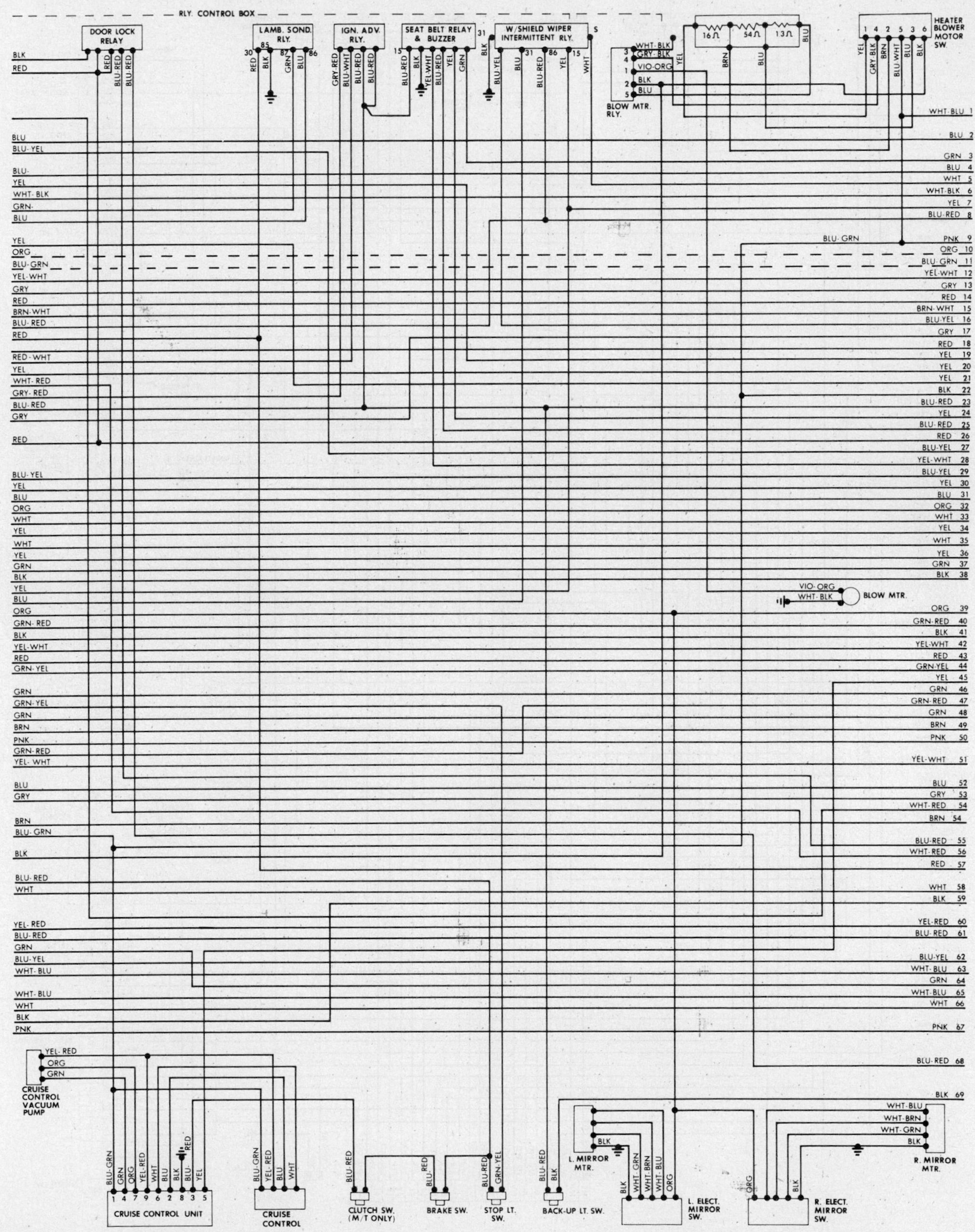
RLY. CONTROL BOX
DOOR LOCK RELAY
LAMB. SOND. RLY.
IGN. ADV. RLY.
SEAT BELT RELAY & BUZZER
W/SHIELD WIPER INTERMITTENT RLY.
HEATER BLOWER MOTOR SW.
BLOW MTR. RLY.
BLOW MTR.
CRUISE CONTROL VACUUM PUMP
CRUISE CONTROL UNIT
CRUISE CONTROL
CLUTCH SW. (M/T ONLY)
BRAKE SW.
STOP LT. SW.
BACK-UP LT. SW.
L. MIRROR MTR.
L. ELECT. MIRROR SW.
R. ELECT. MIRROR SW.
R. MIRROR MTR.

1983 Volvo

760 GLE & 760 GLE TURBO DIESEL (Cont.)

INSTRUMENT PANEL & UNDERDASH

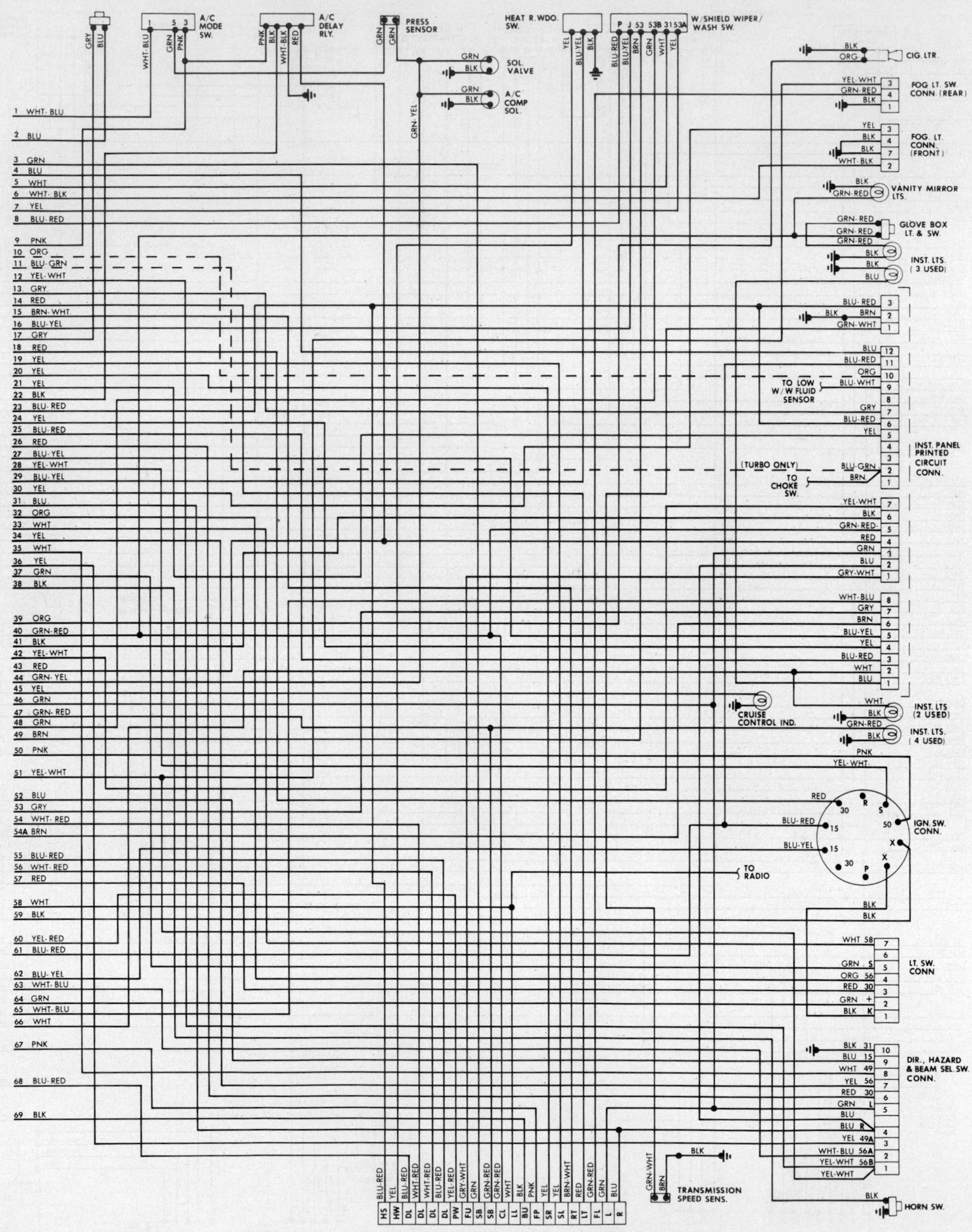
A/C MODE SW.
A/C DELAY RLY.
PRESS SENSOR
SOL. VALVE
A/C COMP SOL.
HEAT R. WDO. SW.
W/SHIELD WIPER/ WASH SW.
CIG. LTR.
FOG LT. SW CONN. (REAR)
FOG. LT. CONN. (FRONT)
VANITY MIRROR LTS.
GLOVE BOX LT. & SW.
INST. LTS. (3 USED)
TO LOW W/W FLUID SENSOR
(TURBO ONLY)
TO CHOKE SW.
INST. PANEL PRINTED CIRCUIT CONN.
CRUISE CONTROL IND.
INST. LTS (2 USED)
INST. LTS. (4 USED)
IGN. SW. CONN.
TO RADIO
LT. SW. CONN
DIR., HAZARD & BEAM SEL. SW. CONN.
TRANSMISSION SPEED SENS.
HORN SW.
1 WHT-BLU
2 BLU
3 GRN
4 BLU
5 WHT
6 WHT-BLK
7 YEL
8 BLU-RED
9 PNK
10 ORG
11 BLU-GRN
12 YEL-WHT
13 GRY
14 RED
15 BRN-WHT
16 BLU-YEL
17 GRY
18 RED
19 YEL
20 YEL
21 YEL
22 BLK
23 BLU-RED
24 YEL
25 BLU-RED
26 RED
27 BLU-YEL
28 YEL-WHT
29 BLU-YEL
30 YEL
31 BLU
32 ORG
33 WHT
34 YEL
35 WHT
36 YEL
37 GRN
38 BLK
39 ORG
40 GRN-RED
41 BLK
42 YEL-WHT
43 RED
44 GRN-YEL
45 YEL
46 GRN
47 GRN-RED
48 GRN
49 BRN
50 PNK
51 YEL-WHT
52 BLU
53 GRY
54 WHT-RED
54A BRN
55 BLU-RED
56 WHT-RED
57 RED
58 WHT
59 BLK
60 YEL-RED
61 BLU-RED
62 BLU-YEL
63 WHT-BLU
64 GRN
65 WHT-BLU
66 WHT
67 PNK
68 BLU-RED
69 BLK
HS HW DL DL DL DL PW FU SB SB CL LL BU FP SR SL RT LT FL L R

760 GLE & 760 GLE TURBO DIESEL (Cont.)

REAR COMPARTMENT & ACCESSORIES

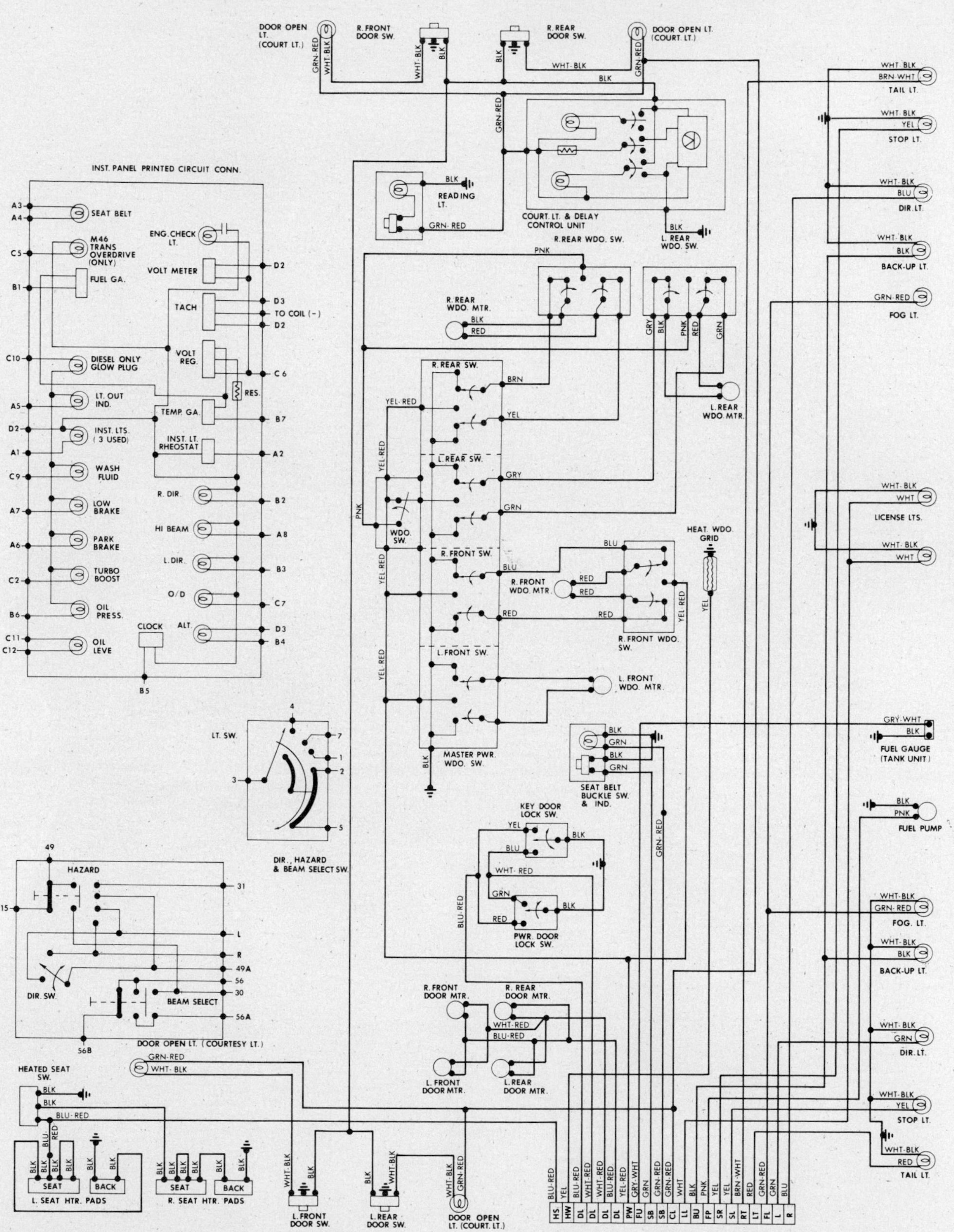
DOOR OPEN LT. (COURT LT.)
R. FRONT DOOR SW.
R. REAR DOOR SW.
DOOR OPEN LT. (COURT. LT.)
TAIL LT.
STOP LT.
DIR. LT.
BACK-UP LT.
FOG LT.
READING LT.
COURT. LT. & DELAY CONTROL UNIT
L. REAR WDO. SW.
R. REAR WDO. SW.
INST. PANEL PRINTED CIRCUIT CONN.
SEAT BELT
M46 TRANS OVERDRIVE (ONLY)
FUEL GA.
ENG. CHECK LT.
VOLT METER
TACH
TO COIL (–)
DIESEL ONLY GLOW PLUG
VOLT REG.
RES.
LT. OUT IND.
TEMP. GA.
INST. LTS. (3 USED)
INST. LT. RHEOSTAT
WASH FLUID
LOW BRAKE
PARK BRAKE
TURBO BOOST
OIL PRESS.
OIL LEVE
R. DIR.
HI BEAM
L. DIR.
O/D
ALT.
CLOCK
R. REAR WDO. MTR.
R. REAR SW.
L. REAR WDO. MTR.
L. REAR SW.
WDO. SW.
R. FRONT SW.
R. FRONT WDO. MTR.
R. FRONT WDO. SW.
HEAT. WDO. GRID
L. FRONT SW.
L. FRONT WDO. MTR.
MASTER PWR. WDO. SW.
LICENSE LTS.
FUEL GAUGE (TANK UNIT)
FUEL PUMP
SEAT BELT BUCKLE SW. & IND.
LT. SW.
DIR., HAZARD & BEAM SELECT SW.
HAZARD
DIR. SW.
BEAM SELECT
KEY DOOR LOCK SW.
PWR. DOOR LOCK SW.
FOG. LT.
DOOR OPEN LT. (COURTESY LT.)
HEATED SEAT SW.
R. FRONT DOOR MTR.
R. REAR DOOR MTR.
L. FRONT DOOR MTR.
L. REAR DOOR MTR.
SEAT
BACK
L. SEAT HTR. PADS
R. SEAT HTR. PADS
L. FRONT DOOR SW.
L. REAR DOOR SW.
DOOR OPEN LT. (COURT. LT.)
HS HW DL DL DL DL PW FU SB SB CL LL BU FP SR SL RT LT FL L R

SECTION 5

ACCESSORIES & EQUIPMENT

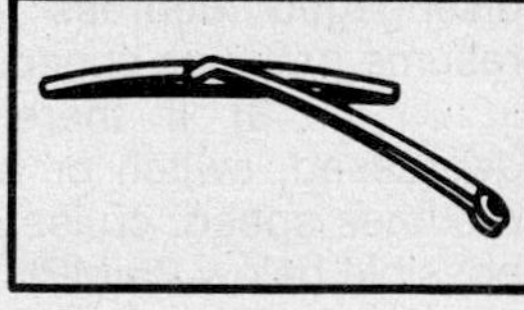

CONTENTS

CRUISE CONTROL

REAR WINDOW DEFOGGER

SWITCHES, GAUGES & INSTRUMENT PANELS

WIPER/WASHER SYSTEMS

NOTE: **ALSO SEE GENERAL INDEX.**

Cruise Control Systems

CHRYSLER CORP. IMPORTS

Challenger, Colt Pickup, Ram-50 Pickup & Sapporo

DESCRIPTION

The cruise control system is electrically actuated and vacuum operated. The speed control switch is located on the instrument panel and consists of 3 buttons; "OFF", "SET" and "RESUME". The system will not operate at speeds under 25 MPH.

Fig. 1: Cruise Control In-Vehicle Components

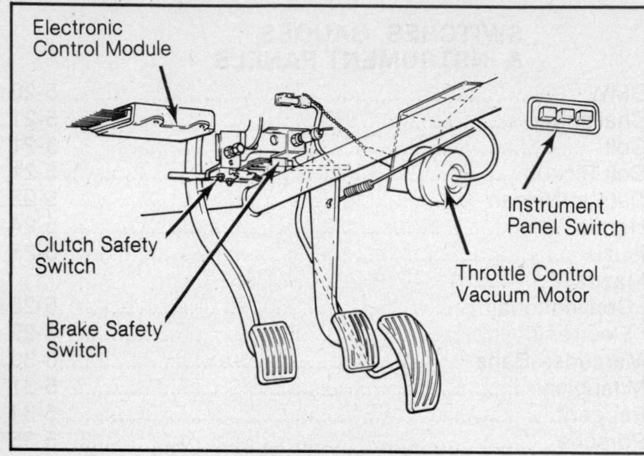
Electronic Control Module
Instrument Panel Switch
Clutch Safety Switch
Throttle Control Vacuum Motor
Brake Safety Switch

OPERATION

The "SET" button incorporates 3 functions. It turns the system on when it is depressed, it sets the vehicle speed when it is released, and it accelerates the vehicle when is is held down. The "OFF" button will deactivate the system. This is accomplished by disengaging the power supply relay located in the instrument panel.

Depressing the brake or clutch deactivates the cruise control function. "RESUME" button can be used after either brake or clutch operation has been depressed. Depressing the button will return the vehicle to the previously set speed at a controlled rate of acceleration, providing the system has not been turned off.

ADJUSTMENTS

BRAKE & CLUTCH SAFETY SWITCHES

Bend actuator lever so that a faint click is heard when the pedal is depressed approximately 1". Be careful not to place a strain on the plastic switch housing.

TROUBLE SHOOTING

1) Set brakes. Place transmission in Neutral or Park. Start engine. If cruise control engages when engine is started, unplug electronic control module. Replace module if condition does not repeat with module unplugged.

2) Release brakes and accelerate vehicle to desired speed. If cruise control engages without accuating "SET" button, electrical circuit or instrument panel switch is faulty.

3) Depress and release "SET" button. Remove foot from accelerator. Speed should be controlled. If speed setting is too high or low, electrical circuit is faulty, there are vacuum leaks at valve body or vacuum motor, there is excessive slack in carburetor cable or speed control chain, or valves in valve body are sluggish.

4) If there is no speed control when button is pressed, fuse is blown, cruise control chain is disconnected, electrical or vacuum circuits are faulty, speed sensor or instrument panel switch is faulty, valve body is faulty, or clutch, brake or speed control switches are improperly adjusted.

5) If there is speedometer noise, excessive needle waver, or erratic servo lock-in performance, speedometer cable is damaged, there is excessive slack in carburetor cable, vacuum source is faulty, valves in cruise control valve body are sticking, or control module is faulty.

6) Drive the vehicle over a rough road. If unit disengages, brake light and speed control switch adjustment is incorrect, or there is a loose connection. Tap brake pedal lightly. If there is no disengagement of system, brake light and cruise control switch adjustment is incorrect, vacuum motor hose is kinked or damaged, cruise control chain is damaged, or electrical circuit is faulty.

7) If in step **6)**, carburetor does not return to normal idle, cruise control chain is damaged, misadjusted, or throttle linkage is faulty. If in step **6)**, cruise control disengaged, depress "RESUME" button. Vehicle should resume previous speed.

8) If there is no resume when button is depressed, switch or electrical circuit is faulty. If vehicle resumes speed, cruise control is okay. If resume speed is possible below 25 MPH, electrical circuit is faulty.

TESTING

QUICK SYSTEM CHECK

1) If the system fails to operate, check the following as possible sources of the problem: Check the brake lights. The entire brake light circuit must be operational for cruise control to work. Check the fuse that powers cruise control circuit.

2) Check the operation of brake and clutch safety switches by listening for a faint click when pedals are depressed. Remove the short section of hose between the vacuum reservoir and valve body at the valve body and check for vacuum.

3) If there is no vacuum, check for loose or cracked hoses. Check all plug-in connections to ensure good contact. Check to make sure speedometer operates.

SYSTEMATIC SYSTEM CHECK

1) Remove 2 screws attaching module to the lower edge of the instrument panel. Allow module to hang down from the wiring harness. Wires on the connector are numbered from 1 to 15 (including blank spaces) starting with the Black ground wire on the end as No. 1.

2) Ground a test lamp and connect to pin No. 2 on circuit board between Black plastic housing and White connector. Lamp should not light. Press "OFF", "SET" and "RESUME" buttons. Lamp should light only when "RESUME" button is pressed.

3) Attach test lamp to pin No. 3. Lamp should light only when "SET" button is pressed. Repeat test with ignition on and test lamp attached to pin No. 9. Lamp

CHRYSLER CORP. IMPORTS (Cont.)

should light only when "OFF" button is pressed. Turn on headlights.

4) Lettering on cruise control switch should be illuminated and should dim and brighten with the instrument panel control. If switch fails any of the tests, test for continuity of electrical connectors. If connectors are okay, replace switch.

BRAKE SAFETY SWITCH TEST

1) Turn on ignition. Check for 12 volts at both terminals on the additional brake safety switch at the back of the connector. If only 1 terminal has 12 volts, operate the brake pedal to check switch adjustment. A click should be heard just before brake pedal arm comes back to the stop.

2) If there is no voltage on either side of switch, check the cruise control fuse. Fuse is the 10-amp fuse for voltage regulator on Challenger and Sapporo, and the 3-amp fuse in cruise control wiring harness on Colt and Ram-50 pickups.

CLUTCH SAFETY SWITCH TEST

Clutch switch is tested in the same manner as brake switch, except that brake pedal must be depressed when testing clutch switch. This supplies power to switch from brake light circuit.

VALVE BODY TEST

1) Turn ignition on. Ground test light and touch terminals on the 5-wire connector 6" from valve body. The 2 White wires chould show 12 volts. The Yellow, Brown and Blue wires should produce a dim light and a faint click should be heard when wires are touched.

2) If no power is found at either wire, check brake switch and cruise control fuse. Fuse is the 10-amp fuse for voltage regulator on Challenger and Sapporo, and the 3-amp fuse in cruise control wiring harness on Colt and Ram-50 pickups. Run engine long enough build up vacuum in reservoir. Shut off engine.

3) Locate 5-wire connector and insert 3 short sections of solid wire into the back of connector so they contact terminals on the Blue, Brown/Yellow and Yellow wires. Connect jumper wires from the valve body bracket.

NOTE: **Do NOT start engine with these jumper wires in place.**

4) Turn ignition on. The accelerator pedal should go to the floor and remain there at least 1 minute. If not, test vaccum supply and vacuum motor.

5) Remove jumper wires. Start engine and check for vacuum supply to valve body by pulling the small hose off the vacuum reservoir. If there is adequate vacuum supply, turn off engine. Remove the small vacuum hose from the center of the valve body (labeled "SERVO") and apply a vacuum source to hose.

6) The accelerator pedal should be pulled directly to the floor. If not, the hose to the vacuum motor has a leak or is pinched, or the vacuum motor has a leak or is jammed.

7) If the valve body has adequate vacuum supply, 12 volts, and vacuum motor operates normally, but valve body will not operate the throttle when valves are grounded in step **3)**, replace valve body.

SPEED SENSOR TEST

Connect ground wire from test light to terminal No. 6 and connect positive probe from the test lamp to terminal No. 10. Jack up the vehicle and rotate the drive wheels. Test lamp should flash on and off as wheels are turned. If not, replace speedometer.

MODULE TEST

NOTE: **Sensor should be tested prior to testing module.**

Connect test lamp from ground to terminal No. 5 (Blue wire) on edge board connector at control module so that lamp can be safely observed while driving vehicle. Lamp should glow dimly. Start the vehicle and drive at 40 MPH. Press "SET" button. Lamp should go out. If not, replace control module.

REMOVAL & INSTALLATION

CONTROL SWITCH

Removal & Installation

Unplug switch at flat 7-wire connector located 6" behind switch under instrument panel. Install a small flat tool under the edge of the control switch and pry the switch out. Be careful not to scar the instrument panel surface. Pull switch and wiring out. To install, reverse removal procedure.

VALVE BODY

Removal (Challenger & Sapporo)

1) Unplug valve body wiring harness. Disconnect large vacuum supply hose from the reservoir. Disconnect small vacuum hose to the vacuum motor from the center of the valve body (labeled "SERVO"). Remove the valve body and reservoir assembly by first pulling up on the radiator overflow tank and laying aside.

2) Loosen the 2 bolts holding the radiator overflow tank bracket and slide the valve body reservoir assembly up and away from the engine. Remove small hose to the reservoir from the valve body. Remove valve body from the bracket by removing 3 nuts holding valve body to bracket.

Installation

To install, reverse removal procedure, making sure small hose from reservoir is placed on outside valve body tube marked "VACUUM".

Fig. 2: Cruise Control Wiring Diagram

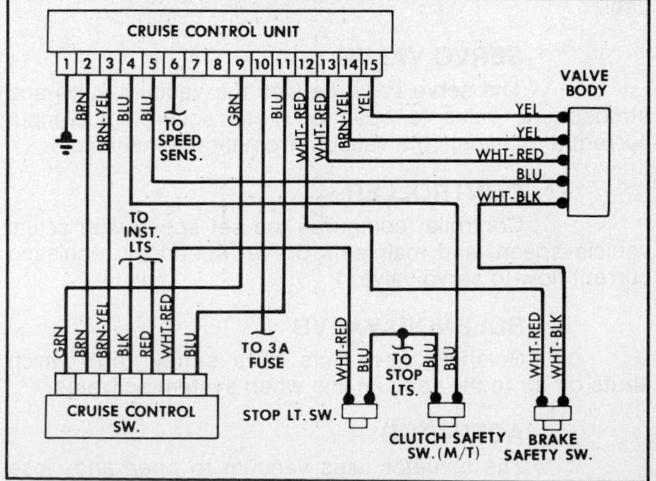
CRUISE CONTROL UNIT
1 2 3 4 5 6 7 8 9 10 11 12 13 14 15
BRN
BRN-YEL
BLU
BLU
TO SPEED SENS.
GRN
BLU
WHT-RED
WHT-RED
BRN-YEL
YEL
VALVE BODY
YEL
YEL
WHT-RED
BLU
WHT-BLK
TO INST. LTS
GRN
BRN
BRN-YEL
BLK
RED
WHT-RED
BLU
TO 3A FUSE
WHT-RED
BLU
TO STOP LTS.
BLU
WHT-RED
WHT-BLK
CRUISE CONTROL SW.
STOP LT. SW.
CLUTCH SAFETY SW. (M/T)
BRAKE SAFETY SW.

DATSUN/NISSAN

Maxima, 200SX, 280ZX

DESCRIPTION

The cruise control system is a combined unit of electronic circuits with vacuum operated mechanisims. Turn signal switch on steering column incorporates a slide switch which has 3 positions: "SET", "RESUME" and "ACCEL". System will not operate at speeds of under 37 MPH.

OPERATION

MAIN SWITCH

When the main switch is turned on and the ignition switch in the "ON" position, the exciting coil of the relay will be energized and the relay will turn on, supplying current to the system. When the ignition switch is turned to "OFF" the relay will also turn off, and remain inoperative even when main switch is turned on.

SET SWITCH

The set switch has an ON-OFF switch type circuit. When the set switch is depressed, "CRUISE" light illuminates. With the switch depressed, the controller cancels the preset vehicle speed. The controller will set the vehicle speed at the speed at which the the vehicle is running when the switch is released.

"ACCEL/RESUME" SWITCH

This switch is designed to increase the set speed, or return it to that speed at which the vehicle was previously being driven before the set speed was canceled. Depressing the "ACCEL" end of the switch causes the speed to increase continuously.

Releasing it will set the vehicle speed at the vehicle's current speed. Depressing the "RESUME" end of the switch momentarily causes the vehicle speed to automatically return to the set speed at which the vehicle was being driven before set speed was canceled. Keeping the "RESUME" switch depressed causes vehicle speed to decrease.

SPEED SENSOR

The speed sensor is an ON-OFF type sensor generating 2 pulses per revolution of the cruise control cable.

SERVO VALVE

The servo valve causes the vacuum valve and atmospheric valve to open or close according to input current and adjusts the vacuum from intake manifold.

CONTROLLER

Controller compares the set speed with actual vehicle speed, and maintains preset speed by regulating current flow to servo valve.

SOLENOID VALVE

Solenoid valve acts as a saftey valve which shuts off air to the vacuum line when system activates.

ACTUATOR

The actuator uses vacuum to open and close the throttle through the servo valve.

STOP SWITCH

Stop switch cuts off power to the cruise control circuit when the brake pedal is depressed.

CLUTCH SWITCH

On manual transmission models only, a clutch switch is used to cut off power to the cruise control circuit when clutch is depressed.

INHIBITOR RELAY

On automatic transmission models only, the inhibitor relay is used to release the cruise control system when the transmission is placed in "N" or "P" position.

TROUBLE SHOOTING

INDICATOR LAMP WILL NOT GLOW

When indicator lamp will not glow with main button depressed and ignition on, problem can be a burnt out bulb, faulty main switch or faulty cruise control relay.

SET SPEED CANCELED

Bent cruise control cable. Faulty controller.

PULSATION OF SET SPEED

Excessive play or binding of cruise control cable. Leakage or clogging in vacuum hose. Binding in actuator. Faulty servo valve. Faulty controller.

EXCESSIVE SETTING ERROR

Excessive play or binding in cruise control cable. Leakage or clogging in vacuum hose. Faulty actuator. Faulty servo valve. Faulty controller. Faulty speed sensor.

SPEED DROPS IMMEDIATELY AFTER SETTING

Excessive play in cruise control cable. Leakage or clogging in vacuum hose. Faulty solenoid valve. Faulty servo valve. Faulty controller.

CANCEL CIRCUIT INOPERATIVE

Faulty controller.

TESTING

INDICATOR LAMP WILL NOT GLOW

1) When indicator lamp will not glow when set switch is depressed and released at proper vehicle speed (main switch on), set automatic transmission selector lever at any position other than "P" and "N". With ignition and main switches on, check for battery voltage at terminals 3 and 7, and 10 and 7 of harness connector. *See Fig. 1.*

2) If battery voltage is present, check for battery voltage between terminals 2 and 7 when set switch is depressed and and ignition and main switches are on. If battery voltage is not present in step **1)**, an open circuit exists. Inhibitor switch, inhibitor relay, or stop switches are faulty, or stop switch is improperly adjusted.

4) If battery voltage is not present in step **2)**, the set switch is faulty. If battery voltage is present, with ignition and main switch on, manually rotate cruise control cable to see if voltages across the harness connector terminals 8 and 7 alternately change from 0 to 7 and vice versa.

5) If voltages change as specified, check controller, coast switch, servo valve, solenoid valve, and actuator. If voltages do not change as specified, speed sensor or controller are faulty.

Fig. 1: Cruise Control Harness Connector Terminals

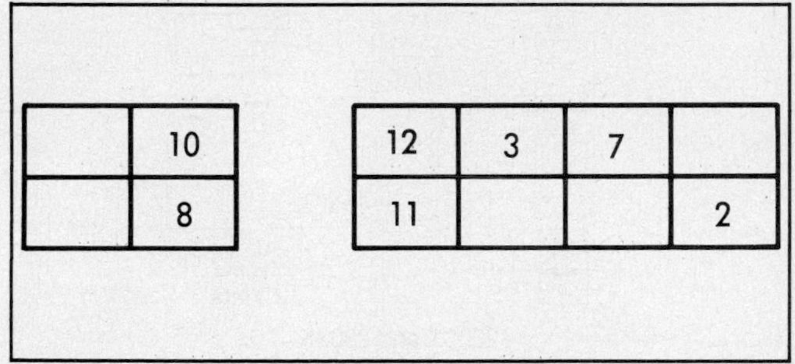
10
8
12
3
7
11
2

VEHICLE WILL NOT ACCELERATE

1) When "ACCEL" is depressed and vehicle will not accelerate, but a constant speed is maintained by the system, set automatic transmission to "P" or "N" position. With ignition, main, and "ACCEL" switches on, test for battery voltage between terminals 12 and 7 of harness connector. *See Fig. 1.*

2) If voltage is not present, "ACCEL" and "RESUME" switch is faulty. If voltage is present, check for 0 volts across terminals 12 and 7 when "ACCEL" end is off. If there is voltage, "ACCEL" and "RESUME" switch is faulty. If there is no voltage, controller is faulty.

VEHICLE WILL NOT DECELERATE

1) When vehicle will not decelerate with "RESUME" on, or will not return to prior speed, but constant speed can be maintained, set automatic transmission to "P" or "N" position. With ignition, main and resume switches on, test for battery voltage between terminals 11 and 7 of harness connector. *See Fig. 1.*

2) If voltage is not correct, "ACCEL" and "RESUME" switch is faulty. If voltage is correct, turn "RESUME" end off and check voltage accross terminals 11 and 7. If voltage is 0, controller is faulty. If voltage is present, "ACCEL" and "RESUME" switch is faulty.

CRUISE LAMP LIGHTS, BUT SPEED IS NOT SET

1) Apply battery voltage to release valve terminal, and check for the following conditions. With port "A" closed, no suction is possible at "B". With "A" open, suction begins at "B". If these conditions are not met, release valve is faulty.

2) If conditions are met, check servo valve for normal operation. If it operates normally, release cruise control cable and check for smooth actuator operation when vacuum is applied to actuator port. If operation is smooth, controller is faulty. If not smooth, actuator is faulty.

SERVO VALVE TEST

Measure the resistance between terminals. Resistance should be 25-30 ohms. Check to make sure valve opens or closes by blowing air through port on actuator side. *See Fig. 2.*

Fig. 2: Testing Servo Valve

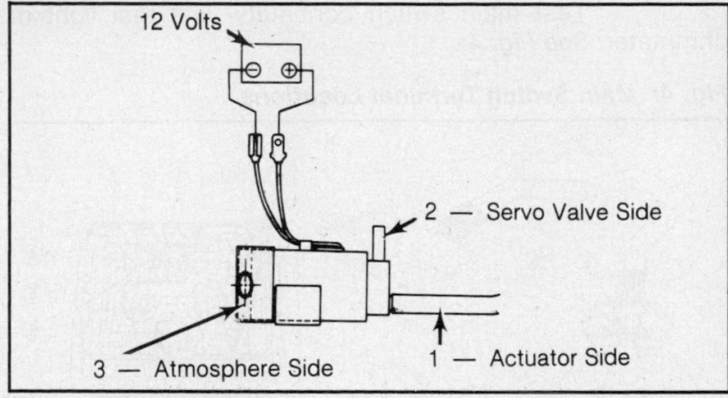
12 Volts
2 — Servo Valve Side
3 — Atmosphere Side
1 — Actuator Side

Test with and without 12 volts applied between terminals.

SERVO VALVE AIR FLOW

Check Ports	Air Flow
Normal Condition	
1-2	Yes
1-3	Yes
2-3	Yes
12 Volts DC Applied Between Terminals	
1-2	Yes
1-3	No
2-3	No

SOLENOID VALVE TEST

Measure resistance between terminals. Resistance should be 25-30 ohms. Check to make sure output vacuum of valve is okay as follows:

1) Disconnect solenoid valve side vacuum hose at solenoid valve and connect vacuum gauge. *See Fig. 3.* Start engine and run until water temperature indicator points to middle of gauge.

2) Apply 0.3 Amp direct current between terminals, using a 20 Ohm, 5 Watt variable resistor to adjust current. Vacuum gauge should read 2.17-3.35" Hg.

Fig. 3: Testing Solenoid Valve

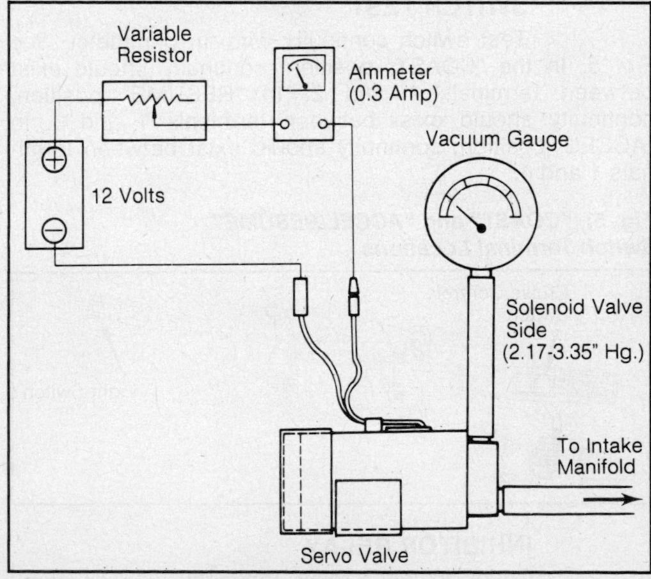
Variable Resistor
Ammeter (0.3 Amp)
Vacuum Gauge
12 Volts
Solenoid Valve Side (2.17-3.35" Hg.)
To Intake Manifold
Servo Valve

Do not apply current with valve connected.

DATSUN/NISSAN (Cont.)

MAIN SWITCH TEST

Test main switch continuity with test light or ohmmeter. *See Fig. 4.*

Fig. 4: Main Switch Terminal Locations

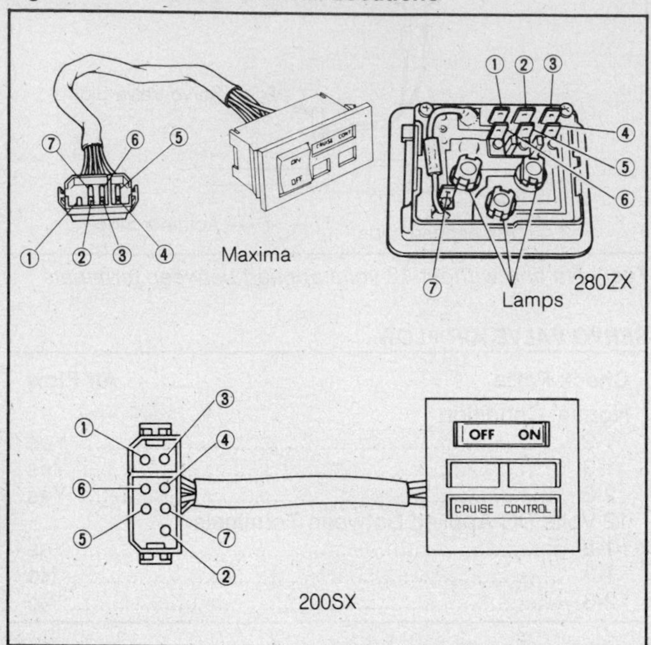

Maxima
280ZX
Lamps
OFF ON
CRUISE CONTROL
200SX

MAIN SWITCH CONTINUITY

Terminals	Normal	ON	OFF
1-2	No	Yes	No
1-6	No	Yes	No
2-6	Yes	Yes	No
3-4	Yes	....	....
5-7	Yes	....	....
6-7	Yes	....	....

"COAST" SWITCH & "ACCEL/RESUME" SWITCH TEST

Test switch continuity with an ohmmeter. *See Fig. 5.* In the "COAST" position, continuity should exist between terminals 1 and 2. In "RESUME" position, continuity should exist between terminals 1 and 3. In "ACCEL" position, continuity should exist between terminals 1 and 4.

Fig. 5: "COAST" and "ACCEL/RESUME" Switch Terminal Locations

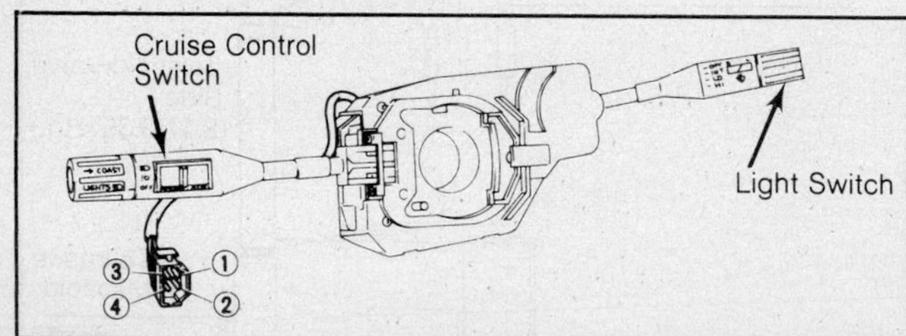

Cruise Control Switch
Light Switch

INHIBITOR RELAY

Check inhibitor relay continuity with an ohmmeter or test light. *See Fig. 6.*

Fig. 6: Inhibitor Relay Test Schematics

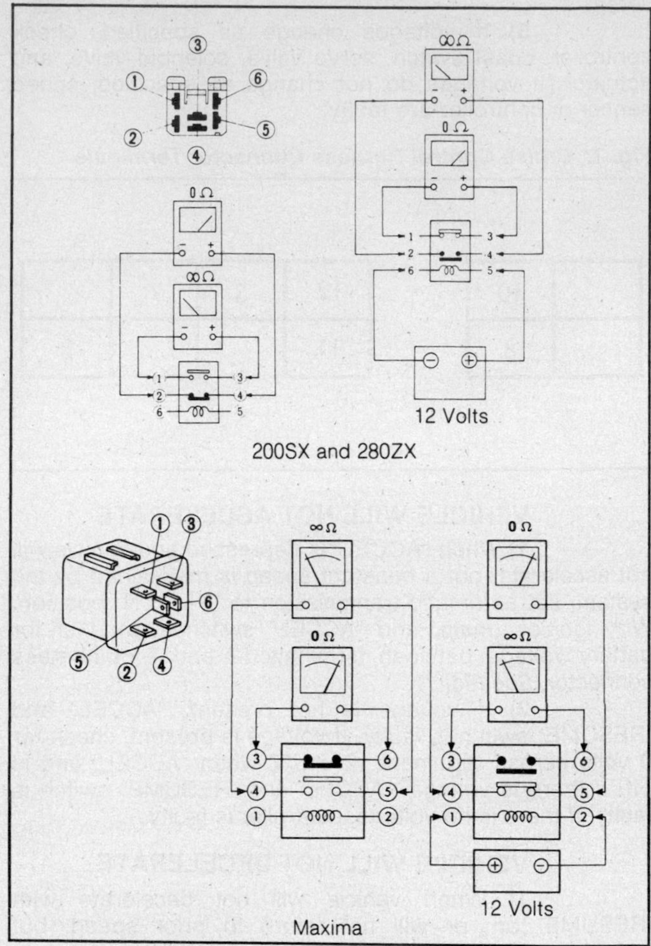

12 Volts
200SX and 280ZX
12 Volts
Maxima

Test with and without 12 volts applied.

INHIBITOR RELAY CONTINUITY

Check Terminals	Continuity
200SX & 280ZX	
Normal Condition	
5-6	Yes
2-4	Yes
1-3	No
With 12 Volts Between 5 and 6	
2-4	No
1-3	Yes
Maxima	
Normal Condition	
3-6	No
4-5	Yes
With With 12 Volts Between 1-2	
3-6	Yes
4-5	No

ADJUSTMENTS

CRUISE CONTROL CABLE

With throttle in idle position, adjust adjusting nut so that there is .08-.12" (2-3 mm) cable free play with no slack of cable. Tighten lock nut.

DATSUN/NISSAN (Cont.)

REMOVAL & INSTALLATION

CRUISE CONTROL CABLE

Removal & Installation

Disconnect cable from actuator. Remove screw attaching cable bracket. Remove rubber boots. Loosen lock nut and remove cable from torsion shaft. To install cable, reverse removal procedure and adjust.

ACTUATOR

Removal & Installation

1) Disconnect battery ground. Disconnect cable from actuator. Disconnect harness connector of servo valve and solenoid valve, and disconnect vacuum hose connecting intake manifold to servo valve. Remove actuator attaching bolt.

2) Remove actuator with servo valve and solenoid valve from vehicle. Disconnect vacuum hose and remove servo valve and solenoid valve. To install, reverse removal procedure.

SOLENOID & SERVO VALVE

Removal & Installation

Disconnect battery ground. Disconnect harness connector and remove valve. To install, reverse removal procedure.

MAIN SWITCH

Removal & Installation

Disconnect battery ground. Push out switch from behind instrument panel. Disconnect harness connector. To install, reverse removal procedure.

BRAKE LIGHT SWITCH, BRAKE & CLUTCH SWITCHES

Removal & Installation

Disconnect battery ground. Remove instrument panel left lower cover and floor assist nozzle. Loosen lock nut and remove switch. To install, reverse removal procedure.

CONTROLLER & CRUISE CONTROL RELAY

Removal & Installation

Disconnect battery ground. Remove passenger seat. Remove controller and cruise control relay. To install, reverse removal procedure.

Fig. 7: 200SX Cruise Control Wiring Diagram

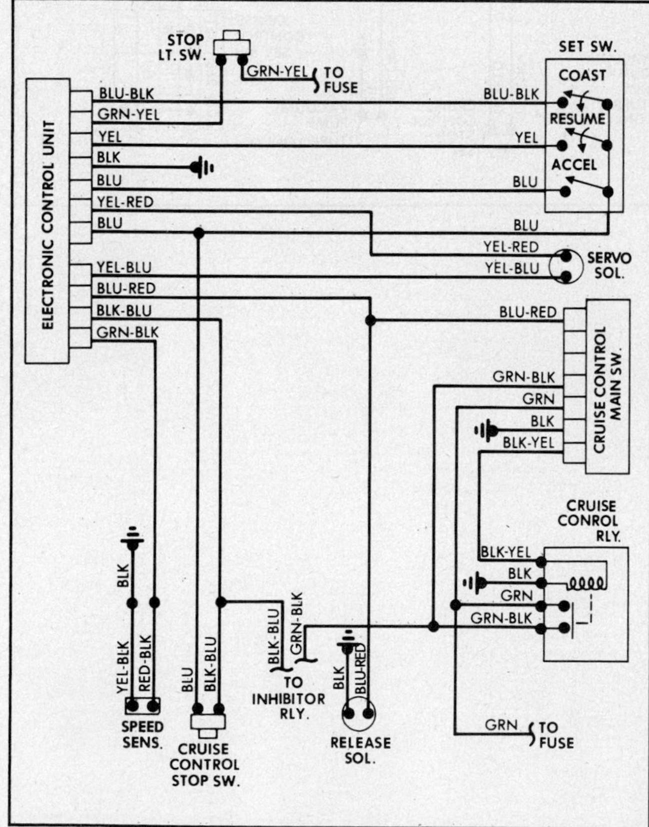

STOP LT. SW.
GRN-YEL
TO FUSE
SET SW.
COAST
RESUME
ACCEL
ELECTRONIC CONTROL UNIT
BLU-BLK
GRN-YEL
YEL
BLK
BLU
YEL-RED
BLU
YEL-BLU
BLU-RED
BLK-BLU
GRN-BLK
SERVO SOL.
CRUISE CONTROL MAIN SW.
GRN-BLK
GRN
BLK
BLK-YEL
CRUISE CONROL RLY.
BLK-YEL
BLK
GRN
GRN-BLK
BLK
YEL-BLK
RED-BLK
BLU
BLK-BLU
BLK-BLU
GRN-BLK
TO INHIBITOR RLY.
BLK
BLU-RED
SPEED SENS.
CRUISE CONTROL STOP SW.
RELEASE SOL.
GRN
TO FUSE

Also see chassis diagram in WIRING DIAGRAM section.

Fig. 8: Maxima Cruise Control Wiring Diagram

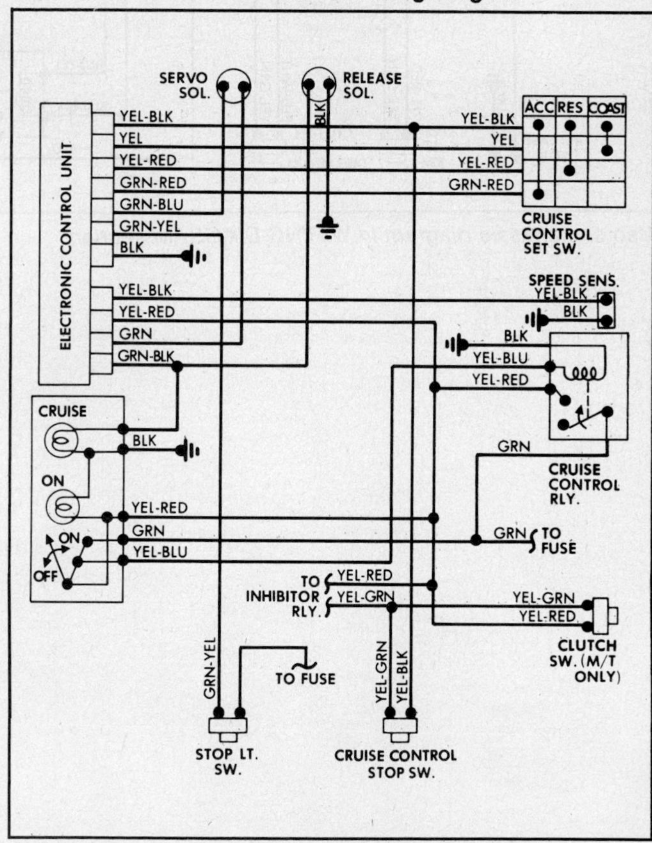

SERVO SOL.
RELEASE SOL.
BLK
ELECTRONIC CONTROL UNIT
YEL-BLK
YEL
YEL-RED
GRN-RED
GRN-BLU
GRN-YEL
BLK
YEL-BLK
YEL-RED
GRN
GRN-BLK
ACC RES COAST
CRUISE CONTROL SET SW.
SPEED SENS.
YEL-BLK
BLK
BLK
YEL-BLU
YEL-RED
GRN
CRUISE CONTROL RLY.
CRUISE
ON
BLK
YEL-RED
GRN
YEL-BLU
ON
OFF
GRN
TO FUSE
TO INHIBITOR RLY.
YEL-RED
YEL-GRN
YEL-GRN
YEL-RED
CLUTCH SW. (M/T ONLY)
GRN-YEL
TO FUSE
YEL-GRN
YEL-BLK
STOP LT. SW.
CRUISE CONTROL STOP SW.

Also see chassis diagram in WIRING DIAGRAM section.

Cruise Control Systems

DATSUN/NISSAN (Cont.)

Fig. 9: 280ZX Cruise Control Wiring Diagram

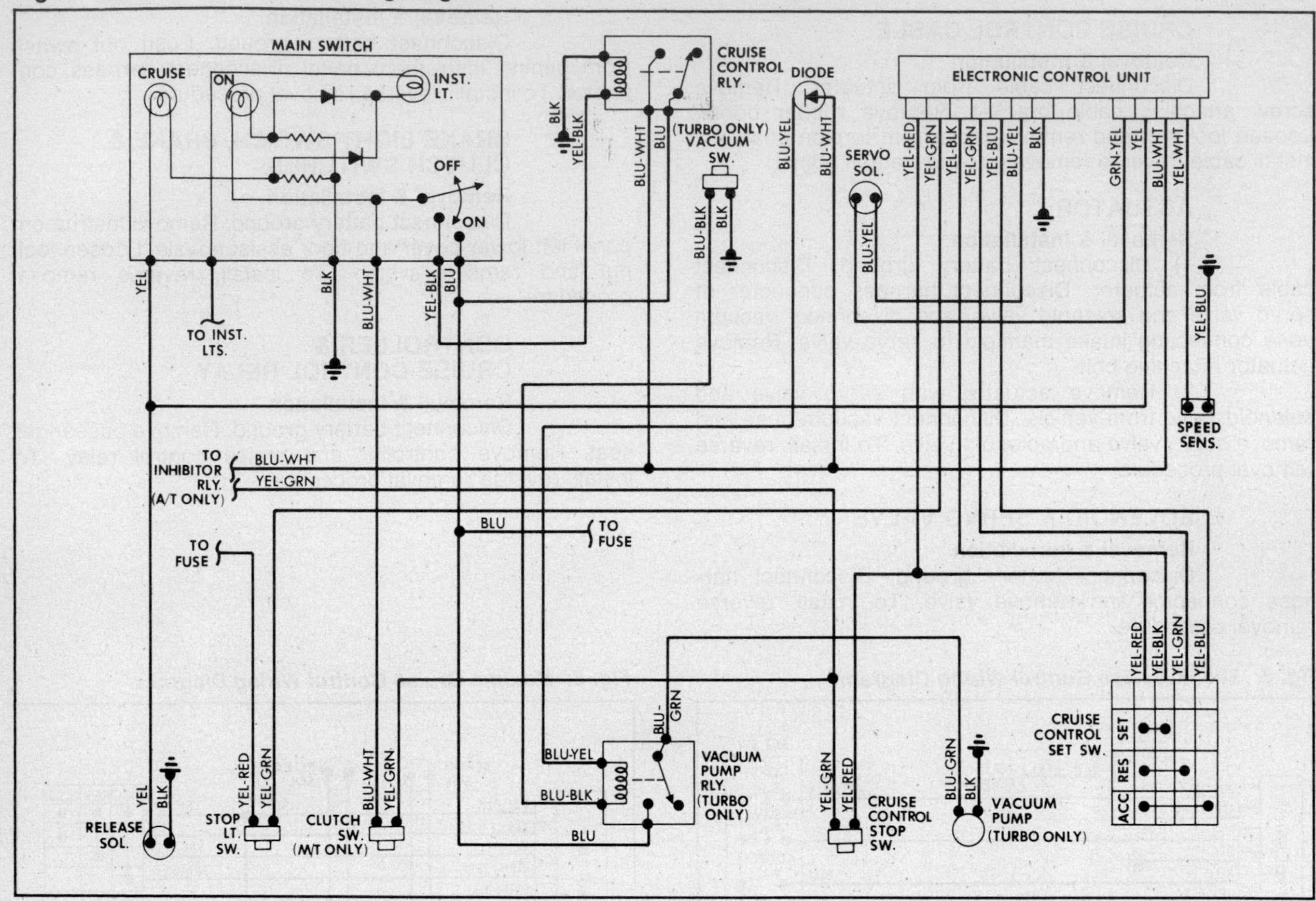
MAIN SWITCH
CRUISE
ON
INST. LT.
OFF
ON
YEL
BLK
BLU-WHT
YEL-BLK
BLU
TO INST. LTS.
CRUISE CONTROL RLY.
BLK
YEL-BLK
BLU-WHT
BLU
(TURBO ONLY) VACUUM SW.
BLU-BLK
BLK
DIODE
BLU-YEL
BLU-WHT
SERVO SOL.
BLU-YEL
ELECTRONIC CONTROL UNIT
YEL-RED
YEL-GRN
YEL-BLK
YEL-GRN
YEL-BLU
BLU-YEL
BLK
GRN-YEL
YEL
BLU-WHT
YEL-WHT
YEL-BLU
SPEED SENS.
TO INHIBITOR RLY. (A/T ONLY)
BLU-WHT
YEL-GRN
BLU
TO FUSE
TO FUSE
BLU-GRN
BLU-YEL
BLU-BLK
BLU
VACUUM PUMP RLY. (TURBO ONLY)
YEL-RED
YEL-BLK
YEL-GRN
YEL-BLU
CRUISE CONTROL SET SW.
SET
RES
ACC
YEL
BLK
RELEASE SOL.
YEL-RED
YEL-GRN
STOP LT. SW.
BLU-WHT
YEL-GRN
CLUTCH SW. (M/T ONLY)
YEL-GRN
YEL-RED
CRUISE CONTROL STOP SW.
BLU-GRN
BLK
VACUUM PUMP (TURBO ONLY)

Also see chassis diagram in WIRING DIAGRAM section.

HONDA

Accord

DESCRIPTION

The cruise control system is a combined unit of electronic circuits and vacuum operated mechanisims. Turn signal switch on steering column incorporates a slide switch which has 3 positions: "SET", "RESUME" and "ACCEL".

OPERATION

When the driver presses and releases the "SET/ACCEL" switch, vehicle speed will be maintained until a new speed is set, brake or clutch pedal is depressed, or system is turned off. When system has 00601102been deactivated by depressing brake or clutch pedal, the driver can re-restablish set speed by pressing and releasing "RESUME" switch.

TROUBLE SHOOTING

ELECTRICAL

1) Turn on ignition and cruise control main switch. If pilot lamp lights, measure voltage across terminals 9 (Black) and 5 (Lt. Green) of control unit connector. *See Fig. 1.*

2) If voltmeter reads 12 volts, control unit is okay. If voltmeter read no voltage, there is an open circuit in wiring harness between main switch and control unit.

Fig. 1: Connectors and Terminal Numbers

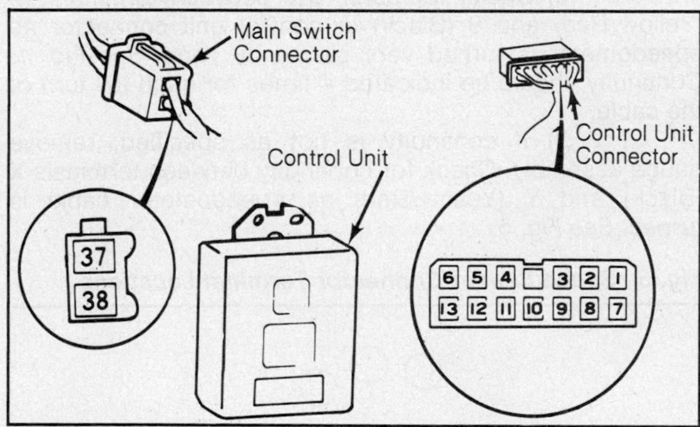
Main Switch Connector
Control Unit Connector
Control Unit
37
38
6 5 4 3 2 1
13 12 11 10 9 8 7

Terminals are viewed from wire side.

3) If pilot lamp in step **1)** did not light, check fuse 20. Replace fuse if defective. If fuse is okay, measure voltage across terminals 31 (Black/Red) and 33 (Black) of main switch connector. If there is no voltage, there is an open circuit in the wiring harness from fuse box to main switch.

4) If voltmeter in step **3)** indicated 12 volts, check for voltage between terminals B and C of main switch. If there there is no continuity, main switch is defective. If there is continuity, bulb is defective.

CONTROL SWITCH

1) Push the horn button. If the horn doesn't blow, the horn circuit is defective. If the horn blows, connect the positive probe of the voltmeter to terminal 6 (Lt. Green/Red) and negative probe to terminal 9 (Black) at control unit connector. Push the "SET" switch. *See Fig. 1.*

2) If there is 12 volts, go to step **4)**. If there is no voltage, connect the voltmeter positive probe to terminal 37 (Lt. Green/Red) of slip ring connector. Connect negative probe to ground. Push the "SET" switch and read voltage with slip ring connector connected.

3) If there is 12 volts, there is an open in wiring harness. If there is no voltage, remove the steering wheel and check control switch as outlined in this article. If switch tests okay, control ring is defective.

4) If in step **1)** there was 12 volts, connect the voltmeter positive probe to terminal 11 (Lt. Green/Black) and the negative probe to terminal 9 (Black) of control unit connector. Push "RESUME" switch. If there is 12 volts, go to step **6)**.

5) If in step **4)** there was no voltage, connect positive probe to terminal 38 (Lt. Green/Black) of control unit connector and negative probe to ground. Push "RESUME" switch. If voltmeter reads 12 volts, there is an open in wiring harness. If there is no voltage, remove steering wheel and check "RESUME" switch as described in this article. If okay, slip ring is defective.

6) If in step **4)** there was 12 volts, check for continuity across terminals 11 (Lt. Green/Black) and 6 (Lt. Green/Red) at control unit connector. If there is no continuity, test is okay. If there is continuity, disconnect slip ring connector and check for continuity between terminals B (Lt. Green/Red) and C (Lt. Green/Black).

7) If there is no continuity, there is a shorted wire in harness from the slip ring connector to the control unit. If there is continuity, check for continuity between terminals B (Lt. Green/Black) and C (Lt. Green/Red) of "SET"/"RESUME" switch connector. If there is continuity, "SET"/"RESUME" switch is defective. If there is no continuity, slip ring is defective.

Fig. 2: Control Switch Terminals and Continuity

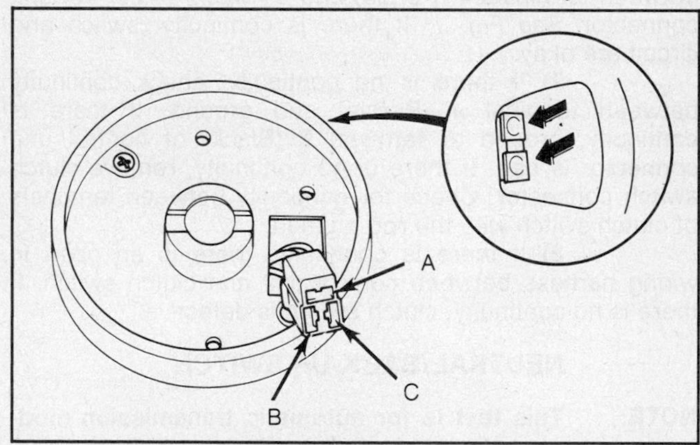
A
B
C

BRAKE SWITCH

1) Apply vehicle brakes. If brake light doesn't go on, check fuse 19 and replace if defective. If okay, check brake light switch. If switch is defective, replace. If switch is okay, brake light is defective.

2) If brake light goes on in step **1)**, connect the positive probe to terminal 12 (Green/White) of control unit connector and negative probe to terminal 9 (Black) with brakes applied. *See Fig. 1.* If there is no voltage, there is an open circuit in wiring harness.

3) If there is 12 volts, connect positive probe to terminal 8 (Green) and negative to terminal 9 (Black) of control unit connector. Turn on ignition and cruise control main switch. Apply and release brake pedal and measure

Cruise Control Systems

HONDA (Cont.)

voltage. With the brakes applied, there should be no voltage. With brakes released, there should be 12 volts.

4) If voltages test out okay in step **3)**, switch and circuits are okay. If not, connect positive probe to terminal 25 (Lt. Green) of brake light switch connector and negative probe to ground. *See Fig. 3.* Measure voltage. If there is no voltage, there is an open circuit in the wiring harness between main switch and brake switch.

Fig. 3: Brake Light Switch and Connector

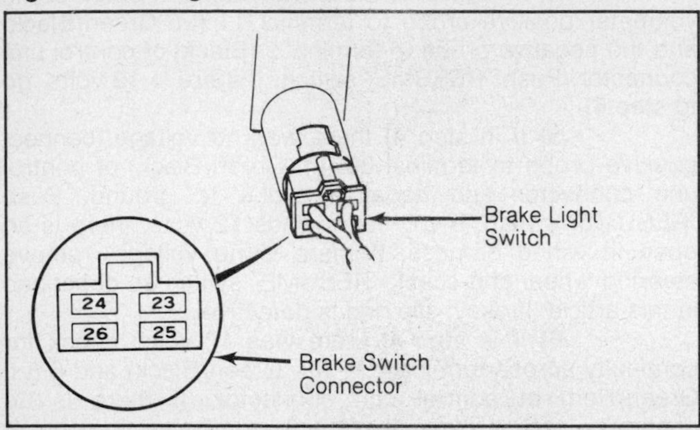
Brake Light Switch
24
23
26
25
Brake Switch Connector

Connector is viewed from wire side.

5) If there is 12 volts, disconnect the brake switch connector and check for continuity between terminals A and D. With brakes released there should be continuity. If okay, there is an open in wiring harness between brake switch and control unit. If not okay, brake switch is defective.

CLUTCH SWITCH

1) With clutch pedal released, check continuity between terminals 4 (Purple) and 9 (Black) of control unit connector. *See Fig. 1.* If there is continuity, switch and circuit are okay.

2) If there is no continuity, check continuity between terminal 4 (Purple) and ground. If there is continuity, ground at terminal 9 (Black) of control unit connector is bad. If there is no continuity, remove clutch switch connector. Check for continuity between terminals of clutch switch with the rod pushed.

3) If there is continuity, there is an open in wiring harness between control unit and clutch switch. If there is no continuity, clutch switch is defective.

NEUTRAL/BACK-UP SWITCH

NOTE: This test is for automatic transmission models only.

1) With the shift lever in the D4, D3 or 2 position, check the continuity between terminals 4 (Purple) and 9 (Black) of control unit connector. *See Fig. 1.* If there is continuity, switch and circuit are okay.

2) If there is no continuity in step **1)**, check continuity between terminal 4 (Purple) of control unit connector and ground. If there is continuity, ground at terminal 9 (Black) of control unit connector is bad.

3) If there is no continuity in step **2)**, check the neutral/back-up switch for continuity. If there is continuity, there is an open in the wiring harness between control unit and neutral/back-up switch. If there is no continuity, switch is defective.

PILOT LAMP

1) Turn ignition and main control switch on. If main switch pilot lamp does not come on, go to Electrical Trouble Shooting. If light comes on, connect terminals 2 (Red) and 9 (Black) in the control unit connector with jumper wire. *See Fig. 1.*

2) If pilot lamp lights, circuit is okay. If pilot lamp does not light, check fuse 9 and replace if defective. If fuse is okay, check that dash gauges are okay. If not okay, check dash wiring. If okay, check for continuity between terminal 2 (Red) of control unit connector and 8 (Red) of pilot lamp connector. *See Fig. 4.*

Fig. 4: Pilot Lamp Connector

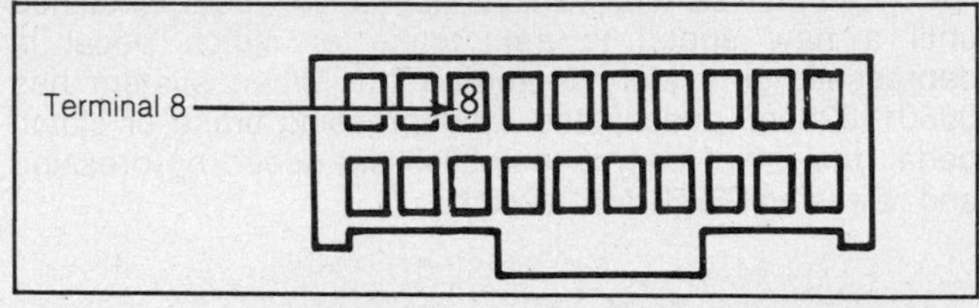
Terminal 8
8

3) If there is no continuity, there is an open circuit in the wiring harness between pilot lamp and control unit. If there is continuity, check bulb. Replace bulb if defective. If bulb is okay, circuit board is defective.

SPEED SENSOR

1) Turn ignition and cruise control main switch on. If main switch pilot lamp does not light, go to Electrical Trouble Shooting. If main switch pilot lamp lights, turn ignition switch off. Disconnect the speedometer cable from transmission.

2) Check for continuity between terminals 13 (Yellow/Red) and 9 (Black) in control unit connector as speedometer is turned very slowly by hand. *See Fig. 1.* Continuity should be indicated 4 times for each full turn of the cable.

3) If continuity is not as specified, remove gauge assembly. Check for continuity between terminals X (Black) and Y (Yellow/Red) as speedometer cable is turned. *See Fig. 5.*

Fig. 5: Speed Sensor Connector Terminal Locations

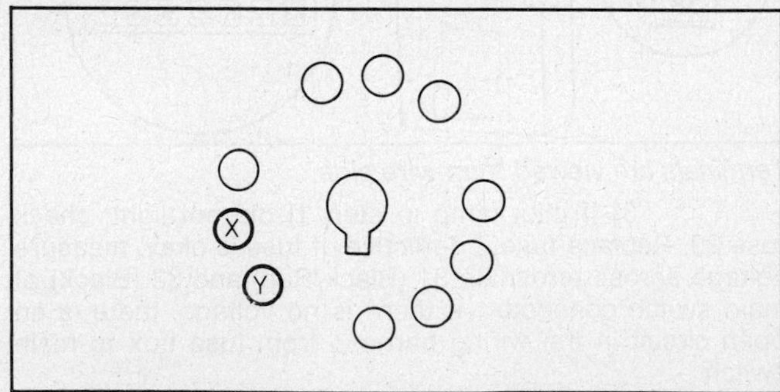
X
Y

Connector is viewed from wire side.

4) Continuity should be indicated 4 times for each full turn of the cable. If okay, there is an open circuit in the wiring harness from gauge to control unit. If not okay, speed sensor is defective.

ACTUATOR

1) Measure the resistance between terminal 3 (Brown) of control unit connector and ground. *See Fig. 1.*

HONDA (Cont.)

Resistance should be 80-120 ohms. If okay, go to step **2)**. If not, disconnect the actuator connector and measure the resistance between terminals A (Black) and C (Brown). *See Fig. 6.* Resistance should be 80-120 ohms.

Fig. 6: Actuator Connector Terminals

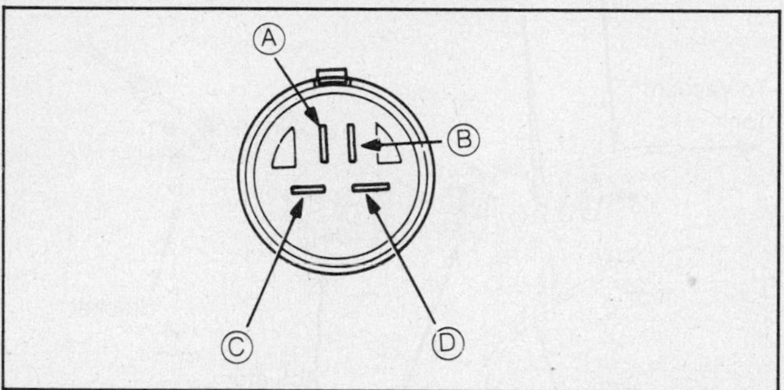
A
B
C
D

View is from the pin side.

2) If actuator resistance is not okay, actuator is defective. If okay, there is an open in the wiring harness from actuator to control unit. If first resistance measured in step **1)** was correct, measure the resistance between ground and terminal 7 (Brown) of actuator connector.

3) Resistance should be 40-60 ohms. If not, disconnect the actuator connector and measure resistance between terminals A (Black) and D (Brown/White). Resistance should be 40-60 ohms. If not, actuator is defective. If okay, there is an open circuit in wiring harness between actuator and control unit.

4) If first resistance measured in step **3)** was okay, measure resistance between terminal 10 (Brown/Black) of actuator connector and ground. Resistance should be 80-120 ohms. If not, disconnect actuator connector and measure resistance between terminals A (Black) and B (Brown/Black).

5) Resistance should be 80-120 ohms. If not, actuator is defective. If okay, there is an open circuit in wiring harness from actuator to control unit. If first resistance measured in step **4)** was okay, disconnect the actuator cable from actuator.

6) Disconnect the actuator connector. Make sure the control unit connector is disconnected. Connect a lead from battery positive terminal to actuator terminal D (Brown/White) and a lead from battery negative terminal to actuator terminals A (Black), B (Brown/Black) and C (Brown). Connect a hand vacuum pump to actuator and draw vacuum.

7) If actuator is not pulled in or is pulled in part way, check the vacuum line for leaks. If line is defective, replace it. If line is okay, actuator is defective. If actuator is pulled in strongly, attempt to pull the actuator rod out by hand.

8) If the rod can be pulled out, actuator is defective. If it can not be pulled out, clean the vent tube and actuator filter, and disconnect the battery negative terminal from actuator terminals A (Black) and B (Brown/Black). If actuator rod does not return, solenoid valve is defective.

TESTING

MAIN SWITCH

Use an ohmmeter to check resistance and continuity across main switch terminals. In both on and off positions, there should be 20 ohms resistance between terminals A and B. In the on position, there should be continuity between terminals B and C. *See Fig. 7.*

Use an ohmmeter to check resistance and continuity across main switch terminals. In both the on and off positions, there should be 20 ohms resistance between terminals A and B. In the on position, there should be continuity between terminals B and C. *See Fig. 7.*

Fig. 7: Main, Brake and Back-Up Switch Terminal Locations

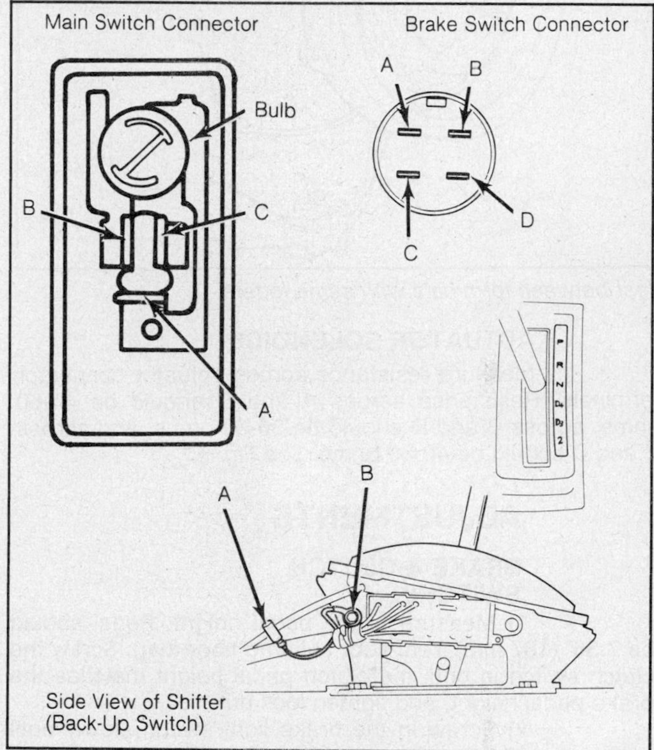
Main Switch Connector
Brake Switch Connector
Bulb
A
B
C
D
Side View of Shifter
(Back-Up Switch)

BRAKE SWITCH

Use an ohmmeter to check continuity across brake switch terminals. In the on or pushed in position, there should be continuity between terminals A and D. In the off or free position, there should be continuity between terminals B and C. *See Fig. 7.*

CLUTCH SWITCH

Check clutch switch continuity. With the rod pushed in, there should be continuity. Release the rod, and there should be no continuity.

NEUTRAL/BACK-UP SWITCH

Check switch for continuity. With the transmission in the D4, D3 or Second gear position, there should be continuity between A and B terminals. In the Park, Reverse or Neutral positions, there should be no continuity. *See Fig. 7.*

CONTROL SWITCH

Check control switch continuity. There should be continuity between terminals A and C when "SET" switch is in the on position, and continuity between terminals A and B with "RESUME" switch in on position. *See Fig. 2.*

HONDA (Cont.)

SLIP RING

Turn the slip ring while checking for continuity between terminals with the same letters. *See Fig. 8.*

Fig. 8: Slip Ring Terminals

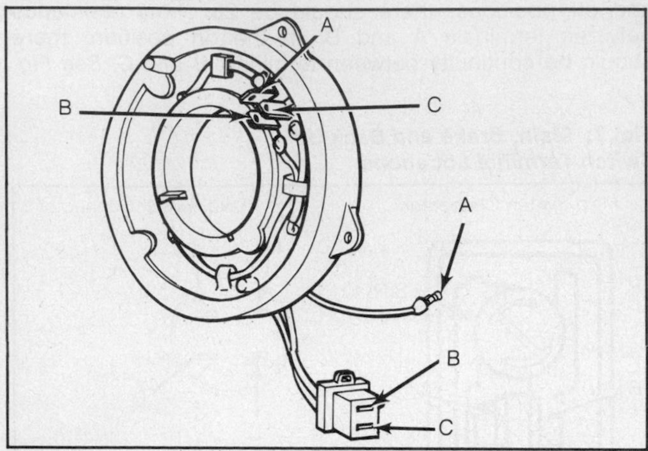
A
B
C
A
B
C

Test between terminals with same letters.

ACTUATOR SOLENOIDS

Measure resistance across actuator connector terminals. Resistance across A and D should be 40-60 ohms, across B and D should be 30-50 ohms, and across C and D should be 40-60 ohms. *See Fig. 6.*

ADJUSTMENTS

BRAKE & CLUTCH SWITCHES

1) Measure brake pedal height. Pedal should be 7.36" (187 mm) from floor (with no floor mat). Screw the clutch switch in until the clutch pedal height matches the brake pedal height, and tighten lock nut.

2) Screw in the brake light switch slowly until the pad on the stop reaches the threads on the switch, and screw the switch in until the pedal has no play. Turn the switch counterclockwise 1/4-1/2 turn from this position, and tighten lock nut.

ACTUATOR CABLE

1) Warm up engine. Loosen the lock nut and cable. Adjust the throttle cable if necessary by loosening lock nut and adjusting nut until deflection is 3/16-3/8" (4-10 mm). Measure deflection with engine running, so that it can be heard when free play ends.

2) To check free play in actuator rod, pull back boot and push the rod slowly until engine RPM begins to rise. Adjust the actuator rod free play by loosening lock nut and turning the adjusting nut. Free play should be adjusted to .25-.37" (6.5-9.5 mm).

3) Tighten lock nut and reinstall boot. Test drive vehicle and make sure cruise control maintains vehicle speed within 2 MPH of set speed.

REMOVAL & INSTALLATION

ACTUATOR & CABLE

Removal & Installation

1) Pull back the boot on cable and loosen the lock nut. Disconnect the cable from the bracket. Disconnect the cable end from the actuator rod. Disconnect the actuator cable from the center arm. *See Fig. 9.*

Fig. 9: Exploded View of Actuator Cable Assembly

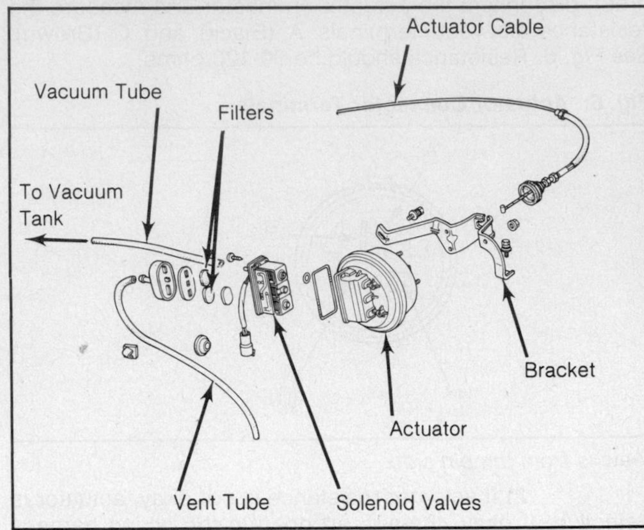
Actuator Cable
Vacuum Tube
Filters
To Vacuum Tank
Bracket
Actuator
Vent Tube
Solenoid Valves

Pull back boot to access lock nut.

2) Turn the grommet 90° in the firewall, and remove the cable. Disconnect the wire connector and vacuum tube. Remove the bolts, and remove actuator. To install, reverse removal procedure.

PEDAL BRACKET

Removal & Installation

1) Disconnect the actuator, throttle and clutch cables from pedal linkage. Drop the steering column by removing nuts from support brackets.

2) Remove the mounting nuts from the front of the pedal bracket. Remove the bolts from the top of the bracket and remove bracket. To install, reverse removal procedure.

Fig. 10: Accord Cruise Control Wiring Diagram

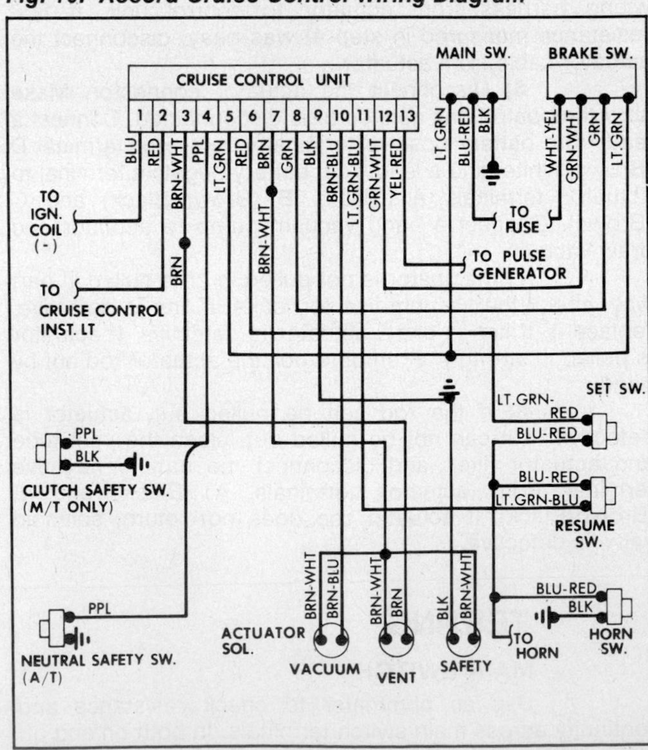
CRUISE CONTROL UNIT
1 2 3 4 5 6 7 8 9 10 11 12 13
BLU
RED
BRN-WHT
PPL
LT.GRN
RED
BRN
GRN
BLK
BRN-BLU
LT.GRN-BLU
GRN-WHT
YEL-RED
MAIN SW.
LT.GRN
BLU-RED
BLK
BRAKE SW.
WHT-YEL
GRN-WHT
GRN
LT.GRN
TO IGN. COIL (-)
TO FUSE
TO PULSE GENERATOR
BRN
BRN-WHT
TO CRUISE CONTROL INST. LT
SET SW.
LT.GRN-RED
BLU-RED
PPL
BLK
CLUTCH SAFETY SW. (M/T ONLY)
BLU-RED
LT.GRN-BLU
RESUME SW.
BRN-WHT
BRN-BLU
BRN-WHT
BRN
BLK
BRN-WHT
BLU-RED
BLK
PPL
ACTUATOR SOL.
NEUTRAL SAFETY SW. (A/T)
VACUUM
VENT
SAFETY
TO HORN
HORN SW.

Cruise Control Systems

MITSUBISHI

Cordia, Starion & Tredia

DESCRIPTION

Cruise control system is electrically-operated and vacuum-actuated. It consists of a cruise control unit, cruise control switch, actuator, speed sensor, vacuum pump or reservoir, vacuum lines and electrical wiring. The system detects the speed of the vehicle through reed switch signals of the speed sensor built into the control switch.

Speed is stored in electronic control unit when the control switch is activated in the "SET" position. Changes in vehicle speed after the set switch is released are compared with the vehicle speed to control the throttle opening through the actuator, so that the set vehicle speed will be maintained at all times. The system includes a vacuum pump to ensure set vehicle speed remains stable when engine vacuum falls.

OPERATION

The cruise control system is operated by a steering column mounted switch. Switch has 4 positions, "ON", "OFF", "SET" and "RESUME". In the "ON" position, current flows to the system, and both system and indicator light are energized. When switch is in the "OFF" position, cruise control is cancelled.

"SET" position sets cruise control by outputting signal to self-holding circuit and memory circuits. It may also be used to reduce or slightly increase vehicle speed. "RESUME" position transmits signal to self-holding circuit to resume speed previously cancelled.

ADJUSTMENTS

NOTE: **Adjustment procedures are for Starion models only.**

SPEED CONTROL CABLE

1) First check adjustment of the accelerator cable. Run engine until it reaches idle RPM. Measure the free play of the pedal. Free play in the cable should be 0-.04" (0-1 mm).

2) If the measured free play is not correct, loosen adjusting nut so the throttle lever is free. Turn adjusting nut to bring free play within specifications.

2) Slide the cruise control cable in the direction of the arrow up to the point just before accelerator pedal begins to move. Secure cruise control cable by inserting clip. Play of cruise control cable should be 0-.1" (0-3 mm).

TESTING

SPEED CONTROL SWITCH

1) Using an ohmmeter or test light, check for continuity between terminals of cruise control switch connector. *See Fig. 1.* With switch in "SET" position, there should be continuity between terminals 1 and 3.

2) With switch in "ON" or "RESUME" position, there should be continuity between terminals 1 and 2 and between terminals 4 and 5. With switch in "RESUME" position, there should be continuity between terminals 1 and 2.

Fig. 1: Cruise Control Switch and Connector

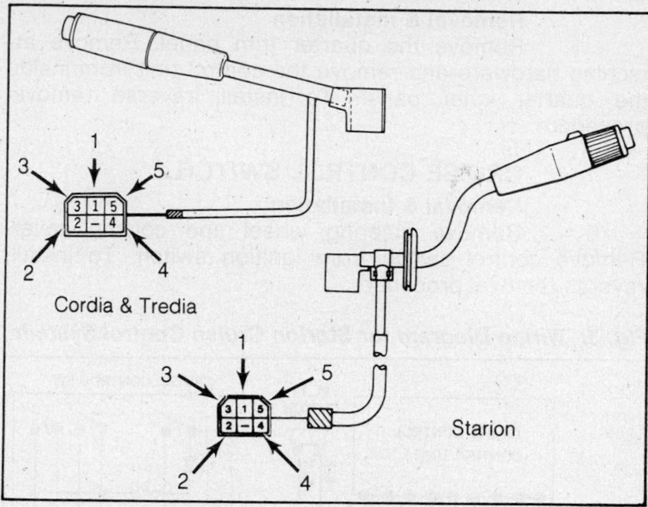
1
3
5
3 1 5
2 – 4
2
4
Cordia & Tredia
1
3
5
3 1 5
2 – 4
Starion
2
4

ACTUATOR

Using an ohmmeter, measure resistance value of release valve coil and control valve coil. For release valve, measure between Yellow and Blue wire terminals. Resistance should be 68 ohms. For control valve coil, measure between Red and Blue wire terminals. Resistance should be 30 ohms.

REMOVAL & INSTALLATION

ACTUATOR

Removal & Installation

To remove the actuator, disconnect it from cruise control cable. Remove actuator from vehicle. To install, reverse removal procedure.

Fig. 2: Wiring Diagram for Cordia and Tredia Cruise Control System

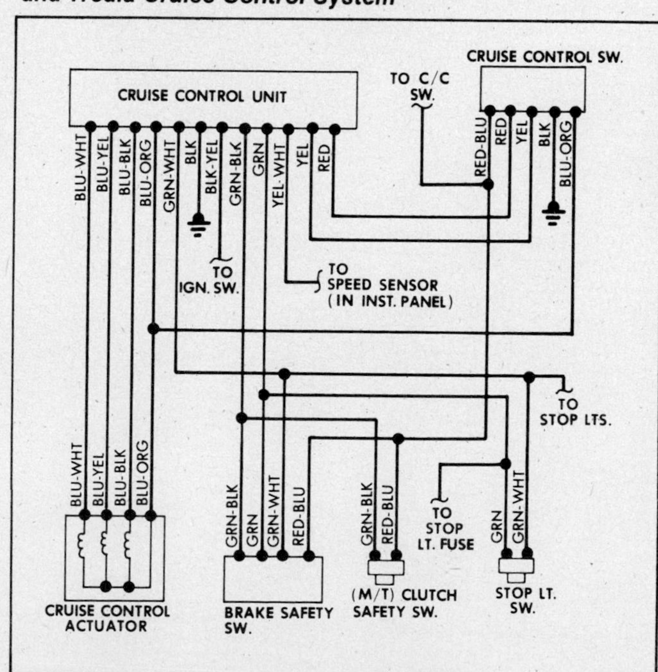
CRUISE CONTROL UNIT
CRUISE CONTROL SW.
TO C/C SW.
BLU-WHT
BLU-YEL
BLU-BLK
BLU-ORG
GRN-WHT
BLK
BLK-YEL
GRN-BLK
GRN
YEL-WHT
YEL
RED
RED-BLU
RED
YEL
BLK
BLU-ORG
TO IGN. SW.
TO SPEED SENSOR (IN INST. PANEL)
TO STOP LTS.
TO STOP LT. FUSE
CRUISE CONTROL ACTUATOR
BRAKE SAFETY SW.
(M/T) CLUTCH SAFETY SW.
STOP LT. SW.

Cruise Control Systems

MITSUBISHI (Cont.)

CRUISE CONTROL CONTROL UNIT

Removal & Installation

Remove the quarter trim panel. Remove attaching hardware and remove the control unit from inside the quarter inner panel. To install, reverse removal procedure.

CRUISE CONTROL SWITCH

Removal & Installation

Remove steering wheel and column cover. Remove control switch from ignition switch. To install, reverse removal procedure.

Fig. 3: Wiring Diagram for Starion Cruise Control System

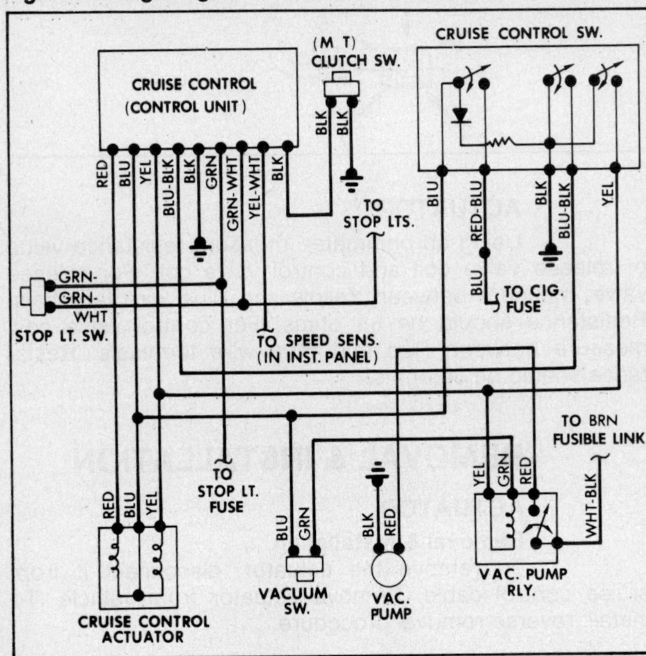

CRUISE CONTROL
(CONTROL UNIT)
(M T)
CLUTCH SW.
CRUISE CONTROL SW.
RED
BLU
YEL
BLU-BLK
BLK
GRN
GRN-WHT
YEL-WHT
BLK
BLK
BLK
TO
STOP LTS.
BLU
RED-BLU
BLK
BLU-BLK
YEL
GRN-
GRN-
WHT
STOP LT. SW.
BLU
TO CIG.
FUSE
TO SPEED SENS.
(IN INST. PANEL)
TO BRN
FUSIBLE LINK
TO
STOP LT.
FUSE
RED
BLU
YEL
BLU
GRN
BLK
RED
YEL
GRN
RED
WHT-BLK
CRUISE CONTROL
ACTUATOR
VACUUM
SW.
VAC.
PUMP
VAC. PUMP
RLY.

Cruise Control System

TOYOTA

Camry, Celica, Cressida, Pickup & Supra

DESCRIPTION

The cruise control system is a unit made up of electronic circuits. A main switch is used to turn the system on and off. An indicator light on main switch shows that system is activated. A control switch with 2 settings, "SET (COAST)" and "RESUME (ACCEL)" is used to set desired vehicle speed. System will not operate at speeds under 25 MPH.

OPERATION

MAIN SWITCH

When the main switch and the ignition switch are in the "ON" positions, the exciting coil of the relay will be energized and the relay will turn on, supplying current to the system. When the ignition switch is turned to "OFF" position, the relay will also turn off, and remain inoperative even when main switch is turned on.

CONTROL SWITCH

The control switch has an ON-OFF switch type circuit. When the control switch is turned to the "SET" position, the "CRUISE" light illuminates. With the switch on "SET", the controller cancels the preset vehicle speed.

The control switch has a "RESUME" position, which is designed to increase the set speed, or return it to the speed at which the vehicle was previously being driven before the set speed was canceled.

Pushing the control switch to the "ACCEL" position causes the vehicle speed to increase continuously. When released, speed will be set at the speed the vehicle is currently traveling.

TROUBLE SHOOTING

CRUISE CONTROL CANNOT BE SET

Meter or stop light fuse is blown. Main switch may be faulty.

DOES NOT CANCEL EVEN WHEN CANCEL OPERATION IS PERFORMED

Parking switch faulty. Speed sensor faulty. Stop light switch faulty.

CANNOT BE RESTORED WITH RESUME SWITCH

Clutch switch or Neutral Start switch faulty. Actuator faulty. "RESUME" switch faulty. Computer faulty. Wiring or ground faulty.

WARNING LIGHT DOES NOT LIGHT

Meter fuse blown. Main switch faulty.

CANNOT OBTAIN DESIRED SPEED

Actuator faulty. Computer faulty.

HUNTING OCCURS BETWEEN ACCELERATION AND DECELERATION

Carburetor or fuel injection problem. Linkage not moving smoothly.

SPEED IS GREATLY REDUCED WHEN ASCENDING SLOPE

Actuator or computer faulty.

TESTING

COMPUTER & SENSOR

Celica, Pickup & Supra

1) Remove side kick panel. Unplug wiring connector from computer. Inspect computer at connector on wire harness side. With ignition switch in the "ON" position and using a voltmeter, measure the voltage between terminal 13 and body ground with the main switch in the "ON" position. *See Fig. 1.* If there is no battery voltage, check the control switch.

2) On Pickup, start the engine. On all models, use a voltmeter to measure the voltage between terminal 8 and body ground. When parking brake lever is pulled, voltage should be 0 volts. When parking brake lever is returned, voltage should be 12 volts.

3) Turn ignition switch to "OFF" position. Using a voltmeter, measure the voltage between terminal 11 and body ground. If battery voltage is not present, check the stop light switch.

4) Using a voltmeter, measure the voltage between terminal 12 and body ground. When brake pedal is depressed, voltage should be 12 volts. When brake pedal is returned, voltage should be 0 volts. If voltage is not correct, check the brake pedal switch.

5) Turn ignition switch to "ACC" position. Using an ohmmeter, check the continuity between terminal 9 and body ground. On manual transmission models, check with clutch pedal depressed. On automatic transmission models, check when shift lever is in neutral position. If there is no continuity, check clutch switch or neutral start switch by measuring the resistance between the terminals.

6) On Celica and Supra, resistance between terminals 6 and 10 should be approximately 68 ohms. Resistance between 4 and 10 should be approximately 30 ohms. On Pickup, resistance between 6 and 10 should be approximately 71 ohms. Resistance between 4 and 10 should be approximately 38 ohms. On all models, if the resistance readings are not correct, check the actuator.

7) Using an ohmmeter, check the continuity between terminal 3 and body ground when control switch is turned to "SET" position. If there is no continuity between terminals, check the control switch.

8) Using an ohmmeter, check the continuity between terminal 7 and body ground when the control switch is turned to "SET" position. If there is no continuity between the terminals, check the control switch.

9) On Celica and Supra, use an ohmmeter to check the continuity between terminal 5 and body ground when the control switch is pushed to the "CANCEL" position. If there is no continuity between the terminals, check the control switch.

10) On all models, use an ohmmeter to check the continuity between terminal 1 and body ground when the vehicle is slightly pushed forward. At this time, the ohmmeter needle should repeatedly move back and forth. If the ohmmeter needle does not deflect, check the speed sensor.

Cruise Control Systems

TOYOTA (Cont.)

Fig. 1: Cruise Control Computer Wiring Connectors

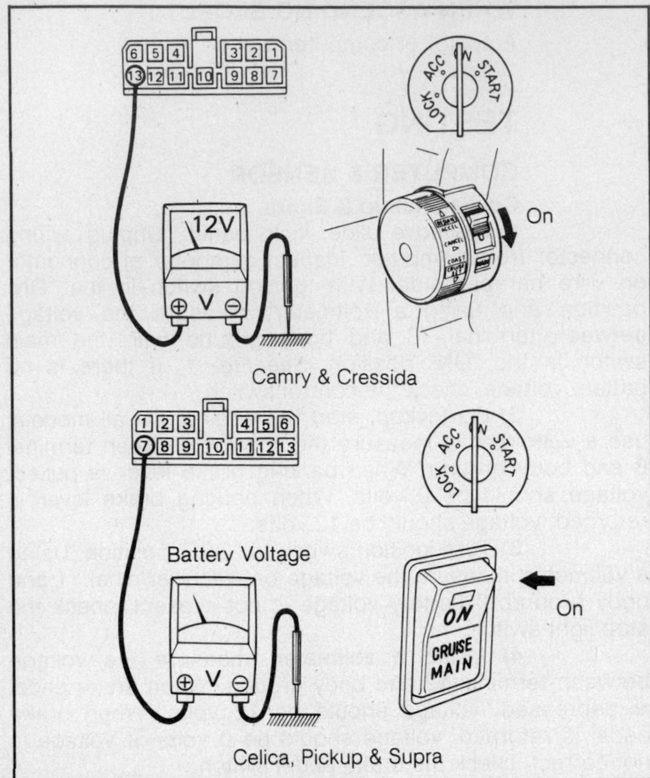
6 5 4 3 2 1
13 12 11 10 9 8 7
ACC ON START
LOCK
12V
V
On
Camry & Cressida
1 2 3 4 5 6
7 8 9 10 11 12 13
ACC ON START
LOCK
Battery Voltage
V
ON
CRUISE MAIN
On
Celica, Pickup & Supra

Camry & Cressida

1) Remove side kick panel. Unplug wiring connector from computer. Inspect computer at connector on wire harness side. With ignition switch in the "ON" position and using a voltmeter, measure the voltage between terminal 7 and body ground with the main switch in the "ON" position. *See Fig. 1.* If there is no battery voltage, check the control switch.

2) Using a voltmeter, measure the voltage between terminal 12 and body ground. When parking brake lever is pulled, voltage should be 0 volts. When parking brake lever is returned, voltage should be 12 volts.

3) Turn ignition switch to the "OFF" position. Using a voltmeter, measure the voltage between terminal 9 and body ground. If there is no battery voltage, check the stop light fuse.

4) Using voltmeter, measure the voltage between terminal 8 and body ground. When brake pedal is depressed, voltage should be 12 volts. When brake pedal is released, voltage should be 0 volts. If voltage is not correct, check the brake pedal switch.

5) Turn ignition switch switch to "ACC" position. Using an ohmmeter, check the continuity between terminal 11 and body ground. On manual transmission models, check with clutch pedal depressed. On automatic transmission models, check when shift lever is in "N" position. If there is no continuity between terminals, check the clutch switch or neutral start switch.

6) Using an ohmmeter, measure the resistance between the terminals. Resistance between terminals 1 and 3 when brake pedal is pressed should be approximately 68 ohms. On Camry, when brake pedal is released, resistance reading should be infinity. On all models, resistance between terminals 2 and 3 should be approximately 30 ohms. If the resistances are not correct, check the actuator.

7) Using an ohmmeter, check the continuity between terminal 4 and body ground when the control switch is turned to the "SET" position. If there is no continuity between terminals, check the control switch.

8) Using an ohmmeter, check the continuity between terminal 13 and body ground when the control switch is pushed to the "RESUME" position. If there is no continuity between the terminals, check the control switch.

9) Using an ohmmeter, check the continuity between terminal 6 and body ground when the vehicle is slightly pushed forward. At this time, the ohmmeter needle should repeatedly move back and forth. If the ohmmeter needle does not deflect, check the speed sensor.

ACTUATOR

Resistance Testing

Disconnect connector from actuator lead wire. Check actuator resistance. Using an ohmmeter, measure the resistance between terminals listed in table. *See Fig. 2.*

ACTUATOR RESISTANCES

Terminal Nos.	Ohms
1-3	
Camry	30
All Others	68-71
1-2	
Camry	68
Celica, Cressida, Supra	30
2-3	
Pickup	38

Fig. 2: Actuator Connector Terminal Numbers

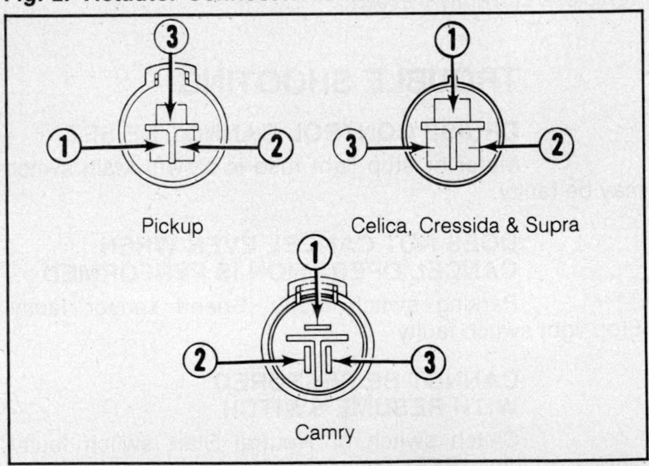
3
1
2
Pickup
1
3
2
Celica, Cressida & Supra
1
2
3
Camry

Operation Testing

1) On all except Camry, disconnect carburetor throttle rod from bell crank. On Camry, disconnect throttle cable from throttle body. On all models, start engine and check actuator operation. Check that the diaphragm makes a smooth reciprocating motion when power is applied to terminals 1 and 2 (Cressida and Pickup) or 2 and 3 (Camry, Celica and Supra).

2) Actuator terminal 1 (Camry), 3 (Cressida and Pickup) or 2 (Celica and Supra) should be grounded to the body or, subsequently, power should be removed from only terminal 2 (2 or 3 on Camry).

TOYOTA (Cont.)

Fig. 3: Speed Sensor Terminal Locations

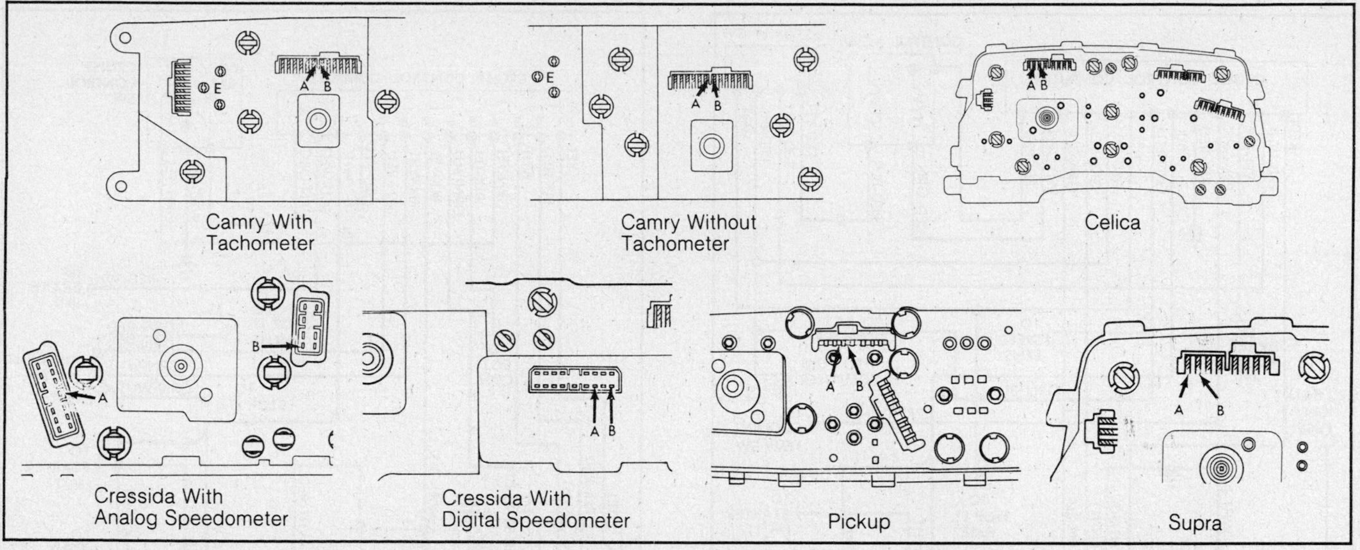
E
A B
Camry With
Tachometer
Camry Without
Tachometer
Celica
Cressida With
Analog Speedometer
Cressida With
Digital Speedometer
Pickup
Supra

3) Confirm that the cable does not return easily when pulled with 4-7 lb. (2-3 kg) of force. Check that the vacuum hose is connected. If the operation is not as specified, replace the actuator.

SPEED SENSOR

Remove combination meter assembly. Using an ohmmeter, check to see that there is continuity between terminals "A" and "B" on circuit board 4 times for each revolution of the magnet shaft. If continuity between the terminals is not as specified, replace the speed sensor.

SWITCHES

NOTE: Test procedures for Cressida were not available from manufacturer.

Camry

1) With main switch in the "ON" position, there should be continuity between terminals 1 and 2, and between 3 and 5. In the "OFF" position, there should be continuity between 3 and 5. With control switch in the "ACCEL (RESUME)" position, there should be continuity between terminals 1 and 2, and between 3 and 4.

2) With control switch in the "CRUISE" position, there should be continuity between terminals 1 and 2, and in the "COAST (SET) position, there should be continuity between terminals 1 and 2 and between 4 and 5.

Celica & Supra

With main switch in the "ON" position, there should be continuity between terminals 1 and 5. With control switch in the "SET" position, there should be continuity between terminals 7 and 8, and in the "RESUME" position, between terminals 3 and 8. With cancel switch in the "ON" position, there should be continuity between terminals 2 and 8.

Pickup

With main switch in the "ON" position, there should be continuity between terminals 1 and 4. With control switch in the "SET" position, there should be continuity between terminals 5 and 6. With control switch in the "RESUME" position, there should be continuity between terminals 2 and 6.

Fig. 4: Switch Connector Terminal Locations

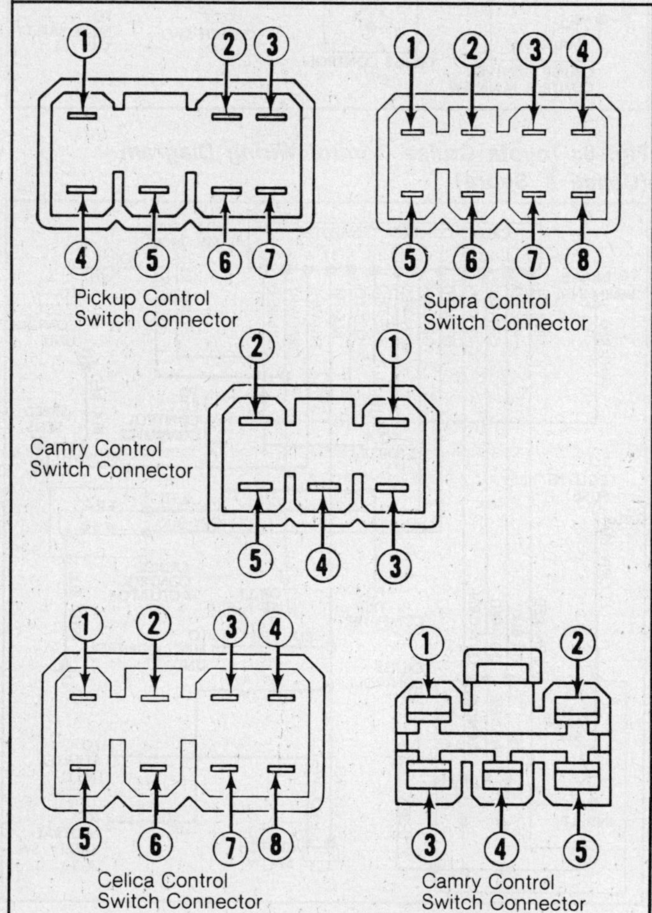
Pickup Control
Switch Connector
Supra Control
Switch Connector
Camry Control
Switch Connector
Celica Control
Switch Connector
Camry Control
Switch Connector

Cruise Control Systems

TOYOTA (Cont.)

Fig. 5: Toyota Cruise Control Wiring Diagram (Camry)

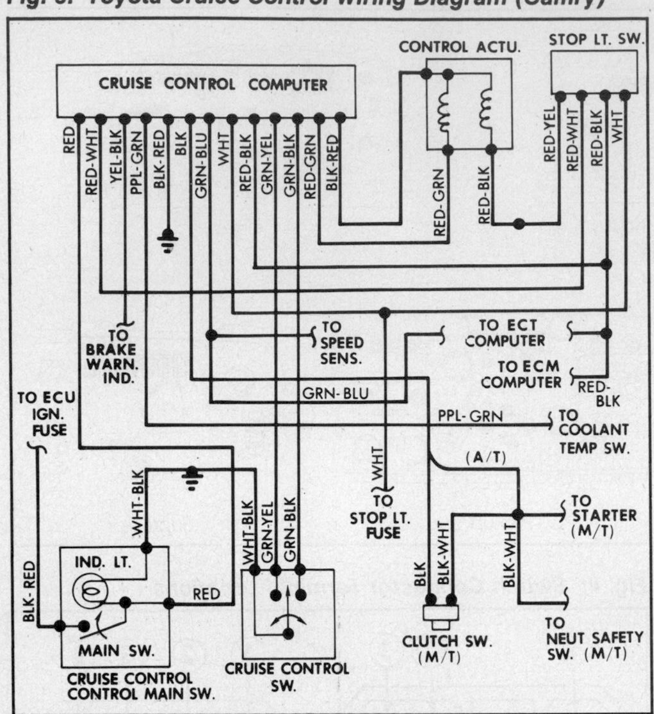
CRUISE CONTROL COMPUTER
CONTROL ACTU.
STOP LT. SW.
RED
RED-WHT
YEL-BLK
PPL-GRN
BLK-RED
BLK
GRN-BLU
WHT
RED-BLK
GRN-YEL
GRN-BLK
RED-GRN
BLK-RED
RED-GRN
RED-BLK
RED-YEL
RED-WHT
RED-BLK
WHT
TO BRAKE WARN. IND.
TO SPEED SENS.
TO ECT COMPUTER
TO ECM COMPUTER
RED-BLK
TO ECU IGN. FUSE
GRN-BLU
PPL-GRN
TO COOLANT TEMP SW.
(A/T)
WHT
TO STOP LT. FUSE
TO STARTER (M/T)
WHT-BLK
BLK-RED
IND. LT.
RED
WHT-BLK
GRN-YEL
GRN-BLK
BLK
BLK-WHT
BLK-WHT
MAIN SW.
CRUISE CONTROL CONTROL MAIN SW.
CRUISE CONTROL SW.
CLUTCH SW. (M/T)
TO NEUT SAFETY SW. (M/T)

Fig. 7: Toyota Cruise Control Wiring Diagram (Cressida)

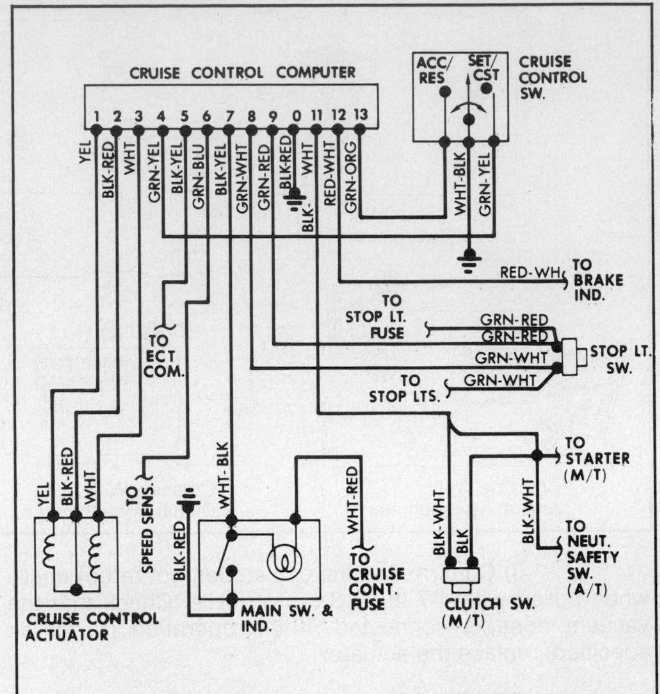
CRUISE CONTROL COMPUTER
1 2 3 4 5 6 7 8 9 0 11 12 13
ACC/RES
SET/CST
CRUISE CONTROL SW.
YEL
BLK-RED
WHT
GRN-YEL
BLK-YEL
GRN-BLU
BLK-YEL
GRN-WHT
GRN-RED
BLK-RED
WHT
BLK
RED-WHT
GRN-ORG
WHT-BLK
GRN-YEL
RED-WH
TO BRAKE IND.
TO STOP LT. FUSE
GRN-RED
GRN-RED
GRN-WHT
STOP LT. SW.
TO ECT COM.
TO STOP LTS.
GRN-WHT
TO STARTER (M/T)
YEL
BLK-RED
WHT
TO SPEED SENS.
BLK-RED
WHT-BLK
WHT-RED
TO CRUISE CONT. FUSE
BLK-WHT
BLK
BLK-WHT
TO NEUT. SAFETY SW. (A/T)
CRUISE CONTROL ACTUATOR
MAIN SW. & IND.
CLUTCH SW. (M/T)

Fig. 6: Toyota Cruise Control Wiring Diagram (Celica & Supra)

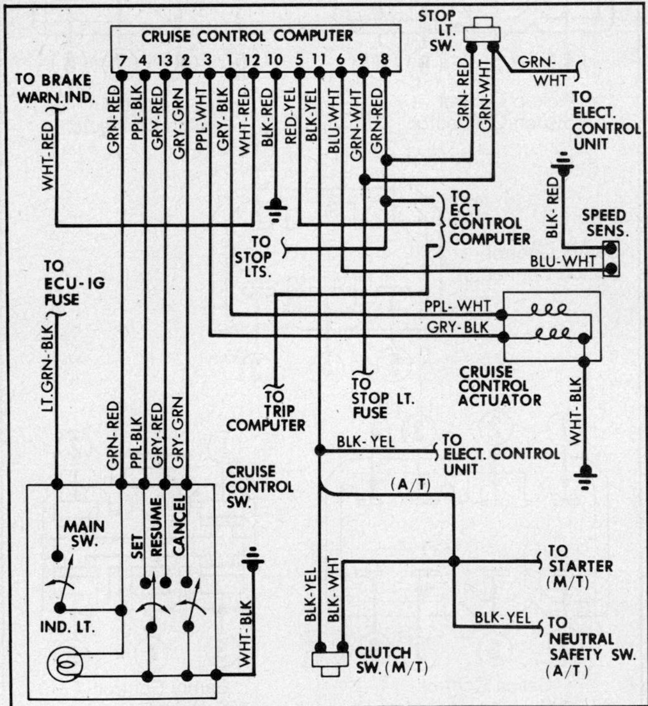
CRUISE CONTROL COMPUTER
7 4 13 2 3 1 12 10 5 11 6 9 8
STOP LT. SW.
TO BRAKE WARN. IND.
GRN-RED
PPL-BLK
GRY-RED
GRY-GRN
PPL-WHT
GRY-BLK
WHT-RED
BLK-RED
RED-YEL
BLK-YEL
BLU-WHT
GRN-WHT
GRN-RED
GRN-RED
GRN-WHT
GRN-WHT
TO ELECT. CONTROL UNIT
WHT-RED
TO ECT CONTROL COMPUTER
BLK-RED
SPEED SENS.
TO STOP LTS.
BLU-WHT
TO ECU-IG FUSE
PPL-WHT
GRY-BLK
LT.GRN-BLK
TO TRIP COMPUTER
TO STOP LT. FUSE
CRUISE CONTROL ACTUATOR
WHT-BLK
GRN-RED
PPL-BLK
GRY-RED
GRY-GRN
CRUISE CONTROL SW.
BLK-YEL
TO ELECT. CONTROL UNIT
(A/T)
MAIN SW.
SET
RESUME
CANCEL
TO STARTER (M/T)
IND. LT.
WHT-BLK
BLK-YEL
BLK-WHT
BLK-YEL
TO NEUTRAL SAFETY SW. (A/T)
CLUTCH SW. (M/T)

Fig. 8: Toyota Cruise Control Wiring Diagram (Pickup)

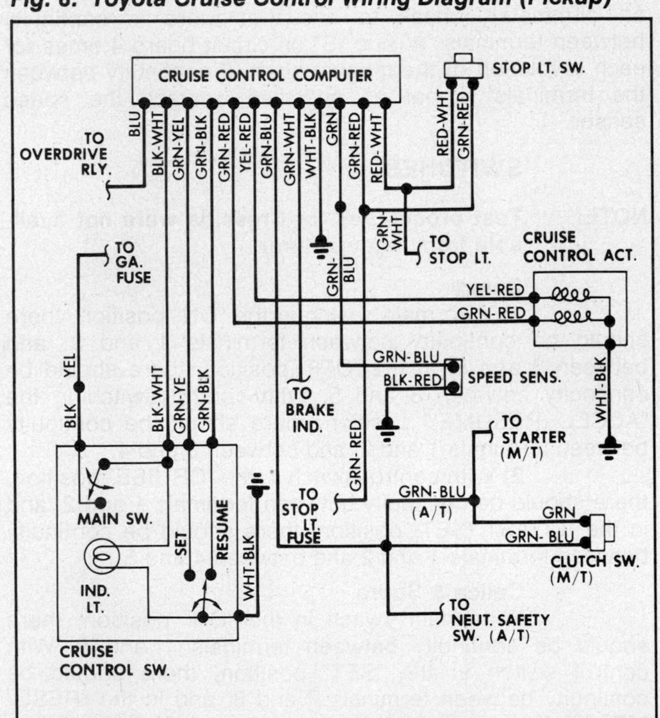
CRUISE CONTROL COMPUTER
STOP LT. SW.
BLU
BLK-WHT
GRN-YEL
GRN-BLK
GRN-RED
YEL-RED
GRN-BLU
GRN-WHT
WHT-BLK
GRN
GRN-RED
RED-WHT
RED-WHT
GRN-RED
TO OVERDRIVE RLY.
GRN-WHT
TO STOP LT.
CRUISE CONTROL ACT.
TO GA. FUSE
GRN-BLU
YEL-RED
GRN-RED
GRN-BLU
BLK-RED
SPEED SENS.
WHT-BLK
TO BRAKE IND.
BLK
YEL
BLK-WHT
GRN-YE
GRN-BLK
TO STARTER (M/T)
GRN-RED
TO STOP LT. FUSE
GRN-BLU
(A/T)
GRN
GRN-BLU
CLUTCH SW. (M/T)
MAIN SW.
SET
RESUME
WHT-BLK
IND. LT.
TO NEUT. SAFETY SW. (A/T)
CRUISE CONTROL SW.

Rear Window Defogger

ALL MODELS

DESCRIPTION

Rear window defogger systems use a heating wire grid bonded to the inside of rear window. Window heat is regulated by a control switch and a relay/timer. An indicator lamp should light to show system is on. Power to the control switch is through a fuse in the fuse block.

OPERATION

Defogger operates when ignition is on and the control switch is moved to "ON". When the switch is turned on, current flows through the wire and evaporates the water from the window. The timer relay will keep power to the grid for a few minutes or until the ignition is turned off.

TROUBLE SHOOTING

DEFOGGER DOES NOT WORK

Blown fuse or poor contact. Defogger switch defective. Poor connections. Broken wire. Relay defective.

INDICATOR LIGHT DOES NOT WORK

Bulb burned out. Open in wiring or poor connection.

TESTING

NOTE: See appropriate chassis wiring diagram in WIRING DIAGRAM section for system wiring diagram.

SYSTEM TESTING

1) Check that all in-line fuses or circuit breakers are operational. Turn ignition and control switches on. Check rear window glass temperature after a few minutes. Glass should feel warm to the touch.

2) If not, use a test lamp or voltmeter to check for battery voltage at grid feed wire. If voltage is not correct, check the wiring harness, control switch or the timer/relay.

FILAMENT TESTING

1) To locate breaks in the grid wire filaments, attach a voltmeter to the middle portion of each filament. Attach the other meter probe to the vertical section of the window grid.

2) If a grid is broken, the meter will register 0 volts or battery voltage. If the wire is unbroken, the meter will register approximately half battery voltage. To the locate the break, move the probe along the wire until the meter needle moves abruptly.

Fig. 1: Voltage Test for Broken Grid Filaments

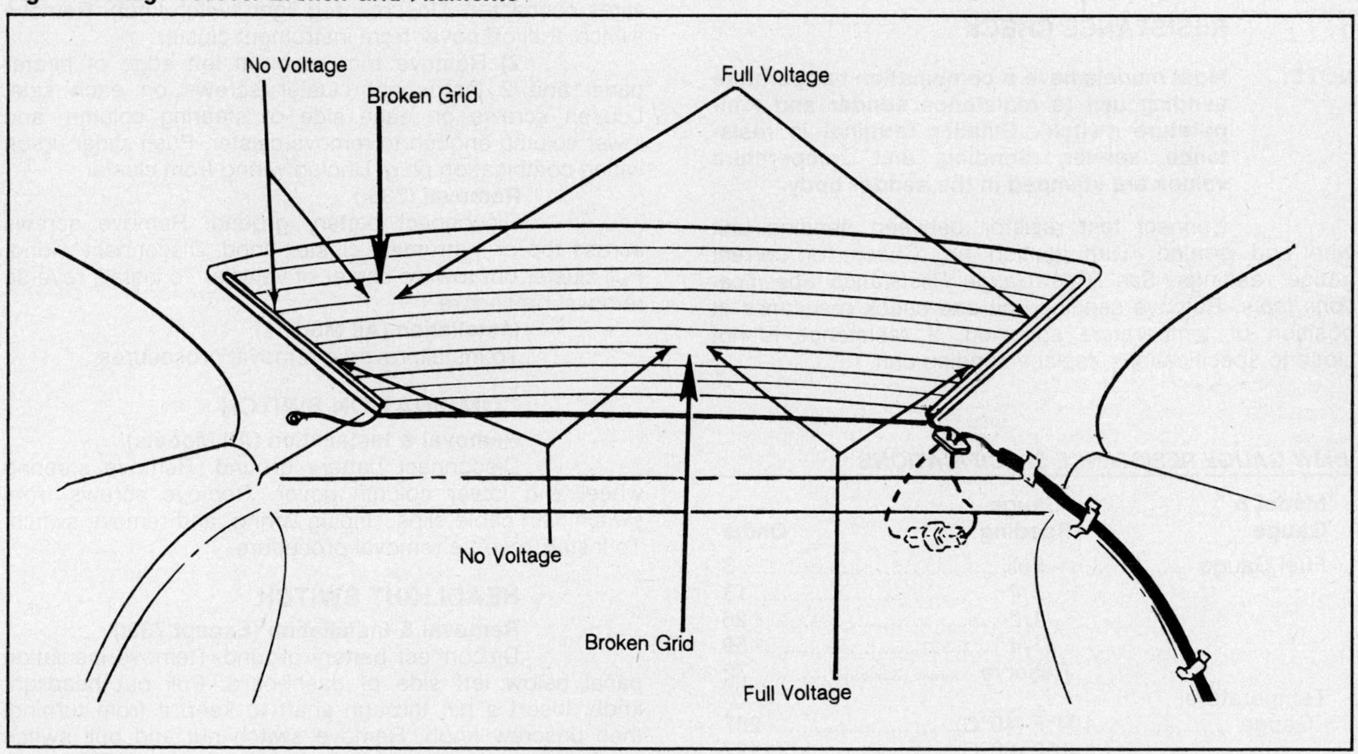
No Voltage
Broken Grid
Full Voltage
No Voltage
Broken Grid
Full Voltage

At the point of break, voltmeter needle will move abruptly.

Switches & Instrument Panels

BMW

DESCRIPTION

All BMW instrument clusters have speedometer, tachometer, fuel gauge and temperature gauge. The headlight switch is on the instrument panel; high beam, turn signals and wiper switch are on steering column levers.

Six-cylinder models have a safety check panel at the lower left side of instrument panel. Gauges use variable resistance sending units. No voltage limiter is used. Electronically-operated speedometers (except 320i) have a sending unit on the rear axle.

TESTING

TEMPERATURE GAUGE

Disconnect sending unit wire and connect it to ground. Turn ignition on briefly. Gauge needle should move into Red zone. If it does, temperature sending unit may be defective. If not, check continuity of sending unit wire. If wiring is good, gauge is inoperative.

FUEL GAUGE

Remove rear seat and tank access cover. Unplug sending unit wire and connect it to ground. Turn ignition on briefly. Gauge needle should move to Full. If it does, sending unit may be defective. If not, check sending unit wire continuity. If wiring is good, gauge is inoperative.

RESISTANCE CHECK

NOTE: **Most models have a combination temperature sending unit (a resistance sender and temperature switch). Smaller terminal is resistance sender. Sending unit temperature values are stamped in the sender body.**

Connect test resistor between sending unit wire and ground. Turn ignition on. Check for correct gauge readings. *See BMW Gauge Resistance Specifications table*. Remove sending unit and check resistance at position or temperature specified. If resistance is not close to specifications, replace sending unit.

BMW GAUGE RESISTANCE SPECIFICATIONS [1]

Model & Gauge	Gauge Reading	Ohms
Fuel Gauge	Full	3
	3/4	13
	1/2	[2] 26
	1/4	[2] 59
	Reserve	72
Temperature Gauge	104°F (40°C)	287
	140°F (60°C)	[3] 127
	250°F (115°C)	25
	262°F (128°C)	18

[1] – 320i resistance values not available.
[2] – 318i resistance, 30 ohms (1/2); 55 ohms (1/4).
[3] – 318i resistance is 132 ohms.

REMOVAL & INSTALLATION

INSTRUMENT CLUSTER

Removal (318i)

1) Disconnect battery ground. Remove steering wheel, insulation panel under left side of dashboard and nuts for trim below instrument cluster. Remove trim.

2) Unscrew screws attaching trim above instrument panel. Pull out trim. Pull out instrument cluster part way. Push slider up on wiring combination plug and unplug wiring from cluster. Remove cluster.

Removal (320i)

Disconnect battery ground. Remove steering wheel and insulation panel under left side of dashboard. Disconnect speedometer cable at middle joint. Do not lose felt ring. Unscrew knurled nut below instrument cluster. Pull out instrument cluster. Unplug wiring from cluster and transmission gear indicator (if equipped). Remove cluster.

Removal (528e & 533i))

Disconnect battery ground. Unscrew trim attaching screws from below steering column and remove trim. Remove steering wheel. Unscrew instrument cluster attaching screws. From behind, press out instrument cluster from instrument panel. Disconnect wiring and remove cluster.

Removal (633CSi)

1) Disconnect battery ground. Remove steering wheel and insulation panel under left side. Pry cover off test panel and remove 3 screws. Pull panel out, leaving wires connected. Unscrew fog light switch knob. Remove switch. Pull off cover from instrument cluster.

2) Remove trim cover at left edge of heater panel and 2 instrument cluster screws on each side. Loosen screws on each side of steering column, and lower column enough to remove cluster. Push slider up on wiring combination plug. Unplug wiring from cluster.

Removal (733i)

Disconnect battery ground. Remove screws across top of instrument cluster hood. Disconnect wiring. Pull cluster out toward center of vehicle. To install, reverse removal procedure.

Installation (All Models)

To install, reverse removal procedures.

COMBINATION SWITCH

Removal & Installation (All Models)

Disconnect battery ground. Remove steering wheel and lower column cover. Remove screws from switch. Cut cable clips, unplug wiring, and remove switch. To install, reverse removal procedure.

HEADLIGHT SWITCH

Removal & Installation (Except 733i)

Disconnect battery ground. Remove insulation panel below left side of dashboard. Pull out headlight knob. Insert a pin through shaft to keep it from turning, then unscrew knob. Remove switch nut and pull switch out from rear. Unplug wiring and remove switch. To install, reverse removal procedure.

Removal & Installation (733i)

Disconnect battery ground. Remove insulation panel below left side of dashboard. Remove knurled nut on back of headlight switch. Unplug wiring and remove switch. To install, reverse removal procedure.

Switches & Instrument Panels

CHRYSLER CORP. IMPORTS

DESCRIPTION & OPERATION

All models have an instrument cluster with speedometer, fuel gauge and temperature gauge. The fuel gauge has a built-in voltage limiter to keep the supply voltage to the gauges at 7 volts.

Some models may also have a shunt type ammeter, oil pressure gauge and tachometer. The pressure gauge is the bimetal type and uses full battery voltage. Control switches are located on the steering column for Challenger and Sapporo. Colt and Pickup models use dashboard switches.

TESTING

VOLTAGE LIMITER

Unplug the fuel or temperature sending unit connector. Connect a voltmeter between the sending unit wire and ground. With the ignition on, voltage should swing between 1 to 7 volts. If not, fuel gauge/limiter must be replaced.

NOTE: **Voltage limiter must be securely grounded or it will be ruined when vehicle is started. Make sure ground connection is tight when installing fuel gauge.**

FUEL GAUGE

1) Disconnect fuel gauge sending unit wire. On Colt models, connect a 17 ohm resistor between wire and ground. On all other models, ground sending unit wire. Fuel gauge should read full.

NOTE: **Keeping the wire grounded too long can damage coils in gauge. Perform test as quickly as possible.**

2) On Colt models, connect a 120 ohm resistor between sending wire and ground. On all other models, connect a 95 ohm resistor between sending wire and ground. Gauge should read empty.

FUEL SENDING UNIT

Connect ohmmeter between gauge terminals. On Colt models, resistance should be 17 ohms with tank full, or 120 ohms with tank empty. On all other models, resistance should be 1-5 ohms with tank full and 103-117 ohms with tank empty. If not, replace sending unit.

TEMPERATURE GAUGE

NOTE: **When performing this test, DO NOT connect sender wire directly to ground.**

1) Unplug temperature sender wire at sending unit. On Challenger and Sapporo, connect a 24 ohm resistor between wire and ground. On all others, use a 70 ohm resistor. Gauge should indicate about 230°F (110°C) for Challenger and Sapporo, and 158°F (70°C) for all others.

2) If gauge tests okay, remove sending unit and place in hot water. The sender should be placed so that its sensing part is .12" (3 mm) from the surface of the water. Resistance should be as shown in table.

OIL PRESSURE GAUGE

1) Unplug sending unit wire. Battery voltage should be present between wire and ground with ignition on. If not, check fuse. On Challenger and Sapporo, connect a 100 ohm resistor between wire and ground. Gauge should indicate about 85 psi (6 kg/cm²).

2) On all other models, connect a 14 volt, 1.4 watt bulb between connector terminal and ground. Bulb should light and gauge should read around 60 psi (4.2 kg/cm²). On all models, if gauges do not have psi marks, needle should point at the second of the 2 center marks.

TEMPERATURE GAUGE RESISTANCE

Application	Temperature °F (°C)	Ohms
Colt	158 (70)	104
All Others	176 (80)	69

AMMETER

1) On Challenger and Sapporo, check ammeter fuse in box at left front fender panel. On all models, remove ammeter. Connect a 3.4 watt bulb (or 60 ohm resistor) in series with a battery and ammeter.

2) If ammeter indicates about 6 amps, it is working correctly. Ammeter is a shunt type that normally passes one-thirtieth of the current being used in vehicle. Do not allow more than 1 amp to pass through ammeter.

REMOVAL & INSTALLATION

INSTRUMENT CLUSTER

Removal & Installation (Colt Pickup & Ram-50 Pickup)

1) Disconnect battery ground. Remove heater and radio knobs. Remove 2 screws under upper edge of cluster. Remove 2 screws inside ashtray opening. Remove 4 screws at corners of cluster. Unplug wiring and speedometer cable and remove cluster.

2) To remove console gauges, remove console floor screws on each side. Pull console back. Remove console gauge mounting screws from inside console. Push gauges toward front of vehicle, unplug wiring and remove. To install, reverse removal procedure.

Removal & Installation (Challenger & Sapporo)

Disconnect battery ground. Remove 4 cluster hood screws. Remove 4 cluster screws. Pull cluster out slightly, then unplug wiring and speedometer cable. Remove cluster. To install, reverse removal procedure.

Removal & Installation (Colt)

1) Disconnect battery ground. Remove steering wheel. Remove heater control knobs. Remove instrument cluster hood mounting screws. Remove light switch, wiper switch, clock and indicator connectors. Remove cluster panel.

2) Remove instrument cluster attaching screws. Pull out instrument cluster slightly, remove speedometer cable and disconnect connectors. To install, reverse removal procedure.

COMBINATION SWITCH

Removal (Challenger & Sapporo)

Disconnect battery ground. Remove steering wheel. Tilt wheel to lowest position and remove column cover. Remove column switch screws. Take off wiring clamp, unplug wiring and remove switch.

Installation

To install, reverse removal procedure. Make sure that turn signal cancel cam pins fit into steering wheel holes.

Switches & Instrument Panels

DATSUN/NISSAN

DESCRIPTION

All models have an instrument cluster that contains the main instrument assembly. This cluster can be removed with all the gauges installed.

A combination switch on the steering column includes the wiper switch, lighting switch and turn signals. Other control switches are located on the instrument panel or console.

TROUBLE SHOOTING

GAUGES NOT WORKING

Blown fuse. Faulty voltage regulator. Loose sender connections. Defective sending unit. Loose connections in instrument cluster.

WARNING LIGHTS NOT WORKING

Burned out bulb. Loose connections. Broken printed circuit. Defective sending unit.

HORN NOT WORKING

Blown fuse. Faulty horn switch. Horn relay inoperative. Loose connection or open circuit. Defective horn.

TESTING

1) Use an ohmmeter to check sensors and switches. Sensors with floats should have continuity when float is in the raised position, and no continuity when float is lowered.

2) Brake lamp and parking brake switches should have continuity when the plunger is in. If sensor does not operate as described, replace it.

REMOVAL & INSTALLATION

COMBINATION SWITCH

Removal & Installation (All Models)

Disconnect battery ground. Remove horn pad and steering wheel. Remove column covers. Unplug connectors, remove mounting screw and slide switch off column. To install, reverse removal procedure.

INSTRUMENT PANEL ASSEMBLY

Removal & Installation (200SX)

1) Disconnect battery ground. Remove steering wheel. Remove steering column covers and combination switch. Remove cover below instruments and disconnect side ventilator air duct.

2) Remove lower left switch assembly below instrument panel. Remove console box. Disconnect wiring connectors from junction box. Disconnect speedometer cable, harness connectors and antenna cable.

3) Remove heater control attaching screws and floor attaching bolts. Remove defroster grille. Remove instrument securing bolts and pull instrument panel out. To install, reverse removal procedure.

Removal & Installation (280ZX)

1) Disconnect battery ground. Remove horn pad, steering wheel and column covers. Remove instrument left lower cover. Disconnect speedometer cable at intermediate connection.

Fig. 1: Exploded View of 200SX Instrument Panel

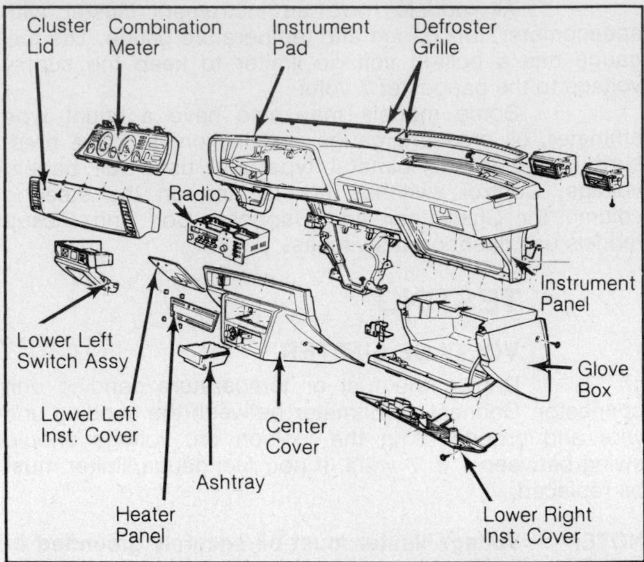
Cluster Lid
Combination Meter
Instrument Pad
Defroster Grille
Radio
Instrument Panel
Lower Left Switch Assy
Glove Box
Lower Left Inst. Cover
Center Cover
Ashtray
Heater Panel
Lower Right Inst. Cover

2) Remove combination switch. Remove combination retaining screws. Carefully pull out instrument panel. Disconnect connector whose leads are connected to instrument panel and remove instrument panel.

3) To remove gauge unit from center of dash, remove glove box. Disconnect instrument harness connector and remove screw retaining combination gauge. Pull out on combination gauge while pushing out toward front of vehicle. To install, reverse removal procedure.

Fig. 2: Exploded View of 280ZX Instrument Panel

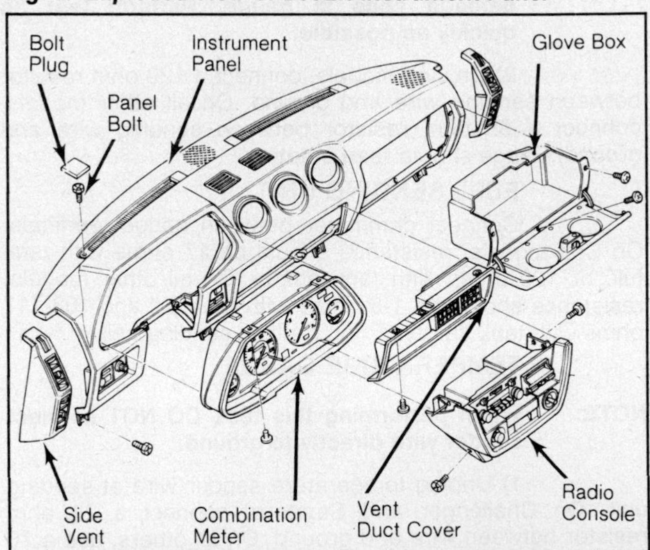
Bolt Plug
Instrument Panel
Glove Box
Panel Bolt
Radio Console
Side Vent
Combination Meter
Vent Duct Cover

Removal & Installation (Maxima)

1) Disconnect battery ground. Remove left lower cover. Remove fuse block and unplug wiring from junction block. Remove steering wheel. Remove column covers and combination switch.

2) Loosen tilt lever and lower column. Disconnect speedometer cable and antenna cable. Remove choke knob. Remove 5 screws under top edge of cluster pad and 2 screws at bottom ends. Remove pad and cluster bezel.

3) Open console box and remove mat. Remove screw inside box. Remove console. Remove heater

DATSUN/NISSAN (Cont.)

control bezel. Remove heater panel screws and radio. Remove defroster grille and heater nozzle on left side.

4) Remove mounting screws for instrument panel and removal panel. To install, reverse removal procedure.

Fig. 3: Exploded View of Maxima Instrument Panel

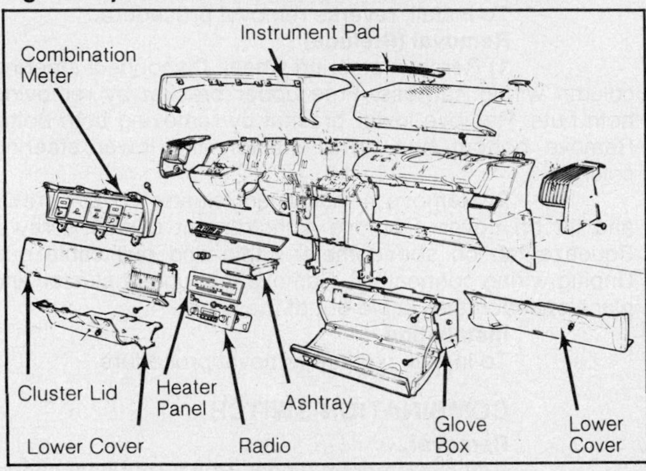

Combination Meter
Instrument Pad
Cluster Lid
Heater Panel
Ashtray
Glove Box
Lower Cover
Lower Cover
Radio

Removal & Installation (Pickup)

1) Disconnect battery ground. Remove steering column cover. Remove package tray (if equipped). Disconnect speedometer cable.

NOTE: Cluster lid and combination meter can be removed at this point if necessary.

2) Unplug wiring for center light, rear defogger, lighter, clock and turn signal switch. Remove 3 instrument panel top bolts (under plugs). Remove bolt above parking brake and bolt in glove box.

3) Remove 2 bolts at each end of instrument panel. Remove panel from vehicle. To install, reverse removal procedure.

Removal & Installation (Pulsar)

1) Disconnect battery ground. Remove steering wheel pad and wheel. Remove steering column cover. Remove attaching screws and instrument cluster bezel. Remove 1 screw above instruments and 1 screw on each side of instrument cluster at bottom.

2) Unplug all wiring and speedometer cable. Lift out combination meter assembly. Gauges can be removed after front bezel and mask are taken off. To install, reverse removal procedure.

Removal & Installation (Stanza)

1) Loosen tilt adjusting lever, and lower steering column completely. Remove steering column cover. Remove retaining screws and tilt cluster lid forward. Then slightly lift the cluster lid while releasing front nails.

2) Remove retaining screws and pull instrument panel out. Disconnect speedometer cable and harness connectors, and remove instrument panel. To install, reverse removal procedure.

Removal & Installation (Sentra)

Remove steering wheel and steering column cover. Remove attaching screws and cluster lid. Remove 4 attaching screws and pull out instrument panel out far enough to disconnect speedometer cable. Remove instrument panel. To install, reverse removal procedure.

Fig. 4: Exploded View of Pulsar Instrument Panel

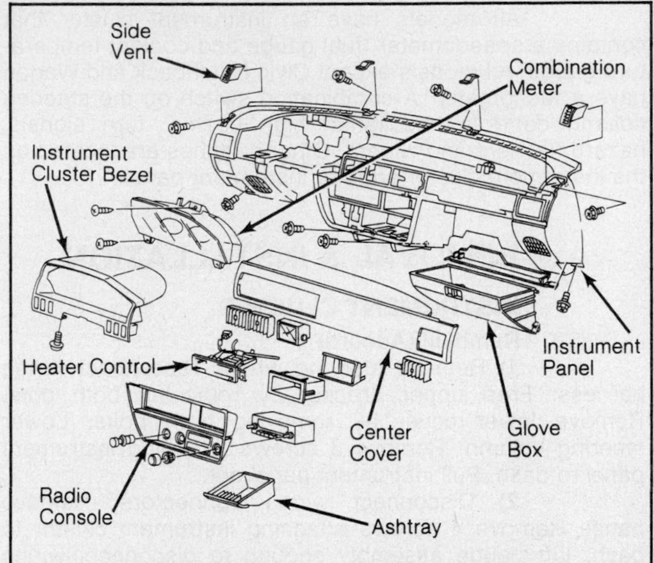

Side Vent
Combination Meter
Instrument Cluster Bezel
Instrument Panel
Heater Control
Center Cover
Glove Box
Radio Console
Ashtray

Fig. 5: Exploded View Stanza Instrument Panel

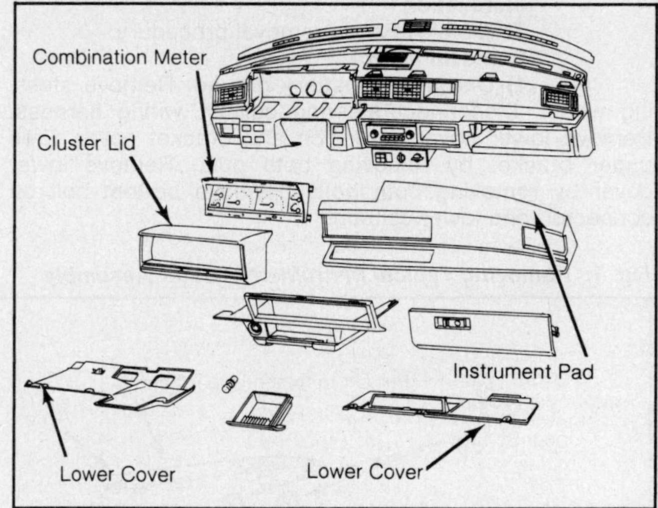

Combination Meter
Cluster Lid
Instrument Pad
Lower Cover
Lower Cover

Fig. 6: Exploded View of Sentra Instrument Panel

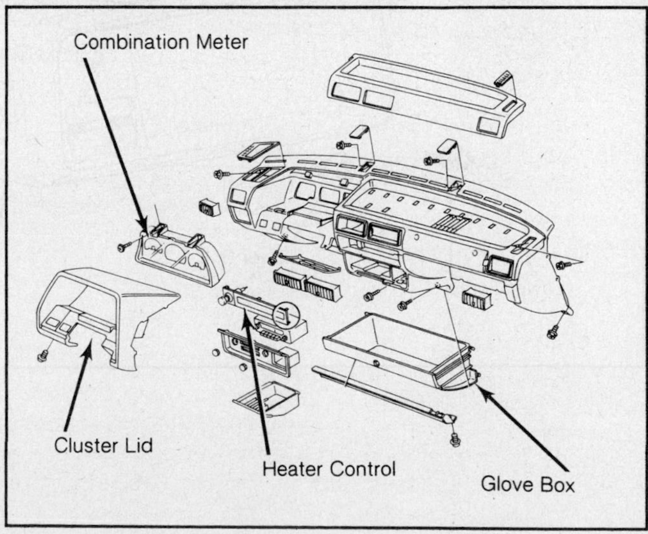

Combination Meter
Cluster Lid
Heater Control
Glove Box

Switches & Instrument Panels

HONDA

DESCRIPTION & OPERATION

All models have an instrument cluster that contains a speedometer, fuel gauge and coolant temperature gauge. All models except Civic Hatchback and Wagon have a tachometer. A combination switch on the steering column controls headlights, high beams, turn signals, hazard flashers and wipers. Other switches are located on the instrument cluster edge or instrument panel.

REMOVAL & INSTALLATION

INSTRUMENT CLUSTER

Removal (Accord)

1) Remove steering wheel. Disconnect wiring harness. Free upper bracket by removing both nuts. Remove lower cover by removing both bolts. Lower steering column. Remove 3 screws attaching instrument panel to dash. Pull instrument panel out.

2) Disconnect wiring connectors. Remove panel. Remove 4 screws attaching instrument cluster to dash. Lift gauge assembly enough to disconnect wiring connectors. Disconnect speedometer cable and remove instrument cluster from vehicle.

Installation

To install, reverse removal procedure.

Removal (Civic)

1) Disconnect battery ground. Remove steering wheel. Disconnect steering column wiring harness. Remove lower cover extension and bracket cover. Free upper bracket by removing both nuts. Remove lower cover by removing both bolts. Remove bottom bolt on connector, and lower column.

2) Remove 4 screws and trim cover. Disconnect speedometer cable from behind dashboard. If equipped, disconnect tachometer cable from behind dashboard. Remove 4 mounting screws and pull the instrument panel part way out. Disconnect connector and remove instrument panel.

Installation

To install, reverse removal procedure.

Removal (Prelude)

1) Remove steering wheel. Disconnect steering column wiring harness. Free upper bracket by removing both nuts. Remove lower bracket by removing both bolts. Remove bottom bolt on connector and lower steering column.

2) Remove 4 instrument cluster cover screws and lift off cover. Remove 4 instrument cluster screws. Squeeze tab on speedometer cable and pull cable out. Unplug wiring connectors. Remove instrument cluster and place speedometer cable out of the way.

Installation

To install, reverse removal procedure.

COMBINATION SWITCH

Removal

Remove steering wheel. Pull turn signal cancel sleeve and washer off steering column. Remove column covers. Unplug wiring connectors and remove clamp screw. Remove combination switch.

NOTE: **Steering column can be lowered to improve access if necessary.**

Installation

To install, reverse removal procedure.

Fig. 1: Removing Typical Instrument Cluster Assembly

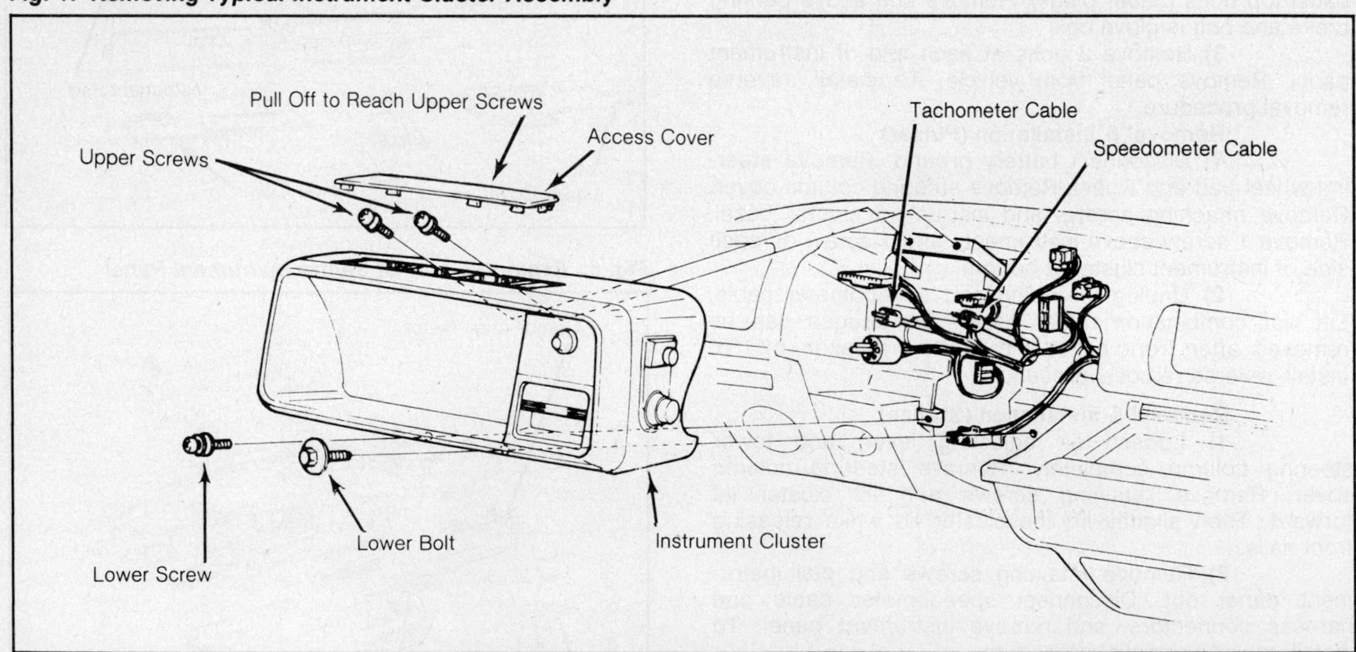
Pull Off to Reach Upper Screws
Access Cover
Upper Screws
Tachometer Cable
Speedometer Cable
Lower Bolt
Instrument Cluster
Lower Screw

ISUZU

DESCRIPTION & OPERATION

All models have instrument cluster with speedometer, fuel gauge and temperature gauge. Impulse and some P'UP models also have oil pressure and system voltage gauges. All gauges use variable resistance sending units. A voltage regulator in the cluster ensures readings stay constant when charging voltage varies.

On P'UP and I-Mark, hazard flashers, windshield wiper/washer and turn signals are controlled by steering column levers. The I-Mark uses 2 combination switches. P'UP models have 1 switch which controls all functions. Impulse has rotary light switch mounted in left satellite switch pod. All other models have a panel-mounted light switch.

TESTING

VOLTAGE REGULATOR

NOTE: **Test procedures were not available for I-Mark and Impulse models.**

P'UP

1) The regulator is built into the fuel gauge. Remove gauge cluster and measure resistance of regulator by connecting ohmmeter leads as shown. *See Fig. 1.* Resistance should measure 110 ohms.

Fig. 1: P'UP Voltage Regulator Resistance Check Points

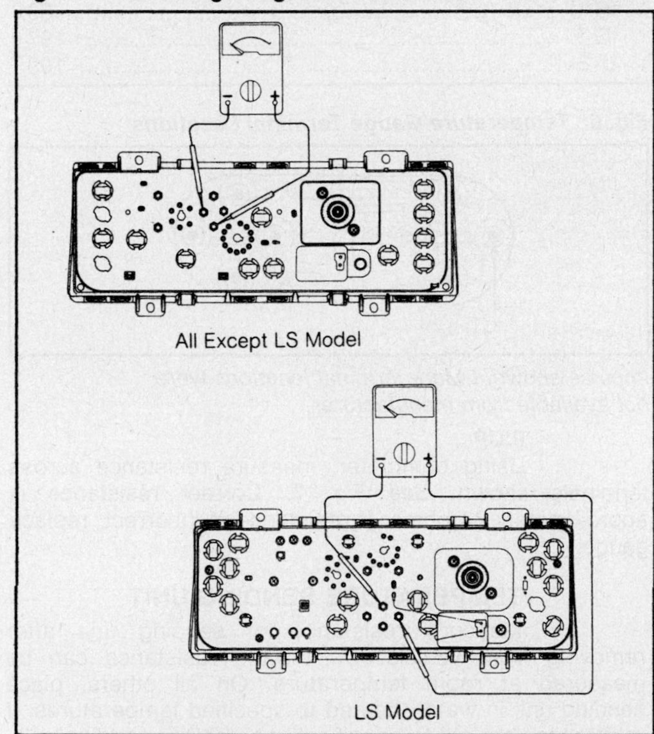
All Except LS Model
LS Model

2) To test regulator operation, connect voltage regulator to battery and check output. Voltmeter at output terminal should swing above and below 7 volts. *See Fig. 2.*

Fig. 2: Testing P'UP Voltage Regulator Operation

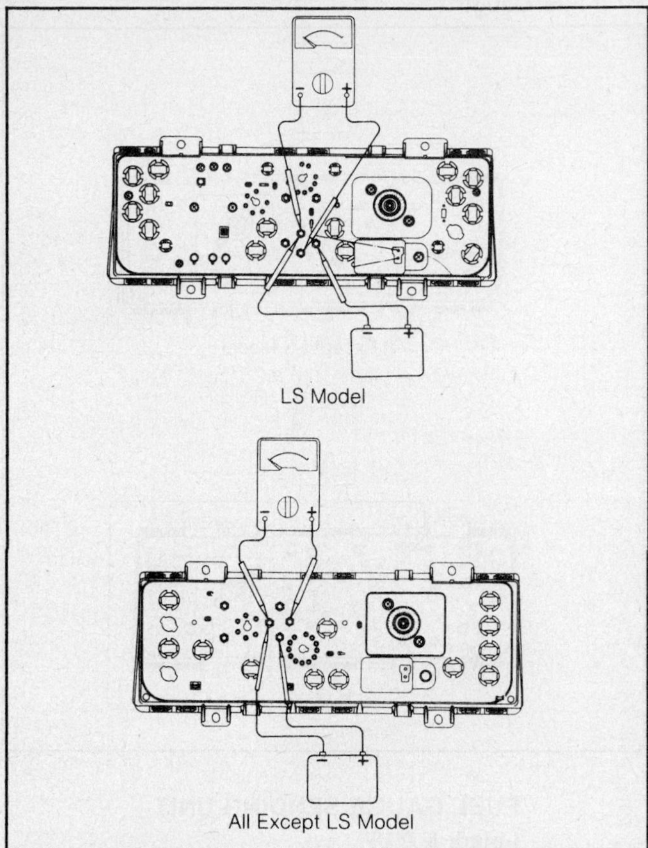
LS Model
All Except LS Model

FUEL GAUGE

I-Mark

Using ohmmeter, measure resistance between fuel gauge terminals. Resistance from IG to U and U to E should be approximately 102 ohms, and resistance from IG to E should be approximately 204 ohms. If resistances are incorrect, replace gauge.

Impulse

Connect ohmmeter to fuel gauge terminals. *See Fig. 3.* Resistance from IG to U should be approximately 260 ohms. From IG to E should be 200 ohms, and from U to E should be 109 ohms. If not, replace gauge.

Fig. 3: Impulse Fuel Gauge Terminals

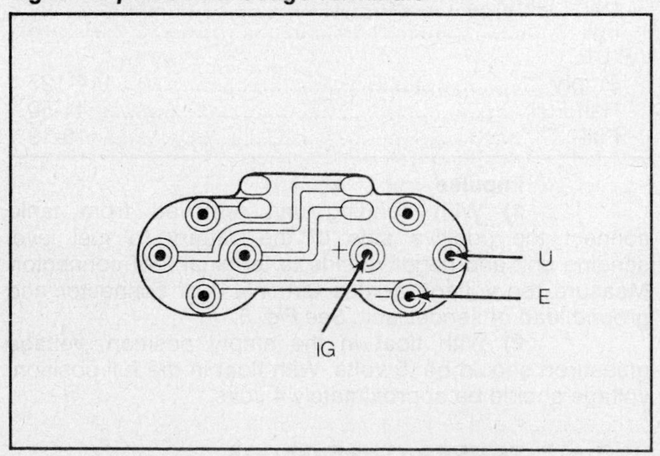
U
E
IG

P'UP

Connect ohmmeter to fuel gauge terminals. Resistance should be 25 ohms. *See Fig. 4.* If not, replace gauge.

ISUZU (Cont.)

Fig. 4: Ohmmeter Hookup Points for Testing P'UP Fuel Gauge

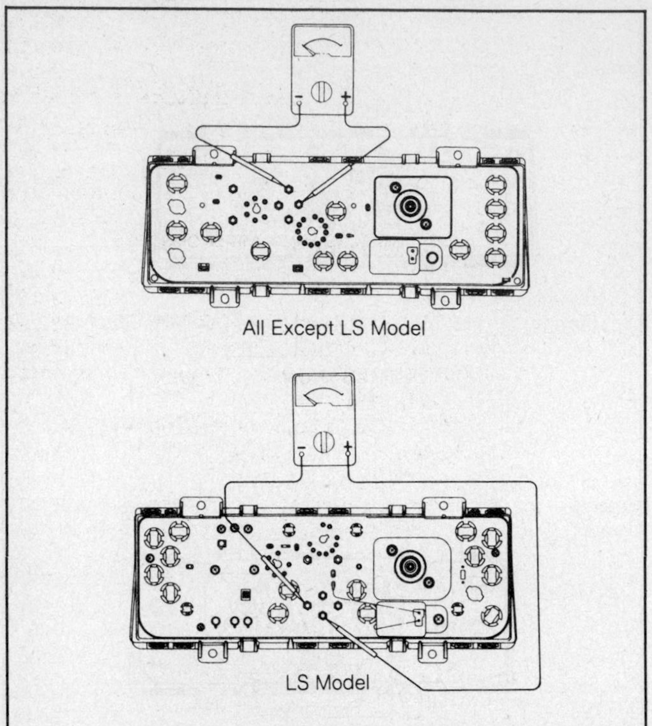
All Except LS Model
LS Model

FUEL GAUGE SENDING UNIT

I-Mark & P'UP

Connect ohmmeter to fuel tank sending unit. As float is moved, resistance reading should change smoothly. Check resistance at 3 positions. If readings are not correct, replace sending unit.

FUEL GAUGE SENDING UNIT RESISTANCE

Application	Ohms
I-Mark	
Empty	97
Half Full	33
Full	6
P'UP	
Empty	114-127
Half Full	41-50
Full	15-19

Impulse

1) With sending unit removed from tank, connect the positive side of the battery to fuel level sending unit and negative side to terminal 2 of connector. Measure the voltage across terminal 4 of connector and ground lead of sender unit. *See Fig. 5.*

2) With float in the empty position, voltage measured should be .5 volts. With float in the full position, voltage should be approximately 4 volts.

TEMPERATURE GAUGE

I-Mark & Impulse

Using ohmmeter, check resistances across lettered terminals as listed in chart. *See Fig. 6.* If resistances are not correct, replace gauge.

Fig. 5: Impulse Fuel Sender Unit and Connector Terminal Locations

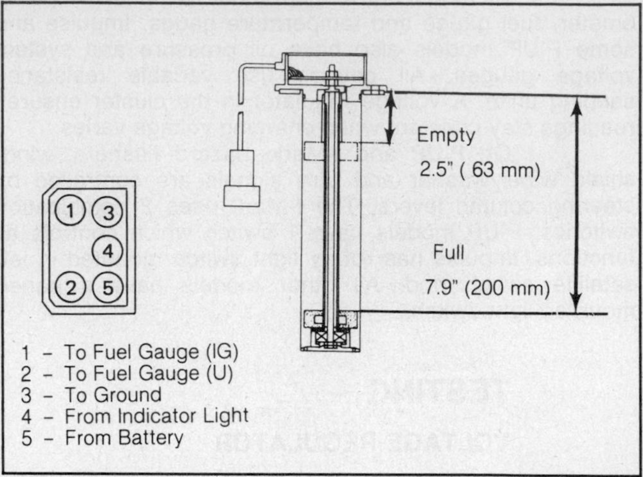
Empty
2.5" (63 mm)
Full
7.9" (200 mm)
1
2
3
4
5
1 – To Fuel Gauge (IG)
2 – To Fuel Gauge (U)
3 – To Ground
4 – From Indicator Light
5 – From Battery

TEMPERATURE GAUGE RESISTANCES

Terminal Position	Ohms
I-Mark	
IG-U	90
IG-E	248
U-E	158
Impulse	
IG-U	88
IG-E	197
U-E	109

Fig. 6: Temperature Gauge Terminal Locations

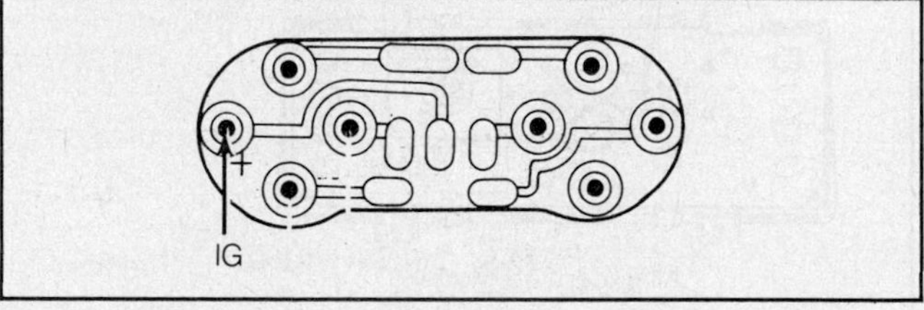
IG

Impulse shown. I-Mark terminal locations were not available from manufacturer.

P'UP

Using ohmmeter, measure resistance across terminals shown. *See Fig. 7.* Correct resistance is approximately 34 ohms. If resistance is incorrect, replace gauge.

TEMPERATURE SENDING UNIT

Measure resistance of sending unit after removing from vehicle. On I-Mark, resistance can be measured at room temperature. On all others, place sending unit in water, heated to specified temperatures. If resistances are not to specifications, replace sending unit.

TEMPERATURE SENDING UNIT RESISTANCE

Application	°F (°C)	Ohms
Impulse	140 (60)	153
	239 (115)	26
P'UP	140 (60)	147
I-Mark	68 (20)	55

ISUZU (Cont.)

Fig. 7: Measuring Temperature Gauge Resistance (P'UP)

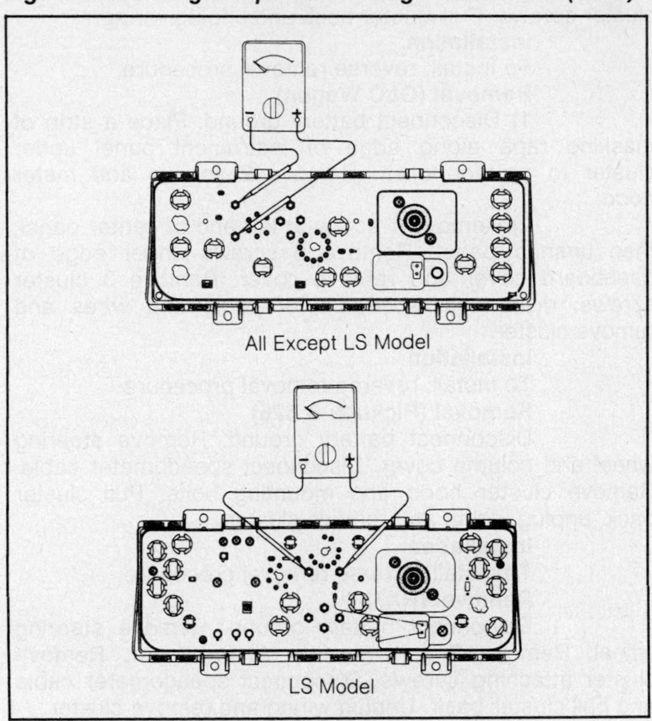
All Except LS Model
LS Model

OIL PRESSURE GAUGE

Impulse

Measure resistance across oil pressure gauge terminals. *See Fig. 8.* If resistances are not correct, replace gauge.

Fig. 8: Impulse Oil Pressure Gauge Terminal Locations

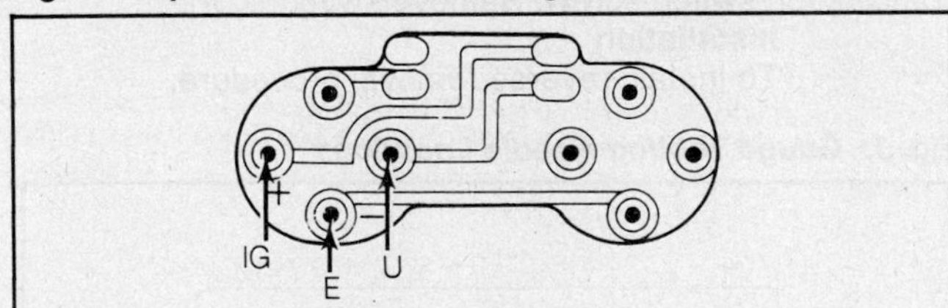
IG
E
U

IMPULSE OIL PRESSURE GAUGE RESISTANCES

Terminal Position	Ohms
IG-U	260
IG-E	200
U-E	124

VOLTMETER

Impulse

Measure resistance across terminals IG and E of voltmeter connector. *See Fig. 9.* Resistance should be approximately 307 ohms. If incorrect, replace gauge.

Fig. 9: Impulse Voltmeter Terminal Locations

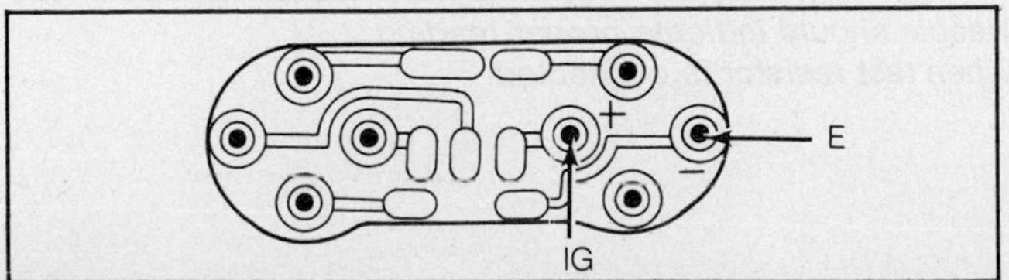
E
IG

P'UP

Apply 12 volts to terminals 2 and 6 of voltmeter connector. *See Fig. 10.* If voltmeter indicates a voltage of 11-13 volts, it is okay. If outside specified range, replace voltmeter.

Fig. 10: P'UP Voltmeter Connector Terminal Locations

7
3
1
6
5
4
2

Viewed from meter side.

REMOVAL & INSTALLATION

INSTRUMENT CLUSTER

Removal (I-Mark)

Disconnect battery ground. Remove cluster panel. Remove cluster attaching screws. Rotate cluster assembly outward, and disconnect the 6 and 12-pole electrical connectors. Disconnect speedometer cable. Remove instrument panel screws or nuts to take out gauges.

Installation

To install, reverse removal procedure.

Removal (Impulse)

1) Disconnect battery ground. Remove steering wheel. Remove attaching screws and steering column cowl set. Remove screws and remove hood above instrument cluster.

2) Remove screws and nuts holding in instrument cluster. Pull out cluster far enough to disconnect speedometer cable and wiring connectors. Remove instrument cluster and satellite switch assembly.

Installation

To install, reverse removal procedure.

Removal (P'UP)

1) Remove radio knobs and nuts. Remove radio bezel. Remove 5 cluster screws and cluster panel.

2) Disconnect speedometer cable. Remove 4 cluster screws. Pull cluster out part way and unplug wiring. Remove cluster.

Installation

To install, reverse removal procedure.

COMBINATION SWITCH

Removal (I-Mark)

Disconnect battery ground. Remove steering wheel. Remove steering column covers. Unplug wiring. Remove 2 screws and wiper switch. Remove 4 screws and left combination switch.

Installation

To install, reverse removal procedure.

Removal (P'UP)

Disconnect battery ground. Remove steering column covers. Unplug wiring. Remove steering wheel with puller (J-29752). Remove 2 screws and combination switch.

Installation

To install, reverse removal procedure.

MAZDA

DESCRIPTION & OPERATION

All models have a steering column mounted combination switch to control turn signals, headlights and wipers. The instrument cluster contains a speedometer, fuel gauge and water temperature gauge.

Some models also have a tachometer, voltmeter and oil pressure gauge. The fuel and temperature gauges operate on 7 volts, supplied by a cluster-mounted voltage regulator. The sending units are variable-resistance type and have the same resistance values on all models.

TESTING

GAUGES

1) Turn ignition on. If gauge needles do not move at all, check for blown fuse or broken power wire. If both gauges are inoperative, voltage regulator may be the cause. If only one gauge does not work, the gauge, sending unit, or connecting wiring may be at fault.

2) To test temperature gauge, disconnect sending unit wire. Connect a resistor between wire and ground, then check gauge reading. Change resistance and recheck. If gauge readings are as shown in tables, replace sending unit. If not, repair wiring or replace gauge.

3) To test fuel gauge, disconnect wire to sending unit at fuel tank (all except GLC Wagon) or unplug connector behind left kick panel (GLC Wagon). Connect resistor between Yellow wire and ground. Check gauge reading.

NOTE: **Allow 2 minutes for gauge reading to stabilize. It should be within 1 pointer width of line on gauge face. See Fig. 1.**

4) If gauge readings are incorrect, replace gauge. If readings are okay, test in-tank sending unit before replacing it. Resistance should measure 0-5 ohms with float raised, and 103-117 ohms with float lowered. If not, replace sending unit.

RESISTANCES FOR FUEL GAUGE TESTING

Needle Position	Test Resistor
Full Line	[1] 7 ohms
Half Tank	33 ohms
Empty Line	[2] 95 ohms

[1] – On Pickup, 3 ohms.
[2] – On Pickup, 110 ohms.

RESISTANCES FOR TEMPERATURE GAUGE TESTING

Model	Cold Line	Hot Line
GLC Wagon & 626	233 ohms	16 ohms
RX7	104 ohms	21 ohms
GLC	154 ohms	12 ohms

REMOVAL & INSTALLATION

INSTRUMENT CLUSTER

Removal (GLC Hatchback)

Disconnect battery ground. Remove steering wheel. Remove meter hood by moving it up and down with hands. Disconnect speedometer cable and remove 4 cluster screws. Pull cluster back and unplug wiring.

Installation

To install, reverse removal procedure.

Removal (GLC Wagon)

1) Disconnect battery ground. Place a strip of masking tape along edge of instrument panel under cluster to protect finish. Remove 2 screws and meter hood.

2) Remove 1 screw at left end of center panel, then unsnap panel. Remove 3 screws under edge of dashboard cover and remove cover. Remove 3 cluster screws, disconnect speedometer cable and wires and remove cluster.

Installation

To install, reverse removal procedure.

Removal (Pickups & 626)

Disconnect battery ground. Remove steering wheel and column cover. Disconnect speedometer cable. Remove cluster hood and mounting bolts. Pull cluster back, unplug wiring and remove cluster.

Installation

To install, reverse removal procedure.

Removal (RX7)

Disconnect battery ground. Remove steering wheel. Remove 2 screws and cluster cover. Remove cluster attaching screws. Disconnect speedometer cable and pull cluster back. Unplug wiring and remove cluster.

Installation

To install, reverse removal procedure.

COMBINATION SWITCH

Removal

Disconnect battery ground. Remove steering wheel. Remove column covers and snap ring at top of column (if equipped). Unplug wiring connectors. Loosen combination switch screw. Remove switch.

Installation

To install, reverse removal procedure.

Fig. 1: Gauge Testing Needle Locations

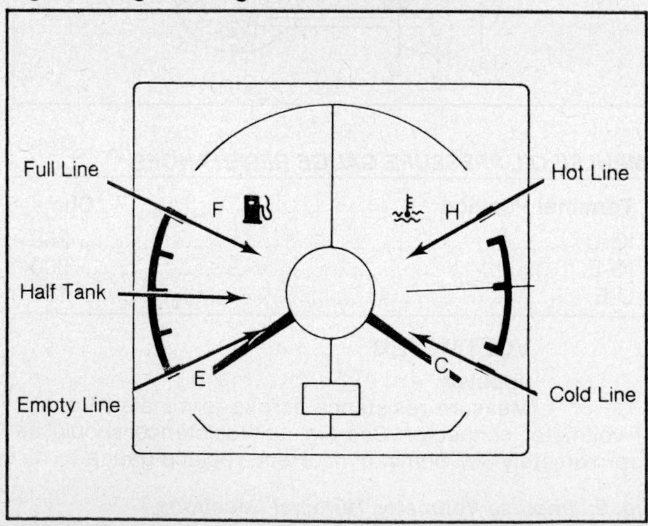
Full Line
Hot Line
F
H
Half Tank
E
C
Empty Line
Cold Line

Needle should indicate proper reading when test resistor is connected.

MAZDA ELECTRONIC INSTRUMENT PANEL

626

DESCRIPTION & OPERATION

Some 626 models may be equipped with microcomputer-operated electronic instrument cluster. The speedometer uses a fluorescent display tube for digital indication /ehicle speed. Tachometer uses Light Emitting Diodes (LEDs) for a zone indication of engine RPM.

Fuel gauge uses fluorescent display tube for zone indication of remaining amount of fuel. Temperature gauge uses fluorescent display tube to indicate coolant temperature. A rheostat is provided to allow adjustment of brightness of displays.

TESTING

TACHOMETER

Connect a known good test tachometer to the negative side of the ignition coil. Start the engine. Compare the indication of vehicle tachometer to test tachometer. If there is a large error, replace vehicle tachometer. See chart for interpetation of tachometer.

TACHOMETER RPM INDICATION

Indication Segments	Indication Range
1 & 2	1-700 RPM
3-25	[1] 701-3000 RPM
26-45	[1] 3001-7000 RPM
46 & 47	[2] 7001-8000 RPM

[1] - One segment for each 200 RPM increase.
[2] - One segment for each 500 RPM increase.

FUEL GAUGE

Disconnect connector from fuel gauge. Connect the "Y" wire from the fuel gauge connector in turn to each of the resistors specified in table and ground resistor to body. *See Fig. 1.* Turn ignition on and confirm that gauge readings are in the correct segment. If not, replace gauge.

Fig. 1: Fuel Level Sender and Connector

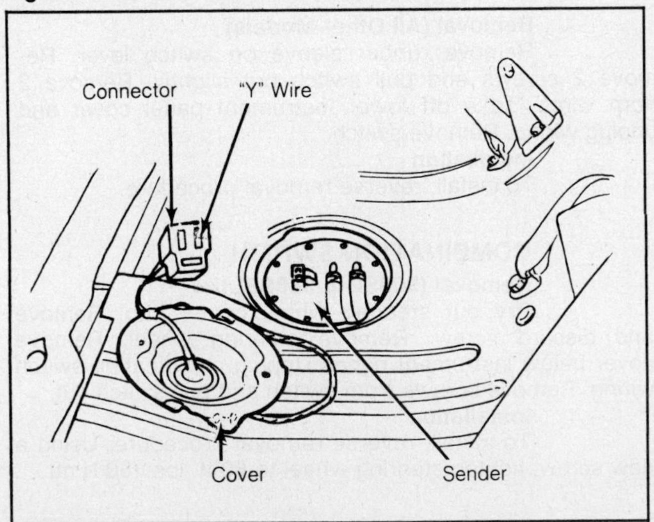
Connector
"Y" Wire
Cover
Sender

FUEL GAUGE RESISTANCE CHECK

Number of Segments Lit	Resistor Used
1	96 or More Ohms
3	56-72 Ohms
5	32-40 Ohms
7	20-28 Ohms
9	8-16 Ohms
10	Less Than 8 Ohms

FUEL LEVEL SENDER

1) Remove rear seat. Remove the service hole cover. Disconnect hose. Use a Phillips screwdriver to remove fuel level sender. *See Fig. 1.* Connect an ohmmeter to the fuel tank unit.

NOTE: If fuel tank is full, fuel may spill when sender is removed.

2) Move the unit arm slowly throughout the range of its travel and check resistance. Resistance should be 3 ohms at the full position, 33 ohms at the half-way point, and 110 ohms at empty position. If incorrect, replace sender.

TEMPERATURE GAUGE

Disconnect connector from temperature sender. Connect the wire from sender in turn to each of the resistors specified in table and ground resistor to body. Turn ignition on, and confirm that gauge readings are in the correct segment. If not, replace gauge.

TEMPERATURE GAUGE RESISTANCE CHECK

Number of Segments Lit	Resistor Used
1	178 or More Ohms
3	121-147 Ohms
5	33-89 Ohms
7	21-24 Ohms
9	Less Than 18 Ohms

TEMPERATURE SENDER

Remove temperature sender from vehicle. Place sender in a container of water, and heat to 176°F (80°C). Measure resistance of sending unit. Resistance should be 49-58 ohms. If not, replace sender.

MERCEDES-BENZ

DESCRIPTION

All models have an instrument cluster with speedometer, clock, fuel gauge, oil pressure gauge and temperature gauge. Some models have a tachometer and 380 models have a vacuum gauge.

The headlight switch is located on the instrument panel. A combination switch on the steering column lever controls the high beams, turn signals and wipers. Additional switches on the console operate other electrical options.

OPERATION

The speedometer on 300SD and 380SEL models is electronic, with a sending unit in the rear of the transmission. All other models use a cable-driven speedometer. The 300SD and 380SEL models also use an electric oil pressure sending unit.

All other models have an oil pressure line to the instrument cluster. Fuel and temperature gauges on all models use variable resistance sending units. Vacuum gauges are connected directly to the intake manifold by a vacuum line.

TESTING

ELECTRONIC SPEEDOMETER

1) Remove screw and pull sender out of transmission tail housing. Turn ignition on. Place a large screwdriver blade across sender tip. Move blade quickly off and on sender. Speedometer needle should move slightly. If not, remove instrument cluster and unplug connector at back of cluster.

2) Connect negative lead of voltmeter on pin 3 and positive lead on pin 5. Repeat test of sender. If voltage is indicated, speedometer is defective. If no voltage, replace sender and harness

VACUUM GAUGE

1) Locate vacuum source hose at 4-way connector near engine. Check for vacuum. If not present, clean vacuum port or repair hose. If vacuum is present, connect directly to vacuum gauge hose and bypass connector.

2) If gauge works, air conditioning system has a vacuum leak. If gauge does not work, repair vacuum line or replace gauge.

ELECTRIC OIL PRESSURE GAUGE

1) Turn ignition on and pull sending unit wire off sending unit. Gauge should indicate about 43 psi (3 kg/cm²). If not, check sending unit wire for short to ground. If wire is okay, replace gauge.

OIL PRESSURE SENDING UNIT RESISTANCE

Pressure psi (kg/cm²)	Resistance (Ohms)
0 (0)	10
14 (1)	70
28 (2)	130
43 (3)	185

2) Connect wire to ground. Gauge should indicate no pressure. If reading remains high, sending unit wire is broken. Check resistance of sending unit as indicated in chart.

FUEL GAUGE

1) Connect ohmmeter between terminal "G" and 31 on fuel gauge sender. Resistance should be between 2 and 70 ohms, depending upon level of fuel in tank. The higher the fuel level, the lower resistance will be.

2) Connect ohmmeter across terminal "W" and 31. Continuity should exist only if tank is empty (low fuel warning contacts). If sender is okay and wire is good, replace fuel gauge.

REMOVAL & INSTALLATION

INSTRUMENT CLUSTER

Removal (380SL & 380SLC)

Pry out steering wheel center cap. Remove and discard screw. Remove steering wheel. Push top of cluster hood up and insert tool to pull cluster out. Unplug wiring, disconnect speedometer cable and remove oil pressure line. Remove cluster.

Installation

To install, reverse removal procedure. Using a new screw, tighten steering wheel to 60 ft. lbs. (80 N.m).

Removal (240D, 300D, 300CD & 300TD)

1) Push top of hood up and slide in pulling hook. Move hook over to right side of cluster (3 o'clock position) and pull cluster out slightly.

2) Loosen speedometer cable clamp (in engine compartment). Pull cluster back, unplug wiring and remove oil pressure line. Disconnect speedometer cable and remove cluster.

Installation

To install, reverse removal procedure.

Removal (300SD & 380SEL)

Pry out steering wheel center cap. Remove and discard screw. Remove steering wheel. Insert pulling hook at left side of cluster and pull cluster out of spring clips. Unplug wiring and remove cluster.

Installation

To install, reverse removal procedure. Using a new screw, tighten steering wheel to 60 ft. lbs. (80 N.m).

Removal (All Other Models)

Remove rubber sleeve on switch lever. Remove 2 screws and pull switch out slightly. Remove 2 horn wires. Take off lower instrument panel cover and unplug wiring. Remove switch.

Installation

To install, reverse removal procedure.

COMBINATION SWITCH

Removal (300SD & 380SEL)

Pry out steering wheel center cap. Remove and discard screw. Remove steering wheel. Remove cover below instrument panel. Unplug combination switch wiring. Remove screws from switch and pull switch out.

Installation

To install, reverse removal procedure. Using a new screw, tighten steering wheel to 60 ft. lbs. (80 N.m).

MITSUBISHI

DESCRIPTION

All models have an instrument cluster with speedometer, fuel gauge and temperature gauge. All models may also be equipped with tachometer. Voltmeter is available on Cordia models. Cordia and Starion models have optional electronic instrument cluster available which includes digital tachometer and electronic gauges.

TROUBLE SHOOTING

GAUGES NOT WORKING

Blown fuse. Faulty voltage regulator. Loose sender connections. Defective sending unit. Loose connections in instrument cluster.

WARNING LIGHTS NOT WORKING

Burned out bulb. Loose connections. Broken printed circuit. Defective sending unit.

HORN NOT WORKING

Blown fuse. Faulty horn switch. Horn relay inoperative. Loose connection or open circuit. Defective horn.

TESTING

VOLTAGE LIMITER

Pickup Models

Unplug the fuel or temperature sending unit connector. Connect a voltmeter between the sending unit wire and ground. With the ignition on, voltage should swing between 1 and 7 volts. If so, the constant voltage limiter may be considered in satisfactory condition.

NOTE: Voltage limiter must be securely grounded or it will be ruined when vehicle is started. Make sure ground connection is tight when installing fuel gauge.

FUEL GAUGE

Disconnect fuel gauge sending unit wire at fuel tank. Connect appropriate resistance between wire and ground. Gauge should read as indicated in table.

NOTE: Keeping the wire grounded too long can damage coils in gauge. Perform test as quickly as possible.

FUEL GAUGE TESTING RESISTANCES

Application	Empty	Full
Montero	120 Ohms	7 Ohms
All Others	95 Ohms	[1] 7 Ohms

[1] – On Cordia and Tredia with vertical gauge, 3 ohms.

TEMPERATURE GAUGE

NOTE: This test is for all models except Cordia & Tredia. When performing this test, DO NOT connect sender wire directly to ground.

1) Unplug temperature sender wire at sending unit. Connect a 24 ohm resistor between wire and ground. Gauge should indicate 240°F (115°C). In a similar manner, connect a 104 ohm resistor. Gauge should read 158°F (70°C).

2) If gauge tests okay, remove sending unit and place in hot water. The sender should be placed so that its sensing part is .12" (3 mm) from the surface of the water. Resistance should be as shown in table.

TEMPERATURE GAUGE RESISTANCE

Application	Temperature °F (°C)	Ohms
Pickup	176 (80)	69
All Others	158 (70)	104

OIL PRESSURE GAUGE

Cordia, Tredia & Starion

Unplug sending unit wire. Battery voltage should be present between wire and ground with ignition on. If not, check fuse. Connect resistor between wire and ground. Gauge should indicate normal pressure (needle should point at the second of the 2 center marks).

OIL PRESSURE GAUGE TEST RESISTANCES

Aplication	Ohms
Cordia & Tredia	40
Starion	120

Pickup

Connect a 14 volt, 1.4 watt bulb between connector terminal and ground. Bulb should light and gauge should read around 60 psi (4.2 kg/cm²). If gauges do not have psi marks, needle should point at the second of the 2 center marks.

AMMETER

1) If ammeter fuse is okay, remove ammeter. Connect a 3.4 watt bulb (or 60 ohm resistor) in series with a battery and ammeter.

2) If ammeter indicates about 6 amps, it is working correctly. Ammeter is a shunt type that normally passes one-thirtieth of the current being used in vehicle. Do not allow more than 1 amp to pass through ammeter.

LIQUID CRYSTAL DISPLAY CIRCUIT

Cordia

Turn ignition to "ACC" position. Depress "CHECK" button for more than 3 seconds and confirm that all lights illuminate (for approximately 2 seconds) in the following manner. Replace liquid crystal display unit if any segments are defective.

1) First, all lights illuminate for approximately 2 seconds.

2) Tachometer segments illuminate in order.

3) Fuel gauge segments illuminate in order.

4) Water temperature gauge segments illuminate in order.

5) MPH lights up, and display ceases with "EE" indication in speed position.

MITSUBISHI (Cont.)

REMOVAL & INSTALLATION

INSTRUMENT CLUSTER

Removal & Installation (Cordia & Tredia)

1) Remove steering wheel, glove box and instrument under cover. Remove lap heater duct and instrument lower cover. Remove defroster duct and 3 heater control cables.

2) On Tredia, remove the fuse block from instrument panel. Remove heater control panel. On all models, remove attaching screws and remove instrument cluster hood by prying on tabs of cluster.

3) Disconnect speedometer cable from back of instrument cluster. Remove cluster mounting screws and pull slightly forward. Disconnect connectors and remove cluster. To install, reverse removal procedure.

Fig. 1: Exploded View of Cordia Instrument Panel

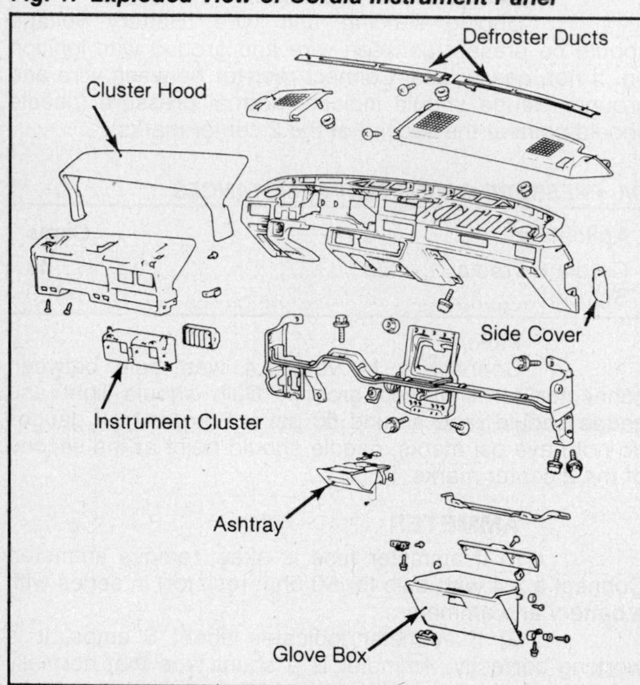
Defroster Ducts
Cluster Hood
Side Cover
Instrument Cluster
Ashtray
Glove Box

Removal & Installation (Montero)

1) Remove instrument cluster cover. Remove screws from bottom of instrument cluster. Remove bolt from upper part of cluster.

2) Disconnect speedometer cable from back of instrument cluster by pushing the stopper of the plug on speedometer cable side of connection.

3) Pull cluster out part way. Disconnect all connectors attaching cluster. Remove cluster. To install, reverse removal procedure.

Removal & Installation (Pickup)

1) Disconnect battery ground. Remove heater fan switch knob, heater control knobs and radio knobs. Remove instrument cluster bezel. Remove mounting screws from 4 corners of cluster.

2) Disconnect speedometer cable and connectors from back of cluster. Remove cluster assembly. To install, reverse removal procedure.

Removal & Installation (Starion)

1) Remove attaching screws from instrument cluster. Pull out both edges of bottom side of cluster hood, and while holding in position, pull up and out.

Fig. 2: Exploded View of Tredia Instrument Panel

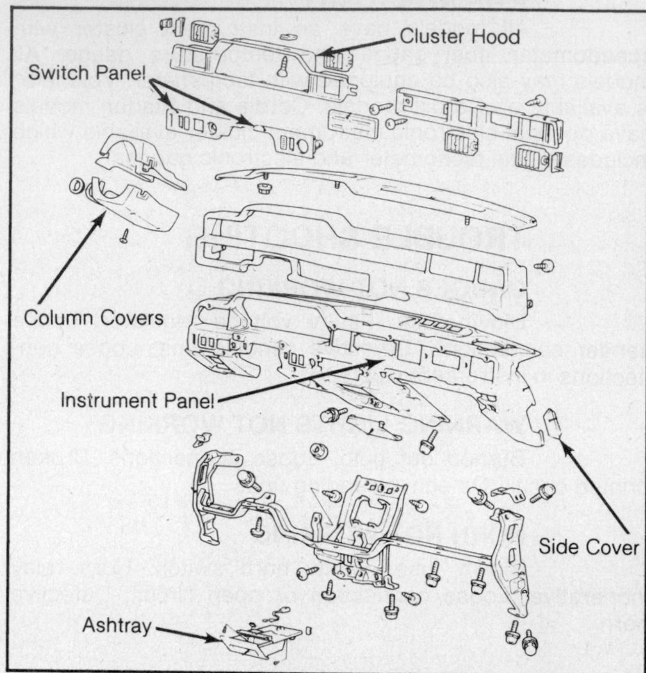
Cluster Hood
Switch Panel
Column Covers
Instrument Panel
Side Cover
Ashtray

Fig. 3: Exploded View of Montero Instrument Panel

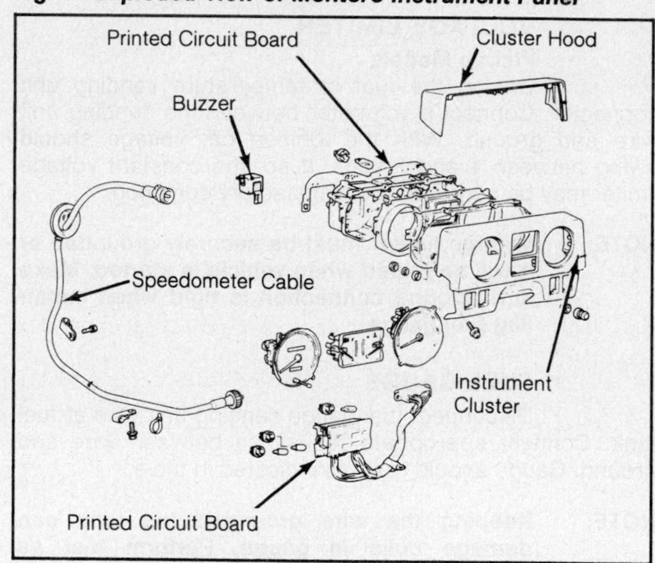
Printed Circuit Board
Cluster Hood
Buzzer
Speedometer Cable
Instrument
Cluster
Printed Circuit Board

Fig. 4: Exploded View of Pickup Instrument Panel

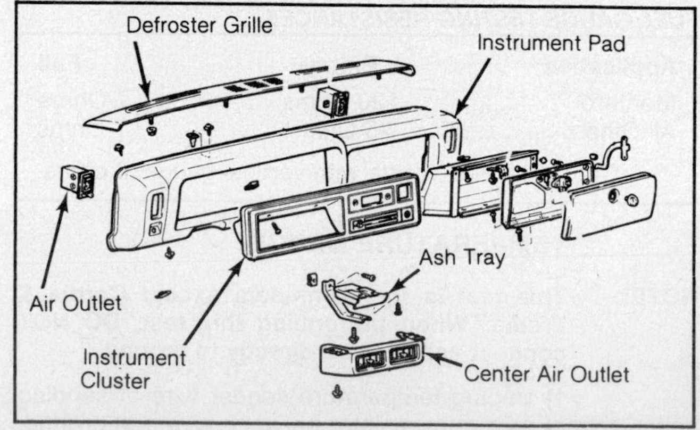
Defroster Grille
Instrument Pad
Ash Tray
Air Outlet
Instrument
Cluster
Center Air Outlet

MITSUBISHI (Cont.)

2) Disconnect cluster switch connectors on both sides of cluster hood. Remove screws from bottom of cluster. Remove nuts from upper part of cluster. Pull both sides of lower part of case up and to the rear.

3) Disconnect speedometer cable from back of instrument cluster by pushing the stopper of the plug on speedometer cable side of connection. Pull cluster out part way. Disconnect all connectors attaching cluster. Remove cluster. To install, reverse removal procedure.

Fig. 5: Exploded View of Starion Instrument Panel

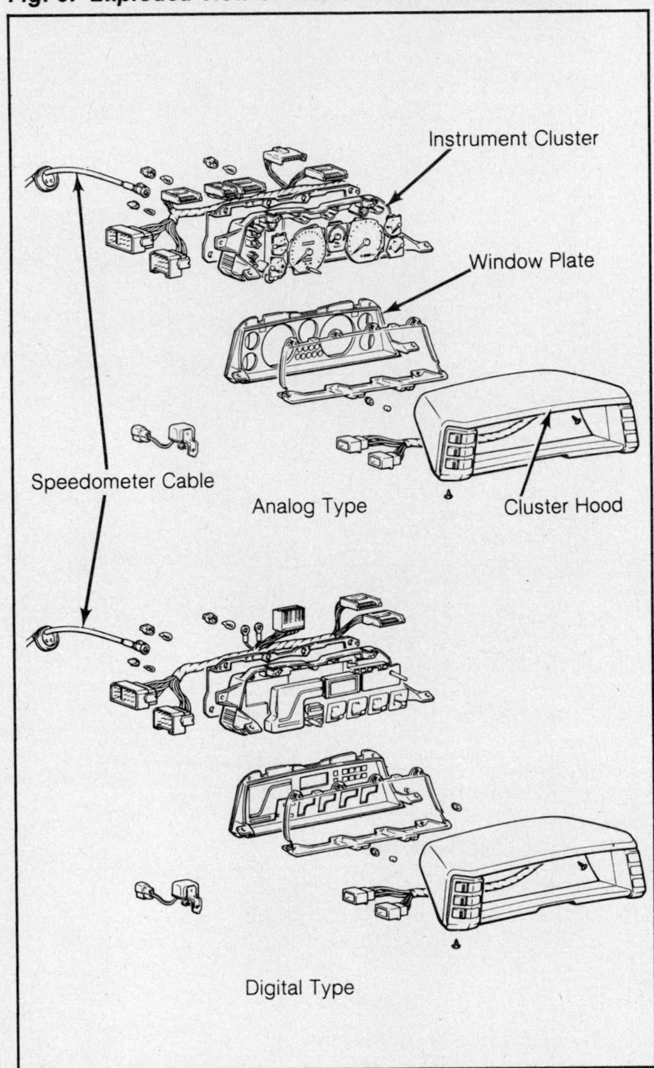

Instrument Cluster
Window Plate
Speedometer Cable
Analog Type
Cluster Hood
Digital Type

PEUGEOT

DESCRIPTION & OPERATION

All models are equipped with an instrument cluster that contains a speedometer, fuel gauge, temperature gauge and tachometer (or clock). Some models are also equipped with a voltmeter. Steering column switches control the lights, wipers, turn signals and cruise control.

The gauges use variable-resistance sending units. When resistance is high, the gauge reads low. When resistance is near zero, the gauge reads high (or full).

TESTING

GAUGES

With ignition turned on, gauge needle should move. Disconnect sending unit wire. Gauge should read low. Connect wire to ground. Gauge should read high. If gauge works as indicated, replace sending unit. If not, check wiring and/or replace gauge.

REMOVAL & INSTALLATION

INSTRUMENT CLUSTER

Removal (505)

Disconnect battery ground. Remove steering wheel. Pull instrument cluster out of place. Disconnect speedometer cable and unplug wiring. Remove cluster.

Installation

To install, reverse removal procedure.

Removal (604)

Disconnect battery ground. Pull sharply on speedometer cable to disconnect it from cluster. Pull release handle under left side of cluster and unhook right side. Unplug wiring and remove cluster. *See Fig. 1.*

Installation

To install, reverse removal procedure, making sure that cable clicks into place.

Fig. 1: Removing 604 Instrument Cluster

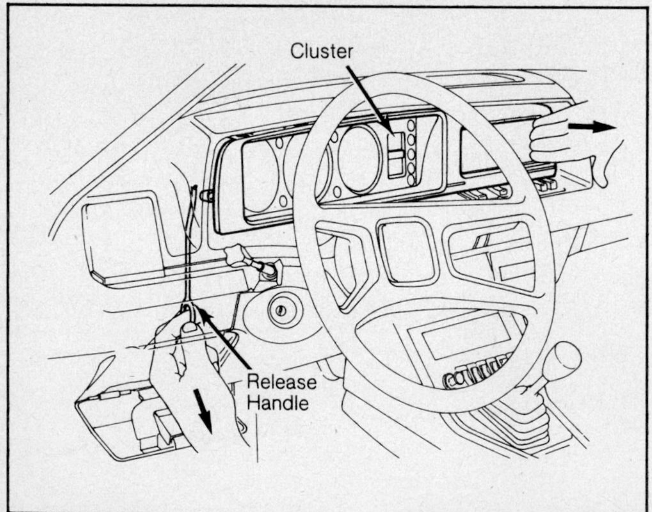
Cluster
Release
Handle

Pull release handle and unhook right side.

COMBINATION SWITCHES

Removal

Remove steering wheel. Remove column covers and unplug wiring. Remove switch screws (if equipped) and remove switch.

Installation

To install, reverse removal procedure.

PORSCHE

DESCRIPTION & OPERATION

All models have a speedometer, tachometer, fuel gauge, oil pressure gauge and clock. All 928S models also have a coolant temperature gauge and voltmeter. The 944 has coolant temperature and fuel consumption gauge. The 911SC has an oil temperature gauge and oil level gauge. The speedometer on 911SC and 928S models is electronic and uses a sensor mounted in the transaxle assembly.

TESTING

ELECTRONIC SPEEDOMETER SENDING UNIT

1) Locate connector for speedometer pickup. On 911SC models, it is beneath an access cover on the tunnel between the rear seats. Connect a test buzzer or voltmeter across the 2 wires.

2) Lift vehicle and rotate right rear wheel, while holding left rear wheel. Buzzer should sound 8 times for each 2 revolutions of the wheel. If vehicle has a limited slip differential, buzzer should sound 8 times for every 1 revolution of the rear wheel. If not, replace sending unit.

3) Make and break the wire connections (between sender and speedometer) as rapidly as possible. Speedometer needle should fluctuate. If not, replace speedometer assembly.

REMOVAL & INSTALLATION

NOTE: Procedures were not available for 911SC and 944 models.

INSTRUMENT CLUSTER

Removal

1) Disconnect battery ground. Remove steering wheel. Remove column switch, cover screws, rear wiper switch and defroster switch. Disconnect both 12-pin plugs at cluster.

2) Remove bolt and screw under cluster, then lift and tilt cluster towards rear. Remove mounting bolt on right side and remove cluster.

Installation

To install, reverse removal procedure.

STEERING COLUMN SWITCH

Removal

Remove steering wheel. Remove cover under steering column switch. Loosen switch mounting screw and cluster cover screws. Lift cluster cover, unplug wiring, and slide off column switch.

Installation

To install, reverse removal procedure.

RENAULT

DESCRIPTION

Le Car models have an instrument cluster with speedometer and fuel gauge. All warning lights are also in the cluster. The headlights, turn signals, and wipers are controlled by 3 steering column levers. The 18i can be equipped with 2 different instrument clusters.

The 18i deluxe model is also used as the standard cluster on Fuego. It has a speedometer, tachometer, temperature gauge, fuel gauge, and an oil level gauge.

In addition, turbo models have a boost gauge in the center console. Three steering column levers are used on all models to control lights, turn signals and wipers. Other switches are on the console or instrument panel.

OPERATION

OIL LEVEL SENSOR

The oil level sensor uses a probe whose resistance changes when it is in a liquid. When the ignition is on and there is no oil pressure, the sensor and a control box compute the oil level and display it on a gauge.

As soon as the oil light goes off, the sensor turns off. The sensor can be removed from the side of the crankcase. The control box is behind the instrument cluster.

REMOVAL & INSTALLATION

INSTRUMENT CLUSTER

Removal (Fuego)

1) Disconnect battery ground. Take off the 2 covers from the sides of the instrument panel. Unscrew the 2 screws from the bottom of the instrument panel cover.

2) Remove bezel from the switches on the right side. Disconnect the switches and remove the switch panel. Squeeze the instrument panel clips and and pull the instrument panel out part way. Unclip the speedometer cable and disconnect wiring.

Installation

To install, reverse removal procedure, pushing in instrument panel hard enough for the speedometer cable to be clipped in place.

Removal (Le Car)

Disconnect battery ground. Remove speedometer cable clip in engine compartment so cable will be slack. Pull off instrument cluster trim. Press side retaining clips back and pull cluster out. Remove speedometer cable and wiring plugs from cluster. Remove cluster.

Installation

To install, reverse removal procedure.

Removal (18i Standard)

Disconnect battery ground. Remove steering column covers. Remove 2 screws under lower front edge of cluster. Unplug wiring and speedometer cable. Carefully insert a screwdriver at top of cluster and pry out at top, while pushing in at the bottom of cluster. Tilt top of cluster out and remove.

Installation

Insert panel so notches pivot on the pins at each side of cluster opening. Tilt cluster back and install 2 screws. Connect wiring and speedometer cable, then install column covers.

Removal (18i Deluxe)

Disconnect battery ground. Remove trim covers from each side of cluster. Remove screw at each side. Remove cluster hood. Disconnect switches. Squeeze panel clips and pull cluster out. Unplug wiring and remove cluster.

Installation

To install, reverse removal procedure. Push cluster in hard enough to snap speedometer cable into place.

COMBINATION SWITCH

Removal (Fuego)

Disconnect battery ground. Remove steering wheel. Remove the 2 steering column half-covers. Remove fixing bolt and screw from switch. Disconnect wiring from switch and remove assembly by pulling upward.

Installation

To install, reverse removal procedure.

Removal (Le Car)

Disconnect battery ground. Remove instrument cluster screws and column lower cover. Remove 4 switch screws, unplug wiring and remove switch.

Installation

To install, reverse removal procedure.

Removal (18i)

Disconnect battery ground. Remove steering wheel and column covers. Remove holding bolt and screw. Unplug wiring and pull switch off. Light switch can be separated from the wiper/turn signal assembly by driving out the pivot pin.

Installation

To install, reverse removal procedure.

SAAB

DESCRIPTION & OPERATION

The instrument cluster contains a speedometer, tachometer, fuel gauge, temperature gauge and clock. Turbo models also have a boost gauge. The control switches are located on the steering column or the instrument panel. The ignition switch is located between the front seat on the floor.

NOTE: **The speedometer cable and most instrument cluster bulbs can be changed by removing the left speaker/defroster grille.**

REMOVAL & INSTALLATION

INSTRUMENT PANEL & HEADLIGHT SWITCH

Removal

1) Disconnect battery ground. Remove steering wheel. Remove 4 screws under edge of instrument panel. Tilt instrument panel back.

CAUTION: **The screws are different lengths. Note positions of screws as instrument panel will be damaged by installing screws in the wrong places.**

2) Remove left speaker/defroster grille. Reach in opening and unplug wiring connectors. Disconnect speedometer cable. Remove instrument panel with switches. Remove cluster screws and remove cluster.

Installation

To install, reverse removal procedure.

INSTRUMENT PANEL LOWER PAD

Removal

Remove lower steering column cover. With engine hood open, remove nut at each edge of lower pad. Remove ashtray. Remove screw inside ashtray opening and remove lower pad.

Installation

To install, reverse removal procedure.

COMBINATION SWITCH

Removal

Remove steering column lower cover. Remove screws under steering column and slide switch bracket off column. Unplug wiring and remove switch.

Installation

To install, reverse removal procedure.

Fig. 1: Dash and Instrument Panel Assembly

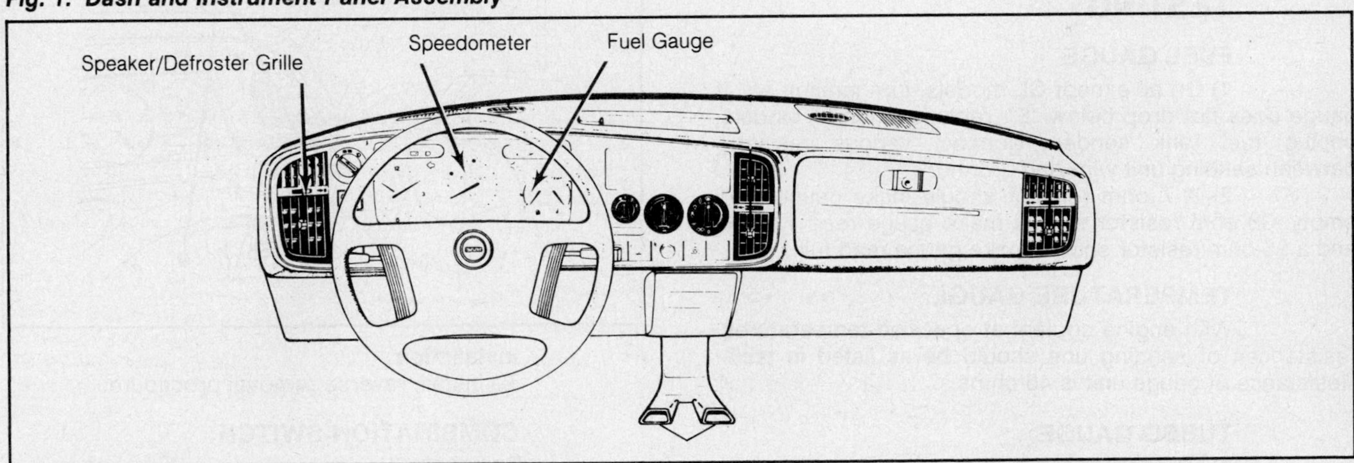
Speaker/Defroster Grille
Speedometer
Fuel Gauge

Remove left speaker/defroster grille to unplug wiring.

SUBARU

DESCRIPTION

Subaru models with conventional dashboards may be equipped with one of 2 different dashboards. Standard and DL models have a speedometer with fuel and temperature gauges. The GL models also have a tachometer, oil pressure gauge and voltmeter.

On turbocharged models, a turbo boost gauge is used to indicate boost pressure inside intake manifold. All models include a telltale graphic monitor with warning lights. The steering column lever operates the turn signals and headlight dimmer. Rotary switches on either side of the instrument cluster control the lights and wipers.

NOTE: Model can be determined by the examining seventh digit of the VIN number. A "1" indicates Standard model, "2" the DL model and "3" the GL model.

OPERATION

On all except GL models, fuel and temperature gauges use a regulated 7 volt supply to ensure accurate readings. The voltage regulator is in the fuel gauge. The oil pressure gauge does not have a regulated voltage supply and operates on 12 volts. All the gauges use variable-resistance sending units.

TESTING

FUEL GAUGE

1) On all except GL models, turn ignition off. If gauge does not drop below "E", replace it. On all models, unplug fuel tank sender. Connect various resistors between sending unit wire and ground.

2) A 7 ohm resistor should make gauge read empty, 33 ohm resistor should make gauge read 1/2 full, and a 95 ohm resistor should make gauge read full.

TEMPERATURE GAUGE

With engine coolant at specified temperatures, resistances of sending unit should be as listed in table. Resistance of gauge unit is 45 ohms.

TURBO GAUGE

1) Disconnect turbo gauge. Hook up wires of a regulated voltage supply to turbo gauge. When supplied with 1.20-1.22 volts, gauge needle should be at the "-" or no boost position.

2) When provided with 2.15-2.23 volts, gauge should register at "0" point. When provided with 3.34-3.54 volts, gauge should indicate the "+" position. If gauge responds incorrectly, replace it.

REMOVAL & INSTALLATION

INSTRUMENT CLUSTER & SWITCHES

Removal

1) Disconnect battery ground. Remove steering column bracket bolts and drop column down. Remove screws from cluster cover and remove after disconnecting any wiring connectors.

2) On GL models, screws are hidden inside vents on either side of cluster. Take out center ventilator control lever by pulling on it. On all models, remove cluster attaching screws. Pull cluster forward and disconnect wiring and speedometer cable. Remove cluster.

Fig. 1: Screw Locations for Removing GL Instrument Cluster Cover

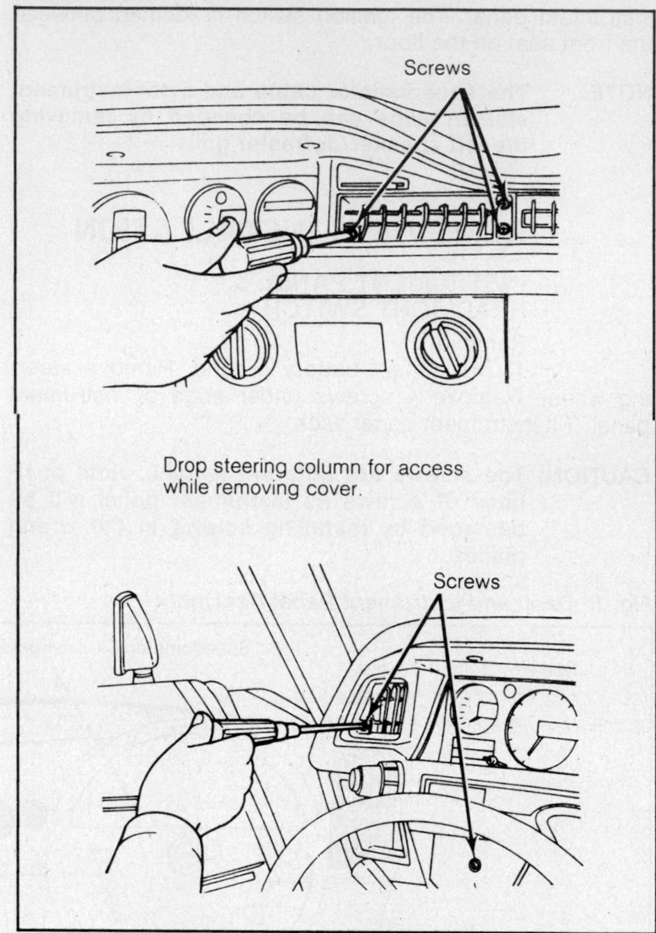
Screws
Drop steering column for access while removing cover.
Screws

Installation

To install, reverse removal procedure.

COMBINATION SWITCH

Removal

1) Remove steering column bracket bolts and pull down steering column. Remove screws from backside of steering wheel. Disconnect wires from horn switch connector.

2) Remove horn pad and steering wheel. Remove steering column cover screws. Unplug wiring connectors. Remove combination switch.

Installation

To install, reverse removal procedure.

SENDING UNIT RESISTANCES

Coolant Temperature	Ohms
GL	
109-129°F (43-54°C)	154
233-245°F (112-119°C)	18
All Except GL	
167-168°F (75-86°C)	52
212-228°F (100-109°C)	24

SUBARU ELECTRONIC INSTRUMENT CLUSTER

DESCRIPTION

Electronic instrument cluster uses 2 microcomputers. A digital computer runs the speedometer, tachometer, fuel gauge and temperature gauge. A trip computer provides driver with information on distance traveled, time and fuel remaining. Vehicle speed, coolant temperature and fuel level are are indicated using fluorescent display tubes.

OPERATION

SPEEDOMETER

Revolutions of the speedometer cable are transmitted to the speed sensor. Pulse signals corresponding to the vehicle speed are produced by photocoupler. Signals are counted by the counter circuit and memorized. This memorized data is sent to the display circuit every half second.

FUEL GAUGE

Fuel sender is provided with a constant current. When resistance of the sender slide resistor changes due to a change in fuel level, the digital signal to the microcomputer changes and indication on bar graph fluorescent display changes.

TEMPERATURE GAUGE

Temperature sender is provided with a constant current. When resistance of the sender resistor changes due to a change in temperature, the digital signal to the microcomputer changes and indication on bar graph fluorescent display changes.

TACHOMETER

Signals from the negative side of the ignition coil are counted by a counter circuit in the microcomputer. This number is memorized by the memory circuit. This data is transferred to the display circuit every .3 seconds to display engine RPM on fluorescent display tubes.

TESTING

FUEL & TEMPERATURE GAUGES

Disconnect connector from sending unit. Connect the appropriate resistor to connector wire, and ground resistor to body. Gauge should illuminate the number of segments indicated in table.

GAUGE RESISTANCE CHECKS

Resistor Used	Number of Segments Illuminated
Fuel Gauge	
7 Ohms	10
62 Ohms	5
97-101 Ohms	1-2
Temperature Gauge	
7 Ohms	10
15-19 Ohms	7-8
300 Ohms	0

TACHOMETER

Hook up a known good test tachometer to engine. If test tachometer and vehicle tachometer indication have a larger variation that specified in table, tachometer is faulty.

TACHOMETER TESTING

Test Tachometer RPM	Vehicle Tachometer RPM
500	400-600
1000	800-1200
2000	1800-2200
3000	2800-3200
4000	3700-4300
5000	4700-5300
6000	5700-6300

TRIP COMPUTER

1) The trip computer contains a test program to check for any malfunction of circuitry or display after power source has been connected. For 200 seconds after power is initially connected, all fluorescent display tubes will be illuminated.

2) Pressing the "RESET" button during the first 200 seconds switches the display tube test program to shift test program, and numbers displayed should change. Pressing "Clock", "Timer", "Trip" or "Range" button during the processing of this test should result in contents corresponding to button pressed being displayed.

3) If each display button is not pressed after the 200 second test period, trip computer will continue to display fuel quantity. With a full tank, resistance of fuel sender should be 5 ohms, and indication on trip computer should read 60-64.

4) With tank half-full, resistance should be 60 ohms and trip computer should read 27-31. With empty tank, resistance should be 105 ohms and indication on trip computer should read 0-4. Arithmetic circuitry and display tube are okay if test is correctly performed.

TOYOTA

DESCRIPTION & OPERATION

GAUGES

All models have a cluster which includes a speedometer, temperature gauge and fuel gauge. The fuel gauge may also have a low fuel warning light. Some models are equipped with a tachometer, oil pressure gauge and voltmeter. A low brake fluid warning light is used on most models.

Gauges may be either the 2-terminal, bi-metallic type or 3-terminal, coil type. Testing procedures for the 2 types vary slightly. All sending units for gauges are the variable resistance type.

SWITCHES

All models have a combination switch on the steering column. The switch controls the headlights, turn signals, wipers, hazard flashers and high beams. The switch can be removed and component switches replaced.

TESTING

FUEL GAUGE & WARNING LIGHT

1) Unplug connector at fuel tank sending unit. Connect a 3.4 watt test lamp between Yellow/Red wire and ground. Turn ignition on. Bulb should start flashing and needle should vibrate.

FUEL & TEMPERATURE GAUGE RESISTANCE

Model	Term. Conn.	Fuel (Ohms)	Temp. (Ohms)
2-Term. Gauge			
Corolla & Starlet		55	55
Land Cruiser		25	25
Pickup		25	25
Tercel			[1] 25
3-Term. Gauge			
Camry	IG-TU		86-106
	TU-E		98-120
	IG-E		184-226
	IG-FU	70-86	
	FU-E	126-154	
	IG-E	115-141	
Celica & Supra	IG-U	102	65
	UE	101	21
	IG-E	203	46
Corolla	IG-FU	102	
	FU-GE	101	
	IG-GE	203	
	IG-TU		90
	TU-GE		58
	IG-GE		248
Cressida	IG-U	83	135
	U-E	156	138
	IG-E	239	273
Tercel	IG-TU		70
	TU-GE		161
	IG-GE		231
	IG-FU	86	
	FU-GE	138	
	IG-GE	224	

[1] – Specificiation is for Yazaki gauge. Denso gauge resistance is 55 ohms.

2) Connect ohmmeter to sending unit terminal and ground. Move sender arm and check that resistance varies smoothly. Pointer of gauge should move when sender is connected to it and float arm is moved.

FUEL SENDING UNIT RESISTANCE

Model	Float Position	Ohms
Camry	Full	1.5-6.5
	Empty	79-87
Land Cruiser	Full	15-19
	Half	35-45
	Empty	111-127
All Other Models	Full	1-5
	Half	28-37
	Empty [1]	102-118

[1] – Pickup models are 92-108 ohms.

3) With gauge connector in place and ignition on, check for voltage at gauge terminals. At one terminal, 2-7 volts should be present. Check gauge resistance by measuring across terminals. Be sure ignition is off and connector unplugged.

4) To check low fuel warning light sensor, remove fuel sender from tank. Connect battery voltage to sensor terminal. Connect a 3.4 watt test lamp between body of sending unit and ground. With sensor dry, light should come on within 40 seconds. With sensor in gasoline or water, light should not come on.

TEMPERATURE GAUGE

1) Unplug connector at coolant temperature sender. Connect a 3.4 watt test lamp between wire and ground. Turn ignition on. Bulb should start flashing and needle of gauge should vibrate.

2) Connect ohmmeter between sender terminal and body of sender. Check resistance at several coolant temperature. Replace sender if inaccurate.

COOLANT TEMPERATURE SENDER RESISTANCE

Model	Temperature F° (°C)	Resistance (Ohms)
Camry	122 (50)	192-260
	176 (80)	65-89
Celica, Cressida & Supra	176 (80)	71
	212 (100)	37
Land Cruiser	122 (50)	226
	240 (115)	26
Pickup	122 (50)	154
	176 (80)	52
	212 (100)	27-28
Starlet	122 (50)	89-260
	240 (115)	24-28
Tercel		
Denso Gauge	122 (50)	189-260
	239 (115)	24-28
Yazaki Gauge	239 (115)	20-27

3) Check gauge resistance by measuring across terminals with ohmmeter. Ignition must be off and connector unplugged. Resistance should be as shown in "Fuel and Temperature Gauge Resistance" table.

4) Connect one end of test lamp to sender terminal and other end to battery voltage. With engine running, test lamp should flash. Lamp should not light when engine is stopped.

TOYOTA (Cont.)

NOTE: Bulb may come on briefly when engine is stopped, but should not remain lit.

REMOVAL & INSTALLATION

COMBINATION SWITCH

Removal

1) Disconnect battery ground. On Corolla, remove instrument cluster bezel. On all models, remove trim under steering column. Remove column covers.

2) Remove horn button and pull off steering wheel. Press in locking tabs on connector and unplug it. Remove mounting screws and combination switch.

3) Remove 2 screws and retainer on light switch. Remove nut and set screw. Be careful not to lose ball and spring from light switch lever. Note position of leads and remove leads from connector.

4) Remove wiper switch, hazard flasher switch and dimmer switch. *See Fig. 1.* Hazard flasher/turn signal switch cannot be removed on Celica.

Installation

1) Install dimmer, hazard flasher and wiper switches. Insert spring in end of arm on light switch. Install nut and screw. Use a small amount of grease to hold ball on end of switch arm, then install retainer.

2) To complete installation, reverse removal procedure.

INSTRUMENT CLUSTER

NOTE: Removal and installation procedures for Camry and Tercel were not available from manufacturer.

Removal (Celica & Supra)

Disconnect battery ground. Remove heater and radio knobs. Pry off heater bezel. Remove cluster bezel and disconnect warning light wires.

Installation

To install, reverse removal procedure

Removal (Corolla)

1) Disconnect battery ground. On sedan and station wagon models, remove cluster trim panel. Remove instrument panel attaching screws. Disconnect speedometer cable and electrical connectors. Remove instrument panel.

2) On coupe and liftback models, remove light control rheostat knob. Remove instrument cluster trim panel. Remove instrument panel attaching screws. Disconnect wiring connectors and speedometer cable. Remove instrument panel.

Installation

On all models, to install, reverse removal procedure.

Removal (Cressida)

1) Disconnect battery ground. Remove trim panel under cluster. Remove rear wiper switch, antenna switch and instrument light dimmer knob.

2) Remove cluster cover panel. Disconnect speedometer cable. Remove cluster screws and pull cluster out. Unplug wiring and remove cluster.

Installation

To install, reverse removal procedure.

Removal (Land Cruiser)

Disconnect battery ground. Remove cluster screws and pull cluster out. Disconnect speedometer cable and wiring. Remove cluster.

Installation

To install, reverse removal procedure.

Removal (Pickup)

Disconnect battery ground. Remove steering column covers. Remove 5 screws and cluster finish panel. Remove screws and pull cluster out. Disconnect wiring and speedometer cable. Remove cluster.

Installation

To install, reverse removal procedure.

Removal (Starlet)

Disconnect battery ground. Remove instrument cluster hood. Disconnect speedometer cable. Remove cluster screws, pull cluster back and unplug wiring. Remove cluster.

Installation

To install, reverse removal procedure.

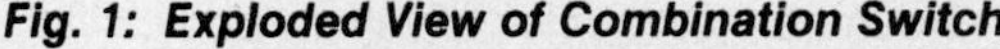

Fig. 1: Exploded View of Combination Switch

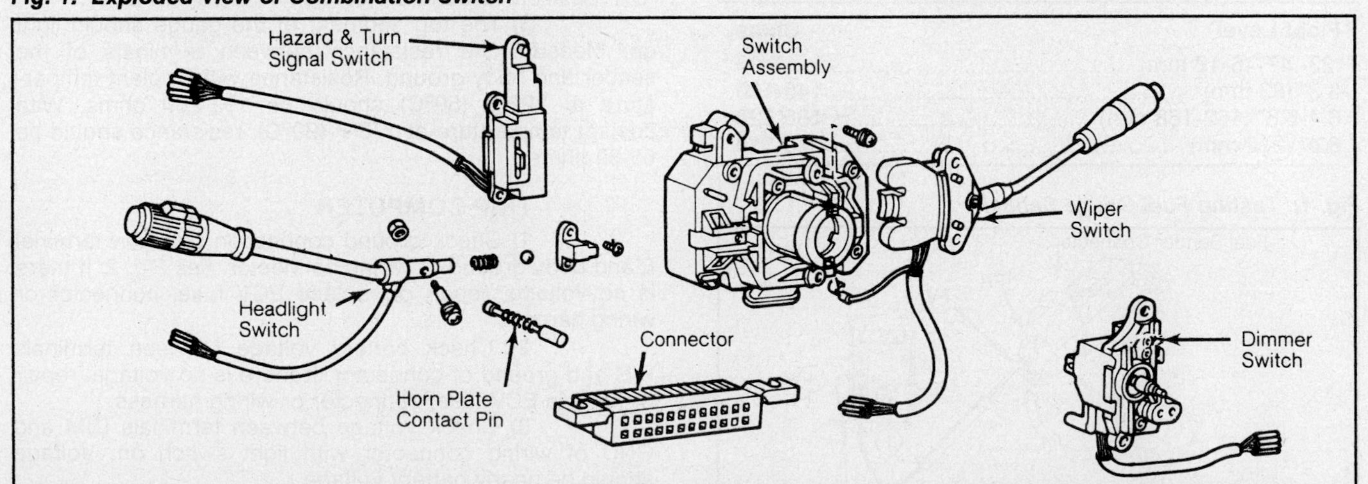
Hazard & Turn Signal Switch
Switch Assembly
Wiper Switch
Headlight Switch
Connector
Horn Plate Contact Pin
Dimmer Switch

TOYOTA ELECTRONIC INSTRUMENT CLUSTER

Cressida & Supra

DESCRIPTION

These models use an electronic instrument cluster. Cluster includes a digital display speedometer and tachometer. Fuel and temperature gauges are displayed in bar graph form. An optional trip computer may be included that can calculate fuel economy, estimated time of arrival (ETA), and distance remaining to destination.

TESTING

NOTE: When testing resistances and voltages, use a high-impedance type tester. Testing is not possible with a standard tester.

TACHOMETER

Connect a known good test tachometer to engine and start engine. Compare the tester and tachometer indications. If error is excessive, replace tachometer.

TACHOMETER TEST CHART

Test RPM	Allowable RPM Range
1000	980-1020
2000	1960-2040
3000	2940-3060
4000	3920-4080
5000	4900-5100

FUEL GAUGE SENDING UNIT

1) Disconnect the connector from the fuel sender. Check that the emergency indicator for receiver gauge and fuel warning light illuminate when the ignition switch is in the "ON" position.

2) Remove sender unit from tank. Raise and lower the float the distances indicated in chart and check resistances between terminals FR and E of connector. *See Fig. 1.*

FUEL SENDER RESISTANCES

Float Level	Ohms
.23-.47" (6-12 mm)	17-33
3.3" (83 mm)	140-180
6.4-6.3" (162-168 mm)	186-226
8.4" (212 mm)	270-310

Fig. 1: Testing Fuel Gauge Sender

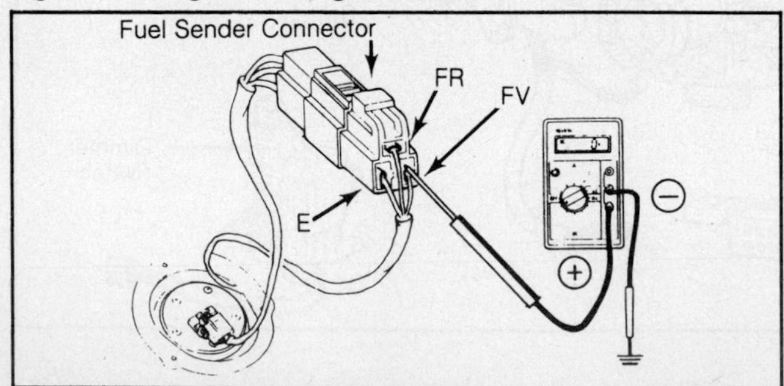
Fuel Sender Connector
FR
FV
E

3) Reconnect connector. Using ohmmeter, check ground connection between terminal E and body ground of the sender gauge connector. *See Fig. 1.* Using a voltmeter, check the power source line between terminal FV and body ground.

NOTE: Make sure not to short the FV terminal.

4) There should be 4.7-5.3 volts present. Check output signal voltage between terminal FR and body ground of the sender gauge connector. Voltages should be as indicated in chart.

FUEL SENDER OUTPUT VOLTAGES

Fuel Level	Voltage
Full	4.4-4.8
1/2 Tank	3.3
1/4 Tank	2.3-2.7
Empty	.3-.5

TEMPERATURE GAUGE

1) Inspect gauge accuracy by comparing actual coolant temperatures against indication on vehicle gauge. Measure coolant temperature with thermometer and check against gauge reading.

TEMPERATURE GAUGE TEMPERATURES

Segment Number	Coolant Temperature °F (°C)
1	Less than 122 (50)
2	122-140 (50-60)
3	140-149 (60-65)
4	149-158 (65-70)
5	158-185 (70-85)
6	185-221 (85-105)
7	221-230 (105-110)
8	230-239 (110-115)
9	239-248 (115-120)
10	More than 250 (120)

2) Warm up engine. Disconnect the connector from the temperature sender unit. Check that the indicator segment is at the lowest point with ignition switch in the "ON" position. Ground the connector to vehicle body.

3) The top segment of the gauge should light up. Measure the resistance between terminals of the sender and body ground. Resistance with coolant temperature at 122°F (50°C) should be 192-260 ohms. With coolant temperature at 176°F (80°C), resistance should be 65-89 ohms.

TRIP COMPUTER

1) Check ground connection between terminal E and body ground of wiring connector. *See Fig. 2.* If there is no voltage, repair or replace ECV fuse, connector or wiring harness.

2) Check battery voltage between terminals +B and ground of connector. If there is no voltage, repair or replace ECV fuse, connector or wiring harness.

3) Check voltage between terminals DIM and GND of wiring connector with light switch on. Voltage should be nearly battery voltage.

TOYOTA ELECTRONIC INSTRUMENT CLUSTER (Cont.)

Fig. 2: Trip Computer Wiring Connector

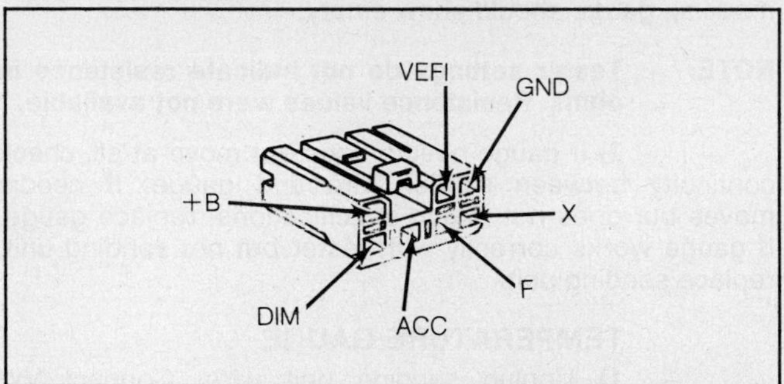
VEFI
GND
+B
X
F
DIM
ACC

4) Check voltage between terminals ACC and GND of wiring connector with ignition switch at "ACC" or "ON" position. Voltage should be nearly battery voltage.

5) Check voltage between terminals VEFI and GND of wiring connector with ignition switch in "ON" position. Voltage should be nearly battery voltage.

6) Check voltage between terminal X and body ground of wiring connector with ignition switch at "ON" position. Voltage should be nearly battery voltage.

7) Check that there is continuity between between terminals F and GND of wiring connector 4 times per revolution of magnet shaft.

VOLKSWAGEN

DESCRIPTION & OPERATION

All models have an instrument cluster that contains a speedometer, fuel gauge and temperature gauge (except Vanagon). Optional instruments include clock, tachometer, voltmeter and oil temperature gauge. The cluster has a printed circuit to power the gauges.

A voltage regulator fits onto the cluster printed circuit and controls voltage to the fuel and temperature gauges. Light emitting diodes (LEDs) are used for most warning lights. The diodes can be replaced by pulling them out of the printed circuit socket.

All models have headlight switch mounted on the dashboard. Other switches on the instrument panel control the hazard flashers, rear window defogger and options. Levers on the steering column control high beams, turn signals and wiper/washers. Most switches are retained in place by spring clips.

TESTING

NOTE: **Specific test procedures for Quantum not available from manufacturer.**

VOLTAGE REGULATOR

1) If both fuel and temperature gauges are inoperative, voltage regulator may be faulty or have a bad ground connection. If only one gauge is inoperative, regulator is not the problem.

2) Partially remove instrument cluster. Position cluster so regulator can be reached with voltmeter probes, but leave chassis harness connected. Check to make sure ground screw on regulator is tight.

3) Turn ignition on. Connect voltmeter negative lead to center terminal of regulator. Connect positive lead to each of the other terminals. Battery voltage should be present at one terminal and 9.5-10.5 volts at the other. If not, replace voltage regulator.

Fig. 1: Testing Voltage Regulator (Vanagon Shown)

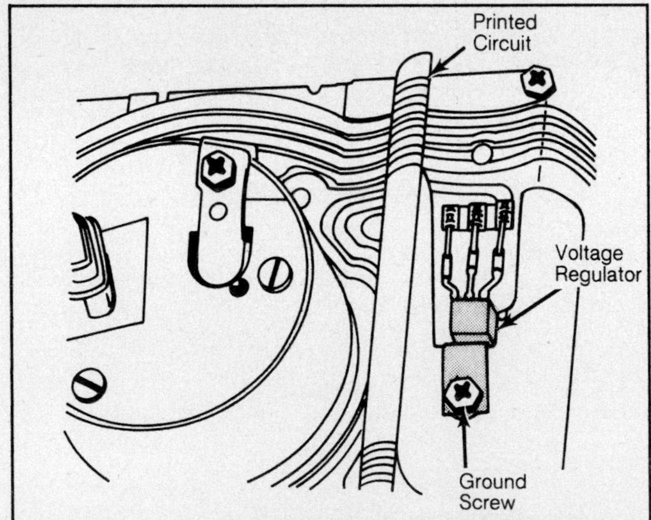
Printed
Circuit
Voltage
Regulator
Ground
Screw

Place negative lead on center terminal.

FUEL GAUGE

1) Unplug wire from fuel tank sending unit. Connect VW tester 1301 between wire and ground. Turn ignition on. With tester set at 60, gauge should show a full tank. With tester at 560 (Vanagon) or 350 (all other models), gauge should show empty.

NOTE: **Tester settings do not indicate resistance in ohms. Resistance values were not available.**

2) If gauge needle does not move at all, check continuity between sender wire and gauge. If needle moves but does not match specifications, replace gauge. If gauge works correctly with tester but not sending unit, replace sending unit.

TEMPERATURE GAUGE

1) Unplug sending unit wire. Connect VW tester 1301 between wire and ground. Turn ignition on. With tester set at 500, gauge should indicate cool. With tester at 60, gauge should indicate hot.

NOTE: **Tester settings do not indicate resistance in ohms. Resistance values were not available.**

2) If gauge needle does not move at all, check continuity between sender wire and gauge. If needle moves but does not match specifications, replace gauge. If gauge works correctly with tester but not sending unit, replace sending unit.

REMOVAL & INSTALLATION

NOTE: **Removal and installation procedures for Quantum not available.**

INSTRUMENT CLUSTER

Removal (Vanagon)

Disconnect battery ground. Reach behind cluster hood and pull back of hood up. Pull hazard flasher switch forward. Pull brake warning light housing toward front of vehicle. Remove 4 mounting screws and remove cluster.

Installation

To install, reverse removal procedure.

Removal (All Except Quantum and Vanagon)

1) Disconnect battery ground. Remove left radio speaker grille and speaker. Pull headlight switch knob out. Reach through speaker grille opening and press button on headlight switch, then pull off headlight knob.

2) Remove radio knobs. Remove 6 screws and pull off cluster bezel. Remove 4 screws and pull instrument cluster back. Disconnect speedometer cable and wiring. Remove cluster.

Installation

To install, reverse removal procedure.

COMBINATION SWITCH

Removal (All Models)

Pull off horn pad and remove steering wheel nut. Remove steering wheel. Remove column cover. Unplug wiring and remove 3 switch screws. Remove switches.

Installation

Install switches on column. Place steering wheel on column and check that clearance between wheel and turn signal switch is about 1/16-1/8" (2-4 mm). If not correct, move spacer sleeve up or down. Tighten steering wheel nut to 36 ft. lbs. (50 N.m) and replace pad.

Switches & Instrument Panels

VOLVO

DESCRIPTION & OPERATION

All models are equipped with an instrument cluster containing a speedometer and combined temperature/fuel gauge. A tachometer or clock is installed in the left side of the cluster.

Additional instruments, depending on model, are mounted to the right of the cluster. Warning lights are at the bottom of the instrument cluster.

TESTING & DIAGNOSIS

TEMPERATURE AND FUEL GAUGE

NOTE: Gauge needle for all models except 760 GLE should be horizontal plus or minus one needle width in the following tests.

Both gauges can be checked with a test resistor. Be sure terminal pins are inserted and mounting nuts are tight before testing gauges. Before replacing gauge, check voltage stabilizer, gauge and sender.

Voltage Stabilizer (All Except 760 GLE)

1) If one gauge is not working, disconnect the sending unit wire from the other (working) gauge. Connect 100 ohm, 1 watt test resistor (Volvo part number 9995158-4) between gauge and ground.

2) With ignition on, gauge pointer should be horizontal. If needle deflection is incorrect, voltage stabilizer or gauge is faulty.

Voltage Stabilizer (760 GLE)

If both the gauges give readings that are too high or give no indication at all, voltage regulator is probably faulty.

Gauges (All Except 760 GLE)

Disconnect sending unit wire from suspected gauge. Connect 100 ohm test resistor between gauge terminal and ground. Gauge needle should be horizontal. If so, sender is bad. If not, gauge is faulty.

Gauges (760 GLE)

1) Disconnect the lead at sensor. Connect 68 ohm test resistor between ground and disconnected lead. If a 75% deflection is obtained, gauge is okay but sensor is defective.

2) For all other readings, gauge or voltage regulator is defective. If problem is with voltage regulator, both gauges will not work.

Fuel Gauge Sending Unit

1) Remove sending unit from tank. Connect an ohmmeter across fuel sending unit leads. Move float up and down and check resistances.

2) For all except 760 GLE, fuel tank sender should have a variable resistance between 230-330 ohms (empty tank) and 35-45 ohms (full tank). For 760 GLE models, see chart. On all models, resistance should vary smoothly as float is moved.

760 GLE FUEL SENDING UNIT RESISTANCES

Float Position	Ohms
Primary Tank	
8.1" (206 mm)	34-38
3.5" (90 mm)	92-104
0" (0 mm)	281-311
Secondary Tank	
Top	1
Bottom	18

Temperature Sending Unit

Heat sensor in water and check resistances at temperatures listed in table. If resistances are incorrect, replace sending unit.

TEMPERATURE SENDER RESISTANCES

Application	Temperature °F (°C)	Ohms
760 GLE	140 (60)	182-252
	194 (90)	72-102
	212 (100)	56-78
All Others	122 (50)	260-310
	212 (100)	55-65

SPEEDOMETER

All Except 760 GLE

If speedometer works and odometer does not, or odometer works and speedometer does not, the unit is faulty and must be replaced. If both stop working at the same time, speedometer drive gear or cable is usually the cause.

760 GLE

If the speedometer does not record speed or distance, the lead between the rear axle sensor and speedometer may be shorted to ground or broken. Check circuit for continuity with an ohmmeter or test light. Check speed sensor resistance. Resistance should be 2750-3150 ohms.

REMOVAL & INSTALLATION

INSTRUMENT CLUSTER

Removal (All Except 760 GLE)

1) Disconnect battery ground. Remove steering column covers. Remove bracket screws and slide bracket down column. Remove cluster screws. Disconnect speedometer cable.

2) Hold speedometer from rear and press up and out until cluster comes loose. Disconnect wiring and remove cluster. To remove instruments, remove retaining screws and carefully pull off. Voltage stabilizer is removed by pulling straight out.

Installation

To install, reverse removal procedure.

Removal & Installation (760 GLE)

Remove soundproofing above the foot pedals. Remove 2 catches and screws holding panel. Press the panel forward. Remove panel. Disconnect connectors and remove instrument panel. To install, reverse removal procedure.

IGNITION SWITCH

Removal (760 GLE)

1) Remove soundproofing underneath instrument panel. Disconnect connector from ignition switch. Remove upper steering column casing and the panel around the ignition switch.

2) Loosen mounting screw for the ignition switch. Insert the key and turn to start position. Through

VOLVO (Cont.)

hole beneath the holder, press in the catch and remove ignition switch.

Installation

Insert the key and turn and depress the locking tab. Remove the key. Position the switch and release the locking tab by inserting the key. Tighten the screw. To complete installation, reverse removal procedure.

Removal (All Others)

Remove hush panel and console side panel. Disconnect switch wiring. Use a short screwdriver to remove switch.

Installation

Reverse removal procedure.

TURN SIGNAL/DIMMER SWITCH

Removal

Remove steering column covers. Remove 2 retaining screws and lift switch out. Mark wires for installation and remove wires.

Installation

To install, reverse removal procedure.

Wiper/Washer Systems

AUDI

DESCRIPTION & OPERATION

All models have 2-speed wiper systems with an intermittent cycle. The washer pump is located in the right side of the fluid reservoir. The system is controlled by the right steering column lever.

On Coupe and 4000 models, the lever operates the intermittent feature when it is moved down from the rest position. Moving the lever up selects the 2 constant speeds.

On 5000 models, moving the lever to the first position selects the intermittent cycle. The second position operates the low speed, and the third selects high speed. On all models, pulling the lever toward the wheel operates the washer pump.

REMOVAL & INSTALLATION

WIPER MOTOR

Removal

Open hood and remove cowl cover if necessary. Pry linkage rods off motor crank arm. Remove crank arm nut and 3 motor bolts. Remove crank arm from the shaft, then remove motor.

Installation

1) Install motor on bracket and connect wiring. Run motor and allow it to park. Install crank arm on Coupe and 4000 models as shown. *See Fig. 1*.

2) On 5000 models, crank arm should be pointing to right side of motor, at a right angle to motor centerline. Install crank arm and motor shaft nut, then slip linkage rods onto crank arm joint.

WIPER SWITCH

Removal & Installation (Coupe & 4000)

Remove steering wheel. Remove steering column cover. Remove 3 screws on turn signal switch. Pull turn signal switch and wiper switch from column. To install, reverse removal procedure.

Removal & Installation (5000)

1) Remove steering wheel. Insert Phillips screwdriver into slot at bottom of column cover and loosen screw.

2) Pull switch and top of cover assembly off column. Remove 2 screws inside cover to remove switch from cover. To install, reverse removal procedure.

Fig. 1: Installing Wiper Crank Arm on Coupe and 4000

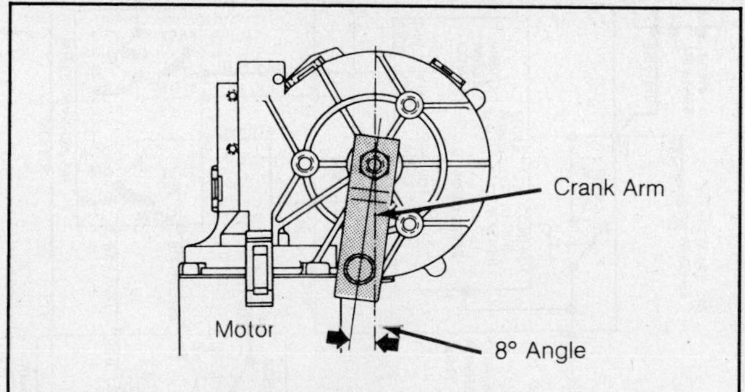
Crank Arm
Motor
8° Angle

Figure applies to Coupe and 4000 models only.

Fig. 2: Audi Coupe and 4000 Wiring Diagram

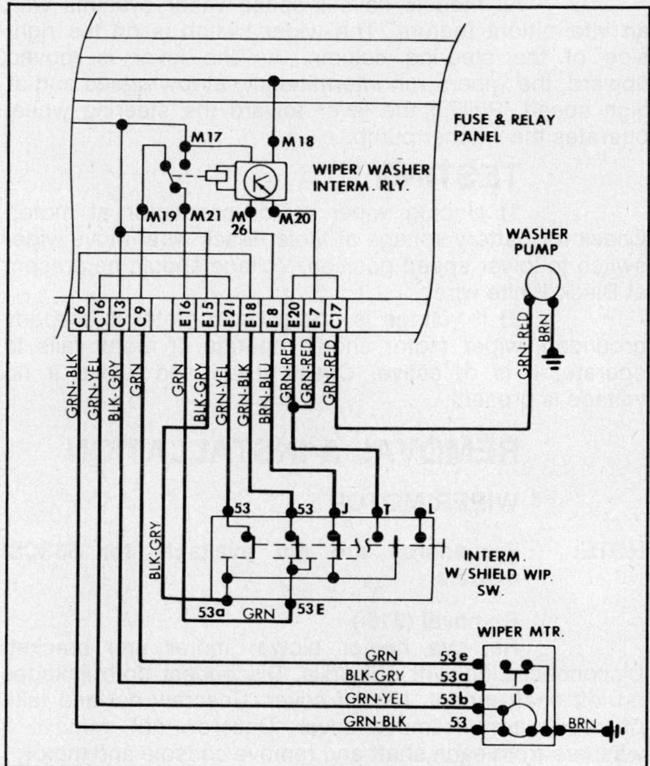
FUSE & RELAY PANEL
M17
M18
WIPER/WASHER INTERM. RLY.
M19
M21
M 26
M20
WASHER PUMP
C6
C16
C13
C9
E16
E15
E21
E18
E8
E20
E7
C17
GRN-BLK
GRN-YEL
BLK-GRY
GRN
GRN
BLK-GRY
GRN-YEL
GRN-BLK
BRN-BLU
GRN-RED
GRN-RED
GRN-RED
GRN-RED
BRN
53
53
J
T
L
BLK-GRY
INTERM. W/SHIELD WIP. SW.
53a
GRN
53E
WIPER MTR.
GRN
53e
BLK-GRY
53a
GRN-YEL
53b
GRN-BLK
53
BRN

Fig. 3: Audi 5000 Wiring Diagram

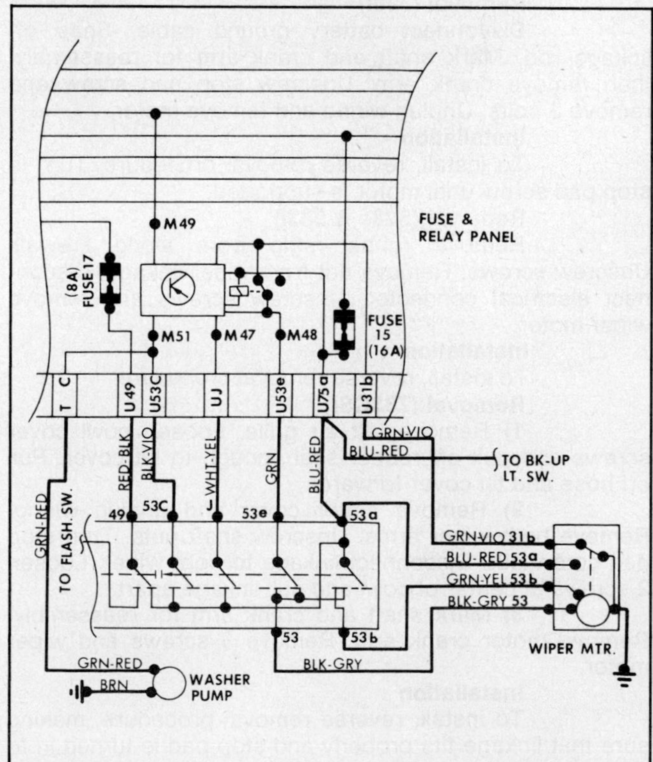
FUSE & RELAY PANEL
M49
(8A) FUSE 17
M51
M47
M48
FUSE 15 (16A)
T
C
U49
U53C
UJ
U53e
U75a
U31b
GRN-VIO
BLU-RED
TO BK-UP LT. SW.
GRN-RED
RED-BLK
BLK-VIO
WHT-YEL
GRN
BLU-RED
TO FLASH. SW.
49
53C
J
53e
53a
GRN-VIO 31b
BLU-RED 53a
GRN-YEL 53b
BLK-GRY 53
53
53b
WIPER MTR.
GRN-RED
BRN
WASHER PUMP
BLK-GRY

Wiper/Washer System

BMW

DESCRIPTION & OPERATION

All models have 2-speed wiper systems with an intermittent feature. The wiper switch is on the right side of the steering column. As the lever is moved upward, the wipers run intermittently, at low speed and at high speed. Pulling the lever toward the steering wheel operates the washer pump.

TESTING

1) Unplug wiper motor connector at motor. Check for battery voltage at Violet/Black wire. Move wiper switch to lower speed position. Voltage should be present at Black/White wire.

2) If voltage is present and motor is properly grounded, wiper motor should operate. If motor fails to operate, it is defective. Check fuses and wiring if no voltage is present.

REMOVAL & INSTALLATION

WIPER MOTOR

NOTE: Procedures are not available for 633CSi models.

Removal (318i)

Remove heater blower motor and bracket. Disconnect plug. Lift out grille. Disconnect both linkages on left shaft mount. Lift off cover. Unscrew nut and take off wiper arm. Remove cover. Unscrew nut, remove 3 washers from each shaft and remove console and motor.

Installation

To install, reverse removal procedure.

Removal (320i)

Disconnect battery ground cable. Snap off linkage rod. Mark shaft and crank arm for reassembly, then remove crank arm. Unscrew stop pad screw and remove 3 bolts. Unplug wiring and remove motor.

Installation

To install, reverse removal procedure. Turn in stop pad screw until motor is supported.

Removal (528e & 533i)

Remove rubber strip from along firewall. Unscrew screws. Remove nut from wiper linkage. Disconnect electrical connector. Unscrew screws and remove wiper motor.

Installation

To install, reverse removal procedure.

Removal (733CSi)

1) Remove left air grille. Loosen cowl cover screws and pull off rubber seal enough to lift cover. Pull off hose and tilt cover forward.

2) Remove motor cover and unplug wiring. Remove both wiper arms. Unscrew shaft nuts. Turn stop pad screw out. Disconnect linkage to right wiper. Loosen 2 screws at center of cowl and pull linkage apart.

3) Mark shaft and crank arm for reassembly. Remove motor crank arm. Remove 3 screws and wiper motor.

Installation

To install, reverse removal procedure, making sure that linkage fits properly and stop pad is turned in to support motor.

WIPER SWITCH

Removal (All Models)

Remove steering wheel. Remove lower column cover. Remove screws on right side of column and pull switch free. If equipped, disconnect vacuum lines from switch. On all models, cut off wiring clips and unplug wiring. Remove switch.

Installation

To install, reverse removal procedure.

Fig. 1: BMW 320i & 633CSi Wiring Diagram

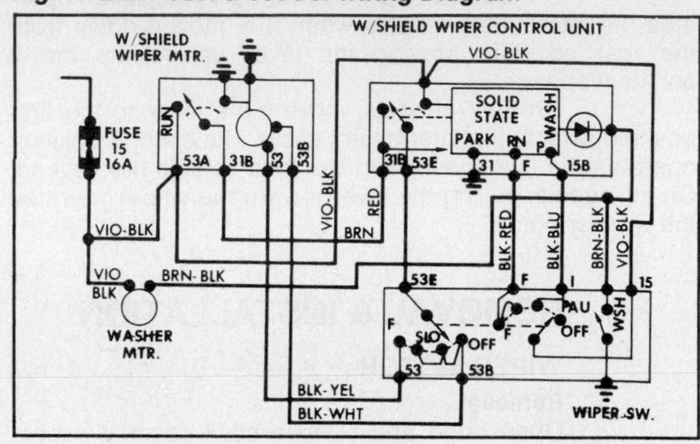
W/SHIELD WIPER CONTROL UNIT
W/SHIELD WIPER MTR.
VIO-BLK
FUSE 15 16A
RUN
53A
31B
53
53B
SOLID STATE
PARK
RN
P
WASH
31B
53E
31
F
15B
VIO-BLK
RED
BRN
BLK-RED
BLK-BLU
BRN-BLK
VIO-BLK
VIO
BLK
BRN-BLK
WASHER MTR.
53E
F
I
15
PAU
OFF
SLO
OFF
WSH
53
53B
BLK-YEL
BLK-WHT
WIPER SW.

Fig. 2: BMW 528e Wiring Diagram

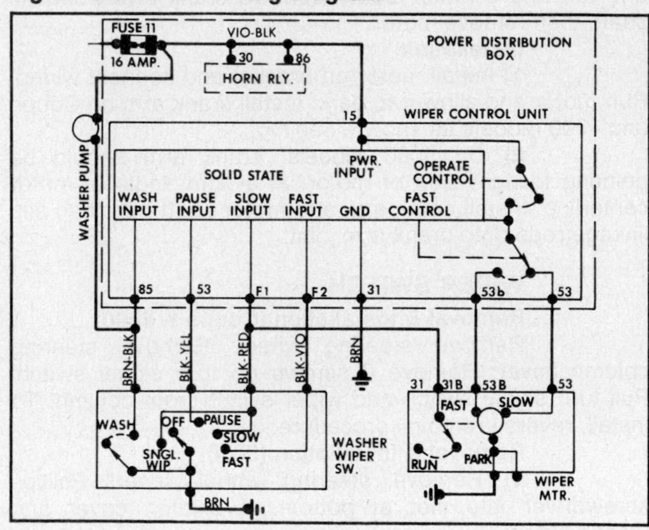
FUSE 11
16 AMP.
VIO-BLK
30
86
HORN RLY.
POWER DISTRIBUTION BOX
15
WIPER CONTROL UNIT
WASHER PUMP
SOLID STATE
PWR. INPUT
OPERATE CONTROL
WASH INPUT
PAUSE INPUT
SLOW INPUT
FAST INPUT
GND
FAST CONTROL
85
53
F1
F2
31
53b
53
BRN-BLK
BLK-YEL
BLK-RED
BLK-VIO
BRN
31
31B
53B
53
FAST
SLOW
WASH
OFF
PAUSE
SLOW
SNGL. WIP
FAST
WASHER WIPER SW.
RUN
PARK
WIPER MTR.
BRN

Fig. 3: BMW 733i Wiring Diagram

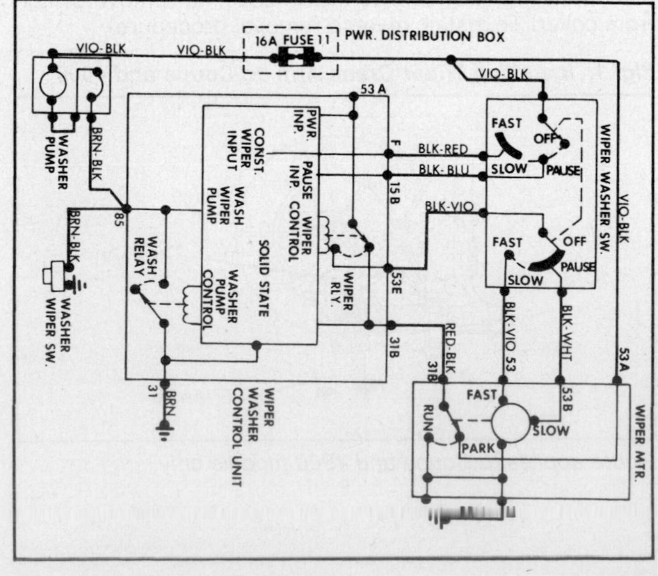
16A FUSE 11
PWR. DISTRIBUTION BOX
VIO-BLK
VIO-BLK
VIO-BLK
53 A
WASHER PUMP
BRN-BLK
PWR. INP.
CONST. WIPER INPUT
PAUSE INP.
WIPER CONTROL
F
15B
BLK-RED
BLK-BLU
BLK-VIO
FAST
OFF
SLOW
PAUSE
WIPER WASHER SW.
VIO-BLK
85
BRN-BLK
WASH RELAY
WASH WIPER PUMP
WASHER PUMP CONTROL
SOLID STATE
WIPER RLY.
53E
FAST
OFF
PAUSE
SLOW
WASHER WIPER SW.
31B
RED-BLK
BLK-VIO 53
BLK-WHT
53A
31B
FAST
53B
RUN
SLOW
PARK
WIPER MTR.
31
BRN
WIPER WASHER CONTROL UNIT

CHRYSLER CORP. IMPORTS

Challenger, Colt, Colt Pickup, Ram-50 Pickup & Sapporo

DESCRIPTION

All models have a 2-speed wiper motor. The washer system uses an electric pump mounted under the fluid reservoir. Challenger and Sapporo models have an intermittent wiper system.

Colt models may be equipped with a rear wiper/washer. On these models, only one washer fluid reservoir is used, but a separate pump under the reservoir is provided for the rear washer.

OPERATION

The wiper systems are operated by a dash-mounted switch on Colt and Pickups, and by a column-mounted switch on Challenger and Sapporo. The intermittent system cycles the washers every 6 seconds. If the washer switch on this system is held for about 5 seconds, the wipers make 2-4 sweeps and turn off.

TESTING

FRONT WIPER MOTOR

Colt

Run wiper motor against a rated load of 1 ft. lb. (.72 N.m). Check number of revolutions per minute. Current value should be correct for both low and high speeds. Make sure wiper motor park positioning is correct. *See Fig. 1.*

COLT WIPER MOTOR TEST

Selected Speed	Motor RPM	Current (Amps)
Low	42-52	Less Than 3.0
High	62-76	Less Than 4.0

Fig. 1: Colt Wiper Motor Park Position

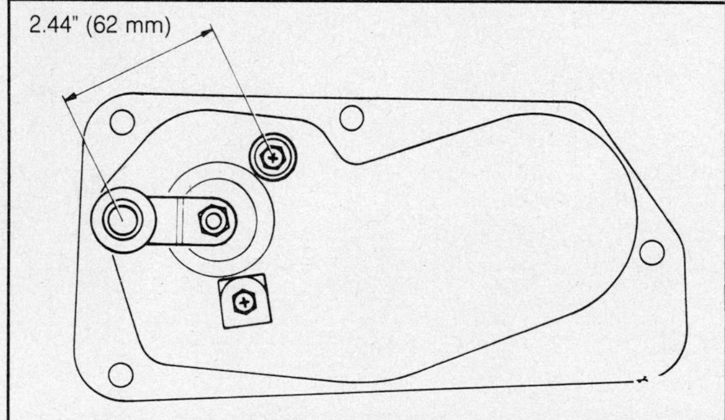
2.44" (62 mm)

Colt Pickup & Ram-50 Pickup

1) If wiper motor operates, perform the following test. Connect an ammeter on the DC 10-amp range to connector Blue/White wire and battery position terminal with wiper motor assembly as a separate unit. Connect a jumper wire from body ground to Blue/Orange wire and then to Blue/Black wire.

2) Run the motor under no load and test for number of revolutions per minute. If the current value is less than 3 amps in both high and low positions, motor is okay. At low speed, motor should turn at 45 RPM, and at high speed at 70 RPM.

Challenger & Sapporo

Raise wiper arms so they do not touch windshield. Unplug motor connector. Confirm that wiper motor operates on low speed when voltage from battery is connected between number 1 and positive terminals. Wiper should operate on high speed when voltage is supplied between number 2 and positive terminals. *See Fig. 2.*

Fig. 2: Challenger and Sapporo Wiper Motor Connector Terminal Locations

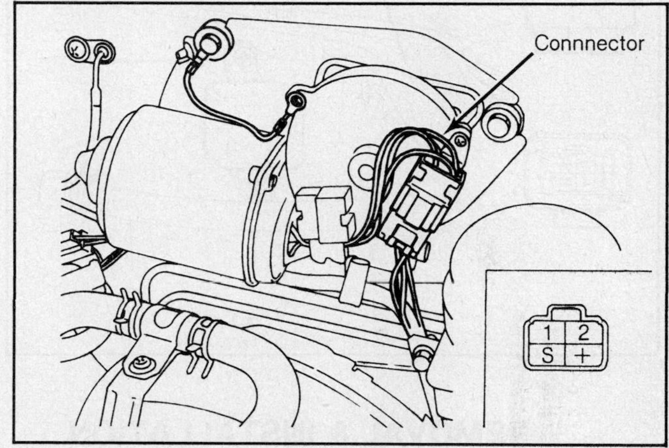
Connnector
1
2
S
+

REAR WIPER MOTOR

Raise wiper arm so motor can operate without load. Connect battery voltage to the Blue wire terminal and connect the Blue/Red wire terminal to ground. Replace motor if it does not run smoothly.

INTERMITTENT RELAY

1) If wipers do not park properly during intermittent operation, or if wipers operate continuously when switch is in intermittent position, check voltage at terminal 3 of the relay to see if voltage oscillates from 0 to 12 volts. Voltage should be 12 volts when wipers are stopped and 0 volts when wipers are in motion. If not, replace relay.

2) If wipers do not operate at all when switch is in intermittent position, connect positive terminal of a voltmeter to number 1 terminal of relay connector. Connect negative terminal of voltmeter to the terminal indicated in table. If voltages are not as indicated, replace relay.

RELAY VOLTAGES

Terminal Number	Voltage
4	12
6	0
3	0

3) If wipers do not operate when washer switch is turned on, connect the positive lead of voltmeter to to the number 1 terminal of the relay. Connect negative terminal of voltmeter to terminal 4. Twelve volts should be indicated. Connect negative terminal of voltmeter to terminal 5. Zero volts should be indicated. If not, replace relay.

CHRYSLER CORP. IMPORTS (Cont.)

4) If wipers do not operate when washer switch is turned on, connect the positive lead of voltmeter to to the number 3 terminal of the relay. There should be battery voltage for 0.6-1.5 seconds. Voltage should drop to zero while wipers operate, and return to 12 volts when wipers stop. If readings are not correct, replace relay.

Fig. 3: Intermittent Wiper Relay Terminal Identification

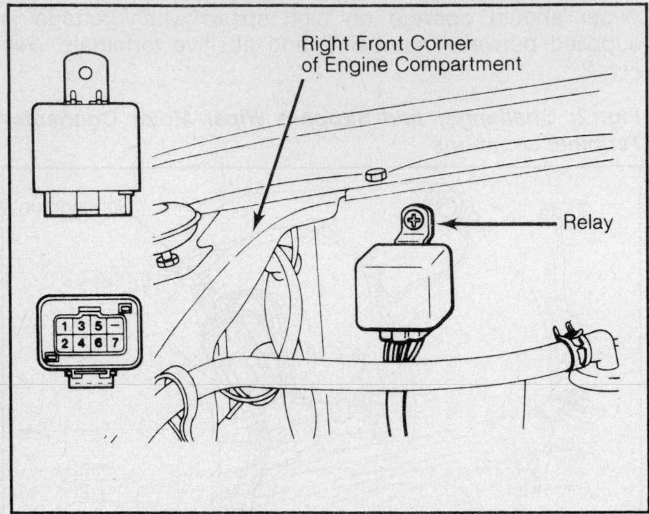

Right Front Corner
of Engine Compartment
Relay
1 3 5 —
2 4 6 7

REMOVAL & INSTALLATION

FRONT WIPER MOTOR

CAUTION: Do not separate crankshaft and motor unless necessary. Be sure to scribe matching marks on shaft and crank arm before disassembly.

Removal (Colt Pickup & Ram-50 Pickup)

1) Remove wiper arm. Remove shaft nut and push shaft into body. Remove wiper access panel on right side of firewall. Remove bolts attaching motor bracket to body and pull wiper motor outward.

2) Disconnect the wiper motor and linkage so that motor shaft and linkage are positioned at right angles to each other. Linkage should be removed while holding shaft.

Installation

To install, reverse removal procedure, making sure stop position of wiper blades is correct.

Removal (Challenger & Sapporo)

1) Lift wiper arm cover and remove shaft nut. Remove wiper arm, seal and nut. Push shaft into body. Unplug motor wiring and remove mounting bolts.

2) Pull motor out and snap free from linkage. Remove motor and linkage. Remove access cover to pull linkage out.

Installation

To install, reverse removal procedure, ensuring that motor is grounded and that wiper blades stop in correct position.

Removal (Colt)

Disconnect wiring at motor. Remove motor bolts and snap motor free from linkage. Remove motor.

Installation

To install, reverse removal procedure.

REAR WIPER MOTOR

Removal (Colt)

Remove wiper arm and shaft nut. Open tailgate and remove inner trim panel. Unplug wiring and remove motor bolts. Remove motor.

Installation

To install, reverse removal procedure.

WIPER SWITCH

NOTE: Procedures were not available for switch removal on Colt Pickup and Ram-50 Pickup.

Removal (Challenger & Sapporo)

Disconnect battery ground cable. Remove steering wheel. Tilt column to lowest position and remove column cover. Remove column switch screws. Unplug wiring, remove wiring clip and remove switch.

Installation

To install, reverse removal procedure, making sure that cancel cam pins are aligned with holes in back of steering wheel.

Removal (Colt)

Remove instrument cluster panel. Pull out the wiper switch knob and remove the knob. Remove the wiper switch attaching screw and connector attaching screw and remove the switch from the cluster panel.

Installation

To install, reverse removal procedure.

Wiper/Washer Systems

DATSUN/NISSAN

Maxima, Pickup, Pulsar, Sentra & Stanza, 200SX, 280ZX

DESCRIPTION & OPERATION

All models are equipped with either 2-speed or intermittent wipers. An optional variable intermittent wiper system may also be used. In the variable system, wiper operation may be varied from 4 to 12 seconds.

Hatchback and station wagon models have a rear wiper/washer system, operated by a dashboard mounted switch. All front wiper/washer systems are operated by a steering column lever.

WIPER MOTOR

All wiper motors include an integral park switch inside the motor housing. The motor cover can be removed and the switch adjusted if wipers do not park correctly. Some models have a circuit breaker (mounted externally) to protect the wiper motor.

INTERMITTENT AMPLIFIER

All models except Maxima use an intermittent amplifier to control the delayed wiper cycle. The amplifier is a solid-state unit which interrupts current flow to the motor. The time delay is either fixed or adjustable with a knob at the end of the wiper stalk.

All Maxima models have a Time Control Unit which controls the delayed wiper cycle. This unit also operates the clock, turn and hazard flashers, seat belt chimes and other circuits.

WASHER

All models have windshield washer systems. A separate pump is used for the rear washer. A common reservoir is used for both washer systems.

DATSUN/NISSAN WIPER SYSTEM COMPONENT LOCATIONS

Model & Component	Connector	Location
200SX		
Intermittent Amplifier	8-Pin	Rear of relay bracket at right front corner engine compartment
Ignition/Accessory Relay	6-Pin & 1-Pin	Right kick panel
Circuit Breaker	2-Wire	Wiper motor connector at cowl
Rear Washer Motor	2-Pin	Right front shock tower
280ZX		
Intermittent Amplifier	6-Pin	Brake Pedal Bracket
Accessory Relay	5-Pin	Right kick panel, top rear
Rear Washer Motor	2-Wire	Left front shock tower
Maxima		
Time Control Unit	8-Pin & 11-Pin	Right kick panel at top
Wiper Relay	5-Pin	Rear outside corner of relay bracket at right front corner engine compartment
Accessory Relay	4-Pin	Front outside corner of relay bracket
Pickup		
Intermittent Amplifier	5-Pin	Steering column bracket
Pulsar		
Intermittent Amplifier	7-Pin	Firewall next to wiper motor
Rear Wiper/Washer Motor	4-Pin	Right rear of panel of hatch area
Sentra		
Intermittent Amplifier	7-Pin	Firewall behind left front shock tower
	6-Pin	Firewall behind left front shock tower
Stanza		
Intermittent Amplifier	7-Pin	Firewall behind left front shock tower
Circuit Breaker		Top of wiper motor plug connector

DATSUN/NISSAN (Cont.)

Fig. 1: Typical Datsun/Nissan Wiper/Washer Components

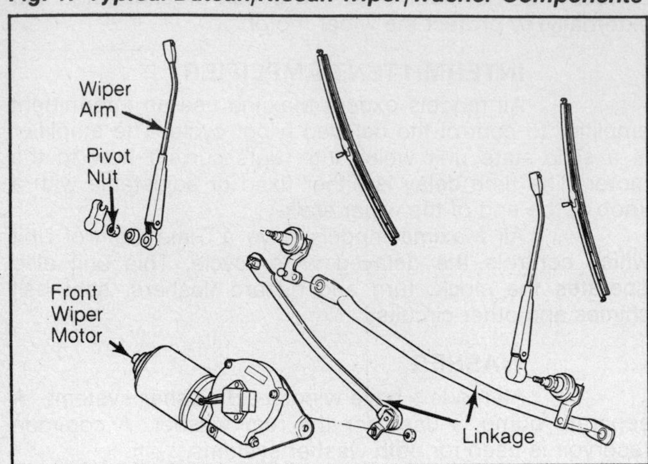
Wiper Arm
Pivot Nut
Front Wiper Motor
Linkage

TESTING

NOTE: Testing procedures for Pulsar models were not available from manufacturer.

FRONT WIPER MOTOR

1) Motor can be tested on the car. Unplug connector and use ohmmeter to check continuity with motor stopped. Using jumper wires, test both motor speeds by applying voltage to terminals shown in "Front Wiper Motor Testing" chart.

2) Finally, check park switch operation by connecting ohmmeter across park terminals while motor is running. Switch should open and close. *See Fig. 2.*

REAR WIPER MOTOR

1) Motor can be tested on the car. Unplug wiring and use ohmmeter to check continuity with motor stopped. Use jumper wires to operate motor by applying voltage to terminals shown in "Rear Wiper Motor Testing" chart.

2) Check park switch operation by connecting ohmmeter across park terminals while motor is running. Switch should open and close. *See Fig. 3.*

FRONT WIPER MOTOR TESTING

Model	Continuity (Motor Off)	Slow Speed Connections	High Speed Connections	Park Switch (On-Off with Motor Running)
200SX	B & L B & H	12v@B L Gnd	12@B H Gnd	P & E
280ZX	1 & 4, 1 & 5	12v@1 4 Gnd	12v@1 5 Gnd	2 & 3, 2 & 6, 7 & 8
Maxima, Sentra & Stanza	B & L B & H	12v@B L Gnd	12v@B H Gnd	P & E
Pickup	1 & 4 1 & 5	12v@1 4 Gnd	12v@1 5 Gnd	2 & 3
Pulsar	12 & 13	12v@13 16 Gnd	12v@15 16 Gnd	....

REAR WIPER MOTOR TESTING

Model	Continuity (Motor Off)	Motor Connections	Park Switch (On-Off with Motor Running)
200SX & Maxima	B & S	12v@B S Gnd	P & E
280ZX	1 & 4	12v@1 4 Gnd	2 & 3, 2 & 4
Pulsar	1 & 2	12v@1 4 Gnd	....
Sentra & Stanza	Red/Blue & Blue/Black	12v@Red/Blue Blue/Black Gnd	Blue/White & Black

DATSUN/NISSAN (Cont.)

Fig. 2: Terminal Identification for Testing Front Wiper Motor

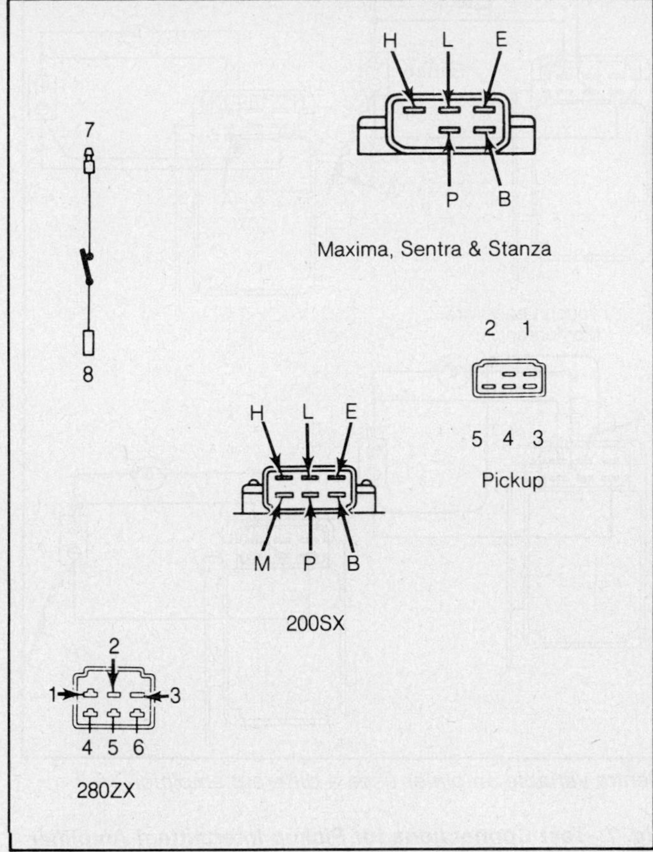
H L E
7
8
P B
Maxima, Sentra & Stanza
8
2 1
5 4 3
Pickup
H L E
M P B
200SX
2
1
3
4 5 6
280ZX

INTERMITTENT AMPLIFIER

1) Remove amplifier from vehicle or position so jumper wires can be connected to terminals. Use care to prevent improper connections since amplifier can be ruined.

2) Connect test lamp and battery as shown in *Figs. 4, 5, 6 & 7.* Correct test procedures must be used for the vehicle being tested.

200SX & 280ZX

Connect jumper wires to amplifier. *See Fig. 4.* When wire "A" is connected, test lamp should come on. Disconnect wire "B". Test lamp should go off, then come back on after a few seconds. If not, replace amplifier.

Pulsar, Sentra & Stanza Variable Intermittent System

Connect jumper wires to amplifier. *See Fig. 5.* When wire "A" is connected, test lamp should come on. Disconnect wire "B". Test lamp should go off, then come back on after a few seconds. If not, replace amplifier.

Sentra Intermittent

Connect test leads to amplifier. *See Fig. 6.* Test lamp must come on when negative lead wire "A" is connected. Momentarily connect lead wire "A" to top center terminal and then disconnect. Test lamp must come on in a few seconds. Replace amplifier if it fails any test.

Pickup

Connect jumper wires to amplifier. *See Fig. 7.* Test lamp should come on when wire is connected to pin 3. Disconnect jumper wire from pin 2. Test lamp should go off, then come back on after 6 seconds. If not, replace amplifier.

TIME CONTROL UNIT

NOTE: **Time Control Unit operates many systems in vehicle. The following tests only check the circuits that control wiper delay operation.**

The Time Control Unit is used on Maxima models only. All tests are made using a voltmeter. Insert voltmeter probes into the REAR of connectors while they are still plugged into control unit. Ensure ignition key is in correct position while testing each circuit. Perform tests in order listed.

Power Circuit

Connect negative lead of voltmeter to pin 2 and positive lead to pin 26. Battery voltage should be present with ignition in "ACC" position. If not, check wiring.

Fig. 3: Terminal Identification for Testing Rear Wiper Motor

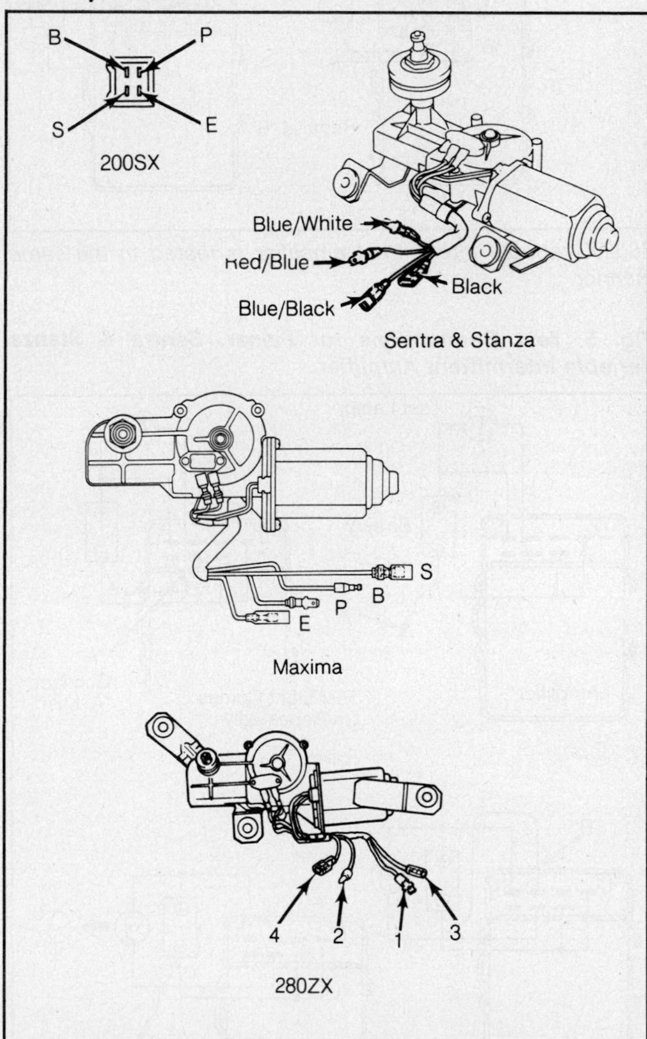
B
P
S
E
200SX
Blue/White
Red/Blue
Black
Blue/Black
Sentra & Stanza
S
B
P
E
Maxima
4
2
1
3
280ZX

Wiper/Washer Systems

DATSUN/NISSAN (Cont.)

Fig. 4: Test Connections for 200SX & 280ZX Intermittent Amplifier

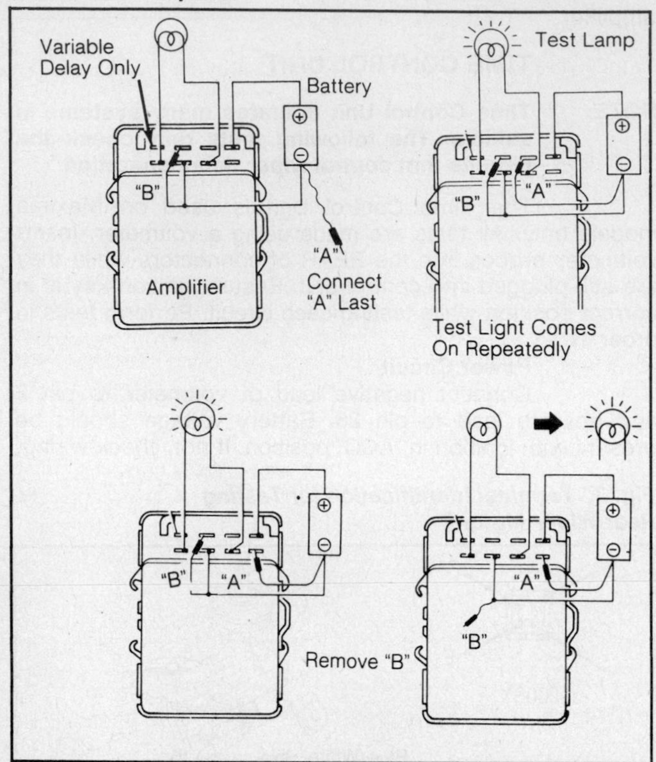
Variable
Delay Only
Battery
Test Lamp
"B"
"A"
"B"
"A"
Connect
"A" Last
Amplifier
Test Light Comes
On Repeatedly
"B"
"A"
"A"
"B"
Remove "B"

280ZX variable intermittent amplifier is tested in the same manner.

Fig. 5: Test Connections for Pulsar, Sentra & Stanza Variable Intermittent Amplifier

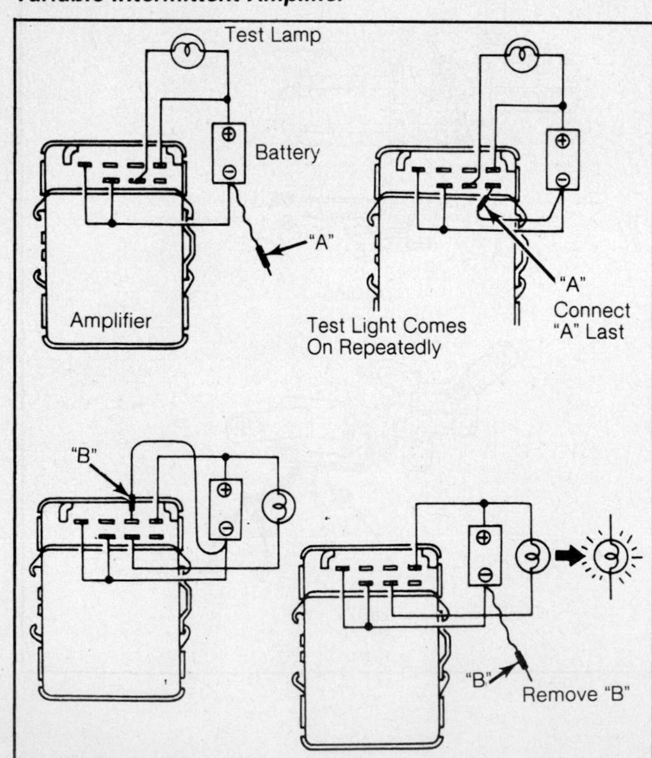
Test Lamp
Battery
"A"
Amplifier
Test Light Comes
On Repeatedly
"A"
Connect
"A" Last
"B"
"B"
Remove "B"

Sentra intermittent system uses a different amplifier.

Fig. 6: Test Connections for Sentra Intermittent Amplifier

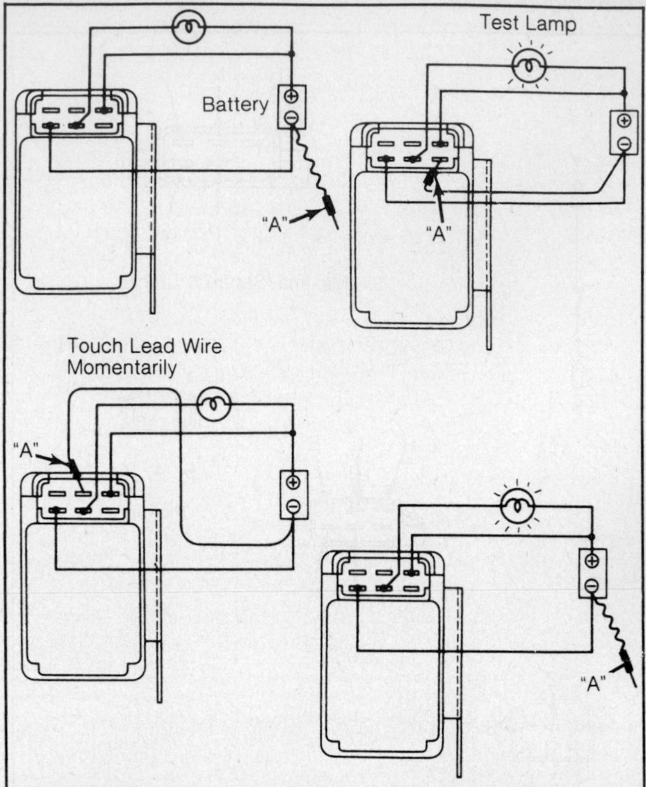
Test Lamp
Battery
"A"
"A"
Touch Lead Wire
Momentarily
"A"
"A"

Sentra variable amplifier uses a different amplifier.

Fig. 7: Test Connections for Pickup Intermittent Amplifier

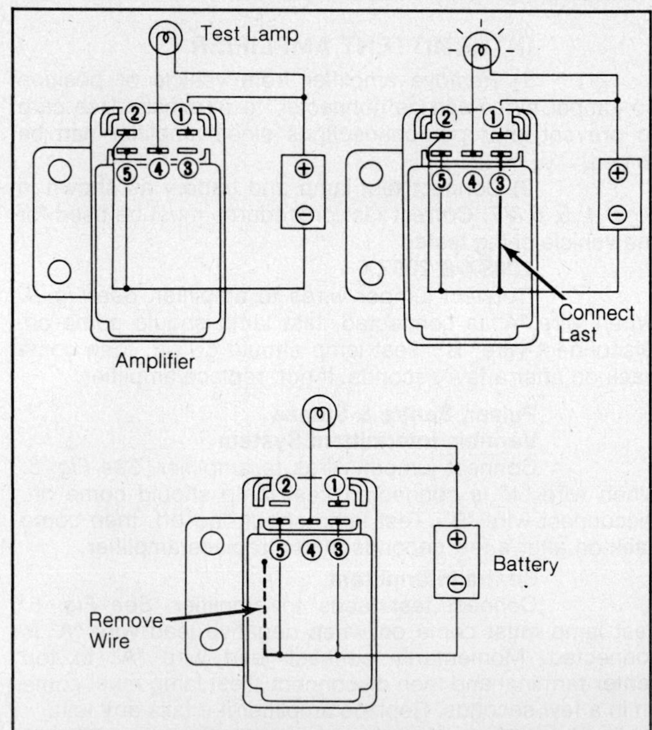
Test Lamp
Connect
Last
Amplifier
Battery
Remove
Wire

Variable intermittent amplifier is tested in the same manner.

DATSUN/NISSAN (Cont.)

Intermittent Circuit

1) Connect negative lead of voltmeter to pin 2 and positive lead to pin 12. Turn ignition "OFF" and set wiper switch to "OFF". Battery voltage should be present. Turn wiper switch to "INT". No voltage should be read. If readings are incorrect, check harness and wiper switch.

2) Connect negative lead of voltmeter to pin 15 and positive lead to pin 1. Turn ignition to "ACC" and wiper switch to "INT". Voltage will vary from 0-12v seconds.

3) Replace time control unit if it does not operate as described. If voltage does not vary, check wiring harness and wiper relay.

4) Connect negative lead of voltmeter to pin 2 and positive lead to pin 16. Turn ignition to "ACC" and wiper switch "ON". Rotate delay adjustment knob at end of wiper lever. Voltage should vary from 0 (short delay) to 8 volts (long delay).

5) If wiper delay cannot be adjusted, but voltage is as described, replace time control unit. If voltage readings are incorrect, check harness and wiper switch.

Fig. 8: Maxima Time Control Unit Connector Pin Locations

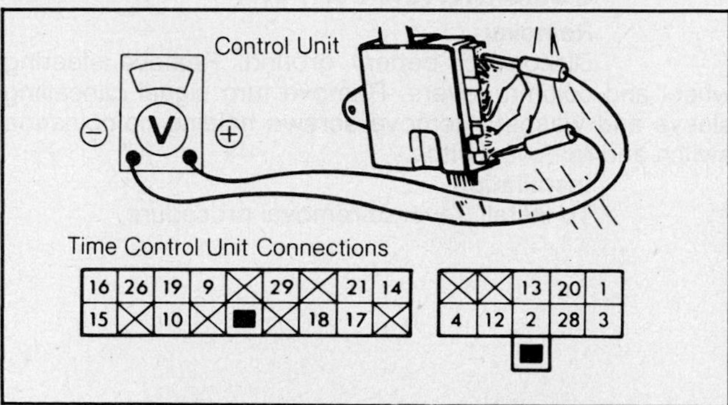
Control Unit
V
Time Control Unit Connections
16 26 19 9 29 21 14
15 10 18 17
13 20 1
4 12 2 28 3

Washer Circuit

1) Connect negative voltmeter lead to pin 2 and positive lead to pin 14. Turn ignition to "ACC" and pull lever to washer position.

2) Battery voltage should be present with washer off, and no voltage present with washer lever pulled. If not, check washer switch and wiring.

3) Connect negative lead of voltmeter to pin 2 and positive lead to pin 26. Battery voltage should be present with ignition in "ACC" position. If not, check wiring.

4) Connect negative lead of voltmeter to pin 15 and positive lead to pin 1. Rotate lever switch fully counterclockwise, with ignition switch at "ACC" position.

5) Battery voltage should be present briefly every 3 seconds. If not, replace amplifier. If amplifier tests okay, problem is in wiper relay.

WIPER RELAY

The wiper relay is used on Maxima models only. Continuity should be present across terminals 3 and 5. With battery voltage applied to 1 and 2, continuity should be present across terminals 3 and 4. *See Fig. 9.*

REMOVAL & INSTALLATION

FRONT WIPER MOTOR & LINKAGE

Removal

1) Disconnect battery ground cable and motor wiring. Remove motor bolts. Remove nut and clip holding linkage arm to motor shaft. Remove motor.

Fig. 9: Wiper Relay Terminal Identification for Testing

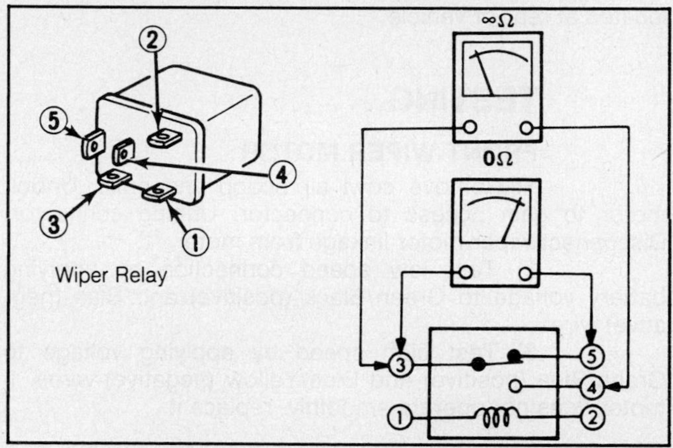
∞Ω
0Ω
Wiper Relay
1
2
3
4
5

2) Remove wiper arm cap and nut. Remove wiper arm and wiper shaft nut. Remove inspection cover (if equipped) and remove linkage.

Installation

To install, reverse removal procedure. Install arms so parked position is .8" (20 mm) from bottom of windshield.

REAR WIPER MOTOR

Removal

Remove wiper shaft nut and wiper arm. Open hatch or tailgate and remove inner panel. Disconnect wiring from motor. Remove wiper motor.

Installation

To install, reverse removal procedure. Install wiper arm so blade is .6-.8" (15-20 mm) from edge of glass when wiper is parked.

COMBINATION SWITCH

Removal

Remove steering wheel pad and steering wheel. Disconnect all wiring. Remove retaining screw and pull switch off column.

Installation

To install, reverse removal procedure. Align tab on switch with hole in column.

Wiper/Washer Systems

HONDA

DESCRIPTION & OPERATION

All models are equipped with a 2-speed front wiper motor with intermittent feature. The washer system uses a small electric pump to spray fluid on the windshield. The wiper switch is part of the combination switch on the steering column.

A rear wiper/washer system is used on Accord and some Civic models. A dashboard switch controls the rear wiper and washer pump. The pump and reservoir are located at rear of vehicle.

TESTING

FRONT WIPER MOTOR

1) Remove cowl air scoop and grille. Unbolt motor to gain access to connector. Unplug connector. Disconnect wiper motor linkage from motor.

2) Test low speed connection by applying battery voltage to Green/Black (positive) and Blue (negative) wires.

3) Test high speed by applying voltage to Green/Blue (positive) and Blue/Yellow (negative) wires. If motor does not operate smoothly, replace it.

REAR WIPER MOTOR

Remove rear wiper motor. Test the wiper motor by applying battery voltage to Green/Black (negative) and Green (positive) wires in motor connector. If motor does not run smoothly, replace it.

WASHER PUMP MOTOR

Connect battery voltage accross the pump terminals. Washer pump should operate and spray from outlet. If not, repair fluid lines or replace pump.

REMOVAL & INSTALLATION

FRONT WIPER MOTOR

Removal

Remove cap on wiper arm. Remove nut and pull arm off. Remove pivot cap, nut, washer and cushion. Remove air scoop and hood seal. Remove linkage nut or clip. Remove motor bolts, unplug wiring and remove motor.

Installation

To install, reverse removal procedure. Operate motor once and allow to park, then install wiper arms.

REAR WIPER MOTOR

Removal

Remove hatch or tailgate inner trim panel. Remove wiper arm cover and nut from wiper shaft. Remove wiper arm, pivot cap (if equipped), nut and bushings. Remove wiper motor bolts, unplug connector and remove motor.

Installation

To install, reverse removal procedure.

COMBINATION SWITCH

Removal

Disconnect battery ground. Remove steering wheel and column covers. Remove turn signal cancelling sleeve and washer. Remove screws holding combination switch and remove switch.

Installation

To install, reverse removal procedure.

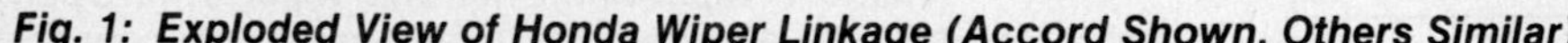

Fig. 1: Exploded View of Honda Wiper Linkage (Accord Shown, Others Similar)

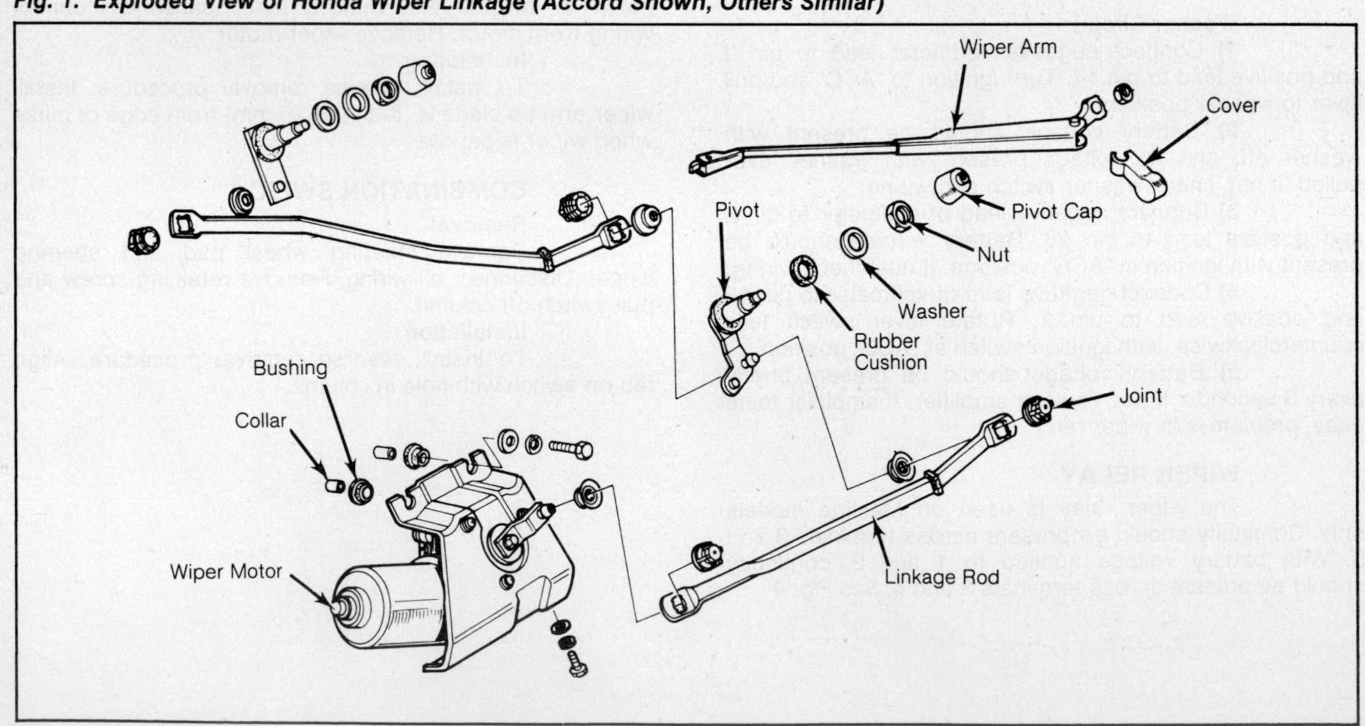
Wiper Arm
Cover
Pivot Cap
Pivot
Nut
Washer
Rubber Cushion
Bushing
Collar
Joint
Wiper Motor
Linkage Rod

ISUZU

DESCRIPTION & OPERATION

All models have a 2-speed wiper system with washer. The control switch is on a steering column lever. All models may have an intermittent system which gives a short delay between wiper cycles.

The delay relay is mounted in a box near the windshield washer reservoir. It cannot be serviced. If defective, the relay must be replaced. Impulse models also have rear window mounted wiper system.

TROUBLE SHOOTING

WIPER ACTION SLUGGISH OR UNEVEN

Worn or binding linkage. Poor ground connection. Worn motor brushes.

WIPER DOES NOT PARK OR DOES NOT STOP

Dirty contact points in park switch at motor. Shorted or open wiring. Bad wiper switch.

WIPER DOES NOT OPERATE

Blown fuse. Open wiring circuit. Bad wiper switch. Defective wiper motor.

REMOVAL & INSTALLATION

FRONT WIPER MOTOR

Removal (I-Mark)

Disconnect battery ground. From underneath instrument panel, remove nut and crankarm from motor. Unplug wiring. Remove 3 nuts and motor assembly.

Installation

To install, reverse removal procedure.

Removal (Impulse)

1) Remove cover and wiper attaching nut. Remove arm and blade assembly. Remove bolts attaching wiper motor to body.

2) Remove bracket assembly with pivot, link and motor. Disconnect linkage from wiper motor and separate motor from linkage and bracket.

Installation

To install, reverse removal procedure.

Removal (P'UP)

Remove 4 motor mounting bolts. Unplug wiring. Pull motor out part of the way and remove shaft nut. Remove motor.

Installation

To install, reverse removal procedure.

REAR WIPER MOTOR

Removal (Impulse)

Remove cover and wiper arm attaching nut. Remove arm and blade assembly. Remove seal, lock nut and collar from behind wiper arm. Remove attaching bolt from wiper motor to body. Remove wiper motor.

Installation

To install, reverse removal procedure.

WIPER LINKAGE

Removal (I-Mark)

1) Disconnect battery ground. Remove wiper arm nuts and wiper arms. Remove steering wheel. Remove instrument cluster. Reach through cluster opening and pry linkage arm from shaft assembly.

2) Remove 3 screws and left shaft assembly. Remove glove box. Pry linkage arm from shaft assembly. Remove 2 screws and right shaft assembly.

Installation

To install, reverse removal procedure.

Removal (Impulse)

1) Remove cover and wiper attaching nut. Remove arm and blade assembly. Remove bolts attaching wiper motor to body.

2) Remove bracket assembly with pivot, link and motor. Disconnect linkage from wiper motor. Disconnect pivot assembly from wiper linkage.

Installation

To install, reverse removal procedure.

Removal (P'UP)

1) Remove wiper arm covers, nuts and wiper arms. Remove pivot shaft nuts and push shafts into cowl. Remove access covers on cowl (in engine compartment).

2) Remove wiper motor bolts. Unplug wiring. Remove motor complete with linkage. Disengage finger on link retainer from hole in link. Disconnect link by turning retainer clockwise.

Installation

To install, reverse removal procedure.

WIPER SWITCH

Removal (I-Mark)

Disconnect battery ground. Remove steering wheel. Remove steering column covers. Unplug wiring. Remove 2 screws and wiper switch.

Installation

To install, reverse removal procedure.

Removal (P'UP)

Disconnect battery ground. Remove steering column covers. Unplug wiring. Remove steering wheel, using "C" clamp puller. Remove 2 screws and combination switch.

Fig. 1: Removing Wiper Motor on P'UP

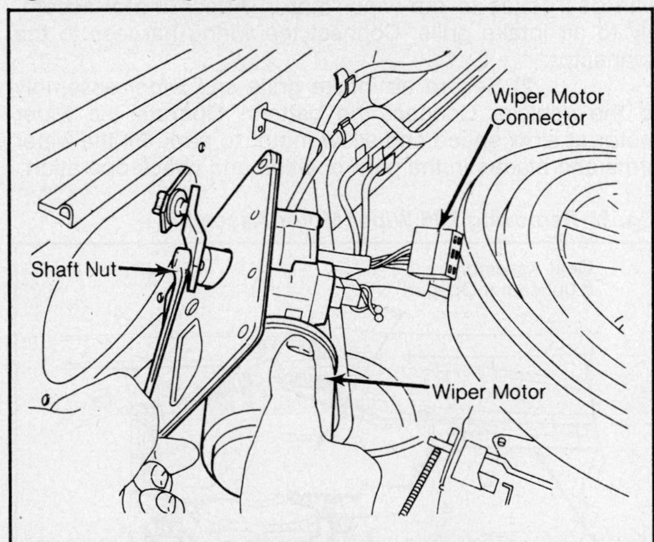
Wiper Motor
Connector
Shaft Nut
Wiper Motor

Do not bend linkage while removing shaft nut.

Wiper/Washer Systems

JAGUAR

DESCRIPTION & OPERATION

Jaguar models have a 2-speed wiper system with intermittent feature. The wipers are controlled by a lever on the right side of the steering column. Moving the lever downward runs the wipers on the intermittent cycle. Moving the lever up operates the low and high speeds.

Pressing the button on the lever operates the washers. When the lever is pulled toward the steering wheel, the wipers work until it is released. The wiper system uses a relay to control the intermittent cycle. The relay is located under the right side of the instrument panel.

REMOVAL & INSTALLATION

WIPER MOTOR

Removal (XJ6)

Remove battery. Lift spring clip on wiper arms and remove arms. Disconnect cable from motor. Remove 2 nuts from motor clamp. Tilt motor towards engine and unplug wiring. Remove motor and drive assembly.

Installation

To install, reverse removal procedure. Run motor and allow wipers to park, then install wiper arms.

Removal (XJS)

1) Disconnect battery. Remove wiper arms and blades. Remove fixing bolts attaching air intake grille and remove grille and wiper assembly complete. Disconnect wiper motor harness. Remove gearbox securing nuts and bushings from gearbox spindles.

2) Separate wiper assembly from air intake grille. Disengage cable rack and connecting tubes from gearbox, and withdraw tubes and gearboxes from cable rack. Withdraw rack from wiper motor shroud and separate plastic shroud from wiper motor.

Installation

1) To install, fit the plastic shroud and tubes with gearboxes to the wiper motor. Attach motor assembly to air intake grille. Connect the wiring harness to the connector.

2) Secure air intake grille and wiper assembly to the vehicle. Connect the battery. Operate the wiper motor at slow speed and allow motor to park. Fit the wiper arms and blades in the park position and check operation.

Fig. 1: Removing XJ6 Wiper Motor Assembly

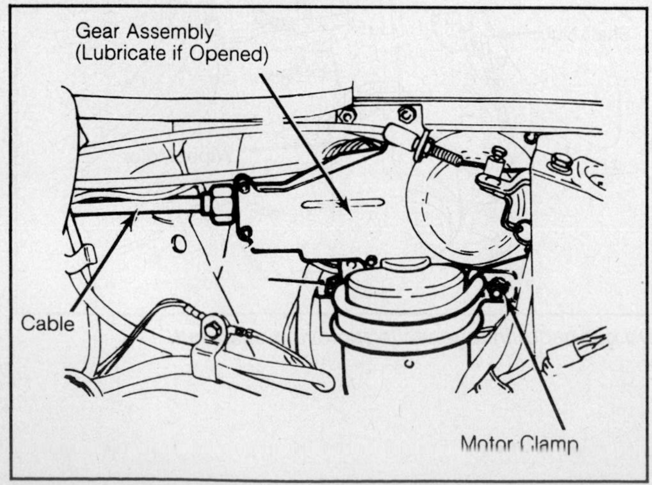
Gear Assembly
(Lubricate if Opened)
Cable
Motor Clamp

Remove battery, cable and motor clamp.

WIPER SWITCH

Removal

1) Disconnect battery ground. Remove steering column lower cover. Remove clamp bolt (beneath column) that holds adaptor. Loosen lock nut and back out set screw 2 turns. Remove steering wheel.

2) Remove insulation panel under left side of dashboard. Remove upper column cover. Loosen clamp and remove switch assembly. Unplug wiring, remove 2 screws and separate wiper switch.

Installation

To install, reverse removal procedure.

Fig. 2: Jaguar Wiper/Washer Wiring Diagram

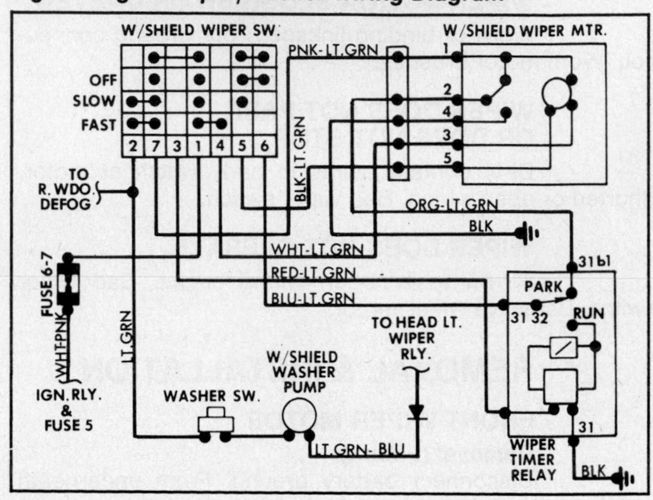
W/SHIELD WIPER SW.
W/SHIELD WIPER MTR.
OFF
SLOW
FAST
2 7 3 1 4 5 6
PNK-LT.GRN
1
2
4
3
5
BLK-LT.GRN
TO
R. WDO.
DEFOG
ORG-LT.GRN
BLK
WHT-LT.GRN
RED-LT.GRN
BLU-LT.GRN
31 b1
PARK
31 32
RUN
FUSE 6-7
WHT-PNK
LT.GRN
TO HEAD LT.
WIPER
RLY.
W/SHIELD
WASHER
PUMP
IGN. RLY.
&
FUSE 5
WASHER SW.
LT.GRN- BLU
31
WIPER
TIMER
RELAY
BLK

MAZDA

DESCRIPTION

All models have a 2-speed wiper motor with intermittent wipe feature. GLC and RX7 models may be equipped with a rear window wiper/washer system. The wiper switch for GLC Wagon is a lever on the left side of the steering column.

On all other models wiper lever is on the right side of column. A time delay relay is used to control the intermittent cycle on all except RX7 models. On RX7, wipers are timed by the "Control Processing Unit" that also operates a number of other accessories.

OPERATION

GLC WAGON

The wiper speeds are controlled by twisting the lever to the left of the steering column. The washer is operated by pressing in on the end of the lever. The rear wiper on GLC Wagon is turned on by pulling out the dash-mounted switch, while the washer operates when the switch is turned.

ALL OTHER MODELS

The wipers are controlled by a lever on the right side of the steering column. As the lever is moved down, it switches the wipers to intermittent, low speed and high speed. If the lever is pulled toward the steering wheel, the washer sprays.

If the lever is pushed away from the steering wheel, the wipers sweep until it is released. The rear wiper/washer on GLC Hatchback is controlled by a rocker switch on the instrument panel. The RX7 rear wiper switch is on the console.

TESTING

WIPER MOTOR

1) Remove wiper motor from vehicle. Connect jumper wires to connector at motor to check both speeds. For low speed, connect battery voltage to Blue wire terminal and ground the Blue/White terminal. For high speed, ground the Blue/Red terminal instead.

MAZDA INTERMITTENT WIPER RELAY LOCATIONS

Model	Connector	Location
GLC		
Hatchback	6-pin	Left of instrument cluster
Wagon	6-pin	Left of instrument cluster
B2000 & B2200	4-pin	Left of instrument cluster
RX7 [1]	17-pin	Left kick panel
626	6-pin [2]	Left of instrument cluster

[1] – Time delay is controlled by "Control Processing Unit".
[2] – For 4-door models. On 2-door and 5-door models, relay has 9-pins.

2) To check the park switch, apply battery voltage to the Blue wire terminal. Connect a jumper wire between Blue/White and Blue/Black. Ground the Black wire. Motor should run briefly and stop.

3) To check rear wiper motor, apply battery voltage to Blue/Red wire and ground the Blue/White wire. Motor should run steadily.

REMOVAL & INSTALLATION

FRONT WIPER MOTOR ASSEMBLY

Removal

1) Run wipers until they are in vertical position, then turn ignition off or disconnect battery cable. Remove wiper arms and shaft nuts.

2) Remove cowl grille or access panel. Unplug at motor. Remove mounting bolts and wiper motor.

Installation

To install, reverse removal procedure.

REAR WIPER MOTOR ASSEMBLY

Removal

Disconnect battery ground. Remove wiper arm and shaft nuts. Remove trim on rear hatch. Remove fasteners and remove wiper hole cover. Disconnect wiring, remove attaching bolts and remove rear wiper motor.

Installation

To install, reverse removal procedure.

WIPER SWITCH

Removal

Disconnect battery ground. Remove steering wheel. Remove column covers and snap ring at top of column (if equipped). Unplug wiring connectors. Loosen combination switch screw. Remove combination switch.

Installation

To install, reverse removal procedure.

Fig. 1: Mazda GLC Hatchback Wiring Diagram

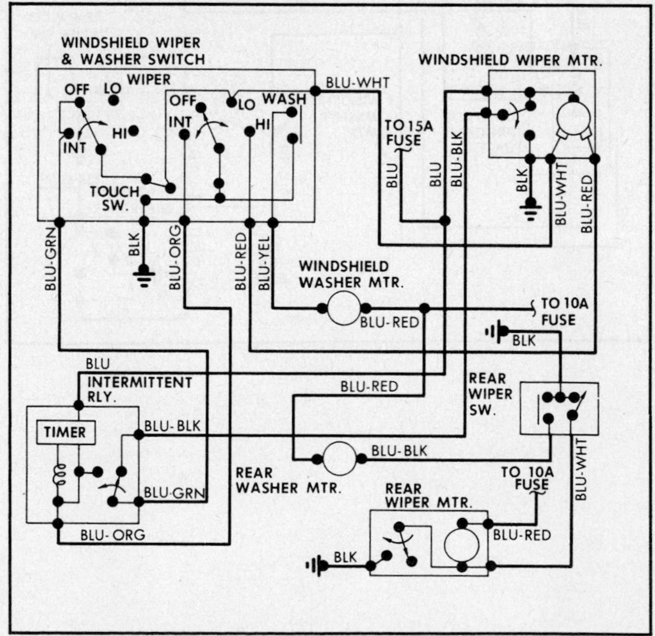
WINDSHIELD WIPER & WASHER SWITCH
WIPER
OFF
LO
HI
INT
OFF
LO
WASH
INT
HI
TOUCH SW.
WINDSHIELD WIPER MTR.
BLU-WHT
TO 15A FUSE
BLU
BLU
BLU-BLK
BLK
BLU-WHT
BLU-RED
BLU-GRN
BLK
BLU-ORG
BLU-RED
BLU-YEL
WINDSHIELD WASHER MTR.
BLU-RED
TO 10A FUSE
BLK
BLU
INTERMITTENT RLY.
TIMER
BLU-BLK
BLU-GRN
BLU-ORG
BLU-RED
REAR WIPER SW.
BLU-BLK
REAR WASHER MTR.
TO 10A FUSE
REAR WIPER MTR.
BLU-WHT
BLU-RED
BLK

MAZDA (Cont.)

Fig. 2: Mazda GLC Wagon Wiring Diagram

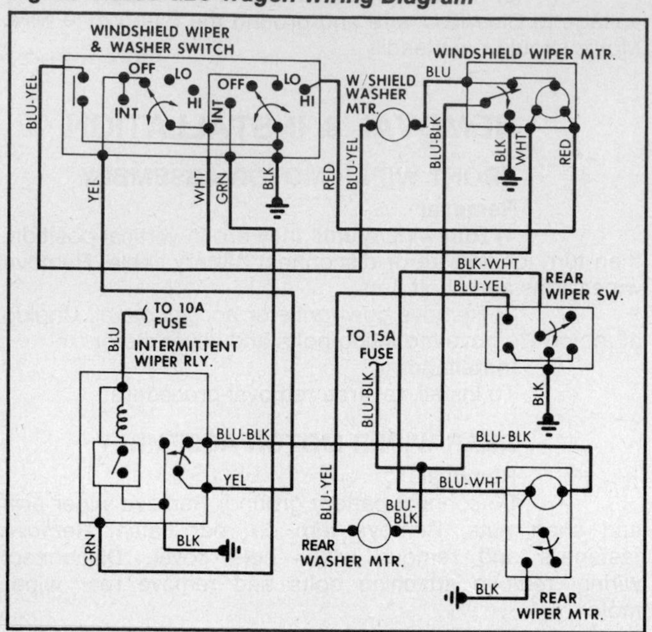
WINDSHIELD WIPER
& WASHER SWITCH
OFF
LO
HI
INT
W/SHIELD
WASHER
MTR.
WINDSHIELD WIPER MTR.
BLU
BLU-YEL
YEL
WHT
GRN
BLK
RED
BLU-BLK
BLK-WHT
BLU-YEL
REAR
WIPER SW.
TO 10A
FUSE
INTERMITTENT
WIPER RLY.
TO 15A
FUSE
BLU-WHT
REAR
WASHER MTR.
REAR
WIPER MTR.

Fig. 3: Mazda RX7 Wiring Diagram

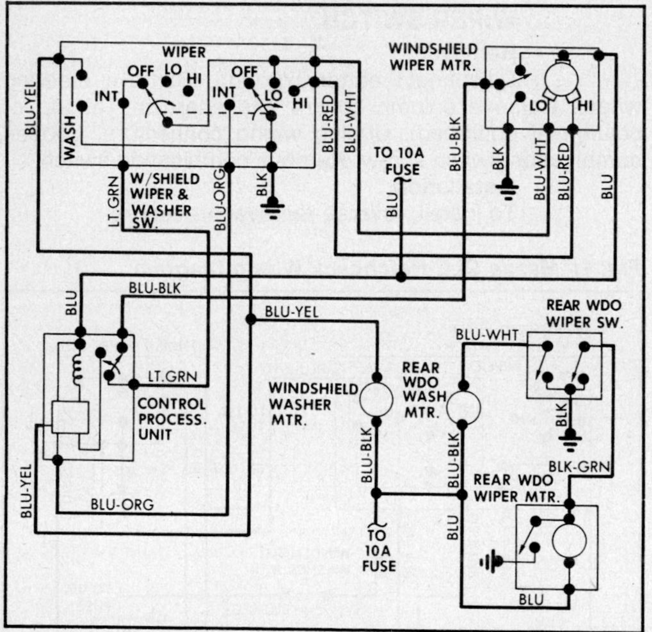
WIPER
OFF
LO
HI
INT
WASH
WINDSHIELD
WIPER MTR.
LT.GRN
W/SHIELD
WIPER &
WASHER
SW.
BLU-ORG
BLU-RED
BLU-WHT
TO 10A
FUSE
BLU-BLK
BLU
BLU-YEL
CONTROL
PROCESS.
UNIT
WINDSHIELD
WASHER
MTR.
REAR
WDO
WASH
MTR.
REAR WDO
WIPER SW.
BLK-GRN
REAR WDO
WIPER MTR.
TO
10A
FUSE

Fig. 4: Mazda B2000 and B2200 Wiring Diagram

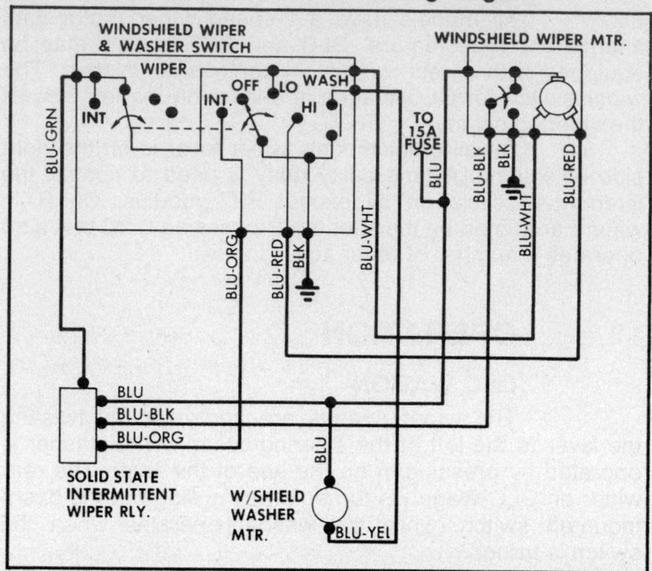
WINDSHIELD WIPER
& WASHER SWITCH
WIPER
INT
INT.
OFF
LO
HI
WASH
WINDSHIELD WIPER MTR.
TO
15A
FUSE
BLU-GRN
BLU-ORG
BLU-RED
BLK
BLU-WHT
BLU-BLK
BLU
BLU-BLK
BLU-ORG
SOLID STATE
INTERMITTENT
WIPER RLY.
W/SHIELD
WASHER
MTR.
BLU-YEL

Fig. 5: Mazda 626 Front Wiper Wiring Diagram (4-Door Models)

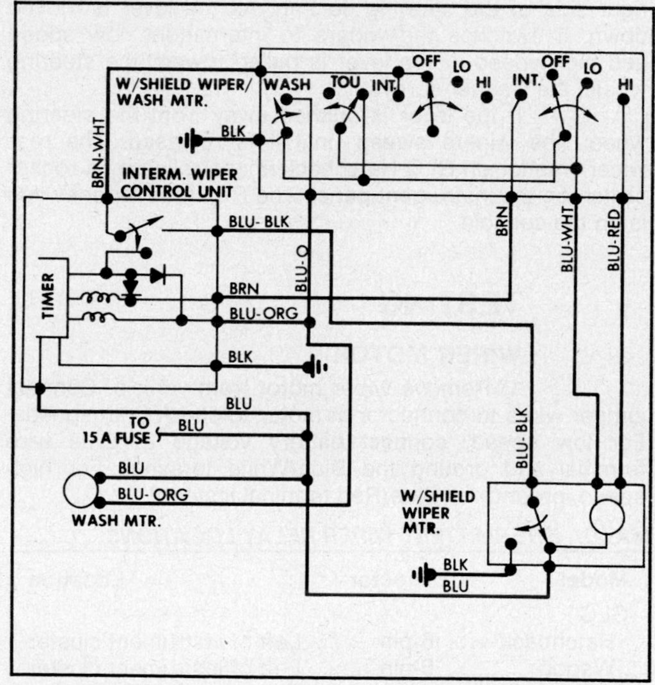
W/SHIELD WIPER/
WASH MTR.
WASH
TOU
INT.
OFF
LO
HI
BRN-WHT
BLK
INTERM. WIPER
CONTROL UNIT
BLU- BLK
TIMER
BLU-O
BRN
BLU-ORG
BLU-WHT
BLU-RED
TO
15 A FUSE
BLU
BLU- ORG
WASH MTR.
W/SHIELD
WIPER
MTR.

Wiper/Washer Systems

MAZDA (Cont.)

Fig. 6: Mazda 626 Front Wiper Wiring Diagram (2 & 5-Door Models)

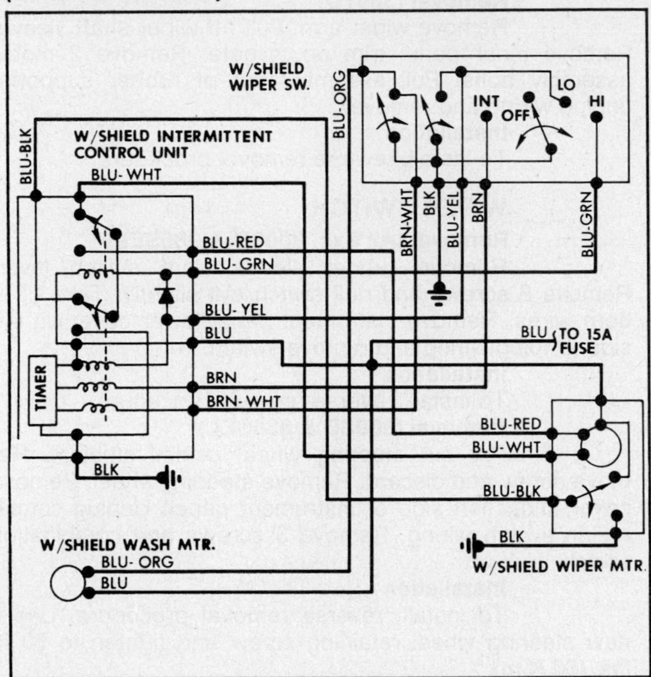
W/SHIELD
WIPER SW.
BLU-ORG
INT
LO
OFF
HI
BLU-BLK
W/SHIELD INTERMITTENT
CONTROL UNIT
BLU-WHT
BRN-WHT
BLK
BLU-YEL
BRN
BLU-GRN
BLU-RED
BLU-GRN
BLU-YEL
BLU
BLU
TO 15A
FUSE
TIMER
BRN
BRN-WHT
BLU-RED
BLU-WHT
BLK
BLU-BLK
W/SHIELD WASH MTR.
BLK
BLU-ORG
W/SHIELD WIPER MTR.
BLU

Fig. 7: Mazda 626 Rear Wiper Wiring Diagram (4-Door Models Only)

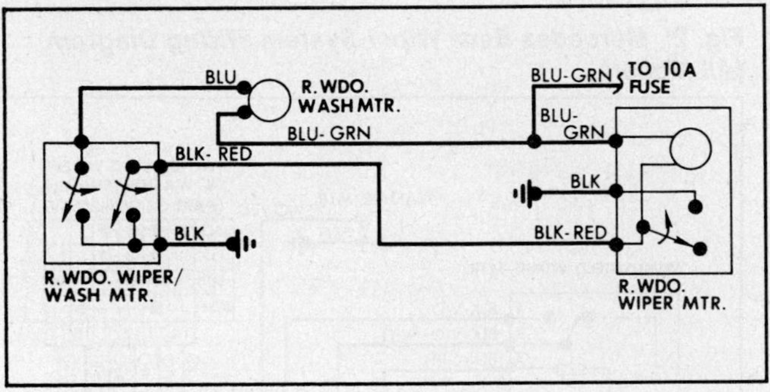
BLU
R.WDO.
WASH MTR.
BLU-GRN
TO 10A
FUSE
BLU-GRN
BLU-
GRN
BLK-RED
BLK
BLK
BLK-RED
R.WDO. WIPER/
WASH MTR.
R.WDO.
WIPER MTR.

Wiper/Washer Systems

MERCEDES-BENZ

DESCRIPTION & OPERATION

All models have a 2-speed wiper system with intermittent feature. The wipers are controlled by a steering column lever. As the lever knob is rotated, it operates the wipers at intermittent, low and high speeds.

Pressing the button at the end of the lever operates the washer system. The intermittent relay is mounted on the wiper motor. Station wagon models have a rear window wiper/washer system. This system has a low speed, intermittent speed and washer.

It is controlled by 3 push buttons at the top left corner of the console. Pressing the washer button operates the washer and wiper until it is released. Pressing either of the other buttons operates the low speed or intermittent speed until the button is pressed a second time.

REMOVAL & INSTALLATION

FRONT WIPER MOTOR

Removal (240D, 300D, 300CD & 300TD)

1) Remove wiper arms. Remove cap and nut from wiper shafts, then remove 4 rivets and left air grille. Remove 2 screws and 4 rivets on center cover, then remove cover.

2) Pull linkage from motor crank arm. Remove water drain from right shaft. Unplug wiring and push plug through panel. Remove motor bolts and motor.

Installation

To install, reverse removal procedure.

Removal (300SD & 380SEL)

Remove wiper arms and air intake covers. Remove 3 linkage mounting bolts. Unplug wiring and push plug through panel. Remove motor with linkage. Remove motor shaft nut, then swivel linkage to one side. Remove motor bolts and motor.

Installation

Install motor on linkage. Place crank arm on motor shaft. Be sure that top of arm is parallel to motor centerline. *See Fig. 1.* Tighten shaft nut. Reverse removal procedures to complete installation.

Fig. 1: Installing Motor Crank Arm Nut

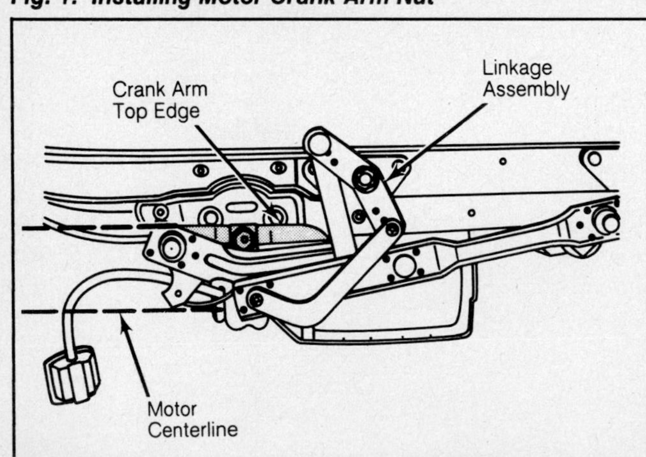
Crank Arm
Top Edge
Linkage
Assembly
Motor
Centerline

Crank arm must be parallel to motor centerline.

NOTE: **Removal and installation procedures for 380SL and 380SLC were not available.**

REAR WIPER MOTOR

Removal (300TD)

Remove wiper arm. Pull off wiper shaft sleeve. Remove inner panel trim on tailgate. Remove 2 motor assembly bolts. Pull assembly out of rubber supports, unplug wiring and remove.

Installation

To install, reverse removal procedure.

WIPER SWITCH

Removal (All Exc. 300SD & 380SEL)

Remove rubber sleeve from switch lever. Remove 2 screws and pull switch out slightly. Take off 2 horn wires. Remove instrument panel lower cover on left side. Unplug wiring and remove switch.

Installation

To install, reverse removal procedure.

Removal (300SD & 380SEL)

Pry out steering wheel center emblem. Remove screw and discard. Remove steering wheel. Remove cover under left side of instrument panel. Unplug combination switch wiring. Remove 3 screws and combination switch.

Installation

To install, reverse removal procedure. Use a new steering wheel retaining screw and tighten to 60 ft. lbs. (80 N.m).

NOTE: **Wiring diagram for rear wiper system on 300TD was not available.**

Fig. 2: Mercedes-Benz Wiper System Wiring Diagram (All Models)

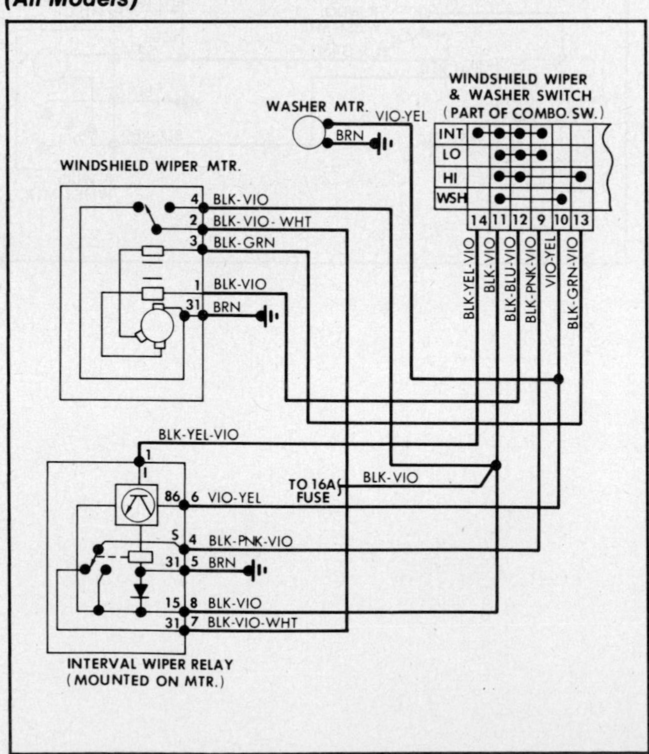
WINDSHIELD WIPER
& WASHER SWITCH
(PART OF COMBO. SW.)
WASHER MTR.
VIO-YEL
BRN
INT
LO
HI
WSH
14 11 12 9 10 13
WINDSHIELD WIPER MTR.
4 BLK-VIO
2 BLK-VIO-WHT
3 BLK-GRN
1 BLK-VIO
31 BRN
BLK-YEL-VIO
BLK-VIO
BLK-BLU-VIO
BLK-PNK-VIO
VIO-YEL
BLK-GRN-VIO
BLK-YEL-VIO
TO 16A
FUSE
BLK-VIO
86 6 VIO-YEL
S 4 BLK-PNK-VIO
31 5 BRN
15 8 BLK-VIO
31 7 BLK-VIO-WHT
INTERVAL WIPER RELAY
(MOUNTED ON MTR.)

Wiper/Washer Systems

MITSUBISHI

DESCRIPTION

All models have a 2-speed wiper motor with intermittent wiper operation feature. The washer system uses an electric pump, mounted under the fluid reservoir. All models except trucks may be equipped with a rear wiper/washer.

OPERATION

The wiper systems are operated by a column-mounted switch. Switch has 4 positions, including off, intermittent operation, and low and high speed wiper operation. On Cordia, Montero and Tredia, intermittent interval is adjustable by rotating the end of switch.

TESTING

FRONT WIPER MOTOR

Pickup

1) If wiper motor operates, perform the following test. Connect an ammeter, set in the DC 10-amp range, to connector Blue/White wire and battery position terminal with wiper motor assembly as a separate unit. Connect a jumper wire from body ground to Blue/Orange wire and then to Blue/Black wire.

2) Run the motor under no load and test for number of revolutions per minute. If the current value is less than 3 amps in both high and low positions, motor is okay. At low speed, motor should turn at 45 RPM, and at high speed at 70 RPM.

WIPER RELAY

Starion

1) Using an ohmmeter, back probe connector to check continuity between relay terminals both while power is being supplied and when it is not. *See Fig. 1.*

Fig. 1: Intermittent Wiper Relay Terminal Locations

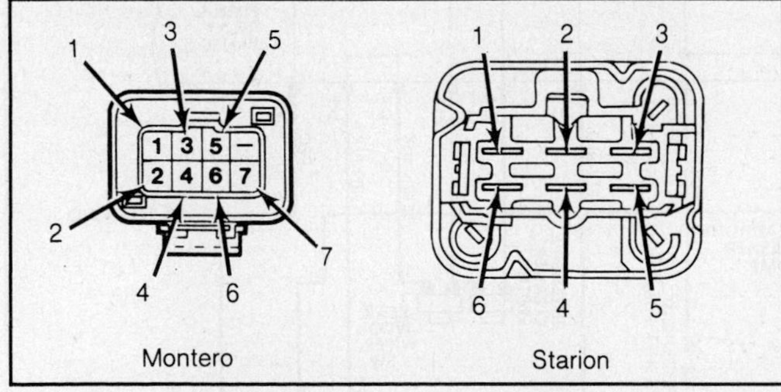
1
3
5
1 3 5 —
2 4 6 7
2
7
4
6
Montero
1
2
3
6
4
5
Starion

2) With power supplied between terminals 4 and 2, there should be continuity between 3 and 5 and no continuity between 3 and 1. With no power supplied, there should be continuity between terminals 3 and 1, and between 4 and 2. There should be no continuity between 3 and 5.

Montero

1) If wipers do not stop in the correct position when the wiper switch is set to the intermittent position, check to see if output voltage from terminal 3 is synchronized with operation of wipers. *See Fig. 1.* When wipers are stopped, voltage should be 12 volts. When wipers are operating, voltage should be zero.

2) If wipers do not operate when wiper switch is set to intermittent position, confirm that power is supplied to terminals 1 and 4. Confirm that voltage between terminal 6 and ground is zero.

3) If wipers do not operate when wiper switch is turned on, confirm that power is supplied to terminals 1 and 4. Confirm that voltage between terminal 5 and ground is zero while washer switch is on.

4) Confirm that voltage between terminal 3 and ground is 12 volts at the moment the washer switch is turned on, and that the voltage is zero approximately one second later. Voltage should be also be zero within 2 to 5 seconds after washer switch is turned off.

REMOVAL & INSTALLATION

FRONT WIPER MOTOR & LINKAGE

Removal (Cordia & Tredia)

1) Remove wiper arm. On Cordia, remove water guide panel, water proof garnish and front deck garnish. Remove pivot shaft mounting nut and push pivot shaft toward the inside.

2) On Tredia, remove the washer nozzle. Loosen the wiper motor assembly mounting bolt and with motor pulled out slightly, disconnect linkage and motor. Remove wiper and motor.

Removal (All Others)

1) Remove wiper arm and pivot shaft mounting nut. Push the pivot shaft toward the inside. Remove cover from wiper access hole on the right side of the front deck (if equipped).

2) Loosen the bolt on the wiper mounting, and with motor pulled out slightly, disconnect motor and linkage. On pickups, disconnect the wiper motor and linkage so that motor shaft and linkage are positioned at right angles to each other.

3) Linkage should be removed while holding shaft. On all models, remove motor and linkage.

Installation (All Models)

To install, reverse removal procedure, making sure stop position of wiper blades is correct.

REAR WIPER MOTOR

Removal (Cordia, Starion & Tredia)

Raise the head cover of the wiper arm pivot, loosen the nut and remove wiper arm and shield cap. Remove the nut and collar. Remove tailgate trim. Remove wiper motor bracket mounting nut, and remove wiper motor from tailgate.

Installation

To install, reverse removal procedure, making sure that wiper blade stops with 1.2" (30 mm) from blade tip to gate lower moulding on Cordia and Tredia, and with 1.8-2.2" (45-55 mm) between blade tip and hatch garnish on Starion.

Removal (Montero)

Remove spare wheel from back door. Remove wiper arm and pivot shaft lock nut. Remove back door trim and water proof film. Remove rear wiper motor mounting bolts and rear wiper motor.

Installation

To install, reverse removal procedure, making sure that blade stops with .8" (20 mm) between blade tip and back door window weather strip.

Wiper/Washer Systems

PORSCHE

DESCRIPTION

Porsche 911SC and 928S models have a 3-speed wiper motor. 944 models have a 2-speed wiper motor. All models have an intermittent cycle. A rear wiper may be installed on all models. A steering column lever is used to control the main wiper system.

A dashboard-mounted switch is used to vary the intermittent cycle. All models may be equipped with headlight washer. On 928S, a special tank of concentrated washer fluid is provided to ensure good windshield cleaning.

OPERATION

FRONT WIPERS

Moving the steering column lever upward selects the wiper speed. Moving the lever downward operates the intermittent feature on 944 and 928S. A switch near the clock selects intermittent operation on 911SC. The interval on the 928S can be varied by rotating a thumbwheel under the right side of the instrument cluster.

REAR WIPERS

The rear wiper on 944 and 928S is controlled by a rocker switch on console. On 911SC, the switch is on the cluster. No rear washer is used. Be sure window glass is wet to prevent scratches.

WINDSHIELD WASHER

The washer sprays when the wiper lever is pulled toward the steering wheel. 928S models also have a special container of solution which ensures good cleaning. This washer is operated by a button under the right side of the cluster (by the intermittent adjustment thumbwheel).

HEADLIGHT WASHER

All models may have a headlight washer. This unit sprays fluid under high pressure directly onto the headlights. It operates only when the headlights are on. It is supplied by the windshield washer reservoir.

A separate pump is provided. Pump is activated by the console switch on 944, by the wiper lever on 928S and cluster mounted button on 911SC.

Fig. 2: 928S Wiper System Wiring Diagram

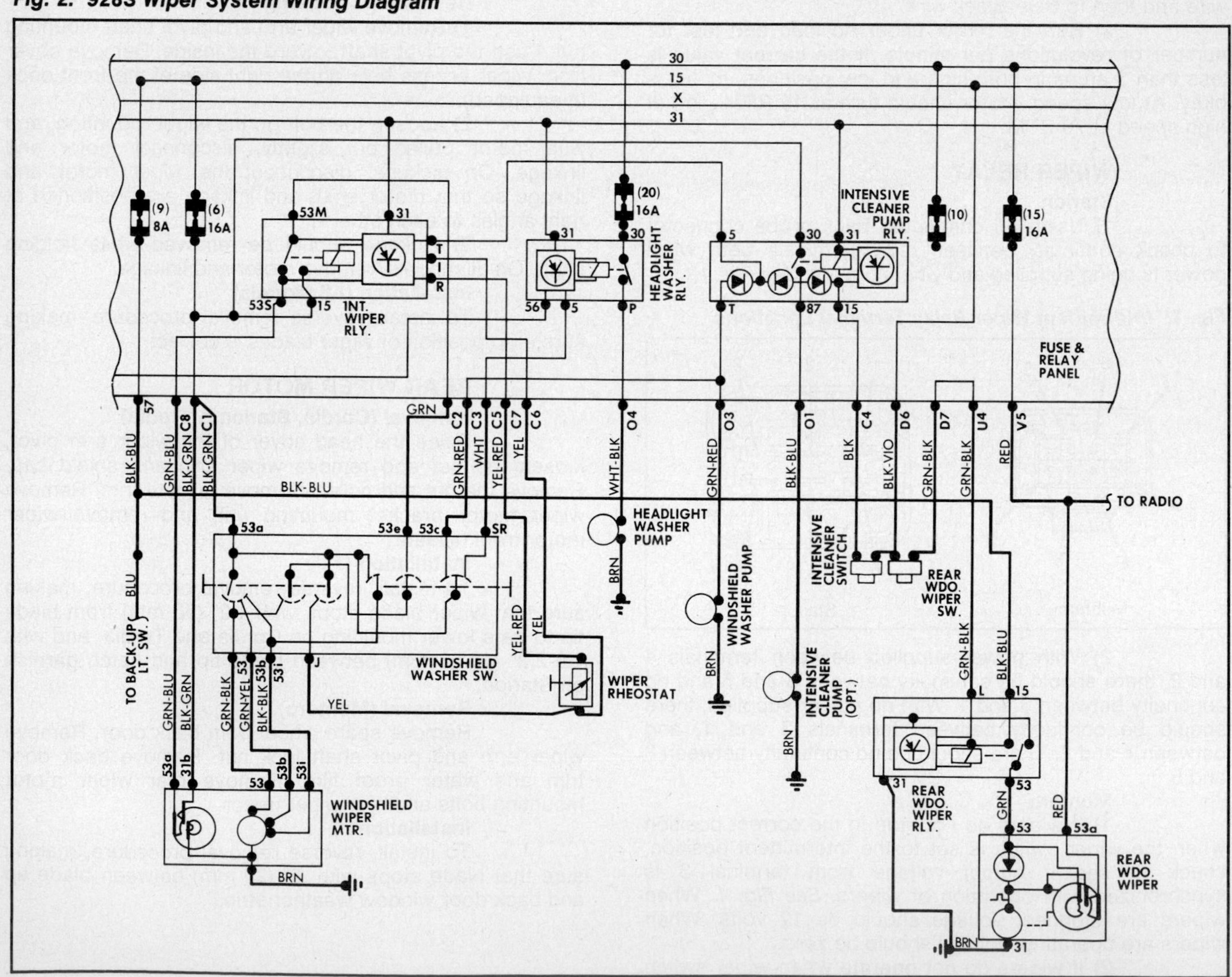

30
15
X
31
(9) 8A
(6) 16A
53M
31
T
I
R
53S
15
INT. WIPER RLY.
(20) 16A
31
30
56
5
P
HEADLIGHT WASHER RLY.
INTENSIVE CLEANER PUMP RLY.
5
30
31
T
87
15
(10)
(15) 16A
FUSE & RELAY PANEL
57
C8
C1
GRN
C2
C3
C5
C7
C6
O4
O3
O1
C4
D6
D7
U4
V5
BLK-BLU
GRN-BLU
BLK-GRN
BLK-GRN
GRN-RED
WHT
YEL-RED
YEL
WHT-BLK
GRN-RED
BLK-BLU
BLK
BLK-VIO
GRN-BLK
GRN-BLK
RED
TO RADIO
53a
53e
53c
SR
HEADLIGHT WASHER PUMP
BRN
INTENSIVE CLEANER SWITCH
REAR WDO. WIPER SW.
BLU
TO BACK-UP LT. SW.
WINDSHIELD WASHER SW.
YEL-RED
YEL
WINDSHIELD WASHER PUMP
J
WIPER RHEOSTAT
INTENSIVE CLEANER PUMP (OPT.)
GRN-BLU
BLK-GRN
GRN-BLK
GRN-YEL 53
BLK-BLK 53b
53i
YEL
53a
31b
53
53b
53i
WINDSHIELD WIPER MTR.
BRN
GRN-BLK
BLK-BLU
L
15
31
REAR WDO. WIPER RLY.
53
GRN
RED
53
53a
REAR WDO. WIPER
BRN
31

PORSCHE (Cont.)

REMOVAL & INSTALLATION

NOTE: Removal and installation information not available for 944 models.

FRONT WIPER MOTOR

Removal (911SC & 928S)

Remove motor cover (if equipped). Remove crank arm nut and unplug wiring. Remove motor bolts. If necessary, loosen motor bracket bolts to slip motor out.

Installation

Install motor on bracket and connect wiring. Let motor run and return to park position, then install crank arm so wiper arms are parked at bottom of windshield. Replace motor cover.

Fig. 1: 911SC Wiper System Wiring Diagram

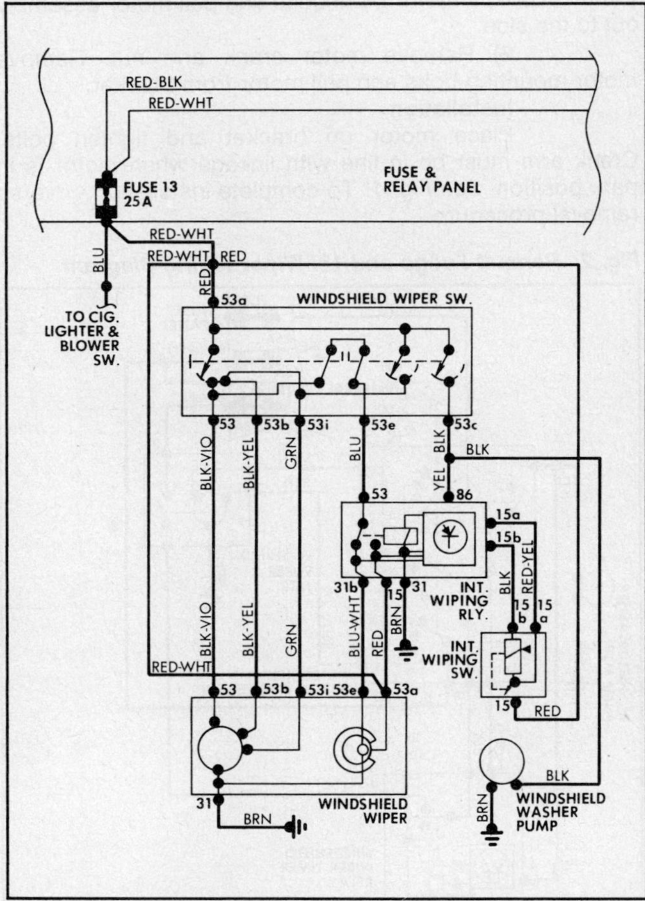

RED-BLK
RED-WHT
FUSE 13
25A
FUSE &
RELAY PANEL
RED-WHT
RED-WHT
RED
BLU
RED
TO CIG.
LIGHTER &
BLOWER
SW.
53a
WINDSHIELD WIPER SW.
53
53b
53i
53e
53c
BLK-VIO
BLK-YEL
GRN
BLU
BLK
YEL
BLK
53
86
15a
15b
31b
15
31
INT.
WIPING
RLY.
BLK
RED-YEL
BLU-WHT
RED
BRN
15 b
15 a
INT.
WIPING
SW.
15
RED
RED-WHT
53
53b
53i
53e
53a
31
BRN
WINDSHIELD
WIPER
BLK
BRN
WINDSHIELD
WASHER
PUMP

Wiper/Washer Systems

RENAULT

DESCRIPTION

All models are equipped with 2-speed wiper motors. The Fuego and 18i also have an intermittent cycle. A rear wiper/washer is available on Fuego, Le Car and 18i Station Wagon.

The Le Car rear washer has a reservoir in the rear of the car, while the 18i uses the front fluid reservoir. The 18i rear pump is inside the pillar behind the left rear door.

NOTE: **Information on Fuego rear washer not available from manufacturer.**

OPERATION

The wipers are controlled by the right column lever. Pulling the lever toward the steering wheel operates the washers. Moving the lever downward operates the intermittent cycle (Fuego and 18i only), low speed and high speed.

The rear wiper is controlled by a push button switch located on instrument panel. Hold the switch to operate the washer and wiper.

TESTING

WASHER MOTOR

1) If motor does not operate, connect a jumper wire from battery to the motor hot wire (ground wire will be Black). If motor still does not work, check pump motor ground connection.

2) If ground is good, replace motor. If motor operates in step **1)**, but not with switch, check wiring or replace switch.

Fig. 1: Wiper Motor Crank Arm Position

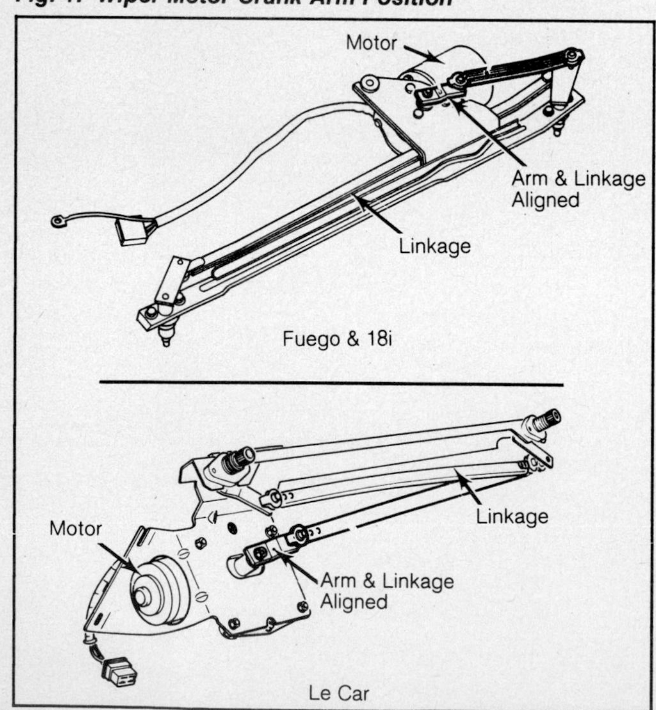
Motor
Arm & Linkage Aligned
Linkage
Fuego & 18i
Linkage
Motor
Arm & Linkage Aligned
Le Car

Motor must be in park position when nut is tightened.

REMOVAL & INSTALLATION

FRONT WIPER MOTOR

Removal (Fuego and 18i)

1) Remove wiper arms and shaft nuts. Remove electrical box, ground wire and motor plate bolt. Push shafts into body and slide motor assembly to the right.

2) Remove crank arm nut and motor bolts. Remove motor from linkage assembly.

Installation

Install motor on linkage assembly. Motor crank arm must be in line with linkage arm when motor is in park position. Reverse removal procedure to complete installation. *See Fig. 1.*

Removal (Le Car)

1) Raise base of wiper arm and remove nut. Pull off wiper arms and remove shaft nuts. Remove electrical box, 2 motor plate bolts and pull motor assembly out to the side.

2) Remove motor crank arm nut. Remove motor mounting bolts and pull motor from bracket.

Installation

Place motor on bracket and tighten bolts. Crank arm must be in line with linkage when motor is in park position. *See Fig. 1.* To complete installation, reverse removal procedure.

Fig. 2: Renault Fuego and 18i Wiper Wiring Diagram

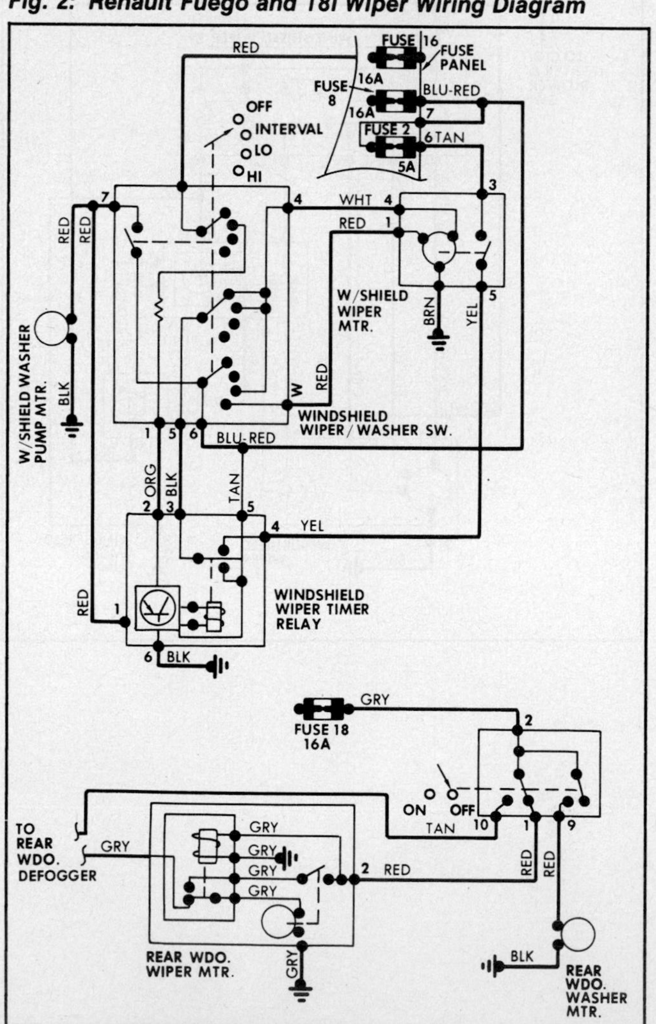
FUSE 16
FUSE PANEL
RED
FUSE 8
16A
BLU-RED
16A
7
FUSE 2
6 TAN
5A
OFF
INTERVAL
LO
HI
7
4
WHT 4
3
RED 1
RED
RED
W/SHIELD WIPER MTR.
BRN
YEL
5
W/SHIELD WASHER PUMP MTR.
BLK
W
RED
WINDSHIELD WIPER/WASHER SW.
1 5 6
BLU-RED
ORG
BLK
TAN
2 3
5
4 YEL
RED
1
WINDSHIELD WIPER TIMER RELAY
6 BLK
GRY
FUSE 18 16A
2
ON
OFF
TAN
10
1
9
TO REAR WDO. DEFOGGER
GRY
GRY
GRY
GRY
GRY
2 RED
RED
RED
REAR WDO. WIPER MTR.
GRY
BLK
REAR WDO. WASHER MTR.

RENAULT (Cont.)

REAR WIPER MOTOR

Removal (All Models)

Remove inner trim panel. Disconnect motor wiring. Remove wiper blade, arm and shaft nuts. Remove motor bolts and motor assembly.

Installation

To install, reverse removal procedure.

Fig. 3: Renault Le Car Wiper Wiring Diagram

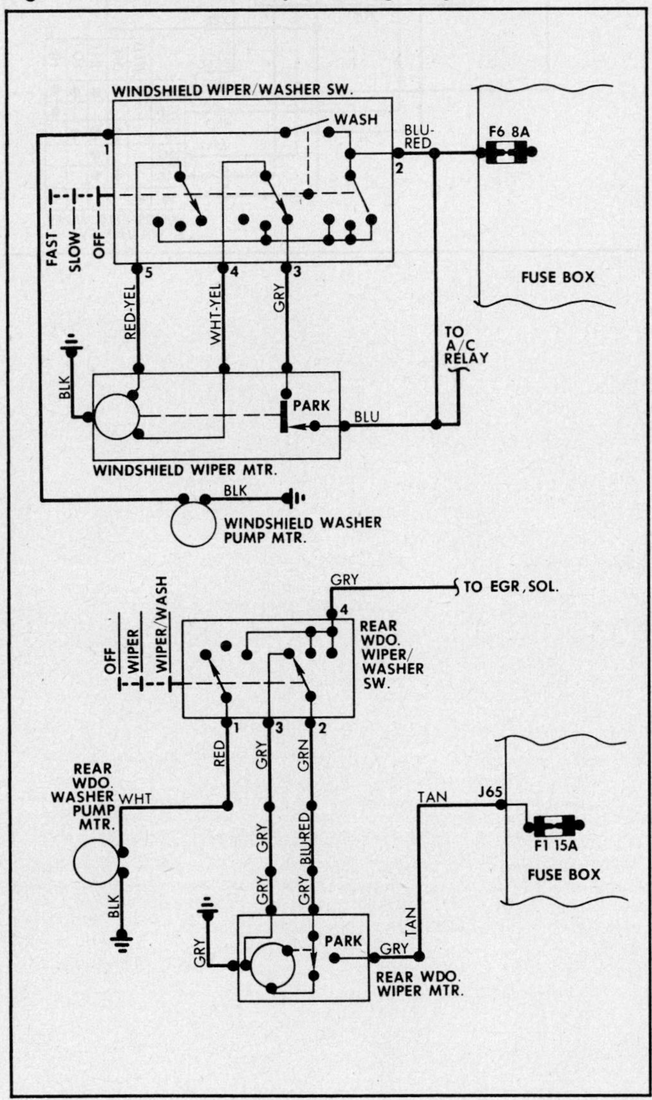
WINDSHIELD WIPER/WASHER SW.
WASH
BLU-RED
F6 8A
FAST
SLOW
OFF
RED-YEL
WHT-YEL
GRY
FUSE BOX
TO A/C RELAY
BLK
PARK
BLU
WINDSHIELD WIPER MTR.
BLK
WINDSHIELD WASHER PUMP MTR.
GRY
TO EGR. SOL.
OFF
WIPER
WIPER/WASH
REAR WDO. WIPER/ WASHER SW.
RED
GRY
GRN
REAR WDO. WASHER PUMP MTR.
WHT
TAN
J65
F1 15A
FUSE BOX
BLU-RED
BLK
PARK
REAR WDO. WIPER MTR.

SAAB

DESCRIPTION & OPERATION

All models have a 2-speed wiper motor that operates the wiper arms through a cable and linkage. The wiper control switch is a steering column lever. The intermittent control relay is located next to the turn signal flasher (on relay bracket under left side of dashboard).

The wiper switch operates the washers when it is pulled toward the steering wheel. As the lever is moved down, the wipers operate intermittently, at low speed and at high speed.

Fig. 1: Saab 900 Wiper Motor Assembly

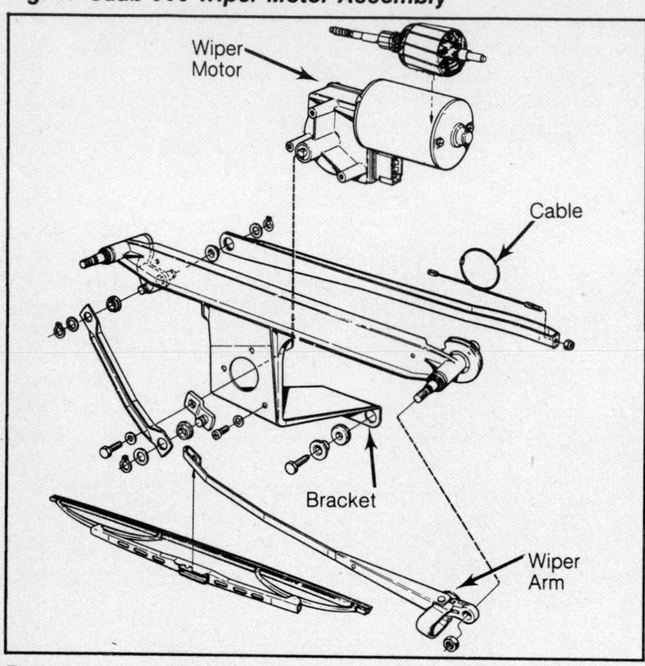
Wiper
Motor
Cable
Bracket
Wiper
Arm

Remove wiper arms and attaching bolts to remove.

Fig. 2: Saab 900 Wiper/Washer System Wiring Diagram

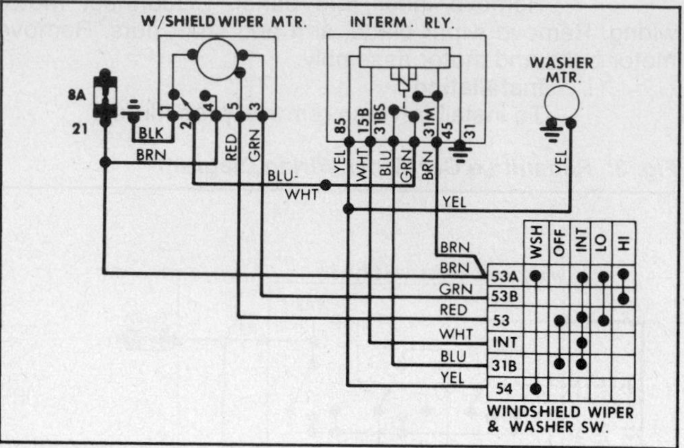
W/SHIELD WIPER MTR.
INTERM. RLY.
WASHER MTR.
8A
21
BLK
BRN
RED
GRN
BLU-
WHT
YEL
WHT
BLU
GRN
BRN
85
15B
31BS
31M
45
31
2
4
5
3
WSH
OFF
INT
LO
HI
53A
53B
53
INT
31B
54
WINDSHIELD WIPER & WASHER SW.

REMOVAL & INSTALLATION

WIPER MOTOR

Removal

Lift wiper arm. Fold cap up and remove wiper shaft nut. Remove wiper arms and rubber shaft covers. Remove bolts at wiper bracket and one bolt at each shaft. Unplug wiring and remove motor assembly with bracket.

Installation

To install, reverse removal procedure.

WIPER SWITCH

Removal

Remove lower steering column cover. Remove screws under steering column and slide switch bracket off steering shaft. Unplug wiring and remove switch.

Installation

To install, reverse removal procedure.

SUBARU

DESCRIPTION

The wiper/washer system includes a 2-speed motor, separate washer pump and rotary switch. The switch is located at the right side of the instrument cluster. GL and GLF models have an intermittent system. Hatchback and Station Wagon models may be equipped with a rear window wiper/washer.

OPERATION

The standard wiper system has 2 speeds. The washer is operated by pushing in the button at the end of the wiper switch. The intermittent system has a third switch position that selects the delayed cycle. No time adjustment is possible.

If the washer button is pressed on this system, the washer will operate and the wipers will run for 4 cycles, then turn off. The rear wiper is operated by the ring on the wiper switch. Turning it to the first position starts the wiper. The second position operates the washer.

REMOVAL & INSTALLATION

FRONT WIPER ASSEMBLY

Removal

1) Disconnect both wiper blades from arms by pulling lever up and sliding them off. Pull up arm shaft covers and remove shaft nuts. Pull off wiper arms. Open hood. Disconnect battery ground. Unplug wiring at motor.

2) Remove cowl panel attaching screws and lift off cowl panel. Cut a short section of metal tubing the same inner diameter as the outer diameter of the plastic joint on motor shaft. Press tubing down over joint to disconnect rod from wiper motor. Remove wiper motor bolts and motor.

Installation

To install, reverse removal procedure. Place wiper arm with Red mark on driver's side. Adjust arms so blades stop about 0.6" (15 mm) above bottom of glass.

REAR WIPER ASSEMBLY

Removal

Lift off arm shaft cover. Remove shaft nut and wiper arm. Remove inside trim from hatch or tailgate. Unplug wiring and remove wiper motor.

Installation

To install, reverse removal procedure.

WASHER TANK

Removal (2-Door Hatchback)

Remove trim and attaching screws. Disconnect hose from washer tank and nozzle. Take out drain hose with cap. Take out washer tank by removing screws. Disconnect electric wires from washer pump at connector.

Installation

To install, reverse removal procedure.

Removal (Station Wagon)

Remove trim and attaching screws. Disconnect hose from washer tank and nozzle. Take out washer tank by pulling it up. Disconnect electric wires from washer pump at connector.

Installation

To install, reverse removal procedure.

Fig. 1: Subaru Front Wiper/Washer Wiring Diagram

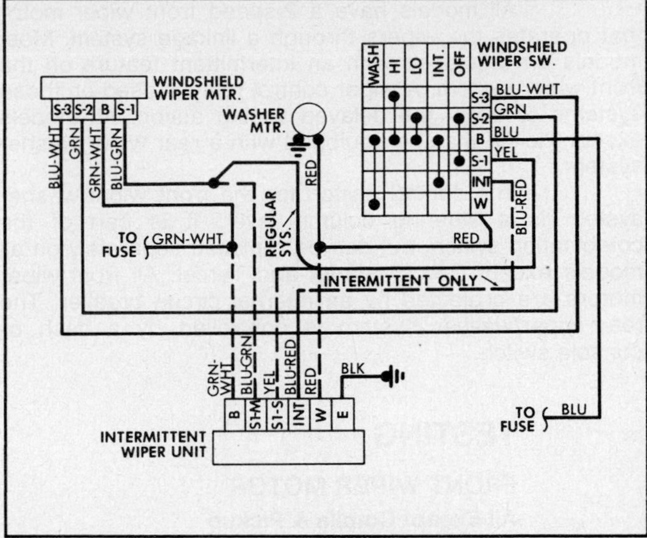
WINDSHIELD WIPER MTR.
S-3 S-2 B S-1
BLU-WHT
GRN
GRN-WHT
BLU-GRN
WASHER MTR.
RED
WINDSHIELD WIPER SW.
WASH HI LO INT. OFF
S-3 BLU-WHT
S-2 GRN
B BLU
S-1 YEL
INT
W
BLU-RED
TO FUSE GRN-WHT
REGULAR SYS.
RED
INTERMITTENT ONLY
GRN-WHT
BLU-GRN
YEL
BLU-RED
RED
BLK
B S1-W S1-S INT W E
INTERMITTENT WIPER UNIT
TO FUSE BLU

Fig. 2: Subaru Rear Wiper/Washer Wiring Diagram

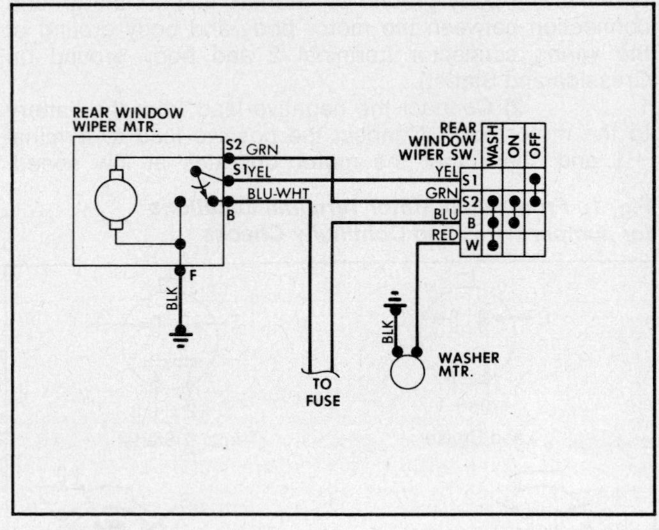
REAR WINDOW WIPER MTR.
S2 GRN
S1 YEL
BLU-WHT
B
F
BLK
REAR WINDOW WIPER SW.
WASH ON OFF
YEL S1
GRN S2
BLU B
RED W
BLK
WASHER MTR.
TO FUSE

Wiper/Washer Systems

TOYOTA

DESCRIPTION & OPERATION

All models have a 2-speed front wiper motor that operates the wipers through a linkage system. Most models are equipped with an intermittent feature on the front wiper system. A wiper control relay is used on those systems to allow the delayed wiping action. All models except Pickup may be equipped with a rear wiper/washer system.

The control switch for the front wiper/washer system is a steering column lever. It is part of the combination switch, but can be replaced separately on all models except Celica, Starlet and Tercel. All front wiper motors are protected by an internal circuit breaker. The rear wiper/washer system is controlled by a dash or console switch.

TESTING

FRONT WIPER MOTOR

All Except Corolla & Pickup

1) Inspect the power source line between terminal B and body ground of the wiring connector (+ terminal and body ground on Starlet). Inspect the ground connection between the motor body and body ground of the wiring connector (terminal 2 and body ground on Cressida and Starlet).

2) Connect the negative lead from the battery to the motor body. Connect the positive lead to terminal +1 and check that the motor operates at low speed.

Fig. 1: Front Wiper Motor Terminal Locations for Jumper Wires and Continuity Checks

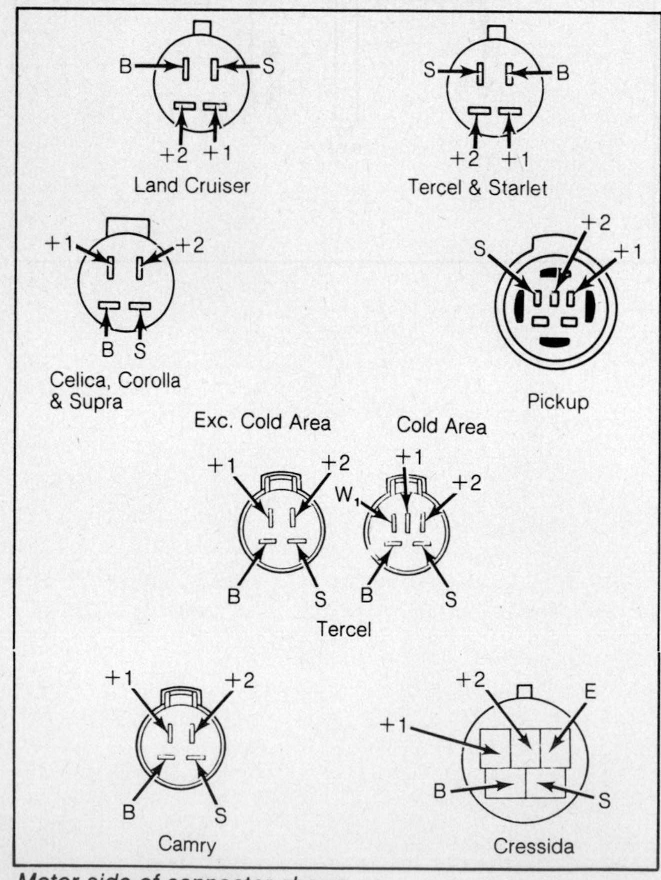
B
S
+2 +1
Land Cruiser
S
B
+2 +1
Tercel & Starlet
+1
+2
B S
Celica, Corolla & Supra
S
+2
+1
Pickup
Exc. Cold Area
Cold Area
+1
+2
+1
W1
+2
B
S
B
S
Tercel
+1
+2
B
S
Camry
+2
E
+1
B
S
Cressida

Motor side of connector shown.

Connect positive lead to terminal +2 and check that the motor turns at high speed.

3) On Camry, connect positive lead to terminal +1 and set wiper in operation. Disconnect positive lead and stop operation halfway. Make sure that the wiper returns to its original position when connecting terminal +1 to terminal S and the positive lead to terminal B. On all models, if motor does not operate properly, replace.

Corolla & Pickup

Place wiper switch in off position. Remove connector from wiper motor. Check for continuity between all terminals except terminal B. If there is no continuity, replace wiper motor.

REAR WIPER MOTOR

All Except Corolla

1) Check the power supply to wipers by checking at between terminal B of wiring connector and body ground (+ terminal and ground on Starlet). On Camry, also check at terminal B' of connector and body ground.

2) Check ground circuit by checking between body ground of wiring connector and the following points: Terminal E (Camry), terminal S (Celica and Supra), terminal 2 (Cressida), – terminal (Starlet), and motor body (Tercel).

3) On Camry, check motor operation by attaching negative battery lead to terminal E. Connect positive lead to terminal Lm. Motor should turn. Disconnect lead and stop wiper operation halfway. Wiper should

Fig. 2: Rear Wiper Motor Terminal Locations for Jumper Wires and Continuity Check

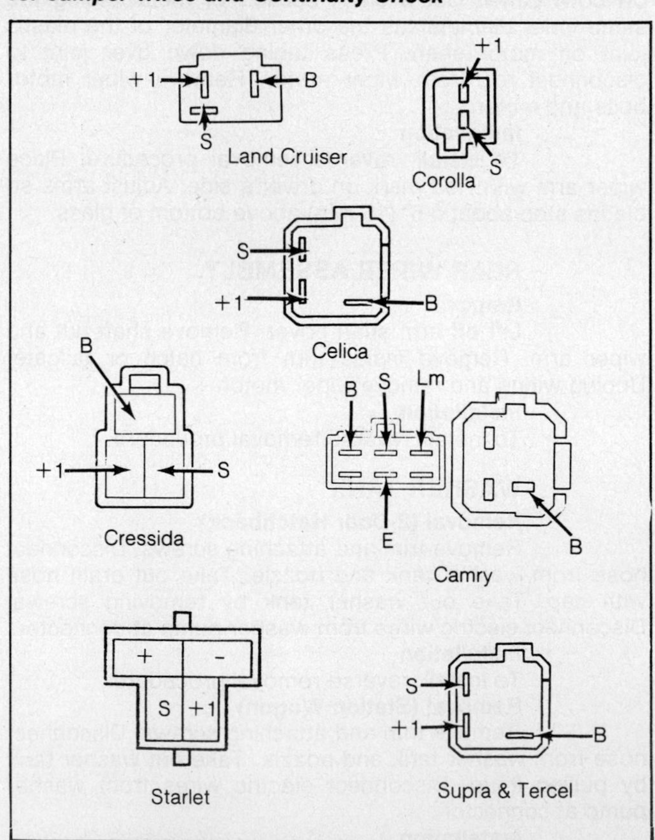
+1
B
S
Land Cruiser
+1
S
Corolla
S
+1
B
Celica
B
+1
S
Cressida
B
S
Lm
E
B
Camry
+
-
S +1
Starlet
S
+1
B
Supra & Tercel

Motor side of connector shown.

TOYOTA (Cont.)

return to original position when connecting terminal Lm to terminal S, and positive lead to terminal B.

4) On all except Camry, check motor operation by connecting the negative lead from battery to the motor body and connect the positive lead to terminal +1. Motor should turn. On all models, if operation is not as described, replace motor.

Corolla

Place rear wiper switch in off position. Remove back door trim. Disconnect connector from wiper motor. Check motor for continuity between terminals S and +1. If there is no continuity, replace wiper motor.

WIPER CONTROL RELAY

Ensure wiper system is operating correctly except for the intermittent wipers. Check that battery voltage is available at wiper relay. If voltage is available and intermittent wipers do not operate properly, replace relay.

WIPER CONTROL RELAY LOCATION

Model	Connector	Location
Camry	[1] 6-pin	Under Instru. Cluster
Celica	4-pin	Right Kick Panel
Corolla	4-pin	Right Kick Panel
Cressida	6-pin	Right Kick Panel
Land Cruiser	5-pin	Under Instru. Cluster
Pickup	4-pin	Right Kick Panel
Starlet	4-pin	Left Corner of Dash
Supra	9-pin	Right Kick Panel
Tercel	4-pin	Left Kick Panel

[1] – Intermittent invariable type. Intermittent variable type has 9 pins.

REMOVAL & INSTALLATION

FRONT WIPER MOTOR

NOTE: **No procedures were available for Tercel models.**

Removal (Pickup & Starlet)

Remove wiper arm shaft nuts and arms. Use screwdriver to pry wiper linkage from motor arm. Disconnect wiring and remove wiper motor. Scribe alignment marks on motor shaft and arm before removing arm. Remove pivot shaft nuts and remove linkage.

Installation

Grease linkage joints and install linkage and motor. Turn wipers on, then off. After motor has parked, install wiper arms.

Removal (Corolla & Cressida)

1) Remove wiper arm shaft nuts and arms. Remove cowl grille panel and access covers. Disconnect wiring and remove wiper motor bolts. Pry wiper arm from linkage.

2) Remove wiper motor. Scribe alignment marks on motor shaft and arm before removing arm. Pry linkage from pivot shaft. Remove arm shaft screw, pivot and linkage.

Installation

Grease linkage joints and install linkage and motor. Turn wipers on, then off. After motor has parked, install wiper arms.

Removal (Land Cruiser)

Remove wiper arm shaft nuts and arms. Remove shaft cover and screw at each wiper shaft. Remove service covers at left and center of cowl. Remove motor plate screws. Pull motor, plate and linkage out to the right. Pry link off motor arm and remove motor plate.

Installation

Lubricate linkage. Insert linkage and motor into cowl opening. Guide link under cowl reinforcement. Run motor and allow to stop in park position, and install wiper.

Removal (Celica & Supra)

Remove wiper arm shaft nuts and wiper arms. Remove cowl grille panel and access hole covers. Pry linkage from wiper motor arm. Unplug wiring and remove wiper motor. Pry linkage from pivot shaft. Remove arm shaft screw. Remove pivot and linkage.

Installation

To install, lubricate linkage points, and reverse removal procedure. Run motor and allow it to stop in park position. Install wiper arm.

REAR WIPER MOTOR REMOVAL

Removal (All Models)

Remove wiper arm shaft nut and wiper arm. Remove shaft bushings. Open rear door and remove inner trim panel. If motor is attached to linkage, disconnect wiper motor arm from linkage. Remove motor.

Installation

To install, reverse removal procedure. Before installing wiper arm, run motor and allow it to stop in park position. Install wiper arm.

WIPER SWITCH

Removal (All Models)

1) Disconnect battery ground. On Corolla, remove instrument cluster bezel. On all models, remove trim panel under steering column. Remove column covers. Remove horn button and pull off steering wheel.

Fig. 3: View of Toyota Combination Switch Showing Wiper Switch Removal

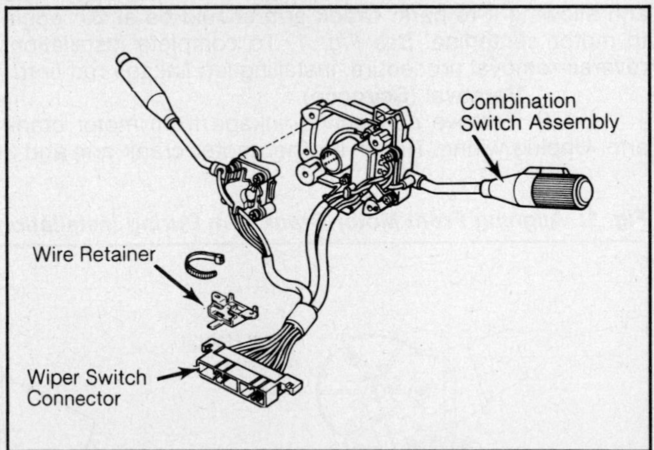
Combination
Switch Assembly
Wire Retainer
Wiper Switch
Connector

2) Press in locking tabs on connector and unplug it. Remove mounting screws and combination switch. On models with multi-piece switch, remove wiper switch screws. Mark wire terminals and remove from connector.

Installation

To install, reverse removal procedure.

Wiper/Washer Systems

VOLKSWAGEN

Jetta, Quantum, Rabbit, Rabbit Pickup, Scirocco & Vanagon

DESCRIPTION

All models are equipped with 2-speed wipers. Rabbit, Rabbit Pickup and Vanagon models have an intermittent feature available as an option. This feature is standard on all other models. The washer motor is located in the side of the fluid reservoir and can be replaced separately.

The wiper control switch is the right-hand lever on the steering column. Rabbit and Scirocco models may be equipped with a rear wiper/washer system, operated by the same column lever.

OPERATION

When the wiper lever is moved up from the rest position, the wipers operate at low speed. Moving the lever another notch starts the high speed. Pulling the lever toward the steering wheel operates the washer.

Pushing the lever toward the dashboard actuates the rear system (wagons only). Pulling the lever down from the rest position selects the intermittent wiper cycle (if equipped). The wipers operate once every 6 seconds.

REMOVAL & INSTALLATION

FRONT WIPER MOTOR

NOTE: **Removal & installation information for Quantum was not available from manufacturer.**

Removal (Jetta, Rabbit & Pickup)

Open hood and unplug wiring connector. Pry linkage off motor crank arm. Remove 4 bolts and motor. Do not remove motor bracket when removing motor.

Installation

Check crank arm alignment by running motor and allowing it to park. Crank arm should be at 20° angle to motor centerline. *See Fig. 1.* To complete installation, reverse removal procedure, installing left linkage rod first.

Removal (Scirocco)

Remove connecting linkage from motor crank arm. Unplug wiring. Remove wiper motor crank arm and 3 motor bolts. Slide motor out from beneath bracket and remove motor.

Installation

Check crank arm alignment by running motor and allowing it to park. Crank arm should be in line with the motor centerline, and linkage ball should point away from motor. *See Fig. 1.* Reverse removal procedure to complete installation.

Removal (Vanagon)

Remove wipers arms and shaft nuts. Remove glove box and instrument cluster. Remove wiper linkage rods by extending fully to passenger side. Remove wiper bracket bolts and bracket. Remove crank arm, 3 bolts and wiper motor.

Installation

Connect motor wiring, run motor and allow it to park. Align crank arm and linkage rod as shown. *See Fig. 1.* Reverse removal procedure to install.

REAR WIPER MOTOR

Removal

Remove inner trim panel on rear hatch. Unplug wiring and pry linkage off motor crank arm. Remove motor crank arm, motor bolts and motor.

Installation

Check crank arm alignment by running motor and allowing it to park. Install crank arm in correct position. *See Fig. 2.* Reverse removal procedure to complete installation.

Fig. 2: Aligning Rear Motor Crank Arm During Installation

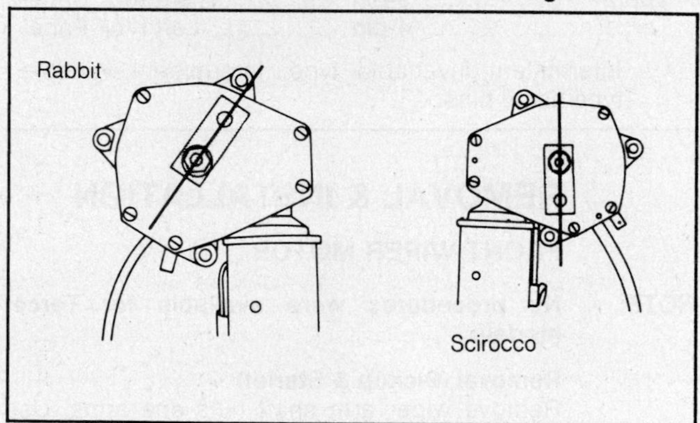
Rabbit
Scirocco

Motor must be in park position.

Fig. 1: Aligning Front Motor Crank Arm During Installation

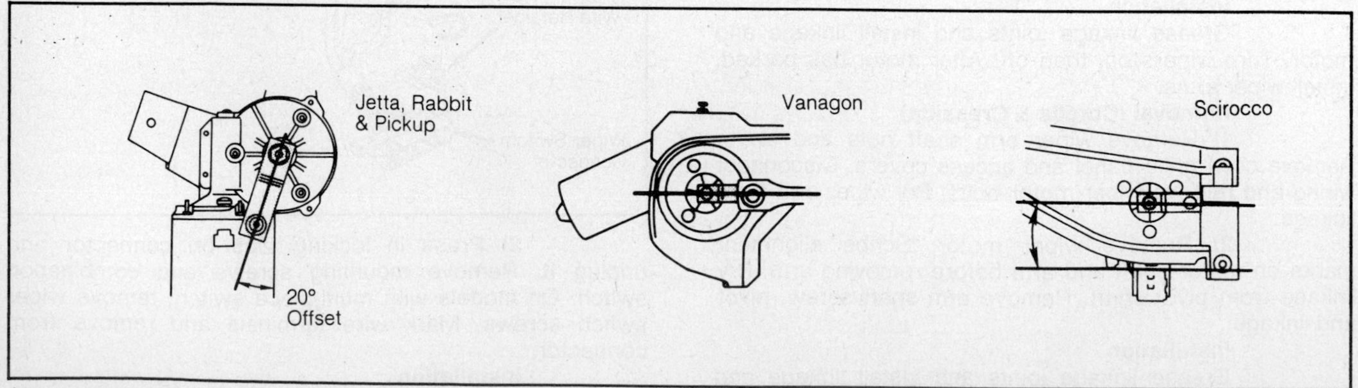
Jetta, Rabbit & Pickup
20° Offset
Vanagon
Scirocco

Motor must be in park position.

Wiper/Washer Systems

VOLKSWAGEN (Cont.)

Fig. 3: Jetta, Quantum & Rabbit Convertible Wiper System Wiring Diagram

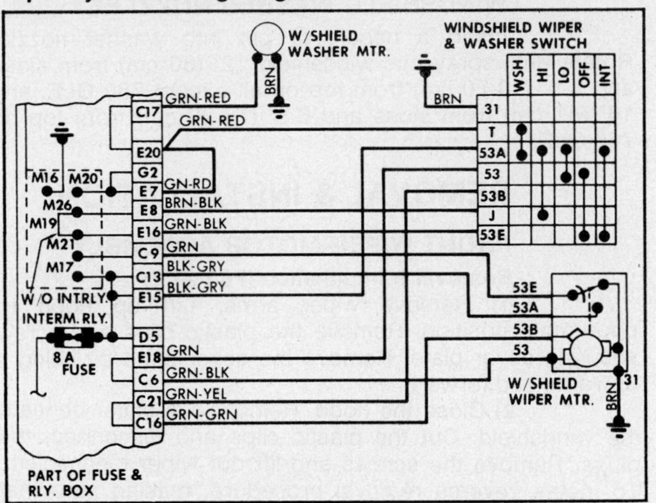

Fig. 4: Rabbit & Rabbit Pickup Wiper System Wiring Diagram

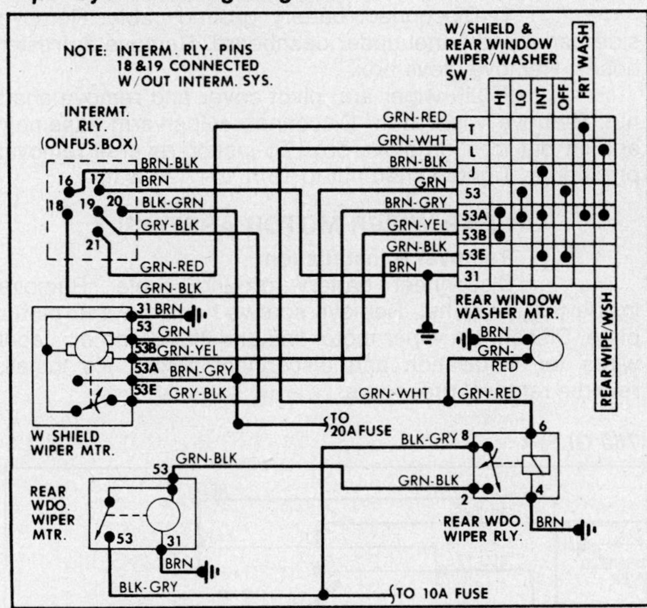

Fig. 5: Vanagon Wiper System Wiring Diagram

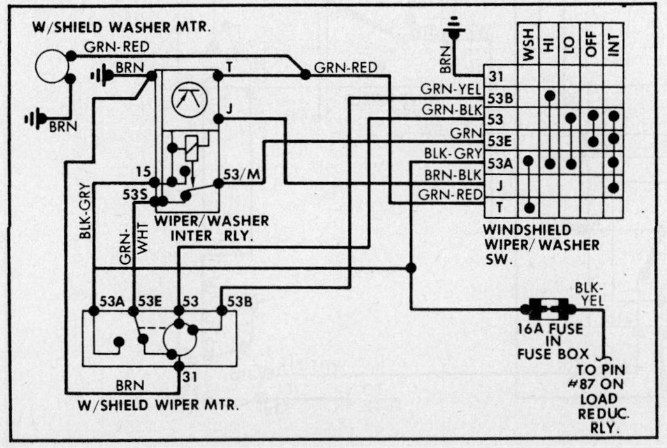

Fig. 6: Scirocco Wiper System Wiring Diagram

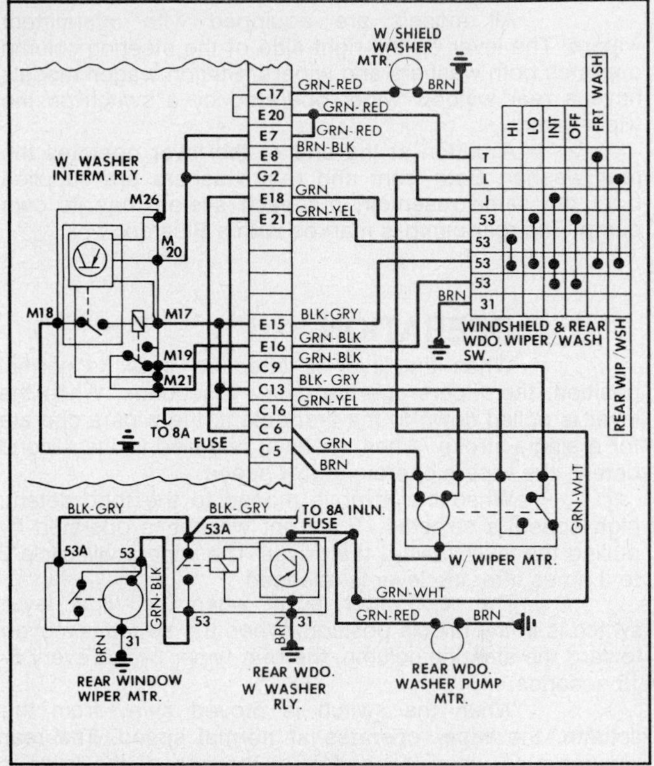

Fig. 7: Quantum Wiper System Wiring Diagram

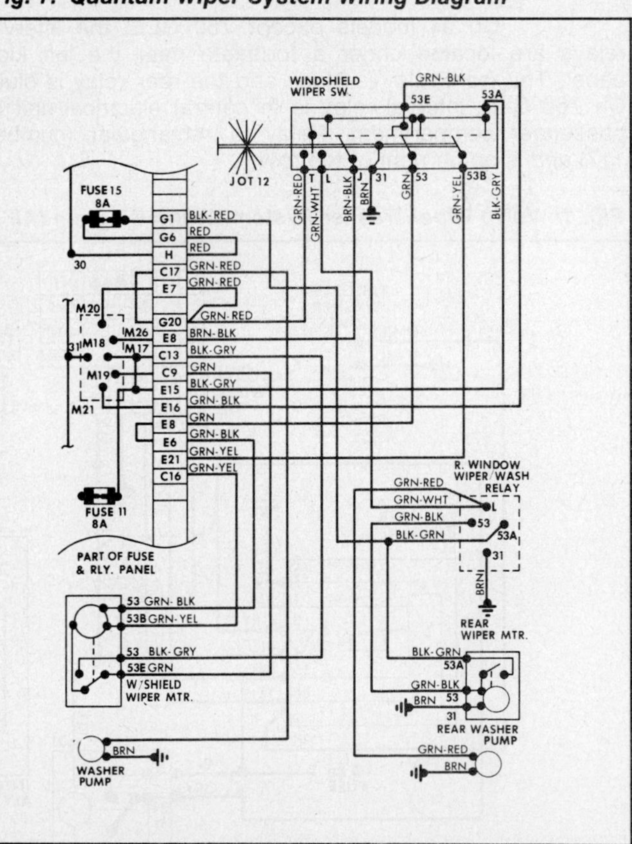

Wiper/Washer Systems

VOLVO

DESCRIPTION

All models are equipped with intermittent wipers. The lever on the right side of the steering column operates both washers and wipers. Station wagon models have a rear window wiper operated by a switch on the wiper lever.

A button at the end of the lever operates the rear washer. Both front and rear washers are supplied from the same reservoir, but each system has its own pump. The rear pump is marked with a Blue dot.

OPERATION

When the lever is lifted up from its normal position, the wipers operate every 7 seconds. When the lever is pulled down to the first detent, the wipers operate for a single stroke. When the lever is pulled to the second detent, the wipers operate at low speed.

When the lever is moved to the third detent, high speed is selected. The front washer is operated by pulling the lever toward the driver. The wipers will cycle 2 to 3 times after the lever is released.

The rear wiper is off when the wiper lever switch is in the middle position. When the switch is moved toward the steering column, the rear wiper cycles every 5-15 seconds.

When the switch is moved away from the column, the wiper operates at normal speed. The rear washer runs when the button at the end of the lever is pressed. The wiper will operate 2 or 3 cycles after the button is released.

On all models except 760 GLE, the interval relays are located under a footplate near the left kick panel. The front relay is black and the rear relay is blue. On 760 GLE, interval relay is in central electrical unit in passenger compartment. Relay is rectangular (number 117) and is on far right of top row.

ADJUSTMENT

WINDSHIELD WASHER NOZZLES

Insert a needle or pin into washer nozzle. Rotate until spray hits windshield 12" (30 cm) from sides and 4-8" (10-20 cm) from top on all except 760 GLE, and 16" (41 cm) from sides and 6-8" (15-20 cm) from top on 760 GLE.

REMOVAL & INSTALLATION

FRONT WIPER MOTOR ASSEMBLY

Removal & Installation (760 GLE)

1) Remove wiper arms. Lift up hood to uppermost position. Remove the plastic clips and screw securing cover plate. Remove the cover plate by lifting it upwards and forward.

2) Close the hood. Remove the cover beneath the windshield. Cut the plastic clips and disconnect the plugs. Remove the screws and lift out wiper mechanism. To install, reverse removal procedure, making sure that wiper motor is in park position.

Removal & Installation (All Other Models)

1) Disconnect battery ground cable. Remove side panel and panel under dashboard. Remove defroster hoses. Remove glove box.

2) Lift wiper arm pivot cover and remove shaft nut. Remove wiper arm. Disconnect wiper arm assembly and lift out through glove box. To install, reverse removal procedure. Tighten shaft nut to 15 ft. lbs. (20 N.m).

REAR WIPER MOTOR ASSEMBLY

Removal & Installation

Disconnect battery ground cable. Remove inside tailgate panel. Remove screws holding wiper motor plate. Disconnect wiper motor link and lift out motor. Label wires for installation and disconnect wiring. To install, reverse removal procedure.

Fig. 1: Volvo Wiper/Washer System Wiring Diagram (All Except 760 GLE)

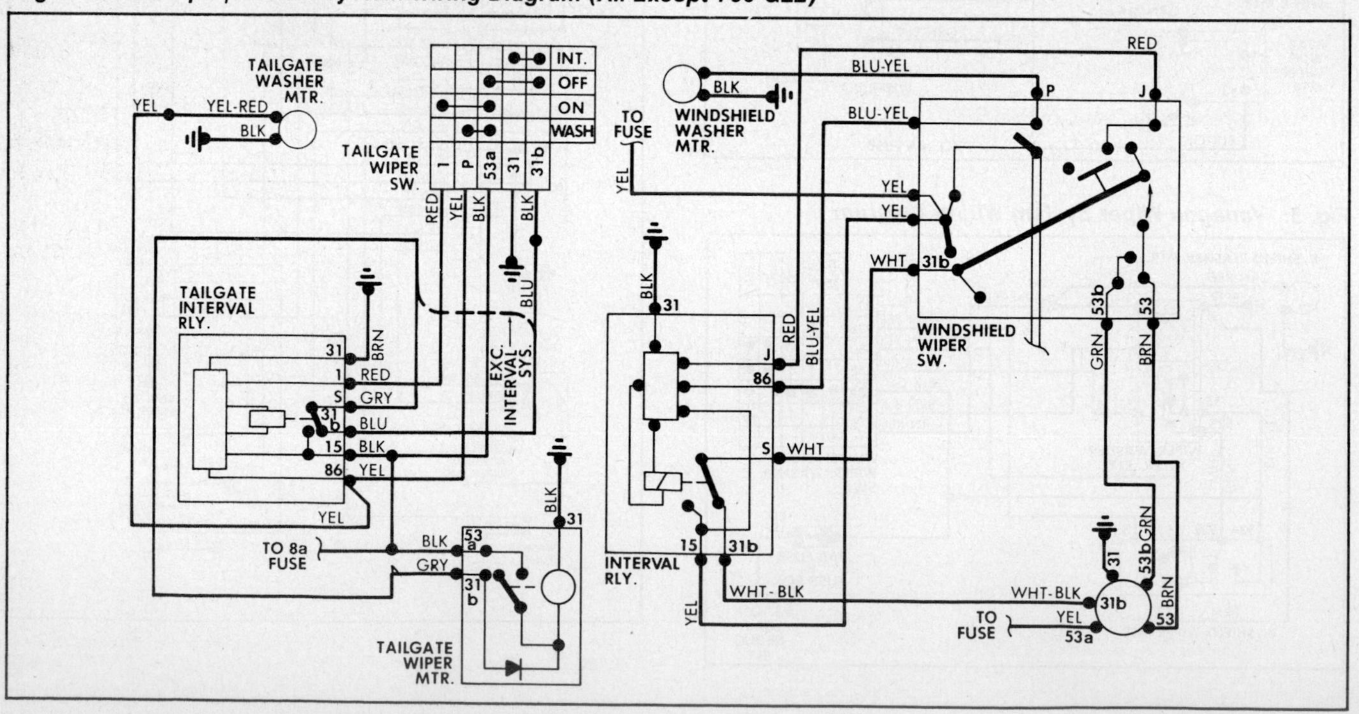

TAILGATE WASHER MTR.
YEL
YEL-RED
BLK
INT.
OFF
ON
WASH
TAILGATE WIPER SW.
1
P
53a
31
31b
RED
YEL
BLK
BLK
BLU
TAILGATE INTERVAL RLY.
31
1
S
31b
15
86
BRN
RED
GRY
BLU
BLK
YEL
EXC. INTERVAL SYS.
TO 8a FUSE
BLK
GRY
53a
31b
31
TAILGATE WIPER MTR.
TO FUSE
WINDSHIELD WASHER MTR.
BLU-YEL
BLU-YEL
RED
P
J
WHT
31b
53b
53
GRN
BRN
WINDSHIELD WIPER SW.
INTERVAL RLY.
J
86
S
15
WHT-BLK
TO FUSE
53a

SECTION 6

ENGINES

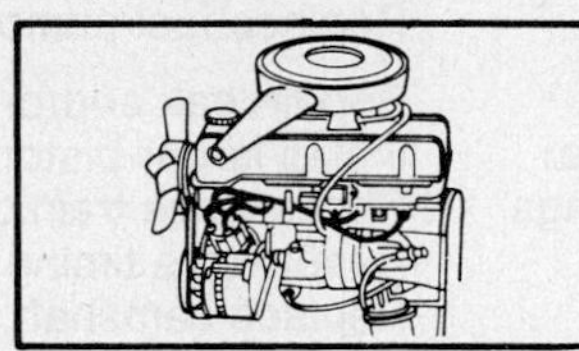

CONTENTS

NOTE: **ALSO SEE GENERAL INDEX.**

Engine Trouble Shooting

GASOLINE ENGINE TROUBLE SHOOTING

CONDITION	POSSIBLE CAUSE	CORRECTION
Engine Lopes At Idle	Intake manifold-to-head leaks	Replace manifold gasket, see ENGINES
	Blown head gasket	Replace head gasket, see ENGINES
	Worn timing gears, chain or sprocket	Replace gears, chain or sprocket
	Worn camshaft lobes	Replace camshaft, see ENGINES
	Overheated engine	Check cooling system, see COOLING
	Blocked crankcase vent valve	Remove restriction
	Leaking EGR valve	Repair leak and/or replace valve
	Faulty fuel pump	Replace fuel pump
Engine Has Low Power	Leaking fuel pump	Repair leak and/or replace fuel pump
	Excessive piston-to-bore clearance	Install larger pistons, see ENGINES
	Sticking valves or weak valve springs	Check valve train components, see ENGINES
	Incorrect valve timing	Reset valve timing, see ENGINES
	Worn camshaft lobes	Replace camshaft, see ENGINES
	Blown head gasket	Replace head gasket, see ENGINES
	Clutch slipping	Adjust pedal and/or replace components, see CLUTCHES
	Engine overheating	Check cooling system, see COOLING
	Auto. trans. pressure regulator valve faulty	Replace pressure regulator valve
	Auto. trans. fluid level too low	Add fluid, see TRANS. SERVICING
	Improper vacuum diverter valve operation	Replace vacuum diverter valve
	Vacuum leaks	Inspect vacuum system and repair as required
	Leaking piston rings	Replace piston rings, see ENGINES
Faulty High Speed Operation	Low fuel pump volume	Replace fuel pump
	Leaking valves or worn valve springs	Replace valves and/or springs, see ENGINES
	Incorrect valve timing	Reset valve timing, see ENGINES
	Intake manifold restricted	Remove restriction
	Worn distributor shaft	Replace distributor
Faulty Acceleration	Improper fuel pump stroke	Remove pump and reset pump stroke
	Incorrect ignition timing	Reset ignition timing, see TUNE-UP
	Leaking valves	Replace valves, see ENGINES
	Worn fuel pump diaphragm or piston	Replace diaphragm or piston
Intake Backfire	Improper ignition timing	Reset ignition timing, see TUNE-UP
	Faulty accelerator pump discharge	Replace accelerator pump
	Improper choke operation	Check choke and adjust as required
	Defective EGR valve	Replace EGR valve
	Fuel mixture too lean	Reset air/fuel mixture, see TUNE-UP
	Choke valve initial clearance too large	Reset choke valve initial clearance
Exhaust Backfire	Vacuum leak	Inspect and repair vacuum system
	Faulty vacuum diverter valve	Replace vacuum diverter valve
	Faulty choke operation	Check choke and adjust as required
	Exhaust system leak	Repair exhaust system leak
Engine Detonation	Ignition timing too far advanced	Reset ignition timing, see TUNE-UP
	Faulty ignition system	Check ignition system, see ELECTRICAL
	Spark plugs loose or faulty	Retighten or replace plugs
	Fuel delivery system clogged	Inspect lines, pump and filter for clog
	EGR valve inoperative	Replace EGR valve
	PCV system inoperative	Inspect and/or replace hoses or valve
	Vacuum leaks	Check vacuum system and repair leaks
	Excessive combustion chamber deposits	Remove built-up deposits
	Leaking, sticking or broken valves	Inspect and/or replace valves
External Oil Leakage	Fuel pump improperly seated or worn gasket	Remove pump, replace gasket and seat properly
	Valve cover gasket broken	Replace valve cover gasket
	Oil filter gasket broken	Replace oil filter and gasket

Engine Trouble Shooting

GASOLINE ENGINE TROUBLE SHOOTING (Cont.)

CONDITION	POSSIBLE CAUSE	CORRECTION
External Oil Leakage (Cont.)	Oil pan gasket broken or pan bent	Straighten pan and replace gasket
	Timing chain cover gasket broken	Replace timing chain cover gasket
	Rear main oil seal worn	Replace rear main oil seal
	Oil pan drain plug not seated properly	Remove and reinstall drain plug
	Camshaft bearing drain hole blocked	Remove restriction
	Oil pressure sending switch leaking	Remove and reinstall sending switch
Excessive Oil Consumption	Worn valve stems or guides	Replace stems or guides, see ENGINES
	Valve "O" ring seals damaged	Replace "O" ring seals, see ENGINES
	Plugged oil drain back holes	Remove restrictions
	Improper PCV valve operation	Replace PCV valve
	Engine oil level too high	Remove excess oil
	Engine oil too thin	Replace with thicker oil
	Valve stem oil deflectors damaged	Replace oil defelctors
	Incorrect piston rings	Replace piston rings, see ENGINES
	Piston ring gaps not staggered	Reinstall piston rings, see ENGINES
	Insufficient piston ring tension	Replace rings, see ENGINES
	Piston ring grooves or oil return slots clogged	Replace piston rings, see ENGINES
	Piston rings sticking in grooves	Replace piston rings, see ENGINES
	Piston ring grooves excessively worn	Replace piston and rings, see ENGINES
	Compression rings installed upside down	Replace compression rings correctly, see ENGINES
	Worn or scored cylinder walls	Rebore cylinders or replace block
	Mismatched oil ring expander and rail	Replace oil ring expander and rail, see ENGINES
	Intake gasket dowels too long	Replace intake gasket dowels
	Excessive main or connecting rod bearing clearance	Replace main or connecting rod bearings, see ENGINES
No Oil Pressure	Low oil level	Add oil to proper level
	Oil pressure sender or gauge broken	Replace sender or gauge
	Oil pump malfunction	Remove and overhaul oil pump, see ENGINES
	Oil pressure relief valve sticking	Remove and reinstall valve
	Oil pump passages blocked	Overhaul oil pump, see ENGINES
	Oil pickup screen or tube blocked	Remove restriction
	Loose oil inlet tube	Tighten oil inlet tube
	Loose camshaft bearings	Replace camshaft bearings, see ENGINES
	Internal leakage at oil passages	Replace block or cylinder head
Low Oil Pressure	Low engine oil level	Add oil to proper level
	Engine oil too thin	Remove and replace with thicker oil
	Excessive oil pump clearance	Reduce oil pump clearance, see ENGINES
	Oil pickup tube or screen blocked	Remove restrictions
	Oil pressure relief spring weak or stuck	Eliminate binding or replace spring
	Main, rod or cam bearing clearance excessive	Replace bearing to reduce clearance, see ENGINES
High Oil Pressure	Improper grade of oil	Replace with proper oil
	Oil pressure relief valve stuck closed	Eliminate binding
	Oil pressure sender or gauge faulty	Replace sender or gauge
Noisy Main Bearings	Inadequate oil supply	Check oil delivery to main bearings
	Excessive main bearing clearance	Replace main bearings, see ENGINES
	Excessive crankshaft end play	Replace crankshaft, see ENGINES
	Loose flywheel or torque converter	Tighten attaching bolts
	Loose or damaged vibration damper	Tighten or replace vibration damper
	Crankshaft journals out-of-round	Re-grind crankshaft journals
	Excessive belt tension	Loosen belt tension

Engine Trouble Shooting

GASOLINE ENGINE TROUBLE SHOOTING (Cont.)

CONDITION	POSSIBLE CAUSE	CORRECTION
Noisy Connecting Rods	Excessive bearing clearance or missing bearing	Replace bearing, see ENGINES
	Crankshaft rod journal out-of-round	Re-grind crankshaft journal
	Misaligned connecting rod or cap	Remove rod or cap and re-align
	Incorrectly tighten rod bolts	Remove and re-tighten rod bolts
Noisy Pistons and Rings	Excessive piston-to-bore clearance	Install larger pistons, see ENGINES
	Bore tapered or out-of-round	Rebore block
	Piston ring broken	Replace piston rings, see ENGINES
	Piston pin loose or seized	Replace piston pin, see ENGINES
	Connecting rods misaligned	Re-align connecting rods
	Ring side clearance too loose or tight	Replace with larger or smaller rings
	Carbon build-up on piston	Remove carbon
Noisy Valve Train	Worn or bent push rods	Replace push rods, see ENGINES
	Worn rocker arms or bridged pivots	Replace rocker arms or pivots, see ENGINES
	Dirt or chips in valve lifters	Remove lifters and remove dirt/chips
	Excessive valve lifter leak-down	Replace valve lifters, see ENGINES
	Valve lifter face worn	Replace valve lifters, see ENGINES
	Broken or cocked valve springs	Replace or reposition springs
	Too much valve stem-to-guide clearance	Replace valve guides, see ENGINES
	Valve bent	Replace valve, see ENGINES
	Loose rocker arms	Retighten rocker arms, see ENGINES
	Excessive valve seat run-out	Re-face valve seats, see ENGINES
	Missing valve lock	Install new valve lock
	Push rod contacting cylinder head	Replace with shorter push rod
	Excessively worn camshaft lobes	Replace camshaft, see ENGINES
	Plugged valve lifter oil holes	Eliminate restriction or replace lifter
	Faulty valve lifter check ball	Replace lifter check ball, see ENGINES
	Rocker arm nut installed upside down	Remove and reinstall correctly
	Valve lifter incorrect for engine	Remove and replace valve lifters
	Faulty push rod seat or lifter plunger	Replace plunger or push rod
Noisy Valves	Improper valve lash	Re-adjust valve lash, see ENGINES
	Worn or dirty valve lifters	Clean and/or replace lifters
	Worn valve guides	Replace valve guides, see ENGINES
	Excessive valve seat or face run-out	Re-face seats or valve face
	Worn camshaft lobes	Replace camshaft, see ENGINES
	Loose rocker arm studs	Re-tighten rocker arm studs, see ENGINES
	Bent push rods	Replace push rods, see ENGINES
	Broken valve springs	Replace valve springs, see ENGINES
Burned, Sticking or Broken Valves	Weak valve springs or warped valves	Replace valves and/or springs, see ENGINES
	Improper lifter clearance	Re-adjust clearance or replace lifters
	Worn guides or improper guide clearance	Replace valve guides, see ENGINES
	Out-of-round valve seats or improper seat width	Re-grind valve seats
	Gum deposits on valve stems, seats or guides	Remove deposits
	Improper sprak timing	Readjust spark timing
Broken Pistons/Rings	Undersize pistons	Replace with larger pistons, see ENGINES
	Wrong piston rings	Replace with correct rings, see ENGINES
	Out-of-round cylinder bore	Re-bore cylinder bore
	Improper connecting rod alignment	Remove and re-align connecting rods
	Excessively worn ring grooves	Replace pistons, see ENGINES
	Improperly assembled piston pins	Re-assemble pin-to-piston, see ENGINES
	Insufficient ring gap clearance	Install new rings, see ENGINES
	Engine overheating	Check cooling system
	Incorrect ignition timing	Re-adjust ignition timing, see TUNE-UP
Excessive Exhaust Noise	Leaks at manifold to head, or to pipe	Replace manifold or pipe gasket
	Exhaust manifold cracked or broken	Replace exhaust manifold, see ENGINES

Engine Trouble Shooting

DIESEL ENGINE TROUBLE SHOOTING

NOTE: **Diesel engine mechanical diagnosis is the same as gasoline engines for items such as noisy valves, bearings, pistons, etc. The following trouble shooting covers only items pertaining to diesel engines**

CONDITION	POSSIBLE CAUSE	CORRECTION
Engine Won't Crank	Bad battery connections or dead batteries	Check connections and/or replace batteries
	Bad starter connections or bad starter	Check connections and/or replace starter
Engine Cranks Slowly, Won't Start	Bad battery connections or dead batteries	Check connections and/or replace batteries
	Engine oil too heavy	Replace engine oil
Engine Cranks Normally, But Will Not Start	Glow plugs not functioning	Check glow plug system, see FUEL
	Glow plug control not functioning	Check glow plug controller, see FUEL
	Fuel not injected into cylinders	Check fuel injectors, see FUEL
	No fuel to injection pump	Check fuel delivery system
	Fuel filter blocked	Replace fuel filter
	Fuel tank filter blocked	Replace fuel tank filter
	Fuel pump not operating	Check pump operation and/or replace pump
	Fuel return system blocked	Inspect system and remove restriction
	No voltage to fuel solenoid	Check solenoid and connections
	Incorrect or contaminated fuel	Replace fuel
	Incorrect injection pump timing	Re-adjust pump timing, see FUEL
	Low compression	Check valves, pistons, rings, see ENGINES
	Injection pump malfunction	Inspect and/or replace injection pump
Engine Starts, Won't Idle	Incorrect slow idle adjustment	Reset idle adjustment, see TUNE-UP
	Fast idle solenoid malfunctioning	Check solenoid and connections
	Fuel return system blocked	Check system and remove restrictions
	Glow plugs go off too soon	See glow plug diagnosis in FUEL
	Injection pump timing incorrect	Reset pump timing, see FUEL
	No fuel to injection pump	Check fuel delivery system
	Incorrect or contaminated fuel	Replace fuel
	Low compression	Check valves, piston, rings, see ENGINES
	Injection pump malfunction	Replace injection pump, see FUEL
	Fuel solenoid closes in RUN position	Check solenoid and connections
Engine Starts/Idles Rough Without Smoke or Noise	Incorrect slow idle adjustment	Reset slow idle, see TUNE-UP
	Injection line fuel leaks	Check lines and connections
	Fuel return system blocked	Check lines and connections
	Air in fuel system	Bleed air from system
	Incorrect or contaminated fuel	Replace fuel
	Injector nozzle malfunction	Test and/or replace nozzles, see FUEL
Engine Starts and Idles Rough Without Smoke or Noise, But Clears After Warm-Up	Injection pump timing incorrect	Reset pump timing, see FUEL
	Engine not fully broken in	Put more miles on engine
	Air in system	Bleed air from system
	Injector nozzle malfunction	Check nozzles, see FUEL
Engine Idles Correctly, Misfires Above Idle	Blocked fuel filter	Replace fuel filter
	Injection pump timing incorrect	Reset pump timing, see FUEL
	Incorrect or contaminated fuel	Replace fuel
Engine Won't Return to Idle	Fast idle adjustment incorrect	Reset fast idle, see TUNE-UP
	Internal injection pump malfunction	Replace injection pump, see FUEL
	External linkage binding	Check linkage and remove binding
Fuel Leaks on Ground	Loose or broken fuel line	Check lines and connections
	Internal injection pump seal leak	Replace injection pump, see FUEL

Engine Trouble Shooting

DIESEL ENGINE TROUBLE SHOOTING (Cont.)

CONDITION	POSSIBLE CAUSE	CORRECTION
Cylinder Knocking Noise	Injector nozzles sticking open	Test injectors and/or replace, see FUEL
	Very low nozzle opening pressure	Test injectors and/or replace
Loss of Engine Power	Restricted air intake	Remove restriction
	EGR valve malfunction	Replace EGR valve
	Blocked or damaged exhaust system	Remove restriction and/or replace components
	Blocked fuel tank filter	Replace filter
	Restricted fuel filter	Remove restriction and/or replace filter
	Blocked vent in gas cap	Remove restriction and/or replace cap
	Tank-to-injection pump fuel supply blocked	Check fuel lines and connections
	Blocked fuel return system	Remove restriction
	Incorrect or contaminated fuel	Replace fuel
	Blocked injector nozzles	Remove nozzle and remove blockage, see FUEL
	Low compression	Check valves, rings, pistons, see ENGINES
Loud Engine Noise With Black Smoke	Basic timing incorrect	Reset timing, see FUEL
	EGR valve malfunction	Replace EGR valve
	Internal injection pump malfunction	Replace injection pump, see FUEL
	Incorrect injector pump housing pressure	Check pressure and adjust, see FUEL
Engine Overheating	Cooling system leaks	Check cooling system and repair leaks
	Belt slipping or damaged	Check tension and/or replace belt
	Thermostat stuck closed	Remove and replace thermostat, see COOLING
	Head gasket leaking	Replace head gasket
Oil Light on at Idle	Low oil pump pressure	Check oil pump operation, see ENGINES
	Oil cooler or line restricted	Remove restriction and/or replace cooler
Engine Won't Shut Off	Injector pump fuel solenoid does not return fuel valve to OFF position	Remove and check solenoid and replace if needed
	VACUUM PUMP DIAGNOSIS	
Excessive Noise	Loose pump-to-drive assembly screws	Tighten screws
	Loose tube on pump assembly	Tighten tube
	Valves not functioning properly	Replace valves
Oil Leakage	Loose end plug	Tighten end plug
	Bad seal crimp	Remove and re-crimp seal

Audi Engines

4000 4-CYLINDER

ENGINE CODING

ENGINE IDENTIFICATION

Engine number is stamped on machined pad near distributor on left side of engine block. Letter prefix indicates engine size.

ENGINE IDENTIFICATION CODE

Engine	Code
1.7L	WT

ENGINE, MANIFOLDS & CYLINDER HEAD

ENGINE

Removal

1) Disconnect battery ground strap. Remove hose from air duct to auxiliary air regulator. Disconnect and remove air intake boot. Remove cold start valve and control pressure regulator with hoses attached.

2) Remove fuel distributor, air flow sensor, fuel injectors, and air cleaner as one unit. Leave fuel lines connected to components. Cap or plug nozzles on fuel injectors and cold start valve.

3) If vehicle is not A/C equipped, proceed to Step **6)**. If A/C equipped, remove grille and condenser. Remove front engine stop bracket located on inner front apron of engine compartment.

4) Loosen nuts on outer half of crankshaft pulley and remove A/C drive belt. Discharge refrigerant from A/C system. Remove hoses from compressor and plug openings. Disconnect wire from compressor clutch.

5) Remove crankcase vent hose from cam cover. Remove compressor-to-mount bolts and remove compressor from vehicle. Remove engine stop from block.

6) Drain coolant by removing lower radiator hose. Remove upper radiator hose and heater hoses from engine. Disconnect electrical plugs from radiator fan and radiator thermo switch. Remove radiator, fan and shroud from vehicle as an assembly.

7) Disconnect clutch cable (if equipped). Label and disconnect all vacuum, ventilation and air hoses connected to engine. Label and disconnect all electrical and ignition wiring connected to engine and accesories.

8) If equipped with cruise control, remove servo and linkage. Remove throttle cable. Remove 3 upper engine-to-transmission bolts. Disconnect exhaust pipe from manifold.

9) Remove cover plate from transmission. If equipped, remove power steering pump after removing drive belt. Lay pump aside with hoses connected. Remove engine stop from lower right front side of engine.

10) Label and disconnect starter cables. Remove starter. Remove right and left engine mount nuts on subframe. On automatic transmission models, remove torque converter bolts through starter hole. Remove bolt from exhaust pipe support.

11) Support transmission with support bar. Position all hoses, linkages and wiring away from engine. Install engine lifting chain. Lift engine until weight is taken off engine mounts. Adjust support bar to bear weight of transmission.

12) Remove remaining engine-to-transmission bolts. Separate engine from transmission. Carefully lift engine from vehicle. Use care not to damage transmission or clutch parts. If equipped with automatic transmission, secure torque converter in place.

Installation

1) To install engine, reverse removal procedure. Carefully guide engine into vehicle and attach to transmission, while keeping weight off engine mounts.

2) Install and tighten upper transmission-to-engine bolts. Remove transmission support bar and lower engine into position on mounts. Install and tighten remaining transmission-to-engine bolts.

3) Final tightening of engine mounts and subframe bolts is done after engine is installed and running at idle speed. Adjust throttle and clutch cables. Recharge A/C if equipped.

CYLINDER HEAD

Removal

1) Disconnect battery ground strap. Remove hose from air intake boot to auxiliary air regulator. Detach and remove air intake boot. Remove cold start valve with hose attached.

2) Remove fuel injectors with lines connected. Unbolt control pressure regulator from block. If possible, leave fuel lines connected to components. Cap or plug nozzles on fuel injectors and cold start valve.

3) Drain coolant from engine. Disconnect coolant hoses which are attached to cylinder head. Label and disconnect all vacuum, air and ventilation hoses attached to cylinder head and intake manifold.

4) Label and disconnect all electrical and ignition wiring attached to cylinder head and intake manifold. Disconnect wire attached to oxygen sensor in exhaust manifold. Remove all drive belts. Remove alternator bracket from cylinder head. Remove upper timing belt cover. Remove cam cover.

5) Remove water pump pulley. Disconnect exhaust pipe from manifold. Disconnect throttle cable. If equipped, remove cruise control servo and linkage. Position No. 1 cylinder on TDC after compression stroke. Loosen timing belt tensioner.

6) Remove timing belt from camshaft sprocket. Loosen head bolts in reverse order of tightening sequence and remove cylinder head with manifolds attached. *See Fig. 1*.

CAUTION: If head bolt(s) require replacement, install new polygon head bolts in complete sets only. Do not retighten polygon head bolts at 1000 mile service or at 1000 mile interval after repairs.

Installation

1) Clean all gasket mating surfaces. Check cylinder head surface for warpage with straight edge. Cylinder head must be resurfaced if distortion exceeds .004" (.10 mm). Minimum thickness of cylinder head after surfacing is 5.219" (132.56 mm). This dimension is measured from face of cylinder head to cam cover gasket surface.

2) Make sure cylinder head bolt holes in block are clean and dry. Place dry cylinder head gasket on cylinder block with word "OBEN" ("TOP") facing upward. Use no sealant on head gasket. Install cylinder head with manifolds. Install head bolts 8 and 10 to align cylinder head, then install remaining head bolts. *See Fig. 1*.

3) Tighten head bolts in 3 steps with engine cold. First step is 29 ft. lbs. (40 N.m). Second step is 43 ft.

4000 4-CYLINDER (Cont.)

lbs. (58 N.m). Third step is to 54 ft. lbs. (73 N.m). Turn bolts an additional 1/4 turn (90°) after final tightening. Install remaining components in reverse order of removal. Ensure valve timing is correct. Adjust timing belt tension and adjust valves.

Fig. 1: Cylinder Head Bolt Tightening Sequence

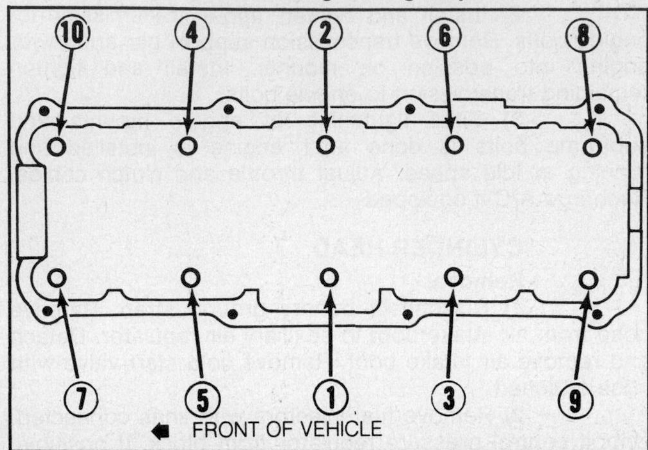
10
4
2
6
8
7
5
1
3
9
FRONT OF VEHICLE

Tighten bolts in 3 steps. Do not retorque polygon bolts following repairs.

CAMSHAFT

TIMING BELT COVER

Removal & Installation

Front cover consists of upper and lower parts. Rear timing belt cover is 1 piece. Remove all drive belts. Remove crankshaft and water pump pulleys. Remove front covers. Install in reverse order of removal.

TIMING BELT & SPROCKET

Removal

1) Remove all drive belts and water pump pulley. Remove upper and lower timing belt covers. Remove cam cover from cylinder head. Turn crankshaft to position No. 1 piston on TDC at end of compression stroke.

Fig. 2: Adjusting Timing Belt Tension

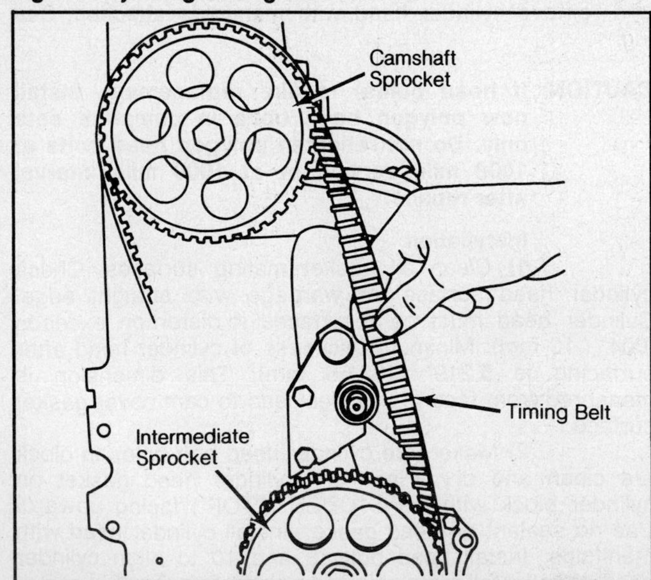
Camshaft
Sprocket
Timing Belt
Intermediate
Sprocket

Tension is correct when belt can be twisted 90° with thumb and finger pressure.

2) Loosen timing belt tensioner to relieve tension on timing belt. Slide timing belt off sprockets. Do not allow camshaft, crankshaft or intermediate sprockets to turn when removing timing belt.

Installation

1) Install new belt onto sprockets. Adjust timing belt tension by turning tensioner clockwise against belt, then tighten.

2) Belt has correct tension when it can be twisted 90° with thumb and finger pressure. Hold belt at point midway between camshaft sprocket and intermediate sprocket. *See Fig. 2.* Ensure valve timing is correct prior to installing remaining components.

VALVE TIMING

1) Turn crankshaft to position No. 1 piston on TDC at end of compression stroke. Zero mark (TDC) on flywheel should align with timing pointer. Distributor rotor should point to notch on distributor housing (No. 1 cylinder).

2) Turn camshaft until mark on camshaft sprocket is aligned with upper edge of timing belt rear cover. Both camshaft lobes of No. 1 cylinder should point upward at 45° to camshaft follower. *See Fig. 3.* Install timing belt and adjust tension. Recheck valve timing.

Fig. 3: Aligning Camshaft Sprocket

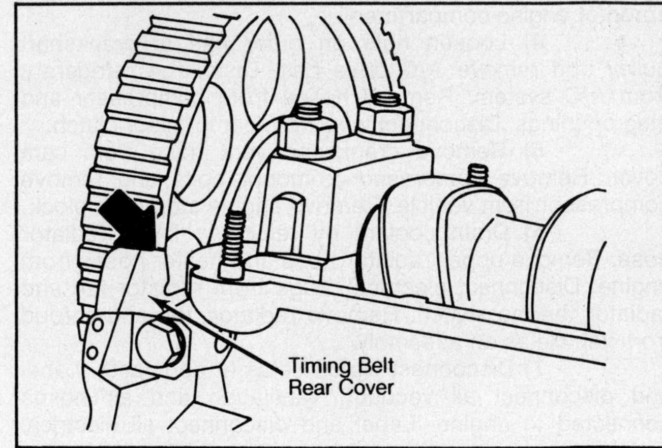
Timing Belt
Rear Cover

Align mark (notch or dot) on camshaft sprocket with upper edge of timing belt rear cover.

CAMSHAFT

Removal

1) If necessary, remove drive belts. Remove upper timing belt cover. Remove cam cover from cylinder head. Turn crankshaft to position No. 1 piston on TDC at end of compression stroke.

2) Loosen timing belt tensioner to relieve tension on timing belt. Remove timing belt from camshaft sprocket.

3) If necessary, mark positions of camshaft bearing caps. Remove bearing caps 1, 3, and 5. In a diagonal pattern, loosen nuts on bearing caps 2 and 4. Make sure to loosen nuts in progressive steps. Remove bearing caps and lift out camshaft.

Installation

1) Prior to installing camshaft, lubricate camshaft journals and bearing surfaces in cylinder head and

4000 4-CYLINDER (Cont.)

caps. Install camshaft. Install caps 2 and 4, making sure caps are not misaligned. *See Fig. 4.* Tigthen cap nuts progressively in diagonal pattern until caps are flush with head surface.

2) Install bearing caps 1, 3 and 5. Ensure caps are not misaligned. Tighten all bearing caps. Install remaining components in reverse order of removal. Make sure valve timing and belt tension are correct before starting engine.

Fig. 4: Checking Camshaft Bearing Cap Alignment

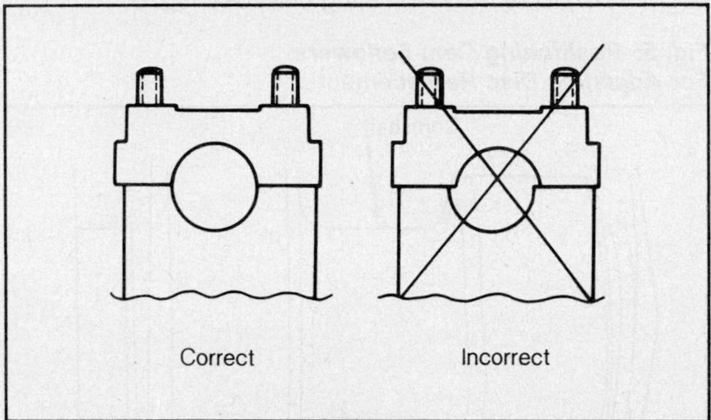
Correct
Incorrect

Tighten camshaft bearing caps to 14 ft. lbs. (20 N.m).

CAMSHAFT OIL SEAL

Removal

1) Remove upper timing belt cover. Position No. 1 piston on TDC at end of compression stroke. Loosen tensioner pulley to relieve tension on timing belt.

2) Remove timing belt and camshaft sprocket. Remove Woodruff key from camshaft. Use seal remover tool (10-221) to remove oil seal.

Installation

1) Install protective sleeve of seal installing tool (10-203) over camshaft. Coat seal lips with oil. Push seal over sleeve and into position.

2) Using seal installing tool (10-203), press seal into bearing cap recess until flush. Install remaining components in reverse order of removal. Check that valve timing is correct.

CAMSHAFT END PLAY

1) Check camshaft end play with cam followers removed. Attach dial indicator with tip on end of camshaft (or sprocket) at 90° to face of sprocket. Push camshaft rearward and zero dial indicator.

2) Push camshaft forward to record maximum movement. If end play exceeds .006" (.15 mm), check camshaft thrust flange and bearing cap for wear. Replace worn components.

INTERMEDIATE SHAFT

1) Use a dial indicator to measure intermediate shaft end play. Maximum end play is .010" (.25 mm). Make sure to remove distributor prior to removing intermediate shaft.

2) If oil seal replacement is necessary, remove oil seal flange and press out seal. Lubricate new seal lips with oil. Install oil seal flange with oil return hole at bottom edge. Use seal installation tool (10-203) to press seal into place.

VALVES

VALVE ARRANGEMENT

E-I-E-I-I-E-I-E (Front-to-rear)

VALVE GUIDE SERVICING

Inspection

1) Clean valve guides. Attach dial indicator and adapting fixture (VW 387 or US 4420A) to mounting surface of cylinder head. Insert a new valve into valve guide. Valve stem end must be flush with upper end of valve guide.

2) Rock valve back and forth against dial indicator point to measure amount of stem-to-guide clearance. Maximum clearance is .039" (1.0 mm) for intake valves and .051" (1.3 mm) for exhaust valves. Check valve seat condition before replacing guides.

Removal

Use press and valve guide remover/installer tool (10-206) to remove and install valve guides. Press guides out from combustion chamber side of head.

Installation

Coat new guide with oil. Press guide into cold cylinder head from camshaft side of head. Do not use more than 1 ton of pressure or guide shoulder may break. Ream guide by hand to proper size.

VALVE & VALVE SEAT SERVICING

1) New design intake and exhaust valves with 3 keeper grooves and chamfered spring retainers have been introduced by manufacturer. Old and new design valves may be installed in same engine, but keepers and spring retainers are not interchangeable.

2) Valves are available with stems shortened by .02" (.5 mm). Use these valves if seats are cut too much during cylinder head servicing. These valves will allow use of thickest valve adjusting disc. Cylinder head must be replaced if correction angle and seat width cannot be maintained.

3) Intake valve seat is cut at 45° angle. Using 30° cutter, narrow intake seat to .079" (2.00 mm). Exhaust valve seat is cut at 45° angle. Using 30° cutter, narrow seat to .094" (2.39 mm). Intake valve seat diameter limit is 1.306" (33.17 mm). Exhaust valve seat diameter limit is 1.212" (30.79 mm).

4) If valves are to be reused, check stem diameter and margin. Minimum intake valve stem diameter is .314" (7.97 mm). Minimum exhaust valve stem diameter is .313" (7.95 mm). Valve head margin cannot be less than .02" (.5 mm). Valve margin is measured from edge of 45° valve face to edge of chamfer on valve head in direction opposite stem. Head margin is same for intake and exhaust valves.

5) Exhaust valves must be lapped by hand. Do not use machine for this purpose. Be sure to remove all traces of grinding compound from valves and guides after valves have been lapped into seats.

VALVE STEM OIL SEALS

NOTE: **Valve stem oil seals may be replaced with cylinder head installed on vehicle.**

Removal

1) Remove camshaft, valve adjusting disc and cam follower. Remove spark plug of cylinder to be

Audi Engines

4000 4-CYLINDER (Cont.)

serviced. Place piston of cylinder to be serviced at bottom of stroke (BDC). Install air hose and adapter (VW 653/3) in spark plug hole and apply air pressure.

CAUTION: Be aware that engine can rotate due to air pressure if piston is not at true BDC. Keep hands clear of belts and pulleys.

2) Do not remove air pressure until valve spring components are reassembled. Using valve spring compressor (VW 541), compress valve spring and remove keepers, retainer, and springs. Lift seal off valve stem.

Installation

Slide plastic protective sleeve onto valve stem. Lubricate new seal and push into place with seal installing tool (10-204). Install remaining components in reverse order of removal. Make sure valve timing is correct.

CAUTION: Installing valve stem oil seal without using plastic protective sleeve of seal installing tool (10-204), may result in seal damage and excessive oil consumption.

VALVE SPRINGS

Valve springs may be replaced with cylinder head installed on vehicle. To replace valve springs, use removal and installation procedure explained in *VALVE STEM OIL SEALS*.

CAM FOLLOWERS

When removing cam followers, keep them in order for reassembly. Remove camshaft and adjusting discs to gain access to cam followers. Remove cam followers and inspect for wear and damage. Replace as necessary. Lightly oil cam followers prior to installing.

VALVE CLEARANCE ADJUSTMENT

NOTE: Cold valve clearances are given for initial settings when engine work has been performed. Recheck valve clearance and make final adjustment with engine coolant temperature about 95°F (35°C).

Measuring Valve Clearance

1) Remove accelerator linkage, upper timing belt cover and cam cover. Turn crankshaft clockwise until cam lobes of cylinder to be adjusted point upward at 45° to follower surface.

CAUTION: Never use camshaft sprocket attaching bolt to turn camshaft, as this may stretch timing belt.

2) Using a feeler gauge, measure valve clearances of each cylinder in firing order 1-3-4-2. Adjust valve clearance if not within specified range.

VALVE CLEARANCE SPECIFICATIONS

Application	In. (mm)
Intake	
Hot	.008-.012 (.20-.30)
Cold	.006-.010 (.15-.25)
Exhaust	
Hot	.016-.020 (.40-.51)
Cold	.014-.018 (.36-.46)

NOTE: When cylinder head service has been performed, valve clearance must be checked and adjusted after 1000 miles.

Adjusting Valve Clearance

1) To remove adjusting disc, cam follower must be depressed using compressing tool (VW 546 or 2078). Make sure correct tool is used as shown in decal on cam cover. Turn cam followers so that grooves are accessible for removing tool. *See Fig. 5.* Using compressing tool, depress cam follower. Use disc remover (10-208 or US 4476) to remove adjusting disc. *See Fig. 6.*

Fig. 5: Positioning Cam Followers For Adjusting Disc Replacement

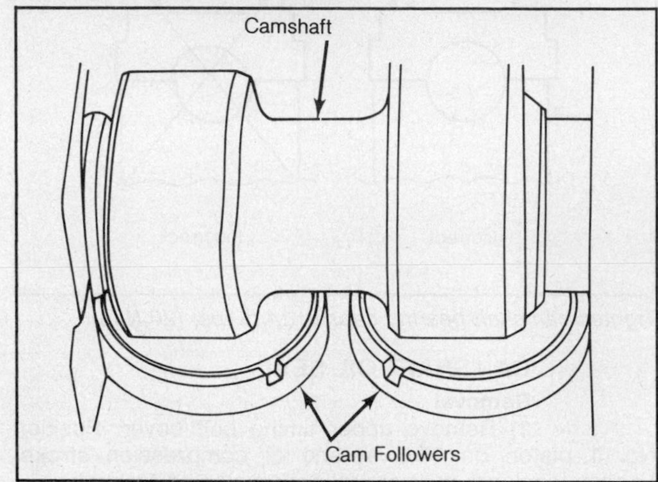
Camshaft
Cam Followers

Fig. 6: Compressing Cam Follower For Adjusting Disc Replacement

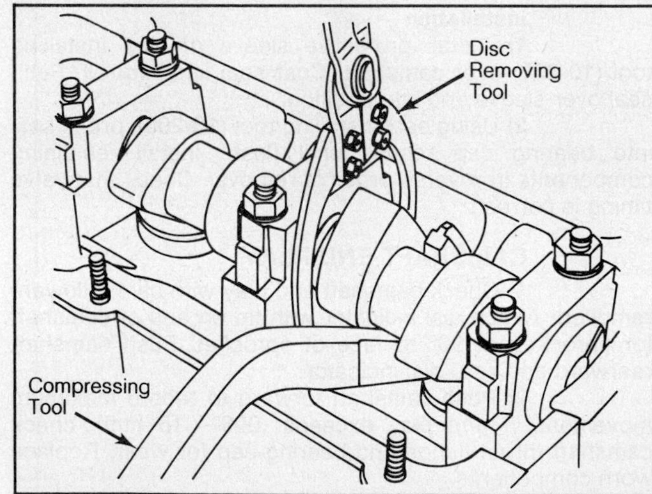
Disc
Removing
Tool
Compressing
Tool

Install adjusting disc with thickness marking on side away from lobe.

2) Thickness of adjusting disc is stamped on bottom of disc. If measured valve clearance is larger than specifications, use a thicker disc. If clearance is less than specification, use a thinner disc.

3) Adjust clearance to middle of tolerance range.Adjusting discs are available in .002" (.05 mm) increments from .118" (3.0 mm) to .167" (4.25 mm).

4) To install discs, depress cam followers and slip discs into place. Ensure side of disc with thickness

4000 4-CYLINDER (Cont.)

marking is installed down, facing cam follower. Repeat procedure until all valves are properly adjusted.

PISTONS, PINS & RINGS

OIL PAN

Removal

Drain engine oil. Attach a lifting device or support bar to engine. Raise engine slightly to support engine weight. Remove cover plate under engine. Remove 4 subframe bolts and lower sub frame out of way. Remove oil pan.

Installation

Assemble connecting rod to piston. Arrow on piston head and forged casting beads on connecting rod must face toward front of engine when assembly is installed. Use piston pin tool (VW 207c) to install piston pin. Install circlip into pin bore groove.

PISTON & ROD ASSEMBLY

NOTE: **All connecting rods must be in same weight class. Connecting rods with same weight class are only available in sets of 4.**

Removal

1) Remove cylinder head, oil pan and oil pump. Place piston to be removed at bottom of cylinder and cover with cloth to collect metal cuttings. Using ridge reamer, remove ridge or deposit from upper end of cylinder bore.

2) Before removing piston and rod from engine, ensure rod and rod cap are marked for cylinder identification. Remove rod cap and carefully push piston and rod out top of cylinder. Install rod cap on rod from which removed.

Installation

1) Coat cylinder bore, piston and rings with engine oil. Ensure ring gaps are spaced 120° apart. Install ring compressor on piston, making sure position of rings does not change.

2) Install piston and rod in its respective bore, with arrow on piston head facing toward front of engine. Forged casting beads on rod and cap must also face toward front of engine. Make sure rod bolts are covered with hose or tape so rod journals on crankshaft are not damaged.

FITTING PISTONS

1) Take 2 cylinder bore measurements with inside micrometer or cylinder bore gauge. Take 1 at 90° to crankshaft centerline and 1 in line with crankshaft centerline as follows: 3/8" from top of bore, at middle of bore and 3/8" from bottom of bore.

2) Difference between the corresponding measurements is cylinder out-of-round. Measure piston diameter 90° to piston pin bore, approximately 9/16" from bottom of piston skirt. Compare this measurement with measurement of corresponding cylinder bore.

3) Install oversize pistons if piston-to-cylinder clearance is excessive. Four sets of pistons are available with 3 sizes in each set. Pistons have 4-digit number marked on face, which gives diameter in millimeters.

FITTING RINGS

1) Place piston rings squarely into cylinder bore about 5/8" from bottom of bore. Use a feeler gauge to measure ring end gap.

2) With rings installed on piston, use a feeler gauge to measure ring side clearance. Take measurement around entire circumference of piston, between top of ring and ring land.

3) Install rings on piston with "TOP" mark facing upward. Recessed edge on outside of center ring must face piston pin. Space ring end gaps 120° apart.

PISTON PIN REPLACEMENT

Removal

Remove circlip from pin bore groove. Use piston pin tool (VW 207c) to remove and install piston pins. If pins are very tight, warm pistons to 140° F (60° C).

Installation

Assemble connecting rod to piston. Arrow on piston head and forged casting beads on connecting rod must face toward front of engine when assembly is installed. Use piston pin tool (VW 207c) to install piston pin. Install circlip into pin bore groove.

CRANKSHAFT MAIN & CONNECTING ROD BEARINGS

CRANKSHAFT MAIN BEARINGS

1) Main bearings are numbered 1 through 5 (front to rear). Never interchange bearing caps. Always measure main bearing clearances 1 at a time.

2) Use Plastigage method for measuring bearing clearances. Ensure oil film is removed from bearing halves and crankshaft journal prior to measuring clearance.

3) With Plastigage in place, install bearing cap and tighten to specification. Do not allow crankshaft to turn. Remove bearing cap. Measure flattened width of Plastigage with scale furnished to determine clearance.

4) When replacing bearings, install grooved bearing halves into cylinder block. Plain bearing halves are installed in main caps. Lubricate crankshaft journal and bearings prior to installing bearings.

CONNECTING ROD BEARINGS

1) Always measure connecting rod bearing clearances 1 at a time. Use Plastigage method for measuring bearing clearances. Ensure oil film is removed from bearing halves and crankshaft journal prior to measuring clearance.

2) With Plastigage in place, install bearing cap and tighten to specification. Do not allow crankshaft to turn. Remove bearing cap. Measure flattened width of Plastigage with scale furnished to determine clearance.

3) Use a feeler gauge to check connecting rod side clearance. Insert feeler gauge between connecting rod and crankshaft thrust face.

CRANKSHAFT END PLAY

Use a feeler gauge to check crankshaft end play. Insert feeler gauge between No. 3 main bearing (thrust bearing) and crankshaft thrust face.

REAR MAIN BEARING OIL SEAL

Removal

Remove transmission and flywheel. Carefully pry oil seal from seal flange.

Audi Engines

4000 4-CYLINDER (Cont.)

Installation

Coat new seal lips with oil. Position seal in place. Place centering sleeve (2003/2A) on crankshaft and start seal into place. Using seal installing tool (2003/1), press in seal until seated. Install remaining components. Use Loctite on flywheel bolts.

FRONT MAIN BEARING OIL SEAL

Removal

1) Remove all drive belts. Remove upper timing belt cover. Set No. 1 piston on TDC after compression stroke. Remove crankshaft pulley. Loosen crankshaft sprocket bolt. Remove water pump pulley.

2) Remove lower timing belt cover. Loosen timing belt tensioner. Remove drive sprocket and timing belt. Using seal removing tool (10-221), carefully pry oil seal from flanged cover.

Installation

Coat lips of new seal with oil. Using installation tool (10-203), press new seal into place. Press in seal to a depth of .08" (2 mm) below outer edge of cover. Install remaining components. Coat timing belt drive sprocket attaching bolt with Loctite before installing. Ensure valve timing is correct.

ENGINE OILING

CRANKCASE CAPACITY

Capacity is 2.6 quarts (2.5L) without filter replacement; 3.2 quarts (3.0L) with filter replacement.

NORMAL OIL PRESSURE

Minimum oil pressure is 29 psi (2.0 kg/cm²) at 2000 RPM, with oil temperature of 176° F (80° C). Specification is for 20W/20 type engine oil.

ENGINE OILING SYSTEM

Oiling system is a pressure feed system. A gear-type oil pump lifts oil from oil pan and pressure feeds it to crankshaft journals, camshaft bearings and intermediate shaft. Other parts of system receive oil lubrication by drainage or splash method.

OIL PUMP

Removal & Disassembly

Remove oil pan. Remove oil pump attaching bolts and lower pump away from engine. Remove pump pickup bolts. Separate pickup from pump body. Remove strainer cover from pickup tube and clean strainer.

Inspection

1) With oil pump gears installed in pump housing, insert feeler gauge between drive gear and driven gear teeth (where teeth mesh). Measure pump gear backlash. Maximum backlash is .002-.008" (.05-.20 mm).

2) Lay a straightedge over pump housing. Insert feeler gauge between pump gears and straightedge. Maximum end play of gears is .006" (.15 mm).

Reassembly & Installation

Assemble pump in reverse order of disassembly. Prime oil pump prior to installing. Install pump in reverse order of removal procedures. Make sure engine has oil pressure after starting.

ENGINE COOLING

CAUTION: Coolant should be used at all times. Only ethylene glycol based (phosphate-free) antifreeze may be used. This coolant protects against corrosion in aluminum/iron engines.

THERMOSTAT

Thermostat begins opening at 194°F (90°C) and is fully open at 216°F (102°C). When installing thermostat, make sure arrow on thermostat housing points toward fender. Always replace "O" ring between water pump housing and thermostat housing.

COOLANT CAPACITY

Capacity is 7.4 quarts (7.0L). 50/50 mixture of antifreeze and water provides protection to -31°F (-35°C).

EXPANSION TANK CAP

Pressure relief valve of cap opens in range of 17-23 psi (1.2-1.6 kg/cm²).

WATER PUMP

Removal & Disassembly

Drain coolant. Remove alternator and drive belt. Remove coolant hoses to pump housing. Remove water pump pulley. Remove pump housing attaching bolts from engine. Remove pump assembly. Remove attaching bolts and separate water pump from pump housing.

Reassembly & Installation

To reassemble, reverse disassembly procedure. Use new gasket between pump and housing. When installing pump assembly, use new "O" ring between pump housing and engine. Open heater control valve fully and fill cooling system. Make sure coolant circulates (thermostat opens) and radiator cooling fan cycles.

TIGHTENING SPECIFICATIONS

Application	Ft. Lbs. (N.m)
Camshaft Bearing Caps	14 (20)
Camshaft Sprocket	58 (80)
Connecting Rod Caps	33 (45)
Crankshaft Pulley	14 (20)
Crankshaft Sprocket [1]	58 (80)
Cylinder Head Bolts (Engine Cold)	
Step 1	29 (40)
Step 2	43 (60)
Step 3 [2]	54 (75)
Engine-to-Transmission Bolts	40 (55)
Flywheel-to-Crankshaft [1]	54 (75)
Manifolds	18 (25)
Intermediate Shaft Sprocket	58 (80)
Main Bearing Caps	47 (65)
Timing Belt Tensioner Nut	33 (45)

[1] – Use Loctite 270.

[2] – After tightening to 54 ft. lbs. (75 N.m), turn bolt an additional 1/4 turn.

4000 4-CYLINDER (Cont.)

ENGINE SPECIFICATIONS

GENERAL SPECIFICATIONS

Year	DISPLACEMENT		Fuel System	HP@RPM	Torque Ft. Lbs.@RPM	Compr. Ratio	BORE		STROKE	
	Cu. In.	Liters					In.	mm	In.	mm
1983	105	1.7	Fuel Inj.	74@5000	94@3000	8.2:1	3.13	79.5	3.40	86.4

VALVES

Engine Size & Valve	Head Diam. In. (mm)	Face Angle	Seat Angle	Seat Width In. (mm)	Stem Diameter In. (mm)	Stem Clearance In. (mm)	Valve Lift In. (mm)
1.7L							
Intake [1]	1.338 (33.99)	45°	45°	.079 (2.01)	.314 Min. (7.98)	.020 Max. (.50)	.....
Exhaust [1]	1.220 (31.00)	45°	45°	.094 (2.40)	.313 Min. (7.95)	.026 Max. (.65)	.....

[1] – Valves are available with stems .02" (.5 mm) shorter than standard size.

PISTONS, PINS, RINGS

Engine	PISTONS	PINS		RINGS		
	Clearance In. (mm)	Piston Fit In. (mm)	Rod Fit In. (mm)	Ring No.	End Gap In. (mm)	Side Clearance In. (mm)
1.7L	.0011 [1] (.028)	[2]	.....	All	.012-.018 [3] (.30-.46)	.0008-.0020 [4] (.020-.050)

[1] – Wear limit is .003" (.07 mm).
[2] – Light press fit at 140°F (60°C).
[3] – Wear limit is .040" (1.02 mm).
[4] – Wear limit is .006" (.15 mm).

CRANKSHAFT MAIN & CONNECTING ROD BEARINGS

Engine	MAIN BEARINGS				CONNECTING ROD BEARINGS		
	Journal Diam. In. (mm)	Clearance In. (mm)	Thrust Bearing	Crankshaft End Play In. (mm)	Journal Diam. In. (mm)	Clearance In. (mm)	Side Play In. (mm)
1.7L							
Std. Size	2.125 [1] (53.97)	.001-.003 [2] (.03-.07)	No. 3	.003-.007 [3] (.07-.17)	1.810 [1] (45.97)	.0011-.0034 [4] (.028-.086)	.015 (.38)
1st U/Size	2.115 (53.72)				1.800 (45.72)		
2nd U/Size	2.105 (53.47)				1.790 (45.47)		
3rd U/Size	2.095 (53.22)				1.780 (45.22)		

[1] – Maximum out-of-round for standard or undersize crankshaft journals is .001" (.03 mm).
[2] – Wear limit is .007" (.17 mm).
[3] – Wear limit is .010" (.25 mm).
[4] – Wear limit is .005" (.12 mm).

4000 4-CYLINDER DIESEL & TURBO DIESEL

ENGINE CODING

ENGINE IDENTIFICATION

Engine number is stamped on machined pad on left side of block, just below head. Letter prefix indicates engine type and size.

ENGINE IDENTIFICATION CODE

Engine	Code
Diesel (1.6L)	JK
Turbo Diesel (1.6L)	CY

ENGINE, MANIFOLDS & CYLINDER HEAD

ENGINE

Removal

1) Disconnect battery ground strap. Remove engine cover plate and transmission cover plate. Fully open heater control valve and open cap on expansion tank. Drain coolant by removing lower radiator hose and heater hose from water pump housing.

2) If A/C equipped, do not loosen any A/C system hoses. Detach radiator cowl from radiator and remove complete with both fans. Remove front grille and detach condensor from radiator. Remove radiator.

3) On models without A/C, disconnect electrical plugs from fan and thermoswitch. Remove radiator with fan attached. Remove fuel supply line and fuel return line from injector pump. Disconnect accelerator cable from pump lever and detach bracket from pump body.

4) Disconnect cold start cable at pin and detach retaining washer from bracket. Disconnect wire from fuel shut-off solenoid. Remove gear shift light switch complete with wiring from bracket.

5) Disconnect wiring from oil pressure switch, coolant temperature sensors, glow plugs and thermoswitch. Detach coolant hose at rear of head. Disconnect clutch cable from bracket and clutch lever.

6) Remove top nuts (1 each) from right and left engine mounts. Remove vacuum pump hose at reservoir. Remove alternator. Remove front engine stop. If A/C equipped, remove crankshaft pulley nuts and compressor belt.

7) Remove bolts attaching compressor bracket to engine. Remove compressor with bracket attached. Secure compressor and bracket assembly away from engine. Ensure A/C hoses are not under tension.

8) Remove exhaust pipe from manifold (or turbocharger). Disconnect starter cable from starter and intermediate plate. Remove bolt from exhaust support bracket at transmission. Remove starter. Remove 2 lower transmission-to-engine bolts. Remove flywheel cover plate bolts.

9) Support transmission with transmission support bar (VW 785/1B or equivalent). Attach lifting chain to engine. Lift engine and transmission until transmission housing touches steering rack. Adjust transmission support bar to contact transmission.

10) Remove remaining transmission-to-engine bolts. Separate engine from transmission. Carefully lift engine from vehicle.

Installation

1) Prior to installing engine, attach intermediate plate to rear of engine (over dowel sleeves). Use grease to hold plate in position. Place starter on engine carrier (support) before installing engine.

2) Install engine in reverse order of removal procedures. Use care not to interchange fuel supply and return union bolts. Fuel return union bolt is marked "OUT" on head. Adjust throttle and clutch cables. Adjust tension of A/C compressor belt with shims on crankshaft pulley.

CYLINDER HEAD

Removal

1) Disconnect battery ground strap. Remove air cleaner, duct and air filter. Drain coolant from engine. Remove cam cover and timing belt cover. Label and disconnect all wires, hoses and lines that may interfere with cylinder head removal.

NOTE: Do not allow diesel fuel to contact coolant hoses. Diesel fuel will damage hoses.

2) Remove and plug fuel lines at injectors. Set No. 1 piston on TDC after compression stroke. Secure camshaft in place by installing camshaft holding tool (2065A) in slot at rear of camshaft.

3) Insert locking pin (2064) through holes in pump sprocket and mounting bracket. This locks pump in place. Check that timing marks on injection pump sprocket, pump body and mounting plate are aligned. Also, ensure TDC mark on flywheel is aligned with reference mark on bell housing.

4) Loosen timing belt tensioner to relieve tension on timing belt. Remove crankshaft pulley. Remove timing belt. Disconnect accelerator cable from injection pump.

5) On non-turbo models, disconnect exhaust pipe support bracket from transmission. Disconnect exhaust pipe from manifold. Remove exhaust manifold from cylinder head. Remove cylinder head. Remove injectors and glow plugs prior to servicing head.

6) On turbocharged models, remove engine and transmission cover plate. Loosen stabilizer bar clamps and push stabilizer bar downward. Disconnect oil return line from turbocharger and engine support. Remove oil return line.

7) Remove turbocharger heat shield. Remove hoses between turbocharger, intake manifold and air cleaner. Remove oil supply line. Disconnect exhaust pipe from turbocharger.

8) Disconnect turbocharger from exhaust manifold and remove. Remove exhaust manifold. Remove cylinder head. Remove injectors and glow plugs prior to servicing head.

9) Measure cylinder head for warpage. Maximum distortion is .004" (.10 mm). Diesel heads must not be resurfaced. Replace head if warping exceeds limit. Always replace injector heat shields. Check injector overflow/return hoses and replace if brittle or splitting.

CAUTION: Cylinder head gaskets have identification notches next to part number. Notches indicate thickness of head gasket. If new pistons or short block is installed, measure the height pistons project above cylinder block deck when piston is at TDC. Select new head gasket according to maximum measured piston height.

10) If piston height is .025-.032" (.63-.82 mm), use head gasket with 1 notch. If piston height is .033-.036"

4000 4-CYLINDER DIESEL & TURBO DIESEL (Cont.)

(.83-.92 mm), use gasket with 2 notches.If piston height is .037-.040" (.93--1.02 mm), use gasket with 3 notches.

CAUTION: Diesel and Turbo-diesel head gaskets do not use the same material. Head gaskets are not interchangeable.

Installation

1) Clean all gasket mating surfaces. Make sure that cylinder head bolt holes are clean and dry. If short block or new pistons have not been installed, install new head gasket that has same amount of identification notches as old gasket. Word "OBEN" on gasket must face upward.

2) Position head over cylinder block. Install head bolts 8 and 10 to align cylinder head. Install remaining bolts and tighten in sequence. *See Fig. 1.*

Fig. 1: Cylinder Head Tightening Sequence

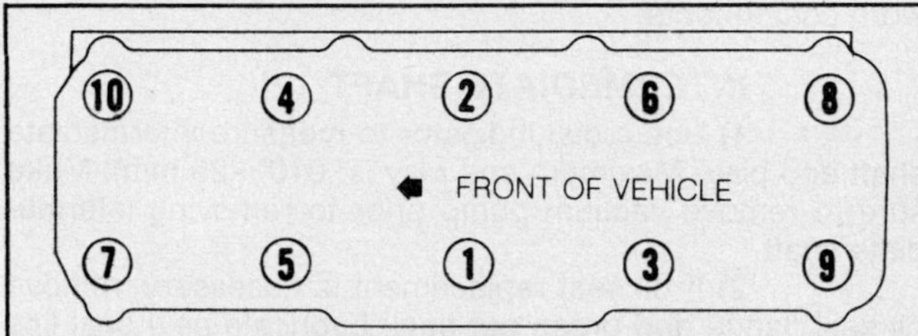
10
4
2
6
8
FRONT OF VEHICLE
7
5
1
3
9

Install bolts 8 and 10 first to align cylinder head.

3) Tighten head bolts in 3 steps, turning bolts an additional 1/2 turn (180°) after final tightening. *See Fig. 1.* Install timing belt. Ensure valve timing and pump timing are correct. Adjust timing belt tension. Adjust valves.

CAUTION: Piston and valve clearance is critical on diesel engines. Internal engine damage will occur if valve timing is incorrect.

4) Before installing turbocharger, coat exhaust manifold-to-turbocharger bolts (heads and threads) with high temperature grease. Also, fill oil supply line connection at top of turbocharger with engine oil prior to installing oil supply line. Run engine at idle for 1 minute to lubricate turbocharger.

5) Install remaining components. Always use new injector heat shields. Tighten injectors to 51 ft. lbs. (69 N.m) and replace injector overflow/return hoses if brittle or cracking. Head bolts must be retightened after engine has been allowed to reach normal operating temperature.

6) With engine warm, tighten head bolts additional 1/4 turn (90°) in sequence. After 1000 miles, tighten head bolts additional 1/4 turn (90°). Do not back off bolts before retightening at any time. Engine may be cold or warm for 1000 mile head bolt retightening. Check valve adjustment.

CAMSHAFT

TIMING BELT & SPROCKET

Removal

1) Remove timing belt cover and cam cover. Turn crankshaft to place No. 1 piston on TDC at end of compression stroke. Lobes of camshaft on No. 1 cylinder must point upward at 45°. Check TDC mark on flywheel aligns with bellhousing reference.

2) Lock camshaft with holding tool (2065A) at rear of camshaft. Tool must be fully installed in slot of camshaft. Align holding tool with feeler gauges between head and tool. Distance from tool to head must be same on both sides of camshaft.

3) Insert locking pin (2064) through holes in pump sprocket and pump bracket. Injection pump is now locked in place and sprocket must not be allowed to move. Check that timing marks on injection pump sprocket, pump body and mounting plate are aligned.

4) Check that TDC mark on flywheel is aligned with reference mark on bell housing. Loosen timing belt tensioner to relieve tension on timing belt. Remove crankshaft pulley. Do not allow crankshaft to turn. Remove timing belt.

Installation

1) Check that TDC mark on flywheel is still aligned with reference mark. Loosen camshaft sprocket bolt 1/2 turn. Loosen sprocket from camshaft by tapping with a rubber mallet.

2) Install timing belt. Remove locking pin from pump sprocket. Apply tension to belt by turning belt tensioner to right.

3) Using tension gauge (VW 210), check timing belt tension midway between camshaft and injection pump sprockets. Tension is correct if tester scale reads 12-13. Tighten camshaft sprocket bolt to 33 ft. lbs. (45 N.m).

4) Remove holding tool from rear of camshaft. Turn crankshaft clockwise 2 turns. Strike timing belt with rubber mallet midway between camshaft sprocket and pump sprocket. Using tension gauge (VW 210), recheck timing belt tension.

5) If necessary, readjust timing belt tension. Check injection pump timing. Install remaining components in reverse order of removal.

VALVE TIMING & INJECTION PUMP TIMING

1) Remove timing belt cover and cam cover. Turn crankshaft to TDC No. 1 cylinder at end of compression stroke. Lobes of camshaft on No. 1 cylinder must point upward at 45° and valves must be closed. Ensure that TDC mark on flywheel is aligned with indicator boss on housing.

2) Check that drive belt tension is correct with tension gauge (VW 210). If marks are aligned and camshaft lobes are in correct position, valve timing is correct. Install holding tool (2065A) in slot at rear of camshaft. Tool must be shimmed with feeler gauges so both ends of tool are same distance from head.

3) Loosen camshaft sprocket bolt 1 turn. Tap back of sprocket with rubber mallet until it is turns freely on camshaft. Tighten sprocket bolt by hand until sprocket has no end play on camshaft but still spins freely. Sprocket and camshaft are wedge fitted and no key is used.

4) Loosen belt tensioner and remove drive belt from pump sprocket. Turn pump sprocket until indexing notches on sprocket, pump and mounting bracket are aligned. Insert locking pin (2064) through holes in pump sprocket and pump bracket. This will lock sprocket and pump in place.

5) Install drive belt and tighten camshaft sprocket bolt to 33 ft. lbs. (45 N.m). Remove holding tool from rear of camshaft. Remove locking pin from pump sprocket. Place tension gauge (VW 210) on belt midway

Audi Engines

4000 4-CYLINDER DIESEL & TURBO DIESEL (Cont.)

between pump and camshaft sprockets. Turn belt tensioner clockwise until tension gauge reads 12-13 and lock tensioner.

6) Remove gauge and rotate crankshaft clockwise 2 full turns (720°). Hit belt 1 time with rubber malletbetween pump and camshaft sprockets to eliminate any play. Recheck belt tension and valve timing. Check that cold start device control knob on dash is pushed in completely.

7) Make sure lever of cold start device is fully off and against stop. Lever is located on engine block side of pump body. Adjust cable at lever if necessary. Remove threaded plug from center of pump cover at end opposite sprocket.

8) Install dial indicator (US 1026) with 0-.118" (0-3.0 mm) range in threaded adapter (2066). Screw adapter into plug hole and preload dial indicator to about .098" (2.50 mm). Slowly rotate engine in counterclockwise direction (opposite operating rotation) until dial indicator needle stops moving.

9) Zero dial indicator. Slowly rotate engine in clockwise direction (operating rotation) until TDC mark on flywheel reaches boss on housing. If pump timing is correct, dial indicator will read .035-.037" (.88-.93 mm). To change injection timing, loosen pump support and mounting plate bolts.

10) Turn pump in brackets until dial indicator reads .034 ± .0007" (.86 ± .020 mm). Tighten pump mounting bolts. Perform injection timing test again. If timing is correct, remove adapter and dial indicator.

11) Install threaded plug with new gasket to avoid fuel leaks. Check that idle speed is 950 ± 30 RPM. Adjust idle speed screw on pump body if necessary. Check that full throttle provides 5300-5400 RPM. Adjust maximum speed stop screw if necessary.

12) Make sure that cold start device is adjusted properly. Adjust accelerator cable by moving clip in slots at pump end of cable housing. With pedal set in full throttle position, pump lever should rest against maximum speed stop without any tension on cable.

CAMSHAFT

Removal

1) Remove timing belt. Mark camshaft bearing caps before removing. Bearing caps are bored off center. Make sure caps are installed correctly. Remove bearing caps No. 1, 3, and 5. Slowly loosen nuts on bearing caps No. 2 and 4 in a diagonal pattern.

2) Remove camshaft. Mount camshaft on lathe or "V" blocks. Position dial indicator with tip slightly preloaded against center camshaft journal. Rotate camshaft and read runout. Maximum runout allowed is .0004" (.010 mm).

Installation

Lubricate bearing surfaces and camshaft journals. To install, reverse removal procedure. Prior to final tightening of bearing cap 5 (thrust bearing cap), align it by tapping end of camshaft with soft-faced hammer. Check valve and pump timing.

CAMSHAFT OIL SEAL

Removal

Remove timing belt cover. Remove timing belt. Remove camshaft sprocket. Using seal remover tool (2085), remove oil seal.

Installation

1) Install protective sleeve of seal installing tool (10-203) over camshaft. Coat seal lips with oil. Push seal over sleeve and into position.

2) Using seal installing tool (10-203), press seal into recess until flush. Install remaining components in reverse order of removal. Ensure valve and pump timing is correct.

CAMSHAFT END THRUST

1) Check camshaft end thrust with cam followers removed. Ensure cam bearing caps are properly tightened. Attach dial indicator to cylinder head. Position indicator point on end of camshaft at 90° to sprocket.

2) Push camshaft rearward and zero dial indicator. Push camshaft forward to record maximum movement. If end thrust exceeds .006" (.15 mm), check camshaft thrust flange and bearing cap for wear. Replace worn components.

INTERMEDIATE SHAFT

1) Use a dial indicator to measure intermediate shaft end play. Maximum end play is .010" (.25 mm). Make sure to remove vacuum pump prior to removing intermediate shaft.

2) If oil seal replacement is necessary, remove oil seal flange and press out seal. Lubricate new seal lips with oil. Install oil seal flange on engine. Position seal into flange recess.

3) Use seal installing tool (10-203) to press seal into place. Install remaining parts in reverse order of removal. Check valve and pump timing.

VALVES

VALVE ARRANGEMENT

E-I-E-I-I-E-I-E (Front-to-rear)

VALVE GUIDE SERVICING

Inspection

1) Clean valve guides. Attach dial indicator and adapting fixture (VW 387 or US 4420A) to mounting surface of cylinder head. Insert a new valve into valve guide. Valve tip must be flush with top of valve guide .

2) Rock valve back and forth against dial indicator point to measure amount of stem-to-guide clearance. Maximum reading on indicator is .039" (1.0 mm) for intake valves and .051" (1.3 mm) for exhaust valves.

Removal

Check head for cracks or excessive wear on seats. Use press and valve guide remover/installer tool (10-206) to remove and install valve guides. Press guides out from combustion chamber side of head.

Installation

Coat new guide with oil. Press into cold cylinder head from camshaft side of head. Do not use more than 1 ton of pressure or guide shoulder may break. Ream guide by hand to proper size.

VALVE STEM OIL SEALS

NOTE: **Valve stem oil seals may be replaced with cylinder head installed on vehicle.**

4000 4-CYLINDER DIESEL & TURBO DIESEL (Cont.)

CAUTION: Installing valve stem oil seal without using plastic protective sleeve of seal installing tool (10-204), may result in seal damage.

Removal

1) Remove camshaft. Remove adjusting disc and cam follower of cylinder to be serviced. Turn crankshaft until piston of cylinder concerned is at TDC. Remove valve springs, allowing valve to rest on piston head.

2) Using valve spring compressor (VW 541), compress valve spring and remove keepers, retainer, and springs. Lift seal off valve stem.

Installation

Slide plastic protective sleeve onto valve stem. Lubricate new seal and push into place with seal installing tool (10-204). Install remaining components in reverse order of removal. Make sure valve and pump timing are correct.

VALVE SPRINGS

Valve springs may be replaced with cylinder head installed on vehicle. To replace valve springs, use removal and installation procedure explained in *Valve Stem Oil Seals*.

CAM FOLLOWERS

Removal

1) Before removing cam followers, mark them for identification. They must be installed in their original locations.

2) Remove camshaft and adjusting discs to gain access to cam followers. Remove cam followers and inspect for wear and damage. Replace as necessary.

Installation

Lightly oil cam followers prior to installing. To install cam followers and remaining components, reverse removal procedure.

VALVE CLEARANCE ADJUSTMENT

NOTE: Cold valve clearances are given for initial settings when engine work has been performed. Recheck valve clearance and make final adjustment with engine coolant temperature about 95° F (35° C).

Measuring Valve Clearance

1) Remove cam cover. Cam lobes of cylinder to be checked must point upward. To turn camshaft, engage transmission in 4th gear and push vehicle.

CAUTION: Never use camshaft sprocket bolt to turn camshaft, as this may stretch timing belt.

2) Using a feeler gauge, measure valve clearances of each cylinder in firing order sequence. *See Fig. 2*. If clearance is not as specified in *Valve Clearance Specifications*, adjustment is necessary.

VALVE CLEARANCE SPECIFICATIONS

Application	In. (mm)
Intake	
Hot	.008-.012 (.20-.30)
Cold	.006-.010 (.15-.25)
Exhaust	
Hot	.016-.020 (.40-.51)
Cold	.014-.018 (.35-.46)

Fig. 2: Measuring Valve Clearance

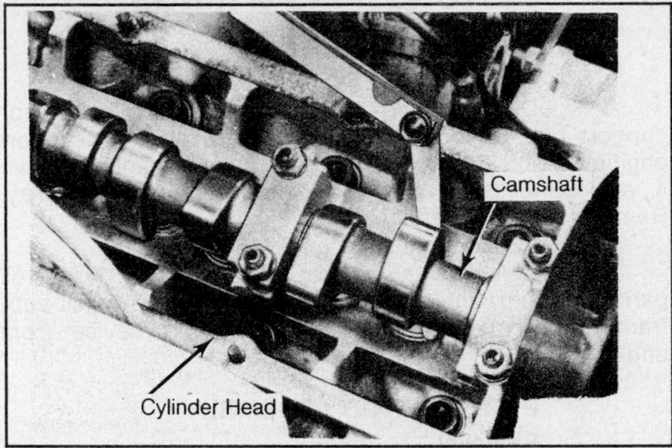
Camshaft
Cylinder Head

Measure clearances in firing order sequence.

NOTE: When cylinder head service has been performed, valve clearance must be checked and adjusted after 1000 miles.

Adjusting Valve Clearance

1) When adjusting valves, piston of cylinder being serviced must not be at TDC. Turn crankshaft about 1/4 turn past piston TDC position. This will keep valves from contacting pistons when cam followers are depressed.

2) To remove adjusting disc, cam follower must be depressed using compressing tool (2078). *See Fig. 3*. Turn cam followers so that grooves are accessible for disc removing tool (US 4476).

Fig. 3: Removing and Installing Adjusting Discs

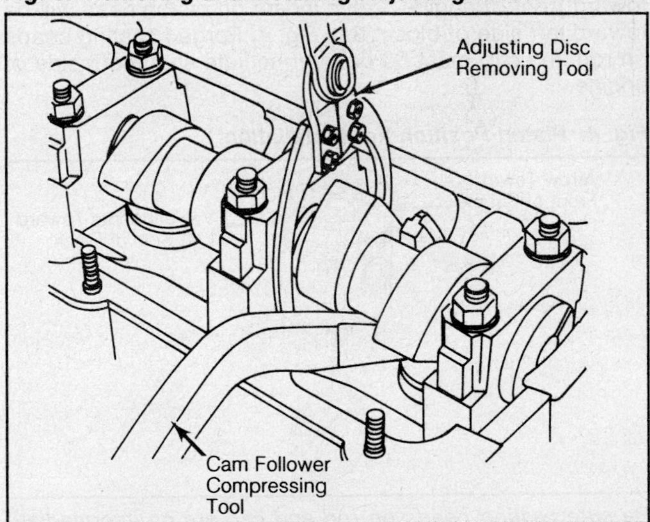
Adjusting Disc
Removing Tool
Cam Follower
Compressing
Tool

Ensure piston of cylinder being serviced is not at TDC.

3) Thickness of adjusting disc is stamped on disc. If measured valve clearance is larger than specifications, use a thicker disc. If clearance is less than specification, use a thinner disc.

4) Adjust clearance to middle of tolerance range. Adjusting discs are available in .002" (.05 mm) increments from .118" (3.0 mm) to .167" (4.25 mm).

5) To install disc, depress cam follower and slip disc into place. Ensure side of disc with thickness marking is installed downward, facing cam follower. Repeat procedure until all valves are properly adjusted.

Audi Engines

4000 4-CYLINDER DIESEL & TURBO DIESEL (Cont.)

PISTONS, PINS & RINGS

OIL PAN

Removal

Drain engine oil. Attach a lifting device or support bar to engine. Raise engine slightly to support engine weight. Remove cover plate under engine. Remove 4 sub-frame bolts and lower sub-frame out of way. Remove oil pan.

Installation

Using a new gasket, install oil pan. Install oil pan bolts and tighten in a crisscross pattern. Install sub-frame and cover plate. Remove support device from engine.

PISTON & ROD ASSEMBLY

Removal

1) Remove cylinder head, oil pan and oil pump. Place piston to be removed at bottom of cylinder and cover with a cloth to collect metal cuttings. Using ridge reamer, remove ridge or deposit from upper end of cylinder bore.

2) Before removing piston and rod from engine, mark piston, rod, and rod cap for cylinder identification. Remove rod cap and carefully push piston and rod out top of cylinder. Keep rod cap and rod together for reassembly.

Installation

1) Coat cylinder bore, piston, and rings with engine oil. Ensure ring gaps are spaced 120° apart. Install ring compressor on piston, making sure rings stay in position.

2) Install piston and rod in its respective bore. Arrow on piston head (with figure 5 beside it) should face toward front of engine. Valve indent on piston head will be toward left side of block. *See Fig. 4*. Forged casting beads on rod and cap must be on intermediate shaft (left) side of engine.

Fig. 4: Piston Position For Installation

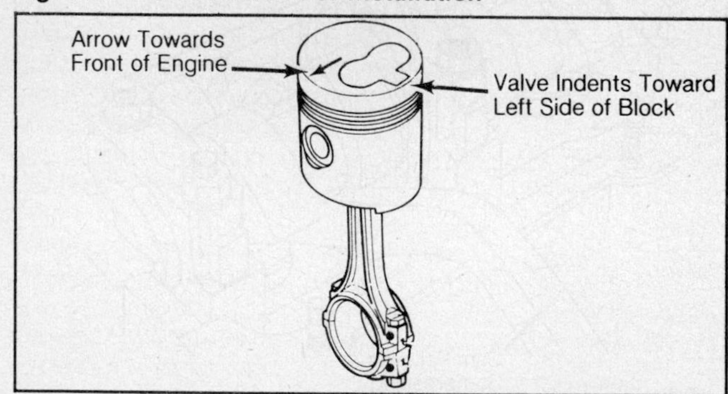
Arrow Towards Front of Engine
Valve Indents Toward Left Side of Block

Be sure casting beads on rod and cap are on intermediate shaft side of engine.

3) Cover threads of connecting rod bolts so that crankshaft journals are not damaged. Turbo diesel rod bolts are stretch type which must be replaced each time rods are disassembled. Tighten stretch bolts to 22 ft. lbs. (30 N.m) and another 1/2 turn (180°).

FITTING PISTONS

1) Take cylinder measurements 90° to crankshaft centerline and in line with crankshaft centerline as follows: 3/8" from top of bore, at middle of bore and 3/8" from bottom of bore. Difference between the corresponding measurements is out-of-round and must not exceed .0016" (.040 mm).

2) Measure piston diameter 90° to piston pin bore, approximately 9/16" from bottom of piston skirt. Compare this measurement with measurement of corresponding cylinder bore. Allowable piston-to-cylinder clearance is .0012" (.030 mm) for a new piston. Wear limit is .0028" (.070 mm).

3) Install oversize pistons if piston-to-cylinder clearance is excessive. Three sets of oversize replacement pistons are available. Each set has 3 different diameter pistons so different cylinder bores may be matched.

FITTING RINGS

1) Place piston rings squarely into cylinder bore about 9/16" from top edge of bore. Use a feeler gauge to measure ring end gap.

2) With rings installed on piston, use a feeler gauge to measure ring side clearance. Take measurement around entire circumference of piston, between top of ring and ring land.

3) Install rings on piston with "TOP" mark facing upward. Space ring end gaps 120° apart.

PISTON PIN REPLACEMENT

Removal

Remove circlip from pin bore groove. Use piston pin tool (VW 222a) to remove and install piston pins. If pins are too tight it may be necessary to warm pistons to about 140° F (60° C).

Installation

1) Assemble connecting rod to piston. Arrow on piston head must face forward and valve indents must be on left side of block. Forged casting beads on connecting rod and cap must be on intermediate shaft side of engine.

2) Use piston pin tool (VW 222a) to install piston pin. Install circlip into pin bore groove.

CRANKSHAFT MAIN & CONNECTING ROD BEARINGS

MAIN BEARINGS

1) Main bearing caps are numbered 1 through 5 (front to rear). Never interchange bearing caps. Always measure main bearing clearances 1 at a time.

2) Use Plastigage method for measuring bearing clearances. Ensure oil film is removed from bearing halves and crankshaft journal prior to measuring clearance.

3) With Plastigage in place, install bearing cap and tighten to specification. Do not allow crankshaft to turn. Remove bearing cap. Measure flattened width of Plastigage with scale furnished to determine clearance.

4) When replacing bearings, install grooved bearing halves into cylinder block. Plain bearing halves are installed in main caps. Lubricate crankshaft journal and bearings prior to installing bearings.

CONNECTING ROD BEARINGS

1) Always measure connecting rod bearing clearances 1 at a time. Use Plastigage method for measuring bearing clearances. Ensure oil film is removed

Audi Engines

4000 4-CYLINDER DIESEL & TURBO DIESEL (Cont.)

from bearing halves and crankshaft journal prior to measuring clearance.

2) With Plastigage in place, install bearing cap and tighten to specification. Do not allow crankshaft to turn. Remove bearing cap. Measure flattened width of Plastigage with scale furnished to determine clearance.

3) Use a feeler gauge to check connecting rod side clearance. Insert feeler gauge between connecting rod and crankshaft thrust face. Wear limit for side clearance is .015" (.37 mm).

CRANKSHAFT END PLAY

Use a feeler gauge to check crankshaft end play. Using feeler gauge, measure thrust clearance between No. 3 main bearing (thrust bearing) and crankshaft thrust face. Wear limit for crankshaft end play is .015" (.37 mm).

REAR MAIN BEARING OIL SEAL

Removal

Remove transmission and flywheel. Carefully pry oil seal from seal flange.

Installation

Coat new seal lips with oil. Position seal in place. Place centering sleeve (2003/2A) on crankshaft and start seal into place. Press in seal until seated, using seal installing tool (2003/1). Install remaining components. Use Loctite on flywheel bolts.

FRONT MAIN BEARING OIL SEAL

Removal

1) Remove all drive belts. Remove timing belt cover. Set No. 1 piston on TDC after compression stroke. Remove crankshaft pulley. On turbo diesel engines, remove vibration damper. Remove timing belt. Remove crankshaft sprocket.

2) For standard diesel engines, use seal removing tool (2085) to remove oil seal. For turbo diesel engines, use seal removing tool (2085) and Allen head bolt from seal installing tool (3083) to remove oil seal.

Installation

1) Coat new seal lips with oil. For standard diesel engines, use tool (10-203) to press new seal into place. For turbo diesel engines, use seal installing tool (3083) to press in seal.

2) Press in seal flush with front cover on standard diesel engines. On turbo diesel engines, press in seal until fully seated. Install remaining components.

3) On turbo diesel engines, be sure to fit notch on drive belt sprocket into slot in crankshaft when installing. Use Loctite on crankshaft sprocket bolt threads on all models.

ENGINE OILING

CRANKCASE CAPACITY

Capacity for standard diesel engine is 2.7 quarts (2.5L) without filter replacement and 3.2 quarts (3.0L) with filter replacement.

Capacity for turbo diesel engine is 4.5 quarts (4.0L) without filter replacement and 5.0 quarts (4.5L) with filter replacement.

OIL PRESSURE

Minimum oil pressure is 29 psi (2.0 kg/cm²) at 2000 RPM. Oil temperature should be 176°F (80°C) for testing. Oil pressure warning light should go out at pressure of 2-6.5 psi (.14-.45 kg/cm²).

ENGINE OILING SYSTEM

1) Oiling system is a pressure feed system. A gear-type oil pump lifts oil from oil pan and pressure feeds it to crankshaft journals, camshaft bearings and intermediate shaft. Other parts of system receive oil lubrication by drainage or splash method.

2) To aid in piston cooling, turbo diesel engines use oil spray from nozzles. Oil nozzles are installed at the bottom of each cylinder. Oil is sprayed into underside of piston to cool piston skirt and head. If oil nozzles have been removed, coat retaining bolt threads with thread adhesive during reassembly.

3) Piston skirts have cutouts to accommodate oiling nozzles. Pressure relief valve in nozzle opens at oil pressure of 22 psi (1.5 kg/cm²) or higher. Oil pressure relief valves are closed at idle speed. Oil filter installation procedure varies with manufacturer. Be sure to follow procedure listed on filter or box.

OIL PUMP

Removal & Disassembly

Remove oil pan. Remove oil pump attaching bolts and lower pump away from engine. Remove pump pickup-to-body bolts and separate pickup from pump body. Remove strainer housing from pickup and clean strainer.

Inspection

1) With oil pump gears installed in pump housing, insert feeler gauge between drive gear and driven gear teeth at point where teeth mesh. Allowable backlash limit is .008" (.20 mm).

2) Lay a straightedge over pump housing. Insert feeler gauge between pump gears and straightedge. End play limit is .006" (.15 mm).

Reassembly & Installation

Assemble pump in reverse order of disassembly. Prime oil pump prior to installing. Install pump in reverse order of removal procedures. Make sure engine has oil pressure after starting.

ENGINE COOLING

THERMOSTAT & THERMOSWITCH

Thermostat begins opening at 185°F (85°C), and is fully open at 221°F (106°C). Radiator fan thermoswitch is on in range of 200-208°F (93-98°C) and goes off in range of 190-200°F (88-93°C).

COOLANT

Capacity is 7.4 quarts (7.0L). Use only ethylene glycol based (phosphate-free) antifreeze for corrosion resistance. Coolant mixture ratio of 50/50 gives antifreeze protection to -30°F (-35°C).

EXPANSION TANK CAP

Expansion tank cap pressure relief valve opens at 13-17 psi (.9-1.2 kg/cm²).

WATER PUMP

Removal & Disassembly

Drain coolant and remove alternator and bracket. Remove coolant hoses to pump housing. Remove pump housing-to-engine bolts. Remove pump assembly.

Audi Engines

4000 4-CYLINDER DIESEL & TURBO DIESEL (Cont.)

Remove attaching bolts and separate water pump from pump housing.

Reassembly & Installation

1) To reassemble, reverse disassembly procedure. Use new gasket between pump and housing. When installing pump assembly, use new "O" ring between pump housing and cylinder block.

2) Remove coolant temperature thermoswitch from hose flange on left side of cylinder head. Fill cooling system with heater control valve in open position. Install thermoswitch in flange.

3) Fill until expansion tank level is .75" (20 mm) above minimum mark. Close tank and start engine. Run engine until radiator cooling fan operates through 1 cycle. Check coolant and top up if necessary.

ENGINE SPECIFICATIONS

GENERAL SPECIFICATIONS

Year	DISPLACEMENT		Fuel System	HP@RPM	Torque Ft. Lbs.@RPM	Compr. Ratio	BORE		STROKE	
	Cu. In.	Liters					In.	mm	In.	mm
1983										
Diesel	97	1.6	Fuel Inj.	52@4800	75@2000	23:1	3.01	76.5	3.40	86.4
Turbo Diesel	97	1.6	Fuel Inj.	68@4500	96.2@2800	23:1	3.01	76.5	3.40	86.4

PISTONS, PINS, RINGS

Engine	PISTONS	PINS		RINGS		
	Clearance In. (mm)	Piston Fit In. (mm)	Rod Fit In. (mm)	Ring No.	End Gap In. (mm)	Side Clearance In. (mm)
1.6L	.0011 [1] (.028)	[2]	.....	Top	.012-.020 [3] (.30-.51)	.002-.004 [4] (.05-.10)
				Center	.012-.020 [3] (.30-.51)	.002-.003 [4] (.05-.08)
				Oil	.010-.016 [3] (.25-.41)	.001-.002 [5] (.03-.05)

[1] – Wear limit is .003" (.07 mm).
[2] – Push fit at 140°F (60°C).
[3] – Wear limit is .039" (1.00 mm).
[4] – Wear limit is .008" (.20 mm).
[5] – Wear limit is .006" (.15 mm).

CRANKSHAFT MAIN & CONNECTING ROD BEARINGS

Engine	MAIN BEARINGS				CONNECTING ROD BEARINGS		
	Journal Diam. In. (mm)	Clearance In. (mm)	Thrust Bearing	Crankshaft End Play In. (mm)	Journal Diam. In. (mm)	Clearance In. (mm)	Side Play In. (mm)
1.6L							
Std. Size	2.125 [1] (53.97)	.0010-.0030 [2] (.025-.076)	No. 3	.0030-.0070 [3] (.076-.178)	1.881 [1] (47.77)	.0011-.0034 [4] (.028-.088)	.014 (.37)
1st U/Size	2.115 (53.72)				1.870 (47.52)		
2nd U/Size	2.105 (53.47)				1.861 (47.27)		

[1] – Maximum out-of-round for standard or undersize crankshaft journals is .001" (.03 mm).
[2] – Wear limit is .007" (.18 mm).
[3] – Wear limit is .015" (.37 mm).
[4] – Wear limit is .005" (.12 mm).

Audi Engines

4000 4-CYLINDER DIESEL & TURBO DIESEL (Cont.)

ENGINE SPECIFICATIONS (Cont.)

VALVES

Engine Size & Valve	Head Diam. In. (mm)	Face Angle	Seat Angle	Seat Width In. (mm)	Stem Diameter In. (mm)	Stem Clearance In. (mm)	Valve Lift In. (mm)
1.6L							
Intake	1.338 (33.99)	45°	45°	.078 (2.00)	.314 Min. (7.97)	.020 Max. (.50)	.....
Exhaust	1.220 (31.00)	45°	45°	.096 (2.40)	.313 Min. (7.95)	.026 Max. (.65)	.....

TIGHTENING SPECIFICATIONS

Application	Ft. Lbs. (N.m)
Camshaft Bearing Caps	15 (20)
Camshaft Sprocket Bolt	33 (45)
Connecting Rod Caps	
Standard Engine	33 (45)
Turbo Engine [3]	22 (30)
Crankshaft Pulley/Vibration Damper	
Standard Engine (Loctite)	110 (150)
Turbo Engine (Lube)	148 (200)
Cylinder Head Bolts	
Step 1	29 (40)
Step 2	43 (60)
Step 3 [1]	54 (75)
Exhaust Manifold-to-Head	19 (25)
Exhaust Manifold-to-Turbocharger [2]	30 (40)
Exhaust Pipe-to-Turbocharger	18 (25)
Flywheel (Loctite)	55 (75)
Glow Plugs	30 (40)
Injection Pump Sprocket	33 (45)
Injectors	52 (70)
Injector Pipes	19 (25)
Intake Manifold	19 (25)
Intermediate Shaft Pulley	33 (45)
Main Bearing Caps	48 (65)
Oil Return Line	
Bracket-to-Turbocharger	19 (25)
Timing Belt Tensioner	33 (45)

[1] – After final tightening, turn bolts an additional 1/2 turn (180°). Run engine to normal operating temperature. Stop engine. Tighten head bolts an additional 1/4 turn (90°). At 1000 mile service, tighten bolts an additional 1/4 turn (90°). Do not back off bolts at any point in sequence.

[2] – Apply high-temperature grease to bolt head and threads before installing.

[3] – Plus additional 180° after torque setting reached.

4000, 5000, COUPE & QUANTUM 5-CYLINDER

ENGINE CODING

ENGINE IDENTIFICATION

Engine number is stamped on machined pad, located on left side of block near control pressure regulator. Letter prefix indicates engine type.

ENGINE IDENTIFICATION CODES

Engine	Code
2.2L	
4000, 5000, Coupe, & Quantum	
Non-turbo	WE
Turbo	WK

ENGINE, MANIFOLDS & CYLINDER HEAD

ENGINE

Removal (4000, Coupe, & Quantum)

1) Disconnect battery ground cable. Open heater control valve fully. Open cap on coolant expansion tank. Drain coolant by disconnecting lower radiator hoses. Remove engine-to-transmission bolt holding coolant pipe. Remove upper coolant hose from pipe (left side of engine).

2) Remove upper radiator cover. Remove upper radiator hose from engine. Remove vacuum hoses at brake booster and at cruise control unit. Remove power steering pump and position aside.

3) Disconnect coolant hose at thermostat housing. Disconnect wires from oil pressure switch and control pressure regulator. Remove control pressure regulator, leaving fuel lines attached. Remove throttle push rod.

4) Remove remaining coolant hose. Remove alternator adjusting bolt and mounting bolt and position alternator aside. Remove alternator bracket from engine block. Remove front engine stop.

5) Loosen clamps and remove air duct. Disconnect electrical plugs from frequency valve and grounding point. Remove distributor vacuum unit hoses. Disconnect electrical plugs at cold start valve, auxiliary air regulator and throttle switch. Remove coil high tension wire at ignition coil.

6) Pull out fuel injectors and remove cold start valve, leaving fuel lines connected. Protect injectors and cold start valve with caps or plugs. Disconnect fuel feed and return lines. Remove fuel distributor with air flow sensor plate. Disconnect breather hose from valve cover.

7) Remove air filter assembly. Disconnect oxygen sensor, thermo switch, thermo-time switch, temperature sending unit, and ignition distributor connectors.

8) If equipped with automatic transmission, remove coolant hoses at oil cooler. Remove coolant hose flange from engine block. Remove heater hoses. Remove cover for right engine mount. Loosen left and right engine mounts.

9) Detach ground strap from mounting bracket. Remove upper engine-to-transmission bolts. Leave 1 bolt installed. Disconnect wire from oil temperature switch.

10) If A/C equipped, remove compressor drive belt. Disconnect wire from compressor clutch. Remove compressor mount bolts from engine and remove compressor. Place compressor aside with hoses connected.

11) Disconnect starter wires. Remove both front subframe bolts. Remove exhaust pipe attaching nuts from manifold. Remove bolt from exhaust pipe support. Remove starter.

12) Working through starter mounting hole, remove 3 torque converter mounting bolts from drive plate. Remove lower engine-to-transmission bolts. Detach shift rod (or clutch cable) from transmission. Support transmission with transmission support bar.

13) Make sure that all wiring, hoses, lines, cables and linkages are disconnected from engine. Attach lifting device to engine. Adjust support bar to contact transmission. Remove remaining upper engine-to-transmission bolt.

14) Lift engine slightly and move away from transmission. Continue to lift engine, while turning it toward the left. Use care when guiding engine out of compartment. Secure torque converter.

Installation

Reverse removal procedure to install engine. Install and tighten starter cable so it does not touch exhaust. Align exhaust system and refill coolant tank. Tighten engine mounting bolts while engine is running at idle speed.

Removal (5000)

1) Disconnect battery ground cable. Remove coolant expansion tank cap. Disconnect bottom hose from expansion tank and drain. Set temperature lever in "COLD" position if vehicle is A/C equipped.

2) Disconnect lower radiator hoses to drain coolant from engine. Remove remaining coolant hoses from engine. Remove control pressure regulator, cold start valve, and fuel injectors with fuel lines attached. Cap injectors and cold start valve.

3) Disconnect air duct and vacuum hoses from throttle valve assembly. Remove air cleaner assembly with fuel distributor and air flow sensor attached, and position aside. If necessary, remove fuel supply and return hoses from fuel distributor.

4) Remove hood latch cable guide from bracket. Remove radiator cowl, shroud, electric fan and radiator. On air conditioned vehicles, remove grille and tilt condenser outward.

5) Remove power steering pump and position aside with hoses connected. Remove ignition coil. Remove windshield washer and power steering reservoirs from holders. Remove distributor cap, rotor, and ignition wires.

6) Disconnect throttle cable (or throttle rod) from engine. Disconnect primary wiring from distributor. Disconnect wiring to oil pressure sender, water temperature sender and oxygen sensor.

7) Remove air conditioning compressor, leaving hoses connected. Secure compressor away from engine. Disconnect exhaust pipe from transmission bracket and from exhaust manifold. If equipped, disconnect turbocharger from exhaust manifold. Remove front engine mount. Remove starter and alternator.

8) Remove torque converter mounting bolts (automatic transmission) from drive plate, doing so through starter mounting hole. Remove lower engine-to-transmission bolts. Install transmission support bar (VW 785/1). Remove upper engine to transmission bolts.

4000 & 5000, COUPE & QUANTUM 5-CYLINDER (Cont.)

9) Remove left engine bracket and loosen right engine bracket from engine mount. With engine lifting device securely attached, lift engine until drive belt pulley is behind grille opening. Support transmission with support bar. Separate engine from transmission.

10) Make sure that all wiring, hoses, lines, cables and linkages are disconnected from engine. While lifting engine upward, turn front of engine toward right side of vehicle. Carefully remove engine.

Installation

1) Reverse removal procedure to install engine. Install and tighten starter cable so it does not touch exhaust. Metal lip of gasket between exhaust manifold and exhaust pipe must face exhaust pipe.

2) Adjust power steering pump, alternator, and air conditioning compressor belt tension. Refill coolant expansion tank. Adjust accelerator cable. Tighten engine mounting bolts with engine running at idle speed.

CYLINDER HEAD

Removal

1) Disconnect battery ground strap. Drain cooling system. Disconnect coolant hoses from head. Label and disconnect all vacuum and air hoses from intake manifold. Label and disconnect all electrical and ignition wires at cylinder head and intake manifold.

2) Remove fuel injectors from head and cold start valve from intake manifold, leaving fuel lines attached. Cap injectors and cold start valve. Remove air duct from throttle housing. Remove all throttle linkage or cables from throttle valve housing.

3) Label and disconnect fuel supply and return lines to fuel distributor. Remove air flow sensor, fuel distributor, injectors, and cold start valve. Disconnect exhaust pipe from manifold or turbocharger.

4) Remove turbocharger unit. Remove exhaust manifold from cylinder head. Remove upper radiator cover. Remove drive belts. Remove power steering pump and position aside with hoses connected. Remove cam cover and timing belt cover.

5) Loosen water pump adjusting bolts to relieve tension on timing belt. Remove timing belt. It is recommended to replace sealing "O" ring between water pump and cylinder block whenever water pump bolts are loosened. Remove water pump to replace "O" ring.

6) Loosen head bolts in reverse order of tightening sequence. *See Fig. 1*. Ensure all wires, hoses, and lines have been removed from cylinder head and intake manifold prior to removing head. Remove cylinder with intake manifold attached.

CAUTION: If head bolt(s) require replacement, install new polygon head bolts in complete sets only. Do not retorque polygon head bolts at 1000 mile service following repair.

Installation

1) Clean gasket mating surfaces and bolt holes in cylinder block. Install head gasket dry with part number facing upward. Use locating pins to hold gasket in place. Before installing cylinder head, turn crankshaft so that pistons are about equal distance from TDC.

2) This will prevent an open valve from hitting a piston. Install head. Install bolts 9 and 11 to align head. Install remaining bolts. Tighten cylinder head bolts in 3 steps. *See Fig. 1*.

Fig. 1: Cylinder Head Tightening Sequence

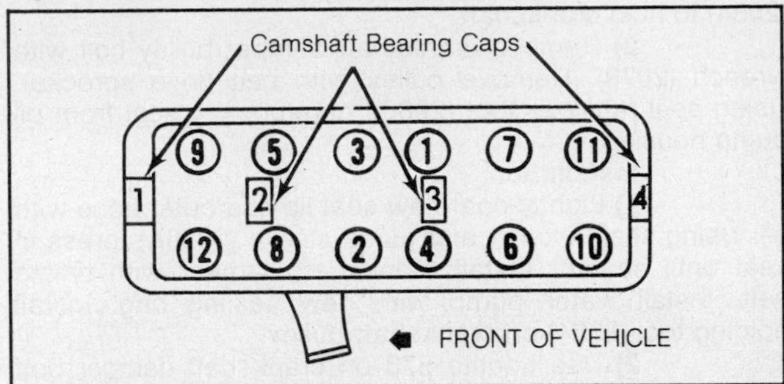
Camshaft Bearing Caps
9
5
3
1
7
11
1
2
3
4
12
8
2
4
6
10
FRONT OF VEHICLE

Tighten bolts in 3 steps.

3) Turn camshaft until timing mark on sprocket is aligned with upper edge of cam cover gasket (or rear timing belt cover). *See Fig. 2*. Turn crankshaft to align TDC mark on flywheel with reference mark on clutch housing.

4) Install water pump with new sealing ring, leaving bolts loose enough to move pump body. Install timing belt and adjust timing belt tension. Turn water pump body counterclockwise to tighten timing belt.

5) Belt has correct tension when it can be twisted 90° with thumb and finger pressure. Measure tension midway between camshaft sprocket and water pump sprocket. Recheck valve timing. Complete installation in reverse order of removal.

Fig. 2: Aligning Camshaft Sprocket

Camshaft
Sprocket
Cam Cover
Gasket

Align mark on camshaft sprocket (arrow) with upper edge of cam cover gasket (or rear timing belt cover).

CAMSHAFT

TIMING BELT COVER

Removal & Installation

Remove upper radiator cover. Remove all drive belts from pulleys. Remove power steering pump with pressure hose connected, and position pump aside. Remove timing belt cover. To install, reverse removal procedure.

FRONT MAIN BEARING OIL SEAL

Removal

1) Remove lower grille. Remove front cover. Loosen water pump to remove timing belt. Remove water pump to check "O" ring. Using crankshaft locking tool (2084) to hold crankshaft.

2) Remove crankshaft damper/pulley bolt with wrench (2079). Remove pulley with belt drive sprocket. Using seal remover tool (2086), carefully pry seal from oil pump housing.

Installation

1) Lightly coat new seal lip and outer edge with oil. Using seal installer and guide sleeve (2080A), press in seal until seated. Install crankshaft damper with timing belt. Install water pump with new sealing ring. Install holding tool (2084) on crankshaft pulley.

2) Use Loctite 573 on crankshaft damper bolt and install. Use wrench (2079) and torque wrench to tighten crankshaft pulley bolt. Torque specification only applies if torque wrench and tool (2079) are parallel.

3) Remove tools and adjust timing belt tension. Make sure valve timing is correct. Install remaining parts in reverse order of disassembly.

TIMING BELT & SPROCKET

Removal

1) Remove upper radiator cover. Remove drive belts. Remove power steering pump with pressure hose connected, and position pump aside. Remove cam cover and timing belt cover.

2) Turn crankshaft clockwise (by crankshaft pulley bolt), until timing mark on camshaft sprocket is aligned with upper edge of cam cover gasket (or rear timing belt cover). *See Fig. 2.*

3) Loosen water pump adjusting bolts to relieve tension on timing belt. Remove timing belt. Remove water pump to check sealing "O" ring. Do not allow crankshaft or camshaft to move.

Installation

1) Install new belt. Install water pump with new sealing ring. Turn water pump counterclockwise to adjust tension of timing belt. Belt has correct tension when it can be twisted 90° with thumb and finger pressure. Measure midway between camshaft sprocket and water pump sprocket.

2) Recheck valve timing. Camshaft lobes on No. 1 cylinder must both point upward. Set crankshaft on TDC for No. 1 cylinder. Ensure that TDC mark is aligned with index point on transmission housing. Make sure that mark on camshaft pulley is aligned with top of camshaft cover gasket or rear timing belt cover. Complete installation in reverse order of removal.

VALVE TIMING

See Timing Belt & Sprocket.

CAMSHAFT

Removal

Remove timing belt. If necessary, mark cam bearing caps 1 to 4 (front to rear). Diagonally loosen bearing caps 2 and 4, then remove caps. Diagonally loosen bearing caps 1 and 3, then remove caps. Remove camshaft from head.

Installation

1) Lubricate bearing surfaces in cam bearing caps. Lubricate camshaft journals and bearing caps. Install camshaft. Install bearing caps in original locations from which removed. Ensure caps are not misaligned. *See Fig. 3.*

2) Lightly tighten bearing caps 2 and 4 in a diagonal pattern. When caps 2 and 4 are snug, tighten all 4 bearing caps. Install remaining components. Set valve timing.

Fig. 3: Proper Cam Bearing Cap Alignment

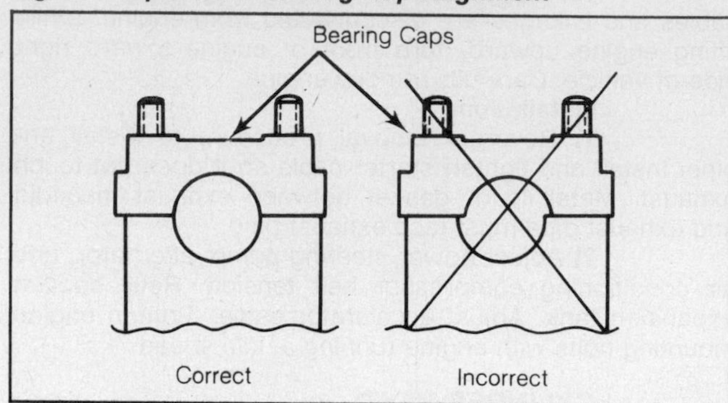
Bearing Caps
Correct
Incorrect

Tighten cam bearing nuts to 14 ft. lbs. (20 N.m).

CAMSHAFT OIL SEAL

Removal

1) Remove timing belt cover and cam cover. Position No. 1 piston on TDC. Loosen camshaft sprocket bolt while keeping camshaft from moving. Loosen water pump adjusting bolts to relieve tension on timing belt.

2) Remove timing belt. Remove water pump to check sealing ring. Remove camshaft sprocket and Woodruff key. Using seal removing tool (2085), remove camshaft oil seal.

Installation

1) Lubricate seal lips with oil. Lubricate seal recess in front cam bearing with oil. Using seal installing tool (10-203), press seal into place until flush with chamfered edge.

2) Do not press seal in any farther, otherwise oil return hole in bearing cap will be blocked. Install water pump and timing belt. Adjust valve timing and belt tension. Install remaining parts in reverse of removal.

CAMSHAFT END THRUST

1) Check camshaft end thrust with cam followers removed. There must be no tension on camshaft for this measurement. Attach dial indicator to cylinder head. Position indicator point at 90° to end of camshaft (or face of sprocket).

2) Push camshaft rearward and zero dial indicator. Push camshaft forward to record maximum movement. If end thrust exceeds .006" (.15 mm), check camshaft thrust flange and bearing cap for wear. Replace worn components.

VALVES

CAUTION: Never rework exhaust valves on a valve grinding machine. Lap exhaust valves by hand only.

4000 & 5000, COUPE & QUANTUM 5-CYLINDER (Cont.)

NOTE: New design intake and exhaust valves with 3 keeper grooves and chamfered spring retainers have been introduced by manufacturer. Old and new design valves may be installed in same engine, but keepers and spring retainers are not interchangeable.

VALVE ARRANGEMENT

E-I-E-I-I-E-I-E-I-E (Front - to - rear).

VALVE GUIDE SERVICING

Inspection

1) Clean valve guides. Attach dial indicator and adapting fixture (VW 387) to mounting surface of cylinder head. Insert new valve into valve guide. Valve tip must be flush with end of valve guide.

2) Rock valve back and forth against dial indicator point to measure amount of stem-to-guide clearance. If reading exceeds .039" (1.0 mm) for intake valves, or .051" (1.3 mm) for exhaust valves, replace guides.

Removal

Use arbor press and valve guide remover/installer tool (10-206) to remove and install guides. Press guides out from combustion chamber side of head.

Installation

Coat new guides with oil. Press into cold (cool if necessary) head from camshaft side. Press guides in as far as they will go. Do not use more than 1 ton pressure once guide shoulder is seated, or guide shoulder may break. Ream guide by hand to proper size.

VALVE STEM OIL SEALS

NOTE: Valve stem seals may be replaced with cylinder head installed on vehicle.

CAUTION: Installing valve stem oil seal without using plastic protective sleeve of seal installing tool (10-204), may result in seal damage.

Removal

1) Remove camshaft, followers and valve adjusting discs. Remove spark plug of cylinder to be serviced. Turn crankshaft until piston of cylinder concerned is at bottom of stroke.

2) Install air hose and adapter (VW 653/3) in spark plug hole and apply air pressure of at least 87 psi. Do not remove air pressure until valve spring components are reassembled.

3) Use spring compressor tool (VW 541/1 or 2036). Compress valve spring and remove keepers, retainers, and springs. Use seal removing pliers (10-218) to remove seals.

Fig. 4: Cylinder Head and Camshaft Assembly with Timing Belt and Cover

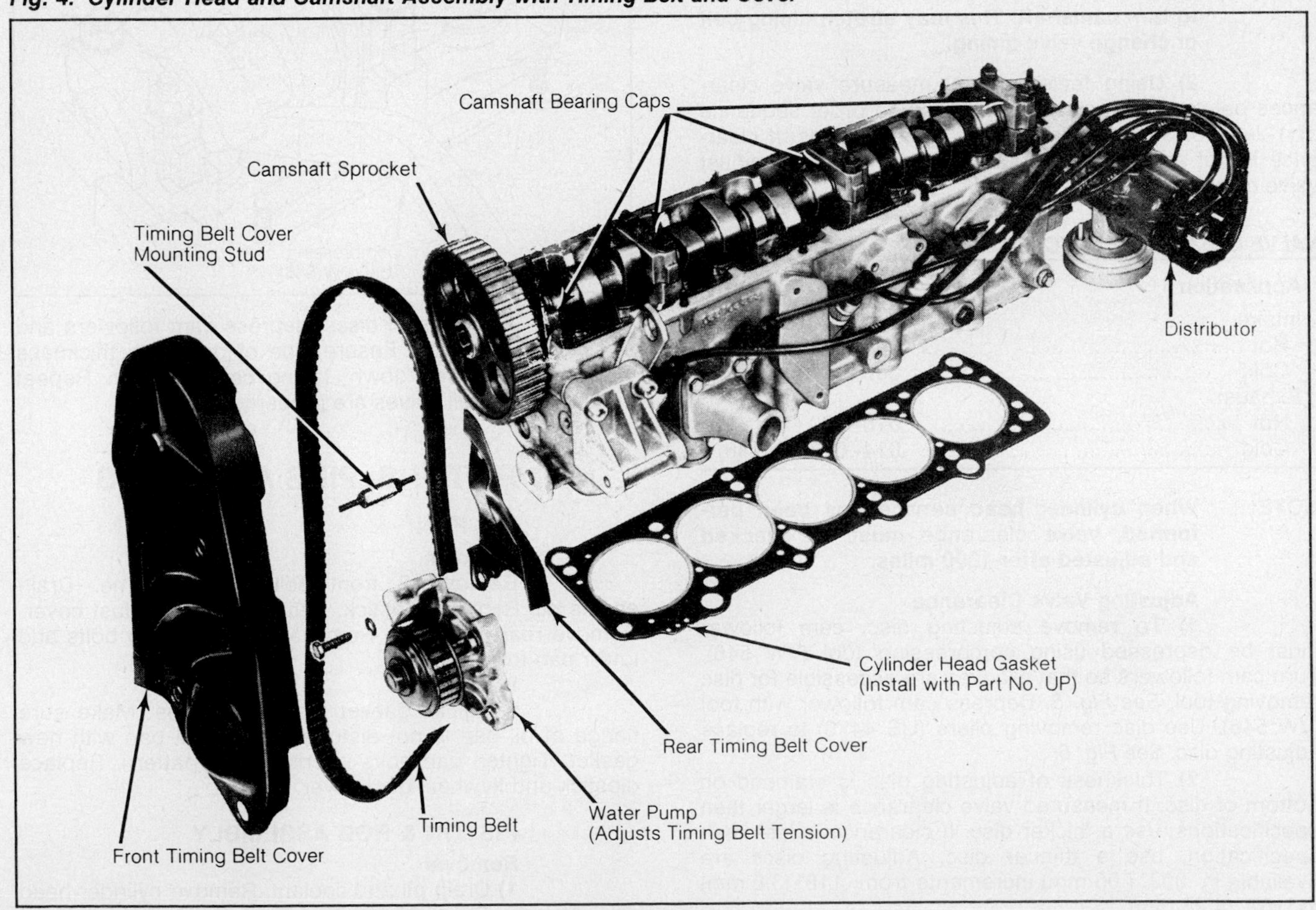
Camshaft Bearing Caps
Camshaft Sprocket
Timing Belt Cover
Mounting Stud
Distributor
Cylinder Head Gasket
(Install with Part No. UP)
Rear Timing Belt Cover
Timing Belt
Water Pump
(Adjusts Timing Belt Tension)
Front Timing Belt Cover

Always check sealing "O" ring whenever water pump moved or loosened.

4000 & 5000, COUPE & QUANTUM 5-CYLINDER (Cont.)

Installation

Place seal protector over valve stem. Lubricate new seal and push seal into place with seal installing tool (10-204). Install remaining valve components.

VALVE SPRINGS

Valve springs may be replaced with cylinder head installed on vehicle. See *Valve Stem Oil Seals* for removal and installation procedure.

CAM FOLLOWERS

When removing cam followers, keep them in order for reassembly in original locations. With camshaft and adjusting discs removed, lift out cam followers. Inspect for wear or damage and replace as necessary. Coat with oil when installing.

VALVE CLEARANCE ADJUSTMENT

NOTE: **Cold valve clearances are given for initial settings, after engine work has been performed. Recheck valve clearance and make final adjustment with engine coolant temperature about 95°F (35°C).**

Measuring Valve Clearance

1) Disconnect accelerator linkage and remove cam cover. Turn crankshaft clockwise until both cam lobes of cylinder to be adjusted point upward.

CAUTION: **Never use camshaft sprocket attaching bolt to turn camshaft. This may stretch timing belt or change valve timing.**

2) Using feeler gauge, measure valve clearances between cam and follower in firing order sequence of 1-2-4-5-3. *See Valve Clearance Specifications.* If clearance is not as specified, change adjusting disc to adjust valve clearance.

VALVE CLEARANCE SPECIFICATIONS

Application	In. (mm)
Intake	
Hot	.008-.012 (.20-.30)
Cold	.006-.010 (.15-.25)
Exhaust	
Hot	.016-.020 (.40-.51)
Cold	.014-.018 (.36-.46)

NOTE: **When cylinder head service has been performed, valve clearance must be checked and adjusted after 1000 miles.**

Adjusting Valve Clearance

1) To remove adjusting disc, cam follower must be depressed using compressing tool (VW 546). Turn cam followers so that grooves are accessible for disc removing tool. *See Fig. 5.* Depress cam follower with tool (VW 546). Use disc removing pliers (US 4476) to replace adjusting disc. *See Fig. 6.*

2) Thickness of adjusting disc is stamped on bottom of disc. If measured valve clearance is larger than specifications, use a thicker disc. If clearance is less than specification, use a thinner disc. Adjusting discs are available in .002" (.05 mm) increments from .118" (3.0 mm) to .167" (4.25 mm).

Fig. 5: Positioning Cam Followers To Replace Adjusting Disc

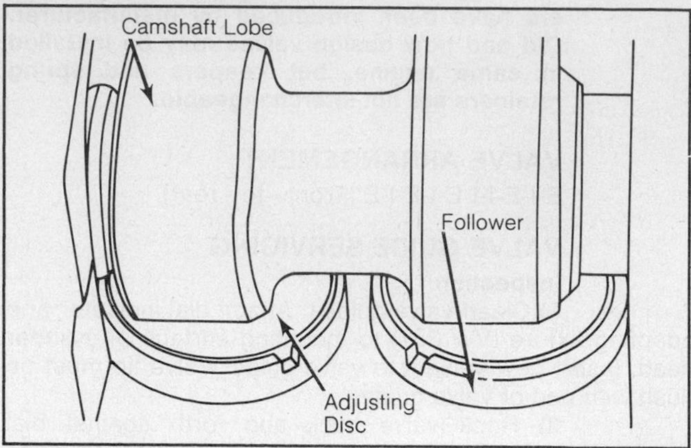
Camshaft Lobe
Follower
Adjusting Disc

Note grooves for disc removing pliers (US 4476).

Fig. 6: Compressing Cam Follower To Replace Adjusting Disc

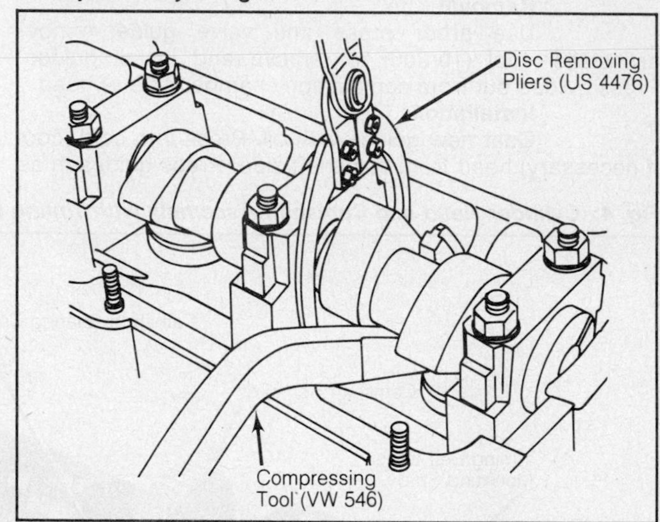
Disc Removing Pliers (US 4476)
Compressing Tool (VW 546)

3) To install discs, depress cam followers and slip discs into place. Ensure side of disc with thickness marking is installed down, facing cam follower. Repeat procedure until all valves are properly adjusted.

PISTONS, PINS AND RINGS

OIL PAN

Removal

Remove 2 front bolts of subframe. Drain engine oil. Remove dipstick. Remove flywheel dust cover. Remove rear pan bolts. Remove remaining pan bolts and lower pan from engine.

Installation

Clean all gasket mating surfaces. Make sure flange of oil pan is not distorted. Install oil pan with new gasket. Tighten pan bolts in criss-cross pattern. Replace dipstick and flywheel dust cover.

PISTON & ROD ASSEMBLY

Removal

1) Drain oil and coolant. Remove cylinder head and oil pan. Place piston to be removed at bottom of cylinder and cover with cloth to collect metal cuttings. Using ridge reamer, remove any ridge or deposit from upper end of cylinder bore.

2) Before removing piston and rod from engine, mark rod and rod cap for cylinder identification. Remove rod cap and carefully push piston and rod out top of cylinder. Install rod cap on rod from which removed.

Installation

1) Coat cylinder bore, piston, and rings with engine oil. Ensure ring end gaps are spaced 120° apart. Install ring compressor on piston, making sure position of rings does not change.

2) Install piston and rod in respective bore. Arrow on piston head faces toward front of engine. Forged marks (lumps) on rod and cap must also face toward front of engine. Make sure connecting rod bolts do not damage bearing journals on crankshaft.

FITTING PISTONS

1) Measure cylinder at 90° to crankshaft centerline and in line with crankshaft centerline as follows: 3/8" from top of bore, at middle of bore and 3/8" from bottom of bore. Difference between corresponding measurements is out-of-round, and must not exceed .0016" (.040 mm).

NOTE: **Cylinder bore dimensions should not be measured with engine mounted on stand. Readings may be incorrect due to distortion of block.**

2) Measure piston diameter 90° to piston pin bore, approximately 9/16" from bottom of piston skirt. Compare this measurement with measurement of corresponding cylinder bore. Maximum allowable piston-to-cylinder clearance is .0010" (.025 mm) for new piston and .0030" (.076 mm) for used piston.

3) Block must be bored and oversize pistons installed if piston-to-cylinder clearance is excessive. Three sizes of pistons are available in each grouping. There are 4 groupings: standard and 3 oversizes.

FITTING RINGS

1) Place piston rings squarely into cylinder bore about 5/8" from bottom of bore. Measure ring end gap with feeler gauge. End gap wear limit is .04" (1.0 mm).

2) With rings installed on piston, use feeler gauge to measure ring side clearance. Measure around entire circumference of piston, between top of ring and ring land. Ring side clearance wear limit is .004" (.10 mm).

3) Install rings on piston with "TOP" mark facing upward. Recessed edge on outside of center ring must face down toward piston pin. Space ring end gaps 120° apart.

PISTON PIN REPLACEMENT

Removal

Remove circlip from pin bore groove. Use piston pin tool (VW 207c) to remove and install piston pins. If pins are too tight it may be necessary to warm pistons to about 140° F (60° C).

Installation

Assemble connecting rod to piston. Arrow on piston head and forged marks on connecting rod must face toward front of engine when assembly is installed. Use piston pin tool (VW 207c) to install piston pin. Install circlip into pin bore groove.

CRANKSHAFT MAIN & CONNECTING ROD BEARINGS

CRANKSHAFT MAIN BEARINGS

1) Main bearing caps are numbered 1 through 6 (front to rear). Never interchange bearing caps. Always measure main bearing clearances 1 at time.

2) Use Plastigage method for measuring bearing clearances. Ensure oil film is removed from bearing halves and crankshaft journal prior to measuring clearance.

3) When replacing bearings, install grooved bearing halves into cylinder block. Plain bearing halves are installed in main caps. Lubricate crankshaft journals and bearings prior to installation.

CONNECTING ROD BEARINGS

1) Always measure connecting rod bearing clearances 1 at time. Use Plastigage method for measuring bearing clearances. Ensure oil film is removed from bearing halves and crankshaft journal prior to measuring clearance.

2) Use feeler gauge to check connecting rod side clearance. Insert feeler gauge between connecting rod and crankshaft thrust face. Wear limit for rod side clearance is .016" (.40 mm).

CRANKSHAFT END THRUST

Use feeler gauge to check crankshaft end play. Insert feeler gauge between No. 4 main bearing (thrust bearing) and crankshaft thrust face. Wear limit is .010" (.25 mm).

REAR MAIN BEARING OIL SEAL

Removal

Remove transmission. Remove clutch parts and flywheel or drive plate on automatic models. Index mark flywheel or drive plate to crankshaft before removal. Using seal remover tool (2086), carefully pry oil seal from seal flange.

Installation

Coat new seal lips with oil. Position seal in place and start by hand. Using seal installing tool (2003/1), press in seal until seated. Install remaining components. Use Loctite on flywheel bolts. Note that notch on outer washer of drive plate faces toward torque converter.

ENGINE OILING

CRANKCASE CAPACITY

For 5000 models, capacity is 4.8 qts. (4.5L) without filter replacement; 5.3 qts. (5.0L) with filter replacement. For 4000, Coupe, and Quantum models, capacity is 3.2 qts. (3.0L) without filter replacement; 3.7 qts. (3.5L) with filter replacement.

NOTE: **Whenever turbocharger is replaced or rebuilt, engine oil and both oil filters must be replaced.**

OIL PRESSURE

Oil pressures should be 14 psi (.98 kg/cm²) at idle speed, and 77 psi (5.3 kg/cm²) at 5500 RPM.

4000 & 5000, COUPE & QUANTUM 5-CYLINDER (Cont.)

Measurements are made with 20W/20 oil at temperature of 176° F (80° C).

OIL PRESSURE RELIEF VALVE

Oil pressure relief valve opens at 77-91 psi (5.3-6.3 kg/cm²).

OIL PRESSURE WARNING SYSTEM

1) Dynamic oil pressure warning system is used on this motor. Control unit with buzzer is mounted on relay panel adapter. Oil pressure switch is on side of block.

2) Switch contact is open with engine off and closes when engine is running and oil pressure reaches 23-29 psi (1.6-2.0 kg/cm²). If oil pressure drops below 23-29 psi (1.6-2.0 kg/cm²) with engine running at 2500 RPM, warning light comes on and buzzer sounds.

ENGINE OILING SYSTEM

Slipper gear type pump is used. Oil pump is mounted at front of engine and driven by crankshaft. *See Fig. 7.* An oil suction tube, extending from oil pump, lifts oil from oil pan. Oil is then fed to internal engine moving parts. Lubrication is either by pressure feed or drainage method.

To aid in piston cooling, turbo engines use oil nozzles which are installed at bottom of each cylinder. Oil is sprayed into underside of piston to cool piston skirt and head. If oil nozzles are removed, coat retaining bolt threads with thread adhesive on installation.

Fig. 7: Engine Oil Pump

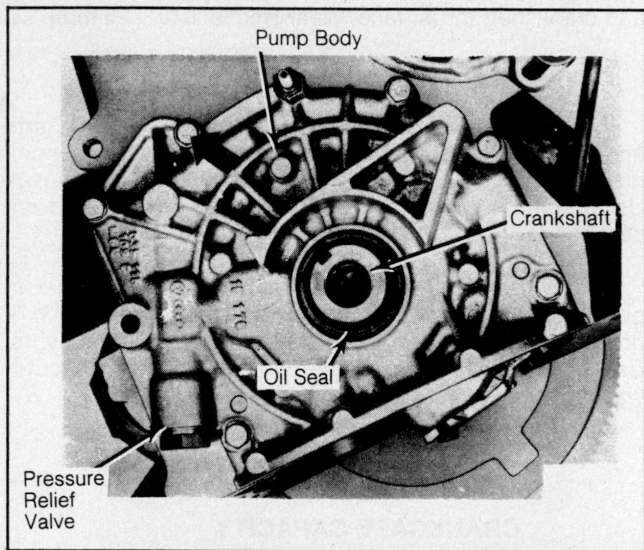
Pump Body
Crankshaft
Oil Seal
Pressure Relief Valve

OIL PUMP

Removal & Disassembly

1) Remove all drive belts from crankshaft pulley. Remove power steering pump (with hoses connected) and position aside. Remove timing belt cover. Loosen crankshaft damper/pulley bolt.

2) Turn crankshaft to position No. 1 piston at TDC after compression stroke. Loosen water pump adjusting bolts. Turn water pump to relieve tension on timing belt.

3) If equipped, remove lower timing belt cover. Ensure crankshaft position has not changed. Remove damper/pulley from crankshaft with drive sprocket attached. Remove dipstick.

4) Drain engine oil and remove oil pan. Remove oil suction tube from oil pump. Remove oil pump. Remove end cover from pump housing. Lift out outer and inner pump gears.

Inspection & Reassembly

Inspect end cover, housing, and gears for wear or scoring. If pump gears require replacement, replace in pairs only. Install gears in pump housing with triangular mark facing end cover. Install end cover.

Installation

Prime oil pump prior to installing. Install oil pump in reverse order of removal procedures. Coat threads of crankshaft damper/pulley bolt with Loctite prior to installing. Adjust timing belt tension. Ensure valve timing is correct.

ENGINE COOLING

THERMOSTAT

Thermostat begins opening at 194°F (90°C), and is fully open at 216°F (102°C). Minimum opening distance of thermostat is .27" (7 mm). When installing, position so arrow on housing points downward across hose connection.

COOLANT CAPACITY

Capacity is 8.6 quarts (8.1L) for non-turbo models, and 10 quarts (9.4L) for turbo models. Always use ethylene glycol based (phosphate-free) antifreeze. A 50/50 mixture protects to about -30°F (-35°C).

EXPANSION TANK CAP

Relief valve opens at 17-19 psi (1.20-1.33 kg/cm²) to relieve pressure.

WATER PUMP

Removal

1) Drain cooling system. Remove timing belt cover. Turn crankshaft to align TDC timing mark with reference mark on clutch housing.

2) Loosen water pump to relieve tension on timing belt. Remove timing belt. Do not allow crankshaft or camshaft to move. Remove water pump.

Installation

Install water pump in reverse order of removal procedure, using new "O" ring. Ensure valve timing is correct prior to installing remaining components.

4000 & 5000, COUPE & QUANTUM 5-CYLINDER (Cont.)

ENGINE SPECIFICATIONS

GENERAL SPECIFICATIONS

Year	DISPLACEMENT		Fuel System	HP@RPM	Torque Ft. Lbs.@RPM	Compr. Ratio	BORE		STROKE	
	Cu. In.	Liters					In.	mm	In.	mm
1983										
Non-Turbo	130.8	2.2	Fuel Inj.	100@5100	118@4000	8.0:1	3.13	79.5	3.40	86.4
Turbo	130.8	2.2	Fuel Inj.	130@5400	142@3000	7.0:1	3.13	79.5	3.40	86.4

VALVES

Engine Size & Valve	Head Diam. In. (mm)	Face Angle	Seat Angle	Seat Width In. (mm)	Stem Diameter In. (mm)	Stem Clearance In. (mm)	Valve Lift In. (mm)
2.2L							
Intake	1.496 (38.00)	45°	45°	.079 (2.00)	.314 (7.98)	.020 Max. (.50)	.....
Exhaust	1.220 (31.00)	45°	45°	.094 (2.40)	.313 (7.95)	.026 Max. (.65)	.....

PISTONS, PINS, RINGS

Engine	PISTONS	PINS		RINGS		
	Clearance In. (mm)	Piston Fit In. (mm)	Rod Fit In. (mm)	Ring No.	End Gap In. (mm)	Side Clearance In. (mm)
2.2L	.001-.003 (.025-.080)	[1]	.....	All	.010-.020 [2] (.25-.51)	.0008-.0030 [3] (.020-.080)

[1] – Push fit at 140°F (60°C).
[2] – Wear limit is .04" (1.0 mm).
[3] – Wear limit is .004" (.10 mm).

CRANKSHAFT MAIN & CONNECTING ROD BEARINGS

Engine	MAIN BEARINGS				CONNECTING ROD BEARINGS		
	Journal Diam. In. (mm)	Clearance In. (mm)	Thrust Bearing	Crankshaft End Play In. (mm)	Journal Diam. In. (mm)	Clearance In. (mm)	Side Play In. (mm)
2.2L							
Std. Size	2.282 [1] (57.97)	.0006-.0030 [2] (.015-.076)	No. 4	.0030-.0070 [3] (.076-.178)	1.810 [1] (45.97)	.0006-.0020 [4] (.015-.051)	.016 (.41)
1st U/Size	2.272 (57.71)				1.800 (45.72)		
2nd U/Size	2.262 (57.45)				1.790 (45.47)		
3rd U/Size	2.252 (57.20)				1.780 (45.22)		

[1] – Maximum out-of-round for standard or undersize crankshaft journals is .001" (.03 mm).
[2] – Wear limit is .006" (.16 mm).
[3] – Wear limit is .010" (.25 mm).
[4] – Wear limit is .005" (.12 mm).

Audi & Volkswagen Engines

4000 & 5000, COUPE & QUANTUM 5-CYLINDER (Cont.)

ENGINE SPECIFICATIONS (Cont.)

TIGHTENING SPECIFICATIONS

Application	Ft. Lbs. (N.m)
Camshaft Bearing Cap	14 (20)
Camshaft Sprocket	58 (80)
Cold Start Valve	7 (10)
Connecting Rod Cap	36 (50)
Crankshaft Damper/Pulley (Loctite)	[1] 258 (350)
Cylinder Head Bolts	
Step 1	29 (40)
Step 2	43 (60)
Step 3 [2]	54 (75)
Exhaust Manifold-to-Head	18 (25)
Exhaust Manifold-to-Turbocharger	43 (60)
Exhaust Pipe-to-Turbocharger	22 (30)
Flywheel (Loctite)	54 (75)
Intake Manifold	18 (25)
Main Bearing Cap	47 (65)
Oil Return Line	
Bracket-to-Turbocharger	18 (25)

[1] – Applies only when using tool 2079 with torque wrench parallel to tool handle.

[2] – After 3rd step, tighten head bolts an additional 1/4 turn. DO NOT retighten after 1,000 miles.

5000 5-CYLINDER DIESEL & TURBO DIESEL

ENGINE CODING

ENGINE IDENTIFICATION

Engine number is stamped on machined pad. Pad is located at left top side of block, between No. 2 and 3 cylinders. Letter prefix indicates engine type.

ENGINE IDENTIFICATION CODES

Engine	Code
2.0L	
Std. Diesel	CN
Turbo Diesel	DE

ENGINE, MANIFOLDS & CYLINDER HEAD

ENGINE

Removal

1) Disconnect battery ground strap. Remove air cleaner. Remove front grille. Remove cover plates under engine and transmission. Remove windshield washer reservoir and place to side.

2) Pull hood latch cable guide out of bracket. Drain cooling system and disconnect coolant and heater hoses attached to engine. Remove power steering pump with hoses connected and lay aside.

3) If equipped with A/C, loosen condenser and tilt outward. Remove auxiliary radiator. Disconnect wiring harness, overheat fuse connector, temperature sender wire, and wires connected to starter.

4) Remove fuel filter bracket and flange. Disconnect fuel return pipe on injection pump. Detach accelerator cable and disconnect idle speed control cable from injection pump lever.

5) Remove right engine mount cover plate. Remove front engine mount from crossmember. If equipped with A/C, remove compressor from engine leaving hoses attached.

6) Remove alternator mounting bracket. Disconnect exhaust pipe from manifold and transmission bracket. If equipped, disconnect exhaust pipe from turbocharger. Remove body ground strap. Remove lower engine-to-transmission bolts.

7) Remove flywheel cover plate from transmission. Install transmission supporting tool (VW 785/1) with slight preload. Attach lifting device to engine.

8) Remove left engine bracket. Loosen right engine bracket from engine mount. Lift engine and transmission until transmission housing contacts steering housing. Adjust transmission support tool until it contacts transmission housing.

9) Remove upper engine-to-transmission bolts. Separate engine from transmission. Turn engine to right (90° from installed position) while lifting from vehicle. Use caution not to damage transmission or clutch parts.

Installation

1) To install engine, reverse removal procedures. Note that metal lip on exhaust manifold flange gasket must face exhaust pipe.

2) After installing upper transmission-to-engine bolts, remove transmission support tool. Tighten engine mounts while engine is running at idle speed.

CYLINDER HEAD

Removal

1) Disconnect battery ground strap. Drain cooling system. Label and disconnect coolant hoses and electrical wiring from head. Disconnect exhaust pipe from manifold (or turbocharger). Remove fuel lines connected to cylinder head. Remove cam cover and front timing belt covers.

2) Remove vacuum pump drive belt from pulley at rear of engine. Remove injection pump belt cover. Set crankshaft to TDC on number 1 cylinder. Timing marks on flywheel and clutch housing must be aligned. Ensure timing marks on injection pump sprocket and injection pump mounting plate are aligned.

3) Lock injection pump sprocket in place with pin tool (2064). Hold vacuum pump pulley and injection pump drive sprocket (camshaft rear sprocket) in place with tool (3036). Remove injection pump drive sprocket retaining bolt. Camshaft must not move. Remove pulley, noting number and position of shims.

4) Remove injection pump drive sprocket and drive belt from rear of camshaft. Install camshaft holding tool (2065A) at rear of camshaft. With camshaft locked in place, loosen front camshaft sprocket bolt 1 turn.

5) Tap sprocket loose and remove sprocket. Loosen and remove head bolts in reverse order of tightening sequence. *See Fig. 1*. Lift off cylinder head with manifolds attached.

CAUTION: Never interchange old style 6-point Allen head bolts with new style polygon Allen head bolts. Polygon bolts are stretch-type bolts and have a different tightening procedure. Turbo-diesel and standard diesel head gaskets do not use same material. Head gaskets are not interchangeable.

CAUTION: Cylinder head gaskets have identification notches next to part number. Notches indicate thickness of head gasket. If new pistons or short block is installed, measure height pistons project above cylinder block deck when piston is at TDC. Select new head gasket according to maximum measured piston height.

Installation

1) Ensure that mating surfaces of engine block and cylinder head are clean. Use gasket with same number of notches as old gasket if installing on original block assembly.

2) Make sure bolt holes in block are clean and dry. Install guide pins in cylinder block at right front and left rear cylinder head bolt holes. Install head gasket dry (no adhesive) with part number facing upward.

3) Install and tighten head bolts in 3 steps. *See Fig. 1*. After 3rd step, turn bolts in sequence additional 180° turn. Install remaining components. Ensure valve and injection timing is correct.

4) Run engine and warm to operating temperature. Tighten head bolts additional 90° further. At 1000 mile service after repairs, tighten cylinder head bolts in sequence additional 90°. Engine may be cold or warm.

5000 5-CYLINDER DIESEL & TURBO DIESEL (Cont.)

Fig. 1: Cylinder Head Tightening Sequence

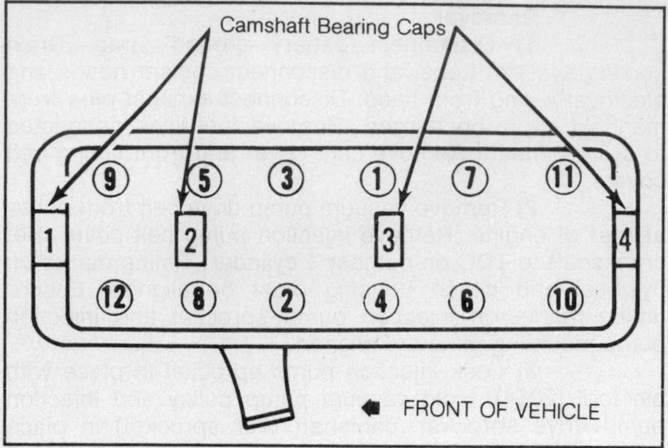
Camshaft Bearing Caps
9
5
3
1
7
11
1
2
3
4
12
8
2
4
6
10
FRONT OF VEHICLE

Loosen cylinder head bolts in reverse order of tightening.

CAMSHAFT

TIMING BELT COVERS

Removal & Installation

Remove drive belts from crankshaft pulley. Remove power steering pump with hoses connected, and position aside. Remove attaching bolts and remove upper and lower timing belt covers. To install, reverse removal procedure.

TIMING BELTS & VALVE TIMING

CAUTION: Valve timing is critical on diesel engines due to limited clearance between valves and pistons. If valve timing is incorrect, major internal engine damage will occur.

Removal

1) Remove drive belts from crankshaft pulley. Remove outer half of vacuum pump pulley and drive belt at rear of engine. Note position and number of shims on pulley.

2) Remove timing belt covers and injection pump belt cover. Remove cam cover. Rotate crankshaft to position No. 1 cylinder at TDC. Timing marks on flywheel and clutch housing must be aligned. Also, timing marks on fuel injection pump sprocket and pump mounting plate must be aligned.

3) Lock injection pump sprocket with pin tool (2064). Hold inner half of vacuum pump pulley and injection pump drive sprocket with tool (3036). Remove sprocket center retaining bolt. Remove inner pulley half, pump sprocket and injection pump drive belt.

4) Secure crankshaft from moving with support tool (2084). Loosen crankshaft damper/pulley center bolt. Install camshaft holding tool (2065A) in slot at rear of camshaft.

5) With camshaft locked in place, loosen water pump bolts to relieve tension on timing belt. Remove crankshaft pulley with timing belt sprocket and timing belt. Remove water pump to check sealing "O" ring.

Installation

1) Ensure crankshaft and injection pump timing marks are aligned. Install crankshaft damper/pulley with sprocket and timing belt. Using tool (2084) to hold crankshaft, install and tighten center bolt.

2) With camshaft still locked in place loosen camshaft sprocket bolt 1 full turn. Using brass drift inserted through hole in rear timing belt cover, tap camshaft sprocket loose from camshaft taper.

3) Install water pump with new sealing ring. Attach timing belt to camshaft sprocket. To adjust timing belt tension, turn water pump until pump sprocket provides tension against timing belt.

4) Using tension tester (VW 210), check timing belt tension midway between camshaft and water pump sprockets. Tension is correct when tester reads 12-13.

5) Check that crankshaft and injection pump timing marks are still aligned. Tighten camshaft sprocket bolt and remove camshaft holding tool.

6) Install injection pump drive sprocket, drive belt, and inner pulley half. Tighten injection pump drive sprocket retaining bolt until it is just possible to turn sprocket on camshaft by hand.

7) Adjust fuel injection pump drive belt tension by loosening mounting bolts and repositioning mounting plate and support on engine. Using tension tester (VW 210), check belt tension midway between fuel injection pump and drive sprockets.

8) If pump drive belt tension is 12-13 on tester (VW 210), tighten fuel injection pump drive sprocket bolt. Remove pin tool (2064) from injection pump sprocket. Install remaining components in reverse order of removal. Ensure injection pump timing is correct.

INJECTION PUMP TIMING

1) Set crankshaft at TDC for No. 1 cylinder. Align marks on flywheel and transmission housing. Align marks on injection pump sprocket and pump mounting plate. Loosen clamp screw on cold start device cable and rotate clamp 90°. Do not loosen screw at end of cable.

2) Remove bolt and sealing washer in center of injection pump. The bolt is in end of pump to which injector lines are connected. Install adapter (2066) and small dial indicator into injection pump. Set dial indicator with .098" (2.5 mm) preload.

3) Slowly rotate crankshaft counterclockwise until needle on dial indicator stops moving. Zero dial indicator with about .04" (1.0 mm) preload. Turn crankshaft clockwise until TDC mark on flywheel aligns with mark on transmission housing. Dial indicator should read lift of .034" (.85 mm).

4) If reading incorrect, loosen bolts holding pump to mounting plate. Turn pump until dial indicator reading is correct. Tighten pump mount bolts and check injection pump lift again.

5) If correct, remove dial indicator and adapter. Replace bolt with new sealing washer. Rotate cold start clamp back 90° to tension cable. Tighten set screw. Start engine. Check that cold start device goes off. Make sure idle is smooth and correct. Check for fuel leaks. Make sure there are no air bubbles in clear fuel line.

CAMSHAFT

Removal

Remove timing belt and fuel injection pump belt. If necessary, mark cam bearing caps 1 to 4 (front to rear). Loosen bearing caps 1 and 4, then remove caps. Diagonally loosen bearing caps 2 and 3, then remove caps. Remove camshaft from head.

Installation

1) Lubricate bearing surfaces in cam bearing caps. Lubricate camshaft journals. Install camshaft. Install cam bearing caps in original locations from which removed. Ensure caps are not misaligned.

2) Lightly tighten bearing caps 2 and 3 in diagonal pattern, then tighten all bearing caps. Install remaining components. Make sure valve timing, valve adjustment, and injection pump timing are correct.

CAMSHAFT FRONT OIL SEAL

Removal

1) Remove timing belt covers and fuel injection pump drive belt cover. Remove cam cover. Position No. 1 cylinder at TDC with timing marks on flywheel and clutch housing aligned. Timing marks on fuel injection pump sprocket and mounting plate must be aligned.

2) Lock injection pump sprocket in place with pin tool (2064). Hold vacuum pump pulley and injection pump drive sprocket (rear camshaft sprocket) with tool (3036). Remove belt pulley, injection pump drive sprocket and drive belt from rear of camshaft.

3) Install camshaft holding tool (2065A) in slot at rear of camshaft to secure in place. Loosen water pump bolts to relieve tension on timing belt. Loosen camshaft sprocket bolt 1 full turn.

4) Using brass drift inserted through hole in rear timing belt cover, tap camshaft sprocket loose from camshaft taper. Remove camshaft sprocket bolt and sprocket. Using seal removing tool (2002), remove camshaft oil seal.

Installation

Lubricate seal lips with oil. Lubricate seal recess in front cam bearing with oil. Using seal installing tool (10-203), press seal into place until seated. Install remaining components in reverse order of removal procedures. Ensure valve timing and injection pump timing are correct.

CAMSHAFT REAR OIL SEAL

Removal

1) Remove vacuum pump belt and pulley. Remove injection pump belt cover. Set No. 1 cylinder on TDC. Timing marks on flywheel and clutch housing, and injection pump sprocket and mounting plate must be aligned.

2) Lock injection pump sprocket in place with pin tool (2064). Hold injection pump drive sprocket in place with tool (3036). Remove injection pump drive sprocket and drive belt from rear of camshaft. Using oil seal removing tool (2002), remove oil seal.

Installation

Lubricate seal lips with oil. Lubricate seal recess in front cam bearing with oil. Using seal installing tool (10-203), press seal into place until seated. Install remaining components in reverse order of removal procedures. Ensure valve timing and injection pump timing are correct.

CAMSHAFT END THRUST

1) Check camshaft end thrust with cam followers and timing belts removed. Attach dial indicator to cylinder head. Position indicator point at 90° to end of camshaft or sprocket. Push camshaft rearward and zero dial indicator.

2) Push camshaft forward to record maximum movement. If end thrust exceeds .006" (.15 mm), check camshaft thrust flange and bearing cap for wear. Replace worn components.

VALVES

CAUTION: **Never rework exhaust valves on valve grinding machine. Lap exhaust valves by hand only.**

NOTE: **New design intake and exhaust valves with 3 keeper grooves and chamfered spring retainers have been introduced by manufacturer. Old and new design valves may be installed in same engine, but keepers and spring retainers are not interchangeable.**

VALVE ARRANGEMENT

E-I-E-I-I-E-I-E-I-E (Front-to-rear)

VALVE GUIDE SERVICING

Inspection

1) Clean valve guides. Attach dial indicator and adapting fixture (VW 387) to mounting surface of cylinder head. Insert new valve into valve guide. Valve tip must be flush with top of valve guide.

2) Rock valve back and forth against dial indicator point to measure amount of stem-to-guide clearance. If wear exceeds .051" (1.3 mm) for intake or exhaust valves, replace guides.

Removal

Use arbor press and valve guide remover/installer tool (10-206) to remove and install guides. Press guides out from combustion chamber side of head.

Installation

Coat new guides with oil. Press into cold head from camshaft side. Press guides in as far as they will go. Do not use more than 1 ton pressure once guide shoulder is seated, or guide shoulder may break. Ream guide by hand to proper size.

VALVE STEM OIL SEALS

NOTE: **Valve stem seals may be replaced with cylinder head installed on vehicle.**

CAUTION: **Installing valve stem oil seal without using plastic protective sleeve of seal installing tool (10-204), may result in seal damage.**

Removal

1) Remove camshaft. Remove followers and valve adjusting discs of cylinder to be serviced. Turn crankshaft until piston of cylinder concerned is at TDC, so valve will rest on piston head when valve springs are removed.

2) Using spring compressor tool (VW 541/1 or 2036), compress valve spring and remove keepers, retainers and springs. Use seal removing pliers (10-218) to remove seal.

Installation

Place seal protector over valve stem. Lubricate new seal and push seal into place with seal installing tool (10-204). Install remaining valve components. Reverse removal procedures to complete installation.

VALVE SPRINGS

Valve springs may be replaced with cylinder head installed on vehicle. See *Valve Stem Oil Seals* for removal and installation procedure.

Audi Engines

5000 5-CYLINDER DIESEL & TURBO DIESEL (Cont.)

CAM FOLLOWERS

When removing cam followers, keep them in order for reassembly in original locations. With camshaft and adjusting discs removed, lift out cam followers. Inspect for wear or damage and replace as necessary. Coat with oil when installing.

VALVE CLEARANCE ADJUSTMENT

NOTE: Cold valve clearances are given for initial settings, after engine work has been performed. Recheck valve clearance and make final adjustment with engine coolant temperature about 95°F (35°C).

Measuring Valve Clearance

1) Remove cam cover. Turn crankshaft clockwise until both cam lobes of cylinder to be adjusted point upward.

CAUTION: Never use camshaft sprocket attaching bolt to turn camshaft, as this may stretch timing belt. Never turn crankshaft counterclockwise.

2) Using feeler gauge, measure valve clearances between cam and follower in firing order sequence. *See Valve Clearance Specifications.* If clearance is incorrect, adjust valves.

VALVE CLEARANCE SPECIFICATIONS

Application	In. (mm)
Intake	
Hot	.008-.012 (.20-.30)
Cold	.006-.010 (.15-.25)
Exhaust	
Hot	.016-.020 (.40-.51)
Cold	.014-.018 (.36-.46)

NOTE: When cylinder head service has been performed, valve clearance must be checked and adjusted after 1000 miles.

Adjusting Valve Clearance

1) When adjusting valves, piston of cylinder being serviced must not be at TDC. Turn crankshaft about 1/4 turn past piston TDC position. This will keep valves from contacting pistons when cam followers are depressed.

2) To remove adjusting disc, cam follower must be depressed using compressing tool (2078). *See Fig. 2.* Use disc remover tool (US 4476) to remove adjusting disc.

3) Thickness of adjusting disc is stamped on bottom of disc. If measured valve clearance is larger than specifications, use thicker disc. If clearance is less than specification, use thinner disc.

4) Adjust clearance to middle of tolerance range. Adjusting discs are available in .002" (.05 mm) increments from .118" (3.0 mm) to .167" (4.25 mm).

5) To install disc, depress cam follower and slip disc into place. Ensure side of disc with thickness marking is installed downward, facing cam follower. Repeat procedure until all valves are properly adjusted.

Fig. 2: Removing and Installing Adjusting Discs

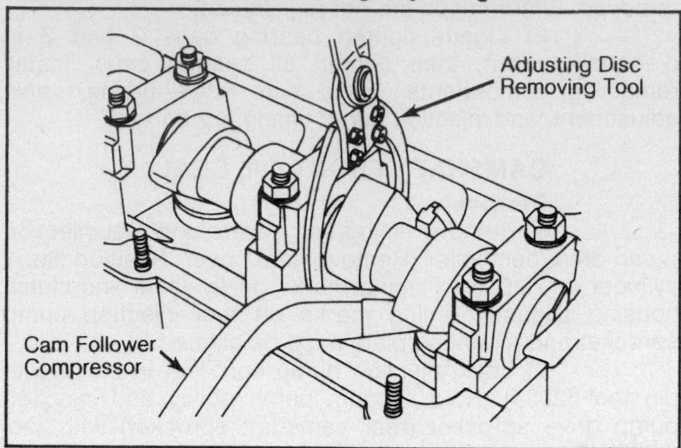
Adjusting Disc
Removing Tool
Cam Follower
Compressor

Ensure piston of cylinder being serviced is not at TDC.

PISTONS, PINS AND RINGS

OIL PAN

Removal

Remove 2 front bolts in subframe. Drain engine oil. Remove flywheel dust cover. Remove both rear pan bolts. Remove remaining pan bolts and lower pan from engine.

Installation

Clean all gasket mating surfaces. Make sure flange of oil pan is not damaged. Using new pan gasket, install oil pan. Tighten pan bolts in criss-cross pattern.

PISTON & ROD ASSEMBLY

Removal

1) Remove cylinder head, oil pan, and oil pump. Place piston to be removed at bottom of cylinder and cover with cloth to collect metal cuttings. Using ridge reamer, remove any ridge or deposit from upper end of cylinder bore.

2) Before removing piston and rod from engine, mark rod and rod cap for cylinder identification. Remove rod cap and carefully push piston and rod out top of cylinder. Install rod cap on rod from which removed.

Installation

1) Coat cylinder bore, piston, and rings with engine oil. Offset ring gaps at 120° apart. Install ring compressor on piston, making sure position of rings does not change.

2) Install piston and rod in its respective bore, with arrow on piston head facing toward front of engine. Forged casting beads on rod and cap will be on oil filter side of engine. Be careful not to damage crankshaft journals with rod bolts.

FITTING PISTONS

1) Take cylinder measurements 90° to crankshaft centerline and in line with crankshaft centerline as follows: 3/8" from top of bore, at middle of bore and 3/8" from bottom of bore.

2) Do not take measurements when engine is mounted on stand as cylinder bore could be distorted.

Difference between corresponding measurements is out-of-round, and must not exceed .0016" (.040 mm).

3) Measure piston diameter 90° to piston pin bore, approximately 9/16" from bottom of piston skirt. Compare this measurement with measurement of corresponding cylinder bore. Maximum allowable piston-to-cylinder clearance is .011" (.03 mm) for new piston, and .027" (.07 mm) for used piston.

4) Install oversize pistons if piston-to-cylinder clearance is excessive. Three sets of oversize replacement pistons are available. Each set has 3 different size pistons.

FITTING RINGS

1) Place piston rings squarely into cylinder bore about 5/8" from bottom of bore. Use feeler gauge to measure ring end gap.

2) With rings installed on piston, use feeler gauge to measure ring side clearance. Take measurement around entire circumference of piston, between top of ring and ring land.

3) Install rings on piston with "TOP" mark facing upward. Space ring end gaps 120° apart.

PISTON PIN REPLACEMENT

Removal

Remove circlip from pin bore groove. Use piston pin tool (10-508) to remove and install piston pins. If pins are too tight it may be necessary to warm pistons to about 140° F (60° C).

Installation

1) Assemble connecting rod to piston. Arrow on piston head must face toward front of engine. Forged casting beads on connecting rod must be on oil filter side of engine when assembly is installed. *See Fig. 3*.

2) Use piston pin tool (VW 207c) to install piston pin. Install circlip into pin bore groove.

Fig. 3: Piston-to-Rod Relationship

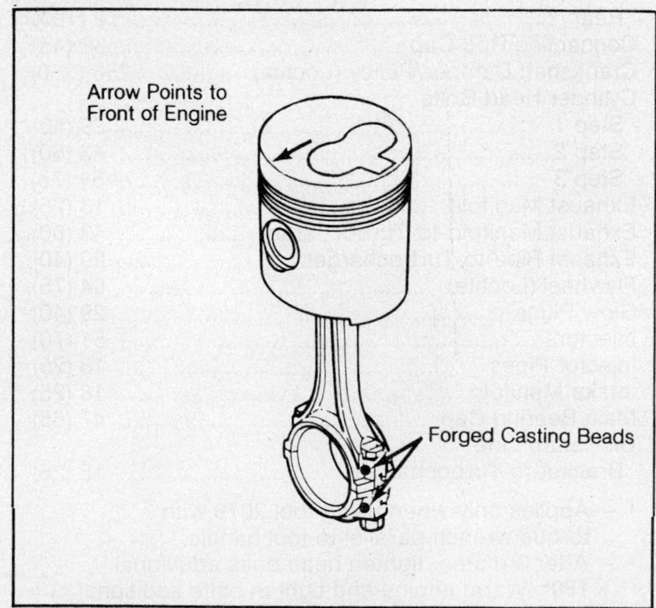

Arrow Points to
Front of Engine
Forged Casting Beads

Forged casting beads on connecting rod must be on oil filter side of engine when assembly is installed.

CRANKSHAFT MAIN & CONNECTING ROD BEARINGS

CRANKSHAFT MAIN BEARINGS

1) Main bearing caps are numbered 1 through 6 (front to rear). Never interchange bearing caps. Always measure main bearing clearances 1 at time.

2) Use Plastigage method for measuring bearing clearances. Clean oil film from bearing halves and crankshaft journal prior to measuring clearance.

3) When replacing bearings, install grooved bearing halves into cylinder block. Plain bearing halves are installed in main caps. Lubricate crankshaft journal and bearings prior to installing bearings.

CONNECTING ROD BEARINGS

1) Always measure connecting rod bearing clearances 1 at time. Use Plastigage method for measuring bearing clearances. Clean oil film from bearing halves and crankshaft journal prior to measuring clearance.

2) Use feeler gauge to check connecting rod side clearance. Insert feeler gauge between connecting rod and crankshaft thrust face. Side clearance wear limit is .015" (.40 mm)

CRANKSHAFT END THRUST

Use feeler gauge to check crankshaft end play. Insert feeler gauge between No. 4 main bearing (thrust bearing) and crankshaft thrust face. End play wear limit is .010" (.25 mm).

REAR MAIN BEARING OIL SEAL

Removal

Remove transmission. Index flywheel or drive plate to crankshaft for reassembly. Remove flywheel or drive plate. Using seal remover tool (2086), carefully pry oil seal from seal flange.

Installation

Coat new seal lips with oil. Position seal in place. Start seal into place by hand. Using seal installing tool (2003/1), press in seal until seated. Install remaining components. Use Loctite on flywheel bolts.

FRONT MAIN BEARING OIL SEAL

Removal

Remove front cover. Remove timing belt. Using crankshaft support tool (2084) to keep crankshaft from moving, remove crankshaft damper/pulley and sprocket. Using seal remover tool (2086), carefully pry seal from oil pump housing.

Installation

Lightly coat new seal lip and outer edge with oil. Using seal installer and guide sleeve (2080), press in seal until seated. Install remaining components in reverse order of removal. Check valve and injection pump timing is correct. Use Loctite on crankshaft damper bolt.

ENGINE OILING

NOTE: Crankcase capacity, oil pressure, and relief valve information for turbo diesel not available at time of printing.

Audi Engines

5000 5-CYLINDER DIESEL & TURBO DIESEL (Cont.)

CRANKCASE CAPACITY

Capacity for standard diesel is 4.2 quarts (4.0L) without filter replacement; 4.8 quarts (4.5L) with filter replacement.

NORMAL OIL PRESSURE

Minimum oil pressure for standard diesel should be 28 psi (1.97 kg/cm²) at 2000 RPM. Measurement is with oil temperature at 176° F (80° C).

OIL PRESSURE RELIEF VALVE

Relief valve opens at 75-90 psi (5.3-6.3 kg/cm²)

ENGINE OILING SYSTEM

A slipper gear type pump is used. Oil pump is mounted at front of engine, and is driven by crankshaft. An oil suction tube, extending from oil pump, lifts oil from oil pan. Oil is then fed to internal engine moving parts. Lubrication is either by pressure feed or drainage method.

To aid in piston cooling, turbo diesel engines use oil nozzles. Oil nozzles are installed at bottom of each cylinder. Oil is sprayed into underside of piston to cool piston skirt and head. If oil nozzles are removed, coat retaining bolt threads with adhesive when reassembling.

OIL PUMP

Removal & Disassembly

1) Remove timing belt covers. Remove timing belt. Using crankshaft support tool (2084) to keep crankshaft from moving, remove crankshaft damper/pulley and sprocket.

2) Drain engine oil and remove oil pan. Remove oil suction tube from oil pump. Remove oil pump. Remove end cover from pump housing. Lift out outer and inner pump gears.

Inspection & Reassembly

Inspect end cover, housing, and gears for wear or scoring. If pump gears require replacement, replace in pairs only. Install gears in pump housing with triangular mark facing end cover. Install and tighten end cover.

Installation

Prime oil pump prior to installing. Install oil pump in reverse order of removal procedures. Coat threads of crankshaft damper/pulley bolt with Loctite prior to installing. Adjust timing belt tension. Check that valve and injection pump timing is correct.

ENGINE COOLING

NOTE: Thermostat, coolant capacity and expansion tank cap information for turbo diesel not available from manufacturer at time of printing.

THERMOSTAT

Standard diesel thermostat begins opening at 188°F (87°C), and is fully open at 202°F (94°C).

COOLANT CAPACITY

Standard diesel capacity is 10 quarts (9.4L).

EXPANSION TANK CAP

Standard diesel relief valve opens at 17-19 psi (1.20-1.33 kg/cm²) to relieve pressure.

WATER PUMP

Removal

1) Drain coolant. Remove power steering pump with hoses connected and lay pump aside. Remove timing belt covers and fuel injection pump drive belt cover.

2) Remove cam cover. Position No. 1 piston on TDC. Timing marks on flywheel and clutch housing must be aligned. Timing marks on fuel injection pump sprocket and mounting plate must be aligned.

3) Lock injection pump sprocket in place with pin tool (2064). Hold vacuum pump pulley and injection pump drive sprocket (rear camshaft sprocket) in place with tool (3036). Remove belt pulley, injection pump drive sprocket, and drive belt from rear of camshaft.

4) Install camshaft holding tool (2065A) to rear of camshaft to secure in place. Loosen water pump bolts to relieve tension on timing belt. Loosen camshaft sprocket bolt 1 full turn.

5) Using brass drift inserted through hole in rear timing belt cover, tap camshaft sprocket loose from camshaft taper. Remove camshaft sprocket. Remove water pump.

Installation

Installation is reverse of removal procedures. Use new sealing "O" ring when installing water pump. Check that timing belts are properly tensioned. Be sure valve timing and injection pump timing is correct.

TIGHTENING SPECIFICATIONS

Application	Ft. Lbs. (N.m)
Camshaft Bearing Cap	15 (20)
Camshaft Sprockets	
Front	33 (45)
Rear	72 (100)
Connecting Rod Cap	33 (45)
Crankshaft Damper/Pulley (Loctite)	[1] 258 (350)
Cylinder Head Bolts	
Step 1	29 (40)
Step 2	43 (60)
Step 3	[2] 54 (75)
Exhaust Manifold	18 (25)
Exhaust Manifold-to-Turbocharger	43 (60)
Exhaust Pipe-to-Turbocharger	29 (40)
Flywheel (Loctite)	54 (75)
Glow Plugs	29 (40)
Injectors	51 (70)
Injector Pipes	18 (25)
Intake Manifold	18 (25)
Main Bearing Cap	47 (65)
Oil Return Line	
Bracket-to-Turbocharger	18 (25)

[1] – Applies only when using tool 2079 with torque wrench parallel to tool handle.

[2] – After 3rd step, tighten head bolts additional 180°. Warm engine and tighten bolts additional 90°. At 1000 miles, tighten bolts additional 90°.

Audi Engines

5000 5-CYLINDER DIESEL & TURBO DIESEL (Cont.)

ENGINE SPECIFICATIONS

GENERAL SPECIFICATIONS

Year	DISPLACEMENT		Fuel System	HP@RPM	Torque Ft. Lbs.@RPM	Compr. Ratio	BORE		STROKE	
	Cu. In.	Liters					In.	mm	In.	mm
1983										
Non-Turbo	121	2.0	Fuel Inj.	67@4800	90@3000	23:1	3.01	76.5	3.40	86.4
Turbo	121	2.0	Fuel Inj.	84@4500	127@2800	23:1	3.01	76.5	3.40	86.4

VALVES

Engine Size & Valve	Head Diam. In. (mm)	Face Angle	Seat Angle	Seat Width In. (mm)	Stem Diameter In. (mm)	Stem Clearance In. (mm)	Valve Lift In. (mm)
2.0L							
Intake	1.417 (36.00)	45°	45°	.078 (2.00)	.314 (7.98)	.026 Max. (.65)	.....
Exhaust	1.220 (31.00)	45°	45°	.096 (2.40)	.313 (7.95)	.026 Max. (.65)	.....

PISTONS, PINS, RINGS

Engine	PISTONS	PINS		RINGS		
	Clearance In. (mm)	Piston Fit In. (mm)	Rod Fit In. (mm)	Ring No.	End Gap In. (mm)	Side Clearance In. (mm)
2.0L	.0012-.0028 (.030-.070)	[1]	.....	Upper	.012-.020 [2] (.30-.51)	.002-.004 [3] (.05-.10)
				Center	.012-.020 [2] (.30-.51)	.002-.003 [3] (.05-.08)
				Oil	.010-.016 [2] (.25-.40)	.001-.002 [4] (.03-.05)

[1] – Push fit at 140°F (60°C). [2] – Wear limit is .04" (1.0 mm). [3] – Wear limit is .008" (.20 mm) [4] – Wear limit is .006" (.15 mm)

CRANKSHAFT MAIN & CONNECTING ROD BEARINGS

Engine	MAIN BEARINGS				CONNECTING ROD BEARINGS		
	Journal Diam. In. (mm)	Clearance In. (mm)	Thrust Bearing	Crankshaft End Play In. (mm)	Journal Diam. In. (mm)	Clearance In. (mm)	Side Play In. (mm)
2.0L							
Std. Size	2.282 [1] (57.97)	.0006-.0030 [2] (.015-.076)	No. 4	.0030-.0070 [3] (.076-.178)	1.881 [1] (47.77)	.0006-.0020 [4] (.015-.051)	.016 (.41)
1st U/Size	2.272 (57.71)				1.871 (47.52)		
2nd U/Size	2.262 (57.45)				1.861 (47.27)		
3rd U/Size	2.252 (57.20)				1.851 (47.02)		

[1] – Maximum out-of-round for standard or undersize crankshaft journals is .001" (.03 mm).
[2] – Wear limit is .006" (.16 mm).
[3] – Wear limit is .010" (.25 mm).
[4] – Wear limit is .005" (.12 mm).

BMW Engines

318i & 320i 4-CYLINDER

ENGINE CODING

ENGINE IDENTIFICATION

Engine identification number is located on engine block at left hand side above starter motor.

TRANSMISSION, ENGINE, MANIFOLDS & CYLINDER HEAD

MANUAL TRANSMISSION

Removal

1) Remove all upper transmission-to-engine mounting bolts. Remove exhaust pipe support bracket. Disconnect exhaust pipe at manifold. Remove front rubber coupling from transmission output flange.

2) Detach center bearing bracket from body after removing heat shield to gain access. Pull down on propeller shaft at center bearing to disengage shaft from transmission flange.

3) Remove speedometer cable. Label and disconnect back-up light switch and 4th gear switch. Remove center console from transmission. Engage transmission in reverse gear, then remove selector rod.

4) Remove clutch slave cylinder and hydraulic line support bracket. Support transmission with transmission jack or stand. Remove crossmember. Remove remaining transmission mounting bolts. Remove transmission.

Installation

To install, reverse removal procedure while noting the following: Install clutch slave cylinder with bleeder valve facing downward. When installing propeller shaft, push center bearing bracket forward .08" (2.0 mm) to preload center bearing, then tighten nuts.

AUTOMATIC TRANSMISSION

Removal

1) Remove accelerator cable and detach from bracket. Remove upper transmission-to-engine mounting bolts. Remove oil filler neck and drain oil.

2) Remove exhaust pipe support bracket. Disconnect exhaust pipe at manifold. Remove speedometer cable from transmission. Remove transmission output flange bolts and detach propeller shaft coupling.

3) Remove heat shield to gain access to center support bearing. Remove center bearing bracket. Pull down on propeller shaft at center bearing to disengage shaft from transmission flange.

4) Remove cover from bottom of transmission. Remove drive plate-to-torque converter bolts. Remove transmission oil cooler lines. Support transmission with transmission jack or stand, then remove crossmember.

5) Remove remaining transmission mounting bolts. Lift off side cover from transmission. Insert a bar through side cover hole, and carefully pry transmission and torque converter away from engine.

Installation

To install, reverse removal procedure. Ensure that torque converter is properly positioned on drive plate. When installing propeller shaft on 320i models, push center bearing bracket forward .08" (2.0 mm) to preload center bearing, then tighten nuts.

ENGINE

Removal

1) Disconnect positive and negative cables from battery. Remove transmission. Drain cooling system and disconnect hoses. Remove oil cooler lines from radiator (if equipped). Remove fan shroud and radiator.

2) If equipped, remove A/C compressor (with hoses connected) and position aside. Remove air cleaner housing. Disconnect fuel feed and return hoses from fuel distributor.

3) Remove hose from charcoal canister. Disconnect ground cable from front axle carrier. Disconnect accelerator cable from throttle valve housing. Label and disconnect all coolant and vacuum hoses from engine.

4) Label and disconnect all electrical and ignition wires between chassis and engine that might interfere with engine removal. Install lifting chain to engine.

5) With engine hoist in place, apply slight supporting tension to engine. Detach left engine mount and upper engine damper. Detach right engine mount. Remove engine from vehicle.

Installation

To install, reverse removal procedure. When filling with coolant, set heater control to "WARM" and fill radiator slowly. Bleed cooling system after engine is warm.

CYLINDER HEAD

Removal

1) Disconnect ground cable from battery. Remove air cleaner housing. Remove fuel line from cold start valve. Remove air hose from auxiliary air regulator.

2) Label and disconnect electrical connections at cylinder head and intake manifold that might interfere with cylinder head removal. Be sure to disconnect harness plug in glove box, and pull wiring through hole in engine compartment wall.

3) Drain cooling system. Disconnect all coolant hoses from cylinder head and intake manifold. Label and disconnect all vacuum hoses from intake manifold.

4) Remove cap from ignition coil. Label and disconnect primary ignition wires from coil and distributor. Remove high tension lead from distributor cap and spark plug wires from spark plugs. Remove distributor cap.

Fig. 1: Timing Mark Alignment for Setting No. 1 Piston at TDC

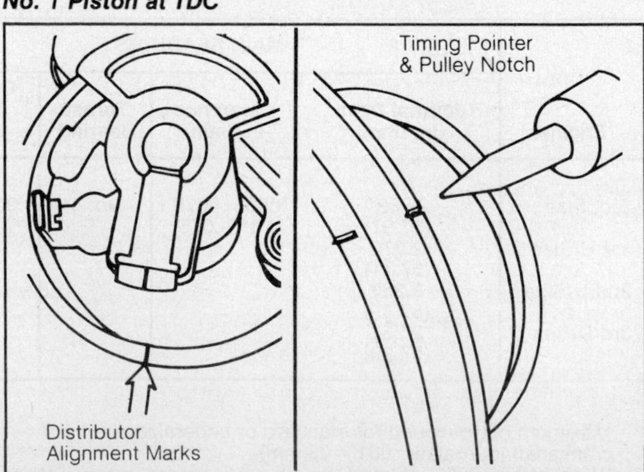
Timing Pointer
& Pulley Notch
Distributor
Alignment Marks

Do not allow crankshaft to move once marks are aligned.

318i & 320i 4-CYLINDER (Cont.)

5) Disconnect accelerator cable. Disconnect oil dipstick tube mount. Label and disconnect fuel lines to fuel injectors. Remove rocker cover. Set No. 1 piston at TDC. Align distributor rotor with notch in distributor housing, and timing pointer with notch in damper. *See Fig. 1.*

6) Remove upper front cover. Using care (because of strong spring pressure), remove timing chain tensioner plug, spring and piston. Remove 4 camshaft sprocket attaching bolts and remove sprocket.

7) Disconnect exhaust support bracket. Disconnect exhaust pipe from manifold. Remove cylinder head bolts in reverse sequence of tightening. *See Fig. 2.* Remove cylinder head with intake manifold attached.

Inspection

Cylinder head may be machined a maximum of .012" (.30 mm). Original height of cylinder head is 5.075-5.083" (128.9-129.1 mm) as measured from engine block mating surface to valve cover surface. If cylinder head is machined, use a .012" (.30 mm) oversize head gasket.

Installation

1) Clean all gasket mating surfaces. Measure distance dowel sleeve (installation guide) projects above cylinder head mounting surface. *See Fig. 3.* Maximum projection should not exceed .197" (5.00 mm).

Fig. 2: Cylinder Head Tightening Sequence

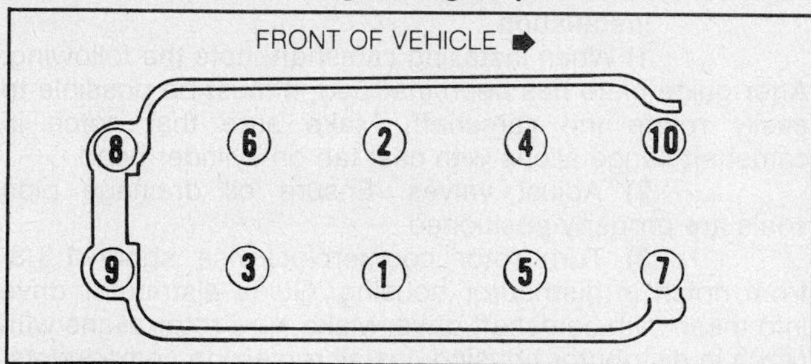
FRONT OF VEHICLE
8
6
2
4
10
9
3
1
5
7

Tighten head bolts in 3 steps, then repeat 3rd step. Retighten head bolts (cold) at 1000 miles.

2) Remove any oil in cylinder head bolt blind holes. Oil in holes may result in incorrect head bolt tightening and possible cylinder head or block damage. Clean cylinder head bolts. Clean threads in block.

Fig. 3: Measuring Dowel Sleeve Projection Above Cylinder Block

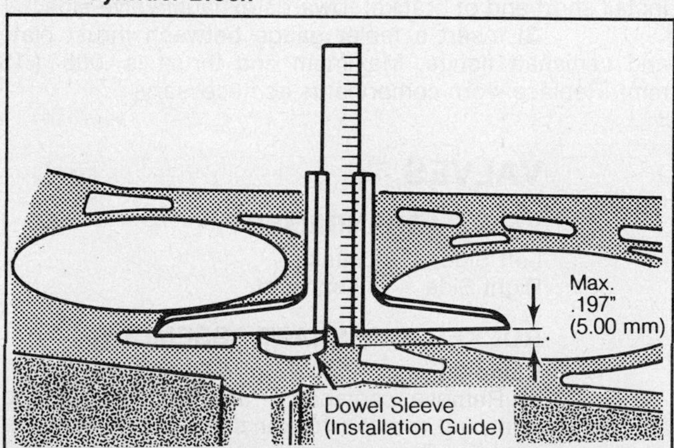
Max.
.197"
(5.00 mm)
Dowel Sleeve
(Installation Guide)

Ensure cylinder block deck surface is clean and free from nicks or burrs.

3) Lubricate head bolt threads and bottom of bolt heads with engine oil. Using new head gasket, install cylinder head. Tighten head bolts in 3 steps. Repeat 3rd step for final tightening. *See Fig. 2.*

4) Install remaining components in reverse order of removal. Ensure valve timing is correct. Adjust valves. At 1000 miles, check torque of head bolts with engine cold. If necessary further tighten head bolts.

CAMSHAFT

ENGINE FRONT COVERS

Removal (Upper Cover)

Remove rocker cover. Disconnect air injection pipe from exhaust manifold. Remove upper front cover attaching bolts. Remove, clean, and inspect cover.

Installation

1) Fill 2 holes in lower front cover (where it junctions with the cylinder head) with sealing compound. Using a new gasket, install front cover.

2) Install attaching bolts. Loosely tighten attaching bolts to lower front cover. Tighten bolts that attach front cover to cylinder head. Tighten bolts that attach upper front cover to lower front cover last.

Removal (Lower Cover)

1) Disconnect battery ground cable. Remove water pump. Remove upper front cover. Using care (because of strong spring pressure), remove timing chain tensioner plug, spring and piston.

2) Disconnect wires from alternator. Remove alternator, mounting bracket and adjusting bracket.

3) Remove oil filter adapter housing. Remove air pump, mounting bracket and adjusting bracket. Remove lifting eye from lower cover. Remove flywheel cover and lock flywheel in place. Remove crankshaft damper.

4) Remove attaching bolts from lower cover and front of oil pan. Loosen remaining oil pan bolts. Carefully separate oil pan gasket from timing case cover with knife blade. Remove lower cover.

Installation

Apply gasket sealer to gaskets. Install lower front cover and remaining components in reverse order of removal. Ensure that chain tensioner take-up land is in oil pocket.

FRONT COVER OIL SEAL

Removal & Installation

1) Remove fan housing from radiator. Loosen alternator and remove drive belt. Remove flywheel cover and lock flywheel in place. Remove damper. Carefully pry seal from recess in cover.

2) Lubricate seal lip with oil. Use seal installing tool to press in seal flush.

TIMING CHAIN & SPROCKETS

Removal

1) Remove distributor cap. Set No. 1 piston at TDC. Align distributor rotor with notch in distributor housing, and timing pointer with notch in damper/pulley. *See Fig. 1.* DO NOT allow crankshaft to move.

2) Remove upper and lower timing case covers. Remove camshaft sprocket. Remove circlip and unscrew pivot pin until chain guide rests on cylinder head gasket. Remove timing chain from sprocket and crankshaft.

318i & 320i 4-CYLINDER (Cont.)

3) Remove chain guide by pulling down and swinging to the right. Remove chain from guide.

4) If crankshaft sprocket removal is necessary, remove oil pan. Remove oil pump sprocket and drive chain. Remove Woodruff key from crankshaft. Using a puller, remove crankshaft sprocket.

Installation

1) If removed, crankshaft sprocket must be heated before installation. Install Woodruff key, crankshaft sprocket, oil pump drive chain, and oil pump sprocket.

2) Oil pump drive chain has correct tension if chain gives under slight thumb pressure midway between sprockets. Two drive chains are available for tension adjustment. If proper tension cannot be obtained with either drive chain, shims are available for installation between oil pump and cylinder block.

3) Install timing chain, camshaft sprocket and remaining components in reverse order of removal. Note that dowel pin bore in camshaft flange must be positioned downward. Notch in camshaft flange must face upward and align with cast tab on cylinder head.

VALVE TIMING

1) Rotate crankshaft to place No. 1 piston on TDC. Timing pointer must align with notch in crankshaft damper. Distributor rotor must align with notch in housing. *See Fig. 1.*

2) Position camshaft so that timing notch on camshaft flange is up, and aligns with cast tab on cylinder head. Dowel pin locating hole in camshaft flange must be positioned downward.

3) Install timing chain components. Without moving crankshaft or camshaft, install camshaft sprocket so that it engages in dowel pin locating hole in camshaft flange.

TIMING CHAIN TENSIONER

CAUTION: Timing chain tensioner piston is under high spring pressure. Use care when removing tensioner plug.

Removal & Disassembly

1) Unscrew tensioner plug, being careful of high spring pressure against plug. Remove spring and piston.

2) Remove piston, check valve and metering disc from piston sleeve. *See Fig. 4.* Clean all parts thoroughly and blow out with compressed air.

Fig. 4: Disassembled View of Tensioner Components

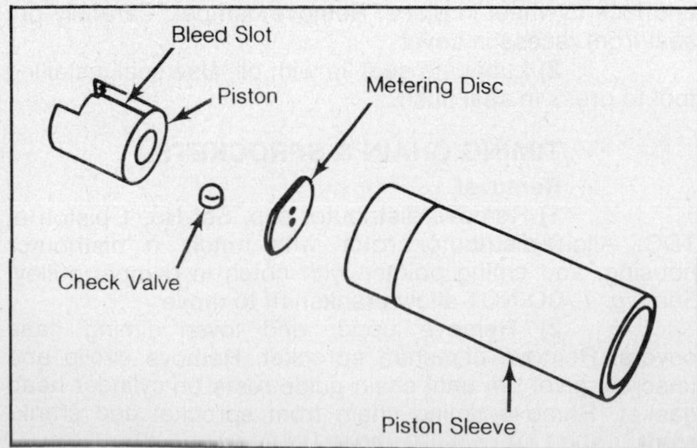
Bleed Slot
Piston
Metering Disc
Check Valve
Piston Sleeve

Piston must be purged of air after installing.

Reassembly & Installation

1) Reassemble piston parts in reverse order. Ensure that metering disc does not block bleed slots in piston. Remove rocker cover.

2) Install piston and spring in lower front cover. Tapered end of spring must face tensioner plug. Install plug and lightly tighten. Fill tensioner piston oil pocket (in lower front cover) with engine oil.

3) Piston must be purged of air. Using a screwdriver, move tensioning rail back and forth against piston until oil runs out around tensioner plug threads. Tighten tensioner plug.

CAMSHAFT

Removal

1) Remove cylinder head. Remove distributor from cylinder head. Mount cylinder head assembly in a holding fixture. Remove oil drain pipe from top of head. Remove cold start valve.

2) Adjust valve clearance to maximum possible to relieve tension on camshaft. Attach compression frame and bracket (11 1 040) to compress rocker arms. Install short end of bracket towards exhaust valve side.

3) Remove thrust plate from cylinder head. Carefully remove camshaft from cylinder head. Leave compression frame tool in place until camshaft has been installed.

Installation

1) When installing camshaft, note the following: After guide plate has been installed, it must be possible to easily rotate the camshaft. Make sure that notch in camshaft flange aligns with cast tab on cylinder head.

2) Adjust valves. Ensure oil drainage pipe seals are properly positioned.

3) Turn rotor counterclockwise about 1 3/8" from notch in distributor housing. Guide distributor drive into mesh with camshaft drive. Make sure rotor aligns with notch in distributor housing. Install remaining components.

CAMSHAFT END THRUST

1) Remove cylinder head. Remove distributor from cylinder head. Mount cylinder head assembly in a holding fixture. Remove oil drain pipe from top of head. Remove cold start valve.

2) Adjust valve clearance to maximum possible to relieve tension on camshaft. Attach a compression frame and bracket (11 1 040) to compress rocker arms. Install short end of bracket towards exhaust valve side.

3) Insert a feeler gauge between thrust plate and camshaft flange. Maximum end thrust is .005" (.13 mm). Replace worn components as necessary.

VALVES

VALVE ARRANGEMENT

Left Side - All intake.
Right Side - All exhaust.

ROCKER ARM SHAFT ASSEMBLY

Removal

1) Remove camshaft. Push back thrust ring and rocker arm and remove rocker shaft circlip. Remove distributor mounting flange.

2) Drive out rocker shafts from rear of head. Retain all springs, washers, rocker arms and thrust rings in proper order for reassembly.

318i & 320i 4-CYLINDER (Cont.)

Inspection

Check rocker arm oil clearance. Standard clearance is .0006-.0030" (.016-.077 mm). Rocker arm bore diameter is .611" (15.52 mm). Rocker arm shaft diameter is .6089-.6096" (15.47-15.48 mm). Replace all worn parts.

Installation

Install all parts in original locations. Use locating pins when installing rocker shafts to align notches for head bolts. Rear end of rocker shaft on intake side is open (no welch plug). Rear end of rocker shaft on exhaust side has welch plug installed. Ensure that welch plug in exhaust side rocker shaft is tight.

VALVE GUIDE SERVICING

1) Check valve guide for wear. If replacement is necessary, press out guide toward combustion chamber side of head. Measure guide bore in cylinder head. If bore exceeds .5512" (14.00 mm), ream head and install oversize guide. Interference fit for oversize bore is .0006-.0017" (.015-.043 mm).

2) Heat cylinder head to 428-482°F (220-250°C). Press in new guide from top of head until tapered groove end protrudes .531" (13.5 mm). Ream guide to obtain specified clearance. *See Replacement Valve Guides* table.

REPLACEMENT VALVE GUIDES

Application	Guide O.D. In. (mm)
Standard	.5525-5529 (14.044-14.033)
1st Oversize	.555 (14.10)
2nd Oversize	.559 (14.20)
3rd Oversize	.563 (14.30)
Modified Length	1.988 (50.50)

VALVE STEM OIL SEALS

Removal

Remove cylinder head from engine. Remove camshaft and rocker arm shaft assembly. Compress valve spring and remove keepers. Remove spring and retainer. Pull off oil seal.

Installation

1) Lubricate new oil seal with oil. Place protective sleeve (11 1 340) over valve stem and install seal. Press seal down until it fits tight against valve spring seat.

2) Install remaining valve components to complete installation. Note that end of valve spring that has tighter coil windings (color coded) is installed facing cylinder head.

VALVE SEAT INSERTS

1) When replacing valve seat, remove old seat by turning out with cutting tool. Drill out bore to appropriate oversize. Note valve seat oversize to be used and rebore head. Interference fit for oversize bore is .004-.006" (.10-.15 mm).

2) When installing new seat, heat head to approximately 392°F (200°C) and chill valve seat to approximately -94°F (-70°C). *See Valve Seat Inserts* table.

VALVE SEAT INSERTS

Application	Measurement In. (mm)
Intake	
1st Oversize	1.864 (47.35)
2nd Oversize	1.872 (47.55)
Exhaust	
1st Oversize	1.589 (40.35)
2nd Oversize	1.596 (40.55)

VALVE SPRINGS

To remove and install valve springs, use procedures explained in *Valve Stem Oil Seals*.

VALVE CLEARANCE ADJUSTMENT

1) Adjust valves in firing order (1-3-4-2), with piston of cylinder concerned on TDC at end of compression stroke. Use a feeler gauge to measure clearance between rocker arm eccentric and tip of valve.

2) To adjust valve clearance, loosen nut of rocker eccentric and insert a rod in eccentric hole. Rotate eccentric until proper clearance is obtained, then tighten lock nut. *See Fig. 5*.

VALVE CLEARANCE ADJUSTMENT

Application	In. (mm)
Intake	.008 (.20)
Exhaust	.010 (.25)

Fig. 5: Adjusting Valve Clearance

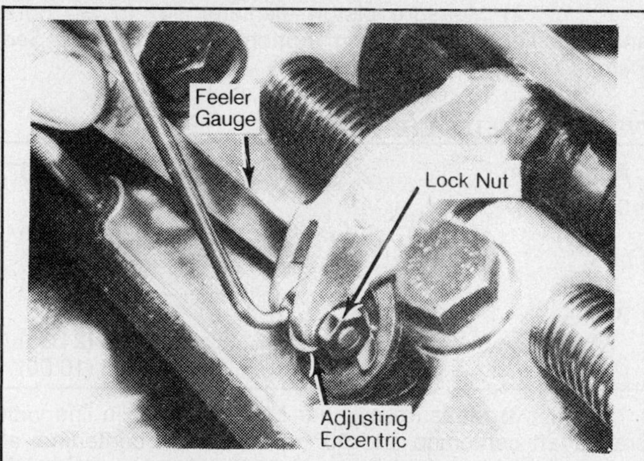
Feeler
Gauge
Lock Nut
Adjusting
Eccentric

Never measure or adjust valve clearance between camshaft lobe and rocker arm.

PISTONS, PINS & RINGS

OIL PAN

Removal & Installation (318i)

To remove upper oil pan section, pull out dipstick. Remove lower oil pan section, reinforcement plate, and ground strap. Remove upper oil pan bolts and remove pan. To install, reverse removal procedure. Coat timing case cover and end cover with sealer.

318i & 320i 4-CYLINDER (Cont.)

Removal (320i)

Remove bolts securing steering to front axle carrier. Pull steering out of way. Drain oil. Remove oil pan bolts. Swing oil pan downward. Turn crankshaft and remove oil pan toward front of engine.

Installation

Clean gasket mating surfaces. Apply sealer to crankcase and oil pan sealing surfaces. Using new gasket, install oil pan in reverse order of removal procedure.

PISTON & ROD ASSEMBLY

Removal

1) Remove oil pan and cylinder head. Place piston to be removed at bottom of its stroke. If necessary, mark rod and rod cap for cylinder identification.

2) Remove rod cap and push piston and rod assembly out top of engine. Install cap on rod from which removed. If replacing pistons or rods, all pistons must be in same weight class. All rods must be in same weight class.

Installation

Install rings on piston with marking "TOP" facing upward. Space ring end gaps 120° apart. Coat piston and cylinder walls with engine oil. Install piston and rod assembly with arrow facing toward front of engine. Install connecting rod cap.

FITTING PISTONS

1) Arrow on piston heads indicate direction of installation. Weight class is indicated by a "+" or "–" sign. All pistons must be in same weight class. Maximum difference in weight between pistons is 10 grams.

2) Measure piston diameter 90° to pin bore and specified distance from bottom of piston skirt. *See Piston Diameter Checkpoint* table.

PISTON DIAMETER CHECKPOINT

Application	In. (mm)
318i	
Alcan	.61 (15.50)
KS	1.22 (30.85)
Mahle	.55 (14.00)
320i	
KS	.96 (24.35)
Mahle	.63 (16.00)

3) Measure cylinder bore diameter in line with crankshaft centerline and 90° to crankshaft centerline, at top, middle, and bottom of cylinder. Maximum out-of-round and taper must not exceed .0004" (.01 mm).

4) If clearance is excessive, bore and hone cylinder block for installation of oversize pistons. *See Piston Guide* table for replacement piston sizes.

PISTON GUIDE

Application (Grade)	Diameter In. (mm)
Standard	3.503 (88.97)
Intermediate	3.506 (89.05)
No. 1 Oversize	3.513 (89.22)
No. 2 Oversize	3.522 (89.47)

FITTING RINGS

Place piston rings squarely into cylinder bore about 9/16" from bottom of bore. When checking ring side clearance, measure around entire circumference of piston, between top of ring and ring land. Install rings on piston with word "TOP" facing up. Space ring end gaps 120° apart.

PISTON PIN REPLACEMENT

Removal & Installation

1) Remove circlip from pin bore groove. Push pin from piston and connecting rod. Piston pins and pistons must be replaced as matched set. All pistons must be in same weight class, as must all connecting rods.

2) If clearance is excessive, press new piston pin bushing into rod. Drill and deburr oil holes, and install bushing so that seam is 90° from rod small end oil hole. Ream bushing so pin slides through under slight pressure.

CAUTION: Connecting rods must not be machined.

3) Assemble connecting rod to piston with oil hole in rod's small end and arrow on piston head on same side. When installed, arrow on piston and rod's small end oil hole will face front of engine.

CRANKSHAFT MAIN & CONNECTING ROD BEARINGS

CRANKSHAFT MAIN BEARINGS

1) Use Plastigage method to measure main bearing clearances. Measure main bearing clearances one at a time. Standard crankshafts are marked with red or blue dots on side of counterweights.

2) Factory ground crankshafts are identified by paint stripes marked on 1st counterweight. Number of paint stripes indicates whether crankshaft has been ground to 1st, 2nd, or 3rd undersize. Bearings are also color coded.

NOTE: Manufacturer recommends crankshaft should only be ground at the factory.

3) Use crankshaft identification number for correct bearing replacement. If red and blue bearing shells are used in combination, be sure to install shells of same color either in main bearing caps or in block.

CONNECTING ROD BEARINGS

Use Plastigage method to measure connecting rod bearing clearances. Measure clearances 1 at a time. Mark connecting rod and cap for cylinder identification before removing caps. Whenever rod bearing caps are removed, cap bolts and nuts should be replaced.

CRANKSHAFT END THRUST

Attach a dial indicator to crankcase with indicator point contacting flywheel. Push flywheel forward and zero dial indicator. Pull flywheel rearward and record crankshaft end thrust. If end thrust is excessive, replace thrust bearing (center main bearing shells).

REAR MAIN BEARING OIL SEAL

Removal

1) Remove transmission and flywheel. Remove 2 rear oil pan bolts and loosen remaining oil pan bolts. Carefully separate oil pan gasket from seal retainer, using a sharp tool.

2) Remove rear main bearing oil seal retainer from rear of crankcase. Remove oil seal from seal retainer.

Installation

Coat oil pan gasket at seal retainer contact surface with sealing compound. Install oil seal into retainer. Coat seal lips with oil and install retainer and seal. Install remaining components.

ENGINE OILING

CRANKCASE CAPACITY

Capacity is 4 quarts (3.8L) without filter replacement; 4.25 quarts (4.0L) with filter replacement.

NORMAL OIL PRESSURE

Oil pressure should be 11-17 psi (0.8-1.2 kg/cm²) at idle. At 4000 RPM, oil pressure should be about 57 psi (4.0 kg/cm²).

OIL PRESSURE RELIEF VALVE

Oil pressure relief valve opens at 59-64 psi (4.1-4.5 kg/cm²).

ENGINE OILING SYSTEM

A rotor type oil pump pressure feeds oil to a full-flow oil filter. From oil filter, oil is circulated through drilled passages to all moving parts of the engine. Oil pump is chain driven off of crankshaft.

OIL PUMP

Removal

Remove oil pan. Remove oil pump sprocket and drive chain. Remove two bolts mounting pump to crankcase and remove oil pump.

Disassembly

1) Unscrew union and remove relief valve spring and plunger from pump body. Remove pick-up tube and cover from pump body. Clean all parts and blow dry with compressed air.

2) If inner rotor replacement is required, remove pump sprocket hub from rotor shaft using a puller. Install new rotor in pump body and press hub onto rotor shaft to a distance of 1.677-1.685" (42.5-42.8 mm) between hub and rotor faces. *See Fig. 6*.

Inspection

1) Using a feeler gauge, measure clearance between outer rotor and pump body. If measurement exceeds specification, replace pump body.

2) Using a feeler gauge, measure clearance between inner and outer rotor. If measurement exceeds specification, replace rotors.

3) Lay a straightedge over pump body. Insert a feeler gauge between straightedge and rotors and measure clearance over rotors. If clearance exceeds specification, replace pump body.

OIL PUMP SPECIFICATIONS

Application	Measurement In. (mm)
Rotor-to-Pump Body	.006-.011 (.15-.27)
Clearance Between Rotors	.0047-.0079 (.119-.200)
Clearance Over Rotors	.0014-.0037 (.035-.095)
Relief Valve Spring	
Free Length	2.677 (67.99)
Installed Length	2.618 (66.50)

Fig. 6: Measuring Distance Between Sprocket Hub and Rotor Face

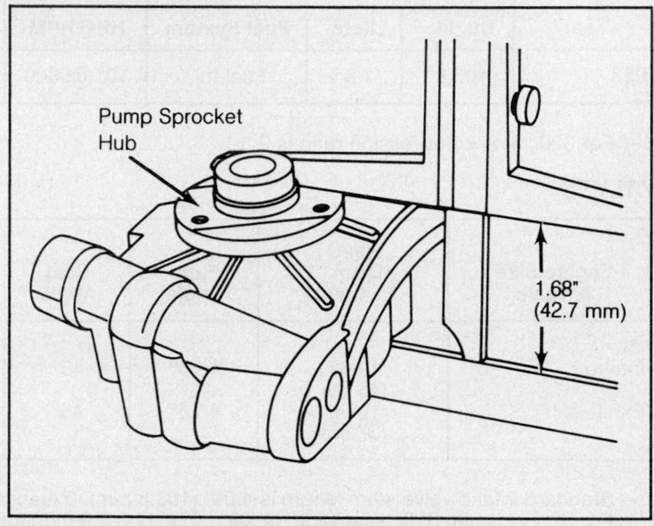
Pump Sprocket
Hub
1.68"
(42.7 mm)

Do not use arbor press to remove sprocket hub. Use a puller to remove hub.

Reassembly

Reassemble oil pump in reverse order of installation, using new parts where required.

Installation

1) Prime oil pump. To install, reverse removal procedure. Check oil pump drive chain tension. Chain tension is correct if chain gives when slight thumb pressure is exerted midway between oil pump and crankshaft sprockets.

2) Two drive chains are available for tension adjustment. If correct tension cannot be obtained with either chain, shims are available for installation between oil pump and cylinder block. Ensure oil hole in shim aligns with oil hole in pump and block.

ENGINE COOLING

THERMOSTAT

Thermostat begins opening at 176°F (80°C), and is fully open at 203°F (95°C).

COOLANT CAPACITY

Capacity is 7.4 quarts (7.0L).

RADIATOR CAP

Radiator cap pressure relief valve opens at 14 psi (1.0 kg/cm²)

BMW Engines

318i & 320i 4-CYLINDER (Cont.)

WATER PUMP

Removal & Installation

Loosen alternator bracket. Remove fan, pulley and drive belt. Remove coolant hoses from water pump. Remove water pump. Using new gasket, install water pump and remaining components in reverse order of removal.

ENGINE SPECIFICATIONS

GENERAL SPECIFICATIONS

Year	DISPLACEMENT		Fuel System	HP@RPM	Torque Ft. Lbs.@RPM	Compr. Ratio	BORE		STROKE	
	Cu. In.	Liters					In.	mm	In.	mm
1983	107.8	1.8	Fuel Inj.	101@5800	100@4500	[1] 8.8:1	3.50	89.0	2.79	71.0

[1] – For 320i, 318i compression ratio is 9.3:1.

VALVES

Engine Size & Valve	Head Diam. In. (mm)	Face Angle	Seat Angle	Seat Width In. (mm)	Stem Diameter In. (mm)	Stem Clearance In. (mm)	Valve Lift In. (mm)
1.8L							
Intake [1]	1.805 (45.85)	45.5°	45°	[2] .059-.083 (1.50-2.10)	.3134-.3139 (7.960-7.975)	.0010-.0020 (.025-.055)	.....
Exhaust [1]	1.490 (37.85)	45.5°	45°	.061-.081 (1.55-2.05)	.3129-.3134 (7.945-7.960)	.0015-.0030 (.040-.070)	.....

[1] – Standard intake valve stem length is 4.09" (103.8 mm). Exhaust valve stem length is 4.11" (104.3 mm).
[2] – For 320i only. On 318i, seat width is .051-.079" (1.3-2.0 mm) for intake andexhaust.

PISTONS, PINS, RINGS

Engine	PISTONS	PINS		RINGS		
	Clearance In. (mm)	Piston Fit In. (mm)	Rod Fit In. (mm)	Ring No.	End Gap In. (mm)	Side Clearance In. (mm)
1.8L Alcan/KS & Mahle Pistons	.0018 (.045)	.00004-.00020 [1] (.0010-.0050)	Push Fit	No. 1	.012-.020 (.30-.50)	.0024-.0036 [2] (.061-.092)
				No. 2	.008-.016 (.20-.40)	.0012-.0024 [3] (.030-.061)
				No. 3	.010-.016 (.25-.40)	.0008-.0020 [4] (.020-.052)

[1] – .00008-.00024" (.0020-.0061 mm) for KS Pistons.
[2] – Side clearance measurement is same for KS Pistons.
[3] – .0016-.0028" (.040-.072 mm) for KS Pistons.
[4] – .0012-.0024" (.030-.061 mm) for KS Pistons.

CRANKSHAFT MAIN & CONNECTING ROD BEARINGS

Engine	MAIN BEARINGS				CONNECTING ROD BEARINGS		
	Journal Diam. In. (mm)	Clearance In. (mm)	Thrust Bearing	Crankshaft End Play In. (mm)	Journal Diam. In. (mm)	Clearance In. (mm)	Side Play In. (mm)
1.8L	2.165 (55.0)	.0012-.0026 (.030-.070)	Center	.0033-.0068 (.085-.174)	1.8898 (48.0)	.0009-.0028 (.023-.070)	.....

BMW Engines

318i & 320i 4-CYLINDER (Cont.)

ENGINE SPECIFICATIONS (Cont.)

VALVE SPRINGS

Engine	Free Length In. (mm)	PRESSURE Lbs. @ In. (Kg @ mm)	
		Valve Closed	Valve Open
1.8L	1.71 [1] (43.5)	64@1.48 (29@37.6)	154@1.12 (70@28.5)

[1] – Depending on spring manufacturer, some springs may be 1.811" (46.0 mm).

CAMSHAFT

Engine	Journal Diam. In. (mm)	Clearance In. (mm)	Lobe Lift In. (mm)
1.8L[1]			
No. 1	1.3769-1.3795 (34.975-35.041)	.0013-.0029 (.034-.074)	.274-.280 (6.95-7.11)
No. 2	1.6525-1.6551 (41.975-42.041)		
No. 3	1.6919-1.6945 (42.975-43.041)		

[1] – End play is .0008-.0051" (.020-.130 mm).

TIGHTENING SPECIFICATIONS

Application	Ft. Lbs. (N.m)
Camshaft Oiler (Hollow Bolt)	8-9 (11-13)
Connecting Rod Bolts	38-41 (51-56)
Crankshaft Damper	101-108 (140-150)
Cylinder Head (Cold) [1]	
Step 1	25-32 (33-44)
Step 2	49-52 (67-71)
Step 3	56-59 (77-81)
Step 4	Repeat Step 3
Exhaust Manifold	22-24 (29-32)
Flywheel Bolts [2]	72-83 (98-113)
Main Bearing Caps	42-45 (57-62)

[1] – Recheck torque at 1000 mile service and retighten if necessary.
[2] – Use Loctite 270 on flywheel bolts.

BMW Engines

528e, 533i, 633CSi & 733i 6-CYLINDER

ENGINE CODING

ENGINE IDENTIFICATION

On 528e models, engine displacement and identification number is stamped on a pad on the lower left side of the engine block. On 533i, 633CSi, & 733i models, displacement and identification numbers are on the top, rear of the engine block on bell housing flange.

ENGINE IDENTIFICATION

Model	Engine
528e	2.7L
533i, 633CSi & 733i	3.2L

TRANSMISSION, ENGINE, MANIFOLDS & CYLINDER HEAD

MANUAL TRANSMISSION

Removal

1) Remove exhaust system and support brackets from vehicle. Disconnect propeller shaft at rear of transmission. Remove heat shield from center support bearing.

2) Remove center support bearing bracket. Lower propeller shaft at center support bearing and pull propeller shaft from transmission. On 533i, 633CSi, and 733i models, remove speed and reference mark sensors.

3) On all models, remove clutch slave cylinder, leaving line connected. Remove speedometer cable and disconnect plug from back-up light switch.

4) Pull up boot from floor shift lever, remove circlip and pull shift lever up and out. Support transmission and remove crossmember. Remove transmission.

Installation

1) To install, reverse removal procedure. When installing propeller shaft, use new lock nuts at rubber coupling. Only tighten nuts (never bolts) to avoid stress on coupling.

2) When installing propeller shaft, push center support bearing forward .08" (2.0 mm) to preload bracket, then tighten nuts.

3) When installing speed and reference mark sensors, note that black plug of speed sensor faces ring gear. Gray ring of reference mark sensor faces flywheel. If plugs are reversed, engine will not start.

AUTOMATIC TRANSMISSION

Removal

1) Disconnect exhaust system and remove support brackets. Disconnect accelerator cable from transmission and disconnect bracket. Drain transmission oil. Remove filler tube and plug opening.

2) Disconnect oil cooler lines from transmission. Label and disconnect all wiring attached to transmission. Remove cover plate from transmission. Mark installed positions of speed and reference mark sensors, then remove.

3) Remove 4 bolts securing torque converter to drive plate. Disconnect shift rod from lever. Disconnect propeller shaft coupling at rear of transmission.

4) Remove heat shield, then remove center support bearing bracket. Lower propeller shaft at center support bearing and pull propeller shaft from transmission. Disconnect speedometer cable. Support transmission.

5) Remove crossmember, then lower transmission to rest on front axle carrier. Place transmission jack under transmission. Separate and remove transmission and torque converter from engine.

Installation

1) To install transmission and remaining components, reverse removal procedures. Before installing transmission, ensure torque converter is properly seated.

2) When installing propeller shaft, push center support bearing forward .08" (2.0 mm) to preload bracket, then tighten nuts.

3) When installing sensors, note that black plug of speed sensor faces ring gear. Gray ring of reference mark sensor faces flywheel. If plugs are reversed, engine will not start.

ENGINE

Removal

1) Remove hood. Disconnect battery cables from battery. Remove transmission. Remove splash guard from under engine. Drain cooling system and remove radiator. Remove power steering pump (leaving hoses connected) and secure away from engine.

2) If equipped, remove A/C compressor (with hoses connected) and secure away from engine. Remove accelerator cable. If equipped, remove cruise control cable from engine.

3) Label and disconnect all electrical and ignition wiring that might interfere with engine removal. Be sure to disconnect wiring harness in glove box, and pull through hole in firewall.

4) Label and disconnect all coolant, ventilation, fuel, and vacuum hoses (or lines) that might interfere with engine removal. Remove air cleaner with air flow sensor.

5) Remove nuts from engine mounts. Ensure no wiring, hoses or lines are attached to engine. Attach a lifting chain and hoist to engine. Carefully lift engine from vehicle.

Installation

To install engine, reverse removal procedures. Ensure that all hoses, lines, and electrical connections are restored to original positions. Bleed cooling system.

CYLINDER HEAD

Removal

1) Disconnect battery ground cable. Drain cooling system. Remove splash guard from bottom of engine. Disconnect exhaust pipes from manifolds.

2) Disconnect accelerator and cruise control cables from throttle valve housing, including cable to automatic transmission (if equipped). Disconnect attached hoses and electrical wiring, then remove air cleaner with air flow sensor.

3) Label and disconnect all coolant hoses attached to cylinder head. Label and disconnect all fuel, ventilation and vacuum hoses (or lines) from cylinder head and intake manifold.

4) Label and disconnect all electrical and ignition wiring that might interfere with head removal. If necessary, disconnect electrical plug in glove box, and pull wiring through hole in firewall.

528e, 533i, 633CSi & 733i 6-CYLINDER (Cont.)

5) Remove valve cover. Remove upper engine front cover (or timing belt cover on 2.7L engine). On 2.7L engine, remove distributor cap.

6) Set No. 1 piston on TDC of compression stroke. Timing pointer and mark on vibration damper should align, and valves of No. 6 cylinder should overlap.

7) On 3.2L engine, remove timing chain tensioner plug, spring and piston. On 2.7L engine, loosen timing belt tensioner bolts. Push tensioner sprocket inward, then tighten adjusting bolt.

8) On 2.7L engine, remove timing belt from camshaft sprocket. On other models, remove camshaft sprocket. Remove cylinder head bolts in reverse of tightening sequence. Install locating pins in bolt holes to keep rocker arm shafts from turning. Remove cylinder head.

Inspection

Cylinder head may be machined if necessary. On 2.7L engine, minimum height from engine block mating surface to valve cover surface is 4.909" (124.70 mm). On 3.2L engine. Minimum height is 5.063" (128.6 mm). Use a .012" (.30 mm) thicker head gasket if cylinder head is machined.

Installation

1) Clean all gasket mating surfaces. Remove oil from head bolt threaded holes in cylinder block. Clean and lubricate bolt heads and threads of head bolts. Using new head gasket, install cylinder head and bolts.

2) On 2.7L engine, tighten head bolts in 2 steps. *See Fig. 1*. Bring engine to normal operating temperature. Using special torque wrench (11 2 110), retighten head bolts to torque angle of 20-30°.

3) On 3.2L engine, tighten head bolts in 2 steps. *See Fig. 2*. Wait 20 minutes and tighten head bolts to final torque. Bring engine to normal operating temperature.

4) Using special torque wrench (11 2 110), retighten head bolts to torque angle of 20-30°. Never loosen bolts during tightening sequence; turn only in tightening direction.

Fig. 1: 2.7L Cylinder Head Tightening Sequence

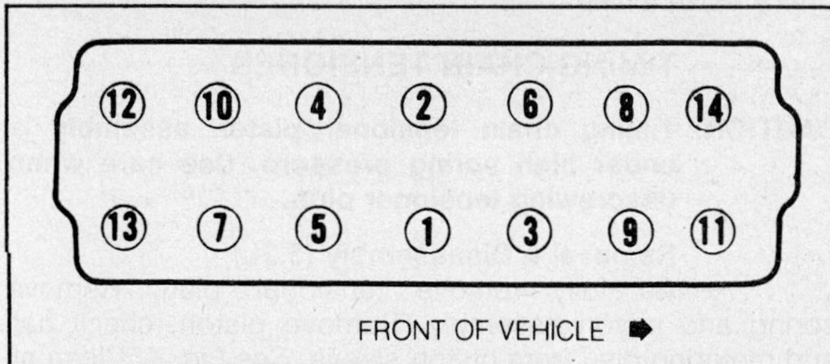

12 10 4 2 6 8 14
13 7 5 1 3 9 11
FRONT OF VEHICLE

Fig. 2: 3.2L Cylinder Head Tightening Sequence

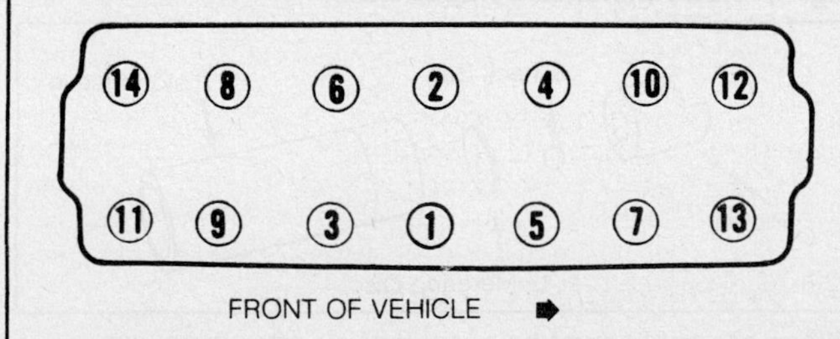

14 8 6 2 4 10 12
11 9 3 1 5 7 13
FRONT OF VEHICLE

Use angle-calibrated torque wrench for final tightening (engine warm).

5) On all models, install camshaft sprocket and timing chain (or timing belt). Ensure valve timing is correct. Install remaining components in reverse order of removal, using new gaskets where required. Adjust valves.

CAMSHAFT

TIMING BELT COVER

Removal (2.7L)

1) Remove all drive belts. Remove pulley and vibration damper. Hold crankshaft in place and remove center bolt from vibration damper hub.

2) Using puller, remove vibration damper hub from crankshaft. Remove crankshaft sprocket from crankshaft using a puller. Hold intermediate shaft sprocket in place and remove attaching bolt, washer and sprocket.

3) Remove 3 oil pan-to-cover bolts, then loosen remaining oil pan bolts. Remove remaining attaching bolts, then remove timing belt cover.

Installation

1) Clean gasket mating surfaces. Coat oil pan-to-cover gasket with gasket sealer. Install centering tool (11 2 211) on crankshaft and centering tool (11 2 212) on intermediate shaft to align front cover.

2) Using new gasket, install and tighten timing belt cover. Note that lettering on crankshaft sprocket must face forward when installing. Install remaining components in reverse order of removal procedure.

UPPER ENGINE FRONT COVER

Removal (3.2L)

Remove valve cover. Partially drain cooling system. Remove thermostat cover. Remove distributor cap, rotor, and cover. Remove upper timing case cover.

Installation

1) Clean gasket mating surfaces. Fill holes in lower front cover (at junction of lower front cover-to-cylinder block) with sealer. Replace oil seal around distributor drive.

2) Using new gasket, install front cover with distributor drive. Install attaching bolts. Tighten bolts to lower cover first, then tighten remaining cover bolts. Install remaining components in reverse order of removal.

LOWER ENGINE FRONT COVER

Removal (3.2L)

1) Remove upper engine front cover. Remove fan. Remove drive belts from crankshaft and fan pulleys. Hold crankshaft in place and remove vibration damper and hub. Remove chain tensioner piston.

2) Remove water pump pulley. Remove alternator and bracket. Remove and set aside power steering pump. Remove oil pan-to-front cover attaching bolts.

3) Loosen remaining oil pan bolts. Remove remaining cover attaching bolts. Carefully separate lower front cover from oil pan.

Installation

Clean gasket mating surfaces. Apply gasket sealer to oil pan gasket and to oil pan-to-cylinder block junction. Install lower engine front cover. Install remaining components in reverse order of installation. Adjust TDC position sensor after installing.

BMW Engines

528e, 533i, 633CSi & 733i 6-CYLINDER (Cont.)

TIMING BELT COVER OIL SEALS

Removal & Installation (2.7L)

Remove timing belt cover. Remove crankshaft and intermediate shaft oil seals from cover. Using seal installing tool, install new seals until flush. Coat seal lips with oil prior to installing cover.

FRONT COVER OIL SEAL

Removal (3.2L)

Remove fan shroud. Remove all drive belts. Remove nut on crankshaft, then remove vibration damper and hub. Pry out oil seal.

Installation

Pack lips of new oil seal with grease. Use seal installing tool (11 1 273) to press in seal. Install remaining components in reverse order of removal.

TIMING BELT & SPROCKET

Removal (2.7L)

1) Remove distributor cap and rotor, then remove cover surrounding distributor. Turn crankshaft to position No. 1 piston on TDC of compression stroke.

2) Ensure timing marks on vibration damper and pointer are aligned. Arrow on camshaft must be aligned with timing mark on cylinder head. *See Fig. 3*.

3) Remove timing belt cover. Loosen tensioner and position away from timing belt to relieve tension. Tighten tensioner adjusting bolt to keep tensioner in retracted position.

4) If installing same timing belt, mark normal direction of rotation on timing belt before removing. Remove timing belt.

Installation

1) Ensure arrow on camshaft sprocket is still aligned with timing mark on cylinder head. Ensure timing mark on crankshaft sprocket is aligned with notch in cover (approximately 1 o'clock position). *See Fig. 3*.

Fig. 3: 2.7L Timing Sprockets Alignment

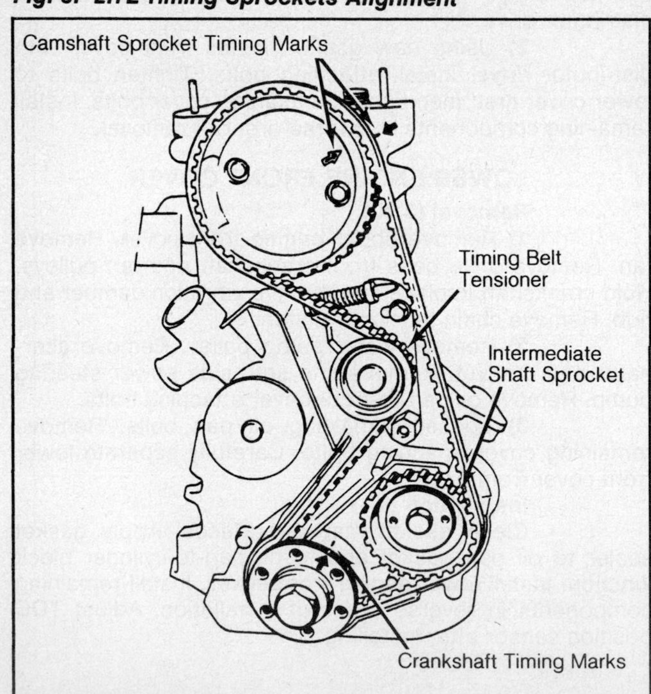
Camshaft Sprocket Timing Marks
Timing Belt Tensioner
Intermediate Shaft Sprocket
Crankshaft Timing Marks

Mark rotation direction on timing belts that will be reused.

2) Install timing belt on sprockets. Loosen tensioner adjusting bolt to allow tension on timing belt. Turn crankshaft in direction of normal rotation until timing belt tightens. Tighten tensioner bolts. Install remaining components in reverse order of removal.

TIMING CHAIN & SPROCKETS

Removal (3.2L)

1) Remove upper and lower engine front cover. Rotate crankshaft until No. 1 cylinder is on TDC at end of compression stroke. Timing mark on front cover should align with notch in vibration damper.

2) Remove camshaft sprocket with timing chain attached. Remove chain from camshaft and crankshaft sprockets.

3) If crankshaft sprocket removal is necessary, remove oil pan. Remove oil pump sprocket and drive chain. Remove Woodruff key from crankshaft. Using a puller, remove crankshaft sprocket.

Installation

1) Install components in reverse order of removal. Oil pump drive chain has correct tension if chain gives under slight thumb pressure midway between sprockets. Adjusting shims are available for adjusting oil pump drive chain tension.

2) Ensure No. 1 piston is still on TDC of compression stroke. When installing timing chain and camshaft sprocket, be sure camshaft flange is correctly positioned. *See Fig. 5*.

VALVE TIMING

For 2.7L engine, valve timing procedures are covered in *Timing Belts & Sprockets*. For all other engines, use procedures explained in *Timing Chain & Sprockets*.

TIMING BELT TENSIONER

Removal & Installation (2.7L)

Remove timing belt cover. Place piston of No. 1 cylinder on TDC of compression stroke. Remove timing belt tensioner. To install, reverse removal procedures. Check valve timing.

TIMING CHAIN TENSIONER

CAUTION: Timing chain tensioner piston assembly is under high spring pressure. Use care when unscrewing tensioner plug.

Removal & Disassembly (3.2L)

Carefully remove tensioner plug. Remove spring and piston assembly. Remove piston, check ball and metering disc from piston sleeve. *See Fig. 4*. Clean all parts thoroughly and blow out with compressed air.

Fig. 4: 3.2L Tensioner Components

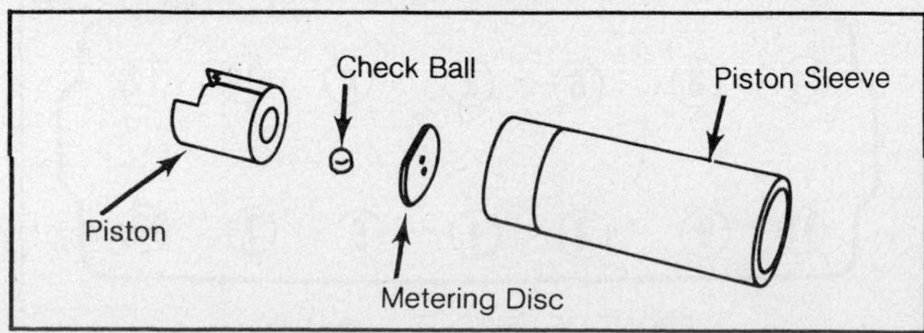
Check Ball
Piston Sleeve
Piston
Metering Disc

Piston assembly must be purged of air after installing.

528e, 533i, 633CSi & 733i 6-CYLINDER (Cont.)

Reassembly & Installation

1) Reassemble piston parts in reverse order of disassembly. Ensure metering disc does not block bleed slots in piston. Remove rocker cover.

2) Install piston assembly and spring in lower front cover. Tapered end of spring must face tensioner plug. Install plug and lightly tighten. Fill tensioner piston oil pocket (in lower front cover) with engine oil.

3) Piston must be purged of air. Using a screwdriver, move tensioning rail back and forth against piston until oil runs out around tensioner plug threads. Tighten tensioner plug. Install remaining components.

CAMSHAFT

Removal (2.7L)

Remove cylinder head. Remove rocker arm shaft assemblies. Remove thrust plate. Pull out camshaft.

Installation

Install camshaft in reverse order of removal. When installing thrust plate, use aligning tool (11 2 212) to properly align. Install remaining components in reverse order of removal.

Removal (3.2L)

1) Remove cylinder head from engine. In vicinity of EGR valve, remove coolant hose and pipe from side of head. Remove EGR valve. Remove 2 hollow attaching bolts, then remove oil distribution pipe from top of head.

2) Loosen all valve adjustments to maximum permissible clearance. Turn camshaft to position camshaft flange as shown in *Fig. 5*. Now rotate camshaft flange approximately 9/16 - 5/8" toward intake side.

3) Install rocker arm compression tool (11 1 060) to relieve tension on camshaft. Tighten nuts on exhaust valve side of tool. Next, tighten nuts on intake valve side of tool. Remove bolts from camshaft thrust plate. Remove camshaft.

Installation

1) Install camshaft in head and tighten thrust plate bolts. Cam must turn easily. Turn camshaft to position camshaft flange as shown in *Fig. 5* (valves of No. 6 cylinder overlap). Remove compression tool.

2) If adapter was removed from front of camshaft, coat bolt threads with Loctite 270 before installation. Install oil pipe so oil bores will spray between rocker arms and cams of intake and exhaust valves.

Fig. 5: 3.2L Camshaft Flange Position for Compression Tool Installation and Removal

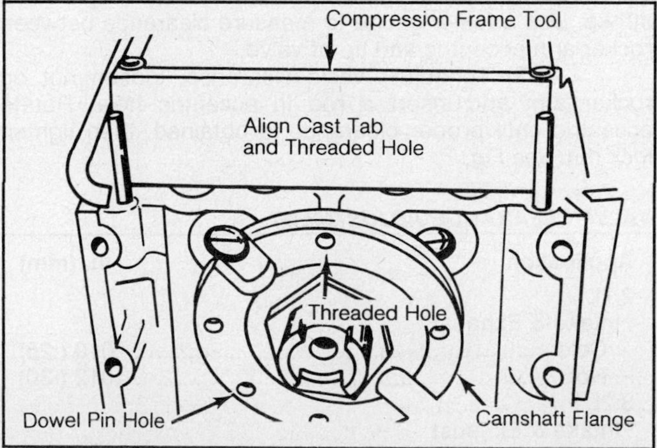
Compression Frame Tool
Align Cast Tab and Threaded Hole
Threaded Hole
Dowel Pin Hole
Camshaft Flange

Position flange as shown when removing and installing camshaft sprocket.

3) Use new seals between oil pipe and rocker supports as well as under head of attaching bolts. Continue assembly in reverse order of removal.

CAMSHAFT OIL SEAL

Removal (2.7L)

Place No. 1 cylinder on TDC of compression stroke. Align ignition timing and valve timing marks. Remove timing belt. Remove camshaft sprocket. Remove thrust plate. Remove oil seal and round cord seal from thrust plate.

Installation

Lubricate oil seals with engine oil. Replace oil seal and round cord seal on thrust plate. Use aligning tool (11 2 212) when installing thrust plate. Install remaining components in reverse order of removal.

CAMSHAFT END THRUST

Insert feeler gauge between thrust plate and camshaft flange (or sprocket on 2.7L). Replace camshaft thrust plate if end thrust is excessive. Recheck end thrust.

INTERMEDIATE SHAFT

Removal & Installation (2.7L)

Remove timing belt cover. Remove guide plate and pull out intermediate shaft. To install, reverse removal procedures. Bearings in engine block are not replaceable.

VALVES

VALVE ARRANGEMENT

Left Side – Intake valves.
Right Side – Exhaust valves.

ROCKER ARM SHAFT ASSEMBLY

Removal (2.7L)

1) Remove cylinder head from engine. Remove camshaft sprocket. Adjust valve clearance of all valves to maximum value. Remove front and rear rubber plugs on either side of rocker shafts.

2) Remove thrust plate from rocker shafts (at front of head). Remove spring clips from rockers. Turn camshaft so valves of cylinder No. 6 overlap.

3) Rotate camshaft 1/4 turn against normal direction of rotation, and at the same time push rockers for cylinders No. 3 and No. 4 to the rear. Push all remaining rockers toward the front of the head.

4) When the camshaft is clear of the rockers, both rocker shafts can be removed. Be sure to keep all rockers in order for later installation in their original locations.

Inspection

Check rocker arms and shaft for excessive wear. Oil clearance should be .0006-.0020" (.016-.052 mm). Replace all worn parts.

Installation

Install rocker arm shaft assembly in reverse order of removal. Install rocker shafts with large oil holes facing downward. Ensure small oil holes and thrust plate grooves in rocker shafts face inward. Straight surface of retaining clips are installed in rocker shaft grooves.

Removal (3.2L)

1) Remove camshaft. Remove end cover and Allen head plugs from end of rocker arm shafts. If necessary, hold shaft with a dowel pin. Push back rocker arms and thrust washers.

528e, 533i, 633CSi & 733i 6-CYLINDER (Cont.)

2) Lift out circlips. Remove dowel pin. Thread slide hammer into end of rocker arm shaft and drive out shaft.

Inspection

Check rocker arms and shaft for excessive wear. Oil clearance should be .0006-.0020" (.016-.052 mm). Replace all worn parts.

Installation

Install rocker arm shaft components in original locations. *See Fig. 6.* Use locating pins to align cutout notches in rocker arm shafts for cylinder head bolts. Oil bores must face valves. Use Loctite on Allen head plugs.

Fig. 6: 3.2L Rocker Arm Assembly

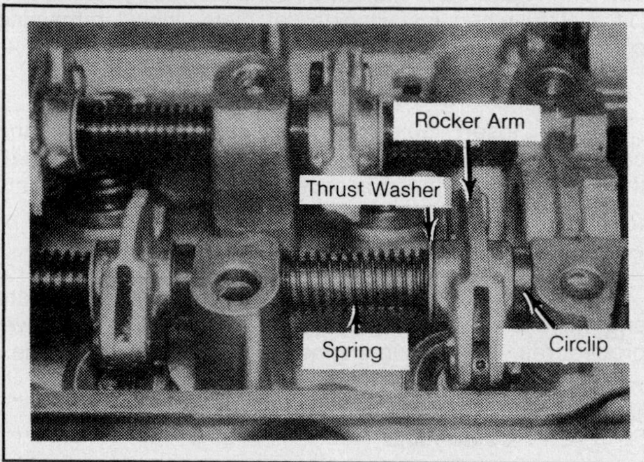
Rocker Arm
Thrust Washer
Spring
Circlip

Keep all components in order for reassembly.

VALVE GUIDE SERVICING

1) If valve-to-guide clearance is excessive, drive out guide toward combustion chamber side of head. Check size of valve guide bore in cylinder head. Valve guide bore diameter should be the same as guide outside diameter.

2) Valve guides are available in 3 oversizes. Oversize diameters are 13.1, 13.2, and 13.3 mm for 2.7L engine. On 3.2L engine, oversize diameters are 14.1, 14.2, and 14.3 mm. When installing guide, heat cylinder head to 122°F (50°C) and, chill valve guide to -238°F (-150°C).

3) Drive guide into cylinder head from top. Stepped end of valve guide must face camshaft. Guide must protrude .551-.591" (14.0-15.0 mm) from top of cylinder head on 2.7L engine and, .513" (13.5 mm) on 3.2L engine. Ream valve guide for correct oil clearance.

VALVE STEM OIL SEALS

Remove valve springs and pull off old seal. When replacing valve stem oil seals, use protective sleeve over valve stem to avoid damage to new seals. Lubricate seal with oil and install.

VALVE SEAT INSERTS

1) When replacing valve seat, remove old seat by turning out with cutting tool. When cutting bore for valve seat inserts, allow for shrink fit. Valve seat insert shrink fit specification is .006" (.15 mm).

2) When installing new seat, heat head to approximately 122°F (50°C) and chill valve seat to approximately -238°F (-150°C). Replacement seats are available in .2 mm and .4 mm oversize outside diameters. *See Valve Seat Diameter* table.

VALVE SEAT DIAMETER

Application	Diameter In. (mm)
2.7L	
Intake	
Standard	1.659 (42.15)
.2 mm O.S.	1.667 (42.35)
.4 mm O.S.	1.675 (42.55)
Exhaust	
Standard	1.482 (37.65)
.2 mm O.S.	1.490 (37.85)
.4 mm O.S.	1.498 (38.05)
3.2L	
Intake	
Standard	1.856 (47.15)
.2 mm O.S.	1.864 (47.35)
.4 mm O.S.	1.872 (47.55)
Exhaust	
Standard	1.581 (40.15)
.2 mm O.S.	1.589 (40.35)
.4 mm O.S.	1.596 (40.55)

VALVE SPRING

Removal

Remove cylinder head. Remove rocker arms and shafts. Compress valve spring with spring compressor and remove keepers. Remove valve spring and retainer.

Inspection

Check spring free length. Check spring pressure in a valve spring tester. Replace defective springs with new springs of same color code.

Installation

Install springs with paint stripe (tight coil end) against head. Install retainer and keepers. All springs must have same color code, wire gauge, and length. Install remaining components to complete installation.

NOTE: On 3.2L engines, the intake valve spring installed height has been changed to 1.457-1.535" (37-39 mm). New cylinder heads which use the modified spring height are marked with an "S" on the intake valve side.

VALVE CLEARANCE ADJUSTMENT

1) Adjust valves in firing order (1-5-3-6-2-4), with piston of cylinder concerned at TDC of compression stroke. Use a feeler gauge to measure clearance between rocker arm eccentric and tip of valve.

2) To adjust valve clearance, loosen nut on rocker arm and insert a rod in eccentric hole. Rotate eccentric until proper clearance is obtained, then tighten lock nut. *See Fig. 7.*

VALVE CLEARANCE ADJUSTMENT

Application	In. (mm)
2.7L	
Intake & Exhaust	
Cold	.010 (.25)
Hot	.012 (.30)
3.2L	
Intake & Exhaust	
Cold	.012 (.30)
Hot	.014 (.35)

Fig. 7: Adjusting Valve Clearance

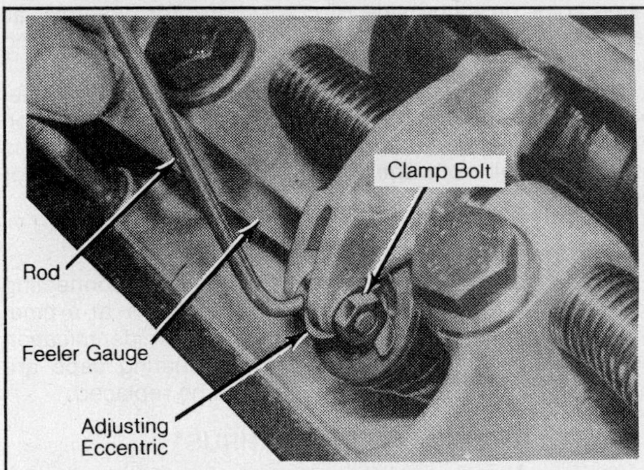
Clamp Bolt
Rod
Feeler Gauge
Adjusting
Eccentric

PISTONS, PINS & RINGS

OIL PAN

Removal (2.7L)

Remove splash guard. Disconnect electrical plug from side of block and remove flywheel cover. Remove oil pan bolts. Remove oil pump and oil pan.

Installation

Clean gasket mating surfaces and coat with gasket sealer. Using new gasket, install oil pump and pan in reverse order of removal. Install remaining components to complete installation.

Removal (3.2L)

1) Drain engine oil and remove wire from oil level switch (if equipped). On 733i models, remove sway bar. On all models, remove power steering pump with hoses connected. Remove mounting bracket attached to oil pan and front cover.

2) Remove alternator and bracket. Remove transmission bell housing cover. Remove engine mount bolts. Raise and support engine from above. Remove oil pan bolts.

3) Lower pan and move toward front of engine. Turn crankshaft until No. 5 and No. 6 connecting rod are above crankcase sealing surface. Remove oil pan..

Installation

Clean gasket mating surfaces and coat with gasket sealer. Using new gasket, install oil pan in reverse order of removal. Install remaining components to complete installation.

PISTON & ROD ASSEMBLY

Removal

1) Remove engine. Remove cylinder head, oil pan, and oil pump. If necessary, mark rod and rod cap for cylinder identification, then remove rod cap.

2) Remove ridge at top of cylinder bore. Push piston and rod assembly out top of block. Install rod cap on connecting rod from which removed.

3) If replacing pistons or rods, be sure they are in the same weight class as existing piston or rods. Weight class is stamped on piston crown with a "+" or "-".

Installation

1) Install rings on piston and space end gaps 120° apart. Coat piston and cylinder walls with engine oil. Install ring compressor on piston.

2) Install piston and rod assembly with arrow on piston head toward front of engine. Install rod bearings. Using new rod bolts and nuts, install and tighten rod caps.

FITTING PISTONS

2.7L

1) Arrow on piston heads indicate direction of installation. Weight class is indicated by a "+" or "–" sign. All pistons must be in same weight class. Maximum weight difference between pistons can be .35 oz. (10 grams).

2) Measure piston diameter 90° to pin bore and at specified height from bottom of piston skirt. *See Piston Diameter Checkpoint* table. Piston crown is stamped with diameter and arrow for installation direction.

PISTON DIAMETER CHECKPOINT

Application	Piston Height In. (mm)	Checkpoint In. (mm)
2.7L		
Mahle	2.71 (68.7)	.315 (8.0)
	3.06 (77.7)	.905 (23)
KS	2.71 (68.7)	.551 (14)
	3.06 (77.7)	.905 (23)

3) Measure cylinder at top, middle, and bottom. Out-of-round must not exceed .0012" (.03 mm). Taper should not exceed .0008" (.02 mm). If oil clearance is excessive, bore and hone cylinder block for installation of oversize pistons.

PISTON DIAMETER SPECIFICATIONS

Application	In. (mm)
2.7L	
Standard	3.3063 (83.98)
Special	3.3094 (84.06)
1st O.S.	3.3161 (84.23)
2nd O.S.	3.3260 (84.48)

3.2L

1) Arrow on piston heads indicate direction of installation. Weight class is indicated by a "+" or "–" sign. All pistons must be in same weight class. Maximum weight difference between pistons can be .35 oz. (10 grams).

2) Measure piston diameter 90° to pin bore and at specified height from bottom of piston skirt. *See Piston Diameter Checkpoint* table. Piston crown is stamped with diameter and arrow for installation direction.

PISTON DIAMETER CHECKPOINT

Application	Checkpoint In. (mm)
3.2L	
Mahle	1.024 (26.00)
KS	1.337 (33.95)

3) Measure cylinder at top, middle, and bottom. Out-of-round must not exceed .0004" (.010 mm). Taper should not exceed .0004" (.010 mm). If oil clearance is excessive, bore and hone cylinder block for installation of oversize pistons.

BMW Engines

528e, 533i, 633CSi & 733i 6-CYLINDER (Cont.)

PISTON DIAMETER SPECIFICATIONS

Application	In. (mm)
3.2L	
Standard	3.5027 (88.97)
Special	3.5059 (89.05)
1st O.S.	3.5126 (89.22)
2nd O.S.	3.5224 (89.47)

FITTING RINGS

1) Place piston rings squarely into cylinder bore about 9/16" from bottom of bore. Use a feeler gauge to measure ring end gap.

2) With rings installed on piston, use a feeler gauge to measure ring side clearance. Take measurement around entire circumference of piston, between top of ring and ring land.

3) Install rings on piston with word "TOP" facing upward. Space ring end gaps 120° apart.

PISTON PIN REPLACEMENT

1) Remove circlip from pin bore groove. Push pin from piston and connecting rod. Piston pins and pistons must be replaced as matched set.

2) All pistons must be in same weight class, as must all connecting rods. Connecting rod weight class is stamped on bearing cap or color coded on rod. Maximum weight difference between connecting rods can be .28 oz. (8 grams).

3) Replacement piston pin bushings are available for all engines. Replacement bushings may be used if pin is not worn. Connecting rods on all engines cannot be machined. Ream bushing so pin slides through under thumb pressure.

4) On 3.2L engine, assemble connecting rod to piston with oil hole in rod's small end and arrow on piston head on same side. When installed, arrow on piston and rod's small end oil hole will face front of engine.

5) On 2.7L engine, assemble connecting rod to piston so rod bearing locating lugs will be on exhaust side of engine, and arrow on piston head will face toward front of engine.

CRANKSHAFT MAIN & CONNECTING ROD BEARINGS

CRANKSHAFT MAIN BEARINGS

NOTE: **Crankshafts are specially treated and can only be ground by the factory.**

1) Use Plastigage method to measure main bearing clearances. Standard crankshafts are marked with red or blue dots on side of counterweights. On 2.7L engine, crankshaft is cast with a "W" on center counterweight. The 3.2L engine has a code "K".

2) Factory ground crankshafts are identified by paint stripes marked on 1st counterweight. This indicates either 1st, 2nd, or 3rd undersize. Two undersizes are available for the 2.7L engine and, 3 undersizes for the 3.2L engine.

3) Factory ground crankshafts are supplied with bearings which are also color coded. If red and blue bearing shells are used in combination, ensure shells of same color on same side of crankshaft. For example, all red bearings in cylinder block and all blue in main bearing caps.

4) If 3 different color (yellow, green, and white) bearings are used, match bearing shells to color codes on bearing journals and crankcase. If crankcase mark is missing, install both shells according to crankshaft color code.

CONNECTING ROD BEARINGS

Use Plastigage method to measure connecting rod bearing clearances. Measure clearances 1 at a time. Mark connecting rod and cap for cylinder identification before removing caps. Whenever rod bearing caps are removed, rod cap bolts and nuts should be replaced.

CRANKSHAFT END THRUST

Attach a dial indicator to crankcase with indicator point contacting flywheel. Push flywheel forward and zero dial indicator. Pull flywheel rearward and record crankshaft end thrust. If end thrust is excessive, replace thrust bearing.

REAR MAIN BEARING OIL SEAL

Removal

1) Remove transmission and flywheel. Remove 2 rear oil pan bolts. Loosen remaining oil pan bolts. Carefully separate seal retainer from oil pan gasket.

2) Remove seal retainer from rear of crankcase. Remove oil seal from seal retainer.

Installation

1) Coat oil pan gasket at seal retainer contact surface with sealing compound. Install oil seal into retainer.

2) Install aligning tool (11 2 213) on crankshaft. Coat seal lips with oil and install retainer and seal. Install remaining components.

ENGINE OILING

CRANKCASE CAPACITY

528e

Capacity is 4.2 quarts (4.0L) without filter replacement; 4.5 quarts (4.3L) with filter replacement.

533i, 633CSi & 733i

Capacity is 5.3 quarts (5.0L) without filter replacement; 6.1 quarts (5.8L) with filter replacement.

NORMAL OIL PRESSURE

528e

Oil pressure should be 7-14 psi (0.5-1.0 kg/cm²) at idle. Maximum oil pressure at top speed should be 72-87 psi (5.0-6.0 kg/cm²).

533i, 633CSi & 733i

Oil pressure should be 7-28 psi (0.5-2.0 kg/cm²) at idle. Maximum oil pressure at top speed should be about 57-71 psi (4.0-5.0 kg/cm²).

OIL PRESSURE RELIEF VALVE

For all models, oil pressure relief valve opens at approximately 68-74 psi (4.8-5.2 kg/cm²).

528e, 533i, 633CSi & 733i 6-CYLINDER (Cont.)

ENGINE OILING SYSTEM

528e

A gear type oil pump is used. Pump shaft is driven by distributor shaft. The pump is attached to the bottom of the crankcase. A safety valve in the oil pump prevents oil pressure from becoming extremely excessive.

A pressure relief valve (screwed into the crankcase) is connected directly into the main oil gallery. When oil pressure reaches predetermined maximum value, valve opens to allow oil to return to crankcase.

Oil pump pressure feeds oil through drilled passages within the block to lubricate all internal engine parts. Upper valve train components are lubricated by drainage method.

533i, 633CSi & 733i

A rotor type oil pump is used. Pump is chain driven off of crankshaft sprocket. Pressure regulating valve is integral with oil pump.

Oil pump pressure feeds oil to full-flow oil filter. From oil filter, oil is circulated through drilled passages to all moving parts of the engine. Upper valve train components and timing chain are lubricated through drainage or splash method.

OIL PUMP

Removal (528e)

Remove oil pan. Remove 3 attaching bolts and remove oil pump.

Disassembly & Inspection

Remove cover to gain access to oil screen and gears. Remove snap ring, spring, and oil pressure relief valve. Check all parts for excessive wear or scoring. Spring length must be 1.724-1.740" (43.8-44.2 mm).

Reassembly & Installation

Assemble oil pump in reverse order of disassembly. To install, reverse removal procedures. Ensure drive shaft engages with distributor shaft when installing.

Removal (533i, 633CSi & 733i)

Remove oil pan. Remove oil pump drive sprocket and detach from chain. Remove oil pump.

Disassembly

1) Unscrew union and remove relief valve spring and plunger from pump body. Remove pick-up tube and cover from pump body. Clean all parts and blow dry with compressed air.

2) If inner rotor replacement is required, remove pump sprocket hub from rotor shaft using a puller. Install new rotor in pump body and press hub onto rotor shaft to a distance of 1.740-1.748" (44.20-44.40 mm) between hub and rotor faces. *See Fig. 8*.

Inspection

1) Using a feeler gauge, measure clearance between outer rotor and pump body. Measure clearance between inner and outer rotor.

2) Lay a straightedge over pump body. Insert a feeler gauge between straightedge and rotors and measure clearance over rotors. Replace all worn parts.

OIL PUMP SPECIFICATIONS

Application	Measurement In. (mm)
Clearance Between Rotors	.005-.008 (.12-.20)
Clearance Over Rotors	.002-.004 (.04-.10)
Outer Rotor-to-Pump Body	.004-.006 (.10-.15)
Spring Free Length	2.677 (67.99)

3) Check free length of relief valve spring. If measurement is less than specified, replace spring.

Fig. 8: Measuring Distance Between Sprocket Hub and Rotor Face

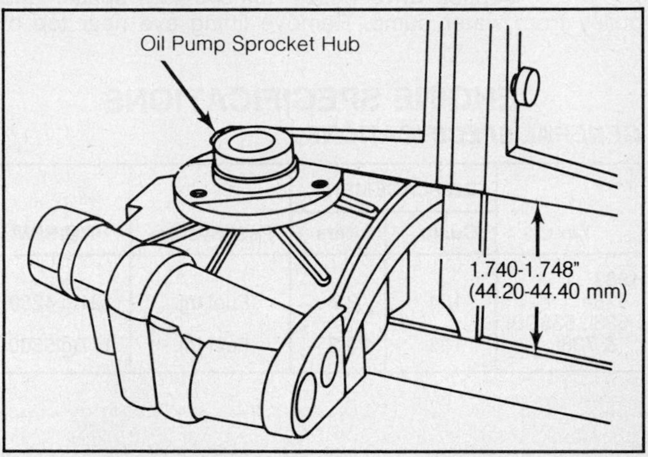
Oil Pump Sprocket Hub
1.740-1.748"
(44.20-44.40 mm)

Use a puller to remove hub.

Reassembly

Reassemble oil pump in reverse order of disassembly, using new parts where required.

Installation

1) Prime oil pump. To install, reverse removal procedure. Check oil pump drive chain tension.

2) Chain tension is correct if chain gives when slight thumb pressure is exerted midway between oil pump and crankshaft sprockets. Shims are available for tension adjustment.

3) Install shims between oil pump and crankcase mounting points. Front and rear shims must be of same thickness.

4) Ensure holes in shims align with corresponding holes in oil pump and crankcase. To install remaining components, reverse removal procedure.

ENGINE COOLING

THERMOSTAT

Thermostat begins opening at 176°F (80°C).

COOLANT CAPACITY

Coolant capacity (including heater system) is 12.7 quarts (12.0L)

RADIATOR CAP

Radiator cap pressure relief valve opens at 12.8-16.4 psi (0.9-1.2 kg/cm²).

WATER PUMP

Removal (528e)

1) Drain coolant. Remove distributor rotor and cap, then remove distributor cover. Remove fan and drive belt from pulley. Remove rubber guard and lift out cover from behind pulley.

2) Remove water pump pulley. Compress tensioner spring and pin near top of water pump and clamp in compressed position. Note installed position of pin to water pump. Remove coolant hoses from water pump. Remove water pump.

BMW Engines

528e, 533i, 633CSi & 733i 6-CYLINDER (Cont.)

Installation

Using new gasket, install water pump. Adjust drive belt tension. Refill and bleed cooling system.

Removal & Installation (533i, 633CSi & 733i)

Loosen drive belts. Remove fan, spacer and pulley from water pump. Remove lifting eye near top of water pump. Remove coolant hose from water pump, then remove pump. Using new gasket, install water pump in reverse order of removal.

ENGINE SPECIFICATIONS

GENERAL SPECIFICATIONS

Year	DISPLACEMENT Cu. In.	DISPLACEMENT Liters	Fuel System	HP@RPM	Torque Ft. Lbs.@RPM	Compr. Ratio	BORE In.	BORE mm	STROKE In.	STROKE mm
1983										
528e	164	2.7	Fuel Inj.	121@4250	16@3250	9.0:1	3.31	84.0	3.19	81.0
533i, 633CSi, & 733i	196	3.2	Fuel Inj.	177@5500	192@4000	8.8:1	3.50	89.0	3.39	86.0

VALVES

Engine Size & Valve	Head Diam. In. (mm)	Face Angle	Seat Angle	Seat Width In. (mm)	Stem Diameter In. (mm)	Stem Clearance In. (mm)	Valve Lift In. (mm)
2.7L [1]							
Intake	1.575 (40.0)	45.5°	45°	.051-.079 (1.3-2.0)	.....	.006 Max. (.15)	.....
Exhaust	1.339 (34.0)	45.5°	45°	.051-.079 (1.3-2.0)	.....	.006 Max. (.15)	.....
3.2L [1]							
Intake	1.811 (46.0)	45.5°	45°	.051-.079 (1.3-2.0)	.....	.006 Max. (.15)	.....
Exhaust	1.496 (38.0)	45.5°	45°	.051-.079 (1.3-2.0)	.....	.006 Max. (.15)	.....

[1] – Minimum valve head margin on intake valves is .051" (1.3 mm) and, .079" (2.0 mm) on exhaust.

PISTONS, PINS, RINGS

Engine	PISTONS Clearance In. (mm)	PINS Piston Fit In. (mm)	PINS Rod Fit In. (mm)	RINGS Ring No.	RINGS End Gap In. (mm)	RINGS Side Clearance In. (mm)
2.7L	.0004-.0015 (.011-.039)	.0002 Max. (.005)	Push Fit	No. 1	.012-.020 (.30-.50)	.0016-.0028 (.040-.072)
				No. 2	.012-.020 (.30-.50)	.0012-.0024 (.030-.062)
				Oil	.010-.020 (.25-.50)	.0008-.0017 (.020-.042)
3.2L	.0008-.002 (.02-.05)	.0002 Max. (.005)	Push Fit	No. 1	.012-.020 (.30-.50)	.0020-.0032 (.050-.082)
				No. 2	.008-.016 (.20-.40)	.0016-.0028 (.040-.072)
				Oil	.010-.020 (.25-.50)	.0008-.0020 (.020-.052)

BMW Engines

528e, 533i, 633CSi & 733i 6-CYLINDER (Cont.)

ENGINE SPECIFICATIONS (Cont.)

CRANKSHAFT MAIN & CONNECTING ROD BEARINGS

	MAIN BEARINGS				CONNECTING ROD BEARINGS		
Engine	Journal Diam. In. (mm)	Clearance In. (mm)	Thrust Bearing	Crankshaft End Play In. (mm)	Journal Diam. In. (mm)	Clearance In. (mm)	Side Play In. (mm)
2.7L [1]							
Red Code	2.3614-2.3618 (59.98-59.99)	.0012-.0028 (.030-.070)	No. 6	.0031-.0064 (.080-.163)	1.7707-1.7713 (44.975-44.991)	.0012-.0028 (.030-.070)	.....
Blue code	2.3610-2.3614 (59.97-59.98)						
3.2L [2]							
Red Code	2.3614-2.3618 (59.98-59.99)	.0012-.0028 (.030-.070)	No. 4	.0033-.0068 (.084-.173)	1.8888-1.8894 (47.975-47.991)	.0012-.0028 (.030-.070)	.....
Blue Code	2.3610-2.3614 (59.97-59.98)						

[1] – On 2.7L engine, maximum crankshaft runout at center journal is .006" (.15 mm).
[2] – On 3.2L engine, maximum crankshaft runout at center journal is .004" (.10 mm).

VALVE SPRINGS

Engine	Free Length In. (mm)	PRESSURE Lbs. @ In. (Kg @ mm) Valve Closed	Valve Open
2.7L	[1]	[1]	[1]
3.2L	1.71 [2] (43.5)	64@1.48 (29@37.6)	154@1.12 (70@28.5)

[1] – Information not available from manufacturer.
[2] – Depending on spring manufacturer, some springs may be 1.811" (46.0 mm).

CAMSHAFT

Engine	Journal Diam. In. (mm)	Clearance In. (mm)	Lobe Lift In. (mm)
2.7L [1]	[2]	[2]	[2]
3.2L [3]			
No. 1	1.3764-1.3770 (34.960-34.975)	.0013-.0029 (.034-.074)	.2922 (7.422)
No. 2	1.7304-1.7310 (43.952-43.967)		
No. 3	1.7704-1.7710 (44.968-44.984)		
No. 4	1.8094-1.8100 (45.959-45.974)		

[1] – End play is .008" (.20 mm)
[2] – Information not available from manufacturer.
[3] – End play is .0012-.0071" (.030-.180 mm).

TIGHTENING SPECIFICATIONS

Application	Ft. Lbs. (N.m)
Camshaft Sprocket	
2.7L Only	41-48 (55-65)
Camshaft Thrust Plate	100-106 (135-144)
Connecting Rod Caps	
2.7L	
Step 1	15 (20)
Step 2	[1]
3.2L	38-41 (51-55)
Cylinder Head Bolts	
2.7L	
Step 1	22-25 (30-34)
Step 2	43-47 (58-64)
Step 3	[2]
3.2L	
Step 1	25-29 (34-40)
Step 2	43-46 (58-62)
Step 3 [3]	57-60 (78-82)
Step 4	[2]
Exhaust Manifold	22-24 (30-32)
Flywheel Bolts (Use Loctite)	75-83 (104-115)
Intermediate Shaft	
Sprocket (2.7L Only)	40-47 (55-64)
Main Bearing Caps	
2.7L	44-49 (60-67)
3.2L	42-45 (57-62)
Vibration Damper Hub	
2.7L	289-318 (392-431)
3.2L	324-339 (440-460)

[1] – Using special (angle-calibrated) torque wrench (11 2 110), tighten bolts an additional 70°.
[2] – Using special (angle-calibrated) torque wrench (11 2 110), tighten bolts an additional 20-30°.
[3] – Wait 20 minutes, then tighten head bolt to final torque.

Datsun/Nissan Engines

PICKUP & 200SX 4-CYLINDER

ENGINE CODING

ENGINE IDENTIFICATION

Engine number is stamped on left side of cylinder block on 200SX and Pickup models.

ENGINE IDENTIFICATION

Application	Code
200SX	
2.2L	Z22E
Pickup	
2.0L	Z20
2.4L	Z24

ENGINE, MANIFOLDS & CYLINDER HEAD

ENGINE

NOTE: **Remove engine and transmission as a unit. Separate engine from transmission after removal.**

Removal (200SX)

1) To reduce fuel pressure to zero, disconnect harness connector at fuel pump relay (with Black/White, Light Green, Light Green/Red and Black wires), while engine is running. After engine stalls, crank 2 or 3 more times. Turn ignition off. Reconnect harness connector.

2) Mark hood and hinges for reassembly reference. Remove hood. Remove battery. Drain cooling system, transmission and crankcase. Disconnect all engine-to-chassis cables, hoses and wires.

3) If equipped, remove air conditioner compressor, power steering belt and pump and set aside. Do not drain oil from pump or discharge systems. Secure units with wire to prevent interference with engine removal.

4) On manual transmission, detach rubber boot. Remove nut from shift lever. Remove lever. On automatic transmission, disconnect joint between control lever and selector rod. Remove oil cooler lines. On all models, remove radiator hoses, shroud and radiator.

5) Disconnect speedometer cable. On automatic transmission, disconnect downshift solenoid, inhibitor switch and vacuum hose. On manual transmission, remove clutch slave cylinder. On all models, index mark drive shaft and remove. Remove front exhaust pipe.

6) Plug end of transmission. Attach lifting hoist to engine. Raise enough to take weight off engine mounts. Remove front and rear engine mount bolts. Pull engine forward. Remove engine and transmission as an assembly.

Removal (Pickup)

1) Disconnect battery. Drain cooling system, transmission and crankcase. Mark hood and hinges for reassembly reference. Remove hood. Detach hoses and tubes and remove air cleaner. Disconnect all engine-to-chassis cables, hoses and wires.

2) If equipped, remove air conditioner compressor, power steering belt and pump and set aside. Do not drain oil from pump or discharge systems. Hold units out of way with wire to prevent interference with engine removal.

3) On manual transmission, detach rubber boot. Remove nut from shift lever. Remove lever. Remove clutch slave cylinder. On automatic transmission, disconnect joint between control lever and selector rod. Remove oil cooler lines. Remove radiator hoses, shroud and radiator.

4) Raise and support vehicle. Remove undercover. Disconnect speedometer cable and switch wires on transmission case. Remove parking brake cable at brake lever. Remove front exhaust pipe from manifold. On automatic transmission, disconnect vacuum hose and oil pipes.

5) On 2WD, index mark drive shaft and remove. Plug end of transmission. On 4WD, index mark and remove front drive shaft assembly from transfer case. On all models, attach lifting hoist to engine. Raise enough to take weight off engine mounts.

6) On 4WD, suspend front differential carrier. Remove front carrier mount bolt. Remove front carrier rear mount bolts and crossmember. Lower front carrier slowly. On all models, remove front and rear engine mount bolts and mounts. Pull engine forward. Remove engine and transmission as an assembly.

Installation (All Models)

Replace any rubber engine mounts showing signs of deterioration or separation. Ensure proper placement of all electrical harnesses and engine mounts. Reverse removal procedures to complete installation.

INTAKE & EXHAUST MANIFOLDS

Removal

1) Disconnect battery. Drain cooling system. Remove air cleaner assembly. On 200SX, disconnect valve cover-to-throttle chamber hose, at cover. On all models, disconnect heater housing-to-water inlet tube, at inlet. Remove bolt holding water and fuel tubes to head.

2) On 200SX, bleed off fuel pressure. On all models, remove heater housing-to-thermostat housing tube. Disconnect fuel line, wiring and related components. On 200SX, remove intake manifold stays, mount bolts and nuts and intake manifold assembly. Discard gasket. *See Fig. 1.*

Fig. 1: Removing 200SX Intake & Exhaust Manifold Assembly

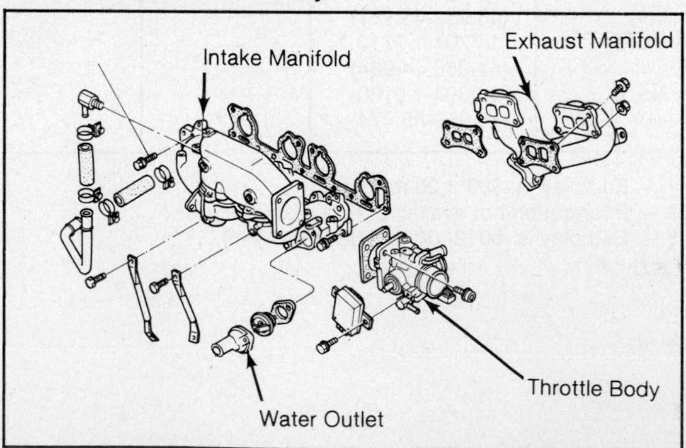
Exhaust Manifold
Intake Manifold
Throttle Body
Water Outlet

Ensure that the fuel pressure is bled before the intake manifold is removed.

3) On Pickup, remove carburetor, mount bolts and nuts and intake manifold assembly. Discard gasket. *See Fig. 2.* On all models, detach front exhaust pipe from exhaust manifold. Remove manifold mount bolts and exhaust manifold assembly. Discard gaskets.

Fig. 2: Removing Pickup Intake & Exhaust Manifolds

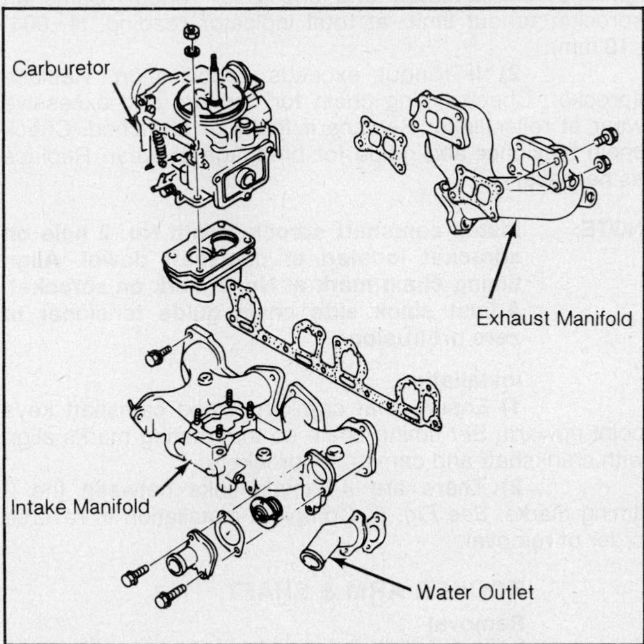
Carburetor
Exhaust Manifold
Intake Manifold
Water Outlet

Replace gaskets whenever manifolds are removed.

Installation

When installing manifolds, use new gaskets. Ensure mating surfaces of cylinder head and manifolds are clean, flat and free of nicks or other damage. Set mount studs in cylinder head, before installing intake manifold, to aid alignment. To complete installation, reverse removal procedure.

CYLINDER HEAD

Removal

1) On 200SX, release fuel system pressure. On all models, disconnect battery. Drain cooling system. Disconnect spark plug wires. Remove radiator and heater hoses. Disconnect drive belts and alternator brackets. Move alternator aside.

2) Remove fan, pulley and water pump. If equipped with air conditioning and/or power steering, remove as outlined in engine removal procedure. Remove air cleaner. Detach throttle linkage. Disconnect cables, hoses and wires from cylinder head-to-chassis or engine. Disconnect hoses and vacuum lines from intake manifold-to-cylinder head or engine block.

3) On Pickup, remove carburetor. On all models, remove intake manifold assembly with EGR valve, air induction tubes and EFI components, if equipped. Remove front exhaust pipe, exhaust manifold assembly and valve cover.

4) Turn crankshaft so No. 1 piston is at TDC on compression stroke. Scribe aligning marks on timing chain and camshaft sprocket, if necessary, for reassembly reference. Remove camshaft sprocket. Use support tool (KV10105800) for timing chain as shown in *Fig. 3*.

5) Remove bolts securing cylinder head-to-front cover. Remove cylinder head mount bolts in reverse of tightening sequence. *See Fig. 4*. Remove cylinder head.

Fig. 3: Holding Timing Chain with Support Tool

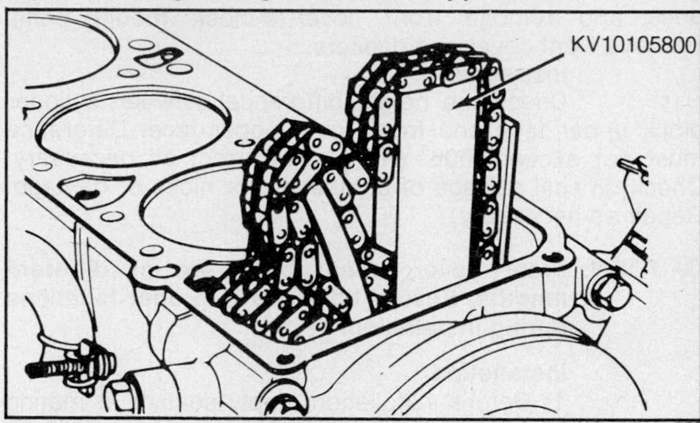
KV10105800

Before removal, ensure timing chain and sprockets are marked for reassembly reference.

Inspection

1) Check cylinder head for cracks, flaws or damage. Replace as necessary. Inspect head and block mating surfaces for warpage. Warpage limit is .004" (.10 mm) or less.

2) If beyond limit, refinish surface. Maximum surface grinding limit of head and/or block is .008" (.20 mm). Replace head and/or block if machined or warped beyond service limit.

Installation

1) Ensure mating surfaces of cylinder head and block are clean. Install head and gasket without sealer. Set No. 1 piston at TDC on compression stroke. Insert head bolts.

2) Tighten No. 1 and No. 2 to 14 ft. lbs. (19 N.m). Install and align sprockets and timing chain. Install remaining components in reverse order of removal, using new seals, gaskets and sealant where required.

3) Tighten head bolts in 3 steps, in sequence shown in *Fig. 4*, to final specified torque. Run engine for several minutes, let it cool down and recheck head bolt torque.

Fig. 4: Cylinder Head Tightening Sequence

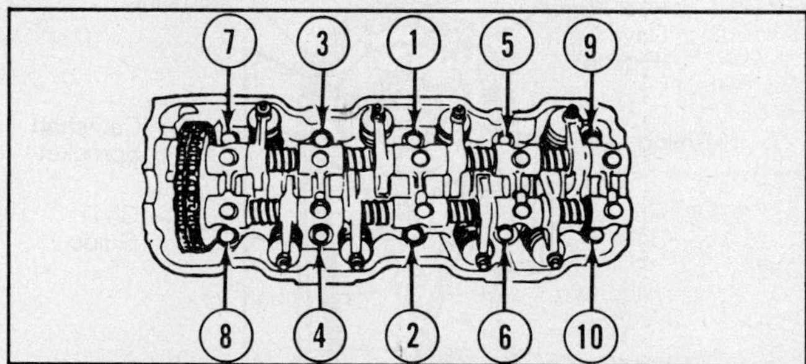
7
3
1
5
9
8
4
2
6
10

Remove the cylinder head mount bolts in reverse of the tightening sequence.

CAMSHAFT

ENGINE FRONT COVER

Removal

1) With engine removed from vehicle and mounted on engine stand, remove oil pan, strainer, oil pump and drive spindle. Remove crankshaft pulley and front cover-to-cylinder head mount bolts.

PICKUP & 200SX 4-CYLINDER (Cont.)

2) Check bolt locations for reassembly reference and remove front cover-to-block mount bolts. Remove front cover and gaskets.

Inspection

Check the height difference between cylinder block upper face and front cover upper face. Difference must not exceed .006" (.15 mm). Correct as necessary. Check oil seal surface of crankshaft for nicks or damage. Repair as necessary.

CAUTION: Front cover mount bolts are of different lengths. Ensure bolts are in proper locations during installation.

Installation

1) Before installation, apply sealant at mating corners of oil pan gasket, cylinder head gasket and front cover gaskets. Press new oil seal in front cover with dust seal lip at outside.

2) Apply lithium grease to sealing lip of oil seal before cover is installed. Using new gaskets, install front cover and related components.

TIMING CHAIN & SPROCKETS

Removal

1) Set No. 1 piston at TDC on compression stroke. Remove fan, belts, crankshaft pulley and valve cover. On 200SX, remove fuel pump and fuel pump drive cam.

2) On all models, scribe reference marks, remove camshaft drive sprocket and carefully lower timing chain. Remove cylinder head-to-front cover mount bolts. Remove cylinder head-to-block mount bolts. Remove head.

3) Set timing chain on support tool (KV10105800). Remove oil pan, strainer, oil pump, drive spindle and engine front cover. Remove timing chain tensioner and guide. Remove timing chain, oil slinger, oil pump drive gear and crankshaft drive sprocket.

Fig. 5: Timing Chain and Sprocket Alignment

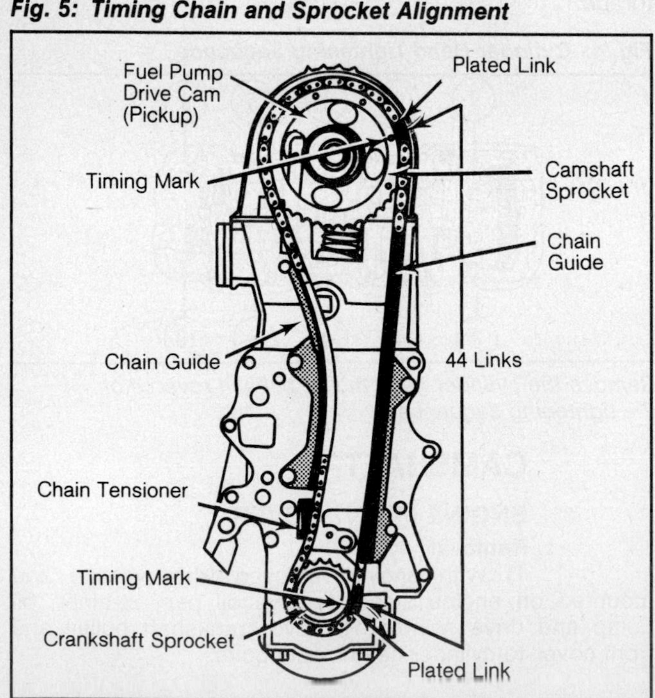
Fuel Pump
Drive Cam
(Pickup)
Plated Link
Timing Mark
Camshaft
Sprocket
Chain
Guide
Chain Guide
44 Links
Chain Tensioner
Timing Mark
Crankshaft Sprocket
Plated Link

There are 44 chain links between the 2 timing marks.

Inspection

1) Check camshaft sprocket tooth surface for flaws and wear. Replace, if any damage is found. Install sprocket on camshaft and check for runout. Camshaft sprocket runout limit, at total indicator reading, is .004" (.10 mm).

2) If runout exceeds specification, Replace sprocket. Check timing chain for damage and excessive wear at roller links. Replace if faulty or stretched. Check chain tensioner and guide for breakage or wear. Replace as necessary.

NOTE: Install camshaft sprocket with No. 2 hole on sprocket located at camshaft dowel. Align timing chain mark at No. 2 mark on sprocket. Adjust slack side chain guide tensioner to zero protrusion.

Installation

1) Ensure that crankshaft and camshaft keys point upward. Set timing chain so that mating marks align with crankshaft and camshaft sprockets.

2) There are 44 chain links between the 2 timing marks. *See Fig. 5*. Complete installation in reverse order of removal.

ROCKER ARM & SHAFT

Removal

With valve cover and gasket removed, loosen rocker arm mount bolts. Do not remove bolts from No. 1 or No. 5 end bracket or rocker and shaft bracket will spring out. Remove rocker arm assembly. Disassemble each rocker arm and shaft carefully. Note component locations for reassembly reference.

Inspection

Check rocker arms and shafts for wear or damage. Standard rocker arm-to-shaft clearance is .0003-.0019" (.007-.049 mm). If excessive wear or damage is found, replace rocker arm and/or shaft.

NOTE: Rocker arm shaft brackets use alphabetical identification marks on each bracket and cylinder head location.

Installation

1) With valve assembly and camshaft installed in cylinder head, make up rocker shaft assembly. Ensure camshaft dowel pin is at front side of head and positioned at 12 o'clock. Install rocker shaft bracket, valve rocker and spring onto shaft. *See Fig. 6*.

2) Intake rocker shaft has an identification slit on front surface. The exhaust rocker shaft does not. Both shafts should be assembled so that punch marks on front surface face up. Marks are used to identify oil hole direction. *See Fig. 7*.

3) Valve rocker is the same for intake and exhaust. Rockers for No. 1 & No. 3 cylinder are marked with "1". Rockers for No. 2 & No. 4 are marked with "2". Do not mix rockers from original locations.

4) Mount rocker shaft assembly onto knock pin in head. Tighten to specification. Set cylinder head on blocks to make space for valves. Otherwise, when shaft assembly is tightened, some valves will open and interfere. After assembling cylinder head, turn camshaft until No. 1 piston is at TDC on compression stroke.

PICKUP & 200SX 4-CYLINDER (Cont.)

Fig. 6: Installing Rocker Arm & Shaft Assembly

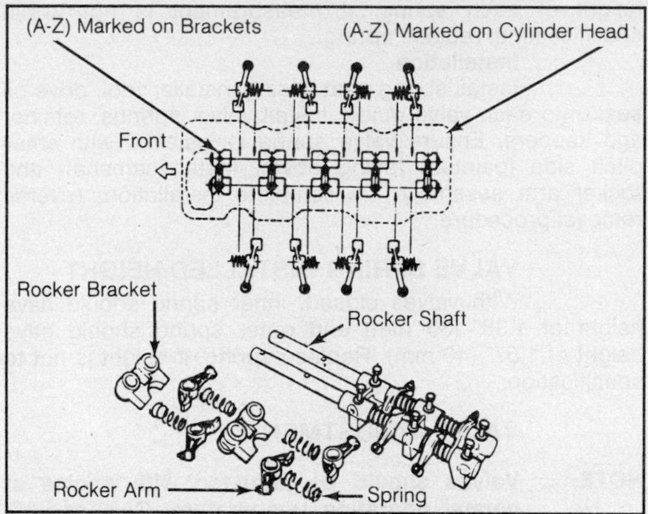
(A-Z) Marked on Brackets
(A-Z) Marked on Cylinder Head
Front
Rocker Bracket
Rocker Shaft
Rocker Arm
Spring

Valve rockers are the same for intake and exhaust.

Fig. 7: Assembling Rocker Arm Shafts Using Identification Marks

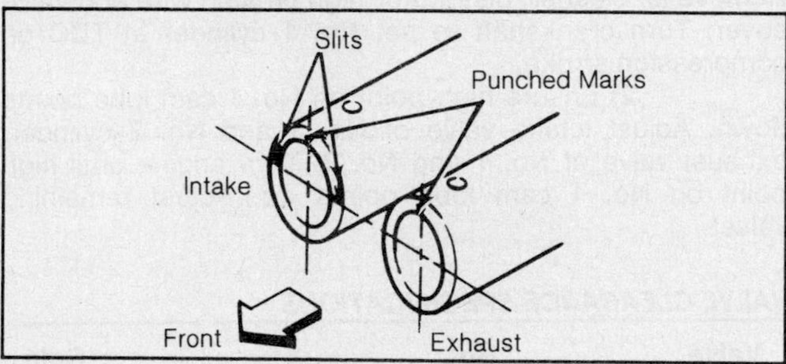
Slits
Punched Marks
Intake
Front
Exhaust

The intake rocker shaft has identification slit on the front surface while the exhaust shaft does not.

CAMSHAFT

Removal

With cylinder head removed, loosen rocker arm bolts evenly, from outside, in sequence. Do not remove bolts from each end bracket of rocker arm shaft assembly or assembly will spring apart. Remove rocker arm assembly. Carefully remove camshaft.

Inspection

1) Check camshaft, journals and cam bracket bearing surfaces for wear or damage. Maximum journal-to-bushing clearance limit is .004" (.10 mm) or less. Check camshaft for bend. With camshaft in "V" blocks, set dial indicator on center journal. Using total gauge reading, bend limit is .008" (.20 mm).

2) Check the camshaft lobe height. Standard height is 1.5150-1.5170" (38.481-38.531 mm) for intake and exhaust lobes. Maximum wear limit of cam lobe is .0098" (.250 mm). Replace camshaft if beyond limits.

3) Check camshaft end play with dial indicator. Maximum end play is .008" (.20 mm). If beyond limit, replace camshaft, brackets and/or cylinder head assembly.

Installation

1) Install camshaft on cylinder head with front camshaft dowel pin at 12 o'clock position. Install rocker arm assembly by aligning to dowel pin on cylinder head.

2) Place cylinder head on wooden blocks to allow for valve space. Tighten rocker arm bolts evenly, in 2 or 3 steps, in outward sequence from center bracket.

CAMSHAFT BEARINGS

Measure inner diameter of camshaft bearing and outer diameter of camshaft journal with micrometer and telescope hole guage. Standard journal diameter is 1.2967-1.2974" (32.935-32.955 mm). Standard bearing clearance is .0018-.0035" (.045-.090 mm). Maximum bearing clearance is .004" (.10 mm). If excessively worn or damaged, replace camshaft and/or cylinder head assembly.

VALVES

VALVE ARRANGEMENT

Right Side - Intake valves.
Left Side - Exhaust valves.

NOTE: **Camshaft MUST be removed to take out valves. See Camshaft Removal & Installation.**

VALVE

Removal

With cylinder head removed, remove camshaft. Remove valves using valve spring compressor tool (ST12070000 or KV101092S0). Keep disassembled parts in order.

Inspection

1) Check valve head diameter, stem diameter and seat angle. Inspect valves for worn, damaged or deformed valve head or stem.

2) If head is worn to .02" (.5 mm) in-margin thickness, replace valve. Valve stem end surface grinding limit is .02" (.5 mm).

Installation

Install valve spring seat and oil seal on valve guide. Place springs in position with close-coiled (painted) end toward cylinder head. Use compressor and install valve retainers and keepers.

VALVE GUIDE

Clearance Check

1) Measure clearance between valve stem and valve guide with micrometer and telescope hole gauge. Check diameter of valve stem at top, center and bottom. Insert hole gauge in guide bore. Measure at center.

2) Standard intake valve stem-to-guide clearance is .0008-.0021" (.020-.053 mm) and exhaust valve stem-to-guide clearance is .0016-.0029" (.040-.073 mm). Maximum stem-to-guide clearance is .004" (.10 mm).

3) Move valve left-to-right in guide. Maximum movement limit at valve tip is .008" (.20 mm), with tip 1.18" (30 mm) from head upper surface. Replace guide if worn beyond limits.

Replacement

1) If clearance is beyond limits and valve stem is not worn, replace guide. To replace, heat head to 302-320°F (150-160°C). Using tool (ST110330000) or equivalent, drive guide out from combustion chamber side.

2) With head at room temperature, ream guide hole to .4797-.4802" (12.185-12.196 mm). Standard guide

PICKUP & 200SX 4-CYLINDER (Cont.)

hole diameter is .4718-.4723" (11.985-11.996 mm). Standard guide outside diameter is .4733-.4738" (12.023-12.034 mm). Interference fit of valve guide-to-head is .0011-.0019" (.027-.049 mm).

NOTE: Valve guides of .20 mm oversize are available for service.

3) To install guide, reheat head. Fit snap ring on new valve guide and press guide into head until snap ring comes in contact with head surface. *See Fig. 8.*

Fig. 8: Installing Intake and Exhaust Valve Guides

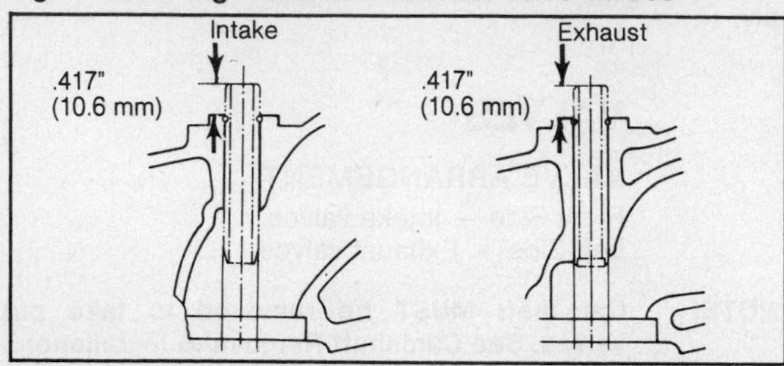
Intake
Exhaust
.417"
(10.6 mm)
.417"
(10.6 mm)

Ensure that the valve guide snap rings are installed to the proper depth.

4) Use reamer (ST110320000) to finish guide bore to .3150-.3157" (8.000-8.018 mm). Reface valve seat surface, as needed, after valve or guide repair or replacement.

VALVE SEAT INSERTS

1) Check valves and valve seat inserts for pitting at valve contact surface. Standard intake valve seat contact is .083" (2.10 mm) and exhaust seat contact is .067" (1.70 mm). Correct valve seat surface or replace if excessively worn.

NOTE: Valve seat inserts of .5 mm oversize are available for service.

2) To remove old inserts, set machine depth stop so that boring cannot continue beyond bottom face of insert recess in head. Machine cylinder head recess diameter, in concentric circles, to valve guide center for correct fit.

3) Heat cylinder head to 302-392°F (150-200°C). Install insert, ensuring that it seats on bottom face of recess. Cut valve seats to correct face angle, seat width and head diameter of valve being installed.

VALVE SPRINGS

Removal

1) With head removed, remove rocker arm assembly and camshaft. Compress valve spring with tool (ST12070000 or KV101092S0). Remove keepers. Detach compressing tool. Remove spring retainer and valve springs.

2) Remove oil seal, using valve lip seal removal and installer tool (KV10107900). Remove valve spring seat. Keep components in correct order for installation.

Inspection

1) Check valve springs for squareness using steel square and surface plate. Standard out of square limit is .087" (2.20 mm) for outer spring and .075" (1.90 mm) for inner spring.

2) Measure free length, tension and assembled height of each spring. If measurement is not within specifications, replace spring.

Installation

Install spring seat. Using installer tool, drive oil seal onto each valve guide. Install valve, springs, retainer and keepers. Ensure valve spring is installed with small pitch side (painted) facing down. Install camshaft and rocker arm assembly. To complete installation, reverse removal procedure.

VALVE SPRING INSTALLED HEIGHT

With valves closed, inner spring should have height of 1.38" (35 mm) and outer spring should have height of 1.57" (40 mm). Replace spring, if height is not to specification.

VALVE ADJUSTMENT

NOTE: Valves should be adjusted with engine at normal operating temperature. Cold specifications are provided for initial settings after assembly.

1) Do not adjust valves with engine running. Remove air cleaner, distributor high tension wire and valve cover. Turn crankshaft to set No. 1 cylinder at TDC on compression stroke.

2) Ensure high point on No. 1 cam lobe points down. Adjust intake valve of No. 1 and No. 2 cylinder; exhaust valve of No. 1 and No. 3. Turn engine until high point on No. 1 cam lobe points up. Adjust remaining valves.

VALVE CLEARANCE SPECIFICATIONS

Valve	Hot	[1] Cold
Intake	.012" (.30 mm)	.008" (.21 mm)
Exhaust	.012" (.30 mm)	.009" (.23 mm)

[1] – Use for initial settings only.

PISTONS, PINS & RINGS

PISTON & ROD ASSEMBLY

Removal

1) With cylinder head, front cover and oil pan removed, remove connecting rod nuts. Remove rod cap with bearing half. Check top of cylinder bore for ridge. If scraper will not remove carbon build-up, remove using ridge reamer.

2) Push piston and rod assembly, with bearing half, out through top of block. Keep rod caps with their respective piston and rod assemblies. Caps are not interchangeable.

Inspection

1) Check connecting rod for bend or torsion using rod aligner tool. Standard bend and torsion limit is .0012" (.030 mm) and maximum limit is .002" (.05 mm) or less, in 3.94" (100 mm) of length.

2) Install rod, with bearings, on crank pin and tighten to specification. Measure rod side thrust clearance. Standard clearance, at rod big end, is .008-.012" (.20-.30 mm). Maximum limit is .024" (.60 mm). Replace rod if not to specifications.

PICKUP & 200SX 4-CYLINDER (Cont.)

Installation

1) To install piston and connecting rod assembly, apply oil to rings, piston and cylinder wall. Ensure ring gaps are approximately 180° apart and not on thrust side of piston or in line with piston pin.

2) Bearing halves must be properly seated in rod and cap. Install ring compressor. Compress rings. Install piston in cylinder. Ensure grade mark stamped in top of piston is toward front of engine and oil hole on rod faces right side of block. *See Fig. 9*.

Fig. 9: Installing Piston & Rod Assembly

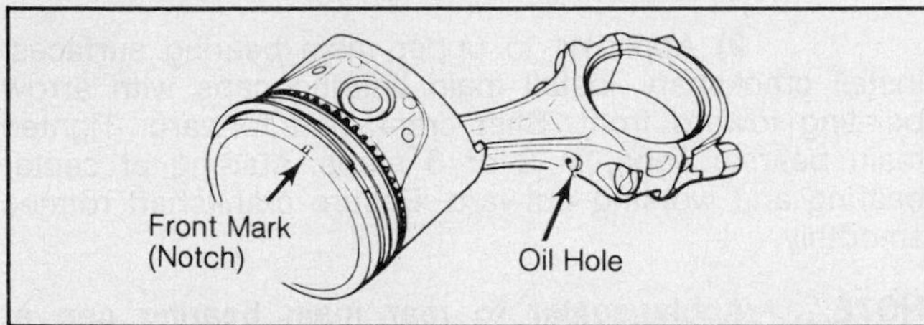
Front Mark
(Notch)
Oil Hole

Ensure the grade mark on piston top faces the front and connecting rod oil hole faces right side of block

3) With piston installed and rod and bearings seated against crankshaft journal, install rod caps to their respective piston and rod assembly. Install cylinder head, front cover and related components. Install new gasket and oil pan. Tighten bolts evenly, in a criss-cross pattern. Do not overtighten.

FITTING PISTONS & RINGS

1) Inspect cylinder block for cracks or flaws. Using bore gauge, measure cylinder bore for out-of-round or excessive taper. If bore out-of-round or taper exceeds .0006" (.015 mm), refinish cylinder bore. When any one cylinder is bored, all cylinders must be bored.

NOTE: Before cylinder block machining operations, ensure main bearing caps are installed and tightened to specification. Bore cylinders in the order of No. 2-4-1-3 to prevent distortion.

2) Determine piston oversize according to amount of wear in cylinder. Standard cylinder bore diameter is 3.3465-3.3484" (85.000-85.050 mm) for Z20, 3.4252-3.4272" (87.000-87.050 mm) for Z22E and 3.5039-3.5059" (89.000-89.050 mm) for Z24. Bore wear limit is .008" (.20 mm). Standard diameter difference between cylinders is .002" (.05 mm) or less and limit is .008" (.02 mm).

3) Measure piston diameter at thrust face. Standard piston diameter is 3.3451-3.3470" (84.965-85.015 mm) for Z20, 3.4238-3.4258" (86.956-87.015 mm) for Z22E and 3.5026-3.5045" (88.965-89.015 mm) for Z24. Add piston-to-cylinder clearance. Finish hone of cylinder may then be determined.

4) After honing cylinder to final fit, measure piston-to-cylinder clearance using pull scale and feeler gauge. With piston and cylinder at room temperature (70°F, 20°C), a force of .4-3.3 lbs. (.2-1.5 kg) should be obtained extracting a .0016" (.04 mm) feeler gauge.

5) If pistons are reused, decarbon piston and ring grooves with scraper and curved steel wire or piece of broken ring. Clean oil slots in bottom land of oil ring groove. Check for scratches, wear or damage. Measure side clearance of rings in grooves as each ring is installed.

NOTE: If only piston rings are replaced, measure gap at bottom of bore. Oversize pistons and rings are available in .02 mm, .5 mm and 1 mm.

6) Standard side clearance for top ring is .0016-.0029" (.040-.073 mm). For 2nd ring, clearance is .0012-.0025" (.030-.063 mm). Maximum side clearance for top and 2nd ring is .004" (.10 mm). If side clearance exceeds limits, replace piston and rings.

7) Check ring end gap. Install ring squarely in cylinder, using piston. Standard end gap is .010-.016" (.25-.40 mm) for top ring, .006-.010" (.15-.30 mm) for second ring and .012-.035" (.30-.90 mm) for oil ring. When installing piston rings, ensure stamped mark on ring faces up. *See Fig. 10*.

Fig. 10: Installation Order of Piston Rings

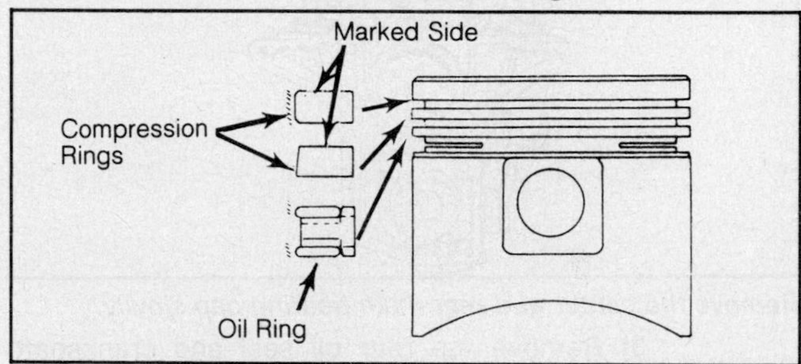
Marked Side
Compression
Rings
Oil Ring

Install the rings with the top mark facing up and the ring gaps spaced properly.

PISTON PINS

1) Piston pin is press fit into connecting rod and has sliding fit in piston. To remove, set piston and rod assembly in hydraulic press (ST13030001) and press pin out of rod. Do not damage piston during removal.

2) Check pin and pin hole for signs of gauling or excessive wear. Using micrometer and telescope hole gauge, measure diameter of piston pin, piston pin hole and rod small end. Determine pin-to-piston and pin-to-rod clearance.

3) Standard piston pin diameter is .8265-.8267" (20.993-20.998 mm). Standard piston pin hole inside diameter is .8268-.8271" (21.001-21.008 mm). Standard rod small end diameter is .8254-.8259" (20.956-20.978 mm).

4) Check pin-to-piston and pin-to-rod clearance in specifications table. To assemble piston and rod, warm piston to room temperature. Insert pin into piston with finger pressure only. Hold piston and rod in proper alignment and press in pin. Assemble with oil hole of rod big end toward right side of block.

CRANKSHAFT & MAIN & CONNECTING ROD BEARINGS

CRANKSHAFT

Removal

1) With engine removed from vehicle, remove cylinder head and oil pan. Remove flywheel and rear plate. Remove oil strainer, oil pump and drive spindle. Remove front cover, chain tensioner, guide and timing chain.

2) Remove oil slinger, oil pump drive gear and crankshaft sprocket. Remove piston and rod assemblies. Remove main bearing caps, from outside, in sequence. Use puller (KV101041SO) to remove center and rear main bearing caps. *See Fig. 11.*

NOTE: **Keep main bearing caps in order for reassembly reference.**

Fig. 11: Removing Center & Rear Main Bearing Caps

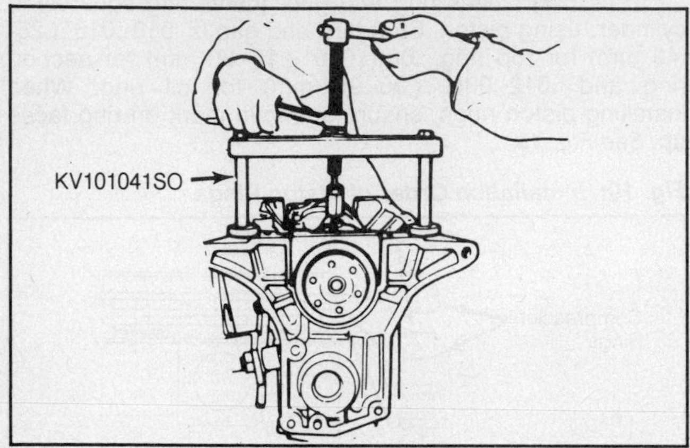
KV101041SO

Remove the center and rear main bearing cap slowly.

3) Remove the rear oil seal and crankshaft. Remove the baffle plate and steel net from the crankcase. *See Fig. 12.*

Fig. 12: Removing Rear Oil Seal

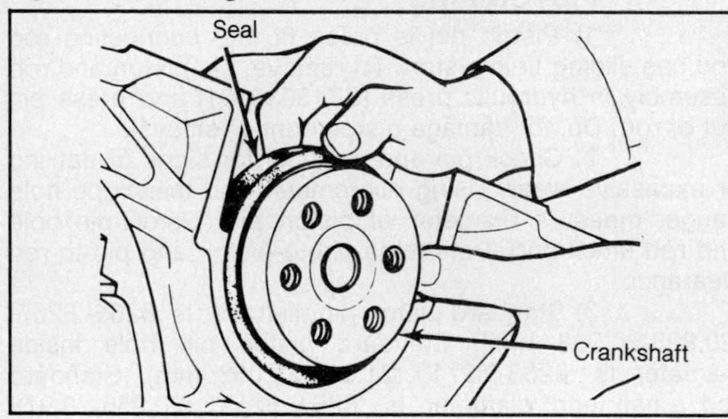
Seal
Crankshaft

Do not damage rear oil seal riding surface of crankshaft during removal or installation.

Inspection

1) Check crankshaft journals and crankpins for scoring, wear, cracks, taper and out of round. Standard taper and out of round limit is .0004" (.010 mm) or less. Maximum taper and out-of-round is .0012" (.030 mm). Check crankshaft for bend by placing on "V" blocks.

2) Use dial indicator at center journal of crankshaft. Standard bend limit is .0010" (.025 mm) or less. If bend exceeds .002" (.05 mm), which is half of indicator reading, replace crankshaft.

3) Check crankshaft pilot bushing for wear or damage. If necessary, pull bushing from crankshaft using pilot bushing puller tool (ST16610001). Clean bushing hole. Insert bushing to .16" (4 mm). Do not damage bushing edge or insert excessively.

4) Check flywheel friction surface for cracks, damage or wear. Measure friction surface runout using a dial indicator. Runout limit is .006" (.15 mm). Resurface or replace flywheel if not within limits. Check tooth surfaces of ring gear for flaws or wear. Replace ring gear if necessary.

Installation

1) Install baffle plate and steel net into crankcase. Install upper main bearing halves into block. Ensure bearings are on correct journal. Journal No. 3 requires a thrust bearing. Bearing for No. 1 is the same as for No. 5. Bearing for No. 2 is the same as for No. 4.

NOTE: **Upper and lower bearings are not interchangeable. Upper bearings have an oil groove.**

2) Apply oil to upper main bearing surfaces. Install crankshaft. Install main bearing caps with arrow pointing toward front. Shift crankshaft forward. Tighten main bearing caps, in 2 or 3 steps, starting at center bearing and working outward. Ensure crankshaft rotates smoothly.

NOTE: **Apply sealer to rear main bearing cap at point where cap contacts cylinder block.**

3) Check crankshaft end play. Standard end play is .002-.007" (.05-.18 mm). End play limit is .012" (.30 mm). If not within specifications, replace center thrust bearing.

4) Apply sealant to side seals and install in rear main bearing cap. Apply oil to outside and sealing lip of oil seal. Install seal, with dust seal lip to outside, using oil seal drift (KV10105500).

5) Wipe oil or foreign matter from fitting surfaces and install rear end plate or drive plate and flywheel. Install piston and rod assemblies. Install remaining components in reverse of removal procedure.

MAIN BEARING CLEARANCE

1) Check bearings for scoring or wear. Replace if damaged. Clean oil from crankshaft. Check clearance using Plastigage method. Standard main bearing clearance is .0008-.0024" (.020-.062 mm). Maximum clearance is .0047" (.120 mm). If not to specifications, replace bearings.

2) Bearings are available in undersizes of .25 mm, .50 mm, .75 mm and 1 mm for Z22E. For Z24, only bearing undersize of .25 mm is available. For Z20, bearings are available in undersizes of .25 mm, .50 mm and .75 mm.

NOTE: **Plastigage should run parallel with crankshaft. Do not block oil hole or turn crankshaft with Plastigage inserted.**

CONNECTING ROD BEARING CLEARANCE

1) Check connecting rod bearing clearance using Plastigage method. Tighten connecting rod caps to 33-40 ft. lbs. (45-54 N.m). Standard rod bearing clearance is .0005-.0021" (.012-.054 mm). Maximum clearance is .0047" (.120 mm). If not to specifications, replace bearings.

2) Bearings are available in undersizes of .25 mm, .50 mm and .75 mm for Z22E. For Z24, only bearing undersize of .25 mm is available. For Z20, bearings are available in undersizes of .25 mm, .50 mm and .75 mm.

PICKUP & 200SX 4-CYLINDER (Cont.)

ENGINE OILING

CRANKCASE CAPACITY

For 200SX & 4WD Pickup, the crankcase capacity is 4.5 qts. (4.3L) with oil filter.

For 2WD Pickup, the crankcase capacity is 4.4 qts. (4.2L) with oil filter.

OIL FILTER

Full-flow, disposable cartridge.

OIL PRESSURE

50-60 psi (3.5-4.2 kg/cm²) at 3000 rpm.

Fig. 13: Cutaway View of Engine Oiling System

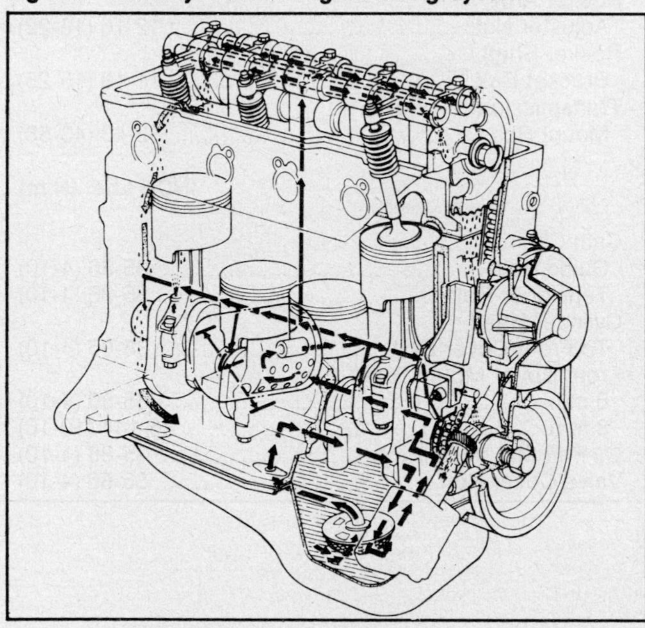

ENGINE OILING SYSTEM

Oil drawn from pan passes through screen to oil pump and is delivered to oil filter and main oil gallery. Main oil gallery supplies oil to crankshaft main bearings and drilled passages in crankshaft.

Oil sprayed from jet holes on connecting rods lubricates cylinders and piston pins. Oil from main gallery lubricates chain tensioner and timing chain. Center hole in crankshaft, center bearing feeds camshaft bearings on cylinder head.

Valve rocker mechanism is lubricated through oil gallery in camshaft and through a small channel at base circle portion of each cam. Rocker arms and valves are lubricated through small holes in oil pipe.

OIL PUMP

Removal

1) Pump assembly is installed at bottom right of front cover and held in place by four bolts. Pump is driven by helical gear on crankshaft and in turn drives distributor shaft.

2) Set No. 1 cylinder at TDC on compression stroke. Check distributor rotor position for reassembly reference. Remove mount bolts. Remove oil pump and drive spindle assembly.

Inspection

1) Remove cover and gasket from oil pump body. Remove gears. Wash parts with solvent. Inspect for wear or damage.

2) With rotor in pump body and gasket installed, clearance between rotor and straight edge, is .0024" (.060 mm) or less.

3) With gasket removed, clearance between pump body and straight edge is .0012" (.030 mm) or less. Ensure clearances are within specifications.

NOTE: Oil pump rotors and body are not serviced separately. If excessively worn or damaged, replace pump rotor set or complete pump assembly.

Installation

1) Install outer pump rotor with larger chamfered portion facing pump body side. Ensure distributor rotor is in same position as before removal. Fill pump housing with oil. Align punch mark on drive spindle with hole in pump. *See Fig. 14.*

Fig. 14: Aligning Oil Pump Timing Marks

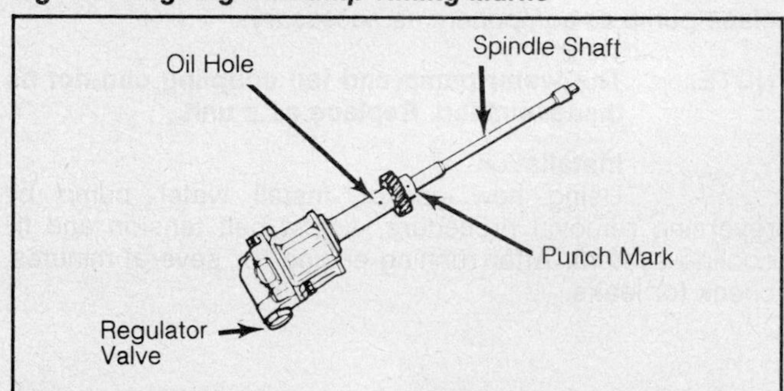
Oil Hole
Spindle Shaft
Punch Mark
Regulator Valve

Ensure that distributor rotor is in same position as it was before oil pump removal.

2) Using new gasket, install oil pump and drive spindle assembly. Ensure drive spindle tip securely fits distributor fitting hole. Tighten all bolts.

OIL PUMP CLEARANCES

Application	[1] In. (mm)
Rotor Side Clearance (Rotor to Bottom Cover) [2]	.008 (.20)
Rotor Tip Clearance	.008 (.20)
Outer Rotor to Body	.012 (.50)

[1] – Wear limit specifications given.
[2] – Clearance is checked with gasket in place.

ENGINE COOLING

THERMOSTAT

Unit begins to open at 180°F (82°C) and is fully open at 203°F (95°C).

Datsun Engines

PICKUP & 200SX 4-CYLINDER (Cont.)

RADIATOR CAP

13 psi (.9 kg/cm²).

COOLING SYSTEM CAPACITY

200SX

11.1 qts. (10.5L) with heater.

Pickup

Auto. transmission, 10 qts. (9.4L).
Manual transmission, 10.8 qts. (10.2L).

WATER PUMP

Removal

To remove pump, open radiator cap and drain cooling system. Remove upper radiator shroud. Loosen alternator bracket and remove fan belt. If equipped, remove power steering belt. Remove fan. Remove pump mount bolts. Remove water pump with fan pulley, fan coupling and gasket.

Inspection

Inspect water pump body and vane for corrosion or rust. Check pump bearing for excessive play or rough operation. Inspect fan coupling for oil leakage or bent bi-metal. Check thermostat for proper operation.Replace pump or component as necessary.

NOTE: **The water pump and fan coupling can not be disassembled. Replace as a unit.**

Installation

Using new gasket, install water pump by reversing removal procedure. Adjust belt tension and fill cooling system. After running engine for several minutes, check for leaks.

TIGHTENING SPECIFICATIONS

Application	Ft. Lbs. (N.m)
Alternator Bracket Bolt	33-40 (44-54)
Camshaft Sprocket Bolt	87-116 (118-157)
Clutch Cover Bolt	12-15 (16-21)
Connecting Rod Nut	33-40 (44-54)
Crankshaft Pulley	87-116 (118-157)
Cylinder Head Mount Bolt [1]	58-65 (78-88)
Flywheel Mount Bolt	101-116 (137-157)
Main Bear Cap Bolt	33-40 (44-54)
Manifold	
Exhaust Mount Bolt	12-15 (16-21)
Intake Mount Bolt	12-15 (16-21)
Oil Pump Mount Bolt	8-11 (11-15)
Rocker Arm	
Adjuster Nut	12-16 (16-22)
Rocker Shaft	
Bracket Bolt	11-18 (15-25)
Transmission-to-Engine	
Mount Bolt	32-43 (43-58)
	INCH Lbs. (N.m)
Cam Chain	
Guide Bolt	35-86 (4-10)
Tensioner Bolt	35-86 (4-10)
Cylinder Head	
To Front Cover Bolt	35-86 (4-10)
Front Cover Mount Bolt	
6 mm	35-86 (4-10)
8 mm	86-144 (10-16)
Oil Pan Mount Bolt	35-86 (4-10)
Valve Cover Bolt	35-86 (4-10)

ENGINE SPECIFICATIONS

GENERAL SPECIFICATIONS

Year	DISPLACEMENT		Fuel System	HP@RPM	Torque Ft. Lbs.@RPM	Compr. Ratio	BORE		STROKE	
	Cu. In.	Liters					In.	mm	In.	mm
1983										
Pickup										
Federal	119.1	2.0	2-Bbl.	95 @ 5200	112 @ 2800	9.4:1	3.35	85	3.39	86
50 States [1]	145.8	2.4	2-Bbl.	103 @ 4800	134 @ 2800	8.3:1	3.50	89	3.78	96
200SX	133.5	2.2	E.F.I. [2]	102 @ 5200	129 @ 2800	8.5:1	3.43	87	3.62	92

[1] – Only gasoline engine available in Calif. Pickups; may also be used in some Federal Pickups.
[2] – Electronic Fuel Injection.

VALVES

Engine Size & Valve	Head Diam. In. (mm)	Face Angle	Seat Angle	Seat Width In. (mm)	Stem Diameter In. (mm)	Stem Clearance In. (mm)	Valve Lift In. (mm)
2.0L, 2.2L & 2.4L							
Intake	1.65 (42)	45°	45.5°	.083 [1] (2.10)	.3136-.3142 (7.965-7.980)	.0008-.0021 (.020-.053)	.....
Exhaust	1.496 (38)	45°	45.5°	.067 (1.70)	.3128-.3134 (7.945-7.960)	.0016-.0029 (.040-.073)	.....

[1] – 2.0L and 2.2L valve seat width shown, 2.4L width is .079" (2 mm).

Datsun Engines

PICKUP & 200SX 4-CYLINDER (Cont.)

ENGINE SPECIFICATIONS (Cont.)

PISTONS, PINS, RINGS

Engine	PISTONS	PINS		RINGS		
	Clearance In. (mm)	Piston Fit In. (mm)	Rod Fit In. (mm)	Ring No.	End Gap In. (mm)	Side Clearance In. (mm)
2.0L, 2.2L & 2.4L	.0010-.0018 (.025-.045)	.0003-.0005 (.008-.012)	.0006-.0014 [1] (.015-.035)	No. 1	.010-.016 (.25-.40)	.0016-.0029 (.040-.073)
				No. 2	.006-.012 (.15-.30)	.0012-.0025 (.030-.063)
				Oil	.012-.035 (.30-.90)	.....

[1] – Interference fit.

CRANKSHAFT MAIN & CONNECTING ROD BEARINGS

Engine	MAIN BEARINGS				CONNECTING ROD BEARINGS		
	Journal Diam. In. (mm)	Clearance In. (mm)	Thrust Bearing	Crankshaft End Play In. (mm)	Journal Diam. In. (mm)	Clearance In. (mm)	Side Play In. (mm)
2.0L, 2.2L & 2.4L	2.1631-2.1636 (54.942-54.955)	.0008-.0024 (.020-.062)	No. 3	.002-.007 (.05-.18)	1.9670-1.9675 (49.961-49.974)	.0005-.0021 (.012-.054)	.008-.012 (.20-.30)

VALVE SPRINGS

Engine	Free Length In. (mm)	PRESSURE Lbs. @ In. (Kg @ mm)	
		Valve Closed	Valve Open
2.0L, 2.2L & 2.4L			
Inner	1.736 [1] (44.10)	24.3@1.38 (11@35)	57@98 (26@25)
Outer	1.959 (49.77)	50.7@1.57 (23@40)	115.3@1.18 (52.3@30)

[1] – Inner spring free length for 2.0L and 2.4L shown. Inner free length for 2.2L is 1.7724" (45.120 mm).

CAMSHAFT

Engine	Journal Diam. In. (mm)	Clearance In. (mm)	Lobe Lift In. (mm)
2.0L, 2.2L & 2.4L	1.2967-1.2974 (32.935-32.955)	.0018-.0035 (.045-.090)	.218 (5.55)

Datsun/Nissan Engines

PULSAR, SENTRA & STANZA 4-CYLINDER

ENGINE CODING

ENGINE IDENTIFICATION

The engine serial number is stamped onto a machined pad, located beneath the exhaust manifold, at left rear side of the engine. The 2nd character of the serial number represents engine model.

ENGINE IDENTIFICATION

Application	Code
Sentra (MPG Model) 1.5L	E15
Pulsar & Sentra 1.6L	E16
Stanza 2.0L	CA20

ENGINE, MANIFOLDS & CYLINDER HEAD

ENGINE

NOTE: Remove the engine and transaxle as a unit. Separate the engine from transaxle after removal.

Removal

1) Mark hood hinge positions. Remove hood. Remove battery and support bracket. On Stanza, remove radiator reservoir tank. On all models, remove air cleaner and fresh air duct. Remove undercover. Drain coolant. Remove radiator and cooling fan.

2) If equipped, remove power steering pump, bracket, air conditioning compressor and idler pulley. Do not discharge systems. Secure components away from engine. Disconnect front exhaust pipe from exhaust manifold.

3) Disconnect accelerator cable. Disconnect all linkages, cables, vacuum hoses and wiring from transaxle. Plug pinion gear hole once speedometer cable is removed. On Stanza, remove EGR vacuum control valve with bracket from body.

4) On all models, remove lower ball joints and discard mount nuts. Drain gear oil from transaxle. Loosen 3 top bolts from struts. Remove both drive shafts from transaxle. Do not damage oil seals.

5) Label and disconnect all vacuum, fuel and air hoses and electrical wiring between engine and chassis. Attach lifting sling and engine hoist to engine. Disconnect engine and transaxle mounts. Lift engine and transaxle from vehicle.

Installation

1) On Stanza, install engine mount brackets and insulators on engine. Align notches in left side mount support and collar when installing support. Ensure no clearance exists between mount support and vehicle body when installed.

2) When installing front mount support, position oblong hole in support so that insulator is in center of bracket. With mount supports installed, tighten buffer rod adjusting bolt to prevent rubber from deforming.

3) On all models, use new nuts when installing ball joints. Reverse removal procedures to install engine and transaxle. Ensure all hoses, cables and wires are properly attached.

INTAKE MANIFOLD

Removal

1) Remove air cleaner and fresh air duct. Disconnect accelerator and choke cables. Disconnect fuel line at carburetor and plug openings. Remove intake manifold support bracket.

2) Remove all wiring, water and vacuum hoses interfering with intake manifold removal. Remove fuel pump and EGR valve assembly, if necessary. Remove intake manifold-to-cylinder head mount nuts. Remove intake manifold assembly with carburetor.

Installation

Install intake manifold assembly using new gaskets. Ensure manifold and head mating surfaces are free of nicks or other damage. To complete installation, reverse removal procedure.

EXHAUST MANIFOLD

Removal

1) Remove exhaust air induction tube bracket and EGR tube at EGR valve side. If necessary, remove distributor and high tension cable. Remove exhaust manifold cover, EGR and exhaust air induction tubes.

2) Detach front exhaust pipe from manifold. When removing exhaust manifold mount bolts, note center mount nut is of different diameter than the others. Remove manifold.

Installation

Install exhaust manifold assembly using new gaskets. Ensure manifold and head mating surfaces are free of nicks or other damage. To complete installation, reverse removal procedure.

CYLINDER HEAD

Removal

1) Turn crankshaft until No. 1 piston is at TDC on compression stroke. Remove alternator and bracket. If equipped, remove power steering pump and A/C compressor. Do not discharge systems. Secure components away from engine.

2) Remove exhaust and intake manifolds as previously described. Remove valve cover and gasket, water pump pulley and pump. On CA20, remove oil and water pumps. Note bolt lengths and locations for reassembly reference.

3) On all models, remove thermostat housing and distributor if necessary. Remove crankshaft pulley and damper. Remove upper and lower outer front dust cover mount bolts. Remove covers and gaskets.

4) Disconnect all hoses, cables and wires interfering with cylinder head removal. On CA20, remove fuel pump mount bolts, spacer and pump. On all models, mark timing belt rotation direction. Loosen timing belt tensioner and remove timing belt.

CAUTION: After timing belt is removed, do not rotate crankshaft or camshaft.

NOTE: On E15 & E16, there are 3 different lengths of cylinder head bolts. Note locations during removal for reassembly reference.

5) On E15 and E16, remove camshaft sprocket, upper inner cover mount bolts and cover. On all models, loosen head bolts gradually, in reverse order of tightening sequence. Remove cylinder head. *See Figs. 2 and 5.*

Inspection

1) Check cylinder head for cracks, flaws or damage. Replace as necessary. Inspect head and block mating surfaces for warpage. Warpage limit is .004" (.10 mm) or less.

2) If beyond limit, refinish surface. Maximum surface grinding limit of head and/or block is .008" (.20 mm). Replace head and/or block if machined or warped beyond service limit.

NOTE: Do not apply sealant to mating surfaces of cylinder block and head.

Installation (E15 & E16)

1) Thoroughly clean mating surfaces of cylinder head and block. Ensure No. 1 piston is at TDC on compression stroke. Install new cylinder head gasket on dowel pins. Install cylinder head assembly.

2) Check camshaft sprocket mark aligns with cylinder head inner cover mark and crankshaft sprocket mark aligns with cylinder block inner cover mark. *See Fig. 1.*

Fig. 1: E15 & E16 Timing Belt Alignment Procedure

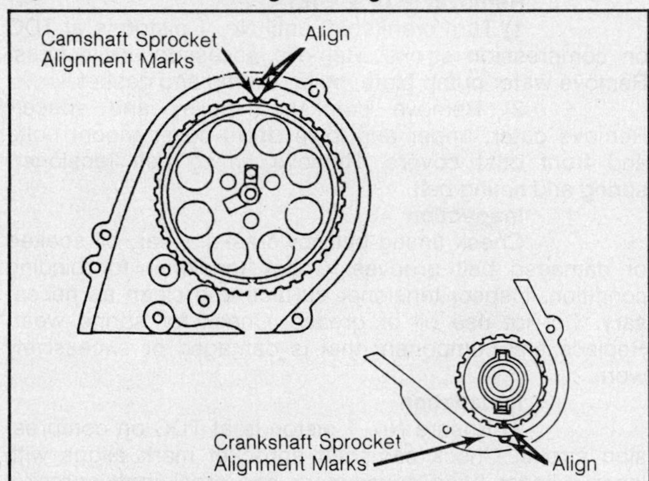
Camshaft Sprocket
Alignment Marks
Align
Crankshaft Sprocket
Alignment Marks
Align

Ensure camshaft and crankshaft timing marks align with the upper and lower inner cover timing marks.

3) Install cylinder head bolts in proper locations. Tighten bolts evenly, in sequence, in 3 steps. *See Fig. 2.* Rotate tensioner clockwise about 70-80° (7-8 cogs). Tighten lock nut. Place timing belt on sprockets.

NOTE: When installing used belt, mount with direction mark facing engine rotating direction.

4) Ensure timing belt is not loose around jack shaft and camshaft sprockets. Loosen tensioner lock nut so tensioner pushes on timing belt. Turn camshaft sprocket about 20° (2 cogs) clockwise.

5) Tighten lock nut while preventing tensioner from moving in "free" direction. Reverse removal procedure to install remaining components. Adjust valve clearance. After engine has run for several minutes, let it cool down and recheck head bolt torque.

Fig. 2: E15 & E16 Cylinder Head Tightening Sequence

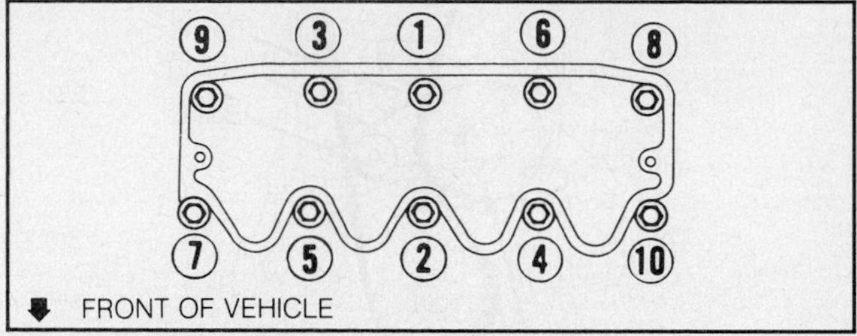
9
3
1
6
8
7
5
2
4
10
FRONT OF VEHICLE

Tighten head bolts evenly, in sequence, in 3 steps.

Installation (CA20)

1) Thoroughly clean head and block mating surfaces. Ensure No. 1 piston is at TDC on compression stroke. Install new cylinder head gasket on dowel pins. Install cylinder head.

2) Install cylinder head bolts. Temporarily tighten 2 center bolts to 14 ft. lbs. (20 N.m). Final tighten head bolts after installing timing belt and front cover.

3) To install distributor, align mark on distributor gear to mark on shaft. Then turn rotor shaft counterclockwise, on distributor cap side, about 15° and install.

4) After checking for proper bolt locations, install water and oil pumps. Install drive belt tensioner. Do not final tighten tensioner bolts before drive belt is installed.

5) Install timing belt plate and crankshaft sprocket with mating marks facing forward. Set timing belt on camshaft and crankshaft sprockets. Align belt mating mark to mating mark on each sprocket. *See Fig. 3.*

Fig. 3: CA20 Timing Belt Alignment Procedure

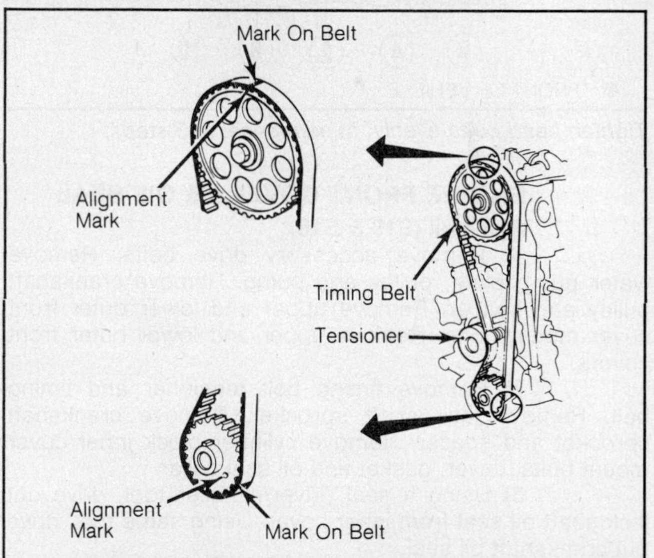
Mark On Belt
Alignment
Mark
Timing Belt
Tensioner
Alignment
Mark
Mark On Belt

Align timing marks on belt with timing marks on sprockets.

6) Tighten belt tensioner and assemble spring. To set spring, hook one end on bolt "B" side. Hook the other end on tensioner bracket pawl. Tighten bolt "B" and then bolt "A". Belt tension will automatically be at the specified value. *See Fig. 4.*

PULSAR, SENTRA & STANZA 4-CYLINDER (Cont.)

Fig. 4: CA20 Timing Belt Tightening Procedure

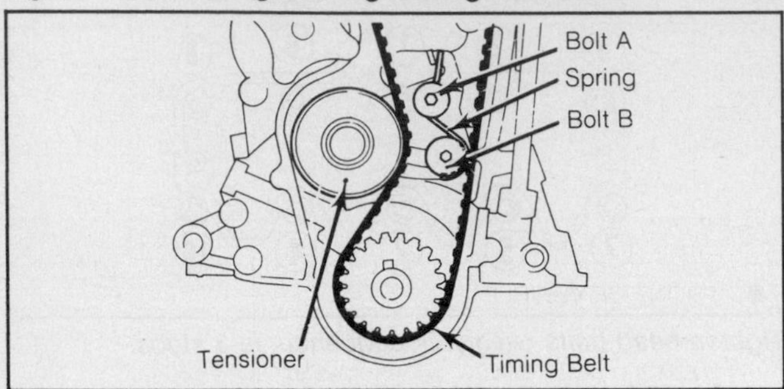
Bolt A
Spring
Bolt B
Tensioner
Timing Belt

Tighten bolt "B" and then bolt "A" to set belt tension.

7) Install new crankshaft front oil seal in oil pump. Install upper and lower front covers with new gaskets. Tighten mount bolts. Install crankshaft plate, pulley damper and pulley.

8) Tighten cylinder head bolts evenly, in sequence, in 3 steps. *See Fig. 5*. To complete installation, reverse removal procedure. After engine has run for several minutes, let it cool down and recheck head bolt torque.

Fig. 5: CA20 Cylinder Head Tightening Sequence

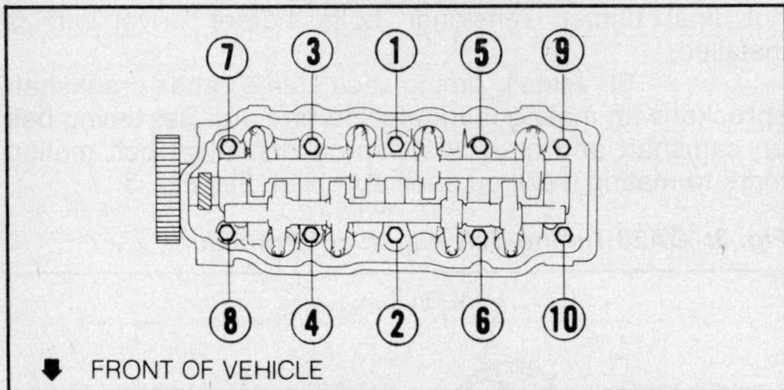
7
3
1
5
9
8
4
2
6
10
FRONT OF VEHICLE

Tighten head bolts evenly, in sequence, in 3 steps.

ENGINE FRONT COVERS & OIL SEAL

Removal (E15 & E16)

1) Remove accessory drive belts. Remove water pump plate, pulley and pump. Remove crankshaft pulley and spacer. Remove upper and lower outer front cover mount bolts. Remove upper and lower outer front covers.

2) Remove timing belt tensioner and timing belt. Remove jack shaft sprocket. Remove crankshaft sprocket and spacer. Remove cylinder block inner cover mount bolts, cover, gasket and oil seal collar.

3) Using a seal driver/installer tool, drive out jack shaft oil seal from inner cover. Using same tool, drive out crankshaft oil seal.

NOTE: Replace front cover seals whenever cylinder block cover is removed.

Installation

1) Lubricate new oil seal lips with oil. Using seal driver/installer tool, drive seals into position. Thoroughly clean mating surfaces. Apply sealer to both sides of cylinder block gasket.

2) Install oil seal collar. Install cylinder block inner cover and tighten mount bolts. Do not damage oil seal lips during installation. Reverse removal procedure to complete installation.

Removal (CA20)

1) Remove accessory drive belts. Drain engine oil. Remove oil pan, oil strainer and gaskets. If necessary, remove water pump. Remove crank pulley, damper and spacer.

2) Remove timing belt tensioner and timing belt. Remove crankshaft sprocket and spacer. Remove oil pump mount bolts and oil pump assembly. Drive out front oil seal from oil pump, using a seal driver/installer tool.

Installation

1) Lubricate new oil seal lip with engine oil. Using seal driver/installer tool, drive seal into position. Align oil pump and crankshaft locating notches and install oil pump assembly.

2) To complete installation, reverse removal procedure. When installing timing belt, ensure crankshaft and camshaft are in proper alignment. *See Timing Belt*.

CAMSHAFT

TIMING BELT

NOTE: After timing belt is removed, do not rotate crankshaft and camshaft.

Removal (E15 & E16)

1) Turn crankshaft until No. 1 piston is at TDC on compression stroke. Remove accessory drive belts. Remove water pump plate, pulley, pump and gasket.

2) Remove crankshaft pulley and spacer. Remove outer, upper and lower front cover mount bolts and front dust covers. Remove timing belt tensioner, spring and timing belt.

Inspection

Check timing belt for cracks, wear, oil soaked or damaged belt grooves. Check tensioner for binding condition. Inspect tensioner surface and clean as necessary. Do not use oil or grease. Check for spring wear. Replace any component that is damaged or excessively worn.

Installation

1) Ensure No. 1 piston is at TDC on compression stroke. Check camshaft sprocket mark aligns with inner cylinder head cover mark and crankshaft sprocket mark aligns with inner cylinder block cover mark. *See Fig. 1*.

2) Install tensioner and rotate clockwise about 70-80°. Tighten lock nut. Place timing belt on sprockets. When installing used belt, mount with direction mark facing engine rotating direction. Ensure belt is not loose around jack shaft and camshaft sprockets.

3) Loosen tensioner lock nut so tensioner pushes on timing belt. Turn camshaft sprocket about 20° (2 cogs) clockwise. Tighten nut while preventing tensioner from turning in "free" direction. To complete installation, reverse removal procedure.

Removal (CA20)

1) Turn crankshaft until No. 1 piston is at TDC on compression stroke. Remove accessory drive belts.

2) Remove upper and lower dust cover mount bolts. Remove upper and lower covers and gaskets. Remove timing belt tensioner, bracket and timing belt.

Installation

1) Do not final tighten tensioner bolts before drive belt is installed. Install timing belt. Align belt mark to camshaft and crankshaft sprocket marks. *See Fig. 3*.

PULSAR, SENTRA & STANZA 4-CYLINDER (Cont.)

2) Tighten belt tensioner and assemble spring. To set spring, hook one end on bolt "B" side. Hook the other end on tensioner bracket pawl. Tighten bolt "B" and then bolt "A". *See Fig. 4*.

3) Belt tension will automatically be at the specified value. Install lower front cover with gaskets and tighten mount bolts. Install plate and front pulley damper. Complete installation by reversing removal procedure.

CAMSHAFT

Removal

1) Turn crankshaft until No. 1 piston is at TDC on compression stroke. Remove accessory drive belts. Remove outer, upper and lower, front dust covers. Remove tensioner and timing belt. Remove valve cover and gasket.

2) On E15 and E16, remove thermostat housing and distributor. Remove camshaft sprocket and upper, inner cylinder head cover. Do not damage oil seal. Remove rocker shaft assembly. Keep all components in order.

3) On CA20, remove fuel pump, spacer, cylinder head rear plate, fuel pump drive cam and camshaft sprocket. Before rocker arm assembly removal, fully loosen rocker arm adjusting screws.

4) When removing rocker arm assembly, loosen mount bolts evenly, from the outside. Remove assembly. Keep all components in order. On all models, pull camshaft from cylinder head.

Inspection

1) Check camshaft, journals and cam lobe surface for bend, wear or damage. Check bend with camshaft in "V" blocks. Set dial indicator on center journal. Using total indicator reading, maximum bend limit is .002" (.05 mm) for E15 and E16. Bend limit is .004" (.10 mm) for CA20.

2) Check camshaft lobe height. Standard lobe heights of E15 and E16 engine are 1.4128-1.4226" (35.884-36.134 mm) for intake and 1.4031-1.4130" (35.640-35.890 mm) for exhaust.

3) Standard lobe height for CA20 engine is 1.5292-1.5309" (38.843-38.884 mm) for intake and exhaust. Maximum wear limit of cam lobe is .008" (.20 mm). Replace camshaft if beyond limits.

4) Check camshaft end play with dial indicator. Maximum end play is .016" (.40 mm) for E15 and E16. End play limit is .008" (.20 mm) for CA20. If beyond limit, replace camshaft and/or cylinder head.

5) Check camshaft journal and cylinder head bearing diameters. Standard journal-to-bearing clearance for CA20 is .002" (.05 mm). For E15 and E16, standard clearance is .0014-.0030" (.035-.076 mm) for journals No. 1, 3 and 5. For journals No. 2 and 4, clearance is .0031-.0047" (.078-.119 mm).

6) Standard inside diameter of camshaft bearings for E15 and E16 is 1.6535-1.6545" (42.000-42.025 mm). If camshaft journal or cylinder head bearing surface is worn to the point that bearing clearance is more than maximum limit, replace camshaft and/or cylinder head.

7) With camshaft sprocket installed, check tooth surface for flaws or excessive wear. Install dial indicator, with pointer mounted to flat surface of sprocket. Check for runout. Standard sprocket runout limit is .004" (.10 mm) or less. Replace sprocket if worn or beyond specification.

Installation

1) Coat camshaft with engine oil and carefully install into engine. Do not damage camshaft bearing surfaces during installation. Install rocker arm assembly.

2) Install upper, inner dust cover (if equipped), camshaft sprocket, tensioner, timing belt and related components. Install outer front covers. To complete installation, reverse removal procedures.

CAMSHAFT BEARINGS

Clearance Check

1) With camshaft removed, measure inside diameter of camshaft bearing surface of cylinder head with telescope hole gauge and outside diameter of camshaft journal with micrometer.

2) Camshaft bearing clearance limit is .004" (.10 mm) for CA20. Clearance limit for E15 and E16 is .006" (.15 mm) for journals No. 1, 3 and 5. For journals No. 2 and 4, limit is .008" (.20 mm).

3) If camshaft journals or bearing surfaces of head are worn beyond clearance limit, replace camshaft and/or cylinder head. Install camshaft as previously outlined.

JACK SHAFT & BEARINGS

Removal (E15 & E16)

1) With drive belts, crankshaft pulley, water pump and front covers removed, detach fuel pump and oil pump. Loosen tensioner. Remove timing belt and jack shaft sprocket.

2) Remove jack shaft locating plate mount bolt and plate. Take out jack shaft. Do not damage bearing surfaces during removal.

Inspection

1) With jack shaft removed, measure inside diameter of jack shaft bearing surfaces, in cylinder block, with inside dial gauge and outside diameter of jack shaft journals with micrometer.

2) Standard outside diameter of jack shaft journal is 1.2593-1.2598" (31.987-32.000 mm) for front and .1.1255-1.1260" (28.587-28.600 mm) for rear. Standard inside diameter of jack shaft bearing is 1.2606-1.2632" (32.020-32.085 mm) for front and 1.1268-1.1293" (28.620-28.685 mm) for rear.

3) Standard journal-to-bushing clearance is .0008-.0039" (.020-.098 mm). Clearance limit is .006" (.15 mm). Replace jack shaft bearings in cylinder block if clearances are beyond limit.

4) With jack shaft and locating plate installed, tighten locating plate mount bolt and check for excessive end play. Mount dial gauge with pointer set on end of jack shaft. Standard end play is .0018-.0041" (.045-.105 mm). If end play is beyond specification, replace locating plate, jack shaft and/or inner bearings.

5) Inspect jack shaft fuel pump cam lobe and oil pump drive gear for excessive wear or damage. Standard lobe height is 1.094-1.098" (27.80-27.90 mm). If lobe or gear is excessively worn, replace jack shaft.

Installation

1) Using bearing removal tool and proper adapters, remove jack shaft bearings. Pull front bearing out from front of block. Using long drift, push out rear freeze plug. Remove rear bearing from rear of engine.

2) Install front and rear jack shaft bearings using bearing installer tool. Ensure bearing oil holes are

PULSAR, SENTRA & STANZA 4-CYLINDER (Cont.)

aligned with cylinder block oil holes. Coat with sealant and install rear jack shaft freeze plug.

3) Coat with engine oil and install jack shaft. Install locating plate and tighten mount bolt. To complete installation, reverse removal procedure.

VALVES

VALVE ARRANGEMENT

Right Side – All Intake.
Left Side – All Exhaust.

VALVE

Check valve head and stem diameter and seat angle. Inspect valves for worn, damaged or deformed valve head or stem. If head is worn to .02" (.5 mm) in-margin thickness, replace valve. Valve stem end surface grinding limit is .008" (.20 mm).

ROCKER ARM & SHAFT ASSEMBLY

NOTE: To prevent rocker shaft springs from slipping out of rocker shafts, insert bracket bolts into end bolt holes.

Removal

1) Remove valve cover and gasket. Fully loosen valve adjusting screws to remove tension. Loosen rocker arm assembly mount bolts evenly, from outside-to-inside.

2) Remove rocker arm and shaft assembly together with mount bolts. On E15 and E16, remove rocker shaft springs, retainers, mount bolts and rocker arms. Keep components in order for reassembly reference. *See Fig. 6.*

Fig. 6: Removing E15 & E16 Rocker Arm and Shaft Assembly

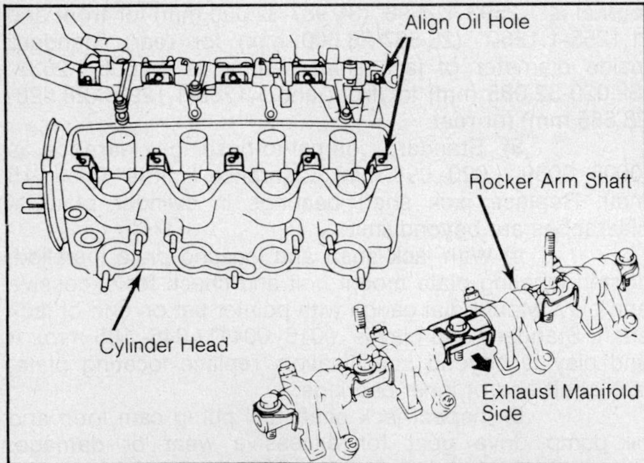
Align Oil Hole
Rocker Arm Shaft
Cylinder Head
Exhaust Manifold
Side

Loosen the rocker arm assembly mount bolts evenly, from outside to inside.

3) On CA20, remove rocker arm springs and shaft mount bolts. Slide rocker arms off rocker shafts. *See Fig. 7.*

Inspection

1) Thoroughly clean components. Inspect rocker arm bore and shaft surface for signs of wear or seizure. Check valve and camshaft end contact surface of rocker arm for excessive wear or scuffing.

2) If valve contact surface is worn, resurface with grinder. If camshaft contact surface is worn, replace rocker arm and/or camshaft.

3) Check clearance between rocker arm and rocker shaft. Standard shaft-to-arm clearance is .0003-.0019" (.007-.049 mm). If worn beyond specifications, replace rocker arm and/or shaft.

Installation

1) Apply oil to rocker shaft and rocker arm bore. On E15 and E16, ensure oil hole in rocker shaft faces down when shaft is installed. Check cutout in center retainer of shaft faces toward exhaust manifold.

2) On CA20, intake rocker shaft has identification mark (slit on front surface) but exhaust shaft does not. Both rocker shafts must be assembled with punched marks on front surface facing 12 o'clock position to identify oil hole direction. *See Fig. 7.*

Fig. 7: Installing CA20 Rocker Arm and Rocker Shaft Assembly

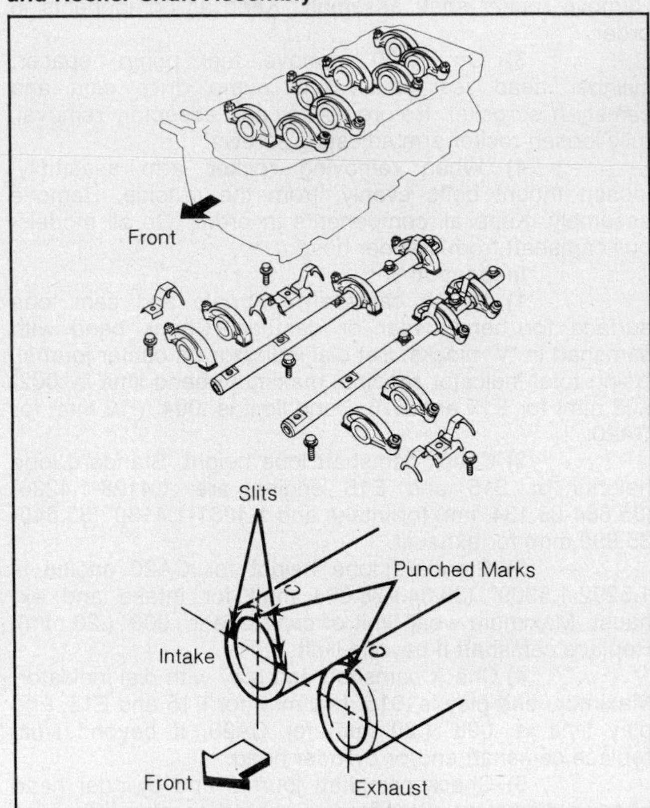
Front
Slits
Punched Marks
Intake
Front
Exhaust

Check the rocker arms for proper location and rocker arm shafts for proper installation position.

3) Reverse disassembly and removal procedures to assemble and install rocker arm assembly. Adjust valve clearance.

VALVE SPRINGS & SEALS

NOTE: Valve stem lip seals are used on all guides. Valve spring seat must be in position before installing seal.

Removal

1) With cylinder head removed, compress valve spring using valve spring compressor tool

PULSAR, SENTRA & STANZA 4-CYLINDER (Cont.)

(KV101072S0) for E15 and E16 and compressor tool (ST12070000) for CA20. *See Fig. 8.*

2) Remove valve keepers. Release spring compressor. Remove spring retainer, springs, oil seal and valve seat. If necessary, use valve lip seal puller tool (KV10107900) to remove oil seals.

Fig. 8: Valve Spring Removal & Replacement

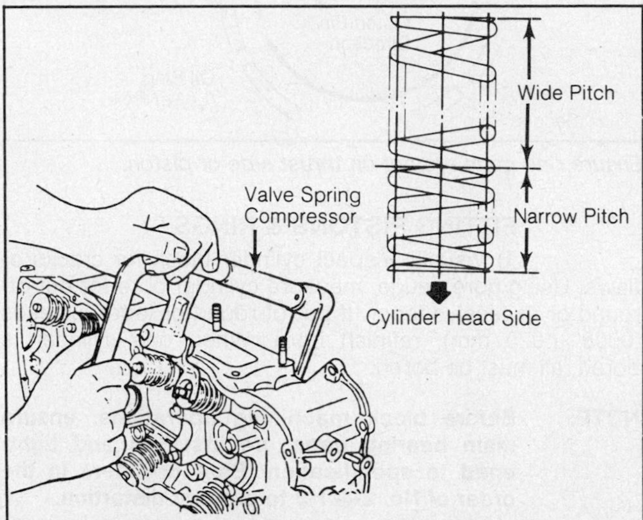
Wide Pitch
Valve Spring
Compressor
Narrow Pitch
Cylinder Head Side

Ensure the valve spring is installed with the narrow pitch side toward cylinder head.

Inspection

1) Check valve spring for squareness using a steel square and surface plate. For E15 and E16, valve spring out of square limit is .079" (2 mm).

2) On CA20, out of square limit is .087" (2.20 mm) on outer spring and .075" (1.90 mm) on inner spring. If out of square measurement is more than specification, replace valve spring.

3) Check valve spring free length and tension. If measurements are more than specified limits, replace valve spring.

Installation

1) Install valve spring seats. Install oil seals using valve lip seal drift tool (KV10107500). Lubricate valve stem end with oil and insert in guide carefully to avoid damaging lip seal.

2) Install valve spring (uneven pitch type) with narrow pitch side toward cylinder head. Using valve spring compressor, compress spring. Install retainer and keepers.

VALVE SPRING INSTALLED HEIGHT

Check valve spring by applying specified load and measuring spring height. If spring height or pressure do not meet specifications, replace spring. *See Valve Spring Specification Table.*

VALVE GUIDE SERVICING

Clearance Check

1) Measure clearance between valve stem and valve guide with micrometer and telescope hole gauge. Check diameter of valve stem at top, center and bottom.

2) Insert hole gauge in valve guide bore and measure at center. Subtract highest reading of valve stem diameter from valve guide bore to determine clearance.

3) Standard valve guide-to-valve stem clearance for E15 and E16 is .0008-.0020" (.020-.050 mm) for intake and .0018-.0030" (.045-.075 mm) for exhaust. Standard guide-to-stem clearance for CA20 is .0008-.0021" (.020-.053 mm) for intake and .0016-.0029" (.040-.073 mm) for exhaust.

4) Maximum guide-to-stem clearance is .004" (.10 mm) for all models. Insert valve into guide and move left and right, parallel with rocker arm. If tip moves .008" (.20 mm) or more, clearance is beyond maximum limit.

Replacement

1) If clearance is beyond limits and valve stem is not worn, the valve guide must be replaced. To replace guide, heat cylinder head to 300-400°F (150-200°C).

2) Using long drift, drive old guide out from combustion chamber side. With head at room temperature, ream cylinder head guide hole to fit new guide. Standard valve guide outside diameter is .4737-.4742" (12.033-12.044 mm) for E15 and E16. Outside diameter is .4340-.4344" (11.023-11.034 mm) for CA20.

3) Interference fit of guide in cylinder head guide hole is .0018-.0029" (.045-.074 mm) for E15 and E16. Interference fit is .0011-.0023" (.027-.059 mm) for CA20. Reheat cylinder head and install new guide.

4) Check guide projects above cylinder head surface .579-.602" (14.70-15.30 mm) for E15 and E16. Guide projection is .402-.409" (10.20-10.40 mm) for CA20. Use reamer to finish guide bore to .2756-.2764" (7.000-7.020 mm). Check and reface valve seat surface as necessary.

VALVE SEAT INSERTS

NOTE: Valve seat inserts are available in .5 mm oversize for service.

1) Check valves and valve seat inserts for contact. Standard seat contact for E15 and E16 intake insert is .059" (1.50 mm). For CA20 intake insert, contact is .071-.083" (1.80-2.10 mm).

2) Standard seat contact for E15 and E16 exhaust insert is .071" (1.80 mm). For CA20 exhaust insert, contact is .055-.071" (1.40-1.80 mm). Check valve seat inserts for pitting at valve contact surface.

3) Correct valve seat surface or replace if excessively worn. When replacing insert, ensure insert is recessed into head 1.6929-1.6935" (43.000-43.016 mm) for intake and 1.4567-1.4573" (37.000-37.016 mm) for exhaust insert.

4) Interference fit of insert is .0032-.0044" (.081-.113 mm) for intake and .0025-.0038" (.064-.096 mm) for exhaust. During installation, ensure insert fits squarely in bore and sets at bottom of recess.

VALVE CLEARANCE

E15 & E16

1) Warm engine to normal operating temperature. With air cleaner and valve cover removed, rotate crankshaft until No. 1 cylinder is at TDC on compression stroke.

NOTE: Valve clearance adjustment is made with engine warm but not running. For assembly purposes, with engine cold, adjust valves to .009" (.22 mm).

2) Loosen valve rocker adjusting screw lock nut and turn adjusting screw until specified clearance of .011" (.28 mm) is obtained. Adjust No. 1 Exhaust and Intake, No. 2 Intake and No. 3 Exhaust.

PULSAR, SENTRA & STANZA 4-CYLINDER (Cont.)

3) Rotate crankshaft and bring No. 4 cylinder to TDC on compression stroke. Adjust remaining valves as follows: No. 2 Exhaust, No. 3 Intake and No. 4 Intake and Exhaust. After adjustment, hold adjusting screw and tighten rocker arm lock nut. Recheck clearances.

CA20

1) With air cleaner and valve cover removed, rotate crankshaft until No. 1 cylinder is at TDC on compression stroke. Loosen valve rocker adjusting screw lock nut.

NOTE: **Valve clearance adjustment is made with engine warm but not running. For assembly purposes, with engine cold, adjust intake valves to .008" (.21 mm) and exhaust valves to .009" (.23 mm).**

2) Turn adjusting screw until specified clearance of .012" (.30 mm) is obtained. Adjust valves as follows: No. 1 Intake and Exhaust, No. 2 Intake and No. 3 Exhaust.

3) Rotate crankshaft until No. 4 cylinder is at TDC on compression stroke. Adjust remaining valves, No. 2 Exhaust, No. 3 Intake and No. 4 Intake and Exhaust. After adjustment, hold adjusting screw and tighten rocker arm lock nut. Recheck clearances.

PISTONS, PINS & RINGS

PISTON & ROD ASSEMBLY

Removal

1) With cylinder head and oil pan removed, remove connecting rod nuts. Remove rod cap with bearing half. Check top of cylinder bore for ridge. If scraper will not remove carbon build-up, remove using ridge reamer.

2) Push piston and rod assembly, with bearing half, out through top of block. Rod caps must be kept with their respective piston and rod assembly and are not interchangeable.

Inspection

1) Check connecting rod for bend or torsion using rod aligner tool. Bend and torsion limit is .004" (.10 mm) or less, in 3.94" (100 mm) of length.

2) Install rod, with bearings, on crank pin. Measure rod side thrust clearance. Play at big end must be .012" (.30 mm) or less. Replace rod if not to specifications.

NOTE: **If connecting rod is replaced, ensure weight difference between rods is no more than .25 oz. (7 grams).**

Installation

1) Oil the rings, piston and cylinder bore. Install piston and rod assembly. Ensure ring gaps are set 180° apart. Do not set on thrust side of piston or in line with piston pin. *See Fig. 9.* Ensure bearing halves are properly seated in rod and cap.

2) Install ring compressor. Install piston in cylinder with notch mark on piston top toward front of engine. With piston installed, ensure rod and bearings are seated against crankshaft journal.

3) Install rod caps to their respective piston and rod assembly. Oil jet of connecting rod should face right side of cylinder block. Install cylinder head and oil pan.

Fig. 9: Positioning Piston Ring End Gaps

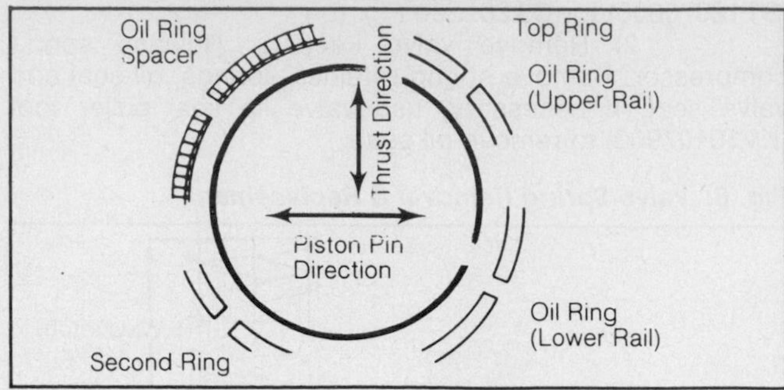
Oil Ring Spacer
Top Ring
Thrust Direction
Oil Ring (Upper Rail)
Piston Pin Direction
Oil Ring (Lower Rail)
Second Ring

Ensure ring gaps are not on thrust side of piston.

FITTING PISTONS & RINGS

1) Visually inspect cylinder block for cracks or flaws. Using bore gauge, measure cylinder bore for out-of-round or excessive taper. If out-of-round or taper exceeds .0008" (.020 mm), refinish bore. When one cylinder is bored, all must be bored.

NOTE: **Before block machining operations, ensure main bearing caps are installed and tightened to specification. Bore cylinders in the order of No. 2-4-1-3 to prevent distortion.**

2) Determine piston oversize according to amount of wear in cylinder (see specifications). By measuring piston at thrust face and adding mean of piston-to-cylinder clearance, finish hone of cylinder may be determined. Measure bore halfway down cylinder and 90° to crankshaft center line.

PISTON DIAMETER SPECIFICATIONS

Application	In. (mm)
E15 & E16	
Standard	2.9908-2.9928 (75.967-76.017)
.02 mm O/S	2.9916-2.9936 (75.987-76.037)
.50 mm O/S	3.0105-3.0125 (76.467-76.517)
CA20	
Standard	3.3254-3.3274 (84.465-84.515)
.5 mm O/S	3.3451-3.3470 (84.965-85.015)
1 mm O/S	3.3648-3.3667 (85.465-85.515)

3) After honing cylinder to final fit, measure piston-to-cylinder clearance using pull scale and feeler gauge. Extracting force to pull scale should be .44-3.31 lbs. (.2-1.5 kg) using .0016" (.040 mm) feeler gauge.

NOTE: **For E15 and E16, pistons and rings are available in .02 mm & .5 mm oversize. For CA20, pistons and rings are available in .5 mm & 1 mm oversize for service. Ensure piston and cylinder are at 68°F (20°C) when checking piston fit.**

4) If pistons are reused, decarbon ring grooves with scraper and curved steel wire or piece of broken ring. Clean oil slots in bottom land of oil ring groove. Check for scratches, wear or damage.

5) Measure piston ring end gap. For all models, end gap limit is .04" (1 mm). Replace rings, if beyond limit. Measure side clearance of rings in grooves as each ring is installed. For E15 and E16, side clearance limit is .008" (.20 mm).

6) Side clearance limit for CA20 is .004" (.10 mm), for all rings. If side clearance exceeds limits, replace piston and rings. When installing rings, ensure stamped mark on each ring faces up.

PISTON PIN REPLACEMENT

1) Piston pin is press fit into connecting rod and has sliding fit in piston. To remove, set piston and rod assembly in hydraulic press (KV101070S0 for CA20 and KV10107400 for E15 and E16). Press pin out of rod. Do not damage piston during removal.

2) Check pin and pin hole for signs of gauling or excessive wear. Using micrometer and telescope hole gauge, measure diameter of piston pin, piston pin hole and rod small end. Determine pin-to-piston and pin-to-rod clearance.

3) For E15 and E16, standard piston pin diameter is .7478-.7480" (18.995-19.000 mm). For CA20, standard pin diameter is .7872-.7874" (19.995-20.000 mm). Standard piston pin hole inside diameter for E15 and E16 is .7481-.7485" (19.003-19.012 mm). For CA20, standard pin hole inside diameter is .7875-.7879" (20.003-20.012 mm).

4) Check pin-to-piston clearance and pin-to-rod interference fit in specifications table. To assemble piston and rod, warm piston to room temperature. Lubricate with oil and insert pin into piston with finger pressure only. Hold piston and rod in proper alignment and press in pin. *See Fig. 10*. Assemble with oil hole of rod big end toward right side of block.

Fig. 10: Removing and Installing Piston Pin

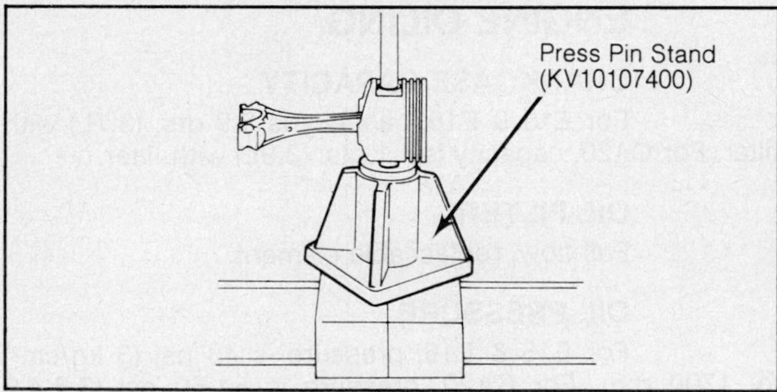

Press Pin Stand
(KV10107400)

Ensure piston and pin are in proper alignment when the pin is pressed into the connecting rod.

CRANKSHAFT & MAIN & CONNECTING ROD BEARINGS

CRANKSHAFT

Removal

1) With engine removed from vehicle, remove cylinder head assembly and oil pan. Remove connecting rod cap nuts. Remove piston and connecting rod assemblies. Remove alternator and engine mount bracket.

2) On E15 and E16, remove water pump and pulley. On all models, remove crankshaft pulley, timing belt covers, belt tensioner, timing belt and crankshaft sprocket. On CA20, remove oil pump and front oil seal.

3) On E15 and E16, remove front inner cylinder block cover and front oil seal. On all models, remove clutch assembly, flywheel and rear plate. Loosen main bearing cap bolts, in 2 steps, and then remove caps. Remove rear oil seal retainer assembly. Carefully lift out crankshaft.

NOTE: **Keep main bearing caps in order for reassembly reference. Check all main and connecting rod bearings, using Plastigage method.**

Inspection

1) Thoroughly clean and inspect crankshaft. Blow out oil passages with compressed air. Check crankshaft journals and crankpins for scoring, wear, cracks, taper and out of round. Standard taper and out of round limit is .0004" (.010 mm) or less. Maximum taper and out-of-round is .0012" (.030 mm).

2) Check crankshaft for bend by placing on "V" blocks. Use dial indicator at center journal of crankshaft. Standard bend is .0010" (.025 mm) or less for CA20 and .002" (.05 mm) or less for E15 and E16. If bend exceeds .002" (.05 mm) for CA20 or .004" (1 mm) for E15 and E16, replace crankshaft.

3) Check crankshaft pilot bushing for wear or damage. If necessary, pull bushing from crankshaft using pilot bushing puller tool (ST16610001) or equivalent. Clean bushing hole. Insert bushing to .16" (4 mm). Do not damage bushing edge or insert excessively.

4) Check flywheel friction surface for cracks, damage or wear. Measure friction surface runout using a dial indicator. Runout limit is .006" (.15 mm). Resurface or replace flywheel if not within limits. Check tooth surfaces of ring gear for flaws or wear. Replace ring gear if necessary.

Installation

1) Install main bearing halves into engine block. Ensure that all bearings are on correct journal. Journal No. 3 requires a thrust bearing. Upper and lower bearings are not interchangeable.

2) Apply oil to main bearing surface and install crankshaft. On E15 and E16, install main bearing caps so number on bearing cap faces toward water pump.

3) On CA20, install main bearing caps so numbers on bearing caps are in a row, starting from front of engine. Tighten main bearing caps in 2 or 3 steps, starting at center bearing and working outward. Ensure crankshaft rotates smoothly.

Fig. 11: Checking Crankshaft End Play

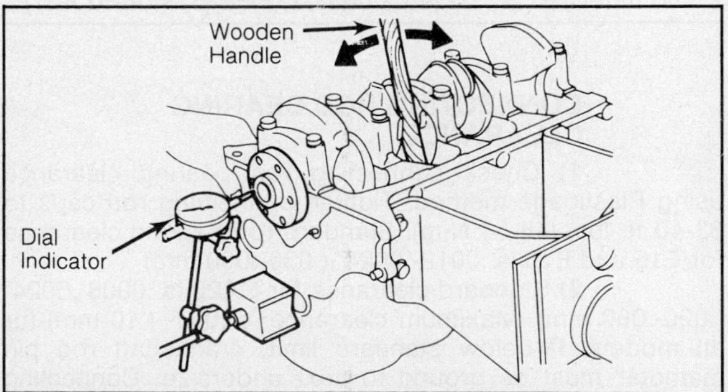

Wooden
Handle
Dial
Indicator

End play should be .002-.007" (.05-.18 mm).

PULSAR, SENTRA & STANZA 4-CYLINDER (Cont.)

4) Check crankshaft end play. *See Thrust Bearing Alignment*. Install rear oil seal retainer. Reverse removal procedure, to complete installation.

THRUST BEARING ALIGNMENT

Thrust bearing is installed on No. 3 main bearing journal. Check crankshaft end play by inserting a feeler gauge between flange of thrust bearing and crankshaft. Standard end play is .002-.007" (.05-.18 mm) and service limit is .012" (.30 mm) for all models. *See Fig. 11*.

NOTE: Plastigage should run parallel with crankshaft. Do not block oil hole or turn crankshaft with Plastigage inserted.

MAIN BEARING CLEARANCE

1) Check bearings for scoring or wear. Replace if damaged. Clean oil from crankshaft. Check clearance using Plastigage method. For E16, standard main bearing clearance for No. 1 and 5 is .0012-.0030" (.031-.076 mm). For No. 2, 3 and 4, standard clearance is .0012-.0036" (.031-.092 mm).

2) For E15, standard main bearing clearance for No. 1, 3 and 5 is .0019-.0030" (.047-.076 mm). For bearings No. 2 and 4, journal clearance is .0012-.0036" (.031-.092 mm).

3) For CA20, standard main bearing clearance is .0016-.0024" (.040-.060 mm) for all main bearings. Maximum clearance for all models is .004" (.10 mm). If below standard limit, crankshaft journal must be ground to next undersize. Main bearing journals may be ground to the undersizes indicated in table.

MAIN BEARING JOURNALS

Application	In. (mm)
E15 & E16	
Standard	1.9663-1.9671 (49.943-49.964)
.25 mm U/S	1.9567-1.9572 (49.701-49.714)
.50 mm U/S	1.9469-1.9474 (49.451-49.464)
.75 mm U/S	1.9370-1.9376 (49.201-49.214)
CA20	
Standard	2.0847-2.0852 (52.951-52.964)
.25 mm U/S	2.0732-2.0737 (52.658-52.671)
.50 mm U/S	2.0633-2.0638 (52.408-52.421)

CONNECTING ROD BEARING CLEARANCE

1) Check connecting rod bearing clearance using Plastigage method. Tighten connecting rod caps to 33-40 ft. lbs. (45-54 N.m). Standard rod bearing clearance for E15 and E16 is .0012-.0024" (.030-.060 mm).

2) Standard clearance for CA20 is .0008-.0024" (.020-.060 mm). Maximum clearance is .004" (.10 mm) for all models. If below standard limit, crankshaft rod pin diameter must be ground to next undersize. Connecting rod bearing pins may be ground to the undersizes indicated in table.

CONNECTING ROD JOURNALS

Application	In. (mm)
E15 & E16	
Standard	1.5730-1.5738 (39.954-39.974)
.08 mm U/S	1.5698-1.5706 (39.874-38.894)
.25 mm U/S	1.5631-1.5639 (39.704-39.724)
.50 mm U/S	1.5533-1.5541 (39.454-39.474)
.75 mm U/S	1.5435-1.5442 (39.204-39.224)
CA20	
Standard	1.7701-1.7706 (44.961-44.974)
.08 mm U/S	1.7657-1.7662 (44.848-44.861)
.25 mm U/S	1.7641-1.7646 (44.808-44.821)
.50 mm U/S	1.7590-1.7595 (44.678-44.691)
.75 mm U/S	1.7492-1.7497 (44.428-44.441)

REAR MAIN BEARING OIL SEAL

NOTE: When replacing front or rear oil seal, note seal mounting direction.

Removal

With engine removed from vehicle, remove clutch assembly. Remove flywheel and engine end plate. Remove oil pan and oil seal retainer assembly. Check oil seal mounting direction for reassembly reference. Drive out old seal from retainer, using a seal driver/installer tool.

Installation

Lubricate seal lips. Using seal driver/installer tool, drive seal into position. Install oil seal retainer. Reverse removal procedure, to complete installation.

ENGINE OILING

CRANKCASE CAPACITY

For E15 & E16, capacity is 3.9 qts. (3.7L) with filter. For CA20, capacity is 4.1 qts. (3.9L) with filter.

OIL FILTER

Full-flow, replaceable element.

OIL PRESSURE

For E15 & E16, pressure is 43 psi (3 kg/cm²) @ 1700 rpm. For CA20, pressure is 54-60 psi (3.8-4.2 kg/cm²)@ 2,000 rpm.

PRESSURE RELIEF VALVE

Non-adjustable, located in oil pump cover.

ENGINE OILING SYSTEM

E15 & E16

Pressure is provided to oiling system by a trochoid rotor type pump. Oil pump is mounted on side of crankcase and is driven by auxilary shaft. Oil pump feeds oil from pan to full flow oil filter.

Oil is then pumped into main oil gallery of crankcase where it is distributed to crankshaft journals, main bearing journals. From this point oil is fed to the camshaft journals and from center camshaft journal to rocker arm shaft to lubricate rocker arms and valves.

PULSAR, SENTRA & STANZA 4-CYLINDER (Cont.)

Cylinder walls and piston pins are lubricated by oil squirt hole in connecting rod. *See Fig. 12.*

Fig. 12: E15 & E16 Engine Oiling System

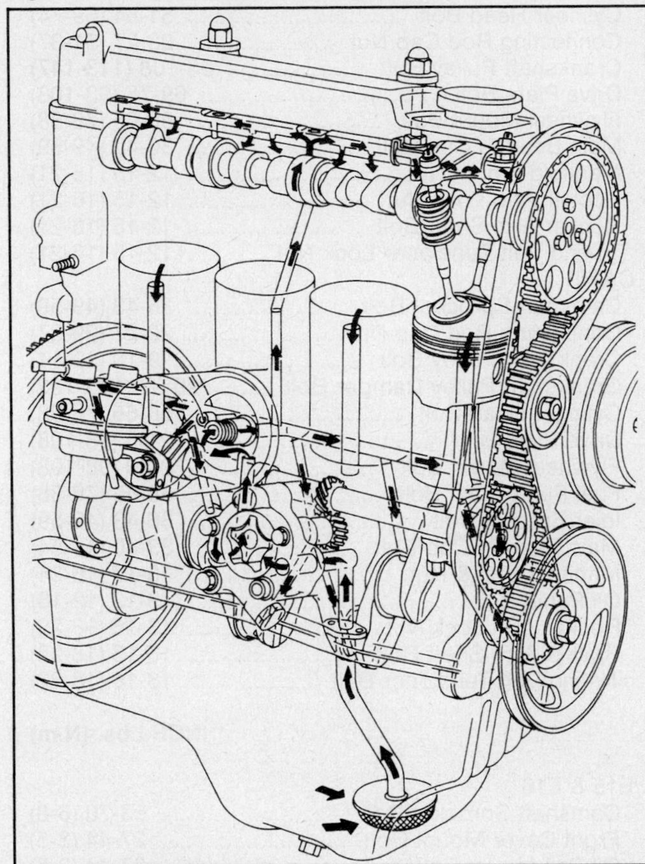

CA20

Pressure is provided to oiling system by a inner gear type pump. Oil pump is mounted on front of crankshaft, and is driven by crankshaft. Oil pump feeds oil from pan to full flow oil filter. Oil is then pumped into main oil gallery of crankcase where it is split into 2 circuits.

Oil is distributed to the main bearings and to the cylinder head oil gallery. From the main bearings oil is fed to connecting rods. Cylinder walls and piston pins are lubricated by oil squirt hole in connecting rod. From the cylinder head oil gallery oil is fed to the number 4 camshaft bracket, which feeds the camshaft, rocker shaft, and the rocker arm. *See Fig. 13.*

Fig. 13: CA20 Engine Oiling System

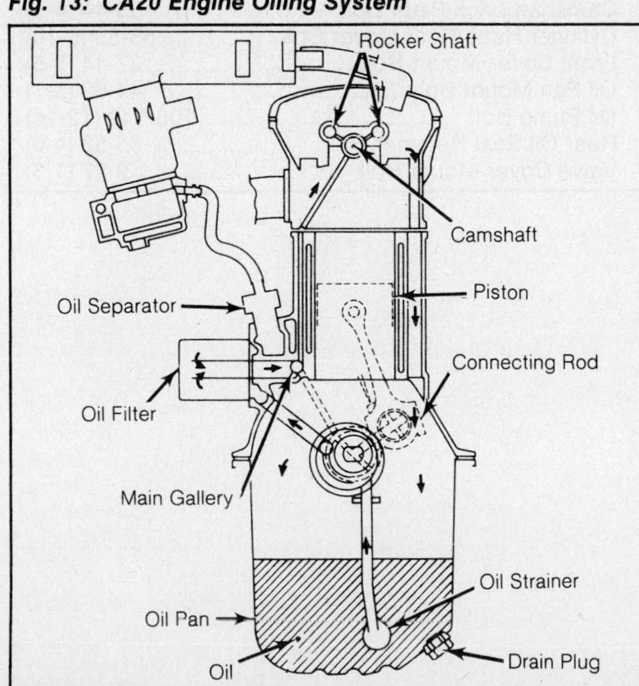
Rocker Shaft
Camshaft
Piston
Oil Separator
Connecting Rod
Oil Filter
Main Gallery
Oil Strainer
Oil Pan
Oil
Drain Plug

OIL PUMP

Removal (E15 & E16)

1) Place drain pan under oil pump assembly. Loosen alternator lower bolts. Remove alternator belt and adjusting bracket bolt. Set alternator aside to gain working clearance.

2) Disconnect oil pressure gauge harness. Remove pump mount bolts and oil pump assembly. Remove pump cover bolts and take out outer rotor. Remove regulator valve. Check all clearances using a feeler gauge. If beyond wear limit, replace entire pump assembly.

NOTE: Inner rotor and drive gear cannot be disassembled. If placed in vise, do not distort pump body and cover.

Inspection

Inspect pump body, cover and pump rotors for cracks and excessive wear. Check inner rotor shaft for looseness in pump body. Check oil pressure regulator valve sliding surface and valve spring. If damaged, replace valve set.

E15 & E16 OIL PUMP CLEARANCES

Application	[1] In. (mm)
Outer Rotor-to-Inner Rotor Tip Clearance	.0047 (.120)
Outer Rotor-to-Pump Body	.006-.008 (.15-.21)
Rotor-to-Straightedge	.002 (.05)
Pump Body-to-Straightedge	.0008 (.020)

[1] – Wear limits shown.

Installation

Apply oil to pump drive gear and shaft. Fill cavity with oil to prime oil pump and install cover with new gasket. Using new gasket, install oil pump assembly. To complete installation, reverse removal procedure.

Removal (CA20)

1) Drain engine oil. Remove oil pan and oil strainer. Remove water pump belt, crankshaft pulley and damper. Remove timing belt tensioner, timing belt and crankshaft sprocket.

NOTE: After timing belt is removed, do not rotate crankshaft and camshaft.

2) Remove oil pump mount bolts and oil pump assembly. Check all gear-to-cresent and gear-to-body clearances with a feeler gauge. Use a straightedge and feeler gauge to check end clearance of gears to housing and cover.

Inspection

Inspect pump body, cover and inner and outer gears for cracks and excessive wear. If beyond wear limit replace entire pump assembly. Check oil pressure regulator valve sliding surface and valve spring. If damaged, replace valve set.

CA20 OIL PUMP CLEARANCES

Application	[1] In. (mm)
Cresent Clearance	
to Outer Gear	.0083-.0126 (.210-.320)
to Inner Gear	.0047-.0091 (.120-.230)
Inner & Outer Gear	
to Housing End Clearance	.002-.004 (.05-.10)
Pump Body Bore	
to Outer Gear Clearance	.004-.008 (.11-.20)

[1] – Wear limits shown.

Installation

1) When installing timing belt, ensure crankshaft and camshaft are in proper positions and locating marks on belt and sprockets align. Apply sealant to outside diameter of oil seal before installation.

2) After installing new oil seal, align locating notches of oil pump and crankshaft and install oil pump assembly. To complete installation, reverse removal procedure.

ENGINE COOLING

COOLING SYSTEM CAPACITY

For E15 & E16 (with heater), capacity is 5 qts. (4.7 L) for manual transmission and 5.6 qts. (5.2L) with automatic transmission.

For CA20 (with heater), the capacity is 7.1 qts. (6.7 L) for manual transmission and 7.5 qts. (7.1L) for automatic transmission.

THERMOSTAT

Opens at 180°F (82°C).

RADIATOR CAP

For all models, the radiator cap pressure is 13 psi. (.9 kg/cm²).

WATER PUMP

NOTE: The water pump cannot be disassembled, replace as a unit.

Removal

1) Drain coolant. On E15 and E16, remove power steering drive belt. Remove power steering pump (if equipped), do not drain oil. Remove alternator drive belt and alternator. Remove A/C compressor drive belt (if equipped).

2) On CA20, remove front cover mount bolts and front cover. On all models, remove water pump pulley. Remove water pump mount bolts, pump and gasket.

Inspection

Inspect water pump body and vane for rust and corrosion. Check pump bearing for excessive end play or rough operation. Replace water pump if any wear or damage is found.

Installation

To install, use new gasket and reverse removal procedure. Ensure gasket contact surfaces are clean.

TIGHTENING SPECIFICATIONS

Application	Ft. Lbs. (N.m)
E15 & E16	
Cylinder Head Bolt	51-54 (69-74)
Connecting Rod Cap Nut	23-27 (31-37)
Crankshaft Pulley Bolt	83-108 (113-147)
Drive Plate Bolt	69-76 (93-103)
Flywheel Mount Bolt	58-65 (78-88)
Main Bearing Cap Bolt	36-43 (49-59)
Manifold Mount Nut	12-15 (16-21)
Rocker Arm Lock Nut	12-15 (16-21)
Rocker Arm Shaft Bolt	12-15 (16-21)
Timing Belt Tensioner Lock Nut	12-15 (16-21)
CA20	
Camshaft Sprocket Bolt	36-43 (49-59)
Connecting Rod Cap Nut	22-27 (29-37)
Crankshaft Pulley Bolt	9-10 (12-14)
Crankshaft Pulley Damper Bolt	90-98 (123-132)
Cylinder Head Bolt	58-65 (78-88)
Drive Plate Bolt	72-80 (98-108)
Flywheel Mount Bolt	72-80 (98-108)
Fuel Pump Cam Bolt	58-65 (78-88)
Idler Bracket Bolt	36-43 (49-59)
Main Bearing Cap Bolt	33-40 (44-54)
Manifold Bolt & Nut	13-17 (18-24)
Oil Pump Bolt	9-12 (12-16)
Rocker Arm Lock Nut	13-16 (18-22)
Rocker Arm Shaft Bolt	13-16 (18-22)
Timing Belt Tensioner Bolt	13-16 (18-22)
	INCH Lbs. (N.m)
E15 & E16	
Camshaft Sprocket Bolt	53-70 (6-8)
Front Cover Mount Bolt	27-44 (3-5)
Oil Pan Mount Bolt	27-44 (3-5)
Oil Pump Mount Bolt & Nut	80-106 (9-12)
Water Pump Pulley Bolt	27-44 (3-5)
Valve Cover Mount Bolt	35-70 (4-8)
CA20	
Camshaft Lock Plate Bolt	35-44 (4-5)
Cylinder Head Rear Cover Bolt	53-89 (6-10)
Front Cover Mount Bolt	27-44 (3-5)
Oil Pan Mount Bolt	44-62 (5-7)
Oil Pump Bolt	106-142 (12-16)
Rear Oil Seal Retainer Bolt	35-53 (4-6)
Valve Cover Mount Bolt	9-27 (1-3)

Datsun/Nissan Engines

PULSAR, SENTRA & STANZA 4-CYLINDER (Cont.)

ENGINE SPECIFICATIONS

GENERAL SPECIFICATIONS

Year	DISPLACEMENT		Fuel System	HP@RPM	Torque Ft. Lbs.@RPM	Compr. Ratio	BORE		STROKE	
	Cu. In.	Liters					In.	mm	In.	mm
1983										
Sentra MPG Model	90.8	1.5	2-Bbl.	67 @ 5200	116 @ 3200	9.0:1	2.99	76.0	3.23	82.0
Pulsar & Sentra [1]	97.5	1.6	2-Bbl.	70 @ 5000	125 @ 2800	9.4:1	2.99	76.0	3.46	88.0
Stanza	120.4	2.0	2-Bbl.	88 @ 5200	112 @ 2800	8.5:1	3.33	84.5	3.46	88.0

[1] – Non-MPG model.

VALVES

Engine Size & Valve	Head Diam. In. (mm)	Face Angle	Seat Angle	Seat Width In. (mm)	Stem Diameter In. (mm)	Stem Clearance In. (mm)	Valve Lift In. (mm)
1.5L & 1.6L							
Intake	1.457 (37)	45.2°-45.7°	45°	.059 (1.50)	.2744-.2750 (6.970-6.985)	.0008-.0020 (.020-.050)	.....
Exhaust	1.181 (30)	45.2°-45.7°	45°	.071 (1.80)	.2734-.2740 (6.945-6.960)	.0018-.0030 (.045-.075)	.....
2.0L							
Intake.	1.575-1.583 (40)	45.5°	45°	.071-.083 (1.80-2.10)	.2742-.2748 (6.965-6.980)	.0008-.0021 (.020-.053)	.....
Exhaust.	1.378-1.386 (35)	45.5°	45°	.055-.071 (1.40-1.80)	.2734-.2740 (6.945-6.960)	.0016-.0029 (.040-.073)	.....

PISTONS, PINS, RINGS

Engine	PISTONS	PINS		RINGS		
	Clearance In. (mm)	Piston Fit In. (mm)	Rod Fit In. (mm)	Ring No.	End Gap In. (mm)	Side Clearance In. (mm)
1.5L & 1.6L	.0009-.0017 (.023-.043)	.0003-.0005 (.008-.012)	.0007-.0015 [1] (.017-.038)	1	.008-.014 (.20-.35)	.0016-.0029 (.040-.070)
				2	.006-.012 (.15-.30)	.0012-.0025 (.030-.063)
				Oil	.012-.035 (.30-.90)	.0020-.0057 (.050-.145)
2.0L	.0010-.0018 (.025-.045)	.0003-.0005 (.008-.012)	.0007-.0015 [1] (.017-.038)	1	.010-.016 (.25-.40)	.0016-.0029 (.040-.073)
				2	.006-.012 (.15-.30)	.0012-.0025 (.030-.063)
				Oil	.012-.035 (.30-.90)	.....

[1] – Interference fit.

CRANKSHAFT MAIN & CONNECTING ROD BEARINGS

Engine	MAIN BEARINGS				CONNECTING ROD BEARINGS		
	Journal Diam. In. (mm)	Clearance In. (mm)	Thrust Bearing	Crankshaft End Play In. (mm)	Journal Diam. In. (mm)	Clearance In. (mm)	Side Play In. (mm)
1.5L	1.9663-1.9671 (49.943-49.964)	.0019-.0030 [1] (.047-.076)	No. 3	.0020-.0071 (.050-.180)	1.5730-1.5738 (39.954-39.974)	.0012-.0024 (.030-.060)	.0040-.0146 (.100-.370)
1.6L	1.9663-1.9671 (49.943-49.964)	.0012-.0030 [2] (.031-.076)	No. 3	.0020-.0071 (.050-.180)	1.5730-1.5738 (39.954-39.974)	.0012-.0024 (.030-.060)	.0040-.0146 (.100-.370)
2.0L	2.0847-2.0852 (52.951-52.964)	.0016-.0024 (.040-.060)	No. 3	.0020-.0071 (.050-.180)	1.7701-1.7706 (44.961-44.974)	.0008-.0024 (.020-.060)	.008-.012 (.20-.30)

[1] – Main bearing clearance for No. 1, 3 and 5 shown, clearance for No. 2 and 4 is .0012-.0036" (.031-.092 mm).
[2] – Main bearing clearance for No. 1 and 5 shown, clearance for No. 2, 3 and 4 is .0012-.0036" (.031-.092 mm).

Datsun/Nissan Engines

PULSAR, SENTRA & STANZA 4-CYLINDER (Cont.)

ENGINE SPECIFICATIONS (Cont.)

CAMSHAFT

Engine	Journal Diam. In. (mm)	Clearance In. (mm)	Lobe Lift In. (mm)
1.5L & 1.6L			
No. 1, 3 & 5	1.6515-1.6522 (41.949-41.965)	.0014-.0030 (.035-.076)	[1]
No. 2 & 4	1.6498-1.6505 (41.906-41.922)	.0031-.0047 (.078-.119)	.....
2.0L	1.8085-1.8092 (45.935-45.955)	.004 [2] (.10)	[3]

[1] – Camshaft lobe height for 1.5L & 1.6L is 1.4128-1.4226" (35.884-36.134 mm) for intake and 1.4031-1.4130" (35.640-35.890 mm) for exhaust.

[2] – Maximum clearance shown.

[3] – Camshaft lobe height for 2.0L is 1.5292-1.5309" (38.843-38.884 mm) for intake and exhaust.

VALVE SPRINGS

Engine	Free Length In. (mm)	PRESSURE Lbs. @ In. (Kg @ mm)	
		Valve Closed	Valve Open
1.5L & 1.6L	1.839 (46.70)	52 @ 1.54 (23 @ 39.2)	.....
2.0L			
Outer	1.968 (49.98)	47 @ 1.58 (21 @ 40.0)	.....
Inner	1.736 (44.10)	24 @ 1.38 (11 @ 35.0)	.....

PICKUP 4-CYLINDER DIESEL

ENGINE CODING

ENGINE IDENTIFICATION

Engine type and serial numbers are located on the right front side and middle of the cylinder block, below mating surface with head. The overhead valve Diesel engine is identified by code number SD25.

ENGINE, MANIFOLDS & CYLINDER HEAD

ENGINE

NOTE: **Remove engine and transmission as a unit. Separate engine after removal.**

Removal

1) Disconnect battery. Mark hood, for reassembly reference and remove. Detach hoses and tubes from air cleaner and remove. Disconnect engine-to-chassis cables, hoses and wires. Remove A/C belt and compressor, if equipped. Do not discharge A/C system.

2) Remove power steering belt and pump, if equipped. Do not drain fluid. Remove reservoir tank. Remove transmission shift linkage. Detach rubber boot. Remove nut from shift lever. Remove lever. Drain cooling system. Remove hoses, shroud and radiator.

3) Raise and support vehicle. Drain transmission and crankcase. Remove undercover. Remove clutch slave cylinder. Disconnect speedometer cable and wires on transmission case. On automatic transmission, remove oil cooler lines. Remove parking brake cable from brake lever side.

4) Index mark rear drive shaft for reassembly reference and then remove. Plug end of transmission. Remove front exhaust pipe. On 4WD, remove front drive shaft. On all models, attach lifting hoist to engine. Raise enough to take weight off engine mounts.

5) On 4WD, suspend front differential carrier. Remove front and rear carrier mount bolts and lower carrier. On all models, remove front and rear engine mount bolts. Turn steering all the way left or right so suspension center link clears oil pan. Pull engine forward and lift assembly up and out.

Installation

1) Replace any rubber engine mounts showing signs of deterioration or separation. Ensure proper placement of all electrical connectors and engine mountings. Install rear engine support bracket-to-rear mount insulator first.

2) Adjust drive belts and accelerator control system. Bleed air from injector pump. Fill oils and coolant to proper levels. Reverse removal procedures to complete installation.

INTAKE & EXHAUST MANIFOLDS

Fuel intake is achieved through injection nozzle assembly mounted directly to cylinder head. Intake manifold is for air only. Remove, with venturi and air duct, as an assembly. Remove exhaust manifold with slinger, breather assembly and gasket. Always replace gasket during manifold installation.

CYLINDER HEAD

Removal

1) Disconnect battery. Drain cooling system. Remove hoses and ducts from air cleaner. Remove air cleaner. Remove drive belts, fan and crank pulley. Remove thermostat housing and water pump. Remove injection pump timer cover. Remove timer with puller tool (ST19530000), if necessary.

2) Remove front cover and vacuum tube assembly. Remove fuel tube assembly. Use 2 wrenches to prevent breakage or striped nuts. Remove injection nozzles, washers and related components. Plug nozzle holes to prevent entry of dust and dirt. Remove alternator and bracket.

3) Disconnect hoses, fuel and vacuum lines from intake manifold, cylinder head and block. Disconnect front exhaust pipe. Remove intake and exhaust manifold assemblies. Drain engine and gear oil. Remove oil filter. Use tool (KV11100300) if necessary. Remove injection rear bracket and oil pipe. Remove main and sub oil cooler assembly.

4) Remove oil filter bracket, injection pump assembly, diesel pump controller assembly, glow plugs, harness and oil cooler hose. Remove valve cover and rocker shaft assembly. Remove push rods. Keep in order for installation. Remove cylinder head bolts. Loosen in several steps, in reverse of tightening sequence. *See Fig. 1.* Remove cylinder head assembly.

Fig. 1: Cylinder Head Bolt Tightening Sequence

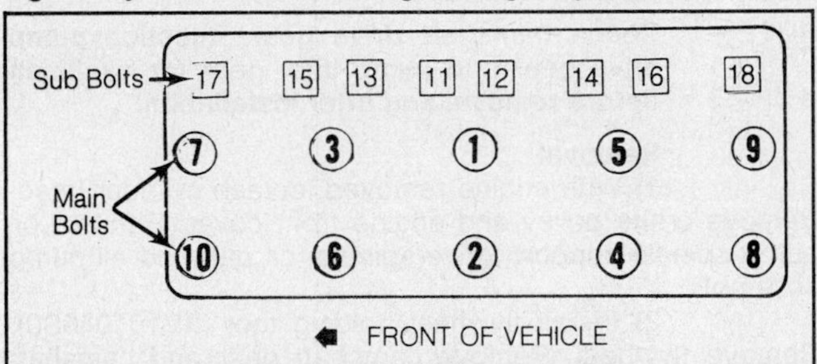
Sub Bolts
17
15
13
11
12
14
16
18
Main Bolts
7
3
1
5
9
10
6
2
4
8
FRONT OF VEHICLE

Remove bolts in the reverse order of tightening sequence.

Inspection

1) Inspect cylinder head, combustion chambers and block for cracks, flaws or melted areas. Replace as necessary. Inspect head and block mating surfaces for warpage, using straight edge and feeler gauge.

2) The head warpage limit is .008" (.20 mm). If beyond limit, correct with surface grinder. After machining operation, cylinder head height should be greater than 3.531" (89.70 mm) or head must be replaced.

3) Check block surface warpage with liners removed. If beyond limit, correct with surface grinder. Longitudinal warpage limit is .004" (.10 mm) or less. Transverse warpage limit is .0008" (.020 mm) or less. After grinding, block height (from upper face of block to crankshaft centerline) should be 10.54" (267.7 mm) or more or block must be replaced.

Installation

1) Clean mating surfaces of cylinder block and head. Install head and new gasket with new rubber "O" rings in water and oil passages. Do not use sealer. Ensure gasket is installed with TOP mark facing up. Insert head bolts. Tighten in sequence, in at least 2 steps. *See Fig. 1.*

2) Install push rods in original position. Twist rod to seat properly in lifter. Install rocker shaft. Tighten shaft bolts in 2 or 3 steps, start from center and work outward. To complete installation, reverse removal procedure.

PICKUP 4-CYLINDER DIESEL (Cont.)

3) After installation, fill oil and coolant to proper levels. Bleed fuel system. Adjust drive belt deflection, injection timing and idle speed. Fully loosen rocker arm adjusting screws. Adjust valves. After engine has run for several minutes, let it cool down and recheck cylinder head bolt torque.

CYLINDER HEAD COMBUSTION CHAMBER

NOTE: **Cylinder head combustion chamber does not normally require removal.**

Replacement

1) Check combustion chamber for cracks or other damage. Note amount of protrusion of chamber for reassembly reference. When removing combustion chamber, be sure cylinder head is not damaged. Using long drift, remove chamber from rocker shaft side.

2) To install combustion chamber, set chamber on ice for several minutes. Align combustion chamber knock pin with cylinder head notch. Drive chamber in, using soft faced hammer. Check amount of protrusion of combustion chamber.

CAMSHAFT

CAMSHAFT

NOTE: **Check camshaft drive gear, injection pump drive gear and pump idler gear for backlash before removal and after installation.**

Removal

1) With engine removed, detach cylinder head. Remove crank pulley and engine front cover. Remove oil pump spindle support, drive spindle, oil pan and oil pump assembly.

2) Install flywheel holding tool (KV101056S0). Remove flywheel. Remove camshaft gear and camshaft locating plate. With engine inverted on stand, carefully remove camshaft.

Inspection

1) Check camshaft journals and cam surface for bend, wear or damage. Check bend with camshaft in "V" blocks. Use a dial indicator with pointer set on center journal. Standard bend limit is .0012" (.030 mm). Maximum bend limit is .0024" (.060 mm). Replace camshaft if bend is greater than maximum limit.

2) Check camshaft lobe height. Standard lobe height is 1.4677-1.4693" (37.280-37.320 mm). Maximum wear limit of cam lobe is .02" (.5 mm). Minimum cam lobe height limit is 1.449" (36.80 mm). Replace camshaft if height is not within limits.

3) Check camshaft end play between locating plate and gear. Standard end play is .003-.011" (.08-.28 mm). Maximum end play is .02" (.5 mm) or less. If beyond limits, replace locating plate.

4) Inspect camshaft and injector pump drive gears and idler gear. If gear teeth and key are scratched or excessively worn, replace gear and/or key. Check gear train backlash using dial indicator. Standard backlash limit is .003-.008" (.07-.20 mm). Maximum limit is .012" (.30 mm). If beyond maximum limit, replace pump gears and/or idler gear as necessary.

5) Check camshaft front locating plate for warpage, using straight edge and feeler gauge. Warpage limit is .008" (.20 mm). If beyond limit, repair or replace front plate.

Installation

Apply oil to bushing surfaces. Install camshaft carefully to avoid damaging cam bushings. Install remaining components in reverse of removal procedure. Tighten all nuts and bolts.

CAMSHAFT BUSHINGS

Removal

With camshaft removed, remove rear camshaft plug from front of engine, using a long drift. Using camshaft bushing replacer tool set (ST16650000), remove camshaft bushings by pulling out through front of engine.

Inspection

Before removal, measure inner diameter of camshaft bearing and outer diameter of camshaft journal. Standard clearance is; .0009-.0040" (.024-.102 mm) for front bushing, .0015-.0045" (.037-.115 mm) for center bushing and .0009-.0040" (.024-.102 mm) for rear bushing. Clearance limit is .0059" (.150 mm) or less. If wear or damage is excessive, replace bushings.

Installation

Install bushings, using bushing replacer set, in reverse order of removal. Align cylinder block and bushing oil holes. Install bushings with beveled end facing front. Apply sealer to new rear plug. Install from the rear, with concave side out, using proper size adapter.

ENGINE FRONT COVER

Removal

To remove cover, follow camshaft removal procedures. Remove crankshaft pulley, using puller if necessary. Remove front cover mount bolts and cover.

Installation

Always use new gasket and oil seal when replacing front cover. Apply sealer to gasket. Reverse removal procedures to install.

GEAR TRAIN OIL JET

Removal & Installation

Drain coolant. Remove radiator shroud, hoses and radiator. Remove crankshaft pulley nut and pulley. Remove front cover. Remove oil jet. Ensure oil holes are not clogged. Clean with wire if necessary. Install in reverse order of removal. Ensure oil jet is installed with oil holes facing crank gear and crankshaft.

VALVES

VALVE ARRANGEMENT

E-I-I-E-E-I-I-E (Front-to-rear).

VALVES

Inspect valves for worn, damaged or deformed valve head or stem. If head is worn below .059" (1.50 mm) in-margin thickness, replace valve. Valve stem end surface grinding limit is .008" (.20 mm).

VALVE GUIDE SERVICE

1) Measure clearance between valve stem and valve guide with micrometer and telescope hole gauge. Check diameter of valve stem at top, center and bottom. Insert hole gauge in guide bore. Measure at center.

2) Maximum stem-to-guide clearance is .006" (.15 mm) or less for intake and .008" (.20 mm) or less for exhaust. If clearance is beyond limits and valve stem is not worn, replace guide.

PICKUP 4-CYLINDER DIESEL (Cont.)

3) To replace, heat head to 300-400°F (150-200°C). Using tool (ST110330000), drive guide out from combustion chamber side. With head at room temperature, ream valve guide hole to .481" (12.20 mm). Reheat head.

4) Install new guide into head until guide projects out .51" (13 mm). Using reamer (ST110320000), finish guide bore to .3150-.3156" (8.000-8.015 mm). Reface valve seat contact surface as needed.

VALVE SEAT INSERTS

1) Check valve seats for pitting or uneven wear at valve contact area. Reface seat if needed. Exhaust valve seats of .008" (.20 mm) and .016" (.40 mm) oversize are available.

2) To remove old inserts, use special seat removing tool (ST10830000). Place soft metal pads under tool, during seat removal, to prevent cylinder head damage. Remove old staking lugs on exhaust side.

3) Place new valve seats on ice for a few minutes to cool. Heat cylinder head to 175°F (80°C). Install valve seats on head with tool (ST10820000). Using a punch and hammer, secure new seat to head in at least 5 places. Ensure seat is punched in new part of head, not over previous marks. *See Fig. 2.*

Fig. 2: Installing Diesel Engine Valve Seat Inserts

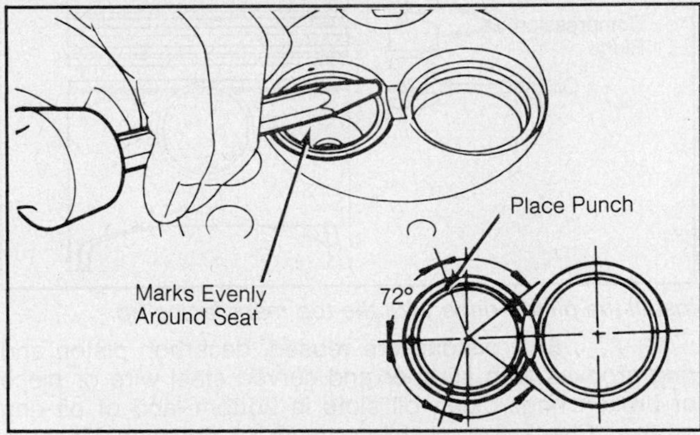
Place Punch
Marks Evenly
Around Seat
72°

Ensure inserts are staked in at least 5 places to locate seat.

VALVE LIFTERS & PUSH RODS

1) Remove valve lifters from cylinder block using lifter remover tool (ST12070000), if necessary. Check lifters for wear, scoring or damage on face and barrel. Replace if excessively worn. Lifter face must be smooth and convex. Check lifter and bore size and lifter-to-bore clearance.

2) Standard clearance is .0006-.0020" (.016-.052 mm). Clearance limit is .004" (.10 mm) or less. Standard lifter outside diameter is .4987-.4994" (12.666-12.684 mm). Standard lifter bore inside diameter is .5000-.5007" (12.700-12.718 mm).

3) Inspect push rod for excessive wear on contact face. Check for bend, using dial indicator. Maximum allowable bend is .02" (.5 mm) or less. Replace push rod if worn excessively or beyond bend limit.

VALVE SPRINGS & OIL SEALS

Removal

With head removed, remove glow plugs. Compress valves with tool (KV101092S0). Remove keepers. Remove compressing tool. Remove spring retainer, valve spring and valve spring seat. Remove valve seal, using remover tool (KV10107900), and discard. Keep components in correct order for installation.

Inspection

Check valve spring for squareness, using steel square and surface plate. Out-of-square limit is .051" (1.30 mm) or less. Check free length and spring tension. If beyond specifications, replace springs.

Installation

Install spring seats. Apply oil to valve stem and oil seal lip. Fit new oil seal onto each valve guide using installer tool (KV10107900). Install valve springs, retainers, keepers and rocker guides. Ensure valve spring is installed with closed coil side (painted Red) on cylinder head side.

VALVE SPRING INSTALLED HEIGHT

With valves closed, spring height should be 1.563" (39.70 mm). See specification chart for free length or pressure with valves open or closed.

VALVE ROCKER ASSEMBLY

1) Check valve rockers, brackets and rocker shafts for scoring, wear or distortion. Replace as necessary. Check clearance between valve rockers and rocker shaft.

2) Standard rocker-to-shaft clearance is .0008-.0020" (.020-.050 mm). Clearance limit is .0059" (.150 mm) or less. Standard shaft outside diameter is .7866-.7874" (19.98-20.00 mm). Standard rocker inside diameter is .7882-.7886" (20.020-20.030 mm). If clearance is exceeded, replace affected rockers and/or shaft.

3) Check rocker shaft bend, at center, using dial indicator. If bend is within limit, shaft may be straightened, if necessary. If bend is beyond limit, replace shaft. Standard bend, using total indicator reading, is .004" (.10 mm). Bend limit is .012" (.30 mm) or less.

VALVE-TO-CYLINDER HEAD SURFACE CLEARANCE

Measure the distance from cylinder head surface to intake and exhaust valves with a depth micrometer. Standard distance for intake valve is .0108-.0266" (.275-.675 mm). Standard distance for exhaust valve is .0120-.0274" (.305-.695 mm). Minimum distance limit for both valves is .0492" (1.250 mm) or less. If specified distance is exceeded, replace valve and/or valve seat.

VALVE CLEARANCE ADJUSTMENT

NOTE: **Valves should be adjusted with engine at normal operating temperature.**

Set No. 1 cylinder at TDC on compression stroke. Adjust clearances on No. 1 and No. 3 exhaust valves and No. 1 and No. 2 intake valves. Bring No. 4 cylinder to TDC on compression stroke. Adjust remaining valves. Clearance is .014" (.35 mm) on intake and exhaust valves.

PICKUP 4-CYLINDER DIESEL (Cont.)

PISTONS, PINS & RINGS

PISTON & ROD ASSEMBLY

Removal

1) With cylinder head, front cover and oil pan removed, detach connecting rod nuts. Remove rod cap with bearing half. Check top of cylinder bore for ridge. If scraper will not remove carbon build-up, remove with a ridge reamer.

2) Push piston and rod assembly, with bearing half, out through top of block. Keep rod caps with their respective piston and rod assemblies. Caps are not interchangeable.

Inspection

1) Check connecting rod for bend or torsion, using rod aligner tool. Bend and torsion limit is .002" (.05 mm) or less, in 3.94" (100 mm) of length.

2) Install rod, with bearings, on crank pin. Measure rod side thrust clearance. Play at rod big end must be .004-.008" (.10-.20 mm) or less. Replace rod and/or bearings if not to specifications.

Installation

1) Reassemble piston and rod assembly so combustion chamber on piston is opposite matching marks on connecting rod big end. *See Fig. 3.* If replacement rods are used (with no matching marks), install with .060" (.15 mm) offset of rod toward front of engine on cylinders No. 1 and 3, and toward rear of engine on cylinders No. 2 and 4.

Fig. 3: Piston and Connecting Rod Assembly Installation

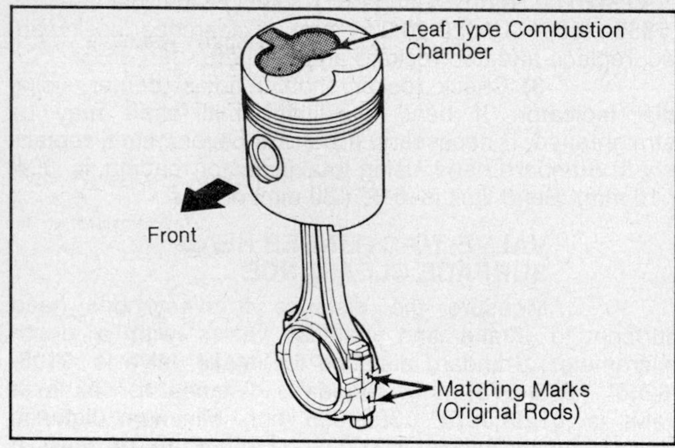
Leaf Type Combustion Chamber
Front
Matching Marks (Original Rods)

Ensure marks on rod and cap match and are on the opposite side of the piston combustion chamber.

2) To install piston and connecting rod assembly, apply oil to rings, piston and cylinder wall. Install piston assemblies on original journal with combustion chamber toward right side of cylinder block.

3) Ensure ring gaps are set approximately 180° apart. Do not set on thrust side of piston or in line with piston pin. Bearing halves must be properly seated in rod and cap. Install ring compressor. Compress rings. Install piston in cylinder.

4) With piston installed and rod and bearings seated against crankshaft journal, install rod caps to their respective piston and rod assembly. Install cylinder head and front cover. Install new gasket and oil pan. Tighten pan bolts evenly, in a criss-cross pattern. Do not over-tighten.

FITTING PISTONS & RINGS

1) Inspect cylinder block for cracks or flaws. Using bore gauge, measure cylinder for out-of-round or excessive taper. If cylinder bore out-of-round or taper exceeds .0008" (.020 mm), replace cylinder liner. Use liner remover/installer tool (KV111023S0) and adapter tool (KV11102320).

2) Check cylinder liner wear by measuring bore diameter. Standard liner bore is 3.5039-3.5053" (89.000-89.035 mm). Liner bore wear limit is .012" (.30 mm). Maximum liner bore diameter is 3.5059-3.5067" (89.050-89.070 mm). Replace liner as necessary.

3) Check amount of liner projection from each cylinder. Standard liner projection is .0008-.0035" (.020-.090 mm). There must be less than .002" (.05 mm) variation between cylinders.

4) Measure piston outside diameter at 2.76" (70 mm) from top of piston. Standard piston diameter is 3.5002-3.5018" (88.905-88.945 mm). Piston wear limit is .006" (.15 mm) or less. If clearance is beyond limit, replace piston. After honing cylinder to final fit, install piston.

5) Measure piston ring end gap and side clearance. Maximum end gap is .059" (1.50 mm). Replace rings as necessary. Install rings on pistons with end gaps 180° apart and so no end gap is in line with thrust face. Install rings with top mark facing upward. *See Fig. 4.*

Fig. 4: Installation Order of Piston Rings

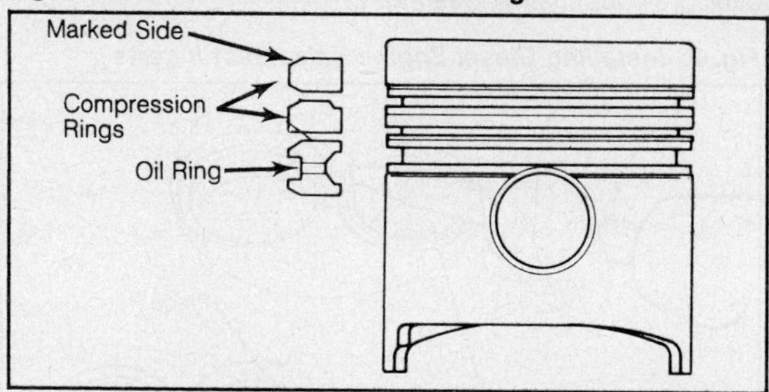
Marked Side
Compression Rings
Oil Ring

Install the piston rings with the top mark facing up.

6) If pistons are reused, decarbon piston and ring grooves with scraper and curved steel wire or piece of broken ring. Clean oil slots in bottom land of oil ring groove. Check for scratches, wear or damage. Measure side clearance of rings in grooves as each ring is installed.

7) Side clearance limit of top ring is .020" (.50 mm), or less. Clearance limit for 2nd ring is .012" (.30 mm), or less. For oil ring, clearance limit is .006" (.15 mm), or less. If side clearance exceeds limits, replace piston and/or rings.

PISTON PINS

1) Check pin, piston pin hole and rod small end bushing for signs of gauling or excessive wear. Using micrometer and telescope hole gauge, measure outside diameter of piston pin and inside diameter of rod bushing. Determine pin-to-rod bushing clearance.

2) Piston pin has an interference fit to piston. Interference fit between piston and pin should be -.0003-.0004" (-.007-.010 mm). Standard piston pin hole diameter is 1.0232-1.0236" (25.990-26.000 mm). Pin-to-rod clearance is .0010-.0018" (.025-.045 mm). If beyond limits, replace piston and pin.

3) To assemble, immerse piston and rod in oil bath at 175°F (80°C). Set pin on ice for several minutes. Ensure combustion chamber on piston top is opposite matching marks on rod and cap. Check rod offset for proper installation. Push in pin by hand. Remove assembly from oil. Install snap rings.

PICKUP 4-CYLINDER DIESEL (Cont.)

CONNECTING ROD SMALL END BUSHING

To replace rod small end bushing, drive out old bushing using piston pin press tool (ST13030001). Install new bushing using pin tool. Be sure to align oil holes. Drive pin bushing in until flush with end surface of rod. After installation, finish hone bushing inside diameter to specification. Standard rod bushing inside diameter is 1.0246-1.0251" (26.025-26.038 mm).

CRANKSHAFT & MAIN & CONNECTING ROD BEARINGS

CRANKSHAFT

Removal

1) With engine removed from vehicle, remove cylinder head and camshaft as previously outlined. Remove valve lifters. Keep components in correct order. Remove camshaft gear, using puller if necessary. Remove engine front plate.

2) Remove piston oil jet bolts, located on bottom side of engine between main bearing caps. Remove oil jets. Remove piston and rod assemblies. Remove rear oil seal assembly. Do not damage crankshaft sealing surface. Remove main bearing caps with bearings. Lift out crankshaft.

NOTE: Keep the main bearing caps in order for reassembly reference.

Inspection

1) Check bearing journals for scoring, excessive wear, cracks or plugged oil passages. Check crankshaft for taper and out-of-round using micrometer. Taper and out-of-round on all journals must be .0008" (.020 mm) or less.

2) Check crankshaft for bend by placing on "V" blocks. Use dial indicator at center journal of crankshaft. Standard bend is .0024" (.060 mm). Using total indicator reading, bend limit is .008" (.20 mm). If beyond limits, replace or regrind crankshaft.

3) If crankshaft is reground, refinish crank journal fillets to a .118" (3 mm) radius and crank pin fillets to a .138" (3.50 mm) radius. Do not attempt to cut counterweight of crankshaft.

4) Check crankshaft pilot bearing for wear or damage. Replace by pulling out bushing using pilot bushing puller tool (ST16610001). Clean bearing hole. Insert new bearing until distance between flange end and bearing is approximately .138" (3.50 mm) deep. Do not oil bushing or insert excessively.

5) Inspect piston oil jets. Blow through outlet of oil jet and be sure air comes out of inlet. Push cut-off valve of oil jet bolt with brass rod and ensure that cut-off valve moves smoothly with proper return.

Installation

1) Mount cylinder block on engine stand. Install front plate. Check front plate for warpage. Maximum warpage limit is .008" (.20 mm). Repair or replace plate if not within specification. Coat with oil. Install lifters and camshaft.

2) Install main bearing halves in block. Block side bearings have oil grooves and are not interchangeable with lower bearing halves. Apply oil to bearing surfaces, crank pins and journals. Install crankshaft. Install main bearing caps with "F" mark toward front of engine.

3) Coat seal-to-crankshaft contact area with grease. Install rear oil seal assembly. Apply sealer to rear main bearing cap at point where cap contacts block. Install cap by aligning marks on cylinder block and main cap.

4) Tighten main caps in several steps. Start at center and work outward. Ensure smooth crankshaft rotation. Install thrust washer at 4th journal from front, with oil groove facing away from cap. *See Fig. 5.*

Fig. 5: Thrust Washer Installation

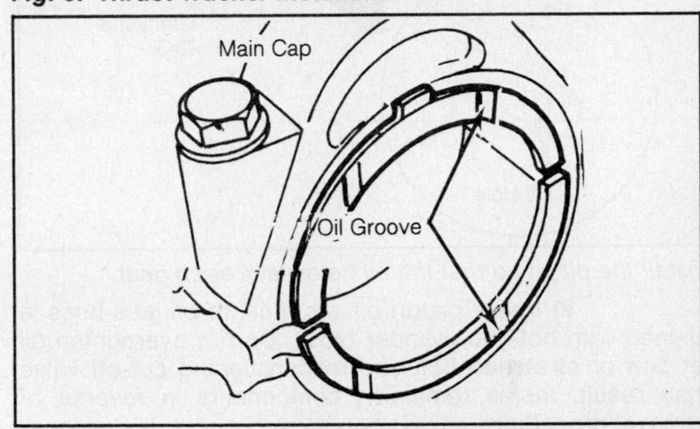
Main Cap
Oil Groove

Install thrust washer so that oil groove faces crankshaft.

5) Measure crankshaft end play. Standard end play is .0024-.0055" (.060-.140 mm). End play limit is .016" (.40 mm), or less. If not to specification, replace thrust washer. Thrust washers are available in .008" (.20 mm) and .016" (.40 mm) oversize.

6) Install piston and rod assemblies. Check rod side clearance. After clearance check, install oil pump. Measure piston top clearance. Set piston to TDC. Measure clearance between top of piston and cylinder block with dial indicator. Check clearance at front and rear of piston.

7) Standard piston top clearance is -.0106-+.0031" (-.27-+.08 mm). Clearance limit is -.016-+.012" (-.40-+.30 mm). Replace components as necessary to achieve proper clearances. Install crankshaft gear through key by aligning crank gear and camshaft gear matching marks. *See Fig. 6*. Measure gear backlash.

Fig. 6: Crankshaft Gear Installation

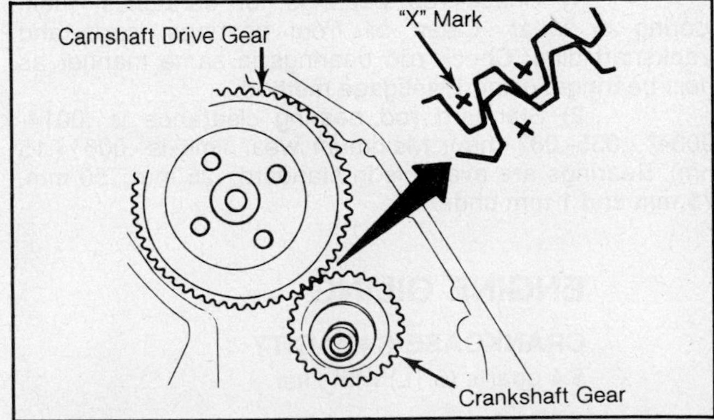
"X" Mark
Camshaft Drive Gear
Crankshaft Gear

Align the "X" mark on the crankshaft gear between the "X" marks on the camshaft gear.

8) Install gear train oil jet so that oil holes face each gear. *See Fig. 7*. Install rear end plate and flywheel.

PICKUP 4-CYLINDER DIESEL (Cont.)

Check flywheel runout using dial indicator. Maximum runout is .006" (.15 mm) or less. Replace or resurface flywheel as necessary.

Fig. 7: Gear Train Oil Jet Installation

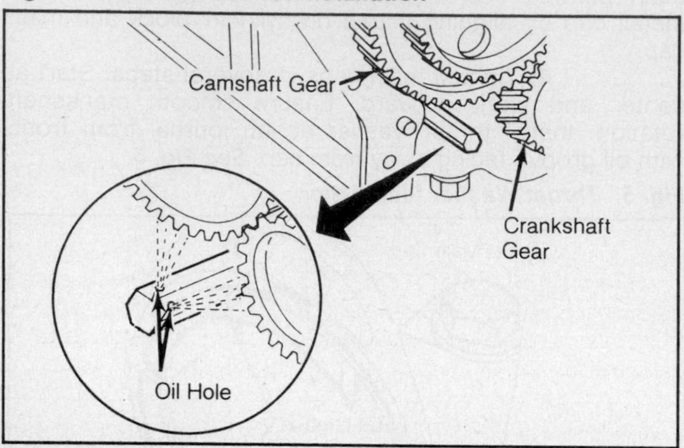

Camshaft Gear
Crankshaft Gear
Oil Hole

Install the oil jet so that the oil holes face each gear.

9) Install piston oil jets. Ensure oil jet's boss is aligned with hole on cylinder block. Do not overtighten oil jet bolt or stretched bolt and malfunctioning cut-off valve may result. Install remaining components in reverse of removal procedure.

NOTE: Gear backlash procedure is detailed in the Camshaft Inspection section.

MAIN BEARINGS

1) Check main bearings for scratches, melt, scoring or wear. Clean oil from bearings, caps and crankshaft journals. Check bearing clearance using Plastigage method. Replace bearings if damage is found or clearance is not to specification.

2) Standard main bearing clearance is .0014-.0037" (.035-.093 mm). Maximum bearing clearance limit is .0059" (.150 mm) or less. Bearings are available in standard, .25 mm, .50 mm and .75 mm undersize.

NOTE: Plastigage should run parallel with crankshaft. Do not block oil hole or turn crankshaft while Plastigage is inserted.

CONNECTING ROD BEARINGS

1) Check rod bearings for scratches, melt, scoring or wear. Clean oil from bearings, caps and crankshaft pins. Check rod bearings in same manner as main bearings, using Plastigage method.

2) Standard rod bearing clearance is .0014-.0034" (.035-.087 mm). Maximum wear limit is .006" (.15 mm). Bearings are available in standard, .25 mm, .50 mm, .75 mm and 1 mm undersize.

ENGINE OILING

CRANKCASE CAPACITY

5.4 quarts (5.1L) with filter.

OIL FILTER

Full-flow, disposable cartridge.

OIL PRESSURE

35-70 psi (2.5-5.0 kg/cm²).

ENGINE OILING SYSTEM

Oil drawn from pan passes through screen to oil pump and is delivered to oil filter, oil cooler and main oil gallery. Main oil gallery supplies oil to crankshaft main bearings and drilled passages in crankshaft.

Oil sprayed from oil jets lubricates drive gear assembly, cylinders and piston pins. Oil from main gallery lubricates injection pump, vacuum pump, camshaft and camshaft bearings. Valve rocker mechanism is lubricated through rocker shaft to rocker arms and down push rods to lifters.

OIL PUMP

Removal

1) Oil pump is located at bottom of engine, enclosed by oil pan. Pump is driven by helical gear on camshaft. Remove oil filter, oil pipe and oil cooler assembly.

2) Remove spindle support and oil pump drive spindle. Drain crankcase. Remove engine undercover and front suspension crossmember. Remove oil pan bolts. With steering wheel all the way right or left, remove pan. Remove oil pump assembly.

NOTE: Do not remove drive gear from drive shaft unless damaged.

Inspection

Disassemble oil pump. Clean parts thoroughly in solvent. Inspect for signs of excessive wear or damage. Check all clearances. Pump is serviced as an assembly only. Replace pump if any part is worn or damaged.

OIL PUMP CLEARANCE

Application	[1] In. (mm)
Gear Side Clearance (Gear to Bottom Cover)	.0059 (.150)
Gear Tooth Clearance (Tooth to Body)	.0098 (.250)
Gear Backlash	.020 (.50)
Shaft Ends to Bottom Cover	.020 (.50)

[1] – Wear limit specifications given.

Installation

Reverse removal procedure to install. Ensure drive spindle aligns properly with camshaft drive gear and drive shaft groove. Install support with new oil seal. Oil hole on support should face cylinder block.

ENGINE COOLING

THERMOSTAT

Thermostat starts to open at 180°F (82°C) and is fully open at 203°F (95°C).

RADIATOR CAP

13 psi (.9 kg/cm²).

COOLING SYSTEM CAPACITY

On 2WD model, capacity is 11.25 quarts (10.6L) with heater and 10.63 quarts (10.1L) without heater. On 4WD model, capacity is 11.38 quarts (10.7L) with heater and 10.75 quarts (10.2L) without heater.

Datsun/Nissan Engines

PICKUP 4-CYLINDER DIESEL (Cont.)

WATER PUMP

Removal

1) The water pump is a centrifugal type with an aluminum body. To remove, drain cooling system. Remove radiator shroud. Loosen fan belt and fan pulley nuts.

2) Loosen alternator upper and lower mount bolts and move alternator toward engine. Remove fan pulley with Tem-coupling and fan. Disconnect coolant hose to thermostat housing side. Loosen water pump mount bolts. Remove pump.

NOTE: The water pump and Tem-coupling cannot be disassembled. Replace as a unit. If excessive mechanical seal squeak occurs when engine is running, use water pump seal lubricant.

Inspection

Inspect pump body for rust and corrosion. Check pump bearing for excessive end play or rough operation. Check clearance between housing and vane. Standard clearance is .016-.039" (.40-1 mm). Check water pump fan coupling for oil leakage or bent bi-metallic component.

Installation

Reverse removal procedures to install. Always use new gaskets.

TIGHTENING SPECIFICATIONS

Application	Ft. Lbs. (N.m)
Camshaft Gear Bolt	33-36 (44-49)
Connecting Rod Cap Nut	49-52 (67-71)
Crankshaft Pulley Nut	217-239 (294-324)
Cylinder Head	
Sub Bolt	33-40 (44-54)
Main Bolt	87-94 (118-127)
Flywheel Bolt	108-123 (147-167)
Injection Pump (In-line) Nut	14-18 (20-25)
Injection Pump Timer Nut	43-51 (59-69)
Intake & Exhaust Manifold Bolt	11-13 (15-18)
Main Bearing Cap Nut	123-127 (167-172)
Oil Jet	22-29 (29-39)
Rocker Pivot Lock Nut	14-18 (20-25)
Rocker Shaft Bolt	14-18 (20-25)
	INCH Lbs. (N.m)
Front Cover	
6 mm Bolt	35-52 (4-6)
8 mm Bolt	84-108 (10-13)
Oil Cooler Mount Bolt	84-108 (10-13)
Oil Pump Mount Bolt	108-168 (13-19)

ENGINE SPECIFICATIONS

GENERAL SPECIFICATIONS

Year	DISPLACEMENT		Fuel System	HP@RPM	Torque Ft. Lbs.@RPM	Compr. Ratio	BORE		STROKE	
	Cu. In.	Liters					In.	mm	In.	mm
1983 Pickup	152	2.5L	Fuel Inj.	70 @ 4000	115 @ 2000	21.4:1	3.50	89	3.94	100

VALVES

Engine Size & Valve	Head Diam. In. (mm)	Face Angle	Seat Angle	Seat Width In. (mm)	Stem Diameter In. (mm)	Stem Clearance In. (mm)	Valve Lift In. (mm)
2.5L							
Intake	1.57 (40)	45.5°	45°	.....	.3138-.3144 (7.970-7.985)	.0006-.0018 (.015-.045)	.....
Exhaust	1.34 (34)	45.5°	45°	.....	.3128-.3134 (7.945-7.960)	.0016-.0028 (.040-.070)	.....

CRANKSHAFT MAIN & CONNECTING ROD BEARINGS

Engine	MAIN BEARINGS				CONNECTING ROD BEARINGS		
	Journal Diam. In. (mm)	Clearance In. (mm)	Thrust Bearing	Crankshaft End Play In. (mm)	Journal Diam. In. (mm)	Clearance In. (mm)	Side Play In. (mm)
2.5L	2.7916-2.7921 (70.907-70.920)	.0014-.0034 (.035-.087)	[1]	.002-.006 (.06-.14)	2.0832-2.0837 (52.913-52.926)	.0014-.0032 (.035-.087)	.004-.008 (.10-.20)

[1] – Utilizes thrust washer on No. 4 crank journal.

Datsun/Nissan Engines

PICKUP 4-CYLINDER DIESEL (Cont.)

ENGINE SPECIFICATIONS (Cont.)

PISTONS, PINS, RINGS

Engine	PISTONS	PINS		RINGS		
	Clearance In. (mm)	Piston Fit In. (mm)	Rod Fit In. (mm)	Ring No.	End Gap In. (mm)	Side Clearance In. (mm)
2.5L	.0031-.0041 (.080-.105)	-.0003-.0004 (.007-.010)	.0010-.0018 [1] (.025-.045)	No. 1	.0118-.0177 (.030-.045)	.0024-.0039 (.060-.100)
				No. 2	.0079-.0138 (.200-.350)	.0016-.0031 (.040-.080)
				Oil	.0005-.0118 (.150-.300)	.0008-.0024 (.020-.060)

[1] – Interference fit.

VALVE SPRINGS

Engine	Free Length In. (mm)	PRESSURE Lbs. @ In. (Kg @ mm)	
		Valve Closed	Valve Open
2.5L Outer & Inner	1.9823 (50.350)	1.563@73 (39.7@33)	1.224@148 (31.1@67)

CAMSHAFT

Engine	Journal Diam. In. (mm)	Clearance In. (mm)	Lobe Lift In. (mm)
2.5L			
Front	1.7887-1.7892 (45.434-45.447)	.0009-.0040 (.024-.102)	.....
Middle	1.7282-1.7287 (43.897-43.910)	.0015-.0045 (.037-.115)	.....
Rear	1.6228-1.6233 (41.218-41.231)	.0009-.0040 (.024-.102)	.....

VALVE TIMING

Engine	INTAKE		EXHAUST	
	Open (BTDC)	Close (ABDC)	Open (BBDC)	Close (ATDC)
2.5L	28°	67°	67°	28°

SENTRA 4-CYLINDER DIESEL

ENGINE CODING

ENGINE IDENTIFICATION

Engine serial number is located on the right front side of the cylinder block below mating surface with head. Overhead camshaft diesel engine is identified by code number CD17.

ENGINE, MANIFOLDS & CYLINDER HEAD

ENGINE

NOTE: Remove engine and transaxle as a unit. Separate engine after removal.

Removal

1) Remove battery. Mark hood for reassembly reference and remove. Remove hoses and tubes to air cleaner. Remove air cleaner. Remove accelerator cable. Remove vacuum and air hoses between engine and vehicle body.

2) Disconnect engine-to-chassis cables, hoses and wires. Remove A/C compressor and idler pulley, if equipped. Do not discharge A/C system. Remove power steering belt and pump, if equipped. Do not drain steering fluid. Drain coolant. Remove radiator and fan.

3) Raise and support vehicle. Detach front exhaust pipe from manifold. On manual transaxle, disconnect control rod link support rod from transaxle. On automatic transaxle, disconnect wire control cable from transaxle. Remove lower ball joints and discard retainer nuts.

4) Drain engine and transaxle oil. Disconnect left and right drive shafts from transaxle. Loosen strut head bolts. Remove drive shafts. Do not damage grease seal on transaxle side. Detach clutch cable. Remove speedometer cable with pinion from transaxle. Plug pinion gear hole to prevent fluid loss.

5) Detach accelerator cable. Disconnect fuel hoses from fuel pump. Attach engine sling to front and rear of cylinder head. Disconnect engine mounts. Lift engine/transaxle assembly up and away from vehicle. Separate engine from transaxle.

Installation

1) Replace any rubber engine mounts showing signs of deterioration or separation. Ensure proper placement of all engine mountings. Install engine, with transaxle, in vehicle. Tighten engine mount attaching bolts.

2) Ensure rubber insulator mounts have proper clearance between sides and center of mount. Automatic transaxle mount clearance is .59-.79" (15-20 mm). Manual transaxle mount clearance is .39-.59" (10-15 mm). To complete installation, reverse removal procedure.

INTAKE & EXHAUST MANIFOLDS

The manifold gasket is of a one-piece construction for intake and exhaust manifolds. The intake manifold is a single piece type with solenoid and EGR control valves mounted. Remove intake manifold and components as an assembly.

The exhaust manifold has a boss for EGR tube. Use care when removing EGR tube. Always replace manifold gasket whenever either manifold is removed. Tab at lower left corner of manifold gasket goes on front side of No. 1 cylinder.

CYLINDER HEAD

Removal

1) Disconnect battery. Drain cooling system. Detach water hose. Remove hoses and ducts from air cleaner. Remove air cleaner. Remove drive belts, fan and crank pulley. Remove thermostat housing and water pump. Remove injection pump and all injection tubes. Remove alternator and bracket.

NOTE: To prevent spill tube from breaking, remove it by gripping nozzle holder with wrench and removing retaining bolt using ratchet and socket.

2) Remove A/C compressor and power steering pump, if equipped. Do not discharge systems. Detach front exhaust pipe and accelerator cable. Remove intake and exhaust manifold assemblies. Remove valve cover assembly.

3) Remove front dust cover and related components. Set No. 1 cylinder at TDC on compression stroke. Remove valve timing belt on front camshaft pulley side. Remove camshaft pulley using puller tool (KV10109300). Remove rear outer cover and injection timing belt. Do not bend belts or rotate from removed position.

NOTE: When removing front inner cover, loosen tensioner to remove bolt at back of tensioner. After installing cover, set tensioner to free side (turn counterclockwise).

4) Remove injection pump pulley with puller tool (ST27180001), if necessary. Remove injection pump bracket and rear inner cover. Remove glow plugs. Loosen head bolts in sequence. Remove cylinder head assembly. *See Fig. 1.*

Inspection

1) Inspect cylinder head, combustion chambers and block for cracks, flaws or melted areas. Replace as necessary. Check cylinder head and block mating surfaces for warpage using straight edge and feeler gauge.

2) The cylinder head warpage limit is .004" (.10 mm) or less. If beyond limit, surface must be refinished. Maximum surface grinding limit of head and/or block is .004" (.10 mm). Replace head and/or block if machined or warped beyond service limit.

NOTE: If injection nozzle and gasket is removed for any reason, ensure new gasket is installed with round shoulder and deepest concave portion of gasket facing combustion chamber.

Installation

1) When replacing head gasket, ensure new gasket has the same identification mark as the old gasket.

Fig. 1: Cylinder Head Bolt Tightening Sequence

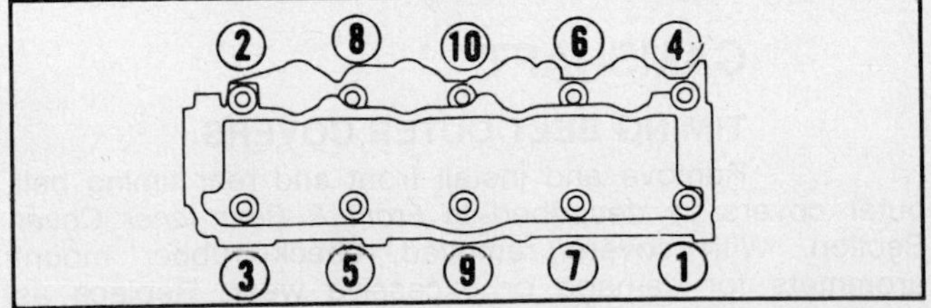

2
8
10
6
4
3
5
9
7
1

Remove bolts in the reverse order of tightening sequence.

SENTRA 4-CYLINDER DIESEL (Cont.)

If pistons, block, rods or crankshaft have been replaced, select new gasket using head gasket selection procedure.

2) To complete installation, reverse removal procedure. Tighten head bolts in at least 2 steps. *See Fig. 1.* Perform final engine adjustments. Bleed fuel system. After engine has run for several minutes, let it cool down and recheck cylinder head bolt torque.

CYLINDER HEAD GASKET

Selection Procedure

1) When pistons, rods, block or crankshaft are replaced, proper head gasket selection procedure must be followed. Clean cylinder block gasket surface. Install dial indicator on block surface and zero gauge. Measure and record length of piston projection at TDC for every cylinder.

2) Measure in three places, across highest point of piston top. Obtain average length of all piston projections. Select suitable gasket. Head gaskets have cutouts for identification purposes.

NOTE: **When maximum length of piston projection is .002" (.05 mm) larger than the average length of piston projections in each grade, use gasket which is 1 grade thicker to prevent piston-to-valve interference.**

CYLINDER HEAD GASKET SELECTION

Piston Projection In. (mm)	Gasket Thickness In. (mm)	Cutouts in Head Gasket
Below .0205 (.52)	.0453 (1.15)	1
.0205-.0224 (.52-.57)	.0472 (1.20)	2
Above .0224 (.57)	.0492 (1.25)	3

CYLINDER HEAD COMBUSTION CHAMBER

NOTE: **Cylinder head combustion chamber does not normally require removal.**

Replacement

1) Remove glow plug connecting plate and glow plugs. Check combustion chamber for cracks or other damage. Note amount of protrusion of chamber for reassembly reference.

2) When removing combustion chamber, be sure cylinder head is not damaged. Using long drift, remove chamber from rocker shaft side. Do not scratch inside of nozzle hole.

3) To install combustion chamber, set chamber on ice for several minutes. Align combustion chamber knock pin with cylinder head notch. Drive chamber in, using soft faced hammer. Check amount of protrusion of combustion chamber.

CAMSHAFT

TIMING BELT OUTER COVERS

Remove and install front and rear timing belt outer covers as described in *Front & Rear Inner Cover* Section. With covers removed, check rubber mount grommets for damage or excessive wear. Replace as necessary.

FRONT INNER COVER

Removal

1) Support engine with jack. Remove right side engine mount. Lift engine to gain working clearance. Set No. 1 cylinder at TDC on compression stroke. Remove drive belts, fan and crankshaft damper pulley.

2) Remove front upper and lower outer covers. Loosen tensioner pulley and set to "free" position. Remove idler pulley. Reference mark and remove valve timing belt, camshaft pulley and related components. Remove mount bolts, rubber grommets and front inner cover.

Installation

1) Inspect and replace damaged or worn rubber mount grommets. Install cover on block. Tighten mount bolts. Install water pump, if removed. Ensure reference marks on belt are at 39th cog.

2) Install crankshaft pulley plate with concave portion facing cylinder block. Align pulley and belt marks. Install pulley and belt. Adjust valve timing belt. Complete installation by reversing removal procedures.

REAR INNER COVER

Removal

1) Remove air cleaner housing with air duct. Set No. 1 cylinder at TDC on compression stroke. Remove rear dust cover. Set tensioner to "free" position. Reference mark belt and pulleys, if necessary. Remove timing belt.

2) Loosen pulley mount nuts. Remove injector timing pulleys, tensioner and related components. Remove mount bolts, rubber grommets and rear inner cover.

Installation

1) To complete installation, reverse removal procedure. Inspect and replace damaged or worn rubber mount grommets. Install water pipe and set pump support before installing rear inner cover.

2) Check injector timing belt, pulleys and related components are free of moisture and oil. Ensure reference marks on belt are at 23rd cog. Align pulley marks. Install pulleys and belt. Adjust timing belt to specification.

CAUTION: **During timing belt adjustment, do not turn crankshaft against normal rotating direction.**

NOTE: **Do not bend, twist or turn timing belt inside out. Check that belt and pulley cogs are free of cracks, burrs, dust, oil and water. Replace belts every 60,000 miles.**

VALVE TIMING BELT ADJUSTMENT

1) With outer dust covers, timing belt and related components removed, inspect belt, tensioners and pulleys for moisture or oil saturation, binding and excessive wear. Replace components as necessary before adjustment. Set No. 1 cylinder on TDC of compression stroke.

2) Ensure tensioner turns freely and spring wear is not excessive. Do not use oil or grease on tensioner. Turn tensioner counterclockwise to set in "free" position. Check that timing pulley and belt marks align. Ensure reference marks are 39 cogs apart.

3) Loosen tensioner mount bolt and give timing belt some tension. Tighten timing belt to specified tension by rotating crankshaft two turns clockwise. Tighten tensioner while holding it in position. Do not allow tensioner to move when tightening or timing belt tension will be too loose or overloaded, shortening service life.

SENTRA 4-CYLINDER DIESEL (Cont.)

INJECTION TIMING BELT ADJUSTMENT

1) With outer dust cover, timing belt and related components removed, inspect belt, tensioner and pulleys for moisture or oil saturation, binding and excessive wear. Replace components as necessary before adjustment. Set No. 1 cylinder at TDC of compression stroke.

2) Check that tensioner turns freely and spring wear is not excessive. Do not use oil or grease on tensioner. Turn tensioner clockwise to set in "free" position. Install belt if necessary. Check that timing pulley and belt marks align. Ensure reference marks are 23 cogs apart.

3) Loosen tensioner mount bolt and give belt some tension. Tighten belt to specified tension by rotating crankshaft two turns, in normal rotation direction. Tighten tensioner while holding it in position. Do not allow tensioner to move when tightening or timing belt tension will be too loose or overloaded, shortening service life.

CAMSHAFT

NOTE: Before and after camshaft removal, measure camshaft end play and camshaft pulley runout.

Removal

1) Disconnect battery. Drain cooling system. Remove air cleaner and related components. Remove belts, fan and crank pulley. Remove hoses, thermostat housing and water pump. Remove alternator.

2) If necessary, remove A/C compressor and power steering pump, if equipped. Do not discharge systems. Remove valve cover assembly. Remove front cover and related components. Set No. 1 cylinder at TDC on compression stroke.

3) Remove valve timing belt on front camshaft pulley side. Hold camshaft pulley with holder tool (KV10109300). Remove mount bolt and pulley. Remove rear outer dust cover, tensioner and injection timing belt. Do not bend belts or rotate from removed position.

4) Remove injection pump timing pulleys using puller tool (ST27180001). Remove injection pump bracket. Remove front and rear inner covers and related components. Remove cylinder head, if necessary.

5) Before removing cam, pry out oil seals. Do not damage cam seal surfaces during removal. Remove camshaft journal caps in the order shown and reference mark, if necessary. *See Fig. 2*. Remove camshaft.

Fig. 2: Camshaft Bearing Journal Bracket Cap Removal

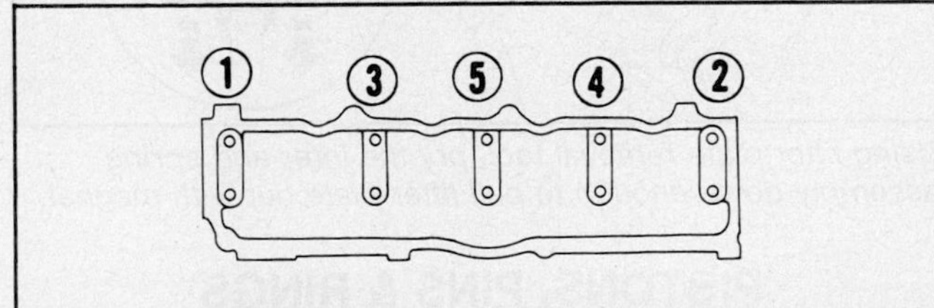

1
3
5
4
2

Install camshaft bracket caps in reverse order of removal.

Inspection

1) Check camshaft journals, cam lobe surfaces and journal caps for bend, wear or damage. Check bend with camshaft in "V" blocks. Use a dial indicator with pointer set on center journal. Standard bend limit is .0008" (.020 mm) or less. Maximum bend limit is .002" (.05 mm). Replace camshaft if bend is greater than maximum limit.

2) Check camshaft lobe height. Standard lobe height for intake is 1.7518-1.7520" (44.496-44.501 mm) and 1.7911-1.7913" (45.494-45.499 mm) for exhaust. Maximum wear limit of cam lobe is .0059" (.150 mm). Replace camshaft if height is not within limits.

3) Check camshaft end play and pulley runout using dial indicator. Maximum end play is .0067" (.170 mm). If beyond limits, replace camshaft and/or cam bearing journal caps. Check camshaft pulley runout. Maximum pulley runout is .004" (.10 mm). If not within limits, replace camshaft pulley.

NOTE: Before camshaft bearing clearance check, ensure journals, head and bearing caps are clean and free of oil. Do not turn camshaft during clearance check.

4) Check clearance at camshaft bearing journals using Plastigage method. Standard cam bearing clearance is .0008-.0024" (.020-.060 mm). Maximum clearance is .004" (.10 mm). If clearance exceeds limits, replace camshaft, bearing caps and/or cylinder head.

5) Inspect camshaft timing belt for fluid contamination, wear or damage. If oil or water soaked, cracked or worn on belt face, replace belt. Check tensioner pulley for wear, cracks or damage on cog face. Check tensioner for smooth rotation, clean surface and spring wear. Clean or replace components as necessary.

Installation

1) To install, reverse removal procedure. Be sure to use proper oil seals. Oil seals are of different diameters. Apply oil to cam seal surface and oil seal lip. Install front seal with arrow pointing clockwise and rear seal with arrow pointing counterclockwise.

2) After installation, check and adjust valve clearance. If out of specification, remove camshaft and replace lifter plate with plate of appropriate size. Ensure lifter rotates smoothly by hand.

VALVES

VALVE ARRANGEMENT

E-I-E-I-I-E-I-E (Front-to-rear).

VALVE

Check valve head diameter, stem diameter and seat angle. Inspect valves for worn, damaged or deformed valve head or stem. If head is worn to .02" (.5 mm) in-margin thickness, replace valve. Valve stem end surface grinding limit is .02" (.5 mm).

VALVE GUIDE SERVICING

Clearance Check

1) Measure clearance between valve stem and valve guide with micrometer and telescope hole gauge. Check diameter of valve stem at top, center and bottom. Insert hole gauge in guide bore. Measure at center.

2) Standard intake valve stem-to-guide clearance is .0008-.0021" (.020-.053 mm) and exhaust valve stem-to-guide clearance is .0016-.0029" (.040-.073 mm). Maximum stem-to-guide clearance is .004" (.10 mm).

3) Move valve left-to-right in guide. Maximum movement limit at valve tip is .008" (.20 mm), with tip 1.18" (30 mm) from head upper surface. Replace guide if worn beyond limits.

Replacement

1) If clearance is beyond limits and valve stem is not worn, replace guide. To replace, heat head to 302-

SENTRA 4-CYLINDER DIESEL (Cont.)

320°F (150-160°C). Using tool (ST110330000) or equivalent, drive guide out from combustion chamber side.

2) With head at room temperature, ream guide hole to .4321-.4329" (10.975-10.996 mm). Standard guide outside diameter is .4340-.4344" (11.023-11.034 mm). Interference fit of valve guide-to-head is .0011-.0023" (.027-.059 mm).

3) To install guide, reheat head. Drive in new guide until it projects out of head .39" (10 mm). Use reamer (ST110320000) to finish guide bore to .2756-.2763" (7.000-7.018 mm). Reface valve seat surface, as needed, after valve or guide repair or replacement.

VALVE SEAT INSERTS

Check valves and valve seat inserts for contact. Standard intake valve seat contact is .067" (1.70 mm) and exhaust seat contact is .071" (1.80 mm). Check valve seat inserts for pitting at valve contact surface. Correct valve seat surface or replace if excessively worn.

VALVE SPRINGS

Removal

1) With head removed, remove glow plug connecting plate and glow plugs. Remove camshaft pulleys, camshaft bracket caps, camshaft and oil seals. Take out valve lifters and lifter plates. If lifters are stuck in bore, remove using lifter puller tool (KV101089S0).

2) Compress valves with tool (KV101092S0). Remove keepers. Detach compressing tool. Remove spring retainer and valve spring. Remove oil seal, using valve lip seal removal and installer tool (KV10107900). Remove valve spring seat. Keep components in correct order for installation.

Inspection

1) Check valve spring for squareness using steel square and surface plate. Standard out of square limit is .083" (2.10 mm) for outer spring and .075" (1.90 mm) for inner spring.

2) Measure free length, tension and assembled height of each spring. If measurement is not within specifications, replace spring.

Installation

Install spring seats. Using installer tool, drive oil seal onto each valve guide. Install valve springs, retainers and keepers. Ensure valve spring is installed with small pitch side (painted Orange) facing down. Install camshaft, seals and bracket caps.

VALVE SPRING INSTALLED HEIGHT

Outer valve spring installed height is 1.555" (39.50 mm) and inner valve spring installed height is 1.417" (35.99 mm), with valve closed. Replace spring, if height is not to specifications.

VALVE LIFTER & LIFTER PLATE

Removal

With camshaft removed, take out lifter plate and lifter. Use lifter removal tool (KV101089S0), if necessary.

Inspection

1) Check valve lifter and lifter plate for scratches and excessive deformation. Remove valve spring assembly and measure inside diameter of lifter bore and outside diameter of lifter body.

2) Standard valve lifter outer diameter is 1.3763-1.3770" (34.959-34.975 mm). Standard lifter bore in head is 1.3775-1.3785" (34.988-34.013 mm).

3) Standard lifter-to-bore clearance is .0005-.0021" (.013-.054 mm). Maximum clearance is .004" (.10 mm). Replace lifter or plate if not to specification.

Installation

When installed, ensure lifter rotates smoothly by hand. Install lifter plate with thickness identification mark facing lifter body.

VALVE CLEARANCE ADJUSTMENT

NOTE: Lifter plates are available in 25 thicknesses, from .120-.165" (3.00-4.20 mm), in .002" (.05 mm) increments.

1) Do not adjust valves with engine running. Cold settings are shown to provide initial clearance after assembly. Warm engine to running temperature. Remove valve cover.

2) Rotate crankshaft so No. 1 cylinder is at TDC on compression stroke. Measure clearance between cam lobe and valve lifter plate on both No. 1 cylinder valves.

3) If clearance is not to specification, replace lifter plate using lifter plate removal tool (KV11102600) and magnet. *See Fig. 3.* Check and adjust valve clearances on remaining cylinders according to firing order.

VALVE CLEARANCE SPECIFICATIONS

Valve	Hot	Cold
Intake	.008-.012" (.20-.30 mm)	.007" (.18 mm)
Exhaust	.016-.020" (.40-.50 mm)	.016" (.40 mm)

Fig. 3: Adjusting Valve Lifter Clearance

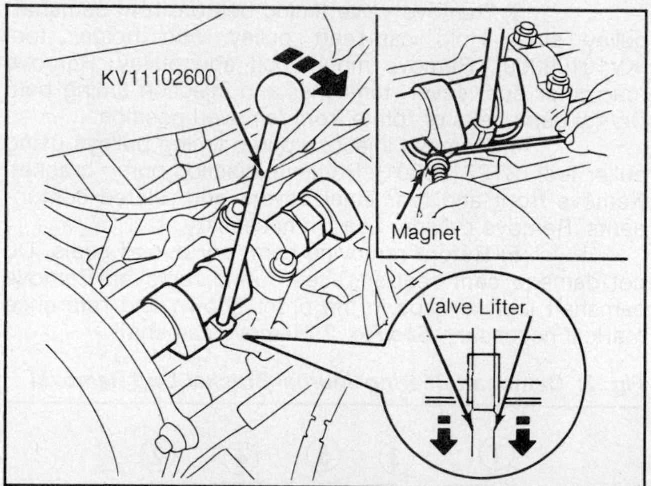
KV11102600
Magnet
Valve Lifter

Using lifter plate removal tool, pry the lifter and spring assembly down enough to pull lifter plate out with magnet.

PISTONS, PINS & RINGS

PISTON & ROD ASSEMBLY

Removal

1) With cylinder head, front and rear covers and oil pan removed, remove connecting rod nuts. Remove rod cap with bearing half. Check top of cylinder bore for ridge. If scraper will not remove carbon build-up, remove using ridge reamer.

SENTRA 4-CYLINDER DIESEL (Cont.)

2) Push piston and rod assembly, with bearing half, out through top of block. Keep rod caps with their respective piston and rod assemblies. Caps are not interchangeable.

Inspection

1) Check connecting rod for bend or torsion using rod aligner tool. Standard bend limit is .0059" (.150 mm) or less, in 3.94" (100 mm) of length. Standard torsion limit is .012" (.30 mm) or less.

2) Install rod, with bearings, on crank pin. Measure rod side thrust clearance. Play at rod big end must be less than .012" (.30 mm). Replace rod if not to specifications.

3) Inspect connecting rod small end bushing for signs of seizing or excessive wear. If necessary, press bushing from rod using press and suitable adapter. Coat new bushing with oil. Align oil holes in rod and bushing.

4) Press bushing into position. Finish grind inside diameter of pin bushing to .9459-.9464" (24.025-24.038 mm). Interference fit of piston pin-to-connecting rod small end bushing is .0010-.0017" (.025-.044 mm).

Installation

1) To install piston and connecting rod assembly, apply oil to rings, piston and cylinder wall. Ensure ring gaps are approximately 180° apart and not on thrust side of piston or in line with piston pin.

2) Bearing halves must be properly seated in rod and cap. Install ring compressor. Compress rings. Install piston in cylinder. Ensure grade mark stamped in top of piston is toward front of engine and oil hole on rod faces right side of block. *See Fig. 4*.

Fig. 4: Installing Piston & Rod Assembly

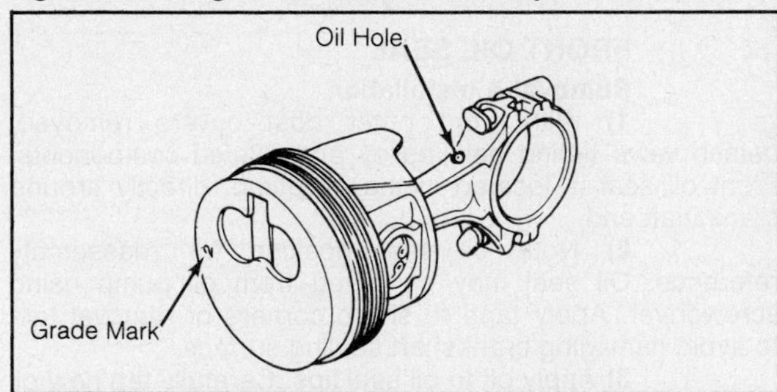
Oil Hole
Grade Mark

Ensure the grade mark on the piston top faces front and connecting rod oil hole faces right side of block.

3) With piston installed and rod and bearings seated against crankshaft journal, install rod caps to their respective piston and rod assembly. Install cylinder head and front and rear covers. Install new gasket and oil pan. Tighten pan bolts evenly, in a criss-cross pattern. Do not over-tighten.

FITTING PISTONS & RINGS

1) Inspect cylinder block for cracks or flaws. Using bore gauge, measure cylinder for out-of-round or excessive taper. If cylinder bore out-of-round or taper exceeds .0008" (.020 mm), refinish cylinder bore. When any one cylinder is bored, all cylinders must be bored.

NOTE: Before cylinder block machining operations, ensure main bearing caps are installed and tightened to specification. Bore cylinders in the order of No. 2-4-1-3 to prevent distortion.

2) Determine piston oversize according to amount of wear in cylinder. Standard piston diameter is 3.1472-3.1492" (79.940-79.990 mm). Standard cylinder bore diameter is 3.1496-3.1516" (80.000-80.050 mm). Bore wear limit is .008" (.20 mm). Measure piston diameter at thrust face. Add piston-to-cylinder clearance. Finish hone of cylinder may then be determined.

3) After honing cylinder to final fit, measure piston-to-cylinder clearance using pull scale and feeler gauge. With piston and cylinder at room temperature (70°F, 20°C), extracting force to pull scale should be 3.3-4.0 lbs. (1.5-1.8 kg) using .0020-.0028" (.050-.070 mm) feeler gauge.

4) If pistons are reused, decarbon piston and ring grooves with scraper and curved steel wire or piece of broken ring. Clean oil slots in bottom land of oil ring groove. Check for scratches, wear or damage. Measure the side clearance of rings in piston grooves as each ring is installed.

5) Maximum side clearance tolerance of top ring is .008" (.20 mm). Maximum clearance for 2nd ring is .0059" (.150 mm) and, for oil ring, clearance is .004" (.10 mm). If side clearance exceeds limits, replace piston and rings. Check ring end gap. Install ring squarely in cylinder, using piston.

6) Standard end gap is .039" (1 mm) for top ring, .028" (.70 mm) for second ring and .024" (.60 mm) for oil ring. When installing piston rings, ensure stamped mark on ring faces up. Install expander ring, behind oil ring. Align teflon tube and ring gap. *See Fig. 5*.

Fig. 5: Installing Piston Rings and Teflon Tube on Piston

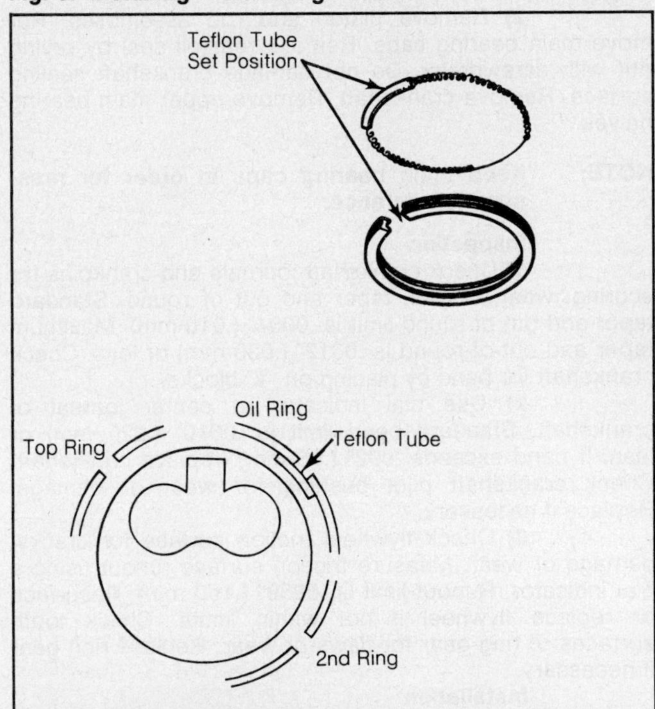
Teflon Tube
Set Position
Oil Ring
Top Ring
Teflon Tube
2nd Ring

Ensure that ring gaps are spaced properly and the expander coil joint is at opposite side of ring gap.

7) Replacement pistons are available in .5 mm and 1 mm oversize. When pistons are replaced, proper head gasket selection procedure must be done. *See CYLINDER HEAD GASKET SELECTION* Section.

PISTON PINS

1) To remove pin, first remove snap rings. Heat piston and rod assembly to about 150°F (65°C).

SENTRA 4-CYLINDER DIESEL (Cont.)

Drive out pin with drift. Do not damage piston during removal. Check pin and pin hole for signs of gauling or excessive wear.

2) Using micrometer and telescope hole gauge, measure diameter of piston pin and piston pin hole. Determine pin-to-piston clearance. Standard piston pin diameter is 23.994-24.000" (.9446-.9449 mm). Standard piston pin hole inside diameter is 23.991-23.999" (.94450.9448 mm). If wear exceeds .0002" (.004 mm), replace piston and pin.

3) To assemble piston and rod, heat piston to 150°F (65°C). Insert pin into piston while holding piston and rod in proper alignment. Assemble with oil hole in rod on same side as combustion chamber in piston top.

CRANKSHAFT & MAIN & CONNECTING ROD BEARINGS

CRANKSHAFT

Removal

1) With engine removed, remove outer parts, install engine attachment and mount assembly on work stand. Remove front and rear outer covers. Remove valve timing and injector timing belts. Remove injector pump pulley and pump. Remove front and rear inner covers. Install flywheel stopper (KV101056S0). Remove flywheel, oil pan, oil pump and cylinder head.

2) Remove piston and rod assemblies. Remove main bearing caps. Remove rear oil seal by prying out with screwdriver. Do not damage crankshaft sealing surface. Remove crankshaft. Remove upper main bearing halves.

NOTE: **Keep main bearing caps in order for reassembly reference.**

Inspection

1) Check crankshaft journals and crankpins for scoring, wear, cracks, taper and out of round. Standard taper and out of round limit is .0004" (.010 mm). Maximum taper and out-of-round is .0012" (.030 mm) or less. Check crankshaft for bend by placing on "V" blocks.

2) Use dial indicator at center journal of crankshaft. Standard bend limit is .0010" (.025 mm) or less. If bend exceeds .002" (.05 mm), replace crankshaft. Check crankshaft pilot bushing for wear or damage. Replace if necessary.

3) Check flywheel friction surface for cracks, damage or wear. Measure friction surface runout using a dial indicator. Runout limit is .0059" (.150 mm). Resurface or replace flywheel if not within limits. Check tooth surfaces of ring gear for flaws or wear. Replace ring gear if necessary.

Installation

1) Install main bearing halves in engine block. Ensure bearings are on correct journal. Upper bearing halves have oil hole and oil groove. Lower bearing halves do not. Do not interchange.

2) Apply oil to main bearing surfaces. Install crankshaft. Apply sealant to each side of rear main bearing cap and corners of cylinder block contact point. Install bearing caps so arrow faces front of engine.

3) Shift crankshaft toward front of engine. Tighten main bearing caps in 2 or 3 steps, starting at center bearing and working outward. Ensure crankshaft rotates smoothly. Check crankshaft end play. End play must be less than .012" (.30 mm). If not within specifications, replace all main bearings as a set. *See Fig. 6.*

Fig. 6: Checking Crankshaft End Play

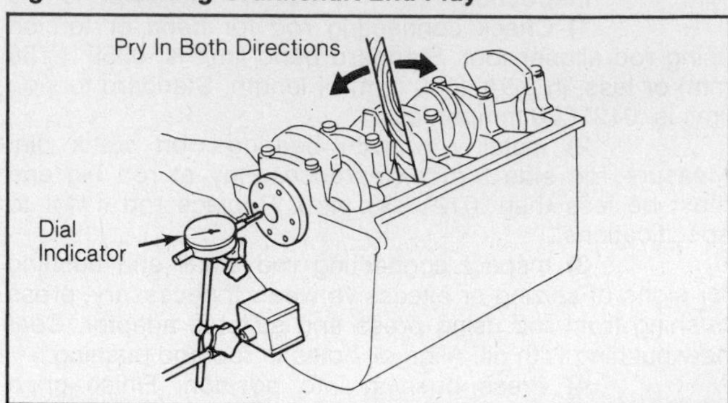
Pry In Both Directions
Dial
Indicator

If end play is incorrect, replace all main bearings as a set.

4) Apply sealer and install rear oil seal and flywheel. Install piston and rod assemblies. To install remaining components, reverse removal procedure.

MAIN & CONNECTING ROD BEARINGS

Check all bearings for scoring or wear. Replace if damage is found. Clean oil from crankshaft journals. Check clearance using Plastigage method. Standard main bearing clearance is .0015-.0026" (.039-.066 mm). Standard connecting rod bearing clearance is .0009-.0026" (.024-.066 mm). Maximum clearance, for all bearings, is .0047" (.120 mm). If clearance is not to specifications, replace bearings.

FRONT OIL SEAL

Removal & Installation

1) With front outer dust covers removed, detach valve timing belt, pulley and related components. Front oil seal is located in the oil pump, directly around crankshaft end.

2) Note oil seal position for reassembly reference. Oil seal may be pryed from oil pump using screwdriver. Apply tape to sharp corners of removal tool to avoid damaging crankshaft sealing surface.

3) Apply oil to oil seal lips. Carefully tap new oil seal into oil pump cavity. Do not damage oil pump body during installation. To complete installation, reverse removal procedure.

REAR OIL SEAL

Removal & Installation

1) With engine and transaxle assembly removed from vehicle, detach transmission assembly. Remove flywheel. Remove oil seal by carefully prying seal away from crankshaft flange and cylinder block.

2) Note oil seal position for reassembly reference. Do not damage flange oil seal surface during removal. Apply tape to sharp corners of removal tool to avoid damaging crankshaft sealing surface.

3) Coat new oil seal with engine oil and tap into position. Do not damage crankshaft flange or cylinder block during installation. Install flywheel and transmission. Complete installation by reversing removal procedure.

ENGINE OILING

ENGINE OILING SYSTEM

Oil drawn from oil pan passes through oil strainer and pipe to oil pump. Oil is delivered to a two-element oil filter, oil cooler, and main oil gallery. Main oil gallery supplies oil to crankshaft main bearings and drilled passages in crankshaft.

Oil sprayed from jet holes on connecting rods lubricates cylinders and piston pins. The main oil gallery supplies oil to camshaft by way of drilled passage which feeds valve lifters, camshaft journals and brackets on cylinder head. Oil is returned to pan by way of oil return hose and pipe. *See Fig. 7.*

Fig. 7: Cutaway View of Engine Oiling System

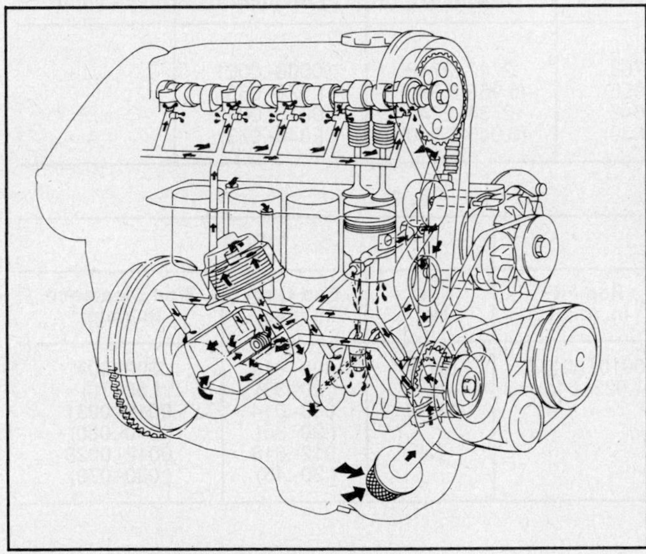

CRANKCASE CAPACITY

4.4 qts. (4.1L) with oil filter.
3.8 qts. (3.5L) without filter.

OIL FILTER

A 2-element filter, with oil return pipe, is used. Filter is a disposable cartridge and combines the function of a main and a bypass filter.

OIL PUMP

Removal

1) An internal gear oil pump assembly is used. Pump is driven directly by crankshaft. The crankshaft front oil seal is installed on the oil pump. Pump is equipped with a pointer which shows TDC of No. 1 cylinder.

NOTE: To prevent oil seal damage when removing oil pump, remove crankshaft key.

2) To remove pump, drain engine oil. Remove valve timing belt and related components. Remove oil pan and pump. *See Fig. 8.*

Inspection

1) Disassemble oil pump. Wash all parts thoroughly in solvent. Inspect for signs of unusual wear or damage. Check all clearances to specifications.

2) Check oil seal for wear or damage. Replace seal by driving out from inside, using drift. To install, coat seal with oil and tap into position. Use care not to damage pump body during installation.

3) Pump is serviced as a complete assembly only. If components are not to specifications, replace entire pump assembly.

Installation

Fill pump with oil and install new cover gasket. Align locating notches and install pump. Apply sealer to new oil pan gasket at 4 corners, where gasket curves down around oil pump and rear plate. To complete installation, reverse removal procedure.

Fig. 8: Exploded View of Oil Pump Assembly

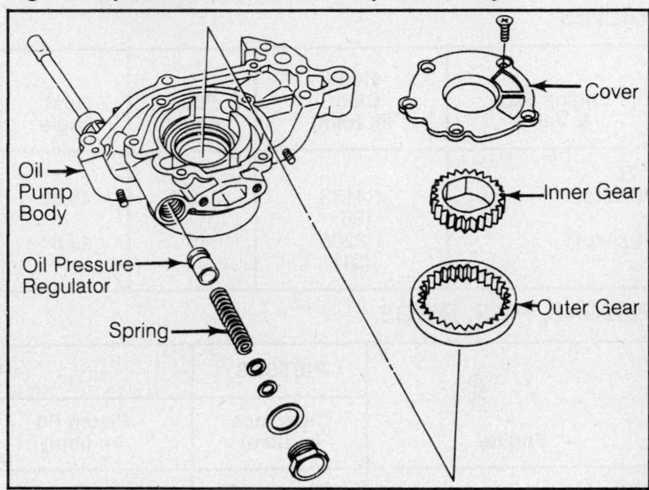
Cover
Oil Pump Body
Inner Gear
Oil Pressure Regulator
Outer Gear
Spring

Pump is serviced as a complete assembly only.

OIL PUMP CLEARANCES

Application	In. (mm)
Outer Gear-to-Body	.0043-.0079 (.11-.20)
Outer Gear-to-Cresent	.0083-.0126 (.21-.32)
Inner Gear-to-Cresent	.0047-.0091 (.12-.23)
Inner & Outer Gear to-Housing Cover	.0020-.0039 (.05-.10)

ENGINE COOLING

THERMOSTAT

180°F (82°C).

COOLING SYSTEM CAPACITY

7.4 quarts (7.0L) with heater.

RADIATOR CAP

13 psi (.9 kg/cm²).

WATER PUMP

Removal & Installation

1) A centrifugal type pump with aluminum body is used. Water pump is driven by valve timing belt located behind front outer dust covers. To remove, drain cooling system and remove fan shroud.

2) Remove belts, pulley, upper and lower outer dust covers. Release tension on idler pulley and remove valve timing belt. Remove water pump and gasket. To install, reverse removal procedure.

SENTRA 4-CYLINDER DIESEL (Cont.)

ENGINE SPECIFICATIONS

GENERAL SPECIFICATIONS

Year	DISPLACEMENT		Fuel System	HP@RPM	Torque Ft. Lbs.@RPM	Compr. Ratio	BORE		STROKE	
	Cu. In.	Liters					In.	mm	In.	mm
1983 Sentra	102.5	1.7L	Fuel Inj.	55 @ 4800	75 @ 2800	21.9:1	3.15	80	3.29	83.6

VALVES

Engine Size & Valve	Head Diam. In. (mm)	Face Angle	Seat Angle	Seat Width In. (mm)	Stem Diameter In. (mm)	Stem Clearance In. (mm)	Valve Lift In. (mm)
1.7L							
Intake	1.4173 (36)	45°	45.5°	.0768 (1.950)	.2742-.2748 (6.965-6.980)	.0008-.0021 (.020-.053)	.....
Exhaust	1.2205 (31)	45°	45.5°	.0642 (1.630)	.2734-.2740 (6.945-6.960)	.0016-.0029 (.040-.073)	.....

PISTONS, PINS, RINGS

Engine	PISTONS	PINS		RINGS		
	Clearance In. (mm)	Piston Fit In. (mm)	Rod Fit In. (mm)	Ring No.	End Gap In. (mm)	Side Clearance In. (mm)
1.7L	.0020-.0028 (.050-.070)	.0-.0002 (.0-.004)	.0010-.0017 [1] (.025-.044)	No. 1	.008-.014 (.20-.35)	.002-.004 (.06-.10)
				No. 2	.008-.014 (.20-.35)	.0016-.0031 (.040-.080)
				Oil	.012-.018 (.30-.45)	.0012-.0028 (.030-.070)

[1] – Interference fit.

CRANKSHAFT MAIN & CONNECTING ROD BEARINGS

Engine	MAIN BEARINGS				CONNECTING ROD BEARINGS		
	Journal Diam. In. (mm)	Clearance In. (mm)	Thrust Bearing	Crankshaft End Play In. (mm)	Journal Diam. In. (mm)	Clearance In. (mm)	Side Play In. (mm)
1.7L	2.0847-2.0852 (52.951-52.964)	.0015-.0026 (.039-.066)	[1]	.0020-.0071 (.050-.180)	1.7701-1.7706 (44.961-44.974)	.0009-.0026 (.024-.066)	.012 (.30)

[1] – Replace all main bearings if end play is not to specification.

VALVE SPRINGS

Engine	Free Length In. (mm)	PRESSURE Lbs. @ In. (Kg @ mm)	
		Valve Closed	Valve Open
1.7L			
Outer	1.83 (46.4)	33.70@1.56 (15.3@39.5)	.....
Inner	1.70 (43.2)	19.20@1.4 (8.7@36)	.....

CAMSHAFT

Engine	Journal Diam. In. (mm)	Clearance In. (mm)	Lobe Lift In. (mm)
1.7L	1.1795-1.1803 (29.960-29.980)	.0008-.0024 (.020-.060)	.....

TIGHTENING SPECIFICATIONS

Application	Ft. Lbs. (N.m)
Camshaft Bracket Nut	13-16 (18-22)
Camshaft Pulley Mount Bolt	68-75 (92-102)
Connecting Rod Nut	23-27 (31-36)
Crankshaft Pulley Mount Bolt	90-98 (123-132)
Cylinder Head Bolt	72-80 (98-108)
Flywheel Mount Bolt	72-80 (98-108)
Front Tensioner Bolt	27-33 (36-44)
Glow Plug	11-14 (15-20)
Idler Pulley Bolt	27-33 (36-44)
Injection Pump Nut	9-13 (13-18)
Injection Nozzle-to-Head Bolt	43-51 (59-69)
Intake/Exhaust Manifold Bolt	13-16 (18-22)
Main Bearing Cap Bolt	33-40 (44-54)
Oil Pump-to-Block Mount Bolt	9-12 (12-16)
Rear Tensioner Bolt	12-15 (16-21)
Spill Tube Nut	29-36 (39-49)
Water Pump Mount Bolt	12-15 (16-21)

MAXIMA, 280ZX & 280ZX TURBO 6-CYLINDER

ENGINE CODING

ENGINE IDENTIFICATION

Engine serial number is stamped on right rear side of cylinder block below mating surface of head.

ENGINE IDENTIFICATION

Application	Engine Size	Code
Maxima	2.4L	L24E
280ZX	2.8L	L28E
280ZX Turbo	2.8L	L28ET

ENGINE, MANIFOLDS & CYLINDER HEAD

ENGINE

NOTE: **Remove engine and transmission as a unit. Separate engine from transmission after removal.**

Removal

1) Remove hood. Mark hinge locations, on hood, for reassembly reference. Bleed off fuel pressure as follows: Remove rear floor carpet and insulator on 280ZX. On all models, start engine. Disconnect fuel pump relay harness connector with engine running. After engine stalls, crank engine 2 or 3 times. Turn ignition switch off. Attach relay connector.

2) Remove battery. Remove power steering pump and A/C compressor, if equipped. Do not disconnect lines. Suspend with wire to prevent hose damage. Drain cooling system and engine crankcase. Remove radiator hoses. Remove air cleaner. Disconnect fuel and canister hoses. Remove canister.

3) On automatic transmission models, disconnect oil cooler lines. Remove radiator and shroud. Remove lower splash guard, if equipped. Disconnect accelerator linkage. Remove wiring to starter, alternator, oil pressure switch, neutral switch, back-up light switch, EGR solenoid valve, electronic fuel injection harness and connector.

4) Disconnect throttle valve switch, cold start valve, air regulator, vacuum cutting solenoid (manual transmission models), auxiliary cooling fan (if equipped), and distributor. Disconnect wiring to boost controlled deceleration solenoid valve. On 280ZX Turbo, remove vacuum control modulator and engine oil cooler hoses at oil filter bracket.

5) On all models, disconnect ground cable to engine. Remove high tension coil wire. Disconnect wire for block terminal. Disconnect fuel return and fuel charge, heater and vacuum hoses. On automatic transmission models, remove wire to inhibitor switch and downshift solenoid. On manual transmission models, remove clutch slave cylinder. Disconnect speedometer cable.

6) Remove center console, "C" ring and control lever pin from transmission rod guide. Remove shift lever from transmission. On 280ZX Turbo, remove heat shield plate beside brake master cylinder. On all models, disconnect exhaust pipe from manifold and exhaust bracket from transmission. Index mark drive shaft and pinion flange. Remove drive shaft.

7) Plug rear of extension housing to prevent oil leakage. Support transmission. Remove rear engine mount. Use hoist to raise engine. Remove front engine mount attaching bolts. Raise engine and transmission. Remove as a unit and set on engine stand. Drain engine oil.

Installation

To install, reverse removal procedures. Ensure rear engine mount is attached to vehicle first. Check proper routing and attachment of electrical harnesses, vacuum and water hoses. Adjust accelerator control system. Refill fluids before starting engine.

MANIFOLDS

Removal

1) Disconnect battery. Drain cooling system. Disconnect valve cover-to-throttle chamber hose, at cover. Disconnect heater housing-to-water inlet tube, at inlet. Remove bolt holding water and fuel tubes to head.

2) Bleed off fuel pressure. Remove heater housing-to-thermostat housing tube. Disconnect fuel line. Remove intake manifold mount bolts. Remove intake manifold assembly. *See Fig. 1*. Detach exhaust pipe from manifold.

Fig. 1: Intake Manifold Assembly

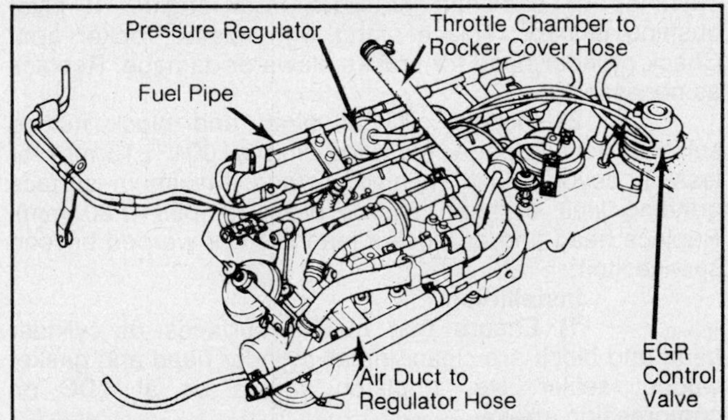
Pressure Regulator
Throttle Chamber to Rocker Cover Hose
Fuel Pipe
EGR Control Valve
Air Duct to Regulator Hose

Non-Turbo shown; 280ZX Turbo is similar.

3) Remove PCV valve hose, sub-heat shield plate and EGR tube. On turbocharged models, disconnect oil passage tube from turbocharger. Remove turbocharger and exhaust outlet as a unit. Remove exhaust manifold mount bolts and manifold.

Installation

To install, use new gaskets and reverse removal procedure.

CYLINDER HEAD

NOTE: **The cylinder head bolts are of 2 different lengths. Note locations during removal for proper reassembly reference.**

Removal

1) Drain cooling system. Disconnect upper radiator hose and heater hoses. Release fuel hose pressure. Remove air regulator and all hoses, as an assembly. Remove spark plug wires at plug end. Remove EGR control valve, vacuum switching valve and hoses, as an assembly.

2) Remove throttle chamber with dash pot and boost controlled deceleration valve. Remove fuel lines, vacuum hoses and canister purge hose pressure regulator. Remove thermostat housing and attached switches, as an assembly. Remove PCV valve hose, sub-heat shield plate and EGR tube.

MAXIMA, 280ZX & 280ZX TURBO 6-CYLINDER (Cont.)

NOTE: Remove clip attaching fuel inlet hose to injector. Do not twist or bend hose during removal.

3) Remove intake manifold and heat shield plate. Remove turbocharger with exhaust outlet, if equipped. Remove exhaust manifold. Remove drive belts. Remove valve cover and camshaft sprocket mount bolt. Rotate crankshaft until No. 1 piston is at TDC of compression stroke.

4) Index mark timing chain and sprocket before removal. Remove sprocket from timing chain. Remove oil pipe. Remove cylinder head mount bolts in reverse of tightening sequence. *See Fig. 2.* Remove bolts securing cylinder head to timing cover. Remove head from engine block.

NOTE: Use tool (ST1740001) to support timing chain. Timing marks should remain unchanged. This simplifies timing mark alignment during reassembly.

Inspection

1) Check but do not remove rocker arm pivot bushings or camshaft brackets from engine. If pivot bushing is bad, replace along with related rocker arm. Check cylinder head for cracks, flaws or damage. Replace as necessary.

2) Inspect cylinder head and block mating surfaces for warpage. Warpage limit is .004" (.10 mm) or less. If beyond limit, refinish surface. Maximum surface grinding limit of head and/or block is .008" (.20 mm). Replace head and/or block if machined or warped beyond service limit.

Installation

1) Ensure that mating surfaces of cylinder head and block are clean. Install cylinder head and gasket without sealer. No. 1 piston should be at TDC on compression stroke.

CAUTION: Do not rotate the crankshaft and camshaft separately.

2) Insert head bolts. Tighten first two in sequence to 14 ft. lbs. (19 N.m). Align sprockets and timing chain. Install remaining components in reverse order of removal. Use new seals, gaskets and sealant where required.

3) Tighten head bolts, in several steps, in sequence. *See Fig. 2.* After engine is assembled and installed; run for several minutes, let it cool down and recheck head torque.

Fig. 2: Cylinder Head Bolt Tightening Sequence

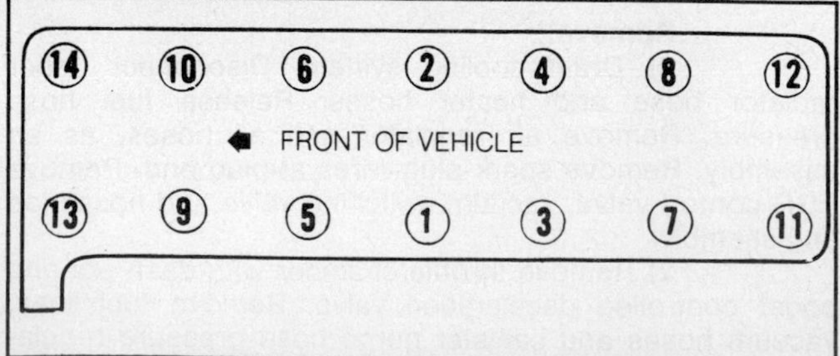
14
10
6
2
4
8
12
FRONT OF VEHICLE
13
9
5
1
3
7
11

Loosen cylinder head bolts in reverse sequence.

CAMSHAFT

CAMSHAFT

Removal

Remove cylinder head. Remove valve rocker springs. Loosen rocker pivot lock nuts. Remove rocker arms by pressing down on spring. Do not lose rocker guide. Carefully remove camshaft from front of head. Do not damage bearings or lobes.

Inspection

1) Check camshaft, journals and cam surface for bend, wear or damage. Check bend with camshaft in "V" blocks, using a dial indicator. Using total indicator reading, maximum bend limit is .004" (.10 mm).

2) Check camshaft lobe height. Standard lobe heights of L24E engine is 1.5728-1.5748" (39.95-40.00 mm). Standard lobe height for L28E & L28ET engine is 1.5728-1.5748" (39.95-40.00 mm) for intake and 1.5866-1.5886" (40.30-40.35 mm) for exhaust.

3) Maximum wear limit of cam lobe is .006" (.15 mm). Replace camshaft if beyond limits. Check camshaft end play with dial indicator. Maximum end play is .015" (.38 mm). If beyond limit, replace thrust plate.

Installation

Carefully install camshaft in head. Install camshaft locating plate with oblong groove of plate facing front of head. Complete installation by reversing removal procedure.

CAMSHAFT BEARINGS

NOTE: Do not remove camshaft bearings. If bearings are removed, bearing centers will be out of alignment. Proper reassembly will be difficult without center boring.

Measure inner diameter of camshaft bearings and outer diameter of camshaft journals. Maximum bearing clearance is .004" (.10 mm). If excessively worn or damaged, replace camshaft and/or cylinder head assembly.

ENGINE FRONT COVER

Removal

1) Drain cooling system. Disconnect hoses. Remove radiator. Remove drive belts, fan and pulley. Disconnect wiring to thermostat housing. Remove housing. Remove crankshaft pulley and water pump. Remove spark plug wires.

2) Mark position of distributor base to engine and position of rotor to distributor. Disconnect distributor wires from coil. Remove distributor. Remove oil pump with drive spindle. Remove front cover mount bolts and front cover.

NOTE: Check height difference between cylinder block upper face and front cover upper face. The difference must be less than .0059" (.150 mm).

Installation

Apply sealant to front cover gasket, front of cylinder block and top of front cover. Install front cover on block. Tighten mount bolts. Install oil pump with drive spindle. Install distributor while aligning index marks. To complete installation, reverse removal procedure.

MAXIMA, 280ZX & 280ZX TURBO 6-CYLINDER (Cont.)

TIMING CHAIN

Removal

Remove front cover. Scribe mating mark on timing chain and sprocket for reassembly reference. Remove camshaft drive sprocket, timing chain, tensioner and chain guide. Remove oil slinger, crankshaft worm gear and sprocket.

Inspection

Check timing chain for damage and excessive wear at roller links. Replace if faulty. Check camshaft sprocket tooth surface for flaws or wear. Install sprocket in position. Check for runout. If runout is more than .004" (.10 mm) or tooth surface is worn, replace sprocket. Inspect chain tensioner and guide for wear or breakage. Replace as necessary.

Installation

1) Install components in reverse of removal procedure. When installing timing chain, camshaft or crankshaft sprocket, ensure camshaft and crankshaft keys point upward.

2) Set timing chain so mating marks match marks on crankshaft and camshaft sprockets on right-hand side. Locate camshaft dowel pin in No. 1 hole in camshaft sprocket.

Fig. 3: Timing Chain and Sprocket Installation

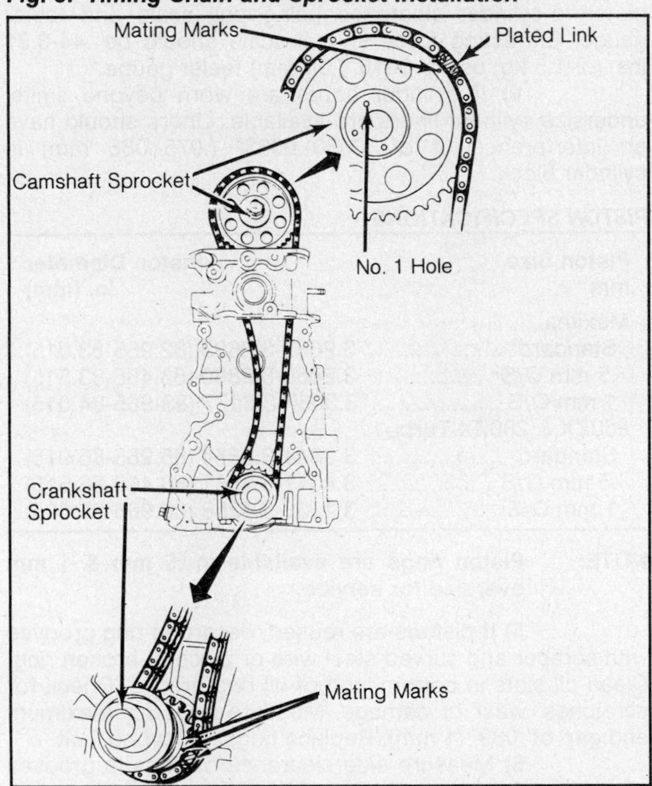
Mating Marks
Plated Link
Camshaft Sprocket
No. 1 Hole
Crankshaft Sprocket
Mating Marks

Ensure that the camshaft and crankshaft keys point upward.

VALVES

VALVE ARRANGEMENT

E-I-I-E-I-E-E-I-E-I-I-E (Front-to-rear).

VALVES

Inspect valves for worn, damaged or deformed valve head or stem. If head is worn to .02" (.5 mm) in-margin-thickness, replace valve. Valve stem end surface grinding limit is .02" (.5 mm).

VALVE GUIDE SERVICING

1) Measure clearance between valve stem and guide with micrometer and telescope hole gauge. Check diameter of stem at top, center and bottom. Insert hole gauge in guide bore. Measure at center.

2) Subtract highest reading of stem diameter from guide bore to obtain clearance. Alternate method is to insert valve in guide and moved left or right. If tip moves .008" (.2 mm) or more, replace guide.

NOTE: Valve guide with .2 mm oversize diameter is available for service, if necessary.

3) Using a press and guide removal tool (ST11320000), force guide from head. Work from combustion chamber side. To ease removal, heat head to 300-400°F (150-200°C). With head at room temperature, ream guide bore to .4812-.4817" (12.223-12.234 mm).

4) Fit snap ring on new guide. Reheat head. Press in guide until ring is in contact with head surface. Ream guide bore, using reamer tool (ST11032000), to .3150-.3157" (8.000-8.018 mm). Correct valve seat surface using new valve guide as axis.

VALVE SEAT INSERTS

Check valve seats for pitting at valve contact surface. Replace as necessary. Valve seat inserts of .5 mm oversize are available for service, if necessary.

VALVE STEM OIL SEALS

An oil seal is installed on all valve guides, located inside of valve spring over valve stem.

VALVE SPRINGS

Removal

1) With cylinder head removed, loosen pivot lock nut. Remove rocker arm by pressing spring down. Do not lose rocker guide. Remove camshaft. Do not damage bearings or cam lobes.

2) Press springs down with compressor tool (ST1207000). Remove valve keepers. Remove compressor tool. Remove spring retainer, inner and outer springs, oil seal and valve spring seat.

Inspection

1) Outer valve spring must be less than .087" (2.20 mm) and inner spring must be less than .047" (1.20 mm) out of square.

2) Valve spring installed height is 1.38" (35 mm) for inner spring and 1.57" (40 mm) for outer spring. Replace spring if not to specifications.

NOTE: Outer valve spring is of an uneven pitch type. Install spring with its narrow pitch side (painted) at cylinder head side.

Installation

1) Install spring seat. Fit oil seal onto valve guide. Install valve springs. Ensure close coil end of White painted outer spring is against head.

2) Install retainers, keepers and rocker guides. Install camshaft. Press valve springs down with screwdriver. Install rocker arms and rocker springs.

MAXIMA, 280ZX & 280ZX TURBO 6-CYLINDER (Cont.)

VALVE ROCKER ARM & OIL PIVOT

Maxima & 280ZX

Remove valve cover and rocker arm. Check pivot head, cam contact surface and pivot contact surface of rocker arm for damage or wear. If necessary, replace pivot and related rocker arm.

NOTE: **Ensure rocker arm and pivot components are kept in order. When installing pivot, clean bolt threads of cylinder head with oil.**

280ZX Turbo

1) Remove valve cover and rocker arm. If oil pivot plunger does not pop up, replace pivot. Do not lift up plunger forcibly. Depress pivot plunger with finger pressure. If it moves about .04" (1 mm), air is inside pivot.

2) Reinstall rocker arm and valve cover. Bleed air by running engine at 1,000 rpm, under no load, for about 10 minutes. Remove valve cover and rocker arm. Check to ensure all air is bleed. If air is still present, replace pivot.

VALVE ADJUSTMENT

1) Do not adjust valves with engine running. Cold settings are shown to provide initial clearance after assembly. Warm engine to operating temperature. Remove valve cover.

2) Rotate crankshaft so No. 1 exhaust cam lobe points up. Adjust exhaust valve clearance on No. 1, 4 and 5 cylinder. Adjust intake valves on No. 2, 4 and 6 cylinder.

3) Rotate crankshaft 360°. Lobe of No. 1 exhaust valve must point down. Adjust exhaust valve clearance on No. 2, 3 and 6 cylinder. Adjust intake clearance on No. 1, 3 and 5 cylinder.

VALVE CLEARANCE SPECIFICATIONS

Valve	Hot	Cold
Intake	.010" (.25 mm)	.007" (.17 mm)
Exhaust	.012" (.30 mm)	.009" (.24 mm)

PISTONS, PINS & RINGS

PISTON & ROD ASSEMBLY

Removal

1) With cylinder head and oil pan removed, remove connecting rod nuts. Remove rod cap with bearing half. Check top of cylinder bore for ridge. If scraper will not remove carbon build-up, remove using ridge reamer.

2) Push piston and rod assembly, with bearing half, out through top of block. Rod caps must be kept with their respective piston and rod assembly and are not interchangeable.

Inspection

Check connecting rod for bend or torsion using rod aligner tool. Bend and torsion limit is .002" (.05 mm) or less, in 3.94" (100 mm) of length. Install rod, with bearings, on crank pin. Measure rod side thrust clearance. Play at big end must be .024" (.60 mm) or less. Replace rod if not to specifications.

Installation

1) Oil the rings, piston and cylinder bore. Install piston and rod assembly. Ensure ring gaps are set 180° apart. Do not set on thrust side of piston or in line with piston pin. Ensure bearing halves are properly seated in rod and cap.

2) Install ring compressor. Install piston in cylinder with notch mark on piston top toward front of engine. With piston installed, ensure rod and bearings are seated against crankshaft journal.

3) Install rod caps to their respective piston and rod assembly. Oil jet of connecting rod should face right side of cylinder block. Install cylinder head and oil pan.

FITTING PISTONS & RINGS

1) Visually inspect cylinder block for cracks or flaws. Using bore gauge, measure cylinder bore for out-of-round or excessive taper. If out-of-round or taper exceeds .0008" (.020 mm), refinish bore. When one cylinder is bored, all must be bored.

NOTE: **Before block machining operations, ensure main bearing caps are installed and tightened to specification. Bore cylinders in the order of No. 1-5-3-6-2-4 to prevent distortion.**

2) Determine piston oversize according to amount of wear in cylinder (see specifications). By measuring piston at thrust face and adding mean of piston-to-cylinder clearance, finish hone of cylinder may be determined.

3) After honing cylinder to final fit, measure piston-to-cylinder clearance using pull scale and feeler gauge. Extracting force to pull scale should be .44-3.31 lbs. (.2-1.5 kg) using .0016" (.04 mm) feeler gauge.

4) If cylinder bores are worn beyond limits, undersize cylinder liners are available. Liners should have an interference fit of .0030-.0033" (.075-.085 mm) in cylinder block.

PISTON SPECIFICATIONS

Piston Size mm	Piston Diameter In. (mm)
Maxima	
Standard	3.2663-3.2683 (82.965-83.015)
.5 mm O/S	3.2860-3.2880 (83.465-83.515)
1 mm O/S	3.3057-3.3077 (83-965-84.015)
280ZX & 280ZX Turbo	
Standard	3.3844-3.3864 (85.965-86.015)
.5 mm O/S	3.4041-3.4061 (86.465-86.515)
1 mm O/S	3.4238-3.4258 (86.965-87.015)

NOTE: **Piston rings are available in .5 mm & 1 mm oversize for service.**

5) If pistons are reused, decarbon ring grooves with scraper and curved steel wire or piece of broken ring. Clean oil slots in bottom land of oil ring groove. Check for scratches, wear or damage. Measure rings for maximum end gap of .039" (1 mm). Replace rings, if beyond limit.

6) Measure side clearance of rings in grooves as each ring is installed. Maximum side clearance tolerance is .004" (.10 mm). If side clearance exceeds limits, replace piston and rings. When installing rings, ensure stamped mark on each ring faces up.

PISTON PINS

1) Using press and adaptors, remove pin from piston and rod. Check pin and bores for signs of sticking, excessive wear or damage. Measure pin bore diameter in piston and outside diameter of pin. Standard pin diameter is .8265-.8267" (20.993-20.998 mm) for 280ZX and .7872-.7874" (19.995-20.000 mm) for Maxima.

MAXIMA, 280ZX & 280ZX TURBO 6-CYLINDER (Cont.)

2) Determine pin-to-piston clearance. Standard clearance is .0002-.0005" (.006-.013 mm) for 280ZX and .0001-.0024" (.003-.062 mm) for Maxima. If wear exceeds specifications, replace both piston and pin. Pin must fit into piston with light thumb pressure at room temperature.

3) Piston pin is press fit in rod. If rod is replaced, ensure new rod is within .247 ounce (7 grams) of defective rod. Install piston pin to piston and rod so that oil hole on rod faces right side of engine and notch on piston head faces forward when installed. *See Fig. 4*.

Fig. 4: Piston and Connecting Rod Alignment

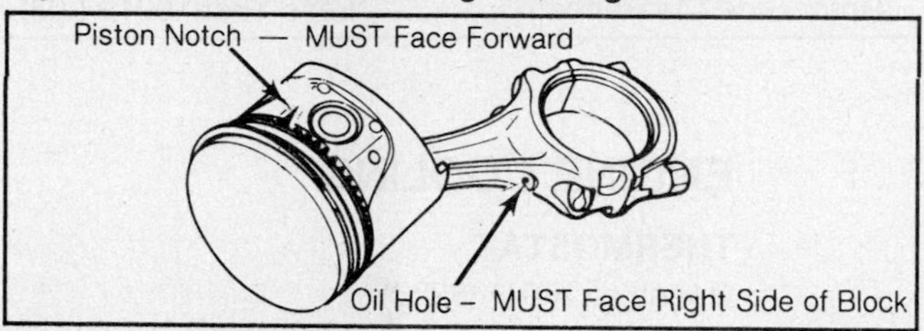
Piston Notch — MUST Face Forward
Oil Hole – MUST Face Right Side of Block

Oil hole on connecting rod faces the right side of engine.

CRANKSHAFT & MAIN & CONNECTING ROD BEARINGS

CRANKSHAFT

Removal

1) With engine removed from vehicle, remove cylinder head and oil pan. Remove flywheel and end plate. Remove oil pump, front cover, chain tensioner and chain guides.

2) Remove timing chain, oil thrower, crankshaft worm gear and chain drive sprocket. Remove piston and rod assemblies. Remove main bearing caps. Use puller (KV10104150) to remove center and rear main bearing caps. *See Fig. 5*.

Fig. 5: Center Main Bearing Cap Removal

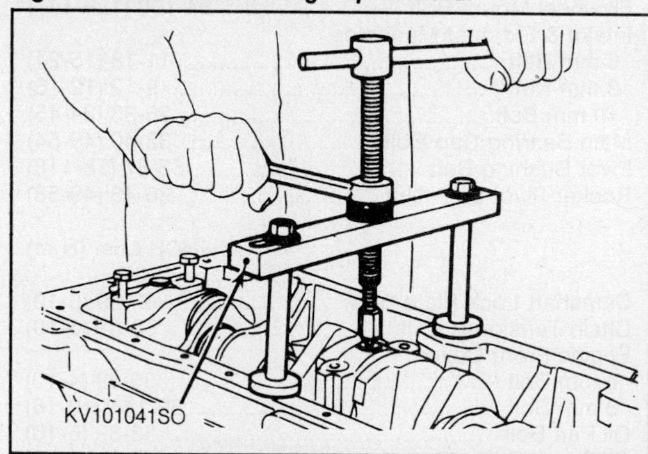
KV101041SO

Remove the center main bearing cap slowly.

3) Remove rear oil seal. Use care not to damage crankshaft sealing surface. Remove crankshaft. Remove baffle plate and steel net from cylinder block.

NOTE: **Keep main bearing caps in order for reassembly reference. Arrows on bearing caps must face front of engine.**

Inspection

1) Check shaft journals and crankpins for scoring, wear, or cracks. Taper and out-of-round of journals and crankpins must not exceed .0012" (.030 mm). Check crankshaft for bend by placing on "V" blocks.

2) Set dial indicator pointer at center journal of crankshaft. If bend exceeds .004" (.10 mm), which is 1/2 of indicator reading, replace crankshaft. Check crankshaft pilot bushing for wear or damage. Replace if necessary.

NOTE: **Do not damage edge of pilot bushing during replacement or inset it excessively.**

3) To remove pilot bushing, pull out using tool (ST16610001). Clean bushing hole. Insert new bushing until distance between flange end and bushing is approximately .157" (4 mm) deep.

Installation

1) Install main bearing halves to engine block. Ensure bearings are on correct journal. Journal No. 4 requires a thrust bearing. Bearing for journal No. 1 is the same as No. 7. Upper bearing halves have an oil groove and are not interchangeable with lower bearing halves.

2) Apply oil to main bearing surface. Install crankshaft. Apply sealant to each side of rear main bearing cap and corners of block contact point. Install bearing caps so arrow faces front of engine.

3) Shift crankshaft toward front of engine. Tighten main bearing caps in 2 or 3 steps. Start at center bearing and work outward. Ensure crankshaft rotates smoothly. Check crankshaft end play. Standard end play is less than .012" (.30 mm). If not within specifications, replace No. 4 center thrust bearing. *See Fig. 6*.

Fig. 6: Checking Crankshaft End Play

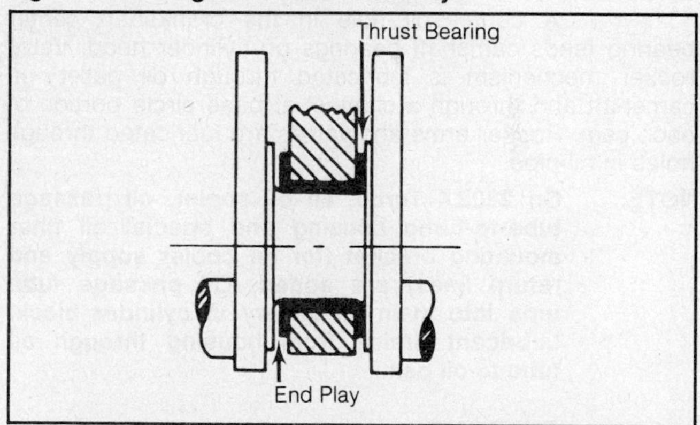
Thrust Bearing
End Play

The crankshaft thrust bearing is located at the No. 4 center main bearing journal.

4) Apply sealer to side seals. Install seals in rear main bearing cap. Apply oil to rear main seal mating surface to prevent scratches and folding seal lip. Install oil seal using installer tools (KV10105500 & ST15310000). Install rear end plate and flywheel. Install piston and rod assemblies. Install remaining components in reverse of removal procedure.

MAIN BEARING CLEARANCE

Check bearings for scoring or wear. Replace if damaged. Clean oil from crankshaft. Check clearance using Plastigage method. Maximum main bearing clearance is .0047" (.120 mm). If not to specifications, replace bearings. Bearings are available in undersizes of .25 mm, .50 mm, .75 mm and 1 mm.

MAXIMA, 280ZX & 280ZX TURBO 6-CYLINDER (Cont.)

NOTE: **Plastigage should run parallel with crankshaft. Do not block oil hole or turn crankshaft with Plastigage inserted.**

CONNECTING ROD BEARING CLEARANCE

Check connecting rod bearing clearance using Plastigage method. Tighten connecting rod caps to 33-40 ft. lbs. (45-54 N.m). Maximum rod bearing clearance is .0047" (.120 mm). If not to specifications, replace bearings. Bearings are available in undersizes of .06 mm, .12 mm, .25 mm, .50 mm, .75 mm and 1 mm.

ENGINE OILING

CRANKCASE CAPACITY

Maxima 5.3 qts. (with filter).
280ZX 4.8 qts. (with filter).
280ZX Turbo 5.5 qts. (with filter).

OIL FILTER

Full-flow, with disposable cartridge.

OIL PRESSURE

50-57 psi (3.5-4.0 kg/cm²) @ 2000 RPM.

ENGINE OILING SYSTEM

Oil drawn from oil pan passes through a screen to oil pump. Oil is delivered to full-flow filter and main oil gallery. Main oil gallery supplies oil to crankshaft main bearings and drilled passages in crankshaft. Oil sprayed from jet holes on connecting rods lubricates chain tensioner and timing chain.

A center oil hole in the crankshaft center bearing feeds camshaft bearings on cylinder head. Valve rocker mechanism is lubricated through oil gallery in camshaft and through a channel at base circle portion of each cam. Rocker arms and valves are lubricated through holes in oil pipe.

NOTE: **On 280ZX Turbo, an oil cooler, oil passage tube-to-turbo housing and special oil filter mounting bracket (for oil cooler supply and return lines) are added. Oil passage tube taps into main oil gallery in cylinder block. Lubricant drains from housing through oil tube to oil pan.**

OIL PUMP

1) Oil pump assembly is installed to bottom of front cover by four bolts. Pump is driven by oil pump drive spindle assembly which is in turn driven by gear on crankshaft.

2) To remove oil pump, first remove distributor. Drain engine oil. Remove oil pump body together with drive spindle. To disassemble, remove pump cover and gasket.

3) Slide pump rotors from pump body. Remove regulator cap, valve and spring. Clean components with solvent. Inspect for wear or damage. Check table and ensure clearances are to specifications.

4) If not to specifications, replace entire pump assembly. Assemble pump in reverse order of disassembly. Align hole in oil pump with punch mark on drive spindle. Fill pump housing with oil before installing to front cover.

OIL PUMP CLEARANCES

Application	In. (mm)
Rotor Tip Clearance	Less Than .0079 (.20)
Outer Rotor-to-Body	Less Than .0197 (.50)
Rotor-to-Cover	Less Than .0024 (.06)
Rotor Side Clearance	Less Than .0012 (.03)

ENGINE COOLING

THERMOSTAT

Opens at 180°F (82°C).

COOLING SYSTEM CAPACITY

11 qts.

RADIATOR CAP

13 psi.

WATER PUMP

Centrifugal type pump with aluminum body. To remove, drain cooling system. Remove shroud. Remove fan belts, fan and pulley. Remove mount bolts and pump from front cover. To install, reverse removal procedure.

TIGHTENING SPECIFICATIONS

Application	Ft. Lbs. (N.m)
Camshaft Sprocket Bolt	94-108 (128-147)
Connecting Rod Nut	33-40 (45-54)
Crankshaft Pulley Bolt	101-116 (137-158)
Cylinder Head Bolt	51-61 (69-83)
Flywheel Mount Bolt	94-108 (128-147)
Intake & Exhaust Manifolds	
8 mm Bolt	11-18 (15-24)
8 mm Nut	9-12 (12-16)
10 mm Bolt	25-33 (34-45)
Main Bearing Cap Bolt	33-40 (45-54)
Pivot Bushing Bolt	58-87 (78-118)
Rocker Pivot Lock Nut	36-43 (49-58)
	INCH Lbs. (N.m)
Camshaft Lock Plate Bolt	53-89 (6-10)
Chain Tensioner Bolt	53-89 (6-10)
Engine Front Cover	
6 mm Bolt	35-89 (4-10)
8 mm Bolt	89-144 (10-16)
Oil Pan Bolt	53-89 (6-10)
Oil Pump Cover Bolt	53-89 (6-10)
Oil Pump-to-Front Cover Bolt	96-132 (11-15)

MAXIMA, 280ZX & 280ZX TURBO 6-CYLINDER (Cont.)

ENGINE SPECIFICATIONS

GENERAL SPECIFICATIONS

Year	DISPLACEMENT Cu. In.	DISPLACEMENT Liters	Fuel System	HP@RPM	Torque Ft. Lbs.@RPM	Compr. Ratio	BORE In.	BORE mm	STROKE In.	STROKE mm
1983										
L24E	146.0	2.4L	Fuel Inj.	120 @ 5200	134 @ 2800	8.9:1	3.27	83	2.90	73.7
L28E	168.0	2.8L	Fuel Inj.	145 @ 5200	156 @ 4000	8.3:1	3.39	86	3.11	79
L28ET	168.0	2.8L	Fuel Inj.	180 @ 5600	202 @ 2800	7.4:1	3.39	86	3.11	79

VALVES

Engine Size & Valve	Head Diam. In. (mm)	Face Angle	Seat Angle	Seat Width In. (mm)	Stem Diameter In. (mm)	Stem Clearance In. (mm)	Valve Lift In. (mm)
2.4L							
Intake	1.65 (42.0)	45.5°	45°	.061 (1.55)	.3136-.3142 (7.965-7.980)	.0008-.0021 (.020-.053)	.....
Exhaust	1.38 (35.0)	45.5°	45°	.055 (1.40)	.3128-.3134 (7.945-7.960)	.0016-.0029 (.040-.073)	.....
2.8L							
Intake	1.73 (44.0)	45.5°	45°	.061 (1.55)	.3136-.3142 (7.965-7.980)	.0008-.0021 (.020-.053)	.....
Exhaust	1.38 (35.0)	45.5°	45°	.061 (1.55)	.3128-.3134 (7.945-7.960)	.0016-.0029 (.040-.073)	.....

PISTONS, PINS, RINGS

Engine	PISTONS Clearance In. (mm)	PINS Piston Fit In. (mm)	PINS Rod Fit In. (mm)	RINGS Ring No.	RINGS End Gap In. (mm)	RINGS Side Clearance In. (mm)
2.4L & 2.8L	.0010-.0018 (.025-.045)	.0002-.0005 (.006-.013)	.0006-.0013 [1] (.015-.033)	No. 1	.010-.016 [2] (.25-.40)	.0016-.0029 (.040-.073)
				No. 2	.006-.012 (.15-.30)	.0012-.0025 (.030-.063)
				Oil	.012-.035 (.30-.90)	.0009-.0028 (.023-.070)

[1] – Interference fit.
[2] – Turbo engine ring end gap is .007-.013" (.19-.33 mm).

CRANKSHAFT MAIN & CONNECTING ROD BEARINGS

Engine	MAIN BEARINGS Journal Diam. In. (mm)	MAIN BEARINGS Clearance In. (mm)	MAIN BEARINGS Thrust Bearing	MAIN BEARINGS Crankshaft End Play In. (mm)	CONNECTING ROD BEARINGS Journal Diam. In. (mm)	CONNECTING ROD BEARINGS Clearance In. (mm)	CONNECTING ROD BEARINGS Side Play In. (mm)
2.4L & 2.8L	2.1631-2.1636 (54.942-54.955)	.0008-.0026 (.020-.066)	Center No. 4	.002-.007 (.05-.18)	1.9670-1.9675 (49.961-49.974)	.0009-.0026 (.024-.066)	.008-.012 (.20-.30)

VALVE TIMING

Engine	INTAKE Open (BTDC)	INTAKE Close (ABDC)	EXHAUST Open (BBDC)	EXHAUST Close (ATDC)
2.4L	22°	38°	54°	6°
2.8L	16°	44°	58°	10°

CAMSHAFT

Engine	Journal Diam. In. (mm)	Clearance In. (mm)	Lobe Lift In. (mm)
2.4L & 2.8L	1.8878-1.8883 (47.949-47.962)	.0015-.0026 (.038-.067)	.....

VALVE SPRINGS

Engine	Free Length In. (mm)	PRESSURE Lbs. @ In. (Kg @ mm) Valve Closed	PRESSURE Lbs. @ In. (Kg @ mm) Valve Open
2.4L & 2.8L			
Inner	1.766 (44.85)	27.1@1.378 (12.3@35)	56.2@.965 (25.5@24.5)
Outer	1.968 (49.98)	47@1.575 (21.3@40)	108@1.161 (49@29.5)

MAXIMA 6-CYLINDER DIESEL

ENGINE CODING

ENGINE IDENTIFICATION

Engine serial number is stamped on right rear side of cylinder block below cylinder head mating surface. Number LD28 identifies diesel engines.

ENGINE, MANIFOLDS & CYLINDER HEAD

ENGINE

NOTE: Remove engine and transmission as a unit. Separate engine from transmission after removal.

Removal

1) Remove hood. Mark hinge locations, on hood, for reassembly reference. Remove battery and air cleaner. Drain coolant from radiator and engine. Remove hoses, shroud and radiator.

2) Remove power steering pump and air conditioning compressor from engine. Do not disconnect lines or hoses. Suspend units with wire to prevent hose damage. On automatic transmission, disconnect oil cooler lines. On all models, remove lower engine splash guard.

3) Disconnect accelerator linkage. Disconnect wiring to starter, alternator, oil pressure switch, neutral switch, back-up light switch, EGR solenoid valve, electronic fuel injection harness and connector, auxiliary cooling fan, distributor and all wiring to thermostat housing.

4) Disconnect wiring to boost controlled deceleration solenoid valve. Remove ground cable from engine. Detach wiring for block terminal. Disconnect fuel return hose, fuel charge hose, heater hoses and vacuum hoses. On automatic transmission, disconnect wire to inhibitor switch and downshift solenoid.

5) On all models, disconnect speedometer cable from rear extension housing. Remove center console, "C" ring and control lever pin from manual transmission striking rod guide. On automatic transmission, remove retaining pin, and disconnect shift lever.

6) If equipped, remove clutch slave cylinder. Plug fluid line. Disconnect front exhaust pipe from manifold. Discard gasket. Disconnect exhaust pipe bracket from rear extension housing.

7) Index mark drive shaft and pinion flange for reassembly reference. Remove drive shaft. Plug rear of extension housing to prevent oil leakage. Support engine with hoist. Raise enough to take weight off engine mounts.

8) Remove diesel engine mounting damper. Remove rear engine mount member bolts and front engine mount attaching bolts. Raise engine and transmission. Remove from vehicle as a unit and set on engine stand.

Installation

To install, reverse removal procedures. Ensure rear engine mount is attached first. Install new exhaust gasket. Check proper routing and attachment of all electrical harnesses, vacuum and water hoses. Refill fluids before starting engine. Bleed air from injection pump.

CYLINDER HEAD

NOTE: The cylinder head bolts are of two different lengths. Note locations during removal for proper reassembly reference.

Removal

1) Disconnect battery ground cable. Remove air cleaner. Drain cooling system. Disconnect upper radiator hose and heater hoses. Disconnect accelerator linkage. Disconnect wiring to EFI harness and connector, distributor and all wiring to thermostat housing.

2) Remove thermostat housing and bottom bypass inlet with hose. Remove intake and exhaust manifolds. Do not separate intake manifold. Remove front engine hoist bracket. Disconnect oil pipe to head and return line to oil pan.

3) Remove injection tube and nozzle assemblies, including return hose and spill tube. Plug nozzle holes and discard nozzle washers. Disconnect injection pump hoses. Remove oil cooler, lines and filter as an assembly. Remove power steering pump bracket.

4) Remove valve cover. Remove blind plug from rear plate. Rotate crankshaft until timing marks on flywheel and rear plate align. Ensure No. 1 piston is at TDC of compression stroke. Index mark timing chain and sprocket before removal.

5) Remove camshaft sprocket mount bolt. Remove camshaft sprocket. Slowly lower timing chain. Remove cylinder head mount bolts gradually, working from outside to inside of head. *See Fig. 1.* Remove cylinder head-to-front cover mount bolts. Remove head from block. Keep disassembled parts in order.

NOTE: Use tool (ST1740001) to support timing chain. Timing marks should remain unchanged. This simplifies timing mark alignment during reassembly.

Inspection

1) Check but do not remove rocker arm pivot bushings or camshaft brackets from engine. If pivot bushing is bad, replace along with related rocker arm. Check combustion chambers for cracks, flaws or melted areas. Replace as necessary.

2) Inspect cylinder head and block mating surfaces for warpage. Warpage limit is .004" (.10 mm) or less. If beyond limit, surface must be refinished. Maximum surface grinding limit of head and/or block is .008" (.20 mm). Replace head and/or block if machined or warped beyond service limit.

Installation

1) Ensure mating surfaces of cylinder head and block are clean. Install head and gasket without sealer. Set No. 1 piston at TDC on compression stroke.

CAUTION: Do not rotate the crankshaft and camshaft separately.

Fig. 1: Cylinder Head Tightening Sequence

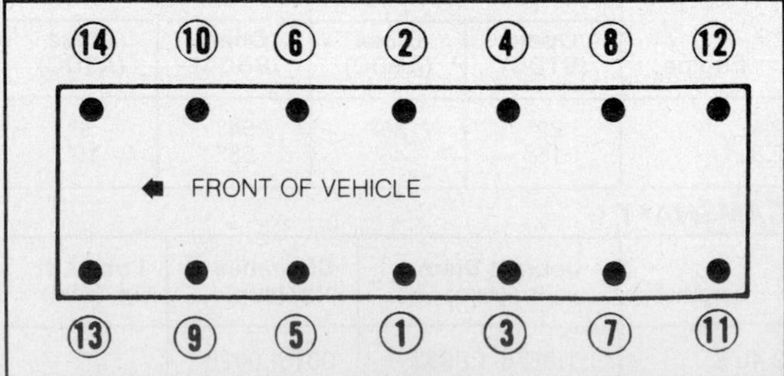

14 10 6 2 4 8 12
FRONT OF VEHICLE
13 9 5 1 3 7 11

Reverse head tightening sequence for removal.

2) Insert head bolts. Tighten two center bolts, in sequence, to 14 ft. lbs. (19 N.m). Align sprockets and timing chain. Install remaining components in reverse order of removal. Use new seals, gaskets, nozzle washers and sealant where required.

3) Tighten head bolts, in several steps, in sequence. *See Fig. 1.* After engine is assembled and installed; run for several minutes, let it cool down and recheck head torque.

CAMSHAFT

CAMSHAFT

Removal

1) Remove cylinder head. Remove glow plug connecting plate and glow plugs. Remove valve rocker springs. Loosen valve rocker pivot lock nuts.

2) Remove rocker arms by pressing down on spring. Do not lose valve rocker guide. Remove camshaft from front of head.

Inspection

1) Check camshaft for bend, wear or damage. Check bend with camshaft in "V" blocks, using a dial indicator. Maximum bend limit is .002" (.05 mm). Check camshaft lobe height.

2) Standard lobe height for LD28 engine is 1.5728-1.5748" (39.95-40 mm) for intake and 1.5866-1.5886" (40.30-40.35 mm) for exhaust. Maximum wear limit of cam lobe is .006" (.15 mm).

3) Check camshaft end play with dial indicator. Maximum end play is .015" (.38 mm). If beyond limits, replace thrust plate.

Installation

1) Carefully install camshaft in head. Do not damage bearings. Install camshaft locating plate with oblong groove of plate facing front of head.

2) Install camshaft sprocket, and tighten mounting bolt. To complete installation, reverse removal procedure.

CAMSHAFT BEARINGS

NOTE: **Do not remove camshaft bearings. If removed, bearing centers will be out of alignment. Proper reassembly will be difficult without center boring.**

Measure inner diameter of camshaft bearings and outer diameter of camshaft journals. If excessively worn or damaged, replace camshaft and/or cylinder head assembly. Camshaft bearing clearance limit is .004" (.10 mm).

ENGINE FRONT COVER

Removal

1) Drain cooling system. Disconnect hoses. Remove radiator. Remove drive belts, fan blade and pulley. Remove crankshaft pulley and water pump. Remove front dust cover, thermostat housing and bottom bypass inlet with hose. Disconnect injection tubes from injection nozzles and hoses to injection pump.

2) Remove front engine hoist bracket and power steering pump bracket. Remove injection pump and injection tubes as an assembly. Pull off injection pump drive crank pulley. Remove oil pump with drive spindle. Remove front cover attaching bolts and front cover.

Installation

Apply sealant to front cover gasket, front of block and top of front cover. Install cover onto block. Tighten front cover-to-cylinder block bolts and head-to-cover bolts. Complete installation by reversing removal procedures.

TIMING CHAIN

Removal

1) Remove engine front cover. Remove rocker arm cover, camshaft sprocket retaining bolt and camshaft sprocket.

2) Remove timing chain, chain tensioner and chain guide. Remove oil slinger, crankshaft oil pump drive gear and crankshaft sprocket.

Installation

1) Install components in reverse of removal procedure. When installing timing chain, camshaft sprocket or crankshaft sprocket, make sure camshaft and crankshaft keys point upward.

2) Set timing chain so that plated links on chain line up with match marks on camshaft and crankshaft sprockets on right-hand side. Locate camshaft dowel pin in No. 1 hole in camshaft sprocket.

Fig. 2: Timing Chain and Sprocket Installation

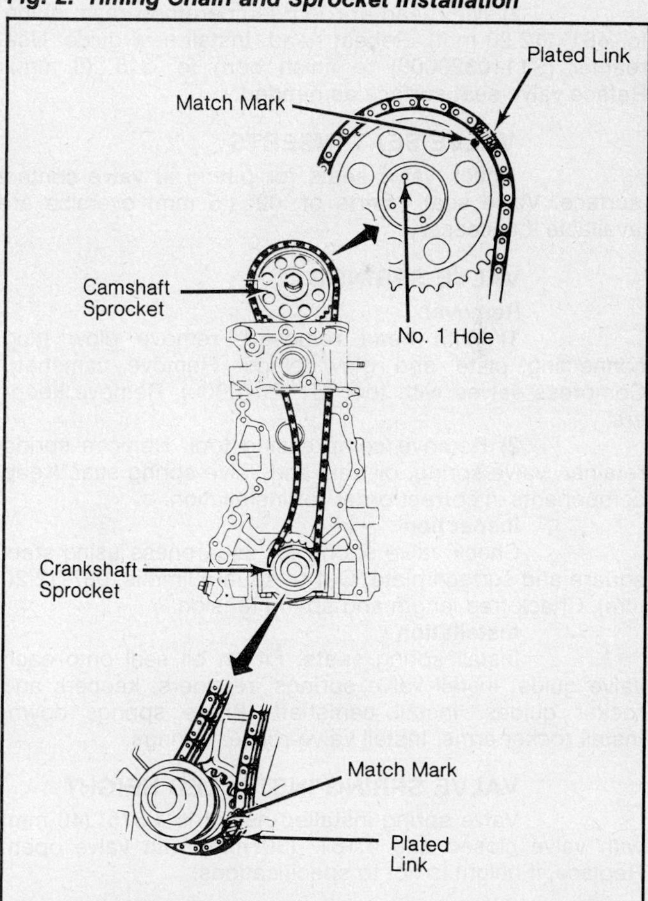
Plated Link
Match Mark
Camshaft Sprocket
No. 1 Hole
Crankshaft Sprocket
Match Mark
Plated Link

Ensure camshaft and crankshaft keys point upward.

MAXIMA 6-CYLINDER DIESEL (Cont.)

VALVES

VALVE ARRANGEMENT

E-I-I-E-I-E-E-I-E-I-I-E (Front-to-rear).

VALVE

Inspect valves for worn, damaged or deformed valve head or stem. If head is worn down to .02" (.5 mm) in-margin thickness, replace valve. Valve stem end surface grinding limit is .02" (.5 mm).

VALVE GUIDE

1) Measure clearance between valve stem and valve guide with micrometer and telescope hole gauge. Check diameter of valve stem at top, center and bottom. Insert hole gauge in guide bore. Measure at center.

2) Maximum stem-to-guide clearance is .004" (.10 mm). Move valve left-to-right in guide. Maximum allowable deflection at valve tip is .008" (.20 mm) with tip 1.18" (30 mm) from head upper surface.

VALVE GUIDE REPLACEMENT

1) If clearance is beyond limits and valve stem is not worn, replace guide. To replace, heat head to 300-400°F (150-200°C). Use tool (ST110330000). Drive guide out from combustion chamber side.

2) With head at room temperature, ream guide to .481" (12.20 mm). Reheat head. Install new guide. Use reamer (ST110320000) to finish bore to .315" (8 mm). Reface valve seat surface as needed.

VALVE SEAT INSERTS

Check valve seats for pitting at valve contact surface. Valve seat inserts of .02" (.5 mm) oversize are available if necessary.

VALVE SPRINGS

Removal

1) With head removed, remove glow plug connecting plate and glow plugs. Remove camshaft. Compress valves with tool (ST12070000). Remove keepers.

2) Remove compressing tool. Remove spring retainer, valve spring, oil seal and valve spring seat. Keep components in correct order for installation.

Inspection

Check valve spring for squareness using steel square and surface plate. Out-of-square limit is .087" (2.20 mm). Check free length and spring tension.

Installation

Install spring seats. Fit an oil seal onto each valve guide. Install valve springs, retainers, keepers and rocker guides. Install camshaft. Press springs down. Install rocker arms. Install valve rocker springs.

VALVE SPRING INSTALLED HEIGHT

Valve spring installed height is 1.575" (40 mm) with valve closed and 1.181" (30 mm) with valve open. Replace, if height is not to specifications.

VALVE CLEARANCE ADJUSTMENT

1) Do not adjust valves with engine running. Cold settings are shown to provide initial clearance after assembly. Warm engine to running temperature. Remove valve cover.

2) Rotate crankshaft so No. 1 exhaust cam lobe is up. Adjust exhaust valve clearance on No. 1, 4 and 5 cylinders. Adjust intake valves on No. 2, 4 and 6 cylinders.

3) Rotate crankshaft 360° so No. 1 exhaust valve lobe is down. Adjust exhaust valve clearance on No. 2, 3 and 6, and intake clearance on No. 1, 3 and 5 cylinders.

VALVE CLEARANCE SPECIFICATIONS

Valve	Hot	Cold
Intake	.010" (.25 mm)	.007" (.18 mm)
Exhaust	.012" (.30 mm)	.010" (.25 mm)

PISTONS, PINS & RINGS

PISTON & ROD ASSEMBLY

Removal

1) With cylinder head, front cover and oil pan removed, remove connecting rod nuts. Remove rod cap with bearing half. Check top of cylinder bore for ridge. If scraper will not remove carbon build-up, remove using ridge reamer.

2) Push piston and rod assembly, with bearing half, out through top of block. Keep rod caps with their respective piston and rod assemblies. Caps are not interchangeable.

Inspection

1) Check connecting rod for bend or torsion using rod aligner tool. Bend and torsion limit is .002" (.05 mm) or less, in 3.94" (100 mm) of length.

2) Install rod, with bearings, on crank pin. Measure rod side thrust clearance. Play at rod big end must be less than .024" (.60 mm). Replace rod if not to specifications.

Installation

1) To install piston and connecting rod assembly, apply oil to rings, piston and cylinder wall. Ensure ring gaps are approximately 180° apart and not on thrust side of piston or in line with piston pin.

2) Bearing halves must be properly seated in rod and cap. Install ring compressor. Compress rings. Install piston in cylinder. Ensure grade mark stamped in top of piston is toward front of engine and oil hole on rod faces right side of block.

3) With piston installed and rod and bearings seated against crankshaft journal, install rod caps to their respective piston and rod assembly. Install cylinder head and front cover. Install new gasket and oil pan. Tighten pan bolts evenly, in a criss-cross pattern. Do not over-tighten.

FITTING PISTONS & RINGS

1) Inspect cylinder block for cracks or flaws. Using bore gauge, measure cylinder for out-of-round or excessive taper. If cylinder bore out-of-round or taper exceeds .0008" (.020 mm), refinish cylinder bore. When any one cylinder is bored, all cylinders must be bored.

NOTE: **Before cylinder block machining operations, ensure main bearing caps are installed and tightened to specification. Bore cylinders in the order of No. 1-5-3-6-2-4 to prevent distortion.**

MAXIMA 6-CYLINDER DIESEL (Cont.)

2) Determine piston oversize according to amount of wear in cylinder (see specifications). By measuring piston at thrust face and adding mean of piston-to-cylinder clearance, finish hone of cylinder may be determined.

3) After honing cylinder to final fit, measure piston-to-cylinder clearance using pull scale and feeler gauge. With piston and cylinder at room temperature (70°F, 20°C), extracting force to pull scale should be 1.3-2.6 lbs. (.6-1.2 kg) using a .0024" (.060 mm) feeler gauge.

PISTON SPECIFICATIONS

Piston Size	Piston Diameter In. (mm)
Standard	3.3244-2.3264 (84.44-84.49)
.5 mm O/S	3.3441-3.3461 (84.94-84.99)
1 mm O/S	3.3638-3.3657 (85.44-85.49)

4) If pistons are reused, decarbon piston and ring grooves with scraper and curved steel wire or piece of broken ring. Clean oil slots in bottom land of oil ring groove. Check for scratches, wear or damage. Measure side clearance or rings in grooves as each ring is installed.

5) Maximum side clearance tolerance of top ring is .008" (.20 mm). Maximum clearance for 2nd ring is .006" (.15 mm) and, for oil ring, clearance is .004" (.10 mm). If side clearance exceeds limits, replace piston and rings.

6) When installing piston rings, ensure stamped mark on ring faces up. Use top and second rings, which have no marks, when bore grade stamped near cylinder block bore is "1" or "2". Use rings with "S" mark when bore grade is "3", "4" or "5". Install expander ring with teflon tube aligned with ring gap. *See Fig. 3.*

Fig. 3: Installation Order of Diesel Engine Piston Rings

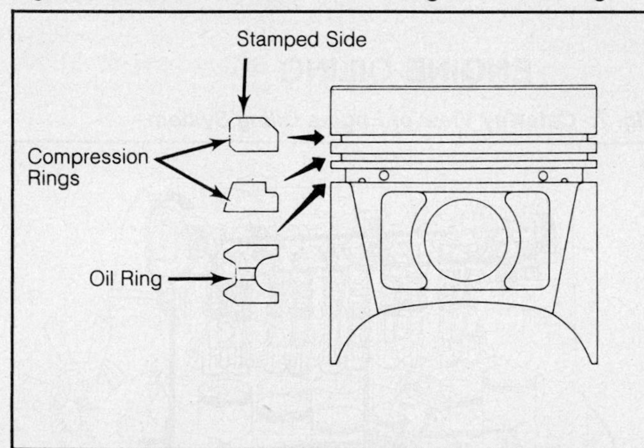
Stamped Side
Compression Rings
Oil Ring

Ensure ring gaps are situated approximately 180° apart.

7) When pistons are replaced, proper head gasket selection procedure must be done. Clean cylinder block gasket surface. Install dial indicator and zero gauge on block surface. Measure and record length of piston projection for every cylinder.

8) Measure in three places across highest point of piston top. Determine maximum length of piston projection and select suitable gasket. Head gaskets have cutouts in them for identification purposes.

CYLINDER HEAD GASKET SELECTION

Piston Projection In. (mm)	Gasket Thickness In. (mm)	Cutouts in Head Gasket
Below .0192 (.487)	.0441 (1.120)	1
.0192-.0226 (.487-.573)	.047 (1.20)	2
Above .0226 (.573)	.0504 (1.280)	3

PISTON PINS

1) To remove pin, first remove snap rings. Heat piston and rod assembly to about 150°F (65°C). Drive out pin with drift. Do not damage piston during removal. Check pin and pin hole for signs of gauling or excessive wear.

2) Using micrometer and telescope hole gauge, measure diameter of piston pin and piston pin hole. Determine pin-to-piston clearance. If wear exceeds .0002" (.004 mm), replace piston and pin.

3) To assemble piston and rod, heat piston to 150°F (65°C). Insert pin into piston while holding piston and rod in proper alignment. Assemble with oil hole in rod on same side as combustion chamber in piston top. *See Fig. 4.*

Fig. 4: Piston and Connecting Rod Assembly Alignment

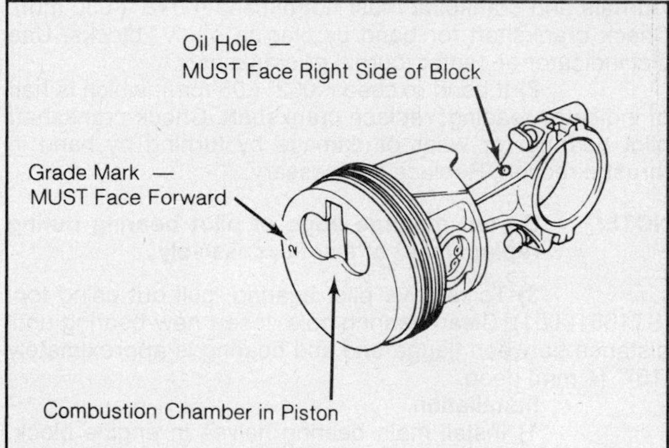
Oil Hole —
MUST Face Right Side of Block
Grade Mark —
MUST Face Forward
Combustion Chamber in Piston

Check that the grade mark on piston top faces forward and the oil hole on the rod faces the right side of block.

CRANKSHAFT MAIN & CONNECTING ROD BEARINGS

CRANKSHAFT

Removal

1) With engine removed, remove cylinder head, front cover and oil pan. Remove flywheel and end plate. Remove oil pump, chain tensioner and chain guides. Remove timing chain, oil slinger, crankshaft oil pump drive gear and crankshaft sprocket.

2) Remove piston and rod assemblies. Remove main bearing caps. Use puller (KV101041SO) to remove center and rear caps. *See Fig 5.* Remove rear oil seal by prying out with screwdriver. Do not damage crankshaft sealing surface. Remove crankshaft. Remove upper main bearing halves.

MAXIMA 6-CYLINDER DIESEL (Cont.)

NOTE: Keep main bearing caps in order for reassembly reference.

Fig. 5: Removing Center & Rear Main Bearing Caps

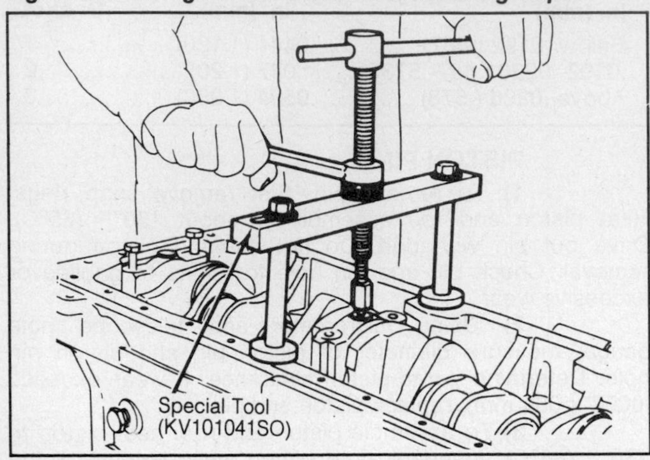
Special Tool
(KV101041SO)

Loosen main bearing cap bolts in sequence, in three steps.

Inspection

1) Check shaft journals and crankpins for scoring, wear, or cracks. Taper and out-of-round of journals and crankpins must not exceed .0012" (.030 mm). Check crankshaft for bend by placing on "V" blocks. Use dial indicator at center journal of crankshaft.

2) If bend exceeds .002" (.05 mm), which is half of indicator reading, replace crankshaft. Check crankshaft pilot bearing for wear or damage by turning by hand in thrust direction. Replace if necessary.

NOTE: Do not damage edge of pilot bearing during replacement or inset excessively.

3) To remove pilot bearing, pull out using tool (ST16610001). Clean bearing hole. Insert new bearing until distance between flange end and bearing is approximately .157" (4 mm) deep.

Installation

1) Install main bearing halves in engine block. Ensure bearings are on correct journal. Journal No. 4 requires a thrust bearing. Bearing for journal No. 1 is the same as journal No. 7. Upper bearing halves have oil hole and oil groove. Lower bearing halves do not. Do not interchange.

2) Apply oil to main bearing surfaces. Install crankshaft. Apply sealant to each side of rear main bearing cap and corners of cylinder block contact point. Install bearing caps so arrow faces front of engine.

3) Shift crankshaft toward front of engine. Tighten main bearing caps in 2 or 3 steps, starting at center bearing and working outward. Ensure crankshaft rotates smoothly. Check crankshaft end play. End play must be less than .012" (.30 mm). If not within specifications, replace center thrust bearing. *See Fig. 6.*

4) Apply sealer and install side seals in rear main bearing cap. Install rear oil seal. Install rear end plate and flywheel. Check flywheel runout using dial indicator. Maximum runout is .006" (.15 mm) or less. Replace or resurface as necessary. Install piston and rod assemblies. To install remaining components, reverse removal procedure.

Fig. 6: Checking Crankshaft End Play

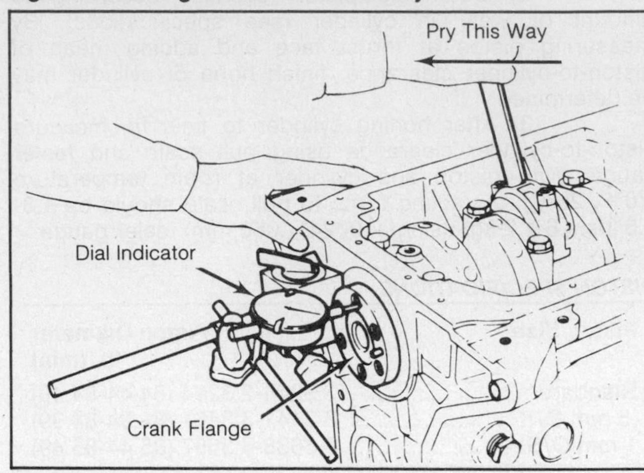
Pry This Way
Dial Indicator
Crank Flange

If end play is incorrect, replace center thrust bearing.

MAIN BEARINGS

1) Check all bearings for scoring or wear. Replace if damage is found. Clean oil from crankshaft. Check clearance using Plastigage method. Maximum main bearing clearance is .0047" (.120 mm).

2) If clearance is not to specifications, replace bearings. Bearings are available in undersizes of .25 mm, .50 mm and .75 mm.

CONNECTING ROD BEARINGS

1) Check connecting rod bearing clearance using Plastigage method. Tighten connecting rod caps to 33-40 ft. lbs. (45-54 N.m). Maximum rod bearing clearance is .0047" (.120 mm).

2) If clearance is not to specifications, replace bearings. Bearings are available in undersizes of .060 mm, .120 mm, .25 mm, .50 mm, .75 mm and 1 mm.

ENGINE OILING

Fig. 7: Cutaway View of Engine Oiling System

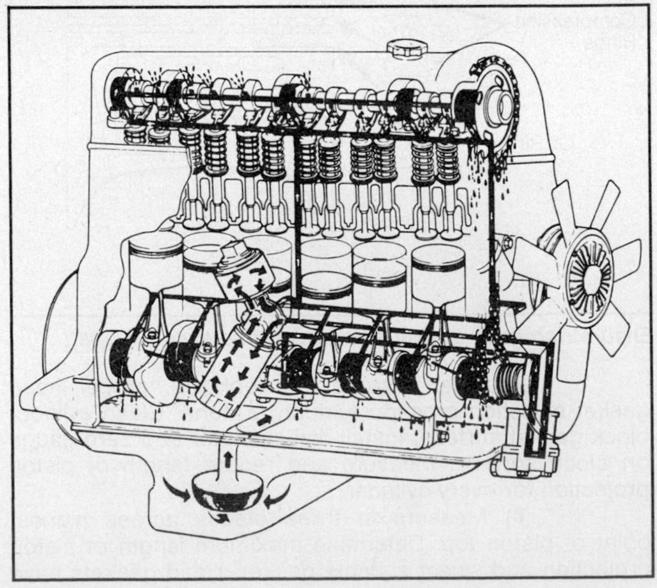

MAXIMA 6-CYLINDER DIESEL (Cont.)

ENGINE OILING SYSTEM

Oil drawn from oil pan passes through a screen to oil pump. Oil is delivered to a two-element oil filter, oil cooler, and main oil gallery. Main oil gallery supplies oil to crankshaft main bearings and drilled passages in crankshaft. Oil sprayed from jet holes on connecting rods lubricates cylinders and piston pins.

Oil from main gallery lubricates chain tensioner and timing chain. A center oil hole in the crankshaft center bearing feeds camshaft bearings on cylinder head. Valve rocker mechanism is lubricated through oil gallery in camshaft and through a small channel at base circle portion of each cam. Rocker arms and valves are lubricated intermittently through small holes or oil pipe.

CRANKCASE CAPACITY

6.5 qts. (6.2L) with oil filter and 6 qts. (5.7L) without filter.

OIL FILTER

A 2-element filter, with oil return pipe, is used. Filter is a disposable cartridge and combines the function of a main and a bypass filter.

OIL PRESSURE

45-55 psi (3.1-3.7 kg/cm²).

OIL PUMP

Removal

1) Oil pump assembly is installed to bottom of front cover by four bolts. Pump is driven by oil pump drive spindle assembly which is in turn driven by gear on crankshaft.

2) To remove pump, drain engine oil, remove 4 retaining bolts and remove oil pump body together with drive spindle. *See Fig. 8.*

Fig. 8: Exploded View of Oil Pump Assembly

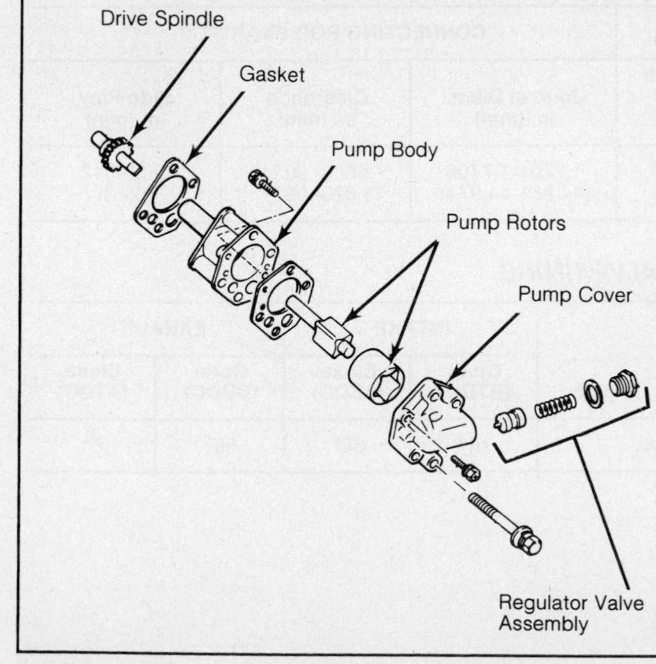

Drive Spindle
Gasket
Pump Body
Pump Rotors
Pump Cover
Regulator Valve Assembly

Pump is serviced as a complete assembly only.

Inspection

1) Disassemble oil pump. Wash all parts thoroughly in clean solvent. Inspect for signs of unusual wear or damage. Check all clearances to specifications.

2) Pump is serviced as a complete assembly only. If components are not to specifications, replace entire pump assembly.

Installation

Fill pump with oil and reverse removal procedure to install.

OIL PUMP SPECIFICATIONS

Application	Clearance In. (mm)
Rotor Tip Clearance	Less Than .008 (.20)
Outer Rotor-to-Body	Less Than .020 (.50)
Rotor-to-Cover	Less Than .002 (.06)
Rotor Side Clearance	Less Than .001 (.03)

ENGINE COOLING

WATER PUMP

A centrifugal type pump with aluminum body is used. To remove, drain cooling system and remove fan shroud. Remove fan belts, fan, and pulley. Remove pump attaching bolts and remove water pump from front cover. To install, reverse removal procedure.

THERMOSTAT

180°F (82°C).

COOLING SYSTEM CAPACITY

11.6 qts. (11L).

RADIATOR CAP

13 psi (.9 kg/cm²).

TIGHTENING SPECIFICATIONS

Application	Ft. Lbs. (N.m)
Camshaft Gear Mount Bolt	87-116 (118-158)
Camshaft Thrust Plate Bolt	4-7 (6-10)
Connecting Rod Nut	33-40 (45-54)
Crankshaft Pulley Mount Bolt	101-116 (137-158)
Cylinder Head Bolt	87-94 (118-128)
Flywheel Mount Bolt	101-116 (137-158)
Glow Plug	14-18 (19-25)
Injection Pump Nut & Bolt	12-15 (16-20)
Intake/Exhaust Manifolds	
8M Bolt	13-16 (18-22)
10M Bolt	25-33 (34-45)
Main Bearing Cap Bolt	51-58 (69-78)
Oil Pump Mounting Bolt	8-11 (11-15)
Rocker Pivot Lock Nut	36-43 (49-59)

Datsun Engines

MAXIMA 6-CYLINDER DIESEL (Cont.)

ENGINE SPECIFICATIONS

GENERAL SPECIFICATIONS

Year	DISPLACEMENT		Fuel System	HP@RPM	Torque Ft. Lbs.@RPM	Compr. Ratio	BORE		STROKE	
	Cu. In.	Liters					In.	mm	In.	mm
1983	170.9	2.8L	Fuel Inj.	80 @ 4600	120 @ 2400	22.7:1	3.33	84.5	3.27	83.0

VALVES

Engine Size & Valve	Head Diam. In. (mm)	Face Angle	Seat Angle	Seat Width In. (mm)	Stem Diameter In. (mm)	Stem Clearance In. (mm)	Valve Lift In. (mm)
2.8L							
Intake	1.54 (39)	45.5°	45°	.075 (1.91)	.3136-.3142 (7.965-7.980)	.0008-.0021 (.020-.053)	.....
Exhaust	1.26 (32)	45.5°	45°	.061 (1.56)	.3128-.3134 (7.945-7.960)	.0016-.0029 (.040-.073)	.....

PISTONS, PINS, RINGS

Engine	PISTONS	PINS		RINGS		
	Clearance In. (mm)	Piston Fit In. (mm)	Rod Fit In. (mm)	Ring No.	End Gap In. (mm)	Side Clearance In. (mm)
2.8L	.0020-.0028 (.05-.07)	.0-.0002 (.0-.004)	.0010-.0017 [1] (.025-.044)	No. 1	.0079-.0114 [2] (.20-.29)	.0024-.0039 (.060-.100)
				No. 2	.0079-.0138 (.20-.35)	.0016-.0013 (.040-.080)
				Oil	.0118-.0177 (.30-.45)	.0012-.0028 (.030-.070)

[1] – Interference fit.
[2] – Without mark. Ring with mark, gap is .0055-.0087" (.14-.22 mm).

CRANKSHAFT MAIN & CONNECTING ROD BEARINGS

Engine	MAIN BEARINGS				CONNECTING ROD BEARINGS		
	Journal Diam. In. (mm)	Clearance In. (mm)	Thrust Bearing	Crankshaft End Play In. (mm)	Journal Diam. In. (mm)	Clearance In. (mm)	Side Play In. (mm)
2.8L	2.1631-2.1636 (54.942-54.955)	.0008-.0024 (.020-.062)	No. 4	.002-.007 (.05-.18)	1.7701-1.7706 (44.961-44.974)	.0008-.0024 (.020-.062)	.008-.012 (.2-.3)

VALVE SPRINGS

Engine	Free Length In. (mm)	PRESSURE Lbs. @ In. (Kg @ mm)	
		Valve Closed	Valve Open
2.8L	1.9594 (49.77)	51@1.575 (23@40.0)	115@1.181 (52@30.0)

VALVE TIMING

Engine	INTAKE		EXHAUST	
	Open (BTDC)	Close (ABDC)	Open (BBDC)	Close (ATDC)
2.8L	14°	38°	60°	8°

CAMSHAFT

Engine	Journal Diam. In. (mm)	Clearance In. (mm)	Lobe Lift In. (mm)
2.8L	1.8878-1.8883 (47.949-47.962)	.0015-.0026 (.038-.067)	

Honda Engines

ACCORD, CIVIC & PRELUDE 4-CYLINDER

ENGINE CODING

ENGINE IDENTIFICATION

Engine serial number is under hood on front left fender and stamped on a machined pad of transaxle. Pad is located on firewall side of engine near the transaxle. Serial number is preceded by engine model number.

ENGINE IDENTIFICATION

Application	Code
Accord (1.75L)	EK1
Civic (1.3L)	EJ1
Civic (1.5L)	EM1
Prelude (1.8L)	ES1

ENGINE, MANIFOLDS & CYLINDER HEAD

ENGINE

Removal

1) Remove battery cables and battery. On Civic, remove battery mounting tray. On Prelude, remove headlight manual retracting knob caps, and turn knobs to bring headlights to "ON" position. On all models, remove grille and bumper apron. On Civic, remove headlight trim.

2) On all models, remove hood brackets and hood. Remove oil filler cap, and drain engine oil from crankcase. Remove radiator cap, and drain coolant from radiator and engine.

NOTE: Engine coolant drain plug is located below No. 2 spark plug.

3) Drain transaxle. Remove air cleaner, filter and all related hoses and ducting. Label and disconnect all vacuum, ventilation and air hoses between engine and chassis. Label and disconnect all electrical wiring between engine and chassis. Disconnect fuel hose at fuel filter.

4) To prevent damage, remove anti-afterburn valve prior to attaching engine hoist lifting chain to engine hoist bracket near valve. Also attach chain to transaxle bracket.

5) Disconnect throttle cable from carburetor, using care not to bend cable. If equipped, remove cruise control actuator bracket bolts, and pull actuator away from body panel. Disconnect vacuum reservoir hose.

CAUTION: When removing throttle cable, ONLY remove lock nut facing throttle lever.

6) Remove radiator hoses and heater hoses from engine. If equipped, detach EGR control box and let hang next to engine. Remove alternator. If A/C equipped, remove compressor (with hoses connected) and bracket, and secure away from engine.

7) On manual transaxle models, loosen clutch cable adjusting nut and disconnect cable from release arm. Remove shift rod yoke attaching bolt and shift lever torque rod at transaxle housing. To remove shift rod on Civic, pull back spring clip, and remove spring pin with a punch.

8) On all automatic transaxle models, remove oil cooling lines at transaxle. Remove shift cable holder at transaxle. On all models, remove cable clip and pull speedometer cable from cable holder. DO NOT remove cable holder. If equipped, remove tachometer cable at engine.

9) If equipped with power steering, remove speed sensor and "V" belt. Disconnect pump and move it to one side. Remove power steering pump bracket.

10) On California and high altitude models, remove air jet controller. On all models, remove connectors and hoses from 3 control boxes. Lift boxes from their brackets, allowing them to hang beside engine. Disconnect ground cable at transmission.

11) Place front of vehicle on jack stands and remove front wheels. On vehicles with automatic transaxle, remove shift console. Place shift lever in reverse, and remove lock pin from end of shift cable. Unscrew cable mounting bolts and remove shift cable holder. Remove exhaust header pipe from manifold.

12) Remove cotter pin and castle nut at tie rod ball joints. On Accord and Prelude, use ball joint remover tool (07941-6920001) to disconnect right and left lower arm bolt and tie rod end ball joints. On Civic, use same tool to remove right and left lower arm ball joints and tie rod ball joints.

13) On all models, turn each steering knuckle outward as far as possible. Using a screwdriver, pry against inner "CV" joint at transaxle housing (move it approximately 1/2") forcing spring clip out of its groove inside differential side gear splines. Remove right and left axles. Coat precision finished surfaces with clean oil or grease. Place plastic bags over drive shaft ends.

CAUTION: When pulling axles, be careful not to damage differential seals.

14) Raise engine enough to relieve load on engine mounts. Remove 3 engine support bolts and push engine support (timing belt side of engine) into shock mount bracket. Remove front and rear engine mounts and torque rods (swing rods out of way).

15) Carefully lift engine and transaxle assembly approximately 6". Check for and remove any hoses, wires or other components which still attached to both engine and chassis. Lift engine and transaxle assembly from vehicle.

Installation

1) Install engine in reverse order of removal. When replacing axles, insert driveshaft until spring clip "clicks" into groove in differential side gear.

NOTE: Always use new spring clips when installing driveshafts.

2) Make sure all wires and hoses are connected properly. Be sure oil cooler hoses are not interchanged during installation. Check that control cables have not been bent or pinched, and that all cables are adjusted properly.

3) When installing speedometer cable, align tab on cable with slot in holder. Install clip so bent leg is on groove side. Pull lightly on cable to make sure it is secure. Readjust clutch pedal free play, and make sure transmission shifts smoothly.

4) Prior to installing, apply sealant to coolant drain plug and a new washer on engine oil drain plug. Restore all fluids to proper levels. Open heater valve and unscrew bleed bolt to bleed air from cooling system.

ACCORD, CIVIC & PRELUDE 4-CYLINDER (Cont.)

CYLINDER HEAD

Removal

CAUTION: DO NOT remove cylinder head until engine temperature drops below 100°F (38°C).

1) Disconnect negative cable from battery. Drain cooling system. Remove upper radiator hose, heater hose and by-pass hose. Remove air cleaner and related hoses and ducting.

2) Label and disconnect all electrical wiring to cylinder head. Disconnect fuel lines, vacuum hoses and throttle cable from carburetor. Remove carburetor. Remove wiring and vacuum hoses from distributor.

3) Remove header pipe from exhaust manifold (on Prelude, remove header pipe bracket). If equipped, remove power steering pump and set aside (DO NOT disconnect hoses). On vehicles without A/C, remove bolt securing alternator bracket to cylinder head and loosen alternator adjusting bolt.

4) On A/C models, remove compressor (with hoses connected) and secure away from engine. Remove compressor bracket. Remove cam cover and timing belt upper cover. Bring No. 1 piston to TDC at end of compression stroke. Loosen timing belt pivot and adjusting bolts. Slip timing belt off camshaft sprocket.

CAUTION: DO NOT crimp or bend timing belt more than 90°. Do not permit belt sides to deflect within 1" (25 mm) of each other.

5) On Civic and Accord, remove oil pump gear cover and pull oil pump shaft out of cylinder head. On Prelude engines, remove carburetors and intake manifold.

Fig. 1: Honda Cylinder Head Tightening Sequences

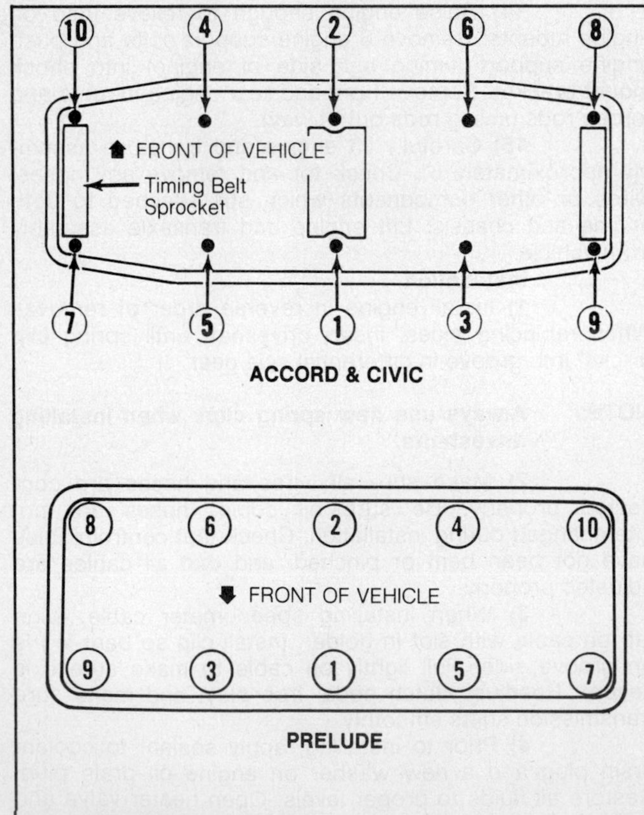
10
4
2
6
8
FRONT OF VEHICLE
Timing Belt
Sprocket
7
5
1
3
9
ACCORD & CIVIC
8
6
2
4
10
FRONT OF VEHICLE
9
3
1
5
7
PRELUDE

Bolts should be tightened in 2 steps.

Remove cylinder head bolts in reverse of tightening sequence by turning 1/3 turn at a time until all bolts are loosened. Remove cylinder head.

Installation

NOTE: Use new gaskets and "O" rings when installing cylinder head.

1) Ensure that all mating surfaces are clean and free of cracks. Check that No. 1 piston is still on TDC. Time valves by aligning camshaft sprocket timing marks. *See Figs. 3 and 4*.

2) Using a new head gasket, install head bolts. Tighten in sequence in 2 steps, first to 22 ft. lbs. (30 N.m), then to 49 ft. lbs. (68 N.m) for Prelude 1.8L engine or 44 ft. lbs. (60 N.m) for all other engines. *See Fig. 1*. To complete installation, reverse removal procedure.

Fig. 2: Honda Manifold Tightening Sequences

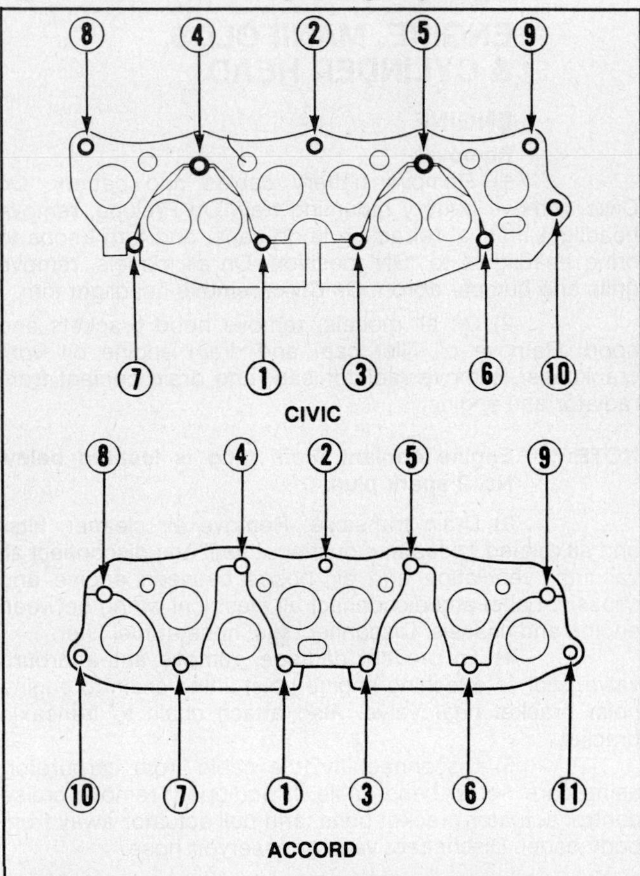
8
4
2
5
9
7
1
3
6
10
CIVIC
8
4
2
5
9
10
7
1
3
6
11
ACCORD

Manufacturer does not indicate sequence for Prelude 1.8L manifolds.

MANIFOLDS

NOTE: Prelude engine has intake manifold on rear side of engine and exhaust manifold on front side of engine. Accord and Civic engines have both manifolds on rear side of engine.

Removal

Disconnect exhaust header pipe from manifold. Loosen 4 intake-to-exhaust manifold bolts on Prelude engine (3 for other models). Remove manifold-to-cylinder head mounting nuts in reverse order of tightening sequence. *See Fig. 2*. Remove and disassemble manifolds.

ACCORD, CIVIC & PRELUDE 4-CYLINDER (Cont.)

Installation (Accord & Civic)

1) Use new gaskets at all locations. Initially, finger tighten exhaust manifold-to-intake manifold bolts. Install manifolds. *See Fig. 2.*

NOTE: **Spring washers used with special nuts must be installed with dished surface facing inward.**

2) Tighten manifolds-to-cylinder head nuts and bolts securing manifolds together, to 7 ft. lbs. (10 N.m). Tighten all manifold nuts and bolts further to 16 ft. lbs. (22 N.m).

Installation (Prelude)

1) Using new gaskets at all locations, install exhaust manifold on cylinder head. Tighten manifold-to-cylinder head nuts to 7 ft. lbs. (10 N.m). Tighten further to 20 ft. lbs. (28 N.m). *See Fig. 2.*

NOTE: **Manufacturer does not indicate tightening sequence for manifold nuts and bolts on Prelude 1.8L engine.**

2) Install exhaust shroud, tightening bolts to 16 ft. lbs. (22 N.m). Using new gaskets, install intake manifold on cylinder head. Tighten all manifold nuts to 16 ft. lbs. (22 N.m).

CAMSHAFT

TIMING BELT & CAMSHAFT PULLEY

Removal

1) Turn crankshaft counterclockwise to position No. 1 piston on TDC at end of compression stroke. Ensure valve timing marks are properly aligned. *See Figs. 3 and 4*. Remove all drive belts from pulleys. Remove water pump pulley and crankshaft pulley.

2) Remove upper timing belt cover from cylinder head. Remove lower timing belt cover from engine block. Loosen timing belt tensioner to relieve tension on timing belt.

CAUTION: **Never expose timing belt to oil or grease, as this will cause belt deterioration.**

3) If same timing belt is to be reused, mark direction of belt rotation before removing. Slide belt off pulleys. Remove camshaft pulley retaining bolt and washer. Pull off pulley.

VALVE TIMING

Be sure No. 1 piston is at TDC (mark on flywheel or driveplate aligned with index mark). Valve timing is correct if camshaft timing marks are properly aligned. *See Figs. 3 and 4*. For timing belt removal and installation procedures, *see Timing Belt and Camshaft Pulley*.

Installation

1) Ensure crankshaft is still at TDC. Install camshaft pulley, special washer and retaining bolt. Tighten to 27 ft. lbs. (38 N.m) on Prelude model; 22 ft. lbs. (30 N.m) on all other models. Check camshaft position has not changed.

2) On Prelude models, position small pulley hole at top. On other models, large pulley hole with cutaway portion should be at top. Timing mark on pulley should align with cylinder head arrow on Accord 1.75L and Civic 1.5L engines; with valve cover surface on Civic 1.3L and Prelude 1.8L engines. *See Figs. 3 and 4*.

3) Loosen tensioner adjusting and pivot bolts. Install timing belt onto sprockets, making sure directional arrow on belt points in original direction of rotation. Use care not to excessively bend or twist belt.

Fig. 3: Positioning Camshaft Timing Marks for 1.3L and 1.8L Engines

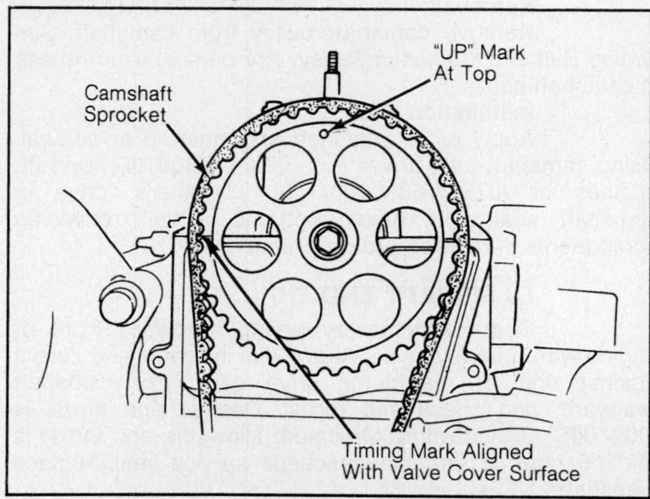
"UP" Mark
At Top
Camshaft
Sprocket
Timing Mark Aligned
With Valve Cover Surface

4) Rotate crankshaft counterclockwise 1/4 turn to create tension on belt. Tighten lower tensioner adjusting bolt. Tighten upper pivot bolt. Reverse removal procedures to complete installation.

Fig. 4: Positioning Camshaft Timing Marks for 1.5L and 1.75L Engines

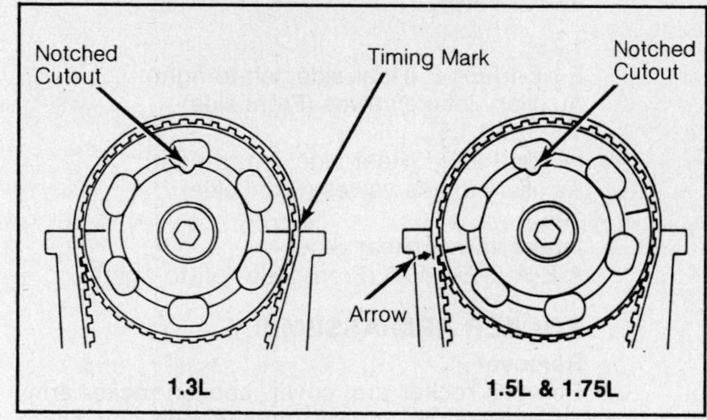
Notched
Cutout
Timing Mark
Notched
Cutout
Arrow
1.3L
1.5L & 1.75L

CAMSHAFT

Removal

Remove timing belt and camshaft pulley. *See Timing Belt and Camshaft Pulley*. Starting at the ends and working toward middle, loosen rocker arm bolts 2 turns at a time in a criss-cross pattern. When fully loosened, remove rocker assembly from cylinder head. Lift out camshaft and seal.

Installation

1) Oil camshaft journals and bearing surfaces in caps and cylinder head. Install camshaft with keyway pointing upward (No. 1 piston at TDC). On 1.8L engine, install oil seal with spring side facing in. Install rocker arm assembly.

2) Starting with bolts at middle of rocker arm assembly and working outward in a circular pattern, tighten all bolts to 9 ft. lbs. (12 N.m). Tighten 8 mm bolts only to 16 ft. lbs. (22 N.m).

3) Install remaining components in reverse order of removal. Before installing cam cover gasket, apply non-hardening sealant to upper rounded surface of front and rear camshaft caps.

CAMSHAFT OIL SEAL

Removal

Remove camshaft pulley from camshaft. *See Timing Belt and Camshaft Pulley*. Pry oil seal from recess in camshaft cap.

Installation

Apply oil to camshaft and inner lip of oil seal. Using camshaft seal driver tool (07947-SB00100) for 1.8L engines or (07947-6890100) for all others, drive in camshaft seal until driver bottoms. Install remaining components in reverse order of removal.

CAMSHAFT END THRUST

Seat camshaft by prying it toward front of engine with a screwdriver. Attach dial indicator and zero it against end of distributor drive gear. Pry camshaft rearward, and check end thrust. Desired end thrust is .002-.006" (.05-.15 mm). Maximum allowable end thrust is .02" (.5 mm). If end play exceeds service limit, replace camshaft.

VALVES

VALVE ARRANGEMENT

NOTE: **Valve arrangement, listed as left-to-right, is as engine sits in vehicle (cylinder No. 4-to-1). Letter A under 1.8L engine indicates auxiliary intake valve.**

1.75L
E-I-E-I-I-E-I-E (Rear side, left-to-right)
Auxiliary intake valves (Front side)
1.3L and 1.5L
I-E-E-I-I-E-E-I (Rear side, left-to-right)
Auxiliary intake valves (Front side)
1.8L
Intake valves (Rear Side)
A-E-A-E-E-A-E-A (Front Side, left-to-right)

ROCKER ARM ASSEMBLY

Removal

Remove rocker arm cover. Loosen rocker arm shaft bolts in criss-cross pattern starting with end caps and working inward. To disassemble 1.3L, 1.5L and 1.75L engines, pull roll pins out of end caps. Keep parts in order for reassembly.

Installation

If shafts were disassembled, reassemble in reverse order of disassembly. Install rocker arm assembly on engine. Tighten support bolts to 16 ft. lbs. (22 N.m) in a circular pattern, starting with center support bolts and working outward.

VALVE GUIDE SERVICING

Inspection

Disassemble cylinder head. Measure inside diameter of valve guide and outside diameter of valve stem to determine stem-to-guide clearance. If clearance is excessive, replace guides and install new valves.

CAUTION: **Use heavy gloves to avoid being burned, when handling heated cylinder head.**

Removal

Heat cylinder head to 300°F (150°C). Using exact valve guide driver and working on combustion chamber side of head, drive guide out top side of head.

NOTE: **It may be necessary to remove some valve guides using an air hammer.**

Installation

Using correct valve guide driver tool and adapter tool, install new valve guides working from top of head. Drive guide in until adapter bottoms on head. To ream valve guides to proper clearance, use cutting oil, valve guide reamer (07984-6890100) for exhaust or (07984-6570100) for intake. After reaming is complete, wash guides thoroughly in detergent and water.

VALVE STEM OIL SEALS

When replacing valve stem oil seals, note that seals for intake valves have a white spring around neck of seal. Oil seals for exhaust valves have a black spring around neck of seal.

VALVE GUIDE DRIVER TOOL SPECIFICATIONS

Application	Tool
1.3L & 1.5L	
Remover	
Exhaust	07942-6570100
Intake	07942-6570100
Installer	
Exhaust	[1] 07943-6890100
Intake	[1] 07943-6890100
1.75L	
Remover	
Exhaust	07742-SA50000
Intake	07742-SA50000
Installer	
Exhaust	[1] 07943-SA50000
Intake	[1] 07943-SA50000
1.8L	
Remover	
Exhaust	07942-8230000
Intake	07942-6570100
Installer	
Exhaust	[2] 07943-SA50000
Intake	[2] 07943-6890100

[1] – Adapter is to be used in conjuction with remover.
[2] – Use with valve guide driver tool (07943-6890100).

VALVE SPRINGS

Removal

Remove cylinder head from engine. Using valve spring compressor, remove valve keepers, retainer and springs. Keep parts in order for installation.

Inspection

Using a steel square and flat surface, check valve springs for squareness. Measure free length of valve springs. Using valve spring tension tester, measure spring tension.

Installation

NOTE: **Before installing valves in cylinder head, coat stems with oil, install and check for smooth movement.**

ACCORD, CIVIC & PRELUDE 4-CYLINDER (Cont.)

Install in reverse of removal procedure. Install springs with closely wound coil end towards spring seat. Check valve spring installed height, and adjust as necessary.

VALVE SPRING INSTALLED HEIGHT SPECIFICATIONS

Application	Measurement In. (mm)
1.3L, 1.5L & 1.75L	
Auxiliary Valve Spring	.98 (25.0)
Intake & Exhaust	
Inner Valve Spring	1.40 (35.6)
Outer Valve Spring	1.49 (37.8)
1.8L	
Auxiliary Valve Spring	.98 (25.0)
Intake	1.66 (42.2)
Exhaust	
Inner Valve Spring	1.46 (37.0)
Outer Valve Spring	1.67 (42.3)

AUXILIARY INTAKE VALVES

Removal

1) Remove auxiliary valve holder nut using special "T" wrench (07907-6570001). Using slide hammer (07741-0010100) and weight (07936-3710200), remove valve holder assembly.

2) Compress spring and remove keepers. Disassemble and inspect valve assembly. Valve seat may be reconditioned, however entire assembly should be replaced if any component exceeds service limit.

NOTE: **An auxiliary chamber is not used on 1.8L engines.**

3) To remove auxiliary chamber, on 1.3L and 1.5L engines, use slide hammer (07936-6340000) and auxiliary chamber remover tool (07940-SA00200) to pull chamber. To remove auxiliary chamber, on 1.75L engines, use slide hammer (07940-6590300) and auxiliary chamber remover tool (07940-6930200) to pull chamber.

Installation

1) Coat valve parts with oil before assembly. On 1.3L, 1.5L and 1.75L engines, install chamber in each auxiliary valve hole with 2 new gaskets. Insert alignment tool (07944-6590000) in spark plug hole to center the chamber.

2) Install new "O" ring on auxiliary valve assembly, then install in chamber. Using "T" wrench tool (07907-6570001), torque lock nut to 58 ft. lbs. (80 N.m).

VALVE CLEARANCE ADJUSTMENT

1) Adjust valves when engine temperature is 100° F (38° C) or less. Remove valve cover. Rotate crankshaft so that No. 1 piston is on TDC at end of compression stroke. Timing marks should align. Adjust valve clearances on No. 1 cylinder.

2) Rotate crankshaft counterclockwise 180° so that No. 3 piston is on TDC at end of compression stroke. Adjust valve clearances on No. 3 cylinder.

3) Rotate crankshaft counterclockwise 180° and adjust valve clearances on No. 4 cylinder. Rotate crankshaft counterclockwise 180° and adjust valve clearances on No. 2 cylinder.

VALVE CLEARANCE SPECIFICATIONS

Application	Clearance In. (mm)
1.3L & 1.5L	
Intake and Auxiliary	.005-.007 (.12-.17)
Exhaust	.007-.009 (.17-.22)
1.75L & 1.8L	
Intake and Auxiliary	.005-.007 (.12-.17)
Exhaust	.010-.012 (.25-.30)

PISTONS, PINS & RINGS

PISTON & ROD ASSEMBLY

Removal

1) Remove oil pan and cylinder head. Remove any ridge from top of cylinder bore. Mark connecting rod and cap for cylinder identification.

NOTE: **Do not confuse number stamped on connecting rod and cap with number indicating position of assembly in engine. This number indicates rod big end bore size only.**

2) Remove rod cap. Push piston and rod assembly out top of cylinder block. Install cap on rod from which removed.

Installation

1) Lubricate piston, rings and cylinder bore with engine oil. Install piston rings and properly space end gaps on piston. *See Fig. 5*.

2) Install piston and rod into cylinder bore. When properly installed, round mark on piston head (triangular mark on 1.75L pistons) and oil hole in connecting rod will be positioned toward intake manifold side. *See Fig. 6*. Install and tighten rod cap.

FITTING PISTONS

1) Measure cylinder bore at 3 places for out-of-round and taper. If either out-of-round or taper exceeds .002" (.05 mm), rebore cylinder for oversize pistons. *See Cylinder Bore Sizes table.*.

NOTE: **Top of 1.8L cylinder block is marked with four letters (either A or B). When read from left-to-right, they indicate cylinder bore size for cylinders No. 1 through 4.**

2) Determine piston-to-cylinder bore clearance. If not within specifications, rebore cylinder and install oversize pistons.

FITTING RINGS

1) Push a ring into cylinder bore approximately 3/4" from bottom of bore. Ring must be square in bore. Using a feeler gauge, measure ring end gap. Compare measurement with specifications.

2) Install rings onto piston. Both compression rings are chamfered. Note that top compression ring has two 30° chamfers on outer edge. Second compression ring's outer edge is slightly chamfered. Using a feeler gauge, measure ring side clearance between ring and ring land.

ACCORD, CIVIC & PRELUDE 4-CYLINDER (Cont.)

CYLINDER BORE SIZES

Application	New Diameter In. (mm)
1.3L	
Standard	[1] 2.834-2.835 (72.00-72.02)
Oversize	2.844-2.845 (72.25-72.27)
1.5L	
Standard	[2] 2.913-2.914 (74.00-74.02)
Oversize	2.923-2.924 (74.25-74.27)
1.75L	
Standard	[3] 13.031-3.032 (77.00-77.02)
Oversize	3.041-3.042 (77.25-77.27)
1.8L [4]	
"A" Standard	[5] 3.1500-3.1504 (80.01-80.02)
"A" .25 O/S	3.1585-3.1594 (80.225-80.248)
"A" .50 O/S	3.1683-3.1692 (80.475-80.498)
"B" Standard	[6] 3.1496-3.1500 (80.00-80.01)
"B" .25 O/S	3.1581-3.1590 (80.215-80.238)
"B" .50 O/S	3.1679-3.1688 (80.465-80.488)

[1] – Service limit is 2.839" (72.10 mm).
[2] – Service limit is 2.917" (74.10 mm).
[3] – Service limit is 3.043" (77.30 mm).
[4] – "A" or "B" designation is located on top surface of cylinder block.
[5] – Service limit is 3.1516" (80.05 mm).
[6] – Service limit is 3.1512" (80.04 mm).

PISTON SIZES AVAILABLE [1]

Application	New Diameter In. (mm)
1.3L	
Standard	2.833-2.835 (71.97-72.00)
Oversize	2.843-2.844 (72.22-72.25)
1.5L	
Standard	2.912-2.913 (73.96-73.99)
Oversize	2.922-2.933 (74.21-74.24)
1.75L	
Standard	3.0299-3.0307 (76.96-76.99)
Oversize	3.0398-3.0405 (77.21-77.23)
1.8L	
"A" Standard	[2] 3.1486-2.1495 (79.975-79-998)
"B" Standard	[3] 3.1482-3.1491 (79.965-79.988)
.25 Oversize	3.1583-3.1594 (80.220-80.248)
.50 Oversize	3.1679-3.1692 (80.465-80.498)

[1] – Measured at bottom of skirt.
[2] – Service limit is 3.1482" (79.965 mm).
[3] – Service limit is 3.1478" (79.955 mm)

3) If ring lands have high steps or are excessively worn, replace piston. Properly space ring end gaps on piston. *See Fig. 5.* Make sure no end gaps are in line with piston pin or thrust face of piston. Install rings with manufacturer's marking facing upward.

PISTON PIN REPLACEMENT

Removal

Using a hydraulic press and piston pin remover/installer tool set (07973-6570002), press piston pin from piston and connecting rod.

NOTE: **When removing or installing piston pin, set piston in press with embossed side facing up. Be sure recessed flat on piston is positioned against lugs on base attachment.**

Fig. 5: Piston Ring End Gaps

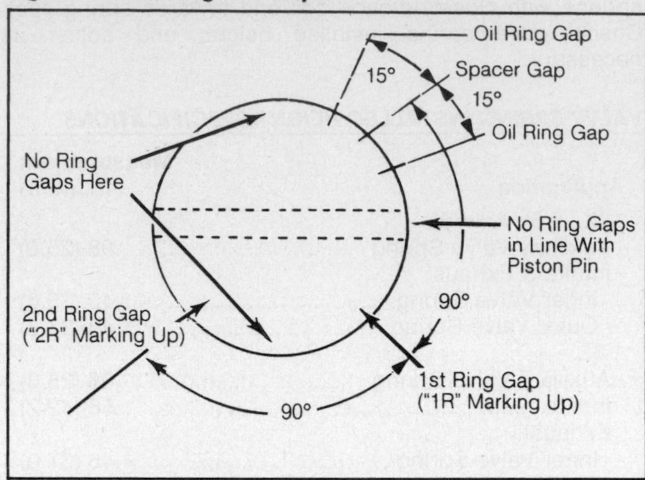
Oil Ring Gap
15°
Spacer Gap
15°
Oil Ring Gap
No Ring Gaps Here
No Ring Gaps in Line With Piston Pin
90°
2nd Ring Gap ("2R" Marking Up)
1st Ring Gap ("1R" Marking Up)
90°

Top compression ring is identified by two 30° chamfers on outer edge.

Installation

Assemble connecting rod to piston so that oil hole in rod and correct round marking on piston head (triangular mark on 1.75L pistons) are on same side. *See Fig. 6.* Lightly lubricate new piston pin with engine oil. Using piston pin installation tool set (07973-6570002), press new pin into piston and connecting rod until pin is centered in rod.

NOTE: **For 1.3L and 1.5L engines, adjust piston pin driver tool (07973-6570201), until lower shoulder of tool is aligned with reference mark for engine. Reference distance for 1.3L engine is 2.13" (54 mm) from end; 2.20" (56 mm) for 1.5L engine.**

Fig. 6: Piston-to-Connecting Rod Relationship

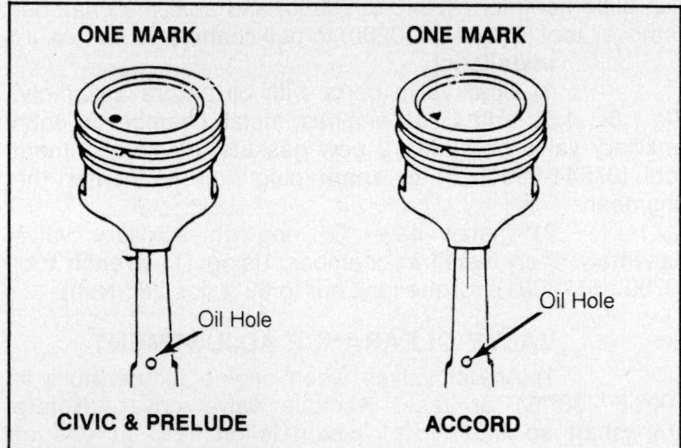
ONE MARK
ONE MARK
Oil Hole
Oil Hole
CIVIC & PRELUDE
ACCORD

Oil hole in connecting rod allows lubrication to thrust side of cylinder wall and piston.

CRANKSHAFT MAIN & CONNECTING ROD BEARINGS

CAUTION: **Replace crankshaft if journals are worn. DO NOT regrind crankshaft, as bearing journals are specially heat-treated.**

ACCORD, CIVIC & PRELUDE 4-CYLINDER (Cont.)

CRANKSHAFT MAIN BEARINGS

1) Prior to disassembly, ensure main bearing caps are marked for identification, for reassembly in their original positions.

2) When using Plastigage method to check bearing clearances, torque main bearings to 29 ft. lbs. (40 N.m) for 1.3L; 33 ft. lbs. (45 N.m) for 1.5L and 48 ft. lbs. (66 N.m) for all others. Ensure oil film is wiped from surfaces to be checked.

3) A code indicating cylinder block bore size for each main journal is stamped into cylinder block. *See Figs. 7 and 8*. Crankshaft main journal sizes are coded, and stamped onto crankshaft. *See Fig. 9*. Use these codes to obtain correct replacement bearings.

4) With crankshaft removed from engine, measure for bend, out-of-round and taper. If any measurement exceeds specifications in Crankshaft Wear Specifications table, replace crankshaft.

Fig. 7: Location of Size Code for Main Journal Bore for 1.75L & 1.8L Engines

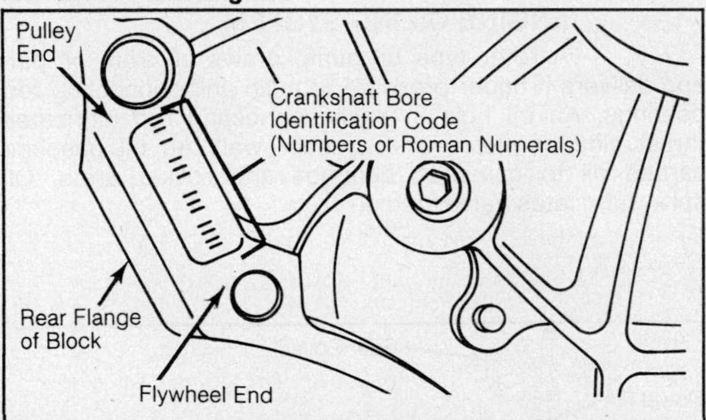
Pulley End
Crankshaft Bore Identification Code (Numbers or Roman Numerals)
Rear Flange of Block
Flywheel End

Roman numerals (letters for 1.5L) indicate journals No. 1-to-5, read from left-to-right.

CONNECTING ROD BEARINGS

1) Prior to disassembly, ensure connecting rod bearing caps are marked for reassembly in their original positions. Also, check connecting rod side play.

CRANKSHAFT WEAR SPECIFICATIONS

Application	Standard In. (mm)	Service Limit In. (mm)
Runout	.0012 (.030)	.0024 (.060)
Taper	.0002 (.005)	.0004 (.010)
Out-of-Round	.0002 (.005)	.0004 (.010)

2) When using Plastigage method to check bearing clearances, torque bearing caps to 23 ft. lbs. (32 N.m) for 1.8L engines; 21 ft. lbs. (29 N.m) for all others. Ensure oil film is wiped from surfaces to be checked.

3) A code is stamped on each connecting rod and cap, indicating bore size of rod's big end. Crankshaft rod journals size codes are stamped on crankshaft counterweight pads. *See Fig. 8*. Use both codes to obtain correct replacement bearings.

Fig. 8: Location of Size Code for Main Journal Bore for 1.3L Engine

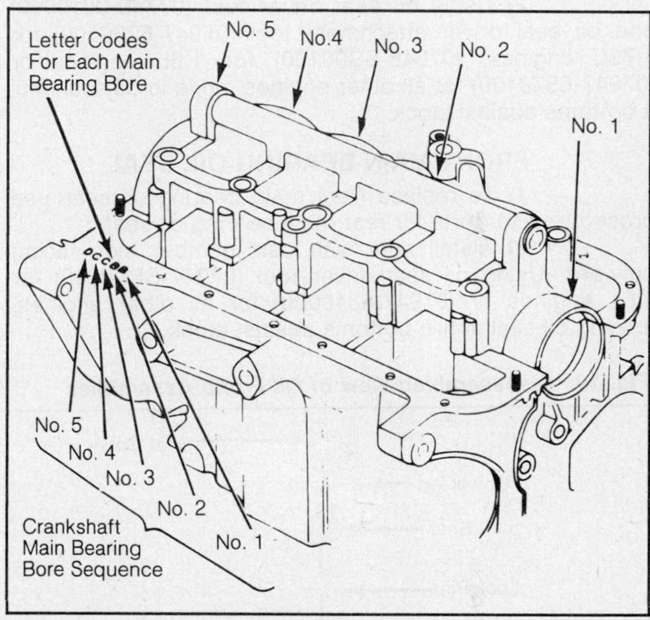
Letter Codes For Each Main Bearing Bore
No. 5
No.4
No. 3
No. 2
No. 1
No. 5
No. 4
No. 3
No. 2
No. 1
Crankshaft Main Bearing Bore Sequence

Fig. 9: Crankshaft Main & Rod Journals Identification Codes

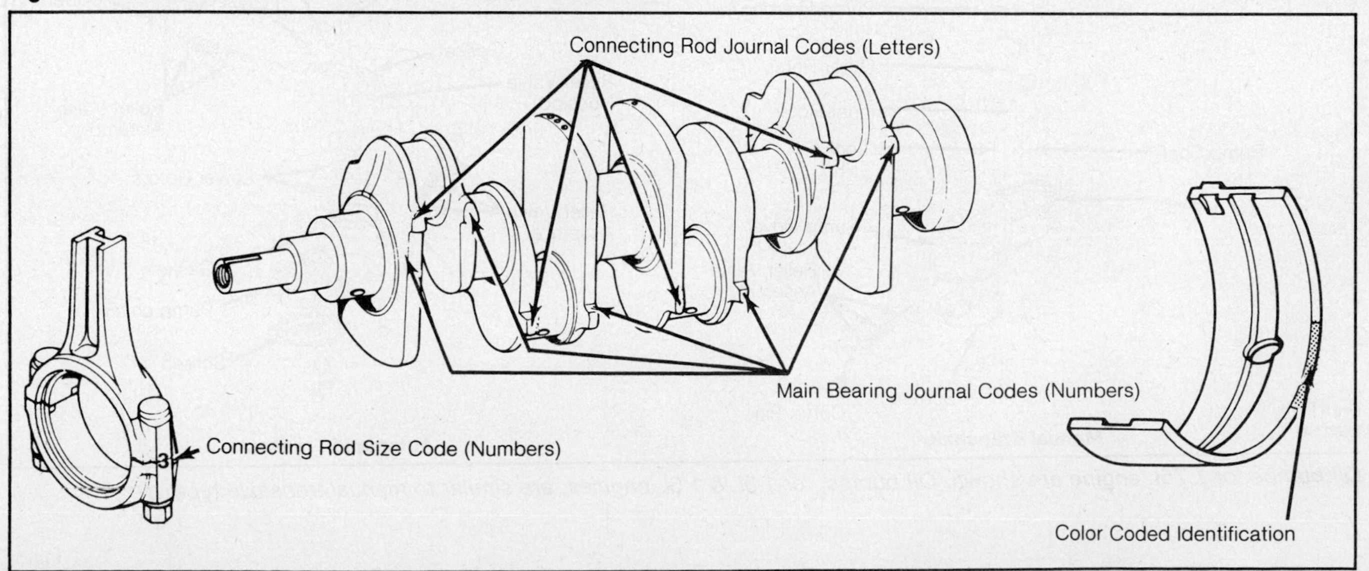
Connecting Rod Journal Codes (Letters)
Main Bearing Journal Codes (Numbers)
Connecting Rod Size Code (Numbers)
Color Coded Identification

ACCORD, CIVIC & PRELUDE 4-CYLINDER (Cont.)

CRANKSHAFT END THRUST

1) Attach a dial indicator to engine with indicator point on end of crankshaft. Push crankshaft away from dial indicator and zero dial indicator.

2) Firmly pull crankshaft towards dial indicator and record measurement. If not within specification, inspect thrust washers and thrust surface of crankshaft.

3) Replace worn parts as necessary. Thrust washer thickness is fixed. Do not change thrust washer thickness by grinding or shimming.

REAR MAIN BEARING OIL SEAL

1) When replacing oil seal, be sure seal bore in cap is dry. Apply non-hardening sealant to inside of seal bore, at cap-to-block parting line. Coat crankshaft and seal lip with engine oil.

2) Using oil seal driver tool (07749-0010000) and oil seal driver attachment tool (07947-6930100) for 1.75L engines, (07948-SB00100) for 1.8L engines or (07947-6570100) for all other engines, drive in oil seal until it bottoms against block.

FRONT MAIN BEARING OIL SEAL

1) To replace front main bearing oil seal, use procedures set forth for rear main bearing oil seal.

2) Install seal with part number side facing outward. Using oil seal driver tool (07947-SB00200) for 1.8L engines or (07947-6340000) for all other engines, drive in oil seal until it bottoms against block.

ENGINE OILING

NOTE: **All oil pumps are driven off camshaft, except for 1.8L engine, which is driven by timing belt. If pump-driven gear is damaged, most likely camshaft drive gear is damaged. In this case, both camshaft and oil pump driven gear must be replaced.**

CRANKCASE CAPACITY

Crankcase capacity for all engines is 3.2 quarts (3.0L) without oil filter replacement; 3.7 quarts (3.5L) when replacing oil filter.

NORMAL OIL PRESSURE

Minimum oil pressure at idle should be 14 psi (.97 kg/cm²) for 1.8L engines or 21 psi (1.45 kg/cm²) for all others. Oil pressure at 3000 RPM should be 48-60 psi (3.4-4.2 kg/cm²), for 1.3L and 1.5L engines or 54-65 psi (3.8-4.6 kg/cm²), for all other engines.

ENGINE OILING SYSTEM

A rotor type oil pump draws oil from oil pan and delivers it under pressure to main and connecting rod bearings. An oil hole in each connecting rod lubricates thrust side of piston and cylinder wall. An oil passage carries oil to camshaft bearings and rocker arms. Oil spray lubricates valve stems.

Fig. 10: Disassembled View of Oil Pump Assemblies

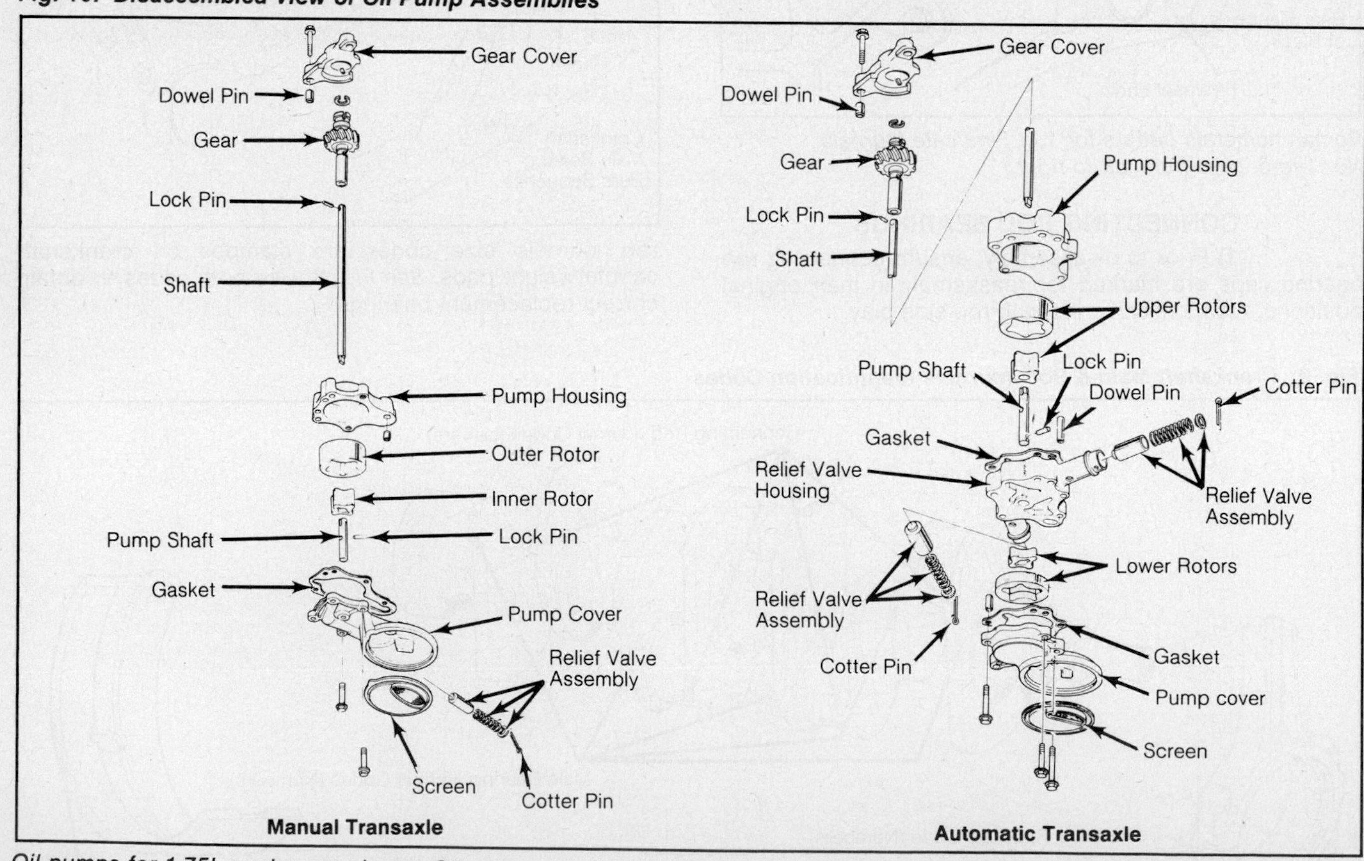
Gear Cover
Dowel Pin
Gear
Lock Pin
Shaft
Pump Housing
Outer Rotor
Inner Rotor
Pump Shaft
Lock Pin
Gasket
Pump Cover
Relief Valve Assembly
Screen
Cotter Pin
Manual Transaxle
Gear Cover
Dowel Pin
Gear
Pump Housing
Lock Pin
Shaft
Upper Rotors
Pump Shaft
Lock Pin
Dowel Pin
Cotter Pin
Gasket
Relief Valve Housing
Relief Valve Assembly
Lower Rotors
Relief Valve Assembly
Cotter Pin
Gasket
Pump cover
Screen
Automatic Transaxle

Oil pumps for 1.75L engine are shown. Oil pumps, for 1.3L & 1.5L engines, are similar to manual transaxle type.

ACCORD, CIVIC & PRELUDE 4-CYLINDER (Cont.)

OIL PUMP

Removal & Disassembly

1) To remove oil pump from 1.8L engine, drain engine oil and remove oil pump drive pulley nut and pulley. Remove 3 bolts and 1 nut holding pump to engine block. Remove oil pump. Remove 2 screws holding cover to pump body and separate.

2) For all others, remove oil pan and oil pump assembly from engine. Remove bolts securing pump cover to pump body.

3) Before removing pump cover, note oil pumps on some models equipped with automatic transaxle have 2 sets of pump rotors. On all models, mark installed position(s) of rotors to ensure installation in their original rotor-to-rotor relation.

4) Disassemble oil pump. To remove relief valve and related components, remove cotter pin from pump cover (or relief valve body). *See Fig. 10.*

Fig. 11: Disassembled View of 1.8L Oil Pump Assembly

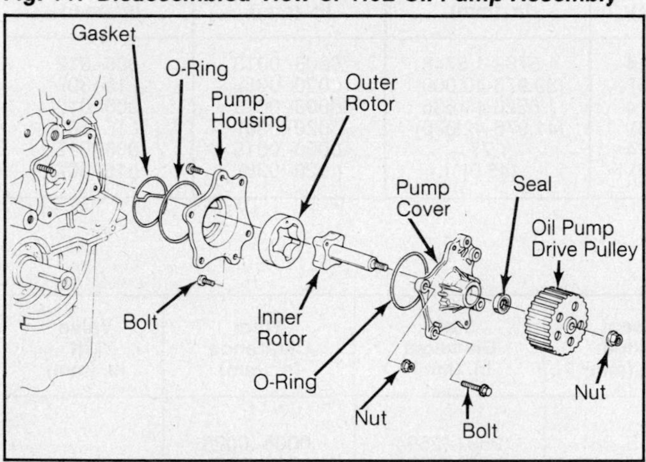
Gasket
O-Ring
Pump Housing
Outer Rotor
Pump Cover
Seal
Oil Pump Drive Pulley
Bolt
Inner Rotor
O-Ring
Nut
Bolt
Nut

Front-mounted pump is operated by timing belt.

Inspection

1) Thoroughly clean and inspect all parts for wear or damage. On pumps with 2 sets of rotors and relief valve assemblies, inspection procedures and specifications apply to both sets.

2) With rotors installed in housing, use a feeler gauge to check clearance between inner rotor lobe and outer rotor. Compare measurement with specifications.

3) With rotors installed in housing, use a feeler gauge to check clearance between outer rotor and housing. Compare measurement with specifications.

4) Place rotors in housing. Lay housing gasket over housing and lay a straightedge over gasket. Insert a feeler gauge between straightedge and rotor assembly to measure rotor end play. Compare measurement with specifications.

5) Check fit of relief valve in its bore. Valve must slide freely in bore. If valve is scored, replace it. Check free length of relief valve spring.

Reassembly & Installation

1) Using new gaskets and "O" rings, reassemble pump in reverse order of disassembly. Make sure rotors are installed in their original positions.

2) Place oil pickup in container of oil and operate pump with screwdriver to prime pump. Place finger over outlet hole and check that pressure is created as pump is turned. Install oil pump in reverse order of removal procedures.

OIL PUMP SPECIFICATIONS

Application	Standard In. (mm)	Service Limit In. (mm)
Rotor Lobe Clearance	.002-.006 (.04-.14)	.008 (.20)
Outer Rotor to Housing	.004-.007 (.10-.18)	.008 (.20)
Rotor End Play	.001-.004 (.03-.10)	.006 (.15)
Spring Free Length	2.00-2.10 (50.8-53.3)	2.00 (50.0)

ENGINE COOLING

THERMOSTAT

Thermostat begins opening about 177-188° F (80-84° C) and is fully open at 203° F (95°C), for all engines. An optional thermostat for 1.8L engines begins to open about 187-194° F (86-90° C) and fully open at 212° F (100° C).

COOLING FAN THERMOSWITCH

At temperatures of 189-197° F (87-92° C), thermoswitch actuates cooling fan. If cooling fan is operating, it should stop at 180-189° F (82-87° C).

COOLANT CAPACITY

Refill capacity (including reserve tank) is 3.6 qts. (3.4L) for 1.3L engines, 4.4 qts. (4.2L) for 1.5L engines and 5.9 qts. (5.6L) for 1.75L engines. Refill capacity (including reserve tank) for 1.8L engines is 7.2 qts. (6.8L) with manual transaxles and 7.9 qts. (7.5L) with automatic transaxles.

WATER PUMP

Removal

Drain radiator and loosen alternator adjusting bolts. Push alternator toward engine and remove drive belt. Remove water pump and "O" ring seal.

Installation

1) Reinstall water pump. Loosen cooling system bleed valve located on thermostat housing. Fill radiator with coolant. When air bubbles no longer appear in coolant, close bleed valve.

2) Start engine. Set heater temperature control lever to high position. Run engine 10 minutes, and open bleed valve again. Allow coolant to drain from bleed valve until air bubbles disappear, then close valve. Refill radiator.

ACCORD, CIVIC & PRELUDE 4-CYLINDER (Cont.)

ENGINE SPECIFICATIONS

GENERAL SPECIFICATIONS

Year	DISPLACEMENT		Fuel System	HP@RPM	Torque Ft. Lbs.@RPM	Compr. Ratio	BORE		STROKE	
	Cu. In.	Liters					In.	mm	In.	mm
1983										
Accord	107	1.75	1 x 3-Bbl.	86@5,800	98.6@3,500	8.8:1	3.03	77.0	3.70	94.0
Civic 1300	81	1.3	1 x 3-Bbl.	60@5,500	73@3,500	9.3:1	2.83	72.0	3.23	82.0
Civic 1500	91	1.5	1 x 3-Bbl.	76@6,000	83.9@3,500	9.3:1	2.91	74.0	3.41	86.5
Prelude	112	1.8	3 x 1-Bbl.	100@5,500	104@4,000	9.4:1	3.15	80.0	5.58	91.0

CRANKSHAFT MAIN & CONNECTING ROD BEARINGS

Engine	MAIN BEARINGS				CONNECTING ROD BEARINGS		
	Journal Diam. In. (mm)	Clearance In. (mm)	Thrust Bearing	Crankshaft End Play In. (mm)	Journal Diam. In. (mm)	Clearance In. (mm)	Side Play In. (mm)
1.3L	1.9676-1.9685 (49.976-50.000)	.0009-.0017 (.024-.043)	No. 4	.004-.014 (.10-.35)	1.5739-1.5748 (39.976-40.000)	.0008-.0015 (.020-.038)	.006-.012 (.15-.30)
1.5L & 1.75L	1.9687-1.9697 (50.006-50.030)	.0010-.0022 (.026-.055)	No. 4	.004-.014 (.10-.35)	1.6526-1.1635 (41.976-42.000)	.0008-.0015 (.020-.038)	.006-.012 (.15-.30)
1.8L	1.9687-1.9697 (50.006-50.030)	.0008-.0019 (.020-.049)	No 3	.004-.014 (.10-.35)	1.77 (45.0)	.0008-.0015 (.020-.038)	.006-.012 (.15-.30)

VALVES

Engine Size & Valve	Head Diam. In. (mm)	Face Angle	Seat Angle	Seat Width In. (mm)	Stem Diameter In. (mm)	Stem Clearance In. (mm)	Valve Lift In. (mm)
1.3L & 1.5L							
Intake	1.366-1.374 (34.70-34.90)	45°	45°	.049-.061 (1.25-1.55)	.2591-.2594 (6.580-6.590)	.0008-.0023 (.023-.058)	.....
Exhaust	1.098-1.106 (27.90-28.10)	45°	45°	.049-.061 (1.25-1.55)	.2574-.2578 (6.537-6.547)	.0025-.0037 (.063-.093)	.....
Auxiliary	.469-.476 (11.90-12.10)	45°	45°	.014-.019 (.35-.49)	.2587-.2593 (6.572-6.587)	.0009-.0023 (.023-.058)	.....
1.75L							
Intake	1.366-1.374 (34.70-34.90)	45°	45°	.049-.061 (1.25-1.55)	.2748-.2751 (6.98-6.99)	.001-.002 (.020-.050)	.....
Exhaust	1.098-1.106 (27.90-28.10)	45°	45°	.049-.061 (1.25-1.55)	.2732-.2736 (6.94-6.95)	.002-.004 (.060-.090)	.....
Auxiliary	.469-.476 (11.90-12.10)	45°	45°	.014-.019 (.35-.49)	.2587-.2593 (6.572-6.587)	.0009-.0023 (.023-.058)	.....
1.8L							
Intake	1.177-1.185 (29.9-30.1)	45°	45°	.049-.061 (1.25-1.55)	.2591-.2594 (6.58-6.59)	.001-.002 (.020-.050)	.....
Exhaust	1.098-1.106 (27.90-28.1)	45°	45°	.049-.061 (1.25-1.55)	.2732-.2736 (6.94-6.95)	.002-.004 (.060-.090)	.....
Auxiliary	469-.476 (11.90-12.10)	45°	45°	.014-.019 (.35-.49)	.2587-.2593 (6.572-6.587)	.0009-.0023 (.023-.058)	.....

ACCORD, CIVIC & PRELUDE 4-CYLINDER (Cont.)

ENGINE SPECIFICATIONS (Cont.)

PISTONS, PINS, RINGS

Engine	PISTONS	PINS		RINGS		
	Clearance In. (mm)	Piston Fit In. (mm)	Rod Fit In. (mm)	Ring No.	End Gap In. (mm)	Side Clearance In. (mm)
1.3L	.0004-.0020 (.010-.050)	.0004-.0009 (.010-.022)	.0006-.0015 (.016-.039)	No. 1 & 2	.006-.014 (.15-.35)	.0012-.0024 (.030-.060)
				Oil	.012-.035 (.30-.90)	.....
1.5L	.0004-.0024 (.010-.060)	.0004-.0009 (.010-.022)	.0006-.0016 (.014-.040)	No. 1 & 2	.006-.014 (.15-.35)	.0012-.0020 (.030-.050)
				Oil	.012-.035 (.30-.90)	.....
1.75L	.0004-.0024 (.010-.060)	.0004-.0009 (.010-.022)	.0007-.0017 (.014-.043)	No. 1 & 2	.006-.014 (.15-.35)	.0008-.0018 (.020-.045)
				Oil	.012-.035 (.30-.90)	.....
1.8L	.0005-.0018 (.012-.045)	.0005-.0009 (.012-.022)	.0006-.0013 (.016-.032)	No. 1 & 2	.008-.014 (.20-.35)	.0008-.0018 (.020-.045)
				Oil	.008-.030 (.20-.70)	.....

CAMSHAFT

Engine	Journal Diam. In. (mm)	Clearance In. (mm)	Lobe Lift In. (mm)
1.8L			
No. 1, 3 & 5	.....	.002-.004 (.05-.09)	.....
No. 2 & 4	.....	.005-.007 (.13-.17)	.....
All Others	.....	.002-.004 (.05-.10)	.....

VALVE SPRINGS

Engine	Free Length In. (mm)	PRESSURE Lbs. @ In. (Kg @ mm)	
		Valve Closed	Valve Open
1.8L			
Intake	1.90 (48.4)	.....	147-170@1.28 (67-77@32.4)
Exhaust			
Inner	1.57 (39.8)	.....	52-60@1.07 (24-27@27.2)
Outer	1.89 (47.9)	.....	.105-120@1.28 (47-55@32.5)
Auxiliary	1.25 (31.7)	.....	35-41@.87 (16-18@22)
All Others			
Intake			
Inner	1.67 (42.3)	.....	28-34@1.008 (12-15@26)
Outer	1.665 (42.30)	.....	99-117@1.09 (45-53@28)
Exhaust			
Inner	1.67 (42.3)	.....	28-34@1.008 (12-15@26)
Outer	1.665 (42.30)	.....	99-117@1.09 (45-53@28)
Auxiliary	1.17 (29.7)	.....	30-36@.87 (13-16@22.0)

TIGHTENING SPECIFICATIONS

Application	Ft. Lbs. (N.m)
Camshaft Sprocket	
1.8L	27 (38)
All Others	22 (30)
Connecting Rod	
1.8L Engines	23 (31)
All Others	21 (28)
Cylinder Head	
1.8L	49 (68)
All Others	44 (60)
Drive Plate	
1.3L & 1.5L Engines	36 (49)
All Others	54 (73)
Flywheel	
1.3L & 1.5L Engines	50 (68)
All Others	76 (103)
Intake & Exhaust Manifold Bolts	
Main Bearing Bolts	
1.3L Engine	29 (39)
1.5L Engine	33 (45)
All Others	48 (65)
Manifold Nuts	
1.8L (Exhaust)	20 (28)
All Others	16 (22)
Rocker Arm Support	
6 mm Bolts	9 (12)
8 mm Bolts	16 (22)
Timing Belt Adjustment Bolt	
1.75L Engine	22 (30)
All Others	32 (44)
Timing Belt Pivot Bolt	
1.75L Engine	22 (30)
All Others	32 (44)

Isuzu Engines

1.8L, 1.9L & 1.95L 4-CYLINDER

I-Mark, Impulse & P'UP

ENGINE CODING

ENGINE IDENTIFICATION

Engine type may be identified by the 8th character of the Vehicle Identification Number (VIN). The VIN is stamped on a metal tab, located on top of instrument panel at lower left of windshield. Engine serial number is stamped on a machined pad on the cylinder block, located near the distributor.

ENGINE IDENTIFICATION CODE

Engine	Code
I-Mark	
1.8L	B
Impulse	
1.95L	A
P'UP	
1.9L	A

NOTE: **Impulse and P'UP engines have the same engine code. These engines share many of the same parts. However, several parts are different and may not interchange. Use correct engine model application whenever service and/or repairs are performed on these engines.**

ENGINE, MANIFOLDS & CYLINDER HEAD

ENGINE

Removal

1) Disconnect battery cables. Remove lower engine cover. Drain crankcase and cooling system. Remove air cleaner assembly. Disconnect accelerator cable and necessary linkages from carburetor. Scribe hinge position on hood and remove hood.

2) Disconnect all coolant and fuel hoses attached to engine. Disconnect and label for reassembly all necessary vacuum lines, electrical, and ignition wiring attached to engine. Disconnect exhaust pipe at manifold. Remove radiator and cooling fan.

3) Disconnect drive shaft, slave cylinder (or clutch cable) and speedometer cable from transmission. If equipped with A/C or power steering, remove from engine and position aside. Do not disconnect refrigerant lines.

4) Remove starter. Remove flywheel inspection cover and bell housing bolts. If equipped with automatic transmission, remove drive plate to torque converter bolts.

5) Support transmission. Attach hoist and lifting chain to engine. Remove front and rear engine mount nuts.

6) Ensure all necessary wiring, hoses, lines, and linkages have been disconnected from engine. Separate engine from transmission and lift out of engine compartment.

Installation

To install engine, reverse removal procedure. Restore all wiring, linkages, cables, hoses, and lines to their original locations.

INTAKE MANIFOLD

Removal

1) Disconnect battery ground cable. Drain cooling system. Remove air cleaner assembly. Remove EGR pipe from manifolds. If necessary, remove EGR valve and bracket assembly from intake manifold.

2) Disconnect all coolant and vacuum hoses attached to intake manifold. Disconnect fuel hose, accelerator cable, vacuum hoses and electrical wiring from carburetor or throttle body.

3) Remove intake manifold and carburetor (or throttle body) as an assembly.

Installation

Clean all gasket surfaces. Using new gasket, install intake manifold. Starting at middle of manifold and working outward, tighten manifold nuts in progressive steps. Install remaining components in reverse order of removal.

EXHAUST MANIFOLD

Removal

1) Disconnect battery ground cable. Remove EGR pipe clamp bolt at rear of cylinder head. Remove EGR pipe from manifolds. Disconnect exhaust pipe support brackets. Disconnect exhaust pipe from manifold.

2) Remove exhaust manifold heat shield and heat stove tube. If equipped, disconnect oxygen sensor wire at exhaust manifold. Remove exhaust manifold.

Installation

Clean gasket mating surfaces. Using new gasket, install and tighten exhaust manifold. Reverse removal procedures to install remaining components.

CYLINDER HEAD

Removal

1) Drain cooling system. Disconnect EGR pipe clamp bolt at rear of cylinder head. Disconnect exhaust pipe from manifold. Disconnect all necessary coolant and vacuum hoses from intake manifold and cylinder head.

2) Disconnect all necessary linkages, cables and electrical wiring from carburetor or fuel injection intake chamber. Disconnnect ignition wires from spark plugs. On I-Mark and P'UP models, remove fuel pump.

3) Remove air cleaner assembly and valve cover. Rotate crankshaft to position No. 4 piston on TDC at end of compression stroke. Remove distributor cap and mark rotor-to-housing relationship.

4) Lock timing chain adjuster by depressing and turning automatic adjuster slide pin 90° clockwise. *See Fig. 1*.

5) Remove camshaft sprocket (with timing chain attached) and fuel pump drive cam. DO NOT allow sprocket and chain to separate. Rest sprocket and chain on chain damper and tensioner.

6) Disconnect air injection pump air hose and check valve at exhaust manifold. Remove cylinder head-to-front cover bolts.

7) Starting with outer bolts and working inward, remove cylinder head bolts. Remove cylinder head with manifolds attached.

Installation

1) Clean gasket mating surfaces. Clean head bolts and threads in cylinder block. Install new head gasket with marking "TOP" upward, and install cylinder head.

1.8L, 1.9L & 1.95L 4-CYLINDER (Cont.)

Fig. 1: Locking Timing Chain Adjuster

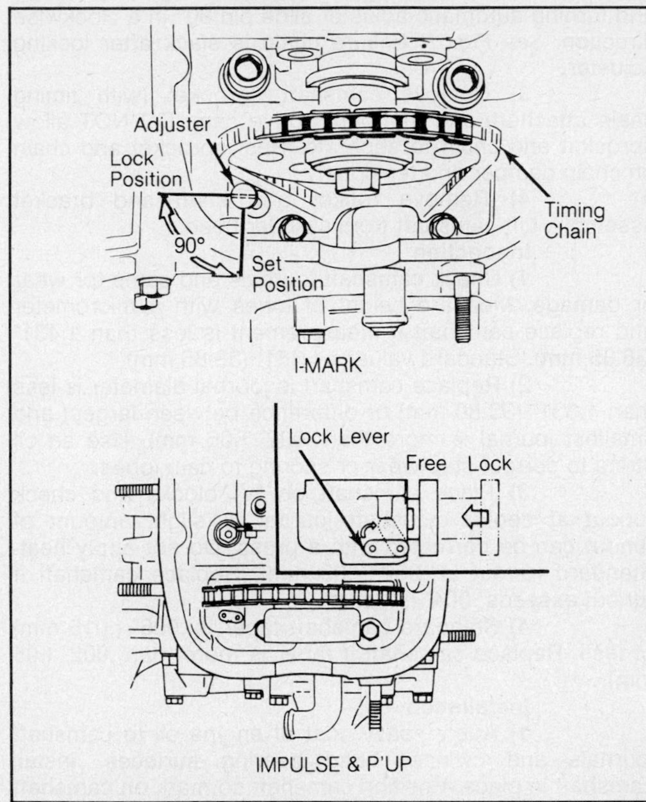
Adjuster
Lock Position
90°
Set Position
Timing Chain
I-MARK
Lock Lever
Free
Lock
IMPULSE & P'UP

2) Install and tighten head bolts in progressive steps to initial specification, then tighten to final specification. *See Fig. 2*. Install remaining components in reverse order of removal. Adjust valves.

Fig. 2: Cylinder Head Tightening Sequence

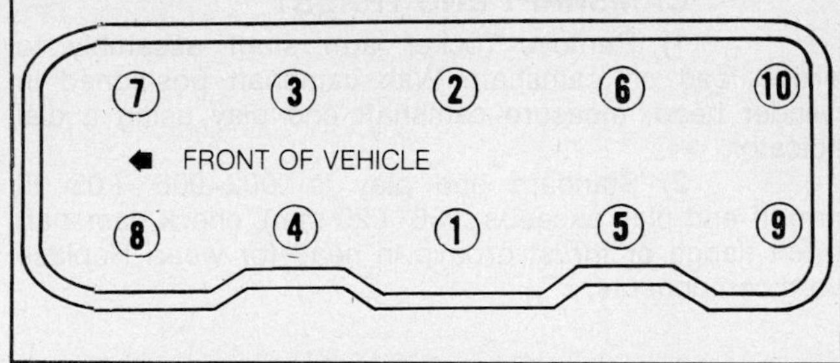
7
3
2
6
10
FRONT OF VEHICLE
8
4
1
5
9

Tighten in progressive steps to 61 ft. lbs. (83 N.m), then tighten to 72 ft. lbs. (98 N.m).

CAMSHAFT

ENGINE FRONT COVER

Removal

1) Remove cylinder head. Remove oil pan. Remove oil pump pickup tube. Remove all drive belts. Remove vibration damper assembly.

2) If A/C equipped, remove compressor and mounting brackets and position aside. Remove distributor. Remove front cover.

Installation

1) Clean gasket mating surfaces. Install new front cover gasket. Align oil pump drive gear punch mark with oil filter side of cover. Align center of dowel pin with alignment mark on oil pump case. *See Fig. 3*.

Fig. 3: Aligning Oil Pump for Front Cover Installation

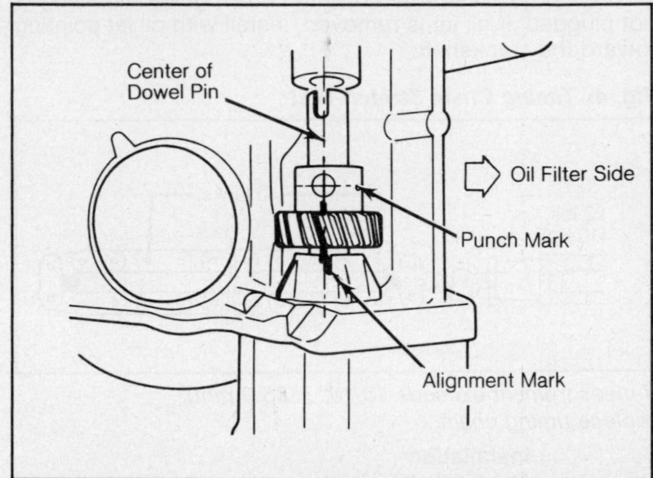
Center of Dowel Pin
Oil Filter Side
Punch Mark
Alignment Mark

Install front cover by engaging pinion gear with oil pump drive gear on crankshaft.

2) Position No. 1 and 4 pistons on TDC. Install front cover by engaging pinion gear with oil pump drive gear on crankshaft.

3) Position punch mark on oil pump drive gear toward engine. Mark may be seen through clearance between front cover and block with oil pan removed.

4) Ensure slot at end of oil pump shaft (as viewed from top of front cover) is parallel with front face of cylinder block. Offset must be forward.

5) Install remaining components in reverse order of removal procedures.

FRONT COVER OIL SEAL

Removal

1) Disconnect negative battery cable. Drain cooling system. Disconnect radiator hoses and remove radiator.

2) Remove all drive belts. Remove fan. Remove vibration damper assembly. Using a screwdriver, carefully pry seal out of front cover.

Installation

Using seal installing tool, install new seal in cover. Coat seal lips with oil. Reverse removal procedure to complete installation.

TIMING CHAIN & SPROCKETS

Removal

Remove front cover. Lock automatic adjuster in retracted position. Remove timing chain from crankshaft sprocket.

Inspection

1) Check camshaft and crankshaft sprockets for wear or damage. If crankshaft sprocket replacement is required, remove sprocket using a puller.

2) Using tension measuring gauge, check timing chain for wear. Using 22 lbs. (10 kg) force, pull chain and measure stretch over a length of 40 chain links. *See Fig. 4*.

3) The standard distance is 15" (381 mm). If distance measured exceeds 15.2" (385 mm), replace chain. Check automatic adjuster, tensioner guide rail, and chain guide for wear. Replace as necessary.

4) Make sure that tensioner guide rail and automatic adjuster move freely on mounting pins. Pins and clips are replaceable.

5) Ensure that oil jet in chain guide mounting is not plugged. If oil jet is removed, install with oil jet pointing toward the crankshaft.

Fig. 4: Timing Chain Stretch Test

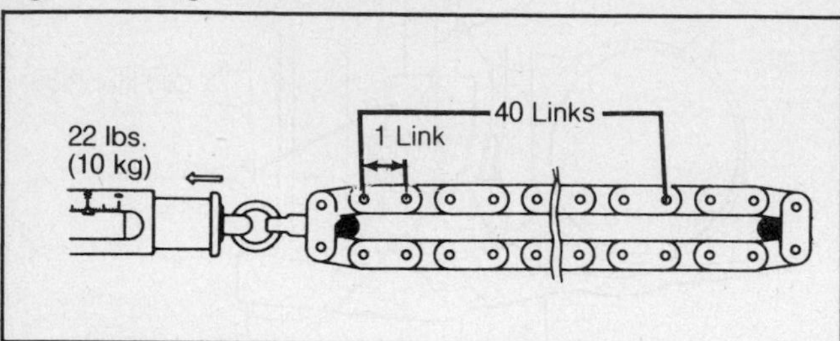
40 Links
1 Link
22 lbs.
(10 kg)

If measurement exceeds 15.16" (385.0 mm), replace timing chain.

Installation

1) Install Woodruff keys, timing sprocket, and oil pump pinion gear (grooved side toward front cover). Turn crankshaft so that Woodruff key is facing upward (No. 1 and No. 4 pistons on TDC).

2) Timing chain has 2 marked link plates that are used for sprocket alignment purposes. The side of the chain with more links between the marked plates must be installed on the chain guide side of the engine.

3) Install chain on crankshaft sprocket, aligning one of the marked link plates with mark on crankshaft sprocket. Position chain around camshaft sprocket, so marked link plate aligns with triangular mark on camshaft sprocket.

4) Install camshaft sprocket on camshaft. Ensure timing marks on sprockets are still aligned with marked plates. *See Fig. 5*. Install remaining components in reverse order of removal.

Fig. 5: Aligning Timing Chain and Sprockets

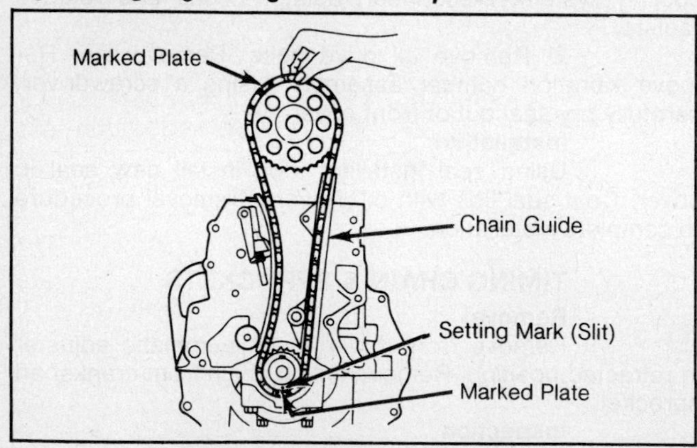
Marked Plate
Chain Guide
Setting Mark (Slit)
Marked Plate

Install timing chain with most links between marked plates towards chain guide side of engine.

CAMSHAFT

Removal

1) Remove valve cover. On I-Mark and P'UP models, remove fuel pump. Position No. 4 piston on TDC at end of compression stroke. Remove distributor cap and mark rotor position on housing.

2) Lock timing chain adjuster by depressing and turning automatic adjuster slide pin 90° in a clockwise direction. *See Fig. 1*. Ensure chain is slack after locking adjuster.

3) Remove camshaft sprocket (with timing chain attached) and fuel pump drive cam. DO NOT allow sprocket and chain to separate. Rest sprocket and chain on chain damper and tensioner.

4) Remove rocker arm shaft and bracket assembly. Lift camshaft from cylinder head.

Inspection

1) Check camshaft journals and cams for wear or damage. Measure height of lobes with a micrometer and replace camshaft if measurement is less than 1.431" (36.35 mm). Standard value is 1.451" (36.85 mm).

2) Replace camshaft is journal diameter is less than 1.331" (33.80 mm) or difference between largest and smallest journal is more than .002" (.05 mm). Use an oil stone to correct step wear or scoring to cam lobes.

3) Place camshaft on "V" blocks and check runout at center camshaft journal. A slight amount of runout can be corrected with a press. Do not apply heat. Standard runout is .002" (.05 mm). Replace camshaft if runout exceeds .004" (.10 mm).

4) Standard camshaft taper is .006" (.015 mm) or less. Replace camshaft if taper is more than .002" (.05 mm).

Installation

1) Apply heavy coat of engine oil to camshaft journals and cylinder head bearing surfaces. Install camshaft in place. Position camshaft so mark on camshaft thrust flange is aligned with mark on No. 1 rocker arm shaft bracket.

2) Check that crankshaft pulley mark is aligned with TDC mark on front cover. Install remaining components in reverse order of removal. Ensure valve timing is correct.

CAMSHAFT END THRUST

1) Remove rocker arm shaft assembly to relieve load on camshaft. With camshaft positioned in cylinder head, measure camshaft end play using a dial indicator.

2) Standard end play is .002-.006" (.05-.15 mm). If end play exceeds .008" (.20 mm), check camshaft thrust flange or thrust groove in head for wear. Replace worn components.

VALVES

VALVE ARRANGEMENT

Right Side - Intake valves.
Left Side - Exhaust valves.

ROCKER ARM SHAFT ASSEMBLY

Removal

1) Remove valve cover. Loosen rocker shaft brackets in progressive steps, working from ends toward center.

2) Disassemble rocker arm shaft assembly by removing springs from the shafts, then remove rocker arm brackets and rocker arms. Keep parts in order for reassembly.

1.8L, 1.9L & 1.95L 4-CYLINDER (Cont.)

Inspection

1) Place rocker arm shafts on "V" blocks and check runout at center of shaft. A slight amount of runout can be corrected with a press. Do not apply heat.

2) Maximum runout should not exceed .008" (.20 mm). Replace rocker arm shaft if runout is greater than .016" (.40 mm).

3) Measure rocker arm shaft at 4 rocker arm locations. Standard diameter is .807" (20.50 mm). Replace rocker arm shaft if less than .801" (20.35 mm).

4) Measure inside diameter of rocker arms. If clearance is greater than .008" (.20 mm) replace either rocker arms or shaft. Replace rocker arms if valve stem contact area is scored or worn.

Installation

1) Reassemble rocker arm shaft components in original positions. Cylinder number on upper face of brackets must point toward front of engine. Longer rocker shaft must be installed on exhaust side. Punch marks on rocker arm shafts must face the front and point up.

2) Coat rocker arm shaft, rocker arms, and valve stems wth engine oil. Install rocker arm shaft assembly on cylinder head. Align camshaft mark with mark on No. 1 rocker arm shaft bracket.

3) Hold rocker arm springs between the jaws of an adjustable wrench, to prevent damage to springs when tightening assembly. Tighten nuts in sequence from center out. Adjust valves.

VALVE SEAT INSERTS

Inspection

With valves installed in cylinder head, check depth of valve head below the cylinder head surface. If depth is more than .067" (1.70 mm), replace valve seat insert.

Removal

1) Weld end of welding rods to several points on inner face of valve seat insert, but away from aluminum alloy parts.

2) Allow cylinder head to cool so that contraction of insert takes place. Apply shock load to welding rods and pull out seats.

Installation

Clean insert recess in cylinder head. Heat seat area in cylinder head with steam to encourage expansion. Chill valve seat in dry ice, then install seat in head. Interference fit is .0031-.0047" (.078-.119 mm).

VALVE GUIDES

Inspection

Measure valve guide and corresponding valve stem for wear. If stem-to-guide clearance is excessive, replace guides. Always replace valves when replacing valve guides.

Removal

Remove valve spring and seal. Working from combustion chamber side of head, use valve guide driver tool (J-26512) to drive guide out towards top side of head. Remove lower spring seat.

Installation

1) Lubricate outside of new guide with engine oil. Working from top side of head, use valve guide driver tool (J-26512) to drive new guide into place until tool bottoms on cylinder head.

2) This should place valve guide at .634-.642" (16.10-16.30 mm) above cylinder head surface. Install lower spring seat and remaining valve components.

VALVE SPRINGS

Removal

1) Remove rocker arm shaft assembly. Remove spark plug of cylinder to be serviced. Install air hose and adapter into spark plug hole and apply air pressure.

2) Use valve spring compressor (J-26513) to remove keepers, retainer, and spring. Remove valve stem oil seal and lower spring seat.

Inspection

1) Measure inner and outer valve spring free length. Test valve spring tension with a valve spring tester. Replace springs that fail tests.

2) Using a flat surface and steel square, check valve spring for out-of-round. Take measurement between top of spring and square, while slowly rotating spring. Out-of-round must not exceed .079" (2.0 mm).

Installation

Lubricate valve stem and lower spring seat. Install lower spring seat, then slide new seal over valve stem and onto guide. Ensure oil seal lip fits into groove in valve guide. Install remaining components.

VALVE CLEARANCE ADJUSTMENT

1) Ensure rocker arm shaft brackets are properly tightened. Set No. 1 piston to TDC of compression stroke. Adjust clearance of No. 1 and No. 2 intake, and No. 1 and No. 3 exhaust valves.

2) Turn crankshaft 1 revolution to place No. 4 piston on TDC of compression stroke. Adjust remaining valves.

VALVE CLEARANCE ADJUSTMENTS

Application	In. (mm)
Cold	
Intake	.006 (.15)
Exhaust	.01 (.25)
Hot	
Intake	.008 (.20)
Exhaust	.012 (.30)

PISTONS, PINS & RINGS

OIL PAN

It is necessary to remove engine from vehicle to remove oil pan. When installing oil pan, apply thin coat of non-hardening sealer to crankcase. *See Fig. 6.*

Fig. 6: Sealer Application Points for Oil Pan Installation

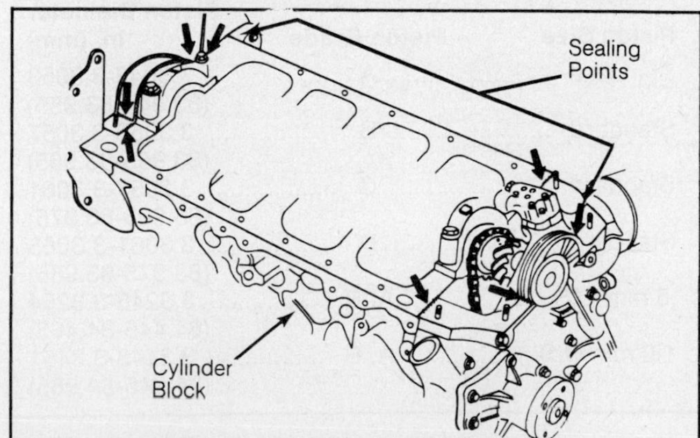
Sealing
Points
Cylinder
Block

Apply non-hardening sealer to points indicated by arrows.

Isuzu Engines

1.8L, 1.9L & 1.95L 4-CYLINDER (Cont.)

PISTON & ROD ASSEMBLY

Removal

1) Remove cylinder head and oil pan. Mark connecting rods and caps (on starter side of engine) for cylinder identification. Remove carbon deposits from upper part of cylinder wall.

2) Remove connecting rod caps. Using a wooden hammer handle, carefully push piston and connecting rod out top of cylinder block.

Installation

Apply clean engine oil to bearings and piston surface. When installing piston and rod assembly, position piston so mark on piston head is facing front of engine and cylinder identification number on connecting rod is on starter side of engine.

FITTING PISTONS

Cylinder Block Inspection

1) Inspect block upper surface for distortion using a straightedge and feeler gauge. Replace block if distortion is more than .016" (.40 mm). If distortion if more than .008" (.20 mm) but less than .016" (.40 mm), block may be resurfaced.

2) Cylinder block must be bored if more than .008" (.20 mm) over standard size. *See Cylinder Bore Size Chart*. Replace cylinder block if bore diameter is greater than 3.466" (88.04 mm) on Impulse and P'UP models, or greater than 3.354" (85.20 mm) on I-Mark models.

CYLINDER BORE SIZE CHART

Application	Standard Size In. (mm)
I-Mark	3.307 (84.0)
Impulse	3.425 (87.0)
P'UP	3.425 (87.0)

Piston Inspection

1) Measure diameter of piston skirt 1.57" (40 mm) below piston head, at a point 90° to piston pin bore. Measure cylinder bore diameter near bottom of bore, where least wear occurs.

2) Difference between cylinder bore diameter and piston diameter must not exceed .0018-.0026" (.045-.065 mm). If clearance exceeds limits, replace pistons. Variation between bore diameters should be .0008" (.02 mm) or less.

I-MARK PISTON SIZE CODE CHART

Piston Size	Piston Grade	Piston Diameter In. (mm)
Standard	A	3.3049-3.3053 (83.944-83.955)
Standard	B	3.3053-3.3057 (83.955-83.965)
Standard	C	3.3057-3.3061 (83.965-83.975)
Standard	D	3.3061-3.3065 (83.975-83.985)
.5 mm O.S.	A, B	3.3246-3.3254 (84.445-84.465)
1.0 mm O.S.	A, B	3.3443-3.3451 (84.945-84.965)

3) Measure weight of all assembled piston and rod assemblies. Variation in weight between assemblies must not exceed .42 oz. (.01 kg). If correction is necessary, adjust by swapping parts between assemblies, other than piston and piston pin.

4) Oversize pistons are available in .020" (0.5 mm) and .040" (1.0 mm) for all models.

IMPULSE PISTON SIZE CHART

Piston Size	Piston Diameter In. (mm)
Standard	3.425-3.426 (87.000-87.040)
.5 mm O.S.	3.444-3.445 (87.500-87.520)
1.0 mm O.S.	3.464-3.465 (88.000-88.020)

P'UP PISTON SIZE CODE CHART

Piston Size	Piston Grade	Piston Diameter In. (mm)
Standard	A	3.4169-3.4173 (86.945-86.955)
Standard	B	3.4173-3.4177 (86.956-86.965)
Standard	C	3.4177-3.4181 (86.966-86.975)
Standard	D	3.4181-3.4185 (86.976-86.985)
.5 mm O.S.	A, B	3.4365-3.4373 (87.445-87.465)
1.0 mm O.S.	A, B	3.4562-3.4570 (87.945-87.965)

FITTING RINGS

1) Position rings into cylinder bore at a point where bore diameter is smallest. Ring must be square in bore. Measure ring end gap with a feeler gauge. Replace rings if end gap is larger than .059" (1.50 mm).

2) Using a feeler gauge, check ring side clearance. Ensure rings turn freely in their ring grooves. Replace pistons and rings if side clearance is greater than .006" (.15 mm).

3) On Impulse models, compression rings will have a piston size mark stamped on top. Standard rings have no marks. A No. 1 compression ring that is .5 mm oversize will have "50" stamped on top. No. 2 compression rings have a "100" stamped on top for the .5 mm oversize. All 1.0 mm oversize rings have a "100" stamped on top.

4) Standard oil rings on Impulse models are painted Red. The .5 mm oversize are painted Blue. The 1.0 mm oversize are painted Yellow.

5) On all models, ensure end gap is correct when installing rings. *See Fig. 7*. Install oil control rings in this order: expander ring, lower side rail, then upper side rail.

6) Position compression rings so that "N", "NPR", or "TOP" mark is upward. Oil control rings are not marked.

1.8L, 1.9L & 1.95L 4-CYLINDER (Cont.)

Fig. 7: Piston Ring Gap Spacing

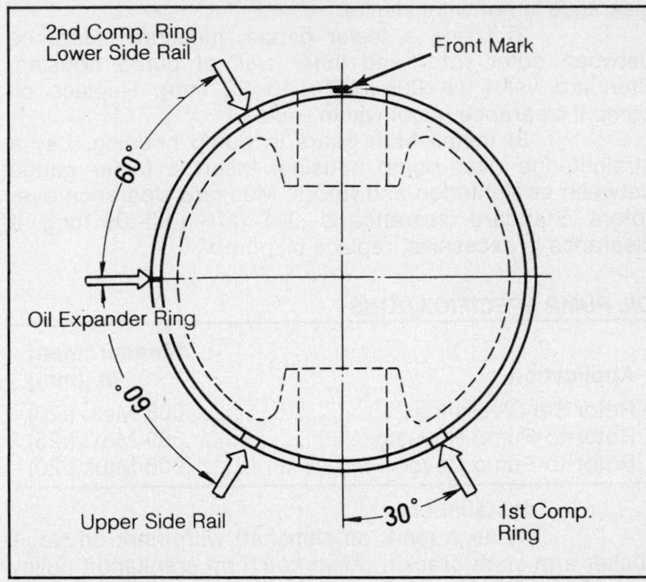
2nd Comp. Ring
Lower Side Rail
Front Mark
60°
Oil Expander Ring
60°
Upper Side Rail
30°
1st Comp.
Ring

Lower side rail and second compression ring share same gap position on piston.

PISTON PIN REPLACEMENT

Removal

Using an arbor press and piston pin remover tool, press piston pin out of piston and connecting rod assembly.

Inspection

1) Correct or replace connecting rod if distortion is greater than .008" (.20 mm) or bend is greater than .006" (.15 mm) per 3.94" (100.0 mm) of length. Standard distortion and bend is .002" (.05 mm) or less.

2) Check piston pin diameter at several points around the circumference. Check interference fit between connecting rod small end and piston. Check fit of pin in piston.

Installation

1) On I-Mark and P'UP models, assemble connecting rod to piston with chamfer on rod's small end on same side as front mark on piston head. *See Fig. 8*.

2) On Impulse models, assemble connecting rod so that front mark on piston and "Isuzu" stamp on connecting rod are on the same side. Lightly oil pin bores in piston and rod. Press pin into piston and rod.

Fig. 8: I-Mark & P'UP Piston-to-Rod Relationship

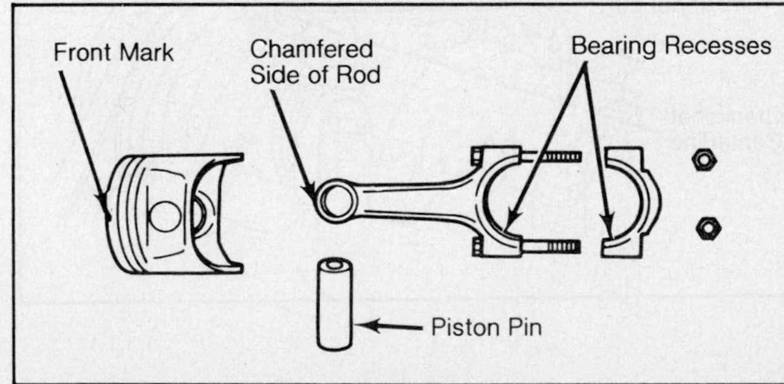
Front Mark
Chamfered
Side of Rod
Bearing Recesses
Piston Pin

Note position of bearing recesses.

CRANKSHAFT MAIN & CONNECTING ROD BEARINGS

NOTE: **To check bearing clearances, remove engine from vehicle. Following procedures are performed with oil pan removed, and oil film removed from surfaces to be checked.**

CRANKSHAFT MAIN BEARINGS

1) Check main bearing clearances using Plastigage method. If clearances are excessive, install undersize bearings. Replacement bearings are available in standard, .010" (.25 mm) undersize and .020" (.50 mm) undersize.

2) To check crankshaft runout, place "V" blocks under crankshaft at No. 1 and No. 5 journals. Position dial indicator point on No. 3 journal.

3) Slowly turn crankshaft at least 1 full revolution, while recording runout. If runout exceeds .0038" (.097 mm), replace or correct crankshaft. Standard runout is .001" (.03 mm).

4) Check taper and out-of-round for main bearing and connecting rod journals. Maximum taper and out-of-round for Impulse is .002" (.05 mm). Maximum taper and out-of-round for I-Mark and P'UP is .003" (.07 mm).

5) Install main caps so arrow on rear face of cap is turned to front of engine. Bearings should be well lubricated prior to installation. Tighten caps in progressive steps, in sequence of 3, 4, 2, 5, and 1.

CONNECTING ROD BEARINGS

1) After ensuring rod caps are marked for cylinder identification, remove rod caps. Use Plastigage method to check for proper clearance. Rod caps must be tightened to specification when measuring clearances.

2) If not within limits, new bearings must be installed. Replacement bearings are available in standard, .010" (.25 mm), and .020" (.50 mm) undersize.

CRANKSHAFT END THRUST

1) To check crankshaft end thrust, install bearings in cylinder block, then lay crankshaft in place. Install thrust bearing on both sides of No. 3 crankshaft journal.

2) Move crankshaft fully endwise and measure clearance between crankshaft thrust face and thrust bearing. If clearance is greater than .012" (.30 mm), replace thrust bearings.

REAR MAIN BEARING OIL SEAL

Removal

Remove starter. Remove transmission. Remove clutch assembly (if equipped). Remove flywheel. Pry oil seal from seal retainer.

Installation

Position new seal into place in retainer. Fill clearance between lips of seal with grease, and coat lips of seal with engine oil. Using installer tool (J-22928-A), install seal into retainer. Reverse removal procedures to complete installation.

1.8L, 1.9L & 1.95L 4-CYLINDER (Cont.)

ENGINE OILING

CRANKCASE CAPACITY

Capacity is 3.4 quarts (3.2L) without filter replacement; 3.8 quarts (3.6L) with filter replacement.

NORMAL OIL PRESSURE

Oil pressure should be approximately 57 psi (4 kg/cm²) at 2800 RPM.

OIL PRESSURE RELIEF VALVE

Oil pressure relief valve opens at approximately 57-71 psi (4-5 kg/cm²).

ENGINE OILING SYSTEM

A trochoid type oil pump is used. The oil pump delivers oil to main gallery, where it is routed to crankshaft journals. Through oil passages in crankshaft, oil is fed to connecting rod journals, connecting rods, and then to piston pins.

A branched oil passage from No. 3 crankshaft journal routes oil to the cylinder head. This oil flows through rocker arm shafts to lubricate rocker arm components. An oil well (located on upper face of cylinder head) provides lubrication to camshaft.

Timing chain and sprockets are lubricated by oil spray from oil jet on chain guide.

Fig. 9: Exploded View of Oil Pump Assembly

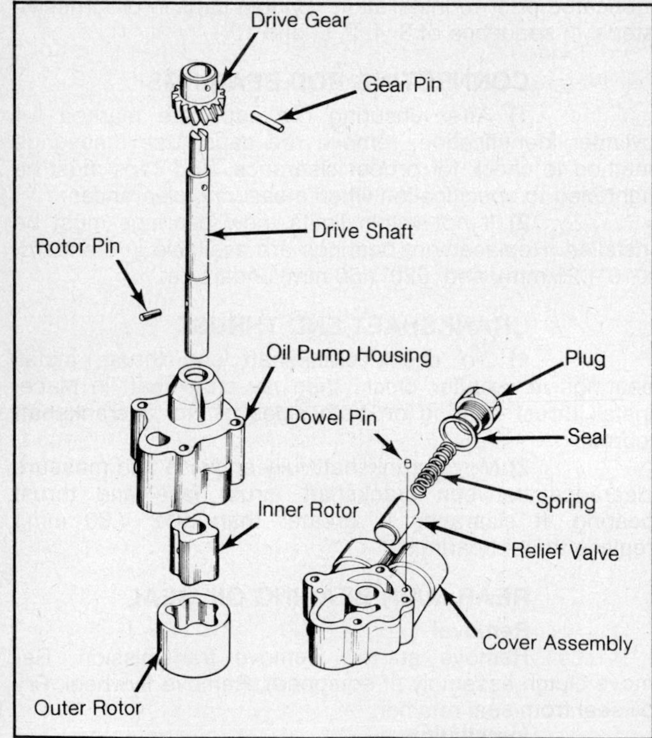
Drive Gear
Gear Pin
Drive Shaft
Rotor Pin
Oil Pump Housing
Plug
Dowel Pin
Seal
Spring
Inner Rotor
Relief Valve
Cover Assembly
Outer Rotor

OIL PUMP

Removal

Remove valve cover and distributor. Remove oil pan. Remove oil pickup tube from block, then remove tube from oil pump. Remove oil pump.

Inspection

1) Using a feeler gauge, measure tip clearance between inner and outer rotors. Standard rotor clearance is .0005-.0059" (.013-.150 mm). Replace oil pump if clearance is not within limits.

2) Using a feeler gauge, measure clearance between outer rotor and inner wall of pump housing. Standard value is .006-.009" (.16-.22 mm). Replace oil pump if clearance is not within limits.

3) Install both gears in pump housing. Lay a straightedge over pump housing. Insert a feeler gauge between straightedge and rotors. Measure clearance over rotors. Standard clearance is .001-.004" (.03-.09 mm). If clearance is excessive, replace oil pump.

OIL PUMP SPECIFICATIONS

Application	Measurement In. (mm)
Rotor Tip Clearance	.008 Max. (.20)
Rotor-to-Pump Housing	.009 Max. (.25)
Rotor-to-Pump Cover	.008 Max. (.20)

Installation

1) Align mark on camshaft with mark on No. 1 rocker arm shaft bracket. Align notch on crankshaft pulley with "O" mark on front cover. When the two sets of marks are aligned, No. 4 piston is at TDC on compression stroke.

2) Ensure alignment marks on oil pump inner and outer rotors are aligned. Prime oil pump. Engage oil pump drive gear with pinion gear on crankshaft, so alignment mark is turned rearward, and is away from crankshaft approximately 20° in a clockwise rotation. *See Fig. 10.*

3) When installing oil pump, make sure mark on drive gear is turned to rear side. Slot at end of drive shaft must be parallel with front face of cylinder block, and offset forward. *See Fig. 11.*

4) Install pump cover by fitting it to the dowel pins, then install mounting bolts. Install remaining components in reverse order of removal procedures.

Fig. 10: Installing Oil Pump

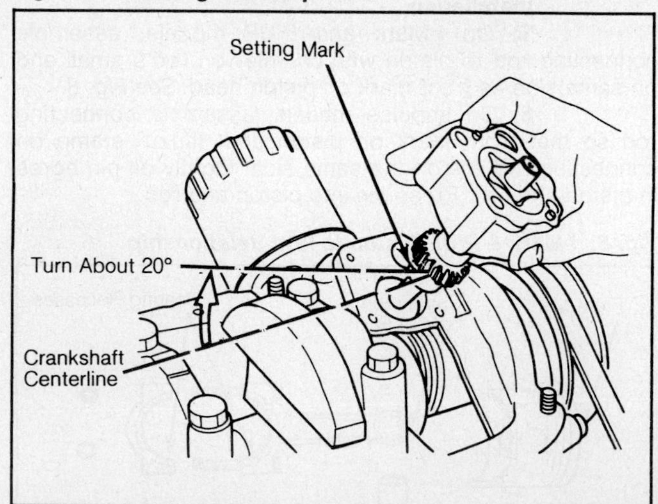
Setting Mark
Turn About 20°
Crankshaft Centerline

1.8L, 1.9L & 1.95L 4-CYLINDER (Cont.)

Fig. 11: Checking Oil Pump Drive Shaft Alignment

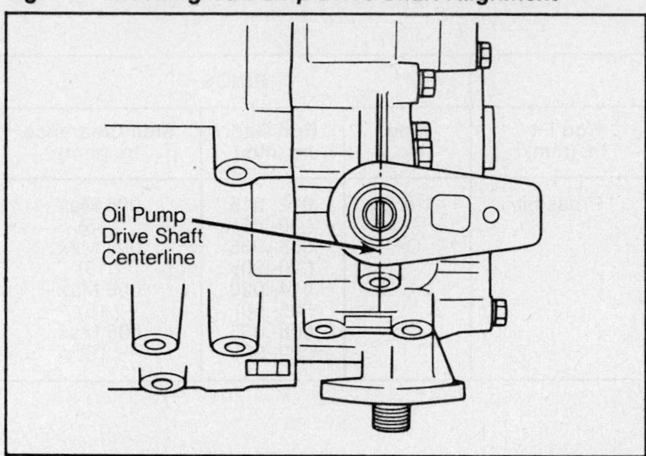
Oil Pump
Drive Shaft
Centerline

RADIATOR CAP

Radiator cap pressure relief valve opens at 15 psi (1.1 kg/cm²).

WATER PUMP

Removal

1) Disconnect negative battery cable. Remove lower cover and drain cooling system. On models without A/C, remove fan. Remove water pump.

2) If A/C equipped, remove fan and air pump drive belt. Remove fan, fan pulley, and air pump drive pulley. Remove fan set plate and pulley. Remove water pump.

Installation

Clean gasket mating surfaces. To install water pump, reverse removal procedures. Adjust belt tensions and fill cooling system.

TIGHTENING SPECIFICATIONS

Application	Ft. Lbs. (N.m)
Camshaft Sprocket	58 (79)
Connecting Rod Caps	43 (58)
Cylinder Head	
Step 1	61 (83)
Step 2	72 (98)
Flywheel	69 (94)
Front Pulley Bolt	18 (25)
Front Pulley Boss Bolt	9 (12)
Intake Manifold	16 (22)
Main Bearing Cap	72 (98)
Rocker Arm Shaft Bracket Nuts	16 (22)

ENGINE COOLING

THERMOSTAT

Thermostat opens at about 180°F (82°C).

COOLANT CAPACITY

I-Mark

The coolant capacity is 7.2 qts. (6.8L) for manual transmission and 7.1 qts. (6.7L) for automatic transmission.

Impulse

The coolant capacity is 6.7 qts. (6.3L) for manual transmission and 6.6 (6.2L) qts. for automatic transmission.

P'UP

The coolant capacity is 8.7 qts. (8.2L) for manual transmission and 8.2 qts. (7.8L) for automatic transmission.

ENGINE SPECIFICATIONS

GENERAL SPECIFICATIONS

Year	DISPLACEMENT		Fuel System	HP@RPM	Torque Ft. Lbs.@RPM	Compr. Ratio	BORE		STROKE	
	Cu. In.	Liters					In.	mm	In.	mm
1983										
I-Mark	110.8	1.8	1x2-Bbl.	78@4800	95@3000	8.5:1	3.31	84.0	3.23	82.0
Impulse	118.9	1.95	Fuel Inj.	90@5000	108@3000	9.3	3.43	87	3.29	83
P'UP	116	1.9	1x2-Bbl.	82@4800	.....	8.4:1	3.43	87	3.23	82

VALVES

Engine Size & Valve	Head Diam. In. (mm)	Face Angle	Seat Angle	Seat Width In. (mm)	Stem Diameter In. (mm)	Stem Clearance In. (mm)	Valve Lift In. (mm)
1.8L, 1.9L, & 1.95L							
Intake	[1] 1.59 (40.3)	45°	[2] 45°	.047-.063 (1.19-1.60)	.310 Min. (7.88)	[3] .0009-.0022 (.023-.056)	.....
Exhaust	[1] 1.34 (34.0)	45°	[2] 45°	.047-.063 (1.19)	.309 Min. (7.85)	[3] .0013-.0031 (.034-.079)	.....

[1] – Values are for I-Mark and P'UP models. Impulse intake valve head diameter is 1.67" (42.4 mm) and exhaust valve head diameter is 1.34" (34.0 mm).
[2] – Correction angles for intake and exhaust valve seats are 15° and 75°.
[3] – Maximum valve stem clearance is .008" (.20 mm) for intake and .009" (.25 mm) for exhaust.

Isuzu Engines

1.8L, 1.9L & 1.95L 4-CYLINDER (Cont.)

ENGINE SPECIFICATIONS (Cont.)

PISTONS, PINS, RINGS

Engine	PISTONS	PINS		RINGS		
	Clearance In. (mm)	Piston Fit In. (mm)	Rod Fit In. (mm)	Ring No.	End Gap In. (mm)	Side Clearance In. (mm)
1.8L	.0018-.0026 (.045-.065)	.0002-.0004 (.006-.011)	[1] Press Fit	1 & 2	.012-.018 (.30-.45)	.006 Max. (.15)
				Oil	.008-.035 (.20-.90)	.006 Max. (.15)
1.9L & 1.95L				1 & 2	.014-.020 (.35-.50)	.006 Max. (.15)
				Oil	.008-.035 (.20-.90)	.006 Max. (.15)

[1] – Interference fit is .0008-.0016" (.030-.041 mm).

CRANKSHAFT MAIN & CONNECTING ROD BEARINGS

Engine	MAIN BEARINGS				CONNECTING ROD BEARINGS		
	Journal Diam. In. (mm)	Clearance In. (mm)	Thrust Bearing	Crankshaft End Play In. (mm)	Journal Diam. In. (mm)	Clearance In. (mm)	Side Play In. (mm)
1.8L, 1.9L, & 1.95L	[1] 2.205 (56)	.0008-.0025 (.020-.064)	No. 3	.002-.009 (.06-.24)	[2] 1.929 (49)	.0007-.0025 (.018-.064)	[3] .008-.013 (.020-.33)

[1] – Minimum main bearing journal diameter for I-Mark and P'UP is 2.156" (54.75 mm). Minimum for Impulse is 2.182" (55.42 mm).
[2] – Minimum connecting rod journal diameter for I-Mark and P'UP is 1.879" (47.75 mm). Minimum for Impulse is 1.906" (48.42 mm).
[3] – Maximum connecting rod side play is .014" (.35 mm).

CAMSHAFT

Engine	Journal Diam. In. (mm)	Clearance In. (mm)	Lobe Lift In. (mm)
1.8,1.9L, & 1.95L [1]	1.3362-1.3366 (33.94-33.95)	[2] .0016-.0035 (.041-.089)	.....

[1] – Standard end play is .002-.006" (.05-.15 mm). Maximum end play is .008" (.20 mm).
[2] – Maximum oil clearance is .006" (.15 mm).

VALVE SPRINGS

Engine	Free Length In. (mm)	PRESSURE Lbs. @ In. (Kg @ mm)	
		Valve Closed	Valve Open
1.8L & 1.9L [1] Inner	[2] 1.78 (45.3)	20 @ 1.5 (9.2 @ 38.5)	.....
Outer	[3] 1.85 (47.0)	35 @ 1.61 (15 @ 41.0)	.....
1.95L [1]	1.89 (48.1)	55 @ 1.6 (25 @ 41)	....

[1] – Replace spring if more than .079" (2.0 mm) out of square.
[2] – Minimum height is 1.72" (43.8 mm).
[3] – Minimum height is 1.79" (45.4 mm).

I-MARK 4-CYLINDER DIESEL

ENGINE CODING

ENGINE IDENTIFICATION

Engine identification code is 8th character of the Vehicle Identification Number (VIN). The VIN is stamped on a metal tab, located on top of instrument panel near lower left side of windshield. Engine serial number is stamped on a machined pad, located at left rear corner of cylinder block.

ENGINE IDENTIFICATION CODE

Engine	Code
Type 4FB1 (1.8L)	P

ENGINE, MANIFOLDS & CYLINDER HEAD

ENGINE

Removal

1) Mark hood hinges for reassembly and remove hood. Disconnect battery cables. Remove cables, battery hold-down and battery. Drain radiator, crankcase and transmission. Remove lower engine splash guard.

2) Remove fan shroud. Disconnect radiator hoses. Remove radiator. Disconnect heater hoses. Remove air connecting hose. Disconnect thermo switch wiring at connectors on thermostat housing.

3) Disconnect alternator wiring at connector. Disconnect vacuum hoses from rear of vacuum pump and at fast idle actuator. Disconnect and remove front exhaust pipe from manifold and mounting bracket.

4) Disconnect accelerator cable from injection pump lever. Disconnect fuel cut solenoid valve switch wiring at connector. If equipped, disconnect tachometer pickup sensor wiring at connector.

5) Disconnect wiring from starter and oil pressure switch. Disconnect fuel hoses from injection pump. Disconnect any remaining engine or transmission to chassis wiring, linkages, cables, lines or hoses.

6) Mark for reinstallation and remove propeller shaft from transmission. Install plug in transmission extension housing to prevent oil spillage. Working inside vehicle, remove console. Pry off shift lever dust boot, then remove shift lever assembly.

7) Remove rear engine mount bolts and bolts attaching exhaust mounting bracket. Attach lifting chain and hoist to engine. Lift engine slightly to remove weight from engine mounts.

8) Remove engine mount nuts and disconnect engine damper from frame. Pull engine forward and carefully remove engine and transmission as an assembly.

Installation

1) Replace any rubber engine mounts showing signs of deterioration or separation. Check engine damper for leakage, worn bushings or any other signs of wear or damage. Replace if needed.

2) Reverse removal procedures to complete installation. Check all fluid levels and purge fuel system of air. Adjust clutch.

INTAKE MANIFOLD

Removal

1) Disconnect negative battery cable. Remove PCV hoses and valve. Remove sensing resistor assembly. Remove 6 injection pipe clips. Remove 8 sleeve nuts attaching injection pipe and remove injection pipe.

2) Remove upper timing belt cover. Remove engine lifting eye. Remove engine stay. Remove attaching bolts and nuts, then remove intake manifold.

Installation

Clean gasket mating surfaces. Using new gasket, install and tighten intake manifold. Install remaining components in reverse order of removal procedures.

CYLINDER HEAD

Removal

1) Open drain plug on cylinder block and drain cooling system. Remove camshaft. Remove sensing resistor assembly. Remove 6 injection pipe clips. Loosen 8 injection pipe nuts and separate injection pipe.

2) Remove fuel leak-off hose, and separate hose from fuel return pipe. Disconnect exhaust pipe from exhaust manifold. Disconnect oil feed pipe from cylinder head. Disconnect heater hose from thermostat housing.

3) Loosen head bolts in reverse order of tightening sequence. *See Fig. 1.* Remove cylinder head and head gasket.

Installation

Clean all gasket mating surfaces. Using new head gasket, install cylinder head. Install head bolts and tighten in 2 steps. *See Fig. 1.* Install remaining components in reverse order of removal.

Fig. 1: Cylinder Head Tightening Sequence

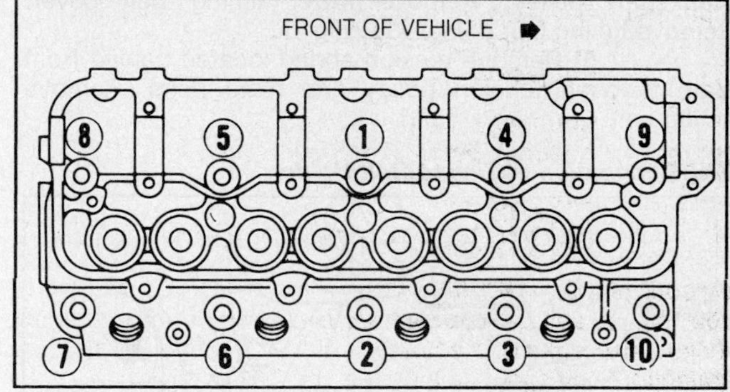
FRONT OF VEHICLE
8
5
1
4
9
7
6
2
3
10

Loosen head bolts in reverse order of tightening.

CAMSHAFT

TIMING BELT COVERS

Removal

Disconnect negative battery cable. Remove fan, pulley and drive belt. Remove crankshaft pulley. Remove 18 attaching bolts, then remove upper and lower timing belt covers.

Installation

To install timing belt covers, reverse removal procedures.

TIMING BELT

Removal

1) Disconnect battery ground cable and drain engine coolant. Remove splash cover from under engine. Remove fan shroud, drive belt, fan and pulley. Remove upper timing belt cover. Remove coolant by-pass hose.

2) With piston of No. 1 cylinder at TDC on compression stroke, check that timing marks on injection

I-MARK 4-CYLINDER DIESEL (Cont.)

pump sprocket and front plate are aligned. Fix sprocket in place by inserting bolt through sprocket and into block. *See Fig. 2*.

Fig. 2: Aligning Injection Pump Timing Marks

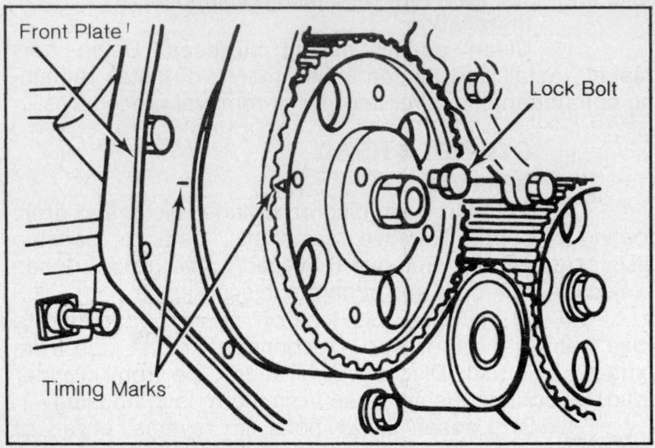
Front Plate
Lock Bolt
Timing Marks

Insert bolt through sprocket and into cylinder block to lock sprocket in place.

3) Remove air connecting hose and PCV hoses, then remove cam cover. Loosen adjusting screws on rocker arms to relieve tension on camshaft. Lock camshaft in place by installing fixing plate (J-29761) in slot at rear of camshaft.

4) Ensure No. 1 piston is still on TDC. Remove crankshaft pulley. Remove lower timing belt cover. Remove timing belt holder. *See Fig. 3*.

5) Remove tension spring located behind front plate. Loosen tension pulley and plate bolts. Remove timing belt.

Fig. 3: Location of Timing Belt Holder

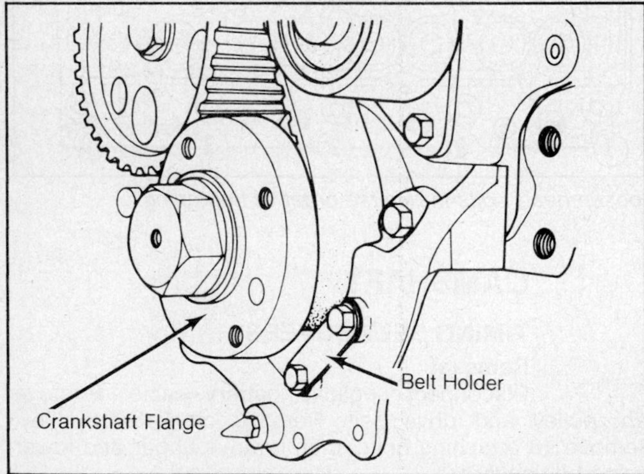
Belt Holder
Crankshaft Flange

When installing holder, make sure it does not rub on timing belt.

Installation

1) Remove camshaft sprocket center bolt. Using a puller, remove sprocket from camshaft, then install sprocket back on camshaft. Lightly tighten center bolt so sprocket can be turned smoothly by hand.

2) Starting with crankshaft sprocket and working in a counterclockwise direction, engage new timing belt over each sprocket and pulley. Check that belt is properly engaged on all sprockets and pulleys.

3) Take up belt slack at tension pulley. To do so, depress tension pulley and install tension spring. Tighten tension pulley pivot bolts just enough to prevent pulley movement. Do not tighten pulley center bolt at this time.

Fig. 4: Location of Tensioner Pulley

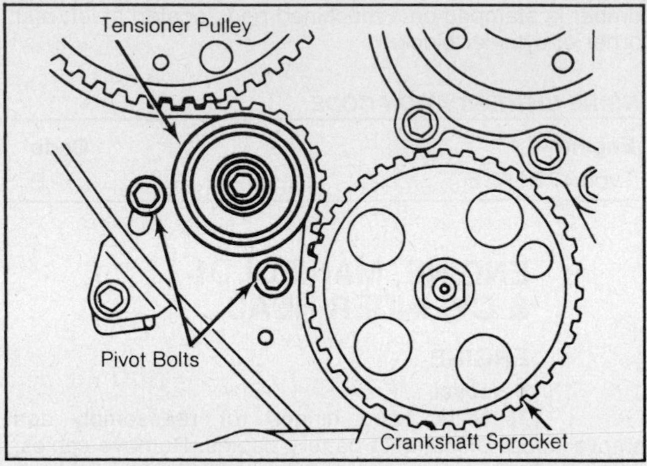
Tensioner Pulley
Pivot Bolts
Crankshaft Sprocket

For preliminary belt adjustment, only tighten pivot bolts. Do not tighten pulley center bolt.

4) Tighten camshaft sprocket. Remove bolt used to lock injection pump sprocket in place. Remove fixing plate tool used to lock camshaft in place. Install crankshaft pulley on crankshaft flange.

5) Check that No. 1 cylinder is still on TDC. Ensure that timing marks on injection pump sprocket and front plate are still aligned. Loosen tensioner pulley pivot bolts and take up timing belt slack.

6) Tighten tensioner pulley center bolt, then tighten pivot bolts. Using tension gauge, check for 47-64 lbs. (21-29 kg) tension between camshaft pulley and injection pump. Reverse removal procedures to complete installation. Ensure timing belt holder does not rub against timing belt. Adjust valves.

VALVE TIMING

To check for correct valve timing, refer to procedures explained in timing belt removal and installation.

INJECTION PUMP TIMING

1) Check that notched line on injection pump flange is aligned with notched line at rear of front plate. With No. 1 cylinder at TDC on compression stroke, check that injection pump timing marks are aligned. *See Fig. 2*.

2) Ensure timing belt is properly tensioned. Remove cam cover and rear plug. Install camshaft fixing plate (J-29761) into slot at rear of camshaft to check for proper valve timing. Fixing plate should fit smoothly into slot. Remove fixing plate.

3) Disconnect injection pipe from pump. Remove distributor head screw and gasket. Install static timing gauge (dial indicator) and set lift approximately .04" (1.0 mm) from the plunger.

4) Turn engine until No. 1 cylinder is 45-60° BTDC, then calibrate dial indicator to zero.

5) The crankshaft has a total of 7 notched lines on the crankshaft pulley, divided into 2 groups. The group with 4 notched lines is used for static timing. Disregard the group of 3 notched lines (dynamic timing marks).

I-MARK 4-CYLINDER DIESEL (Cont.)

6) Turn crankshaft in normal direction of rotation until 12° BTDC timing mark (next to last notch on pulley) is aligned with timing pointer. Dial indicator should read .020" (.50 mm).

7) If indicator reading is not correct, loosen the 2 injection pump flange retaining nuts and rotate pump housing until a correct reading is obtained. Tighten nuts and recheck reading.

CAMSHAFT

Removal

1) Remove cam cover. Remove timing belt. Hold camshaft in place and remove camshaft sprocket center bolt. Using a puller, remove camshaft sprocket. Remove 4 retaining bolts and remove front head plate.

2) Remove rocker arm shaft assembly. Remove cam bearing caps and bearings. Keep in order for later installation. Remove camshaft oil seal. Remove camshaft.

Installation

1) Using engine oil, heavily lubricate camshaft and journal surfaces in cylinder head. Install camshaft and new oil seal.

2) Apply gasket sealer to No. 1 cam bearing cap-to-cylinder head contact surface. Reverse removal procedures to complete installation. Adjust valves.

CAMSHAFT OIL SEAL

To replace camshaft oil seal, use procedures explained in camshaft removal and installation.

VALVES

VALVE ARRANGEMENT

Intake Valves (Right side)
Exhaust Valves (Left side)

ROCKER ARM SHAFT ASSEMBLY

Removal

Remove cam cover. Starting at the ends and working inward, gradually loosen rocker arm shaft bracket bolts and nuts. Remove rocker arm shaft bracket and rocker arm assembly. Keep parts in order if disassembly is required.

Installation

Heavily lubricate rocker arm shaft, rocker arms and valve tips with engine oil. Install assembly in reverse order of removal. Starting at center and working outward in a circular pattern, tighten brackets. Adjust valves.

VALVE GUIDE SERVICING

Inspection

Using dial indicator method, check valve stem-to-guide clearance. Position dial indicator point about .40" (10 mm) above end of guide. Rock valve stem back and forth and measure movement. If movement exceeds .008" (.20 mm), replace valve guide and valve.

Removal

Working from combustion chamber side of cylinder head, drive out old guide with valve guide driver tool (J-26512).

Installation

Coat outer surface of guide with engine oil. Working from top side of head, drive guide into head with driver tool (J-26512). Guide should project from cylinder head .583" (14.8 mm). Always replace valve guide and valve as a set.

VALVE STEM OIL SEALS

Removal

Remove rocker arm shaft assembly. Position piston of cylinder concerned to TDC. Using spring compressor tool (J-29760), compress spring and remove valve locks. Release pressure and remove spring retainer and springs. Remove valve stem oil seal.

Installation

Apply engine oil to inner face of new oil seal and to valve stem. Install oil seal. Install inner and outer springs with green painted side (closed-coil end) toward cylinder head. Using spring compressor tool, install remaining components in reverse order of removal.

VALVE SEAT INSERTS

Removal

To remove seat, arc-weld a bead of metal around inner face of seat. Allow to cool a few minutes. Using screwdrivers, pry out valve seat.

Installation

Using arbor press, install new seat. Grind seat to correct width and angle. Lap valve and seat to complete installation.

VALVE SPRINGS

To remove and install valve springs, use procedures outlined in valve stem oil seal removal and installation. Always replace inner and outer springs as a set.

Inspection

1) Measure inner and outer valve spring free length. Test valve spring tension with a valve spring tester. Replace springs that fail tests.

2) Using a flat surface and steel square, check valve spring for squareness. Take measurement between top of spring and square, while slowly rotating spring. Out-of-square must not exceed .04" (1.0 mm).

SWIRL CHAMBER REPLACEMENT

Removal

Measure chamber depth in head with straight edge and feeler gauge. If depth exceeds .0008" (.020 mm), chamber must be replaced. Use a small diameter drift (1/8 - 3/16") to drive out old chamber. Insert drift through injection nozzle hole to swirl chamber and drive out with hammer.

Installation

Install lock ball into groove in swirl chamber. Align lock ball in chamber with groove in cylinder head and drive in. Use press to seat chamber. A piece of metal should be placed between press and chamber to prevent damage. Grind face of swirl chamber flush with face of cylinder head to complete installation.

VALVE CLEARANCE ADJUSTMENT

1) Ensure rocker arm shaft brackets are properly tightened. Cold or hot valve clearances are as follows: .010" (.25 mm) for intake valves, and .014" (.35 mm) for exhaust valves.

2) Turn crankshaft to position No. 1 piston at TDC on compression stroke. Adjust valve clearance as listed in valve clearance setting sequence table.

Isuzu Engines

I-MARK 4-CYLINDER DIESEL (Cont.)

3) Turn crankshaft 1 revolution to place No. 4 piston on TDC at end of compression stroke and adjust remaining valves.

VALVE CLEARANCE SETTING SEQUENCE

Piston On TDC	Adjust Int. Nos.	Adjust Exh. Nos.
1	1, 2	1, 3
4	3, 4	2,4

PISTONS, PINS & RINGS

OIL PAN

Oil pan removal and installation is performed with engine removed from vehicle.

PISTON AND ROD ASSEMBLY

Removal

1) Remove engine from vehicle. Remove cylinder head and oil pan. Remove carbon deposits from upper edge of cylinder wall. Remove rod cap.

2) Push piston/rod assembly out top of cylinder block. Install rod cap on its respective piston/rod assembly.

Installation

1) Apply oil to rings, piston and cylinder wall. Make sure ring gaps are properly spaced. *See Fig. 5.* Make sure bearing halves are properly seated in connecting rod and cap.

Fig. 5: Piston Ring Gap Locations

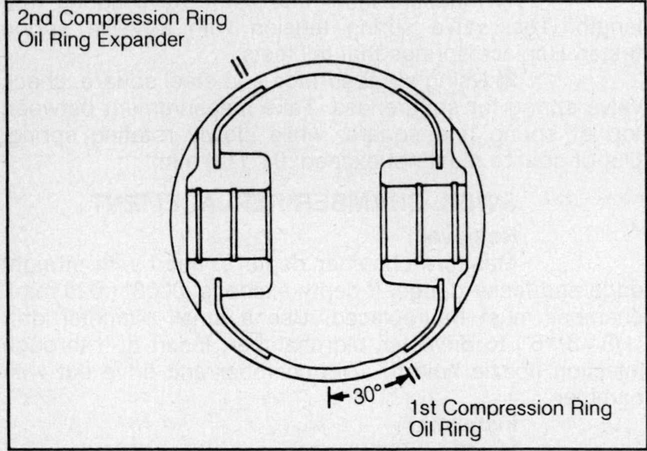
2nd Compression Ring
Oil Ring Expander
30°
1st Compression Ring
Oil Ring

2) Install a ring compressor and compress rings. Install piston in cylinder. Ensure notched mark on piston head points toward front of engine. Install and tighten rod cap. Reverse removal procedures to complete installation.

FITTING PISTONS

1) Measure cylinder bore diameter at a point 5 1/2" below cylinder block deck surface. Take measurements in line with and 90° to crankshaft centerline. If wear is excessive, cylinder should be bored for installation of oversize piston.

2) Measure piston (skirt) diameter at right angle to piston pin. Take piston skirt measurement about 1 3/4" from top of piston head. Subtract this figure from cylinder diameter to determine piston-to-cylinder wall clearance.

REPLACEMENT PISTON SPECIFICATIONS

Piston Size	Piston Diameter In. (mm)
Standard	3.307-3.309 (84.00-84.05)
.020" O/S	3.326-3.328 (84.50-84.54)
.040" O/S	3.346-3.348 (85.00-85.04)

FITTING RINGS

1) Position rings into cylinder bore at a point where bore diameter is smallest. Ring must be square in bore. Measure ring end gap with a feeler gauge.

2) Using a feeler gauge, check ring side clearance. Ensure rings turn freely in their ring grooves. When installing rings on piston, ensure gaps are correct. *See Fig. 5.*

3) Install rings on piston in this order: expander ring, oil ring, 2nd compression ring, then 1st compression ring. The "N" mark on compression rings must be facing upward.

PISTON PIN REPLACEMENT

Removal

To remove pin, use snap ring pliers and remove snap rings from piston. Push out piston pin with finger. Piston pin bushing in rod's small end is replaceable.

Installation

1) Assemble rod to piston so front mark on piston head and Isuzu mark on rod are on same side. Also, match marks on rod will be on combustion chamber side of piston head. *See Fig. 6.*

2) Coat pin with oil and install in piston and rod. Install snap rings to secure piston pin in place.

Fig. 6: Positioning Rod to Piston

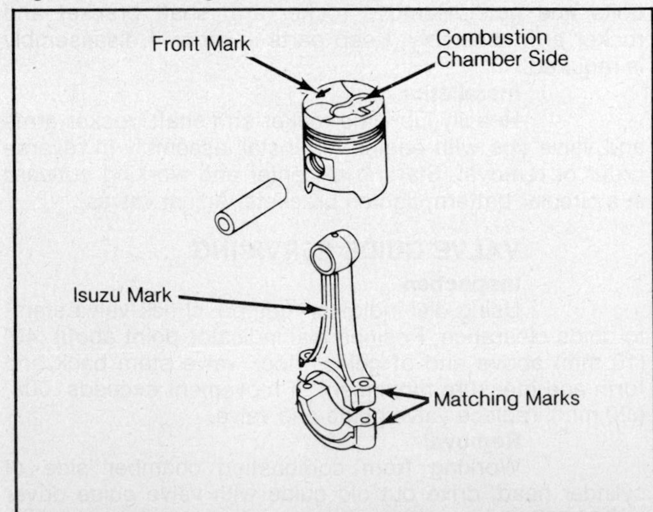
Front Mark
Combustion
Chamber Side
Isuzu Mark
Matching Marks

Note positions of identification markings when assembling rod to piston.

I-MARK 4-CYLINDER DIESEL (Cont.)

CRANKSHAFT MAIN & CONNECTING ROD BEARINGS

NOTE: To check bearing clearances, remove engine from vehicle. Following procedures are performed with oil pan removed, and oil film removed from surfaces to be checked.

CRANKSHAFT MAIN BEARINGS

1) If necessary, mark all bearing caps for cylinder identification. Check clearances 1 at a time. With all bearing caps (except one being checked) tightened, check clearances using Plastigage method.

2) If clearances are excessive, replace crankshaft and bearings. Taper must not exceed .0010" (.025 mm). Crankshaft journals and crankpins cannot be reground.

3) To check crankshaft for straightness, place "V" blocks under crankshaft at No. 1 and No. 5 journals. Position dial indicator point on No. 3 journal.

4) Slowly turn crankshaft at least 1 full revolution, while recording runout. If runout exceeds .0024" (.060 mm), replace crankshaft and bearings.

5) When installing thrust bearing on No. 3 journal, oil grooved thrust faces must be turned outward.

6) Coat joining faces of No. 5 main bearing cap and cylinder block with silicone sealer. *See Fig. 7*. No. 1 and No. 5 main bearing caps are installed flush with face of cylinder block.

7) Apply engine oil to threads and seating face of cap bolts. Install all bearing caps. Tighten caps in progressive steps, in sequence of 3, 2, 4, 1 and 5.

Fig. 7: No. 5 Main Bearing Cap Sealer Application

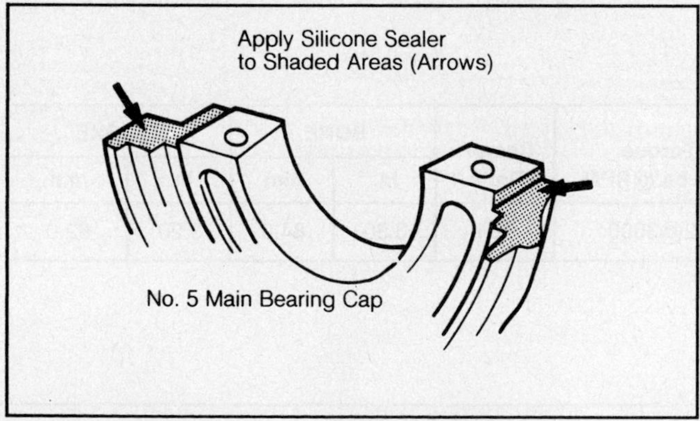
Apply Silicone Sealer
to Shaded Areas (Arrows)
No. 5 Main Bearing Cap

Install bearing cap before sealer sets up.

CONNECTING ROD BEARINGS

1) After ensuring rod caps are marked for cylinder identification, remove rod caps. Use Plastigage method to check for proper clearance.

2) If not within limits, install new bearings if crankpin is not worn beyond limits.

CRANKSHAFT END THRUST

Using a feeler gauge, measure crankshaft end thrust. Move crankshaft fully endwise and measure clearance between crankshaft thrust face and thrust bearing. If clearance is greater than .012" (.30 mm), replace thrust bearings.

REAR MAIN BEARING OIL SEAL

Removal

Remove transmission from engine. If equipped, remove clutch cover and disc. Remove flywheel. Pry rear oil seal from bearing cap.

Installation

Coat seal lip with engine oil. Using seal installer tool, install new seal. Reverse removal procedures to install remaining components.

CRANKSHAFT FRONT OIL SEAL

Removal

Remove timing belt. Remove center bolt from crankshaft flange. Using a puller, remove flange from crankshaft, then use puller to remove crankshaft sprocket. Pry out front oil seal.

Installation

Coat seal lip and fitting face of oil seal with engine oil. Using seal installer, install oil seal into seal retainer. Install remaining components in reverse order of removal.

ENGINE OILING

CRANKCASE CAPACITY

Capacity is 5.5 quarts (5.2L) with oil filter replacement; 5.0 quarts (4.7L) without filter replacement.

NORMAL OIL PRESSURE

Normal oil pressure should be approximately 50-60 psi (3.5-4.5 kg/cm²).

ENGINE OILING SYSTEM

Oil pump is sprocket driven off of timing belt. Oil drawn from pan passes through a strainer to oil pump. Oil is delivered to full flow oil filter, oil cooler, and main oil gallery.

Main oil gallery supplies oil to crankshaft main bearings. Drilled passages in crankshaft route oil to lubricate connecting rods and bearings.

Oil gallery feeds oil to vacuum pump and rocker arm shaft to lubricate rocker arms and cam bearings. Oil is fed from gallery to oil jet pipe which sprays oil from below piston to lubricate and cool cylinder walls and piston.

OIL PUMP

Removal

Remove timing belt. Remove 4 Allen head bolts through access holes in oil pump sprocket, and remove oil pump. *See Fig. 8*.

Inspection

1) Disassemble oil pump. Thoroughly clean pump parts and dry with compressed air. Visually inspect disassembled parts for wear, damage or other abnormal conditions.

2) Measure outside diameter of oil pump sprocket hub. If measurement is less than 1.100" (27.94 mm), replace sprocket.

3) Insert outer rotor into recess in cylinder block. Lay a straightedge over cylinder block and outer rotor. Using a feeler gauge, measure outer rotor end clearance.

I-MARK 4-CYLINDER DIESEL (Cont.)

Fig. 8: Oil Pump Assembly

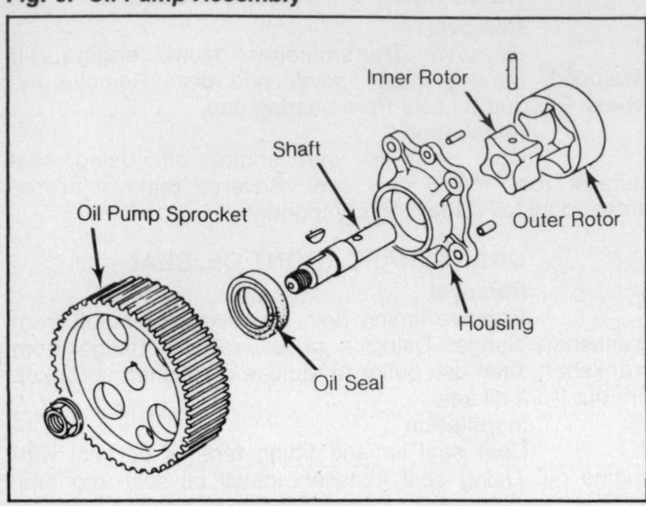
Inner Rotor
Shaft
Oil Pump Sprocket
Outer Rotor
Housing
Oil Seal

4) With outer rotor inserted into recess in cylinder block, use a feeler gauge to measure side clearance between rotor and recess in cylinder block.

5) Install inner rotor into outer rotor. Using a feeler gauge, measure clearance between rotors.

6) Reassemble pump in reverse order of disassembly.

Installation

Apply engine oil to outer rotor, then install with tapered side turned toward cylinder block. Apply engine oil to new oil seal and install into housing. Install inner rotor after lubricating with engine oil. Install remaining components in reverse order of removal.

OIL PUMP SPECIFICATIONS

Application	[1] Clearance In. (mm)
Outer Rotor End Clearance	.008 (.20)
Outer Rotor Side Clearance	.016 (.40)
Clearance Between Rotors	.008 (.20)

[1] — Clearances given are maximum wear limits.

ENGINE COOLING

THERMOSTAT

Thermostat opens at about 180°F (82°C).

COOLING SYSTEM CAPACITY

Cooling system capacity is 7.4 quarts (7.0L).

RADIATOR CAP

Pressure relief valve opens at approximately 13 psi (.9 kg/cm²).

WATER PUMP

Removal

1) Disconnect negative battery cable. Drain cooling system by opening drain plugs on radiator and cylinder block. Remove fan, fan pulley and drive belt.

2) Remove crankshaft pulley. Remove upper and lower timing belt covers. Remove coolant by-pass hose. Remove water pump and gasket.

Installation

Clean gasket mating surfaces. Using new gasket, install water pump in reverse order of removal.

ENGINE SPECIFICATIONS

GENERAL SPECIFICATIONS

Year	DISPLACEMENT Cu. In.	DISPLACEMENT Liters	Fuel System	HP@RPM	Torque Ft. Lbs.@RPM	Compr. Ratio	BORE In.	BORE mm	STROKE In.	STROKE mm
1983	110.8	1.8	Fuel Inj.	51@5000	72@3000	22:1	3.30	84.0	3.20	82.0

CRANKSHAFT MAIN & CONNECTING ROD BEARINGS

Engine	MAIN BEARINGS Journal Diam. In. (mm)	MAIN BEARINGS Clearance In. (mm)	MAIN BEARINGS Thrust Bearing	MAIN BEARINGS Crankshaft End Play In. (mm)	CONNECTING ROD BEARINGS Journal Diam. In. (mm)	CONNECTING ROD BEARINGS Clearance In. (mm)	CONNECTING ROD BEARINGS Side Play In. (mm)
1.8L	2.201-2.202 (55.92-55.93)	.0015-.0031 (.039-.080)	No. 3	.0024-.0094 (.061-.239)	1.926-1.927 (48.920-48.946)	.0016-.0031 (.040-.080)	.....

Isuzu Engines

I-MARK 4-CYLINDER DIESEL (Cont.)

ENGINE SPECIFICATIONS (Cont.)

PISTONS, PINS, RINGS

	PISTONS	PINS		RINGS		
Engine	Clearance In. (mm)	Piston Fit In. (mm)	Rod Fit In. (mm)	Ring No.	End Gap In. (mm)	Side Clearance In. (mm)
1.8L	.0002-.0017 (.005-.045)	.0001-.0005 (.002-.012)	.0003-.0078 [1] (.008-.020)	No. 1	.0078-.0157 (.200-.400)	.0035-.0049 (.090-.125)
				No. 2	.0078-.0157 (.200-.400)	.0014-.0020 (.035-.050)
				Oil	.0078-.0157 (.200-.400)	.0012-.0028 (.030-.070)

[1] – Clearance between pin and bushing in rod.

VALVES

Engine Size & Valve	Head Diam. In. (mm)	Face Angle	Seat Angle	Seat Width In. (mm)	Stem Diameter In. (mm)	Stem Clearance In. (mm)	Valve Lift In. (mm)
1.8L							
Intake	.....	45°	45°	.0472-.0590 (1.200-1.500)	.313 (7.95)	.0016-.0028 (.040-.070)	.....
Exhaust	.....	45°	45°	.0472-.0590 (1.200-1.500)	.313 (7.95)	.0020-.0031 (.05-.08)	.....

CAMSHAFT

Engine	Journal Diam. In. (mm)	Clearance In. (mm)	Lobe Lift In. (mm)
1.8L	1.1004-1.1011 (27.95-27.97)	.0008-.0035 (.020-.090)	.....

VALVE SPRINGS

Engine	Free Length In. (mm)	PRESSURE Lbs. @ In. (Kg @ mm)	
		Valve Closed	Valve Open
1.8L			
Inner	1.783 (45.3)	17-20@1.52 [1] (7-9@38.5)	.....
Outer	1.846 (46.9)	31-35@1.61 [1] (14-16@41.0)	.....

[1] – Compressed height as measured in tester.

TIGHTENING SPECIFICATIONS

Application	Ft. Lbs. (N.m)
Cylinder Head	
Step 1	21-36 (30-50)
Step 2	
New Bolt	83-98 (113-133)
Used Bolt	90-105 (122-142)
Camshaft Bearing Caps	15-22 (20-30)
Camshaft Sprocket	43-50 (58-68)
Connecting Rod	54-61 (73-83)
Crankshaft Sprocket	98-119 (133-161)
Engine Rear Plate	25-33 (34-45)
Exhaust Manifold	11-18 (15-24)
Flywheel	36-43 (49-59)
Main Bearing Caps	65-72 (88-98)
Idler Pulley Center Bolt	47-61 (64-83)
Injection Pump Timing Pulley	43-50 (58-68)
Intake Manifold	25-32 (34-43)
Oil Jet Pipe (1)	40-54 (54-73)
Oil Pump	11-18 (15-24)
Rocker Arm Shaft Assembly	15-22 (20-30)
Tension Pulley Center Bolt	47-61 (64-83)

Isuzu Engines

P'UP 4-CYLINDER DIESEL

ENGINE CODING

ENGINE IDENTIFICATION

Engine identification code is 8th character of the Vehicle Identification Number (VIN). The VIN is stamped on a metal tab, located on top of instrument panel near lower left of windshield. Engine serial number is stamped on a machined pad, located at front of the cylinder block.

ENGINE IDENTIFICATION CODE

Engine	Code
C-223 (2.2L)	S

ENGINE, MANIFOLDS & CYLINDER HEAD

TRANSMISSION

Removal (4WD Only)

1) Disconnect battery negative cable. Drain transmission oil. Remove transmission and transfer shift levers. Remove return spring from transfer shift lever. Remove starter. Disconnect exhaust pipe from manifold, then remove bracket at transmission.

2) Disconnect speedometer cable and ground cable. Disconnect rear propeller shaft at differential. Remove center bearing mount bolts, then remove 1st and 2nd rear propeller shafts together. On long wheel base 4WD models, remove shafts separately.

3) Disconnect front propeller shaft at both ends. Remove return spring and clutch cable from clutch release lever. Remove flywheel cover. Remove rear transmission mount bolts. Raise engine and transmission, then remove transmission support crossmember.

4) Lower engine and transmission and support rear of engine. Remove transfer side case from transmission. Disconnect electrical wiring to transmission. Remove shift cover from top of transmission.

5) Before removing transmission from vehicle make sure transmission is positioned approximately 4 inches lower than it was when it was mounted. Measurement should be taken at tail shaft housing. Remove transmission from engine. When removing transmission, turn side case surface downward and pull case straight back until it is completely disengaged.

Installation

To install transmission, reverse removal procedures. Install gear shift lever with transmission in neutral. Install transfer shift lever in position "4L" or "2H". Adjust clutch.

ENGINE

NOTE: **On 4WD models, transmission must be removed prior to removing engine. On 2WD models, transmission and engine must be removed as a unit.**

Removal

1) Remove hood. Disconnect battery cables. Remove cables, battery hold-down and battery. Drain engine cooling system, crankcase and transmission. Remove cover from under engine.

2) Remove air cleaner assembly. Disconnect all coolant hoses. Remove all drive belts. Remove fan, fan shroud, radiator grill and radiator. Disconnect accelerator control cable. If A/C equipped, disconnect compressor control cable.

3) Disconnect fuel hoses (or lines). Disconnect all transmission wiring. Disconnect vacuum hose at fast idle actuator and wire connector at fuel cut solenoid. Detach electrical connectors from sensing resistor, thermoswitch and A/C compressor.

4) Disconnect vacuum hoses from vacuum pump. Disconnect alternator wiring. Disconnect exhaust pipe from manifold and remove mounting bracket from engine backing plate. Remove all wiring from starter.

5) Working inside passenger compartment, remove transmission shift lever. Remove return spring and clutch cable from clutch release lever. Remove cable through stiffener bracket.

6) Disconnect speedometer and ground cables from transmission. Mark for reassembly, then remove propeller shaft. Remove 2 rear transmission mount bolts. Attach engine hoist and raise engine and transmission for clearance, then remove crossmember-to-frame bracket bolts.

7) On 2WD models, remove transmission rear extension mounting nuts. Remove engine mounting bolt and nuts. Disconnect any remaining engine or transmission to chassis wiring. Pull engine forward, then carefully remove engine and transmission as an assembly.

Installation

Replace any rubber engine mounts showing signs of deterioration, separation or unusual wear. Reverse removal procedures to complete installation. Check all fluid levels. Adjust clutch.

CYLINDER HEAD

Removal

1) Drain cooling system. Remove air cleaner. Remove intake manifold. Disconnect exhaust pipe from exhaust manifold. Remove exhaust manifold.

2) Disconnect upper radiator hose from engine. Remove fan and fan shroud. Disconnect injection pipes. Remove nozzle holder retaining nuts and nozzle holder assembly. Remove rocker arm shaft assembly.

3) Remove push rods. Remove joint bolt and disconnect the leak-off pipe. Loosen head bolts in reverse of tightening sequence. Remove cylinder head and gasket.

Fig. 1: Cylinder Head Tightening Sequence

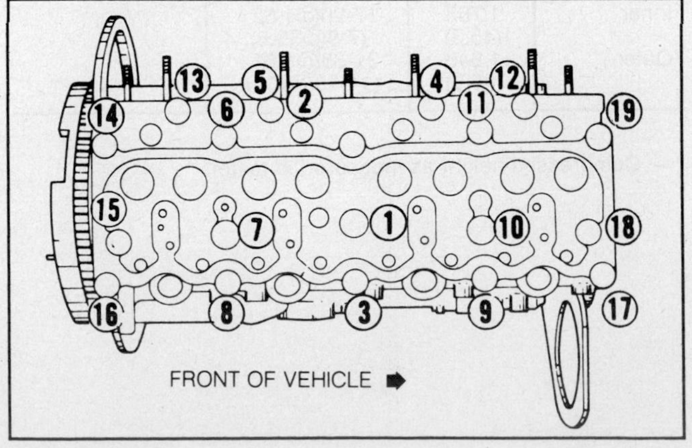
13
5
4
12
14
6
2
11
19
15
7
1
10
18
16
8
3
9
17
FRONT OF VEHICLE

P'UP 4-CYLINDER DIESEL (Cont.)

Installation

Install new head gasket with "TOP" mark facing upward. Install and tighten cylinder head. *See Fig. 1*. Install push rods. Install and tighten rocker arm shaft assembly. *See Fig. 2*. Reverse removal procedure to complete installation.

Fig. 2: Rocker Arm Shaft Assembly Tightening Sequence

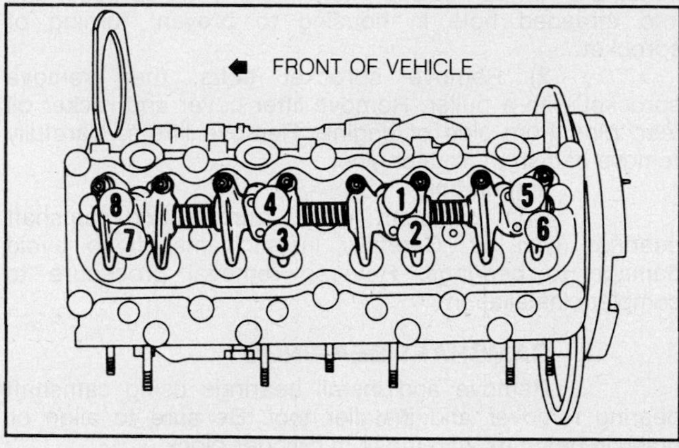
FRONT OF VEHICLE
8
7
4
3
1
2
5
6

CAMSHAFT

TIMING BELT COVER

Removal

Drain cooling system. Remove battery. Remove fan and fan shroud. Disconnect radiator hoses at engine. Remove radiator grille and radiator. Remove all drive belts. Remove crankshaft pulley. Remove timing belt cover in 2 pieces.

Installation

Install timing belt cover in reverse order of removal procedures.

TIMING BELT

Removal

1) Remove timing belt cover. Position No. 1 piston at TDC on compression stroke. Ensure injection pump sprocket and camshaft sprocket timing marks are aligned. *See Fig. 3*.

Fig. 3: Sprocket Alignment for Timing Belt Removal & Installation

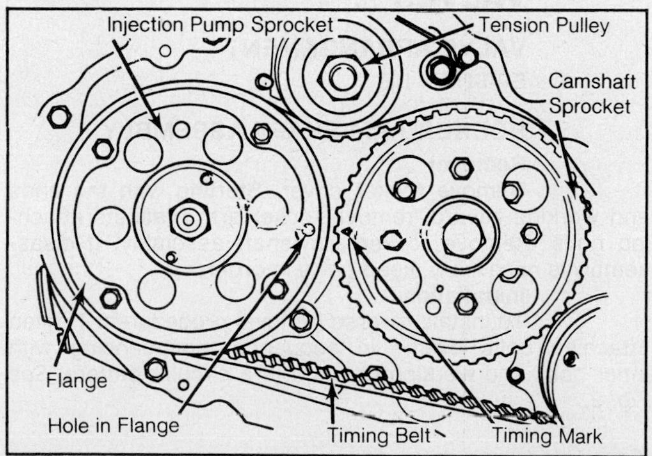
Injection Pump Sprocket
Tension Pulley
Camshaft Sprocket
Flange
Hole in Flange
Timing Belt
Timing Mark

Timing pointer and crankshaft pulley timing mark must be aligned for removal & installation

2) Remove injection pump timing pulley flange bolts and remove flange. When removing tension spring, avoid using excess force on spring. Remove tension pulley and center. Remove timing belt. Ensure sprocket positions do not change.

Installation

1) Before installing timing belt, check that the timing marks on injection pump and camshaft sprockets are aligned, as well as crankshaft pulley and timing pointer. *See Fig. 4*. Install timing belt over crankshaft sprocket first, then camshaft sprocket and injection pump sprocket.

Fig. 4: Timing Mark Alignment

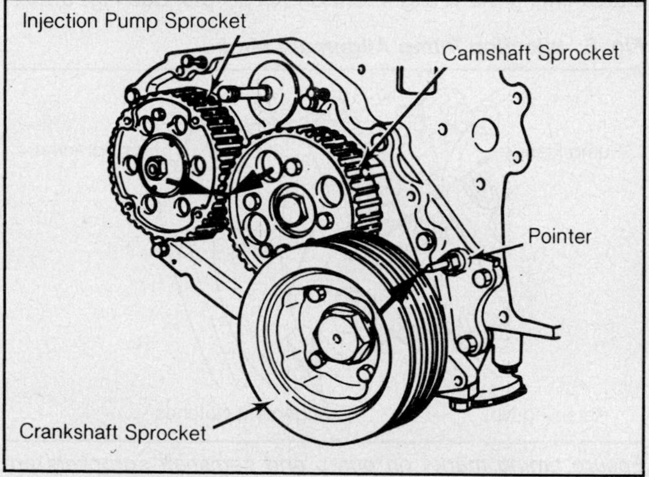
Injection Pump Sprocket
Camshaft Sprocket
Pointer
Crankshaft Sprocket

Heavy black arrows show points of timing mark alignment.

2) Install tension pulley center and tension pulley. The end of the tension pulley center must be in contact with 2 pins on the timing pulley housing. *See Fig. 5*. Hand tighten nut, install tension spring and tighten nut to 22-36 ft. lbs. (30-50 N.m).

Fig. 5: Tension Pulley Installation

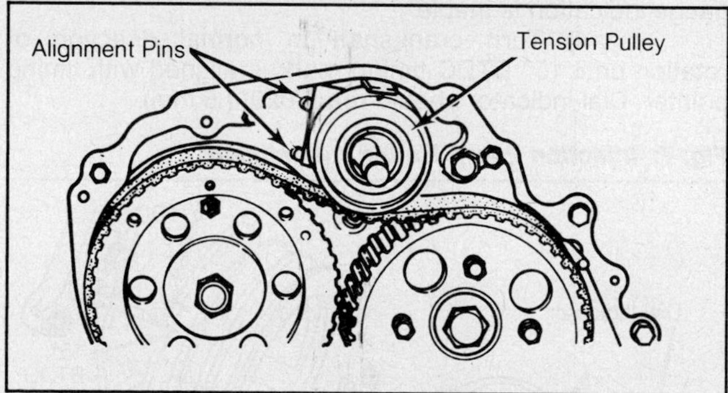
Alignment Pins
Tension Pulley

Ensure end of tension pulley center is in contact with 2 pins.

3) Turn crankshaft 2 complete revolutions in direction of normal rotation. Further turn 90° past TDC. Loosen tension pulley nut completely and allow pulley to take up slack. Tighten nut.

4) Install and tighten injection pump pulley flange. Ensure hole in flange lines up with triangular timing mark on pump sprocket. *See Fig. 3*.

5) Turn crankshaft 2 turns more, bringing No. 1 cylinder to TDC on compression stroke. Check timing mark alignment.

P'UP 4-CYLINDER DIESEL (Cont.)

6) Check belt tension with tension tester (J-29771). Tension should be 33-55 lbs. (15-25 kg). Adjust valve clearance. Reverse removal procedure to complete installation.

VALVE TIMING

To check for correct valve timing, refer to procedures explained in Timing Belt removal and installation.

INJECTION PUMP TIMING

1) Check that notched lines on injection pump flange and injection pump front bracket are aligned. *See Fig. 6*. With No. 1 cylinder at TDC on compression stroke, check timing mark alignment on sprockets. *See Fig. 3*.

Fig. 6: Injection Pump Alignment Marks

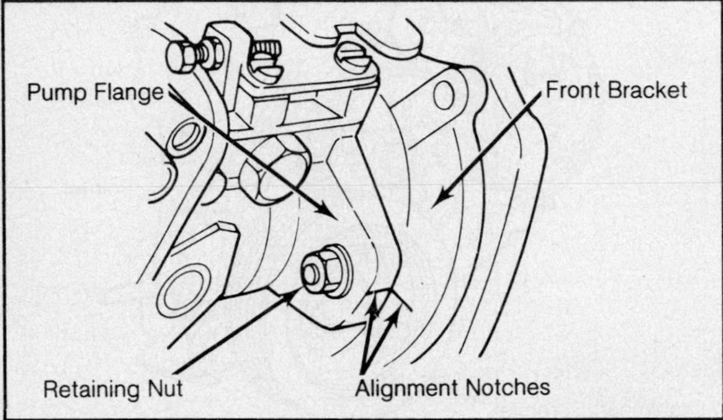
Pump Flange
Front Bracket
Retaining Nut
Alignment Notches

Ensure timing marks on pump and camshaft sprockets are also aligned.

2) Disconnect injection pipe from pump and remove distributor head screw. Install static timing gauge (dial indicator) and set lift approximately .04" (1 mm) from the plunger.

3) Turn engine until No. 1 cylinder is 45-60° BTDC, then calibrate dial indicator to zero. Turn crankshaft pulley slightly in both directions and check that gauge indication is stable.

4) Turn crankshaft in normal direction of rotation until 15° BTDC timing mark is aligned with timing pointer. Dial indicator should read .020" (.5 mm).

Fig. 7: Injection Pump Timing Adjustment

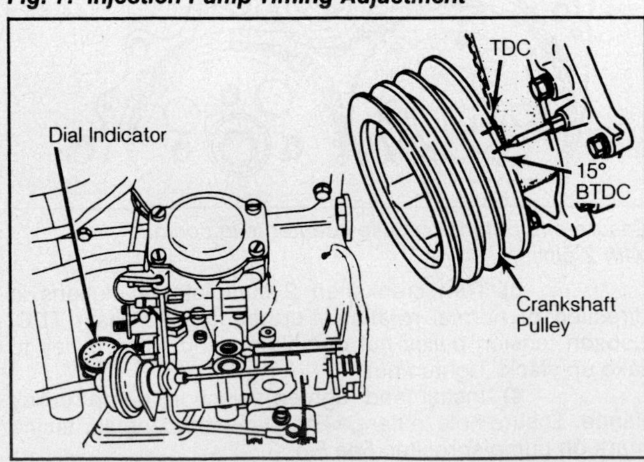
TDC
Dial Indicator
15°
BTDC
Crankshaft
Pulley

5) If indicator reading is not correct, loosen the 2 injection pump flange retaining nuts and rotate housing until a correct reading is obtained. Tighten nuts and recheck reading.

CAMSHAFT

Removal

1) Remove engine from vehicle. Remove timing belt. Remove rocker arm shaft assembly and push rods. Install a 6 mm bolt through hole in camshaft sprocket and into threaded hole in housing to prevent turning of sprocket.

2) Remove sprocket bolts, then remove sprocket with a puller. Remove lifter cover and rocker oil feed pipe from side of engine. Remove lifters. Carefully remove camshaft from engine.

Installation

Coat camshaft lobes, journals and camshaft bearings with oil. Carefully install camshaft to avoid damage to bearings. Reverse removal procedure to complete installation.

CAMSHAFT BEARINGS

Remove and install bearings using camshaft bearing remover and installer tool. Be sure to align oil holes in bearings with those in cylinder block.

CAMSHAFT OIL SEAL

Removal

1) Remove timing belt. Install a 6 mm bolt through hole in camshaft sprocket and into threaded hole in housing to prevent turning of sprocket.

2) Remove sprocket bolts, then remove sprocket with a puller. Remove oil seal retainer. Remove oil seal.

Installation

Using seal installer, install oil seal into retainer until seated. Install remaining components in reverse order of removal.

CAMSHAFT END THRUST

Remove timing belt cover. Attach a dial indicator to cylinder block with indicator point on camshaft sprocket center bolt. Push camshaft rearward and zero dial indicator. Use a screwdriver to pry camshaft forward and record end thrust. Maximum end thrust is .008" (.20 mm).

VALVES

VALVE ARRANGEMENT

E-I-I-E-E-I-I-E

ROCKER ARM SHAFT ASSEMBLY

Removal

Remove rocker cover. Starting with the ends and working inward, remove rocker arm brackets attaching bolts. Remove rocker arm shaft assembly. If disassembly is necessary, keep parts in order.

Installation

To install, reverse removal procedures. Tighten attaching bolts evenly in sequence, commencing with inner bolts and working outward in a circular pattern. *See Fig. 2*.

P'UP 4-CYLINDER DIESEL (Cont.)

VALVE GUIDE SERVICING

Inspection

Using dial indicator method, check valve stem-to-guide clearance. Position dial indicator point about .40" (10 mm) above end of guide. Rock valve stem back and forth and measure movement. If movement exceeds .008" (.20 mm) replace valve and worn guide.

Removal

Working from combustion chamber side of cylinder head, drive out old guide with driver tool (J-26512).

Installation

Coat outer surface of guide with engine oil. Working from top side of head, drive guide into head with driver tool (J-26512). Guide should project from cylinder head .472" (12.0 mm). Always replace valve guide and valve as a set.

VALVE STEM OIL SEALS

Removal

Remove rocker arm shaft assembly. Position piston of cylinder concerned to TDC. Using spring compressor tool (J-29760), compress spring and remove valve locks. Release pressure and remove spring retainer and springs. Remove valve stem oil seal.

Installation

Apply engine oil to inner face of new oil seal and to valve stem. Install oil seal. Install inner and outer springs with green painted side (closed-coil end) toward cylinder head. Using spring compressor tool, install remaining components in reverse order of removal.

VALVE SEAT INSERTS

Removal

To remove seat, arc-weld a bead of metal around inner face of seat. Allow to cool a few minutes. Using screwdrivers, pry out valve seat.

Installation

Using arbor press, install new seat. Grind seat to correct width and angle. Lap valve and seat to complete installation.

VALVE SPRINGS

Removal & Installation

To remove and install valve springs, use procedures outlined in Valve Stem Oil Seal removal and installation.

Inspection

1) Measure inner and outer valve spring free length. Test valve spring tension with a valve spring tester. Replace springs that fail tests. Always replace inner and outer springs as a set.

2) Using a flat surface and steel square, check valve spring for squareness. Take measurement between top of spring and square, while slowly rotating spring. Out-of-square must not exceed .04" (1.0 mm). Replace inner and outer springs as a set.

SWIRL CHAMBER REPLACEMENT

Removal

Measure chamber depth in head with straight edge and feeler gauge. If depth exceeds .0008" (.020 mm), chamber must be replaced. Use a small diameter drift (1/8 - 3/16") to drive out old chamber. Insert drift through injection nozzle hole to swirl chamber and drive out with hammer.

Installation

Install lock ball into groove in swirl chamber. Align lock ball in chamber with groove in cylinder head and drive in. Use press to seat chamber. A piece of metal should be placed between press and chamber to prevent damage. Grind face of swirl chamber flush with face of cylinder head to complete installation.

VALVE CLEARANCE ADJUSTMENT

1) Ensure rocker arm shaft brackets are properly tightened. Cold valve clearance is .016" (.40 mm) for intake and exhaust valves. Hot valve clearance is .015" (.37 mm) for intake and exhaust valves.

2) Turn crankshaft to position No. 1 piston on TDC at end of compression stroke. Adjust valve clearance as listed in valve clearance setting sequence table.

3) Turn crankshaft 1 revolution to place No. 4 piston on TDC at end of compression stroke and adjust remaining valves.

VALVE CLEARANCE SETTING SEQUENCE

Piston On TDC	Adjust Int. Nos.	Adjust Exh. Nos.
1	1, 2	1, 3
4	3, 4	2,4

PISTONS, PINS & RINGS

OIL PAN

Oil pan removal and installation is performed with engine removed from vehicle.

PISTON AND ROD ASSEMBLY

Removal

1) Remove engine from vehicle. Remove cylinder head. Remove crankcase and oil pan as an assembly. Detach oil pipe sleeve nut from crankcase. Remove 2 attaching bolts, then remove oil pump with oil pipe attached.

2) Remove carbon deposits from upper edge of cylinder wall. Remove rod cap. Push piston/rod assembly out top of cylinder block. Install rod cap on its respective piston/rod assembly.

Installation

1) Lightly oil rings, piston and cylinder wall. Make sure ring gaps are properly spaced. *See Fig. 8.* Make sure bearing halves are properly seated in connecting rod and cap.

Fig. 8: Piston Ring Gap Locations

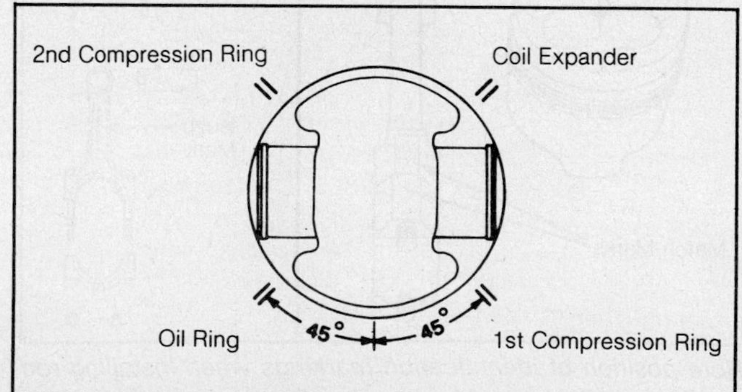
2nd Compression Ring
Coil Expander
Oil Ring
45°
45°
1st Compression Ring

P'UP 4-CYLINDER DIESEL (Cont.)

2) Install a ring compressor and compress rings. Install piston in cylinder. Ensure mark on piston head points towards front of engine. Install and tighten rod cap. Reverse removal procedures to complete installation.

FITTING PISTONS

1) Measure cylinder bore diameter at points 5/8" and 4 1/2" below cylinder block deck surface. Take measurements in line with and 90° to crankshaft centerline. If wear is excessive, cylinder should be bored for installation of oversize piston.

2) Measure piston diameter at right angle to piston pin. Subtract this figure from cylinder diameter to determine piston-to-cylinder wall clearance.

PISTON DIAMETER SPECIFICATIONS

Application	In. (mm)
Standard	3.457-3.458 (87.83-87.85)
.5 mm Oversize	3.477-3.478 (88.33-88.35)
1 mm Oversize	3.497-3.498 (88.83-88.85)

FITTING RINGS

1) Position rings into cylinder bore at a point where bore diameter is smallest. Ring must be square in bore. Measure ring end gap with a feeler gauge.

2) Using a feeler gauge, check ring side clearance. Ensure rings turn freely in their ring grooves. When installing rings on piston, ensure gaps are correct. *See Fig. 8*.

3) Install rings on piston in this order: expander ring, oil ring, 2nd compression ring then 1st compression ring. The "N" mark on compression rings must be upward.

PISTON PIN REPLACEMENT

Removal

To remove pin, use snap ring pliers and remove snap rings from piston. Use a brass rod to drive out pin. Piston pin bushings in rod's small end are replaceable.

Installation

1) Heat piston to about 175°F (80°C). Assemble rod to piston so front mark on piston head and Isuzu mark on rod are on same side. Also, match marks on rod will be on combustion chamber side of piston head. *See Fig. 9*.

2) Coat pin with oil and install in piston and rod. Install snap rings to secure pin in place.

Fig. 9: Positioning Rod to Piston

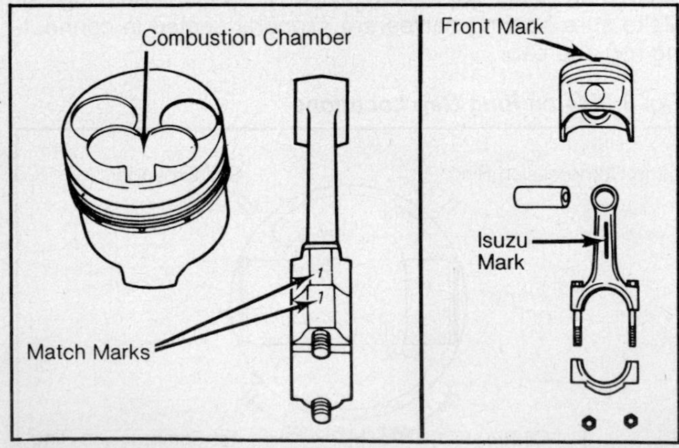
Combustion Chamber
Front Mark
Isuzu Mark
Match Marks

Note position of identification markings when installing rod to piston.

CRANKSHAFT MAIN & CONNECTING ROD BEARINGS

NOTE: **To check bearing clearances, remove engine from vehicle. Following procedures are performed with oil pan removed, and oil film removed from surfaces to be checked.**

MAIN BEARINGS

1) If necessary, mark all bearing caps for cylinder identification. Check clearances 1 at a time. With all bearing caps (except one being checked) tighted, check clearances using Plastigage method.

2) If clearances are excessive, replace crankshaft and bearings. Taper must not exceed .0010" (.025 mm). Crankshaft journals and crankpins cannot be reground.

3) To check crankshaft for straightness, place "V" blocks under crankshaft at No. 1 and No. 5 journals. Position dial indicator point on No. 3 journal.

4) Slowly turn crankshaft at least 1 full revolution, while recording runout. If runout exceeds .0024" (.060 mm), replace crankshaft and bearings.

5) When installing thrust bearing (No. 3 journal), oil grooved thrust faces must be turned outward.

6) Install arch gaskets on bearing caps 1 and 5. Use liquid gasket sealer to hold gasket in place while installing caps. Gasket should not project more than .002" (.05 mm) from fitting face of cap. *See Fig. 10*.

7) Apply thin coat of silicone sealer to fitting face of bearing caps 1 and 5. *See Fig. 10*. Install all bearing caps. Ensure arch gasket protrusions fit properly, when installing bearing caps 1 and 5.

8) No. 2 and No. 4 bearing caps are identical. Install bearing cap with the mark "A" in the No. 2 position. Tighten caps in progressive steps, in sequence of 3, 4, 2, 5 and 1.

Fig. 10: Arch Gasket & Sealer Installation

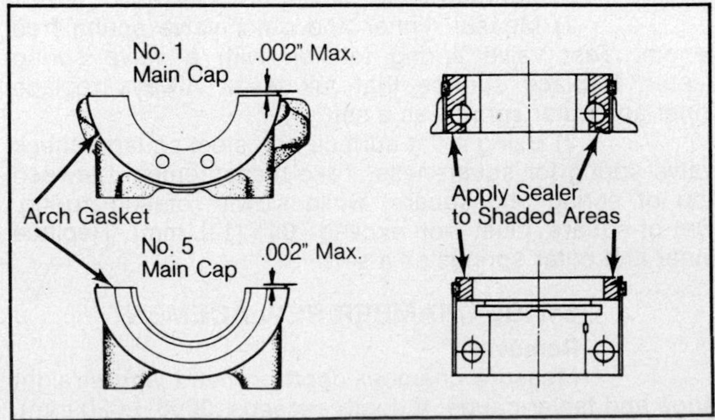
No. 1
Main Cap
.002" Max.
Arch Gasket
No. 5
Main Cap
.002" Max.
Apply Sealer
to Shaded Areas

Install bearing caps before sealer sets up.

P'UP 4-CYLINDER DIESEL (Cont.)

CONNECTING ROD BEARINGS

1) After ensuring rod caps are marked for cylinder identification, remove rod caps. Use plastigage method to check for proper clearance.

2) If crankpin is not worn and clearance is beyond maximum, replace bearings.

CRANKSHAFT END THRUST

Using a feeler gauge, measure crankshaft end thrust between thrust bearing and thrust face of crankshaft. Move crankshaft fully endwise and measure clearance between crankshaft thrust face and thrust bearing. If clearance is greater than .012" (.30 mm), replace thrust bearings.

REAR MAIN BEARING OIL SEAL

Removal

Remove engine from vehicle. If equipped, remove clutch cover and disc. Remove flywheel. Remove rear oil seal.

Installation

Coat seal lip with engine oil. Using seal installer tool, install new seal. Reverse removal procedures to install remaining components.

CRANKSHAFT FRONT OIL SEAL

Removal

Remove camshaft oil seal retainer. Hold crankshaft from turning and remove crankshaft pulley. Using a puller, remove crankshaft sprocket. Remove front oil seal dust cover, then remove oil seal.

Installation

Coat seal lip with engine oil. Using seal installer, install oil seal. Install remaining components in reverse order of removal.

ENGINE OILING

CRANKCASE CAPACITY

Capacity is 5.1 quarts (4.8L) with oil filter replacement; 4.2 quarts (4.0L) without filter replacement.

NORMAL OIL PRESSURE

Normal oil pressure for all models is 50-60 psi (3.5-4.5 kg/cm²), at high engine speeds.

ENGINE OILING SYSTEM

A rotor-type oil pump is used on 2WD models and 4WD models use a gear-type oil pump. Oil drawn from crankcase passes through a strainer, then to oil pump.

Oil is delivered to full flow oil filter, oil cooler, and main oil gallery. By-pass valves are incorporated into oil filter and oil cooler.

Main oil gallery supplies oil to lubricate crankshaft, main and connecting rod bearings. Oil gallery feeds oil to vacuum pump and camshaft. From camshaft, oil is routed to feed rocker arm shaft assembly and upper valve train components.

Oil is fed from oil gallery to oil jet pipe, which sprays oil from below pistons to lubricate cylinder walls and piston pins. Oil spray from oil jets also aids in piston cooling.

OIL PUMP

Removal

To remove, first remove oil pan and crankcase. Remove oil pipe sleeve nut and the 2 bolts holding pump in place. Remove oil pump.

Fig. 11: Oil Pump Assemblies

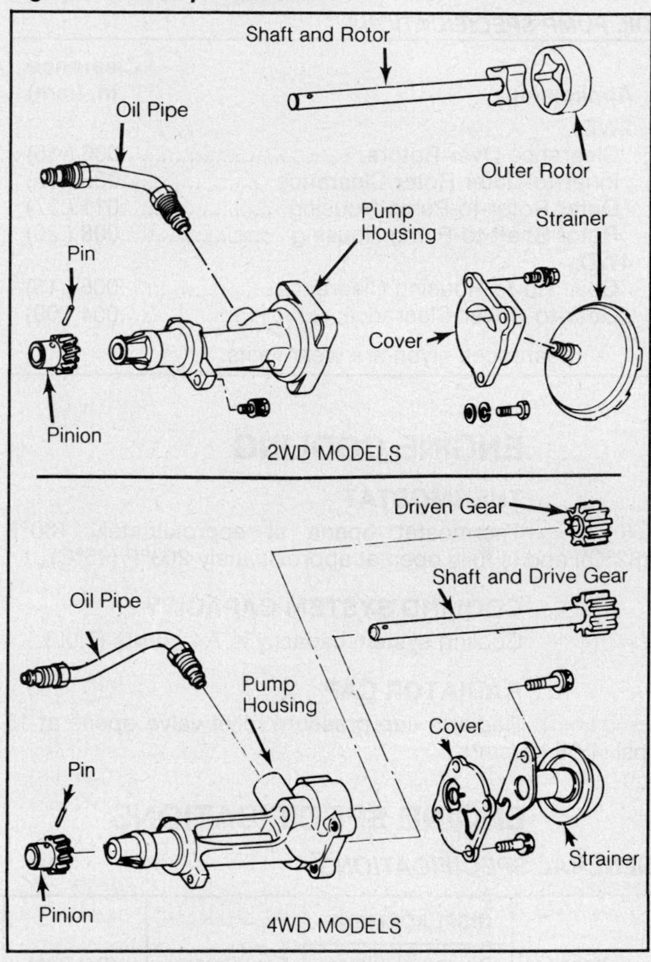
Shaft and Rotor
Oil Pipe
Outer Rotor
Pump Housing
Strainer
Pin
Cover
Pinion
2WD MODELS
Driven Gear
Shaft and Drive Gear
Oil Pipe
Pump Housing
Cover
Pin
Strainer
Pinion
4WD MODELS

Thoroughly clean all parts prior to measuring clearances.

Inspection (2WD Models)

1) Disassemble oil pump and clean all parts thoroughly. Inspect for signs of unusual wear or damage.

2) With rotors installed in pump, lay a straightedge over pump housing. Use a feeler gauge to measure clearance between rotors and straightedge. If clearance over rotors is excessive, replace rotor set.

3) Using a feeler gauge, measure clearance between inner and outer rotors. If clearance is beyond limits, replace rotor set.

4) Using feeler gauge, measure clearance between outer rotor and pump housing. If clearance is excessive, replace entire pump assembly.

5) Check clearance between rotor shaft and pump body. If beyond limits, replace entire pump assembly.

Inspection (4WD Models)

1) Using a feeler gauge, check clearance between pump body inner wall and tip of each gear. If clearance is beyond limits, replace entire gear set.

Isuzu Engines

P'UP 4-CYLINDER DIESEL (Cont.)

2) With gears installed, lay a straightedge over pump housing. Use a feeler gauge to measure clearance between gears and straightedge. If gear-to-cover clearance is excessive, replace entire pump assembly.

Installation

Reverse removal procedures to install.

OIL PUMP SPECIFICATIONS

Application	[1] Clearance In. (mm)
2WD	
Clearance Over Rotors	.006 (.15)
Inner-to-Outer Rotor Clearance	.006 (.15)
Outer Rotor-to-Pump Housing	.011 (.27)
Rotor Shaft-to-Pump Housing	.008 (.20)
4WD	
Gear Tip-to-Housing Clearance	.006 (.15)
Gear-to-Cover Clearance	.004 (.09)

[1] – Clearances given are wear limits.

ENGINE COOLING

THERMOSTAT

Thermostat opens at approximately 180°F (82°C), and is fully open at approximately 203°F (95°C).

COOLING SYSTEM CAPACITY

Cooling system capacity is 7.4 quarts (7.0L).

RADIATOR CAP

Radiator cap pressure relief valve opens at 15 psi (1.05 kg/cm²).

WATER PUMP

Removal

Drain cooling system and remove battery, fan, fan shroud and upper radiator hose. Remove drive belts and fan pulley. Remove water pump retaining bolts and remove pump.

Installation

Clean gasket mating surfaces. Using new gasket, install water pump in reverse order of removal.

TIGHTENING SPECIFICATIONS

Application	Ft. Lbs. (N.m)
Cylinder Head	
Step 1	40-47 (54-64)
Step 2	
New Bolt	54-61 (76-85)
Used Bolt	61-69 (85-97)
Camshaft Sprocket	72-87 (101-122)
Connecting Rod	58-65 (81-91)
Crankshaft Sprocket	124-151 (174-211)
Engine Rear Plate	55-67 (77-94)
Flywheel	65-72 (91-101)
Main Bearing Caps	116-130 (162-182)
Manifolds (Intake & Exhaust)	10-17 (14-24)
Injection Pump Timing Pulley	42-52 (59-73)
Oil Jet Pipe	24-27 (34-38)
Oil Jets	22 (31)
Oil Cooler	54-61 (76-85)
Rocker Arm Shaft Assembly	10-17 (14-24)
Tension Pulley	78-95 (109-133)

ENGINE SPECIFICATIONS

GENERAL SPECIFICATIONS

Year	DISPLACEMENT		Fuel System	HP@RPM	Torque Ft. Lbs.@RPM	Compr. Ratio	BORE		STROKE	
	Cu. In.	Liters					In.	mm	In.	mm
1983	136.6	2.2	Fuel Inj.	62@4300	96@2000	21:1	3.46	88	3.62	92

VALVES

Engine Size & Valve	Head Diam. In. (mm)	Face Angle	Seat Angle	Seat Width In. (mm)	Stem Diameter In. (mm)	Stem Clearance In. (mm)	Valve Lift In. (mm)
2.2L							
Intake	.....	45°	45°	.047-.059 (1.20-1.50)	.310-.315 (7.88-8.00)	.0015-.0027 (.039-.068)	.....
Exhaust	.....	45°	45°	.047-.059 (1.20-1.50)	.309-.315 (7.85-8.00)	.0025-.0037 (.064-.093)	.....

Isuzu Engines

P'UP 4-CYLINDER DIESEL (Cont.)

ENGINE SPECIFICATIONS (Cont.)

CRANKSHAFT MAIN & CONNECTING ROD BEARINGS

	MAIN BEARINGS				CONNECTING ROD BEARINGS		
Engine	Journal Diam. In. (mm)	Clearance In. (mm)	Thrust Bearing	Crankshaft End Play In. (mm)	Journal Diam. In. (mm)	Clearance In. (mm)	Side Play In. (mm)
2.2L	2.3591-2.3594 (59.92-59.93)	.0011-.0033 (.029-.085)	No. 3	.0018 Max. (.300)	2.0835-2.0839 (52.92-52.93)	.0016-.0047 (.040-.120)	.....

PISTONS, PINS, RINGS

	PISTONS	PINS		RINGS		
Engine	Clearance In. (mm)	Piston Fit In. (mm)	Rod Fit In. (mm)	Ring No.	End Gap In. (mm)	Side Clearance In. (mm)
2.2L	.0062-.0070 (.157-.177)	.0002 (.004)	.0003-.0008 (.008-.020)	No. 1	.008-.016 (.20-.40)	.002-.003 (.05-.07)
				No. 2	.008-.016 (.20-.40)	.001-.002 (.03-.06)
				Oil	.008-.016 (.20-.40)	.0008-.0021 (.020-.054)

VALVE SPRINGS

		PRESSURE Lbs. @ In. (Kg @ mm)	
Engine	Free Length In. (mm)	Valve Closed	Valve Open
2.2L			
Inner	1.89 (47.9)	12-14@1.45 [1] (5.5-6.3@37.0)	.....
Outer	1.86 (47.3)	43-49@1.54 [1] (19.7-22.2@39.0)	.....

[1] – Compressed height as measured in spring tension tester.

CAMSHAFT

Engine	Journal Diam. In. (mm)	Clearance In. (mm)	Lobe Lift In. (mm)
2.2L	1.87-1.89 (47.6-48.0)	.0047 Max. (.002)	.....

VALVE TIMING

	INTAKE		EXHAUST	
Engine	Open (BTDC)	Close (ABDC)	Open (BBDC)	Close (ATDC)
2.2L	16°	54°	56°	14

XJ6 6-CYLINDER

ENGINE CODING

ENGINE IDENTIFICATION

Engine can be identified by the number stamped on top of cylinder block at rear of engine and on identification plate in engine compartment.

ENGINE, MANIFOLDS & CYLINDER HEAD

CAUTION: **The fuel injection system must always be depressurized before disconnecting any fuel system component. Disconnect fuel pump relay and crank engine for a few seconds to depressurize system.**

ENGINE

NOTE: **Engine and transmission are removed as an assembly.**

Removal

1) Remove hood and disconnect battery. Drain engine oil and cooling system. Disconnect radiator hoses and remove radiator and lower cowl. Remove right hand harness cover and disconnect headlamps. Disconnect wiring and A/C hoses from fender support rods and remove rods.

2) Disconnect fuel lines from fuel cooler, and plug all openings. Disconnect wiring from A/C compressor. Remove drive belt and remove A/C compressor. Do not disconnect refrigerant hoses. Disconnect wiring from alternator.

3) Disconnect exhaust pipes from exhaust manifolds. Remove engine ground strap. Remove transmission oil cooler from firewall. Remove air cleaner. Disconnect air-flow meter wiring. Remove air-flow meter and bracket. Disconnect and plug fuel line.

4) Remove power steering pump and move out of the way. Do not disconnect power steering hoses. Disconnect wiring, hoses, vacuum pipes and throttle cable from top of engine. Disconnect injector harness, ground lead and starter lead. Lift fresh air intake out of position and remove heater hose and water valve.

5) Install engine support (MS 53A). Jack up front of vehicle and support with safety stands. Remove rear and intermediate heat shields. Disconnect plate between oil pan and transmission. Place floor jack under rear engine mount and raise it slightly. Remove engine mount attaching bolts and remove engine mount.

6) Remove propeller shaft attaching bolts and remove propeller shaft. Disconnect selector lever cable and speedometer cable. Jack up vehicle, remove safety stands and lower vehicle.

7) Disconnect front lifting eye from right hand studs and replace with lifting eye (C 37851). Install lifting eye on second row of studs from front of engine. Attach engine sling and support engine.

8) Place floor jack with a piece of wood under transmission. Remove front engine mounts. Carefully raise the engine and move it forward to clear steering gear housing. Remove engine/transmission assembly.

Installation

Carefully lower engine/transmission assembly into vehicle. Ensure that engine clears steering gear housing. Reverse removal procedure to complete installation. Check all fluid levels.

INTAKE MANIFOLD

Removal

1) Depressurize fuel system. Remove air cleaner assembly. Remove airflow meter and disconnect hoses from throttle housing. Disconnect cable from airflow meter throttle switch. Remove throttle cable, kickdown cable and service interval counter cable, if used.

2) Remove breather and fuel tubes from fuel rail. Remove thermostat housing. Disconnect ignition coil harness and remove coil. Remove distributor cap and remove spark plug wires. Remove connector from auxiliary air valve cold start injector, coolant temperature sensor and thermostatic switch.

3) Remove fuel injection harness and disconnect fuel hoses from cold start injector regulator and fuel rail. Remove intake manifold attaching nuts. Remove intake manifold and gasket.

Installation

Install intake manifold gasket. Reverse removal procedure to complete installation.

EXHAUST MANIFOLD

Removal

1) Remove screws securing hot air duct to camshaft covers and remove hot air duct from exhaust manifold heat shield. Remove hardware attaching air delivery pipe clip to exhaust manifold heat shield. Remove air delivery pipe from air pump outlet elbow.

2) Loosen air pump drive belt and move pump as far as possible away from cylinder head. Disconnect nut securing EGR pipe. Remove hardware securing steering pinion heat shield. Remove hardware securing heat shield to exhaust manifold. Remove A/C compressor heat shield, if used.

3) Remove hardware securing exhaust pipes to exhaust manifolds. Remove hardware securing exhaust manifold to cylinder head and remove manifold. Remove screws securing hot air pickup from rear of exhaust manifold.

Installation

Install exhaust manifold gasket. Reverse removal procedure to complete installation.

Fig 1: Camshaft Timing

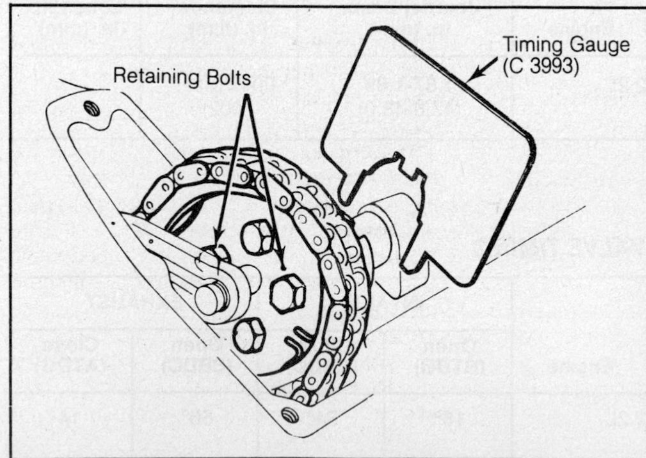
Timing Gauge
(C 3993)
Retaining Bolts

Fit timing gauge into front flange slot of camshaft.

XJ6 6-CYLINDER (Cont.)

CYLINDER HEAD

NOTE: The crankshaft must not be rotated while the camshaft sprockets are disconnected and cylinder head is still in place. Support cylinder head on wooden blocks to prevent damaging valves.

Removal

1) Depressurize fuel injection system and drain cooling system. Disconnect wiring and A/C hoses from fender support rods and remove rods. Disconnect radiator hoses. Remove camshaft covers. Remove nuts attaching breather housing to front of cylinder head and remove breather.

2) Remove bolt securing dipstick tube to inlet manifold. Disconnect exhaust pipes from exhaust manifold. Disconnect fuel lines from fuel cooler, and plug all openings. Disconnect spark plug wires, temperature lead and engine ground from manifold.

3) Remove air cleaner. Disconnect air-flow meter hoses and remove air-flow meter. Disconnect throttle and kickdown cables. Disconnect heater hoses and remove camshaft oil feed tubes by removing banjo bolts from back of cylinder head.

4) Jack up front of vehicle and support with safety stands. Turn the crankshaft until the two camshaft timing notches are below the camshafts. Remove the two accessible bolts from each camshaft flange. Turn the crankshaft one complete revolution and loosen two remaining bolts.

5) Loosen lock nut on idler sprocket shaft. Slacken timing chain tension by pressing in on serated adjuster plate and rotating timing chain adjuster (JD 2B) in a clockwise direction. *See Fig 2.* Remove remaining bolts.

6) Remove sprockets from camshaft and slide sprockets up the support brackets. Mark "fit" holes in adjuster plates. Remove cylinder head domed nuts and six nuts securing front of cylinder head. Lower vehicle and remove cylinder head.

Fig. 2: Adjusting Upper Timing Chain

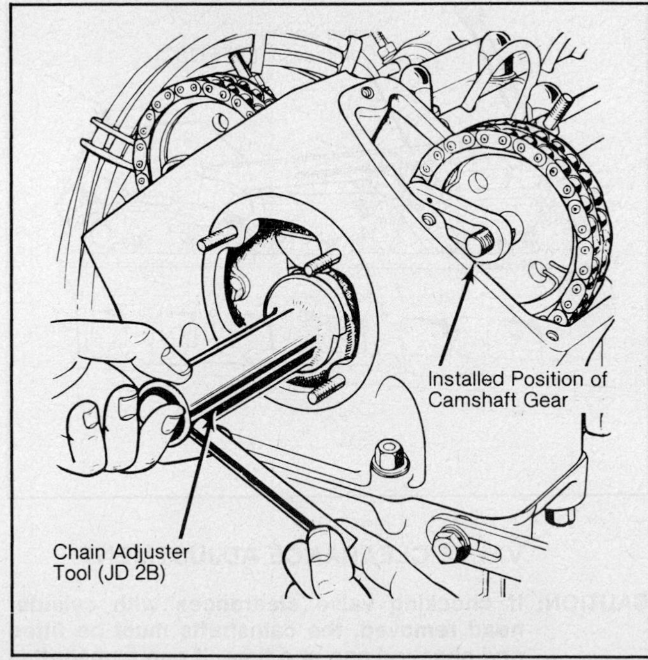
Installed Position of
Camshaft Gear
Chain Adjuster
Tool (JD 2B)

Do not use excessive force to tighten chain.

Installation

1) Install new head gasket, ensure that "TOP" mark is upward. Rotate crankshaft until No. 6 (front) cylinder is at TDC, with distributor rotor pointing approximately forward in-line with engine. Rotate camshafts until timing gauge (C 3993) can be located in front flange slots. *See Fig. 1.*

2) Lower cylinder head into position and install spark plug wire and lifting brackets. Install cylinder head domed nuts and six nuts securing front of cylinder head. Tighten nuts to specified torque and in proper sequence. *See Fig. 3.*

3) Locate sprockets on camshaft flanges and ensure both holes in each flange are in alignment with "fit" holes marked during removal. If necessary, remove snap ring and reposition adjuster plate. *See Fig. 4.*

4) Secure adjuster plates to camshaft, using two bolts and lock plates. Rotate engine until remaining holes are accessible. Install bolts and bend up lock plate tabs. Set timing chain tension by turning timing chain adjuster (JD 2B) in a counter-clockwise direction. Tighten lock nut.

5) Ensure that No. 6 (front) cylinder is at TDC (with pointer opposite "0" on timing scale) and recheck position of camshafts using timing gauge (C 3993). Reverse removal procedure to complete installation. Check ignition timing and perform exhaust emission test.

Fig 3: Jaguar XJ6 Cylinder Head Tightening Sequence

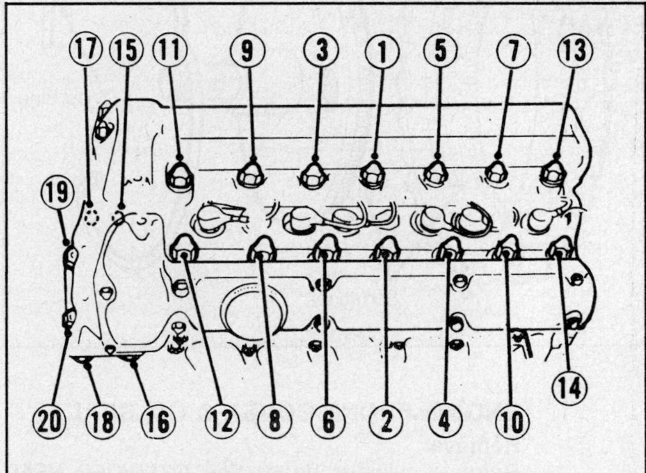
17
15
11
9
3
1
5
7
13
19
14
20
18
16
12
8
6
2
4
10

Tighten cylinder head bolts in 3 steps.

CAMSHAFTS

CAMSHAFTS

NOTE: The crankshaft must not be rotated while the camshaft sprockets are disconnected and cylinder head is still in place.

Removal

1) Remove camshaft covers. Remove nuts attaching breather housing to front of cylinder head and remove breather. Loosen lock nut on idler sprocket shaft. Remove the two accessible bolts from camshaft flange. Rotate crankshaft until valve timing gauge can be fitted into slot of camshaft. *See Fig 1.* Remove remaining bolts.

2) Slacken timing chain tension by rotating timing chain adjuster (JD 2B) in a clockwise direction. *See Fig 2.* Remove sprockets from camshaft and slide

Jaguar Engines

XJ6 6-CYLINDER (Cont.)

sprockets up the support brackets. Mark "fit" holes in adjuster plates. Remove camshaft bearing caps and remove camshaft.

Installation

1) Install camshaft bearings. Install camshaft with keyway in front flange pointing upward. Install and tighten bearing caps. Align camshaft using timing chain gauge (C 3993). Install camshaft sprocket on camshaft and ensure that "fit" holes line up.

2) Secure camshaft sprocket to camshaft, using two bolts and lock plates. Rotate engine until remaining holes are accessible. Install bolts and bend up lock plate tabs. Set timing chain tension by turning timing chain adjuster (JD 2B) in a counter-clockwise direction. Tighten lock nut.

3) Ensure that No. 6 (front) cylinder is at TDC (with pointer opposite "0" on timing scale) and recheck position of camshafts using timing gauge (C 3993). Reverse removal procedure to complete installation. Check tappet adjustment, ignition timing and perform exhaust emission test.

Fig. 4: Exploded View of Camshaft Sprocket Assembly

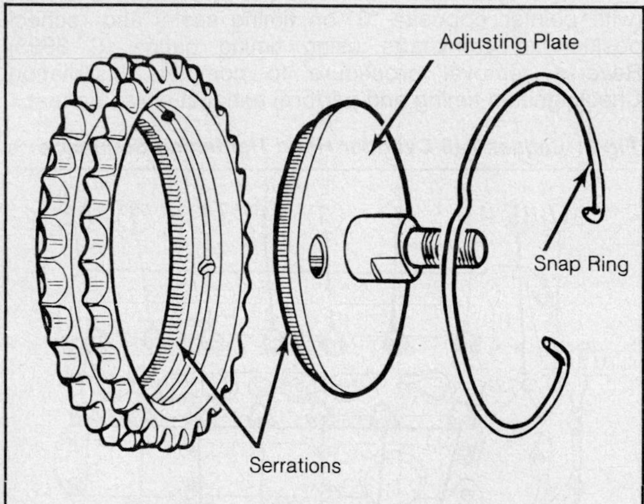
Adjusting Plate
Snap Ring
Serrations

ENGINE FRONT COVER & OIL SEAL

Removal

Remove cylinder head. *See CYLINDER HEAD removal in this article.* Remove water pump. Remove oil pan. Remove vibration damper, cone and crankshaft Woodruf key. Remove front engine cover and timing pointer. Remove spacer and front oil seal.

Installation

To install, reverse removal procedures.

VALVES

VALVE ARRANGEMENT

Right Side – Intake valves.
Left Side – Exhaust valves.

VALVE GUIDES

NOTE: **When installing oversize replacement guides, check O.D. of guide to be used. If necessary, ream cylinder head bore to obtain proper interference fit.**

Removal

Check valve stem clearance. Replace valve guide if stem clearance is more than 0.001-0.004" (0.025-0.10 mm). Replace valve guides by heating head in boiling water for 30 minutes. Drive guides out of head from combustion chamber end.

Installation

Coat new guide with graphite grease and install snap ring. Reheat cylinder head and drive in new guides from top until snap ring is seated in groove.

REPLACEMENT VALVE GUIDES

Application	Size Mark	Dimension In. (mm)
Standard	No Mark	.501-.502 (12.73-12.75)
1st Oversize	1 Groove	.503-.504 (12.78-12.80)
2nd Oversize	2 Grooves	.506-.507 (12.85-12.88)
3rd Oversize	3 Grooves	.511-.512 (12.98-13.00)

VALVE SPRINGS

NOTE: **Support cylinder head on wooden blocks to prevent damaging valves.**

Removal

Remove camshaft, tappets and adjusting pads. Keep camshaft bearing caps, tappets and pads in proper order. Install spring compressor (JD 6118C). Compress springs, remove valve keepers and remove valve springs.

Installation

Replace springs, if necessary. Reverse removal procedure to complete installation.

Fig. 5: Valve Spring Compressor Tool Installation

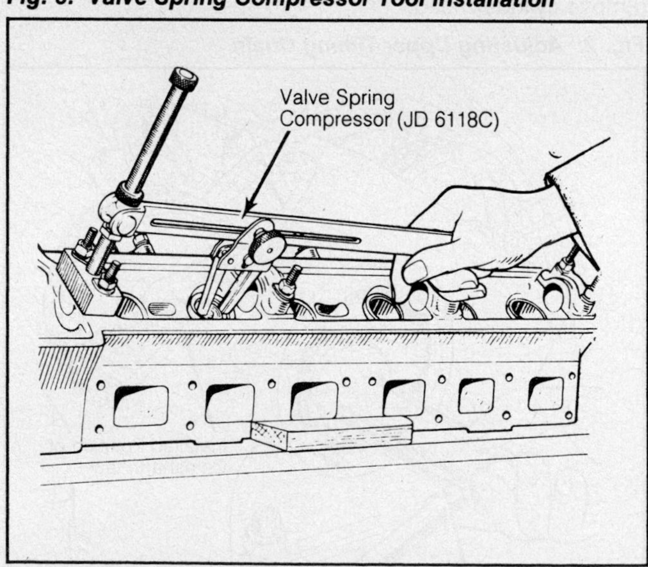
Valve Spring
Compressor (JD 6118C)

VALVE CLEARANCE ADJUSTMENT

CAUTION: **If checking valve clearances with cylinder head removed, the camshafts must be fitted and checked one at a time. If one camshaft is**

XJ6 6-CYLINDER (Cont.)

rotated while the other is in position, interference between inlet and exhaust valves is likely to occur. Keep camshaft bearing shells, tappets and pads in proper order.

1) Remove camshaft covers, if necessary. Rotate camshafts and record clearance between cam lobe and tappets. Remove camshaft, if adjustment is required. *See CAMSHAFT removal in this article.* Remove tappets and adjusting pads from valves that need adjustment.

Fig 6: Valve Tappet and Guide Assembly

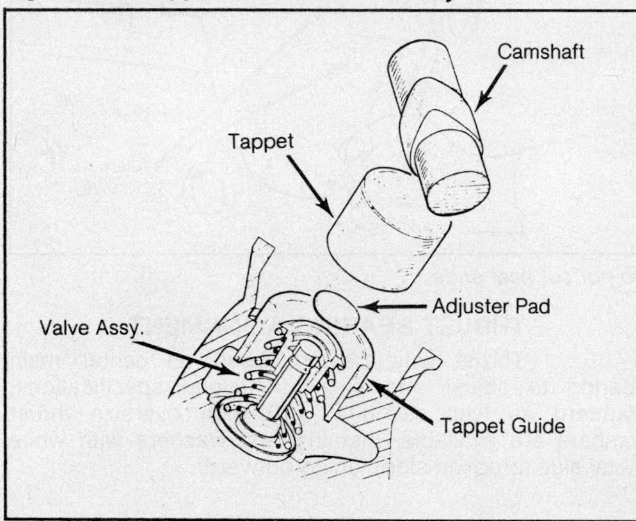
Camshaft
Tappet
Adjuster Pad
Valve Assy.
Tappet Guide

2) Subtract specified valve clearance from actual (measured) valve clearance. Select a new adjusting pad that is equal to difference between the two readings. Adjusting pads are available in increments of .001" (0.03 mm), from .085" (2.16 mm) to .110" (2.79 mm) and are marked with letters from "A" to "Z" respectively.

3) Install correct adjusting pads and tappets. Reverse removal procedure to complete valve clearance adjustment.

VALVE CLEARANCE SPECIFICATIONS

Application	In. (mm)
Intake	0.012-0.014 (0.305-0.356)
Exhaust	0.012-0.014 (0.305-0.356)

PISTONS, PINS & RINGS

OIL PAN

NOTE: **Oil pan removal is best accomplished with engine out of vehicle. Following procedures may be used with engine installed.**

Removal

Remove front suspension. Drain engine oil. Remove oil return pipe and transmission oil cooler line clips. Remove hardware attaching pan to engine and remove oil pan. Remove strainer box, if necessary.

Installation

Ensure that "O" ring is installed in oil return pipe. Lightly grease new "O" ring and press into oil pan groove until ends are flush. Do not trim ends. Reverse removal procedure to complete installation.

PISTON & ROD ASSEMBLY

NOTE: **Piston and connecting rod assemblies are numbered to their corresponding position in engine. No. 1 cylinder is at rear of engine.**

Removal

Remove cylinder head and oil pan. Remove nuts from connecting rods and remove bearing caps. Push piston and rod assembly out of cylinder.

Installation

Coat bearing shells and journals with oil. Compress piston rings and insert piston and rod assembly so that "FRONT" stamp on piston is toward front of engine. If new piston and rods are being installed they should be stamped with the number of the bore in which they are to be installed. Reverse removal procedure to complete installation.

PISTON RINGS

Check ring end gap and side clearance. Install oil control ring in bottom groove. Ensure that expander ends do not overlap. Install compression rings in top two grooves with "TOP" side up. The top compression ring is chrome-plated and cargraph coated, the Red coating must not be removed.

PISTON PINS

Remove snap rings and push piston pin out of piston. Piston pins and pistons are a matched set, do not mix. Piston pins are color coded. The O.D. of Red piston pins is 0.8751-0.8752" (22.228-22.230 mm), the O.D. of Green piston pins is 0.8750-0.8751" (22.225-22.228 mm). Install new snap rings.

FITTING PISTONS

1) Check piston-to-cylinder wall clearance to determine if proper clearance exists. If it is necessary to rebore cylinder, ensure that reboring does not to exceed .020" (.51 mm) as oversize pistons are available in .51 mm only.

2) If replacing pistons with standard sizes (no reboring), note the following list of piston grades and select replacement piston of same grade. Piston grade is stamped in piston crown and on top face of block adjacent to cylinder.

3) Grade "S" pistons are 3.6252-3.6262" (92.080-92.105 mm) in diameter across bottom of skirt and at right angles to piston pins. Honed diameter of bore must be 0.007-0.0013" (0.018-0.033 mm) greater than measured diameter of piston.

STANDARD PISTON GRADING

Stamp Mark	Cylinder Diameter In. (mm)
F	3.6250-3.6253 (92.075-92.083)
G	3.6254-3.6257 (92.085-92.093)
H	3.6258-3.6261 (92.095-92.103)

CYLINDER LINERS

1) Should reboring require more than .020" (.51 mm), new cylinder liners must be installed. Press out worn cylinder liners from below. Lightly coat block cylinder wall and outer top half of cylinder liner with a jointing compound.

2) Press in new liner until it is flush with top of block. Bore out and hone liner to correspond with grade of piston being installed. Following reboring, the plugs in the main oil gallery should be removed and cylinder block oilways thoroughly cleaned. When dry, coat interior of crankcase with an oil and heat resistant paint.

Fig. 7: Cylinder Liner Removing and Installing Block

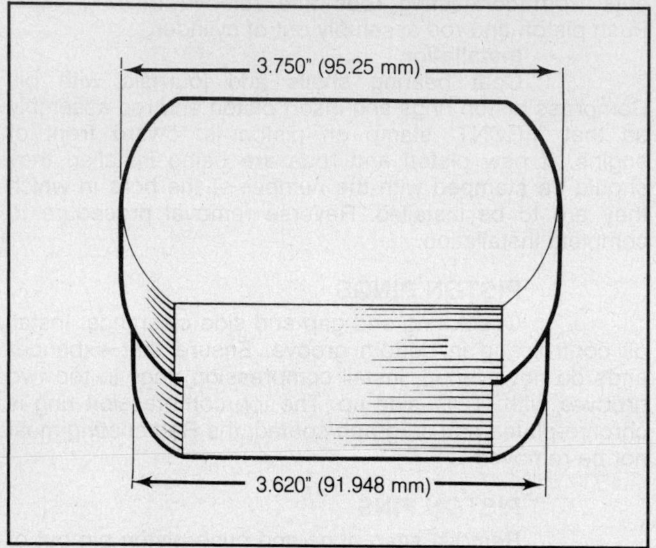
3.750" (95.25 mm)
3.620" (91.948 mm)

CRANKSHAFT MAIN & CONNECTING ROD BEARINGS

MAIN & CONNECTING ROD BEARINGS

1) Remove connecting rod and main bearing caps, keeping parts in order for reassembly. Measure bearing clearances, using Plastigage. If wear or out-of-round exceeds .003" (.08 mm), grind crankshaft and install undersize bearings.

2) Undersize bearings are available in .010" and .020" (.25 mm and .51 mm) only. If grinding exceeds .020" (.51 mm), replace crankshaft. Install main and connecting rod caps and tighten to specified torque.

REAR MAIN BEARING OIL SEAL

NOTE: **The following procedure must be performed before crankshaft is installed.**

1) Apply a thin coat of Hermetite to oil seal grooves for 1 inch from parting face. Carefully tap new rear oil seal halves into position, then roll seal into retainer until ends do not protrude. Do not cut seal ends.

2) When both halves are properly in place, secure oil seal retainer with Allen head screws. Attach rear main bearing cap without bearings and torque to 72 ft. lbs. (98 N.m). Attach rear oil seal housing to cylinder block, using three Allen head screws.

3) Apply a thin coat of graphite grease to inside surface of oil seal and insert sizing tool (JD 17B). *See Fig. 8.* Press tool inward and turn until it is fully seated. Remove sizing tool by pulling and twisting in opposite direction. Remove oil seal retainer and install crankshaft.

Fig. 8: Rear Oil Seal Installation

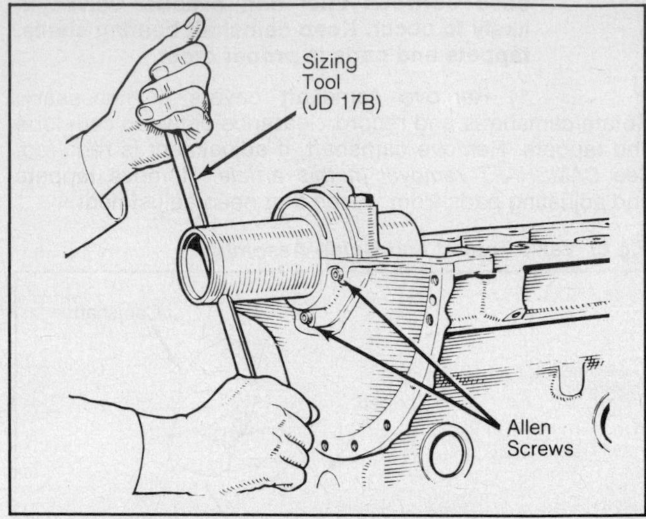
Sizing
Tool
(JD 17B)
Allen
Screws

Do not cut seal ends.

THRUST BEARING ALIGNMENT

Thrust washers are used on center main bearing to adjust end play. If beyond specifications, standard as well as .004" (.10 mm) oversize thrust washers are available. Install thrust washers with white metal side (grooved side) facing outward.

TIMING CHAIN

TIMING CHAIN REPLACEMENT

Removal

1) Remove cylinder head *See CYLINDER HEAD removal in this article.* Remove water pump and oil pan. Remove vibration damper, cone and crankshaft Woodruff key. Remove timing gear cover, timing pointer, spacer, and front oil seal.

2) Remove oil slinger from crankshaft. Remove bottom timing chain tensioner and chain guide retaining screws. Remove conical filter behind tensioner. Loosen four set screws securing top timing chain assembly. Do not remove set screws at this point.

3) Remove crankshaft timing sprocket and chain assembly. Be sure to remove spacers, top timing chain dampers, and top timing chain retainer. Disengage camshaft sprockets from top chain. Remove nut and serrated washer from idler shaft. Remove serrated plate, plunger, and spring.

4) Remove nuts retaining front mounting bracket to rear mounting bracket. Remove timing chains from intermediate and idler sprockets. Remove idler shaft, idler sprocket, and bushing from rear mounting bracket. Remove snap ring and press intermediate shaft from rear mounting bracket. Note location of bushing and shim under intermediate sprocket.

Installation

1) Insert eccentric idler shaft in hole of front mounting bracket. Position spring and plunger in bracket and install serrated plate on shaft. Loosely secure plate using washer and nut.

2) Attach idler sprocket (21 teeth) to idler shaft. Install intermediate sprocket (large gear forward) on

XJ6 6-CYLINDER (Cont.)

Fig. 9: Exploded View of Timing Gear and Chain Assembly

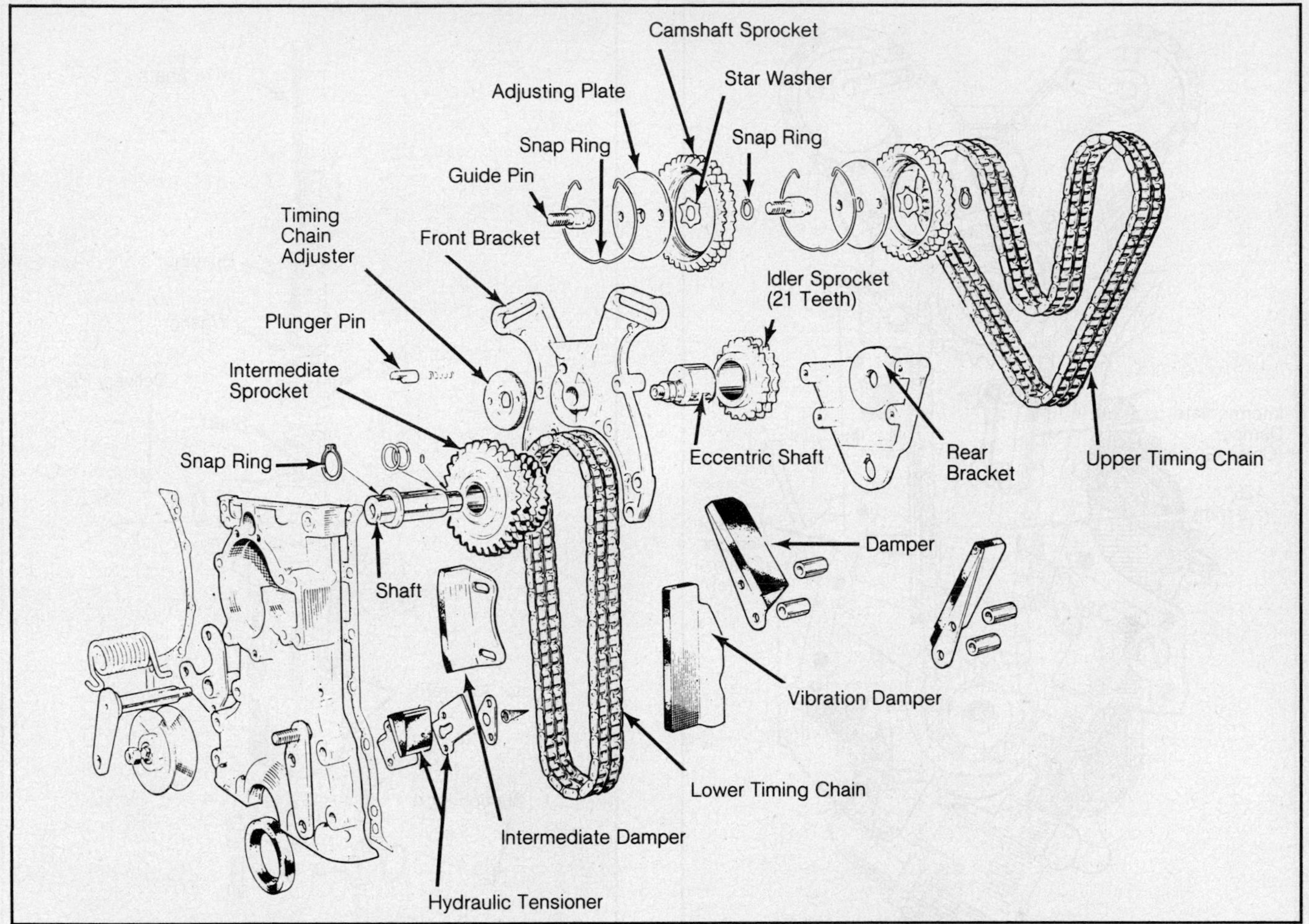
Camshaft Sprocket
Star Washer
Adjusting Plate
Snap Ring
Snap Ring
Guide Pin
Timing Chain Adjuster
Front Bracket
Idler Sprocket (21 Teeth)
Plunger Pin
Intermediate Sprocket
Snap Ring
Eccentric Shaft
Rear Bracket
Upper Timing Chain
Damper
Shaft
Vibration Damper
Lower Timing Chain
Intermediate Damper
Hydraulic Tensioner

intermediate shaft. Install shim in rear mounting bracket. Install shaft assembly in rear mounting bracket, ensuring roll pin engages in slot. Install snap ring.

3) Install top timing chain (longer chain) on small intermediate sprocket, and lower timing chain on large sprocket. Loop top chain beneath idler sprocket and secure top mounting bracket to rear bracket.

4) Install four long set screws and spring washers to front mounting bracket and attach dampers, chain support plate, and spacers to set screws. Equalize loops of top timing chain and locate camshaft sprockets in loops. Rotate eccentric idler shaft to lift idler sprocket to its highest position between camshaft sprockets.

5) Ensure Woodruff key is installed in crankshaft. Install crankshaft sprocket, but do not fully seat at this time. Loop bottom timing chain beneath crankshaft sprocket, then tap sprocket until it is fully seated. Position and secure crankshaft sprocket assembly.

6) Install, but do not tighten, bottom timing chain guides. Insert conical filter into hole of cylinder block. Screw slipper into tensioner until .125" (3.2 mm) exists between slipper and body. Locate tensioner on shims as necessary to ensure slipper runs central on chain, and secure using two set screws and lock plate.

7) Place slip gauge or spacer card supplied with new tensioner between slipper and body of tensioner to maintain a clearance of .125" (3.2 mm), then adjust intermediate damper to touch chain.

8) Tighten set screws and bend up tabs of lock plate. Remove slip gauge and tap chain or tensioner slipper to release ratchet. Position oil slinger on crankshaft. Install timing cover, oil pan and cylinder head to complete installation.

ENGINE OILING

ENGINE OILING SYSTEM

Lubrication is provided by a gear driven eccentric rotor type pump.

CRANKCASE CAPACITY

8.7 qts. (8.2L).

OIL FILTER

Full-flow, disposable canister. Located on right side of engine.

NORMAL OIL PRESSURE (HOT)

40 psi @ 3000 RPM.

OIL PUMP

Removal

Remove oil pan. Remove suction and delivery pipes. Remove bolts attaching oil pump to front main

Fig. 10: Lower Timing Chain Adjustment Measuring Point

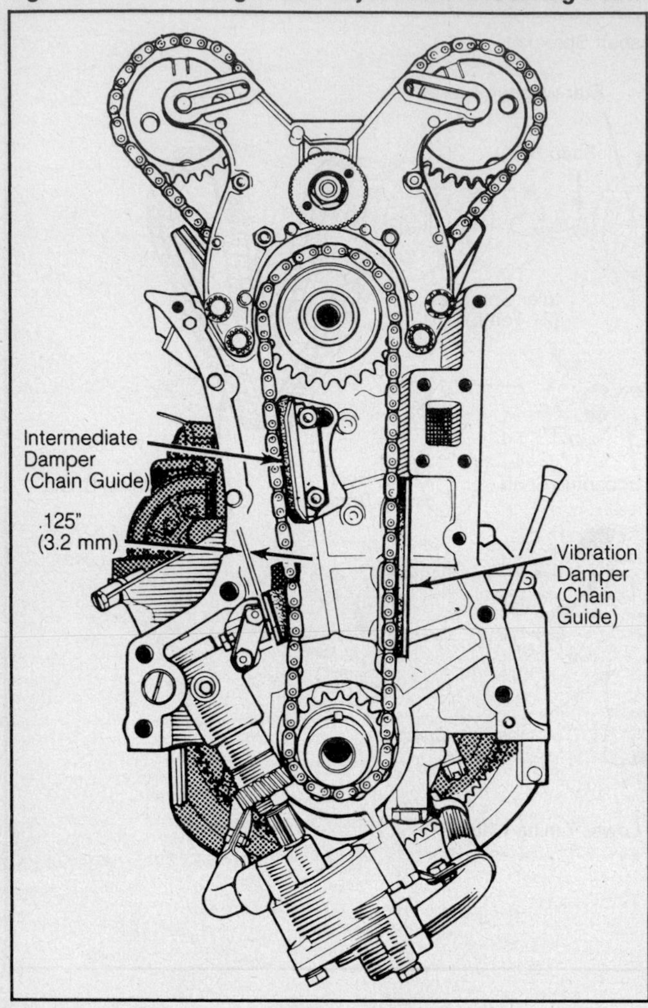
Intermediate Damper (Chain Guide)
.125" (3.2 mm)
Vibration Damper (Chain Guide)

Fig. 11: Exploded View of Oil Pump

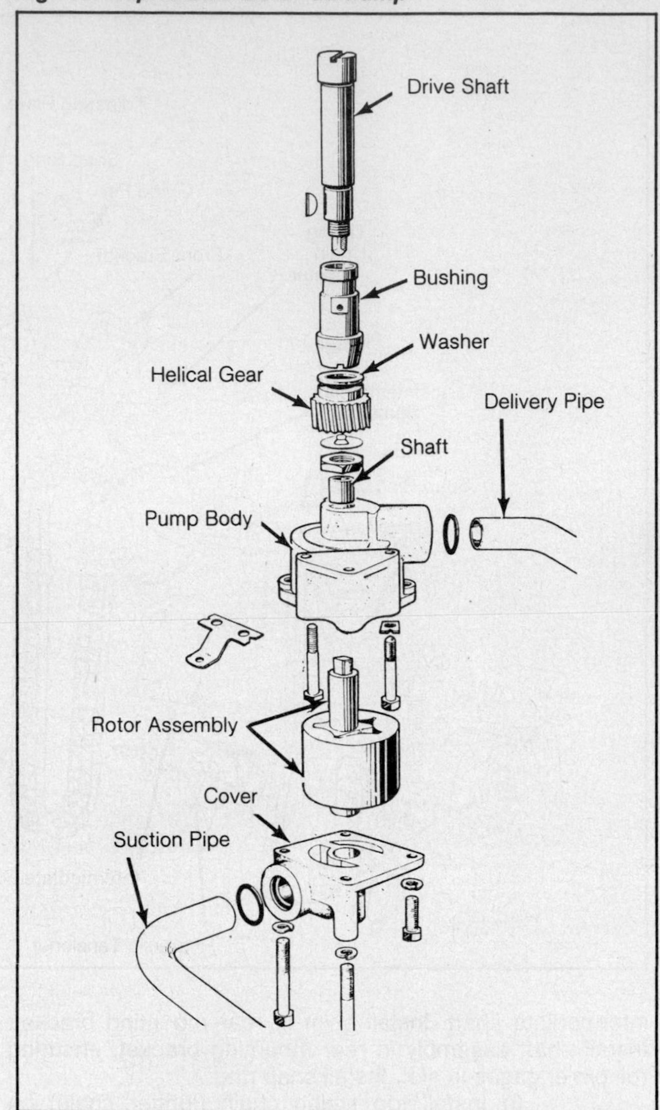
Drive Shaft
Bushing
Washer
Helical Gear
Delivery Pipe
Shaft
Pump Body
Rotor Assembly
Cover
Suction Pipe

bearing cap. Remove pump and coupling sleeve at top of drive shaft.

Disassembly

1) Remove bolts and take off bottom cover. Remove inner and outer rotors. Inner rotor is pinned to drive shaft and cannot be disassembled.

2) Check clearances of inner and outer rotor lobes, outer rotor-to-body and rotor-to-cover plate. Place drive shaft in a soft-jawed vise and check that rotor is tight on pin.

Reassembly

Install outer rotor to pump body with chamfered end first. Reassemble oil pump in reverse order of disassembly.

Installation

Replace "O" rings on suction and delivery pipes. Ensure that suction pipe is on center line of engine. Reverse removal procedure to complete installation.

OIL PUMP CLEARANCES

Application	In. (mm)
Inner-to-Outer Rotor	.006 (.15)
Outer Rotor-to-Body	.010 (.25)
Rotor-to-Cover (End Play)	.0025 (.06)

ENGINE COOLING

WATER PUMP

Removal

1) Drain radiator. Remove radiator and lower cowl. Loosen fan belt and remove fan assembly. Remove idler adjusting bolt. Remove hardware securing idler pulley to housing and remove studs.

2) Remove steering pump belt. Remove A/C compressor belt, if used. Loosen steering pump bolts and remove adjustment bolt from special stud. Remove special stud. Remove set screws securing thermostatic switch housing. Remove housing and bottom hose as an assembly.

3) Remove crankshaft pulley and damper assembly, by tapping with a mallet. Remove cone and

Jaguar Engines

XJ6 6-CYLINDER (Cont.)

save Woodruff key. Loosen upper clip to engine cross pipe. Remove set screws securing water pump and remove pump.

Installation

Tighten set screws evenly to avoid distortion. Reverse removal procedure to complete installation.

COOLING SYSTEM CAPACITY

19.2 qts. (18.2L).

TIGHTENING SPECIFICATIONS

Application	Ft. Lbs. (N.m)
Camshaft Cover (Domed Nuts)	7-8 (9-11)
Camshaft Bearing Caps	9 (12)
Connecting Rod Caps	36-38 (49-52)
Crankshaft Damper Bolt	125-150 (169-203)
Cylinder Head Nuts	50-52 (68-71)
Front Engine Mount	14-18 (19-24)
Main Bearing Caps	69-72 (94-98)
Radiator-to-Front Crossmember	22-26 (30-35)
Rear Engine Mount	
5/16" Bolt	8-10 (11-14)
3/8" Bolt	27-32 (37-43)

ENGINE SPECIFICATIONS

GENERAL SPECIFICATIONS

Year	DISPLACEMENT		Fuel System	HP@RPM	Torque Ft. Lbs.@RPM	Compr. Ratio	BORE		STROKE	
	Cu. In.	Liters					In.	mm	In.	mm
1983	258.4	4.2	Fuel Inj.	176 @ 4750	219 @ 2500	8.1:1	3.625	92.07	4.173	106

VALVES

Engine Size & Valve	Head Diam. In. (mm)	Face Angle	Seat Angle	Seat Width In. (mm)	Stem Diameter In. (mm)	Stem Clearance In. (mm)	Valve Lift In. (mm)
4.2 L							
Intake	1.87-1.88 (47.50-47.75)	45°	44.5°	.....	.310-.3125 (7.87-7.94)	.001-.004 (.025-.10)	.375 (9.525)
Exhaust	1.620-1.630 (41.15-41.40)	45°	44.5°	.....	.310-.3125 (7.87-7.94)	.001-.004 (.025-.10)	.375 (9.525)

CRANKSHAFT MAIN & CONNECTING ROD BEARINGS

Engine	MAIN BEARINGS				CONNECTING ROD BEARINGS		
	Journal Diam. In. (mm)	Clearance In. (mm)	Thrust Bearing	Crankshaft End Play In. (mm)	Journal Diam. In. (mm)	Clearance In. (mm)	Side Play In. (mm)
4.2 L	2.750-2.7505 (69.85-69.86)	.0008-.0025 (.020-.064)	Center	.004-.006 (.10-.15)	2.086-2.0866 (52.98-53.00)	.001-.0027 (.025-.069)	.0058-.0087 (.147-.221)

PISTONS, PINS, RINGS

Engine	PISTONS	PINS		RINGS		
	Clearance In. (mm)	Piston Fit In. (mm)	Rod Fit In. (mm)	Ring No.	End Gap In. (mm)	Side Clearance In. (mm)
4.2 L	.0007-.0013 (.018-.033)	Full Floating	Full Floating	No. 1	.015-.020 (.38-.51)	.0015-.0035 (.038-.089)
				No. 2	.009-.014 (.23-.35)	.0015-.0035 (.038-.089)
				Oil	.015-.045 (.38-1.14)	[1]

[1] – Self-expanding.

Jaguar Engines

XJ6 6-CYLINDER (Cont.)

ENGINE SPECIFICATIONS (Cont.)

VALVE SPRINGS

Engine	Free Length In. (mm)	PRESSURE Lbs. @ In. (Kg @ mm)	
		Valve Closed	Valve Open
4.2 L			
Inner	1.66-1.72 (42.0-43.7)	.....	.....
Outer	1.94-2.00 (49.3-50.8)	.....	.....

VALVE TIMING

Engine	INTAKE		EXHAUST	
	Open (BTDC)	Close (ABDC)	Open (BBDC)	Close (ATDC)
4.2 L	15°	57°	57°	15°

CAMSHAFT

Engine	Journal Diam. In. (mm)	Clearance In. (mm)	Lobe Lift In. (mm)
4.2 L	.9990-.9995 (25.375-25.387)	.0005-.002 (.013-.051)	.....

XJS V12

ENGINE CODING

ENGINE IDENTIFICATION

Engine number is stamped on cylinder block at rear of engine, between cylinder heads.

ENGINE, MANIFOLDS & CYLINDER HEAD

CAUTION: **The fuel injection system must always be depressurized before disconnecting any fuel system component. Disconnect fuel pump relay and crank engine for a few seconds to depressurize system.**

ENGINE

NOTE: **Engine and transmission are removed as an assembly.**

Removal

1) Remove hood and drain cooling system. Depressurize fuel and air conditioning systems. Disconnect battery. Remove right-hand harness cover and disconnect headlamps. Remove harness clips from right-hand fender support rod and move harness out of the way.

2) Disconnect coil, pick-up module, ballast resistor and move harness out of the way. Remove receiver-drier clamps and relays from top rail. Remove the fan cowl-to-top rail attaching nuts. Disconnect the thermostatic switch harness and move out of the way. Remove right-hand fender support rod.

3) Remove air cleaner assemblies. Remove the air anti-recirculation panel and fan attaching nuts. Remove lower radiator grille and grommets. Remove oil cooler to radiator attaching screws. Carefully position A/C condenser assembly out of the way.

4) Remove top radiator hose and disconnect remaining hoses from thermostat housings. Disconnect transmission cooler hoses from radiator and plug all openings. Disconnect expansion pipe and heater return hoses from radiator. Remove engine oil cooler and carefully move radiator forward.

5) Loosen fan belt and remove fan/clutch assembly. Disconnect bottom radiator hose and coolant level probe from radiator. Carefully remove radiator assembly. Remove battery and left-hand fender support rod.

6) Disconnect fuel hoses from fuel cooler and plug all openings. Disconnect fuel compressor hose and plug all openings. Remove fuel cooler from air cleaner backplate.

7) Loosen power steering pump belt and remove power steering pump. Position pump out of the way and remove pump bracket. Disconnect A/C hoses from receiver-drier and condenser assembly. Plug all openings and remove condenser assembly.

8) Disconnect engine and alternator harness. Disconnect fuel feed hoses from engine and plug all openings. Disconnect vacuum hoses from brake vacuum reservoir. Disconnect brake servo hose and manifold one-way valve. Remove hose from firewall and move brake hose assembly out of the way.

9) Disconnect vacuum tubes from rear of right-hand intake manifold. Remove bolt securing transmission dipstick tube and remove tube assembly. Disconnect starter solenoid from relay and starter feed wire from firewall connector.

10) Disconnect throttle switch, oil pressure switch, temperature sensor and ballast resistor. Disconnect cruise control harness, if used. Remove fresh air grille and remove hardware securing water valve to fire wall. Disconnect hoses from water valve and remove valve.

11) Remove starter relay from firewall. Disconnect vacuum feed tube from manifold cross pipe. Disconnect kickdown switch wires and throttle cable from engine. Disconnect cruise control cable, if used. Install engine support (MS 53A) above rear engine lifting eyes and support engine.

12) Raise and support vehicle. Remove steering gear heat shields and disconnect exhaust pipes from exhaust manifolds. Place floor jack under rear engine mount and raise it slightly. Remove engine mount attaching bolts and remove engine mount.

13) Remove intermediate and rear heat shields. Remove crossmember attaching bolts and remove crossmember. Remove propeller shaft attaching bolts and remove propeller shaft. Disconnect speedometer cable. Lower engine slightly and disconnect selector cable. Disconnect ground strap and lower vehicle.

14) Place floor jack with a piece of wood under transmission and remove engine support. Attach engine sling and support engine, being careful not to damage thermostatic vacuum switch or tubes.

NOTE: **Chains of engine hoist must be of sufficient length to ensure that distance between lifting eyes and hook of hoist is 34.5" (876 mm) from front eyes to hook and 41" (1041 mm) from rear eyes to hook.**

15) Remove nuts from front engine mounts. Loosen lower nuts on right-hand engine mount. Carefully raise engine 2-3 inches. Push engine off to one side until engine clears steering gear.

16) The rear of the engine must be kept as high as possible to allow oil pan to clear steering gear housing. Continue to raise engine being careful not to damage A/C expansion valve or evaporator unions. Remove engine/transmission assembly.

Installation

Ensure that engine mount fiber discs are installed. Carefully lower engine into position and tighten front engine mounts. Reverse removal procedure to complete installation. Check all fluid levels and charge A/C system.

INTAKE MANIFOLDS

Removal (Right Side)

1) Disconnect battery and drain cooling system. Remove air cleaner and depressurize fuel system. Remove screws securing pipe to fuel injection overflow valve. Remove spacer from left-hand valve. Disconnect manifold pressure hose from "T" and manifold.

2) Release clip securing fuel pipe to fuel rail and disconnect hose. Release throttle linkage from bellcrank. Disconnect vacuum hoses from throttle housing. Release clamp securing air pipe to rubber elbow and disconnect pipe.

3) Remove plastic clips securing harness to fuel rail. Disconnect electrical connectors from fuel injectors and cold start injector. Disconnect ground strap from manifold ram tube. Disconnect brake vacuum hose from one way valve. Disconnect transmission, diverter valve and heater vacuum hose from rear of intake manifold.

4) Remove throttle return spring. Remove hardware securing intake manifold to cylinder head. Release clip securing air rail to check valve connecting hose. Remove air rail and discard "O" rings. Release clamp securing hose fuel crossover pipe and disconnect hose at fuel rail.

5) Remove EGR valve from throttle housing. Remove intake manifold stud spacers. Carefully remove intake manifold assembly. Plug inlet ports and transfer components to replacement intake manifold, if necessary.

Installation

Install new air rail sealing rings. Reverse removal procedure to complete installation. Check throttle linkage adjustment.

Removal (Left Side)

1) Disconnect battery and drain cooling system. Remove air cleaner and depressurize fuel system. Remove fender support rod. Remove screws securing pipe to fuel injection overflow valve. Remove spacer from left-hand valve.

2) Release clamp securing prssure regulator return hose to fuel rail and disconnect hose. Disconnect manifold pressure hose from intake manifold. Disconnect vacuum hose from throttle housing and electrical connectors from kickdown switch. Release throttle linkage from bellcrank.

3) Remove plastic clips securing harness to fuel rail. Disconnect electrical connectors from fuel injectors and cold start injector. Disconnect brake vacuum hose from one way valve. Remove throttle return spring. Release clamp securing bleed pipe to rubber elbow and disconnect pipe.

4) Remove hardware securing intake manifold to cylinder head. Remove screws securing air rail clips to manifold ram tubes. Release clip securing air rail to check valve connecting hose. Remove air rail and discard "O" rings.

5) Remove EGR valve from throttle housing. Remove intake manifold stud spacers. Carefully remove intake manifold assembly. Plug inlet ports and transfer components to replacement intake manifold, if necessary.

Installation

Install new air rail sealing rings. Reverse removal procedure to complete installation. Check throttle linkage adjustment.

EXHAUST MANIFOLDS

Removal

1) Disconnect battery. Remove nuts securing exhaust pipe to exhaust manifold. Remove bolts securing exhaust pipe to exhaust tube and allow exhaust pipe to rest on front suspension crossmember. Remove intake manifold from side being serviced.

2) Remove self-tapping screws securing starter solenoid heat shield to main heat shield from right-hand exhaust manifold. Remove set screws securing heat shield to exhaust manifolds. Remove nuts securing exhaust manifolds to cylinder heads and carefully remove exhaust manifolds.

Installation

To install, reverse removal procedure.

CYLINDER HEAD

NOTE: **The following procedure may be used for removal of either cylinder head.**

Removal

1) Disconnect battery and drain cooling system. Remove air filters and remove right-hand intake manifold, if either head is to be removed. Remove left-hand intake manifold, only if left cylinder head is to be removed. Remove right-hand camshaft cover, if either head is to be removed. Remove left-hand camshaft cover, only if left-hand cylinder head is to be removed.

NOTE: **Align camshaft using timing gauge on cylinder head being removed. If both heads are to be removed, align right-hand camshaft.**

2) Remove battery, only if it is next to cylinder head being removed. Remove rubber grommet from front of timing cover. Insert blade of screwdriver (JD 42-2) through timing cover hole and release timing chain tensioner. Rotate crankshaft until valve timing gauge (C 3993) can be inserted in slot in camshaft front flange.

Fig. 1: Valve Timing Gauge in Position for Timing Chain Removal or Installation

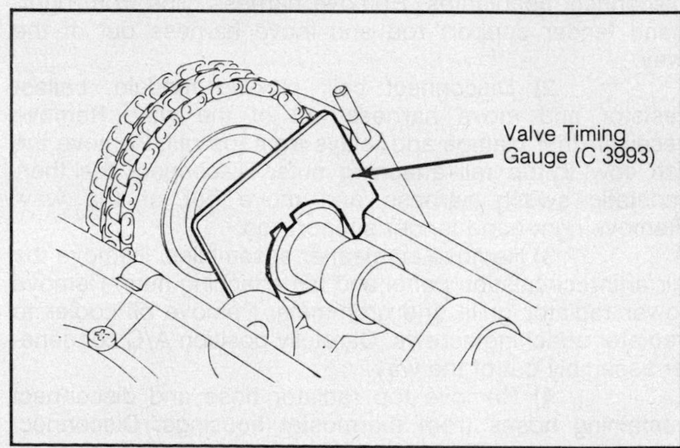
Valve Timing
Gauge (C 3993)

3) Using tensioner retractor tool (JD 44), fully retract timing chain tensioner. Remove special tools, as soon as the locking catch engages on step. Disconnect camshaft sprocket from camshaft and install sprocket retaining tool (JD 40).

4) Remove self-tapping screws securing starter solenoid heat shield from right cylinder head. Remove set screws securing heat shield to exhaust manifold. Remove nuts securing exhaust pipe to exhaust manifold. Remove bolts securing exhaust pipe to exhaust tube and allow exhaust pipe to rest on front suspension crossmember.

5) Remove camshaft oil feed banjo bolts. Remove A/C compressor. Remove hardware securing cylinder heads to timing cover. Remove cable clips from studs. Loosen cylinder head nuts, working from center of head outward. Remove cylinder heads and place on wooden blocks to prevent damaging valves. Discard old gaskets.

NOTE: **Do not rotate engine, unless cylinder liner retainers (JD 41) have been attached to cylinder heads.**

XJS V12 (Cont.)

Fig. 2: Retracting Timing Chain Tensioner

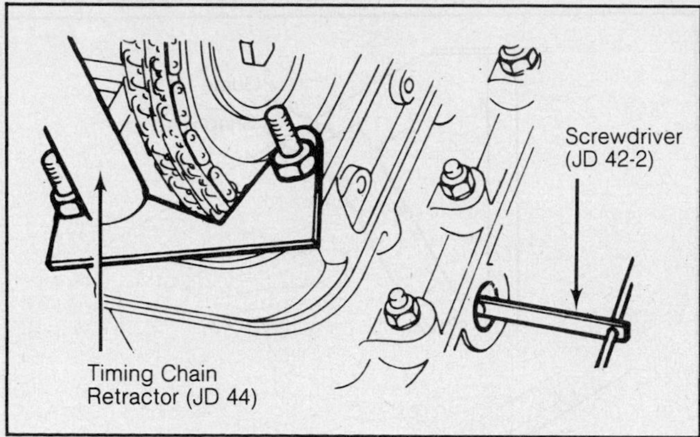

Screwdriver
(JD 42-2)
Timing Chain
Retractor (JD 44)

Installation

1) Remove distributor cover. Attach a dial indicator to cylinder head stud. Rotate crankshaft to set No. 1 piston (right bank) to TDC of compression stroke. The distributor rotor will point at approximately 5° from pickup module.

2) Turn camshaft until timing gauge (C 3993) can be inserted in slot in camshaft front flange. Remove cylinder liner retainer. Install cylinder head gasket with "TOP" side up. Install cylinder head and tighten nuts to specified torque. *See Fig. 3.*

Fig. 3: Cylinder Head Tightening Sequence

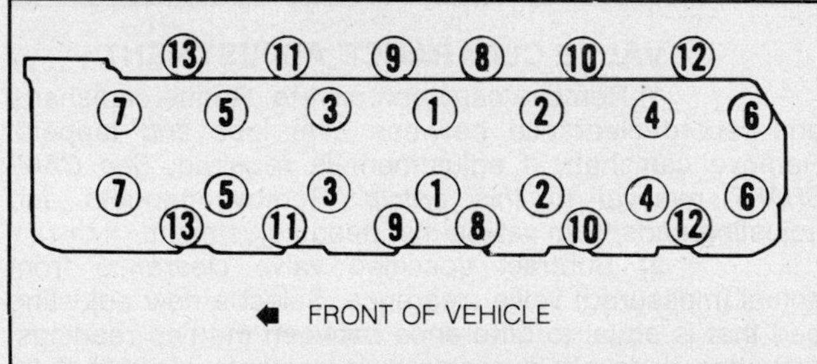

13 11 9 8 10 12
7 5 3 1 2 4 6
7 5 3 1 2 4 6
13 11 9 8 10 12
FRONT OF VEHICLE

4) Tighten cylinder head-to-timing cover nuts. Remove sprocket retainer and check alignment of sprocket holes. If camshaft and sprocket holes are not in alignment, remove snap ring which holds camshaft coupling to sprocket and disengage coupling from splines.

5) Rotate coupling until access to retaining bolt holes can be obtained. Bolt coupling to camshaft. Engage sprocket with coupling and install snap ring. Remove timing gauge (C 3993). Repeat procedures in steps **2)** through **5)** on left cylinder head.

6) Rotate engine until remaining camshaft sprocket retaining bolts can be installed. Insert blade of screwdriver (JD 42-2) through hole in timing cover and trip locking catch. Install rubber grommet. Reverse removal procedure to complete installation. Check all fluid levels and set ignition timing.

CAMSHAFT

ENGINE FRONT COVER & OIL SEAL

Removal

1) Remove cylinder heads and oil pan. Remove oil pump adapter tubes and oil pump adapter. Remove alternator and power steering pump. Remove air injection (smog) pump and A/C compressor, if used.

2) Remove water pump. Remove crankshaft damper bolt and strike damper sharply with leather mallet. Remove damper and cone. Remove hardware securing alternator and smog pump brackets.

3) Remove bolts securing timing cover. Note lenght and relative position of bolts and dowel pins. Remove timing cover. Discard oil seal and gaskets.

Installation

To install, reverse removal procedure.

Fig. 4: Detail of Front Cover & Oil Seal

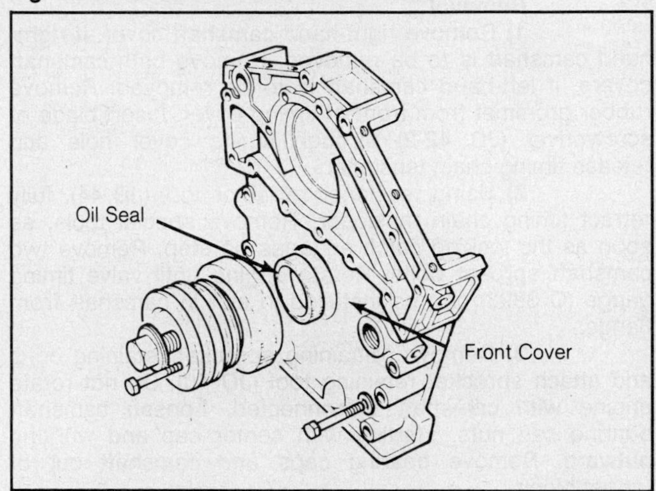

Oil Seal
Front Cover

TIMING CHAIN

Removal

Remove timing cover. Install intermediate shaft retainer (JD 39) on intermediate shaft (jackshaft). *See Fig. 5.* Disconnect timing chain from camshaft and jackshaft sprockets. Remove crankshaft sprocket and chain. Do not turn crankshaft with timing chain removed.

Installation

To install, reverse removal procedure.

Fig. 5: View of Timing Chain Installation

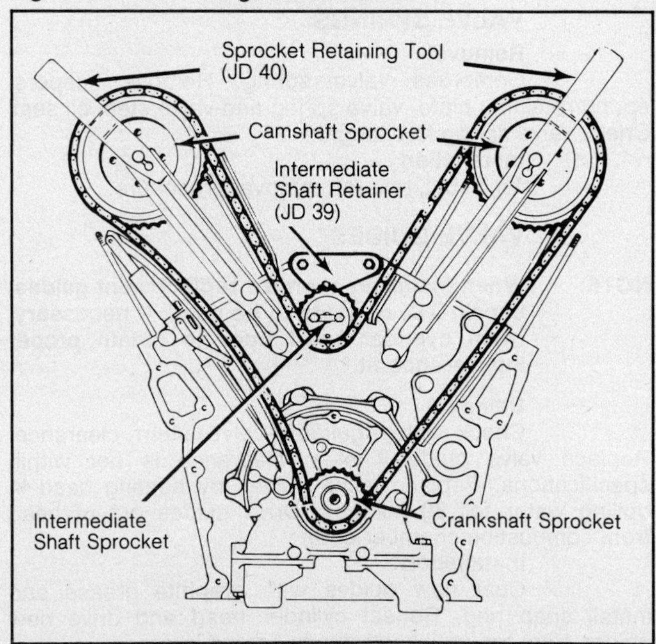

Sprocket Retaining Tool
(JD 40)
Camshaft Sprocket
Intermediate
Shaft Retainer
(JD 39)
Intermediate
Shaft Sprocket
Crankshaft Sprocket

Jaguar Engines

XJS V12 (Cont.)

VALVE TIMING

Remove distributor cover. Attach a dial indicator to cylinder head stud. Rotate crankshaft to set No. 1 piston (right bank) to TDC of compression stroke. The distributor rotor will point at approximately 5° from pickup module. Turn camshaft until timing gauge (C 3993) can be inserted in slot in camshaft front flange. *See Fig. 1.* Repeat procedure on left bank.

CAMSHAFT

Removal

1) Remove right-hand camshaft cover, if right-hand camshaft is to be removed. Remove both camshaft covers, if left-hand camshaft is to be removed. Remove rubber grommet from front of timing cover. Insert blade of screwdriver (JD 42-2) through timing cover hole and release timing chain tensioner.

2) Using tensioner retractor tool (JD 44), fully retract timing chain tensioner. Remove special tools, as soon as the locking catch engages on step. Remove two camshaft sproket bolts. Rotate engine until valve timing gauge (C 3993) can be installed in slot in camshaft front flange.

3) Remove remaining sprocket retaining bolts and attach sprocket retaining tool (JD 40). Do not rotate engine with camshaft disconnected. Loosen camshaft bearing cap nuts, starting with center cap and working outward. Remove bearing caps and camshaft out of tappet block.

Installation

To install, reverse removal procedure.

VALVES

VALVE ARRANGMENT

Right Side

E-I-I-E-E-I-I-E-E-I-I-E (Front-to-rear).

Left Side

E-I-I-E-E-I-I-E-E-I-I-E (Front-to-rear).

VALVE SPRINGS

Removal

Compress valve spring. Remove keepers, spring retaining plate, valve spring and valve stem oil seal. Check valve spring free lenght.

Installation

To install, reverse removal procedure.

VALVE GUIDES

NOTE: **When installing oversize replacement guides, check O.D. of guide to be used. If necessary, ream cylinder head bore to obtain proper interference fit.**

Removal

Check valve guide-to-valve stem clearance. Replace valve guide if stem clearance is not within specifications. Replace valve guides by heating head in boiling water for 30 minutes. Drive guides out of head from combustion chamber end.

Installation

Coat new guides with graphite grease and install snap ring. Reheat cylinder head and drive new guides from top until snap ring is seated in groove.

Fig. 6: View Showing Correct Valve Guide Installation

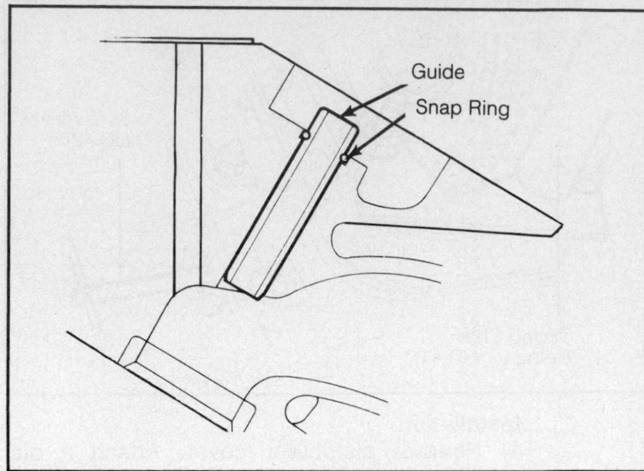
Guide
Snap Ring

Drive valve guide in until circlip is seated in groove.

REPLACEMENT VALVE GUIDES

Application	Size Mark	Dimension In. (mm)
1st Oversize	2 Grooves	.506-.507 (12.85-12.88)
2nd Oversize	3 Grooves	.511-.512 (12.98-13.00)

VALVE CLEARANCE ADJUSTMENT

1) Remove camshaft covers. Rotate camshafts and record clearance between cam lobe and tappets. Remove camshaft, if adjustment is required. *See CAMSHAFT removal in this article.* Remove tappets and adjusting pads from valves that need adjustment.

2) Subtract specified valve clearance from actual (measured) valve clearance. Select a new adjusting pad that is equal to difference between the two readings. Adjusting pads are available in increments of .001" (0.03 mm), from .085" (2.16 mm) to .110" (2.79 mm). Adjusting pads are marked with letters "A" to "Z" respectively.

3) Install correct adjusting pads and tappets. Reverse removal procedure to complete valve clearance adjustment.

VALVE CLEARANCE SPECIFICATIONS

Application	In. (mm)
Intake	0.010-0.012 (0.25-0.30)
Exhaust	0.010-0.012 (0.25-0.30)

PISTON, RINGS & PINS

OIL PAN

Removal

Drain engine oil. Remove power steering-to-rack pipe to gain access to front oil pan bolts. Remove oil pan retaining bolts, and remove oil pan.

Installation

To install, reverse removal procedure.

XJS V12 (Cont.)

PISTON & ROD ASSEMBLY

Removal

Remove cylinder heads and oil pan. Remove oil pump adapter tubes and oil pump adapter. Rotate crankshaft until bearing cap to be removed is accessible. Remove nuts, bearing cap and bearing. Push piston and rod assembly out of cylinder.

Installation

Coat all parts with engine oil and make sure that piston ring gaps are evenly spaced around circumference of piston. Compress piston rings and insert piston and rod assembly so that "FRONT" stamp faces front of engine. Reverse removal procedure to complete installation.

Fig. 7: Exploded View of Piston Assembly

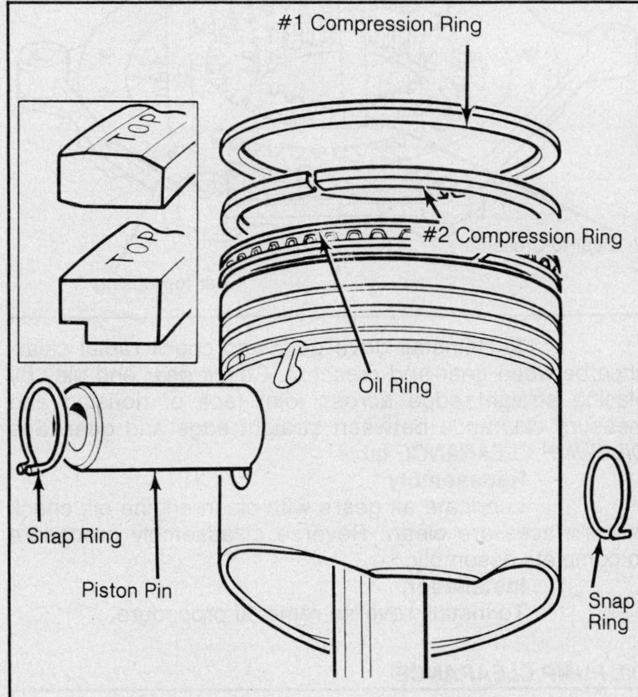
#1 Compression Ring
TOP
TOP
#2 Compression Ring
Oil Ring
Snap Ring
Piston Pin
Snap Ring

Piston must be fitted so the "FRONT" stamp faces front of engine.

PISTON RINGS

Check ring end gap and side clearance. Install oil control ring in bottom groove. *See Fig. 7.* Ensure that expander ends do not overlap. Install compression rings in top two grooves with "TOP" side up. The top compression ring is chrome-plated and cargraph coated, the RED coating must not be removed.

PISTON PINS

Remove snap rings and push piston pin out of piston. Piston pins and pistons are a matched set, do not mix. The connecting rods must be installed so that "FRONT" stamp on piston faces front of engine. The chamfer on crankshaft end of connecting rod should face the crank pin radius.

FITTING PISTONS

Check piston-to-cylinder wall clearance to determine if proper clearance exists. If liner or piston is worn, replacement must be of standard size.

CYLINDER LINERS

NOTE: **If new liners are to be installed, they must be of same grade designation as old liners. Grade A-Red 3.543" (89.98 mm), or B-Green 3.544" (90.01 mm).**

Press out cylinder liners from below. Smear cylinder liners with Hylomar, prior to installation. Press cylinder liners into cylinder block. Remove excessive sealant. Ensure liners are correctly seated and install cylinder liner retainers (JD 41).

CRANKSHAFT MAIN & CONNECTING ROD BEARINGS

CRANKSHAFT MAIN BEARINGS

NOTE: **While it is possible to replace main bearing shells with engine in vehicle, this should only be done when it is certain that crankshaft is not damaged.**

Removal

Remove cylinder heads and oil pan. Remove oil pump adapter tubes and remove oil pump adapter. Remove crankshaft undershield. Remove bolt, washer and nut securing oil delivery pipe elbow to oil pump adapter. Disconnect delivery pipe from crankcase and oil pump adapter. Remove main bearing caps, as required.

NOTE: **Due to extremely hard surface of crankshaft journals, it is not possible to grind crankshaft satisfactorily. Crankshafts are available on exchange basis and are supplied complete with matching bearings. Bearings are available only in standard size.**

Fig. 8: Exploded View of Main Bearings & Rear Oil Seal Assembly

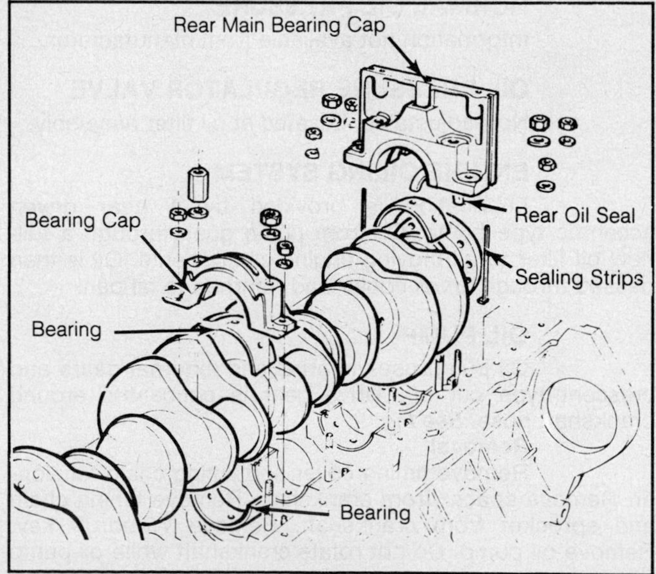
Rear Main Bearing Cap
Bearing Cap
Rear Oil Seal
Sealing Strips
Bearing
Bearing

Jaguar Engines

XJS V12 (Cont.)

Installation

1) Rear and center main bearing shells must not be interchanged with one another. The rear main bearing shell has an oil groove while the center main bearing shell does not. Apply sealant to outer grooves of rear main bearing cap.

2) Install bolt securing delivery pipe elbow in a downward direction. Install new "O" rings on suction and delivery pipes. Reverse removal procedure to complete installation.

REAR MAIN OIL SEAL REPLACEMENT

NOTE: **Rear oil seal replacement must be performed before installation of crankshaft.**

1) Apply sealant to outer grooves of rear main bearing cap. Apply one drop of Loctite to oil seal grooves. Install new oil seal halves in grooves of rear main bearing cap. Install main bearing cap on cylinder block and tighten.

2) Apply a small amount of graphite grease to oil seal. Insert oil seal installer (JD 17B and JD 17B-1). Press tool inward and rotate until fully seated. Remove rear main bearing cap. Coat oil seal with graphite grease. Position crankshaft and install main bearing caps.

THRUST BEARING ALIGNMENT

Measure crankshaft end play. Thrust bearing washers are used on center main bearing cap to adjust end play. Select thrust washers that bring end play within specification. Install thrust washers with grooved side facing outward.

ENGINE OILING

CRANKCASE CAPACITY

11 qts. (10.2L) with filter.

OIL FILTER

Full-flow, disposable element.

NORMAL OIL PRESSURE

Information not available from manufacturer.

OIL PRESSURE REGULATOR VALVE

Non-adjustable. Located at oil filter assembly.

ENGINE OILING SYSTEM

Lubrication is provided by a gear driven eccentric type pump. Oil from pump goes through a full-flow oil filter to all moving engine components. Oil is then passed through an oil cooler and returned to oil pan.

OIL PUMP

Oil pump uses internal and external gears and crescent type cut off. Drive gear is concentric around crankshaft nose. *See Fig. 9.*

Removal

Remove timing cover and timing chain tensioner. Remove spacer from crankshaft. Remove timing chain and sprocket from crankshaft. Remove Woodruff key. Remove oil pump. Do not rotate crankshaft while oil pump is removed.

Disassembly

1) Remove 8 bolts and lock washers and remove pump cover from gear housing. Mark drive and driven gear faces for reassembly reference. Remove both gears, and clean thoroughly.

2) Check condition of all gears. Remove burrs with fine file. Reinstall driven gear and check radial clearance between gear and housing. Checks should not be taken at any of the 6 radial flats on the gear.

Fig. 9: Correct Procedure to Measure Oil Pump Clearances

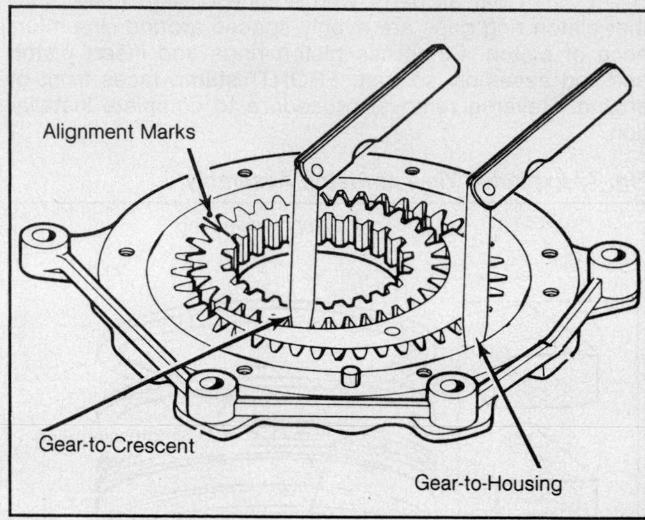
Alignment Marks
Gear-to-Crescent
Gear-to-Housing

3) Reinstall drive gear and check radial clearance between gear and crescent. Check gear end play by placing straight edge across joint face of housing and measure clearance between straight edge and gear. *See OIL PUMP CLEARANCE table.*

Reassembly

Lubricate all gears with clean engine oil, check that surfaces are clean. Reverse disassembly procedure to complete assembly.

Installation

To install, reverse removal procedure.

OIL PUMP CLEARANCE

Application	In. (mm)[1]
Driven Gear-to-Housing	.005 (.127)
Drive Gear-to-Crescent	.006 (.152)
Gear End Play	.005 (.127)

[1] – Wear limit specifications given.

ENGINE COOLING

COOLANT CAPACITY

22 qts. (21.2L)

THERMOSTAT

Two thermostats are used. Opening temperature is 174-181°F (79-83°C).

WATER PUMP

NOTE: **Exchange water pumps do not come with pulley, therefore pulley must be removed before sending in defective pump. Pulley must then be installed on pump before placing on engine.**

Jaguar Engines

XJS V12 (Cont.)

Removal

1) Drain and remove radiator. Remove lower cowl and mounting bracket and move out of the way. Remove fan/clutch assembly. Remove fan belt. Remove idler pulley adjusting bolt. Remove hardware attaching idler pulley housing. Remove studs. Remove steering pump.

2) Remove A/C compressor pump belt, if used. Loosen steering pump pivot bolts enough to remove adjustment bolt from stud. Remove stud. Remove thermostatic switch housing and bottom hose assembly. Remove crankshaft pulley and damper assembly.

3) Loosen upper hose clamp on engine cross pipe. Remove set screws and washers attaching water pump. Pull pump out and downward to clear cross pipe hose.

Installation

To install, reverse removal procedure.

TIGHTENING SPECIFICATIONS

Application	Ft. Lbs. (N.m)
Cylinder Head	
7/16" Nuts	49-52 (71)
3/8" Nuts	27-28 (38)
Crankshaft Main Bearing Nuts	
1/2"	59-62 (73)
3/8"	27-28 (38)
Connecting Rod Nuts	40-41 (54)
Camshaft Cap Nuts	10 (14)
Crankshaft Pulley Bolts	125-150 (169-203)
Flywheel-to-Crankshaft Bolts	63-66 (89)

ENGINE SPECIFICATIONS

GENERAL SPECIFICATIONS

Year	DISPLACEMENT		Fuel System	HP@RPM	Torque Ft. Lbs.@RPM	Compr. Ratio	BORE		STROKE	
	Cu. In.	Liters					In.	mm	In.	mm
1983	326	5.3	Fuel Inj.	262@5000	290@3000	11.5:1	3.543	90	2.756	70

VALVES

Engine Size & Valve	Head Diam. In. (mm)	Face Angle	Seat Angle	Seat Width In. (mm)	Stem Diameter In. (mm)	Stem Clearance In. (mm)	Valve Lift In. (mm)
5.3 L							
Intake	1.620-1.630 (41.15-41.40)	45°	44.5°	.....	.3092-.3093 (7.854-7.856)	.001-.004 (.03-.10)	.375 (9.5)
Exhaust	1.355-1.365 (34.42-34.67)	45°	44.5°	.....	.3092-.3093 (7.854-7.856)	.001-.004 (.03-.10)	.375 (9.5)

PISTONS, PINS, RINGS

Engine	PISTONS	PINS		RINGS		
	Clearance In. (mm)	Piston Fit In. (mm)	Rod Fit In. (mm)	Ring No.	End Gap In. (mm)	Side Clearance In. (mm)
5.3 L	.0012-.0017 (.030-.040)	Push Fit	.0000-.0002 (.000-.005)	1	.014-.020 (.36-.51)	.0029 (.074)
				2	.010-.015 (.25-.38)	.0034 (.086)
				Oil	.015-.045 (.38-1.14)	[1]

[1] – Oil ring is self expanding.

Jaguar Engines

XJS V12 (Cont.)

ENGINE SPECIFICATIONS (Cont.)

CRANKSHAFT MAIN & CONNECTING ROD BEARINGS

Engine	MAIN BEARINGS				CONNECTING ROD BEARINGS		
	Journal Diam. In. (mm)	Clearance In. (mm)	Thrust Bearing	Crankshaft End Play In. (mm)	Journal Diam. In. (mm)	Clearance In. (mm)	Side Play In. (mm)
5.3 L	3.0007-3.0012 (76.218-76.230)	.0015-.003 (.038-.076)	Center	.004.006 (.10-.15)	2.2994-2.3000 (58.40-58.42)	.0015-.0034 (.038-.086)	.007-.013 (.18-.33)

VALVE SPRINGS

Engine	Free Length In. (mm)	PRESSURE Lbs. @ In. (Kg @ mm)	
		Valve Closed	Valve Open
5.3 L			
Inner	1.734 (44.0)	.....	.....
Outer	2.103 (53.4)	.....	.....

CAMSHAFT

Engine	Journal Diam. In. (mm)	Clearance In. (mm)	Lobe Lift In. (mm)
5.3 L	1.0615-1.0620 (26.96-26.97)	.001-.003 (.03-.08)	.....

VALVE TIMING

Engine	INTAKE		EXHAUST	
	Open (BTDC)	Close (ABDC)	Open (BBDC)	Close (ATDC)
5.3 L	17°	59°	59°	17°

Mazda Engines

GLC & B2000 4-CYLINDER

ENGINE CODING

ENGINE IDENTIFICATION

Engine number is stamped on a machined pad. On B2000, engine number is located on right front side of engine block. On GLC, engine number is located on block, near distributor.

ENGINE, MANIFOLDS & CYLINDER HEAD

ENGINE

Removal (RWD Models)

1) Remove hood after marking hinge location. Drain cooling system and crankcase. On GLC, remove cooling fan. On all models, remove battery and air cleaner. Disconnect accelerator cable and wiring from carburetor.

2) Disconnect fuel lines at fuel pump and carburetor. On automatic transmission models, disconnect and plug transmission cooler lines at radiator. On all models, remove radiator hoses and radiator.

3) Disconnect all engine vacuum hoses. Disconnect wires from temperature sending unit, oil pressure switch, alternator, distributor, back-up light switch and starter. Disconnect exhaust pipe from manifold.

4) On manual transmission models, remove cover plate from clutch housing and clutch slave cylinder. On automatic transmission models, remove drive plate-to-torque converter bolts.

5) On all models, support transmission with a jack and remove nuts and bolts attaching transmission to engine. On manual transmission models, remove clutch slave cylinder.

6) On all models, remove engine mount attaching nuts and bolts. Install alifting sling to engine lifting brackets. Attach an engine hoist and raise slightly. Pull engine forward until clear of transmission. Lift engine from vehicle.

Removal (FWD Models)

1) Remove hood and battery. Raise and support vehicle. Remove engine undercover. Drain engine oil, transaxle oil and coolant. Remove the crossmember. Lift engine slightly and remove front wheels.

2) Detach steering knuckles. Remove driveshafts from transaxle. Disconnect shifting rod and extension bar (if equipped) from transaxle. Remove lower hose from radiator. Remove transaxle mounting rubbers. Disconnect exhaust pipe from front catalytic converter.

3) Remove transaxle bracket. Remove air cleaner. Disconnect all electrical wiring from engine. Disconnect accelerator cable. Remove speedometer cable from transaxle. Disconnect clutch cable and bracket (if equipped), and ground cable from transaxle.

4) Remove upper radiator hose and heater hose. Disconnect all remaining hoses from engine. Remove canister. Disconnect engine mounting brackets. Lift engine and transaxle from vehicle at the same time.

Installation (All Models)

To install, reverse removal procedures.

CYLINDER HEAD

NOTE: **Check timing chain for stretch prior to removing cylinder head. See Timing Chain & Sprockets procedures.**

Removal

1) Remove engine lifting brackets from cylinder head. Disconnect exhaust pipe, then remove exhaust manifold. Disconnect ignition wires from spark plugs and remove cap from distributor.

2) Remove necessary vacuum hoses and wiring from distributor, then remove distributor. Disconnect hoses and remove air pump with bracket. Loosen drive belt, then remove water pump fan and pulley. Remove water pump.

3) If equipped, disconnect anti-afterburn valve. Label and disconnect all coolant, fuel and vacuum hoses from cylinder head, manifold and carburetor.

4) Label and disconnect all necessary wiring and cables from cylinder head, manifold and carburetor. Remove intake manifold and carburetor as an assembly.

5) Remove rocker arm cover. On RWD models, remove cover from timing chain tensioner. Install chain adjuster guide (49-3953-260) on tensioner to secure snubber in place. *See Fig. 1*. On FWD models, remove chain adjuster from front cover.

Fig. 1: Installing Chain Adjuster Guide on Timing Chain Tensioner

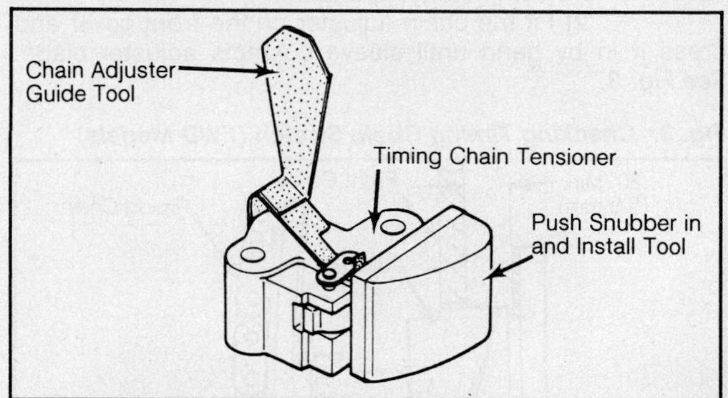
Chain Adjuster
Guide Tool
Timing Chain Tensioner
Push Snubber in
and Install Tool

Snubber must be held in retracted position when removing cylinder head, timing chain or camshaft.

6) Secure flywheel in place to prevent crankshaft and camshaft from moving. Remove distributor drive gear from camshaft. Remove camshaft sprocket lock nut. Remove the 1 cylinder head-to-front cover attaching bolt.

7) Gradually loosen cylinder head bolts in reverse order of tightening sequence, then remove bolts. Wire camshaft sprocket and timing chain together for correct chain-to-sprocket relationship during reassembly.

8) Remove rocker arm assembly. Keeping upward tension on timing chain, carefully remove camshaft from sprocket and cylinder head. Remove cylinder head.

Installation

1) Clean all gasket mating surfaces. Install new head gasket. Place cylinder head on aligning dowels. If removed, install camshaft bearings in cylinder head and bearing caps. Lubricate bearings and camshaft journals with engine oil.

2) Install camshaft on cylinder head and engage with camshaft sprocket and timing chain. Install rocker arm assembly and head bolts.

3) Install the 1 cylinder head-to-front cover bolt. Tighten cylinder head bolts in sequence. *See Fig. 2*. Install and tighten remaining components in reverse order of removal. Ensure valve timing is correct. Adjust timing chain tension. Adjust valves.

GLC & B2000 4-CYLINDER (Cont.)

Fig. 2: Cylinder Head Tightening Sequence

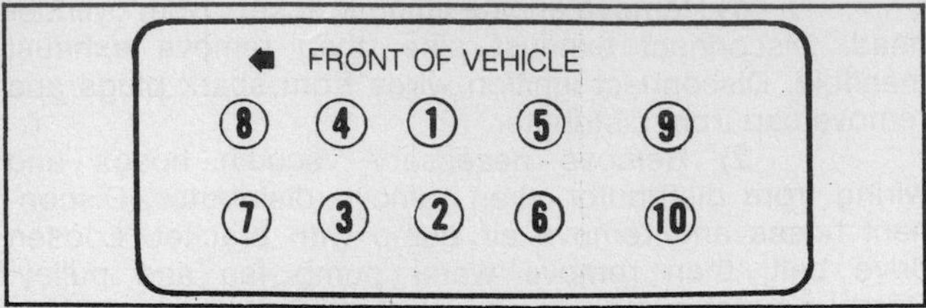
FRONT OF VEHICLE
8 4 1 5 9
7 3 2 6 10

Loosen bolts in reverse order of tightening sequence.

CAMSHAFT

ENGINE FRONT COVER

Manufacturer does not give procedures for front cover removal and installation.

TIMING CHAIN & SPROCKETS

Checking for Stretch (FWD Models)

1) Remove timing chain adjuster from front cover. Make sure sleeve is not locked. This would be the case if it were completely expanded.

2) Fit the chain adjuster on the front cover and press it in by hand until sleeve contacts adjuster blade. *See Fig. 3*.

Fig. 3: Checking Timing Chain Stretch (FWD Models)

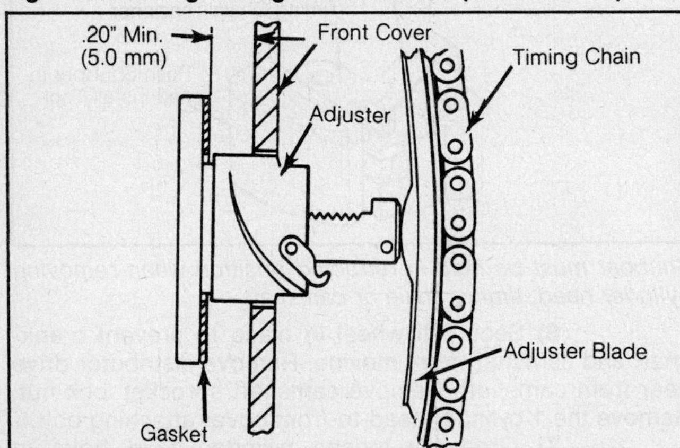
.20" Min.
(5.0 mm)
Front Cover
Timing Chain
Adjuster
Adjuster Blade
Gasket

3) Measure distance between the chain adjuster gasket and front cover. *See Fig. 3*. If measurement is .2" (5 mm) or less, replace timing chain.

Checking for Stretch (RWD Models)

1) Remove cover from timing chain tensioner. Remove 2 blind plugs from front of front cover, then loosen chain guide strip screws.

2) On 2.0L engines, remove blind plug on right side of front cover. Adjust timing chain tension by slightly rotating crankshaft in normal direction of rotation, then proceeding as follows:

3) Insert a screwdriver through access hole in side of front cover (or through top of cylinder head on 1.5L engines) and press in on top of chain guide strip. DO NOT use excessive pressure.

4) While retaining pressure on guide strip, tighten guide strip screws through 2 holes in front cover. Chain is now adjusted.

5) To check for stretch, measure distance between rear face of snubber and tensioner housing. *See Fig. 4*. If distance exceeds .07" (17 mm), replace the chain.

Fig. 4: Checking Timing Chain for Wear (RWD Models)

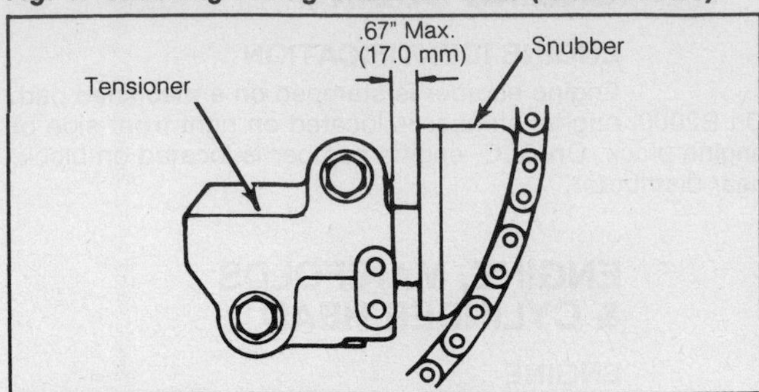
.67" Max.
(17.0 mm)
Snubber
Tensioner

Adjust chain tension prior to taking measurement.

Removal

1) On FWD models, remove chain adjuster from front cover. On all models, remove cylinder head, oil pan and engine front cover. On RWD models, remove chain adjuster from cylinder block. Loosen chain guide strip screws through access holes in front cover.

2) On RWD models, remove oil pump driven sprocket and drive chain from pump, then remove pump drive sprocket from crankshaft. Remove crankshaft timing sprocket and chain. On FWD models, remove crankshaft sprocket and timing chain.

Installation (RWD models)

1) Position crankshaft with keyway up. Place timing chain on crankshaft sprocket. On 2.0L engines, 2 plated links of chain straddle timing mark on sprocket. On 1.5L engines, plated link aligns with timing mark on crankshaft sprocket. *See Fig. 5*.

Fig. 5: Alignment Marks of Timing Chain & Sprockets

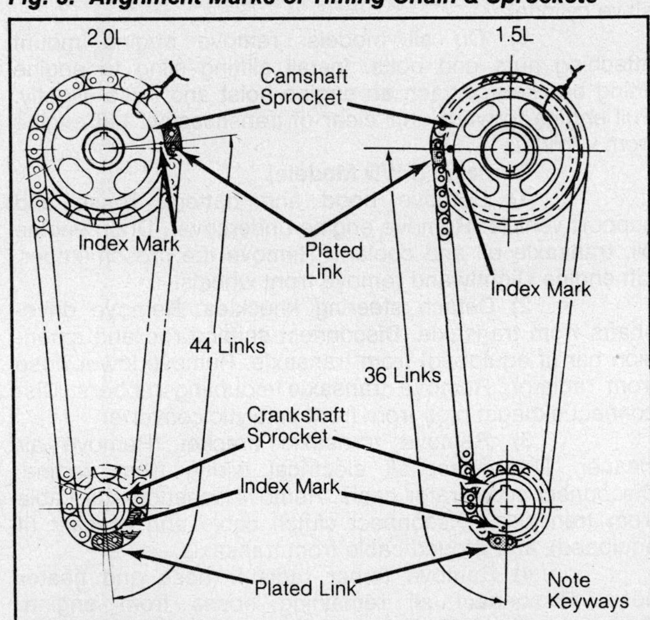
2.0L
1.5L
Camshaft
Sprocket
Index Mark
Plated
Link
Index Mark
44 Links
36 Links
Crankshaft
Sprocket
Index Mark
Plated Link
Note
Keyways

2) Install crankshaft sprocket and chain onto crankshaft, ensuring chain-to-sprocket positioning does not change. Install oil pump drive sprocket onto crankshaft. Install and tighten oil pump sprocket and drive chain on oil pump.

3) Install chain adjuster guide (49-3953-260) onto chain tensioner to keep snubber retracted. Install chain tensioner onto cylinder block. Using new head gasket, place cylinder head onto cylinder block.

GLC & B2000 4-CYLINDER (Cont.)

4) Place timing chain around camshaft sprocket with timing mark and plated link aligned. Lay camshaft on cylinder head and engage camshaft with sprocket and chain. Ensure all timing marks are aligned. *See Fig. 5*.

5) Tighten camshaft sprocket. Install rocker arm assembly and cylinder head bolts. Tighten cylinder head bolts. Install front cover and oil pan.

6) Adjust timing chain tension by slightly rotating the crankshaft in the direction of engine rotation, then proceeding as follows:

7) Insert a screwdriver through access hole in side of front cover (or through top of cylinder head on 1.5L engines) and press in on top of guide strip. DO NOT use excessive pressure. While retaining light pressure on guide strip, tighten guide strip screws through 2 holes in front cover.

8) Remove the timing chain adjuster guide from tensioner to release snubber. Install tensioner cover. Using new gaskets where required, install oil pan and remaining components in reverse order of removal.

Installation (FWD models)

1) Install timing chain and crankshaft sprocket with timing marks aligned. *See Fig. 5*. Install front cover and oil pan. Using new gasket, place cylinder head in position on block.

2) Align camshaft sprocket timing mark with plated link on timing chain. Place camshaft onto cylinder head and engage camshaft into camshaft sprocket. Ensure timing marks are still aligned. *See Fig. 5*.

3) Install and tighten rocker arm assembly and head bolts. Install and tighten camshaft sprocket lock nut. Install crankshaft pulley, applying sealer to inside of pulley bolt.

4) Push sleeve of timing chain adjuster into adjuster body and lock pin with hook. *See Fig. 6*. Install and tighten timing chain adjuster to front cover.

Fig. 6: Locking Timing Chain Adjuster (FWD Models)

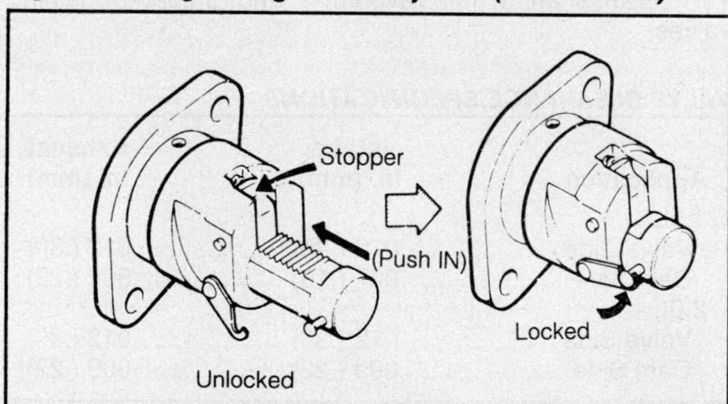
Stopper
(Push IN)
Locked
Unlocked

NOTE: **Adjuster unlocks automatically and adjusts chain tension after engine is cranked once or twice.**

5) Using new gaskets where necessary, install and tighten remaining components in reverse order of removal. If necessary, adjust valves.

CAMSHAFT

Removal

1) Remove rocker arm cover. On RWD models, remove cover from timing chain tensioner. Install chain adjuster guide (49-3953-260) on tensioner to secure snubber in place. On FWD models, remove chain adjuster from front cover.

2) Secure flywheel in place to prevent crankshaft from moving. Remove distributor drive gear from camshaft. Remove camshaft sprocket lock nut. Remove cylinder head-to-front cover attaching bolt.

3) Gradually loosen cylinder head bolts in reverse order of tightening sequence, then remove bolts. Wire camshaft sprocket and timing chain together to ensure correct chain-to-sprocket relationship upon reassembly.

4) Remove rocker arm assembly. Keeping upward tension on timing chain, carefully remove camshaft from sprocket and cylinder head.

Inspection

1) Inspect camshaft journals and lobes for wear or scoring. Using a micrometer, measure cam lobe height. If measured height is less than specification, replace camshaft.

CAM LOBE HEIGHT SPECIFICATIONS

Application	[1] Lobe Height In. (mm)
1.5L	
FWD Models	1.7289 (43.914)
RWD Models	1.7288 (43.912)
2.0L	
Intake Lobes	1.7652 (44.837)
Exhaust Lobes	1.7639 (44.804)

[1] – Minimum allowable measurement.

2) Measure diameter of camshaft journals. If wear is more than .002" (.05 mm) below minimum standard diameter, camshaft must be ground or replaced.

3) Using a dial indicator, check camshaft out-of-round. Camshaft must not exceed .0012" (.030 mm) out-of-round.

Installation

To install, reverse removal procedure. Adjust timing chain tension as explained in Timing Chain & Sprockets.

CAMSHAFT BEARINGS

Removal & Installaion

Remove camshaft. Remove bearing inserts from cylinder head and camshaft caps. To install, reverse removal procedures.

CAMSHAFT END THRUST

Using a feeler gauge, check camshaft end thrust between sprocket and thrust plate. If end thrust measurement exceeds .008" (.20 mm), replace thrust plate.

VALVES

VALVE ARRANGEMENT

1.5L FWD Engine

Firewall Side – Intake valves.
Exhaust Manifold Side – Exhaust valves.

1.5L RWD Engine

Right Side – Intake valves.
Left Side – Exhaust valves.

2.0L Engine

Left Side – Intake valves.
Right Side – Exhaust valves.

GLC & B2000 4-CYLINDER (Cont.)

ROCKER ARM SHAFT ASSEMBLY

1) When disassembling rocker arm shaft assembly, keep all parts in order for reassembly. *See Figs. 7 and 8*. Inspect all components for wear or damage.

Fig. 7: 1.5L Rocker Arm Assembly

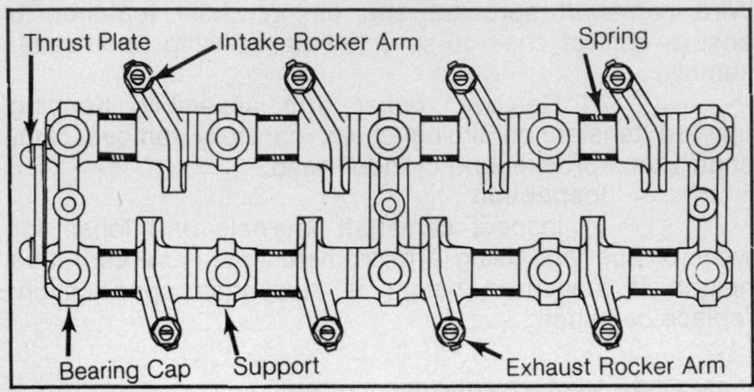
Thrust Plate
Intake Rocker Arm
Spring
Bearing Cap
Support
Exhaust Rocker Arm

Fig. 8: 2.0L Rocker Arm Assembly

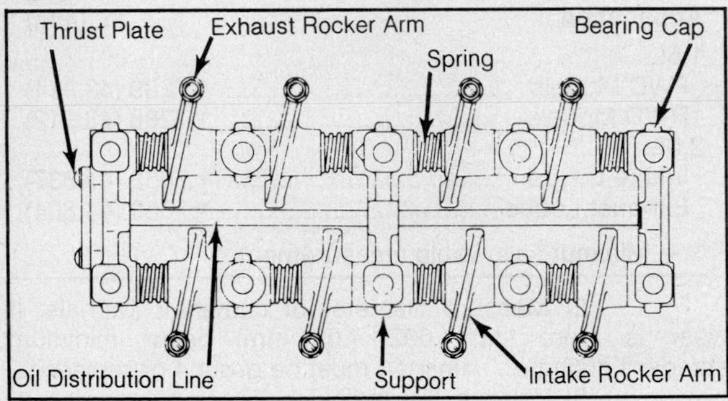
Thrust Plate
Exhaust Rocker Arm
Bearing Cap
Spring
Oil Distribution Line
Support
Intake Rocker Arm

2) Standard clearance between rocker arm bore and shaft is .0008-.0029" (.020-.074 mm) for 1.5L engines, and .0011-.0032" (.027-.081 mm) for 2.0L engines. If clearance is more than .004" (.10 mm) replace worn components.

3) On 2.0L engines, note that 2 rocker shafts are used on intake side. Install center bearing cap with oil hole on intake side.

4) 2.0L engines use an "O" ring on oil distribution pipe to absorb vibration. Slide "O" ring onto pipe. Install pipe, then work "O" ring into hole in center camshaft cap. Be sure oil holes in pipe face downward.

Fig. 9: Rocker Arm Offset

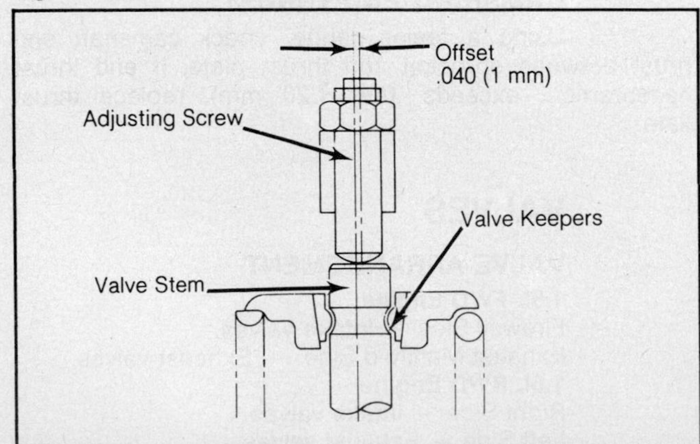
Offset
.040 (1 mm)
Adjusting Screw
Valve Keepers
Valve Stem

Move rocker arm supports to offset screws of intake and exhaust rocker arms.

5) Align rocker shaft assembly with dowels and install onto cylinder head. Before tightening cylinder head bolts, offset each rocker arm .040" (1.02 mm) from valve stem center, by shifting rocker shaft supports slightly. *See Fig. 9*.

VALVE GUIDE SERVICING

CAUTION: The valve keepers for intake and exhaust valves are not interchangeable. Care must be taken not to interchange them. See Fig. 10.

Fig. 10: Intake & Exhaust Valve Keepers

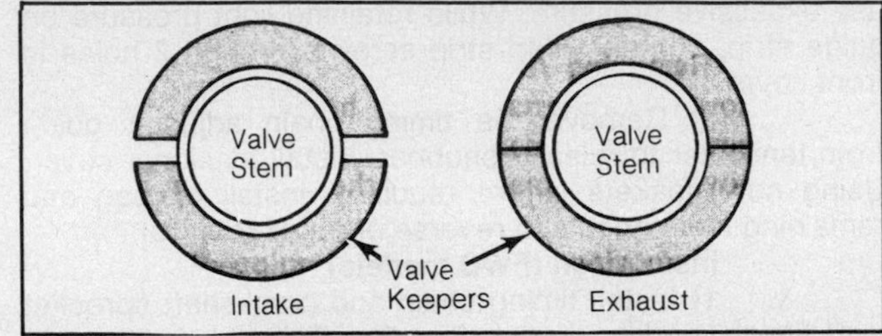
Valve Stem
Valve Stem
Valve Keepers
Intake
Exhaust

Do not interchange keepers.

Use valve guide driver tool (49-0221-251A) to remove and install guides. When installing new guide, drive guide in until ring of guide just touches cylinder head. Always install new oil seal when valve components have been disassembled.

VALVE CLEARANCE

1) Ensure head bolts are properly tightened. Warm engine to operating temperature. Valves can be adjusted at camshaft or valve stem.

2) Set No. 1 piston on TDC at end of compression stroke. Adjust intake valves of No. 1 and 2 cylinders, and exhaust valves of No. 1 and 3 cylinders. Turn crankshaft 1 full revolution and adjust remaining valves.

VALVE CLEARANCE SPECIFICATIONS

Application	Intake In. (mm)	Exhaust In. (mm)
1.5L		
Valve Side	.010 (.25)	.012 (.30)
Cam Side	.007 (.18)	.009 (.22)
2.0L		
Valve Side	.012 (.30)	.012 (.30)
Cam Side	.009 (.22)	.009 (.22)

VALVE STEM OIL SEALS

Remove cylinder head from vehicle and disassemble valve components to replace oil seals.

VALVE SPRINGS

Removal

Remove all carbon from inside of combustion chamber. Using a valve spring compressor, compress springs and remove keepers, retainers, valve springs and seats.

Inspection

1) With valve springs removed, inspect for damage. Use a valve spring tester test spring tension.

GLC & B2000 4-CYLINDER (Cont.)

Measure valve spring free length and compare with specifications.

2) Use a steel square and flat surface to check squareness of spring. If more than .056" (1.43 mm) out-of-square, replace spring.

Installation

To install valve springs and remaining components, reverse removal procedures.

PISTONS, PINS & RINGS

OIL PAN

Removal

1) Remove protective cover from under engine. Drain engine oil. On FWD models, remove oil pan.

2) On RWD models, remove clutch release cylinder (if equipped). Leave hydraulic line attached. Remove clutch cover (if equipped). Remove oil pan.

Installation

Clean all gasket mating surfaces. Apply sealer to oil pan sealing surface. Using new gasket, install oil pan in reverse order of removal.

PISTON & ROD ASSEMBLY

Removal

1) Remove oil pan, cylinder head, and oil pump. Make sure connecting rods and caps are marked so they can be replaced in their original positions.

2) Remove rod caps. Push piston and rod assembly out top of cylinder. Take care not to damage crankshaft journal.

Fig. 11: 1.5L Engine Ring Gap Locations

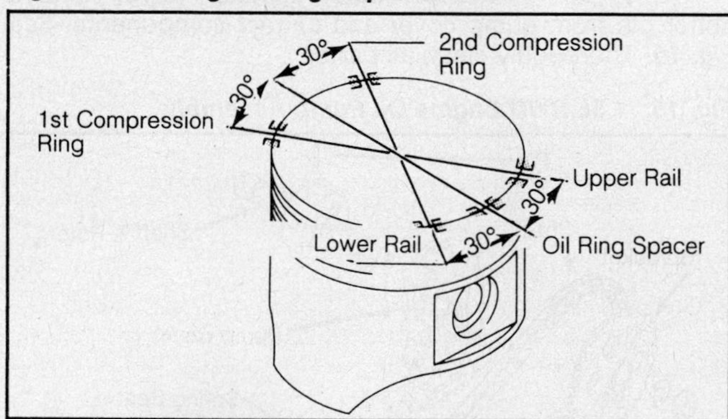

2nd Compression Ring
30°
30°
1st Compression Ring
Upper Rail
30°
Lower Rail
30°
Oil Ring Spacer

Installation

1) Install piston rings on piston and properly space ring gaps. *See Figs. 11 and 12*. Lubricate piston rings, pistons and cylinder walls with engine oil. Install ring compressor onto piston without changing position of rings.

Fig. 12: 2.0L Engine Ring Gap Locations

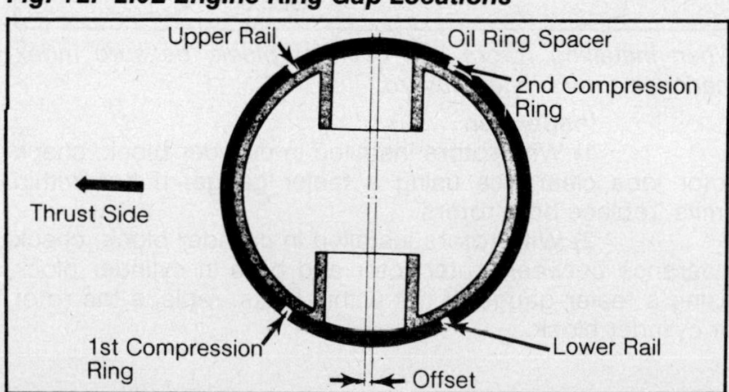

Upper Rail
Oil Ring Spacer
2nd Compression Ring
Thrust Side
1st Compression Ring
Lower Rail
Offset

2) Install piston and rod assembly. Make sure "F" mark on pin boss is facing front of engine. Install rod caps and tighten rod bolts. Install oil pump, oil pan and cylinder head.

FITTING PISTONS

1) Measure cylinder bore diameter at top, middle and bottom of bore. Take measurements in line with and 90° to crankshaft centerline. *See Fig. 13*.

Fig. 13: Cylinder Bore Measuring Points

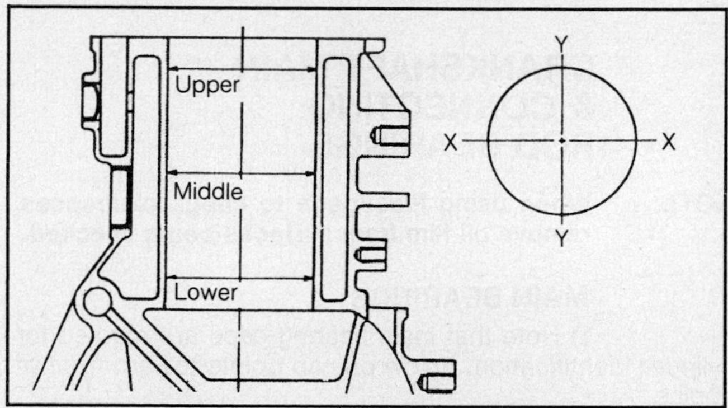

Upper
Middle
Lower
Y
X
X
Y

If difference between minimum and maximum bore measurements exceeds .006" (.15 mm), bore cylinders.

2) Difference between minimum and maximum bore diameters must not exceed .006" (.15 mm). If wear exceeds limits, bore and hone cylinders for installation of oversize pistons.

3) Inspect pistons and replace those severely damaged due to scoring, scratching or burning. Measure piston diameter 90° to pin bore, about 11/16" below lower ring groove. Use piston diameter and bore measurements to determine piston-to-cylinder bore clearance.

FITTING RINGS

1) Position rings near bottom of bore at a point where bore diameter is smallest. Ring must be square in bore. Measure ring end gap with a feeler gauge.

2) Using a feeler gauge, check ring side clearance. Ensure rings turn freely in their ring grooves.

3) When installing rings on piston, ensure gaps are correct. *See Figs. 11 and 12*. Install compression rings with marking upward.

Fig. 14: Correct Piston-to-Rod Relationship

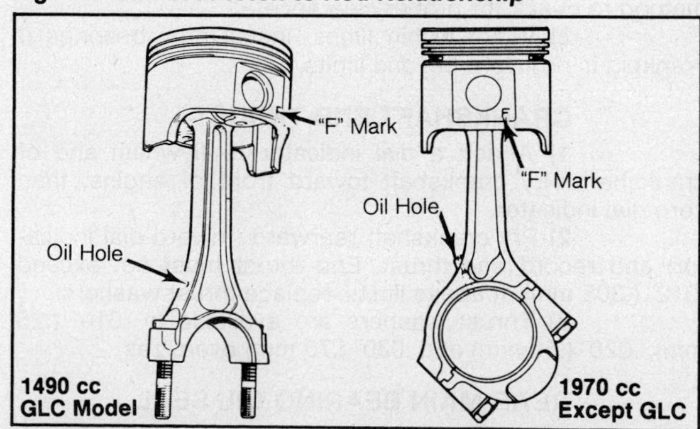

"F" Mark
"F" Mark
Oil Hole
Oil Hole
1490 cc
GLC Model
1970 cc
Except GLC

When installed in engine, "F" marking on pin boss will face front and oil hole in rod will be on right side.

GLC & B2000 4-CYLINDER (Cont.)

PISTON PIN REPLACEMENT

1) Piston pin is press fit in connecting rod. Use pin remover/installer tool and adapters for removal and installation.

2) Assemble connecting rod to piston. *See Fig. 14*. When installed in engine, "F" mark on pin boss will face front of engine, and oil hole in connecting rod will be on right side of engine.

3) When installing pins, a press load of 1102-3307 lbs. (500-1500 kg) is required. If the press load is not within load range, replace the pin or connecting rod.

CRANKSHAFT MAIN & CONNECTING ROD BEARINGS

NOTE: When using Plastigage to check clearances, remove oil film from surfaces being checked.

MAIN BEARINGS

1) Note that main bearing caps are marked for cylinder identification. Arrow on cap points toward front of engine.

2) When removing rear main bearing cap, note installed position of cap side seals with relation to seal holes. Also, note position of thrust washers.

3) Check clearances 1 at a time. With all bearing caps tightened (except one being checked), check clearances using Plastigage method.

4) Using a micrometer, check crankshaft journals for taper. Taper must not exceed .002" (.05 mm).

5) To check crankshaft for straightness, place "V" blocks under crankshaft journals at both ends. Position dial indicator point on center journal.

6) Slowly turn crankshaft at least 1 full revolution, while recording crankshaft runout. Maximum runout is .0012" (.030 mm).

7) When installing thrust washers, be sure oil-grooved sides face thrust sides of crankshaft.

8) Install side seals between cylinder block and rear main bearing cap as follows: On RWD models, install seals with hole facing sideways. On FWD models, install seals with hole facing front or rear of engine.

CONNECTING ROD BEARINGS

1) After ensuring rod caps are marked for cylinder identification, remove rod caps. Use Plastigage method to check for proper clearance.

2) If not within limits, install new bearings if crankpin is not worn beyond limits.

CRANKSHAFT END THRUST

1) Attach a dial indicator to flywheel end of crankshaft. Pry crankshaft toward front of engine, then zero dial indicator.

2) Pry crankshaft rearward (toward dial indicator) and record end thrust. End thrust must not exceed .012" (.305 mm). If above limits, replace thrust washers.

3) Thrust washers are available in .010" (.25 mm), .020" (.50 mm) and .030" (.75 mm) oversizes.

REAR MAIN BEARING OIL SEAL

With flywheel and oil pan removed, remove rear main bearing cap. Note installed positions of rubber side seals. Lubricate new seal lips and install onto crankshaft. Install rear main bearing cap and new rubber side seals.

ENGINE OILING

CRANKCASE CAPACITY

1.5L Engines

Capacity is 3.2 quarts (3.0L) without filter replacement; 3.9 quarts (3.7L) with filter replacement.

2.0L Engines

Capacity is 4.1 quarts (3.9L) without filter replacement; 4.7 quarts (4.5L) with filter replacement.

NORMAL OIL PRESSURE

Oil pressure at 3000 RPM should be 50-64 psi (3.5-4.5 kg/cm²).

ENGINE OILING SYSTEM

Oil is circulated by a rotor-type pump. On RWD model 1.5L engines, pump is assembled to front of cylinder block. On all other models, pump is mounted to bottom of crankcase at front of engine. On all models, pumps are chain driven.

OIL PUMP

Removal (1.5L RWD)

Remove front cover. Remove sprocket and drive chain from oil pump. Remove pump cover. Note and record positions of index marks on rotors. Remove lock pin, pump shaft and rotors from cylinder block.

Disassembly

To remove pressure regulator valve, remove cotter pin from pump cover and extract components. *See Fig. 15*. Thoroughly clean all parts.

Fig. 15: 1.5L RWD Engine Oil Pump Assembly

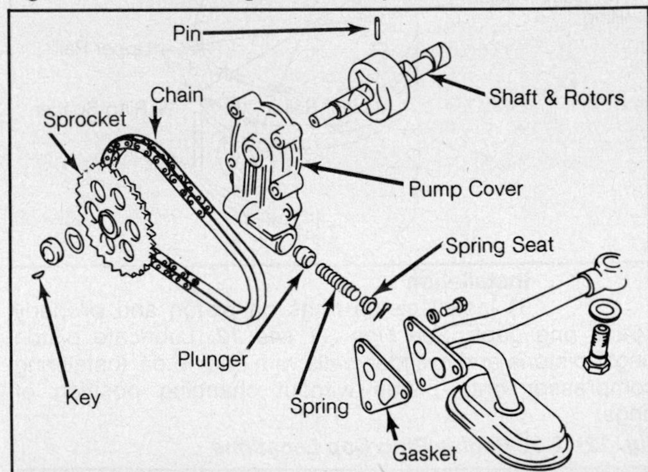
Pin
Shaft & Rotors
Chain
Sprocket
Pump Cover
Spring Seat
Plunger
Key
Spring
Gasket

When installing rotors into cylinder block, be sure index marks on rotors face outward.

Inspection

1) With rotors installed in cylinder block, check rotor lobe clearance using a feeler gauge. If not within limits, replace both rotors.

2) With rotors installed in cylinder block, check clearance between outer rotor and bore in cylinder block using a feeler gauge. If not within limits, replace the rotor or cylinder block.

GLC & B2000 4-CYLINDER (Cont.)

3) Place a straightedge over rotors and cylinder block. Using a feeler guage, measure clearance between rotors and straightedge. Record measurement.

4) Now lay a straightedge over pump cover at point where rotors and shaft contact cover. Using a feeler gauge, measure clearance between straightedge and cover.

5) To determine end play of rotors, combine measurements taken in steps **3)** and **4)**. If combined measurements exceed limits, grind (resurface) pump cover until correct clearance is obtained.

1.5L RWD OIL PUMP CLEARANCE

Application	In. (mm)
Rotor Lobe Clearance	.010 (.25) Max.
Outer Rotor to Body	.012 (.30) Max.
Rotors End Play	.006 (.15) Max.

Reassembly & Installation

Lubricate pump parts, and reassemble in reverse order of disassembly. Install rotors into cylinder block so index marks face outward. Install remaining parts in reverse order of removal.

Removal (1.5L FWD & 2.0L)

Remove oil pan. Remove oil pump sprocket and detach chain from sprocket. Remove oil pump from cylinder block. Remove pump cover. Note and record positions of rotors index marks. Extract shaft and rotors. *See Figs. 16 and 17.*

Fig. 16: 1.5L FWD Engine Oil Pump Assembly

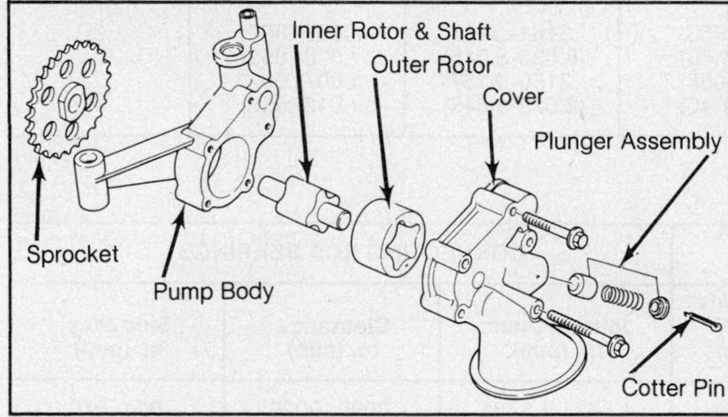
Inner Rotor & Shaft
Outer Rotor
Cover
Plunger Assembly
Sprocket
Pump Body
Cotter Pin

Disassembly

To remove oil pressure regulator components, remove cotter pin from pump body and extract spring seat, spring and plunger. Thoroughly clean all parts.

Inspection

1) Install rotors in pump body. Using a feeler gauge, measure clearance between rotor lobes. If excessive, replace both rotors.

2) Install rotors in pump body. Using feeler gauge, measure clearance between outer rotor and pump body. If beyond limits, replace rotor or pump body.

3) With rotors installed in pump body, lay a straightedge over pump body. Using a feeler gauge, measure clearance between rotors and straightedge. Record measurement.

4) Now lay a straightedge over pump cover and measure clearance between cover and straightedge at middle of cover. Record measurement.

5) Combine measurements in steps **3)** and **4)** to determine rotors end play. If sum of measurements exceeds specified limit, repair or replace pump body and/or cover.

Fig. 17: 2.0L Engine Oil Pump Assembly

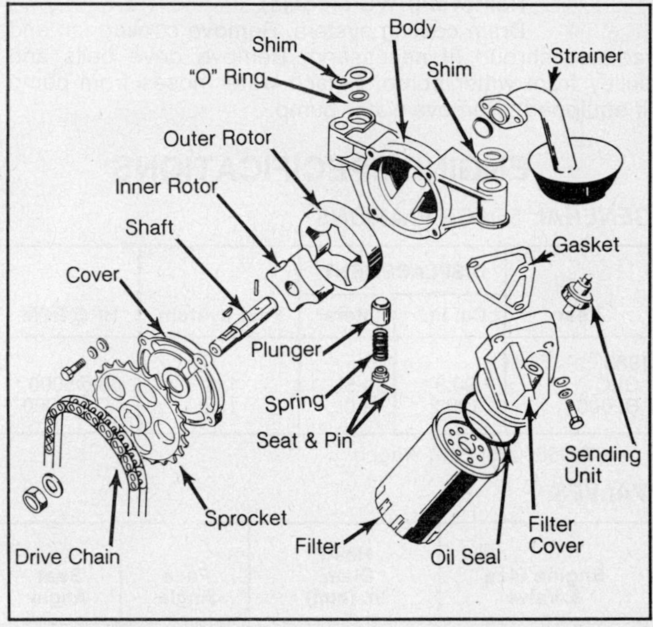
Body
Shim
"O" Ring
Shim
Strainer
Outer Rotor
Inner Rotor
Shaft
Gasket
Cover
Plunger
Spring
Seat & Pin
Sending
Unit
Sprocket
Filter
Cover
Drive Chain
Filter
Oil Seal

Reassembly

Lubricate pump parts and reassemble in reverse order of disassembly. When installing rotors into pump body, be sure index marks on rotors are positioned toward pump cover.

Installation

Install oil pump in reverse order of removal. Check tension of oil pump drive chain, by pushing in on chain at a point midway between sprockets. If chain slack exceeds 5/32", install adjusting shims between pump and block.

1.5L FWD & 2.0L OIL PUMP CLEARANCE

Application	In. (mm)
Rotor Lobe Clearance	.010 (.25) Max.
Outer Rotor to Body	
FWD 1.5L	.014 (.35) Max.
2.0L	.012 (.30) Max.
Rotors End Play	.006 (.15) Max.

ENGINE COOLING

THERMOSTAT

On RWD 1.5L engine, thermostat begins to open at 190°F (88°C) and is fully open at 212°F (100°C). On all other models, thermostat begins to open at 180°F (82°C) and fully opens at 203°F (95°C).

COOLANT CAPACITY

Coolant capacity (including heater) is 5.8 quarts (5.5L) for 1.5L engines. For 2.0L engines, coolant capacity is 7.6 quarts (7.2L) for B2000 models.

RADIATOR CAP

Radiator cap pressure relief valve opens at approximatey 13 psi (.9 kg/cm²).

Mazda Engines

GLC & B2000 4-CYLINDER (Cont.)

WATER PUMP

NOTE: It may be necessary to remove radiator to facilitate water pump removal.

Removal (RWD Models)

Drain cooling system. Remove cooling fan and radiator shroud (if necessary). Remove drive belts and pulley from water pump. Detach water hoses from pump (if equipped). Remove water pump.

Removal (FWD Models)

Drain coolant. Remove engine undercover. Remove pump drive belt. Remove radiator hose, bypass hose and "O" ring. Remove water pump.

Installation (All Models)

Using a new gasket, install water pump by reversing removal procedure.

ENGINE SPECIFICATIONS

GENERAL SPECIFICATIONS

Year	DISPLACEMENT		Fuel System	HP@RPM	Torque Ft. Lbs.@RPM	Compr. Ratio	BORE		STROKE	
	Cu. In.	Liters					In.	mm	In.	mm
1983										
GLC	90.9	1.5L	1x2	68@5000 [1]	82@3000	9.0:1	3.03	77	3.15	80
B2000	120.2	2.0L	1x2	77@5000	82@3000	8.6:1	3.15	80	3.86	98

[1] – 63@5000 for GLC Wagon.

VALVES

Engine Size & Valve	Head Diam. In. (mm)	Face Angle	Seat Angle	Seat Width In. (mm)	Stem Diameter In. (mm)	Stem Clearance In. (mm)	Valve Lift In. (mm)
1.5L							
Intake	1.4153-1.4193 (35.950-36.050)	45°	45°	.055 (1.40)	.3161-.3167 (8.030-8.045)	.0007-.0021 (.018-.053)	.....
Exhaust	1.2185-1.2225 (30.950-31.050)	45°	45°	.055 (1.40)	.3159-.3167 (8.025-8.045)	.0007-.0023 (.018-.058)	.....
2.0L							
Intake	1.6495-1.6575 (41.900-42.100)	45°	45°	.055 (1.40)	.3161-.3167 (8.030-8.045)	.0007-.0021 (.018-.053)	.....
Exhaust	1.2952-1.3032 (32.900-33.100)	45°	45°	.055 (1.40)	.3159-.3167 (8.025-8.045)	.0007-.0023 (.018-.058)	.....

CRANKSHAFT MAIN & CONNECTING ROD BEARINGS

Engine	MAIN BEARINGS				CONNECTING ROD BEARINGS		
	Journal Diam. In. (mm)	Clearance In. (mm)	Thrust Bearing	Crankshaft End Play In. (mm)	Journal Diam. In. (mm)	Clearance In. (mm)	Side Play In. (mm)
1.5L	1.9661-1.9668 (49.938-49.956)	.0009-.0017 (.023-.042)	No. 5	.004-.006 (.10-.15)	1.5724-1.5731 (39.940-49.956)	.0009-.0026 (.024-.066)	.004-.010 (.11-.26)
2.0L	2.4780-2.4786 (62.940-62.955)	.0012-.0020 (.031-.050)	No. 5	.003-.009 (.08-.24)	2.0842-2.0848 (52.939-52.952)	.0011-.0030 (.027-.077)	.004-.008 (.11-.21)

PISTONS, PINS, RINGS

Engine	PISTONS	PINS		RINGS		
	Clearance In. (mm)	Piston Fit In. (mm)	Rod Fit In. (mm)	Ring No.	End Gap In. (mm)	Side Clearance In. (mm)
1.5L	.0015-.0020 (.026-.052)	.0003-.0010 (.008-.026)	[1]	1 & 2	.006-.012 (.15-.30)	.0012-.0028 (.030-.070)
				Oil	.012-.035 (.31-.89)	.....
2.0L	.0019-.0025	1-.0009	[1]	1 & 2	.008-.016 (.020-.40)	.0012-.0028 [2] (.030-.070)
				Oil	.012-.035 (.31-.89)	.....

[1] – Interference Fit
[2] – Ring No. 2 side clearance is .0012-.0025" (.030-.064 mm).

Mazda Engines

GLC & B2000 4-CYLINDER (Cont.)

ENGINE SPECIFICATIONS (Cont.)

CAMSHAFT

Engine	Journal Diam. In. (mm)	Clearance In. (mm)	Lobe Lift In. (mm)
1.5L			
Front & Rear	1.6515-1.6522 (41.949-41.965)	.0014-.0030 (.035-.076)	.....
Center	1.6504-1.6510 (41.919-41.935)	.0026-.0042 (.065-.106)	.....
2.0L			
Front & Rear	1.7695-1.7701 (44.945-44.960)	.0007-.0027 (.019-.069)	.....
Center	1.7691-1.7697 (44.935-44.950)	.0011-.0031 (.029-.079)	.....

VALVE SPRINGS

Engine	Free Length In. (mm)	PRESSURE Lbs. @ In. (Kg @ mm)	
		Valve Closed	Valve Open
1.5L	1.71 (43.3)	63@1.32 (28.7@33.5)	.....
2.0L			
Inner	1.45 (36.8)	21@1.26 (9.5@32)	.....
Outer	1.47 (37.3)	31@1.34 (14.3@34.0)	.....

TIGHTENING SPECIFICATIONS

Application	Ft. Lbs. (N.m)
1.5L	
Camshaft Sprocket and Distributor Drive Gear	22-25 (30-35)
Connecting Rod Cap	22-26 (30-35)
Crankshaft Pulley	81-88 (110-120)
Cylinder Head	58-60 (78-82)
Exhaust Manifold	14-19 (19-26)
Flywheel	61-66 (83-90)
Intake Manifold	14-19 (19-26)
Main Bearing Cap	49-52 (66-70)
Oil Pump Sprocket	22-26 (30-35)
2.0L	
Camshaft Sprocket	52-59 (70-80)
Connecting Rod Cap	30-34 (41-46)
Crankshaft Pulley	101-108 (140-149)
Cylinder Head	
Cold	66-70 (90-95)
Hot	70-74 (95-100)
Distributor Drive Gear	52-59 (70-80)
Exhaust Manifold	16-21 (22-29)
Flywheel	114-120 (155-163)
Intake Manifold	14-19 (19-26)
Main Bearing Cap	62-66 (84-90)
Oil Pump Sprocket	22-26 (30-35)

626 4-CYLINDER

ENGINE CODING

ENGINE IDENTIFICATION

The 626 4-cylinder engine can be identified by the engine code number, stamped in a pad on the left side of the cylinder block, behind the alternator and below No. 1 spark plug (front right side of engine compartment).

ENGINE IDENTIFICATION CODE

Engine	Code
626 (2.0L)	FE

ENGINE, MANIFOLDS & CYLINDER HEAD

ENGINE

Removal

1) Remove hood after marking hinge location. Drain engine oil, transaxle fluid, and coolant. Disconnect battery negative terminal. Remove air cleaner. Disconnent fuel supply hose, return hose and accelerator cable.

2) Disconnect speedometer cable and clutch or control cable. Remove engine ground wire, vacuum hose from power brake unit, and 3-way valve vacuum switch and bracket.

3) Disconnect both heater hoses. Remove duty solenoid valve and vacuum sensor. Disconnect wiring to engine and transaxle. Remove electric fan, radiator and washer tank. On models with air conditioning, remove subtank, alternator and A/C compressor.

4) Remove front wheels, splash shields, power-steering pump and drive shafts. Disconnect shift linkage and shifter extension bar.

5) Remove flexible joints, bolts and nuts. Remove torque stopper, engine and transaxle mounting nuts. Remove engine and transaxle from vehicle.

Installation

To install, reverse removal procedure. Check all fluid levels.

MANIFOLDS & CYLINDER HEAD

Removal

1) Turn crankshaft to position No. 1 cylinder at TDC. Drain cooling system. Remove air cleaner, distributor, thermostat and fuel pump.

2) Disconnect accelerator cable from carburetor. Remove intake manifold mounting hardware and remove manifold and carburetor assembly.

3) On vehicles equipped with air conditioning, remove alternator, alternator mounting strap, A/C compressor and alternator bracket installation bolts.

4) Disconnect engine ground wire. Remove timing belt upper cover. Disconnect timing belt from cam gear. Remove secondary air pipes. Disconnect oxygen sensor connector.

5) Remove exhaust manifold shroud. Disconnect exhaust pipe from manifold by removing 3 attaching nuts and gasket. Remove exhaust manifold-to-cylinder head mounting hardware and remove manifold from vehicle.

6) Remove valve cover and gasket. Remove cylinder head bolts in reverse order of installation sequence. Break cylinder head loose from engine block and remove head from vehicle.

Installation

To install, reverse removal procedure. Tighten head bolts in sequence. *See Fig. 1.* Refill cooling system and change oil and filter. Adjust valves.

Fig. 1: Cylinder Head Tightening Sequence

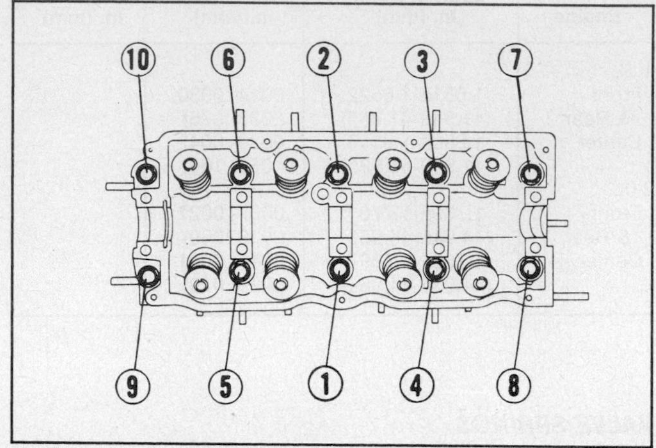
10
6
2
3
7
9
5
1
4
8

To loosen bolts, reverse tightening sequence.

CAMSHAFT

TIMING BELT

Removal

Remove fan belt and upper timing belt cover. For reassembly, mark an arrow on timing belt to indicate direction of travel. Remove lower timing belt cover, crankshaft pulley and damper. Remove tensioner lock bolt, tensioner and spring. Remove timing belt from vehicle.

Inspection

Check timing belt for wear, cracks, oil or grease. Replace timing belt every 60,000 miles (100,000 km) or as needed. Be careful not to twist, crimp or sharply bend a timing belt.

Installation

1) Align cam gear mark "A" with pointer on front housing. *See Fig. 2.* Align crank gear mark with pointer on oil pump body. *See Fig. 3.* Apply tensioner by turning tensioner lock bolt. Attach tensioner spring. Apply maximum tensioner to outer side and partially tighten lock bolt.

Fig. 2: Camshaft Gear Alignment

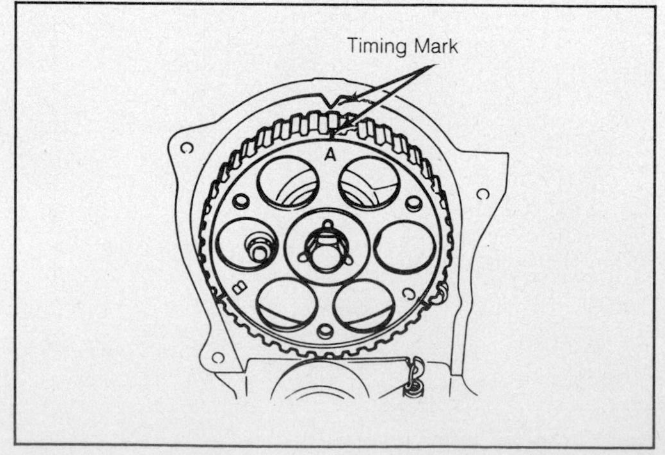
Timing Mark
A

Fig. 3: Crankshaft Gear Alignment

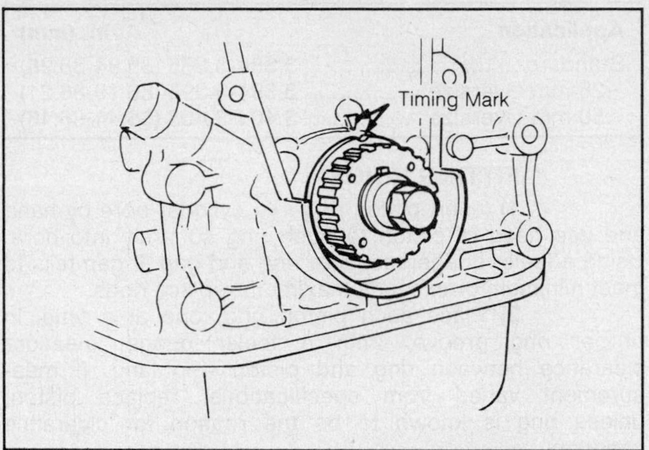
Timing Mark

2) So that tension is not lost, install timing belt onto crankshaft gear and camshaft gear, doing so from tension side (right side, as viewed from engine front). If timing belt is being reused, be sure arrow is pointing in direction of travel.

3) Loosen tensioner lock bolt to apply tension. To apply equal tension to each side of timing belt, turn crankshaft 2 revolutions in direction of travel. Tighten tensioner lock bolt. Check for proper alignment of timing marks.

4) To check for proper tension, measure amount of deflection .47-.55" (12-14 mm) midway between crank gear and cam gear when force of 22 lbs. (10 kg) is applied. If tension is incorrect, repeat step **3)**.

CAMSHAFT OIL SEAL

Removal

Turn crankshaft so that No. 1 cylinder is at TDC. Remove upper timing belt cover, tensioner and spring. Disconnect timing belt from camshaft gear and remove gear. Place a shop towel below oil seal to keep any oil from dripping on timing belt. With a flat blade screwdriver, pry oil seal from housing.

Installation

Apply a thin coat of oil to lip of seal before installation. Using a 1 3/8" (35 mm) socket and hammer, tap seal into place. Make sure front edge of oil seal is flush with front edge of housing. To complete installation, reverse removal procedure. See Timing Belt installation for adjustment and alignment procedures.

CRANKSHAFT OIL SEAL

Removal

1) Turn crankshaft so that No. 1 cylinder is at TDC. Raise and support vehicle. Remove tire and wheel assembly from right side. Remove wheel well splash shield. Remove fan belt, crankshaft pulley and damper.

2) Remove timing belt upper and lower covers, tensioner and timing belt. Remove crankshaft gear attaching bolt and gear. Using a flat blade screwdriver, pry oil seal from oil pump body.

Installation

Apply a thin coat of oil to lip of seal before installation. Using a 1 3/8" (35 mm) socket and hammer, tap seal into pump body until front edge of oil seal is flush with front edge of pump body. To complete installation, reverse removal procedure. See Timing Belt installation for adjustment and alignment procedures.

CAMSHAFT

Removal

1) Remove valve cover, gasket and fuel pump. Remove distributor and rear housing assembly from head. Remove upper timing belt cover, tensioner and spring. Remove bolt attaching cam gear to camshaft and remove gear.

2) Place a shop towel below oil seal to keep any oil from dripping on timing belt. Remove front housing assembly from head. Remove rocker arm assembly. Remove camshaft from head.

Installation

To install, reverse removal procedure. Adjust valves. See Timing Belt installation for adjustment and alignment procedures.

VALVES

VALVE ARRANGEMENT

I-E-E-I-I-E-E-I (Front-to-rear).

ROCKER ARM SHAFT ASSEMBLY

See Camshaft removal and installation procedures. Also be sure to adjust the valves.

VALVE SPRINGS & SEALS

Removal

With cylinder head removed from engine, compress valve spring with a "C" type valve spring compressor. Remove keepers and retainer. Remove spring and seal from cylinder head. It may be necessary to use a pair of pliers to remove seal from guide.

Inspection

Inspect for cracks or other damage. Check free length and angle. Replace if necessary. Outer spring free length is 1.984" (50.4 mm). Inner spring free length is 1.744" (44.3 mm). Angle limit is .071" (1.81 mm).

Installation

To install, reverse removal procedure using a new seal.

VALVE GUIDE SERVICING

Removal

With cylinder head removed from engine, remove valve springs and stem seals. Measure valve stem-to-valve guide movement with a dial indicator placed near guide. If measurement exceeds .008" (.20 mm) replace guide.

Installation

1) To replace guide, remove valve and drive out guide from combustion chamber side of head using guide installer (49 0221 51A).

2) To install guide, place clip on guide. Using guide installer (49 0221 251A), drive guide into head, from the side opposite the combustion chamber, until clip barely contacts cylinder head. Reassemble head.

VALVE CLEARANCE ADJUSTMENT

1) With engine warm, torque cylinder head bolts in sequence to proper specification. Bring No. 1 piston to TDC and adjust No. 1 and No. 2 intake valves, and No. 1 and No. 3 exhaust valves.

2) Turn crankshaft one revolution to bring No. 4 piston to TDC and adjust the clearance of the remaining valves. *See Valve Clearance Specifications Table.*

VALVE CLEARANCE SPECIFICATIONS [1]

Application	Intake In. (mm)	Exhaust In. (mm)
2.0L		
Valve Side	.012 (.30)	.012 (.30)
Cam Side	.009 (.20)	.009 (.20)

[1] – With engine warm.

PISTONS, RINGS & PINS

OIL PAN

Removal

Raise and support vehicle. Drain engine oil. Remove torque stopper and right front wheel and tire assembly. Remove wheel well splash shield and front exhaust pipe. Remove motor mount and inspection cover. Remove bolts attaching oil pan to engine and remove oil pan from vehicle.

Installation

To install, reverse removal procedure. Add oil before starting engine. Start engine and check for leaks.

PISTON & ROD ASSEMBLY

Removal

1) Drain engine oil and coolant. Remove cylinder head. Remove oil pan and oil strainer. Turn crankshaft so that the rod cap of the rod and piston to be removed is at BDC.

2) Remove 2 nuts attaching rod cap to rod and remove cap and bearing. Using a wooden hammer handle, push the large end of the connecting rod through the top side of cylinder block.

CAUTION: Make sure connecting rod bolt threads do not damage rod journal on crankshaft.

Installation

1) Apply a coat of oil to cylinder wall and rod bearing halves. Be sure piston ring gaps are spaced and not in alignment. Place piston ring compressor over piston and tighten to compress rings. If more than one piston was removed, be sure that each piston is installed in proper cylinder.

2) Place rubber tubing over rod bolts to protect crank journals during installation. With "F" mark on piston facing forward, position piston in cylinder bore with ring compressor resting on cylinder block surface. Tap piston into bore with wooden hammer handle.

3) Guide large end of rod over crank journal. Install rod cap. Make sure marks on connecting rod and connecting rod cap are in alignment. To complete installation, reverse removal procedure.

FITTING PISTONS

Measure cylinder bore for out-of-round and taper. Cylinder bore standard value is 3.3859-3.3866" (86.000-86.019 mm). Cylinder bore maximum wear limit is .0059" (.15 mm). If readings exceed maximum, rebore cylinder to next oversize. *See Piston Diameter Specifications table.*

PISTON DIAMETER SPECIFICATIONS

Application	In. (mm)
Standard	3.384-3.385 (85.94-85.96)
.25 mm Oversize	3.394-3.395 (86.19-86.21)
.50 mm Oversize	3.404-3.405 (86.44-86.46)

FITTING RINGS

1) Insert piston ring into cylinder bore by hand and use head of piston to push ring squarely into bore. Using a feeler guage, measure ring end gap. If gap fails to meet minimum or exceeds maximum replace rings.

2) Place each piston ring, one at a time, in proper ring groove. With a feeler guage, measure clearance between ring and piston ring land. If measurement varies from specifications, replace piston, unless ring is known to be the reason for clearance variation.

PISTON PIN REPLACEMENT

Place piston and rod assembly in a hydraulic press and press pin from piston and rod. To install, reverse removal procedure.

CRANKSHAFT MAIN & CONNECTING ROD BEARINGS

MAIN BEARINGS

1) Install main bearing halves into cylinder block. Be sure that back surface of bearings are free from oil and dirt before installing them in block. Place crank in block. With bearing halves in main caps, install and tighten all caps.

2) Remove one cap at a time and position Plastigage on top of journal. Set main cap in position and tighten. Remove main cap and measure clearance.

3) Standard clearance is .0012-.0019" (.031-.049 mm). Maximum clearance should not exceed .0031" (.08 mm). If clearance exceeds limit, repair crankshaft by grinding, and use undersize bearings. Place a film of oil on bearing halves and crank journals at final assembly.

CONNECTING ROD BEARINGS

1) Install rod bearing halves into connecting rod and install rod and piston assembly. Position Plastigage on journal and set rod cap and bearing in position and tighten. Ensure mating marks on cap and on rod are aligned.

2) Remove cap and check clearance. Standard clearance is .0010-.0026" (.027-.067 mm). Maximum clearance should not exceed .0039" (.10 mm). If clearance exceeds limit, repair crankshaft by grinding, and use undersize bearings. Place a film of oil on bearing halves and rod journals at final assembly.

CRANKSHAFT END PLAY

1) This step is to be performed with main caps installed, but without rods installed. Attach a dial indicator to engine with indicator point at end of crankshaft.

2) Push crankshaft away from indicator and set indicator at zero. Firmly pull crankshaft towards dial indicator and record measurement. If measurement is not within specifications, inspect thrust bearing and thrust

626 4-CYLINDER (Cont.)

surface of crankshaft. Replace thrust bearing or grind crankshaft as necessary.

REAR MAIN BEARING OIL SEAL

Remove 6 bolts attaching rear cover assembly and remove from crankshaft. Pry oil seal from cover. Replace with a new seal and reinstall cover assembly. Be sure to oil lip of seal before installation.

ENGINE OILING

CRANKCASE CAPACITY

Crankcase capacity is 3.8 quarts (3.6L) without oil filter replacement; 4.1 quarts (3.9L) when replacing oil filter.

NORMAL OIL PRESSURE

Oil pressure should be 43-57 psi (3-4 kg/cm²) at 3,000 rpm.

OIL PRESSURE RELIEF VALVE

Oil pressure relief valve opens at 11-17 psi (.8-1.2 kg/cm²).

ENGINE OILING SYSTEM

For illustration of engine oil system, see Fig. 4.

Fig. 4: View of Engine Oiling System

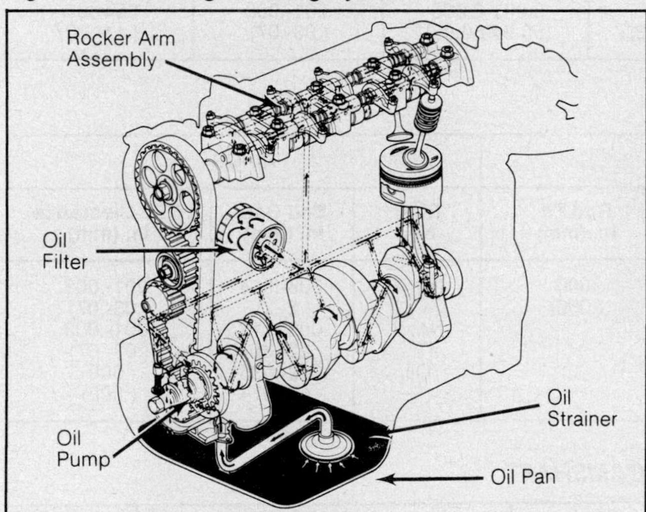
Rocker Arm Assembly
Oil Filter
Oil Strainer
Oil Pump
Oil Pan

OIL PUMP

Removal

Turn crankshaft to No. 1 TDC. Raise and support vehicle. Drain engine oil. Remove timing belt crank pulley. *See Timing Belt removal and installation for details.* Remove oil pan, oil pump and oil strainer.

Disassembly

Separate oil strainer from oil pump. Remove pump cover from back of pump. Remove inner and outer pump gears. Remove snap ring to access plunger assembly. Remove oil seal from front of oil pump body.

Inspection

1) Check pump for distortion or damage to pump body or cover, worn or damaged plunger, weak or broken plunger spring, and measure clearances.

2) Outer gear tooth tip-to-crescent maximum clearance is .013" (.35 mm). Inner gear tooth tip-to-crescent maximum clearance is .016" (.40 mm). Outer gear-to-pump body maximum clearance is .008" (.20 mm).

3) With both gears in place, position a straightedge across pump body above both gears and measure side clearance with a feeler guage. Maximum side clearance is .004" (.10 mm).

Reassembly

To reassemble, reverse disassembly procedure. Replace any worn or damaged parts.

Installation

To install, reverse removal procedure. *See Timing Belt installation for alignment and adjustment procedures.* Add engine oil.

ENGINE COOLING

COOLANT CAPACITY

7.4 qts. (7.0L)

THERMOSTAT

The thermostat is a wax type. Opening temperature is 190°F (88°C) and full-open temperature is 212°F (100°C).

RADIATOR CAP

Relief valve pressure for the radiator cap is 13 psi (.9 kg/cm²).

WATER PUMP

Removal

Turn crankshaft to No. 1 TDC. Drain coolant. Remove fan belt and timing belt upper cover. Remove wheel well splash shield, crankshaft pulley and timing belt lower cover. Remove tensioner and timing belt. Remove water pump inlet pipe. Remove water pump and gasket.

Installation

To install, reverse removal procedure. During assembly, apply a coating of vegetable oil to "O" ring. See Timing Belt installation for alignment and adjustment procedures. Fill cooling system.

TIGHTENING SPECIFICATIONS

Application	Ft. Lbs. (N.m)
Cylinder Head	
Warm	69-80 (95-110)
Cold	59-64 (82-88)
Main Bearing Caps	61-65 (84-90)
Connecting Rod Caps	37-41 (51-56)
Camshaft Pulley	35-48 (48-66)
Oil Pan	5-9 (7-12)
Crankshaft Pulley	80-87 (110-120)
Front Housing	14-19 (19-26)
Timing Tensioner	28-39 (38-53)
End Plate	13-22 (19-31)
Rear Cover	6-9 (8-12)
Rear Housing	14-19 (19-26)
Fuel Pump	14-19 (19-26)
Oil Pump	14-19 (19-26)
Water Pump	14-19 (19-26)
Intake Manifold	14-19 (19-26)
Exhaust Manifold	16-21 (22-29)
Flywheel	71-76 (98-105)
Pressure Plate	15-20 (22-27)
Rocker Shaft	13-20 (18-27)

Mazda Engines

626 4-CYLINDER (Cont.)

ENGINE SPECIFICATIONS

GENERAL SPECIFICATIONS

Year	DISPLACEMENT		Fuel System	HP@RPM	Torque Ft. Lbs.@RPM	Compr. Ratio	BORE		STROKE	
	Cu. In.	Liters					In.	mm	In.	mm
1983	121.9	2.0	2-Bbl	83@4800	110@2500	8.6:1	3.39	86	3.39	86

VALVES

Engine Size & Valve	Head Diam. In. (mm)	Face Angle	Seat Angle	Seat Width In. (mm)	Stem Diameter In. (mm)	Stem Clearance In. (mm)	Valve Lift In. (mm)
2.0L							
Intake	.019 (.5)	45°	45°	.047-.063 (1.2-1.6)	.316-.317 (8.03-8.05)	.001-.002 (.03-.06)	.....
Exhaust	.040	45°	45°	.047-.063 (1.2-1.6)	.316-.317 (8.03-8.04)	.001-.002 (.03-.06)	.....

CRANKSHAFT MAIN & CONNECTING ROD BEARINGS

Engine	MAIN BEARINGS				CONNECTING ROD BEARINGS		
	Journal Diam. In. (mm)	Clearance In. (mm)	Thrust Bearing	Crankshaft End Play In. (mm)	Journal Diam. In. (mm)	Clearance In. (mm)	Side Play In. (mm)
2.0L	2.359-2.360 (59.94-59.96)	.001-.002 (.031-.049)	No. 3	.003-.007 (.08-.18)	2.005-2.006 (50.94-50.96)	.001-.003 (.03-.07)	.004-.010 (.11-.26)

PISTONS, PINS, RINGS

Engine	PISTONS	PINS		RINGS		
	Clearance In. (mm)	Piston Fit In. (mm)	Rod Fit In. (mm)	Ring No.	End Gap In. (mm)	Side Clearance In. (mm)
2.0L	.001-.003 (.036-.075)	.001 (.024)	.000 (.000)	No. 1	.008-.014 (.2-.3)	.001-.003 (.03-.07)
				No. 2	.006-.012 (.2-.3)	.001-.003 (.03-.07)
				Oil	.012-.035 (.3-.9)	.000 (.000)

VALVE SPRINGS

Engine	Free Length In. (mm)	PRESSURE Lbs. @ In. (Kg @ mm)	
		Valve Closed	Valve Open
2.0L			
Inner	1.80 (45.7)	101 (1.81)	.....
Outer	2.063 (52.4)	101 (1.81)	.....

CAMSHAFT

Engine	Journal Diam. In. (mm)	Clearance In. (mm)	Lobe Lift In. (mm)
2.0L			
Front & Rear	1.257-1.258 (31.94-31.97)	.001-.003 (.04-.09)	.....
Center	1.256-1.257 (31.91-31.94)	.003-.005 (.07-.12)	.....

VALVE TIMING

Engine	INTAKE		EXHAUST	
	Open (BTDC)	Close (ABDC)	Open (BBDC)	Close (ATDC)
2.0L	17°	56°	64°	15°

Mazda Engines

B2200 4-CYLINDER DIESEL

ENGINE CODING

ENGINE IDENTIFICATION

Engine identification code is stamped on left side of engine block just below the intake manifold and above the injection pump. The VIN is stamped on a metal tab located on top of the instrument panel near lower left hand side of windshield. The following table indicates engine block code only.

ENGINE IDENTIFICATION CODE

Engine	Code
B2200 Diesel (2.2L)	S2

ENGINE, MANIFOLDS & CYLINDER HEAD

ENGINE

Removal

1) Remove hood after marking hinge location. Drain cooling system and crankcase. Remove battery and air cleaner. Disconnect accelerator cable at injection pump.

2) Disconnect fuel lines. Disconnect oil cooler lines at crankcase. Remove radiator hoses and radiator. Disconnect engine vacuum hoses.

3) Disconnect wires from temperature sending unit, oil pressure switch, alternator, back-up light switch and starter. Disconnect exhaust pipe from manifold.

4) Remove cover plate from clutch housing and clutch slave cylinder. Support transmission with a jack and remove nuts and bolts attaching transmission to engine. Remove starter. Remove clutch slave cylinder.

5) Remove engine mount attaching nuts and bolts. Install a lifting sling to engine lifting brackets. Attach an engine hoist and raise slightly. Pull engine forward until clear of transmission. Lift engine from vehicle.

Installation

To install reverse removal procedure, and check all fluid levels before starting engine.

MANIFOLDS & CYLINDER HEAD

Removal

1) Remove engine lifting brackets from cylinder head. Disconnect exhaust pipe, then remove exhaust manifold. Drain cooling system. Remove coolant hoses at engine. Remove thermostat housing retaining bolts, and remove housing.

2) Remove vacuum sensing tube. Loosen drive belt, then remove water pump fan and pulley. Remove 5 water pump retaing bolts and water pump. Remove alternator and bracket retaining bolts, and remove as an assembly.

3) Label and disconnect all necessary wiring and cables from cylinder head and manifolds. Disconnect and remove injection nozzle. Remove intake manifold retaining bolts and remove manifold.

4) Remove rocker arm cover. Gradually loosen cylinder head bolts in reverse order of tightening sequence, then remove bolts. Remove rocker arm assembly, and push rods. Lift off cylinder head.

Installation

1) Clean all gasket mating surfaces. Install new head gasket, and install cylinder head. Install rocker arm assembly, and head bolts.

2) Tighten cylinder head bolts in sequence. *See Fig. 1.* Install and tighten remaining components in reverse order of removal. Adjust valves.

Fig. 1: Cylinder Head Tightening Sequence

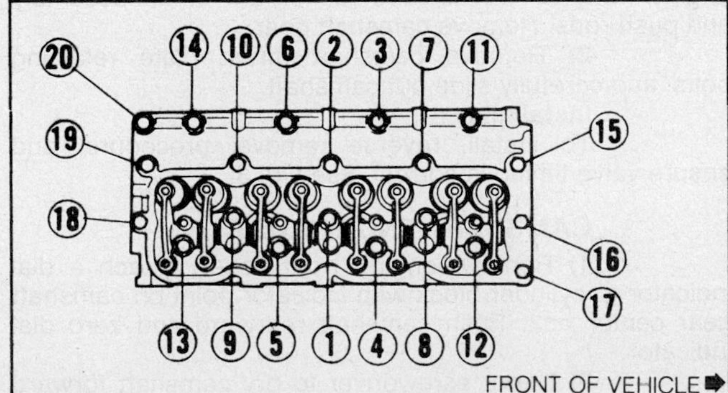
14
10
6
2
3
7
11
20
19
18
15
16
17
13
9
5
1
4
8
12
FRONT OF VEHICLE

Loosen bolts in reverse order of tightening sequence.

VALVES

VALVE ARRANGEMENT

I-E-I-E-I-E-I-E (Front-to-rear).

ROCKER ARM SHAFT ASSEMBLY

Removal

Remove rocker arm cover. Starting with the ends and working inward, remove rocker arm shaft attaching bolts. Remove rocker arm shaft assembly.

Installation

Tighten attaching bolts evenly in sequence, starting with inner bolts and working outward in a circular pattern.

VALVE SPRINGS

Removal & Installation

To remove and install valve springs, use procedures outlined in Valve Stem Oil Seal removal and installation.

Inspection

1) Measure inner and outer valve spring free length. Outer valve spring free length is 1.717" (43.6 mm). Inner valve spring free length is 1.654" (42.0 mm). If not within specifications, replace springs. Always replace inner and outer valve springs as a set.

2) Measure valve spring squareness. Place the valve spring on a surface plate and measure the squareness with a square. Measure the squareness at the upper part of valve spring.

3) Outer valve spring squareness limit is .054" (1.37 mm). Inner valve spring squareness limit is .049" (1.25 mm). If not within specifications, replace springs. Always replace inner and outer valve springs as a set.

VALVE STEM OIL SEALS

Removal

1) Remove rocker arm cover, and remove rocker arm shaft assembly. Position piston of cylinder concerned to TDC.

B2200 4-CYLINDER DIESEL (Cont.)

2) Using spring compressor tool, compress spring and remove valve locks (taper sleeves). Release pressure and remove spring retainer and springs. Remove valve stem oil seal.

Installation

When installing new stem seals, apply grease to stem of valve. Reverse removal procedure, to complete installation.

VALVE GUIDE SERVICING

Inspection

1) Using dial indicator, check valve stem-to-guide clearance. Position dial indicator point about .40" (10 mm) above end of guide.

2) Rock valve stem back and forth and measure movement. If clearance exceeds .0050" (.127 mm) replace valve and valve guide.

Removal

Using a valve guide installer tool (49 0636 165A), drive out old valve guide toward combustion chamber side of cylinder head.

Installation

1) Coat outer surface of guide with engine oil. Working from top side of head, drive guide into head with valve guide installer tool (49 0636 165A).

2) Guide should project from cylinder head .650" (16.5 mm). Always replace valve guide and valve as a set.

VALVE CLEARANCE ADJUSTMENT

1) Ensure rocker arm shaft is properly tightened. Hot valve clearance is .012" (.30 mm) for intake and exhaust valves. *See Fig. 2.*

2) Turn crankshaft to position No. 1 piston to TDC compression stroke. Adjust intake valve clearance on No. 1 and No. 2 cylinder, and exhaust valve clearance on No. 1 and No. 3 cylinder.

3) Turn crankshaft 1 revolution to place No. 4 piston to TDC compression stroke and adjust intake valve clearance on No. 3 and No. 4 cylinder, and exhaust valve clearance on No. 2 and No. 4 cylinder.

Fig. 2: Valve Adjustment Sequence

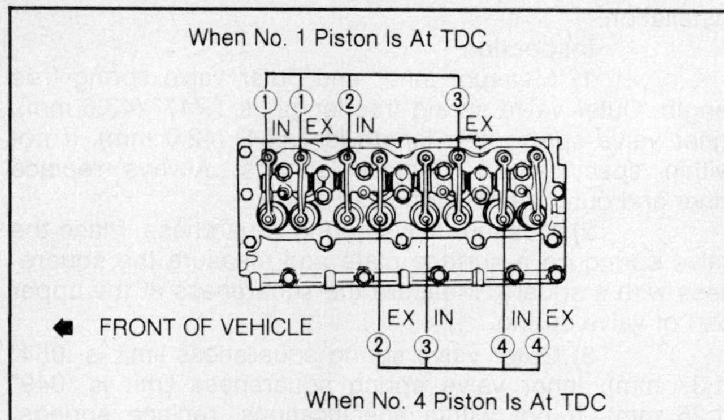
When No. 1 Piston Is At TDC
① ① ② ③
IN EX IN EX
FRONT OF VEHICLE
EX IN IN EX
② ③ ④ ④
When No. 4 Piston Is At TDC

CAMSHAFT

ENGINE FRONT COVER

Removal

1) Drain cooling system. Remove battery. Disconnect radiator hoses at engine. Remove radiator. Remove alternator belt.

2) Remove crankshaft pulley retaining bolt, and remove pulley. Remove front cover retaining bolts and remove front cover.

Installation

To install, reverse removal procedure.

CRANKSHAFT FRONT OIL SEAL

Removal

Remove front engine cover. Using a screwdriver, carefully pry oil seal out of front cover.

Installation

Coat seal lip with engine oil. Using seal driver, install seal. Install remaining components in reverse order of removal.

TIMING GEAR

Removal

Remove front engine cover. Remove gear retaining nut. Using a gear puller, remove gear(s).

Installation

To install reverse removal procedure, and ensure timing gears are in proper alignment. *See Fig. 3.*

VALVE TIMING

To check for correct valve timing, refer to procedures explained in Timing Gear removal and installation.

Fig. 3: Timing Gear Alignment Marks

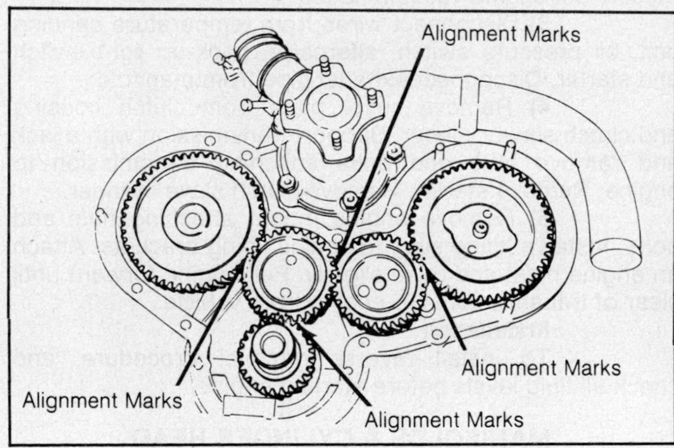
Alignment Marks
Alignment Marks
Alignment Marks
Alignment Marks

Ensure marks are in correct alignment.

CAMSHAFT

Removal

1) Remove engine from vehicle. Remove engine front cover. Remove rocker arm shaft assembly and push rods. Remove camshaft gear.

2) Remove camshaft thrust plate retaining bolts, and carefully slide out camshaft.

Installation

To install, reverse removal procedure, and ensure valve timing is correct. *See Fig. 3.*

CAMSHAFT END THRUST

1) Remove engine front cover. Attach a dial indicator to cylinder block with indicator point on camshaft gear center bolt. Push camshaft rearward and zero dial indicator.

2) Use a screwdriver to pry camshaft forward and record end thrust. Maximum end thrust is .0118" (.3 mm). If not within specifications, replace thrust plate.

B2200 4-CYLINDER DIESEL (Cont.)

INJECTION PUMP TIMING

1) Check that notched lines on injection pump flange and injection pump front bracket are aligned. With No. 1 cylinder at TDC on compression stroke, check timing mark alignment of timing gears. *See Fig. 3*.

2) Disconnect injection pipe from pump and remove hydraulic head plug. Rotate the crankshaft pulley until the 2°ATDC mark on the pulley is aligned with the pointer. Install a dial indicator so that the pointer touches the plunger end of the pump, and dial gauge indicates approximetly .08" (2.0 mm).

3) Turn crankshaft counterclockwise (opposite of engine rotation) until timing mark on crankshaft pulley moves from the original position (2°ATDC) to the counterclockwise side by 30-50°. *See Fig. 4*.

4) Ensure that the dial indicator pointer has stopped moving. Zero dial indicator. Turn crankshaft pulley slightly in both directions and see that guage indication is stable.

5) Turn crankshaft in normal direction of rotation until timing mark is aligned with timing pointer. Dial indicator should read .04" (1.0 mm).

Fig. 4: Injection Pump Adjustment

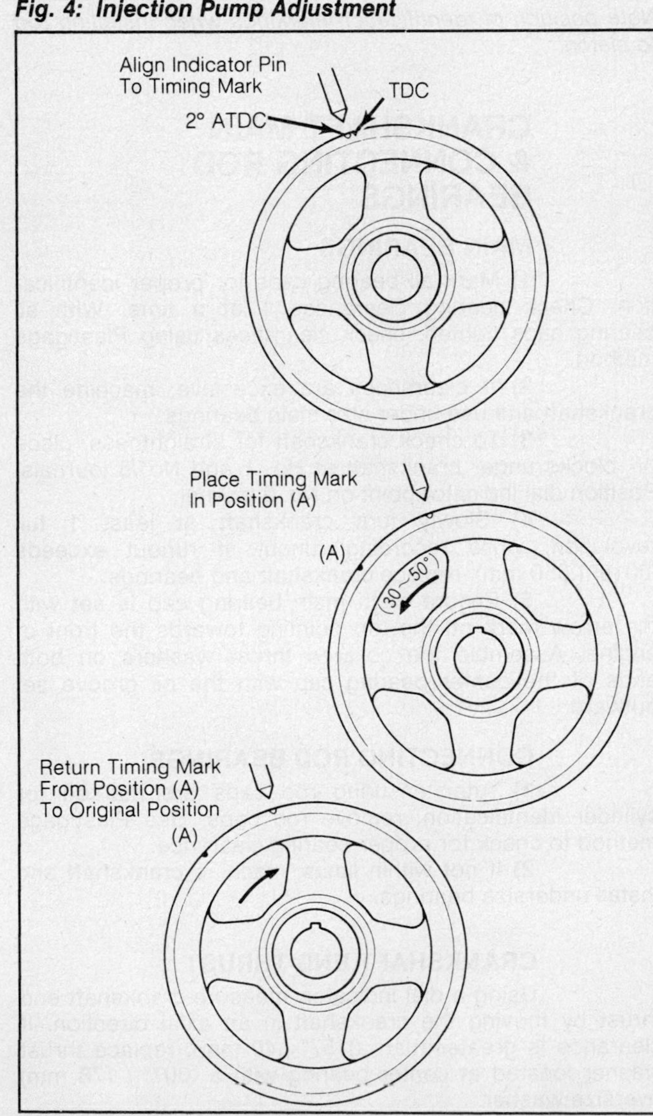
Align Indicator Pin
To Timing Mark
TDC
2° ATDC
Place Timing Mark
In Position (A)
(A)
(30~50°)
Return Timing Mark
From Position (A)
To Original Position
(A)

Ensure pump flange nuts are loose, when adjusting pump.

6) If indicator reading is not within specifications, loosen the injection pump flange retaining nuts, and rotate housing until correct specifications are obtained. Tighten nuts and recheck reading.

PISTONS, PINS & RINGS

OIL PAN

Raise vehicle, and remove engine under cover. Drain engine oil. Remove the oil pan nuts and bolts, and remove oil pan.

PISTON AND ROD ASSEMBLY

Removal

1) Remove cylinder head. Remove oil pan. Remove oil pump set screw at side of cylinder block. Remove oil pipe attaching bolts, then remove oil pump with oil pipe attached.

2) Remove carbon deposits from upper edge of cylinder wall. Remove rod cap. Push piston/rod assembly out top of cylinder block. Install rod cap on its respective piston/rod assembly.

Installation

1) Lightly oil rings, piston and cylinder wall. Ensure ring gaps are properly spaced. *See Fig. 5*. Make sure bearing halves are properly seated in connecting rod and cap.

Fig. 5: Piston Ring Gap Locations

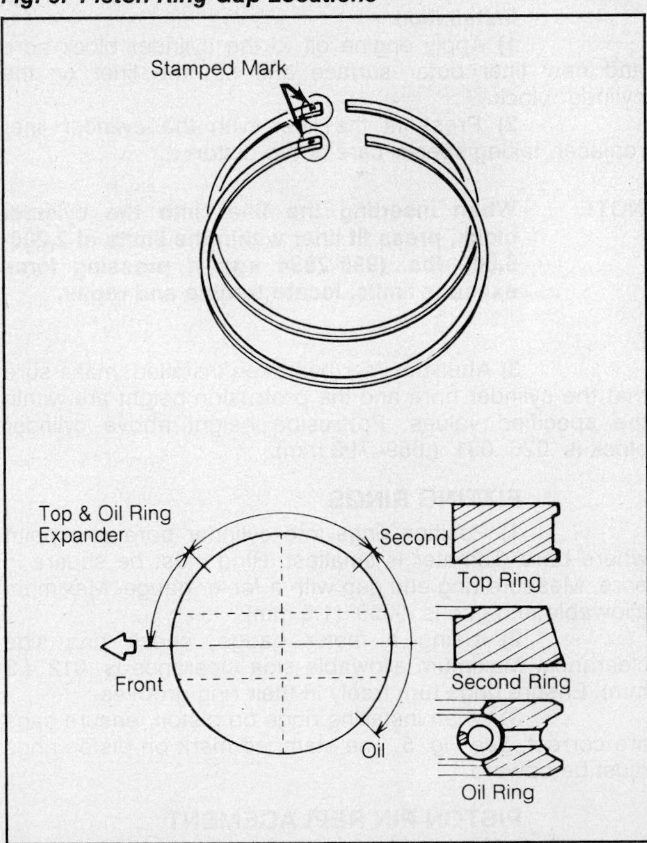
Stamped Mark
Top & Oil Ring
Expander
Second
Top Ring
Front
Second Ring
Oil
Oil Ring

The ring gap should not be directed toward the thrust side or counter thrust side.

Mazda Engines

B2200 4-CYLINDER DIESEL (Cont.)

2) Install a ring compressor and compress rings. Install piston in cylinder. Ensure piston/connecting rod assembly is installed in proper direction. *See Fig. 6.* Install and tighten rod cap. Reverse removal procedure to complete installation.

FITTING PISTONS

Measure the clearance between the piston and cylinder liner. If the clearance exceeds .0021-.0031" (.054-.080 mm), measure the piston diameter in the thrust direction, .6299" (16 mm) above the bottom of piston. Piston diameter should be 3.4985-3.4994" (88.867-88.893 mm). If not within specifications, replace the piston.

CYLINDER LINERS

Inspection

1) Measure the inner diameter of cylinder liners and determine the extent of wear. Measure the cylinder liner diameter at 3 positions, top, middle and bottom.

2) Standard diameter is 3.5001-3.5020" (88.90-88.95 mm), maximum wear limit (beyond standard diameter) is .0079" (.20 mm). If not within specifications, replace liner.

Removal

Press out old liner, using cylinder liner replacement tool (49 0636 015). Check cylinder block bore for any scratches. If any scratches are found, remove with an oil soaked fine emery cloth.

Installation

1) Apply engine oil to the cylinder block bore and new liner outer surface and set the liner on the cylinder block.

2) Press fit the liner with the cylinder liner replacer, taking special care not to distort it.

NOTE: **When inserting the liner into the cylinder block, press fit liner within the limits of 2,200-6,600 lbs. (998-2994 kg). If pressing force exceeds limits, locate trouble and repair.**

3) After the liner has been installed, make sure that the cylinder bore and the protrusion height are within the specified values. Protrusion height above cylinder block is .026-.031" (.659-.790 mm).

FITTING RINGS

1) Position rings into cylinder bore at a point where bore diameter is smallest. Ring must be square in bore. Measure ring end gap with a feeler gauge. Maximum allowable end gap is .0059" (1.5 mm).

2) Using a feeler gauge, check ring side clearance. Maximum allowable side clearance is .012" (.3 mm). Ensure rings turn freely in their ring grooves.

3) When installing rings on piston, ensure gaps are correct. *See Fig. 5.* The stamped mark on piston rings must be upward.

PISTON PIN REPLACEMENT

Removal

To remove pin, use snap ring pliers and remove snap rings from piston. Press piston pin out. Piston pin bushings in rod's small end are replaceable.

Installation

1) Assemble rod to piston so that sub-combustion chamber side of piston head is oposite locking groove on connecting rod. *See Fig. 6.*

2) Coat pin with oil and install in piston and rod. Install snap rings to secure pin in place.

Fig. 6: Positioning Rod to Piston

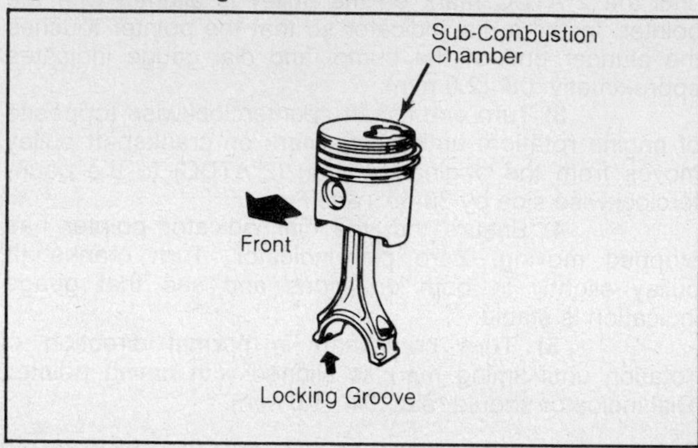
Sub-Combustion
Chamber
Front
Locking Groove

Note position of identification markings when installing rod to piston.

CRANKSHAFT MAIN & CONNECTING ROD BEARINGS

MAIN BEARINGS

1) Mark all bearing caps for proper identification. Check bearing clearances 1 at a time. With all bearing caps tighted, check clearances using Plastigage method.

2) If clearances are excessive, machine the crankshaft and use under size main bearings.

3) To check crankshaft for straightness, place "V" blocks under crankshaft at No. 1 and No. 5 journals. Position dial indicator point on No. 3 journal.

4) Slowly turn crankshaft at least 1 full revolution, while recording runout. If runout exceeds .0019" (.050 mm), replace crankshaft and bearings.

5) Ensure each main bearing cap is set with the arrow mark on the top pointing towards the front of engine. Assemble the collared thrust washers on both ends of the center bearing cap with the oil groove set outward.

CONNECTING ROD BEARINGS

1) After ensuring rod caps are marked for cylinder identification, remove rod caps. Use Plastigage method to check for proper bearing clearance.

2) If not within limits, machine crankshaft and install undersize bearings.

CRANKSHAFT END THRUST

Using a dial indicator, measure crankshaft end thrust by moving the crankshaft in an axial direction. If clearance is greater than .0157" (.40 mm), replace thrust washer located at center bearing with a .007" (.178 mm) oversize washer.

B2200 4-CYLINDER DIESEL (Cont.)

REAR MAIN BEARING OIL SEAL

Removal

Remove transmission, and flywheel assembly. Remove 8 bolts attaching rear oil seal housing to cylinder block, and remove housing. Using a screwdriver carefully pry seal out of housing.

Installation

Coat seal lip with engine oil. Using seal installer tool, install new seal. Reverse removal procedures to install remaining components.

ENGINE OILING

CRANKCASE CAPACITY

Capacity is 7.9 qts. (7.5L).

NORMAL OIL PRESSURE

Normal oil pressure is 57 psi (4.1 kg/cm²), at 3600 RPM.

ENGINE OILING SYSTEM

A rotor-type oil pump. Oil drawn from crankcase passes through a strainer, then to oil pump. Oil is delivered to full flow oil filter, oil cooler, and main oil gallery. By-pass valves are incorporated into oil filter and oil cooler.

Main oil gallery supplies oil to lubricate crankshaft, main and connecting rod bearings. Oil gallery feeds oil to camshaft. From cam, oil is routed to feed rocker arm shaft assembly and upper valve train components.

OIL PUMP

Removal

Remove oil pan. Remove oil pump set screw, located at side of cylinder block. Remove oil pipe attaching bolts, and remove oil pump.

Fig. 7: Oil Pump Assembly

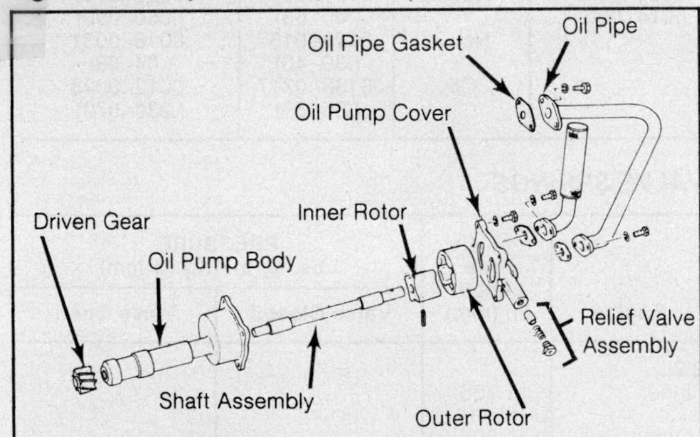
Oil Pipe Gasket
Oil Pipe
Oil Pump Cover
Driven Gear
Inner Rotor
Oil Pump Body
Relief Valve
Assembly
Shaft Assembly
Outer Rotor

Thoroughly clean all parts prior to measuring clearances.

Inspection

1) Disassemble oil pump and clean all parts thoroughly. Inspect for signs of unusual wear or damage.

2) With rotors installed in pump, place a straightedge over pump housing. Use a feeler gauge to measure clearance between rotors and straightedge. If clearance over rotors is excessive, replace rotor set.

3) Using a feeler gauge, measure clearance between inner and outer rotors. If clearance is beyond limits, replace rotor set.

4) Using feeler gauge, measure clearance between outer rotor and pump housing. If clearance is excessive, replace entire pump assembly.

5) Check clearance between rotor shaft and pump body. If beyond limits, replace entire pump assembly.

Inspection

1) Using a feeler gauge, check clearance between pump body inner wall and tip of each gear. If clearance is beyond limits, replace entire gear set.

2) With gears installed, lay a straightedge over pump housing. Use a feeler gauge to measure clearance between gears and straightedge. If gear-to-cover clearance is excessive, replace entire pump assembly.

Installation

To install, reverse removal procedures.

OIL PUMP SPECIFICATIONS

Application	[1] Clearance In. (mm)
Clearance Over Rotors	.006 (.15)
Inner-to-Outer Rotor Clearance	.012 (.30)
Outer Rotor-to-Pump Housing	.012 (.30)
Rotor Shaft-to-Pump Housing	.0039 (.1)

[1] — Clearances given are wear limits.

ENGINE COOLING

THERMOSTAT

Thermostat opens at approximately 180°F (82°C), and is fully open at approximately 203°F (95°C).

COOLING SYSTEM CAPACITY

Cooling system capacity is 11.1 qts. (10.5L).

RADIATOR CAP

Radiator cap pressure relief valve opens at 13 psi (.914 kg/cm²).

WATER PUMP

Removal

Drain cooling system. Remove fan, fan shroud and upper radiator hose. Remove drive belt and fan pulley. Remove water pump retaining bolts and remove pump.

Installation

Clean gasket mating surfaces. Using new gasket, install water pump in reverse order of removal.

TIGHTENING SPECIFICATIONS

Application	Ft. Lbs. (N.m)
Cylinder Head	80-85 (110-117)
Camshaft Gear	45-51 (62-70)
Connecting Rod	50-54 (69-75)
Crankshaft Pulley	145-181 (200-250)
Engine Rear Plate	23-34 (33-48)
Flywheel	95-137 (131-190)
Main Bearing Caps	80-85 (110-117)
Manifolds (Intake & Exhaust)	11-17 (16-24)
Injection Pump Timing Gear	29-51 (40-70)
Rocker Arm Shaft Assembly	80-85 (110-117)
Idle Gear	16-23 (23-32)

Mazda Engines

B2200 4-CYLINDER DIESEL (Cont.)

ENGINE SPECIFICATIONS

GENERAL SPECIFICATIONS

Year	DISPLACEMENT		Fuel System	HP@RPM	Torque Ft. Lbs.@RPM	Compr. Ratio	BORE		STROKE	
	Cu. In.	Liters					In.	mm	In.	mm
1983	134.8	2.2	Fuel Inj.	.....	.....	.....	3.50	88.9	3.50	89.0

VALVES

Engine Size & Valve	Head Diam. In. (mm)	Face Angle	Seat Angle	Seat Width In. (mm)	Stem Diameter In. (mm)	Stem Clearance In. (mm)	Valve Lift In. (mm)
2.2L							
Intake	1.591-1.599 (40.4-40.6)	45°	45°	.079 (2.0)	.3150-.3197 (7.880-8.050)	.0015-.0055 (.038-.140)	.....
Exhaust	1.412-1.422 (35.987-36.013)	30°	30°	.079 (2.0)	.3150-.3197 (7.867-8.088)	.0020-.0055 (.051-140)	.....

CRANKSHAFT MAIN & CONNECTING ROD BEARINGS

Engine	MAIN BEARINGS				CONNECTING ROD BEARINGS		
	Journal Diam. In. (mm)	Clearance In. (mm)	Thrust Bearing	Crankshaft End Play In. (mm)	Journal Diam. In. (mm)	Clearance In. (mm)	Side Play In. (mm)
2.2L	2.5586-2.5591 (64.987-65.000)	.0016-.0047 (.040-.120)	No. 3	.0055-.0157 (.140-.40)	2.0861-2.0866 (52.987-53.000)	.0014-.0039 (.036-.100)	.0094-.0157 (.239-.400)

PISTONS, PINS, RINGS

Engine	PISTONS	PINS		RINGS		
	Clearance In. (mm)	Piston Fit In. (mm)	Rod Fit In. (mm)	Ring No.	End Gap In. (mm)	Side Clearance In. (mm)
2.2L	.0021-.0031 (.054-.080)	.0006 (.016)	.0006-.0017 (.014-.050)	No. 1	.0157-.0217 (.40-.55)	.0020-.0035 (.050-.090)
				No. 2	.0118-.0157 (.30-.40)	.0016-.0031 (.04-.08)
				Oil	.0138-.0217 (.35-.55)	.0012-.0028 (.030-.070)

CAMSHAFT

Engine	Journal Diam. In. (mm)	Clearance In. (mm)	Lobe Lift In. (mm)
2.2L			
No. 1	2.0473 (52.00)	.0024-.0047 (.060-.120)	.....
No. 2	2.0374 (51.75)	.0024-.0047 (.060-.120)	.....
No. 3	2.0177 (51.25)	.0024-.0047 (.060-.120)	.....

VALVE SPRINGS

Engine	Free Length In. (mm)	PRESSURE Lbs. @ In. (Kg @ mm)	
		Valve Closed	Valve Open
2.2L			
Inner	1.736 (44.1)	.....	.....
Outer	1.807 (45.9)	.....	.....

Mazda Engines

RX7 ROTARY ENGINE

ENGINE CODING

ENGINE IDENTIFICATION

Engine identification number is stamped on front engine housing behind the distributor.

ENGINE IDENTIFICATION

Application	Code
RX7	12A

ENGINE

REMOVAL & INSTALLATION

Removal

1) Remove hood and disconnect battery ground cable. Drain engine oil and coolant. Remove engine under cover.

2) Disconnect following electrical wires: Primary and secondary ignition wires at coils, pick-up coil wiring connections, condensor lead, oil level sensor lead, temperature sensor and oil thermo sensor (except California vehicles).

3) Remove air cleaner assembly. Disconnect the following tubes and hoses: Oil hoses at cooler, radiator hoses, automatic transmission cooler lines (if equipped), heater hoses, fuel supply and return lines, vacuum and evaporative hoses, and air pipe at rear of intake manifold.

4) Remove cooling fan and drive assembly, radiator, and radiator shroud assembly. Disconnect connector and "B" terminal wire from alternator. Disconnect connector from throttle sensor.

5) Without disconnecting refrigerant lines, remove compressor and air conditioning condensor (if equipped) and tie out of the way.

6) Disconnect choke heater connector. Disconnect accelerator, choke and hot start assist cables. Disconnect any remaining wires, tubes or linkages between engine and chassis at top of engine. Remove upper engine-to-transmission bolts.

7) Raise and support vehicle. Remove starter. Remove lower engine-to-transmission bolts. Remove exhaust pipe front cover. Remove nuts and bolts, and disconnect exhaust pipe from exhaust manifold. Support front catalytic converter.

8) Support front of transmission with jack and remove left and right engine mount nuts. Attach sling to engine and take up slack. Pull engine forward to clear clutch shaft, then lift engine from vehicle.

Installation

To install engine, reverse removal procedure ensuring that linkages, tubes and electrical connections are restored in original position. Refill all fluids to specified levels, warm up engine and check for leaks.

Fig. 1: Exploded View of Rotors & Eccentric Shaft Assembly

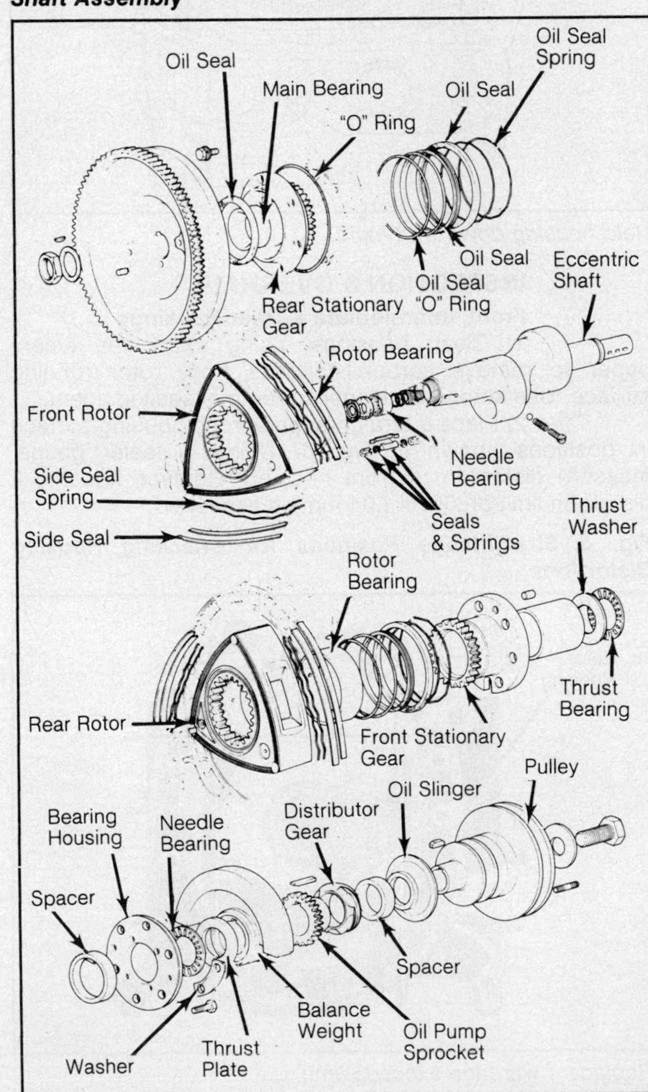
Oil Seal
Main Bearing
"O" Ring
Oil Seal
Oil Seal Spring
Oil Seal
Oil Seal
Eccentric Shaft
Rear Stationary Gear
"O" Ring
Rotor Bearing
Front Rotor
Needle Bearing
Side Seal Spring
Side Seal
Seals & Springs
Thrust Washer
Rotor Bearing
Thrust Bearing
Rear Rotor
Front Stationary Gear
Pulley
Oil Slinger
Distributor Gear
Bearing Housing
Needle Bearing
Spacer
Spacer
Balance Weight
Oil Pump Sprocket
Thrust Plate
Washer

DISASSEMBLY

NOTE: To ease engine disassembly, manufacturer recommends use of special engine stand (49 0107 680A) and hanger (49 1114 005).

1) Loosen drive belts and hoses, and remove air pump and alternator. Disconnect metering oil pump connecting rod and hoses at metering oil pump outlets. Remove exhaust manifold cover. Remove intake manifold and carburetor. Remove gasket and "O" ring.

2) Remove exhaust manifold, engine mount and distributor . Remove, oil filter and cover from front housing. Remove water pump and drive pulley for air conditioning compressor (if equipped).

3) Turn engine over, and remove oil pan and strainer. Install flywheel brake (49 1881 060) on manual transmission models or stopper (49 1881 055) on automatic transmission models.

4) Remove eccentric shaft pulley. Take off front cover with gasket, and slide distributor gear off shaft. Remove "O" ring from oil passage. Remove oil pump sprocket nut. *See Fig. 2.* Slide oil pump sprocket, eccentric shaft sprocket and drive chain off together. Remove oil pump.

RX7 ROTARY ENGINE (Cont.)

Fig. 2: Oil Pump Drive and Sprocket Removal

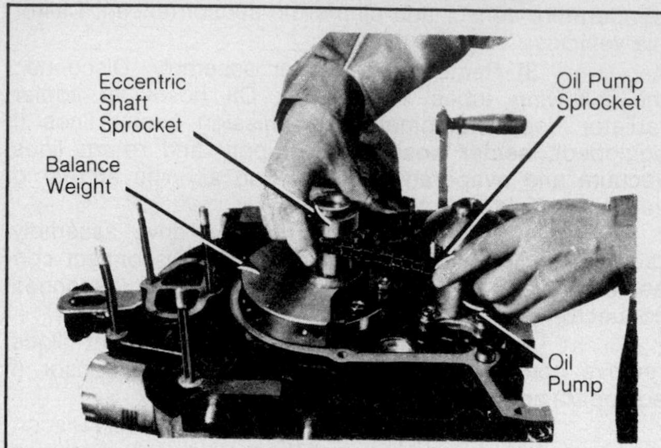
Eccentric
Shaft
Sprocket
Oil Pump
Sprocket
Balance
Weight
Oil
Pump

Pump drive and sprocket must be removed together.

5) Remove balance weight and following parts in order: Thrust washer, needle bearing, bearing housing, needle bearing, spacer and thrust plate.

6) On manual transmission models, remove clutch assembly. Use puller to remove flywheel. On automatic transmission models, remove drive plate. Use puller to remove counterweight.

7) Remove tension bolts on rear housing in sequence. *See Fig. 3.* Loosen in 2 or 3 steps. Lift rear housing off shaft. Remove any seals stuck to rotor sliding surface, and place them back in original positions. Remove seals and "O" rings from face of rear rotor housing.

Fig. 3: Loosening Sequence of Tension Bolts

3
6
7
10
11
15
14
18
17
16
12
13
8
9
2
4
5
1

Loosen in 2 or 3 steps.

8) Attach dowel puller (49 0813 215A), and pull tubular dowels off rear rotor housing. *See Fig. 4.* Hold rotor housing by hand to keep it from moving up, and remove rear rotor housing. Use caution to avoid dropping apex seals and side pieces of rear rotor. Remove seals and "O" ring from front side of rear rotor housing.

9) Remove side pieces, apex seals and springs from rear rotor and store in order for reassembly. Remove all corner seals, corner seal springs, side seals and side seal springs and store in order for reassembly. Remove rear rotor, and place on clean pad with internal gear side down.

10) Remove seals and springs on remaining side of rotor, and store in order for reassembly. Place protector on seal inner lip, and remove outer seal with remover (49 0813 225). Remove inner seal. Remove seals and springs and store in order for reassembly. Mark rear rotor for assembly identification.

11) Attach puller, and while holding housing down, pull tubular dowels off intermediate housing. Remove intermediate housing by sliding beyond rear rotor journal on eccentric shaft. Carefully lift out eccentric shaft to avoid damage to rotor bearing and main bearing. Repeat steps **6)** through **8)** to remove front rotor housing and rotor assembly.

Fig. 4: Extracting Tubular Dowels from Engine

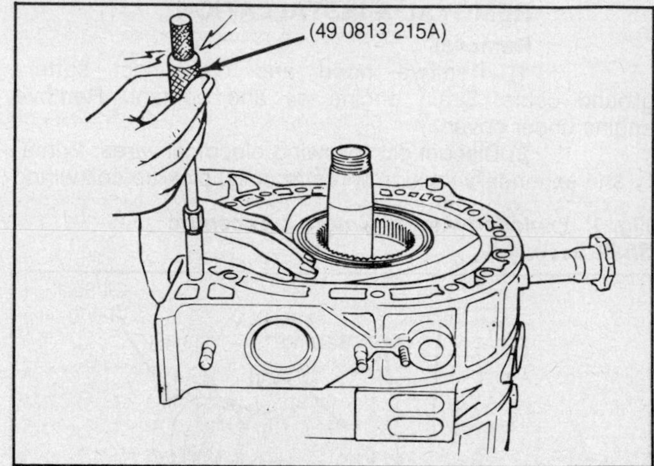
(49 0813 215A)

Hold housing down with hand.

INSPECTION & OVERHAUL

Front, Intermediate & Rear Housings

1) Clean housings, using extra fine emery paper to remove carbon deposits from rotor running surface. Use ketone or thinner to remove sealing agent.

2) Place a straightedge across housing surface in positions shown in *Fig. 5.* Using a feeler gauge, measure distortion of front housing. Replace housing if distortion limit of .0016" (.04 mm) is exceeded.

Fig. 5: Straightedge Positions for Checking Housing Distortions

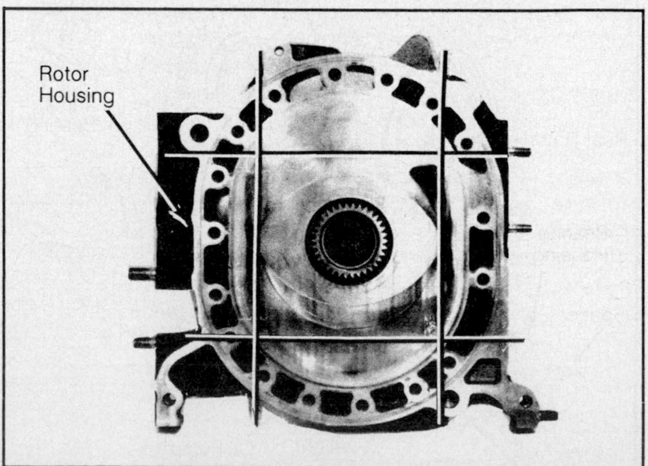
Rotor
Housing

Replace if warpage exceeds limit.

RX7 ROTARY ENGINE (Cont.)

3) Remove oil pressure control valve and spring from front cover. Check for damage or corrosion. Replace if defective. Measure control valve spring free length. Free length must be 2.74" (69.6 mm).

NOTE: Cap bolt and valve spring for 1983 models are painted yellow. Never use a control valve spring from a 1982 or earlier year in 1983 models.

4) Check for stepped wear on rotor sliding surfaces of the 3 housings . Measurements are made using a dial indicator and gauge body. *See Fig. 6*.

Fig. 6: Measuring Housing Wear with Dial Indicator

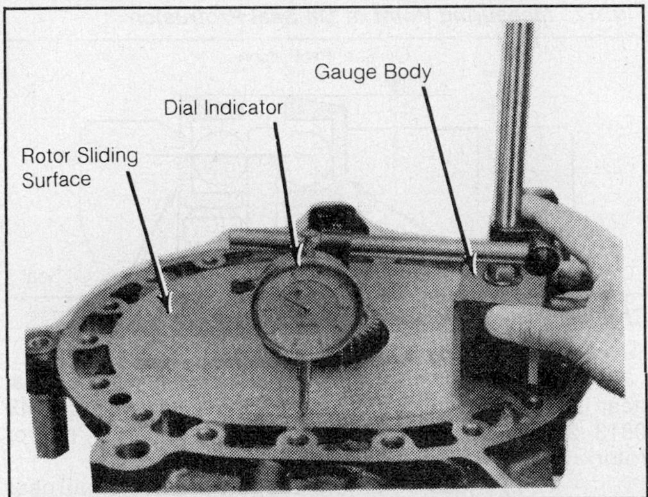
Gauge Body
Dial Indicator
Rotor Sliding
Surface

Check entire circumference of housing.

5) Side seal step wear must be checked on the inside and outside of oil seal tracing mark. *See Fig. 7*.

Fig. 7: Checking Side Seal Step Wear

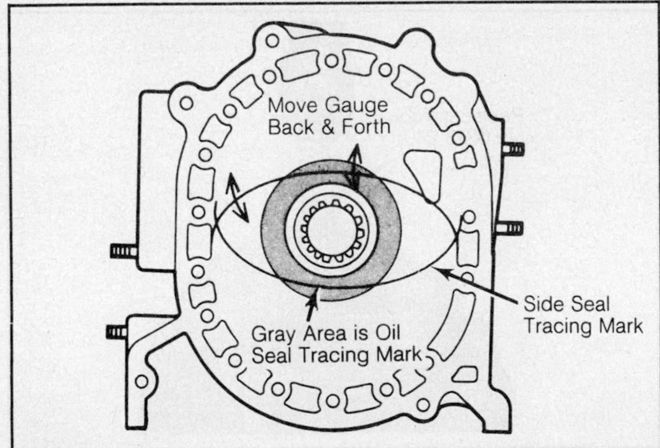
Move Gauge
Back & Forth
Side Seal
Tracing Mark
Gray Area is Oil
Seal Tracing Mark

Replace housing if step wear exceeds limit.

SIDE SEAL STEP WEAR

Location	Limit
Inside Oil Seal Tracing Mark	.0004" (.01 mm)
Outside Oil Seal Tracing Mark	.004" (.10 mm)

6) Check oil seal step wear. Limit is .0008" (.02 mm). *See Fig. 8*.

Fig. 8: Oil Seal Step Wear

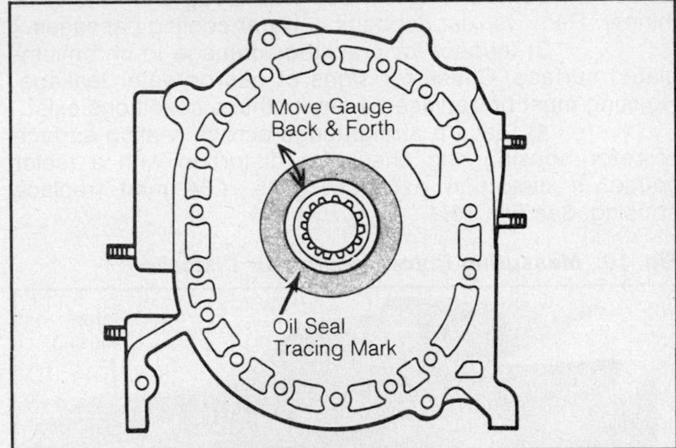
Move Gauge
Back & Forth
Oil Seal
Tracing Mark

Step wear limit is .0008" (.02 mm)

7) Measure inner diameter of main bearing and outer diameter of bearing journal on eccentric shaft. Standard clearance is .0016-.0028" (.04-.07 mm). If clearance exceeds .0039" (.10 mm), replace bearing.

8) To replace front or rear main bearing, remove stationary gear retaining bolts. Using a mandrel (49 0813 235), drive stationary gear with bearing out of housing .

9) Place stationary gear in a press. Use same mandrel and press main bearing out of stationary gear.

10) Install new bearings while aligning tang bearing with a slot of stationary gear. Press bearing into gear until adapter of mandrel just contacts stationary gear flange. Install the stationary gear into the housing, aligning the slot of the gear flange with the dowel pin on the housing. *See Fig. 9*.

NOTE: When installing rear main bearing, check condition of "O" ring and replace if necessary. Apply sealing agent on stationary gear flange prior to installing it on rear housing. Align pin and slot.

Fig. 9: Stationary Gear Slot & Dowel Alignment

Rear Housing
Slot
"O" Ring
Dowel

Illustration applies to front and rear housings.

Rotor Housing

1) Inspect rotor housing for signs of water or gas leakage. Check for wear or damage to rotor running surface or stationary gear. Check main bearings for signs of scoring or flaking.

RX7 ROTARY ENGINE (Cont.)

2) To clean housing, wipe off sealing agent or carbon in rotor running surface with a rag and ketone or thinner. Remove rust deposits in water cooling passages.

3) Inspect for cracks or damage to chromium-plated surface. Check for signs of gas or water leakage. Housing must be replaced if any of these conditions exist.

4) Place a straightedge across sealing surface of rotor housing and check for distortion with a feeler gauge. If distortion exceeds .0016" (.04 mm), replace housing. *See Fig. 10.*

Fig. 10: Measuring Rotor Housing for Distortion

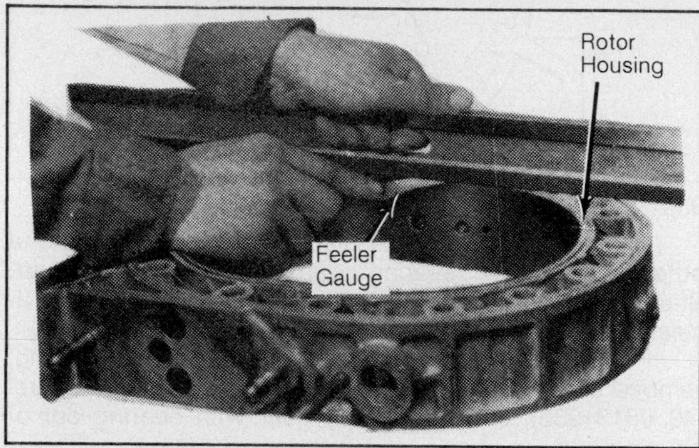
Rotor
Housing
Feeler
Gauge

Replace if distortion exceeds limit.

5) Check rotor housing thickness at points A, B, C, and D in *Fig. 11.* If micrometer readings vary between point A and minimum value for B, C, and D by more than .0024" (.06 mm), replace rotor housing.

NOTE: **This excessive clearance would indicate a possibility of gas or water leakage.**

Fig. 11: Rotor Housing Thickness Check Points

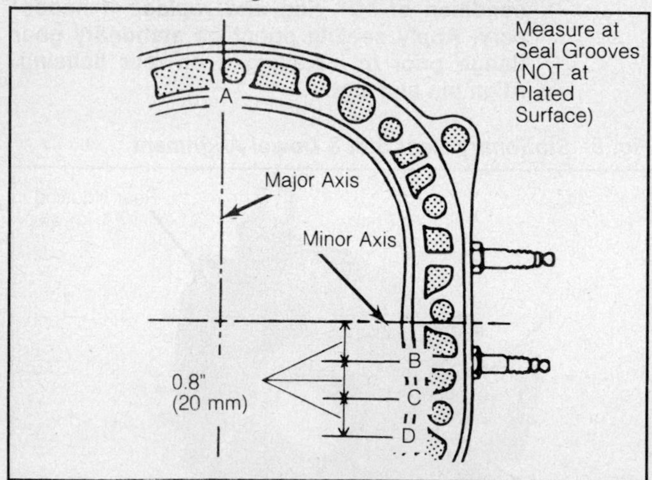
Measure at
Seal Grooves
(NOT at
Plated
Surface)
A
Major Axis
Minor Axis
B
C
D
0.8"
(20 mm)

Check thickness at A, B, C & D.

Rotors

1) Inspect rotor for wear or damage, and check internal gear for chips, cracks or scoring. Measure rotor width at 3 points, and subtract maximum width from width of rotor housing at point "A" in *Fig. 11*.

2) Clearance between side housing and rotor should be .0047-.0071" (.12-.18 mm). If clearance is excessive or rotor is damaged, replace rotor assembly.

3) If clearance is less than specified, internal gear may have come out. Strike internal gear lightly with plastic hammer and remeasure.

4) Measure inner diameter of rotor bearing and outside diameter of rotor bearing journal on eccentric shaft. Replace rotor bearing if clearance exceeds .0039" (.10 mm) or any damage is shown. See Rotor Bearing Replacement.

Rotor Oil Seal

With oil seal installed in rotor, measure contact lip width of seal. Seal must be replaced if contact width exceeds .020" (0.5 mm). Measure seal protrusion, and replace seal spring if protrusion is less than .020" (0.5 mm). *See Fig. 12.*

Fig. 12: Measuring Point of Oil Seal Protrusion

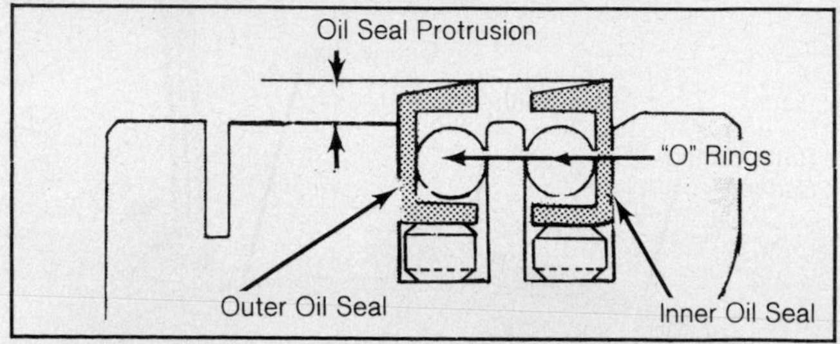
Oil Seal Protrusion
"O" Rings
Outer Oil Seal
Inner Oil Seal

Check for free movement of seals in groove.

Rotor Bearing Replacement

1) Place rotor bearing on support so internal gear is facing downward. Using rotor bearing replacer (49 0813 240), without adapter ring, press bearing out of rotor.

2) Place rotor on support with internal gear facing upward. Place a new rotor bearing so slot in rotor bore is in line with bearing lug. Press new bearing (using tool with adapter) until bearing is flush with rotor boss. *See Fig. 13.*

Fig. 13: Pressing Rotor Bearing from Rotor

Replacer Tool
(49 0813 240)

Slot in rotor bore must be in line with bearing lug.

Apex Seal

1) Clean all carbon from apex seal and spring with a cleaning solution (not emery paper). Measure height of apex seal with a micrometer. *See Fig. 14.* Replace seal if height is less than .275" (7.0 mm).

RX7 ROTARY ENGINE (Cont.)

Fig. 14: Measuring Apex Seal Height

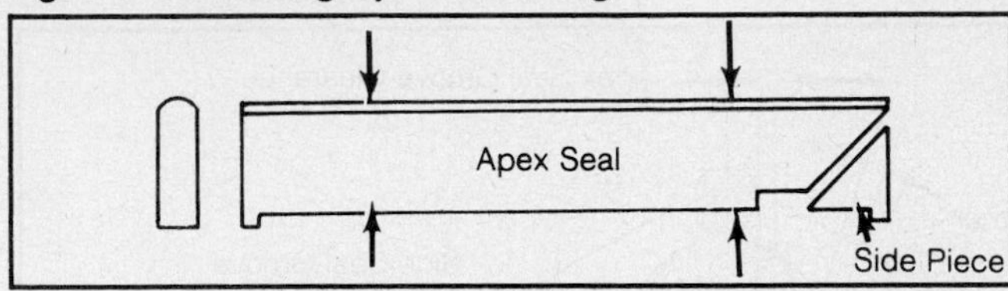
Apex Seal
Side Piece

Clean thoroughly before measuring.

2) Check for warpage by measuring the clearance between the top surfaces of 2 apex seals with a feeler gauge. Replace all 3 seals if clearance exceeds .0024" (.06 mm). *See Fig. 15.*

Fig. 15: Apex Seal Warpage

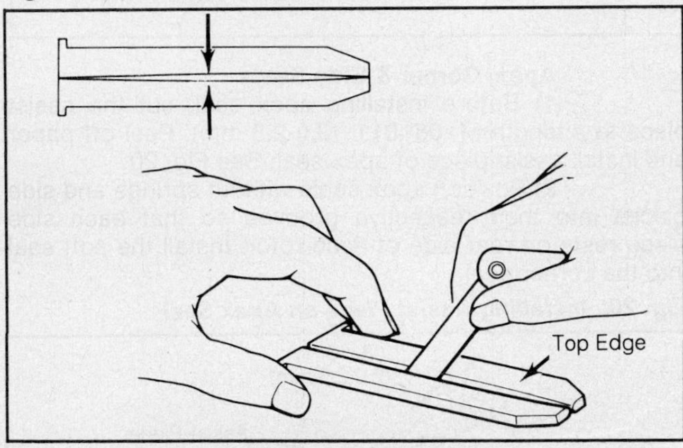
Top Edge

Replace if the clearance exceeds limits.

3) Using a feeler gauge, check gap between apex seal and groove in rotor. Feeler gauge should be inserted until tip of feeler gauge reaches bottom of groove.

4) Standard clearance is .0020-.0035" (.05-.09 mm). Replace apex seal if gap exceeds .0059" (.15 mm). Check seal spring height as shown in *Fig. 16.* Replace spring if free height is less than .2165" (5.5 mm).

Fig. 16: Measuring Free Height of Apex Seal Spring

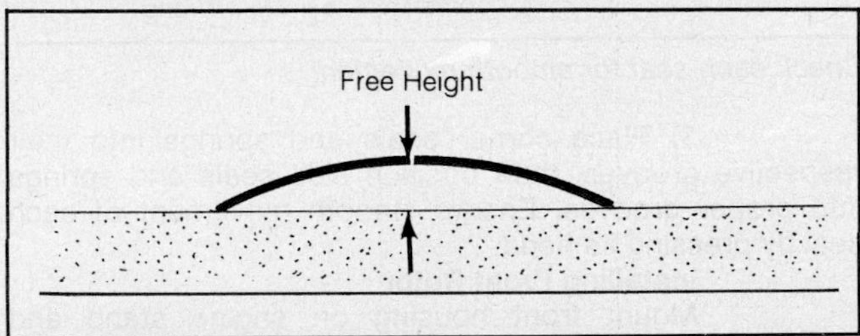
Free Height

Height must be more than .2165" (5.5 mm).

Side Seal

1) Remove all carbon from side seal and spring. Check side seal protrusion from rotor surface, and confirm free movement by pressing with finger. Protrusion should be more than .02" (.5 mm).

2) Check gap between side seal and groove with a feeler gauge. Standard gap is .0012-.0031" (.03-.08 mm). If wear limit of .004" (.10 mm) is measured, replace side seal.

3) Check gap between side seal and corner seal with seals installed on rotor. Insert feeler gauge between end of side seal (against rotating direction of rotor) and the corner seal. If gap exceeds .016" (.4 mm), replace side seal.

4) When side seal is replaced, adjust gap between side seal and corner seal by grinding one end of side seal along round shape of corner seal, using a fine file. Adjust gap .002-.006" (.05-.15 mm).

Corner Seal

1) Clean carbon from corner seal. Check corner seal protrusion from rotor surface, and check free movement by pressing with finger. Protrusion should be more than .02" (.5 mm).

2) Extent of corner seal groove wear is determined by using special Bar Limit Gauge (49 0839 165) shown in *Fig. 17*, and is classified according to the following.

Fig. 17: Checking Corner Seal Groove Measurement

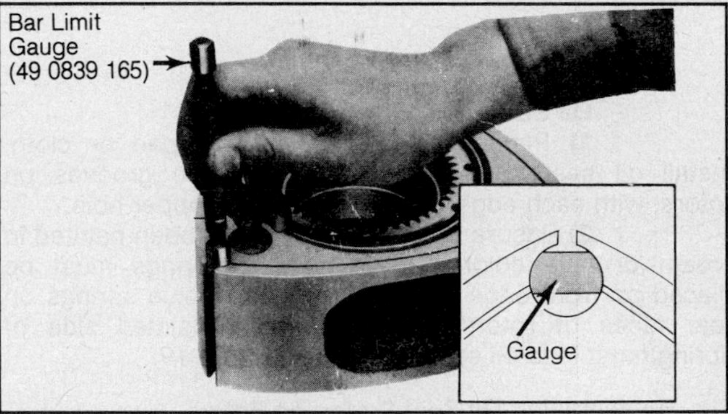
Bar Limit Gauge (49 0839 165)
Gauge

Replace rotor if both ends of gauge fit in gap.

3) If neither end of gauge goes into groove, it indicates that gap conforms to specifications. If "Go" end of gauge goes into groove, it indicates that gap is more than standard, but less than wear limit. In this case replace corner seal. *See Fig. 18.*

4) If both ends of gauge (both the "Go" and "No Go" ends) fit in groove, it indicates that gap exceeds wear limit. Replace rotor.

Eccentric Shaft

1) Thoroughly clean eccentric shaft in a cleaning solution and blow out oil passages with compressed air. Inspect shaft for scratching or scoring of bearing journals and possible blocked oil passages.

2) Check rotor bearing clearance by measuring inner diameter of the rotor bearing and outer diameter of the eccentric shaft rotor journal. Clearance should be .0016-.0031" (.04-.08 mm).

3) Replace the bearing if clearance exceeds .0039" (.10 mm). Replace eccentric shaft if journal diameters are under specified limits.

4) Place eccentric shaft in 2 "V" blocks. Mount a dial indicator and check runout of both ends by rotating shaft slowly. If runout exceeds .0024" (.06 mm), replace shaft.

5) Oil passages in eccentric shaft are sealed by a blind plug in rear of shaft. Inspect plug for possible oil leakage. If leakage is detected, remove plug with an Allen wrench, and install new "O" ring. Tighten plug.

6) Inspect needle bearings in end of shaft for wear or damage. Check for spring weakness, stuck, or damaged steel ball at the oil jets. Inspect front needle bearing, bearing housing, and thrust plate for wear or damage. Inspect front and rear oil seals for leaks, replace as necessary.

Fig. 18: Measuring Clearance of Apex, Side & Corner Seals

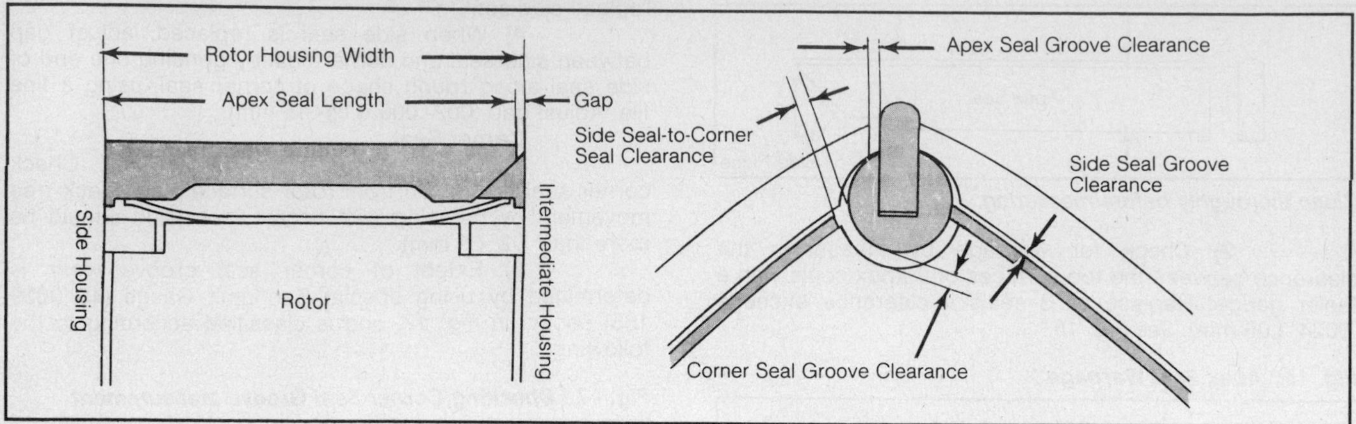
Rotor Housing Width
Apex Seal Length
Gap
Side Housing
Rotor
Intermediate Housing
Apex Seal Groove Clearance
Side Seal-to-Corner Seal Clearance
Side Seal Groove Clearance
Corner Seal Groove Clearance

REASSEMBLY

Oil Seals

1) Place the rotor on rubber pad or cloth. Install oil seal springs in their respective grooves on rotors, with each edge of spring fitted in stopper hole.

2) Ensure oil seal springs have been painted in cream or blue color: Cream colored springs must be placed on front edge faces of rotors and blue springs on rear faces of rotors. When installing, painted side of spring must face oil seal (upward). *See Fig. 19*.

Fig. 19: Installing Oil Seal Spring on Rotor

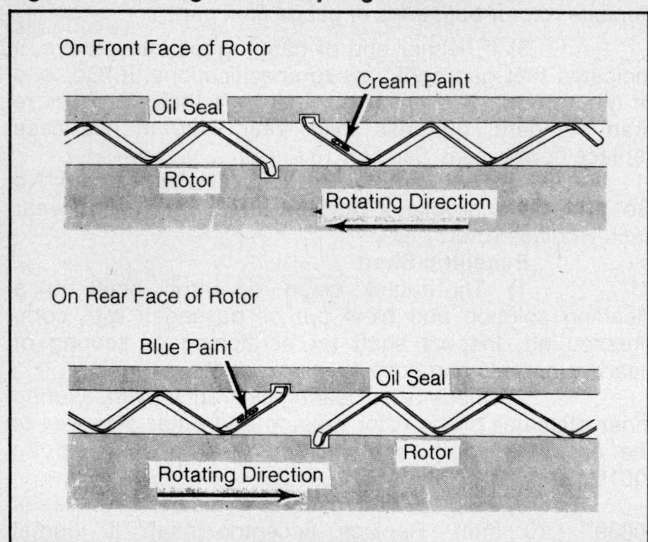
On Front Face of Rotor
Cream Paint
Oil Seal
Rotor
Rotating Direction
On Rear Face of Rotor
Blue Paint
Oil Seal
Rotor
Rotating Direction

Painted side of spring must face oil seal.

3) Insert new "O" ring in each oil seal. Install inner oil seal to each side of rotor as follows: Position oil seal to groove so square edge of spring fits in stopper notch of oil seal. Press into position by using a used inner oil seal so lip of inner oil seal sinks into position approximately .016" (.4 mm) below surface of rotor.

4) Install outer oil seal so square edge of spring fits in stopper notch of oil seal. Slowly push oil seal in position with fingers. Confirm smooth movement of each oil seal by pressing oil seal.

5) Check oil seal protrusion. Install oil seal springs and oil seals on the other side of rotor. Take care not to deform lip of oil seal.

Apex, Corner & Side Seals

1) Before installing apex seal, cut the assist piece to a length of .08-.011" (2.0-2.8 mm). Peel off paper and install assist piece of apex seal. See Fig. 20.

2) Position apex seals without springs and side pieces into their respective grooves so that each side piece rests on rear side of each rotor. Install the soft seal into the corner seal.

Fig. 20: Installing Assist Piece on Apex Seal

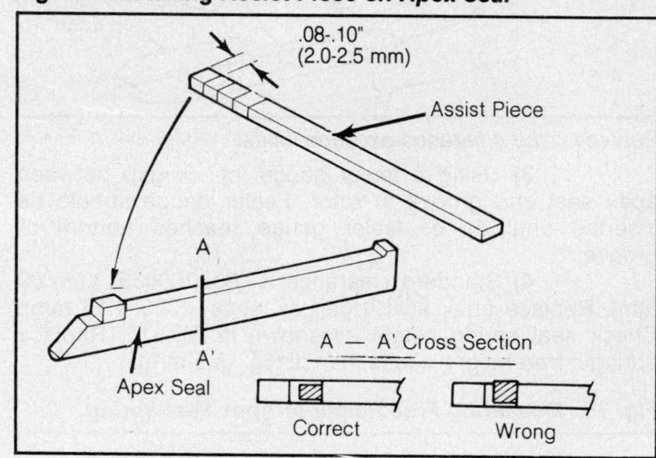
.08-.10"
(2.0-2.5 mm)
Assist Piece
A
A'
Apex Seal
A — A' Cross Section
Correct
Wrong

Check each seal for smooth movement.

3) Place corner seals and springs into their respective grooves, then position side seals and springs into proper grooves. Ensure smooth movement of each seal by pressing its head.

Installing Front Rotor

Mount front housing on engine stand and place front rotor assembly on housing. Use care not to drop seal into port. Mesh internal and stationary gears so that one rotor apex is set to one of 4 positions shown in *Fig. 21*.

Mazda Engines

RX7 ROTARY ENGINE (Cont.)

Fig. 21: Positioning Rotor Apex for Reassembly

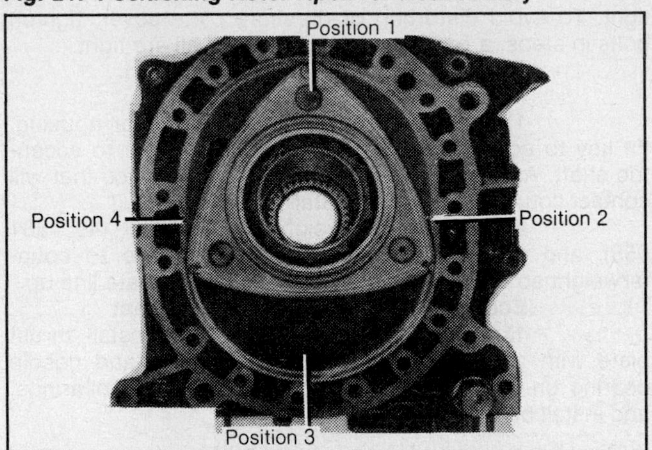
Position 1
Position 4
Position 2
Position 3

Use care not to drop seal into port.

Installing Eccentric Shaft

Lubricate front rotor journal and main journal on shaft with engine lubricant. Being careful not to damage rotor and main bearings, insert eccentric shaft.

Installing Front Rotor Housing

1) As front and rear rotor housings are not interchangeable, be sure they are installed in correct sequence. Apply sealing agent to front side of rotor housing. *See Fig. 22.*

Fig. 22: Applying Sealing Agent to Rotor Assembly

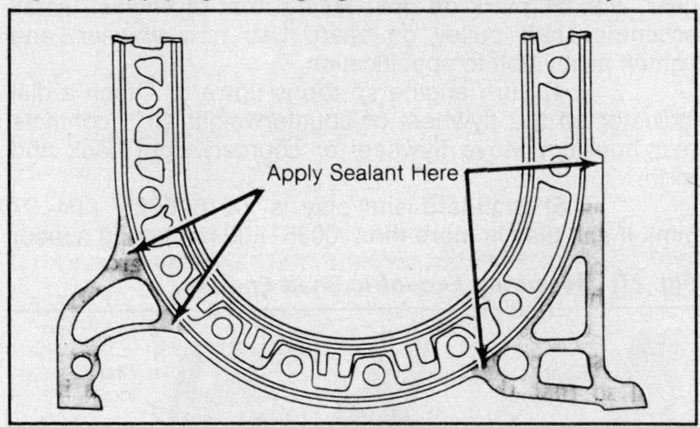
Apply Sealant Here

2) To provide greater durability to sealing rubbers, install a protector behind each inner sealing rubber. *See Fig. 23.* Install a new "O" ring, sealing rubbers and protector in front side of engine housing. Apply light coat of petroleum jelly to hold seals in place.

NOTE: Inner sealing rubber is square type. The wider white line of sealing rubber should face toward combustion chamber and seam of rubber should be placed as shown in Fig. 24. Do not stretch sealing rubbers.

3) Invert front rotor housing using care that seals remain in position, and install on front housing. Lubricate tubular dowels and insert through front rotor housing holes.

Fig. 23: Installing Protectors for Inner Sealing Rubbers

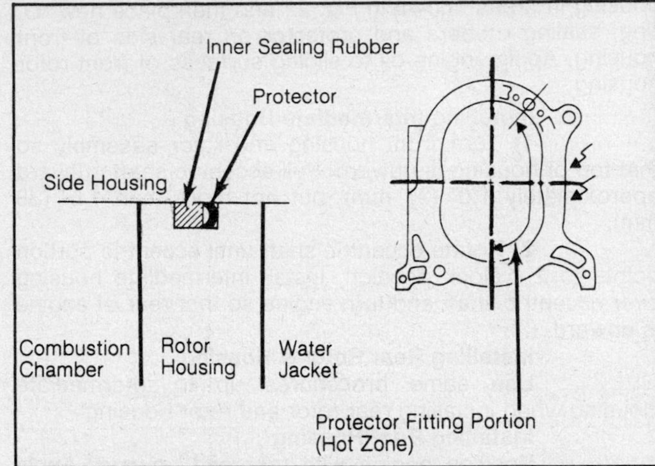
Inner Sealing Rubber
Protector
Side Housing
Combustion Chamber
Rotor Housing
Water Jacket
Protector Fitting Portion (Hot Zone)

Apply light coat of petroleum jelly to hold seals in place.

Fig. 24: Positioning Inner Sealing Rubber

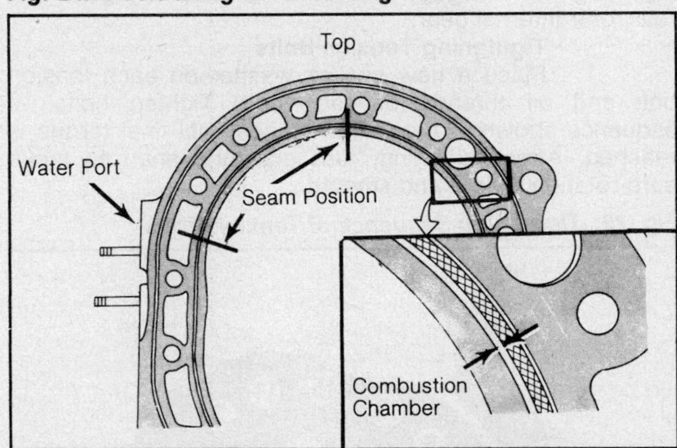
Top
Water Port
Seam Position
Combustion Chamber

Wider white line of sealing rubber should face toward combustion chamber.

4) Insert apex seal springs so that both ends of spring may support the back side of the apex seal. Install the soft seal into corner seal. Install corner seal springs and seals into their respective grooves. Fit side pieces to original positions and lubricate with engine oil.

5) Confirm that spring is set correctly on side piece. *See Fig. 25.* Confirm smooth movement of each seal by pressing on head.

Fig. 25: Positioning of Apex Seal and Spring

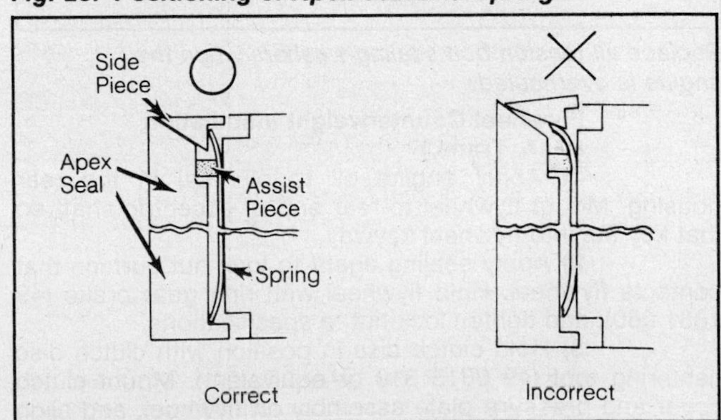
Side Piece
Apex Seal
Assist Piece
Spring
Correct
Incorrect

Check side piece for correct installation.

RX7 ROTARY ENGINE (Cont.)

6) Apply sealing agent on the rear side of front housing in areas shown in *Fig. 22* and then place new "O" ring, sealing rubbers and protector on rear side of front housing. Apply engine oil to sliding surfaces of front rotor housing.

Installing Intermediate Housing

1) Turn front housing and rotor assembly so that top of housing is upward. Pull eccentric shaft outward approximately 1.0" (25 mm), but not more than 1.5" (38 mm).

2) Rotate eccentric shaft until eccentric portion points to 2 o'clock position. Install intermediate housing over eccentric shaft and turn engine so that rear of engine is upward.

Installing Rear Rotor & Housing

Use same procedures up to Intermediate Housing when installing rear rotor and rotor housing.

Installing Rear Housing

Position engine with rear end upward. Apply sufficient lubricant onto stationary gear and main bearing. Install rear housing onto rear rotor housing, and turn rear rotor slightly to engage rear housing stationary gear with rear rotor internal gear.

Tightening Tension Bolts

Place a new sealing washer on each tension bolt and oil threads of each bolt. Tighten bolts, in sequence shown in *Fig. 26*, in stages until final torque is reached. After tightening, turn eccentric shaft to make sure rotation is light and smooth.

Fig. 26: Tightening Sequence of Tension Bolts

15
11
13
7
9
5
3
1
2
4
8
6
12
10
17
16
14
18

Replace all tension bolt sealing washers when the engine is overhauled.

Flywheel Counterweight Installation (Man. Trans.)

1) Apply engine oil to oil seal in the rear housing. Mount flywheel to rear end of eccentric shaft so that key fits into flywheel keyway.

2) Apply sealing agent to lock nut surface that contacts flywheel. Hold flywheel with ring gear brake (49 1881 060), and tighten lock nut to specifications.

3) Hold clutch disc in position with clutch disc centering tool (49 0813 310 or equivalent). Mount clutch cover and pressure plate assembly on flywheel, and align the "O" marks of clutch cover and flywheel.

4) Install 4 standard and 2 reamer bolts finger tight. To avoid distortion of pressure plate cover, tighten bolts in steps, a few turns at a time, until all are tight.

Flywheel Counterweight Installation (Auto. Trans.)

1) Apply engine oil to oil seal in rear housing. Fit key to eccentric shaft. Install counterweight to eccentric shaft. Apply sealing agent to lock nut surface that will contact counterweight and install lock nut.

2) Hold counterweight with stopper (49 1881 055), and tighten lock nut. Install drive plate to counterweight so hole in counterweight and drive plate line up.

Eccentric Shaft End Play Adjustment

1) Turn engine so front is up. Install thrust plate with chamfer downward. Slide spacer and needle bearing on eccentric shaft. Lubricate shaft and bearings, and install bearing housing.

NOTE: If bearing housing has not been removed, use care that center of needle bearing in bearing housing comes to center of eccentric shaft and that spacer is seated to thrust plate.

2) Lubricate and install needle bearing, thrust washer, and balance weight on shaft. Install keys in oil pump and eccentric shaft keyways. Place oil pump drive chain on oil pump sprocket and eccentric shaft sprocket. Install sprockets on shafts.

3) Align the keyways of eccentric shaft sprocket and balance weight. Install key. Install distributor drive gear, with "F" mark on gear facing front of engine. Install eccentric shaft pulley on shaft. Use new washer, and tighten pulley bolt to specification.

4) Turn engine so top is upward. Attach a dial indicator on the flywheel or counterweight so it contacts rear housing. Move flywheel or counterweight back and forth.

5) Standard end play is .0016-.0028" (.04-.07 mm). If end play is more than .0035" (.09 mm) grind spacer

Fig. 27: Measuring Eccentric Shaft End Play

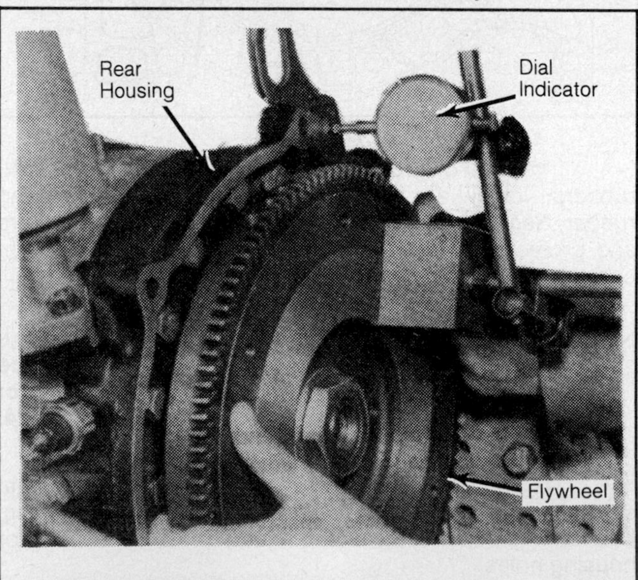
Rear
Housing
Dial
Indicator
Flywheel

Standard end play is .0016-.0028" (.04-.07mm).

RX7 ROTARY ENGINE (Cont.)

on surface plate with emery paper or install thinner spacer. If end play is less than .0016" (.04 mm), install thicker spacer.

6) Oversize spacers are available in 5 sizes from .3181" to .3150" (8.08 mm to 8.00 mm) and are identified by stamped letter "X", "K", "Y", "V", and "Z" respectively. When spacer has been installed, recheck end play.

NOTE: If end play is below specified amount, spacer thickness is too small. If end play is beyond specifications, spacer is too thick.

Installing Front Cover & Eccentric Shaft Pulley

1) Turn engine so front is upward. Remove eccentric shaft pulley. Tighten oil pump sprocket nut and bend tab of lock washer.

2) Check oil pump drive chain slack by pressing finger against chain. *See Fig. 29* Chain slack measurement should not exceed .47" (12 mm). If the slack exceeds the limit, replace drive chain.

3) Install new "O" ring on front housing oil passage. Install front cover and gasket on front housing. Lubricate oil seal in front cover. Install eccentric shaft pulley on shaft. Use new washer and tighten pulley bolt.

Installing Oil Strainer & Oil Pan

1) Invert engine so that bottom of engine is up. Install oil strainer gasket and strainer on front housing. Cut off excess gasket along mounting surface of oil pan.

2) Apply a .16-.24" (4-6 mm) bead of sealer on mounting surface of oil pan (to the inside of pan bolt holes) and install gasket. Apply a similar bead of sealant to gasket. Install pan and tighten bolts.

Installing Water Pump

Turn engine upright, position gasket and water pump on front housing and tighten attaching bolts.

NOTE: For further information on cooling system components, see Cooling System in this article.

Installing Distributor

1) Rotate eccentric shaft until yellow mark (leading timing mark) on pulley aligns with indicator pin on front cover. Align notch on distrubutor housing with punch mark on driven gear.

2) Insert distributor and lock nut. Turn distributor housing until a trigger wheel blade aligns with pick-up coil. Tighten lock nut.

Installing External Components

1) Install exhaust manifold, engine mount, intake manifold with carburetor, and alternator and drive belt. Check clearance between alternator support and bracket. Limit is .0059" (.15 mm). Adjust with shim if necessary.

2) Install air pump and drive belt. oil filter assembly and all other external components. Before removing engine from stand, install engine hanger bracket to front cover.

ENGINE OILING

CRANKCASE CAPACITY

The crankcase capacity is 4.9 quarts (4.6L), including filter.

OIL FILTER

A full-flow, disposable cartridge-type filter is mounted on the rear housing.

NORMAL OIL PRESSURE

Normal oil pressure is 10-26 psi (.7-1.8 kg/cm²) at idle speed, 64-78 psi (4.5-5.5 kg/cm²) at 3000 RPM.

ENGINE OILING SYSTEM

Engine oiling system is forced circulation using a 2 rotor type oil pump. Oil pump is mounted on front housing and is chain driven through eccentric shaft. The oil pressure is maintained through a regulator valve and pressure control valve. A full flow oil filter and oil cooler are mounted on the rear housing.

Oil is directed from the oil pump to the oil pressure control valve in the front cover. The oil then flows to the oil filter/cooler assembly on the rear cover which directs lubricating oil to all internal parts. The pressure regulator valve in the rear cover acts as a secondary pressure regulation device.

The oil pressure control valve is designed to open at 114 psi (8 kg/cm²). The free length of the control valve spring should be 2.74" (69.6 mm). Never use an oil pressure control spring from a previous year in a 1983 model. The cap bolt and spring are painted yellow in 1983. The oil pressure regulator valve will relieve pressure at 71.1 psi (4.9 kg/cm²). Its spring free length should be 1.83" (46.4 mm).

The engine is equipped with a metering oil pump which regulates the amount of oil pumped to the float chamber of the carburetor. The oil enters the combustion chamber with the air/fuel mixture to lubricate the seals within the chamber. The amount of oil increases as engine RPM increases. The metering pump control lever is actuated by a rod connected to the throttle lever.

Fig. 28: Mazda RX7 Engine Oiling System

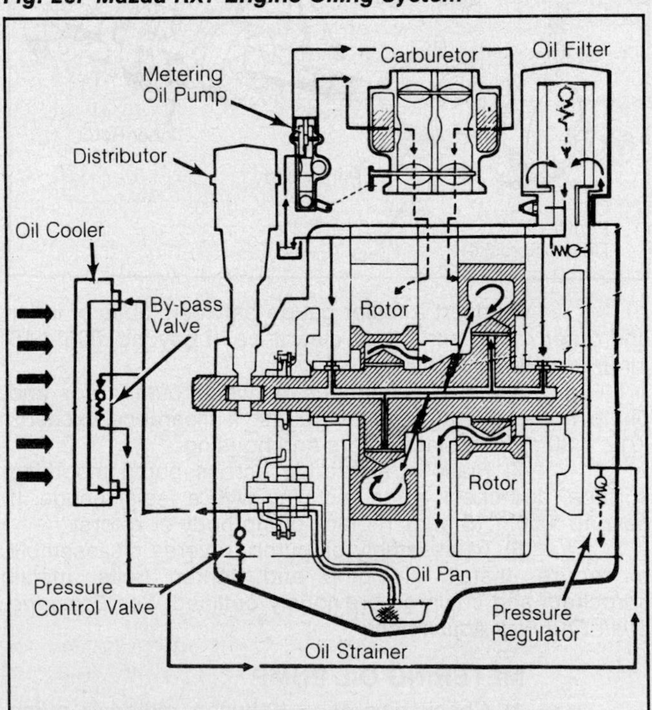
Carburetor
Oil Filter
Metering Oil Pump
Distributor
Oil Cooler
By-pass Valve
Rotor
Rotor
Oil Pan
Pressure Control Valve
Pressure Regulator
Oil Strainer

RX7 ROTARY ENGINE (Cont.)

OIL PUMP

NOTE: **Oil pump is mounted on the front engine housing and must be overhauled wiht front engine cover removed.**

1) Remove front engine cover. Check oil pump drive chain slack by pressing finger against chain and measuring slack. If measurement exceeds .47" (12 mm), replace drive chain. *See Fig. 29.*

Fig. 29: Measuring Oil Pump Drive Chain Slack

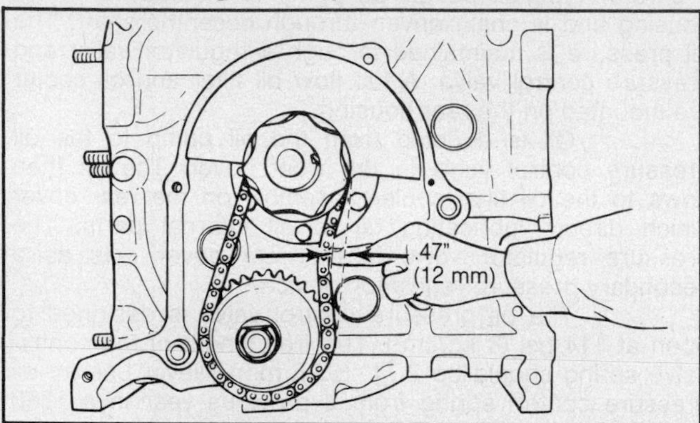
.47"
(12 mm)

Replace chain if slack exceeds limit.

2) Diassemble oil pump in following order: Remove snap ring, rear outer rotor, rear inner rotor, key, and middle plate. Remove front inner rotor, key shaft, spring pin, and front outer rotor. *See Fig. 30.*

Fig. 30: Exploded View of Oil Pump Assembly

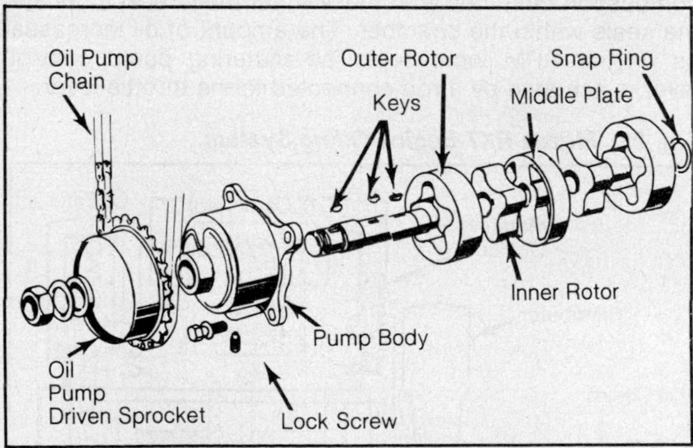
Oil Pump
Chain
Outer Rotor
Snap Ring
Keys
Middle Plate
Inner Rotor
Pump Body
Oil
Pump
Driven Sprocket
Lock Screw

3) Insert a feeler gauge between lobes of inner and outer rotors and check clearance. If beyond .006" (.15 mm), replace both rotors.

4) Check clearance between outer rotor and pump housing with a feeler gauge. If clearance exceeds .012" (.30 mm), replace rotors and housing.

5) Place straightedge across pump mounting surface, and check rotor end play with a feeler gauge. If beyond .006" (.15 mm), replace pump body or rotors.

6) To assembly oil pump, reverse disassembly procedure. Install oil pump and tighten bolts. Install sprockets and chain as previously outlined. *See Eccentric Shaft End Play Adjustment.*

METERING OIL PUMP

1) Check clearance between metering pump lever and washer. *See Fig. 31.* Clearance must be no more than .04" (1.0 mm).

Fig. 31: Adjusting Metering Pump Control Rod

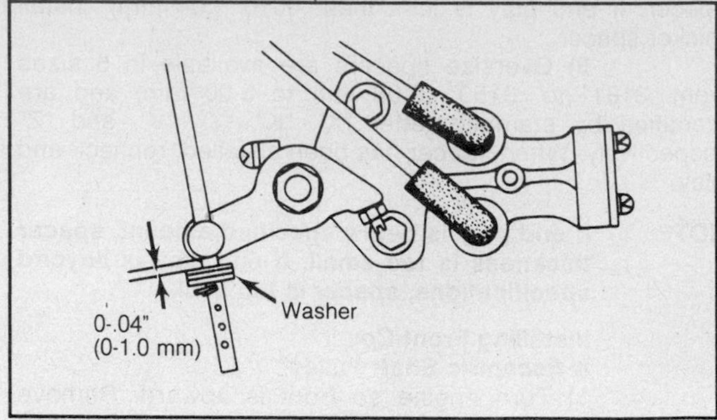
Washer
0-.04"
(0-1.0 mm)

Adjust clearance by changing washers.

2) To check oil discharge, detach connecting rod. Disconnect oil lines at carburetor. Start engine and adjust idle to 2000 RPM. Once oil flow from hoses becomes steady, measure volumn discharged. Pump should discharge .07-.08 oz. (2.0-2.4 cc) in 6 minutes.

CAUTION: **Carburetor will not be receiving oil during test. Add small amount of clean oil to carburetor to provide proprer lubrication during testing.**

3) To adjust oil metering pump, turn the adjusting screw clockwise to increase flow or counterclockwise to decrease flow. One completer turn will change oil discharge flow by .007-.011" oz. (.2-.3 cc) for 6 minutes of operation.

4) Ensure lock nut on adjustment screw is tight. Recheck metering oil pump discharge rate.

OIL COOLER

Inspection

Check the oil cooler for damage, cracks, or leaks. Replace the oil cooler if defective.

Removal & Installation

1) Remove water hoses installed on the inlet and outlet sides of cooler. Remov oil pipe and sealing washer. Remove oil cooler and filter housing as an assembly.

2) Remove "O" rings. Do not disassemble. Replace as an assembly if necessary. To install, reverse removal procedure. Use new filter, "O" rings, and sealing washer. Add engine oil and coolant. Start engine and check for leaks.

ENGINE COOLING

THERMOSTAT

Thermostat is a wax pellet type which starts to open at 180°F (82°C) and fully opens at 203°F (95°C).

PRESSURE CAP

The radiator pressure cap is rated at 13 psi (.9 kg/cm²).

WATER PUMP

Removal

1) Drain coolling system. Remove air cleaner, water temperature switch connector, air conditioner drive belt, and air pump drive belt.

RX7 ROTARY ENGINE (Cont.)

2) Remove alternator, cooling fan, and drive belts. Remove air conditioning pulley (if equipped). Disconnect radiator hoses and remove water pump.

Disassembly

1) Press the pulley boss off of the pump shaft. Remove the snap ring.

2) Supporting the pump body, apply pressure to the rear end of the shaft to press the shaft, spacer, and bearing assembly out through the front of the pump body. *See Fig. 32*.

3) Remove impeller and seal assembly from the pump body. Press bearings and spacer from the shaft.

Fig. 32: Exploded View of Water Pump

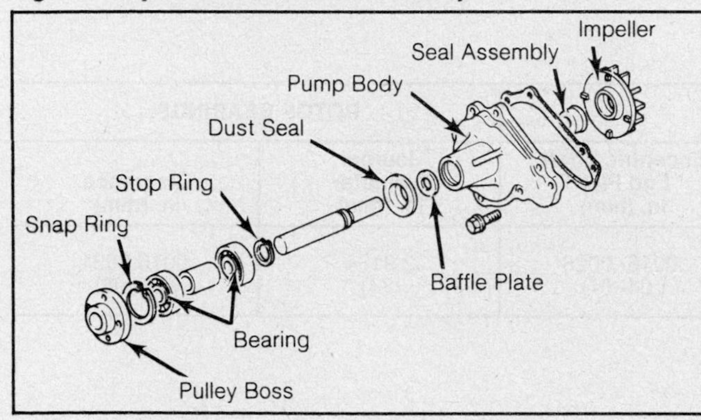
Impeller
Seal Assembly
Pump Body
Dust Seal
Stop Ring
Snap Ring
Baffle Plate
Bearing
Pulley Boss

Reassembly

1) Install stop ring and dust seal on the shaft. Drive baffle plate onto the taper of the shaft.

2) Press the rear bearing onto the shaft with sealed side rearward until it contacts the stop ring. Press shaft and bearing assembly into the pump body.

3) Place spacer on the shaft fill with grease. Install front bearing (sealed side forward) until the snap ring can be installed. Press pulley boss onto pump shaft.

4) Install the seal assembly into the body. Press impeller onto the shaft until it is flush with the end of the shaft.

Installation

To install, reverse removal procedure. Adjust drive belt tension and refill cooling system.

TIGHTENING SPECIFICATIONS

Application	Ft. Lbs. (N.m)
Eccentric Shaft Pulley	72-87 (98-118)
Flywheel Lock Nut	289-362 (393-492)
Intake Manifold	14-19 (19-26)
Oil Pump Sprocket	23-34 (32-47)
Pressure Plate	13-20 (18-27)
Water Pump	13-20 (18-27)

ENGINE SPECIFICATIONS

GENERAL SPECIFICATIONS

Year	Cu. In.	Liters	Fuel System	HP@RPM	Torque Ft. Lbs.@RPM	Compr. Ratio	ROTOR HOUSING WIDTH	
							In.	mm
1983	70.0	1.1	4 Bbl.	.....	.....	9.4:1	2.7559	70

ROTOR HOUSING, INTERMEDIATE HOUSING & ROTOR

Engine	ROTOR HOUSING		FRONT, INTERMEDIATE & REAR HOUSING		ROTOR		
	Width In. (mm)	Distortion Limit In. (mm)	Width In. (mm)	Distortion Limit In. (mm)	Width In. (mm)	Housing-to-Rotor Clearance In. (mm)	Land Protrusion In. (mm)
1.1L							
Front	2.7559 (70)	.0016 (.04)	1.576 (40)	.0016 (.40)	2.748 (69.8)	.0047-.0074 (.12-.19)	.....
Center			1.969 (50)	.0016 (.40)			
Rear	2.7559 (70)	.0016 (.04)	2.362 (60)	.0016 (.40)	2.748 (69.8)	.0047-.0074 (.12-.19)	

APEX SEAL

Engine	Length In. (mm)	Seal Width In. (mm)	Height In. (mm)	SEAL-TO-HOUSING		SEAL-TO-ROTOR	
				Clearance In. (mm)	Wear Limit In. (mm)	Groove Clearance In. (mm)	Wear Limit In. (mm)
1.1L	2.748 (69.8)	.1181 (3.0)	.3347 (8.5)	.....	.....	.0020-.0035 (.05-.09)	.0059 (.15)

Mazda Engines

RX7 ROTARY ENGINE (Cont.)

ENGINE SPECIFICATIONS (Cont.)

SIDE SEAL

Engine	Thickness In. (mm)	Width In. (mm)	SEAL-TO-GROOVE		SIDE SEAL-TO-CORNER SEAL	
			Clearance In. (mm)	Limit In. (mm)	Clearance In. (mm)	Limit In. (mm)
1.1L	.0394 (1.0)	.1378 (3.5)	.0012-.0031 (.03-.08)	.0039 (.10)	.0020-.0059 (.05-.15)	.0157 (.40)

ECCENTRIC SHAFT MAIN & ROTOR BEARINGS

Engine	MAIN BEARINGS			ROTOR BEARINGS	
	Journal Diameter In. (mm)	Clearance In. (mm)	Eccentric Shaft End Play In. (mm)	Journal Diameter In. (mm)	Clearance In. (mm)
1.1L	1.6929 (43)	.0016-.0031 (.04-.08)	.0016-.0028 (.04-.07)	2.9134 (74)	.0016.0031 (.04-.08)

CORNER SEAL

Engine	Diameter In. (mm)	Height In. (mm)	SEAL-TO-GROOVE		SIDE SEAL-TO-CORNER SEAL	
			Clearance In. (mm)	Limit In. (mm)	Clearance In. (mm)	Limit In. (mm)
1.1L	.4331 (11.0)	.2756 (7.0)	.....	.....	.0020-.0059 (.05-.15)	.0157 (.40)

OIL SEAL

Engine	Height In. (mm)	SEAL LIP CONTACT WIDTH	
		Standard In. (mm)	Limit In. (mm)
1.1L	.2205 (5.6)	Less than .02 Less than (.5)	.....

PORT TIMING

Engine	INTAKE		EXHAUST	
	Open (ATDC)	Close (ABDC)	Open (BBDC)	Close (ATDC)
1.1L	32°	40°	75°	38°

Mercedes-Benz Engines

4-CYLINDER DIESEL & 5-CYLINDER TURBO DIESEL

ENGINE CODING

ENGINE IDENTIFICATION

Engine identification number is stamped on left side of cylinder block. First 6 digits of this number are used for engine identification purposes.

ENGINE IDENTIFICATION

Application	Chassis Type	Engine Code
240D (4-Cyl.)	123.123	616.912
300D (5-Cyl. Turbo)	123.130	617.912
300CD (5-Cyl. Turbo)	123.150	617.912
300SD (5-Cyl. Turbo)	126.120	617.951
300TD (5-Cyl. Turbo)	123.193	617.952

ENGINE, MANIFOLDS & CYLINDER HEAD

ENGINE

Removal

1) Drain cooling system. Disconnect negative battery cable. Remove engine hood, radiator and fan shroud. (On some models, hood may be raised 90° to allow for engine removal.) Remove air filter with intake duct.

2) Draw oil from power steering pump reservoir and disconnect hoses. If equipped with air conditioning, dismount and set compressor aside, do not disconnect refrigerant hoses.

3) Remove control linkage with shaft and set aside. Disconnect all coolant, vacuum, oil, fuel, electrical lines and hoses which lead to engine. On turbocharged models, loosen oil filter cover and raise slightly. Disconnect exhaust system at turbocharger.

4) On all other models, disconnect exhaust pipe at exhaust manifold. On all models, remove lateral support for exhaust pipe at transmission. If equipped with level control, remove pump and set aside, leaving lines connected.

5) Remove engine mount bolts at chassis. Remove drive shaft shield and disconnect drive shaft at transmission. Disconnect engine shock absorbers at chassis. Disconnect shift lever and all electrical connections at transmission.

6) Remove transmission cross-member retaining bolts, and remove cross-member. Attach sling to lifting eyes and hoist engine/transmission assembly out at an angle of approximately 45°. Separate engine/transmission assembly.

Installation

Lower engine/transmission assembly into position, and reverse removal procedure to complete installation.

NOTE: **Ensure that oil cooler, lines and filter housing have been flushed if installing new engine as a result of bearing failure.**

TURBOCHARGER

Removal (Turbo Diesel Only)

1) Remove air filter assembly and all ducting. Disconnect wire from temperature switch. Remove vacuum line and crankcase breather pipe. Disconnect engine oil supply line to turbocharger.

2) Remove air filter mounting bracket. Disconnect exhaust flange at exhaust manifold. Remove exhaust pipe bracket on automatic transmission and move exhaust pipe to rear.

3) Remove intermediate flange mounting bracket. Remove 4 mounting nuts holding turbocharger to manifold and remove turbocharger. Cover oil return pipe.

Installation

1) Install new flange gasket so that reinforcing bead is towards exhaust manifold. Ensure that center housing is filled with approximately 1/4 pint of oil.

2) Install intermediate flange and oil return pipe and install turbocharger. To complete installation, reverse removal procedure.

INTAKE & EXHAUST MANIFOLDS

Removal

Remove air cleaner assembly. Remove all vacuum lines and electrical connections that would interfere with manifold removal. Remove manifold retaining bolts, and remove manifold.

Installation

Clean gasket mating surfaces. Install manifold, using new gasket. Reverse removal procedure to complete installation.

CYLINDER HEAD

Removal

NOTE: **Ensure engine has cooled down before removing cylinder head.**

1) Drain cooling system. Disconnect negative battery cable and water hoses attached to cylinder head. Remove air cleaner. If equipped with level control, remove pump and set aside, leaving lines connected.

2) If equipped with power steering, remove pump with bracket and fuel filter and set aside. On turbocharged models, loosen and pull up oil filter cover slightly, and remove turbocharger.

3) Detach all remaining electrical connections, water, fuel and vacuum lines from cylinder head and intake manifold. Unbolt dipstick guide tube of automatic transmission from intake manifold.

4) Disconnect exhaust pipe from manifold or turbocharger and at transmission support. Remove throttle control linkage and set aside. Remove injection lines, and cover all connections.

5) Remove exhaust manifold support at manifold. Remove camshaft cover. Loosen, but do not remove camshaft sprocket bolt. Rotate crankshaft by using socket tool on crankshaft pulley so that No. 1 cylinder is at TDC on compression stroke.

6) Loosen, and remove rocker arm assembly bracket bolts evenly. Remove rocker arm assemblies. Mark camshaft sprocket and timing chain for proper assembly. Remove chain tensioner plug, and remove tensioner spring.

7) Remove timing chain guide rail from cylinder head. Remove camshaft sprocket. Loosen and remove head bolts in reverse order of tightening sequence. *See Fig. 1.* Attach sling to lifting eyes on head and lift head from engine. Thoroughly clean all mating surfaces of head and cylinder block.

4-CYLINDER DIESEL & 5-CYLINDER TURBO DIESEL (Cont.)

NOTE: Injection nozzles must be removed prior to removing the 5 head bolts next to nozzles.

Fig. 1: Cylinder Head Tightening Sequence

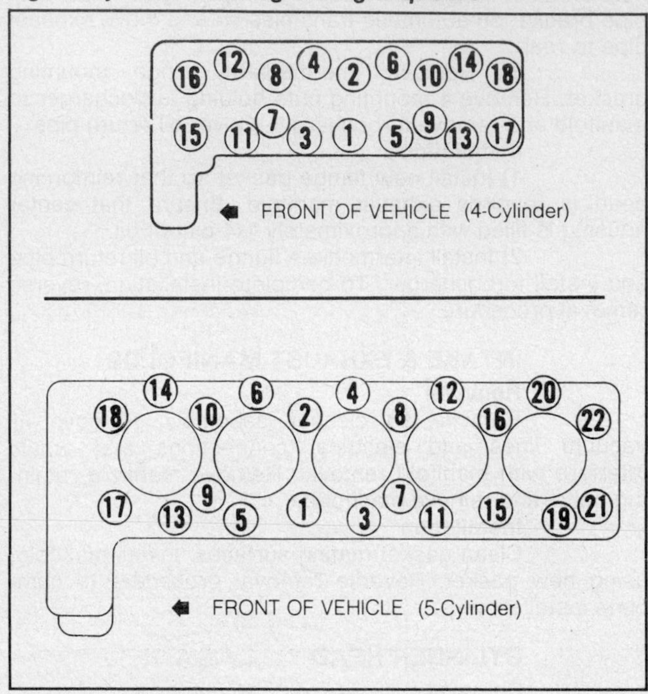
16 12 8 4 2 6 10 14 18
15 11 7 3 1 5 9 13 17
FRONT OF VEHICLE (4-Cylinder)
14 6 4 12 20
18 10 2 8 16 22
17 13 9 5 1 3 7 11 15 19 21
FRONT OF VEHICLE (5-Cylinder)

When removing cylinder head, loosen bolts in reverse order.

Installation

1) Ensure that No. 1 piston is still at TDC. Place new head gasket into position, ensuring that locating dowels are in correct position. Install cylinder head on block. Install cylinder head bolts, ensuring there of proper length. Tighten cylinder head bolts.

2) To complete installation, reverse removal procedure, and note the following. Adjust valve clearance. Use new seals and gaskets when installing all components. Run engine until warm, then loosen each head bolt 1/4 turn and tighten in sequence. *See Fig. 1.*

CAMSHAFT

TIMING CHAIN

Removal & Installation

1) A split link timing chain is available for repairs without dismantling engine. Remove glow plugs, and camshaft cover. Remove air cleaner adapter. Cover chain guard with cloth and grind open both pins of a link in the timing chain.

2) Remove old link and insert new split link with new chain attached. Turn crankshaft slowly in normal direction while feeding new chain in, and old chain out. Ensure that chain does not slip on sprockets and install master (split) link from rear so that retainer will be at front of engine.

3) Install link spring lock with closed end facing direction of rotation. Rotate crankshaft through one complete revolution and check that all timing marks still agree. To complete installation, reverse removal procedure.

Fig. 2: Timing Chain and Related Components

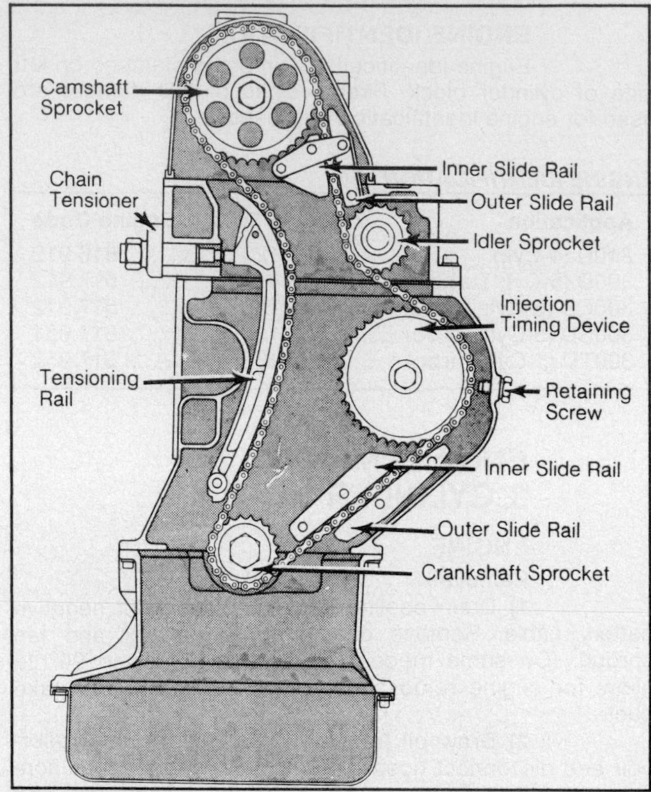
Camshaft Sprocket
Chain Tensioner
Inner Slide Rail
Outer Slide Rail
Idler Sprocket
Injection Timing Device
Tensioning Rail
Retaining Screw
Inner Slide Rail
Outer Slide Rail
Crankshaft Sprocket

Timing chain can be replaced without major dismantling of engine.

VALVE TIMING

1) Rotate No. 1 piston to TDC of compression stroke. Align camshaft timing mark with mark on No. 1 camshaft bearing support bracket. Install camshaft sprocket.

2) If correct valve timing is not achieved when camshaft sprocket is installed, offset Woodruff keys are available to make timing corrections, see following table:

Fig. 3: Camshaft Timing Mark Locations

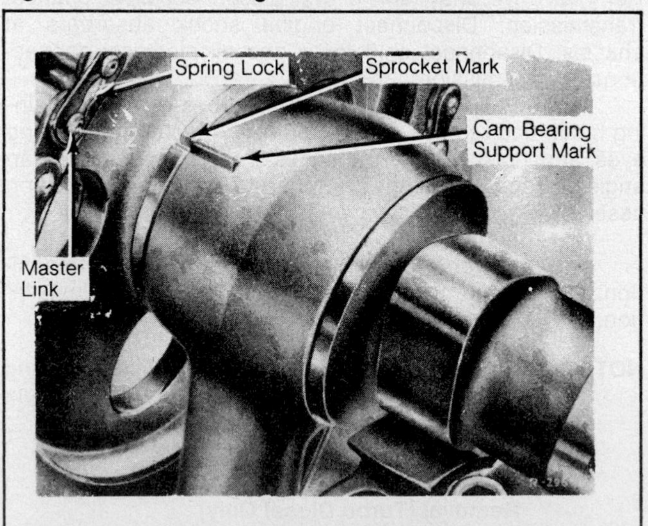
Spring Lock
Sprocket Mark
Cam Bearing Support Mark
Master Link

Ensure timing marks are correctly aligned.

4-CYLINDER DIESEL & 5-CYLINDER TURBO DIESEL (Cont.)

OFFSET WOODRUFF KEYS

Offset	Crankshaft Correction
.0275" (.7 mm)	4°
.0354" (.9 mm)	6 1/2°
.0433" (1.1 mm)	8°
.0511" (1.3 mm)	10°

INJECTION PUMP TIMING

1) To check injection pump timing (start of fuel delivery), turn crankshaft in normal direction until 24° BTDC mark is at pointer with No. 1 piston on compression stroke. Remove first pumping element pipe connection and valve ports and install overflow pipe in their place.

2) Set control lever to full throttle position. Attach auxiliary fuel container to pump inlet fitting. Rotate engine until fuel stream stops from overflow pipe and drips are at least 10-15 seconds apart. Delivery should occur when pipe stops dripping and crankshaft is on 24° BTDC mark.

3) Turn crankshaft 2 more full turns and check that fuel stops dripping at end of second full turn if pump timing is correct. If adjustment is required, loosen pump mounting nuts and turn pump toward engine to advance delivery and away from engine to retard start of delivery.

4) When timing is correct, tighten mounting nuts and recheck start of delivery. Disconnect auxiliary fuel container and overflow pipe. Connect normal fuel line and install first pumping element with fittings.

CAMSHAFT

Removal

Remove camshaft cover and camshaft sprocket. See Cylinder Head in this article. Remove shim from camshaft together with bearings and oil pipe. To install apply engine oil to camshaft bearings, camshaft journals and cams. Place camshaft into bearings from rear.

Installation

Reverse removal procedure, ensuring that camshaft supports and dowel pins are aligned.

CAMSHAFT BEARING REPLACEMENT

1) Inspect camshaft bearings for wear. If worn, grind bearing journals and fit undersize bearings.

Fig. 4: Detailed View of Camshaft

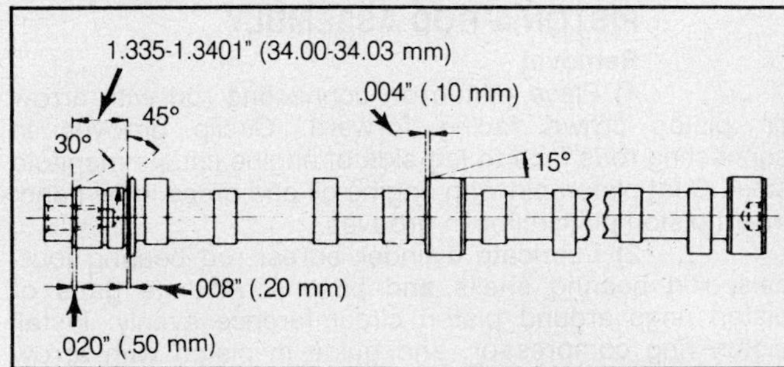
1.335-1.3401" (34.00-34.03 mm)
45°
30°
.004" (.10 mm)
15°
.008" (.20 mm)
.020" (.50 mm)

Install camshaft into bearings from rear.

2) Bearing on No. 1 journal controls camshaft end play. Width of journal is 1.3385-1.3401" (34.0-34.03 mm). Place bearing on camshaft and install retaining ring.

3) Using a feeler gauge, measure clearance between camshaft flange and bearing. Lap bearing to proper fit. The following table lists camshaft bearing journal diameters for standard and undersize bearings:

CAMSHAFT JOURNAL DIAMETERS

Application	Bearing No. 1 In. (mm)	No. 2 & 3 In. (mm)	[1] No. 4 In. (mm)
Standard	1.375 (34.94)	1.831 (46.51)	1.926 (48.94)
Intermediate (Grey)	1.371 (34.84)	1.824 (46.34)	1.923 (48.84)
1st Undersize (Red)	1.365 (34.69)	1.818 (46.19)	1.916 (48.69)

[1] — Only applies to 5-cylinder engine.

VALVES

VALVE ARRANGEMENT

4-Cylinder

E-I-I-E-E-I-I-E (Front-to-rear).

5-Cylinder

E-I-I-E-E-I-I-E-E-I (Front-to-rear).

ROCKER ARM ASSEMBLIES

Removal

1) Remove air cleaner, and camshaft cover. Loosen rocker arm bracket bolts and rotate camshaft so there is no load on rocker arms being removed.

2) Remove front assembly (serving 2 front cylinders), then rotate camshaft so that rear assembly can be removed without tension. Disassemble and replace parts as requied.

Installation

To install, reverse removal procedure. Adjust valve clearance.

Fig. 5: Detailed View of Rocker Arm Assembly

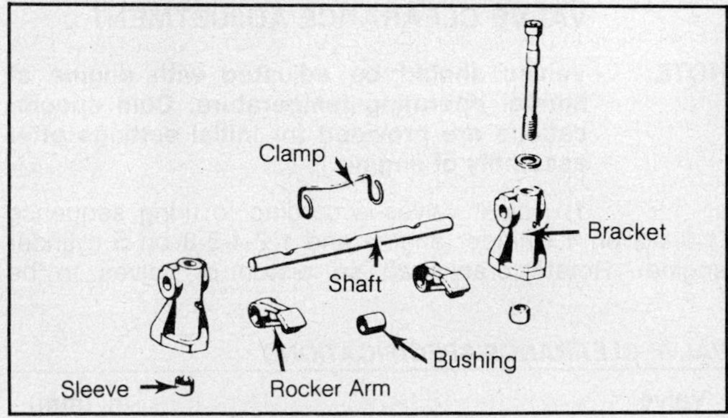
Clamp
Bracket
Shaft
Bushing
Sleeve
Rocker Arm

Loosen and/or tighten bolts evenly.

VALVE SPRINGS & OIL SEALS

Removal

With rocker arms and brackets removed from head, install spring compressor and remove adjusting cap and lock nut from valve stem. Remove collar and valve spring. Old seal may be pried off with screwdriver or pulled off with pliers.

4-CYLINDER DIESEL & 5-CYLINDER TURBO DIESEL (Cont.)

Installation

Note that intake seals are color coded Black and exhaust seals are Green. Position assembly sleeve over valve stem and press new seal onto guide with tool (617 589 00 43 00). Replace valve spring, collar, lock nut and adjusting cap.

VALVE GUIDE SERVICING

Checking Valve Guides

After removal of valve spring and valve stem seal, the wear on valve guide can be determined by moving valve stem crosswise in relation to engine. Maximum movement of .004" (.12 mm) is allowed.

Removing & Inserting Guides

1) Drive out valve guide with knock-out mandrel from direction of combustion chamber or press out. Insert valve guide into liquid oxygen for approximately 3-4 minutes. Insert immediately into respective bore, and drive in with a hammer.

2) If no liquid oxygen is available, heat head in a water bath, or heat in an oven to a maximum of 176°F (80°C). Coat valve guide with lubricant, and drive in with knock-in mandrel until circlip or knock-in mandrel rests against cylinder head. Guides are pressed in from rocker side. Check guide bores and ream for proper clearance as required.

3) Valve guides are available in standard and 1 oversize (color Red). An interference fit of .0004-.0015" (.010-.040 mm) is used. If guide does not meet specifications, replace. Note that intake guides are 2.362" (60 mm) long and exhaust guides are 1.909" (48.5 mm) long.

VALVE GUIDES SPECIFICATIONS

Application	Guide O.D. In. (mm)	Cyl. Head Bore In. (mm)
Standard	.5522-.5527 (14.03-14.04)	.5511-.5518 (14.00-14.02)
Oversize (Red)	.5601-.5605 (14.23-14.24)	.5590-.5597 (14.20-14.22)

VALVE CLEARANCE ADJUSTMENT

NOTE: **Valves should be adjusted with engine at normal operating temperature. Cold specifications are provided for initial settings after assembly of engine.**

1) Adjust valves according to firing sequence (1-3-4-2 on 4 cylinder engine and 1-2-4-5-3 on 5 cylinder engine). Rotate crankshaft so piston of valves to be adjusted is at TDC on compression stroke. Measure clearance between surface of camshaft and rocker arm.

2) To adjust, fit holding wrench on valve retainer. Loosen cap nut while holding hex nut and adjust clearance by turning cap nut. After adjustment, lock cap nut by tightening hex nut and recheck valve clearance.

VALVE CLEARANCE SPECIFICATIONS

Valve	In. (mm)
Intake	
Cold	.004 (.10)
Warm	.006 (.15)
Exhaust	
Cold	[1] .012 (.30)
Warm	[1] .014 (.35)

[1] — Clearances for Turbo Diesel are .04" (.10 mm) for intake, and .016" (.40 mm) for exhaust.

PISTONS, RINGS & PINS

OIL PAN

Removal

1) Drain engine oil and remove or raise engine hood to 90° position. Disconnect air cleaner corrugated duct and remove throttle control shaft. Remove fan shroud, and place over fan. Remove oil dipstick tube bracket at power steering pump bracket.

2) Remove A/C compressor, and loosen clamp for air/oil cooler lines. Disconnect engine shock absorbers at chassis. Loosen exhaust system lateral support at transmission. Remove engine mounting bolts from chassis. Remove oil cooler lines for automatic transmission at transmission, between intermediate flange and upper section of pan.

3) Remove 4 lower bolts on intermediate flange and remove intermediate flange shield. Remove lower oil pan retaining bolts, and remove pan. Use drift and drive oil dipstick guide tube out as far as it will go. Remove strainer extension with strainer from oil pump. Remove upper oil pan bolts.

4) Attach engine sling and hoist to front of engine, and raise enough to remove oil pan upper section. Pull out oil dipstick guide tube. Turn crankshaft until counterweights and connecting rods clear pan, and lower and remove pan from block.

Installation

1) Install new radial seal in groove at rear of pan. Ensure that mating surfaces are clean. Coat upper pan section with gasket compound. Place upper pan in position and insert dipstick guide tube. On turbocharged engine, insert oil return line from turbocharger.

2) Bolt upper section of pan to engine. Mount strainer extension and strainer to oil pump. Use new gasket and bolt lower pan to upper pan. To complete installation, reverse removal procedure.

PISTON & ROD ASSEMBLY

Removal

1) Place piston on connecting rod with arrow on piston crown facing forward. Circlip grooves in connecting rods face to left side of engine (intake manifold side). Coat piston pin with engine oil and press in by hand. Insert piston pin circlips in grooves.

2) Lubricate cylinder bores, rod bearing journals, rod bearing shells and pistons. Arrange gaps of piston rings around piston circumference evenly. Install piston ring compressor, and guide in piston with arrow facing forward.

3) Place connecting rod bearing caps on connecting rods, with cap code numbers aligning with connecting rod code numbers. Tighten rod cap nuts. Measure piston protrusion above top of cylinder block with piston at TDC. Piston should project at least .020" (.50 mm), but not more than .035" (.90 mm) above block.

4-CYLINDER DIESEL & 5-CYLINDER TURBO DIESEL (Cont.)

FITTING PISTONS & RINGS

1) Measure piston and cylinder diameters to determine running clearance. Piston diameter is measured at 90° to piston pin bore near bottom of piston skirt.

2) There are 2 compression rings, and 1 oil ring. Install compression rings with markings "top" or "F" and oil ring with marking "GOE" or "F" facing upward.

CRANKSHAFT MAIN & CONNECTING ROD BEARINGS

MAIN BEARING SERVICE

Measure main bearing and connecting rod journals for out-of-round and taper. Out-of-round must not exceed .0002-.0004" (.005-.010 mm) and taper must not exceed .0004-.0006" (.010-.015 mm). Select proper undersize (if required), and grind crankshaft to diameters shown in Crankshaft Journal Diameters table.

CRANKSHAFT JOURNAL DIAMETERS

Application	Main In. (mm)	Con. Rod In. (mm)
Standard	2.7541-2.7545 (69.95-69.96)	2.0454-2.0458 (51.95-51.96)
1st Undersize	2.7442-2.7446 (69.70-69.71)	2.0356-2.0360 51.70-51-71)
2nd Undersize	2.7344-2.7348 (69.45-69.46)	2.0257-2.0261 (51.45-51.46)
3rd Undersize	2.7246-2.7249 (69.20-69.21)	2.0159-2.0163 (51.20-51.21)
4th Undersize	2.7147-2.7151 (68.95-68.96)	2.0060-2.0064 (50.95-50.96)

THRUST BEARING ALIGNMENT

1) Third main bearing is equipped with separate shells and thrust washers in place of 2 one piece bearing inserts. Two identical thrust washers are inserted in cylinder block, and 2 remaining halves are fitted in bearing cap.

2) Bottom halves have 2 tabs to prevent turning and avoid incorrect installation. Following size thrust washers are available to adjust crankshaft end play: .085" (2.15 mm), .087" (2.20 mm), .089" (2.25 mm), .092" (2.35 mm) and .094" (2.40 mm).

REAR MAIN BEARING OIL SEAL

Removal

With oil pan and crankshaft removed, pull old seal from groove in crankcase and oil pan.

Installation

Insert new radial seal in groove and press into place using an oiled hammer handle. To provide overlap, cut seal off .040" (1 mm) above separation surface. Coat seal halves with engine oil.

FRONT OIL SEAL

Removal

Remove radiator and fan shroud. Remove front pulley and vibration dampener. Pry old oil seal from front cover,using a screwdriver. If fitted with original seal, remove spacer washer with puller (616 589 00 33 00).

NOTE: **On some engines, chrome plated spacer ring will not be required. Replacement seals for Turbo Diesel are of Green Viton inside and Black acrylic outside. Other seals are Black outside and White inside.**

Installation

Install new spacer ring (if required) and lubricate seal lips with engine oil. Ensure that seal cavity is clean and free of nicks and scratches. Place seal squarely into recess, and use seal installation tool to press seal into proper position.

Fig. 6: Sectional View of Crankshaft Front Oil Seal

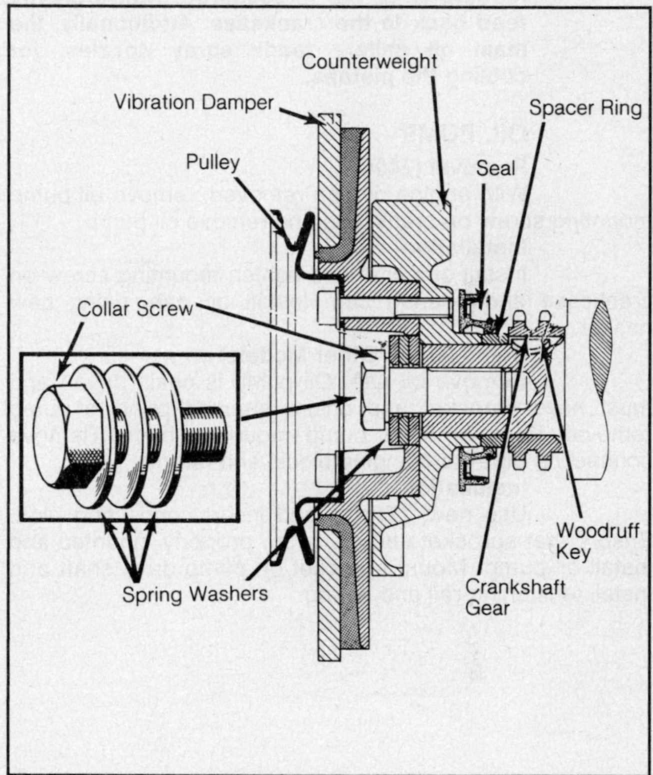
Counterweight
Vibration Damper
Spacer Ring
Pulley
Seal
Collar Screw
Woodruff Key
Crankshaft Gear
Spring Washers

Lubricate oil seal lips with engine oil.

ENGINE OILING

CRANKCASE CAPACITIES

4 & 5-Cylinder — 7.0 qts. (6.6L).
5-Cylinder Turbo — 7.9 qts. (7.5L).

NORMAL OIL PRESSURE

7.1 psi. (.5 kg/cm²) at 700-780 RPM idle speed; 42 psi. (3 kg/cm²) at 3000 RPM.

OIL FILTER

Oil filter is vertically mounted and contains a single cartridge composed of a main and by-pass section.

PRESSURE REGULATOR VALVE

Non-adjustable.

ENGINE OILING SYSTEM

Engine lubrication is provided by a gear type oil pump, which force feeds oil through an oil filter to oil

4-CYLINDER DIESEL & 5-CYLINDER TURBO DIESEL (Cont.)

gallery. From oil gallery, oil flows to main and connecting rod bearings. Pistons, wrist pins and connecting rod bushings are splash lubricated.

A vertical oil passage from oil gallery has a transverse passage which supplies oil to intermediate sprocket shaft and bearings. Another oil passage supplies oil to oil pump drive shaft and helical gear.

Vertical passage also supplies oil to No. 1 camshaft bearing. An external oil tube attached to No. 1 camshaft bearing support, lubricates other camshaft bearings and rocker arms.

NOTE: **Turbo Diesel models have an external line feeding oil to the turbocharger with a gravity feed back to the crankcase. Additionally, the main oil gallery feeds spray nozzles, for cooling the pistons.**

OIL PUMP

Removal (240D)

With engine oil pan removed, remove oil pump mounting screw on crankcase and remove oil pump.

Installation

Install oil pump and tighten mounting screw on crankcase and bearing cap. Install oil pan, using new gasket.

Removal (All Other Models)

Remove oil pan. Oil pump is chain driven and must have sprocket and chain removed prior to pump removal. Remove 5 oil pump mounting bolts. Remove connecting pipe from engine block, and remove pump.

Installation

Use new "O" ring and insert connecting pipe. Ensure that sprocket and chain are properly mounted and install oil pump. Mount sprocket on pump drive shaft and install tensioning rail and spring.

ENGINE COOLING

THERMOSTAT

Opens at 172-180°F (78-82°C).

COOLING SYSTEM CAPACITY

4-Cylinder 10.6 qts. (10.3L).
5-Cylinder 11.6 qts. (11.0L).
5-Cylinder Turbo 12.7 qts. (12.0L).

WATER PUMP

Removal

Drain cooling system and loosen "V" belts. Remove fan and drive pulley. Disconnect hoses from pump. Remove mounting bolts, and remove pump.

Installation

Coat new gasket with sealer, and mount pump on engine. Install fan and hub, and adjust belts. Fill radiator and expansion tank to mark and run engine. After temperature reaches approximately 140°F (60°C), install radiator cap and check for leaks.

TIGHTENING SPECIFICATIONS

Application	Ft. Lbs. (N.m)
Cylinder Head (Hex Head Bolts) [1]	
Step 1	51 (70)
Step 2	66 (90)
Step 3	73 (100)
Cylinder Head (12-Point Head Bolts)	
Step 1	30 (40)
Step 2	[2] 51 (70)
Rocker Arm Support Bolts	29 (39)
Prechamber in Cyl. Head	108-130 (157-177)
Nozzle Holder in Prechamber	51-58 (69-79)
Glow Plugs	36 (49)
Connecting Rod Caps	36 (49)
Main Bearing Caps	65 (88)
Crankshaft Front Hex Bolt	195-239 (265-325)
Camshaft Sprocket Bolt	58 (79)

[1] — Setting time between steps 2 & 3 is 10 minutes.
[2] — Loosen head bolts 1/4 turn, and retighten in sequence to final torque after engine is warm.

ENGINE SPECIFICATIONS

GENERAL SPECIFICATIONS

Year	DISPLACEMENT		Fuel System	HP@RPM	Torque Ft. Lbs.@RPM	Compr. Ratio	BORE		STROKE	
	Cu. In.	Liters					In.	mm	In.	mm
1983										
4-Cylinder	146.4	2.4	Fuel Inj.	67@4000	97@2400	21.0:1	3.57	90.9	3.64	92.4
5-Cylinder	183.0	3.0	Fuel Inj.	120@4350	170@2400	21.5:1	3.57	90.9	3.64	92.4

VALVES

Engine Size & Valve	Head Diam. In. (mm)	Face Angle	Seat Angle	Seat Width In. (mm)	Stem Diameter In. (mm)	Stem Clearance In. (mm)	Valve Lift In. (mm)
2.4L & 3.0L							
Intake	1.563-1.571 (39.70-39.90)	30°	30°	.051-.063 (1.3-1.6)	.3906-.3913 (9.92-9.94)	.0030 (.075)	.....
Exhaust	1.343-1.350 (34.10-34.30)	30°	30°	.098-.114 (2.5-2.9)	.3906-.3913 (9.92-9.94)	.0030 (.075)	.....

4-CYLINDER DIESEL & 5-CYLINDER TURBO DIESEL (Cont.)

ENGINE SPECIFICATIONS (Cont.)

PISTONS, PINS, RINGS

Engine	PISTONS	PINS		RINGS		
	Clearance In. (mm)	Piston Fit In. (mm)	Rod Fit In. (mm)	Ring No.	End Gap In. (mm)	Side Clearance In. (mm)
2.4L & 3.0L	.0007-.0015 (.018-.0138)	[1]	Push Fit	No. 1	.0079-.0138 (.20-.35)	.004-.005 (.100-.132)
				No. 2	.0079-.0138 (.20-.35)	.003-.004 (.070-.102)
				No. 3	.0098-.0157 (.25-.40)	.001-.002 (.030-.062)

[1] – Interference fit. See Piston & Rod Assembly in this article.

CRANKSHAFT MAIN & CONNECTING ROD BEARINGS

Engine	MAIN BEARINGS				CONNECTING ROD BEARINGS		
	Journal Diam. In. (mm)	Clearance In. (mm)	Thrust Bearing	Crankshaft End Play In. (mm)	Journal Diam. In. (mm)	Clearance In. (mm)	Side Play In. (mm)
2.4L & 3.0L	2.7541-2.7545 (69.95-69.96)	.0012-.0027 (.031-.068)	Center	.0039-.0090 (.10-.22)	2.0454-2.0458 (51.95-51.96)	.0012-.0027 (.031-.068)	.005-.010 (.12-.26)

VALVE SPRINGS

Engine	Free Length In. (mm)	PRESSURE Lbs. @ In. (Kg @ mm)	
		Valve Closed	Valve Open
2.4L & 3.0L	2.015 (51.2)	.....	130.1@1.102 (59.0@28.0)

CAMSHAFT

Engine	Journal Diam. In. (mm)	Clearance In. (mm)	Lobe Lift In. (mm)
2.4L & 3.0L			
No. 1	1.375 (34.94)	.0010-.0026 (.025-.066)	.003-.006 (.070-.149)
No. 2, 3 & 4	1.926 (48.94)	.0010-.0026 (.025-.066)	.....

VALVE TIMING

Engine	INTAKE		EXHAUST	
	Open (BTDC)	Close (ABDC)	Open (BBDC)	Close (ATDC)
2.4L & 3.0L	13.5°	15.5°	19°	17°

Mercedes-Benz Engines

3.8 LITER V8

ENGINE CODING

ENGINE IDENTIFICATION

Identification number is located on tag attached to engine crankcase. First six digits of code are used to identify engine, as follows:

ENGINE IDENTIFICATION

Application	Chassis Type	Engine Code
380 SEC	126.043	116.963
380 SL	107.045	116.962
380SEL	126.033	116.963

ENGINE, MANIFOLDS & CYLINDER HEADS

ENGINE

Removal

1) Remove engine hood. Drain cooling system, using both left and right engine block drains. Disconnect and remove battery and frame. Remove air conditioning system and remove pipe set at compressor.

2) Disconnect and remove all water hoses. Remove all vacuum, fuel and electrical lines leading to engine. On model 126 remove exhaust pipe at manifold. On all other models completely remove exhaust system. Remove right drag link end from ball-stud.

3) On all models, drain power steering reservoir and disconnect hoses. Remove TDC test socket, and remove cable from TDC transmitter. Remove left and right engine shock absorbers.

4) Attach engine sling and hoist, to engine. Remove engine mount bolts. Remove rear engine carrier with engine mount. Remove driveshaft retaining bolts, and remove driveshaft.

5) Remove transmission linkages, at transmission. Lift engine/transmission assembly at a 45° angle, and carefully remove from vehicle. Separate engine from transmission assembly.

Installation

1) Ensure that oil cooler and all hoses have been flushed and are free from contamination. Renew engine mounts and components as required.

2) Reverse removal procedure, to complete installation. Recharge air conditioning system, and check for leaks.

INTAKE MANIFOLD

Removal

1) Disconnect negative battery cable. Partially drain coolant, at cylinder block drain plug. Disconnect injection lines and fuel lines. Pull off air lines. Remove bowden wire from automatic transmission.

2) Remove bearing bracket from linkage regulation and bearing bracket from longitudinal regulating shaft. Pull off connecting cables and plug. Disconnect vacuum lines from automatic transmission, and brake power unit.

3) remove cooling system hoses. Remove intake manifold attaching bolts, and remove intake manifold toward the rear. Clean intake manifold and check flange surfaces for warpage with straightedge.

Installation

To install, reverse removal procedure.

EXHAUST MANIFOLD

Removal

Disconnect negative battery cable. Disconnect exhaust pipe from manifold and exhaust gas return line at 90° fitting. Remove exhaust manifold retaining bolts, and remove exhaust manifold.

Installation

To install, reverse removal procedure.

CYLINDER HEAD

Removal

1) Remove left and right cylinder block drain plugs, and drain cooling system. Remove air cleaner, and battery. Remove fuel line and injectors. Disconnect fuel injection linkage.

NOTE: **Cylinder head removal should not be attempted until engine has cooled down. Several specially shaped Allen wrenches are required for cylinder head bolt removal and replacement.**

2) Disconnect and remove intake manifold. Remove A/T fluid filler pipe from attachment at cylinder head. Remove alternator and mounting bracket. Remove distributor, and power steering pump with mounting bracket.

3) Disconnect exhaust pipe from manifold and exhaust gas return line at 90° fitting. Remove chain tensioner and slide rails. Mark camshaft sprocket and timing chain position for assembly reference. Remove sprocket from camshaft. Using specially shaped Allen wrenches, remove head bolts and lift off head.

Installation

1) Ensure that all mating surfaces are clean and install new cylinder head gasket. Tighten cylinder head bolts. *See Fig. 1.*

2) To complete installation, reverse removal procedure and note the following: and run engine until normal operating temperature is reached. Slightly loosen head bolts individually, then retighten.

Fig. 1: Cylinder Head Tightening Sequence

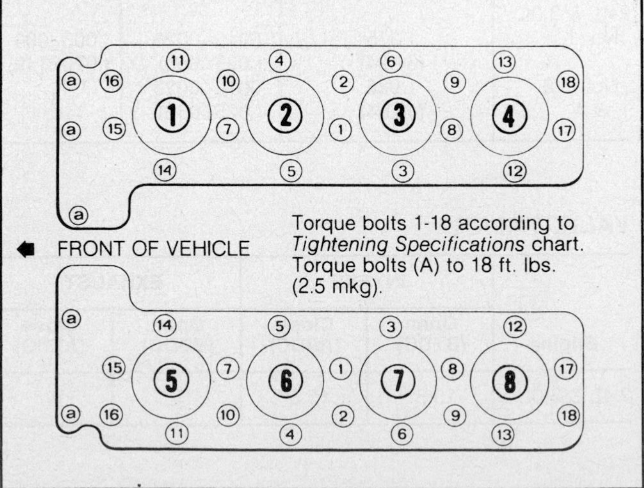
FRONT OF VEHICLE
Torque bolts 1-18 according to *Tightening Specifications* chart. Torque bolts (A) to 18 ft. lbs. (2.5 mkg).

Loosen cylinder head in reverse order.

CAMSHAFT

FRONT MAIN BEARING OIL SEAL

Removal

1) With engine removed from vehicle. Remove all V-belts, mark hub and crankshaft with paint or chalk.

2) Remove vibration damper, pulley and hub. Remove oil seal, making sure that crankshaft and receiving bore are not damaged.

Installation

1) Ensure there are no burrs on edge of receiving bore, before installing new seal. Lubricate receiving bore and seal lip with oil.

2) Install oil seal with installation sleeve (110 589 07 61 00). To complete installation, reverse removal procedure.

TIMING CHAIN

Removal & Installation

1) A split link timing chain is available for repairs without dismantling engine. Remove spark plugs, and camshaft covers. Remove air cleaner adapter. Cover chain guard with cloth and grind open both pins of a link in the timing chain.

2) Remove old link and insert new split link with new chain attached. Turn crankshaft slowly in normal direction while feeding new chain in, and old chain out. Ensure that chain does not slip on sprockets and install master (split) link from rear so that retainer will be at front of engine.

Fig. 2: Timing Chains and Sprockets

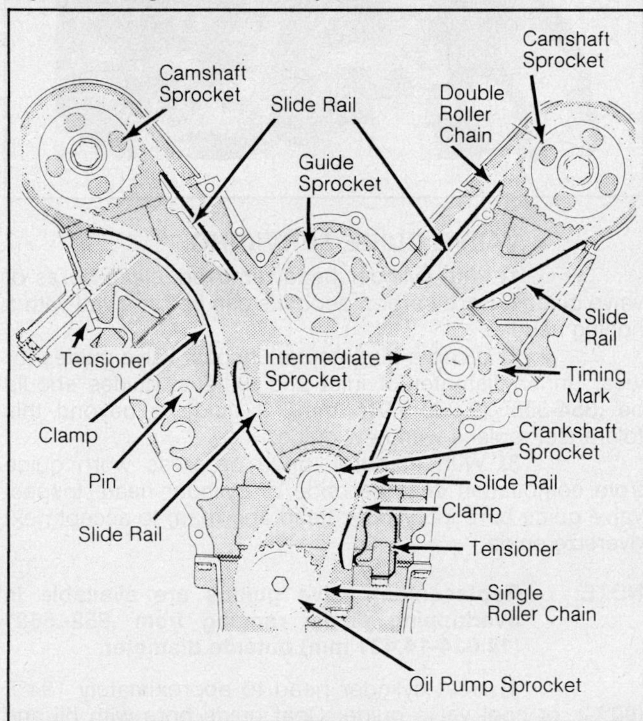
Camshaft Sprocket
Slide Rail
Double Roller Chain
Camshaft Sprocket
Guide Sprocket
Slide Rail
Tensioner
Intermediate Sprocket
Timing Mark
Clamp
Crankshaft Sprocket
Pin
Slide Rail
Clamp
Slide Rail
Tensioner
Single Roller Chain
Oil Pump Sprocket

When installing new chain, ensure that chain does not slip on sprockets.

3) Install link spring lock with closed end facing direction of rotation. Rotate crankshaft through one complete revolution and check that all timing marks still agree. To complete installation, reverse removal procedure.

CHAIN TENSIONER

1) Remove air injector pipe, and 3 bolts fastening tensioner. Remove chain tensioner.

NOTE: **In all instances chain tensioner is lubricated and connected to oiling circuit.**

2) To check tensioner, place in container of oil vertically so that oil covers flange. Actuate plunger to fill tensioner with oil. After filling and venting, plunger should allow compression very slowly and evenly, and with considerable force.

3) To install, use new gasket and tighten bolts evenly. Pressure pin of tensioner must press against lug of tensioning rail.

VALVE TIMING

1) Measure timing periods on inlet valves of cylinder 1 and 6. Remove hydraulic valve lifters and replace with adjusting screws (116 050 11 20). Adjust each screw so rocker arm just touches the base circle of the cam.

2) Attach dial indicator so that pointeer rests vertically on valve spring retainer. Pin should have .118" (3 mm) preload and dial should be set to zero.

3) Rotate engine in direction of normal rotation, until pointer moves .0787" (2 mm), leaving a preload of .039" (1 mm). Readings should be in accordance with valve timing chart. Repeat for No. 6 intake valve.

4) If timing requires correction, install an offset Woodruff Key or new chain. Keys are available in 4 offsets providing corrections of 4°, 6 1/2°, 8°, and 10°.

5) After checking and adjusting valve timing, reinstall hydraulic lifters and adjust for proper base setting.

CAMSHAFT & BEARINGS

Removal

1) With cylinder head covers removed, set No. 1 piston at TDC compression stroke and remove rocker arms. Mark sprockets and timing chain for reassembly.

2) Remove camshaft sprockets. Remove camshaft bearings, oil tube and camshaft as an assembly.

Installation

1) Assemble bearings on camshaft. Note that smooth bearing journals must fit in bearings with an oil groove, and camshaft journals with an oil groove must fit in bearings without an oil groove.

2) Place camshaft and bearing assembly on head. Note that outer screw of left camshaft rear bearing must be inserted in bearing prior to mounting due to interference from brake unit. Oil pipe connections on bearings must be renewed to ensure proper oil pressure.

3) Tighten camshaft bearing mounting bolts, and check that camshaft rotates freely. Mount compensating washer so that both inner and outer notches align with Woodruff key in camshaft. Assemble sprockets to camshaft so that white color faces camshaft and timing marks are aligned.

4) Install rocker arms and check basic clearance of lifters. See Adjusting Lifters to Base Setting, in this article. To complete installation, reverse removal procedure.

3.8 LITER V8 (Cont.)

NOTE: Whenever it is necessary to install either new rocker arms or camshaft, both rocker arms and camshaft must be replaced. Camshaft journals may be reground and undersize bearings installed.

DISTRIBUTOR DRIVE GEAR

Removal

1) With engine front cover removed, disconnect slide rails as needed and timing chain tensioners.

2) Remove chain from intermediate sprocket and pull sprocket from engine. Use puller to extract bushing from crankcase and cover.

Installation

1) Press new bushings in position so that lubricating groove is at bottom. Lubricate bushings and install intermediate sprocket.

2) Note that mark on sprocket must align with mark on crankcase with number 1 cylinder at TDC position on it's compression stroke. To complete installation, reverse removal procedure.

VALVES

VALVE ARRANGEMENT

Right Bank — E-I-E-I-E-I-I-E (Front-to-rear).
Left Bank — E-I-I-E-I-E-I-E (Front-to-rear).

ROCKER ARMS

1) Rocker arms are individually mounted on the 16 valves, without use of a shaft. They are in constant contact with the camshaft, thrust plates above the valve stems, and hydraulic valve lifters. To remove, compress spring on each valve using compressor (123 589 03 61 00). Mark each arm for installation in original position.

NOTE: Whenever it is necessary to install either new rocker arms or camshaft, both rocker arms and camshaft must be replaced. Camshaft journals may be reground and undersize bearings installed.

2) Rocker arms have a chamfer behind ball socket (lifter end). This prevents rocker arm from striking retaining cap of lifters in extreme cases. Do not use rocker arms unless they have this chamfer.

3) Whenever camshaft is replaced, new rocker arms must also be installed. Likewise, when new rocker arms are installed, replace the camshaft, as well. When making replacements, check base setting of hydraulic valve lifters using test gauge (100 589 04 23 00).

4) Correct, as required, using new thrust piece. Thrust pieces are available in steps of .0014" (.35 mm), from .147" (3.7 mm) to .228" (5.8 mm). See Adjusting Lifters to Base Setting, in this article.

VALVE SPRINGS & STEM SEALS

Removal

Using spring compressor (123 589 03 61 00) remove rocker arms. Lift out thrust plate and, using special magnet (116 589 06 63 00), remove valve keepers. Remove spring retainer, inner and outer valve springs, valve stem seals and rotocaps.

Fig. 3: Removing Valve Keepers

(123 589 03 61 00)
Spring Compressor Tool
(116 589 06 63 00)
Special Magnet

Use special magnet (116 589 06 63 00) to remove valve keepers.

Installation

Replacement valve stem seals are supplied in a kit which includes assembly sleeves. Place sleeve over stem and install lubricated seal with installing tool. Install remaining components in reverse order of removal.

Fig. 4: Installing Valve Stem Seals

(116 589 00 43 00)

VALVE GUIDE SERVICING

1) With cylinder head removed, clean bores of valve guides. Hard carbon deposits can be removed with a honing needle.

2) Using a plug gauge, inspect valve guides for wear. Inner diameter of inlet and exhaust guides should be .354-355" (9.000-9.015 mm). If guide is beyond this tolerance, replace with new guide.

3) With mandrel, drive or press worn guide from combustion chamber side of cylinder head. Inspect valve guide bore in cylinder head and ream to accept next oversize guide.

NOTE: Replacement valve guides are available in overlapping sizes, ranging from .552-.568" (14.014-14.431 mm) outside diameter.

4) Heat cylinder head to approximately 194°F (90°C), or cool valve guide. Coat guide bore with oil and using mandrel, seat new guide in bore.

NOTE: Be sure snap ring is properly installed. Recheck valve guide clearance and that valve moves freely in guide.

3.8 LITER V8 (Cont.)

VALVE SEAT RING

1) Check valve guide prior to removing seat ring. See Valve Guide Servicing in this section. If seat ring is worn, carefully remove it by machining with a valve seat ring turning tool.

2) Thoroughly clean the receiving bore, and check its diameter. If diameter is within specifications, install a new valve seat ring of the same size. If diameter is not within specifications, 1.811-1.812" (46.0-46.02 mm) for intake or 1.575-1.576" (40.0-40.01 mm) for exhaust, machine bore to next oversize.

3) To install, heat cylinder head in water to approximately 140°F (60°C). Place pre-cooled seat ring into bore. To position seat ring, lightly tap ring, using a mandrel and hammer.

4) Machine valve seat to correct width and correct for runout. Do not machine rounded bead on lower part of valve seat. Valve seat runout should not exceed .0016" (.04 mm).

HYDRAULIC VALVE LIFTERS

1) Hydraulic valve lifters eliminate the need to adjust valve clearance. Constant contact of rocker arms with camshaft, valves and lifters not only reduces noise, but also compensates for wear or temperature changes.

NOTE: **Always keep hydraulic valve lifters in an upright position. Rocker arms and valve lifters should always be reinstalled in original locations. When checking and adjusting lifter settings, crank engine for 30 seconds with starter contact switch.**

2) The ball valve closes when the cam lobe exerts pressure on rocker arm. Trapped oil in pressure chamber forms a solid hydraulic connection which prevents the plunger from moving fully downward. Leak-off vents permit air and excess oil to escape.

3) To check hydraulic lifter performance, press on rocker arm at lift end with valves in closed position. If pressure bleeds off too rapidly, replace faulty lifter(s). If lifters are removed, they should be stored in an upright position and reinstalled in original location.

ADJUSTING LIFTERS TO BASE SETTING

1) When replacing compensating element (hydraulic lifters) or camshaft and rocker arms, basic position of compensating element must be checked. Rotate engine so that cam lobe of element to be checked is in the upright position and install test gauge (100 589 04 23 00).

2) Set measuring pin of gauge through rocker arm hole so that it rests on ball pin of lifter. Basic position is correct when red groove of pin is aligned with measuring edge of tool.

3) If groove is below measuring edge, a plus (+) deviation is indicated, requiring a thinner thrust piece. Entire groove showing above measuring edge indicates a minus (-) deviation, and requires a thicker thrust piece.

4) To correct setting, remove rocker arm and thrust piece. Install thinner or thicker thrust piece as required, and reinstall rocker arm. Repeat measuring procedure. Position is correct when center of measuring groove aligns with edge of gauge.

PISTONS, RINGS & PINS

OIL PAN

Removal (Model 107)

1) Remove radiator, and shroud. Remove front axle assembly. Remove A/C compressor and mounting bracket.

2) Remove supporting angle bracket between pan and transmission. Remove oil pan bolts and lower oil pan along with dipstick guide tube from engine.

Installation

To install, apply grease to clean mating surfaces and install new gasket. Place pan in position and reverse removal procedure, to complete installation.

Removal (Model 126)

1) Remove A/C compressor and mounting bracket from engine. Remove drive belt tensioning pulley. Unbolt and remove oil pan lower half. Remove oil pump drive sprocket and mounting bolts. Remove oil pump.

2) Remove oil pan upper half retaining bolts, and remove upper pan. Remove engine mount bolts. Loosen both engine shock absorbers. Remove radiator shell. Lift engine until oil pan can be removed.

Installation

To install, ensure that all mating surfaces are clean and apply thin layer of grease. Use new gasket and install oil pan upper half. To complete installation, reverse removal procedure.

PISTON & ROD ASSEMBLY

Removal

1) With cylinder head and oil pan removed, remove connecting rod nuts and bearing caps. Push piston and rod assembly out top of cylinder. Use care not to damage any bearing surface, during removal procedure.

2) Remove piston pin snap ring and push out piston pin. Retain all components in proper order for reassembly.

Installation

1) Check rings for gap and end clearance. Replace if not within specifications. Lubricate piston pins and connecting rod bushings. Push in piston pin (do not heat piston), and insert snap rings.

2) Stagger ring gaps on piston and fit ring compressor. Install piston and rod assembly with arrow on piston facing toward front of engine.

3) Install rod caps, matching code numbers to and facing rod numbers. Tighten rod cap nuts and check all clearances.

FITTING PISTONS

Measure cylinder bores at top, bottom and center of bore in at least 2 directions. If greater than .004" (.10 mm) from standard, cylinders must be bored and new pistons fitted.

CYLINDER BORE SPECIFICATIONS

Application	In. (mm)
Standard	3.6220-3.6228 (92.0-92.02)
1st Oversize	3.6417-3.6425 (92.50-92.52)
2nd Oversize	3.6614-3.6622 (93.0-93.02)

3.8 LITER V8 (Cont.)

PISTON RINGS

1) Check rings for gap and end clearance. Stagger ring gaps on piston and fit ring compressor. Install piston and rod assembly with arrow on piston facing toward front of engine.

2) Install rod caps, matching code numbers to and facing rod numbers. Tighten rod cap nuts and check all clearances.

PISTON PINS

Removal

Piston pins are retained with circlips in pistons. To remove pins, remove circlips and push out pins.

Installation

To install, ensure that arrow on piston crown faces front (timing chain end) and that bearing retaining notch in connecting rod faces toward outside of engine. Lubricate pin and push into piston and rod assembly by hand.

NOTE: Do not heat piston to install piston pin.

CRANKSHAFT MAIN & CONNECTING ROD BEARINGS

MAIN & CONNECTING ROD BEARINGS

1) Mount main bearing cap to cylinder block without bearings in place. Measure inside diameter at 3 locations, as shown in *Fig. 5*. Be sure cap is properly positioned when taking reading. Offset bearing caps can be moved into center position by lightly tapping them with a plastic hammer.

2) All three measurements should agree. If basic bores exceed specifications and the required overlap of bearing shell halves is not assured, remove .008" (.02 mm) from contact surfaces, using a surface plate.

Fig. 5: Location for Measuring Main Bearing Bore Diameter

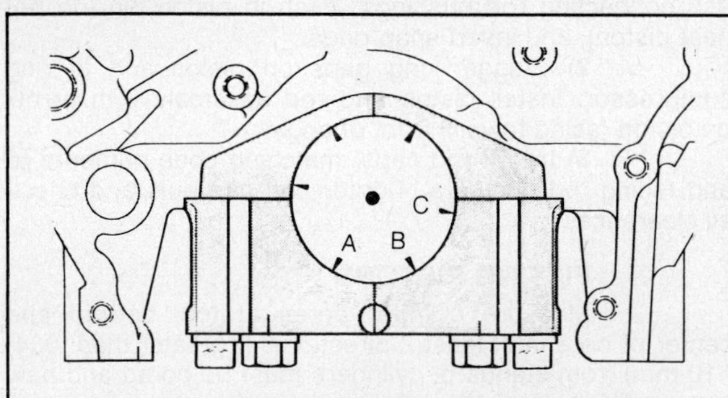
A
B
C

Be sure cap is properly positioned, when taking reading.

3) Measure main bearing and connecting rod bearings at front and rear to check for taper. If beyond .0006" (.015 mm), remove excess material from one side of bearing cap, using surface plate.

4) Use proper bearing shells to match measurements obtained. Several overlapping bearing sizes are available. Fit bearing halves into bearing bore and tighten bolts.

5) Measure inner diameter of bearings and outer diameter of journals. Difference in measurements should be within bearing clearance specifications. If not, change bearing shell halves.

6) When proper clearance is calculated, clean and oil all parts and install crankshaft. Tighten main cap bolts according to sequence. *See Fig. 6.*

Fig. 6: Crankshaft Main Bearing Tightening Sequence

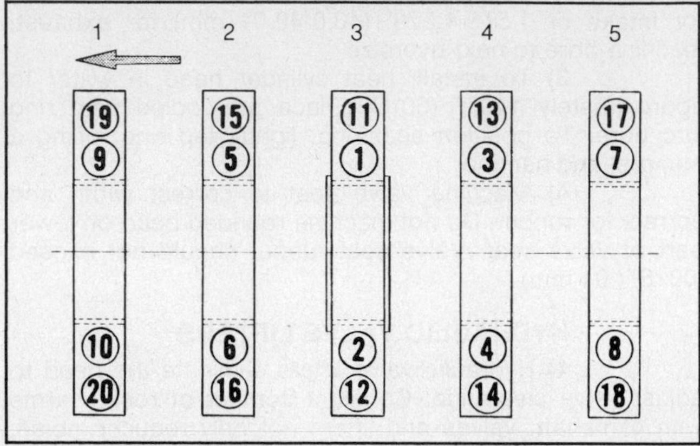
1
2
3
4
5
19
9
15
5
11
1
13
3
17
7
10
20
6
16
2
12
4
14
8
18

Tighten bolts in 2 steps.

7) With crankshaft properly installed, check for free rotation and for proper end play. Install connecting rods.

THRUST BEARING ALIGNMENT

Use a feeler gauge to check crankshaft end play. Insert feeler gauge between No. 3 main bearing (thrust bearing) and crankshaft thrust face. Crankshaft end play should be .004-.009" (.10-.23 mm).

REAR MAIN BEARING OIL SEAL

Removal

1) Remove engine from vehicle. Remove flywheel assembly. Force out old oil seal. Clean sealing surfaces.

2) Check crankshaft running surface for scoring. Oil seal with sealing lip offset inward is available in case of scored crankshaft.

Fig. 7: Installing Rear Cover and Seal

Conical Sleeve
(116 589 03 43 00)

Seal can be installed, without removing rear engine plate.

3.8 LITER V8 (Cont.)

Installation

1) Lubricate lip of seal, and place seal into position in rear engine cover. Place conical sleeve (116 589 03 43 00) over crankshaft end and place cover in position.

2) Use care so that pan gasket is not damaged, during this procedure. Install drive plate (flywheel).

NOTE: **Drive plate (flywheel) can only be mounted in one position due to offset of 1 of the 8 fastening bolts.**

ENGINE OILING

CRANKCASE CAPACITY

8.5 qts. (8.0L) with filter.

OIL FILTER

Disposable cartridge type. Located near front of engine. Some models use upright oil filters (canister type).

NORMAL OIL PRESSURE

7.1 psi (.5 kg/cm²) at idle; 42.6 psi (3.0 kg/cm²) at 3000 RPM.

BY-PASS VALVE

Valve is located in crankcase and enters into main oil gallery. When filter becomes severely contaminated valve will open and oil will enter in an unfiltered state.

ENGINE OILING SYSTEM

Lubrication is provided by a gear type oil pump directly driven by crankshaft. Oil is picked up through a strainer from lower portion of oil pan and forced to oil filter through a gallery in timing casing.

After passing through filter, oil flows to center main gallery, to crankshaft and through rod bearings up rods to piston pin bushing. Oil galleries run to cylinder head, valve assemblies and to camshafts. Circuit also oils timing chain tensioner.

OIL PUMP

Removal

Remove oil pan, as previously outlined. Oil pump is chain driven and must have sprocket and chain removed prior to pump removal. Remove 4 oil pump mounting bolts. Slide pump off drive shaft..

Installation

Mount oil pump on sprocket. The clamping sleeve in sprocket should enter cutout of drive shaft. Install oil pump.

NOTE: **Lock tensioning spring of chain tensioner with a screwdriver, against rotation when tightening Pump retaining bolt.**

ENGINE COOLING

COOLING SYSTEM CAPACITY

15.8 qts. (14.9L).

THERMOSTAT

1) Opens at 162-169°F (72-76°C). Thermostat is located in water pump housing. *See Fig 8.*

2) To remove, drain cooling system, remove air cleaner, disconnect battery and alternator. Remove housing and thermostat. When installing ensure ball-valve is mounted at highest point.

Fig. 8: Thermostat Installation

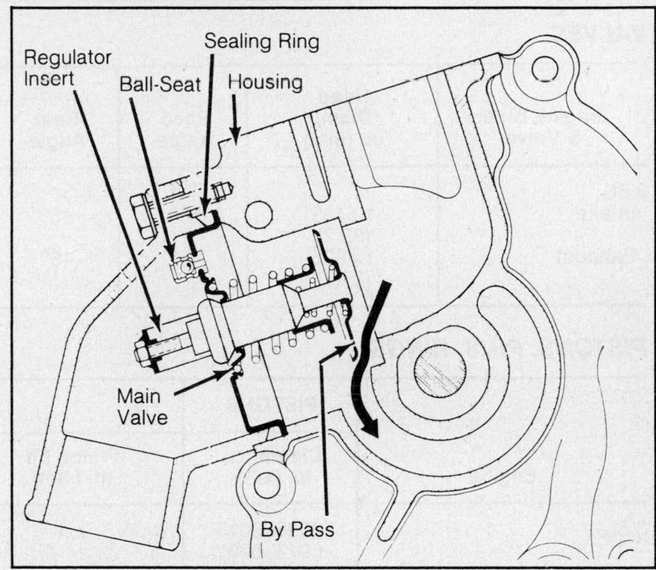
Sealing Ring
Regulator Insert
Ball-Seat
Housing
Main Valve
By Pass

When installing, ensure ball-valve is mounted at highest point.

WATER PUMP

Removal

1) Disconnect all necessary water hoses and any remaining components from water pump housing.

2) Remove distributor, and 8 water pump mounting bolts. Remove pump from vehicle.

Installation

Clean gasket mating surfaces, and install water pump with new gasket. To complete installation, reverse removal procedure.

TIGHTENING SPECIFICATIONS

Application	Ft. Lbs. (N.m)
Cylinder Head Bolts	
Cold Step 1	22 (30)
Cold Step 2	43 (58)
Warm Step 3	43 (58)
Camshaft Bracket Bolts	36 (49)
Camshaft Sprocket Bolts	72 (98)
Connecting Rod Bolts	33 (45)
Main Bearing Caps	
Large Bolts	72 (98)
Small Bolts	47 (64)
Crankshaft Bolts	195-239 (265-325)
Oil Pressure Relief Valve	29 (39)
Flywheel (Drive Plate)	[1] 25 (35)
Hydraulic Valve Lifters	36 (49)
Chain Tensioner Nut	80 (109)

[1] — After torque values are achieved, torque an additional 90-100°.

Mercedes-Benz Engines

3.8 LITER V8 (Cont.)

ENGINE SPECIFICATIONS

GENERAL SPECIFICATIONS

Year	DISPLACEMENT		Fuel System	HP@RPM	Torque Ft. Lbs.@RPM	Compr. Ratio	BORE		STROKE	
	Cu. In.	Liters					In.	mm	In.	mm
1983	234	3.8	Fuel Inj.	155@4750	196@2750	8.3:1	3.46	88	3.11	78.1

VALVES

Engine Size & Valve	Head Diam. In. (mm)	Face Angle	Seat Angle	Seat Width In. (mm)	Stem Diameter In. (mm)	Stem Clearance In. (mm)	Valve Lift In. (mm)
3.8L							
Intake	1.5433 (39.2)	45°	45°	.051-.078 (1.3-2.0)	.3523-.3531 (8.95-8.97)	.003 (.075)	.....
Exhaust	1.4606 (37.1)	45°	45°	.059-.079 (1.5-2.0)	.3523-.3531 (8.95-8.97)	.003	.....

PISTONS, PINS, RINGS

Engine	PISTONS	PINS		RINGS		
	Clearance In. (mm)	Piston Fit In. (mm)	Rod Fit In. (mm)	Ring No.	End Gap In. (mm)	Side Clearance In. (mm)
3.8L	.0005-.0015 (.013-.023)	.....	.0002-.0007 (.005-.018)	No. 1	.014-.022 (.35-.55)	.002-.0036 (.050-.092)
				No. 2	.014-.022 (.35-.55)	.0016-.0030 (.040-.082)
				Oil	.010-.016 (.25-.40)	.0012-.0030 (.030-.072)

CRANKSHAFT MAIN & CONNECTING ROD BEARINGS

Engine	MAIN BEARINGS				CONNECTING ROD BEARINGS		
	Journal Diam. In. (mm)	Clearance In. (mm)	Thrust Bearing	Crankshaft End Play In. (mm)	Journal Diam. In. (mm)	Clearance In. (mm)	Side Play In. (mm)
3.8L	2.517-2.2519 (63.93-63.98)	.0018-.0033 (.045-.084)	.....	.004-.009 (.10-.23)	2.031 (51.6)	.0008-.0027 (.021-.068)	.009-.015 (.233-.39)

VALVE TIMING

Engine	INTAKE		EXHAUST	
	Open (BTDC)	Close (ABDC)	Open (BBDC)	Close (ATDC)
3.8L	24°	75°	4°	125°

CAMSHAFT

Engine	Journal Diam. In. (mm)	Clearance In. (mm)	Lobe Lift In. (mm)
3.8L			
No. 1	1.376-1.377 (34.96-34.98)	.0004-.0023 (.02-.06)	.....
No. 2 & 3	1.935-1.936 (49.16-49.18)	.0011-.0027 (.03-.07)	.....
No. 4 & 5	1.943-1.944 (49.36-49.38)	.0011-.0027 (.03-.07)	.....

VALVE SPRINGS

Engine	Free Length In. (mm)	PRESSURE Lbs. @ In. (Kg @ mm)	
		Valve Closed	Valve Open
3.8L			
Inner	1.77 (45)	24.7@1.3 (11.2@33)	50.7@846 (23@21.5)
Outer	1.95 (49.5)	67.24@1.65 (30.5@42)	194@1.2 (88@30.5)

Mitsubishi Engines

1.4L & 1.6L 4-CYLINDER

Chrysler Corp. Imports: Colt

ENGINE CODING

ENGINE IDENTIFICATION

Engine model code and serial number are stamped on engine block just below No. 1 spark plug on right side of block. Model codes are listed in table.

ENGINE IDENTIFICATION

Application	Engine Model	[1] Engine VIN Code
1.4L (86.0")	G12B	2
1.6L (97.5")	G32B	3

[1] – Eighth digit of VIN code.

ENGINE, MANIFOLDS & CYLINDER HEAD

ENGINE

Removal

1) Drain cooling system and remove battery and tray. Remove air cleaner assembly. Remove purge control valve bracket from battery support and disconnect vacuum hose from valve. Remove windshield washer tank, radiator reservoir and damping canister.

2) Remove radiator assembly and cooling fan. Disconnect the following from the engine/transaxle: clutch, accelerator and speedometer cables, heater hose, fuel hoses, PCV vacuum hose, high altitude compensator vacuum hose (California models), bowl vent purge hose,

3) Remove wires from starter, engine ground, alternator, coolant temperature, ignition coil, high temperature sensor, neutral start switch, back-up light and oil pressure switch.

4) Remove ignition coil. From under vehicle, remove undercover and drain transaxle. Remove right and left drive shafts from transaxle case and suspend with wire to prevent damaging joints. Cover holes in transaxle case to prevent entry of foreign matter.

NOTE: **Drive shaft retainer rings should be replaced whenever drive shafts are removed from transaxle.**

5) Remove assist rod, control rod and range selector cable from manual transaxle. Remove shift control cable from automatic transaxle. Disconnect and suspend exhaust pipe.

6) Remove front roll rod bolts and loosen transaxle mounting bracket attaching nuts. Remove bolts and nuts from front and rear engine insulators and disconnect rear roll rod.

7) Suspend engine from chains attached to hoisting brackets and remove mounting bracket nuts loosened previously. Lift engine-transaxle assembly from vehicle using care that assembly does not hit battery bracket during removal.

Installation

Reverse removal procedures and tighten mounting bolts and nuts to specifications with weight of engine on insulators. Ensure projection on roll rod lower bolt is inserted into slot in bracket. Replace all fluids and adjust all cables and linkages.

CYLINDER HEAD & MANIFOLDS

Removal (1.4L)

1) Drain cooling system and disconnect upper radiator hose. Remove breather hose and air cleaner. Disconnect vacuum hose at distributor, fuel hose and water hose.

2) Disconnect accelerator linkage and spark plug wires. Remove distributor, carburetor and intake manifold. Remove heat cowl, exhaust manifold assembly and timing belt cover.

3) Move timing belt tensioner toward water pump and secure it. Remove timing belt from camshaft sprocket, ensuring belt is left on crankshaft sprocket. Remove rocker arm cover.

4) Loosen cylinder head bolts, in steps, in reverse of tightening sequence. *See Fig. 1.* Remove bolts and cylinder head making certain gasket pieces do not fall into engine.

Removal (1.6L)

1) Drain cooling system and disconnect upper radiator hose. Remove breather and purge hoses. Remove air cleaner and fuel line. Remove vacuum hose at distributor and purge control valve.

2) Detach spark wires and remove distributor. Disconnect heater hose intake manifold and water hose between cylinder head and carburetor. Disconnect water gauge wire and remove fuel pump.

3) Remove exhaust manifold. Remove intake manifold and carburetor as an assembly. Remove timing belt upper front cover. Turn crankshaft so number 1 piston is at TDC on compression stroke.

4) Mark timing belt with marker in line with camshaft sprocket timing mark. Remove camshaft sprocket bolt and remove camshaft sprocket with timing belt attached. Position on sprocket holder.

5) If there is a large gap present between camshaft sprocket and sprocket holder, insert a 2" (50 mm) piece of timing belt or similar material into the gap to prevent belt from disengaging from crankshaft or oil pump sprockets.

6) Loosen cylinder head bolts, in steps, in reverse of tightening sequence. *See Fig. 1.* Remove bolts and lift cylinder head from engine being careful not to twist sprocket and belt.

Installation (1.4L & 1.6L)

1) To install cylinder head and intake manifold, reverse removal procedures. Gasket surfaces must be clean and new gaskets used. Use sealer on both sides of intake manifold gasket around water passages.

NOTE: **Avoid sliding cylinder head when installing in order to prevent damage to gasket and aligning dowels (when installed). Engine should not be run with valve cover off due to oil spray from rocker arms.**

2) Tighten cylinder head bolts in tightening sequence to initial torque of 25 ft. lbs. (34 N.m). *See Fig. 1.* Repeat procedure, tightening bolts to final torque.

3) Complete installation by reversing removal procedures. Temporarily set valve clearance to cold engine settings. Readjust to hot engine settings when engine reaches normal operating temperature. Install valve cover, air cleaner and breather hoses.

Mitsubishi Engines

1.4L & 1.6L 4-CYLINDER (Cont.)

Fig. 1: Cylinder Head Tightening Sequence

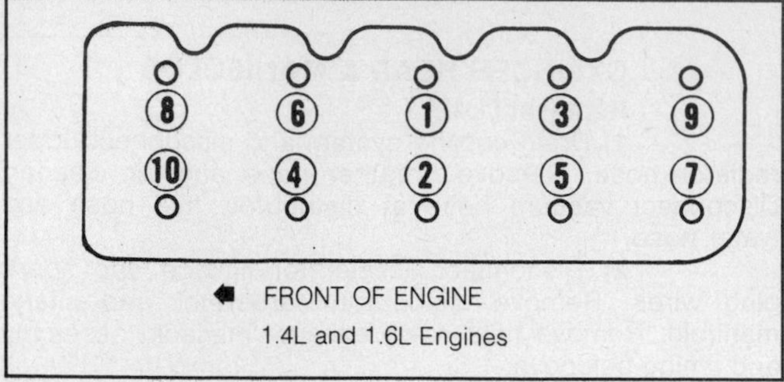

8
6
1
3
9
10
4
2
5
7
FRONT OF ENGINE
1.4L and 1.6L Engines

Remove bolts in reverse order during removal.

CAMSHAFT

ROCKER ARMS & SHAFTS

Removal (1.4L)

1) Remove breather hose and air cleaner. Remove timing belt from camshaft sprocket only. Remove camshaft sprocket and valve covers.

2) Loosen rocker shaft mounting bolts and lift off rocker shaft, rocker arms and springs as an assembly. Remove bolts from shafts and slide off springs and rocker arms.

Installation

To install reverse removal procedure, ensuring short springs for exhaust valves, are used with right-hand rocker arm parts.

Fig. 2: Installing Timing Belt on 1.4L Engine

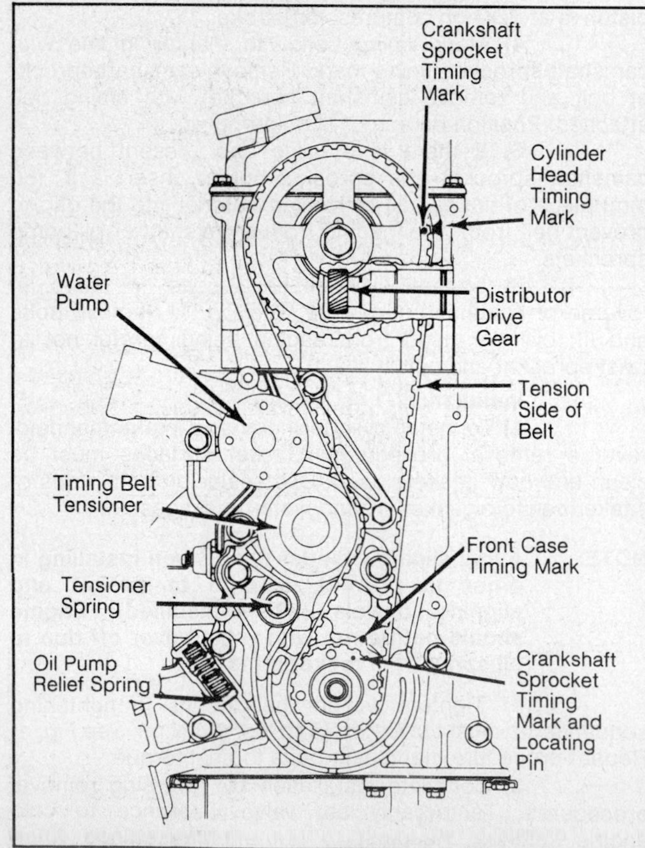

Crankshaft Sprocket Timing Mark
Cylinder Head Timing Mark
Water Pump
Distributor Drive Gear
Tension Side of Belt
Timing Belt Tensioner
Front Case Timing Mark
Tensioner Spring
Oil Pump Relief Spring
Crankshaft Sprocket Timing Mark and Locating Pin

Make certain sprocket timing marks are in alignment before installing belt.

CAMSHAFT

Removal (1.4L)

1) Remove rocker arms and shafts as previously described. Remove timing belt cover and move belt tensioner fully toward water pump, ensuring camshaft sprocket mark is aligned with timing mark on cylinder head. *See Fig. 2.*

2) Remove timing belt and camshaft sprocket from camshaft. Remove distributor and fuel pump. Remove camshaft rear cover from rear of head and thrust case tightening bolt from top of head.

3) Remove camshaft from rear of head. Check thrust case for camshaft end play. If excessive, replace thrust case and recheck. If rear of camshaft journal is badly worn, replace camshaft.

Installation

To install, thoroughly lubricate camshaft and seal lips and reverse removal procedure.

Fig. 3: Rocker Arm Identification on 1.4L & 1.6L Engines

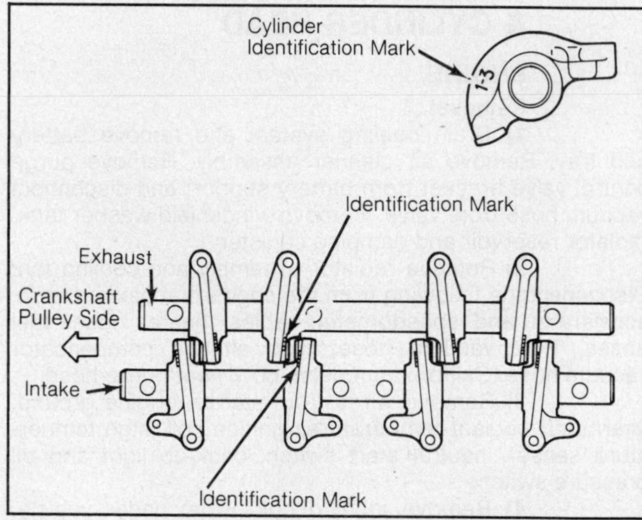

Cylinder Identification Mark
1-3
Identification Mark
Exhaust
Crankshaft Pulley Side
Intake
Identification Mark

Numbers on rocker arms indicate cylinder application.

ROCKER ASSEMBLY & CAMSHAFT

Removal (1.6L)

1) Remove breather hoses, purge line and air cleaner. Disconnect spark plug wires and remove upper front cover. Turn crankshaft to TDC of compression stroke on No. 1 cylinder.

2) Make mating mark on timing belt in alignment with timing mark on camshaft sprocket and upper inner cover. *See Fig. 4.* Slide camshaft sprocket, with belt attached, off camshaft and allow sprocket to rest on sprocket holder.

3) If there is a large gap present between camshaft sprocket and sprocket holder, insert a 2" (50 mm) piece of timing belt or similar material into the gap to prevent belt disengagement from crankshaft or oil pump sprocket.

4) Remove camshaft spacer and upper inner cover. Remove camshaft bearing caps, rocker arms and rocker shafts as an assembly. Remove oil seal and distributor drive gear from camshaft. Remove camshaft.

Installation

1) Lubricate camshaft lobes and camshaft bearing journals and install camshaft into cylinder head. Check camshaft endplay. Endplay should be .002"-.006" (.05-.15 mm).

1.4L & 1.6L 4-CYLINDER (Cont.)

Fig. 4: Aligning Camshaft Timing Marks on 1.6L Engine

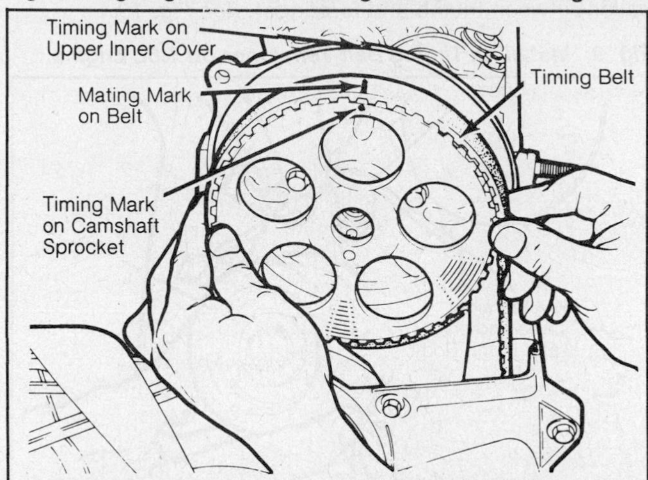

Timing Mark on Upper Inner Cover
Mating Mark on Belt
Timing Belt
Timing Mark on Camshaft Sprocket

2) Install distributor drive gear. Install rocker arm assembly to cylinder head. Camshaft should be positioned with keyway at 41° position. *See Fig. 5.*

Fig. 5: Installing Camshaft Woodruff Key on 1.6L Engine

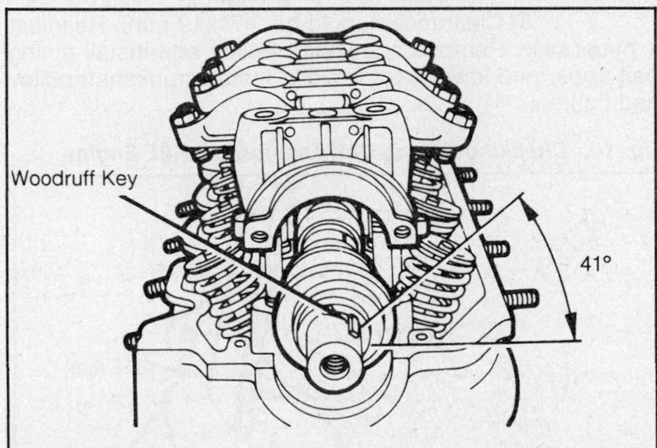

Woodruff Key
41°

Align key as shown for installation.

3) Insert camshaft bearing caps and tighten bolts to 7 ft. lbs. (10 N.m) in sequence of center, 2, 4, front and rear. Repeat sequence, tightening to specified torque.

4) Using seal installer (MD998248), drive camshaft oil seal in until installer touches distributor drive gear. Install upper inner cover, camshaft spacer and camshaft sprocket.

5) If dowel pin hole on camshaft sprocket is not in alignment with dowel pin, lightly strike projections at No. 2 exhaust cam with a screwdriver to turn camshaft.

6) Complete installation by reversing removal procedure. Temporarily set valve clearance to cold engine settings. Readjust to hot engine settings when engine reaches normal operating temperature. Install valve cover, air cleaner and breather hoses.

TIMING BELT & SPROCKETS

Removal (1.4L)

1) Remove fan, spacer, water pump pulley and belt. Remove timing belt cover and move timing belt tensioner upward toward water pump and secure. Remove timing belt from camshaft sprocket.

2) Remove camshaft sprocket and crankshaft pulley. Mark belt with an arrow indicating direction of rotation for installation reference and remove timing belt.

Installation

1) Install spacer, flange and crankshaft sprocket. *See Fig. 6.* Insert camshaft sprocket and tighten retaining bolt. Align camshaft and crankshaft sprockets timing marks with No. 1 piston at TDC on compression stroke.

Fig. 6: Mounting Timing Belt Flange and Sprocket

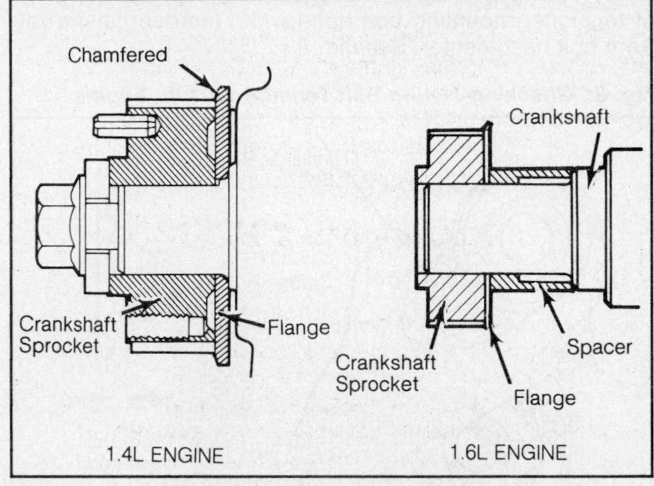

Chamfered
Crankshaft
Crankshaft Sprocket
Flange
Crankshaft Sprocket
Spacer
Flange
1.4L ENGINE
1.6L ENGINE

Installing flange incorrectly could result in a damaged belt.

2) Mount belt tensioner, spring, spacer and temporarily tighten bolt. Position spring against tensioner first, then against case and tighten bolt. *See Fig. 7.* Positon and secure tensioner toward water pump.

Fig. 7: Installing Timing Belt Tensioner on 1.4L Engine

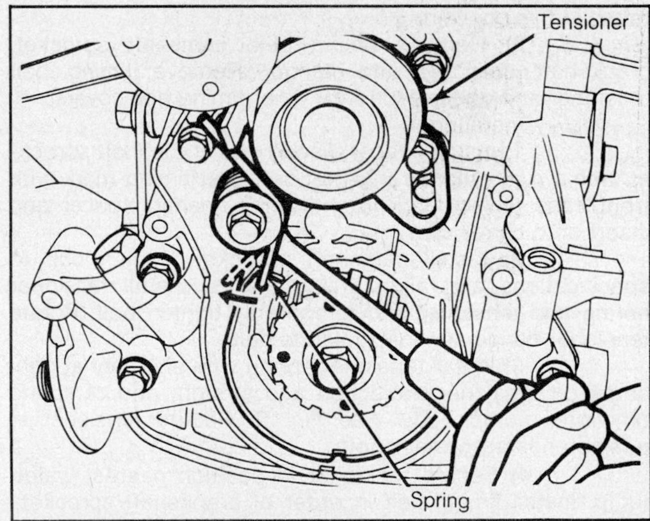

Tensioner
Spring

Use care when winding spring to prevent damage to the front cover.

3) Install timing belt on crankshaft and camshaft sprockets. Ensure tension side is tight and timing marks are aligned when pressure is applied to turn camshaft in reverse direction.

4) Align dowel and install crankshaft pulley. Loosen tensioner bolt. Ensure proper mesh of belt and sprocket. With only spring tension applied to belt, tighten tensioner spring bolt first and slotted adjustment hole bolt last.

5) Slowly turn crankshaft one revolution clockwise and realign crankshaft sprocket timing mark at TDC.

1.4L & 1.6L 4-CYLINDER (Cont.)

Do not push or shake belt while turning nor turn crankshaft in counterclockwise direction.

6) Loosen tensioner spring bolt first then slotted adjustment hole bolt. Tighten tensioner bolts to 15-18 ft. lbs. (20-24 N.m) by tightening slotted adjustment hole bolt first and tensioner spring bolt last.

7) Check belt tension by pushing tension side of timing belt in horizonatally using about 11 lbs. (5 kg) force. Timing belt tooth end should be approximately 1/4 of tensioner mounting bolt head width (across flats) away from bolt head center. *See Fig. 8.*

Fig. 8: Checking Timing Belt Tension on 1.4L Engine

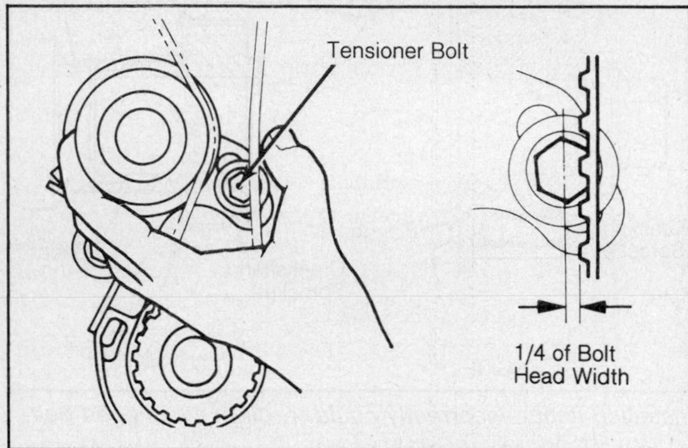
Tensioner Bolt
1/4 of Bolt
Head Width

Use moderate force when checking belt tension.

Removal (1.6L)

1) Remove crankshaft pulley, upper and lower front timing belt covers and crankshaft sprocket bolt. Move tensioner to release belt tension and tighten nut to retain in this position.

2) Remove timing belt, camshaft sprocket, crankshaft sprocket and flange. Remove timing belt tensioner and upper and lower inner timing belt covers.

Installation

1) Install spacer, flange and crankshaft sprocket. *See Fig. 6.* Align crankshaft sprocket timing mark with front case timing mark. Lightly oil camshaft spacer and insert onto camshaft.

2) Install camshaft sprocket, tighten bolt to specifications and align timing marks. Install tensioner spring and tensioner and temporarily tighten bolt. Rotate tensioner flange and install flange bolts.

3) Install tensioner spring with end bent at right angle on tensioner projection and straight end of spring on water pump body. *See Fig. 9.* Secure tensioner in position nearest water pump.

4) Secure tensioner in position nearest water pump. Install timing belt in order of crankshaft sprocket, oil pump sprocket and camshaft sprocket, while keeping belt slackening.

5) Ensure all individual timing marks are aligned and that tension side of belt is tight. Align dowel and temporarily install crankshaft pulley. Lightly push tensioner by hand to ensure belt and sprocket are in complete mesh.

6) Tighten tensioner nut then tighten bolt. Turn crankshaft one revolution clockwise, smoothly without pushing, jerking or turning counterclockwise. Loosen tensioner bolt and nut to allow spring pressure to tighten belt.

7) Tighten tensioner nut, then tighten bolt to 16-21 ft. lbs. (22-29 N.m). Check tensioner adjustment by holding center of tension side of belt and seal line of inner cover between thumb and forefinger. *See Fig. 10.*

Fig. 9: Installing Timing Belt Tensioner on 1.6L Engine

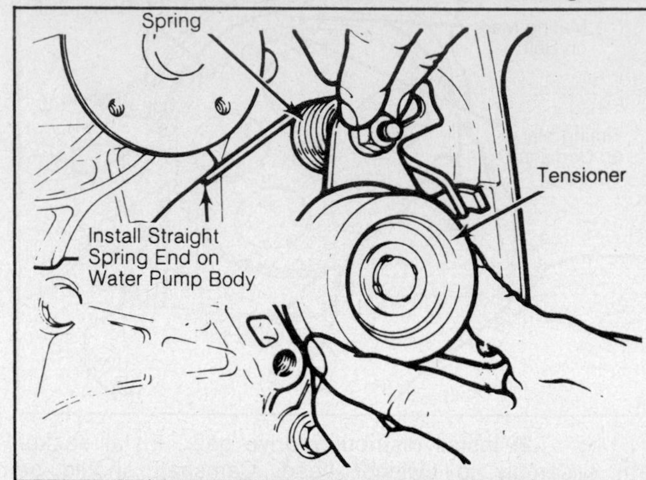
Spring
Tensioner
Install Straight
Spring End on
Water Pump Body

Install straight end of spring on water pump body; bent end on tensioner projection.

8) Clearance should be .47" (12 mm). Readjust if necessary. Remove crankshaft pulley and install timing belt upper and lower front covers. Install crankshaft pulley and tighten.

Fig. 10: Checking Timing Belt Tension on 1.6L Engine

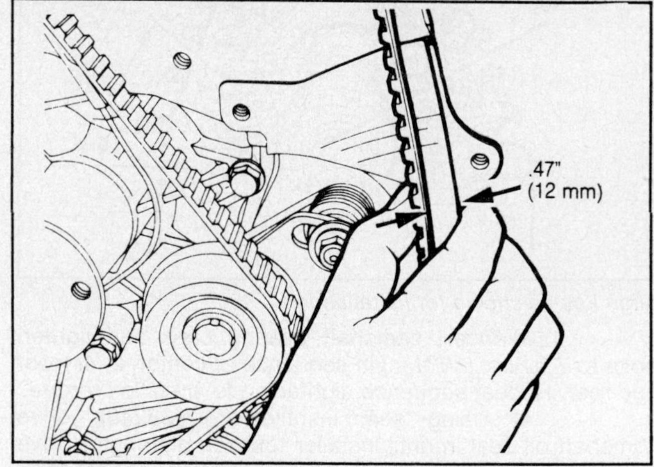
.47"
(12 mm)

Do not twist or push belt to test its tension.

VALVES

VALVE ARRANGEMENT

Left Side - Intake and Jet
Right Side - Exhaust

JET VALVES

1) Remove rocker arms and shafts as previously described. Using special Jet Valve Socket Wrench (MD998310), remove jet valves. Disassemble valve using spring pliers (MD998309) to compress spring and remove retainer lock.

2) Make certain jet valve socket wrench is not tilted with respect to center of valve when used. If tool is tilted, stem may be bent resulting in defective valve operation and a broken wrench.

1.4L & 1.6L 4-CYLINDER (Cont.)

3) Check valve head and seat for damage and make sure jet valve slides smooth in body without play. Do not disturb jet valve and body combination. If defective, jet valve and body should be replaced as an assembly.

VALVE SPRINGS

1) With camshaft and rocker arm assembly removed, use valve spring compressor to remove retainer locks. Remove all retainers, springs, spring seats and valves, keeping in proper order for reassembly.

2) Check valve spring free length and installed height. Installed height is measured between spring seat and bottom of retainer. Measurement should be 1.417-1.456" (36-37 mm). Standard spring squareness should be 1.5° or less. If beyond 3° replace spring.

VALVE GUIDE SERVICING

1) Ensure valve stem is to specifications and check valve stem clearance. If clearance exceeds service limits as listed in table, replace valve guide with next oversize.

VALVE GUIDE OVERSIZES

Size Mark	Guide Size mm	Cyl. Head Bore In. (mm)
1.4L		
5	.05	.4766-.4770 (12.105-12.115)
25	.25	.4844-.4848 (12.304-12.314)
50	.50	.4943-.4947 (12.555-12.565)
1.6L		
5	.05	.5138-.5145 (13.05-13.07)
25	.25	.5216-.5224 (13.25-13.27)
50	.50	.5315-.5323 (13.50-13.52)

Fig. 11: Installing Valve Guide and Checking Protrusion

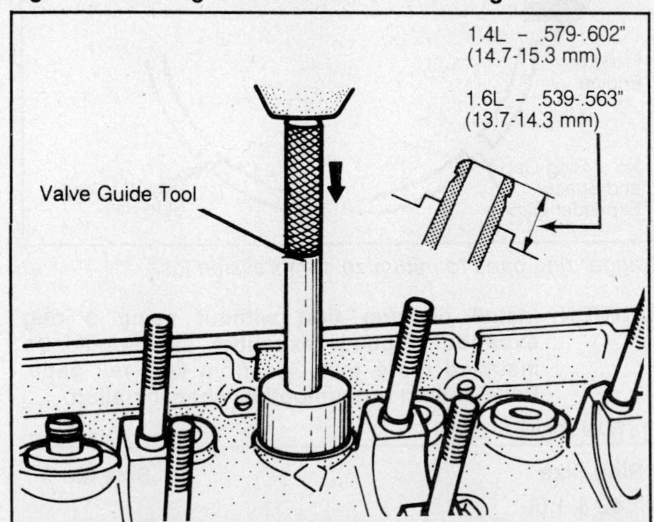
1.4L - .579-.602"
(14.7-15.3 mm)
1.6L - .539-.563"
(13.7-14.3 mm)
Valve Guide Tool

Cylinder head must be heated prior to installation.

2) Heat cylinder head to approximately 480°F (249°C), then use a valve guide tool to drive out each guide toward the combustion chamber. After head has cooled, ream guide bore in cylinder head to specified size.

3) To install new guides, reheat head to same temperature, quickly insert and drive guides into head.

4) Guide should protrude above head surface .579-.602" (14.7-15.3 mm) on 1.4L engines; .539-.563" (13.7-14.3 mm) on 1.6L engines when properly installed. Check guide I.D. and ream as necessary.

VALVE SEAT SERVICING

1) Check valve seat for damage or wear. Replace or rework seat, as necessary. If reworking seat, check valve guide first. Make proper replacement, if required.

2) Check seat for necessary corrections. Recondition valve seat with grinder or cutter to specified contact width. After rework, valve and seat should be lapped with compound.

3) Valve seat sink (wear of seat inward allowing valve to seat too deep in head) must be checked by measuring installed height of spring between the spring seat and retainer with oil spring components installed.

4) Standard dimension is 1.417" (36 mm) for 1.4L engine and 1.469" (37.3 mm) for 1.6L engine, with an additional wear limit of .039" (1.0 mm). Replace valve seat if beyond limit.

5) Remove valve seat by thinning down with a cutter, then machine seat bore to proper size for replacement seat. Heat head to approximately 480°F (250°C) and press in oversize seat.

6) Replacement seats are available in .30 mm and .60 mm oversizes, marked "30" and "60" respectively. After installing valve seat, machine to specifications.

VALVE STEM OIL SEALS

After installing valve spring seat, place stem seal on guide. Use installer to lightly hammer seal into correct position as tool bottoms on head. Do not use old seals and avoid twisting seals when installing.

VALVE CLEARANCE ADJUSTMENT

NOTE: Jet valve clearance adjustment must be made before intake valve is adjusted and after cylinder head is retightened.

1) Remove valve cover and position cylinder No. 1 at TDC of compression stroke. Adjust clearance on valves marked "A". *See Fig. 12.*

2) Loosen adjustment screw lock nut on jet valve and intake valve 2 or more turns. Adjust clearance between jet valve stem and adjustment screw.

3) Hold adjustment screw with screwdriver and tighten lock nut. Check adjustment and readjust if necessary. Jet valve spring is comparatively weak and must not be forced in when making adjustment.

4) Adjust intake valve next, using same procedure, except jet valve lock nut remains tight. Check to ensure lock nuts are tight and clearance is correct. Continue adjusting remaining valves marked "A" using same sequence.

5) Position cylinder No. 4 at TDC of compression stroke. Adjust valves marked "B", using same procedure previously outlined. *See Fig. 12.* After completing adjustment, check idle speed and readjust if necessary.

Mitsubishi Engines

1.4L & 1.6L 4-CYLINDER (Cont.)

Fig. 12: Adjusting Valve Clearance

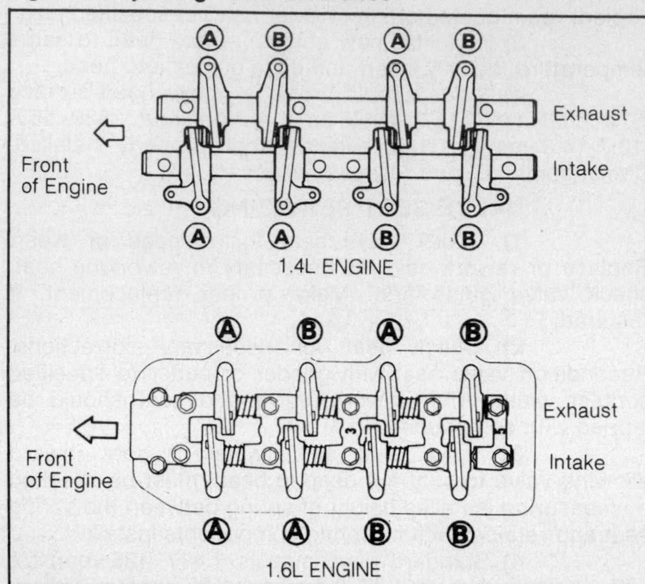

A
B
A
B
Exhaust
Front of Engine
Intake
A
A
B
B
1.4L ENGINE
A
B
A
B
Exhaust
Front of Engine
Intake
A
A
B
B
1.6L ENGINE

Ensure intake valve adjustment screw is fully loosened, when adjusting jet valve.

VALVE CLEARANCE SPECIFICATIONS

Application	Cold In. (mm)	Hot In. (mm)
Intake	.003 (.07)	.006 (.15)
Exhaust	.007 (.17)	.010 (.25)
Jet Valve	.003 (.07)	.006 (.15)

PISTONS, PINS & RINGS

PISTON & CONNECTING ROD ASSEMBLY

Removal

1) Remove cylinder head, oil pan and screen. Check to ensure connecting rods and rod caps are marked to aid in assembling components to their original position.

2) Remove carbon ridge from cylinder bores. Remove connecting rod caps. Remove connecting rod and piston assembly through top of cylinder block.

Installation

1) To install, lubricate all internal surfaces with engine oil before installation. Make sure "front" mark on piston head faces front of engine.

2) Use ring compressor and compress rings, without changing their position. Install piston and connecting rod assembly into cylinder block in their original position.

3) Tap lightly on piston dome with wooden handle tool while guiding connecting rod onto crankshaft. Install rod cap onto proper piston and connecting rod assembly. Tighten attaching bolts. Install cylinder head and oil pan.

FITTING PISTONS

1) After checking block for distortion, cracks, scratches or other abnormalities, measure bores at 3 levels. If any distortion exceeds .001" (.02 mm) from standard bore size, block must be rebored and oversize pistons installed.

NOTE: **Replacement pistons are available in standard, .25 mm, .50 mm, .75 mm and 1.0 mm oversizes. Oversize pistons are stamped on crown to indicate oversize.**

2) Check outside diameter of piston by measuring at a point .079" (2 mm) from bottom of skirt and at 90° to pin bore. Determine amount of cylinder reboring required to meet specified clearance.

NOTE: **Pin-to-rod fit at normal temperature requires 1,102-3,306 lbs. (500-1500 kg) to press pin through rod.**

PISTON PINS

1) Check piston pin-to-bore fit. Pin should press in smoothly by hand at room temperature. When assembling, apply engine oil to outside of pin and to piston pin bore.

2) Position rod to piston with "front" mark upward. Align pin with pressing tool, and press pin into piston and rod.

PISTON RINGS

1) Measure piston ring side and end clearance for all pistons and replace rings as necessary. When replacing ring in cylinder bore not needing reconditioning, check ring end gap at lower part of cylinder that is less worn.

2) When replacing a ring, be sure to use one of the same size. Install rings on piston with end gaps staggered at 120° intervals, but make sure no ring gap is in line with thrust face of pin bore. Also be sure the manufacturer's marks are facing upward when rings are installed.

Fig. 13: Positioning Piston Ring Gap

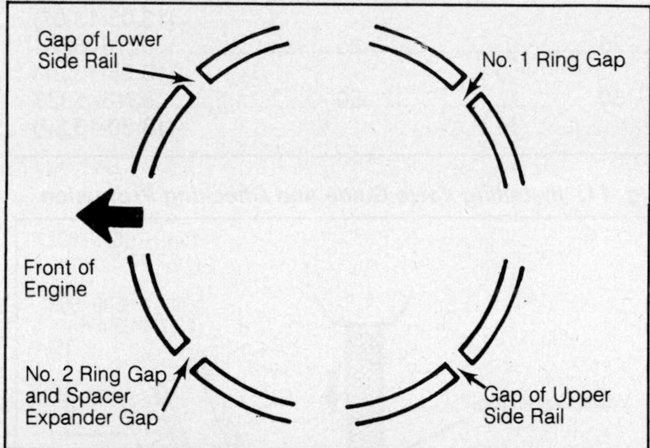

Gap of Lower Side Rail
No. 1 Ring Gap
Front of Engine
No. 2 Ring Gap and Spacer Expander Gap
Gap of Upper Side Rail

Stagger ring gaps to minimize compression loss.

CAUTION: **Install oil ring first without using a ring expander. Spacer expander gap should be installed more than 45° from side rail gaps. Rails should turn smoothly when installed.**

PISTON RING SIZES

Ring Size	Size Mark
1.4L & 1.6L	
Standard	No Mark
.25 mm Oversize	25
.50 mm Oversize	50
.75 mm Oversize	75
1.0 mm Oversize	100

1.4L & 1.6L 4-CYLINDER (Cont.)

CRANKSHAFT MAIN & CONNECTING ROD BEARINGS

MAIN & CONNECTING ROD BEARINGS

1) Inspect each bearing for peeling, melting, seizure or improper contact. Replace defective bearings. Measure outside diameter of crankshaft and connecting rod journals to determine if out-of-round or tapered.

2) Use Plastigage method to measure bearing clearance. If clearance exceeds limits, bearing should be replaced or undersize bearing installed. Undersize bearings are available in .25 mm, .50 mm, and .75 mm undersizes.

THRUST BEARING

With crankshaft bearing caps installed, check thrust clearance (end play) by inserting feeler gauge between center main bearing and crankshaft thrust face. If clearance exceeds specified limits, replace center main bearing.

ENGINE OILING

ENGINE OILING SYSTEM

All engines use force-feed type lubrication system. 1.4L engines uses gear-crescent type pump, 1.6L engine uses a trochoid type pump.

CRANKCASE CAPACITY

1.4L - 3.7 quarts (3.5L) including filter.
1.6L - 4.2 quarts (4.0L) including filter.

OIL PRESSURE

6 psi (.42 kg/cm²) @ curb idle;
45 psi (3.15 kg/cm²) @ 3000 RPM.

OIL PUMP

Removal (1.4L)

Gear-crescent type pump is mounted on front of engine assembly and driven directly by the crankshaft. Oil pan, oil screen and timing belt must be removed prior to removing front cover/oil pump assembly. Remove mounting bolts and pump assembly.

Installation

Inspect gears, case and seal for wear or damage. Ensure that gears are assembled in same direction as originally installed. Use new gaskets and install pump and pan. Use sealer at joint faces and seams.

OIL PUMP CLEARANCE SPECIFICATIONS

Application	In. (mm)
1.4L Gear-To-Crescent Type	
Outer Gear-to-Case	.0039-.0079 (.10-.20)
Outer Gear-to-Crescent	.0087-.0134 (.22-.34)
Gear End Play	.0016-.0039 (.04-.10)
Inner Gear-to-Crescent	.0083-.0126 (.21-.32)
1.6L Trochoid Type	
Side Clearance	.0024-.0047 (.06-.12)
Tip Clearance	.0016-.0047 (.04-.12)
Body Clearance	.0039-.0063 (.10-.16)
Drive Shaft-to-Cover Clear.	.0008-.0020 (.02-.05)

Removal & Installation (1.6L)

Mounted at lower left of engine, driven by camshaft drive belt. Cover and rotor assembly may be removed after removing drive sprocket by taking out cover bolts and lifting assembly out. Pump may also be removed with engine front cover as an assembly. To install, reverse removal procedure.

CAUTION: **Prior to installing oil pump, fill with sufficient amount of engine oil to prime pump.**

ENGINE COOLING

THERMOSTAT

190°F (88°C).

RADIATOR CAP

9.2 psi (.64 kg/cm²).

COOLANT CAPACITY

1.4L - 4.7 quarts (4.5L).
1.6L - 5.3 quarts (5.0L).

WATER PUMP

Removal

1) Drain cooling system and disconnect battery. Remove drive belt, fan, pulley, and lower radiator hose to pump. Ensure that number 1 piston is at TDC on compression stroke.

2) Remove camshaft pulley, timing belt covers, timing belt, camshaft sprocket, upper inner cover and timing belt tensioner. Remove mounting bolts and remove pump from engine.

Installation

To install, use new gasket and reverse removal procedure.

TIGHTENING SPECIFICATIONS

Application	Ft. Lbs. (N.m)
Camshaft Bearing Caps	
1.6L	14-15 (19-20)
Camshaft Sprocket	
1.4L	47-54 (64-73)
1.6L	44-57 (60-78)
Intake Manifold	11-14 (15-19)
Main Bearing Caps	37-39 (50-53)
Connecting Rod Caps	24-25 (33-34)
Crankshaft Sprocket Bolt	
1.4L	37-43 (50-58)
1.6L	44-50 (60-68)
Cylinder Head	51-54 (69-73)
Flywheel-to-Crankshaft	94-101 (128-137)
Drive Plate-to-Crankshaft	94-101 (128-137)
Jet Valve	13-15 (18-20)
Rocker Arm Shaft	15-19 (20-26)
	INCH Lbs. (N.m)
Oil Pump Cover	
1.4L	72-108 (8-10)
Crankshaft Pulley Bolt	90-102 (10-11)

Mitsubishi Engines

1.4L & 1.6L 4-CYLINDER (Cont.)

ENGINE SPECIFICATIONS

GENERAL SPECIFICATIONS

Year	DISPLACEMENT		Fuel System	HP@RPM	Torque Ft. Lbs.@RPM	Compr. Ratio	BORE		STROKE	
	Cu. In.	Liters					In.	mm	In.	mm
1983	86.0 97.5	1.4 1.6	2-Bbl. 2-Bbl.	64@5000 72@5000	78@3000 85@3000	8.8:1 8.5:1	2.91 3.03	74.0 76.9	3.23 3.39	82.0 86.0

VALVES

Engine Size & Valve	Head Diam. In. (mm)	Face Angle	Seat Angle	Seat Width In. (mm)	Stem Diameter In. (mm)	Stem Clearance In. (mm)	Valve Lift In. (mm)
1.4L & 1.6L							
Intake	[1] 1.34 (34)	45°	45°	.035-.051 (.9-1.3)	.315 (8.0)	.0012-.0024 (.03-.06)	[2] .346 (8.8)
Exhaust	[3] 1.18 (30)	45°	45°	.035-.051 (.9-.13)	.315 (8.0)	.0020-.0035 (.05-.09)	[4] .346 (8.8)

[1] – On 1.6L engine 1.50" (38 mm).
[2] – On 1.6L engine .362" (9.2 mm).
[3] – On 1.6L engine 1.22" (33 mm).
[4] – On 1.6L engine .362" (9.2 mm).

PISTONS, PINS, RINGS

Engine	PISTONS	PINS		RINGS		
	Clearance In. (mm)	Piston Fit In. (mm)	Rod Fit In. (mm)	Ring No.	End Gap In. (mm)	Side Clearance In. (mm)
1.4L & 1.6L	.0008-.0016 (.02-.04)	[1]	Locked in Rod	No. 1	.008-.016 (.2-.4)	.0012-.0028 (.03-.07)
			[2]	No. 2	.008-.016 (.2-.4)	.0008-.0024 (.02-.06)
				Oil	.008-.020 (.2-.5)	.....

[1] – Thumb press fit without rod installed.
[2] – Press in at 1100-3300 lbs. at room temp.

CRANKSHAFT MAIN & CONNECTING ROD BEARINGS

Engine	MAIN BEARINGS				CONNECTING ROD BEARINGS		
	Journal Diam. In. (mm)	Clearance In. (mm)	Thrust Bearing	Crankshaft End Play In. (mm)	Journal Diam. In. (mm)	Clearance In. (mm)	Side Play In. (mm)
1.4L & 1.6L	[1] 1.890 (48)	.0008-.0028 (.02-.07)	No. 3	.002-.007 (.05-.18)	[2] 1.653 (42)	.0004-.0024 (.01-.06)	.004-.010 (.10-.25)

[1] – On 1.6L engine 2.244" (57 mm).
[2] – On 1.6L engine 1.772" (45 mm).

1.4L & 1.6L 4-CYLINDER (Cont.)

ENGINE SPECIFICATIONS (Cont.)

CAMSHAFT

Engine	Lobe Height In. (mm)	Wear Limit In. (mm)	Lobe Lift In. (mm)
1.4L			
Intake	1.500 (38.1)	.020 (.51)	.....
Exhaust	1.504 (38.2)	.020 (.51)	.....
1.6L			
Int. & Exh.	1.433 (36.4)	.020 (.51)	.359 (.92)

1 – Journal oil clearance .002-.004" (.05-.09 mm).
2 – End play 1.4L engine .002-.008" (.05-.20 mm), 1.6L engine .002-.006" (.05-.15 mm).

VALVE SPRINGS

Engine	Free Length In. (mm)	PRESSURE Lbs. @ In. (Kg @ mm)	
		Valve Closed	Valve Open
1.4L	1.697 (43.1)	69@1.417 (31.1@36)	.....
1.6L	1.823 (46.3)	62.0@1.469 (27.2@37.3)	.....

Mitsubishi Engines

1.8L 4-CYLINDER

Mitsubishi: Cordia & Tredia

ENGINE CODING

ENGINE IDENTIFICATION

Engine model code and serial number are stamped on top edge of right front side of cylinder block behind power steering pump.

ENGINE IDENTIFICATION

Application	Engine Model	[1] Engine VIN Code
1.8L (109.5")	G62B	4

[1] – Eighth digit of VIN code.

ENGINE & CYLINDER HEAD

ENGINE

Removal

1) Disconnect negative battery cable and remove hood. Drain coolant, transaxle, power steering pump and A/C refrigerant. Remove radiator and windshield washer reservoir. Remove radiator assembly and battery tray.

2) Remove air cleaner and disconnect heater and brake booster hoses. Disconnect transaxle cooler lines, if equipped. Disconnect accelerator, speedometer and clutch or shift cable.

3) Disconnect power steering and A/C compressor hoses, if equipped. Disconnect necessary engine wiring. Detach vacuum and fuel hoses from engine. Detach exhaust pipe from manifold and suspend with wire.

4) Disconnect strut and stabilizer bars from lower control arms. Remove shift control rod, extension and range selector control cable, if equipped with manual transaxle.

5) Remove left and right lower control arm-to-crossmember bolts. Remove drive shafts from transaxle, plug holes and lower drive shafts and lower control arms to crossmember.

6) Attach lifting cables to engine and raise engine enough to pull cable tight. Remove left mount insulator nut, front roll rod upper mounting bolt on No.1 crossmember side and rear roll insulator mounting bolt.

CAUTION: Do not remove left mount insulator bolt. Only remove the nut.

7) Remove left mount insulator-to-fender nuts. Detach cap from within right fender shield. Remove transaxle insulator bracket mounting bolts and bolts connecting insulator and bracket.

8) Remove select control valve bolts, detach wiring connector and disconnect vacuum hoses. Remove transaxle insulator bracket. Lift engine weight off mountings.

9) Maintaining this position, remove rear roll stopper and left mount bracket insulator bolts. With engine tilted upward, lift engine-transaxle assembly from vehicle.

Installation

Reverse removal procedure to reinstall engine-transaxle assembly. Replace all fluids and adjust all cables and linkages.

CYLINDER HEAD

1) Drain cooling system. Remove breather hose and air cleaner. Disconnect necessary wiring. Detach vacuum and water hoses. Disconnect accelerator linkage and spark plug wires.

2) Place piston in cylinder No. 1 at TDC of compression stroke. Remove distributor, carburetor, intake manifold and exhaust manifold assembly. Remove crankshaft and water pump pulleys.

3) Remove timing belt front upper and lower covers. Mark timing belt, indicating direction of rotation, if belt is to be reused. Remove timing belt, camshaft sprocket and valve cover.

4) Loosen camshaft cap bolts, in steps, and remove bolts. Remove rocker shaft assembly and camshaft. Loosen cylinder head bolts, in steps, in reverse of tightening sequence. *See Fig. 1.*

Inspection

Check cylinder head gasket surface for warpage by using straightedge and feeler gauge. If warpage exceeds .004" (.1 mm), lightly machine head surface or replace cylinder head.

Installation

1) Install cylinder head gasket with gasket identification mark "62" facing cylinder head. Do not apply sealant to gasket or mating surfaces. Install cylinder head and head bolts.

2) Tighten bolts in sequence to 1/2 of tightening specification, then tighten to final specification. *See Fig. 1.* Install camshaft sprocket and timing belt, ensuring timing mark alignment and belt tension are correct.

3) Reverse removal procedure to complete installation. Replace coolant and adjust belts, valves and accelerator cable. With engine at operating temperature, adjust timing and carburetor.

Fig. 1: Cylinder Head Tightening Sequence

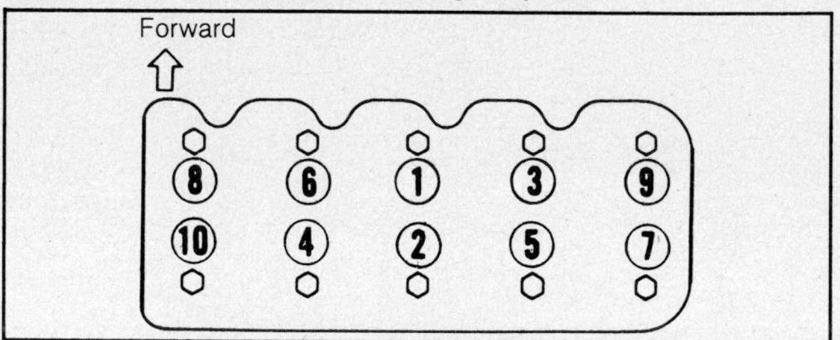
Forward
8
6
1
3
9
10
4
2
5
7

Reverse sequence when removing bolts.

CAMSHAFT

ROCKER SHAFT ASSEMBLY & CAMSHAFT

Removal

1) Camshaft removal is possible without removing lower timing belt cover. *See procedure under Timing Belts and Sprockets.* If belt requires detailed inspection or replacement, use following procedure.

2) Disconnect negative battery cable and remove crankshaft and water pump pulleys. Remove upper and lower front timing belt covers. Disconnect spark plug wires and remove valve cover.

3) Position cylinder No. 1 at TDC of compression stroke. Camshaft sprocket timing mark should be alignment with timing mark on cylinder head. *See Fig. 2.*

1.8L 4-CYLINDER (Cont.)

12) Hold belt and seal line of under cover, between thumb and forefinger, at center of tension side. Measure clearance between belt and seal line. Clearance should be .55" (14 mm). Reverse removal procedure to complete reassembly.

VALVES

VALVE ARRANGEMENT

Left Side - Intake and Jet
Right Side - Exhaust

JET VALVES

Removal

1) Remove rocker arms and shafts as previously described. Using special jet valve socket wrench (MD998310), remove jet valves. Disassemble valve using spring pliers (MD998309) to compress spring and remove retainer lock.

2) Make certain jet valve socket wrench is not tilted with respect to center of valve when used. If tool is tilted, stem may be bent resulting in defective valve operation and a broken wrench.

Inspection

1) Check valve head and seat for damage. Make sure jet valve slides smooth in body without play. Check jet valve face and jet body seat for seizure or damage. Check jet valve spring for deterioration, cracks or wear.

2) Do not disturb jet valve and body combination. If defective, jet valve and body should be replaced as an assembly. Spring can be replaced separately, if defective.

Installation

1) Install new jet valve oil seal using installer (MD998308). Apply oil to jet valve stem and carefully insert jet valve into body. Ensure valve slides smoothly after installation.

2) Compress spring and install retainer lock, using care to prevent damaging valve stem. Install "O" ring on jet body. Lubricate "O" ring, jet body threads and seat surface.

3) Install jet valve assembly hand tight, then tighten to specifications using special socket wrench. Use care to avoid tilting wrench and damaging jet valve assembly.

VALVE CLEARANCE ADJUSTMENT

NOTE: Jet valve clearance adjustment must be made before intake valve is adjusted and after cylinder head is retightened.

1) Remove valve cover and position cylinder No. 1 at TDC of compression stroke. Adjust clearance on valves marked "A". *See Fig. 8.*

2) Loosen adjustment screw lock nut on jet valve and intake valve 2 or more turns. Adjust clearance between jet valve stem and adjustment screw.

3) Hold adjustment screw with screwdriver and tighten lock nut. Check adjustment and readjust if necessary. Jet valve spring is comparatively weak and must not be forced in when making adjustment.

4) Adjust intake valve next, using same procedure used for jet valve adjustment, except jet valve lock nut remains tight. Check to ensure lock nuts are tight

Fig. 8: Adjusting Valve Clearance

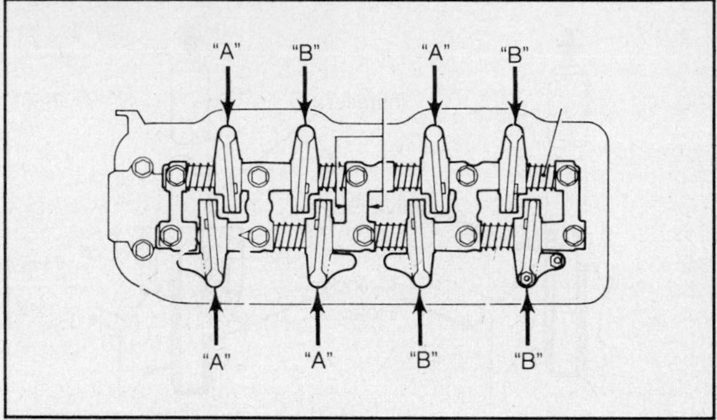
"A"
"B"
"A"
"B"
"A"
"A"
"B"
"B"

Ensure intake valve adjustment screw is fully loosened, when adjusting jet valve.

and clearance is correct. Continue adjusting remaining valves marked "A" using same sequence.

5) Position cylinder No. 4 at TDC of compression stroke. Adjust valves marked "B", using same procedure previously outlined. *See Fig. 8.* After completing adjustment, check idle speed and readjust if necessary.

VALVE CLEARANCE SPECIFICATIONS

Application	Cold In. (mm)	Hot In. (mm)
Intake	.003 (.07)	.006 (.15)
Exhaust	.007 (.17)	.010 (.25)
Jet Valve	.003 (.07)	.006 (.15)

VALVE GUIDE SERVICING

1) Ensure valve stem is to specifications and check valve stem clearance. If clearance exceeds service limits listed in table, replace valve guide with next oversize.

VALVE GUIDE OVERSIZES

Size Mark	Guide Size (mm)	Cylinder Head Bore In. (mm)
1.8L		
5	.05	.5138-.5145 (13.05-13.07)
25	.25	.5216-.5224 (13.25-13.27)
50	.50	.5315-.5322 (13.50-13.52)

2) Using a valve guide tool (MD998115), drive out each guide toward combustion chamber. Machine guide bore in cylinder head to outside diameter of guide being installed.

3) To install, drive new guides into top of head, using installer (MD98115) with adapter, to ensure guide is installed to predetermined height. Guide should protrude .591" (15 mm) above head surface when properly installed. Check guide I.D. and ream as necessary.

1.8L 4-CYLINDER (Cont.)

Fig. 9: Removing and Installing Valve Guide

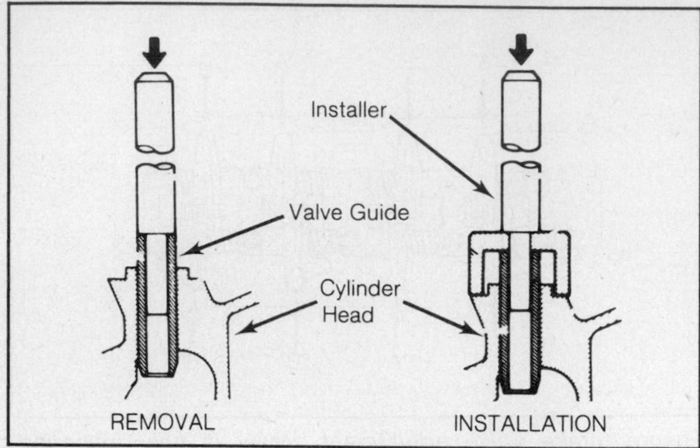
Installer
Valve Guide
Cylinder
Head
REMOVAL
INSTALLATION

Install valve guide at room temperature.

VALVE SEAT SERVICING

1) Check valve seat for evidence of overheating or improper contact with valve face. Replace or rework seat, as necessary. If reworking seat, check valve guide first.

2) Make proper replacement, if required, then check seat for necessary corrections. Recondition valve seat with grinder or cutter to specified contact width. After rework, valve and seat should be lapped with compound.

3) Remove valve seat ring by thinning down with a cutter, then machine seat bore to outside diameter and height of oversize valve seat ring. See *Valve Seat Oversizes* table for seat hole diameter.

NOTE: **Do not install valve seat ring at room temperature. This will damage seat hole and prevent seat from fitting tightly.**

4) Cool valve seat ring with dry ice and press seat into cylinder head. After installing valve seat ring, machine to specifications. After rework, valve and valve seat should be lapped with compound.

VALVE SEAT OVERSIZES

Oversize	Seat Hole Diameter In. (mm)
Intake	
.30	1.744-1.745 (44.30-44.33)
.60	1.756-1.757 (44.60-44.63)
Exhaust	
.30	1.508-1.509 (38.30-38.33)
.60	1.520-1.521 (38.60-38.63)

VALVE STEM OIL SEALS

After installing valve spring seat, place new stem seal on guide. Use installer (MD998377) to lightly tap seal into position as tool bottoms on spring seat.

VALVE SPRINGS

1) With camshaft and rocker arm assembly removed, use valve spring compressor to remove retainer locks. Remove all retainers, springs, spring seats and valves, keeping in proper order for reassembly.

2) Check valve spring load, free length and spring squareness. Standard spring squareness should be 1.5° or less. If beyond 3° replace spring. Install spring with identification color upward toward retainer.

PISTONS, PINS & RINGS

PISTON & CONNECTING ROD ASSEMBLY

Removal

1) Remove cylinder head, oil pan and screen. Check to ensure connecting rods and rod caps are marked on big end side surface to aid in installing components to their original position.

2) Remove carbon ridge from cylinder bores. Remove connecting rod caps. Remove connecting rod and piston assembly through top of cylinder block.

Installation

1) To install, lubricate all internal surfaces with engine oil before installation. Make sure "arrow" mark on piston head faces front of engine.

2) Use ring compressor to compress rings, without changing ring gap position. Install piston and connecting rod assembly into cylinder block in original position.

3) Tap lightly on piston dome with wooden handle tool while guiding connecting rod onto crankshaft. Install rod cap onto proper piston and connecting rod assembly. Tighten attaching bolts. Install cylinder head and oil pan.

FITTING PISTONS

1) After checking block for distortion, cracks, scratches or other abnormalities, measure bores at top, center and bottom of No. 1 piston ring travel for taper and out-of-round.

2) If any cylinder has more than .0008" (.02 mm) taper or out-of-round, or if cylinder walls are badly scuffed or scored, block must be rebored or honed and new oversized pistons and rings fitted.

3) Bore or hone all cylinders to same oversize. Do not bore only one cylinder. Bore or hone cylinders in sequence, skipping adjacent cylinders to prevent heat distortion.

NOTE: **Replacement pistons are available in standard, .25 mm, .50 mm, .75 mm and 1.0 mm oversizes. Oversize pistons are stamped on crown to indicate oversize.**

4) Measure outside diameter of piston by measuring at a point .079" (2 mm) from bottom of skirt below pin boss, and at 90° to pin bore. Determine cylinder boring finish dimension.

PISTON PINS

1) Check piston pin-to-bore fit. Pin should press in smoothly by hand at room temperature. When assembling, apply engine oil to outside of pin and piston pin bore.

2) Position rod in piston with "arrow" mark on piston and "G6" mark on connecting rod facing upward. Align pin with pressing tool, and press pin into piston and rod.

NOTE: **Pin-to-rod fit at normal temperature requires 1,653-3,858 lbs. (750-1750 kg) to press pin through rod.**

PISTON RINGS

1) Measure piston ring side and end clearance for all pistons and replace rings as necessary. When replacing ring in cylinder bore not needing reconditioning, check ring end gap at lower part of cylinder that is less worn.

2) When replacing a ring, be sure to use one of the same size. Compression rings differ in scraping edge design. From a cross sectional view, ring No. 1 has a barrel shaped scraping edge and ring No. 2 has a tapered edge.

3) Install rings on piston with end gaps staggered at 120° intervals, but make sure no ring gap is in line with thrust face of pin bore. Also ensure manufacturer's marks are facing upward when rings are installed.

Fig. 10: Positioning Piston Ring Gaps

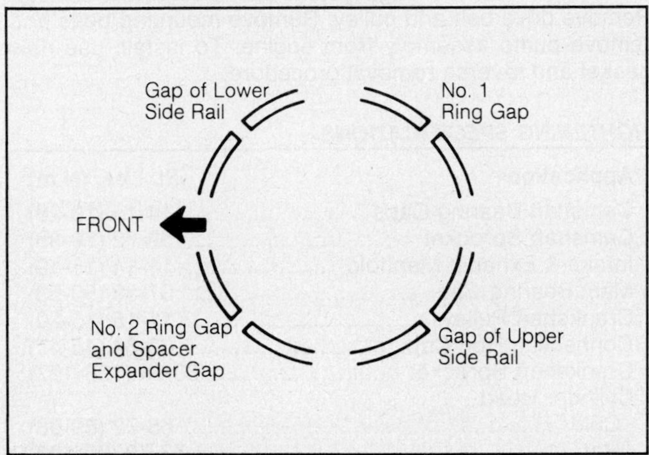
Gap of Lower
Side Rail
No. 1
Ring Gap
FRONT
No. 2 Ring Gap
and Spacer
Expander Gap
Gap of Upper
Side Rail

Stagger ring gaps to minimize compression loss.

4) Install oil ring first without using a ring expander. Spacer expander gap should be installed more than 45° from side rail gaps. Rails should turn smoothly when installed.

PISTON RING SIZES

Ring Size	Size Mark
1.8L	
Standard	No Mark
.25 mm Oversize	25
.50 mm Oversize	50
.75 mm Oversize	75
1.0 mm Oversize	100

CRANKSHAFT MAIN & CONNECTING ROD BEARINGS

MAIN & CONNECTING ROD BEARINGS

1) Inspect each bearing for peeling, melting, seizure or improper contact. Replace defective bearings. Measure outside diameter of crankshaft and connecting rod journals to determine if out-of-round or tapered.

2) Use Plastigage method to measure bearing clearance. If clearance exceeds limits, bearing should be replaced or undersize bearing installed. Undersize bearings are available in .25 mm, .50 mm, and .75 mm undersizes.

3) Main bearing caps are installed with "arrow" directed toward front of engine and cap number in correct order. Gradually tighten cap bolts in 2 or 3 steps, before tightening to specifications.

4) Connecting rod bearing caps are installed with bearing insert locking tabs, located on same side of rod. Ensure crankshaft turns freely and end play is within specifications, after completely bearing installation.

THRUST BEARING

With crankshaft bearing caps installed, check crankshaft end play by inserting feeler gauge between shoulder of center main bearing and crankshaft thrust face. If clearance exceeds specified limits, replace No. 3 main bearing.

ENGINE OILING

ENGINE OILING SYSTEM

Engine uses force-feed type lubrication system, utilizing a gear-type pump. Pump assembly is mounted on front of engine assembly. Oil pump driven gear is bolted to left silent shaft and driven by camshaft timing belt.

CRANKCASE CAPACITY

4.2 quarts (4.0L) including filter.

OIL PRESSURE

6 psi (.42 kg/cm²) @ curb idle;
45 psi (3.15 kg/cm²) @ 3000 RPM.

OIL PUMP

Removal

1) Oil pan, oil screen, timing belts and oil filter bracket must be removed prior to removing front cover-oil pump assembly. Remove oil pump sprocket by removing plug at left side of cylinder block. *See Fig. 11.*

2) With cylinder No. 1 at TDC of compression stroke, insert screwdriver, with .3" (8 mm) shaft, 2.36" (60 mm) into hole to keep silent shaft in position.

Fig. 11: Removing Oil Pump Sprocket

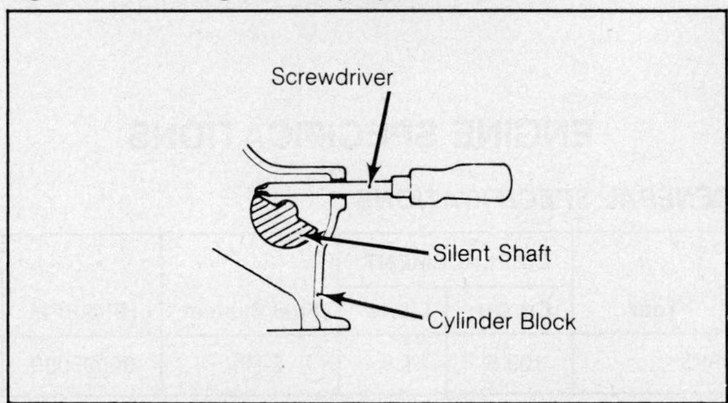
Screwdriver
Silent Shaft
Cylinder Block

Silent shaft should be repositioned if screwdriver fails to insert 2.36" (60 mm).

Inspection

1) Inspect gears, case and seal for wear or damage. Reinstall gears as originally installed in front case and measure gear side clearance. Clearance should not exceed .005" (.13 mm).

2) Check gear contacting surfaces of front cover and oil pump cover for step wear. Replace front case assembly if either excessive clearance or step wear is evident.

Mitsubishi Engines

1.8L 4-CYLINDER (Cont.)

Installation

1) Install oil pump gears in front case and align timing marks on gears with timing marks facing toward oil pump cover. *See Fig. 12.* Install pump cover and tighten bolts.

Fig. 12: Aligning Oil Pump Timing Marks

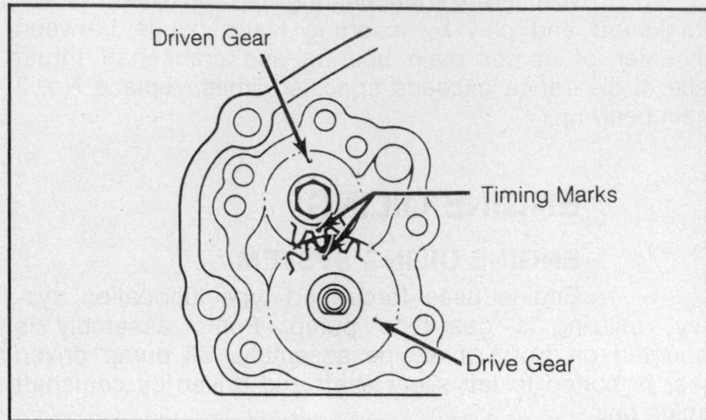
Driven Gear
Timing Marks
Drive Gear

Timing marks face toward pump cover.

2) Insert left silent shaft in oil pump drive gear and temporarily tighten bolt. Install guide (MD99285) on end of crankshaft with smaller diameter toward front of engine. Lightly oil guide.

3) Install new front case gasket and insert left silent shaft with front case. Insert screwdriver in left side of block to keep left silent shaft in position. Tighten driven gear-to-silent shaft bolt.

4) Install oil filter bracket and tighten front case bolts. Apply sealant to 4 locations on cylinder block where oil seal case and front case join cylinder block. Install oil pan with new gasket. Reverse removal procedure to complete installation.

CAUTION: Prior to installing oil pump, fill with sufficient amount of engine oil to prime pump.

ENGINE COOLING

THERMOSTAT

190°F (88°C).

RADIATOR CAP

11-15 psi (.77-1.05 kg/cm²).

COOLANT CAPACITY

7.4 quarts (7.0L)

WATER PUMP

Removal and Installation

Drain cooling system and disconnect battery. Remove drive belt and pulley. Remove mounting bolts and remove pump assembly from engine. To install, use new gasket and reverse removal procedure.

TIGHTENING SPECIFICATIONS

Application	Ft. Lbs. (N.m)
Camshaft Bearing Caps	14-15 (19-20)
Camshaft Sprocket	59-72 (79-98)
Intake & Exhaust Manifold	11-14 (15-19)
Main Bearing Cap	37-39 (50-53)
Crankshaft Pulley	11-15 (15-20)
Connecting Rod Cap	33-34 (45-47)
Crankshaft Sprocket	80-94 (108-127)
Cylinder Head	
Cold	65-72 (89-98)
Hot	73-79 (99-107)
Flywheel-to-Crankshaft	94-101 (127-137)
Drive Plate-to-Crankshaft	94-101 (127-137)
Jet Valve	13-15 (18-20)
Oil Pump Cover	11-13 (15-18)
Oil Pump Sprocket	25-28 (34-39)
Rocker Arm Shaft	15-19 (20-26)
Water Pump	
M8 X 65	15-19 (20-26)
Others	9-11 (12-15)
	INCH Lbs. (N.m)
Oil Pan	54-66 (6-7)

ENGINE SPECIFICATIONS

GENERAL SPECIFICATIONS

Year	DISPLACEMENT		Fuel System	HP@RPM	Torque Ft. Lbs.@RPM	Compr. Ratio	BORE		STROKE	
	Cu. In.	Liters					In.	mm	In.	mm
1983	109.5	1.8	2-Bbl.	80@5000	93@3000	8.5:1	3.17	80.5	3.46	87.9

VALVES

Engine Size & Valve	Head Diam. In. (mm)	Face Angle	Seat Angle	Seat Width In. (mm)	Stem Diameter In. (mm)	Stem Clearance In. (mm)	Valve Lift In. (mm)
1.8L							
Intake	1.70 (43)	45°	45°	.035-.051 (.9-1.3)	.315 (8.0)	.0012-.0024 (.03-.06)	.....
Exhaust	1.38 (35)	45°	45°	.047-.063 (1.2-1.6)	.315 (8.0)	.0020-.0035 (.05-.09)	.....

Mitsubishi Engines

1.8L 4-CYLINDER (Cont.)

ENGINE SPECIFICATIONS (Cont.)

PISTONS, PINS, RINGS

Engine	PISTONS	PINS		RINGS		
	Clearance In. (mm)	Piston Fit In. (mm)	Rod Fit In. (mm)	Ring No.	End Gap In. (mm)	Side Clearance In. (mm)
1.8L	.0008-.0016 (.02-.04)	[1]	Locked in Rod	No. 1	.010-.018 (.25-.45)	.002-.004 (.05-.10)
			[2]	No. 2	.008-.016 (.20-.41)	.001-.002 (.02-.05)
				Oil	.008-.020 (.20-.51)	.....

[1] – Thumb press fit without rod installed.
[2] – Press in at 1653-3858 lbs. at room temp.

CRANKSHAFT MAIN & CONNECTING ROD BEARINGS

Engine	MAIN BEARINGS				CONNECTING ROD BEARINGS		
	Journal Diam. In. (mm)	Clearance In. (mm)	Thrust Bearing	Crankshaft End Play In. (mm)	Journal Diam. In. (mm)	Clearance In. (mm)	Side Play In. (mm)
1.8L	2.244 (57)	.0008-.0020 (.02-.05)	No. 3	.002-.007 (.05-.18)	1.772 (45)	.0008-.0020 (.02-.05)	.004-.010 (.10-.25)

CAMSHAFT [1]

Engine	Journal Diam. In. (mm)	Clearance In. (mm)	Lobe Lift In. (mm)
1.8L	1.496 (38)	.002-.004 (.05-.09)	.....

[1] – Cam lobe height 1.66" (42.2 mm).

VALVE SPRINGS

Engine	Free Length In. (mm)	PRESSURE Lbs. @ In. (Kg @ mm)	
		Valve Closed	Valve Open
1.8L	[1] 1.870 (47.5)	62@1.591 (28.1@40.4)	.....

[1] – Maximum out-of-square 1.5°.

Mitsubishi Engines

2.0L & 2.6L 4-CYLINDER

Chrysler Corp. Imports: Challenger, Colt Pickup, Ram-50 Pickup & Sapporo
Mitsubishi: Montero, Pickup & Starion

ENGINE CODING

ENGINE IDENTIFICATION

Engine model code and serial number are stamped on right side of engine block, just below No. 1 spark plug on 2.6L engines and above engine oil dipstick on 2.0L engines.

Eighth digit of Vehicle Identification Number, located on upper left side of instrument panel, can also be used to identify vehicle's engine size. Engine model and VIN codes are listed in table.

ENGINE IDENTIFICATION

Application	Engine Model	[1] Engine VIN Code
2.0L (121.8")	[2] G63B	5
2.6L (155.9")	[3] G54B	7

[1] – Eighth digit of VIN code.
[2] – Referred to by Chrysler Corp. as "U" engine.
[3] – Referred to by Chrysler Corp. as "F" engine for Sapporo and Challenger; "W" engine for Pickups.

ENGINE, MANIFOLDS & CYLINDER HEAD

ENGINE

Removal (Challenger & Sapporo)

1) Disconnect negative battery cable, and remove engine undercover and hood. Drain coolant and transmission fluid. Remove air cleaner and disconnect necessary vacuum hoses.

2) Detach accelerator cable from carburetor and disconnect wiring from: coil, alternator, starter, gauges and switches. Disconnect radiator and heater hoses, fuel lines, and brake booster vacuum hoses.

3) If equipped with automatic transmission, disconnect oil cooler lines. Detach power steering pump, and without bending hoses, suspend with wire. Remove lower radiator shroud. Remove radiator attaching bolts, and lift out radiator. Mark mating flanges, remove flange bolts and remove drive shaft.

4) If equipped with manual transmission, disconnect clutch cable or shift lever. Lower transmission and remove shifter assembly. If equipped with automatic transmission, disconnect control rod. On all models, disconnect speedometer cable and back-up light switch.

5) Remove front exhaust pipe-to-rear catalytic converter bolts. Support transmission and remove rear engine support bracket and insulator. Remove both engine support brackets and insulators. Attach lifting cables. With front of engine tilted upward, lift out engine-transmission assembly.

Removal (Colt Pickup, Montero & Ram-50 Pickup)

1) Disconnect negative battery cable. Remove hood and air cleaner. Disconnect heater and brake booster vacuum hoses. Disconnect fuel hoses and accelerator cable.

2) Disconnect wiring from starter, alternator, coil and water temperature and oil pressure sending units. Remove radiator assembly. Disconnect clutch cable and remove front exhaust pipe.

3) Remove power steering pump, if equipped. Remove undercover and other protective transmission covers, if equipped. Disconnect speedometer cable, back-up light harness and 4WD indicator light switch (if equipped).

4) Mark for reference, and remove drive shafts. Remove gear shift lever assembly. Support transmission, detach rear insulator from transmission and remove crossmember.

5) Detach and remove transfer case mounting bracket and support insulator from transfer case. Remove front engine insulator mounting nuts. Attach lifting cables. With front of engine tilted upward, lift out engine-transmission assembly.

Removal (Starion)

1) Disconnect negative battery cable and remove hood. Remove air cleaner and detach accelerator cable. Disconnect heater, fuel, boost sensor and brake booster hoses.

2) Disconnect starter, alternator, ECI, ignition and gauge wiring. Remove power steering pump and radiator assembly. Remove rear catalytic converter. Disconnect speedometer cable and back-up light switch wiring.

3) Remove drive shaft, clutch release cylinder, engine mount bolts and gearshift lever assembly. Support transmission, remove insulator bolts and crossmember. Attach lifting cables and remove engine-transmission assembly.

Installation (All Models)

To install, reverse removal procedures. Use care to align front engine mount locating holes without twisting insulator rubber. Using new tab lock washers, tighten mounting bolts and nuts to specifications with weight of engine on insulators. Replace all fluids, adjust all cables and linkages and check operation of gauges and meters.

CYLINDER HEAD & MANIFOLDS

Removal

1) Drain cooling system and disconnect water hoses at cylinder head and intake manifold. Remove breather and purge hose, vacuum hose at distributor and purge control valve.

2) Disconnect accelerator linkage, spark plug wires, water temperature gauge unit and exhaust manifold flange. Remove air cleaner, fuel line, distributor and fuel pump. Remove exhaust manifold, then intake manifold and carburetor assembly.

3) Remove rocker cover and breather. Remove semi-circular seal. Turn crankshaft so No. 1 piston is at TDC on compression stroke. Mark chain for reference, in line with sprocket mark.

4) Remove distributor drive gear and camshaft sprocket. Remove cylinder head bolts in three stages, reversing the sequence shown in *Fig. 1.* Lift off cylinder head, using care not to slide it, nor to twist sprocket and chain.

Installation

1) Clean mating surfaces and use a new cylinder head gasket. Do not apply sealant to gasket.

2.0L & 2.6L 4-CYLINDER (Cont.)

Install cylinder head. To prevent damage to gasket, mating surfaces and alignment dowels, avoid sliding cylinder head.

2) Tighten cylinder head bolts to initial torque of 35 ft. lbs. (48 N.m). Follow sequence in *Fig. 1*. Repeat procedure, tightening bolts to final torque.

Fig. 1: Cylinder Head Bolt Tightening Sequence

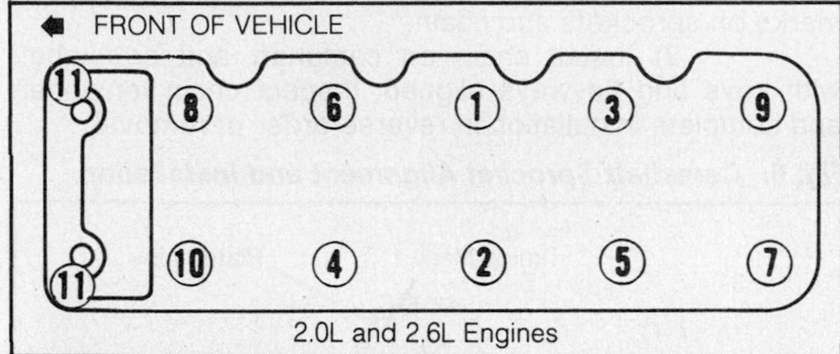
FRONT OF VEHICLE
11
8
6
1
3
9
10
4
2
5
7
11
2.0L and 2.6L Engines

Reverse order when removing cylinder head.

3) Temporarily set valve clearance to cold engine settings. Readjust to hot engine settings after engine is at normal operating temperature. Install rocker cover, air cleaner and breather hoses.

CAMSHAFT

ROCKER ASSEMBLY & CAMSHAFT

Removal

1) Remove air cleaner, breather hoses and purge line. Remove fuel pump and line. Disconnect spark plug wires and remove rocker cover. Remove breather and semi-circular seal.

2) Slightly loosen camshaft sprocket bolt and turn engine to TDC of compression stroke on No. 1 cylinder. Make mating mark on timing chain and camshaft sprocket.

3) Remove camshaft sprocket and hang sprocket on sprocket holder provided on timing chain lower front cover. Remove distributor drive gear, camshaft bearing caps, rocker arms and rocker shafts as an assembly. Remove camshaft.

NOTE: **If front and rear bearing cap bolts are left inserted, rocker shaft assembly can be removed without separation of pieces.**

Installation

1) Lubricate camshaft lobes and camshaft bearing journals and install camshaft to cylinder head. Install rocker arm assembly to cylinder head. Camshaft should be positioned with dowel in the 12 o'clock position. *See Fig. 2.*

2) Insert camshaft bearing cap bolts and tighten to 7 ft. lbs. (10 N.m) in sequence of center, 2, 4, front and rear. Repeat sequence, tightening to specified torque.

3) Install camshaft sprocket and distributor drive gear to camshaft. Turn crankshaft backwards about 90° and tighten camshaft locking bolt. To complete installation, reverse removal procedures.

COUNTERBALANCE DRIVE CHAIN

Removal

1) Drain coolant and engine oil. Disconnect negative battery cable. Remove rocker cover, breather

Fig. 2: Camshaft Installation Position, and Bearing Cap and Rocker Arm Shaft Mating Marks

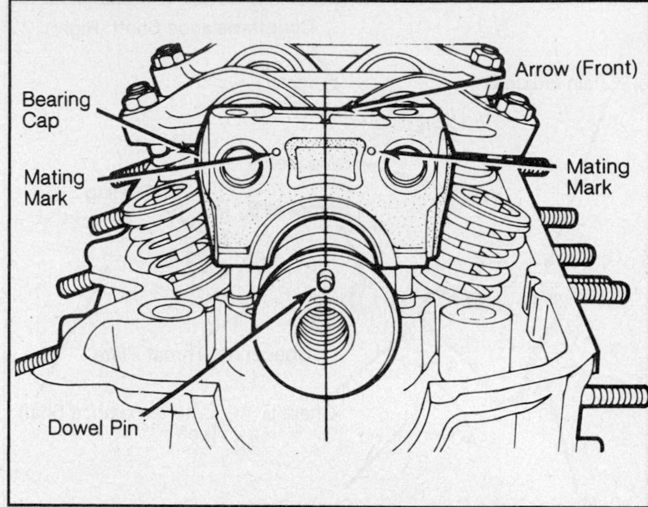
Arrow (Front)
Bearing Cap
Mating Mark
Mating Mark
Dowel Pin

Ensure camshaft dowel is in 12 o'clock position.

and semi-circular seal. Remove alternator, fan belt, fan, water pump pulley and water pump. Remove distributor and oil pan.

Fig. 3: Exploded View of Rocker Assembly

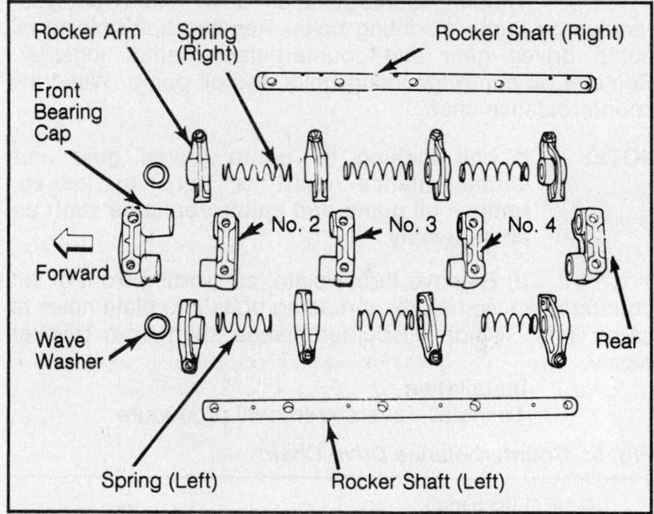
Rocker Arm
Spring (Right)
Rocker Shaft (Right)
Front Bearing Cap
No. 2
No. 3
No. 4
Forward
Wave Washer
Rear
Spring (Left)
Rocker Shaft (Left)

Check rocker arms for wear or damage on all contact surfaces.

2) Remove crankshaft pulley and timing chain case. Remove chain guides "A", "B", and "C", sprocket locking bolts and crankshaft sprocket. Remove both counterbalance shaft sprockets and drive chain. *See Figs. 4 and 5.*

Installation

1) Refer to *Figs. 4 and 5* for component location, and reverse removal procedure. Ensure that mating marks on sprockets align with plated links on counterbalance chain.

2) Adjust tension by installing guides "A" and "C". Shake counterbalance shaft sprockets to take slack from chain. Adjust guide "B" so there will be .040-.140" (1.0-3.5 mm) clearance between guide and chain at point "P". Tighten guide mounting bolts and complete assembly.

2.0L & 2.6L 4-CYLINDER (Cont.)

Fig. 4: Exploded View of Counterbalance Shafts and Drive Chain

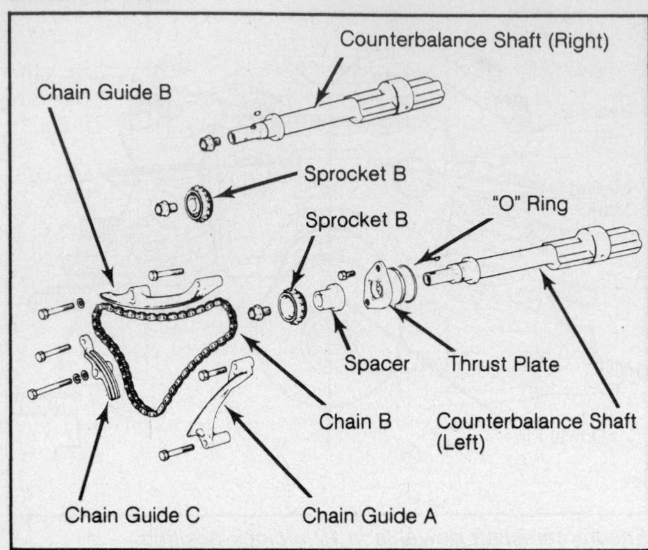
Counterbalance Shaft (Right)
Chain Guide B
Sprocket B
"O" Ring
Sprocket B
Spacer
Thrust Plate
Chain B
Counterbalance Shaft (Left)
Chain Guide C
Chain Guide A

Right counterbalance shaft is driven off of oil pump.

COUNTERBALANCE SHAFTS

Removal

1) With counterbalance drive chain removed, remove oil pump mounting bolts. Remove bolt holding oil pump driven gear and counterbalance shaft together. Remove oil pump mounting bolts and oil pump. Withdraw counterbalance shaft.

NOTE: If bolt locking oil pump driven gear and counterbalance shaft is hard to loosen, remove oil pump and counterbalance shaft as an assembly.

2) Remove thrust plate, supporting front of left counterbalance shaft, by threading bolts into plate holes at same time. Withdraw counterbalance shaft from cylinder block.

Installation

To install, reverse removal procedure.

Fig. 5: Counterbalance Drive Chain

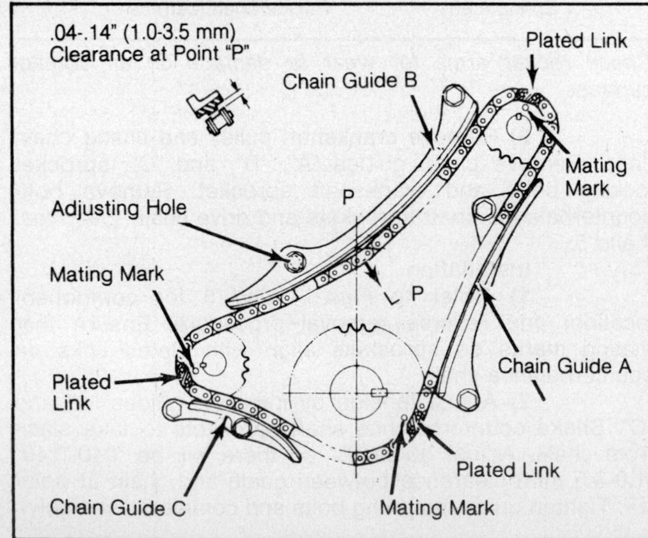
.04-.14" (1.0-3.5 mm)
Clearance at Point "P"
Plated Link
Chain Guide B
Mating Mark
P
Adjusting Hole
Mating Mark
P
Chain Guide A
Plated Link
Plated Link
Chain Guide C
Mating Mark

Align plated links with mating marks.

TIMING CHAIN

Removal

With counterbalance drive chain removed, take off chain tensioner and right and left chain guides. Remove camshaft sprocket and timing chain.

Installation

1) To install, rotate crankshaft until No. 1 piston is at TDC on compression stroke. Align mating marks on sprockets and chain.

2) Install chain on camshaft and crankshaft with keys and keyways aligned. Inspect chain tensioner, and complete installation in reverse order of removal.

Fig. 6: Camshaft Sprocket Alignment and Installation

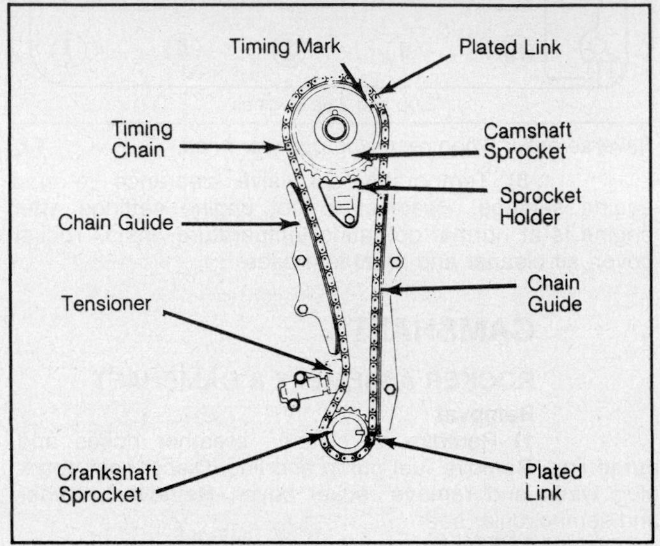
Timing Mark
Plated Link
Timing Chain
Camshaft Sprocket
Sprocket Holder
Chain Guide
Chain Guide
Tensioner
Crankshaft Sprocket
Plated Link

Align plated links with timing marks on sprockets.

VALVES

VALVE ARRANGEMENT

Left Side – Intake and Jet
Right Side – Exhaust

JET VALVES

Using special Jet Valve Socket Wrench (MD998310), remove jet valves. Disassemble valve using spring pliers (MD998309) to compress spring and remove retainer lock. Check valve head and seat for damage and make sure jet valve slides smooth in body without play.

CAUTION: Make certain that jet valve socket wrench is not tilted with respect to center of valve. If tool is tilted, stem may bend and result in improper valve operation. Do not attempt to repair jet valve and body combination. If defective, replace as an assembly.

VALVE SPRINGS

1) With camshaft and rocker arm assembly removed, compress valve spring and remove retainer locks (keepers). Remove all retainers, springs, spring seats and valves, keeping in proper order for reassembly.

2) Check valve spring free length and pressure. Standard spring squareness should be 1.5° or less. Replace if beyond 3°.

2.0L & 2.6L 4-CYLINDER (Cont.)

VALVE GUIDE SERVICING

1) Check valve stem-to-guide clearance, and if clearance exceeds service limits as listed in table, replace valve guide with next oversize component. Guides are available in the following oversizes:

VALVE GUIDE OVERSIZES

Size Mark	Guide Oversize mm	Cyl. Head Bore mm
5	.05	.5138-.5145 (13.05-13.07)
25	.25	.5216-.5224 (13.25-13.27)
50	.50	.5315-.5323 (13.50-13.52)

2) Heat cylinder head to approximately 480°F (249°C), and use a valve guide tool to drive out each guide toward the combustion chamber.

3) After head has cooled to room temperature, ream guide bore in cylinder head to specified size. To install new guides, reheat head to same temperature, quickly insert and drive guides into head.

4) When properly installed, guide should protrude .591" (15 mm) above head surface on 2.0L engines and .551" (14 mm) on 2.6L engines. See Fig. 7. Check guide I.D. and ream as necessary.

Fig. 7: Valve Guide Installation and Height

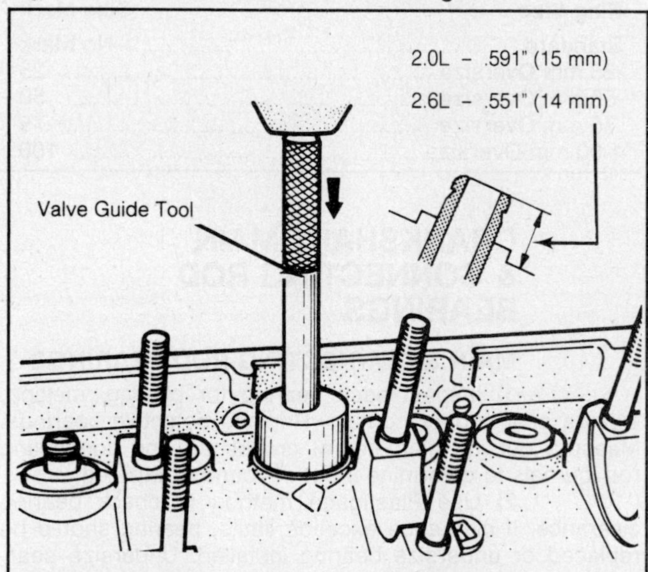
2.0L - .591" (15 mm)
2.6L - .551" (14 mm)
Valve Guide Tool

Cylinder head must be heated prior to installation.

VALVE STEM OIL SEALS

After installing valve spring seat, place stem seal on guide. Use installer to lightly hammer seal into correct position as tool bottoms on head. Do not use old seals and do not twist seals when installing.

VALVE SEAT SERVICING

1) Check valve seat for damage or wear. Replace or rework seat, as necessary. If reworking seat, check valve guide first. Make proper replacement, if required, then check seat for necessary corrections.

2) Recondition valve seat with grinder or cutter to specified contact width. After rework, valve and seat should be lapped with compound.

3) Valve seat sink (wear of seat inward allowing valve to seat too deep in head) must be checked by measuring installed height of spring between the spring seat and retainer with all spring components installed.

4) Standard dimension is 1.590" (40.4 mm) with an additional wear limit of .039" (1.0 mm). Replace valve seat if beyond limit.

5) To remove valve seat, thin down with a cutter. Machine seat bore to proper size for replacement seat. Heat head to approximately 480°F (250°C) and press in oversize seat.

6) Replacement seats are available in .012" (.305 mm) and .024" (.610 mm) oversizes, marked "30" and "60" respectively. After installing, machine valve seat to specifications.

VALVE CLEARANCE ADJUSTMENT

1) Ensure timing marks on camshaft sprocket and chain are aligned. With head assembly installed, adjust valves in 1-3-4-2 cylinder sequence, according to following procedure.

2) At compression stroke TDC, for cylinder being adjusted, loosen rocker arm nuts; then, turning adjusting screw, adjust valve clearance to specifications.

3) Complete engine assembly and temporarily install rocker cover. Warm engine until coolant temperature is 170 to 180°F. With piston at TDC on compression stroke, back intake valve adjusting screw off 2 or more turns.

4) Adjust jet valve clearance, intake valve clearance, and finally exhaust valve clearance. Assure that all adjusting screw lock nuts are tightened securely.

VALVE CLEARANCE

Application	Cold In. (mm)	Hot In. (mm)
Intake	.003 (.07)	.006 (.15)
Exhaust	.007 (.17)	.010 (.25)
Jet Valve	.003 (.07)	.006 (.15)

NOTE: **Jet valve spring is comparatively weak and must not be forced in when making adjustment. Final valve clearance should be adjusted after cylinder head bolts have been tightened to final torque.**

PISTONS, PINS & RINGS

PISTON & CONNECTING ROD ASSEMBLY

Removal

1) Remove cylinder head and oil pan. Check to ensure connecting rods and rod caps are marked to aid in assembling components to their original position. Remove rear main seal housing.

2) Remove carbon ridge from cylinder bores. Remove connecting rod caps. Remove connecting rod and piston assembly through top of cylinder block.

2.0L & 2.6L 4-CYLINDER (Cont.)

Installation

1) To install, lubricate all internal surfaces with engine oil before installation. Make sure front mark on piston head faces front of engine.

2) Use a ring compressor to compress rings (without changing their position) and install piston and connecting rod assembly into cylinder block in their original position.

3) Tap lightly on piston dome with wooden handle tool while guiding connecting rod onto crankshaft. Install rod cap onto proper piston and connecting rod assembly with bearing insert notches on same side. Tighten attaching bolts and install cylinder head, rear main seal housing and oil pan.

FITTING PISTONS

1) After checking block for distortion, cracks, scratches or other abnormalities, measure bores at 3 levels. If any distortion exceeds .001" (.02 mm) from standard bore size, block must be rebored and oversize pistons installed.

NOTE: **Pistons are available in standard, .25 mm, .50 mm, .75 mm and 1.0 mm oversizes. Oversize pistons are stamped on crown to indicate oversize amount.**

2) Check outside diameter of piston by measuring at a point .079" (2 mm) from bottom of skirt and at 90° to pin bore. Determine amount of cylinder reboring required to meet specified clearance.

NOTE: **Pin-to-rod fit at normal temperature will require 1,653-3,858 lbs. (750-1,750 kg) to press piston through rod.**

PISTON PINS

NOTE: **Identification mark on connecting rod faces toward front of engine.**

Check pin fit in piston bore without rod. At room temperature, pin should press in smoothly by hand. When assembling, apply engine oil to outside of pin and to piston pin bore. Position rod and piston marks (indicating front) upward. Align pin with pressing tool, and press pin into piston and rod.

PISTON RINGS

NOTE: **Compression rings differ in scraping edge design. From a cross sectional view, ring No. 1 has a barrel shaped scraping edge and ring No. 2 has a tapered edge.**

1) Measure piston ring side and end clearance for all pistons and replace rings as necessary. When replacing a ring without correcting the cylinder bore, check ring end gap at lower part of cylinder that is less worn. When replacing a ring, be sure to use one of the same size.

2) Install rings on piston with end gaps staggered at 120° intervals, but make sure no ring gap is in line with thrust face of pin bore. Also be sure the manufacturer's marks are facing upward when rings are installed.

Fig. 8: Piston Ring Gap Positions

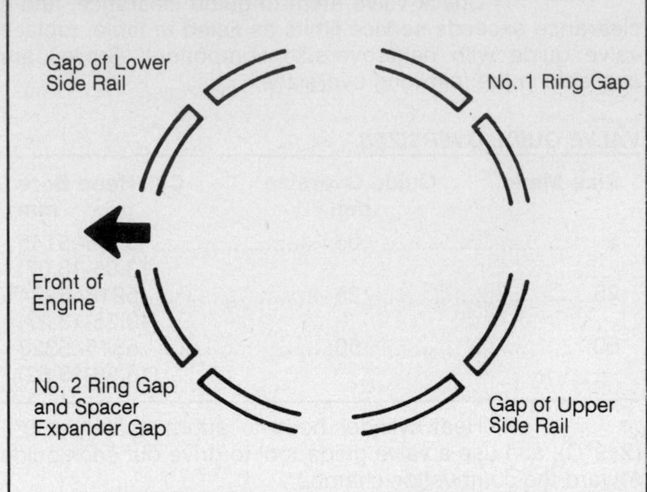
Gap of Lower Side Rail
No. 1 Ring Gap
Front of Engine
No. 2 Ring Gap and Spacer Expander Gap
Gap of Upper Side Rail

Stagger ring gaps to minimize compression loss.

CAUTION: **Install oil ring first without using a ring expander. Spacer expander gap should be installed more than 45° from side rail gaps, and rails should turn smoothly when installed.**

PISTON RING SIZES

Ring Size	Size Mark
Standard	No Mark
.25 mm Oversize	25
.50 mm Oversize	50
.75 mm Oversize	75
1.00 mm Oversize	100

CRANKSHAFT MAIN & CONNECTING ROD BEARINGS

MAIN & CONNECTING ROD BEARINGS

1) Inspect each bearing for peeling, melting, seizure or improper contact. Replace defective bearings. Measure outside diameter of crankshaft and connecting rod journals to determine if out-of-round or tapered.

2) Use Plastigage method to check bearing clearance. If clearance exceeds limits, bearing should be replaced or undersize bearing installed. Undersize bearings are available in .25 mm, .50 mm, and .75 mm undersizes.

NOTE: **Do not turn crankshaft with Plastigage installed.**

THRUST BEARING

With crankshaft bearing caps installed, check thrust clearance (end play) by inserting feeler gauge between center main bearing and crankshaft thrust face. If clearance exceeds specified limits, replace center main bearing.

2.0L & 2.6L 4-CYLINDER (Cont.)

ENGINE OILING

ENGINE OILING SYSTEM

A force-feed type lubrication system is used. The pump is a gear type pump that is driven off counterbalance shaft chain. Driven gear of pump drives the counterbalance shaft.

CRANKCASE CAPACITY

Montero and Pickups
2.0L (Pickups Only).
RWD - 4.2 quarts (4.0L).
4WD - 5.2 quarts (5.0L).
2.6L
RWD - 5.2 quarts (5.0L).
4WD - 6.1 quarts (5.8L).
Challenger, Sapporo and Starion
2.6L
4.5 quarts (4.3L)

OIL PRESSURE

6 psi (.42 kg/cm²) @ curb idle and 45 psi (3.15 kg/cm²) @ 3000 RPM.

OIL PUMP

Removal

Pump is mounted at lower right side of engine block, and driven by countershaft drive chain. For removal, *see Counterbalance Shafts.*

Installation

To install, reverse removal procedure, assuring that oil pump gear mating marks are aligned and that Woodruff key on counterbalance shaft fits in keyway of driven gear.

CAUTION: Prior to installing oil pump (all models), fill with .33 oz. (10 cc) of engine oil to prime pump.

Fig. 9: Mating Marks of Oil Pump Gears

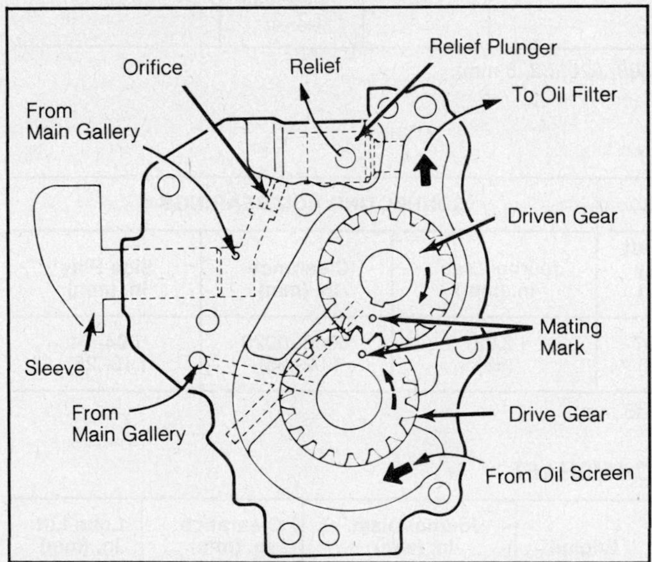
Relief Plunger
Orifice
Relief
To Oil Filter
From
Main Gallery
Driven Gear
Mating
Mark
Sleeve
From
Main Gallery
Drive Gear
From Oil Screen

Align marks during assembly.

OIL PUMP SPECIFICATIONS

Application	Clearance In. (mm)
Gear Tip-to-Body Clearance	.0043-.0059 (.11-.15)
Gear End Play	.0024-.0047 (.06-.12)
Drive Gear-to-Bearing	.0008-.0020 (.02-.05)
Drive Gear-to-Rear Bearing	.0016-.0028 (.04-.07)

ENGINE COOLING

THERMOSTAT

190°F (88°C).

RADIATOR CAP

11-15 psi (0.8-1.1 kg/cm²).

COOLANT CAPACITY

8.5-9.7 quarts (8.0-9.2L).

WATER PUMP

Removal & Installation

Drain cooling system and disconnect battery. Remove fan shroud if so equipped and remove lower radiator hose. Remove drive belt, cooling fan, fan clutch and pulley. Remove water pump. To install, reverse removal procedure using new gasket.

TIGHTENING SPECIFICATIONS

Application	Ft. Lbs. (N.m)
Camshaft Bearing Caps	14-15 (19-20)
Camshaft Sprocket	
2.0L	37-43 (49-58)
2.6L	59-72 (79-98)
Connecting Rod Caps	33-34 (45-47)
Crankshaft Sprocket	80-94 (108-127)
Cylinder Head (Cold)	65-72 (89-98)
Cylinder Head (Hot)	73-79 (98-107)
Flywheel or Drive Plate-to-Crankshaft	94-101 (127-137)
Jet Valve	13-15 (18-20)
Main Bearing Cap	
2.0L	37-39 (49-53)
2.6L cc	55-61 (75-83)
	INCH Lbs. (N.m)
Oil Pump Mounting	72-74 (8-10)

Mitsubishi Engines

2.0L & 2.6L 4-CYLINDER (Cont.)

ENGINE SPECIFICATIONS

GENERAL SPECIFICATIONS

Year	DISPLACEMENT		Fuel System	HP@RPM	Torque Ft. Lbs.@RPM	Compr. Ratio	BORE		STROKE	
	Cu. In.	Liters					In.	mm	In.	mm
1983 Challenger & Sapporo	155.9	2.6	2-Bbl.	100@5000	137@2500	8.2:1	3.58	91.1	3.86	98.0
[1] Montero & Pickups	121.9 155.9	2.0 2.6	2-Bbl. 2-Bbl.	90@5000 105@5000	103@2500 139@2500	8.5:1 8.2:1	3.35 3.59	85.0 91.1	3.46 3.86	88.0 98.0
Starion	155.9	2.6	EFI	145@5000	185@2500	7.0:1	3.59	91.1	3.86	98.0

[1] – Montero only uses 2.6L engine.

VALVES

Engine Size & Valve	Head Diam. In. (mm)	Face Angle	Seat Angle	Seat Width In. (mm)	Stem Diameter In. (mm)	Stem Clearance In. (mm)	[1] Valve Lift In. (mm)
2.0L & 2.6L							
Intake	[2] 1.69 (43)	45°	45°	.035-.051 (.9-1.3)	.315 (8.0)	.0012-.0024 (.03-.06)	.390 (9.9)
Exhaust	[3] 1.38 (35)	45°	45°	.047-.063 (1.2-1.6)	.315 (8.0)	.0020-.0035 (.05-.09)	.390 (9.9)

[1] – On 2.6L engine: .413" (10.5 mm).
[2] – On 2.6L engine: 1.81" (46 mm).
[3] – On 2.6L engine: 1.50" (38 mm).

PISTONS, PINS, RINGS

Engine	PISTONS	PINS		RINGS		
	Clearance In. (mm)	Piston Fit In. (mm)	Rod Fit In. (mm)	Ring No.	End Gap In. (mm)	Side Clearance In. (mm)
2.0L & 2.6L	.0008-.0016 (.02-.04)	[1]	[2] Locked in Rod	No. 1	.010-.018 (.25-.45)	.0024-.0039 (.06-.10)
				No. 2	.010-.018 (.25-.45)	.0008-.0024 (.02-.06)
				Oil	[3] .008-.035 (.2-.9)	.....

[1] – Thumb press fit without rod installed.
[2] – Press in at 1653-3858 lbs. at room temp.
[3] – On 2.0L engine: .008-.020" (.2-.5 mm).

CRANKSHAFT MAIN & CONNECTING ROD BEARINGS

Engine	MAIN BEARINGS				CONNECTING ROD BEARINGS		
	Journal Diam. In. (mm)	Clearance In. (mm)	Thrust Bearing	Crankshaft End Play In. (mm)	Journal Diam. In. (mm)	Clearance In. (mm)	Side Play In. (mm)
2.0L & 2.6L	[1] 2.362 (60)	.0008-.0020 (.02-.05)	No. 3	.002-.007 (.05-.18)	[2] 2.087 (53)	.0008-.0020 (.02-.05)	.004-.01 (.10-.25)

[1] – On 2.0L engines: 2.244" (57 mm).
[2] – On 2.0L engines: 1.772" (45 mm).

VALVE SPRINGS

Engine	Free Length In. (mm)	PRESSURE Lbs. @ In. (Kg @ mm)	
		Valve Closed	Valve Open
2.0L & 2.6L	[1] 1.869 (47.5)	62@1.59 (27.6@40.4)	.....

[1] – Not exceeding 1.5° out of square.

CAMSHAFT

Engine	Journal Diam. In. (mm)	Clearance In. (mm)	Lobe Lift In. (mm)
2.0L & 2.6L Int. & Exh.	1.339 (34)	.002-.004 (.05-.09)	[1] .393 (10.0)

[1] – On 2.6L engine: .413" (10.5 mm)

2.3L 4-CYLINDER TURBO DIESEL

Chrysler Corp. Imports: Colt Pickup & Ram-50 Pickup
Mitsubishi: Pickup

ENGINE CODING

ENGINE IDENTIFICATION

Engine model code and serial number are stamped on left side of cylinder block near engine oil dipstick.

ENGINE IDENTIFICATION

Application	Engine Model	[1] Engine VIN Code
2.3L (143.2")	[2] 4D55	9

[1] – Eighth digit of VIN code.
[2] – Referred to by Chrysler Corp. as "TBD" engine.

ENGINE, MANIFOLDS & CYLINDER HEAD

ENGINE

Removal

1) Disconnect negative battery cable and drain engine oil. Remove hood and air cleaner duct. Disconnect heater hoses, water level sensor and throttle cable. Disconnect fuel hoses and remove fuel filter.

2) Remove power steering pump, if equipped. Disconnect glow cable, gauge-unit harness connectors, engine ground cable and starter motor wiring harness. Detach clutch release cylinder from transmission.

3) Disconnect engine oil cooler lines and brake booster vacuum hose. Disconnect alternator wiring and oil pressure switch or gauge wiring. Remove radiator assembly and front exhaust pipe.

4) On rear-wheel drive models, remove under cover, disconnect speedometer cable, back-up light switch harness. On 4WD models, remove under cover, under skid plate, transfer case protector and disconnect speedometer cable.

5) Disconnect back-up light switch and 4WD indicator light switch. On all models, remove driveshafts and gearshift lever assembly. Support transmission with jack and detach rear insulator from transmission.

6) Remove No. 2 crossmember. On 4WD models, support transfer case and remove transfer case mounting bracket, support insulator and plate from side frame. Detach mounting bracket from transfer case.

7) On all models, remove nuts from front engine insulators. Attach lifting device and remove engine-transmission assembly from vehicle.

Installation

Reverse removal procedure to reinstall engine-transmission assembly. Replace all fluids. Adjust throttle cable and clutch pedal.

CYLINDER HEAD

1) Place cylinder No. 1 at TDC of compression stroke. Drain cooling system and disconnect necessary wiring, cables and hoses. Disconnect and plug fuel line to injectors.

2) Disconnect necessary turbocharger and boost compensator connections. Remove timing belt front upper cover. Remove access plug from front lower timing belt cover and relieve timing belt tension.

3) Remove camshaft sprocket, valve cover, rocker arm assembly and camshaft. Using wrench (MD998051) gradually loosen cylinder head bolts, in reverse of tightening sequence. *See Fig. 1.*

Inspection

Inspect cylinder head for cracks and damage; combustion chamber for damage and looseness and gasket surface for warpage. Use a straightedge and feeler gauge to measure warpage. If warpage exceeds .004" (.1 mm), lightly machine head surface or replace cylinder head.

Installation

1) Install cylinder head gasket carefully as it has no identification mark. Do not apply sealant to gasket or mating surfaces. Install cylinder head and head bolts.

2) Tighten bolts in sequence to 1/2 of tightening specification, then tighten to final specification. *See Fig. 1.*Reverse removal procedure to complete installation.

Fig. 1: Cylinder Head Tightening Sequence

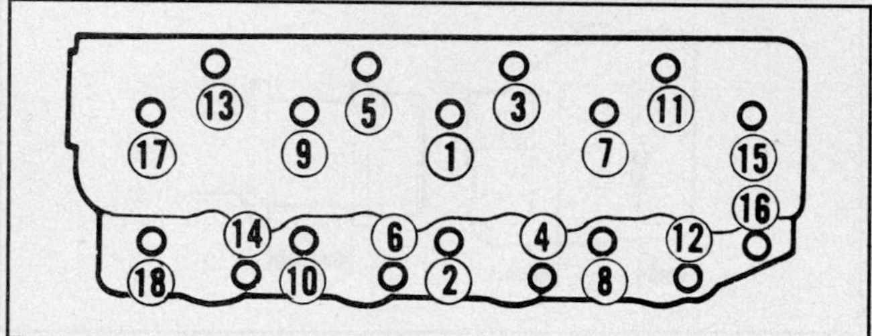

13
5
3
11
17
9
1
7
15
16
14
6
4
12
18
10
2
8

Reverse sequence when removing bolts.

CAMSHAFT

ROCKER SHAFT ASSEMBLY & CAMSHAFT

Removal

1) Disconnect negative battery cable. Remove upper front timing belt cover. Position cylinder No. 1 at TDC of compression stroke. Camshaft sprocket dowel should be at topmost position and sprocket timing marks should be in alignment. *See Fig. 2.*

Fig. 2: Aligning Camshaft Sprocket Timing Marks

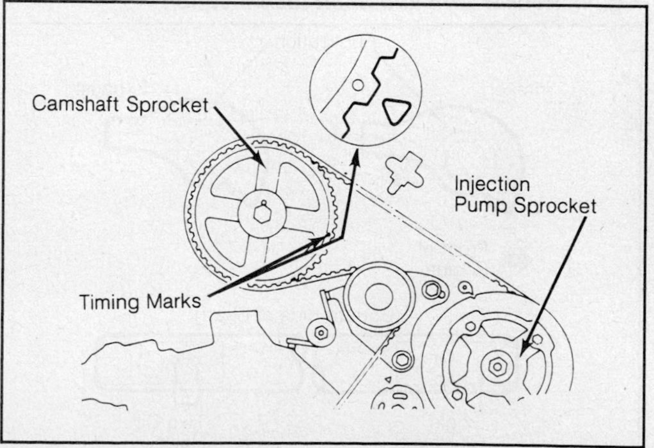

Camshaft Sprocket
Injection Pump Sprocket
Timing Marks

Camshaft sprocket dowel pin should be at topmost position, with cylinder No. 1 at TDC of compression stroke.

2.3L 4-CYLINDER TURBO DIESEL (Cont.)

2) Disconnect breather and boost compensator hose. Remove valve cover. Remove access cover and relieve tensioner pressure on timing belt. Remove camshaft sprocket, rocker shaft assembly and camshaft.

Inspection

1) Inspect rocker arm cam contact surface for dents and wear; adjustment screw contact surface for wear and out-of-round and rocker shaft bore for loose fit on shaft.

2) Inspect rocker arm shaft for wear on rocker arm contact surfaces. Inspect camshaft for wear and damage on: journals, lobes, fuel pump drive cam, distributor drive gear and oil seal contact surface.

3) Ensure oil holes in rocker arms and rocker shafts are clear. Inspect camshaft bearing for wear. Replace cylinder head if bearing is excessively worn. Inspect oil seal lip for damage and replace if required.

Installation

1) Before installing camshaft, determine camshaft end play by subtracting dimension 'A" of front bearing cap from dimension "B" of camshaft. *See Fig. 3.*

Fig. 3: Measuring Camshaft End Play

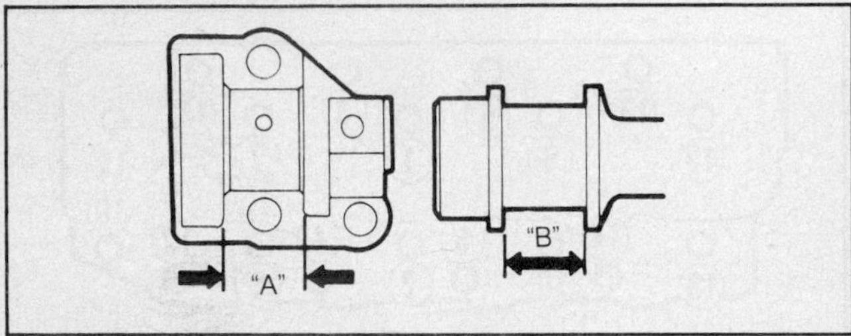
"A"
"B"

Subtract dimension "A" from dimension "B" to determine camshaft end play.

2) Lubricate camshaft journals and lobes. Install camshaft. Install bearing caps, with numbers stamped on cap, in numerical order starting at front of engine. Tighten cap bolts to specifications.

3) Install camshaft oil seal using installer (MD998381). Ensure injection pump sprocket and crankshaft sprocket timing marks are in proper alignment. Install belt on camshaft sprocket and install sprocket.

4) Identify rocker arms and determine correct installation of rocker arm shaft. *See Fig. 4.* Lubricate shaft and inner bore of rocker arm. Assemble rocker shaft assembly with oil holes down and single oil hole forward.

Fig. 4: Rocker Arm and Shaft Identification

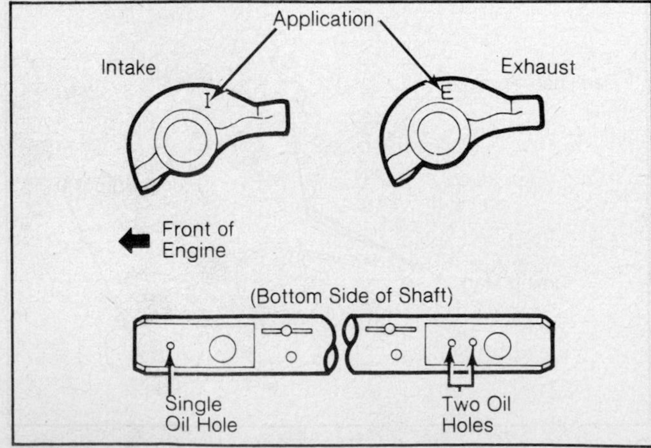
Application
Intake
Exhaust
I
E
Front of Engine
(Bottom Side of Shaft)
Single Oil Hole
Two Oil Holes

Install rocker shaft with oil holes down and single oil hole toward front of engine.

5) Install rocker shaft bolts and gradually tighten to specifications. Install camshaft sprocket and timing belt. Ensure timing mark alignment and belt tension are correct.

6) Reverse removal procedure to complete installation. Adjust valves. *See Valve Clearance Adjustment.* Apply sealant to top surface of cylinder block above semi-circular packing at rear of head and install valve cover.

TIMING BELTS & SPROCKETS

Removal

1) Disconnect negative battery cable and remove drive belts, fan, pulleys and timing belt covers. Position cylinder No. 1 at TDC of compression stroke and ensure timing marks are in alignment. *See Fig. 5.*

Fig. 5: Aligning Timing Marks

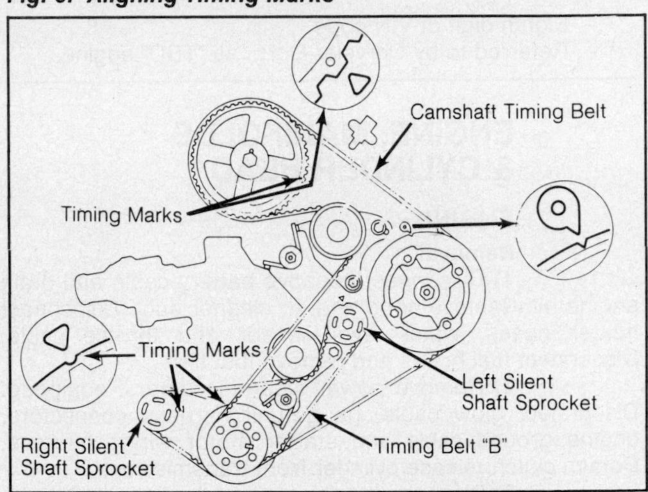
Camshaft Timing Belt
Timing Marks
Timing Marks
Left Silent Shaft Sprocket
Right Silent Shaft Sprocket
Timing Belt "B"

Proper alignment of timing marks with cylinder No. 1 at TDC of compression stroke.

2) Mark belts indicating direction of rotation. Loosen nuts and bolts securing belt tensioners. Pivot tensioners toward water pump and secure. Remove timing belts and necessary sprockets.

3) Remove silent shaft sprockets by removing plug from right side of block and cover from left side of block. Insert screwdriver and socket extension into holes to hold silent shafts in place. *See Fig. 6.*

Inspection

1) Inspect back of belt for being hard, non-elastic and having a glossy surface. If no mark is produced when finger nail is forced into it, replace belt.

2) Check for rounded sides on belt. Sides of belt should be straight and clear-cut. Flaking, peeling, cracking and separating rubber from canvas also indicates belt replacement. Cracks are most evident at base of tooth.

3) Abnormal wear most often occurs on load side of tooth. Fluffy canvas, unclear canvas texture, belt color changed to white from rubber missing, reduced tooth width or a missing tooth, warrant belt replacement.

Installation

1) Install crankshaft sprocket and flange ensuring flange on crankshaft sprocket "B" is installed correctly. *See Fig. 7.* Mount injection pump sprocket, if removed, and tighten nut to specifications.

2.3L 4-CYLINDER TURBO DIESEL (Cont.)

Fig. 6: Removing Silent Shaft Sprockets

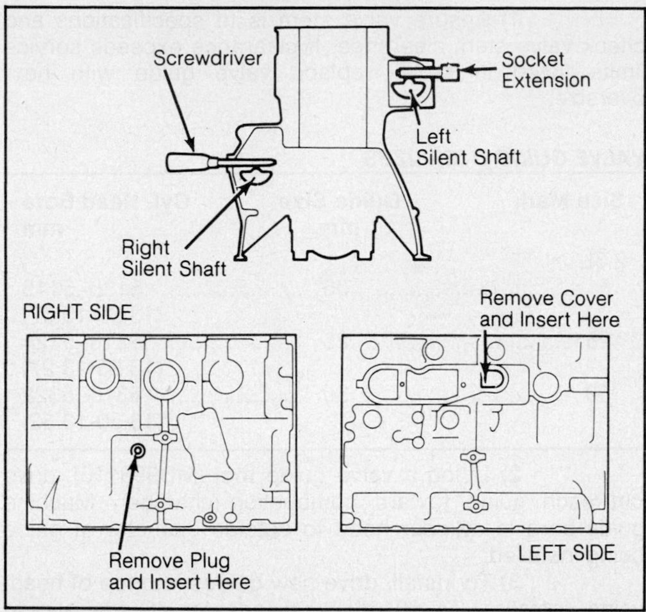
Screwdriver
Socket Extension
Left Silent Shaft
Right Silent Shaft
RIGHT SIDE
Remove Cover and Insert Here
Remove Plug and Insert Here
LEFT SIDE

Remove cover from left side and plug from right side of cylinder block to gain access of silent shafts.

Fig. 7: Installing Crankshaft Sprocket

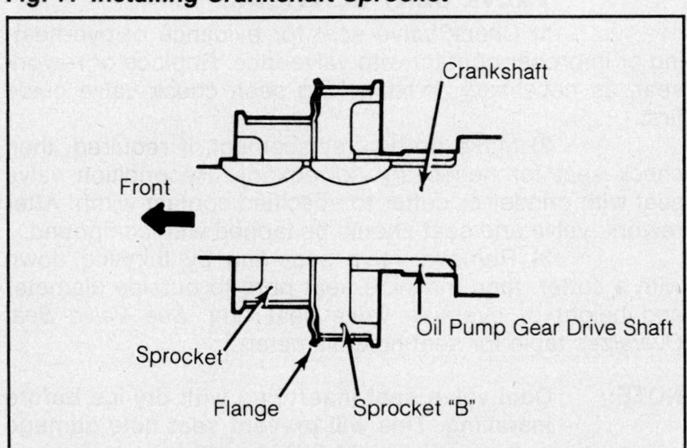
Crankshaft
Front
Oil Pump Gear Drive Shaft
Sprocket
Flange
Sprocket "B"

Note mounting position of flange, incorrect installation could result in a broken belt.

2) Install flange to injection pump sprocket, noting flange holes are offset to aid in correct installation. Lightly oil left silent shaft spacer and insert spacer with chamfered end toward seal.

3) Install both silent shaft sprocket, if removed, and tighten nut and bolt to specifications. Keep silent shafts from turning by using method described in removal procedure.

4) Position and secure tensioner "B" fully toward water pump. Align timing marks on crankshaft sprocket and silent shaft sprockets. *See Fig. 8.* Install timing belt "B", noting reference mark if refitting old belt.

5) Install timing belt "B", ensuring tension side has no slack. Check alignment of timing marks. Loosen tensioner "B" mounting nut and bolt, and allow tensioner spring pressure to adjust belt.

6) Tighten nut first, then tighten bolt. Make certain bolt is not tightened first. Using index finger, press belt at center of tension side inward and measure belt deflection. Deflection should be .16-.20" (4-5 mm).

Fig. 8: Aligning Sprocket Timing Marks for Timing Belt "B"

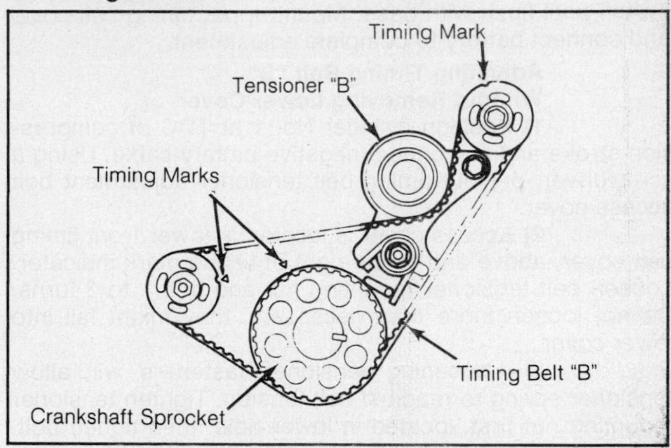
Timing Mark
Tensioner "B"
Timing Marks
Timing Belt "B"
Crankshaft Sprocket

7) Position and secure camshaft timing belt tensioner fully toward water pump. Align camshaft, crankshaft and injection pump timing marks. *See Fig. 5.* Install timing belt in order of crankshaft sprocket, injection pump sprocket and camshaft sprocket.

8) Ensure tension side of belt is taut and injection pump sprocket does not turn. If reusing old belt, make certain belt is installed according to rotation reference mark.

9) While keeping belt taut, loosen tensioner mounting bolts and allow tensioner spring pressure to tighten belt. Check to ensure timing belt and camshaft sprocket are still in mesh.

10) Tighten upper, slot-side, bolt first before tightening lower, fulcrum-side bolt. Tightening bolts in sequence other than indicated will over-tighten belt. After tightening tensioner mounting bolts check sprocket alignment.

11) Turn crankshft clockwise until second tooth past timing mark on camshaft sprocket is in alignment with "triangle" timing mark. Turn crankshaft counterclockwise and realign timing marks.

12) Using forefinger, press belt on tension side of belt between camshaft sprocket and injection pump sprocket. Measure belt deflection. Deflection should be .16-.20" (4-5 mm). Reverse removal procedure to complete installation.

Adjusting Camshaft Timing Belt Without Replacing Belt

1) Remove upper front timing belt cover and disconnect negative battery cable. Inspect entire belt for conditions listed in inspection procedure. If belt condition is satisfactory, position cylinder No. 1 at TDC of compression stroke.

2) Ensure timing marks are in alignment. *See Fig. 5.* Loosen tensioner mounting bolts 1 to 2 turns. Smoothly and accurately, turn crankshaft in clockwise direction only, until second tooth past timing mark on camshaft sprocket, is in alignment with "triangle" timing mark.

3) Tighten 2 tensioner mounting bolts in order of upper bolt first and lower bolt last to prevent rotation of tensioner bracket. Turn crankshaft counterclockwise and realign timing marks.

4) Check belt tension by pushing down on timing belt, with forefinger, at center of belt between camshaft sprocket and injection pump sprocket. Belt deflection should measure .16-.20" (4-5 mm).

2.3L 4-CYLINDER TURBO DIESEL (Cont.)

5) Readjust belt tension if deflection is not correct. Reset timing belt switch by pressing knob on switch until flush with base. Mount upper timing belt cover and connect battery to complete adjustment.

Adjusting Timing Belt "B" Without Removing Lower Cover

1) Position cylinder No. 1 at TDC of compression stroke and disconnect negative battery cable. Using a screwdriver, pry out timing belt tensioner adjustment bolt access cover.

2) Access cover is located in lower front timing belt cover, above and to the right of timing mark indicator. Loosen belt tensioner mounting nut and bolt 1 to 2 turns. Do not loosen more than necessary, they might fall into lower cover.

3) Loosening tensioner fasteners will allow tensioner spring to readjust belt tension. Tighten tensioner mounting nut first, located in lower hole, then tighen bolt, located in upper hole, to specifications. Install access cover and connect battery.

VALVES

VALVE ARRANGEMENT

E-I-E-I-E-I-E-I (Front-to-rear)

VALVE CLEARANCE ADJUSTMENT

1) Remove valve cover and position cylinder No. 1 at TDC of compression stroke. Adjust clearance on valves marked "A" as follows. *See Fig. 9.*

Fig. 9: Adjusting Valve Clearance

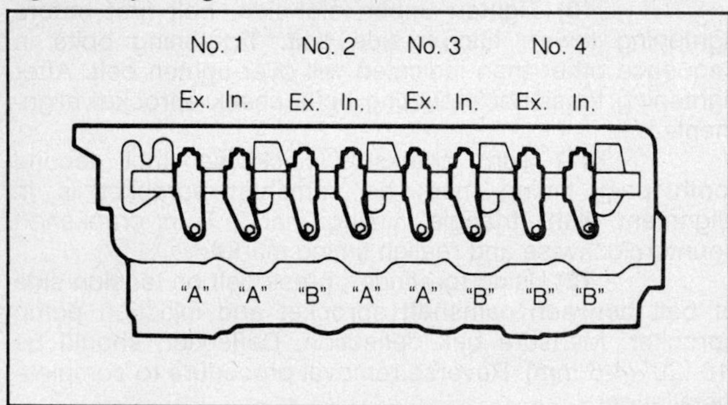
No. 1
No. 2
No. 3
No. 4
Ex. In. Ex. In. Ex. In. Ex. In.
"A" "A" "B" "A" "A" "B" "B" "B"

Adjust valves marked "A" with cylinder No. 1 at TDC of compression stroke; valves "B" with No. 4 at TDC.

2) Loosen adjustment screw lock nut 2 or more turns. Adjust clearance between valve stem and adjustment screw. Hold adjustment screw with screwdriver and tighten lock nut.

3) Check adjustment and readjust if necessary. Check to ensure lock nut is tight and clearance is correct. Continue adjusting remaining valves marked "A" using same procedure.

4) Position cylinder No. 4 at TDC of compression stroke. Adjust valves marked "B", using same procedure previously outlined. *See Fig. 8.* After completing adjustment, check idle speed and readjust if necessary.

VALVE CLEARANCE SPECIFICATIONS

Application	Clearance In. (mm)
Intake & Exhaust	.010 (.25)

VALVE GUIDE SERVICING

1) Ensure valve stem is to specifications and check valve stem clearance. If clearance exceeds service limits listed in table, replace valve guide with next oversize.

VALVE GUIDE OVERSIZES

Size Mark	Guide Size mm	Cyl. Head Bore mm
2.3L		
5	.05	.5138-.5145 (13.05-13.07)
25	.25	.5216-.5224 (13.25-13.27)
50	.50	.5315-.5322 (13.50-13.52)

2) Using a valve guide tool (MD998115), drive out each guide toward combustion chamber. Machine guide bore in cylinder head to outside diameter of guide being installed.

3) To install, drive new guides into top of head, using installer (MD98115) with adapter. Guide should protrude .591" (15 mm) above head surface when properly installed. Check guide I.D. and ream as necessary.

VALVE SEAT SERVICING

1) Check valve seat for evidence of overheating or improper contact with valve face. Replace or rework seat, as necessary. If reworking seat, check valve guide first.

2) Make proper replacement, if required, then check seat for necessary corrections. Recondition valve seat with grinder or cutter to specified contact width. After rework, valve and seat should be lapped with compound.

3) Remove valve seat ring by thinning down with a cutter, then machine seat bore to outside diameter and height of oversize valve seat ring. *See Valve Seat Oversizes* table for seat hole diameter.

NOTE: **Cool valve seat insert ring with dry ice before installing. This will prevent seat hole damage and ensure a tight fitting seat ring.**

4) Press seat into cylinder head. After installing valve seat ring, machine to specifications. After rework, valve and valve seat should be lapped with compound.

VALVE SEAT OVERSIZES

Oversize	Seat Hole Diameter In. (mm)
Intake	
.30 mm	1.705-1.706 (43.30-43.33)
.60 mm	1.717-1.718 (43.60-43.63)
Exhaust	
.30 mm	1.469-1.470 (37.30-37.33)
.60 mm	1.480-1.481 (37.60-37.63)

VALVE STEM OIL SEALS

After installing valve spring seat, place new stem seal on guide. Use installer (MD998377) to lightly tap seal into position as tool bottoms on spring seat.

VALVE SPRINGS

1) With camshaft and rocker arm assembly removed, use valve spring compressor to remove retainer

2.3L 4-CYLINDER TURBO DIESEL (Cont.)

locks. Remove all retainers, springs, spring seats and valves. Keep parts in proper order for reassembly.

2) Check valve spring load, free length and spring squareness. Standard spring squareness should be 1.5° or less. If beyond 3° replace spring. Install spring with identification color upward toward retainer.

PISTONS, PINS & RINGS

PISTON & CONNECTING ROD ASSEMBLY

Removal

1) Remove cylinder head, oil pan and screen. Ensure connecting rods and rod caps are marked on big end side surface to aid in installing parts to their original position.

2) Remove carbon ridge from cylinder bores. Remove connecting rod caps. Remove connecting rod and piston assembly through top of cylinder block.

Installation

1) To install, lubricate all internal surfaces with engine oil before installation. Make sure "arrow" mark on piston head faces front of engine. Use ring compressor to compress rings, without changing ring gap position.

2) Install piston and connecting rod assembly into cylinder block in original position. Tap lightly on piston dome with wooden handle tool while guiding connecting rod onto crankshaft.

3) Do not allow connecting rod to contact oil jet. Install rod cap onto proper piston and connecting rod assembly. Tighten attaching bolts. Install cylinder head and oil pan.

FITTING PISTONS

1) After checking block for distortion, cracks, scratches or other abnormalities, measure bores at top, center and bottom of No. 1 piston ring travel for taper and out-of-round.

2) If any cylinder has more than .0008" (.02 mm) taper or out-of-round, or if cylinder walls are badly scuffed or scored, block must be rebored or honed and new oversized pistons and rings fitted.

3) Measure outside diameter of piston by measuring at a point .079" (2 mm) from bottom of skirt below pin boss, at 90° to pin bore.

4) Calculate cylinder boring dimension by adding piston O.D. to the piston-to-cylinder clearance specification and subtracting the honing margin of .0008" (.02 mm).

5) Bore or hone all cylinders to same oversize. Do not bore only one cylinder. Bore or hone cylinders in sequence, skipping adjacent cylinders to prevent heat distortion.

NOTE: Replacement pistons are available in standard, .25 mm, .50 mm, .75 mm and 1.0 mm oversizes. Oversize pistons are stamped on crown to indicate oversize.

PISTON PINS

1) Check piston pin rod-fit and piston-fit. Accurate pin clearance is necessary due to high cylinder compression. If pin-to-rod clearance is excessive replace connecting small end bushing.

2) Using tool (MD998386), press bushing from connecting rod. Lightly oil bushing and bore. Press bushing into rod on side with chamfered bore. Ensure oil hole in rod and bushing are aligned.

3) Ream or hone bushing to fit size of pin. Position rod in piston with "arrow" mark on piston and "D" mark on connecting rod facing upward. Insert pin and snap rings. Check piston assembly for smooth full-floating movement.

PISTON RINGS

1) Measure piston ring side and end clearance for all pistons and replace rings as necessary. When replacing ring in cylinder bore not needing reconditioning, check ring end gap at lower part of cylinder that is less worn.

2) When replacing a ring, be sure to use one of the same size. Compression rings differ in scraping edge design. From a cross sectional view, ring No. 1 has a barrel shaped scraping edge and ring No. 2 has a tapered edge.

3) Install oil ring first using a ring expander. Install rings on piston with manufacturer's marks facing upward and end gaps staggered at 120° intervals. Make certain that no end gap is in line with thrust face of pin bore. *See Fig. 10.*

Fig. 10: Positioning Piston Ring Gaps

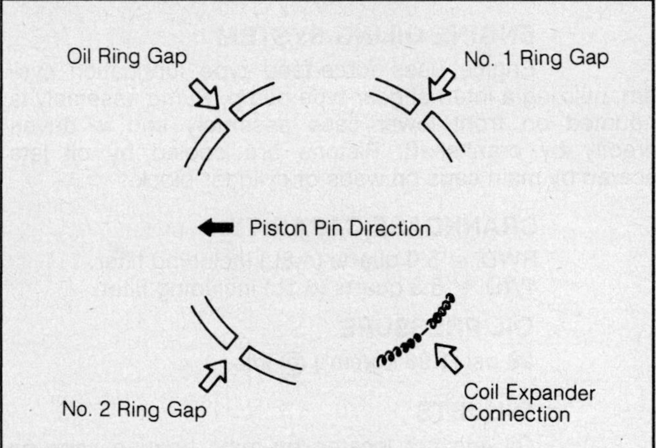
Oil Ring Gap
No. 1 Ring Gap
Piston Pin Direction
No. 2 Ring Gap
Coil Expander
Connection

Make sure end gaps are not positioned in line with thrust face of pin bore.

PISTON RING SIZES

Ring Size	Size Mark
2.3L	
Standard	No Mark
.25 mm Oversize	25
.50 mm Oversize	50
.75 mm Oversize	75
1.0 mm Oversize	100

CRANKSHAFT MAIN & CONNECTING ROD BEARINGS

MAIN & CONNECTING ROD BEARINGS

1) Inspect each bearing for peeling, melting, seizure or improper contact. Replace defective bearings. Measure outside diameter of crankshaft and connecting rod journals to determine if out-of-round or tapered.

2) Use Plastigage method to measure bearing clearance. If clearance exceeds limits, bearing should be

2.3L 4-CYLINDER TURBO DIESEL (Cont.)

replaced or undersize bearing installed. Undersize bearings are available in .25 mm, .50 mm, and .75 mm undersizes.

3) Main bearing caps are installed with "arrow" directed toward front of engine and cap number in correct order starting at front. Tighten cap bolts in sequence of center, No. 2, No. 4, front and rear.

4) Gradually tighten cap bolts in 2 or 3 steps, before tightening to specifications. Connecting rod bearing caps are installed with bearing insert locking tabs, located on same side of rod.

5) After completely bearing installation, ensure crankshaft turns freely and crankshaft end play and connecting rod side clearance are within specifications.

THRUST BEARING

With crankshaft bearing caps installed, check crankshaft end play by inserting feeler gauge between shoulder of center main bearing and crankshaft thrust face. If clearance exceeds specified limits, replace No. 3 main bearing.

ENGINE OILING

ENGINE OILING SYSTEM

Engine uses force-feed type lubrication system, utilizing a internal gear-type pump. Pump assembly is mounted on front lower case assembly and is driven directly by crankshaft. Pistons are cooled by oil jets located by main caps on webs of cylinder block.

CRANKCASE CAPACITY

RWD - 5.0 quarts (4.8L) including filter.
4WD - 6.3 quarts (6.1L) including filter.

OIL PRESSURE

28 psi (1.96 kg/cm²) @ idle.

OIL JETS

Oil jets are located by main bearing caps on webs of cylinder block. Two types of jets are used, one type is for cylinders No. 1 and No. 3 and other for cylinders No. 2 and No. 4. Mount oil jets facing center of cylinder and directed toward crown of piston. Improperly mounted oil jet will greatly reduce piston cooling.

OIL PUMP

Removal

1) Oil pan, oil screen and front upper case assembly must be removed prior to removing front cover-oil pump assembly. Remove silent shaft driven gear bolt. *See procedure in Timing Belts and Sprockets*

2) Remove front cover-oil-pump assembly. Remove oil pump cover, make alignment marks on gears for installation reference and remove gears from front cover assembly.

Inspection

1) Check gear contact surfaces of front cover and oil pump cover for step wear. Inspect gears, case and seal for wear or damage.

2) Reinstall gears as originally installed in front case and measure gear side clearance. *See Fig. 11.* Replace front case assembly if either step wear or excessive clearance is evident.

Fig. 11: Oil Pump Clearance

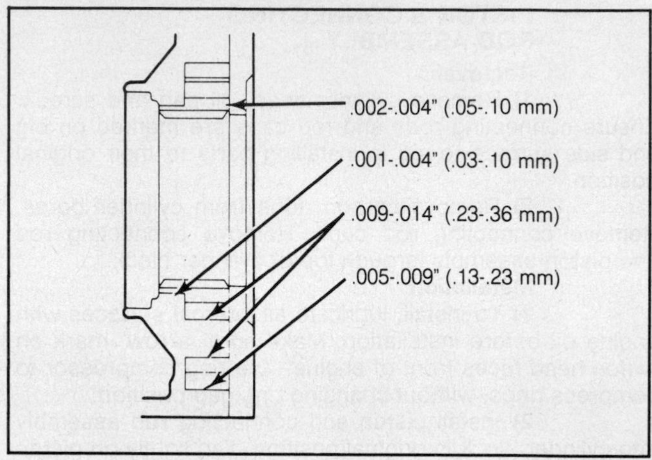
.002-.004" (.05-.10 mm)
.001-.004" (.03-.10 mm)
.009-.014" (.23-.36 mm)
.005-.009" (.13-.23 mm)

Replace front case assembly if side clearance is excessive.

Installation

Install oil pump gears in front case and align marks made during disassembly. Install pump cover and tighten bolts to specifications. Reverse disassembly procedure to complete installation. *See Timing Belts and Sprockets and Valve Clearance Adjustment* for adjustment procedures.

CAUTION: Prior to installing oil pump, fill with sufficient amount of engine oil to prime pump.

ENGINE COOLING

THERMOSTAT

190°F (88°C).

RADIATOR CAP

10.7-14.9 psi (.77-1.05 kg/cm²).

COOLANT CAPACITY

8.5 quarts (8.0L)

WATER PUMP

Drain cooling system and disconnect battery. Remove lower radiator hose, drive belt, cooling fan, fan clutch and pulley. Remove mounting bolts and remove pump assembly from engine. To install, use new gasket and reverse removal procedure.

ENGINE SPECIFICATIONS

GENERAL SPECIFICATIONS

Year	DISPLACEMENT		Fuel System	HP@RPM	Torque Ft. Lbs.@RPM	Compr. Ratio	BORE		STROKE	
	Cu. In.	Liters					In.	mm	In.	mm
1983	143.2	2.3	Fuel Inj.	.....	.....	21.0:1	3.59	91.1	3.54	90.0

Mitsubishi Engines

2.3L 4-CYLINDER TURBO DIESEL (Cont.)

ENGINE SPECIFICATIONS (Cont.)

VALVES

Engine Size & Valve	Head Diam. In. (mm)	Face Angle	Seat Angle	Seat Width In. (mm)	Stem Diameter In. (mm)	Stem Clearance In. (mm)	Valve Lift In. (mm)
2.3L							
Intake	1.57 (40)	45°	45°	.035-.051 (.9-1.3)	.315 (8.0)	.0012-.0024 (.03-.06)	.....
Exhaust	1.34 (34)	45°	45°	.047-.063 (1.2-1.6)	.315 (8.0)	.0020-.0035 (.05-.09)	.....

PISTONS, PINS, RINGS

Engine	PISTONS	PINS		RINGS		
	Clearance In. (mm)	Piston Fit	Rod Fit In. (mm)	Ring No.	End Gap In. (mm)	Side Clearance In. (mm)
2.3L	.0016-.0024 (.04-.06)	.0001-.0002	Full-Floating	No. 1	.010-.016 (.25-.40)	.001-.002 (.02-.04)
				No. 2	.010-.016 (.25-.40)	.001-.003 (.03-.07)
				Oil	.010-.018 (.25-.45)	.001-.003 .02-.07

CRANKSHAFT MAIN & CONNECTING ROD BEARINGS

Engine	MAIN BEARINGS				CONNECTING ROD BEARINGS		
	Journal Diam. In. (mm)	Clearance In. (mm)	Thrust Bearing	Crankshaft End Play In. (mm)	Journal Diam. In. (mm)	Clearance In. (mm)	Side Play In. (mm)
2.3L	2.598 (66)	.0008-.0020 (.02-.05)	No. 3	.0008-.0020 (.02-.05)	2.087 (53)	.0008-.0024 (.02-.06)	.004-.010 (.10-.25)

CAMSHAFT [1]

Engine	Journal Diam. In. (mm)	Clearance In. (mm)	Lobe Lift In. (mm)
2.3L	1.181 (30)	.002-.004 .05-.09	.....

[1] – Cam lobe height 1.46" (37.1 mm).

VALVE SPRINGS

Engine	Free Length In. (mm)	PRESSURE Lbs. @ In. (Kg @ mm)	
		Valve Closed	Valve Open
2.3L	[1] 1.933 (49.1)	61@1.591 (27.6@40.4)	.....

[1] – Maximum out-of-square 1.5°.

TIGHTENING SPECIFICATIONS

Application	Ft. Lbs. (N.m)
Belt Tensioner	16-21 (22-29)
Camshaft Bearing Caps	14-15 (19-20)
Camshaft Sprocket	47-54 (64-73)
Connecting Rod Cap	33-34 (45-47)
Crankshaft Pulley	33-34 (45-47)
Crankshaft Sprocket	123-137 (167-186)
Cylinder Head	
Cold	76-83 (103-112)
Hot	84-90 (113-122)
Drive Plate-to-Crankshaft	94-101 (127-137)
Flywheel-to-Crankshaft	94-101 (127-137)
Front Case	15-19 (20-26)
Intake & Exhaust Manifold	11-14 (15-19)
Main Bearing Cap	55-61 (74-83)
Rocker Arm Shaft	25-28 (34-39)
Silent Shaft Sprocket	25-28 (34-39)
	INCH Lbs. (N.m)
Oil Pan	53-62 (6-7)
Valve Cover	44-53 (5-6)

505 4-CYLINDER

ENGINE CODING

ENGINE IDENTIFICATION

Engine serial number is stamped on left side of engine block, and is also located on identification plate attached to top panel, above center of grille.

Engine identification number is stamped on camshaft tunnel on left side of block, near the starter. The letters at the beginning and end of the number are used for identification as follows:

ENGINE IDENTIFICATION CODES

Application	Transmission	Engine Codes
XN6 Engine	Manual	BVM
XN6 Engine	Automatic	BVA

ENGINE, MANIFOLDS & CYLINDER HEAD

ENGINE

Removal

1) Remove engine hood, battery and fan shroud. Drain radiator and remove upper and lower hoses. Remove electrical lead from cooling fan switch, and remove radiator lower mounting bolts. Remove rubber duct hose at mixture regulator throttle plate housing.

2) Remove fuel supply and return hoses and hose from cold start injector. Remove PCV hose and electrical connectors from cold start injector and fuel distributor. Remove fuel hoses and electrical connector from control pressure regulator.

3) Remove fuel injectors, mixture regulator and air filter. If equipped, remove A/C compressor and freon hose clamp near alternator. Disconnect accelerator cable and electrical harness near brake master cylinder.

Fig. 1: Positioning Support Plate for Torque Converter During Engine Removal

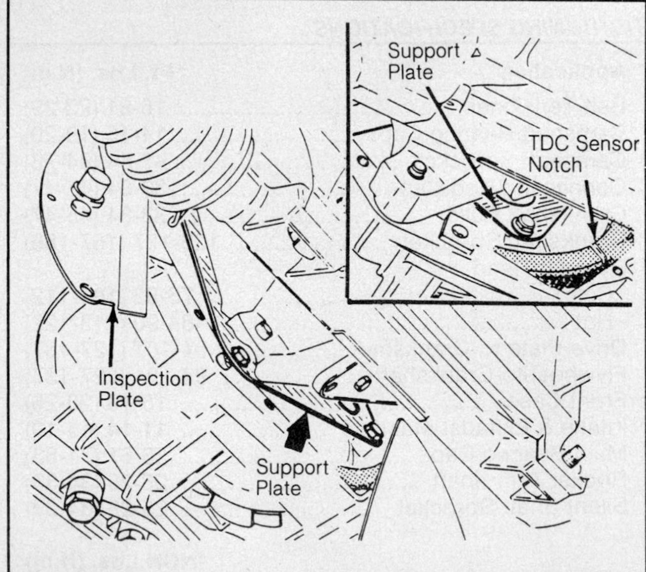
Support Plate
TDC Sensor Notch
Inspection Plate
Support Plate

Mark TDC sensor notch in reference to support plate.

4) Remove diagnostic plug for TDC sensor, located near ignition coil. Remove high tension lead from coil. Remove vacuum hoses from charcoal canister.

5) Remove heater hose near charcoal canister and fan. Remove oxygen sensor (Lambda) wire near vacuum switches, and disconnect air injection hose to catalytic converter. Remove vacuum switches support and 3-wire electrical connector nearby. Install engine sling assembly.

6) Remove starter, clutch housing bolts, and left engine mount. Remove right engine mount. Remove 3 power steering pump bolts and set pump aside. Remove exhaust header pipe.

7) Remove inspection plates from clutch housing. On vehicles with automatic transmission, remove inspection plate without altering TDC sensor adjustment. To do so, position torque converter support plate as shown in *Fig. 1.* Mark TDC sensor notch in reference to support plate. Support torque converter with special clamp (8.0315-A).

8) Remove A/C condenser and set to left side, keeping hoses connected. Remove and set receiver-drier to one side. Lift engine with engine sling assembly until top of bell housing contacts lower firewall. *See Fig. 2.*

Fig. 2: Removing Engine from Vehicle

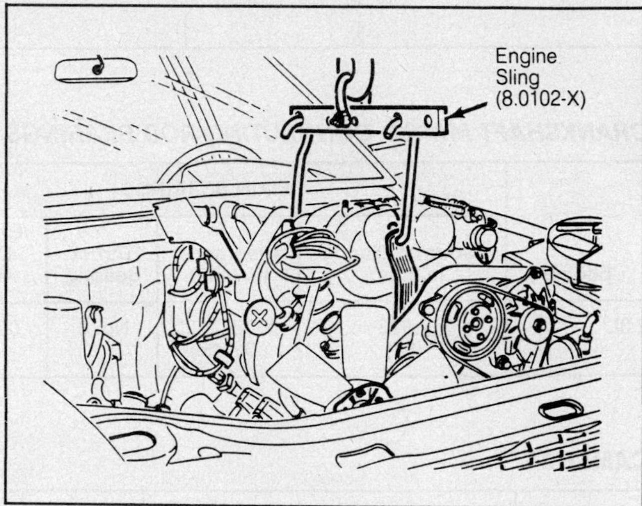
Engine Sling (8.0102-X)

Carefully lift engine out of engine compartment.

9) Install transmission support. Disengage engine from transmission and lift engine carefully out of engine compartment. Check for electrical leads, cables, hoses or pipes which have not been detached from engine.

Installation

1) To install engine, reverse removal procedures. On vehicles with automatic transmissions, lubricate torque converter centering nipple with Calysol grease (F 3015).

2) Position TDC sensor notch, and align reference marks made during removal. Coat 4 torque converter bolts with Loctite and tighten. Use ring gear locking pawl (8.0110-J) when tightening bolts.

3) On vehicles with manual transmissions, lightly lubricate splines, front and mainshaft pilot bushings with Molykote 321. Place gearshift lever in gear. Tighten engine mount-to-crossmember bolts and engine-to-clutch housing bolts.

4) Adjust TDC sensor, if new, by bringing 3 nipples in contact. If reusing TDC sensor, deburr 3 nipples so gap of .067" (1.7 mm) exists between sensor and ring gear.

5) Refill radiator, cooling system, engine crankcase and automatic transmission. Check power steering fluid reservoir level.

6) To adjust accelerator cable, depress accelerator pedal against its stop, placing a .20" (5 mm) spacer between pedal and stop (full throttle position). Connect cable to throttle drum.

7) Rotate drum to full throttle position. Exert slight pull on cable housing stop to place control under slight load. Install clip to obtain minimum gap between clip and common manifold.

8) To adjust kick-down cable, place throttle plate in idle position. Extend cable to obtain a maximum play of .02" (.5 mm) between cable housing stop and cable travel limiter. Tighten cable on drum.

CYLINDER HEAD

Removal

1) Drain cooling system including cylinder block. Disconnect battery. Remove exhaust header pipe and oxygen sensor. Remove mounting brackets for common manifold and intake manifold.

2) Pull common manifold off pipes. Remove distributor cap, injectors, and diagnostic plug bracket. Disconnect electrical connector near ignition coil and remove high tension lead from coil. Remove all clamps, and wire ties from vicinity of ignition coil. Remove vacuum hoses from charcoal canister.

3) Remove air pump outlet hose at pump. Remove upper wire and lower connector from thermo-time switch. Remove sliding bolt from air pump-to-alternator bracket. Remove upper and lower radiator hoses. Remove heater hose and power steering reservoir.

4) Remove radiator, fan and fan shroud. Remove water pump belt from pulley. Remove thermostatic air slide valve bracket. Remove vacuum hoses, coolant hoses, and thermostatic wire from valve. Remove 2 large hoses from diverter valve. Remove bracket from valve. Remove air injection assembly.

5) Remove heater hose near dipstick and remove auxiliary air device. Remove remaining electrical connectors from switches or sensors mounted in cylinder head. Remove rocker arm oil feed pipe. Disconnect all vacuum hoses remaining on intake manifold side of engine, including hose at diverter valve.

6) Remove spark plug wire brackets and wires at spark plug. Remove valve cover. Remove cooling fan brush holder. Remove sealing rings from spark plug tubes. Remove rocker arm assembly and push rods.

7) Use prying tool to break cylinder head loose. Install cylinder liner retainers (8.0132) to prevent liners from moving.

Inspection

1) Plug passages in cylinder block for valve lifters and oil return. Clean and scrape cylinder block gasket surface, and run a tap in cylinder block bolt holes.

2) Check liner protrusion above block (.0028-.0055" or .07-.14 mm) at engine centerline. No liner should protrude more than .0015" (.04 mm) above adjacent liner. If not to specifications, replace liner gaskets.

3) Using a gasket scraper, clean cylinder head gasket surface. Clean cylinder head bolts. Check for cylinder head warpage, maximum allowable is .004" (.10 mm).

4) Check cylinder head thickness. Original thickness is 3.636-3.648" (92.35-92.65 mm), with minimum permissable thickness being 3.616" (91.85 mm). If cylinder head must be surfaced, check thickness before and after surfacing to be sure thickness is within tolerances.

5) Clean and check valve lifters, using caution not to mix them. DO NOT scrape carbon off piston tops, as liner damage could result.

Installation

1) Install cylinder head in reverse of removal sequence, noting the following: When installing cylinder head, use 2 locating guides (8.-115-BZ). Install new head gasket, "DESSUS", "ALTO" or "TOP" facing up (toward cylinder head).

2) Install cylinder head and rocker arm assembly. Lightly tighten cylinder head bolts (with flat washers), using a drop of engine oil on threads. Lightly tighten rocker shaft nuts. Remove 2 head guides. Install last 2 head bolts.

NOTE: **Do not get oil in cylinder head bolt holes, as this could cause hydraulic blockage and prevent proper tightening.**

3) Using tightening sequence shown in *Fig. 3*, tighten head bolts to 36 ft. lbs. (50 N.m) and rocker shaft nuts to 11 ft. lbs. (15 N.m). Place angular head torquing tool (8.0129) on 2 center bolts (1 and 2). Completely loosen No. 1 bolt and retighten to 14 ft. lbs. (20 N.m). Keep tool in place and maintain tension on torque wrench.

Fig. 3: Cylinder Head Bolt Tightening Sequence

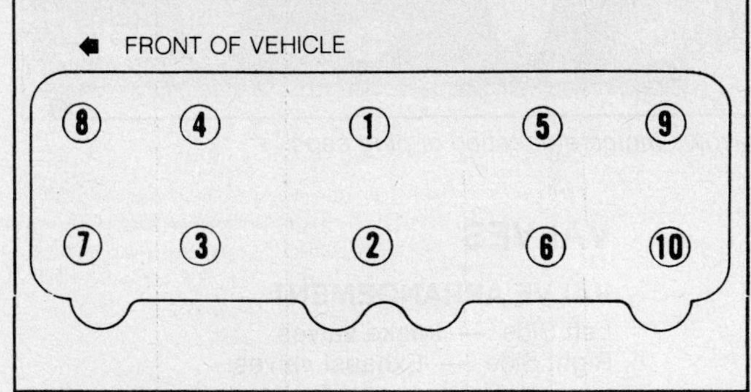
FRONT OF VEHICLE
8
4
1
5
9
7
3
2
6
10

Head bolts must be retorqued after 1000-1500 miles.

4) Position pointer on tool at "O" notch by moving spring loop. Continue torquing until pointer lines up with "90" notch. Repeat entire procedure with No. 2 bolt. Then move tool and complete tightening procedure in proper sequence.

5) If there is any doubt concerning torque of any one bolt, loosen it completely and repeat all tightening procedures for that one head bolt. Adjust valves. Reverse removal procedure, and note the following: Refill cooling system.

NOTE: **Adjust intake valve clearance to .006" (.15 mm) and exhaust valves to .012" (.30 mm). After 1000-1500 miles, retorque cylinder head bolts (after engine has cooled for 6 hours), and adjust valve clearances to standard specifications. See Valve Clearance Adjustment.**

6) Adjust air pump and alternator belt tension at idler pulley. Loosen both idler pulley mounting bolts. Apply 36 ft. lbs. (50 N.m) torque to nut directly above idler pulley.

7) Tighten mounting bolts. Turn engine 1 full turn to align belt on idler pulley. Loosen mounting bolts. Tighten idler pulley nut to 58 ft. lbs. (79 N.m). Retighten mounting bolts.

SPARK PLUG TUBE REPLACEMENT

Removal

With cylinder head supported, screw in plugs without springs to prevent dirt from falling into cylinder. Remove tubes using mallet or extractor.

NOTE: **If spark plug tubes are removed, new tubes MUST be installed.**

Installation

To install tubes, coat with sealing compound and insert so plug caps are facing as shown in *Fig. 4*. When tube is fully seated, it will protrude 2.835" (72 mm) upward from cylinder head.

Fig. 4: Position of Spark Plug Tubes for Installation

Front
Tube

Arrows indicate direction of plug caps.

VALVES

VALVE ARRANGEMENT

Left Side — Intake valves.
Right Side — Exhaust valves.

NOTE: **Cylinders and valves are numbered with number 1 cylinder at flywheel end of engine.**

VALVE SPRING REPLACEMENT

Intake Valve

1) Turn crankshaft in direction of engine rotation and position where exhaust valve just begins to open. Slide rocker arm off intake valve then bring piston to TDC on compression stroke.

2) Using valve spring compressor, compress spring and remove keepers, spring retainer and spring.

Exhaust Valve

1) Remove spark plug from cylinder requiring attention. Rotate crankshaft in direction of engine rotation and bring intake valve to fully closed position. Slide rocker arm off exhaust valve.

2) Insert hinged tool (0-0136) into spark plug hole and bring piston to TDC without forcing as tool is between piston and valve. Using spring compressor, compress spring and remove keepers, spring retainer and spring.

Fig. 5: Removing Valve Spring with Valve Held in Place

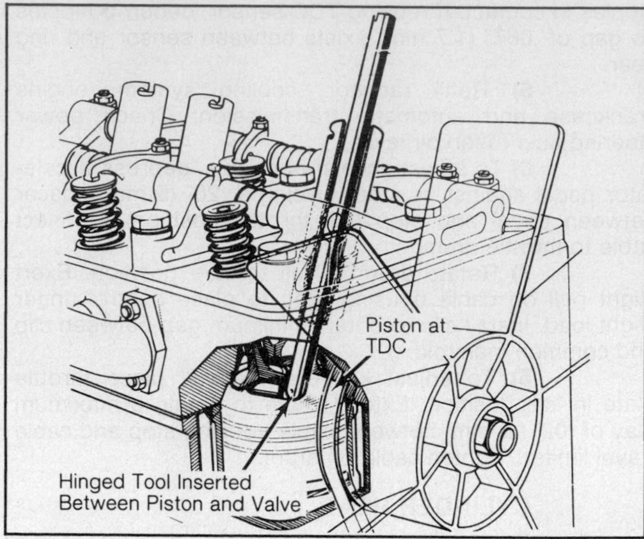
Piston at TDC
Hinged Tool Inserted Between Piston and Valve

VALVE CLEARANCE ADJUSTMENT

NOTE: **Engine must be allowed to cool at least 6 hours before adjusting valves. Adjust valves in firing order sequence (1-3-4-2). No. 1 cylinder is on flywheel end of engine.**

1) Rotate engine until exhaust valve number one is fully opened, then adjust intake valve number three and exhaust valve number four.

2) Rotate crankshaft one half turn (180°) until next number valve is fully opened and adjust corresponding valves. See Valve Adjustment Sequence Table. Continue this procedure until all valves have been adjusted.

VALVE ADJUSTMENT SEQUENCE

Valve Open	Adjust Valves
E 1	I 3 & E 4
E 3	I 4 & E 2
E 4	I 2 & E 1
E 2	I 1 & E 3

VALVE CLEARANCE SPECIFICATIONS [1]

Application	Intake [2] In. (mm)	Exhaust [3] In. (mm)
All Models	.004 (.10)	.010 (.25)

[1] – Tolerance range of +0 to +.002" (+0 to +.05 mm).

[2] – Adjust to .006" (.15 mm) after installing cylinder head. Retorque to above specifications after 1000-1500 miles.

[3] – Adjust to .012" (.30 mm) after installing cylinder head. Retorque to above specifications after 1000-1500 miles.

505 4-CYLINDER (Cont.)

CAMSHAFT

ENGINE FRONT COVER & OIL SEAL

Removal

1) Drain engine oil, and remove oil sump pan (if necessary). Remove radiator, and fan belt. Remove crankshaft pulley retaining bolt, and pulley. Remove idler pulley assembly.

2) Unscrew front cover retaining bolts, and remove cover. Using a seal driver tool, drive out old seal from front cover.

Installation

Using a seal driver tool, drive new oil seal into front cover. Install new gasket on front cover, and install front cover. Reverse removal procedure to complete installation.

TIMING CHAIN

Removal

1) Remove radiator, fan belt and spark plugs. Remove crankshaft pulley and timing chain cover. Disengage chain tensioner by removing plug and turning 3 mm Allen bolt clockwise.

2) Position camshaft as shown in *Fig. 6* to avoid any possible contact of valves and pistons when rotating crankshaft with timing chain removed. Remove camshaft sprocket, timing chain, crankshaft sprocket and Woodruff key.

Fig. 6: Proper Alignment of Camshaft and Crankshaft for Removing Timing Chain

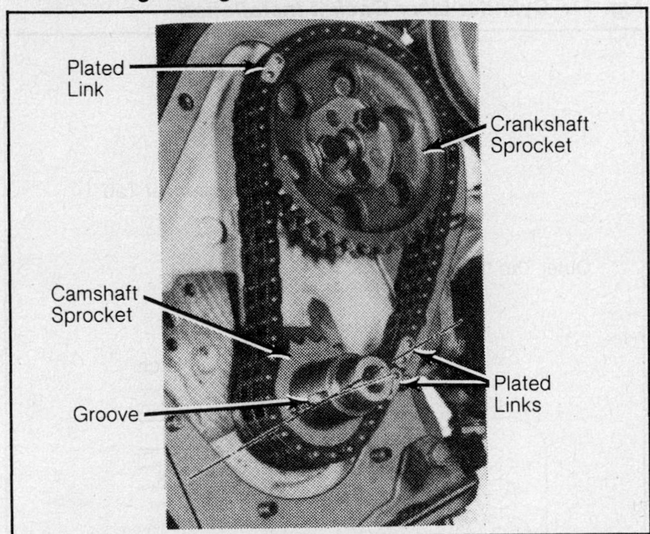
Plated
Link
Crankshaft
Sprocket
Camshaft
Sprocket
Groove
Plated
Links

Ensure timing marks are in correct alignment.

Installation

1) Hold crankshaft in original position and install Woodruff key and sprocket. Position camshaft and then crankshaft as shown in *Fig. 7*.

2) Install timing chain first on camshaft sprocket, then on crankshaft sprocket. Ensure timing marks are in correct alignment. Fit camshaft with a new washer and tighten bolts. Bend up tabs.

3) Engage chain tensioner by adjusting Allen wrench in a clockwise manner. Install a new tab washer on plug and bend tab.

4) Install thrust washers (if required) and timing chain cover. Install timing chain cover on 2 centering pins, being careful to protect seal. Install crankshaft pulley after cover bolts are tightened.

Fig. 7: Proper Alignment of Camshaft and Crankshaft

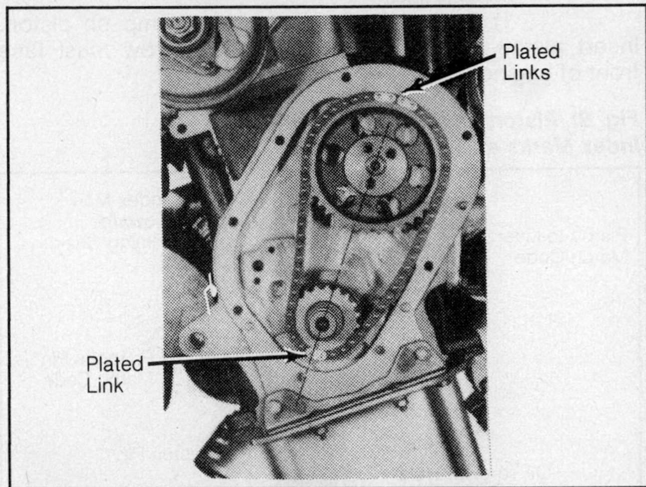
Plated
Links
Plated
Link

Ensure timing marks are in correct alignment.

PISTONS, PINS & RINGS

PISTON & ROD ASSEMBLY

Removal

1) With engine removed and mounted on engine stand, remove intake and exhaust manifolds. Remove all auxiliary equipment, including alternator, air pump and fuel pump. *See Fig. 8*.

2) Remove cylinder head. See Cylinder Head Removal in this article. Remove oil pan and oil pump.

Fig. 8: Cylinder Block and Cylinder Head Assembly

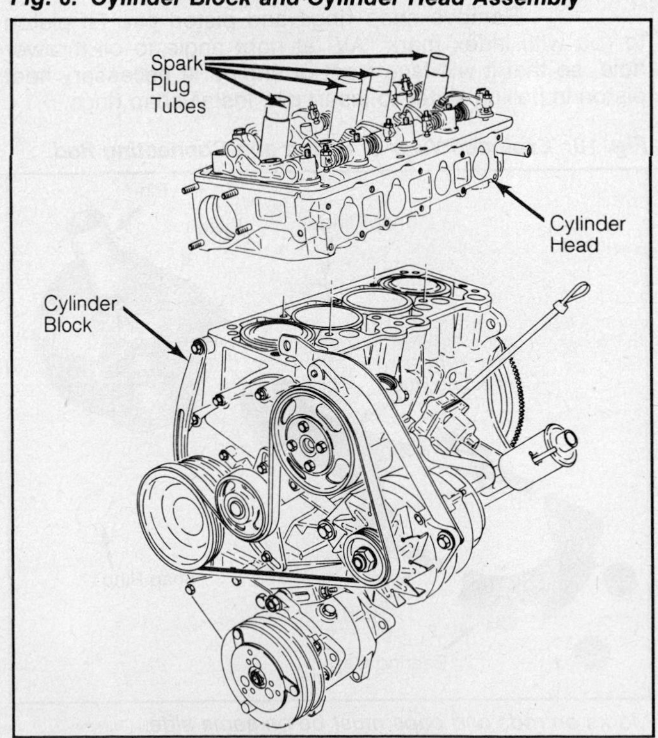
Spark
Plug
Tubes
Cylinder
Head
Cylinder
Block

505 4-CYLINDER (Cont.)

Remove bearing caps, keeping them in original order. Remove pistons and connecting rods. Attach connecting rods to matching cap, mark rod assemblies 1-4.

Installation

1) To install, fit piston ring clamp on piston. Insert piston and rod assembly. Index arrow must face front of engine.

Fig. 9: Piston and Rod Assembly with Index Marks and Codes

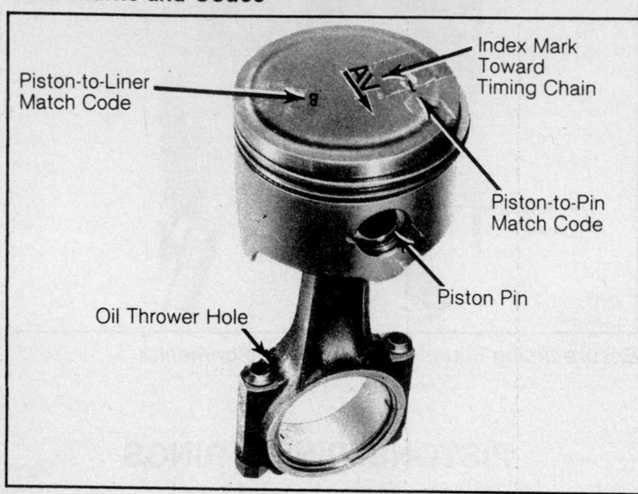
Piston-to-Liner
Match Code
Index Mark
Toward
Timing Chain
Piston-to-Pin
Match Code
Piston Pin
Oil Thrower Hole

Index arrow must face front of engine.

2) Push piston down cylinder and guide connecting rod with bearing over crankshaft journal. Install bearing cap and tighten.

NOTE: **Marks on rods and caps must be positioned on the same side.**

PISTON PIN REPLACEMENT

Remove snap rings and piston pin. Fit piston to rod with index mark "AV" at right angle to oil thrower hole, so that it will face front of engine. If necessary heat piston in boiling water to insert pin. Install snap rings.

Fig. 10: Exploded View of Piston and Connecting Rod

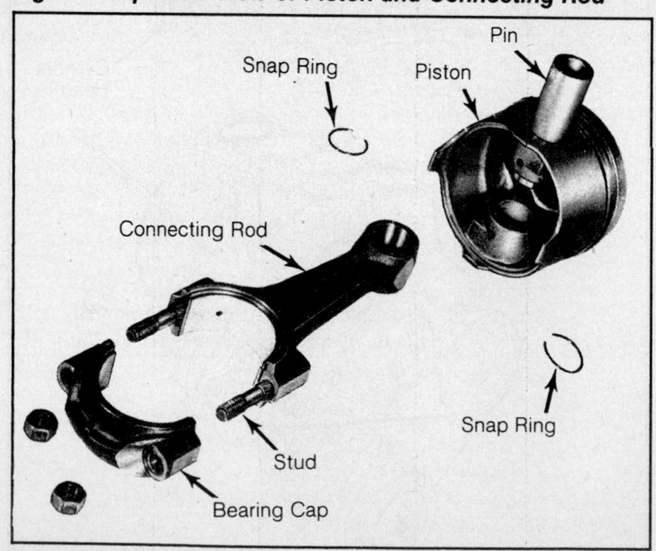
Pin
Snap Ring
Piston
Connecting Rod
Snap Ring
Stud
Bearing Cap

Marks on rods and caps must be on same side.

NOTE: **The "AV" mark on piston top must face front of engine. Pistons and liners must be matched by letter code. Number on top of piston refers to piston pin code (1 — Blue, 2 — White, and 3 — Red).**

CYLINDER LINER REPLACEMENT

1) Remove cylinder liners, using extractor if required. Before installing liners, clean and inspect for burrs. Insert liners, without base gaskets, with flats on shoulder of liners 1-2 and 3-4 being parallel.

NOTE: **Do not alter piston/liner pairings.**

2) Place a dial gauge and support on block face. Synchronize dial at 0 and 5. Check each liner at 4 different points, noting the highest reading. Maximum allowable difference between 2 opposite points must be less than .003" (.07 mm). If specification is exceeded, it may be necessary to change position of liners.

3) Select a base gasket for each liner which will give a protusion of approximately .005" (.12 mm). Gaskets are available in 4 different sizes. Use only 1 gasket on each liner.

4) Fit gasket on liner. Engage gasket inner tabs in liner grooves. *See Fig. 11.* Position tab with reference mark at right angles to flat. Position liners with outer tabs in position. Install liner compressor tools to block. Seat liners and ensure protrusion is correct. Remove compressor tools and install liner locks.

Fig. 11: Cylinder Liner Gasket Installation

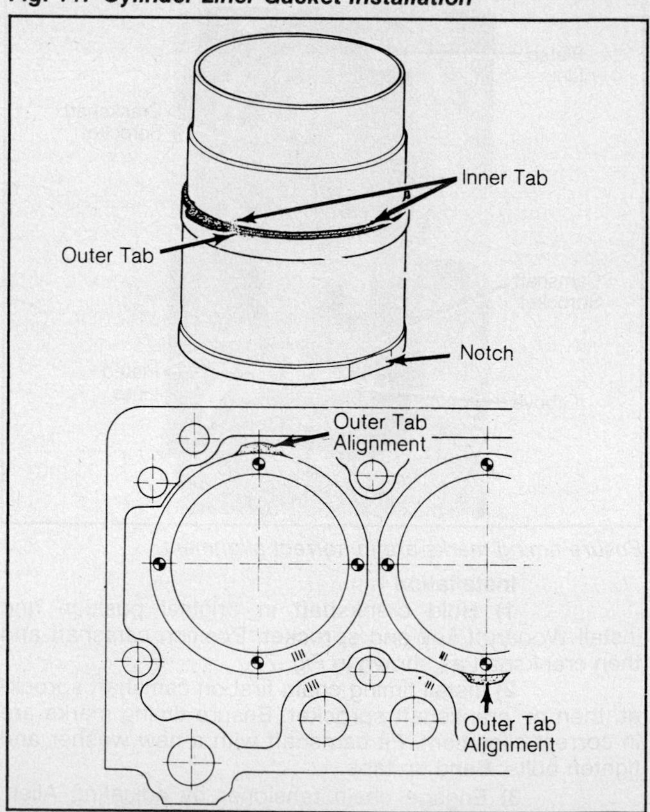
Inner Tab
Outer Tab
Notch
Outer Tab
Alignment
Outer Tab
Alignment

Gaskets are available in 4 different sizes.

NOTE: **Difference in protrusion of adjoining cylinders must not exceed .0015" (.04 mm).**

505 4-CYLINDER (Cont.)

CRANKSHAFT MAIN & CONNECTING ROD BEARINGS

MAIN BEARINGS

1) With engine removed from vehicle, remove oil sump. Remove cylinder head. See Cylinder Head Removal in this section. Scribe a reference mark on connecting rod caps, and main bearing caps.

2) Remove piston/rod assemblys. Remove front cover, and timing chain assembly. Remove clutch/flywheel assembly. Remove main bearing caps, and carefully remove crankshaft.

NOTE: Counter balance weights are bolted on crankshaft, if removed ensure they are replaced in their original position.

3) Fit the main bearing half shells into the cylinder block, and main bearing caps. Lubricate the main bearings, and carefully place the crankshaft in position.

4) Install main bearing caps, and bolts. Tighten main bearing cap bolts in 2 or 3 steps, starting at center bearing and working outward. Ensure crankshaft rotates smoothly.

5) Use Plastigage method to measure main bearing clearances. Measure main bearing clearances 1 at a time. Wipe oil from surfaces to be checked. DO NOT allow crankshaft to turn once Plastigage is in place and bearing cap is tightened.

6) Remove bearing cap. Measure flattened width of Plastigage with scale furnished to determine clearance.

THRUST BEARING WASHERS

After installing crankshaft, check end play. End play must not exceed .008" (.20 mm). If specification is exceeded, oversize thrust washers are available in .094" (2.40 mm), .096" (2.45 mm), and .098" (2.50 mm) sizes.

REAR MAIN BEARING OIL SEAL

1) Crankshaft must be removed to replace oil seal. Work seal packing manually into cylinder block and into bearing cap grooves. Place seal forming mandrel (8.0110 A) onto packing and form packing into groove by tapping mandrel with a hammer.

2) Make sure packing is correctly seated in is groove without being crushed. Cut seal packing clean flush with mating surface and follow same procedure for bearing cap.

3) Place side seals in grooves of bearing cap and hold seals in place with shim tool (8.0110 BZ). Lubricate shims and bring into place in cylinder block, tapping down with hammer handle.

4) Install and tighten bearing cap bolts and check that bearing cap has seated properly. Remove shim tool (8.0110 BZ). Trim side seals with knife so they protrude .020" (.50 mm) above lower crankcase mating surface. Gauge (8.0110 D) can be used for measurement.

ENGINE OILING

ENGINE OILING SYSTEM

A high output, gear type oil pump is mounted to engine block lower surface and is operated by camshaft.

CRANKCASE CAPACITY

Approximately 4.2 qts. (3.9L).

OIL FILTER

Full-flow cartridge type.

NORMAL OIL PRESSURE

28-51 psi (2-3.6 kg/cm²) at idle; 44-67 psi (3-4.7 kg/cm²) at 4000 RPM.

ENGINE COOLING

COOLING SYSTEM CAPACITY

Auto. Trans. — 7.7 qts. (7.2L)
Man. Trans. — 7.5 qts. (7.1L)

THERMOSTAT

Opens at 180°F (82°C).

RADIATOR CAP

14.3 psi (1.0 kg/cm²).

WATER PUMP

Removal & Installation

Remove radiator, and fan belt. Disconnect heater hose from pump and self-engaging fan brush holder. Remove water pump. To install, reverse removal procedure and ensure contact surfaces are clean before installing new gasket.

SELF-DISENGAGING FAN

Driven by water pump shaft and controlled by a thermal contact-breaker. Fan engages at approximately 190°F (88°C) and disengages at 174°F (79°C).

TIGHTENING SPECIFICATIONS

Application	Ft. Lbs. (N.m)
Belt Tension Nut	[1] 58 (79)
Camshaft Retaining Plate Bolts	12 (16)
Camshaft Sprocket Bolts	16 (22)
Connecting Rod Nuts	29 (39)
Crankshaft Main Bearing Bolts	54 (73)
Crankshaft Pulley Bolts	123 (167)
Cylinder Head	See Text
Engine-to-Clutch Housing	40 (54)
Engine-to-Converter Housing	22 (30)
Engine Mounts-to-Crossmember	22 (30)
Flywheel-to-Crankshaft Bolts	49 (67)
Oil Pump Mounting Bolts	7 (10)
Rocker Arm Support Nut	11 (15)

[1] – First step, tighten to 36 ft. lbs. (50 N.m), turn engine one full turn, and retighten to 58 ft. lbs. (79 N.m).

Peugeot Engines

505 4-CYLINDER (Cont.)

ENGINE SPECIFICATIONS

GENERAL SPECIFICATIONS

Year	DISPLACEMENT		Fuel System	HP@RPM	Torque Ft. Lbs.@RPM	Compr. Ratio	BORE		STROKE	
	Cu. In.	Liters					In.	mm	In.	mm
1983	120.3	2.0	K-Jetronic	96@4900	116@3300	8.3:1	3.465	88	3.189	81

CRANKSHAFT MAIN & CONNECTING ROD BEARINGS

Engine	MAIN BEARINGS				CONNECTING ROD BEARINGS		
	Journal Diam. In. (mm)	Clearance In. (mm)	Thrust Bearing	Crankshaft End Play In. (mm)	Journal Diam. In. (mm)	Clearance In. (mm)	Side Play In. (mm)
2.0L							
No. 1 (Rear)	2.1616-2.1646 (54.905-54.980)	.....	Rear	.003-.008 (.08-.20)	2.1123-2.1131 (53.652-53.673)	.0006-.003 (.016-.076)	.....
No. 2	2.2102-2.2112 (56.140-56.165)						
No. 3	2.2509-2.2515 (57.174-57.189)						
No. 4	2.3050-2.3060 (58.548-58.573)						
No. 5	2.3386-2.3392 (59.401-59.416)						

4-CYLINDER DIESEL & TURBO DIESEL

ENGINE CODING

ENGINE IDENTIFICATION

Engine identification number is stamped on front left side of engine block, just below cylinder head. Engine identification number corresponds with Vehicle Identification Number, and runs from number 1340000 upward on non-turbo models and 8000000 on turbo models.

ENGINE IDENTIFICATION

Application	Code
504 & 505 Diesel	XD2C
505 & 604 Turbo Diesel	XD2S

ENGINE, MANIFOLDS & CYLINDER HEAD

ENGINE

NOTE: Specific engine removal and installation procedures were not available for 504 diesel and 604 Turbo diesel engines. Procedures for Turbo should be similar to normally aspirated engines. Disconnect any additional components necessary for removal.

Removal

1) Drain cooling system. Remove battery, battery tray, radiator expansion tank. Remove air filter and intake pipe on vacuum pump. Remove upper and lower radiator hoses and mountings. Disconnect power steering hoses from pump and transmission cooler lines at radiator, and suspend high enough to prevent drainage.

2) Remove radiator. Remove starter and clutch housing sealing plates. Remove fan and belt tensioners. On air conditioned models, protect condenser with plywood. Remove air conditioner compressor, and using some wire hang along inner fender with hoses attached. Route refrigerant hoses to back of engine.

3) On all models, remove sound proofing panel clips on the cowl panel and remove degassing tank bracket. Remove mounting bolts on front header pipe to manifold, intermediate exhaust muffler and lower the compressor cut-out switch (if equipped). Lower front crossmember after having removed mounting bolts. Suspend crossmember with two 12x150 bolts approximately 2 3/4-4" (70-100 mm) long (P.N. 6902.77).

4) On automatic transmission models, remove the torque converter bolts (accessible through starter motor opening). Move torque converter back from flywheel. Loosen 3 engine-to-clutch housing bolts slightly using a hex socket (8.0208). Remove the top converter bolt.

5) On all models, remove the 4 mounting bolts of the engine mounts on the main crossmember. Install engine hoist, and lift until transmission touches tunnel. Install engine support bracket (8.0125). Disconnect the power steering line leading to the distribution valve.

6) Remove the 2 lower engine-to-transmission mounting bolts, clear engine and lift, being careful not to pull on refrigerant lines. On automatic transmission models, ensure torque converter is fully disengaged, and install torque converter retaining clamp.

Installation

On manual transmission models, coat mainshaft splines with Molykote 321. On automatic transmission models, coat converter nipple with Calysol F3015 grease. To complete installation, reverse removal procedures.

CYLINDER HEAD

CAUTION: Cylinder head bolts must not be loosened while engine is warm.

Removal

1) Drain cooling system. Disconnect and remove battery. Disconnect exhaust pipe from manifold, vacuum pump, overflow reservoir, electrical connections and harness securing clips from engine. Disconnect heater hose, rocker oil feed pipe at cylinder head, and remove upper power steering pump bracket mounting bolt.

2) Remove water pump bolt, valve cover, rocker shaft assembly and push rods. Gradually loosen cylinder head bolts in sequence shown in *Fig. 1.* Remove cylinder head using levers (0.0149).

Fig. 1: Cylinder Head Bolt Tightening Sequence

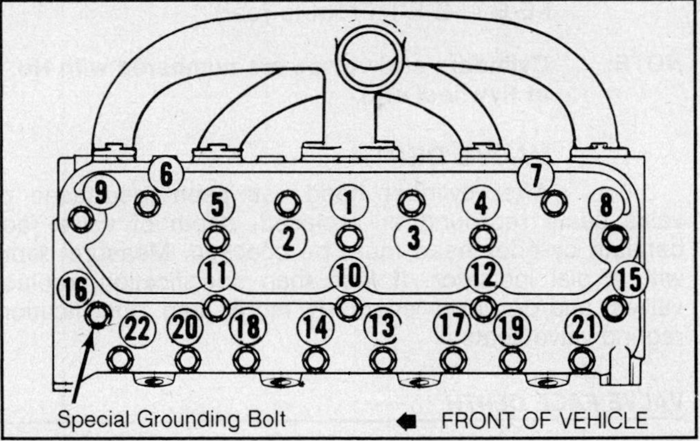
9
6
5
1
4
7
8
2
3
11
10
12
15
16
22
20
18
14
13
17
19
21
Special Grounding Bolt
FRONT OF VEHICLE

Installation

1) Run an 11x150 tap through bolt holes to clean threads and clean all foreign material and oil from threads. Brush clean bolt threads. Use new domed washers on non-Turbo engines with dome installed up (on Turbo engines, use flat washers). Carefully clean mating surfaces of cylinder head and block.

2) Check amount of piston protrusion to determine correct head gasket thickness. Measure the amount of piston protrusion with a dial indicator and tool (8.011 P). Select the maximum amount of protrusion (all 4 cylinders). If protrusion is greater to or equal to .030" (.79 mm) for Turbo, or more than .033" (.84 mm) for non-Turbo engines, gasket thickness needed is .067" (1.7 mm).

3) Reference mark for this gasket is 3 notches. If protrusion is less than .030" (.79 mm) for Turbo, or less than .033" (.84 mm) for non-Turbo engines, gasket thickness required is .067" (1.58 mm). Reference mark for this gasket is 2 notches.

4) Install cylinder head guides (8.0114) in bolt holes 15 and 16. *See Fig. 1.* Install the correct thickness gasket dry. Place cylinder head over guides and install remaining bolts, noting that 8 short bolts are installed on injector side, 7 medium length bolts are installed on manifold side and 6 long bolts are installed in center.

4-CYLINDER DIESEL & TURBO DIESEL (Cont.)

5) Bolt threads and contact faces should be lightly lubricated with Molykote 6 Rapid. Install remaining bolts. Special ground bolt is installed in No. 16 position.

6) Tighten cylinder head bolts in 1st step to 22 ft. lbs. (30 N.m) in sequence. *See Fig. 1.* In 2nd step, tighten in sequence turbo bolts to 51 ft. lbs. (69 N.m), non-turbo to 47 ft. lbs. (64 N.m). Loosen each bolt (1 at a time in sequence) 1/4 turn and retighten.

7) Install injector holders with new seals, injector shields and washers. Install push rods to original positions. Install rocker arm assembly. Adjust valves.

8) Run engine at 3000 RPM for 10 minutes. Allow to cool for 3 1/2 hours. In sequence, loosen head bolts 1/4 turn and retorque to specifications. Immediately repeat retorque procedure a 2nd time.

NOTE: **Non-turbo engines with Yellow (class 10.9) head bolts, must have head bolts retightened after 1000-1500 miles. Retighten head bolts using procedure described previously.**

VALVES

VALVE ARRANGEMENT

I-E-E-I-I-E-E-I (Front-to-rear).

NOTE: **Cylinders and valves are numbered with No. 1 at flywheel end.**

VALVE DEPTH

After cylinder head has been resurfaced or valve seats reground or replaced, depth of valve face beneath cylinder head must be checked. Measure depth with a dial indicator. If less than specification, replace valves and/or valve seats. If more than specification, regrind valve seats.

VALVE FACE DEPTH

Application	Depth In. (mm)
Non-Turbo	.033-.047 (.85-1.20)
Turbo	
Intake	.041-.047 (2.05-1.40)
Exhaust	.033-.047 (.85-1.20)

ROCKER ARM ASSEMBLY

1) To remove rocker arm assembly, remove rocker arm cover and remove rocker shaft support bolts. Lift rocker arm assembly noting oil line union sealing washer.

2) To disassemble rocker arm assembly, remove end shaft supports and remove rocker arms, supports, springs and washers. Remove locating screw on lubrication fitting, then remove shaft.

3) Check shaft diameter at areas where rocker arms contact shaft. Minimum diameter of shaft is .746" (18.95 mm). Replace shaft and/or rocker arms if excessive wear or scoring is evident.

4) To assemble rocker arm assembly, slide rocker shaft into lubrication fitting noting that oil holes in shaft are on same side as screw hole in fitting. Line up screw hole in shaft with threaded hole in fitting and install locating screw and copper washer.

Fig. 2: Assembled View of Rocker Arm Assembly with Oil Holes Detailed

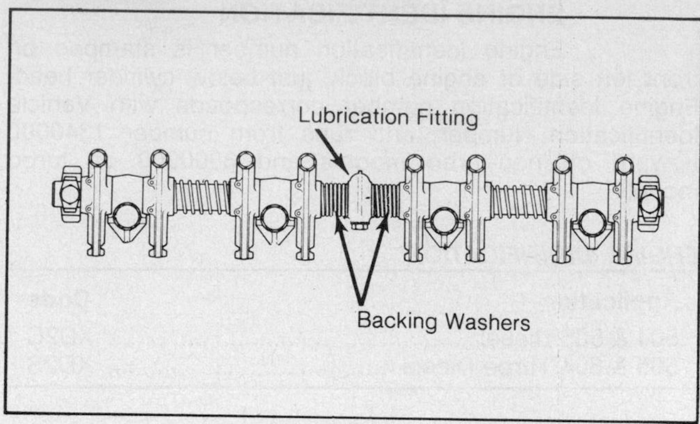
Lubrication Fitting
Backing Washers

Fig. 3: Installing Rocker Arm Assembly to Cylinder Head

Oil Union
Sealing Washer

5) Lubricate rocker shaft and install washers, springs, rocker arms and supports. Install push rods and install rocker shaft assembly to cylinder head. Install .004" (.10 mm) shims between each of the end rocker shaft bearing blocks and on Turbo, between No. 1 & 4 intake rockers.

6) Install new oil union seal washer. Tighten intermediate bearing blocks (nuts), then tighten end supports (bolts). Remove shims and check for free movement of the 2 end rockers. There should be .004" (.10 mm) play at the 2 end rocker arms.

VALVE CLEARANCE ADJUSTMENT

NOTE: **Engine must be allowed to cool at least six hours before adjusting valves.**

Rotate engine until exhaust valve number one is fully opened, then adjust intake valve number three and exhaust number four. Rotate engine one half turn until next number valve is fully opened and adjust corresponding valves. *See table.* Continue until all valves have been adjusted.

VALVE ADJUSTING SEQUENCE

Valve Open	Adjust Valves
E1	I3 & E4
E3	I4 & E2
E4	I2 & E1
E2	I1 & E3

4-CYLINDER DIESEL & TURBO DIESEL (Cont.)

VALVE CLEARANCE SPECIFICATIONS

Application	Intake In. (mm)	Exhaust In. (mm)
Turbo	.006 (.15)	.010 (.25)
Non-Turbo	.010-.012 (.250-.255)	.010-.012 (.250-.255)

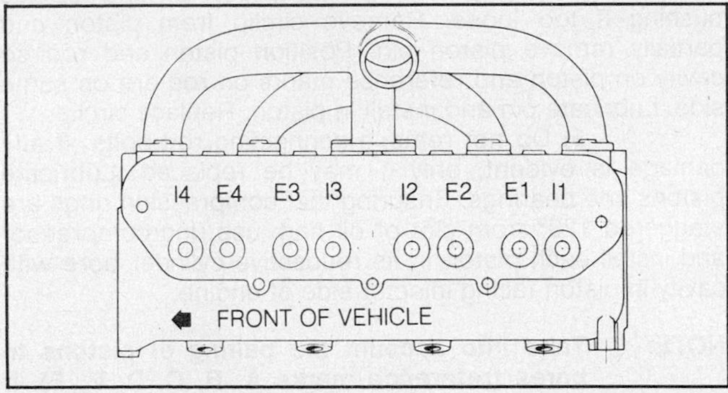
I4 E4 E3 I3 I2 E2 E1 I1
FRONT OF VEHICLE

Fig. 4: View of Intake and Exhaust Valve Arrangement

COMBUSTION (SWIRL) CHAMBERS

Removal

Remove cylinder head from vehicle and remove injectors, injector studs, rocker arms, rocker arm mounting studs, manifolds and glow plugs. Using drift (see illustration) carefully drive swirl chambers down and out of cylinder head. Tap drift LIGHTLY so as not to damage inner face of chamber.

CAUTION: If the swirl chamber twists and/or sticks in its bore, turn head over, tap chamber back into place with soft mallet, and start over again.

Fig. 5: Removing Valve Spring with Valve Held in Place

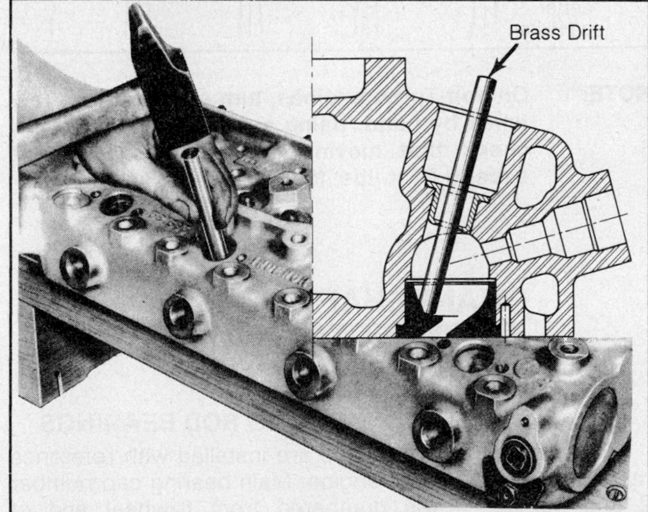
Brass Drift

Ensure piston is at TDC.

Inspection

1) Inspect swirl chambers for distortion and cracks. Small cracks around the gas outlet are acceptable and do not affect engine operation. Replace all doubtful chambers. Measure thickness of shoulder and overall height of chamber.

Fig. 6: View Showing Acceptable Cracks in Combustion Chamber

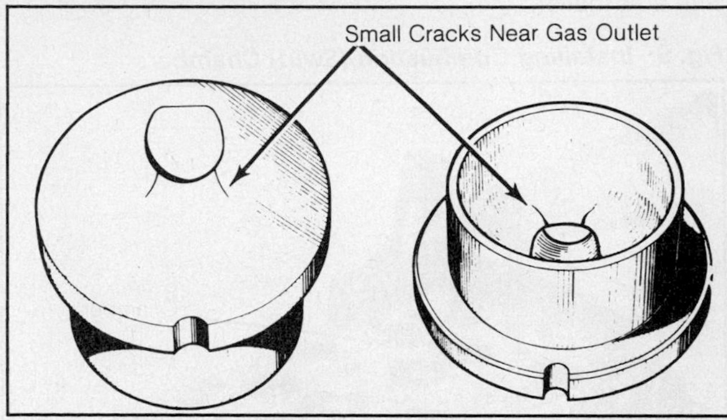
Small Cracks Near Gas Outlet

2) Place truing punch (0.0139) over chamber bore in cylinder head, making sure dowel pin in punch is correctly located in head. Tap truing punch to make sure shoulder surface of bore is parallel with cylinder head. Slightly chamfer the edges of the chamber bore.

Fig. 7: Cross-Sectional View Showing Combustion Chamber Clearance and Protrusion

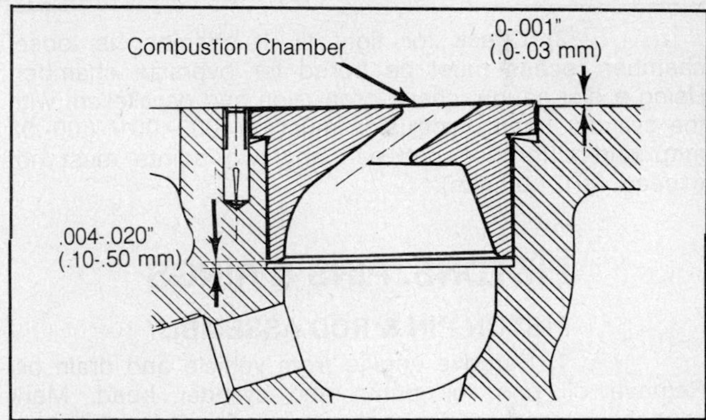
Combustion Chamber
.0-.001"
(.0-.03 mm)
.004-.020"
(.10-.50 mm)

3) Measure depth of bore and depth to shoulder. Swirl chamber should protrude from cylinder head surface .000-.001" (.00-.03 mm) and clearance from swirl chamber to bottom of chamber bore should be .004-.020" (.10-.50 mm). To adjust clearances, chamber may be machines on shoulder surface and on bottom surface. Never machine face of chamber.

Fig. 8: Combustion (Swirl) Chamber with Detail of Machinable Surfaces

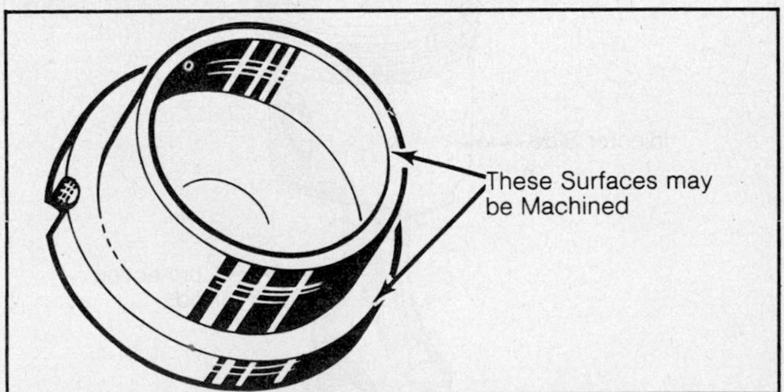
These Surfaces may be Machined

Installation

1) Insert new wedge pins into the cylinder head and using chamfered drift, drive pins .028" (.7 mm)

4-CYLINDER DIESEL & TURBO DIESEL (Cont.)

below cylinder head surface. Carefully insert the swirl chambers in the original bores and lightly tap into place with soft mallet.

Fig. 9: Installing Combustion (Swirl) Chambers

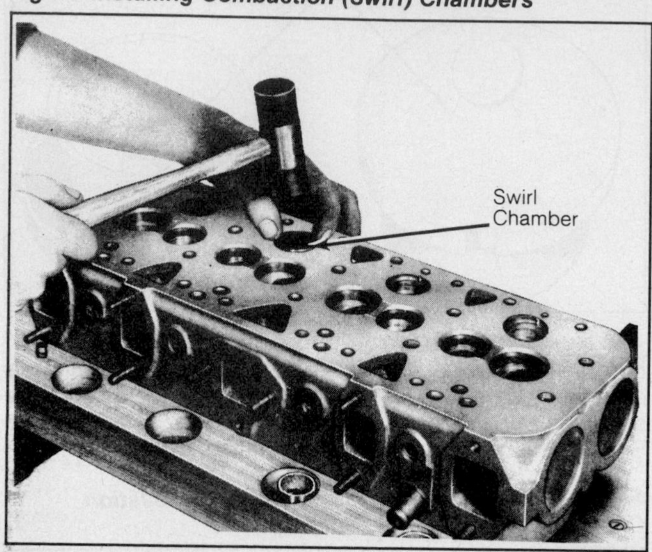
Swirl
Chamber

2) Check for tight fit. If chamber is loose, chamber recess must be bored for oversize chamber. Using a dial gauge, check protrusion and parallelism with the cylinder head. Protrusion must be .000-.001" (.00-.03 mm) and difference between any two points must not exceed .001" (.03 mm).

PISTONS, PINS & RINGS

PISTON PIN & ROD ASSEMBLY

1) Remove engine from vehicle and drain oil. Remove oil pan, oil pump and cylinder head. Mark connecting rods for replacement in original location and remove connecting rod caps.

2) Push pistons up through top of cylinder block and replace connecting rod caps so they do not become mixed. Remove piston pin circlip and remove piston pin.

Fig. 10: Assembled View of Piston and Connecting Rod

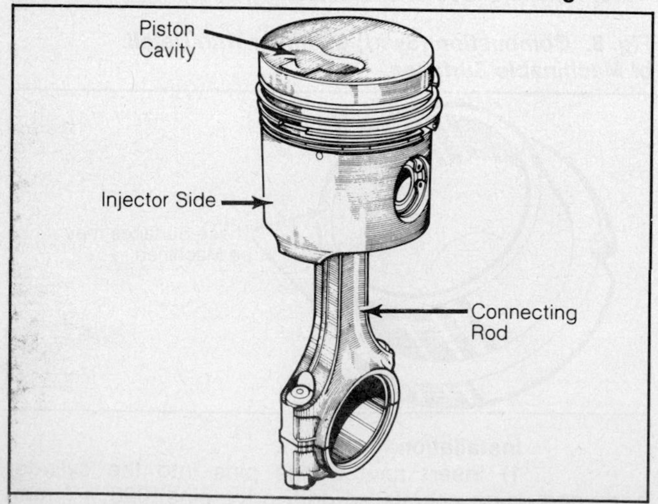
Piston
Cavity
Injector Side
Connecting
Rod

NOTE: **Pistons, pins and rings are matched at factory and must not be intermixed.**

3) Clean new piston assemblies with trichlorethylene. Do not remove piston rings to clean pistons. Make sure all protective coating has been removed from ring grooves. Blow with compressed air and check that piston rings move freely in grooves.

4) Check fit of piston pin in connecting rod small end bushing. Ream bushing if too tight and replace bushing if too loose. Remove circlip from piston and partially remove piston pin. Position piston and rod so cavity on piston and reference marks on rod are on same side. Lubricate pin and install in piston. Replace circlip.

5) Do not remove connecting rod bolts. If any damage is evident, only 1 may be replaced. Lubricate pistons and bearings. Ensuring that compression rings are staggered 120° from slot of oil ring, use ring compressor and install each piston in its respective cylinder bore with cavity in piston facing injector side of engine.

NOTE: **Take into account the pairing of pistons to bores (reference marks A, B, C, D, E, F). If only 1 reference mark is evident, all 4 bores are identical. "A" and "B" are standard sizes, all others oversize. See Fig. 11.**

Fig. 11: Matching Pistons to Cylinder Bores

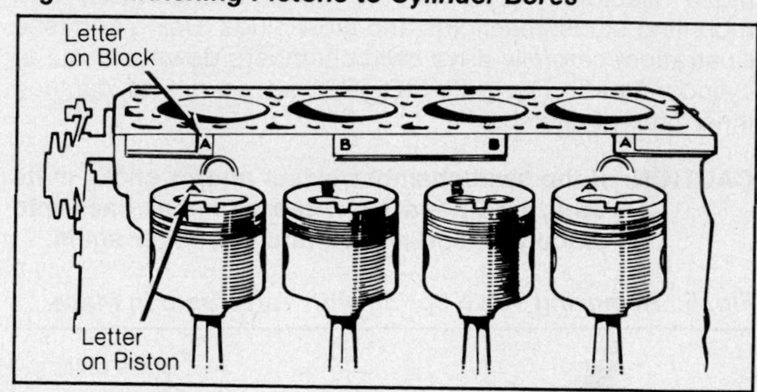
Letter
on Block
A
B
B
A
Letter
on Piston

NOTE: **On non-Turbo engines, turn engine over a few times by hand. Using a driving pawl (8.0110), check that moving parts torque does not exceed 44 ft. lbs. (59 N.m).**

CRANKSHAFT MAIN & CONNECTING ROD BEARINGS

MAIN & CONNECTING ROD BEARINGS

Main bearing caps are installed with reference mark on injector side of engine. Main bearing cap number 2 and number 4 (as numbered from flywheel end of engine) are nearly identical. Bearing cap number 2 can be identified by a letter after the part number.

THRUST BEARING ALIGNMENT

Thrust washers are located on each side of center main bearing. Measure end play, and replace thrust washers as required. Thrust washers are available in standard thickness .091-.092" (2.30-2.33 mm) and oversize

.098-.100" (2.50-2.53 mm). Install washers with oil grooves toward crankshaft.

REAR MAIN BEARING OIL SEAL

1) Crankshaft must be removed to replace oil seal. Work seal packing manually into cylinder block and into bearing cap grooves. Place seal forming mandrel (8.0110 A) onto packing and form packing into groove by tapping mandrel with a hammer.

2) Make sure packing is correctly seated in it's groove without being crushed . *See Fig. 12.* Cut seal packing clean flush with mating surface and follow same procedure for bearing cap.

3) Place side seals in grooves of bearing cap and hold seals in place with shim tool (8.0110 CZ and 8.0110 B). Lubricate shims and bring into place in cylinder block, tapping down with hammer handle.

4) Install and tighten bearing cap bolts and check that bearing cap has seated properly. Trim side seals with knife so they protrude .020" (.50 mm) above lower crankcase mating surface. Gauge (8.0110 D) can be used for measurement.

Fig. 12: Using a Mandrel and Mallet to Install Upper Rear Main Oil Seal

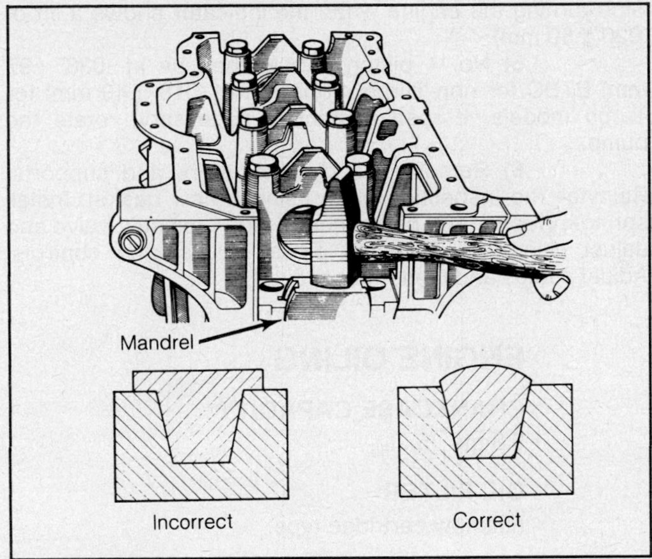
Mandrel
Incorrect
Correct

CAMSHAFT

TIMING CHAIN

Removal

1) Remove the radiator. Remove water pump, power steering and alternator belts. Remove the alternator and the cooling fan blade. If equipped with air conditioning, remove drive belt and protect condenser with plywood.

2) Remove the damper pulley. Lock crankshaft using ring gear locking pawl (8.0110 L) on vehicle. Remove the timing chain housing. Turn crankshaft to bring keyway to vertical position. Unload chain tensioner as follows:

3) For non-automatic loading tensioner (Sedis) unload by placing the lock in position No. 1. Push pad in all the way. Place lock in position No. 2. DO NOT attempt to dismantle the lock. *See Fig. 13.* For automatic loading tensioner (Brampton) wrap with wire.

4) To unload, remove wire. Retrieve the pad, spring and piston. Reassemble and lock together using a 3 mm hex wrench. Insert the assembly into the housing leaving a gap of .080" (2 mm). *See Fig. 13.*

Fig. 14: Timing Chain Installation

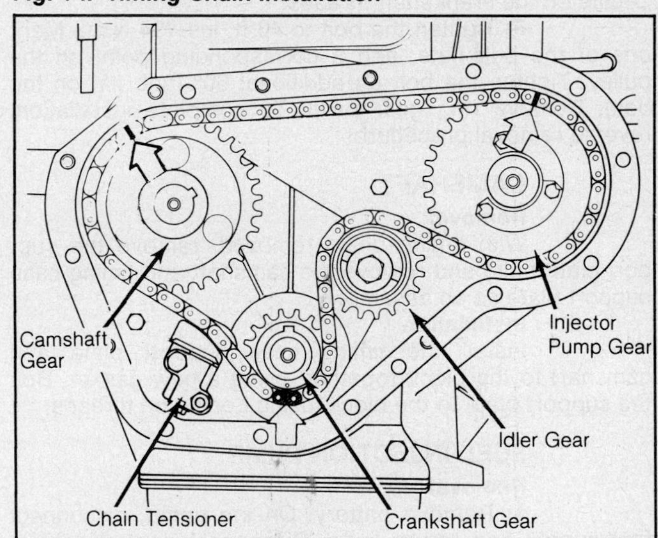
Camshaft Gear
Injector Pump Gear
Idler Gear
Chain Tensioner
Crankshaft Gear

Allow the tensioner to lightly tension the chain.

Fig. 13: Hydraulic Chain Tensioners

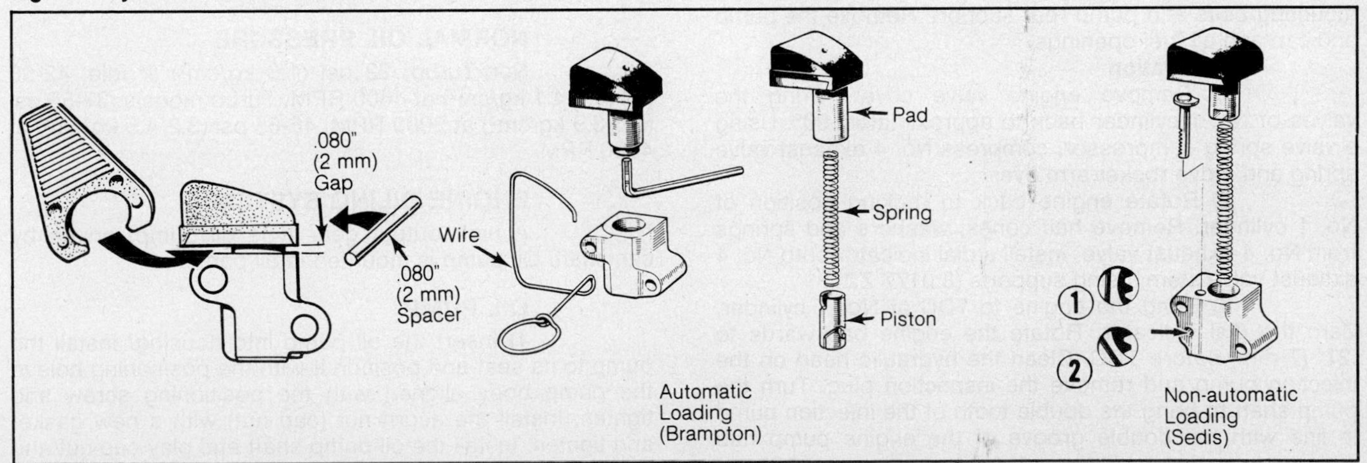
.080" (2 mm) Gap
Wire
.080" (2 mm) Spacer
Pad
Spring
Piston
1
2
Automatic Loading (Brampton)
Non-automatic Loading (Sedis)

4-CYLINDER DIESEL & TURBO DIESEL (Cont.)

Installation

1) Install the chain ensuring that the reference links align with each of the pinion references. *See Fig. 14.* If it becomes necessary to turn the camshaft, bring the crankshaft keyway to the horizontal plane (1/2 stroke of the piston).

2) Reinstall the hydraulic tensioner and support plate. Install the eccentric idler pinion and turn it in the direction of chain rotation until a play between chain and tensioner of .020-.040" (.5-1 mm) is obtained for Turbo, .040-.080" (1-2 mm) for non-Turbo engines.

3) Mount the tensioner to the engine. For non-automatic loading tensioner, place lock in position No. 1 and let pad release pad freely. For automatic loading tensioner, remove the spacer, push the pad in all the way, and release freely.

4) Allow the tensioner to lightly tension the chain (both types of tensioners). Rotate the crankshaft 1 full turn to ensure there is no piston-to-valve contact.

5) Reinstall the timing chain housing with a new gasket. After carefully cleaning the crankshaft pulley bolt threads, crankshaft threads, pulley, spacer and bearing faces, install the pulley. Lock the crankshaft, using ring gear locking pawl (8.0110 L). Put a few drops of Loctite on the crankshaft threads.

6) Tighten the bolt to 40 ft. lbs. (54 N.m). Mark one of the bolt flats, and a corresponding point on the pulley. Tighten the bolt an additional 60° (one flat on the bolt). Remove ring gear pawl. To complete installation, reverse removal procedures.

CAMSHAFT

Removal

With timing chain removed, remove the support plate bolts and remove the camshaft and timing case support plate as an assembly.

Installation

Install the timing case support plate and camshaft to the block together, using a new gasket. Bolt the support plate to the block, using Loctite on threads.

FUEL INJECTION PUMP

Removal

1) Remove battery. On the pump, disconnect fuel supply and return lines. Disconnect control cables, fuel shut-off electrovalve wire, and load sensor harness (if equipped).

2) Remove injector pipes. Remove 2 front mounting bolts and pump rear support. Remove the pump and cap and all fuel openings.

Installation

1) Remove engine valve cover. Bring the valves of No. 1 cylinder back to approximately 90°. Using a valve spring compressor, compress No. 4 exhaust valve spring and move rocker arm over.

2) Rotate engine back to rocking position of No. 1 cylinder. Remove half cones, washers and springs from No. 4 exhaust valve. Install a dial indicator onto No. 4 exhaust valve stem, using supports (8.0177 ZZ).

3) Bring the engine to TDC at No. 4 cylinder. Zero the dial indicator. Rotate the engine backwards to .27" (7 mm) before TDC. Clean the hydraulic head on the injection pump and remove the inspection plug. Turn the pump shaft to bring the double tooth of the injection pump in line with the double groove of the engine pump hub pinion.

4) Coat new gasket with grease and install on pump flange. Install pump on engine and install mounting bolts without tightening. Adjust timing as outlined in Adjustments.

Adjustment

1) Loosen injection pump mounting bolts. Attach dial indicator to No. 4 cylinder exhaust valve. With engine at .27" (7 mm) before TDC, rotate the injection pump body away from engine. Install dial indicator to pump using adapters (8.0117T, P, and S).

2) Turn engine and locate BDC and TDC points on the dial indicator. At BDC the pump dial indicator should have some preload. Zero the pump dial indicator at BDC. Bring piston No. 4 to TDC of compression stroke. Check zero point of engine dial indicator.

3) Turn engine 90° in reverse, and recheck pump dial indicator. Turn engine in normal direction of rotation and bring No. 4 piston to .038" (.97 mm) BTDC for non-Turbo models, and to .016" (.40 mm) BTDC for Turbo models. Rotate the pump toward the engine until the dial indicator indicates a lift of .020" (.50 mm).

4) Tighten pump mounting bolts. Check timing by rotating the engine the normal direction 2 turns. Turn the engine back approximately 90°. Rotate engine slowly in normal direction while watching the pump dial indicator. Stop turning the engine when the indicator shows a lift of .020" (.50 mm).

5) No. 4 piston should then be at .038" (.97 mm) BTDC for non-Turbo models, and .016" (.40 mm) for Turbo models. If readjustment is necessary, rotate the pump.

6) Remove the dial indicators and supports. Reinstall the inspection plug, using a new gasket. Install springs, washer and half cones of No. 4 exhaust valve and adjust clearance. Reinstall pipes, hoses, and controls. Adjust cables and bleed fuel circuit.

ENGINE OILING

CRANKCASE CAPACITY

5.3 qts. (5.0L).

OIL FILTER

Full-flow cartridge type.

PRESSURE REGULATOR VALVE

Located in oil pump.

NORMAL OIL PRESSURE

Non-Turbo, 22 psi (1.6 kg/cm²) at idle, 42-58 psi (3.0-4.1 kg/cm²) at 4000 RPM. Turbo models, 37-55 psi (2.6-3.9 kg/cm²) at 2000 RPM, 46-65 psi (3.2-4.5 kg/cm²) at 4000 RPM.

ENGINE OILING SYSTEM

A high output gear type oil pump, driven by camshaft. Oil pump is mounted in oil pan.

OIL PUMP

1) Insert the oil pump into housing. Install the pump to its seat and position it with the positioning hole in the pump body aligned with the positioning screw and tighten. Install the acorn nut (cap nut) with a new gasket and tighten. Install the oil pump shaft end play cap nut and tighten lightly without any shims.

4-CYLINDER DIESEL & TURBO DIESEL (Cont.)

Fig. 15: Sectional View of Engine Oiling Circuit

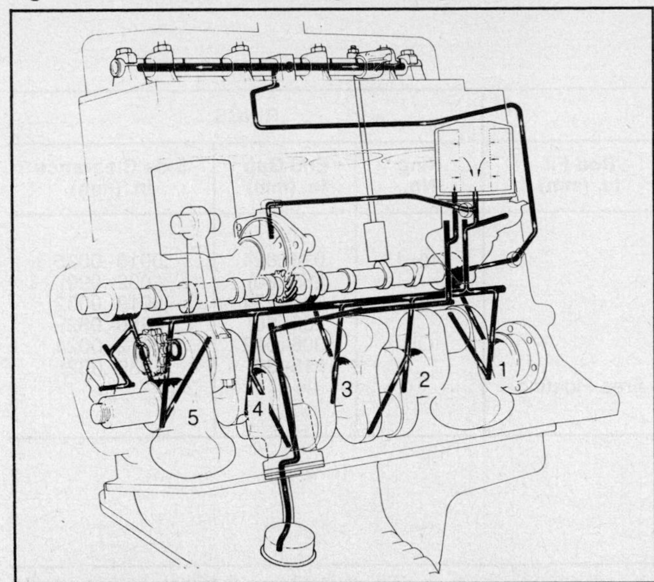
1
2
3
4
5

Non-Turbo model shown, Turbo model is similar.

2) Using a feeler gauge, measure the gap between the cap nut bearing face and the cylinder block through the slot provided. Remove the cap nut, and install a shim to obtain correct end play. For Turbo models, shim should be .020-.040" (.05-.1 mm) greater than feeler gauge reading. For non-Turbo models, shim should be .040" (1 mm) greater than feeler gauge reading. Reinstall cap nut and tighten.

ENGINE COOLING

COOLING SYSTEM CAPACITY

10.5 qts. (9.9L).

THERMOSTAT

Opens at 167°F (72°C) for non-Turbo models, 176°F (80°C) for Turbo models.

WATER PUMP

Removal

Remove radiator, top hose, and fan belt. Disconnect heater hose from water pump, and the self-disengaging fan brush holder. Remove water pump.

Installation

To install, reverse removal procedures, while noting the following: Clean contact surfaces before installing new gasket.

SELF-DISENGAGING FAN

Driven by water pump shaft and controlled by a thermal contact-breaker. Fan engages at 178-182°F (81-83°C) and disengages at 151-158° (66.5-70°C).

TIGHTENING SPECIFICATIONS

Application	Ft. Lbs. (N.m)
Clutch Housing-to-Block	43 (58)
Connecting Rod Caps	43 (58)
Cylinder Head	[1]
Injection Pump Mounting Bolts	14 (19)
Main Bearing Caps	80 (109)
Eccentric Idler Gear	16 (12)
Crankshaft Pulley	[2] 40 (54) plus 60°
Flywheel Bolts	56 (76)
Glow Plugs	16 (22)
Oil Pump Cap Nut	65 (88)
Rocker Arm Supports	
End Supports	14 (19)
Center Supports	34 (46)

[1] – See Cylinder Head Installation in this article.
[2] – See Timing Chain Installation in this article.

ENGINE SPECIFICATIONS

GENERAL SPECIFICATIONS

Year	DISPLACEMENT Cu. In.	DISPLACEMENT Liters	Fuel System	HP@RPM	Torque Ft. Lbs.@RPM	Compr. Ratio	BORE In.	BORE mm	STROKE In.	STROKE mm
1983										
Turbo	140.6	2.3	Fuel Inj.	80@4150	136@2000	21:1	3.700	94	3.267	83
Non-Turbo	140.6	2.3	Fuel Inj.	71@4500	99@2500	23:1	3.700	94	3.267	83

VALVES

Engine Size & Valve	Head Diam. In. (mm)	Face Angle	Seat Angle	Seat Width In. (mm)	Stem Diameter In. (mm)	Stem Clearance In. (mm)	Valve Lift In. (mm)
2.3L							
Turbo							
Intake	1.594 (40.5)	45°	45°	.....	.3339-.3344 (8.480-8.495)	.0024 (.062)	.....
Exhaust	1.319 (33.5)	45°	45°	.....	.3330-.3337 (8.460-8.475)	.0032 (.082)	.....
Non-Turbo							
Intake	1.594 (40.5)	30°	30°	.....	.3336-.3344 (8.473-8.495)	.0018 (.047)	.243 (6.173)
Exhaust	1.319 (33.5)	45°	45°	.....	.3328-.3337 (8.453-8.475)	.0026 (.067)	.243 (6.173)

Peugeot Engines

4-CYLINDER DIESEL & TURBO DIESEL (Cont.)

ENGINE SPECIFICATIONS (Cont.)

PISTONS, PINS, RINGS

Engine	PISTONS	PINS		RINGS		
	Clearance In. (mm)	Piston Fit In. (mm)	Rod Fit In. (mm)	Ring No.	End Gap In. (mm)	Side Clearance In. (mm)
2.3L Non-Turbo	.005-.006 (.13-.16)	Press Fit	.....	No. 1	.014-.024 (.35-.60)	.0013-.0035 (.032-.090)
				No. 2	.014-.024 (.35-.60)	.0019-.0032 (.050-.082)
				Oil	.006-.012 (.16-.30)	.0012-.0024 (.030-.062)
Turbo	.005-.006 (.13-.16)	Free Floating	Free Floating	[1]	[1]	[1]

[1] – Turbo specifications not available from manufacturer.

CRANKSHAFT MAIN & CONNECTING ROD BEARINGS

Engine	MAIN BEARINGS				CONNECTING ROD BEARINGS		
	Journal Diam. In. (mm)	Clearance In. (mm)	Thrust Bearing	Crankshaft End Play In. (mm)	Journal Diam. In. (mm)	Clearance In. (mm)	Side Play In. (mm)
2.3L	2.1651-2.1661 [1] (54.994-55.021)	.002-.004 (.05-.10)	Center	.003-.011 (.08-.29)	1.9678-1.9689 (49.984-50.011)	.002-.004 (.05-.10)	.....

[1] – Turbo journal diameter is 2.1651-2.1661" (54.994-55.021 mm).

VALVE TIMING

Engine	INTAKE		EXHAUST	
	Open (BTDC)	Close (ABDC)	Open (BBDC)	Close (ATDC)
2.3L				
Turbo	12°	16°	56°	12°
Non-Turbo	12°	40°	56°	12°

VALVE SPRINGS

Engine	Free Length In. (mm)	PRESSURE Lbs. @ In. (Kg @ mm)	
		Valve Closed	Valve Open
2.3L			
Inner [1]	1.61 (41)	16.87@1.22 (7.64@31)	34.88@.87 (15.8@22)
Outer [1]	1.76 (44.6)	49@1.38 (22.2@35)	101.3@1.02 (46@26)

[1] – Tight coils face toward cylinder head.

944 4-CYLINDER

ENGINE CODING

ENGINE IDENTIFICATION

Engine identification number is stamped on the left side of the engine block near the clutch housing.

ENGINE CODES

Application	Code
With Auto. Trans.	44/04
With Man. Trans.	44/02

ENGINE, MANIFOLDS & CYLINDER HEAD

ENGINE

Removal

1) Engine is removed from underneath the vehicle. On manual transmission the clutch bell housing is removed with the engine. Raise and support vehicle. Disconnect negative battery cable. Remove front wheels. Disconnect battery positive cable and push through splash wall with rubber grommet.

2) Disconnect 2 plugs for engine wiring harness. Unplug control unit harness connector. Control unit is in passenger compartment near steering column. Push control unit plug and wiring through firewall.

3) Disconnect throttle cable, oxygen sensor wire, brake booster vacuum hose, air cleaner with air flow sensor. Remove distributor cap, rotor, and dust cap. Disconnect engine ground strap.

4) Disconnect and plug fuel feed and return lines. Drain cooling system. Remove splash shield. Disconnect exhaust system from engine. Remove starter. On manual transmission, remove clutch slave cylinder and line.

5) Support engine from above with VW support tool (10-222) or engine hoist. Remove stabilizer bar on front suspension. Remove shield for right engine mount on front crossmember.

6) Disconnect universal joint on steering gear, tie rod ends, hydraulic engine mounts, and left and right control arms on front crossmember. Remove front crossmember from underneath.

7) Remove air conditioner belt (if equipped). Remove air conditioner compressor and mount and suspend from spring strut. Do not disconnect refrigerant lines.

8) Disconnet coolant hoses from radiator, expansion tank, and heater. Remove radiator and cooling fans. Remove lower central tube mounting bolts. Lower engine, pull forward and remove from underneath.

Installation

To install, reverse removal procedure. On manual transmission models, insert bell housing bolts finger tight. Tighten bell housing bolts after hydraulic engine mount and front crossmember have been mounted.

MANIFOLDS & CYLINDER HEAD

Removal

1) Disconnect battery ground. Remove cap on coolant expansion tank. Remove splash guard. Drain coolant. Remove poly-rib belt. Remove drive belt cover. Set No. 1 cylinder to TDC of compression stroke.

2) Remove distributor cap, unscrew distributor arm and remove protective cap. Remove mount for distributor cap. Relax belt tension, and pull camshaft belt off of camshaft sprocket. Unscrew 2 mounting bolts on rear drive belt cover.

3) Disconnect fuel lines. Remove plastic cover on fuel collection tube. Pull off wire plugs on fuel injectors, and lay wire harness aside. Unscrew aluminum plugs, coolant line and bolts. Remove camshaft housing from cylinder head. Make sure hydraulic valve lifters do not fall out and are not mixed up.

4) Remove air cleaner assembly. Remove intake brace bolt. Remove intake distributor by dismantling holder on brake booster, hose on intake distributor, retaining clamp on accelerator cable, and mounting bolts of intake distributor and cylinder head.

5) Unscrew bolts of the exhaust manifold-to-catalytic converter flange. Unscrew hose on heater regulating valve and 2 screws on neck for coolant circuit. Unscrew mounting nuts for cylinder head. Unscrew crosswise from outside to inside. Remove cylinder head.

Inspection

1) Check cylinder head for distortion with a straightedge and feeler gauge. Maximum warpage is .0012" (.03 mm). Cylinder head can be resurfaced.

2) A maximum of .0079" (.2 mm) may be removed from cylinder head surface. To determine if cylinder head has already been machined, measure distance "A". *See Fig. 1.* The minimum dimension of "A" is .937" (23.8 mm).

Fig. 1: Checking Cylinder Head

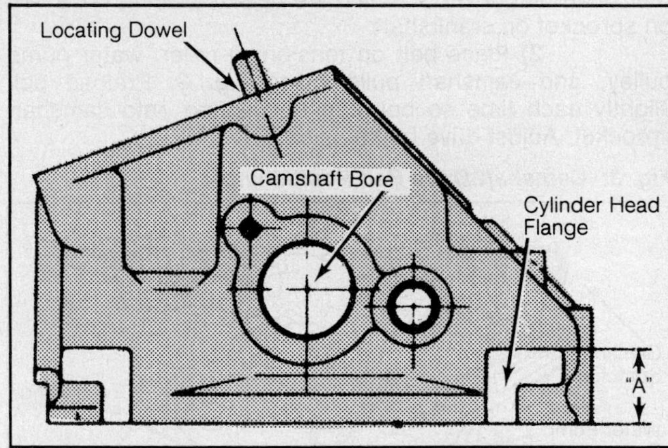
Locating Dowel
Camshaft Bore
Cylinder Head
Flange
"A"

Minimum distance "A" is .937" (23.8 mm).

3) If combustion end sealing surface must be machined, camshaft end sealing surface must also be surfaced. Before machining, plug oil bore of check valve and remove dowel pins.

Installation

1) Place cylinder head in position on cylinder block. Mount cylinder head on block. Install cylinder head nuts and tighten to specifications in 3 stages. *See Fig. 2.*

2) Leave cylinder head in this pre-loaded state for 30 minutes. Unscrew all nuts, in sequence, by 1/4 turn. Tighten to final torque of 61 ft. lbs. (85 N.m). Mount camshaft housing. Tighten bolts and aluminum plugs.

3) Install drive belt. *See Camshaft.* To complete installation, reverse removal procedure. Adjust poly-rib belt.

944 4-CYLINDER (Cont.)

Fig. 2: Cylinder Head Nut Tightening Sequence

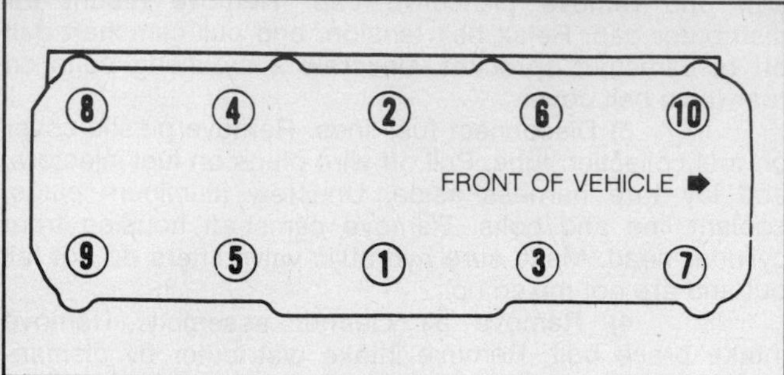
8
4
2
6
10
FRONT OF VEHICLE
9
5
1
3
7

Loosen cylinder head in reverse order.

CAMSHAFT

CAMSHAFT DRIVE BELT

Removal

1) Disconnect battery ground. Remove poly-rib belt. Remove drive belt cover. Set No. 1 cylinder to TDC compression stroke.

2) Remove distributor cap, unscrew distributor arm and remove protective cap. Remove mount for distributor cap. Relax belt tension and pull camshaft belt off of camshaft sprocket.

Installation

1) Ensure No. 1 cylinder is still at TDC. TDC marks on flywheel and cast clutch housing must be aligned. Align mark on camshaft sprocket with mark on rear drive belt cover. Install drive belt by placing drive belt on sprocket on crankshaft.

2) Place belt on tensioning roller, water pump pulley, and camshaft pulley. *See Fig. 3.* Preload belt slightly each time so belt can be pushed onto camshaft sprocket. Adjust drive belt tension.

Fig. 3: Camshaft Drive Belt Positioning

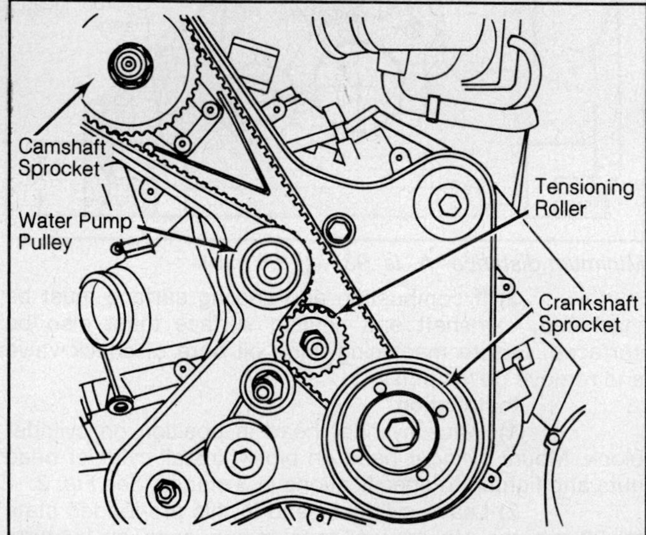
Camshaft Sprocket
Water Pump Pulley
Tensioning Roller
Crankshaft Sprocket

Preload belt slightly by hand when installing.

NOTE: Drive belt tension can only be adjusted on a cold engine.

Adjusting Camshaft Drive Belt Tension

1) Turn crankshaft counterclockwise by about 10° on crankshaft, which equals approximately 1.5 teeth to mark on camshaft sprocket. Prepare tension gauge (9201) for testing. *See Fig. 4.*

Fig. 4: Drive Belt Tension Gauge

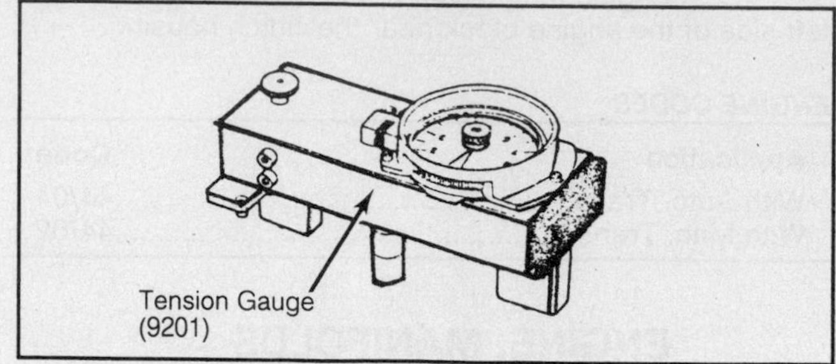
Tension Gauge (9201)

2) Pull out on lock pin on gauge, and completely push out gauge pin (opposite lock pin). Zero the telltale needle. Slide tension gauge onto belt. Push in measuring needle slowly, until lock pin can be heard to engage. Read value from dial gauge. Belt tension should be 2.4-3.0 dial value.

3) If adjustment is necessary, turn tensioner clockwise to tighten, or counterclockwise to loosen. Tighten mounting nut while counterholding. Turn engine 2 revolutions clockwise.

4) Align the TDC mark on the camshaft sprocket with cast mark in mount for the distributor cap. Turn engine counterclockwise from this position by approximately 10° on crankshaft. Recheck belt tension and adjust if necessary. Belt tension must be rechecked after 500-2000 miles.

BALANCE SHAFT DRIVE BELT

Removal

Remove splash guard. Loosen bolts of pressure rod slightly prior to unscrewing lock nuts. Remove poly-rib belt. Unscrew vent hose and take off drive belt cover. Loosen idler pulley so that pulley does not touch drive belt. Remove belt.

Installation

1) Turn crankshaft clockwise until TDC mark on camshaft sprocket is aligned with cast mark on mount for distributor cap. TDC marks on flywheel and cast clutch housing should be aligned.

2) Turn both balance shafts until marks of balance shaft sprockets align with rear drive belt cover. Install drive belt so that side of belt with color coded tooth faces out. Adjust belt tightness.

NOTE: Drive belt tension can only be adjusted on a cold engine.

Balance Shaft Drive Belt Adjustment

1) Remove plug from mount on distributor cap. Turn crankshaft clockwise until TDC mark on camshaft sprocket is aligned with cast mark in mount for distributor cap. TDC marks on flywheel and clutch cast housing must also be aligned. Check basic position of balance shaft sprockets.

2) Marks on sprockets should be aligned with marks on rear of rear drive belt cover. For upper shaft, align groove "O" with Woodruff key. For lower shaft, align groove "U" with Woodruff key. *See Fig. 5.* Prepare tension gauge (9201) for testing. Pull out lock pin on tension gauge and push out gauge pin opposite lock pin completely. Zero telltale needle.

944 4-CYLINDER (Cont.)

Fig. 5: Balance Shaft Drive Belt Positioning

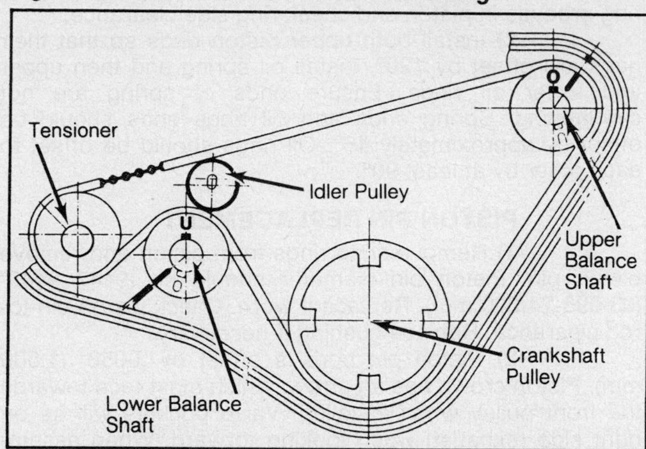
Tensioner
Idler Pulley
Upper Balance Shaft
Crankshaft Pulley
Lower Balance Shaft

Marks on sprockets should align with marks on rear cover.

3) Slide tension gauge onto belt. Push in gauge needle until lock pin is heard to engage and read value from dial gauge. On engines without slotted guide roller, tension should be 2.4-3.0 dial value for both new and used belts.

4) If adjustment is necessary, turn tensioner clockwise to tighten. Turn tensioner counterclockwise to loosen. Tighten tensioner nut.

5) After adjusting drive belt tension, adjust idler pulley. Use .02" (.5 mm) feeler gauge to maintain .02" (.5 mm) clearance between drive belt and pulley when upper portion of drive belt is preloaded .04-.08" (1 to 2 mm). Tighten idler pulley in this position. *See Fig. 6.*

Fig. 6: Preload Clearance of Balance Shafts

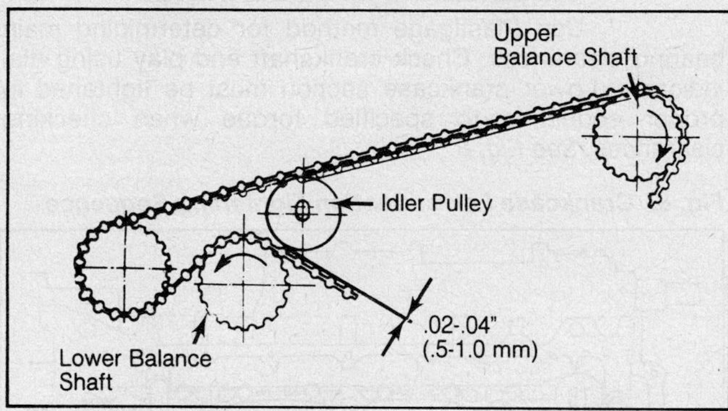
Upper Balance Shaft
Idler Pulley
.02-.04"
(.5-1.0 mm)
Lower Balance Shaft

Set clearance with preload at .04-.08" (1.0-2.0 mm).

6) If correct gap cannot be reached, turn idler pulley 180° and repeat adjustment. Tighten mounting nut. Install and adjust poly-rib belt.

NOTE: **The tension gauge should not be turned or moved on belt during test procedures.**

POLY-RIB BELT

Adjustment

1) Prepare tension gauge (9201) for testing. Pull out lock pin on tension gauge and push out gauge pin opposite lock pin completely. Zero telltale needle. Slide gauge carefully onto belt. Push in gauge needle until lock pin is heard to engage and read value from dial gauge.

2) Pull out lock pin and remove gauge. Poly-rib belt should have a tension of 9.2-9.8 dial value for both new and used belts. To adjust belt tension, slightly loosen bolts at end of adjusting rod. Loosen adjusting rod lock nuts and turn rod to obtain correct tightness of belt.

VALVES

VALVE ARRANGEMENT

I-E-I-E-I-E-I-E (Front-to-rear).

HYDRAULIC VALVE LIFTERS

Valve train uses bucket type hydraulic lifters. Cam lobes depress the lifters which are filled with engine oil under pressure through internal passages. With hydraulic lifters, no further valve clearance adjustment is necessary.

NOTE: **Use caution to make sure lifters are always installed in original positions. DO NOT mix up lifter order.**

VALVE SPRINGS

1) Valve springs may be removed using conventional overhead valve type compressor. Remove keepers and lift off retainer and springs.

2) To install, reverse removal procedure. Make sure to note the number of shims between valve springs and cylinder head and replace in same position.

Fig. 7: Installed Valve Spring Length

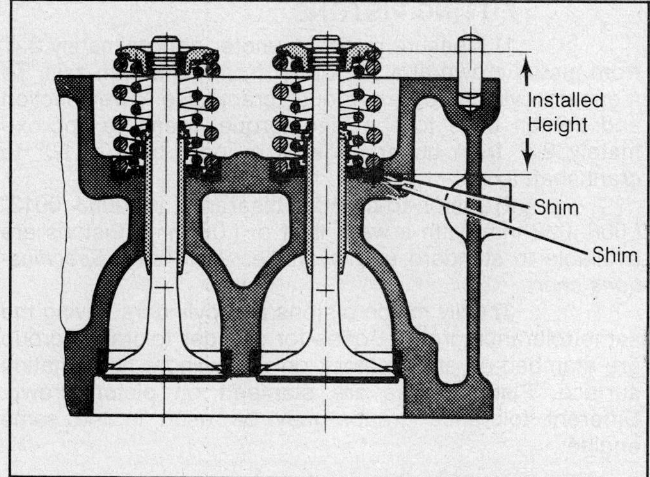
Installed Height
Shim
Shim

Replace shims to adjust length.

VALVE SPRING INSTALLED LENGTH

To check valve spring installed height, install tool (9138) with shims for applicable valve, spring retainer and keepers. Read distance from tool and correct, if required, by adding or removing shims.

VALVE SPRING INSTALLED HEIGHT SPECIFICATIONS

Application	In. (mm)
Intake Valve	1.61-1.63 (41.0-41.5)
Exhaust Valve	1.57-1.59 (40.0-40.5)

VALVE STEM OIL SEALS

With valve springs removed, pry off old seal using caution to prevent marring guide. Place plastic sleeve on valve stem, lubricate seal and push into place.

Porsche Engines

944 4-CYLINDER (Cont.)

VALVE GUIDE SERVICING

Removal

Using spot facer, grind off enough of valve guides protruding from the cylinder head so that guides are flush with cylinder head. Do not damage guide collars for spring retainers. Press out valve guides toward combustion chamber.

Inspection

Measure valve guide bores in cylinder head. Grind off replacement valve guide (928 104 328 52) to obtain a press fit of .0024-.0031" (.06-.08 mm).

Installation

Coat valve guide with talcum powder. Align and press into cylinder head against stop from the camshaft end. Ream valve guides for proper valve stem clearnace.

VALVE SEAT INSERTS

1) Valve seats may be machined until wear limit is reached. Wear limit must be checked using a new valve. Install new valve with springs and keepers.

2) Measure height of valve stem tip above camshaft housing mating surface. Maximum height is .57" (14.5 mm). If beyond specification, replace with oversize valve seat insert. Grind seats to specified angle and width.

PISTON, PINS & RINGS

FITTING PISTONS

1) Measure piston diameter approximately 2.4" from piston crown at a 90° offset from piston pin axis. To measure cylinder bores, mount crankcase lower section and tighten bolts to specified torque. Measure approximately 2.4" from upper edge of cylinder bore at 90° to crankshaft axis.

2) Piston-to-cylinder clearance is .0003-.0013" (.008-.032 mm) with a wear limit of (.08 mm). Pistons are available in standard and oversize. *See Piston Specifications chart*.

3) Only match pistons and cylinders having the same tolerance group. Codes for cylinder tolerance group are stamped on engine block on the cylinder head mating surface. Piston codes are stamped on piston crown. Different tolerance groups may be used in the same engine.

PISTON SPECIFICATIONS

Application	Tolerance Group	Diameter In. (mm)
Standard	0	99.98
	1	99.99
	2	100.00
1st Oversize	I0	100.48
	I1	100.49
	I2	100.50
2nd Oversize	II0	100.98
	II1	100.99
	II2	101.00

FITTING RINGS

1) Position rings into cylinder bore at a point where bore diameter is smallest. Ring must be square in bore. Measure ring end gap with a feeler gauge. Clean ring grooves in piston and check ring side clearance.

2) Install both upper piston rings so that their gaps are offset by 120°. Install oil spring and then upper and lower oil rings. Ensure ends of spring are not overlapping. Spring ends and oil rings ends should be offset by approximately 45°. Oil rings should be offset to each other by at least 90°.

PISTON PIN REPLACEMENT

1) Remove snap rings from piston and remove piston pin. Piston pin diameter should be .9447-.9448" (23.996-24.000 mm). Replace if worn. Check piston pin-to-rod clearance. Replace bushing if necessary.

2) Piston pin bore is offset by .0058" (1.500 mm). Piston crown has an arrow, which must face towards the front pulley when installed. Valve pockets will be on right side (exhaust) when looking forward. When assembling pistons, codes of connecting rod upper and lower sections must be mounted together and all face one side.

CAUTION: Some 1983 models are equipped with lighter connecting rods. They are stamped with the code "4G" and have a yellow paint dot near the crankshaft end. Lighter version rods are not available as spare parts. In case of repairs, replace with complete set of standard rods.

CRANKSHAFT MAIN & CONNECTING ROD BEARINGS

CRANKSHAFT MAIN BEARINGS

Use Plastigage method for determining main bearing clearances. Check crankshaft end play using dial indicator. Lower crankcase section must be tightened in proper sequence to specified torque when checking clearances. *See Fig. 8*.

Fig. 8: Crankcase Lower Section Tightening Sequence

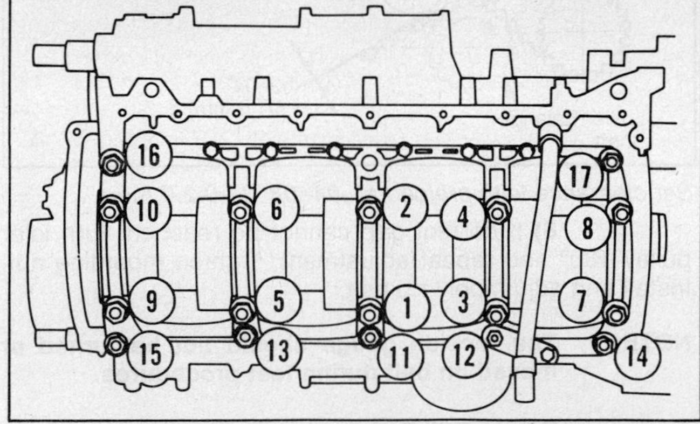
16
17
10
6
2
4
8
9
5
1
3
7
15
13
11
12
14

2) On final assembly of engine, throughly clean lower crankcase section. Apply a very thin coat of Loctite 574 to lower crankcase section in oil intake area and sealing surface in flywheel area. Tighten bolts in sequence to specifiec torque.

CONNECTING ROD BEARINGS

Throughly clean connecting rod cap and bearing shell of all oil. Use Plastigage method for

944 4-CYLINDER (Cont.)

determining connecting rod clearances. Ensure that connecting rods are installed to piston correctly. The 12-point nuts may be used only once.

NOTE: **Crankcase upper and lower sections as well as balance shaft cover are machined together and must be installed together. Codes of both balance shaft covers must be visible from above after installation.**

BALANCE SHAFT

BALANCE SHAFT BEARINGS

1) The rear of the balance shaft is supported by bearing shells in crankcase and balance shaft cover. Front of balance shaft is supported by a bushing in the shaft front housing. Front balance shaft bushing may be replaced by pressing out of housing. Both balance shafts are identical.

2) Balance shaft diameter should be 1.2195-1.2201" (30.975-30.991 mm). The diameter of the bore for rear balance shaft bearings in crankcase and balance shaft cover must be 1.3386-1.3393" (34.000-34.019 mm).

3) The bushing bore in front bearing housing should be 1.3386-1.3393" (34.000-34.019 mm). Balance shaft bearing surface diameter must be 1.2195-1.2201" (30.975-30.991 mm).

4) On final assembly, throughly clean balance shaft covers and apply a thin coat of Loctite 638 on sealing surfaces. Install on engine and tighten all nuts and bolts finger tight. Mount front bearing housing with a lightly oiled "O" ring. Do not tighten front bearing housing bolts.

5) Tighten bearing housing cover small (M6) bolts to 6 ft. lbs. (8 N.m). Tighten remaining nuts and bolts to specification in 2 steps. Check movement of balance shaft between each tightening step.

BALANCE SHAFT DRIVE PULLEYS

Installation

1) Install upper and lower balance shaft seals. Seals have different diameters. Also, arrow stamped on front of seal must point in rotating direction of balance shafts.

2) Install upper balance shaft pulley with groove code "O" on Woodruff key. Install lower balance shaft with groove code "U" aligned with Woodruff key. On both pulleys, mount collar so that codes "O" and "U" can be seen in large bores.

3) Coat mounting bolts with Loctite 574. Tighten to specification using spanner wrench to hold drive pulley.

ENGINE OILING

CRANKCASE CAPACITY

Oil capacity is 5.8 qts. (5.5L) with filter change.

OIL FILTER

Oil filter is full-flow, spin-on replaceable type.

NORMAL OIL PRESSURE

Oil pressure at normal operating temperature and 5000 RPM should be 58 psi (4.08 kg/cm²).

ENGINE OILING SYSTEM

Engine utilizes a wet sump with an oil cooler located in a housing on the right side of the engine, using engine coolant as a heat exchanger. Cooler housing is also used as a mount for the oil filter and oil pressure sending unit.

Pressure relief valve is inside the housing. Oil pump is a crescent gear type. It is located in a separate housing, bolted to the front of the crankcase. A splined drive sleeve drives the oil pump by way of an axial connection with the inner gear.

The oil pump draws in oil from the oil pan through oil filter screen. The filter screen tube is mounted on the crankcase lower section and is sealed with a rubber ring. The oil continues to the oil pump through a suction bore in the crankcase upper and lower sections.

The sealing surface around the suction bore should be coated with Loctite 574. Oil delivered by the pump enters a short bore in the crankcase upper section. From there oil reaches the pressure relief valve arranged transverse to the bore and passes through a riser to inlet side of oil cooler.

The oil, after being cooled passes through the oil filter and pressure sending unit, reaches the main bore by way of a cross bore. The main bearings are supplied by the main bore. Connecting rod bearings recieve oil from inclined bores in crankshaft.

Oil for the rear bearing of the left upper balance shaft comes from the crankshaft thrust bearing (No. 3). Right balance shaft is supplied by a separate bore off of the main bore. An oil bore in each balance shaft supplies oil to the front flange bearings.

A gallery passes through the crankcase to the cylinder head and camshaft housing. Camshaft housing has branching bore to supply camshaft and lifters. A check valve is installed to prevent oil from flowing down cam supply bore when engine is shut off.

OIL PUMP

Oil pump can be disassembled by driving out insert through the rear of the housing. Inspect all parts for excessive wear or damage. When assembling pump, punch mark on outer rotor must face the front of the engine. Coat outer surface of rear housing insert with Loctite 574 before assembly.

ENGINE COOLING

COOLANT CAPACITY

Coolant capacity is about 8.5 qts. (8.0L).

RADIATOR CAP

Radiator cap opens at 14.5 psi (1.02 kg/cm²).

THERMOSTAT

Thermostat opens at 181°F (83°C).

WATER PUMP

Water pump is mounted on front of crankcase. It is driven from the rear of camshaft toothed drive belt. Manufacturer does not provide specific removal and installation procedure.

Porsche Engines

944 4-CYLINDER (Cont.)

ENGINE SPECIFICATIONS

GENERAL SPECIFICATIONS

Year	DISPLACEMENT		Fuel System	HP@RPM	Torque Ft. Lbs.@RPM	Compr. Ratio	BORE		STROKE	
	Cu. In.	Liters					In.	mm	In.	mm
1983	151	2.5	Fuel Inj.	143@5500	137@3000	9.5:1	3.94	100.0	3.11	78.9

VALVES

Engine Size & Valve	Head Diam. In. (mm)	Face Angle	Seat Angle	Seat Width In. (mm)	Stem Diameter In. (mm)	Stem Clearance In. (mm)	Valve Lift In. (mm)
2.5L							
Intake	1.77 (45.0)	45°	45° [1]	.067 (1.7)	.353 (8.97)	.031 (.80)	....
Exhaust	1.57 (40.0)	45°	45° [1]	.079 (2.0)	.352 (8.95)	.031 (.80)	....

[1] – Inner correction angle is 60°; outer correction angle is 30°.

PISTONS, PINS, RINGS

Engine	PISTONS	PINS		RINGS		
	Clearance In. (mm)	Piston Fit In. (mm)	Rod Fit In. (mm)	Ring No.	End Gap In. (mm)	Side Clearance In. (mm)
2.5L	.0003-.0013 [1] (.008-.032)	.....	.0007-.0013 (.018-.032)	1	.0079-.0177 (.20-.45)	.0019-.0032 (.05-.082)
				2	.0079-.0177 (.2-.45)	.0016-.0028 (.04-.072) [2]
				Oil	.0149-.0557 (.38-1.4)	.0009-.0054 (.023-.137)

[1] – Wear limit is .0031" (.080 mm).
[2] – For rings manufactured by KS, side clearance is .0019-.0032" (.050-.082 mm).

CRANKSHAFT MAIN & CONNECTING ROD BEARINGS

Engine	MAIN BEARINGS				CONNECTING ROD BEARINGS		
	Journal Diam. In. (mm)	Clearance In. (mm)	Thrust Bearing	Crankshaft End Play In. (mm)	Journal Diam. In. (mm)	Clearance In. (mm)	Side Play In. (mm)
2.5L [1]	2.755-2.756 (69.971)	.0008-.0038 (.020-.098)	No. 3	.0043-.0122 (.110-.312)	2.0461-2.0468 (51.971-51.990)	.0013-.0036 (.034-.092)	.0039-.0157 (.100-.400)

[1] – Crankshaft bore diameter is 2.953-2.954" (75.000-75.019 mm).

944 4-CYLINDER (Cont.)

ENGINE SPECIFICATIONS (Cont.)

VALVE SPRINGS

Engine	Free Length In. (mm)	PRESSURE Lbs. @ In. (Kg @ mm) Valve Closed	Valve Open
2.5L			
Outer	2.03 (51.5)	....	....
Inner	1.73 (44.0)	....	....

VALVE TIMING

Engine	INTAKE Open (BTDC)	INTAKE Close (ABDC)	EXHAUST Open (BBDC)	EXHAUST Close (ATDC)
2.5L	1°	49°	43°	3°

TIGHTENING SPECIFICATIONS

Application	Ft. Lbs. (N.m)
Balance Shaft Cover Bolt	
M8	
Step 1	11 (15)
Step 2	14 (20)
Balance Shaft Cover Bolt	
M6	6 (8)
Balance Shaft Cover Stud	
Step 1	11 (15)
Step 2	22 (30)
Balance Shaft Sprockets	33 (45)
Camshaft Housing	14 (20)
Camshaft Plugs (Aluminum)	29 (40)
Camshaft Sprocket	33 (45)
Crankcase Lower Section Studs	
M 12	
Step 1	14 (20)
Step 2	29 (40)
Step 3	55 (75)
M 10	
Step 1	14 (20)
Step 2	36 (50)
M8	14 (20)
M6	6 (8)
Connecting Rod Bolts	41-44 (57-62)
Crankshaft Sprocket	160 (210)
Cylinder Head-to-Crankcase	
Step 1	14 (20)
Step 2	36 (50)
Step 3	611 (85)
Flywheel-to-Crankshaft	65 (90)
Guide Roller-to-Water Pump Housing	33 (45)
Tensioner-to-Bearing Housing	33 (45)
Tensioner-to-Oil Pump Housing	33 (45)

911SC 6-CYLINDER

ENGINE CODING

ENGINE IDENTIFICATION

Engine identification number is die-stamped on blower fan support near oil temperature sensor. Second digit of number identifies engine.

ENGINE IDENTIFICATION

Application	Code
911SC (3.0L)	4

ENGINE, MANIFOLDS & CYLINDER HEADS

ENGINE

Removal

1) Place vehicle on jack stands. Disconnect battery ground. Remove air cleaner. Detach air conditioning compressor from brackets, but leave hoses attached.

2) Disconnect all electrical wires running between engine and engine compartment. Remove the fuel lines at filter and return line. Disconnect the accelerator linkage.

3) Remove rear center tunnel cover in passenger compartment. Remove rubber boot in tunnel by pulling forward over the selector rod. Loosen shift rod coupling and pull coupling off of transmission inner shift rod.

4) Disconnect speedometer sensor wires in tunnel. Remove rubber plug with wire plug. Drain crankcase and plug hoses on engine and oil tank. Remove heater hoses at exchangers. Remove rear stabilizer.

5) Disconnect ground strap at body and battery wires at starter. Disconnect accelerator linkage from pedal and clutch cable from transmission. Loosen propeller shaft flange socket head screws at transmission.

6) Place a jack under engine and transmission assembly and apply a little upward pressure to relieve tension on motor mounts. Remove transmission and engine mount bolts. Lower engine and transmission assembly out of vehicle. Do not move vehicle unless propeller shafts are suspended horizontally.

Installation

To install, reverse removal procedure. Do not clamp heater hoses. Slide heater hoses onto the exchangers just before the engine and transmission assembly is in final installation position.

CYLINDER HEADS

Removal

1) With fuel injection system removed, take off distributor cap and spark plug wires. Remove cooling air ducts, cover shrouds, ducts connecting air blower outlets and heat exchanger inlets with cover shrouds.

2) Remove rear engine mount from holder. Remove exhaust system, engine mounting bracket, blower pulley and drive belt. Loosen both screws of band strap attaching alternator to blower housing and pull housing rearward. Disconnect alternator cables and remove blower housing along with alternator.

3) Remove heat exchanger using special wrenches (P 205 & P 217). Disconnect camshaft oil lines between crankcase and chain housing covers. Remove covers. Remove chain tensioner, pivot lever and chain sprocket as an assembly.

4) Remove camshaft sprocket nuts using wrenches (P 202 & P 203). Withdraw sprocket dowel pin with removal tool (P 212). Use a screwdriver to lift spring retainers from groove and remove chain guides. Remove camshaft sprockets and flanges. Pry Woodruff keys from camshafts.

NOTE: **Each cylinder has a separate head. If camshaft housing is removed, any single head may be removed. If camshaft housing is left attached to cylinder heads, cylinder heads and camshaft housing may be removed as an assembly.**

5) To remove a single head, rotate camshaft to take load off of rocker arm shaft to be removed. Loosen and remove rocker arm shafts and remove camshaft housing. With special tool (P 119), remove cylinder head nuts and lift off cylinder head.

6) Mark cylinder heads, cylinders and camshaft housings for reassembly in original positions. To remove all 3 cylinder heads and camshaft housing as an assembly, evenly loosen and unscrew cylinder head nuts with special tool (P 119).

Installation

1) Place cylinder head gaskets on cylinders with perforated side of steel insert facing cylinder. Install cylinder heads and oil return tubes at same time. Coat oil return tubes with engine oil for easier installation. Lightly tighten cylinder head nuts.

2) Split (2 piece) oil return pipes may be installed without removing and disassembling the engine. If using this type, all "O" rings and seals must be lightly oiled and pipe telescoped.

3) Extend pipe until end seals are seated and place retaining ring in its groove. Short pipe must be installed in crankshaft housing.

Fig. 1: Cross Section of Rocker Arm Shaft Assembly

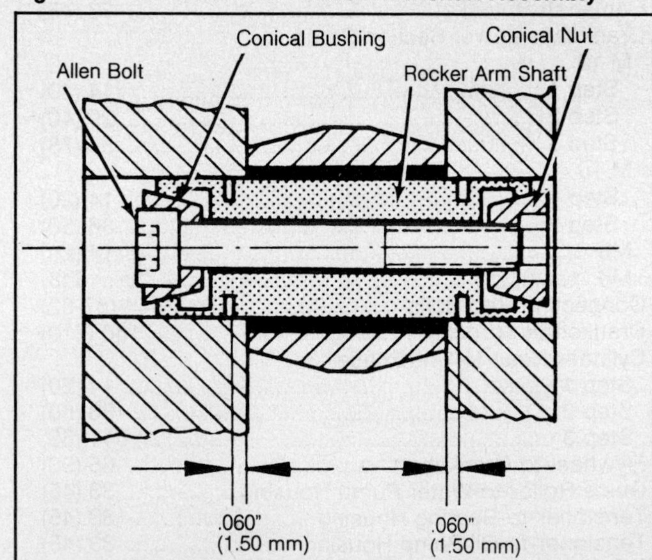
Conical Bushing
Conical Nut
Allen Bolt
Rocker Arm Shaft
.060"
(1.50 mm)
.060"
(1.50 mm)

Shafts should be recessed into bores.

4) Install cool air shrouds and attach with clamps. Use Loctite 573 as a sealing compound between

911SC 6-CYLINDER (Cont.)

camshaft housing and cylinder head. Slide camshaft housing onto mounting studs.

5) Tighten camshaft housing nuts down a few turns to ensure seal. Install Allen screws in proper location and tighten camshaft housing in a crosswise pattern.

NOTE: **Camshaft housings are interchangeable, but camshafts are not. Camshafts must be positioned on their proper side. See Fig. 6.**

6) Tighten cylinder head nuts in a crosswise pattern, checking that camshaft does not bind in housing. If camshaft binds, loosen cylinder head nuts and tighten in a different sequence. With cylinder head nuts tight, camshaft must be free to rotate.

7) Install rocker shafts and arms so grooves in shafts are recessed approximately .060" (1.52 mm) into bores. *See Fig. 1.* Tighten Allen bolts using wrenches (P 210 and P 211).

8) Install gasket, "O" ring, sealing flange, thrust plate, spacer, Woodruff key and camshaft sprocket flange as shown in *Fig. 2.* If sealing flange is worn, replace it.

Fig. 2: Assembling Components to Install Camshaft Sprocket Flange and Sprocket

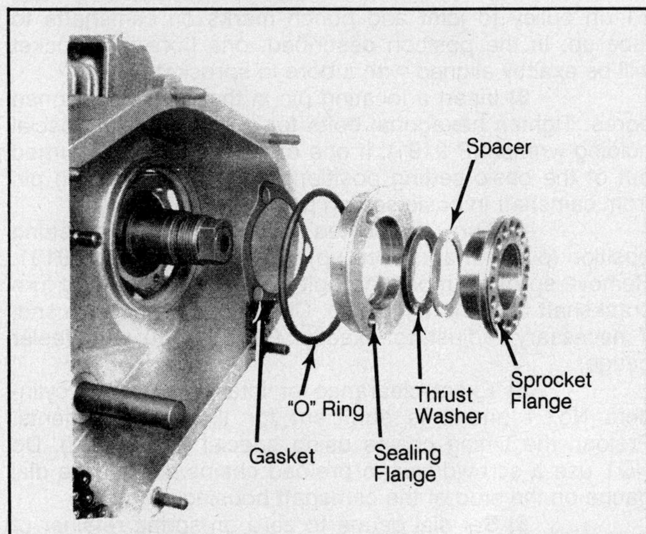
Spacer
Sprocket Flange
Thrust Washer
"O" Ring
Gasket
Sealing Flange

Replace camshaft sealing flange if worn.

9) Install camshaft sprockets and check chain alignment. *See Fig. 4 or Fig. 5.* Install heat exchanger, then chain tensioner. Slide chain guides on mounting studs. Lift retaining spring with screwdriver and slide chain guide into place. Install chain tension pivot lever and sprocket. Ensure that oil holes in pivot stud face upward.

10) Fill and bleed chain tensioners. Depress and install tensioners. Left tensioner may be positioned in only far enough to let camshaft nut be installed after valve timing. *See Valve Timing.* Install chain housing covers and camshaft oil lines. To complete installation, reverse removal procedure.

CAMSHAFTS

CAMSHAFTS

Removal

1) With engine out of vehicle, remove rocker covers and rocker arm assemblies. Remove muffler, oil hose from crankcase to chain housing cover, chain tensioner and chain tensioner sprocket.

2) Remove belt pulley from left camshaft. Remove bearing and chain housing covers. Remove ball bearing from camshaft with a puller.

3) Unscrew nuts attaching camshaft sprocket with special tools (P 202 & P 203). Remove dowel pin from camshaft sprocket with puller (P 212). Pull sprocket and sprocket flange from camshaft. Remove 3 attaching screws and sealing flange with "O" ring, and withdraw camshaft rearward.

Installation

To install, reverse removal procedure. Note that camshafts are not symetrical and must be replaced on side they were removed from during disassembly. *See Fig. 3 and Fig. 6.*

Fig. 3: Camshaft Sprocket Position

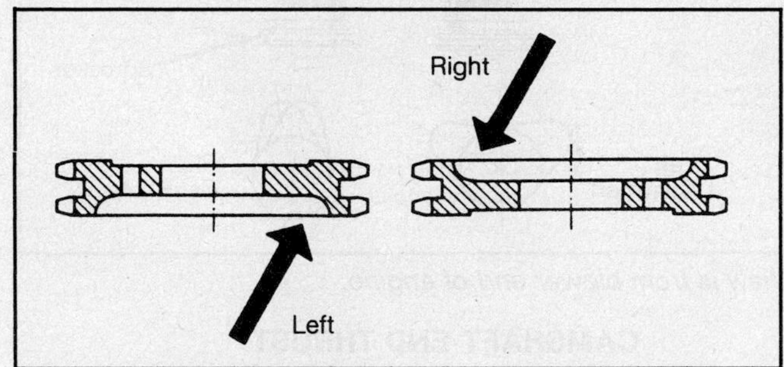
Right
Left

View is from blower end of engine.

Fig. 4: Top View Showing Timing Chain Alignment

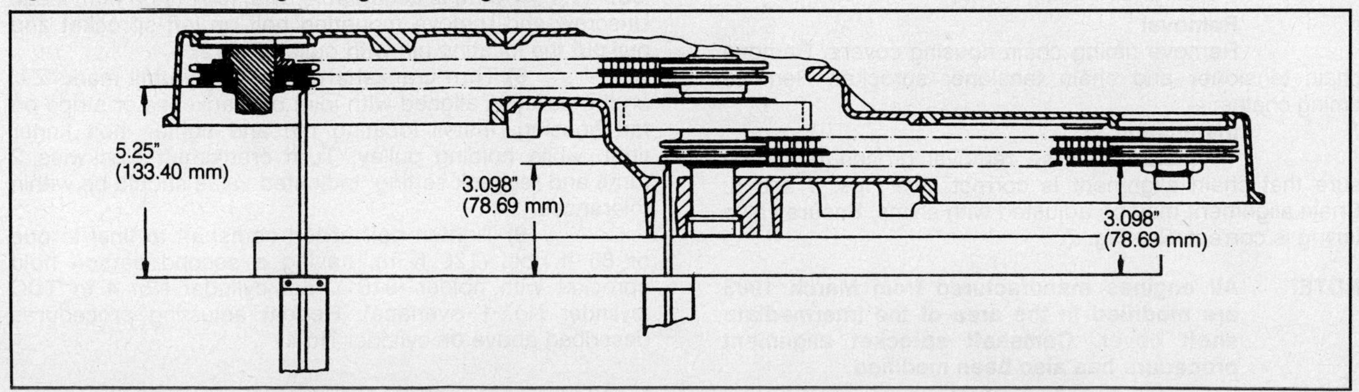
5.25"
(133.40 mm)
3.098"
(78.69 mm)
3.098"
(78.69 mm)

911SC 6-CYLINDER (Cont.)

Fig. 5: Top View Showing Modified Chain Alignment

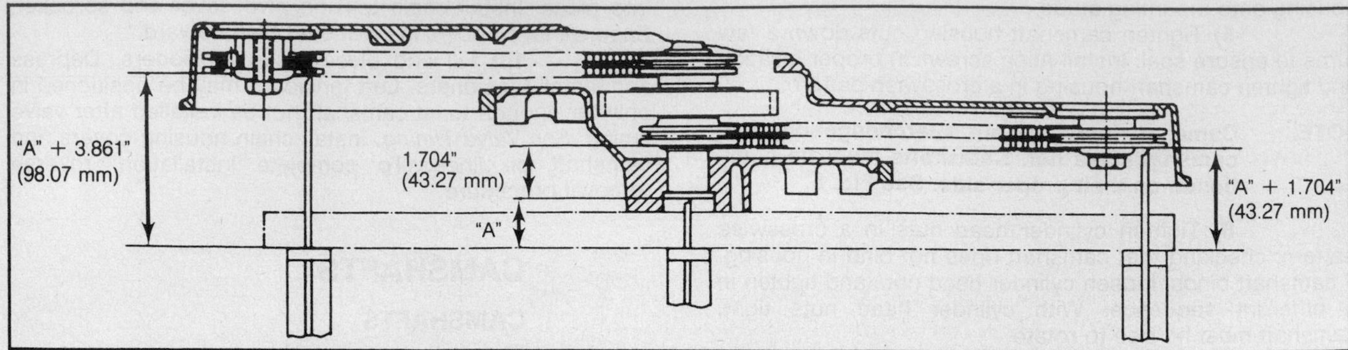
"A" + 3.861"
(98.07 mm)
1.704"
(43.27 mm)
"A"
"A" + 1.704"
(43.27 mm)

Illustration applies to all engines manufactured in March 1983 and later.

NOTE: **Camshaft housings are interchangeable, but camshafts are not. Camshafts must be positioned on their proper side. See Fig. 6.**

Fig. 6: Camshaft and Housing

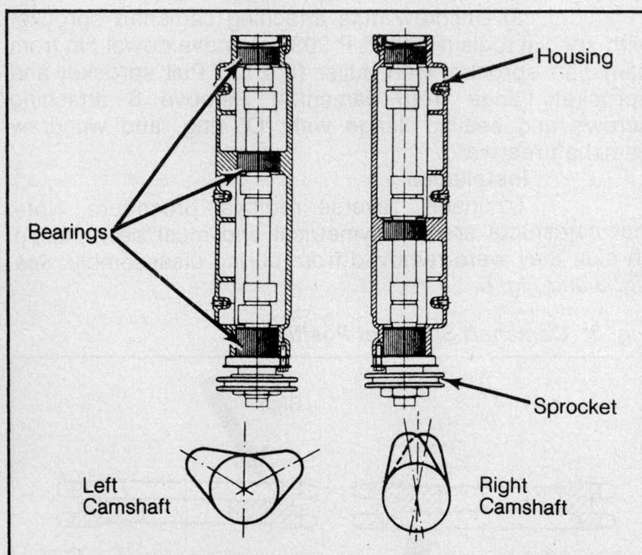
Housing
Bearings
Sprocket
Left
Camshaft
Right
Camshaft

View is from blower end of engine.

CAMSHAFT END THRUST

Measure camshaft end play with a dial indicator. If play is excessive, replace aluminum thrust washer located behind camshaft sprocket flange.

TIMING CHAIN

Removal

Remove timing chain housing covers. Remove chain tensioner and chain tensioner sprocket. Remove timing chains.

Installation

To install. reverse removal procedure. Make sure that chain alignment is correct. *See Figs. 4 and 5.* Chain alignment may be adjusted with shims. Ensure valve timing is correct. *See Fig. 7*.

NOTE: **All engines manufactured from March 1983 are modified in the area of the intermediate shaft cover. Camshaft sprocket alignment procedure has also been modified.**

VALVE TIMING

1) Rotate crankshaft until mark "Z1" on crankshaft pulley aligns with joint of crankcase or stripe on fan housing. Position both camshafts so that punch marks face up. *See Fig. 7.*

2) Engine has its basic setting (cylinder No. 1 = TDC and cylinder No. 4 = overlap) by adjusting mark Z1 on pulley to joint and punch marks on camshafts to face up. In the position described, one bore in sprocket will be exactly aligned with a bore in sprocket flange.

3) Insert a locating pin in these exactly aligned bores. Tighten hexagonal bolts for sprockets with special holding wrench (P 9191). If one of the camshafts is turned out of the basic setting position, remove the locating pin from camshaft in basic setting position.

4) Turn mislocated camshaft to basic setting position (punch marks face up) with holding wrench 9191. Remove sprocket mounting bolt and locating pin, and turn crankshaft to mark "Z1" again. Check valve clearance and, if necessary, adjust to exactly .04" (.1 mm) with feeler gauge.

5) Exact clearance of intake valves on cylinders No. 1 and 4 is sufficient for timing adjustments. Preload the timing chains using special lever (9182). Do NOT use a screwdriver to preload chains. Mount the dial gauge on the stud of the camshaft housing.

6) Set dial gauge to zero on spring retainer of intake valve for cylinder No. 1 with valve closed and approximately .40" (10 mm) preload. Slowly turn the crankshaft clockwise from "Z1" about 1 turn and observe dial gauge at the same time.

7) Continue turning until the mean value of the adjusting tolerance (valve lift) is reached. A range of .055-.067" (1.4-1.7 mm) is acceptable, with .061 (1.55 mm) ideal. Unscrew and remove mounting bolt on left sprocket and pull out the locating pin with puller (P 212).

8) Turn crankshaft accordingly until mark "Z1" on the pulley is aligned with joint of crankcase or stripe on fan housing. Install locating pin and tighten bolt finger tight, while holding pulley. Turn crankshaft clockwise 2 turns and recheck setting. Indicated value should be within tolerances.

9) Tighten bolt of left camshaft to final torque of 86 ft. lbs. (120 N.m), having a second person hold sprocket with holder (9191). Set cylinder No. 4 to TDC (cylinder No. 1 overlaps). Repeat adjusting procedures described above on cylinder No 4.

911SC 6-CYLINDER (Cont.)

Fig. 7: View of Engine from Blower End (Rear of Vehicle) Showing Valve Timing Marks

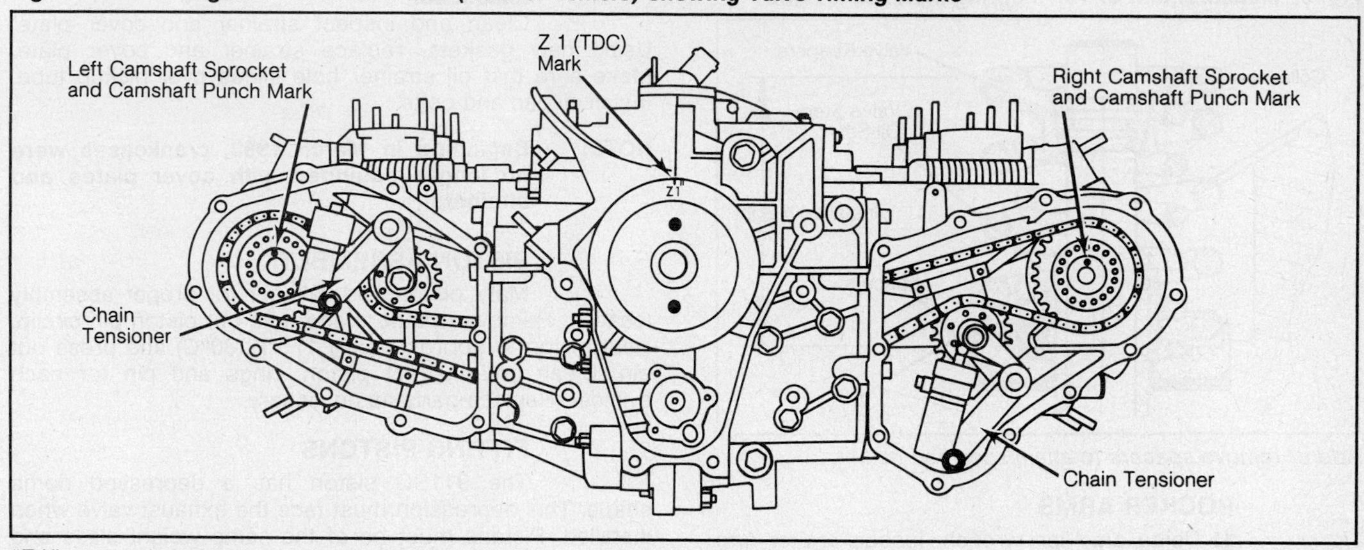
Z 1 (TDC)
Mark
Left Camshaft Sprocket
and Camshaft Punch Mark
Right Camshaft Sprocket
and Camshaft Punch Mark
Z1
Chain
Tensioner
Chain Tensioner

"Z1" on crankshaft pulley should align with joint of crankcase or stripe on fan housing.

INTAKE VALVE LIFT

Application	In. (mm)
911SC	.055-.067 (1.4-1.7)

VALVES

VALVE ARRANGEMENT

All upper valves are intake valves. All lower valves are exhaust valves.

VALVE GUIDE SERVICING

1) In order to avoid spreading the end of the valve guide when removing it, mill the guide down to the head on the camshaft side. A .433" (11 mm) drill bit may be used if milling tool is not available. Drive valve guide out into combustion chamber.

2) Using a hole gauge, measure bore in cylinder head. Turn oversize guide down in a lathe so that O.D. gives an interference fit of .0024-.0035" (.060-.090 mm).

3) Press valve guide into head from camshaft side until a measurement of .5196" (13.200 mm) is reached. *See Fig. 8.* Use grease as a lubricant when pressing in valve guides. Ream valve guide I.D. to .3543-.3549" (8.990-9.010 mm).

Fig. 8: Cross Section of Valve Guide Installed in Head

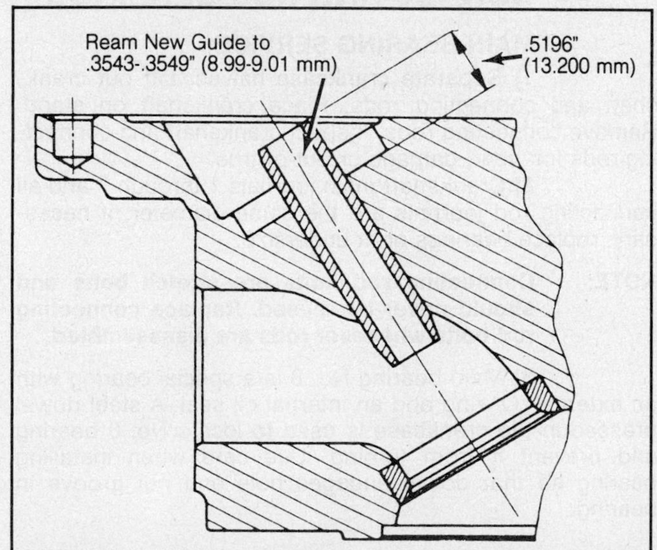
Ream New Guide to
.3543-.3549" (8.99-9.01 mm)
.5196"
(13.200 mm)

Use lubricant when installing guides.

VALVE STEM OIL SEALS

Removal

Using a spring compressor, remove valve keepers and take off valve springs with collar. Remove valve stem oil seal from end of valve guide.

Installation

Install new seal over stem, using caution to avoid damage to seal as it passes over keeper grooves. Force seal over end of valve guide evenly. Install remaining components in reverse order of removal.

VALVE SPRING SERVICING

1) Remove valve springs as previously described and check for wear or fatigue. Replace as necessary and install with closely wound coils next to cylinder head.

2) Check installed height with special tool (P 10) and add or remove spacers under the valve spring to attain specified installed height. Installed height for all valve springs should be 1.346-1.358" (34.20-34.50 mm) with valve closed.

Fig. 9: Measurement of Valve Spring Installed Height

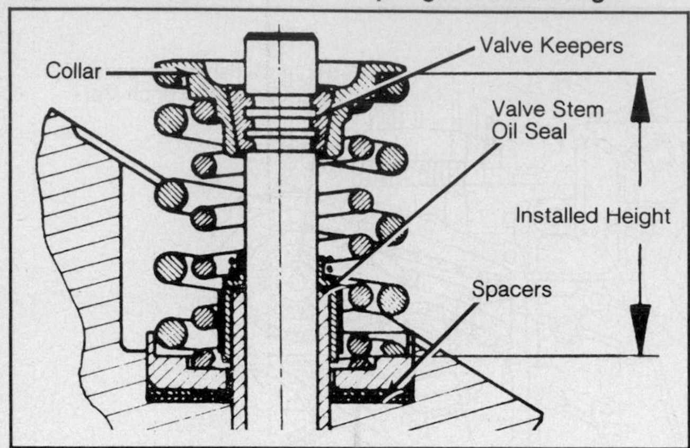
Collar
Valve Keepers
Valve Stem
Oil Seal
Installed Height
Spacers

Add or remove spacers to attain specified height.

ROCKER ARMS

1) Using an Allen wrench, loosen rocker arm shaft bolt. Slide rocker shaft out of cylinder head and remove arm. Check rocker arm shaft and bushing for wear and replace as required.

2) Install rocker arm shaft with Allen bolt facing either No. 2 or No. 5 cylinder. Center shaft in housing and tighten Allen bolt. *See Fig. 1.*

ROCKER ARM SPECIFICATIONS

Application	Diameter In. (mm)	Wear Limit In. (mm)
Rocker Arm Bushing	.7090-.7094 (18.009-18.019)	.7106 (18.049)
Rocker Arm Shaft	.7080-.7084 (17.983-17.993)	.7074 (17.968)
Rocker Arm Width	1.015-1.019 (25.78-25.88)	1.011 (25.68)
Housing Width	1.023-1.029 (25.98-23.14)	1.033 (26.24)

VALVE CLEARANCE ADJUSTMENT

1) Valve clearance should be set to .004" (.10 mm) with engine cold. If valves or seats have been reground, set clearances to .010" (.25 mm), run engine for 1/2 hour, then reset valves to original cold clearance.

2) Adjust valves in firing order sequence: 1,6,-2,4,3 and 5. Rotate to TDC of firing stroke on No. 1 cylinder and adjust clearance. Rotate crankshaft 120° for each cylinder to be adjusted until complete.

NOTE: **Cylinders are numbered 1, 2, and 3 from pulley end on driver's side of vehicle. Cylinders No. 4, 5, and 6 are on passenger's side of vehicle. No. 6 is at flywheel end.**

PISTONS, PINS & RINGS

OIL PAN

Removal

Remove nuts attaching oil pan (strainer cover plate) and remove strainer plate gaskets and strainer.

Installation

Clean and Inspect strainer and cover plate. Using new gaskets, replace strainer and cover plate. Make sure that oil strainer hole slides over pickup tube. Install oil pan and bolts.

NOTE: **Beginning in March 1983, crankcases were no longer equipped with cover plates and strainers.**

PISTON ASSEMBLY

Mark piston and cylinder for proper assembly location. Remove cylinders and take out piston pin circlip. Heat piston to approximately 176°F (80°C) and press out pin. Clean and inspect piston, rings and pin for each cylinder. Replace parts as necessary.

FITTING PISTONS

The 911SC piston has a depressed dome shape. This depression must face the exhaust valve when installed. Pistons must be of the same weight class and cylinders of same size in order to prevent unbalance of the engine.

1) Measure cylinder for wear and out-of-round. Cylinders and pistons are marked according to size. "O" indicates standard, while "1" or "2" indicates first or second oversize. Measure cylinder diameter 1.18" (30.0 mm) below top edge of cylinder.

2) Take one measurement in line with thrust face and another at 90° to this measurement. Cylinder is worn if diameter measurement is more than .004" (.10 mm) beyond diameter specification. If difference in the 2 measurements is more than .0016" (.040 mm), then cylinder has exceeded its ovality limit.

3) Position piston rings in bottom of cylinder and measure ring gap. Check side clearance in piston ring grooves. Install rings on piston with marking "TOP" facing upward.

CRANKSHAFT MAIN & CONNECTING ROD BEARINGS

MAIN BEARING SERVICE

1) Separate crankcase halves. Lift out crankshaft and connecting rods. Place crankshaft on stand. Remove connecting rods. Inspect crankshaft and connecting rods for wear, damage or out-of-true.

2) Crankshaft main journals 1 through 7 and all connecting rod journals are the same diameter. If necessary, replace bearings or fit undersize.

NOTE: **Connecting rod bolts are stretch bolts and should never be reused. Replace connecting rod bolts whenever rods are disassembled.**

3) Main bearing No. 8 is a special bearing with an external "O" ring and an internal oil seal. A steel dowel pressed in the crankcase is used to locate No. 8 bearing and prevent it from turning. Use care when installing bearing so that dowel engages hole and not groove in bearing.

911SC 6-CYLINDER (Cont.)

Fig. 10: Crankshaft Assembly with Component Locations

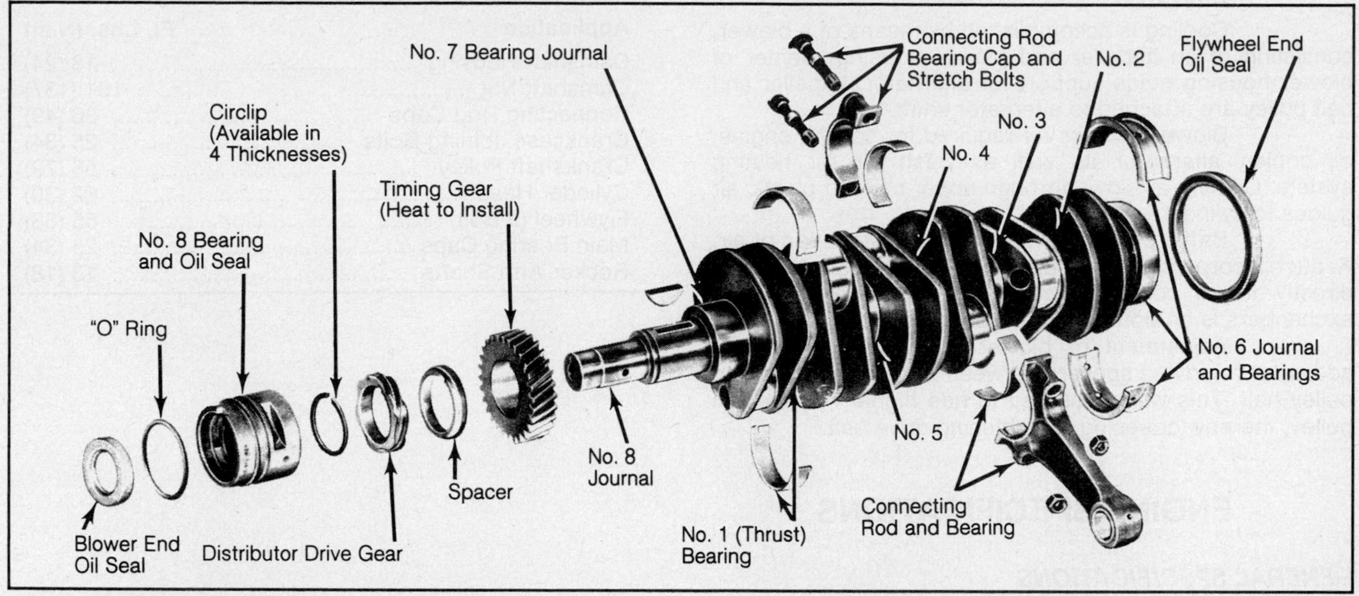
No. 7 Bearing Journal
Connecting Rod Bearing Cap and Stretch Bolts
No. 2
Flywheel End Oil Seal
Circlip (Available in 4 Thicknesses)
No. 3
No. 4
Timing Gear (Heat to Install)
No. 8 Bearing and Oil Seal
"O" Ring
No. 6 Journal and Bearings
No. 5
No. 8 Journal
Spacer
Connecting Rod and Bearing
No. 1 (Thrust) Bearing
Blower End Oil Seal
Distributor Drive Gear

THRUST BEARING ALIGNMENT

Check end play at No. 1 main bearing. Width of No. 1 bearing is 1.1024-1.1044" (28.000-28.0500 mm). Maximum wear limit is .011" (.28 mm) beyond specifications. Replace main bearing or crankshaft if excessive wear is present.

MAIN BEARING OIL SEALS (BLOWER END)

Remove belt pulley. Using a screwdriver, pry out old seal. Coat new seal with oil and press in place with installation tool (P 216).

MAIN BEARING OIL SEALS (FLYWHEEL END)

Remove flywheel. Displace oil seal with a chisel or drift and pry out with screwdriver. Coat outer seal edges with sealing compound and press into crankcase with driver (P 215) until seal is flush with face of crankcase.

INTERMEDIATE SHAFT BEARING SERVICE

With crankcase halves separated, lift out intermediate shaft and bearings. Inspect shaft and bearings for wear or damage and replace as necessary. Undersize bearings are NOT available.

ENGINE OILING

OIL CAPACITY

Capacity is 13.7 qts. (13.L) total, 10.6 qts. (10.L) for oil change.

OIL FILTER

Oil filter is the disposable, spin-on type.

NORMAL OIL PRESSURE

Oil pressure should be 65 psi (4.6 kg/cm) at 5000 RPM with an oil temperature of 194°F (90°C).

PRESSURE RELIEF AND SAFETY VALVES

Identically constructed coil spring operated valves. Safety valve is set to operate at a higher pressure than relief valve.

ENGINE OILING SYSTEM

Lubrication is dry sump type. Two independent oil pumps provide for pressure and suction in system. Pressure pump takes oil from externally mounted oil tank, and forces oil through passages to main, connecting rod and intermediate shaft bearings.

Camshaft bearings are oiled by external oil lines leading to camshaft housing. Oil splashes against valve cover to drip on rocker arms and valve stems. Suction pump takes oil from sump through strainer and forces it through oil filter to oil tank.

Oil from lower part of camshaft housing is returned to crankcase by oil return pipes. Pressure is controlled by 4 separate valves. At low temperatures, a thermostatically controlled valve directs oil to engine. At higher temperatures, oil first flows through cooler and then to bearings.

A pressure and relief valve directs oil into crankcase if pressure rises above 76.9-99.6 psi (5.4-7.0 kg/cm²). Additional safety and by-pass valves are built into the system to prevent damage from excess pressure.

OIL PUMP

Oil pump may be removed when crankcase halves are separated. No repair of pump is possible. Replace if defective.

NOTE: Engine manufactured as of March 1983 use a modified oil pump. Oil screen is now part of oil pick-up pipe.

Porsche Engines

911SC 6-CYLINDER (Cont.)

ENGINE COOLING

Cooling is accomplished by means of a blower, consisting of an impeller and blower housing. Center of blower housing holds support for alternator. Impeller and belt pulley are attached to alternator shaft.

Blower delivers air required for cooling engine, oil cooler, alternator as well as fresh air for heating system. Cooling air flows through upper molded plastic air guides to cylinders and heads.

Baffle plates provide uniform distribution of air. A duct incorporated into upper air guide leads air flow directly to oil cooler. Ducting for air delivery to heat exchangers is on both sides of blower housing.

Adjustment of blower drive belt is done by adding or removing spacers between impeller housing and pulley half. This will cause belt to ride higher or lower on pulley, thereby loosening or tightening drive belt.

TIGHTENING SPECIFICATIONS

Application	Ft. Lbs. (N.m)
Camshaft Housing	18 (24)
Camshaft Nut	101 (137)
Connecting Rod Caps	36 (49)
Crankcase Joining Bolts	25 (34)
Crankshaft Pulley	58 (79)
Cylinder Head	22 (30)
Flywheel (9 Bolt)	65 (88)
Main Bearing Caps	25 (34)
Rocker Arm Shafts	13 (18)

ENGINE SPECIFICATIONS

GENERAL SPECIFICATIONS

Year	DISPLACEMENT		Fuel System	HP@RPM	Torque Ft. Lbs.@RPM	Compr. Ratio	BORE		STROKE	
	Cu. In.	Liters					In.	mm	In.	mm
1983	182.7	3.0	Fuel Inj.	172@5500	175@4200	9.3:1	3.74	95.0	2.77	70.4

VALVES

Engine Size & Valve	Head Diam. In. (mm)	Face Angle	Seat Angle	Seat Width In. (mm)	Stem Diameter In. (mm)	Stem Clearance In. (mm)	Valve Lift In. (mm)
3.0L							
Intake	....	45°	45°	....	....	....	....
Exhaust	....	45°	45°	....	....	....	....

CRANKSHAFT MAIN & CONNECTING ROD BEARINGS

Engine	MAIN BEARINGS				CONNECTING ROD BEARINGS		
	Journal Diam. In. (mm)	Clearance In. (mm)	Thrust Bearing	Crankshaft End Play In. (mm)	Journal Diam. In. (mm)	Clearance In. (mm)	Side Play In. (mm)
3.0L							
Jrnls. 1-7	2.362 (60.00)	.0003-.0028 (.008-.070)	No. 1	.0043-.0076 (.110-.190)	2.085 (53.00)	.001-.0034 (.028-.086)	....
Jrnl. 8	1.220 (31.00)	.004 (.10)					

Porsche Engines

911SC 6-CYLINDER (Cont.)

ENGINE SPECIFICATIONS (Cont.)

PISTONS, PINS, RINGS

Engine	PISTONS	PINS		RINGS		
	Clearance In. (mm)	Piston Fit In. (mm)	Rod Fit In. (mm)	Ring No.	End Gap In. (mm)	Side Clearance In. (mm)
3.0L	.001-.002 (.023-.044)	Press Fit	.0007-.0015 (.018-.038)	No. 1	.004-.008 (.10-.20)	.003-.004 (.07-.10)
				No. 2	.004-.008 (.10-.20)	.001-.003 (.04-.07)
				Oil	.006-.012 (.15-.30)	.0008-.0020 (.02-.05)

VALVE TIMING

Engine	INTAKE		EXHAUST	
	Open (BTDC)	Close (ABDC)	Open (BBDC)	Close (ATDC)
3.0L	7°	47°	49°	3°

Porsche Engines

928S V8

ENGINE CODING

ENGINE IDENTIFICATION

Engine code and identification number is stamped on the front reinforcing rib in the top half of the crankcase.

ENGINE IDENTIFICATION

Application	Code
928S (4664 cc)	M 28

ENGINE & CYLINDER HEADS

ENGINE

Removal

1) With car standing on all 4 wheels, loosen engine compartment cross braces. Disconnect battery ground at spare wheel well. Detach windshield washer hoses and engine compartment light wires. Remove engine hood. Remove cap from coolant expansion tank.

2) Remove air intake hoses and entire air cleaner assembly. Raise car on hoist at specified pick up points. Place wooden block between central tube and rear tunnel brace. Detach splash shield at bottom and drain radiator. Remove left and right water drain plugs from crankcase.

3) Drain engine oil and remove lower body brace. Disconnect exhaust pipes at manifolds and remove left and right heat shields. Detach ground cable at body. Install and tighten drain plugs.

4) Unscrew clutch slave cylinder at clutch housing and remove with line connected. Remove mounting strap for pressure line to slave cylinder. Disconnect wires at starter and remove clutch housing with starter.

5) Disconnect clutch lever by pressing down in direction of clutch. Release starter wire from clamps on steering crossmember. Remove socket head bolts and push propeller shaft coupling back on propeller shaft. Unscrew throwout bearing sleeve mounting bolts and push sleeve toward flywheel.

6) Detach left and right engine shock absorbers at control arms, then at upper mountings. Disconnect air conditioner temperature switch wires on radiator and compressor clutch at connector plug. Loosen compressor and remove from console but do not disconnect hoses.

7) Suspend compressor with wire. Remove air pump filter housing and alternator cooling hose. Remove lower fan shroud. Disconnect all coolant hoses and bottom oil hose at radiator. Remove engine mounts separately by lifting with hydraulic jack and wooden block on oil pan.

8) Lower engine to front crossmember carefully. Move jack and pad to second side and remove mount in same manner. Remove clutch-to-engine mounting bolts and lower car. Remove remaining coolant hoses. Disconnect upper oil hose at radiator.

9) Remove radiator mounting bolts and lift out radiator. Disconnect engine wire harness and distributor wire transmitter plugs. Disconnect B+ wire and remove control unit. Detach and place ignition coil aside. Disconnect fuel feed and return lines.

10) Detach power steering pump lines at pump and supply tank. Drain oil and remove tank. Disconnect brake booster vacuum hose at manifold. Disconnect accelerator and cruise control cable, remove holder and clamp and place cables outside.

11) Cover A/C condenser with a thin board to prevent damage when removing engine. With engine adapter (9137) in eyelets provided, lift until snug with car resting on its wheels.

12) Remove upper engine block-to-clutch housing mounting bolts. Pull engine forward carefully and remove short propeller shaft with guide tube. Lift engine out of car.

Installation

To install, reverse removal procedure noting that heater lever should be in "warm" position when filling cooling system. Coolant level must reach center of expansion tank with engine warm.

CYLINDER HEADS

NOTE: **Manufacturer does not furnish removal and replacement procedures for cylinder heads. Heads may be removed with engine in vehicle. Following items must be noted when performing cylinder head operations.**

1) Allow engine to cool prior to draining coolant and removing heads. Remove camshaft housing, then loosen cylinder head nuts in reverse of tightening sequence.

2) Inspect cylinder heads for cracks and warpage. Measure warpage using straightedge and feeler gauge. Maximum warpage is .003" (.08 mm). Maximum machining to head surface is .012" (.3 mm).

3) Left and right cylinder head gaskets are different. Arrow must face forward and "TOP/OBEN" marking must face up. Tighten head bolts in 3 steps according to tightening specifications, following tightening sequence. *See Fig. 1.*

Fig. 1: Cylinder Head Tightening Sequence

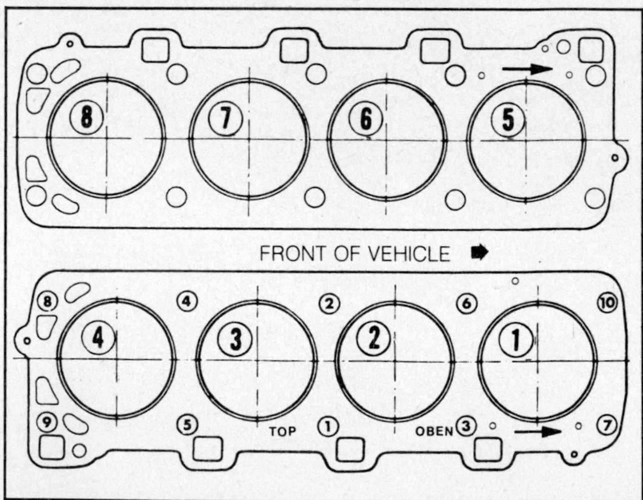
8
7
6
5
FRONT OF VEHICLE
8
4
2
6
10
4
3
2
1
9
5
TOP
1
OBEN
3
7

Loosen in reverse order.

NOTE: **Washers must not turn while tightening cylinder head nuts. Control by making paint marks if necessary.**

4) Flat gasket between cylinder head and camshaft housing must be placed properly to ensure that oil supply bore to camshaft is not blocked. Camshaft housing must be completely assembled prior to installation.

CAMSHAFT & DRIVE BELT

CAMSHAFTS

Camshafts run in 5 bearings without shells in camshaft housing. Housing cover plates must be removed in order to remove rubber plugs covering top row of bolts.

Camshaft housing assembly must be completely assembled before installation. Housing is located on heads with 2 dowel pins and mounted with socket head bolts.

CAMSHAFT DRIVE BELT INSTALLATION

1) Rotate crankshaft clockwise and align TDC mark on vibration damper with red indicator on cover. With timing belt and tensioner removed, turn both camshafts until notches in drive sprockets align with marks cast on camshaft bearing caps.

2) Preload belt by hand and install belt on sprockets in order of crankshaft, oil pump, left camshaft, water pump, right camshaft and tension roller. Ensure belt and camshaft sprocket teeth match.

3) If necessary, rotate camshaft counterclockwise until teeth match. Tighten timing belt to specifications. *See Camshaft Drive Belt Adjustment.* Rotate engine 2 revolutions and align cylinder No. 1 at TDC of compression stroke.

4) Check camshaft timing marks for proper alignment and retighten camshaft drive belt. Ensure tester is not turned or pushed when during tension measurement. Recheck belt adjustment at least once.

Fig. 2: View of Camshaft Drive Belt Installation

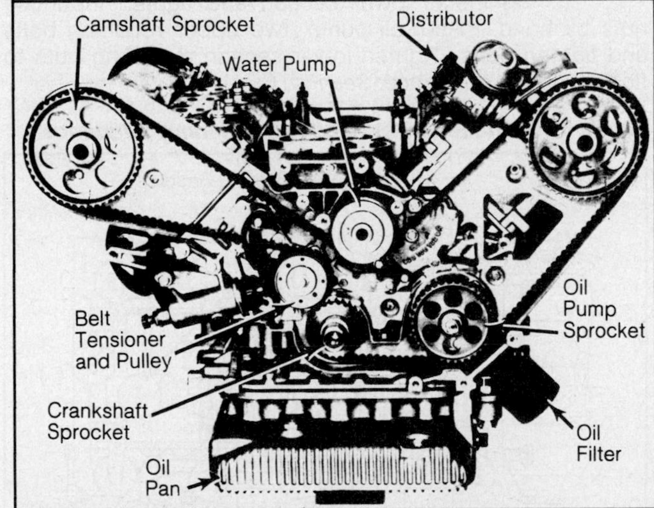
Camshaft Sprocket
Distributor
Water Pump
Belt
Tensioner
and Pulley
Oil
Pump
Sprocket
Crankshaft
Sprocket
Oil
Filter
Oil
Pan

Measure belt tension between tension roller and lower camshaft sprocket.

CAMSHAFT DRIVE BELT ADJUSTMENT

1) Rotate crankshaft in direction of rotation and position cylinder No. 1 at TDC of compression stroke. Mark on vibration damper should be in alignment with red indicator on cover.

2) Remove timing belt upper cover. Ensure each camshaft sprocket timing mark is in alignment with mark cast on camshaft bearing cap. Turn engine over 2 more times until TDC is reached again.

3) Check timing belt for damage and wear. Pull out lock-pin and push out gauge pin, opposite lock pin, on tester (9201). Move telltale to "0" position on gauge. *See Fig. 3.*

Fig. 3: Belt Tension Tester

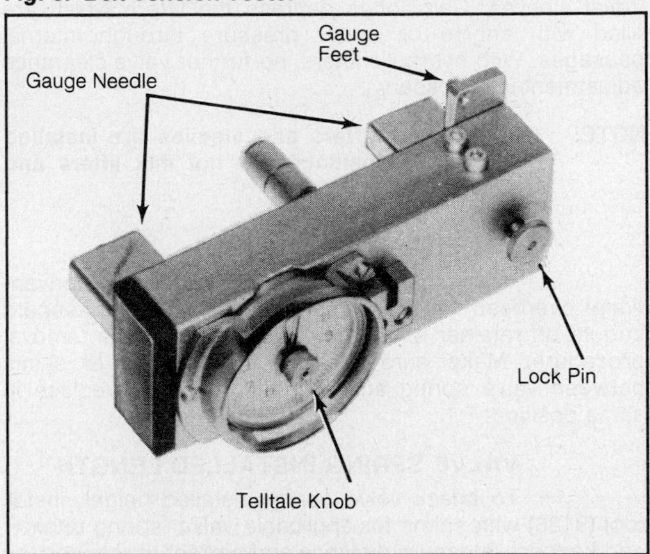
Gauge
Feet
Gauge Needle
Lock Pin
Telltale Knob

Belt tension adjustments are based on scale values of tester.

4) Slide tool onto belt section between tension roller and lower camshaft sprocket. Ensure measuring pin is resting in groove of belt. Push tester down on side closer to tensioner, until gauge needle, resting on air pump bracket, engages.

5) Read measured value while keeping tester horizontal to belt and free of tension. Tester must not touch plastic cover. Move telltale to "0" position on gauge.

6) Pull out lockpin to disengage gauge needle again. Remove tester from timing belt and read measured value. Correct belt tension if necessary. Adjustment screw is located on bottom of engine at front right-hand side.

7) To adjust, loosen adjustment screw lock nut and turn adjustment screw until tension is correct. Tighten lock nut and turn engine 2 revolutions. Recheck tension adjustment.

CAMSHAFT DRIVE BELT TENSION

Application	Scale Value
New or used	4.5

DRIVE BELT TENSIONER

1) Drive belt tensioner uses hydraulic damper and belt guide pulley to reduce belt load. Tensioner is filled with engine oil. Space between tensioner housing and engine block is used as an oil reservoir.

2) To fill, remove oil filler (larger) and bleeder Allen head bolts on tensioner housing. Using an oil can, slowly pour engine oil into filler hole until air-free oil flows from bleeder hole.

3) Install and tighten filler and bleeder bolts. Check fluid level after 1000 miles and at 15,000 intervals thereafter. To check, remove filler bolt. If oil can be seen, level is okay.

928S V8 (Cont.)

VALVES

VALVE ARRANGEMENT

I-E-I-E-I-E-I-E (Both Banks, Front-to-rear).

HYDRAULIC VALVE LIFTERS

Bucket type hydraulic lifters operate in sintered metal sleeves. Cam lobes depress the lifters which are filled with engine oil under pressure through internal passages. With hydraulic lifters, no further valve clearance adjustment is necessary.

NOTE: **Ensure that lifters and sleeves are installed in original positions. Do not mix lifters and sleeves.**

VALVE SPRINGS

Valve springs may be removed using conventional overhead valve type compressor. Remove keepers and lift off retainer and spring. To install, reverse removal procedure. Make sure to note the number of shims between valve spring and cylinder head and replace in same position.

VALVE SPRING INSTALLED LENGTH

To check valve spring installed height, install tool (9138) with shims for applicable valve, spring retainer and keepers. Measure distance and correct, if required, by adding or removing shims. Correct spring length is 1.492-1.516 (37.90-38.50).

Fig. 4: Measuring Installed Valve Spring Length

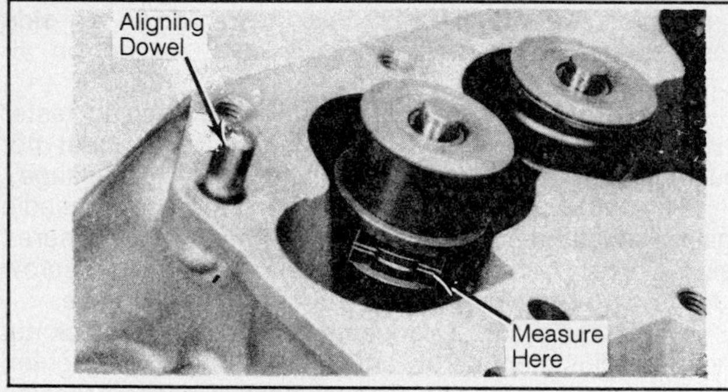
Aligning
Dowel
Measure
Here

Correct distance with shims.

VALVE STEM OIL SEALS

With valve springs removed, pry off old seal using caution to prevent marring guide. Place plastic sleeve on valve stem, lubricate seal and push into place using valve seal installation tool.

PISTONS, PINS & RINGS

OIL PAN

Oil pan is of cast aluminum design with ribs for reinforcing and cooling. Pan attaches to lower crankcase section with gasket and cap screws. Manufacturer does not provide specific removal and replacement instructions.

PISTONS

1) Piston and pins are paired according to weight. Mark pistons and pins to ensure parts are not interchanged. If parts are mixed up, rearrange by checking total weight of piston.

2) Piston total weight is measured with pin, rings and pin retainers. Piston weigh should be 718-726 grams 25.1-25.4 ounces. An oversize piston has same weight as standard piston.

3) Piston repair sizes are standard, .50 mm oversize and 1.0 mm oversize (98 mm), with 3 tolerance groups for each size. Each tolerance group is stamped on piston crown "0", "1" or "2".

4) Tolerance group stampings indicate if piston is the standard, .01 mm or .02 mm oversize of its particular repair size. Piston diameter measurements should be taken 2.4" (61 mm) from crown of piston, 90° to pin bore.

PISTON RINGS

Install compression rings so gaps are offset by 120°. Install oil scraper ring with spring gap offset 45° from side rails and side rail gaps offset 90° from each other. Ensure no ring gap is in line with thrust face of pin bore.

CRANKSHAFT MAIN & CONNECTING ROD BEARINGS

CRANKCASE LOWER SECTION

1) Crankcase lower section provides saddles for main bearings. When replacing, it is not necessary to remove old sealant. Clean grease from surfaces and apply Loctite 573 (Green) with a short-pile roller.

NOTE: **Use seal nuts for crankcase mounting to avoid oil seapage and possible oil pressure loss.**

2) Install lower section and tighten mounting nuts by hand. Install oil pump, two upper retaining bolts and tighten bolts. Tighten lower section mounting nuts to final torque in sequence. *See Fig. 5.*

Fig. 5: Crankcase Lower Section Tightening Sequence

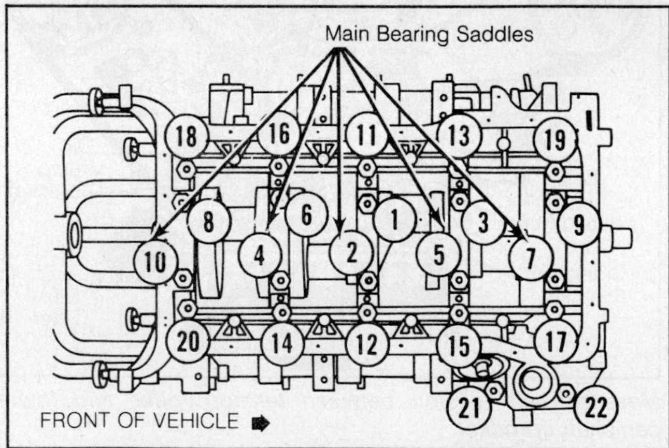
Main Bearing Saddles
18
16
11
13
19
8
6
1
3
9
10
4
2
5
7
20
14
12
15
17
21
22
FRONT OF VEHICLE

MAIN & CONNECTING ROD BEARINGS

1) Use Plastigage method for determining bearing clearance. Check crankshaft end play using dial indicator. Replacement bearings are available in standard and .25 mm, .50 mm and 75 mm oversize and undersize.

Porsche Engines

928S V8 (Cont.)

2) Install piston and connecting rod assembly with rounded edges of valve relief facing down. Ensure small chamfer on connecting rod faces rod on same journal and larger chamfer faces web of crankshaft.

CRANKSHAFT OIL SEALS

Crankshaft oil seals are installed with crankcase lower half removed. Use alignment tool (9126) to align flywheel end seal, and installation tool (9125) to install pulley end oil seal.

ENGINE OILING

ENGINE OILING SYSTEM

Engine utilizes a wet sump with an oil cooler integrated in the vehicle radiator as a heat exchanger. Sickle type oil pump is located in a separate cast iron housing bolted to the left front of the engine. Pump is driven by toothed belt.

Full pressure system pumps oil to pressure relief valve, thermostat, main oil passage, filter, crankcase upper section, cylinder heads and camshaft housings. All main oil passages are cast into the mating surface of the crankcase lower section.

OIL FILTER

Full-flow spin-on type oil filter is easily changed from beneath vehicle.

NORMAL OIL PRESSURE

Normal pressure is 87 psi (6.09 kg/cm²) at 4000 RPM and 178°F (80°C).

CRANKCASE CAPACITY

Capacity is approximately 7.9 qts. (7.5L) with filter change.

OIL PUMP

Removal

Hold oil pump drive gear with locking tool (9157) and loosen mounting nuts. Remove drive gear, oil pump mounting bolts and oil pump.

Inspection

With oil pump dry, check end play using tool (387), threaded adapter and dial indicator. End play should be .003-.005" (.08-.12 mm).

Installation

To install, reverse removal procedure.

ENGINE COOLING

An aluminum radiator and a mechanically driven visco-fan are utilized on 928S. Water pump is driven by the back side of the toothed timing belt.

An expansion tank with filler opening and water level sending unit is mounted at the right rear of the engine compartment. Water level is indicated on the instrument cluster.

COOLING SYSTEM CAPACITY

Capacity is 17.0 qts. (16.1 L).

THERMOSTAT

Thermostat opens at 178-185°F (81-85°C).

RADIATOR CAP

Radiator cap pressure relief valve opens at 12.8-16.4 psi (.9-1.2 mm).

ENGINE SPECIFICATIONS

GENERAL SPECIFICATIONS

Year	DISPLACEMENT		Fuel System	HP@RPM	Torque Ft. Lbs.@RPM	Compr. Ratio	BORE		STROKE	
	Cu. In.	Liters					In.	mm	In.	mm
1983	273	4.7	Fuel Inj.	234@5250	263@4000	9.3:1	3.82	97.0	3.11	78.9

PISTONS, PINS, RINGS

Engine	PISTONS	PINS		RINGS		
	Clearance In. (mm)	Piston Fit In. (mm)	Rod Fit In. (mm)	Ring No.	End Gap In. (mm)	Side Clearance In. (mm)
4.7L	.001-.002 [1] (.024-.050)	Interference	.0007-.0012 (.019-.032)	No. 1	.008-.015 (.20-.40)	.002-.003 [2] (.050-.082)
				No. 2	.008-.015 (.20-.40)	.002-.003 [2] (.050-.082)
				No. 3	.015-.055 (.40-1.4)	.0009-.0050 [2] (.023-.137)

[1] – Wear limit .003" (.080 mm).

[2] – For KS piston rings. For Mahle piston rings, No . 1 clearance is .002-.004" (.060-.102 mm), No. 2 clearance is .0015-.0026" (.040-.072 mm) and No. 3 clearance is (.013-.127 mm). Piston manufacturer must match ring manufacturer.

928S V8 (Cont.)

ENGINE SPECIFICATIONS (Cont.)

VALVES

Engine Size & Valve	Head Diam. In. (mm)	Face Angle	Seat Angle	Seat Width In. (mm)	Stem Diameter In. (mm)	Stem Clearance In. (mm)	Valve Lift In. (mm)
4.7L							
Intake	1.692 (43.00)	45°	45°	.067 (1.70)	.3498 (8.97)	.0010-.0020 (.030-.057)	....
Exhaust	1.496 (38.00)	45°	45°	.078 (2.00)	.3490 (8.95)	.0200-.0028 (.050-.077)	....

CRANKSHAFT MAIN & CONNECTING ROD BEARINGS

Engine	MAIN BEARINGS				CONNECTING ROD BEARINGS		
	Journal Diam. In. (mm)	Clearance In. (mm)	Thrust Bearing	Crankshaft End Play In. (mm)	Journal Diam. In. (mm)	Clearance In. (mm)	Side Play In. (mm)
4.7L	2.754-2.755 (69.97-69.99)	.0008-.0038 (.020-.098)	No. 3	.0039-.0157 (.100-.400)	2.046-2.047 (51.97-51.99)	.001-.004 (.034-.092)	.004-.016 (.10-.40)

CAMSHAFT [1]

Engine	Journal Diam. In. (mm)	Clearance In. (mm)	Lobe Lift In. (mm)
4.7L	2.38 (60.5)	.....	.....

[1] – End Play .004-.007" (.10-.18 mm).

VALVE TIMING

Engine	INTAKE		EXHAUST	
	Open (BTDC)	Close (ABDC)	Open (BBDC)	Close (ATDC)
4.7L	12°	48°	32°	6°

TIGHTENING SPECIFICATIONS

Application	Ft. Lbs. (N.m)
Cylinder Head Bolts	
Phosphated [1]	
Step 1	14 (20)
Step 2	36 (50)
Step 3	65 (90)
Zinc Coated [2]	
Step 1	14 (20)
Step 2	[3]
Step 3	[4]
Main Bearing Carrier	
10 mm Bolt	
Step 1	14 (20)
Step 2	29-33 (40-45)
12 mm Bolt	
Step 1	14 (20)
Step 2	29 (40)
Step 3	44-47 (60-65)
Connecting Rod Nuts	42-46 (58-63)
Camshaft	33 (45)
Camshaft Housing	14 (20)
Flywheel	65 (90)
Front Pulley	213 (295)
Camshaft Pulley	33 (45)
Oil Pump	
Step 1	11 (15)
Step 2	14 (20)
Spark Plugs	18-22 (25-30)
Oil Drain Plug	44 (60)

[1] – Grayish black color.
[2] – Yellowish gold color.
[3] – Turn nuts 90°.
[4] – Turn nuts additional 90°.

FUEGO, FUEGO TURBO & 18i 4-CYLINDER

ENGINE CODING

ENGINE IDENTIFICATION

Engine identification plate is located on left side of engine block above starter. First 3 characters show engine type.

ENGINE IDENTIFICATION

Application	Code
Fuego Turbo (1.57L)	A7L
Fuego and 18i (1.65L)	843

ENGINE, MANIFOLDS & CYLINDER HEAD

ENGINE

Removal

1) Remove battery. On 18i, remove engine undercover. On all models, drain cooling system at engine and radiator. Drain engine oil. Remove radiator grille (on 18i, remove parking light bulbs first), grille upper crossmember, radiator and cooling fan.

2) If equipped with air conditioning, remove cooling fans, disconnect condensor from radiator and place on bumper. Remove starter and exhaust heat shields, catalytic converter and air intake hose. Remove clutch cable and bracket. On 18i, remove alternator.

3) On all models, if equipped with power steering, remove pump and place it with lines attached on frame rail. If equipped with air conditioning, disconnect compressor and place on frame rail with lines. Disconnect all electrical leads, control cables, vacuum lines and coolant hoses that might interfere with engine removal.

4) Disconnect fuel lines and clamp to prevent tank drainage. Remove sending units from cylinder head. Remove upper engine-to-transaxle bolts. On Fuego and Fuego Turbo, remove electronic ignition module and sensor from clutch or converter housing.

5) On all models, remove flywheel shield, lower engine-to-transaxle bolts, and side engine bolts. If equipped with automatic transmission, remove converter shield and converter fixing bolts on drive plate. Clamp plate with converter locking tool (Mot. 582).

6) Attach lifting sling (Mot. 597) and raise engine until transaxle touches steering crossmember. Secure transaxle. Pull engine forward to disengage from transaxle. Remove engine from vehicle. If equipped with automatic transmission, attach retaining plate (B. Vi. 465) to prevent converter movement.

Installation

1) To install, reverse removal procedure. On manual transmission models, lightly grease clutch shaft splines and surface of clutch thrust plate with Molykote BR 2 grease.

2) Adjust clutch cable clearance. On automatic transmission models, lubricate converter centering housing in crankshaft with Molykote BR 2 grease.

3) Line up paint mark on converter facing part of driving plate blade sharp edges. Replace driving plate converter bolts. On Fuego Turbo, first tighten bolts and springs on catalytic converter flange, then loosen 1 1/2 turns.

CYLINDER HEAD

Removal

1) Disconnect battery. Remove radiator grille and upper crossmember. Drain cooling system at cylinder block and radiator. Disconnect wiring, cables and heater hoses at water pump. Remove catalytic converter. Remove water pump belt and air intake hose.

2) Remove distributor, valve cover, and diagnostic socket. Disconnect fuel lines and clamp to prevent tank drainage. On Fuego Turbo, disconnect connecting hose between turbo and air cooler. Disconnect oil feed line from turbo. Disconnect EGR hose.

3) On all models, unscrew rocker arm adjusting screws and remove push rods, arranging in proper sequence. Loosen cylinder head bolts and remove 6 inner bolts. Remove rubber washers and cups in spark plug recesses. Clamp rocker arm assembly with a rubber band or string around 4 end bolts.

4) Remove rocker arm assemblies. Unstick cylinder head from block by rotating cylinder head around centering dowel on distributor side. Tap each end of cylinder head with a plastic mallet on both right and left sides. *See Fig. 1.* DO NOT merely lift off cylinder head.

Fig. 1: Rotating Cylinder Head Around Centering Dowel

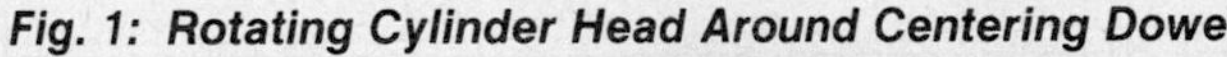

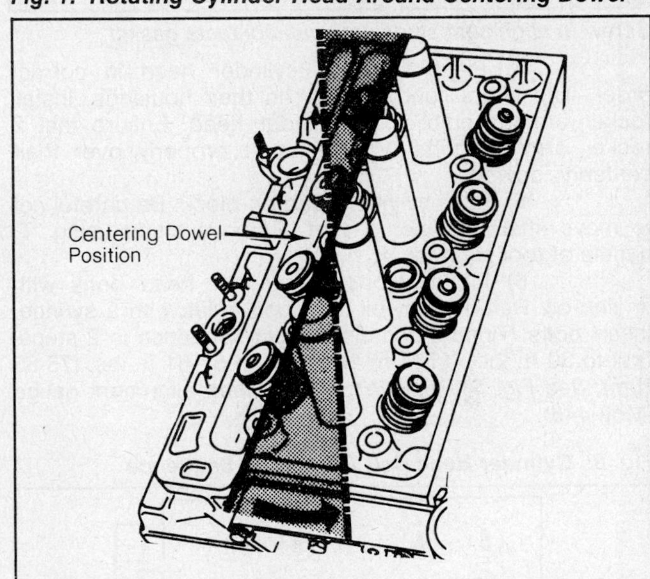
Centering Dowel
Position

DO NOT merely lift off cylinder head.

5) Raise cylinder head slightly and remove lifters, arranging them in sequence. Remove cylinder head and lifter chamber seal. Place liner clamp (Mot. 521-01) in position on cylinder block.

Installation

1) Remove old gasket pieces with Magnus "Magstrip" or Decaplock "88" liquid. Remove any oil from cylinder head bolt holes with a syringe. Check cylinder liner protrusion as outlined under Pistons, Pins & Rings.

2) Remove liner clamp. Ensure centering dowel and distributor drive gear are properly positioned in cylinder block. *See Camshaft & Timing Chain in this article.* Position cylinder head gasket. *See Fig. 2.*

3) Screw alignment studs (Mot. 451) into indicated positions until ball makes contact with cylinder head gasket. Install lifter chamber gasket, ensuring ends

FUEGO, FUEGO TURBO & 18i 4-CYLINDER (Cont.)

do not overlap with cylinder head gasket. Place alignment gauge (Mot. 446) in cylinder block hole. *See Fig. 2.*

Fig. 2: Alignment Gauge, Studs and Centering Dowel Positioning

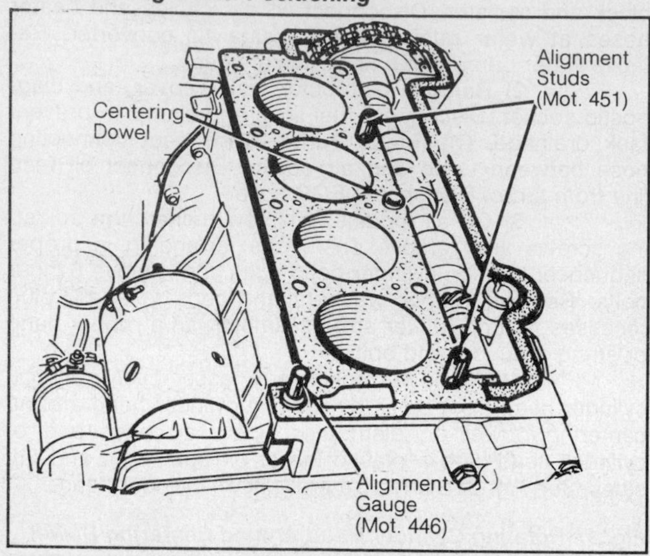
Alignment
Studs
(Mot. 451)
Centering
Dowel
Alignment
Gauge
(Mot. 446)

Screw in alignment studs until ball contacts gasket.

4) Place lifters in cylinder head in correct order. Tap lifters lightly to seat in their housings. Install rocker arm assemblies to cylinder head. Ensure that 2 rocker arm supports with holes fit properly over their centering dowels.

5) Place cylinder head on block. Be careful not to move lifter chamber gasket. Remove studs using "T" handle of tool set (Mot. 451).

6) Lightly lubricate cylinder head bolts with engine oil. Remove any oil from bolt holes with a syringe. Insert bolts. Tighten bolts in correct sequence in 2 steps, first to 30 ft. lbs. (41 N.m) and then to 57-61 ft. lbs. (78-83 N.m). *See Fig. 3.* Remove cylinder head alignment gauge (Mot. 446).

Fig. 3: Cylinder Head Bolt Tightening Sequence

8 4 1 5 9
FRONT OF VEHICLE
7 3 2 6 10

7) Insert push rods. Install remaining components in reverse order of removal and adjust valve clearance. Run engine until thermostat opens and allow to cool 2 1/2 hours. Loosen bolt No. 1 a half turn and retighten to 57-61 ft. lbs. (78-83 N.m). Repeat for remaining bolts in correct sequence.

CAMSHAFT

CAMSHAFT & TIMING CHAIN

Removal

1) Remove cylinder head, distributor and camshaft end bearing cover plate. Remove oil pan and crankshaft pulley. Remove timing cover and timing chain tensioner with thrust plate and filter. Remove 2 chain guides.

2) Remove crankshaft pulley key. Remove crankshaft sprocket and chain together using puller (Mot. 49). Screw bolt (Mot. 525) into crankshaft and then remove camshaft.

Installation

1) Lubricate camshaft bearings and slide camshaft in, but not all way. Place chain over camshaft sprocket. Line up mark on sprocket with center of crankshaft and camshaft. *See Fig. 4.*

Fig. 4: Alignment of Camshaft and Crankshaft Sprockets

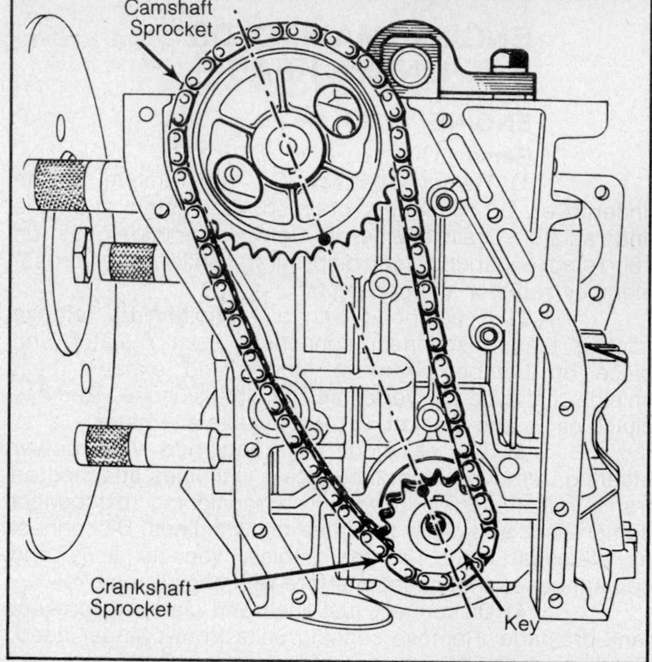
Camshaft
Sprocket
Crankshaft
Sprocket
Key

Line up mark on sprocket with cam and crankshaft centers.

2) Place key on crankshaft. Rotate crankshaft to bring key to top. Place crankshaft sprocket on chain. Timing mark must line up with camshaft sprocket mark as well as center of camshaft and crankshaft. *See Fig. 4.*

3) Place sprocket on crankshaft. Use tool (Mot. 525) to install sprocket, while gradually pushing camshaft into position. Insert and tighten 2 camshaft clamp bolts. Install chain tensioner with oil filter and thrust plate. Tighten bolts.

4) Install chain guides. If chain gauge (Mot. 420) is available, place on chain. Push 2 guides against gauge, tighten bolts and remove gauge. *See Fig. 5.* If gauge is not available, stretch chain and position guides so there is .012-.020" (.30-.50 mm) between chain and guides. Tighten bolts.

5) Install crankshaft pulley key. Install timing cover centering dowels and install timing cover to block. Install new oil seal as follows: Place oil seal over assembly sleeve of installation tool (Mot. 525).

6) Place assembly against timing cover and screw bolt into crankshaft until seal contacts timing cover. Install remaining components in reverse order of removal.

Fig. 5: Adjusting Timing Chain Tension Using Gauge

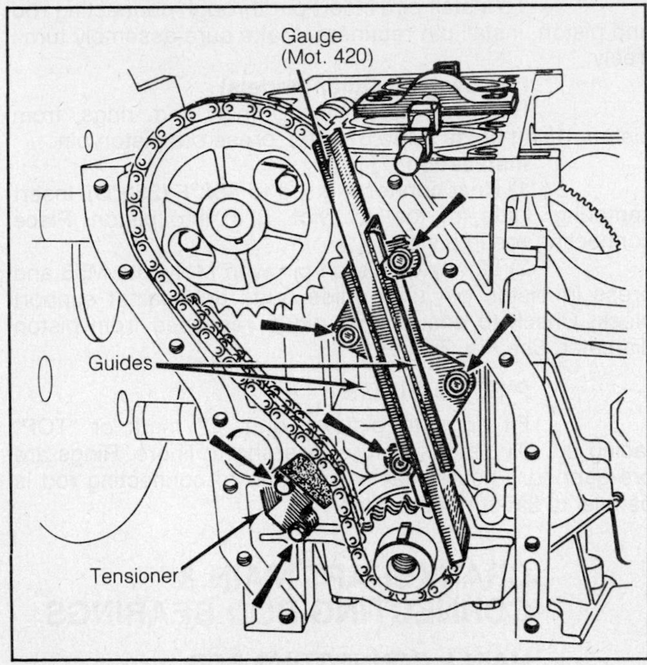

Gauge
(Mot. 420)
Guides
Tensioner

Broad arrows indicate tensioner and guide bolts.

DISTRIBUTOR DRIVE GEAR

1) Rotate engine to bring No. 1 cylinder to TDC. Install distributor drive gear with smaller offset toward camshaft. Drive gear slot should be in line with lube hole in cylinder block.

2) Angle formed by drive gear slot and a line perpendicular to camshaft should be 53°. Fill camshaft oil galley with oil and install rear camshaft bearing cover plate and gasket.

VALVES

VALVE ARRANGEMENT

Right Side – Intake valves.
Left Side – Exhaust valves.

VALVE GUIDE SERVICING

1) With cylinder head removed, lay cylinder head on wedge shaped block so guide is vertical. Valve guide angles are 23° for intake valves, 26° for exhaust valves. Push guide out with arbor press, using mandrel from (Mot. 356) tool set.

2) Examine valve guide and determine whether it is original or a replacement. Replace with next oversize. First oversize has 1 groove mark, 2nd oversize has 2 groove marks. Turn cylinder head over on block and ream guide bore for valve guide.

3) Ream to .519" (13.20 mm) for 1st oversize, .526" (13.35 mm) for 2nd oversize. Fit valve guide on end of mandrel with chamfer facing outward. Lubricate guide and press in until positioned correctly.

4) Distance between valve seat and end of valve guide should be 1.575" (40.00 mm) for intake valves, 1.220" (31.00 mm) for exhaust valves. Ream valve guide bore to accept valve stem using (Mot. 357). Recut valve seat.

VALVE SPRINGS

Removal

Disconnect battery. Remove valve cover and distributor. Remove cylinder head and mount on support stand (Mot. 330.01). Unscrew appropriate rocker arm screws. Compress valve spring with spring compresser (Faucom U 43-L). Remove split keepers, cap and springs.

Installation

To install, reverse removal procedure. Make sure valve spring is installed with closest coil spring spacing toward cylinder head.

ROCKER SHAFT

Disassembly

Remove retaining roll pin from rocker shafts. Note relative positions of parts, remove and clean them.

NOTE: Cup plugs at ends of shafts must not be removed.

Reassembly

Install 2 shafts into supports at clutch end of head. Install intake shaft retaining pin. Install remaining parts and install exhaust shaft retaining pin.

NOTE: Supports 1 and 4 are identical, with lubrication holes and locating dowel. Supports 2, 3 and 5 are identical, with no lubrication hole. The 2 shafts are also identical.

VALVE CLEARANCE ADJUSTMENT

Set valves cold. To adjust, rotate crankshaft until valve listed in column 1 of table is fully open, then adjust valves specified in second column of table. Set intake valves to .008" (.20 mm) and exhaust valves to .010" (.25 mm). Note that valves and cylinders are numbered from rear to front.

VALVE ADJUSTMENT SEQUENCE

Valve Open	Adjust
No. 1 Exhaust	No. 3 Intake & No. 4 Exhaust
No. 3 Exhaust	No. 4 Intake & No. 2 Exhaust
No. 4 Exhaust	No. 2 Intake & No. 1 Exhaust
No. 2 Exhaust	No. 1 Intake & No. 3 Exhaust

PISTONS, PINS & RINGS

CYLINDER LINERS & PISTON ASSEMBLY

Removal

Remove cylinder head, oil pan, and oil pump. Mark connecting rods and caps on camshaft side. Remove caps and bearings. Remove liner clamp. Remove piston and rod assembly from block with liner.

Installation

1) Check cylinder liner protrusion WITHOUT sealing "O" ring installed on liner base. Install dial indicator (Mot. 251-01) and measuring block (Mot. 252-01), measure protrusion. It should be .004-.007" (.10-.17 mm). *See Fig. 6.* If protrusion is incorrect, check with a new set of liners to determine if problem is block or liners.

FUEGO, FUEGO TURBO & 18i 4-CYLINDER (Cont.)

Fig. 6: Checking Cylinder Liner Protrusion

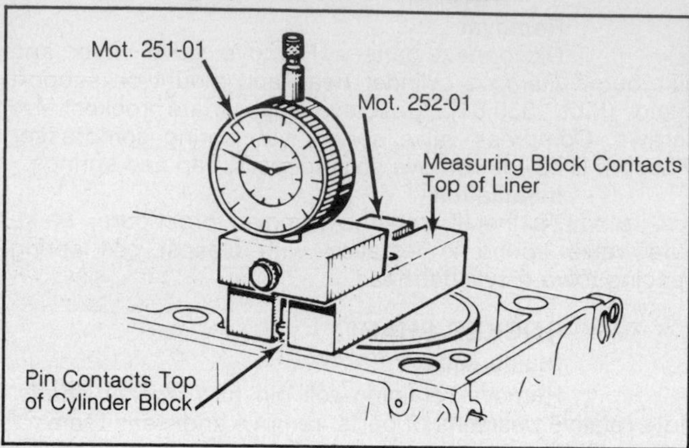
Mot. 251-01
Mot. 252-01
Measuring Block Contacts Top of Liner
Pin Contacts Top of Cylinder Block

Check protrusion without "O" ring installed.

2) Position liners with "O" rings installed so that difference in protrusion is not greater than .002" (.04 mm) on any 2 adjacent cylinders. Liners should also be stepped down from front-to-rear or rear-to-front. Oil piston and connecting rod assembly. Place piston assembly in liner using ring compressor (Mot. 851).

3) Tops of pistons are marked with an arrow pointing toward flywheel and have a spot facing same way. Flat surface of big end of connecting rod must be parallel to flat surface at top of liner. Connecting rod markings face camshaft.

4) Install liner clamp (Mot. 521-01). Place connecting rods with bearings on lubricated rod bearing journals and install matching rod caps and bearings. Install remaining components in reverse order of removal.

PISTON PIN

Removal (Fuego Turbo)

Piston pins are free fitting in both piston and connecting rods, and are held in by retainers. To remove piston pin, remove retainers and push out piston pin.

Fig. 7: Piston Mounting and Identification Marks

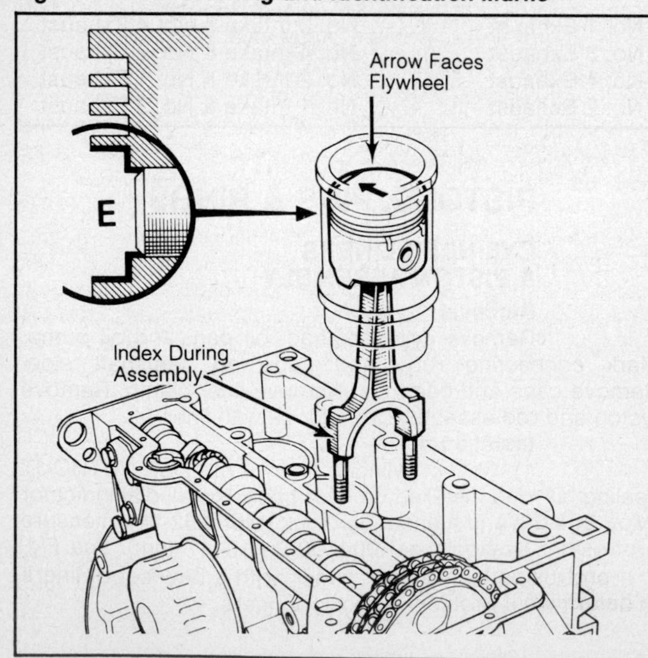
Arrow Faces Flywheel
E
Index During Assembly

Make sure piston pin is recessed in piston.

Installation

To install pin, insert pin through connecting rod and piston, install pin retainers. Make sure assembly turns freely.

Removal (All Other Models)

Remove piston from liner and rings from piston. Using press (Mot. 574-07), press out piston pin.

Installation

1) Heat connecting rod to 482°F (250°C). Insert centering guide (of tool kit Mot. 574) into piston. Place connecting rod in piston.

2) Lightly oil piston pin with Molykote M55 and press in piston pin until guide butts up against support block. Check to ensure that pin is recessed from piston diameter. *See Fig. 7.*

PISTON RINGS

Fit rings to pistons with "O" mark or "TOP" facing up. Oil pistons before inserting to liners. Rings are pre-gapped. Ensure that flat surface of connecting rod is parallel to flat surface on liner.

CRANKSHAFT MAIN & CONNECTING ROD BEARINGS

MAIN & CONNECTING ROD BEARING SERVICE

1) Remove cylinder head and oil pan. Invert engine and mark bearing caps. Remove connecting rod bearing caps and all main bearing caps except No. 1. Remove all bearing shells.

2) Remove No. 1 main bearing cap by tapping underneath with a hammer at each end. Remove oil seals, crankshaft, main bearings and thrust washers.

3) Use a micrometer and measure crankshaft journals. If any main bearing journal is worn beyond 2.148" (54.55 mm) or any connecting rod journal is worn beyond 1.880" (47.75 mm), crankshaft must be reground and fitted with new bearings.

NOTE: **Journals are roll-hardened. Make sure roll-hardening remains intact over a 140° section facing rotational centerline of crankshaft. See Fig. 8.**

4) Install upper main bearings (they have lubrication holes). Lubricate bearings and crankshaft journals. Fit crankshaft to block. Insert thrust washers with White metal face toward crankshaft. Fit main bearings No. 2, 3, 4, and 5 to caps (they have no lubrication holes).

5) Lubricate bearings and install caps without tightening bolts. Fit rear main bearing and cap. *See Rear Main Bearing Cap & Oil Seal procedure*. Use a dial indicator and check crankshaft end play.

6) If end play exceeds .009" (.23 mm) replace thrust washers to obtain correct specification. Fit upper connecting rod bearings and slide onto crank shaft. Fit lower half of bearing and tighten all caps. Ensure crankshaft is free to turn.

FUEGO, FUEGO TURBO & 18i 4-CYLINDER (Cont.)

Fig. 8: Crankshaft MUST Maintain Roll-Hardened Surfaces as Shown

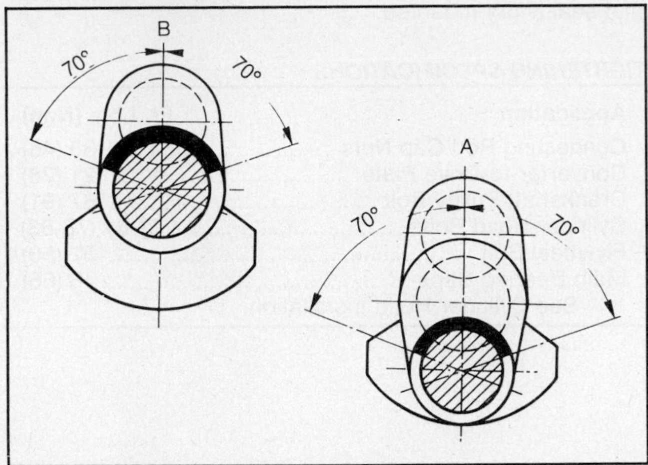

B
70°
70°
A
70°
70°

Roll-hardening must cover a 140° section.

REAR MAIN BEARING CAP & OIL SEAL

1) Insert bearing to cap. Temporarily install cap and tighten bolts. Measure dimension "C" between cylinder block and main bearing seal housing. *See Fig. 9.* If less than .20" (5.0 mm) select seals .201" (5.1 mm) thick. If greater than .20" (5.0 mm), select seals .213" (5.4 mm) thick (White marking).

Fig. 9: Measurement for Seal Selection

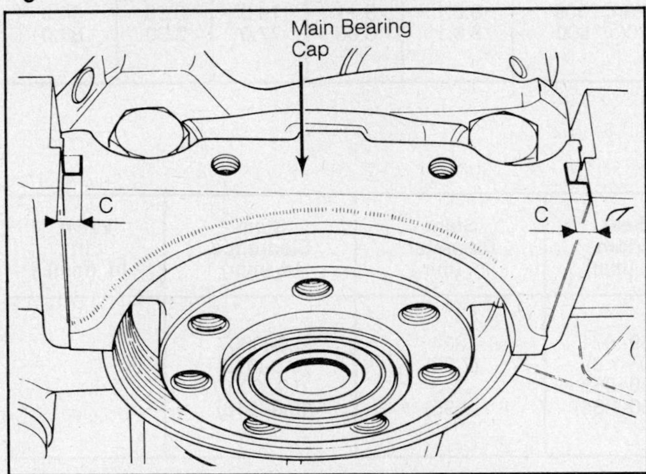

Main Bearing Cap
C
C

Measure between cylinder block and seal housing.

2) Remove cap. Place 2 side seals on cap with seal groove facing outward. Seal protrusion on cylinder block side should be .031" (.20 mm). Lubricate seals and bearing and install cap over 2 centering studs, placing foil shims between block and seals to protect seals.

3) When cap is almost in place, use a ruler to ensure seals still protrude slightly. Remove shims and studs and tighten bolts. After checking end play, lubricate new oil seal lips and drive in seal with (Mot. 259-01). Be careful of oil seal lip.

ENGINE OILING

CRANKCASE CAPACITY

Capacity is 4.5 quarts (4.3L) with filter change.

OIL FILTER

Oil filter is disposable canister type.

NORMAL OIL PRESSURE

Oil pressure should be 29 psi (2.1 kg/cm²) at idle, 58 psi (4.0 kg/cm²) at 4000 RPM.

ENGINE OILING SYSTEM

Engine oil is picked up in pan and pumped by oil pump through oil filter to passages in lifter chamber. It then travels upward through passages to lubricate camshaft bearings and downward through passages to lubricate crankshaft and connecting rod bearings.

It travels upward through a passage at rear of lifter chamber to rocker shafts to lubricate valve train and drains back to lifter chamber. At front of lifter chamber it travels through a passage to timing chain tensioner. Oil then drains back to oil pan.

Fig. 10: Engine Oiling System

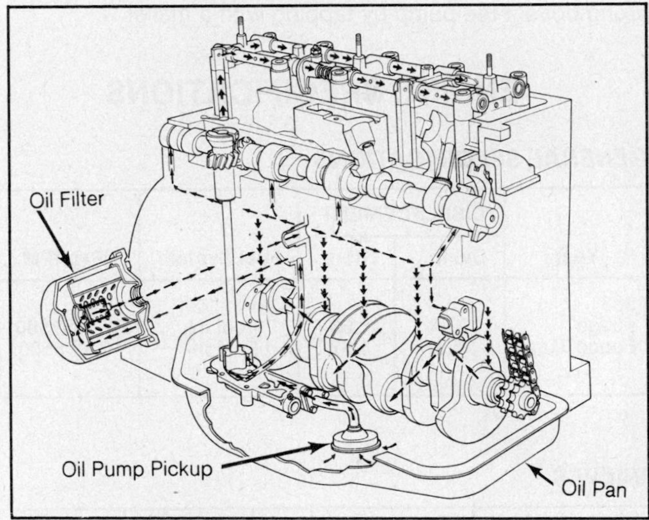

Oil Filter
Oil Pump Pickup
Oil Pan

OIL PUMP

Removal

Drain oil pan and remove flywheel protective cover (if necessary). Remove oil pan, oil pump and 2 pump rotors.

Disassembly

Unscrew suction pipe bolts. Remove cotter pin from pressure relief valve and remove spring cup, spring and piston.

Inspection

Check clearance of 2 rotors in positions shown in *Fig. 11.* Dimension "A" should be .002-.011" (.05-.28 mm). Dimension "B" should be .001-.006" (.02-.15 mm). If clearance exceeds specifications, replace rotors.

Fig. 11: Oil Pump Rotor Clearances

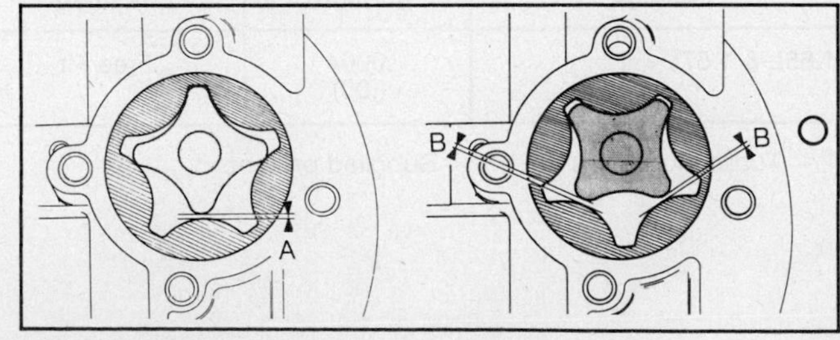

A
B
B

FUEGO, FUEGO TURBO & 18i 4-CYLINDER (Cont.)

Reassembly

Place piston, spring, and spring cup in pump body. Install cotter pin, suction pipe and gasket. Tighten bolts and bend lock plate over.

Installation

Install assembly with rotors to block. Install oil pan and new gasket.

ENGINE COOLING

COOLING SYSTEM CAPACITY

Capacity is about 7.5 quarts (7.3L). Fill at reservoir tank.

WATER PUMP

Removal

Disconnect battery. Drain cooling system and remove upper grille crossmember, grille, radiator and cooling fan. Remove water pump drive belt and pump fixing bolts. Free pump by tapping with a mallet.

Installation

To install, reverse removal procedure. Note that seal is dry mounted.

TIGHTENING SPECIFICATIONS

Application	Ft. Lbs. (N.m)
Connecting Rod Cap Nuts	33 (45)
Converter-to-Drive Plate	21 (28)
Crankshaft Pulley Bolt	67 (91)
Cylinder Head Bolts	[1] 57-61 (78-83)
Flywheel Bolt	37 (50)
Main Bearing Caps	48 (65)

[1] – See Cylinder Head Installation.

ENGINE SPECIFICATIONS

GENERAL SPECIFICATIONS

Year	DISPLACEMENT		Fuel System	HP@RPM	Torque Ft. Lbs.@RPM	Compr. Ratio	BORE		STROKE	
	Cu. In.	Liters					In.	mm	In.	mm
1983										
Fuego	100.5	1.65	Fuel Inj.	86.3@5500	86.3@2500	8.6:1	3.11	79.0	3.30	84.0
Fuego Turbo	95.5	1.57	Fuel Inj.	107@5500	120@2500	8.0:1	3.03	77.0	3.30	84.0

VALVES

Engine Size & Valve	Head Diam. In. (mm)	Face Angle	Seat Angle	Seat Width In. (mm)	Stem Diameter In. (mm)	Stem Clearance In. (mm)	Valve Lift In. (mm)
1.65L & 1.57L							
Intake	1.524 38.7	90°	90°	.059-.071 (1.5-1.8)	.314 (7.98)	0.0-.0007 (0.0-.018)	....
Exhaust	1.358 (34.5)	90°	90°	.039-.053 (1.00-1.35)	.313 (7.95)	0.0-.0007 (0.0-.018)	....

PISTONS, PINS, RINGS

Engine	PISTONS	PINS		RINGS		
	Clearance In. (mm)	Piston Fit In. (mm)	Rod Fit In. (mm)	Ring No.	End Gap In. (mm)	Side Clearance In. (mm)
1.65L & 1.57L	.0004 (.05)	Free Fit	Press Fit [1]	All	[2]	....

[1] – Turbo motor free fit. [2] – Supplied pre-set.

FUEGO, FUEGO TURBO & 18i 4-CYLINDER (Cont.)

ENGINE SPECIFICATIONS (Cont.)

CRANKSHAFT MAIN & CONNECTING ROD BEARINGS

Engine	MAIN BEARINGS				CONNECTING ROD BEARINGS		
	Journal Diam. In. (mm)	Clearance In. (mm)	Thrust Bearing	Crankshaft End Play In. (mm)	Journal Diam. In. (mm)	Clearance In. (mm)	Side Play In. (mm)
1.65L & 1.57L	2.157 [1] (54.80)	....	No. 3	.002-.009 (.05-.23)	1.890 [2] (48.00)	....	.012-.022 (.31-.57)

[1] – Limit 2.148" (54.55 mm). [2] – Limit 1.880" (47.75 mm).

VALVE SPRINGS

Engine	Free Length In. (mm)	PRESSURE Lbs. @ In. (Kg @ mm)	
		Valve Closed	Valve Open
1.65L & 1.57L			
Outer	2.138 (54.3)	....	117@1.201 (53@30.5)
Inner [1]	1.843 (46.8)	36@.95 (16.3@24.5)	....

[1] – Turbo motor has outer spring only.

CAMSHAFT

Engine	Journal Diam. In. (mm)	Clearance In. (mm)	Lobe Lift In. (mm)
1.65L & 1.57L	....	[1]	....

[1] – End play .002-.005" (.05-.12 mm).

VALVE TIMING

Engine	INTAKE		EXHAUST	
	Open (BTDC)	Close (ABDC)	Open (BBDC)	Close (ATDC)
1.57L Turbo	10°	50°	50°	10°
1.65L	21°	59°	59°	21°

LE CAR 4-CYLINDER

ENGINE CODING

ENGINE IDENTIFICATION

Type of vehicle and engine number is marked on a number plate riveted to the left rear side of the engine block. Plate is located just below cylinder head mating surface. First 5 digits indicate engine type.

ENGINE IDENTIFICATION

Application	Code
Le Car (1.4L)	847-25

ENGINE MANIFOLDS & CYLINDER HEAD

ENGINE

NOTE: **Engine and transaxle are removed as an assembly.**

Removal

1) Remove battery. Drain coolant from engine and radiator. Drain engine oil. Take out grille. Remove hood and inner fender support. Remove air cleaner.

2) Disconnect all electrical leads, control cables, vacuum lines and coolant hoses that might interfere with engine removal. Mark each item as it is disconnected. Remove transaxle cover.

3) Remove exhaust pipe flange. Remove radiator mounting nuts. Lift out radiator, cooling fan, and expansion tank. Disconnect steering shaft at flexible coupling. Do not lose rubber bushing.

4) Remove front wheels. Remove brake calipers without disconnecting hoses and support out of way. Disconnect tie rods at rack. Use tool and separate upper ball joints. Remove steering gear box. Be sure to index steering box shims.

5) Remove air pump complete with bracket. Remove top transaxle bolts on bell housing. Attach hydraulic hoist to engine. Remove nuts from engine mounts. Remove shift rod support bolts.

6) Disconnect clutch cable. Remove front transaxle mounting bracket. Slide transaxle to left, then to right to free axle drive shafts. Remove engine assembly from vehicle.

Installation

To install, reverse removal procedure. Grease transaxle input shaft and axle drive shafts. Do not damage oil seals on axle drive shafts. Make sure axle drive shafts fully seat. Adjust clutch. Refit steering rubber bushing. Bleed cooling system.

INTAKE & EXHAUST MANIFOLD

Removal

1) Disconnect battery ground. Remove air filter hose. Disconnect and plug carburetor heating hose. Disconnect choke, accelerator, fuel lines and vacuum lines. Take off carburetor. Separate exhaust pipe.

2) Remove manifold nuts and starter heat shield. Pull manifold from engine. It may be necessary to remove nut on left engine mount and tilt engine to right to gain enough clearance for removal.

Installation

To install, reverse removal procedure, replacing all gaskets.

CYLINDER HEAD

Removal

1) Disconnect battery ground. Drain cooling system. Remove air cleaner. Disconnect all hoses, vacuum lines, wires, and cables from cylinder head. Loosen air pump and take off belt. Disconnect exhaust pipe at the manifold.

2) Disconnect hood lock control cable and place out of way. Take off valve cover. Remove cylinder head bolts, only loosening bolt next to distributor 1/2 turn. Tap head until free. Remove bolt and head.

Fig. 1: Cylinder Head Tightening Sequence

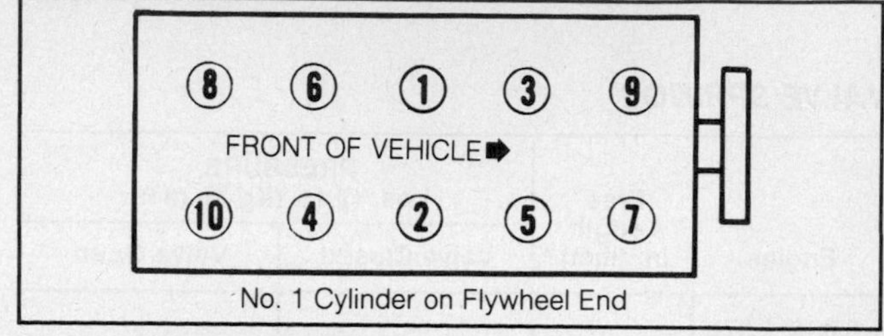
8 6 1 3 9
FRONT OF VEHICLE
10 4 2 5 7
No. 1 Cylinder on Flywheel End

Loosen in reverse order.

Installation

To install cylinder head, reverse removal procedure. Make sure new head gasket is installed with "HAUT-TOP" marking facing up.

CAMSHAFT

TIMING CHAIN

Removal

With engine removed and supported, remove timing cover. Wire tensioner shoe away from chain. *See Fig. 2.* Remove camshaft sprocket lock bolt. Use a puller to remove camshaft sprocket with timing chain. Chain will come off without disturbing crankshaft sprocket.

Fig. 2: Views of Timing Chain Tensioner

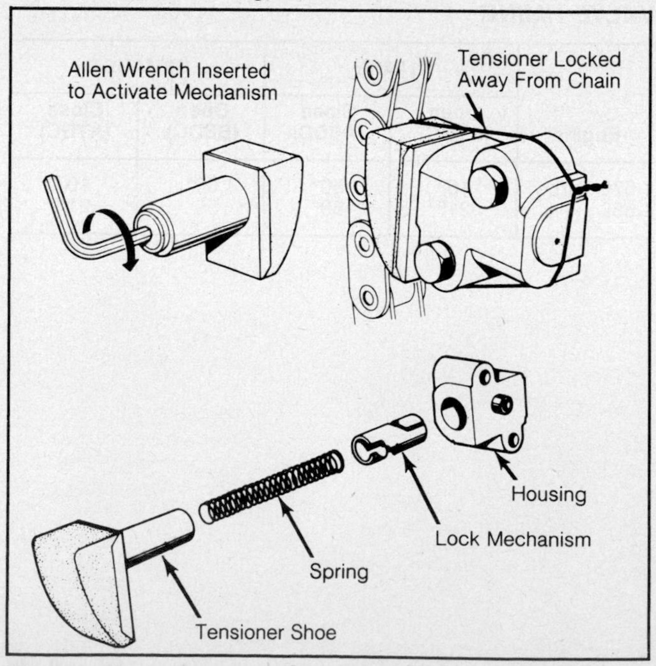
Allen Wrench Inserted
to Activate Mechanism
Tensioner Locked
Away From Chain
Housing
Lock Mechanism
Spring
Tensioner Shoe

Wire tensioner shoe away from chain during removal.

LE CAR 4-CYLINDER (Cont.)

Installation

1) Position chain on camshaft sprocket. Align camshaft reference mark with mark on crankshaft. Note position of camshaft and crankshaft keyway shown in *Fig. 3.* Using a small hex wrench, activate the tensioner mechanism.

Fig. 3: Index Mark and Keyway Positions for Timing Chain Installation (Engine Inverted)

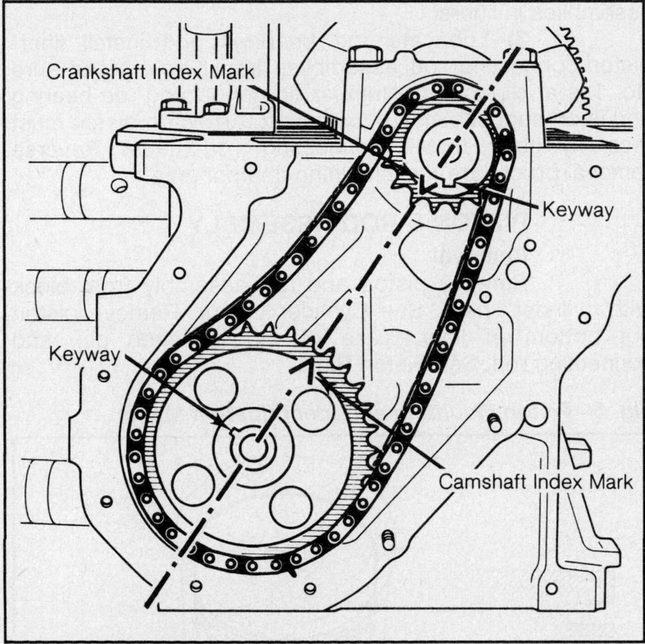
Crankshaft Index Mark
Keyway
Keyway
Camshaft Index Mark

Align reference marks to install chain.

2) Refit chain tensioner with thrust plate. Tighten mounting bolts and release load on automatic wear compensator tensioner. Release load by pressing down on bottom of tensioner body. Install new timing chain tensioner.

CAMSHAFT

Removal

Remove engine and support on stand. Remove cylinder head, distributor drive gear, oil pan, timing chain cover, and timing chain. Work through access slots in camshaft sprocket and remove 2 flange bolts. Carefully slide camshaft from engine.

Installation

1) Check clearance between camshaft sprocket and flange. Clearance must not exceed .002-.005" (.05-.12 mm). Lubricate camshaft journals and lobes, then refit the camshaft.

2) Install flange and tighten. Refit sprocket and tighten mounting bolt. Make sure all camshaft and crankshaft alignment marks are matched. *See Fig. 3.* Reverse removal procedure for remaining components.

CAMSHAFT OIL SEAL

Removal

1) Remove engine air cleaner, air pump, pump support and drive belt. Remove the serrated pulley from the camshaft. Remove camshaft bearing using puller (Mot. 876). Install a spacer of 1.0" (25 mm) diameter and 1.75" (45 mm) length between the camshaft and the bolt of tool Mot. 500.02.

2) Install tool with spacer and push past the seal. Expand the tool ends by moving ring expander as far in as possible. Screw in bolt and remove seal.

Installation

Place the new seal on tool Mot. 500.02. Install the seal on the camshaft and tap gently into place all the way to the centering spacer. Install the bearing using tool Mot. 876 with the tool grip facing outward. Install the remaining components in reverse order of removal.

VALVES

VALVE ARRANGEMENT

E-I-I-E-E-I-I-E (Front-to-rear).

VALVE GUIDE SERVICING

1) Measure O.D. of worn guide and replace with nearest oversize. Standard valve guide O.D. is .433" (11 mm). First oversize is .437" (11.10 mm) and is identified by 1 groove mark. Second oversize is .443" (11.25 mm) and is identified by 2 groove marks.

2) Ream valve guide hole in head to accept new guide. Size of reamer must be equal to outside diameter of new valve guide. To install new guide, lightly lubricate with oil. Fit guide to press with chamfer facing out. Seat guide completely in head. Finish ream valve guide bore to accept valve.

VALVE SPRINGS

Removal (Cylinder Head Installed)

Remove valve cover. Remove spark plug of cylinder requiring work. Loosen rocker arm as far as possible and remove push rod. Fit valve retaining tool in spark plug hole. Compress valve spring. Remove keepers, top cup, spring, and base washer. Check spring at free length and under a load.

Installation

To install, reverse removal procedure. Make sure valve spring is installed with closest coil spacing toward cylinder head.

ROCKER SHAFT

After cleaning rocker shaft components, remove clips and take off springs, rocker arms, and support

Fig. 4: Exploded View of Rocker Arm and Shaft Assembly

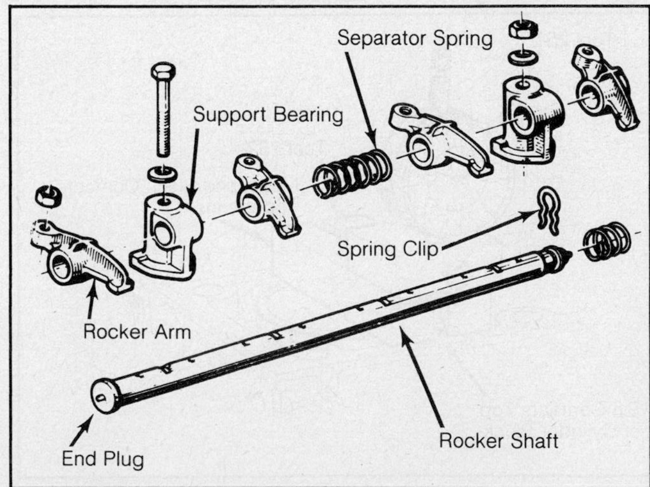
Separator Spring
Support Bearing
Spring Clip
Rocker Arm
End Plug
Rocker Shaft

LE CAR 4-CYLINDER (Cont.)

bearings. End plugs are press fit and cannot be removed. For correct reassembly sequence refer to *Fig. 4.*

VALVE CLEARANCE

Set intake valve clearance to .006" (.15 mm) cold or .007" (.18 mm) hot. Set exhaust valve clearance to .008" (.20 mm) cold or .010" (.25 mm) hot. Hot refers to an engine that has been operated at normal engine temperature and allowed to cool for 50 minutes.

VALVE ADJUSTING SEQUENCE

Valve Open	Valve to Adjust
No. 1 Exhaust	No. 3 Int. & No. 4 Exh.
No. 3 Exhaust	No. 4 Int. & No. 2 Exh.
No. 4 Exhaust	No. 2 Int. & No. 2 Exh.
No. 2 Exhaust	No. 1 Int. & No. 3 Exh.

PISTONS, PINS & RINGS

OIL PAN

Removal

1) Drain oil. Remove sway bar "U" brackets and pull bar down. Remove lower transaxle metal cover. Remove transaxle bolts that mount through gear shift bracket. Clutch protective cover must be removed.

2) Place a jack under front of transaxle to support it. Remove front pad. Raise transaxle front. Remove mounting bolts and tilt pan toward back of vehicle. Rotate crankshaft to provide clearance. Clean gasket surfaces.

Installation

To install, reverse removal procedure. Apply gasket sealer to rubber gaskets. Make sure pan side gaskets overlap bearing gaskets.

CYLINDER LINERS

Removal

1) Disconnect battery ground. Drain cooling system and oil pan. Remove air cleaner, cylinder head, oil pan, and oil pump. Fit liner clamp on head.

2) Index connecting rods and bearing caps. Remove connecting rod caps and bearings. Remove liner clamp and liner-piston-rod assembly.

Fig. 5: Checking Cylinder Liner Protrusion

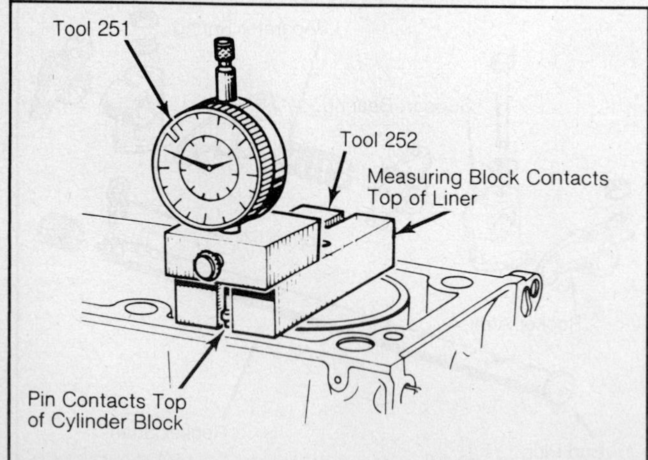
Tool 251
Tool 252
Measuring Block Contacts Top of Liner
Pin Contacts Top of Cylinder Block

Measure protrusion without "O" ring installed.

Installation

1) Check cylinder liner protrusion WITHOUT sealing "O" ring installed on liner base. Install dial indicator (Mot. 251) and measuring block (Mot. 252) as shown in *Fig. 5.* Protrusion must be .001-.004" (.02-.09 mm). If protrusion is incorrect, substitute a new set of liners to determine if defect is in liners or cylinder block.

2) Remove liners from cylinder block and install "O" rings on base of liners. Install the piston assemblies in liners.

3) Lubricate rod bearings and install liner-piston-connecting rod assemblies into block. Make sure No. 1 is at clutch end. Number on connecting rod bearing end is on opposite side of camshaft. Arrow on piston must face flywheel. Install connecting rod caps. Reverse removal procedure for remaining components.

PISTON & ROD ASSEMBLY

Removal

Remove piston and rod assembly from block with cylinder liners. See Cylinder Liners. Remove piston out bottom of liner. Take off rings, piston pin, and connecting rod. See Piston Pins.

Fig. 6: Piston Mounting and Identification Marks

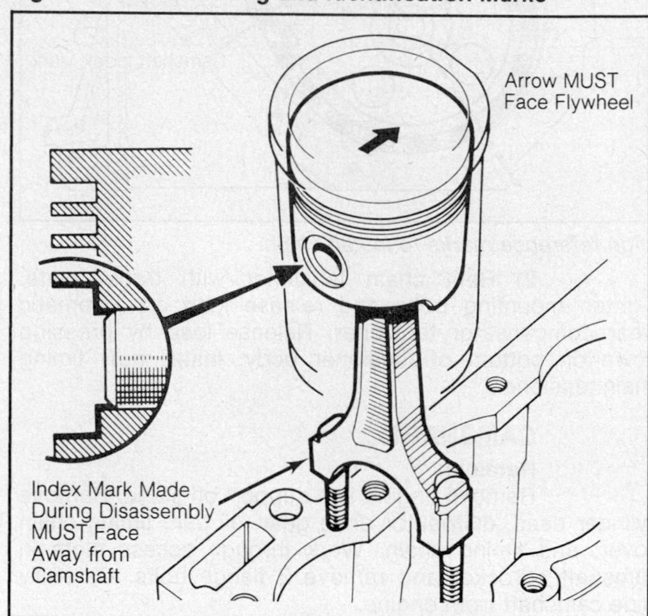
Arrow MUST Face Flywheel
Index Mark Made During Disassembly MUST Face Away from Camshaft

Reassemble piston and connecting rod as shown.

Installation

Fit piston pin. Fit rings. Piston rings are pregapped. Assemble with "O" mark or "TOP" facing up. Lubricate connecting rod assemblies with oil and fit to liner. Make sure machined side of connecting rod bearing is parallel with flat edge on liner top.

PISTON PIN

Removal

Remove piston assembly from liner. Remove rings. Using pin tool (Mot. 574), extract piston pin.

Installation

1) Position piston with arrow facing flywheel. Index mark made during removal on connecting rod must face away from camshaft. Heat connecting rod to 482°F (250°C). Slide new piston over installing mandrel and screw in locating plug (part of tool kit Mot. 574).

LE CAR 4-CYLINDER (Cont.)

2) Lightly oil piston pin. Push mandrel, pin guide, and pin assembly through piston by hand, until piston pin makes contact with rod. This procedure will automatically center and correctly space the pin.

CRANKSHAFT MAIN & CONNECTING ROD BEARINGS

MAIN BEARING SERVICE

1) Remove cylinder head and oil pan. Invert engine. Remove connecting rod bearing caps. Mark position of main bearing to block. Remove main bearing caps. Remove crankshaft, upper main bearings, and thrust washers.

2) Use a micrometer and measure crankshaft journals. If any main bearing journal is worn beyond 2.147" (54.55 mm) or any connecting rod journal is worn beyond 1.722" (43.73 mm), crankshaft must be reground and fitted with new bearings.

NOTE: **Connecting rod journals are roll hardened. Make sure roll hardening remains intact over a 140° section facing rotational centerline of crankshaft.**

Fig. 7: Crankshaft MUST Maintain Roll Hardened Surfaces as Shown in Illustration

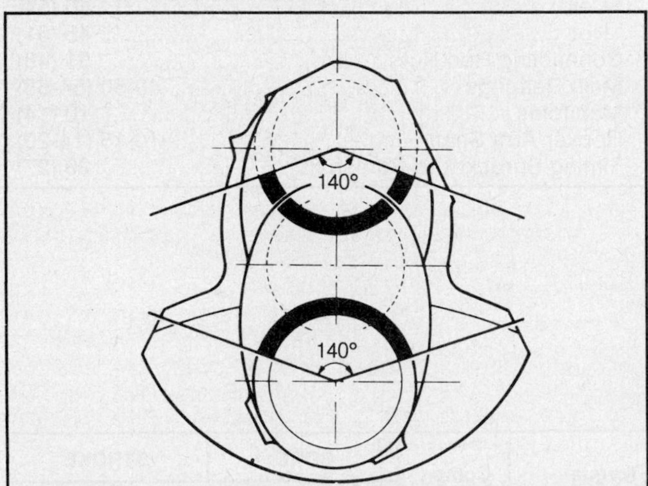
140°
140°

Hardening must cover a 140° segment.

3) Fit upper main bearings. Nos. 1 and 3 are identical. Nos. 2, 4, and 5 have 2 oil holes. Lubricate main bearing journals and fit crankshaft into position. Fit thrust washers with White metal toward crankshaft. Fit bearing to main bearing caps (those with no oil holes). Fit caps being sure to align with previously made reference marks.

4) Fit upper connecting rod bearings and slide over crankshaft. Fit lower half of bearing in cap, then tighten cap. Make sure crankshaft is free to turn.

5) Use a dial indicator to check crankshaft end play. Crankshaft should not have more than .002-.009" (.05-.23 mm) end play. Replace thrust washers if end play is beyond specification.

REAR MAIN BEARING OIL SEAL

With New Crankshaft

Fit new seal to installation tool Mot. 259-01 (or equivalent). Lubricate outer seal lip. Install seal in original position, seating it until the tool lip just contacts the cylinder block.

With Original Crankshaft

Offset new seal approximately 1/8" to position seal so it does not rest in same place as original. Drive seal into place with tool Mot 259-01 (or equivalent). Seal is seated when tool edge just touches block. Remove tool, insert 1/8" thick spacer, and repeat seating process to correctly seat seal into position.

ENGINE OILING

CRANKCASE CAPACITY

Capacity is 3.5 qts. (3.3L) with filter change.

OIL FILTER

Filter is the disposable canister type.

NORMAL OIL PRESSURE

Oil pressure should be 10 psi (.7 kg/cm²) at idle speed, and 50 psi (3.5 kg/cm²) at 4000 RPM.

ENGINE OILING SYSTEM

Oil is picked up in the pan and pumped through the oil pump and filter to a gallery with passages leading to main, connecting rod and camshaft bearings.

Oil from the front main bearing supplies the chain tensioner and returns to the pan. At the back of the main gallery, oil travels up a passage to the rocker arms and valve train.

Fig. 8: Engine Oiling System

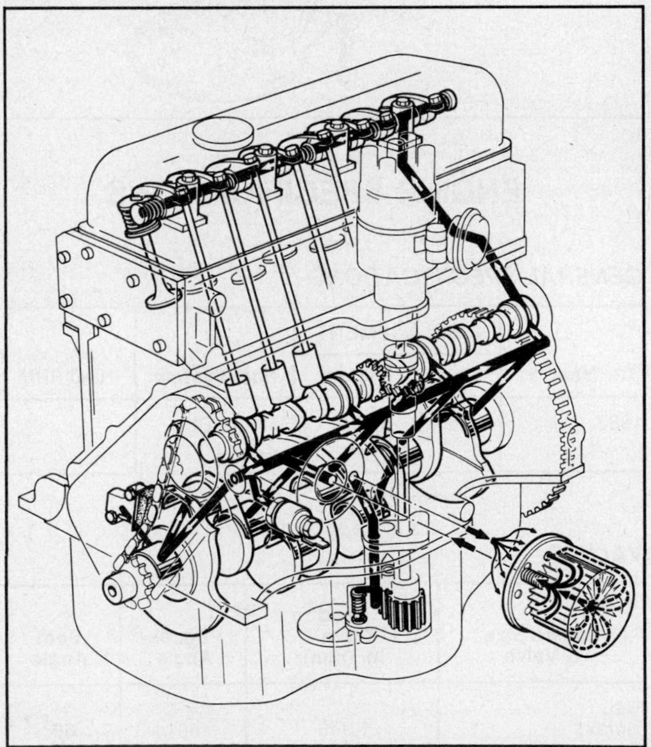

OIL PUMP

Removal

Drain oil and remove oil pan. Take out 3 bolts mounting oil pump and remove pump.

LE CAR 4-CYLINDER (Cont.)

Disassembly

Remove 4 pump cover bolts. Remove cover slowly, as relief valve is under spring tension. Remove driven gear, drive gear, and drive gear shaft.

Inspection

Examine splines on drive shaft. Check ball seat for damage. Check pressure relief spring for fatigue. Check clearance between gears and body. Replace gears if clearance exceeds .008" (.20 mm).

Reassembly

To reassemble oil pump, reverse disassembly procedure.

Fig. 9: Exploded View of Oil Pump Assembly

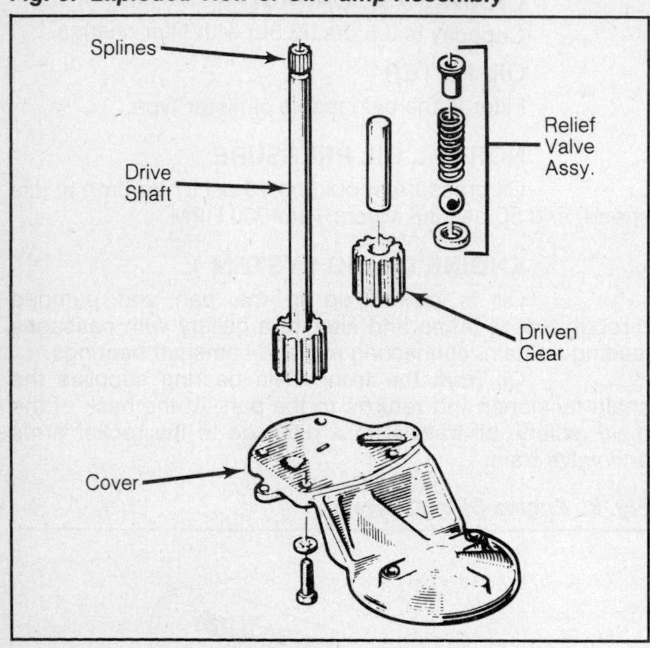

Splines
Drive Shaft
Relief Valve Assy.
Driven Gear
Cover

Installation

Install pump and mounting bolts. Do not use gasket between oil pump and block. Tighten the mounting bolts. To complete installation, reverse the removal procedure.

ENGINE COOLING

WATER PUMP

Removal

Disconnect battery. Disconnect hoses. Drain block at plug near timing cover. Loosen alternator. Remove water pump drive belt. Remove A.I.R. pump, water pump pulley, grooved belt, and temperature sending unit. Remove mounting bolts and tap pump free.

Installation

To install, reverse removal procedure. Be sure to bleed air from cooling system.

COOLING SYSTEM CAPACITY

Capacity is approximately 6.5 quarts (6.2L), including heater.

TIGHTENING SPECIFICATIONS

Application	Ft. Lbs. (N.m)
Cylinder Head Bolts	
Cold	40 (54)
Hot	45 (61)
Connecting Rod Nuts	35 (48)
Main Bearings	40-50 (54-68)
Manifolds	10 (14)
Rocker Arm Shaft	10-15 (14-20)
Timing Sprocket-to-Camshaft	20 (27)

ENGINE SPECIFICATIONS

GENERAL SPECIFICATIONS

Year	DISPLACEMENT		Fuel System	HP@RPM	Torque Ft. Lbs.@RPM	Compr. Ratio	BORE		STROKE	
	Cu. In.	Liters					In.	mm	In.	mm
1983	85.4	1.4	1x2-Bbl.	....	....	8.8:1	2.99	76.0	3.03	77.0

VALVES

Engine Size & Valve	Head Diam. In. (mm)	Face Angle	Seat Angle	Seat Width In. (mm)	Stem Diameter In. (mm)	Stem Clearance In. (mm)	Valve Lift In. (mm)
1.4L							
Intake	1.346 (34.2)	60°	60°	.043-.055 (1.1-1.4)	.276 (7)	....	....
Exh.	1.141 (29.0)	45°	45°	.055-.067 (1.4-1.7)	.267 (7)	....	....

LE CAR 4-CYLINDER (Cont.)

ENGINE SPECIFICATIONS (Cont.)

CRANKSHAFT MAIN & CONNECTING ROD BEARINGS

Engine	MAIN BEARINGS				CONNECTING ROD BEARINGS		
	Journal Diam. In. (mm)	Clearance In. (mm)	Thrust Bearing	Crankshaft End Play In. (mm)	Journal Diam. In. (mm)	Clearance In. (mm)	Side Play In. (mm)
1.4L	2.157 (54.80)	....	No. 3	.002-.009 (.05-.23)	1.731 (43.97)	....	.012-.022 (.30-56)

PISTONS, PINS, RINGS

Engine	PISTONS	PINS		RINGS		
	Clearance In. (mm)	Piston Fit In. (mm)	Rod Fit In. (mm)	Ring No.	End Gap In. (mm)	Side Clearance In. (mm)
1.4L	....	Free Fit	Press Fit	....	[1]	....

[1] – Pre-set gap. Do not alter.

CAMSHAFT

Engine	Journal Diam. In. (mm)	Clearance In. (mm)	Lobe Lift In. (mm)
1.4L	....	[1]	....

[1] – End play .002-.005" (.05-.12 mm).

VALVE TIMING

Engine	INTAKE		EXHAUST	
	Open (BTDC)	Close (ABDC)	Open (BBDC)	Close (ATDC)
1.4L	22°	62°	65°	25°

VALVE SPRINGS

Engine	Free Length In. (mm)	PRESSURE Lbs. @ In. (Kg @ mm)	
		Valve Closed	Valve Open
1.4L	1.65 (42.0)	....	80@1.0 (36@25)

900 & 900 TURBO 4-CYLINDER

ENGINE CODING

ENGINE IDENTIFICATION

Engine number is stamped on engine block and is located in the left front corner of the engine compartment. The 4th character of the number indicates whether the engine is turbo-charged or normally aspirated, the 5th character indicates automatic or manual transmission.

ENGINE IDENTIFICATION

Application	Code
900	
Man. Trans.	B20IMUC
Auto. Trans.	B20IAUC
900 Turbo	
Man. Trans.	B20SMUC
Auto. Trans.	B20SAUC

ENGINE, MANIFOLDS & CYLINDER HEAD

ENGINE

NOTE: Engine and transaxle assembly are removed as a unit. Transaxle housing is engine lower crankcase (pan).

Removal

1) Disconnect and remove battery. Disconnect windshield washer hose. Remove hood and drain cooling system.

2) Disconnect ground strap between engine and chassis and disconnect positive cable from starter motor. Disconnect servo vacuum hose at manifold and remove bellows between air flow sensor and intake manifold.

3) Clean area around fuel distributor lines and detach at connectors. Cover openings and plug fuel line ends. Remove air cleaner assembly along with mixture control unit. Disconnect EGR system (if equipped). Disconnect upper and lower radiator hoses and heater hoses.

4) Disconnect all ignition wiring connectors as well as sensors, emission control and electrical power connections between chassis and engine. Disconnect heating system and vacuum hoses.

5) Disconnect throttle control wire. Disconnect 2 hydraulic lines at power steering pump (if equipped).

6) On manual transmission models, disconnect clutch line from slave cylinder. Cap hose and slave cylinder opening, put gear lever in neutral, and drive front taper pin from shift rod joint. Separate joint from gear shift rod.

7) On automatic transmission models, remove protective cover from exhaust manifold (if equipped), and place gear selector in "P" position. Remove selector cable retaining screw, push back spring loaded sleeve on shift rod, and disconnect cable.

8) On all models, disconnect exhaust pipe at manifold. Disconnect speedometer cable at transmission.

9) Loosen clamps and remove bellows from inner universal joints at transaxle. Place spacer tool (83 93 209) between upper control arm and body so front suspension will be unloaded when car is raised.

10) Raise and support vehicle, then remove lower end piece from right side control arm. Remove rear engine mounting bolts and loosen the front engine mounting nut so mount can be lifted from the bracket. Attach lifting sling and slightly raise engine.

11) Move engine to the right and remove left universal joint, then move engine to left and remove right universal joint. Ensure that all cables and lines are free from engine and remove entire power unit from vehicle.

Installation

1) Ensure that universal joints are packed with grease. Fit new gaskets to the exhaust pipe flanges. Suspend engine and balance it so the front engine mount will locate in its bracket before the rear.

2) Lower the assembly, guiding the front mount into its bracket and continue to lower engine until rear of engine is 2" (50-60 mm) above mountings.

3) Move the engine to the right and guide in the left universal joint. Lower the engine carefully, guiding it into the mountings, and at the same time aligning the right universal joint. Ensure that exhaust pipe flanges line up.

4) Refit the right end piece to the control arm. Tighten universal joints and install rear engine mounting bolts. Tighten all engine mountings. To complete installation, reverse removal procedures.

CYLINDER HEAD & MANIFOLDS

Removal

1) Remove battery leads. Drain cooling system. Remove upper radiator hose. Remove PCV hose from valve cover. Remove wiring from distributor and temperature sending unit. Remove warm-up regulator and auxiliary air valve from cylinder head.

2) Rotate crankshaft to TDC position on firing stroke of No. 1 cylinder. Remove valve cover. Place a jack under the transmission case. Detach the stay between right engine mount and cylinder head and rotate it to one side.

3) Jack up engine slightly and support it with a piece of wood between cross member and transmission case. Detach and support the intake and exhaust manifolds. Detach the chainwheel from the camshaft but keep the chain hanging on the chainwheel.

4) Place the chainwheel between the chain guide and tensioner. Remove 2 timing cover-to-cylinder head bolts. Remove cylinder head bolts in the reverse of sequence shown in *Fig. 1.* Lift the cylinder head off block and remove from vehicle.

Fig. 1: Cylinder Head Tightening Sequence

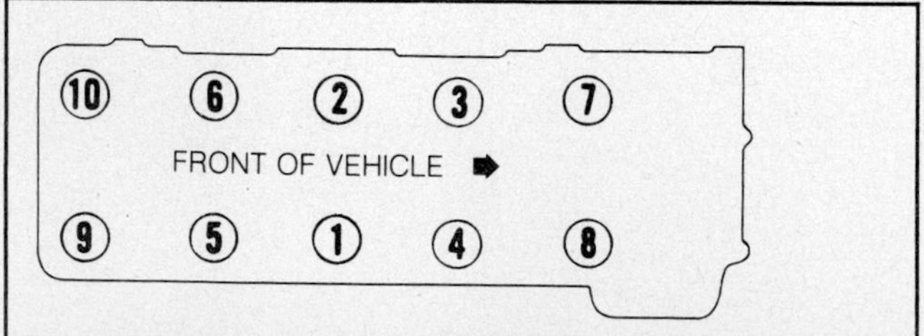
10
6
2
3
7
FRONT OF VEHICLE
9
5
1
4
8

Loosen in reverse order.

Installation

1) Place a new gasket on engine block. With crankshaft at "O" position, temporarily install the camshaft chainwheel and place camshaft at TDC position on No. 1

900 & 900 TURBO 4-CYLINDER (Cont.)

cylinder firing stroke. Position the chain on the chainwheel and place chain between chain guide and tensioner.

2) Install the cylinder head and tighten the bolts in 2 stages in the sequence shown in *Fig. 1.* Install the cylinder head-to-timing cover bolts. Take tension off of timing chain tensioner by inserting tool (83 93 357) into tensioner catch and pulling upward. *See Fig. 2.*

Fig. 2: Chain Tensioner and Tensioner Tool

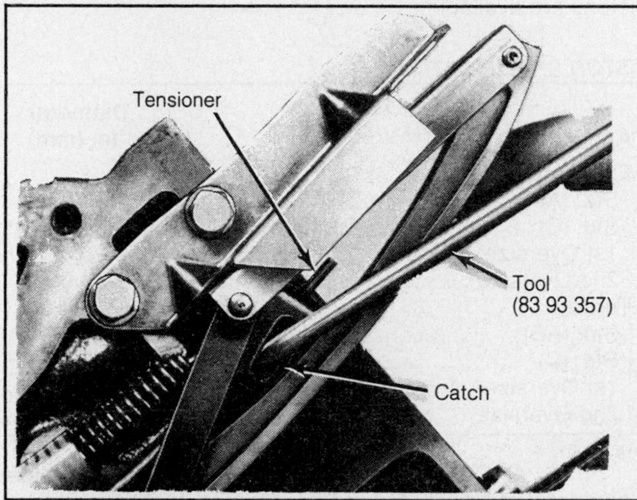
Tensioner
Tool
(83 93 357)
Catch

Shown in tension release position.

3) Place the chainwheel on the camshaft so that the marks on bearing cap, chainwheel, and screw holes align. If necessary, alter position of chain. Install the camshaft chainwheel retaining bolts using flat washers.

4) Using tool (83 93 357), push tensioner catch down to tension chain. To complete installation, reverse removal procedures.

NOTE: **Cylinder head bolts should be retightened in the following manner. Run engine until warm. Then, allow it to cool 30 minutes. Loosen each head bolt slightly, following proper sequence. Retighten bolts. Then, tighten each bolt an additional 1/4 turn (90°), following the proper sequence.**

CAMSHAFT

TIMING CHAIN ASSEMBLY

Removal

1) With engine removed from vehicle, place cylinder No. 1 at TDC of compression stroke. Remove valve cover. Remove chainwheel from camshaft and hang between tensioner and chain guide.

2) Remove crankshaft pulley and oil pump. Remove water pump. See Oil Pump and Water Pump Removal procedures. Remove 2 cylinder head-to-timing cover bolts.

3) Remove timing cover bolts and remove timing cover. Remove timing chain, camshaft chainwheel, tensioner and chain guide.

Installation

1) Ensure that both crankshaft and camshaft are in TDC position for No. 1 cylinder compression stroke. Install chain tensioner and chain guide.

2) Temporarily install camshaft chainwheel. Position the chain on the camshaft and crankshaft chainwheels and between the tensioner and chain guide.

3) Install the timing cover, oil pump and water pump. Take the tension off of the timing chain by inserting tool (83 93 357) into tensioner catch and pressing down.

4) Place the chainwheel on the camshaft sprocket so that marks on the camshaft bearing cap, chainwheel and screw holes align. Install the camshaft chainwheel using flat washers.

5) Tension chain by inserting tool (83 93 357) into tensioner catch and pushing down to turn catch over latch arm. *See Fig. 2.* To complete installation, reverse removal procedures.

CAMSHAFT

Removal

Remove valve cover and camshaft chainwheel. Hang chainwheel and chain between tensioner and chain guide. Remove camshaft bearing caps and lift out camshaft.

Fig. 3: Camshaft Timing Marks

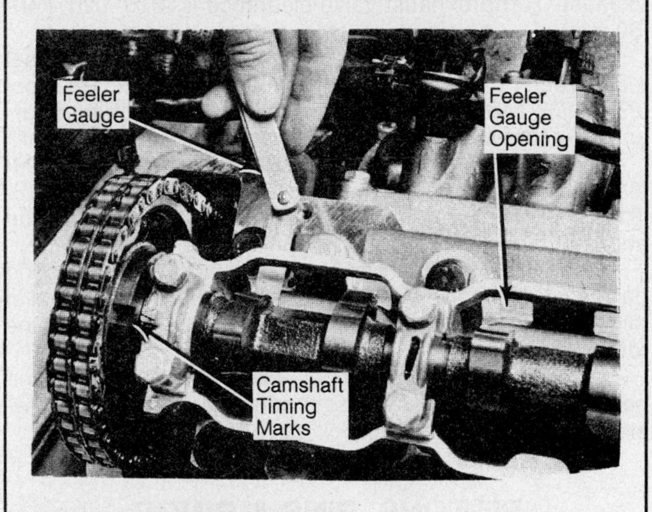
Feeler
Gauge
Feeler
Gauge
Opening
Camshaft
Timing
Marks

Align arrow on sprocket with mark on bearing cap.

Installation

Install camshaft and bearing assembly so that feeler gauge openings are at top. Ensure that crankshaft is still at TDC for No. 1 cylinder and reverse removal procedure.

VALVES

VALVE ARRANGEMENT

E-I-I-E-E-I-I-E (Front-to-rear).

VALVE SPRINGS

NOTE: **Valve spring replacement is possible without removing cylinder head from engine.**

Removal

1) Remove camshaft as previously described. Remove camshaft bearing support assembly. With cylinder head installed, take spark plug out of cylinder and fit air hose connector.

900 & 900 TURBO 4-CYLINDER (Cont.)

2) Supply air pressure to keep valve from dropping into cylinder. Remove valve depressors and adjusting pallets. Use a valve compressor and remove retainers (keepers) with a magnet.

Installation

To install, reverse removal procedures.

VALVE GUIDE SERVICING

1) To check for wear, pull valve about .12" (3 mm) from its seat and check radial play at valve head. If play exceeds .020" (.5 mm), replace valve and/or guide.

2) To replace guide, run hot water through head and pull guide from head using puller (8392631). To install, ensure that head is warm as in removal. Use guide tool (8392631) and press in new guide from the top.

VALVE CLEARANCE ADJUSTMENT

1) Check clearance with valve cover removed by rotating crankshaft so that cam lobe of valve to be measured points away from valve. Measure clearance with feeler gauge between heel of cam and follower.

2) Clearance should be between .006-.012" (.15-.30 mm) for intake and .014-.020" (.35-.50 mm) for exhaust. Turbo exhaust valve clearance is .016-.020" (.40-.50 mm).

3) If any valve clearance is beyond limits, direct measurement of all valve clearance is required. Use tool (8391450) and a dial indicator to measure actual clearance. Record clearance readings on all valves.

4) Adjust intake clearances if beyond .008-.010" (.20-.25 mm) and exhaust clearances if beyond .016-.018" (.40-.45 mm). Turbo exhaust clearance should be adjusted if beyond .018-.020" (.45-.50 mm).

5) Remove camshaft, followers and adjusting pallets of any valve requiring adjustment. Measure pallet thickness and add noted valve clearance to determine total clearance.

6) Subtract proper valve clearance to find needed pallet thickness. Install new pallets. Install followers and camshaft and recheck valve clearance.

PISTONS, PINS & RINGS

PISTON & ROD ASSEMBLY

Removal

With cylinder head and pan removed, note that rods and rod caps are numbered. Remove carbon or wear ridge from top of cylinders. Remove bearing caps and place plastic sleeves over rod bolts. Push piston/rod assembly out of cylinder.

Installation

Ensure that ring gaps are staggered and install ring compressor. Compression ring gaps should be equally spaced from each other. Notch on piston top must face timing cover and connecting rod numbers face exhaust side.

PISTON PIN REPLACEMENT

Piston pins are retained by circlips. Remove circlips and press out piston pins. Check pins and bearings for wear or damage and replace as required.

FITTING PISTONS

1) To fit pistons to cylinder bores, use a feeler gauge .500" (12.7 mm) wide and .0005-.0016" (.014-.040 mm) thick. Oil cylinder lightly and insert piston without rings.

2) Attach feeler gauge to a spring scale. Insert feeler gauge between piston and cylinder wall at right angles to piston pin. When feeler gauge can be pulled out of cylinder with a force of 1.8-2.6 lbs. (.816-1.18 kg), piston clearance has been determined.

3) Repeat test at several different depths in cylinder bore. Graded standard and non-graded oversize pistons are available.

PISTON SPECIFICATIONS

Application	Diameter In. (mm)
Exc. Turbo	
Std. (AB)	3.5425-3.5427 (89.980-89.986)
Std. (C)	3.5433-3.5437 (89.999-90.010)
1st Oversize	3.5619-3.5625 (90.472-90.487)
2nd Oversize	3.5816-3.5822 (90.972-90.987)
Turbo	
Std. (AB)	3.5421-3.5424 (89.970-89.976)
Std. (C)	3.5427-3.5434 (89.986-90.002)
1st Oversize	3.5614-3.5620 (90.460-90.475)
2nd Oversize	3.5811-3.5817 (90.960-90.975)

4) Check piston rings for end gap and side clearance, using an inverted piston to position ring in bore. On worn bores, measure at lower end of bore.

5) Install rings on pistons, staggering ring gaps. Compression ring gaps should be located above piston pin (180° from each other). Oil ring gaps should be equally spaced from each other.

CRANKSHAFT MAIN & CONNECTING ROD BEARINGS

BEARING SERVICE

1) Remove connecting rods and main bearing caps. Measure journals with a micrometer. Out-of-round should not exceed .002" (.051 mm). If crankshaft is near or over stated limit of wear, regrind journals and fit undersize bearings.

2) Using "V" blocks and a dial indicator check crankshaft for bend. If bend exceeds .002" (.051 mm), replace or repair crankshaft.

3) Using Plastigage method, check main bearing and connecting rod bearing journals. If clearance is found excessive, combine undersize bearings to correct clearance. Undersize bearings are available in various thicknesses.

THRUST BEARING ALIGNMENT

Center main bearing is thrust bearing. Check crankshaft end play. If beyond specifications, replace thrust washers with oil grooves facing crankshaft.

ENGINE OILING

CRANKCASE CAPACITY

3.7 quarts (3.5L) with filter for engines without turbo. 4.5 quarts (4.3L) for turbocharged engine.

900 & 900 TURBO 4-CYLINDER (Cont.)

OIL FILTER

Full-flow type.

NORMAL OIL PRESSURE

43 psi (3.0 kg/cm²) @2000 RPM.

PRESSURE REGULATOR VALVE

Valve is non-adjustable. It opens at 51-74 psi (3.6-5.2 kg/cm²).

ENGINE OILING SYSTEM

Oil pressure is generated by a gear type oil pump with one gear wheel and an eccentric ring gear. The pump is mounted on the timing cover and is driven by a crankshaft mounted driving plate. Oil is forced through a full flow filter and oil channels to crankshaft main and connecting rod bearings and valve train.

OIL PUMP

Removal

Clean area around pump. Immobilize crankshaft by attaching locking device (83 92 987) to flywheel ring gear. Remove crankshaft pulley retaining bolt and remove pulley from crankshaft. Remove oil pump retaining bolts and extract the pump.

Inspection

Using a straight edge and feeler gauge, check end float between pump body and gear wheel.

Installation

Oil the gear wheels. Install the ring gear so that the mark on its face is visible. Fit a new sealing ring in groove in pump body. Prime pump with oil and install to engine. Remove oil filter adapter casting and fill passage with oil. Reinstall casting.

NOTE: **It may be necessary to extract the pump gear slightly to locate it on driving plate.**

ENGINE COOLING

COOLING SYSTEM CAPACITY

10.8 qts. (10.0L).

THERMOSTAT

Thermostat begins to open at 190°F (88°C).

RADIATOR CAP

Opens at 12.9-17.1 psi (0.9-1.2 kg/cm²).

WATER PUMP

Removal

Drain coolant. Remove driving belt. Remove water pump attaching screws and remove water pump.

Installation

Clean gasket mating surfaces and install a new gasket. Install pump to timing cover. Install pulley and driving belt.

TIGHTENING SPECIFICATIONS

Application	Ft. Lbs. (N.m)
Main Bearings	79 (108)
Rod Bearings	40 (54)
Camshaft Bearing Caps	13 (18)
Crankshaft Pulley	137 (190)
Cylinder Head [1]	
Step 1	45 (60)
Step 2	65 (90)
Flywheel	43 (59)
Oil Pump	13 (18)
Camshaft Sprocket	14 (20)
Intake Manifold	13 (18)
Exhaust Manifold	18 (25)

[1] — Retighten as described in Installation procedure.

ENGINE SPECIFICATIONS

GENERAL SPECIFICATIONS

Year	DISPLACEMENT		Fuel System	HP@RPM	Torque Ft. Lbs.@RPM	Compr. Ratio	BORE		STROKE	
	Cu. In.	Liters					In.	mm	In.	mm
1983										
900	121	2.0	Fuel Inj.	110@5250	119@3500	9.25:1	3.54	90	3.07	78
Turbo	121	2.0	Fuel Inj.	135@4800	160@3500	7.20:1	3.54	90	3.07	78

VALVES

Engine Size & Valve	Head Diam. In. (mm)	Face Angle	Seat Angle	Seat Width In. (mm)	Stem Diameter In. (mm)	Stem Clearance In. (mm)	Valve Lift In. (mm)
2.0L							
Intake	1.654 (42.0)	44.5°	45°	.004-.008 (1-2)	.313-.314 (7.960-7.975)	0.02 (0.5)	.....
Exhaust	1.398 (35.5)	44.5°	45°	.004-.008 (1-2)	.313-.314 (7.955-7.980)	0.02 (0.5)	.....

900 & 900 TURBO 4-CYLINDER (Cont.)

ENGINE SPECIFICATIONS (Cont.)

PISTONS, PINS, RINGS

Engine	PISTONS	PINS		RINGS		
	Clearance In. (mm)	Piston Fit In. (mm)	Rod Fit In. (mm)	Ring No.	End Gap In. (mm)	Side Clearance In. (mm)
2.0L	.0006-.0016 [1] (.014-.040)	.0002-.0006 (.005-.014)	[2]	No. 1	.014-.021 (.35-.55)	.002-.003 (.050-.082)
				No. 2	.012-.018 (.30-.45)	.0016-.003 (.040-.072)
				Oil	.015-.055 (.38-1.40)	.....

[1] – Turbo clearance .0009-.0020" (.024-.050 mm).
[2] – Interference fit.

CRANKSHAFT MAIN & CONNECTING ROD BEARINGS

Engine	MAIN BEARINGS				CONNECTING ROD BEARINGS		
	Journal Diam. In. (mm)	Clearance In. (mm)	Thrust Bearing	Crankshaft End Play In. (mm)	Journal Diam. In. (mm)	Clearance In. (mm)	Side Play In. (mm)
2.0L	2.283-2.284 (57.981-58.000)	.001-.002 (.020-.062)	Center	.003-.011 (.08-.28)	2.046-2.047 (51.981-52.000)	.001-.002 (.026-.062)	.....

VALVE TIMING

Engine	INTAKE		EXHAUST	
	Open (BTDC)	Close (ABDC)	Open (BBDC)	Close (ATDC)
2.0L				
900	10°	54°	46°	18°
Turbo	12°	40°	62°	2°

VALVE SPRINGS

Engine	Free Length In. (mm)	PRESSURE Lbs. @ In. (Kg @ mm)	
		Valve Closed	Valve Open
2.0L	1.700 (43.1)	.....	170-183@1.161 (77-83@29.5)

CAMSHAFT

Engine	Journal Diam. In. (mm)	Clearance In. (mm) [1]	Lobe Lift In. (mm) [2]
2.0L	1.139 (28.94)	.....	Int. .425 (10.8) Exh. .433 (11.0)

[1] – End play is .003-.010" (.08-.25 mm).
[2] – Turbo lobe lift is .358" (9.1 mm) for intake, .413" (10.5 mm) for exhaust.

Subaru Engines

1600, 1800 & 1800 TURBO 4-CYLINDER

ENGINE CODING

ENGINE IDENTIFICATION

The engine can be identified by the sixth digit in the VIN on all models except those equipped with turbo. Turbo models can be identified by the sixth and seventh digits. The VIN is stamped on a metal tab located on top of the instrument panel near the lower left corner of the windshield.

ENGINE IDENTIFICATION CODES

Application	Code
1.6L 2WD	2
1.6L 4WD	3
1.8L 2WD	4
1.8L 4WD Non-Turbo	5
1.8L 4WD Turbo	55

ENGINE, MANIFOLDS & CYLINDER HEAD

ENGINE

Removal (Non-Turbo Models)

NOTE: **It is possible to remove engine with transmission fitted. Removal procedure given is with transmission remaining in vehicle.**

1) Disconnect battery cable. Remove spare wheel from engine compartment. Remove air cleaner assembly.

2) Disconnect fuel line from fuel pump intake. Allow fuel to drain into a suitable container. Drain radiator and engine block. Disconnect radiator hose at engine.

3) Disconnect all wiring to engine and accessories. On automatic transmission models disconnect oil cooler pipes. Remove all control cables and vacuum hoses from engine.

4) Remove upper radiator bolts, and lift out radiator. Remove nuts on each of engine-to-firewall struts. Remove strut by moving to rear to clear engine hanger. On vehicles with power steering, remove pump assembly and bracket.

5) On automatic transmission models, disconnect torque converter from engine by rotating crankshaft to allow removal of 4 bolts through timing hole. Use care that bolts do not fall into housing.

6) On manual transmission models, remove clutch return spring. Remove nuts from brackets on engine and firewall, and remove engine stabilizer.

7) On all models, remove engine-to-transmission bolts and nuts and disconnect exhaust pipe. Remove bolts securing front engine mounts to engine. Slightly hoist engine with chain hoist attached to front and rear hangers, and separate engine from transmission.

8) When separating engine from transmission, ensure that torque converter remains with transmission (automatic transmission only). Slightly jack up transmission during removal procedure. Remove engine completely and place on engine stand.

Removal (Turbo Models)

1) Open and support hood. Remove spare tire. Decrease fuel pressure. Remove ground cable. Disconnect air temperature sensor connector and remove spare tire supporter.

2) Remove fuel and evaporation hoses. Remove vacuum hoses and disconnect wiring. Remove link assembly and accelerator cable. Disconnect window washer tank and place behind right strut tower.

3) Remove power steering pump assembly and place on bulkhead. Remove air duct and air flowmeter boot. Cover openings to keep out dirt and dust. Remove upper cover.

4) Remove center exhaust pipe. Loosen bolts attaching converter cover and remove cover. Remove turbo charger body. Disconnect oxygen sensor connector.

5) Remove torque converter to flex plate bolts. Remove nuts and bolts from upper joint of engine with transmission. Drain coolant and remove radiator assembly.

6) Disconnect oil cooler hoses from pipe assembly. Disconnect heater hoses at engine. Remove front engine mount. Remove lower nuts joining engine to transmission. Connect sling to power steering bracket and pitching stopper bracket. Raise engine and remove from vehicle.

Installation (All Models)

To install, reverse removal procedure.

NOTE: **It is possible to remove engine with transmission fitted. Removal procedure given is with transmission remaining in vehicle.**

INTAKE MANIFOLD

Removal (Non-Turbo Models)

1) Disconnect negative battery cable. Remove air cleaner assembly. Drain coolant and disconnect all hoses from manifold. Disconnect throttle linkages, vacuum lines, fuel lines and electrical connections to manifold.

2) Remove EGR pipe from rear of manifold. Remove 6 manifold-to-cylinder head bolts, and remove manifold.

Removal (Turbo Models)

1) Remove wiring harness from intake manifold by disconnecting at: auxiliary air valve, throttle switch, FICD solenoid valve, thermometer CP, coolant thermosensor, and ground terminal at pressure regulator stay.

2) Remove pressure regulator and the following from intake manifold and throttle body: vacuum hoses, blow by hose, heater hoses, throttle body hot water preheat hose, and EGR pipe.

3) Disconnect at the manifold: throttle body assembly, auxiliary air valve, thermostat cover, thermostat and hose, thermometer CP, coolant thermosensor, PCV valve, air relief valve assembly, and vacuum pipe CP.

Installation (All Models)

After cleaning mating surfaces and installing new gaskets, reverse removal procedure.

EXHAUST MANIFOLD

Removal

1) Remove hot air intake hose from exhaust pipe. Disconnect O_2 sensor harness. Remove nuts which secure front exhaust manifold assembly to exhaust port of engine.

2) Remove bolts connecting front exhaust pipe with rear exhaust pipe. Remove bolt connecting front exhaust pipe with bracket of body.

1600, 1800 & 1800 TURBO 4-CYLINDER (Cont.)

Installation

1) When installing exhaust manifold, always use new gaskets and lock nuts. The manifold-to-engine gasket is installed with the FLAT side toward engine

2) To install, reverse removal procedure and tighten bolts to specified torque.

CYLINDER HEAD

Removal

1) Remove intake and exhaust manifolds. Remove valve covers, rocker arm shafts and push rods.

NOTE: Keep push rods in order for installation in original position.

2) Loosen cylinder head bolts in the sequence shown in *Fig. 1.* Remove cylinder heads.

Fig. 1: Cylinder Head Loosening Sequence

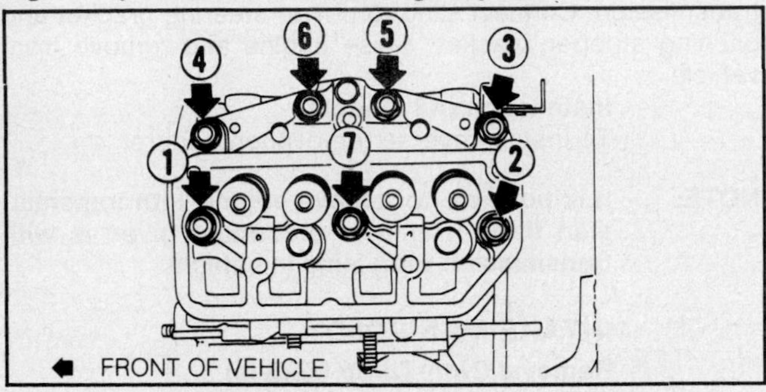
FRONT OF VEHICLE

Installation

1) Clean mating surfaces of cylinder head and crankcase so that they are free of oil, grease and dirt.

NOTE: Apply head gasket sealant Three Bond 1201 or Dow Corning 92-024 to both sides of new cylinder head gasket. Install gasket quickly after applying sealant.

2) Before installing cylinder heads, coat all nut and bolt threads with oil. Reverse removal procedure, tightening nuts and bolts in 3 successive steps. *See Tightening Specifications table for torque.*

3) After tightening all the cylinder head nuts and bolts, retighten the center nut (No. 1) to ensure it is correctly torqued.

CRANKCASE

DISASSEMBLY

1) Remove intake and exhaust manifolds and cylinder heads. Remove oil pump, oil pan and crankcase Allen head plugs. Working through hole in camshaft hole, straighten lock washers and remove bolts.

2) Position pistons at bottom dead center and remove circlip with long-nosed pliers. Access to No. 1 and No. 2 piston pins is through front crankcase plug holes. Access to No. 3 and No. 4 piston pins is through rear service holes. Remove pins and pistons, marking for reassembly.

3) To prevent upper crankcase lifters from falling out, use valve lifter clips (899804100). Separate crankcase halves by removing nuts and bolts.

Fig. 2: Cylinder Head Tightening Sequence

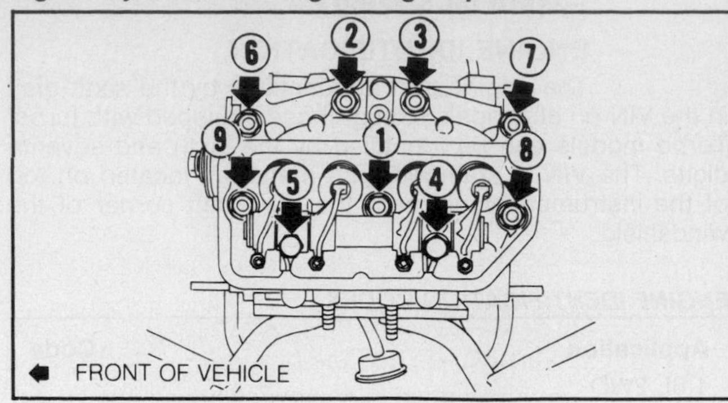
FRONT OF VEHICLE

Tighten all bolts to 47 ft. lbs. (64 N.m).

REASSEMBLY

1) Before reassembly, check for loose or bent stud bolts. When replacing stud bolts, coat threads with a torque-holding sealant (Loctite 270) before installation. Check crankcase-to-cylinder head mating surface for warpage, and correct by grinding if necessary. Warping limit is .002" (.05 mm).

2) Lubricate all friction surfaces with engine oil prior to reassembly. With bearings installed on the crankcase half having No. 2 and No. 4 cylinders, install crankshaft and camshaft.

3) Clean mating surfaces of crankcase and apply liquid gasket. Install "O" ring and backup ring on the crankcase half having No. 2 and No. 4 cylinders. Reverse disassembly procedure. Tighten crankcase halves and cylinder heads in sequence shown in Figs. 2 and 3.

Fig. 3: Crankcase Tightening Sequence

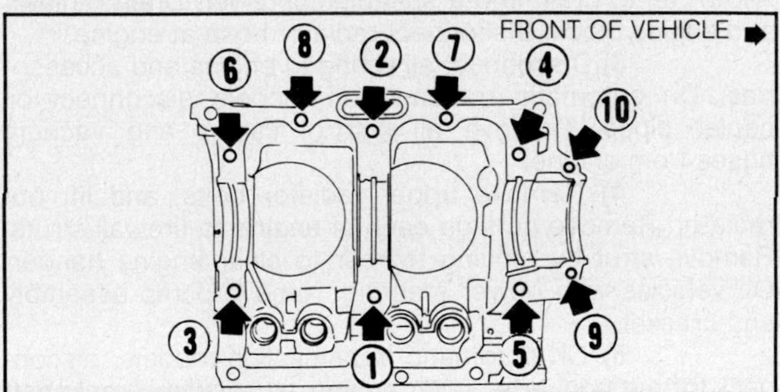
FRONT OF VEHICLE

Torque varies with bolt size.

CAMSHAFT

FRONT COVER OIL SEAL

Removal

Remove front pulley bolt and tap pulley lightly to disengage. Drive out old seal.

Installation

Install new seal using installer tool (499067000). Install crank pulley. Apply oil to pulley bolt threads and liquid gasket (Three Bond 1215) on the flange seat. Torque to specifications.

1600, 1800 & 1800 TURBO 4-Cylinder (Cont.)

TIMING GEAR

Measure camshaft gear runout with dial indicator. Replace camshaft if runout exceeds .010" (.25 mm). Measure backlash between camshaft gear and crankshaft gear. If backlash exceeds .0039" (.10 mm), replace camshaft gear. Standard value of backlash is .0004-.0020" (.01-.05 mm).

CAMSHAFT BEARINGS

See Crankcase in this article.

VALVE TIMING

With crankcase halves split, install crankshaft and camshaft so punch mark on camshaft gear is visible through chamfered hole in crankshaft gear.

Fig. 4: Aligning Camshaft with Crankshaft

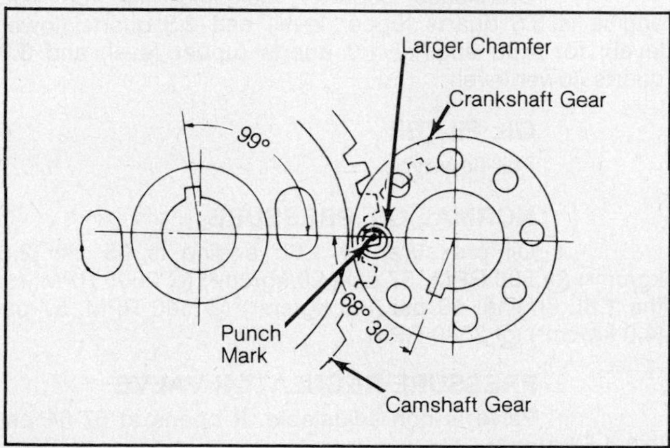
Larger Chamfer
Crankshaft Gear
99°
68° 30'
Punch Mark
Camshaft Gear

Camshaft gear mark should be visible through crankshaft gear chamfered hole.

CAMSHAFT

Camshaft may be removed when crankcase has been split. Check for wear or damage, replace camshaft if necessary. Using a dial indicator, check that bend does not exceed .002" (.051 mm).

NOTE: **If camshaft is replaced, all valve lifters should also be replaced. Check identification marks. The 1.6L engine uses camshaft marked "51", while 1.8L engine uses camshaft marked "72".**

CAMSHAFT END THRUST

Measure thrust clearance between camshaft and camshaft plate. Standard clearance is .0008-.0035" (.02-.09 mm). If clearance exceeds limit of .008" (.20 mm), replace camshaft plate.

CAM LOBE LIFT

Measure camshaft lobe height. If less than 1.269-1.273" (32.23-32.33 mm) overall, replace camshaft.

VALVES

VALVE ARRANGEMENT

I-E-E-I (Both banks, front-to-rear).

ROCKER ARM SHAFT ASSEMBLY

Check rocker arm shaft, rocker arm and bushing for wear or damage. Replace any worn parts. Pay special attention to the position and number of all spring washers, plain washers, spacers and rocker arms.

VALVE SPRINGS

Using a spring compressor, remove "O" ring, valve keepers and spring retainer. Check spring under pressure and at free length. Spring squareness must be within .083" (2.10 mm). Replace if necessary. Install spring with wide spaced coil (paint marks) facing valve spring retainer.

VALVE STEM OIL SEALS

Valve stem oil seals are used only on intake valves. Slide seal off of valve guide and replace with a new seal. When inserting stem, use care not to damage seal.

VALVE GUIDE SERVICING

1) Check valve guide for wear or damage. Using a drift punch, drive defective guides out through top of head. Press in new guide from top of head until it projects .689-.709" (17.50-18.00 mm) for intake valves and .886-.906" (22.50-23.01 mm) for exhaust valves.

2) Ream valve guide to provide correct clearance. Inspect valve seat to make sure it is true with guide. Reface valve seat if necessary.

VALVE LIFTERS

Remove lifters from crankcase. Inspect lifter for wear or clogged oil hole. Replace if lifter-to-crankcase clearance exceeds .004" (.10 mm). Standard clearance is .0012-.0028" (.030-.07 mm).

VALVE CLEARANCE ADJUSTMENT

With engine cold, rotate engine to TDC of firing stroke. Insert feeler gauge between rocker arm and valve stem. Clearances should be as follows:

VALVE CLEARANCE SPECIFICATIONS

Application	Intake In. (mm)	Exhaust In. (mm)
1.6L & 1.8L	.010 (.25)	.014 (.35)

PISTONS, PINS & RINGS

FITTING PISTONS

1) Measure cylinder bore .028" (.7 mm) from top of cylinder in line with crankshaft and again 90° from centerline of crankshaft. Also measure bore 1.48" (37 mm) and then 2.65" (67 mm) from top of cylinder.

2) After boring and honing, if cylinder bore diameter is .0197" (.50 mm) more than standard bore of 3.6205-3.6216" (91.960-91.990 mm), replace crankcase.

3) Measure piston 1.04" (26.3 mm) from bottom of skirt, 90° from piston pin hole.

NOTE: **Measurement of both pistons and cylinder bores should be performed at 68°F (20°C). All cylinders must be bored to same size and use same size pistons.**

1600, 1800 & 1800 TURBO 4-CYLINDER (Cont.)

4) Check piston ring end gap and side clearance. Check gap at bottom of cylinder bore. Fit piston rings with "R" or "N" facing up.

Fig. 5: Piston Ring Gap Position

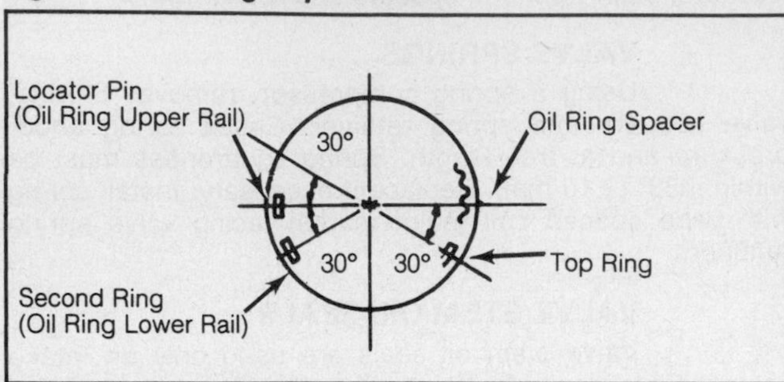
Locator Pin
(Oil Ring Upper Rail)
Oil Ring Spacer
30°
30°
30°
Top Ring
Second Ring
(Oil Ring Lower Rail)

PISTON PINS

Check piston pins for damage, cracks, wear or distortion. Check connecting rod bushing for wear. If pin or bushing are worn beyond specification, replace bushing in connecting rod, and ream to fit standard pin. Piston pin is a thumb push fit at 68°F (20°C).

CRANKSHAFT MAIN & CONNECTING ROD BEARINGS

MAIN & CONNECTING ROD BEARINGS

1) Check connecting rod side play with a feeler gauge. If side play exceeds specifications, replace connecting rod.

2) Use Plastigage method to measure both main and connecting rod bearing clearances. Main bearing inserts are available in standard, .001" (.03 mm), .002" (.05 mm) and .010" (.25 mm) undersize. Connecting rod bearing inserts are available in standard, .002" (.005mm) and .010" (.25mm) undersize.

NOTE: Position each connecting rod with the marked side facing forward. Make sure connecting rods are assembled correctly by checking their matching number. See Fig. 6.

Fig. 6: Connecting Rod Alignment Marks

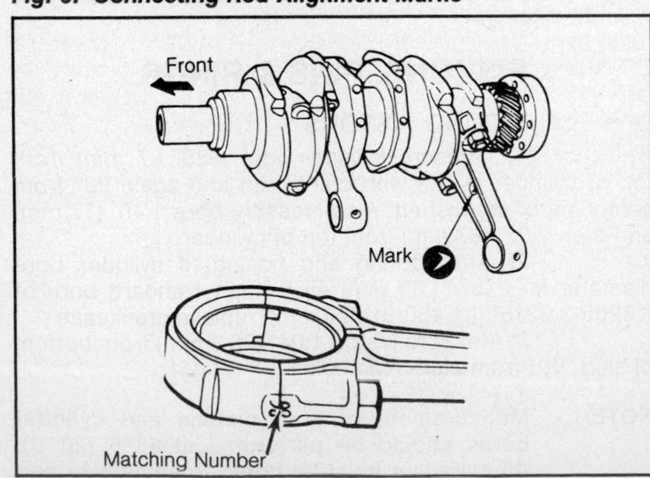
Front
Mark
Matching Number

Connecting rod mark should face front of engine.

3) Check crankshaft for bend by placing front and rear main journals on "V" blocks and fitting a dial indicator on center journal. Correct or replace crankshaft if bend exceeds .0014" (.035 mm).

REAR MAIN BEARING OIL SEAL SERVICE

Remove engine from vehicle. Flywheel or torque converter flex plate must be removed to gain access to rear seal. Pry oil seal from flywheel housing and coat new seal with oil before installation.

ENGINE OILING

CRANKCASE CAPACITY

Crankcase capacity including filer for 1.6L engine is 3.5 quarts (upper level) and 2.5 quarts (lower level); for 1.8L engine, 4.0 quarts (upper level) and 3.0 quarts (lower level).

OIL FILTER

Full-flow type.

NORMAL OIL PRESSURE

Oil pressure for 1.6L engine is 35 psi (2.5 kg/cm²) @ 500 RPM, 57 psi (4.0 kg/cm²) @ 2500 RPM; for the 1.8L engine, 50 psi (3.5 kg/cm²) @ 500 RPM, 57 psi (4.0 kg/cm²) @ 2500 RPM.

PRESSURE REGULATOR VALVE

Valve is non-adjustable. It opens at 57-64 psi (4.0-4.5 kg/cm²).

ENGINE OILING SYSTEM

Oil is pressure fed by a camshaft driven trochoid type oil pump. Pump incorporates an oil relief and by-pass valve in its body. Oil pump is located externally on engine. Oil from pump passes from main oil gallery to journals of camshaft and crankshaft. From there, oil goes to main bearings, piston pin bushings and cylinder walls. Oil passes through valve lifters and push rods to oil rocker arms.

OIL PUMP

Removal

Remove 4 attaching bolts and pull pump and filter forward. Remove oil filter from pump.

Disassembly

Remove screws, lift cover and rotor from pump body. Remove "O" ring. Remove by-pass spring and ball. Unscrew plug and remove washers, spring and pressure relief valve.

Inspection

1) Measure rotor-to-drive gear and rotor-to-body clearance. Measure rotor side clearance and measure diameters of rotor and drive gear. Replace any component that exceeds wear limits.

2) Inspect relief valve spring, valve and pump body for wear or damage.

NOTE: Make sure oil pump shaft is aligned with slot in camshaft when reassembling.

Reassembly

Reassemble in reverse order, using all new gaskets and "O" rings.

1600, 1800 & 1800 TURBO 4-CYLINDER (Cont.)

Installation

Install oil filter on pump. Using rearward movement reinstall oil pump and four attaching bolts.

OIL PUMP CLEARANCES

Application	In. (mm)
Rotor-to-Drive Gear	.0008-.0047 (.02-.11)
Outer Rotor-to-Body	.0012-.0051 (.03-.13)
Rotor Side Clearance	.0059-.0083 (.15-.21)

OIL PUMP DIMENSIONS

Application	In. (mm)
Drive Gear O.D.	1.1693-1.1709 (29.70-29.74)
Rotor O.D.	1.5957-1.5968 (40.53-40.56)
Relief Valve Spring Free Length	1.851 (47.10)

ENGINE COOLING

COOLANT DRAINING

A coolant drain plug is provided at the lower right corner of the radiator.

COOLANT CAPACITY

The coolant capacity is 5.6 qts. (5.3L) for 1.6L engine and 5.8 qts. (5.5L) for the 1.8L engine.

THERMOSTAT

For both 1.6L and 1.8L engines, the thermostat starts to open at 190°F (88°C) and fully opens at 208°F (98°C).

WATER PUMP

Removal

Drain coolant and disconnect main radiator outlet hose and by-pass hose. Remove drive belt and attaching bolts. Remove water pump.

Disassembly

1) Remove 4 screws attaching cover plate and gasket. Press pulley off shaft.

NOTE: **To prevent bearing damage, do not press the shaft. Press the bearing outer race during disassembly or assembly.**

2) Pressing on outer race, press pump shaft from body. Press the impeller from pump shaft, and remove mechanical seal.

Reassembly

1) Before assembly, heat pump body to 176-212°F (80-100°C). Pressing on outer race, press pump shaft into body. Apply liquid gasket to outer edge of seal, and press into pump body with carbon washer facing impeller.

2) Press impeller onto shaft until impeller-to-body clearance is .020-.028" (.5-.7 mm).

3) Support impeller side of pump shaft. Press on pulley until distance between center of pulley groove and rear face of pump housing is 2.524-2.547" (64.1-64.7 mm) for 1600 cc engine or 2.406-2.429" (61.1-61.7mm) for 1800 cc engine.

Installation

Install water pump, new gasket, drive belt and hoses. Gradually tighten bolts alternately and evenly in several steps to prevent leakage. The clamps for the water hose should be positioned low to prevent interference with EGR pipe.

Fig. 7: Exploded View of Water Pump

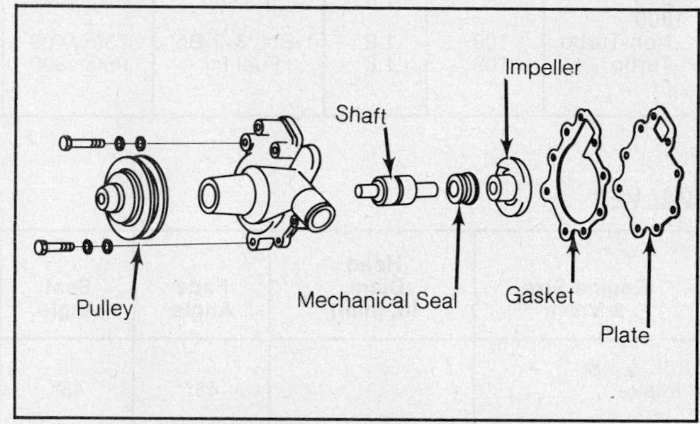
Impeller
Shaft
Pulley
Mechanical Seal
Gasket
Plate

ELECTRIC COOLING FAN

All models are equipped with an electric cooling fan motor. Two different fan motors (Hitachi and Mitsuba) are used on vehicles. They are not interchangeable.

TIGHTENING SPECIFICATIONS

Application	Ft. Lbs. (N.m)
Cylinder Head	
Step 1	22 (30)
Step 2	43 (58)
Step 3	47 (64)
Connecting Rod Nuts	29-31 (39-42)
Crankshaft Pulley	47-54 (64-73)
Crankcase Plug	46-56 (63-76)
Crankcase Halves	
6 mm Bolts	3-4 (4-5)
8 mm Bolts	17-20 (23-27)
10 mm Bolts	29-35 (39-48)
Intake Manifold	13-16 (18-22)
Flywheel	30-33 (41-45)
Rocker Arm	47 (64)

1600, 1800 & 1800 TURBO 4-CYLINDER (Cont.)

ENGINE SPECIFICATIONS

GENERAL SPECIFICATIONS

Year	DISPLACEMENT		Fuel System	HP@RPM	Torque Ft. Lbs.@RPM	Compr. Ratio	BORE		STROKE	
	Cu. In.	Liters					In.	mm	In.	mm
1983										
1600	97	1.6	2-Bbl.	69@4800	86@2800	9.0: 1	3.62	92	2.36	60
1800										
Non-Turbo	109	1.8	1-Bbl. & 2-Bbl.	73@4400	94@2400	8.7: 1	3.62	92	2.64	67
Turbo	109	1.8	Fuel Inj.	95@4800	123@2000	7.7: 1	3.62	92	2.64	67

VALVES

Engine Size & Valve	Head Diam. In. (mm)	Face Angle	Seat Angle	Seat Width In. (mm)	Stem Diameter In. (mm)	Stem Clearance In. (mm)	Valve Lift In. (mm)
1.6L & 1.8L							
Intake	.....	45°	45°	.028-.051 (.7-1.3)	.3130-.3136 (7.950-7.965)	.0014-.0026 (.035-.065)	.....
Exhaust	.....	45°	45°	.039-.071 (1.0-1.8)	.3128-.3134 (7.945-7.960)	.0016-.0028 (.040-.070)	....

PISTONS, PINS, RINGS

Engine	PISTONS	PINS		RINGS		
	Clearance In. (mm)	Piston Fit In. (mm)	Rod Fit In. (mm)	Ring No.	End Gap In. (mm)	Side Clearance In. (mm)
1.6L & 1.8L	.0004-.0016 (.010-.040)	.0002-.0004 (.004-.010)	0-.0009 (0-.022)	No.1	.0079-.0138 [1] (.20-.35)	.0016-.0031 [3] (.04-.08)
				No. 2	.0079-.0138 [1] (.20-.35)	.0012-.0028 [3] (.03-.07)
				No. 3	.0079-.0354 [2] (.20-.90)	.....

[1] – Limit .0591" (1.5mm). [2] – Limit .07987" (2.0 mm). [3] – Limit .0059" (.15 mm).

CRANKSHAFT MAIN & CONNECTING ROD BEARINGS

Engine	MAIN BEARINGS				CONNECTING ROD BEARINGS		
	Journal Diam. In. (mm)	Clearance In. (mm)	Thrust Bearing	Crankshaft End Play In. (mm)	Journal Diam. In. (mm)	Clearance In. (mm)	Side Play In. (mm)
1.6L							
Front & Rear	1.9668-1.9673 (49.957-49.970)	.0004-.0014 [1] (.010-.035)	Center	.0004-.0037 [2] (.010-.095)	1.7715-1.7720 (44.995-45.010)	.0008-.0028 [3] (.020-.070)	.0028-.013 [4] (.07-.33)
Center	1.9673-1.9678 (49.970-49.982)	.0004-.0012 (.010-.030)					
1.8L							
Front & Rear	2.1636-2.1642 (54.995-54.970)	.0004-.0012 (.010-.030)	Center	.0004-.0037 (.010-.095)	1.7715-1.7720 (44.995-45.010)	.0008-.0028 (.020-.070)	.0028-.013 (.07-.33)
Center	2.1636-2.1642 (54.995-54.970)	.0004-.0010 (.010-.025)					

[1] – Limit front and rear, .0022" (.55mm); limit center, .0018" (.045 mm). [2] – Limit .0118" (.30 mm). [3] – Limit .0039" (.10 mm).
[4] – Limit .016" (.40 mm).

1600, 1800 & 1800 TURBO 4-CYLINDER (Cont.)

ENGINE SPECIFICATIONS (Cont.)

VALVE TIMING

Engine	INTAKE		EXHAUST	
	Open (BTDC)	Close (ABDC)	Open (BBDC)	Close (ATDC)
1.6L	20°	60°	60°	20°
1.8L				
Manual	20°	60°	60°	20°
Automatic	20°	64°	64°	20°
Turbo	16°	68°	68°	20°

VALVE SPRINGS

Engine	Free Length In. (mm)	PRESSURE Lbs. @ In. (Kg @ mm)	
		Valve Closed	Valve Open
1.6L & 1.8L			
Inner	1.921 (48.8)	19.0-22.1@1.476 (8.6-10.0@37.5)	41.7-48.3@1.122 (18.9-21.9@28.5)
Outer	1.783 (45.3)	32.9-38.1@1.555 (14.9-17.3@39.5)	112.5-127.9@1.20 (51.0-58.0@30.5)

CAMSHAFT

Engine	Journal Diam. In. (mm)	Clearance In. (mm)	Lobe Lift In. (mm)
1.6L			
Front & Center	1.022-1.0226 (25.959-25.975)	.0010-.0023 [1] (.025-.059)	.210 (5.34)
1.8L			
Front & Center	1.2582-1.2589 (31.959-31.975)	.0010-.0023 (.025-.059)	.210 (5.34)
1.6L & 1.8L Rear	1.4157-1.4163 (35.959-35.975)	.0010-.0023 (.025-.059)	.210 (5.34)

[1] – Limit – .0039" (.1 mm).

2S-E 4-CYLINDER

ENGINE CODING

ENGINE IDENTIFICATION

The engine serial number is stamped onto a machined pad, located on the right side of the engine block.

ENGINE IDENTIFICATION

Application	Code
Camry (2.0L)	2S-E

ENGINE, MANIFOLDS & CYLINDER HEAD

ENGINE

NOTE: Remove the engine and transaxle as a unit. Separate the engine from the transaxle after removal.

Removal

1) Mark hood hinge positions. Remove hood. Remove battery. Drain cooling system. On automatic transmission; disconnect throttle cable, with bracket, from throttle body. On manual transmission, disconnect accelerator cable from throttle body.

2) If equipped with cruise control, remove actuator cover. Disconnect wiring connector and vacuum hose. Remove actuator with bracket. If equipped with air conditioning, disconnect main and sub fan motor connectors. Disconnect reservoir and upper and lower radiator hoses.

3) On automatic transmission: disconnect oil cooler hoses. Remove radiator supports, rubber cushions and radiator. Remove air cleaner assembly with air flow meter and hose.

4) Mark for reassembly reference and remove all electrical connectors, cables and vacuum hoses that interfer with engine removal. Pull out EFI wire harness to right side fender apron. Disconnect 2 heater hoses. Detach fuel inlet hose from filter and return hose from return pipe.

5) Remove speedometer cable from transaxle. On manual transmission, detach clutch slave cylinder and hose bracket. Do not disconnect hoses for the clutch hydraulic system. Disconnect transmission control cable. If equipped, detach A/C belt, compressor, power steering belt and pump with bracket. Set assemblies aside. Do not discharge systems.

6) Raise and support vehicle. Drain oil from engine and/or transaxle. Wrap drive axle boots with shop towels. Remove 6 nuts from each drive shaft flange while depressing brake pedal. Disconnect both front drive shafts.

7) Disconnect front exhaust pipe and remove 2 gaskets from manifold. Remove exhaust pipe stay from cylinder block. Remove 2 hole covers and disconnect front and rear engine mounts. Remove crossmember if necessary. Lower vehicle.

NOTE: Do not damage power steering gear housing or neutral start switch during removal. Ensure all wiring, hoses and cables are clear of engine before lifting.

8) Attach engine hoist to lift brackets on engine. Remove engine and transaxle mounts from brackets. Remove left side transaxle mount bracket. Carefully lift engine/transaxle assembly out of vehicle and place on work stand.

Installation

1) With engine hoist chained to lift brackets, slowly lower engine/transaxle assembly into engine compartment. Tilt transaxle down while lowering to clear neutral start switch, engine mount brackets and power steering gear housing.

2) Install engine mounts, brackets and crossmembers. To complete installation, reverse removal procedures. Connect all wiring and fuel and vacuum hoses. Adjust drive belts. Fill radiator with coolant and engine/transaxle with oil.

INTAKE & EXHAUST MANIFOLDS

Removal

1) Disconnect battery. Drain coolant if necessary. On automatic transmission, disconnect throttle cable, with bracket, from throttle body. On manual transmission, disconnect accelerator cable from throttle body.

2) Remove air cleaner assembly. Disconnect alternator, wiring and bracket as necessary. Mark components for reassembly reference. Disconnect vacuum hose from air intake chamber to power brake booster.

3) Detach A/C vacuum hoses. If necessary, remove A/C and power steering units and set aside. Mark for reassembly reference and remove emission control hoses and EFI wiring.

4) If necessary, remove water outlet housing, rear end housing and heater pipe. Disconnect fuel hoses. Raise vehicle. Disconnect intake manifold stay, power steering vane pump vacuum hoses and front exhaust pipe.

5) Lower vehicle. Detach fasteners and remove intake manifold with air chamber assembly and gasket. Remove 4 bolts and exhaust manifold heat insulator. Remove remaining exhaust manifold mount bolts and nuts, exhaust manifold and gasket.

Inspection

1) Inspect air intake chamber and intake and exhaust manifold gasket surfaces for nicks, warpage or damage. Intake and exhaust manifold warpage limit is .012" (.30 mm).

2) Air intake chamber warpage limit is .012" (.30 mm). If warpage is beyond maximum limits, resurface or replace components as necessary.

Installation

Install intake and exhaust manifolds using new gaskets. Complete installation by reversing removal procedure.

CYLINDER HEAD

Removal

1) Disconnect battery. Drain coolant. On automatic transmission, disconnect throttle cable with bracket from throttle body. On manual transmission, disconnect accelerator cable from throttle body.

2) Remove air cleaner, pipe and hoses. Disconnect alternator, wiring and bracket. Mark components for reassembly reference. On manual transmission, detach water temperature sending unit.

3) On automatic transmission, detach water temperature switch connector. Disconnect vacuum hose from air intake chamber-to-power brake booster. Detach A/C vacuum hose from dash panel. Disconnect A/C idle up hoses. Remove cruise control actuator vacuum hose from 3-way "T" fitting.

4) If necessary, remove A/C and power steering units and set aside. Do not discharge systems. Mark for reassembly reference and disconnect emission control hoses and EFI wiring. Pull out EFI wire harness to right side fender apron.

5) Remove integrated ignition assembly. Disconnect upper radiator hose and by-pass hose. Remove water outlet housing mount bolts, housing and gasket. Disconnect heater water outlet hose.

6) Detach air hoses from air valve. Disconnect No. 2 water by-pass hose. Remove rear end housing mount bolts and housing with air valve and gasket. Disconnect heater water inlet hose. Detach No. 1 water by-pass hose. Remove clamps, heater pipe mount bolts, pipe and gasket. Disconnect fuel hoses.

7) Raise vehicle. Drain engine oil. Disconnect intake manifold stay, power steering vane pump vacuum hoses and front exhaust pipe. Lower vehicle. Remove timing belt from camshaft timing sprocket.

NOTE: **Do not allow timing belt to come in contact with oil, water or dust.**

8) Remove No. 1 idler pulley and tension spring. Remove throttle body. Disconnect PCV hoses and remove valve cover and gasket. Loosen camshaft housing mount bolts gradually, in 3 steps, in sequence shown in *Fig. 1*. Remove camshaft housing with camshaft.

Fig. 1: Removing Camshaft Housing With Camshaft

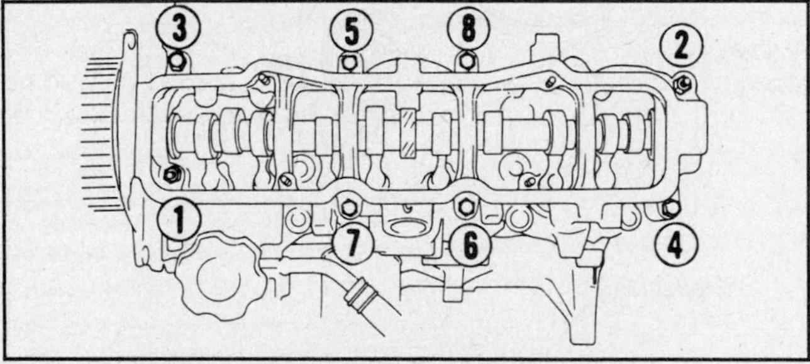
3
5
8
2
1
7
6
4

Camshaft housing warpage or cracking may result if mount bolts are removed in incorrect order.

9) If necessary, remove rocker arms and hydraulic valve lifters. Note locations for proper reassembly reference. Loosen and remove cylinder head bolts gradually, in 3 steps, in sequence shown in *Fig. 2*.

Fig. 2: Cylinder Head Removal Sequence.

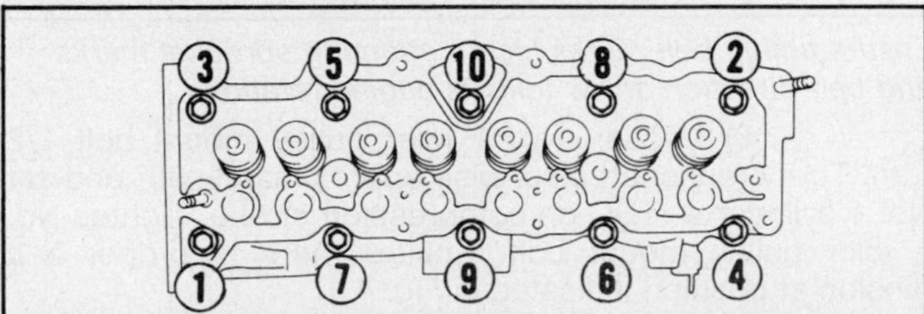
3
5
10
8
2
1
7
9
6
4

Cylinder head warpage or cracking may result if mount bolts are removed in incorrect order.

10) Lift cylinder head from dowel pins on block and place on work stand. If head is difficult to remove, pry with bar at proper spot between head and block projection. Remove intake manifold mount bolts and intake manifold with air chamber assembly. Remove exhaust manifold mount bolts, heat insulator, exhaust manifold and gasket.

NOTE: **Do not damage cylinder head or block surface on head gasket side during prying operation.**

Inspection

1) Clean all gasket material from top of cylinder block. Blow out carbon and oil from bolt holes. Using wire brush and gasket scraper, remove carbon and gasket material from combustion chambers, head and manifold surfaces. Do not scratch or damage gasket contact surfaces.

NOTE: **Do not clean cylinder head in a "hot tank" or it may be damaged.**

2) Using straightedge and feeler gauge, check cylinder head and block for warpage. Measure head on all four sides and diagonally. Measure block lengthwise across head bolt holes on gasket surface and diagonally.

3) Maximum warpage on block side and camshaft housing side of head is .002" (.05 mm). On manifold sides of head, warpage limit is .0031" (.080 mm). Maximum warpage of block is .002" (.05 mm). If warped beyond limits, resurface or replace cylinder head and/or block.

4) Using a dye penetrant, check combustion chambers, intake and exhaust ports, head surface and top of head for cracks. If crack is found, replace cylinder head.

NOTE: **Before installing cylinder head and camshaft housing mount bolts, apply oil to threads and under bolt head. Ensure no oil is on cylinder head installation surfaces.**

Installation

1) With intake manifold, air intake chamber assembly and exhaust manifold installed on head, apply gasket sealant to new head gasket and install. Tighten cylinder head bolts gradually, in 3 steps, in reverse of sequence shown in *Fig. 2*.

2) Install hydraulic valve lifters and rocker arms in correct order. Remove any old packing material from installation surfaces. Apply No. 102 seal packing, or equivalent, to camshaft housing. Install housing immediately after seal packing has been applied.

3) Tighten camshaft housing mount bolts gradually, in 3 steps, in sequence shown in *Fig. 1*. To complete installation, reverse removal procedures. Adjust timing and drive belts. ensure all wiring, vacuum hoses and cables are installed in correct order.

4) Ensure inlet hose is connected to fuel filter with new gaskets. Fill cooling system. Refill engine with oil. Check and set ignition timing and idle speed. Start engine and check for leaks. Run engine for several minutes, let it cool down and recheck cylinder head mount bolt torque.

CAMSHAFT

ENGINE FRONT COVERS

Removal

1) Raise and support vehicle. Remove right front wheel and tire. Remove right fender apron seal.

2S-E 4-CYLINDER (Cont.)

Loosen alternator pivot, adjusting lock and adjusting bolts. Remove alternator drive belt. If equipped, remove cruise control actuator with bracket.

2) Remove power steering pump and belt. Do not drain pump or disconnect hoses. Using jack, raise engine enough to remove weight from right side engine mount. Remove right side engine mount insulator and bracket. Remove No. 2 (upper) timing belt cover and gasket.

3) Secure crankshaft and remove crankshaft pulley mount bolt. Use pulley removal tool (SST09213-31021) or equivalent, to remove pulley. Remove No. 1 (lower) timing belt cover with gaskets.

Installation

1) Check timing belt directional arrow points in direction of engine revolution and marks on belt and sprockets are aligned. Install timing belt guide with cup side facing out. Install No. 1 timing belt cover with new gaskets.

2) Install crankshaft pulley and tighten mount bolt. Pull timing belt upward and align preset mark on No. 1 cover with crankshaft pulley groove. If removed, install No. 1 idler pulley, tension spring, camshaft timing pulley and timing belt.

3) Ensure valve timing and belt tension are correct. Install No. 2 timing belt cover and new gaskets. To complete installation, reverse removal procedures. Install and adjust drive belts as necessary.

TIMING BELT

Removal

1) With engine upper front cover (No. 2) removed, align camshaft oil seal retainer preset mark with center of small hole on camshaft sprocket by turning crankshaft pulley clockwise until No. 1 cylinder is at 90° BTDC on compression stroke.

NOTE: **If reusing old timing belt, draw directional arrow on belt in direction of engine revolution. Place match marks on crankshaft and camshaft sprockets and belt. Ensure belt is not contaminated with water, oil or dust.**

2) Loosen No. 1 idler pulley mount bolt and shift pulley as far left as it will go. Retighten mount bolt. Remove timing belt from camshaft sprocket. Using camshaft sprocket holding tool (SST09278-54011) or equivalent, hold sprocket and remove mount bolt.

3) Remove No. 1 idler pulley and tension spring. Using crankshaft pulley removal tool, secure crankshaft and remove pulley mount bolt and pulley. Remove front lower timing belt cover with gaskets. Remove timing belt and guide.

4) Remove No. 2 idler pulley. Remove crankshaft timing sprocket. If necessary, sprocket may be carefully pryed off using 2 flat bars with cloth between bars and cylinder block.

Inspection

1) Check timing belt teeth for cracks or damage. If tooth damage is found, ensure camshaft, water pump or oil pump are not locked. If wear or cracks on flat belt face are found, check for nicks on one side of idler pulley lock.

2) If wear or damage to only one side of belt is found, check the belt guide and alignment of each pulley and sprocket. If noticeable wear is found on belt teeth, check timing cover gasket for damage and proper installation. Ensure there is no foreign material on sprocket teeth.

3) Check idler pulleys for smooth rotation. Replace if roughness or noise is found. Inspect tension spring free length. Free length is 2.01" (51 mm). Installed tension and length is 16-19 lbs. @ 2.36" (7.4-8.6 kg @ 60 mm).

Installation

1) Install crankshaft timing sprocket over crankshaft key. Install No. 2 idler pulley. Align marks and install timing belt on sprocket. Install belt guide with cup side outward. Install No. 1 timing belt cover with new gaskets.

2) Install crankshaft pulley, secure crankshaft and tighten mount bolt. Pull timing belt upward and align preset mark on No. 1 timing belt cover with crankshaft sprocket groove. *See Fig. 3.*

3) Install No. 1 idler pulley and tension spring. Pry pulley as far left as it will go and tighten. Align camshaft knock pin with camshaft timing sprocket during installation. Hold sprocket with tool and install sprocket mount bolt.

4) Align camshaft oil seal retainer preset mark with center of small hole on camshaft timing sprocket.*See Fig. 3*. Install timing belt. Ensure belt has proper tension between crankshaft timing sprocket, water pump pulley and camshaft timing sprocket.

Fig. 3: Installing Engine Timing Belt And Sprockets

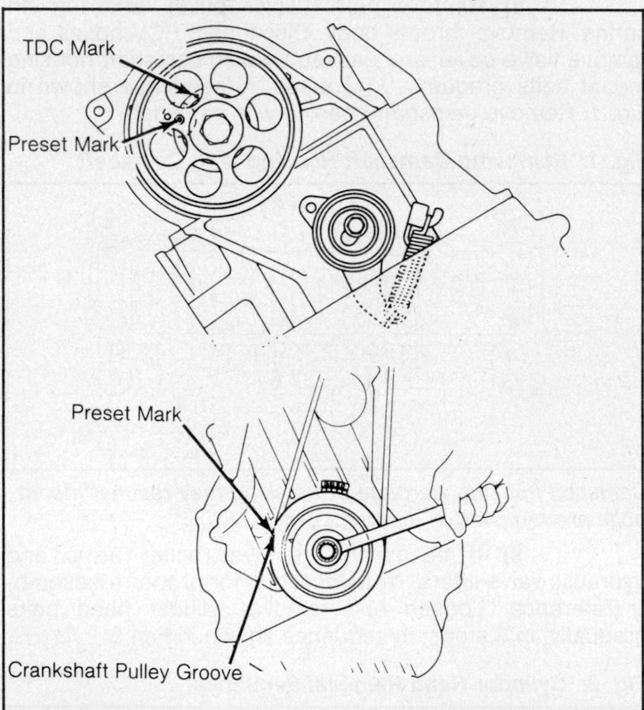
TDC Mark
Preset Mark
Preset Mark
Crankshaft Pulley Groove

Ensure timing belt marks locate at timing sprocket marks and belt direction arrow follows engine rotation.

5) Loosen No. 1 idler pulley mount bolt 1/2 turn. Turn crankshaft clockwise approximately 90° and set No. 1 cylinder at TDC on compression stroke. Tighten No. 1 idler pulley mount bolt. Ensure there is proper belt tension at position indicated in *Fig. 4*.

6) Turn crankshaft two revolutions clockwise from TDC to TDC. Check valve timing. Ensure sprocket marks align with belt and cover marks and belt has proper tension. *See Fig. 3 & 4.*

2S-E 4-CYLINDER (Cont.)

NOTE: Changing the timing belt meshing by one tooth will change crankshaft sprocket angle by 18°.

7) Readjust belt position if necessary. Install No. 2 timing belt cover with new gasket. Complete installation by reversing removal procedure.

Fig. 4: Checking Timing Belt Tension

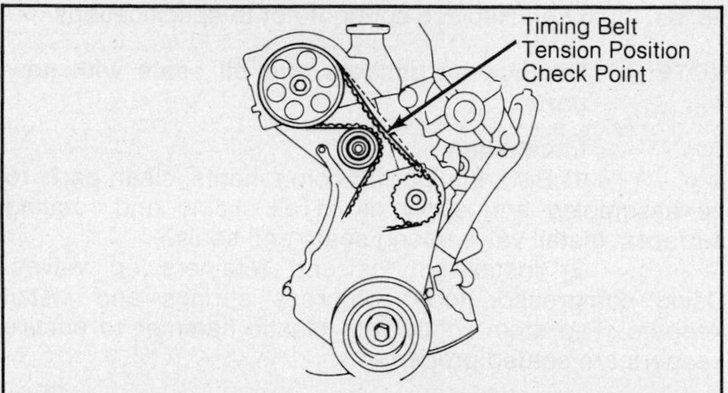
Timing Belt
Tension Position
Check Point

After installation, ensure the timing belt has proper tension at position indicated.

CAMSHAFT & CAMSHAFT HOUSING

NOTE: Before camshaft removal, check camshaft end play using dial indicator.

Removal

1) With engine upper front cover removed, install camshaft sprocket holding tool (SST09278-54011) or equivalent. Hold sprocket and remove mount bolt. Remove sprocket. With valve cover removed, remove rocker arms and hydraulic valve lifters.

2) Remove oil seal retainer mount bolts. Remove oil seal retainer and "O" ring. While slowly turning camshaft, remove without damaging camshaft housing bearing surfaces. If necessary, remove camshaft housing as described in cylinder head removal procedure.

Inspection

1) Before camshaft removal, check camshaft end play. Standard end play is .0031-.0091" (.080-.230 mm). Maximum end play is .0138" (.350 mm). If clearance is greater than maximum specification, replace camshaft and/or housing.

2) With camshaft housing removed, measure cylinder head contact surface for warpage using a straightedge and feeler gauge. Maximum warpage limit is .0031" (.080 mm). If warpage is greater than specification, replace camshaft housing.

3) Check for bend by placing camshaft in "V" blocks. Using dial indicator, set pointer on center journal. Rotate camshaft and measure total runout. Maximum bend limit is .0016" (.040 mm). If beyond limit, replace camshaft.

4) Using micrometer, check camshaft lobe heights for excessive wear. Standard lobe height is 1.5325-1.5365" (38.926-39.026 mm). Minimum lobe height is 1.5268" (38.780 mm). If worn below limit, replace camshaft.

5) Using micrometer and telescope hole gauge, measure camshaft journals and camshaft housing bearing bores for excessive wear. Standard bearing-to-journal clearance is .0010-.0026" (.025-.067 mm). Maximum clearance is .004" (.10 mm). If clearance is more than maximum limit, replace camshaft and/or housing.

Installation

1) Insert camshaft into camshaft housing. Place new "O" ring into oil seal retainer. Apply "Three Bond 1324" anaerobic adhesive and sealant to 2 or 3 threads of bolt ends and install oil seal retainer. Install rocker arms and valve lifters.

2) Align camshaft knock pin with camshaft timing sprocket. Using sprocket holding tool, install and tighten mount bolt. Ensure timing sprocket is free of oil or water. Complete installation by reversing removal procedure.

CAMSHAFT OIL SEAL

Removal & Installation

1) With camshaft oil seal retainer removed for housing, tap oil seal out using hammer and drift. Do not damage oil seal contact surface of retainer. Apply grease to new oil seal. Install seal using installer tool (SST09214-60010).

2) With camshaft oil seal retainer installed, use a knife to cut off lip of oil seal. Using screwdriver, carefully pry out seal. Do not damage seal lip contact surface of camshaft or seal contact surface of retainer.

3) Inspect seal contact surface of camshaft for cracks or damage and replace as necessary. Apply grease to new oil seal lip. Using installed tool, replace oil seal.

CRANKSHAFT FRONT OIL SEAL

Removal & Installation

1) With oil pump removed from block, tap oil seal out using hammer and drift. Do not damage oil seal contact surface of oil pump. Apply grease to new oil seal. Install seal using installer tool (SST09226-10010).

NOTE: During installation, ensure oil seal is flush with oil pump body outer surface.

2) With oil pump installed, use a knife to cut off lip of oil seal. Using screwdriver, carefully pry out seal. Do not damage seal contact surface of oil pump or seal lip contact surface of crankshaft.

3) Inspect seal lip contact surface of crankshaft for cracks or damage and replace as necessary. Apply grease to new oil seal lip. Using installed tool, replace oil seal. Do not set seal more than .04" (1 mm) into oil pump body.

VALVES

VALVE ARRANGEMENT

I-E-I-E-E-I-E-I (Front-to-rear).

VALVE

1) Using gasket scraper, chip any carbon from valve head. Using wire brush, clean valve thoroughly. Inspect valves for worn, damaged or deformed valve head or stem.

2) Check valve head in-margin thickness. If valve head is worn to .02" (.5 mm) in-margin thickness for intake or .04" (1 mm) for exhaust, replace valve.

3) Check surface of valve stem tip for excessive wear. Standard overall valve length is 4.319" (109.70 mm) for intake and 4.303" (109.30 mm) for exhaust.

4) Valve stem end surface grinding limit is .02" (.5 mm). If valve stem tip is worn, resurface with grinder or replace valve.

2S-E 4-CYLINDER (Cont.)

VALVE GUIDE SERVICING

Clearance Check

1) Using valve guide brush and solvent, clean valve guides. Measure clearance between valve stem and guide with micrometer and telescope hole gauge. Check diameter of stem at top, center and bottom. Insert hole gauge in guide bore. Measure at center.

2) Subtract highest reading of stem diameter from guide bore to obtain clearance. Maximum valve stem-to-guide clearance is .0031" (.080 mm) for intake and .004" (.10 mm) for exhaust. If clearance is beyond limits and valve stem is not worn, replace guide.

NOTE: **Replacement valve guides are available in .05 mm oversize.**

Replacement

1) Using hammer and drift, tap valve guide firmly enough to break guide off flush with cylinder head surface. Remove snap ring. Gradually heat head to 176-212°F (80-100°C). Using valve guide removal and installer tool (SST09201-60011) or equivalent, drive guide out from camshaft side.

2) Measure cylinder head hole for valve guide. Standard guide hole diameter is .5118-.5129" (13.000-13.027 mm). Standard guide outside diameter is .5134-.5138" (13.040-13.051 mm). If guide hole measures more than specification, machine guide hole for oversized guide.

3) With head at room temperature, ream guide hole to .5138-.5148" (13.050-13.077 mm). Oversize guide outside diameter is .5154-.5158" (13.090-13.101 mm). To install valve guide, reheat cylinder head.

4) Drive in new guide using guide removal and installer tool until snap ring comes in contact with cylinder head. *See Fig. 5.* Using 8 mm reamer, finish guide bore to specified clearance between guide and valve. Reface valve seat surface, as needed, after valve or guide repair or replacement.

Fig. 5: Installing Oversize Valve Guide

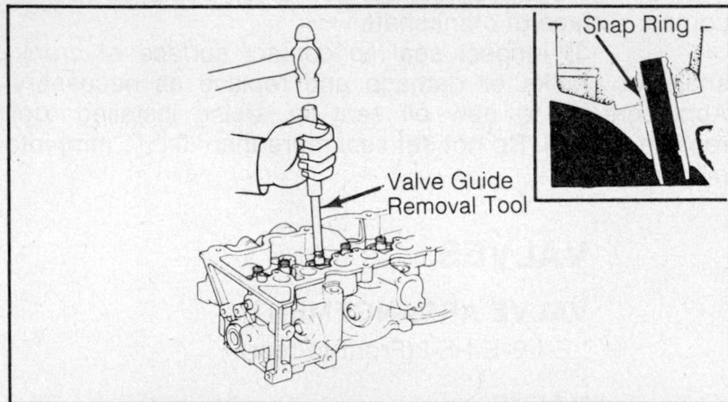
Snap Ring
Valve Guide
Removal Tool

If stem-to-guide clearance is more than maximum limit, bore guide hole and install oversize valve guide.

VALVE SPRINGS

Removal

1) With cylinder head, camshaft housing and camshaft removed, remove rocker arms and hydraulic valve lifters. Keep components in order for reassembly reference.

2) Press valve spring down with compressor tool (SST09202-43013). Remove valve keepers. Remove compressor tool. Remove spring retainer, spring, valve, oil seal and valve spring seat. Keep components in order for reassembly reference.

Inspection

1) Using steel square, check squareness of valve springs. Spring must be less than .079" (2 mm) out of square. Check free length of spring and replace any not within limits.

2) Using spring tester, check tension of each spring at specified installed height. Valve spring installed height is 1.555" (39.50 mm). Minimum installed tension is 68 lbs. (30.5 kg). Replace spring if not to specifications.

NOTE: **Replace all gaskets and oil seals with new parts.**

Installation

1) Before installing components, clean parts to be assembled and apply oil to all sliding and rotating surfaces. Install valve spring seats and seals.

2) Install springs and retainers on valves. Using compressor tool, compress springs and install keepers. Tap stem lightly with plastic hammer to ensure keepers are seated properly.

ROCKER ARM

Removal

With camshaft housing and camshaft removed, remove rocker arms and hydraulic lifters. Keep all components in order for reassembly reference.

Inspection

Check the contact surface of valve rocker arm, valve stem end and/or camshaft lobe. If contact surface is excessively worn, replace rocker arm.

Installation

With cylinder head installed, assemble and install rocker arms and hydraulic lifters in proper order. Install camshaft housing and camshaft. Complete installation by reversing removal procedure.

HYDRAULIC VALVE LIFTERS

Removal

With camshaft housing and camshaft removed, remove rocker arms and hydraulic lifters. Keep all components in order for reassembly reference.

NOTE: **Do not disassemble hydraulic lifter. Replace unit if lifter stroke or leak down exceeds specification.**

Inspection

1) To check hydraulic lifters, bleed unit by immersing in light oil. Insert lifter tool (SST09276-70010) into lifter plunger hole. Slide plunger up and down several times while pushing on check ball lightly.

2) If plunger stroke exceeds .020" (.50 mm), repeat step **1)**. If plunger stroke exceeds limit after repeated bleeding, replace component.

3) If lifter plunger stroke is within limit, use a leak down tester to check lifter. Apply 44 lbs. (20 kg) of pressure to plunger and measure its slide down speed after plunger has moved approximately .08" (2 mm).

4) Standard leak down time is 2-7 seconds with a plunger movement of .04" (1 mm). If lifter leak down is not to specification, replace unit.

Installation

With cylinder head installed, assemble and install rocker arms and hydraulic lifters in proper order. Install camshaft housing and camshaft. Complete installation by reversing removal procedure.

2S-E 4-CYLINDER (Cont.)

PISTONS, PINS & RINGS

PISTON & ROD ASSEMBLY

Removal

1) With cylinder head and oil pan removed, remove connecting rod nuts. Remove rod cap with bearing half. Check top of cylinder bore for ridge. If scraper will not remove carbon build-up, remove using ridge reamer.

2) Push piston and rod assembly, with bearing half, out through top of block. Rod caps must be kept with their respective piston and rod assembly and are not interchangeable.

Inspection

1) Check connecting rod for bend or torsion using rod aligner tool. Bend limit is .002" (.05 mm) or less, in 3.94" (100 mm) of length. Torsion limit is .006" (.15 mm) or less, in 3.94" (100 mm) of length.

2) Install rod, with bearings, on crank pin. Measure rod side thrust clearance. Maximum play at rod big end must be .012" (.30 mm) or less. Replace rod if not to specifications.

Installation

1) Oil the rings, piston and cylinder bore. Install piston and rod assembly. Ensure ring gaps are set 180° apart and code marks face up. Do not set on thrust side of piston or in line with piston pin. *See Fig. 6.* Ensure bearing halves are properly seated in rod and cap.

Fig. 6: Assembling Piston Rings

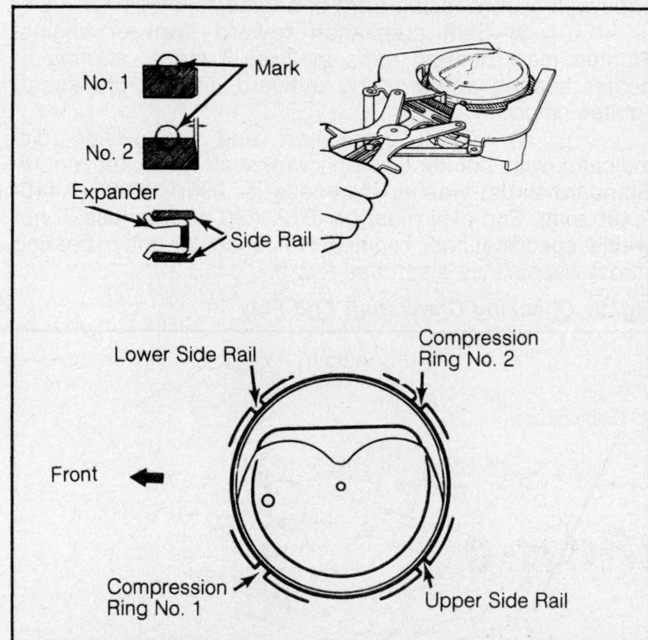
No. 1
Mark
No. 2
Expander
Side Rail
Lower Side Rail
Compression
Ring No. 2
Front
Compression
Ring No. 1
Upper Side Rail

Ensure ring gaps do not align and code marks face up.

2) Install ring compressor. Install piston in cylinder with cavity on piston top aligned with straight edge of rod and facing toward front of engine. *See Fig. 7.* With piston installed, ensure rod and bearings are seated against crankshaft journal.

3) Install rod caps to their respective piston and rod assembly. Install cylinder head. Install new gasket and oil pan. Tighten pan bolts evenly, in a criss-cross pattern. Do not over-tighten. Complete installation by reversing removal procedure.

Fig. 7: Checking Piston and Rod Alignment Position

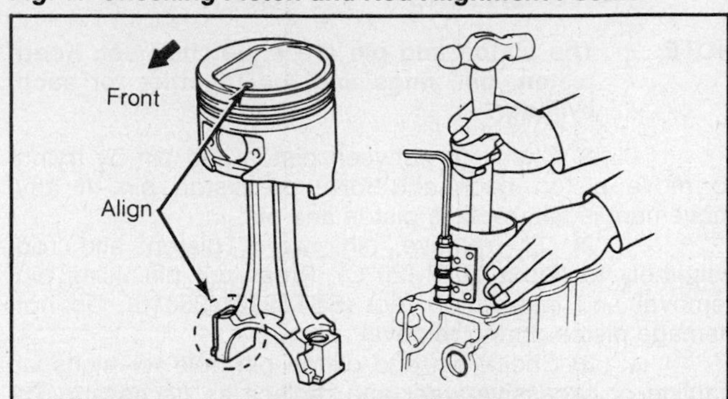
Front
Align

Ensure cavity on piston top aligns with straight edge of rod and faces front of engine.

FITTING PISTONS & RINGS

1) Inspect cylinder block for cracks or flaws. Using bore gauge, measure cylinder for out-of-round or excessive taper. If cylinder bore out-of-round or taper exceeds .0008" (.020 mm), refinish cylinder bore. When any one cylinder is bored, all cylinders must be bored. Check cylinder block-to-head contact surface for warpage. Maximum warpage limit is .002" (.05 mm).

NOTE: **Before cylinder block machining operations, ensure main bearing caps are installed and tightened to specification. Bore cylinders in the order of No. 2-4-1-3 to prevent distortion.**

2) Determine piston oversize according to amount of wear in cylinder. Standard piston diameter is 3.3061-3.3073" (83.975-84.005 mm). Standard cylinder bore diameter is 3.3071-3.3083" (84.000-80.030 mm). Bore wear limit is 3.3181" (84.280 mm). Measure piston diameter at thrust face. Add piston-to-cylinder clearance. Finish hone of cylinder may then be determined.

NOTE: **Pistons and rings are available in .50 mm, .75 mm and 1 mm oversize for service.**

PISTON SPECIFICATIONS

Piston Size	Piston Diameter In. (mm)
Standard	3.3061-3.3073 (83.975-84.005)
.50 mm O/S	3.3258-3.3270 (84.475-84.505)
.75 mm O/S	3.3356-3.3368 (84.725-84.755)
1 mm O/S	3.3455-3.3466 (84.975-85.005)

3) After honing cylinder to final fit, measure piston-to-cylinder clearance with piston and cylinder at room temperature of 70°F (20°C). Maximum clearance limit is .002" (.05 mm). Ensure that difference of bore limit between cylinders is .002" (.05 mm) or less. If more than limit, cylinders must be bored.

4) If pistons are reused, decarbon piston and ring grooves with scraper and curved steel wire or piece of broken ring. Clean oil slots in bottom land of oil ring groove. Check for scratches, wear or damage.

5) Measure side clearance of rings in grooves as each ring is installed. If side clearance exceeds limits, replace piston and rings. Check ring end gap. Install ring squarely in cylinder, using piston. When installing piston rings, ensure code mark on ring faces up.

2S-E 4-CYLINDER (Cont.)

PISTON PINS

NOTE: The piston and pin are a matched set. Keep piston, pin, rings and rod together for each cylinder.

1) Check fit between piston and pin by trying to move piston back and forth on piston pin. If any movement is felt, replace piston and pin.

2) To remove pin, warm piston and rod assembly to about 70°F (20°C). Press out pin using pin removal and installation tool (SST09221-25016). Do not damage piston during removal.

3) Check pin and piston pin hole for signs of gauling or excessive wear and replace as necessary. To assemble piston and rod, reheat piston to 70°F (20°C). Align the cavity on piston with straight edge on connecting rod.

4) Coat with oil and insert pin into piston using pin removal and installation tool while holding piston and rod in proper alignment. Check to ensure there is no movement of piston on pin.

CRANKSHAFT & MAIN & CONNECTING ROD BEARINGS

CRANKSHAFT

Removal

1) With engine removed, remove outer parts, install engine attachment and mount assembly on work stand. Remove drive belts and front covers. Remove valve timing belt.

2) Secure crankshaft and remove flywheel or drive plate, oil pan, oil pump and cylinder head. Remove piston and rod assemblies. Using punch, mark rods and caps for reassembly reference.

3) Remove main bearing caps and arrange caps, inserts and thrust washers in order for reassembly reference. Remove rear oil seal retainer. Do not damage crankshaft sealing surface. Remove crankshaft. Remove upper main bearing halves.

NOTE: If replacing main bearing, replace with one having the same number as marked on cylinder block. There are three sizes of standard bearings, marked 1, 2 or 3 accordingly. See Fig. 8.

Fig. 8: Checking Standard Main Bearing Sizes

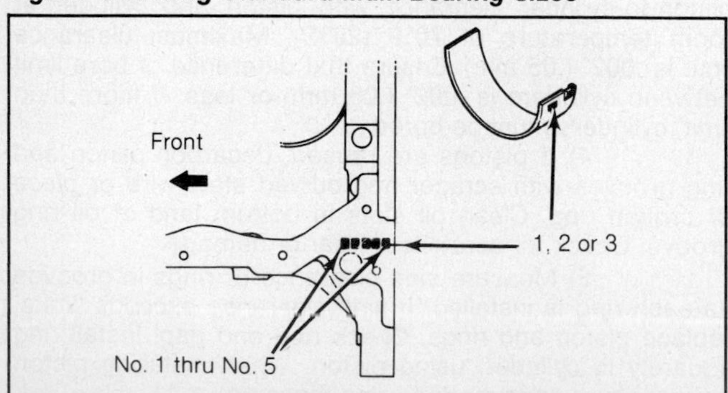
Front
1, 2 or 3
No. 1 thru No. 5

When checking main bearings, arrange inserts, thrust washers and bearing caps in proper order.

Inspection

1) Check crankshaft journals and crankpins for scoring, wear, cracks, taper and out of round. Maximum taper and out of round limit is .0008" (.020 mm). If taper and out of round exceeds specification, replace crankshaft.

2) Check crankshaft for bend by placing on "V" blocks. Use dial indicator at center journal of crankshaft. Maximum bend limit is .0024" (.060 mm) or less. If bend exceeds specification, replace crankshaft.

3) Check flywheel friction surface for cracks, damage or wear. Measure friction surface runout using a dial indicator. Runout limit is .004" (.10 mm). Resurface or replace flywheel if not within limits. Check tooth surfaces of ring gear for flaws or wear. Replace as necessary.

NOTE: Main bearing caps are numbered and must be installed with arrows facing forward.

Installation

1) Install main bearing halves in engine block. Ensure bearings are on correct journal. Upper bearing halves have oil hole and oil groove. Lower bearing halves do not. Do not interchange inserts or crankshaft journal damage will result.

2) Apply oil to main bearing surfaces. Install the upper thrust washers on center bearing and lower thrust washers on No. 3 main bearing cap with oil grooves facing outward. Install crankshaft. Install main bearing caps with arrows facing front of engine.

3) Shift crankshaft toward front of engine. Tighten main bearing caps in 2 or 3 steps, starting at center bearing and working outward. Ensure crankshaft rotates smoothly.

4) Check crankshaft end play using dial indicator with pointer set on crankshaft sprocket mount. Standard thrust washer thickness is .0961-.0980" (2.440-2.490 mm). End play must be .012" (.30 mm) or less. If not within specifications, replace No. 3 center main bearing thrust washers as a set. *See Fig. 9*.

Fig. 9: Checking Crankshaft End Play

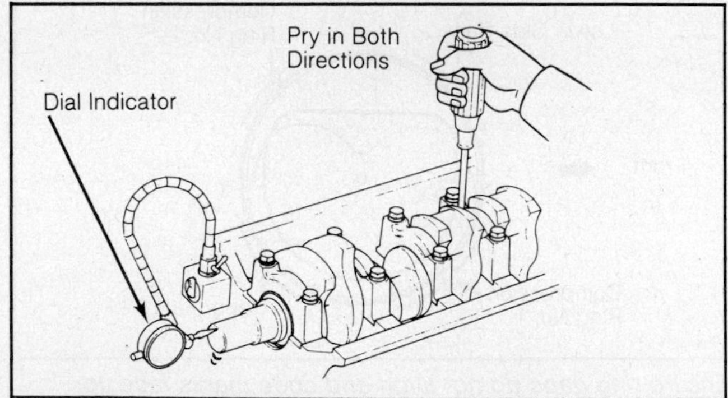
Pry in Both Directions
Dial Indicator

If clearance is more than specification, replace No. 3 main bearing thrust washers as a set.

5) Install rear oil seal retainer. Install flywheel or drive plate. Install piston and rod assemblies. To install remaining components, reverse removal procedure.

MAIN BEARING CLEARANCE

1) Check bearings for scoring or wear. Replace if damaged. Clean oil from crankshaft. Check bearing clearance using Plastigage method. Maximum main bearing clearance is .0031" (.080 mm).

2S-E 4-CYLINDER (Cont.)

2) If not to specifications, replace main bearing inserts with ones having same number as marked on cylinder block. There are three sizes of standard main bearings, marked 1, 2 and 3 accordingly.

NOTE: Plastigage should run parallel with crankshaft. Do not block oil hole or turn crankshaft with Plastigage inserted.

CONNECTING ROD BEARING CLEARANCE

1) Check bearings for scoring or wear. Replace if damaged. Clean oil from crankshaft. Check bearing clearance using Plastigage method. Tighten rod caps to 33-39 ft. lbs. (45-53 N.m). Maximum connecting rod bearing clearance is .0031" (.080 mm).

2) If not to specifications, replace rod bearing inserts with ones having the same number as marked on bearing cap. Three sizes of standard rod bearing are available, marked 1, 2 and 3 accordingly.

CRANKSHAFT REAR OIL SEAL

Removal & installation

1) Remove engine/transaxle assembly and separate. Remove flywheel or drive plate. With rear oil seal retainer removed from block, tap oil seal out using hammer and drift. Do not damage oil seal contact surface of retainer. Apply grease to new oil seal. Install seal using installer tool (SST09223-41020).

NOTE: During installation, do not install oil seal slantwise.

2) With rear oil seal retainer installed, use a knife to cut off lip of oil seal. Using screwdriver, carefully pry out seal. Do not damage seal contact surface of retainer or seal lip contact surface of crankshaft.

3) Inspect seal lip contact surface of crankshaft for cracks or damage and replace as necessary. Apply grease to new oil seal. Using installed tool (SST09223-63010), replace oil seal.

ENGINE OILING

CRANKCASE CAPACITY

4.2 qts. (4.0L) with filter.

OIL FILTER

Full-flow, with disposable cartridge.

OIL PRESSURE

36-71 psi (2.5-5.0 kg/cm²) @ 3000 RPM.

OIL PUMP

Removal

1) Raise and support vehicle. Drain engine oil. Remove right side engine under cover and oil level gauge. Remove oil pan, using care not to damage oil pan flange when prying.

2) Remove oil strainer mount bolts, strainer and "O" ring. Remove timing belt. Remove oil pump housing mount bolts and carefully tap housing with plastic hammer to dislodge.

Disassembly

1) Remove oil pump body mount bolts, pump body, driven rotor and "O" ring. Hold sprocket in soft jaw vise. Remove nut, sprocket, drive rotor and pump body.

2) Using snap ring pliers, remove the snap ring. Remove the retainer, spring and relief valve piston. *See Fig. 11.*

Inspection

1) Using feeler gauge, measure clearance between driven rotor and pump body. Standard clearance is .004-.007" (.10-.17 mm). Maximum clearance is .008" (.20 mm). If clearance is greater than maximum limit, replace oil pump rotor set and/or pump body. *See Fig. 10.*

2) Measure clearance between both rotor tips. Standard clearance is .0016-.0063" (.040-.160 mm). Maximum clearance limit is .008" (.20 mm). If clearance is greater than maximum limit, replace oil pump rotor set. *See Fig. 10.*

Fig. 10: Checking Oil Pump Clearances

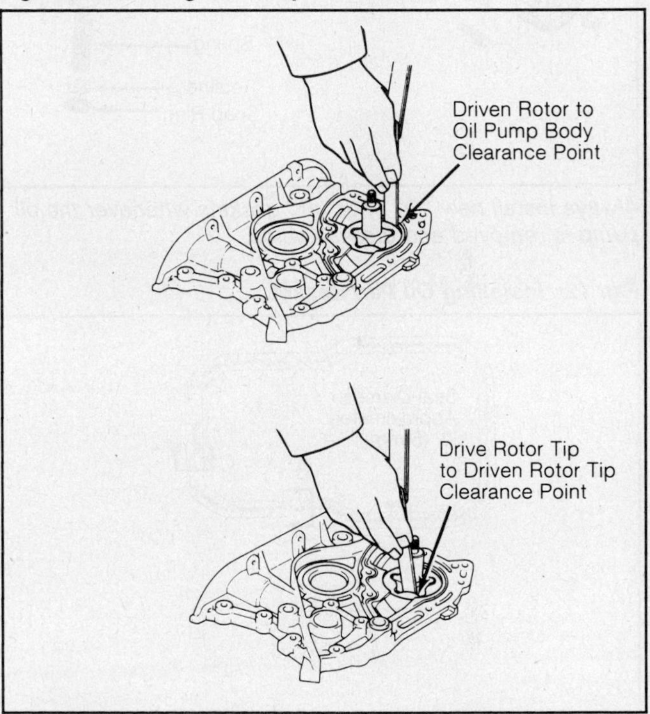
Driven Rotor to
Oil Pump Body
Clearance Point
Drive Rotor Tip
to Driven Rotor Tip
Clearance Point

If clearance between pump driven rotor and body or rotor tips is not within limits, replace rotor set and/or body.

3) Inspect relief valve components for wear or damage. Check relief valve operating pressure is within limits. Standard pressure is 51-63 psi (3.6-4.4 kg/cm²). Inspect oil seal for wear or damage and replace as necessary.

Assembly

1) Install relief valve piston, spring and retainer into pump body and secure with snap ring. Insert sprocket in drive rotor and install nut loosely. Hold sprocket in soft jaw vise and tighten nut to 16-23 ft. lbs. (22-31 N.m).

2) Place driven rotor into pump body with mark facing up. Install new "O" ring in body groove. Install pump body on pump housing. *See Fig. 11.*

Installation

1) Using new gasket, install pump housing onto cylinder block. Install timing belt. Install oil strainer with new "O" ring.

2) Clean old packing material from oil pan and apply new No. 102 seal packing or equivalent to oil pan. *See Fig. 12.* Install oil pan as soon as seal packing is applied.

2S-E 4-CYLINDER (Cont.)

Fig. 11: Checking Oil Pump Body and Housing Assembly

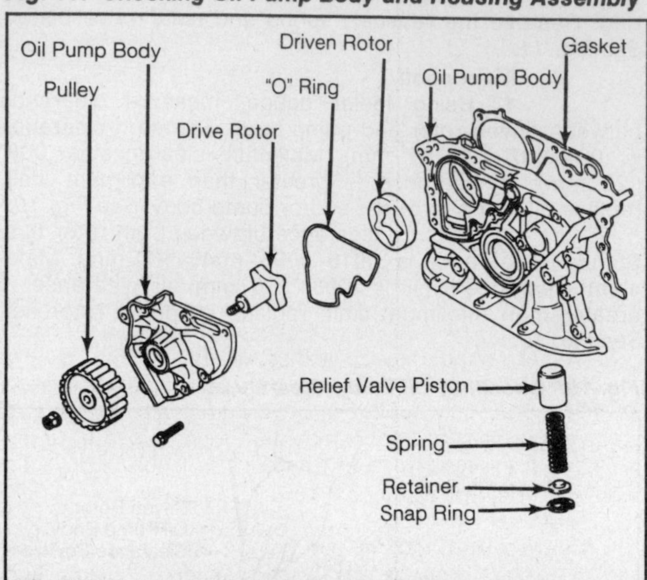
Oil Pump Body
Pulley
Driven Rotor
"O" Ring
Drive Rotor
Oil Pump Body
Gasket
Relief Valve Piston
Spring
Retainer
Snap Ring

Always install new "O" rings and gaskets whenever the oil pump is removed and disassembled.

Fig. 12: Installing Oil Pan Gasket

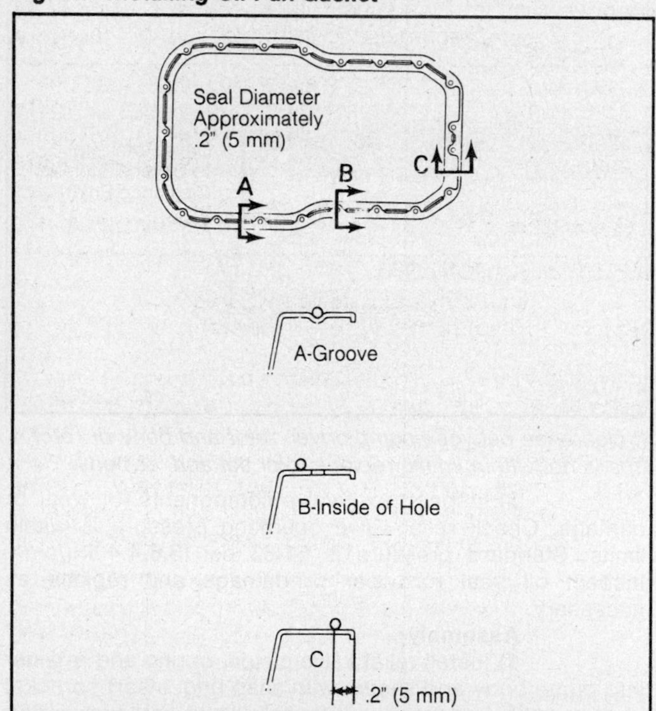
Seal Diameter
Approximately
.2" (5 mm)
A
B
C
A-Groove
B-Inside of Hole
C
.2" (5 mm)

Install the oil pan as soon as the seal packing is applied.

3) Install remaining components in reverse of removal procedure. Fill with oil, start engine and check for leaks.

ENGINE COOLING

THERMOSTAT

Thermostat opens at 176-183°F (80-84°C).

COOLING SYSTEM CAPACITY

The cooling system capacity is 7.4 qts. (7.0L) with heater or air conditioner.

RADIATOR CAP

11-15 psi. (.75-1.05 kg/cm²).

WATER PUMP

Removal

1) Drain coolant. Remove drive and timing belts. Remove alternator adjusting bar. Disconnect radiator inlet hose. Disconnect water temperature switch connector from water inlet housing.

2) Disconnect water by-pass hose from water pump. Remove heater pipe mount bolts, heater pipe and gasket. Remove 3 water pump assembly mount bolts in sequence shown in *Fig. 13*.

3) Remove remaining mount bolts and tap water pump housing with plastic hammer to dislodge. Remove pump, "O" ring and gasket.

Inspection

1) Check water pump impeller and pump body for cracks and damage of the contact surfaces. Replace water pump assembly if worn or damaged.

2) Inspect pump bearing for roughness or noise and replace as necesaary. Check that there is no sign of coolant leakage from drain hole. Check thermostat and radiator to ensure proper cooling system function.

Installation

1) Assemble water pump with new gasket. Install pump with 3 bolts. Place new "O" ring into pump cover groove. Install pump assembly with remaining mount bolts in reverse of removal sequence. *See Fig. 13.*

Fig. 13: Removing Water Pump Assembly Mount Bolts

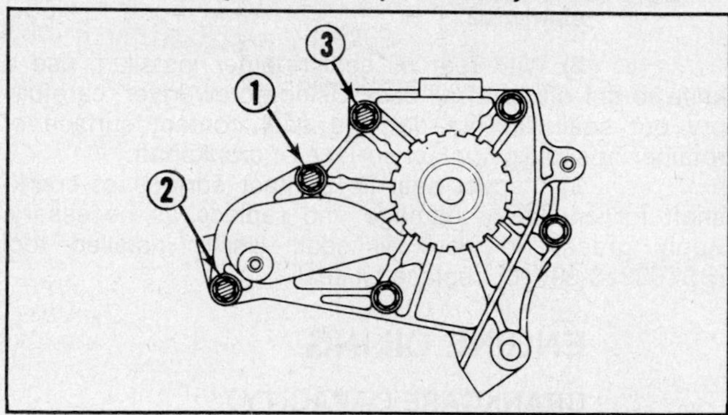
3
1
2

Remove water pump assembly mount bolts in proper sequence.

2) Install heater pipe with new gasket. Connect related hoses and switch. Install timing and drive belts. Reverse removal procedure to install remaining components. Fill cooling system with coolant, start engine and check for leaks.

Toyota Engines

2S-E 4-CYLINDER (Cont.)

ENGINE SPECIFICATIONS

GENERAL SPECIFICATIONS

Year	DISPLACEMENT		Fuel System	HP@RPM	Torque Ft. Lbs.@RPM	Compr. Ratio	BORE		STROKE	
	Cu. In.	Liters					In.	mm	In.	mm
1983 Camry	121.7	2.0	E.F.I. [1]	92 @ 4200	113 @ 2400	8.7:1	3.31	84	3.54	90

[1] – Electronic fuel injection.

VALVES

Engine Size & Valve	Head Diam. In. (mm)	Face Angle	Seat Angle	Seat Width In. (mm)	Stem Diameter In. (mm)	Stem Clearance In. (mm)	Valve Lift In. (mm)
2.0L							
Intake	.....	45.5°	45°	.047-.063 (1.20-1.60)	.3138-.3144 (7.970-7.985)	.0010-.0024 (.025-.060)	.....
Exhaust	.....	45.5°	45°	.047-.063 (1.20-1.60)	.3136-.3142 (7.965-7.980)	.0012-.0026 (.030-.065)	.....

PISTONS, PINS, RINGS

Engine	PISTONS	PINS		RINGS		
	Clearance In. (mm)	Piston Fit In. (mm)	Rod Fit In. (mm)	Ring No.	End Gap In. (mm)	Side Clearance In. (mm)
2.0L	.0006-.0014 (.015-.035)	Press Fit [1]	Press Fit [1]	No. 1	.011-.020 (.28-.50)	.0012-.0028 (.030-.070)
				No. 2	.008-.017 (.20-.45)	.0012-.0028 (.030-.070)
				Oil	.008-.031 (.20-.79)	.0012-.0028 (.030-.070)

[1] – The piston and pin are available only as a matched set.

CRANKSHAFT MAIN & CONNECTING ROD BEARINGS

Engine	MAIN BEARINGS				CONNECTING ROD BEARINGS		
	Journal Diam. In. (mm)	Clearance In. (mm)	Thrust Bearing	Crankshaft End Play In. (mm)	Journal Diam. In. (mm)	Clearance In. (mm)	Side Play In. (mm)
2.0L	2.1648-2.1654 (54.985-55.000)	.0008-.0019 [1] (.020-.047)	No. 3	.0008-.0087 (.020-.220)	1.8892-1.8898 (47.985-48.000)	.0009-.0022 (.024-.055)	.0063-.0083 (.160-.210)

[1] – The main bearing clearance for journal No. 3 is .0012-.0022" (.030-.057 mm).

VALVE SPRINGS

Engine	Free Length In. (mm)	PRESSURE Lbs. @ In. (Kg @ mm)	
		Valve Closed	Valve Open
2.0L	1.8390 (46.710)	68 @ 1.56 (30.8 @ 39.5)	.....

2S-E 4-CYLINDER (Cont.)

ENGINE SPECIFICATIONS (Cont.)

CAMSHAFT

Engine	Journal Diam. In. (mm)	Clearance In. (mm)	Lobe Lift In. (mm)
2.0L			
No. 1	1.8291-1.8297 (46.459-46.475)	.0010-.0026 (.025-.067)	.....
No. 2	1.8192-1.8199 (46.209-46.225)	.0010-.0026 (.025-.067)	.....
No. 3	1.8094-1.8100 (45.959-45.975)	.0010-.0026 (.025-.067)	.....
No. 4	1.7996-1.8002 (45.709-45.725)	.0010-.0026 (.025-.067)	.....
No. 5	1.7897-1.7904 (45.459-45.475)	.0010-.0026 .025-.067)	.....
No. 6	1.7799-1.7805 (45.209-45.225)	.0010-.0026 (.025-.067)	.....

TIGHTENING SPECIFICATIONS

Application	Ft. Lbs. (N.m)
Camshaft Housing Mount Bolt	9-13 (26-49)
Camshaft Sprocket Mount Bolt	37-43 (50-58)
Connecting Rod Cap Bolt	33-39 (45-53)
Crankshaft Main Bearing Cap Bolt	40-47 (54-64)
Crankshaft Sprocket Mount Bolt	73-86 (99-117)
Cylinder Head Mount Bolt	44-50 (60-68)
Drive Plate Mount Bolt	61 (83)
Drive Shaft Bearing Bracket to Cylinder Block Mount Bolt	40 (54)
Intake & Exhaust Manifold Mount Bolt	31 (42)
Integrated Ignition Assembly to Camshaft Housing	8-11 (11-15)
Flywheel Mount Bolt	65-72 (88-98)
No. 1 Idler Pulley to Cylinder Block Mount Bolt	26-36 (35-49)
No. 2 Idler Pulley to Oil Pump Mount Bolt	26-36 (35-49)
Transaxle-to-Engine Mount Bolt	
10 mm	29 (39)
12 mm	47 (64)
	INCH Lbs. (N.m)
Oil Pump Assembly to-Cylinder Block Mount Bolt	66-99 (8-11)
Water Pump assembly to Cylinder Block Mount Bolt	66-99 (8-11)
Oil Strainer to Cylinder Block	35-60 (4-7)
Oil Pan to Cylinder Block Mount Bolt	35-60 (4-7)

3A-C & 4A-C 4-CYLINDER

ENGINE CODING

ENGINE IDENTIFICATION

The serial number and code are stamped on the left rear side of the engine block.

ENGINE IDENTIFICATION

Application	Code
Corolla RWD (1.6L)	4A-C
Tercel FWD (1.5L)	3A-C

ENGINE, MANIFOLDS & CYLINDER HEAD

ENGINE

NOTE: **On 3A-C, separate engine from transaxle before removal. On 4A-C, remove engine and transmission as a unit. Separate engine from transmission and remove starter after assembly removal.**

Removal

1) Mark hinge locations. Remove hood. Remove battery and carrier. Remove air cleaner assembly. Drain coolant. On 3A-C, wrap drive shaft boots with shop towels. Remove fan shroud (A/C only). On all models, remove radiator, alternator, brackets, drive belts, fan, water pump (3A-C only) and hoses as necessary.

2) If equipped, detach A/C belt, compressor, condenser, power steering belt and pump with bracket. Set assemblies aside. Do not discharge systems. Remove engine sub wiring harness and set aside. On 3A-C, remove 4 upper transaxle-to-engine mount bolts. On automatic transmission, disconnect throttle linkage and oil cooler lines.

3) On 4A-C, remove emission control valve set. Disconnect oxygen sensor and air hose from air suction reed valve. From inside of vehicle, remove console box and disconnect shift lever. On all models, raise and support vehicle. Drain engine oil. On 3A-C, remove front exhaust pipe and bracket, differential plate bolts and oil cooler pipe (if equipped).

4) On 4A-C, remove front exhaust pipe and brackets from catalytic converter. Scribe alignment marks on differential and drive shaft flanges. Disconnect 4 drive shaft flange mount bolts. Remove center bearing carrier mount bolts. Remove drive shaft assembly. Insert transmission tool (SST09325-12010), or equivalent, to prevent oil leakage.

5) On all models, identify and disconnect engine-to-chassis electrical connections at engine. Disconnect carburetor linkage, fuel lines and heater hoses. On 3A-C manual transmission, remove starter cable and windshield washer tank. Disconnect clutch pedal tension spring and release cable. On automatic transmission, remove starter and torque converter cover.

6) On 4A-C, disconnect fuel line at fuel pump and front exhaust pipe at manifold flange. Disconnect speedometer cable and back-up light switch connector. Remove clutch slave cylinder. On automatic transmission, disconnect oil cooler lines and remove power steering gear housing. Place jack under transmission.

7) Remove engine rear mount and ground cable. Remove engine mount bolts from both side mounts. Attach hoist chain to engine and take up slack. Lift engine/transmission assembly from vehicle. Use caution to avoid damage to clutch and brake fluid reservoirs. Disconnect transmission and starter from engine after removal.

8) On 3A-C, support transmission with floor jack. Remove engine mounts. Attach hoist to engine hangers. With hoist supporting engine, remove remaining lower transaxle mount bolts. Check all wiring and hoses are detached from engine before removal.

9) On manual transmission, carefully lift and remove engine. On automatic transmission, remove 4 torque converter mount bolts. Pull engine about 2" forward, disconnect torque converter and remove engine. Suspend clutch or converter housing.

Installation

1) With 4A-C engine connected to transmission, install starter. Carefully lower engine into position. Replace engine mount bolts and nuts. On manual transmission, install clutch slave cylinder and bleed hydraulic system as necessary. On 3A-C, install engine and connect to transaxle.

2) On all models, install all wiring, heater and vacuum hoses. Adjust drive belts. Add proper amount of engine and transmission oil and coolant. To complete installation, reverse removal procedure. Reinstall hood, start engine and check for leaks.

INTAKE & EXHAUST MANIFOLDS

NOTE: **Intake and exhaust manifolds are removed and installed as an assembly.**

Removal

1) Disconnect battery. Remove air cleaner assembly. Disconnect fuel and vacuum lines, choke and throttle linkage or cable at carburetor. On air conditioner, remove vacuum idle up hose.

2) On all models, identify and disconnect fuel, brake booster, emission control and heater inlet vacuum hoses. Remove heat insulator, PCV valve and PCV hose. Identify and disconnect all hoses and wiring related to removal of manifolds.

3) Disconnect exhaust pipe at manifold. Remove manifold stay from exhaust manifold. Remove intake and exhaust manifold mount nuts and bolts. Remove manifolds with carburetor as an assembly. Separate carburetor from manifolds as necessary.

Inspection

1) Inspect intake and exhaust manifold gasket surfaces for nicks or damage. Using straightedge and feeler gauge, check manifolds for warpage. Warpage limit for 4A-C intake manifold is .008" (.20 mm).

2) For 4A-C exhaust manifold and 3A-C intake and exhaust manifolds, warpage limit is .012" (.30 mm). If warpage is beyond limits, resurface or replace manifolds as necessary.

Installation

To install, reverse removal procedure. Ensure mating surfaces are clean and new gaskets are used. Tighten 2 center bolts first. Tighten remainder in a front-to-rear, top-to-bottom pattern.

3A-C & 4A-C 4-CYLINDER (Cont.)

CYLINDER HEAD

Removal

1) Disconnect battery. Remove air cleaner assembly. Drain coolant and engine oil. Remove upper radiator hose. Disconnect heater inlet hose from cylinder head rear plate. Remove drive belts and water pump pulley. Detach manifold stay from exhaust manifold. On A/C, remove idle-up vacuum hose.

2) If equipped, detach A/C belt, compressor, condenser fan, power steering belt and pump with bracket. Set assemblies aside. Do not discharge systems. On 4A-C, disconnect oxygen sensor wire. On all models, identify and remove remaining wiring, heater and vacuum hoses related to cylinder head. Remove intake and exhaust manifolds and carburetor as an assembly.

3) Remove spark plugs, wires and distributor as an assembly. Remove valve cover with gasket and half circle plug, alternator upper bracket and water outlet. Remove fuel lines to fuel pump and pump. Position No. 1 cylinder at TDC on compression stroke. Ensure rocker arms for No. 1 are loose. If not, rotate crankshaft one revolution.

4) Remove alternator as necessary. Using puller, remove crankshaft pulley. On 4A-C, remove air suction reed valve and components. On all models, remove timing belt covers, gasket and (3A-C only) water pump. Mark position of camshaft timing sprocket and timing belt. Loosen idler pulley mount bolt and retighten pulley in far left position. Remove timing belt.

NOTE: Do not bend or twist timing belt. Keep belt free of oil, water or dust. Loosen head bolts in proper sequence or warpage and cracking may result.

5) Loosen cylinder head bolts, in 2 or 3 steps, in reverse of sequence shown in *Fig. 1*. Lift head from dowels on block and set on wood blocks on work bench. If difficult to remove, pry with flat bar between cylinder head and block projection.

NOTE: Do not damage cylinder head or block surface during prying operation.

Inspection

1) Clean all gasket material from top of block. Blow out carbon and oil from bolt holes. Using wire brush and gasket scraper, remove carbon and gasket material from combustion chambers, head and manifold surfaces. Do not scratch or damage gasket contact surfaces.

NOTE: Do not clean cylinder head in a "hot tank" or it may be damaged.

2) Using straightedge and feeler gauge, check head and block for warpage. Measure head on all four sides and diagonally. Measure block lengthwise across head bolt holes on gasket surface and diagonally.

3) Maximum warpage on block side of head is .002" (.05 mm). On manifold surfaces, warpage limit is .004" (.10 mm). Maximum warpage of block is .002" (.05 mm). Maximum resurfacing limit is .004" (.10 mm). If warped beyond limits, resurface or replace cylinder head and/or block.

4) Using a dye penetrant, check combustion chambers, intake and exhaust ports, head surface and top of head for cracks. If crack is found, replace cylinder head.

Installation

1) Ensure that mating surfaces are clean and camshaft caps and rocker arm assembly are tightened properly. Apply oil to all sliding and rotating surfaces. On 4A-C, install head gasket with sealer side facing up.

2) On all models, install new head gasket and cylinder head. Tighten head bolts gradually, in 3 steps, in the sequence shown in *Fig. 1*. Install timing belt and check valve timing and timing belt tension. Complete installation in reverse order of removal.

3) Set valve clearance. Fill cooling system. Refill engine with oil. Check and set ignition timing and idle speed. Start engine and check for leaks. Run engine for several minutes, let it cool down and recheck cylinder head mount bolt torque.

Fig. 1: Cylinder Head Bolt Tightening Sequence

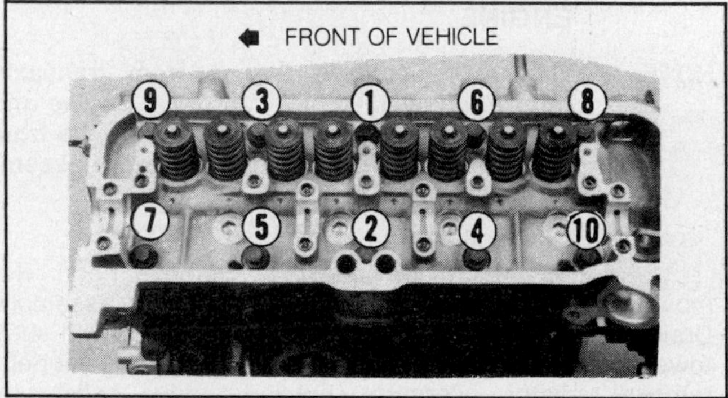
FRONT OF VEHICLE
9
3
1
6
8
7
5
2
4
10

Loosen the head bolts in reverse of tightening sequence.

CAMSHAFT

ENGINE FRONT COVERS

Removal

1) Drain cooling system. Remove radiator and air cleaner assembly. Remove alternator upper bracket and water outlet, if necessary. On air conditioner, remove drive belt, idler pulley, fan shroud, fan and bracket.

2) On all models, remove drive belts, water pump pulley and valve cover. Remove upper engine front cover mount bolts, cover and gasket. Set No. 1 cylinder at TDC on compression stroke.

NOTE: Check rocker arms on No. 1 cylinder are loose. If not, turn crankshaft 1 turn clockwise.

3) On 4A-C, remove crankshaft pulley No. 2 (power steering only). On all models, secure camshaft and remove crankshaft pulley bolt. Using puller tool (SST09213-31021), remove crankshaft pulley. Remove lower engine front cover.

Installation

Clean all gasket surfaces thoroughly. Install front covers and new gasket. Reverse removal procedure to complete assembly.

TIMING BELT & SPROCKETS

NOTE: If reusing old timing belt, draw directional arrow on belt in direction of engine revolution. Place match marks on crankshaft and camshaft sprockets and belt. Ensure belt is not contaminated with water, oil or dust.

3A-C & 4A-C 4-CYLINDER (Cont.)

Removal

1) Drain cooling system. Remove fan shroud (A/C only). Remove radiator and air cleaner assembly. Remove drive belts, fan, water pump drive pulley (on 3A-C) and valve cover with gasket.

2) Set No. 1 cylinder at TDC on compression stroke and check No. 1 rocker arms are loose. If not, rotate crankshaft 1 turn. On 4A-C, remove crankshaft pulley No. 2 (power steering only). Using puller tool, remove crankshaft pulley.

3) Remove upper and lower engine front cover mount bolts, gasket and covers. Loosen idler pulley mount bolt, position pulley at far left and retighten mount bolt. Remove timing belt.

Inspection

1) Check belt teeth for cracks or damage. If tooth damage is found, ensure camshaft is not locked. If wear or cracks on flat belt face are found, check for nicks on one side of idler pulley lock.

2) If wear or damage to only one side of belt is found, check belt guide and alignment of each pulley and sprocket. If noticeable wear is found on belt teeth, check timing cover gasket for damage and proper installation.

3) Ensure there is no foreign material on sprocket teeth. Check timing belt idler pulley for smooth rotation. Replace if roughness or noise is found.

Installation

1) Loosen timing belt idler pulley mount bolt, move pulley as far left as possible and retighten bolt. Do not bend or twist belt. Install timing belt.

2) If reusing old belt, align marks made during removal. Install belt with arrow pointing in direction of revolution. Release idler pulley and place tension on belt.

3) If installing new belt, align crankshaft timing pulley and TDC mark on oil pump cover. Align front cam bearing cap mark and center of small hole on camshaft timing sprocket. *See Fig. 2.*

4) Slowly turn crankshaft 2 revolutions clockwise. Recheck timing marks. Measure belt tension on side opposite idler pulley. Pushing belt toward pulley.

5) Deflection should be .24-.28" (6-7 mm), at tension of 4.4 lbs. (2 kg). *See Fig. 2.* If tension incorrect, readjust with idler pulley. Complete installation by reversing removal procedure.

Fig. 2: Aligning Valve Timing Marks

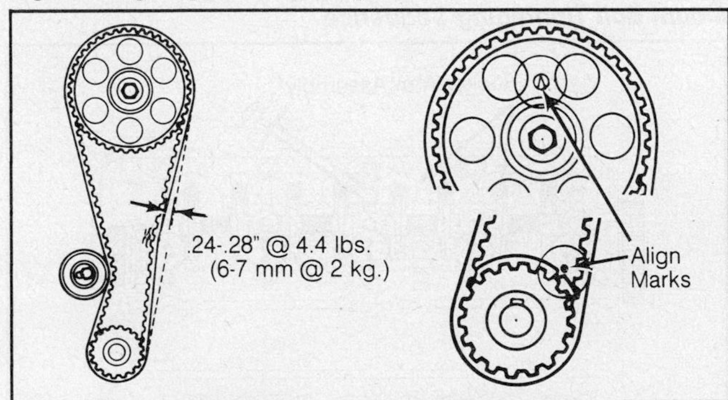
.24-.28" @ 4.4 lbs.
(6-7 mm @ 2 kg.)
Align
Marks

Check the timing belt tension after installation.

CAMSHAFT

Removal

1) Remove air cleaner assembly. Identify and remove all wiring and hoses interfering with valve cover removal. Remove valve cover and gasket. Remove engine front covers, gasket and timing belt. Loosen rocker arm support bolts in 3 to 4 steps, in reverse order of tightening sequence. *See Fig. 3.*

2) Remove rocker arm assembly. Secure camshaft. Remove camshaft timing sprocket. Before camshaft removal, measure end play. Remove camshaft bearing caps in the following sequence: front, rear, front center and rear center.

3) Keep bearing caps in order for reassembly reference. Remove camshaft and oil seal. Detach distributor drive gear mount bolt from camshaft and remove drive gear.

NOTE: The camshaft rides directly on cylinder head bearing surfaces and caps. There are no replaceable cam bearings in the head.

Inspection

1) Before removal, check camshaft end play. Standard end play is .0031-.0071" (.080-.180 mm). Maximum end play is .0098" (.250 mm). If clearance is beyond limits, replace camshaft and/or cylinder head assembly.

2) Check for bend by placing camshaft in "V" blocks. Using dial indicator, set pointer on center journal. Rotate camshaft and measure total runout. Maximum bend limit for 3A-C is .0024" (.060 mm). On 4A-C, bend limit is .10" (.004 mm). If beyond limit, replace camshaft.

3) Using micrometer, check camshaft lobe heights for excessive wear. Standard lobe height is 1.5366-1.5370" (39.030-39.040 mm) for 3A-C with 4-speed transmission and 1.5528-1.5531" (39.440-39.450 mm) for all others. Minimum lobe height is 1.5248" (38.730 mm) for 3A-C with 4-speed transmission and 1.5409" (39.140 mm) for all others. If worn below limit, replace camshaft.

4) Using micrometer, measure camshaft bearing journals. Replace camshaft if journals show nicks, scores or wear. Inspect cam bearing caps for flaking or scoring. If caps are damaged or excessively worn, replace head and camshaft.

5) Check camshaft oil clearance, with camshaft and bearing caps tightened in place, using Plastigage method. Do not turn camshaft during measurement. Maximum clearance is .004" (.10 mm). If clearance is beyond limit, replace camshaft and cylinder head.

Installation

1) Coat camshaft and bearing caps with oil. Apply grease to new oil seal lip and sealant on outside edge of seal. Install oil seal. Do not set slantwise. Install camshaft.

2) Apply sealer to No. 1 bearing cap-to-head junction points and install. Install remaining bearing caps with arrows on No. 2, 3 and 4 caps facing forward.

3) Tighten bearing cap bolts gradually, in 3 or 4 steps. *See Fig. 3.* To complete installation, reverse removal procedure.

CAMSHAFT OIL SEAL

Removal & Installation

1) Remove air cleaner, valve cover, front covers and timing belt. Loosen rocker arm support bolts in 3 to 4 steps, in reverse order of sequence shown in *Fig. 3.* Remove rocker arm assembly.

2) Secure camshaft and remove camshaft timing sprocket. Remove camshaft bearing caps in the following sequence: front, rear, front center and rear center.

3A-C & 4A-C 4-CYLINDER (Cont.)

3) Keep caps in order for reassembly reference. Remove camshaft and oil seal. Inspect seal contact surface of camshaft for cracks or damage. Replace as necessary. Apply grease to new oil seal lip and sealant to outside of seal.

4) Install oil seal. Ensure seal is not installed slantwise. Install No. 1 bearing cap with sealant applied at cap-to-head junction points. Tighten bearing caps in 3 to 4 steps, in sequence shown in *Fig. 3*.

CRANKSHAFT FRONT OIL SEAL

Removal & Installation

1) With oil pump removed from block, tap oil seal out using hammer and drift. Do not damage seal contact surface of pump. Apply grease to new oil seal. Replace using seal installer tool (SST09517-30011 for 3A-C and SST09517-30010 for 4A-C).

NOTE: **During installation, ensure oil seal is flush with oil pump body outer surface.**

2) With pump installed, use knife to cut off lip of seal. Using screwdriver, carefully pry out seal. Do not damage seal contact surface of pump or seal lip contact surface of crankshaft.

3) Inspect seal lip contact surface of crankshaft for cracks or damage. Replace as necessary. Apply grease to new seal lip. Using installer tool, replace oil seal. Do not install the seal slantwise or set the seal more than .04" (1 mm) into oil pump body.

VALVES

VALVE ARRANGEMENT

I-E-E-I-I-E-E-I. (Front-to-rear).

VALVES

1) Using gasket scraper, chip carbon from valve head. Using wire brush, clean valve thoroughly. Inspect valves for worn, damaged or deformed head or stem.

2) Check valve head in-margin thickness. If head is worn to .02" (.5 mm) in-margin thickness for intake or .04" (1 mm) for exhaust, replace valve. Check surface of valve stem tip for excessive wear.

3) Standard valve length is 4.208" (106.88 mm) for intake and 4.204" (106.78 mm) for exhaust. Valve stem end surface grinding limit is .02" (.5 mm). If valve stem tip is worn, resurface with grinder or replace valve.

VALVE SPRINGS

Removal

1) With cylinder head, rocker arms and shaft assembly removed, remove cam bearing caps, seal and camshaft. Keep components in order for reassembly reference.

2) Press valve spring down with compressor tool (SST09202-43013). Remove valve keepers. Remove compressor tool. Remove spring retainer, spring, valve, oil seal and valve spring seat.

NOTE: **Keep all valve train and camshaft components in order for reassembly reference.**

Inspection

1) Using steel square, check squareness of valve springs. Spring must be .08" (2 mm) or less out of square. Check free length of springs. Replace any not within limits.

2) Using spring tester, check tension of each spring at specified installed height. Valve spring installed height is 1.52" (38.6 mm). Minimum installed tension is 46.3 lbs. (21 kg). Replace spring if not to specifications.

Installation

1) Before installing components, clean parts to be assembled. Apply oil to sliding and rotating surfaces. Install valve spring seats and new oil seals.

2) Install springs and retainers on valves. Using compressor tool, compress springs and install keepers. Tap stem lightly with plastic hammer to ensure keepers are seated properly.

ROCKER ARMS & SHAFT ASSEMBLY

Removal

1) Remove air cleaner and valve cover. Loosen valve adjuster lock nuts. Back off adjuster screws. Loosen rocker arm support bolts in 3 to 4 steps, in reverse of tightening sequence. *See Fig. 3*. Remove rocker arm assembly.

2) Check arm-to-shaft clearance by twisting rocker arm on shaft. Little or no movement should be felt. If movement is felt, disassemble rocker arm assembly and measure oil clearance. During disassemble, mark parts for proper reassembly.

Inspection

1) Using dial indicator, measure inside diameter of rocker arm. Using micrometer, measure outside diameter of rocker shaft. Subtract rocker diameter from shaft diameter.

2) Determine clearance. Standard rocker arm-to-shaft clearance is .0004-.0019" (.010-.048 mm). If clearance exceeds .0024" (.060 mm), replace rocker arm and/or shaft.

3) Check cam end contact surface of rocker arm and valve contact surface of rocker arm adjusting screw. If worn excessively, grind or replace rocker arm and/or adjusting screw as necessary.

Installation

1) To install, reverse removal procedure. Tighten rocker arm support bolts gradually, in 3 to 4 steps, in proper sequence. *See Fig. 3*.

Fig. 3: Rocker Arm Assembly and Bearing Cap Mount Bolt Tightening Sequence

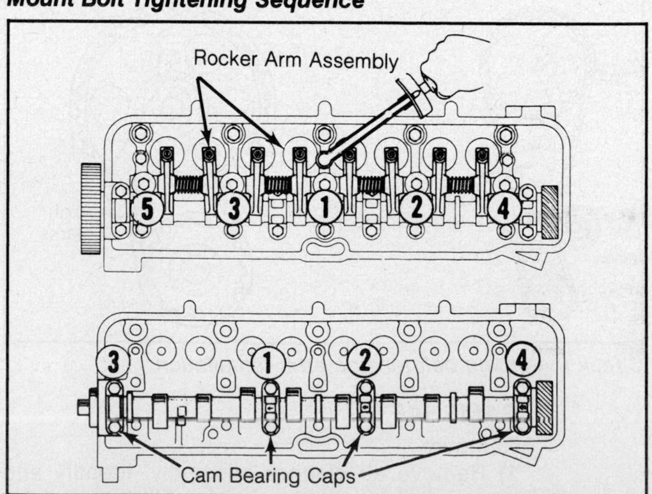

Rocker Arm Assembly
5
3
1
2
4
3
1
2
4
Cam Bearing Caps

Loosen the rocker arm assembly and cam bearing cap mount bolts in reverse of the tightening sequence.

3A-C & 4A-C 4-CYLINDER (Cont.)

2) If necessary, loosen adjusting screws and nuts prior to installation of assembly. When assembling rocker shaft, shaft oil holes must face right, left and bottom. *See Fig. 4.*

Fig. 4: Assembling Rocker Arms and Shaft Assembly

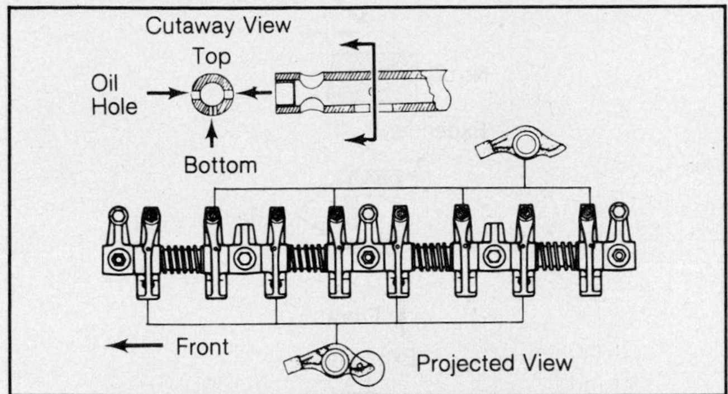

Cutaway View
Top
Oil Hole
Bottom
Front
Projected View

Face oil holes of rocker shaft to right, left and bottom.

VALVE GUIDE SERVICING

Clearance Check

1) Using valve guide brush and solvent, clean guides. Measure clearance between valve stem and guide with micrometer and telescope hole gauge. Check diameter of stem at top, center and bottom. Insert hole gauge in guide bore. Measure at center.

2) Subtract highest reading of stem diameter from guide bore to obtain clearance. Standard guide inside diameter is .2760-.2768" (7.010-7.030 mm). Maximum stem-to-guide clearance is .0031" (.080 mm) for intake and .004" (.10 mm) for exhaust. If clearance is beyond limits and stem is not worn, replace guide.

NOTE: **Replacement valve guides are available in .05 mm oversize.**

Replacement

1) Using hammer and drift, tap guide firmly enough to break guide off flush with cylinder head surface. Remove snap ring. Gradually heat head to 194°F (90°C). Using valve guide removal tool (SST09201-60011) or equivalent, drive guide out from camshaft side.

2) Measure cylinder head valve guide hole. Standard guide outside diameter is .4543-.4548" (11.540-11.551 mm). If hole-to-guide clearance is excessive, machine hole for oversized guide.

3) With head at room temperature, ream guide hole to fit new guide. Oversize guide outside diameter is .4563-.4567" (11.590-11.601 mm). To install valve guide, reheat cylinder head.

4) Drive in new guide, using installer tool, until snap ring contacts head. Using 7 mm reamer, finish guide bore to specified clearance. Reface valve seat surface, as needed, after valve or guide repair or replacement.

VALVE CLEARANCE ADJUSTMENT

NOTE: **Valves should be adjusted with engine at normal operating temperature but not running. Cold specifications are provided for initial settings after assembly.**

1) With engine at normal operating temperature, stop engine and remove valve cover. Bring No. 1 piston to TDC of compression stroke. Ensure rockers on No. 1 are loose and No. 4 are tight.

2) If not, rotate crankshaft 1 revolution. Realign cutout on damper pulley with 0° timing mark on timing belt cover. Adjust No. 1 & 2 intake valves and No. 1 & 3 exhaust valves.

3) Rotate crankshaft one full turn (360°) clockwise to realign timing mark on damper pulley with "O" mark on timing cover. Adjust No. 3 & 4 intake valves and No. 2 & 4 exhaust valves.

VALVE CLEARANCE SPECIFICATIONS

Valve	Hot In. (mm)	Cold In. (mm)
Intake	.008 (.20)	.007 (.18)
Exhaust	.012 (.30)	.011 (.28)

PISTONS, PINS & RINGS

PISTON & ROD ASSEMBLY

Removal

1) With cylinder head and oil pan removed, remove connecting rod nuts. Remove rod cap with bearing half. Check top of cylinder bore for ridge. If scraper will not remove carbon build-up, remove using ridge reamer.

2) Cover rod bolts with short pieces of rubber hose to protect crankshaft journals from damage. Push piston/rod assembly, with bearing half, out through top of block.

NOTE: **Rod caps must be kept with their respective piston and rod assembly and are not interchangeable.**

Inspection

1) Check connecting rod for bend or torsion using rod aligner tool. Bend and torsion limit is .002" (.05 mm) or less, in 3.94" (100 mm) of length.

2) Install rod, with bearings, on crank pin. Measure side thrust clearance. Maximum play at big end must be .012" (.30 mm) or less. Replace rod if not to specifications.

Installation

1) Install rings with code marks up. Ensure ring gaps are set 180° apart and are not on thrust side of piston or in line with pin. *See Fig. 5.* Apply oil to rings, piston and bore. Install piston and rod assembly. Ensure bearing inserts are properly seated.

2) Install ring compressor. Install piston/rod assembly with cavity on piston top aligned with protrusion of rod and facing toward front of engine. *See Fig. 6.* With piston installed, ensure rod and bearings are seated against crankshaft journal.

3) Ensure rod and cap marks align. Tighten caps to specification. Install cylinder head. Install new gasket and oil pan. Tighten pan bolts evenly, in a criss-cross pattern. Do not over-tighten. Complete installation by reversing removal procedure.

FITTING PISTONS & RINGS

NOTE: **Pistons and rings are available in .50 mm, .75 mm and 1 mm oversize for 3A-C and .01 mm and .02 mm oversize for 4A-C engines.**

1) Inspect cylinder block for cracks or flaws. Using bore gauge, measure for out-of-round or excessive

3A-C & 4A-C 4-CYLINDER (Cont.)

taper. If measurements exceed .0008" (.020 mm), refinish bore. When one cylinder is bored, all must be bored. Check head gasket surface for warpage. Maximum limit is .002" (.05 mm).

NOTE: **Before cylinder block machining operations, ensure main bearing caps are installed and tightened to specification. Bore cylinders in order of No. 2-4-1-3 to prevent distortion.**

2) Determine piston oversize according to cylinder wear. Standard bore diameter is 3.0512-3.0524" (77.500-77.530 mm) for 3A-C and 3.1890-3.1894" (81.000-81.010 mm) for 4A-C. Bore wear limit is .008" (.20 mm). Measure piston diameter at right angle to pin and .20" (5 mm) below oil ring groove. Add piston-to-cylinder clearance. Determine finish hone of cylinder.

PISTON DIAMETER SPECIFICATIONS

Application	In. (mm)
3A-C	
Standard	3.0468-3.0480 (77.390-77.420)
.50 mm Oversize	3.0665-3.0677 (77.890-77.920)
.75 mm Oversize	3.0764-3.0776 (78.140-78.170)
1 mm Oversize	3.0862-3.0874 (78.390-78.420)
4A-C	
Standard	3.1846-3.1850 (81.890-81.900)
.01 mm Oversize	3.1850-3.1554 (80.900-80.910)
.02 mm Oversize	3.1854-3.1858 (80.910-80.920)

3) After honing cylinder to final fit, measure piston-to-cylinder clearance with parts at 70°F (20°C). Ensure difference of bore limit between cylinders is .002" (.05 mm) or less. If beyond limit, cylinders must be bored.

4) If reusing pistons, decarbon ring grooves with scraper and curved steel wire or piece of broken ring. Clean oil slots in bottom land of oil ring groove. Check for scratches, wear or damage.

5) Measure side clearance of rings in grooves as each is installed. Check ring end gap. Install ring squarely in cylinder, using piston. If beyond limits, replace piston and/or rings. When installing rings, ensure code mark faces up. *See Fig. 5.*

PISTON PINS

NOTE: **The piston and pin are a matched set. Keep piston, pin, rings and rod together for each cylinder.**

1) Check fit between piston and pin by moving piston back and forth on piston pin. If any movement is felt, replace piston and pin.

2) To remove, warm piston and rod assembly to about 70°F (20°C). Press out pin using pin removal/installer tool (SST09221-25014 for 3A-C and SST09221-25015 for 4A-C). Do not damage piston during removal.

3) Check pin and piston pin hole for signs of gauling or excessive wear. Replace as necessary. To assemble, reheat piston to 70°F (20°C). Align the cavity on piston top with protrusion on rod.

Fig. 5: Positioning Piston Ring Gaps

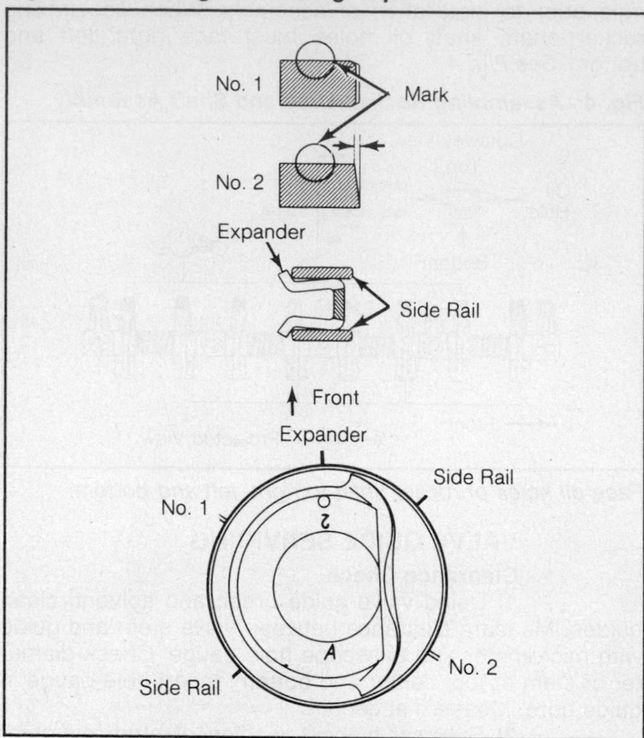
No. 1
Mark
No. 2
Expander
Side Rail
Front
Expander
Side Rail
No. 1
No. 2
Side Rail

Ensure ring gaps are not on thrust side of piston and code marks on rings face up.

4) Coat pin with oil. Insert into piston using pin installer tool while holding parts in proper alignment. Check for no movement of piston on pin. *See Fig. 6.* Press pin until centered in rod.

Fig. 6: Assembling Piston & Connecting Rod

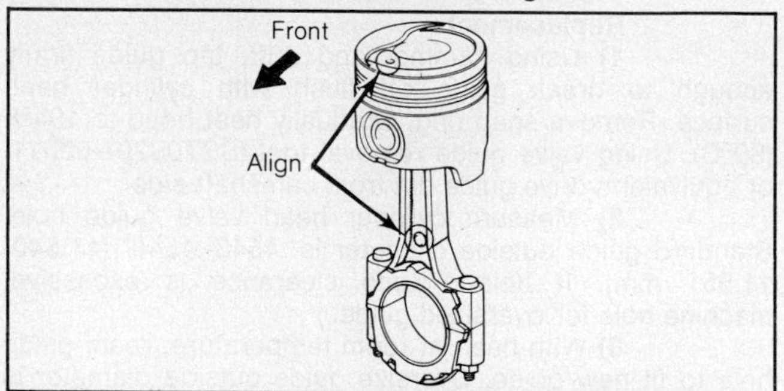
Front
Align

Align the piston cavity with connecting rod protrusion.

CRANKSHAFT & MAIN & CONNECTING ROD BEARINGS

CRANKSHAFT

NOTE: **The cylinder block bearing marks are near the No. 5 main bearing cap. The number stamped closest to flywheel edge of block corresponds to No. 5 main bearing.**

3A-C & 4A-C 4-CYLINDER (Cont.)

Removal

1) With engine removed, remove outer parts, install engine attachment and mount assembly on work stand. Remove drive belts and front covers. Remove valve timing belt.

2) Secure crankshaft and remove flywheel or drive plate, oil pan, oil pump and cylinder head. Remove piston and rod assemblies. Using punch, mark rods and caps for reassembly reference.

3) Remove main bearing caps and arrange caps, inserts and thrust washers in order. Remove rear oil seal retainer. Do not damage crankshaft sealing surface. Remove crankshaft. Remove upper main bearing halves.

NOTE: **If replacing main bearing, replace with one having the same number as marked on cylinder block. There are three sizes of standard bearings, marked 1, 2 or 3 accordingly.**

Inspection

1) Check crankshaft journals and crankpins for scoring, wear, cracks, taper and out of round. Maximum taper and out of round limit is .0008" (.020 mm). If beyond limits, replace crankshaft.

2) Check crankshaft for bend by placing on "V" blocks. Use dial indicator at center journal. Maximum limit is .0024" (.060 mm) or less for 3A-C and .0012" (.030 mm) or less for 4A-C. If beyond limits, replace crankshaft.

NOTE: **The pilot bearing in the crankshaft rear opening is permanently lubricated and requires no cleaning or lubrication.**

3) Inspect crankshaft rear end pilot bearing. If damaged or excessively worn, replace pilot bearing using removal tool (SST09303-35011) and installer tool (SST09304-30012).

4) Check flywheel friction surface for cracks, damage or wear. Measure runout using dial indicator. Runout limit is .008" (.02 mm). Resurface or replace if beyond limits. Check tooth surfaces of ring gear for flaws or wear. Replace as necessary.

NOTE: **Main bearing caps are numbered and must be installed with arrows facing forward.**

Installation

1) Install main bearing inserts in block. Ensure bearings are on correct journal. Upper and lower bearing inserts have oil holes. Check insert oil holes are in proper alignment with block and bearing cap oil holes.

2) Apply oil to main bearing surfaces. Install upper thrust washers on center bearing and lower thrust washers on No. 3 main bearing cap with oil grooves facing out. Install crankshaft. Install bearing caps with arrows facing front of engine.

3) Shift crankshaft toward front of engine. Tighten bearing caps in 2 or 3 steps, starting at center bearing and working outward. Ensure crankshaft rotates smoothly. *See Fig. 7*.

4) Check end play using dial indicator with pointer set on crankshaft sprocket mount. Standard thrust washer thickness is .0961-.0980" (2.440-2.490 mm). End play must be .012" (.30 mm) or less. If beyond limits, replace thrust washers as a set.

5) Install rear oil seal retainer. Install flywheel or drive plate. Install piston and rod assemblies. To install remaining components, reverse removal procedure.

Fig. 7: Main Bearing Cap Tightening Sequence

FRONT OF VEHICLE
5
3
1
2
4

Loosen the main bearing cap bolts in reverse order.

MAIN BEARING CLEARANCE

1) Check bearings for scoring or wear. Replace if damaged. Clean oil from crankshaft. Check bearing clearance using Plastigage method. Maximum main bearing clearance is .0031" (.080 mm).

2) If beyond limit, replace main bearing inserts with ones having same number as marked on cylinder block. There are three sizes of standard main bearings, marked 1, 2 and 3 accordingly.

NOTE: **Plastigage should run parallel with crankshaft. Do not block oil hole or turn crankshaft with Plastigage inserted.**

CONNECTING ROD BEARING CLEARANCE

1) Check bearings for scoring or wear. Replace if damaged. Clean oil from crankshaft. Check bearing clearance using Plastigage method. Tighten rod caps to 26-32 ft. lbs. (35-43 N.m). Maximum connecting rod bearing clearance is .0031" (.080 mm).

2) If beyond limit, replace rod bearing inserts with ones having same number as marked on bearing cap. There are three sizes of standard rod bearings, marked 1, 2 and 3 accordingly.

CRANKSHAFT REAR OIL SEAL

Removal & Installation

1) Remove engine/transaxle assembly and separate. Remove flywheel or drive plate. With seal retainer removed from block, tap oil seal out using hammer and drift. Do not damage seal contact surface of retainer. Apply grease to new oil seal. Install using installer tool (SST09218-56010 for 3A-C and SST09223-41020 for 4A-C).

NOTE: **During installation, do not install oil seal slantwise.**

2) With retainer installed, use knife to cut off lip of seal. Using screwdriver, carefully pry out seal. Do not damage seal contact surface of retainer or seal lip contact surface of crankshaft.

3) Inspect seal lip contact surface of crankshaft for cracks or damage. Replace as necessary. Apply grease to new oil seal. Using installer tool, replace oil seal.

ENGINE OILING

CRANKCASE CAPACITY

The crankcase capacity is 3.5 qts. (3.3L) with filter. Refill without filter is 3.2 qts. (3.0L).

3A-C & 4A-C 4-CYLINDER (Cont.)

NORMAL OIL PRESSURE

The normal oil pressure 4.3 psi (.3 kg/cm²) at idle. At 3000 RPM the oil pressure should be 35.6-71.1 psi (2.5-5.0 kg/cm²).

OIL PRESSURE REGULATOR VALVE

The oil pressure regulator valve is located in the oil pump cover. It is a nonadjustable type valve.

ENGINE OILING SYSTEM

Oil is forced from a gear type oil pump to full-flow oil filter. From the filter, oil is directed to crankshaft main bearings which feeds connecting rod bearings. The oil passage above No. 1 main bearing feeds camshaft and rocker arm shaft through No. 1 rocker support. Oil is then returned to the pan. *See Fig. 8*.

Fig. 8: 4-Cylinder Engine Oiling System

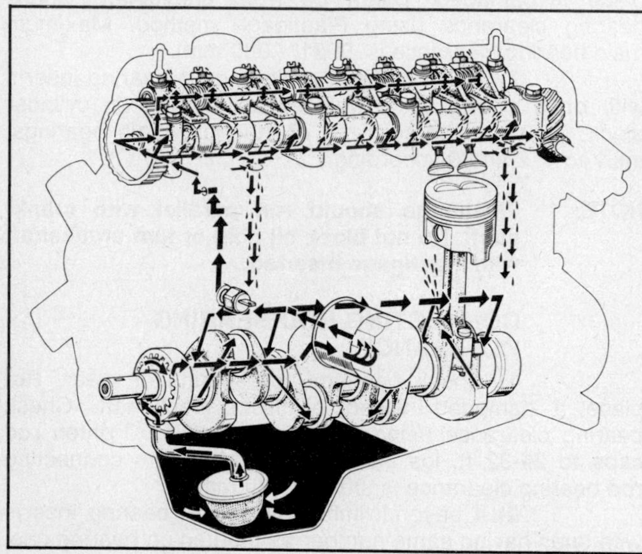

Typical Toyota 4-Cylinder engine oiling system.

OIL PUMP

NOTE: When repairing oil pump, the oil pan and screen should be removed and cleaned.

Removal

1) Raise and support vehicle. Drain engine oil. Remove timing covers and timing belt. Using oil pan prying tool (SST09032-00100), remove oil pan. Do not use prying tool on pump side. Do not damage pan flange.

2) Remove oil strainer mount bolts and strainer. Remove dipstick and tube. Remove oil pump by tapping pump body with plastic hammer. Disassemble pump cover, drive gear, driven gear, oil seal and relief valve. *See Fig. 9*.

Inspection

1) Check gears for wear or damage. Install new oil seal using seal installer tool (09517-30011 for 3A-C and 09517-30010 for 4A-C). Do not install seal slantwise.

2) Measure clearances between drive gear and driven gear, side clearance, and gear-to-body clearance. If beyond limits, replace necessary parts. Check relief valve for wear or damage. *See Fig. 9*.

Fig. 9: Exploded View of Oil Pump Assembly

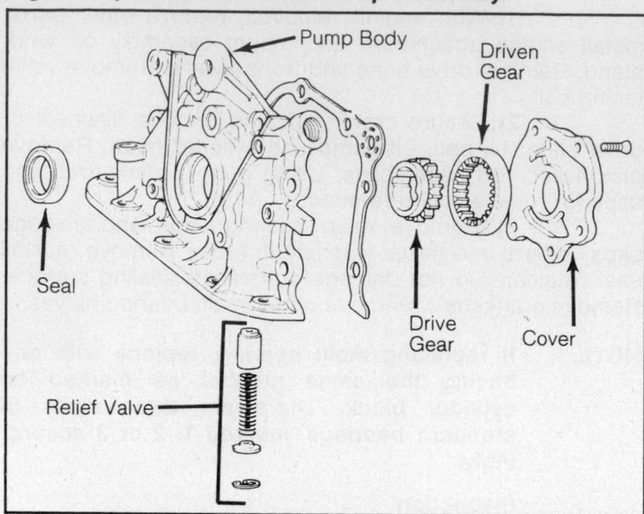
Pump Body
Driven Gear
Seal
Drive Gear
Cover
Relief Valve

Replace oil seal and any gear that shows excessive wear, damage or is beyond clearance limits.

Installation

1) Check that mating surfaces are clean. Ensure pump drive gear spline teeth engage with large teeth of crankshaft.

2) Using new seal packing No. 102 pan gasket or silicone base sealant, install oil pan. Complete installation by reversing removal procedures.

OIL PUMP CLEARANCES

Application	In. (mm)
Drive Gear Tip-to-Cresent	.004-.010 (.11-.25)
	Limit .014 (.35)
Driven Gear Tip-to-Cresent	.002-.012 (.06-.31)
	Limit .014 (.35)
Gear Side	.001-.003 (.03-.08)
	Limit .004 (.10)
Driven Gear-to-Body	.004-.008 (.10-.19)
	Limit .008 (.20)

ENGINE COOLING

COOLANT CAPACITY

Total coolant capacity with heater is 5.7 qts. (5.4L) for manual transmission and 6.6 qts. (6.2L) for automatic transmission..

THERMOSTAT

The thermostat starts to open at 176-183°F (80-84°C) and is fully open at 203°F (95°C).

FAN THERMOSWITCH

The fan thermoswitch operates between 181-194°F (83-90°C).

RADIATOR CAP

10.7-14.9 psi. (.75-1.05 kg/cm²).

3A-C & 4A-C 4-CYLINDER (Cont.)

WATER PUMP

NOTE: Do not allow coolant onto timing belt during replacement or repair.

Removal

1) Drain cooling system. Loosen alternator pivot bolt, swing unit toward engine and remove drive belt. Remove fan shroud (A/C only). Remove fluid coupling with fan, water pump pulley and drive belt.

2) Remove water outlet housing, by-pass pipe, water inlet housing, thermostat, timing belt upper cover and oil dip stick tube. Disconnect heater outlet hose from pipe and remove heater outlet pipe mounting bolt. Remove water pump.

Disassembly

1) Remove water pump suction cover mount bolts and pry off cover. Remove 4 stud bolts from pulley seat. Using hydraulic press and service tool (SST09236-00100), press pulley seat off of pump bearing shaft.

2) Heat pump body to about 185°F (85°C). Press out bearing, with impeller, from pump body. Press impeller off of pump shaft/bearing assembly. Remove seal set from bearing assembly.

Reassembly

1) Heat pump body to 185°F (85°C). Press bearing/shaft assembly into body until bearing race is flush with body top surface. Apply sealant to new seal set and press onto bearing assembly.

2) Press pulley seat onto pump bearing shaft. Distance between face of pulley seat and rear of pump body should be 2.99" (76 mm) for 3A-C and 3.34-3.40" (84.8-86.2 mm) for 4A-C.

3) Install new packing and seat into impeller. Apply oil to seal lip and rotor contact surfaces. Press impeller onto shaft to depth of .236" (6 mm). Install 4 stud bolts to pulley seat. After assembly, ensure impeller turns smoothly. *See Fig. 10.*

Installation

1) To install, mount heater outlet pipe, with new gasket, to pump. Place new "O" ring gasket on clean block surface and mount pump. Install new "O" ring onto dipstick tube and mount to block.

2) Complete installation by reversing removal procedures. Adjust drive belt tensions, fill coolant system, start engine and check for leaks.

Fig. 10: Installing Impeller to Specified Depth

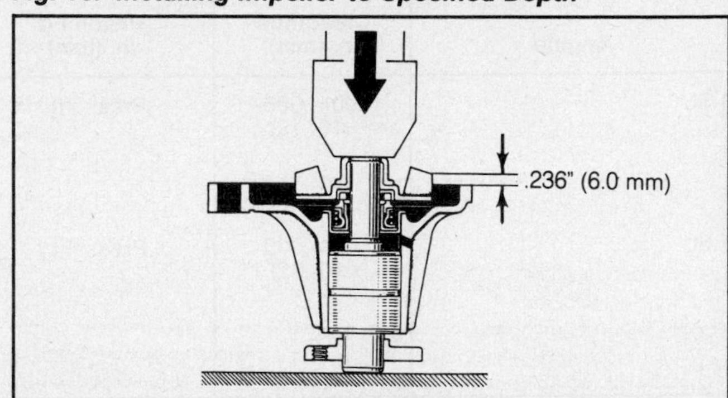
.236" (6.0 mm)

Impeller will not clear housing if depth is not correct.

TIGHTENING SPECIFICATIONS

Application	Ft. Lbs. (N.m)
Camshaft Bearing Cap Bolt	8-10 (11-14)
Camshaft Sprocket Bolt	29-39 (39-53)
Connecting Rod Cap Nut	26-32 (36-44)
Crankshaft Pulley Bolt	80-94 (109-128)
Cylinder Head Bolt	40-47 (54-64)
Distributor Drive Gear Mount Bolt	20-23 (27-31)
Exhaust Pipe-to-Manifold Mount Bolt	26-32 (36-44)
Flywheel Bolt	55-61 (75-83)
Main Bearing Cap Bolt	40-47 (54-64)
Manifold Nut	15-21 (20-29)
Oil Pump Mount Bolt	13-18 (18-24)
Rocker Shaft Support Bolt	17-19 (23-26)
Timing Belt Idler Mount Bolt	
3A-C	22-32 (30-43)
4A-C	26-36 (35-49)

ENGINE SPECIFICATIONS

GENERAL SPECIFICATIONS

Year	DISPLACEMENT Cu. In.	DISPLACEMENT Liters	Fuel System	HP@RPM	Torque Ft. Lbs.@RPM	Compr. Ratio	BORE In.	BORE mm	STROKE In.	STROKE mm
1983										
Corolla	96.8	1.6	2-Bbl.	70 @ 4800	85 @ 2800	9.0:1	3.19	81.0	3.03	77.0
Tercel	88.6	1.5	2-Bbl.	62 @ 4800	76 @ 2800	9.0:1	3.05	77.5	3.03	77.0

VALVES

Engine Size & Valve	Head Diam. In. (mm)	Face Angle	Seat Angle	Seat Width In. (mm)	Stem Diameter In. (mm)	Stem Clearance In. (mm)	Valve Lift In. (mm)
1.5L & 1.6L							
Intake	.....	44.5° [1]	45°	.047-.063 (1.20-1.60)	.2744-.2750 (6.970-6.985)	.0010-.0024 (.025-.060)	.....
Exhaust	.....	44.5° [1]	45°	.047-.063 (1.20-1.60)	.2742-.2748 (6.965-6.980)	.0012-.0026 (.030-.065)	.....

[1] – 1.6L valve face angle is 45.5°.

Toyota Engines

3A-C & 4A-C 4-CYLINDER (Cont.)

ENGINE SPECIFICATIONS (Cont.)

PISTONS, PINS, RINGS

Engine	PISTONS	PINS		RINGS		
	Clearance In. (mm)	Piston Fit In. (mm)	Rod Fit In. (mm)	Ring No.	End Gap In. (mm)	Side Clearance In. (mm)
1.5L	.004-.005 (.10-.12)	Press Fit [1]	Press Fit [1]	No. 1	.008-.016 [2] (.20-.40)	.0016-.0031 (.04-.08)
				No. 2	.006-.014 (.15-.35)	.0012-.0028 (.03-.07)
				Oil	.004-.024 (.10-.60)	.....
1.6L	.004-.005 (.10-.12)	Press Fit [1]	Press Fit [1]	No. 1	.010-.014 [2] (.25-.35)	.0016-.0031 (.040-.080)
				No. 2	.006-.012 (.15-.30)	.0012-.0028 (.030-.070)
				Oil	.008-.028 (.20-.70)	.....

[1] – Piston and pin are available only as a set.
[2] – End gap for "TP" brand rings shown; for "Riken" brand, end gap is .008-.014" (.20-.35 mm) for top ring, .006-.012" (.15-.30 mm) for second ring and .012-.035" (.30-.90 mm) for oil ring.

CRANKSHAFT MAIN & CONNECTING ROD BEARINGS

Engine	MAIN BEARINGS				CONNECTING ROD BEARINGS		
	Journal Diam. In. (mm)	Clearance In. (mm)	Thrust Bearing	Crankshaft End Play In. (mm)	Journal Diam. In. (mm)	Clearance In. (mm)	Side Play In. (mm)
1.5L & 1.6L	1.8892-1.8898 (47.985-48.000)	.0005-.0019 (.012-.049)	Center	.0008-.0073 (.020-.185)	1.5742-1.5748 (39.985-40.000)	.0008-.0020 (.020-.051)	.006-.010 (.15-.25)

CAMSHAFT

Engine	Journal Diam. In. (mm)	Clearance In. (mm)	Lobe Lift In. (mm)
1.5L & 1.6L	1.1015-1.1022 (27.979-27.995)	.0015-.0029 (.037-.073)	.....

VALVE SPRINGS

Engine	Free Length In. (mm)	PRESSURE Lbs. @ In. (Kg @ mm)	
		Valve Closed	Valve Open
1.5L & 1.6L	1.756 (44.60)	52@1.52 (23.6@38.6)	.....

4K-E 4-CYLINDER

ENGINE CODING

ENGINE IDENTIFICATION

Engine serial number and code are stamped on right side of block above oil filter. First 3 digits are engine code.

ENGINE IDENTIFICATION

Application	Code
Starlet	4K-E

ENGINE, MANIFOLDS & CYLINDER HEAD

ENGINE

Removal

1) Disconnect negative battery cable. Remove hood. Disconnect air cleaner hose. Drain coolant and disconnect all coolant hoses. Remove radiator. Disconnect and label all electrical wiring and vacuum hoses.

2) Disconnect throttle cable. Remove air cleaner with air flow meter. Remove radiator upper baffle with fan and motor. Remove shift lever from inside vehicle.

3) Raise and support vehicle. Remove drive shaft, starter, speedometer cable, and clutch release cable. Remove engine mount bolts. Place wood block between oil pan and front crossmember.

4) Attach chain hoist to engine. Remove rear engine mount. Lower vehicle. Remove engine and transmission from vehicle. Separate engine from transmission.

Installation

To install reverse removal procedure. Restore all wiring, linkages, cables, hoses, and lines to original locations.

INTAKE & EXHAUST MANIFOLDS

Removal

1) Disconnect negative battery cable. Disconnect air cleaner hose and throttle cable. Disconnect and label all fuel, coolant, and vacuum lines from intake chamber.

2) Remove PCV hose from valve cover. Remove air intake chamber brackets. Remove air intake pipe with air intake chamber and air valve. Remove fuel injection wire harness from manifold.

3) Remove heater outlet hose with pipe. Disconnect exhaust pipe from manifold. Remove intake and exhaust manifolds. Maximum intake and exhaust manifold warp limit is .008" (.20 mm).

Installation

To install, reverse removal procedure, ensuring that mating surfaces are clean and new gaskets are used. Tighten 2 center bolts first, then top front, bottom rear, bottom front, and top rear in that order.

CYLINDER HEAD

Removal

1) Drain cooling system and remove upper radiator hose. Remove intake-exhaust manifold assembly as previously outlined. Disconnect all coolant hoses from cylinder head. Remove valve cover.

2) Loosen rocker arm support bolts in 3 or 4 steps. Follow sequence of front, rear, front center and rear center bolts.

3) Remove bolts and shaft assembly. Remove push rods and keep in order for reassembly in original position. Disconnect spark plug wires. Loosen and remove head bolts in 2 or 3 steps in reverse of tightening sequence. *See Fig. 1*. Lift cylinder head from engine.

Fig. 1: Cylinder Head Tightening Sequence

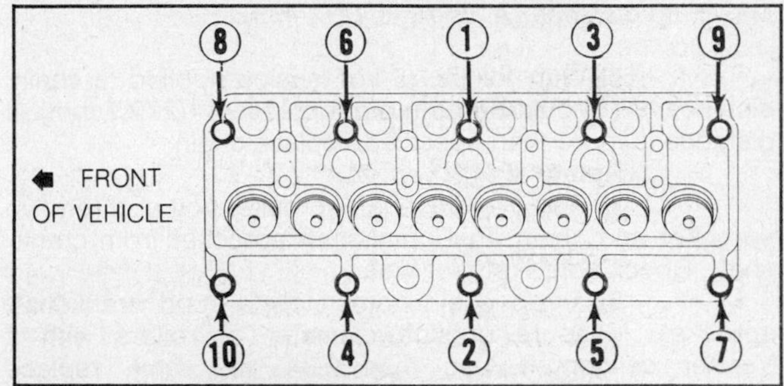
8
6
1
3
9
FRONT
OF VEHICLE
10
4
2
5
7

Remove in reverse order of tightening sequence.

Installation

1) Ensure that mating surfaces are clean. Install new gasket with "FRONT" side facing up. Continue assembly in reverse order of removal. Tighten head bolts gradually in 2 or 3 steps in sequence. *See Fig. 1*.

2) Install push rods and rocker shaft assembly. Tighten rocker support bolts in 3 or 4 steps. Adjust valves.

CAMSHAFT

FRONT COVER OIL SEAL

Removal

Remove all fan belts. Remove crankshaft pulley center bolt. Using gear puller, remove crankshaft pulley. Being carefull not to damage crankshaft, pry out old seal.

Installation

Coat the lip of the new seal with multipurpose grease. Using seal driver, install new oil seal. Reverse removal procedure to complete installation.

TIMING CHAIN & GEAR

Checking for Stretch

1) Remove timing chain cover. With timing chain installed on engine, attach a spring scale to timing chain on tensioner side. Pull out on chain with pressure of 22 lbs. (10 kg). If distance between chain tensioner plunger and tensioner body exceeds .531" (13.5 mm), chain and sprockets must be removed and checked.

CAUTION: When checking distance between tensioner plunger and body, note thickness of tensioner head. If tensioner head is worn beyond limits, measurement will be inaccurate. See Timing Chain Tensioner.

2) Timing chain may be checked off the engine. Secure 1 link of timing chain and attach spring tension gauge to opposite end. *See Fig. 2*.

4K-E 4-CYLINDER (Cont.)

Fig. 2: Checking Timing Chain Elongation

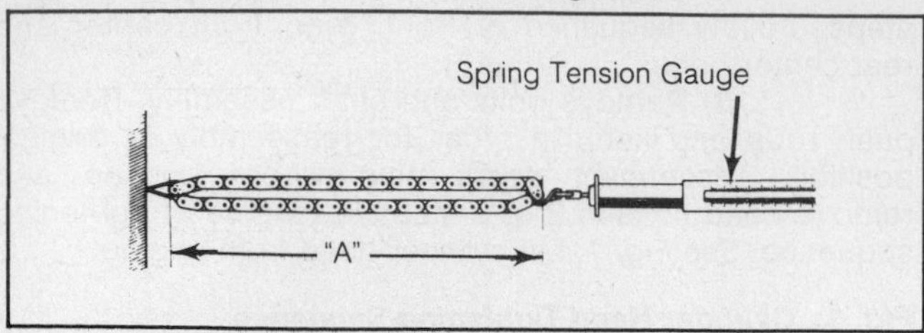
Spring Tension Gauge
"A"

Maximum distance "A" is 10.7" (272 mm).

3) With 11 lbs. (5 kg) tension applied to chain, distance "A" should be no more than 10.74" (272.7 mm). If distance is more than specified, replace chain.

Removal

1) Remove camshaft sprocket bolt and remove sprocket and chain. Pull crankshaft sprocket from crankshaft. Check sprockets for wear.

2) Wrap chain completely around crankshaft sprocket. Measure outside diameter of rollers with a Vernier caliper. If less than 2.34" (59 mm), replace sprocket. Measure camshaft sprocket in the same manner. If less than 4.48" (114 mm), replace sprocket.

3) To correctly install sprockets and timing chain, set No. 1 piston to TDC of compression stroke. Align camshaft dowel pin with mark on thrust plate. Align chain timing marks with those on sprockets. *See Fig. 3.*

Fig. 3: Aligning Marks for Timing Chain and Sprocket Installation

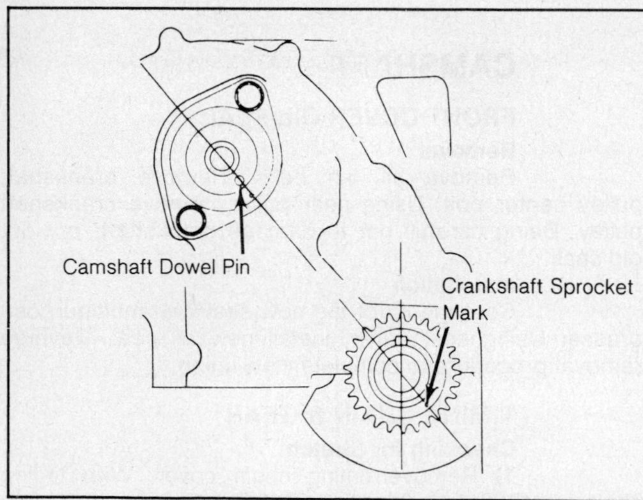
Camshaft Dowel Pin
Crankshaft Sprocket Mark

No. 1 piston set to TDC of compression stroke.

4) Install timing chain and sprockets together. Apply a light coat of oil to camkshaft sprocket bolt and tighten. Install chain tensioner and vibration damper. Install timing chain cover and crankshaft pulley.

TIMING CHAIN TENSIONER & DAMPER

1) Inspect surfaces of tensioner plunger and bore of tensioner body. To test clearance, lubricate plunger and insert it into plunger body. Cover two oil passages with fingers and pull plunger about half way out. Vacuum strong enough to return plunger should be felt.

2) Measure thickness of tensioner head and chain damper wall. Head should be minimum .47" (12 mm) and chain damper should be minimum .28" (7 mm).

CAMSHAFT

Removal

1) Remove timing chain and sprockets. See Timing Chain. Take off camshaft thrust plate. Remove front end plate from engine block.

2) Remove cylinder head, valve lifters and distributor as previously described. Pull camshaft straight out, using care not to damage bearings or journals.

3) Check camshaft runout at number 2 journal by using a dial indicator. Maximum runout limit is .0012" (.03 mm), and maximum journal out-of-round or taper is .0008" (.02 mm).

Installation

After installing camshaft, set valve timing. See Timing Chain. Install cylinder head with new gasket. See Cylinder Head. Reverse removal procedure to complete assembly.

CAMSHAFT END THRUST

With sprocket installed, check clearance between thrust plate and first bearing journal. If clearance exceeds .012" (.3 mm), replace thrust plate. If clearance is still excessive after replacing thrust plate, it will be necessary to replace the camshaft.

CAM LOBE HEIGHT

Total height of camshaft lobe is 1.436-1.440" (36.47-36.57 mm) for intake lobe. Height of exhaust lobe is 1.432-1.436" (36.37-36.47 mm). If less than 1.429" (36.29 mm) for intake or 1.421" (36.10 mm) for exhaust lobes, replace camshaft.

CAMSHAFT BEARINGS

Removal

1) To replace bearings, remove expansion plug from rear of engine. Use bearing replacement tool (09215-22010) to remove old bearings and insert new ones. Measure camshaft journal diameter and subtract from measured diameter of bearing bore to determine clearance.

2) Bearings should be replaced if clearance exceeds .004" (.1 mm). Journals may be ground and .005" (.125 mm) or .010" (.250 mm) undersized bearings installed if necessary.

Installation

Oil holes in bearings must be aligned with oil holes in cylinder block. Install new expansion plug, coated with sealer, when all bearings have been installed.

VALVES

VALVE ARRANGEMENT

E-I-I-E-E-I-I-E (Front-to-rear).

ROCKER ARM ASSEMBLY

Disassembly

1) Remove air intake chamber and valve cover. Remove rocker arm assembly retaining bolts in 3 or 4 steps. Loosen in sequence of front, rear, front center and rear center bolts. Remove rocker arm assembly.

2) Remove retaining clips from both ends of rocker arm shaft. Keeping in order for reassembly, remove conical spring, rocker arms, springs and support stands

4K-E 4-CYLINDER (Cont.)

3) Thoroughly clean and inspect all components. Check rocker arm-to-shaft clearance. If clearance exceeds .0024" (.061 mm), replace rocker arms or shafts as necessary. Reface valve end of rocker arm if worn. Lubricate all components before assembly.

Reassembly

1) Assemble rocker arm assembly in reverse order of disassembly. Install rocker arm so that protruding side of valve end of rocker arm faces support stand.

2) Tighten rocker support bolts in 3 or 4 steps. Tighten in following sequence: Rear center, front center, rear and front.

VALVE SPRINGS

Removal

Use compressor (09202-43012) to compress valve springs and retainers. Remove valve spring retainer locks (keepers), then remove retainer, spring, seal and washer. Mark and remove valves and components for reassembly.

Installation

Install components in original location and order. Use new seals on valve stems. Compress springs and install keepers.

Fig. 4: Exploded View of Valve Train Components

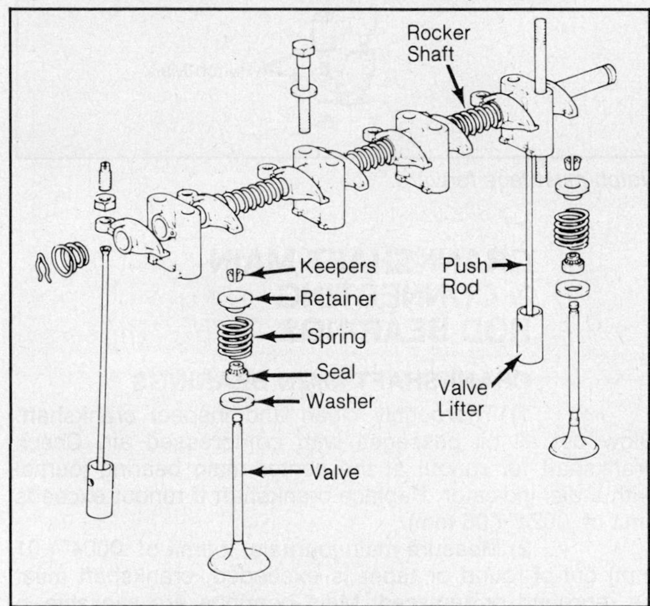

Rocker Shaft
Keepers
Retainer
Spring
Seal
Washer
Valve
Push Rod
Valve Lifter

VALVE SPRING INSTALLED HEIGHT

1) With valve spring removed, check length under specified load (see specifications) in a spring tester. Check free length. If less than 1.83" (46.5 mm), replace valve spring.

2) Check valve spring squareness with a steel square. Replace spring if out of square more than .063".

VALVE STEM LENGTH

Valve stem tips may be resurfaced on a valve grinder. DO NOT grind more than .020" (.5 mm). Standard intake valve length is 3.933" (99.9 mm). Exhaust valve length is 3.941" (100.1 mm).

VALVE GUIDE SERVICING

1) Measure valve guide inner diameter and valve stem outer diameter. If clearance exceeds .003" (.08 mm) for intake or .004" (.10 mm) for exhaust valves, replace valves and/or guides.

NOTE: **Cylinder head should be heated to about 212°F (100°C) before removal or replacement of valve guide.**

2) To replace valve guide, break off upper portion of guide at snap ring. Drive remaining portion of guide out of head through combustion chamber with driver (09201-60011).

3) Install snap ring on guide and install from top with driver. Drive in until snap ring contacts head. Guide projects .07" (18 mm) when properly installed. Ream guide for proper stem clearance.

NOTE: **Oversize guides .002" (.05 mm) larger than original guides are available if required to obtain proper fit between guide and head.**

HYDRAULIC VALVE LIFTERS

1) Using a leak down tester, apply 44 lbs. (20 kg.) of pressure to the plunger. Measure the leak down time after the 1st .02" (.5 mm) of travel. Leak down time should be 20-500 seconds for .04" (1 mm) at a temperature of 68°F (20°C).

2) Check clearance between valve lifter and bore in crankcase. If clearance exceeds .004" (.1 mm), replace lifter with an oversize tappet.

3) Oversize lifter is .002" (.05 mm) over standard. Ream bore in crankcase until clearance of .0006-.0020" (.015-.029 mm) is obtained.

VALVE CLEARANCE ADJUSTMENT

1) Set No. 1 cylinder to TDC of compression stroke. Ensure No. 2 and No. 4 exhaust and, No. 3 and No. 4 intake valves are sunk lower than the other valves.

2) Adjust clearance of No. 1 intake and exhaust, No. 2 intake, and No. 3 exhaust valves. Turn adjusting screw until rocker arm just touches valve stem. Turn adjusting screw 1 more turn. Tighten locknut. Turn crankshaft 1 revolution and adjust remaining valves.

PISTONS, RINGS & PINS

PISTON & ROD ASSEMBLY

NOTE: **Remove ridge from top of cylinder bore before removing pistons.**

Removal

1) With engine out of vehicle, remove cylinder head and oil pan. Mark each connecting rod and mating cap for reassembly.

2) Remove connecting rod cap and place a short length of hose over rod bolt to prevent damage to crankshaft.

3) Push piston and connecting rod assembly up and out through top of block. Mark piston to insure that it is installed in same cylinder.

Installation

1) To install piston and rod assembly, make sure ring gaps are in correct position. *See Fig. 5.* Coat piston and rings with oil.

2) Compress piston rings with a ring compressor and install piston and rod assembly in crankcase with notch in piston facing front of engine. Apply oil to

4K-E 4-CYLINDER (Cont.)

crankshaft journals. Make sure bearings are properly seated in connecting rod and cap.

3) Install connecting rod cap in correct position and tighten nuts to specifications. Install cylinder head, oil pan and engine as previously outlined.

FITTING PISTONS

1) Check cylinder head mating surface of engine block with a straightedge and feeler gauge. Replace block if warpage is more than .002" (.05 mm). Rebore engine block if taper and out-of-round exceeds .0008" (.02 mm).

2) Measure cylinder bores in 3 places at 90° to and parallel with crankshaft. If more than .008" (.20 mm) over standard, cylinders must be rebored.

3) When reboring, finish to final dimension by honing the last .0008" (.02 mm). Pistons and rings are available in .020", .030" and .040" (.50, .75 and 1.00 mm) oversize.

4) Measure diameter of piston .91" (23.0 mm) from top of piston at 90° to piston pin. Normal clearance is .0012-.0020" (.03-.05 mm). Check piston ring side clearance in pistons. See Fitting Rings.

PISTON DIAMETER TABLE

Oversized Piston	In. (mm)
.50 mm	75.46-75.51 (2.9709-2.9728)
.75 mm	75.71-75.76 (2.9807-2.9827)
1.00 mm	75.96-76.01 (2.9905-2.9925)

FITTING RINGS

1) Measure ring end gap at the lowest part of piston travel. Clean piston ring grooves and measure ring side clearance. If clearance exceeds limit, replace ring and/or piston.

2) When installing rings, the size and manufacturer marks must face upward. Position ring gaps as shown in *Fig. 5*.

Fig. 5: Arranging Piston Ring Gaps

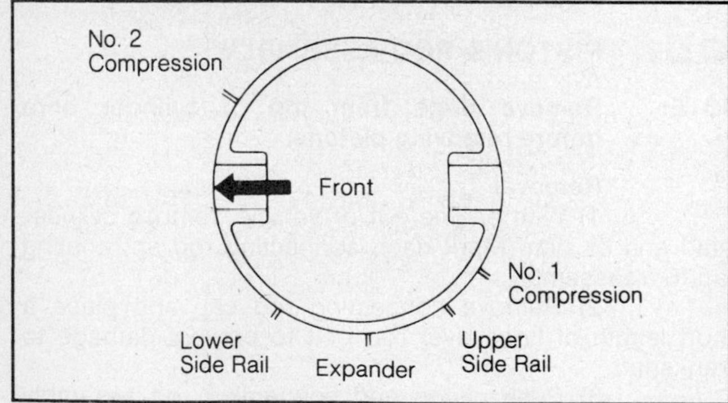
No. 2
Compression
Front
No. 1
Compression
Lower
Side Rail
Expander
Upper
Side Rail

Size & manufacturer marks must face upward.

PISTON PIN REPLACEMENT

1) Check the pin fit by rocking the piston at right angle to pin. If any movement is felt, replace the piston and pin.

2) Remove circlips from pin hole in piston. Heat piston to approximately 158-176°F (70-80°C). Drive out piston pin. Make sure pins, pistons and connecting rods are marked for reassembly.

3) Thoroughly clean and inspect all components. Coat pin with engine oil and heat piston to 158-176°F (70-80°C). Pin should push fit with thumb pressure through piston. If fit is too loose, replace piston and pin.

4) Check piston pin-to-connecting rod clearance. If more than .002" (.05 mm), replace bushing. Press bushing out and install new bushing with press and driver (09222-30010). Make sure to align bushing and connecting rod oil holes. Refinish new bushing with pin hole grinder.

5) Thoroughly lubricate all components before assembly. Position piston on connecting rod with notch in piston and front mark on connecting rod facing the same direction. Heat piston and install piston pin and circlips. *See Fig. 6*.

Fig. 6: Assembling Piston & Rod

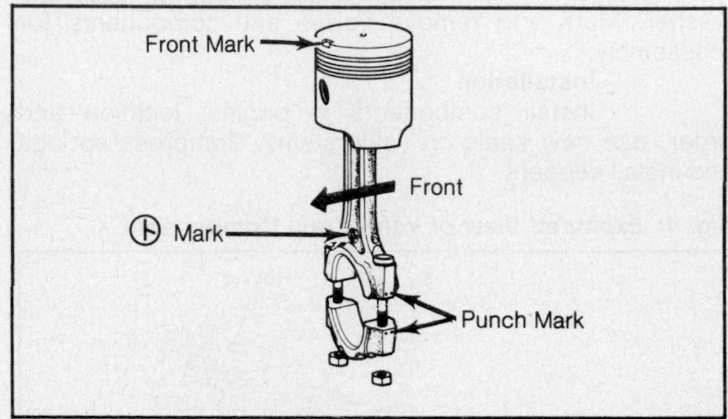
Front Mark
Front
Mark
Punch Mark

Notch must face forward.

CRANKSHAFT MAIN & CONNECTING ROD BEARINGS

CRANKSHAFT MAIN BEARINGS

1) Thoroughly clean and inspect crankshaft. Blow out all oil passages with compressed air. Check crankshaft for runout at the center main bearing journal with a dial indicator. Replace crankshaft if runout exceeds limit of .0024" (.06 mm).

2) Measure main journals. If limit of .0004" (.01 mm) out-of-round or taper is exceeded, crankshaft must be reground or replaced. Main bearings are available in .002", .010", and .020" (.05, .25, and .50 mm) undersize.

3) Main bearing clearance is checked by the Plastigage method.If clearance is excessive, crankshaft must be ground to next undersize. The limit of bearing clearance on both main and connecting rod bearings is .004" (.1 mm).

4) Install bearing halves in crankcase and main bearing caps. Lubricate bearings and install crankshaft. Install main bearing caps with arrows toward front.

5) Tighten cap bolts in 2 or three steps. Tighten cap bolts in the following order: Bearing cap No. 3, 4, 2, 5 and 1. Install remaining components in reverse order of removal, noting proper alignment of timing marks. *See Timing Chain*.

4K-E 4-CYLINDER (Cont.)

CONNECTING ROD BEARINGS

1) Measure connecting rod journals. If taper or out-of-round exceeds .0004" (.01 mm), crankshaft must be reground or replaced.

2) Connecting rod bearings are available in .010", .020", and .030" (.25, .50 and .75 mm) undersizes.

3) Make sure bearing halves and crankshaft journals are thoroughly clean. Check oil clearance by Plastigage method. Install connecting rod cap and tighten nuts to specifications.

THRUST BEARING ALIGNMENT

1) Check crankshaft end play with number 3 main bearing cap and original thrust washers installed. Pry crankshaft back and forth and measure clearance with a feeler gauge.

2) Standard clearance is .002-.009" (.04-.24 mm) with a maximum limit of .012" (.3 mm). Excessive clearance may be reduced with .002" (.125 mm) or .004" (.250 mm) oversize bearings. Install with grooves toward crankshaft.

REAR MAIN BEARING OIL SEAL

Removal & Installation

1) Oil seal may be replaced with engine in vehicle and crankshaft installed. Remove transmission, clutch assembly and flywheel. *See appropriate Toyota article in CLUTCHES Section*. Remove rear oil seal retainer. Drive old seal out of retainer.

2) Drive new seal into position with tool (09250-10011). Coat seal lips with multi-purpose grease and install seal assembly. Install flywheel and tighten to specifications. Install remaining components in reverse of removal procedure.

ENGINE OILING

CRANKCASE CAPACITY

The crankcase capacity is 3.7 qts. (3.5L) with filter and 3.2 qts. (3L) without filter.

OIL FILTER

The oil filter is a full flow type, mounted on outside of crankcase next to distributor.

NORMAL OIL PRESSURE

With engine at 212°F, normal oil pressure is 35.6-71.1 psi (2.5-5.0 kg/cm²) @ 3000 RPM.

OIL PRESSURE REGULATOR VALVE

The pressure regulator valve is a non-adjustable type, mounted in oil pump.

ENGINE OILING SYSTEM

Oil is circulated through the engine by pressure provided by a trochoid rotor type oil pump. Pump is mounted on bottom of crankcase and is driven by camshaft through the distributor drive. Oil is drawn from oil pan and is circulated through a full flow oil filter into the main oil gallery. Oil is then distributed to main and connecting rod bearing journals and camshaft bearing journals.

Cylinders and piston pins are lubricated by oil squirting from hole in connecting rod. Oil is supplied to timing chain by oil from timing chain tensioner. Oil flows from number 2 cam bearing journal to rocker arm shaft to lubricate rocker arms. Excess oil from rocker arm shaft lubricates valves and valve stems.

Fig. 7: Engine Oiling System

OIL PUMP

Disassembly

Remove oil strainer, pump cover and pressure regulator plug from side of pump body. Remove spring, piston and rotors from pump body. Thoroughly clean and inspect all components.

Fig. 8: Exploded View of Oil Pump

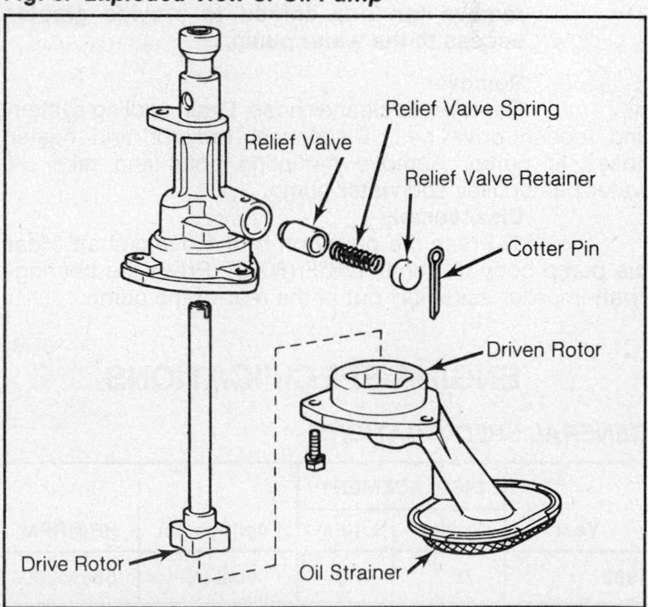
Relief Valve Spring
Relief Valve
Relief Valve Retainer
Cotter Pin
Driven Rotor
Drive Rotor
Oil Strainer

Inspection

1) Check rotor tip clearance. If tip clearance is more than limit, replace rotors. Check clearance between drive rotors and cover using a straightedge and feeler

4K-E 4-CYLINDER (Cont.)

gauge. If clearance exceeds limit, replace cover, pump body or rotors.

2) Check clearance between outer rotor and pump body with feeler gauge. If more than limit replace pump body or rotors. Check pressure regulator spring and piston for wear or damage. Replace as necessary.

Reassembly

To assemble pump, reverse disassembly procedure. Install rotors with punch marks toward body (upward). With pump assembled, submerge in clean motor oil and rotate drive shaft to check flow of oil from outlet port.

OIL PUMP CLEARANCE SPECIFICATIONS

Application	In. (mm)
Rotor Tip Clearance	.002-.006 (.04-.16) Limit .008 (.2)
Rotor Side Clearance	.001-.004 (.03-.09) Limit .006 (.15)
Rotor-to-Body Clearance	.004-.006 (.10-.16) Limit .008 (.2)

ENGINE COOLING

COOLANT CAPACITY

The coolant capacity is 5.5 qts. (5.2L).

THERMOSTAT

Begins to open at 187°F (86°C) and fully opens at 212°F (100°C).

WATER PUMP

NOTE: **Cooling fan is electrically driven and may run at any time the ignition is on if coolant temperature is high. It may be necessary to remove fan and shroud to provide greater access to the water pump.**

Removal

Remove air cleaner hose. Drain cooling system and loosen drive belt. Disconnect radiator and heater hoses at pump. Remove mounting bolts and take off water pumppulley and water pump.

Disassembly

1) Press the pulley off of the pump shaft. Heat the pump body to about 176°F (80°C). Press the bearing-shaft-impeller assembly out of the rear of the pump.

2) Press the impeller off of the pump shaft. Remove the seal from the pump shaft.

Fig. 9: Exploded View of Water Pump

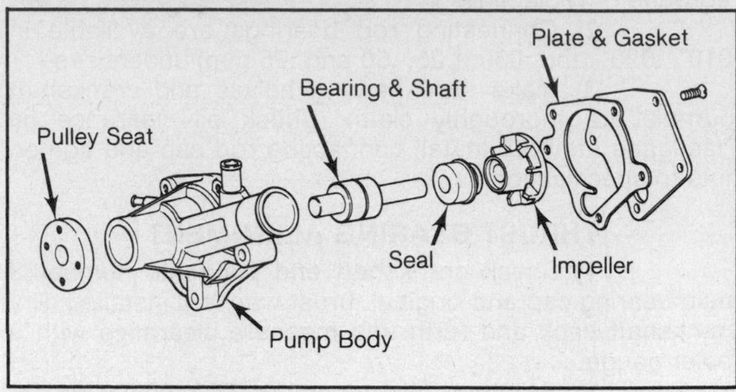
Plate & Gasket
Bearing & Shaft
Pulley Seat
Seal
Impeller
Pump Body

Reassembly

1) Heat pump body to 176°F (80°C). Press the bearing and shaft into the body. Bearing should be flush with the front edge of the neck of the body. Press in the seal and impeller. Rear face of body and impeller should be flush.

2) Press the pulley seat on the pump shaft to the specified depth. The pump shaft should protrude .283" (7.2 mm) above the front face of the pulley seat.

Installation

To install, clean mating surfaces, coat new gasket with sealer and install water pump.

TIGHTENING SPECIFICATIONS

Application	Ft. Lbs. (N.m)
Cylinder Head Bolts	40-47 (55-64)
Manifold Nuts	15-21 (20-29)
Main Bearing Cap Bolts	40-47 (55-64)
Connecting Rod Cap Nuts	29-37 (39-50)
Camshaft Sprocket Bolt	40-47 (55-64)
Crankshaft Pulley Bolt	55-75 (75-102)
Flywheel Bolts	40-47 (55-64)
	INCH Lbs. (N.m)
Camshaft Thrust Plate Bolts	53-78 (6-9)

ENGINE SPECIFICATIONS

GENERAL SPECIFICATIONS

Year	DISPLACEMENT		Fuel System	HP@RPM	Torque	Compr.	BORE		STROKE	
	Cu. In.	Liters			Ft. Lbs.@RPM	Ratio	In.	mm	In.	mm
1983	78.7	1.3	Fuel Inj.	58@5200	74@3400	9.5:1	2.95	75	2.87	73

Toyota Engines

4K-E 4-CYLINDER (Cont.)

ENGINE SPECIFICATIONS (Cont.)

VALVES

Engine Size & Valve	Head Diam. In. (mm)	Face Angle	Seat Angle	Seat Width In. (mm)	Stem Diameter In. (mm)	Stem Clearance In. (mm)	Valve Lift In. (mm)
1.3L							
Intake	.....	44.5°	[1] 45°	.043-.071 (1.1-1.8)	.3136-.3142 (7.965-7.980)	.0012-.0026 (.030-.065)	.....
Exhaust	.....	44.5°	[1] 45°	.047-.071 (1.2-1.8)	.3134-.3140 (7.960-7.975)	.0014-.0028 (.035-.070)	

[1] – Correction angles are 30° and 65°.

PISTONS, PINS, RINGS

Engine	PISTONS	PINS		RINGS		
	Clearance In. (mm)	Piston Fit In. (mm)	Rod Fit In. (mm)	Ring No.	End Gap In. (mm)	Side Clearance In. (mm)
1.3L	.0012-.0020 (.03-.05)	Thumb Pressure	.0002-.0003 (.004-.008)	No. 1	.0039-.0110 (.10-.28)	.0012-.0028 (.03-.07)
				No. 2	.0059-.0118 (.15-.30)	.0008-.0024 (.02-.06)
				Oil	[1] .008-.028 (.2-.7)	.....

[1] – Specification is for TP type rings. Riken oil ring end gap is .012-.035" (.30-.90 mm).

CRANKSHAFT MAIN & CONNECTING ROD BEARINGS

Engine	MAIN BEARINGS				CONNECTING ROD BEARINGS		
	Journal Diam. In. (mm)	Clearance In. (mm)	Thrust Bearing	Crankshaft End Play In. (mm)	Journal Diam. In. (mm)	Clearance In. (mm)	Side Play In. (mm)
1.3L	1.9676-1.9685 (49.976-49.999)	.0006-.0016 (.016-.040)	No. 3	.0016-.0095 (.040-.242)	1.6526-1.6435 (41.976-42.000)	.0006-.0016 (.016-.040)	.0079-.0150 (.200-.382)

VALVE TIMING

Engine	INTAKE		EXHAUST	
	Open (BTDC)	Close (ABDC)	Open (BBDC)	Close (ATDC)
1.3L	22°	44°	56°	10°

VALVE SPRINGS

Engine	Free Length In. (mm)	PRESSURE Lbs. @ In. (Kg @ mm)	
		Valve Closed	Valve Open
1.3L	1.831 (46.5)	77.2©1.512 (35.0@38.4)	.....

CAMSHAFT

Engine	Journal Diam. In. (mm)	Clearance In. (mm)	Lobe Lift In. (mm)
1.3L [1]			
No. 1	1.7011-1.7018 (43.209-43.225)	.0010-.0026 (.025-.066)	.....
No. 2	1.6911-1.6917 (42.954-42.970)	.0016-.0030 (.040-.076)	
No. 3	1.6813-1.6819 (42.704-42.720)	.0016-.0030 (.040-.076)	
No. 4	1.6716-1.6722 (42.459-42.475)	.0010-.0026 (.025-.066)	

[1] – Maximum camshaft runout measured at center journal is .0024" (.06 mm).

Toyota Engines

22R & 22R-E 4-CYLINDER

ENGINE CODING

ENGINE IDENTIFICATION

Engine serial number is stamped on left side of cylinder block, behind the alternator. Last group of characters designates engine type.

ENGINE IDENTIFICATION

Application	Code
Celica (2.4L)	
Carburetor	22R
Fuel Injection	22R-E
Pickup (2.4L)	22R

ENGINE, MANIFOLDS & CYLINDER HEAD

ENGINE

Removal

1) Remove engine hood, and disconnect negative battery cable. Drain cooling system. Remove air cleaner. Remove fan, radiator, shroud, hoses, and upper bracket. If equipped with air conditioning, remove compressor but DO NOT disconnect refrigerant hoses.

2) Disconnect heater hoses, fuel lines, and brake booster hose from intake manifold. Disconnect and label all electrical wiring and emission control hoses to ensure proper installation.

3) On fuel injected models, remove EGR modulator and air intake chamber with throttle body. Disconnect the actuator, accelerator, and throttle cables. Disconnect and label all fuel injection wiring and vacuum hoses. On other models, disconnect accelerator linkage from carburetor.

4) On all models equipped with automatic transmission, disconnect automatic transmission throttle cable. On vehicles with power steering, remove pump from engine. Do not disconnect hoses. Remove shift lever and clutch slave cylinder on manual transmission models.

5) Raise and support vehicle. Remove exhaust pipe at manifold. Remove engine undercover. Disconnect transmission shift linkage. If equipped with automatic transmission, disconnect cooler lines.

6) On Celica models, remove lower side engine shock absorber. Remove steering gear housing from crossmember and suspend under vehicle.

7) On all models, remove drive shaft. Remove motor mount bolts (above crossmember). Attach engine hoist to engine. Place jack under transmission. Place wood block between firewall and cylinder head to prevent damage to heater hose.

8) Remove rear transmission mounting bracket. Lift engine and transmission from vehicle.

Installation

To install, reverse removal procedure. Be sure to check all fluid levels and linkage adjustments prior to starting engine.

CYLINDER HEAD

Removal

1) Disconnect negative battery cable. Drain engine oil and cooling system. Disconnect exhaust pipe at manifold flange. Remove air cleaner. Remove and label all hoses and linkages to intake manifold, carburetor (or air intake chamber on fuel injection), and cylinder head.

2) Disconnect upper radiator and heater hoses from cylinder head. Remove water by-pass tube bolts. Disconnect and label all electrical wiring, fuel lines, and vacuum hoses from cylinder head. Remove fuel pump from cylinder head (if equipped). Remove distributor with cap and wires.

3) If equipped, remove power steering pump and set aside. On fuel injected vehicles, remove EGR modulator with bracket and air intake chamber with throttle body. Disconnect and label all fuel injection wiring and linkages.

4) On all models, remove valve cover. Set No. 1 piston to TDC on compression stroke. Paint mating marks on camshaft sprocket and timing chain. Remove rubber half circle seal and cam sprocket retaining bolt.

5) Pull distributor drive gear and fuel pump drive cam off sprocket. Remove sprocket from camshaft. Allow sprocket and chain to rest in cylinder head.

6) Remove chain cover bolt in front of camshaft sprocket. Remove cylinder head bolts in reverse of tightening sequence. *See Fig. 1.*

7) Pry equally at front and rear of rocker arm assembly to clear locating dowels. Lift head carefully to clear locating dowels. DO NOT pry between head and block.

Installation

1) Apply liquid sealer at 2 front corners of engine block and position head gasket over locating dowels. Place head in position and turn camshaft so dowel is at top.

2) Install rocker arm assembly over locating dowels and tighten head bolts in 3 steps. Continue installation in reverse of removal sequence. Ensure valve and ignition timing is properly set. Adjust valves.

Fig. 1: Cylinder Head/Rocker Arm Bolt Tightening Sequence

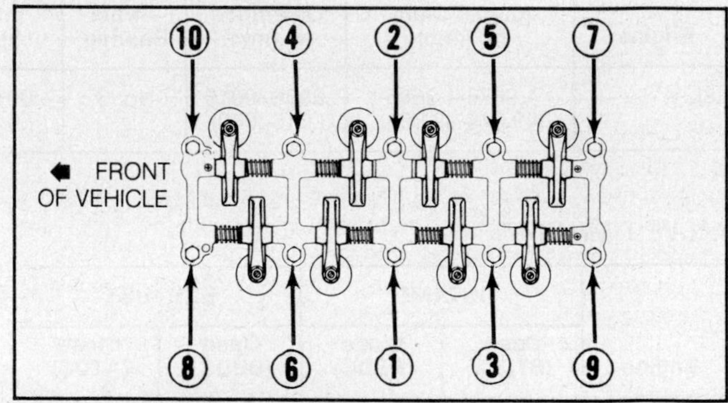
10
4
2
5
7
FRONT
OF VEHICLE
8
6
1
3
9

Loosen head bolts in reverse order.

CAMSHAFT

ENGINE FRONT COVER OIL SEAL

Removal & Installation

1) Seal is a press fit in oil pump body at front of crankshaft. Remove crankshaft pulley set bolt. Using gear puller, remove crankshaft pulley. Pry out seal with screwdriver.

2) Drive new seal into position using installer tool (09223-50010). Lubricate seal lip lightly with multipurpose grease after installation. Tighten crankshaft pulley bolt to specification.

22R & 22R-E 4-CYLINDER (Cont.)

TIMING CHAIN

Removal

1) Remove cylinder head and oil pan. Remove radiator, drive belts, air pump, and alternator bracket. Set No. 1 cylinder to TDC of compression stroke. Remove crankshaft pulley and water by-pass tube bolts. Remove timing chain cover assembly.

2) Remove chain from damper. Remove cam sprocket and chain. Using gear puller, remove both oil pump drive and chain sprocket.

Inspection

1) Check chain, sprockets, tensioner, and chain dampers for wear. Replace chain tensioner if width is less than .43" (11 mm). Minimum size for left and right side chain dampeners is .02" (.5 mm).

2) Measure length of timing chain with chain fully stretched. Maximum distance between 17 links should be 5.79" (147.0 mm). *See Fig. 2.*

Fig. 2: Checking Timing Chain Stretch

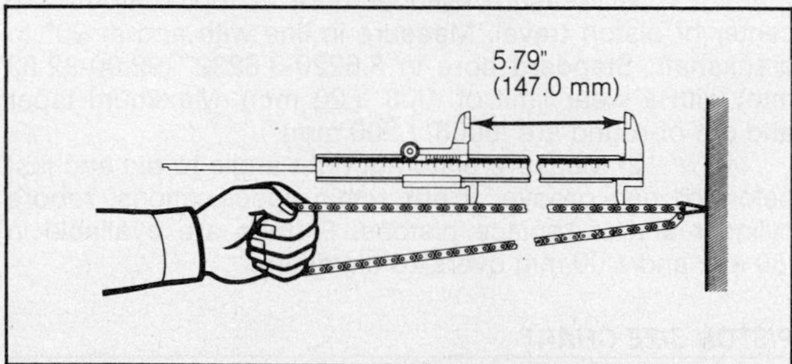
5.79"
(147.0 mm)

Check chain length between 17 links.

3) Wrap timing chain completely around camshaft sprocket. Using a Vernier caliper held parallel to the sprocket, measure the outer sides of the chain rollers. Using the same method, measure the crankshaft sprocket and chain.

4) The minimum dimension for crankshaft sprocket and chain is 2.339" (59.4 mm). The minimum dimension for camshaft sprocket and chain is 4.48" (113.8 mm). If either measurement is less than minimum, replace chain and both sprockets.

Installation

1) Ensure No. 1 cylinder is at TDC (crankshaft Woodruff key will be facing up). Position sprocket on crankshaft. Place chain on sprocket with single bright link aligned with the timing mark on sprocket.

2) Install cam sprocket in chain so that timing mark on sprocket is located between 2 chromed links. *See Fig. 3.* Slide oil pump drive spline over crankshaft key. Install cover assembly with new gasket over dowels and pump spline.

3) Continue installation in reverse of removal procedure. Set camshaft timing as follows: With No. 1 cylinder at TDC on compression stroke, position camshaft so that dowel on sprocket flange is at 12 o'clock position.

VALVE TIMING

1) Turn crankshaft so No. 1 piston is at TDC of compression stroke (align mark on crankshaft with pointer on chain cover). Turn camshaft to locate dowel pin and stamped mark on camshaft at 12 o'clock position.

2) Timing mark on camshaft sprocket must be between 2 plated links on timing chain. Plated link on timing chain must be aligned with crankshaft sprocket timing mark.

Fig. 3: Aligning Camshaft Sprocket and Timing Chain

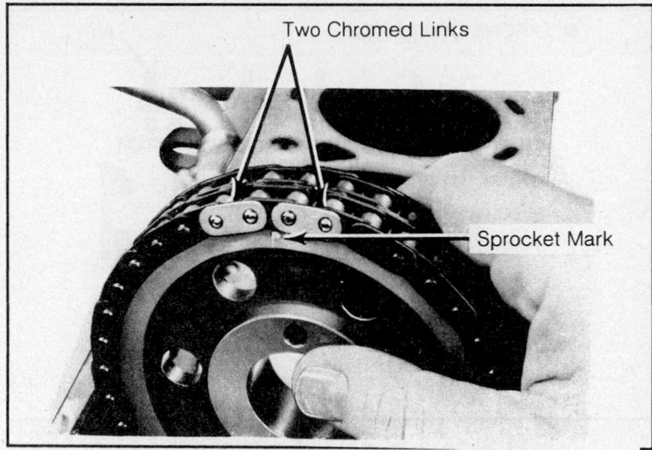
Two Chromed Links
Sprocket Mark

Camshaft dowel pin should be in 12 o'clock position.

CAMSHAFT

Removal

Remove cylinder head and rocker arm assembly. Remove camshaft bearing caps and lift out camshaft.

Inspection

1) Camshaft bearing clearance may be checked using Plastigage method. If clearance exceeds specifications, replace cylinder head and/or camshaft. Measure journal diameter.

2) Maximum camshaft runout at center journal is .008" (.2 mm). Replace camshaft if runout is beyond limit. Replace camshaft if intake lobe height is less than 1.678-1.682" (42.63-42.72 mm), or exhaust height is less than 1.681-1.684" (42.69-42.78 mm).

Installation

To install, reverse removal procedure. Install bearing caps in numbered order with arrows pointing toward the front. Adjust valves.

VALVES

VALVE ARRANGEMENT

Right Side – Intake valves.
Left Side – Exhaust valves.

ROCKER ARM ASSEMBLY

1) If rocker arms appear loose, disassemble rocker arm assembly and measure rocker arm-to-shaft clearance. Clearance should be .0004-.0020" (.01-.05 mm), with a maximum limit of .0031" (.08 mm).

2) If clearance exceeds maximum limit, replace rocker arms and/or shafts. Reassemble in reverse of disassembly, noting that all rocker arms are identical, but that all rocker stands are different. *See Fig. 4.*

VALVE SPRINGS

Check valve spring free length and squareness. If less than 1.8" (45.8 mm) long or out of square more than .063" (1.6 mm), replace spring. Use a spring tester and measure tension at installed height. Replace spring if less than specified.

VALVE STEM OIL SEALS

Removal & Installation

1) Using a spring compressor, remove valve keepers. Withdraw spring retainer and springs. Remove valve stem oil seal from end of valve guide.

Fig. 4: Disassembled View of Rocker Arm Assembly

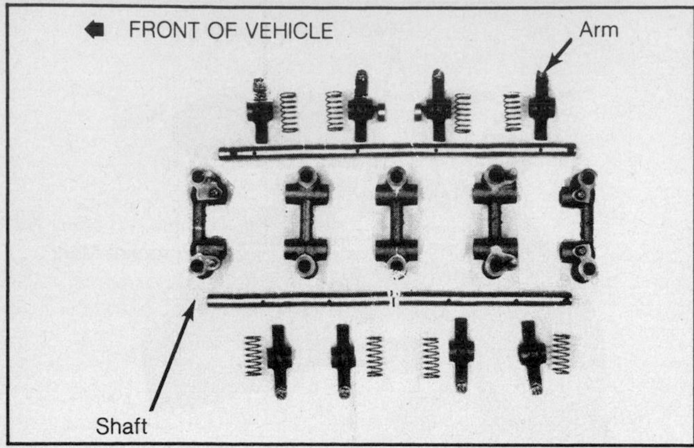
FRONT OF VEHICLE
Arm
Shaft

2) Slide a new oil seal over valve stem, using care not to damage seal as it passes over keeper grooves. Force seal over end of valve guide. Reverse removal procedure for remaining components.

VALVE GUIDE SERVICING

Removal & Installation

1) If valve stem oil clearance exceeds specifications, valve guides must be replaced. Break off end of guide using punch and hammer. Heat cylinder head to about 194°F (90°C).

2) Using driver (09201-60011), drive old guide out through combustion chamber. Install new valve guide from top of head until snap ring contacts cylinder head. Guide should have .75" (19 mm) protrusion above cylinder head. Ream valve guide for proper stem clearance.

VALVE CLEARANCE ADJUSTMENT

1) Engine must be at normal operating temperature. Remove valve cover and rotate crankshaft until No. 1 piston is TDC on the compression stroke. Measure clearance between rocker arm and valve stem. Adjust No. 1 and No. 2 intake valves and No. 1 and No. 3 exhaust valves.

2) Rotate crankshaft one complete revolution (360°) and align timing mark at TDC. Adjust remaining valves.

VALVE CLEARANCE ADJUSTMENT

Valve	In. (mm)
Intake	.008 (.20)
Exhaust	.012 (.30)

PISTONS, PINS & RINGS

OIL PAN

Removal

1) Drain engine oil. Remove engine undercover. On Pickup models, detach steering idler arm bracket. Remove pitman arm and front crossmember. Remove oil pan.

2) On Celica, remove engine shock absorber and engine mount bolts. Jack engine up about 1" (25 mm). Remove oil pan bolts and nuts. Remove oil pan.

Installation

Place gasket on pan and apply sealer to 4 corners where front cover and rear seal retainer join cylinder block. Install pan. To complete installation, reverse removal procedure.

PISTON & ROD ASSEMBLY

Removal

1) Remove cylinder head and oil pan. Machine ring ridge from top of cylinder. Mark rods and caps for correct assembly, then remove rod caps.

2) Cover rod bolts with short length of hose to prevent crankshaft damage, then push piston/rod assembly out of block.

Installation

Lubricate piston, cylinder and journal with clean engine oil. Position rings, and install ring compressor. *See Fig. 5.* Stamped mark on ring must face upward. Install piston/rod assembly in proper position with notch on piston top facing forward.

FITTING PISTON

1) Measure cylinder bore at top, bottom, and center of piston travel. Measure in line with and at 90° to crankshaft. Standard bore in 3.6220-3.6232" (92.00-92.03 mm) with a wear limit of .008" (.20 mm). Maximum taper and out-of-round are .0008" (.200 mm).

2) Measure piston at right angle to pin and just below oil ring groove. If not within specifications, rebore cylinder and/or replace pistons. Pistons are available in .50 mm and 1.00 mm oversize diameters.

PISTON SIZE CHART

Application	In. (mm)
Standard	3.6196-3.6208 (91.938-91.968)
.5 mm O/S	3.6393-3.6405 (92.438-92.468)
1.0 mm O/S	3.6590-3.6602 (92.938-92.968)

FITTING RINGS

1) Measure compression ring end gap at bottom of ring travel. If not within specification, replace the ring. Do not file ring end. Check clearance of ring in land groove. If side clearance is greater than maximum, replace piston.

2) Position rings on piston with code marks facing up. Position ring end gaps correctly. *See Fig. 5.*

Fig. 5: Correct Piston Ring Gap Arrangement

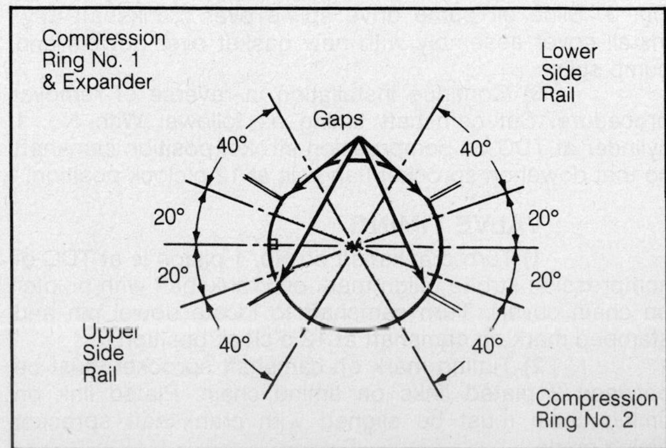
Compression
Ring No. 1
& Expander
Lower
Side
Rail
Gaps
40°
40°
20°
20°
20°
20°
Upper
Side
Rail
40°
40°
Compression
Ring No. 2

Stamped mark on ring must face upward.

22R & 22R-E 4-CYLINDER (Cont.)

PISTON PIN REPLACEMENT

Removal

Try to move piston back and forth on the piston pin. If any movement is felt, replace piston and pin. Heat piston to 176°F (80°C). Using hammer and driver, push piston pin out of piston and connecting rod.

Inspection

1) Measure clearance between rod bushing and piston pin. Replace rod bushing if clearance if greater than .0006" (.015 mm).

2) At 176°F (80°C), pin should push into piston with thumb pressure. If pin can be installed at lower temperature, replace pin and piston. The maximum rod bend and twist limit is .002" (.05 mm) per 3.94" (100 mm). If rod is bent or twisted, replace rod.

NOTE: Piston and pin are a matched set. Use new snap rings for reassembly.

Installation

Heat piston to 176°F (80°C) and position piston and connecting rod so manufacturer's mark on rod and indent on piston crown face same direction. Push piston pin into piston and rod assembly. Install snap rings.

Fig. 6: Correct Alignment of Piston and Rod Assembly

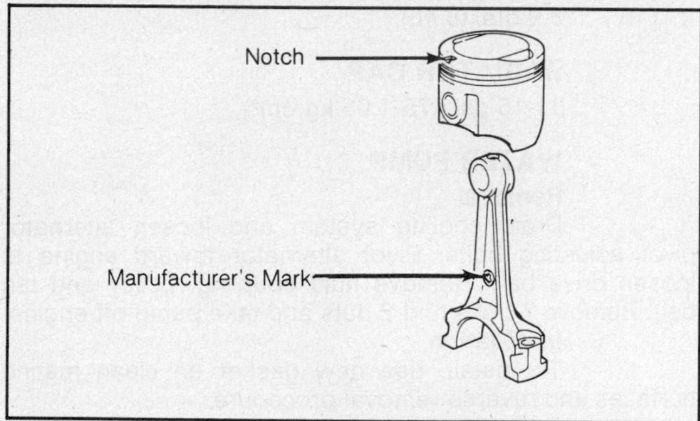
Notch
Manufacturer's Mark

Mark on rod and indent on piston crown must face same direction.

CRANKSHAFT MAIN & CONNECTING ROD BEARINGS

MAIN BEARINGS

1) Measure crankshaft runout at center bearing journal. If runout exceeds .004" (.1 mm), replace crankshaft.

2) Inspect all journals for wear or scoring. Out-of-round or taper limit is .004" (.1 mm). If crankshaft is worn excessively, grind journals for undersize bearings.

3) Measure bearing clearances using Plastigage method. If clearance exceeds specifications, grind journals for undersize bearings. Main bearings are available .25 mm undersize. Main journal finish diameter for undersize bearings is 2.3504-2.3508" (59.70-59.71 mm).

CONNECTING ROD BEARINGS

1) Measure connecting rod bearing clearance using Plastigage method. Replace bearings or grind crankshaft if clearance is greater than .004" (.10 mm).

2) Regrind crankshaft to .010" (.25 mm) undersize if taper or out-of-round is greater than .0004" (.01 mm). Connecting rod journal diameter for undersize is 2.0748-2.0752" (52.70-52.71 mm).

THRUST BEARING ALIGNMENT

Check crankshaft end play at thrust bearing using a feeler gauge. If end play exceeds limit of .012" (.30 mm), replace thrust washers. Thrust washers are available in .125" (3.2 mm) and .250" (6.3 mm) oversizes.

REAR MAIN BEARING OIL SEAL

Rear main bearing oil seal may be replaced with engine in vehicle. Remove transmission. Pry out old seal from retainer. Using tool (09223-41010), drive oil seal in place. After installing new seal, coat seal lip lightly with multi-purpose grease.

ENGINE OILING

CRANKCASE CAPACITY

4.9 qts. (4.6L) including filter.

OIL FILTER

Full-flow type with paper elements. Located at right side of engine.

OIL PRESSURE

Oil pressure at idle speed is 4.3 psi (.3 kg/cm²) and 36-71 pis (2.5-5.0 kg/cm²) at 3000 RPM.

PRESSURE RELIEF VALVE

64 psi (4.5 kg/cm²) operating pressure.

ENGINE OILING SYSTEM

Oiling system is force fed, utilizing a gear and crescent type oil pump, driven from front of crankshaft. Oil from oil pan is pumped through a full flow oil filter and then to oil galleries in cylinder block. Oil is fed to crankshaft bearings, timing chain assembly, camshaft and rocker arm assembly.

Fig. 7: Engine Oiling System

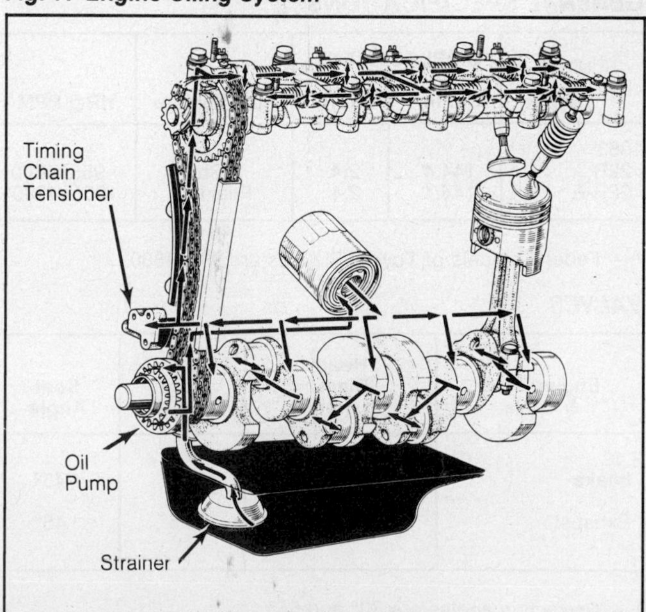
Timing
Chain
Tensioner
Oil
Pump
Strainer

Toyota Engines

22R & 22R-E 4-CYLINDER (Cont.)

OIL PUMP

Removal

1) Remove oil pan and strainer. Remove drive belts and crankshaft pulley. Remove 5 bolts and oil pump assembly.

2) Remove oil pump drive spline from crankshaft and "O" ring from engine block. Remove relief valve plug, spring and piston from pump body. Remove driven and drive gear from pump body.

Fig. 8: Exploded View of Oil Pump

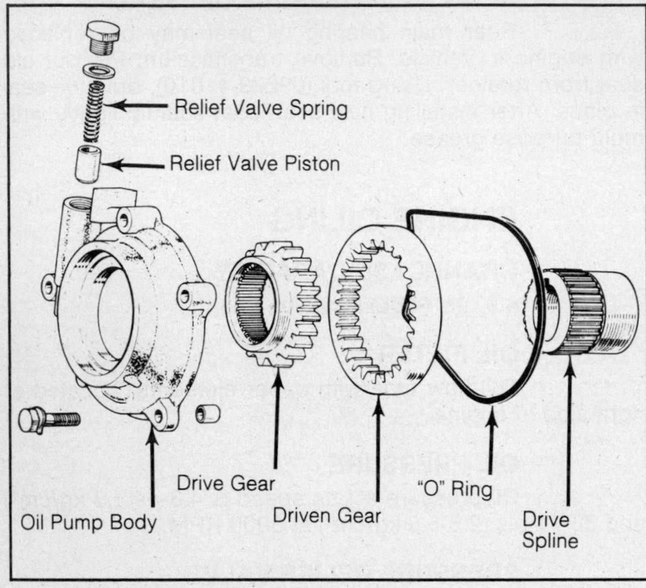
Relief Valve Spring
Relief Valve Piston
Drive Gear
"O" Ring
Oil Pump Body
Driven Gear
Drive
Spline

Install new "O" ring in block and apply sealer to upper bolt.

Installation

Reassemble pump and lubricate seal lip. Install new "O" ring in block and apply sealer to upper bolt. Install and tighten pump. Complete installation in reverse of removal procedure.

OIL PUMP SPECIFICATIONS

Application	Clearance In. (mm)
Drive Gear-to-Crescent	
Standard	.0087-.0098 (.220.25)
Wear Limit	.012 (.30)
Driven Gear-to-Crescent	
Standard	.0059-.0083 (.15-.21)
Wear Limit	.012 (.30)
Driven Gear-to-Body	
Standard	.0035-.0059 (.09-.15)
Wear Limit	.008 (.20)
Gear Faces-to-Body	
Standard	.0012-.0035 (.03-.09)
Wear Limit	.0059 (.15)

ENGINE COOLING

THERMOSTAT

On Federal models except Cab and Chassis Pickup, starts to open at 190°F (88°C) and is fully open at 212°F (100°C).

COOLING SYSTEM CAPACITY

8.9 qts. (8.4L).

RADIATOR CAP

11-15 psi (.75-1.05 kg/cm²).

WATER PUMP

Removal

Drain cooling system and loosen alternator pivot adjusting bolts. Pivot alternator toward engine to loosen drive belt. Remove fluid coupling, pulley and fan belt. Remove 7 bolts and 2 nuts and take pump off engine.

Installation

To install, use new gasket on clean mating surfaces and reverse removal procedure.

ENGINE SPECIFICATIONS

GENERAL SPECIFICATIONS

Year	DISPLACEMENT		Fuel System	HP@RPM	Torque Ft. Lbs.@RPM	Compr. Ratio	BORE		STROKE	
	Cu. In.	Liters					In.	mm	In.	mm
1983										
22R	144.4	2.4	2-Bbl.	[1] 95@4800	129@2800	9.0:1	3.62	92.0	3.50	89.0
22R-E	144.4	2.4	Fuel Inj.	105@4800	137@2800	9.0:1	3.62	92.0	3.50	89.0

[1] – Federal models of Toyota Pickups are 99@4800.

VALVES

Engine Size & Valve	Head Diam. In. (mm)	Face Angle	Seat Angle	Seat Width In. (mm)	Stem Diameter In. (mm)	Stem Clearance In. (mm)	Valve Lift In. (mm)
2.4L							
Intake	.....	44.5°	[1] 45°	.047-.063 (1.19-1.60)	.3138-.3144 (7.970-7.985)	.0008-.0024 (.0020-.060)	.....
Exhaust	.....	44.5°	[1] 45°	.047-.063 (1.19-1.60)	.3136-.3142 (7.965-7.980)	.0012-.0028 (.030-.070)	.....

[1] – Correction angles are 30° and 65°.

22R & 22R-E 4-CYLINDER (Cont.)

ENGINE SPECIFICATIONS (Cont.)

PISTONS, PINS, RINGS

Engine	PISTONS	PINS		RINGS		
	Clearance In. (mm)	Piston Fit In. (mm)	Rod Fit In. (mm)	Ring No.	End Gap In. (mm)	Side Clearance In. (mm)
2.4L	.0020-.0028 (.050-.071)	Press Fit	.0002-.0004 (.005-.011)	No. 1	[1] .0094-.0142 (.24-.36)	.008 (.20)
				No. 2	[1] .0071-.0154 (.18-.39)	.008 (.20)
				Oil	.....	.....

[1] – Specifications are for pickup, Celica compression ring end gaps are .0071-.0142" (.18-.36 mm).

CRANKSHAFT MAIN & CONNECTING ROD BEARINGS

Engine	MAIN BEARINGS				CONNECTING ROD BEARINGS		
	Journal Diam. In. (mm)	Clearance In. (mm)	Thrust Bearing	Crankshaft End Play In. (mm)	Journal Diam. In. (mm)	Clearance In. (mm)	Side Play In. (mm)
2.4L	2.3614-2.3622 (59.98-60.00)	.0010-.0022 (.025-.055)	Center	.0008-.0087 (.020-.220)	2.0865-2.0866 (52.998-53.000)	.0010-.0022 (.025-.055)	.0063-.0102 (.160-.259)

CAMSHAFT

Engine	Journal Diam. In. (mm)	Clearance In. (mm)	Lobe Lift In. (mm)
2.4L [1]	1.2984-1.2992 (32.98-33.00)	.0004-.0020 (.010-.050)	.....

[1] – End play is .0031-.0071" (.08-.18 mm).

VALVE SPRINGS

Engine	Free Length In. (mm)	PRESSURE Lbs. @ In. (Kg @ mm)	
		Valve Closed	Valve Open
2.4L	1.803 (45.80)	55@1.59 (25@40.5)	.....

TIGHTENING SPECIFICATIONS

Application	Ft. Lbs. (N.m)
Camshaft Bearing Bolts	13-16 (18-22)
Camshaft Sprocket Bolt	51-65 (69-88)
Connecting Rod Cap Bolts	40-47 (54-64)
Crankshaft Pulley Bolt	102-130 (139-177)
Cylinder Head Bolts	53-63 (72-86)
Exhaust Manifold	29-36 (39-49)
Flywheel Bolts	73-86 (99-117)
Intake Manifold	13-19 (18-26)
Main Bearing Cap Bolts	69-83 (94-113)
Timing Cover Bolts	
8 mm	9 (12)
10 mm	29 (39)

Toyota Engines

L 4-CYLINDER DIESEL

ENGINE CODING

ENGINE IDENTIFICATION

Engine identification tag is located on engine valve cover. It contains engine identification code.

ENGINE IDENTIFICATION

Application	Code
Pickup (2.2L)	L

ENGINE, MANIFOLDS & CYLINDER HEAD

ENGINE

NOTE: **Remove the engine/transmission assembly as a unit. Detach starter and separate engine from transmission after removal.**

Removal

1) Mark hood hinge positions. Remove the hood, air cleaner and both batteries. Drain cooling system. Disconnect and remove radiator hoses, fan shroud and radiator.

2) If equipped with air conditioning, remove drive belt and compressor bracket bolts. Lay compressor aside. Do not discharge system. Remove fan belt, fan, and fan pulley.

3) Disconnect fuel hoses from injection pump, heater hoses at left side of engine and vacuum reservoir hose. If equipped with air conditioning, disconnect idle-up vacuum hose.

4) Identify and disconnect wires to alternator, starter, oil pressure switch, thermo switch and terminal "B+" from glow plug relay No. 1. Disconnect wiring harness to engine at left fender.

5) Disconnect accelerator wire from injector pump. Using service tool (SST09305-20012), remove transmission shift lever from inside vehicle. Raise and support vehicle. Drain engine oil. Remove engine under cover panel.

6) Disconnect back-up light switch wire from transmission. Remove engine shock absorber and drive shaft. Disconnect speedometer cable. Disconnect exhaust pipe clamp from transmission housing.

7) Disconnect exhaust pipe mount nuts at manifold and remove pipe. Remove clutch slave cylinder but do not discharge system. Lower vehicle and remove mount bolts on each side of engine. Place jack under transmission.

NOTE: **During engine removal, ensure all wiring, hoses and lines are clear before lifting.**

8) If vehicle is air conditioned, do not damage condenser. Remove rear engine mount bracket at cross-member. Attach chain to engine brackets and position hoist over engine. Remove engine and transmission together as a unit.

Installation

1) If separated, attach transmission-to-engine and install starter. Install assembly into vehicle. Complete installation by reversing removal procedure.

2) Connect wiring and hoses, adjust drive belts, add coolant and oil, start engine and check for leaks.

INTAKE & EXHAUST MANIFOLDS

NOTE: **Fuel intake is achieved through injection nozzle assembly mounted directly to cylinder head. Intake manifold is for air only.**

Removal

1) Identify and remove all wiring, hoses and lines interfering with intake and/or exhaust manifold removal. Remove intake manifold and gasket, with venturi and air duct, as an assembly.

2) Remove front exhaust pipe mount bolts and pipe from exhaust manifold. Remove exhaust manifold mount bolts, manifold and gasket.

Inspection

Check and clean manifold-to-head contact surfaces. Inspect gasket surfaces for scratches, damage or warpage. Manifold warpage limit is .016" (.40 mm). Replace manifold if it exceeds warpage limit.

Installation

Always replace gaskets during intake and/or exhaust manifold installation. To complete installation, reverse removal procedure.

CYLINDER HEAD

Removal

1) Using starter, turn engine over until No. 1 cylinder is at TDC on compression stroke. Disconnect negative battery terminals. Remove glow plug bracket and glow plugs.

2) Disconnect and remove injection and fuel pipes from engine. Arrange parts in order for correct reassembly. Remove injection nozzle holders using service tool (SST09268-46011 of set SST09260-46011) or equivalent. Remove linkage pipe.

3) Remove intake and exhaust manifolds. Remove fan belt, fan and fan pulley. Remove crankshaft damper bolt. Do not apply tension to timing belt during damper bolt removal. Using puller tool (SST09213-60016), remove damper. Remove timing belt cover mount bolts, cover and gasket.

NOTE: **Do not allow dirt, oil or water to contact timing belt. Do not bend, twist or turn belt inside out.**

4) If timing belt is re-used, mark belt rotation direction, belt/camshaft sprocket timing marks and belt/injection pump sprocket timing marks before removing belt, to ensure correct reassembly.

5) Remove timing belt guide and valve cover. Loosen idler pulley mount bolt, move pulley to relaxed position and retighten. Remove timing belt.

Fig. 1: Rocker Arm Assembly Tightening Sequence

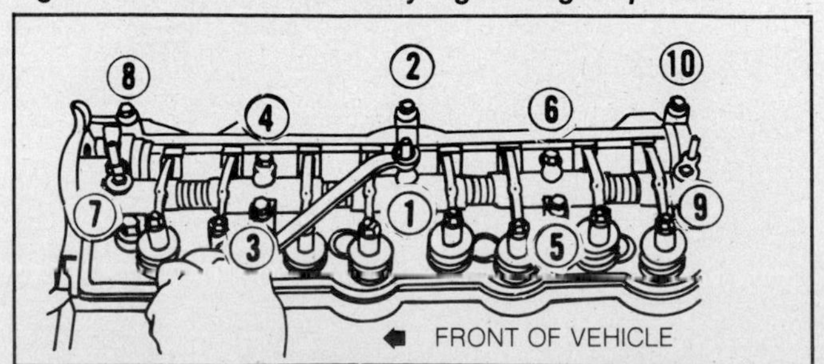
8
2
10
4
6
7
1
9
3
5
FRONT OF VEHICLE

Loosen rocker arm mount bolts in reverse of tightening sequence to disassemble.

L 4-CYLINDER DIESEL (Cont.)

6) Using sprocket holding tool (SST09278-54011) or equivalent, hold camshaft timing sprocket while removing mount bolt. Carefully tap camshaft sprocket with plastic hammer to remove.

7) Loosen and remove camshaft oil seal retainer mount bolts in 2 or 3 steps. Remove oil seal retainer. Loosen rocker shaft assembly mount bolts, in 2 or 3 steps, in reverse order of tightening sequence. *See Fig. 1.*

8) Remove rocker shaft assembly and camshaft. Gradually loosen cylinder head bolts in reverse order of tightening sequence. *See Fig. 2.* Remove cylinder head.

Fig. 2: Cylinder Head Tightening Sequence

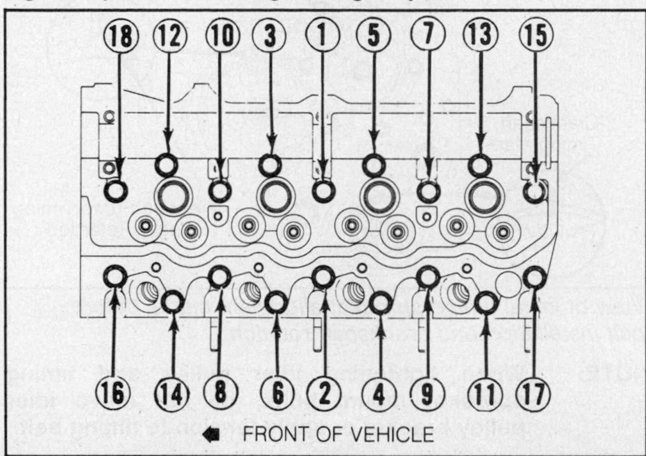
18 12 10 3 1 5 7 13 15
16 14 8 6 2 4 9 11 17
FRONT OF VEHICLE

Loosen cylinder head mount bolts in reverse of tightening sequence to disassemble.

Inspection

1) Inspect the cylinder head, combustion chambers and block for cracks, flaws or melted areas. Replace as necessary.

2) Check cylinder head gasket surface, intake and exhaust manifold mount surface and cylinder block head gasket surface for warpage using straightedge and feeler gauge.

3) The cylinder head gasket surface warpage limit is .008" (.20 mm). Intake and exhaust manifold mount surface warpage limit is .016" (.40 mm).

4) Cylinder block warpage limit is .008" (.20 mm). Replace the cylinder head and/or block if machined or warped beyond service limit.

Installation

1) Clean cylinder head and manifold mount bolt holes using compressed air. Ensure that all mating surfaces are clean and free from oil, grease, dirt and all foreign materials.

2) Set No. 1 cylinder at TDC on compression stroke. Position head on block. Coat bolt threads and under bolt head lightly with oil. Install and tighten mount bolts, in 2 or 3 steps, in sequence. *See Fig. 2.* Install camshaft and rocker arm assembly.

3) Apply sealant to projecting end of camshaft timing sprocket and install mount bolt to proper torque. Use service tool to hold sprocket during mount bolt installation. Do not use impact wrench to install timing sprocket mount bolt.

NOTE: **When installing fuel injection nozzle holder, ensure concave portion of new holder gasket faces up.**

4) Install timing belt with engine cold. Ensure belt and sprocket match marks aligned. Reverse removal procedure to complete installation. Install nozzle holders and new gaskets. Adjust valve clearance, drive belts and check injection timing.

COMBUSTION CHAMBERS

NOTE: **Cylinder head combustion chamber does not normally require removal.**

Removal

1) Remove cylinder head and glow plugs. Drive out the cylinder head combustion chambers with a thin drift punch inserted through the glow plug hole.

2) Keep combustion chambers in order for reassembly reference. When removing combustion chamber, be sure cylinder head is not damaged.

Inspection

Clean and check the combustion chambers for cracks and damage. Replace any defective chambers.

Installation

1) To install combustion chamber, set chamber on ice for several minutes. Align the combustion chamber knock pin with the cylinder head notch. Drive in the chamber with a soft faced hammer.

NOTE: **Combustion chamber shims are available in .05 mm, .10 mm, .15 mm and .20 mm sizes.**

2) Check combustion chamber protrusion above the cylinder head. Protrusion should be .0024" (.060 mm) or less. If protrusion is more than specification, adjust with shims.

CAMSHAFT

TIMING BELT COVER

Removal

1) Disconnect battery. Remove air cleaner assembly. Drain cooling system. Remove radiator hoses, shroud and radiator as necessary. Remove drive belt, fan and pulley.

2) Identify and remove any wiring, hoses and lines interfering with timing belt cover removal. Remove crankshaft damper bolt. Do not apply tension to timing belt during damper bolt removal.

3) Remove crankshaft damper pulley using pulley removal tool (SST09213-60016) or equivalent. Detach timing belt cover mount bolts and remove belt cover and gasket.

Installation

Install engine timing belt cover with new gasket. Complete installation by reversing removal procedure.

CAMSHAFT OIL SEAL

NOTE: **Camshaft oil seal may be replaced with No. 2 seal retainer installed on engine.**

Removal

1) Identify and remove any wiring, hoses and lines interfering with front cover removal. Set No. 1 cylinder at TDC on compression stroke. With engine front parts and drive belts removed, detach crankshaft damper pulley mount bolt. Do not tension timing belt during pulley mount bolt removal.

L 4-CYLINDER DIESEL (Cont.)

2) Using puller tool (SST09213-60016) or equivalent, remove damper pulley. Remove engine timing belt cover and gasket. Loosen idler pulley mount bolt and set to relaxed position. Mark belt-to-sprockets position and rotation direction if reusing belt. Remove timing belt.

3) Use sprocket holding tool (SST09278-54011) or equivalent, to hold camshaft and remove sprocket mount bolt. Lightly tap sprocket with plastic hammer to remove. Carefully pry out old seal from camshaft oil seal retainer.

Installation

Coat the lip of the new seal with multipurpose grease. Install new seal using seal driver tool (SST09223-22010) or equivalent. Ensure No. 1 cylinder is at TDC on compression stroke. Reverse removal procedure to complete assembly.

TIMING BELT

Removal

1) Using starter, turn engine over until No. 1 piston is at TDC on compression stroke. Disconnect negative battery terminals. Remove fan belts, fan and pulley.

2) Remove damper pulley mount bolt. Do not tension timing belt during damper mount bolt removal. Using puller tool (SST09213-60016), remove damper. Remove timing belt cover mount bolts. Remove timing belt cover and belt guide.

CAUTION: Before removing bolts securing camshaft, crankshaft and injection pump sprockets, release tension on timing belt. Do not bend or twist belt. Keep free from oil, water or dust.

3) Loosen idler pulley bolt and set pulley in relaxed position. Remove timing belt. To remove crankshaft timing sprocket, secure flywheel and remove mount bolt. Using gear puller, remove crankshaft timing sprocket.

4) To remove injection pump sprocket, use sprocket holding tool to secure injection pump drive sprocket. Remove mount bolt. Use gear puller to remove injection pump sprocket. Do not drop sprocket as it may spring out during removal.

5) A nonadjustable, belt tensioning idler pulley is used between the crankshaft and oil pump timing pulleys. Remove center mount bolt to remove pulley if necessary.

Inspection

1) Check timing belt for wear, cracks or missing teeth. If defective, check if injection pump camshaft is locked or there are nicks on belt side of idler pulley lock. Replace belt and components as needed.

2) Inspect belt for excessive wear on one side only. if damaged, check the belt guide and the alignment of each sprocket. Before installing new belt, remove idler pulleys and spring. Check idler pulley bearings for noise or roughness.

3) Inspect spring for proper free length and tension. Standard free length is 1.563" (39.70 mm). Standard tension is 2.05" @ 8.8 lbs. (52 mm @ 4 kg). Replace idler pulley and/or spring as necessary.

4) Check camshaft, injection pump and crankshaft timing sprockets for wear or damage. If noticeable wear on belt teeth, check timing belt cover gasket for damage and proper installation. Replace components as necessary.

Installation

1) Before installing timing belt, engine should be cold. Always turn crankshaft clockwise. Install adjustable idler pulley loose enough so it may be moved side to side by hand.

2) Check alignment of timing marks on each pulley. *See Fig. 3*. Note that injection pump timing is normally in the retarded position.

Fig. 3: Aligning Camshaft, Crankshaft & Injection Pump Sprocket Timing Marks

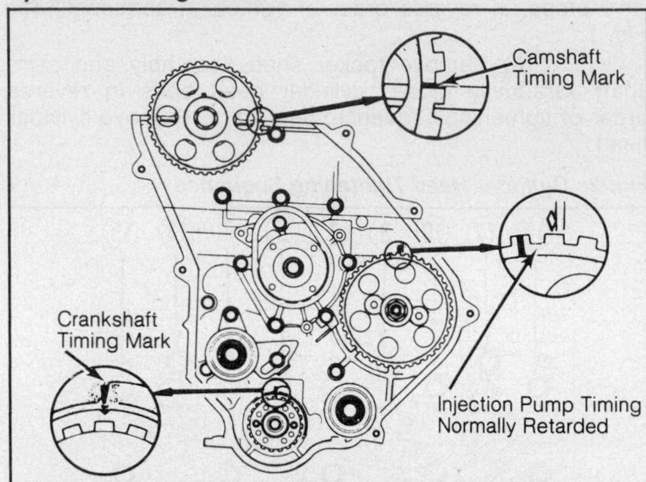
Camshaft
Timing Mark
Crankshaft
Timing Mark
Injection Pump Timing
Normally Retarded

View of initial timing sprocket alignment marks before belt installation and crankshaft rotation.

NOTE: When tightening idler pulley and timing sprocket mount bolts, do not move idler pulley bracket or apply tension to timing belt.

3) Install nonadjustable idler pulley, timing belt and adjustable idler pulley spring. Turn the crankshaft 2 revolutions clockwise from TDC to TDC. While turning crankshaft ensure adjustable idler pulley bracket is moving.

4) Ensure that each pulley aligns with timing mark. *See Fig. 4*. Tighten timing belt idler pulley bolts. Reverse removal procedure to complete installation.

Fig. 4: Realigning the Camshaft, Crankshaft & Injection Pump Sprocket Timing Marks

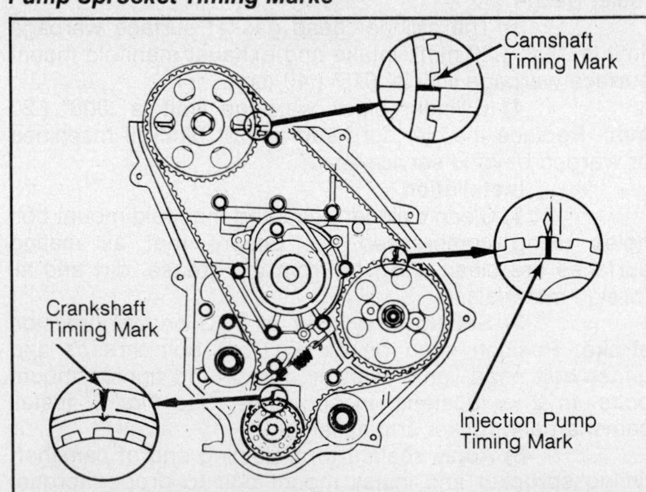
Camshaft
Timing Mark
Crankshaft
Timing Mark
Injection Pump
Timing Mark

View of timing sprocket and belt alignment marks after turning crankshaft two revolutions.

CAMSHAFT

Removal

1) Before removal, set No. 1 cylinder at TDC on compression stroke. Remove valve cover, gasket and

L 4-CYLINDER DIESEL (Cont.)

front engine parts. Place timing match marks and belt direction on belt. Loosen adjustable idler pulley and remove timing belt.

2) Check camshaft end play before removal. Secure camshaft with holding tool (SST09278-54011) and remove camshaft timing sprocket mount bolt. Remove sprocket by lightly tapping with plastic hammer.

3) Remove No. 2 oil seal retainer mount bolts and retainer assembly. Gradually loosen rocker arm assembly bolts in reverse order of tightening sequence. *See Fig. 1*. Remove rocker arm assembly. Remove camshaft bearing caps, bearing inserts and camshaft.

Inspection

1) Check camshaft journals and cam lobe surface for bend, wear or damage. Check bend with camshaft in "V" blocks. Use a dial indicator with pointer set on center journal. Standard bend limit is .0016" (.040 mm). Maximum bend limit is .002" (.05 mm). Replace camshaft if bend is greater than maximum limit.

2) Check camshaft lobe height. Standard lobe height is 1.6948" (43.048 mm) for intake and 1.7020" (43.232 mm) for exhaust. Minimum cam lobe height limit is 1.681" (42.70 mm) for intake and 1.690" (42.90 mm) for exhaust. Replace camshaft if height is not within limits.

3) Check camshaft end play with the camshaft bearing caps installed and tightened to specifications. Standard end play is .0022-.0061" (.055-.155 mm). The maximum end play limit is .012" (.30 mm). If clearance is beyond limits, replace camshaft and/or cylinder head assembly.

4) Using micrometer, measure camshaft bearing journals. Replace camshaft if journals show nicks, scores or wear. Inspect cam bearing inserts for flacking or scoring and replace as necessary.

5) Check camshaft oil clearance with camshaft and bearing caps tightened in place, using Plastigage method. Do not turn camshaft during measurement. Standard oil clearance is .0009-.0029" (.022-.074 mm). Maximum clearance is .004" (.10 mm). If clearance is beyond limit, adjust with suitable size bearing.

Installation

1) Install camshaft with sprocket locating pin in the 12 o'clock position. Loosen adjusting screw lock nuts on rocker arms when installing rocker arm assembly.

2) Install new gaskets and seals. Reverse removal procedures to complete installation. Adjust valve clearance with engine at normal operating temperature.

VALVES

VALVE ARRANGEMENT

E-I-E-I-E-I-E-I (Front-to-rear).

VALVE

1) Using gasket scraper, chip carbon from valve head. Using wire brush, clean valve thoroughly. Inspect valves for worn, damaged or deformed head or stem.

2) Check valve head in-margin thickness. If head is worn to .035" (.90 mm) in-margin thickness for intake or .039" (1 mm) for exhaust, replace valve. Check surface of valve stem tip for excessive wear.

3) Standard valve length is 4.8405" (122.950 mm) for intake and 4.8327" (122.750 mm) for exhaust. Valve stem end surface grinding limit is .02" (.5 mm). If valve stem tip is worn, resurface with grinder or replace valve.

4) Check valve face and seat for pitting, uneven wear, proper contact width and position with valve face contact area. Resurface valve and/or seat if needed.

VALVE SPRINGS

Removal

1) With cylinder head, rocker arm/shaft assembly, camshaft timing sprocket and No. 2 oil seal retainer removed, remove cam bearing caps and camshaft. Keep components in order for reassembly reference.

2) Press valve spring down with compressor tool (SST09202-43012). Remove valve keepers. Remove compressor tool. Remove spring retainer, spring, valve, oil seal and valve spring seat.

NOTE: Keep all valve train and camshaft components in order for reassembly reference.

Inspection

1) Using steel square, check squareness of valve springs. Spring must be .08" (2 mm) or less out of square. Check free length of springs. Replace any not within limits.

2) Using spring tester, check tension of each spring at specified installed height. Valve spring installed height is 1.547" (39.30 mm). Minimum installed tension is 44.1 lbs. (20 kg). Replace spring if not to specifications.

Installation

1) Before installing components, clean parts to be assembled. Apply oil to sliding and rotating surfaces. Install valve spring seats and new oil seals.

2) Install springs and retainers on valves. Using compressor tool, compress springs and install keepers. Tap stem lightly with plastic hammer to ensure keepers are seated properly.

VALVE STEM OIL SEALS

1) New oil seals should be installed whenever the valve is disassembled. Pry off old oil seal without damaging valve guide. Coat new seal lip with engine oil.

2) Using seal driver tool (09201-54010) or equivalent, install seal so that bottom of seal is .374-.390" (9.50-9.90 mm) above valve spring seat on cylinder head.

VALVE GUIDE SERVICING

Clearance Check

1) Using valve guide brush and solvent, clean guides. Measure clearance between valve stem and valve guide with micrometer and telescope hole gauge. Check diameter of valve stem at top, center and bottom.

2) Insert hole gauge in guide bore. Measure at several places and use maximum wear for calculation. Standard intake valve stem-to-guide clearance is .0008-.0022" (.021-.057 mm) and exhaust valve stem-to-guide clearance is .0016-.0030" (.040-.076 mm).

3) Maximum stem-to-guide clearance is .004" (.10 mm) for intake and .0047" (.120 mm) for exhaust. Replace guide if worn beyond limits.

Replacement

1) If clearance is beyond limits and valve stem is not worn, replace guide. To replace, heat cylinder head. Using service tool (SST09201-60011) or equivalent, drive guide out from top end toward the combustion chamber.

2) To install guide, reheat head. Ensure guide hole is clean. Apply oil to guide hole and guide. Using service tool, drive in new guide until tip projects out of head .642-.657" (16.30-16.70 mm).

L 4-CYLINDER DIESEL (Cont.)

3) Use reamer to finish guide bore to specified clearance. Reface valve seat surface, as needed, after valve or guide repair or replacement.

ROCKER ARMS & SHAFT ASSEMBLY

Removal

1) Remove valve cover and gasket. Loosen rocker arm assembly mount bolts in reverse of tightening sequence. *See Fig. 1.* Remove rocker arm assembly. Disassemble rocker assembly components and check rocker arm-to-shaft clearance.

2) Keep all parts in order when disassembling rocker arm shaft. Rocker arms and adjusting screws may be refaced if scored lightly. Measure clearance between the rocker arm and shaft. See Rocker Arm Assembly Specifications Table.

ROCKER ARM ASSEMBLY SPECIFICATIONS

Application	In. (mm)
Oil Clearance	.0008-.0024 (.020-.060)
Limit	.004 (.10)
Rocker Arm Bore	
Limit	.732 (18.60)
Shaft Diameter	
Limit	.726 (18.44)

Installation

After all clearances have been checked, reverse removal procedures to complete installation. Check that front rocker support and shaft oil holes are aligned. *See Fig. 5.*

Fig. 5: Assembling Rocker Arm Shaft

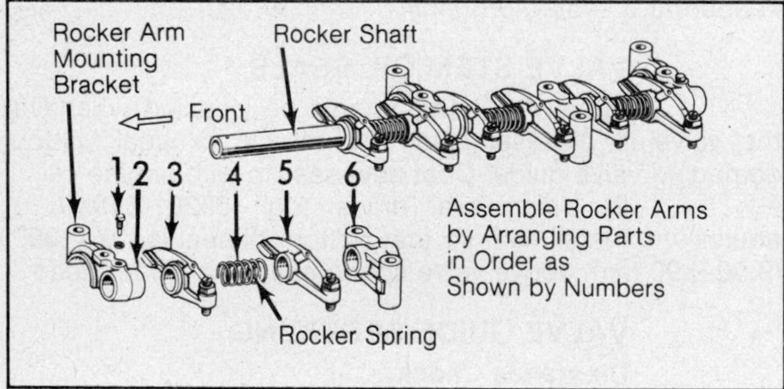

Rocker Arm Mounting Bracket
Rocker Shaft
Front
1 2 3 4 5 6
Assemble Rocker Arms by Arranging Parts in Order as Shown by Numbers
Rocker Spring

Oil holes of front rocker support and shaft must be aligned.

VALVE CLEARANCE ADJUSTMENT

NOTE: **Valves should be adjusted with engine at normal operating temperature but not running. Cold specifications are provided for initial settings after assembly.**

1) With engine at normal operating temperature, stop engine and remove valve cover and gasket. Bring No. 1 piston to TDC of compression stroke. Ensure rockers for No. 1 cylinder are loose.

2) If rocker arms are not loose, rotate crankshaft one revolution and realign timing notch on damper pulley with pointer on timing cover. Adjust No. 1 & 2 intake valves and No. 1 & 3 exhaust valves.

3) Rotate crankshaft one full turn (360°) clockwise to realign pulley timing notch with pointer. Adjust No. 3 & 4 intake valves and No. 2 & 4 exhaust valves. After adjustment, install new gasket and valve cover. Do not start engine with valve cover removed.

VALVE CLEARANCE SPECIFICATIONS

Valve	Hot In. (mm)	Cold In. (mm)
Intake	.010 (.25)	.011 (.27)
Exhaust	.014 (.36)	.015 (.38)

NOTE: **After valve clearance adjustment, injection pump timing should be checked. Refer to Toyota Diesel Fuel Injection article in the FUEL SYSTEMS Section.**

PISTONS, PINS & RINGS

PISTON & ROD ASSEMBLY

Removal

1) Remove front engine parts, cylinder head, injection pump, oil pump housing, oil pan and strainer. Before piston/rod assembly removal, check rod side thrust clearance.

NOTE: **Before injection pump removal, check position of oil pump housing and pump body marks for reassembly reference.**

2) Detach connecting rod nuts. Mark for identification and remove rod cap with bearing half. Cover rod bolts with short pieces of rubber hose to protect crankshaft journals during removal and installation.

3) Check top of cylinder bore for ridge. If scraper will not remove carbon build-up, remove with a ridge reamer. Push piston and rod assembly, with bearing half, out through top of block. Keep rod caps with their respective piston and rod assemblies. Caps are not interchangeable.

Inspection

1) Check connecting rod for bend or torsion, using rod aligner tool. Bend and torsion limit is .002" (.05 mm) or less, in 3.94" (100 mm) of length.

2) Install rod, with bearings, on crank pin. Measure rod side thrust clearance. Standard play at rod big end is .003-.008" (.08-.20 mm).

3) Maximum side play is .012" (.30 mm). Replace the rod and/or bearings if not to specifications.

Installation

1) Reassemble piston and rod assembly so notch on piston and identification mark on connecting rod faces front. Connecting rod cap mark must also face front. *See Fig. 6.*

2) To install piston and connecting rod assembly, apply oil to rings, piston and cylinder wall. Install piston assemblies on original journal with combustion chamber angled toward left side of block. *See Fig. 7.*

3) Ensure ring gaps are set approximately 180° apart. Do not set on thrust side of piston or in line with piston pin. Set expander coil joint at opposite side from oil ring gap. *See Fig. 7.* Bearing halves must be properly seated in rod and cap.

4) Install ring compressor on piston and rings. Install piston assembly in cylinder bore. With piston assembly installed and rod and bearings seated against crankshaft journal, install rod caps to their respective piston and rod assemblies.

5) Install cylinder head, oil pump housing, injection pump and front engine parts. Install new gasket

L 4-CYLINDER DIESEL (Cont.)

and oil pan. Tighten pan bolts evenly, in a criss-cross pattern. Do not over-tighten.

Fig. 6: Piston and Connecting Rod Assembly Installation

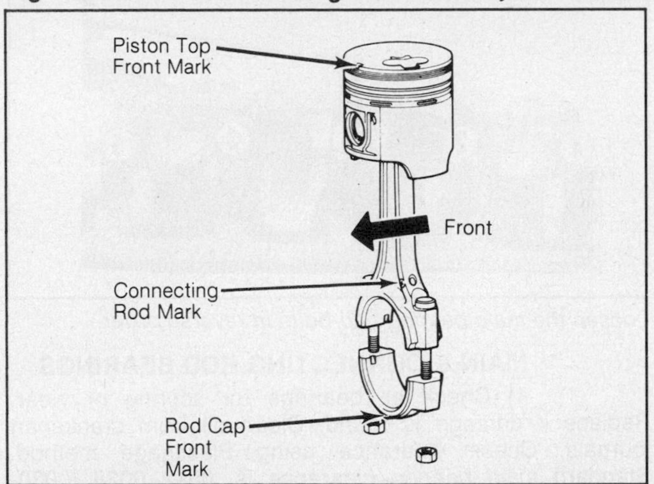
Piston Top
Front Mark
Front
Connecting
Rod Mark
Rod Cap
Front
Mark

Ensure identification marks on rod and cap match and the notch on piston top and mark on rod and cap faces front.

FITTING PISTONS & RINGS

1) Inspect cylinder block and liners for cracks, vertical scores or flaws. Using bore gauge, measure liner at top, center and bottom for cylinder bore wear. If bore wear is excessive or liner is heavily scored, replace using liner remover/installer tool (SST09218-54011).

NOTE: **When removing cylinder liner, press out from bottom of block. Do not use more than 4400-6600 lbs. (2000-3000 kg) of pressure.**

2) Check cylinder liner wear by measuring bore diameter. Standard bore diameter is 3.5433-3.5445" (90.000-90.030 mm). Liner bore wear limit is .008" (.20 mm). When replacing liner, coat bore with oil and press liner in through top of block. Rebore and hone new liner to fit standard piston.

3) With piston at room temperature, measure outside diameter at 1.34" (34 mm) from bottom of piston skirt. Standard piston diameter is 3.5413-3.5425" (89.950-89.980 mm). Measure cylinder bore and subtract piston size. If clearance is beyond limit, replace piston. After honing cylinder to final fit, install piston.

4) Check amount of liner projection from each cylinder. Standard liner projection is .0004-.0039" (.010-.100 mm). There must be less than .0016" (.040 mm) projection variation between cylinders. If protrusion is not within specification, adjust with liner shims.

NOTE: **Cylinder liner shims are available in .05 mm and .10 mm thicknesses.**

5) If pistons are reused, decarbon piston and ring grooves with scraper and curved steel wire or piece of broken ring. Clean oil slots in bottom land of oil ring groove. Check for scratches, wear or damage. Measure side clearance of rings in grooves as each ring is installed.

6) Measure piston ring end gap. Replace pistons and/or rings as necessary if clearances are beyond limits. Install rings on pistons with end gaps 180° apart and not in line with thrust face. Ensure expander coil joint is set at opposite side from oil ring ends. Install rings with code mark facing upward. *See Fig. 7.*

Fig. 7: Installation Order of Piston Rings

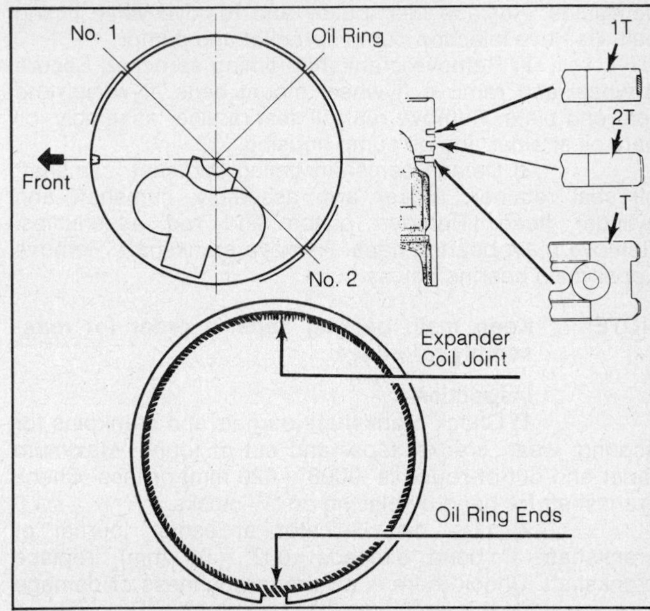
No. 1
Oil Ring
1T
2T
T
Front
No. 2
Expander
Coil Joint
Oil Ring Ends

Install the piston rings with the code marks facing up and the end gaps 180° apart.

PISTON PINS

1) Check piston pin fit by rocking piston at right angle to pin. If any movement is felt, replace piston and pin. To remove pin, first remove snap rings. Heat piston and rod assembly to about 140°F (60°C). Press out pin using piston pin removal tool (SST09221-46010). Do not damage piston during removal.

2) Check pin, piston pin hole and rod bushing for signs of gauling or excessive wear. Using micrometer and telescope hole gauge, measure outside diameter of piston pin and inside diameter of connecting rod pin bushing and piston pin hole. Determine pin-to-rod bushing and pin-to-piston pin hole clearance.

3) Standard pin diameter is 1.0630-1.0634" (27.000-27.010 mm). Standard pin-to-bushing clearance is .0006-.0009" (.014-.022 mm). Standard pin-to-piston pin hole is .0002-.0005" (.004-.012 mm). If wear exceeds .002" (.05 mm), replace bushing, pin and/or piston as necessary. Press rod bushing out using bushing removal/installer tool (SST09222-40011).

NOTE: **When installing rod bushing, align bushing oil hole with rod oil hole.**

4) Install bushing with service tool and machine bore with pin hole grinder. Ensure fit between bushing and pin is such that, at room temperature, oil coated pin may be pushed in with finger pressure.

5) To assemble piston and rod, reheat piston. Insert oil coated pin into piston with finger pressure while holding piston and rod in proper alignment. Assemble with identification mark on rod and notch on piston top facing front. *See Fig. 6.* Install snap rings.

CRANKSHAFT & MAIN & CONNECTING ROD BEARINGS

CRANKSHAFT

Removal

1) With engine removed, remove outer parts, install engine attachment and mount engine assembly on work stand. Remove damper pulley, timing belt cover and belt guide. Release idler pulley and remove valve timing belt. Remove injection pump sprocket and pump.

2) Remove crankshaft timing sprocket. Secure flywheel and remove flywheel mount bolts, flywheel and rear end plate. Remove rear oil seal retainer assembly, oil pan, oil strainer and oil pump housing.

3) Detach camshaft timing sprocket, camshaft oil seal retainer, rocker arm assembly, camshaft and cylinder head. Remove piston and rod assemblies. Remove main bearing caps. Remove crankshaft. Remove upper main bearing halves.

NOTE: **Keep main bearing caps in order for reassembly reference.**

Inspection

1) Check crankshaft journals and crankpins for scoring, wear, cracks, taper and out of round. Maximum taper and out-of-round is .0008" (.020 mm) or less. Check crankshaft for bend by placing on "V" blocks.

2) Use dial indicator at center journal of crankshaft. If bend exceeds .002" (.05 mm), replace crankshaft. Check there is no drag, roughness or damage to crankshaft pilot bushing.

NOTE: **Do not damage edge of pilot bearing during replacement or inset excessively.**

3) If necessary, note installation depth and remove pilot bearing using bearing puller tool (SST09303-35010). Drive in bearing using installer tool (SST09304-30012) or equivalent. Check flywheel friction surface for cracks, damage or wear.

4) Measure friction surface runout using a dial indicator. Runout limit is .008" (.20 mm). Resurface or replace flywheel if not within limits. Check tooth surfaces of ring gear for flaws or wear. Replace ring gear if necessary.

NOTE: **Main bearing caps are numbered and must be installed with arrows facing forward.**

Installation

1) Install main bearing inserts in block. Ensure bearings are on correct journal. Upper and lower bearing inserts have oil holes. Check insert oil holes are in proper alignment with block and bearing cap oil holes.

2) Apply oil to main bearing surfaces. Install upper thrust washers on center bearing and lower thrust washers on No. 3 main bearing cap with oil grooves facing out. Install crankshaft. Install bearing caps with arrows facing front of engine.

3) Shift crankshaft toward front of engine. Tighten bearing caps in 2 or 3 steps, starting at center bearing and working outward. Check rotation after each bearing cap is installed to ensure crankshaft rotates smoothly. *See Fig. 8.*

4) Check end play using dial indicator with pointer set on crankshaft sprocket mount. Standard thrust washer thickness is .0961-.0980" (2.440-2.490 mm). Standard end play is .0016-.0098" (.040-.250 mm). Maximum end is .012" (.30 mm). If beyond limits, replace thrust washers as a set.

5) Install rear oil seal retainer. Install flywheel or drive plate. Install piston and rod assemblies. To install remaining components, reverse removal procedure.

Fig. 8: Main Bearing Cap Tightening Sequence

4
2
1
3
5

Loosen the main bearing cap bolts in reverse order.

MAIN & CONNECTING ROD BEARINGS

1) Check all bearings for scoring or wear. Replace if damage is found. Clean oil from crankshaft journals. Check clearance using Plastigage method. Standard main bearing clearance is .0012-.0028" (.030-.070 mm). Maximum clearance is .004" (.10 mm).

NOTE: **Plastigage should run parallel with crankshaft. Do not block oil hole or turn crankshaft with Plastigage inserted.**

2) Standard connecting rod bearing clearance is .0012-.0028" (.030-.070 mm). Maximum clearance, for rod bearings, is .004" (.10 mm). If clearance is not to specifications, replace bearings.

NOTE: **The main bearings have replacement inserts of .25 mm, .50 mm, .75 mm and 1 mm undersize available for service.**

MAIN BEARING JOURNALS

Application	In. (mm)
2.2L Diesel	
Standard	2.4402-2.4409 (61.980-62.000)
.25 mm U/S	2.4307-2.4311 (61.740-61.750)
.50 mm U/S	2.4209-2.4213 (61.490-61.500)
.75 mm U/S	2.4110-2.4114 (61.240-61.250)
1 mm U/S	2.4012-2.4016 (60.990-61.000)

NOTE: **The rod bearings have replacement inserts of .25 mm and .50 mm undersize available for service.**

CONNECTING ROD JOURNALS

Application	In. (mm)
2.2L Diesel	
Standard	2.0858-2.0866 (52.980-53.000)
.25 mm U/S	2.0764-2.0768 (52.740-52.750)
.50 mm U/S	2.0665-2.0669 (52.490-52.500)

CRANKSHAFT FRONT OIL SEAL

Removal & Installation

1) With damper pulley and timing belt cover removed, detach valve timing belt, crankshaft timing sprocket and related components. Front oil seal is located in the oil pump housing, directly around crankshaft end.

2) Note oil seal position for reassembly reference. Oil seal may be pryed from pump housing using

L 4-CYLINDER DIESEL (Cont.)

screwdriver. Apply tape to sharp corners of removal tool to avoid damaging crankshaft sealing surface.

3) Apply grease to oil seal lips. Carefully tap new oil seal into oil pump cavity using seal installer tool (SST09223-22010) or equivalent. Do not damage oil pump housing during installation. To complete installation, reverse removal procedure.

CRANKSHAFT REAR OIL SEAL

Removal & Installation

1) With engine and transmission assembly removed from vehicle, detach transmission. Remove flywheel and rear end plate. Remove oil seal from retainer by carefully prying seal away from crankshaft flange and cylinder block.

2) Note oil seal position for reassembly reference. Do not damage crankshaft oil seal surface during removal. Apply tape to sharp corners of removal tool to avoid damaging crankshaft sealing surface.

3) Coat new oil seal with grease and tap into position using seal installer tool (SST09223-56010). Do not damage crankshaft flange or cylinder block during installation. Install flywheel, rear end plate and transmission. Complete installation by reversing removal procedure.

ENGINE OILING

CRANKCASE CAPACITY

The crankcase capacity is 6.1 qts. (5.8L) with filter. Refill without filter is 5.1 qts. (4.8L).

NORMAL OIL PRESSURE

11.4 psi (.8 kg/cm²) at idle.

OIL PRESSURE REGULATOR VALVE

There are two oil pressure regulator valves. Both are located in the oil cooler. One is the oil pump relief valve and the other is the oil cooler relief valve.

ENGINE OILING SYSTEM

Oil is forced from a gear type oil pump to full-flow oil filter. From the filter, oil is directed to crankshaft main bearings which feeds connecting rod bearings. The oil passage above the rear main bearing feeds camshaft and rocker arm shaft through No. 5 rocker support. Oil is then returned to the pan. *See Fig. 9.*

Fig. 9: Toyota 4-Cylinder Diesel Engine Oiling System

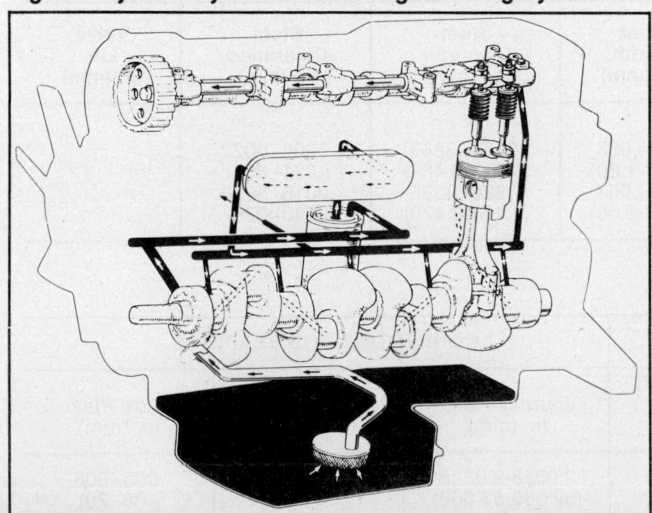

OIL PUMP

NOTE: **When repairing oil pump, the oil pan and screen should be removed and cleaned.**

Removal

1) Raise and support vehicle. Drain engine oil. Remove timing belt cover and timing belt. Using oil pan prying tool (SST09032-00100), remove oil pan. Do not use prying tool on pump side. Do not damage pan flange.

2) Remove oil strainer mount bolts and strainer. Remove dipstick and tube. Remove oil pump by tapping pump housing with plastic hammer. Disassemble pump cover, drive gear, driven gear, oil seal and relief valve. *See Fig. 10.*

Inspection

1) Check the oil pump gears and housing for wear or damage. Install new oil seal using seal installer tool (SST09223-22010) or equivalent. Do not install seal slantwise.

2) Measure clearances between drive gear and cresent, driven gear and cresent, side clearance and gear-to-body clearance. *See Fig. 10.* If beyond limits, replace necessary parts.

3) Check relief valve components for wear or damage. Standard oil pump relief valve spring free height is 2.335-2.374" (59.30-60.30 mm). Installed height is 1.974" @ 10.1 lbs. (50.15 mm @ 4.58 kg).

4) Standard oil cooler relief valve spring free height is 2.335-2.374" (59.30-60.30 mm). Installed height is 2.217" @ 3.6 lbs. (56.30 mm @ 1.65 kg).

Fig. 10: Exploded View of Oil Pump Assembly

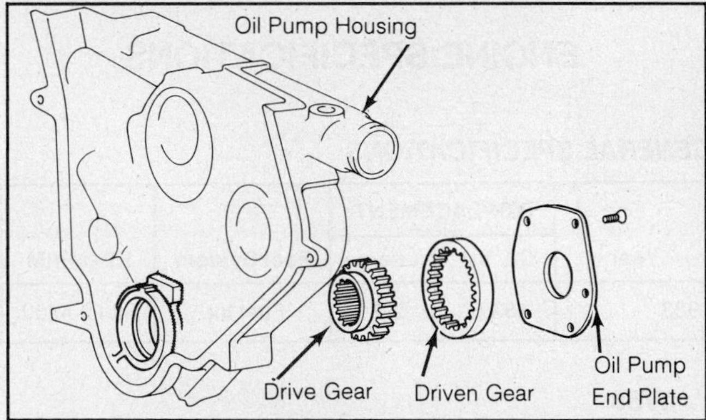
Oil Pump Housing
Drive Gear
Driven Gear
Oil Pump
End Plate

Replace oil seal and any gear that shows excessive wear, damage or is beyond clearance limits.

Installation

1) Check that mating surfaces are clean. Ensure pump drive gear spline teeth engage with large teeth of crankshaft.

2) Using new seal packing pan gasket or silicone base sealant, install oil pan. Complete installation by reversing removal procedures.

OIL PUMP CLEARANCES

Application	In. (mm)
Drive Gear Tip-to-Cresent	.009-.010 (.22-.25)
	Limit .012 (.30)
Driven Gear Tip-to-Cresent	.006-.008 (.15-.21)
	Limit .012 (.30)
Gear Side	.0012-.0035 (.030-.090)
	Limit .006 (.15)
Driven Gear-to-Body	.0024-.0059 (.060-.150)
	Limit .008 (.20)

Toyota Engines

L 4-CYLINDER DIESEL (Cont.)

ENGINE COOLING

COOLANT CAPACITY

The total coolant system capacity, with heater, is 11.1 qts. (10.5L).

THERMOSTAT

The thermostat starts to open at 190°F (88°C). At 208°F (98°C), the thermostat should be open more than .39" (10 mm).

RADIATOR CAP

10.7-14.9 psi. (.75-1.05 kg/cm²).

WATER PUMP

NOTE: **Do not allow coolant onto timing belt during replacement or repair.**

Removal

Drain cooling system. Remove fan belt, fan and fan pulley. Remove water pump mount bolts and pump.

Disassembly

1) Support pulley seat and press from pump shaft using removal tools (SST09236-28011 and SST09236-36010). Heat pump body to 167-176°F (75-85°C). Using shaft removal tool (09236-28011), press pump bearing from rotor.

2) Press out the bearing, shaft and impeller through the rear of the housing. Press the impeller off of the water pump shaft. Remove seal from pump shaft. Check all parts for wear, cracks or damage. *See Fig. 11*.

Fig. 11: Exploded View of Water Pump

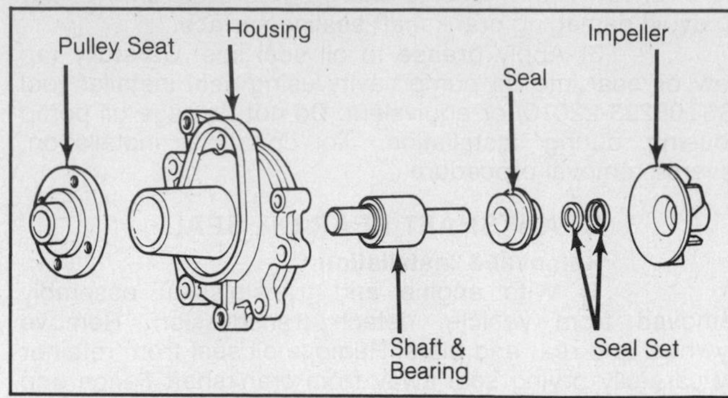
Pulley Seat
Housing
Impeller
Seal
Shaft &
Bearing
Seal Set

When installing impeller, ensure depth is correct or impeller will not clear housing.

Reassembly

1) Reheat pump body. Press bearing and shaft assembly into pump housing. Bearing should be flush with front edge of housing neck. Apply liquid sealer to outside edge of the seal and press into pump body.

2) Coat face of seal set that contact seal in body and install seal set into the rotor. Press the impeller onto pump shaft. Press pulley seat on the pump shaft to specified depth. Depth is 2.60" (66 mm) measured from front face of pulley to rear face of pump housing.

Installation

Clean gasket surfaces and install new gaskets. To complete installation, reverse removal procedures. After assembling pump, ensure the rotor turns smoothly with pump plate installed. Adjust drive belt tensions, fill coolant system, start engine and check for leaks.

ENGINE SPECIFICATIONS

GENERAL SPECIFICATIONS

Year	DISPLACEMENT		Fuel System	HP@RPM	Torque Ft. Lbs.@RPM	Compr. Ratio	BORE		STROKE	
	Cu. In.	Liters					In.	mm	In.	mm
1983	133.5	2.2	Fuel Inj.	62 @ 4200	93.3 © 2400	21.5:1	3.54	90	3.39	86

VALVES

Engine Size & Valve	Head Diam. In. (mm)	Face Angle	Seat Angle	Seat Width In. (mm)	Stem Diameter In. (mm)	Stem Clearance In. (mm)	Valve Lift In. (mm)
2.2L							
Intake	.....	44.5°	45°	.051-.063 (1.30-1.60)	.3336-.3342 (8.473-8.489)	.0008-.0022 (.021-.057)	.....
Exhaust	.....	44.5°	45°	.051-.063 (1.30-1.60)	.3328-.3335 (8.454-8.470)	.0016-.0030 (.040-.076)	.....

CRANKSHAFT MAIN & CONNECTING ROD BEARINGS

Engine	MAIN BEARINGS				CONNECTING ROD BEARINGS		
	Journal Diam. In. (mm)	Clearance In. (mm)	Thrust Bearing	Crankshaft End Play In. (mm)	Journal Diam. In. (mm)	Clearance In. (mm)	Side Play In. (mm)
2.2L	2.4402-2.4409 (61.980-62.000)	.0012-.0028 (.030-.070)	No. 3	.002-.010 (.04-.25)	2.0858-2.0866 (52.980-53.000)	.0012-.0028 (.030-.070)	.003-.008 (.08-.20)

L 4-CYLINDER DIESEL (Cont.)

ENGINE SPECIFICATIONS (Cont.)

PISTONS, PINS, RINGS

Engine	PISTONS	PINS		RINGS		
	Clearance In. (mm)	Piston Fit In. (mm)	Rod Fit In. (mm)	Ring No.	End Gap In. (mm)	Side Clearance In. (mm)
2.2L	.0014-.0022 (.035-.055)	.0002-.0005 [1] (.004-.012)	.0006-.0009 [1] (.014-.022)	No. 1	.008-.016 (.20-.40)	.0024-.0039 (.060-.100)
				No. 2	.012-.020 (.30-.50)	.0016-.0031 (.040-.080)
				Oil	.012-.020 (.30-.50)	.0012-.0028 (.030-.070)

[1] – Oil coated piston pin must be pressed in using finger pressure only.

VALVE TIMING

Engine	INTAKE		EXHAUST	
	Open (BTDC)	Close (ABDC)	Open (BBDC)	Close (ATDC)
2.2L	14°	44°	51°	11°

VALVE SPRINGS

Engine	Free Length In. (mm)	PRESSURE Lbs. @ In. (Kg @ mm)	
		Valve Closed	Valve Open
2.2L	1.81-1.83 (45.9-46.6)	53.4@1.547 (24.2@39.30)	.....

TIGHTENING SPECIFICATIONS

Application	Ft. Lbs. (N.m)
Camshaft Bearing Cap Bolt	8-10 (11-14)
Camshaft Sprocket Bolt	69-75 (94-102)
Connecting Rod Cap Nut	37-43 (50-58)
Crankshaft Pulley Bolt	69-75 (94-102)
Cylinder Head Bolt	84-90 (114-122)
Delivery Valve Holder	26-32 (35-43)
Exhaust Manifold	11-15 (15-20)
Flywheel Bolt	84-90 (114-122)
Injection Pipe Union Nut	15-21 (20-28)
Intake Manifold	8-11 (11-15)
Main Bearing Cap Bolt	71-81 (96-110)
Nozzle Holder Mount Bolt	51-65 (69-88)
Nozzle Retaining Nut	44-57 (60-77)
Rocker Shaft Support Bolt	11-15 (15-20)

Toyota Engines

2F 6-CYLINDER

ENGINE CODING

ENGINE IDENTIFICATION

Engine number is stamped on right side of cylinder block above starter motor. First 2 characters indicate engine type.

ENGINE IDENTIFICATION

Application	Code
Land Cruiser	
4.2L	2F

ENGINE, MANIFOLDS & CYLINDER HEAD

ENGINE

Removal

1) Drain crankcase and cooling system and remove battery. Remove hood and tip grill forward. Disconnect radiator and heater hoses and remove radiator. Remove air cleaner assembly and cover carburetor.

2) Disconnect throttle and choke controls to carburetor. If equipped with air conditioning, remove compressor and condenser. DO NOT disconnect refrigerant lines.

3) Disconnect alternator and ignition wiring between engine and chassis. Tag all vacuum and emission control hoses for identification and disconnect from engine.

4) If equipped with power steering, remove pump and reservoir from engine and tie out of way, but do not disconnect hoses.

5) Remove engine and transmission undercovers. Remove front propeller shaft and winch drive shaft. Place jack or supporting device under transmission and transfer case.

6) Remove bolts attaching transmission to bell housing. Disconnect exhaust pipe from manifold and fuel line at pump.

7) Attach hoist and sling to engine, and remove engine mount bolts and nuts. Move engine forward and up, using care to avoid damage to engine compartment components.

Installation

Use guide dowels in transmission bolt holes and lower into position. Use care when aligning clutch assembly over transmission pilot shaft. Continue installation in reverse sequence of removal.

INTAKE & EXHAUST MANIFOLDS

Removal

1) Disconnect battery and remove air cleaner. Disconnect throttle rod, choke rod, accelerator wire, vacuum line, and fuel line from carburetor.

2) Disconnect magnetic valve wire from ignition coil terminal, and remove carburetor assembly. Disconnect exhaust pipe from exhaust manifold. Remove manifold nuts, manifolds and gaskets.

Installation

1) Thoroughly clean all gasket surfaces and install new gaskets. Replace intake or exhaust manifold if warpage limit of .079" (2 mm) is exceeded.

2) Install manifold assembly, and gradually tighten bolts working from center out. *See Fig. 1.* Install remaining components in reverse of removal procedure.

Fig. 1: Intake-Exhaust Manifold Tightening Sequence

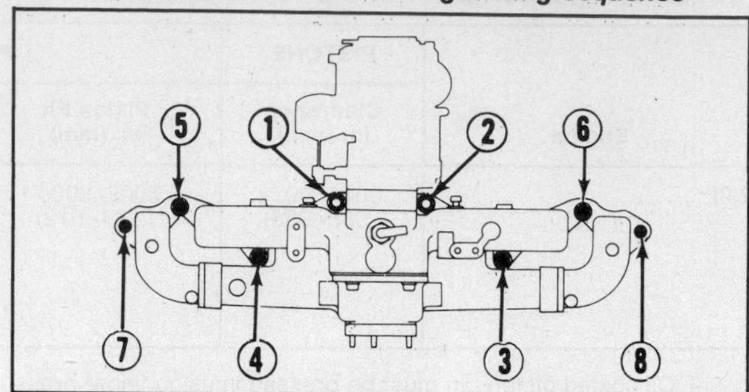
5
1
2
6
7
4
3
8

Check for warpage before installation.

CYLINDER HEAD

Removal

1) Drain cooling system and remove air cleaner assembly. After marking for identification, disconnect spark plug wires, electrical connectors and vacuum hoses from head. Remove intake and exhaust manifold.

2) Remove valve cover and rocker arm assembly. Take out push rods, keeping them in order for installation. Loosen head bolts in 2 or 3 steps in reverse of tightening sequence. *See Fig. 2.* Remove cylinder head.

Inspection

1) The limit of head surface warpage is .0059" (.15 mm). The manifold mounting surface warpage limit is .0039" (.1 mm).

2) If warpage exceeds the limit, correct by machining or replacement. The maximum reface limit for both surfaces is .0079" (.2 mm).

Installation

1) Ensure that all mating surfaces are clean. Place new head gasket on cylinder block. Ensure mating oil hole on push rod side is between No. 4 and 5 cylinder.

2) Install cylinder head and tighten bolts in 2 or 3 steps. *See Fig. 2.* Complete installation in reverse sequence of removal.

Fig. 2: Cylinder Head Tightening Sequence

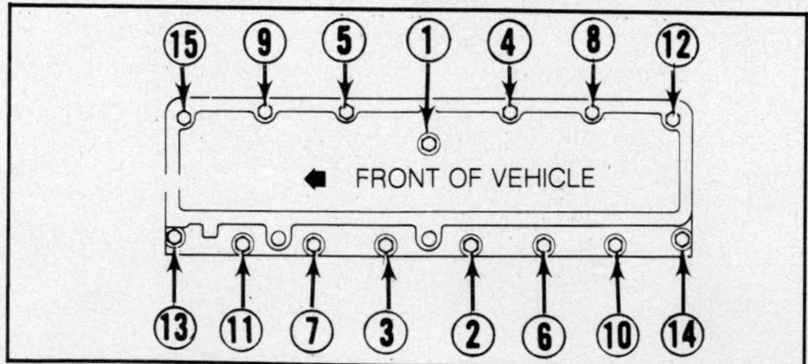
15
9
5
1
4
8
12
FRONT OF VEHICLE
13
11
7
3
2
6
10
14

Loosen in reverse order.

CAMSHAFT

ENGINE FRONT COVER

Removal

Drain cooling system and remove radiator. Take off all fan belts. Using a gear puller, remove

Toyota Engines

2F 6-CYLINDER (Cont.)

crankshaft pulley. Remove timing gear cover bolts, and take off cover.

Installation

1) Install cover and gasket. Ensure that bolts of proper length are used, and liquid sealer is used on threads of lower 2 bolts.

2) Drive pulley into position with tool (09214-60010) to locate cover properly. Tighten cover bolts. Reverse disassembly procedure.

FRONT COVER OIL SEAL

Removal & Installation

Pry old oil seal out using screwdriver. Install new oil seal so open end of seal is toward inside of timing gear cover. Drive seal in place with tool (09515-35010).

TIMING GEAR

NOTE: Camshaft must be removed from engine for gear replacement. Due to model variations, engine may have to be removed from vehicle.

Checking for Wear

1) Set engine to TDC of No. 1 cylinder. Drain cooling system and remove radiator. Remove engine front cover as previously described.

2) Replace camshaft and crankshaft timing gears if gear backlash exceeds .008" (.2 mm).

Removal

1) Align the timing marks, and remove the camshaft thrust plate aligning bolts. *See Fig. 3.*

Fig. 3: Aligning Timing Marks on Gears

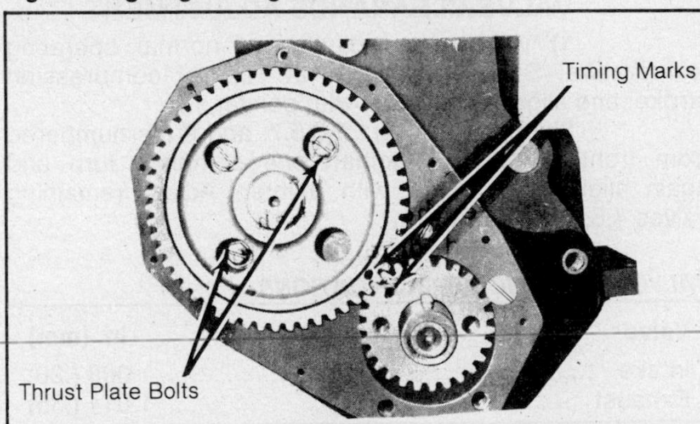
Timing Marks
Thrust Plate Bolts

Use puller to remove gears.

2) Remove valve cover and engine side cover. Remove rocker arm shaft. Noting position for reinstallation, remove push rods and valve lifters. Pull out the camshaft.

3) Remove the snap ring and press timing gear off of camshaft. Pry pulley key from crankshaft. Using a gear puller, pull timing gear off of crankshaft.

Installation

1) Install crankshaft timing gear and pulley key. Press new timing gear on camshaft. Oil camshaft journals and bearings and install camshaft.

2) Align timing marks on camshaft and crankshaft timing gears. *See Fig. 3.*

3) If oil nozzle was removed, screw in and stake in two places. Oil hole must face gears. *See Fig. 4.*

4) Reverse disassembly procedure and reinstall engine. Refill cooling system with 50-50 mixture of antifreeze and water.

Fig. 4: Adjusting Oil Nozzle so Hole Faces Gears

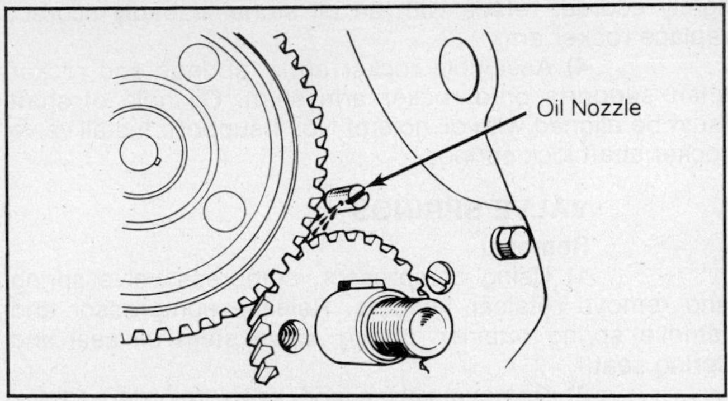
Oil Nozzle

Screw nozzle in and stake at 2 places.

CAMSHAFT

Removal & Installation

See Timing Gear in this article.

CAMSHAFT END THRUST

1) Measure end thrust with feeler gauge. Measurement is taken between thrust plate and first cam journal.

2) Thrust should be .0079-.0103" (.200-.261 mm). If thrust exceeds .012" (.30 mm), replace camshaft thrust plate.

CAM LOBE HEIGHT

Measure height of cam lobe. If wear exceeds specification limit, replace camshaft. Intake lobe limit is 1.496" (38 mm). Exhaust lobe limit is 1.492" (37.9 mm).

CAMSHAFT BEARING

Removal

1) Check camshaft for runout at center journal. If runout exceeds .0059" (.15 mm), replace camshaft. Inspect camshaft journals and bearings for wear or damage.

2) If clearance exceeds specifications, replace camshaft bearings and/or camshaft. Bearings are available in standard .010" and .020" (.25 and .50 mm) oversizes.

3) Drive out camshaft rear expansion plug from cylinder block. Remove bearings using camshaft bearing remover/installer tool (09215-00010).

Installation

When installing new bearings, ensure that oil holes of bearing align with oil holes in cylinder block. Coat rear expansion plug with sealer, and reinstall plug in block.

VALVES

VALVE ARRANGEMENT

E-I-I-E-E-I-I-E-E-I-I-E (Front-to-rear).

ROCKER ARM ASSEMBLY

1) When disassembling, note position of rocker arms and supports. Check rocker arms and shaft for damage or wear.

2) Measure the oil clearance between rocker arms and shaft. Clearance should be .0007-.0017" (.018-.043 mm).

3) Check contact surface of rocker arm. If only lightly scored, reface with an oil stone. If badly scored, replace rocker arm.

4) Assemble rocker arms, springs and rocker shaft supports onto rocker arm shaft. Oil hole of shaft must be aligned with oil hole of No. 4 support. Install valve rocker shaft lock springs.

VALVE SPRINGS

Removal

1) Using compressor, compress valve spring and remove retainer keepers. Release compressor and remove spring retainer, spring, valve stem oil seal and spring seat.

2) Remove valves and keep in order. Check spring squareness, free height and tension at installed height. Spring should be square within .072" (1.8 mm).

Installation

1) Insert valve into valve stem guide, and install valve spring seat, valve spring, valve stem oil seal and valve spring retainer onto valve stem.

2) Compress valve spring using valve spring compressor, and install valve spring retainer locks. Make sure retainer locks seat properly in valve stem groove.

VALVE STEM LENGTH

Valve stem tips may be resurfaced to a limit of .02" (.5 mm) if necessary. The overall valve length limit is 4.894" (124.3 mm) for intake and 4.902" (124.5 mm) for exhaust.

VALVE STEM OIL SEALS

Cup-type oil seals are used on all valves. Coat new seals with engine oil, and install with seal installer tool (09201-31010). Drive in a distance of .386-.406" (9.8-10.2 mm) above cylinder head. *See Fig. 5.*

Fig. 5: Measuring Valve Seal Installed Height

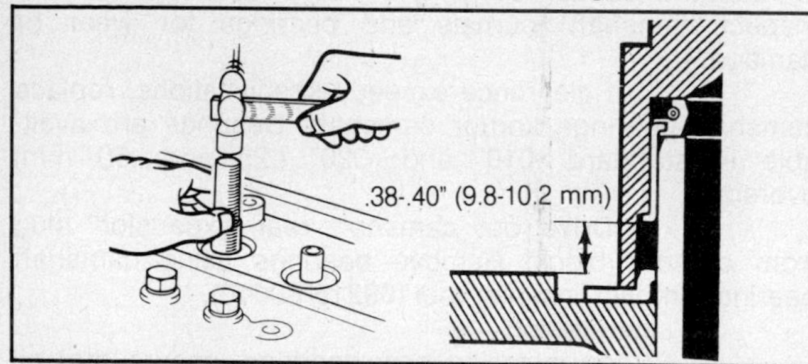
.38-.40" (9.8-10.2 mm)

Coat seals with oil before installation.

VALVE GUIDE SERVICING

1) Check clearance between valve stems and valve guides. If clearance exceeds .004" (.10 mm) for intake or .005" (.12 mm) for exhaust, replace valve and/or valve guide.

2) To replace valve guide, drive toward combustion chamber with installer/remover tool (09201-60011).

3) After removing guide, measure valve guide bore in cylinder. If guide bore is more than .5519" (14.018 mm), machine the bore to .5531-.5539" (14.050-14.068 mm).

4) Install .002" (.05 mm) oversize valve guide. Install from top of cylinder head. When properly installed guide should extend .689" (17.5 mm) from top of cylinder head.

5) Intake valve guide length is 2.13" (54 mm) and exhaust guide is 2.32" (59 mm) long. After installing, ream guide for proper clearance.

Fig. 6: Installing Valve Guides to .689" (17.5 mm) Depth

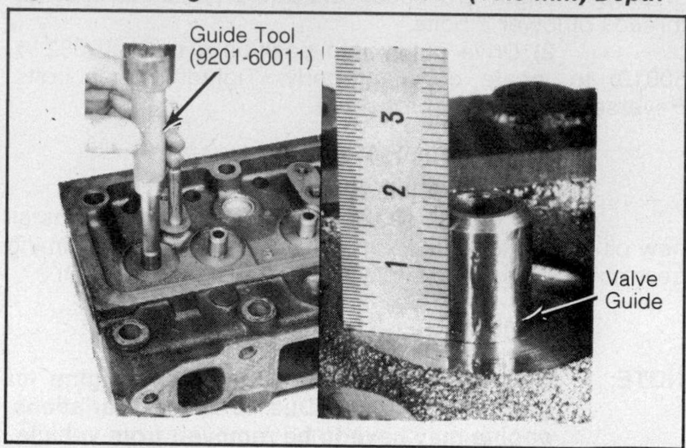
Guide Tool
(9201-60011)
Valve
Guide

Protrusion is the same for intake and exhaust guides.

VALVE LIFTERS

1) Check the lifters and bores for wear or damage. Valve lifter standard diameter is .9902" (25.15 mm).

2) The standard oil clearance is .0007-.003" (.019-.075 mm). If clearance exceeds limit, replace lifter with oversize lifter. Oversize lifters are available in .002" (.05 mm).

VALVE CLEARANCE ADJUSTMENT

1) Valves are adjusted at normal operating temperature. Set No. 1 piston at TDC of compression stroke, and align timing mark with pointer.

2) Adjust valves 1,2,3,5,7, and 9 (as numbered from front). Rotate crankshaft one complete turn and again align timing mark with pointer. Adjust remaining valves 4,6,8,10,11, and 12.

VALVE CLEARANCE SPECIFICATIONS

Valve	In. (mm)
Intake	.008 (.20)
Exhaust	1.014 (.35)

PISTONS, PINS & RINGS

OIL PAN

Removal

Remove engine undercovers. Remove flywheel side and undercover. Remove front propeller shaft. Drain oil, remove oil pan attaching bolts and oil pan.

Installation

Thoroughly clean all gasket mating surfaces. Apply liquid sealer onto both oil pan gasket surfaces. Install oil pan and tighten bolts. Reverse removal procedure for remaining components.

PISTON & ROD ASSEMBLY

Removal

With cylinder head and oil pan removed, remove connecting rod caps and remove bearings. Remove ridge from top of cylinder. Push piston and rod

2F 6-CYLINDER (Cont.)

assembly up through cylinder block. Mark all components with cylinder numbers for correct reassembly.

NOTE: Cover rod bolts with a short piece of hose during removal and installation to prevent damage to crankshaft.

Installation

1) Lubricate piston and rings and position ring gaps. *See Fig. 7.* Use a ring compressor and install piston/rod assembly in proper position. Notch on piston must face FRONT and Toyota trademark on rod should face REAR.

2) Oil hole in rod faces right (camshaft) side. Install bearings and caps. Check for smooth rotation of crankshaft after tightening each bearing cap.

FITTING PISTONS

1) Measure cylinder bores at 90° and parallel to crankshaft centerline. Also measure bores at top, center and bottom of piston travel.

2) If cylinder bore is worn beyond specifications, cylinder must be bored and oversize pistons installed. Oversize pistons are available in .020", .040" and .060" (.50, 1.00 and 1.50 mm).

3) Measure piston with micrometer at bottom of skirt at right angles to piston pin. Standard piston diameter is 3.6992-3.7012" (93.96-94.01 mm). If worn beyond limits, replace piston.

CYLINDER BORE SPECIFICATIONS

Application	Wear Limits In. (mm)
Standard Bore	3.701-3.703 (94.00-94.05)
Bore Wear Limit	.008 (.20)
Taper	.0008 (.020)
Difference Between Cylinders.	.002 (.05)

FITTING RINGS

1) Measure ring gaps in cylinder. If cylinder has not been bored, check gap with ring in lowest part of cylinder.

NOTE: Two types of rings are used: NP & Riken. Check specifications for ring gap.

2) Check clearance of piston ring in ring groove. If groove worn beyond limit, replace piston. Install rings with marks facing upward.

Fig. 7: Spacing Piston Ring Gaps

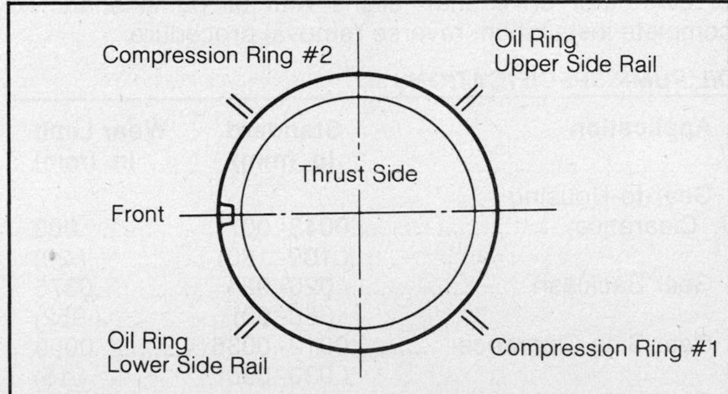
Compression Ring #2
Oil Ring
Upper Side Rail
Thrust Side
Front
Oil Ring
Lower Side Rail
Compression Ring #1

Code marks on rings will face upward.

PISTON PINS

Removal

Remove piston pin bolt and push piston pin from piston and connecting rod. Mark all parts for correct assembly order.

Inspection

1) Coat piston pin with engine oil. The piston pin should push into piston hole with thumb pressure.

2) The oil clearance limit between piston and piston pin is .0028" (.07 mm). If clearance is exceeded, replace piston and piston pin as a set .

3) Check connecting rod for bending or twisting. The bend limit per 3.94" (100 mm) is .002" (.05 mm). The twist limit per 3.94" (100 mm) is .006" (.15 mm).

Installation

1) Position piston and connecting rod so that when notch on top of piston faces forward, oil hole in connecting rod faces camshaft side.

2) Push pin into assembly, and center pin in piston. Center connecting rod between piston pin bosses and tighten piston pin bolt.

Fig. 8: Proper Assembling of Piston and Rod

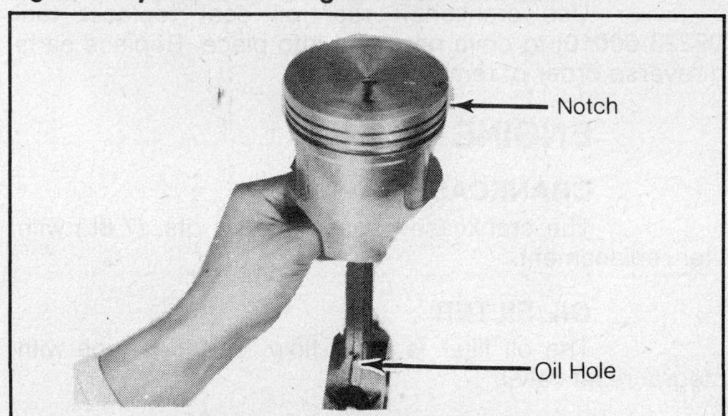
Notch
Oil Hole

Notch on top of piston must face forward.

CRANKSHAFT MAIN & CONNECTING ROD BEARINGS

MAIN BEARINGS

1) Thoroughly clean crankshaft, and blow out oil passages with compressed air. Inspect crankshaft for scoring or wear.

2) Check crankshaft for runout with a dial indicator on second or third main bearing journal. If runout exceeds .004" (.10 mm), replace crankshaft.

3) If main bearing journal taper or out-of-round exceeds .0004" (.01 mm), grind crankshaft to next undersize.

4) Main bearing oil clearance is checked by the Plastigage method. If clearance cannot be brought to specifications by use of new standard size bearings, grind crankshaft to next undersize.

5) Crankshaft bearings are available in .002", .010", and .020" (.05, .25, and .50 mm) undersize.

NOTE: All main bearings are different. No. 1 (front) and No. 4 (rear) have oil holes and must be installed on block side. Arrow on connecting rod cap must face front.

Toyota Engines

2F 6-CYLINDER (Cont.)

CONNECTING ROD BEARINGS

1) Check connecting rod journals for wear, taper or out-of-round. The taper and out-of-round limit is .0004" (.01 mm). Grind crankshaft if worn beyond limit.

2) Check connecting rod oil clearance by Plastigage method. Grind crankshaft if new standard size bearings will not restore proper clearance. Undersize bearings are available in .002", .010", and .020" (.05, .25 and .50 mm).

THRUST BEARING ALIGNMENT

Install main bearing caps and tighten to specifications. Check crankshaft end play at No. 3 main bearing. If clearance exceeds .012" (.3 mm), replace No. 3 crankshaft bearings.

REAR MAIN BEARING OIL SEAL

Removal

Remove transmission and transfer case assembly. Mark position of pressure plate relative to flywheel for later installation. Remove pressure plate, clutch and flywheel. Pry out oil seal with a screwdriver.

Installation

Use crankshaft rear oil seal replacer tool (09223-60010) to drive new seal into place. Replace parts in reverse order of removal.

ENGINE OILING

CRANKCASE CAPACITY

The crankcase capacity is 8.2 qts. (7.8L) with filter replacement.

OIL FILTER

The oil filter is a full-flow, cartridge-type with integral relief valve.

NORMAL OIL PRESSURE

The oil pressure is maintained at 50-64 psi (3.5-4.5 kg/cm²) by safety valve in oil pressure regulator.

OIL PRESSURE REGULATOR VALVE

The oil pressure regulator valve is located in the oil pump. It is non-adjustable.

ENGINE OILING SYSTEM

Force-feed system ensures positive lubrication through oil holes and galleries in engine block. *See Fig. 9.*

OIL PUMP

Removal

With oil pan removed, remove bolts attaching oil strainer to crankcase. Remove oil pump mounting bolt and oil pump line. Remove pump from engine.

Disassembly

Remove oil pump cover, regulator valve plug and disassemble pump. Inspect all parts for wear or damage.

Inspection

Inspect regulator valve in valve bore for smooth operation. Install gears in housing and check for proper clearances.

Reassembly

1) Reassemble in reverse order of disassembly. Ensure that the pump cover discharge hole faces toward the pump body bolt hole.

Fig. 9: Toyota 2F Engine Oiling System

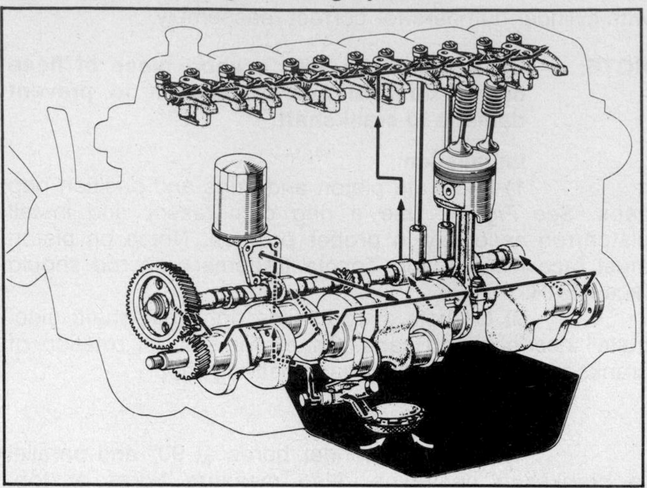

2) Prior to installing assembled pump, check operation by submerging inlet line in fresh engine oil. Turn shaft clockwise with a screwdriver and check for oil flow from discharge hole.

3) Cover the discharge hole with thumb, and turn shaft. Turning resistance should be felt.

Fig. 10: Exploded View of Oil Pump Assembly

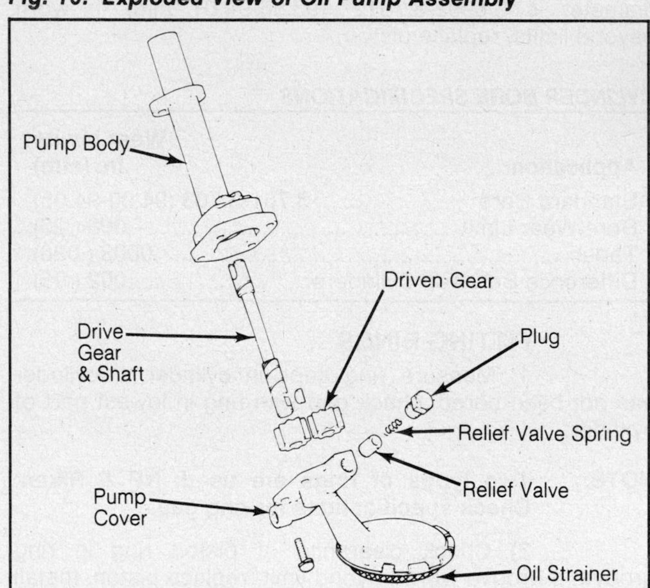
Pump Body
Driven Gear
Drive Gear & Shaft
Plug
Relief Valve Spring
Relief Valve
Pump Cover
Oil Strainer

Installation

Install pump on engine, noting that lower end of distributor drive shaft aligns with oil pump shaft. To complete installation, reverse removal procedure.

OIL PUMP SPECIFICATIONS

Application	Standard In. (mm)	Wear Limit In. (mm)
Gear-to-Housing Clearance	.0043-.0071 (.109-.180)	.008 (.20)
Gear Backlash	.020-.024 (.50-.60)	.0375 (.952)
Gear Side Clearance	.0012-.0035 (.030-.090)	.0059 (.15)
Cover Wear		.0059 (.15)

Toyota Engines

2F 6-CYLINDER (Cont.)

ENGINE COOLING

COOLANT CAPACITY

Coolant capacity is 17.4 qts. (16.5L).

THERMOSTAT

The thermostat is a wax pellet type. It begins to open at 187°F (86°C) and is fully opened at 212°F (100°C).

WATER PUMP

Removal

Drain cooling system, and loosen alternator adjusting bar. Remove fan, fan pulley and fan belt. Remove lower radiator hose and heater hose from pump. Remove water pump retaining bolts, pump and gasket.

Disassembly

1) Remove the rear plate and gasket. Press the pulley seat off of the pump shaft.

2) Heat the pump housing to approximately 176°F (80°C). Press shaft and bearing assembly out through the rear of the housing.

3) Press the impeller off of the pump shaft and remove seal set. Inspect all parts for wear, cracks, or damage.

Reassembly

1) Press bearing and shaft into pump housing. Apply liquid sealer to outside edge of seal set and press into pump housing.

2) Install the packing and seal into the impeller. Press impeller onto pump shaft. The impeller-to-housing clearance should be .03" (.75 mm).

3) Press pulley seat onto pump shaft to specified depth. Measurement is from front face of pulley seat to rear face of pump housing.

PULLEY SEAT INSTALLATION DEPTH

Type	Depth
Direct Drive	6" (152.3 mm)
Fan Clutch	4.6" (117.3 mm)

Installation

Ensure that mating surfaces are clean and free from pitting or damage. Install pump with new gasket and tighten mounting bolts. Complete installation in reverse sequence of removal and adjust belt tension.

TIGHTENING SPECIFICATIONS

Application	Ft. Lbs. (N.m)
Camshaft Thrust Plate Bolts	8-11 (11-15)
Connecting Rod Bearing Caps	35-54 (48-73)
Crankshaft Main Bearing Caps	
No. 1 - No. 3	91-108 (124-147)
No. 4	76-94 (103-128)
Crankshaft Pulley	116-144 (158-196)
Cylinder Head	84-97 (114-132)
Flywheel Bolts	58-79 (79-107)
Manifold Nuts	29-36 (39-49)
Piston Pin Bolt	40-50 (54-68)
Rocker Arm-to-Cyl. Head	
8 mm Bolt	15-21 (20-29)
10 mm Bolt	22-32 (30-44)

ENGINE SPECIFICATIONS

GENERAL SPECIFICATIONS

Year	DISPLACEMENT		Fuel System	HP@RPM	Torque Ft. Lbs.@RPM	Compr. Ratio	BORE		STROKE	
	Cu. In.	Liters					In.	mm	In.	mm
1983	257.9	4.2	2-Bbl.	125©3600	271@1800	8.3:1	3.70	94	4.00	101.6

VALVES

Engine Size & Valve	Head Diam. In. (mm)	Face Angle	Seat Angle	Seat Width In. (mm)	Stem Diameter In. (mm)	Stem Clearance In. (mm)	Valve Lift In. (mm)
4.2L [1]							
Intake	1.81 (46.0)	45.5°	45°	.055 (1.4)	.3138-.3144 (7.970-7.985)	.0012-.0024 (.030-.060)	.....
Exhaust	1.48 (37.5)	45.5°	45°	.067 (1.7)	.3134-.3140 (7.960-7.975)	.0016-.0028 (.040-.071)	.....

[1] – Maximum clearance for intake guides is .004" (.10 mm) and, .005" (.12 mm) for exhaust.

Toyota Engines

2F 6-CYLINDER (Cont.)

ENGINE SPECIFICATIONS (Cont.)

PISTONS, PINS, RINGS

Engine	PISTONS	PINS		RINGS		
	Clearance In. (mm)	Piston Fit In. (mm)	Rod Fit In. (mm)	Ring No.	End Gap In. (mm)	Side Clearance In. (mm)
4.2L	.0012-.0020 (.034-.050)	.0003-.0005 (.008-.012)	Locked in Rod	No. 1	.0079-.0157 (.200-.400)	.0012-.0028 (.030-.071)
				No.2	.0079-.0157 (.200-.400)	.0008-.0024 (.020-.060)
				Oil (NP)	.0079-.0197 (.200-.500)	.0016-.0075 (.040-.190)
				Oil (Riken)	.0118-.0354 (.30-.90)	.0016-.0075 (.040-.190)

CRANKSHAFT MAIN & CONNECTING ROD BEARINGS

Engine	MAIN BEARINGS				CONNECTING ROD BEARINGS		
	Journal Diam. In. (mm)	Clearance In. (mm)	Thrust Bearing	Crankshaft End Play In. (mm)	Journal Diam. In. (mm)	Clearance In. (mm)	Side Play In. (mm)
4.2L							
No. 1	2.6367-2.6376 (66.972-66.996)	.0008-.0017 (.020-.044)	No. 3	.002-.006 (.06-.16)	2.1252-2.1260 (53.98-54.00)	.0008-.0024 (.020-.060)	.003-.009 (.08-.24)
No. 2	2.6957-2.6967 (68.472-68.496)						
No. 3	2.7548-2.7557 (69.972-69.996)						
No. 4	2.8139-2.8148 (71.472-71.496)						

VALVE SPRINGS

Engine	Free Length In. (mm)	PRESSURE Lbs. @ In. (Kg @ mm)	
		Valve Closed	Valve Open
4.2L	2.028 (51.5)	71@1.693 (32.5@43.0)	.....

CAMSHAFT

Engine	Journal Diam. In. (mm)	Clearance In. (mm)	Lobe Lift In. (mm)
4.2L			
No. 1	1.8810-1.8888 (47.955-47.975)	.001-.003 (.025-.075)	.....
No. 2	1.8289-1.8297 (46.455-46.475)		
No. 3	1.7699-1.7707 (44.955-44.975)		
No. 4	1.7108-1.7116 (43.455-43.475)		

5M-GE 6-CYLINDER

ENGINE CODING

ENGINE IDENTIFICATION

Engine number is stamped on a machined pad on the front, right side of engine block. Engine code is also printed on a sticker attached to cylinder head cover.

ENGINE IDENTIFICATION CODE

Application	Code
Cressida & Supra (2.8L)	5M-GE

ENGINE, MANIFOLDS & CYLINDER HEAD

ENGINE

Removal

1) Disconnect battery and drain cooling system. Remove hood and fan shroud. Remove radiator hoses, radiator, heater hoses, and all oil cooler hoses. Remove oil pressure sending wire and alternator wiring.

2) Remove air cleaner and air intake ducting. Disconnect brake booster vacuum hose. Disconnect distributor primary wiring and coil secondary wiring.

3) Label and disconnect all fuel lines, vacuum hoses and electrical wiring between engine and engine compartment. If equipped, remove A/C compressor. Leave refrigerant lines connected.

4) Disconnect starter wiring and accelerator connecting rod. If equipped with manual transmission, disconnect clutch flexible hose from master cylinder tube Cap hose end to prevent fluid leakage.

5) Remove power steering pump. Leave hoses connected. Raise and support vehicle. Disconnect exhaust pipe from manifold, and remove exhaust pipe supports and insulator.

6) Disconnect speedometer drive cable and back-up light wiring. On manual transmission models, remove console box and gear shift lever.

7) On automatic transmission models, remove connecting rod swivel nut and disconnect control rod from shift lever. On all models, remove propeller shaft and plug rear of transmission to prevent oil leakage.

8) On Supra models, lower power rack and pinion steering gear. On both models, take off rear engine undercover. Remove front engine mount bolts. Support transmission with jack. Remove rear engine mount and crossmember.

9) Place wood block between firewall and cylinder head rear end to prevent damage to heater hose. Lower jack supporting transmission and remove stands. Using an engine hoist, remove engine and transmission assembly from vehicle.

Installation

To install, reverse removal procedure. Check all fluid levels and linkage adjustments prior to starting engine.

INTAKE MANIFOLD

Removal

1) Disconnect battery and drain coolant. Remove No. 1 and No. 2 air valve hoses from air intake chamber. Remove air intake connector and throttle body hose.

2) Disconnect No. 1 and No. 2 water by-pass hoses from throttle body. Disconnect 2 PCV hoses from valve cover. Disconnect fuel hose from hose support.

3) Label and disconnect emission control hoses from the throttle body and air intake chamber. Remove air intake chamber bracket, EGR cooler, and vacuum pipe.

4) Label and disconnect all wiring from air intake chamber and intake manifold. Disconnect cold start fuel hose from delivery hose.

5) Remove air intake chamber. Remove pulsation damper, No. 1 fuel pipe, and water outlet housing. Remove bolts and lift off intake manifold.

Inspection

Check air intake chamber and intake manifold for surface warpage. Maximum surface warpage is .004" (.1 mm) for both. Replace if beyond limits.

Installation

Thoroughly clean all gasket surfaces and install new gasket. Install manifold assembly. Gradually tighten bolts working from center outward. Install remaining components in reverse of removal procedure.

EXHAUST MANIFOLD

Removal & Inspection

Remove the 2 heat insulators. Disconnect oxygen sensor and exhaust pipe. Remove exhaust manifold and gasket. Maximum exhaust manifold surface warpage is .0295" (.75 mm). Replace if beyond limits.

Installation

Clean manifold and cylinder head mating surfaces. Install exhaust manifold and new gasket. Tighten nuts to specifications.

CYLINDER HEAD

Removal

1) Remove intake and exhaust manifolds. Remove distributor and spark plug wires from cylinder head. Without disconnecting hoses, remove power steering pump bracket and set aside.

2) Disconnect and label all electrical wiring. Remove timing belt and camshaft timing pulleys. Remove inner timing belt cover.

3) To prevent head warpage or cracking, cylinder head bolts must be removed in correct order. Loosen cylinder head bolts in 2 or 3 steps in reverse of tightening sequence. *See Fig. 1.*

Fig. 1: Cylinder Head Tightening Sequence

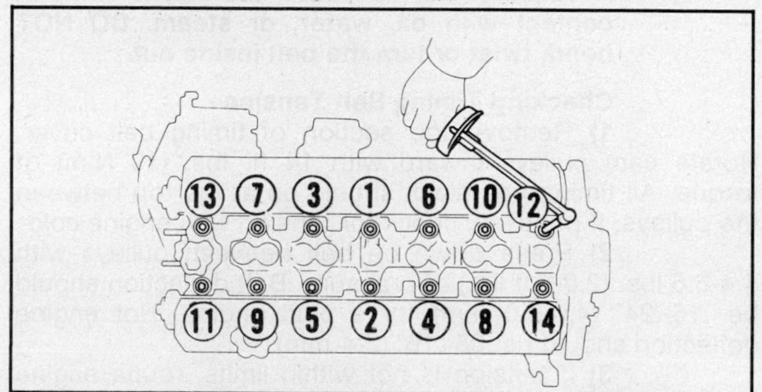
13
7
3
1
6
10
12
11
9
5
2
4
8
14

Tighten in sequence in 3 steps.

Toyota Engines

5M-GE 6-CYLINDER (Cont.)

Inspection

Using a feeler gauge and precision straight-edge, check cylinder head for warp. Warp limit for intake and exhaust manifold, cylinder head, and camshaft housing surfaces is .004" (.10 mm).

Installation

1) Clean all gasket surfaces, and apply sealer to both top front corners of block. Install new head gasket over dowels on block.

2) Clean all foreign matter from bolt hole, and place cylinder head on block. Tighten cylinder head bolts in sequence in 3 steps. *See Fig. 1*.

3) Install timing belt and camshaft timing pulleys. See Timing Belt. Reverse removal procedure to complete assembly.

CAMSHAFT

TIMING BELT COVERS

Removal

1) Engine front cover consists of 2 sections. Remove top section by removing 4 bolts and lifting off front of block.

2) Loosen and remove all drive belts. Remove crankshaft pulley bolt. Using a gear puller, remove the crankshaft pulley. Remove lower timing belt cover section.

Installation

Thoroughly clean front covers and block mating surfaces. Use liquid sealer on front cover gaskets when assembling. Install crankshaft pulley and tighten to specifications.

ENGINE FRONT COVER OIL SEAL

Removal

Remove upper and lower timing belt covers and timing belt. Remove crankshaft timing pulley with a gear puller. Remove oil pump drive shaft pulley bolt and pulley. Pry old seals out without damaging cover or retainer.

Installation

Apply engine oil to seal lip. Install oil seals using seal driver. Install pulleys. Tighten oil pump pulley bolt to specifications. Install timing belt, covers, and drive belts.

TIMING BELT & GEAR

NOTE: **Check timing belt for cracks, damaged or missing teeth and excessive wear. Replace if necessary. DO NOT allow the belt to come in contact with oil, water, or steam. DO NOT bend, twist or turn the belt inside out.**

Checking Timing Belt Tension

1) Remove top section of timing belt cover. Rotate cam pulleys inward with 14 ft. lbs. (19 N.m) of torque. All timing belt slack should be at the top between the pulleys. If possible, check for tension with engine cold.

2) Press down on belt between pulleys with 4.4-6.6 lbs. (2.0-3.0 kg.) of pressure. Belt deflection should be .16-.24" (4.0-6.0 mm) for a cold engine. Hot engine deflection should be .08-.16" (2-4 mm).

3) If tension is not within limits, rotate engine clockwise so as to move belt slack to idler pulley side of engine.

4) Loosen the idler pulley lock bolt, and allow spring to take up belt slack. Tighten bolt to 36 ft. lbs. (49 N.m). Check tension, and readjust if necessary.

Removal

1) Disconnect negative battery cable. Remove all drive belts. Set No. 1 cylinder to TDC of compression stroke. Remove top section of engine front cover.

2) Loosen idler pulley set bolt, and relieve the timing belt tension. Using gear puller, remove crankshaft pulley. Remove lower section of engine front cover.

3) If timing belt is to be reused, place a rotation direction mark on the belt. Remove timing belt.

CAUTION: **BEFORE removing camshaft timing pulleys, note position of pulley and match pin on camshaft. Pulley may be installed in more than one position.**

4) If necessary, remove camshaft timing pulley or oil pump drive pulley by holding the pulley with a spanner wrench and loosening set bolt. Remove exhaust valve cover and oil filler cap. If necessary, use a gear puller to remove crankshaft timing pulley.

Inspection

Inspect drive belt for wear, cracks or damage to teeth. Check pulleys for wear or damage. Check idler pulley bearing for smooth operation. Idler pulley tension spring free length must be 2.67" (67.8 mm) or less. If not as specified, replace spring.

Installation

1) If removed, install oil pump drive pulley. Tighten bolt to specifications. Install crankshaft timing pulley, idler pulley, and idler pulley tension spring.

2) Install timing belt on crankshaft pulley, noting position of rotation direction mark if reusing old belt. Install lower section of engine front cover with gasket.

3) Install crankshaft pulley and tighten bolt to specification. Ensure No. 1 cylinder is on TDC of compression stroke. Ensure match holes of No. 2 journal of camshaft housing are aligned with camshaft match holes. *See Fig. 3*.

4) Install camshaft timing pulleys and match pins in original position. Exhaust side pulley is installed with belt guide toward rear of engine. Intake side pulley is installed with belt guide toward front of engine.

5) With match holes in camshaft and camshaft housing aligned, camshaft timing pulley match marks should align with rear cover. *See Fig. 2*. If not, remove pin from camshaft timing pulley. Align pulley and rear cover match marks. Install pin into an overlapped hole.

6) Install camshaft timing pulley bolts. Install the timing belt. Tighten camshaft pulley bolts to specification.

CAUTION: **Do not use belt tension to hold pulleys when tightening.**

7) Adjust belt tension as described in *Checking Timing Belt Tension*. Turn crankshaft clockwise 2 times. Ensure all match marks and holes are aligned. Retighten idler pulley set bolt. Reverse removal procedure to complete assembly.

5M-GE 6-CYLINDER (Cont.)

Fig. 2: Aligning Timing Belt.

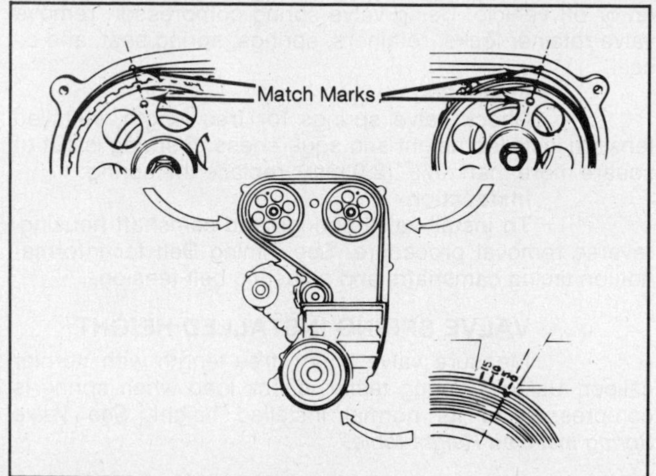
Match Marks

Check belt tension after alignment.

VALVE TIMING

Checking Valve Timing

1) Set No. 1 cylinder to TDC of compression stroke. Remove top timing belt cover. Remove oil filler cap and exhaust side valve cover.

2) Ensure match hole of camshafts are aligned with those of camshaft housing by turning crankshaft pulley. *See Fig. 3.* Intake and exhaust camshafts should be aligned separately.

Fig. 3: Aligning Camshaft Match Holes.

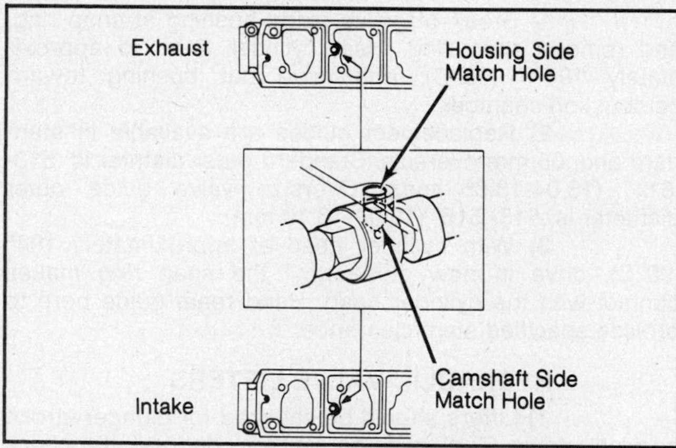
Exhaust
Housing Side
Match Hole
Intake
Camshaft Side
Match Hole

No. 1 cylinder set at TDC of compression stroke.

3) If the crankshaft pulley timing mark is within 5° of No. 1 cylinder TDC compression stroke, no alignment is necessary. If crankshaft pulley mark is not within 5° of TDC, realign holes.

4) Using a spanner wrench, remove camshaft pulley set bolt. Never use timing belt tension to loosen or tighten set bolt.

5) Make sure that match holes of camshaft and housing are aligned. Using a magnet, remove the match pin from the hole of camshaft timing pulley. Ensure No. 1 cylinder is at TDC of compression stroke and camshaft timing pulley mark is aligned with mark on rear timing cover case.

6) There are five holes on the camshaft and timing pulley. Select one overlapped hole, and insert the match pin into it. *See Fig. 4.*

Fig. 4: Aligning Camshaft & Pulley.

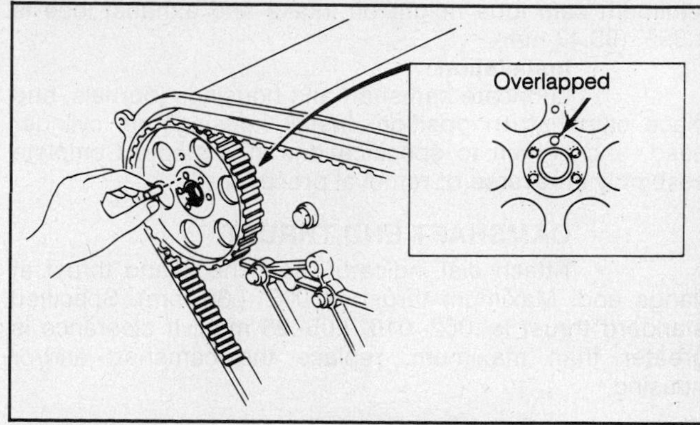
Overlapped

No. 1 cylinder set to TDC of compression stroke.

7) If no hole overlaps, rotate crankshaft slightly so pin will fit into most closely overlapped hole. *See Fig. 4.* Changing pin position will change crankshaft pulley angle by approximately 3°. Install and tighten camshaft pulley set bolt. Adjust belt tension.

CAMSHAFT

Removal

1) Remove air cleaner assembly, spark plug wires, distributor, and top section of timing belt cover. Disconnect all air intake, water, and fuel hoses that will interfere with removal of camshaft housings.

CAUTION: BEFORE removing camshaft timing pulleys, note position of pulley and match pin on camshaft. Pulley may be installed in more than one position.

2) Relieve tension on timing belt. Using a spanner wrench, remove camshaft timing pulley set bolts. Noting position for reassembly, remove timing pulleys and match pins.

3) Remove valve covers. Loosen camshaft housings in reverse of tightening sequence. *See Fig. 5.* Lift off camshaft housings. Remove housing rear covers and pull out camshaft.

Fig. 5: Camshaft Housing Tightening Sequence

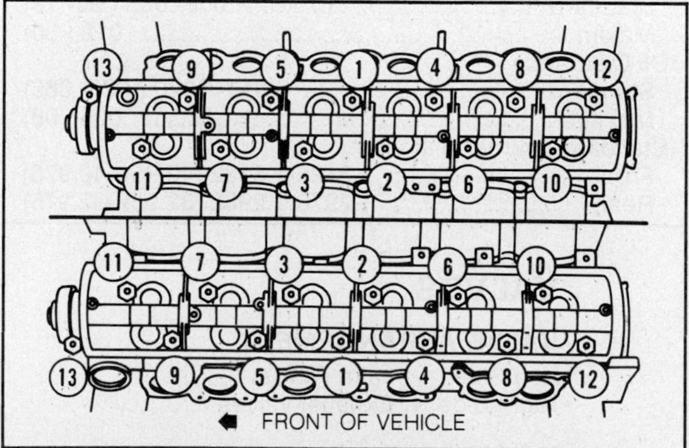
13
9
5
1
4
8
12
11
7
3
2
6
10
11
7
3
2
6
10
13
9
5
1
4
8
12
FRONT OF VEHICLE

Tighten housing in sequence in 3 steps.

Inspection

Check camshaft runout at center journal. Maximum allowable runout is .002" (.04 mm). Check

Toyota Engines

5M-GE 6-CYLINDER (Cont.)

journal diameter. Check for scoring or excessive wear. Minimum cam lobe height on intake and exhaust lobe is 1.396" (35.47 mm).

Installation

Lubricate camshaft and housings journals, and place camshaft in position. Install housings on cylinder head, and tighten to specifications in 3 steps. Complete assembly in reverse of removal procedure.

CAMSHAFT END THRUST

Attach dial indicator, and check end thrust at flange end. Maximum thrust is .012" (.30 mm). Specified standard thrust is .002-.010" (.05-.25 mm). If clearance is greater than maximum, replace the camshaft and/or housing.

CAMSHAFT BEARINGS

There are no camshaft bearings in the camshaft housings. If clearance is beyond limits, replace housing.

OIL PUMP SHAFT

Removal

1) Oil pump shaft can be removed with engine in vehicle. Set No. 1 cylinder to TDC of compression stroke. Drain cooling system, and remove radiator and fan. Remove all drive belts.

2) Remove engine timing belt as previously described. Using gear puller, remove crankshaft timing gear. Remove oil pump drive shaft pulley.

3) Remove bolts along right half of water pump. Remove timing belt case with water pump. Remove thrust plate bolt. Carefully pull oil pump shaft from engine block.

Inspection

1) Check end play between collar and thrust plate with feeler gauge. If beyond limits, replace thrust plate and collar.

2) Measure bearing bore diameter and journal diameter for oil clearance. Replace bearings if necessary.

OIL PUMP SHAFT SPECIFICATIONS

Application	In. (mm)
Thrust Clearance	
Standard	.002-.005 (.06-.13)
Maximum	.012 (.30)
Oil Clearance	
Standard	.0010-.0026 (.025-.066)
Maximum	.003 (.08)
Standard Journal Diameter	
Front	1.6126-1.6132 (40.959-40.975)
Rear	1.2976-1.2982 (32.959-32.975)

VALVES

VALVE ARRANGEMENT

Left Side – Intake valves.
Right Side – Exhaust valves.

VALVE SPRINGS

Removal

1) Remove air cleaner assembly and valve cover. Remove camshaft housings. Keep ALL parts in order for installation. Remove rocker arms and hydraulic lifters.

2) Springs may be removed with cylinder head on or off vehicle. Using valve spring compressor, remove valve retainer locks, retainers, springs, spring seat, and oil seal.

Inspection

Check valve springs for free length, installed tension, installed height and squareness. If spring is out of square more than .079" (2.0 mm), replace the spring.

Installation

To install valve springs and camshaft housing, reverse removal procedure. See Timing Belt for information on timing camshafts and adjusting belt tension.

VALVE SPRING INSTALLED HEIGHT

Measure valve spring free length with Vernier caliper. Using a spring tester, check load when spring is compressed to its normal installed height. *See Valve Spring Installed Height table.*

VALVE SPRING INSTALLED HEIGHT

Application	In. (mm)
Exhaust	1.69 (43.0)
Intake	1.57 (40.0)

VALVE STEM LENGTH

If the valve stem tip is worn, resurface with a valve grinder. DO NOT grind more than .020" (.5 mm). The overall valve length is 4.232" (107.5 mm) for intakes. The overall exhaust valve length is 4.319" (109.7 mm).

VALVE GUIDE SERVICING

1) Break off valve guide bushing at snap ring, and remove snap ring. Heat cylinder head to approximately 194°F (90°C), and drive out bushing toward combustion chamber.

2) Replacement guides are available in standard and .05 mm oversize. Standard outer diamter is .513-.514" (13.04-13.05 mm). Oversize valve guide outer diameter is .515-.516" (13.09-13.10 mm).

3) With cylinder head at approximately 194° (90°C), drive in new guide until the snap ring makes contact with the cylinder head. Hand ream guide bore to provide specified stem clearance.

HYDRAULIC VALVE LIFTERS

1) Lifters should be checked for plunger stroke and leak-down. Tool must be made to depress the check ball for plunger stroke check. *See Fig. 6.*

Fig. 6: Checking Plunger Stroke

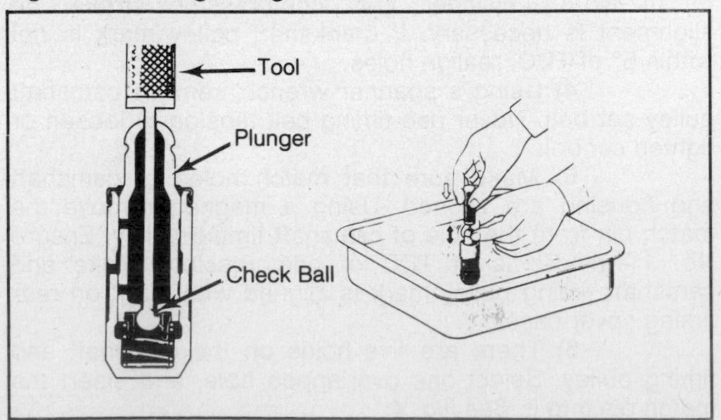
Tool
Plunger
Check Ball

Immerse lifter in light oil.

2) Immerse lifter in light oil, and depress the check ball. Slide plunger up and down several times. Replace lifter if stroke exceeds .020" (.50 mm).

CAUTION: DO NOT disassemble the hydraulic lifter.

3) Using a leak-down tester, measure the leak-down speed after checking that the plunger has been depressed about .08" (2 mm). Apply a pressure of 44.1 lbs. (20 kg.).

4) The leak-down time, with pressure applied, is 2-7 seconds for a distance of .04" (1 mm).

VALVE CLEARANCE ADJUSTMENT

The valve clearance is automatically adjusted by use of hydraulic valve lifters.

PISTONS, RINGS & PINS

OIL PAN

Removal

1) Raise and support vehicle. Drain engine oil and coolant. Disconnect air connector pipe from air cleaner. Remove oil level gauge.

2) Disconnect upper radiator hose, and loosen fan belts. Remove clutch fan and shroud.

3) Remove engine and flywheel housing under-covers. Remove exhaust pipe clamp and stiffener plates. Remove motor mount bolts on both sides of engine. Place a jack under the transmission, and raise the engine approximately 2 inches. Remove oil pan.

Installation

Clean oil pan and block thoroughly. Apply sealer to corners of new oil pan gasket. Install oil pan and gasket. Install remaining parts in reverse of removal sequence.

PISTON & ROD ASSEMBLY

Removal

1) Remove cylinder head and oil pan. Remove connecting rod caps. Place a short length of hose over rod bolts to prevent damage to crankshaft. Keep all parts in order for reassembly.

2) Remove bearings. If there is a ridge at the top of cylinder, use a ridge reamer before removing piston and rod. Push piston and rod assembly up through cylinder head side.

Installation

1) Apply oil to piston and piston rings. Using ring compressor, install piston and rod assembly in cylinder block. Make sure notch on piston faces front.

2) Replace connecting rod caps with mating marks aligned. Tighten nuts evenly in 2 or 3 steps, and check connecting rod side play. Reverse removal procedure to complete assembly.

FITTING PISTONS

1) Measure at top, center, and bottom of cylinder bore. Measure at 90° and parallel to crankshaft center. If measurements are not within specifications, rebore the cylinder. *See Bore Diameter Specifications* table.

2) Cylinder block surface warp limit is .002" (.05 mm). If taper or out-of-round exceeds .0008" (.020 mm), cylinders must be rebored. Cylinders must be bored to achieve piston clearance of .0020-.0028" (.05-.07 mm).

BORE DIAMETER SPECIFICATIONS

Application	Maximum Diameter In. (mm)
Standard	3.2776 (83.25)
Oversize	
.50 mm	3.2972 (83.75)
.75 mm	3.3071 (84.00)
1.00 mm	3.3169 (84.25)

3) Measure piston diameter at right angles to piston pin centerline, .98" (25 mm) from piston head. *See Piston Diameter Specifications* table.

PISTON DIAMETER SPECIFICATIONS

Application	Diameter In. (mm)
Standard	3.2650-3.2669 (82.93-82.98)
Oversize	
.50 mm	3.2846-3.2866 (83.43-83.48)
.75 mm	3.2945-3.2965 (83.68-83.73)
1.00 mm	3.3043-3.3063 (83.93-83.98)

4) Finish to final dimension by honing the last .0008" (.020 mm). Allow bore to cool after boring and honing to avoid erroneous readings while measuring.

FITTING RINGS

Check piston ring end gap at lowest part of cylinder. Measure ring groove clearance in piston. Replace pistons and/or rings if they will not meet specifications. Install rings with mark on side of ring facing upwards. Position piston ring gaps. *See Fig. 7.*

Fig. 7: Positioning Ring Gaps

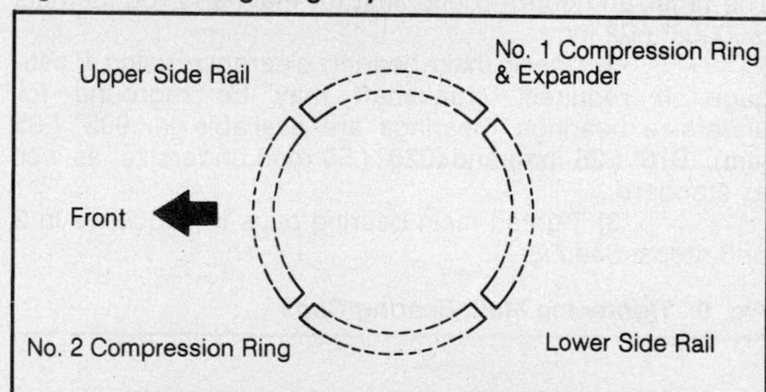
No. 1 Compression Ring & Expander
Upper Side Rail
Front
No. 2 Compression Ring
Lower Side Rail

Install piston with notch facing forward.

PISTON PIN REPLACEMENT

Removal

1) Try to move the piston back and forth on the piston pin. If any movement is felt, replace the piston and pin. To disassemble piston and rod, remove circlips in piston pin hole with needle nose pliers.

2) Heat piston to about 140°F (60°C), and remove pin by tapping lightly with plastic hammer. Keep piston, pin and rod together as a set.

Inspection

1) Check pistons and pins for wear or scoring. Inspect rod for bend or twist. The rod bend limit is .002"

5M-GE 6-CYLINDER (Cont.)

(.05 mm) per 3.94" (100 mm). The rod twist limit is .006" (.15 mm) per 3.94" (100 mm).

2) The oil clearance between piston pin and rod bushing must not be over .0006" (.015 mm). If clearance is greater than limit, replace rod bushing. Hone new rod bushing so that oil clearance is .0002-.0004" (.005-.011 mm).

Fig. 8: Assembling Piston & Rod

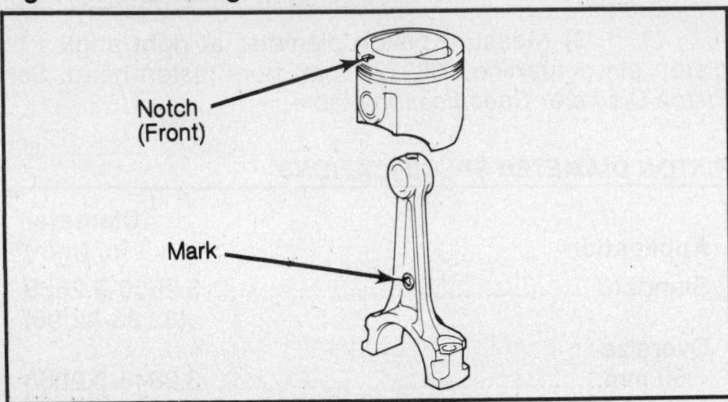
Notch
(Front)
Mark

Notch and mark must be aligned.

Installation

Install one circlip in piston, and heat to about 140°F (60°C). Align piston notch with rod mark. Coat piston pin with engine oil and push pin in with thumb. Install remaining circlip.

CRANKSHAFT MAIN & CONNECTING ROD BEARINGS

MAIN BEARINGS

1) Check crankshaft runout with dial indicator. If runout exceeds .0024" (.060 mm), replace crankshaft. The taper and out-of-round limit for main and rod journals is .0008" (.02 mm).

2) Check main bearing clearance using Plastigage. If required, crankshaft may be reground for undersize bearings. Bearings are available in .002" (.05 mm), .010" (.25 mm) and .020" (.50 mm) undersize, as well as standard.

3) Tighten main bearing caps in sequence in 2 or 3 steps. *See Fig. 9.*

Fig. 9: Tightening Main Bearing Caps

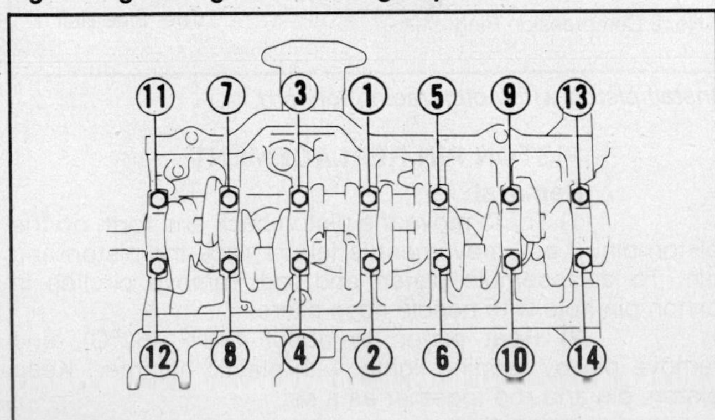
11
7
3
1
5
9
13
12
8
4
2
6
10
14

Tighten caps in 2 or 3 steps.

CONNECTING ROD BEARINGS

1) Measure connecting rod side play with dial indicator. If greater than .012" (.30 mm), rod must be replaced. Wipe off bearing journal, then check clearance with Plastigage.

2) If clearance exceeds .003" (.08 mm) and cannot be corrected with .002" (.05 mm) undersize bearings, or if taper or out-of-round exceeds .0008" (.020 mm), grind crankshaft to next undersize.

3) Connecting rod bearings are available in .002" (.05 mm), .010" (.25 mm), and .020" (.50 mm) undersize.

THRUST BEARING ALIGNMENT

1) Measure crankshaft end play with center (number 4) main bearing and cap installed. If clearance exceeds .012" (.30 mm), replace thrust washers to achieve standard clearance of .0020-.0098" (.050-.248 mm).

2) Standard thickness of thrust washer is .115" (2.92 mm) with .005" (.13 mm) and .010" (.25 mm) oversizes available.

NOTE: **Install thrust washers with oil grooves facing outward.**

REAR MAIN OIL SEAL

1) Rear main oil seal may be replaced without removing oil pan. Remove transmission and flywheel for access to seal.

2) Inspect oil seal lip and replace if worn or damaged. Pry old seal out without damaging cover or retainer. Install seal, using replacer tool (09223-41010). Apply multipurpose lubricant to seal lip.

ENGINE OILING

CRANKCASE CAPACITY

The crankcase capacity is 5.4 qts. (5.1L) with filter, 4.9 qts. (4.6L) without filter.

OIL FILTER

The oil filter is a full-flow, spin-on type.

NORMAL OIL PRESSURE

Oil pressure at idle should be more than 3.6 psi (.25 kg/cm²). At 3000 RPM oil pressure is 35.6-71.1 psi (2.5-5.0 kg/cm²).

OIL PRESSURE RELIEF VALVE

The oil pressure relief valve is a nonadjustable type located in the oil pump. The oil pressure relief valve operating pressure is 63-71 psi (4.4-5.0 kg/cm²). There is also an oil pressure regulator valve for the hydraulic lifters. It is located on top of the engine in front of No. 1 spark plug.

ENGINE OILING SYSTEM

System is force-feed type, with a full-flow filtering unit. Pressure is delivered by a gear-driven oil pump. From filter oil travels through cylinder block passages by which internal components are lubricated.

5M-GE 6-CYLINDER (Cont.)

OIL PUMP

Removal

Raise and support vehicle. Remove oil pan as previously described. Unbolt and remove oil pump.

Disassembly

Disassemble pump by removing (in order) snap ring, spacer, drive shaft gear, Woodruff key, pump cover, pump shaft sub-assembly, driven gear, relief valve plug, gasket, spring and relief valve.

Inspection

Check oil pump for signs of wear or scoring. Measure body and side clearance. Measure gear backlash.

Fig. 10: Exploded View of Oil Pump

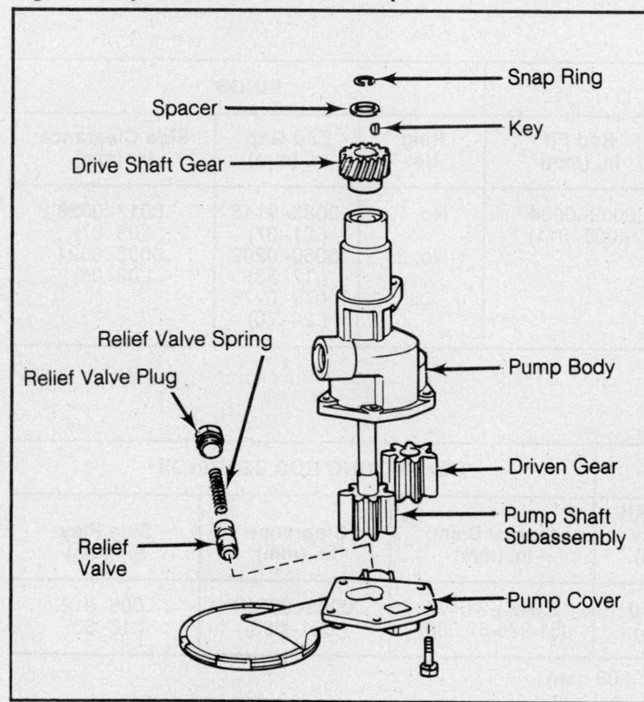
Snap Ring
Spacer
Key
Drive Shaft Gear
Relief Valve Spring
Relief Valve Plug
Pump Body
Driven Gear
Pump Shaft Subassembly
Relief Valve
Pump Cover

Reassembly

After inspection is finished, reassemble pump. Check pump operation by immersing inlet tube in engine oil. Turn pump shaft counterclockwise and check for oil discharge.

Installation

Install oil pump. Clean gasket from oil pan and block. Install oil pan with new gasket and reverse removal procedure.

OIL PUMP SPECIFICATIONS

Application	Wear Limit In. (mm)
Body Clearance	.008 (.20)
Gear Backlash	.035 (.90)
Shaft Diameter	.55 (13.9)
Side Clearance	.006 (.15)

OIL PUMP GUIDE BUSHING

Oil pump drive bushing may be pressed out of cylinder block if worn. Install bushing with oil hole facing crankshaft and front mark facing front of cylinder block.

ENGINE COOLING

COOLANT CAPACITY

The coolant capacity is 8.8 qts. (8.3L).

THERMOSTAT

Wax pellet type, begins to open at 186-194°F (86-90°C) and should open to more than .32" (8 mm) at 212°F (100°C).

WATER PUMP

Removal

Drain cooling system. Loosen and remove drive belts and fan shroud. Remove 8 pump bolts and take off pump assembly.

Installation

Install water pump with water drain hole positioned downward. Use new gasket and reverse removal procedure.

TIGHTENING SPECIFICATIONS

Application	Ft. Lbs. (N.m)
Camshaft Housing	16 (22)
Camshaft Timing Pulley	51 (69)
Connecting Rod Cap	33 (45)
Crankshaft Pulley	108 (146)
Cylinder Head	58 (79)
Exhaust Manifold	29 (39)
Flywheel	54 (73)
Intake Manifold	16 (22)
Main Bearing Caps	75 (102)

ENGINE SPECIFICATIONS

GENERAL SPECIFICATIONS

Year	DISPLACEMENT Cu. In.	DISPLACEMENT Liters	Fuel System	HP@RPM	Torque Ft. Lbs.@RPM	Compr. Ratio	BORE In.	BORE mm	STROKE In.	STROKE mm
1983	168.4	2.8	Fuel Inj.	145@5200	155@4400	8.8:1	3.27	83	3.35	85

Toyota Engines

5M-GE 6-CYLINDER (Cont.)

ENGINE SPECIFICATIONS (Cont.)

VALVES

Engine Size & Valve	Head Diam. In. (mm)	Face Angle	Seat Angle	Seat Width In. (mm)	Stem Diameter In. (mm)	Stem Clearance In. (mm)	Valve Lift In. (mm)
2.8L							
Intake [1]	.....	45°	45° [2]	.047-.063 (1.2-1.6)	.3138-.3144 (7.970-7.985)	.0010-.0024 (.025-.060)	.....
Exhaust	.....	45°	45° [2]	.047-.063 (1.2-1.6)	.3136-.3142 (7.965-7.980)	.0012-.0026 (.035-.065)	.....

[1] – Minimum intake valve margin is .02" (.50 mm). Minimum exhaust valve margin is .04" (1.0 mm).
[2] – Correction angles for valve seats are 30° and 60°.

PISTONS, PINS, RINGS

Engine	PISTONS Clearance In. (mm)	PINS Piston Fit In. (mm)	PINS Rod Fit In. (mm)	RINGS Ring No.	RINGS End Gap In. (mm)	RINGS Side Clearance In. (mm)
2.8L	.0020-.0028 (.050-.071)	.....	.0002-.0004 [1] (.005-.011)	No. 1	.0083-.0146 (.21-.37)	.0012-.0028 (.03-.07)
				No. 2	.0060-.0209 (.17-.53)	.0008-.0024 (.02-.06)
				Oil	.0079-.0276 (.20-.70)	

[1] – Limit is .0006" (.015 mm).

CRANKSHAFT MAIN & CONNECTING ROD BEARINGS

Engine	MAIN BEARINGS Journal Diam. In. (mm)	MAIN BEARINGS Clearance In. (mm)	MAIN BEARINGS Thrust Bearing	MAIN BEARINGS Crankshaft End Play In. (mm)	CONNECTING ROD BEARINGS Journal Diam. In. (mm)	CONNECTING ROD BEARINGS Clearance In. (mm)	CONNECTING ROD BEARINGS Side Play In. (mm)
2.8L	2.3617-2.3627 (59.988-60.012)	.0013-.0023 [1] (.034-.058)	No. 4	.002-.010 (.05-.25)	2.0463-2.0472 (51.976-52.000)	.0008-.0021 [1] (.021-.053)	.006-.012 (.16-.30)

[1] – Maximum oil clearance for main and connecting rod bearings is .003" (.08 mm).

VALVE TIMING

Engine	INTAKE Open (BTDC)	INTAKE Close (ABDC)	EXHAUST Open (BBDC)	EXHAUST Close (ATDC)
2.8L	15°	53°	56°	12°

VALVE SPRINGS

Engine	Free Length In. (mm)	PRESSURE Lbs. @ In. (Kg @ mm) Valve Closed	PRESSURE Lbs. @ In. (Kg @ mm) Valve Open
2.8L			
Intake	1.93 (49.02)	76.5-84.4@1.58 (34.7-38.3@40.0)	.....
Exhaust	2.07 (52.58)	73.4-80.9@1.69 (33.3-36.7@43.0	.....

CAMSHAFT

Engine	Journal Diam. In. (mm)	Clearance In. (mm)	Lobe Lift In. (mm)
2.8L			
No. 1	1.4944-1.4951 (37.959-37975)	.0010-.0026 (.025-.066)	.....
No. 2	1.6913-1.6919 (42.595-42.975)		
No. 3	1.7110-1.7116 (43.595-43.475)		
No. 4	1.7307-1.7313 (43.959-43.975)		
No. 5	1.7504-1.7510 (44.459-44.475)		
No. 6	1.7700-1.7707 (44.959-44.975)		
No. 7	1.7897-1.7904 (45.459-45.475)		

Volkswagen Engines

JETTA, QUANTUM, RABBIT, RABBIT PICKUP & SCIROCCO 4-CYLINDER

ENGINE CODING

ENGINE IDENTIFICATION

Engine identification number is stamped on left side of engine block near ignition distributor.

ENGINE IDENTIFICATION

Application	Code
Quantum	WT
All Others	EN

ENGINE, MANIFOLDS & CYLINDER HEAD

ENGINE

NOTE: **On all except Quantum, engine and transmission must be LOWERED out of vehicle as an assembly.**

Removal (Quantum)

1) Disconnect battery ground. Set heater temperature control to warm position. Open radiator cap. Remove power steering pump attaching bolts. Remove drive belt and place power steering pump to the side leaving hoses connected.

NOTE: **Never drain coolant while engine is hot. Doing so could cause engine block or cylinder head to warp.**

2) Drain engine coolant and remove hose from coolant outlet on head. Disconnect electrical connectors from thermo-time switch, alternator and control pressure regulator. Disconnect vacuum hoses from ignition distributor. Remove bolts and place control pressure regulator aside with fuel lines connected.

3) Disconnect wires from radiator fan switch and fan. Loosen radiator bracket bolt and remove radiator assembly complete with air duct and fan. Remove clip on clutch cable and unhook cable. Remove nut on left engine mount. Disconnect wire for Hall sending unit at distributor.

4) Disconnect coil wire, wire from ignition distributor, wire from coolant temperature sender and wire for oxygen sensor thermo-switch. Disconnect coolant hoses. Disconnect electrical wires for cold start valve, frequency valve and oxygen sensor. Remove charcoal filter valve from air duct and remove air duct.

5) Remove preheater hose and cold start valve (with fuel line connected). Disconnect vacuum hose for ignition distributor from intake manifold. Remove accelerator cable, crankcase breather hose and brake booster hose. Remove electrical connector from auxiliary air regulator.

6) Pull out the injectors and protect with caps (leave fuel lines connected). Remove fuel distributor with air filter housing and lay aside (leave fuel lines connected). Lay aside cold start valve, control pressure regulator and fuel injectors (leave all fuel lines connected).

7) On models without air conditioning, remove front engine mount. On all models, remove exhaust pipe from manifold. Disconnect electrical wiring from starter. Remove nuts from right engine mount. Remove starter bolts. Remove lower engine-to-transmission bolts and flywheel cover plate.

8) On models with automatic transmission, remove starter. Remove 3 torque converter mounting bolts. On all models, support transmission with special support tool (VW 785/1B). On models with air conditioning, remove front engine mount. Loosen nuts on outer half of crankshaft pulley and remove drive belt.

9) Remove upper air conditioning compressor mounting bracket bolts. Remove 3 lower compressor mounting bracket bolts. Remove compressor with bracket and place aside with wiring connected. Remove throttle valve housing, auxiliary air regulator and horn bracket. Remove condensor with hoses and lay aside.

10) On all models, attach engine sling (US 1105) to engine and lift engine until all engine mounts are free. Remove right engine mount. Tension transmission supporting tool again. Remove upper engine-to-transmission bolts.

11) Separate engine from transmission. Lift and turn engine to remove from vehicle. On automatic transmissions, secure torque converter to transmission to keep it from falling out.

Installation

To install engine, reverse removal procedures using care to observe all tightening specifications. Engine mounts must be properly aligned and free of tension before tightening.

Removal (All Except Quantum)

1) Disconnect battery cables at battery. Loosen fuel filler cap to relieve tank pressure. Remove rubber duct connecting throttle valve assembly to mixture control unit. Drain engine coolant by removing hose from thermostat flange.

NOTE: **Never drain coolant while engine is hot. Doing so could cause engine block or cylinder head to warp.**

2) Disconnect radiator fan motor and thermoswitch. Remove radiator with fan motor and ducts. On air conditioned vehicles, remove air conditioner compressor and tie aside without disconnecting hoses.

3) On all models, disconnect the following electrical connectors: Alternator, thermoswitch, oil pressure switch, warm-up regulator, coolant temperature sensor, coil and condensor wires, cold start valve, auxiliary air regulator and starter solenoid harness.

4) Remove intake air pre-heating duct. Remove injectors. Remove fuel lines for cold start valve and warm-up regulator. Disconnect remaining fuel, coolant, emission control and vacuum lines and position out of the way. Have a container ready to catch leaking fuel in case system is still under pressure.

5) Disconnect and remove accelerator linkage from engine. Disconnect speedometer cable and ground cable from transmission. Detach selector cable and bracket on automatic transmission models. Detach the clutch cable from the clutch operating lever on manual transmission models.

6) On all models, disconnect starter wires and back-up light switch. Raise vehicle. Remove exhaust flex-pipe nuts or spring clip. On manual transmission models, remove shift lever from shift linkage. On all models, remove the starter. Disconnect the drive shafts from the drive flanges.

7) Remove horn and place out of the way. Remove engine front mount. Lower vehicle and remove axle nuts. Raise vehicle and disconnect lower ball joints from bearing housings. Remove drive shaft while holding strut assembly away from vehicle.

8) Reconnect ball joints and lower vehicle onto wheels. Attach lifting sling (US 1105) to engine and lift slightly. Remove complete rear mount. Remove right front wheel. On manual transmission models, remove relay shaft and gearshift lever rods.

9) On all models, remove bolts holding side mounts to body and lower engine and transmission assembly to the dolly. Raise vehicle to clear engine and remove assembly from beneath vehicle.

Installation

To install, reverse removal procedure using caution to observe all tightening specifications. Engine mounts must be properly aligned and free of tension before tightening.

CYLINDER HEAD & MANIFOLDS

Removal

1) Disconnect duct connecting throttle valve housing to mixture control unit. Remove radiator cap. Remove thermostat housing from water pump. Remove thermostat and drain cooling system.

NOTE: **Never drain coolant while engine is hot. Doing so could cause engine block or cylinder head to warp.**

2) Remove camshaft drive belt. Remove injectors from manifold tubes. Disconnect all hoses, cables and wires attached to throttle valve housing and intake air distributor. Disconnect exhaust pipe.

3) Remove nuts and bolts that hold exhaust manifold and intake manifold (air intake distributor) to cylinder head. Remove manifolds. Remove any screws, bolts or clips attaching air conditioning components to cylinder head (if equipped).

4) Remove upper alternator mounting bolt and adjusting bracket. Disconnect all coolant hoses. Disconnect temperature gauge wire. Remove spark plug wires and spark plugs. Remove the wire from the oil pressure sending unit.

5) Remove valve cover. Remove head bolts in reverse order of installation. Remove cylinder head. If head is stuck, pry off with a block of wood placed in each outboard exhaust port.

Installation

To install, reverse removal procedure. Make sure head gasket is positioned with "OBEN" mark facing up. Tighten head bolts in sequence and according to step outlined in table.

CYLINDER HEAD TIGHTENING STEPS

Application	Ft. Lbs. (N.m)
Step No. 1	29 (40)
Step No. 2	44 (60)
Step No. 3	Additional 1/2 Turn

NOTE: **Polygon (12 point) socket head bolts are set to final torque while cold and do not need to be retightened when hot. Tighten in sequence to 54 ft. lbs. (75 N.m) plus an additional 1/4 turn.**

Fig. 1: Cylinder Head Tightening Sequence

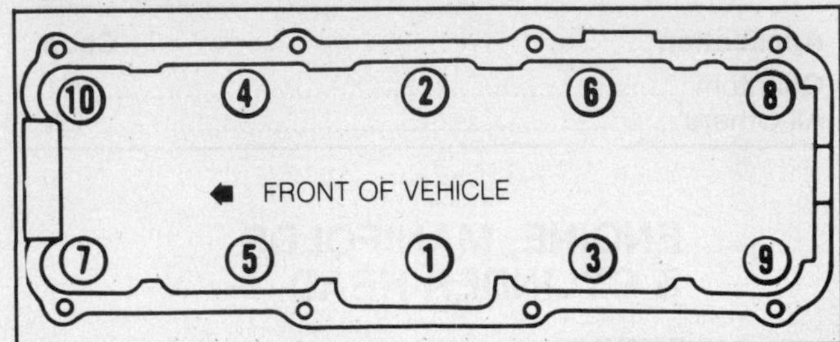
10
4
2
6
8
FRONT OF VEHICLE
7
5
1
3
9

Loosen in reverse order.

CAMSHAFT

TIMING BELT

NOTE: **Sprockets DO NOT have to be removed to replace camshaft drive belt.**

Removal

Remove alternator belt, water pump pulley, and upper and lower drive belt covers. If equipped, remove air conditioning compressor drive belt. Loosen belt tensioner, and work belt off sprockets toward front of engine.

Fig. 2: Intermediate Shaft Alignment

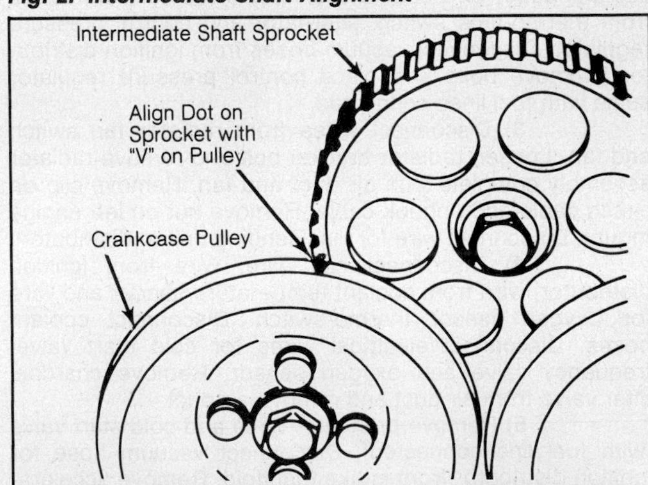
Intermediate Shaft Sprocket
Align Dot on Sprocket with "V" on Pulley
Crankcase Pulley

Rotate intermediate shaft and crankshaft to align marks.

Installation

1) Rotate camshaft sprocket until index punch mark on camshaft sprocket is lined up with top surface of valve cover mounting flange on spark plug side of head. Rotate crankshaft and intermediate shaft until index punch mark on intermediate shaft sprocket aligns with "V" notch on crankshaft pulley.

2) Use care not to move any sprocket. Fit belt on bottom first and then at top. There should be no slack between sprockets. Tighten tensioner so belt can just be twisted 90° halfway between camshaft and intermediate sprockets. Tighten adjuster lock nut and reverse removal procedure for remaining components.

CAMSHAFT

Removal

1) Remove camshaft cover. Loosen and remove bearing caps in following sequence: 5, 1, and 3. Then loosen bearing caps 2 and 4 diagonally. Bearing caps are numbered front to rear.

2) Check camshaft end play. Remove camshaft and lift out cam followers. Install camshaft using only bearing caps 1 and 5. Fit dial indicator so tip of gauge touches front of camshaft. Pry camshaft back and forth. Reading should not exceed .006" (.150 mm). If end play is beyond limits, replace either camshaft or cylinder head.

3) Check camshaft runout. Fit dial indicator so gauge pin is against camshaft center journal. Turn camshaft and record runout range. Runout must not exceed .0004" (.010 mm). Replace camshaft as necessary.

4) Inspect camshaft lobes for wear. Worn lobes usually indicate lack of lubrication. Check engine oiling passages to make sure they are not restricted. If worn, replace camshafts and discs.

5) Inspect cam followers for signs of seizure or lack of lubrication. If any aluminum particles from head are found on cam followers, replace followers. Cylinder head must be replaced if any follower bores are worn or excessively rough.

Installation

1) Lightly lube cam follower bores, then fit followers in their original bores. Install adjusting discs. Place camshaft on cylinder head. Loosely attach No. 2 and No. 4 bearing caps.

2) Gradually tighten caps. Fit No. 5 and No. 3 bearing caps. Install new oil seal in front of camshaft. Install No. 1 bearing cap. Make sure all caps are torqued to proper specifications.

VALVE TIMING

1) With timing belt removed as previously described, rotate crankshaft and intermediate shaft until index mark (punch mark) on intermediate shaft is positioned in "V" notch on crankshaft pulley. *See Fig. 2.*

2) This is firing point of No. 1 cylinder. Next, turn camshaft until timing mark on rear of camshaft sprocket is in line with top of cylinder head cover flange. *See Fig. 3.* Replace timing belt.

Fig. 3: Camshaft Sprocket Positioning

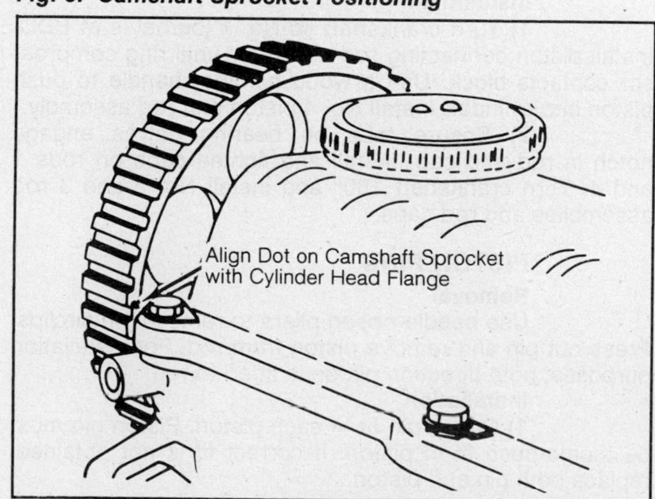
Align Dot on Camshaft Sprocket
with Cylinder Head Flange

Align dot on sprocket with cylinder head flange.

VALVES

VALVE ARRANGEMENT

E-I-E-I-I-E-I-E (Front-to-rear).

VALVE GUIDE SERVICING

1) Clean valve guides before making measurements. To measure guide, attach a mounting device with a dial gauge (VW689/1) to mounting surface of cylinder head. Insert a new valve until end of stem is flush with end of valve guide.

2) Rock valve head against dial indicator and check amount of rock recorded. Maximum allowable rock is .039" (1.0 mm) for intake valves and .051" (1.30 mm) for exhaust valves. Proper valve guide diameter is .315"-.316" (8.01-8.04 mm).

3) Use a press and adaptor (10-206) to remove and install valve guides. To remove guides, press out from combustion chamber side of head.

4) Coat new valve guides with engine oil. Press new guides into cold head from camshaft side. Make sure shoulder of guide meets firmly with top of cylinder head. Ream guides to uniform inside diameter.

NOTE: **Do not use more than 1 ton pressure once guide shoulder is seated or shoulder may break.**

VALVE SPRINGS

NOTE: **Although normal maintenance on valve system is performed with head removed, it is possible to replace stem seals, keepers, retainers or broken springs with cylinder head installed.**

Removal (Head Installed)

With camshaft and tappets removed, turn crankshaft until piston of cylinder being worked on is at BDC. Apply steady air pressure of at least 85 psi through spark plug hole adapter to keep valves seated. Compress spring with tool (VW 541) and remove valve keepers. Remove and replace damaged or worn parts.

Removal (Head Removed)

With camshaft and tappets removed, use compressor (VW 541) to depress retainer and remove keepers. Take out retainer and springs.

Installation

1) Before installation, check springs on spring tester and inspect for cracks or distortion. Lower edge of valve spring retainer should be chamfered to prevent valve stem scoring.

2) If necessary, grind a chamfer using stone or other tool. To install, reverse removal procedure. When installing the springs, make sure closely spaced coils of outer springs are against spring seats.

Volkswagen Engines

JETTA, QUANTUM, RABBIT, RABBIT PICKUP & SCIROCCO 4-CYLINDER (Cont.)

VALVE STEM OIL SEALS

With tappet, adjuster pad, keepers, springs, and spring seats removed, extract valve stem oil seal. When installing new seal, first position protective plastic sleeve on valve stem, lubricate seal, and use a mandrel (10-204) to push seal onto valve guide.

VALVE CLEARANCE ADJUSTMENT

1) Adjust valves with engine at normal operating temperature. Clearance adjustments are to be checked and made according to firing order. Using a wrench on the crankshaft pulley bolt, turn clockwise to bring No. 1 piston to TDC (cam lobes pointing up).

Fig. 4: Assembled View of Valve and Camshaft

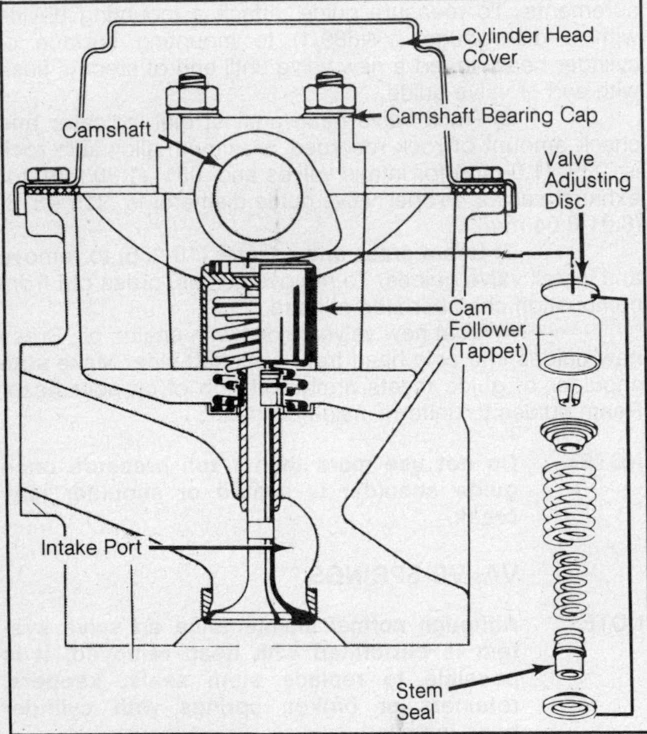
Cylinder Head Cover
Camshaft Bearing Cap
Camshaft
Valve Adjusting Disc
Cam Follower (Tappet)
Intake Port
Stem Seal

2) Determine valve clearance by inserting a feeler gauge between cam lobe heel and adjusting disc.Rotate crankshaft pulley 180° at a time, and check cylinder Nos. 3, 4 and 2, consecutively.

3) If necessary, adjust to specifications by installing thicker or thinner adjusting discs. Discs are available in 26 different thicknesses in increments of .0019" (.050 mm). Disc thickness is stamped on bottom, and ranges from .1181" (3.00 mm) to .1673" (4.25 mm).

4) To install, press cam follower down with follower depressing tool (VW 546). Remove old disc with special pliers (VW 208), and insert new disc with stamped thickness marking toward cam follower.

NOTE: **Cold settings are given for reference, as initial settings to be used during cylinder head rework. Final adjustments are made at normal operating temperature, and should be rechecked after approximately 1000 miles of operation.**

VALVE CLEARANCE SPECIFICATIONS

Application	In. (mm)
Intake	
Hot	.008-.012 (.20-.30)
Cold	.006-.010 (.15-.25)
Exhaust	
Hot	.016-.020 (.40-.50)
Cold	.014-.018 (.35-.45)

PISTONS, PINS & RINGS

OIL PAN

NOTE: **Removal and installation procedure not available for Quantum.**

Removal & Installation

1) Drain oil, remove bolts and remove oil pan. Remove nuts holding engine mounts on subframe and bolts holding subframe to body. Pull subframe downward to separate engine mounts and body.

2) Drain oil, remove mounting bolts and remove oil pan. To install, reverse removal procedure. Make sure gasket surfaces are clean before installing new gaskets.

PISTON & ROD ASSEMBLY

NOTE: **Piston and rod assemblies can be removed with engine in vehicle. Manufacturer recommends engine removal for extensive overhaul work.**

Removal

1) Mark cylinder number on crown of each piston. If necessary, mark arrows pointing toward front of block on piston crowns. Remove rod cap bolts and push piston out top of cylinder. Use wooden hammer handle for this operation.

2) If a ridge at top of cylinder prevents piston removal, use a ridge reamer to cut down the ridge. DO NOT force piston out of cylinder. Mark connecting rods and bearing caps for proper reinstallation.

Installation

1) Turn crankshaft so No. 1 journal is at BDC. Install piston connecting rod assembly until ring compressor contacts block. Use a wood hammer handle to push piston into cylinder. Install No. 4 piston and rod assembly.

2) Ensure tabs on bearing halves engage notch in rod and cap. Install and tighten caps on rods 1 and 4. Turn crankshaft 180° and install No. 2 and 3 rod assemblies and rod caps.

PISTON PINS

Removal

Use needle-nosed pliers to remove pin circlips. Press out pin and remove piston from rod. For installation purposes, note direction piston is fitted to rod.

Installation

1) Check pin fit in each piston. Piston pin must be thumb-push fit in piston. If correct fit is not obtained, replace both pin and piston.

2) Check pin fit in connecting rod. Wear limit is .0016" (.040 mm). Rebush connecting rod and hone bushing to obtain correct clearance.

NOTE: **If pin is too tight, heat piston to approximately 140°F (60°C) in an oil bath.**

FITTING PISTONS

1) Measure cylinder at 3 points: 3/8" (10 mm) from top and bottom, and at center of bore. Take measurements in line with, and at 90° to thrust face. Maximum cylinder taper or out-of-round is .0016" (.040 mm) beyond standard dimensions. If excessive, cylinder reboring and oversize pistons are necessary.

Fig. 5: Codes Stamped on Piston Head

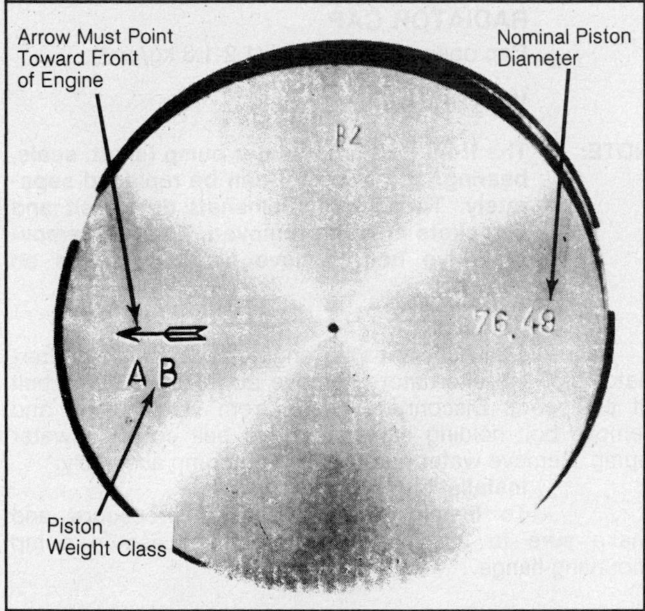

Arrow Must Point Toward Front of Engine
Nominal Piston Diameter
76.48
A B
Piston Weight Class

Fig. 6: Piston Ring Installation

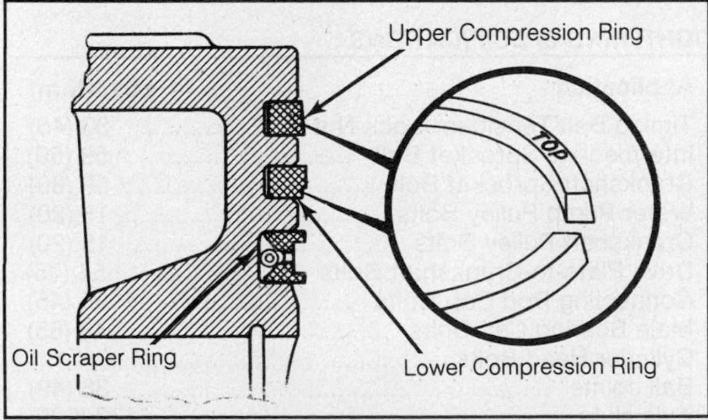

Upper Compression Ring
TOP
Oil Scraper Ring
Lower Compression Ring

Word TOP must face piston crown.

2) Measure pistons at .63" (16.0 mm) from bottom of piston skirt (measuring 90° to pin bore). Combining this measurement with measurement of corresponding cylinder bore, note piston-to-cylinder clearance. If this exceeds .0028" (.070 mm), oversize pistons must be installed.

3) Place rings squarely in cylinder bore about .6" (15 mm) down from top edge and measure end gap. Install rings on piston and measure side clearance. Position ring gaps 120° offset to each other (start with oil ring gap directly to the rear). Ensure stamp mark "TOP" on rings is facing upward.

CRANKSHAFT MAIN & CONNECTING ROD BEARINGS

MAIN & CONNECTING ROD BEARINGS

1) Push crankshaft toward one end and measure crankshaft end play at No. 3 (thrust) bearing. Main bearing caps are stamped "1" to "5" (front to rear), and must be returned to original positions upon reassembly. Measure end play (side play) of connecting rods.

2) Remove all bearing caps and check bearing clearance using Plastigage. Measure crankshaft journals with a micrometer to determine journal out-of-round and taper. The maximum allowable wear is .0012" (.030 mm).

3) Install main bearing inserts with oil groove in the engine block, making sure anti-rotation tabs engage in saddle notches. Lubricate new bearings, place crankshaft in block, and install lower main shells and caps in proper order.

CRANKSHAFT JOURNAL DIAMETERS

Size	Main Bearing In. (mm) [1]	Rod Bearing In. (mm) [1]
Standard	2.25 (53.97)	1.810 (45.97)
1st US	2.115 (53.72)	1.800 (45.72)
2nd US	2.105 (53.47)	1.790 (45.47)
3rd US	2.095 (53.22)	1.780 (45.22)

[1] — Journal diameter is ± .0004" (.010 mm).

REAR MAIN BEARING OIL SEAL

NOTE: **Rear main bearing oil seal may be replaced with engine in vehicle. Transmission and flywheel must be removed.**

Fig. 7: Using Special Tool to Install Rear Main Oil Seal

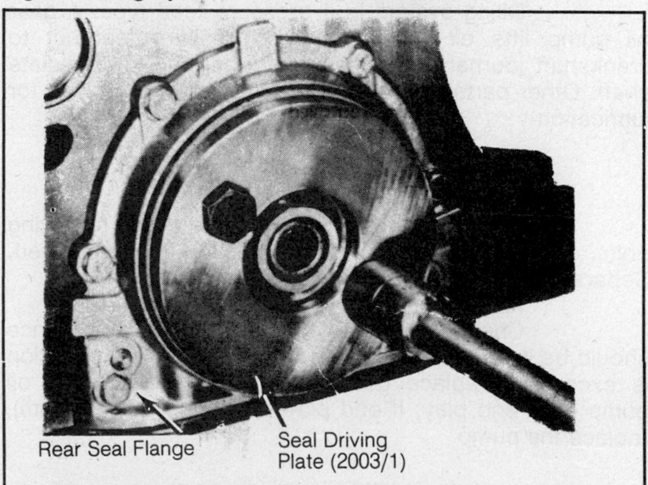

Rear Seal Flange
Seal Driving Plate (2003/1)

Volkswagen Engines

JETTA, QUANTUM, RABBIT, RABBIT PICKUP & SCIROCCO 4-CYLINDER (Cont.)

Removal

Insert a large screwdriver between crankshaft flywheel flange and inside lip of oil seal. Pry out old seal.

Installation

Install seal guide sleeve (2003/2A or equivalent) over crankshaft flange. Start new seal over guide sleeve, and into recess in seal carrier. Remove guide sleeve and bolt seal driving plate (2003/1 or equivalent) to flywheel mounting flange. Tighten bolts evenly to bring seal flush with carrier.

FRONT MAIN BEARING OIL SEAL AND INTERMEDIATE SHAFT OIL SEAL

Removal

Remove camshaft belt. Remove crankshaft sprocket. Pry seal from seal carrier, being careful not to damage carrier. Use removing tool (10-219 or equivalent) to remove seal.

Installation

Using installing tool (10-203 or equivalent), press in new seal until flush with seal carrier. If tool 10-203 was used, remove it and using aluminum part of tool, press seal in until recessed .080" (2.0 mm) in seal carrier.

NOTE: **Same procedure applies to intermediate shaft oil seal except: Remove intermediate shaft sprocket. Only press new seal in until flush with seal carrier.**

ENGINE OILING

CRANKCASE CAPACITY

Capacity is 4.2 quarts (4.7 quarts with filter change) on all except Quantum. On Quantum, capacity is 2.6 quarts (3.0 quarts with filter change).

OIL FILTER

Replaceable spin-on type.

NORMAL OIL PRESSURE

Minumum of 28 psi (1.97 kg/cm²) with engine at normal operating temperature.

ENGINE OILING SYSTEM

Oiling system is a pressure feed type. A gear oil pump lifts oil from pan and pressure feeds it to crankshaft journals, camshaft bearings, and intermediate shaft. Other parts of system receive oil mist or splash for lubrication

OIL PUMP

Removal

With oil pan removed remove pump mounting bolts. Remove oil pump, leaving pickup tube attached. Separate pickup tube from pump.

Inspection

Check oil pump gear backlash. Clearance should be between .002-.008" (.05-.20 mm). If specification is exceeded, replace gears or pump. Measure the oil pump gear end play. If end play exceeds .006" (.15 mm), replace the pump.

Installation

To install, reverse removal procedure. Make sure all mating surfaces are clean before installing gaskets. Oil pump drive shaft must align with distributor drive gear.

ENGINE COOLING

COOLING SYSTEM CAPACITY

Coolant capacity is 7.3 quarts (6.9L) on Rabbit Pickup and Quantum, 4.9 quarts (4.6L) on all others.

THERMOSTAT

Thermostat begins to open at 176°F (80°C), fully open at 201°F (94°C).

RADIATOR CAP

Cap opens at 17-19 psi (1.2-1.3 kg/cm²).

WATER PUMP

NOTE: **The front portion of water pump (shaft, seals, bearing, and housing) can be replaced separately. To do this, camshaft drive belt and sprockets must be removed. To avoid removing drive belt, remove water pump as an assembly.**

Removal

Drain coolant with engine cool. Remove alternator belt and alternator. Remove air injection pump belt (if equipped). Disconnect hoses from water pump and remove bolt holding camshaft drive belt cover to water pump. Remove water pump bolts and pump assembly.

Installation

To install, reverse removal procedure and make sure to use new "O" ring in recess in pump mounting flange.

NOTE: **Do not use sealer between water pump mounting flange and engine block.**

TIGHTENING SPECIFICATIONS

Application	Ft. Lbs. (N.m)
Timing Belt Tensioner Lock Nut	33 (45)
Intermediate Sprocket Bolt	[1] 59 (80)
Crankshaft Sprocket Bolt	59 (80)
Water Pump Pulley Bolts	15 (20)
Crankshaft Pulley Bolts	15 (20)
Drive Plate-to-Crankshaft Bolts	[1 4] 55 (75)
Connecting Rod Cap Bolts	[1] 33 (45)
Main Bearing Cap Bolts	[2] 48 (65)
Cylinder Head Bolts	[3]
Ball Joints	36 (49)
Axle Nuts	173 (235)
Manifold-to-Cylinder Head Bolts	18 (25)
Water Pump Bolts	15 (20)

[1] – Use Loctite.
[2] – To check clearance, tighten to 26 ft. lbs. (45 N.m) only.
[3] – In 3 steps. See text.
[4] – Bolt with shoulder 72 ft. lbs. (100 N.m).

Volkswagen Engines

JETTA, QUANTUM, RABBIT, RABBIT PICKUP & SCIROCCO 4-CYLINDER (Cont.)

ENGINE SPECIFICATIONS

GENERAL SPECIFICATIONS

Year	DISPLACEMENT		Fuel System	HP@RPM	Torque Ft. Lbs.@RPM	Compr. Ratio	BORE		STROKE	
	Cu. In.	Liters					In.	mm	In.	mm
1983	105	1.7	Fuel Inj. [1]	74@5000	90@3000	8.2:1	3.13	79.5	3.40	86.4

[1] – Some Rabbit models have Carter TYF 1-Bbl. carburetor.

VALVES

Engine Size & Valve	Head Diam. In. (mm)	Face Angle	Seat Angle	Seat Width In. (mm)	Stem Diameter In. (mm)	Stem Clearance In. (mm)	Valve Lift In. (mm)
1.7L							
Intake	1.338 (33.9)	45°	45°	.079 (2.0)	.314 (7.98)	.001-.002 (.03-.05)	....
Exhaust	1.220 (31.0)	45°	45°	.095 (2.4)	.313 (7.95)	.002-.003 (.05-.07)	....

PISTONS, PINS, RINGS

Engine	PISTONS	PINS		RINGS		
	Clearance In. (mm)	Piston Fit In. (mm)	Rod Fit In. (mm)	Ring No.	End Gap In. (mm)	Side Clearance In. (mm)
1.7L	.0012 [1] (.03)	Push Fit	.0004-.0008 [2] (.01-.02)	Comp.	.012-.018 [3] (.30-.45)	.0008-.002 [4] (.02-.05)
				Oil	.010-.016 [3] (.25-.40)	.0008-.002 [4] (.02-.05)

[1] – Wear limit .027" (.07 mm). [2] – Wear limit .0015" (.04 mm). [3] – Wear limit .039" (1 mm). [4] – Wear limit .006 (.15 mm).

CRANKSHAFT MAIN & CONNECTING ROD BEARINGS

Engine	MAIN BEARINGS				CONNECTING ROD BEARINGS		
	Journal Diam. In. (mm)	Clearance In. (mm)	Thrust Bearing	Crankshaft End Play In. (mm)	Journal Diam. In. (mm)	Clearance In. (mm)	Side Play In. (mm)
1.7L	2.124-2.125 (53.96-53.98)	.001-.003 [1] (.025-.076)	No. 3	.003-.007 [2] (.07-.17)	1.809-1.810 (45.96-45.98)	.0011-.0033 [3] (.028-.088)	.014 [4] (.37)

[1] – Wear limit .007" (.17 mm). [2] – Wear limit .0015" (.37 mm). [3] – Wear limit .0047" (.12 mm). [4] – Wear limit indicated.

CAMSHAFT

Engine	Journal Diam. In. (mm)	Clearance In. (mm)	Lobe Lift In. (mm)
1.7L	....	.0008-.002 [1] (.02-.05)	....

[1] – End play .006" (.15 mm).

VALVE SPRINGS

Engine	Free Length In. (mm)	PRESSURE Lbs. @ In. (Kg @ mm)	
		Valve Closed	Valve Open
1.7L			
Inner	....	46-51@.719 (21-32@18.3)	....
Outer	....	96-106@.916 (43.5-48@22.3)	....

VANAGON 1.9L WATER-COOLED 4-CYLINDER

ENGINE CODING

ENGINE IDENTIFICATION

Engine code number is stamped on right crankcase half below breather. First 2 digits indicate engine type and size. This 1.9L 4-cylinder engine is horizontally opposed and water-cooled.

ENGINE IDENTIFICATION

Application	Engine Code
Vanagon (1.9L)	DH

ENGINE, MANIFOLD, & CYLINDER HEAD

ENGINE

Removal

1) Disconnect battery ground strap. Disconnect wiring and remove air flow sensor, air cleaner, and air intake boot. Disconnect wires at rear of alternator. Disconnect wiring from fuel injectors, throttle valve switch, and auxiliary air regulator.

2) Disconnect vacuum hoses at charcoal filter valve. Disconnect and plug fuel return line at pressure regulator. Disconnect and plug fuel supply line at "T" in fuel ring. On models with automatic transmission, remove circlip and spring from accelerator rod.

3) Disconnect coil lead and wiring plug at distributor. Disconnect wiring at oxygen sensor, oil pressure switch, temperature sensor, and temperature sender. Unplug wiring to coolant level warning switch (in expansion tank). Disconnect grounds on top left side of crankcase.

4) Clamp off both radiator hoses at thermostat housing. Clamp off both heater hoses at right rear side of engine compartment. Open expansion tank, remove drain plugs in bottom of cylinder heads, and drain coolant. Disconnect coolant hoses from expansion tank at engine end. Remove expansion tank.

5) Disconnect brake booster vacuum line at check valve. Remove both upper engine-to-transmission nuts. On models with automatic transmission, remove 3 torque converter-to-drive plate bolts. These bolts are reached through hole on top of transmission housing.

6) Disconnect wiring at starter. On models with automatic transmission, remove accelerator rod from lever on transmission. Remove lower sheet metal plates on left and right side of engine. Remove bolts from rear cover plate, leaving plate in place.

7) Loosen transmission mount bolt so transmission can pivot. Attach support bar (VW 785/1B) so support pad is about 4.75" (120 mm) below transmission housing. Support engine with adapter (US 612/5) and transmission jack. Remove 4 engine carrier-to-frame bolts.

8) Lower engine/transmission assembly until transmission rests on support bar. While lowering, keep wiring out of way and adjust angle of engine to clear oil filler tube.

9) Remove 2 lower engine-to-transmission nuts. Separate engine from transmission and remove from vehicle. On models with automatic transmission, secure torque converter in place.

Installation

1) Installation procedure is reverse of removal. Check throw-out bearing for wear or roughness. Lubricate throw-out bearing and main shaft splines lightly with high temperature grease. Do not lubricate throw-out bearing guide sleeve.

2) Replace all self-locking nuts on engine mounts. Check and adjust accelerator cables and linkage. Replace coolant drain plug gaskets. Fill and bleed cooling system. Make sure engine develops oil pressure after starting.

INTAKE MANIFOLD

Removal

1) Intake manifold and throttle valve housing are removed as assembly. Assembly can be removed with engine in vehicle. Disconnect battery ground strap. Disconnect wires and remove air cleaner with air sensor and intake boot. Clamp and disconnect coolant hoses from crossover pipe. Remove fuel supply and return lines.

2) Disconnect all wiring connectors to injectors, temperature sensor, throttle switches, and air auxiliary regulator. Disconnect accelerator cable at throttle valve lever. On models with automatic transmission, remove circlip and spring from accelerator rod.

3) Disconnect all vacuum lines from intake air distributor. Remove metal coolant crossover pipe. Remove intake manifold-to-cylinder head bolts. Lift intake manifold and throttle valve housing off engine as unit.

Installation

Installation procedure is reverse of removal. Always use new gaskets between heads and manifold ends. Make sure all hose clamps are tight. Bleed cooling system and check for leaks. Adjust accelerator cable or rod (models with automatic transmission).

CYLINDER HEAD

NOTE: Cylinder head may be removed with engine installed.

Removal

1) Remove rocker arm cover with gasket. Loosen rocker arm retaining nuts so tension is relieved evenly. Remove intake manifold assembly if both heads are to be removed. Remove intake manifold runners and connected hoses from 1 side if only 1 head is being removed.

2) Remove expansion tank cap and drain plugs under heads. Drain cooling system. Disconnect coolant hoses attached to head. Remove front and rear exhaust pipes from both heads. Remove push rods and keep in order for reassembly.

Fig. 1: Cylinder Head Nut Tightening Sequence

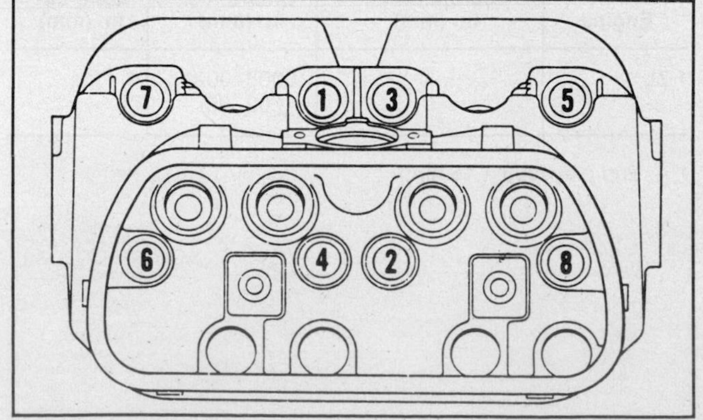
7
1
3
5
6
4
2
8

Loosen in reverse order.

VANAGON 1.9L WATER-COOLED 4-CYLINDER (Cont.)

3) Remove 8 cap nuts holding cylinder head to block. Loosen nuts gradually in diagonal sequence from outside to center. *See Fig. 1.* Remove cylinder head and gasket. Remove push rod tubes. Remove metal sealing ring and thin green "O" ring from cylinder sleeve.

Installation

1) Make sure push rod tube is correct length. Tube should be about 7.64" (194 mm) between inside edges of tube sealing "O" rings. *See Fig. 2.* Seam of tube faces up and small end is toward cylinder head. Always use new sealing rings. Sand sealing substance on cylinder head until smooth.

Fig. 2: Push Rod Tube Length

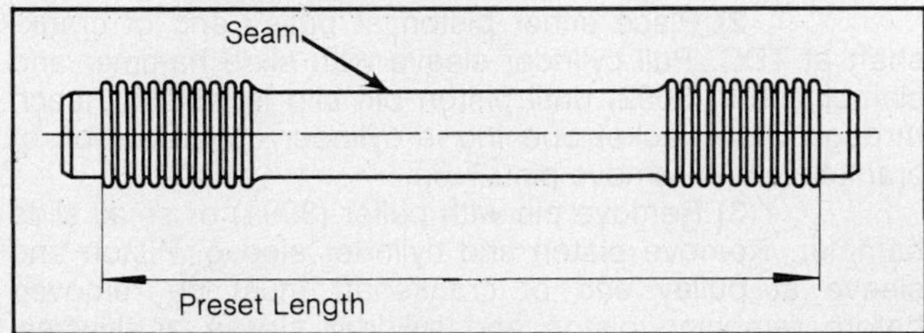
Seam
Preset Length

Install small end to cylinder head with seam up.

2) Clean sealing surface with solvent. Install new thin green "O" ring and metal gasket on cylinder sleeves. Install new water jacket gasket on crankcase surface. Apply I-2 mm wide bead of sealing compound (VW No. D 000 400) in center of new water jacket gasket. Install push rod tubes with small end toward head.

NOTE: **Manufacturer specifies only VW No. D 000 400 sealing compound and G-11 coolant. Cylinder head must be installed within 45 minutes of application of sealing compound. Excessive sealant will plug coolant passages in cylinder head.**

3) Coat sealing face of cap nuts with waterproof compound. Install and snug cap nut at No. 1 stud enough to install remaining cap nuts. Tighten cap nuts to first stage of 7 ft. lbs. (9.5 N.m) in sequence shown. *See Fig. 1.* Make sure push rod tubes are correctly seated.

4) Tighten cap nuts to final setting of 25 ft. lbs. (34 N.m). Install push rods, making sure that push rods fit into cups of lifters. Install rocker assembly with slots facing upward on shaft supports. Adjust hydraulic lifters after rocker assembly-to-head nuts are tight. Install rocker cover with new gasket.

5) Reassemble remaining parts in reverse order of removal. Use new exhaust flange gaskets with metal surface toward head. Always use new locking nuts. Use new gaskets on drain plugs. Fill and bleed cooling system. Make sure engine develops oil pressure after starting.

VALVES

VALVE ARRANGEMENT

E-I-I-E (Both heads).

VALVE GUIDE SERVICING

NOTE: **Check heads for cracks before performing service work on head. Cracks between valve seats or between seat and spark plug thread are acceptable, according to manufacturer. Cracks may not exceed .019" (.48 mm) in width. Cracks may not extend beyond first coil of plug thread.**

1) Clean carbon from seats and port areas around guides. Insert new valve into guide to be measured. Tip of valve stem must be flush with valve guide end. Mount dial indicator with tip against side of valve head. Rock valve back and forth.

2) Maximum reading or wear limit is .047" (1.19 mm). This reading is double valve stem clearance, which has a wear limit of .024" (.61 mm). If guides are to be replaced, mount head on plate (US 4401A). Drill guides out with shouldered drill to depth of 1.575-1.968" (40-50 mm).

3) Press remaining portion of guide out with drift (US 4408 or 4417) toward combustion chamber side. Coat new guide with oil and press in with drift (US 4410) from side opposite combustion chamber. Maximum pressure to be used is 2 tons. Ream guides to size with reamer (US 4412 or 4413).

4) Valve seats must be refaced after replacement of guides. Damaged or burned seats may be refaced if seat width can be maintained. Also, upper angle (15° chamfer) must not exceed outer diameter of valve seat insert at widest point (where outer edge of seat meets cylinder head).

5) Cut seat at 45° angle until seat is completely clean. Cut 75° angle to slightly chamfer lower edge of valve seat. Cut 15° angle until correct seat width is obtained. Seat width range of 45° angle is .055-.098" (1.39-2.49 mm). Lap valves into seats. Remove all lapping compound from valves and heads before reassembly.

VALVE SPRINGS

Removal

1) Valve springs may be removed with head installed or removed. If head is installed, apply air pressure to cylinder through spark plug hole to hold valves closed. Compress spring retainer and springs.

2) Remove keepers and release compressor. Remove retainer and both springs (inner and outer). Make sure springs are not cracking and are of equal length.

Installation

Install inner and outer springs over valve stem. Install compressor and retainer. Compress retainer and springs. Install keepers, making sure that keepers fit properly in grooves of valve stem. Release compressor and remove air pressure if used.

ROCKER ARM ASSEMBLY

Removal

Remove rocker arm cover and gasket. Remove nuts holding rocker shaft. Loosen nuts gradually to relieve spring tension evenly. Check adjusting screw surfaces for pitting or mushrooming. Make sure threads of adjusting screws and lock nuts move freely.

Installation

Install rocker arm assembly on studs of head. Make sure slot in shaft support faces up. Make sure push rods are properly seated in cups of lifters and cups at base of rockers. Tighten 2 nuts holding shaft down evenly. Adjust hydraulic lifter clearance. Install rocker arm cover with new gasket.

HYDRAULIC VALVE LIFTERS

Removal

1) Lifters may be removed and replaced without removal or disassembly of engine. Replacement

VANAGON 1.9L WATER-COOLED 4-CYLINDER (Cont.)

push rod tubes must be used if cylinder head is not removed.

2) Remove rocker arm covers, push rods, push rod tubes, and sheet metal under push rod tubes. Remove lifters with magnet extended into lifter bore. Keep lifters in order and mark for reassembly in same location.

CAUTION: Failure to install lifters in same location will cause premature failure of camshaft.

Inspection

1) Check lifter face for pitting or excessive wear. If such wear is evident, try to examine lobes of camshaft through lifter bore in case side. Check side of lifter for galling. Check that lifter moves freely in bore. Do not repair lifter.

2) If damaged or worn, lifter must be replaced with new part. Make sure lifter is bled properly. Apply firm thumb pressure against push rod socket. Try to push socket into lifter body. Lifter must be bled if socket moves.

3) Pry out lock ring. Remove push rod socket, plunger, ball check valve with spring, check valve retainer, and plunger spring from lifter valve body. Fill valve body with oil up to bleed hole. Insert plunger spring. Install plunger with ball check valve, check valve spring, and valve retainer.

4) Push downward and open ball check valve with scribe. Insert push rod socket and slowly compress in vise, using valve guide or shortened push rod against socket. Bleed hole must face up with lifter in horizontal position. Compress socket until lock ring can be installed.

Installation

1) Lightly oil lifter body and slide into lifter bore of crankcase. Install replacement push rod tube with new sealing rings at each end. Compress replacement tube and position between head and crankcase from underside of head. Seam must face up and small end of tube must be at cylinder head end.

2) Release push rod tube and allow it to expand between case and head. Make sure seals seat properly. Install push rods. Make sure push rods seat fully in lifter sockets.

CAUTION: If push rod rides on edge of lifter, initial adjustments will be incorrect. Valve lifter will be damaged when engine is started.

3) Install rocker arm assembly. Tighten nuts down evenly to avoid binding. Adjust hydraulic lifter clearance. Install rocker cover with new gasket.

NOTE: Intermittent lifter noise upon starting, during sudden acceleration, and with high temperature or high engine speed is considered normal, per manufacturer.

VALVE CLEARANCE ADJUSTMENT

1) Valve or hydraulic lifter clearance must be adjusted any time rocker shafts have been removed and installed. Loosen lock nuts and back out adjusting screw until rounded face is flush with surface of rocker arm. Rotate crankshaft until No. 1 cylinder is at TDC.

2) Distributor rotor will point to notch on distributor housing. Turn adjusting screws of No. 1 cylinder in until just touching tip of valve stem. Turn adjusting screws in 2 turns (720°) and tighten lock nuts. Rotate crankshaft 180° and adjust next cylinder.

3) Repeat until all screws have been adjusted. Install rocker arm cover with new gasket. Start engine and let idle until no lifter or valve noise is heard. Idle should be smooth and engine should have oil pressure.

PISTONS, PINS, & RINGS

CYLINDERS

Removal

1) Remove engine from vehicle and mount on stand. Remove cylinder heads. Mark pistons and cylinder sleeves with matching numbers. Note arrow on crown of piston points to flywheel. Note bosses on cylinder sleeves face each other. Clean all scale deposits and sealing compound from cylinder head and crankcase surfaces.

2) Place either piston at pulley end of crankshaft at TDC. Pull cylinder sleeve with slide hammer and clamping bar (3092) until piston pin clip is visible. Reach through water jacket opening in cylinder cover portion of crankcase and remove pin circlip.

3) Remove pin with puller (3091) or small slide hammer. Remove piston and cylinder sleeve. Piston and sleeve at pulley end of crankshaft must be removed before removing piston and cylinder sleeve at flywheel end of crankshaft. Remove rubber sealing rings from cylinder sleeve. Clean deposits from cylinder sleeves and crankcase.

Installation

1) Put new rubber sealing rings on sleeve. Thick black ring always goes at base of sleeve (by crankcase) while thin green ring always goes at top of sleeve (by cylinder head). Piston and sleeve assembly at flywheel end of crankshaft must be installed first on each side of engine.

2) Compress piston rings and install piston into sleeve. Check that arrow on piston crown points to flywheel end of crankshaft. Gap of oil scraper (bottom) ring must be up. Gaps of rings must be offset by 180°. Install circlip for pin in flywheel side of piston.

3) Mount connecting rod support (3090) on lower center head stud. Note "L" and "R" markings on tool for left and right side usage. Support connecting rod in horizontal position with crankshaft at TDC. Install piston with sleeve and align connecting rod with holes in piston.

4) Install piston pin with tool (3091) and insert circlip. Make sure pin is not galled. Make sure piston and rod move freely on pin. Push cylinder sleeve into crankcase opening until it bottoms out. Install cylinder head with proper sealant. *See Cylinder Head Installation.* Install remaining parts in reverse order of removal.

FITTING PISTONS

1) Measure piston diameter at bottom of skirt about 9/16" (15 mm) from edge. Take measurement at 90° to pin bore. Measure internal diameter of cylinder sleeve with cylinder bore gauge or internal micrometer. Take measurement 3/8-5/8" (l0-16 mm) from top of sleeve.

2) Piston skirt clearance is difference between sleeve diameter and piston diameter. Wear limit is .008" (.20 mm) while new clearance is .001-.002" (.03-.06 mm). Measure piston recess depth, from top face of crown to bottom of recess in crown. *See Fig. 3.* This measurement should be .458" (11.65 mm).

3) Push ring squarely into lower end of sleeve about 3/16 (4-5 mm) and measure ring end gap. Upper and lower compression ring gap wear limit is .035" (.90 mm). Oil scraper ring gap wear limit is .037" (.95 mm).

Install rings with "TOP" mark facing crown of piston. *See Fig. 4.*

Fig. 3: Piston Recess Depth Measurement

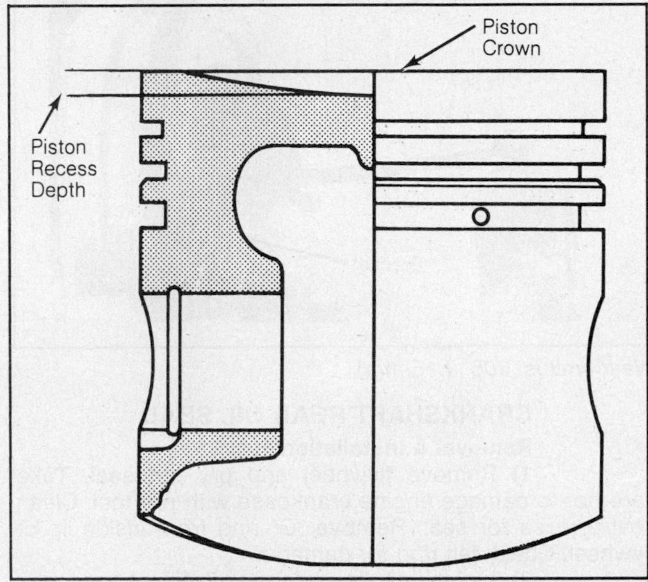

Piston
Crown
Piston
Recess
Depth

4) Measure side clearance between face of ring and side of ring land. Upper compression ring side clearance has wear limit of .005" (.12 mm). Lower compression and oil scraper ring side clearance wear limit is .004" (.10 mm).

5) Size, weight, and installation direction are marked on crown of piston. Arrow must point to flywheel when piston is installed. Weight group is indicated by "+" or "-" mark. Pistons marked "+" weigh 16.12-16.37 ozs. (457-464 g). Pistons marked "-" weigh 15.80-16.08 ozs. (448-456 g).

6) Maximum weight difference between pistons is .35 ozs. (10 g). Paint dot (Blue for standard) is for matching sleeve diameter size to piston diameter. Piston diameter is measured in millimeters and given as 4 digit number stamped into face.

Fig. 4: Piston Ring Installation

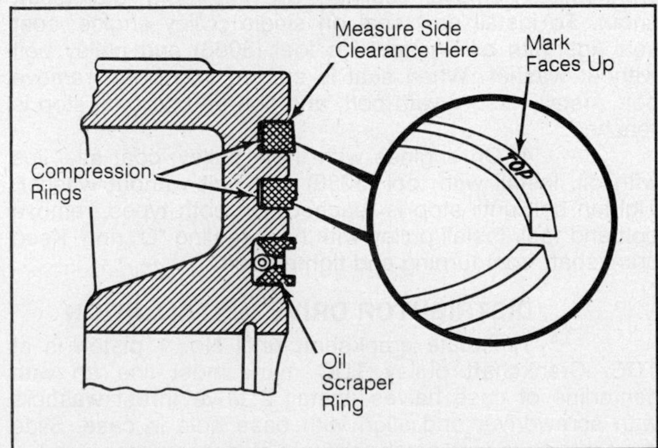

Measure Side
Clearance Here
Mark
Faces Up
Compression
Rings
TOP
Oil
Scraper
Ring

Measure side clearance between face of ring and piston groove.

CRANKCASE, CRANKSHAFT & CAMSHAFT

CRANKCASE

Disassembly

1) Remove engine from vehicle after draining oil. Place on engine stand with sturdy frame head attached to left case half. Remove manifolds, cylinder heads, pistons and cylinder sleeves, and engine carrier assembly. Note directional arrows on carrier for reassembly.

2) Remove flywheel or drive plate, crankshaft pulley, and breather tower. Remove distributor, distributor drive gear, 2 drive gear shims, and oil filter. Remove oil pump assembly. *See Oil Pump Removal.* Pry out front and rear crankshaft oil seals. Remove oil filler tube. Remove alternator and bracket.

3) Remove water pump and thermostat housing as assembly. Remove hydraulic lifters and keep in marked order for reassembly. Remove 10 mm nuts on case through studs. There are 10 mm cap nuts inside cylinder cover portion of right case half. Remove all 8 mm nuts and bolts holding case halves together.

4) Separate case halves. Use rubber mallet if case will not separate easily. DO NOT use prying tools or levers between case halves as machine surfaces will be damaged. Oil leaks will occur even if no other damage is done. Lift camshaft and crankshaft with connecting rods out of left case half.

5) If bearings are to be reused, remove from case halves and keep in order for reassembly. Remove main bearing locating dowels. Remove metal camshaft plug. Unbolt oil pickup tube and remove.

Reassembly

1) Clean all sealing compound off cases, bolts, nuts, and washers. Blow out all oil galleys with compressed air. Check studs for tightness. Install oil pickup after blowing clear with compressed air, making sure pickup is tight fit in case.

2) Make sure bearing locating dowels are snug fit in case. Install main and camshaft bearings in cases, making sure tangs locate properly in grooves. Lay crankshaft, with connecting rods attached, into left case half. Make sure main bearings and locating dowels line up properly.

3) Install camshaft, making sure valve timing is correct. *See Camshaft Installation.* Install metal camshaft plug in left case after coating edge of plug with sealer. Spread sealer over mating surfaces of both halves of crankcase. Place right half of case over through studs and press case halves together.

4) Coat both sides of washers or faces of cap nuts with sealing compound and install all 8 and 10 mm nuts. Tighten 8 mm nut above and behind No. 1 exhaust lifter bore first. Tighten all 10 mm nuts and then tighten all remaining 8 mm nuts. Install distributor drive gear and distributor. *See Distributor Drive Installation.*

5) Install carrier assembly, making sure arrow points to front of vehicle. Install flywheel or drive plate, front, and rear crankshaft oil seals after checking crankshaft end play. *See Crankshaft End Play.*

6) Install remaining parts in reverse order of disassembly. Always use new gaskets and sealing rings. Make sure engine develops oil pressure after starting. Bleed and top up cooling system.

VANAGON 1.9L WATER-COOLED 4-CYLINDER (Cont.)

CRANKSHAFT & BEARINGS

Disassembly

1) Remove No. 1 main (thrust) bearing from crankshaft. Mount assembled crankshaft on holding tool (VW 801) and clamp tool in vise. Remove oil slinger, main bearing No. 4, and circlip. Remove connecing rods, keeping rods and bearings in order for reassembly.

2) Place stripped crankshaft in press. Use press plate (VW 402) or bearing separator behind steel gear and press off steel crankshaft/camshaft timing gear, spacer, and brass distributor drive gear as set. Remove No. 3 main bearing.

3) Thoroughly clean crankshaft and blow out oil passages with compressed air. Measure runout of crankshaft. If runout exceeds .0008" (.020 mm), crankshaft must be turned to next undersize. Measure bearing journals, using micrometer or Plastigauge method.

4) If journals show more than .0012" (.030 mm) wear, turn crankshaft to next undersize. Check small end bushings in connecting rods. Always replace connecting rod nuts. Check pilot bearing. Remove with puller.

Reassembly

1) Mount crankshaft and holding tool (VW 801) in vise. Heat steel and brass gears in oil bath to about 175°F (80° C). Oil No. 3 Main bearing and place on crankshaft with dowel locating hole away from gears.

2) Place heated gears and spacer on crankshaft. Timing marks (2 dots) on steel gear face No. 4 bearing. Only light pressure should be needed to seat gears if heated properly. Install circlip. Oil No. 4 main bearing and install with groove toward oil slinger.

3) Install oil slinger and Woodruff key. Put connecting rod bearings in rods and caps with tangs engaging notches. Install connecting rods with forged mark on rods faceing up. Match numbers stamped on rod and cap must be next to each other. Tap both sides of rod lightly to keep bearing shells from pinching.

4) Check side clearance of connecting rods. Maximum side play is .028 " (.70 mm). Connecting rods should only be replaced in sets of 4 with maximum weigth difference of .35 ozs. (10 g). Install crankshaft pilot bearing with marked side of bearing cage facing out. Grease rollers with molybdenum disulfide. Replace felt ring.

CRANKSHAFT END PLAY

1) Crankshaft end play is adjusted by shims between flywheel and thrust surface of rear main (No. 1) bearing. Always use 3 shims to set end play. To check end play of crankshaft, mount dial indicator with tip at 90° to face of flywheel. *See Fig. 5.*

2) Move flywheel in and out, recording measurement. End play range for new parts is .003-.005" (.07-.13 mm) with a wear limit of .006" (.15 mm). When setting end play, install flywheel with 2 shims. Do not install "O" ring or rear crankshaft oil seal at this time.

3) Mount dial indicator and measure end play. Determine thickness of third shim, using .004" (.10 mm) as desired end play setting. Thickness of shims is marked on shim. Always check reading with micrometer. Remove flywheel and install 3 shims.

4) Install new rear oil seal, "O" ring in flywheel, and felt ring. Install flywheel and tighten bolts. Recheck crankshaft end play with dial indicator. Mount clutch disc and pressure plate on flywheel if end play is correct. Use clutch pilot to align disc with pilot bearing.

Fig. 5: Measuring Crankshaft End Play

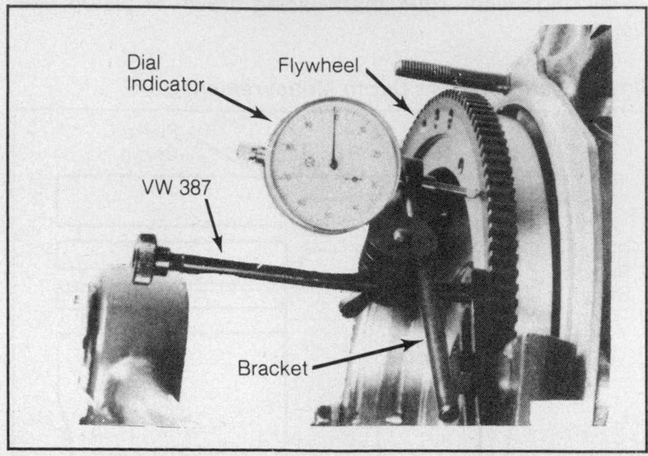
Dial
Indicator
Flywheel
VW 387
Bracket

Wear limit is .006" (.15 mm)

CRANKSHAFT REAR OIL SEAL

Removal & Installation

1) Remove flywheel and pry out seal. Take care not to damage engine crankcase with pry tool. Clean seating area for seal. Remove "O" ring from inside lip of flywheel. Check felt ring for damage.

2) Lightly oil lips of new flywheel seal and install on guide tool (VW 191). Attach base of tool (VW 191) to crankshaft. Press seal and guide tool in until seal seats. Put new "O" ring into flywheel, lube lightly, and install flywheel.

CRANKSHAFT FRONT OIL SEAL

Removal & Installation

1) Remove drive belt(s) and pulley. If pulley is single "V" belt type, hold flywheel or drive plate through hole in crankcase while loosening or tightening pulley bolt. If pulley is triple "V" belt type (vehicles with A/C and power steering), use holding tool (3102).

2) Holding tool (3102) locks into smaller hole on triple pulley and bolt hole from carrier-to-right mount bolt. Smaller hole must be up when loosening bolt and down when tightening bolt. Bolt must be removed from carrier-to-mount location to allow tool installation.

3) Pry seal out, being careful not to damage crankcase. Remove sealing "O" ring from crankshaft snout. To install new seal on single pulley engine, coat seal lips with oil. Install with tool (3088) and pulley bolt without washer. When seal is started into bore, remove bolt, install washer with bolt, and tighten bolt until stop is reached.

4) On engines with triple pulley, coat seal lips with oil. Install with tool (3088) and bolt without washer. Tighten bolt until stop is reached. On both types, remove bolt and tool. Install pulley with new sealing "O" ring. Keep crankshaft from turning and tighten bolt.

DISTRIBUTOR DRIVE INSTALLATION

1) Rotate crankshaft until No. 1 piston is at TDC. Crankshaft pulley TDC mark must line up with centerline of case halves. Install 2 drive thrust washers with screwdriver and align with base hole in case. Slide drive into case with small segment closer to water pump.

2) Slot on top of drive must point to bolt just behind and right of water pump flange. *See Fig. 6.* Line of slot will be almost parallel to centerline of case halves.

VANAGON 1.9L WATER-COOLED 4-CYLINDER (Cont.)

Take care not to damage soft teeth of brass drive gear on crankshaft. Put small spring into top of drive.

Fig. 6: Installing Distributor Drive Gear

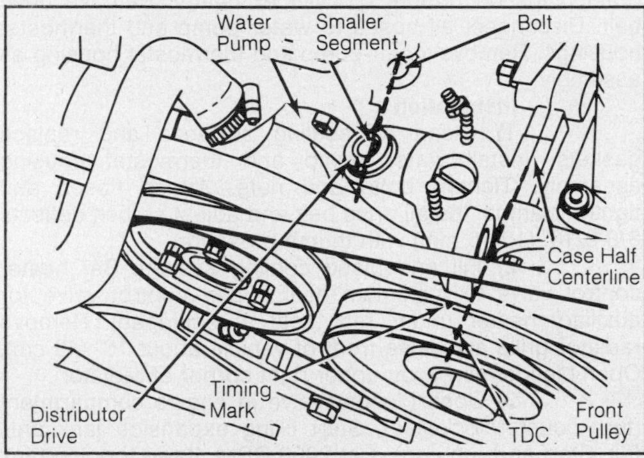
Water Pump
Smaller Segment
Bolt
Case Half Centerline
Timing Mark
Distributor Drive
TDC
Front Pulley

Small segment faces water pump.

3) Align mark on distributor rotor with notch on lip of distributor housing. This is No. 1 position of distributor. Slide distributor into crankcase, making sure that lugs on bottom of distributor mate with slot on top of drive. Tighten 8 mm nut on distributor hold-down clamp.

CAMSHAFT

Inspection

With camshaft removed from engine, check rivets holding gear to shaft. Replace camshaft if rivets are loose or worn on heads. Mount camshaft in "V" blocks or lathe and check runout with dial indicator. Maximum runout allowed is .0015" (.040 mm) measured at center bearing journal of camshaft.

Installation

1) Place camshaft into left case half. Bearing shells must be installed properly with tabs engaged in case notches. Crankshaft should not be in place for camshaft end play measurement. Mount dial indicator with plunger at 90° to face of camshaft gear.

2) Move camshaft back and forth in case. Maximum end play is .006" (.16 mm). Camshaft thrust bearing (behind gear) controls end play. Bearing set must be replaced if end play is excessive. Remove camshaft and dial indicator. Install crankshaft into left half of crankcase. *See Crankcase Reassembly.*

3) Install camshaft in left half of case. "O" mark on OUTER face of camshaft must be between 2 dots on face of steel crankshaft gear. Mount dial indicator with tip at 90° to tooth on camshaft gear. Rock camshaft gear against crankshaft gear to measure backlash.

4) Backlash of camshaft gear to crankshaft gear may range from 0-.002" (0-.05 mm). If backlash is correct, rotate crankshaft counterclockwise (opposite running rotation). Camshaft must not lift out of bearings. If camshaft does lift, fit a camshaft with a smaller gear.

5) Markings for camshaft gear sizes are on INNER face of gear. Markings range from "+5" to zero to "-5". More positive numbers give a tighter fit while more negative numbers give a looser fit. Numbers indicate how much pitch radius varies from standard pitch radius "0" or zero in 1/100 mm steps.

6) Perform backlash and "walking" checks each time different camshaft is fitted. This is a critical measurement. Crankshaft steel gear is available in 1 size. Steel gear must be checked carefully for galling or heat distortion.

ENGINE OILING

OIL CAPACITY

Oil capacity is 4.2 qts. (4.0L) without filter change, 4.7 qts. (4.5L) with filter change. Filter is full flow spin-on type.

OIL PRESSURE

Minimum oil pressure should be 29 psi (2 kg/cm²) at 2000 RPM with oil temperature of 176°F (80°C). Oil pressure warning light should go out at pressure of 2-6.5 psi (.15-.45 kg/cm²). Spring loaded pressure relief valve opens when oil pressure becomes excessive.

ENGINE OILING SYSTEM

1) Gear-type oil pump at front of engine is driven by camshaft. Oil flows under full pressure from pump to filter to main bearing journals through oil galleys in crankcase casting. Crankshaft is cross-drilled to provide oil to connecting rod journals.

2) Oil galleys bring full pressure to camshaft journals and hydraulic valve lifters. Oil flows through hollow push rods to lubricate rocker arm assembly. Splash oil lubricates valve stems. Excess oil returns to crankcase through push rod tubes. Cylinder walls and piston pins are splash lubricated.

OIL PUMP

Removal

Remove engine. Remove exhaust and engine carrier. Remove oil pump cover with 4 sealing nuts. Remove gears from pump body. Install oil pump puller (VW 201) in pump body and slowly draw pump from crankcase opening.

Inspection

1) Check pump body for scoring. Make sure post for driven gear is tight in pump body. Check lug of drive gear for excessive wear. Make sure machine surface of pump cover is smooth and flat.

2) Place gears into pump body. Place straightedge across pump body and face of gears. Measure end play of gears to straightedge with feeler gauge. Maximum end play is .004" (.10 mm).

Installation

1) Lightly coat THICK oil pump body gasket with sealer. Place over studs against crankcase. Carefully tap pump body into crankcase with soft mallet. Make sure to align studs and pump body. Avoid tearing gasket edge.

2) Place drive gear in pump body and rotate until lug fits into groove on face of camshaft. Install driven gear, rotating crankshaft slightly to align gear teeth. Install dry THIN oil pump cover gasket over studs.

3) Place pump cover plate on studs. Tighten new sealing nuts in diagonal pattern. Sealing ring of nut faces oil pump cover. Install remaining parts in reverse of removal. Install engine. Make sure engine has oil pressure after starting.

ENGINE COOLING

NOTE: **All parts of cooling system can be removed and installed with engine installed.**

VANAGON 1.9L WATER-COOLED 4-CYLINDER (Cont.)

COOLANT CAPACITY

Cooling system capacity is 18.4 qts. (17.5L). Coolant mixture of 50/50 water/antifreeze protects to about -30°F (-35°C). Use only ethylene glycol (phosphate free) antifreeze (VW No. ZVW 237 102) to prevent damage to water jacket sealing surfaces of cylinder head.

THERMOSTAT

1) Thermostat is located in left half of water pump housing. Thermostat begins to open at 185°F (85°C) and is fully open at 221°F (105°C). Minimum opening distance of thermostat is .315"(8.00 mm). *See Fig. 7.*

2) Radiator fan thermoswitch is located at lower left side of radiator. Switch has 2 stages with first stage coming in at 199-208°F (93-98°C) and shutting off at 190-199°F (88-93°C). Second stage comes in at 210-221°F (99-105°C) and shuts off at 196-206°F (91-97°C).

Fig. 7: Cooling System Component Location

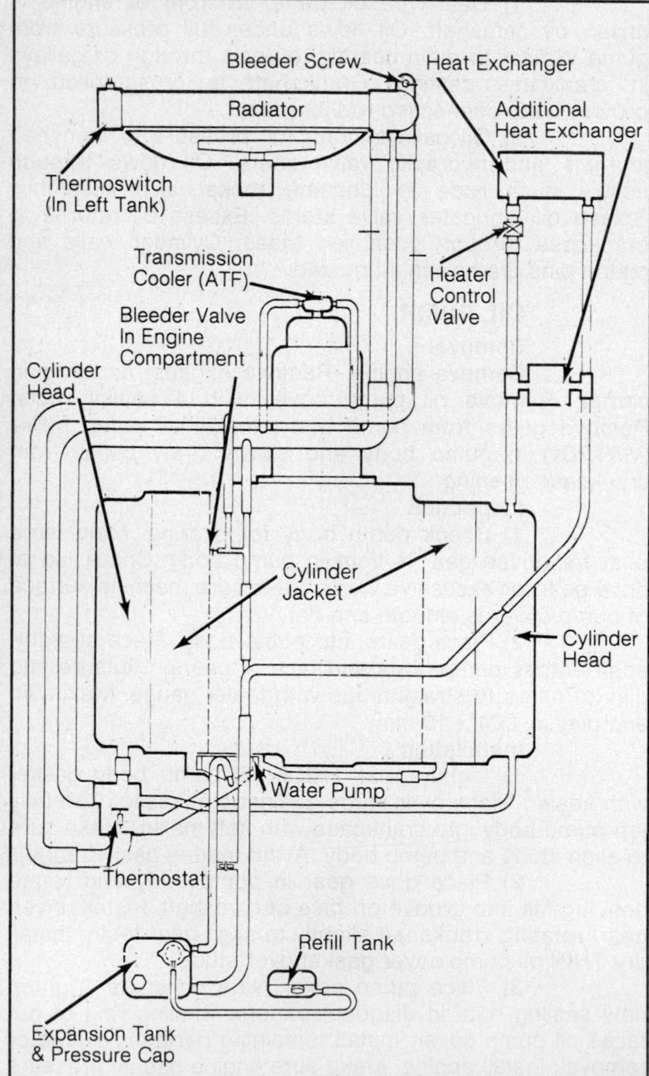
Bleeder Screw
Heat Exchanger
Radiator
Additional Heat Exchanger
Thermoswitch (In Left Tank)
Transmission Cooler (ATF)
Heater Control Valve
Bleeder Valve In Engine Compartment
Cylinder Head
Cylinder Jacket
Cylinder Head
Water Pump
Thermostat
Refill Tank
Expansion Tank & Pressure Cap

RADIATOR CAP

Radiator cap is located on expansion tank at left side of engine compartment. Cap opens at 13-17 psi (.9-1.2 kg/cm²) to allow flow to expansion tank. Cap also opens at vacuum of .3-1.45 psi (.02-.10 kg/cm²) to allow flow from expansion tank.

WATER PUMP

Removal

Remove expansion tank cap. Drain coolant at drain plugs on bottom of cylinder heads. Remove drive belt. Disconnect all hoses to water pump and thermostat housings. Remove water pump and thermostat housing as assembly.

Installation

1) Clean all sealing surfaces and replace gaskets. Install water pump and thermostat housing assembly. Tighten bolts and nuts. Attach hoses and tighten clamps. Install drive belt and adjust so belt deflects 3/8-9/16" (10-15 mm) with thumb pressure.

2) Fill and bleed cooling system. Set heater control valve to maximum heat. Open control valve for auxiliary heater under rear seat (if equipped). Remove radiator grille and raise front of vehicle about 16" (40 cm). Open bleeder screw on upper right corner of radiator.

3) Open bleeder valve in engine compartment (turn counterclockwise). Start filling expansion tank until full. Start and run engine at 2000 RPM. Keep topping tank until coolant flows bubble-freefrom bleeder screw on radiator. Add coolant until tank is full and install cap on tank.

4) Turn engine off and restart after 20 seconds. Open expansion tank cap with engine running at 2000 RPM. Close bleeder screw on radiator when coolant is flowing out. Add coolant to expansion tank until full and close tank tightly.

5) Close bleeder valve in engine compartment. Switch engine off. Top up refill tank to maximum mark. Attach pressure tester to expansion tank and run engine until cooling fan has cycled. Check for leaks, remove tester, and tightly install cap on expansion tank.

RADIATOR & COOLING FAN

Removal

Remove spare tire bracket and radiator grille. Remove hoses and wires from radiator tanks. Remove radiator. Radiator cooling fan may be removed without draining coolant. Lower radiator with hoses attached and remove fan and fan shroud.

Installation

Install radiator or cooling fan in reverse of removal. Bleed cooling system and pressure test for leaks. Make sure that radiator cooling fan cycles properly.

TIGHTENING SPECIFICATIONS

Application	Ft. Lbs. (N.m)
Connecting Rod Nut	33 (45)
Crankcase Half Nuts (8 mm)	15 (19)
Crankcase Half Sealing Nuts (10 mm)	26 (35)
Cylinder Head Nuts	26 (35)
Rocker Shaft-to-Cylinder Head Nuts	19 (25)
Exhaust Flange-to-Cylinder Head	15 (20)
Coolant Pipe-to-Cylinder Head	15 (20)
Drain Plug-to-Crankcase	19 (25)
Drive Plate-to-Crankshaft	66 (90)
Flywheel-to-Crankshaft	81 (110)
Pulley-to-Crankshaft Bolt	
Single "V" Pulley	44 (60)
Triple "V" Pulley	258 (350)
Engine-to-Transmission	22 (30)
Oil Pump-to-Crankcase	19 (25)
Water Pump-to-Crankcase	15 (20)
Torque Converter-to-Drive Plate	15 (20)
Pressure Plate-to-Flywheel	15 (20)

Volkswagen Engines

VANAGON 1.9L WATER-COOLED 4-CYLINDER (Cont.)

ENGINE SPECIFICATIONS

GENERAL SPECIFICATIONS

Year	DISPLACEMENT		Fuel System	HP@RPM	Torque Ft. Lbs.@RPM	Compr. Ratio	BORE		STROKE	
	Cu. In.	Liters					In.	mm	In.	mm
1983	116	1.9	Fuel Injection	82@4800	.....	.....	3.70	94	.....	.....

VALVES

Engine Size & Valve	Head Diam. In. (mm)	Face Angle	Seat Angle	Seat Width In. (mm)	Stem Diameter In. (mm)	Stem Clearance In. (mm)	Valve Lift In. (mm)
1.9L							
Intake	1.575 (40.0)	45°	45°	.055-.098 (1.40-2.50)	.314 (7.97)	.024 (.60)	.....
Exhaust	1.339 (34.00)	45°	45°	.055-.098 (1.4-2.5)	.351 (8.92)	.024 (.60)	.....

PISTONS, PINS, RINGS

Engine	PISTONS	PINS		RINGS		
	Clearance In. (mm)	Piston Fit In. (mm)	Rod Fit In. (mm)	Ring No.	End Gap In. (mm)	Side Clearance In. (mm)
1.9L	.001-.002 (.02-.05)	Full Floating	Full Floating	1	.012-.018 (.30-.45)	.002-.003 (.05-.08)
				2	.012-.020 (.30-.50)	.002-.003 (.05-.08)
				3	.010-.016 (.25-.40)	.001-.002 (.02-.05)

CRANKSHAFT MAIN & CONNECTING ROD BEARINGS

Engine	MAIN BEARINGS				CONNECTING ROD BEARINGS		
	Journal Diam. In. (mm)	Clearance In. (mm)	Thrust Bearing	Crankshaft End Play In. (mm)	Journal Diam. In. (mm)	Clearance In. (mm)	Side Play In. (mm)
1.9L							
No. 1	2.3614-2.3618 (59.980-59.990)	....	No. 1	.003-.005[2] (.07-.13)	2.1646-2.1652 (54.983-54.996)	.....	[1]
No. 2	2.1642-2.1650 (54.971-54.990)	....					
No. 3	2.1646-2.1650 (54.980-54.990)	....					
No. 4	1.5742-1.5748 (39.984-40.000)	....					

[1] – Limit .028" (.70 mm). [2] – Limit .006" (.15 mm)

VANAGON 2.0L AIR-COOLED 4-CYLINDER

ENGINE CODING

ENGINE IDENTIFICATION

Engine code number is stamped on crankcase below breather. First 2 digits of number are engine code. This 2.0L 4-cylinder engine is horizontally opposed. Air cooling is by fan bolted to crankshaft.

ENGINE IDENTIFICATION

Application	Engine Code
Vanagon (2.0L)	CV

ENGINE, MANIFOLD & CYLINDER HEAD

ENGINE

Removal

1) Disconnect battery. Remove air cleaner with air flow sensor and air intake duct. Remove rubber boot to heater booster. Disconnect electrical wiring to following components: alternator, distributor, and oil pressure sending unit. Disconnect plug at control unit. Remove oil dipstick.

2) Disconnect vacuum hose for brake booster. Disconnect remaining vacuum hoses and electrical wiring leads running between engine and body. Remove nuts of upper engine mounting bolts and disconnect accelerator cable. On automatic transaxle models, remove plug on top of transaxle housing.

3) Pull ATF dipstick and remove ATF filler tube grommet. Remove three 8 mm bolts of torque converter through hole on top of transaxle housing. To gain access to bolts of torque converter, rotate crankshaft with adapter (3052) so each bolt appears in hole at top of transmission housing.

4) On all models, remove heater flap housing clamp bolt. Clamp and detach fuel lines by starter and from pressure regulator. Disconnect wiring from starter. Loosen transaxle front mount bolt so transaxle can pivot.

5) On automatic transaxle models, loosen accelerator cable at selector lever and detach. Loosen transmission carrier bolt. On all models, place support (VW 785/1) under transaxle. Place floor jack with adapter (VW 612/5) under engine. Raise jack until engine is just supported.

6) Remove nuts from lower engine mounting bolts. Remove engine carrier-to-frame bolts. Lower engine/transaxle assembly until transaxle rests on support (VW785/1). Slide engine assembly slightly to rear until it clears input shaft. Lower engine with floor jack.

Installation

1) To install, reverse removal procedure. Replace all self-locking nuts. On manual transaxle models, check clutch release bearing for wear. Lubricate splines on main drive shaft, contact points of clutch release bearing and clutch release lever.

2) Do not lubricate clutch release bearing guide sleeve. Adjust accelerator cable at full throttle position. On automatic transaxle models, adjust accelerator cable at selector lever.

INTAKE MANIFOLD

Removal

1) Fuel injection manifold can be removed with engine in vehicle. Remove air cleaner, hoses, and pressure regulator. Disconnect wires on fuel injectors and remove retaining nuts. Pull injectors off with hoses and retainers.

2) Disconnect hoses on injectors and remove. Remove intake manifold cover plate. Remove nuts and washers securing manifold to cylinder head. Lift up on manifold and remove runners from air distributor.

Installation

To install manifold, reverse removal procedure. Use new gaskets and tighten intake manifold mounting nuts uniformly.

CYLINDER HEAD

NOTE: **Engine must be removed from vehicle and manifolds removed before removing cylinder heads. If cylinders are not to be removed, use retaining device to keep cylinders from pulling free.**

Removal

1) Remove rocker arm cover and gasket. Remove rocker arm shaft retaining nuts, loosening gradually to relieve spring tension evenly. Remove rocker arm assemblies.

2) Remove push rods, keeping in order for reassembly. Remove pushrod tubes. Remove sheet metal and exhaust system. Loosen cylinder head nuts gradually working in sequence from outside toward center.

Fig. 1: Cylinder Head Nut Tightening Sequence

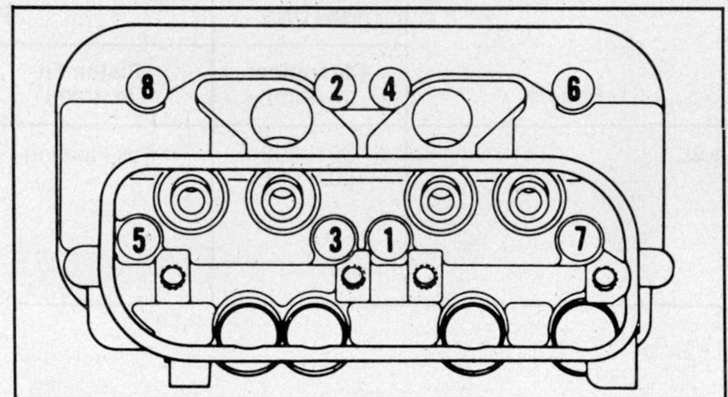
8
2
4
6
5
3
1
7

Loosen in reverse order.

Installation

1) Place new metal gasket rings in outside edges of combustion chambers. Install head over cylinder studs. Tighten nuts lightly by hand. Tighten to specification in diagonal sequence from center of head outward. *See Fig. 1.*

2) Install push rod tube through cylinder head with small end to crankcase and large end at head. Install remaining components in reverse order of removal. Ensure push rod tube retaining spring bears against end of tubes.

3) Engage spring in slots of rocker arm supports. Adjust hydraulic valve lifters. Install cylinder head cover with new gasket.

VALVES

VALVE ARRANGEMENT

E-I-I-E (Both heads).

VALVE GUIDE SERVICING

1) Clean carbon and oil from cylinder head. Check head for cracks in ports, seats, and combustion

VANAGON 2.0L AIR-COOLED 4-CYLINDER (Cont.)

chamber before servicing guides. Place new valve in guide with stem end flush with end of guide. With dial indicator, measure valve rock at valve head. If rock exceeds .047" (1.20 mm), replace guide.

2) Mount head in fixture (US 4401A). Drill guides with shouldered drill to a depth of 1.575-1.968" (40.00-50.00 mm). Drive remaining part of guide out through combustion chamber. Coat new guide with engine oil. Press in from rocker arm side of head using mandrel (US 4410).

3) Maximum pressure must not exceed 2 tons. Do not use a hammer and drift to replace guides. Damage to cylinder head may occur. Ream guide to proper size after installation.

VALVE SPRINGS

NOTE: **Valve spring may be removed with cylinder head installed. Apply a minimum of 85 psi (6.0 kg/cm²) air pressure to cylinder through spark plug hole to hold valve in place while compressing spring.**

Removal

Remove cylinder head cover and rocker arm shaft. Install valve spring compressor tool (VW 311S with cylinder head removed). Compress spring retainer and spring and remove valve keepers. Release compressor and remove spring retainer and spring.

Fig. 2: Using Spring Compressor to Remove Valve Spring

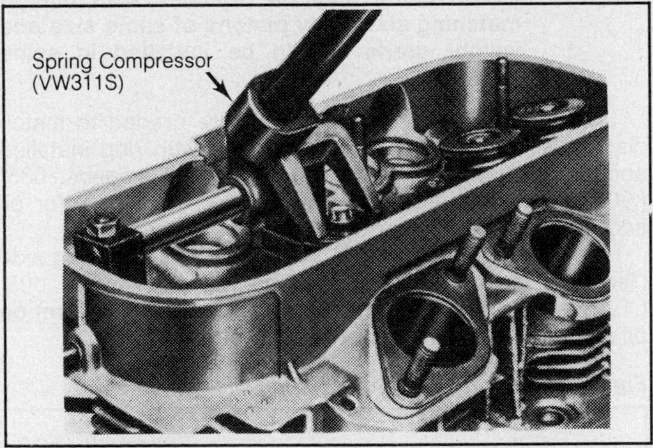

Spring Compressor
(VW311S)

Use compressed air to hold valve shut.

Installation

Install valve spring and valve spring retainer. Compress spring and install valve keepers. Remove compressor tool. Make sure keepers seat fully in grooves of valve stem.

ROCKER ARM ASSEMBLY

Removal

Remove valve cover clip. Remove valve cover. Remove 4 rocker shaft retaining nuts. Each side has 2 separate shafts. Make sure mounting nuts are gradually and evenly loosened until spring tension is completely relieved.

Inspection

Check rocker arms and shafts for wear. Check valve adjusting screws for pitting or flat spots. Make sure adjusting screws and lock nuts are free and move easily.

Installation

To install, reverse removal procedure. Rocker arm supports are installed with slot facing down. Chamfered face must face outward. Make sure push rod tube retaining spring is reinstalled. Adjust valve clearance.

Fig. 3: Sectional View of Valve with Related Parts

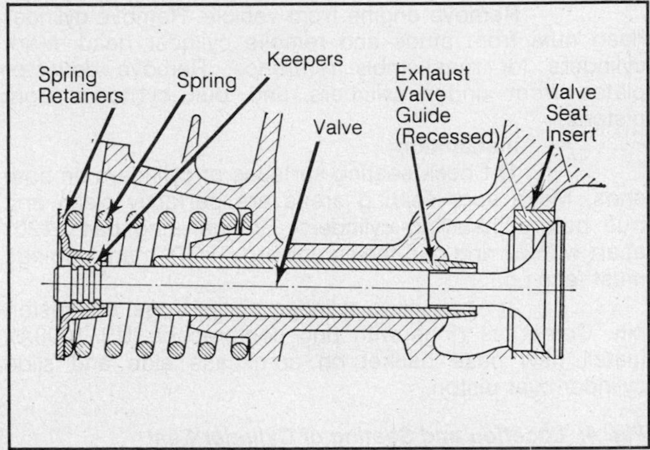

Spring
Retainers
Spring
Keepers
Valve
Exhaust
Valve
Guide
(Recessed)
Valve
Seat
Insert

HYDRAULIC VALVE LIFTERS

Removal

Valve lifters may be removed and installed without removing or disassembling engine. Remove valve covers, rocker arms, push rods, and push rod tubes from engine. Remove lifters with magnetic tool. Mark lifters for installation in original position.

Inspection

Lifters should never be repaired. If lifters are found to be worn or damaged, replace them. Intermittent valve noise (clatter) is normal during starting, sudden acceleration, high temperatures, or high engine speed. If metal particles are found in sump, remove, disassemble, and clean all lifters.

Installation

1) Ensure that lifters are bled properly. Press on push rod socket with firm thumb pressure. If no resistance is felt, bleed lifter. Fill tin can with engine oil. Cut old Type I push rod in half.

2) Remove lock ring, push rod socket, plunger, ball check valve with spring, and plunger spring from body. Put valve lifter body in can, making sure it is completely covered with oil. Reinstall all parts removed except push rod socket and lock ring.

3) Open ball check valve with scribe so oil can pass out of bottom of plunger. Install push rod socket. Keeping lifter covered with oil, use Type 1 push rod with press to force push rod socket into lifter body. Install lock ring when push rod socket is compressed enough.

4) Install lifters in crankcase bores. Install remaining parts in reverse of disassembly. Make sure that push rods are located in socket of lifters and rocker arms. Adjust valve lifters.

VALVE CLEARANCE ADJUSTMENT

1) Back out adjusting screws until ball end is flush with under side of rocker arm. Turn crankshaft until No. 1 cylinder is in firing position (No. 1 mark on distributor body aligned with rotor). Turn adjusting screws for both rocker arms of No. 1 cylinder until tips just touch valve stems (zero clearance).

2) Turn screws 2 additional turns clockwise and tighten lock nuts. Turn crankshaft so rotor moves counterclockwise in 90° increments and repeat adjustment for remaining cylinders.

VANAGON 2.0L AIR-COOLED 4-CYLINDER (Cont.)

PISTONS, PINS & RINGS

CYLINDERS

Removal

Remove engine from vehicle. Remove cylinder head nuts from studs and remove cylinder head. Mark cylinders for reassembly reference. Remove deflector plates from under cylinders and pull cylinders from pistons.

Installation

1) Check seating surfaces of cylinders on both ends. Make sure seating areas are perfectly clean and true before installing cylinders. Stagger ring gaps 120° apart with oil ring gap facing upward. "TOP" mark on rings must face up.

2) Apply oil to cylinder, piston rings, and piston pin. Compress rings with ring compressor (US 1008A). Install new base gasket on crankcase side and slide cylinder over piston.

Fig. 4: Location and Seating of Cylinder Seal

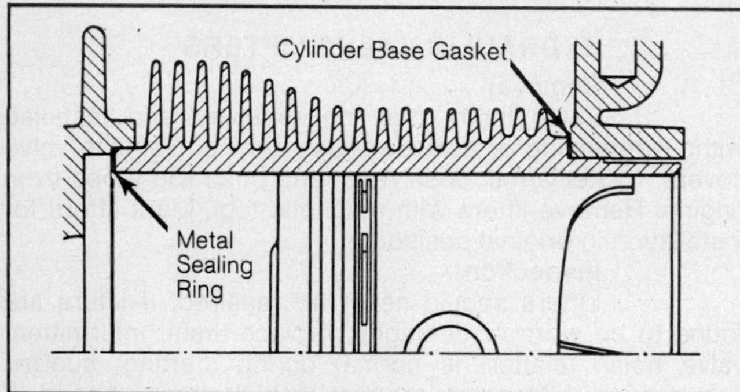
Cylinder Base Gasket
Metal Sealing Ring

Install new seal when installing cylinder.

3) Make sure studs do not contact cooling fins when cylinder is completely seated against crankcase. Install cylinder deflector plates and remaining components in reverse of removal.

Fig. 5: Installing Cylinder Assembly

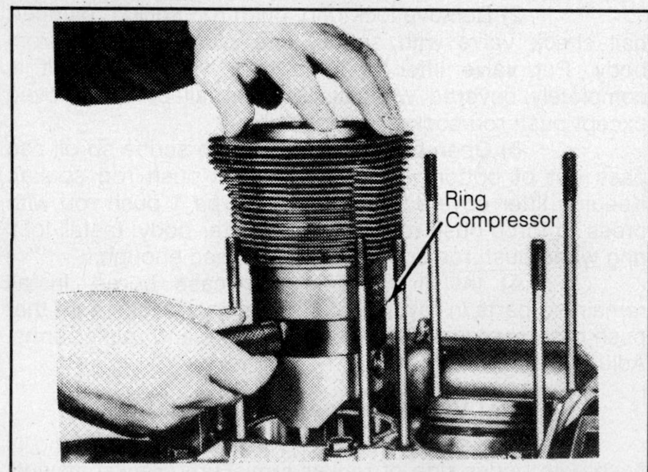
Ring Compressor

Make sure studs do not contact cooling fins.

FITTING PISTONS

1) With piston and cylinder removed, measure clearance between piston and cylinder. Measure piston at 90° to piston pin about 3/8" (16 mm) from edge of skirt. Measure cylinder at several points with bore gauge, using largest reading to determine clearance.

2) If clearance exceeds .008" (.20 mm) replace piston and cylinder as a set. New piston must be of same weight grade as original or within 10 g of original piston weight.

3) Piston size, weight and installation position are marked on top of piston. Pistons and cylinders are available in .020" (.50 mm) and .040 (1.00 mm) oversizes. *See Fig. 6.*

Fig. 6: Top of Piston with Detail of Markings

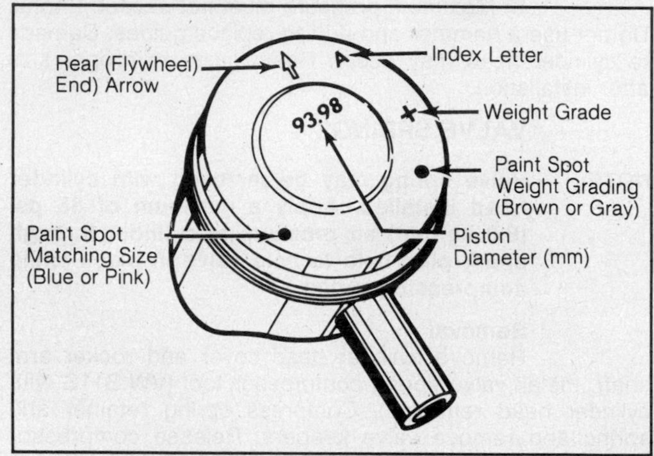
Rear (Flywheel) End) Arrow
Index Letter
A
93.98
Weight Grade
Paint Spot Weight Grading (Brown or Gray)
Paint Spot Matching Size (Blue or Pink)
Piston Diameter (mm)

Oversizes of .020" (.50 mm) and .040" (1.0 mm) available.

NOTE: Piston alone may be replaced with one of matching size. Only pistons of same size and weight grade should be installed in same engine.

4) New piston rings are size graded to match piston/cylinder sets. Measure ring gap with ring installed about 3/16" into cylinder. If ring end gap exceeds .035" (.90 mm) for compression rings or .037" (.95 mm) for oil scraper, replace cylinder or rings.

5) Install rings on piston and measure ring side clearance using feeler gauge. If clearance exceeds .005" (.12 mm) on upper and middle rings or .004" (.10 mm) on oil scraper ring, piston must be replaced.

Fig. 7: Measuring Piston Ring Side Clearance

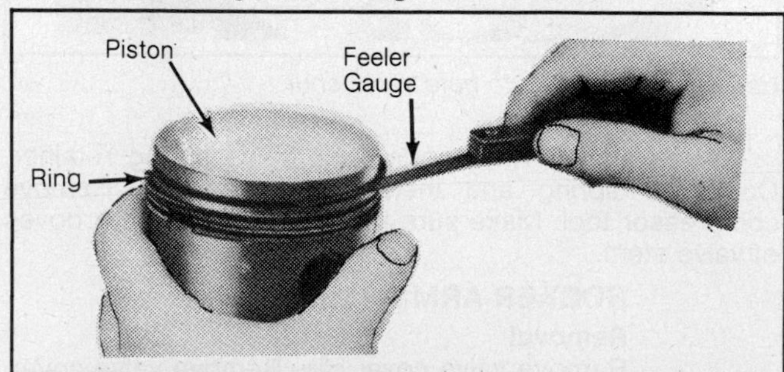
Piston
Feeler Gauge
Ring

If limit is exceeded, replace piston.

PISTON PINS

Removal

Mark cylinders and pistons for proper reassembly. Remove cylinders. Remove piston pin circlips. Push piston pin out of piston.

Installation

1) Check fit of pin in piston. At room temperature piston pin should be light push fit. If pin is too loose, both pin and piston must be replaced.

VANAGON 2.0L AIR-COOLED 4-CYLINDER (Cont.)

2) Install 1 circlip in piston on side facing flywheel. Position piston on connecting rod. Arrow on crown of piston must point to flywheel. Push piston pin through piston. Replace remaining circlip. Replace remaining components in reverse of removal.

NOTE: Piston may be heated to ease pin installation.

CRANKCASE, CRANKSHAFT, MAIN & CONNECTING ROD BEARINGS

CRANKCASE

Crankcase must be taken apart to replace connecting rods, connecting rod bearings, and main bearings. It is also necessary to disassemble crankcase to remove crankshaft, camshaft, and camshaft bearings.

Disassembly

1) Remove engine from vehicle. Mount securely in engine stand. Remove exhaust system and both heat exchangers. Remove cylinder heads, cylinders, and pistons. Remove clutch, flywheel (drive plate on automatic models), and fan with pulley. Remove distributor, distributor drive, and fuel pump.

2) Remove blower housing with alternator. Remove engine carrier with support bracket. Remove oil cooler, oil filter, flange, and oil pump assembly. *See Oil Pump Removal.* Remove oil strainer cover and filler pipe. Remove valve lifters and keep in order for reassembly.

3) Remove six 10 mm case half nuts and bolts. Remove all 8 mm nuts and bolts from crankcase flange. DO NOT insert tools between crankcase flanges to separate halves. Damage to machine surfaces will occur. If stuck together, use rubber hammer to loosen right half from left.

Reassembly

1) Thoroughly clean and inspect both crankcase halves. Remove oil sealing compound from mating surfaces, case bolts, studs, and washers. Blow out oil passages with compressed air. Check studs for tightness. Replace "O" ring on oil suction pipe.

2) Install crankshaft, with connecting rods, in left side crankcase half. Make sure dowel pins are properly aligned with bearing holes. Install camshaft bearings and camshaft. *See Camshaft Installation.* Coat camshaft plug edge using liquid sealer. Spread liquid sealer over mating surfaces of crankcase halves.

3) Coat case half bolt (10 mm) heads and washers with sealer and install in left crankcase. Install new plastic vibration dampers (part No. 021 101 107) on shank of case half bolts whether or not originally equipped. Mate case halves. Make sure oil pickup mount hole is aligned with bolt hole in case.

4) Coat locking nuts and washers for case half bolts with sealer. Install nuts with locking rings outward. Tighten case half nuts while holding bolts stationary. Turn crankshaft to check for free movement. Coat bolt heads and nuts of 8 mm bolts with sealer. Install bolts and tighten.

CAUTION: Do not tighten oil strainer cover nut beyond 9 ft. lbs. (12 N.m). Internal case damage will occur if torque exceeds specification.

5) Always use new sealing washer on 8 mm through bolt that secures oil pickup. Install flywheel and check crankshaft end play. *See Crankshaft End Play.* Install new crankshaft oil seals. *See Crankshaft Front Oil Seal Replacement and Crankshaft Rear Oil Seal Replacement.* Install distributor drive. *See Distributor Drive Installation.* Install remaining components in reverse of removal procedure.

MAIN & CONNECTING ROD BEARING SERVICE

1) Mount crankshaft and connecting rod assembly securely in vise. Remove hub, slinger, and No. 4 main bearing. Remove snap ring securing brass distributor drive gear and steel crankshaft gear to crankshaft. Remove distributor drive gear and crankshaft gear on press with plates (VW 457) or using puller.

2) Remove number 3 bearing. Remove connecting rods, keeping caps and rods together for proper reassembly. Thoroughly clean and inspect crankshaft. Blow out oil passages with compressed air. Check runout of crankshaft. If runout exceeds .0008" (.020 mm), turn crankshaft to next undersize.

3) Check crankshaft journals for wear. If journals are worn more than .0012" (.030 mm), turn crankshaft to next undersize. Lubricate and install number 3 bearing with hole for locating dowel toward rear (flywheel) end of crankshaft.

4) Heat steel and brass crankshaft gears to approximately 176°F (80°C) in an oil bath and install on crankshaft over Woodruff key. Chamfer on steel gear bore must face number 3 main bearing journal. Install spacer, brass distributor drive gear and circlip.

5) Lubricate and install No. 1 and No. 4 main bearings on crankshaft. Install lower bearing half of No. 2 in crankcase, ensuring that dowel in crankcase engages hole in bearing shell. Turn bearings on crankshaft to properly position oil holes and dowel holes.

6) Install bearing halves in cap and rod so that tangs in shells engage notches in rod end. Fit to crankshaft with numbers on rod and cap on same side.

NOTE: Lightly tap both sides of connecting rod with hammer to eliminate slight pinching of bearing shells when installing connecting rod.

Fig. 8: Checking Connecting Rod Side Clearance

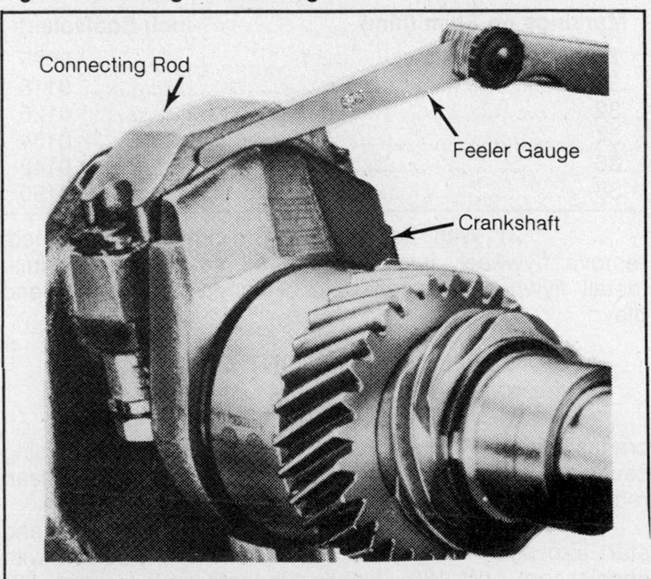
Connecting Rod
Feeler Gauge
Crankshaft

Side play limit is .028" (.70 mm).

VANAGON 2.0L AIR-COOLED 4-CYLINDER (Cont.)

7) Check connecting rod side play with feeler gauge. If side play exceeds .028" (.70 mm), replace connecting rod. Install crankshaft and connecting rod assembly. Check crankshaft end play. *See Crankshaft End Play.*

CRANKSHAFT END PLAY

1) Crankshaft end play is checked with engine assembled. Install flywheel with 2 shims, but do not install "O" ring and crankshaft oil seal. Attach dial indicator to crankcase and measure back and forth movement of crankshaft.

Fig. 9: Checking Crankshaft End Play

Flywheel
VW387
Adjust End
Play With Shims

End play limit is .005" (.13 mm).

2) Calculate necessary thickness of third shim. Install third shim and recheck end play. Thickness of shim is etched on face of shim. Always use 3 shims to obtain correct end play.

END PLAY SHIMS

Markings on Shim (mm)	Inch Equivalent
.24	.0095
.30	.0118
.32	.0126
.34	.0134
.36	.0142
.38	.0150

3) With correct shim thickness determined, remove flywheel. Install O-ring, oil seal, and 3 shims. Install flywheel. Tighten bolts. Recheck crankshaft end play.

CRANKSHAFT FRONT OIL SEAL

Removal & Installation

1) Remove cooling fan. Pull fan hub off crankshaft with puller (VW 185). Pry old seal out, using caution to avoid damaging crankshaft or crankcase. Clean recess and chamfer edges of seal seat, if necessary.

2) Coat outside of seal lightly with sealer and start into position by hand. Press into final position with special tool (VW 190). Lightly lubricate new fan hub "O" ring before completing installation. Install fan and tighten bolts.

CRANKSHAFT REAR OIL SEAL

Removal & Installation

1) Remove flywheel and carefully pry out old seal. Clean seat and chamfer edges if necessary. Apply thin film of sealer to outside edges and start seal into recess by hand.

2) Seal lip must point toward crankcase. Complete installation with special tool (VW 191). Lubricate contact surface on flywheel "O" ring. Install flywheel.

DISTRIBUTOR DRIVE INSTALLATION

1) When crankcase has been assembled and remaining components installed, distributor drive must be installed. Rotate crankshaft until No. 1 piston is at TDC of compression stroke.

2) Align timing mark on pulley with 0° mark on ignition timing scale. Insert distributor drive with slot at a 12° angle to center line of engine. Small segment of slot faces coil (left) side. *See Fig. 10.*

Fig. 10: Engine Distributor Drive Installation Position

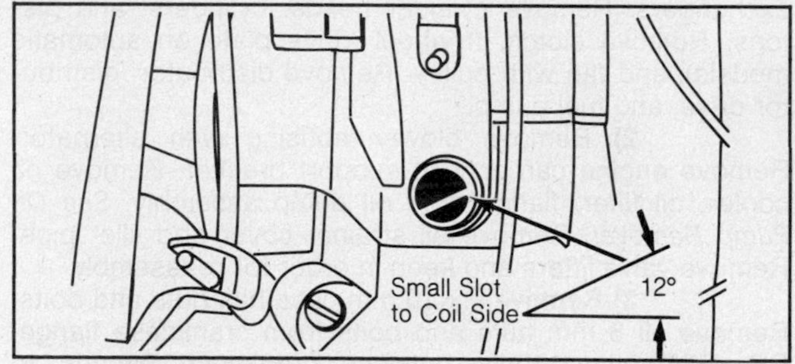
Small Slot
to Coil Side
12°

Insert with slot at 12° to engine centerline.

CAMSHAFT

CAMSHAFT INSTALLATION

1) With camshaft removed, check riveting of camshaft gear to camshaft. Measure camshaft runout on center bearing journal. Maximum allowable runout is .0015" (.040 mm). If beyond limit, replace camshaft.

2) Check gear backlash with camshaft and crankshaft installed in crankcase half. Correct backlash is 0-.002" (0-.05 mm). When backlash is correct, rotate crankshaft backwards (counterclockwise). Gears have correct fit if camshaft does not try to lift ("walk") out of bearings.

Fig. 11: Position of Camshaft Timing Gear

Camshaft
Gear
Crankshaft
Gear

The "O" must be between punch marks.

VANAGON 2.0L AIR-COOLED 4-CYLINDER (Cont.)

3) If camshaft "walks" out of bearings, teeth on camshaft gear have wrong pitch radius for crankshaft gear. Camshafts with gears that have various pitch radii are available. Pitch radius is stamped on inner face of timing gear. Range of radii is "-5" to zero to "+5".

4) Install camshaft with "O" stamped in tooth on outside of camshaft gear between 2 teeth with punch marks on crankshaft gear. Assemble crankcase halves as previously outlined. *See Fig. 11.*

CAMSHAFT END PLAY

Camshaft end play is checked with camshaft installed in left crankcase half. Crankshaft is not installed for this measurement. Measure back and forth movement of camshaft with a dial indicator. If end play exceeds .006" (.16 mm), replace camshaft and/or bearings.

VALVE TIMING

Install camshaft with "O" stamped in tooth on outside of camshaft gear between 2 teeth with punch marks on steel crankshaft gear. *See Fig. 11.*

ENGINE OILING

OIL CAPACITY

Oil capacity is 3.2 qts. (3.0L) without filter change, 3.7 qts. (3.5L) with filter change. Oil filter is full-flow, throw-away type.

OIL PRESSURE

Oil pressure should be 29 psi (2.0 kg/cm²) at 2000 RPM with oil temperature at 176°F (80°C). Oil pressure warning light should go out at pressure of 2-6.5 psi (.15-.45 kg/cm²).

PRESSURE REGULATOR VALVES

Oil pressure relief valve, used to protect oil cooler from excessive pressure, is located in crankcase between oil pump and oil filter. Oil pressure control valve, used to control oil pressure to bearings, is located in side of crankcase.

Fig. 12: Exploded View of Relief Valve Components

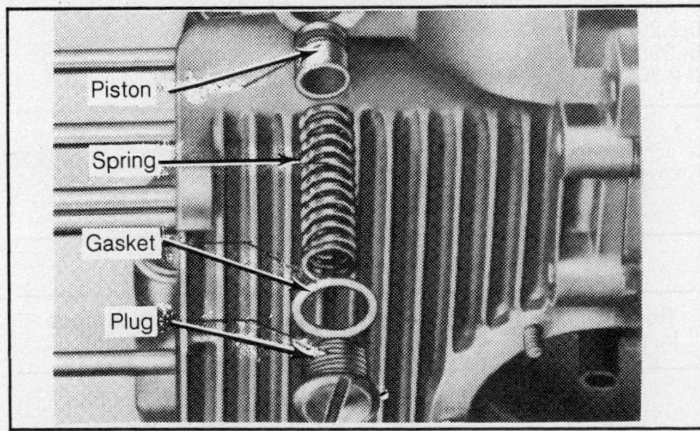
Piston
Spring
Gasket
Plug

ENGINE OILING SYSTEM

Full pressure lubrication system utilizes a gear-type oil pump and is installed in front of engine and driven by camshaft. Oil is pumped through oil filter, oil cooler and into main oil galleys in crankcase.

Crankshaft main and connecting rod journals are oiled through cross-drilled oil passages in crankshaft. Oil is pumped to camshaft through oil passages that also lubricate hydraulic lifters. Oil flows through push rods to lubricate rocker arms and shafts.

Valve stems are lubricated by splash oil from rocker arms. Excess oil flows back into crankcase through push rod tubes. Cylinder walls and piston pins are lubricated by splash oil.

Fig. 13: Distribution of Oil For Engine Lubrication

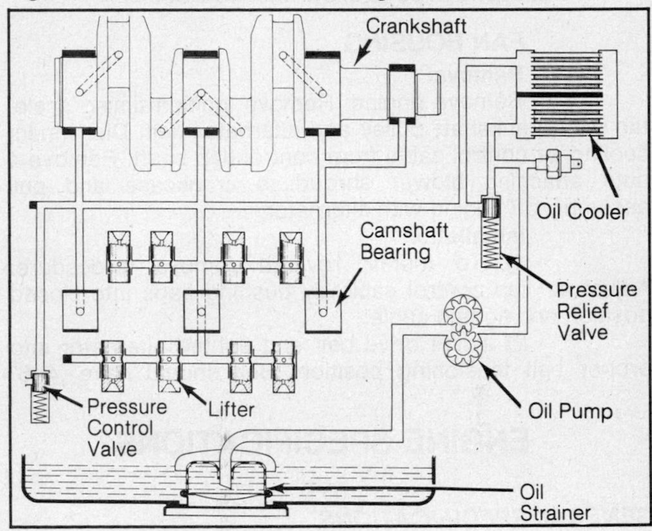
Crankshaft
Oil Cooler
Camshaft Bearing
Pressure Relief Valve
Pressure Control Valve
Lifter
Oil Pump
Oil Strainer

OIL COOLER

Removal

To remove oil cooler, remove cooling fan housing with alternator. Remove three 6 mm nuts with washers attaching oil cooler to front of crankcase. Remove support strap and oil cooler as a unit.

Installation

Oil cooler should be pressure tested before installation. Maximum test pressure is 85 psi (5.9 kg/cm²) measured with tester (VW 661/2). To install, reverse removal procedure. Always use new rubber seals when installing oil cooler.

OIL PUMP

Removal

Remove engine. Remove 4 nuts holding oil pump housing. Using 2 levers, pry oil pump out of crankcase. Oil pump insert can be removed with puller (VW 803). Always use new 6 mm locking nuts when reinstalling pump insert.

Inspection

Check housing for wear. Make sure fixed post on pump insert has not moved in case. Measure gear backlash for wear. Backlash must not exceed .008" (.20 mm). Replace "O" ring on insert before reassembly of pump.

Installation

Install new gasket to block. Hand turn engine until oil pump drive shaft is fully engaged in camshaft. Reverse removal procedure for remaining components.

ENGINE COOLING

THERMOSTAT

At 185-194°F (85-90°C), thermostat length should be at least 1 13/16" (46 mm) measured from shoulders on bellows shaft.

Volkswagen Engines

VANAGON 2.0L AIR-COOLED 4-CYLINDER (Cont.)

COOLING SYSTEM

Engine is cooled by a radial blower mounted to front end of crankshaft. Blower draws air through opening in fan housing at front of engine. Fan housing is 2-piece unit, mounted around blower and attached to crankcase.

As air is drawn in, it is directed over finned cylinders and cylinder heads. Air flow is controlled by flaps attached to thermostat by cable. As engine warms up, thermostat opens flaps to allow total flow of air.

FAN HOUSING

Removal

Remove engine. Remove ignition timing scale, fan with crankshaft pulley and alternator belt. Disconnect cooling air control cable from control flap shaft. Remove 4 nuts attaching blower shroud to crankcase and pull assembly off engine with alternator.

Installation

1) To install, reverse removal procedure. Adjust air flap control cable by pushing flaps into closed position and tighten cable.

2) Install drive belt and tighten alternator into proper belt tensioning position. Belt should have .4-.6" (10-15 mm) deflection when pressed firmly in middle with thumb. Install cover plates and engine.

TIGHTENING SPECIFICATIONS

Application	Ft. Lbs. (N.m)
Connecting Rod Nut	25 (34)
Crankcase Half Nuts (8 mm)	14 (19)
Crankcase Half Locking Nuts (10 mm)	22 (30)
Cylinder Head Nuts	22 (30)
Rocker Shaft-to-Cylinder Head Nuts	11 (15)
Heat Exchanger-to-Cylinder Head	14 (19)
Oil Cover Plate-to-Crankcase Nut [1]	9 (12)
Drive Plate-to-Crankshaft	65 (90)
Hub-to-Crankshaft Bolt	22 (30)
Fan-to-Hub	14 (19)
Engine-to-Transmission	22 (30)
Oil Pump-to-Crankcase	18 (25)
Oil Cooler-to-Crankcase	14 (19)
Flywheel-to-Crankshaft	80 (110)
Torque Converter-to-Drive Plate	18 (25)
Pressure Plate-to-Flywheel	18 (25)

[1] – Crankcase damage will occur if torque exceeded.

ENGINE SPECIFICATIONS

GENERAL SPECIFICATIONS

Year	DISPLACEMENT		Fuel System	HP@RPM	Torque Ft. Lbs.@RPM	Compr. Ratio	BORE		STROKE	
	Cu. In.	Liters					In.	mm	In.	mm
1983	120	2.0	Fuel Injection	67@4200	101@3000	7.3:1	3.70	94	2.80	71

VALVES

Engine Size & Valve	Head Diam. In. (mm)	Face Angle	Seat Angle	Seat Width In. (mm)	Stem Diameter In. (mm)	Stem Clearance In. (mm)	Valve Lift In. (mm)
2.0L							
Intake	1.547 (39.3)	29.5°	30°	.070-.086 (1.80-2.20)	.313 (7.95)	.024 (.60)	....
Exhaust	1.299 (33.0)	45°	45°	.070-.098 (1.80-2.50)	.351 (8.92)	.024 (.60)	....

PISTONS, PINS, RINGS

Engine	PISTONS	PINS		RINGS		
	Clearance In. (mm)	Piston Fit In. (mm)	Rod Fit In. (mm)	Ring No.	End Gap In. (mm)	Side Clearance In. (mm)
2.0L	.001-.002 (.03-.06)	[1]	[1]	1	.016-.026 (.40-.65)	.002-.003 (.04-.07)
				2	.016-.026 (.40-.65)	.002-.003 (.04-.07)
				3	.010-.016 (.25-40)	.001-.002 (.02-.05)

[1] – Push fit with light thumb pressure at room temperature.

VANAGON 2.0L AIR-COOLED 4-CYLINDER (Cont.)

ENGINE SPECIFICATIONS (Cont.)

CRANKSHAFT MAIN & CONNECTING ROD BEARINGS

	MAIN BEARINGS				CONNECTING ROD BEARINGS		
Engine	Journal Diam. In. (mm)	Clearance In. (mm)	Thrust Bearing	Crankshaft End Play In. (mm)	Journal Diam. In. (mm)	Clearance In. (mm)	Side Play In. (mm)
2.0L							
No. 1	2.3609-2.3617 (59.967-59.987)	.0016-.0039 (.041-.099)	No. 1	.003-.005 (.07-.13)	1.9677-1.9685 (49.98-50.00)	.0008-.0027 (.020-.069)	.004-.016 [1] (.10-.41)
No. 2	2.3609-2.3617 (59.967-59.987)	.0012-.0035 (.030-.089)					
No. 3	2.3609-2.3617 (59.967-59.987)	.0016-.0039 (.041-.099)					
No. 4	1.5739-1.5748 (39.977-40.025)	.0020-.0039 (.051-.099)					

[1] – Limit .028" (.7 mm).

Volkswagen Engines

4-CYLINDER DIESEL & TURBO-DIESEL

Jetta, Quantum, Rabbit, Rabbit Pickup & Vanagon

ENGINE CODING

ENGINE IDENTIFICATION

Engine identification is stamped on left side of cylinder block on machined pad near No. 3 cylinder.

ENGINE IDENTIFICATION

Application	Code
Quantum & Jetta, Turbo Diesel	CY
Vanagon	CS
All Others	JK

ENGINE, CYLINDER HEAD & MANIFOLDS

ENGINE

NOTE: **Engine and transmission assembly must be LOWERED out of Rabbit models as a unit. Removal and installation procedures for Quantum not available from manufacturer.**

Removal (All Except Quantum & Vanagon)

1) Disconnect battery ground. Open coolant expansion tank. Open heater valve and drain all coolant from system at thermostat flange (engine cool). Remove radiator with fan. Remove alternator and detach fuel filter from body.

NOTE: **Never drain coolant while engine is hot. Doing so could cause engine block or cylinder head to warp.**

2) Disconnect wires for fuel shut-off solenoid, glow plugs, oil pressure switch and coolant temperature sensor. Disconnect hoses for heater and expansion tank. Remove fuel supply and return lines and disconnect accelerator cable with bracket from injection pump. Disconnect cold start cable.

3) On air conditioned vehicles, remove air conditioner compressor and mounting brackets and set out of way without disconnecting hoses. On all models, disconnect wires from starter and back-up light switch and ground from transmission mount. On manual transmission models, detach clutch cable and remove relay shaft lever.

4) Remove exhaust flex pipe nuts or spring clips. Disconnect drive shafts from drive flanges. Remove starter, horn, oil filter and front engine mount. Remove axle nuts (vehicle must be on ground) and disconnect lower ball joints from bearing housings. Remove drive shaft while holding strut assembly away from vehicle.

5) Reconnect ball joints so vehicle may be lowered onto wheels. Remove complete rear mount. Remove right front wheel. Attach sling (US 1105) to engine and lift slightly. On manual transmission models, remove relay shaft and gearshift lever rods.

6) On all models, remove bolts holding side mounts to body. Lower engine and transmission assembly to dolly. Raise vehicle to clear and remove assembly.

Installation

To install, reverse removal procedures noting that fuel supply and return union screws are not interchanged. Fuel return pipe union screw is marked "OUT" on hexagonal head.

Removal (Vanagon)

1) Disconnect battery ground. Remove top of air cleaner. Remove lower engine cover. Open coolant expansion tank cap. Drain cooling system (engine cool). Disconnect lower hose from water pump at connecting pipe to radiator. Disconnect center hose from water pump.

NOTE: **Never drain coolant while engine is hot. Doing so could cause engine block or cylinder head to warp.**

2) Disconnect wiring from oil pressure switch, temperature sensors and glow plugs. Disconnect all remaining fuel, coolant, emission control and vacuum lines and position out of way. Disconnect accelerator cable from pump lever and bracket. Disconnect cold start cable.

3) Disconnect wire from fuel shut-off solenoid. Remove coolant reservoir. Remove oil fill cap and dipstick. Remove nuts from rear engine mounts (leave bolts in place). Remove all (7) engine and transmission mounting bolts. Remove bolts. Remove support member. Support engine with a crane and adapter (3058 or equivalent).

4) Remove nuts from front engine mount and remove engine mount bolts. Lower engine and transmission assembly until engine can be separated from transmission. Support transmission, remove engine from transmission and lower out of vehicle.

Installation

To install, reverse removal procedures noting that fuel supply and return union screws are not interchanged. Fuel return pipe union screw is marked "OUT" on hexagonal head.

CYLINDER HEAD & MANIFOLDS

NOTE: **Cylinder head may be removed and installed with engine in vehicle. Complete removal and installation procedures for Quantum and Vanagon not available from manufacturer.**

Removal (All Except Quantum & Vanagon)

1) Remove air cleaner and ducting, then drain cooling system (engine cool). Remove camshaft drive belt. Unbolt thermostat housing from water pump. Disconnect battery ground strap.

NOTE: **Never drain coolant while engine is hot. Doing so could cause engine block or cylinder head to warp.**

2) Disconnect accelerator cable from injection pump. Detach fuel lines at injectors by unscrewing unions. Disconnect wire from glow plug bus, temperature sending wire and any other wires which could interfere with removal of cylinder head.

3) Remove spring clips holding exhaust pipe to manifold using clip remover tool (3059 or equivalent). Unbolt exhaust pipe support from engine and transaxle assembly (if equipped). From underneath vehicle, remove bolts and nuts holding exhaust manifold to cylinder head. Remove manifold from head.

4) Disconnect coolant hoses from head and remove any other hoses which may interfere with head

4-CYLINDER DIESEL & TURBO-DIESEL (Cont.)

removal. Remove cylinder head cover bolts and retaining plate. Carefully lift off cover and gasket. Loosen head bolts in reverse order of tightening sequence. *See Fig. 2.* Lift off head. Remove injectors and glow plugs to prevent damage while working on head.

5) Remove combustion chamber inserts by placing drift through injector hole and tapping out with hammer. Prior to installation, pre-chamber inserts must be reinstalled. When installing injectors, new heat shields must be installed between each injector and cylinder head. Place new shield in position with recess upward, toward injector. Tighten injector.

NOTE: Combustion chamber inserts are NOT supplied as spare parts on latest models. If inserts are damaged it will be necessary to replace cylinder head.

Installation

1) Clean gasket surface and ensure that cylinder head and block are not warped. Maximum distortion of .004" (.010 mm) is allowed. If installing on original piston and block assembly select a new head gasket that has the same marks as the original.

2) To determine proper gasket, measure projection of piston above block when at TDC. Select proper gasket from following table. Gasket must be installed with word "OBEN" facing up.

AVAILABLE CYLINDER HEAD GASKETS

Piston Projection In. (mm)	Gasket Thickness In. (mm)	Ident. Notches
Quantum		
.026-.031 (.67-.80)	....	1
.032-.035 (.81-.90)	....	2
.036-.040 (.91-1.02)	....	3
All Others		
.025-.032 (.63-.82)	.055 (1.40)	1
.033-.036 (.83-.92)	.059 (1.50)	2
.037-.040 (.93-1.02)	.063 (1.60)	3

NOTE: Due to the aluminum construction of the head, do not use metal brushes or scrapers to clean gasket sealing surface or combustion chambers. Use solvent and wooden or plastic scrapers to remove foreign material. Do not mar piston tops when cleaning cylinder block. Ensure that all bolt holes and cylinder bores are absolutely free of debris prior to installation head or bolts.

Fig. 1: Measuring Piston Projection

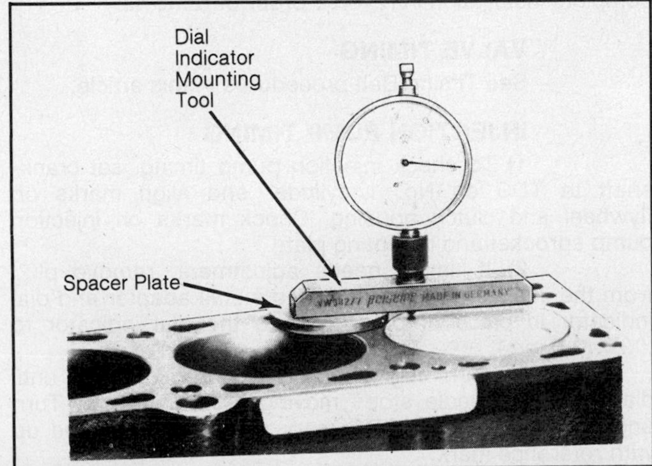
Dial Indicator Mounting Tool
Spacer Plate

3) Lower head carefully onto gasket. Use guide pins (3070) or 2 of the outermost bolts and washers to keep gasket and head aligned with block. Diesel engines use either 6-point, head 11 mm bolts or 12-point, 12 mm head bolts. The 12-point bolts must be replaced with every engine repair.

4) On the 6-point bolts, tighten in 3 steps to specifications listed in table. After the third step, warm up engine until fan cycles on. Torque once again, without backing off, to third step specification. After 1000 miles of use, retorque by loosening bolts 30° at a time and then tighten again to third step specification.

5) On the 12-point bolts, tighten in 3 steps to specifications listed in table. After the second step, tighten the bolts an additional 1/2 turn. Warm up engine until fan cycles on. Tighten an additional 1/4 turn. After 1000 miles of use, retorque an additional 1/4 turn. To complete installation, reverse removal procedure.

CYLINDER HEAD BOLT TIGHTENING

Application	Ft. Lbs. (N.m)
6-Point Bolts	
Step No. 1	35 (50)
Step No. 2	50 (70)
Step No. 3	65 (90)
12-Point Bolts	
Step No. 1	29 (40)
Step No. 2	43 (75)
Step No. 3	[1]

[1] – For third step of procedure, see cylinder head installation procedure.

Fig. 2: Cylinder Head Tightening Sequence

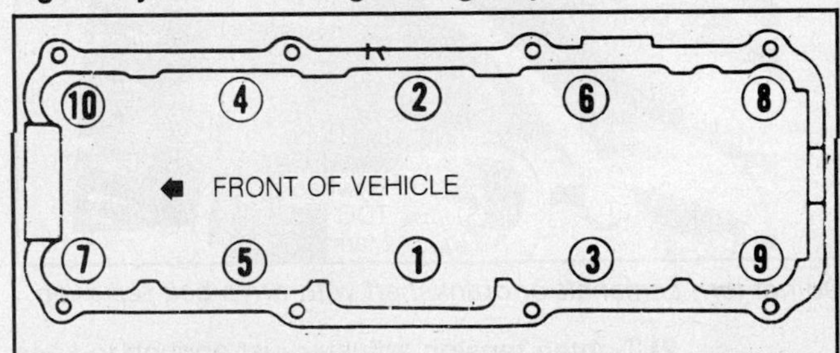
10
4
2
6
8
FRONT OF VEHICLE
7
5
1
3
9

Loosen in reverse order.

CAMSHAFT

TIMING BELT

NOTE: Sprockets do not have to be removed to replace drive belt.

Removal

1) Loosen alternator and remove V-belt. Remove crankshaft V-belt pulley. Remove air cleaner and ducting. Remove drive belt and cylinder head cover. Remove timing plug on top of bell housing. Rotate engine to bring No. 1 piston to TDC. Check that TDC mark on flywheel is aligned with reference.

4-CYLINDER DIESEL & TURBO-DIESEL (Cont.)

2) Using locking tool (2065A for Vanagon, 2065 for other models) lock camshaft in position. Align tool by turning camshaft until one end of tool touches cylinder head. Measure gap at other end with feeler gauge. Insert feeler gauges of 1/2 thickness measured between tool and cylinder head at each end of tool.

3) Lock injection pump sprocket at TDC with special pin (2064). Loosen belt tensioner and remove timing belt from sprockets.

CAUTION: Do not TURN camshaft or crankshaft with drive belt removed.

Installation

1) Ensure that flywheel is still aligned with TDC mark. With camshaft and injection pump locked in place, loosen camshaft sprocket bolt 1/2 turn. Lightly tap camshaft gear loose from camshaft. Install drive belt so there is no slack between camshaft sprocket and injection pump and injection pump and crankshaft sprocket.

Fig. 3: Flywheel TDC Mark and Camshaft Locking Tool

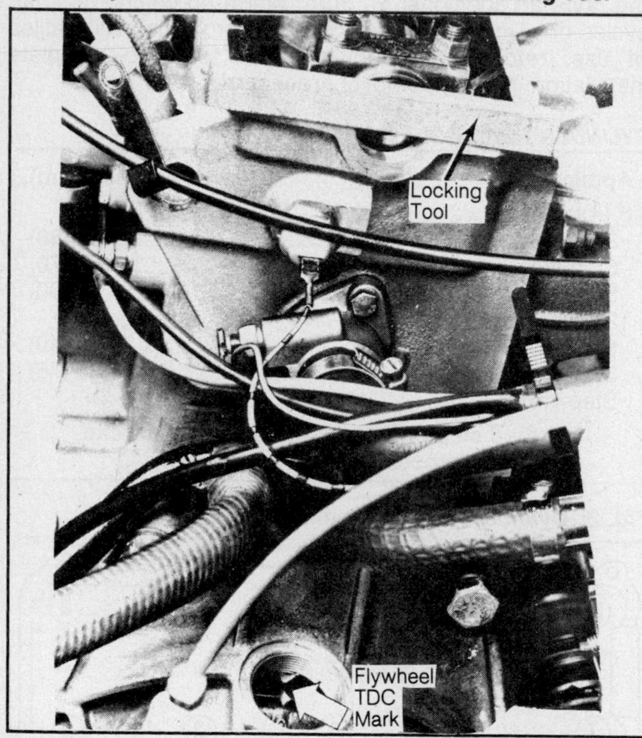
Locking Tool
Flywheel TDC Mark

Do not turn camshaft or crankshaft with drive belt removed.

2) Tighten tension adjuster just enough to keep belt firmly in place. Remove injection pump locking pin. Adjust belt tension by turning tensioner until scale reads 12-13 on tension adjuster tool (VW 210). Tighten camshaft sprocket bolt and tensioner adjuster lock nut. Remove lock from camshaft.

3) Turn crankshaft 2 revolutions in direction of engine rotation. Using a rubber hammer, strike belt once between camshaft sprocket and injection pump sprocket. Recheck belt tension and install remaining components in reverse order of removal. Check injection pump timing.

CAMSHAFT

Removal

Remove timing belt. Loosen bearing caps in following sequence: 5, 1, and 3, then loosen caps 2 and 4 diagonally. Bearing caps are numbered front (sprocket end) to rear (flywheel end).

Inspection

1) Number and remove cam followers, then reinstall camshaft using only end (1 and 5) bearing caps. Check axial play of camshaft with dial indicator. If play exceeds .006" (.15 mm), either head or camshaft is worn and must be replaced.

2) To measure camshaft bearing clearance, install caps 1 at a time and check with either a dial indicator or Plastigage. Check camshaft runout by installing shaft between centers and applying dial indicator at center bearing journal. Runout must not exceed .0004" (.010 mm) when camshaft is rotated.

Fig. 4: Measuring Camshaft End Play

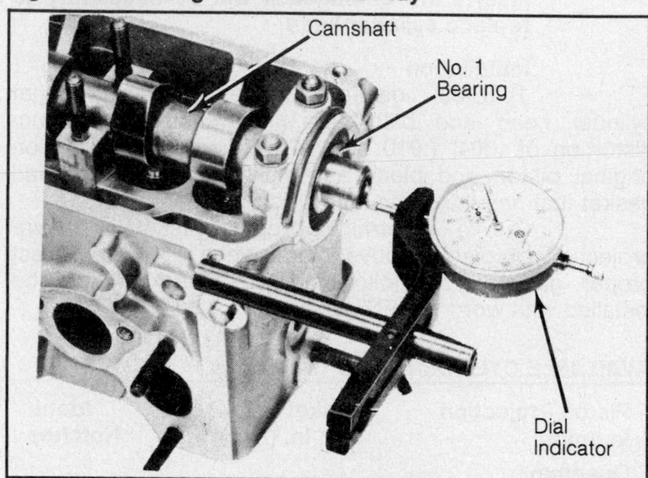
Camshaft
No. 1 Bearing
Dial Indicator

End play must not exceed .006" (.15 mm).

3) Inspect cam lobes, followers, and all bearing surfaces. Ensure that all oil passages are clean. Replace any components showing signs of pitting, galling or signs of seizure.

Installation

1) Lightly lubricate all components for assembly. Install cam followers in original bores with matching adjusting discs. Place camshaft and number 2 and 4 bearing caps in position with cam lobes of No. 1 cylinder pointing upward.

2) Gradually tighten all 4 bearing cap nuts until camshaft is fully seated. Install caps 5, 3, and 1. Use seal installer (10-203 or equivalent) to install front oil seal and complete installation in reverse order of removal.

VALVE TIMING

See Timing Belt procedures in this article.

INJECTION PUMP TIMING

1) To check injection pump timing, set crankshaft to TDC on No. 1 cylinder and align marks on flywheel and clutch housing. Check marks on injection pump sprocket and mounting plate.

2) If timing needs adjustment, remove plug from the injection pump cover and install adapter and dial indicator in place of plug. Preload the dial indicator to .097" (2.5 mm).

3) Turn engine slowly counterclockwise until dial indicator needle stops moving. Zero indicator. Turn engine clockwise until TDC mark on flywheel is lined up with reference mark.

4-CYLINDER DIESEL & TURBO-DIESEL (Cont.)

4) Check dial indicator against specifications listed in table. If out of adjustment, loosen bolts on mounting plate and support. Turn pump to adjust timing and tighten bolts.

INJECTION PUMP TIMING SPECIFICATIONS

Application	Range In. (mm)
Quantum	[1] .037-.041 (.95-1.05)
Rabbit & Rabbit Pickup	
With no paint dot	[2] .033-.037 (.83-.93)
With yellow paint dot	[3] .043-.047 (1.10-1.20)
Vanagon	[2] .031-.035 (.78-.88)

[1] – Set to .039" (1.00 mm).
[2] – Set to .034" (.86 mm).
[3] – Set to .045" (1.15 mm).

VALVES

VALVE ARRANGEMENT

E-I-E-I-I-E-I-E (Front-to-rear).

Fig. 5: End View of Camshaft and Valve Assembly

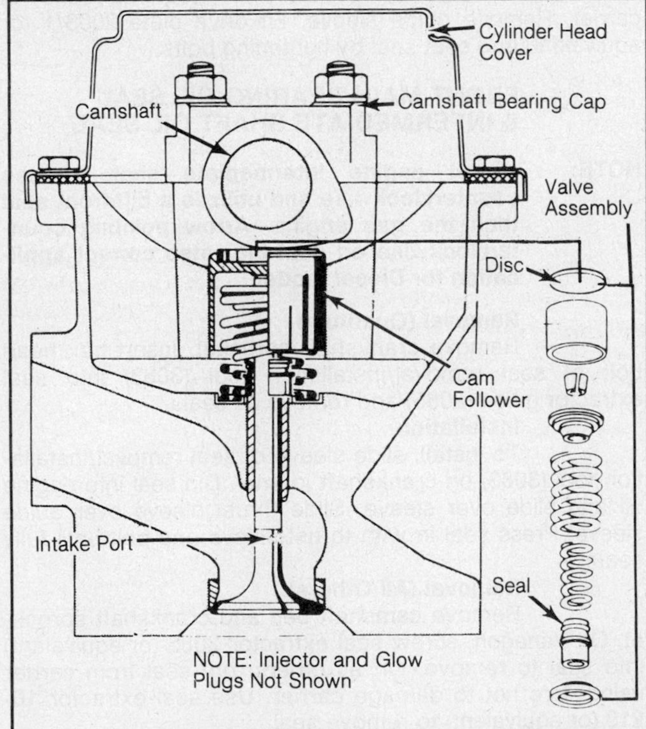
Cylinder Head Cover
Camshaft
Camshaft Bearing Cap
Valve Assembly
Disc
Cam Follower
Intake Port
Seal
NOTE: Injector and Glow Plugs Not Shown

VALVE GUIDE SERVICING

1) To check for wear, insert NEW valve in clean valve guide until stem end is flush with spring end of guide. Use dial indicator to check that lateral (rocking) movement is not more than .051" (1.3 mm) when moved back and forth against indicator.

2) Prior to replacing worn guides, check that head is not cracked and that valve seats can be refaced. Press out old guides and coat new guides with oil. Press new guides in up to shoulder but do not use more than one ton of pressure once shoulder is seated. Hand ream the guides to a uniform diameter of .315-.316" (8.013-8.035 mm).

VALVE STEM SEALS AND SPRINGS

NOTE: **It is possible to replace valve springs and seals with head installed provided camshaft and tappets are removed. Piston of cylinder concerned must be at top dead center position**

Use spring compressor to depress spring and retainer. Remove keepers, then remove retainer and springs. Remove stem seal. Use protective sleeve over valve stem and install new seal. Complete assembly in reverse order of disassembly.

VALVE CLEARANCE ADJUSTMENT

1) Engine should be near operating temperature. Rotate crankshaft so that cam lobes for No. 1 cylinder (curb side) point upward. Check intake and exhaust clearance between heel of cam lobe and follower.

2) Use crankshaft pulley to rotate crankshaft 180° at a time and check No. 3, No. 4, and No. 2 clearance. If clearances are not within specifications, use thinner or thicker adjusting discs to increase or decrease clearance.

NOTE: **Do not turn engine by camshaft pulley as this will stretch drive belt. Use a wrench to turn crankshaft or push vehicle in fourth gear to move crankshaft and valve train.**

3) Twenty-six different thicknesses of discs are available in increments of .0019" (.05 mm) from .1181" (3.0 mm) to .1673" (4.25 mm). To install, turn crankshaft about 1/4 turn past TDC and press cam follower down with tool (VW 546). Remove old disc with special pliers (VW 10-208) and insert new disc with etched thickness marking toward cam follower.

VALVE CLEARANCE SPECIFICATIONS

Application	In. (mm)
Intake	
Hot	.008-.012 (.20-.30)
Cold	.006-.010 (.15-.25)
Exhaust	
Hot	.016-.020 (.40-.50)
Cold	.014-.018 (.35-.45)

NOTE: **Cold settings are given for reference as initial settings to be used during cylinder head rework. Final adjustments are made at normal operating temperatures and should be checked after 1000 miles of operation**

PISTONS, PINS & RINGS

PISTON & ROD ASSEMBLY

Removal

1) Mark cylinder number on crown of each piston. If necessary, mark arrows pointing toward front of block on piston crowns. Remove rod cap bolts and push piston out top of cylinder using wooden hammer handle.

4-CYLINDER DIESEL & TURBO-DIESEL (Cont.)

2) If ridge at top of cylinder prevents piston removal, use ridge reamer prior to further disassembly. DO NOT force piston out of cylinder. Mark rods and bearing caps for proper installation.

Installation

1) Turn crankshaft so No. 1 journal is at BDC. Install piston and rod assembly until ring compressor contacts block. Guide rod over journal and use wooden handle of hammer to push piston into cylinder.

2) Repeat with No. 4 piston and rod assembly ensuring that tabs on bearing halves engage notches in respective rod and cap. Tighten caps on rods 1 and 4, then rotate crankshaft 180° and install No. 2 and No. 3 piston and rod assemblies.

PISTON PINS

Removal

Use needle-nose pliers to remove circlips. Press out pin and remove piston, noting direction piston is fitted to rod. If pin is too tight, heat piston to approximately 140°F (60°C) and then press out.

Installation

Check piston and pin fit for thumb push fit. Connecting rod and pin wear limit is .0015" (.040 mm). Connecting rod may be rebushed and honed to proper size if required. If pin is too loose in piston, replace both pin and piston.

FITTING PISTONS

Measure cylinder at 3 points: 3/8" (10 mm) from top and bottom, and at center of bore. Measure in line with and at 90° to thrust face. Cylinder wear limit is .0015" (.040 mm) out of round. If limit is exceeded, cylinders must be honed and new pistons fitted.

Fig. 6: Side and Top View of Diesel Piston

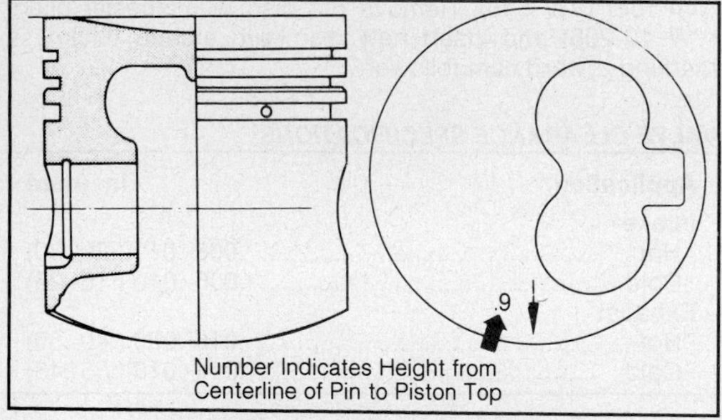
.9
Number Indicates Height from
Centerline of Pin to Piston Top

Quantum pistons have notch in skirt for oil jet.

CRANKSHAFT MAIN & CONNECTING ROD BEARINGS

MAIN & CONNECTING ROD BEARINGS

1) Push crankshaft toward one end and measure end play at No. 3 (thrust) bearing. Main bearing caps are numbered "1" through "5" with "1" at drive belt end and "5" at flywheel end. Measure connecting rod end play (side play). Check all bearing clearances with Plastigage, tightening bearings to 26 ft. lbs. (35 N.m).

2) Measure crankshaft journals to determine size and any out-of-round. Maximum allowable out of round is .0012" (.030 mm). Install main inserts with bearing half having oil groove into block. Lubricate bearings and install caps in original positions.

CRANKSHAFT JOURNAL DIAMETERS

Size	Main Bearing In. (mm) [1]	Rod Bearing In. (mm) [1]
Standard	2.125 (53.97)	1.810 (45.97)
1st US	2.115 (53.72)	1.800 (45.72)
2nd US	2.105 (53.47)	1.790 (45.47)
3rd US	2.095 (53.22)	1.780 (45.22)

[1] — Journal diameter is ± .0004" (.010 mm).

REAR MAIN BEARING OIL SEAL

NOTE: **Rear main bearing oil seal may be replaced with engine in vehicle. Transmission and flywheel must be removed.**

Removal

Insert screwdriver between crankshaft and flywheel flange and inside lip of seal. Pry seal out.

Installation

Install guide sleeve tool 2003/2A (or equivalent) over crankshaft flange. Start new seal into recess in carrier. Remove guide sleeve. Fit drive plate 2003/1 (or equivalent) and seat seal by tightening bolts.

FRONT MAIN BEARING OIL SEAL & INTERMEDIATE SHAFT OIL SEAL

NOTE: **Diesel engine intermediate shaft rotates counterclockwise and utilizes a different seal than the gas engine. Arrow pointing counterclockwise on seal indicates correct application for Diesel model.**

Removal (Quantum)

Remove crankshaft sprocket. Insert hex head bolt of seal removal/installation tool (3083) into seal extractor guide (2085) and remove oil seal.

Installation

To install, slide sleeve of seal removal/installation tool (3083) on crankshaft journal. Dip seal into engine oil and slide over sleeve. Slide thrust sleeve over guide sleeve. Press seal in with thrust sleeve and bolt until fully seated.

Removal (All Others)

Remove camshaft belt and crankshaft sprocket. On Vanagon, screw seal extractor 2085 (or equivalent) into seal to remove. On all others, pry seal from carrier using care not to damage carrier. Use seal extractor 10-219 (or equivalent) to remove seal.

Installation

Coat seal lips with oil and press into carrier until flush. Use special tool 10-203 (or equivalent). Remove steel sleeve from carrier and use aluminum part of the tool to drive seal in to a depth of .08" (2 mm) from front of carrier.

NOTE: **Same procedures are used for intermediate shaft seal except that intermediate shaft sprocket is removed. Seal is pressed in only until flush with carrier.**

4-CYLINDER DIESEL & TURBO-DIESEL (Cont.)

ENGINE OILING

CRANKCASE CAPACITY

OIL CAPACITY

Application	Qts. (L)
Quantum	
With Filter Change	3.7 (3.5)
Without Filter Change	3.2 (3.0)
Jetta, Rabbit & Rabbit Pickup	
With Filter Change	4.7 (4.5)
Without Filter Change	4.2 (4.0)
Vanagon	
With Filter Change	4.2 (4.0)
Without Filter Change	3.7 (3.5)

OIL FILTER

Oil filter is the replaceable, spin-on type.

NORMAL OIL PRESSURE

For Quantum, the oil pressure at normal operating temperature should be 7 psi (.49 kg/cm²) @ 1000 RPM, and 74 psi (5.2 kg/cm²) @ 5000 RPM. On all others, the oil pressure should be a minimum of 28 psi (2.0 kg/cm²) @ 2000 RPM and at normal operating temperature.

ENGINE OILING SYSTEM

Gear type oil pump provides oil for pressure feed to crankshaft journals, camshaft bearings, and intermediate shaft. A larger, heavy-duty oil filter and revised oil pump drive are used in the Diesel. Other lubrication characteristics are similar to the spark ignition engines.

OIL PUMP

Removal

Drain oil and remove oil pan. Remove pump mounting bolts and pump along with pick-up tube. Install in vise and remove pick-up tube.

Inspection

Check oil pump gear backlash with feeler gauge. Clearance should be between .002-.008" (.05-.20 mm). Measure the pump gear end play using a machinist's square and feeler gauge for .006" (.15 mm) clearance or less. If specifications are exceeded, replace the gears or the pump.

Installation

To install, make sure that all mating surfaces are clean. Install gaskets and reverse removal procedure.

ENGINE COOLING

COOLING SYSTEM CAPACITY

COOLANT CAPACITY

Application	Qts. (L)
Jetta	6.9 (6.5)
Quantum, Rabbit & Rabbit Pickup	7.3 (7.0)
Vanagon	16.9 (16.0)

THERMOSTAT

NOTE: Thermostat information not available for Quantum.

Thermostat to open at 185°F (85°C) on Vanagon and 176°F (80°C) on all others. Fully open at 221°F (105°C) on Vanagon and 201°F (94°C) on all others. Fan thermoswitch starts fan at 200-208°F (93-98°C).

RADIATOR CAP

Cap opens at 17-21 psi (1.2-1.5 kg/cm²) for Quantum, 11-16 psi (.8-1.1 kg/cm²) for Vanagon, and 17-19 (1.2-1.3 kg/cm²) for all others.

WATER PUMP

NOTE: Never drain the coolant while the engine is hot. Cylinder head or engine block could warp if not allowed to cool prior to draining.

Removal

Drain cooling system. Disconnect battery ground cable and unplug alternator wires. Remove alternator and bracket. Disconnect thermostat housing and hoses from water pump. Remove bolts holding pump to camshaft belt cover and engine block and remove pump.

Installation

To install, reverse removal procedure. Use new "O" ring in recess in pump mounting flange.

NOTE: Do NOT use sealer between water pump mounting flange and engine block.

TIGHTENING SPECIFICATIONS

Application	Ft. Lbs. (N.m)
Timing Belt Tensioner Lock Nut	33 (45)
Intermediate Sprocket Bolt	33 (45)
Crankshaft Sprocket Bolt	[1] 81 (110)
Water Pump Pulley Bolts	15 (20)
Crankshaft Pulley Bolts	15 (20)
Main Bearing Cap Bolts	48 (65)
Flywheel-to-Crankshaft Bolts	[2] 55 (75)
Connecting Rod Caps	33 (45)
Camshaft Sprocket Bolt	33 (45)
Camshaft Bearing Cap Bolts	15 (20)
Cylinder Head Bolts	See Text
Manifolds-to-Cylinder Head	18 (25)

[1] – Vanagon 110 ft. lbs. (150 N.m).
[2] – Bolts with shoulder 72 ft. lbs. (100 N.m.)

Volkswagen Engines

4-CYLINDER DIESEL & TURBO-DIESEL (Cont.)

ENGINE SPECIFICATIONS

GENERAL SPECIFICATIONS

Year	DISPLACEMENT		Fuel System	HP@RPM	Torque Ft. Lbs.@RPM	Compr. Ratio	BORE		STROKE	
	Cu. In.	Liters					In.	mm	In.	mm
1983	97.0	1.6	Fuel Inj.	52@4800 [1]	72@2000 [2]	23:1	3.012	76.5	3.40	86.40

[1] – Quantum 68@4500 RPM, Vanagon 48@4200 RPM. [2] – Quantum 98@2800 RPM.

VALVES

Engine Size & Valve	Head Diam. In. (mm)	Face Angle	Seat Angle	Seat Width In. (mm)	Stem Diameter In. (mm)	Stem Clearance In. (mm)	Valve Lift In. (mm)
1.6L							
Intake	1.338 (40.00)	45°	45°	.079 (2.00)	.314 (7.97)	.051 (1.30)	....
Exhaust	1.220 (31.00)	45°	45°	.095 (2.40)	.313 (7.95)	.051 (1.30)	....

PISTONS, PINS, RINGS

Engine	PISTONS	PINS		RINGS		
	Clearance In. (mm)	Piston Fit In. (mm)	Rod Fit In. (mm)	Ring No.	End Gap In. (mm)	Side Clearance In. (mm)
1.6L	.001 [1] (.03)	Push Fit	.0004-.0008 [2] (.01-.02)	No. 1	.012-.020 [3] (.30-.50)	.002-.004 [4] (.06-.09)
				No. 2	.012-.020 [3] (.30-.50)	.002-.003 [4] (.06-.08)
				No. 3	.010-.016 [3] (.25-.40)	.001-.002 [5] (.03-.06)

[1] – Wear limit .028" (.07 mm). [2] – Specification not available for Quantum. [3] – Wear limit .039" (1.0 mm).
[4] – Wear limit .008" (.20 mm). [5] – Wear limit .006" (.15 mm).

CRANKSHAFT MAIN & CONNECTING ROD BEARINGS

Engine	MAIN BEARINGS				CONNECTING ROD BEARINGS		
	Journal Diam. In. (mm)	Clearance In. (mm)	Thrust Bearing	Crankshaft End Play In. (mm)	Journal Diam. In. (mm)	Clearance In. (mm)	Side Play In. (mm)
1.6L	2.124-2.125 (53.96-53.98)	.001-.003 [1] (.03-.08)	No. 3	.003-.007 [2] (.07-.17)	1.880-1.881 (47.76-47.78)	.0011-.0035 [3] (.028-.088)	.014 (.37)

[1] – Wear limit .007" (.17 mm). [2] – Wear limit .015" (.37 mm). [3] – Wear limit .0047" (.12 mm).

VALVE SPRINGS

Engine	Free Length In. (mm)	PRESSURE Lbs. @ In. (Kg @ mm)	
		Valve Closed	Valve Open
1.6L			
Inner	....	46-51@.719 (21-23@18.3)	....
Outer	....	96-106@.875 (43.5-48@22.3)	....

CAMSHAFT

Engine	Journal Diam. In. (mm)	Clearance In. (mm)	Lobe Lift In. (mm)
1.6L	....	.0008-.002 [1] (.02-.05)	....

[1] – 1984 Models = .004 (.10)
End play .006" (.1 mm).

Volvo Engines

B21FT & B23F 4-CYLINDER

ENGINE CODING

ENGINE IDENTIFICATION

Engine identification number is located on a label on the camshaft timing belt cover and stamped in the block behind the distributor. Last 3 digits identify engine. The Vehicle Identification Number also carries an engine code as its 7th and 8th digits. The code is 47 for the B23F engine and 88 for the B21FT.

ENGINE IDENTIFICATION

Application	Code
B23F (2.3L)	
Non-Turbo Models	
Man. Trans.	499-802
Auto. Trans.	499-803
B21FT (2.1L)	
Turbo	
Man. Trans.	499-800
Auto. Trans.	499-801

ENGINE, MANIFOLDS & CYLINDER HEAD

ENGINE

Removal

1) Remove battery. Disconnect windshield washer hose and engine compartment lamp. Remove hood. Remove rubber boot and snap ring at base of gearshift lever (manual transmission only).

2) Remove cap from expansion tank. Open radiator drain cock and drain coolant. Disconnect lower radiator hose at radiator, crankcase ventilation hose at cylinder head, and upper radiator hose at engine. Detach expansion tank hoses from radiator.

3) Disconnect oil cooler lines for automatic transmission at radiator. On Turbo, disconnect oil cooler lines. On all models, remove fan shroud screws, disconnect radiator, and lift radiator and fan shroud from vehicle.

4) Remove air cleaner and hose asssembly. Loosen tensioner nut and remove belt from air pump. Disconnect hoses at pump and remove pump and bracket assembly.

5) Remove vacuum pump after disconnecting hoses, including hose to brake power cylinder. Remove tensioner bar bolts, drive belt and power steering pump.

6) If equipped with air conditioning, remove crankshaft pulley and A/C drive belt. Reinstall pulley loosely. Disconnect and remove compressor and bracket.

7) Mark and disconnect 4 vacuum hoses at engine and 2 carbon filter hoses. Remove wire or connector from distributor, high tension lead from coil, and starter motor cables and clutch cable clamp from starter.

8) Detach wiring harness from voltage regulator. Disconnect throttle cable at pulley and A/C wire at solenoid on intake manifold.

9) Remove fuel cap to relieve pressure, and remove fuel hoses from filter and return pipe. Remove guard plate for ballast resistor, and disconnect 2 wire connectors from intake manifold micro switch, 4 in wiring harness, and 2 at ballast resistor.

10) Disconnect heater hoses at firewall and drain oil from engine. Remove exhaust pipe flange nuts and gasket.

11) Remove front engine mounting bolts and front exhaust pipe mounting bracket. Disconnect gearshift control rod (automatic transmission) or clutch cable (manual transmission).

12) Disconnect speedometer cable, propeller shaft "U" joint, and gearshift selector from control rod. If manual transmission has overdrive, disconnect wire to gearshift selector. Using a wooden block, place jack under transmission. Remove transmission support member.

13) Attach lifting yoke assembly (5035) to 3 engine lifting eyes, and adjust lifting beam (2810) to its rearmost position.

14) Hoist slightly to release front engine mount dowels. Check for wires or hoses, and disconnect as necessary. Adjust lifting beam to forward position and lift engine from car.

Installation

To install, reverse removal procedure and check for proper installation of all lines, hoses and electrical leads.

INTAKE & EXHAUST MANIFOLDS

Removal

1) Disconnect battery ground cable. Remove air bellows from CI unit to intake manifold. Disconnect PCV hoses at intake manifold and flame arrester.

2) Disconnect vacuum pump hose at intake manifold. Disconnect diverter valve hoses. Disconnect air pump with tensioner and position to one side.

3) Disconnect the following fuel lines: Control pressure regulator (1 hose), cold start injector (1 hose), distributor pipe to engine (2 hoses) front fuel filter to engine (2 hoses), and injector hoses (4 hoses).

4) Disconnect wiring at control pressure regulator, cold start injector, and auxiliary air valve.

5) Remove air injection pipe. Disconnect throttle cable from intake manifold. Disconnect charcoal canister hoses and EGR valve hose from intake manifold. Remove intake manifold brace, attaching nuts, and intake manifold.

6) Disconnect transmission fill pipe from flywheel housing (automatic transmissions only). Remove attaching nuts and exhaust manifold.

Installation

To install, reverse removal procedure and use new manifold gaskets. Tighten nuts and bolts to specifications.

CYLINDER HEAD

Removal

1) Drain cooling system at radiator and cylinder block. Disconnect battery ground cable. Disconnect upper radiator hose at engine.

2) Disconnect air bellows between CI unit and air cleaner. Remove PCV hoses from intake manifold and oil trap on block. Disconnect vacuum pump hose at intake manifold.

3) Disconnect diverter valve hoses. Remove air pump and bracket. Disconnect the following fuel lines: Control pressure regulator (1 hose), cold start injector (1 hose), distributor pipe to engine (2 hoses), front fuel filter to engine (2 hoses), and injector hoses (4 hoses).

Volvo Engines

B21FT & B23F 4-CYLINDER (Cont.)

4) Disconnect wires at following components: Control pressure regulator, cold start injector, auxiliary air valve, and temperature sender. Disconnect throttle cable from intake manifold.

5) Disconnect charcoal canister hoses and EGR valve hose from intake manifold. Disconnect transmission fill pipe from transmission housing (automatic transmissions only).

6) Remove water pipe rear clamp from manifold. Remove exhaust manifold to exhaust pipe attaching nuts. Remove intake manifold brace. Disconnect spark plug cables at plugs, then disconnect upper water hose at firewall.

7) Remove timing belt cover, slacken timing belt tensioner and remove timing belt. Remove valve cover and cylinder head bolts. Lift cylinder head from engine.

Installation

1) Install new head gasket with "TOP" mark upward. Be sure all contact surfaces are clean. Position cylinder head over gasket.

2) Dip head bolts and washers in engine oil before installation. Install and tighten bolts in 3 steps in sequence shown in *Fig. 1.* First tighten bolts to 15 ft. lbs. (20 N.m). Tighten next to 44 ft. lbs. (60 N.m). Angle tighten an additional 90°.

3) Adjust valves. Reverse remainder of removal procedure and make final valve adjustment after running engine for 10 minutes. See Valve Clearance Adjustment. Retorque cylinder head bolts.

Fig. 1: Cylinder Head Tightening Sequence

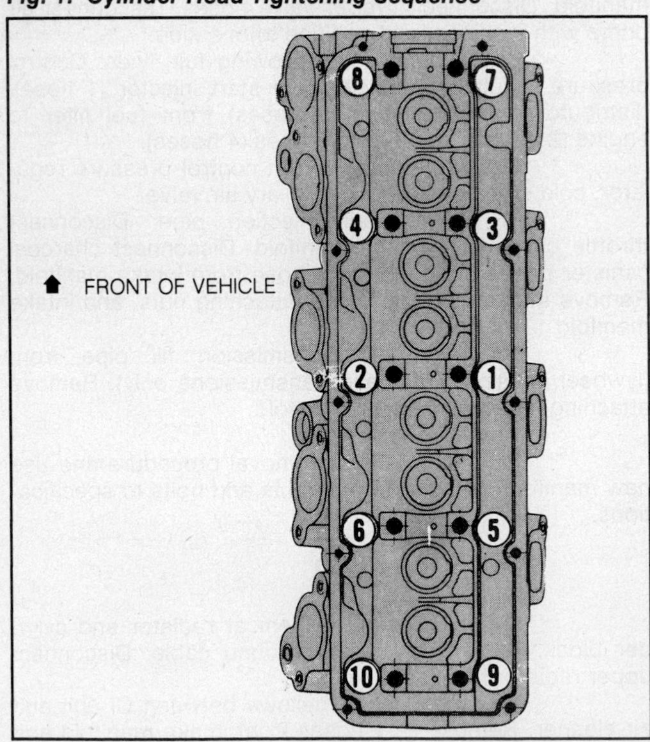
8
7
4
3
FRONT OF VEHICLE
2
1
6
5
10
9

Tighten to final torque in 3 steps.

CAMSHAFT

NOTE: **Rear end of camshafts for B21FT engine are stamped with the letter "T". Camshafts for B23F are stamped with letter "M".**

Removal

1) Remove valve cover and gasket. Check and note markings on camshaft bearing caps. Remove center bearing cap and install holder tool (5021) to hold camshaft in place while removing remaining bearing caps.

2) Remove timing belt cover and slacken drive belt tensioner. Pull off drive belt and remove camshaft sprocket. Remove remaining bearing caps and take out front camshaft oil seal. Release screw on holder tool and lift out camshaft.

Inspection

Inspect bearing surfaces for damage. Camshaft bearings should have an inner diameter of 1.811-1.823" (30.00-30.02 mm).

Installation

Ensure that dowel for sprocket is UP (12 o'clock position) and lubricate all bearing and friction surfaces. To complete installation, reverse removal procedure.

TIMING BELT INSTALLATION

1) Install belt tensioner if previously removed. Align notch in crankshaft belt guide with timing mark on front cover.

2) Rotate intermediate shaft so timing mark on sprocket aligns with mark on belt guard. Align marks on camshaft belt guide wtih timing mark on valve cover.

3) New drive belts have yellow markings. Two lines should fit toward crankshaft marks and next mark toward intermediate shaft mark.

4) Place belt over crankshaft sprocket first, then intermediate shaft. Stretch belt on tension side and fit over camshaft sprocket. Slide back of belt inside tension roller.

5) Loosen nut on belt tensioner to permit spring tension to act against drive belt. Recheck timing marks for proper location and tighten tensioner nut. Attach pulley to front hub on crankshaft.

VALVES

NOTE: **The exhaust valves on turbocharged engines are stellite-coated and must not be machined. They may be ground on the seat. Use extreme care when disposing damaged or worn sodium-filled exhaust valves. If the sodium contained in the valve comes into contact with water, a violent reaction will occur.**

VALVE ARRANGEMENT

E-I-E-I-E-I-E-I (Front-to-rear).

VALVE GUIDE SERVICING

Removal & Installation

1) Heat cylinder head to 140°F (60° C) and press old guides out with drift (2818). To install, use intake guide drift (5027) and exhaust guide drift (5028) to press in new guides.

2) Valve guides are available in standard size (no grooves) and 3 oversizes (1, 2 or 3 grooves). Ream oversize guides with proper reamer (5161, 5162, or 5163 respectively).

3) Press in until drift contacts cylinder head to give proper height above cylinder head. Installed height

B21FT & B23F 4-CYLINDER (Cont.)

Fig. 2: Timing Marks for Crankshaft, Intermediate Shaft and Camshaft

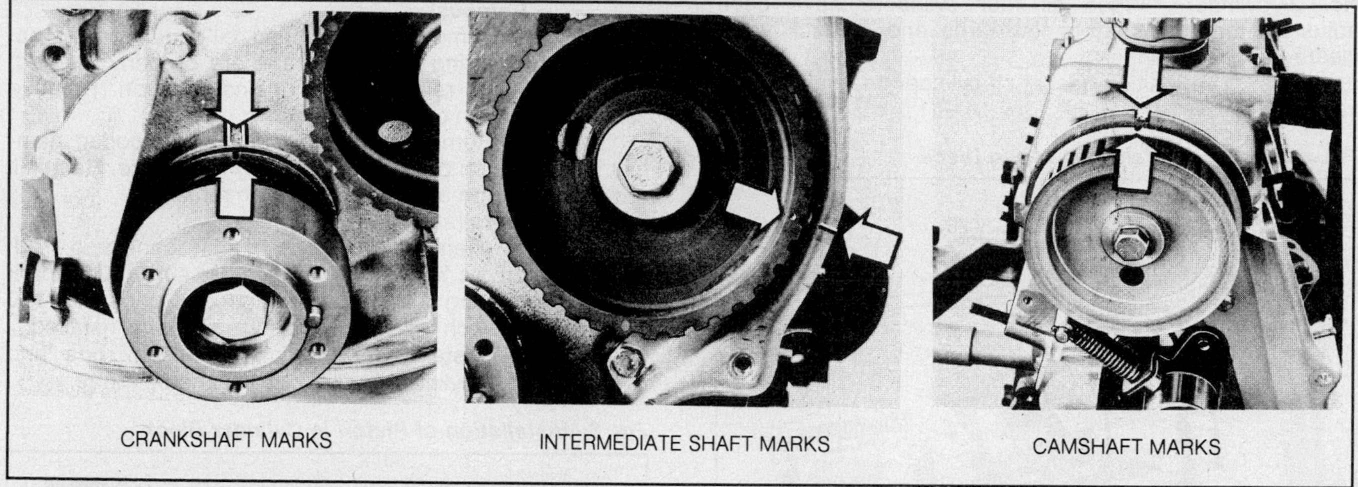
CRANKSHAFT MARKS
INTERMEDIATE SHAFT MARKS
CAMSHAFT MARKS

Align marks as shown before installing timing belt.

for intake guide is .606-.614" (15.4-15.6 mm) and .705-.713" (17.9-18.1 mm) for exhaust guide.

NOTE: **Ensure that replacement guide is same size as old guide. At least 1980 lbs. (898 kg) force should be required to press in new guide; if not, head must be fitted with oversize guide.**

VALVE SPRINGS

Removal

With cylinder head removed, compress valve springs using valve spring compression tool, and remove valve retainers. Disassemble valve spring components and place valves in order in valve rack.

Installation

To install, place valves in position, fit valve guide seal, valve spring, upper washer and retainer.

Fig. 3: Valve and Guide Assembly

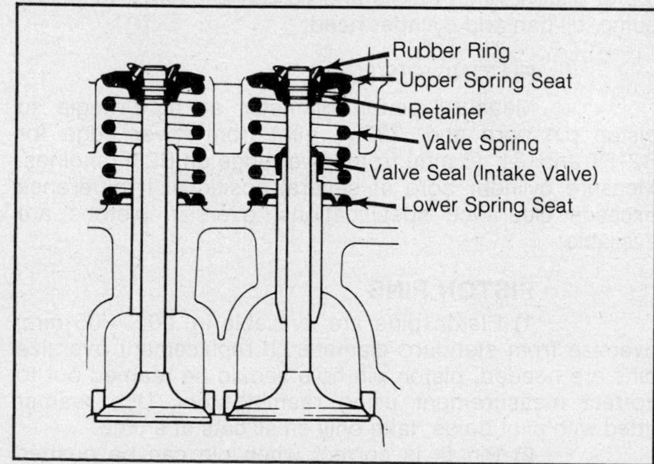
Rubber Ring
Upper Spring Seat
Retainer
Valve Spring
Valve Seal (Intake Valve)
Lower Spring Seat

VALVE SPRING INSTALLED HEIGHT

Valve spring ends must be square. Installed height of valve spring cannot exceed specifications. Measure spring height from base of spring pad on cylinder head to underside of spring retainer.

VALVE CLEARANCE ADJUSTMENT

1) Valve clearance is adjusted with engine off, and may be done either warm or cold. Remove valve cover.

2) Turn crankshaft center bolt until camshaft is in position for firing No. 1 cylinder. Both cam lobes should point up at equally large angles. Pulley timing mark should be on 0°.

3) Using feeler gauge, check valve clearance of No. 1 cylinder, measuring between camshaft lobe and discs. Intake and exhaust valves should have same clearances.

VALVE CLEARANCE SPECIFICATIONS

When Checking	In. (mm)
Cold engine	.012-.016" (.30-.40 mm)
Hot engine	.014-.018" (.35-.45)
When Setting	**In. (mm)**
Cold Engine	.014-.016" (.35-.40 mm)
Hot Engine	.016-.018" (.40-.45 mm)

4) If clearance is incorrect, line up notches in valve depressors, so they are at right angles to engine center line.

5) Install valve adjustment tool (5022) and turn handle downward until depressor groove is just above edge of cylinder head. Remove adjusting disc with special pliers (5026).

6) Using micrometer, measure thickness of disc. Then determine proper thickness required of new disc to bring clearance within specifications. For example, measure existing clearance and subtract correct clearance.

7) Difference should be added to thickness of old disc to determine thickness of new disc required. Discs are available in thicknesses ranging from .130" (3.30 mm) to .177" (4.50 mm) in increments of .002" (.05 mm).

8) Discs should be oiled and installed with marks down. Remove valve adjustment tool (5022), rotate crankshaft to correct firing position for No. 3 cylinder and repeat procedure.

B21FT & B23F 4-CYLINDER (Cont.)

9) Then adjust valve clearance for No. 4 and No. 2 cylinders. When all four cylinders have been adjusted, turn camshaft a few turns and recheck valve clearance at all cylinders.

10) Position gasket on cylinder head and install valve cover.

Fig. 4: Removing Valve Adjusting Discs

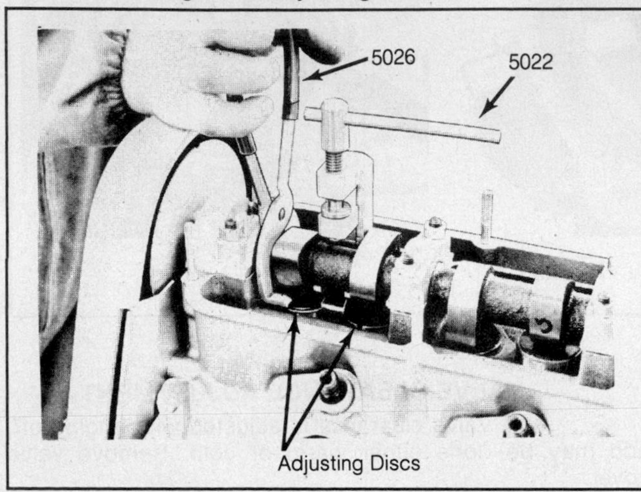
5026
5022
Adjusting Discs

Adjust clearance by altering disc thickness.

PISTONS, PINS & RINGS

OIL PAN

Removal

1) Raise and support front of vehicle. Remove splash guard. Remove engine mount nuts from underside of crossmember.

2) Disconnect steering shaft at steering gear. Remove steering "U" joint lower bolt, loosen upper bolt and slide "U" joint up on shaft.

3) Position lifting tools (5006, 5033 and 5115) and lift engine slightly. *See Fig. 5.* Take out crossmember bolts. Lower crossmember.

4) Remove left engine mount. Remove support bracket (located between rear of oil pan and clutch housing). Remove oil pan bolts. Turn and lower oil pan.

Installation

To install oil pan, reverse removal procedure.

Fig. 5: Lifting Tools Installed for Oil Pan Removal

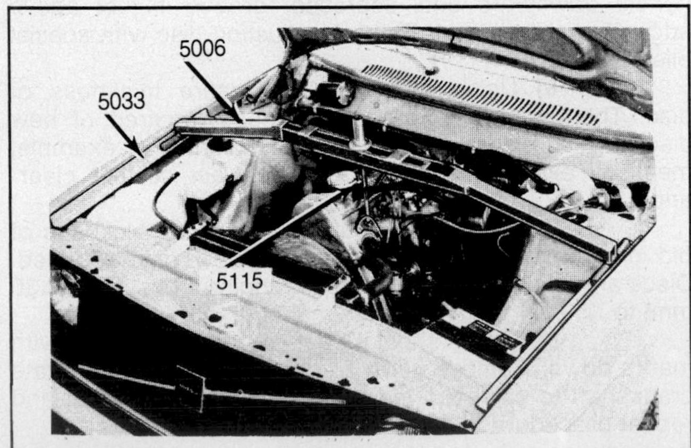
5006
5033
5115

Support engine before removing pan.

PISTON & ROD ASSEMBLY

Removal

1) Remove cylinder head, oil pan and oil pump. Be sure connecting rods and caps are properly marked, so they may be reinstalled in original location. Remove carbon ridge from cylinder bores.

2) Remove rod cap, and using wooden hammer handle, push piston out top of cylinder bore. Reinstall rod cap on piston and rod from which removed.

Installation

1) Remove rod cap from connecting rod. Secure piston pin with retaining rings. Be sure "TOP" mark on rings is facing top of piston and end gaps are 120 degrees from each other and rings are properly installed.

2) Install bearings in connecting rods and caps. Lubricate cylinder bores, pistons and bearings.

Fig. 6: Installation of Piston in Cylinder Block

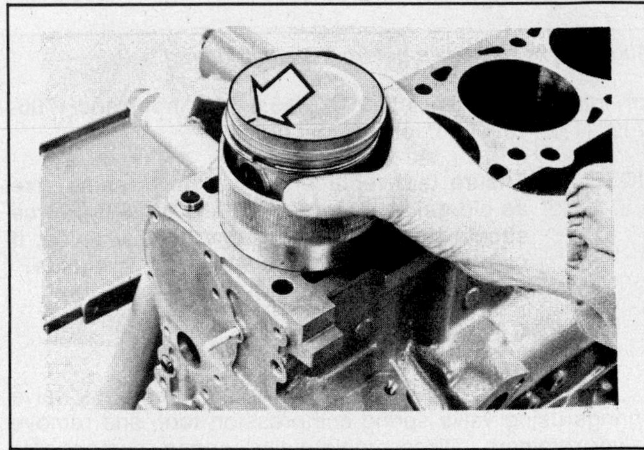

Align arrow toward front of block.

3) Using piston ring compressor (5031), insert rod and piston into bore, with mark on top of piston and on connecting rod toward front of engine.

4) Using wooden hammer handle, tap lightly on top of piston. Align marks and tighten end caps. Install oil pump, oil pan and cylinder head.

FITTING PISTONS

Measure piston diameter ar right angle to piston pin bore and .28" (7 mm) from lower edge for B21FT and .31" (8 mm) from lower edge on B23F engines. Measure cylinder bore at several positions. If difference exceeds clearance specifications, oversize pistons are available.

PISTON PINS

1) Piston pins are available in .002" (.05 mm) oversize from standard diameter. If replacement oversize pins are needed, piston pin hole should be reamed out to correct measurement using reaming tool. Use reamer fitted with pilot guide, take only small cuts at a time.

2) Pin fit is correct when pin can be pushed through connecting rod hole with only light thumb pressure (close running fit). Pin should push easily through piston.

B21FT & B23F 4-CYLINDER (Cont.)

CRANKSHAFT MAIN & CONNECTING ROD BEARINGS

MAIN & CONNECTING ROD BEARINGS

Removal

1) Remove oil pan and related parts. See Oil Pan Removal. Identify and mark connecting rod caps and main bearing caps to ensure correct replacement.

Fig. 7: Piston Pin Installation

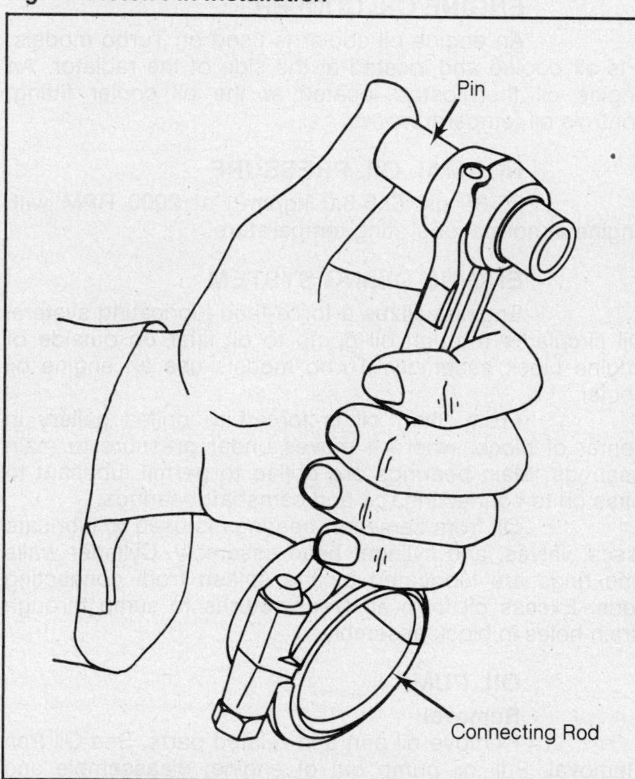
Pin
Connecting Rod

Pin should fit through rod using thumb pressure only.

2) Remove connecting rod caps and push pistons towards top of cylinders. Remove main bearing caps (one at a time) and thoroughly clean all bearing surfaces.

Installation

1) Measure all journals, using a micrometer. Out-of-roundness on main bearing journals should not exceed .003" (.0 mm) and on connecting rod journals, it should not exceed .002" (.05 mm).

2) If values obtained are close to, or in excess of wear limits, crankshaft must be reground to next suitable undersize.

3) If all journals check out to standard size, refit with replacement bearings. Reinstall main bearing caps, refit connecting rods to crankshaft and tighten all nuts and bolts to specifications. Reassemble engine in reverse order of removal.

REAR MAIN BEARING OIL SEAL

Removal

Remove transmission, clutch, and flywheel from engine. Remove 2 bolts from oil pan (into rear flange). Slacken 2 bolts on each side of flange, and remove flange. Use a drift (2817) to remove oil seal.

Installation

1) Clean flange area thoroughly and inspect seal mating surface of crankshaft. Install new seal to flange using drift (2817).

NOTE: **If a new crankshaft has been installed, screw center bolt of tool in fully and install seal at outer position of flange. If crankshaft has not been replaced, install seal with center bolt of tool screwed out a couple of turns.**

2) Oil new seal and install flange with new gasket to cylinder block. Install attaching bolts and tighten. Install oil pan attaching bolts and tighten. Install flywheel, clutch, and transmission.

ENGINE FRONT COVER OIL SEAL

Removal

1) Remove fan shroud, fan belt and fan pulley. Remove water pump pulley and camshaft drive belt cover. Remove crankshaft hub, sprocket and belt guide. Remove sprocket from intermediate shaft.

Fig. 8: Oiling System Components

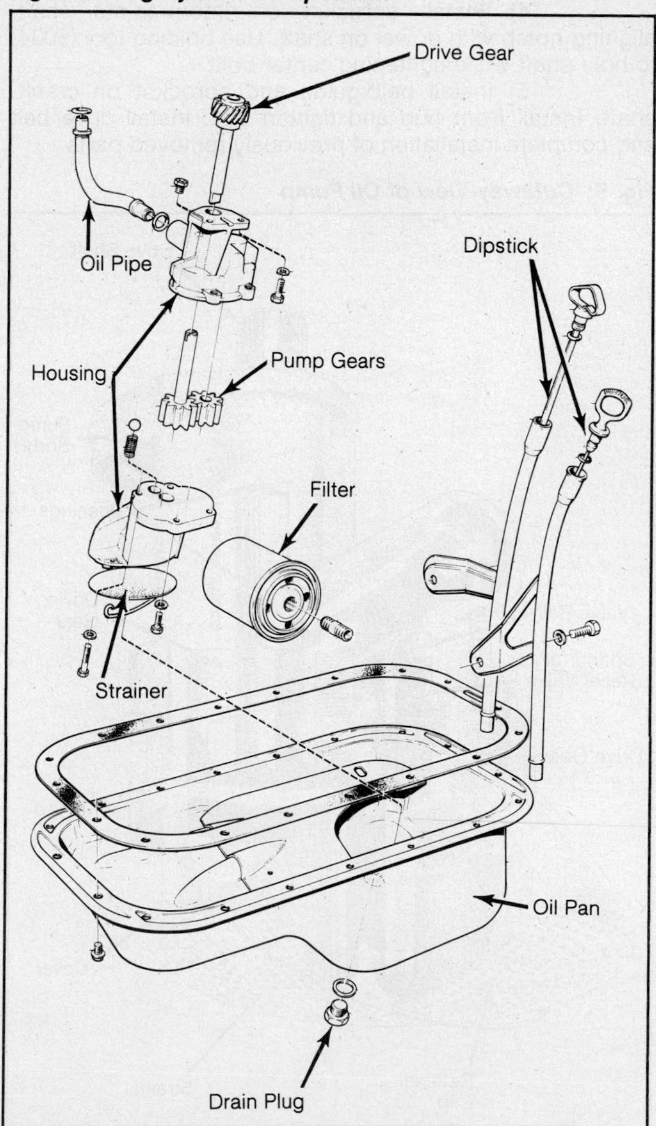
Drive Gear
Oil Pipe
Dipstick
Housing
Pump Gears
Filter
Strainer
Oil Pan
Drain Plug

B21FT & B23F 4-CYLINDER (Cont.)

2) Detach wiring harness across front of engine. Remove two oil pan bolts from base of front cover and loosen two on each side of them. Remove drive belt guard plate and front cover.

NOTE: Front cover removal is not necessary if only the seals are being replaced. Pry old seals out and proceed to step 2) of installation.

3) Using seal driver (5025), press out intermediate shaft seal from front cover. Using similar driver (5024) press out crankshaft seal. Use same tools to install new seals.

Installation

1) Using new gasket, install front cover. Install oil pan, drive belt guard plate, and wiring harness.

2) Using driver (5024), install crankshaft seal. Using similar driver (5025), install intermediate shaft seal in front cover. Install inner belt guide on camshaft (collar facing away from belt).

3) Install camshaft sprocket, aligning notch with dowel on camshaft. Install outer belt guide, washer and center bolt. Hold sprocket with holding tool (5034) and tighten bolt.

4) Install sprocket on intermediate shaft, aligning notch with dowel on shaft. Use holding tool (5034) to hold shaft while tightening center bolt.

5) Install belt guide and sprocket on crankshaft. Install front hub and tighten bolt. Install drive belt and complete installation of previously removed parts.

Fig. 9: Cutaway View of Oil Pump

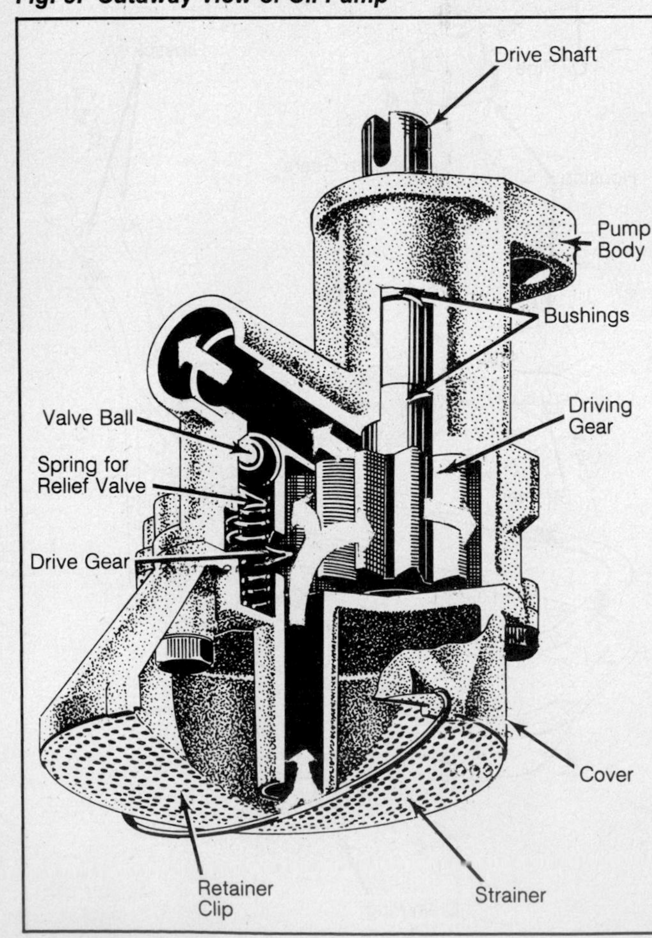
Drive Shaft
Pump Body
Bushings
Valve Ball
Driving Gear
Spring for Relief Valve
Drive Gear
Cover
Retainer Clip
Strainer

Prime pump before installing.

ENGINE OILING

CRANKCASE CAPACITY

B23F with filter change 4.0 quarts (3.8L). Without filter change 3.5 quarts (3.3L). B21FT (Turbo) with filter change 4.7 quarts (4.4L). Without filter change 4.2 quarts (3.9L).

OIL FILTER

Full-flow canister, disposable type.

ENGINE OIL COOLER

An engine oil cooler is used on Turbo models. It is air cooled and located at the side of the radiator. An engine oil thermostat, located at the oil cooler fitting, controls oil temperature.

NORMAL OIL PRESSURE

35-85 psi (2.6-6.0 kg/cm²) at 2000 RPM with engine at normal operating temperature.

ENGINE OILING SYSTEM

Engine utilizes a force-feed lubricating system. Oil circulates through oil pump to oil filter on outside of engine block assembly. Turbo models use an engine oil cooler.

From filter, oil is forced to drilled gallery in center of block, where it moves under pressure to main bearings. Main bearings are drilled to permit lubricant to pass on to connecting rod and camshaft bearings.

Oil from camshaft bearings is used to lubricate discs, valves, and cylinder head assembly. Cylinder walls and rings are lubricated by the splash from connecting rods. Excess oil from all areas returns to sump through drain holes in block assembly.

OIL PUMP

Removal

Remove oil pan and related parts. See Oil Pan Removal. Pull oil pump out of engine, disassemble and clean all parts thoroughly. Check all parts for excessive wear or signs of fatigue.

Inspection

1) Measure backlash (clearance excluding bearings) between pump gears. It should be .006-.014" (.15-.35 mm). Also measure end play of gears. Allowable end play is .0008-.0048" (.02-.12 mm).

2) Side clearance excluding bearings is .0008-.0035" (.02-.09 mm). Drive shaft bearing clearance is .0013-.0028" (.032-.070 mm). Idling shaft bearing clearance is .0006-.0016" (.014-.043 mm).

3) Relief valve spring free length should be 1.543" (39.2 mm). When loaded to 10.1-11.9 lbs. (4.5-5.4 kg), spring length should be 1.033" (26.3 mm). When loaded to 13.6-17.2 lbs. (6.2-7.8 kg), spring length should be .827" (21.0 mm).

4) If any parts show excessive wear or play, replace necessary components. Drive shaft and gear are matched set and must be replaced as an assembly.

Installation

Reinstall oil pump, making sure that sealing rings on oil delivery pipe are securely in place. Be sure oil pump properly engages pump drive shaft. Replace oil pan and related components.

Volvo Engines

B21FT & B23F 4-CYLINDER (Cont.)

ENGINE COOLING

WATER PUMP

Removal

1) Remove expansion tank cap, open engine block drain cock, and disconnect lower radiator hose at radiator. Remove fan shroud and fan. Loosen alternator and air pump and remove drive belts.

2) Remove water pump pulley, timing gear cover, and lower radiator hose. Remove retaining bolt and slide coolant pipe rearward. Remove pump.

Installation

Clean all surfaces. Place new sealing ring on coolant pipe. Install new gasket when mounting pump. Install other components previously removed. Fill with coolant.

THERMOSTAT

Standard wax type (marked 87°) opens at 197 (92°C); fully open at 207°F (97°C).

COOLANT CAPACITY

10 qts. (9.4L).

TIGHTENING SPECIFICATIONS

Application	Ft. Lbs. (N.m)
Cylinder Head Bolts [1]	
Step 1	15 (20)
Step 2	44 (60)
Step 3	Angle tighten additional 90°
Main Bearing Caps	85-91 (115-124)
Connecting Rod Caps	43-48 (58-65)
Camshaft Bearing Caps	13-16 (18-22)
Exhaust Pipe-to-Turbo	16-19 (22-26)
Exhaust & Intake Manifold Bolts	15 (20)
Flywheel Bolts	47-54 (64-73)
Engine Mount Bolts	15 (20)
Sprockets	
Camshaft	37 (50)
Intermediate Shaft	37 (50)
Crankshaft	122 (166)
Fan Bolt	33 (45)
Drive Belt Tensioner Nut	37 (50)

[1] – Torques apply to oiled screws, bolts and nuts. Cleaned fasteners must be oiled prior to installation.

ENGINE SPECIFICATIONS

GENERAL SPECIFICATIONS

Year	DISPLACEMENT Cu. In.	DISPLACEMENT Liters	Fuel System	HP@RPM	Torque Ft. Lbs.@RPM	Compr. Ratio	BORE In.	BORE mm	STROKE In.	STROKE mm
1983										
B21FT	130.0	2.1	Fuel Inj.	127@5400	150@3750	7.5:1	3.623	92	3.150	80
B23F	141.0	2.3	Fuel Inj.	107@5400	127@3500	10.3:1	3.780	96	3.150	80

VALVES

Engine Size & Valve	Head Diam. In. (mm)	Face Angle	Seat Angle	Seat Width In. (mm)	Stem Diameter In. (mm)	Stem Clearance In. (mm)	Valve Lift In. (mm)
2.1L & 2.3L							
Intake	1.732 (44)	44.5°	45°	.051-.075 (1.3-1.9)	.3132-.3138 (7.96-7.97)	.0012-.0024 (.030-.060)	.....
Exhaust	1.380 (35)	44.5°	45°	.066-.091 (1.7-2.3)	.3128-.3134 (7.94-7.96)	.0024-.0035 (.060-.090)	.....

PISTONS, PINS, RINGS

Engine	PISTONS Clearance In. (mm)	PINS Piston Fit In. (mm)	PINS Rod Fit In. (mm)	RINGS Ring No.	RINGS End Gap In. (mm)	RINGS Side Clearance In. (mm)
2.1L & 2.3L	[1] .0008-.0016 (.020-.040)	[2] Push Fit	[2] Push Fit	2 Comp.	[3] .0138-.0260 (.35-.65)	.0015-.0028 (.040-.072)
				Oil	.010-.024 (.25-.60)	.0012-.0024 (.030-.062)

[1] – The B23F engine with piston height of 3.1654" (80.4 mm) has clearance of .0002-.0003" (.005-.007 mm). B23F engines with piston height of 3.0079" (76.4 mm) has clearance of .0004-.0016" (.010-.040 mm).
[2] – Pin secured with circlip at each end. Push fit in piston; light thumb pressure (close running fit) in rod.
[3] – Lower compression ring end gap is .0138-.0217" (.35-.55 mm).

Volvo Engines

B21FT & B23F 4-CYLINDER (Cont.)

ENGINE SPECIFICATIONS (Cont.)

CRANKSHAFT MAIN & CONNECTING ROD BEARINGS

	MAIN BEARINGS				CONNECTING ROD BEARINGS		
Engine	Journal Diam. In. (mm)	Clearance In. (mm)	Thrust Bearing	Crankshaft End Play In. (mm)	Journal Diam. In. (mm)	Clearance In. (mm)	Side Play In. (mm)
2.1L & 2.3L [1]	[2] 2.4981-2.4986 (63.451-63.464)	.0011-.0033 (.028-.083)	.....	.001 Max. (.25) Max.	2.1255-2.1260 (53.987-54.000)	.0009-.0028 (.024-.070)	.006-.014 (.15-.35)

[1] – Diameter of intermediate shaft front journal should be 1.8494-1.8504" (46.97-47.00 mm); middle journal, 1.6939-1.6949" (43.03-43.05 mm), and rear journal, 1.6900-1.6909" (42.92-42.95mm). Intermediate shaft bearing clearances should be .0008-.0030" (.020-.075 mm). End play should be .008-.018" (.20-.46 mm).

[2] – Maximum out-of-round is .0028" (.07 mm); taper limit is .002" (.05 mm).

CAMSHAFT

Engine	Journal Diam. In. (mm)	Clearance In. (mm)	Lobe Lift In. (mm)
2.1L & 2.3L [1]	1.1437-1.1445 (29.050-29.070)	[2] .0012-.0028 (.030-.071)	.....

[1] – Rear end of 2.1L camshaft is stamped with letter "T"; 2.3L is stamped with letter "M".

[2] – End play is .004-.006" (.1-.4 mm).

VALVE SPRINGS

Engine	Free Length In. (mm)	PRESSURE Lbs. @ In. (Kg @ mm)	
		Valve Closed	Valve Open
2.1L & 2.3L	1.77 (45)	62-70@1.50 (28-32@38)	156-174@1.06 (71-80@27)

B28F V6

ENGINE CODING

ENGINE IDENTIFICATION

Engine identification number is located on plate on front left side of engine block, in front of oil filter and on decal at right rear side of cylinder head. Vehicle Identification Number (VIN) is located on right side center door pillar and on top of instrument panel at lower left of windshield.

ENGINE, MANIFOLDS & CYLINDER HEADS

ENGINE

Removal

1) Remove hood, air cleaner, grille, grille crossmember, fan shroud and engine splash guard. Drain engine and transmission oil. Drain cooling system (each side of block) and disconnect all coolant hoses. Disconnect AC compressor and move to 1 side (DO NOT disconnect hoses).

2) Remove radiator. Disconnect throttle cable, speedometer and battery ground cable. Disconnect and mark all electrical connections, hoses and tubing that will interfere with engine removal.

3) If equipped with manual transmission, lift rear wheels off ground and operate vehicle with overdrive engaged. Depress clutch pedal and stop engine. Remove ash tray and holder assembly.

4) Remove frame from around gear shift lever. Disconnect gearshift lever cover from floor. Remove snap ring holding shift lever. Using tool (5181), remove lock nut and pin at gear shift lever rod under vehicle. Cover gearshift lever with paper or cloth.

5) If equipped with automatic transmission, move gear selector to "PARK" and disconnect kickdown cable at throttle pulley. Drain transmission oil by disconnecting oil filler tube at oil pan.

6) Disconnect automatic transmission oil cooler pipes at radiator. Disconnect control rod at transmission lever. Disconnect reaction rod at transmission housing. On model AW71, disconnect solenoid wire.

7) Attach a lifting cradle crossmember tool (2810) and 2 lifting cradle sling tools (5100) to engine, then support lifting cradle on engine hoist. Using tool (5244), disconnect propeller shaft at transmission.

8) Disconnect exhaust pipe at joint in front of catalytic converter and remove exhaust pipe from exhaust pipe bracket. Remove rear engine mount and crossmember assembly. Remove nuts from front engine mounts and lift engine/transmission assembly from car.

NOTE: **When removing engine, check for hoses and wires not previously removed.**

Installation

To install, reverse removal procedures.

CYLINDER HEAD & MANIFOLDS

Removal

1) Disconnect battery ground cable. Release any pressure in fuel tank. Remove air cleaner. Remove air intake duct, oil filler cap and hoses, fuel lines from fuel filter, fuel return pipe and air control valve from inlet manifold.

2) Remove spark plug wires from spark plugs, ignition coil and wire holders, then move aside. Remove injectors from cylinder head and plug holes. Loosen retaining clips from distributor cap.

3) Remove vacuum hoses from charcoal filter, intake manifold at left rear corner, intake manifold at right rear corner and T-connector. Remove front section of intake manifold and stuff manifold holes with paper.

4) Remove throttle cable, kick-down cable (automatic transmission) and cruise control cable (if equipped). Disconnect and move wiring harness aside. Remove bolts from pressure regulator and lay regulator on top of intake manifold.

5) Remove 4 intake manifold bolts and intake manifold, then plug ports in cylinder head. From right cylinder head, remove AC compressor and secure out of way.

6) Remove oil dipstick and tube, upper radiator hose, hose between cylinder head and coolant pump, connection to ignition timing sender, cylinder head ground lead and coolant hose from cylinder head. Remove distributor cap and ignition cables (turn crankshaft to ignition position cylinder 1) and remove distributor.

7) Remove intake manifold. From left cylinder head, remove vacuum pump, intake air heater tube, lower radiator hose from coolant pump and hose between coolant pump and cylnder head.

8) When removing either cylinder head, remove exhaust crossover pipe flange nuts, exhaust pipe support bolts at transmission, pry off rubber support rings at center silencer and slide exhaust system backwards.

9) Remove valve cover and cover plate from rear of cylinder head. Using an 8 mm Allen wrench, remove timing gear timing plug from left cylinder head (right cylinder head has cover plate). Remove 4 upper timing gear cover bolts. Using a 10 mm Allen wrench, loosen timing gear sprocket bolt.

NOTE: **If both cylinder heads are removed, mark rocker arm assemblies to avoid interchange.**

10) Loosen rocker arm shaft assembly bolts in same sequence as for tightening and remove rocker arm shaft assembly. Loosen camshaft lock plate and move to one side. Using timing chain tensioner tool (5213), apply tension to timing chain.

NOTE: **Timing chain tensioner tool (5213) will hold timing chain in stretched position when camshaft is removed. If timing chain is slackened, chain tensioner under timing gear cover will take up chain slack making it impossible to reinstall camshaft.**

11) Remove camshaft from sprocket (left side bolt can be unscrewed but not removed). Move camshaft to rear to free it from sprocket. Remove cylinder head bolts *See Fig. 1.* Pry cylinder head up with a wooden hammer handle on inner edge to loosen before removing.

NOTE: **When removing cylinder heads, make sure cylinder liners DO NOT separate from seals at lower seat. If this happens, coolant can flow into crankcase necessitating a complete engine tear down and cleaning.**

12) When cylinder head is removed, place it on wooden blocks on work bench. Remove gasket and install

B28F V6 (Cont.)

cylinder liner holder tool (5093). Use needle nose pliers to remove guide sleeves. Stuff paper around cylinder liners to prevent dirt from entering engine. When cleaning, remove cylinder liners one-at-a-time.

CAUTION: When cleaning, use plastic scraper to prevent scratching. Use compressed air to blow clean cylinder head bolt holes.

13) If both cylinder heads are removed or crankshaft is to be turned, install timing chain support bracket tool (5105) and remove timing gear chain holder tool (5213). *See Fig. 2.*

14) When ONLY replacing cylinder head gasket, clean gasket surfaces and check for warpage. Clean valve cover. Use a steel rule and feeler gauge to check warpage, maximum warpage is .002" (.05 mm) over 4.0" (100 mm) length. If warpage exceeds measurement, replace head.

Fig. 1: Cylinder Head Tightening Sequence

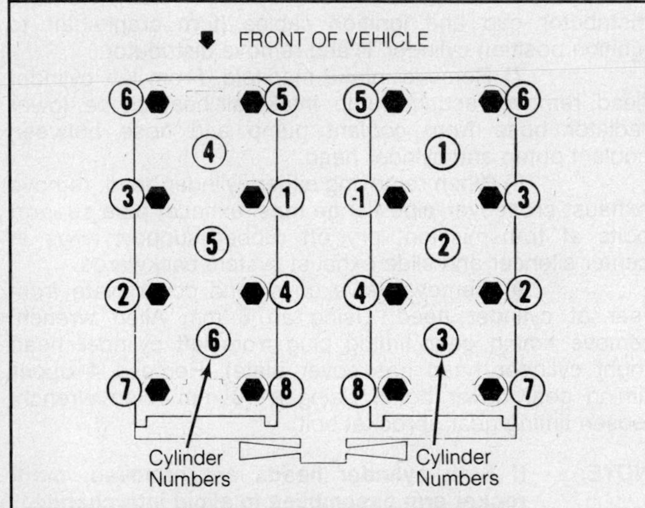
FRONT OF VEHICLE
Cylinder Numbers
Cylinder Numbers

Reverse sequence when removing cylinder head bolts.

Installation

1) Install timing gear chain holder tool (5213) and remove timing gear chain support bracket tool (5105) from cylinder block face. Close cylinder block drain cocks. Install guide sleeves and insert a .118" (3 mm) drill bit under each sleeve.

2) Remove cylinder liner holder tools (5093) and protective paper, then install cylinder head gasket. Position cylinder head on block face. Install cylinder head with one bolt and push camshaft into timing gear sprocket. Install timing gear sprocket bolt but do not torque.

NOTE: Make sure camshaft does not catch on locking plate and sprocket fits correctly on camshaft groove.

3) Remove drill bits from under guide sleeves. Position rocker arm shaft assemblies (right and left rocker arm assemblies) and install cylinder head bolts. Torque all bolts in sequence in three stages. *See Fig. 1.*

4) Remove timing gear chain holder tool (5213). Position camshaft locking plate and tighten bolt. Using a 10 mm Allen wrench and screwdriver to hold chain, torque timing gear sprocket bolt to 52-66 ft. lbs. (70-90 N.m).

CYLINDER HEAD TIGHTENING SPECIFICATIONS

Sequence	Ft. Lbs. (N.m)
First Step	7 (10)
Second Step	22 (30)
Third Step [1]	44 (60)

[1] – After third step, tightening must be completed using a protractor tool (5098).

5) Apply sealer to timing gear cover. Install timing gear cover and replace 4 upper bolts. Using an 8 mm Allen wrench, install timing gear plug on left cylinder head. Replace cover plate on right side using a new "O" ring. Install cover plate at rear of cylinder head using a new gasket.

Fig. 2: Removing Cylinder Head With Special Tools

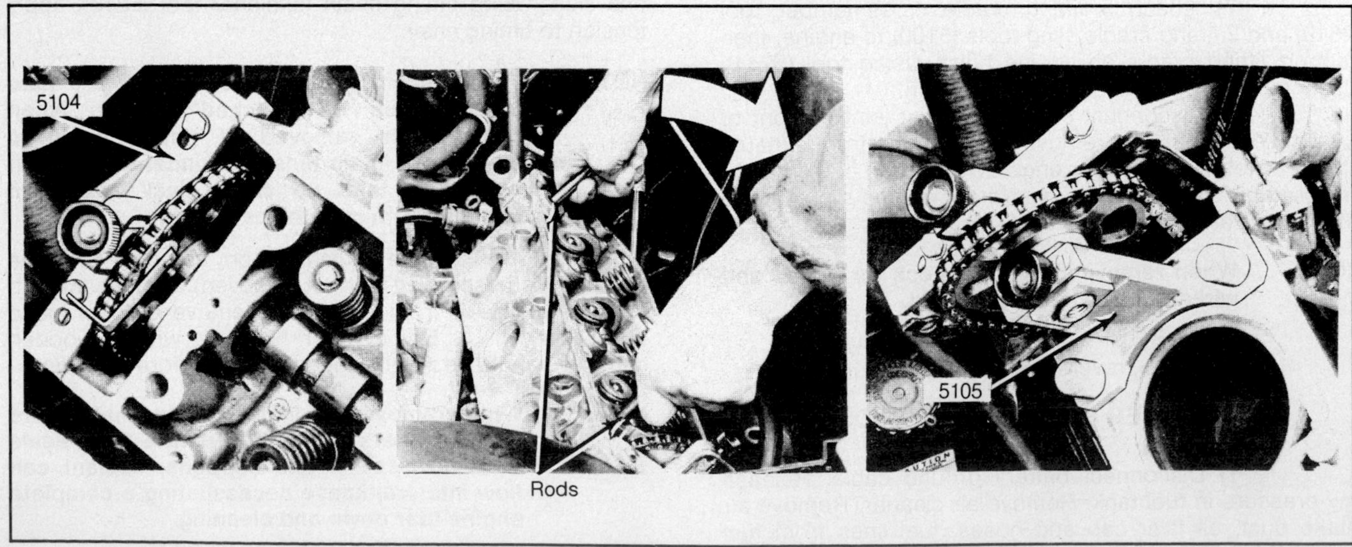
5104
Rods
5105

Use of special tools indicated will aid in removal and installation.

Volvo Engines

B28F V6 (Cont.)

6) Wait 10-15 minutes after torquing head bolts. Loosen all head bolts in sequence and retorque to 11-15 ft. lbs. (15-20 N.m). Using protractor tool (5098) on a standard socket, angle torque head bolts to 113-117° in sequence using rocker arm shaft as a reference line.

7) Adjust valve clearance *See Fig. 8.* when engine is cold. Refer to *Valve Clearance Adjustment* in this section. Turn crankshaft until No. 1 cylinder is at TDC, then install distributor with rotor pointing toward notch on housing. *See Figs. 3 & 5.*

Fig. 3: Installing Volvo V6 Distributor

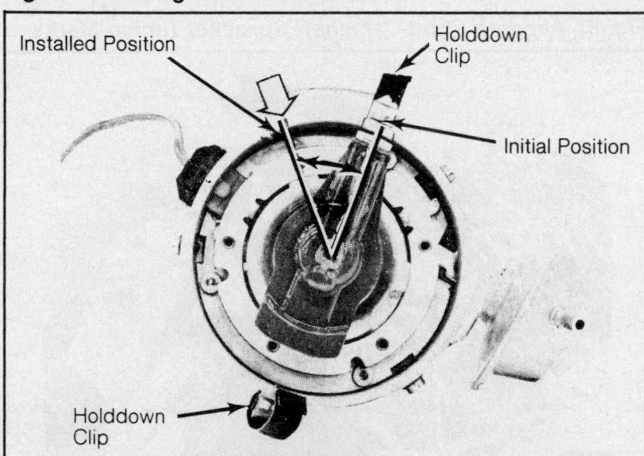
Installed Position
Holddown Clip
Initial Position
Holddown Clip

Align rotor as shown prior to installation.

8) Install valve covers and gaskets. Complete reassembly procedures by reversing removal procedures. After engine is assembled, run engine for 15 minutes and cool for 30 minutes. Back off head bolts once more and torque to 11-15 ft. lbs. (15-20 N.m).

9) Using protractor tool (5098), torque to 113-117° in sequence. *See Fig. 4.* Reinstall valve covers and torque to 7-11 ft. lbs. (10-15 N.m). Check and adjust throttle control cable, ignition timing, idle speed and CO%.

Fig. 4: Final Tightening of Cylinder Head Bolts

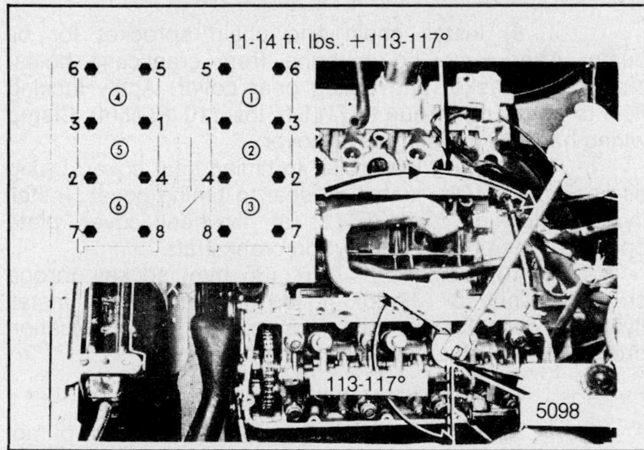
11-14 ft. lbs. +113-117°
6 5 5 6
4 1
3 1 1 3
5 2
2 4 4 2
6 3
7 8 8 7
113-117°
5098

Perform this step only after running and cooling engine.

CAMSHAFT

CAMSHAFT

Removal

1) Remove valve cover and cover plate from rear of cylinder head. Using an 8 mm Allen wrench, remove timing gear timing plug from left cylinder head (right cylinder head has cover plate). Remove 4 upper timing gear cover bolts. Using a 10 mm Allen wrench, loosen timing gear sprocket bolt.

NOTE: If both cylinder heads are removed, mark rocker arm assemblies to avoid interchange.

2) Loosen rocker arm shaft assembly bolts in same sequence as for tightening and remove rocker arm shaft assembly. Loosen camshaft lock plate and move to one side. Using timing gear chain tensioner tool (5213), apply tension to timing chain.

NOTE: Timing gear chain tensioner tool (5213) will hold timing chain in stretched position when camshaft is removed. If timing chain is slackened, chain tensioner under timing gear cover will take up chain slack making it impossible to reinstall camshaft.

3) Remove camshaft from timing gear sprocket (left side bolt can be unscrewed but not removed). Replace timing gear chain tensioner tool (5213) with timing gear support bracket tool (5105). Move camshaft to rear to free it from sprocket.

Installation

1) Install timing gear chain tensioner tool (5213) and remove timing gear chain support bracket tool (5105) from cylinder block face. Push camshaft into timing gear sprocket. Install timing gear sprocket bolt but do not torque.

NOTE: Make sure camshaft does not catch on locking plate and sprocket fits correctly on camshaft groove.

2) Remove timing gear chain tensioner tool (5213). Position camshaft locking plate and tighten bolt. Using a 10 mm Allen wrench and screwdriver to hold chain, torque timing gear sprocket bolt to 52-66 ft. lbs. (70-90 N.m).

3) Place sealer on timing gear cover. Install timing gear cover and replace 4 upper bolts. Using an 8 mm Allen wrench, install timing gear plug on left cylinder head.

4) Check camshaft end play, it should not exceed .02" (.15 mm), if so replace lock plate. Install cover plate on right side using a new "O" ring. Install cover plate at rear of cylinder head using a new gasket.

TIMING GEAR COVER

Removal

1) Disconnect battery ground cable. Remove splash guard, AC compressor, oil tube from oil cooler, electrical leads from thermal sensor on radiator, fan shroud, radiator and hoses, alternator and power steering pump belts.

2) Remove power steering pump from bracket, fan, water pump pulley and drive belts, air intake duct, vacuum pump, oil filler cap, control pressure regulator and ignition system connector. Turn crankshaft so pulley mark No. 1 is opposite 0° mark. Remove both valve covers and flywheel cover a left side of transmission.

3) Install flywheel locking tool (5112) at fly-wheel opening of transmission. Using a 1 7/16" (36 mm) socket, remove crankshaft nut. Remove pulley while key is on top of shaft (prevents dropping key in crankcase). Remove timing gear cover. Plug hole in oil pan with paper. Tap out timing gear seal.

B28F V6 (Cont.)

Installation

1) Clean surfaces and place gaskets on block and timing gear cover. Install cover and tighten bolts to 7-11 ft. lbs. (10-15 N.m). Using a crankshaft oil seal driver tool (5103), install crankshaft oil seal.

2) Using flywheel locking tool (5112) and a 1 7/16" (36 mm) socket, install crankshaft pulley and tighten crankshaft nut to 177-207ft. lbs. (240-280 N.m). Complete installation procedures by reversing removal procedures.

CHAINS & SPROCKETS

Removal

1) Remove timing gear cover. Using a 10 mm Allen wrench and screwdriver, remove camshaft bolts. Turn each timing gear chain tensioner lock 1/4 turn counterclockwise and push in piston to slacken camshaft chains.

2) Remove oil pump sprocket and chain, both tensioners, oil strainers, and curved and straight dampers. Remove camshaft sprockets and chains. Stuff rags in holes near crankcase to keep key from falling in crankcase. From crankshaft, remove outer sprocket, inner double sprocket and key (either by hand or with puller).

Installation

1) Place inner key on crankshaft. Install inner double sprocket (line on sprocket should face outward). Install outer key and outer sprocket, new strainers, chain tensioners, curved and straight dampers. Apply locking fluid to bolts.

2) Rotate crankshaft so key aligns with camshaft in left bank (No. 1 cylinder at TDC). Position camshaft so key points upward (rocker arms for No. 1 cylinder should have no clearance).

3) Place chain on camshaft sprocket so that mark on sprocket is between 2 marks on timing chain. *See Fig. 6.* Place chain on inner crankshaft sprocket so timing mark on sprocket is facing mark on crankshaft sprocket.

4) Chain should be stretched on tension side (side against straight chain damper). Install left camshaft sprocket onto camshaft so that pin on sprocket slips into recess in camshaft. Use a screwdriver to hold sprocket and tighten center bolt to 52-66 ft. lbs. (70-90 N.m).

Fig. 5: Aligning Crankshaft Timing Marks

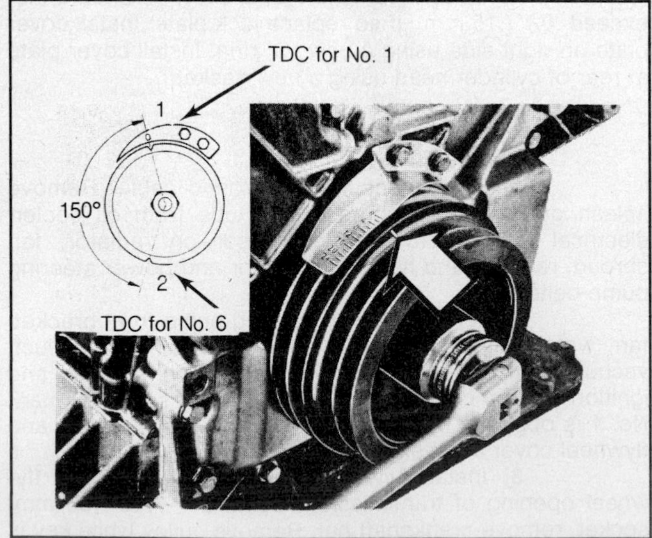
TDC for No. 1
1
150°
2
TDC for No. 6

Set crankshaft to firing position for No. 1 cylinder.

5) Rotate crankshaft clockwise so that key points straight downward. Set right side camshaft so keyway is in position shown in *Fig. 6.* Place chain on crankshaft center sprocket so mark on crankshaft aligns with mark on timing chain. Place chain on camshaft sprocket so that mark on sprocket is between 2 marks on timing chain.

6) Fit sprocket on camshaft with chain stretched on tension side. Pin on sprocket should slip into camshaft recess. Use a screwdriver to hold sprocket and torque center bolt to 52-66 ft. lbs. (70-90 N.m).

Fig. 6: Aligning Right Camshaft Sprocket Timing Marks

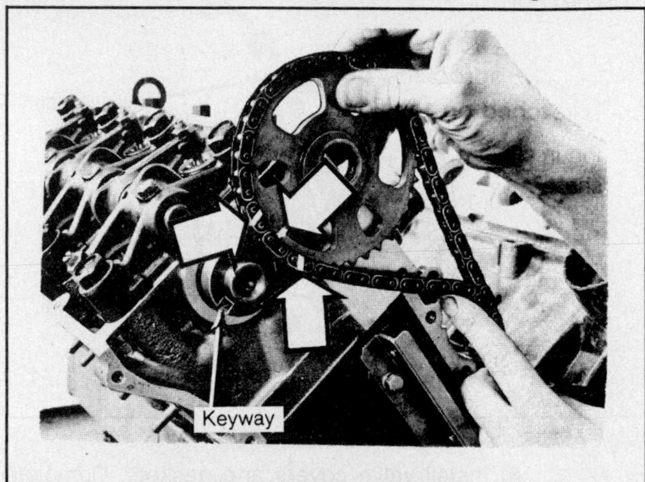
Keyway

Align timing marks and keyway as shown.

7) Turn lock on each chain tensioner 1/4 turn clockwise. Set chain tension by rotating crankshaft 2 full turns in direction of rotation (clockwise).

NOTE: **After rotating crankshaft, marks on chains and sprockets will not coincide. It may be necessary to rotate crankshaft several times before marks will coincide.**

8) Install chain and chain sprocket for oil pump. After removing covering from crankcase holes, install new gasket and timing gear cover. Apply locking fluid to bolts and torque to 7-11 ft. lbs. (10-15 N.m). Clamp wiring harness to timing gear cover.

9) Fit off-load roller to timing gear cover. Using oil seal tool (5103), install oil seal to timing cover. Install flywheel locking tool (5112) at flywheel cover plate opening. Place pulley and nut on crankshaft.

10) Using a 1 7/16" (36 mm) socket, torque crankshaft nut to 177-207 ft. lbs. (240-280 N.m). Install flywheel cover plate at transmission. Complete installation procedures by reversing removal procedures.

IGNITION TIMING PLATE

1) Remove intake manifold and coolant pump. Remove rear plug at top front of engine block. Rotate crankshaft so that TDC of No. 1 cylinder is at 20° mark on timing plate. *See Fig. 5.*

2) Insert a long 5/16" (8 mm) drill bit or similar rod into hole and against crankshaft counterweight. *See Fig. 7.* Rotate crankshaft in direction of normal rotation until drill bit can drop into recess in counterweight (TDC for No. 1 cylinder).

B28F V6 (Cont.)

NOTE: Do not drop drill bit into engine. Use drill or rod up to 10" long.

Fig. 7: Locating Top Dead Center of No. 1 Cylinder

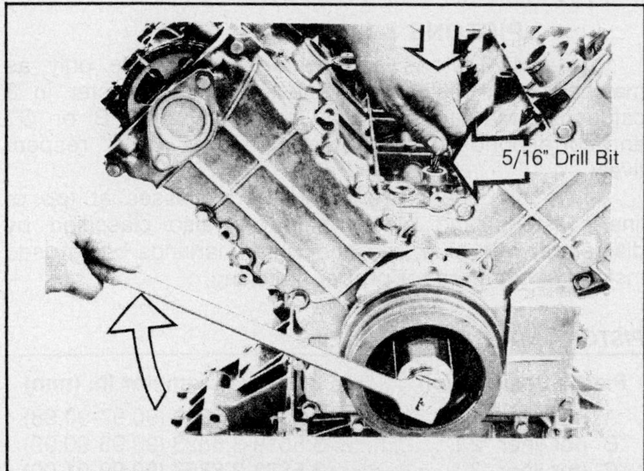
5/16" Drill Bit

Use a 5/16" (8 mm) rod or drill bit up to 10" long.

3) Loosen two bolts and adjust timing plate so that 0° mark is aligned with pulley mark. Tighten 2 bolts and remove drill bit or rod. Install plug with new seal and torque to 26-30 ft. lbs. (35-40 N.m). Reinstall coolant pump and intake manifold.

ROCKER ARM ASSEMBLY

Removal

1) Remove valve cover from rear of cylinder head. Loosen rocker arm shaft assembly bolts in same sequence as for tightening and remove rocker arm shaft assembly. Remove lock ring from end of shaft. Remove rocker arms, shaft supports, spacer sleeves and springs.

2) Keep all parts in order for correct assembly. Remove lock bolt and rocker shaft support from rocker shaft. Check shaft-to-arm clearance. New part clearance is .0005-.002" (.012-.054 mm). Replace worn parts as necessary.

Installation

1) Install rocker shaft support on rocker shaft with lubricating holes pointing downward. Flat top surface should face toward lock ring groove in other end of shaft. Tighten lock bolt.

2) Install thick spacer, exhaust rocker arm, thin spacer, intake rocker arm, spring and rocker shaft support, in order. After installing rocker arm parts, install lock ring in rocker shaft groove.

VALVES

VALVE ARRANGEMENT

Right Bank - E-I-E-I-E-I (Front-to-rear).
Left Bank - I-E-I-E-I-E (Front-to-rear).

VALVE STEM OIL SEALS AND VALVE SPRINGS

With cylinder head removed from engine, remove spark plugs, injectors, rear cover plate, lock plate and camshaft. Using a valve spring compressor, remove valve keepers, spring retainer, spring, lower spring seat and valve. Remove valve guide seal from guide. Place valves in order in rack.

VALVE GUIDE SERVICING

1) Check valve guides for wear. If replacement is necessary, press out old guide using drift tool (5218). Ream hole in cylinder head to oversize class 1 or 2.

2) Heat cylinder head to 300° F (150° C) and cool valve guides to -95° F (-70° C). Press valve guides into cylinder heat quickly (3-4 seconds, because of high temperature loss.

3) Using drift tool (5108) for intake or (5109) for exhaust, press in new guides. Using reamer tool (5224), ream guides to .3150-.3158" (8.00-8.02 mm). Check for burrs and be sure valves move freely in guides. Using drift tool (5218), install valve guide seals

RECONDITIONING VALVES

1) After inspection, grind valves, mill or grind valve seats and lap valves with grinding paste, as necessary. Check valve springs for proper length and tension.

2) Install seals, valves, spring seats, spring and spring retainers. Compress spring and install keepers. Remove spring compressor tool and reinstall all parts previously removed from cylinder head.

VALVE CLEARANCE ADJUSTMENT

1) Rotate crankshaft with 1 7/16" (36 mm) wrench to bring No. 1 piston to TDC. *See Fig. 5.* In this position, both rocker arms for No. 1 cylinder should have clearance.

2) Check and adjust following cylinders for clearance: Intake valves on cylinders 1, 2, and 4; exhaust valves on cylinders 1, 3, and 6. *See Fig. 8.*

Fig. 8: Valve Clearance Adjustment Sequence

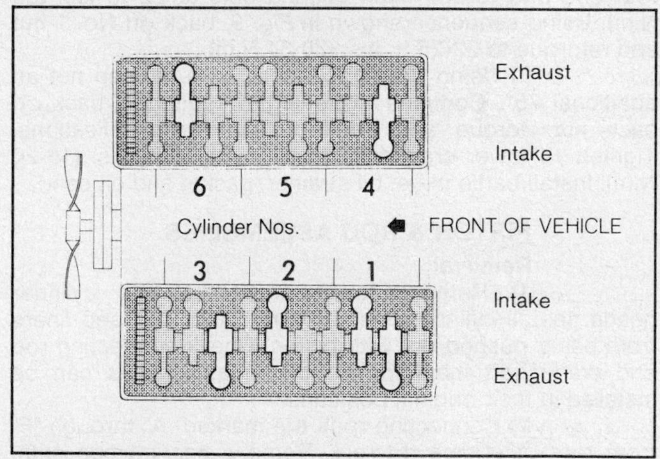
Exhaust
Intake
6
5
4
Cylinder Nos.
FRONT OF VEHICLE
3
2
1
Intake
Exhaust

Adjust valves with engine cold.

VALVE CLEARANCE SPECIFICATIONS [1]

Valve	In. (mm)
Intake	.004-.006" (.10-.15 mm)
Exhaust	.010-.012" (.25-.30 mm)

[1] - Cold engine.

3) Rotate crankshaft one full turn so marking is again opposite 0° mark. Rocker arms for No. 1 cylinder will now have clearance. Check and adjust following cylinders for clearance: Intake valves on cylinders 3, 5, and 6; exhaust valves on cylinders 2, 4, and 5. *See Fig. 8.*

B28F V6 (Cont.)

PISTONS, PINS & RINGS

LOWER CRANKCASE

Removal

Remove oil pan, gasket, oil strainer and baffle plate. Remove 14 crankcase bolts and 8 main bearing nuts. Lift off lower crankcase. Install main bearing cap retainers (5096) on two outer bearings.

Installation

1) Install rubber ring for oil channel. Clean and apply sealing compound to crankcase and block surfaces. Remove main bearing cap retainers and install lower crankcase.

Fig. 9: Main Bearing Cap Tightening Sequence

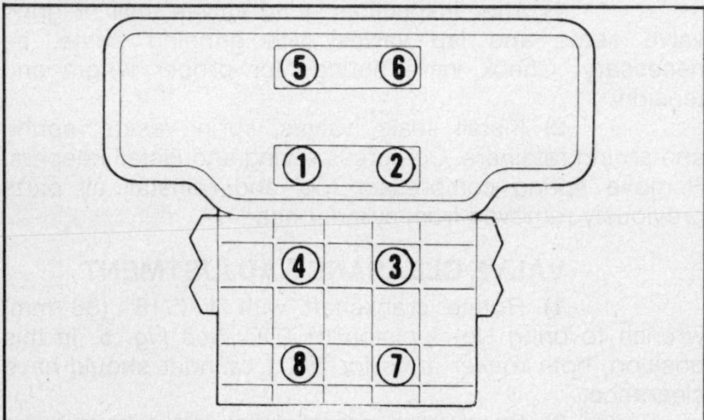
5
6
1
2
4
3
8
7

Follow sequence shown when tightening main bearing caps.

2) Be sure crankcase and block are flush at rear end and torque main bearing nuts to 22 ft. lbs. (30 N.m). Using sequence shown in *Fig. 9,* back off No. 1 nut and retorque to 22-25 ft. lbs. (30-34 N.m).

3) Using protractor tool (5098), tighten nut an additional 75°. Continue tightening in sequence, back off each nut, torque and angle tighten to specifications. Tighten 14 lower crankcase bolts to 11-15 ft. lbs. (15-20 N.m). Install baffle plate, oil strainer, gasket and oil pan.

PISTON & ROD ASSEMBLIES

Removal

1) Remove lower crankcase and cylinder heads. Install cylinder liner holders (5093) to keep liners from being pushed out with piston. Check connecting rod and crankshaft markings so piston assemblies can be installed in their original positions.

2) Connecting rods are marked "A" through "F" from rear of engine to front. Remove bearing cap nuts, bearing caps and push piston assembly out through top of bore. Remove big end bearing.

3) Remove piston rings. Clean ring grooves and piston of any carbon deposits. Measure side clearance and end gap of piston rings with a feeler gauge. Replace any components not within specifications.

Installation

1) Install piston rings with end gaps at 120° angles from each other. Offset gaps on oil control rings. Note position marking on compression rings and install with markings pointing up. *See Fig. 10.*

2) Lightly lubricate rings. Using installation tool (5106), press piston into proper bore. Make sure that stamped arrow on top of piston is pointing toward front of engine. This will produce a clearance between big end bearing and crankshaft journal.

3) This clearance should be positioned behind for cylinders 1, 2 and 3, and in front for cylinders 4, 5 and 6. Install bearing cap and tighten to 33-37 ft. lbs. (45-50 N.m).

PISTONS & LINERS

1) Pistons and liners are available only as matched sets. Pistons are classified by diameter in 3 categories. Marking on piston top is either "A", "B" or "C", and corresponds to liners marked "1", "2" or "3" respectively.

2) Liners are marked in recesses at top of liner. Pistons and piston pins are also classified by diameters, with blue, red and white markings being used instead of numbers for proper matching.

PISTON AND LINER DIAMETERS

Piston Designation	Diameter In. (mm)
"A" (for liner "1")	3.5815-3.5819 (90.97-90.98)
"B" (for liner "2")	3.5819-3.5823 (90.98-90.99)
"C" (for liner "3")	3.5823-3.5827 (90.99-91.00)
Liner Designation	**Diameter In. (mm)**
"1" (for piston "A")	3.5827-3.5831 (91.00-91.01)
"2" (for piston "B")	3.5831-3.5835 (91.01-91.02)
"3" (for piston "C")	3.5835-3.5839 (91.02-91.03)

3) Measure piston diameter at right angles to pin bore. Take measurements .32" (8.0 mm) above lower edge. With an inside dial indicator, check cylinder liner taper, wear and out-of-round.

4) Take measurement for maximum wear immediately below top dead center and at a right angle to engine center line. Take measurement for minimum wear at bottom dead center of piston stroke.

5) To determine piston-to-cylinder clearance, subtract piston diameter from maximum and minimum bore diameters. Do not remove pistons from connecting rods, unless piston and liner replacement is necessary.

6) If liner is to be removed for cleaning or inspection, mark liner and block with colored pen. Do not damage gasket surface. Remove liner holders and pull up liners.

7) When installing liners, be sure contact surfaces on block and liner are clean and without defect. Install No. 1 liner first (without shims) using previous pen markings for alignment.

8) Tighten liner by hand, using two liner holders (5093). Using a dial indicator, measure liner height above block at three points. Largest measurement should not exceed smallest measurement by more than .002" (.05 mm).

9) Liner should be as close to .006-.009" (.16-.23 mm) above block face as possible. Use correct shims to achieve dimension.

LINER SHIM THICKNESSES [1]

Color	Thickness - In. (mm)
Blue	.0028-.0041 (.070-.105)
White	.0033-.0047 (.085-.120)
Red	.0041-.0055 (.105-.140)
Yellow	.0051-.0065 (.130-.165)

[1] – Use same thickness shims for all liners.

Volvo Engines

B28F V6 (Cont.)

Fig. 10: Installing Piston Rings

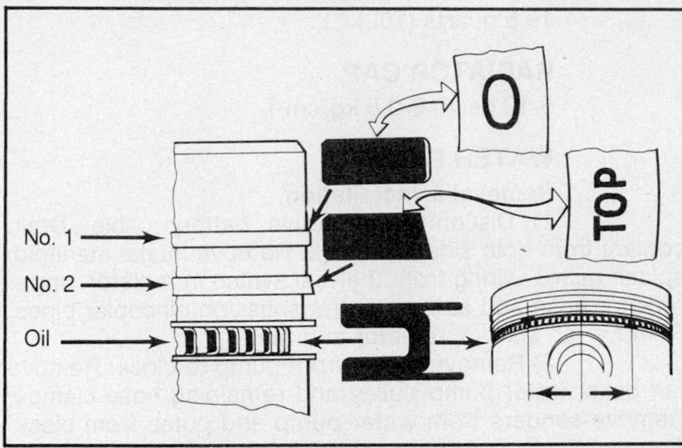
O
TOP
No. 1
No. 2
Oil

Install rings with identification mark facing upward.

10) Install shims with color marking up and positioned as shown in *Fig. 11*. Inner tabs on shims should be in liner groove.

Fig. 11: Positioning Shims on Liners

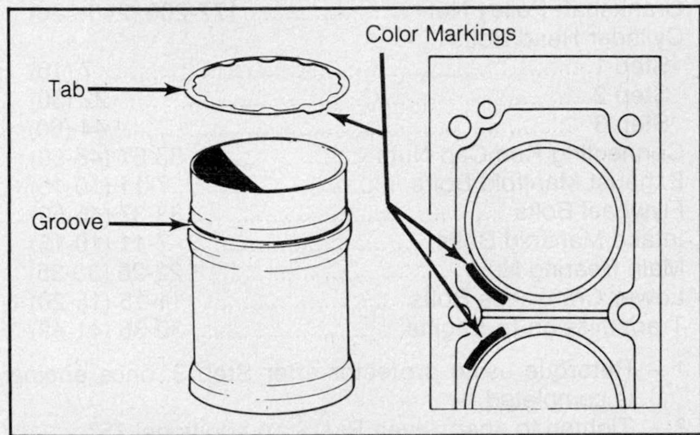
Color Markings
Tab
Groove

Tabs on shim should engage groove on liner.

11) After shimming, install four liner holders (5093) for each bank. Again measure each liner at three points. Largest and smallest dimensions should be within .002" (.05 mm).

12) Measure three liners at points shown in *Fig. 12*. Difference in measurements between points "1" and "2" and between "3" and "4" should not exceed .006-.009" (.16-.23 mm). If height difference is excessive, change shims.

Fig. 12: Checking Liner Height Above Block Face

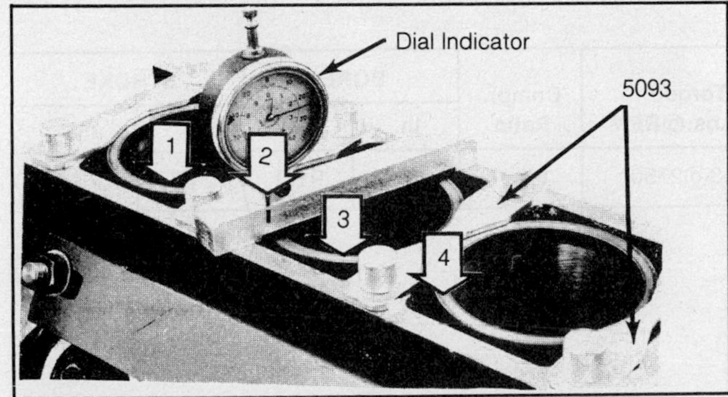
Dial Indicator
5093
1
2
3
4

Liner should protrude .006-.0091" (.16-.23 mm) above block.

CRANKSHAFT MAIN & CONNECTING ROD BEARINGS

MAIN AND CONNECTING ROD BEARINGS

Removal

1) Remove oil pan, lower crankcase, cylinder heads, clutch, drive plate or flywheel, spacer (automatic transmission) and input shaft pilot bearing (manual transmission). Remove seal holder and use a screwdriver to pry out oil seal. Press new seal in flush with retainer.

2) Check main bearing cap markings (marked 1 through 4, from rear-to-front). Remove main bearing retainers and caps. Remove upper and lower thrust bearings and lift out crankshaft. Remove main bearings from block and caps.

NOTE: **Thrust bearing is located on flywheel end of crankshaft.**

Installation

1) After inspecting crankshaft and measuring journals for wear, position oiled main bearings with oil holes to engine block. Carefully set crankshaft into place. Oil and install thrust bearings with notched ends in engine block groove.

2) Oil and install unnotched thrust bearings on crankshaft. Noting that cap identification number faces front of engine, lubricate bearing shell and position in bearing cap. Install bearing cap and bearing retainers (5096).

3) Using a dial indicator, measure crankshaft end play and install thrust washers to bring end play to .0028-.0106" (.07-.27 mm). Oil remaining bearing shells, place in caps and install, noting that cap number points toward front of engine.

4) Install main bearing retainer on rear main cap and 1 nut on each remaining bearing cap to keep them in place until ready to install lower crankcase. Install lower crankcase and torque main caps. See Lower Crankcase.

ENGINE OILING

CRANKCASE CAPACITY

6.9 quarts (6.5L) with oil filter change, and 6.3 quarts (6.0L) without filter change.

OIL FILTER

Full-flow type, disposable, spin-on element.

OIL PRESSURE

With engine warm and a new filter installed, minimum 14.2 psi (1.0 kg/cm²) @ 900 RPM, and 57 psi (4 kg/cm²) @ 3000 RPM.

ENGINE OILING SYSTEM

Engine utilizes a force-feed lubrication system. Oil moves from oil pan through strainer to oil pump and full-flow oil filter mounted outside of engine block assembly. Oil is pressure fed from filter to drilled galleries in block.

Volvo Engines

B28F V6 (Cont.)

Lubricant moves under pressure to main bearings, which are drilled to pass oil on to connecting rod and camshaft bearings, upward in block to rocker arm shafts.

Excess or run-off oil drains back down into oil pan through drain holes in cylinder head. Cylinder walls and piston rings are lubricated by splash from connecting rods.

OIL PUMP SPECIFICATIONS

Dimension Application	In.(mm)
Backlash	[1] .007-.011 (.17-.27)
Bearing Clearance, Driving Shaft	.0006-.0021 (.015-.053)
Bearing Clearance, Trailing Shaft	.0006-.0020 (.015-.051)
Clearance Tooth-to-Housing	[1] .0043-.0073 (.110-.185)
End Play	.0010-.0033 (.025-.084)
Relief Valve Spring Length, No Load	3.52 (89.5)

[1] – Excluding bearing clearance.

OIL PUMP

Oil pump is stocked as a complete unit (housing cover with impeller and relief valve). Inspect housing, cover and gears for damage or wear. Replace if necessary.

Removal

Remove drive belts, crankshaft pulley and timing gear cover. Remove oil pump drive sprocket and chain. Remove 4 retaining bolts and lift out oil pump with gears.

Installation

Place gears on shaft and lubricate pump housing, gears and shaft. Install pump assembly, ensuring pump gears and shafts are centered in housing before tightening bolts. Install pump drive sprocket and chain. Install remaining components in reverse of removal order.

ENGINE COOLING

THERMOSTAT

Wax-type. Begins to open at 196-200°F (91-93°C); fully open at 215°F (102°C). Marking, 198°F (92°C).

COOLING SYSTEM CAPACITY

10.5 quarts (10L).

RADIATOR CAP

9-12 psi (0.6-0.8 kg/cm²).

WATER PUMP

Removal & Installation

1) Disconnect negative battery cable. Drain coolant from both sides of block. Remove intake manifold, splash guard, wiring from thermal switch in radiator, upper radiator hose and automatic transmission oil cooler pipes. Remove fan shroud, radiator and fan.

2) Remove hoses from pump to block. Remove fan belts, water pump pulley and remaining hose clamps. Remove senders from water pump and pump from block. Remove cover and thermostat from pump body. Install in reverse order.

TIGHTENING SPECIFICATIONS

Application	Ft. Lbs. (N.m)
Camshaft Center Bolt	52-66 (70-90)
Crankshaft Pulley Nut	177-206 (240-280)
Cylinder Head Bolts	
Step 1	7 (10)
Step 2	22 (30)
Step 3	[1] 44 (60)
Connecting Rod Cap Nuts	33-37 (45-50)
Exhaust Manifold Bolts	7-11 (10-15)
Flywheel Bolts	33-37 (45-50)
Intake Manifold Bolts	7-11 (10-15)
Main Bearing Nuts	[2] 22-26 (30-35)
Lower Crankcase Bolts	11-15 (15-20)
Transmission-to-Engine	30-36 (41-49)

[1] – Retorque using protector after Step 3, once engine is completed.

[2] – Tighten to spec. given PLUS an additional 75°.

ENGINE SPECIFICATIONS

GENERAL SPECIFICATIONS

Year	DISPLACEMENT		Fuel System	HP@RPM	Torque Ft. Lbs.@RPM	Compr. Ratio	BORE		STROKE	
	Cu. In.	Liters					In.	mm	In.	mm
1983	174	2.8	Fuel Inj.	130@5500	153@2750	8.8:1	3.58	91.0	2.87	73.0

Volvo Engines

B28F V6 (Cont.)

ENGINE SPECIFICATIONS (Cont.)

VALVES

Engine Size & Valve	Head Diam. In. (mm)	Face Angle	Seat Angle	Seat Width In. (mm)	Stem Diameter In. (mm)	Stem Clearance In. (mm)	Valve Lift In. (mm)
2.8L							
Intake	1.73 (44)	29.5°	30°	.051-.067 (1.3-1.7)	.3139-.3145 (7.97-7.99)	.006-.008 (.15-.20)	.2142 (5.44)
Exhaust	1.46 (37)	44.5°	45°	.079-.094 (2.0-2.4)	.3136-.3142 (7.96-7.98)	.012-.014 (.30-.35)	.2339 (5.94)

1 – Stem diameter gets larger from head of valve toward stem, where above measurement is taken.

PISTONS, PINS, RINGS

Engine	PISTONS	PINS		RINGS		
	Clearance In. (mm)	Piston Fit In. (mm)	Rod Fit In. (mm)	Ring No.	End Gap In. (mm)	Side Clearance In. (mm)
2.8L	.0008-.0016 (.020-.040)	.0004-.0006 (.010-.015)	.0008-.0016 (.020-.041)	Comp. 1	.016-.024 (.40-.60)	.0018-.0029 (.045-.074)
				Comp. 2	.016-.024 (.40-.60)	.0010-.0021 (.025-.054)
				Oil	.016-.057 (.40-1.45)	.0004-.0092 (.009-.233)

CRANKSHAFT MAIN & CONNECTING ROD BEARINGS

Engine	MAIN BEARINGS				CONNECTING ROD BEARINGS		
	Journal Diam. In. (mm)	Clearance In. (mm)	Thrust Bearing	Crankshaft End Play In. (mm)	Journal Diam. In. (mm)	Clearance In. (mm)	Side Play In. (mm)
2.8L	2.7576-2.7583 (70.043-70.062)	.0015-.0035 (.038-.088)	.....	.0028-.0106 (.070-.270)	2.0578-2.0585 (52.267-52.286)	.0012-.0031 (.030-.080)	.008-.015 (.20-.38)

VALVE SPRINGS

Engine	Free Length In. (mm)	PRESSURE Lbs. @ In. (Kg @ mm)	
		Valve Closed	Valve Open
2.8L	1.854 (47.1)	52-60@1.57 (24-27@40)	132-152@1.181 (61-69@30)

CAMSHAFT

Engine	Journal Diam. In. (mm)	Clearance In. (mm)	Lobe Lift In. (mm)
2.8L			
Front	1.5921-1.5931 (40.440-40.465)	1 .0014-.0033 (.035-.085)	.....
2nd	1.6157-1.6173 (41.040-41.065)		
3rd	1.6394-1.6404 (41.640-41.665)		
4th	1.6630-1.6640 (42.240-42.265)		

1 – End play should be .0028-.0057" (.070-.144 mm)

Volvo Engines

D24 & D24T 6-CYLINDER DIESEL

ENGINE CODING

ENGINE IDENTIFICATION

The Volvo 6-cylinder diesel engine is designated D24 and the diesel turbo is designated D24T. The engine serial number is stamped in the block under the vacuum pump on left side of engine block. Digits 6 and 7 of the Vehicle Identification Number (VIN), located on top of instrument panel at lower left of windshield, also denotes engine usage. D24T engines are coded "76", and the D24, "77".

ENGINE IDENTIFICATION

Application	Code
D24	
Man. Trans.	498704
Auto. Trans.	498705
D24T	
Man. Trans.	.....
Auto. Trans.	.....

ENGINE, MANIFOLDS & CYLINDER HEAD

ENGINE

Removal

1) If equipped with a manual transmission, remove (at console) 4 clips and fold up rubber bellows, 3 back-up light connectors, blue wire at switch, bracket for reverse inhibitor and lock ring on gear lever. Move lock ring, rubber ring and plastic journal up on gear lever.

2) If equipped with automatic transmission, move selector to "PARK". Disconnect battery. Disconnect windshield washer hoses and remove hood. Remove splash guard and gas cap. Remove lower radiator hose, drain coolant and remove coolant hoses attached to engine. Disconnect lower hose at cold start device and turn end down to drain coolant.

3) If equipped with automatic transmission, disconnect oil tubes at radiator. Disconnect expansion tank. Remove radiator and any attached hoses. Disconnect electrical connector at firewall, hoses at heater control valve, hose at vacuum pump and accelerator cable from pulley and bracket.

4) Remove and plug fuel lines at filter and return line of injection pump (at clamp). Disconnect thin black wire of glow plug relay. Remove relay, hang it and wire bundle on engine. Remove power steering belt and pump with bracket, then move out-of-way.

5) Remove cooling fan, spacer, pulleys and drive belts. Remove air cleaner cover with hoses attached. Remove voltage regulator connector, screw holding wire bundle to wheel housing and place wire bundle on engine. Disconnect exhaust pipes at front and rear manifolds on all except turbocharged models.

6) If equipped with turbocharger, remove inlet hose from turbo pipe, air cleaner assembly and preheater hose. Remove snap rings from intake pipe and hose to blow-off valve. Remove snap ring from compressor intake pipe and plug hole immediately. Remove bolts retaining oil return pipe and oil delivery pipe, and plug holes.

7) Press turbocharger compressor pipe into intake pipe. Remove exhaust pipe from turbocharger. Remove exhaust pipe from transmission support bracket and disconnect joint. With mounting nuts removed, lower front end of turbocharger and remove.

8) For all vehicles, drain engine oil. Disconnect drive shaft, speedometer cable and gear lever from transmission. On vehicles with manual transmission, disconnect clutch cable and pull out from clutch lever and housing. If equipped with automatic transmission, disconnect shift lever.

9) Disconnect speedometer and drive shaft. Position jack under transmission, raise slightly and remove transmission crossmember. Detach engine mounts; remove nuts on left front axle member and lower nut from right front rubber pad. Attach lift beam tool (2810) and lift hook tools (5185 and 5186) or a lifting device to engine.

10) Move hoist to rear position on lift beam tool (2810) and hoist engine enough to off-load left engine mount. Remove jack from under transmission. Move hoist to front position and carefully lift out engine, ensuring all wires and hoses clear assembly.

Installation

To install engine, reverse removal procedures. Adjust clutch cable clearance to .063-.125" (1-3 mm). If equipped with manual transmission, engage 1st gear, adjust clearance between shifting yoke and gear shift lever to .020-.060" (.5-1.5 mm). If equipped with automatic transmission, place selector lever in "DRIVE" and adjust

CYLINDER HEAD

Removal

1) Remove splash guard, expansion tank cap and lower radiator hose. Drain radiator and disconnect battery. Disconnect exhaust pipe from transmission bracket. Disconnect exhaust pipe from rear and front exhaust manifold of engine. If equipped with turbocharger, refer to steps **6)** and **7)** of *Engine, Manifolds and Cylinder Head*.

2) Disconnect air cleaner cover with intake and crankcase hose. Disconnect lower hose of cold start device, turn hose down and drain coolant. Disconnect upper radiator hose and cold start device hose. Disconnect vacuum pump and move to wheel housing. Remove vacuum pump plunger from cylinder head.

3) Using compressed air, blow dirt away from fuel delivery pipe area. Remove and plug fuel delivery pipes. Disconnect at cylinder head, temperature gauge sender wire, glow plug wire, rear glow plugs wire bundle, rear injector return hose and temperature gauge sender wire attachment at rear of cylinder head.

4) Remove valve cover and (front and rear) timing belt covers. Using a 1 1/16" (27 mm) socket on damper pulley bolt, set No. 1 piston at TDC (timing mark on flywheel at 0°). At front camshaft, remove 2 screws holding belt shield to cylinder head.

5) Loosen water pump and idler pulley bolts to remove timing belt from camshaft gear. Using spanner wrench tool (5199), hold front camshaft drive gear in place and remove center retaining bolt. *See Fig. 1.* Tap gear loose from camshaft tapered end.

NOTE: Camshaft MUST NOT rotate or damage to valves and pistons may result.

6) Remove injection pump drive belt by loosening retaining bracket bolts. Tighten 1 screw to hold pump in upper position. Use spanner wrench (5199) to hold rear camshaft sprocket and wrench (5201) to remove center retaining bolt. *See Fig. 1.* Tap gear loose from camshaft.

Volvo Engines

D24 & D24T 6-CYLINDER DIESEL (Cont.)

Fig. 1: Using Camshaft Gear Retaining Wrench

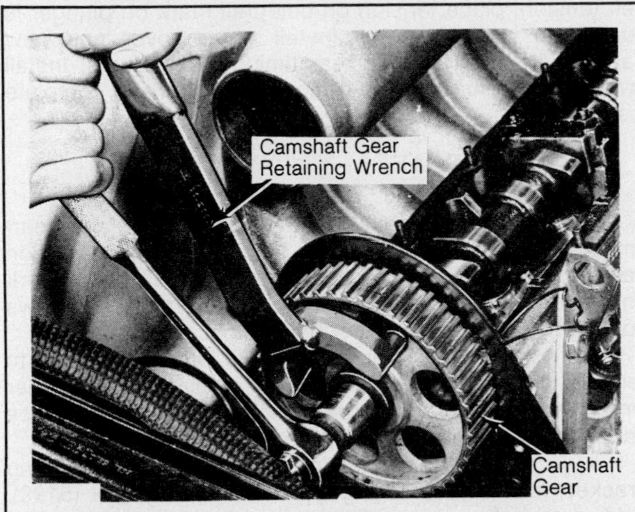
Camshaft Gear
Retaining Wrench
Camshaft
Gear

Camshaft MUST NOT rotate, or damage to valves and pistons could result.

7) Using a .394" (10 mm) Allen wrench, loosen cylinder head bolts in reverse order of tightening sequence. Carefully lift cylinder head from engine. Make sure rear glow plug clears injection pump bracket and valves do not touch cylinder walls. Set cylinder head on wooden blocks so it does not rest on valves.

Inspection

Clean all mating surfaces and check that cylinder head is not warped. Maximum allowable distortion is .008" (.2 mm) diagonally and .002" (.05 mm) crosswise.

NOTE: **Cracks between valve seats not wider than .02" (.5 mm) do not warrant replacement of cylinder head, as they do not impair engine function.**

Installation

1) Select a head gasket with same number of notches as previous gasket. If pistons, rods, or crankshaft were disassembled or repaired, piston projection above engine block must be measured. Use a dial indicator to measure each piston while at TDC. Select a proper gasket from Available Cylinder Head Gasket table.

AVAILABLE CYLINDER HEAD GASKETS

Piston Projection	Notches	Gasket Thickness
.026-.031" (.67-.80 mm)	1	.055" (1.4 mm)
.032-.035" (.81-.90 mm)	2	.059" (1.5 mm)
.036-.04" (.91-1.02 mm)	3	.063" (1.6 mm)

2) Remove rear glow plug to keep it from getting damaged when installing cylinder head. Install 2 dowel pin tools (5189), to outer bolt holes to guide cylinder head into position. With engine positioned at TDC, set camshaft for injection on cylinder No. 1 (both cam lobes of No. 1 cylinder should point up at equally large angles).

3) Carefully set cylinder head into place. Install head bolts with new washers, cone side facing up and oil threads and washers. Torque cylinder head bolts in 4 stages. Place camshaft lock gauge tool (5190) in camshaft groove at rear of cylinder head. Place a .08" (.2 mm) feeler gauge under left side of tool (5190). *See Fig. 3.*

NOTE: **Feeler gauge placed under camshaft lock gauge tool (5190) is to compensate for timing gear clearance.**

4) Install and set injection pump. See *Injection Pump Timing*. Position belt tension gauge tool (5197) on timing belt and set gauge to .50" (12.5 mm).

5) Using coolant pump to adjust timing gear belt tension, place tension on belt until mark on plunger is flush with gauge sleeve. Install valve cover and new gaskets. Install front and rear timing gear covers. Install and torque delivery pipes to 18 ft. lbs. (25 N.m).

CYLINDER HEAD TIGHTENING SPECIFICATIONS

Sequence	Ft. Lbs. (N.m)
Stage 1	30 (40)
Stage 2	44 (60)
Stage 3	50 (75)
Stage 4	Additional 1/2 turn

Fig. 2: Tightening Sequence For Cylinder Head

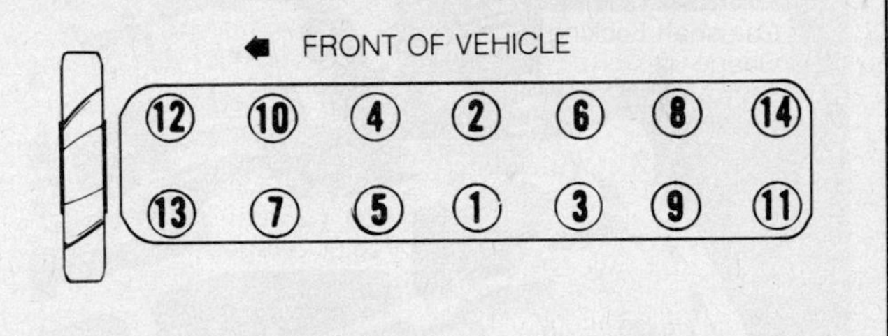
FRONT OF VEHICLE
12 10 4 2 6 8 14
13 7 5 1 3 9 11

Loosen in reverse order.

6) Complete installation by reversing removal procedure. Run engine until it reaches operating temperature. Remove valve cover, vacuum pump and vacuum pump plunger. Tighten cylinder head bolts in proper sequence an additional 1/4 turn.

NOTE: **After 600-1200 miles, cylinder head bolts must be retorqued. Vacuum pump and plunger must be removed to gain access to cylinder head bolt. With engine cool, tighten each bolt, in sequence, an additional 1/4 turn.**

CAMSHAFT

TIMING BELT

Removal

1) Remove splash guard, cooling fan, spacer, pulley, fan and power steering pump belts, power steering pump and expansion tank cap. Drain and remove radiator. Disconnect battery ground cable.

2) Remove valve cover and (front and rear) timing belt covers. Using a 1 1/16" (27 mm) socket on damper pulley bolt, set No. 1 piston at TDC (timing mark on flywheel at 0°). Loosen water pump and idler pulley bolts to remove timing belt from camshaft gear.

3) Using damper pulley wrench (5187) and damper pulley bolt tool (5188), remove damper pulley bolt. Using a .236" (6 mm) socket, remove 4 screws from damper pulley and pulley (it may be necessary to tap pulley from shaft). Remove lower belt shield and timing gear belt.

D24 & D24T 6-CYLINDER DIESEL (Cont.)

4) Remove center bolt from idler pulley. Using idler pulley removal tool (5202), remove idler pulley. Replace and tap new idler pulley into position. Using spanner wrench tool (5199), hold front camshaft drive gear in place and remove center retaining bolt. *See Fig. 1.*

NOTE: **Idler pulley must be replaced when replacing timing gear belt. Use puller (5202) or equivalent to remove pulley.**

NOTE: **Camshaft MUST NOT rotate or damage to valves and pistons may result.**

5) Tap gear loose from camshaft tapered end. Remove injection pump drive belt by loosening retaining bracket bolts. Tighten 1 screw to hold pump in upper position. Use spanner wrench tool (5199) to hold rear camshaft sprocket and wrench (5201) to remove center retaining bolt. Tap gear loose from camshaft. *See Fig. 1.*

Fig. 3: Setting Timing Using Camshaft Locking Gauge

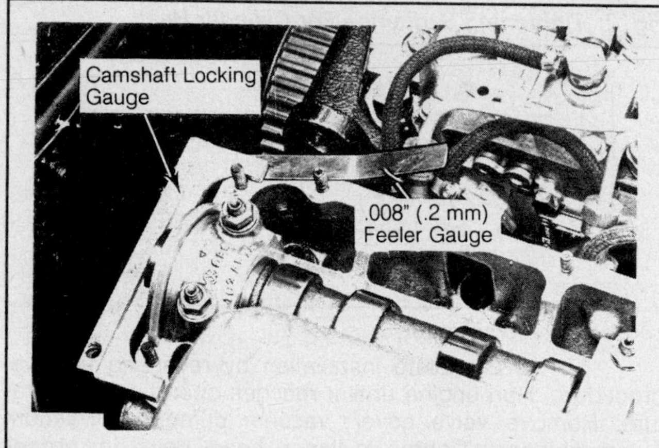
Camshaft Locking Gauge
.008" (.2 mm) Feeler Gauge

Installation

1) Check that No. 1 piston is at TDC, timing mark on flywheel is at 0° and camshaft lobes for No. 1 cylinder are faced up with equally large angles in comparison with cylinder head. Place camshaft lock gauge tool (5190) in camshaft groove at rear of cylinder head.

2) Place a .08" (.2 mm) feeler gauge under left side of camshaft lock gauge tool (5190). *See Fig. 3.* Install timing gear belt and damper pulley. Replace 4 damper pulley bolts and torque to 15 ft. lbs. (20 N.m).

NOTE: **Feeler gauge placed under camshaft lock gauge tool (5190) is to compensate for timing gear clearance.**

3) Using damper pulley wrench tools (5187 and 5188), install and torque center bolt (use sealing agent on center bolt threads) of damper pulley to 255 ft. lbs. (350 N.m). Install front timing gear belt and camshaft timing gear (make certain camshaft does not turn), torque to 33 ft. lbs. (45 N.m), after setting timing marks.

4) Remove camshaft gauge tool (5190) and feeler gauge from rear of camshaft. Install rear camshaft gear and injection pump belt. Set injection pump. See *Injection Pump Timing*.

5) Position belt tension gauge tool (5197) on timing and injection pump belt, set gauge to .50" (12.5 mm). Place tension on belt until mark on plunger is flush with gauge sleeve and tighten bolts.

6) Using coolant pump to adjust timing gear belt tension, place tension on belt until mark on plunger is flush with gauge sleeve. Install valve cover and new gaskets. Install front and rear timing gear covers. Install lower belt shield. Reverse removal procedure to complete installation.

CAMSHAFT

Removal

1) Remove valve cover and (front and rear) timing gear covers. Using a 1 1/16" (27 mm) socket on damper pulley bolt, set No. 1 piston at TDC (timing mark on flywheel at 0°). At front camshaft, remove 2 screws holding belt shield to cylinder head.

2) Loosen water pump and idler pulley bolts to remove timing belt from camshaft gear. Using spanner wrench tool (5199), hold front camshaft drive gear in place and remove center retaining bolt. *See Fig. 1.*

3) Loosen retaining bolts of injection pump bracket and remove timing gear belt. Using tool (5199), hold camshaft rear gear and remove center bolt with wrench tool (5201).

4) Remove camshaft drive gear, vacuum pump (place pump on wheel housing) and vacuum pump plunger. With engine at TDC, remove bearing caps 1 and 4. Alternately loosen cap nuts on caps 2 and 3. Lift out camshaft and remove seals.

Installation

1) Lightly lubricate bearings and contact surfaces. Place camshaft lock gauge tool (5190) in camshaft groove at rear of cylinder head. Place a .08" (.2 mm) feeler gauge under left side of camshaft lock gauge tool (5190). *See Fig. 3.* Position camshaft on cylinder head.

Fig. 4: Referencing Top Dead Center Mark of No. 1 Cylinder

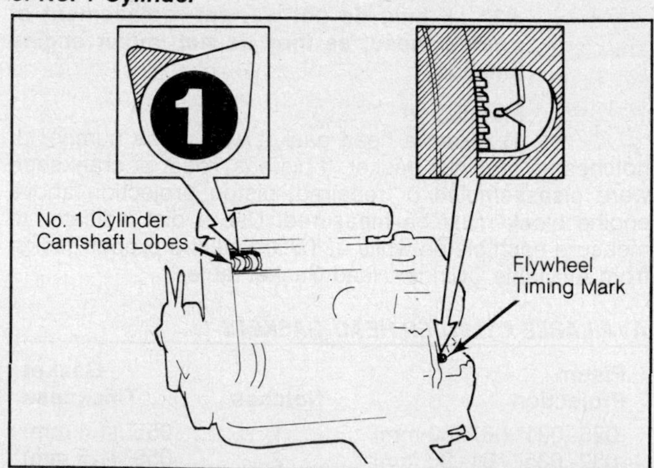
1
No. 1 Cylinder Camshaft Lobes
Flywheel Timing Mark

2) Cam lobes for cylinder No. 1 should point up at equally large angles. Install bearing caps 2 and 3, tighten cap nuts alternately. Use camshaft lock gauge tool (5190) to guide rear end when tightening. Remove gauge.

3) Install new oil seals on camshaft, but do not press them to bottom. Make sure seals are not cocked. Install bearing caps 1 and 4. Torque bearing cap nuts to 15 ft. lbs. (20 N.m). Use oil seal installation tool (5200) and camshaft retaining bolt to press rear seal into position.

4) Use oil seal installation tool (5200) and a mallet to drive front seal into position. Reverse removal procedure to complete installation. Set injection pump timing. See *Injection Pump Timing*.

D24 & D24T 6-CYLINDER DIESEL (Cont.)

INJECTION PUMP

Removal

1) Pinch off hoses to cold start device and disconnect. Disconnect accelerator cable and automatic transmission kickdown cable (if equipped). Remove rear timing gear cover, vacuum pump, vacuum pump plunger and fuel delivery pipes. Plug all fuel lines and connections to prevent contamination of fuel system.

2) Turn crankshaft pulley to bring No. 1 piston to TDC. Loosen injection pump bracket bolts to relieve belt tension and remove drive belt. Tighten one bolt to retain pump in an upright position.

3) Using wrench (5199) to hold camshaft rear gear and wrench (5201) on gear nut, loosen center nut enough to allow gear to rotate on camshaft without letting camshaft rotate. Lock injection pump gear with stop tool (5193) and remove gear nut, using wrench (5201).

4) Using puller tool (5204), remove injection pump gear. Remove bolts retaining front injection pump bracket to engine. Bracket comes out with pump. Remove .236" (6 mm) Allen screws retaining injection pump and remove pump.

Installation

To install, reverse removal procedure, noting that mark on injection pump and bracket coincide. Install key on shaft correctly before replacing gear.

INJECTION PUMP TIMING

1) To check pump timing remove rear timing belt cover and set No. 1 piston to TDC. Disconnect cold start device by loosening screw nearest to lever and push lever forward. Rotate sleeve 90° and push lever back against stop. DO NOT loosen clamp screw at end of cable.

NOTE: DO NOT loosen screw farthest from lever. If it is loosened, cold start device must be re-set on test bench.

2) Install a dial indicator with adaptor tool (5194) in place of plug at injector pump distributor. Set dial indicator with .08" (2 mm) preload between plunger and pump shaft. Turn crankshaft counterclockwise until dial indicator is at minimum reading.

3) Set dial indicator to zero. Install stop tool (5193) to lock injector pump gear. If necessary, loosen injection pump retaining screws and turn pump so line on housing and bracket align. Dial indicator reading should now be .028" (.70 mm).

4) Tighten screws and rotate crankshaft 2 complete turns, bringing No. 1 piston back to TDC. Dial indicator should still read .028" (.70 mm). Readjust and recheck as necessary to obtain proper setting. Remove dial indicator and stop tool. Install timing gear cover. Push cold start device lever forward, turn sleeve 90° and tighten screw.

VALVES

VALVE ARRANGEMENT

E-I-E-I-E-I-I-E-I-E-I-E (Front-to-rear).

VALVE CLEARANCE ADJUSTMENT

1) Remove valve cover and rotate crankshaft so No. 1 piston is at TDC (cam lobes point up at equally large angles). Flywheel mark should be at 0° mark. Check intake and exhaust clearance between heel of cam lobe and cam follower. Check remaining cylinders in firing order sequence.

2) If adjustment is required, turn crankshaft 1/4 turn clockwise from piston TDC, as there is no room to depress valves. Using valve depressor tool (5196), press down on valve depressor and remove disc with special pliers (5195).

3) Calculate thickness of disc required to reach proper setting. Discs are available in thicknesses of .130-.167" (3.30-4.25 mm) in increments of .002" (.05 mm). Lubricate and position new disc with stamped marking down. Rotate crankshaft several times and recheck all settings. Install valve cover.

VALVE CLEARANCE SPECIFICATIONS

Application	In. (mm)
Intake	
Hot	.008-.012 (.20-.30)
Cold	.006-.010 (.15-.25)
Exhaust	
Hot	.016-.020 (.40-.50)
Cold	.014-.018 (.35-.45)

VALVE GUIDE SERVICING

1) With cylinder head, camshaft and lifters removed from engine, attach a valve spring compressor to each valve. Compress valve spring and remove retaining lock, upper valve spring washer, valve springs and valve. Remove valve guide seals and lower valve spring washers.

2) Using a dial indicator, measure valve guide clearance by placing a new valve in guide bore with a valve stem end edge to edge with valve guide. Use proper intake or exhaust valve for bores as stem diameters are different.

3) Rock valve back and forth and observe dial indicator reading. Clearance must not exceed .051" (1.3 mm). If clearance is excessive, replace valve guides. Press out old guides from combustion chamber side of cylinder head using a drift tool (5218 or equivalent).

4) Oil replacement valve guide and press in place from camshaft side of cylinder head until guide flange bottoms in cylinder head. Do not use more than 1 ton force or flange may break off of guide. Ream guides using hand reamer tool (5224 or equivalent). Replace valve components, camshaft and cylinder head in reverse order of removal.

NOTE: Valves and seats must be reground if valve guides are replaced.

PISTONS, PINS & RINGS

PISTON & ROD ASSEMBLY

Removal

With oil pan and cylinder head removed, mark each piston assembly for proper installation. Ream any ridge from cylinder bores using a ridge reamer. Place a rag on top of piston to collect cuttings. Remove connecting rod cap and bearing shells, push piston assembly out through top of cylinder bore.

Volvo Engines

D24 & D24T 6-CYLINDER DIESEL (Cont.)

Installation

1) Fit bearing shells in connecting rod and rod cap. Lubricate cylinder bores, pistons and bearing shells. Turn crankshaft so journal for piston being serviced is at bottom of stroke.

2) Using a ring compressor, fit piston to bore noting that arrow on piston crown faces forward. Push piston down and locate connecting rod to crankshaft. Fit rod cap to connecting rod and tighten new nuts. Install all pistons and check that crankshaft rotates freely.

FITTING PISTONS

1) Using a bore indicator, measure each cylinder bore at 3 points, both parallel and at right angles to crankshaft. Measure .393" (10 mm) from top, bottom and at center of cylinder bore. Cylinder bore reading must not deviate by more than .002" (.04 mm) from basic value.

2) Measure piston diameter at right angle to piston pin .59" (15 mm) from lower edge. Subtract reading from that taken of cylinder bore. If specifications are exceeded, reboring or oversize pistons must be used.

NOTE: **Pistons with rounded edges on pressure side MAY NOT be used again. Round edges are caused by faulty injectors, which must be serviced before installation.**

3) Place each piston ring squarely into bottom of cylinder bore and measure ring gap. Place ring approximately .59" (15 mm) from lower edge of cylinder.

PISTON PINS

Removal

Remove circlips retaining piston pin. Push out pin with a drift. If pin moves stiffly, heat piston to approximately 140° F (60° C)

Installation

1) Assemble in reverse order. If piston pin bushing warrants replacement, press bushing out using drift (5017 or equivalent). Press in new bushing until edges are flush with connecting rod.

2) Drill out lubricating hole in bushing and ream bushing with a reamer. Piston pin must be loose, but still able to slide through hole with slight resistance.

PISTON RINGS

Removal

Using ring pliers, remove rings from piston. Remove any carbon deposits from ring lands and piston.

Installation

1) Fit expander ring in lowest groove of piston. Fit oil ring so ring gap is opposite spring opening. Install lower compression ring with "TOP" marking upward.

2) Install upper compression ring. Turn compression rings so all gaps are 120° apart. Do not turn oil control ring.

CRANKSHAFT MAIN & CONNECTING ROD BEARINGS

MAIN & CONNECTING ROD BEARINGS

Removal

1) Check markings on main and connecting rod bearings and remark if necessary. Using Plastigage method, check main and connecting rod bearing clearance.

2) If clearance is excessive, replace bearings. Do not mix old and new bearings. Replace only in sets.

Installation

1) Fit main bearing shells in engine block and main bearing caps. Install bearing shells with oil hole to engine block. Lubricate bearings and place crankshaft in position.

2) Fit main bearing caps with No. 1 toward vibration damper and No. 7 toward flywheel. *See Piston and Rod Assembly* for connecting rod installation procedure.

CRANKSHAFT FRONT SEAL

With vibration damper removed, pull old seal from housing using puller tool (5205 or equivalent). Grease seal lips and press into place by hand. Use adapter tool (5200), a thick washer and camshaft center bolt to press seal into housing until seated.

CRANKSHAFT REAR SEAL

With flywheel removed, pry out old seal with a screwdriver. Coat seal contact surfaces and lips with oil and hand start into position. Tap seal into housing until it bottoms, using drift tool (5208 or equivalent).

ENGINE OILING

CRANKCASE CAPACITY

7.4 qts. (7.0L) with filter change and 6.5 qts. (6.2L) without filter change.

OIL FILTER

Replaceable spin-on type.

NORMAL OIL PRESSURE

Minimum of 28 psi (2 kg/cm²) @ 2000 RPM with engine at normal operating temperature.

ENGINE OILING SYSTEM

Gear-type oil pump pressure lubricates pistons, piston pins and crankshaft. Three nozzles in head distribute oil to cam lobes, valve depressors and vacuum pump piston.

OIL PUMP

Oil pump cannot be removed without removing engine. No repairs can be made in vehicle. Oil pump must be replaced as an assembly as there are no separate replaceable parts.

ENGINE COOLING

COOLANT CAPACITY

Man. Trans. – 11.5 qts. (11.0L).
Auto. Trans. – 10.5 qts. (10.0L).

THERMOSTAT

Begins to open at 189°F (87°C).
Fully open at 216°F (102°C).

Volvo Engines

D24 & D24T 6-CYLINDER DIESEL (Cont.)

NOTE: When filling cooling system, air must be bled out of system by disconnecting upper hose from cold start device and setting heater in high position. Fill system, run engine for 5 minutes while continuing to fill system. Reconnect hose and complete filling.

WATER PUMP

Removal

Mark alignment position on belt, camshaft and crankshaft gears. Also, mark belt as to which parts face upward and forward. Remove timing belt. *See Timing Belt Removal*. Remove protective plate and pump retaining bolts and remove water pump.

Installation

Making sure all gasket surfaces are clean, lightly grease a new "O" ring and fit it to pump. DO NOT use any other sealing agent. Install pump with longest retaining bolt in upper hole. Reverse removal procedure to complete installation.

TIGHTENING SPECIFICATIONS

Application	Ft. Lbs. (N.m)
Camshaft Gear Bolt (Front)	33 (45)
Camshaft Gear Bolt (Rear)	74 (100)
Camshaft Bearing Caps	15 (20)
Crankshaft Pulley Nut	258 (350)
Cylinder Head Bolts	
Step 1	30 (40)
Step 2	44 (60)
Step 3	55 (75)
Step 4	Additional 1/2 turn
Hot torque	Additional 1/4 turn
After 600-1200 miles	Additional 1/4 turn
Connecting Rod Cap Nuts	35 (45)
Exhaust Manifold Bolts	18 (25)
Flywheel Bolts	55 (75)
Injectors-to-Cylinder Head	52 (70)
Injector Pump Gear	33 (45)
Intake Manifold Bolts	18 (25)
Main Bearing Cap Bolts	48 (65)
Transmission-to-Engine	33 (48)
Turbo-to-Exhaust Manifold	44 (60)
Turbo-to-Exhaust Pipe	18 (25)

ENGINE SPECIFICATIONS

GENERAL SPECIFICATIONS

Year	DISPLACEMENT		Fuel System	HP@RPM	Torque Ft. Lbs.@RPM	Compr. Ratio	BORE		STROKE	
	Cu. In.	Liters					In.	mm	In.	mm
1983										
Diesel	145	2.4	Fuel Inj.	76@4800	98@2800	23.0:1	3.01	76.5	3.40	86.4
Diesel Turbo	145	2.4	Fuel Inj.	103@4800	139@2400	23.0:1	3.01	76.5	3.40	86.4

VALVES

Engine Size & Valve	Head Diam. In. (mm)	Face Angle	Seat Angle	Seat Width In. (mm)	Stem Diameter In. (mm)	Stem Clearance In. (mm) [1]	Valve Lift In. (mm)
2.4L							
Intake	1.417 (36.0)	44.5°	45°	.079 (2.0)	.314 (7.97)	.0118 (.30)	.335 (8.5)
Exhaust	1.221 (31.0)	45°	45°	.094 (2.4)	.313 (7.95)	.0118 (.30)	.354 (9.0)

[1] – Wear limit .05" (1.3 mm)

PISTONS, PINS, RINGS

Engine	PISTONS	PINS		RINGS		
	Clearance In. (mm) [1]	Piston Fit In. (mm)	Rod Fit In. (mm)	Ring No.	End Gap In. (mm) [2]	Side Clearance In. (mm)
2.4L	.0012-.0019 (.03-.05)	Push Fit	Close Running Fit	Comp. 1	.012-.020 (.30-.50)	.0043-.0055 [3] (.06-.09)
				Comp. 2	.012-.020 (.30-.50)	.0028-.0039 [3] (.07-.10)
				Oil	.010-.016 (.25-.40)	.0012-.0028 [4] (.03-.07)

[1] – Wear limit .0051" (.13 mm) [2] – Wear limit .040" (1.0 mm) [3] – Wear limit .008" (.2 mm) [4] – Wear limit .006" (.15 mm)

Volvo Engines

D24 & D24T 6-CYLINDER DIESEL (Cont.)

ENGINE SPECIFICATIONS (Cont.)

CRANKSHAFT MAIN & CONNECTING ROD BEARINGS

Engine	MAIN BEARINGS				CONNECTING ROD BEARINGS		
	Journal Diam. In. (mm)	Clearance In. (mm) [1]	Thrust Bearing	Crankshaft End Play In. (mm) [2]	Journal Diam. In. (mm)	Clearance In. (mm) [3]	Side Play In. (mm)
2.4L	2.283 (58.0)	.0006-.0029 (.016-.075)	No. 4	.003-.007 (.07-.18)	1.88 (47.8)	.0006-.0024 (.015-.062)	.0157 (.40)

[1] – Wear limit .0063" (.16 mm) [2] – Wear limit .010" (.25 mm) [3] – Wear limit .0047" (.12 mm)

CAMSHAFT

Engine	Journal Diam. In. (mm)	Clearance In. (mm) [1]	Lobe Lift In. (mm)
2.4L			
Front	1.257-1.258 (31.92-31.95)	.002-.004 (.05-.10)	.....
Others	1.1786-1.1795 (29.94-29.96)	.002-.004 (.05-.10)	

[1] – End play .006" (.15 mm)

VALVE SPRINGS

Engine	Free Length In. (mm)	PRESSURE Lbs. @ In. (Kg @ mm)	
		Valve Closed	Valve Open
2.4L			
Inner	1.33 (33.9)	16.2@1.13 (7.3@28.6)	49.4@.72 (22.0@18.3)
Outer	1.58 (40.2)	40.0@1.28 (18.0@32.6)	102.5@.88 (46.0@22.3)

SECTION 7

CLUTCHES

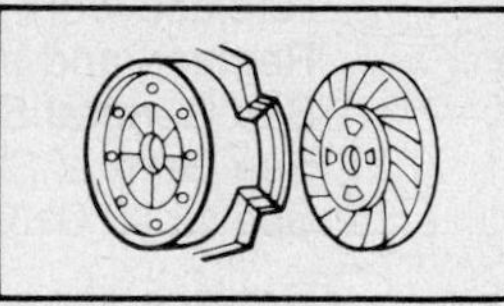

CONTENTS

NOTE: ALSO SEE GENERAL INDEX.

Clutches

CLUTCH TROUBLE SHOOTING

CONDITION	POSSIBLE CAUSE	CORRECTION
Chattering or Grabbing	Incorrect lever adjustment	See adjustment in CLUTCHES
	Oil, grease or glaze on facings	Disassemble and clean or replace
	Loose "U" joint flange	See DRIVE AXLES & TRANSFER CASES
	Worn input shaft spline	See CLUTCHES
	Binding pressure plate	See CLUTCHES
	Binding release lever	See CLUTCHES
	Binding disc hub	See Removal in CLUTCHES
	Unequal pressure plate contact	Replace worn/misaligned components
	Loose/bent clutch disc	See Removal & Installation in CLUTCHES
	Incorrect transmission alignment	See Removal in MANUAL TRANSMISSION
	Worn pressure plate, disc or flywheel	See Removal & Installation in CLUTCHES
	Broken or weak pressure springs	Replace pressure plate
	Sticking clutch pedal	See General Servicing in CLUTCHES
	Incorrect disc facing	Replace and match components
	Engine loose in chassis	Tighten all mounting bolts
Spinning	Dry or worn bushings	Lubricate and replace worn parts
	Misaligned clutch housing	See Removal in MANUAL TRANSMISSION
	Bent or distorted clutch disc	Replace and match components
	Excessive pedal free play	See Adjustment in CLUTCHES
Dragging	Oil or grease on facings	Clean and replace if necessary
	Incorrect lever or pedal adjustment	See Adjustment in CLUTCHES
	Dust or dirt on clutch	See General Servicing in CLUTHCES
	Worn or broken facings	Replace worn/damaged components
	Bent clutch disc or pressure plate	Replace and match components
	Clutch disc hub binding on shaft	See General Servicing in CLUTCHES
	Binding pilot bushing	See Gereral Servicing in CLUTCHES
	Sticking release bearing sleeve	See CLUTCHES
Rattling	Weak or broken release lever spring	Replace spring and check alignment
	Damaged pressure plate	Replace and match components
	Broken clutch return spring	Replace spring
	Worn splines on disc or input shaft	Replace disc and/or input shaft
	Worn clutch release bearing	Replace spring and check alignment
	Dry or worn pilot bushing	Lubricate or replace bushing
	Unequal release lever contact	Align or replace lever
	Incorrect pedal free play	See Adjustment in CLUTCHES
	Warped clutch disc	Replace and match components
Slipping	Pressure springs worn or broken	Replace damaged components
	Oily, greasy or worn clutch facings,	Clean or replace components
	Incorrect clutch alignment	See CLUTCHES
	Warped clutch disc or pressure plate	Replace and match damaged components
	Binding release levers or clutch pedal	See General Servicing in CLUTCHES
Squeaking	Worn or damaged release bearing	Replace worn/damaged parts
	Dry or worn pilot/release bearing	Lubricate or replace if necessary
	Pilot bearing turning in crankshaft	See Removal in CLUTCHES
	Worn input shaft bearing	Replace bearing and seal
	Incorrect transmission alignment	See Removal in MANUAL TRANSMISSION
	Dry clutch fork between pivot	See General Servicing in CLUTCHES
Heavy and/or Stiff Pedal	Sticking release bearing sleeve	See General Servicing in CLUTCHES
	Dry or binding pedal hub	Lubricate and align components
	Floor mat interference with pedal	Lay mat flat in proper area
	Dry or binding ball/fork pivots	Lubricate and align components
Grinding	Dry release bearing	See General Servicing in CLUTCHES
	Dry or worn pilot bearing	Lubricate or replace bearing
	Worn input shaft bearing	Replace bearing
Whirring	Incorrect pedal free play	See Adjustment in CLUTCHES
	Incorrect transmission alignment	See Removal in MANUAL TRANSMISSION

ALFA ROMEO GTV-6 2.5

DESCRIPTION

The clutch is a twin, dry plate type. Pressure plate is a diaphragm spring type. A prelubricated release bearing is used. Bearing is operated by a master cylinder connected by fluid line to the slave cylinder. Slave cylinder is connected, in turn, to a release lever.

REMOVAL & INSTALLATION

Removal and installation procedures for the clutch-gearbox-differential assembly were not available from the manufacturer at the time of publication.

OVERHAUL

CLUTCH UNIT

Disassembly

1) With the clutch-gearbox-differential assembly removed, mount assembly on work stand (R.4.0151) with clamps (R.4.0154) and fasten with bracket (R.4.0150). Remove slave cylinder release fork.

2) Loosen lock nut. Remove rear shift lever from clutch assembly housing. Remove clutch unit mount bolts from gearbox housing. Disengage clutch unit from primary input shaft.

3) Mount clutch unit on work stand. Using extractor tool (A.3.0600), pull yoke off shaft. Remove dust guard and clutch unit cover. Index mark flywheel, intermediate and rear pressure plate for reassembly reference. Remove rear pressure plate mount bolts.

4) Remove rear pressure plate, release bearing and rear clutch plate. Remove intermediate pressure plate and front clutch plate. Remove gearbox input shaft needle bearing, using puller (A.3.0402). Remove flywheel mount bolts. Remove flywheel from input shaft.

5) Place rear pressure plate on work table with friction surface up. Apply pressure to spring. Remove circlip holding release bearing retaining ring. Remove rear pressure plate from bearing. Discard Belleville (spring) washer.

6) To dismantle clutch cover, remove shift lever dust cover. Remove 2 lock nuts holding rear bearing. Remove front ball bearing. Discard "O" ring. Remove rear ball bearing using puller (A.3.0401). Replace Belleville washer and "O" ring upon installation.

NOTE: **If pressure plates are excessively worn or damaged, manufacturer recommends entire clutch assembly be replaced with new or rebuilt unit.**

Inspection

1) Check clutch discs for wear, damage, burnt or oil-saturated linings. Inspect components for loose rivets, distorted friction surfaces or uneven lining wear. Replace both discs even if defects are found on only one disc.

2) Check release bearing for excessive noise or roughness by turning by hand in thrust direction. Bearing must have no excess play and should slide freely on guide sleeve. Inspect input shaft needle bearing for seizing marks or excessive wear. Replace components as necessary.

3) Inspect flywheel shaft. Replace if working surfaces are worn. Check flywheel shaft bearings. Replace if seized or excessively worn. Inspect flywheel for wear, cracks, grooves or burnt friction surface. Friction surface must be parallel to flywheel shaft mount surface within .0024" (.060 mm).

4) Standard thickness, from friction surface-to-flywheel shaft side surface, is .43" (11 mm). If flywheel is resurfaced, ensure radius is remachined at outer edge of friction surface. If flywheel was reground or wear is more than .008" (.20 mm), replace entire clutch assembly with new or rebuilt unit.

Reassembly

1) To assemble clutch cover, drive rear bearing in using bearing installer (A.3.0282). Lock in place using lock nuts. Install spacer with beveled side toward front cover. Install new "O" ring in seat. Install front ball bearing.

2) Refit shift lever dust boot. Install release bearing. Apply Loctite to flywheel shaft mount bolts. Install flywheel-to-shaft. If needle bearing was removed, install using bearing installer (A.3.0405). Match index marks. Install front drive plate, intermediate pressure plate and rear driven plate.

3) Line up slots of 2 driven plates with clutch alignment tool (A.4.0205). Install rear pressure plate with release bearing. Install pressure plate mount bolts onto flywheel. Check that pressure plates and driven plates are tight to each other and true to the flywheel, ensuring clutch has initial idle travel. Remove alignment tool. Install clutch cover and dust guard.

4) Apply Loctite to clutch shaft and tighten yoke lock nut. Lubricate release bearing guide sleeve, ball spindle and contact surface of release lever with grease. Install shift lever and tighten. To complete installation, reverse removal procedure. When installing release lever, ensure it is properly located on ball spindle seat and release bearing seat.

ADJUSTMENTS

The clutch wear, pedal stroke and free play are automatically adjusted by operation of hydraulic system. No periodic adjustment is required.

TIGHTENING SPECIFICATIONS

Application	Ft. Lbs. (N.m)
Clutch Cover Assembly Mount Bolt	21-23 (29-32)
Clutch Shaft Yoke Lock Nut	69-76 (93-103)
Flywheel-to-Shaft Flange Bolt	20-22 (28-31)
Pressure Plate-to-Flywheel Bolt [1]	13-16 (18-22)
Shift Lever Lock Nut	20-23 (28-32)

[1] – Tighten mount bolts evenly, in a diagonal pattern.

Clutches

AUDI COUPE & 4000

DESCRIPTION

Clutch is single plate, dry disc type, using diaphragm type pressure plate and pre-lubricated clutch release bearing. Clutch is cable-actuated.

REMOVAL & INSTALLATION

CLUTCH ASSEMBLY

Removal

1) Disconnect battery. Disconnect exhaust header pipe at manifold, front exhaust pipe from front muffler, and bracket on transmission. Remove upper transmission-to-engine bolts and engine support bolts. Disconnect backup light wiring. Remove air cleaner.

NOTE: **On models equipped with 5-cylinder engine and 5-speed transmission, engine must be supported from above while removing and installing transmission.**

2) Remove bolt attaching the shift rod coupling to rear of transmission shifting shaft. Separate assemblies. Unhook clutch cable at release lever. Disconnect speedometer cable.

3) Disconnect axle drive shafts at inner drive flanges. Remove starter. Take off front clutch housing cover plate. Remove remaining transmission-to-engine bolts. On some models, removal of certain steering brackets are necessary to remove transmission.

4) Support transmission with jack and lift slightly, if necessary. Remove transmission rear mounts and brackets. Remove front support bolts. Pry transmission away from engine and slide it out of vehicle.

5) Install Holding Tool (10-201) onto flywheel. Index mark pressure plate and flywheel for proper installation in original position. Loosen pressure plate bolts 1/4 turn at a time in diagonal pattern. Slide pressure plate off flywheel dowels, and separate clutch disc. *See Fig. 1.*

Fig. 1: Exploded View of Clutch Assembly

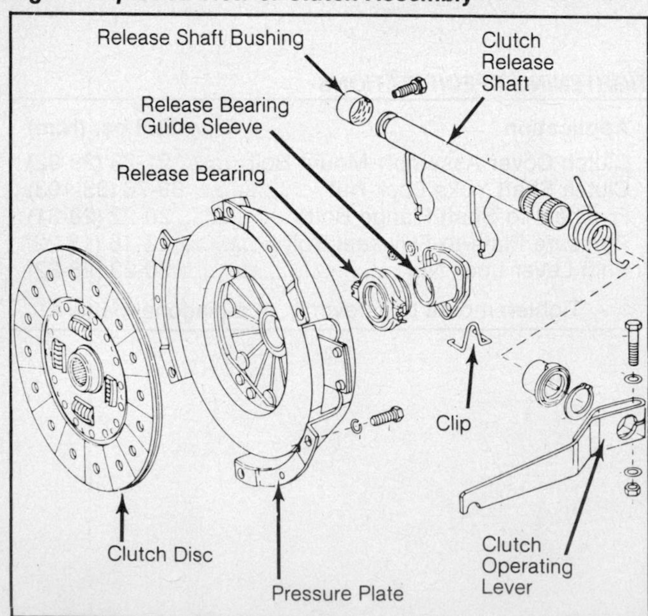
Release Shaft Bushing
Clutch Release Shaft
Release Bearing Guide Sleeve
Release Bearing
Clip
Clutch Disc
Pressure Plate
Clutch Operating Lever

Check pressure plate and disc for cracks and wear.

Inspection

1) Clean and check pressure plate surface for cracks, burns and wear. Maximum clutch surface inward taper is .012" (.30 mm). Check diaphragm spring ends for wear or scores. Pressure plate may be used with scratches or scores up to .012" (.30 mm) in depth. Replace if more wear is evident.

2) Check straps between pressure plate and cover for cracks. Check tightness of rivets. Check clutch disc lining and splines for wear. Check clutch disc runout. Maximum runout is .016" (.40 mm). Check rivets for tightness.

Installation

To install, reverse removal procedure and note the following: Lubricate clutch disc splines lightly with grease before assembly. Use clutch alignment tool to fit pressure plate and disc. Ensure flywheel and pressure plate index marks are aligned.

CLUTCH RELEASE BEARING

1) With transmission separated from engine, remove retaining springs and clips securing release bearing to clutch fork. As bearing is prelubricated, do not clean in solvent. Rotate bearing and check for roughness or noise, replace as necessary.

2) Apply Molykote paste to bearing contact points on clutch fork. Install retaining springs in retaining clips before sliding clips onto release shaft. To install clutch components, reverse removal procedure.

CLUTCH RELEASE SHAFT

1) Check clutch release shaft and pedal bushings for free movement. If shaft is loose or binds, check and replace clutch pedal bushings as necessary. Remove retainer clip, pedal pivot pin and pedal assembly. On 4-speed transmission, drive out old bushings with drift. On 5-speed transmissions, use Bushing Removal Tools (VW 401, VW 408a & VW 434).

NOTE: **Always use new self-locking nuts and retainer clips during assembly. Lubricate bolts lightly with Molykote grease.**

2) Press in rubber bushing first. Lightly coat plastic bushing and, on 4-speed transmission, press in with vise. On 5-speed transmissions, use Bushing Installer Tools (VW 401, VW 411, VW 416b & VW 436a). Lubricate shaft and bushings. Do not grease guide sleeve. Install pedal assembly.

CLUTCH RELEASE SHAFT BUSHING

1) With transmission out of vehicle and clutch components removed, install bushing removal tools. On 5-speed transmissions, use Bushing Removal Tools (VW 771/15 & VW 771) or equivalent.

2) Using slide hammer, tap bushing out of housing. Install new bushing with bearing installer tools. On 5-speed transmission (093), use installer tool (VW 295). On 5-speed transmission (013), use tools (VW 439 & VW 431).

3) Lubricate bushing and shaft with Molykote and install. Do not grease guide sleeve. Install clutch components and complete transmission installation.

AUDI COUPE & 4000 (Cont.)

PILOT BEARING

1) Lock flywheel in place, using Flywheel Holding Tool (10-201) or equivalent, on all engines to prevent rotation. On 4 & 5-cylinder gas engines and 4-cylinder diesel engine, install Pilot Bearing Remover Tool (10-202) or equivalent. Remove bearing.

2) Install pilot bearing with letters on bearing face out, using Pilot Bearing Installer Tool (VW 207c) for 4-cylinder gas and diesel engines. Use Pilot Bearing Installer Tool (2026) or equivalent, for 5-cylinder engine.

3) Seat bearing until distance from flywheel recess to bushing edge is 1/16" (1.5 mm) for 4-cylinder gas and diesel engines and 7/32" (5.5 mm) for 5-cylinder engine. Lubricate bearing, complete clutch and/or transmission repair.

ADJUSTMENT

CLUTCH PEDAL FREE PLAY

1) Adjust clutch pedal free play by loosening and adjusting both lock nuts at clutch cable. Pedal free play is .59" (15 mm), measured at clutch pedal for 4-speed and 5-speed transmissions. On some models, lock nuts are replaced by spring clips.

2) Clutch operating lever distance, from outside edge of clutch cable mount bracket (near oil filter) to flat upper edge of lever, is 6.625" (168 mm) for 4-speed. Measurement is 6.656" (169 mm) for 5-speed (013) and 7.594" (193 mm) for 5-speed (093) transmission. Tip of lever (where cable attaches) should be at same height as bottom of horizontal boss on lower left front of transmission case.

TIGHTENING SPECIFICATIONS

Application	Ft. Lbs. (N.m)
Clutch Assembly-to-Flywheel Bolts	18 (25)
Clutch Release Shaft Retaining Bolt	11 (15)
Clutch Operating Lever Retaining Bolt	18 (25)
Guide Sleeve Mount Bolt	
4-Speed	7 (10)
5-Speed	11 (15)
Transmission-to-Engine Bolts	40 (55)
Flywheel-to-Crankshaft	45 (75)

Clutches

AUDI 5000

DESCRIPTION

Clutch is a single plate, dry disc type. Pressure plate is a diaphragm spring type. A pre-lubricated release bearing is used. Bearing is operated by slave cylinder push rod and release lever.

The slave cylinder is mounted to top of clutch housing and extends to inside of housing. Clutch pedal is hooked directly to clutch master cylinder push rod fork using a clevis pin. Master cylinder is secured to clutch and brake pedal mounting brace.

REMOVAL & INSTALLATION

CLUTCH ASSEMBLY

Removal

1) Disconnect the battery. On diesel models, remove air cleaner. Remove windshield washer bottle and upper engine-to-transmission bolts. Disconnect speedometer cable. Remove tensioning clip from slave cylinder. Using a punch, drive out slave cylinder lock pin. Remove cylinder with fluid line connected.

2) Support weight of engine. On diesel models, remove splash shield. Remove exhaust pipe heat shield. Disconnect exhaust pipe at manifold. Disconnect axle drive shafts at transaxle and hang out of way. Disconnect back-up light wire. Pry off both shifting and adjusting rods.

3) Remove the lower engine-to-transmission mounting bolts. Remove starter and subframe cover shield. Slightly raise transmission. Remove transmission support bolts and bushings from both sides of subframe. Loosen both rear subframe mounting bolts. Remove right side transmission bracket.

4) Slide transmission off dowels and remove from vehicle. Index mark position of pressure plate on flywheel. Insert Flywheel Retainer Tool (10-201) or equivalent. Loosen pressure plate mounting bolts evenly in diagonal pattern. Remove pressure plate and clutch disc.

Inspection

1) Check surface of clutch diaphragm spring fingers that contact release bearing for scores or wear. Pressure plate may be used if scores are no deeper than .012" (.30 mm).

2) Check pressure plate for cracks, burn marks and scoring. Replace pressure plate if inward taper of disc contact face exceeds .012" (.30 mm) or if any rivets are damaged or loose.

3) The maximum runout of clutch disc face is .020" (.50 mm), measured at outer edge. Check disc splines for wear and rivets for tightness.

Installation

To install, reverse removal procedure and note the following: Clutch disc spring cage must face pressure plate. Clutch disc must slide freely with no radial play on input shaft. Lubricate input shaft splines with molybdenum grease. Align pressure plate index marks. Use Clutch Disc Alignment Tool (10-213) to center disc.

CLUTCH RELEASE BEARING

Removal

1) Remove the transmission. Remove cap bolt (attaching 2 retainer pieces) at lower edge of release lever. Slide release lever and bearing out of slave cylinder push rod and off guide sleeve.

2) Disengage circlip and retainer clips securing release bearing to lever. Separate bearing from lever. If necessary, guide sleeve can also be removed.

Inspection

Check clutch release bearing for wear or unusual noise. Do not wash bearing in solvent. If bearing is excessively rough or noisy, replace. Inspect release lever and guide sleeve for excessive wear, replace as necessary.

Installation

To install, reverse removal procedure. Lubricate ball cap located in clutch housing with grease. Do not grease plastic guide sleeve. Ensure clutch release lever locates directly into slave cylinder push rod tip. Push rod tip should be lubricated.

Fig. 1: Clutch Release Bearing with Related Components

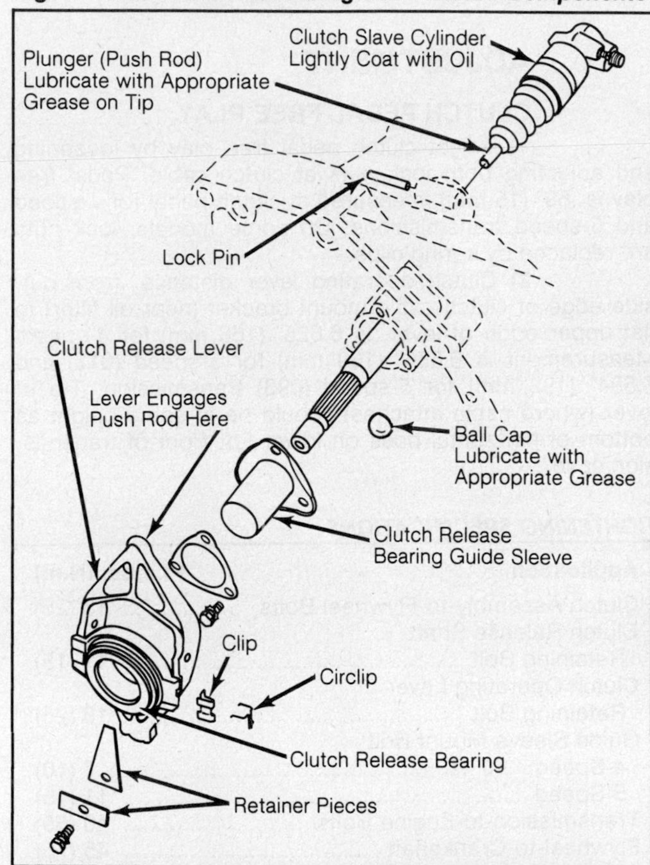
Clutch Slave Cylinder
Lightly Coat with Oil
Plunger (Push Rod)
Lubricate with Appropriate
Grease on Tip
Lock Pin
Clutch Release Lever
Lever Engages
Push Rod Here
Ball Cap
Lubricate with
Appropriate Grease
Clutch Release
Bearing Guide Sleeve
Clip
Circlip
Clutch Release Bearing
Retainer Pieces

Lubricate ball stud, release bearing surface and slave cylinder push rod tip with Molykote grease.

CLUTCH PEDAL BUSHING

1) Check the clutch pedal bushings for free movement. If shaft is loose or binds, check and replace clutch pedal bushings as necessary. Detatch slave cylinder clip at clevis and remove from pedal assembly. Remove retainer clip, pedal pivot pin and pedal assembly.

2) Drive out old bushings with drift. Install new bushings by pressing with vise. Ream to size. Install clutch pedal assembly, replace all circlips and self-locking nuts. Bleed and adjust system as necessary.

AUDI 5000 (Cont.)

NOTE: Do not add or mix DOT 5 silicone type brake fluid to system or severe component corrosion may result. Replace all internal components when repairing master or slave cylinder. Coat cups and piston with brake paste before installing. Replace all circlips and self-locking nuts.

MASTER CYLINDER

Removal

Disconnect and plug the fluid lines. Separate cylinder from clutch pedal by removing circlip and clevis pin. Note circlip location for proper reassembly. Remove 2 bolts mounting master cylinder to pedal bracket and take out cylinder.

Fig. 2: Exploded View of Master Cylinder

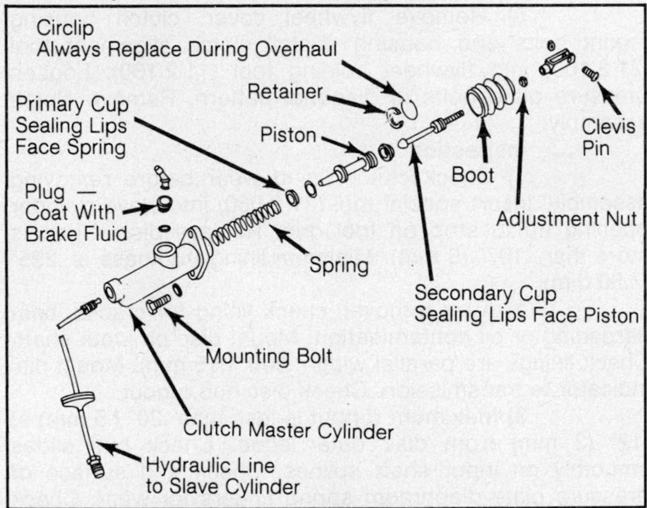
Circlip
Always Replace During Overhaul
Retainer
Primary Cup
Sealing Lips
Face Spring
Piston
Clevis
Pin
Boot
Plug —
Coat With
Brake Fluid
Adjustment Nut
Spring
Secondary Cup
Sealing Lips Face Piston
Mounting Bolt
Clutch Master Cylinder
Hydraulic Line
to Slave Cylinder

Replace all rubber components during overhaul.

Inspection

With rubber boot, clevis and push rod removed, unclip snap ring. Remove snap ring spacer and piston with cups and spring. Check piston and cylinder bore for wear, nicks and/or corrosion. Replace clutch master cylinder assembly if light honing does not clean up bore. Replace all rubber parts during overhaul. Note secondary cup sealing lips face piston and primary cup sealing lips face spring.

Installation

To install master cylinder, reverse removal procedure and bleed air from fluid line. Do not use more than 35 psi (2.4 kg/cm²) in pressure bleeder when bleeding system. Check for proper clutch operation. Road test vehicle.

SLAVE CYLINDER

Removal

Working from under vehicle, remove tensioning clamp. Drive out slave cylinder lock pin located on top of transmission. Slide cylinder back until push rod clears; then maneuver cylinder until fluid line can be disconnected and plugged.

Inspection

Remove slave cylinder push rod, rubber boot and retaining ring (note ring location for proper installation). Remove piston, cup and spring. Check cylinder bore and piston for wear, nicks and/or corrosion. Replace all internal components during slave cylinder overhaul. If corrosion in cylinder is evident and light hone will not clean up, replace slave cylinder assembly. Coat all internal rubber parts with brake paste before installation.

Fig. 3: Exploded View of Slave Cylinder

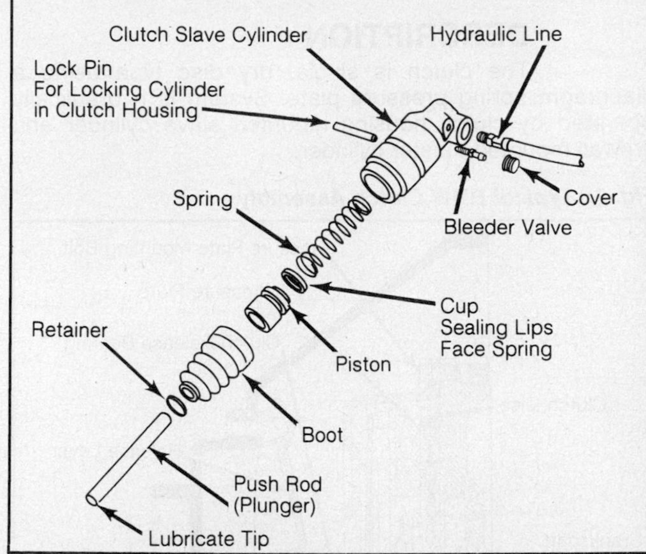
Clutch Slave Cylinder
Hydraulic Line
Lock Pin
For Locking Cylinder
in Clutch Housing
Spring
Cover
Bleeder Valve
Cup
Sealing Lips
Face Spring
Retainer
Piston
Boot
Push Rod
(Plunger)
Lubricate Tip

During installation, ensure clutch release lever locates directly into slave cylinder push rod tip.

Installation

To install, reverse removal procedure. Coat outer machined surface of cylinder with grease before inserting into place. Bleed air from fluid line. Check for proper clutch operation and pedal height.

ADJUSTMENTS

CLUTCH PEDAL

Adjust master cylinder push rod so that in rest position clutch pedal stands 3/8" (10 mm) above brake pedal. Ensure return spring moves clutch pedal to end position after releasing. Pedal should not rest on pedal mounting or excessive clutch plate wear will occur.

NOTE: If clutch pedal is correctly adjusted but fails to properly return, check hydraulic system for air, tight pedal bushing or jammed return spring.

TIGHTENING SPECIFICATIONS

Application	Ft. Lbs. (N.m)
Pressure Plate Bolt	18 (25)
Drive Shaft-to-Transmission Bolt	32 (43)
Slave Cylinder Mount Bolt	14 (20)
Engine-to-Transmission Bolt	
Upper Bolt	40 (54)
Lower Bolt	
Inner Bolt	33 (45)
Outer Bolt	14 (20)
Guide Sleeve Mount Bolt	11 (15)
Master Cylinder Mount Bolt	14 (20)
Pedal Mount Assembly Bolt	18 (25)
Release Lever Retainer Bolt	11 (15)
Starter Bolt	40 (54)

Clutches

BMW

318i, 320i, 528e, 533i, 633CSi & 733i

DESCRIPTION

The clutch is single, dry disc type using a diaphragm spring pressure plate. System is hydraulically operated by clutch housing mounted slave cylinder and firewall mounted master cylinder.

Fig. 1: Typical BMW Clutch Assembly

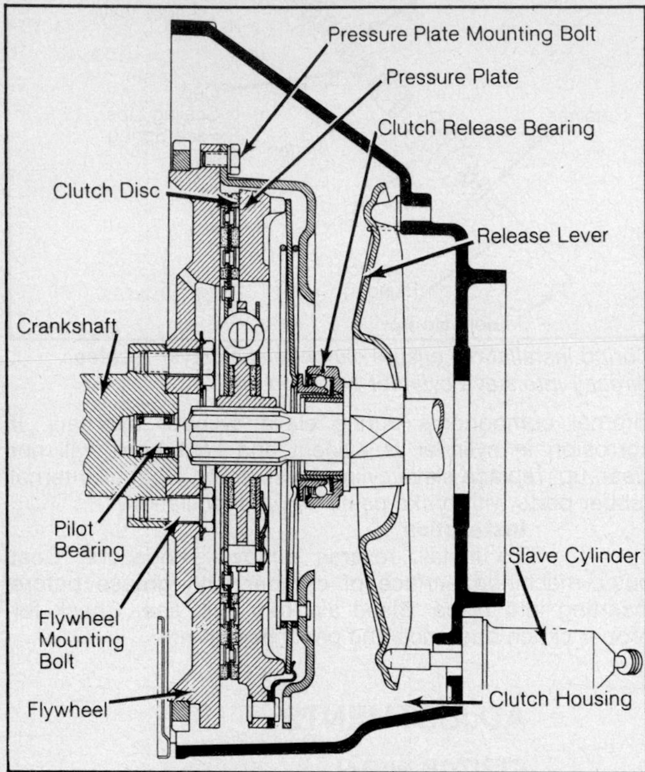
Pressure Plate Mounting Bolt
Pressure Plate
Clutch Release Bearing
Clutch Disc
Release Lever
Crankshaft
Pilot Bearing
Slave Cylinder
Flywheel Mounting Bolt
Clutch Housing
Flywheel

Do not allow oil, grease or dirt to contaminate the clutch component friction surfaces.

REMOVAL & INSTALLATION

CLUTCH ASSEMBLY

NOTE: **Check lining wear, described in Inspection section in this article, before clutch assembly removal.**

Removal

1) From inside engine compartment, remove accessable, upper clutch housing mount bolts and bracket. On 318i & 320i models, engage Reverse gear. On all models, from inside vehicle, lift shift lever dust boot. Remove circlip holding lever in place. Detach selector rod from gearshift lever.

2) After noting component locations, remove shift lever. Raise and support vehicle. Detach front exhaust system components. Fit clamp tool (26 1 011) to drive shaft flange. Remove bolts and discard lock nuts holding drive shaft flange-to-transmission shaft flange. Remove heat shield.

3) On 733i, remove web under drive shaft tunnel. On all models, remove center support bearing and bracket. Remove drive shaft from front flange. Position out of way. Support transmission with jack. Detach crossmember from body. Remove speedometer cable from transmission.

4) Detach clutch slave cylinder from clutch housing and set aside, leaving hydraulic line attached. Disconnect electrical connections from transmission. Remove transmission mount bolts. Pull transmission straight back and lower lower from vehicle.

NOTE: **On vehicles with speed and referance mark sensors, check component locations for proper reassembly referance. Black plug goes to starter ring gear and Gray plug goes to flywheel. Check and replace "O" rings as necessary. Do not mix sensors or engine will not start.**

5) Remove flywheel cover, clutch housing mount bolts and housing. Install clutch alignment tool (21 2 100) and flywheel holding tool (11 2 160). Loosen pressure plate bolts in diagonal pattern. Remove clutch assembly.

Inspection

1) Check clutch lining wear before removing assembly. Insert special tool (21 2 060) into slave cylinder opening up to stop on tool grip. Replace disc if gap is more than .197" (5 mm). Minimum lining thickness is .295" (7.50 mm).

2) After removal, check lining for cracks, heat hardening or oil contamination. Mount disc on input shaft. Check linings are parallel within .006" (.15 mm). Mount dial indicator to transmission. Check disc hub runout.

3) Maximum runout is less than .20" (.5 mm) at .12" (3 mm) from disc outer edge. Check hub slides smoothly on input shaft splines. Check end surface of pressure plate diaphragm spring fingers for wear. Check unevenness of spring finger height is less than .024" (.60 mm).

4) Check diaphragm springs for heat distortion, loosened rivets, wear or damage. Inspect pressure plate and flywheel friction surfaces for cracks, distortion and proper thickness. Minimum flywheel thickness is .988" (25.10 mm) for 318i, 320i and 528e and 1.047" (26.60 mm) for 633i and 733i models.

5) Resurface or replace flywheel if runout is more than .004" (.10 mm). Pressure plate friction surface must be level. Light roughness may be dressed with fine emery cloth. If surfaces are deeply scored, resurface or replace defective parts.

Installation

1) Using alignment tool, install clutch disc and pressure plate. Install flywheel holding tool. Tighten pressure plate mount bolts evenly, in diagonal pattern. On all except 318i & 320i, install clutch housing.

2) Lightly apply molybdenum grease on contact surfaces of release bearing, disc hub splines, pressure plate and release lever. Install slave cylinder with bleeder screw at bottom.

3) Install drive shaft. To preload center bearing, move bracket .078" (2 mm) forward in slots. Install and tighten NEW drive shaft flange lock nuts. On 320i, install clutch housing. To complete installation, reverse removal procedure.

BMW (Cont.)

RELEASE BEARING & LEVER

Removal

With transmission and clutch housing removed from engine, remove spring from pivot end of release arm. Slide off arm and bearing assembly. Separate release bearing. Measure for overall length of 1.93-1.97" (49.1-49.9 mm).

Inspection

Check release bearing for noise, excessive play or lubrication loss by turning by hand in thrust direction. Check release lever for excessive wear or damage at bearing and pivot contact faces. Replace components as necessary.

Installation

Coat contact points and pack lubricating groove of release bearing with molybdenum grease. To complete installation, reverse removal procedure.

CLUTCH MASTER CYLINDER

Removal

1) Remove trim under left side of instrument panel. On 318i & 320i models, remove accelerator cable. Remove bolt attaching master cylinder push rod-to-clutch pedal. Siphon off brake fluid from reservoir.

2) Detach reservoir and hydraulic lines from clutch master cylinder. On 733i models only, remove windshield washer tank. On all models, remove master cylinder mount bolts at firewall. Remove master cylinder from vehicle.

Installation

To install, reverse removal procedures. Bleed hydraulic system. On 633CSi and 733i, ensure that pedal over-center spring is engaged in pedal guide before attaching push rod.

CLUTCH SLAVE CYLINDER

Removal & Installation

Siphon off fluid from reservoir. Detach slave cylinder from clutch housing. Disconnect hydraulic line. Remove cylinder. To install, reverse removal procedure. Ensure cylinder is mounted with bleeder screw at bottom. Fill reservoir and bleed system.

OVERHAUL

CLUTCH MASTER CYLINDER

Remove master cylinder. Slide off dust boot. Remove circlip holding push rod. Remove piston assembly. Clean components with denatured alcohol. Inspect cylinder bore for corrosion or scoring. Replace all rubber parts. Lubricate internal parts with brake fluid and reassemble. Adjust push rod length to approximately 5.5" (140 mm). *See Fig. 2.*

Fig. 2: Sectional View of Clutch Master Cylinder

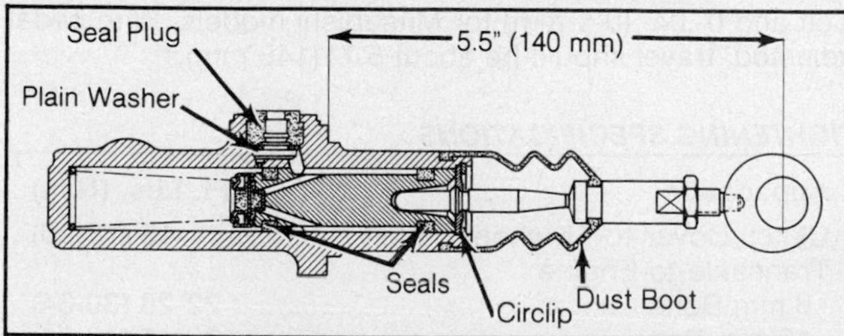
Seal Plug
5.5" (140 mm)
Plain Washer
Seals
Circlip
Dust Boot

Check that clearance between piston assembly and master cylinder bore is within specification.

NOTE: **Coat all pivot points on clutch pedal assembly with Molykote 2 (or equivalent) prior to assembly.**

CLUTCH SLAVE CYLINDER

Remove retaining ring. Remove push rod, boot and piston assembly. Clean internal parts with alcohol. Inspect bore for scoring and corrosion. Replace all rubber parts. Lubricate internal parts with brake fluid and reassemble.

Fig. 3: Sectional View of Clutch Slave Cylinder

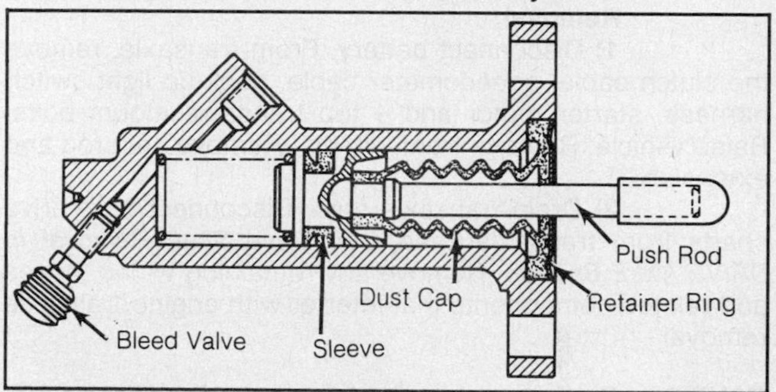
Push Rod
Dust Cap
Retainer Ring
Bleed Valve
Sleeve

Replace all rubber components during overhaul.

ADJUSTMENT

NOTE: **The clutch pedal stroke and free play are automatically adjusted for disc wear by operation of hydraulic system.**

HYDRAULIC SYSTEM BLEEDING

Ensure that fluid reservoir is full. Attach bleeder hose to bleed screw on slave cylinder. Submerge end of hose in partly filled container of brake fluid. Slowly pump clutch pedal several times.

Hold pedal down on last stroke. Loosen bleeder screw to allow air to escape. Close bleeder screw and repeat until air is bled from system. Ensure fluid reservoir does not run dry during bleeding operation or complete hydraulic system must be rebleed.

TIGHTENING SPECIFICATIONS

Application	Ft. Lbs. (N.m)
Clutch Housing-to-Engine Bolt	
8 mm Bolt	18-20 (24-27)
10 mm Bolt	35-38 (47-51)
Cover-to-Clutch Housing Bolt	
6 mm Bolt	6-7 (8-9)
8 mm Bolt	18-20 (24-27)
Clutch-to-Flywheel Bolt	16-17 (22-23)
Drive Shaft Flange Bolt	72 (98)
Master Cylinder Mount Bolt	16-17 (22-23)
Slave Cylinder-to-Housing Mount Bolt	18-20 (24-27)

CHRYSLER CORP. IMPORTS & MITSUBISHI FWD MODELS

Chrysler Corp Imports: Colt
Mitsubishi: Cordia & Tredia

DESCRIPTION

The clutch is a diaphragm spring, single disc type. Operation is mechanically-controlled by cable. The clutch release bearing is sealed and permanently lubricated.

REMOVAL & INSTALLATION

CLUTCH ASSEMBLY

Removal

1) Disconnect battery. From transaxle, remove the clutch cable, speedometer cable, back-up light switch harness, starter motor and 4 top transaxle mount bolts. Raise vehicle. Remove front wheels. Remove shift rod and extension.

2) Drain transaxle fluid. Disconnect both drive shafts from transaxle case. *See Drive Shaft Removal in DRIVE AXLE Section*. Remove any remaining wiring ,hoses and related components that interfer with engine/transaxle removal.

CAUTION: Replace drive shaft retainer ring if removed. Do not damage drive shaft boots.

3) Disconnect range selector cable (if equipped). Remove engine rear cover. Support engine with lifting device. Remove remaining engine-to-transaxle mount bolts. Detach transaxle mount insulator bolt and remove transaxle assembly from vehicle.

4) Insert Clutch Disc Guide Tool (MD998017 for Chrysler Corp. & MD998245 for Mitsubishi) in clutch center hole. Loosen pressure plate mount bolts diagonally. Remove clutch assembly.

Fig. 1: Exploded View of Clutch Assembly

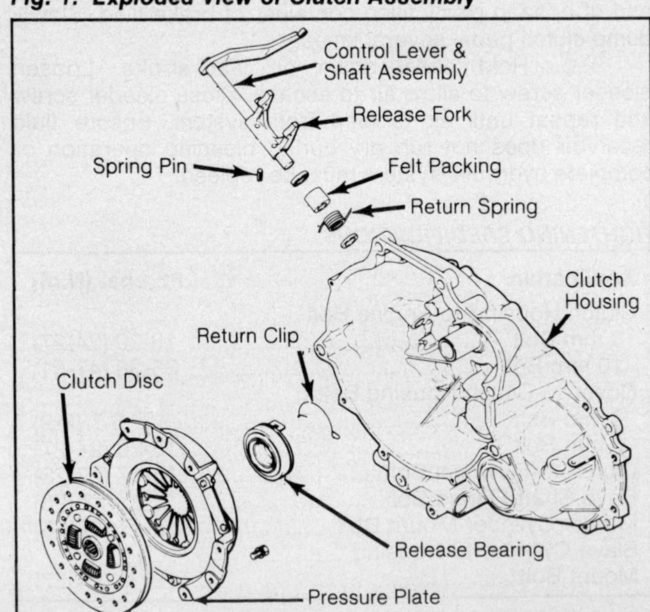
Control Lever &
Shaft Assembly
Release Fork
Spring Pin
Felt Packing
Return Spring
Clutch
Housing
Return Clip
Clutch Disc
Release Bearing
Pressure Plate

Install clutch disc with manufacturer's stamped mark on the pressure plate side.

5) Remove return clip on transaxle side. Remove release bearing carrier and bearing. Using lock pin extractor (MD998019), remove shift arm spring pins and control lever assembly.

6) Remove clutch shift arm, 2 felt packings and 2 return springs. Clean clutch disc and check for wear, damage, loose rivets or oil-soaked lining. Replace if lining-to-rivet distance is less than .012" (.30 mm). *See Fig. 1*.

Installation

1) To install, reverse removal procedure. Insert clutch control lever and shaft assembly into transaxle case from left side. Install shift arm, packings and return springs on shaft.

NOTE: Do not reuse old spring lock pins.

2) Grease inside surface of bushing and oil seal lips. Apply oil to packings. Align lock pin holes of shift arm and control shaft. Drive in lock pins using installer tool (MD998245) or punch.

3) Check that spring pin slot direction is at right angle to center line of control shaft. Grease disc spline and main drive gear spline. Use guide tool to center disc and cover assembly on flywheel.

4) Ensure disc surface with manufacturers stamped mark is on pressure plate side. Install release bearing and carrier. Mount return clip. Grease inside diameter of carrier and groove. Install transaxle.

5) If equipped, loosen front roll rod bolt to unload roll rod. Retighten to 22-29 Ft. Lbs. (29-39 N.m). Ensure no axial load is applied to rod. Adjust clutch cable and clutch pedal.

CLUTCH CABLE

Removal

Loosen cable adjusting wheel in engine compartment. Loosen clutch pedal adjusting bolt lock nut. Back off adjusting bolt. Disconnect cable from release lever and clutch pedal.

Installation

To install, reverse removal procedure. Grease cable contact areas of clutch pedal and release lever. Check pedal travel, free play and position. Adjust as necessary.

ADJUSTMENTS

PEDAL HEIGHT & FREE PLAY

Adjust clutch pedal height (measured from top of clutch pedal to floor board) to 6.9-7.2" (175-183.5 mm) by turning clutch pedal adjusting bolt. Free play (measured at center of pedal pad) must be .8-1.2" (20-30 mm).

CLUTCH CABLE

Pull outer cable toward engine. Clearance between adjusting nut and holder is .20-.24" (5-6 mm) for Colt and 0-.04" (0-1 mm) for Mitsubishi models. With pedal adjusted, travel should be about 5.7" (145 mm).

TIGHTENING SPECIFICATIONS

Application	Ft. Lbs. (N.m)
Clutch Cover-to-Flywheel	11-15 (15-20)
Transaxle-to-Engine	
8 mm Bolts	22-25 (30-34)
10 mm Bolts	32-40 (43-54)
Starter Mount Bolt	16-23 (22-31)

CHRYSLER CORP. IMPORTS & MITSUBISHI RWD MODELS

Chrysler Corp. Imports: Challenger, Colt Pickup, Ram-50 Pickup & Sapporo
Mitsubishi: Montero, Pickup & Starion

DESCRIPTION

The clutch is a diaphragm spring, single disc type. On Mitsubishi Gas Pickup and all Chrysler Corp. models except Diesel Pickups, operation is mechanically-controlled by cable.

On Diesel Pickups, Montero and Starion, the clutch operation is controlled by hydraulic release cylinder connected, by a hydraulic line, to clutch master cylinder. Pedal connects to master cylinder by adjustable rod. On all models, the clutch release bearing is permanently lubricated and sealed.

REMOVAL & INSTALLATION

CLUTCH ASSEMBLY

Removal

1) Disconnect the battery. Remove the air cleaner assembly and the starter. On Sapporo, Starion and Challenger, place a rag between valve cover and firewall to protect the components when engine is moved.

2) Place shift lever in Neutral. Do not place lever in Reverse. On Pickups, remove 2 upper transmission mount bolts from bell housing. From inside the passenger compartment of Pickups, remove lock bolts and lift up console box, if equipped.

3) Remove the carpet. Remove dust cover retaining plate bolts and plate. Lift up dust cover. Remove the extension housing mount bolts and the shift lever assembly.

NOTE: **When removing shift lever assembly on Montero models, keep transmission shift lever in Neutral and transfer case shift lever in 4WD/high range position.**

4) On all models, raise and support vehicle. On Montero, remove transfer case protector. On all models, drain transmission and/or transfer case oil. Scribe mating marks on drive shaft flange yoke and differential flange.

5) On 4WD Pickups, set free-wheeling hubs to "Free" position. Set transfer case gear shift lever to "2H" position. On all models, disconnect drive shaft-to-differential pinion flange bolts.

6) On 2WD Pickups, remove center bearing assembly. On all models, remove drive shaft(s) from transmission by pulling straight out. Do not damage oil seal lip at rear of transmission. Plug opening of extension housing after drive shaft removal.

NOTE: **Ensure vehicle is level during drive shaft removal to prevent excessive loss of transmission or transfer case oil from rear of extension housing.**

7) On all models, disconnect speedometer cable and back-up light connector from transmission. If equipped, disconnect ground cable. On 4WD Pickups, disconnect 4WD indicator light switch harness.

8) On all Pickups, disconnect front exhaust pipe from exhaust manifold. On all models except Diesel Pickups, Montero and Starion, remove clutch cable from release lever.

9) On Diesel Pickups, Montero and Starion, remove hydraulic clutch release cylinder. On all models except 4WD Pickups, remove bell housing cover. Support rear of engine on service jack. Remove rear engine support bracket. Tilt transmission back slightly and remove control housing, if equipped.

10) On 4WD Pickups, remove retainer plate, transfer case mount bracket, No. 2 crossmember and bell housing cover. On all models, remove the remaining transmission-to-bell housing mount bolts. Pull transmission assembly rearward from engine and remove from vehicle.

CAUTION: **Use care not to bend or twist front end of main drive gear shaft.**

11) Insert clutch centering tool (MD998017 for Chrysler Corp. & MD998127 for Mitsubishi models) or main drive gear shaft into clutch center hole to prevent dropping disc. Scribe mating marks on clutch cover and flywheel for proper reassembly.

12) Alternately loosen clutch mount bolts diagonally. Remove clutch cover assembly. Separate pressure plate and clutch disc. Handle carefully to prevent contamination of friction surfaces. *See Fig. 1*. Detach two clips on transmission side and remove release bearing.

NOTE: **When removing release lever, slide in direction of arrow to disengage fulcrum from clip. Attempting to remove lever by sliding in other direction will result in damage to clip.**

Fig. 1: Exploded View of Clutch Assembly – All Except Diesel Pickup & Mitsubishi Models

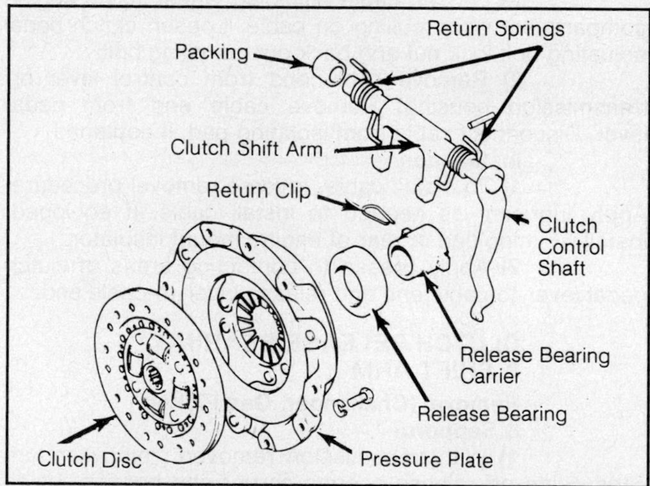
Return Springs
Packing
Clutch Shift Arm
Return Clip
Clutch Control Shaft
Release Bearing Carrier
Release Bearing
Clutch Disc
Pressure Plate

Install clutch disc with manufacturer's stamped mark on the pressure plate side.

NOTE: **Use vacuum cleaner or shop towel to clean asbestos dust from clutch housing during inspection and repair. Do not use compressed air.**

Inspection

1) Check for excessive wear, warpage or damage of clutch components. On all models, replace clutch disc if lining is worn to within .012" (.30 mm), measured from rivet heads to friction surface.

2) Inspect diaphragm spring for excessive wear of fingers and looseness of strap rivets. Check pressure plate for scoring. Ensure flatness is within .020"

(.50 mm). Using dial indicator, check flywheel runout is no more than .004" (.10 mm). Resurface or replace as necessary.

3) Check release bearing for rough rotation and excessive noise and diaphragm spring contact portions for abnormal wear. Inspect the bearing and fulcrum contact points of release lever for abnormal wear. Replace worn components as necessary.

4) Inspect hydraulic system components. Disassemble master and release cylinders. Inspect for rust and scoring of cylinder bore and piston, deformation and excessive wear of piston cups and clogging of hydraulic lines.

NOTE: Do not disassemble master cylinder piston assembly, if worn, replace as an assembly. If release cylinder components are worn, replace complete cylinder assembly.

Installation

1) To install, reverse removal procedure. Ensure clutch disc surface with manufacturers stamped mark is on pressure plate side. Use centering tool to center disc on flywheel.

2) Apply light coating of grease to disc and input shaft splines, groove of release bearing inside diameter, release lever fulcrum hole and release cylinder pushrod hole. Do not allow grease to contact clutch friction surfaces.

CLUTCH CABLE

Removal (Except Diesel Pickup & Mitsubishi Models)

1) Loosen cable adjusting wheel inside engine compartment while pulling on cable. Loosen clutch pedal adjusting bolt lock nut and back out adjusting bolt.

2) Remove cable end from control lever on transmission housing. Remove cable end from pedal lever. Disconnect cable from isolating pad, if equipped.

Installation

1) To install cable, reverse removal procedure. Apply lubricant as needed to install cable. If equipped, install isolating pad at rear of engine mount insulator.

2) Apply grease to contacting areas of clutch pedal lever-to-cable end and release lever-to-cable end.

CLUTCH RELEASE BEARING & SHIFT ARM

Removal (Challenger, Gas Pickup & Sapporo)

1) With transmission removed, remove return clips. Slide off release bearing carrier and bearing. Using a punch, remove shift arm spring pin and release lever assembly. Remove shift arm, 2 felt packings and 2 return springs. *See Fig. 2*.

2) Check release bearing turns freely under light load with no evidence of roughness. Replace bearing if noisy, rough or dry. DO NOT clean in solvent, use compressed air only.

Installation

1) Insert lever and shaft into left side of transmission case. Place shift arm, felt packings and return springs on shaft assembly. Apply grease to inside of bushing and oil seal lips. Apply oil to felt packings.

NOTE: Spring pin slot direction must be at right angle to control shaft centerline.

2) Align shift arm pin and control shaft pin holes. Drive spring pins into position. Complete clutch assembly installation. Check pedal height, travel & free play. Adjust as necessary.

Fig. 2: Removing Shift Arm Spring Pins

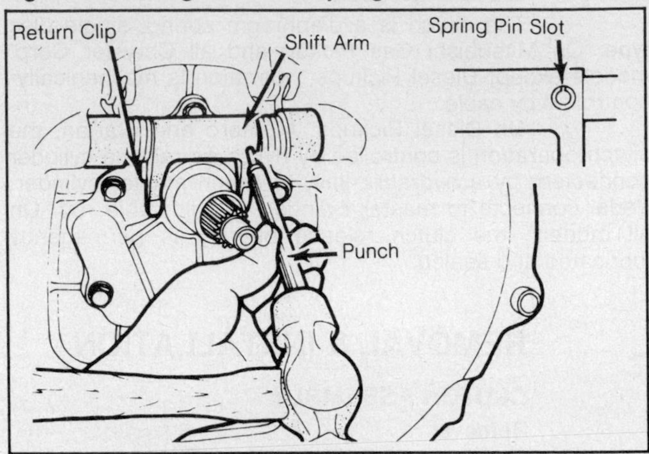
Return Clip
Shift Arm
Spring Pin Slot
Punch

The spring pin slot must face upward when arm is installed.

Removal (Diesel Pickup & Mitsubishi Models)

1) Remove clutch release cylinder boot and detach release cylinder from transmission case. When removing release lever, slide lever in direction of arrow to disengage fulcrum from clip.

2) DO NOT slide in oposite direction of arrow or damage to clip will result. Remove release bearing and related components.

Installation

1) Apply grease to release lever where it contacts fulcrum and install. Install release lever boot to transmission case. Install release cylinder assembly to transmission case.

2) Fill groove of bearing inside diameter with grease. Install remaining components. Check adjustments. On Diesel Pickup, Montero and Starion, check that release bearing free play is .06" (1.6 mm).

CLUTCH MASTER CYLINDER

Removal & Disassembly (Diesel Pickup & Mitsubishi Models)

1) Disconnect hydraulic line at clutch master cylinder. Slowly depress clutch pedal to drain fluid. Remove cotter pin retaining cylinder push rod-to-pedal.

2) Remove mount bolts and master cylinder. Remove piston stop ring. Pull out piston assembly. Wash master cylinder, piston and cup in brake fluid. *See Fig. 3*.

CAUTION: Do not disassemble piston assembly, replace worn or damaged components. During installation, ensure new piston assembly is not damaged. Use DOT 3 or higher grade brake fluid to bleed hydraulic system.

Inspection

1) Check inner surface of master cylinder and outer surface of piston for wear, corrosion or damage. Check cylinder bore-to-piston clearance. Check piston cup for damage, deformation or wear. Check return springs for loss of tension and damage. Replace any parts not within specifications.

2) Standard master cylinder inside diameter is .6248-.6265" (15.870-15.913 mm). Standard piston outside diameter is .6231-.6248" (15.827-15.870 mm). Standard master cylinder-to-piston clearance is 0-.0034" (0-.086 mm). Service limit is .006" (.15 mm).

Fig. 3: Exploded View of Hydraulic Clutch Assembly for Diesel Pickup & Mitsubishi Models

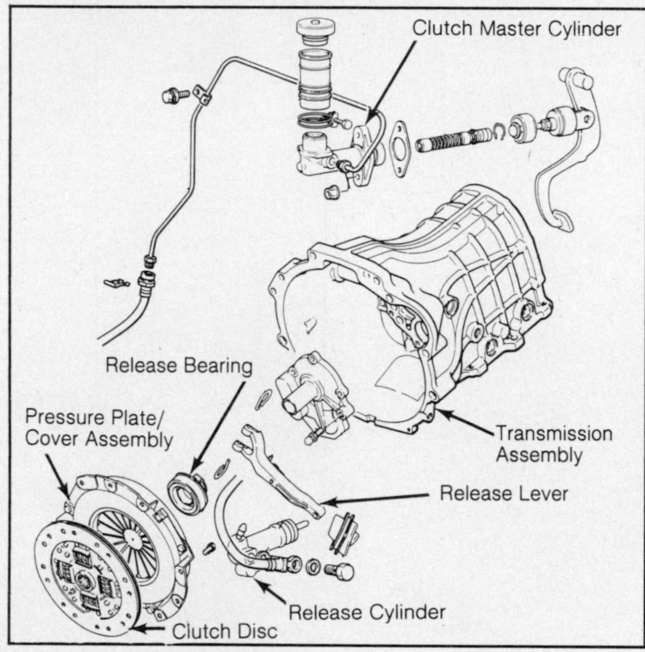
Clutch Master Cylinder
Release Bearing
Pressure Plate/
Cover Assembly
Transmission
Assembly
Release Lever
Release Cylinder
Clutch Disc

Handle the clutch components carefully to prevent any contamination of friction surfaces.

Assembly & Installation

1) Apply clean brake fluid to cylinder bore and piston assembly before installation. Do not to damage piston cup during installation in bore.

2) Mount cylinder to the fire wall. Tighten mount bolts and fluid line. Bleed clutch hydraulic system and adjust pedal height, travel and free play.

CLUTCH RELEASE CYLINDER

Removal & Installation

1) Remove release cylinder. Disassemble and inspect cup, piston and cylinder bore. Standard release cylinder bore is .750" (19.05 mm) for Montero and Starion.

2) If cup edge or bore is worn or damaged, replace complete release cylinder with new assembly. If components are in good condition, coat outer surface of piston and piston cup with rubber grease.

3) Install spring, piston assembly and retainer in cylinder. Install push rod and boot. Install release cylinder assembly into transmission case. Install remaining components. Bleed hydraulic system and check clutch pedal height, travel and free play.

ADJUSTMENTS

CAUTION: Insufficient pedal travel will result in poor clutch release and/or slippage. On Montero & Starion, no clutch pedal free play or travel adjustment is possible.

PEDAL HEIGHT, TRAVEL & FREE PLAY

1) Rotate adjusting bolt (at pedal top) so pedal height is as indicated in table. Ensure adjuster wheel-to-insulator clearance is .12-.16 (3-4 mm) for all models.

2) Pedal height is measured between floor board and top of pedal pad. After pedal height and travel adjustment, check for proper free play. *See Fig. 4*.

Fig. 4: Clutch Pedal Adjustment Procedure

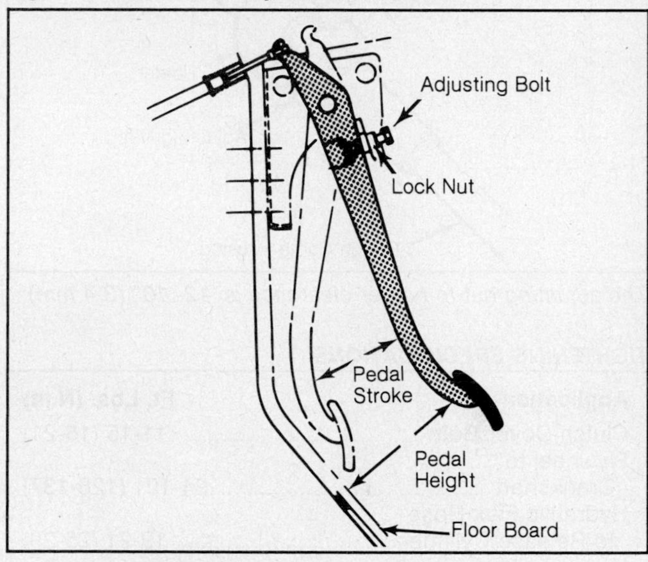
Adjusting Bolt
Lock Nut
Pedal
Stroke
Pedal
Height
Floor Board

Clutch pedal adjustment is the same for all models.

CLUTCH PEDAL HEIGHT AND TRAVEL

Application	Height In. (mm)	Travel In. (mm)
Challenger		
& Sapporo	7.5 (190)	6.0 (150)
Montero	7.4 (187.5) [1]	[2]
Pickups		
2.0L (Gas)	6.5 (166)	5.5 (140)
2.6L (Gas)	6.9 (176)	5.9 (150)
2.3L (Diesel)	6.9 (176)	5.9 (150)
Starion	7.6 (192.5) [1]	[2]

[1] – May vary by .10" (2.5 mm) either way.

[2] – Montero and Starion have no pedal travel or free play adjustment. Free play is built into hydraulic sytem. If not to specification, bleed system.

CLUTCH PEDAL FREE PLAY

Application	In. (mm)
Pickup (All Gas)	.8-.14 (20-35)
Pickup (Chrysler Corp. Diesel)	.2-.4 (5-10)
Pickup (Mitsubishi Diesel)	.4-.5 (10-15)
Challenger & Sapporo	.6-.8 (15-20)

CLUTCH CABLE

Adjustment (Except Diesel Pickup & Mitsubishi Models)

Pull clutch cable housing toward engine compartment. Rotate cable adjusting nut until .12-.16" (3-4 mm) clearance is obtained between adjusting nut and holder. *See Fig. 5*. Check for proper free play.

CHRYSLER CORP. IMPORTS & MITSUBISHI RWD MODELS (Cont.)

Fig. 5: Adjusting Clutch Pedal Free Play – All Except Diesel Pickup & Mitsubishi Models

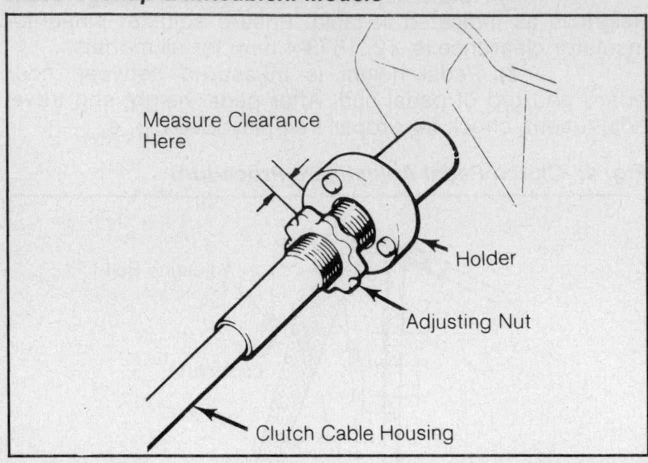
Measure Clearance
Here
Holder
Adjusting Nut
Clutch Cable Housing

The adjusting nut-to-holder clearance is .12-.16" (3-4 mm).

TIGHTENING SPECIFICATIONS

Application	Ft. Lbs. (N.m)
Clutch Cover Bolt	11-15 (15-21)
Flywheel to Crankshaft	94-101 (128-137)
Hydraulic Flex Hose to Release Cylinder	19-21 (25-29)
Hydraulic Line (Steel) to Clutch Master Cylinder	10-12 (13-16)
Transmission-to-Engine Flange Bolt	32-39 (43-53)
Starter Mount Bolt	16-23 (22-31)

DATSUN/NISSAN – PULSAR, SENTRA & STANZA

DESCRIPTION

Clutch assembly is a single, dry disc type with diaphragm spring pressure plate. Actuation is mechanical, using an adjustable cable connected to the pedal and release fork. The release bearing is prelubricated and sealed.

REMOVAL & INSTALLATION

CLUTCH ASSEMBLY

Removal

1) Remove battery and battery holding plate. Remove radiator reservoir tank. Raise vehicle and remove front wheels. Drain transaxle gear oil. Remove bolts attaching steering knuckle to strut assembly. Pull drive shaft ends out of transaxle.

CAUTION: **When removing drive shaft, do not damage lip of oil seal. After removal of shafts, insert bar to prevent side gears from rotating or falling into differential case.**

2) Remove wheel house protector plate bolts and plate. Separate control rod and support rod from transaxle. On Stanza models, disconnect exhaust pipe from engine manifold and frame bracket. On all models, remove engine gusset mount bolts and transmission protector.

3) Disconnect clutch and speedometer cables, back-up and neutral switch wires. Support rear of engine with jack. Remove starter. Support transaxle with jack. Remove engine mount bolts. Remove engine-to-transaxle bolts. Slide transaxle away from engine. Loosen pressure plate bolts evenly in crisscross pattern. Remove disc and pressure plate. *See Fig. 1.*

Fig. 1: Exploded View of Clutch Assembly

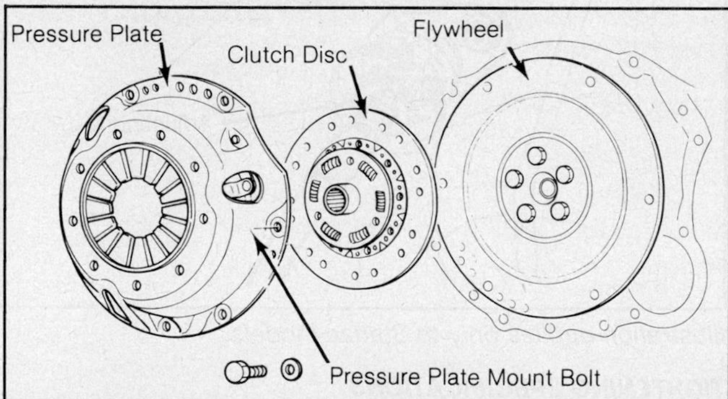
Pressure Plate
Clutch Disc
Flywheel
Pressure Plate Mount Bolt

Ensure friction surfaces are oil and grease free.

NOTE: **Wash all clutch components except disc and bearings in solvent. Release bearing and pilot bearing are prelubricated, do not wash with solvents. Clean only with compressed air.**

Inspection

1) Light roughness on pressure plate and flywheel may be dressed with fine emery cloth. If surfaces are deeply scored, replace defective parts. Check clutch disc for wear. Standard clutch lining thickness is .138" (3.5 mm). Minimum height of lining above rivet heads is .012" (.3 mm).

2) For all models, compressed disc thickness is .315-.331" (8.0-8.4 mm) and free thickness is .350-.378" (8.90-9.60 mm). Mount disc onto input shaft. Mount dial indicator to transmission case. Check disc runout. For Stanza, maximum runout should be less than .20" (.5 mm), at a radius of 3.74" (95 mm) from shaft axis. For Sentra and Pulsar, measure at radius of 3.35" (85 mm).

3) Check disc hub fit on input shaft splines. Disc should slide smoothly. If backlash at outer edge of disc exceeds .016" (.4 mm), replace disc and/or input shaft. Check end surface of pressure plate diaphragm springs for wear. Check height of springs by placing spacer plate tool (ST20050100) onto base plate tool (ST20050010). Tighten clutch cover assembly onto base plate with retainer bolts (ST20050051).

4) Measure spring height at several points with depth gauge. Spring height is 1.142-1.220" (29-31 mm) for Sentra and Pulsar. Height for Stanza is 1.220-1.299" (31-33 mm). Replace components as necessary. If height of spring end is beyond specification, adjust height and unevenness with spring adjustment tool (ST20050240).

5) Check unevenness of diaphragm spring toe height. Unevenness must be less than .02" (.5 mm). Inspect thrust rings for wear or damage by shaking cover assembly up and down. Listen for chattering noise. Lightly tap on rivets. Listen for crackling noise. Replace complete assembly if noise is heard.

Installation

1) Apply grease to input shaft splines and contact surfaces of release fork and bearing. Slide disc onto spline shaft several times, remove and wipe excess grease from components. Install clutch assembly and align with clutch assembly centering tool (KV30101000).

NOTE: **Take special care to prevent grease or oil from contaminating clutch facing and other friction surfaces.**

2) Tighten bolts evenly in a diagonal pattern. Remove clutch assembly centering tool. Reinstall transaxle in reverse order of removal procedure. Refill transaxle with oil. Adjust pedal height and free play.

CLUTCH CABLE

Removal

Remove instrument lower cover. On Stanza, remove left side heater duct. On all models, disconnect cable from release lever and clutch pedal. Remove bolts holding cable housing to engine side of firewall. Lift out cable.

Installation

To install cable, reverse order of removal. Apply grease to both ends of cable and return spring.

CLUTCH RELEASE FORK & BEARING

Removal

Remove transaxle from engine. Disconnect spring from release bearing and note location for proper installation. Remove bearing. Align release fork retaining pins with cavity in clutch housing. Using a pin punch, drive out retaining pins. Pull out clutch control shaft. Release lever and spring can now be removed. *See Fig. 2.*

Inspection

Check contact areas of release bearing and fork for excessive wear. Check release bearing for noise or roughness by rotating by hand in thrust direction. Inspect return spring and release bearing spring for wear. Replace components as necessary.

DATSUN/NISSAN – PULSAR, SENTRA & STANZA (Cont.)

Fig. 2: Removing Release Fork Retaining Pins

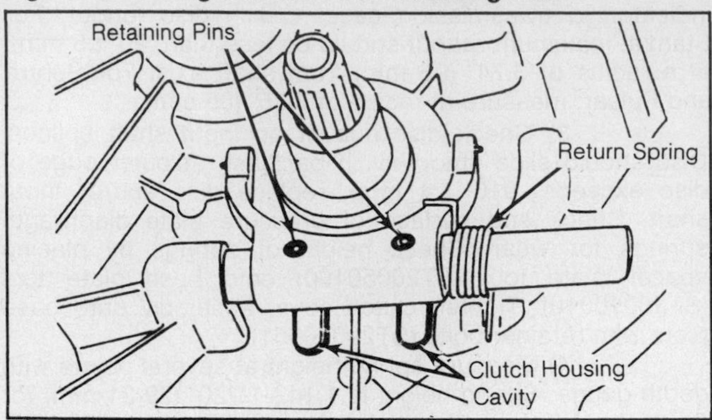
Retaining Pins
Return Spring
Clutch Housing
Cavity

Align pins with housing cavity and drive out with punch.

Installation

1) Using a lithium based grease, lubricate inner groove of release bearing. Lubricate contact surfaces of release fork and bearing and contact surfaces of control shaft and housing.

NOTE: Do not use excessive lubricant on clutch component sliding surfaces or melting grease will contaminate friction surfaces.

2) Install release fork, return spring and control shaft. Align holes in control shaft and release fork. Drive in retaining pins. Install release bearing spring on bearing. When installing release bearing, ensure that bearing spring is secured on fork.

ADJUSTMENTS

PEDAL HEIGHT

The clutch pedal height is adjusted by means of an adjustable pedal stopper. Loosen the lock nut and adjust stopper for correct pedal height "H". *See Fig. 3.*

Fig. 3: Measuring Pedal Height & Free Play

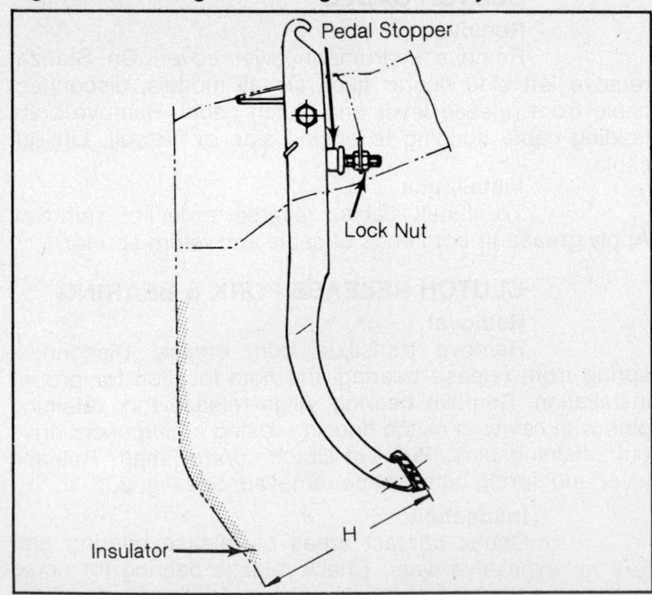
Pedal Stopper
Lock Nut
Insulator
H

Adjustment applies to Pulsar, Sentra & Stanza models.

The pedal height for Sentra and Pulsar is 7.64-8.03" (194-204 mm). On Stanza models, height is 5.85-6.24" (148.5-158.5 mm).

PEDAL FREE PLAY

Pulsar & Sentra

Free play is adjusted at the release lever end of clutch cable. Loosen lock nut and adjust cable until free travel is .43-.83" (11-21 mm). *See Fig. 4.*

Fig. 4: Adjusting Pedal Free Play

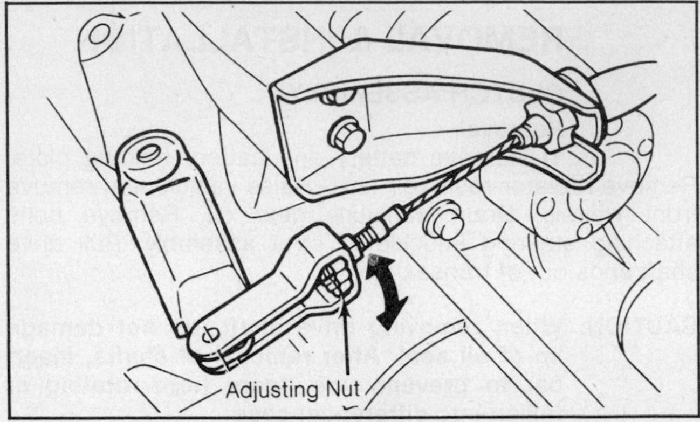
Adjusting Nut

Illustration applies to Pulsar & Sentra models.

Stanza

The free play is adjusted on the engine side of the firewall. An adjustment nut is located where clutch cable housing is bolted to firewall. Adjust cable until free travel is .43-.63" (11-16 mm). *See Fig. 5.*

Fig. 5: Adjusting Pedal Free Play

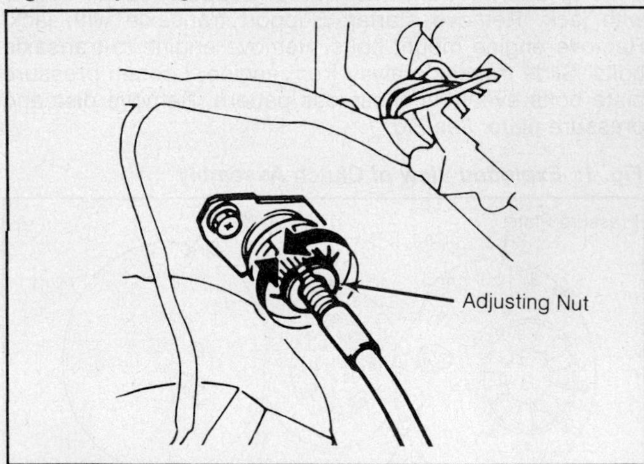
Adjusting Nut

Illustration applies only to Stanza models.

TIGHTENING SPECIFICATIONS

Applications	Ft. Lbs. (N.m)
Flywheel-to-Crankshaft Bolt	
Pulsar & Sentra	58-65 (78-88)
Stanza	72-80 (98-108)
Pressure Plate-to-Flywheel Bolt [1]	
Pulsar	16-22 (22-29)
Sentra & Stanza	12-15 (16-21)
Pedal Stopper Bolt Locknut	
Pulsar & Sentra	9-11 (12-15)
Stanza	12-19 (16-25)

[1] – Tighten mount bolts evenly, in a diagonal pattern, to final torque.

DATSUN/NISSAN – EXC. PULSAR, SENTRA & STANZA

DESCRIPTION

Clutch is dry, single disc type. All models use diaphragm spring type pressure plate and prelubricated clutch release bearing. Clutch operates by firewall mounted master cylinder and clutch housing mounted slave cylinder. All models use nonadjustable slave cylinder assembly.

REMOVAL & INSTALLATION

CLUTCH ASSEMBLY

Removal

1) Disconnect battery and accelerator linkage. Remove console box. Place shift lever in neutral. Remove shift lever boot, snap ring or nut, shift lever pin and shift lever. Raise and support vehicle. Disconnect exhaust pipe from manifold. If required, remove bolts mounting exhaust pipe bracket-to-extension housing or rear engine crossmember. If equipped, remove exhaust pipe insulator.

2) Disconnect back-up light, neutral, overdrive and transmission controlled spark connectors (if equipped). Disconnect speedometer cable on all except 4WD models. Index mark drive shafts and companion flanges prior to removal. On 4WD models, remove primary and front drive shafts. Remove front differential carrier crossmember.

3) Remove slave cylinder. On all except 4WD, separate center support bearing from crossmember. Remove drive shaft. On all models, plug rear of transmission to prevent fluid loss. Support engine and transmission with jacks. Loosen rear engine mount attaching bolt.

4) Remove rear engine mount bracket. Remove starter and engine-to-transmission bolts. Slide transmission rearward and remove. Install clutch alignment tool (KV30100100) or equivalent. Loosen pressure plate bolts, using a criss-cross pattern, until spring pressure is relieved. Remove pressure plate and clutch disc.

Fig. 1: Typical Datsun/Nissan Hydraulic Clutch System

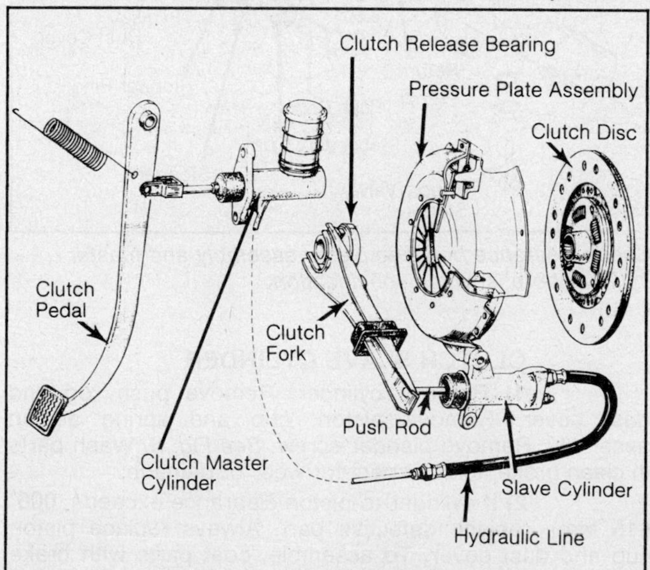
Clutch Release Bearing
Pressure Plate Assembly
Clutch Disc
Clutch Pedal
Clutch Fork
Push Rod
Clutch Master Cylinder
Slave Cylinder
Hydraulic Line

Clutch systems on different models may vary slightly.

NOTE: Handle clutch components carefully to prevent contamination of friction surfaces.

Inspection

1) Install disc on input shaft spline. Backlash measured at outside edge must be .016" (.40 mm) or less. Replace disc and/or shaft if backlash is excessive.

2) Check runout at specified radius from centerline of hub. *See Clutch Disc Runout Specifications* table. Replace if runout exceeds limit. Check flywheel-to-clutch disc surface runout. Limit is .006" (.15 mm) or less. Replace or resurface flywheel as necessary.

CLUTCH DISC RUNOUT SPECIFICATIONS

Application	Radius In. (mm)	Runout In. (mm)
200SX	4.25 (108)	.20 (.5)
Maxima	4.25 (108)	.20 (.5)
280ZX		
Non-Turbo	4.25 (108)	.20 (.5)
Turbo	4.53 (115)	.20 (.5)
Pickup	4.25 (108)	.20 (.5)

3) Check friction surface of disc for wear, grease or oil. Standard clutch lining thickness is .14" (3.5 mm). Standard disc free thickness for all except 280ZX 2+2 seater and Turbo is .325-.352" (8.25-8.95). Compressed thickness is .299-.315" (7.6-8.0 mm).

4) Standard disc free thickness for 280ZX 2+2 seater and Turbo is .337-.364" (8.55-9.25 mm). Compressed thickness is .307-.323" (7.80-8.20 mm). On all models, minimum distance from rivet head-to-disc surface is .012" (.3 mm).

5) Check end surface of clutch cover diaphragm springs for wear and replace if excessive. Measure height of springs by assembling spacer tool (ST20050100) onto base plate tool (ST200500100) and retain cover assembly with mount bolts (ST20050051). Measure spring height-to-base plate at several points with depth gauge.

6) If height is beyond specification, adjust with diaphragm adjusting tool (ST20050240). Standard spring height for all models except 280ZX Turbo is 1.299-1.378" (33-35 mm). Standard spring height of 280ZX Turbo is 1.476-1.555" (37.50-39.50 mm).

7) On all models, unevenness specification of diaphragm spring toe height is less than .02" (.5 mm). Replace cover assembly if adjustments do not bring components within specification.

8) Inspect thrust rings for wear or damage by shaking cover assembly and listen for chattering noise. Lightly tap on rivets and listen for crackling noise. Either noise indicates worn thrust rings and complete assembly must be replaced.

Installation

1) Lightly lubricate clutch disc splines with molybdenum grease. Slide onto mainshaft splines several times. Remove disc and wipe off excess grease. Slip clutch assembly over guide dowels. Use clutch aligning tool to center disc and pressure plate.

2) Tighten bolts evenly, one turn at a time, in a criss-cross pattern. To complete installation, reverse removal procedure. Adjust linkage and pedal. Check and refill transmission lubricant. Bleed clutch hydraulic system.

DATSUN/NISSAN – EXC. PULSAR, SENTRA & STANZA (Cont.)

CLUTCH MASTER CYLINDER

Removal & Installation

Disconnect master cylinder push rod at clevis by removing snap ring. Disconnect hydraulic line from master cylinder-to-slave cylinder. On 280ZX models only, remove windshield washer tank and electronic fuel injection resistor. On all models, remove master cylinder mount bolts and remove cylinder. Remove master cylinder dust cover if equipped. To install, reverse removal procedure. Bleed hydraulic system. Adjust pedal height and free play.

CLUTCH DAMPER

Removal & Installation (Diesel Engine)

Remove hydraulic lines from clutch damper. Remove clutch damper from bracket. To install, reverse removal procedure. Bleed hydraulic system and adjust pedal height and free play.

CLUTCH SLAVE CYLINDER

Removal & Installation

Remove clutch fork return spring (if equipped). Disconnect hydraulic line from slave cylinder. Remove bolts attaching cylinder to clutch housing and remove slave cylinder. To install, reverse removal procedure. Bleed hydraulic system and adjust pedal height and free play.

CLUTCH RELEASE BEARING & LEVER

Removal

With transmission removed from vehicle, remove dust boot from clutch housing. Disconnect release lever return spring and retaining clips holding release bearing to lever. Remove bearing and lever as an assembly through front of clutch housing. Remove bearing from collar using a puller.

Inspection

Check for excessive wear on contact surfaces of release lever, ball pin and bearing sleeve. Replace components as necessary. Check release bearing by rotating in thrust direction by hand. If bearing rotation is rough or noisy, replace bearing.

Installation

Assemble bearing onto inner sleeve using a press. Do not press on outer race. Apply molybdenum grease to inside surface of bearing collar, release bearing contact points, release bearing, ball pin in clutch housing and ball contact points on release lever. To complete installation, reverse removal procedure.

PILOT BEARING

Removal

With transmission, clutch assembly and release bearing components removed, pull pilot bearing from crankshaft with bearing puller tool (ST16610001) or equivalent. Do not lubricate bearing or wash in solvent, clean only with compressed air.

Inspection

Check bearing for fit in bore of crankshaft. Check inner surface of pilot bearing for wear, roughness or bell-mouth condition. Check transmission main drive gear. Replace worn components.

Installation

Before installing new bearing, clean crankshaft bearing hole and check for nicks or damage. Insert bearing into crankshaft until distance between flange end and bearing is .16" (4 mm) for all models. Do not damage edge of pilot bearing or insert to deep into crankshaft bore.

OVERHAUL

NOTE: **More than one manufacturer supplies master and slave cylinders. Do not interchange parts. Ensure overhaul kit matches cylinder. Do not use mineral oil to clean components or rubber parts will be destroyed.**

CLUTCH MASTER CYLINDER

1) Remove cylinder and filler cap. Drain fluid. Remove dust cover and stopper ring. Remove push rod and stopper. Remove supply valve stopper, piston, spring seat and return spring. *See Fig. 2.*

2) Wash parts in clean brake fluid. Blow dry with compressed air. Inspect for excessive wear or damage. If cylinder-to-piston clearance exceeds .006" (.15 mm), replace defective part. Replace rubber piston cup and dust cover during overhaul.

3) Ensure internal passages are clear. To assemble, coat parts with brake fluid and reverse disassembly procedure. Bleed hydraulic system. Adjust pedal height and free play.

Fig. 2: Exploded View of Clutch Master Cylinder

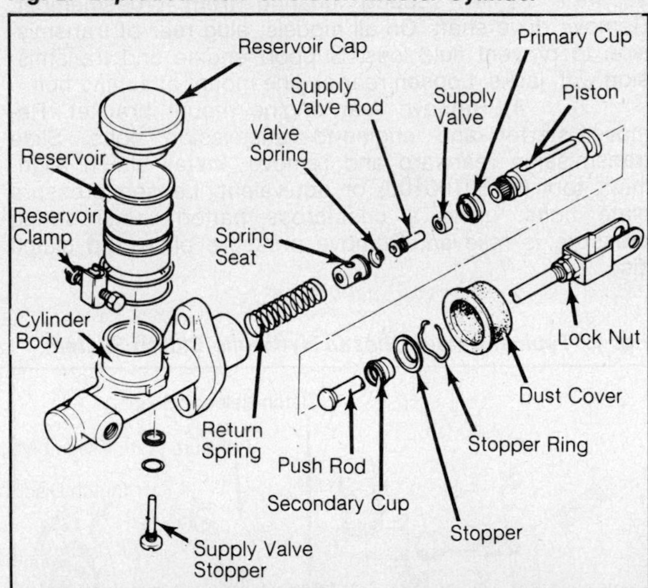
Reservoir Cap
Primary Cup
Supply Valve Rod
Supply Valve
Piston
Valve Spring
Reservoir
Reservoir Clamp
Spring Seat
Cylinder Body
Lock Nut
Dust Cover
Return Spring
Stopper Ring
Push Rod
Secondary Cup
Stopper
Supply Valve Stopper

Check clearance between piston assembly and master cylinder bore is within specification.

CLUTCH SLAVE CYLINDER

1) Remove cylinder. Remove push rod and dust cover. Remove piston, cup and spring as an assembly. Remove bleeder screw. *See Fig. 3*. Wash parts in clean brake fluid. Inspect for wear or damage.

2) If cylinder-to-piston clearance exceeds .006" (.15 mm), replace defective part. Always replace piston cup and dust cover. To assemble, coat parts with brake fluid and reverse disassembly procedure. Ensure piston cup is installed properly. Bleed hydraulic system.

DATSUN/NISSAN – EXC. PULSAR, SENTRA & STANZA (Cont.)

Fig. 3: Clutch Slave Cylinder Assembly

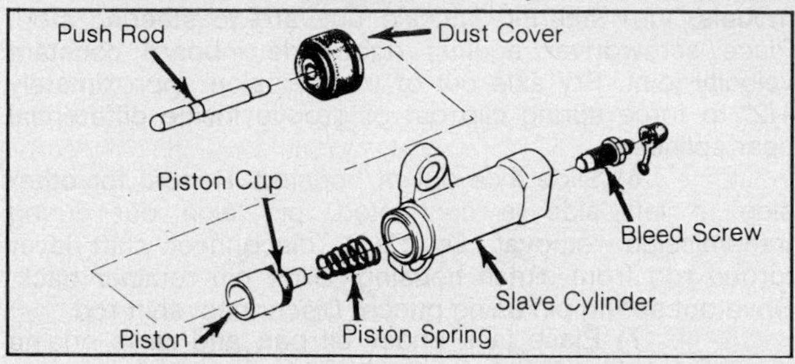
Push Rod
Dust Cover
Piston Cup
Bleed Screw
Slave Cylinder
Piston
Piston Spring

Replace rubber slave cylinder components during overhaul.

3) To assemble, coat all parts with brake fluid and reverse disassembly procedure. Ensure piston cup is installed properly and bleed hydraulic system.

CLUTCH DAMPER

Maxima & Pickup (Diesel Engine)

1) Remove four cover mount screws. Do not let oil touch damper rubber. Remove damper rubber, piston and cup. Clean parts in brake fluid. Check cylinder bore and piston for wear or damage. If cylinder-to-piston clearance exceeds .006" (.15 mm), replace defective parts. Replace piston cup during overhaul.

2) Check damper rubber for cracks, deformation and elasticity. Replace as necessary. To assemble, reverse disassembly procedure. Lubricate parts in brake fluid. Bleed hydraulic system. Adjust pedal height and free play.

ADJUSTMENT

PEDAL HEIGHT & FREE PLAY

1) Adjust pedal height on all models except 280ZX and Pickup by turning pedal stopper adjusting nut. Pickup models are adjusted by turning clutch switch adjusting nut. *See Fig. 4*.

2) On 280ZX models, adjustment is made by first setting adjusting rod length to 6.10" (155 mm). *See Fig. 5*. Then adjust master cylinder push rod so that pedal height is 8.03" (204 mm).

3) Turn pedal stopper or clutch switch until pedal height is down to 7.91" (201 mm). *See Fig. 6*. On all models, free play is adjusted to .04-.20" (1-5 mm) by turning master cylinder push rod in or out.

Fig. 4: Adjusting Clutch Pedal Height & Free Play

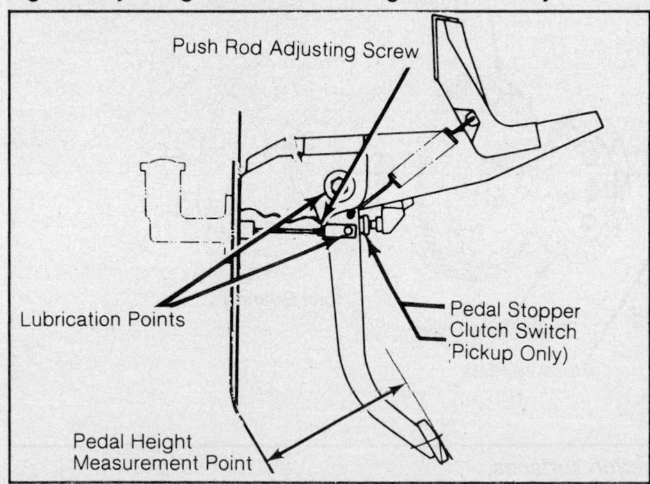
Push Rod Adjusting Screw
Lubrication Points
Pedal Stopper
Clutch Switch
(Pickup Only)
Pedal Height
Measurement Point

Illustration applies to all models except 280ZX.

PEDAL HEIGHT SPECIFICATIONS

Application	In. (mm)
200SX	6.38-6.77 (162-172)
280ZX	7.91 (201)
Maxima	
Gas	6.69-7.09 (170-180)
Diesel	6.89-7.28 (175-185)
Pickup	
Gasoline	6.73-6.97 (171-177)
Diesel	7.05-7.28 (179-185)

Fig. 5: Adjusting 280ZX Clutch Pedal Rod

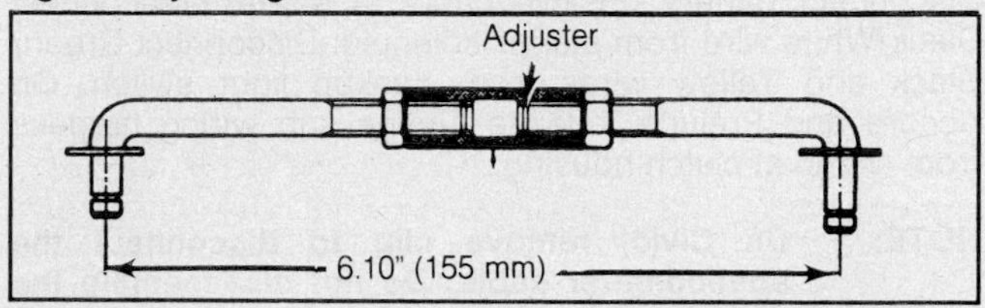
Adjuster
6.10" (155 mm)

Fig. 6: Adjusting 280ZX Clutch Pedal Height & Free Play

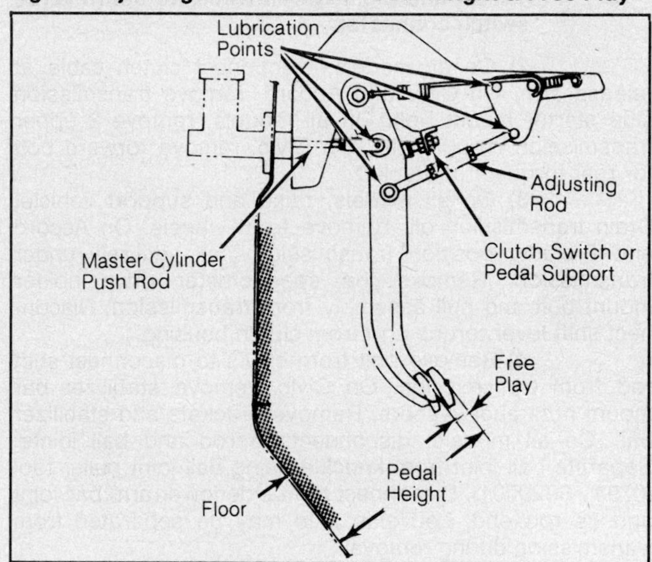
Lubrication
Points
Adjusting
Rod
Clutch Switch or
Pedal Support
Master Cylinder
Push Rod
Free
Play
Pedal
Height
Floor

HYDRAULIC SYSTEM BLEEDING

NOTE: **On diesel engine with clutch damper, bleed hydraulic system in sequence of slave cylinder, clutch damper and master cylinder.**

TIGHTENING SPECIFICATIONS

Application	Ft. Lbs. (N.m)
Clutch Cover Mount Bolt	12-15 (16-21)
Clutch Cover-to-Flywheel Bolt [1]	12-15 (16-21)
Crossmember-to-Body	23-31 (31-42)
Engine-to-Transmission Bolt	
Maxima	29-35 (39-47)
All Others	32-43 (43-58)
Flex Hose-to-Slave Cylinder Nut	12-15 (16-21)
Slave Cylinder Mount Bolt	22-30 (30-40)
Starter Motor-to-Housing	22-29 (30-39)

[1] – Tighten bolts evenly, in a diagonal pattern.

HONDA ACCORD, CIVIC & PRELUDE

DESCRIPTION

Clutch is single plate dry disc type, using a diaphragm spring to engage pressure plate. Clutch has a mechanical release system consisting of clutch pedal, cable, release lever and release bearing.

REMOVAL & INSTALLATION

CLUTCH ASSEMBLY

Removal

1) Place the shift lever in Neutral. Disconnect the battery ground cable at battery and transmission. Disconnect battery positive cable at starter. Disconnect Black/White wire from starter solenoid. Disconnect Green/Black and Yellow wires from backup light switch. On Accord and Prelude, release engine sub wiring harness from clamp at clutch housing.

NOTE: **On Civic, remove clip to disconnect the speedometer cable. Do not disassemble the speedometer gear holder. On the Civic 1300 5-Speed transmission, disconnect the Black/Yellow and Light Green wires for 5th/Reverse switch connector.**

2) On all models, disconnect clutch cable at release arm. On Civic and Accord, remove transmission side starter mount bolt. On all models, remove 2 upper transmission mount bolts. On Civic, remove forward bolt for rear torque arm bracket.

3) On all models, raise and support vehicle. Drain transmission oil. Remove front wheels. On Accord and Prelude, position transmission jack securely under transmission. Remove the speedometer drive holder mount bolt and pull assembly from transmission. Disconnect shift lever torque arm from clutch housing.

4) Remove bolt from clevis to disconnect shift rod from transmission. On Civic, remove stabilizer bar mount nuts and washers. Remove brackets and stabilizer bar. On all models, disconnect tie rod and ball joints. Separate ball joint from knuckle using ball joint puller tool (07941-6920001). Disconnect right side lower arm ball joint and tie rod end. Left side axle may be separated from transmission during removal.

5) On Prelude, remove damper fork bolt. On all models, turn steering knuckle outward to steering stop. Place screwdriver against right side inboard constant velocity joint. Pry axle out of transmission approximately 1/2" to force spring clip out of groove inside differential gear splines.

6) Slide axle out of housing. Repeat for other side. If left side is connected, pry axle out during transmission removal. On Civic, disconnect shift lever torque rod from clutch housing. Slide pin retainer back. Drive out spring pin using punch. Disconnect shift rod.

7) Place jack under oil pan and raise engine enough to unload mounts. Remove front and rear torque rods and rear torque rod bracket. Remove engine damper bracket from center transmission crossmember. Remove rear engine mount and bracket. Place 1" x 2" x 4" block of wood between center crossmember and oil pan. Lower jack and rest engine on crossmember.

8) On Accord and Prelude, remove clutch housing bolts from front and rear transmission mount brackets. Remove clutch cover. On all models, remove engine side starter mount bolt and lower starter through chassis. Remove remaining transmission mount bolts.

9) Lift transmission with jack enough to take weight off engine. Slide transmission away from engine until mainshaft clears clutch pressure plate. Lower jack and remove transmission. If reusing clutch, mark pressure plate position on flywheel.

10) Check pressure plate diaphragm spring finger height before removing clutch assembly. Install ring gear holder tool (07924-6340100 or 07924-SA00000). Loosen bolts in a crisscross pattern and lift off clutch assembly. *See Fig. 1 & 2.*

Inspection

1) Check pressure plate diaphragm spring fingers for wear or unevenness at release bearing contact points. Check spring finger height using clutch disc alignment tool and feeler gauge. For Accord and Prelude, use alignment tool (07974-6890100 or 07974-6890101).

2) For Civic, use alignment tool (07924-6890101). Check that distance between tool flange and fingers is no more than .04" (1 mm). Unevenness service limit of spring fingers is .04" (1 mm) maximum. Inspect pressure plate surface for wear, cracks, burning or

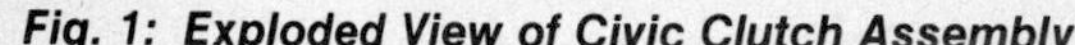

Fig. 1: Exploded View of Civic Clutch Assembly

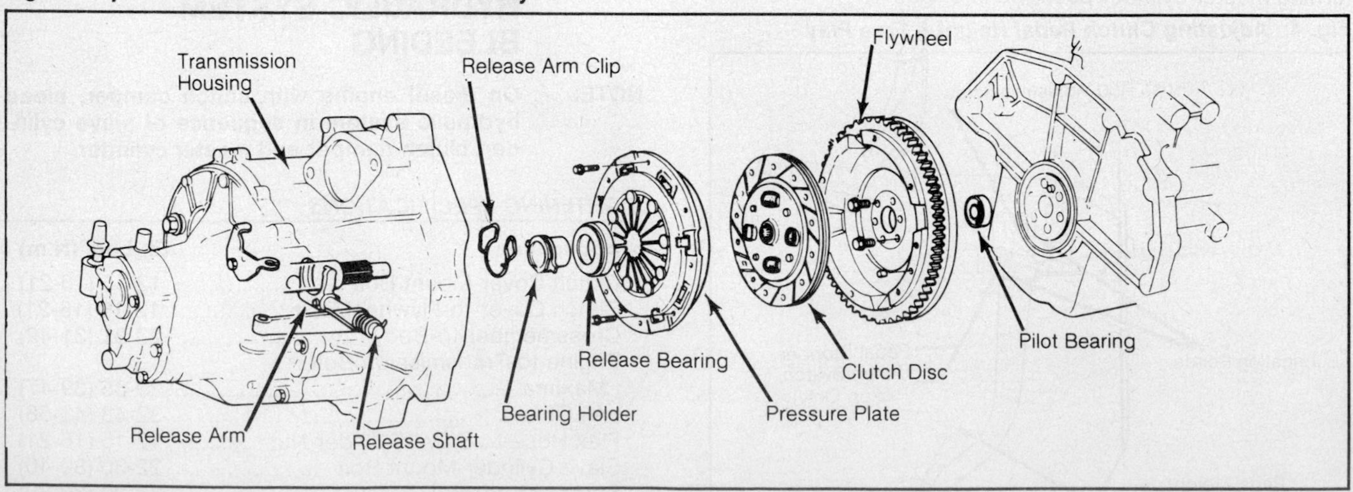
Transmission Housing
Release Arm Clip
Flywheel
Release Bearing
Clutch Disc
Pilot Bearing
Bearing Holder
Pressure Plate
Release Arm
Release Shaft

Do not allow oil, grease or dirt to contaminate clutch component friction surfaces.

warpage. Maximum face warpage is .006" (.15 mm). Measure with a straight edge and feeler gauge at several points.

3) Check pressure plate surface for inward taper. Standard taper is .001" (.03 mm). Taper service limit for Civic is .003" (.08 mm) and for Accord and Prelude is .006" (.15 mm). Check clutch disc lining for excessive wear, burned or oil soaked condition. Measure disc thickness.

4) Standard disc thickness is .32-.35" (8.1-8.8 mm) for Accord and Prelude and .34-.37" (8.7-9.4 mm) for Civic. Service limit is .22" (5.7 mm) for Accord and Prelude and .24" (6.1 mm) for Civic. Check clutch disc for loose rubber torsion dampers. Replace disc if any are loose. Measure depth of rivets, on both sides, from lining surface.

5) Standard rivet depth is .051" (1.30 mm) for all models. The minimum height of lining above rivet heads is .008" (.20 mm). Place disc on input shaft and check runout. Standard disc runout is .032" (.80 mm). Maximum runout is .039" (1 mm). Inspect flywheel ring gear teeth for wear or damage. Check clutch disc-to-flywheel friction surface for wear, cracks or burning.

6) Measure flywheel runout, using dial indicator, through two or more revolutions. Push in on flywheel while turning to take up crankshaft thrust washer clearance. Standard runout is .002" (.05 mm). Maximum runout is .006" (.15 mm). Replace or resurface flywheel if not to specification.

Installation

1) Using clutch alignment tool and ring gear holder, install disc and pressure plate. Tighten bolts evenly, in a crisscross pattern, to final torque. Ensure that 2 dowel pins are installed in clutch housing.

2) Clean release bearing sliding surfaces. Apply molybdenum grease to release bearing contact points, clutch disc and transmission mainshaft splines.

CAUTION: **New spring clips must be used on both axle shafts. Slide axles in until spring clips engage differential.**

3) Complete installation in reverse order of removal. Ensure drain plug is tight and refill transmission with SE or SF grade oil. Adjust clutch pedal height, travel and free play.

CLUTCH RELEASE BEARING

CAUTION: **Release bearing is packed with grease. Do not wash in solvent, clean with compressed air only.**

Removal (Accord & Prelude)

Remove bolt holding release fork-to-release shaft. Remove release shaft and bearing assembly. Separate release arm from bearing by removing clip from holes in release bearing. Note clip location for proper installation.

Installation

1) Lightly coat contact surfaces with Molybdenum grease. Align release arm with locating holes of bearing and install release arm clip in holes. Install release shaft and bearing. Align release shaft and arm.

2) Install new lock plate and bolt. After installation, move release arm up and down to ensure fork fits properly against bearing and bearing slides freely. To complete installation, reverse removal procedure.

Removal (Civic)

1) Using small screwdriver, pry ends of release bearing clip out of holes in fork. Slide bearing and holder off shaft sleeve. To prevent damaging clip, DO NOT bend further than necessary. Note clip location for proper installation. Check release bearing for excessive play by spinning by hand in thrust direction. If there is excessive play, replace bearing.

2) To replace bearing, drive holder out of release bearing by using small end of drive attachment tool (driver 07749-0010000 with attachment 07947-6340300). Drive new bearing onto holder using large end of driver attachment. Rounded shoulder on bearing inner race faces down.

Installation

1) Position clip in front of side tabs on bearing holder. Slide bearing assembly onto transmission shaft sleeve. Using screwdriver, pry out ends of clip and guide them into holes in fork. If clutch fork shaft was removed, assemble bearing, fork and clip together first.

2) Slide assembly onto transmission shaft sleeve. Reinstall clutch fork shaft and spring. Secure shaft using new lock plate and bolt. After installation, move release arm up and down to be sure fork fits properly against bearing holder and holder slides freely on sleeve. To complete installation, reverse removal procedure.

Fig. 2: Exploded View of Accord & Prelude Clutch Assembly

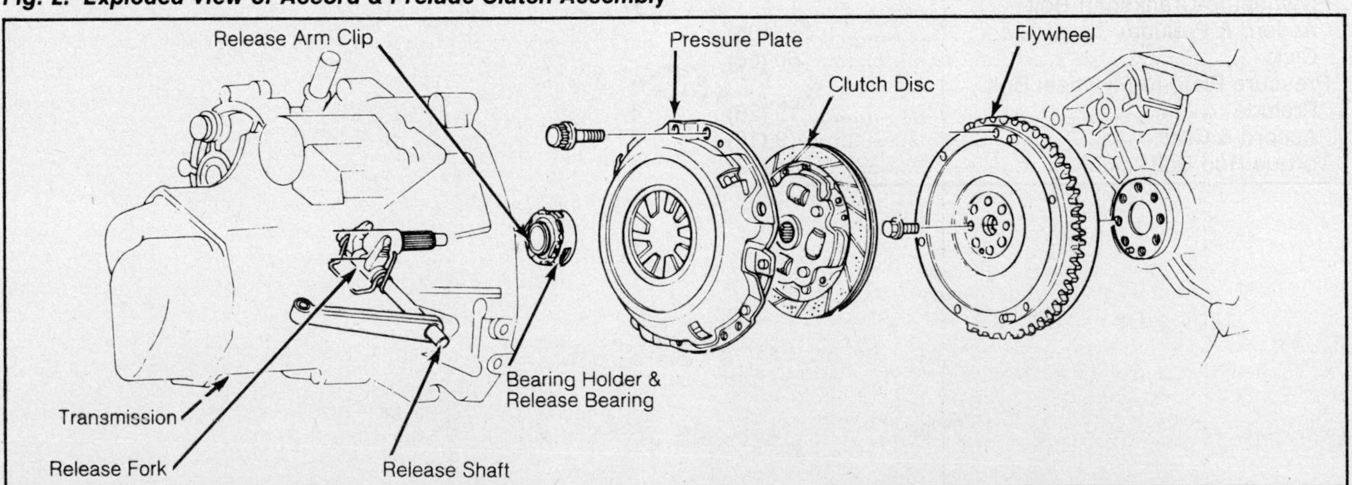

Release Arm Clip
Pressure Plate
Flywheel
Clutch Disc
Bearing Holder &
Release Bearing
Transmission
Release Fork
Release Shaft

Check clutch disc and flywheel for excessive wear, cracks or damage and release bearing for noise or roughness.

HONDA ACCORD, CIVIC & PRELUDE (Cont.)

ADJUSTMENT

CLUTCH PEDAL

1) Ensure that pedal return spring holds clutch pedal against stop pad. Turn adjusting nut to give 3/16-7/32" (4.4-5.4 mm) free play at release arm on Civic and 13/64-1/4" (5.2-6.4 mm) on Accord and Prelude. *See Fig. 3.*

Fig. 3: Clutch Adjustment Nut Location

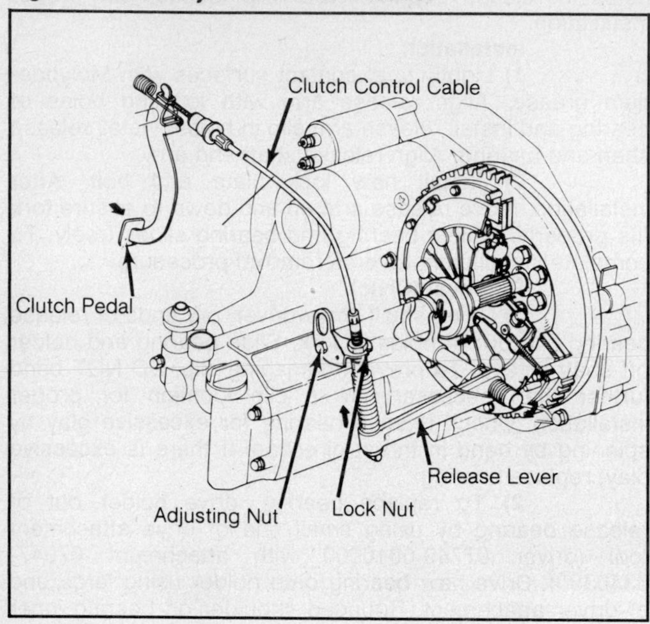
Clutch Control Cable
Clutch Pedal
Release Lever
Lock Nut
Adjusting Nut

Turn adjusting nut in or out for free play at release arm tip.

2) Free play at pedal should be 3/8-1 3/16" (10-30 mm) for Accord and 7/8-1 1/8" (23-28 mm) for Civic and Prelude. Disengagement height for Civic is 1 3/16" (30 mm) from floor and height for Accord and Prelude is 1 1/4" (32 mm).

3) If pedal play and/or pedal disengagement height exceed these specifications, clutch components may require replacement.

TIGHTENING SPECIFICATIONS

Application	Ft. Lbs. (N.m)
Flywheel-to-Crankshaft Bolt	
Accord & Prelude	76 (105)
Civic	50 (68)
Pressure Plate-to-Flywheel Bolt	
Prelude	19 (26)
Accord & Civic	9 (12)
Torque Rod Bolt	54 (73)

ISUZU I-MARK & P'UP

DESCRIPTION

Clutch assembly is a single plate, dry disc type, using a diaphragm spring to engage pressure plate with a prelubricated release bearing. Clutch has a mechanical release system consisting of clutch pedal, cable, yoke and release bearing.

On P'UP models, the clutch components are riveted together to prevent disassembly. The entire clutch assembly must be replaced if pressure plate or disc is worn beyond limits.

REMOVAL & INSTALLATION

CLUTCH ASSEMBLY

Removal (Except 4WD P'UP)

1) Disconnect battery. From inside, remove shift lever assembly. Loosen clutch cable adjusting nuts and remove upper starter mount nuts at left side of engine compartment. Remove starter wiring. Raise and support vehicle. Remove drive shaft.

2) Remove speedometer and clutch cable. Remover starter lower bolt and starter. Disconnect exhaust pipe from manifold. Remove exhaust pipe bracket. Remove flywheel inspection cover and rear transmission support mount bolt. Support transmission. Remove rear transmission support from frame.

3) On 2WD P'UP, remove 2 lower flywheel cover mount bolts. Remove 2 bolts mounting frame bracket-to-rear mount. Using a jack, slightly raise transmission. Remove 4 crossmember-to-frame bolts. Remove 2 bolts mounting transmission extension housing. Lower engine and transmission assembly. Support rear of engine. Disconnect electrical leads at transmission. Remove transmission-to-engine mount bolts and transmission.

4) On I-Mark, lower transmission. Position about 4" lower than when mounted. Disconnect back-up light switch and coasting fuel cut switch wires (gasoline models only). Remove transmission housing-to-engine bolts. Move transmission straight back. Lower from vehicle.

5) On all models, index mark clutch assembly-to-flywheel for reassembly reference. Install clutch assembly aligning tool (J-24547). Remove retaining bolts evenly in a criss-cross pattern. *See Fig. 1*.

Removal (4WD P'UP)

1) Disconnect battery. Drain transmission oil. Slide transmission and transfer case shift lever boots upward on levers. Remove gearshift lever mount bolts. Remove spring from transfer case shift lever and both levers. Remove starter mount bolts and starter.

2) Raise and support vehicle. Disconnect exhaust pipe from manifold. Remove exhaust hanger from transmission. Disconnect speedometer and ground cable at transmission. Disconnect rear drive shaft at differential. Remove 2 center bearing mount bolts.

3) Remove first and second rear drive shafts together. Disconnect front drive shaft at both ends. Remove return spring at clutch fork. Disconnect clutch cable from clutch fork. Pull forward through stiffener bracket. Remove 2 lower flywheel guard mount bolts.

4) Remove 2 frame bracket-to-transmission rear mount bolts and nuts. Raise engine and transmission assembly slightly. Remove 4 crossmember-to-frame bracket bolts. Remove 2 rear mount bolts from transfer case. Lower assembly. Support rear of engine.

5) Remove side case mount bolts and nuts. Remove side case. Use care not to lose shift rod detent spring and detent ball during side case removal. Disconnect electrical connectors from transmission. Remove shift cover and gasket from top of transfer case. Remove transmission-to-engine bolts.

NOTE: **When removing 4WD transmission, turn side case fitting face down. Pull transmission back to clear clutch assembly.**

6) Pull transmission straight back to clear clutch assembly. Tilt front down. Remove transmission. Index mark pressure plate and flywheel for reassembly reference. Loosen pressure plate attaching bolts evenly until pressure is relieved. Support clutch assembly with clutch aligning tool (J-24547). Remove clutch assembly. *See Fig. 1*.

Fig. 1: Exploded View of I-Mark & P'UP Clutch Assembly

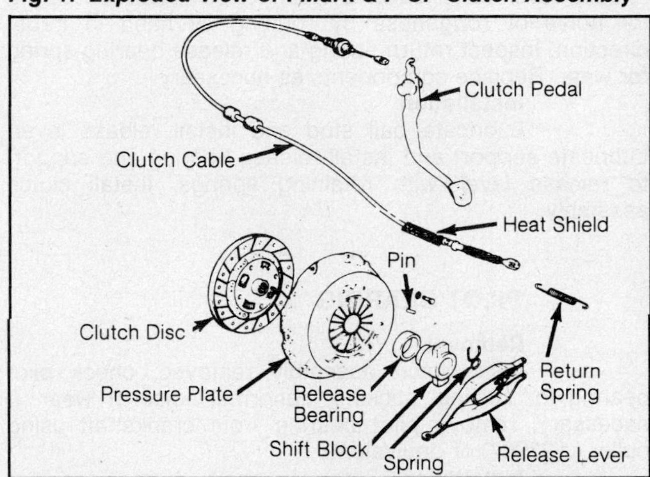
Clutch Pedal
Clutch Cable
Heat Shield
Pin
Clutch Disc
Pressure Plate
Release Bearing
Return Spring
Shift Block
Spring
Release Lever

Check that clutch friction surfaces are not contaminated with oil, grease or dirt.

Inspection

1) Check clutch disc for burned, worn or damaged lining, loose rivets or very loose torsional springs. Check for smooth sliding fit of disc hub by installing on input shaft splines. Measure backlash, in direction of rotation, at outer edge with dial indicator. Replace disc and/or input shaft if backlash exceeds .113" (2.9 mm).

2) Check clutch lining for signs of oil or grease contamination. Check lining thickness. Standard thickness of lining per side is .141" (3.57 mm). Standard compressed lining thickness is .313" (8 mm). Standard free lining thickness is .344" (8.70 mm). Minimum lining depth is .008" (.20 mm) above rivet heads.

3) Measure clutch disc runout, at outer edge, with dial indicator. Maximum runout is .039" (1 mm). Check friction surfaces of flywheel and pressure plate for scoring or roughness. Smooth slight roughness with fine emery cloth.

4) If surfaces are deeply scored, resurface or replace components as necessary. Inspect release lever ball socket, release bearing contact face and ball retaining spring for damage. Spring must hold release lever tightly to ball stud.

Installation (All Models)

1) Using aligning tool, install clutch assembly in original position. Tighten bolts evenly, in criss-cross pattern. Lightly lubricate input shaft splines, clutch hub and release bearing contact surfaces with moylbdenum grease.

Clutches

ISUZU I-MARK & P'UP (Cont.)

2) To complete installation, reverse removal procedure. Readjust clutch pedal height and free play. Refill transmission with SAE 30 engine oil.

NOTE: The pilot and release bearings are permanently lubricated. Do not wash in solvent, clean only with compressed air and shop towel.

RELEASE BEARING

Removal

With clutch assembly removed, remove release bearing-to-lever retaining spring. Remove release bearing with support. Remove release lever from transmission ball stud.

Inspection

Check contact areas of release bearing and release lever for excessive wear. Check release bearing for noise or roughness by rotating by hand in thrust direction. Inspect return spring and release bearing spring for wear. Replace components as necessary.

Installation

Lubricate ball stud and install release lever. Lubricate support and install release bearing and support to release lever with retaining springs. Install clutch assembly.

PILOT BEARING

Removal

With clutch assembly removed, check pilot bearing for seizing, sticking, abnormal noise or wear. If necessary, remove pilot bearing from crankshaft using puller (J-23907) or equivalent.

Installation

Install pilot bearing in crankshaft bore using driver (J-26516) or equivalent. Bearing must be fitted against bottom face of bearing fitting hole. Install remaining parts by reversing removal procedure.

CLUTCH CABLE

Removal

1) Loosen clutch cable lock and adjusting nuts. Remove cable clip in engine compartment. Raise vehicle. Remove return spring from release lever. Remove clutch cable from release lever and slide it through retaining bracket. Disconnect cable from clutch pedal and remove.

2) On P'UP, disconnect cable from hooked portion of clutch pedal and pull out toward engine compartment together with damper rubber. Use care not to damage rubber damper during removal. On all models, check cable assembly and/or damper rubber for fatigue or damage. Replace as necessary.

Installation

Slide cable through firewall and install clutch pedal. Install cable in original position through retaining bracket to release lever. Install clutch return spring. Adjust clutch cable and tighten lock nut.

ADJUSTMENTS

CLUTCH PEDAL HEIGHT

Adjust clutch switch setting so pedal height, from floor, is 6.20" (157.5 mm) for I-Mark and 6.5-6.8" (164-174 mm) for P'UP. Lock switch in position with lock nut.

CLUTCH PEDAL FREE PLAY

I-Mark

Loosen lock and adjusting nuts on clutch cable. Pull cable toward front of vehicle to take up slack. Turn adjusting nut inward until free play is 5/8" (16 mm). Tighten lock nut.

P'UP

Pull cable into engine compartment. Rotate adjuster nut until washer damper assembly is brought back into contact with firewall. Work pedal several times. Pull cable out again. Fully tighten nut. Back adjusting nut off until there is .2" (5 mm) between adjusting nut and boot. Tighten lock nut. *See Fig. 2.*

Fig. 2: Adjusting Clutch Pedal Free Play

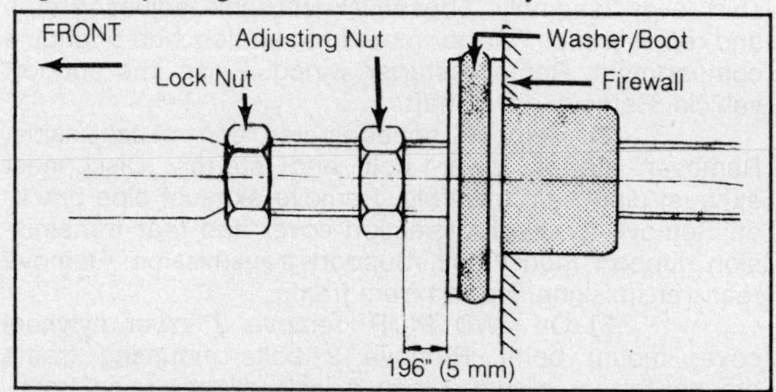
FRONT
Adjusting Nut
Washer/Boot
Lock Nut
Firewall
.196" (5 mm)

Check pedal free play if clutch is dragging or slipping.

TIGHTENING SPECIFICATIONS

Application	Ft. Lbs. (N.m)
Flywheel-to-Crankshaft Bolt	69 (93)
Pressure Plate-to-Flywheel Bolt	
I-Mark	14 (19)
P'UP	13 (18)
Release Lever Ball Stud	29 (39)

ISUZU IMPULSE

DESCRIPTION

Clutch assembly is a single plate, dry disc type, using diaphragm spring to engage pressure plate with prelubricated release bearing. Clutch is operated by firewall-mounted master cylinder and clutch housing mounted slave cylinder.

REMOVAL & INSTALLATION

CLUTCH ASSEMBLY

Removal

1) Disconnect negative battery cable. From inside of vehicle, remove gear shift knob. Remove boot cover assembly from shift lever. Remove console assembly. Raise and support vehicle. Drain transmission oil. Remove front exhaust pipe assembly.

2) Remove parking brake cable adjusting nut. Disconnect rear cable from front cable. Remove cable locating clip. Remove center exhaust pipe assembly. Using jack, raise front of differential carrier. Remove mount bolts.

3) Remove 4 front drive shaft flange mount bolts. Remove front drive shaft. Remove mount bolts for drive shaft crossmember. Remove rear drive shaft assembly. Remove speedometer cable assembly. Disconnect and plug fluid line to slave cylinder. Remove cylinder.

4) Remove cover under transmission case. Position jack under transmission. Remove engine rear mount bolts. Lower transmission slightly. Remove bolts retaining shifter quadrant cover-to-transmission case. Disconnect wiring from transmission.

5) Remove transmission mount bolts. Lower transmission from vehicle. Ensure starter is moved forward to prevent it from falling out when mount bolts are removed. Index mark clutch assembly to flywheel for reassembly reference. Install clutch assembly alignment tool (J-24547). Remove mount bolts evenly, in a diagonal pattern. Remove clutch assembly. *See Fig. 1.*

Fig. 1: Exploded View of Impulse Clutch Assembly

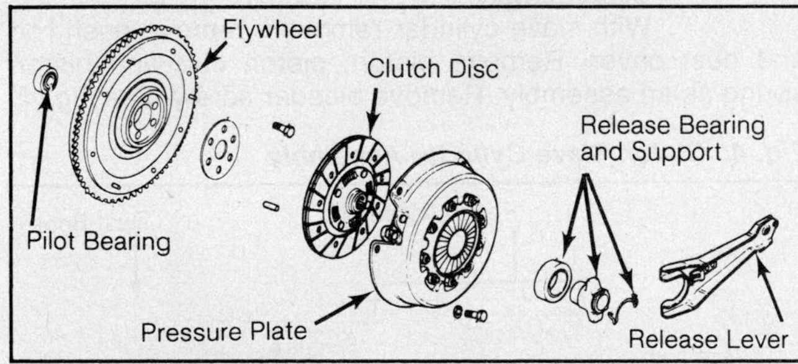
Flywheel
Clutch Disc
Release Bearing
and Support
Pilot Bearing
Pressure Plate
Release Lever

Check that clutch friction surfaces are not contaminated with oil, grease or dirt.

Inspection

1) Check clutch disc friction surfaces for cracks, heat hardening or contamination by dirt, oil or grease. Inspect damper springs. Replace disc if excessive play is found. Check depression of rivet heads-to-lining surface. Standard head depth is .047" (1.20 mm). Minimum depth is .008" (.20 mm).

2) Check disc lining thickness. Standard lining thickness per side is .138" (3.50 mm). Standard compressed thickness .307" (7.80 mm). Free thickness is .338" (8.60 mm). Measure disc runout. Mount dial gauge 90° to lining surface. Standard runout is .028" (.70 mm). Service limit is .039" (1 mm).

3) Check disc hub spline wear. Mount disc to top gear shaft splines. Measure wear at outside diameter. Standard movement is .02" (.5 mm). Service limit is .039" (1 mm). Inspect pressure plate friction surfaces for cracks, distortion and proper thickness. Standard thickness is .51" (13 mm).

4) Check diaphragm springs for heat distortion, loosened rivets, wear or damage. Check wire ring for wear. Measure spring tension. Invert clutch cover assembly. Mount new clutch disc or .307" (7.80 mm) plate to pressure plate. Compress assembly until transmission side of disc surface is flush with pressure plate top surface.

5) Note reading of pressure gauge. Standard spring pressure is 838 lbs. (3728 N.m). With springs compressed, measure height of fingers at tip ends. Standard height is 1.26-1.34" (32-34 mm). Replace pressure plate if height or spring pressure is less than standard.

6) Inspect flywheel friction surface. Resurface or replace if heavy wear marks or damage is evident. Standard surface depth is 1.26" (32 mm). Service limit is 1.22" (31 mm). Replace ring gear if teeth are worn or damaged.

NOTE: Wash all clutch components except disc and release bearing in solvent. Blow dry with compressed air.

Installation

Lightly lubricate clutch release lever assembly, disc hub and top gear shaft splines and release bearing contact surfaces with molybdenum grease. Install release lever, spring and bearing assembly. Mount alignment tool. Install clutch assembly.

Tighten mount bolts evenly, in a diagonal pattern. With transmission mounted, clean and install magnetic drain plug and fill transmission. To complete installation, reverse removal procedure.

CLUTCH MASTER CYLINDER

Removal & Installation

Remove hydraulic line from reservoir-to-master cylinder and plug opening. Disconnect hydraulic line from master cylinder-to-slave cylinder. From inside of vehicle, disconnect master cylinder push rod at clevis. Remove master cylinder mount bolts. Remove cylinder. *See Fig. 2.* Remove dust cover and check for fluid leakage. To install, reverse removal procedure. Bleed hydraulic system. Check pedal stroke and free play.

CLUTCH SLAVE CYLINDER

Removal & Installation

Disconnect hydraulic line from slave cylinder-to-master cylinder and plug opening. Remove bolts attaching slave cylinder to clutch housing. Remove cylinder. To install, reverse removal procedure. Bleed hydraulic system. Check pedal stroke and free play.

ISUZU IMPULSE (Cont.)

Fig. 2: Exploded View of Clutch Control Components

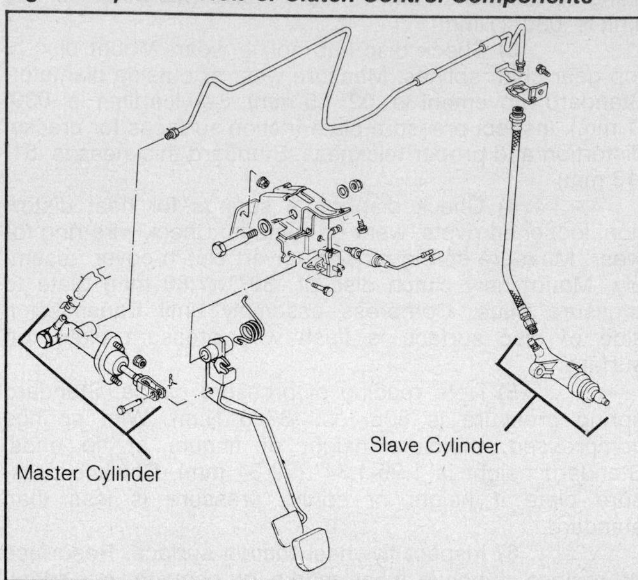
Slave Cylinder
Master Cylinder

Inspect clutch hydraulic components for leakage and replace or repair as necessary.

RELEASE BEARING & LEVER

NOTE: Release bearing is permanently lubricated. Do not wash in solvent. Clean only with compressed air.

Removal

With clutch assembly removed, remove release bearing-to-lever retaining spring. Remove release bearing with support. Remove release lever from ball stud.

Inspection

Check release bearing for noise, excessive play or lubrication loss by turning by hand in thrust direction. If replacement is needed, remove bearing from support using puller (J-22888) and adaptor (J-2241-11).

Check and replace release lever if excessive wear or damage is found on shift collar or pivot contact faces. Inspect return spring and release bearing spring for wear. Replace components as necessary.

Installation

To install release bearing to support, lightly coat mating surfaces with molybdenum grease and press together. Lubricate ball stud. Install release lever. Lubricate support. Install release bearing and support to release lever with retaining spring. Install clutch assembly.

PILOT BEARING

NOTE: The pilot bearing is permanently lubricated. Do not wash in solvent. Clean only with compressed air.

Removal

With clutch assembly removed, check pilot bearing for seizing, sticking, abnormal noise or wear by turning in thrust direction. If necessary, remove pilot bearing from crankshaft using puller (J-23907) or equivalent.

Installation

Install pilot bearing in crankshaft bore using driver (J-26516-A) and adaptor (J-8092). Bearing must be fitted against bottom face of bearing bore. To complete installation, reverse removal procedure.

OVERHAUL

CLUTCH MASTER CYLINDER

Disassembly

With master cylinder out of vehicle, remove push rod, dust cover, snap ring and piston stopper. Remove piston, spring seat and return spring. *See Fig. 3.* Wash all parts in clean brake fluid and blow dry with compressed air.

Fig. 3: Exploded View of Clutch Master Cylinder

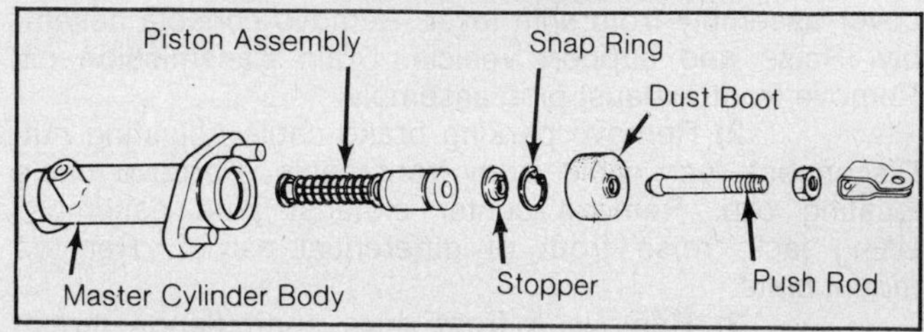
Piston Assembly
Snap Ring
Dust Boot
Master Cylinder Body
Stopper
Push Rod

Check that clearance between piston assembly and master cylinder bore is within specification.

Inspection

Inspect all components for excessive wear or damage. Standard clearance between master cylinder bore and piston is .0028" (.070 mm). If cylinder-to-piston clearance exceeds .0059" (.150 mm), replace defective part. Replace rubber piston cup and dust cover during overhaul.

Reassembly

Ensure all recesses, openings and internal passages are clear of foreign matter. To assemble, coat parts with brake fluid. Reverse disassembly procedure. Bleed hydraulic system. Check pedal height and free play.

CLUTCH SLAVE CYLINDER

Disassembly

With slave cylinder removed, remove push rod and dust cover. Remove piston, piston cup and piston spring as an assembly. Remove bleeder screw. *See Fig. 4.*

Fig. 4: Clutch Slave Cylinder Assembly

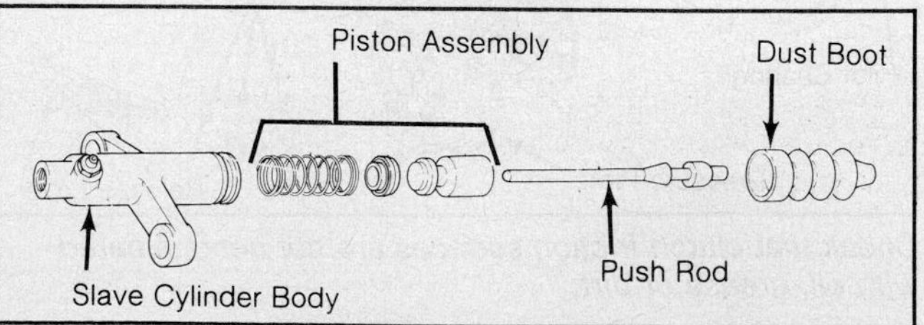
Piston Assembly
Dust Boot
Push Rod
Slave Cylinder Body

Replace all rubber components during overhaul.

Inspection

Wash parts in clean brake fluid. Inspect for wear or damage. Standard clearance between slave cylinder bore and piston is .0028" (.070 mm). If cylinder-to-piston clearance exceeds .0059" (.150 mm), replace defective part. Replace piston cup and dust cover during overhaul.

ISUZU IMPULSE (Cont.)

Reassembly

To assemble, coat all parts with brake fluid and reverse disassembly procedure. Ensure piston cup is installed properly and bleed hydraulic system.

ADJUSTMENTS

CLUTCH PEDAL STROKE & FREE PLAY

The clutch pedal stroke and free play are automatically adjusted by operation of hydraulic system.

CLUTCH PEDAL HEIGHT

Adjust clutch pedal height by turning master cylinder push rod after lock nut has been loosened. Adjust clearance between clutch switch and pedal to .020-.059" (.50-1.50 mm). After adjustment, check that push rod is in contact with master cylinder piston.

HYDRAULIC SYSTEM BLEEDING

Fill reservoir with brake fluid. Fit bleeder hose to bleeder screw. Place opposite end of hose into clear container partially filled with brake fluid. Slowly pump clutch pedal two or three times and hold to floor. Break bleeder screw loose. Allow air to vent. Close bleeder screw. Allow pedal to return.

Repeat procedure until no air bubbles are present in discharged fluid. Do not let fluid reservoir run dry during bleeding operation or complete hydraulic system must be rebleed. After bleeding system, check clutch pedal free play, disengagement and position.

TIGHTENING SPECIFICATIONS

Application	Ft. Lbs. (N.m)
Drive Shaft Flange Mount Bolt	18-22 (24-30)
Flywheel-to-Crankshaft Bolt	65-72 (88-98)
Pressure Plate-to-Flywheel Bolt	12-14 (16-19)
Release Lever Ball Stud	30 (39)

MAZDA - FWD

DESCRIPTION

Clutch is a single, dry disc, diaphragm spring type. The release mechanism is cable actuated. A prelubricated release bearing is used and is located in transmission housing.

REMOVAL & INSTALLATION

CLUTCH ASSEMBLY

Removal

1) Disconnect negative battery cable and speedometer cable. On GLC, remove EGR pipe and water pipe bracket. On all models, detach clutch cable from release lever. Remove clutch cable brackets and harness clips. Raise and support vehicle. Drain transaxle oil.

2) Remove front wheels. Remove under and side covers. On 626, remove control link of stabilizer bar. On all models, remove lower arm ball joints. To remove drive shaft, pull straight out on caliper while lightly prying and/or tapping shaft. Do not damage oil seal or bend drive shaft ball joint to maximum extent.

3) Support engine at transaxle end. Separate shift control rod and shift rod. Remove extension bar from transaxle. Remove crossmember. Remove starter. Support transaxle with a jack. Remove transaxle mount bolts and transaxle. Install flywheel holding tool (49 E301 060).

4) Install clutch disc alignment tool (49 E301 310 for GLC and 49 SE01 310 for 626). Loosen pressure plate mount bolts evenly, in diagonal pattern. Index mark pressure plate-to-flywheel. Remove clutch assembly and note component locations for proper reassembly. *See Fig. 1.*

Fig. 1: Exploded View of FWD Clutch Assembly

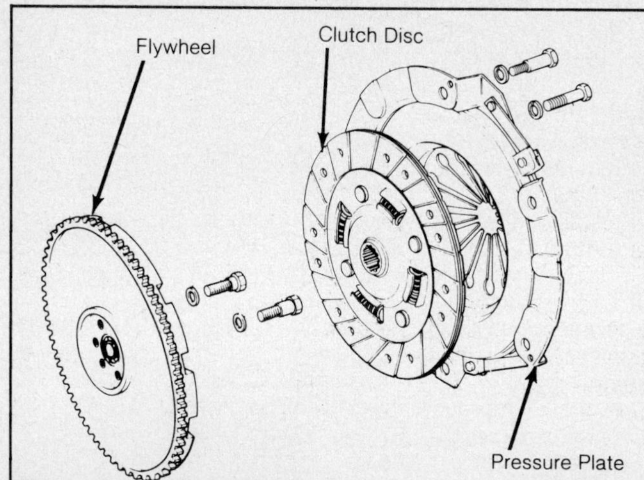
Flywheel
Clutch Disc
Pressure Plate

Ensure clutch friction surfaces are not contaminated with grease, oil or dirt.

Inspection

1) Check disc for loose rivets, worn springs or oil contamination. Minimum lining height above rivet heads is .012" (.30 mm). Standard disc free thickness is .319-.343" (8.10-8.70 mm). The GLC lining thickness per side is .138" (3.50 mm). The 626 lining thickness per side is .150" (3.80 mm).

2) Inspect flywheel and pressure plate friction surfaces for burns, scoring or grooves. Flywheel friction surface warpage limit is .008" (.20 mm). Resurface flywheel and/or pressure plate as necessary. If flywheel ring gear is replaced, ensure chamfer on teeth faces engine.

3) Mount clutch disc on input shaft. Check runout using dial indicator. Maximum runout is .039" (1 mm). Check disc hub and input shaft splines for excessive wear. Hub must slide smoothly on input shaft splines.

NOTE: **Mount clutch disc with largest projected portion of hub toward transaxle.**

Installation

1) Lightly lubricate clutch component contact points and splines with molybdenum grease. Center clutch assembly with alignment tool. Align pressure plate and flywheel index marks.

2) Install flywheel holding tool and tighten pressure plate bolts evenly, in a diagonal pattern. To complete installation, reverse removal procedure.

CLUTCH RELEASE BEARING & FORK

NOTE: **On GLC models, release bearing and collar are of single unit construction. On all models, bearing is prelubricated, do not wash in solvent. Clean only with compressed air.**

Removal & Installation

1) Disconnect return spring from fork. Twist release lever and separate from fork. Remove release bearing. Remove bolt holding release lever and fork together. Pull release lever and remove key and release fork.

2) Inspect release bearing for uneven rotation, abnormal noise or wear by turning by hand in thrust direction. Check for worn or damaged diaphrgm spring or release fork contact surface.

3) Install bearing on front cover of transaxle and check for smooth sliding movement. Check for cracked or bent release fork or lever. Replace components as necessary.

4) Lightly apply molybdenum grease to clutch component contact areas and sliding surfaces. To complete installation, reverse removal procedures.

CLUTCH CABLE

Removal & Installation

1) On 626, remove blower air duct from below instrument panel. On all models, remove lock nut, adjusting nut, plain washer, damper and roller from release lever. *See Fig. 3.* Pull cable out of bracket. On GLC, remove cover from inner panel. On all models, disconnect cable from pedal assembly.

2) Disconnect clip. Remove cable from master cylinder bracket. Remove cable boot from firewall on engine compartment side. Inspect cable for damage to boot, inner and outer cable. Check cable function.

3) To install, reverse removal procedure. Grease bushings, pedal hook and roller. Seal boot to firewall. Adjust pedal free play.

PILOT BEARING

Removal & Installation

1) Pilot bearing is pressed into flywheel. If loose or rough, replace bearing. On GLC, remove flywheel and use round rod to drive out bearing. On 626, remove bearing using puller (49 1285 071).

MAZDA – FWD (Cont.)

2) Pack bearing with lithium grease before installation. On GLC, install by press-fitting until bearing is flush with flywheel surface. On 626, press bearing into flywheel to a depth of .086-.110" (2.20-2.80 mm).

ADJUSTMENTS

NOTE: Adjust pedal height first; then adjust clearance between release lever and roller. Check clutch disengagement distance last.

CLUTCH PEDAL HEIGHT

1) On GLC, remove cover under instrument panel. On 626, remove blower air duct from under instrument panel. Loosen clutch switch lock nut. Rotate switch to obtain height. *See Fig. 2.*

Fig. 2: FWD Clutch Pedal Height Adjustment

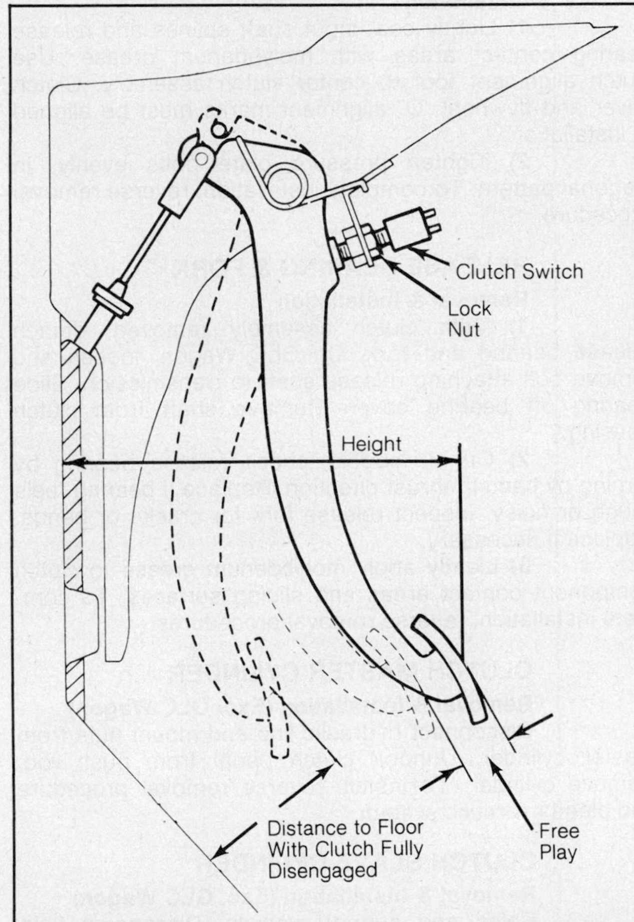
Clutch Switch
Lock Nut
Height
Distance to Floor With Clutch Fully Disengaged
Free Play

Adjust pedal height first; then adjust the clearance between the release lever and roller.

2) The GLC pedal height is 9.05-9.25" (230-235 mm). The 626 pedal height is 8.43-8.63" (214-219 mm). After adjustment, tighten lock nut and install cover.

CLUTCH PEDAL FREE PLAY

1) Clutch pedal free play is .43-.67" (11-17 mm). Release lever free play is .08-.12" (2-3 mm). Play is set at release lever. Depress lever and pull roller while measuring gap. Turn adjusting nut to obtain clearance. Tighten lock nut. *See Fig. 3.*

Fig. 3: Exploded View of Clutch Release Lever and Cable

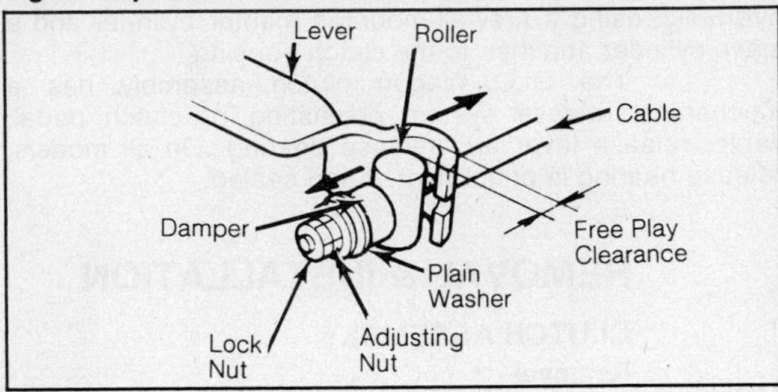
Lever
Roller
Cable
Damper
Free Play Clearance
Plain Washer
Lock Nut
Adjusting Nut

Depress release lever and pull roller while measuring gap.

2) On 626, adjust the installation length of the clutch pedal assist spring located at the top of the clutch pedal. Turn adjusting nut to bring spring length to 1.14-1.54" (33.5-34.5 mm). After adjustment, install air duct.

CLUTCH PEDAL DISENGAGEMENT DISTANCE

Check that distance from floor to center of pedal pad upper surface is within specification when clutch is fully disengaged. Standard distance is 3.2" (80 mm) or more. *See Fig. 2.*

TIGHTENING SPECIFICATIONS

Application	Ft. Lbs. (N.m)
Flywheel-to-Crankshaft Bolt	
GLC	60-65 (82-88)
626 [1]	71-76 (98-105)
Pressure Plate-to-Flywheel Bolt	
GLC	13-20 (18-27)
626	15-20 (22-27)
Release Lever and Fork	
GLC	13-20 (18-27)
626	6-8 (8-11)

[1] – Lightly apply sealant to the flywheel mount bolts to prevent oil leakage.

Clutches

MAZDA - RWD

DESCRIPTION

The clutch assembly for all models is a single plate, dry disc, diaphragm spring type. The clutch release system used on the RX7 and B2000 and B2200 Pickups is hydraulic, using a firewall-mounted master cylinder and a slave cylinder attached to the clutch housing.

The GLC Wagon clutch assembly has a mechanical release system consisting of clutch pedal, cable, release lever and release bearing. On all models, release bearing is prelubricated and sealed.

REMOVAL & INSTALLATION

CLUTCH ASSEMBLY

Removal

1) Disconnect negative battery cable. Place shift lever in Neutral. Remove shift knob. Remove console box (if equipped). Remove shift lever dust boot, lever and related components. On RX7, remove air cleaner. On GLC Wagon, remove 2 upper clutch housing mount bolts.

2) On all models, raise and support vehicle. Drain transmission. Remove drive shaft. Remove under covers. Remove any interfering exhaust components. On all except GLC Wagon, remove clutch slave cylinder and set aside without removing fluid line.

3) On all models, remove starter, speedometer cable and related electrical connections. Place jack under rear end of engine. Protect oil pan with wood block. Position jack under transmission. Remove transmission-to-engine mount bolts.

4) If equipped, remove transmission-to-cross-member bolts, crossmember-to-frame bolts and cross-member. Slide transmission back until input shaft is cleared and remove from vehicle.

5) Install flywheel holding tool (49 0118 271A for GLC Wagon and B2000 Pickup, 49 E301 060 for B2200 Pickup and 49 1881 060 for RX7). Index mark pressure plate-to-flywheel.

6) Install clutch assembly alignment tool (49 SE01 310 for all models). Loosen pressure plate mounting bolts evenly, in a diagonal pattern. Separate clutch disc and pressure plate. Remove release bearing and fork. *See Fig. 1.*

Fig. 1: Exploded View of RWD Clutch Assembly

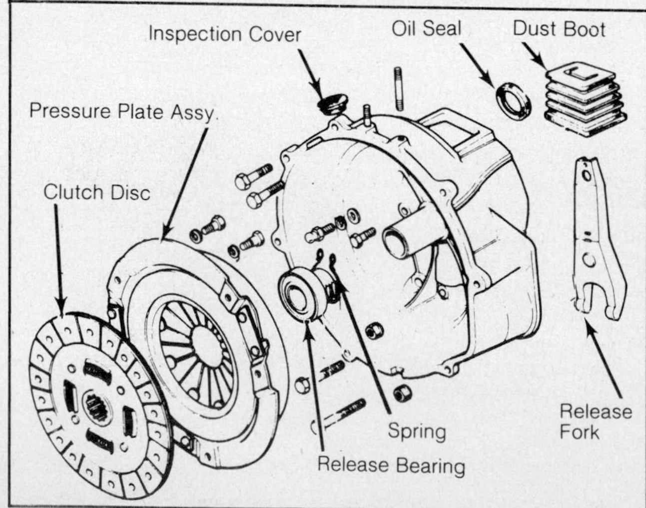
Inspection Cover
Oil Seal
Dust Boot
Pressure Plate Assy.
Clutch Disc
Spring
Release Fork
Release Bearing

Check clutch disc and flywheel for excessive wear, cracks or damage and release bearing for noise or roughness.

Inspection

1) Check disc for loose rivets, worn springs or oil contamination. Minimum lining height above rivet heads is .012" (.30 mm). On RX7, minimum disc free thickness is .276" (7 mm).

2) Inspect flywheel and pressure plate friction surfaces for burns, scoring or grooves. Friction surface warpage limit is .002" (.05 mm). Resurface or replace flywheel and/or pressure plate as necessary. If flywheel ring gear is replaced, ensure chamfer on teeth faces engine.

3) On RX7, inspect pressure plate diaphragm spring fingers for excessive wear or out of alignment. Maximum out of alignment limit is .039" (1 mm). Finger groove wear limit is .039" (1 mm).

4) Mount clutch disc on input shaft. Check runout using dial indicator. Maximum runout is .039" (1 mm). Check disc hub and input shaft splines for excessive wear. Hub must slide smoothly on input shaft splines.

Installation

1) Lightly coat input shaft splines and release bearing contact areas with molybdenum grease. Use clutch alignment tool to center clutch assembly. Clutch cover and flywheel "O" alignment marks must be aligned at installation.

2) Tighten pressure plate bolts evenly, in diagonal pattern. To complete installation, reverse removal procedure.

RELEASE BEARING & FORK

Removal & Installation

1) With clutch assembly removed, detach release bearing and fork. On GLC Wagon, loosen and remove bolt attaching release shaft to transmission. Slide bearing off bearing cover. Remove shaft from clutch housing.

2) On all models, check release bearing by turning by hand in thrust direction. Replace if bearing feels rough or noisy. Inspect release fork for cracks or bends. Replace if necessary.

3) Lightly apply molybdenum grease to clutch component contact areas and sliding surfaces. To complete installation, reverse removal procedures.

CLUTCH MASTER CYLINDER

Removal & Installation (Exc. GLC Wagon)

Disconnect hydraulic line and mount nuts from master cylinder. Unhook clutch pedal from push rod. Remove cylinder. To install, reverse removal procedure and bleed hydraulic system.

CLUTCH SLAVE CYLINDER

Removal & Installation (Exc. GLC Wagon)

Raise and support vehicle. Disconnect fluid hose and plug. Remove slave cylinder-to-clutch housing mount nuts. Detach cylinder. To install, reverse removal procedure and bleed hydraulic system.

CLUTCH CABLE

Removal & Installation (GLC Wagon)

1) Loosen clutch release cable lock nuts at stop ring on engine side of firewall. Pull inner cable toward clutch pedal. Disconnect inner cable from pedal assembly.

2) Pull and remove cable through stop ring from engine side of firewall. Disconnect inner cable at

MAZDA – RWD (Cont.)

release lever. Remove retaining clip, pull outer cable and remove from clutch housing bracket. *See Fig. 2.*

Fig. 2: GLC Wagon Clutch Cable Assembly

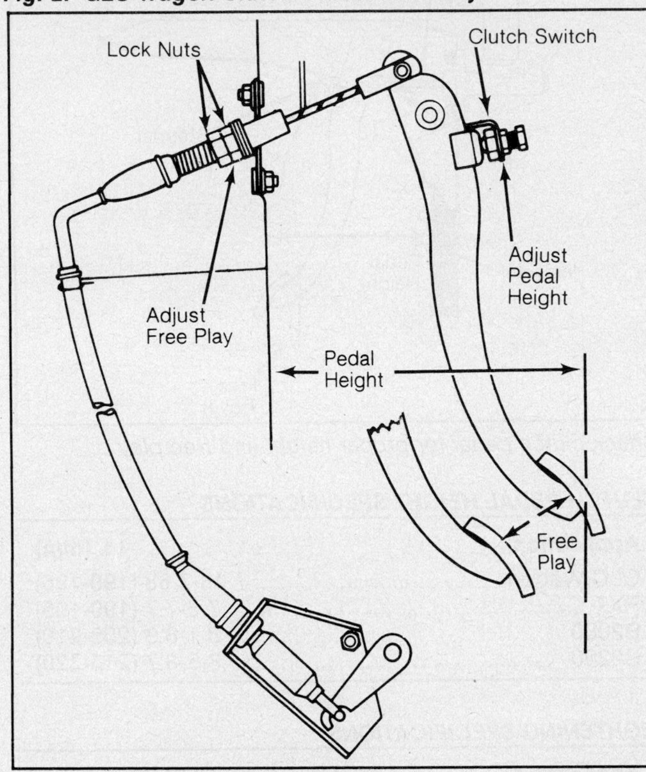
Lock Nuts
Clutch Switch
Adjust Pedal Height
Adjust Free Play
Pedal Height
Free Play

3) Inspect for damage to stop ring, cable ends and inner and outer cable. Check cable function. Before installing, apply molybdenum grease to bushings, pedal hook and roller. To complete installation, reverse removal procedure. Adjust cable for proper pedal free play.

PILOT BEARING

Removal & Installation (RX7)

With clutch components removed, check pilot bearing for roughness, looseness and any damage. If necessary, remove bearing and oil seal with puller tool (49 1285 071). To install new bearing, use installer tool (49 0823 072A). Apply multipurpose grease to bearing and install oil seal.

Removal & Installation (All Other Models)

Pilot bearing is pressed into flywheel. To replace, install flywheel holding tool and remove flywheel. Using arbor press and driver, press old bearing out. Press new bearing in until it is flush with flywheel surface. Lubricate with multipurpose grease. Install flywheel and holder. Tighten mount bolts evenly, in a diagonal pattern.

FLYWHEEL

Removal & Installation (RX7)

1) With clutch assembly removed, lock flywheel in position using holding tool. Loosen and remove lock nut with box wrench (49 0820 035). Remove flywheel using puller tool (49 0823 300A). Turn tool handle and lightly tap puller head. Once lock nut is loose, do not drop flywheel.

2) Inspect rear oil seal for leakage and replace as necessary. Before installing flywheel, apply sealer to surface of lock nut that contacts flywheel and install. Tighten lock nut to specification. To complete install, reverse removal procedure.

Tighten lock nut to specification. To complete install, reverse removal procedure.

OVERHAUL

CLUTCH MASTER CYLINDER

NOTE: **Master cylinders used on B2000 & B2200 Pickup have a different external appearance, but procedures are the same.**

Disassembly (Exc. GLC Wagon)

1) Remove reservoir cap assembly. Drain brake fluid. On RX7, remove reservoir connector bolt and reservoir. On B2000 & B2200 Pickups, remove hydraulic line adapter, washer, 1-way valve, spring and pin.

2) Remove piston stop ring, washer and piston assembly. Separate piston, cups and return spring. *See Fig. 3.* Clean parts in denatured alcohol or brake fluid. Blow dry with compressed air.

3) Check all parts for wear, damage or deformation. Standard piston-to-cylinder bore clearance is .001-.004" (.032-.102 mm). If clearance exceeds .006" (.15 mm), replace defective part. Coat all components with clean brake fluid before assembly.

Fig. 3: Exploded View of Clutch Master Cylinder

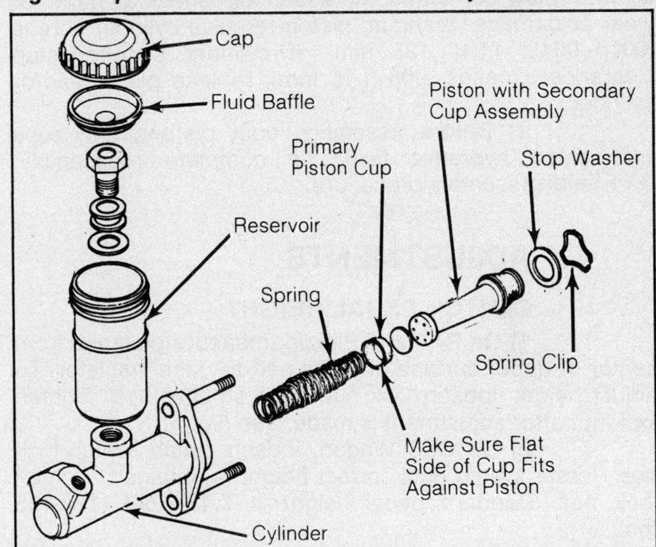
Cap
Fluid Baffle
Piston with Secondary Cup Assembly
Primary Piston Cup
Stop Washer
Reservoir
Spring
Spring Clip
Make Sure Flat Side of Cup Fits Against Piston
Cylinder

B2000 & B2200 master cylinder external appearance is slightly different.

Reassembly

1) Install primary cup with flat side against piston. Ensure compensating port is open. To complete assembly, reverse disassembly procedure. After assembly, fill reservoir with clean brake fluid.

2) Bench bleed master cylinder by holding finger over outlet port and operating piston with screwdriver. Pump piston until air is ejected at outlet port and fluid pressure is felt. Install master cylinder and bleed hydraulic system.

CLUTCH SLAVE CYLINDER

Disassembly (Exc. GLC Wagon)

With slave cylinder removed, detach dust boot and release rod. Remove piston and cup assembly from

MAZDA – RWD (Cont.)

cylinder, using compressed air if required. Remove spring, bleeder screw and valve. *See Fig. 4.*

Fig. 4: Exploded View of Clutch Slave Cylinder

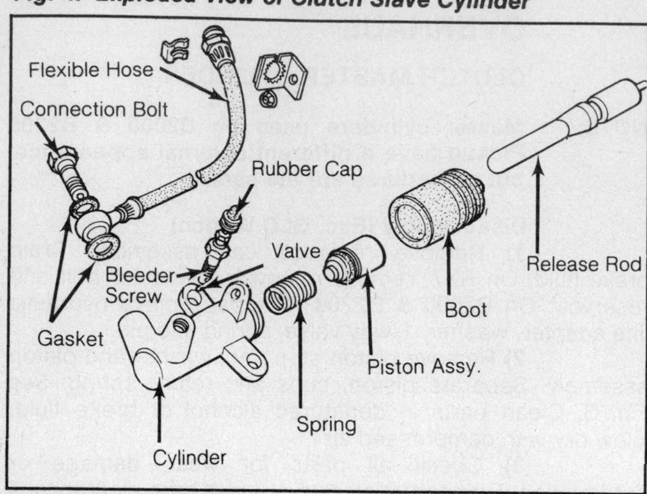
Flexible Hose
Connection Bolt
Rubber Cap
Valve
Bleeder Screw
Gasket
Release Rod
Boot
Piston Assy.
Spring
Cylinder

Inspect clutch hydraulic components for leakage and repair or replace as necessary.

Reassembly

1) Wash parts in clean brake fluid or denatured alcohol. Blow dry with compressed air. Check all parts for wear or damage. Standard piston-to-slave cylinder bore is .0016-.0049" (.040-.125 mm). If cylinder bore-to-piston clearance exceeds .006" (.15 mm), replace piston and/or cylinder.

2) Before assembly, coat pistons and cups with clean hydraulic fluid. To complete reassembly, reverse disassembly procedure.

ADJUSTMENTS

CLUTCH PEDAL HEIGHT

1) On RX7 and Pickup, measure distance from center of upper surface of pedal pad-to-dash insulator. To adjust height, loosen lock nut. Turn stopper bolt. Tighten lock nut after adjustment is made. *See Fig. 5.*

2) On GLC Wagon, loosen clutch switch lock nut. Rotate switch until correct height is obtained. Tighten lock nut. Standard pedal height is 7.48-7.68" (190-195 mm).

CLUTCH PEDAL FREE PLAY

1) On RX7 and Pickups, adjust clutch pedal free play, measured at pedal pad, to .02-.12" (0.6-3.0 mm). Loosen lock nut and turn pedal stopper bolt to specification. Tighten lock nut. *See Fig. 5.*

2) On GLC Wagon, clutch pedal free play is .39-.59" (10-15 mm). Adjust by setting release cable clearance at engine side of firewall. Loosen lock nut, pull outer cable and turn adjusting nut until clearance is .06-.09" (1.5-2.3 mm). Tighten lock nut. Check pedal free play. *See Fig. 2.*

Fig. 5: Clutch Adjustment Locations (Exc. GLC Wagon)

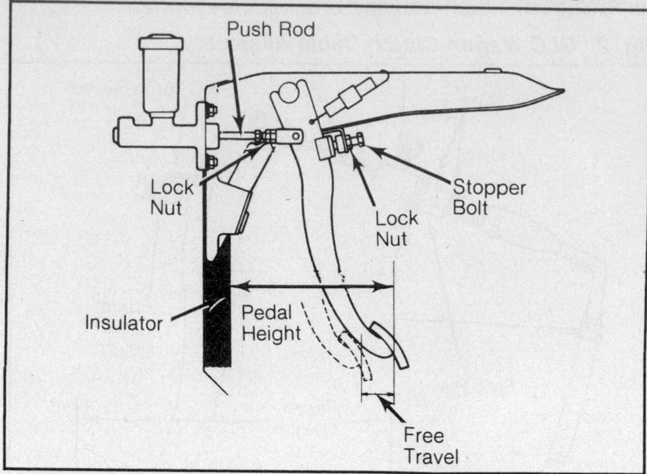
Push Rod
Lock Nut
Stopper Bolt
Lock Nut
Insulator
Pedal Height
Free Travel

Check clutch pedal for proper height and free play.

CLUTCH PEDAL HEIGHT SPECIFICATIONS

Application	In. (mm)
GLC Wagon	7.48-7.68 (190-195)
RX7	7.5-7.7 (190-195)
B2000	8.1-8.3 (205-210)
B2200	8.5-8.7 (215-220)

TIGHTENING SPECIFICATIONS

Application	Ft. Lbs. (N.m)
Flywheel-to-Crankshaft	
B2000	112-118 (155-163)
B2200	95-137 (131-190)
GLC Wagon	60-65 (83-90)
Flywheel-to-Eccentric Shaft	
RX7 Rotary Engine	289-362 (393-492)
Pressure Plate-to-Flywheel	13-20 (18-27)

MERCEDES-BENZ 240D

DESCRIPTION

Dry single disc type clutch uses a diaphragm spring type pressure plate. Clutch actuation is hydraulic, using a clutch pedal mounted master cylinder and a clutch housing mounted slave cylinder.

Clutch free play is adjusted automatically. A pedal mounted over center spring assists in clutch pedal actuation. A sealed prelubricated clutch release bearing is also used.

REMOVAL & INSTALLATION

Removal

1) Disconnect battery ground cable, support transmission with jack, then remove rear crossmember, exhaust support bracket, exhaust pipe and clamp. Loosen, DO NOT remove, propeller shaft center bearing.

2) Remove propeller shaft-to-transmission bolts. Ensuring that companion plate remains attached to propeller shaft, push propeller shaft towards rear. Remove speedometer drive from rear of transmission.

3) Remove clutch slave cylinder and pull towards the rear with lines connected, until rod is released from clutch housing. Remove shift linkage from transmission shift levers. Remove starter.

4) Remove transmission-to-intermediate flange attaching bolts (removing two upper bolts last). Pull transmission out until input shaft is clear of clutch assembly. Remove transmission.

5) Loosen pressure plate attaching bolts 1 to 1 1/2 turns at a time until tension is released, then remove all bolts, pressure plate and clutch disc.

Installation

1) Place slave cylinder and line above transmission. Using an aligning tool, center clutch disc on flywheel and install pressure plate. Tighten bolts 1 to 1 1/2 turns at a time until tight.

NOTE: **When installing propeller shaft to transmission, raise engine and transmission with jack. Torque propeller shaft center bearing clamp nut to 22-29 ft. lbs (30-39 N.m).**

2) During installation, make sure that clutch is fully seated in flywheel recess. To complete installation, reverse removal procedure. Bleed hydraulic system. Check clutch pedal and shift linkage adjustment.

RELEASE BEARING & LEVER

Removal

Remove release bearing from bearing tube on front transmission cover. Move release lever down and to the left, then pull from ball pin on clutch housing.

Installation

To install, apply light coat of lubricant to all bearing and lever contact surfaces, and reverse removal procedure.

CLUTCH MASTER CYLINDER

Removal

1) Remove floor mats and lining from driver compartment. Remove cover under instrument panel. Siphon fluid from reservoir to below minimum mark and loosen input line by pulling elbow out of rubber clamping ring on master cylinder.

2) Disconnect pressure line from master cylinder and unscrew master cylinder from pedal assembly. Remove master cylinder and connecting hose, leaving push rod on clutch pedal.

Installation

To install, reverse removal procedure. Refill fluid level in reservoir and bleed hydraulic system. Adjust master cylinder push rod clearance. See Adjustments.

CLUTCH SLAVE CYLINDER

Removal

Disconnect hydraulic line from slave cylinder, then plug line with a rubber cap to prevent loss of fluid. Remove bolts attaching cylinder to clutch housing, then remove slave cylinder and push rod from housing as an assembly.

CAUTION: **Take care not to loose plastic shim installed between cylinder and housing. Shim is recessed to accommodate inspection gauge.**

Fig. 1: Mercedes-Benz 240D Clutch Assembly

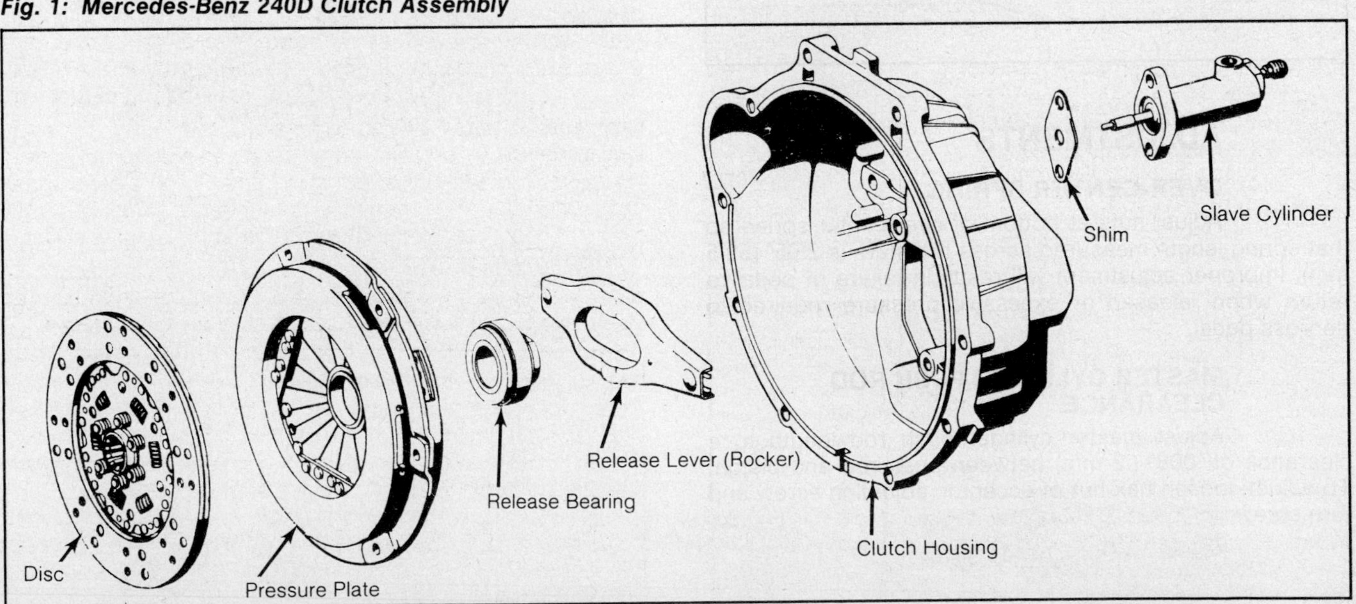
Slave Cylinder
Shim
Release Lever (Rocker)
Release Bearing
Clutch Housing
Disc
Pressure Plate

MERCEDES-BENZ 240D (Cont.)

Installation

1) To install, place shim with grooved end against clutch housing and hold in position. Notches in shim must face outward.

2) Insert slave cylinder with push rod into clutch housing, and install and tighten mounting bolts. Connect hydraulic line to cylinder and bleed hydraulic system.

Fig. 2: Exploded View of Clutch Pedal Assembly

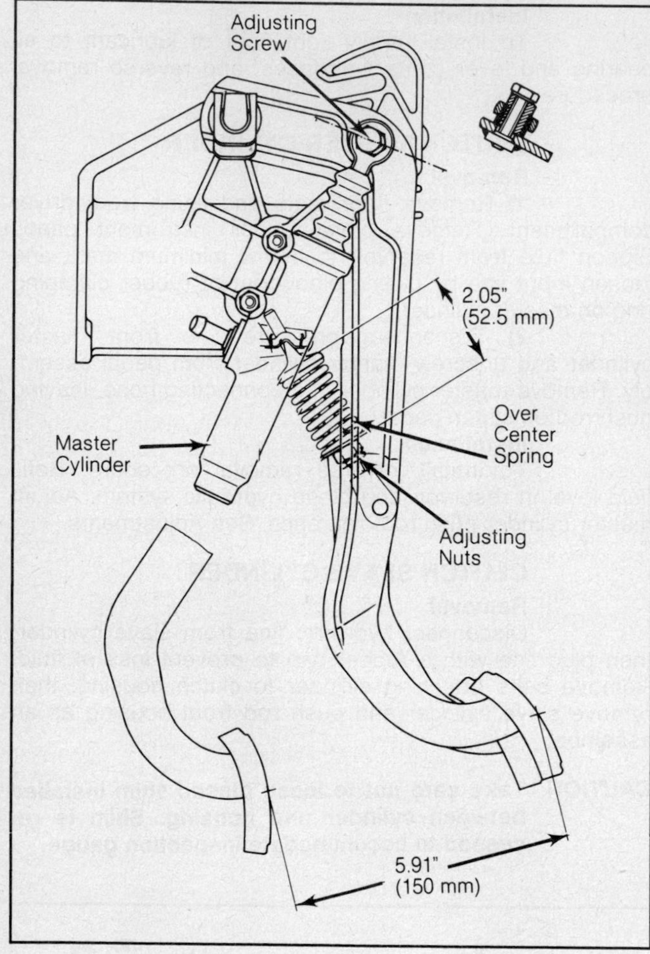
Adjusting Screw
2.05" (52.5 mm)
Master Cylinder
Over Center Spring
Adjusting Nuts
5.91" (150 mm)

CHECKING CLUTCH DISC WEAR

Wear on clutch disc may only be checked using special inspection gauge. With slave cylinder installed on clutch housing, insert inspection gauge in groove of plastic shim. Disc is serviceable if notches on gauge disappear in flange. If notches remain visible, wear limit is exceeded and disc must be replaced. *See Fig. 3.*

Fig. 3: Checking for Clutch Disc Wear

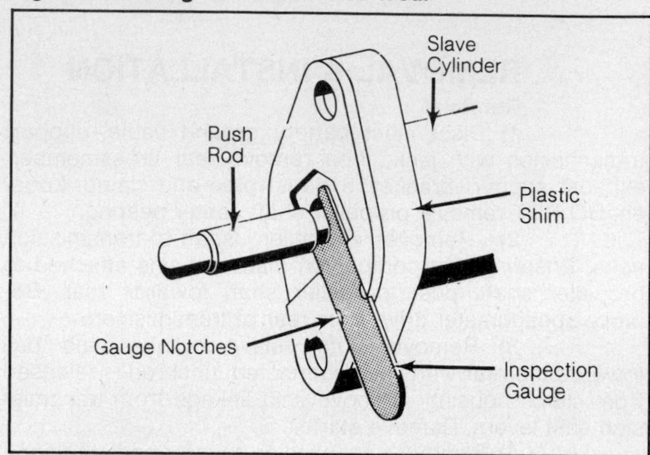
Slave Cylinder
Push Rod
Plastic Shim
Gauge Notches
Inspection Gauge

Disc is servicable if notches disappear in flange.

ADJUSTMENTS

OVER-CENTER SPRING

Adjust nuts at bottom of over-center spring so that spring length measured across retainers is 2.05" (52.5 mm). Improper adjustment will result in failure of pedal to return when released or excessive pressure required to depress pedal.

MASTER CYLINDER PUSH ROD CLEARANCE

Adjust master cylinder push rod length to a clearance of .008" (.2 mm) between push rod and piston. To adjust, loosen hex nut of eccentric adjusting screw and turn screw.

PEUGEOT 504, 505 & 604

DESCRIPTION

Clutch is a dry, single disc, diaphragm spring type. Clutch actuation is hydraulic, using a firewall mounted master cylinder and a bell housing mounted slave cylinder.

A prelubricated clutch release bearing is also used. Due to hydraulic system design, no adjustments, with the exception of bleeding hydraulic system, is necessary.

Fig. 1: Sectional View of Clutch Assembly

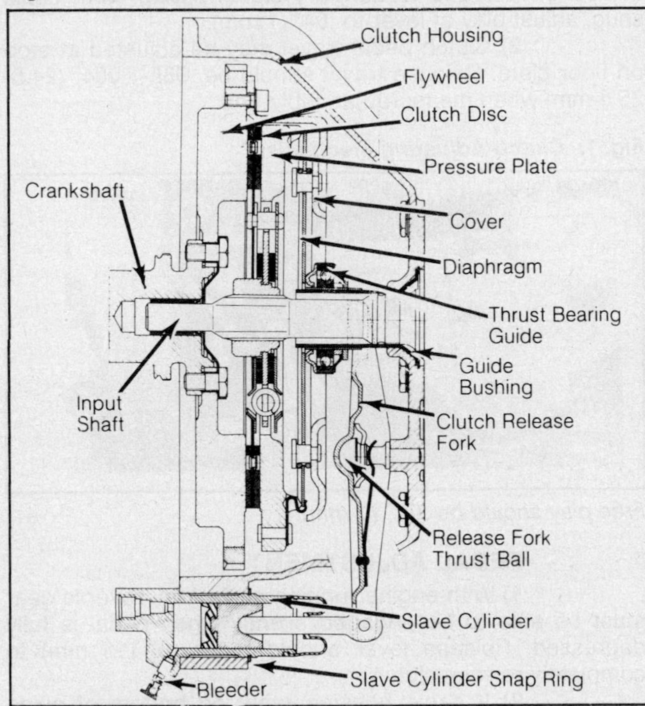
Clutch Housing
Flywheel
Clutch Disc
Pressure Plate
Crankshaft
Cover
Diaphragm
Thrust Bearing
Guide
Guide
Bushing
Input
Shaft
Clutch Release
Fork
Release Fork
Thrust Ball
Slave Cylinder
Slave Cylinder Snap Ring
Bleeder

REMOVAL & INSTALLATION

CLUTCH ASSEMBLY

NOTE: **Engine and transmission must be removed as an assembly.**

Removal

1) Remove hood, battery with tray, ignition coil, starter, radiator, expansion tank, and windshield washer bottle. Disconnect heater hoses, fuel lines, throttle controls, vacuum lines, and all chassis-to-engine electrical wires.

2) Remove air cleaner and ducting to fuel injection or carburetion system. On models equipped with air conditioning, DO NOT disconnect hoses or pressure connections. Remove and set aside under hood components of the air conditioning system.

3) Disconnect electrical leads to compressor, pressure switch, thermostat, and electric cooling fan. Free receiver-drier, condenser and compressor from their mountings and move to right side of vehicle.

4) If equipped with power steering, remove power steering pump and set aside without disconnecting hoses. On all models, remove upper clutch housing-to-engine mounting bolts and inspection plates.

5) Disconnect exhaust pipe from manifold and remove muffler and exhaust pipe supporting brackets with heat deflector. Attach hoisting sling and raise engine until transmission contacts tunnel.

6) Disconnect and remove drive shaft. On 504 & 505 models, support rear of transmission. Remove steering coupling clamp bolts and replace with slightly longer bolts. Lower front cross member about 1.2" (30 mm) with steering rack attached.

7) On all models, remove lower clutch housing-to-engine bolts. Pull engine slightly forward and carefully lift from vehicle. Separate engine and transmission.

8) Mark pressure plate and flywheel for reassembly reference. Remove pressure plate mounting bolts evenly in a crisscross pattern and remove clutch assembly.

Installation

1) Lubricate transmission input splines and clutch release bearing guide with Molykote (or equivalent). Use centering tool to align clutch assembly on flywheel.

2) Clutch disc must be installed with flexible hub toward transmission. Replace pressure plate mounting bolt washers during installation.

3) Torque pressure plate bolts evenly to 11 ft. lbs. (15 N.m). To complete installation, reverse removal procedure, ensuring that all reference marks are aligned.

CLUTCH RELEASE BEARING & FORK

Removal

Remove slave cylinder from clutch housing. Remove release bearing from fork by turning it counterclockwise. Remove clutch fork by pulling it outward until backing spring is disengaged from ball stud.

NOTE: **Bearing is self-lubricated. DO NOT wash in any cleaning solution. Lubricate with motor oil when installing.**

Installation

Pack rubber cup on ball stud with grease. To complete installation, reverse removal procedure.

PILOT BUSHING

Bushing is press fit in rear of crankshaft. Bushing must be replaced if excessive clearance with transmission input shaft is evident. Remove and install bushing using puller and driver.

CLUTCH MASTER CYLINDER

Removal & Installation

Disconnect and plug master cylinder hydraulic lines from fluid reservoir and to slave cylinder. Remove bolts securing master cylinder to pedal assembly and remove master cylinder. To install, reverse removal procedure and bleed hydraulic system.

CLUTCH SLAVE CYLINDER

Removal & Installation

Disconnect hydraulic line at slave cylinder. Remove snap ring securing cylinder in clutch housing, then slide slave cylinder from clutch housing mounting. To install, reverse removal procedure and bleed hydraulic system.

NOTE: **Overhaul procedures for clutch slave cylinder and master cylinder not provided by manufacturer.**

Clutches

PORSCHE 911SC

DESCRIPTION

Clutch is a single, disc dry type with a diaphragm spring pressure plate. The clutch release mechanism is operated by an adjustable cable.

REMOVAL & INSTALLATION

CLUTCH ASSEMBLY

Removal

1) Raise and support vehicle. Disconnect negative battery cable. Remove air cleaner. Remove engine block vent hose. Plug vent cover hole. If equipped, remove air conditioning compressor and set aside. Do not remove hoses.

2) Remove relay plate cover. Disconnect engine wires at relay plate, adapter plug, relay plate socket, and ignition control unit. Remove fuel hoses at filter and return line. Disconnect accelerator linkage.

3) Remove rear center tunnel cover in passenger compartment. Slide boot forward over shift selector rod. Disconnect coupling from inner shift rod. Disconnect speedometer sensor wires in tunnel. Drain engine oil. Plug hoses on engine and oil tank.

4) Remove heater hoses at exchangers. Remove rear stabilizer. Disconnect ground strap at body and battery wires at starter. Disconnect accelerator linkage from pedal and clutch cable at transmission. Remove axle shafts from flanges at transmission.

5) Place jack under engine/transmission assembly. Lift slightly. Do not damage secondary air injection pipes. Loosen transmission and engine mount bolts. Lower assembly from vehicle.

6) Remove circlip from clutch release lever shaft. Remove lever and rubber ring. Remove mount bolts. Pull transmission from engine. Mark pressure plate and flywheel for reassembly. Insert clutch alignment tool. Loosen bolts evenly, in a diagonal pattern. Separate clutch assembly from engine.

Inspection

Check disc for loose rivets, worn springs or oil contamination. Inspect flywheel and pressure plate friction surfaces for burns, scoring or grooves. Resurface or replace flywheel and/or pressure plate as necessary. Mount disc on input shaft. Check runout. Check disc hub splines for excessive wear. Hub must slide smoothly on input shaft splines.

Installation

1) Ensure marks on flywheel and clutch are aligned. Tighten pressure plate bolts evenly, in a diagonal pattern. Use clutch alignment tool to center disc. If installing new clutch, balancing marks on clutch and flywheel should be offset 180°.

2) With transmission installed, pull release lever away from engine. There must be at least .78" (19.8 mm) clearance between release lever and transmission housing. To complete installation, reverse removal procedure.

CLUTCH RELEASE BEARING

Removal

Bearing is removed with pressure plate. Remove by laying pressure plate on bearing and removing snap ring on flywheel side of clutch fingers. Remove bearing along with washers. Check bearing for roughness or noise by turning by hand in thrust direction.

Installation

Apply thin coat of lubricant to guide tube and friction surfaces. Complete installation by reversing removal procedures.

ADJUSTMENT

CLUTCH ADJUSTMENT

1) Clutch free play is checked at transmission adjusting lever due to auxiliary clutch spring. With cable snug, adjust play at lever to .04" (1 mm).

2) Clutch pedal travel may be adjusted at stop on floor plate. Release travel should be .965-1.004" (24.5-25.5 mm) when measured at cable end.

Fig. 1: Clutch Adjusting Mechanism

Free Play

Free play should be .04" (1 mm).

PEDAL ADJUSTMENT

1) With engine running and warm, reverse gear must be able to be engaged silently when pedal is fully depressed. Release lever should move .6" (15 mm) to completely release clutch.

2) If cable housing rests on bottom of guide clamp when pedal is fully depressed, inner cable must be adjusted at yoke end. Measure from threaded cable end of yoke to outer edge of lock nut.

3) Adjust if not within .7-.9" (17-22 mm). If arc of cable is too large and allows cable to come out of guide clamp when pedal is released, inner cable must be shortened at yoke end.

TIGHTENING SPECIFICATIONS

Application	Ft. Lbs. (N.m)
Engine Bracket Mount Bolt	30 (40)
Flywheel Mount Bolt	
10 mm Bolt	66 (90)
12 mm Bolt	111 (150)
Pilot Bearing Mount Bolt	7 (10)
Starter Mount Nut	33-35 (46-48)

PORSCHE 928S & 944

DESCRIPTION

The 928S model uses a double, dry disc clutch with a diaphragm spring pressure plate. The 944 utilizes a single, dry disc clutch and a diaphragm spring pressure plate. The clutch release mechanism is operated hydraulically on both models.

REMOVAL & INSTALLATION

CLUTCH ASSEMBLY

Removal (928S)

1) Disconnect battery ground strap. Raise and support vehicle. Remove lower body brace. Remove clutch slave cylinder, leaving line attached. Remove lower clutch housing with starter attached and suspend from stabilizer bar. Remove catalytic converter, if equipped.

2) Remove coupling bolts and push coupling back on drive shaft. If equipped with long coupling, remove plug from central tube to reach rear bolt. Remove release bearing sleeve mount bolts and push sleeve toward flywheel.

3) Mark pressure plate, intermediate plate and flywheel for reassembly reference. For dowel pin-centered clutches, drive dowel pins in direction of pressure plate with a punch until they are beyond centering bore of flywheel.

4) Check dowel positions visually at opening on intermediate plate. Loosen pressure plate mount bolts evenly, in a diagonal pattern. Disconnect release lever at ball stud by pushing lever down toward flywheel. Push entire clutch assembly and short drive shaft back and remove downward.

NOTE: **Clutch pressure plates and intermediate plates cannot be overhauled or repaired. Clean only with compressed air and visually inspect to determine condition.**

Inspection

1) Check clutch discs for loose rivets, worn springs or oil-contaminated lining. Since clutch discs will be subject to different degrees of wear, lining thickness will vary. On unsprung disc, flywheel end lining, between flywheel and intermediate plate, will be thinner.

2) Inspect flywheel and pressure plate friction surfaces for burns, scoring or grooves. Surfaces grooved more than .012" (.30 mm) must be replaced. Check pressure plate deflection with steel ruler and feeler guage. Maximum inward deflection is .012" (.30 mm).

3) Mount discs on input shaft. Check disc hub splines for excessive wear. Hub must slide smoothly on input shaft splines. Check lateral runout. Maximum runout is .016" (.40 mm) measured at 7.48" (190 mm) from center axis.

NOTE: **Differences in tolerances may make it necessary to preload clutch to install release bearing and lever.**

Installation

1) Assemble and install clutch as a unit. Prior to installation, push intermediate plate at the 3 adjusting elements in direction of release bearing to preload pressure plate. When assembling clutches, ensure that hubs of discs face release bearing. Front disc hub length is .787" (20 mm) and rear hub length is 1.141" (29 mm).

2) To assemble, place pressure plate on a level plate in a press. Slide clips (US 8039) under bolt heads. Check protrusion of centering pins. They should protrude .12" (3 mm) over bearing surface of intermediate plate.

3) Push intermediate plate in the direction of release bearing on the 3 adjusting elements. Assemble clutch, noting that disc with long hub is installed in the rear. Ensure that the Yellow arrow mount marks on discs heavy side are 180° from each other.

4) Check that White mark on disc, without spring-loaded liner, faces flywheel. Drive pressure plate on to centering pins of intermediate plate with a plastic hammer far enough that drive plate between them can still be moved with short drive shaft.

5) Recheck protrusion of centering pins. Lubricate contact areas and guide centering pins on to flywheel. Ensure pressure plate and intermediate plate White markings are 180° from each other.

6) Insert and tighten mount bolts. Ensure short drive shaft moves easily. Remove clips from under pressure plate bolt heads. To complete installation, reverse removal procedure. Check that protruding support plate on lower body brace faces forward.

Removal (944)

1) Disconnect ground wire at battery and clutch housing. Remove mount bolts, reference mark sensor and speed sensor for DME ignition system from clutch housing. Remove air cleaner and starter wiring harness. Raise vehicle and remove exhaust system. Disconnect wires from backup light switch and oxygen sensor.

2) Remove catalytic convertor heat shield, splash guard and rear exhaust pipe bracket. Push back dust cover of selector rod. Remove locking wire and bolt. Remove shift lever holding clamp and knob. Remove lever circlip. Pull off selector rod and washer of lever bolt.

3) Remove insulator above shift lever console. Remove console rear mount bolt. Mark console location. Turn shift lever 180° and remove. Push down on insulation sheet. Push selector rod forward in tunnel cavity about 12" (300 mm). Remove 2 upper clutch housing mount bolts.

4) Remove end cap from central tube housing. Insert screwdriver through opening into housing. Press in retainer on protective tube. Push back selector rod far enough so that it is outside of central tube housing. Remove clamping sleeve bolts through the openings. Move clamping sleeve toward transmission.

5) Detach axle shafts from transmission and suspend to prevent damage to boots. Place jack under transmission and lift slightly. Remove transmission-to-central tube housing mount bolts. Remove transmission mount bolts. Lower transmission, with central tube, until tube rests on rear axle cross tube.

6) Remove transmission-to-central tube flange bolts. Remove transmission from below. Remove starter. Remove clutch hydraulic line clamp and slave cylinder. Disconnect starter wiring harness on clutch housing. Loosen nut and remove release lever shaft mount bolt. Pull out shaft with 8 mm bolt.

7) Detach 4 central tube-to-clutch housing mount bolts. Pull back selector rod to prevent damage when moving central tube. Support engine with lifting tool (VW 10-222). Move central tube back to rest on transmission carrier. Remove clutch housing guard.

8) Remove engine mount nuts and push engine to the right. Remove lower clutch housing mount

PORSCHE 928S & 944 (Cont.)

bolts. Move clutch housing back. Turn until clutch release lever is located below cast boss on oil pan. Loosen pressure plate mount bolts evenly, in a diagonal pattern. Remove clutch assembly from flywheel.

Inspection

1) Check clutch disc for loose rivets, worn springs or oil-contaminated lining. Standard lining free thickness is .307-.331" (7.80-8.40 mm). Minimum free thickness is .248" (6.30 mm).

2) Inspect flywheel and pressure plate friction surfaces for burns, scoring or grooves. Surfaces grooved more than .012" (.30 mm) must be resurfaced or replaced as necessary. Check pressure plate deflection with steel ruler and feeler guage. Maximum inward deflection is .012" (.30 mm).

3) Mount disc on input shaft. Check runout. Check disc hub splines for excessive wear. Maximum lateral runout is .023" (.60 mm) measured at .078-.118" (2-3 mm) from outside edge. Hub must slide smoothly on input shaft splines. Check and replace selector rod protective tube if retainer is deformed excessively.

NOTE: **Mount release lever with clutch housing together on engine and release bearing before installing release lever shaft. When installing shaft, do not use force. Move shaft back and forth slightly to align needle bearing and bore in housing. Shaft machined surface faces mounting bolt against stop.**

Installation

1) Ensure that marks on flywheel and clutch are aligned. Tighten pressure plate bolts evenly, in a diagonal pattern. Use clutch alignment tool or old input shaft to center disc. If installing new clutch, balancing marks on clutch and flywheel should be offset 180°.

NOTE: **To avoid tension in drivetrain during installation, tighten central tube-to-clutch housing mount bolts only after bolting engine and transmission together.**

2) Place selector rod protective tube in transmission case. Install transmission. Push selector rod tube foreward until retainer engages in transmission case.

3) Mount selector rod on intermediate lever and lock with steel safety wire. When installing shift lever, mount lever so that incline is at 85°. Complete installation by reversing removal procedure.

CLUTCH RELEASE BEARING & FORK

Removal (928S)

Bearing is removed with pressure plate. To remove, lay pressure plate on bearing. Apply pressure. Remove snap ring located on flywheel side of clutch fingers. Remove bearing and washers.

Inspection

Clean components with compressed air only. Check release bearing for roughness or noise by turning by hand in thrust direction. Check clutch component contact surfaces for excessive wear or damage.

Installation

Apply thin coat of lubricant to guide tube and friction surfaces. To complete installation, reverse removal procedures.

Removal (944)

Remove clutch housing and release components together. Pull out release lever shaft retaining bolt. Remove release lever shaft. Detach release bearing and fork.

Inspection

Clean components with compressed air only. Check release bearing for roughness or noise by turning by hand in thrust direction. Check clutch component contact surfaces for excessive wear or damage. Check release fork needle bearings for looseness, wear or damage. Replace components as necessary.

Installation

Apply thin coat of lubricant to friction surfaces. If removed, press release fork needle bearings in flush with fork surface and lubricate with molybdenum grease. To complete installation, reverse removal procedures.

BALL STUD

NOTE: **Clutch rattling noise can be cause by worn plastic ball stud bushing on clutch release lever. Replace as necessary. Ball stud is retained with Loctite. Unscrew carefully. If necessary, remove clutch housing. Heat housing no more than 450° and remove ball stud.**

Removal & Installation (928S)

With clutch and release lever removed, unscrew old ball stud with 15 mm socket wrench. Apply Loctite to new ball stud threads and tighten. Complete installation by reversing removal procedure.

CLUTCH MASTER CYLINDER

Removal & Installation

Disconnect and plug hydraulic lines from fluid reservoir and to slave cylinder. Remove master cylinder mount bolts. Remove cylinder. To install, reverse removal procedure and bleed hydraulic system.

CLUTCH SLAVE CYLINDER

Removal & Installation

Raise and support vehicle. Disconnect fluid line and plug. Remove slave cylinder-to-clutch housing mount nuts. Remove cylinder. To install, reverse removal procedure and bleed hydraulic system.

OVERHAUL

CLUTCH SLAVE CYLINDER

Disassembly

With slave cylinder removed, detach dust boot and circlip. Remove piston and cup assembly from cylinder, using compressed air if required. Remove spring and bleeder screw.

Reassembly

Wash parts in clean brake fluid or denatured alcohol. Blow dry with compressed air. Check all parts for wear or damage. Before assembly, coat piston assembly and cylinder bore with brake paste. Replace circlip and all rubber components. To complete reassembly, reverse disassembly procedure.

Clutches

PORSCHE 928S & 944 (Cont.)

ADJUSTMENTS

CLUTCH FREE PLAY

No adjustment is necessary due to automatic adjustment by slave cylinder. There must be .02" (.5 mm) play between end of push rod and master cylinder piston. This gives approximately .12" (3 mm) free play at pedal pad. If necessary, correct play by adjusting push rod.

CLUTCH SPRING LENGTH

928S

The distance between the inside of spring retainer and center of pin must be 1.7" (43 mm). Measurement is taken with clutch engaged and pedal against final stop. Adjust by turning wing nut. *See Fig. 1*.

Fig. 1: Adjusting 928S Clutch Spring Length

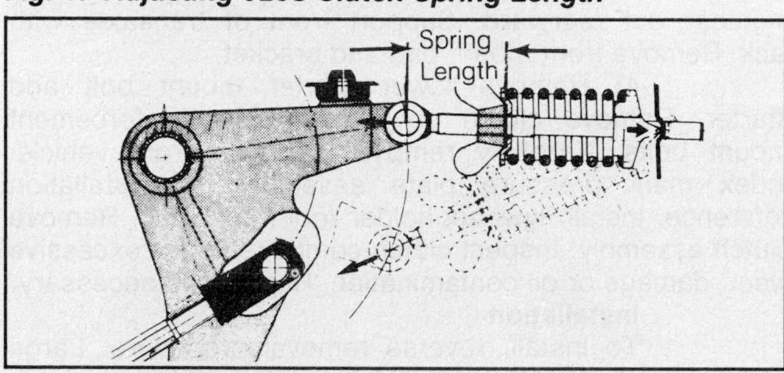
Spring
Length

944

Clutch spring length is checked with clutch engaged and pedal against final stop. The distance between outer edge of plate and the knife-edge bearing must be 2.36" (60 mm). Adjust by turning hexagon nut. *See Fig. 2*.

Fig. 2: Adjusting 944 Clutch Spring Length

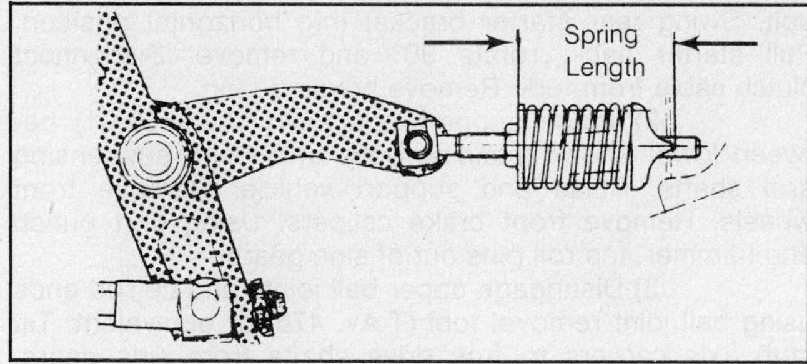
Spring
Length

INSPECTION

CLUTCH DISC WEAR

928S

Remove inspection plug located below slave cylinder. The clutch disc is worn when front edge of release lever just appears in the inspection hole.

944

Remove inspection plug in clutch housing next to slave cylinder. Measure distance from inside edge of inspection hole to release lever. Standard distance "A" with new disc is .70" (18 mm). The clutch disc must be replaced if the distance "A" is 1.34" (34 mm) or more. *See Fig. 3*.

Fig. 3: Checking 944 Clutch Disc Wear

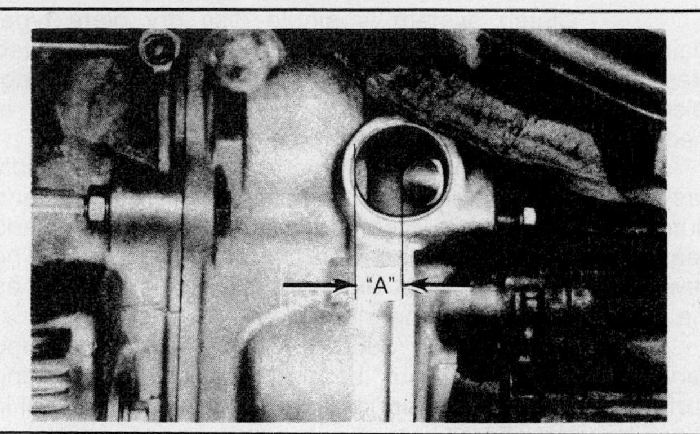
"A"

TIGHTENING SPECIFICATIONS

Application	Ft. Lbs. (N.m)
Backup Light Switch	
928S	16 (22)
944	22 (30)
Ball Stud-to-Clutch Housing	
6 mm	7 (10)
8 mm	17 (23)
Clutch-to-Flywheel	
928S	14-17 (19-23)
Clutch Housing-to-Engine	
928S	51-60 (70-83)
944	54 (75)
Drive Shaft Flange-to Differential Bolt	
944	18 (25)
Drive Shaft Flange-to-Transmission Shaft	
944	58 (80)
Flywheel-to-Crankshaft Bolt	
928S & 944	65 (90)
Guide Sleeve Mount Bolt	
944	11 (15)
Joint Flange-to-Transmission Outlet	
928S	31 (43)
Master Cylinder-to-Firewall Bolt	
944	15 (21)
Pressure Plate-to-Flywheel Bolt	
944	18 (25)
Slave Cylinder Mount Bolt	
928S	14-17 (19-23)
944	15 (21)

RENAULT

DESCRIPTION

Clutch system is single disc dry plate type. Main components are: Disc, diaphragm spring operated pressure plate, ball bearing type clutch release bearing, release fork, and pilot bearing. Clutch operation is mechanical through cable actuation.

A combination oil seal and bearing assembly has replaced the separate crankshaft pilot bearing and clutch housing oil seal in some models. The new seal and bearing assembly is mounted in clutch housing bore. The new short shaft does not extend into crankshaft bore as the long shaft with pilot bearing does.

An extended outer track ring on the bearing serves as the throw-out bearing support and sliding surface. The bearing is lubricated through an oil channel in clutch housing and oil hole in outer track ring.

REMOVAL & INSTALLATION

NOTE: **On all models, replace flywheel bolts if removed. Clean the flywheel-to-crankshaft mating flange and coat with sealer. When installing flywheel, coat new bolts with Loctite.**

CLUTCH ASSEMBLY

Removal (Fuego & Fuego Turbo)

1) Disconnect battery. Remove 3 starter mount bolts. Disengage clutch from release fork. Remove housing stop. Place support spacers (T.Av. 509-01) between lower shock pins and lower suspension arm shafts. Raise and support vehicle. Ensure support spacers remain in place.

2) Remove front wheels. Detach brake calipers and set aside. Disconnect upper ball joints and tie rod ends at steering knuckle. Use ball joint puller tool (T.Av. 476) or equivalent, if necessary. Using pin drift, drive out drive shaft roll pins on side gear shafts.

3) Tilt stub axle carrier. Disengage drive shaft from side gear shaft. Remove from vehicle. Disconnect speedometer cable, shift linkage, backup light wires and emission control switches.

4) Remove clutch cover. Note top dead center sensor location, if equipped, for reassembly reference. Support transmission with a jack. Remove left and right transmission mounts. Remove transmission-to-engine mount bolts. Remove starter.

5) Slide transmission back and away from engine. Use caution not to bind on clutch components. Index mark pressure plate and flywheel for reassembly reference. Install flywheel holder tool (Mot. 582). Remove clutch assembly. Inspect clutch components for excessive wear, damage or oil contamination. Replace as necessary.

Installation

1) Lightly coat input shaft splines with molybdenum grease. Install disc with damper flange toward transmission. Center disc visually on flywheel. Install pressure plate. Tighten bolts evenly, in a diagonal pattern.

2) Drive shaft and side gear alignment holes must be aligned. Install drive shaft roll pins. Reverse removal procedure to complete assembly. Adjust release bearing clearance.

Removal (LeCar)

1) Disconnect battery. Detach speedometer cable at transmission. Remove water pump belt, camshaft pulley and air injection components. Remove 2 upper starter mount bolts. If necessary, use special wrench (Ele. 565).

2) Remove clutch housing mount bolts. Lower left mount bolt may need special wrench (Mot. 253). Detach brake calipers and set aside. Disconnect tie rods at steering rack end. Disconnect upper ball joints. Remove drive shafts from side gears by tilting stub axle carriers downward and out.

NOTE: **Do not damage oil seal lips on differential adjusting ring nuts while removing drive shafts.**

3) Remove mount bolts from support tab on transaxle. Disconnect clutch cable at lever. Push against sleeve retainer with screwdriver to free it from support tab. Remove tubular crossmember bolts. Slide crossmember out rearward. Support front of transaxle with jack. Remove front mount pad and bracket.

4) Remove lower starter mount bolt and starter. Remove clutch cover and side reinforcement mount bolts. Carefully remove transaxle from vehicle. Index mark pressure plate assembly for installation reference. Install flywheel holder tool (Mot. 582). Remove clutch assembly. Inspect clutch components for excessive wear, damage or oil contamination. Replace as necessary.

Installation

To install, reverse removal procedure. Large end of clutch disc hub should face engine. Using clutch assembly alignment tool (Emb. 319) or equivalent, align pressure plate and disc. Lightly grease input shaft and axle drive shaft splines. Make sure axle drive shafts fully seat into side gears.

Removal (18i)

1) Disconnect negative battery cable. Disconnect battery cables at starter and starter solenoid. Remove starter mount bolts. Loosen top engine mount bolt. Swing rear starter bracket into horizontal position. Pull starter back, rotate 90° and remove. Disconnect clutch cable from fork. Remove housing stop.

2) Place support spacers (T.Av. 509.01) between lower shock retaining bolts and lower suspension arm shafts. Raise and support vehicle. Remove front wheels. Remove front brake calipers. Using drift punch and hammer, tap roll pins out of side gears.

3) Disengage upper ball joints and tie rod ends using ball joint removal tool (T.Av. 476) or equivalent. Tilt stub axle carriers to free drive shafts from side gears. Disconnect back-up light wires, emission control wires and speedometer cable from transmission.

4) Disconnect shift linkage by removing bolt in linkage ball joint. Do not remove ball joint from its housing. Remove pivot bolt. Remove clutch cover and note position of top dead center sensor for reassembly reference. Support transmission with jack. Remove left and right transmission mounts.

5) Remove transmission-to-engine mount bolts. Pull transmission rearward. Remove from vehicle. Index mark pressure plate assembly for installation reference. Install flywheel holder tool (Mot. 582). Remove clutch assembly. Inspect clutch components for excessive wear, damage or oil contamination. Replace as necessary.

Installation

To install, reverse removal procedure. Larger end of clutch disc hub should face engine. Using clutch assembly alignment tool (Emb. 786) or equivalent, align

RENAULT (Cont.)

pressure plate and disc. Lightly grease input shaft and axle drive shaft splines. Make sure axle drive shafts fully seat into side gears.

CLUTCH CABLE

Removal & Installation

(Fuego, Fuego Turbo & 18i)

Disconnect cable from lever on transaxle. Detach the cable from clutch pedal. Installation is reverse of removal procedure.

Removal (LeCar)

Remove locknut and adjusting nut. Remove left glove compartment tray. Detach clutch pedal return spring. Remove pedal retaining clip and cable-to-pedal clevis pin. Slide pedal off of pivot rod. Free cable from sleeve stop on pedal bracket. Remove cable.

Installation

Lubricate pedal bore, shaft and retaining pin with molybdenum grease. To complete installation, reverse removal procedure. Adjust free play.

CLUTCH RELEASE BEARING & FORK

Removal

With transaxle removed, disconnect return spring from release bearing and fork. Slide bearing off transmission input shaft. To extract fork retaining roll pins on Fuego and Fuego Turbo, use slide hammer tool (Emb. 880) or equivalent. On LeCar & 18i, use pin remover tool (Emb. 384). Remove fork shaft, fork and return spring.

Installation

1) Lubricate fork shaft with molybdenum grease. Slide shaft into transaxle housing (fitted with rubber seal) and through release fork and return spring.

2) Align holes in shaft with holes in fork. Install roll pins. Ensure pins protrude .039" (1 mm) on forward side of fork. *See Fig. 1.*

Fig. 1: Installing Release Fork Pins

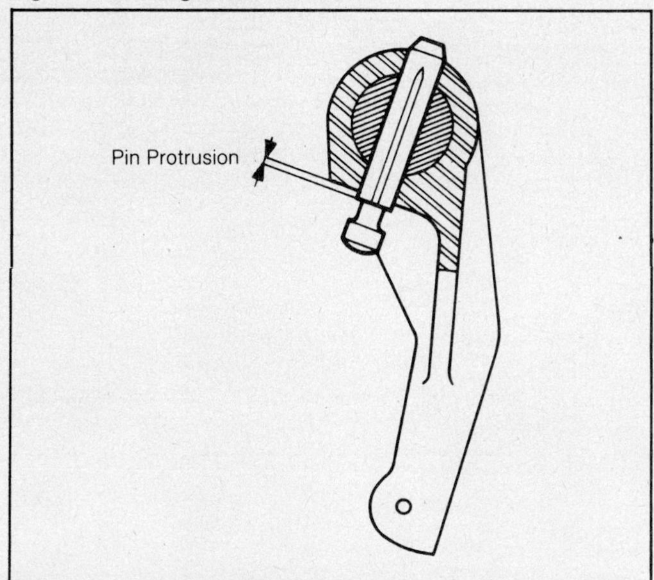
Pin Protrusion

Pin protrusion must be .039" (1 mm).

3) Lubricate bearing sleeve and fork fingers with molybdenum grease. Slide bearing onto transmission input shaft. Install return spring, placing ends in holes of release bearing support and in fork.

4) Lubricate bearing face and portion of clutch diaphragm spring which bearing contacts with molybdenum grease. Install transmission. Adjust clutch free play.

PILOT BEARING

Removal

Remove transaxle, clutch assembly and flywheel. Using extractor tool (Mot. 11) or equivalent, remove bearing from crankshaft. Note that bearing is prelubricated and factory sealed. Do not clean in solvent. Inspect for noise and roughness by turning by hand in thrust direction. Replace as necessary.

NOTE: **Pilot bearing is not used on models with new short clutch shaft and combination oil seal and bearing assembly. Short shaft may be used on crankshaft drilled for pilot bearing.**

Installation

Coat pilot bearing housing surface of crankshaft with Loctite. Using driver, install bearing into crankshaft. Install flywheel, clutch assembly and transaxle. Adjust free play.

OIL SEAL

NOTE: **Two types of oil seal and bearing assemblies will be used in service. Ensure proper parts identification before repair. Clutch assembly alignment tool is not needed when new short shaft, oil seal and bearing assembly are installed.**

Removal

Remove transaxle. Remove clutch housing mount bolts and housing. Remove oil seal or combination oil seal/bearing assembly from clutch housing.

Installation (Long Shaft Models)

Fit seal in place over special tool (B.Vi. 526) for 18i or (B.Vi. 488) for LeCar. Coat paper gasket with sealer. Place tool inside release bearing guide to spread seal lip. Refit clutch housing on transaxle and slide tool along clutch shaft. Remove tool. Tighten clutch housing nuts and complete installation.

Fig. 2: Short Clutch Shaft With Oil Seal/Bearing Assembly

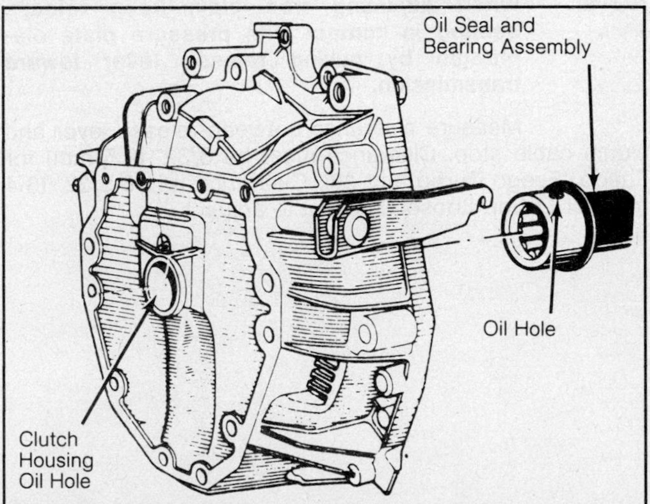
Oil Seal and
Bearing Assembly
Oil Hole
Clutch
Housing
Oil Hole

Ensure proper parts identification before beginning repair.

Clutches

RENAULT (Cont.)

Installation (Short Shaft Models)

Coat bearing bore in the clutch housing with molybdenum grease. Align oil holes in the clutch housing and new seal/bearing assembly. *See Fig. 2*. Press assembly into clutch housing. Ensure seal is flush against housing. Mount clutch housing on transaxle and complete installation.

OVERHAUL

FLYWHEEL

LeCar

1) LeCar is equipped with a stepped flywheel. Check flywheel runout with a dial indicator. Maximum runout must not exceed .0024" (.060 mm). If resurfacing is necessary, check dimension "C" first. If "C" is less than .894" (22.7 mm), flywheel must be replaced. *See Fig. 3*.

Fig. 3: Flywheel Resurfacing Tolerances

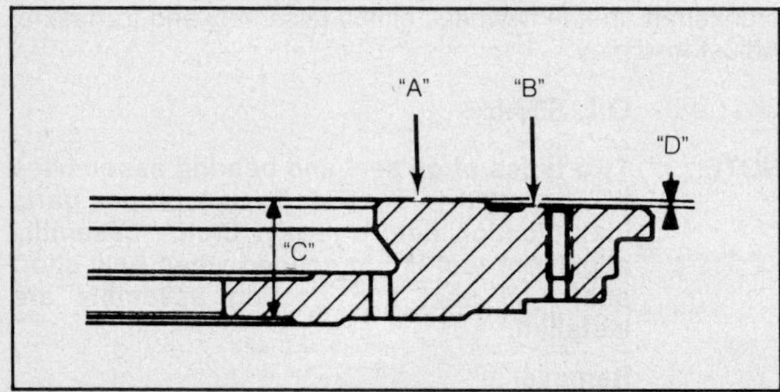
"A"
"B"
"D"
"C"

Replace flywheel if "C" is less than .894" (22.7 mm).

2) Remove dowel pins. When resurfacing flywheel, dimension "D" between surfaces "A" and "B" must be .020" (.5 mm). Dowels must protrude .276" (7 mm) above flywheel face.

ADJUSTMENT

CLUTCH FREE PLAY

NOTE: **When adjusting free play, keep release bearing in contact with pressure plate diaphragm by pulling release lever toward transmission.**

Measure clearance between release lever and clutch cable stop. Clearance must be 3/32" (2.5 mm) for Fuego, Fuego Turbo and 18i. Clearance is 1/8-5/32" (3-4 mm) for LeCar. Loosen lock nut to adjust.

TIGHTENING SPECIFICATIONS

Application	Ft. Lbs. (N.m)
Brake Caliper Bracket Bolt	
Fuego	44 (60)
18i	74 (100)
Clutch Housing-to-Transmission	
LeCar	
8 mm Bolts	15 (20)
10 mm Bolts	30 (41)
18i	
8 mm Bolts	18 (24)
10 mm Bolts	26 (35)
Flywheel-to-Crankshaft Mount Bolt	
All Models [1]	37 (50)
Steering Ball Joint Nut	
Fuego	29 (39)
18i	26 (35)
Upper Suspension Ball Joint Nut	
Fuego	48 (65)
18i	37 (50)
Wheel Lug Bolts	
All Models	59 (80)

[1] – Replace the flywheel bolts whenever they are removed. Apply Loctite to new bolt threads before installation.

SAAB

DESCRIPTION

Clutch is single dry plate, diaphragm spring type. Components consist of riveted lining clutch disc, pressure plate assembly and release bearing. Clutch operation is hydraulic. Pedal activates master cylinder, connected by flex hose, to slave cylinder.

Slave cylinder is inside clutch cover, around input shaft, and acts directly on release bearing. Clutch adjustment is automatic. On 5-speed models, clutch hub is equipped with a pre-damper.

REMOVAL & INSTALLATION

CLUTCH ASSEMBLY

Removal

1) Remove clutch cover housing. Disengage clutch and fit spacer ring (83 90 023) between diaphragm spring fingers and pressure plate cover. Spacer ring will keep clutch disengaged while removing components.

NOTE: **If clutch cannot be disengaged normally, compress diaphragm spring with tool (83 93 175) to fit spacer. Pressure plate assembly is integral. Do not disassemble.**

2) Unhook spring clip. Remove input shaft cover and plastic propeller. Install 8 mm bolt in end of input shaft. Pry out shaft with tool (83 93 175).

3) Remove 3 slave cylinder mount bolts. Remove pressure plate mount bolts. Simultaneously lift out clutch disc, pressure plate assembly, slave cylinder and release bearing. *See Fig. 1.*

Fig. 1: Clutch Assembly Removal

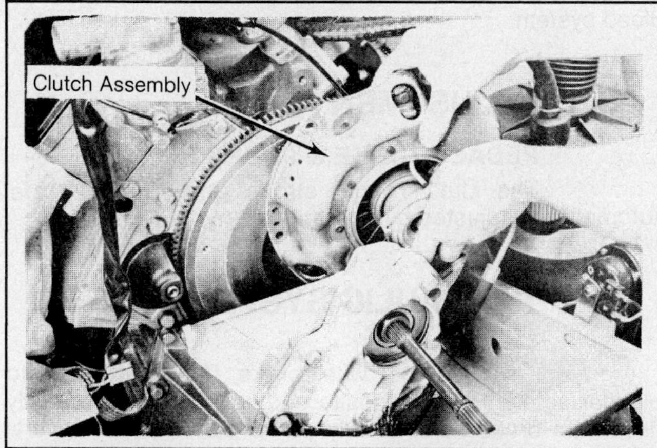
Clutch Assembly

Ensure plastic sleeve is not damaged during removal.

Inspection

1) With clutch assembly installed, remove inspection plate on top of clutch cover and look through inspection hole. On Early Design slave cylinder, slowly disengage clutch and than release. Release bearing should be in contact with pressure plate fingers.

2) Check sliding lock ring on piston in slave cylinder is in contact with cylinder walls. The minimum distance between sliding lock ring and lock ring behind release bearing is .04" (1 mm). On Late Design, measure distance between plastic sleeve front edge and front edge of machined surface of slave cylinder housing.

3) Replace worn clutch disc if distance is less than .08" (2 mm). Distance with new disc is .354" (9 mm). Check that loaded, compressed thickness of disc is .28-.30" (7.1-7.6 mm) for Non-Turbo models and .27-.29" (6.9-7.4 mm) for Turbo models. Check unloaded disc-to-pressure plate gap is .050" (1.27 mm).

4) Check flywheel and pressure plate friction surfaces for burns, cracks or scoring. Measure surface warpage with straightedge and feeler gauge. At pressure plate inner edge, maximum taper is .0012" (.030 mm). Resurface as necessary.

5) Outer edge has no clearance allowable. Check at several points. Check release bearing turns freely under light load. Replace bearing if noisy, rough or dry. Do not clean in solvent, use compressed air only.

NOTE: **Flywheel bolt heads on 5-speed transmissions are thinner than 4-speed bolts. If replacing, use correct bolts.**

Installation

1) Before clutch installation, ensure input shaft seal, in primary gear case, is in good condition. Reassemble clutch assembly. Install components simultaneously. Loosely install pressure plate mount bolts.

2) Ensure hardened side of release bearing faces clutch assembly. Coat input shaft splines with molybdenum grease. Tap shaft into position. Ensure shaft engages splines of disc and flywheel bearing. Coat slave cylinder bolts with Loctite. Install slave cylinder.

NOTE: **Do not depress clutch pedal farther than necessary. Seal lip may be pressed too far, causing hydraulic leak and seal damage.**

3) Tighten pressure plate bolts. On early design models, with pedal depressed, install sliding lock ring toward slave cylinder. On late design models, ensure plastic sleeve with circlip is installed with slave cylinder. Depress clutch pedal. Remove spacer. To complete installation, reverse removal procedure.

CLUTCH MASTER CYLINDER

Removal

1) From inside vehicle, remove access cover under left side of instrument panel. Remove safety padding. Remove push rod pin at clutch pedal. Remove master cylinder mount nuts from firewall.

2) From engine compartment, remove fluid flex hose from reservoir-to-cylinder and plug opening. Remove hydraulic line at rear of cylinder. Remove master cylinder.

Installation

To install, reverse removal procedure and bleed system.

CLUTCH SLAVE CYLINDER

Slave cylinder removal is accomplished during clutch assembly removal. *See Clutch Assembly Removal* in this article.

OVERHAUL

NOTE: **Wash cylinder components with clean brake fluid. Do not use any form of mineral oil for cleaning or permanent damage to rubber components will result.**

CLUTCH MASTER CYLINDER

Disassembly

1) Pull back rubber cover. Remove circlip, push rod and stop washer. Remove piston assembly, convex washer, rear piston seal and return spring. Inspect cylinder bore and piston assembly.

2) Replace complete master cylinder assembly if components are worn or damaged. Replace rubber seals whenever cylinder is disassembled. *See Fig. 2.*

Fig. 2: Exploded View of Clutch Master Cylinder

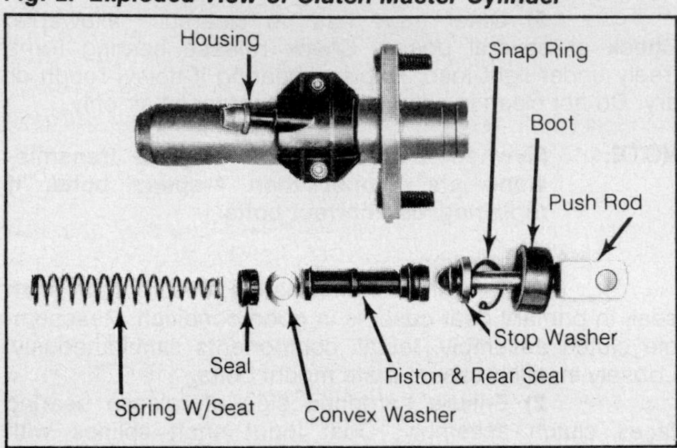
Housing
Snap Ring
Boot
Push Rod
Stop Washer
Seal
Piston & Rear Seal
Spring W/Seat
Convex Washer

Replace master cylinder if bore or piston assembly shows signs of excessive wear or damage.

Reassembly

1) Install return spring and retainer. Lubricate piston and seals with clean brake fluid. Install seals, convex washer and piston. *See Fig. 3.*

Fig. 3: Master Cylinder Convex Washer Installation

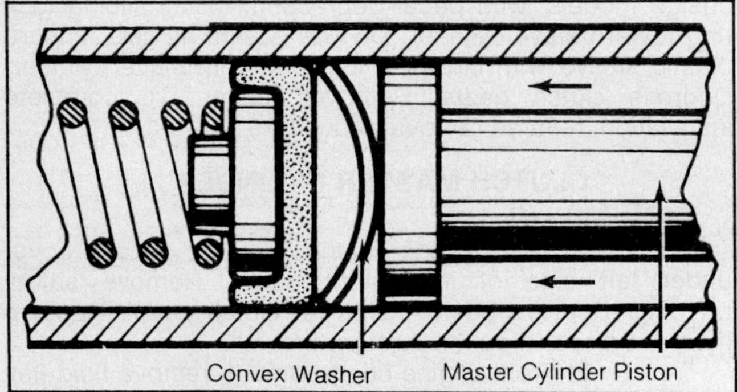
Convex Washer
Master Cylinder Piston

Convex side of washer must face master cylinder piston.

2) Install push rod, washer and retaining ring. Install rubber cover. Install cylinder and bleed system.

CLUTCH SLAVE CYLINDER

NOTE: **On Late Design slave cylinder: A plastic sleeve, with circlip, replaces sliding circlip. Sleeve rides on machined surface of cylinder body and doubles as dust cover.**

Disassembly

1) Remove clutch release bearing from slave cylinder. Set slave cylinder with release bearing end facing up. Press cylinder sleeve out. Remove "O" ring from sleeve flange. Remove piston, lip seal and related components.

2) Clean and inspect slave cylinder housing-to-sleeve bore, sleeve inside bore and outside surface, piston assembly and all rubber components for wear and damage. *See Fig. 4.*

Fig. 4: Clutch Slave Cylinder (Early Design)

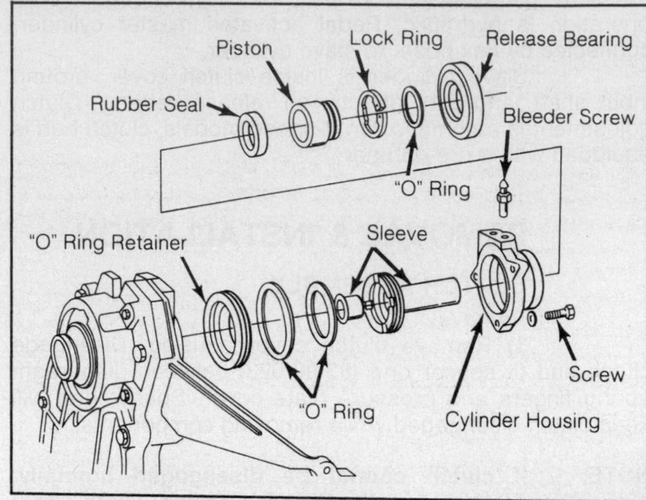
Piston
Lock Ring
Release Bearing
Rubber Seal
Bleeder Screw
"O" Ring
"O" Ring Retainer
Sleeve
Screw
"O" Ring
Cylinder Housing

Replace slave cylinder assembly if cylinder bore, sleeve or piston assembly are excessively worn or damaged.

Reassembly

1) Before beginning reassembly, lightly coat lip seal and piston with rubber grease. DO NOT coat "O" ring. Fit "O" ring to sleeve flange. Slide seal lip on sleeve. Coat sleeve flange with brake fluid. Insert sleeve into cylinder. Push seal lip part way into cylinder.

2) Guide sleeve and cylinder together by pushing on piston until lock rings and "O" ring are fitted. Place slave cylinder on support and seat sleeve into cylinder. Fit release bearing to piston. Install cylinder. Bleed system.

ADJUSTMENTS

PEDAL STROKE & FREE PLAY

The clutch pedal stroke and free play are automatically adjusted by operation of hydraulic system.

HYDRAULIC SYSTEM BLEEDING

Fill reservoir with brake fluid. Fit hose to bleeder screw. Place opposite end into container partially filled with brake fluid. Slowly pump clutch pedal several times and hold to floor. Break bleeder screw loose. Allow air to vent. Close bleeder screw. Allow pedal to return.

Repeat procedure until no air bubbles are present in discharged fluid. Do not let reservoir run dry or complete system must be rebleed. After bleeding system, check clutch pedal free play, disengagement and position.

TIGHTENING SPECIFICATIONS

Applications	Ft. Lbs. (N.m)
Flywheel-to-Crankshaft Bolt	43 (59)
Slave Cylinder Nut	4-10 (6-14)
8 mm Mount Bolt	15-18 (20-25)

SUBARU

DESCRIPTION

Clutch is a single, dry disc type with a diaphragm spring pressure plate. Mechanical actuation is by a cable. Sealed release bearing requires no lubrication.

REMOVAL & INSTALLATION

CLUTCH ASSEMBLY

Removal

1) Remove spare tire and support bracket. Remove negative cable from battery. Do not remove positive battery cable from starter. Disconnect clutch cable return spring, lock nut, adjusting nut and outer cable retainer clip. Disconnect rubber boot.

2) Disconnect speedometer cable and retainer clip at transmission. Disconnect back-up lamp switch connector, starter harness and ground cable on vehicle body. Remove starter with battery cable attached. Remove upper engine-to-transmission bolts and loosen lower nuts.

3) Loosen transmission side torque rod stopper nut by .39" (10 mm) and tighten engine side nut by same amount. DO NOT move side torque rod stopper more than specification. Slightly tilt engine backward to facilitate transmission removal. On all models except 4WD, remove bolts from two places which secure gear shift system to transmission.

4) On 4WD models, remove hand brake tray cover and hand brake cover. Remove rod cover. Set gear selector lever at 4WD position. Remove nut connecting gear selector rod with 4WD selector rod. Remove 2 nuts connecting 4WD selector rod and lever from plate.

5) Remove boot retainer screws. Remove nut connecting gear shift lever and pull up shift lever with boot. Separate both gear selector lever and 4WD selector lever system from transmission. Disconnect oxygen sensor and harness. Use care not to strike oxygen sensor against any parts during removal.

6) On all models, raise and support front end of vehicle. Remove front exhaust pipe assembly. On 4WD models, remove transmission cover. On all models, remove bolts retaining drive shaft-to-differential flange and detach rear drive shaft. Do not damage oil seal during drive shaft removal. Plug rear of transmission to prevent oil leakage.

7) Remove stabilizer bar. Remove bolts and lower left and right transverse links. Remove clamp on left side of hand brake cable. Remove nuts from left and right transmission mounting pads. Drive spring pins from inner ends of axle shafts and discard pins. Pull wheels out until axles separate from driving splines.

CAUTION: Do not reuse axle shaft spring pins and transverse link nuts.

8) Remove nuts securing left and right transmission mount rubber cushions. Support transmission with jack and remove center crossmember. Remove remaining nuts securing transmission-to-engine. Move transmission away from engine enough to prevent main shaft from interfering with engine. Lower jack and remove transmission. Remove pressure plate mount bolts. Remove clutch assembly. *See Fig. 1.*

Fig. 1: Exploded View of Subaru Clutch Assembly

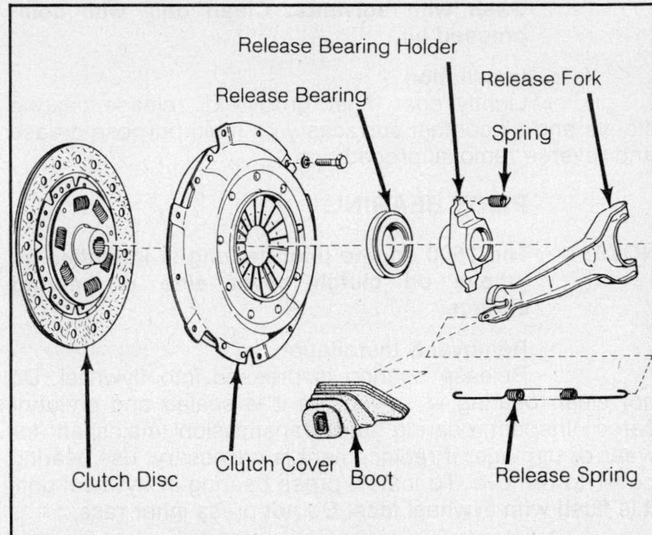
Release Bearing Holder
Release Fork
Release Bearing
Spring
Clutch Cover
Boot
Release Spring
Clutch Disc

Ensure that dirt or oil does not contaminate the clutch component friction surfaces.

Inspection

1) Standard depth of rivet heads, below friction surface, is .055" (1.40 mm). Minimum depth is .012" (.30 mm). Standard clutch disc compressed thickness is .307" (7.80 mm). Disc free thickness, for 1600 engine, is .346" (8.80 mm) and .335" (8.50 mm) for 1800 engine.

2) Install disc on input shaft and check that it slides smoothly. Check runout at specified point, measured from shaft center axis to radius point on outer circumference of disc face. Measurement point for 1600 and non-4WD 1800 engines is 3.74" (95 mm) and 4.21" (107 mm) for 1800 4WD engine. Maximum disc runout is .028" (.70 mm).

3) Check pressure plate surface for cracks, burns or scoring. Check pressure plate for loose rivets or worn diaphragm spring fingers. Check release bearing and pilot bearing for excessive noise, looseness, wear or damage by turning by applying hand pressure in thrust direction. Do not wash permanently lubricated bearings in solvent, clean with compressed air only. Replace components as necessary.

Installation

1) Reverse removal procedure to complete installation. Using molybdenum disulphide grease, lubricate the following: inner groove of release bearing, contact surface of fork and pivot, contact surface of fork and holder and transmission main shaft splines.

2) Using clutch disc alignment tool (499747000), place disc and pressure plate in position on flywheel. Ensure that there is a gap of 120° or more between "O" balance marks on flywheel and pressure plate. Tighten bolts to 10.50-12.70 ft. lbs. (14.2-17.2 N.m) gradually in a criss-cross pattern. Adust clutch pedal free play.

CLUTCH RELEASE BEARING

Removal

With transmission separated from engine, disconnect return springs from transmission and remove bearing assembly. Bearing may be removed from or installed on sleeve using press. Do not press on outer race.

NOTE: Release bearing is prelubricated, do not wash with solvents. Clean only with compressed air.

Installation

Lightly coat inner groove of release bearing sleeve and all contact surfaces with multi-purpose grease and reverse removal procedures.

PILOT BEARING

NOTE: The 1600 engine pilot bearing is identified by groove on clutch cover side of bearing surface.

Removal & Installation

Release bearing is pressed into flywheel. Do not clean bearing in solvent as it is sealed and prelubricated. Inspect bearing and transmission mainshaft for wear or damage. If replacement is necessary, use bearing puller to remove. To install, press bearing in flywheel until it is flush with flywheel face. Do not press inner race.

ADJUSTMENT

CLUTCH FREE PLAY

Remove release fork return spring. Adjust spherical nut so that there is .08-.12" (2-3 mm) play at fork end. *See Fig. 2.* Do not twist cable during adjustment. Attach return spring and ensure that cable is routed without kinks or sharp bends. On 1600 engine, hook long spring side of release spring to release fork.

Fig. 2: Adjusting Clutch Cable at Release Lever

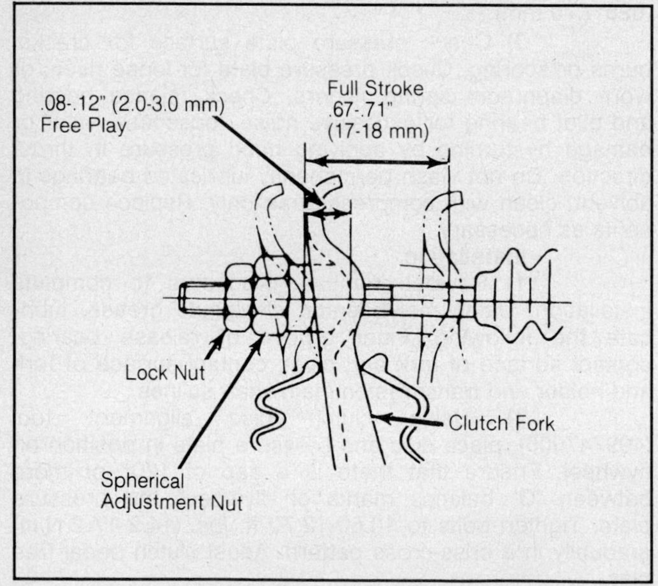
.08-.12" (2.0-3.0 mm)
Free Play
Full Stroke
.67-.71"
(17-18 mm)
Lock Nut
Clutch Fork
Spherical
Adjustment Nut

Both 1600 & 1800 models are adjusted in the same manner.

CLUTCH ADJUSTMENT SPECIFICATIONS

Application	In. (mm)
Clutch Pad Surface Position [1]	.59" (15)
Clutch Pedal Stroke	5.1-5.4 (129-137)
Release Fork Stroke	.67-.71 (17-18)
Release Fork Free Play	.08-.12 (2.0-3.0)
Pedal Free Play	.50-.80 (13-20)

[1] – Above brake pedal level.

TIGHTENING SPECIFICATIONS

Application	Ft. Lbs. (N.m)
Engine-to-Transmission Bolt	34-40 (46-54)
Stabilizer Bar	13-16 (18-22)
Transverse Link Nut	43-50 (59-69)
Pressure Plate Mount Bolt [1]	11-13 (14-17)

[1] – Tighten bolts gradually, in a crisscross pattern, to specified torque.

TOYOTA – EXCEPT STARLET & TERCEL

DESCRIPTION

Clutch is a dry, single plate, diaphragm spring type which is hydraulically operated by a firewall mounted master cylinder and clutch housing mounted slave cylinder. Slave cylinders are nonadjustable and clearance is automatically compensated for by internal design of cylinder.

Fig. 1: Exploded View of Typical Clutch Arrangement

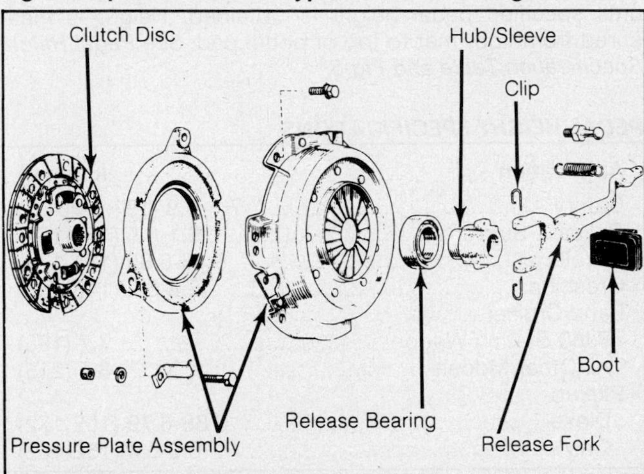
Clutch Disc
Hub/Sleeve
Clip
Boot
Release Bearing
Pressure Plate Assembly
Release Fork

Pressure plate assembly and hub/sleeve retainer springs vary between models.

REMOVAL & INSTALLATION

CLUTCH ASSEMBLY

NOTE: **Clutch removal procedures are of a general nature written to cover all Toyota models listed.**

Removal

1) Disconnect battery cable. Remove air cleaner and drain cooling system. Remove upper radiator hose. On Land Cruiser, remove cowl side trim, heater duct on transmission hump and front carpet or mat. On all models, remove shift lever boot, shifter assembly and on Land Cruiser remove transfer case levers. Remove starter.

2) Raise vehicle and support at front and rear with jack stands. If equipped, remove protective cover from under engine.

3) Remove clutch slave cylinder, but only disconnect hydraulic line if necessary. Disconnect front exhaust pipe from manifold and front clamp from mounting. Disconnect front pipe from converter and remove pipe from vehicle. Disconnect speedometer cable and electrical leads from transmission.

4) Scribe index marks on drive shafts and couplings for reinstallation reference, then remove drive shafts. Insert appropriate plug into extension housing to prevent oil spillage.

5) Support engine with a jack, using a wooden block to protect oil pan. Support transmission with transmission jack and remove rear support crossmember. Lower transmission jack slightly and remove transmission-to-engine bolts. Pull transmission (including transfer case on Land Cruiser) to rear. Lower and remove from vehicle. Do not drain transmission oil.

6) Mark pressure plate and flywheel for reassembly reference. Loosen pressure plate attaching bolts alternately and evenly until pressure plate is released. Separate clutch disc and pressure plate.

Installation

1) Use appropriate aligning tool to center clutch disc on flywheel. Tighten clutch pressure plate attaching bolts alternately and evenly in a diagonal progression until 11-15 ft. lbs. (15-20 Nm) of torque are meet.

2) Using a feeler gauge and tool (#SST 09301-00013), measure gap between spring tips and tool. If gap is larger than .02 in (.5 mm), use tool (#SST 09301-00012) to bend springs until alignment is correct. *See Fig. 2.*

Fig. 2: Diaphragm Spring Tip Alignment Check

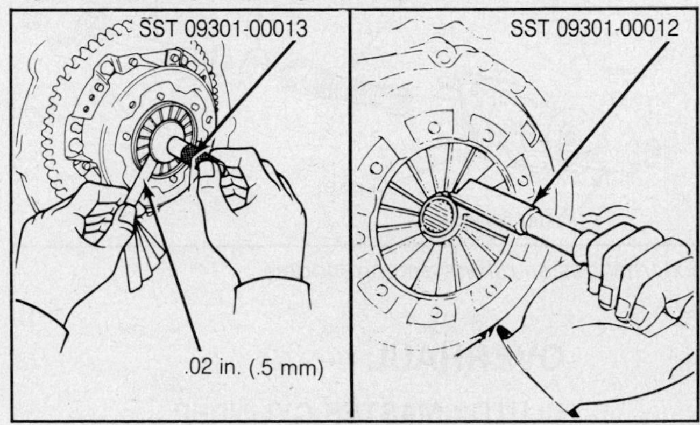
SST 09301-00013
SST 09301-00012
.02 in. (.5 mm)

3) Apply molybdenum disulphide grease to the following contact points: release fork and hub, hub and lever, hub and oil seal, and hub and bushing. Also apply grease to inside of bearing and inside of clutch disc splines. Reverse removal procedure to complete installation and bleed hydraulic system if necessary.

CLUTCH MASTER CYLINDER

Removal & Installation

Disconnect master cylinder push rod at clutch pedal by removing cotter pin and clevis. Disconnect hydraulic line at cylinder. Remove cylinder attaching nuts and remove cylinder from firewall. To install, reverse removal procedure and adjust pedal height and free play. Bleed hydraulic system and check for leaks.

CLUTCH SLAVE CYLINDER

Removal & Installation

Raise and support vehicle on safety stands. Disconnect hydraulic line and clip. Remove slave cylinder attaching bolts and remove slave cylinder. To install, reverse removal procedure and bleed hydraulic system.

CLUTCH RELEASE BEARING

Removal

With transmission removed, check release bearing for freedom of rotation with bearing still installed on hub. To remove, disconnect retaining clips from bearing collar and slide assembly off transmission input shaft. If bearing does not rotate smoothly, press off collar with appropriate driver.

Installation

Use press and driver to install new bearing on sleeve. Lightly grease inner groove of bearing collar and all contact surfaces and reverse removal procedures.

Clutches

TOYOTA – EXCEPT STARLET & TERCEL (Cont.)

PILOT BEARING

Removal & Installation

If pilot bearing is worn or damaged, pull from crankshaft with puller. Coat new bearing with multi-purpose grease and drive into crankshaft with appropriate driver.

Fig. 3 Exploded View of Clutch Master Cylinder

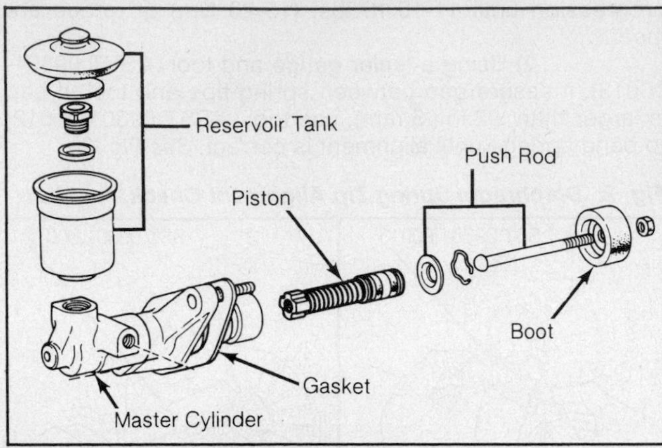

Reservoir Tank
Push Rod
Piston
Boot
Gasket
Master Cylinder

External design differs among models.

OVERHAUL

CLUTCH MASTER CYLINDER

NOTE: Brake fluid will damage painted surfaces, wash off immediately.

Disassembly

With cylinder removed from vehicle, clamp in a soft-jawed vise. Remove hold-down bolt and pull off reservoir. Pull back boot and remove snap ring on push rod. Pull out push rod, piston, cup and remaining internal components.

Reassembly

Wash all parts in clean brake fluid and inspect for wear or damage. Dip cylinder cups into clean brake fluid or coat with rubber grease before assembly. Assemble piston components in reverse order of disassembly. Install piston assembly, push rod, snap ring and reservoir into master cylinder.

CLUTCH SLAVE CYLINDER

Disassembly

Remove rubber boot and push rod. Remove piston assembly and spring from bore. If necessary, remove bleeder screw.

Reassembly

Wash all parts in clean brake fluid and inspect for wear or damage. Dip piston into clean brake fluid or coat with brake grease. Install spring and piston assembly into cylinder bore and install rubber boot. Install push rod and bleeder screw.

Fig. 4: Exploded View of Slave Cylinder

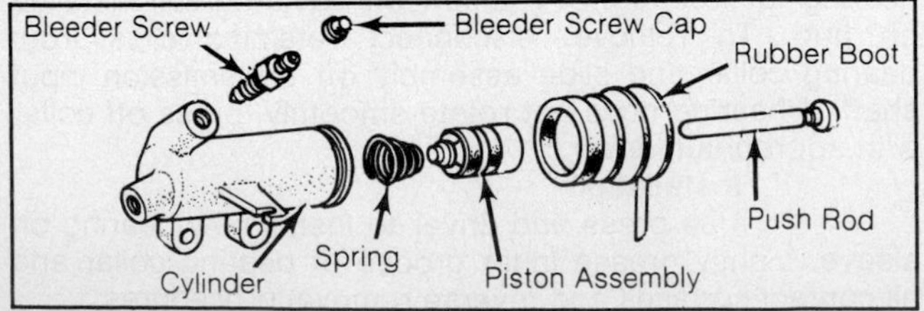

Bleeder Screw
Bleeder Screw Cap
Rubber Boot
Push Rod
Spring
Cylinder
Piston Assembly

External design differs among models.

ADJUSTMENT

PEDAL HEIGHT

Adjust pedal stop bolt at top of pedal assembly until specified pedal height is obtained. Height is measured from floor mat to top of pedal pad. *See Pedal Height Specification Table and Fig 5.*

PEDAL HEIGHT SPECIFICATIONS

Application	In. (mm)
Camry	7.5-7.9 (191.5-201.5)
Celica & Supra	6.1-6.5 (154-164)
Corolla	6.46-6.85 (164-174)
Cressida	5.8-6.2 (148-158)
Land Cruiser	
FJ60 Station Wagon	7.7 (195)
All Other Models	8.5 (215)
Pickup	
Diesel	6.38-6.79 (162-172)
Gas	6.0-6.4 (152-162)

Fig. 5: Pedal Height and Free Play Measuring Points

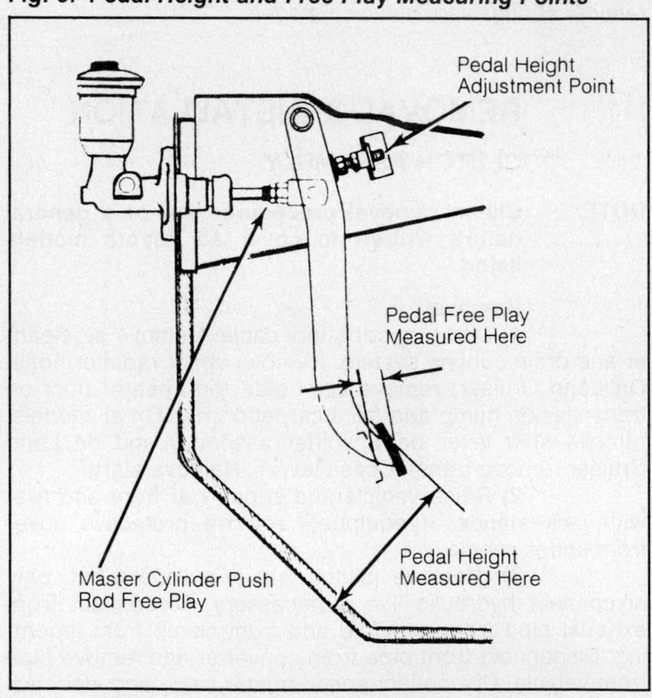

Pedal Height
Adjustment Point
Pedal Free Play
Measured Here
Pedal Height
Measured Here
Master Cylinder Push
Rod Free Play

PUSH ROD FREE PLAY

Land Cruiser

Push rod play is distance pedal moves before moving piston in master cylinder. Adjust by turning push rod. Play at pedal top should be .04-.20 (1.0-5.0 mm).

PEDAL FREE PLAY

To adjust free play (measured at pedal pad), loosen lock nut on master cylinder push rod and turn push rod in or out until free play is within specifications. Tighten lock nut. *See Fig. 5 and Pedal Free Play Table.*

TOYOTA – EXCEPT STARLET & TERCEL (Cont.)

PEDAL FREE PLAY

Application	In. (mm)
Camry, Celica, Cressida, Pickup & Supra	.2-.6 (5-15)
Corolla	.5-.9 (13-23)
Land Cruiser	1.2-2.0 (30-50)

CLUTCH FORK FREE PLAY

Land Cruiser

Clutch fork free play is distance slave cylinder push rod moves before moving clutch fork. To adjust clutch fork free play, loosen lock nut at slave cylinder and turn push rod tip while holding push rod nut with wrench. Free play should be .16-.20" (4-5 mm). Tighten lock nut and check clutch pedal free play.

HYDRAULIC SYSTEM BLEEDING

1) Raise and support vehicle on safety stands. Check master cylinder reservoir often during bleeding operation; add fluid as required. Remove slave cylinder bleeder screw cap and connect flexible hose to bleeder.

2) Immerse opposite end of tube in jar partially filled with brake fluid. Pump clutch pedal several times. With pedal depressed, loosen screw 1/3-1/2 turn, exhaust air and close before pressure is depleted.

3) Repeat operation until no air bubbles are seen in discharged fluid. Close bleeder screw on down stroke of pedal. Check system for leaks and fill master cylinder reservoir.

NOTE: Brake fluid will damage painted surfaces, wash off immediately.

Clutches

TOYOTA STARLET & TERCEL

DESCRIPTION

Clutch is single dry disc using diaphragm spring type pressure plate. Actuation is mechanical, using an adjustable cable connected to clutch pedal and release fork. A permanently lubricated release bearing is used.

Fig. 1: Exploded View of Clutch Components

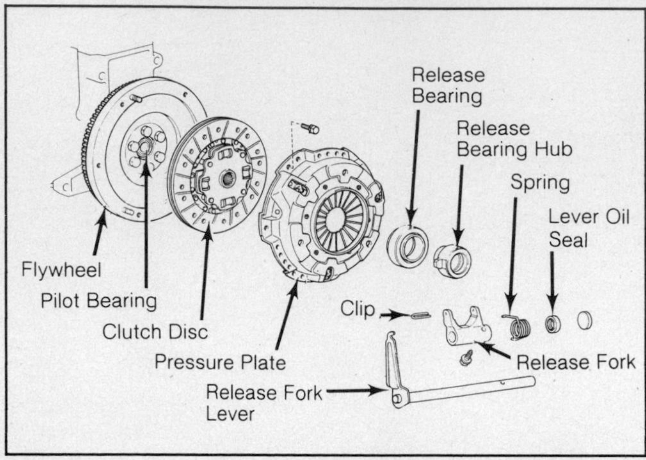
Release Bearing
Release Bearing Hub
Spring
Lever Oil Seal
Flywheel
Pilot Bearing
Clutch Disc
Pressure Plate
Clip
Release Fork
Release Fork Lever

REMOVAL & INSTALLATION

CLUTCH ASSEMBLY

NOTE: **Clutch removal procedures are of a general nature written to cover both Starlet & Tercel.**

Removal

1) Disconnect battery ground. Remove air cleaner inlet duct and disconnect clutch cable. Drain cooling system and disconnect upper hose from engine. Remove upper transaxle set bolt and remove both drive shafts. Remove starter.

2) On Starlet and 4WD vehicles, remove console box and remove shift lever from inside vehicle using snap ring pliers to remove snap ring. Raise vehicle, making sure that it is securely supported. Remove drive shaft and insert appropriate tool into extension housing, to prevent oil spillage. Disconnect 4WD link and 4WD switch wire.

3) With vehicle raised, remove front exhaust pipe by removing flange nuts and clamp on the side of transaxle. Remove stiffener plate, disconnect back-up light switch wire and speedometer cable.

4) On 2WD Tercel, remove number 1 gear shift rod and lever housing rod.

5) Place a jack under transaxle with wood block to prevent damage and remove rear support member. Put a wooden block between engine and dash panel. Remove transaxle four set bolts, disconnect rear bond cable and remove transaxle. Do not drain transaxle oil.

6) Loosen pressure plate bolts one turn at a time until spring pressure is released, then remove pressure plate and disc.

Installation

1) Assemble disc and pressure plate to flywheel using appropriate aligning tool. Finger tighten mounting bolts initially, then tighten bolts in a triangular pattern, one turn at a time to a final torque of 14 ft. lbs. (19 N.m).

2) Using a feeler gauge and tool (#SST 09301-00013), measure gap between spring tips and tool. If gap is larger than .02 in (.5 mm), use tool (#SST 09301-00012) to bend springs until alignment is correct. *See Fig. 2.*

Fig. 2: Diaphragm Spring Tip Alignment Check

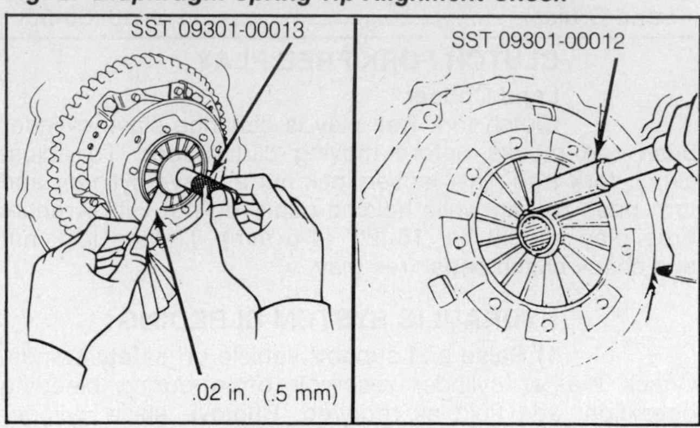
SST 09301-00013
SST 09301-00012
.02 in. (.5 mm)

3) Apply molybdenum disulphide grease to the following contact points: release fork and hub, hub and lever, hub and oil seal, and hub and bushing. Also apply grease to inside of bearing and inside of clutch disc splines. Reverse removal procedure to complete installation.

CLUTCH CABLE

Removal & Installation

1) Disconnect clutch pedal sector tension spring (vertical) from pedal side. Disconnect clutch release cable end from release fork lever. Turn the release sector toward the front side and disconnect the clutch release cable end from the release sector.

Fig. 3: Clutch Cable, Pedal and Release Sector Assembly

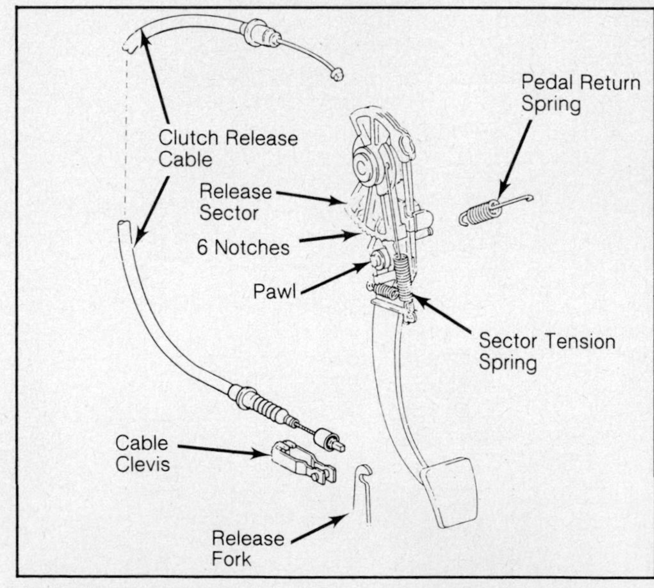
Pedal Return Spring
Clutch Release Cable
Release Sector
6 Notches
Pawl
Sector Tension Spring
Cable Clevis
Release Fork

At least 6 notches must remain on sector.

2) Remove clutch release cable and remove clevis from the release cable. To install, install cable clevis to the clutch release cable. Run the cable through hole in floor. Turn the release sector and connect the inner release cable end to the groove of the release sector.

TOYOTA STARLET & TERCEL (Cont.)

3) Connect cable end to release fork lever. Connect pedal tension spring. Check pedal free play. Check clutch release sector and pawl position. There must be at least 6 notches remaining on the release sector. If there are less, replace clutch disc. *See Fig. 3.*

CLUTCH RELEASE BEARING

Removal

With transmission removed, check release bearing for freedom of rotation with bearing still installed on hub. To remove, disconnect retaining clips from bearing collar and slide assembly off transmission input shaft. If bearing does not rotate smoothly, press off collar with driver (#SST 09315-00010).

Installation

Use press and driver to install new bearing on sleeve. Lightly grease inner groove of bearing collar and all contact surfaces and reverse removal procedures.

PILOT BEARING

Removal & Installation

If pilot bearing is worn or damaged, pull from crankshaft with a puller. Coat new bearing with multi-purpose grease and drive into crankshaft with appropriate driver.

ADJUSTMENTS

PEDAL HEIGHT

Measure distance from floor panel to upper surface of clutch pedal. Adjust pedal stopper bolt to give proper pedal height specifications. *See Pedal Height Specifications table and Fig 4.*

PEDAL HEIGHT SPECIFICATIONS

Application	In. (mm)
Starlet	6.9-7.3 (174.5-184.5)
Tercel	7.4-7.8 (187-197)

Fig. 4: Pedal Height and Free Play Measurement Points

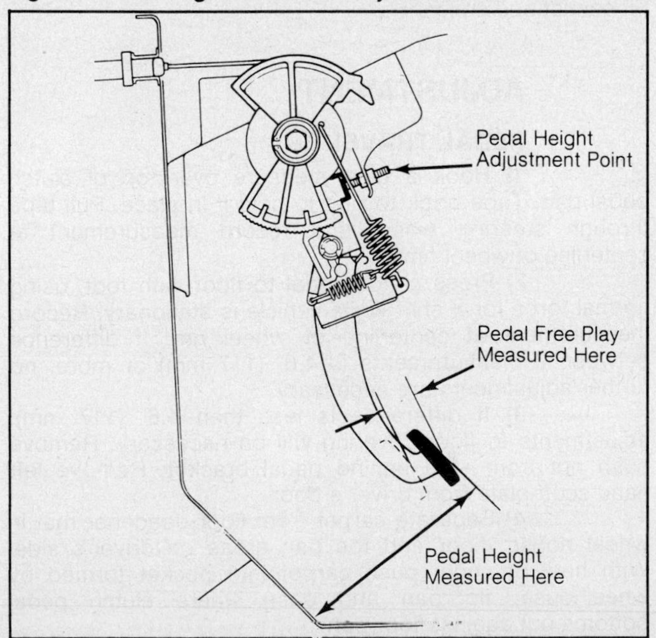
Pedal Height
Adjustment Point
Pedal Free Play
Measured Here
Pedal Height
Measured Here

CLUTCH PEDAL FREE PLAY

With release bearing contacting pressure plate, check pedal play and adjust as necessary. To adjust, pull slightly on release cable and turn adjusting nut. Ensure that adjusting nut protrusion and cable holder inner notch are aligned, then depress pedal several times and recheck pedal play. *See Pedal Free Play table and Fig 4.*

PEDAL FREE PLAY

Application	In. (mm)
Starlet	.08-1.38 (2-35)
Tercel	.08-1.10 (2.0-28.0)

VOLKSWAGEN JETTA, PICKUP, RABBIT & SCIROCCO

DESCRIPTION

Clutch is a single plate dry disc type, using a diaphragm type pressure plate and a transmission mounted clutch release bearing. Clutch is cable operated.

REMOVAL & INSTALLATION

TRANSAXLE & CLUTCH ASSEMBLY

Removal

1) Disconnect battery ground. Attach an engine support assembly. Remove left transaxle mount bolts and mount. Disconnect back-up light wires, speedometer drive cable (plug hole) and clutch cable.

Fig. 1: Clutch Cable Routing and Adjusting Location

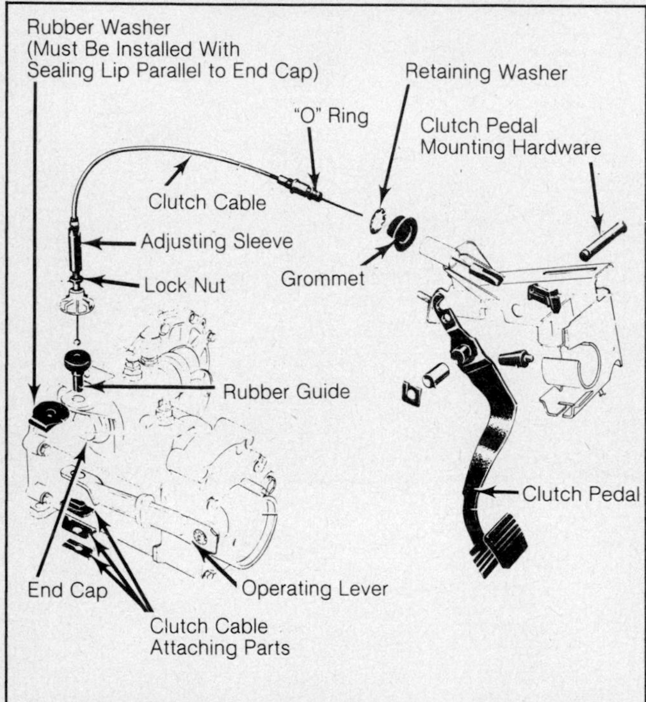
Rubber Washer
(Must Be Installed With
Sealing Lip Parallel to End Cap)
Retaining Washer
"O" Ring
Clutch Pedal
Mounting Hardware
Clutch Cable
Adjusting Sleeve
Lock Nut
Grommet
Rubber Guide
Clutch Pedal
End Cap
Operating Lever
Clutch Cable
Attaching Parts

2) Remove upper clutch housing-to-transaxle bolts. Remove starter. On models equipped with flywheel which has cutouts, align flywheel lug with boss on bell housing. On all models, disconnect shift linkage at rod lever and relay lever and remove front selector rod.

NOTE: **Vehicles with cutouts in flywheel can be identified by a stud/nut at right engine-to-transaxle mounting position. Flywheel on this type vehicle MUST be aligned before separating engine/transaxle.**

3) Remove exhaust pipe bracket. Remove transaxle rear mount and support transaxle on jack. Disconnect left and right drive shafts at transaxle and wire up out of way. Remove large plate cover bolts (plate remains on engine). Remove small cover bolts and cover.

4) Remove the right engine-to-transaxle bolt (stud/nut). On vehicles with cutouts in flywheel, pull transaxle away from engine to clear dowels and lower and remove transaxle. On all other vehicles, pull transaxle away from engine, while cocking engine so right side drive flange clears flywheel. Lower and remove transaxle.

5) With transaxle removed from engine, install holding tool (VW558) to ring gear or pressure plate. Remove bolts in a diagonal manner until flywheel can be removed. Pry retaining ring from release plate and lift release plate from pressure plate. Remove pressure plate bolts in a diagonal manner and separate clutch disc.

Installation

To install, coat pressure plate bolts with Loctite 270 or 271 (or equivalent) and reverse removal procedure. Retaining ring ends must be between 2 slots in release plate. Use centering tool (VW547) to center clutch disc on flywheel.

NOTE: **If new flywheel is to be installed, a new timing mark must be cut into flywheel 1/4" (6 mm) to right of TDC mark.**

CLUTCH RELEASE BEARING & OPERATING LEVER ASSEMBLY

Removal

1) Remove 4 bolts and washers mounting clutch release cover to the far left end of transaxle case. Cover is waffle patterned. Remove 2 circlips located at each side of clutch lever.

2) Pull operating lever and release shaft assembly out of case. Lift return spring along with clutch lever out of transaxle case. Take out release bearing, guide sleeve and push rod. Check all seals and bearing. Replace defective parts.

Installation

1) Coat ends of push rod with multi-purpose grease and insert back into position. Grease sliding surface of bearing and guide sleeve.

2) Position return spring and clutch lever inside transaxle case. Return spring center hook should fit on top of clutch lever lug. Spring end hooks must point down to hold clutch lever away from release bearing.

3) Lightly coat release shaft with multi-purpose grease. Fit shaft. Work operating lever until splines on release shaft mesh with those in clutch lever.

4) Install circlips. Make sure when operating lever is in normal position that return spring has tension. Fit gasket and cover.

ADJUSTMENT

PEDAL TRAVEL

1) Hook a tape measure over top of clutch pedal pad. Tape hook to pad to hold it in place. Pull tape through steering wheel and record measurement at centerline of wheel rim.

2) Press clutch pedal to floor with foot, using normal force for a shift while vehicle is stationary. Record measurement at centerline of wheel rim. If difference between 2 measurements is 4.6" (117 mm) or more, no further adjustments are necessary.

3) If difference is less than 4.6" (117 mm), adjustments to floor covering will be necessary. Remove push nut from stud behind pedal bracket. Remove left hand scuff plate from driver's door.

4) Separate carpet from floor deadener mat in wheel house, floor and toe pan areas on driver's side. With heel of shoe, push carpet into pocket formed by wheelhouse, floorpan and dash where clutch pedal bottoms out against floor pan.

VOLKSWAGEN JETTA, PICKUP, RABBIT & SCIROCCO (Cont.)

5) Lay carpet back into position and measure to see if required amount of travel has been obtained. If so, finish by tucking carpet under hinge pillar and scuff plate.

6) If clutch pedal travel is still short of 4.6" (117 mm), pull back carpet again and cut away portion of floor deadener that is between floorpan and area where pedal bottoms out. Reinstall carpet by pressing into pocket and reinstall trim pieces.

CLUTCH PEDAL FREE PLAY

1) Clutch pedal free play should be 27/32"-1" (21-25 mm) at clutch pedal. Loosen lock nut. Depress pedal at least 5 times. Insert adjusting gauge (US 5043) and adjust sleeve until zero free play is obtained.

2) Tighten lock nut. Remove adjusting gauge. Depress clutch pedal several times. Check free play at pedal.

TIGHTENING SPECIFICATIONS

Application	Ft. Lbs. (N.m)
Cover Plate	11 (15)
Drive Shaft-to-Transmission	32 (44)
Flywheel Bolts	14 (19)
Pressure Plate Bolts	54 (73)
Transmission-to-Engine	47 (64)

VOLKSWAGEN QUANTUM

DESCRIPTION

Clutch is single plate dry disc type, using a diaphragm type pressure plate and a prelubricated clutch release bearing. Clutch is cable actuated.

Fig. 1: Exploded View of Clutch Assembly

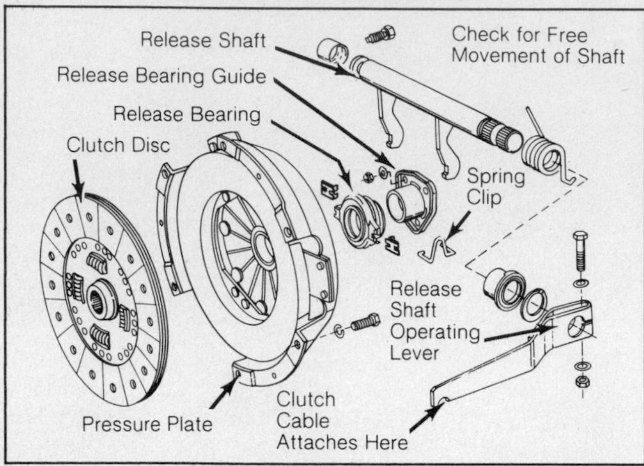
Release Shaft
Check for Free Movement of Shaft
Release Bearing Guide
Release Bearing
Clutch Disc
Spring Clip
Release Shaft Operating Lever
Clutch Cable Attaches Here
Pressure Plate

REMOVAL & INSTALLATION

TRANSAXLE & CLUTCH ASSEMBLIES

Removal

1) Disconnect battery ground. Remove upper engine-to-transaxle bolts. Detach speedometer cable. Unhook clutch cable. Disconnect exhaust pipe at manifold. Remove engine support bolts. Remove front muffler and exhaust pipe.

2) Remove drive shafts at transaxle. Disconnect back-up light wiring. Remove cover plate bolts. Remove starter bolt. Remove shift rod couping bolt. Pry off shift rod couping ball. Pull off shift rod coupling from shift rod.

3) Position transmission lift under transmission and lift up slightly. Loosen bolt "A" and remove bolt "B" from rear transaxle mount. Remove rubber mount. *See Fig. 2.* Remove 3 front transaxle support bolts. Remove lower engine-to-transaxle bolts.

Fig. 2: Transmission Support Assembly

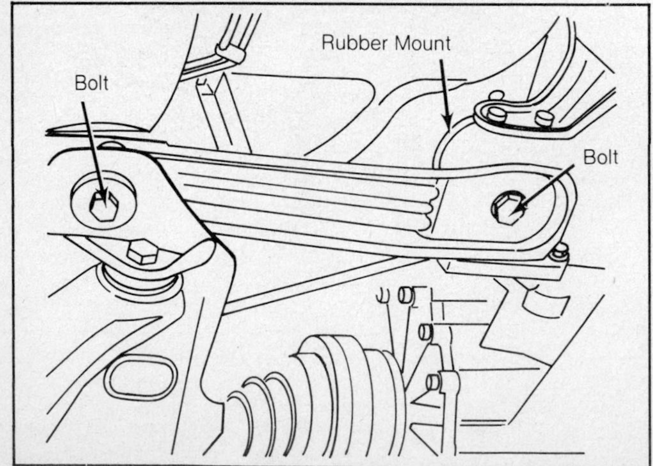
Rubber Mount
Bolt
Bolt

Pivot support to the rear.

4) Pry transmission away from engine. Remove transaxle by lowering transmission support 2071 or US 618 with US 618/1. Lock flywheel to prevent rotation and index mark pressure plate and flywheel. Loosen pressure plate bolts 1/4 turn at a time, working in a diagonal pattern. Slide pressure plate off dowels on flywheel.

Installation

1) Using a clutch alignment tool, fit pressure plate with clutch. Make sure alignment marks are observed. Loosely attach assembly with 6 bolts.

2) Tighten pressure plate bolts in criss-cross pattern about 2 turns at a time. Position transaxle to engine. Make sure mainshaft splines are clean and lubricated lightly with molybdenum disulphide grease.

3) Reverse removal procedure to install remaining components. Make sure all engine-to-transaxle mounts are aligned and free of tension before tightening bolts and nuts.

CLUTCH RELEASE BEARING

Removal

With transaxle removed, remove retaining clips and springs from release bearing. Slide bearing off bearing guide.

Installation

To install, lubricate metal guide sleeve with molybdenum disulphide paste. Coat pivoting points between bearing and operating shaft with multi-purpose grease. Position bearing to shaft and install retaining clips and springs.

NOTE: Bearing is pre-lubricated. DO NOT wash in solvent.

CLUTCH CABLE

Removal

Loosen cable adjusting nuts and free clutch cable housing from support bracket. Separate cable from clutch operating lever (mounted on side of clutch housing). Disconnect cable at pedal and force cable and housing into passenger compartment and remove.

Installation

To install new cable, reverse removal procedure and adjust pedal free play.

NOTE: If new clutch cable has been installed, make sure to recheck clutch pedal free play after 300 miles.

ADJUSTMENT

CLUTCH PEDAL FREE PLAY

Clutch pedal free play (measured at pedal pad) should be 9/16" (15 mm). Adjust free play at support bracket on transmission case by adjusting cable housing length with lock nuts on cable housing.

TIGHTENING SPECIFICATIONS

Application	Ft. Lbs. (N.m)
Clutch Assembly-to-Flywheel	18 (24)
Clutch Lever-to-Transmission	18 (24)
Drive Shaft-to-Transmission	33 (45)
Transmission-to-Engine	40 (54)

VOLKSWAGEN VANAGON

DESCRIPTION

Clutch is single disc, dry diaphragm spring type which is hydraulically operated by a firewall mounted master cylinder and a clutch housing mounted slave cylinder. Slave cylinder is nonadjustable and clearance is automatically compensated for by internal design of cylinder.

Transmission model identification code is located on left rear side of transmission case. First 3 numbers of code indicate transmission model.

TRANSMISSION IDENTIFICATION

Application	Model
2.0L (Gas) 4-Speed	091
1.6L (Diesel)	
4-Speed	091
5-Speed	094
1.9L (Gas) 4-Speed	091/1

REMOVAL & INSTALLATION

CLUTCH ASSEMBLY

Removal

1) Disconnect battery ground cable. Remove upper engine-to-transmission bolts. Remove clutch line bracket from transmission. Remove clutch slave cylinder from mounting bracket and hang on a wire (DO NOT disconnect line).

2) On transmission models 091/1 and 094, remove bracket for accelerator cable. Remove 6 hex bolts from both drive shafts, separate drive shafts from transmission and suspend both from wires. Disconnect back-up lights wires.

3) Disconnect starter wires and remove starter. Using an engine support (VW 785/1), remove rubber plugs from wheel housing to hook in support chain.

4) Remove shift linkage and shift rod support from transmission. Disconnect ground strap from body. Remove front transmission mount from body. Remove lower transmission bolts.

5) Support transmission using transmission jack (US 618 and 618/5). Pull transmission off of guide pins. Lower front of transmission by loosening engine support (loosen spindle on VW 785/1) until there is enough room to remove transmission.

6) Lock flywheel with flywheel lock (VW 215C). Mark pressure plate and flywheel for reassembly reference. Loosen pressure plate-to-flywheel bolts evenly in a diagonal fashion and remove clutch assembly.

Installation

1) Apply molybdenum disulphide grease to release bearing. Lubricate transmission input shaft with molybdenum disulphide powder. Position clutch disc against flywheel and align using a centering tool.

2) Install pressure plate and tighten bolts evenly in a diagonal fashion. Replace transmission by reversing removal procedure. Insert rear bolt for slave cylinder before installing. Position air deflector plates correctly.

NOTE: **Never drain coolant while engine is hot. Doing so could cause engine block or cylinder head to warp.**

CLUTCH RELEASE BEARING

Removal

Remove transmission as outlined in Clutch Assembly in this article. Pry off clip retainers from bearing and disengage spring clips. Remove release bearing by sliding off guide tube.

NOTE: **Do not wash bearing in solvent or cleaning solution. Wipe with dry cloth to clean.**

Installation

Lubricate release shaft and release bearing pivot points with molybdenum disulphide grease. Position bearing on shaft and install spring clips and retainers. Make sure clips are correctly positioned.

Fig. 1: Clutch Release Bearing Assembly

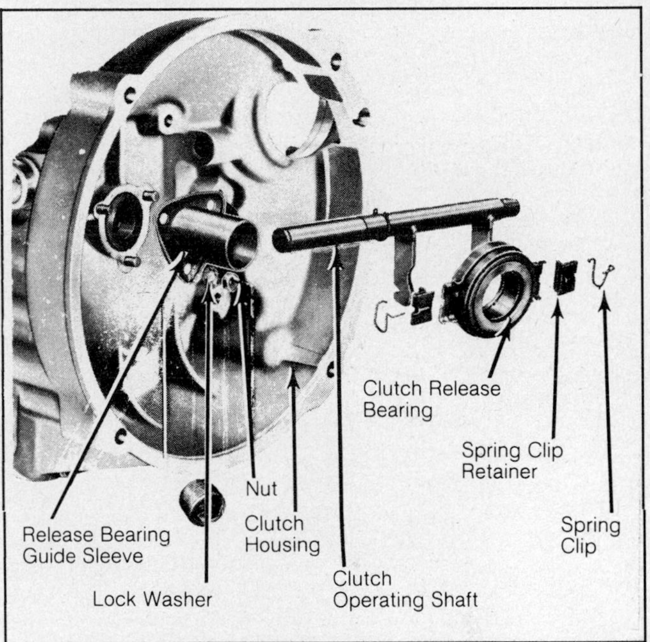
Clutch Release Bearing
Spring Clip Retainer
Nut
Clutch Housing
Spring Clip
Release Bearing Guide Sleeve
Clutch Operating Shaft
Lock Washer

CLUTCH MASTER CYLINDER

Removal

Disconnect master cylinder push rod at clutch pedal by removing cotter pin and clevis. Disconnect hydraulic line at cylinder. Remove cylinder attaching bolts and remove cylinder from firewall.

Installation

To install, reverse removal procedure and pressure bleed system following manufacturer's bleeding instructions.

CLUTCH SLAVE CYLINDER

Removal

Disconnect hydraulic line from slave cylinder. To disconnect slave cylinder, push rod from clutch lever ball. Remove mounting bolts and remove cylinder.

Installation

Grease clutch lever ball lightly. Insert rear bolt to slave cylinder and install on vehicle. Install front bolt, attach hydraulic line and clutch lever. Pressure bleed system following manufacturer's bleeder instructions.

Clutches

VOLKSWAGEN VANAGON (Cont.)

TIGHTENING SPECIFICATIONS

Application	Ft. Lbs. (N.m)
Engine-to-Transmission Nuts & Bolts	
Gasoline Models	22 (30)
Diesel Models	
10 mm Bolts	33 (45)
12 mm Bolts	58 (80)
Drive Shaft-to-Transmission	
Bolts (Gasoline Models)	33 (45)
Pressure Plate-to-Flywheel Bolts	18 (24)

VOLVO

DESCRIPTION

Clutch is single dry disc type, using a diaphragm spring type pressure plate. All DL, GL and Turbo models use a 8.5" (216 mm) clutch disc. The 760 GLE models use a 9.5" (241 mm) pressure plate and a 9" (229 mm) clutch disc.

REMOVAL & INSTALLATION

CLUTCH ASSEMBLY

Removal

1) Disconnect battery ground cable and back-up light wiring harness connector. Working from under vehicle, disconnect gearshift lever from gearshift rod. Remove lock screw and pin, and hold lever to avoid exerting force on transmission. On hydraulic clutch systems, unbolt slave cylinder from housing and disconnect from release arm. On mechanical clutch systems, unhook clutch fork spring and separate cable from housing.

2) Separate shift boot from carpet. Remove reverse gear detent plate. Remove snap ring with snap ring pliers, and lift out gearshift lever. Remove front exhaust pipe bracket and position a support under engine.

3) Remove crossmember at rear of transmission. Index mark propeller shaft and disconnect from transmission. Disconnect speedometer cable from transmission. Remove starter motor bolts, and free starter from clutch housing. Remove clutch housing cover plates and all bolts except two at bottom.

4) Install transmission jack and remove last two clutch housing bolts. Pull transmission to rear, and turn to clear propeller shaft tunnel. Lower transmission from vehicle. Loosen pressure plate bolts gradually in a diagonal pattern and remove clutch assembly. Check pilot bearing and flywheel surface for any cracks or excess wear.

Installation

Reverse removal procedure, making sure that flywheel and pressure plate are free from grease. Using alignment tool, install clutch disc with long side of hub facing back. Install pressure plate, and tighten bolts gradually in a diagonal pattern. Adjust clutch fork free travel.

NOTE: **Since differences in pressure plates and bearings exist between models, components must never be interchanged.**

CLUTCH CABLE

Removal

1) Raise vehicle, disconnect return spring and loosen cable. Disconnect cable from fork, bellhousing and clamp at fuel filter.

NOTE: **There is no return spring on Turbo models.**

2) Remove underdash panel. Remove locking pin and rubber bushing. Pull cable out of firewall.

Installation

Reverse removal procedure. Adjust clutch fork free play to specifications.

Fig. 1: Volvo Mechanical Linkage Clutch System

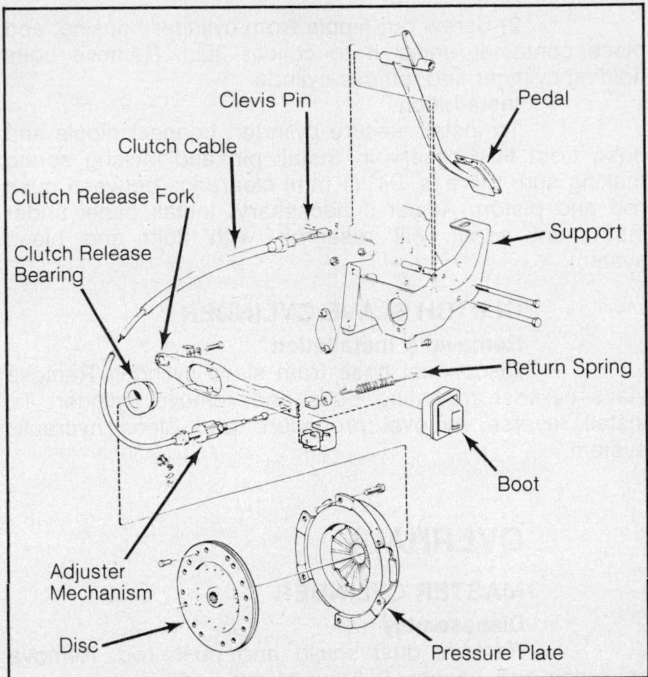
Clevis Pin
Pedal
Clutch Cable
Clutch Release Fork
Support
Clutch Release Bearing
Return Spring
Boot
Adjuster Mechanism
Disc
Pressure Plate

CLUTCH MASTER CYLINDER

Removal

1) Remove panel under instrument panel. Remove pin and locking spring from clutch pedal. Disconnect hose from clutch fluid reservoir.

Fig. 2: Volvo Hydraulic Clutch System

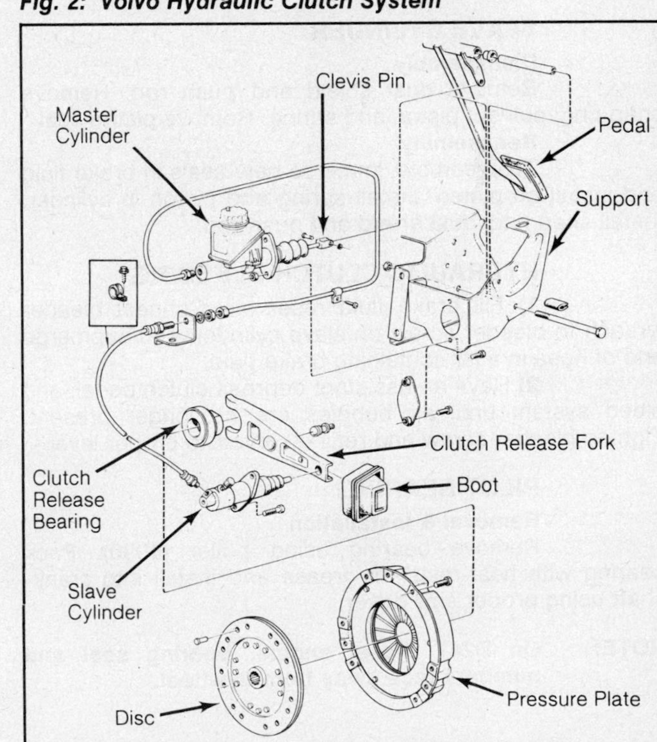
Clevis Pin
Master Cylinder
Pedal
Support
Clutch Release Fork
Boot
Clutch Release Bearing
Slave Cylinder
Pressure Plate
Disc

VOLVO (Cont.)

NOTE: Clutch fluid may damage vehicle paint.

2) Screw out nipple from cylinder housing, and place container under it to collect fluid. Remove bolts holding cylinder and remove cylinder.

Installation

To install, secure cylinder, connect nipple and hose from fluid reservoir. Install pin and locking spring making sure there is .04" (1 mm) clearance between push rod and piston. Adjust if necessary. Install panel under instrument panel. Fill reservoir with fluid and bleed system.

CLUTCH SLAVE CYLINDER

Removal & Installation

Disconnect hose from slave cylinder. Remove slave cylinder mounting bolts and remove cylinder. To install reverse removal procedure and bleed hydraulic system.

OVERHAUL

MASTER CYLINDER

Disassembly

Remove dust shield and push rod. Remove snap ring and washer. Pull out piston and remove spring. Remove seals from piston and thoroughly clean and inspect.

Reassembly

To assemble, immerse new piston seals in brake fluid, and install on piston. Install spring and piston in cylinder. Install washer and snap ring. Install dust shield and push rod.

SLAVE CYLINDER

Disassembly

Remove dust shield and push rod. Remove snap ring, pull out piston and spring. Remove piston seal.

Reassembly

To assemble, immerse new seals in brake fluid and install on piston. Install spring and piston in cylinder. Install snap ring, dust shield and push rod.

HYDRAULIC CLUTCH BLEEDING

1) Fill brake fluid reservoir. Connect bleeder wrench to bleeder screw on slave cylinder, and submerge end of hose in a jar containing brake fluid.

2) Have an assistant depress clutch pedal, and bleed system until air bubbles are no longer present. Tighten bleeder screw and refill reservoir to proper level.

PILOT BEARING

Removal & Installation

Remove bearing using puller (4090). Pack bearing with heat-resistant grease and install into crankshaft using proper size driver.

NOTE: On D24T diesel engine, bearing seal and numbers face away from flywheel.

ADJUSTMENT

CLUTCH FREE PLAY

Using adjustment mechanism attached to clutch housing, set free play. Adjustment is correct when approximately .04-.12" (1-3 mm) clutch fork free play is obtained. Hydraulic systems are not adjustable.

Fig. 3: Adjusting Clutch Free Play

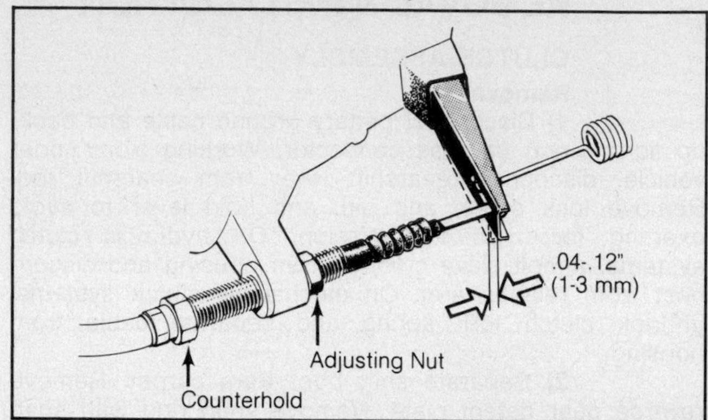
.04-.12"
(1-3 mm)
Adjusting Nut
Counterhold

SECTION 8

DRIVE AXLES

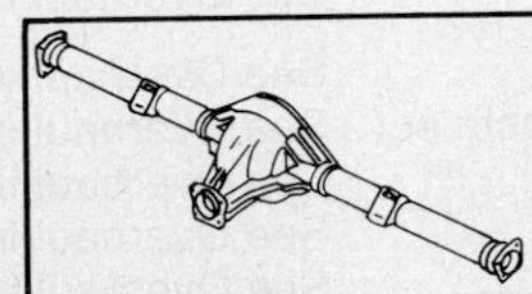

CONTENTS

TROUBLE SHOOTING

GEAR TOOTH PATTERNS

FWD AXLE SHAFTS & CV JOINTS

DRIVE AXLES

LOCKING HUBS

NOTE: ALSO SEE GENERAL INDEX.

Drive Axles

TROUBLE SHOOTING

CONDITION	POSSIBLE CAUSE	CORRECTION
General Knocking or Clunking	Excessive differential side gear clearance	See Overhaul in DRIVE AXLES
	Worn rear axle pinion shaft	See Overhaul in DRIVE AXLES
	Worn case or differential cross shaft in case	See Overhaul in DRIVE AXLES
	Excessive end play of axle shafts-to-differential cross shaft	See Overhaul in DRIVE AXLES
	Gear teeth mutilitated	See Overhaul in DRIVE AXLES
	Improper axle shaft spline fit	See Overhaul in DRIVE AXLES
	Total axle backlash too great	See Overhaul in DRIVE AXLES
	Incorrect driveline angle	See Adjustment in PROPELLER SHAFT ALIGNMENT
Clunking During Initial Engagement	Excessive differential side gear clearance	See Overhaul in DRIVE AXLES
	Excessive ring and pinion backlash	See Overhaul in DRIVE AXLES
	Worn or loose pinion shaft	See Overhaul in DRIVE AXLES
	Worn or damaged inboard joint	See Overhaul in DRIVE AXLES
Gear Howl or Whine	Improper pinion depth	See Overhaul in DRIVE AXLES
	Improper ring gear backlash adjustment	See Overhaul in DRIVE AXLES
	Improper ring gear runout	See Overhaul in DRIVE AXLES
	Impropr bearing preload	See Overhaul in DRIVE AXLES
	Excessive pinion bearing wear	See Overhaul in DRIVE AXLES
Clicking or Chatter on Turns	Wrong lubricant in differential	Drain and refill differential
	Clutch plates worn	See Overhaul in POSITIVE TRACTION DIFFERENTIALS
	Worn or damaged outboard joints	See Overhaul in DRIVE AXLES
	Differential side gears or pinion worn	See Overhaul in DRIVE AXLES
Knock or Click Approximately Every Second Revolution	Flat spot on rear wheel bearing	See Overhaul in DRIVE AXLES
Grunt Noise on Stops	Lack of lubricant in propeller shaft slip yoke	See UNIVERSAL JOINTS
Groan in Forward or Reverse	Wrong lubricant in differential	Replace lubricant
Knock in Drive Line in High Gear at 10 MPH	Worn or damaged universal joints	See UNIVERSAL JOINTS
	Side gear hub counterbore in differential worn oversize	See Overhaul in DRIVE AXLES
Ping, Snap or Click in Drive Line	Loose upper or lower control arm bushing bolts	See Replacement in FRONT SUSPENSION
	Loose companion flange	See Overhaul in DRIVE AXLES
Scraping Noise	Slinger, companion flange or end yoke rubbing on rear axle carrier	See Overhaul in DRIVE AXLES
Car Will Not Move	Broken axle shaft	See Overhaul in DRIVE AXLES
	Broken pinion stem	See Overhaul in DRIVE AXLES
	Broken welds	See Overhaul in DRIVE AXLES
	Axle lock up	See Overhaul in DRIVE AXLES
	Broken gear teeth	See Overhaul in DRIVE AXLES
	Broken wheel bearing	See Overhaul in DRIVE AXLES
Axle Backlash	Excessive ring and pinion clearance	See Overhaul in DRIVE AXLES
	Loose fitting differential pinion shaft	See Overhaul in DRIVE AXLES
	Excessive side gear-to-case clearance	See Overhaul in DRIVE AXLES
Leakage at Differential or Driveshaft	Rough outside surface on splined yoke	See Overhaul in DRIVE AXLES
	Drive pinion seal or nut	See Overhaul in DRIVE AXLES
	Axle cover gasket, or axle shaft seal	See Overhaul in DRIVE AXLES
	Bad welds or improper axle vent hose	See Overhaul in DRIVE AXLES
	Case porosity	Apply heat resistant silicone sealer to case

Drive Axles

TROUBLE SHOOTING (Cont.)

CONDITION	POSSIBLE CAUSE	CORRECTION
Roughness, Shudder or Vibration Upon Heavy Acceleration	Double cardan joint ball seats worn, and ball set spring may be broken	See UNIVERSAL JOINTS
	Excessive joint angle	See Propeller Shaft Alignment in DRIVE AXLES
	Sticking inboard joint assembly	See UNIVERSAL JOINTS
	Worn or damaged inboard or outboard joints	See UNIVERSAL JOINTS
Roughness, Vibration or Body Boom Experienced at Any Speed	Rough rear wheel bearings	See Overhaul in DRIVE AXLES
	Unbalanced or damaged propeller shaft	Check and/or balance propeller shaft
	Unbalanced or damaged tires	Check and/or balance tires
	Worn or damaged universal joints	See UNIVERSAL JOINTS
	Bent of damaged drive shaft, or undercoating on drive shaft	Check drive shaft balance
	Tight universal joints	Lubricate or replace as necessary
	Burrs or gouges on companion flange	Resurface or replace flange
	Drive shaft or companion shaft runout too great	Repair or replace as necessary
	Excessive looseness at slip yoke spline	See Overhaul in DRIVE AXLES

GEAR TOOTH PATTERNS

GEAR CONTACT PATTERNS

PRELIMINARY INSPECTION

1) Clean lubricant from internal parts, then rotate gears and inspect for wear or damage. Mount a dial indicator to housing and check backlash at several points around ring gear.

2) Backlash must be within specifications at all points. If no defects are found, check gear tooth pattern.

CHECKING TOOTH PATTERNS

NOTE: Drive pattern should be well centered on ring gear teeth. Coast pattern should be centered but may be slightly toward toe of ring gear teeth. On some models, gear tooth pattern has priority over pinion and backlash specifications

1) Paint ring gear teeth with a marking compound, then wrap a cloth or rope around drive pinion flange to act as a brake. Rotate ring gear until a clear tooth pattern is obtained.

2) Gear tooth contact pattern will disclose whether correct pinion bearing mounting shim has been installed and drive gear backlash set properly.

3) Backlash between drive gear and pinion must be maintained within specified limits until correct tooth pattern is obtained.

GEAR BACKLASH & PINION SHIM CHANGES

NOTE: Change in tooth pattern is directly related to change in shim and backlash.

1) With no change in backlash, moving pinion further from ring gear moves drive pattern toward heel and top of tooth, and moves coast pattern toward toe and top of tooth.

2) With no change in backlash, moving pinion closer to ring gear moves drive pattern toward toe and bottom of tooth, and moves coast pattern toward heel and bottom of tooth.

3) With no change in pinion shim thickness, an increase in backlash moves ring gear further from pinion. Drive pattern moves toward heel and top of tooth, and coast pattern moves toward heel and top of tooth.

4) With no change in pinion shim thickness, a decrease in backlash moves ring gear closer to pinion gear. Drive pattern moves toward toe and bottom of tooth, and coast pattern moves toward toe and bottom of tooth.

Fig. 1: Gear Tooth Contact Pattern

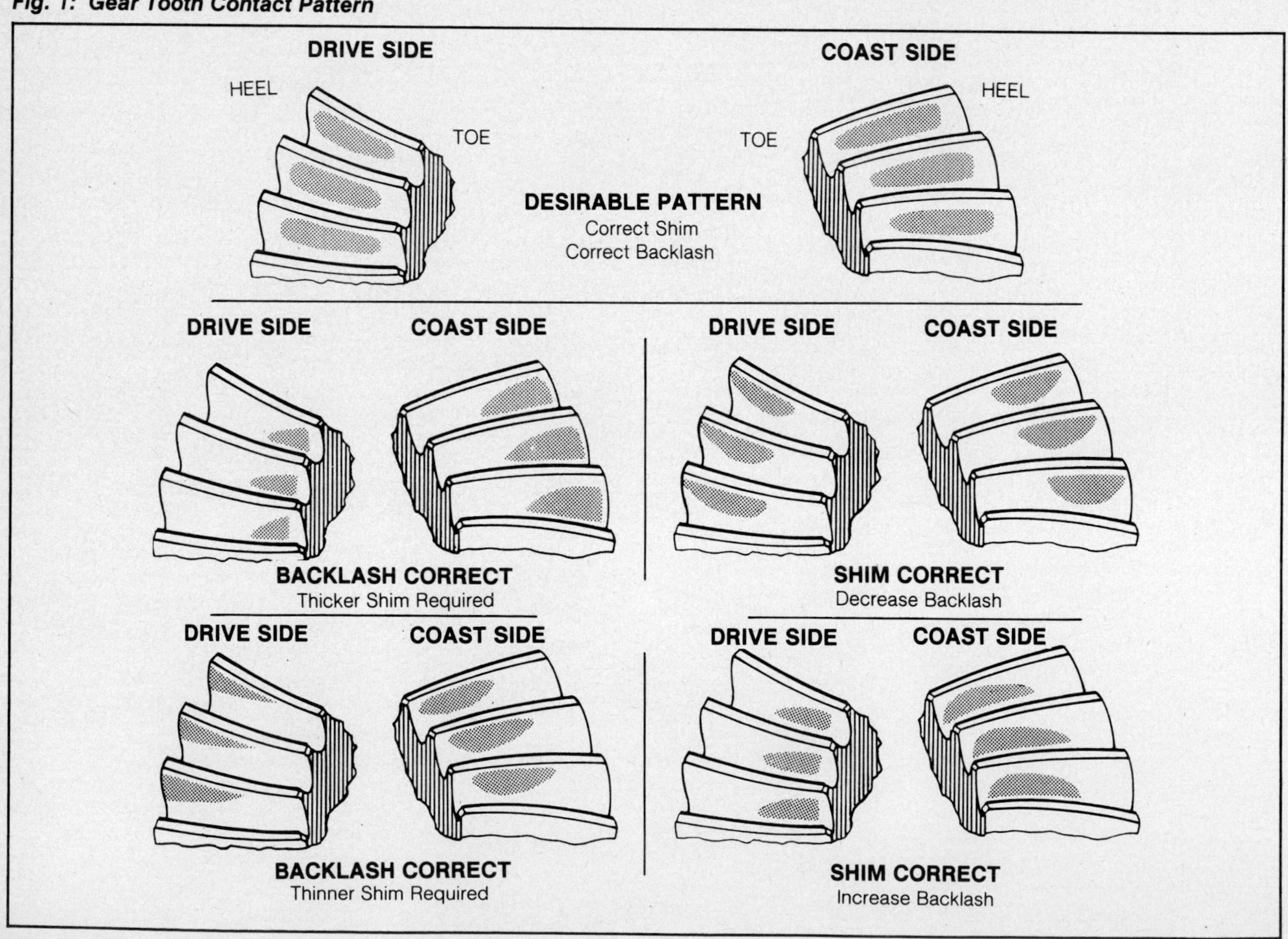
DRIVE SIDE
HEEL
TOE
COAST SIDE
TOE
HEEL
DESIRABLE PATTERN
Correct Shim
Correct Backlash
DRIVE SIDE
COAST SIDE
BACKLASH CORRECT
Thicker Shim Required
DRIVE SIDE
COAST SIDE
SHIM CORRECT
Decrease Backlash
DRIVE SIDE
COAST SIDE
BACKLASH CORRECT
Thinner Shim Required
DRIVE SIDE
COAST SIDE
SHIM CORRECT
Increase Backlash

FWD Axle Shafts & CV Joints

ALL MODELS

Audi, Chrysler Corp. Imports, Datsun/Nissan, Honda, Mazda, Mitsubishi, Renault, Saab, Toyota & Volkswagen Models with Front Wheel Drive

DESCRIPTION

Axle shafts transfer power from the transaxle-to-driving wheels. All axle shafts consist of a shaft and flexible Constant Velocity (CV) joints at each end. The inner CV joint is splined or bolted to the transaxle. The outer CV joint is splined to the wheel bearing hub and secured by a nut.

The CV joints may be either Double Offset or Birfield Joints (DOJ or BJ), or Tripot-Rzeppa Joints (TJ) design type. The DOJ joint type consists of equally spaced balls between an inner and outer race. The TJ joint type consists of a triangle yoke within a housing.

On Audi, Toyota Camry and Volkswagen models the inner CV joint is bolted to differential case drive flanges. On Renault and Subaru models the inner CV joint is splined onto differential output shafts and secured with a pin (except LeCar). On Saab models the inner CV joint housing is pressed into the differential side gear and secured with a snap ring. On all other models the inner CV joint is splined into the differential side gear and held with a spring clip.

TROUBLE SHOOTING

TROUBLE SHOOTING CHART

Condition	Possible Cause
Grease Leaks	CV boot torn or cracked.
Clicking Noise on Cornering	Damaged outer CV.
Clunk Noise on Acceleration	Damaged inner CV.
Vibration or Shudder on Acceleration	Sticking, damaged or worn CV. Misalignment or spring height.

SERVICE (IN-VEHICLE)

REMOVAL

CAUTION: Vehicle weight must not be allowed to rest on wheel bearings and hub, without axle shaft installed and axle shaft nut tightened to specification.

Audi & Volkswagen

1) Remove hub cap. Loosen axle shaft nut. Raise and support vehicle. Remove axle nut and wheel. Disconnect and remove exhaust pipe from exhaust manifold and transaxle as required. Remove Allen bolts connecting inner CV joint to differential case drive flange.

2) On 5000 models with automatic transmission, remove sway bar brackets. On all other models, mark position of both ball joint flanges on the control arms. Remove ball joint from control arm and pull pivot mounting outward while removing axle shaft. Press axle shaft out of hub and guide past transaxle.

NOTE: Axle shafts should be disassembled ONLY to replace defective rubber boots. If boots are replaced, check all components for wear or damage and replace as complete assembly.

Chrysler Corp. Imports, Honda & Mitsubishi

1) Remove front wheel dust cap and loosen lock nut. Raise vehicle and remove tires and undercover panel. Remove lower ball joint and strut from lower control arm. Drain transaxle fluid.

2) On Prelude models, remove spring strut-to-support and support-to-spindle bolts. Separate lower ball joint.

3) On all models, insert pry bar between transaxle case and BJ or TJ type CV joint. Apply pressure to the tool handle and force axle shaft from transaxle.

Fig. 2: View of Axle Shaft Removal

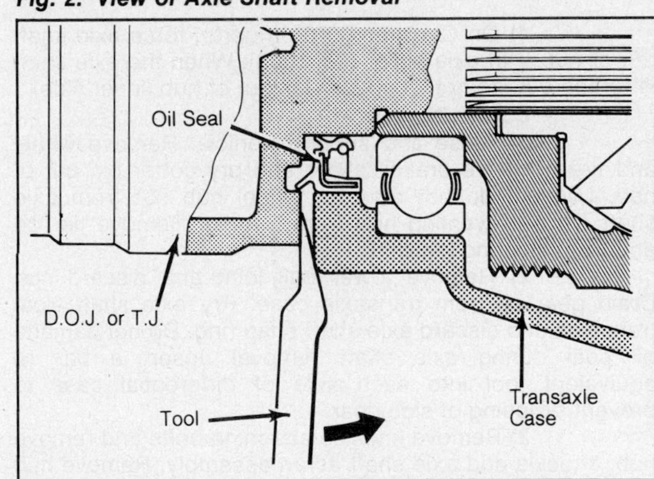
Oil Seal
D.O.J. or T.J.
Transaxle Case
Tool

Fig. 1: Exploded View of Typical Audi & Volkswagen Axle Shaft Assembly

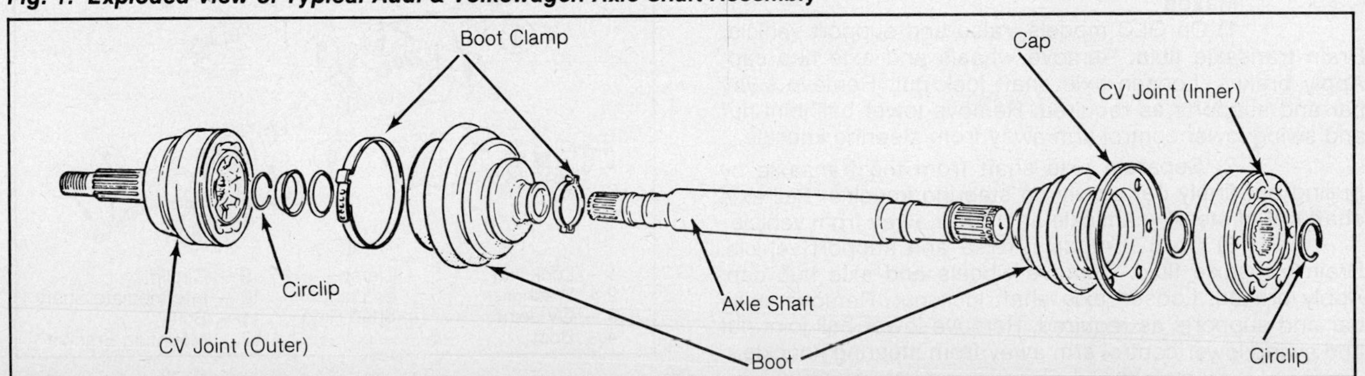
Boot Clamp
Cap
CV Joint (Inner)
Circlip
Axle Shaft
CV Joint (Outer)
Boot
Circlip

FWD Axle Shafts & CV Joints

ALL MODELS (Cont.)

Fig. 3: Exploded View of Datsun/Nissan Axle Shaft Assemblies

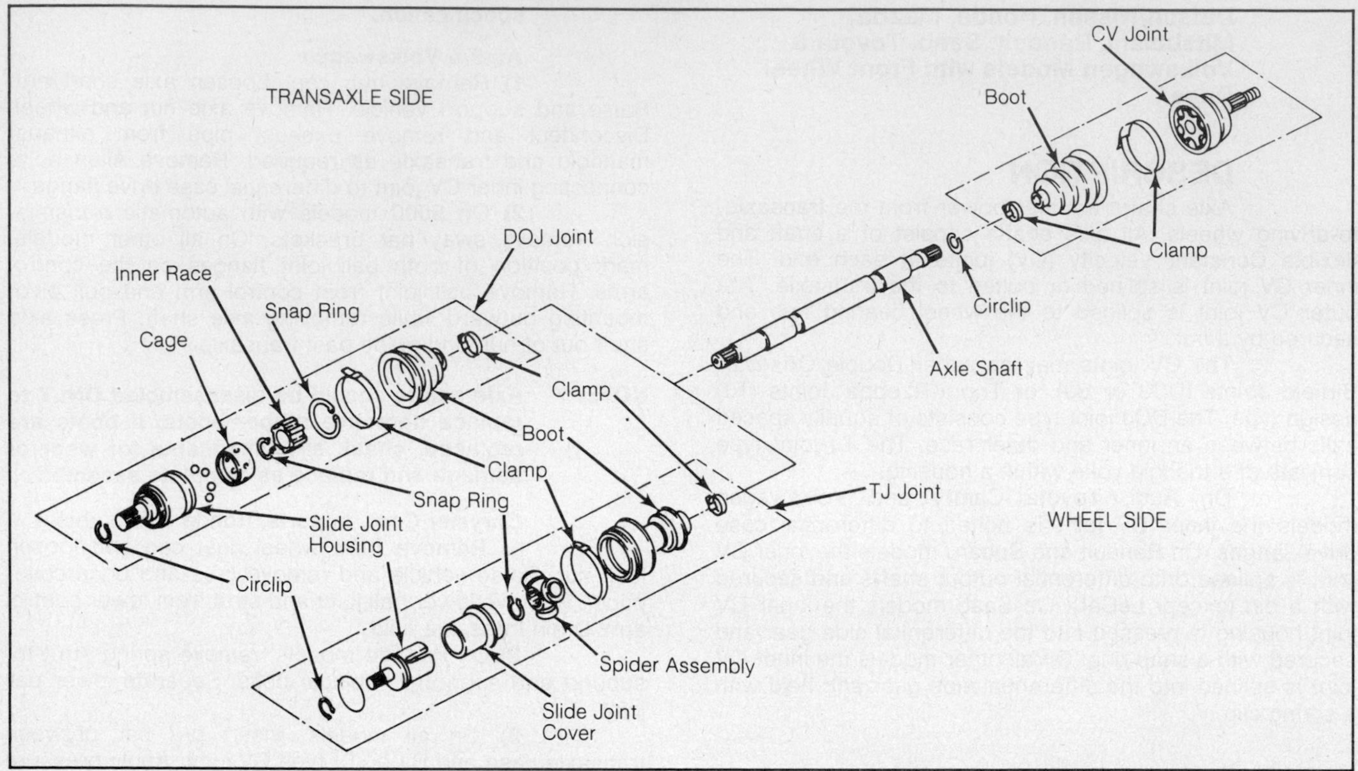

TRANSAXLE SIDE
CV Joint
Boot
Clamp
Circlip
Axle Shaft
DOJ Joint
Inner Race
Snap Ring
Cage
Clamp
Boot
Clamp
Snap Ring
Slide Joint
Housing
Circlip
TJ Joint
WHEEL SIDE
Spider Assembly
Slide Joint
Cover

NOTE: Replace side retainer ring each time the axle shaft is removed from transaxle case.

4) On Chrysler Corp. Imports, force axle shaft out of hub with axle puller (CT-1003). When the axle shaft is forced out, do not let spacer fall out of hub (inner side).

Datsun/Nissan

1) Raise and support vehicle. Remove wheel and tire. Remove brake caliper and pry cotter pin out of hub. Loosen, do not remove, wheel hub nut from axle shaft while preventing hub from turning. Remove tie rod end from steering knuckle.

2) Remove lower ball joint and discard nut. Drain gear oil from transaxle case. Pry axle shaft from transaxle and discard axle shaft snap ring. Do not damage oil seal during axle shaft removal. Insert a bar or equivalent tool into each side of differential case to prevent dropping of side gear.

3) Remove knuckle attaching bolts and remove hub, knuckle and axle shaft as an assembly. Remove hub nut and pull hub off shaft. Using a ball joint remover, separate lower ball joint from knuckle, if necessary.

Mazda

1) On GLC models, raise and support vehicle. Drain transaxle fluid. Remove wheels and axle hub cap. Apply brakes. Loosen axle shaft lock nut. Remove sway bar and supports as required. Remove lower ball joint nut and swing lower control arm away from steering knuckle.

2) Separate axle shaft from the transaxle by pulling out firmly but slowly on steering knuckle. Pull axle shaft out of steering knuckle and lower away from vehicle.

3) On 626 models, raise and support vehicle. Drain transaxle fluid. Remove wheels and axle hub cap. Apply brakes. Loosen axle shaft lock nut. Remove sway bar and supports as required. Remove lower ball joint nut and swing lower control arm away from steering knuckle.

4) On manual transmission models, insert pry bar between left inner CV joint and transmission. Hit pry bar to remove shaft. *See Fig. 5.* On automatic transmission models, insert chisel between left inner CV joint and transmission. Hit chisel to remove shaft. *See Fig. 6.*

Fig. 4: View of Mazda 626 Axle Shafts & Intermediate Shaft

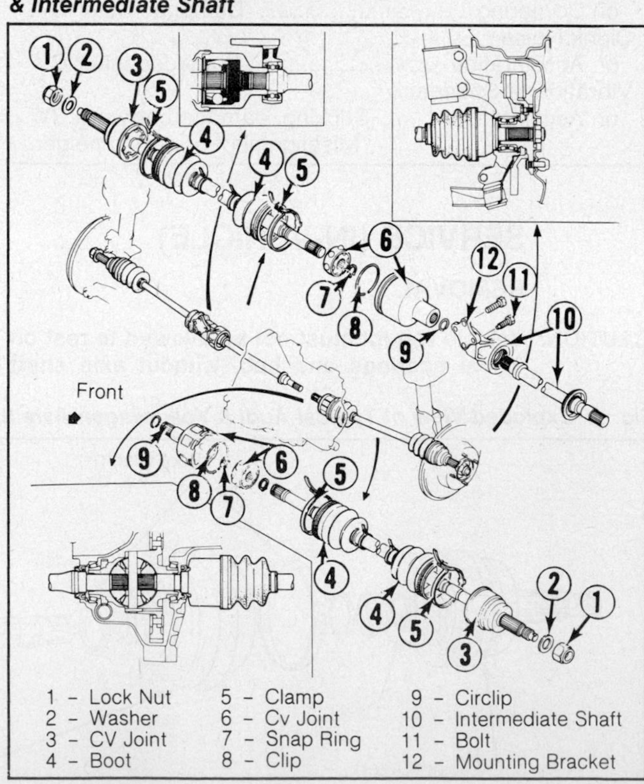

Front
1 - Lock Nut
2 - Washer
3 - CV Joint
4 - Boot
5 - Clamp
6 - Cv Joint
7 - Snap Ring
8 - Clip
9 - Circlip
10 - Intermediate Shaft
11 - Bolt
12 - Mounting Bracket

FWD Axle Shafts & CV Joints

ALL MODELS (Cont.)

Fig. 5: Removing Mazda 626 Axle Shaft With Manual Transmission

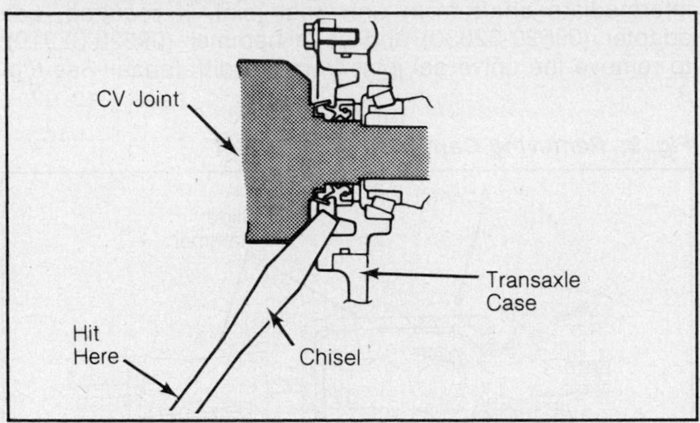
CV Joint
Transaxle
Case
Hit
Here
Chisel

Fig. 6: Removing Mazda 626 Axle Shaft With Automatic Transmission

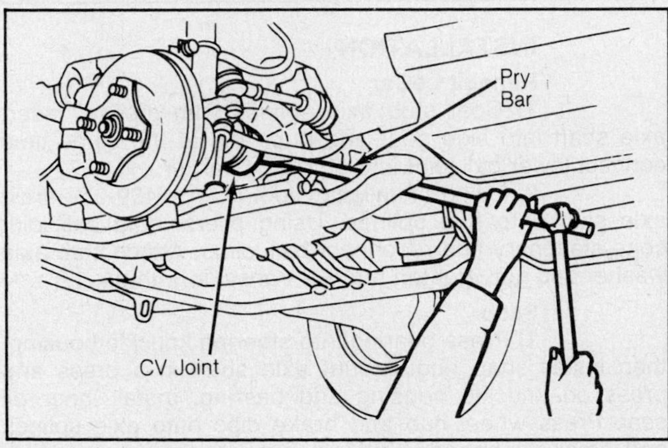
Pry
Bar
CV Joint

5) Use pry bar on right inner CV joint to uncouple axle shaft from intermediate shaft. Pull axle shaft out of wheel hub. If required, unbolt intermediate shaft mounting bracket and remove from vehicle.

Renault

1) On Fuego and 18i models, raise and support vehicle. Compress control arm assembly and insert spacer (T. Av. 509-01) between lower control arm pivot shaft and bottom of shock absorber. Hold hub stationary and remove hub nut. Loosen upper ball joint nut and tie rod end nut, but do not remove.

2) Press on ball joint and tie rod end studs to loosen from steering knuckle. Remove brake caliper, but do not disconnect hydraulic line. Remove ball joint and tie rod end nuts.

3) Tilt steering knuckle outward to allow removal of axle shaft. Separate axle shaft from hub. Drive roll pin out of inner CV joint and separate axle shaft from transaxle.

4) On LeCar models, remove stub axle nut and washer using hub locking tool (Rou. 436-01). Using ball joint extender tool (T. Av. 476), disconnect upper and lower suspension and steering arm ball joints.

5) Mount axle shaft extracting tool (T. Av. 235) on hub. Push out axle shaft far enough for lower ball joint to clear stub axle. Withdraw axle shaft. Repeat on other side.

NOTE: **If components show excessive or abnormal wear, complete axle shaft must be replaced.**

Fig. 7: Cutaway View of Renault Outer CV Joint

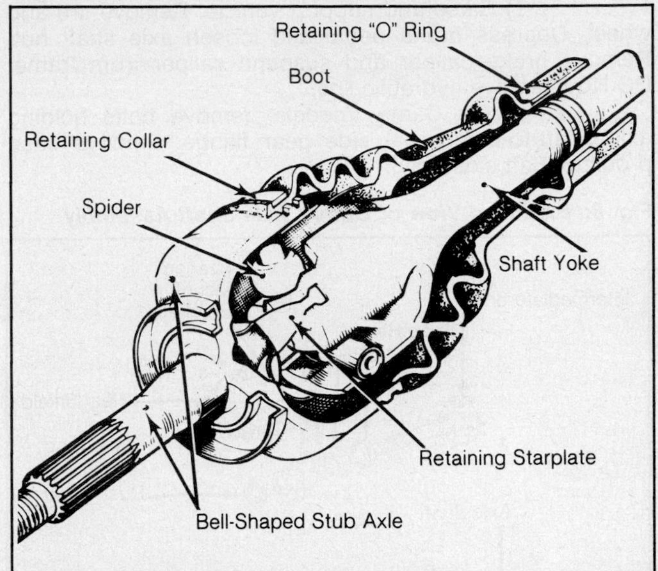
Retaining "O" Ring
Boot
Retaining Collar
Spider
Shaft Yoke
Retaining Starplate
Bell-Shaped Stub Axle

Saab

NOTE: **Downward movement of the control arms is limited by rubber buffer inside of shock absorber. Therefore, it will be necessary either to remove shock absorber before raising vehicle or to support control arm with a jack at outer end of lower control arm.**

1) Remove hub cap, loosen hub nut and loosen wheel lugs. Raise and support vehicle. Remove wheels. Rotate brake disc to align recess in disc edge with brake pads. Disconnect parking brake cable. Remove caliper mounting bolts and hang caliper out of way with wire. DO NOT disconnect hydraulic line.

2) Remove hub and disc assembly with extractor (8996084). Remove larger clamp on inner universal joint bellows. Remove steering arm and upper ball joint with remover (8995409). Disconnect screws on lower control arm bracket. Separate inner CV joint from axle flange. Cover end of rubber bellows to prevent needle bearings from falling onto floor.

3) Grasp wheel splash guard and pull axle assembly through wheel housing to remove. Thoroughly clean axle assembly. Place steering knuckle housing in a press and press out axle shaft. Remove snap ring from bearing housing. Press out and discard bearing.

NOTE: **Axle shafts cannot be disassembled. If damaged or defective, replace as complete assembly.**

Subaru

1) Disconnect negative battery cable. Apply parking brake. Remove front wheel cap and cotter pin, and loosen castle nut and wheel nuts. Raise and support vehicle and remove front tires and wheels. Release parking brake. Remove parking brake cable bracket from transverse link.

2) Drive out spring pin of DOJ. Remove disc brake assembly, disconnect tie-rod, transverse link and dampner strut. Remove axle shaft from differential spindle along with housing. Remove housing from axle shaft by using puller (921121000).

FWD Axle Shafts & CV Joints

ALL MODELS (Cont.)

Toyota

1) Raise and support vehicle. Remove tire and wheel. Depress brake pedal and loosen axle shaft nut. Remove brake caliper and suspend caliper from frame. DO NOT remove hydraulic line.

2) On Camry models, remove bolts holding axle shaft-to-differential side gear flange. Remove case protector (left side only).

Fig. 8: Exploded View of Camry Axle Shaft Assembly

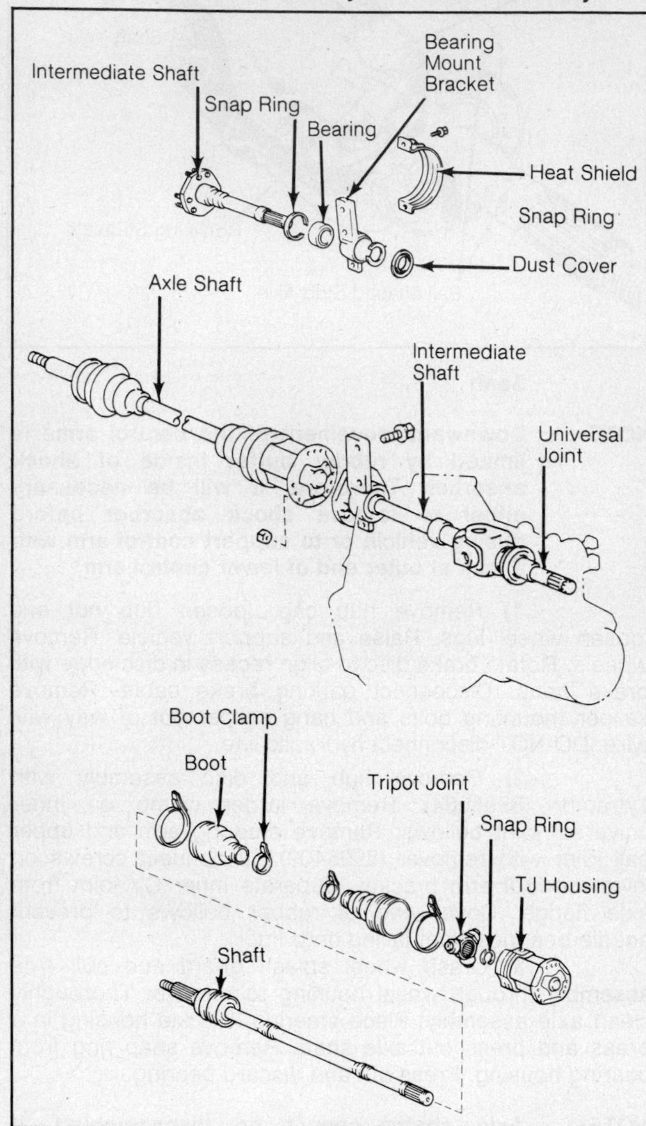
Intermediate Shaft
Snap Ring
Bearing
Bearing Mount Bracket
Heat Shield
Snap Ring
Dust Cover
Axle Shaft
Intermediate Shaft
Universal Joint
Boot Clamp
Boot
Tripot Joint
Snap Ring
TJ Housing
Shaft

3) On Tercel models, disconnect nut holding stabilizer bar end to suspension arm. Put alignment marks on steering knuckle-to-suspension strut for reassembly. Remove upper steering knuckle-to-suspension strut bolts.

4) On all models, remove axle shaft nut. Pull axle shaft out of hub with puller (SST09950-20014).

5) On Tercel models, separate steering knuckle from strut and draw out axle shaft from rear of hub. Remove stiffener plate (left side only). Tap shaft out from differential with remover (SST09648-16010) and hammer. Install stopper (SST09563-16010) in differential case to prevent oil leakage.

NOTE: **Do not damage rubber boots of axle shaft Always carry and store shaft in level position.**

6) On Camry models, remove the intermediate shaft mounting bolts. Remove the bearing bracket. Pull intermediate shaft from universal joint. If required, use adapter (09520-32030) and slide hammer (09520-32010), to remove the universal joint from the differential. *See Fig. 9.*

Fig. 9: Removing Camry Universal Joint

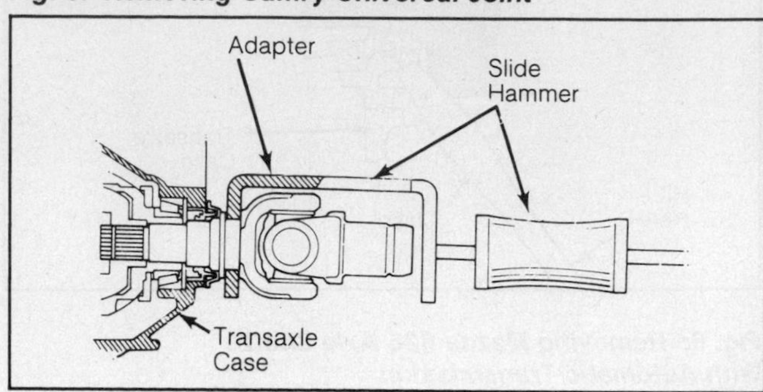
Adapter
Slide Hammer
Transaxle Case

INSTALLATION

Renault LeCar

1) Coat stub axle splines with grease. Insert axle shaft into side gear and hub, and at the same time connect lower ball joint into stub axle carrier.

2) Using installation tool (T. Av. 409-01), draw axle shaft into hub splines. Using pliers, hold ball joint cone stationary and reconnect ball joints. Attach stub axle washer and nut. Tighten nut. Fill transaxle with oil.

Saab

1) Press bearing into steering knuckle housing, then install snap ring. Mount axle shaft in a press and press on knuckle housing and bearing. Install inner oil seal. Press wheel hub and brake disc onto axle splines and install washer and new lock nut.

NOTE: **Do not tighten lock nut at this time.**

2) Install axle shaft through wheel housing. Mount any needle bearings which may have fallen out of inner CV joint on ends of "T" piece. Attach inner CV joint to axle flange. Install upper ball joint to steering knuckle and reinstall lower control arm bracket. Mount tie rod end to steering arm. Mount brake caliper.

3) Reinstall front wheel and lower vehicle. Tighten hub lock nut. Secure in place by peening into locking groove. Pump brake pedal several times to seat brake pads.

All Other Models

1) To install, reverse removal procedure and note the following: Install a new side retainer ring. Check the seals at both ends of the axle shaft and replace prior to installation if necessary. Lubricate the transaxle seal lip with transaxle oil.

NOTE: **Always install new cotter pins, washers and suspension nuts.**

2) Install axle shaft. On all models with snap ring retained axle shafts, try to pull axle shaft out of differential by hand to ensure proper engagement of snap ring. On Renault Fuego and 18i models, apply locking compound to axle shaft roll pins before installing.

3) On Audi Coupe models, apply (D6) locking compound to splines. On all models, install axle shafts into wheel hub. Align suspension marks made at removal and tighten nuts. Check camber setting and adjust if

ALL MODELS (Cont.)

necessary. Stake the axle shaft nut in place with a blunt punch after tightening.

4) Bleed brake system and replace transaxle fluid, if required. On Tercel models, measure the distance between drive shafts at transaxle. Distance should be less than 7.6" (194 mm).

OVERHAUL

AUDI & VOLKSWAGEN

Disassembly

1) On inner CV joint, remove circlip from axle shaft and drive protective cap from CV joint. Place axle shaft in holder (VW402) and press CV joint from shaft with adapter (VW408a), supporting hub to prevent damage. Pivot hub and cage assembly out of inner joint. Push out and remove balls. Align ball hub grooves with cage and remove hub.

NOTE: Inner CV joint and ball hub are matched sets. DO NOT interchange with outer joint. Also, balls of CV joints cannot be interchanged between CV joints.

Fig. 10: Removing Audi & Volkswagen Inner CV Joint Ball Hub

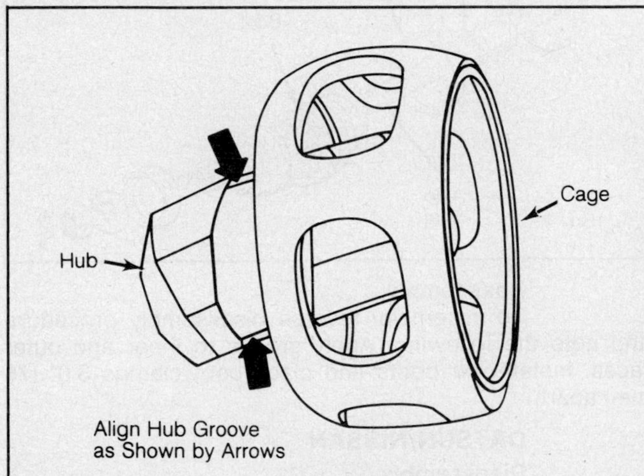
Cage
Hub
Align Hub Groove
as Shown by Arrows

2) Remove and discard inner boot clamp and boot. On outer CV joint, spread circlip inside ball hub and drive CV joint off axle shaft with brass drift by tapping on hub. Mark position of ball hub and outer joint. Tilt cage and remove each ball.

3) Align cage perpendicular to joint. Align 2 large openings of cage with raised portions of joint and remove cage and hub. Position 1 retainer of hub in large opening and remove hub by tilting outward. Remove and discard outer boot and clamp.

Reassembly

1) To reassemble CV joints, reverse disassembly procedure and note the following: Lubricate joints with 3 ozs. of molybdenum disulphide grease. After inserting balls into inner CV joint hub and cage, insert hub and cage into joint perpendicularly.

2) Chamfer of ball hub splines must face larger diameter of joint. Rotate ball and cage into position and ensure CV joint wide ball groove and narrow hub groove are on same side of joint. *See Fig. 11.* Joint is correctly assembled if hub can move over shaft splines by hand.

Fig. 11: Installing Audi & Volkswagen Ball Hub and Cage in Inner CV Joint

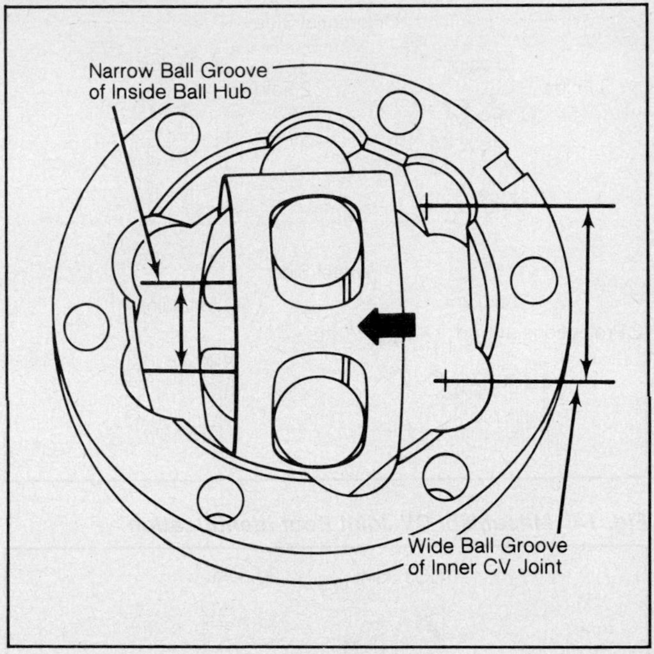
Narrow Ball Groove
of Inside Ball Hub
Wide Ball Groove
of Inner CV Joint

3) Outer CV joint alignment marks must match after reassembly. Replace dust boots and clamps. Install CV joints onto axle shaft with inside ball hub chamfer facing shaft.

4) Outer CV joint must be assembled with dished washer concave side facing thrust washer and convex side of thrust washer facing CV joint. *See Fig. 12.*

5) Inner CV joint must be assembled with dished washer concave side facing CV joint when installed on shaft. Install boot clamps with open end facing opposite direction of normal rotation. Always use new circlips to retain CV joints on shafts.

Fig. 12: Cutaway View of Audi & Volkswagen Outer CV Joint Showing Installation of Dished and Thrust Washers

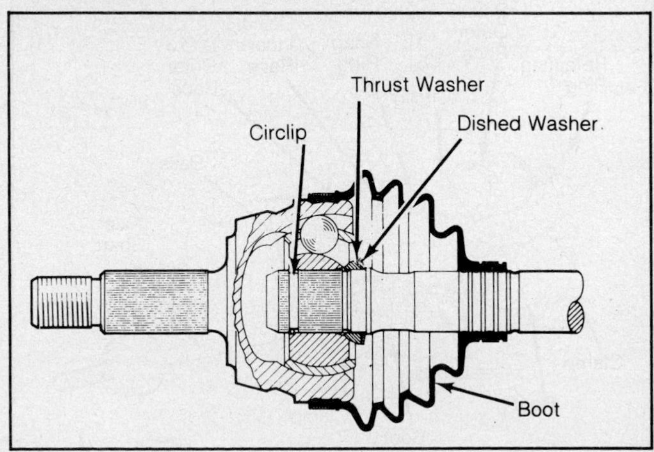
Thrust Washer
Circlip
Dished Washer
Boot

CHRYSLER CORP. IMPORTS & MITSUBISHI

NOTE: See accompanying CV Joint Boot Identification illustrations to identify CV joint and boot application.

ALL MODELS (Cont.)

Fig. 13: Chrysler Corp. Imports CV Joint Boot Identification

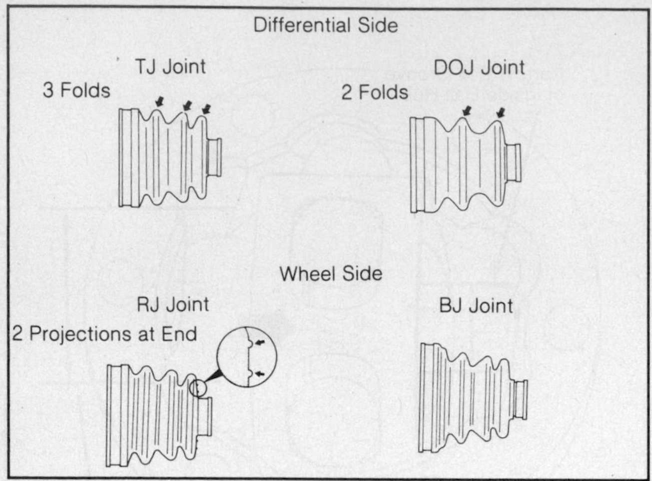
Differential Side
TJ Joint
3 Folds
DOJ Joint
2 Folds
Wheel Side
RJ Joint
2 Projections at End
BJ Joint

Fig. 14: Mitsubishi CV Joint Boot Identification

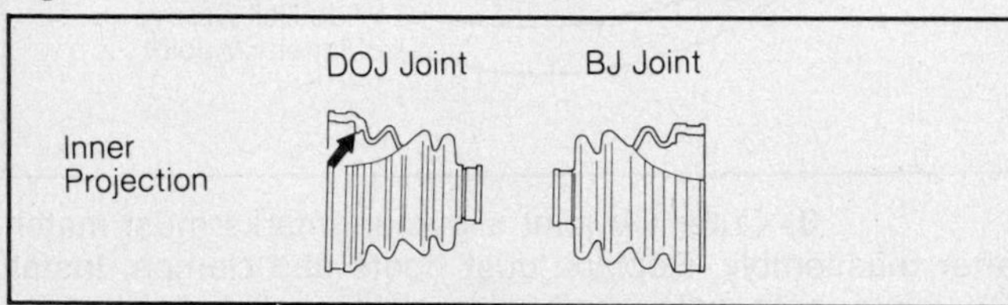
DOJ Joint
BJ Joint
Inner
Projection

Disassembly (BJ Type)

Remove inner joint boot. Remove circlip from joint and remove outer race. Remove snap ring and inner race. Remove cage and balls as an assembly.

NOTE: **Do not disassemble inner bearing assembly as they are mated parts and should not be disturbed.**

Fig. 15: Exploded View of Axle Shaft (BJ Type)

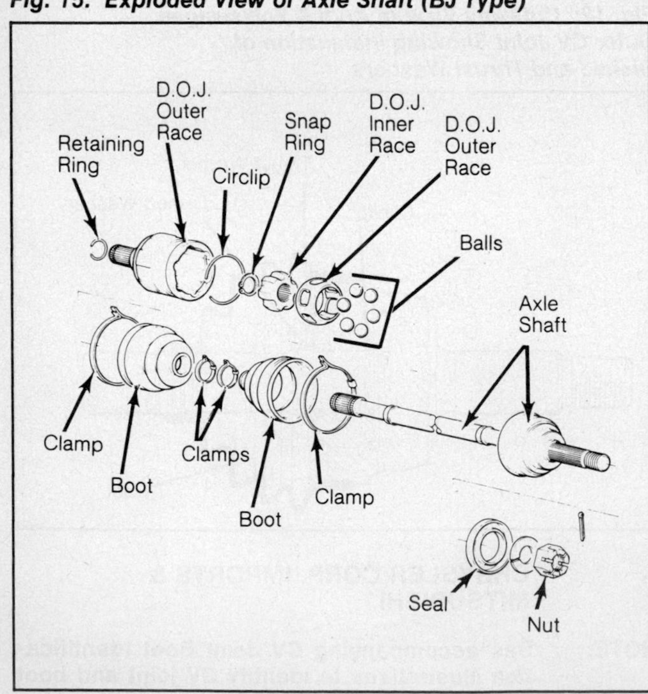
D.O.J.
Outer
Race
Retaining
Ring
Circlip
Snap
Ring
D.O.J.
Inner
Race
D.O.J.
Outer
Race
Balls
Axle
Shaft
Clamp
Boot
Clamps
Boot
Clamp
Seal
Nut

Reassembly

To assemble, reverse disassembly procedure and note the following: Apply grease to inner and outer races. Install CV joint assembly on shaft with chamfered edge of inner race facing outer edge of shaft. Install new boots and place boot clamps 3.5" (90 mm) apart.

Disassembly (TJ Type)

Remove inner joint boots. Pull axle shaft out from inner case. Remove snap ring and take out spider assembly. Clean, but do not disassemble, spider assembly. Remove remaining boots.

Fig. 16: Exploded View of Axle Shaft (TJ Type)

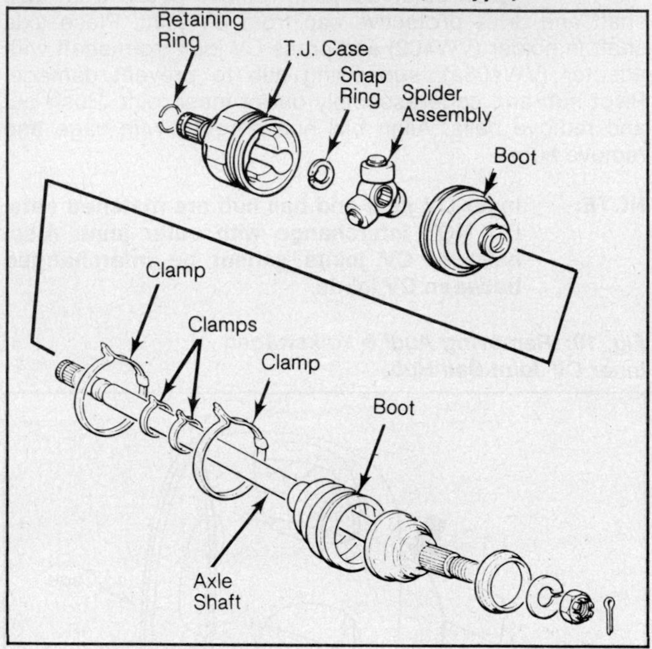
Retaining
Ring
T.J. Case
Snap
Ring
Spider
Assembly
Boot
Clamp
Clamps
Clamp
Boot
Axle
Shaft

Reassembly

To assemble, reverse disassembly procedure and note the following: Apply grease to inner and outer races. Install new boots and place boot clamps 3.0" (75 mm) apart.

DATSUN/NISSAN

Disassembly

NOTE: **Manufacturer does not recommend disassembly of outer CV joints. If defective, replace joint assemblies as complete components.**

1) Place axle shaft in soft-jawed vise with inner CV joint facing up. Remove and discard boot bands from inner boot. Remove inner CV joint housing and stub axle from axle shaft.

2) On TJ type joints, mark spider assembly-to-shaft position for reassembly reference. Remove and discard snap ring and press off spider assembly without dropping axle shaft. Remove dust boot. Using a saw blade, make several cuts down side of CV joint cover. Remove and discard cover by bending it off housing. Remove and discard "O" ring.

3) On BJ type joints, remove large snap ring. Slide outer race off axle shaft. Remove balls from cage. Turn cage 1/2 turn and slide off inner race. Remove small snap ring and tap inner race off axle shaft.

FWD Axle Shafts & CV Joints

ALL MODELS (Cont.)

Fig. 17: Datsun/Nissan CV Joint Disassembly

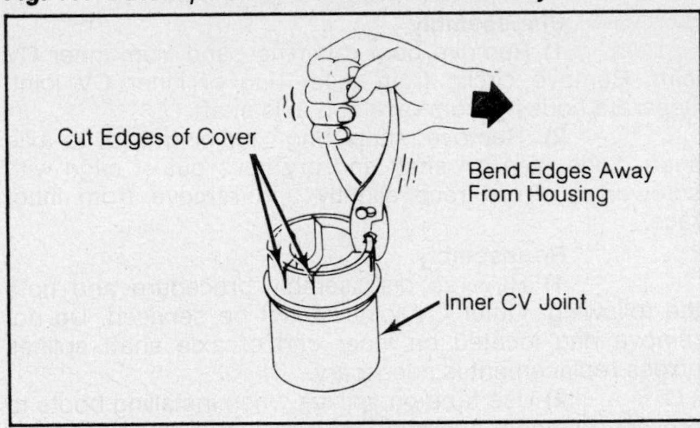
Cut Edges of Cover
Bend Edges Away From Housing
Inner CV Joint

4) To remove outer CV joint, place axle shaft in vise so outer CV joint faces up. Remove and discard boot bands. Mark outer CV joint-to-shaft position for reassembly reference. Lightly tap joint with plastic mallet to separate joint from axle shaft. Remove and discard snap ring. Remove boot.

Reassembly

1) Mount axle shaft in soft-jawed vise with outer end facing out. Position dust boot and new small boot band on shaft without tearing boot on shaft splines. Install new snap ring. Slide outer CV joint onto shaft, aligning marks made during disassembly. Seat joint by lightly tapping with plastic mallet.

2) Pack joint assembly with grease (1/2 ozs. on outer side and 3 ozs. on inner side). Install new large boot band. Wrap band around boot 2 times and tighten using screwdriver and pliers. Using a punch, lock band in position. Cut off excess band, leaving amount equal to band width. Bend excess back over itself.

3) Position dust boot on shaft so its length is 3.94" (100 mm) for TJ type joints or 3.54" (90 mm) for BJ type joints. Secure small band in position without deforming or buckling dust boot. Turn axle shaft in vise so inner end faces up.

4) On inner TJ type joint, coat new "O" ring with grease and install on CV joint housing. Install new cover on housing and bend outer edge at 2 points (180° apart) using block of wood to prevent damage. Housing cover should not rattle. Apply sealant at outer edge of housing and cover.

5) Position boot and new small band on axle shaft. Slide spider assembly onto shaft, aligning marks made during disassembly. Press spider assembly into position with splined chamfer facing axle shaft. Retain in position with new snap ring (round surface facing spider assembly).

6) Pack CV joint assembly with 6.5 ozs. of grease. Install new large boot band and secure in same manner as for inner CV joint. Position dust boot on shaft so its length is 4.40" (112 mm). Secure small band in position without deforming or buckling dust boot.

7) On inner BJ type joints, reverse disassembly procedure. Pack joint with 3.5 ozs. of grease. Install boot and secure as for inner CV joint. Position boot on shaft so its length is 3.30" (84 mm).

HONDA

Disassembly

CAUTION: Outer CV joint on all models cannot be serviced. If joint is found to be worn or damaged, complete axle shaft assembly must be replaced. Always replace inboard housing spring clip when axle shafts are removed.

1) Remove dust boot retaining band from inner CV joint. Slide boot back away from joint. Remove and discard inner CV joint spring clip. Separate joint housing from axle shaft.

2) On Civic models, wipe grease from joint. Remove large snap ring and separate shaft with ball bearing from housing. On Accord and Prelude models, remove snap ring. Slide spider and rollers off shaft. On all models, remove inner retaining band from dust boot and slide boot off shaft.

3) On Civic models, remove retaining band from damper weight and slide weight off shaft. On all models, remove outer retaining band from outer CV joint and clean joint of grease to check operation of joint.

Fig. 18: Honda Civic Axle Shaft Assembly

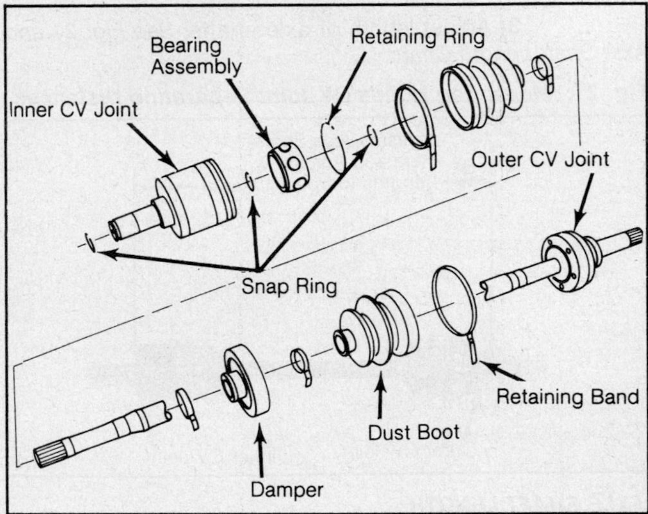
Bearing Assembly
Retaining Ring
Inner CV Joint
Outer CV Joint
Snap Ring
Retaining Band
Dust Boot
Damper

Fig. 19: Honda Accord & Prelude Axle Shaft Assembly

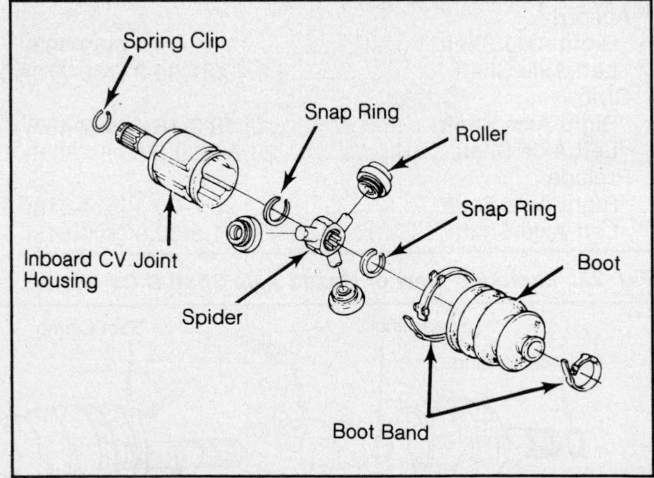
Spring Clip
Snap Ring
Roller
Snap Ring
Inboard CV Joint Housing
Boot
Spider
Boot Band

Reassembly

1) To reassemble, reverse disassembly procedure. For Civic models, vibration dampener must be installed .08" (2 mm) from start of taper on outer axle shaft end. *See Fig. 20.* Press ball bearings into race until firmly seated.

FWD Axle Shafts & CV Joints

ALL MODELS (Cont.)

Fig. 20: Adjusting Damper Position on Honda Civic Axle Shaft

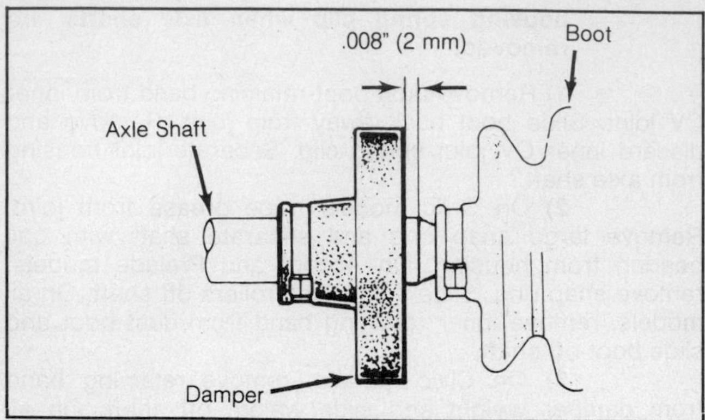
.008" (2 mm)
Boot
Axle Shaft
Damper

2) Install ball bearing race with chamfered end toward small end of bearing cage. Thoroughly pack both inner and outer CV joints with grease. Install new bands on all boots.

3) Adjust length of axle shafts. *See Fig. 21 and Axle Shaft Length Chart.*

Fig. 21: Measuring Honda CV Joint Separating Distances

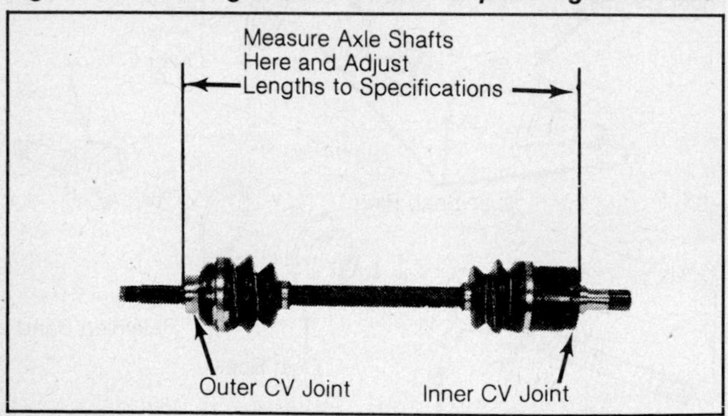
Measure Axle Shafts
Here and Adjust
Lengths to Specifications
Outer CV Joint
Inner CV Joint

AXLE SHAFT LENGTH

Application	Length In. (mm)
Accord	
Right Axle Shaft	19.2-19.4 (489-493)
Left Axle Shaft	30.1-30.3 (766-770)
Civic	
Right Axle Shaft	18.2-18.4 (462-467)
Left Axle Shaft	29.7-29.9 (755.5-760.5)
Prelude	
Right Axle Shaft	20.2-20.4 (514-518)
Left Axle Shaft	31.8-32.0 (809-813)

MAZDA

Disassembly

1) Remove boot retaining band from inner CV joint. Remove circlip from outer ring of inner CV joint. Separate housing from race and axle shaft.

2) Remove snap ring retaining race-to-axle shaft. Slide race off shaft and pry balls out of cage with screwdriver. Turn race slightly and remove from inner race.

Reassembly

1) Reverse disassembly procedure and note the following: Outer CV joint cannot be serviced. Do not remove ring located on inner end of axle shaft splines unless replacement is necessary.

2) Use tape on splines when installing boots to prevent damage. Vibration damper on right axle shaft should be 14.45" (367 mm) from outer CV joint.

RENAULT

Disassembly (Outer CV Joint)

Remove boot retaining collar from CV joint. Remove as much grease as possible from joint. Remove bell shaped stub axle from axle shaft by lifting arms of retaining starplate one at a time. Do not twist arms off of starplate. Separate stub axle from axle shaft and remove boot if necessary.

Fig. 23: Separating Retaining Starplate from Outer End of Renault Axle Shaft

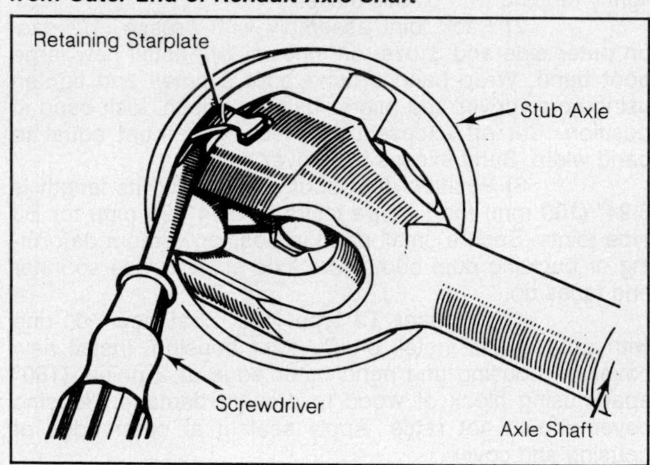
Retaining Starplate
Stub Axle
Screwdriver
Axle Shaft

Be careful not to break off arms when removing plate.

Disassembly (Inner CV Joint)

1) Protect sealing surface of CV joint with tape or a plastic cap. Cut retaining collar and boot off CV joint. Remove as much grease as possible.

Fig. 22: Exploded View of Mazda Axle Shaft & CV Joints

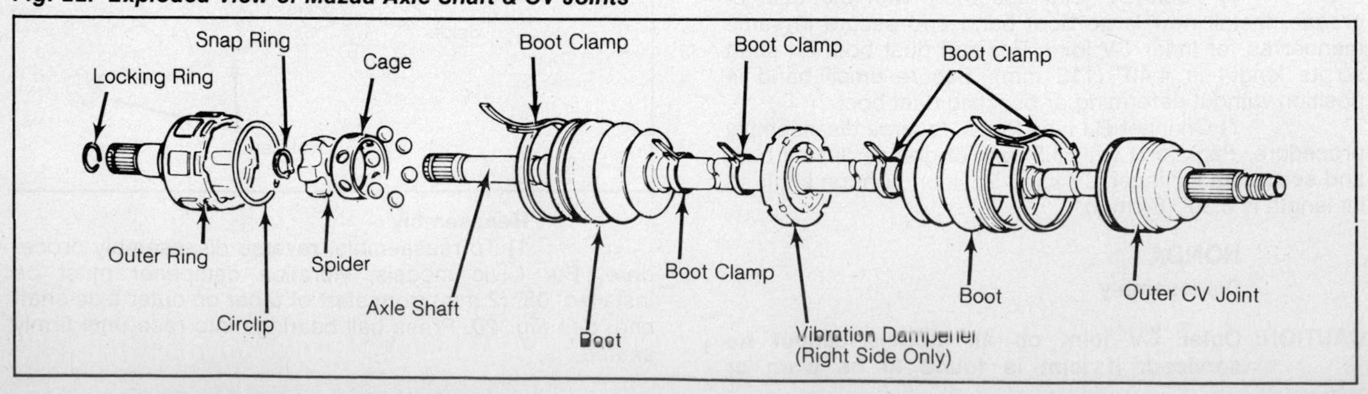
Snap Ring
Cage
Locking Ring
Boot Clamp
Boot Clamp
Boot Clamp
Outer Ring
Spider
Circlip
Axle Shaft
Boot
Boot Clamp
Vibration Dampener
(Right Side Only)
Boot
Outer CV Joint

ALL MODELS (Cont.)

2) Bend 3 locking plate tabs out of the way and remove yoke. Do not remove rollers from their journals. If necessary, use tape to secure rollers. Using a press, remove axle shaft from inner CV joint spider.

Fig. 24: Cutaway View of Renault Inner CV Joint

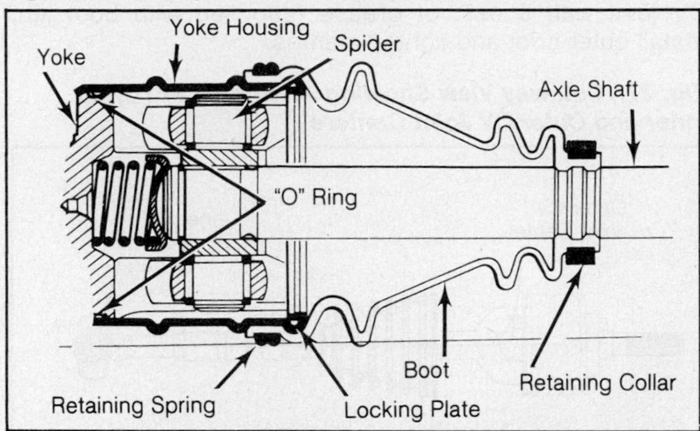
Yoke Housing
Spider
Yoke
Axle Shaft
"O" Ring
Boot
Retaining Collar
Retaining Spring
Locking Plate

NOTE: **Never use thinner to clean any components.**

Reassembly (Outer CV Joint)

1) Install seal expander (T. Av. 537-02) over outer end of axle shaft. Place axle shaft in soft-jawed vise. Using motor oil, lubricate entire surface of tool and inside of boot. Slide boot onto end of tool and smooth out first fold of boot.

2) Move boot as close as possible toward axle shaft, then let it slide back on tool. Repeat 4 to 5 times to stretch boot, adding oil as necessary. When boot becomes easier to slide back and forth, slide it all the way into position on axle shaft. Remove tool.

3) Install spring and thrust ball joint into spider. Position roller cages in center of joint. Align retaining starplate so that each arm is between 2 roller cages. Reinstall axle shaft into bell-shaped stub axle. Fill boot and spider with about 5.3 ozs. of grease for Fuego and 18i models, or 6.4 ozs. for LeCar models of grease. Secure boot with retaining rings.

Reassembly (Inner CV Joint)

1) If yoke and any other parts are replaced, lubricate axle shaft and slide on boot with retaining collar. Slide metal yoke housing onto axle shaft. Install spider onto axle shaft splines and stake in place at 3 equally spaced points around shaft.

2) Install new "O" ring onto yoke perforation. Install yoke into metal housing by tapping in until fully seated and hold with a press. Crimp end of housing that faces transaxle onto housing. Proceed to step **5)**.

3) If only boot or spider was replaced, lubricate axle shaft and slide on boot with retaining collar. Install spider onto axle shaft and stake in place at 3 equally spaced points around shaft. Remove tape from roller cages and engage spider with yoke.

4) Fabricate a shim from .098" (2.5 mm) flat stock measuring 1.575" (40 mm) long, .236" (6 mm) at each end and having a 1.772" (45 mm) radius across one of the long sides. Insert this shim under each of the locking tabs on yoke while tapping tabs back into place using a drift punch.

5) To complete assembly of CV joint, fill yoke and boot with about 5 ozs. of grease. Position lips of boot in grooves of axle shaft and yoke housing. Place retaining collar on axle shaft end of boot. Insert a smooth round-ended rod under yoke end of boot to allow air to escape.

6) Extend or compress joint until distance from back of yoke housing (not splined coupling) to axle shaft end of boot is to specification. *See Renault Axle Boot Specifications Chart.* Remove rod from boot. Place retaining spring around yoke end of boot being careful not to stretch spring.

RENAULT AXLE BOOT SPECIFICATIONS

Application	Length In. (mm)
Fuego & 18i	
GI 76	6.14 (156)
GI 82	6.34-6.42 (161-163)
LeCar	
Round Housing	6.34-6.42 (161-163)
Triangle Housing	6.00-6.08 (152-155)

SAAB

Disassembly (Outer CV Joint)

Install wheel assembly in a press to remove axle shaft with outer CV joint. Peel the boot back. Wipe grease from inner race. Use circlip pliers to open snap ring and remove axle shaft.

Disassembly (Inner CV Joint)

Remove snap ring. Remove TJ joint and boot. The differential side cover must be removed to service inner CV joint housing.

Fig. 25: Sectional View of Saab Steering Knuckle

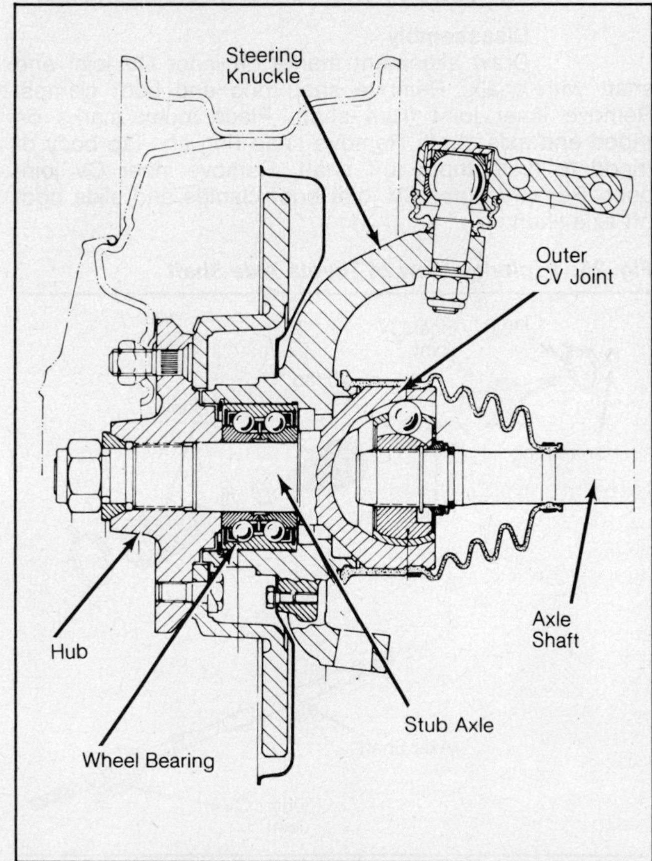
Steering Knuckle
Outer CV Joint
Hub
Axle Shaft
Stub Axle
Wheel Bearing

Reassembly

Pack the CV joints with Lithium-Lead based EP grease. To reassemble, reverse disassembly procedure.

FWD Axle Shafts & CV Joints

ALL MODELS (Cont.)

SUBARU

Disassembly

1) Straighten bent claw of larger end of boot on double offset joint side. Loosen band by means of screwdriver or pliers taking care not to damage boot. Remove boot band on the small end of DOJ boot in the same manner.

2) Remove the larger end of boot on DOJ side. Pry and remove round circlip located at the neck of outer race on DOJ side with a screwdriver. Take out the outer race on DOJ side from the shaft assembly.

3) Wipe off grease and remove balls. Move the cage to the boot side. Remove snap ring with snap ring pliers. Take out the inner race of DOJ.

4) Take out the cage of the DOJ from the shaft and remove the boot from DOJ with care not to damage it. Pull out the boot on the CV joint side.

Inspection

Examine CV joint for corrosion, damage or wear. Ensure axle shaft does not have excessive deflection, twist or wear. Replace components as necessary.

Reassembly

To reassemble, reverse disassembly procedure. Grease CV joint and DOJ with Molylex No. 2 grease.

TOYOTA

NOTE: **Before disassembling axle shaft, check outer CV joint for any play. If play exists at outer CV joint, replace complete axle shaft assembly. Outer CV joint cannot be disassembled.**

Disassembly

Draw alignment marks on inner CV joint and shaft with chalk. Remove snap ring and boot clamps. Remove inner joint from shaft. Place index marks on tripod and axle shaft. Remove snap ring and tap body of tripod to drive tripod off shaft. Remove inner CV joint boot. Remove outer CV joint boot clamps and slide boot off axle shaft.

Fig. 26: Exploded View of Toyota Axle Shaft

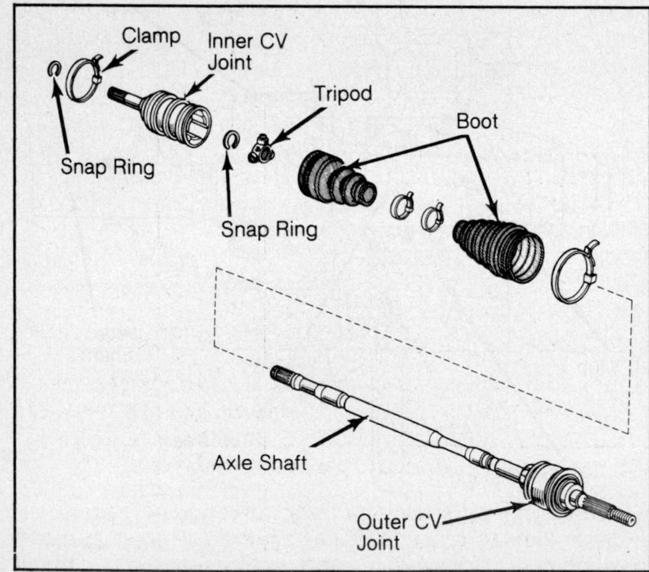
Clamp
Inner CV Joint
Tripod
Boot
Snap Ring
Snap Ring
Axle Shaft
Outer CV Joint

Reassembly

1) Slide new boots onto axle shaft. Place clamping rings loosely over boots with open end of clamp away from direction of rotation. Do not tighten clamps at this time. Place beveled side of tripod onto shaft with beveled splines facing outer joint and align reference marks.

2) Before tapping tripod into final position, align centers of inner and outer joints. *See Fig. 27.* Tap tripod into position and install new snap ring. Pack outer CV joint with 8 ozs. of grease (supplied with boot kit). Install outer boot and tighten clamps.

Fig. 27: Cutaway View Showing Alignment of Toyota Inner and Outer CV Joint Centers

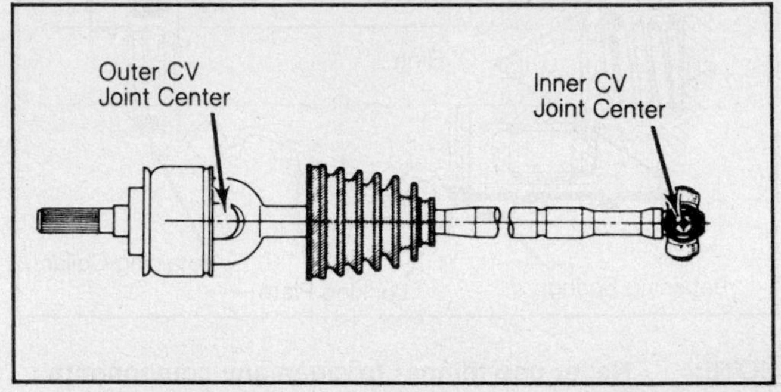
Outer CV Joint Center
Inner CV Joint Center

3) Pack inner CV joint with 5 ozs. of grease (supplied with boot kit). Align reference marks made at disassembly and install inner CV joint. Install inner CV joint boot and tighten clamps. Install new snap ring on axle shaft.

Fig. 28: Standard Length of Toyota Camry Axle Shaft

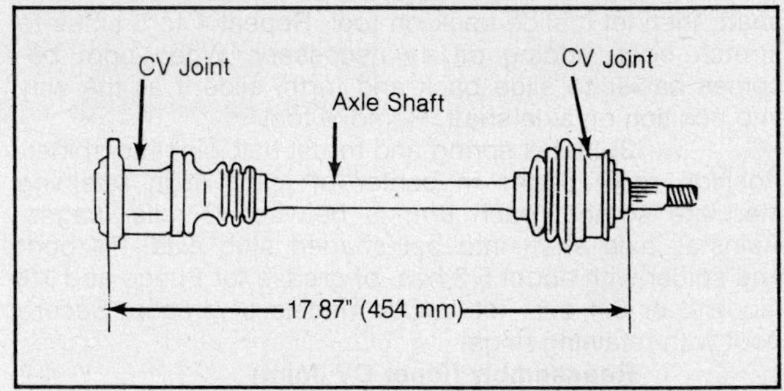
CV Joint
CV Joint
Axle Shaft
17.87" (454 mm)

4) On Camry models, standard axle shaft length is 17.87" (454 mm). Ensure boots are not deformed when axle shaft is at standard length. *See Fig. 28.*.

5) On Tercel models, install balancer to left axle shaft. Position balancer 15.98" (406 mm) from end of outer CV joint. Tighten clamps. *See Fig. 29.*

Fig. 29: Locating Toyota Tercel Damper on Axle Shaft

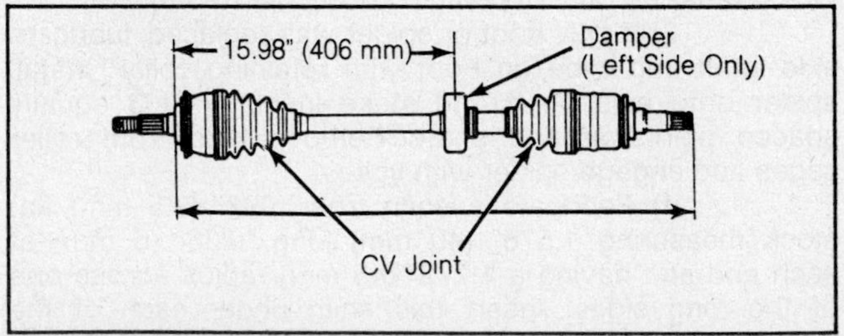
15.98" (406 mm)
Damper
(Left Side Only)
CV Joint

Damper is on left axle shaft only.

NOTE: **On Tercel models, right axle shaft is 28.5" (724 mm) long. Left shaft is 24.6" (625 mm) long. If axle shaft does not meet length specification, replace axle shaft assembly.**

FWD Axle Shafts & CV Joints

ALL MODELS (Cont.)

TIGHTENING SPECIFICATIONS

Application	Ft. Lbs. (N.m)
Audi & Volkswagen	
All Models Except 5000	
Axle Shaft Nut	167 (230)
Ball Joints	47 (64)
CV Joint Bolts	32 (43)
5000	
Axle Shaft Nut	200 (274)
CV Joint Bolts	32 (43)
Chrysler Corp. Imports	
Axle Shaft Nut	167 (230)
Ball Joints	78 (105)
Datsun/Nissan	
Axle Shaft Nut	115 (157)
Ball Joint Nuts	44 (58)
Honda	
Axle Shaft Nut	137 (185)
Ball Joints	40 (55)
Support-To-Strut	32 (43)
Support-to-Spindle	47 (64)
Mazda	
Axle Shaft Nut	140 (200)
Ball Joints	36 (48)
Sway Bar Link	11 (15)
Mitsubishi	
Axle Shaft Nut	167 (230)
Ball Joints	47 (64)
Renault	
Axle Shaft Nut	
Fuego & 18i	185 (250)
LeCar	90 (122)
Ball Joints	48 (65)
Tie Rod Ends	30 (40)
Saab	
Axle Shaft Nut	260 (350)
Subaru	
Axle Shaft Nut	145 (197)
Ball Joint Nut	25 (34)
Tie Rod Ends	22 (30)
Toyota	
Camry	
Axle Shaft Nut	137 (185)
Brake Caliper	70 (96)
CV Joint Bolts	25 (34)
Intermediate Shaft Mount	40 (54)
Tercel	
Axle Shaft Nut	137 (185)
Brake Caliper	70 (96)
Spring Strut-to-Knuckle	105 (142)
Sway Bar	35 (47)
Tie Rod End	32 (43)

Drive Axles

BMW INTEGRAL CARRIER

318i, 320i, 528e, 533i, 633CSi, 733i

DESCRIPTION

Final drive assembly has hypoid type ring and pinion gear. Assembly may have a multi-disc, self-locking differential (ZF DL-175). Housing has a removable rear cover. Differential carrier is retained in the sides of the housing by bearing caps and is supported by tapered roller bearings.

Shims under the bearing caps maintain proper carrier bearing preload. Drive pinion gear is supported by roller bearings and preload is maintained by a collapsible spacer between the bearings.

AXLE RATIO & IDENTIFICATION

The ring and pinion gear set with Klingelnberg tooth design can be identified by the letter "K" stamped on the drive pinion gear; Gleason teeth are noted by an "H" stamping. Letter "S" indicates a self-locking differential.

To determine axle ratio, divide number of ring gear teeth by number of drive pinion gear teeth. The number of teeth on ring and drive pinion gears is stamped on forward right side of differential housing.

REMOVAL & INSTALLATION

CONSTANT VELOCITY JOINT

Removal

Remove cover from joint housing. Remove snap ring from end of drive shaft. Remove clamps from boot. Press drive shaft from joint and note position of thrust washer, if equipped. Remove dust boot.

Installation

To install, reverse removal procedure. Convex side of thrust washer faces joint, if equipped. When repacking "CV" joints, use only "Moly" type grease.

DRIVE AXLES & BEARINGS

Removal

1) Raise and support vehicle. Remove wheel and brake drum assembly. Remove drive shaft. Loosen castellated nut (all 6-cyl. models) securing flange to drvieaxle. Using a puller, remove flange.

2) On all models, install castellated nut on axle shaft and drive out drive axle using a soft-headed mallet. Remove bearings and seals. Remove spacer sleeve and shim, if equipped.

Installation

1) To install, reverse removal procedure. Install inner bearing. Determine distance between outer races of inner and outer bearings.

2) Measure spacer and shim. Install a spacer and shim that will obtain specified axle shaft end play. Pack bearings and hub with grease. Using new seals, complete installation procedure.

DRIVE PINION COMPANION FLANGE OIL SEAL

Removal

1) Remove final drive assembly and mount on holding fixture. Remove lock washer. Using a prick punch, mark installed position of companion flange. Using an INCH lb. torque wrench, measure and record pinion gear preload.

2) Hold flange stationary and remove lock nut. Pull off companion flange. Check bearing surface of flange. Replace flange if deeply scored. Pull out seal and discard.

Installation

1) Dip new seal in gear oil. Drive seal into case until flush. Press companion flange onto pinion gear, aligning punch marks made during removal.

2) Loosely install lock nut. Using INCH lb. torque wrench, tighten lock nut. Tighten lock nut to preload value measured during removal PLUS 2 INCH lbs. (.23 N.m) for new seal.

Fig. 1: Exploded View of BMW Integral Carrier Assembly

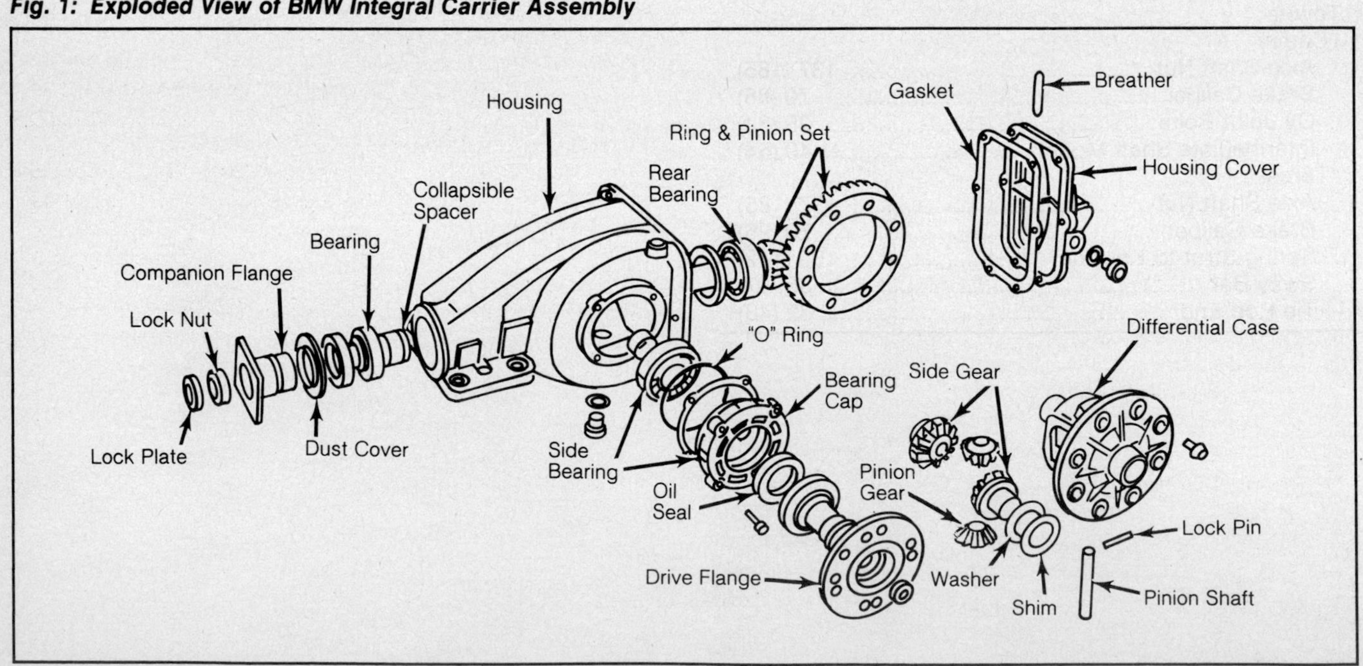
Housing
Ring & Pinion Set
Rear Bearing
Collapsible Spacer
Bearing
Companion Flange
Lock Nut
Lock Plate
Dust Cover
Gasket
Breather
Housing Cover
Differential Case
"O" Ring
Bearing Cap
Side Gear
Side Bearing
Oil Seal
Pinion Gear
Lock Pin
Drive Flange
Washer
Shim
Pinion Shaft

BMW INTEGRAL CARRIER (Cont.)

Fig. 2: Sectional View of Axle Shaft Assembly

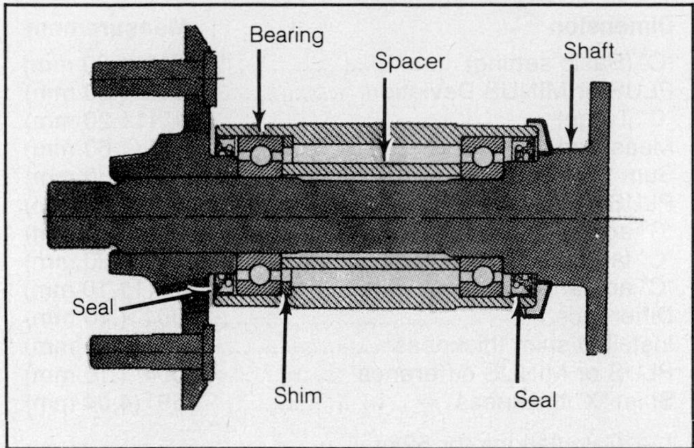
Bearing
Spacer
Shaft
Seal
Shim
Seal

Wheel bearing play is adjusted by spacer length and shim.

3) If lock nut can not be tightened to specified torque value or if preload value (measured during removal) is exceeded, removal and installation of drive pinion is required (always replace "Crush" sleeve). If preload value is obtained, install lock washer.

AXLE FLANGE & OIL SEAL

Removal

With final drive assembly mounted in holding fixture, pry off drive flanges with tire irons. Mark flanges for installation in original positions. Check flanges. Flanges with scored bearing or seal surfaces must be replaced. Remove and discard flange snap ring. Remove seal with puller.

Installation

Dip seal in gear oil. Drive seal into case until it rests against stop. Insert new snap ring into recessed groove in case. Replace drive flange and ensure snap ring engages groove in flange.

DIFFERENTIAL ASSEMBLY

Removal

Detach propeller shaft and drive shafts from final drive. Suspend shafts out of way. Detach self-aligning support at final drive. Remove electrical connectors. Support final drive on jack and remove final drive mounting bolts. Lower jack and remove final drive assembly.

Installation

To install, reverse removal procedure. Ensure that assembly is stress-free when tightened to specified torque.

OVERHAUL

DISASSEMBLY

Differential Housing (Conventional)

1) Remove final drive assembly and mount in holding fixture. Using an INCH lb. torque wrench, measure and record preload of pinion gear and differential gears.

2) Drain oil and remove rear cover plate. Discard gasket. Remove drive flanges as previously described. Remove both bearing caps, keeping right and left parts separated. Record number and location of shims under bearing caps. Remove differential assembly from case.

3) Remove multi-tab pulse ring. Remove side bearings with puller. Remove bolts securing ring gear to carrier. Remove ring gear. Drive out pinion shaft lock pin. Remove pinion shaft and gears. Remove side gears with shims and thrust washers.

Differential Housing (Limited Slip)

1) With differential removed from housing. Remove 8 retainer plate bolts and turn case upside down, letting plate assembly slide out. Remove thrust washer, diaphragm spring, outer and inner plates.

2) Lift off pressure member and take off pinion side gear. Remove pinion gears with shafts. Check and replace any components that show scoring, easy movement or being worn. Keep all components in order for reassembly.

Drive Pinion Gear

1) Remove lock washer. Using a prick punch, mark installed position of companion flange. Using an INCH lb. torque wrench, measure and record pinion gear preload.

2) Hold flange stationary and remove lock nut. Pull off companion flange. Check bearing surface of flange. Replace flange if deeply scored. Pull out seal and discard. Press drive pinion from housing. Remove collapsible spacer and using special tools (33 1 350 & 33 1 371) remove front housing bearing .

3) Remove drive pinion shaft oil seal. Using special tools, (33 1 350, 33 1 356, 33 1 362 and 33 1 363) remove pinion inner bearing race from case. Note shim "X" thickness under bearing race. *See Fig. 3.*

Fig. 3: Sectional View of Drive Pinion Gear Assembly

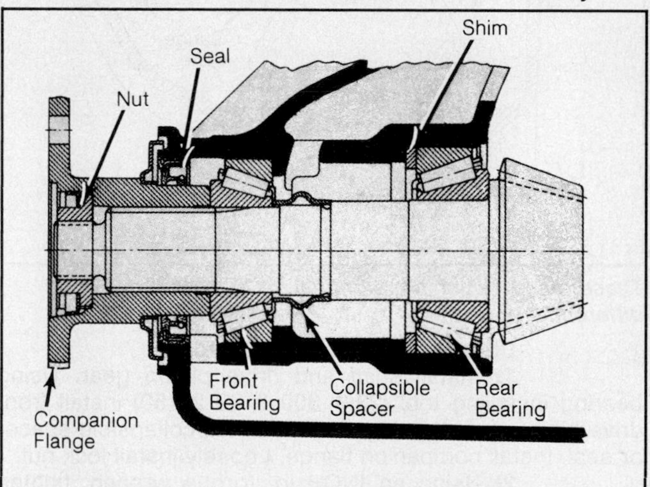
Shim
Seal
Nut
Front Bearing
Collapsible Spacer
Rear Bearing
Companion Flange

Note position of collapsible spacer and shim.

REASSEMBLY & ADJUSTMENT

Drive Pinion Gear

1) Using bearing race installing tool, install front and rear bearing races in housing. *See Fig. 4.* Press rear bearing onto drive pinion. Note any deviations ("+" or "-") stamped on drive pinion. This amount must be added (if "+") or subtracted (if "-") from measurement "C". *See Fig. 5.*

2) If original ring and pinion gear set is being installed, install drive pinion gear using original shim and new collapsible spacer. If new ring and pinion gear set is being installed, install new shim that is same thickness as original shim.

BMW INTEGRAL CARRIER (Cont.)

Fig. 4: Bearing Race Installing Tool

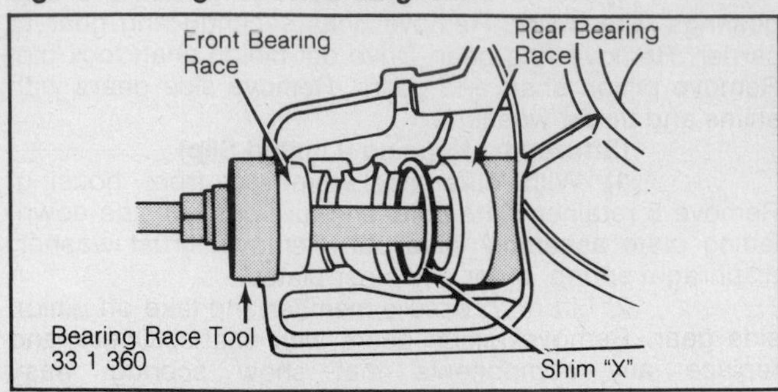
Front Bearing Race
Rear Bearing Race
Bearing Race Tool 33 1 360
Shim "X"

Both bearing races are pulled in together.

Fig. 5: Pinion Shim Measuring Points

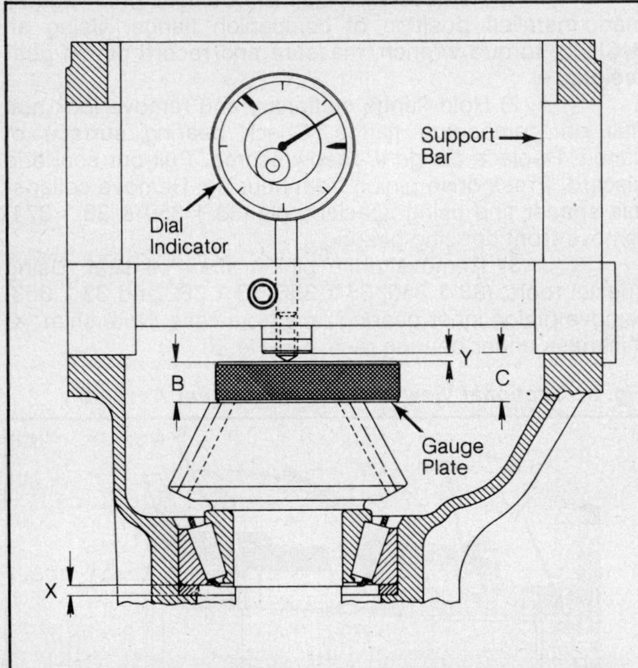
Support Bar
Dial Indicator
Y
B
C
Gauge Plate
X

These measurements are critical for correct differential operation.

Drive Pinion Bearing Preload

1) Install shim and drive pinion gear. Using bearing installing tool (23 1 300 & 23 2 150) install front drive pinion gear bearing. Do not install collapsible spacer or seal. Install companion flange. Loosely install lock nut.

2) Using an INCH lb. torque wrench, tighten lock nut to obtain preload of 13 INCH lbs. (1.5 N.m) on 318i and 320i models or 22 INCH lbs. (2.5 N.m) on all other models.

3) Mount dial indicator on support bar (33 1 381). Place support bar and dial indicator over gauge plate (33 1 382). Zero dial indicator with .157" (4 mm) preload. Place gauge plate on drive pinion in housing. Place support bar with dial indicator in housing. Measure distance between support bar and gauge plate (dimension "Y").

4) Basic setting adjustments are: 318i & 320i models, .434" (11.02 mm); 528e, 533i & 633CSi models, .453" (11.50 mm); and 733i models, .728" (18.50 mm). Using dimensions in Fig. 5., determine required shim thickness "X" by using the sample calculation chart.

SAMPLE PINION BEARING PRELOAD CALCULATION

Dimension	Measurement
"C" (Basic setting)	[1].453" (11.50 mm)
PLUS or MINUS Deviation	- .012" (.30 mm)
"C" Target	.441" (11.20 mm)
Measured value "Y"	.063" (1.60 mm)
Sum "B" (Gauge plate)	.374" (9.50 mm)
PLUS measured value "Y"	+ 1.063" (27.00 mm)
"C" actual	.437" (11.10 mm)
"C" target	.441" (11.20 mm)
"C" actual	- [2] .437" (11.10 mm)
Difference =	.004" (.10 mm)
Installed shim thickness	.163" (4.14 mm)
PLUS or MINUS difference	- .004" (.10 mm)
Shim "X" thickness =	.159" (4.04 mm)

[1] – Calculations for 528e.
[2] – If "C" target is greater than "C" actual, difference is subtracted from shim thickness. If "C" target is smaller than "C" actual, difference is added to shim thickness.

5) Remove tools, companion flange and drive pinion gear. Install shims of calculated thickness. Shims are available in .0004-.0012" (.01-.03 mm) thicknesses.

6) Install shims, drive pinion gear, collapsible spacer and seal. Install companion flange and tighten lock nut to obtain specified pinion gear bearing preload. If preload is exceeded, new collapsible spacer must be installed and procedure repeated.

Differential Housing (Conventional)

1) Press on side bearings. Install both differential side gears with thrust washers and shims. Ensure concave side of thrust washers face gears. Using drive flanges, center side gears.

2) Mount differential assembly in vise. Install spreader tool (33 1 430). *See Fig. 6.* Spread side gears by tightening spindle until drive flange can just be turned. Remove drive flange and install pinion gears. Remove spreader tools. Install pinion shaft and lock pin.

drive flanges, center side gears.

Fig. 6: Spreading Differential Side Gears

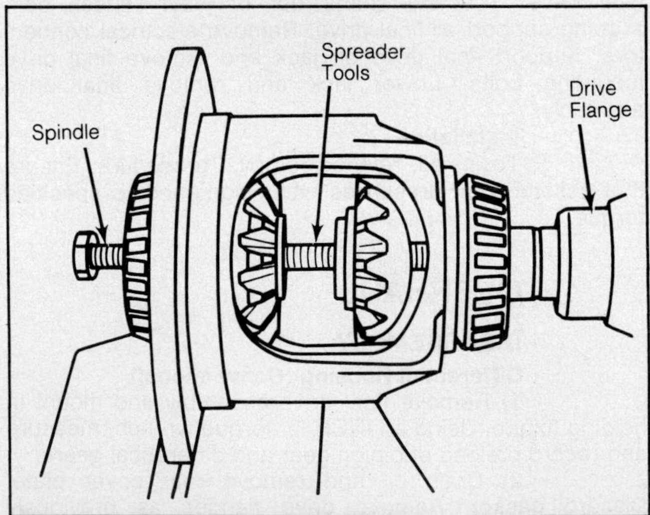
Spreader Tools
Drive Flange
Spindle

Spread gears until drive flange can just be turned.

3) Install side gear gauge plate and spindle. Hand tighten spindle. Mount dial indicator on differential

BMW INTEGRAL CARRIER (Cont.)

case. Zero dial indicator. Tighten spindle until thrust washer is pressed flat.

4) Loosen spindle. Turn side gear and repeat measurement at various points. Repeat procedure on opposite side gear. Adjust specified clearance by installing thicker or thinner shims.

5) Shims are available in .002" (.05 mm) increments. Remove gauge plate and spindle, pinion shaft, pinion gears and side gears. Install shims of calculated thickness and repeat procedure.

NOTE: **Ring gear tooth pattern has priority over backlash and preload adjustments. After setting backlash and preload, perform tooth contact pattern and adjust shims accordingly.**

Differential Bearing Preload

1) Install INCH lb. torque wrench on companion flange lock nut. Measure total preload of drive pinion gear and ring gear, with seals installed. Compare preload reading with that measured during disassembly. Add 2 INCH lbs. (.23 N.m) for new drive pinion gear seal.

2) Preload should meet specifications. If not, perform tooth contact pattern check and adjust total shim thicknesses. After final adjustments or changing shim thicknesses or positions, always verify adjustments with tooth contact pattern check. Install new rear cover gasket, cover and fill with lube oil. *See Gear Tooth Contact Pattern at beginning of this section.*

Limited Slip Differential

1) To reassemble, reverse disassembly procedures. Place diaphragm spring and thrust washer in case. Oil grooves of thrust washer are face up. Install in order diaphragm spring, outer plate, inner plate, pressure ring and differential side gear in case. *See Fig. 7.*

2) Install drive flanges. Check slip torque while holding one differential side gear and driving the other. Slip torque is adjusted with outer plates which are available in 3 different thicknesses.

Fig. 7: Limited Slip Plate Assembly

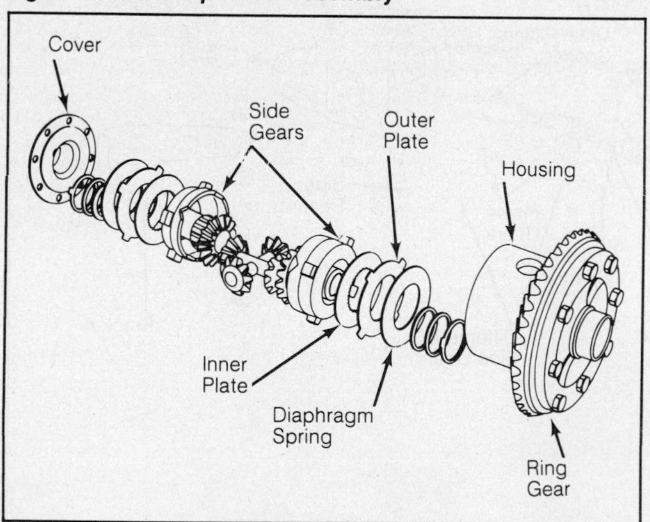
Cover
Side Gears
Outer Plate
Housing
Inner Plate
Diaphragm Spring
Ring Gear

Outer plates adjust slip torque.

AXLE ASSEMBLY SPECIFICATIONS

Application	In. (mm)
Axle Shaft End Play	.002-.004 (.05-.10)
Max. Axle Drive	
Flange Runout	.006 (.15)
Ring Gear-to-Pinion	
Gear Backlash	
All Models	.028-.051 (.7-1.3)

TIGHTENING SPECIFICATIONS

Application	Ft. Lbs. (N.m)
Rear Housing Cover Bolts	29-36 (40-50)
Companion Flange Nut (Minimum)	
318i & 320i	11 (15)
528e, 533i & 633CSi	108 (146)
733i	228 (310)
Drive Flange Cap Bolts	16-20 (22-26)
Drive Flange Nuts	43-50 (58-66)
Axle Shaft Nuts	
318i & 320i	295-346 (400-469)
528e, 533i & 633CSi	170-190 (230-260)
733i	290-365 (420-495)
Ring Gear Bolts	
318i & 320i	63-74 (85-100)
528e, 533i & 633CSi	36-40 (49-54)
733i	119-141 (161-191)
Final Drive Mounting Bolts	
318i & 320i	60-66 (81-89)
528e, 533i & 633CSi	89 (121)
733i	101-112 (137-152)

CHRYSLER CORP. IMPORTS & MITSUBISHI INTEGRAL HOUSING

Chrysler Corp. Imports Colt 4WD Pickup, Ram-50 4WD Pickup; Mitsubishi Montero & 4WD Pickup

DESCRIPTION

The front axle assembly consists of a differential carrier, housing tube, inner shaft, and 2 drive axles. Drive axles are of full-floating design. Birfield Joints (BJ) and Double Offset Joints (DOJ) are used at opposite ends of each drive axle. Torsion bar suspension is used on these models. *See Fig. 1.*

AXLE RATIO & IDENTIFICATION

Chrysler Corp. and Mitsubishi use one type of front axle assembly. Final drive gear ratio is 4.625:1 on Montero and 3.909:1 on all other models. Any differences in removal and installation or overhaul procedures will be noted where they occur.

REMOVAL AND INSTALLATION

NOTE: References to BJ refer to Birfield Joint; DOJ to Double Offset Joint.

Fig. 1: Front Drive Axle and Suspension (4WD)

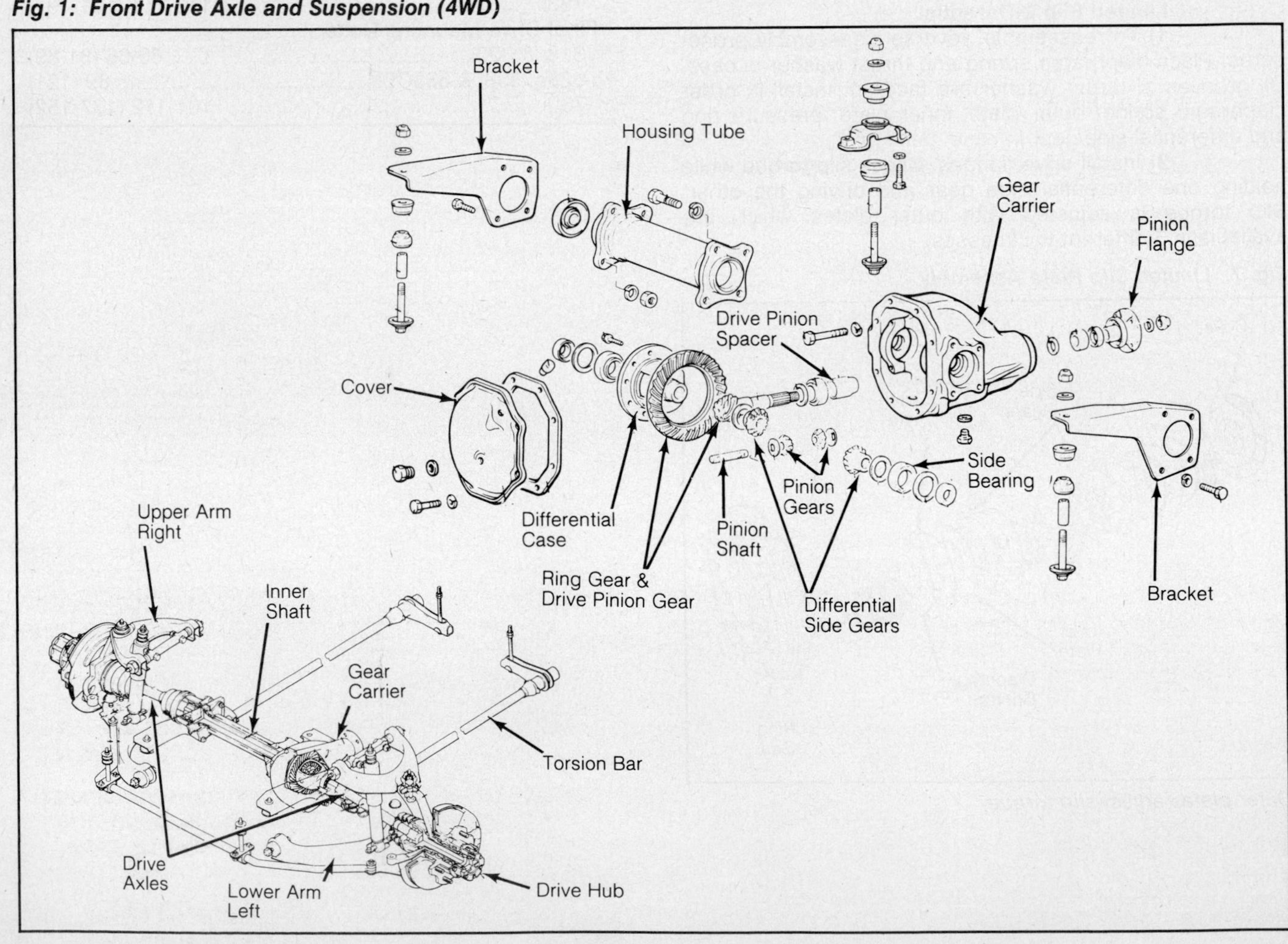
Bracket
Housing Tube
Gear Carrier
Pinion Flange
Drive Pinion Spacer
Cover
Side Bearing
Pinion Gears
Upper Arm Right
Differential Case
Pinion Shaft
Ring Gear & Drive Pinion Gear
Bracket
Inner Shaft
Differential Side Gears
Gear Carrier
Torsion Bar
Drive Axles
Lower Arm Left
Drive Hub

DRIVE AXLES & BEARINGS

Removal

1) Raise and support vehicle. Remove wheels. Remove brake calipers with hoses attached and support out of way. Remove cover of locking hub and take snap ring from drive axle. Remove cotter pins and slotted nuts from tie rod end, upper ball joint, and lower ball joint.

2) Using pullers (C-3894-A and MB990635), disconnect tie rod and ball joints from knuckle. Remove knuckle and locking hub as unit, being careful of BJ boot. Pull left drive axle assembly from differential carrier. Avoid damage to differential oil seal when removing drive axle spline section.

3) Raise right lower control arm with jack. Disconnect upper shock mount nuts and remove shock from arm post on side frame. Disconnect right drive axle from inner shaft and remove.

CAUTION: Do not remove or lower jack under control arm until shock has been reconnected.

4) Remove inner shaft from differential carrier assembly. Pry dust seal from housing tube assembly. *See Fig. 2.*

CHRYSLER CORP. IMPORTS & MITSUBISHI INTEGRAL HOUSING (Cont.)

Fig. 2: Exploded View of Front Drive Axles (4WD)

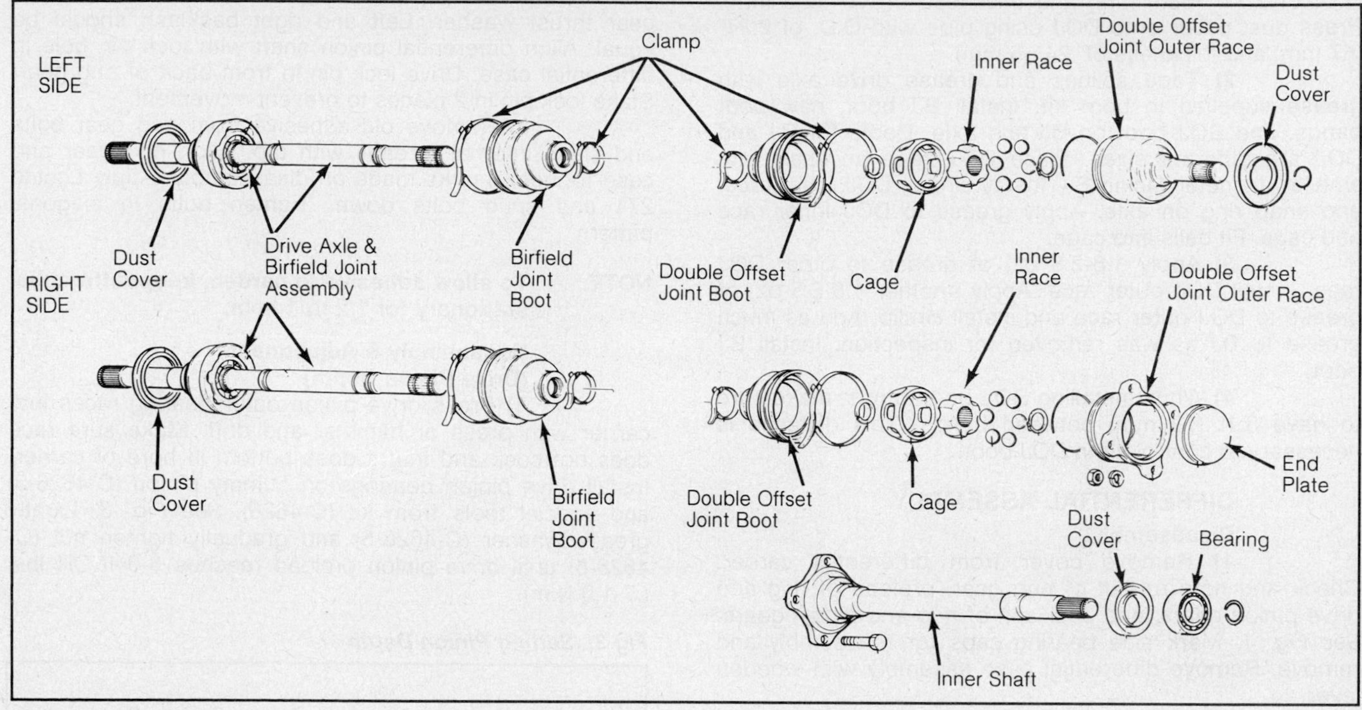
LEFT SIDE
RIGHT SIDE
Clamp
Dust Cover
Drive Axle & Birfield Joint Assembly
Birfield Joint Boot
Double Offset Joint Boot
Cage
Inner Race
Double Offset Joint Outer Race
Dust Cover
Double Offset Joint Boot
Cage
Inner Race
Double Offset Joint Outer Race
End Plate
Dust Cover
Bearing
Inner Shaft
Dust Cover
Birfield Joint Boot

Large opening of boot clamps to outer race of joint.

Installation

1) Install new dust seal in housing tube and apply grease to seal lip. Install inner shaft to differential, driving shaft in after splines mate. Be careful not to damage oil seal. Replace circlip on BJ spline and attach right drive axle to inner shaft and torque nuts to specification.

2) Connect right shock to arm post of side frame. Tighten adjusting nut (bottom) until stud of shock extends .81" (20.5 mm) past lower edge of nut. Tighten lock nut to 9-13 ft. lbs. (12-18 N.m). Drive left drive axle into differential after mating splines. Replace circlip on BJ side spline. Take care not to damage oil seal.

3) Reinstall knuckle with front hub assembly. To adjust drive axle axial play, install snap ring on drive axle without outer spacer. Install dial indicator at right angle to end of drive axle. Measure axial travel of shaft and select spacer so value of .008-.020" (.2-.5 mm) is reached.

DIFFERENTIAL CARRIER

Removal

1) Drain gear oil. Support carrier assembly. Disconnect drive axles and inner shaft. Index mark propeller shaft and pinion flange for reassembly. Disconnect propeller shaft. Remove left and right differential mounting brackets at differential and frame.

2) Disconnect front suspension crossmember from support bracket of side frame. Remove differential carrier assembly with front crossmember attached. Remove carrier assembly from suspension crossmember.

Installation

To install, reverse removal procedure. Make sure to align index marks on propeller shaft and pinion flange. Fill assembly with gear oil.

OVERHAUL

NOTE: References to BJ refer to Birfield Joint; DOJ to Double Offset Joint.

DRIVE AXLES & BEARINGS

Disassembly

1) Remove boot bands. *See Fig. 2.* Remove circlip from outer race of DOJ. Pull drive axle away from DOJ outer race. Remove balls from DOJ cage and turn cage 30° from position in which balls are installed. Push cage toward BJ and remove snap ring holding inner DOJ race on axle. Remove DOJ inner race and cage from axle. Remove circlip behind cage from axle. After taping splines of axle, remove DOJ and BJ boots from drive axle.

CAUTION: Do not try to disassemble BJ. Drive axle and BJ are supplied as unit.

2) Remove dust cover from BJ and DOJ. Bend over outer lip of dust cover on inner shaft. With puller (MB990560) and press, remove bearing from inner shaft. Remove dust cover.

Inspection

Inspect inside of BJ for rust, dirt, water, or damage to balls and races. Inspect drive axles and inner shaft for bending or damage to splines. Check boots for cracks or wear. Inspect DOJ inner and outer races for wear or damage. Check DOJ cage and balls for rust, dirt, or wear damage. Check inner shaft bearing for seizure, roughness, or discoloration.

Reassembly

1) Using a pipe with O.D. of 2.95" (75 mm) and wall thickness of .16" (4 mm), press dust cover onto inner shaft. Press bearing onto inner shaft using puller

CHRYSLER CORP. IMPORTS & MITSUBISHI INTEGRAL HOUSING (Cont.)

(MB990560). Press dust cover onto BJ using pipe with O.D. of 2.71" (68.9 mm) and thickness of .09" (2.3 mm). Press dust cover onto DOJ using pipe with O.D. of 2.24" (57 mm) and thickness of .24" (6 mm).

2) Tape splines and grease drive axle with grease supplied in boot kit. Install BJ boot, new boot bands, and DOJ boot on BJ and axle. Boots for BJ and DOJ are different sizes. Place DOJ cage on shaft with smaller diameter facing BJ. Install circlip, DOJ inner race, and snap ring on axle. Apply grease to DOJ inner race and cage. Fit balls into cage.

3) Apply 1.8-2.8 oz. of grease to outer DOJ race. Install DOJ outer race. Apply another 1.8-2.5 oz. of grease to DOJ outer race and install circlip. Add as much grease to BJ as was removed for inspection. Install BJ boot.

4) When installing DOJ boot bands, make sure to have 3.1" (79 mm) between bands. This distance is necessary to control air in DOJ boot.

DIFFERENTIAL ASSEMBLY

Disassembly

1) Remove cover from differential carrier. Check and note runout of ring gear, preload of ring and drive pinion gears, and backlash of ring and pinion gears. *See Fig. 1.* Mark side bearing caps for reassembly and remove. Remove differential case assembly with wooden lever.

2) Using bearing puller, remove side bearings from case. Keep left and right side bearings and side bearing shims together for reassembly. Mark position of ring gear to differential case for reassembly. Loosen ring gear bolts in diagonal sequence and remove.

3) Drive out differential pinion shaft lock pin from ring gear side. Pull out differential pinion shaft and pinion gears. Remove side gears and thrust spacers, keeping left and right gears and spacers separate.

4) Hold pinion flange and remove self-locking nut. Mark pinion flange-to-pinion position and remove flange. Tap drive pinion end with plastic hammer to force out drive pinion with height adjusting shim, front bearing inner race, spacer, and preload adjusting shim still installed on drive pinion.

5) Using puller, remove drive pinion front bearing inner race and height adjusting shim at same time. Save shim for reassembly. Remove outer pinion bearing races from carrier. When removing pinion rear outer race, remove oil seal and rear inner race at same time.

Inspection

1) Check differential gear tooth contact. Replace damaged or worn parts. Check bearings and races for heat discoloration, seizure, and rough surfaces. Replace any bearing that is defective.

2) Install side gear and circlip on spline end of left drive axle or inner shaft. Measure play of side gear-to-splines with dial indicator. Maximum play allowed is .020" (.5 mm). Check differential pinion gear and shaft for wear or seizure.

Reassembly & Adjustment (Differential Case Assembly)

1) Place side gear thrust spacers behind side gears in original position. Assemble left and right side gears in differential case. Install both pinion gears, with washers attached, at same time. Rotate pinion gears to mesh with side gears. Install differential pinion shaft.

2) Check backlash between pinion and side gears. If limit of .006" (.15 mm) is exceeded, change side gear thrust washer. Left and right backlash should be equal. Align differential pinion shaft with lock pin hole in differential case. Drive lock pin in from back of ring gear. Stake lock pin in 2 places to prevent movement.

3) Remove old adhesive from ring gear bolts and clean internal threads with tap. Align ring gear and case to index marks made on disassembly. Apply Loctite 271 and snug bolts down. Tighten bolts in diagonal pattern.

NOTE: To allow adhesive to harden, keep differential stationary for 1/2 to 1 hour.

Reassembly & Adjustment (Drive Pinion Depth)

1) Press drive pinion outer bearing races into carrier with press or hammer and drift. Make sure race does not cock and that it does bottom in bore of carrier. Install drive pinion bearings on dummy pinion (C-4626-3) and special tools from kit (C-4626). *See Fig. 3.* Lightly grease washer (C-4626-5) and gradually tighten nut (C-4626-6) until drive pinion preload reaches 6-9 INCH lbs. (.7-1.0 N.m).

Fig 3: Setting Pinion Depth

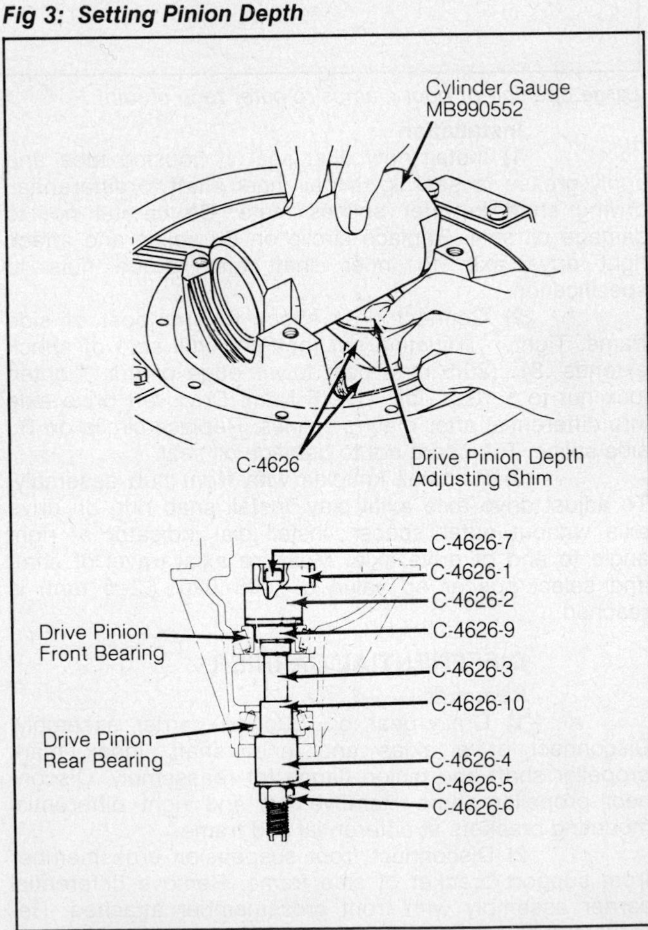
Cylinder Gauge
MB990552
C-4626
Drive Pinion Depth
Adjusting Shim
C-4626-7
C-4626-1
C-4626-2
Drive Pinion
Front Bearing
C-4626-9
C-4626-3
C-4626-10
Drive Pinion
Rear Bearing
C-4626-4
C-4626-5
C-4626-6

Position special tools as shown.

2) Mount special tool (MB990552) in side bearing seat. Make sure side bearing seat is clean and that tool firmly contacts seat. Also make sure cutouts on

Drive Axles

CHRYSLER CORP. IMPORTS & MITSUBISHI INTEGRAL HOUSING (Cont.)

special tool are in position shown. *See Fig. 3.* Select drive pinion depth adjusting shim that just fits gap between tools (MB990552 and C-4626-1).

3) Install selected drive pinion depth adjusting shim between drive pinion and front pinion bearing. Using tool (MB990802), press front pinion bearing onto drive pinion.

Reassembly & Adjustment (Pinion Bearing Preload)

1) Install drive pinion in carrier. Install drive pinion preload shim between pinion spacer and rear pinion bearing. Tighten pinion flange nut to specified torque and check preload.

2) If preload is incorrect, change shim and/or spacer until standard preload value of 6-9 INCH lbs. (.7-1.0 N.m) is reached without oil seal in place. After preload is correct, remove pinion flange.

3) Lightly grease outer edge of oil seal and drive into gear carrier. Lightly grease (50% or more molybdenum disulfide) seal contact surface of pinion flange. Install flange and tighten self-locking nut.

Reassembly & Adjustment (Side Bearing)

1) Press side bearing inner race onto differential case, using special tool (MB990802). Select 2 side bearing adjusting shims that are thinner than those removed and equal to each other. Place shims on each side of case assembly and install case assembly into gear carrier.

2) Push case assembly fully to one side of carrier. Measure clearance between carrier and side bearing shim using 2 feeler gauges at opposite sides of bearing. Remove test shims and measure with micrometer. Select 2 pairs of shims that equal thickness of test shims plus 1/2 of clearance measured plus .002" (.05 mm). Install one pair on each side of case assembly.

NOTE: Make sure no clearance exists between gear carrier and adjusting shim.

3) Install side bearing shims and differential case assembly into gear carrier. Tap side bearing shims with brass bar to fit them to side bearing outer race. Shims cannot be installed later because edge of inner race surface extends beyond surface of outer race.

4) Align marks made on disassembly of carrier side bearing caps and gear carrier. Tighten carrier cap bolts to specification. Set up dial indicator and check ring and drive pinion backlash.

5) If not within standard value of .005-.007" (.13-.18 mm), change side bearing adjusting shims. If backlash is too small, place a thinner shim behind ring gear and a thicker shim opposite ring gear. If backlash is too great, place a thicker shim behind ring gear and a thinner shim opposite the ring gear.

NOTE: Be sure to change shims so that total thickness of all shims remains the same as value determined in step 2).

6) Check runout of ring gear in at least 4 places with a dial indicator. If runout exceeds limit of .002" (.05 mm), change mounting position of ring gear-to-case and remeasure. If runout remains excessive, ring gear or differential case must be replaced.

7) Apply semi-drying sealer to gear carrier surface and cover surface. Install gasket. Tighten cover bolts.

AXLE ASSEMBLY SPECIFICATIONS

Application	In. (mm)
Drive Axle	
Axial Play	.008-.020 (.2-.5)
Double Offset Joint	
Boot Bands (Spacing)	3.1 (79)
Side Gear-to-Drive Axle	
Spline Backlash Limit	.020 (.5)
Differential Pinion-to-Side	
Gear Backlash	.006 (.15)
Ring Gear-to-Drive	
Pinion Backlash	.005-.007 (.13-.18)
Ring Gear Runout (Backside)	.002 (.05)
Shock Stud Adjusting Nut	[1] .81 (20.6)
	INCH Lbs. (N.m)
Drive Pinion Preload	
With Oil Seal	9-11 (1.0-1.2)
Without Oil Seal	6-9 (.7-1.0)

[1] – Measured from top of shock stud to bottom face of adjusting nut.

TIGHTENING SPECIFICATIONS

Application	Ft. Lbs. (N.m)
Knuckle-to-Ball Joint	
Upper	44-65 (60-88)
Lower	87-130 (118-176)
Shock Absorber Jam Nut	6-8 (8-11)
Right Drive Axle-to-	
Inner Shaft Assembly	37-43 (50-58)
Pinion Flange Lock Nut	116-159 (157-215)
Side Bearing Carrier Cap Bolts	40-47 (54-64)
Differential Carrier-to-	
Housing Tube	58-72 (79-98)
Differential Carrier-to-Bracket	58-72 (79-98)
Front Crossmember	73-86 (99-117)
Ring Gear-to-Case Bolts	[1] 58-65 (79-88)
Cover-to-Carrier Bolts	11-15 (15-20)

[1] – Threads coated with Loctite 271.

Drive Axles

CHRYSLER CORP. IMPORTS & MITSUBISHI SEPARATE CARRIER

Chrysler Corp. Imports Challenger Colt Pickup, Ram-50 Pickup & Sapporo; Mitsubishi Pickup & Montero

DESCRIPTION

Rear axle features a rigid banjo type axle housing and semi-floating rear axle shafts. Differential consists of hypoid reduction gears and straight bevel differential gears. A limited slip differential is available in Pickup and Montero models.

Side bearing preload is adjusted by side bearing nuts. Pinion bearing preload, pinion depth, and differential side gear adjustments are made with shims and/or spacers.

AXLE RATIO & IDENTIFICATION

Challenger and Sapporo use a 3.308:1 ratio for both manual and automatic transmissions. Colt and Ram-50 Pickups use a 3.909:1 ratio differential with 4-speed manual transmissions, and a 3.545:1 ratio differential with 5-speed manual and automatic transmissions.

Montero uses a 4.625:1 ratio differential. All other 4-wheel drive models use a 3.909:1 ratio differential with all transmissions. Ratio is determined by dividing number of ring gear teeth by number of drive pinion teeth.

REMOVAL & INSTALLATION

AXLE SHAFTS & BEARINGS

Removal (Pickup & Montero)

1) Raise and support rear axle housing so rear wheels clear ground. Remove rear wheel and brake drum. Disconnect hydraulic line from wheel cylinder.

2) Disconnect bearing case from axle housing. Remove backing plate, bearing case, and axle shaft as an assembly, using puller if required.

3) Remove "O" ring and shims and retain shims for reassembly. Remove and discard inner axle shaft oil seal. Mount backing plate, bearing case, and axle shaft assembly in a vise.

4) Loosen axle shaft bearing lock washer. Remove lock nut from rear of backing plate with spanner (MB990785). Remove washers and reinstall lock nut on axle shaft approximately 3 turns.

5) Attach puller (MB990787-A) at rear of backing plate to remove axle shaft from bearing case. Tighten puller nuts diagonally with equal pressure to avoid binding. Using a hammer and drift, remove bearing outer race from bearing case. Remove oil seal from bearing case.

6) Inspect axle shaft for runout, measuring deflection at face of axle flange with a dial indicator. Maximum axle shaft runout is .004" (0.1 mm). Replace axle shaft if limit is exceeded. Inspect sealing surfaces and splines for wear grooves or cracks. Inspect wheel hub bolts for tightness and bearing outer retainer for deformation. Replace defective parts as necessary.

Installation

1) Apply grease to outer surface of bearing outer race and to lip of new outer oil seal. Drive seal into bearing case. Slide bearing case and bearing over rear axle shaft. Apply grease on bearing rollers. Press bearing inner race onto axle shaft.

2) Install washer, lock washer, and lock nut. Tighten lock nut to specifications. Bend tab on lock washer into groove on lock nut. Apply grease to lip of inner oil seal. Drive oil seal into rear axle housing end.

3) Before assembly operations, remove old sealer and any rust from mating face of bearing case and housing. Insert a .04" (1.0 mm) shim and "O" ring into left side of housing.

4) Apply sealer to mating face of bearing case. Fit left side axle shaft assembly into left side of housing. Tighten bearing case to specifications.

5) Fit right side shaft assembly into right side housing. Do not use a shim or an "O" ring. Temporarily tighten bearing case nuts with a torque of 4 ft. lbs. (6 N.m). Measure gap between bearing case and axle housing with a feeler gauge.

6) Loosen bearing case nuts and separate axle shaft assembly from housing. Select 1 shim with a thickness equivalent to gap measured in step **5)**, and a second shim with a thickness of from .0020-.0079" (.05-.20 mm). Insert selected shims and "O" ring into housing. Apply sealer to mating face of bearing case.

Fig. 1: Exploded View of Pickup Axle Assembly

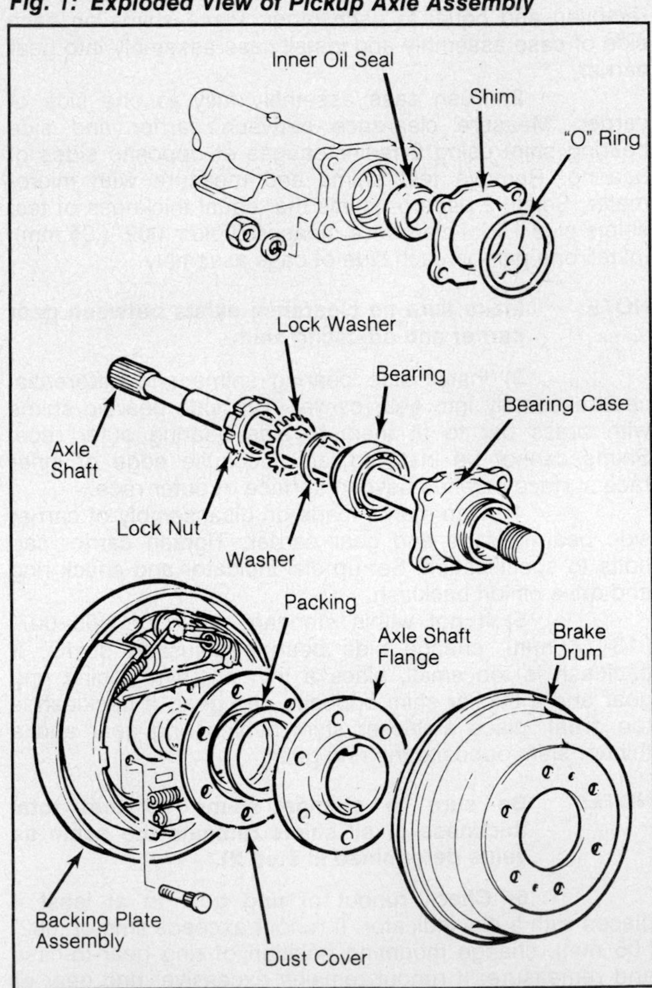
Inner Oil Seal
Shim
"O" Ring
Lock Washer
Bearing
Bearing Case
Axle Shaft
Lock Nut
Washer
Packing
Axle Shaft Flange
Brake Drum
Backing Plate Assembly
Dust Cover

CHRYSLER CORP. IMPORTS & MITSUBISHI SEPARATE CARRIER (Cont.)

7) Fit right side axle shaft assembly into housing and tighten bearing case and bearing to specifications. Check axial play of axle shaft with a dial indicator. Axial play of rear axle shaft should be .002-.008" (.05-.20 mm).

Removal (Except Pickup & Montero)

1) Raise and support rear axle housing so rear wheels clear ground. Remove rear wheel and backing plate nuts.

2) If equipped with disc brakes, remove caliper support together with parking brake rear cable, caliper assembly, and brake hose. Support with wire. Remove brake disc.

3) Remove bolts attaching bearing outer retainer to axle housing through hole in flange. Using puller, remove axle shaft from housing. Set brake backing plate with parking brake attached out of way. Remove oil seal.

4) Inspect axle shaft for runout, measuring at face of axle flange with a dial indicator. Maximum axle shaft runout is .004" (0.1 mm). Check sealing surfaces and splines for grooves or cracks.

5) Replace axle shaft if limit is exceeded or damage is evident. Rear axle bearing should be replaced when bearing noise is detected. Inspect wheel hub bolts for tightness and bearing outer retainer for deformation. Replace as necessary.

6) To remove bearing, grind down bearing retainer at 1 point until retainer thickness is .04-.06" (1.0-1.5 mm). Chisel ground portion and remove retainer. Using bearing puller or press, remove bearing from axle.

Fig. 2: Exploded View of Axle Shaft Assembly (Except Pickup & Montero)

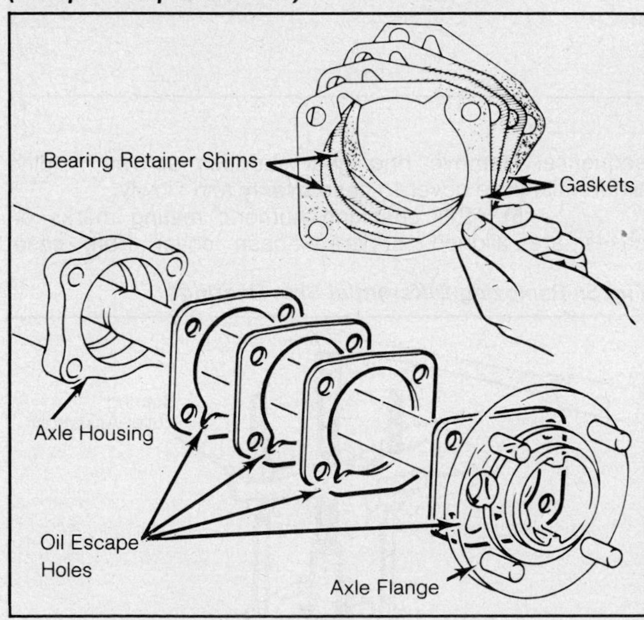
Bearing Retainer Shims
Gaskets
Axle Housing
Oil Escape Holes
Axle Flange

Oil escape holes must face downward.

Installation

1) Install bearing outer retainer, rear wheel bearing, and bearing inner retainer on rear axle shaft. Press rear axle shaft bearing inner retainer until its face is firmly pressed against rear wheel bearing. Make sure pressure applied to install bearing inner retainer is less than 13,200 lbs. (58,800 N).

2) Clean rear axle housing oil seal and apply multi-purpose grease. Tap new oil seal into axle housing until it contacts rear of axle housing. Apply grease to oil seal lip and to oil seal surface which contacts bearing inner retainer.

3) Insert rear axle assembly into rear axle housing, taking care not to damage oil seal. Attach bearing outer retainer, without gasket(s) and shim(s), by tightening in a criss-cross pattern. Tighten to specifications.

4) On models with drum rear brakes, remove rear brake shoes from backing plate. Measure clearance between bearing outer retainer and backing plate. According to measurement obtained, select gasket(s) and bearing retainer shim(s) so that clearance is within standard value of 0-.01" (0-.25 mm).

5) Remove rear axle shaft assembly and install selected gasket(s) and bearing retainer shim(s) with oil escape holes downward. Reassemble as previously described.

6) Check axial play of rear wheel bearing with dial indicator. Axial play limit is .03" (0.8 mm)

DIFFERENTIAL CARRIER

Removal

1) Drain oil from rear axle differential housing. Mark flange yoke-to-pinion flange position and disconnect propeller shaft.

2) Pull out both rear axle shafts 3" (70 mm). Remove differential gear housing mounting nuts and withdraw differential gear carrier. *See Fig. 3*. It may be necessary to tap outside of housing to break gear carrier loose.

Fig. 3: Removing Differential Gear Housing

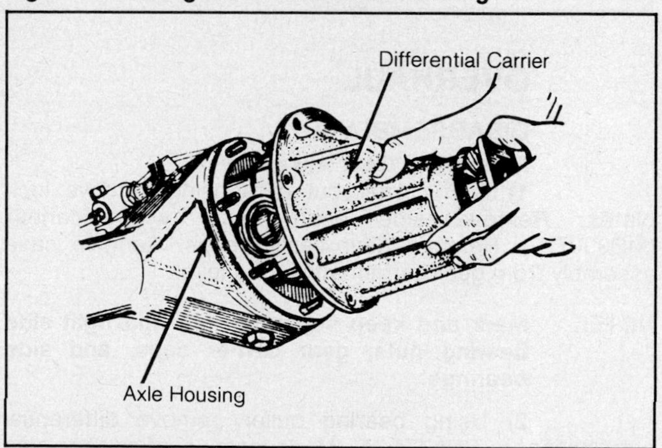
Differential Carrier
Axle Housing

Tap on housing to break loose.

Installation

1) Lightly coat bearings and gears with oil. Apply sealing compound to gear carrier, gasket, and axle housing mating surfaces.

2) Assemble gear carrier to axle housing with nuts and tighten. Fill differential gear housing with 1.4 quarts of multi-purpose gear oil.

CHRYSLER CORP. IMPORTS & MITSUBISHI SEPARATE CARRIER (Cont.)

Fig. 4: Exploded View of Differentials (4WD & RWD)

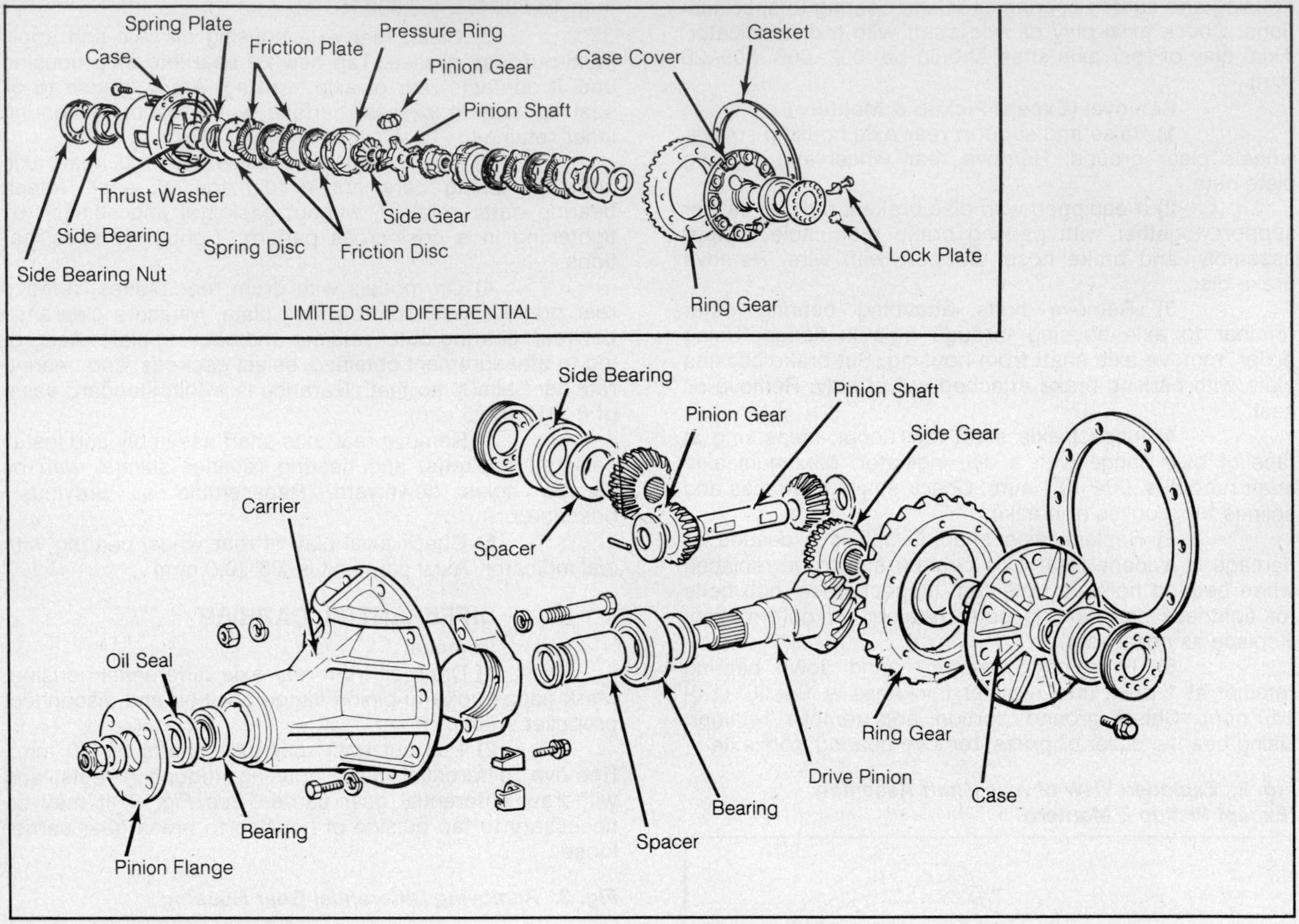

OVERHAUL

DISASSEMBLY

Differential Gear Assembly

1) With carrier out of housing, remove lock plates. Remove side bearing nut with spanner (MB990722). Remove gear carrier caps. Remove case assembly from gear carrier with wood lever.

NOTE: Mark and keep separated left and right side bearing nuts, gear carrier caps, and side bearings.

2) Using bearing puller, remove differential side bearings. *See Fig. 5*. Mark location of case-to-ring gear for reassembly.

3) On conventional units, remove ring gear lock plate tabs and loosen bolts in diagonal sequence. Remove ring gear. Drive out pinion shaft lock pin from differential case with a long punch. Remove differential pinion shaft and pinion gears. Pinion side gears and spacers are now accessible. Note placement of pinion side gear and spacers to ensure reassembly in same position.

4) On limited slip units, mark ring gear-to-case position. *See Fig. 4*. Loosen ring gear bolts in diagonal sequence. Remove ring gear. Loosen screws holding differential case cover to case evenly and slowly.

5) After checking numeric mating marks on cases are aligned, separate case cover from case.

Fig. 5: Removing Differential Side Bearings

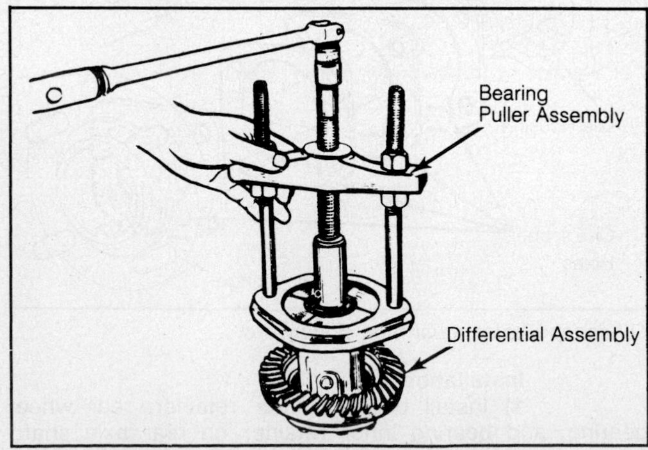
Bearing Puller Assembly
Differential Assembly

Note location of side bearings and spacers for reassembly.

CHRYSLER CORP. IMPORTS & MITSUBISHI SEPARATE CARRIER (Cont.)

Keeping left and right components separate for reassembly, remove components from case.

Drive Pinion

1) Hold pinion flange and remove lock nut. Mark drive pinion-to-flange position for reassembly. Remove pinion flange. Using a wheel puller, force out drive pinion with adjusting shim, rear inner bearing race, spacer and preload adjusting shim.

Fig. 6: Removing Rear Drive Pinion Bearing

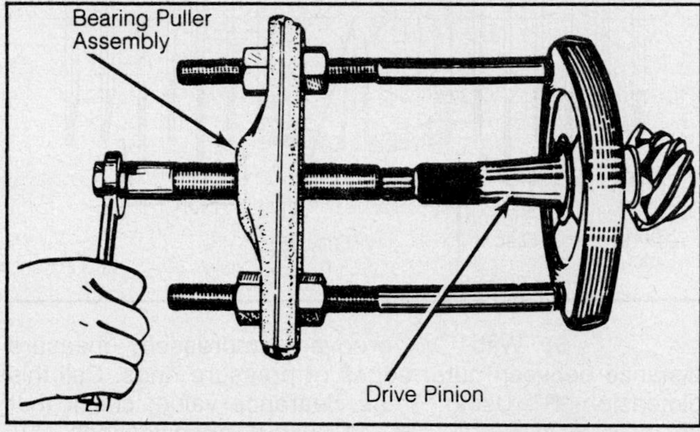
Bearing Puller
Assembly
Drive Pinion

Rear bearing outer race is removed by same method.

2) With bearing puller, remove rear bearing inner race and pull off drive pinion adjusting shim. *See Fig. 6.* Retain depth adjusting shim for reassembly. Using drift, remove front drive pinion bearing outer race, oil seal, and rear bearing outer race.

INSPECTION

Conventional Differential

1) Check differential gears for correct tooth contact and replace gears if wear is excessive. Inspect bearing races for roughness or score marks and replace bearing assembly, if necessary.

2) Ensure splines of side gears and rear axle shafts fit correctly, checking with dial indicator. Backlash limit for axle shaft-to-side gear wear is .024" (0.6 mm) on Pickup and Montero and .02" (0.5 mm) on all other models. Check pinion gears and pinion shaft for seizure or excessive wear, replacing components if necessary.

NOTE: To check gear tooth contact using paint impression method, refer to beginning of this section.

Limited Slip Differential

1) In addition to inspection performed on conventional differentials, all internal contact and sliding surfaces must be checked for wear. Friction discs, friction plates, spring plates, and spring discs should be replaced if signs of seizure, color change from excessive heat, or severe friction are evident.

NOTE: Heavier contact wear on inner circumference of friction surfaces is due to spring plate and spring disc pressure and is considered normal.

2) Check 6 projections on inner circumference of friction disc. Repair nicks or dents with an oil stone. Replace friction disc if damage is too severe.

3) Check 4 projections on outer edge of friction plate. Repair nicks or dents with oil stone. Replace plate if necessary. Check friction surface of pressure ring. Repair nicks and scratches. First grind with oil stone and then polish with rubbing compound on surfacing plate.

4) Check sliding surfaces of thrust washers, differential case, hole in pressure rings, outer circumference of side gears, and thrust blocks. Check contact surfaces of spring-to-case, outer circumference of pressure rings, and inner circumference of case. Check outer projections of pressure rings, spherical surface of pinion gears, and inner diameter of pressure rings.

5) Check "V" shape in pressure rings and pinion shaft. Check outer diameter of pinion shaft and hole in pinion gears. Check outer circumference groove of side gears and inner circumference groove of differential case. Repair any nicks or burrs found with oil stone.

6) Measure warping of friction plates and discs on surfacing plate, using a dial indicator. Maximum warping allowed is .003" (.08 mm). Measure thicknesses of projections and friction surfaces of friction plates and discs at several points, using a micrometer. Maximum wear allowed (difference between thickness of projection and thickness of friction surface) is .004" (0.1 mm).

7) Measure thickness of thrust washer at several points, using a micrometer. Minimum thickness of thrust washer is .055" (1.4 mm).

REASSEMBLY & ADJUSTMENT

Case Assembly (Conventional)

1) Install thrust spacers behind side gears in their original position and assemble pinion and side gears in differential. Insert both pinion gears, with pinion washers attached, so they mesh with side gears. It may be necessary to slightly rotate pinions to achieve desired meshing. Insert differential pinion shaft without lock pin.

2) Check pinion and side gear backlash as shown in *Fig. 7*. If backlash is beyond .002-.005" (.05-.127 mm) on Pickup and Montero or .006" (.15 mm) on all other models, adjust by selecting a side gear thrust washer (spacer) of correct size. If backlash is to be adjusted, ensure right and left sides are equally shimmed.

Fig. 7: Checking Differential and Side Gear Backlash

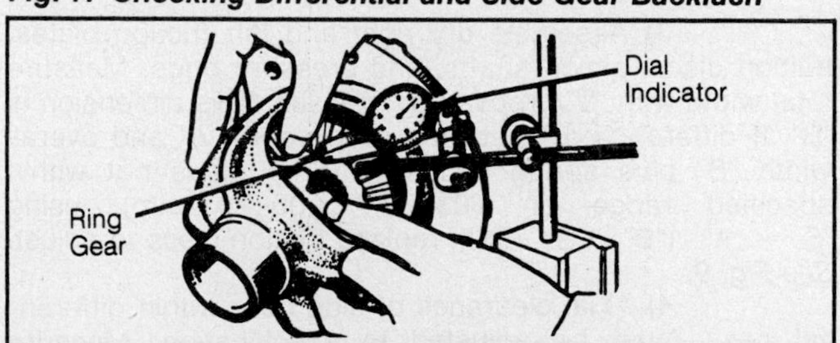
Dial
Indicator
Ring
Gear

Right and left sides must be equally shimmed.

3) Align drive pinion shaft with drive pinion shaft lock pin hole in differential case and drive lock pin into hole from back side of ring gear. Securely stake lock pin in 2 places to prevent movement.

4) Remove old adhesive from ring gear mounting bolts and gear mounting surface. Clean internal threads with tap. Apply Loctite 271 to bolts and install.

CHRYSLER CORP. IMPORTS & MITSUBISHI SEPARATE CARRIER (Cont.)

Make certain to align mating marks on differential case and ring gear. Tighten bolts alternately in diagonal sequence to specified torque.

NOTE: To harden adhesive, keep differential stationary for 1/2 to 1 hour.

Case Assembly (Limited Slip)

1) Before assembly, clearance between clutch plates and differential case must be adjusted to specifications. Determine depth "A" of differential case, using formula "A" = "E" - "F" + "G". *See Fig. 8.*

Fig. 8: Measuring Case Depth

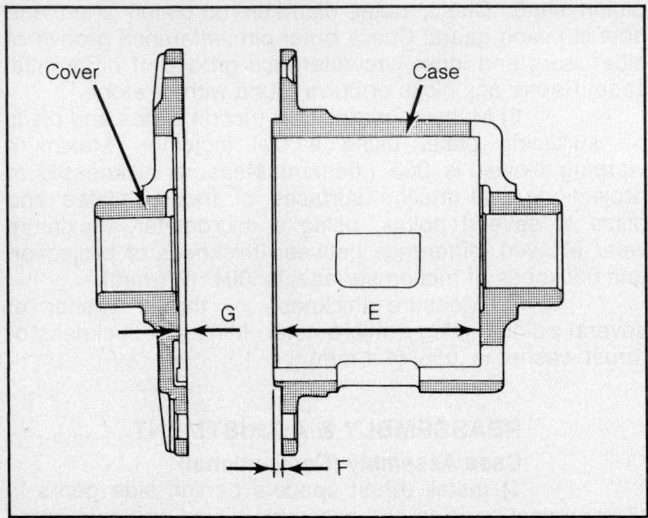

Cover
Case
G
E
F

This applies to limited slip models.

2) Place spring disc over spring plate with both facing same direction. Measuring with a micrometer, arrange them so that difference between right-hand set (Sr) and left-hand set (Sl) is as small as possible. Combine 2 friction discs and 2 friction plates from right-hand set (Fr) and 2 friction discs and 2 friction plates from left-hand set (Fl). Rotate discs and plates until minimum difference between Fr and Fl is reached. *See Fig. 9.*

NOTE: Difference between (Sr + Fr) and (Sl + Fl) must be .002" (.05 mm) or less.

3) Assemble dry right and left friction plates, friction discs, pinion shafts, and pressure rings. Measure total width with "V" groove compressed. This dimension is "B". If difference "S" between case depth "A" and overall width "B" plus spring thickness (Sr+ Sl) is not within specified range of .003-.007" (.06-.20 mm), using "S" = "A" - ("B" + Sr + Sl), replace friction discs to adjust. *See Fig. 9.*

4) Axial clearance of side gear within differential case must be adjusted to specification. Measure depths of thrust washer contact surfaces of cases. Call these dimensions "C" and "D". Assemble pressure rings, pinion gears, side gears, pinion shafts, and thrust washers.

5) With calipers, measure from outer face of pressure rings to outer edge of thrust washers while compressing "V" groove manually. Thrust washers should be selected so difference between right and left measured values is less than .002" (.05 mm).

Fig. 9: Assembling Order and Direction

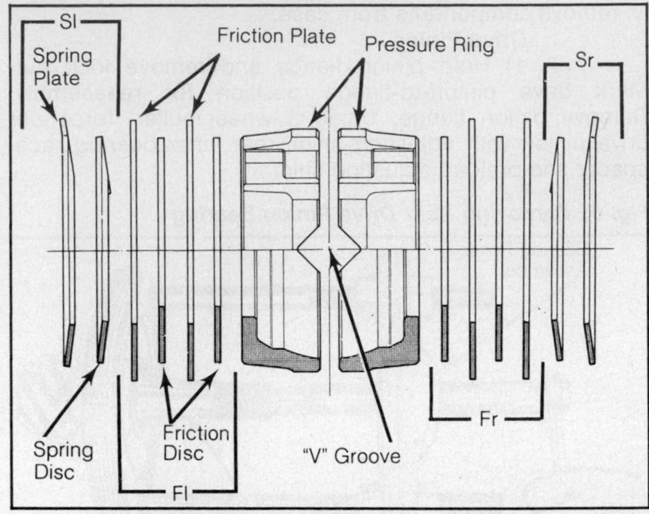

Sl
Spring Plate
Friction Plate
Pressure Ring
Sr
Spring Disc
Friction Disc
"V" Groove
Fr
Fl

6) With "V" groove compressed, measure distance between outer edges of pressure rings. Call this dimension "R". Using "T" as clearance value, check that "T" = "A" + "C" + "D" - "R" is within specifications. "T" value is .002-.007" (.05-.20 mm). If "T" is not within specification, replace thrust washers to adjust.

7) Before assembling, apply gear oil to all components. Ensure assembly order and direction of spring plates is correct. *See Fig. 9.* Align marks on differential cases. After assembly, use special tool (MB990988) to check starting torque necessary to overcome frictional force of clutch plates.

8) Clutch plate starting torque for new plates is 44-72 ft. lbs. (60-98 N.m). For plates that are being reused, starting torque value is 22-57 ft. lbs. (30-77 N.m). Clean old adhesive from ring gear bolts and internal threads (with tap). Apply Loctite 271 to bolts, tighten evenly, and then torque to specification in a diagonal pattern.

NOTE: To harden adhesive, keep differential stationary for 1/2 to 1 hour.

Drive Pinion Depth

1) Using a drift and hammer or a press, seat front and rear pinion bearing outer races into gear carrier ensuring that outer races do not cock. Be sure bearing races are completely seated in bore of gear carrier before proceeding.

2) Install drive pinion bearings with dummy pinion shaft (C-4626-3) and special tools from kit (C-4626) into gear carrier. Apply light grease to washer (C-4626-5) before tightening. *See Fig. 10.* Gradually increase preload of drive pinion bearings by tightening special tool to a standard value of 6-9 INCH lbs. (.7-1.0 N.m) on Pickup and Montero or 7-13 INCH lbs. (.8-1.5 N.m) on all other models.

3) Clean side bearing seats thoroughly and mount special tool (MB990552) in side bearing seats. Make sure that cutout flats on special tool (MB990552) are in position shown and that tool is contacting side bearing seat firmly. *See Fig. 10.* Select drive pinion depth adjusting shim with same thickness as gap between special tools (MB990552 and C-4626).

CHRYSLER CORP. IMPORTS & MITSUBISHI SEPARATE CARRIER (Cont.)

Fig. 10: Setting Pinion Depth

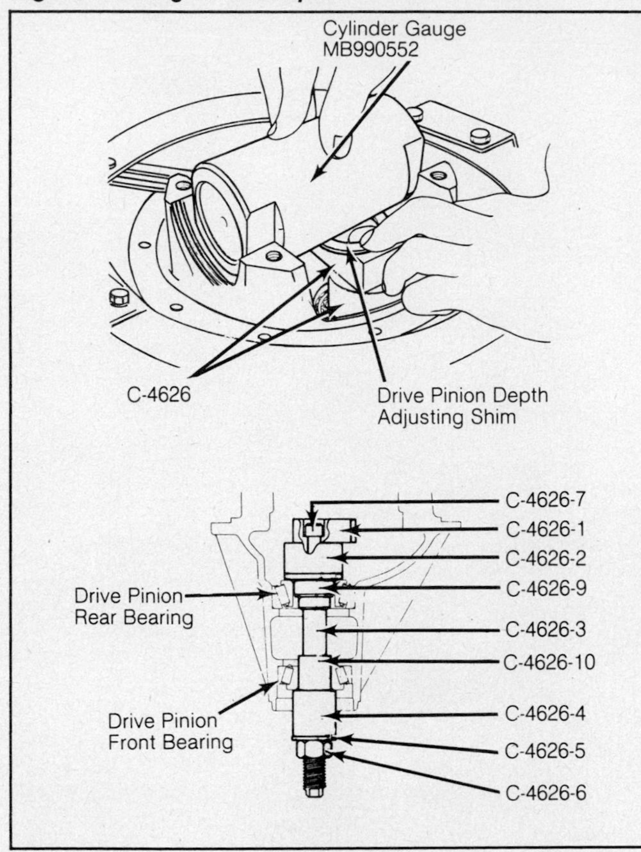
Cylinder Gauge
MB990552
C-4626
Drive Pinion Depth
Adjusting Shim
C-4626-7
C-4626-1
C-4626-2
C-4626-9
Drive Pinion
Rear Bearing
C-4626-3
C-4626-10
Drive Pinion
Front Bearing
C-4626-4
C-4626-5
C-4626-6

Position special tools as shown.

4) Install selected drive pinion depth adjusting shim between drive pinion gear and rear drive pinion bearing. Press rear pinion bearing onto pinion shaft with special tool (MB990802 for Pickup and Montero or MB990728 for all other models).

Drive Pinion Preload

1) Install drive pinion in gear carrier. From front side of gear carrier, install pinion spacer, pinion spacer front shim, front pinion bearing inner race, and pinion flange in order listed. Holding pinion flange, tighten lock nut to specified torque.

2) Measure preload of drive pinion front and rear bearings and compare to standard value (without oil seal) of 6-9 INCH lbs. (.7-1.0 N.m) on Pickup and Montero or 7-13 INCH lbs. (.8-1.5 N.m) on all other models. If measurement is not within standard value, adjust bearing preload by changing pinion spacer shim and/or pinion spacer.

3) Remove pinion flange and drive pinion from gear carrier. Lightly grease outer edge of new pinion oil seal and drive it into gear carrier. Apply a molybdenum disulfide grease to oil seal lip. Install drive pinion carefully through seal and insert pinion flange. Lightly greasing flange washer, install washer and new lock nut. Tighten new lock nut to specified torque.

4) Measure preload of drive pinion front and rear bearings and compare to standard value (with oil seal) of 10-16 INCH lbs. (1.1-1.8 N.m).

Side Bearing

1) Press side bearing inner races onto differential case, using special tool (MB990802 on Pickup and Montero and MB990728 on all other models). Install differential carrier in housing and install outer races. Align bearing cap index marks and snug carrier cap bolts with fingers.

2) Install side bearing nuts. Torque carrier cap-to-carrier bolts. Screw in side bearing nut on each side of drive gear using special tool (MB990201) to adjust standard backlash value. Turn bearing nuts in and out until rotation is smooth and then tighten to 11 lbs. (50 N.), using tension gauge at end of special tool (MB990201).

3) Set up dial indicator to measure backlash at ring gear tooth. Check that backlash is within standard value of .005-.007" (.13-.18 mm). If backlash is less than standard value, loosen side bearing nut at back of ring gear and tighten side bearing nut on tooth side of gear by same amount.

4) After adjusting backlash, tighten both side bearing nuts by 1/2 pitch to preload side bearings. One pitch is distance between 2 adjacent holes on face of side bearing nuts. Recheck backlash and, if correct, choose and install proper type lockplate and tighten to specified torque.

Ring Gear Runout

Set up dial indicator to back side of ring gear and measure runout at 4 or more points. If ring gear has excessive runout, change mounting position of ring gear-to-differential case. Replace ring gear or differential case as necessary if runout still exceeds .002" (.05 mm).

NOTE: **Check gear tooth contact using paint impression method described at beginning of this section.**

Final Inspection & Assembly

1) Lightly coat each gear and bearing before and during reassembly with gear oil. After installing each component, ensure all rotating parts are free to move smoothly.

2) Install differential gear assembly to axle housing after applying sealing agent and tighten gear carrier mounting nuts in diagonal sequence. Make sure embossed portion of gear assembly is on vent side of axle housing on Pickup models.

3) Tighten brake backing plate lock nuts on Pickup and Montero or bearing outer retainer nuts on all other models. Bleed brake hydraulic system completely. Fill axle housing with gear oil (SAE 90 above -10°F). On limited slip models, gear oil additive-friction modifier must be used in addition to hypoid gear oil.

4) On models with limited slip, preload of differentia! must be checked. Put transmission in neutral, lock front wheels, and release parking brake fully. One rear wheel should be on ground and other raised up. Remove raised wheel.

5) Mount special tool (MB990767) to hub bolts with hub nuts. Measure axle shaft starting torque in forward direction with torque wrench. Standard value for limited slip differential preload is 11 ft. lbs. (15 N.m) using special tool (MB990767). Without using special tool, value for preload is 20 ft. lbs. (27 N.m). If preload torque value is less than specified, limited slip differential must be removed and repaired.

Drive Axles

CHRYSLER CORP. IMPORTS & MITSUBISHI SEPARATE CARRIER (Cont.)

AXLE ASSEMBLY SPECIFICATIONS

Application	In. (mm)
Axial Play of Axle Shaft	
Pickup & Montero	.002-.008 (.05-.20)
All Others	0-.01 (0-.25)
Differential Pinion and Side Gear Backlash	
Pickup & Montero	.002-.005 (.05-.013)
All Others	.006 (.15) Max.
Drive Pinion and Ring Gear Backlash	
Pickup & Montero	.005-.007 (.13-.18)
All Others	.004-.006 (.11-.16)
Ring Gear Runout (Backside)	0-.002 (0-.05)

TIGHTENING SPECIFICATIONS

Application	Ft. Lbs. (N.m)
Outer Bearing Retainer	25-36 (34-49)
Ring Gear-to-Differential Case	58-65 (79-88)
Pinion Flange-to-Pinion (Final Torque)	
Pickup & Montero	138-180 (187-244)
All Others	137-181 (186-245)
Differential Carrier Cap	
Pickup & Montero	40-47 (54-64)
All Others	25-29 (34-39)
Differential Gear Carrier Assembly-to-Axle Housing	18-22 (25-29)
Lock Plate	11-16 (15-22)

DATSUN/NISSAN INTEGRAL HOUSING

280ZX & Maxima Sedan (Rear)
4WD Pickup (Front)

DESCRIPTION

The axle assembly is a hypoid gear-type with integral carrier housing. The pinion bearing preload adjustment is made with a spacer and washer between the front and rear bearing cones.

The differential side bearing preload and pinion depth adjustment are made by shims. Driving power is transmitted to the axle by ball spline type drive shaft with universal joints at both ends.

AXLE RATIO & IDENTIFICATION

Datsun does not identify axles with a particular external identification marking. One basic type of axle assembly is used, with differences in ring gear diameter between model applications.

The R180 (180 mm ring gear) is used as the rear axle assembly on all Maxima sedans, all automatic transmission 280ZX models, and 2-seater 280ZX models with manual transmission. The R180 is also used as the front axle in all 4WD Pickups.

The R200 (200 mm ring gear) is used in all 280ZX Grand Luxury and Turbo models with manual transmission. To determine axle ratio, divide the number of ring gear teeth by the number of drive pinion gear teeth.

REMOVAL & INSTALLATION

FRONT AXLE DRIVE SHAFTS & BEARINGS

Removal (4WD Pickup)

NOTE: To remove locking hub, refer to Locking Hubs article in this section, then proceed with removal procedure. Ensure locking knob is set to "Lock" before removal.

1) Raise and support vehicle. Remove tire and wheel. Remove caliper assembly. Remove locking hub cover retaining screws, and remove cover. Remove drive clutch snap ring and drive clutch. Remove rebound bumper and stabilizer bar-to-lower link bolt.

2) Remove axle shaft-to-differential carrier bolts and remove axle shaft. To ease removal, turn steering wheel in opposite direction.

3) Remove knuckle arm-to-knuckle bolt. Support lower control arm with a jack and remove nuts holding upper and lower ball joints to control arms. Remove knuckle.

4) Using a screwdriver, straighten lock washer. Remove front wheel lock nut. Remove and discard lock washer and special washer. Remove inner grease seal. Push wheel bearing support out of wheel hub.

5) Separate hub from knuckle, using a slide hammer type puller. Remove bearing collar from spindle.

6) Drive out inner wheel bearing and grease seal by tapping outer race with brass drift and hammer. Separate hub and rotor. Remove outer wheel bearing and grease seal. Remove drive shaft bearing from bearing support with a drift.

Fig. 1: Exploded View of 4WD Pickup Front Axle

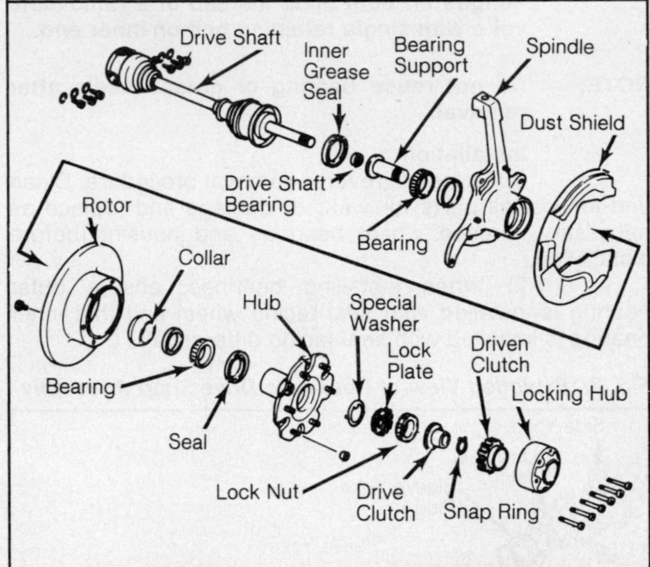
Drive Shaft
Inner Grease Seal
Bearing Support
Spindle
Dust Shield
Drive Shaft Bearing
Rotor
Bearing
Collar
Hub
Special Washer
Lock Plate
Driven Clutch
Locking Hub
Bearing
Seal
Lock Nut
Drive Clutch
Snap Ring

Installation

1) To install, reverse removal procedure. Coat bearings and seals with grease and ensure seals are installed properly. Install same bearing collar that was removed, or use new bearing collar of same number. Always use new lock washer.

2) Tighten lock nut to specifications, and turn hub several times in both directions to seat bearing. Attach a spring gauge to steel stud, and check that wheel bearing preload is 2.2-9.5 lbs. (1.0-4.3 kg).

3) If preload is higher than specified, replace bearing collar with a thicker collar (increase stamped number by 1).

4) If preload is lower than specified, replace bearing collar with a thinner collar (decrease stamped number by 1). Repeat procedure until correct preload is obtained.

5) When bearing preload is correct, bend lock washer tab up into lock nut groove, and install hub and knuckle assembly.

6) Before installing locking hub cover, adjust drive axle end play to .004-.012" (.1-.3 mm) by using a snap ring of proper thickness. Snap rings are available in 5 thicknesses from .043-.075" (1.1-1.9 mm) in .008" (.2 mm) increments.

REAR AXLE DRIVE SHAFTS & BEARINGS

Removal (Except 4WD Pickup)

1) Raise and support vehicle. Remove tire and wheel. On Maxima models, remove brake drum. On 280ZX models, disconnect hydraulic line at caliper, and remove caliper and disc.

2) Disconnect drive shaft from axle shaft. Remove wheel bearing lock nut using rear axle adapter (KV40101000) and bar.

3) Draw out axle shaft using rear axle adapter and slide hammer. Remove companion flange. Remove grease seal and inner bearing using a drift. Withdraw outer bearing from rear axle shaft using bearing puller.

DATSUN/NISSAN INTEGRAL HOUSING (Cont.)

NOTE: 280ZX models with R200 differential use flanges on both ends instead of a removable yoke with single retaining bolt on inner end.

NOTE: Do not reuse bearing or grease seals after removal.

Installation

1) To install, reverse removal procedure. Clean and inspect all parts for wear or damage and replace as necessary. Grease wheel bearings and housing before installation.

2) When installing bearings, ensure outer bearing is installed with seal facing wheel and that inner bearing is installed with seal facing differential.

Fig. 2: Exploded View of Rear Axle Drive Shaft Assembly

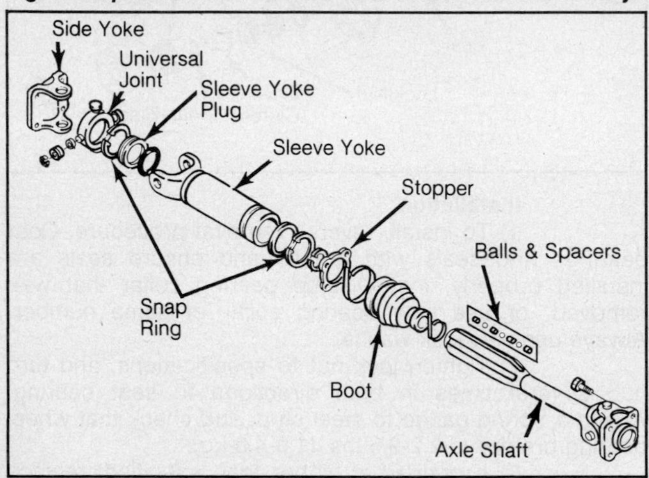
Side Yoke
Universal Joint
Sleeve Yoke Plug
Sleeve Yoke
Stopper
Balls & Spacers
Snap Ring
Boot
Axle Shaft

R200 differential shown.

3) Axle housings are stamped with letter "M", "N" or "P". Be sure bearing spacer of same stamping is installed. Tighten lock nut to specifications and check that axle shaft end play is 0-.012" (0-.3 mm).

Fig. 3: Exploded View of Maxima Sedan Rear Axle

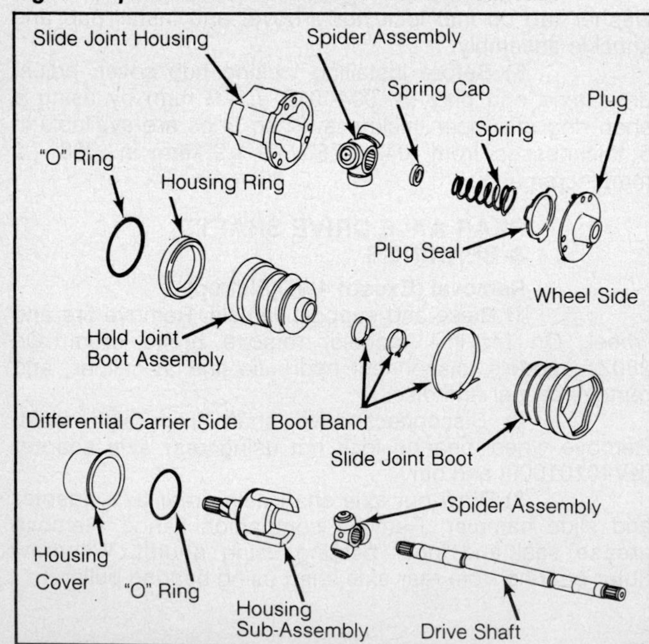
Slide Joint Housing
Spider Assembly
Spring Cap
Plug
Spring
"O" Ring
Housing Ring
Plug Seal
Wheel Side
Hold Joint Boot Assembly
Differential Carrier Side
Boot Band
Slide Joint Boot
Spider Assembly
Housing Cover
"O" Ring
Housing Sub-Assembly
Drive Shaft

Datsun 4WD Pickup front axle similar.

4) If either adjustment is not correct, replace bearing spacer and repeat procedure. Bleed and adjust brakes.

PINION FLANGE & OIL SEAL

Removal

Raise and support vehicle. Drain differential. Disconnect propeller shaft from pinion flange. Hold pinion flange and remove pinion nut. Remove flange with puller. Remove oil seal.

Installation

1) To install, reverse removal procedure. Apply grease between seal lips before installation. Tighten pinion nut to specifications.

2) Be sure pinion bearing preload is correctly adjusted. Fill differential to proper level with gear oil.

AXLE ASSEMBLY

NOTE: Drive shafts of 280ZX models are connected to R180 differential with yokes and to R200 differential with companion flanges.

Removal

1) Raise and support rear of vehicle. Drain differential gear oil. Disconnect propeller shaft at companion flange. Disconnect drive shafts at each wheel, and remove side yoke fixing bolts at differential. Remove side yokes and drive shaft assemblies.

2) On 280ZX, remove front shield. On all models, support differential on jack, and remove mounting bolts at suspension members. On Maxima models, remove nut on end of differential bracket. On all models, lower assembly on jack and remove from vehicle.

NOTE: Support suspension member on a stand to prevent damage to insulators.

Installation

To install, reverse removal procedure. Tighten all nuts and bolts to specifications. Fill assembly to correct level with gear oil.

OVERHAUL

FRONT AXLE DRIVE SHAFT

NOTE: Manufacturer does not recommend disassembly of front drive shaft on 4WD Pickup. Replace as complete assembly only.

REAR AXLE DRIVE SHAFT

Disassembly (Except 4WD Pickup)

1) Remove universal joint from differential end of drive shaft. Remove snap ring from sleeve yoke plug and remove plug. Compress drive shaft, and remove snap ring from stopper. Remove stopper.

2) Disconnect boot, and separate drive shaft carefully so as not to lose balls and spacers.

Cleaning & Inspection

1) Check rubber boot and oil seals for damage, and replace as necessary. Inspect drive shaft for straightness, cracks, damage, and distortion. Replace drive shaft if necessary.

2) Check all other components for wear, damage, and distortion. Replace complete drive shaft

DATSUN/NISSAN INTEGRAL HOUSING (Cont.)

assembly if any faulty part is found. Check drive shaft play as shown in *Fig. 4*. Replace complete assembly if play exceeds .04" (1 mm) on Maxima or .008" (.2 mm) on 280ZX.

NOTE: **Measurement should be taken with drive shaft fully compressed.**

Fig. 4: Measuring Play in Rear Drive Shaft

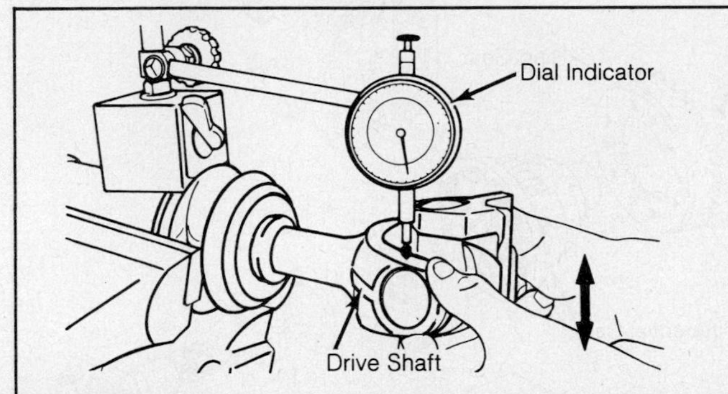
Dial Indicator
Drive Shaft

Move shaft up and down with dial indicator installed.

Reassembly

1) To reassemble, reverse disassembly procedure, and note the following. Align yokes. Be sure steel balls and spacers are installed in correct order.

2) Adjust distance between spider journals (measured from center-to-center) to length of 13.54" (344 mm). Cover sleeve yoke with boot, and secure with boot band.

3) Adjust axial play of universal joint to within .008" (.2 mm) by use of snap rings. Snap rings of equal thickness must be installed on each end of yoke sleeves.

4) Apply grease to ball grooves and oil grooves with about 1 1/4 ozs. (35 g) of oil in bottom end of sleeve yoke.

DIFFERENTIAL

NOTE: **Front axle assembly of 4WD Pickup is overhauled in same manner as that for Maxima models (R180 differential).**

Disassembly

1) Mount differential carrier assembly in holding fixture, and remove rear mounting member and cover

Fig. 5: Exploded View of Datsun R180 Integral Carrier Differential Assembly

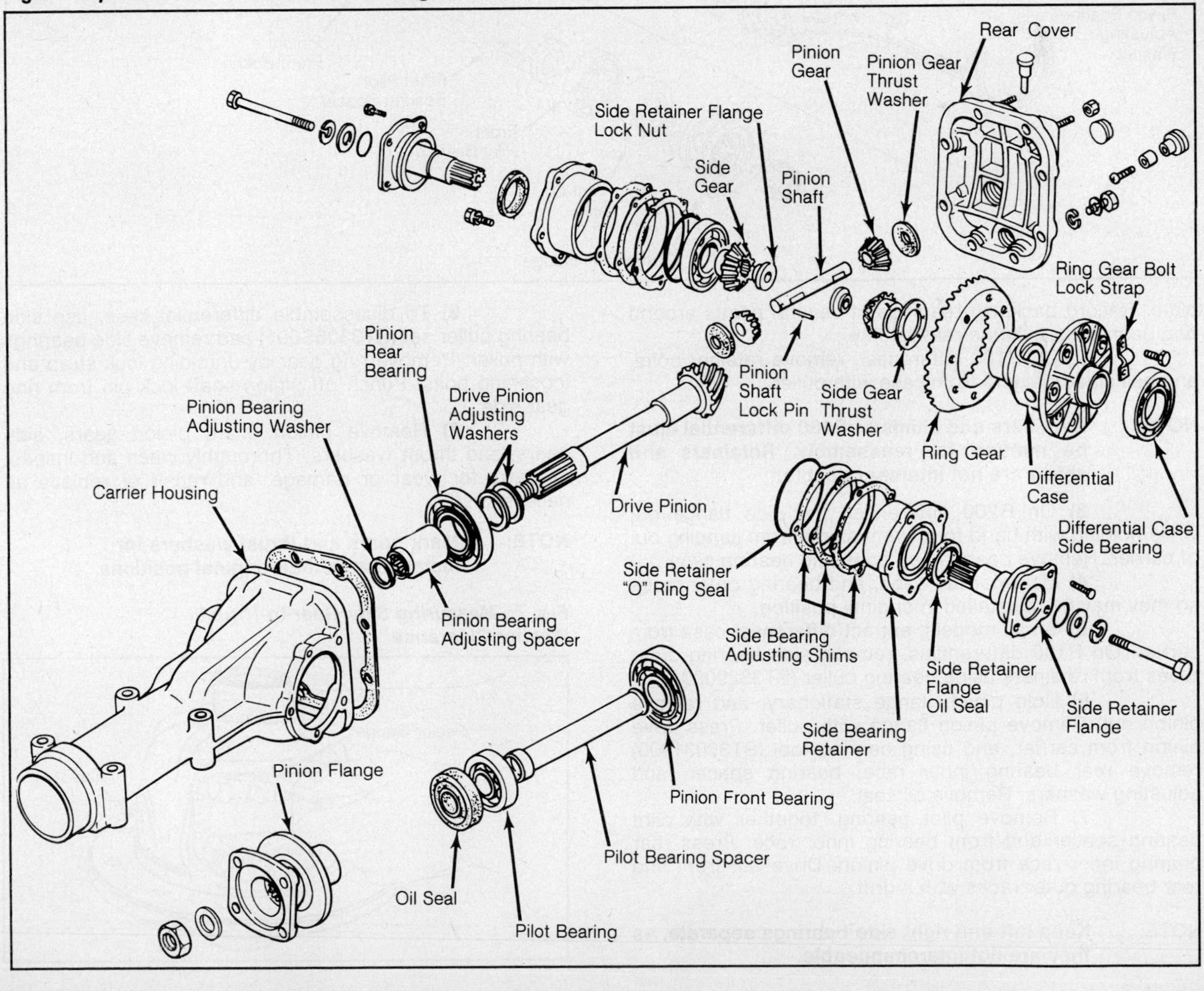

DATSUN/NISSAN INTEGRAL HOUSING (Cont.)

Fig. 6: Exploded View of Datsun R200 Integral Carrier Differential Assembly

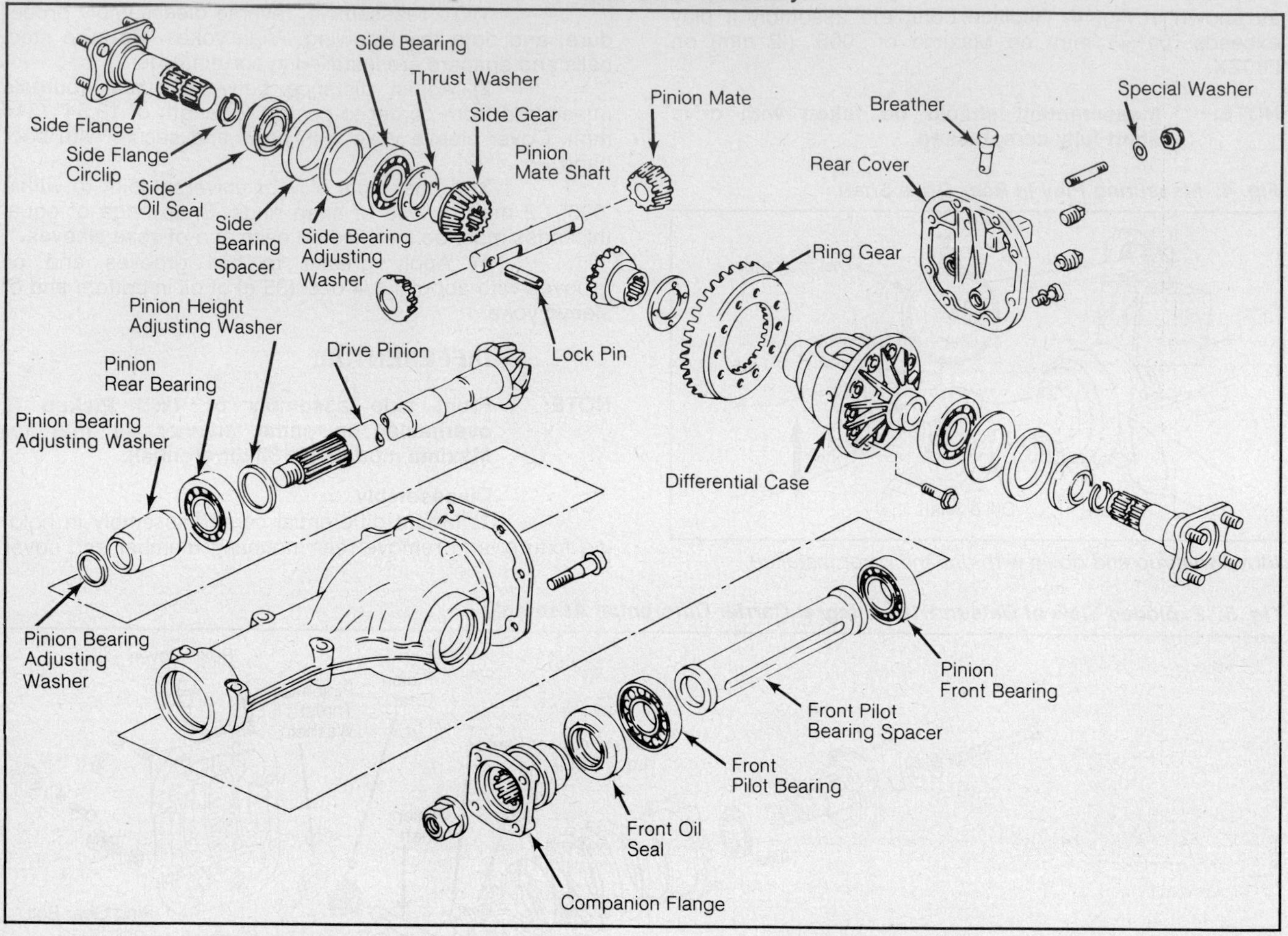

plate. Record backlash readings at several points around ring gear for use during reassembly.

2) On R180 differential, remove retainer bolts, and pull side retainers from case with puller.

NOTE: Retainers and shims of R180 differential must be marked for reassembly. Retainers and shims are not interchangeable.

3) On R200 differential, pry side flange out while holding with hand to prevent shims from jumping out of carrier. Remove bearing cap bolts and bearing caps.

4) Mark carrier, caps, and bearing outer races so they may be reinstalled in original position.

5) On all models, extract differential case from carrier. On R180 differentials, remove side bearing outer races from retainers using bearing puller (ST33290001).

6) Hold pinion flange stationary, and remove pinion nut. Remove pinion flange with puller. Press drive pinion from carrier, and using bearing tool (ST30031000) remove rear bearing inner race, bearing spacer, and adjusting washers. Remove oil seal.

7) Remove pilot bearing, together with pilot bearing spacer and front bearing inner race. Press rear bearing inner race from drive pinion. Drive out front and rear bearing outer races with a drift.

NOTE: Keep left and right side bearings separate, as they are not interchangeable

8) To disassemble differential case, use side bearing puller set (ST3306S001) and remove side bearings with puller. Remove ring gear by unfolding lock strap and loosening bolts. Punch off pinion shaft lock pin from ring gear side.

9) Remove pinion shaft, pinion gears, side gears, and thrust washers. Thoroughly clean and inspect all parts for wear or damage, and repair or replace as necessary.

NOTE: Mark gears and thrust washers for installation in their original positions.

Fig. 7: Measuring Side Gear-to-Thrust Washer Clearance

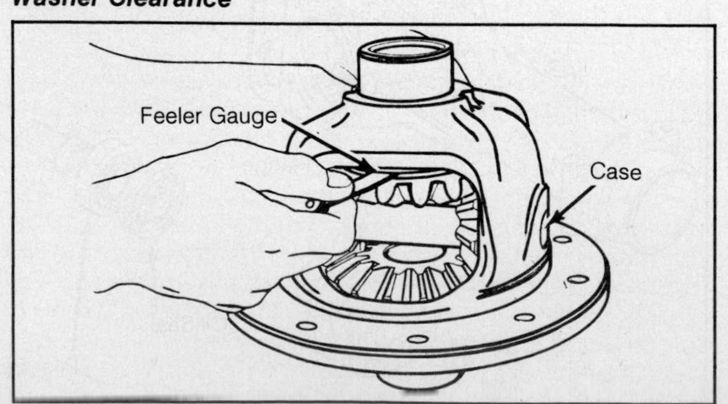
Feeler Gauge
Case

Drive Axles

DATSUN/NISSAN INTEGRAL HOUSING (Cont.)

Reassembly & Adjustment
(Differential Case Assembly)

1) Assemble pinion gears, side gears, and thrust washers in original positions in differential case. Fit pinion shaft to differential case so that it aligns with lock pin holes.

2) Adjust side gear-to-pinion gear backlash, or adjust clearance between rear face of side gear and thrust washer. Install pinion shaft lock pin and lock in place with punch.

3) Apply gear oil to gear tooth surface and thrust surfaces, and ensure gears rotate smoothly. Install ring gear on differential case, and install bolts and new lock washers.

NOTE: Tighten ring gear bolts diagonally, while tapping around bolt heads with hammer.

4) When replacing side bearings, measure bearing thickness with a .787" (20 mm) gauge and weight block (ST32501000). Bearing thickness should be slightly smaller than gauge. *See Fig. 8.*

5) Using adapter, (ST33061000) press fit side bearing inner race on differential case and side bearing outer race into side retainers. Install new oil seal on side retainer, and apply grease to cavity between seal lips.

NOTE: R200 differential has non-removable side bearing retainers. R200 bearings are .827" (21 mm) wide.

Fig. 8: Measuring Side Bearing Thickness

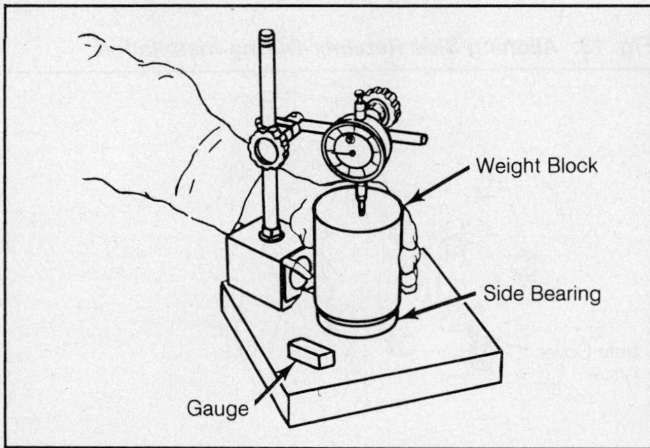
Weight Block
Side Bearing
Gauge

Bearing width should be smaller than gauge.

Reassembly and Adjustment
(Drive Pinion Bearing Preload)

1) Using outer race drift set, (ST30611000, ST30621000 and ST30701000) install front and rear bearing outer races into carrier. Install dummy pinion shaft (ST31212000) with rear bearing and original pinion depth washer between bearing and pinion head.

2) If ring and pinion gear contact pattern was NOT correct at time of disassembly, use new pinion depth washer .122" (3.09 mm) thick.

3) Install pinion bearing preload spacer (ST31851000) and washer, front bearing cone, drive pinion dummy collar, (ST31214000) companion flange, and nut onto dummy shaft. Do not install oil seal at this time. Tighten nut to specified torque.

4) If pinion shaft cannot be turned by hand during entire process of tightening nut, replace preload spacer and washer with thicker ones.

5) Using an INCH Lb. torque wrench, check rotating torque of pinion shaft. If preload is not within specification, install a thicker adjusting washer to decrease preload torque or a thinner washer to increase preload torque.

Fig. 9: Checking Drive Pinion Bearing Preload

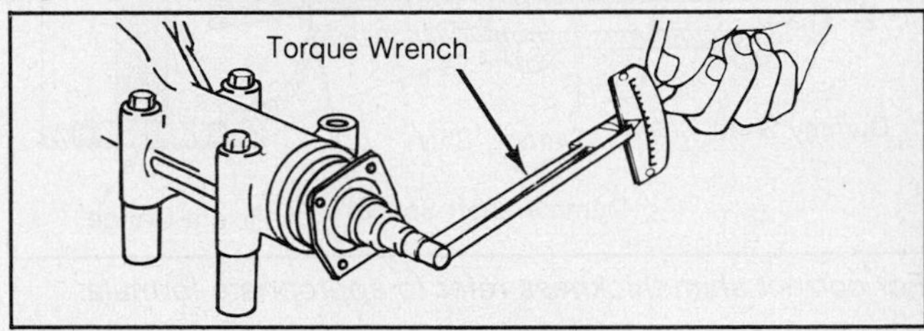
Torque Wrench

Preload torque is adjusted with shims.

Reassembly & Adjustment
(Drive Pinion Gear Installed Height)

1) Leave dummy drive shaft installed (as described under Preload Adjustment), and install height gauge (ST31211000) into bearing bores of carrier. Measure clearance between end of pinion gear head and height gauge using feeler gauge.

2) Thickness of drive pinion height adjusting shim can be determined by the appropriate formula in the Pinion Height Shim Formulas table.

NOTE: Formula values are given in millimeters. If values signifying H, D, and S are not given, regard them as zero.

PINION HEIGHT SHIM FORMULAS

Differential Application	Formula
R180	T = W + N - ((H - D' - S) x .01) - .2
R200	T = N - ((H - D') x .01) + 3.0

T = Thickness of adjusting washer needed.
W = Thickness of washer temporarily installed.
N = Clearance between gauge and dummy shaft.
H = Figure marked on drive pinion head.
D = Figure marked on dummy shaft.
S = Figure marked on height gauge.

3) After determining correct thickness of required pinion height adjusting washer, remove dummy shaft and height gauge. Fit correct pinion height adjusting washer on drive pinion gear, and using adapter (ST30901000) press fit rear bearing inner race.

4) Lubricate pinion bearings, Install drive pinion gear, pinion bearing spacer and washer, pilot bearing race, pilot bearing spacer, pilot bearing, and oil seal. Install pinion flange, and tighten pinion nut to specified torque.

Drive Axles

DATSUN/NISSAN INTEGRAL HOUSING (Cont.)

Fig. 10: Measuring Drive Pinion Gear Installed Height

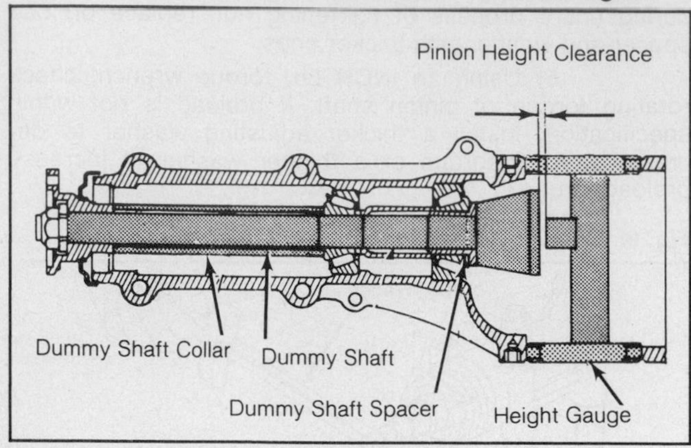
Pinion Height Clearance
Dummy Shaft Collar
Dummy Shaft
Dummy Shaft Spacer
Height Gauge

For correct shim thickness refer to appropriate formula.

Reassembly & Adjustment (Side Bearing Preload)

1) Required thickness of left and right side retainer shims can be obtained by using the appropriate formula in the Side Bearing Shim Formulas table.

NOTE: Formula values are given in millimeters. If value signifying A, B, C, D, G_1, and G_2 are not given, regard them as zero.

Fig. 11: Side Bearing Preload Formula Values

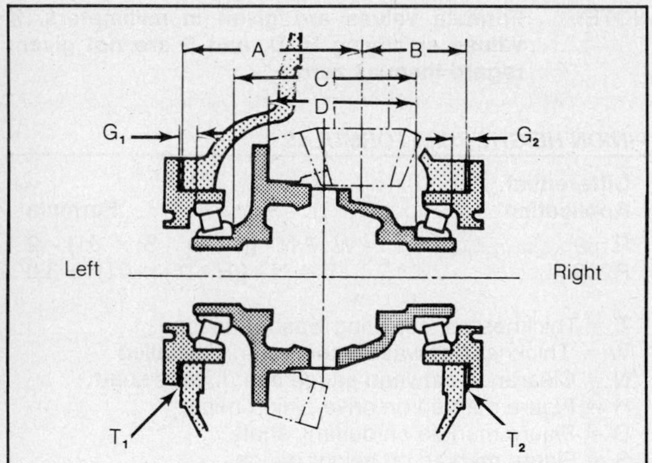
A
B
C
D
G_1
G_2
Left
Right
T_1
T_2

SIDE BEARING SHIM FORMULAS

Differential Application	Formula
R180	$T_1 = (A + C + G_1 - D) \times .01 + .76 - E$
	$T_2 = (B + D + G_2) \times .01 + .76 - F$
R200	$T_1 = (B - D + H') \times .01 + E + 2.05$
	$T_2 = (B - D + H') \times .01 + F + G + 1.95$

T_1 = Required thickness of left side retainer shim.
T_2 = Required thickness of right side retainer shim.
A & B = Figure marked on gear carrier.
C & D = Figure marked on differential case.
E & F = Difference in width of left or right bearing.
G_1 & G_2 = Figure marked on left or right retainers.
G = Standard spacer (8.10 mm) thickness difference.
H' = Variation figure marked on ring gear.

2) On R180 differentials, install differential case assembly in gear carrier in reverse order of disassembly. Fit correct shims and "O" ring seal in both side retainers in carrier. Arrow should point as shown in *Fig. 13*.

3) On R200 differentials, install differential case assembly with side bearing outer races into gear carrier. Insert side bearing washers, and drive in spacer between right side washer and housing.

4) Align marks on bearing cap and carrier and install bolts. Tighten to specifications.

NOTE: Use care in installing spacer to avoid tilting side bearing outer race.

Fig. 13: Aligning Side Retainer During Installation

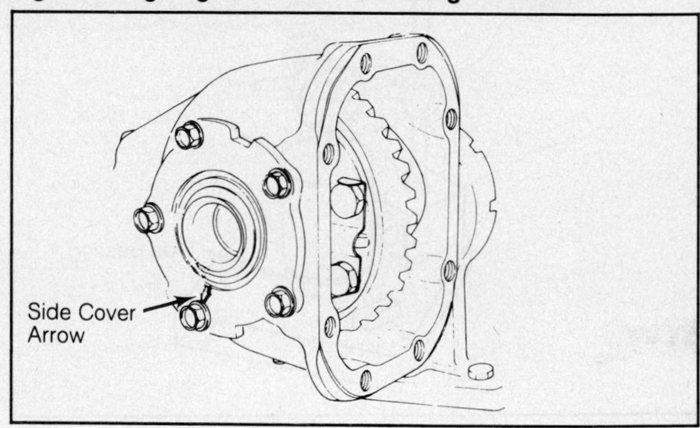
Side Cover Arrow

Fig. 12: Side Bearing Preload Identification Marks (R180 Differential Shown)

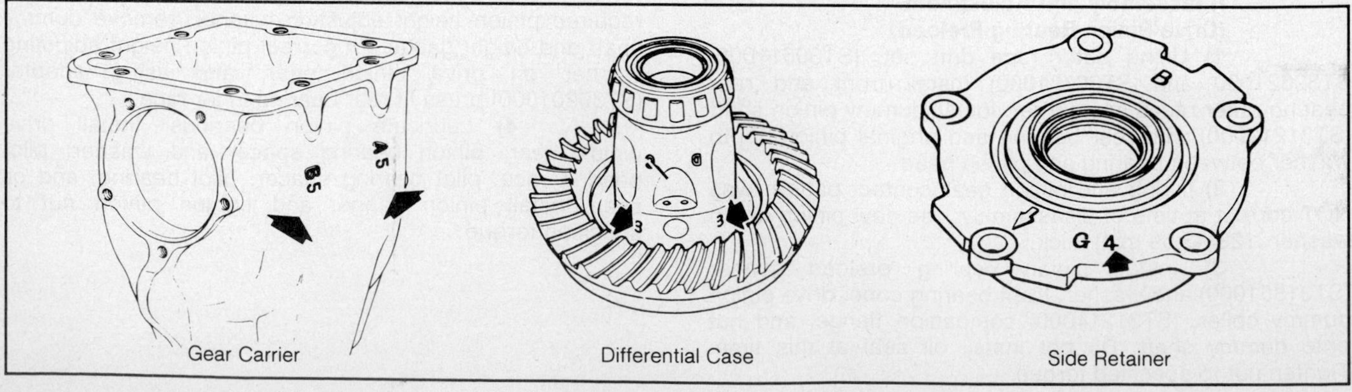
B5
A5
3
3
B
G 4
Gear Carrier
Differential Case
Side Retainer

DATSUN/NISSAN INTEGRAL HOUSING (Cont.)

5) Using dial indicator, measure ring gear-to-drive pinion backlash and adjust if necessary. Check side bearing preload, and adjust if necessary by adding or removing side retainer shims.

Fig. 14: Measuring Ring Gear Backlash

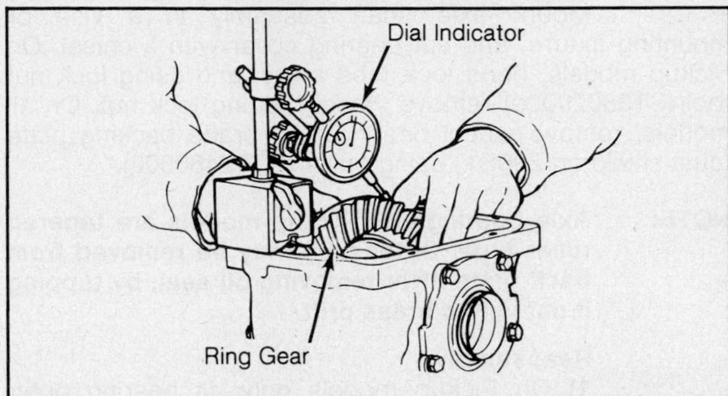
Dial Indicator
Ring Gear

NOTE: If side bearing preload is readjusted, ring gear-to-drive pinion backlash must be checked and, if necessary, adjusted.

Final Inspection & Reassembly

1) After all adjustments are to specifications, make tooth contact pattern test and make any necessary corrections. *See Gear Tooth Contact Pattern at beginning of this section.*

2) Install rear cover and tighten nuts to specifications. Refill axle assembly to correct level with gear oil.

AXLE ASSEMBLY SPECIFICATIONS

Application	INCH Lbs. (N.m)
Pinion Bearing Preload	
Without Oil Seal	
All Models	9-11 (1.0-1.2)
With Oil Seal	
Pickup	8-15 (.90-1.7)
All Others	9.5-12 (1.07-1.3)
	In. (mm)
Ring Gear-to-Pinion Backlash	
280ZX (R180 Differential)	.004-.008 (.10-.20)
All Others	.005-.007 (.13-.18)
Side Gear Backlash	.004-.008 (.10-.20)

TIGHTENING SPECIFICATIONS

Application	Ft. Lbs. (N.m)
Wheel Bearing Lock Nut	
Pickup (Front)	108-145 (147-196)
All Others	181-239 (246-325)
Drive Shaft Flange Bolts	
R180 Differential	23-31 (31-42)
R200 Differential	36-43 (49-58)
Pinion Flange-to-Propeller Shaft Flange	
Maxima Sedan	17-24 (23-37)
All Others	25-33 (34-45)
Rear Cover Bolts	
280ZX (R200 Differential)	12-17 (16-23)
Maxima Sedan	14-19 (19-26)
All Others	29-30 (39-41)
Rear Cover-to-Mount	
R180 Differential	43-58 (58-78)
R200 Differential	65-87 (88-118)
Drive Pinion Nut	
R180 Differential	123-145 (167-197)
R200 Differential	137-159 (186-216)
Ring Gear Bolts	
R180 Differential	65-72 (88-98)
R200 Differential	43-51 (58-69)
Side Bearing Retainer Bolts	
R180 Differential	6.5-8.7 (9-12)
Side Bearing Cap Bolts	
R200 Differential	65-72 (88-98)

Drive Axles

DATSUN/NISSAN SEPARATE CARRIER

200SX, Maxima Wagon,
2WD & 4WD Pickups (Rear)

DESCRIPTION

Differential gear carrier assembly has a hypoid type ring and pinion gear set. The gear carrier is constructed of cast iron. The drive pinion is mounted in 2 tapered roller bearings, preloaded by a collapsible spacer.

Drive pinion is aligned into position with a shim, located between shoulder on drive pinion and rear bearing.

Differential case is supported in carrier by 2 tapered roller side bearings. The side bearings are preloaded by inserting shims between bearings and differential. Case houses 2 side gears that mesh with 2 pinion gears, mounted on a lock pin. Pinion and side gears are set in front of thrust washers.

AXLE RATIO & IDENTIFICATION

Datsun/Nissan does not identify rear axle with a particular outside identification marking. However, all models use same basic type of removable carrier rear axle.

It should be noted, that part or model numbers may vary between vehicle models, but internal design is similar.

Various axle ratios are available, depending on model and whether vehicle is equipped with manual or automatic transmission. Ratio may be determined by dividing number of ring gear teeth by number of pinion gear teeth.

REMOVAL & INSTALLATION

AXLE SHAFTS & BEARINGS

Removal

1) Raise and support vehicle. Remove tire and wheel. Disconnect parking brake linkage and hydraulic line. On 200SX, remove brake caliper. On all other models, remove brake drum.

2) Remove brake backing plate retaining nuts (dust shield nuts on 200SX), and pull assembly from housing with a slide hammer.

Disassembly

Mount axle shaft assembly in a vise or mounting fixture, and cut bearing collar with a chisel. On Pickup models, bend lock tabs away, and using lock nut tool (ST38020000) remove wheel bearing lock nut. On all models, remove wheel bearing with brake backing plate (dust shield on 200SX) using puller (HT72480000).

NOTE: **Axle bearings on Pickup models are tapered roller type. Outer race may be removed from back plate after removing oil seal, by tapping it out with a brass drift.**

Reassembly

1) On Pickup models only, fit bearing outer race into position in backing plate using brass drift. Install oil seal. Pack seal lips with grease, and install bearing and new lock washers. Tighten lock nut to specifications. Bend up lock tabs on washer.

2) On all other models, use a press to install bearing spacer, bearing, and new collar.

Installation

1) To install, reverse removal procedure. On all models except Pickup, insert axle shaft. Adjust gap between wheel bearing and axle tube end to 0-.004" (.1 mm) by installing appropriate shim. *See Fig. 2.*

2) On Pickup models, insert shims between back plate and axle tube end so that measured axle shaft end play is .0008-.006" (.02-.15 mm).

3) On all other models, mount dial gauge and check axle shaft end play. End play should be .002-.016" (.05-.41 mm) on 200SX; .008-.020" (.20-50 mm) on Maxima.

Fig. 1: Exploded View of Datsun/Nissan Separate Carrier Differential Assembly

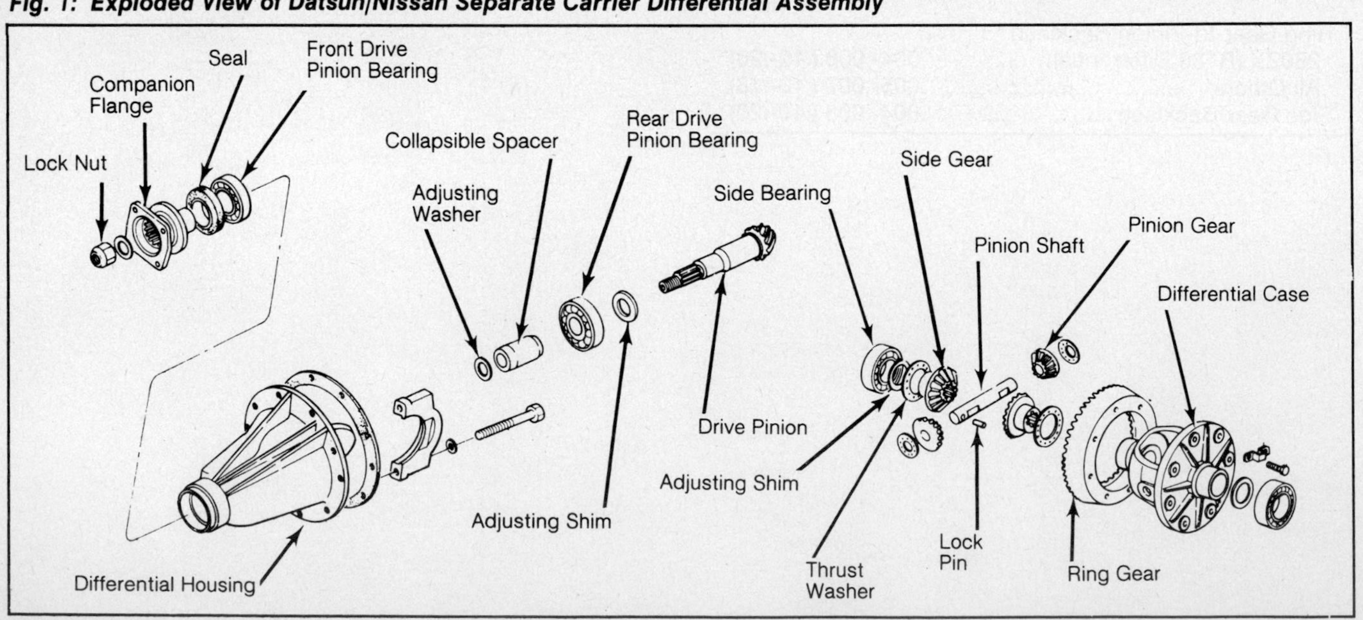
Seal
Front Drive
Pinion Bearing
Companion
Flange
Lock Nut
Collapsible Spacer
Rear Drive
Pinion Bearing
Adjusting
Washer
Side Gear
Side Bearing
Pinion Gear
Pinion Shaft
Differential Case
Drive Pinion
Adjusting Shim
Adjusting Shim
Lock
Pin
Thrust
Washer
Ring Gear
Differential Housing

DATSUN/NISSAN SEPARATE CARRIER (Cont.)

Fig. 2: Checking Clearance Between Wheel Bearing & Axle Tube End (Except Pickup Models)

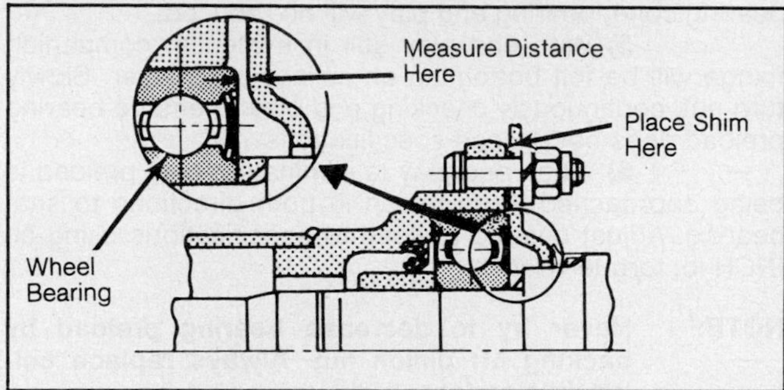
Measure Distance Here
Place Shim Here
Wheel Bearing

PINION FLANGE SEAL

Removal

Raise and support rear end of vehicle. Drain gear oil. Scribe an index mark on propeller shaft and companion flange. Detach shaft, and wire out of way. Remove drive pinion nut and companion flange. Remove oil seal.

Installation

Set new oil seal into position, and pack grease between seal lips. Position companion flange and flat washer on drive pinion. Tighten nut, and check bearing preload.

DIFFERENTIAL CARRIER

Removal

1) Raise and support vehicle on safety stands placed under rear axle housing. Drain gear lubricant.

2) Scribe an index mark on propeller shaft, and remove. Withdraw rear axle shafts as previously described.

3) Remove nuts mounting differential gear carrier to rear axle housing, and lift out gear carrier.

Installation

To install differential gear carrier, reverse removal procedure and tighten nuts.

OVERHAUL

DISASSEMBLY

NOTE: **Inspection of ring gear backlash and gear tooth contact prior to disassembly can indicate where possible problems may exist. See Gear Tooth Contact at beginning of this section.**

Differential

1) Mount differential carrier in a holding fixture, scribe index marks on side bearing caps and carrier. Remove bearing caps, and lift out differential assembly.

2) Remove drive pinion lock nut, and pull companion flange off with gear puller (SPDO14). Remove drive pinion together with rear bearing inner race, spacer, and washer. Drive pinion can be freed by tapping front end of assembly. If necessary, extract oil seal, and withdraw front bearing inner race.

3) Using inner race remover (ST33051001) and press, extract bearing from drive pinion gear. Using a drift, remove front and rear bearing races. Disassemble differential case as follows. Using puller (ST33051001 & ST33061000), remove side bearings. Keep right and left side components separate for reassembly reference.

4) Bend back ring gear retaining bolt lock tabs, and remove bolts by loosening in a diagonal sequence. Tap ring gear off gear case, using a soft hammer.

5) Drive out pinion shaft lock pin. Remove pinion gears, side gears, and thrust washers. Identify gears and thrust washers for installation in original positions.

CLEANING & INSPECTION

Clean all disassembled parts and visually inspect for excessive wear. Check all gears for wear and replace if necessary. Inspect thrust washer surfaces and be sure they are free from surface scratches.

NOTE: **Drive pinion and ring gear are replaced only as a set.**

REASSEMBLY & ADJUSTMENT

Case Assembly

1) Fit pinion, side gears, and thrust washers in differential case. Assemble pinion shaft to differential case, so that lock pin holes align with shaft.

2) To obtain specified clearance, insert side gear thrust washers of proper thickness between rear face of side gear and thrust washer. Insert pinion shaft lock pin and secure by peening with a punch.

3) Lightly oil gear tooth areas and all thrust surfaces. Check that gears turn freely and smoothly. Fit ring gear on differential case, tighten bolts in diagonal manner, and bend over lock tabs.

4) If side bearing is to be replaced, measure thickness of new one, using tool set as shown in *Fig. 3.* Normal bearing thickness should be as specified. Using a press, seat side bearing cone into differential case.

Fig. 3: Measuring Side Bearing Thickness

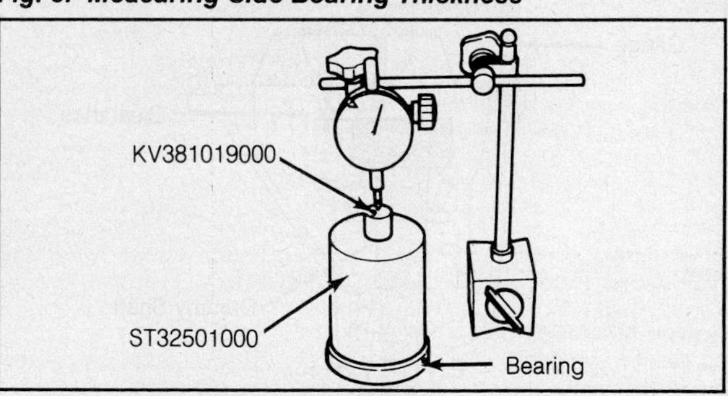
KV381019000
ST32501000
Bearing

Drive Pinion Height

1) Pinion height is adjusted with drive pinion adjusting washer placed behind drive pinion gear. Variation from the standard size to the drive gear center is marked on drive pinion gear head. If tolerance is greater than standard size, number is marked in "+", if less than standard size, marking is "–".

2) Install front and rear drive pinion outer races in gear carrier. Fit drive pinion adjusting washers and rear bearing on dummy shaft (ST31942000). *See Fig. 4.* Position dummy shaft in final drive housing without drive pinion adjusting spacer. Install front pinion bearing and companion flange.

3) Tighten drive pinion nut to specified preload setting. DO NOT overtighten pinion nut. Install drive pinion

DATSUN/NISSAN SEPARATE CARRIER (Cont.)

height gauge (ST31941000) on final drive housing. Measure clearance between end of gauge and surface of dummy shaft as shown in *Fig. 4*.

4) To calculate thickness of needed drive pinion adjusting shim, use the appropriate formula in the Drive Pinion Shim Thickness table.

DRIVE PINION SHIM THICKNESS

Application	Formula
200SX	T = N - (H - D' - S) x .01 + 2.98
Maxima & Pickup	T = N - (H - D' - S) x .01 + 2.18

T = Thickness of needed shim.
W = Thickness of temporary shim.
N = Clearance between depth gauge and dummy shaft.
H = Figure stamped on drive pinion head.
D = Figure stamped on dummy shaft.
S = Figure marked on height gauge.

NOTE: Formula values are expressed in millimeters.

5) Remove dummy shaft from gear carrier. Take pinion rear bearing out of dummy shaft. Select correct shims, based upon calculations. Refit pinion rear bearing and drive pinion. Ensure face side of shims are toward back of pinion gear.

NOTE: Pinion nut, oil seal, and collapsible spacer must NEVER be reused. Always use new parts during overhaul.

Fig. 4: Measuring Clearance Between Height Gauge and Dummy Shaft

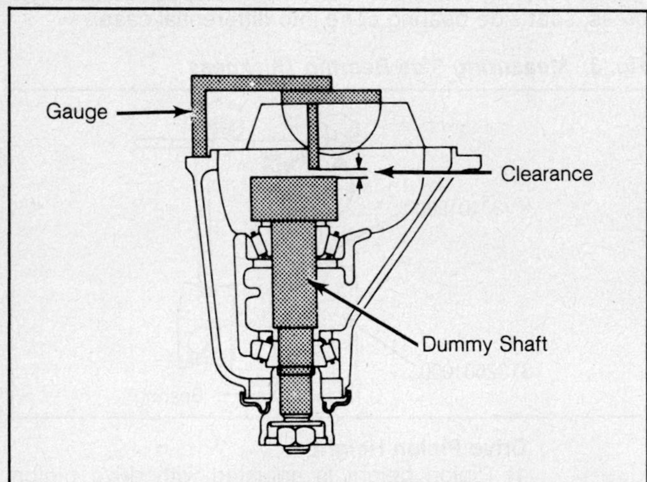
Gauge
Clearance
Dummy Shaft

Drive Pinion Preload

1) After obtaining final pinion bearing height, lubricate front bearing and place into carrier. Fit new oil seal in carrier, and fill space between seal lips with grease.

2) Slip new collapsible spacer on drive pinion. Lubricate pinion rear bearing. Insert companion flange in oil seal, while holding flange tightly against pinion front bearing cone.

3) Working from rear of carrier, insert drive pinion into companion flange. Ensure drive pinion threads and mounting nut are dirt free. Holding companion flange with flange tool (ST31530000), tighten nut.

4) This will pull drive pinion into front bearing cone and flange. When drive pinion is pulled into front bearing cone, bearing end play will be reduced.

5) With end play still in evidence, companion flange will be felt bottoming on collapsible spacer. Slowly turn nut, continuously checking end play to ensure bearing preload does not exceed specifications.

6) When end play is eliminated, final preload is being approached. Turn pinion in both directions to seat bearing. Adjust bearing preload to specifications using an INCH lb. torque wrench.

NOTE: Never try to decrease bearing preload by backing off pinion nut. Always replace collapsible spacer.

Backlash & Side Bearing Preload

1) Preload is adjusted with shims after overhaul work has been completed on differential assembly. When assembling without changing side bearings, install shims of original thickness.

2) If bearings are being replaced, use the appropriate formula in the *Side Bearing Shim Thickness table* to determine required shim thickness.

SIDE BEARING SHIM THICKNESS

Application	Formula
200SX	T1 = (A - C + D - H') x .01 + .20 + E
	T2=(B - D + H') x .01 + .09 + F
Maxima	
& Pickup	T1 = (A - C + D - H') x .01 + .175 + E
	T2 = (B - D + H') x .01 + .150 + F

T1 = Left shim thickness.
T2 = Right shim thickness.
A = Figure marked on left bearing carrier.
B = Figure marked on right bearing carrier.
C & D = Figure stamped on differential case (+ or –number).
E & F = Deviation from standard bearing thickness.
H' = Figure stamped on ring gear.

NOTE: Formula values are expressed in millimeters.

Fig. 5: Calculating Side Bearing Shim Thickness

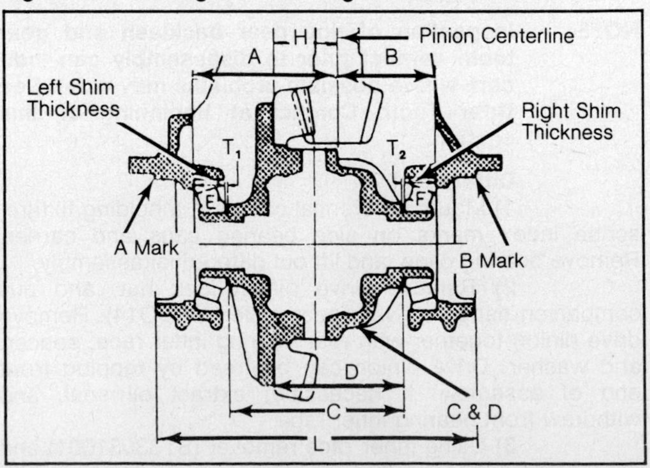
H
Pinion Centerline
A
B
Left Shim Thickness
Right Shim Thickness
T_1
T_2
E
F
A Mark
B Mark
D
C
C & D
L

3) Side bearing thickness is measured using gauge and weight block (ST32501000 & KV001019000). Measure thickness in at least 3 locations.

DATSUN/NISSAN SEPARATE CARRIER (Cont.)

4) Fit side bearing shim of differential case, and press in both side bearing inner races. Place differential case assembly into gear carrier, using a rubber mallet. Align index marks on bearing cap and gear carrier. Install bearing cap on carrier.

5) As a second check, measure distance between bearing caps with a micrometer. *See Fig. 6.* Specification obtained should be as indicated in table. Correct any deviation with shim of proper thickness.

Fig. 6: Measuring Distance Between Bearing Caps

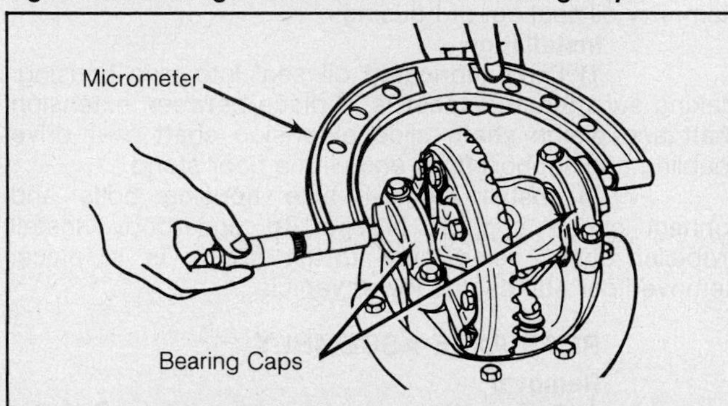
Micrometer
Bearing Caps

6) Using a dial indicator, measure ring gear-to-drive pinion backlash. Measurement should be as indicated in specifications. If backlash is less than specified, decrease thickness of left shim and increase thickness of right shim by same amount.

7) If backlash is more than specified, reverse placement of shims in procedure above. Using same dial indicator, check ring gear deflection. Runout should be as specified.

Fig. 7: Measuring Ring Gear Backlash

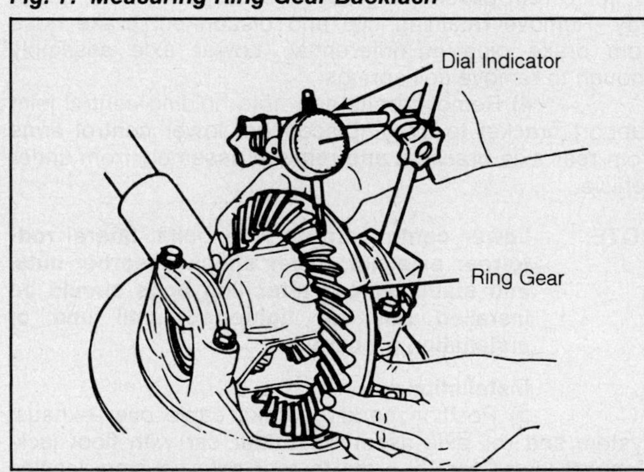
Dial Indicator
Ring Gear

8) Check drive pinion preload by measuring the amount of rotating torque needed to turn companion flange. *See Fig. 8.* Check gear tooth contact pattern and correct any problem.

NOTE: **See Gear Tooth Patterns at beginning of this section.**

Fig. 8: Measuring Drive Pinion Preload

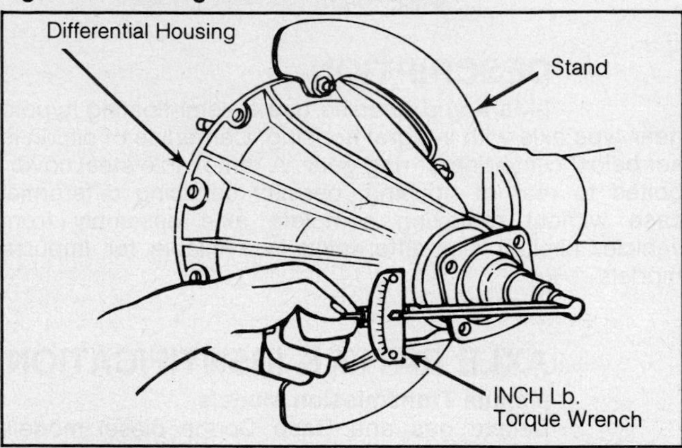
Differential Housing
Stand
INCH Lb.
Torque Wrench

AXLE ASSEMBLY SPECIFICATIONS

Application	INCH Lbs. (N.m)
Drive Pinion Preload	
With Oil Seal Installed	
200SX	6-9 (.7-1.0)
Maxima Wagon	6-13 (.7-1.5)
Pickup	9.5-14 (1.1-1.6)
	In. (mm)
Ring Gear-to-Pinion Backlash	
200SX	.005-.007 (.13-.18)
All Others	.006-.008 (.15-.20)
Pinion Gear-to-Side Gear Backlash	
All Models	.006-.008 (.15-.20)
Ring Gear Backface Runout	
200SX	.0016 (.04)
Pickup	.0031 (.08)
Standard Side Bearing Thickness	
200SX	.7283 (18.5)
All Others	.7874 (20)
Distance Between Bearing Cap Edges	
All Models	7.811-7.817 (198.40-198.55)

TIGHTENING SPECIFICATIONS

Application	Ft. Lbs. (N.m)
Drive Pinion Nut	94-217 (127-294)
Ring Gear Retaining Bolts	
200SX, Maxima Wagon, & Pickup	65-72 (88-98)
Side Bearing Cap Bolts	
All Models	36-43 (49-59)
Differential Carrier-to-Axle Housing	
200SX & Maxima Wagon	18-25 (25-34)
Pickup	12-18 (17-25)
Companion Flange-to-Propeller Shaft	25-33 (34-44)

Drive Axles

ISUZU INTEGRAL HOUSING

I-Mark & Impulse

DESCRIPTION

I-Mark and Impulse use a semi-floating hypoid gear type axle with integral housing. Centerline of pinion is set below centerline of ring gear. A removable steel cover, bolted to rear of housing, permits servicing differential case without removing complete axle assembly from vehicle. Limited slip differential is available for Impulse models.

AXLE RATIO & IDENTIFICATION

Manual Transmission Models

Deluxe gas and Base Coupe diesel models have a 3.154:1 gear ratio. LS gas and all diesel models except Base Coupe have a 3.308:1 gear ratio.

Automatic Transmission Models

All gas models with automatic transmissions have a 3.308:1 gear ratio. Diesel automatic transmission models have a 3.583 gear ratio.

To determine axle ratio, divide number of ring gear teeth by number of pinion teeth.

REMOVAL & INSTALLATION

AXLE SHAFTS

Removal

1) Raise and support vehicle. Remove wheel and brake drum. On Impulse, remove caliper and rotor. Working through access holes in axle shaft flange, remove 4 nuts and washers that retain axle shaft bearing retainer.

2) Install slide hammer on axle shaft flange and remove axle shaft. To replace bearing parts, first remove retaining ring by cutting off with a chisel. Press off bearing.

3) Check axle shaft for radial runout at bearing seat. Maximum radial runout allowed is .002" (.05 mm) for I-Mark and .04" (1.0 mm) for Impulse. Check lateral runout at largest flange diameter. Maximum lateral runout is .004" (.10 mm) for I-Mark and .006" (.15 mm) for Impulse. Check axle splines for distortion or wear. Replace axle shaft if damaged or worn.

NOTE: **When removing axle shaft from housing, make sure axle shaft or splines do not rest on or tear axle seal.**

Installation

1) Press on bearing so that seal groove on bearing faces shaft splines. Press on retainer ring so that shoulder faces bearing.

2) Check axle shaft end play. Using depth gauge, measure depth of rear axle bearing seat in housing with backing plate in place. Measure width of bearing outer race. Difference between measurements is required shim thickness to set end play. End play should be 0-.008" (0-.2 mm)

CAUTION: No end play (too tight) will cause loose backing plate fit.

3) Lubricate splines and insert axle shaft into housing. Drive shaft into housing with mallet after splines engage. Install lock washers and nuts. Install brake drum (rotor and caliper on Impulse) and wheel assembly.

PINION FLANGE & OIL SEAL

Removal

1) Raise and support vehicle. Disconnect propeller shaft from pinion flange and remove shaft from transmission. Plug transmission extension housing to prevent lubricant loss. Place a floor stand under front of rear axle housing.

2) Support extension housing and disconnect center support bracket from underbody. Remove bolts attaching extension housing to axle housing and separate them. Pry oil seal out of housing.

Installation

1) Drive lubricated oil seal into axle housing. Making sure thrust washer is in place between extension shaft and pinion shaft, slide extension shaft over drive coupling and support front end with a floor stand.

2) Install flange-to-axle housing bolts and connect center support bracket to underbody. Install propeller shaft, being sure thrust spring is in place. Remove floor stands and lower vehicle.

REAR AXLE ASSEMBLY

Removal

1) Raise vehicle and support at frame. Remove wheels. Disconnect parking brake cable equalizer and return spring from brake rod. Remove parking brake cable clamps. Position a jack under rear axle and raise axle only enough to support weight.

2) Disconnect rear stabilizer bar-to-body clamps. On LS coupe model only, loosen stabilizer-to-axle bracket bolts and nuts. Disconnect shock absorbers at bottom. Disconnect lateral rod at left end. Unhook exhaust system brackets.

3) After marking for reassembly, disconnect "U" joint from pinion flange and tie propeller shaft out of way. Remove retaining clip and disconnect brake hose from brake pipe at differential. Lower axle assembly enough to remove coil springs.

4) Remove bolts and nuts holding central joint support bracket to body. Disconnect lower control arms from rear axle brackets and remove assembly from under vehicle.

NOTE: **Lower control arm-to-axle bolts, lateral rod-to-rear axle nut, lower shock absorber nuts, and stabilizer bar attaching bolts should be installed but not tightened until end of installation procedure.**

Installation

1) Position parking brake cable over exhaust system and roll axle assembly under car with floor jack. Connect lower control arms to rear axle housing, leaving bolts hand tight. Attach central joint support to body and tighten nuts to specification.

2) Lowering axle assembly, install coil springs with upper and lower damper rings. Position springs and damper rings correctly. Install lateral rod to axle housing, leaving bolts loose. On LS Coupe, attach rear stabilizer bar-to-body clamps, leaving bolts loose.

3) Attach exhaust system brackets. Connect brake hose to brake pipe and install retaining clip. Attach propeller shaft to pinion flange, making sure to align marks made on disassembly. Tighten bolts to specification.

ISUZU INTEGRAL HOUSING (Cont.)

Fig. 1: Exploded View of I-Mark Rear Axle Assembly

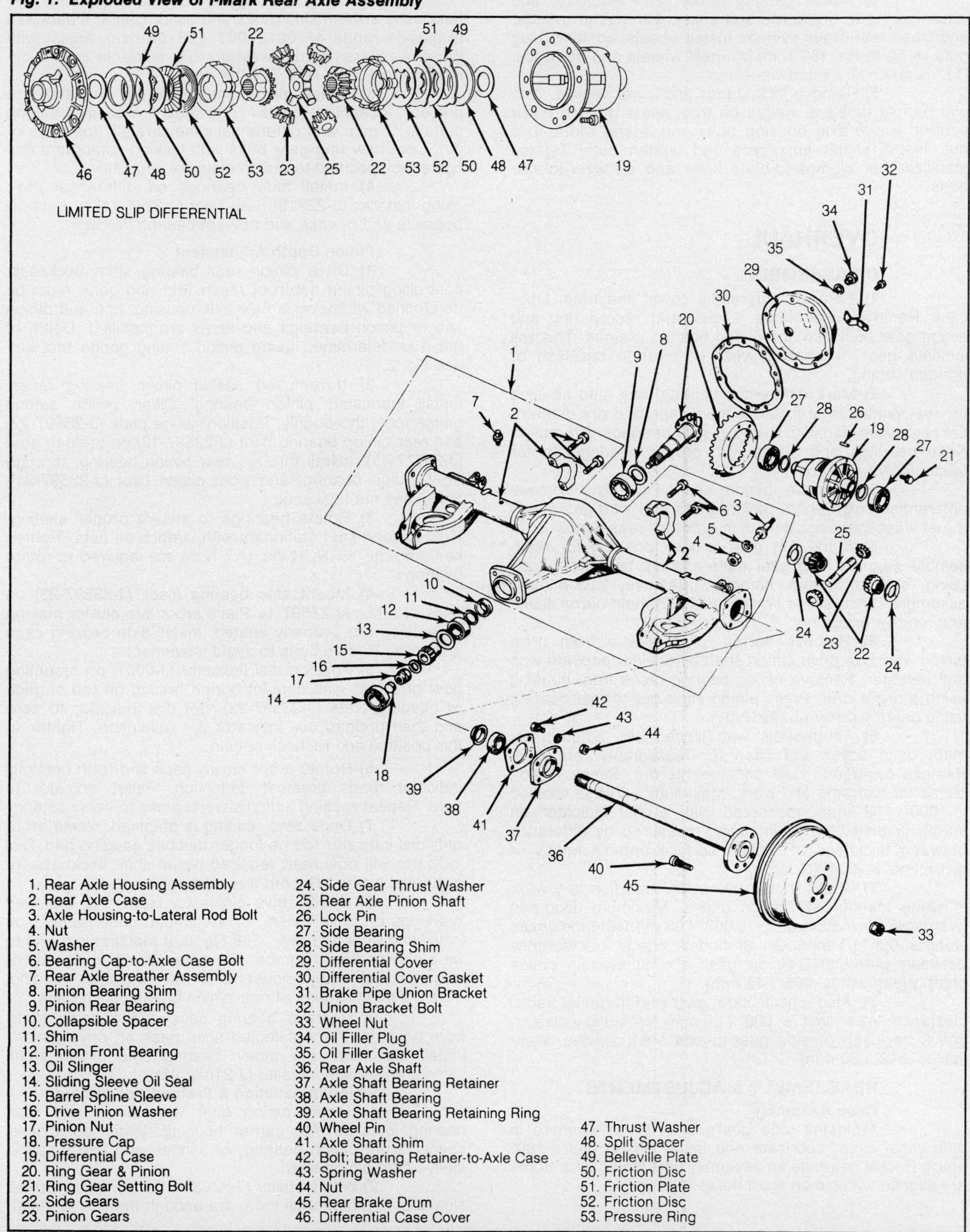

LIMITED SLIP DIFFERENTIAL
1. Rear Axle Housing Assembly
2. Rear Axle Case
3. Axle Housing-to-Lateral Rod Bolt
4. Nut
5. Washer
6. Bearing Cap-to-Axle Case Bolt
7. Rear Axle Breather Assembly
8. Pinion Bearing Shim
9. Pinion Rear Bearing
10. Collapsible Spacer
11. Shim
12. Pinion Front Bearing
13. Oil Slinger
14. Sliding Sleeve Oil Seal
15. Barrel Spline Sleeve
16. Drive Pinion Washer
17. Pinion Nut
18. Pressure Cap
19. Differential Case
20. Ring Gear & Pinion
21. Ring Gear Setting Bolt
22. Side Gears
23. Pinion Gears
24. Side Gear Thrust Washer
25. Rear Axle Pinion Shaft
26. Lock Pin
27. Side Bearing
28. Side Bearing Shim
29. Differential Cover
30. Differential Cover Gasket
31. Brake Pipe Union Bracket
32. Union Bracket Bolt
33. Wheel Nut
34. Oil Filler Plug
35. Oil Filler Gasket
36. Rear Axle Shaft
37. Axle Shaft Bearing Retainer
38. Axle Shaft Bearing
39. Axle Shaft Bearing Retaining Ring
40. Wheel Pin
41. Axle Shaft Shim
42. Bolt; Bearing Retainer-to-Axle Case
43. Spring Washer
44. Nut
45. Rear Brake Drum
46. Differential Case Cover
47. Thrust Washer
48. Split Spacer
49. Belleville Plate
50. Friction Disc
51. Friction Plate
52. Friction Disc
53. Pressure Ring

ISUZU INTEGRAL HOUSING (Cont.)

4) Attach parking brake cable equalizer and return spring to brake rod and adjust. Fill master cylinder and bleed rear brake system. Install wheels, tightening lug nuts to 50 ft. lbs. (68 N.m) on steel wheels and 86 ft. lbs. (117 N.m) on aluminum wheels.

5) Remove jack stands and lower vehicle. With two people or equal weight on front seats, tighten lower control arm-to-axle housing bolts and lateral rod-to-axle nut. Install shock absorbers and tighten nuts. Tighten stabilizer bar clamps-to-body bolts and stablizer-to-axle bolts.

OVERHAUL

DISASSEMBLY

1) Remove differential cover and drain lubricant. Remove axle shafts. Check and record ring and pinion gear backlash and pinion bearing preload. This will indicate gear or bearing wear or error in backlash or preload setting.

2) Mark differential bearing caps and housing for reassembly reference. Remove caps and pry differential case from housing. Remove side bearings with puller. Keep bearings and shims with proper bearing cap for reassembly reference.

3) Remove pinion shaft lock pin. Remove differential pinion shaft, pinion gears and side gears with thrust washers keeping them in order for reassembly.

4) Mark ring gear-to-case position for reassembly. Remove ring gear bolts and tap gear from case using soft drift and hammer. Remove torque tube assembly. Using spline holder (J-22932), hold barrel spline and remove pinion nut.

5) Remove barrel spline sleeve from drive pinion. Remove drive pinion shaft by driving rearward with soft hammer. Remove pinion bearing races from housing using a brass drift. Press pinion shaft out of rear bearing using bearing puller (J-22912-01).

6) On models with limited slip differentials, mark case cover and case for reassembly reference. Remove cover and take components out. Check friction plates for warpage and wear. Maximum warpage allowed is .003" (.08 mm), measured with a dial indicator on surfacing plate. Maximum wear, measured by difference between thickness of friction surface and thickness of projection, is .004" (.1 mm).

7) Check friction discs for distortion and wear in same manner as friction plates. Maximum distortion (warpage) for friction discs is.003" (.08 mm) and maximum wear is .004" (.1 mm). On all models, check for clearance between differential pinion gear and differential pinion shaft. Wear limit is .006" (.15 mm).

8) Also check side gear-to-differential radial clearance. Wear limit is .008" (.20 mm). With dial indicator, check backlash of side gear-to-axle shaft splines. Wear limit is .012" (.30 mm)

REASSEMBLY & ADJUSTMENTS

Case Assembly

1) Install side gears and thrust washers in differential case. Lubricate and install pinion gears 180° apart. Rotate gears as an assembly until pinion gear bores are aligned with pinion shaft bores in case.

2) With one side gear held stationary, measure backlash between side gears and pinion gears. If backlash is outside range of .0012-.003" (.03-.08 mm), adjust with thrust washers. Thrust washers are available in 9 thicknesses from .039-.055" (1.0-1.4 mm).

3) Install pinion shaft lock pin and stake to prevent loosening. Install ring gear, checking mating surface of gear and differential case carefully for burrs or dirt. Coat new ring gear bolts with locking compound and tighten to specified torque in diagonal sequence.

4) Install side bearings on differential case using installer (J-22919). Use pilot (J-2241-11) to support opposite end of case and prevent bearing damage.

Pinion Depth Adjustment

1) Drive pinion rear bearing shim thickness, controlling pinion depth of mesh with ring gear, must be determined whenever a new axle housing, ring and pinion set, or pinion bearings and races are installed. Depth of mesh is determined using pinion setting gauge tool set. *See Fig. 2*.

2) If removed, install pinion bearing races. Install lubricated pinion bearing. Clean pinion setting gauge tools thoroughly. Position gauge plate (J-23597-22) and rear pinion bearing pilot (J-23597-12) on preload stud (J-21777-43). Install through rear pinion bearing, through front pinion bearing, and front pinion pilot (J-23597-21). Install hex nut until snug.

3) Rotate bearings to ensure proper seating. Hold preload stud stationary with wrench on flats. Tighten hex nut until 15 INCH lbs. (1.7 N.m) are required to rotate bearings.

4) Mount side bearing discs (J-23597-23) on ends of arbor (J-23597-1). Place arbor into carrier making sure discs are properly seated. Install side bearing caps and bolts. Tighten bolts to avoid movement.

5) Position dial indicator (J-8001) on mounting post of arbor, with contact button resting on top surface of gauging plate (J-23597-22). Set dial indicator to zero and then preload dial indicator 3/4 revolution. Tighten in this position and recheck setting.

6) Rotate arbor slowly back and forth until dial indicator reads greatest deflection. Reset indicator to zero. Repeat rocking action several times to verify setting.

7) Once zero reading is obtained, rotate arbor until dial indicator rod no longer touches gauging pad. Dial indicator will now read required pinion shim thickness for a "normal pinion." Record this reading.

8) Check drive pinion for painted or stamped markings on pinion stem, or a stamped code number on small end of pinion gear. *See Fig. 3*. If marking is found to be a plus or minus number (for instance +2 or -5), add or subtract that many thousandths from indicator reading. This will be thickness of rear pinion bearing shim pack.

9) Remove bearing caps and gauging tools from housing. Place selected shim pack on drive pinion. Install lubricated rear pinion bearing onto pinion shaft using a press with installer (J-21022-02).

Pinion Installation & Preload Adjustment

1) Install pinion gear with shims and rear bearing installed into carrier housing. Install collapsible spacer, front pinion bearing, oil slinger, and barrel spline sleeve onto pinion shaft.

2) With installer (J-22938-01) draw barrel spline sleeve onto pinion until there are enough threads to install

ISUZU INTEGRAL HOUSING (Cont.)

drive pinion washer and nut. Do not use installer (J22938-01) to adjust preload. Torque pinion nut to 108 ft. lbs. (146 N.m).

Fig. 2: Pinion Depth Gauge Set

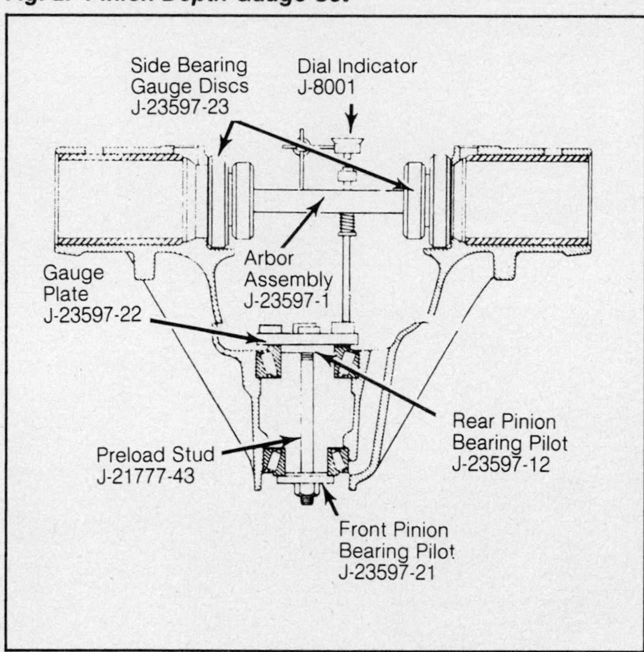

Side Bearing
Gauge Discs
J-23597-23
Dial Indicator
J-8001
Gauge
Plate
J-23597-22
Arbor
Assembly
J-23597-1
Rear Pinion
Bearing Pilot
J-23597-12
Preload Stud
J-21777-43
Front Pinion
Bearing Pilot
J-23597-21

Add dial indicator reading to number in thousandths marked on pinion gear.

Fig. 3: Pinion Marking Locations

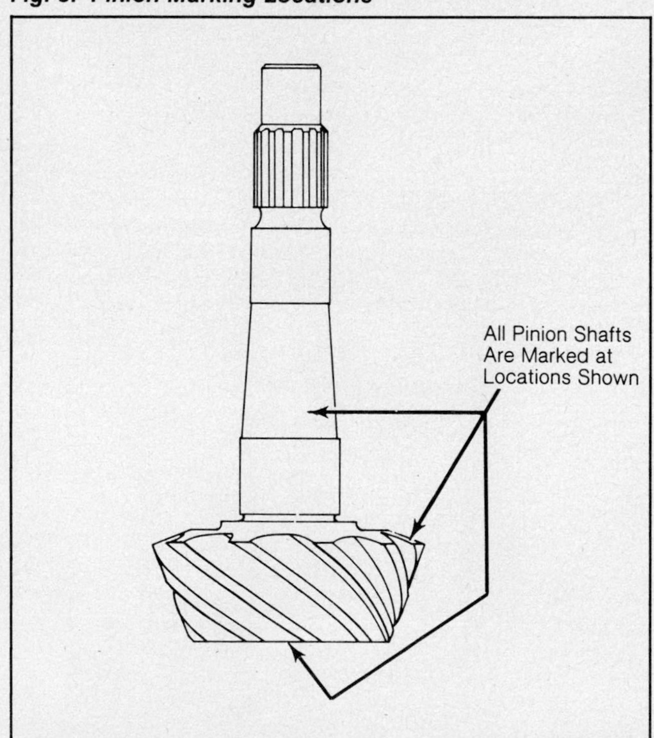

All Pinion Shafts
Are Marked at
Locations Shown

If no markings are found on pinion, use dial indicator reading as shim thickness.

3) Continue to tighten pinion nut until a preload of 6-11 INCH lbs. (.7-1.2 N.m) with 9 INCH lbs. (1.0 N.m) preferred for new bearings, and 5-8 INCH lbs. (.6-.9 N.m) with 6 INCH lbs (.7 N.m) preferred for old bearings, is required to rotate drive pinion. Install new oil seal that has been soaked in gear oil.

CAUTION: Do not back off nut to loosen preload. If preload is exceeded, a new collapsible spacer must be installed and nut retightened until preload is obtained.

Side Bearing Preload

1) Place differential case assembly without shims into side bearing bores of carrier. Using 2 feeler gauge sets, insert feeler stock of sufficient thickness between each bearing outer race and carrier to remove all end play. Make sure feeler stock is pushed to bottom of bearing bores.

2) Mount dial indicator (J-8001) on carrier so indicator stem is at right angles to a tooth on ring gear. Adjust feeler gauge thickness on both sides until ring gear backlash is .005-.007" (.13-.18 mm) with .006" (.15 mm) preferred.

3) With zero end play and correct backlash, remove feeler gauges. Determine thickness of required shims and add .002" (.051 mm) to each shim pack to provide side bearing preload.

4) Remove case assembly and both side bearings. Install shim packs with respective side bearing. Position case assembly and outer races in carrier. Use a soft faced hammer to drive case into carrier until side bearing outer races bottom in their bores.

5) Install side bearing caps in their original location and tighten bolts to 36 ft. lbs. (49 N.m). Rotate case assembly several times to seat bearings. Check lateral runout of installed ring gear. Maximum runout is .003" (.08 mm). If runout limit is exceeded, either differential case or ring gear and drive pinion gear will need to be replaced.

6) Check backlash and preload using torque wrench on ring gear attaching bolt. Torque should be 20-30 INCH lbs. (2.3-3.4 N.m) for new bearings or 10-20 INCH lbs. (1.1-2.3 N.m) for used bearings.If torque is incorrect, it will be necessary to reshim side bearings. *See Fig. 4*. Install axle housing cover with new gasket, using sealer on center bolts at top and bottom of plate.

Fig. 4: Adjusting Backlash

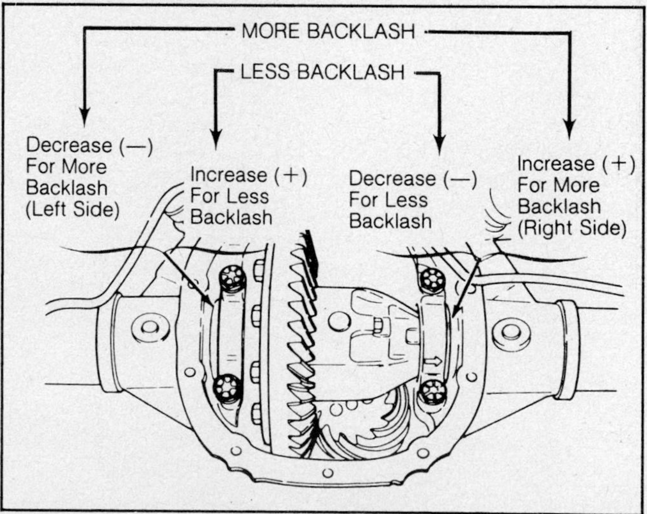

MORE BACKLASH
LESS BACKLASH
Decrease (—)
For More
Backlash
(Left Side)
Increase (+)
For Less
Backlash
Decrease (—)
For Less
Backlash
Increase (+)
For More
Backlash
(Right Side)

Shim subtracted from one side must be added to other side to maintain preload.

Drive Axles

ISUZU INTEGRAL HOUSING (Cont.)

AXLE ASSEMBLY SPECIFICATIONS

Application	INCH Lbs. (N.m)
Pinion Bearing Preload	
New Bearings [1]	6-11 (.7-1.2)
Used Bearings [1]	5-8 (.6-.9)
	In. (mm)
Ring Gear Backlash	.005-.007 (.13-.18)
Ring Gear Runout	.003 (.08)
Side Bearing Preload [2]	Slip fit Plus .004 (.10)
Axle Shaft Radial Runout	
I-Mark	.002 (.05)
Impulse	.04 (1.0)
Axle Shaft Flange Lateral Runout	
I-Mark	.004 (.10)
Impulse	.006 (.15)
Axle Shaft End Play	0-.008 (0-0.2)

[1] – Measured with new seal without ring gear installed.
[2] – Add .002" to each side to preload bearings.

TIGHTENING SPECIFICATIONS

Application	Ft. Lbs. (N.m)
Axle Shaft Flange Nuts	28 (38)
Propeller Shaft-to-Pinion Flange	18 (24)
Side Bearing Cap Bolt	
I-Mark	36 (49)
Impulse	29-36 (39-49)
Housing Cover Bolts [1]	22 (30)
Pinion Preload Nut	
I-Mark	108 (146)
Impulse	101-116 (137-157)
Ring Gear-to-Case Bolt	
I-Mark	50 (68)
Impulse	58-65 (79-88)

[1] – Lower center bolt only, 16 ft. lbs. (21 N.m).

ISUZU P'UP

DESCRIPTION

Rear axle housing is banjo type with removable differential carrier and semi-floating axle shafts. Front axle has removable differential carrier and full-floating axle shafts.

Both differentials are hypoid type ring and pinion gears. The axle shafts are retained in housing by cone-type roller bearings and bearing retainers at axle housing outer ends.

AXLE RATIO & IDENTIFICATION

All models are equipped with 1 type of rear axle. The front axle on 4WD models is similar to rear axle. Rear axle ratio on 2WD vehicles with manual transmission is 3.42:1 for gasoline model, and 3.73:1 for diesel model.

The gear ratio on automatics and 4WD vehicles front and rear is 4.10:1. Gear ratio is determined by dividing the number of ring gear teeth by the number of drive pinion gear teeth.

REMOVAL & INSTALLATION

NOTE: References to BJ refer to Birfield Joint; DOJ to Double Offset Joint.

DRIVE AXLES & BEARINGS

NOTE: Front axle assembly must be removed prior to removal of drive axles and bearings.

Removal (Front)

1) Disconnect propeller shaft at front differential. Raise front of vehicle on hoist until weight is removed from springs. Support frame on jack stands. Remove wheels and skid plate.

2) Completely loosen torsion bar by turning height control arm adjusting bolts. Remove strut bars. Remove stabilizer bar-to-lower control arm bolts and disconnect stabilizer.

3) Remove brake calipers from supports and hang on frame with wire. Disconnect ball joints at outer tie rods. Remove upper control arms from frame brackets by removing bolts from upper pivot shafts.

4) Tape shim packs together and mark for reinstallation for proper camber and caster adjustments. Remove lower control arm link ends, shock absorber-to-lower control arm bolts and lower control arms.

5) Move transfer shift lever into "2H" position and set locking hub knob to "FREE" position. Remove locking hub assembly. Remove snap ring and shims from end of spindle.

6) Remove hub and rotor assembly along with upper link and front axle (both sides). Disconnect pitman arm and idler arm. Remove steering linkage assembly.

NOTE: See Locking Hub article in this section for complete removal and installation procedures of locking hubs.

Fig. 1: Exploded View of Isuzu Rear Axle Assembly

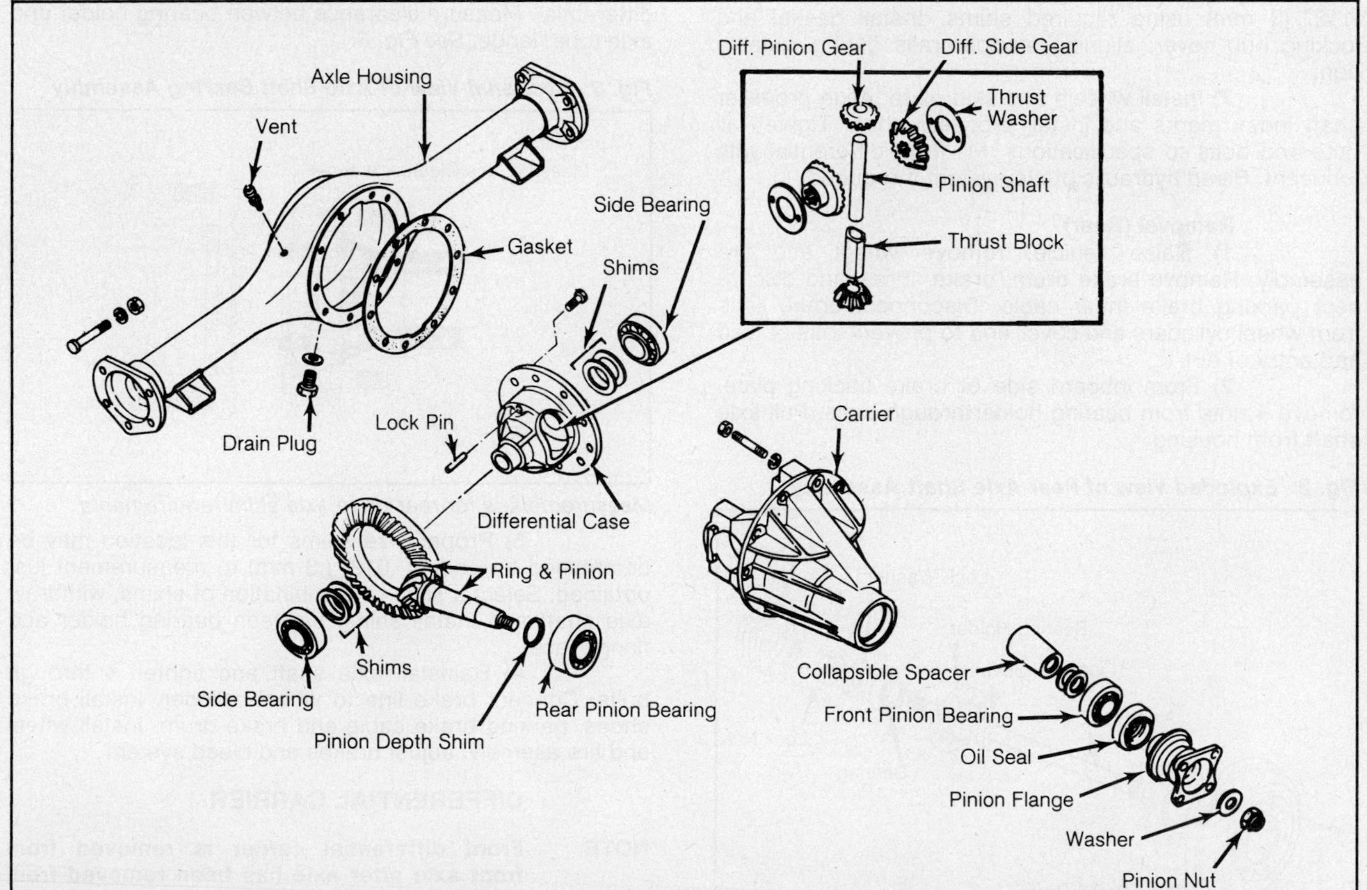
Axle Housing
Vent
Gasket
Drain Plug
Diff. Pinion Gear
Diff. Side Gear
Thrust Washer
Pinion Shaft
Thrust Block
Side Bearing
Shims
Lock Pin
Carrier
Differential Case
Ring & Pinion
Shims
Side Bearing
Rear Pinion Bearing
Pinion Depth Shim
Collapsible Spacer
Front Pinion Bearing
Oil Seal
Pinion Flange
Washer
Pinion Nut

Drive Axles

ISUZU P'UP (Cont.)

7) Support front axle assembly on floor jack and remove 4 axle case mounting bolts. Lower and remove front axle assembly. DO NOT damage Birfield or double offset joints.

8) Drain differential housing, remove 4 axle mounting bracket-to-axle housing bolts. Pull axle shafts from both sides of housing.

9) Remove axle shaft bearing from steering knuckle using a puller. Drive out bearing races with brass drift and replace races with hydraulic press. Install new bearings.

Installation

1) Install axle shafts in housing and tighten 4 axle mounting bracket-to-axle housing bolts. Place front axle assembly on floor jack and position under vehicle frame.

2) Install axle assembly and tighten case mounting bracket bolts. Install Pitman arm to steering sector shaft and idler arm to pivot shaft. Tighten bolts.

3) Install hub and rotor assemblies with upper control arms to axle shaft ends. Install pivot shaft to frame bracket. Install camber and caster adjusting shims in original positions.

4) Refit shock absorbers. Connect lower control arms to frame brackets. Connect ball joints to knuckle arms and tighten castellated nuts.

5) Install strut bars and stabilizer bar ends. Tighten control arm adjusting bolts. Install disc brake caliper assemblies. Thoroughly lubricate locking hub body and lock washer. Install snap ring.

6) Push axle shaft with hand pressure and set clearance between locking hub body and snap ring to .112" (3 mm) using required shims. Install gasket and locking hub cover, aligning stopper rails during installation.

7) Install wheels and skid plate. Align propeller shaft index marks and install propeller shaft. Tighten all nuts and bolts to specifications. Fill front differential with lubricant. Bleed hydraulic brake system if required.

Removal (Rear)

1) Raise vehicle, remove wheel and tire assembly. Remove brake drum, brake shoes and disconnect parking brake inner cable. Disconnect brake lines from wheel cylinders and cover end to prevent loss of fluid and entry of dirt.

2) From inboard side of brake backing plate, remove 4 nuts from bearing holderthrough bolts. Pull axle shaft from housing.

Fig. 2: Exploded View of Rear Axle Shaft Assembly

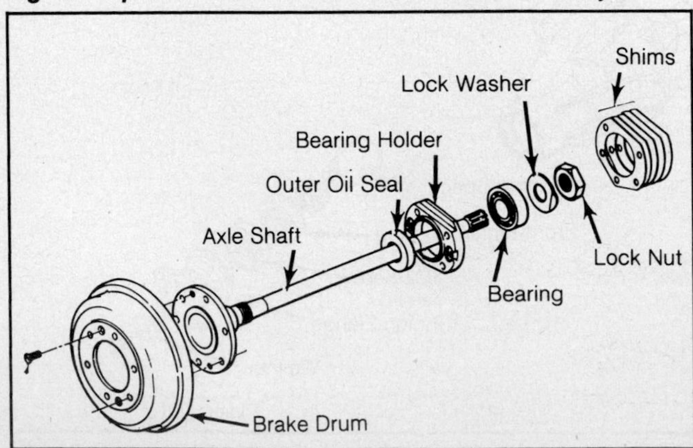
Shims
Lock Washer
Bearing Holder
Outer Oil Seal
Axle Shaft
Lock Nut
Bearing
Brake Drum

Bearing Replacement

1) To replace rear bearing, flatten locking tab of lock washer, mount axle shaft in a vise, clamping vise jaws around lock nut.

2) Using a puller positioned on lug bolts, turn axle shaft loose from lock nut, lock washer, bearing and holder and brake backing plate. Remove oil seal from outboard side of bearing holder. Drive off bearing outer race with a drift.

3) Install bearing outer race and grease seal into holder. Apply wheel bearing grease to bearing holder, rear axle tube and bearing inner race.

4) Insert 4 through bolts into backing plate. Install bearing holder to backing plate, making sure oil seal side of bearing holder is against backing plate.

5) Place backing plate assembly over axle shaft, position bearing over axle shaft and press into bearing holder. Install new lock washer with dished side away from bearing. Thread lock nut onto shaft.

6) Place lock nut between vise jaws and using tool used during disassembly, tighten lock nut securely. Bend over portion of lock washer opposite to locating tab to prevent lock nut from turning.

Installation

1) If both axle shafts were removed, insert a .079" (2 mm) shim between bearing holder and axle tube flange of first axle shaft to be installed. Insert shaft into axle tube and install and tighten bearing holder-to-flange bolts.

2) For the second axle shaft (or if only one shaft was removed), insert shaft without shims into axle tube until it comes into contact with thrust block in differential. Measure clearance betwen bearing holder and axle tube flange. *See Fig. 3.*

Fig. 3: Sectional View of Axle Shaft Bearing Assembly

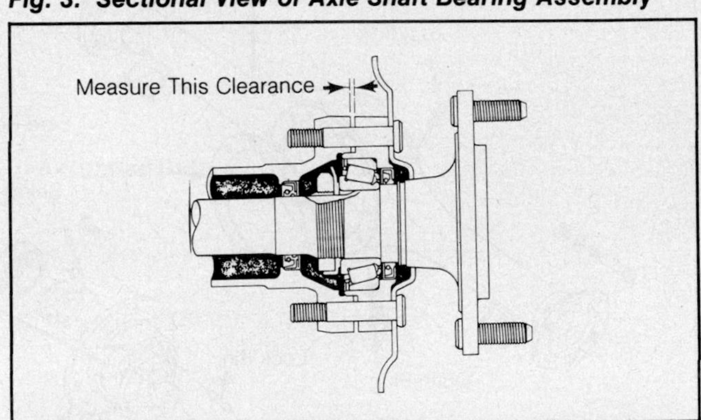
Measure This Clearance

Measurement is for rear drive axle shim requirements.

3) Proper size shims for this location may be determined by adding .012" (.3 mm) to measurement just obtained. Select a shim or combination of shims, withdraw axle shaft and install shims between bearing holder and flange face.

4) Reinstall axle shaft and tighten 4 through bolts. Connect brake line to wheel cylinder. Install brake shoes, parking brake cable and brake drum. Install wheel and tire asembly, adjust brakes and bleed system.

DIFFERENTIAL CARRIER

NOTE: **Front differential carrier is removed from front axle after axle has been removed from vehicle.**

ISUZU P'UP (Cont.)

Removal (Rear)

1) Raise rear of vehicle and support with jack stands. Remove wheels and brake drums. Disconnect brake lines at wheel cylinders and plug. Disconnect parking brake cable brackets at rear spring location. Drain differential oil.

2) Remove 4 through bolts from each end flange and partially withdraw axle shafts from axle tubes. Disconnect propeller shaft from pinion flange and place out of way. Remove nuts attaching carrier to axle housing and remove carrier assembly.

Installation

To install, reverse removal procedure. Make sure to refill axle with lubricant.

OVERHAUL

FRONT AXLE SHAFTS

NOTE: Axle shaft assembly is an integral unit and should be disassembled only to replace defective parts.

Fig. 4: Exploded View of Front Axle Shafts

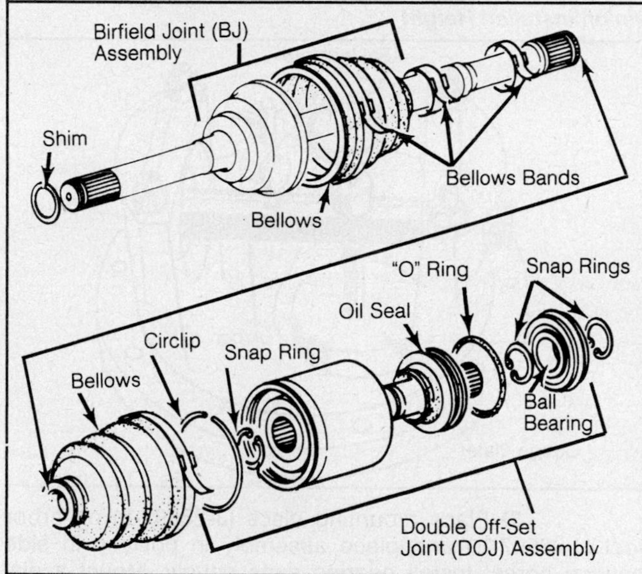

Birfield Joint (BJ)
Assembly
Shim
Bellows Bands
Bellows
"O" Ring
Snap Rings
Oil Seal
Circlip
Snap Ring
Bellows
Ball
Bearing
Double Off-Set
Joint (DOJ) Assembly

Birfield joint (BJ) and double offset joint (DOJ) shaft assemblies shown.

Disassembly

1) Remove front axle assembly and axle shafts as previously described. Using a screwdriver, lift hooked end of bellows band on larger diameter end of double offset joint (DOJ) and carefully remove bellows. Repeat procedure to remove band on smaller end. Discard bellows bands.

2) Slide bellows toward Birfield joint (BJ) side and pry off circlip. Hold DOJ case with hand and withdraw shaft. Remove grease. Remove 6 balls by prying out with screwdriver inserted against shaft.

3) Rotate bearing cage 1/2 pitch to align cage ball guide with ball retainer projection. Slide bearing cage toward bellows. Remove ball retainer. Remove bearing cage and bellows. *See Fig. 5.*

Fig. 5: Removing Bearing Cage and Retainer

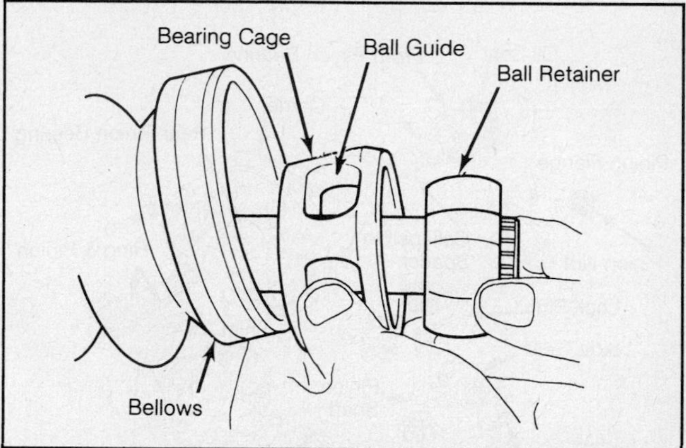

Bearing Cage
Ball Guide
Ball Retainer
Bellows

Bearing cage cannot be removed in reverse direction.

NOTE: BJ assembly is secured in position with axle shaft and cannot be disassembled. BJ assembly should be removed from DOJ assembly only to replace bellows.

Inspection

1) Clean all parts and inspect the BJ and DOJ assemblies for play in normal direction of rotation. If variance exceeds 2 1/2°, replace entire axle shaft.

2) If axle shaft-to-case contact is found, check steering angle. If axle shaft-to-circlip or bottom case contact is found, check for transverse misalignment of front axle assembly.

Reassembly

1) Carefully install bellows to BJ assembly and fill half of the cavity with specified grease. Fill bearing cage with specified grease and seat bellows.

2) Install new bellows band. During installation of bellows, equalize air pressure on both sides to prevent premature wear due to collapse of bellows.

3) Working from DOJ assembly side, push bellows band and bellows onto shaft. Slide bearing cage onto shaft (smaller diameter side toward BJ end). Slide ball retainer onto shaft.

4) Secure ball retainer with snap ring. Align ball guide of bearing cage with ball retainer projection. Turn cage 1/2 pitch. Press ball bearings into position with fingers.

5) Fill half the clearance of DOJ case with grease and position case over DOJ bearing assembly. Install circlip in groove with ends positioned at inner circumference, away from ball bearing groove. Pack DOJ assembly with grease and install bellows as previously described for BJ assembly.

DIFFERENTIAL ASSEMBLIES

NOTE: Overhaul procedures of front and rear differentials are similar.

Disassembly

1) Mark side bearing caps for reassembly reference. Remove nuts and bearing caps. Remove differential case assembly. Remove differential side bearings from case. Record thickness of each side bearing and shim pack and place with appropriate bearing race.

ISUZU P'UP (Cont.)

Fig. 6: Exploded View of Front Differential Assembly

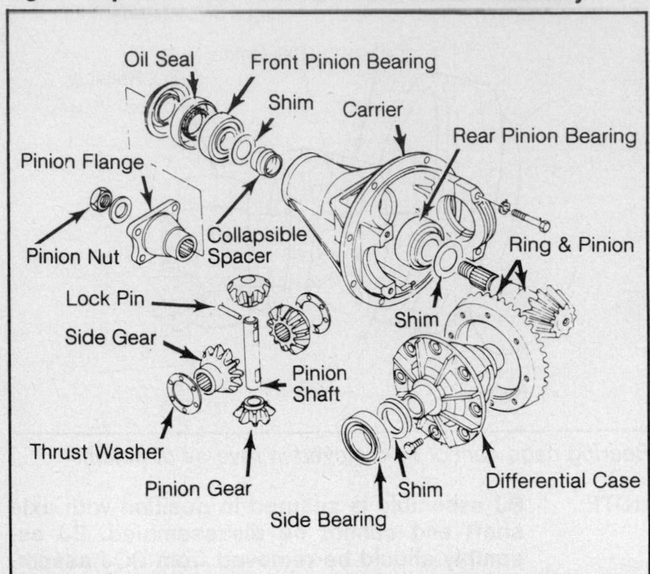
Oil Seal
Front Pinion Bearing
Shim
Carrier
Rear Pinion Bearing
Pinion Flange
Collapsible Spacer
Pinion Nut
Ring & Pinion
Lock Pin
Shim
Side Gear
Pinion Shaft
Thrust Washer
Pinion Gear
Shim
Differential Case
Side Bearing

Keep right and left side bearing races with respective bearings.

2) Remove ring gear bolts and separate ring gear from case. Drive out pinion shaft lock pin using a long drift. Remove pinion shaft using a drift, then withdraw thrust block (rear differential), pinion gears, side gears and thrust washers.

Fig. 7: Removing Pinion Shaft Lock Pin

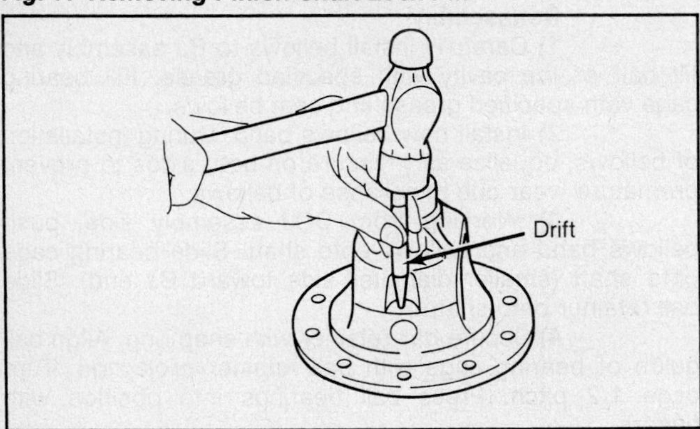
Drift

It may be necessary to remove caulking in lock pin using a 5 mm drill.

3) Remove pinion nut and pinion flange. Drive the pinion gear from carrier using a soft hammer or drift. Withdraw front pinion bearing and oil seal.

4) Using a drift, remove pinion bearing races from carrier. Mount pinion gear in a press and remove rear pinion bearing and depth shim from pinion gear.

Reassembly & Adjustment (Case Assembly)

1) Install side gears and thrust washers in case. Position thrust washers 180° apart, then roll gears into position making sure they are in alignment to allow installation of pinion shaft.

2) Place thrust block between pinion gears (rear differential only). Drive pinion shaft into position, making sure lock pin hole aligns with hole in case. Measure backlash between side gears and pinion gears; if greater than .007" (.18 mm), install selective thrust washers to bring backlash within specifications.

3) Washers are available in thicknesses of .041" (1.04 mm), .045" (1.14 mm), .049" (1.24 mm) and .053" (1.35 mm).

NOTE: **Increasing washer thickness decreases backlash; decreasing washer thickness increases backlash.**

4) Install lock pin in pinion shaft and caulk end to prevent loosening. Install ring gear in position on case, apply Loctite to threads and tighten bolts in diagonal sequence to 72-87 ft. lbs. (98-118 N.m) on rear differential or to 51-65 lbs. (69-88 N.m) on front differential.

Reassembly & Adjustment (Drive Pinion Depth)

1) Install front and rear pinion bearing races into carrier bores. Lubricate pinion bearings and position in respective races. Install gauge plate, preload stud and pilot through front and rear bearing and tighten nut securely.

2) Rotate bearing to ensure proper seating. Tighten lock nut until 20 INCH lbs. (2.3 N.m) of torque are required to rotate new bearing, or 8-10 INCH lbs. (1.0-1.2 N.m) are required to rotate used bearings.

Fig. 8: Tool Arrangement for Measuring Drive Pinion Installed Height

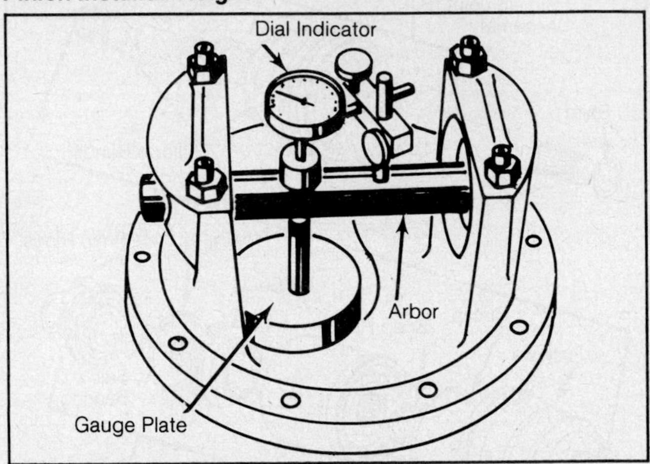
Dial Indicator
Arbor
Gauge Plate

3) Place mounting discs (J-23597-8) on arbor tool (J-23597-1) and place assembly in position in side bearing bores. Install bearing caps snugly. Mount a dial indicator on arbor post and preload dial 1/2 revolution, then tighten indicator in this position.

4) Position indicator plunger on gauge plate, slowly swing across until highest reading is obtained, then "zero" indicator on highest reading of gauge plate.

5) Carefully swing plunger off gauge plate and note indicator reading. Reading is the correct thickness of rear pinion depth shim for a nominal drive pinion.

NOTE: **Front differential pinion shims are available in sizes ranging from .059-.077" (1.5-1.95 mm). Rear differential pinion shims are available in sizes ranging from .086-.101" (2.18-2.56 mm). A rear differential indicator reading of 0 (zero) or .001" (.03 mm) requires shims of .100" (2.54 mm) and .101" (2.56 mm) respectively.**

Fig. 9: Pinion Depth Code Location on Pinion Head

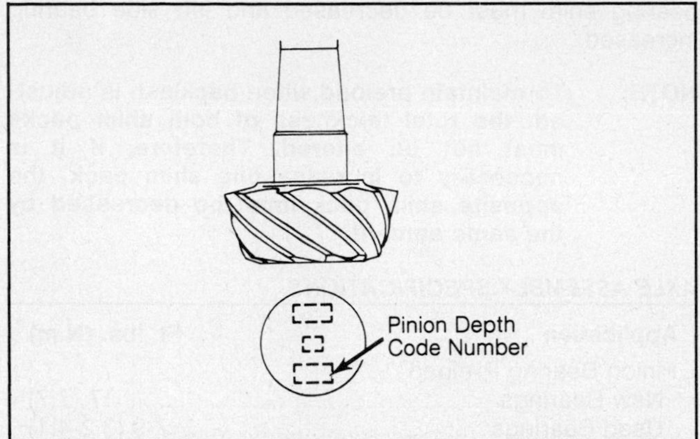

Pinion Depth
Code Number

If pinion depth code is "0", the pinion is "nominal" and no dial indicator correction is required.

6) Examine head of drive pinion. Pinion depth code is stamped by chemical ink and is the lower of three numbers. A " + " (plus) number indicates need for greater mounting distance (decreased shim thickness).

7) A " – " (minus) number indicates need for smaller mounting distance (increased shim thickness). See appropriate chart to determine proper shim variation to compensate for plus or minus markings.

FRONT DIFFERENTIAL PINION DEPTH SHIMS

Pinion Code	Correction Required
+6	Subtract .0024" (.06 mm)
+4	Subtract .0016" (.04 mm)
+2	Subtract .0008" (.02 mm)
0	No Correction Required
–2	Add .0008" (.02 mm)
–4	Add .0016" (.04 mm)
–6	Add .0024" (.06 mm)

REAR DIFFERENTIAL PINION DEPTH SHIMS

Pinion Code	Correction Required
+10	Subtract .005" (.13 mm)
+8	Subtract .004" (.10 mm)
+6	Subtract .003" (.08 mm)
+4	Subtract .002" (.05 mm)
+2	Subtract .001" (.03 mm)
0	No Correction Required
–2	Add .001" (.03 mm)
–4	Add .002" (.05 mm)
–6	Add .003" (.08 mm)
–8	Add .004" (.10 mm)
–10	Add .005" (.13 mm)

8) Using bearing installing tool (J-6133-01), place selected shim on drive pinion and press rear bearing onto pinion. Remove gauging tools from carrier.

NOTE: DO NOT press on roller cage. Press only on bearing inner race.

Pinion Bearing Preload

1) Place drive pinion and collapsible spacer into carrier. Install front pinion bearing and oil seal. Mount pinion flange on drive pinion, apply lubricant to pinion threads and install pinion nut. Tighten rear differential nut to 85 ft. lbs. (115 N.m) and front differential nut to 108-145 ft. lbs. (146-197 N.m).

2) Rotate pinion to ensure bearings are seated. Wind a small amount of string (approximately 4-6 windings) around pinion flange. Using a pull scale, note reading required to rotate flange.

Fig. 10: Using Pull Scale to Measure Drive Pinion Bearing Preload

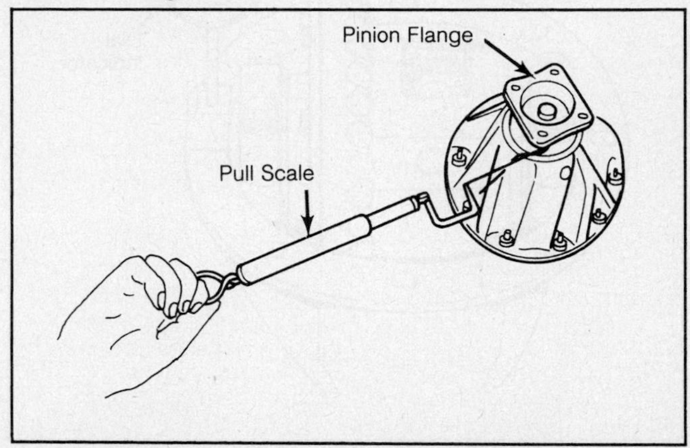

Pinion Flange
Pull Scale

3) Continue tightening nut in small increments until pull required to rotate flange is 17 lbs. (7.7 kg) for new bearings or 8-9 lbs. (3.6-4.1 kg) for used bearings.

CAUTION: Preload builds quickly. Nut should be tightened only in small increments and pull scale used after each small amount of tightening. If preload is exceeded, a new collapsible bearing spacer must be installed.

Backlash & Side Bearing Preload

1) If original side bearings, differential case, ring and pinion, and differential carrier are being reused, the original shims may be reinstalled in their respective positions.

2) If only new side bearings are being installed, measure new bearings with a micrometer and compare thickness with original bearings. If new bearing is thicker, SUBTRACT difference from shim pack. If new bearing is thinner, ADD difference to shim pack.

3) If new bearings, and/or differential case, ring and pinion, or differential carrier are being installed, new shims must be selected as follows. Install side bearings onto differential case, but do not install shims at this time.

4) Mount case into carrier bores. Move ring gear tightly against carrier on ring gear side (away from pinion), and hold in this position. Using a feeler gauge, measure clearance between bearing and differential carrier on side opposite ring gear. Record clearance.

5) Proper preload is established using the predetermined dimension of .002" (.05 mm). Therefore, ADD this dimension to clearance obtained in step **3)** for proper preload. This will give required total thickness of both shim packs. Equally divide the total dimension for required shim pack thickness for each side.

6) Remove case from carrier, remove side bearings and install shim packs, then reinstall bearings. Install differential case into carrier, tapping carefully into place.

7) Install side bearing caps in original positions, install and tighten attaching bolts. Measure runout

Drive Axles

ISUZU P'UP (Cont.)

of ring gear. If runout exceeds .002" (.05 mm), correct by cleaning or replacing parts. See Fig. 11.

Fig. 11: Checking Ring Gear Backface Runout

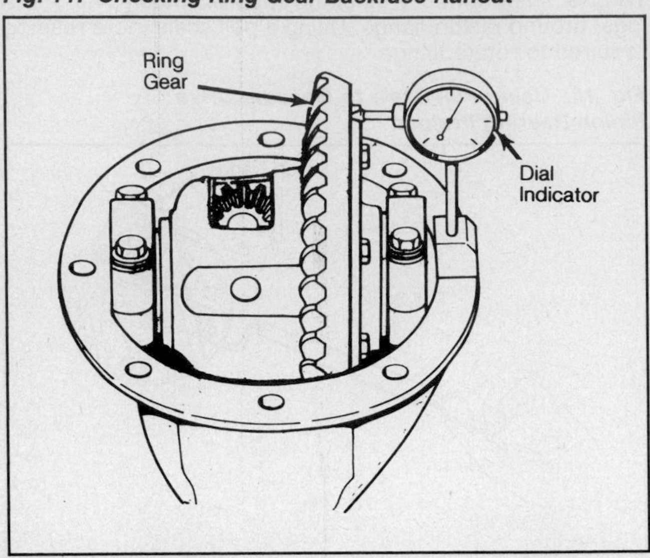
Ring Gear
Dial Indicator

NOTE: **Backlash changes approximately .002" (.05 mm) for each .003" (.08 mm) shim change.**

8) Mount a dial indicator against ring gear teeth and measure backlash in three locations. Backlash should be .005-.007" (.13-.18 mm) on rear differential and .004-.006" (.10-.15 mm) on front differential.

9) If not within specifications, shims behind side bearings must be adjusted. To increase backlash, right side bearing shim must be increased and left side bearing decreased. To decrease backlash, right side bearing shim must be decreased and left side bearing increased.

Fig. 12: Checking Ring Gear-to-Drive Pinion Gear Backlash

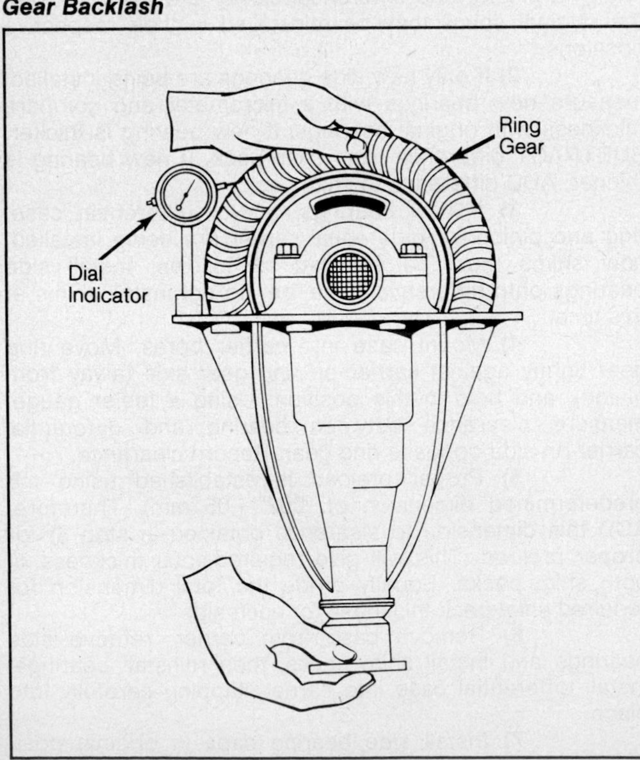
Ring Gear
Dial Indicator

NOTE: **To maintain preload when backlash is adjusted, the total thickness of both shim packs must not be altered. Therefore, if it is necessary to increase one shim pack, the apposite shim pack must be decreased by the same amount.**

AXLE ASSEMBLY SPECIFICATIONS

Application	Ft. lbs. (N.m)
Pinion Bearing Preload [1]	
New Bearings	17 (7.7)
Used Bearings	7-9 (3.2-4.1)
	In. (mm)
Side & Pinion Gear	
Backlash	.001-.003 (.025-.08)
Side Bearing Preload	[2] .002 (.05)
Ring Gear Backface Runout	.002 (.05)
Ring Gear Backlash	
Front & Rear	.005-.007 (.13-.18)

[1] – Measured with pull scale.
[2] – Add to side bearing "zero clearance" shim pack.

TIGHTENING SPECIFICATIONS

Application	Ft. Lbs. (N.m)
Ball Joint Stud Nuts [1]	75 (102)
Ball Joint-to-Lower Arm	45 (61)
Control Arm Pivot-to-Frame	
Upper	76 (103)
Lower	130 (177)
Upper Control Arm Pivot Shaft Bushing	87 (118)
Lower Control Arm-to-Crossmember	94 (128)
Rotor-to-Hub	36 (49)
Strut Bar-to-Lower Arm	45 (61)
Strut Bar-to-Frame	
Lock Nut	50 (68)
Nut	15 (20)
Pitman Arm-to-Steering Shaft	160 (217)
Idler Arm-to-Pivot Shaft	87 (118)
Front Axle Mounting Bolts	15 (20)
Rear Propeller Shaft-to-Pinion Flange	18 (24)
Rear Axle Shaft Lock Nut	190 (258)
Rear Axle Bearing Through Bolt	52 (71)
Ring Gear-to-Case Bolts [2]	
Front	44-58 (60-79)
Rear	85 (116)
Bearing Cap Nuts	
Front	50 (68)
Rear	75 (102)
Pinion Flange Nut [3]	
Front	108-145 (147-197)
Rear	85 (116)
Carrier-to-Housing Bolts	18 (24)
Front Axle Shaft-to-Axle Case	44 (60)

[1] – Plus additional torque to align cotter pin hole. NEVER back off to align cotter pin.
[2] – Threads coated with Loctite.
[3] – Initial torque only.

JAGUAR

XJ6, XJS

DESCRIPTION

The differential assembly is of hypoid ring and pinion design with center line of drive pinion gear set below centerline of ring gear. A collapsible spacer is used to set drive pinion bearing preload and all other differential adjustments are accomplished using shims.

Stub axles transmit power out of differential, through independent rear suspension, to drive wheels. A limited slip unit, is used on some models.

AXLE RATIO & IDENTIFICATION

Jaguar uses an integral carrier rear axle which may be equipped with a limited slip differential. Limited slip differential can be identified by the letters "PL" on a tag under the axle cover bolt.

Two different axle ratios are used. A 3.07:1 gear ratio is used as standard on 12-cylinder models and as an alternative on 6-cylinder models. A 3.31:1 gear ratio is used as standard on 6-cylinder models. To determine axle ratio, divide number of ring gear teeth by number of pinion gear teeth.

REMOVAL & INSTALLATION

REAR SUSPENSION ASSEMBLY

NOTE: **This procedure is provided since many operations on the final drive require removal of rear suspension assembly before starting work on final drive.**

Removal

1) Raise and support vehicle. Place stands forward of radius arms on body with wood blocks between body and stands. Remove wheels. Remove mufflers from tail pipes.

2) Remove safety wire and bolts securing safety strap to body. Remove radius arm securing bolt, safety strap and radius arm from body mounting post. Disconnect and plug brake lines at body.

3) Remove clevis pin securing hand brake cable to actuating levers on crossmember. Loosen lock nut and remove outer hand brake cable screw from adjuster block. Detach drive shaft from differential.

4) Place jack under rear suspension. Remove bolts and lock nuts securing crossmember mounts to frame. Lower and remove rear suspension from vehicle.

Installation

To install, reverse removal procedures. Bleed brakes. Tighten radius arm nuts on lower control arm when weight of vehicle is on wheels.

HALF SHAFT

Removal

1) Remove rear suspension assembly. Remove rear hub as follows. Remove fulcrum shaft grease fitting. Withdraw cotter pin and remove nut and washers from splined end of half shaft. Using puller (JD 1D), pull hub and carrier from half shaft.

2) Remove spacer from half shaft and examine inner oil seal track. Replace track if necessary. Remove 1 nut from outer suspension arm fulcrum shaft and using soft hammer, drive out shaft. Remove hub and carrier assembly from car.

Fig. 1: Hub and Carrier Assembly Removal from Half Shaft

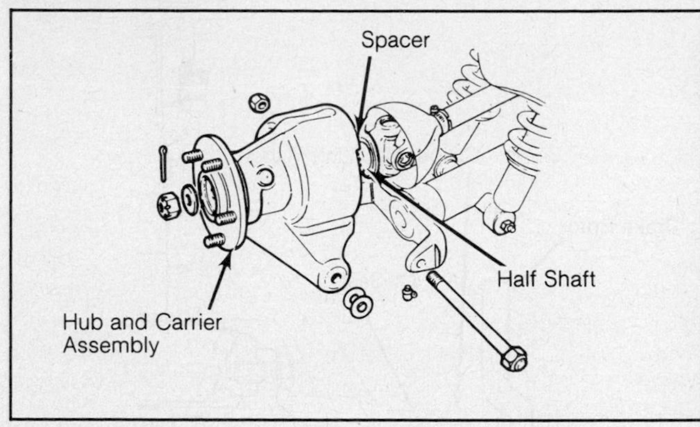
Spacer
Half Shaft
Hub and Carrier
Assembly

A puller must be used to remove hub and carrier from half shaft.

3) Support suspension arm with jack and remove nut and bolt securing top of forward shock absorber. Remove nuts and washer securing shock absorber to suspension arm and remove shock. Remove 4 nuts securing half shaft flange to stub axle flange and brake rotor.

4) Pull half shaft from suspension unit noting number of camber shims installed between half shaft flange and brake rotor. If necessary, remove joint shields by drilling out rivets.

Installation

1) To install, reverse removal procedure. If necessary, replace joint shield, positioning grease nipple access hole correctly.

2) Cover joint lines in shield with non-hardening waterproof sealing compound. Be sure to replace camber shims.

3) To reinstall rear hub, install dummy shaft in hub carrier fulcrum. Install carrier on suspension arm, installing shims removed from between carrier and suspension arm. Replace outer suspension arm fulcrum shaft, displacing dummy shaft. Secure shaft with nut and reinstall grease nipple.

4) If necessary, install oil seal track to half shaft splined flange, replace spacer. Thoroughly clean and degrease splines of half shaft and bore of hub.

5) Using a small brush, sparingly apply Loctite to outer two thirds of half shaft splines. Assemble hub carrier to half shaft. Install washer and tighten hub carrier assembly nut. Install new cotter pin.

6) Install dial indicator so it bears against hub and zero indicator. Using 2 pry bars, pry out on hub and measure hub bearing end play. If end play exceeds specifications, overhaul rear hub and carrier assembly. After installation of rear suspension in vehicle, check rear wheel camber.

STUB AXLE OIL SEAL

NOTE: **To remove stub axle it is necessary to remove the inboard end of the drive shaft, the forward attachment of the radius rod, and the brake caliper and disc.**

JAGUAR (Cont.)

Fig. 2: Sectional View of Stub Axle Assembly

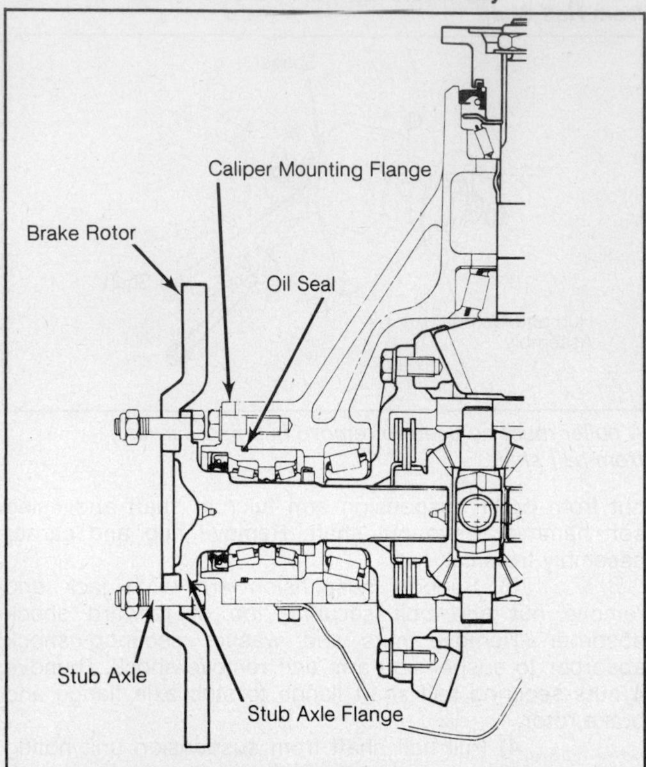
Caliper Mounting Flange
Brake Rotor
Oil Seal
Stub Axle
Stub Axle Flange

Remove stub axle, caliper mounting shims, bearing, and oil seal as a unit.

Removal

1) Remove half shaft. Remove locking wire securing caliper mounting bolts. Remove caliper mounting bolts and caliper. Remove brake rotor, noting number of shims removed between rotor and stub axle flange. Remove safety wire and 5 bolts securing caliper mounting flange (bearing housing) to final drive.

2) Withdraw stub axle, together with caliper mounting shims, bearings and oil seal. Discard oil seal. Turn down tab washer and remove nut from stub axle. Remove bearings and caliper mounting flange from stub axle.

Installation

1) Lightly oil new seal and position carefully in drive case. Press seal squarely and fully seat in case groove. DO NOT remove protruding portion of seal.

2) Coat seal with hypoid oil and place caliper mounting flange and seal assembly over stub axle. Slide bearings on drive shaft followed by new tab washer and nut. Ensure bearings seat square to stub axle shoulder and tighten nut. Turn tab up on washer.

3) Lightly oil stub axle splines and install shaft in final drive housing. Install bolts securing mounting bracket finger tight. Using feeler gauge, measure dimension between inside face of mounting bracket and final drive housing.

4) The measurement obtained determines shim thickness required. Remove stub axle and select shims of required thickness, and thinly coat mating faces and shims with sealant. Tighten bolts in a diagonal sequence.

5) Safety wire securing bolts to tension in clockwise direction. Install brake rotors and half shaft flange, using shims removed from between rotor and flange. Install caliper on mounting bracket.

6) Install distance spacers (oversize nuts) to rotor studs and tighten nuts. Use feeler gauges to ensure that rotor is centrally located between jaws of caliper. If necessary add to or remove from shim pack between flange and disc to center rotor. Continue assembly in reverse of disassembly procedure.

PINION FLANGE & SEAL

Removal

1) Disconnect propeller shaft. Check and record torque required to turn drive shaft flange clockwise (viewed from front) through backlash movement.

2) Block rear wheels and remove flange securing nut and washer. Remove flange. Pry oil seal out of final drive case. Lightly score oil seal recess with tang of file.

Installation

1) Ensure oil seal recess is clean and free of oil. Lightly tap new oil seal into recess ensuring seal is square with case. Reinstall flange, washer and nut.

2) Tighten nut to specifications while rotating flange to ensure bearing seats correctly. Recheck pinion preload.

3) If preload is below specifications, continue tightening flange nut until specified preload is obtained. If preload exceeds maximum specified value, new collapsible spacer must be installed. *See Overhaul*. Reconnect propeller shaft and remove wheel chocks.

REAR AXLE ASSEMBLY

Removal

1) Drain final drive unit and remove rear suspension assembly. Remove final drive mounting plate and shock absorber/spring units. Remove nuts securing half shaft inner universal joint to brake rotor.

2) Disconnect half shaft, noting shims removed. Remove nut from inner suspension arm fulcrum shaft and drive out shaft. Repeat for other side of unit. Disconnect hand brake levers from compensator.

3) Remove safety wire from final drive mounting bolts, remove bolts and tilt crossmember forward over pinion. Remove calipers from final drive unit. Remove brake rotors, noting number of shims removed from between rotor and stub axle flange.

Installation

To install, reverse removal procedure. Make sure brake rotor is centered between jaws of caliper and safety wire tension bolts in clockwise direction.

OVERHAUL

DISASSEMBLY

1) Remove rear cover and discard gasket. Remove safety wire and bolts securing caliper mounting flange. Withdraw stub axle along with caliper mounting flange shims, bearings and oil seal. Turn down tab washer and remove nut, bearings and caliper mounting flange from stub axle.

2) Repeat procedure for second stub axle. Remove bolts securing differential bearing caps and lift off caps. Pry out differential assembly using 2 pry bars, taking care not to damage housing.

3) Remove drive pinion nut and washer. Mark relative positions of flange and remove flange. Using a press, remove pinion from differential housing.

Fig. 3: Exploded View of Jaguar Limited Slip Differential Assembly

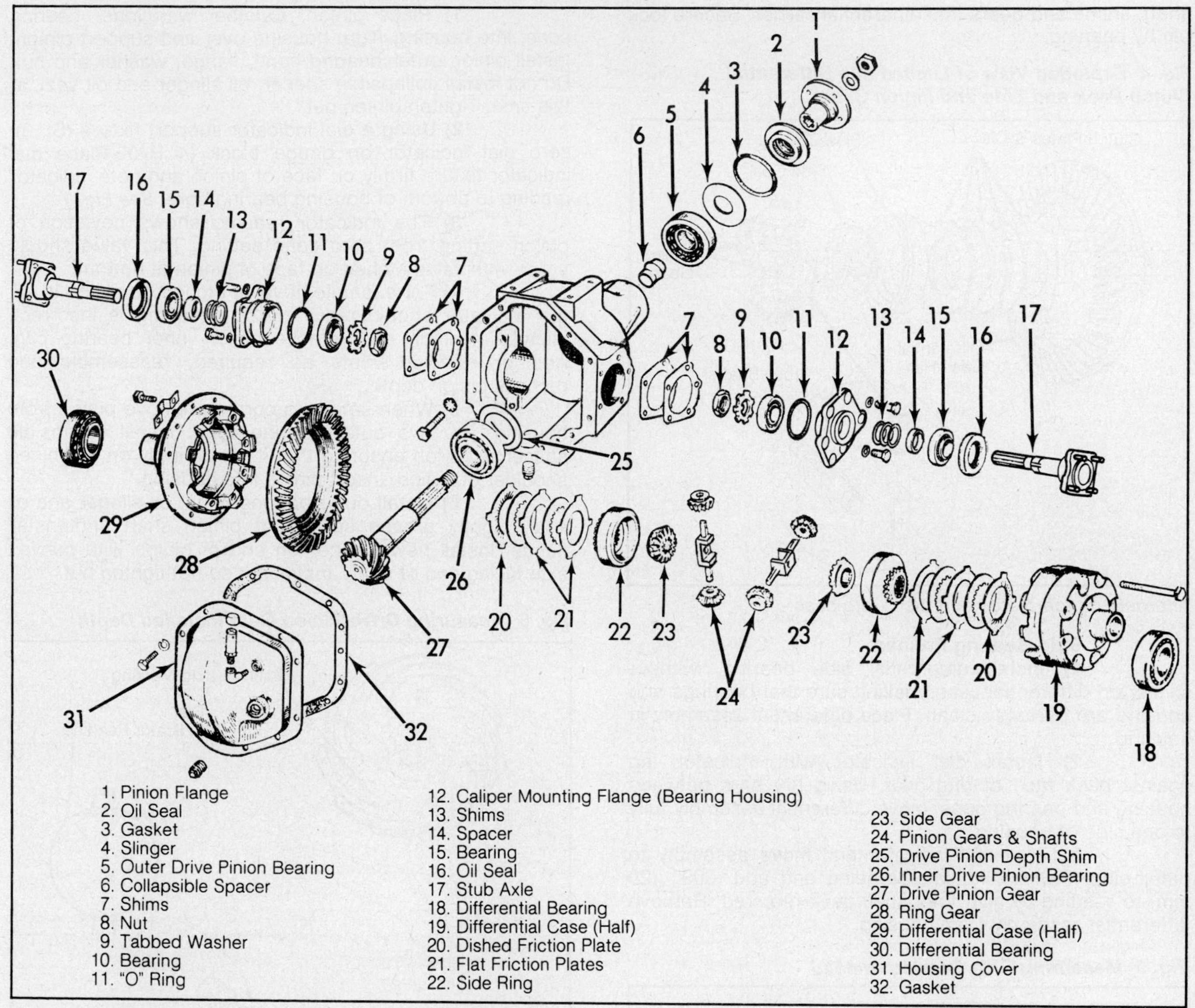

1. Pinion Flange
2. Oil Seal
3. Gasket
4. Slinger
5. Outer Drive Pinion Bearing
6. Collapsible Spacer
7. Shims
8. Nut
9. Tabbed Washer
10. Bearing
11. "O" Ring
12. Caliper Mounting Flange (Bearing Housing)
13. Shims
14. Spacer
15. Bearing
16. Oil Seal
17. Stub Axle
18. Differential Bearing
19. Differential Case (Half)
20. Dished Friction Plate
21. Flat Friction Plates
22. Side Ring
23. Side Gear
24. Pinion Gears & Shafts
25. Drive Pinion Depth Shim
26. Inner Drive Pinion Bearing
27. Drive Pinion Gear
28. Ring Gear
29. Differential Case (Half)
30. Differential Bearing
31. Housing Cover
32. Gasket

4) Remove oil seal, oil slinger and outer bearing cone. Examine inner and outer bearing cups for wear. If replacement is required, remove cups using a puller.

5) On limited slip differentials, remove differential side bearings using output shaft bearing remover (SL 47). If no reference marks are present, scribe a line across both halves of differential case to ensure correct reassembly.

6) Remove bolts securing both halves of differential case. Split case and remove clutch discs and plates from one side.

7) Remove differential side ring, pinion side gear and pinion cross shafts complete with gears. Remove remaining side gear and ring and remove remaining clutch discs and plates.

8) On conventional differentials, remove peening and drive pinion shaft lock out of carrier. Remove gears, shaft and shims from carrier.

REASSEMBLY & ADJUSTMENT

Case Assembly

1) On limited slip differentials, install clutch plates and discs alternately into flange half of case. Install 2 Belleville clutch plates so that convex sides are against case.

2) Install side ring and position 1 side gear into ring recess. Install pinion cross shafts complete with pinion gears, ensuring that ramps on shafts coincide with mating ramps in case.

3) Assemble differential case halves ensuring that reference marks are lined up and clutch friction plate tongues are aligned with grooves in differential case. Install bolts, but do not tighten. Check alignment of splines by inserting both stub axles.

4) On limited slip differentials, tighten differential case bolts with stub axles in position. With 1 stub axle locked, other axle must not turn more than .75" (19 mm) measured on a 6" (152 mm) radius.

JAGUAR (Cont.)

5) On conventional differentials, install pinion shaft, shims and gears into differential carrier. Secure lock pin by peening.

Fig. 4 Exploded View of Limited Slip Differential Clutch Pack and Side and Pinion Gears

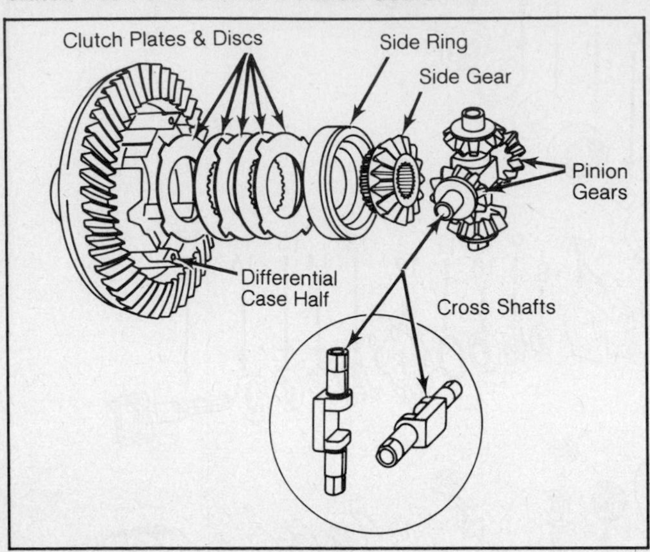
Clutch Plates & Discs
Side Ring
Side Gear
Pinion Gears
Differential Case Half
Cross Shafts

Alternate clutch plates and discs into case.

Side Bearing Preload

1) Install differential side bearing, without shims, on differential case, making sure that bearings and housing are perfectly clean. Place differential assembly in housing.

2) Install dial indicator with indicator leg against back face of ring gear. Using pry bars between housing and bearing cups, move differential assembly fully to one side of housing.

3) Zero dial indicator and move assembly to other side. Record indicator reading and add .009" (.20 mm) to reading to give total shim pack required. Remove differential assembly from housing.

Fig. 5 Measuring Side Bearing Preload

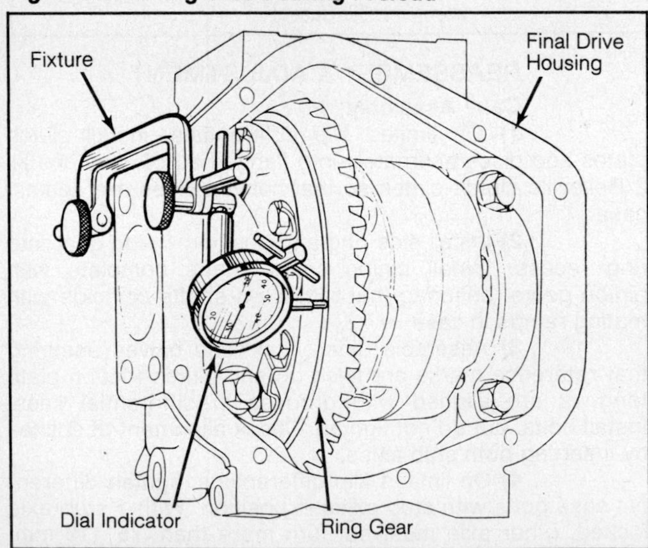
Fixture
Final Drive Housing
Dial Indicator
Ring Gear

Record indicator reading and add .009" (.20 mm) to give total shim pack required.

Drive Pinion Depth

1) Place pinion, together with inner bearing cone, into housing. Turn housing over and support pinion. Install pinion outer bearing cone, flange, washer and nut. Do not install collapsible spacer, oil slinger and oil seal, at this time. Tighten pinion nut.

2) Using a dial indicator support fixture (SL 3), zero dial indicator on gauge block (4 HA). Place dial indicator fixture firmly on face of pinion and note indicator reading to bottom of housing bearing bore. *See Fig. 7.*

3) The indicator reading shows deviation of pinion setting from zero cone setting. This value should agree with value etched on face of pinion at bottom.

4) For example, if value etched on pinion is -2, dial indicator should read -.002". If setting is incorrect, dismantle pinion and remove pinion inner bearing cup. Add or remove shims as required, reassemble and recheck pinion depth.

5) When setting is correct, remove pinion from housing. Remove outer bearing cone. Install collapsible spacer to pinion ensuring that it seats firmly on machined shoulder of pinion. Insert pinion into housing.

6) Install outer bearing cone, oil slinger and oil seal. Lightly grease splines of pinion shaft and install flange. Install new washer on end of pinion with convex side facing end of shaft. Install but do not tighten nut.

Fig. 6 Measuring Drive Pinion Gear Installed Depth

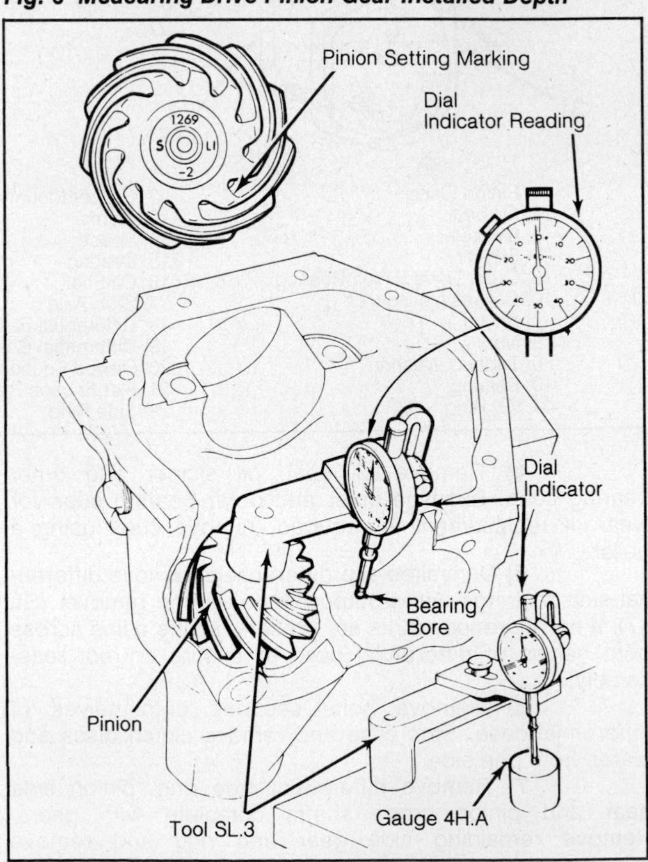
Pinion Setting Marking
Dial Indicator Reading
1269
S
LI
-2
Dial Indicator
Bearing Bore
Pinion
Tool SL.3
Gauge 4H.A

Pinion deviation from zero cone setting is etched on face of pinion.

JAGUAR (Cont.)

Backlash Adjustment

1) Place differential assembly, complete with side bearings but less shims, in housing. Ensure that bearings and housing are clean. Install dial indicator on housing with feeler on back face of ring gear.

2) Pry differential case and ring gear assembly away from pinion until opposite side bearing is seated against housing. Zero dial indicator at this point.

3) Move differential assembly towards pinion until ring gear is deeply meshed with pinion. Note indicator reading and from this value, subtract the backlash allowance etched on drive gear (example: B/L.007 denotes .007").

4) This result will yield the thickness of shims (in inches) to be placed between differential case and side bearing on ring gear side of differential.

5) Install this thickness of shims, taking shims from pack determined previously under "Side Bearing Preload". Install balance of total shims required on opposite side of case. *See Example of Calculations table.*

6) With shims calculated installed, lower differential assembly into position, lightly tapping bearings home with soft hammer. Make sure ring and pinion gears mesh as installation proceeds.

7) Install side bearing caps, ensuring proper cap is placed on proper bearing. Tighten cap bolts. Mount dial indicator on housing with plunger against back face of ring gear.

EXAMPLE OF CALCULATIONS:

Side Bearing Preload Reading	.080"
PLUS Preload Value	.009"
Total Shim Pack	.089"
Pinion-to-Ring Gear Clearance	.042"
MINUS Etched Backlash Value	.007"
Total Ring Gear Side Shims	.035"
Total Shim Pack	.089"
MINUS Ring Gear Side Shims	.035"
Opposite Ring Gear Shim Pack	.054"

8) Turn pinion by hand and check ring gear run out. If run out exceeds specification, disassemble differential, clean all mounting surfaces and check for burrs.

9) Now place dial indicator to measure ring gear backlash. Move ring gear and check that backlash is to the specification etched on ring gear. If backlash is not to specification, transfer necessary shims from side of differential case to the other.

NOTE: **To increase backlash, remove shims from ring gear side and install on opposite side and visa versa. Finally, run a gear tooth contact pattern and adjust shims as necessary.**

Pinion Bearing Preload

1) Install pinion and stub axle oil seals. Install stub axles following procedure given under stub axle removal and installation. Tighten flange nut to specified torque. During tightening process, rotate flange to ensure correct seating of taper roller bearings.

2) Use care not to over tighten nut. If nut is over tightened, install a new collapsible spacer as pinion bearing preload will otherwise be incorrect. Install final drive rear cover using new gasket and sealer (Hylomar).

Fig. 7 Measuring Ring Gear-to-Drive Pinion Gear Backlash

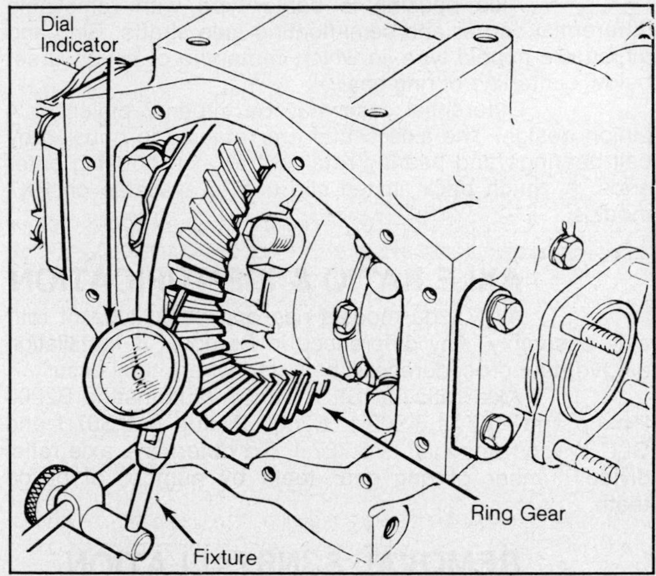
Dial Indicator
Ring Gear
Fixture

If nut is over tightened a new collapsible spacer must be installed.

AXLE ASSEMBLY SPECIFICATIONS

Application	In. (mm)
Rear Hub Bearing Endplay	
Preferred	.001-.003" (.03-.08)
Acceptable	[1] .005" (.13)
Zero Cone Setting	[2] 2.625" (66.67)
Drive Pinion Preload	
Preferred	.001-.003" (.03-.08)
Acceptable	[1] .005" (.13)
Side Bearing Preload	[1] .009" (.23)
Ring Gear Run Out	[1] .005" (.13)

[1] – Maximum clearance.
[2] – Distance from centerline of differential bearing bores to pinion face.

TIGHTENING SPECIFICATIONS

Application	Ft. Lbs. (N.m)
Radius Arm & Safety Strap-to-Body	40-45 (54-61)
Half Shaft Flange Nuts	49-55 (67-75)
Outer Suspension Arm	
Fulcrum Nut	95-105 (129-143)
Hub Carrier Assembly Nut	100-120 (136-163)
Stub Axle Nut	90-110 (122-150)
Caliper Bracket-to-Final Drive Housing	60-69 (81-93)
Pinion Flange Nut	120-130 (163-177)
Differential Case Bolts	43-50 (58-68)
Bearing Cap Bolts	63-70 (86-96)

Drive Axles

MAZDA

GLC Wagon, RX7,
B2000 Pickup, B2200 Diesel Pickup

DESCRIPTION

Axle housing is banjo type with removable differential carrier and semi-floating axle shafts. Ring and pinion are hypoid type, in which centerline of pinion is set below centerline of ring gear.

Differential case may be either 2 pinion or 4 pinion design. The axle shafts are retained in housing by ball bearings and bearing retainers at axle housing outer ends. A clutch pack limited slip unit is available on RX7 models.

AXLE RATIO & IDENTIFICATION

All Mazda models use one basic type of rear axle assembly. Any differences in Removal & Installation or Overhaul procedures will be noted where they occur.

Axle ratio on GLC Wagon (automatic), B2200 Pickup and RX7 is 3.909:1. B2000 Pickup is 3.307:1 and GLC Wagon (manual) is 3.727:1. To determine axle ratio, divide number of ring gear teeth by number of pinion teeth.

REMOVAL & INSTALLATION

AXLE SHAFTS & BEARINGS

Removal

1) Raise and support vehicle. Remove wheel. Remove brake drum and brake shoes. Disconnect and plug hydraulic line from wheel cylinder. Disconnect parking brake cable.

2) From inboard side of backing plate, remove 4 nuts from axle housing through bolts. Pull drive axle, backing plate, bearing housing (Pickups) and shims (if equipped) from axle housing with drive axle puller (49 0223 630B). Remove oil seal from axle housing.

3) On Pickup models, flatten locking tabs of lock washer. Loosen lock nut with spanner wrench. Remove lock nut and washer.

4) Using bearing pullers (49 8531 746 & 49 0259 747), remove bearing and housing assembly from drive axle. Remove backing plate. Remove bearing and oil seal from housing.

Installation

1) Install backing plate and spacer on shaft with chamfered edge of spacer must face drive axle flange. Using bearing attachment, (49 0259 748) press

Fig. 2: Exploded View of Axle Shaft Assembly for All Models Except Pickups

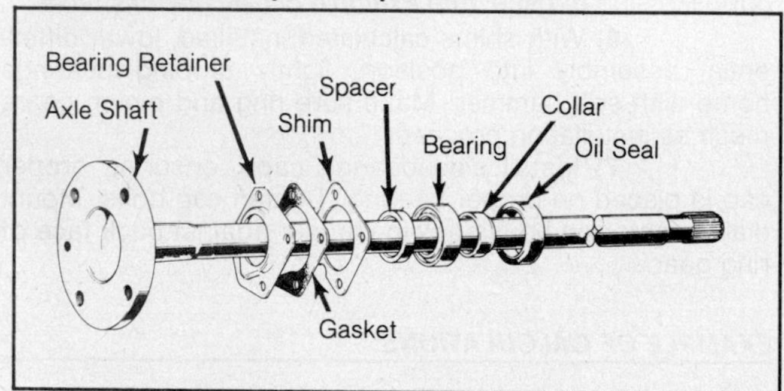
Bearing Retainer
Axle Shaft
Spacer
Shim
Collar
Bearing
Oil Seal
Gasket

Chamfered edge of spacer must face axle shaft flange.

Fig. 1: Exploded View of Mazda Rear Axle Assembly

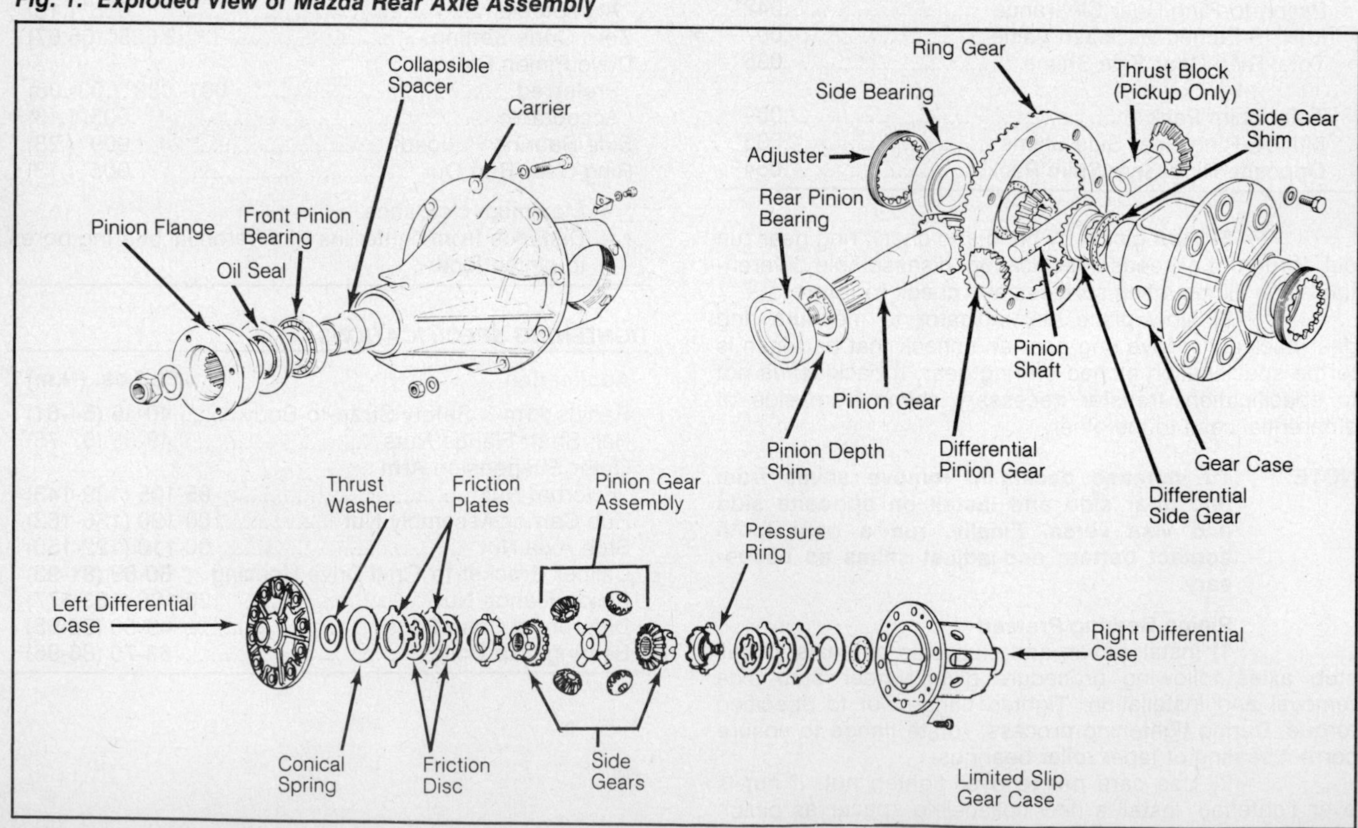
Collapsible
Spacer
Carrier
Pinion Flange
Front Pinion
Bearing
Oil Seal
Ring Gear
Thrust Block
(Pickup Only)
Side Bearing
Side Gear
Shim
Adjuster
Rear Pinion
Bearing
Pinion
Shaft
Pinion Gear
Pinion Depth
Shim
Differential
Pinion Gear
Gear Case
Differential
Side Gear
Thrust
Washer
Friction
Plates
Pinion Gear
Assembly
Pressure
Ring
Left Differential
Case
Right Differential
Case
Conical
Spring
Friction
Disc
Side
Gears
Limited Slip
Gear Case

Drive Axles

MAZDA (Cont.)

bearing onto shaft until seated. Press new bearing collar onto shaft without any lubricant.

CAUTION: Do not press bearing and collar onto shaft at the same time. If bearing collar is installed with less than 2.7 tons pressure (2,451 kg), replace bearing collar.

2) Apply a light coat of grease to oil seal and install oil seal in housing. Temporarily mount drive axle and backing plate on axle housing with mounting nuts.

3) Install dial indicator on backing plate and check drive axle end play. End play should be .002-.006" (.05-.15 mm) on Pickups and 0-.004" (0-.1 mm) on all other models.

4) On Pickup models only, if both drive axles were removed, the end play of each shaft must be measured separately. The end play for first drive axle installed should be .026-.033" (.65-.85 mm).

5) The end play for the second drive axle installed should be set to normal end play clearance of .002-.006" (.05-.15 mm).

6) After installing correct shim pack, install and tighten all attaching bolts and nuts. Install brake shoes and drum. Connect hydraulic lines to wheel cylinders, adjust brakes and bleed hydraulic system.

DIFFERENTIAL CARRIER

Removal

1) Raise and support vehicle with jack stands. Remove drain plug and drain rear axle lubricant. Remove axle shafts.

2) Mark propeller shaft and pinion flange for reassembly reference. Disconnect propeller shaft. Remove carrier attaching nuts and withdraw carrier from axle housing.

Installation

To install, reverse removal procedure. Make sure to refill axle with lubricant.

OVERHAUL

DISASSEMBLY

1) Mount carrier in a repair stand. Punch identification marks on side bearing supports of carrier, differential bearing caps and side bearing adjusters. Remove adjuster lock plates, loosen bearing cap attaching nuts or bolts, and slightly back off adjusters to relieve preload.

2) Remove bearing caps and adjusters, then withdraw differential assembly from carrier, making sure side bearing races remain with their respective bearings.

3) Using puller, (49 0839 425C) remove side bearings from gear case. Straighten lock tabs, remove ring gear attaching bolts, and separate ring gear from gear case.

4) On limited slip differentials, gradually loosen attaching screws until distance between left and right half of differential case is about 0.12" (3 mm). Then carefully separate differential halfs. Remove following parts: Thrust washer, conical spring, friction plate, friction disc, pressure ring, side gear, pinion gear and spider. Keep parts in order for reassembly. *See Fig. 1.*

5) On conventional differentials, drive out differential pinion shaft lock pin with a punch and remove

Fig. 3: Exploded View of Axle Shaft Assembly for Pickups

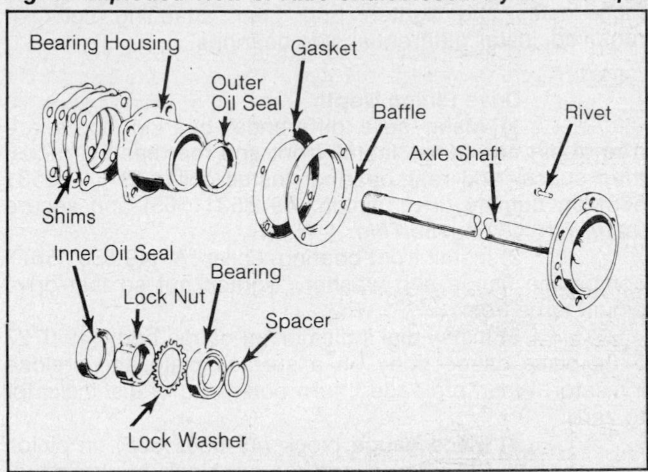
Bearing Housing
Gasket
Outer
Oil Seal
Baffle
Rivet
Axle Shaft
Shims
Inner Oil Seal
Bearing
Lock Nut
Spacer
Lock Washer

If both axle shafts were removed, the end play of each shaft must be measured separately.

pinion shaft. Rotate pinion gears 90° and remove gears, thrust washer, thrust block (if equipped) and differential side gears.

6) Remove pinion nut and pinion flange. Remove drive pinion and rear bearing assembly, adjusting shims (if equipped), spacer and bearing collar (if used). Remove front oil seal and withdraw front pinion bearing.

7) Using a press, remove rear bearing from drive pinion, then lift off pinion adjusting shim. If necessary for replacement, use a drift punch and remove pinion bearing races from carrier.

8) Inspect all parts for chipped or worn teeth, damaged bearing journals, cracks, flaking or any damage. Replace defective parts as necessary.

NOTE: It may be necessary to tap end of pinion with a soft hammer to remove from carrier.

REASSEMBLY & ADJUSTMENT

Case Assembly

1) Install a thrust washer on each differential side gear and install into case. Through openings in gear case, insert pinion gears exactly 180° opposite each other. Rotate pinion gears 90° so holes in gears line up with pinion shaft holes in gear case. Insert pinion shaft through case and pinion gears.

2) On limited slip differential, install parts in the following order: Thrust washer, conical spring, friction plate, friction disc, friction plate, friction disc and pressure ring. *See Fig. 1.*

3) Check backlash between side gears and pinion gears. Backlash should be less than .008" (.2 mm) on Pickups and less than .004" (.1 mm) on all other models. If not, install selective thrust washers to bring backlash within specifications.

NOTE: Always use same thickness thrust washer for both side gears.

4) If equipped with thrust block, remove pinion shaft, install thrust block and reinstall pinion shaft. On all models, install lock pin into case to secure pinion shaft. Using a punch, stake lock pin hole to prevent pin from working loose.

MAZDA (Cont.)

5) On all models, mount ring gear on case, then install and tighten ring gear attaching bolts. If removed, install differential side bearings.

Drive Pinion Depth

1) Make sure differential bearing bores are free of dirt and burrs. Install front and rear bearing races, then spacer and rear bearing. Install collar "B" (49 8531 568) on dummy drive pinion (49 8531 565) and secure them with "O" ring. *See Fig. 4.*

2) Install front bearing, collar "A" (49 8531 567), companion flange and washer. Tighten nut so that drive pinion turns freely.

3) Install dial indicator on gauge body (49 0727 570), place gauge body on a surface plate and preload indicator. When preloaded, turn outer ring of dial indicator to zero.

4) Place gauge block (49 0305 555) on pinion and position indicator assembly on block so button of indicator contacts lowest portion of differential bearing support bore.

NOTE: **DO NOT install collapsible spacer.**

5) Record the amount the indicator moves in a "+" (plus) or "–" (minus) direction from zero. Remove gauging assembly and pinion from carrier. Check rear face of pinion for the machining correction figure.

6) If pinion is marked "+" (plus), SUBTRACT amount specified on pinion from dial indicator reading; if marked "–" (minus), ADD amount to indicator reading.

NOTE: **Figures on pinion are hundredth millimeters.**

7) Select correct pinion depth adjusting shim to be used for reassembly by adding or subtracting the amount determined in steps **3)** through **5)** from the thickness of the original pinion depth shim used during gauging process. Position correct shim (from chart) on pinion and install pinion bearing.

Fig. 4: Dummy Pinion Shaft and Gauge Block

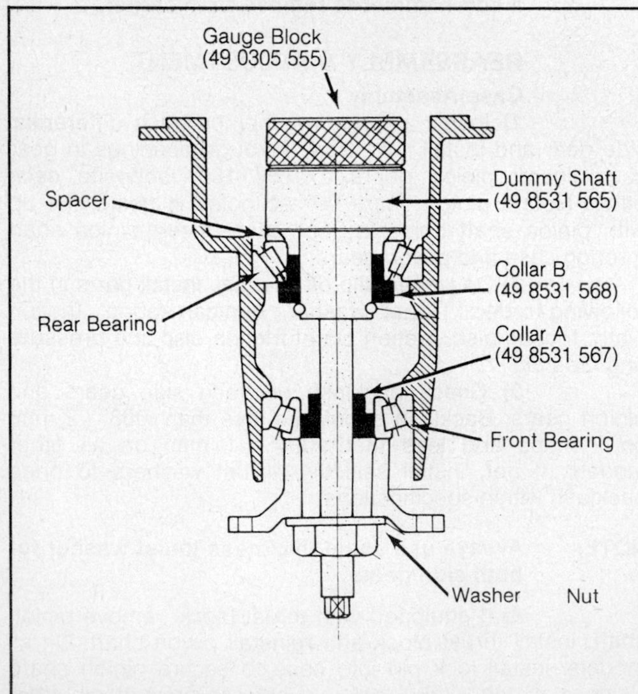
Gauge Block
(49 0305 555)
Spacer
Dummy Shaft
(49 8531 565)
Collar B
(49 8531 568)
Rear Bearing
Collar A
(49 8531 567)
Front Bearing
Washer
Nut

Never use collapsible spacer when checking pinion depth.

Fig. 5: Measuring Drive Pinion Installed Height

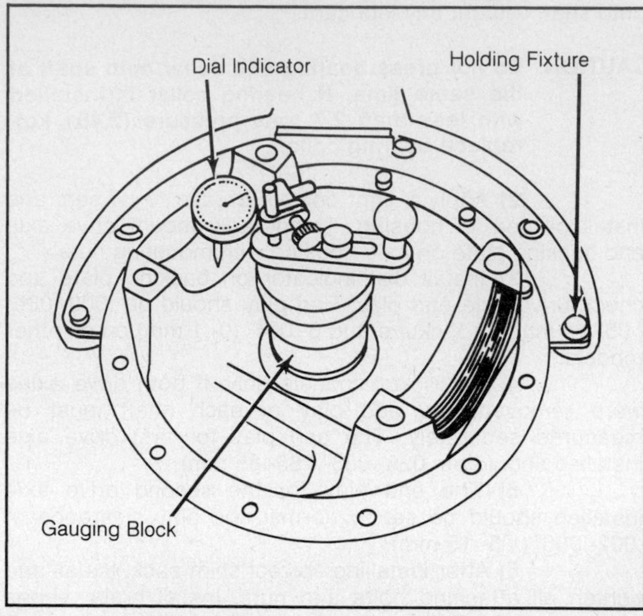
Dial Indicator
Holding Fixture
Gauging Block

The use of a dial indicator, pinion gauge set and gauge block are required for this procedure.

PINION DEPTH ADJUSTING SHIMS

Identification Mark	Thickness In. (mm)
08	.121 (3.08)
11	.122 (3.11)
14	.124 (3.14)
17	.125 (3.17)
20	.126 (3.20)
23	.127 (3.23)
26	.128 (3.26)
29	.130 (3.29)
32	.131 (3.32)
35	.132 (3.35)
38	.133 (3.38)
41	.134 (3.41)
44	.135 (3.44)
47	.137 (3.47)

Pinion Bearing Preload

1) Install collapsible spacer onto drive pinion assembly and install in carrier. Place front bearing in position on pinion. Hold pinion fully forward and drive pinion bearing over pinion until seated.

2) Apply grease to pinion oil seal lip and install seal into carrier. Install flange on pinion by tapping with soft hammer. Install pinion washer and nut.

3) Before tightening nut (when pinion preload is zero), check oil seal drag using a torque wrench. Tighten pinion nut to initial torque specifications as shown in chart.

MAZDA (Cont.)

INITIAL PINION NUT TORQUE

Application	Ft. Lbs. (N.m)
GLC Wagon	87-130 (118-176)
Pickups	145-253 (197-343)
All Others	94-130 (127-176)

4) With nut tightened to initial torque value, check preload using a torque wrench mounted on pinion nut. If preload is not as specified in specification table, continue tightening nut and checking preload until specified preload is obtained.

CAUTION: Preload builds quickly. Nuts should be tightened a little at a time and preload checked after each slight amount of tightening.

Backlash & Side Bearing Preload

1) Place differential case assembly into carrier making sure index marks on ring and pinion gears are aligned. *See Fig. 7.* Install bearing adjusters and bearing caps, then tighten bearing cap nuts or bolts finger tight.

2) Turn adjusters with a spanner wrench until bearing end play is eliminated and some backlash exists between ring gear and pinion. Slightly tighten one bearing cap nut or bolt on each side of carrier and measure backlash.

3) Mount a dial indicator to carrier flange so button of indicator contacts one of the ring gear teeth at a right angle. Check backlash between ring and pinion gears.

4) Using the spanner wrench, turn both bearing adjusters equally until backlash is as specified in Axle Assembly Specifications.

5) Differential bearing preload (case spread) is obtained by tightening both bearing adjusters equally. Tighten adjusters until distance between pilot sections of side bearing caps is 6.5133-6.5158" (165.437-165.50 mm) on GLC Wagon, 7.3004-7.3033" (185.43-185.50 mm) on RX7 or 8.485-8.0513" (204.428-204.50 mm) on Pickups.

Fig. 6: Installing Drive Pinion Bearing Collapsible Spacer

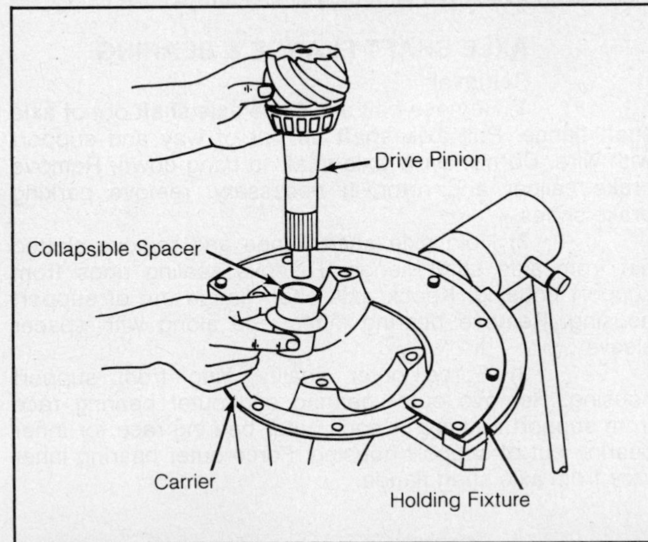
Drive Pinion
Collapsible Spacer
Carrier
Holding Fixture

If preload specifications are exceeded, collapsible spacer must be replaced.

Fig. 7: Adjusting Differential Bearing Preload (Case Spread)

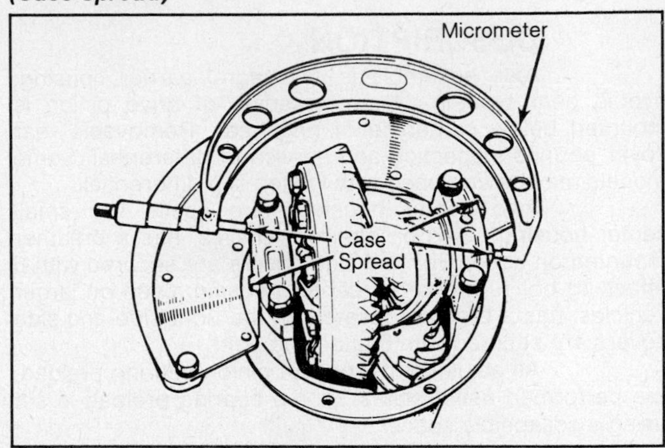
Micrometer
Case
Spread

When adjusting side bearing preload, care must be taken not to affect the ring and pinion gear backlash.

AXLE ASSEMBLY SPECIFICATIONS

Application	INCH Lbs. (N.m)
Pinion Bearing Preload [1]	
GLC Wagon	2.6-6.1 (.29-.68)
Pickups	11.3-15.6 (1.27-1.76)
All Others	7.8-12.2 (.88-1.37)
Side Bearing Preload	
GLC Wagon	4-9 (.45-1.01)
Pickups	4-13 (.45-1.47)
All Others	5-18 (.56-2.03)
	In. (mm)
Ring & Pinion Backlash	
GLC Wagon	.0059-.0067 (.15-.17)
Pickups	.0075-.0083 (.19-.21)
All Others	.0035-.0043 (.09-.11)
Side Gear & Pinion Backlash	
Pickups	0-.008 (0-0.2)
All Others	0-.004 (0-0.1)
	Qts. (L)
Oil Capacity	
GLC	.8 (.8)
Pickups	1.4 (1.3)
RX7	1.3 (1.2)

[1] – Without oil seal installed.

TIGHTENING SPECIFICATIONS

Application	Ft. Lbs. (N.m)
Pinion Nut	
GLC Wagon	87-130 (118-177)
Pickups	145-253 (197-344)
All Others	94-130 (128-177)
Ring Gear-to-Differential Case	
RX7	51-61 (69-83)
All Others	54-61 (72-83)
Differential Bearing Cap Bolts	
GLC Wagon	23-34 (31-46)
Pickups	41-59 (56-80)
All Others	27-38 (37-52)

MERCEDES-BENZ INTEGRAL CARRIER

240D, 300 Series, 380 Series

DESCRIPTION

Axle assembly is of integral carrier housing, hypoid gear type in which centerline of drive pinion is mounted below centerline of ring gear. Removable rear cover permits inspection and service of differential. Some models may be equipped with limited slip differential.

Two center housings are used. The small center housing, used on smaller vehicles, has a breather mounted on end cover and side covers are secured with 6 attaching bolts. The larger center housing, used on larger vehicles, has a breather located on the right side and side covers are secured with 8 attaching bolts.

All adjustments, except pinion bearing preload, are performed using shims. Pinion bearing preload is set using a collapsible spacer.

AXLE RATIO & IDENTIFICATION

All models use integral carrier rear axle with semi-trailing arm rear suspension. To determine axle ratio, divide the number of ring gear teeth by the number of pinion gear teeth.

REMOVAL & INSTALLATION

AXLE SHAFTS

Removal

1) Drain lubricant from rear axle. Remove brake caliper and suspend with wire. Remove axle shaft-to-axle shaft flange bolt. Force axle shaft out of axle shaft flange. If additional clearance is required to aid in axle shaft removal, remove upper shock absorber mount and lower suspension arm to stop.

2) Support axle housing and remove rubber mount from body. Lower axle housing slightly. Clean housing and remove rear cover plate. Remove and discard "C" lock holding axle shaft to differential side gear. Pull shaft from gear along with spacer.

Fig. 1: Axle Shaft "C" Lock Removal

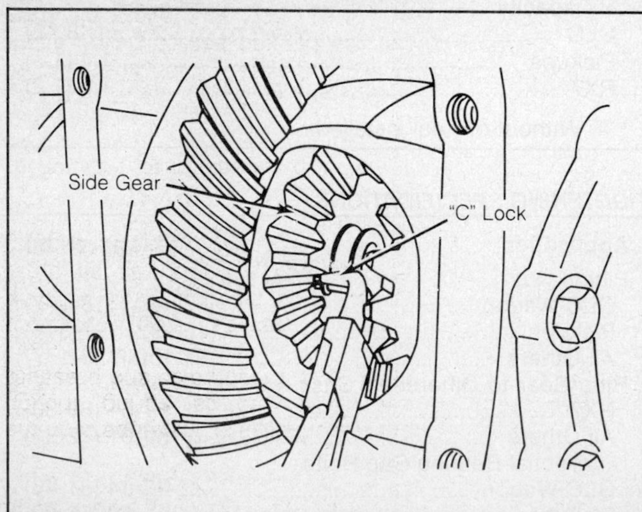
Side Gear
"C" Lock

Always use new "C" lock for installation.

Installation

1) Face of universal joint spider carries a stamped "R" for right or "L" for left. Make sure that correct axle is used on correct side. Place old spacer ring on constant velocity joint. Slide axle shaft into differential side gear and install new "C" lock onto shaft.

2) Check end play between inner universal joint and axle housing. There should be no perceptible end play. In addition, lock ring should still turn in groove. If necessary, install a thicker or thinner lock ring to achieve desired results.

3) Completely telescope axle shaft and install axle shaft flange. Tighten attaching nut. Mount end cover, with sealing compound, and tighten attaching bolts. Raise axle housing and install rubber mount to axle housing. Attach rubber mount to body.

CONSTANT VELOCITY JOINT

Removal

1) Remove axle shaft. Cut stop sleeve of constant velocity ("CV") joint on beaded edge and pull sleeve from spider joint. Remove spider from hub along with 6 balls. Remove locking ring from groove in axle shaft. Press spider from shaft.

2) Pull stop sleeve and rubber sleeve from shaft. Loosen hose clamps and pull second rubber sleeve across disassembled end of axle shaft. Carefully clean joint. Inspect balls and other parts for wear or damage.

Installation

1) Slide new rubber sleeve onto shaft up to bead. Place assembly sleeve (115 589 01 63 00) on splines to protect against damage. Place new stop sleeve on shaft and press spider onto axle shaft. Install locking ring. Assemble universal spider and 6 balls using magnetic ball holders for assistance.

2) Place new sealing rings on universal spider and attach new protective sleeve. Insert complete axle shaft into beading tool (115 589 36 63 00) and install split supporting ring. Attach beading ring and bead edge of sleeve while tightening nuts against stop of beading tool.

3) Remove axle shaft from tool and fill "CV" joint with 8.1 ozs. (230 grams) of "CV" joint oil (supplied with rubber sleeve repair kit). Attach rubber sleeve to stop sleeve and axle shaft with new hose clamps.

AXLE SHAFT FLANGE & BEARING

Removal

1) Remove bolt and force axle shaft out of axle shaft flange. Pull axle shaft up out of way and support with wire. Do not allow axle shaft to hang down. Remove brake caliper and rotor. If necessary, remove parking brake shoes.

2) Hold axle shaft flange and remove slotted nut from axle shaft flange. Remove sealing rings from support housing. Knock axle shaft flange out of support housing. Remove bearing inner race along with spacer sleeve.

3) Force outer sealing ring from support housing. Remove outer bearing and outer bearing race from support housing. Knock outer bearing race for inner bearing out of support housing. Force outer bearing inner race from axle shaft flange.

MERCEDES-BENZ INTEGRAL CARRIER (Cont.)

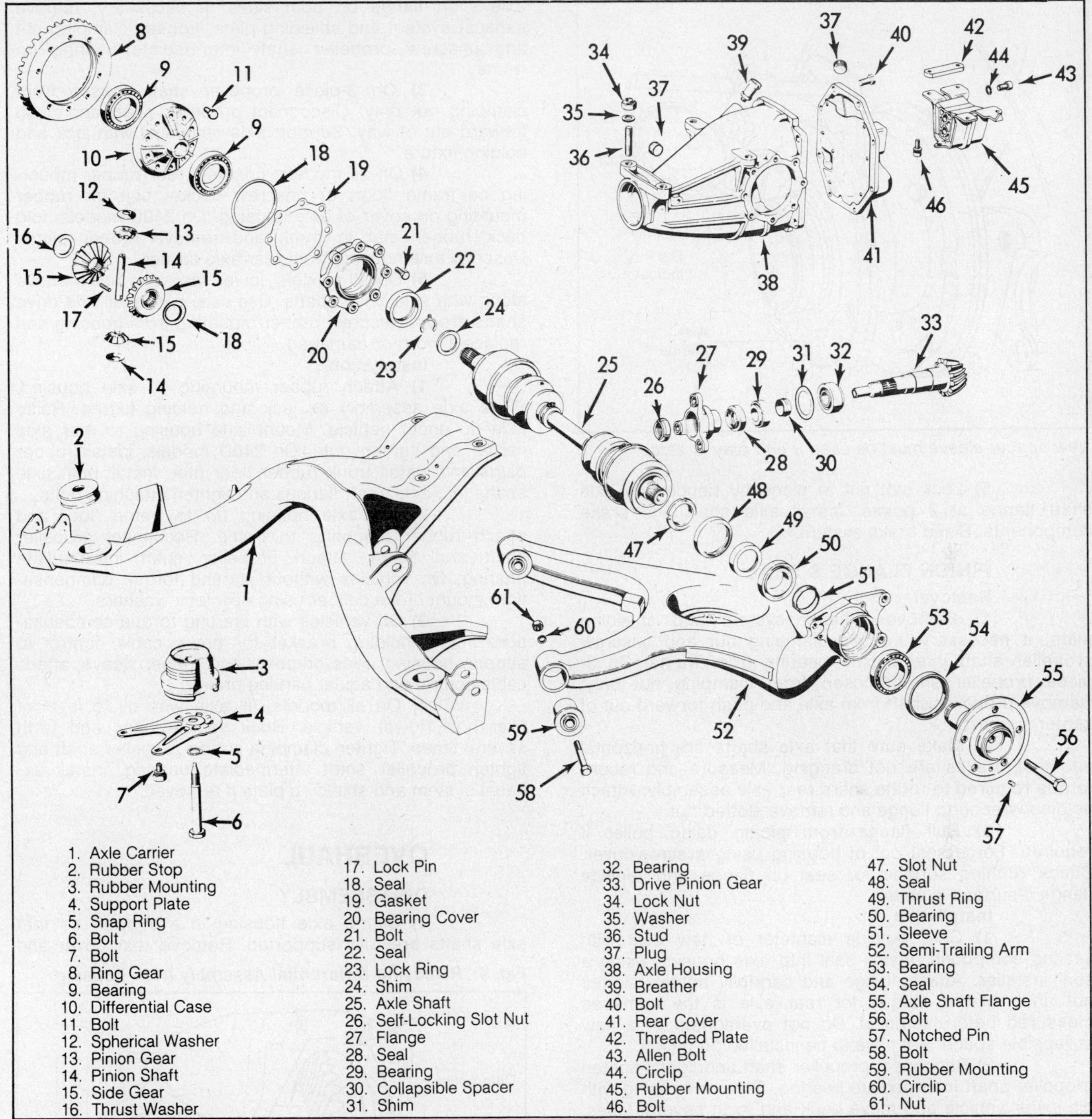

1. Axle Carrier
2. Rubber Stop
3. Rubber Mounting
4. Support Plate
5. Snap Ring
6. Bolt
7. Bolt
8. Ring Gear
9. Bearing
10. Differential Case
11. Bolt
12. Spherical Washer
13. Pinion Gear
14. Pinion Shaft
15. Side Gear
16. Thrust Washer
17. Lock Pin
18. Seal
19. Gasket
20. Bearing Cover
21. Bolt
22. Seal
23. Lock Ring
24. Shim
25. Axle Shaft
26. Self-Locking Slot Nut
27. Flange
28. Seal
29. Bearing
30. Collapsible Spacer
31. Shim
32. Bearing
33. Drive Pinion Gear
34. Lock Nut
35. Washer
36. Stud
37. Plug
38. Axle Housing
39. Breather
40. Bolt
41. Rear Cover
42. Threaded Plate
43. Allen Bolt
44. Circlip
45. Rubber Mounting
46. Bolt
47. Slot Nut
48. Seal
49. Thrust Ring
50. Bearing
51. Sleeve
52. Semi-Trailing Arm
53. Bearing
54. Seal
55. Axle Shaft Flange
56. Bolt
57. Notched Pin
58. Bolt
59. Rubber Mounting
60. Circlip
61. Nut

Fig. 2: Exploded View of Mercedes-Benz Drive Axle Assembly

Installation

1) Ensure axle shaft flanges are installed on correct sides. Right flange is marked with "R" and left flange is marked with "L". Press inner race for outer bearing onto axle shaft flange. Install both outer bearing races in support housing.

2) Coat seat for outer sealing ring on support housing with sealing compound and install seal. Make sure that seal rests straight against chamfer at bottom of housing. Fill cavity between bearing races in support housing with grease.

3) Attach new spacer sleeve to axle shaft flange and install into carrier housing. Attach inner race for inner bearing to axle shaft. Fill new sealing ring with anti-friction grease and coat outer edge with sealing compound. Press inner race and sealing ring into housing. Install seal running ring and install new slot nut.

4) Attach dial indicator to support housing and adjust end play of axle shaft flange while rotating axle shaft flange back and forth. If slot nut is overtightened, reducing end play to zero, install new spacer sleeve and retighten slot nut.

MERCEDES-BENZ INTEGRAL CARRIER (Cont.)

Fig. 3: Checking Axle Shaft Flange End Play

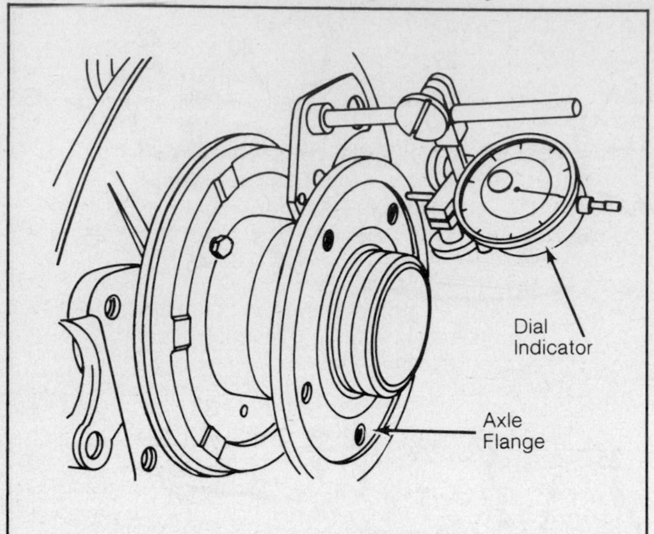
Dial
Indicator
Axle
Flange

New spacer sleeve must be used if end play is zero.

5) Lock slot nut in place by bending in axle shaft flange at 2 points. Install axle shaft and brake components. Bleed brake system.

PINION FLANGE & SEAL

Removal

1) Remove exhaust system and shielding plate, if necessary. Loosen clamping nut and unscrew propeller shaft intermediate bearing from frame. On 3-piece propeller shaft, loosen front clamping nut only. Remove propeller shaft from axle and push forward out of center support.

2) Make sure that axle shafts are horizontal and that brakes are not dragging. Measure and record torque required to rotate entire rear axle assembly. Attach holding wrench to flange and remove slotted nut.

3) Pull flange from pinion using puller if required. Force seal out of housing using a screwdriver. Check running surface for seal on flange and replace flange if surface is worn.

Installation

1) Coat outside diameter of new seal with sealing compound. Install seal into axle housing using a seal installer. Attach flange and carefully tighten slotted nut until rotating torque for rear axle is the same as measured before removal. Do not overtighten or a new collapsible spacer will have to be installed on pinion.

2) Reconnect propeller shaft and lightly tighten propeller shaft intermediate bearing. Fill axle housing with oil, lower vehicle and move back and forth several times. Tighten clamping nut on universal and propeller shaft intermediate bearing. Reinstall shielding plate and exhaust system, if removed.

AXLE ASSEMBLY

Removal

1) Drain oil from rear axle. On vehicles without starting torque compensation, remove right brake caliper and suspend out of way. On vehicles with starting torque compensation, disconnect brake control cable. Remove holding bracket on support housing, remove rubber sleeve and push cover back.

2) On all models, disconnect axle shafts from axle shaft flange on both sides. If necessary, remove exhaust system and shielding plate. Loosen clamping nut and unscrew propeller shaft intermediate bearing on frame.

3) On 3-piece propeller shaft, loosen front clamping nut only. Disconnect propeller shaft and push forward out of way. Support axle assembly with jack and holding fixture.

4) On all models, unscrew rear rubber mounting on frame floor, or unscrew socket bolt for rubber mounting on cover of axle housing. On 240D models, fold back rubber mat in trunk and remove rubber plugs. Unscrew axle housing from rear axle carrier.

5) On all models, lower rear axle and remove along with axle drive shafts. Use care not to let axle drive shafts droop. Unscrew rubber mounting from housing and replace if worn or damaged.

Installation

1) Attach rubber mounting to axle housing. Place axle assembly on jack and holding fixture. Raise axle up under vehicle. Mount axle housing to rear axle carrier and tighten nuts. On 240D models, install rubber plugs and install trunk rubber floor mat. Install both axle shafts into axle shaft flanges and tighten attaching bolts.

2) Lift axle housing up to frame floor and attach rubber mounting to frame. Reconnect propeller shaft and lightly attach propeller shaft intermediate bearing. On vehicles without starting torque compensation, mount brake caliper using new lock washers.

3) On vehicles with starting torque compensation, mount holding bracket for brake cable control to support housing, slide on cover and rubber sleeve, attach cable control and adjust parking brake.

4) On all models, fill axle with oil to level of filler hole, lower vehicle. Rock vehicle back and forth several times. Tighten clamping nut on propeller shaft and tighten propeller shaft intermediate bearing. Install exhaust system and shielding plate if removed.

OVERHAUL

DISASSEMBLY

1) Clamp axle housing in a support so that axle shafts are fully supported. Remove rear cover and

Fig. 4: Removing Differential Assembly from Housing

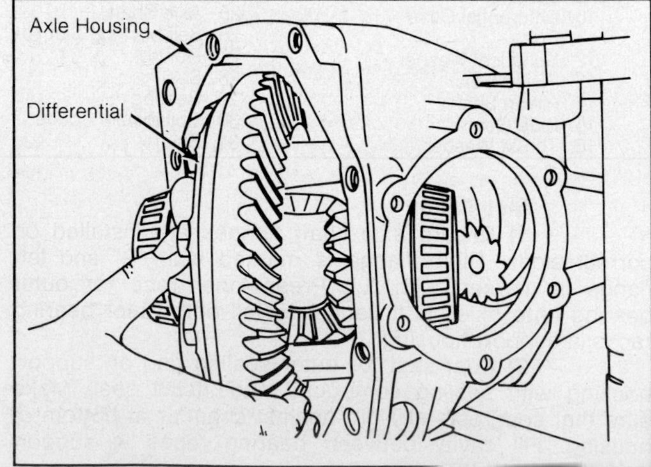
Axle Housing
Differential

MERCEDES-BENZ INTEGRAL CARRIER (Cont.)

axle shafts. Remove bearing side cover bolts and push out of housing along with seal rings and shims. Mark all parts for correct left and right side assembly.

2) Tilt case slightly and remove differential from housing. Mark relative position of ring gear to differential case. Remove ring gear attaching bolts and carefully remove ring gear from case. To disassemble case, pull roller bearings from case using a puller. Knock pinion shaft lock pin out of case and remove pinion shaft.

3) On limited slip differentials, insert assembly mandrels (115 589 04 61 00) through case and side gears. Remove pinions and spherical washers. Remove right side gear and friction discs, keeping all parts in order for reassembly. Then repeat procedure for left side. On standard differentials, lift out side gears, thrust washers and spherical washers.

4) To remove drive pinion, remove flange nut and flange. Drive pinion out of housing. Pry seal out of housing with screwdriver. Press front bearing outer race out of housing using press and mandrel. Pull rear bearing outer race out of case using adapter. Press roller bearing inner race from pinion using press plate.

REASSEMBLY & ADJUSTMENT

Case Assembly (Standard Differential)

1) Place thrust washers on side gears and insert assembled gears in case. Insert assembly mandrels (116 589 18 61 00) into side gears and mount both pinions along with spherical washers. Insert dummy pinion shaft into case to locate pinion gears and spherical washers.

2) Check torque required to rotate side gears. If necessary, change side gear thrust washers to obtain specified torque. When side gear preload is correct, insert pinion shaft in place of mandrel. Install new clamping sleeve and press bearing inner races on case using a mandrel.

Case Assembly (Limited Slip Differential)

1) Mount friction discs on side gears in correct order. *See Fig. 5.* Install left side gear (ring gear side) with discs and insert assembly mandrel (116 589 18 61 00).

Fig. 5: Friction Disc Installation Sequence

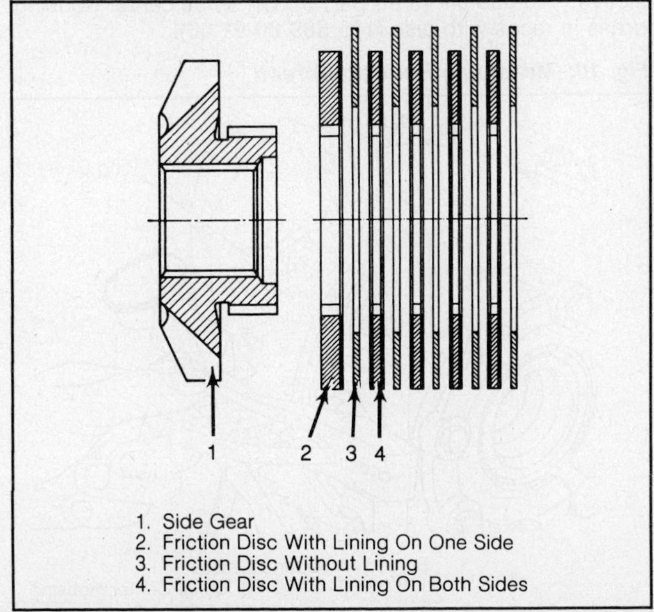
1
2
3
4
1. Side Gear
2. Friction Disc With Lining On One Side
3. Friction Disc Without Lining
4. Friction Disc With Lining On Both Sides

Assemble components in order.

Make sure that disc lugs align properly in case. Repeat procedure for right side gear. Install pinions with new spherical washers.

2) Insert mandrel (116 589 07 61 00) through case, pinions and spherical washers. Check torque required to rotate side gears. If necessary, change side gear thrust washers to obtain specified torque.

3) When side gear preload is correct, insert pinion shaft in place of mandrel. Install new clamping sleeve and press bearing inner races on case using press and mandrel.

Fig. 6: Zeroing Dial Indicator for Pinion Depth Adjustment

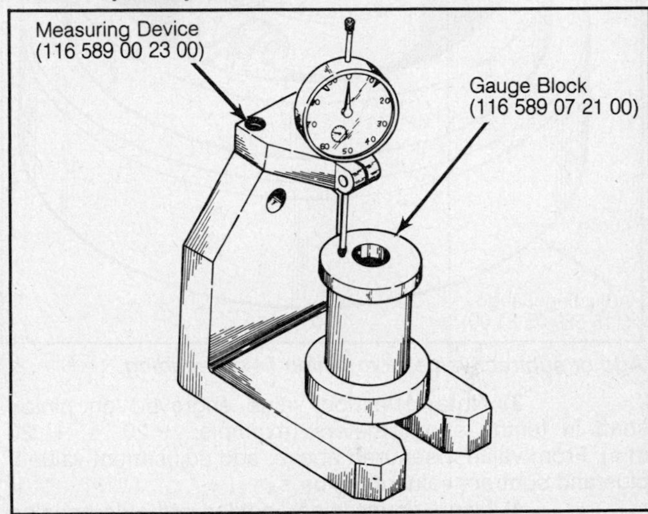
Measuring Device
(116 589 00 23 00)
Gauge Block
(116 589 07 21 00)

Zero dial indicator after preloading with .12" (3 mm).

Drive Pinion Depth

1) Mount dial indicator in measuring device (116 589 00 23 00). Insert gauge block (116 589 07 21 00). Place tip of dial indicator on top of gauge block. Allow dial indicator tip to depress about .12" (3 mm) on gauge block and zero dial indicator. *See Fig. 6.*

2) Press inner tapered roller bearing on drive pinion and place bearing outer race on roller cage of

Fig. 7: Measuring Pinion Height

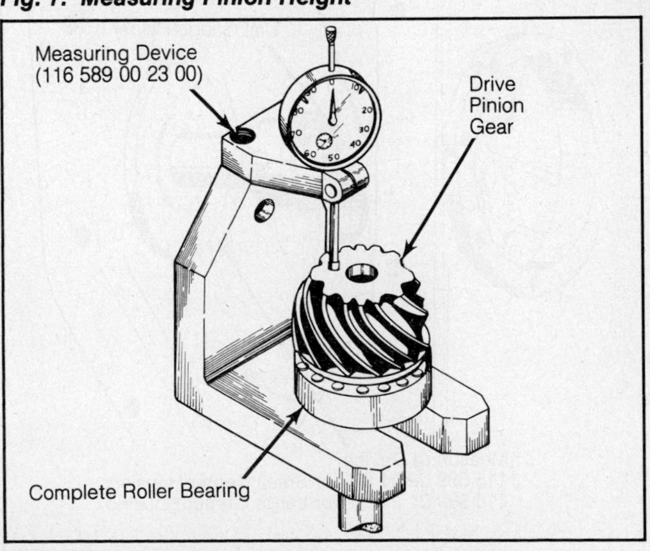
Measuring Device
(116 589 00 23 00)
Drive
Pinion
Gear
Complete Roller Bearing

Add or subtract pinion deviation value on pinion.

MERCEDES-BENZ INTEGRAL CARRIER (Cont.)

bearing. Insert pinion assembly into measuring device. On pinions from large center housings, place magnetic plate (116 589 01 21 00) on top of pinion. Place indicator stem on head of pinion and note reading.

Fig. 8: Zeroing Dial Indicator

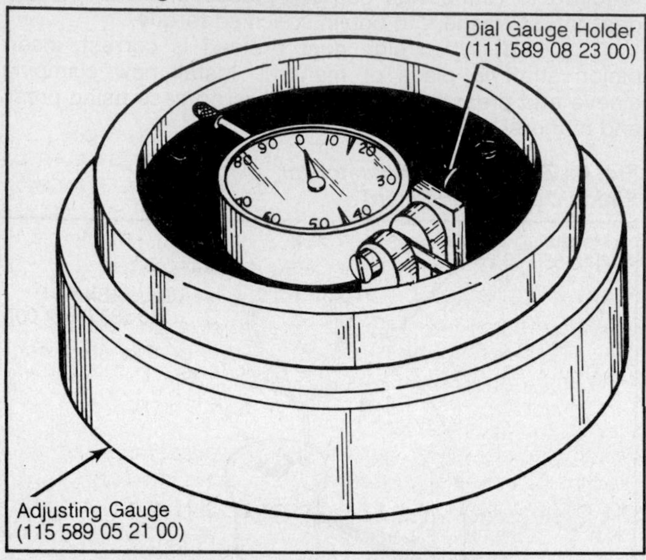
Dial Gauge Holder
(111 589 08 23 00)
Adjusting Gauge
(115 589 05 21 00)

Add or subtract value from pinion height reading.

3) Note deviation value engraved on pinion shaft in tenths of millimeters (example: + 20 = + .20 mm). From value measured above, add adjustment value if plus and subtract value if minus.

4) Insert gauge block holder into axle housing and screw on appropriate gauge block (116 589 07 21 00). Insert dial gauge holder into adjusting gauge and zero indicator with stem depressed about .12" (3 mm).

Fig. 9: Measuring Housing Depth

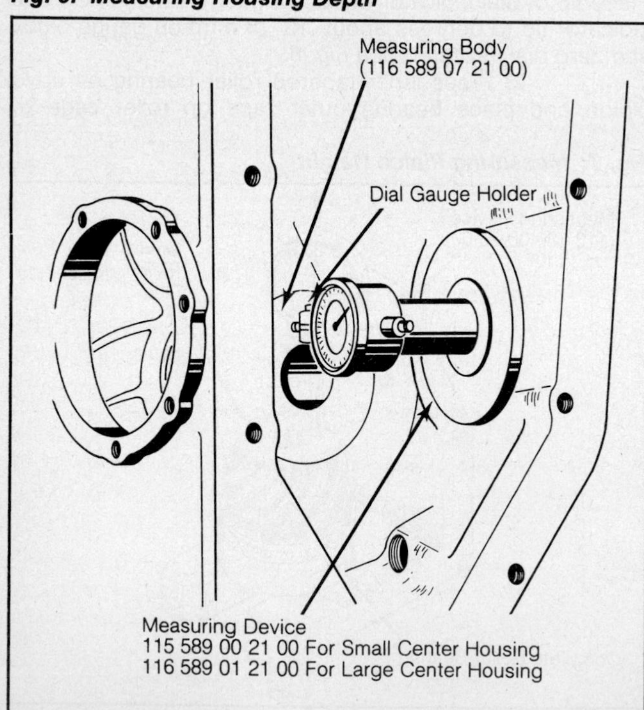
Measuring Body
(116 589 07 21 00)
Dial Gauge Holder
Measuring Device
115 589 00 21 00 For Small Center Housing
116 589 01 21 00 For Large Center Housing

Measure depth with calculated shim installed.

5) Insert adjusting gauge together with dial gauge holder into right bore of housing and screw down. Read indicator reading difference between adjusting gauge and gauge block face end.

6) If value is plus, it must be subtracted from result obtained in step **3)** and if minus, must be added to above result (example: If measured deviation is +.16 mm, subtract this value from 1.70 mm to obtain 1.54 mm). This result is thickness of required shim.

7) Remove all tools from axle housing. Insert shim of calculated thickness into axle housing. If necessary, a thicker washer may be ground down to required thickness. Install outer races of bearings in housing. Lubricate bearings on drive pinion with hypoid gear oil and insert pinion and new collapsible spacer into housing.

8) Install front bearing inner race. Coat new seal on circumference with sealing compound and press into cover using mandrel. Coat running surface of pinion flange with molybdenum disulphide paste and slide flange on drive pinion, making sure alignment marks are lined up.

Pinion Bearing Preload

1) Check that runout of pinion flange does not exceed specification. If runout is excessive, reposition flange. Hold flange and install new locking slot nut. Gradually tighten nut while turning pinion and applying light hammer blows to axle housing. Continue tightening nut until specified pinion turning torque is obtained.

2) Do not exceed specified preload. If preload is exceeded, remove pinion from housing and replace collapsible spacer.

3) Insert measuring device and dial indicator holder into right bore of housing. Place magnetic measuring plate (052 C) on head of pinion. Dial indicator should read value engraved on pinion shaft. Maximum error is .0008" (.02 mm). If error is higher, disassemble pinion and install correct shim.

Backlash & Side Bearing Preload

1) On small center housing axles, press out sealing rings and outer bearing bores from side covers using a mandrel. On large center housing axles remove sealing rings from covers. Remove bearing outer race.

2) On all axles, press in new outer races with sleeve (116 589 04 43 00 part 5). On small center housing, press in races with disc (115 589 00 61 00).

Fig. 10: Measuring Housing Spread

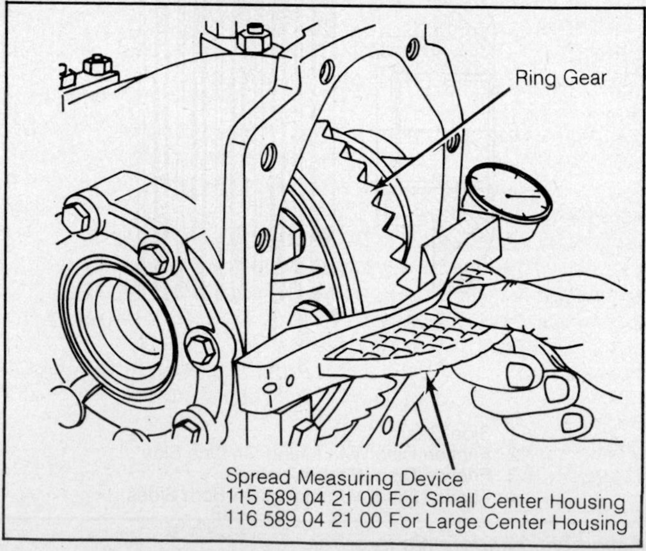
Ring Gear
Spread Measuring Device
115 589 04 21 00 For Small Center Housing
116 589 04 21 00 For Large Center Housing

3) Coat outer edge of new seals with sealing compound and press into bearing covers with a punch. Place previously used shims on bearing covers and install new sealing rings in grooves of covers. Carefully clean bore of ring gear and seat on differential case as ring gear is removed from case.

4) Heat ring gear to about 140-158°F (60-70°C) and install gear on case. Make sure installation markings are lined up if old ring gear and case are being used. If necessary, tap gear on case using rubber hammer. Tighten ring gear bolts uniformly and in a criss-cross pattern.

5) Place differential case into housing. Place assembly fixture (116 589 06 61 00) into housing. Place both bearing covers with shims on centering surface of fixture and slide into housing on same side from which they were removed. Turn both covers so that marking "bottom" ("unten") faces downward.

6) Remove assembly fixture and install cover attaching bolts, but do not tighten. Mount case spread measuring device and support blocks on housing. Zero dial indicator.

7) Tighten bearing cover bolts. Place spread measuring device on support blocks and measure spread of axle. Spread should not exceed specification. Adjust size of shims as necessary to obtain the specified case spread. Install backlash measuring device into right side bearing bore and clamp down.

8) Measure backlash at 4 points on ring gear. Adjust shims from side-to-side as necessary to obtain specified backlash. When preload and backlash are correct, install both axle drive shafts with new "C" lock rings. Clean end cover mating surfaces and coat with sealing compound. Install cover and tighten bolts.

Fig. 11: Measuring Ring-to-Pinion Gear Backlash

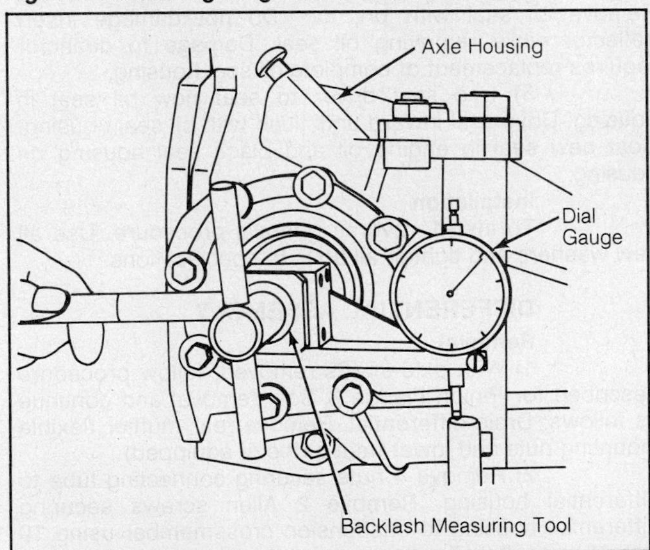
Axle Housing
Dial Gauge
Backlash Measuring Tool

Adjust shims from side-to-side to obtain specified backlash.

AXLE ASSEMBLY SPECIFICATIONS

Application	In. (mm)
Axle Shaft	
Flange End Play	.0016-.0024 (.04-.06)
Housing Spread	
Small Center Housing	.004-.006 (.10-.15)
Large Center Housing	.006-.008 (.15-.20)
Pinion Flange Runout	.001 (.03)
Ring Gear Runout	.0008 (.02) Max.
Ring & Pinion Backlash	.0030-.0055 (.08-.14)
	Ft. Lbs. (N.m)
Side Gear Turning Torque	
Standard Differential	22-66 (30-90)
Limited Slip Diff.	59-103 (80-140)
	INCH Lbs. (N.m)
Pinion Turning Torque	
New Bearings	10.6-12.4 (1.2-1.4)
Used Bearings	4.4-8.9 (0.5-1.0)

TIGHTENING SPECIFICATIONS

Application	Ft. Lbs. (N.m)
Axle Housing-to-Axle Carrier	74 (100)
Axle Shaft-to-Axle Shaft Flange	22 (30)
Bearing Cover-to-Axle Housing	15 (20)
Brake Caliper Bolt	15 (20)
Front Rubber Mount-to-Frame	37 (50)
Housing Rear Cover	33 (45)
Propeller Shaft Clamping Nut	
2-Piece Shaft	22-30 (30-40)
3-Piece Shaft	
Front	22-30 (30-40)
Rear	148 (200)
Rear Rubber Mount-to-Frame	18 (25)
Ring Gear Bolts	
Small Center Housing	
Standard Bolt	59 (80)
Self-Locking Bolt	74 (100)
Large Center Housing	89 (120)
Rubber Mount-to-Axle Housing	89 (120)

Drive Axles

PEUGEOT SPLIT HOUSING – I.R.S.

504, 505, 604

DESCRIPTION

All models use a hypoid type limited slip differential. Unit is housed in ribbed aluminum alloy split case, which is bolted to rear suspension crossmember. A torque tube houses the propeller shaft, which is splined to the drive pinion. Drive axles are driven by differential side gears through tripod type constant velocity ("CV") joints.

AXLE RATIO & IDENTIFICATION

Two basic design axle housings are used on all models. One type has thrust washers on both sides of housing; the other has thrust washer on 1 side only. To determine axle ratio, divide number of ring gear teeth by number of pinion gear teeth.

REMOVAL & INSTALLATION

AXLE SHAFTS & BEARINGS

Removal

1) Raise rear of vehicle, and support under rear suspension arms. Remove rear wheels. Loosen but do not remove hub nut.

2) On drum brake models, remove brake drum. Disconnect parking brake cable from operating lever. Remove 4 axle hub bearing support-to-suspension arm bolts.

3) On disc brake models, disconnect brake line from clip on suspension arm. Remove brake caliper and suspend from vehicle without distorting brake line. If equipped, mark position of rotor retaining screw and remove screw. Remove 4 axle hub bearing support-to-suspension arm bolts.

4) To remove axle, using 2 guides (B 1 & B 2) screw in until splines are fully released. Compress "CV" joint at differential and remove axle shaft. Free axle shaft from hub using, if necessary a universal type puller. *See Fig. 1.*

Fig. 1: Removing Rear Axle Assembly

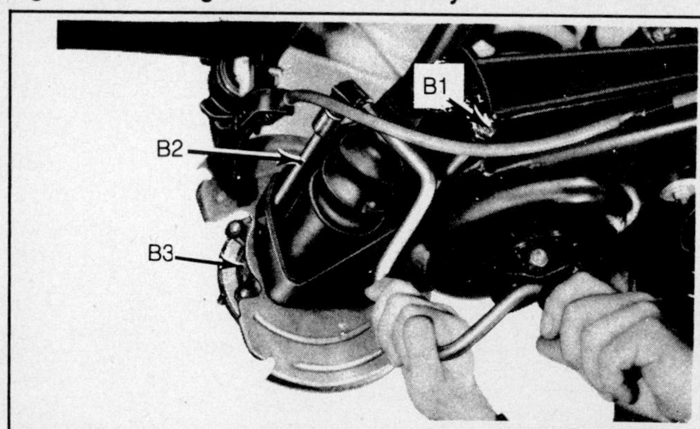
B1
B2
B3

Axle hub and bearing support are removed with axle shaft.

5) With axle assembly pressed out of control arm, remove axle assembly from rear housing without damaging housing seals. Remove axle assembly through lower control arm. With axle removed, place axle assembly in press, with adapter plate located just below hub. Remove hub nut and washer. Press axle out of hub.

Installation

1) To install, reverse removal procedures. Before assembling hub to axle bearing support, grease spline of axle stub. Before installing axle assembly into housing, make sure housing side seal is in perfect condition. Apply grease between lips of seal and to axle shaft splines.

2) Use new washer when assembling bearing support-to-lower control arm. Tighten bolts to specifications. Install brake caliper with new washers. Install brake anti-chatter spring onto caliper with arrow facing normal direction of rotation.

3) When installing hub nut, tighten to specification and stake the nut. After installing wheels, check level of lubricant in housing.

PINION FLANGE & SEAL

Removal

1) Raise and support vehicle. Remove exhaust pipe assembly and allow it to rest on rear crossmember. Remove both Allen screws securing housing. Allow housing to rest on rear crossmember.

2) Inside vehicle, remove rear seat cushions. Loosen 3 nuts on "T" shaped metal bracket and remove first nut. Bend up "T" bracket, and remove plastic plug from guide hole. Insert special guide pin (K1) into guide hole and tighten pin with special bar (K2).

3) Leave special bar (K2) in guide pin and remove other 2 lock nuts. Lower crossmember until special bar (K2) is resting on floorboard. Repeat operation on opposite side. Remove 4 nuts securing housing to propeller shaft tube. Move housing rearward and allow it to rest on wooden block.

4) Remove spring located inside propeller shaft. Remove seal support plate from front of housing. Place housing in vise. Clean front oil seal housing. Remove oil seal with pry bar. Do not damage insert deflector while removing oil seal. Damage to deflector requires replacement of complete oil seal housing.

5) Use seal driver to seat new oil seal in housing. Drive seal inward until flush with oil seal housing. Coat new seal in engine oil and place seal housing on housing.

Installation

To install, reverse removal procedure. Use all new washers and tighten all bolts to specifications.

DIFFERENTIAL ASSEMBLY

Removal

1) With axle shafts removed, follow procedure described for Pinion Flange & Seal removal and continue as follows: Drain differential. Remove rear muffler flexible mounting nuts and lower heat baffle (if equipped).

2) Remove 4 nuts securing connecting tube to differential housing. Remove 2 Allen screws securing differential housing to suspension crossmember using 10 mm Allen socket. To disengage differential housing, pull it first to rear and then to left, and remove unit from vehicle.

Installation

To install, reverse removal procedures. Grease splines before installation. Ensure propeller shaft spring is placed into rear end of propeller shaft.

PEUGEOT SPLIT HOUSING — I.R.S. (Cont.)

Fig. 2: Exploded View of Peugeot Independent Rear Suspension (I.R.S.) Drive Axle Assembly

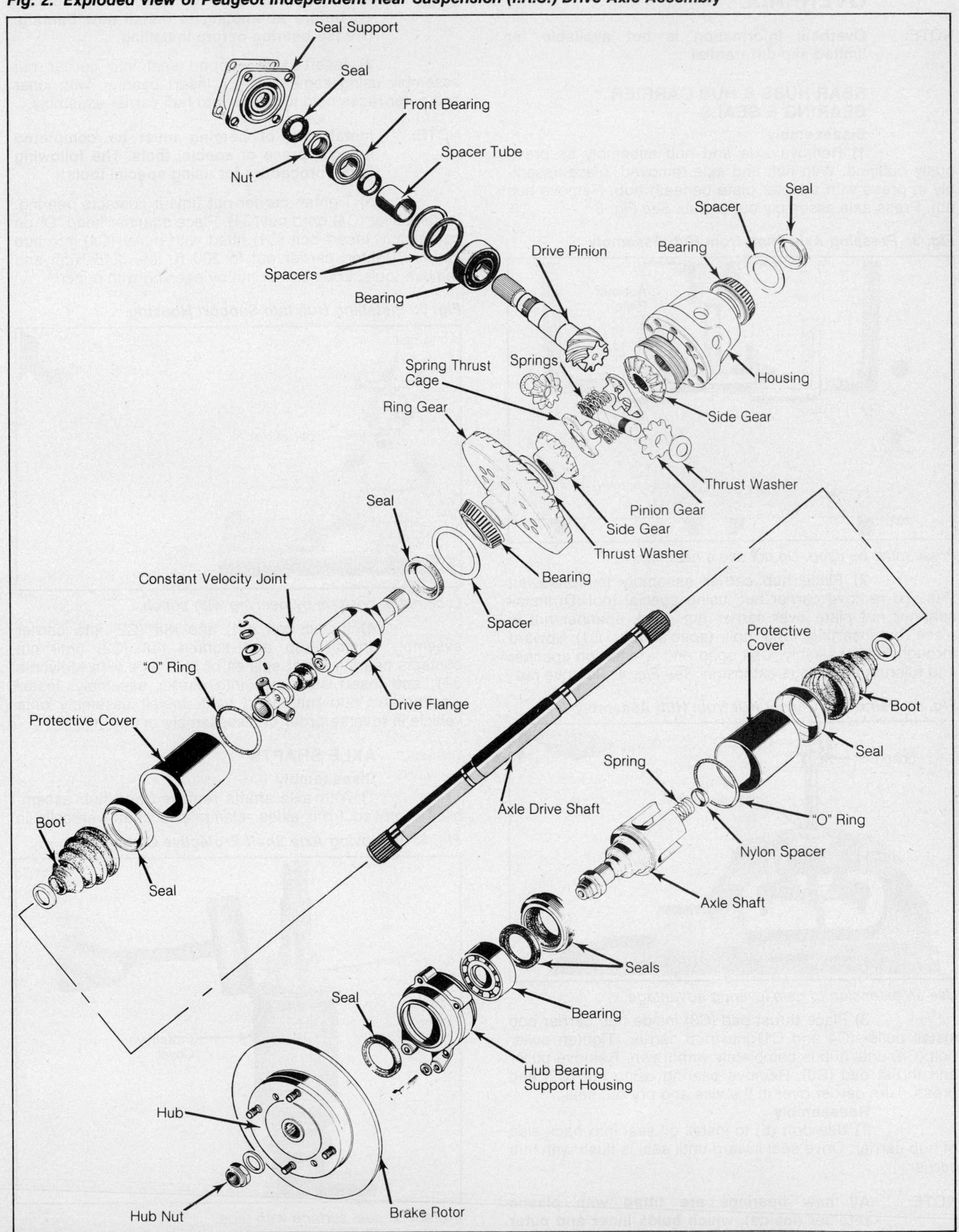
Seal Support
Seal
Front Bearing
Nut
Spacer Tube
Spacers
Bearing
Drive Pinion
Bearing
Spacer
Seal
Housing
Springs
Spring Thrust Cage
Ring Gear
Side Gear
Thrust Washer
Pinion Gear
Side Gear
Thrust Washer
Seal
Bearing
Spacer
Constant Velocity Joint
"O" Ring
Drive Flange
Protective Cover
Boot
Seal
Axle Drive Shaft
Protective Cover
Boot
Seal
Spring
"O" Ring
Nylon Spacer
Axle Shaft
Seals
Bearing
Seal
Hub Bearing Support Housing
Hub
Hub Nut
Brake Rotor

Drive Axles

PEUGEOT SPLIT HOUSING – I.R.S. (Cont.)

OVERHAUL

NOTE: **Overhaul information is not available for limited slip differential.**

REAR HUBS & HUB CARRIER BEARING & SEALS

Disassembly

1) Remove axle and hub assembly as previously outlined. With hub and axle removed, place assembly in press with adapter plate beneath hub. Remove hub nut. Press axle assembly out of hub. *See Fig. 3.*

Fig. 3: Pressing Axle Shaft from Hub Assembly

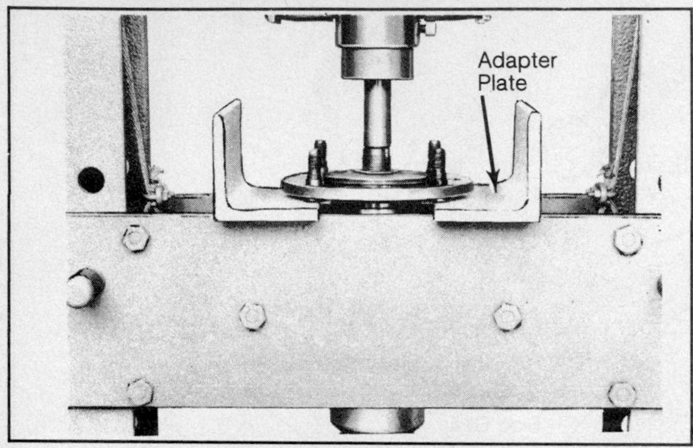
Adapter
Plate

Press must be used. Do not use a hammer.

2) Place hub carrier assembly in soft-jawed vise. To remove carrier nut, using special tool (D) install spanner nut plate over carrier nut. Lock spanner nut in place by inserting long bolt (special tool C1) upward through hub assembly. Use open end wrench on spanner and fulcrum advantage extension. *See Fig. 4.* Remove nut.

Fig. 4: Removing Carrier Nut from Hub Assembly

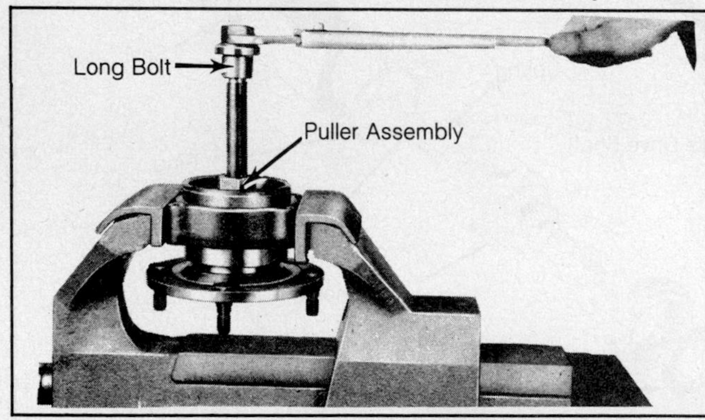
Long Bolt
Puller Assembly

Use an extension to gain levering advantage.

3) Place thrust pad (C3) inside hub carrier and install puller (C4 and C1) into hub carrier. Tighten puller bolt (C4) until hub is completely withdrawn. Remove puller and thrust pad (C3). Remove bearing using nut (C2) and press. Turn carrier over in the vise and pry out seal.

Reassembly

1) Use drift (E) to install oil seal into back side of hub carrier. Drive seal inward until seal is flush with hub carrier.

NOTE: **All new bearings are fitted with plastic retainer (inside), which holds inner and outer races together. This retainer must be removed before attempting to install new bearing. Grease bearing before installing.**

2) Insert double-lipped seal into carrier nut assembly using same drift (E). Insert bearing, with inner and outer races held together, into hub carrier assembly.

NOTE: **Installation of bearing must be completed using a press or special tools. The following is the procedure for using special tools.**

3) Tighten carrier nut until it contacts bearing. Install puller (C4) onto nut (C1). Place spanner head "D" on carrier nut. Insert bolt (C1) fitted with puller (C4) into hub carrier. Tighten carrier nut to 200 ft. lbs. (246 N.m) and remove tools. Lock carrier nut by peening with punch.

Fig. 5: Installing Hub into Support Housing

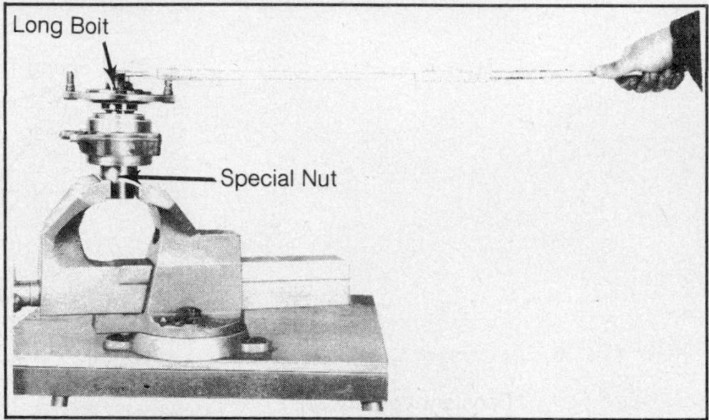
Long Bolt
Special Nut

Lock nut in position by peening with punch.

4) Install bolt (C1) and nut (C2) into carrier assembly. Install hub and tighten nut (C2) until nut contacts bearing. Coat splines of stub axle with Molycote 321, and insert stub axle into carrier assembly. Install washer and hub nut, hand tight. Install assembly onto vehicle in reverse order of disassembly.

AXLE SHAFTS

Disassembly

1) With axle shafts removed and hub assemblies removed from axles, clamp axle shaft vertically in

Fig. 6: Removing Axle Shaft Protective Cover

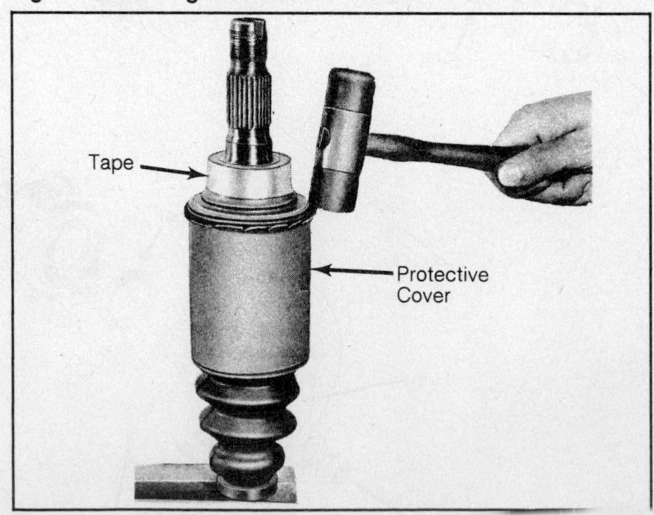
Tape
Protective
Cover

Protect oil seal surface with tape.

soft-jawed vise. Place adhesive tape on oil seal bearing surface. Using pliers, uncrimp edge of metal cover.

2) Using soft-faced hammer, gently tap downward on cover to expose "CV" joint. Place adhesive tape around "CV" joint. "CV" joint is not repairable and must be replaced as a unit.

3) Remove as much grease as possible, but do not dip components in degreasing agent. Use press to remove "CV" joint. There is no need to remove 3 punch marks on end of shaft as they will disappear during removal procedure.

Fig. 7: Removing Constant Velocity ("CV") Joint

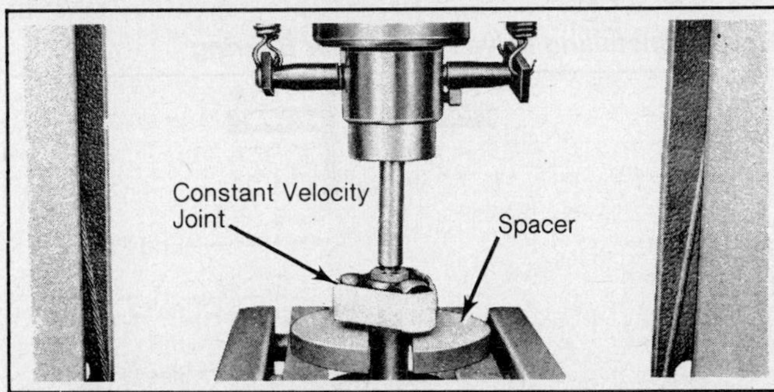
Constant Velocity
Joint
Spacer

Wrap tape around constant velocity joint.

4) Remove protective metal cover and rubber ring. Remove other constant velocity joint in same manner as previously described. From outside joint housing, remove "O" ring. From inside, remove all grease. If nylon bushing on inside of "CV" joint housing is damaged, remove bushing with chisel.

5) Remove retaining washer with screwdriver. Use small stone and drill to remove any burrs in housing. When this operation is complete, clean inside of housing. Blow dry with compressed air.

Reassembly

1) To reassemble, reverse disassembly procedure. When installing metal cover, note there are 2 different sizes. The shorter one fits on differential side of axle shaft. Protective stopper must be installed on wheel side of axle shaft.

2) After installing "CV" joints onto respective shafts, use punch to peen shaft at 3 equidistant places on shaft end. If nylon bushing was removed, insert new bushing. Insert washer over bushing and peen washer in 3 equidistant places.

3) Before installing the cover over the "CV" joint housing, grease inside of housing and replace "O" ring. With cover over housing and assembly placed in press to hold tension, peen over cover. Install axle assembly as previously outlined.

Fig. 8: Disassembled View of Constant Velocity Joint Protective Covers

"O" Ring
Protective Cover
Seal
Boot
Collar

Shorter cover fits on differential side of axle shaft.

DIFFERENTIAL

Disassembly

1) With differential removed, remove front oil seal support plate and gasket. Install mounting plate on bottom 2 studs of housing. Place housing in vise (rear of housing up) by clamping mounting plate. Loosen all bolts and nuts on rear housing.

2) Remove front attaching screws of bearing side plates. Remove 6 bolts and 4 nuts holding housing halves together. Lift off rear half of housing. If necessary, use soft faced mallet to assist in removing rear housing half.

3) Loosen vise and rotate housing to allow front of housing to be in horizontal position. Install special spanner (N), hex sleeve with bolt tang, over end of drive pinion nut. Secure spanner to front oil seal support plate stud with a nut. *See Fig. 9.*

4) Install adapter (N) on input pinion nut and secure it to stud with a nut. Place splined socket (M) over pinion and then unscrew nut clockwise.

Fig. 9: Using Special Socket to Remove Drive Pinion

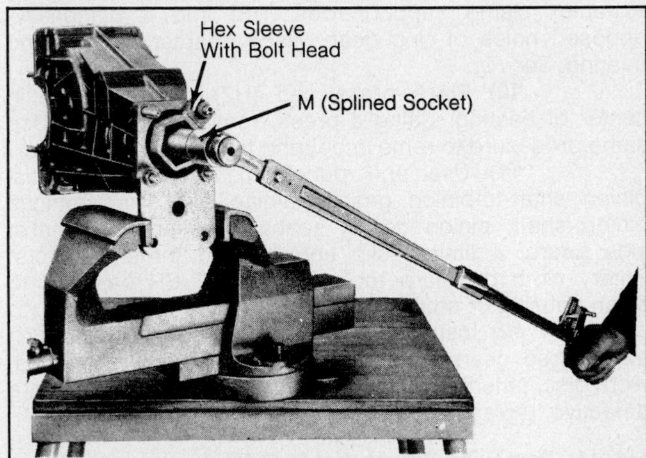
Hex Sleeve
With Bolt Head
M (Splined Socket)

Lock nut does not have to have stakes removed.

5) Remove housing from vise and rotate housing. Press on drive end of pinion to remove drive pinion assembly. Do not use a hammer to remove pinion assembly.

6) To remove drive pinion rear bearing outer race, install parts of special puller/driver (L). Install bolt (L1), extractor (L4) and support plate (D). Turn bolt counterclockwise and remove rear outer bearing race first.

7) To remove drive pinion front bearing outer race, install parts of special puller/driver (L). Install bolt (L1) and extractor (L3). Turn bolt clockwise to remove front outer race.

8) Place drive pinion in vise and press off drive pinion rear bearing. Special collar (SZ) is designed for this purpose and fits over drive pinion gear and against rear bearing shoulder.

CAUTION: As parts are separated in following step, catch differential side gear and thrust washer to prevent damage.

9) To disassemble differential assembly, remove ring gear-to-case bolts. Remove ring gear. Insert 4

PEUGEOT SPLIT HOUSING – I.R.S. (Cont.)

Fig. 10: Removing Pinion Rear Outer Bearing Race

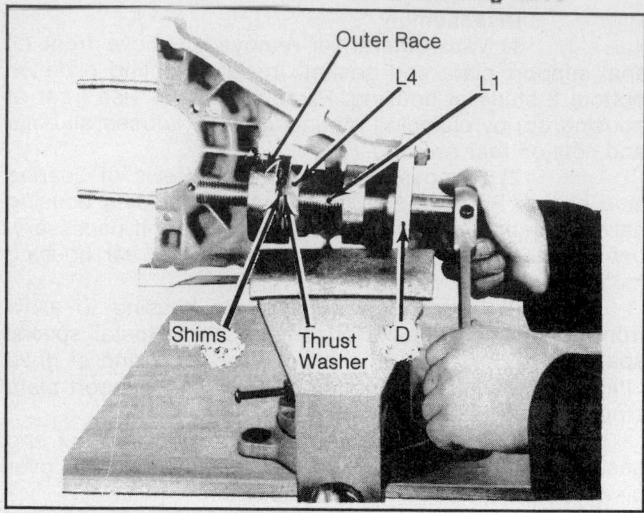
Outer Race
L4
L1
Shims
Thrust
Washer
D

Case is split to show assembled view of tools.

extractor clamp support rods (H3) into 4 diagonally-opposed holes of ring gear. Place adapter (H1) around bearing. *See Fig. 11.*

10) Place press pad (H2) on ring gear, in center of bearing. Using a press, remove ring gear. Use same procedure to remove bearing from differential case.

11) Use drift punch to remove differential pinion shaft-to-pinion gear retaining pin. Then remove pinion shaft, pinion gears, spacer washers, differential side gears, 4 limited slip springs and thrust washers. Emery cloth or sharp tools should NEVER be used to clean housing or other differential parts.

12) Inspect all components for damage such as cracked gears, broken limited slip pressure springs, worn disc, pitted or scored bearings. If any componets are defective, replace as necessary.

Fig. 11: Removing Differential Side Bearings

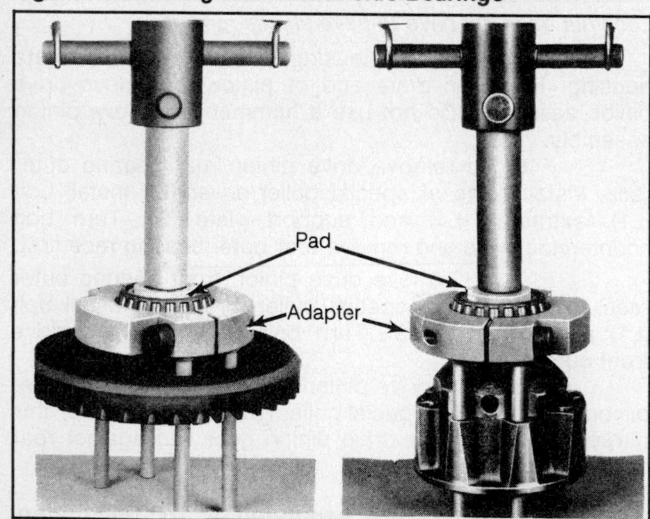
Pad
Adapter

Never use a hammer to remove bearings.

Reassembly & Adjustment

1) Clean all parts in solvent and blow dry with compressed air. Spray Molykote 321 into drive pinion housing. Do not heat housing.

2) Ring gear and drive pinion must be replaced as an assembly. Use new differential side bearings, drive pinion bearings, flex washers, drive pinion nut, differential assembling bolts, drive pinion seal and all other "O" rings and differential seals.

3) Before installing drive pinion rear bearing, check that front bearing slides freely on drive pinion shaft. If any difficulty is experienced, polish shaft bearing surface with fine abrasive until bearing just slides (as free fit) onto shaft.

4) Smooth front of drive pinion shaft with stone to remove any burrs. Front end of shaft serves as contact point during various adjustments. With front bearing fit correct, install pinion rear bearing by using special sleeve (C) and end pad (H2).

Fig. 12: Installing Drive Pinion Rear Bearing

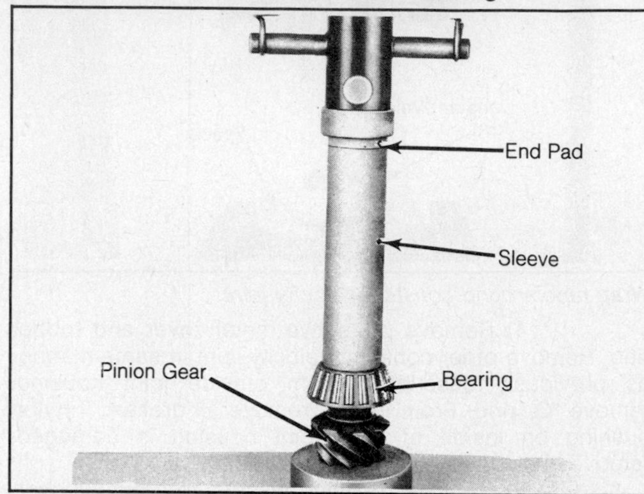
End Pad
Sleeve
Pinion Gear
Bearing

Press until bearing contacts drive pinion gear shoulder.

5) Install mounting plate on front housing half. Place housing in vise in horizontal position. Using puller/driver, install thrust washer, outer bearing races (back-to-back) into housing. Use bolt (L1), thrust plate (L2) and nut (L5). Tighten bolt head of (L1) to 101 ft. lbs. (137 N.m). Oil bearing with specified oil.

Fig. 13: Installing Drive Pinion Bearing Outer Race

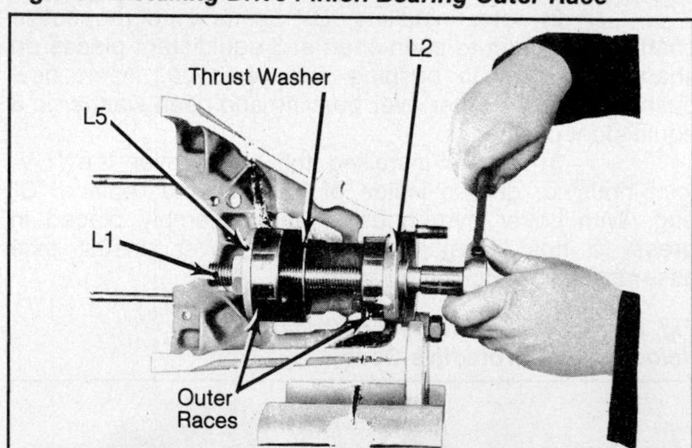
L2
Thrust Washer
L5
L1
Outer
Races

Case is split to show assembled view of tools.

6) Install drive pinion into housing with rear bearing, long spacer, front bearing and nut. Install spanner (hexagon sleeve with bolt tang) over end of drive pinion nut. Secure spanner to stud bolt with nut. *See Fig. 13.*

7) Install splined drive pinion holding socket (M) over pinion spline. Torque nut to 7.2 ft. lbs. (10 N.m).

PEUGEOT SPLIT HOUSING – I.R.S. (Cont.)

Rotate drive pinion in both directions and again tighten nut. Continue operation until nut can no longer be tightened without exceeding the torque specification.

Pinion Depth Adjustment

1) Install pinion depth measuring tool (AZ) into front half of housing. Retain in position with bridge clamp (A3). *See Fig. 14.* Tighten nuts of clamp to 7.2 ft. lbs. (10 N.m). Equalize distance between bridge pads and housing on both sides by using feeler gauges. Free feeler assembly (A2) and ensure there is contact with drive pinion.

Fig. 14: Measuring Drive Pinion Installed Depth

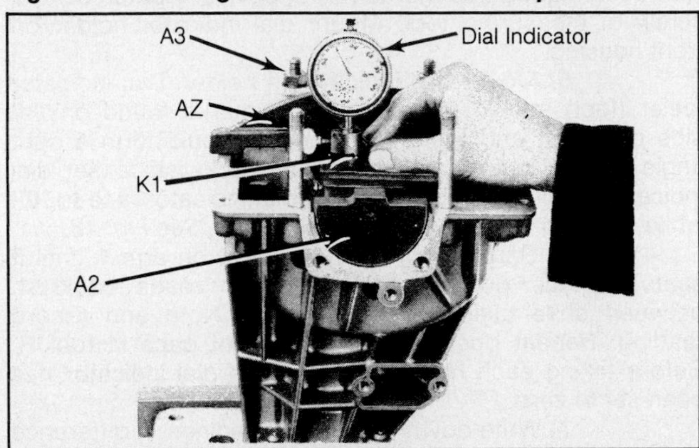
A3
Dial Indicator
AZ
K1
A2

Equalize distance between bridge pads and housing.

2) Install dial indicator on holder (K1). Position indicator so foot is resting on upper surface of feeler assembly (A2). Adjust height of indicator so small hand reads "3" (for example). Zero dial indicator. Slide holder (K1) so indicator foot contacts machined surface of pinion depth measuring tool (AZ). Movement of dial indicator indicates depth of feeler assembly (A2). Record value obtained.

3) There are 2 reference marks on hypoid gear end of drive pinion. The first indicates pinion depth and second corresponds with number of ring gear (matched set). Write down reference number (bottom number). To this number, whether positive or negative, add + .012" (+ .30 mm) to find corresponding guide number.

4) Compare dial indicator reading previously obtained with guide number. The difference between 2 numbers represents thickness of shims to be installed between drive pinion rear bearing outer race and thrust washer. To find corresponding guide number and to calculate thickness of shims, use procedure outlined in sample calculation:

Sample Calculation

Dimension	Measurement
Constant Added to Determine Guide Number	.012" (.30 mm)
Number on End of Drive Pinion	- .0015" (.04 mm)
Resulting Guide Number	.010" (.26 mm)
Dial Indicator Reading from Step **2)**	.026" (.67 mm)
Subtract Guide Number (Obtained Above)	- .010" (.26 mm)
Total Shim Thickness Required	.016" (.41 mm)

Fig. 15: Identification Marks on Drive Pinion Gear

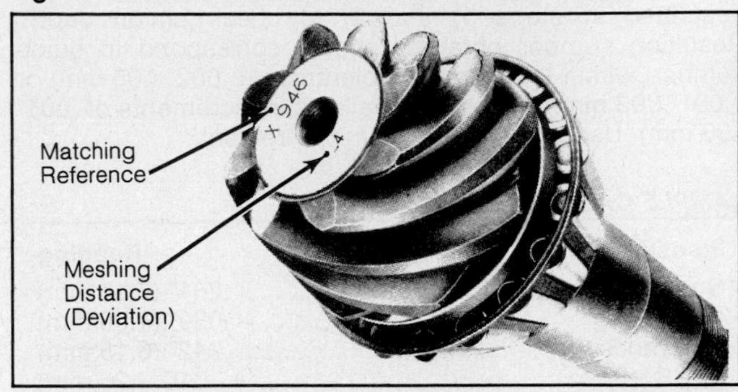
Matching Reference
Meshing Distance (Deviation)
x 946

Always replace ring and pinion gears in matched pairs.

5) Remove tool (AZ) and drive pinion from housing. Use puller/driver to remove drive pinion rear bearing outer race from housing. Install thrust washer and shims (previously determined). Reinstall rear bearing outer race. Torque puller/driver to 101 ft. lbs. (137 N.m) to seat.

6) Place drive pinion vertically on work bench and make colored chalk mark down full length of 1 spline. Install long spacer, front bearing and nut (J). Place holding fixture (N) over nut (J). Use socket (C) to torque pinion to 203 ft. lbs. (276 N.m).

7) Screw dial indicator onto extension (K2). Place dial indicator on end of drive pinion. Make sure extension (K2) faces chalk mark on pinion spline and rests on machined surface of nut J. Move dial indicator to bring small hand to "1" and big hand to "0".

8) Remove dial indicator and lay aside, making sure reading is not changed. Remove nut (J) and front bearing. Place pinion into front housing with long spacer and front bearing. Torque nut (J) to 7.2 ft. lbs. (10 N.m). Rotate pinion 10 turns counterclockwise and retorque.

Fig. 16: Measuring Drive Pinion Depth

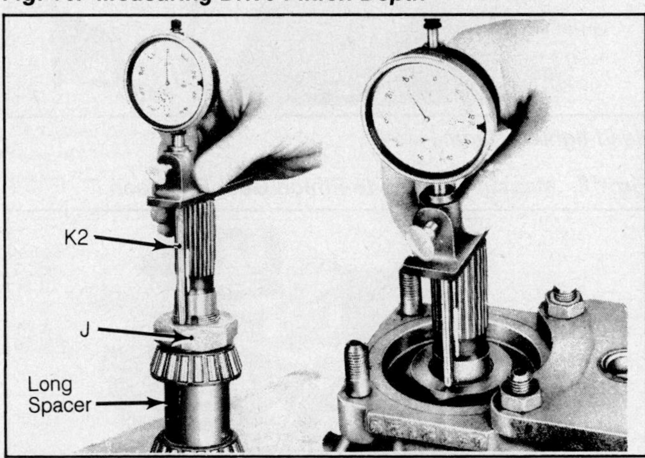
K2
J
Long Spacer

Subtract difference to determine shim size.

9) With colored chalk, mark as reference and take another reading. Place dial indicator between end of shaft and nut J. Find difference between 2 readings and subtract .002" (.06 mm). The number obtained is the thickness of shims necessary between front bearing and long spacer.

10) Install pinion into housing with long spacer, adjusting shims and new nut. Torque nut to 203 ft. lbs. (276 N.m). Use speed wrench attached to socket (C) to turn pinion by hand.

PEUGEOT SPLIT HOUSING – I.R.S. (Cont.)

11) Use tools (AZ and K1) and dial indicator as described in steps **1)** and **2)** to check pinion depth. Resulting number obtained should correspond to guide number, within the following tolerance: +.002" (.05 mm) or –.001" (.03 mm.) Shims are available in increments of .001" (.03 mm). Use shim closest to measurement.

SAMPLE CALCULATION

Measurement	Reading
On Machined Surface	.281" (7.15 mm)
In Housing	- .039" (1.00 mm)
Difference	.242" (6.15 mm)
PLUS	+ .010" (.25 mm)
Total	.252" (6.40 mm)

SAMPLE CALCULATION

Measurement	Reading
On Machined Surface	.287" (7.29 mm)
On Thrust Plate	- .039" (1.00 mm)
Height Of Collar	.248" (6.29 mm)

Fig. 17: Installing Clamp on Right Side

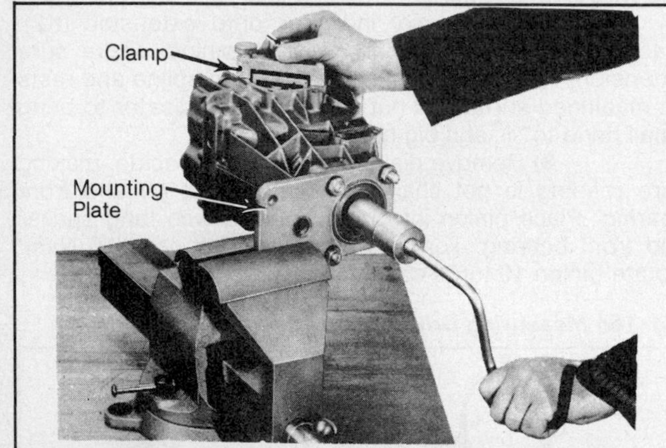
Clamp
Mounting Plate

Hand tighten clamp.

Fig. 18: Measuring Ring-to-Pinion Gear Backlash

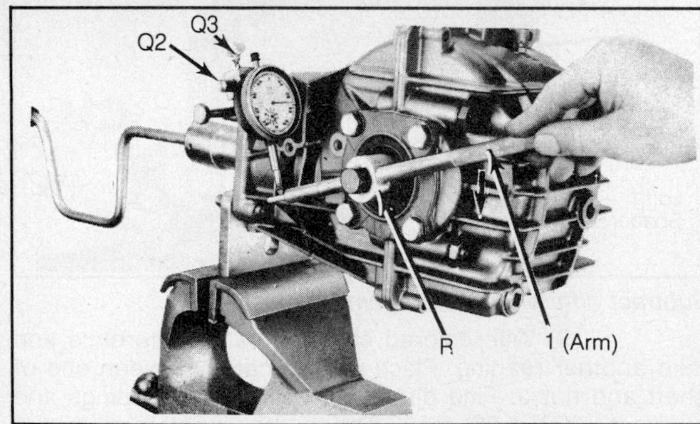
Q3
Q2
R
1 (Arm)

Perform measurement at 3 different locations.

Differential Backlash Adjustment

1) Install mounting plate on bottom 2 studs of front housing and mount housing in vise with rear housing up. Oil bearing housings. Install differential assembly. Install base shim of .053" (1.35 mm) behind bearing without thrust plate. Measure and record thickness of shim with micrometer before installation.

2) Install and hand tighten rear cover with 4 nuts and new washers. Loosen vise and install housing in vertical position with right side up. *See Fig. 17.*

3) Install clamp (P) and hand tighten only. Rotate pinion spline 5 turns in both directions and recheck tightness of clamp. Retighten rear cover nuts to 4 ft. lbs. (5 N.m). Move assembly in vise to its normal upright position.

4) Install backlash measuring tool (R) horizontally. Ensure 1 radial groove in ring gear face is aligned with double quotation marks (" ") of device. Tighten central screw of measuring tool. Mount dial indicator holder on front housing.

5) Mount dial indicator in holder. Dial indicator feeler (foot) should rest between 2 marks found on flat side of tool R and feeler and tool R should form a right angle. Carefully turn pinion counterclockwise to set dial indicator small hand to "5". Adjust dial indicator face to "0", while applying upward pressure on arm 1. *See Fig. 18.*

6) Carefully press downward on arm 1 until it seats. In this position, dial indicator reads backlash between drive pinion and ring gear. Note and record reading. Repeat operation at 3 different gaps in tool R. Before taking each reading, make sure dial indicator has been set to zero.

7) Write down 2 extreme readings. If difference between maximum and minimum reading exceeds .003" (.07 mm), check for dirt or burrs on teeth. Record minimum backlash reading. From the Backlash Adjustment Table, determine amount to be added or subtracted from base shim.

BACKLASH ADJUSTMENT TABLE

Reading Recorded In. (mm)	Adjustment to Base Shim In. (mm)
.0070-.0086 (.18-.22)	+ .0039 (.10)
.0090-.0106 (.23-.27)	+ .0020 (.05)
.0110-.0126 (.28-.32)	0
.0129-.0138 (.33-.35)	- .0020 (.05)
.0150-.0165 (.38-.42)	- .0039 (.10)
.0169-.0185 (.43-.47)	- .0059 (.15)
.0189-.0205 (.48-.52)	- .0079 (.20)
.0209-.0224 (.53-.57)	- .0098 (.25)
.0228-.0244 (.58-.62)	- .0118 (.30)
.0248-.0264 (.63-.67)	- .0157 (.40)
.0268-.0283 (.68-.72)	- .0177 (.45)
.0287-.0303 (.73-.77)	- .0197 (.50)
.0307-.0323 (.78-.82)	- .0236 (.60)

Bearing Preload Adjustment

1) Install a .79" (20 mm) stem to dial indicator. Mount dial indicator on mounting plate (K1). Place mounting plate over thrust plate with feeler (foot) touching outer bearing surface. Set small hand of dial indicator to "5" and zero dial face.

2) Place mounting plate on flat surface of left front housing with dial indicator feeler (foot) resting on outer bearing race. Make sure mounting plate does not rest on both front and rear housings, only on front housing. Record reading.

3) Subtract readings obtained in steps **1)** and **2)**, rounded off to nearest .002" (.05 mm), to determine

PEUGEOT SPLIT HOUSING – I.R.S. (Cont.)

difference. To this figure, add the amount recorded during Backlash adjustment for final shim thickness (step **7)** of Backlash adjustment). Also add .0059" (.15 mm). The final figure is shim thickness required.

4) Mount assembly in vise with rear housing up. Remove backlash measuring tool (R), dial indicator, clamp and rear housing half. Remove base shim. Do not use a shim pack of more than 2 shims to obtain required shim thickness.

5) Coat rear housing half with sealant. Attach rear housing to front housing with 4 nuts and new washers. Hand tighten nuts. Coat new oil seal with oil and install in thrust plate. Install shims of calculated thickness between right bearing and housing (end opposite ring gear).

6) Install new greased "O" ring between thrust plate and housing. Install thrust plate and hand tighten bolts. Tighten bolts to 4 ft. lbs. (5 N.m) in sequence. *See Fig. 19.* Rotate differential gear train in both directions. Tap housing with soft mallet to ensure mating. Tighten bolts to specification in sequence.

Fig. 19: Tightening Sequence for Housing

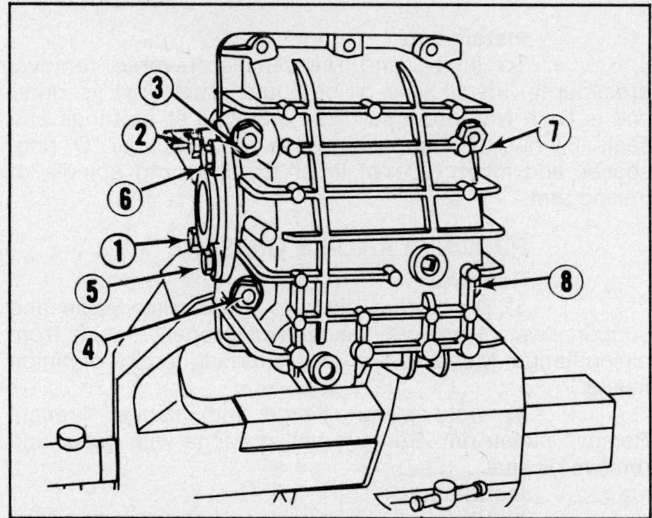
3
2
6
1
5
4
7
8

Tighten bolts to specifications.

7) Using steps described above, check backlash. If backlash is incorrect, repeat backlash adjustment. Install and tighten 6 housing retaining bolts.

8) Coat new oil seal with oil and install in left side of case (ring gear side). Remove mounting plate on front housing. Remove and clean oil seal plate. Remove and discard gasket and oil seal.

9) Ensure oil seal deflector is staked in position. Using a center punch, stake deflector at 3 points at 120° intervals. Soak new seal in oil and install. Install gasket and oil seal plate.

AXLE ASSEMBLY SPECIFICATIONS

Application	Specification
Pinion Depth	
All Models ..	[1] - .001" to + .002" (- .03 to + .05 mm)
Ring Gear-to-Pinion	
Gear Backlash	[2] .008" (.20 mm)

[1] – Deviation from guide used.
[2] – Maximum. With deviation from - .0020" to + .0023" (- .05 to +.06 mm)

TIGHTENING SPECIFICATIONS

Application	Ft. Lbs. (N.m)
Hub Carrier-to-Lower Control Arm	29 (40)
Rear Caliper Retaining Bolts	37 (50)
Rear Hub Nut	189 (257)
Differential Housing-to-Subframe	
Allen Heads	27 (37)
Ring Gear-to-Differential Assembly	96 (130)
Differential Side Plate Bolts	6 (8)
Propeller Shaft (Torque Tube Nuts)	44 (60)
Body-to-Crossmember Bolts	48 (65)
Rear Housing-to-Front Housing	
Nuts	48 (65)
6 Bolts (3 Upper & 3 Lower)	7 (10)
Bolts	26 (35)

Drive Axles

SUBARU 4WD REAR AXLE

DESCRIPTION

The rear axle assembly of all 4WD vehicles is a hypoid type with integral carrier housing. The pinion bearing preload adjustment is made by a selective spacer and washer.

The differential side bearing preload and pinion depth adjustments are made with shims. Driving power is transmitted to rear axle by ball spline type drive shafts with Double Offset Joints (DOJ) at each end.

AXLE RATIO & IDENTIFICATION

All 4WD vehicles use one basic type rear axle assembly. To determine axle ratio, divide number of ring gear teeth by number of pinion teeth.

REMOVAL & INSTALLATION

AXLE SHAFT & BEARINGS

Removal

1) Apply hand brake. Remove wheel cap and cotter pin. Loosen castle nut and wheel nuts. Disconnect lower bolt of shock absorber. Loosen locking bolts of crossmember outer bushing.

2) Raise and support vehicle. Remove wheel and tire assembly. Remove castle nut and brake drum.

3) Drive out spring pins of inner and outer Double Offset Joint (DOJ) by using 6 mm diameter steel rod. Remove outer DOJ from spindle of trailing arm with trailing arm lowered fully. Remove inner DOJ from differential spindle.

Fig. 1: Exploded View of Rear Drive Axle Assembly

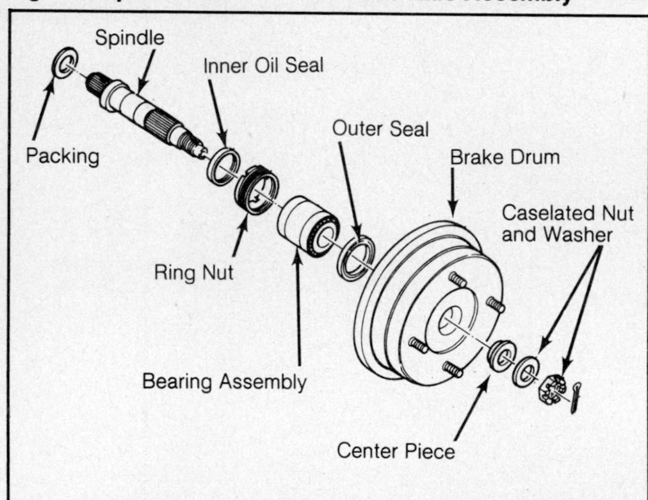
Spindle
Inner Oil Seal
Packing
Outer Seal
Brake Drum
Caselated Nut
and Washer
Ring Nut
Bearing Assembly
Center Piece

4) Remove rear exhaust pipe, muffler and covers. Disconnect brake line and plug end. Remove brake assembly from trailing arm by removing 4 bolts.

5) Remove bolt from inner bushing of inner trailing arm. Remove 3 bolts from inner arm and outer arm, remove inner arm.

6) Place inner arm in vise. Straighten staked portion of housing. Remove ring nut and remove spindle inward by tapping from outside with a soft hammer.

7) Remove oil seal. Insert spindle from outside of housing and press outer bearing out by pushing inner race through housing. Press out inner race of spindle.

Fig. 2: Driving Spring Pins Out of Double Offset Joint (DOJ)

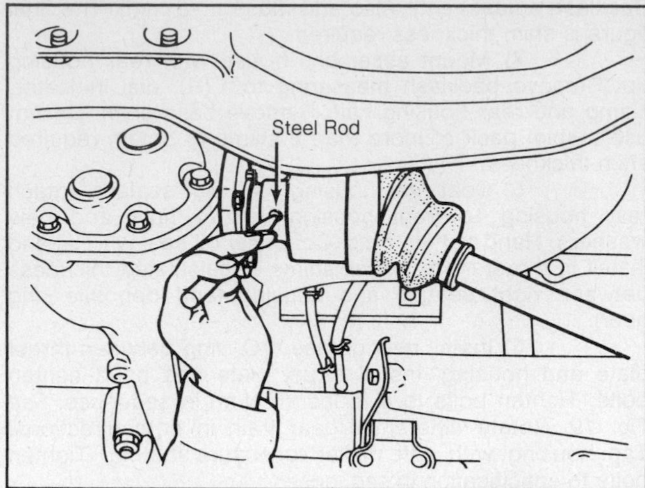
Steel Rod

Drive out springs of double offset joint using a 6 mm diameter steel rod.

Installation

To install and reassemble, reverse removal procedures. Install new oil seal into drum until its outer end is flush with drum surface. Lubricate all bearings and seals. Fill hub of drum with grease. Install spacer "O" ring, spacer and inner race of inner bearing onto spindle of trailing arm.

PINION FLANGE & OIL SEAL

Removal

1) Drain gear oil from differential. Raise and support rear of vehicle. Disconnect propeller shaft from pinion flange. Measure and record turning torque of pinion flange.

2) Hold pinion flange with flange wrench. Remove pinion nut. Remove pinion flange with puller and remove oil seal.

Installation

1) Apply grease between oil seal lips. Install oil seal using drift tool (398417700). Install pinion flange.

2) Hold flange with flange wrench (398427700) and tighten nut until turning torque is same as recorded before removal. Install remaining components in reverse order of removal procedure.

DIFFERENTIAL ASSEMBLY

Removal

1) Raise and support rear of vehicle. Drain gear oil. Remove exhaust pipe, muffler, propeller shaft and drive shafts.

2) Support axle assembly with a jack. Remove nuts on mounting member. Remove 2 bolts retaining front end of differential carrier. Lower jack and remove axle assembly.

Installation

To install, reverse removal procedure. Tighten bolts to specification and fill unit with gear oil.

SUBARU 4WD REAR AXLE (Cont.)

OVERHAUL

DRIVE AXLE SHAFT

Disassembly

Hold drive shaft in a vise and remove rubber boot. Remove snap ring and stopper. Remove snap ring and outer race of DOJ. Remove snap ring and inner race DOJ. Carefully remove DOJ boot.

Inspection

1) Check DOJ for corrosion, damage, seizure, and excessive play. Inspect drive shaft for straightness, cracks, damage and distortion. Replace drive shaft if ball spline portion is worn or damaged.

2) Check drive shaft play at DOJ. Maximum play of DOJ is .04" (1 mm).

Fig. 3: Exploded View of Drive Axle Shaft

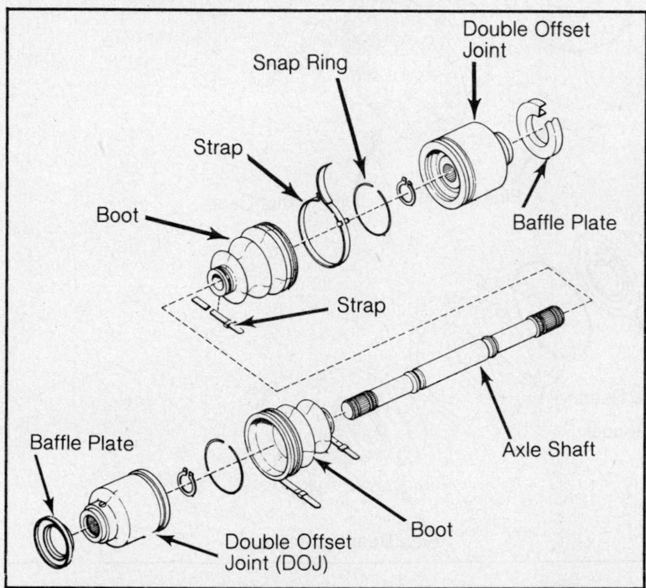

Double Offset Joint
Snap Ring
Strap
Boot
Baffle Plate
Strap
Axle Shaft
Baffle Plate
Boot
Double Offset Joint (DOJ)

Drive axle should be disassembled only to inspect and lubricate (DOJ).

Reassembly

1) To reassemble, reverse disassembly procedure. Apply grease to axle splines and install DOJ. Be careful not mix inner and outer DOJ.

2) Adjust axial play to within .0008" (.02 mm) by selecting proper size snap ring. Tighten all bolts.

DIFFERENTIAL CASE

NOTE: **Mark side retainers for reassembly reference. Left and right retainers are not interchangeable.**

Disassembly

1) Mount carrier on holding fixture. Remove rear cover and inspect differential before disassembly. Check following: Tooth contact of ring and pinion and backlash. Runout of drive gear at its back surface and rotation torque of drive pinion. Using puller, remove side retainer. Remove differential case assembly from carrier.

2) If side bearings are to be replaced, using puller and attachment (398457700) remove bearing side retainers.

3) Remove side bearings from differential case with puller. Pull out differential carrier. Remove ring gear by unfolding lock strap and loosening bolts. Unstake pinion shaft lock pin and punch pin out from flange side.

4) Hold pinion flange stationary using flange tool (398427700) and remove pinion nut. Remove pinion flange with puller. Press drive pinion from carrier and remove rear bearing inner race, bearing spacer and adjusting washer.

5) Remove pinion shaft, pinion gears, side gears and thrust washer. Thoroughly clean all parts and inspect for wear or damage; replace as necessary.

Reassembly & Adjustment

1) Assemble pinion gears, side gears and thrust washers in original positions in differential case. Fit pinion shaft to differential case so that it aligns with lock pin holes.

2) Adjust clearance between differential case and back of side gear to .004-.008" (.1-.2 mm) by selecting proper thrust washer. Thrust washers are available in the following sizes, .030-.032" (.75-.80 mm), .032-.034 (.80-.85 mm), and .034-.036" (.85-.90 mm).

3) Install pinion shaft lock pin and lock in place on both sides. Apply gear oil to gear tooth surface and thrust surfaces and make sure gears rotate smoothly. Install ring gear on differential case and install bolts and new lock washers.

NOTE: **Tighten ring gear bolts diagonally while tapping around bolt heads with a hammer.**

Fig. 4: Measuring Side Bearing Width

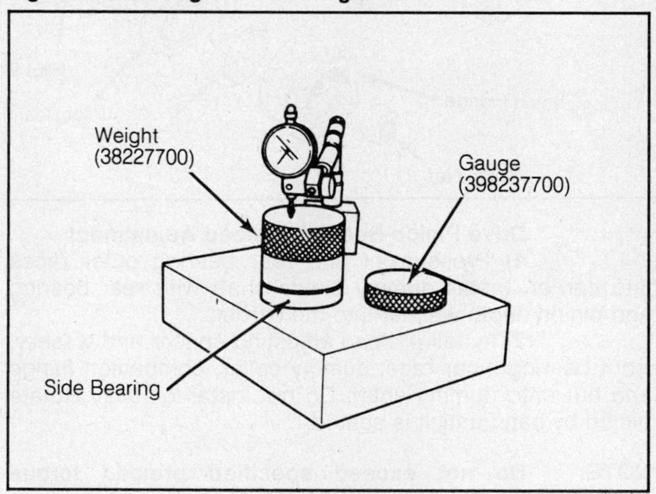

Weight (38227700)
Gauge (398237700)
Side Bearing

Standard bearing width is .787" (20 mm).

4) When replacing side bearings, measure bearing width by using a weight block (398227700) or equivalent. *See Fig. 6.* Standard bearing width is .787" (20 mm).

5) Press side bearing inner race onto differential case and bearing outer race into side retainer. Install new oil seal on side retainer and apply grease to cavity between seal lips.

SUBARU 4WD REAR AXLE (Cont.)

Fig. 5: Exploded View of Subaru 4WD Differential Assembly

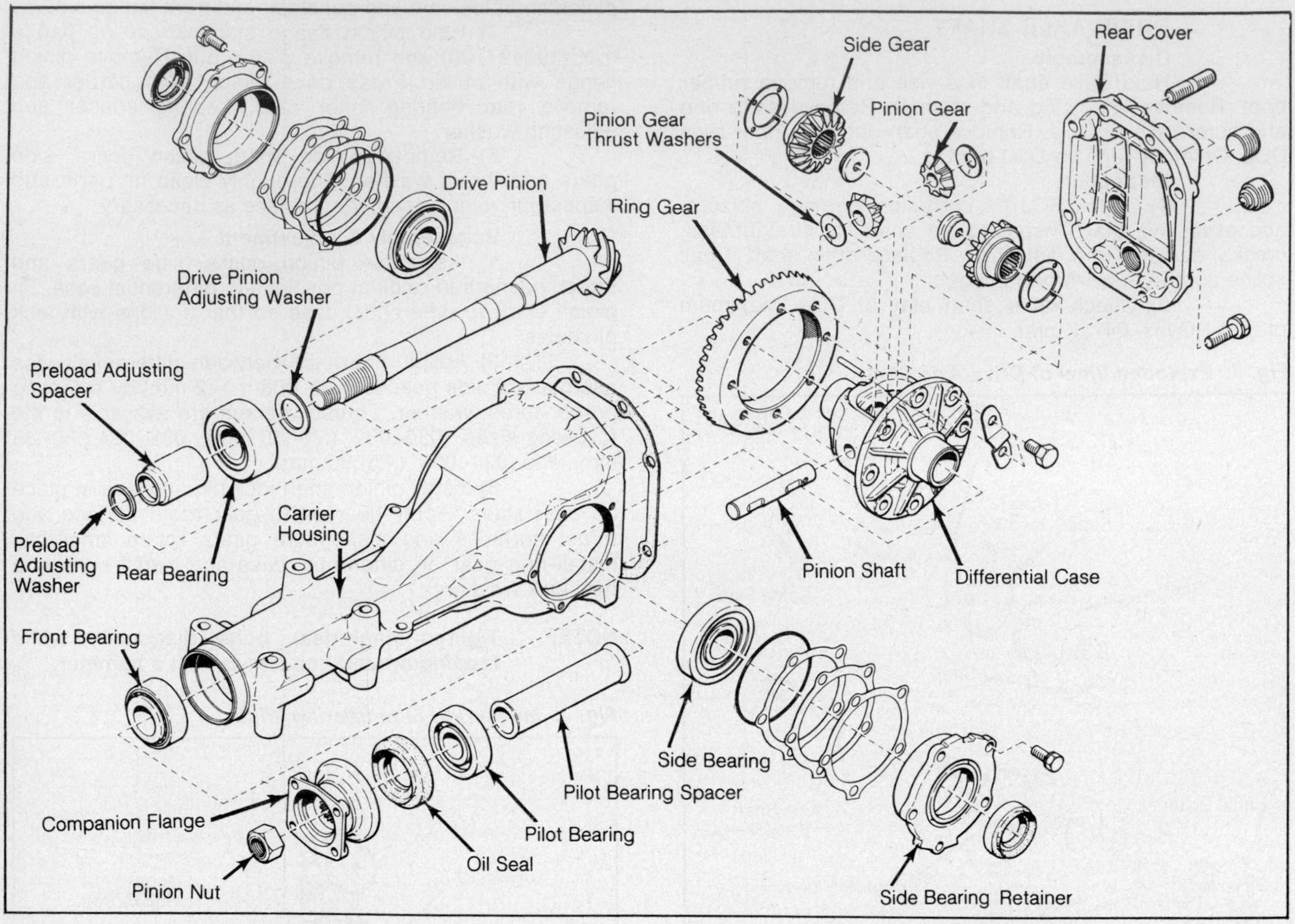

Drive Pinion Bearing Preload Adjustment

1) Press front and rear bearing outer races into carrier. Install dummy pinion shaft with rear bearing and pinion depth washer into the carrier.

2) Install preload adjusting spacer and washer, front bearing inner race, dummy collar, companion flange and nut onto dummy shaft. Do not install oil seal. Rotate pinion by hand until it is seated.

NOTE: **Do not exceed specified preload torque during preload adjustment.**

Fig. 6: Installing Dummy Shaft

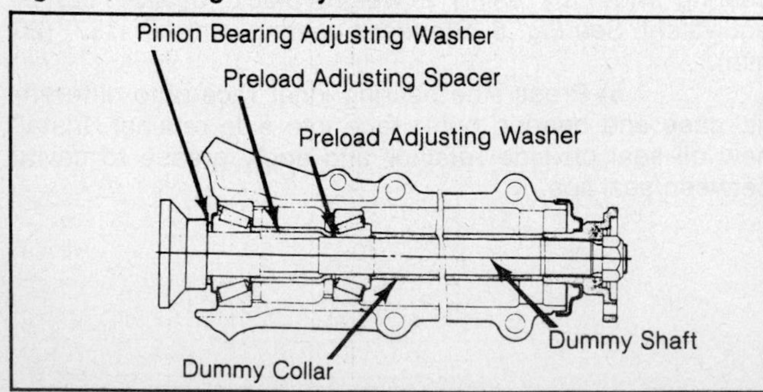
Pinion Bearing Adjusting Washer
Preload Adjusting Spacer
Preload Adjusting Washer
Dummy Shaft
Dummy Collar

If ring and pinion gear tooth contact pattern show normal pattern, reuse original washer.

3) Tighten nut to specified torque. Using an INCH lb. torque wrench, check rotating torque of pinion shaft. If preload is not within specification, select the correct washer and spacer so that specified preload is obtained when nut is tightened to correct torque.

4) Spacers are available in lengths from 2.213" (56.2 mm) to 2.252" (57.2 mm) in increments of .008" (.20 mm). Washers are available in thicknesses from .102" (2.59 mm) to .0909" (.231 mm) in increments of .0008" (.02 mm).

Drive Pinion Gear Installed Height

1) Leave dummy drive pinion shaft installed, and install height gauge. *See Preload Adjustment*. Using a feeler gauge, measure clearance between end of pinion gear head and height gauge.

2) Determine the thickness of the pinion height adjusting washer to be installed using the following formula.

NOTE: **Formula values are given in millimeters.**

$$T = To + N - (H \times .01) - .20$$

T = Thickness of adjusting washer needed.
To = Thickness of washer temporarily installed.
N = Clearance between gauge and dummy shaft.
H = Figure marked on drive pinion head.

Drive Axles

SUBARU 4WD REAR AXLE (Cont.)

3) After determining the correct thickness of required pinion height adjusting washer, remove dummy shaft and height gauge. Install pinion height adjusting washer on drive pinion, then press rear bearing inner race into position.

4) Insert drive pinion into gear carrier. Install previously selected preload adjusting spacer, washer, oil seal, companion flange, and pinion nut. Tighten pinion nut to specification.

Fig. 7: Measuring Drive Pinion Gear Installed Height

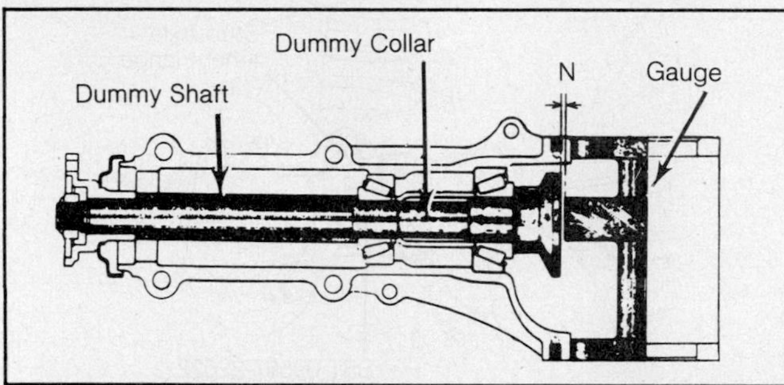
Dummy Collar
N
Gauge
Dummy Shaft

Using a feeler gauge, measure clearance (N) between end of pinion gear head and height gauge.

Side Bearing Preload

1) Use the following formula to obtain the proper thickness of left and right side retainer shims.

NOTE: **Formula values are given in millimeters.**

T_1 **(Left) = (A + C + G_1 – D) x .01 + .76 – E**

T_2 **(Right) = (B + D + G_2) x .01 + .76 – F**

T_1 = Required thickness of left side retainer shim.

T_2 = Required thickness of right side retainer shim.

A & B = Figure marked on gear carrier.
C & D = Figure marked on differential case.
E & F = Difference in width of left or right bearing.
G_1 = Figure marked on left side retainer.
G_2 = Figure marked on right side retainer.

Fig. 8: Location of Identification Marks

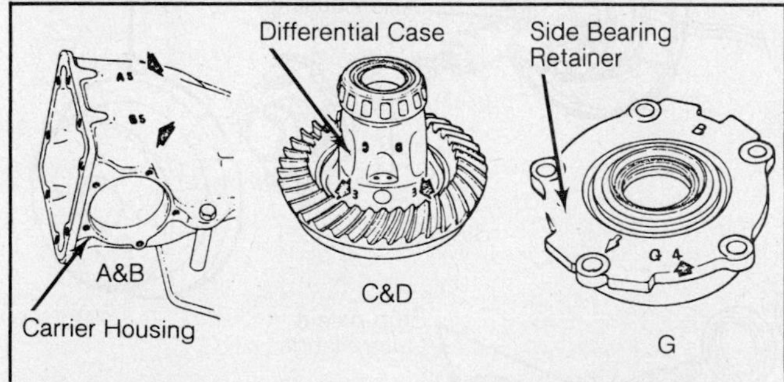
Differential Case
Side Bearing Retainer
A&B
Carrier Housing
C&D
G

If the identification mark is not present, regard it as zero.

2) Install differential case assembly into differential carrier in reverse order of disassembly. Fit selected shims and "O" ring on the side retainer and install retainers in carrier with arrow pointing as shown in *Fig. 11.*

3) Measure drive gear-to-drive pinion backlash. If reading is not within specification, correct by decreasing the shim thickness on one side and increasing the shim thickness on other side the same amount. Total shim thickness must be the same to maintain proper preload.

4) Check tooth contact of drive gear. If tooth contact is incorrect, recheck shim measurements.

Fig. 9: Aligning Side Retainer

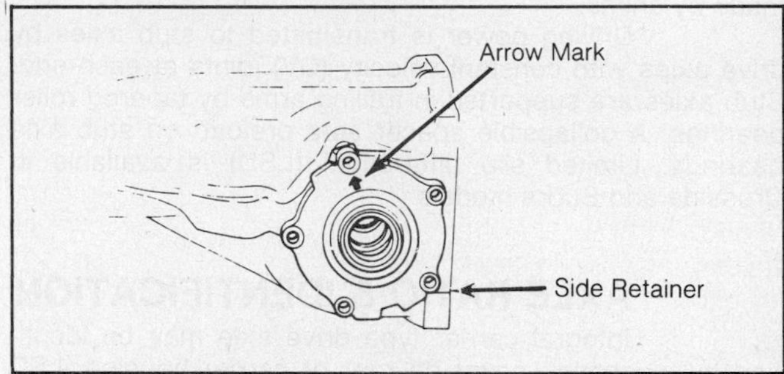
Arrow Mark
Side Retainer

Arrow must point as shown for proper alignment.

AXLE ASSEMBLY SPECIFICATIONS

Application	INCH Lbs. (N.m)
Pinion Bearing Preload	
New Bearing	4.4-6.4 (6.0-8.7)
Used Bearing	1.9-3.7 (2.6-5.0)
Side Bearing Clearance	.004-.008 (.1-.2)
Drive Gear-to-Pinion Backlash	.004-.008 (.1-.2)
Drive Gear Backface Runout [1]	.002 (.05)

[1] – Maximum Clearance.

TIGHTENING SPECIFICATIONS

Application	Ft. Lbs. (N.m)
Pinion Nut	123-145 (167-197)
Ring Gear Bolts	51-58 (69-79)
Side Bearing Retaining Bolt	7-9 (9-12)
Side Yoke Retaining Bolt	14-19 (19-26)
Rear Cover Bolts	14-19 (19-26)
Front Carrier Mounting Bolts	58-72 (79-98)
Rear Carrier Mounting Bolts	43-51 (58-69)
Propeller Shaft Flange Bolts	13-18 (18-24)
Companion Flange Bolts	13-18 (18-24)
Axle Nut	174 (237)
Rear Drive Shaft Spindle Ring Nut	130-160 (177-217)

Drive Axles

TOYOTA INTEGRAL HOUSING

Celica, Cressida, & Supra

DESCRIPTION

Drive axle assembly is hypoid type with integral carrier housing. Drive pinion bearing preload adjustment is made with collapsible spacer between front and rear pinion bearing inner races. Differential side bearing preload and drive pinion depth adjustment are made by shims.

Driving power is transmitted to stub axles by drive axles with constant-velocity (CV) joints at each end. Stub axles are supported in trailing arms by tapered roller bearings. A collapsible spacer sets preload on stub axle bearings. Limited slip differential (LSD) is available in Cressida and Supra models.

AXLE RATIO & IDENTIFICATION

Integral carrier type drive axle may be identified by inspection cover on rear of carrier housing. LSD uses 2-piece case while conventional differential uses 1-piece case. To determine axle ratio, divide number of ring gear teeth by number of pinion gear teeth.

REMOVAL & INSTALLATION

STUB AXLE & BEARINGS

Removal

1) Raise vehicle. Remove rear wheel. Disconnect outer CV joint from stub axle inner flange. Remove caliper and support out of way, being careful of brake line. Release parking brake fully and remove rotor.

2) Loosen staked portion of flange nut with chisel. Remove flange nut and washer. Remove inner flange and plate washer from stub axle shaft using puller (09557-22022). *See Fig. 2.* Remove stub axle with seal and outer bearing, using puller.

Fig. 2: Removing Stub Axle Inner Flange

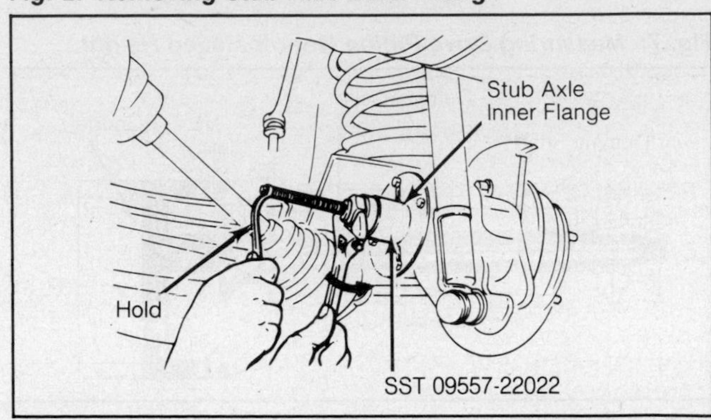
Stub Axle
Inner Flange
Hold
SST 09557-22022

Do not lose plate washer at end of flange (bearing side).

3) Remove inner seal from housing and take out inner bearing. Drive stub axle bearing outer races from housing with brass drift. Press outer bearing off stub axle shaft and remove seal.

Inspection

1) Inspect stub axle shaft and outer flange for damage or wear. Measure runout of stub axle outer flange. If flange runout exceeds .004" (.10 mm), stub axle must be replaced. *See Fig. 3.*

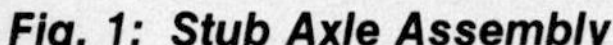

Fig. 1: Stub Axle Assembly

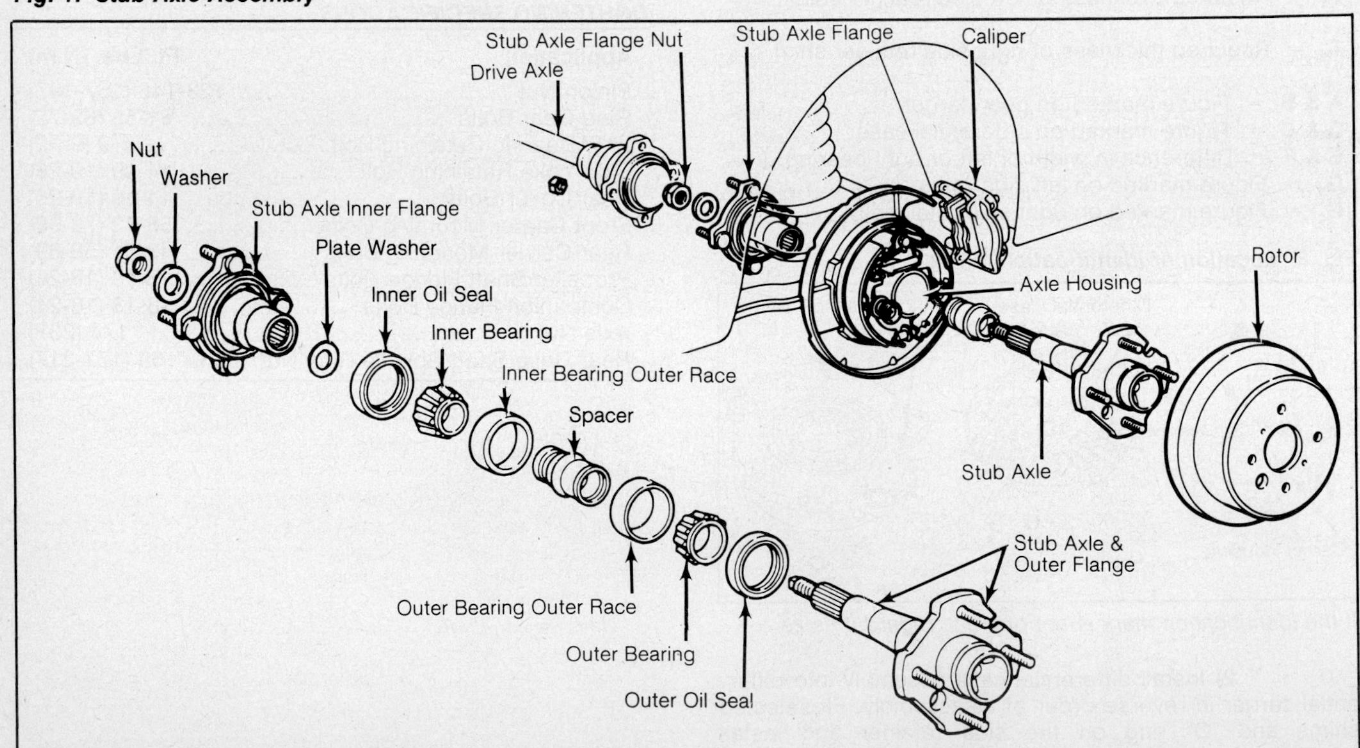
Stub Axle Flange Nut
Drive Axle
Stub Axle Flange
Caliper
Nut
Washer
Stub Axle Inner Flange
Plate Washer
Inner Oil Seal
Inner Bearing
Inner Bearing Outer Race
Spacer
Rotor
Axle Housing
Stub Axle
Stub Axle &
Outer Flange
Outer Bearing Outer Race
Outer Bearing
Outer Oil Seal

Note drum-type parking brake located inside disc brake rotor.

TOYOTA INTEGRAL HOUSING (Cont.)

Fig. 3: Checking Axle Flange Runout

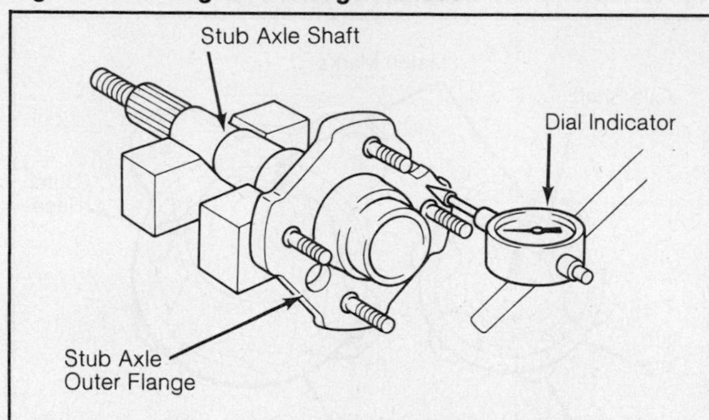
Stub Axle Shaft
Dial Indicator
Stub Axle
Outer Flange

If runout exceeds .004" (.10 mm) replace axle shaft.

2) Clean and dry bearings and races. Inspect for pits, scoring, or heat damage. Bearing and outer race must be replaced as set if either is damaged.

Installation

1) Pack bearings with MP grease No. 2. Drive outer race of inner bearing into housing. Place inner bearing in race. Drive new inner seal into housing to correct depth. *See Seal Depth table.* Drive outer race of outer bearing into housing.

2) Pack inside of housing and coat outside of new spacer with MP grease No. 2. Install new spacer in hub. Place outer bearing in race and drive new outer seal in to correct depth. Coat seal lips with No. 2 grease.

3) Install stub axle shaft in bearings. Install inner flange with plate washer in housing after lightly coating flange with grease. Use puller (09557-22022) to align inner flange and axle shaft tip, making sure no grease gets on shaft threads. *See. Fig. 4.*

Fig. 4: Aligning Axle Shaft and Inner Flange

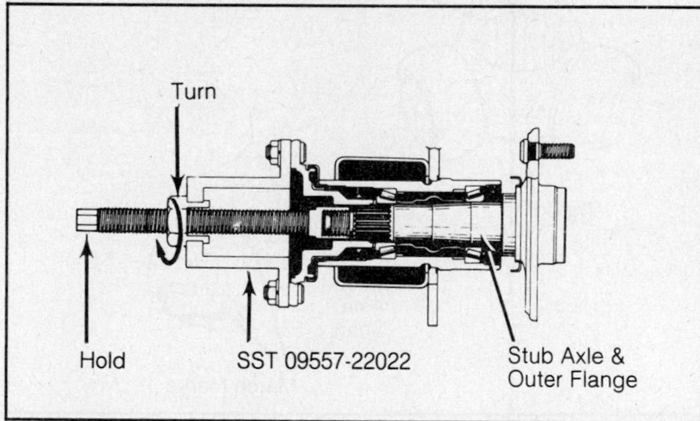
Turn
Hold
SST 09557-22022
Stub Axle &
Outer Flange

Use Puller (09557-22022).

4) Install new flange nut with washer and torque nut to 22-36 ft. lbs. (30-49 N.m), making sure that axle shaft has axial play. Rotate shaft in both directions and measure rotational resistance with torque wrench. Torque flange nut to 58 ft. lbs. (79 N.m).

5) Check with torque wrench that preload rotation of bearings is .9-3.5 INCH Lbs. (.10-.40 N.m). Turn flange one revolution per 6 seconds while measuring. If preload is too low, tighten nut 5-10° at a time until specified preload is reached.

6) Maximum torque on flange nut is 145 ft. lbs. (197 N.m). If maximum torque is exceeded, new spacer must be installed and preload procedure repeated. Stake flange nut.

7) Install rotor and check parking brake adjustment. Install caliper. Attach outer CV to inner stub axle flange and torque nuts to specification. Install rear wheel and tighten lug nuts.

DRIVE AXLE ASSEMBLY

NOTE: **There are two types of drive axle assemblies. Toyota type has outer joint with tripod inner race and stops on axle shaft for locating joints. NTN type has outer joint with round CV inner race and 2 snap rings locating joints. Confirm which you have before beginning work. See Fig. 5.**

Fig. 5: Two Types of Drive Axles

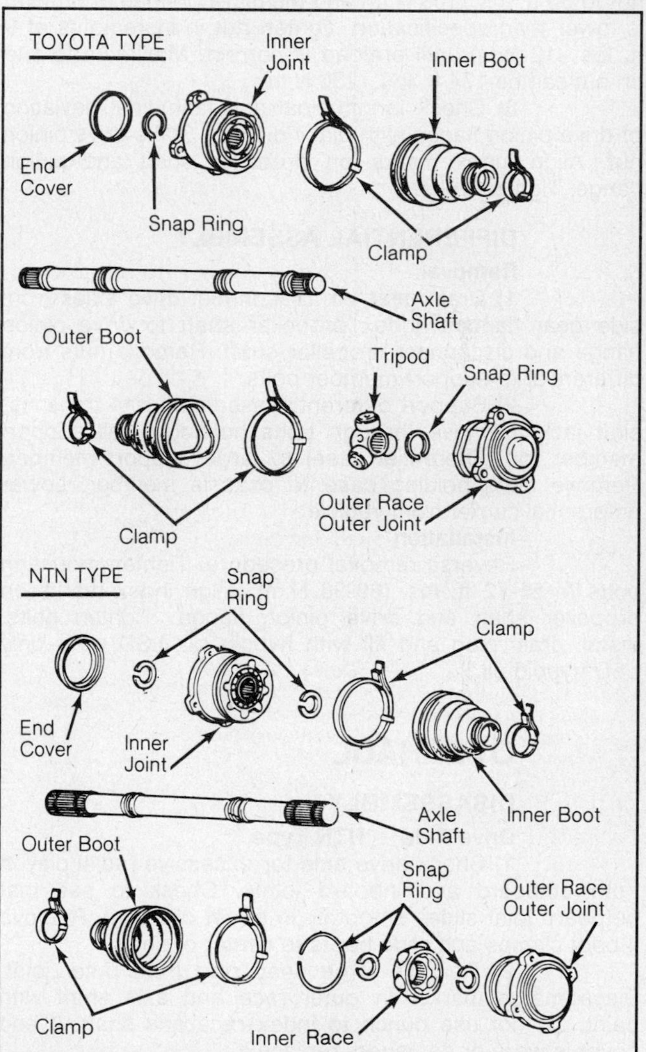
TOYOTA TYPE
Inner
Joint
Inner Boot
End
Cover
Snap Ring
Clamp
Axle
Shaft
Outer Boot
Tripod
Snap Ring
Outer Race
Outer Joint
Clamp
NTN TYPE
Snap
Ring
Clamp
End
Cover
Inner
Joint
Axle
Shaft
Inner Boot
Outer Boot
Snap
Ring
Outer Race
Outer Joint
Clamp
Inner Race

Toyota outer joint is tripod type while NTN outer joint is round CV type.

Removal

Disconnect drive axle from differential side gear flange and from stub axle flange.

Installation

Install drive shaft with narrow distance between flange and boot band at differential side. Use care to avoid damage to boots when installing drive shaft. Tighten nuts 44-57 ft. lbs. (60-77 N.m).

DRIVE PINION FLANGE & OIL SEAL

Removal

1) Index propeller shaft to drive pinion flange and remove propeller shaft. Loosen staked portion of drive pinion flange nut. Remove nut and flange. Remove oil seal from housing and remove oil slinger.

2) Remove front bearing from housing with puller. Remove collapsible bearing spacer and discard.

Installation

1) Install new spacer and front bearing. Install oil slinger with concave side facing front drive pinion bearing . Apply grease to seal lips and install new oil seal to correct depth. *See Seal Depth table.* Install flange and lightly coat drive pinion threads with grease.

2) Install flange nut and hold flange. Tighten nut to 80 ft. lbs. (108 N.m) and measure preload. If preload is lower than specification, tighten nut in increments of 9 ft. lbs. (12 N.m) until preload is correct. Maximum torque on nut can be 174 ft. lbs. (236 N.m).

3) Check longitudinal and latitudinal deviation of drive pinion flange with dial indicator. Stake drive pinion nut. Align index marks on propeller shaft and pinion flange. Tighten bolts.

DIFFERENTIAL ASSEMBLY

Removal

1) Drain gear oil. Disconnect drive axles from side gear flanges. Index propeller shaft to drive pinion flange and disconnect propeller shaft. Remove nuts from differential-to-support member bolts.

2) Support differential assembly with transmission jack. Remove through bolts holding small support member (on differential case) to large support member. Remove bolts holding case to chassis member. Lower differential carrier from vehicle.

Installation

Reverse removal procedure. Tighten mounting bolts to 51-72 ft. lbs. (69-98 N.m). Align index marks on propeller shaft and drive pinion flange. Tighten bolts. Install drain plug and fill with hypoid oil. LSD uses only LSD hypoid oil.

OVERHAUL

DISASSEMBLY

Drive Axle - NTN Type

1) Check drive axle for excessive radial play in both outboard and inboard joints. Check to see that outboard joint slides smoothly in thrust direction. Remove 4 boot clamps and slide boots to center of shaft.

2) Remove large snap ring from outer joint. Place match marks on outer race and axle shaft with paint. Do not use punch to index race and shaft. If end cover is worn or damaged, replace it.

3) Remove balls from inner race of outer joint by tapping edge of cage in axial direction of shaft, using a soft hammer. Move bearing cage to center of axle shaft. Remove outer snap ring and press inner race from axle shaft. Remove inner snap ring and cage. Remove both dust boots.

4) Pry end cover from inner joint. Place match marks on inner joint and axle shaft with paint. Remove snap ring and press joint from axle shaft. Clean all parts. Check parts for cracks, wear, or damage. Replace as necessary.

Fig. 6: Match Mark Location on NTN Type

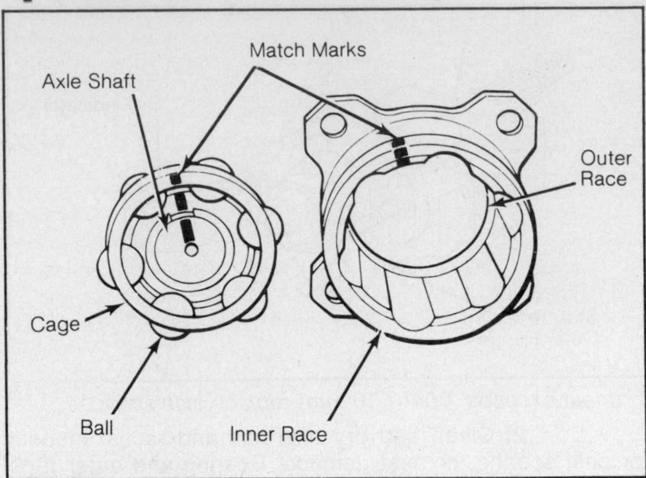
Match Marks
Axle Shaft
Outer Race
Cage
Ball
Inner Race

Use paint, not punch, to make match marks on outer race and axle shaft.

Drive Axle - Toyota Type

1) Check drive shaft for excessive radial play in both outer and inner joints. Check to see that outer joint slides smoothly in thrust direction. Remove 4 boot clamps and slide boots to center of shaft.

2) Place match marks on outer race of outer joint and axle shaft with paint. Do not punch marks. Remove outer race. If end cover is worn or damaged, replace it. Place match marks on tripod and shaft.

Fig. 7: Match Mark Location on Toyota Type

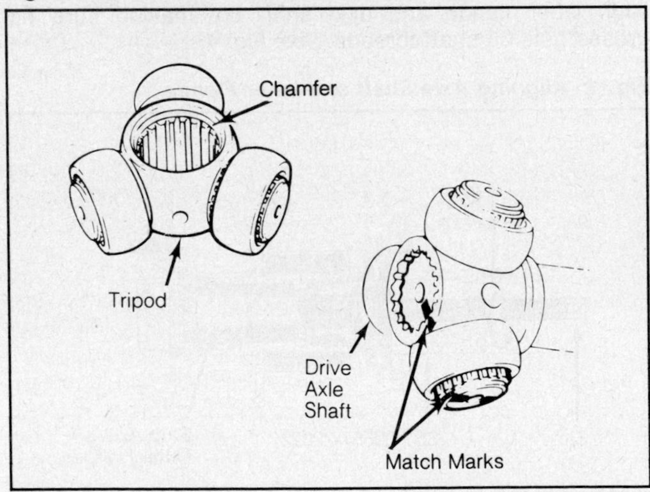
Chamfer
Tripod
Drive Axle Shaft
Match Marks

Do not press on roller.

3) Remove snap ring and remove tripod from axle shaft with press. Do not press on roller. Remove both dust boots.

4) Pry end plate from inner joint. Place match marks on inner joint outer race and drive shaft. Remove snap ring and press inner joint from shaft. Clean all parts. Check parts for cracks, wear, or damage, and replace as necessary.

TOYOTA INTEGRAL HOUSING (Cont.)

Fig. 8: Exploded View of Differentials

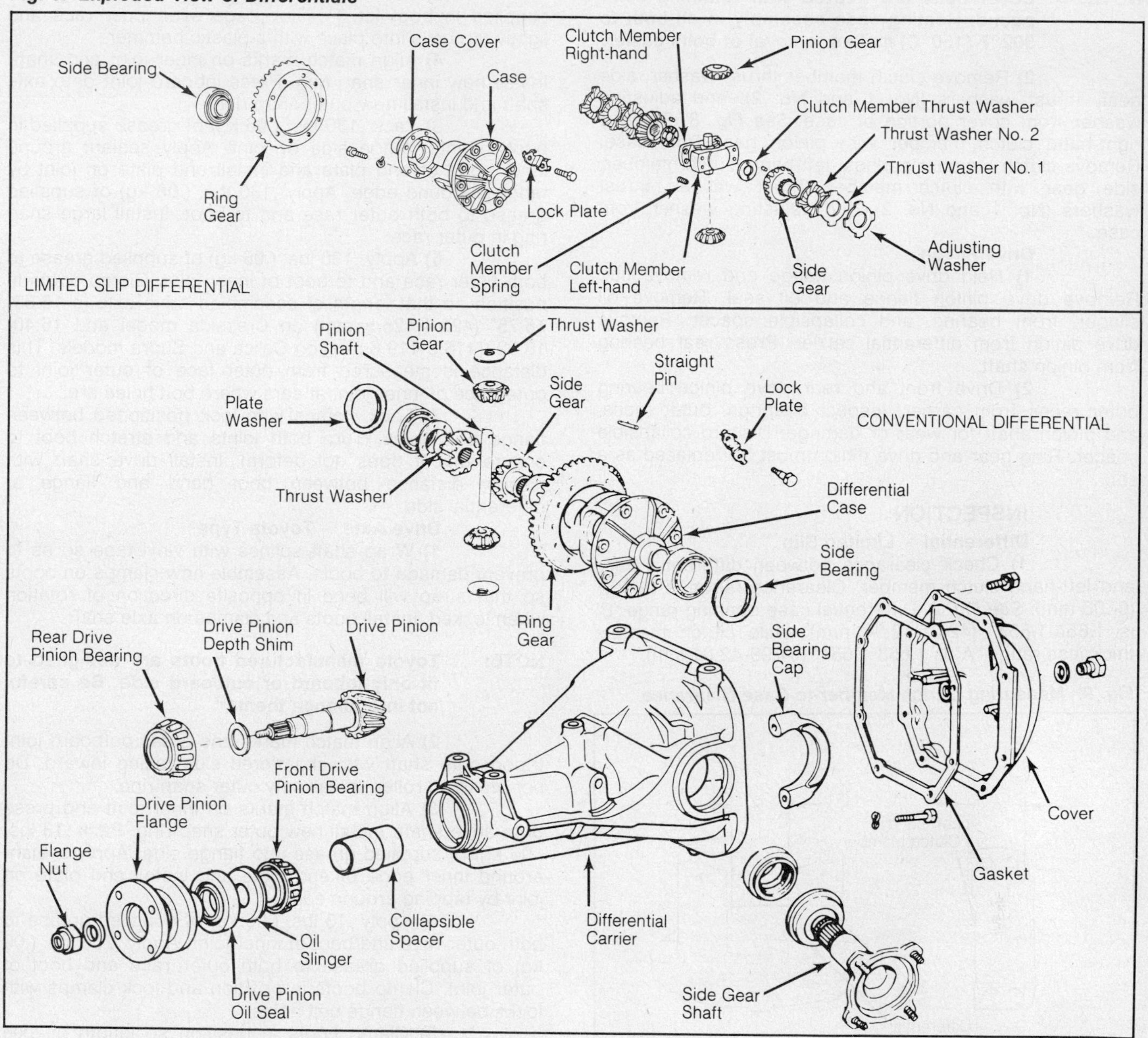

Side Bearing
Case Cover
Case
Ring Gear
Lock Plate
Clutch Member Right-hand
Pinion Gear
Clutch Member Thrust Washer
Thrust Washer No. 2
Thrust Washer No. 1
Adjusting Washer
Side Gear
Clutch Member Left-hand
Clutch Member Spring
LIMITED SLIP DIFFERENTIAL
Pinion Shaft
Pinion Gear
Thrust Washer
Straight Pin
Lock Plate
Side Gear
Plate Washer
CONVENTIONAL DIFFERENTIAL
Thrust Washer
Differential Case
Side Bearing
Ring Gear
Side Bearing Cap
Rear Drive Pinion Bearing
Drive Pinion Depth Shim
Drive Pinion
Front Drive Pinion Bearing
Drive Pinion Flange
Flange Nut
Oil Slinger
Collapsible Spacer
Differential Carrier
Drive Pinion Oil Seal
Side Gear Shaft
Cover
Gasket

Differential Case - Conventional

1) Remove differential carrier cover. Remove side gear shaft and oil seal. Check ring gear runout and backlash. Check gear tooth contact pattern. Check side gear backlash while holding one pinion gear toward case. Measure drive pinion preload and total preload.

2) Put alignment marks on bearing cap and differential carrier. Remove caps. Remove two side bearing preload adjusting plate washers. Measure plate washers and record thicknesses. Remove differential case and ring gear. Remove differential case side bearing outer races.

NOTE: **Mark bearings, gears, and thrust washers for installation in their original position.**

3) Remove side bearings from case with puller. Keep side bearings with correct outer races and mark for reassembly. Put alignment marks on ring gear and differential case. Remove ring gear bolts and locking tabs. Remove ring gear by tapping on gear with a plastic hammer.

4) Using hammer and punch, drive out straight pin holding pinion shaft to case. Remove pinion shaft, pinion gears, side gears, and thrust washers. Thoroughly clean and inspect all parts for wear or damage. Repair or replace parts as necessary.

Differential Case - Limited Slip

1) Perform steps **1)** through **3)** as previously described for conventional case disassembly. Index case cover and case for reassembly. Ensure left and right clutch member numbers match. Loosen case cover bolts in diagonal sequence.

TOYOTA INTEGRAL HOUSING (Cont.)

NOTE: Cover bolts are treated with retaining compound. Heating case assembly in oil bath to 302°F (150°C) makes removal of bolts easier.

2) Remove clutch member thrust washer, side gear, thrust washers (No. 1 and No. 2), and adjusting washer from cover portion of case. *See Fig. 8.* Remove right-hand clutch member with pinion gear from case. Remove clutch member springs, left-hand clutch member, side gear with clutch member thrust washer, thrust washers (No. 1 and No. 2), and adjusting washer from case.

Drive Pinion

1) Hold drive pinion flange and remove nut. Remove drive pinion flange and oil seal. Remove oil slinger, front bearing, and collapsible spacer. Remove drive pinion from differential carrier. Press rear bearing from pinion shaft.

2) Drive front and rear drive pinion bearing outer races from carrier. Inspect bearings, outer races, and pinion shaft for wear or damage. Discard collapsible spacer. Ring gear and drive pinion must be replaced as a set.

INSPECTION

Differential - Limited Slip

1) Check clearance between differential case and left-hand clutch member. Clearance range is 0-.002" (0-.05 mm). *See Fig. 9.* Differential case opening range "B" is 1.654-1.655" (42.01-42.04 mm) while clutch member thickness range "A" is 1.653-1.654" (41.99-42.01 mm).

Fig. 9: Measuring Clutch Member-to-Case Clearance

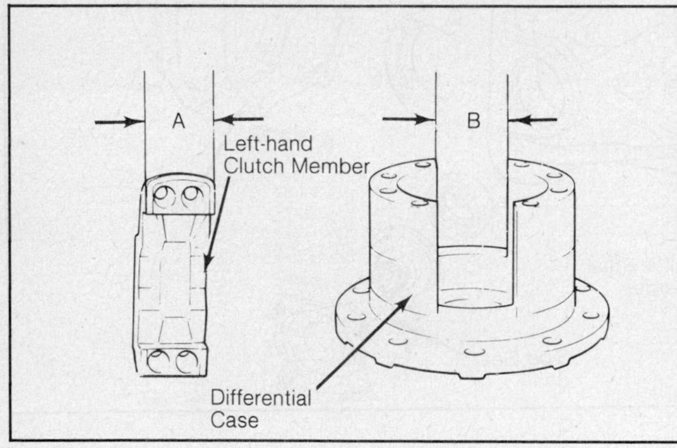
A
B
Left-hand
Clutch Member
Differential
Case

Clearance should be 0-.002" (0-.05 mm).

2) Check side gear thrust washers for heat damage or excessive wear. Check springs for tension. If side gear or clutch member needs to be replaced, thrust washer touching that part must also be replaced. Any reused parts must be installed in original position.

REASSEMBLY & ADJUSTMENT

Drive Axle - NTN Type

1) Wrap shaft splines with vinyl tape so as to prevent damage to boots. Assemble new clamps on boots so that straps will bend opposite to direction of rotation. Install boots and clamps on shaft. Install new inner snap rings.

2) Place cage of outer joint onto shaft with larger diameter facing outward. Align match marks and press inner race onto drive shaft. Install new outer snap ring.

3) Coat inner race, cage, and balls with grease supplied in boot kit. Position cage over inner race and lightly tap balls into place with a plastic hammer.

4) Align match marks on inner joint and shaft. Install new inner snap ring. Press inboard joint onto axle shaft and install new outer snap ring.

5) Pack .130 lbs. (.06 kg) of grease supplied in boot kit into flange side of joint. Apply sealant around inner edge of end plate and install end plate on joint by tapping around edge. Apply .130 lbs. (.06 kg) of supplied grease to both outer race and to boot. Install large snap ring in outer race.

6) Apply .130 lbs. (.06 kg) of supplied grease to both outer race and to boot of inner joint. Clamp boots in position so that length of assembled drive axle is 16.63-16.75" (422.4-425.5 mm) on Cressida model and 16.40-16.52" (416.6-419.6 mm) on Celica and Supra models. This distance is measured from outer face of outer joint to outer face of inner joint at ears where bolt holes are.

7) Lock clamps with lock positioned between flange bolt holes. Turn both joints and stretch boot to ensure that it does not deform. Install drive shaft with narrow distance between boot band and flange at differential side.

Drive Axle - Toyota Type

1) Wrap shaft splines with vinyl tape so as to prevent damage to boots. Assemble new clamps on boots so that strap will bend in opposite direction of rotation when locked. Install boots and clamps on axle shaft.

NOTE: Toyota manufactured boots are designed to fit only inboard or outboard side. Be careful not interchange them.

2) Align match marks and press outboard joint tripod onto shaft with chamfered side facing inward. Do not press on roller. Install new outer snap ring.

3) Align match marks on inner joint and press onto drive shaft. Install new outer snap ring. Pack .13 lbs. (.06 kg) of supplied grease into flange side. Apply sealant around inner edge of end plate and install end plate on joint by tapping around edge.

4) Apply .13 lbs. (.06 kg) of supplied grease to both outer race and boot of inner joint. Apply .200 lbs. (.09 kg) of supplied grease to both outer race and boot of outer joint. Clamp boots in position and lock clamps with locks between flange bolt holes.

5) Clamp boots in position so length of axle assembly is 16.36" (415.5 mm). This measurement is made from outer face of inner joint to outer face of outer joint, at ears in flange where bolt holes are located. Turn both joints and stretch boots to ensure that boots do not deform.

Differential Case - Conventional

1) Install side gears and thrust washers in case. Thrust washers should be same size for both sides if possible. Install pinion gears with thrust washers and tap pinion shaft into place. Check side gear backlash while holding 1 pinion gear toward case.

2) If backlash is incorrect, change thickness of thrust washers until backlash is within range of .002-.008" (.05-.20 mm). Install straight pin through case and hole in pinion shaft. Stake pin to differential case. Press side bearings onto case.

3) Clean contact surfaces of differential case. Heat ring gear to 212°F (100°C) in oil bath. Clean ring gear contact surface with solvent and install on case while still

TOYOTA INTEGRAL HOUSING (Cont.)

hot. Align index marks on ring gear and case. Coat ring gear bolts with hypoid oil and install with lock plates.

CAUTION: Do not heat ring gear above 230°F (110°C).

4) Tighten ring gear bolts gradually in diagonal sequence. When bolts are snug, tighten to 67-75 ft. lbs. (91-102 N.m). Stake lock plates with 1 tab flush against flat of bolt head. Tab resting on point should be staked on tightening side of point.

5) Install case with side bearings into carrier. Snug down adjusting nut until there is no play in bearing. Check ring gear runout with a dial indicator against back of gear (opposite teeth) in 4 places.

6) Maximum runout allowed is .003" (.07 mm). If runout is excessive, rotate ring gear on case and remeasure. If runout cannot be brought within specified range, case or ring gear must be replaced.

Differential Case - Limited Slip

1) Side gear thrust clearance (axial clearance inside case) must be determined first. Clean all parts. Set up measuring tool (09411-22011) and install parts in order

Fig. 10: Measuring for Selection of Side Gear Thrust Washers

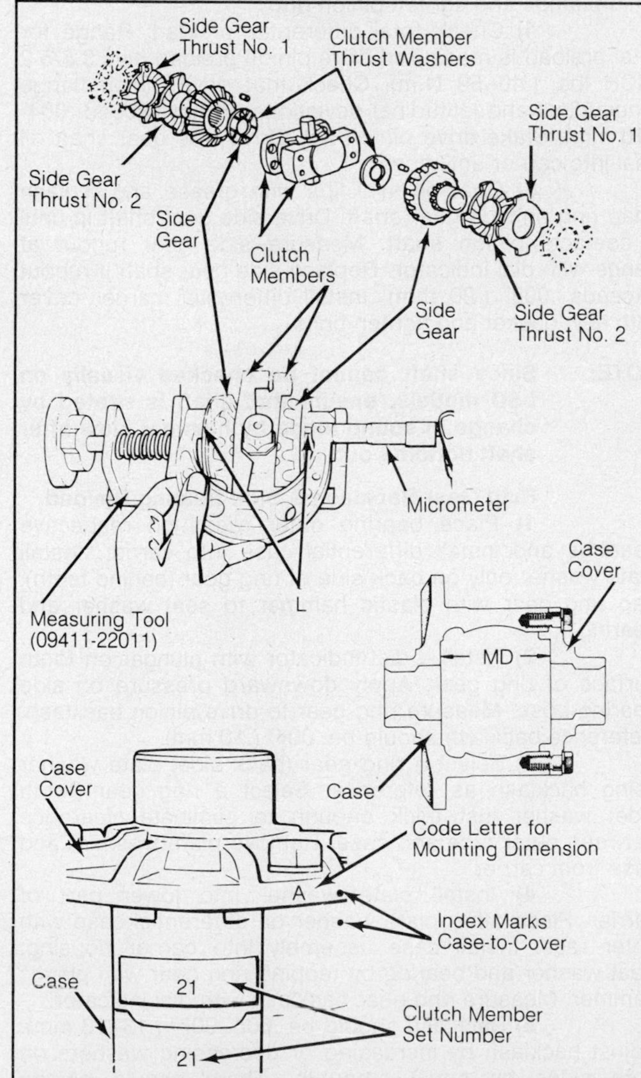
Side Gear Thrust No. 1
Clutch Member Thrust Washers
Side Gear Thrust No. 1
Side Gear Thrust No. 2
Side Gear
Clutch Members
Side Gear
Side Gear Thrust No. 2
Micrometer
Case Cover
Measuring Tool (09411-22011)
MD
Case Cover
Case
Code Letter for Mounting Dimension
A
Index Marks Case-to-Cover
Case
21
Clutch Member Set Number
21

Adjusting washers and clutch member springs are not assembled in measuring tool.

shown. *See Fig. 10.* Do not assemble adjusting washers or clutch member springs at this time.

2) Loosen clamping nut on measuring tool and hold parts with spring tension of tool. Measure "L" dimension with micrometer. Dimension "L" is assembled distance from outer face of left-hand thrust washer No. 1 to outer face of right-hand thrust washer No. 1.

3) Make sure parts are aligned in tool and measure "L" dimension several times. Take average of readings. Differential case mounting dimension is classified at time of manufacture. Code letters "A" through "E" are stamped onto edge of case cover. *See Case Mounting Dimension table.*

CASE MOUNTING DIMENSION

Code Letter [1]	In. (mm)
A	2.952-2.953 (74.98-75.01)
B	2.953-2.954 (75.01-75.03)
C	2.954-2.956 (75.03-75.08)
D	2.956-2.957 (75.08-75.11)
E	2.957-2.958 (75.11-75.13)

[1] - Letter stamped in edge of case cover.

4) Adjusting washers are selected by correlating mounting dimension (from code letter stamped on edge of case cover) and dimension "L" in table. *See Adjusting Washer Selection Table.* Adjusting washers are available in 6 thicknesses and reference numbers "1" through "6" are stamped on 1 ear of washer. *See Adjusting Washer Size table.*

ADJUSTING WASHER SIZE

Number [1]	In. (mm)
1	.071 (1.80)
2	.073 (1.85)
3	.075 (1.90)
4	.077 (1.95)
5	.079 (2.00)
6	.081 (2.05)

[1] - Number stamped on ear of adjusting washer.

5) Install in differential case 1 selected adjusting washer, thrust washer No. 1, thrust washer No. 2, side gear, clutch member thrust washer, and left-hand clutch member in order as named. Do not install clutch member springs at this time. Install right-hand clutch member with pinion gear.

6) Install in case cover other selected adjusting washer, thrust washer No. 1, thrust washer No. 2, side gear, and clutch member thrust washer. Assemble case and cover with "L" dimension measured parts and tighten bolts to 44-50 ft. lbs. (60-68 N.m).

7) Turn side gears with side gear shaft (after removal of snap ring from shaft) to make sure gears turn smoothly. Thrust washers must be changed if side gears do not turn smoothly. Remove cover from case and take out all internal parts. Wash differential case, cover, and case bolts with strong degreasing solvent, such as trichloroethylene.

TOYOTA INTEGRAL HOUSING (Cont.)

TOYOTA LIMITED SLIP DIFFERENTIAL ADJUSTING WASHER TABLE

Measurement "L" In. (mm)	REQUIRED ADJUSTING WASHERS FOR SPECIFIC DIFFERENTIAL CASE CODE				
	A	B	C	D	E
2.7917-2.7925 (70.91-70.93)	5 + 5	5 + 5	6 + 5	6 + 6	6 + 6
2.7929-2.7937 (70.94-70.96)	5 + 4	5 + 5	5 + 5	6 + 5	6 + 6
2.7941-2.7949 (70.97-70.99)	5 + 4	5 + 4	5 + 5	5 + 5	6 + 5
2.7953-2.7961 (71.00-71.02)	4 + 4	5 + 4	5 + 4	5 + 5	5 + 5
2.7965-2.7972 (71.03-71.05)	4 + 3	4 + 4	5 + 4	5 + 4	5 + 5
2.7976-2.7984 (71.06-71.08)	4 + 3	4 + 3	4 + 4	5 + 4	5 + 4
2.7988-2.7996 (71.09-71.11)	3 + 3	4 + 3	4 + 3	4 + 4	5 + 4
2.8000-2.8008 (71.12-71.14)	3 + 2	3 + 3	4 + 3	4 + 3	4 + 4
2.8012-2.8020 (71.15-71.17)	3 + 2	3 + 2	3 + 3	4 + 3	4 + 3
2.8024-2.8031 (71.18-71.20)	2 + 2	3 + 2	3 + 2	3 + 3	4 + 3
2.8035-2.8043 (71.21-71.23)	2 + 2	2 + 2	3 + 2	3 + 2	3 + 3
2.8047-2.8055 (71.24-71.26)	2 + 1	2 + 2	2 + 2	3 + 2	3 + 2
2.8059-2.8067 (71.27-71.29)	2 + 1	2 + 1	2 + 2	2 + 2	3 + 2
2.8071-2.8079 (71.30-71.32)	1 + 1	2 + 1	2 + 1	2 + 2	2 + 2

8) Coat internal parts with LSD hypoid oil. Install 1 adjusting washer into case with oil groove away from case. Install thrust washer No. 1, thrust washer No. 2, side gear, clutch member thrust washer (oil groove faces clutch member), left-hand clutch member, clutch member spring, and right-hand clutch member with pinion gears in case.

9) Install second adjusting washer in case cover with oil groove facing away from cover. Install thrust washer No. 1, thrust washer No. 2, side gear, and clutch member thrust washe. (with oil groove facing clutch member) in cover.

10) Place cover on case and align index marks. Apply locking compound to cover bolts. Tighten bolts evenly in diagonal sequence. Turn side gear with side gear shaft to ensure gears turn smoothly. Press side bearings onto differential case.

Drive Pinion Bearing Preload

1) Install front and rear bearing outer races into carrier. Press rear drive pinion bearing onto drive pinion with depth shim under bearing. Install drive pinion into carrier. Install front bearing.

NOTE: Drive pinion preload is set in 2 stages. Initial adjustment is made without spacer, oil slinger, or oil seal installed. Final adjustment is made after differential case is installed and ring and pinion backlash have been set.

2) Install drive pinion flange and lightly grease threads of pinion flange nut. Install flange nut and adjust drive pinion preload by slowly tightening nut. Measure preload with torque wrench. Preload range is 10.4-16.5 INCH lbs. (1.17-1.86 N.m) for new bearings and 5.2-8.7 INCH lbs. (.58-.98 N.m) for used bearings.

CAUTION: As there is no spacer installed at this time, tighten pinion nut slowly until desired preload is obtained. Be careful not to overtighten.

3) Install differential case and adjust ring gear-to-drive pinion backlash. *See Ring Gear Backlash & Side Bearing Preload procedure in this article.* Remove drive pinion flange and front bearing. Install new bearing spacer, front bearing, oil slinger, and oil seal. Install drive pinion flange and tighten pinion nut.

4) Check total differential preload. Range for total preload is measured drive pinion preload plus 3.5-5.2 INCH lbs. (.40-.59 N.m). Check that drive pinion flange longitudinal and latitudinal deviations do not exceed .004" (.10 mm). Stake drive pinion nut. Drive side gear shaft oil seal into carrier until flush.

5) Coat oil seal lips with grease and replace snap ring on side gear shaft. Drive side gear shaft in until it contacts pinion shaft. Measure side gear runout at flange with dial indicator. Replace side gear shaft if runout exceeds .008" (.20 mm). Install differential carrier cover with new gasket and tighten bolts.

NOTE: Since shaft cannot be checked visually on LSD models, ensure that shaft is seated by change in sound made by hammer blow after shaft bottoms out.

Ring Gear Backlash & Side Bearing Preload

1) Place bearing outer races on respective bearings and install differential case into carrier. Install plate washer only on back side of ring gear (behind teeth). Tap ring gear with plastic hammer to seat washer and bearing.

2) Install a dial indicator with plunger on tooth surface of ring gear. Apply downward pressure on side bearing boss. Measure ring gear-to-drive pinion backlash. Reference backlash should be .004" (.10 mm).

3) Select a ring gear (back side) plate washer using backlash as reference. Select a ring gear (tooth side) washer just thick enough to eliminate clearance between outer race and case. Remove plate washers and case from carrier.

4) Install plate washer into lower part of carrier. Place other plate washer on differential case with outer race. Install case assembly into carrier housing. Seat washer and bearing by tapping ring gear with plastic hammer. Measure ring gear backlash with dial indicator.

5) Backlash should be .005-.007" (.13-.18 mm). Adjust backlash by increasing or decreasing washers on both sides by equal amounts. There should be no

TOYOTA INTEGRAL HOUSING (Cont.)

clearance between plate washer and case. Ring gear backlash must exist at all times.

6) After adjustment of plate washers has been made, remove ring gear (tooth side) washer and measure thickness. Install washer .002-.004" (.05-.10 mm) thicker than washer removed.

NOTE: Select washer which can be pressed 2/3 of way in by finger.

7) Using a plastic hammer, tap washer in place. Recheck ring gear backlash. Backlash range is .005-.007" (.13-.18 mm). Adjust as necessary. Align index marks on caps and carrier. Install cap bolts and tighten to 51-65 ft. lbs. (69-88 N.m).

8) Measure total preload. Total preload must equal drive pinion preload plus 3.5-5.2 INCH lbs. (.39-.59 N.m). Coat 3 or 4 teeth at 3 different positions on ring gear with red lead.

9) Hold companion flange firmly and rotate ring gear in both directions. Inspect gear tooth contact pattern. Adjust as necessary by changing shims on drive pinion. *See GEAR TOOTH PATTERNS article at beginning of this section.*

AXLE ASSEMBLY SPECIFICATIONS

Application	In. (mm)
Stub Axle Flange Runout	.004 (.10)
Drive Pinion Flange Deviation	
Longitudinal	.004 (.10)
Latitudinal	.004 (.10)
Ring Gear Backlash	.005-.007 (.13-.18)
Ring Gear Runout	.003 (.07)
Side Gear Backlash	.002-.008 (.05-.20)
Side Gear Shaft Runout	.008 (.20)
	INCH Lbs. (N.m)
Drive Pinion Preload	
Celica	
New Bearings	8.7-13.9 (.9-1.6)
Used Bearings	4.3-6.9 (.5-.8)
Cressida & Supra	
New Bearings	10.4-16.5 (1.2-1.9)
Used Bearings	5.2-8.7 (.6-1.0)
Assembled Preload [1]	
Celica	2.7-4.3 (.3-.5)
Cressida & Supra	3.5-5.2(.04-.58)
Stub Axle Bearing Preload	.9-3.5 (.1-.4)

[1] – Add this amount to Drive Pinion Preload to obtain Total Preload which is sum of Drive Pinion Preload and Side Bearing Preload.

SEAL DEPTH

Application	In. (mm)
Drive Pinion Seal	
Celica & Supra	.08 (2.0)
Cressida	.06 (1.5)
Inner Stub Axle Seal	1.22 (31.0)
Outer Stub Axle Seal	.217 (5.5)
Side Gear Shaft Seal	Flush with Case

TIGHTENING SPECIFICATIONS

Application	Ft. Lbs. (N.m)
Stub Axle Flange Nut	58-144 (79-195)
Differential Carrier Bolts	51-72 (69-98)
Differential Support Member	
Mounting Bolt	51-72 (69-98)
Propeller Shaft Flange Bolts	44-57 (60-77)
Drive Pinion Flange Nut	80-174 (108-236)
Ring Gear Bolts	67-75 (91-102)
Side Bearing Cap Bolts	51-65 (69-88)

TOYOTA SEPARATE CARRIER

**Celica, Corolla, Cressida,
Land Cruiser, Pickup, Starlet,
& Tercel (Rear)**

NOTE: **Cab and chassis models will be referred to as C & C within this article.**

DESCRIPTION

The axle assembly is a hypoid gear type with a separate carrier housing. Limited slip differentials are available in Cressida and Land Cruiser models. One-piece differential cases use 2 pinion gears. Two-piece differential cases use 4 pinion gears.

Differential side bearing preload is set with adjusting nuts on all models. Pinion bearing preload can be set with either a solid spacer and adjusting shim or with a collapsible spacer.

AXLE RATIO & IDENTIFICATION

Toyota uses only 1 basic type of separate carrier axle assembly. Any differences in removal & installation or overhaul procedures between vehicle models will be noted where they occur. To determine axle ratio, divide number of ring gear teeth by number of pinion gear teeth.

REMOVAL & INSTALLATION

FRONT AXLE SHAFTS & BEARINGS

NOTE: **On vehicles equipped with locking hubs, refer to Locking Hubs article in this section. Ensure locking knob is set to "FREE" position before removal.**

Fig. 1: Exploded View of Front Axle Shaft Assembly (Land Cruiser and 4WD Pickup)

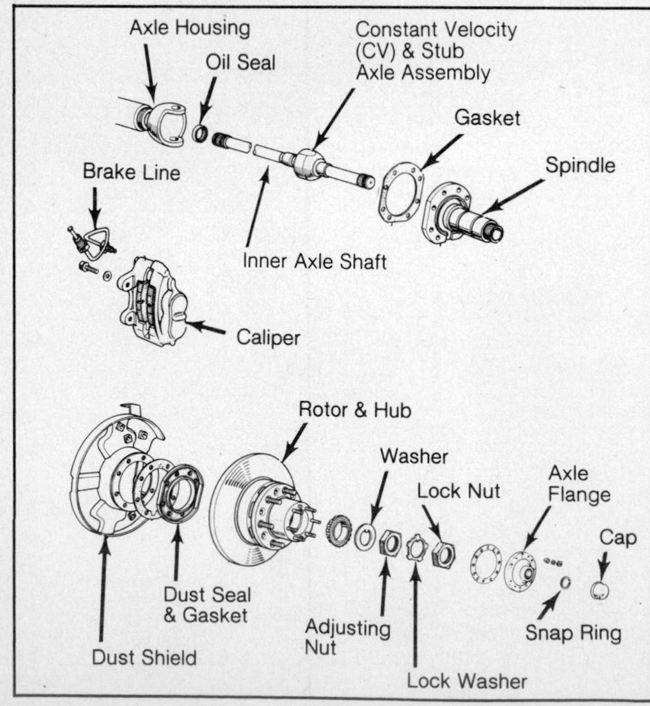
Axle Housing
Oil Seal
Constant Velocity (CV) & Stub Axle Assembly
Gasket
Spindle
Brake Line
Inner Axle Shaft
Caliper
Rotor & Hub
Washer
Lock Nut
Axle Flange
Cap
Dust Seal & Gasket
Adjusting Nut
Snap Ring
Dust Shield
Lock Washer

Removal (Land Cruiser and 4WD Pickup)

1) Raise and support vehicle. Remove wheel and tire assembly. Disconnect brake line at brake caliper and remove caliper assembly.

2) Remove dust cover and snap ring. *See Fig. 1.* Remove axle flange cone washers with punch. Install bolts in threaded flange holes and turn bolts equally to remove axle flange.

3) Release lock plate and remove outer lock nut. Remove lock plate and bearing adjusting nut. Remove outer bearing and thrust washer. Remove axle hub with disc.

4) To remove inner wheel bearing, pry out oil seal and remove bearing. Drive outer bearing races from hub if replacement is necessary.

5) Remove dust shield retaining bolts. Remove dust seal, gasket, and shield. Remove spindle assembly by tapping with a brass drift if necessary. Remove gasket.

6) Position 1 flat of constant velocity (CV) joint so it is pointing upward. Remove axle shaft assembly. Clean assembly with solvent.

NOTE: **Do not disconnect steering knuckle. Front end alignment and knuckle bearing preload settings will be affected and require readjustment.**

Installation

1) Install axle shaft with one flat of CV pointing upward. Pack steering knuckle cavity with molybdenum disulphide lithium base grease to about 3/4 of knuckle volume. Install spindle on knuckle with new gasket.

2) Put dust cover, new gasket, and dust seal on spindle. Tighten 8 spindle mounting bolts. Pack front hub bearings with multipurpose grease and coat inside of hub also. Place inner bearing in hub and drive oil seal into hub. Lightly coat lips of seal with grease.

3) Install axle hub on spindle. Install outer bearing and thrust washer. Torque adjusting nut to 43 ft. lbs. (58.3 N.m) with spanner (09607-60020). Rotate hub several times in each direction. Loosen adjusting nut until hand tight. Retighten adjusting nut to 35-60 INCH Lbs. (4-6.8 N.m).

4) Check starting preload with spring scale. If preload is within range of 6.2-12.6 lbs. (2.8-5.7 kg), install lock washer and lock nut. Tighten lock nut to 58-72 ft. lbs. (79-98 N.m) and secure by bending 1 tab of lock washer in and 1 tab out.

5) Place gasket on hub and install flange or locking hub. Install cone washers and nuts. Tighten nuts evenly. If using flange, pull stub axle shaft out of hub far enough to install snap ring. Drive dust cap onto flange.

REAR AXLE SHAFTS

NOTE: **Land Cruiser models with semi-floating rear axles require removal of axle housing inspection cover BEFORE attempting removal of axle shaft.**

Removal (Land Cruiser - Semi-Floating)

Raise and support vehicle. Remove tire, wheel, and brake drum. Drain axle housing and remove inspection cover. *See Fig. 2.* Remove differential pinion shaft lock pin. Remove pinion shaft and spacer. Push axle shaft to center of vehicle and remove axle lock circlip. Remove axle shaft, taking care not to damage bearing oil seal.

TOYOTA SEPARATE CARRIER (Cont.)

Fig. 2: Exploded View of Land Cruiser Rear Axle Shaft Assembly

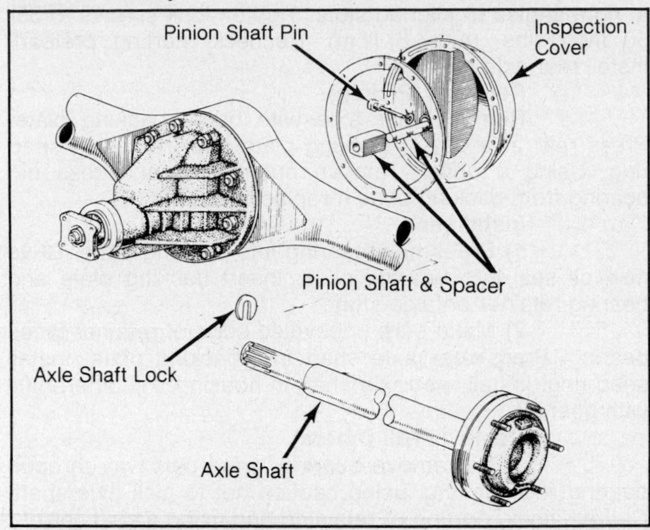

Pinion Shaft Pin
Inspection Cover
Pinion Shaft & Spacer
Axle Shaft Lock
Axle Shaft

Semi-floating axle shafts shown.

Installation

To install, reverse removal procedure. Check axle shaft end thrust clearance. Select pinion shaft spacer that gives clearance of .0024-.0183" (.060-.465 mm). Fill differential with hypoid gear oil. Use limited slip additive if equipped with limited slip differential.

Removal (Land Cruiser - Full Floating)

Remove axle flange nuts. Using punch, remove lock washer cones. Use bolts in threaded flange holes to remove axle shaft. Remove oil seal with puller.

Installation

To install, replace flange gasket and oil seal. Reverse removal procedure.

Removal (Pickup)

1) Raise and support vehicle. Remove tire and wheel. Drain differential housing. Remove parking brake cable guide clip and clamp bolt at crossmember and frame.

2) Disconnect parking brake cable from intermediate lever on 2WD models. On 4WD models, remove pin and disconnect parking brake rear cable from bellcrank. Disconnect and cap brake line at wheel cylinder. Remove brake drum mounting bolts and drum.

3) Remove 4 backing plate-to-axle housing nuts behind backing plate. Remove axle shaft and backing plate together. Avoid damaging oil seal in axle housing.

4) Remove axle shaft snap ring. Remove and discard "O" ring. Press out axle shaft from backing plate. Remove bearing retainer.

Fig. 3: Exploded View of Toyota 2-Pinion Rear Differential Assembly

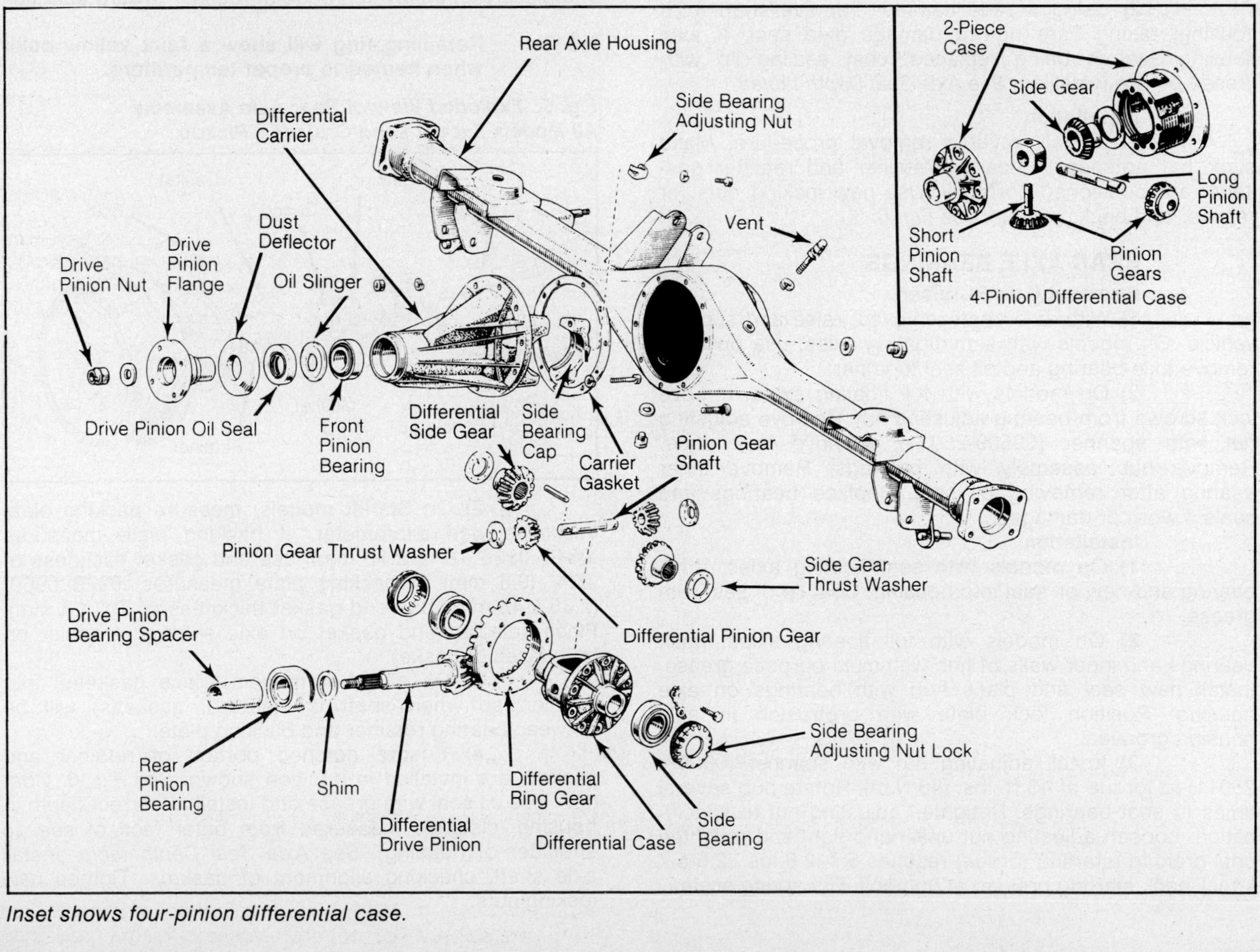

Inset shows four-pinion differential case.

TOYOTA SEPARATE CARRIER (Cont.)

Fig. 4: Exploded View of Pickup Rear Axle

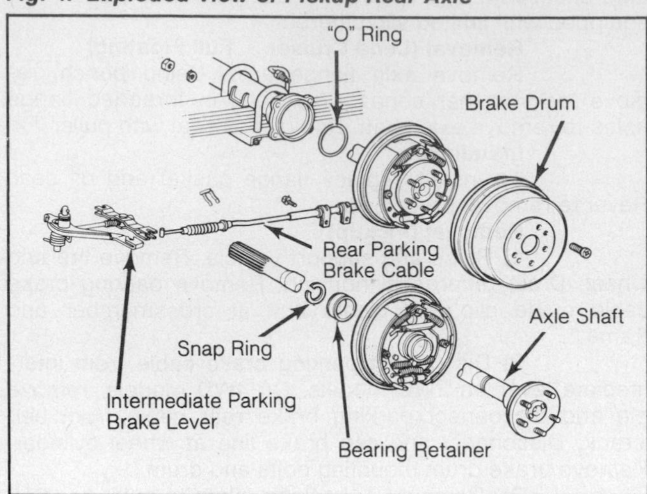
"O" Ring
Brake Drum
Rear Parking
Brake Cable
Axle Shaft
Snap Ring
Intermediate Parking
Brake Lever
Bearing Retainer

Installation

To install, reverse removal procedure. Install new "O" ring and fill differential with hypoid gear oil. Make sure bearing retainer is installed with flat unbeveled edge toward bearing.

Removal (All Others)

1) Raise and support vehicle. Remove tire, wheel, and brake drum. Working through hole in axle flange, remove bearing retainer-to-axle housing bolts.

2) Using a slide hammer, remove shaft from housing, taking care not to damage axle seal. If axle housing seal is being replaced, coat sealing lip with grease before installing. *See Axle Seal Depth table.*

Installation

To install, reverse removal procedure. Make sure that notches in bearing retainer and retainer gasket(s) are positioned correctly. Use new locking nuts for retainer and backing plate. *See Fig. 6.*

REAR AXLE BEARINGS

Removal (Land Cruiser)

1) With axle shaft removed, raise and support vehicle. On models with semi-floating axles, use puller to remove axle bearing and oil seal together.

2) On models with full floating axles, remove lock screws from bearing adjusting nut. Remove adjusting nut with spanner (09509-25011). Remove lock plate. Remove hub assembly with bearings. Remove inner bearing after removing oil seal. Replace bearings and seals if worn or damaged.

Installation

1) On models with semi-floating axles, drive bearing and new oil seal into housing. Coat lip of seal with grease.

2) On models with full floating axles, pack bearings and inner walls of hub with multi-purpose grease. Install new seal and place hub with bearings on axle housing. Position lock plate with protrusion in axle housing groove.

3) Install adjusting nut with spanner (09509-25011) to torque of 43 ft. lbs. (58 N.m). Rotate hub several times to seat bearings. Retighten adjusting nut to specification. Loosen adjusting nut until hand tight and retighten until preload (starting torque) reaches 5.7-l2.6 lbs. (2.6-5.7 kg.). Check starting preload at hub bolt with spring scale.

4) Align 1 axle housing slot with any 1 adjusting nut slot. Install lock screws into holes which are at right angles to aligned slots. Tighten lock screws to 35-60 INCH lbs. (4.0-6.8 N.m). Recheck starting preload. Install rear axle shaft.

Removal (Pickup)

Remove rear axle with brake backing plate. Press rear axle out of backing plate after removing snap ring. Using a puller, remove outer oil seal. Press old bearing from backing plate if replacing it.

Installation

1) Press new bearing into backing plate. Drive new oil seal into bearing case. Insert backing plate and bearing retainer on axle shaft.

2) Make sure unbeveled edge of retainer faces bearing. Press rear axle shaft into backing plate. Install snap ring. Install rear axle shaft in housing. Fill differential with gear oil.

Removal (All Others)

1) To remove bearing, grind part way through bearing retainer ring, using caution not to nick axle shaft. Cut remaining portion of retaining ring using a cold chisel.

2) Remove split retaining ring and press bearing off shaft. Remove spacer from shaft. Remove oil seal from axle housing with puller.

Installation

1) To install, place outer retainer and bearing onto shaft. Press bearing onto axle shaft. Heat new inner bearing retainer to about 300°F (150°C) in oil bath. Press into place with unbeveled edge of retainer toward bearing.

NOTE: **Retaining ring will show a faint yellow color when heated to proper temperature.**

Fig. 5: Exploded View of Rear Axle Assembly
All Models Except Land Cruiser & Pickup

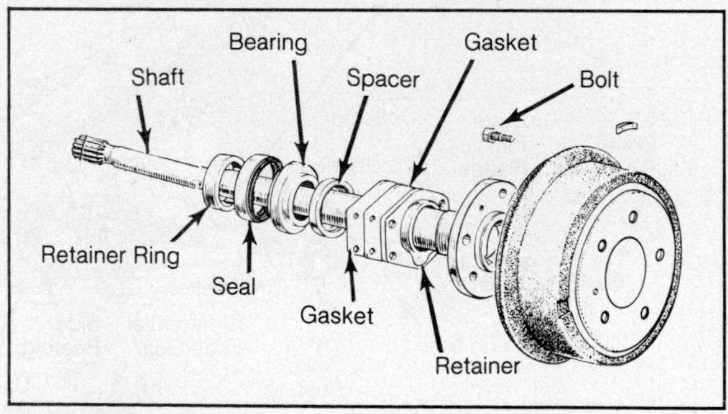
Bearing
Gasket
Shaft
Spacer
Bolt
Retainer Ring
Seal
Gasket
Retainer

2) On Starlet models, measure backing plate thickness with micrometer. If backing plate measures .0843-.0929" (2.14-2.36 mm), use end gasket thickness of .024" (0.6 mm). If backing plate measures .0929-.0969" (2.36-2.46 mm), use end gasket thickness of .01" (.3 mm). Place selected end gasket on axle shaft. Put sealer on both faces of gasket.

3) On all other models, place gasket(s) into position so when shaft is installed, gasket(s) will be between bearing retainer and backing plate.

4) Ensure notched portion of retainer and gaskets are installed in position shown. *See Fig. 6.* Coat new axle oil seal with grease and install to correct depth in housing (distance measured from outer face of seal to shoulder of housing). *See Axle Seal Depth table.* Install axle shaft, checking alignment of gaskets. Tighten new locking nuts.

TOYOTA SEPARATE CARRIER (Cont.)

Axle Seal Depth

Application	In. (mm)
Celica	.24 (6.0)
Corolla	
Sedan	.23 (5.9)
Wagon	.20 (5.0)
Cressida	.24 (6.0)
Starlet	.22 (5.6)
Tercel	.22 (5.6)

Fig. 6: Exploded View of Rear Axle Shaft

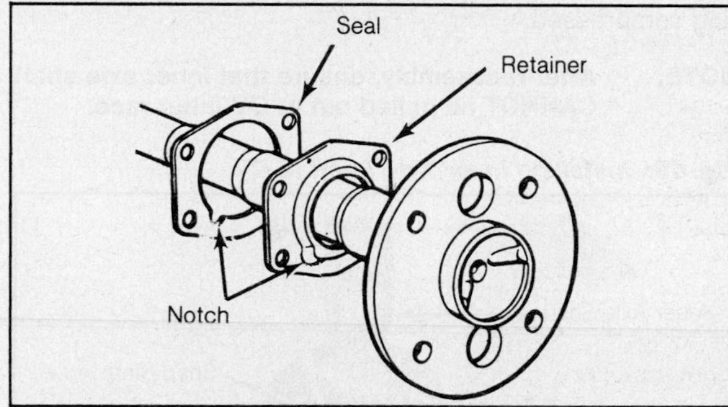
Seal
Retainer
Notch

Note notch in flange gasket.

PINION SEAL REPLACEMENT (ON VEHICLE)

Removal (Except Land Cruiser)

1) Index mark propeller shaft and drive pinion flange. Set parking brake. Disconnect and remove propeller shaft.

2) On Pickup models, measure and record total pinion preload with torque wrench attached to pinion flange nut. If preload is not within limits, adjust with shim before installing new seal. Measurement is made within backlash of drive pinion and ring gear. Axle shafts are locked by parking brake.

3) On all models, loosen staked portion of pinion shaft nut. Install holding tool to flange, and remove nut. Using flange puller, remove pinion flange. Remove oil seal using puller and remove oil slinger (plate washer on 4WD Pickup). Remove bearing with bearing puller. Remove collapsible spacer (rigid spacer and shim on C & C and 4WD Pickup models)

Fig. 7: Removing Drive Pinion Front Bearing

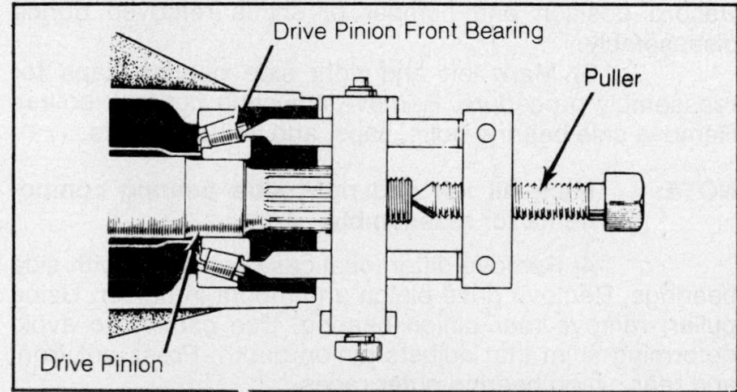
Drive Pinion Front Bearing
Puller
Drive Pinion

NOTE: Toyota recommends installing new spacer for Celica, Corolla, Cressida, 2WD Pickup, Starlet, and Tercel models whenever oil seal is replaced.

Installation (Pickup Models)

1) On C & C and 4WD Pickup models, install bearing spacer, shim(s), front bearing, and plate washer. Apply grease to seal lip and install to proper depth. *See Pinion Seal Depth table.* Install pinion flange. Install new nut after lightly greasing threads. Tighten nut to 123-151 ft. lbs. (167-205 N.m) while holding the pinion flange stationary.

2) Rotate pinion several times to seat bearing. Measure preload of backlash (starting torque). If preload is incorrect, adjusting shim(s) must be changed. Stake pinion flange nut with punch when adjustments are complete.

3) On 2WD models, install new bearing spacer, front bearing, and oil slinger. Drive new oil seal to correct depth after lightly greasing seal edges. *See Pinion Seal Depth table.* Install pinion flange. Coat threads of new nut with grease and torque to 80 ft. lbs. (108 N.m) while holding pinion flange. Turn flange several times to seat bearing.

4) Using torque wrench, measure preload of backlash. If preload is insufficient, gradually tighten nut in increments of 5-10°, until preload is obtained. If maximum torque value of 173 ft. lbs. (234 N.m) is exceeded, replace spacer and repeat procedure. If preload is exceeded, replace bearing spacer.

5) Complete installation by reversing removal procedure. Add lubricant as required.

Installation (All Others)

1) Install spacer, bearing, and oil slinger. Apply grease to seal lip and install to proper depth in housing. *See Pinion Seal Depth table.* Using plastic hammer, install pinion flange. Install new nut and tighten to specified torque.

2) Rotate pinion in both directions to seat bearing. Measure bearing preload. If preload is excessive, replace spacer and repeat procedure.

3) If preload is insufficient, gradually tighten nut in increments of 5-10° until preload is obtained. If preload is exceeded, replace spacer and repeat procedure. Complete installation by reversing removal procedure. Add lubricant if required.

PINION SEAL DEPTH

Application	In. (mm)
Celica	.08 (2.0)
Corolla	0-.02 (0-0.5)
Cressida	.24 (6.0)
Pickup	
2WD	.06 (1.5)
C & C and 4WD	.04 (1.0)
Starlet	.04 (1.0)
Tercel	.04 (1.0)

DIFFERENTIAL CARRIER

Removal

Drain oil from axle housing. Remove wheels. Index propeller shaft to pinion flange and remove propeller shaft. Remove axle shafts as previously described. Loosen bolts and remove differential carrier.

NOTE: Do not damage oil seal during removal of axle shaft if seal is not to be replaced.

Drive Axles

TOYOTA SEPARATE CARRIER (Cont.)

Installation

To install, reverse removal procedure, noting following. Coat both sides of carrier-to-housing gasket with sealer before installation. Fill axle housing with gear oil. Use limited slip additive on models with limited slip differentials.

OVERHAUL

FRONT AXLE SHAFT & SPINDLE

Disassembly (Land Cruiser & 4WD Pickup)

1) Mount spindle in vise. Remove bushing with puller. Install new bushing with press. Inspect axle shaft for wear or damage. Carefully inspect constant velocity (CV) joint for rust, dirt, or excessive looseness.

Fig. 8: Removing & Installing CV Cage & Inner Race

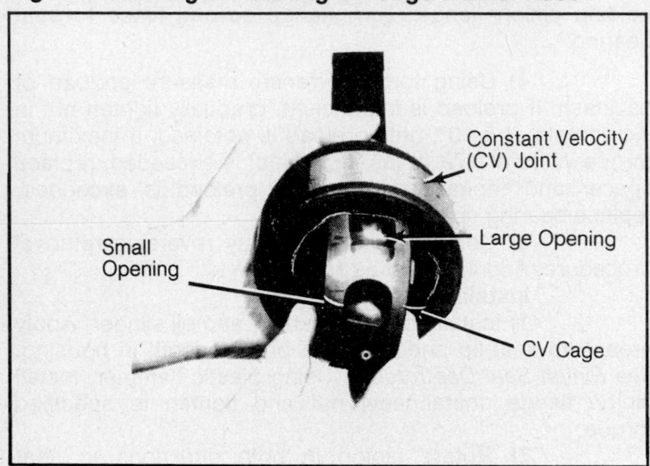
Constant Velocity
(CV) Joint
Large Opening
Small
Opening
CV Cage

2) Mount inner axle shaft in a vise with CV pointing upward. Place a brass drift against CV inner race and drive CV off inner shaft. Do not allow CV to drop.

3) Remove snap rings from inner axle shaft. Tilt cage and inner race outward from housing. Remove 6 ball bearings one at a time.

4) Turn cage and inner race 90° from outer CV race. Align 2 larger openings of cage with 2 protrusions of outer CV race. Remove inner race and cage. Separate by turning inner race perpendicular to large cage openings and pulling out.

Fig. 9: Exploded View of CV Cage & Inner Race

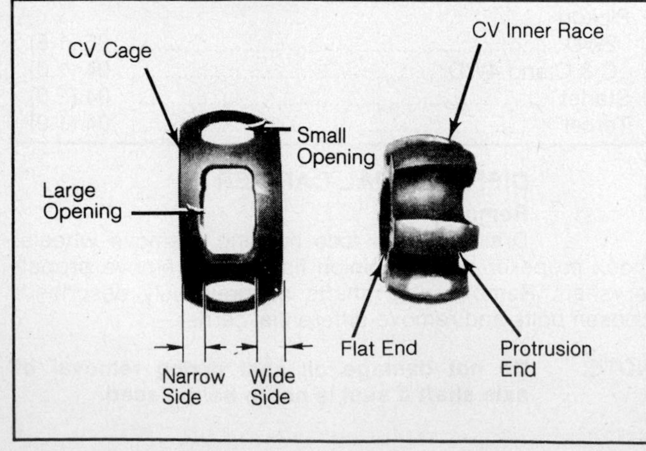
CV Cage
CV Inner Race
Small
Opening
Large
Opening
Flat End
Protrusion
End
Narrow
Side
Wide
Side

Reassembly

1) Coat inner race, cage, and balls with molybdenum disulphide lithium base grease. Reverse disassembly procedure. Make sure protruding end of inner race is covered by wide portion of cage during reassembly.

2) When installing inner race and cage into outer race, wide side of cage must face outward. Fit 6 balls into cage. After reassembly, pack stub axle end with lithium base grease.

3) Install new snap rings on axle shaft. Insert inner axle shaft into CV inner race, keeping inner snap ring compressed.

NOTE: **After reassembly, ensure that inner axle shaft CANNOT be pulled out of CV inner race.**

Fig. 10: Installing Inner Axle Shaft to CV

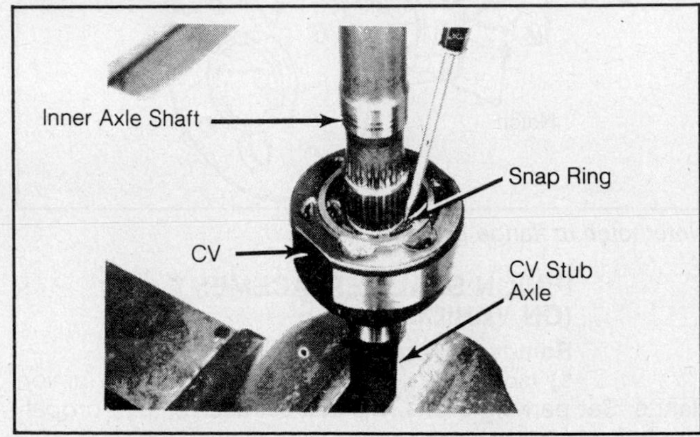
Inner Axle Shaft
Snap Ring
CV
CV Stub
Axle

DIFFERENTIAL

NOTE: **4WD front differentials are overhauled using same procedures as those described for rear differentials.**

Case Disassembly (Conventional)

1) Mount carrier in holding fixture. Before disassembling differential, check tooth contact pattern, ring gear runout (measured at back of gear in 4 places), ring gear-to-drive pinion backlash, and total preload. Record readings.

2) Loosen staked portion of pinion shaft nut. Install holder and remove nut. Using flange puller, remove pinion flange. Remove oil seal, bearing, and slinger. Record position and number of shims removed during disassembly.

3) Mark left and right side bearing caps for reassembly procedure. Remove adjusting nut lock bolt(s). Remove side bearing bolts, caps, and adjusting nuts.

NOTE: **Mark all left and right side bearing components for reassembly.**

4) Remove differential case assembly with side bearings. Remove drive pinion and mount in holder. Using puller, remove rear pinion bearing. Use caution to avoid deforming shim that adjusts pinion depth. Press out front and rear pinion bearing outer races.

5) Remove side bearings from differential case. Index ring gear to case. Straighten ring gear bolt lock plates. Remove bolts. Mount case assembly in vise so ring gear teeth are pointed down.

TOYOTA SEPARATE CARRIER (Cont.)

Fig. 11: Removing Differential Case

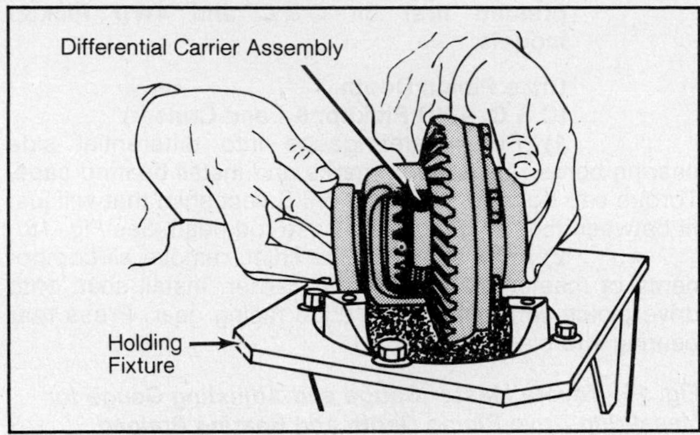
Differential Carrier Assembly
Holding Fixture

Mark all components for reassembly.

6) Tap ring gear from case using a soft faced hammer. On 2-pinion differentials, remove pinion gear shaft retaining pin, and drive out gear shaft. Remove pinion gears, side gears, and thrust washers.

7) On 4-pinion differentials, index differential case cover to case. Remove cover attaching bolts. Drive out 3 pinion shafts. Remove pinion gears, pinion shaft holder, side gears, and thrust washer(s).

NOTE: **Three longer differential cover bolts are used to secure pinion shafts in 4-pinion differentials.**

Fig. 12: Removing Rear Pinion Bearing

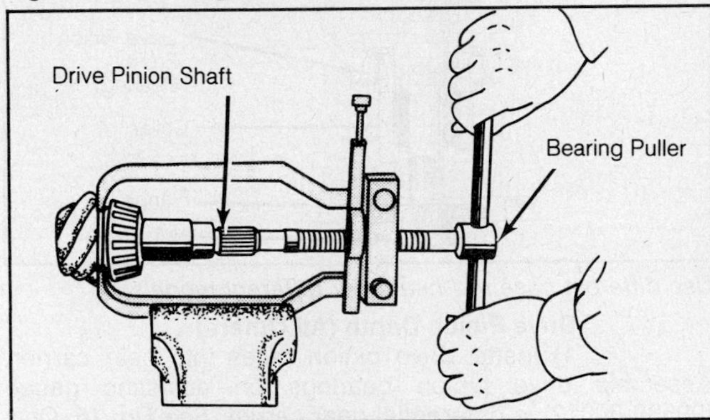
Drive Pinion Shaft
Bearing Puller

Do not allow pinion gear to fall from puller.

Case Reassembly

1) Lubricate all components with hypoid gear lubricant. On 2-pinion models, assemble side gears and pinion gears into differential case. Make sure oil groove, if present on side gear thrust washer, faces toward gear.

2) On 4-pinion models, install side gears, thrust washers, differential pinions, pinion shaft holder, differential shaft, and pinion shaft. Install differential case cover, aligning index marks, and tighten bolts. Note location of 3 longer bolts (pinion shaft bolts).

3) Check backlash between side gears and pinion gears. If not within specifications, install selective fit thrust washers. Install equal thickness thrust washers on each side, if possible.

4) Press differential side bearings onto differential case. Heat ring gear in oil bath to approximately 212°F (100°C). Wipe off gear and press onto differential case.

Fig. 13: Installing Side Bearing On Differential Case

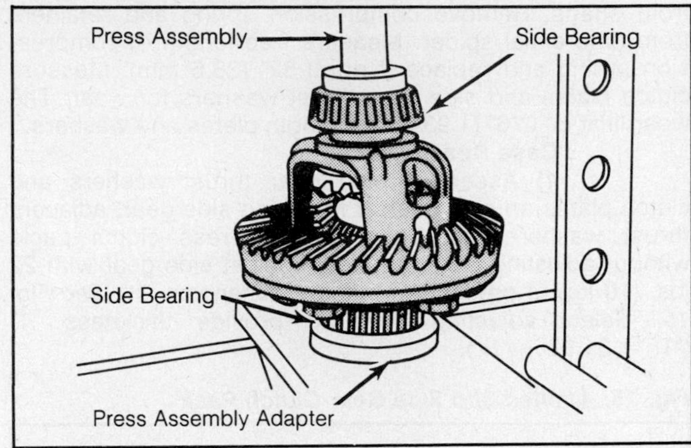
Press Assembly
Side Bearing
Side Bearing
Press Assembly Adapter

Oil groove on side gear thrust washer must face gear.

5) Fit bolts, tighten evenly, and bend over lock tabs. Install differential case assembly on differential carrier. Measure ring gear runout. If runout exceeds specifications, remount ring gear 180° from original position on differential case.

6) If this fails to bring ring gear into specifications, remove ring gear from case, and examine case runout. If case runout is within range specified for ring gear, ring gear is at fault, and should be replaced. Remove ring gear and case assembly from carrier.

Case Disassembly (Limited Slip)

1) Index mark left and right case halves for reassembly. Loosen through bolts in diagonal sequence. Open case and remove side gears with thrust washers, clutch plates, and adjusting plates. Keep left and right side components separate and mark for reassembly in same order. *See Fig. 14*.

Fig. 14: Exploded View of Limited Slip Differential

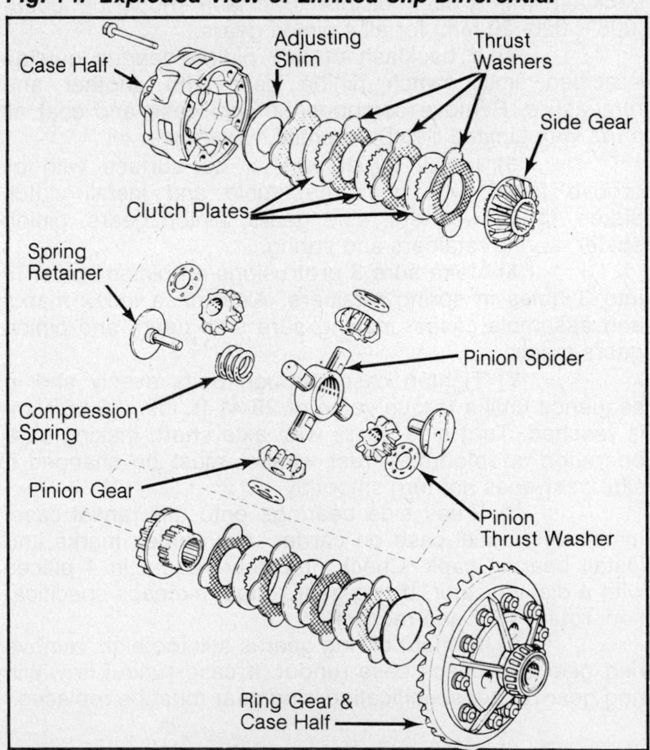
Case Half
Adjusting Shim
Thrust Washers
Side Gear
Clutch Plates
Spring Retainer
Pinion Spider
Compression Spring
Pinion Gear
Pinion Thrust Washer
Ring Gear & Case Half

2) Remove pinion gears and thrust washers from shafts. Remove compression spring and retainers from differential spider. Measure free length of compression spring and replace if not 1.52" (38.6 mm). Measure clutch plates and side gear thrust washers for wear. The wear limit is .076" (1.93 mm) for both plates and washers.

Case Reassembly

1) Assemble side gear thrust washers and clutch plates on side gear. If replacing side gear, adjacent thrust washer must be replaced. Press clutch pack, without adjusting shim in place, against side gear with 22 lbs. (10 kg) of pressure. Measure dimension "H". *See Fig. 15.* Select adjusting shim to provide thickness "T" ("T" = 31.02 – "H").

Fig. 15: Limited Slip Side Gear Clutch Pack

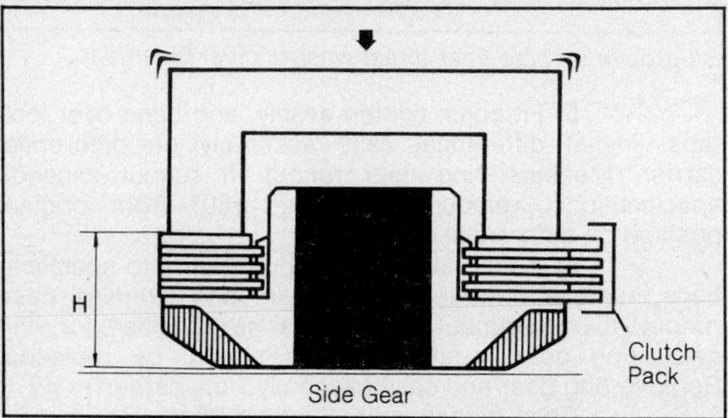
H
Clutch
Pack
Side Gear

Assemble clutch pack without adjusting shim.

2) Install side gear with clutch plates, thrust washers, and adjusting shim into differential case. Install pinion spider with pinion gears, thrust washers, spring retainers, and spring.

3) Holding side gear and applying pressure against spring retainer, measure pinion gear-to-side gear backlash with a dial indicator. Backlash should be .0008-.008" (.020-.20 mm) for all 4 pinion gears.

4) If backlash of any pinion gear is outside specified limit, switch pinion gear with another and remeasure. Remove components from case and coat all parts with Limited Slip Differential hypoid gear oil.

5) Install thrust washer so surface with oil groove faces side gear. Assemble and install clutch plates, thrust washers, side gears, pinion gears, pinion spider, spring retainers and spring.

6) Make sure 3 protrusions on pinion spider fit into 3 holes in spring retainers. Align case index marks and assemble cases, making sure side gears and pinion gears mesh.

7) Tighten case through bolts evenly and in sequence until a torque value of 29-41 ft. lbs. (39-56 N.m) is reached. Turn side gears with axle shaft, making sure operation is smooth. Thrust washer must be changed if side gear does not turn smoothly.

8) Press side bearings onto differential case. Install differential case on carrier. Align index marks and install bearing caps. Check ring gear runout in 4 places with a dial indicator. If ring gear runout exceeds specification, rotate 180° and recheck.

9) If runout of ring gear is still too high, remove ring gear and check case runout. If case runout is within ring gear runout specification, ring gear must be replaced.

NOTE: Toyota recommends adjusting pinion bearing preload first on C & C and 4WD Pickup models.

Drive Pinion Depth
(C & C, 4WD Pickup, & Land Cruiser)

1) Put master gauge into differential side bearing bores. Align index marks and install bearing caps. Torque cap bolts to specification. Select shim that will just fit between master gauge and base rod head. *See Fig. 16.*

2) After selecting the shim, remove all components of master gauge kit from carrier. Install shim onto drive pinion with chamfered edge facing gear. Press rear bearing into place.

Fig. 16: Toyota Master Gauge and Adjusting Gauge for Measuring Drive Pinion Depth and Bearing Preload

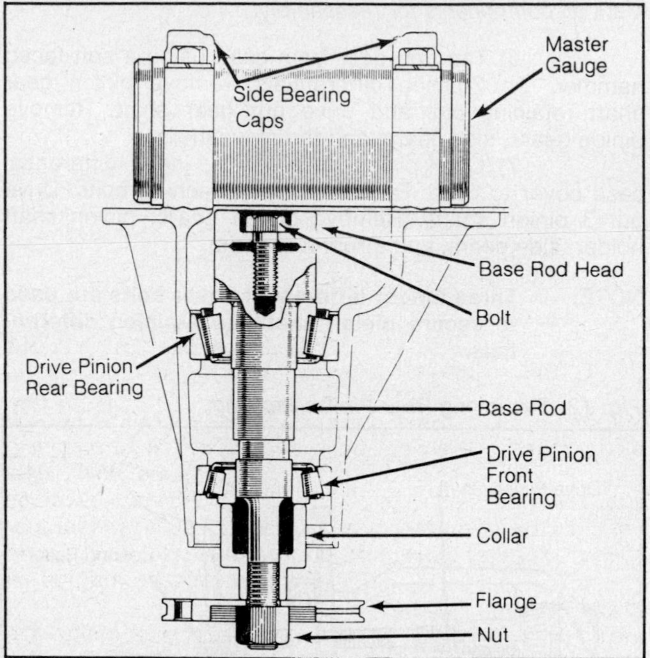
Master
Gauge
Side Bearing
Caps
Base Rod Head
Bolt
Drive Pinion
Rear Bearing
Base Rod
Drive Pinion
Front
Bearing
Collar
Flange
Nut

Use different base rod heads for different models.

Drive Pinion Depth (All Others)

1) Install drive pinion races into gear carrier. Assemble drive pinion bearings on adjusting gauge (09530-30012) in differential gear carrier. *See Fig. 16.* Only tighten bolt of gauge until drive pinion has no play.

2) Place master gauge in differential side bearing bores. Align index marks and install caps. Torque cap bolts. Select depth adjusting shim that will just fit between master gauge and base rod head. Remove special tools.

3) Press selected depth adjusting shim and rear bearing onto drive pinion. Chamfered side of shim faces toward gear.

Pinion Bearing Preload
(C & C, 4WD Pickup, & Land Cruiser)

1) Install drive pinion bearings, spacer, shim, and adjusting gauge (09530-30012) in differential carrier. *See Fig. 16.* Do not install drive pinion depth adjusting shim at this time. Hold collar and tighten pinion flange nut to specification.

2) Measure drive pinion preload with torque wrench. *See Pinion Bearing Preload table.* If preload is

TOYOTA SEPARATE CARRIER (Cont.)

incorrect, change by increasing or decreasing number of shims between front bearing and spacer.

3) Starting preload for new bearings will be higher than starting preload for used bearings. Check pinion flange deviation with a dial indicator. If longitudinal or latitudinal deviation is more than .004" (.10 mm), bearings must be checked. Stake drive pinion nut.

PINION BEARING PRELOAD [1]

Application	INCH Lbs. (N.m)
Celica & Corolla	
New Bearings	8.7-13.9 (1.0-1.6)
Used Bearings	4.3-6.9 (.5-.8)
Cressida	
New Bearings	13.9-19.1 (1.6-2.2)
Used Bearings	6.9-9.5 (.8-1.1)
Pickup (C & C & 4WD) & Land Cruiser	
New Bearings	16.5-22.6 (1.9-2.6)
Used Bearings	7.8-11.3 (.9-1.3)
Pickup (2WD)	
New Bearings	10.4-16.5 (1.2-1.9)
Used Bearings	5.2-8.7 (.6-1.0)
Starlet & Tercel	
New Bearings	5.6-10.9 (.6-1.2)
Used Bearings	3.5-6.1 (.4-.7)

[1] – Record torque reading.

Pinion Bearing Preload (All Others)

1) Install drive pinion with rear bearing and depth shim into differential carrier. Install new bearing spacer, front bearing, and oil slinger onto drive pinion shaft.

2) Drive lightly greased new oil seal to proper depth in gear carrier. *See Pinion Seal Depth table.* Install pinion flange and new nut with light coat of grease on threads. Hold flange and torque nut to 80 ft. lbs. (108 N.m). Rotate flange to seat bearings.

3) Using a torque wrench, measure pinion bearing preload. Starting preload for new bearings is higher than starting preload for used bearings. *See Pinion Bearing Preload table.* If preload is too high, replace spacer and repeat procedure.

4) If preload is too low, tighten nut 5-10° at a time until preload is reached. If maximum torque on nut of 173 ft. lbs. (234 N.m) is exceeded, replace spacer and repeat procedure. Do not back off nut to reduce preload.

5) Check pinion flange deviation with a dial indicator. If longitudinal or latitudinal deviation is more than .004" (.10 mm), bearings must be checked. Stake drive pinion nut.

Backlash & Side Bearing Play

1) Place side bearing outer races on their respective bearings. Install differential assembly into carrier and fit adjusting nuts. Make sure adjusting nuts are threaded properly. Put bearing caps on in original position as marked. Make sure there is some backlash between drive pinion and ring gear.

2) Thread bolts in 2 or 3 turns and press down on bearing cap by hand. If cap does not fit tightly to carrier face, adjusting nuts are not threaded correctly. Reinstall adjusting nuts if necessary.

3) Install dial indicator so plunger touches face of ring gear tooth at 90°. Tighten bearing cap bolts until spring washers are slightly compressed. Using spanner (09504-00010), tighten adjusting nut on ring gear side of differential case. Stop when ring gear backlash of .008" (.2 mm) is reached.

4) Tighten adjusting nut on drive pinion side of carrier. If ring gear backlash increases, loosen nut until additional backlash is gone. Place dial indicator against bearing cap on ring gear side so that sideways movement can be measured.

5) Tighten adjusting nut on drive pinion side until dial indicator just starts to move. This point is zero preload on the side bearing. Tighten adjusting nut another l-1.5 notches past zero preload point. Remount dial indicator at 90° to ring gear tooth.

6) Set ring gear backlash by turning left and right adjusting nuts by the same amount. Maintain the preload by turning one nut in while turning the other out by the same distance. When backlash measures .0051-.0071" (.13-.18 mm), torque bearing cap bolts to 51-65 ft. lbs. (69-88 N.m). Recheck ring gear backlash.

7) Measure total preload of ring gear and drive pinion. Starting torque should be greater than measured preload of drive pinion alone. Different models have different amounts of additional preload. *See Additional Bearing Preload Torque table.* Select proper adjusting nut lock (1 or 2 teeth) and install lock on each bearing cap.

ADDITIONAL BEARING PRELOAD TORQUE [1]

Application	INCH Lbs. (N.m)
Celica	2.6-4.3 (.3-.5)
Corolla, Starlet, & Tercel	1.7-3.5 (.2-.4)
Cressida, Land Cruiser, & Pickup	3.5-5.2 (.4-.6)

[1] – Add this amount to measurement recorded when setting drive pinion preload.

Fig. 17: Measuring Ring Gear Backlash

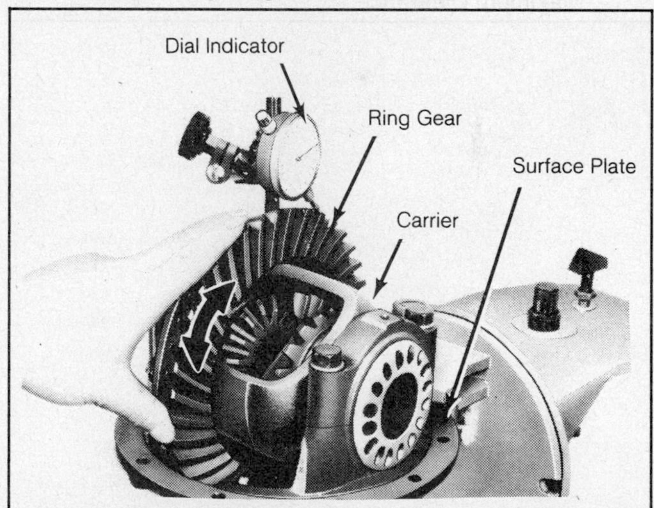
Dial Indicator
Ring Gear
Surface Plate
Carrier

Drive Axles

TOYOTA SEPARATE CARRIER (Cont.)

AXLE ASSEMBLY SPECIFICATIONS

Application	In. (mm)
Side Gear-to-Pinion Gear Backlash	
Corolla	.0008-.008 (.020-.20)
Land Cruiser	
Conventional	.0008-.008 (.020-.20)
Limited Slip	.0008-.009 (.020-.24)
Starlet & Tercel	.0008-.006 (.020-.15)
All Others	.002-.008 (.05-.20)
Drive Pinion-to-Ring Gear Backlash	
Land Cruiser	.006-.008 (.15-.20)
Starlet & Tercel	.004-.006 (.10-.15)
All Others	.005-.007 (.13-.18)
Ring Gear Backface Runout [1]	
Land Cruiser	.004 (.10)
Pickup	
2WD	.003 (.07)
C & C & 4WD	.004 (.10)
All Others	.003 (.07)
Drive Pinion Flange Deviation (All Models)	
Longitudinal & Latitudinal	.004 (.10)
Axle Shaft Runout	
Celica & Cressida	.059 (1.50)
Corolla, Pickup (All), Starlet, & Tercel	.079 (2.00)
Axle Shaft Flange Runout	
Celica & Cressida	.004 (0.10)
All Others	.008 (0.20)
	Lbs. (kg)
Axle Hub Preload Starting Torque	
Land Cruiser (Rear)	5.7-12.6 (2.6-5.7)
Land Cruiser & Pickup Front	6.2-12.6 (2.9-5.7)

[1] – Maximum Clearance.

TIGHTENING SPECIFICATIONS

Application	Ft. Lbs. (N.m)
Drive Pinion Flange Nut	
Celica, Corolla, & Cressida	80-174 (109-236)
Land Cruiser	145-174 (197-236)
Pickup	
2WD	80-174 (109-236)
C & C & 4WD	123-152 (167-207)
Starlet & Tercel	69-144 (93-195)
Differential Bearing Cap Bolts	
Celica, Cressida, & Pickup	51-65 (69-88)
Corolla	36-51 (49-69)
Land Cruiser	65-80 (88-109)
Starlet & Tercel	40-47 (54-64)
Ring Gear-to-Case Bolts	
Celica & Cressida, Pickup (All) Starlet, & Tercel	65-76 (88-103)
Corolla	51-58 (69-79)
Land Cruiser	76-87 (103-118)
Carrier-to-Axle Housing	
Pickup (All)	14-22 (19-30)
Axle Retainer Flange Bolts	
Celica, Corolla, Cressida Starlet, & Tercel	43-54 (58-73)
Land Cruiser (Rear)	21-25 (29-34)
Land Cruiser (Front)	29-39 (39-53)
Pickup (All)	44-57 (60-77)
Adjusting Nut Lock Plates	
Starlet & Tercel	3-5 (4-7)
All Others	8-11 (11-15)
Differential Case Through Bolts	
Corolla	21-25 (29-34)
Land Cruiser (LSD)	29-41 (39-56)
Front Spindle Bolts [1]	29-39 (39-53)
Front Hub-to-Flange [1]	20-25 (27-34)
Bearing Adjusting Nut [1]	3-5 (4-7)
Wheel Nuts [1]	65-87 (88-118)

[1] – Pickup 4WD & Land Cruiser.

VOLVO

DL, GL, Turbo, & 760 GLE

DESCRIPTION

Axle shafts are semi-floating. Axle shaft outer bearings are pressed onto shafts and attached to axle housing by outer retainers. Axle shaft bearing clearance is not adjustable and is determined by bearing design.

Hypoid type drive pinion and ring gear set uses a 2-pinion differential with a 1-piece case. Limited slip differential is available. Limited slip cases are of 2-piece design and use 4 pinion gears mounted on a spider. Differential adjustments are made with shims.

AXLE RATIO & IDENTIFICATION

Standard (Type 1030) and heavy-duty (Type 1031) rear axles are available. Several different ratios are used. Plate attached to left front side of final drive housing gives axle ratio, part number, and serial number. Divide number of ring gear teeth by number of drive pinion gear teeth to determine axle ratio.

REMOVAL & INSTALLATION

AXLE SHAFTS & BEARINGS

NOTE: **Although axle shaft bearing end play is not adjustable, it should be checked prior to disassembly.**

Checking Procedure

1) Raise vehicle and remove rear wheel. Remove brake pads. Put steel ball in center hole of axle shaft, using small amount of grease to hold ball in place. Mount dial indicator with plunger tip against steel ball, using tip with flat surface. Plunger must be at 90° to axle flange.

2) Rotate axle shaft at least 1 full revolution in each direction. Measure total end play. If end play exceeds specification, check axle bearing, axle housing, and outer retainer for wear or damage.

Removal

1) Remove rear wheels and collision guards, if equipped. Disconnect brake line and bracket from axle housing. Remove caliper and support to side with wire, being careful not to damage brake line. Make sure parking brake is fully released.

2) Remove brake rotor set screws. Take off rotors, tapping with soft mallet if necessary. Remove parking brake shoes, unhooking retaining springs. Disconnect parking brake cables by driving out lock pin at lever.

3) Remove bolts for bearing retainer through holes in axle flange. Remove axle shaft using puller. Pry inner seal from housing. Press bearing and snap ring off axle shaft. Remove oil seal.

Installation

1) Pack new bearing and new seal lip groove with high temperature wheel bearing grease. Place bearing retainer and oil seal on axle shaft. Press new bearing and new snap ring onto axle shaft. Always use a new snap ring. Narrow side of taper fits into axle housing.

2) Clean axle housing and drive in new inner seal. Install axle shaft and tighten bearing retainer bolts. Install parking brake shoes and reconnect cables. Install rotors and tighten set screws.

3) Check parking brake adjustment. Install brake caliper, pads, and collision guard, if used. Reconnect brake line and bracket to axle housing. Install wheels and tighten lug nuts.

PINION FLANGES & SEAL

Removal

1) Disconnect propeller shaft at pinion flange. Check drive pinion and bearings for excessive play. Before new seal is installed, final drive must be removed and repaired if loose or rough.

2) Remove flange nut from drive pinion while holding flange. Remove flange using puller. Remove old oil seal and dust shield.

Installation

1) Drive new seal into housing after packing seal spring and lips with grease. Unless packed, seal spring could jump out of position. Press flange onto drive pinion.

2) Install flange washer and nut and tighten to proper torque specification. There are 3 different nuts used and torque ratings differ. Reconnect propeller shaft to drive pinion flange.

AXLE ASSEMBLY

NOTE: **On models equipped with limited slip differential (LSD), rotational friction of LSD must be checked with axle assembly in vehicle.**

Checking Procedure

Raise 1 rear wheel and block opposite side. Place transmission in neutral and release parking brake. Remove raised wheel. Attach torque wrench to axle flange. Rotate axle flange and measure friction torque of LSD. If rotational friction is below minimum specification, friction discs and plates in LSD must be replaced.

Removal

1) Raise vehicle and remove wheels. Remove intermediate exhaust pipe. Loosen trailing arm retaining bolts so arms can pivot at front ends. Remove stabilizer bar and track (Panhard) rod. Remove collision guards, if used.

2) Disconnect ventilation hose from axle housing. Disconnect brake line brackets from axle housing. Remove calipers and hang on springs, being careful not to damage lines. Fully release parking brake and remove rotors. Remove parking brake shoes and disconnect cables from levers.

3) Disconnect propeller shaft from pinion flange. Disconnect parking brake cables from axle housing. Only remove plastic tube if axle housing is being replaced. Disconnect reaction rods at axle housing. Support axle assembly securely with transmission jack.

4) Compress springs and disconnect shock absorbers at upper mounts. Remove spring compressors. Remove bolts holding axle housing to trailing arms. Lower and remove axle assembly.

Installation

1) Move axle assembly under vehicle on transmission jack and raise into position. Connect trailing arms with stabilizer bar brackets to axle housing, leaving bolts finger tight. Compress springs and connect shock absorbers to upper mounts. Release springs.

2) Remove transmission jack. Connect reaction rods to axle housing, leaving bolts finger tight. Attach parking brake cables to axle housing. Attach propeller shaft to pinion flange. Connect parking brake cables to levers and install parking brake shoes.

3) Install rotors and check parking brake adjustment. Install calipers and attach brake line brackets to axle housing. Attach ventilation hose to axle housing. Install collision guards, if used. Connect Panhard rod and stabilizer bar to axle housing and trailing arms, leaving bolts finger tight.

4) Install wheels and tighten lug nuts. Lower and rock vehicle to settle suspension. With full weight of vehicle on suspension, tighten bolts on trailing arms, reaction rods, Panhard rod, and stabilizer bar.

OVERHAUL

DISASSEMBLY

Drive Pinion & Carrier

1) Support axle assembly with pinion flange down and bottom of housing toward work stand. Remove axle shafts and inner seals. Remove inspection cover.

2) If final drive is being reconditioned because of noise, run a tooth contact pattern check before disassembly as this may assist in locating fault.

Fig. 1: Exploded View of Volvo Drive Axle Assembly

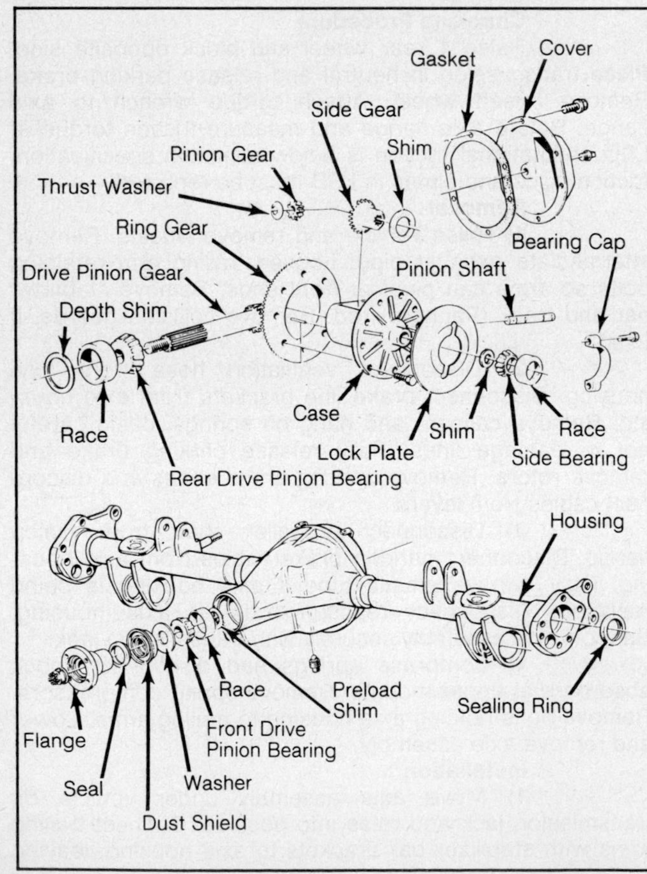
Gasket
Cover
Side Gear
Shim
Pinion Gear
Thrust Washer
Ring Gear
Bearing Cap
Drive Pinion Gear
Pinion Shaft
Depth Shim
Race
Case
Shim
Race
Lock Plate
Side Bearing
Rear Drive Pinion Bearing
Housing
Race
Preload Shim
Sealing Ring
Front Drive Pinion Bearing
Flange
Seal
Washer
Dust Shield

3) Check alignment markings on side bearing caps and carrier. Index caps to carrier for reassembly if necessary. Remove side bearing caps. Attach differential housing spreader (2394 and 2601) to carrier housing. Align pins on spreader with holes in housing and screw retainer bolts into housing.

4) Tighten tensioning screw until spreader fits snugly in housing. Slowly tighten tensioning screw until differential case assembly can be removed from carrier. Do not tighten screw more than 3.5 turns. Carefully pry differential assembly out of carrier.

CAUTION: Excessive or prolonged tension by spreader can distort carrier housing.

5) Remove spreader tool from housing. Turn axle assembly over and drain oil. Remove drive pinion flange nut, holding flange. Remove flange, using puller. Force drive pinion from carrier housing using a plastic hammer. Hold drive pinion with free hand to avoid damage.

6) Drive out front drive pinion bearing, with seal and washer, from back of housing. Drive out rear drive pinion bearing race from front of housing. Press rear drive pinion bearing off drive pinion or use puller (5215 on Type l030 axle assembly or 5216 and 5214 on Type 1031 axle assembly).

Case Assembly - Limited Slip

1) Remove side bearings with puller (2483), taking care not to damage shims. Mark left and right bearings and shims for reassembly. Index differential case halves and mark differential gear shafts for reassembly.

Fig. 2: Exploded View of Limited Slip Differential

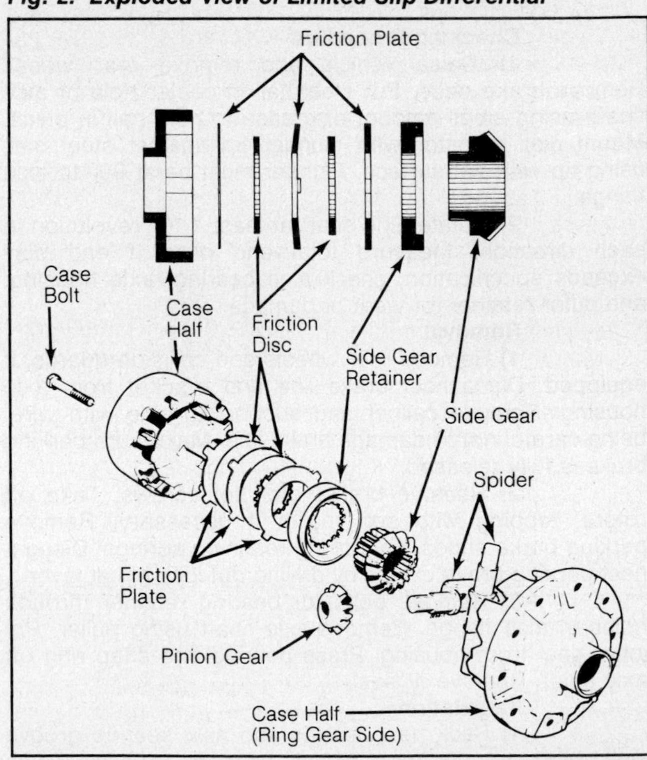
Friction Plate
Case Bolt
Case Half
Friction Disc
Side Gear Retainer
Side Gear
Spider
Friction Plate
Pinion Gear
Case Half (Ring Gear Side)

Note size and shape of friction plates for reassembly reference.

2) Remove bolts holding case halves together, noting that Type 1030 axle uses bolts with left-hand threads. Open differential case and remove side gears, side gear retainers, friction plates, friction discs, and pinion gears with spider.

3) Index ring gear to differential case half for reassembly. Remove and discard bolts holding ring gear to case. Remove ring gear from differential case.

Case Assembly - Conventional

1) Remove side bearings with puller (2483), taking care not to damage shims. Mark left and right bearings and shims for reassembly in correct position. Hold case assembly securely and remove lock plate over ring gear bolts.

2) Index ring gear to differential case for reassembly. Loosen bolts holding ring gear to case. Tap bolts to push ring gear from case. Discard old bolts. Drive out lock pin holding differential gear shaft.

3) Drive out differential gear shaft. Remove differential pinion gears by rolling them out of case. Remove pinion gear shims. Lift out differential side gears with shims.

INSPECTION

1) Inspect all parts for wear or damage. Bearings that have any damage from heat or scoring must be replaced. If drive pinion or ring gear show tooth damage from seizing, they must be replaced as a set.

2) If differential side or pinion gears show any damage, gears must be replaced as a complete set (2 side gears and 2 pinion gears in conventional models or 2 side gears and 4 pinion gears in LSD models).

3) Flat and thrust washers for differential gears should be replaced. Bolts holding ring gear to case must always be replaced. Pinion flange locking nut must be checked carefully as it loses locking capacity after being removed several times.

4) Replace drive pinion flange if worn or scored on sealing surface. Always use new oil seals and gaskets. Check axle housing for cracks. Check all brackets on housing for broken welds or damage.

5) On models with LSD, all friction discs should be replaced if any discs show excessive wear or heat damage. *See Checking Procedure for rotational friction under Axle Assembly in this article.*

REASSEMBLY & ADJUSTMENT

Case Assembly - Conventional

1) Place differential side gears together with thrust washers in differential case. Compress thrust washers so that pinion gears and thrust washers can be rolled into case as an assembly.

2) Drive in differential pinion shaft. Drive in shaft lock pin, using punch to stake pin in place. Line up index marks on ring gear and case. Install ring gear, making sure that contact surfaces are clean and without any burrs. Install new ring gear bolts with locking compound. Tighten to specification in diagonal pattern.

Case Assembly - Limited Slip

1) Line up index marks on ring gear and case half. Install ring gear on case, making sure contact surface is clean and free of burrs. Install new ring gear bolts with locking compound. Tighten to specification in diagonal pattern.

2) Lubricate parts in hypoid oil with limited slip additive. Install side gear and retainer, spider with pinion gears, side gear and retainer, and friction plates onto ring gear half of case. *See Fig. 2 for assembly order and direction.*

NOTE: **On earlier differentials that have side gears and side gear retainers splined for axle shafts, splines must be aligned using axle shafts while case through bolts are being tightened.**

3) Align ears on friction plates and fit smaller half of case to ring gear half. Make sure index marks on case halves are aligned. Install case through bolts and torque to specification in diagonal pattern.

Drive Pinion Depth & Bearing Preload

1) Clean shoulder on drive pinion with emery cloth. Install adjusting ring and wrench (Type 1030 uses ring 2685 and wrench 2841; Type 1031 uses ring 2840 and wrench 2841) on drive pinion. Make sure locking screw on adjusting ring is not covered by drive pinion head. *See Figs. 3 & 4.* Place drive pinion in carrier so screw on adjusting ring faces large side of carrier.

Fig. 3: Drive Pinion Adjusting Ring and Wrench

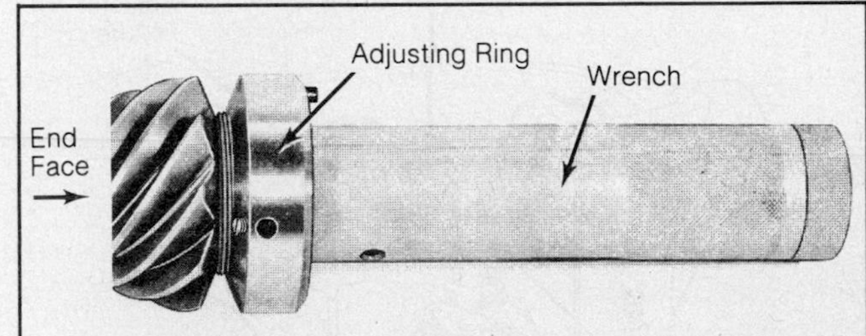
Adjusting Ring
Wrench
End
Face

Drive pinion gear installed in adjusting ring and wrench.

2) Make sure pin on adjusting ring fits into carrier recess. Drive pinion has a certain nominal measurement to center line of ring gear from face of drive pinion head. Due to manufacturing tolerances, deviations from this nominal measurement occur.

3) On rear axles made by Volvo, deviation is always positive and is indicated in hundredths of a millimeter. The plus sign is not used. Deviation from nominal measurement is recorded on drive pinion.

Fig. 4: Measuring Drive Pinion Gear Installed Height

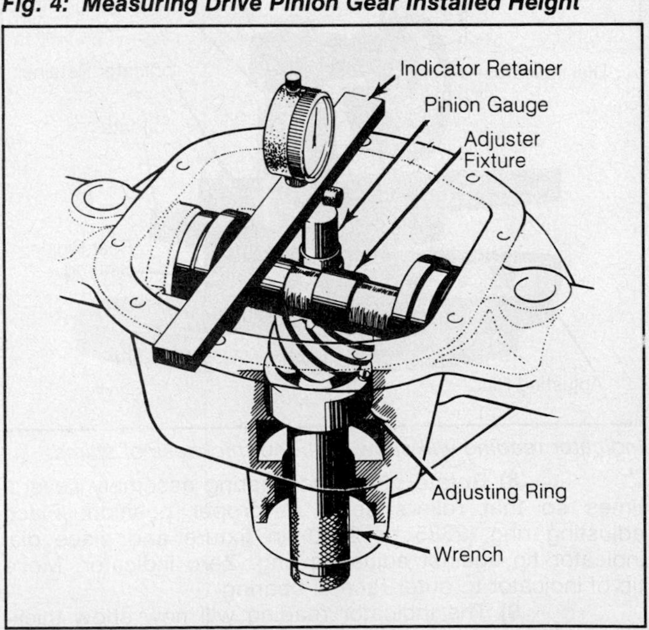
Indicator Retainer
Pinion Gauge
Adjuster
Fixture
Adjusting Ring
Wrench

Pinion gear and adjusting ring tool installed in housing.

VOLVO (Cont.)

4) Place measuring tool (2393) in carrier, with pinion gauge on end face of pinion and adjuster fixture set in differential bearing positions. Place dial indicator retainer so retainer sits on gasket face of axle housing with dial indicator tip touching adjuster fixture.

5) Zero dial indicator against adjuster fixture. Move indicator over until tip touches pinion gauge. For example, if drive pinion is marked 0.33, the pinion gauge should lie .013" (.33 mm) under adjuster fixture. *See Fig. 5.*

6) Adjust indicated reading by turning wrench on drive pinion until dial indicator shows correct value. Lock wrench with set screw on adjusting ring.

7) Remove measuring tools and drive pinion. Place complete rear pinion bearing with outer race in measuring fixture (2600). Assemble plate, spring, and nut with flat side of nut facing up.

Fig. 5: Dial Indicator Zeroing Location

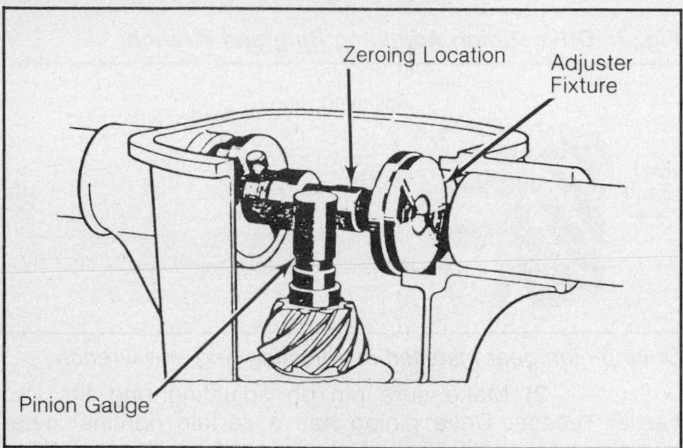
Zeroing Location
Adjuster Fixture
Pinion Gauge

Dial indicator retainer is not installed.

Fig. 6: Determining Pinion Depth Shim Thickness

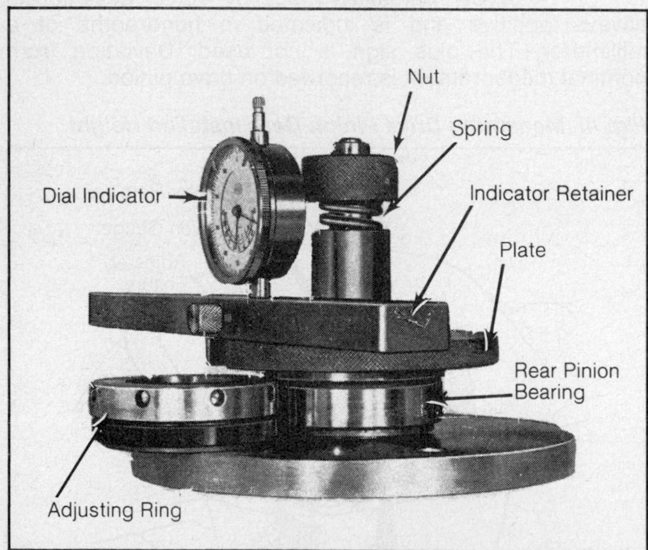
Nut
Spring
Dial Indicator
Indicator Retainer
Plate
Rear Pinion Bearing
Adjusting Ring

Indicator reading will show required thickness of shims.

8) Rotate plate and bearing assembly several times so that rollers settle in proper position. Place adjusting ring (2685 or 2840) in fixture and place dial indicator tip against adjusting ring. Zero indicator. Move tip of indicator to outer race of bearing.

9) The indicator reading will now show thickness of rear drive pinion bearing shims. *See Fig. 6.* Measure shims for correct thickness with micrometer. As it is difficult to find shim of exact thickness required, shim may be .002" (.05 mm) thicker or .0008" (.020 mm) thinner than measured value.

10) Press rear bearing on drive pinion. Place measured shim in axle carrier housing. Press in outer races of rear and front drive pinion bearings.

CAUTION: The spacer washer found under rear bearing inner race during first time disassembly must not be reinstalled when overhauling.

11) Insert drive pinion in housing and install three .03" (.75 mm) thick shims and front pinion bearing. Pull pinion into housing, using wrench (2404) and press tool (1845 or 5156). Install washer and nut on pinion shaft and tighten to specifications.

Fig. 7: Measuring Installed Depth of Pinion Gear

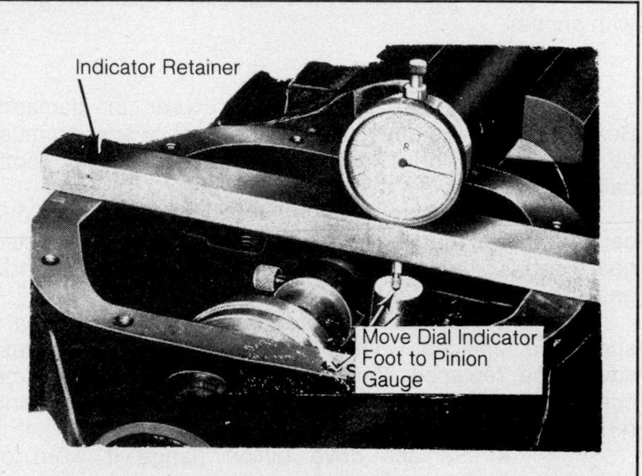
Indicator Retainer
Move Dial Indicator Foot to Pinion Gauge

Adjust shim thickness as necessary to obtain specified torque.

12) Install pinion gauge, dial indicator, and dial indicator retainer. *See Fig. 7.* Pull down on drive pinion while rotating it back and forth. Zero dial indicator. Press pinion up while rotating it back and forth. Record dial indicator reading.

13) Tap drive pinion from housing and remove shims equal to the dial indicator reading plus .0035" (.090 mm) for new bearings or .0028" (.071 mm) for used bearings. Install pinion with selected shim pack and front bearing. Press drive pinion in with wrench (2404) and press tool (1845 or 5156).

14) Install pinion nut with washer and torque to specification. Check drive pinion bearing preload with torque wrench. Adjust shim thickness if required to obtain specified torque. Recheck pinion depth using measuring tools as described in steps **4)** and **5)**.

Backlash & Side Bearing Preload

1) Lubricate inside of adjusting ring tools (2595) and install them on differential carrier. Black oxidized adjusting ring should be placed on ring gear side of differential case. Oil bearing bores in carrier. Install differential with adjusting rings in axle housing.

2) Adjust rings apart until differential is held firmly without any preload. Set dial indicator tip against ring gear tooth and adjust rings so that specified backlash is obtained. Turn both rings in same direction. Backlash range is .005-.007" (.13-.18 mm). Preferred setting is .006" (.15 mm).

VOLVO (Cont.)

NOTE: **Keep bearings and shims separate so that they are installed on correct side.**

3) After correct backlash is obtained, lock adjusting rings in position. Remove differential with adjusting rings. Position centering plate on measuring fixture (2600). Place side bearing in fixture. Install plate, spring, and nut (flat side of nut faces up). Rotate plate and bearing back and forth to settle rollers.

4) Place adjusting ring on measuring fixture. Install retainer (2284) with dial indicator. Zero dial indicator with tip against adjusting ring. Move tip of dial indicator to inner race of side bearing. Record measurement.

5) Measure shim thickness with micrometer. Total thickness of shim(s) should be measured value plus .0028" (.071 mm). Repeat measuring procedure for opposite side bearing shim pack.

6) Install shim pack and press side bearing opposite ring gear on first. Install lock plate for ring gear bolts. Install shim pack and press on side bearing by ring gear. Use press tools on both side bearings to prevent damage to side bearings.

7) Install housing spreader (2394 and 2601) on carrier and expand until tool pins are flush against hole edges in carrier. Tighten tension screw additional 3.5 turns maximum. Install differential carrier with side bearing outer races in place. Remove housing spreader.

8) Check index marks and install side bearing caps. Torque cap bolts to specification. Check ring gear backlash to make sure no change has occurred. Set dial indicator on back of ring gear and check runout in 4 places.

9) Install oil slinger. Drive pinion oil seal into housing after packing seal spring with grease. Press drive pinion flange onto drive pinion. Install pinion flange nut and washer. Torque nut to specification. Install inspection cover with new gasket on back of carrier housing.

10) If inner oil seals for axle shafts were removed, drive them into housing ends after packing lips with grease. Fill space between retainer and inner race of axle bearing with grease. Reinstall axle shafts and tighten bearing retainer bolts. Fill with correct lubricant.

AXLE ASSEMBLY SPECIFICATIONS

Application	In. (mm)
Ring Gear Runout [1]	.003 (.08)
Pinion-to-Ring Gear	
Backlash Preferred	.006 (.15)
Backlash Range	.005-.007 (.13-.18)
Axle Shaft Bearing End Play [1]	.004-.014 (.10-.36)
Differential Side Bearing Preload	.005-.008 (.13-.20)
	INCH Lbs. (N.m)
Pinion Bearing Preload Torque	
Used Bearing	5-10 (.6-1.1)
New Bearings	21-39 (2.4-4.4)
	Ft. Lbs. (N.m)
Limited Slip Friction Torque	40-110 (54-149)

[1] – Maximum deviation allowed.

TIGHTENING SPECIFICATIONS

Application	Ft. Lbs. (N.m)
Pinion Flange Nut	
88626 (3/4" UNF)	175-220 (237-298)
946831 (3/4" UNF)	145-185 (197-251)
947855 (M20 x 15)	145-185 (197-251)
Side Bearing Cap Bolts	35-50 (47-68)
Ring Gear Bolts	
Standard Head	50-58 (68-79)
Flanged Head	65-80 (88-108)
Wheel Lug Nuts	85 (115)
Axle Shaft Bearing Retainer Bolts	22-36 (30-49)
LSD Case Through Bolts	44-55 (60-75)

Locking Hubs

ALL MANUFACTURERS

Chrysler Corp. Imports, Datsun/Nissan, Isuzu, Mitsubishi, & Toyota 4WD Pickups; Mitsubishi Montero & Toyota Land Cruiser

DESCRIPTION

Locking hubs engage and disengage front wheels from axle shafts on 4WD vehicles. When hubs are engaged or locked, wheels and axle shafts rotate together. When hubs are disengaged or unlocked, front wheels free wheel on hub bearings and axle shafts are not turned by wheels.

Engagement is accomplished through action of gears and springs within hub. When hub is locked, hub clutch engages inner hub, which is always connected to axle shaft by inner splines of hub. Hub clutch is always connected by outer splines to hub body. Control handle applies or releases spring tension to control hub clutch position.

Automatic hubs are engaged by rotational force of axle shaft when 4WD is selected at transfer case. Automatic hubs disengage when 2WD is selected and vehicle is driven in reverse. Cams, brakes, and springs are used to lock or unlock automatic hubs.

IDENTIFICATION

Several different makes of hub are used. Manufacturer's name is on control handle of manual hubs if marked. Automatic hubs have no handle on cover. Manual hubs have control handle marked with "LOCK" and "FREE" directions. Outer edge of hub cover on manual hubs is marked with "LOCK" and "FREE" positions.

REMOVAL & INSTALLATION

MANUAL HUBS

Removal

With control knob set to "FREE" position and transfer shift lever set in 2WD position, remove cover-to-body bolts and cover assembly. Remove outer snap ring and shims (if equipped) from axle shaft. Remove hub body-to-hub bolts or nuts and cone washers (if equipped). Remove hub body and inner clutch from axle shaft.

Installation

Place new gasket on axle hub and install hub body with bolts or nuts and cone washers (if equipped). Tighten fasteners. Install snap ring, making sure snap ring fits groove on axle shaft. Apply grease to splines of inner hub. Set control handle and clutch in "FREE" position. Install new gasket and cover assembly and tighten bolts. Check control handle for smooth operation.

AUTOMATIC HUBS

Removal

Make sure hub is in "FREE" position and transfer case is in 2WD. Remove hub cover and gasket. Unscrew cover on Montero. Remove cover-to-hub body bolts on Isuzu. Remove snap ring and shims from axle shaft. Unbolt hub body from axle hub and remove drive clutch and inner cam with hub body.

Installation

1) On Isuzu, apply Loctite 515 to flange surface of driven clutch assembly. Install inner cam and drive clutch assembly on axle shaft and tighten bolts. On Montero, apply nonhardening sealant to hub surface. Align key of brake B with slot on spindle, make sure axle hub-to-housing fit is tight, and tighten bolts. *See Fig. 1.*

Fig. 1: Exploded View of Automatic Hubs

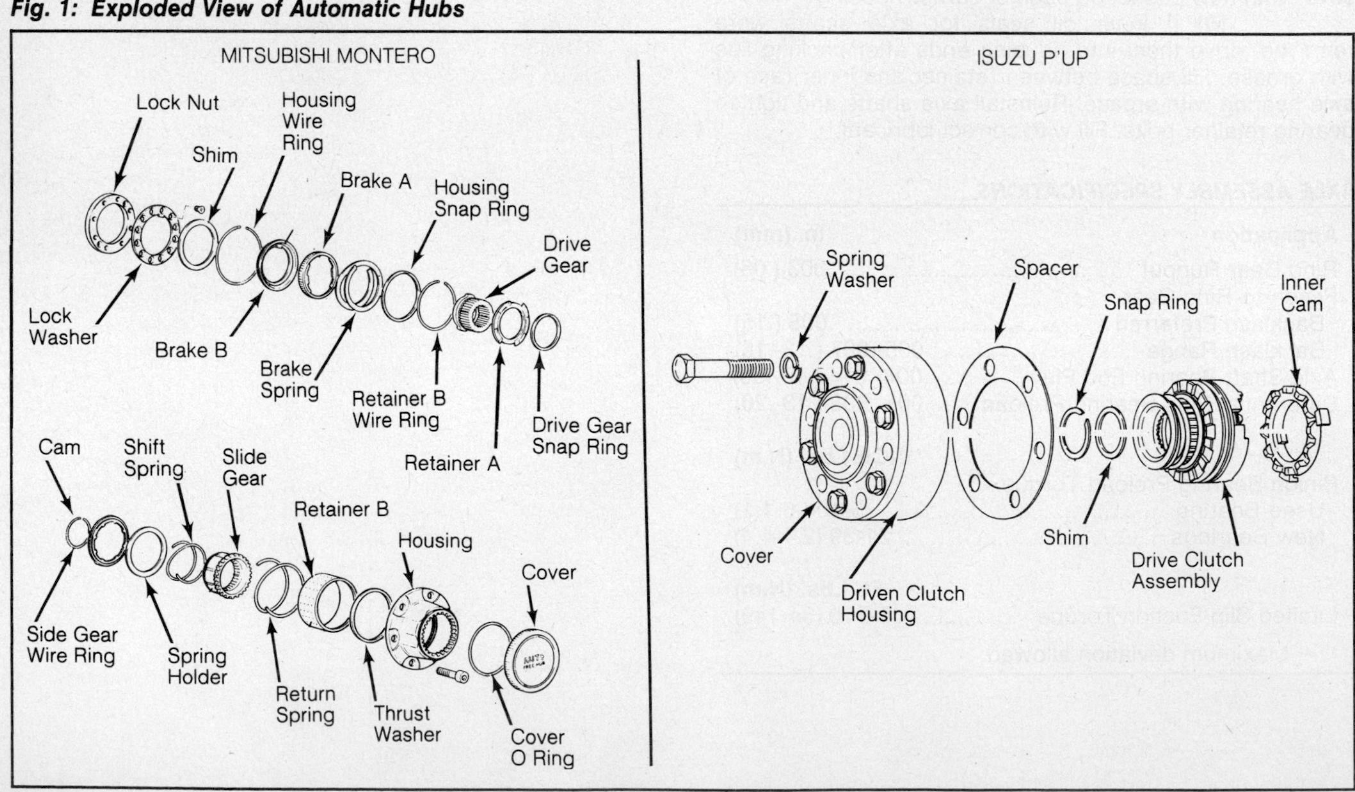
MITSUBISHI MONTERO
Lock Nut
Housing Wire Ring
Shim
Brake A
Housing Snap Ring
Drive Gear
Lock Washer
Brake B
Brake Spring
Retainer B Wire Ring
Drive Gear Snap Ring
Retainer A
Cam
Shift Spring
Slide Gear
Retainer B
Housing
Cover
Side Gear Wire Ring
Spring Holder
Return Spring
Thrust Washer
Cover O Ring
ISUZU P'UP
Spring Washer
Spacer
Snap Ring
Inner Cam
Cover
Shim
Drive Clutch Assembly
Driven Clutch Housing

Reassemble with Loctite 515 on Isuzu and nonhardening sealer on Montero.

Locking Hubs

ALL MANUFACTURERS (Cont.)

2) On all models, make sure axle shaft end play is correct. Install snap ring with shim. On Isuzu, apply Loctite 515 to driven clutch flange surface. Install driven clutch flange and tighten bolts. On Montero, grease "O" ring and screw hub cover on tightly by hand.

OVERHAUL

MANUAL HUB

Disassembly

1) On Datsun/Nissan, set hub in "LOCK" position. Use magnet to pull and turn driven clutch in clockwise direction to remove. Remove locking pin from inside hub case. *See Fig. 2.*

Fig. 2: Using Magnet to Remove Datsun/Nissan Driven Clutch

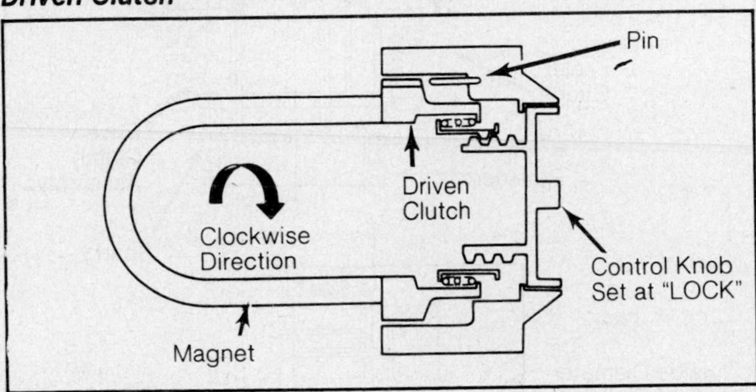
Pin
Driven Clutch
Clockwise Direction
Control Knob Set at "LOCK"
Magnet

2) On all other models, remove snap ring and control handle from hub cover. Remove detent ball and spring from control handle. Remove snap ring, inner hub, and hub ring from body. Remove snap ring, hub ring, and spacer from inner hub. *See Fig. 3.*

Inspection

1) Clean all hard parts in solvent. Inspect all parts for excessive wear or damage. Make sure control handle moves smoothly in cover. Check that clutch moves smoothly in hub body.

2) On Toyota models, measure inside diameter of hub ring at point "A" with vernier caliper. Measure outside diameter of inner hub at point "B" where hub ring rides. *See Fig. 4.* Value of "A" - "B" is oil clearance. Maximum clearance is .012" (.31 mm). Replace inner hub or hub ring if clearance is excessive.

Fig. 4: Measuring Toyota Inner Hub Oil Clearance

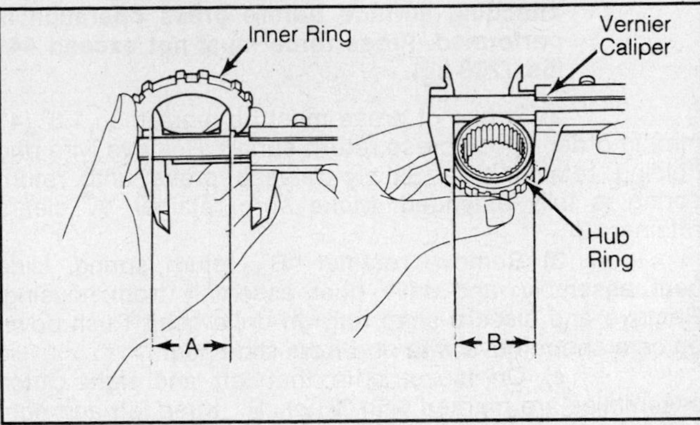
Inner Ring
Vernier Caliper
Hub Ring
A
B

Maximum clearance is .012" (.31 mm).

Reassembly

1) On Datsun/Nissan, install lock pin in hub. Set control knob in "FREE" position. Screw driven clutch (in counterclockwise direction) into hub assembly until it stops. Back out until groove in driven clutch lines up with bolt hole in hub assembly.

2) On all other models, apply grease to sliding surface of all parts. Install seal, detent ball, and compression spring into control handle. Insert handle in cover and install snap ring. Install retaining spring in clutch with end of spring aligned with first groove cut in full width spline.

3) Install follower pawl on retaining spring with bent spring end hooked against 1 of large tabs on pawl. Top ring of retaining spring rides on small tabs. Place compression spring between clutch and cover with large end of spring against cover. Install clutch with pawl tab fitted to control handle.

4) Install spacer and hub ring on inner hub. Install snap ring. Insert inner hub and hub ring assembly in hub body. Install snap ring. Set control handle and clutch to "FREE" position. Install cover temporarily and make sure hub turns smoothly. Remove cover for installation procedure.

AUTOMATIC HUB

Disassembly

1) On Montero, pry wire ring from housing after pressing on brake "B". *See Fig. 1.* Remove brake "B", brake "A", and brake spring. Remove housing snap ring. Compress return spring by slowly pushing in on drive gear with press.

Fig. 3: Exploded View of Toyota Manual Hub

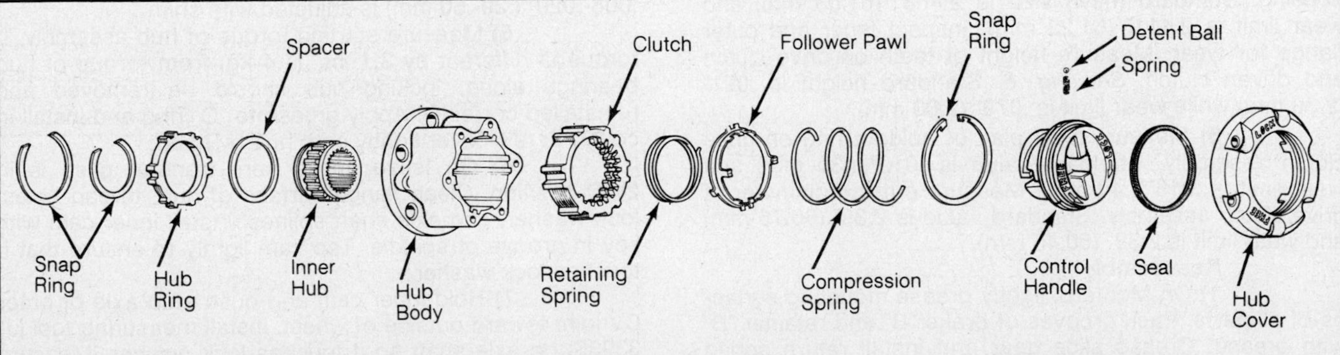
Spacer
Clutch
Follower Pawl
Snap Ring
Detent Ball
Spring
Snap Ring
Hub Ring
Inner Hub
Hub Body
Retaining Spring
Compression Spring
Control Handle
Seal
Hub Cover

All makes are similar but note differences during disassembly procedure.

ALL MANUFACTURERS (Cont.)

CAUTION: Use protective mat or covering under cover attaching surface before press operation is performed. Press force must not exceed 441 lbs. (200 kg).

2) Stroke of press must be more than 1.6" (41 mm) in order to compress return spring. Remove wire ring holding retainer "B". Slowly release press until return spring is fully extended. Make sure retainer "A" clears retainer "B".

3) Remove retainer "B", return spring, slide gear assembly, and drive gear assembly from housing. Remove and discard snap ring on drive gear. Push down on cam and remove wire ring from slide gear.

4) On Isuzu, note that left and right clutch assemblies are marked with "L" or "R". Keep left and right side parts separated for reassembly.

Inspection

1) On Montero, check drive gear and slide gear for wear or damage. Check cam portion of retainer "A". Check cam, slide gear, and housing teeth. Check retainer "B" and housing contact surfaces.

2) Assemble brakes "A" and "B" and set vernier caliper with jaws on both lugs of brake "A" at same time. Measure combined brake thickness. If measurement is less than .35" (9.0 mm), replace both brakes as a set.

3) Measure return spring and shift spring. *See Fig. 5.* Measure dimension shown from outside of 1 wire diameter to outside of other wire diameter. Return spring must be replaced if it measures less than 1.4" (36 mm). Replace shift spring if it measures less than 1.2" (30.5 mm).

Fig. 5: Measuring Points for Montero Automatic Hub

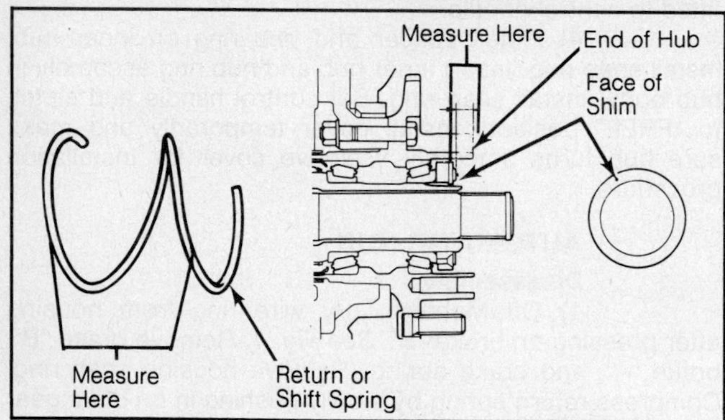
Measure Here
End of Hub
Face of
Shim
Measure
Here
Return or
Shift Spring

Replace springs if dimension shown is below limit.

4) On Isuzu, measure inside diameter of housing. Standard (new) size is 2.403" (61.03 mm) and wear limit is 2.411" (61.23 mm). Inspect inner and outer flange for wear. Measure height of teeth on drive clutch and driven clutch. *See Fig. 6.* Standard height is .091" (2.30 mm) while wear limit is .079" (2.00 mm).

5) Measure axial play of holdout ring on drive clutch assembly. Standard value is .012" (.30 mm) and wear limit is .016" (.40 mm). Measure outside diameter of drive clutch assembly. Standard value is 2.39" (60.75 mm) and wear limit is 2.38" (60.45 mm).

Reassembly

1) On Montero, lightly grease mounting surfaces of all parts. Pack grooves of brake "B" and retainer "B" with grease. Grease slide gear and install return spring with smaller coil diameter toward seat. Measure starting torque of front hub assembly with spring scale.

Fig. 6: Wear Point Measurements of Isuzu Automatic Hub

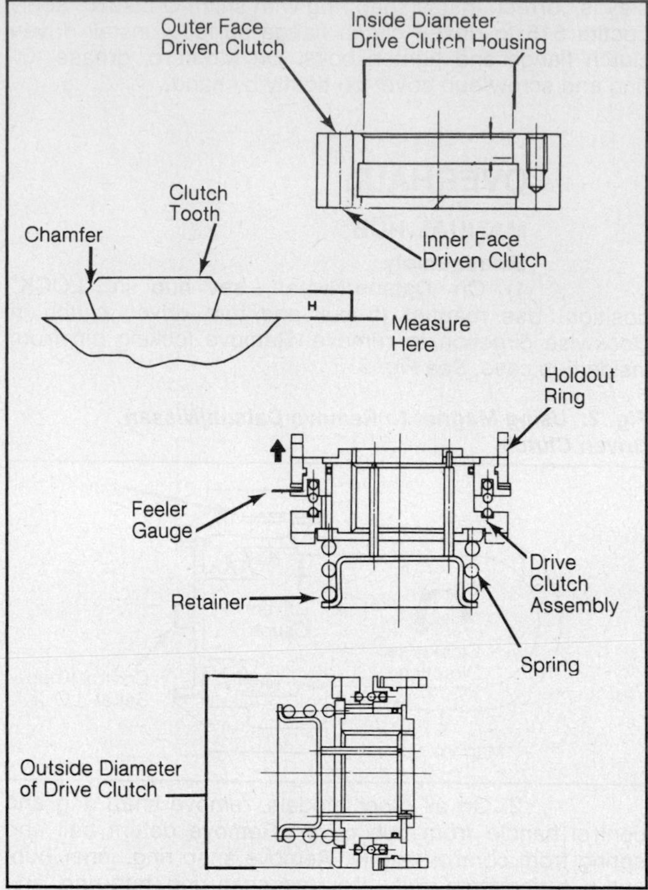
Outer Face
Driven Clutch
Inside Diameter
Drive Clutch Housing
Clutch
Tooth
Chamfer
Inner Face
Driven Clutch
H
Measure
Here
Holdout
Ring
Feeler
Gauge
Drive
Clutch
Assembly
Retainer
Spring
Outside Diameter
of Drive Clutch

2) If torque is outside range of 0.9-4.1 lbs. (.4-1.9 kg), adjust with lock nut setting. Measure depth of brake contact surface. *See Fig. 5.* Range of depth is .46-.48" (11.7-12.2 mm) and is adjusted by shims. Apply nonhardening sealant to hub surface.

3) Align key on brake "B" with slot in spindle and loosely install hub assembly. Check that hub surface and hub assembly face fit closely when hub assembly is pressed lightly against hub. Rotate hub until close fit is obtained. Tighten hub assembly-to-hub bolts.

4) Install snap ring on axle shaft without shims. Mount dial indicator with tip on end of axle shaft and plunger at 90° to rotor. Turn axle shaft back and forth until resistance is felt to find center of turning stroke. At this point, measure axial play (end play) of shaft. Range of .008-.020" (.20-.50 mm) is adjusted with shim.

5) Measure starting torque of hub assembly. If torque is different by 3.1 lbs. (1.4 kg) from torque of hub bearings alone, locking hub should be removed and reinstalled correctly. Apply grease to "O" ring and install in cover. Screw cover tightly onto hub by hand.

6) On Isuzu, make sure transfer case is in 2WD position. Clean flange surface of hub, thread holes, lock washer, and axle shaft splines. Install inner cam with key in groove of spindle. Tap cam lightly to ensure that it touches lock washer.

7) Hold inner cam and push stub axle of outer CV joint toward outside of wheel. Install measuring tool (J-33935) on axle shaft so it touches lock washer. Measure clearance between outer face of tool and outer edge of

Locking Hubs

ALL MANUFACTURERS (Cont.)

snap ring groove. *See Fig. 7.* Adjust clearance with shims to range of 0-.004" (0-.10 mm).

Fig. 7: Measuring Points for Isuzu Automatic Hub

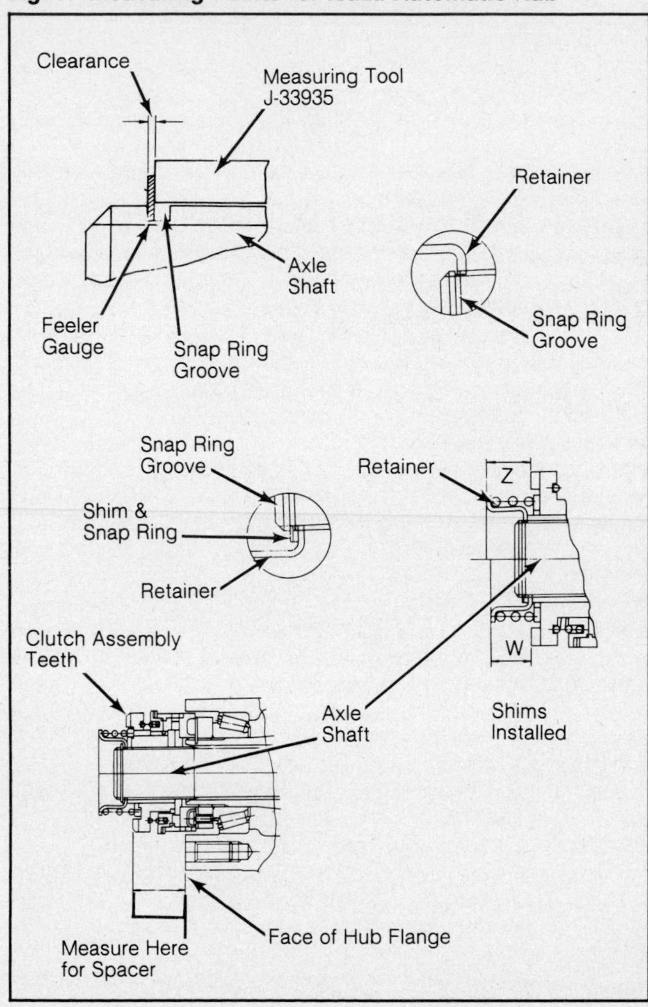

Clearance
Measuring Tool
J-33935
Retainer
Axle
Shaft
Snap Ring
Groove
Feeler
Gauge
Snap Ring
Groove
Snap Ring
Groove
Retainer
Z
Shim &
Snap Ring
Retainer
Clutch Assembly
Teeth
W
Axle
Shaft
Shims
Installed
Face of Hub Flange
Measure Here
for Spacer

8) Remove special tool, making sure that inner cam remains in place. Install drive clutch assembly. Check that assembly marked "L" is on left side and assembly marked "R" is on right side of vehicle. Lightly grease axle splines, inside of driven clutch, back and side grooves of drive clutch assembly.

9) Align cut portion of holdout ring with convex part of drive clutch assembly. Align clutch assembly with inner cam and engage teeth of drive clutch with inner cam teeth. Measure distance from outer face of spring retainer on drive clutch assembly to outer face of teeth on drive clutch assembly. Record distance as "Z".

10) Install shims selected with measuring tool and install new snap ring. Ensure that snap ring fits properly in groove of axle shaft. Measure distance from outer face of spring retainer to outer face of teeth on drive clutch assembly after installing snap ring and shims. Record distance as "W".

11) If "Z" - "W" is larger than .0079" (.200 mm), shim selection is correct. Measure distance from face of hub flange to outer face of clutch assembly teeth. *See Fig. 7.* For a distance of 1.00-1.04" (25.4-26.3 mm), no spacer is used. For a distance of 1.04-1.07" (26.3-27.2 mm), use 1 mm spacer. For a distance of 1.07-1.11" (27.2-28.1 mm), use 2 mm spacer.

12) Apply Loctite 515 to both sides of spacer and flange surface of driven clutch assembly. Install flange to driven clutch assembly. Tighten bolts. Apply Loctite 515 to flange surface of housing assembly. Install housing assembly with bolts and spring washers. Ensure that housing assembly turns smoothly and tighten bolts.

TIGHTENING SPECIFICATIONS

Application	Ft. Lbs. (N.m)
Hub Body-to-Hub	
Chrysler Corp. & Mitsubishi	
All Models	36-43 (49-58)
Isuzu	39.8-47.0 (54-64)
Toyota Pickup	21-25 (29-34)
Toyota Land Cruiser	18-25 (24-34)
Cover-to-Hub Body	
Chrysler Corp. & Mitsubishi	
All Models	7-10 (9-14)
Datsun/Nissan	18-25 (24-34)
Isuzu	17.4-21.7 (24-29)
Toyota Land Cruiser	3-5 (4-7)
Toyota Pickup	6-8 (8-11)

SECTION 9

BRAKES

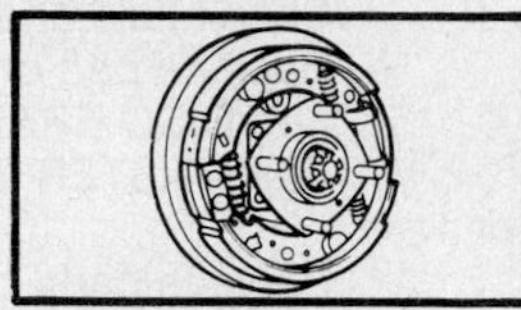

CONTENTS

NOTE: **ALSO SEE GENERAL INDEX.**

Brakes

TROUBLE SHOOTING

CONDITION	POSSIBLE CAUSE	CORRECTION
Brakes Pull Left or Right	Incorrect tire pressure	Inflate tires to proper pressure
	Front end out of alignment	See WHEEL ALIGNMENT
	Mismatched tires	Check tires sizes
	Restricted brake lines or hoses	Check hose routing
	Loose or malfunctioning caliper	See DISC BRAKES
	Bent shoe or oily linings	See DRUM BRAKES
	Malfunctioning rear brakes	See DRUM or DISC BRAKES
	Loose suspension parts	See SUSPENSION
Noises Without Brakes Applied	Front linings worn out	Replace linings
	Dust or oil on drums or rotors	See DRUM or DISC BRAKES
Noises with Brakes Applied	Insulator on outboard shoe damaged	See DISC BRAKES
	Incorrect pads or linings	Replace pads or linings
Brake Rough, Chatters or Pulsates	Excessive lateral runout	Check rotor runout
	Parallelism not to specifications	Reface or replace rotor
	Wheel bearings not adjusted	See SUSPENSION
	Rear drums out-of-round	Reface or replace drums
	Disc pad reversed, steel against rotor	Remove and reinstall pad
Excessive Pedal Effort	Malfunctioning power unit	See POWER BRAKES
	Partial system failure	Check fluid and pipes
	Worn disc pad or lining	Replace pad or lining
	Caliper piston stuck or sluggish	See DISC BRAKES
	Master cylinder piston stuck	See MASTER CYLINDERS
	Brake fade due to incorrect pads or linings	Replace pads or linings
	Linings or pads glazed	Replace pads or linings
	Worn drums	Reface or replace drums
Excessive Pedal Travel	Partial brake system failure	Check fluid and pipes
	Insufficient fluid in master cylinder	See MASTER CYLINDERS
	Air trapped in system	See BLEEDING
	Rear brakes not adjusted	See Adjustment in DRUM BRAKES
	Bent shoe or lining	See DRUM BRAKES
	Plugged master cylinder cap	See MASTER CYLINDER
	Improper brake fluid	Replace brake fluid
Pedal Travel Decreasing	Compensating port plugged	See MASTER CYLINDERS
	Swollen cup in master cylinder	See MASTER CYLINDERS
	Master cylinder piston not returning	See MASTER CYLINDERS
	Weak shoe retracting springs	See DRUM BRAKES
	Wheel cylinder piston sticking	See DRUM BRAKES
Dragging Brakes	Master cylinder pistons not returning	See MASTER CYLINDERS
	Restricted brake lines or hoses	Check line routing
	Incorrect parking brake adjustment	See DRUM BRAKES
	Parking brake cables frozen	See DRUM BRAKES
	Incorrect installation of inboard disc pad	Remove and replace correctly
	Power booster output rod too long	See POWER BRAKE UNITS
	Brake pedal not returning freely	See DISC or DRUM BRAKES
Brakes Grab or Uneven Braking Action	Malfunction of combination valve	See CONTROL VALVES
	Malfunction of power brake unit	See POWER BRAKE UNITS
	Binding brake pedal	See DISC or DRUM BRAKES
Pulsation or Roughness	Uneven pad wear caused by caliper	See DISC BRAKES
	Uneven rotor wear	See DISC BRAKES
	Drums out-of-round	Reface or replace drums

HYDRAULIC BRAKE BLEEDING

DESCRIPTION

Hydraulic system bleeding is necessary any time air has been introduced into system. Bleed brakes at all 4 wheels if master cylinder lines have been disconnected or master cylinder has run dry.

Bleeding may be done either by using pressure bleeding equipment or by manually pumping brake pedal and using bleeder tubes.

MANUAL BLEEDING

1) Fill master cylinder, then install bleeder hose to first bleeder valve to be serviced. See Bleeding Sequence. Place other end of hose in clean glass jar.

2) Partially fill jar with clean brake fluid, so end of hose is submerged in fluid. Open bleeder valve 3/4-1 turn.

3) Depress brake pedal slowly through its full travel (except as noted in Bleeding Sequence Chart). Close bleeder valve, then release pedal. Repeat procedure until flow of fluid shows no signs of air bubbles.

NOTE: Check fluid level in master cylinder frequently during bleeding sequence to ensure air does not enter system.

PRESSURE TANK BLEEDING

1) Clean master cylinder cap and surrounding area, then remove cap. With pressure tank at least 1/3 full, connect master cylinder using adapters.

2) Attach bleeder hose to first bleeder valve to be serviced. See Bleeding Sequence. Place other end of hose in clean glass jar. Partially fill jar with clean brake fluid, so end of hose is submerged in fluid.

3) Open release valve on pressure bleeder. Unscrew valve 3/4-1 turn, noting fluid flow. When fluid flow from bleeder valve into container is free of bubbles, close bleeder valve securely.

4) Bleed remaining cylinders in correct sequence and in same manner. Remove pressure tank from master cylinder and check fluid level of master cylinder reservoir.

BLEEDING PRESSURES [1]

Application	psi (kg/cm²)
BMW	
733i	56 (3.9)
All Others	28 (2.0)
Porsche	32 (2.3)
Renault	30 (2.1)
Volvo	50-60 (3.5-4.2)

[1] – For models not listed, refer to pressure tank manufacturer's specifications.

BLEEDING SEQUENCE

Before bleeding system, exhaust all vacuum from power unit by depressing brake pedal several times. Bleed hydraulic system in the following sequence:

BLEEDING SEQUENCE

Application [1]	Cylinder or Line
Audi & Volkswagen	RR,LR,RF,LF
BMW	Longest Line First
Chrysler Corp. Imports	
Colt	LR,RF,RR,LF
All Others [2]	RR,LR,RF,LF
Datsun	
Maxima	RR,LR,RF,LF
Pickup	Master Cyl., Comb. Valve, Longest Line First
Pulsar & Sentra	RR,LF,LR,RF
All Others	Master Cyl., Longest Line First
Honda	LF,RR,RF,LR
Isuzu	
I-Mark, P'UP	Shortest Line First
Impulse	RR,LR,RF,LF
Jaguar [3]	LR,RR, Front
Mazda [4]	Longest Line First
Mercedes-Benz	Longest Line First
Mitsubishi	
Cordia, Tredia	LR,RF,RR,LF
All Others	RR,LR,RF,LF
Peugeot [5]	Longest Line First
Porsche [6]	LR,RR,RF,LF
Renault	Longest Line First
Saab	LR,RF,RR,LF
Subaru	Master Cyl.,FR,RF,RR,LF
Toyota	Longest Line First
Volvo [7]	LF,RF,LR,RR

[1] – Before bleeding rear brakes, push brake pressure regulator in direction of rear axle.

[2] – Pickup models do not require bleeding of RR.

[3] – Engine running at idle speed.

[4] – GLC Wagon has independent front and rear circuits. Bleed each circuit separately.

[5] – If pressure tank is used, bleed all wheels at the same time.

[6] – If equipped with inner and outer caliper bleed valves, bleed outer valves first, then inner valves.

[7] – Rear wheels must be higher than front wheels. Front calipers are each equipped with 3 bleed valves. Bleed all 3 valves at same time.

Brakes

AUDI

Coupe, 4000, 4000 Turbo Diesel, 5000, 5000 Turbo, 5000 Turbo Diesel

DESCRIPTION

Brake system is hydraulically-operated, using a tandem master cylinder and power brake unit. Front brakes are sliding caliper disc on all models. Rear brakes on 5000 Turbo models are sliding caliper disc. All other models use leading/trailing shoe drum brakes.

Brake hydraulic system incorporates a brake pressure regulator to prevent premature lock-up of rear wheels. All service brake systems are self-adjusting. Parking brake is cable-actuated on rear brake system.

ADJUSTMENTS

STOP LIGHT SWITCH

1) On 5000 Turbo, remove connector, loosen lock nut and turn switch until tip is just touching brake pedal. Attach ohmmeter, and turn switch until reading is infinite (switch open). Turn switch 2 additional turns and tighten lock nut.

2) On all other models, loosen lock nut and turn switch until distance between tip and switch body is .087-.098" (2.2-2.5 mm). *See Fig. 1.* Tighten lock nut, and check operation of switch.

Fig. 1: Adjusting Stop Light Switch

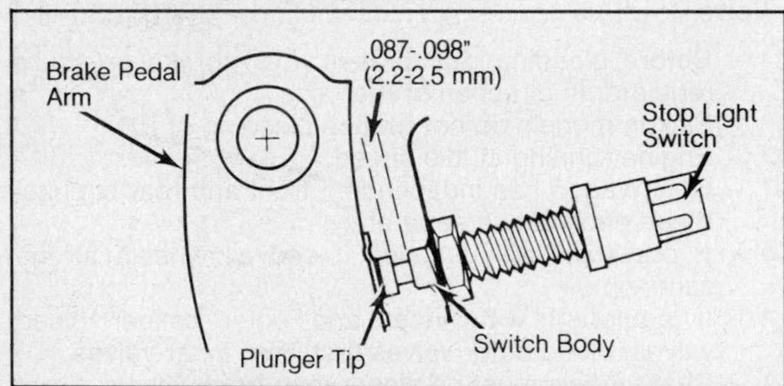
Brake Pedal Arm
.087-.098" (2.2-2.5 mm)
Stop Light Switch
Plunger Tip
Switch Body

Dimensions refer to Non-Turbo models only.

PARKING BRAKE

NOTE: Parking brake adjustment on 5000 Turbo is required only if rear calipers or parking brake parts are replaced.

5000 Turbo

1) Raise and support vehicle. Release parking brake lever, and ensure parking brake levers at each rear wheel are resting on caliper stops. Loosen parking brake cable adjustment if necessary. Depress brake pedal several times, then pull parking brake lever up to 3rd notch.

2) Tighten adjusting nut at equalizer until both wheels can just be turned by hand. Release parking brake lever, and check that wheels rotate freely and levers on calipers return to stops. *See Fig. 2.*

4000 & 5000 Models

1) Raise and support vehicle. Firmly depress brake pedal once. Set parking brake lever at 3rd notch (2nd on 4000) from fully released position.

Fig. 2: 5000 Turbo Rear Disc Brake Caliper Parking Brake Lever Resting Position

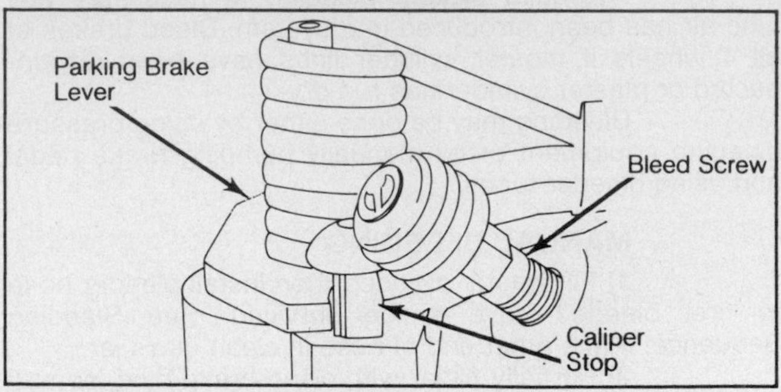
Parking Brake Lever
Bleed Screw
Caliper Stop

Brake levers should be against stops.

2) Tighten adjusting nut at equalizer until both wheels can just be turned by hand. Release parking brake lever, and ensure both wheels rotate freely.

BRAKE WARNING LIGHT

A dual warning light is mounted on dash. Light should glow when parking brake lever is pulled 1 notch, and go off when lever is fully released (ignition on).

To check circuit warning sensor, release parking brake (ignition on) and ensure light is off. Open bleeder screw on 1 wheel and depress brake pedal. Light should glow.

BRAKE PRESSURE REGULATOR

Checking & Adjusting

1) Regulator is located on rear frame. Empty vehicle, fill fuel tank, and load driver's seat to 165 lbs. (74.8 kg). Bounce rear of car several times, and allow vehicle to settle normally. Firmly depress brake pedal and release quickly. Regulator should have moved.

2) Measure distance from top of tire rim to lower edge of fender lip (both sides). Install left spring tensioner. Raise vehicle on hoist, and insert right spring tensioner (upper end only). Lower vehicle and bounce rear of car several times. Allow car to settle normally, and attach right spring tensioner to axle.

NOTE: Spring tensioners and measurement are not required if drive-on type hoist is used to support vehicle.

3) Raise vehicle and check measurement. Adjust if necessary. Connect one 1500 psi (110 kg/cm²) gauge to left front caliper and another to right rear wheel cylinder (caliper). Bleed gauges, and depress brake pedal firmly several times. Depress brake pedal until front gauge reaches reading listed in table. Check rear gauge reading.

BRAKE PRESSURE REGULATOR PRESSURES

Application	Front Gauge psi (kg/cm²)	Rear Gauge psi (kg/cm²)
4000		
1st Reading	725 (51)	457-566 (32-40)
2nd Reading	1450 (102)	725-914 (51-64)
All Other Models		
1st Reading	725 (51)	493-566 (35-40)
2nd Reading	1450 (102)	827-899 (58-63)

AUDI (Cont.)

4) If pressures are consistently high at rear gauge, loosen regulator clamp bolt and REDUCE spring tension. If pressures were consistently low, INCREASE spring tension. If specified pressures cannot be obtained after adjustment, replace regulator.

Fig. 3: Brake Pressure Regulator Adjustment

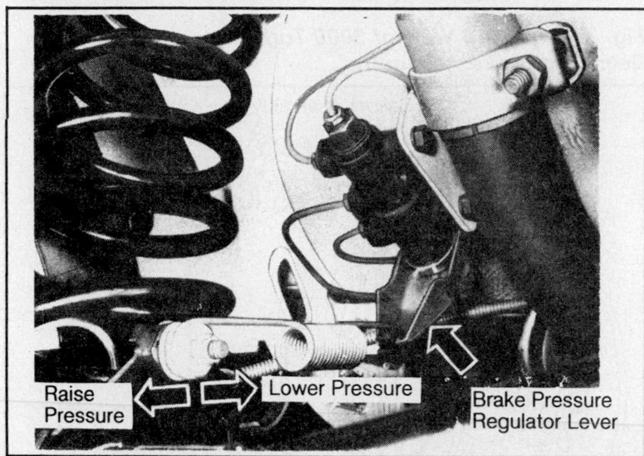
Raise Pressure
Lower Pressure
Brake Pressure Regulator Lever

4000 regulator is mounted in reverse direction.

REMOVAL & INSTALLATION

NOTE: **During removal or installation of brake pads or calipers, siphon small amount of brake fluid from master cylinder reservoir BEFORE pushing caliper piston into cylinder bore. This will prevent overflowing. Also, when reusing brake pads, mark the pads to ensure replacement in their original locations.**

NOTE: **Whenever brake pads or shoes are replaced and when brake rotors or drums are resurfaced or replaced, prevent uneven braking by making sure the part is replaced or resurfaced on both sides of the vehicle.**

FRONT DISC BRAKE PADS

Removal (5000)

1) Raise and support vehicle, remove tire and wheel. Remove plug from end of caliper guide pin. Remove Allen head bolts from top of caliper mounting frame. Thread 8 mm bolts into caliper guide pins, and pull to remove guide pins.

2) Remove caliper from mounting frame and lay aside. Remove brake pads (outer pad first), and push piston into housing.

Installation

1) Install brake pads in caliper (inner pad first) making sure to align pegs on outer brake pad with holes in caliper.

2) Install caliper assembly into mounting frame. Push caliper guide pins into mounting frame as far as possible. Install new Allen head guide pin retaining bolts in mounting frame, and replace plugs in ends of guide pins.

Removal (Coupe, 4000, 5000 Turbo)

1) Raise and support vehicle. Remove tire and wheel. Using hand pressure, force caliper to slide outward (toward outer wheel bearing) to seat piston in caliper bore.

Fig. 4: Exploded View of 5000 Front Disc Brake Assembly

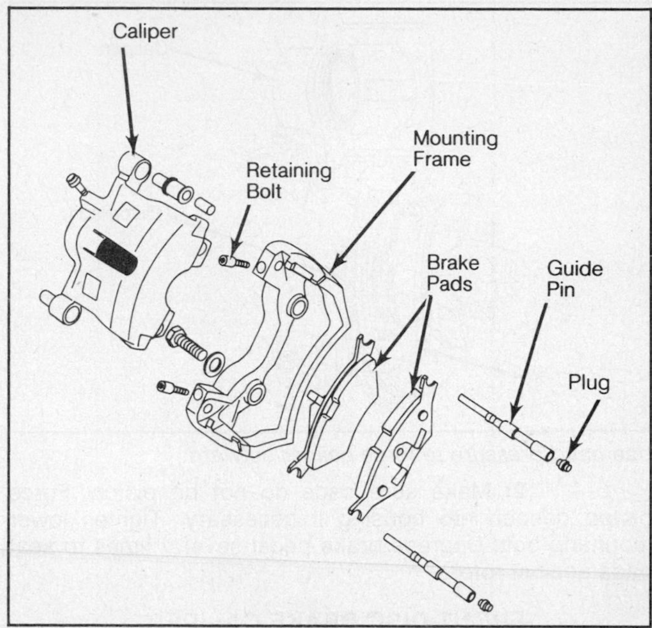
Caliper
Retaining Bolt
Mounting Frame
Brake Pads
Guide Pin
Plug

Fig. 5: Location of Guide Pins and Retaining Bolts

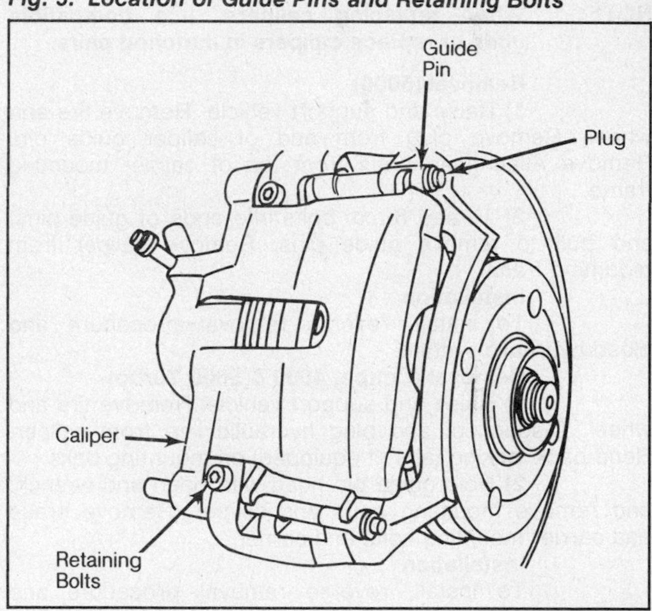
Guide Pin
Plug
Caliper
Retaining Bolts

2) Hold guide pin head with open end wrench while removing lower mounting bolt. Rotate caliper assembly upward. *See Fig. 6.* Remove disc pads from carrier.

Installation

1) Clean area where pads rest. Make sure grommets on guide pins are not damaged. Guide pins must slide smoothly in housing. Install brake pads. Swing caliper housing down.

NOTE: **When replacing disc pads on Coupe, 4000 and 5000 Turbo models, install heat shield (furnished with repair kit) on piston side of inner pad.**

AUDI (Cont.)

Fig. 6: Coupe, 4000 & 5000 Turbo Front Disc Pad Removal

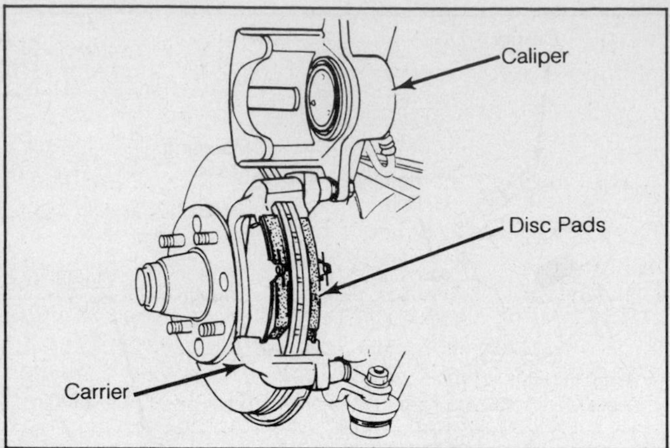
Caliper
Disc Pads
Carrier

Use hand pressure to force caliper outward.

2) Make sure pads do not hit piston. Force piston deeper into housing if necessary. Tighten lower mounting bolt. Depress brake pedal several times to seat pads against rotor.

FRONT DISC BRAKE CALIPER

NOTE: **When replacing calipers, use compatible units or replace calipers in matched pairs.**

Removal (5000)

1) Raise and support vehicle. Remove tire and wheel. Remove plug from end of caliper guide pin. Remove Allen head bolts from top of caliper mounting frame.

2) Thread 8 mm bolts into ends of guide pins, and pull to remove guide pins. Remove caliper from mounting frame.

Installation

To install, reverse removal procedure and bleed hydraulic system.

Removal (Coupe, 4000 & 5000 Turbo)

1) Raise and support vehicle. Remove tire and wheel. Disconnect and plug hydraulic line from caliper. Bend back locking tabs (if equipped) on mounting bolts.

2) Hold guide pin head with open end wrench. and remove mounting bolts and caliper. Remove brake pad carrier mounting bolts and carrier.

Installation

To install, reverse removal procedure and bleed hydraulic system.

FRONT DISC BRAKE ROTOR

Removal

1) Raise and support vehicle. Remove tire and wheel. Remove caliper as previously described and hang from vehicle frame with wire. DO NOT disconnect hydraulic line unless necessary.

2) Remove screw securing rotor to spindle (4000 modles) and pull rotor from spindle.

Installation

To install rotor assembly, reverse removal procedure. Bleed hydraulic system if necessary.

REAR DISC BRAKE PADS

NOTE: **When reusing brake pads, mark the pads to ensure replacement in their original locations.**

Removal

1) Raise and support vehicle. Remove tire and wheel. Hold guide pin head with open end wrench while removing mounting bolts.

2) Remove caliper, and hang from vehicle frame with wire. DO NOT disconnect or damage hydraulic line. Remove disc pads from carrier.

Fig. 7: Exploded View of 5000 Turbo Rear Disc Brake Assembly

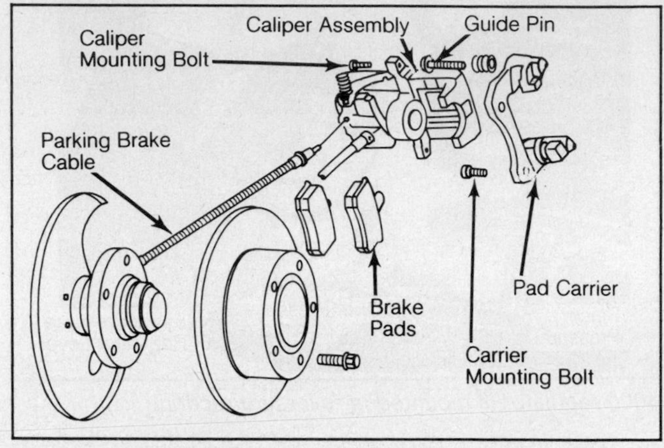
Caliper Assembly
Guide Pin
Caliper
Mounting Bolt
Parking Brake
Cable
Pad Carrier
Brake
Pads
Carrier
Mounting Bolt

Installation

1) Using an Allen wrench, turn piston in clockwise rotation while pushing it into caliper bore. Install brake pads in carrier.

2) Install caliper assembly, and tighten mounting bolts. Pump brake pedal several times to seat pads. Check parking brake adjustment, and bleed hydraulic system if necessary.

REAR DISC BRAKE CALIPER

Removal

1) Raise and support vehicle. Remove tire and wheel. Disconnect parking brake cable from caliper assembly. Disconnect and plug hydraulic line from caliper.

2) Remove caliper mounting bolts while holding guide pin head with open end wrench. Remove caliper. Remove pad carrier mounting bolts and carrier.

Installation

1) Fill caliper cylinder with brake fluid and pre-bleed caliper. Install brake pad carrier, then install caliper assembly. Tighten mounting bolts.

2) Reconnect hydraulic line and parking brake cable to caliper. Pump brake pedal 40 times to seat pads. Check parking brake adjustment and bleed hydraulic system.

REAR DISC BRAKE ROTOR

Removal

Raise and support vehicle. Remove tire and wheel. Remove caliper as previously described, and hang from frame with wire. DO NOT disconnect hydraulic line. Remove rotor from spindle.

Installation

To install, reverse removal procedure.

REAR BRAKE DRUM

Removal

1) Raise and support vehicle. Remove tire. Before removing right drum, release spring pressure on pressure regulator. Remove 1 wheel bolt.

AUDI (Cont.)

2) Using a screwdriver inserted through wheel bolt hole, push adjusting wedge upward. Reinstall wheel bolt. Remove wheel bearing hardware. Remove drum assembly without dropping thrust washer or outer bearing.

Installation

To install, reverse removal procedure and adjust wheel bearings. *See appropriate Rear Suspension article in SUSPENSION Section.* Depress brake pedal firmly to set self-adjusting mechanism.

REAR BRAKE SHOES

Removal

1) Remove brake drum. Remove hold-down springs and pins. Remove brake shoes from anchor pins and remove return springs.

2) Disconnect parking brake cable from lever. Disconnect adjusting wedge spring and upper return spring. Remove brake shoes. Place adjuster strut and shoe in vise. Remove tension spring. Separate shoe and components.

Installation

To install, reverse removal procedure and note the following: Lug on adjusting wedge faces backing plate. Adjust wheel bearings. *See appropriate Rear Suspension article in SUSPENSION Section.* Install drum and depress brake pedal firmly to set self-adjusting mechanism.

Fig. 8: Exploded View of Rear Drum Brake Assembly

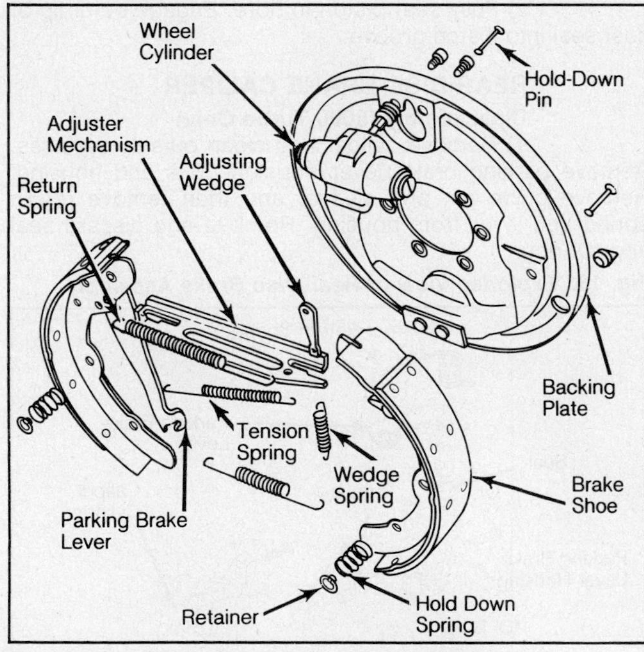
Wheel Cylinder
Hold-Down Pin
Adjuster Mechanism
Adjusting Wedge
Return Spring
Backing Plate
Tension Spring
Wedge Spring
Brake Shoe
Parking Brake Lever
Retainer
Hold Down Spring

This applies to Coupe, 4000 and 5000 models.

MASTER CYLINDER

Removal

Siphon brake fluid from reservoir and remove hydraulic lines from master cylinder. Disconnect warning light electrical lead. Remove mounting bolts, and separate master cylinder from power brake unit.

Installation

Replace "O" ring between master cylinder and power brake unit. Reverse removal procedure and bleed hydraulic system.

POWER BRAKE UNIT

Removal (Coupe, 4000 & 5000)

1) Remove master cylinder from power brake unit. Remove pin at brake pedal, and disconnect operating rod.

2) Remove mounting nuts from firewall. Disconnect vacuum line, and remove power unit.

Fig. 9: Hydraulic Power Brake Unit

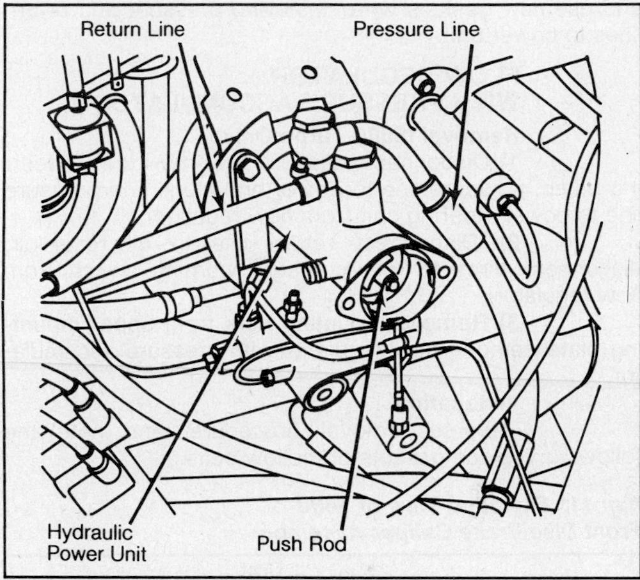
Return Line
Pressure Line
Hydraulic Power Unit
Push Rod

This applies to 5000 Turbo models.

Installation

To install, reverse removal procedure and note the following: Replace filter at operating rod end.

NOTE: **Clevis and brake lever each have 2 holes. Install clevis pin only in holes nearest front of vehicle.**

Fig. 10: Flow Regulator With Pressure Accumulator

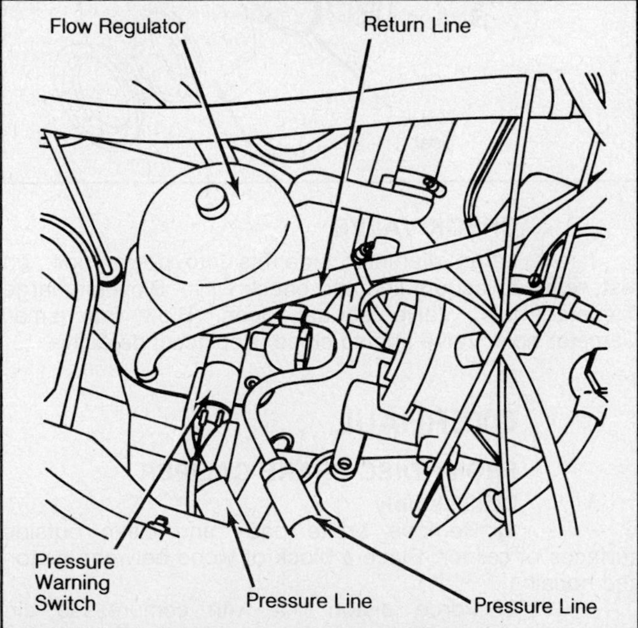
Flow Regulator
Return Line
Pressure Warning Switch
Pressure Line
Pressure Line

Flow regulator is located near master cylinder.

Removal (5000 Turbo)

1) Remove master cylinder from power brake unit. Disconnect pressure line and return line from power unit.

2) Remove push rod clevis pin. Remove power unit mounting bolts and power unit.

Installation

To install, reverse removal procedure and note the following: Install new lock clip on push rod clevis pin and use new gaskets when installing pressure and return lines to power unit.

FLOW REGULATOR WITH PRESSURE ACCUMULATOR

Removal (5000 Turbo Only)

1) Disconnect pressure line from power steering pump, pressure line to power brake unit and pressure line to power steering unit from flow regulator.

2) Disconnect return line to oil reservoir, disconnect wires to low pressure warning switch from flow regulator.

3) Remove mounting nuts from upper mounting plate, remove flow regulator with pressure accumulator.

Installation

Reverse removal procedure, and note the following: replace gaskets on hollow bolts.

Fig. 11: Exploded View of 5000 Front Disc Brake Caliper Assembly

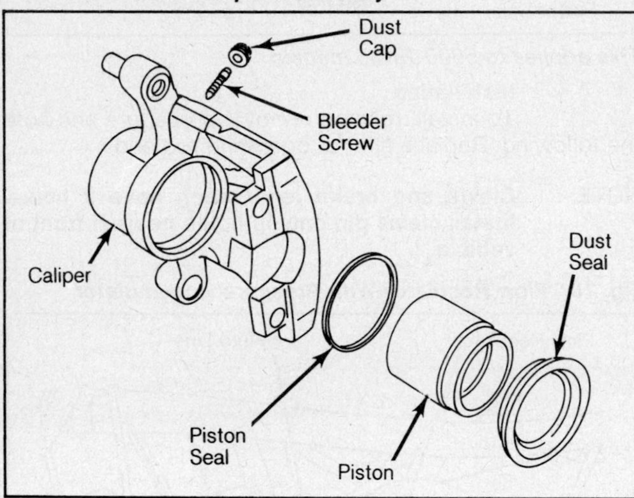
Dust Cap
Bleeder Screw
Caliper
Dust Seal
Piston Seal
Piston

CHECK VALVE

Large diameter side fits into power unit. To test, remove vacuum line and check valve. Blow into large diameter hole. Valve should open. Blow into small diameter hole. Valve should close. Replace if defective.

OVERHAUL

FRONT DISC BRAKE CALIPER

Disassembly

1) Remove brake pads and clean outside surfaces of caliper. Place a block of wood between piston and housing.

2) Force piston out with compressed air. Remove dust seal. Remove piston seal without damaging bore or groove.

Cleaning & Inspection

Clean all parts in alcohol only. Check cylinder bore and piston for wear or damage. Parts are serviced by replacement only. Boots, guide pins and other minor parts are only available with new pad carrier.

Fig. 12: Exploded View of Coupe, 4000 and 5000 Turbo Front Disc Brake Caliper Assembly

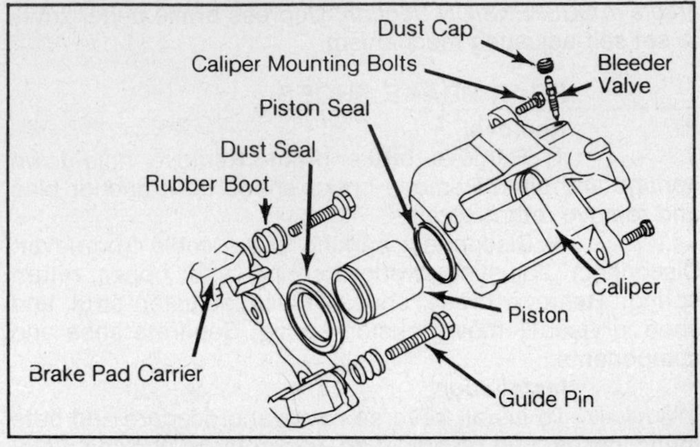
Dust Cap
Caliper Mounting Bolts
Bleeder Valve
Piston Seal
Dust Seal
Rubber Boot
Caliper
Piston
Brake Pad Carrier
Guide Pin

Reassembly

1) Coat piston, cylinder bore, and new seal with brake paste. Fit seal into cylinder. Slide dust seal onto piston. Slowly insert piston into bore, fitting inner lip of dust seal into caliper housing groove.

2) Fully seat piston in bore. Engage outer lip of dust seal into piston groove.

REAR DISC BRAKE CALIPER

Disassembly (5000 Turbo Only)

1) Remove caliper and clean outside surfaces. Remove parking brake lever housing bolts and housing. Remove guide pin and sleeve, and then remove return spring and lever from housing. Remove and discard seal and "O" ring.

Fig. 13: Exploded View of Rear Disc Brake Assembly

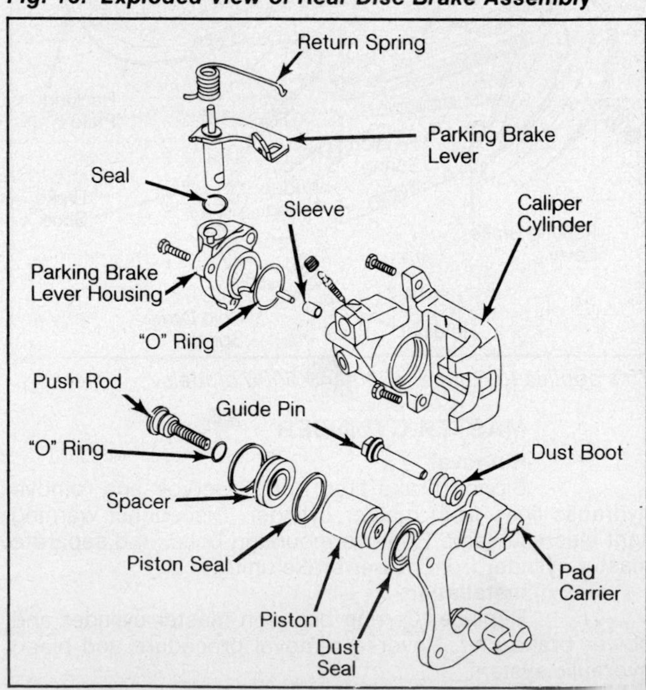
Return Spring
Parking Brake Lever
Seal
Sleeve
Caliper Cylinder
Parking Brake Lever Housing
"O" Ring
Push Rod
Guide Pin
"O" Ring
Dust Boot
Spacer
Piston Seal
Pad Carrier
Piston
Dust Seal

Ensure that push rod pin aligns with housing.

AUDI (Cont.)

2) Using hand pressure, push piston out rear of caliper asembly. Remove push rod from rear of piston, then "O" ring, seals and spacer. Carefully remove piston seal without damaging bore or groove.

Cleaning & Inspection

Clean all parts in alcohol only. Check all parts for wear or damage. Guide pins, dust boots, seals, "O" rings and pad carrier are the only serviceable parts. Any damage to other parts requires replacement of caliper assembly.

Reassembly

1) Coat piston, piston seal and parking brake guide pin with brake paste. Fit seal into cylinder groove. Slide dust seal onto piston. Install spacer, "O" ring and seal onto push rod. Fit push rod into piston. Push piston into caliper bore from rear.

2) Replace seals on parking brake lever assembly, and then install return spring and brake lever into housing. Install guide pin and sleeve in housing. Fit parking brake lever housing to rear of caliper and ensure push rod pin aligns with housing. Install and tighten bolts. Pre-bleed caliper assembly.

REAR WHEEL CYLINDER

Disassembly

Thoroughly clean outside of cylinder. Remove boots, piston assemblies, cups and spring. Remove dust cap and bleeder screw.

Cleaning & Inspection

Clean all parts in alcohol only. Check all parts for rust, corrosion or wear. If necessary, replace complete cylinder.

Fig. 15: Exploded View of Rear Wheel Cylinder

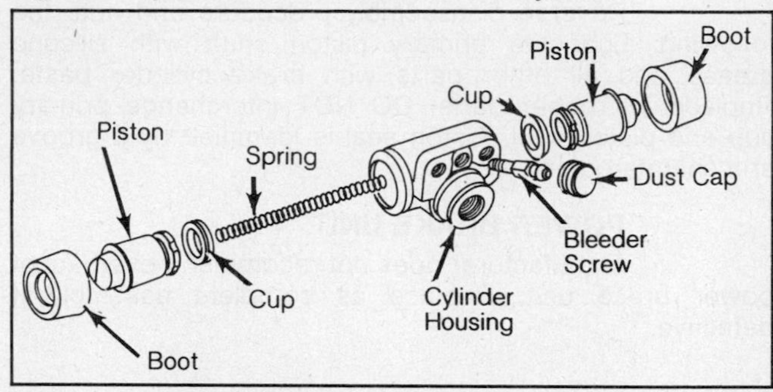

Boot
Piston
Cup
Piston
Spring
Dust Cap
Bleeder
Screw
Cup
Cylinder
Housing
Boot

Reassembly

Reverse disassembly procedure and note the following: *Refer to Fig. 15* for correct installation position of wheel cylinder pistons.

MASTER CYLINDER

Disassembly

1) Remove "O" ring from master cylinder housing. Remove piston stop screw. Remove retaining ring and both pistons from housing.

2) Remove pressure valves and reservoir from master cylinder housing. Disassemble piston assemblies as necessary.

Cleaning & Inspection

Clean all parts in alcohol and check for rust, corrosion, or other damage. Replace parts as necessary. Make sure compensating and filler holes are not plugged.

Fig. 14: Master Cylinder Component Relationship

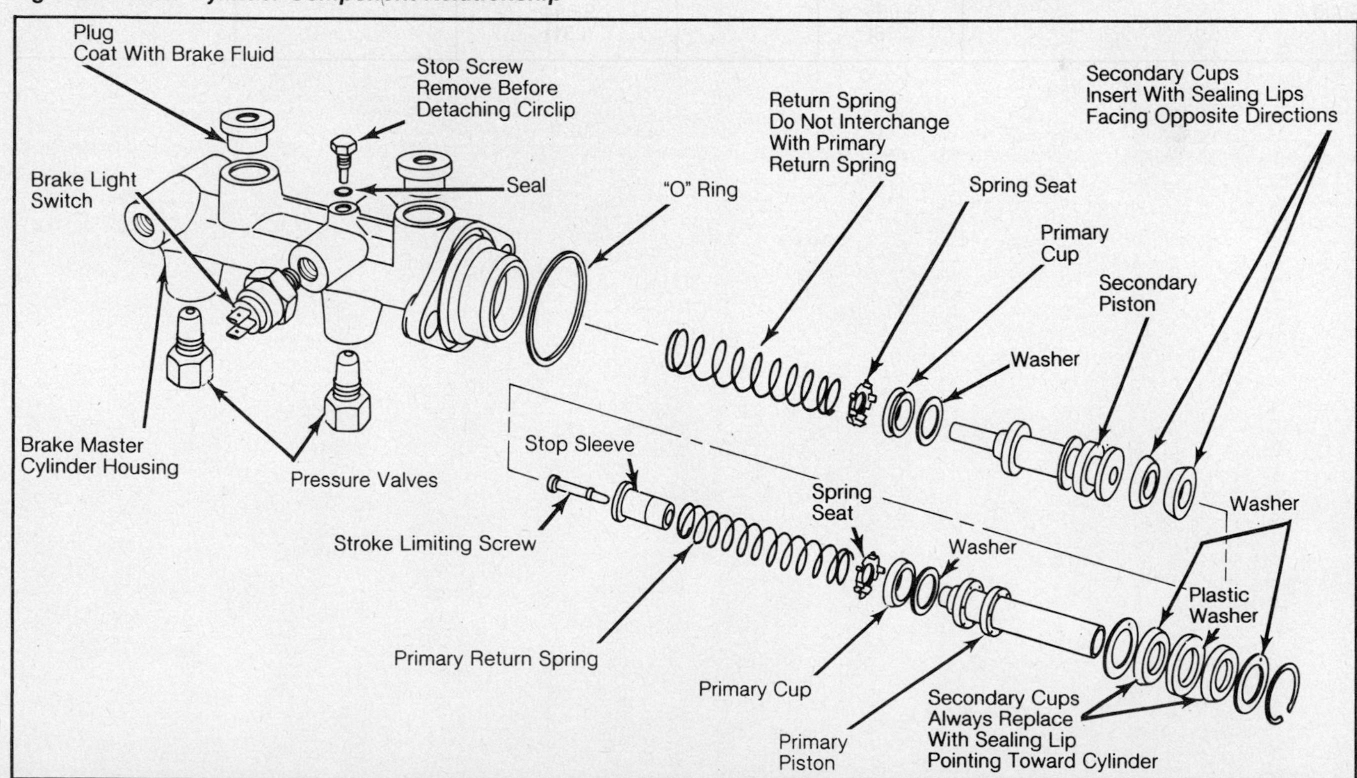

Plug
Coat With Brake Fluid
Stop Screw
Remove Before
Detaching Circlip
Return Spring
Do Not Interchange
With Primary
Return Spring
Secondary Cups
Insert With Sealing Lips
Facing Opposite Directions
Brake Light
Switch
Seal
"O" Ring
Spring Seat
Primary
Cup
Secondary
Piston
Washer
Brake Master
Cylinder Housing
Pressure Valves
Stop Sleeve
Spring
Seat
Washer
Stroke Limiting Screw
Washer
Plastic
Washer
Primary Return Spring
Primary Cup
Secondary Cups
Always Replace
With Sealing Lip
Pointing Toward Cylinder
Primary
Piston

Audi 4000 housing external design differs — internal parts are identical.

Brakes

AUDI (Cont.)

Reassembly

Reverse disassembly procedure and note the following: Lubricate primary piston shaft with silicone grease and all other parts with brake cylinder paste. Replace all rubber parts. DO NOT interchange primary cup and piston seal. Piston seal is identified by a groove and chamfered end.

POWER BRAKE UNIT

Manufacturer does not recommend overhaul of power brake unit. Replace as complete assembly if defective.

TIGHTENING SPECIFICATIONS

Application	Ft. Lbs. (N.m)
Caliper-to-Carrier Bolts	
4000 & 5000 Turbo (Front & Rear)	25 (34)
Carrier Mounting Bolts	
4000	36 (49)
5000 Turbo	
Front	83 (112)
Rear	47 (64)
Caliper Mounting Frame Bolts (5000)	83 (112)
Caliper Guide Pin Retaining Bolts (5000)	18 (24)

DISC BRAKE ROTOR SPECIFICATIONS

Application	Disc Diameter In. (mm)	Lateral Runout In. (mm)	Parallelism In. (mm)	Original Thickness In. (mm)	Min. Refinish Thickness In. (mm)	Discard Thickness In. (mm)
Coupe & 4000	.....	.002 (.06)	.0008 (.02)	.472 (12)	.....	.394 (10)
5000	.....	.002 (.06)	.0008 (.02)	.866 (22)	.....	.787 (20)
5000 Turbo						
Front	.....	.002 (.06)	.0008 (.02)	.866 (22)	.....	.787 (20)
Rear	.....	.002 (.06)	.0008 (.02)	.394 (10)	.....	.315 (8)

DRUM BRAKE SPECIFICATIONS

Application	Drum Diam. In. (mm)	Drum Width In. (mm)	Max. Drum Refinish Diam. In. (mm)	Wheel Cyl. Diam. In. (mm)	Master Cyl. Diam. In. (mm)
Coupe & 4000	7.874 (200)	.....	7.894 (200.5)	.....	.....
5000	9.055 (230)	.....	9.094 (231)	.....	.....

BMW

318i, 320i, 528e, 533i, 633CSi, 733i

DESCRIPTION

Brake system is hydraulically-operated, using a tandem master cylinder and power brake unit. All models, except 318i and 320i, are equipped with 4 piston ATE front and rear disc calipers. The 318i and 320i models are equipped with rear drum brakes and Girling front disc brake calipers.

Disc pad wear indicators are mounted on the instrument panel to indicate need for pad replacement. An optional brake pressure regulator may be installed to reduce fluid pressure to rear brakes. Parking brake is cable-actuated on drum brake of 318i and 320i models, and consists of internally-mounted parking brake shoes on all rear disc brake systems.

ADJUSTMENT

BRAKE PEDAL HEIGHT

1) Brake pedal height (measured from firewall to pedal pad center) should be 9.4-9.8" (239-249 mm) on 318i and 320i; 9.1-9.5" (230-241 mm) on 528e, 533i and 633CSi; and 9.9-10.2" (251-260 mm) on 733i.

2) To adjust pedal height, loosen stop light switch lock nut, and position stop light switch out of way. Loosen brake operating rod lock nut, and turn operating rod until correct pedal height is obtained. Tighten lock nut. Reposition and adjust stop light switch. Tighten stop light switch lock nut.

STOP LIGHT SWITCH

Stop light switch is located under instrument panel in front of brake pedal arm. To adjust stop light switch, loosen lock nut. Turn adjusting nut so contact plunger just touches pedal arm and extended length of plunger is .20-.24" (5-6 mm). Tighten lock nut.

PARKING BRAKE

NOTE: Before adjusting parking brake (except 320i), pull parking brake lever until resistance is felt; then 1 additional notch. With parking brake lever engaged as described, drive vehicle a maximum of 1/4 mile.

318i

1) Lift out front clamp. Pull off rubber cap. Disconnect rear clamp. Unscrew adjusting bolts. Operate brake pedal several times. Basic clearance is automatically adjusted. Listen for clicking noise on rear wheels.

2) Pull up parking brake lever by 5 teeth. Adjust adjusting nuts enough so that rear wheels can just be turned evenly. Release lever. Check that wheels can be turned easily and that indicator light goes out with ignition switch on. Adjust switch, if necessary.

320i

1) Raise and support rear of vehicle. Fully release parking brake. Tighten brake shoes until wheel is locked. Back off adjusters about 1/8 turn or until wheel can just barely turn.

2) Working inside passenger compartment, tighten nuts on lever until parking brake holds vehicle securely before 6th ratchet stop is reached.

528e, 533i, 633CSi, 733i

1) Raise and support vehicle. Remove tire and wheel, and release parking brake. Insert a screwdriver into rotor inspection hole. Turn adjuster until parking brake shoes lock rotor. Back off adjuster 4-6 notches.

2) Working inside driver's compartment, tighten adjustment nuts on lever until parking brake holds vehicle securely before 5th ratchet stop is reached.

BRAKE WARNING LIGHT

1) A dual warning light is mounted on instrument panel. Light should glow when parking brake lever is pulled 1 notch (ignition on) and go off when lever is fully released.

2) To check circuit warning sensor, fully release parking brake, and ensure light is off (ignition on). Raise master cylinder filler cap. Warning lamp should glow. If not, check bulb or circuit connections.

REMOVAL & INSTALLATION

DISC PADS

Removal

1) Raise and support vehicle. Remove wheel and tire. Disconnect pad wear sensors. Bend open fastener, and pull out. Drive out retaining pin toward inside of vehicle. Remove cross spring.

2) Using extractor tool, remove pads from caliper. If pad thickness has worn to .080" (2 mm), replace pads. Only replace pads in matched sets.

Installation

1) Using a cylinder brush, clean guide surface and support surface in caliper. Siphon sufficient fluid from master cylinder reservoir to prevent overflowing. Press pistons to bottom of bores.

2) On rear calipers, ensure machined position of piston face makes a 20° angle with caliper wall. *See Fig. 1.* Rotate piston with tool (341050), if necessary.

3) On ATE front calipers, install disc pads, shims (if required), cross spring and retaining pins. After installation, depress brake pedal several times to seat pads.

4) On Girling calipers, adjust shoulders of pistons so that guards are located at machined shoulders of piston. If necessary, use guard as adjusting template.

5) Install pads, cross spring, and retaining pins. Replace fastener, bending straight side. After installation, depress pedal several times to seat pads.

CALIPER ASSEMBLY

Removal

Drain brake fluid from master cylinder reservoir. Remove caliper mounting bolts. Disconnect disc pad wear indicator electrical lead. Disconnect brake fluid inlet lines. Lift caliper off rotor.

Installation

Reverse removal procedure and then bleed the hydraulic system.

ROTOR

Removal

Raise and support vehicle. Remove tire and wheel. On front calipers, separate bracket from strut. On all models, remove caliper, and hang from frame with wire.

Brakes

BMW (Cont.)

DO NOT disconnect hydraulic line. On rear calipers, slip hydraulic line out of holding clamp. Remove rotor mounting bolt, and remove brake rotor.

NOTE: **Front brake rotors are balanced. DO NOT remove or reposition balance clips. If any rotor must be replaced, replace rotors in axle sets.**

Fig. 1: Piston Alignment for Rear Brake Calipers

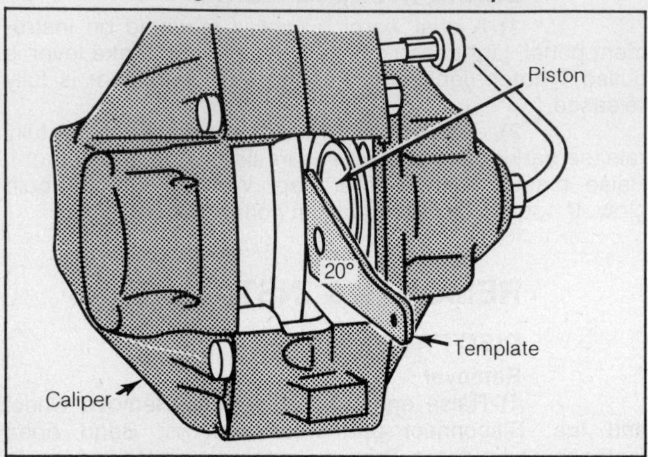
Piston
20°
Template
Caliper

Use template to achieve 20° angle.

Installation

To install, reverse removal procedure.

PARKING BRAKE SHOES

Removal

With rear caliper and rotor removed, disconnect upper return spring using brake spring pliers. Using brake spring removal tool (34 4 000), turn retaining springs 90°. Set spring aside. Pull brake shoes apart at bottom and lift upward.

Installation

To install, reverse removal procedure, adjust parking brake shoes, and check operation.

BRAKE DRUM

Removal & Installation

Loosen brake adjuster cams. Remove countersunk Allen bolt, and slide off brake drum. To install, reverse removal procedure and note: If one brake drum is reground, drum on other side must also be reground.

BRAKE SHOES

Removal

Remove brake drum. Disengage mounting spring and hold-down spring clip from each shoe. Disconnect bottom return spring. Pull shoes apart and out of each wheel cylinder. Disconnect parking brake cable, and remove brake shoes. If brake shoe lining has worn to .118" (3.0 mm) or less, replace brake shoes.

Installation

Reverse removal procedure and note: Connect long end of spring between parking brake lever and brake shoe.

REAR AXLE SEALS & BEARINGS

Removal

1) Raise and support vehicle. Remove wheel and brake drum assembly. Remove drive shaft. Loosen castellated nut (all 6-cyl. models) securing flange to drvieaxle. Using a puller, remove flange.

Fig. 2: Exploded View of Rear Drum Brake Assembly

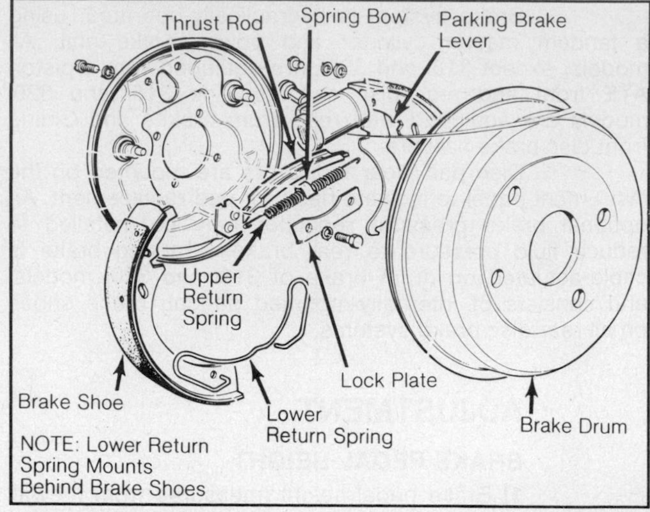
Thrust Rod
Spring Bow
Parking Brake Lever
Upper Return Spring
Lock Plate
Brake Shoe
Lower Return Spring
Brake Drum
NOTE: Lower Return Spring Mounts Behind Brake Shoes

320i models shown; 318i models similar.

2) On all models, install castellated nut on axle shaft and drive out drive axle using a soft-headed mallet. Remove bearings and seals. Remove spacer sleeve and shim, if equipped.

Installation

To install, reverse removal procedure. Install inner bearing. Determine distance between outer races of inner and outer bearings.

MASTER CYLINDER

NOTE: **On 320i models only, mixture control unit must be removed to take off master cylinder.**

Removal

1) Siphon off brake fluid from reservoir. On 318i, 528e and 533i models, pull off plugs and clutch hydraulic hose. On 320i, disconnect clutch hose connection. On 633CSi, remove brake fluid tank.

2) On all models, disconnect all hydraulic lines from master cylinder. Remove nuts mounting master cylinder to power booster. On 320i models, remove nuts mounting master cylinder support to inner fender panel. On all models, remove support and master cylinder.

Installation

To install, reverse removal procedure and note: Make sure "O" ring on master cylinder is not damaged. An imperfect fit will not allow correct vacuum build-up.

POWER BRAKE UNIT

NOTE: **Power brake unit must be removed with master cylinder attached. On 320i, mixture control unit must be removed prior to removal of power brake unit.**

Removal

1) Siphon brake fluid from master cylinder reservoir. On all models except 320i, remove left portion of lower dash panel. On all models, remove operating rod clevis pin from brake pedal arm. Disconnect and plug hydraulic lines at master cylinder, including clutch hose.

BMW (Cont.)

2) Disconnect vacuum hose from power brake unit (hydraulic lines on 733i). Remove power brake unit mounting bolts. On 320i only, separate master cylinder support from inner fender panel. Remove power unit/master cylinder assembly from vehicle. Separate master cylinder from power brake unit.

NOTE: On 533i, 633CSi and 733i models, power steering pump also supplies hydraulic pressure through hydraulic accumulator to the power brake unit. If power steering fails, there will be sufficient pressure in the hydraulic accumulator to provide a few brake applications with full power.

Installation

To install, mount master cylinder to power brake unit, and reverse removal procedure. Bleed hydraulic system after installation.

Check Valve Replacement (318i & 320i)

Check valve is located in vacuum line between power unit and intake manifold. To remove, loosen hose clamps, remove vacuum lines, and remove valve. To install, reverse removal procedure. Make sure arrow or black portion of valve faces intake manifold.

OVERHAUL

BRAKE CALIPER

NOTE: DO NOT disassemble 4-piston caliper halves.

Disassembly

With pads removed from caliper, remove retaining ring and dust boot. Using clamp, hold one piston in position, and insert wooden block in caliper cavity. Apply compressed air to fluid inlet to force out opposite piston. Repeat procedure for each piston. Remove piston seals without damaging caliper bore.

Fig. 3: Disassembled View of 2-Piston Caliper

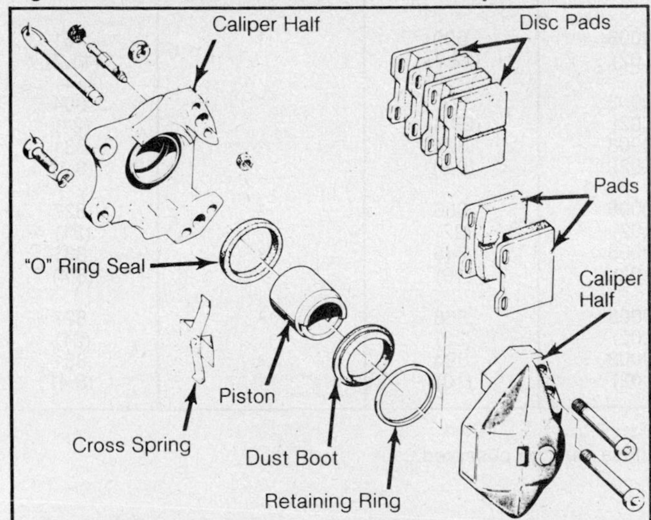
Caliper Half
Disc Pads
Pads
"O" Ring Seal
Caliper Half
Piston
Cross Spring
Dust Boot
Retaining Ring

Caliper is used as rear caliper on 528e, 533i, 633CSi and 733i models and front caliper on 318i and 320i models.

Cleaning & Inspection

Clean components in clean brake fluid, and blow dry. Inspect caliper bore and pistons for wear or damage. Replace caliper assembly if corroded or worn. DO NOT hone. Replace piston seals and dust boots at each overhaul.

Reassembly

Coat pistons and calipers bores with brake cylinder paste. Install piston seals, then install pistons. Make sure pistons are not tilted when inserting. On 2-piston calipers, ensure 20° piston angle is preset. Install dust boots and retaining rings.

Fig. 4: Disassembled View of 4-Piston Caliper

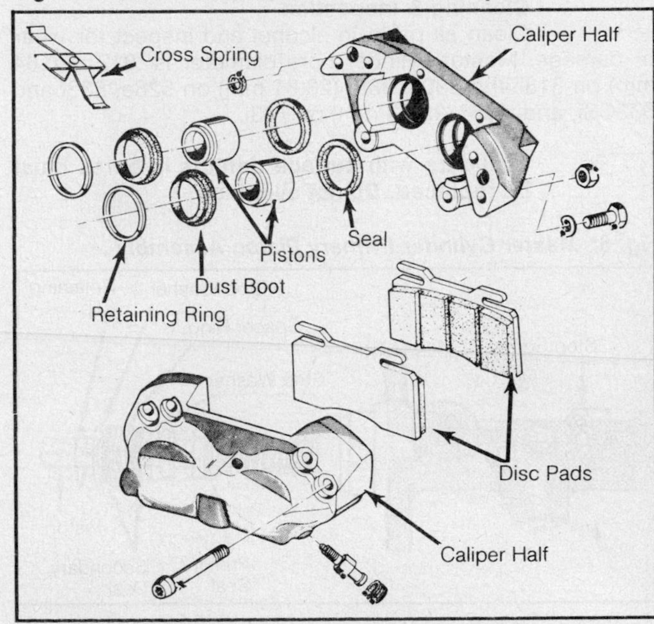
Caliper Half
Cross Spring
Seal
Pistons
Dust Boot
Retaining Ring
Disc Pads
Caliper Half

Caliper is used as front caliper on 528e, 533i, 633CSi and 733i.

REAR WHEEL CYLINDER

Disassembly

Remove dust boots and force out pistons and return spring. Separate and discard cylinder cups from pistons.

Cleaning & Inspection

Clean all parts in clean brake fluid. Check cylinder bore and dust boot retaining grooves for rust and corrosion. Replace wheel cylinder assembly if defective. DO NOT hone. Replace all rubber parts during overhaul.

Reassembly

Coat all parts with brake cylinder paste. Reassemble wheel cylinder by reversing disassembly procedure.

Fig. 5: Exploded View of 320i Rear Wheel Cylinder

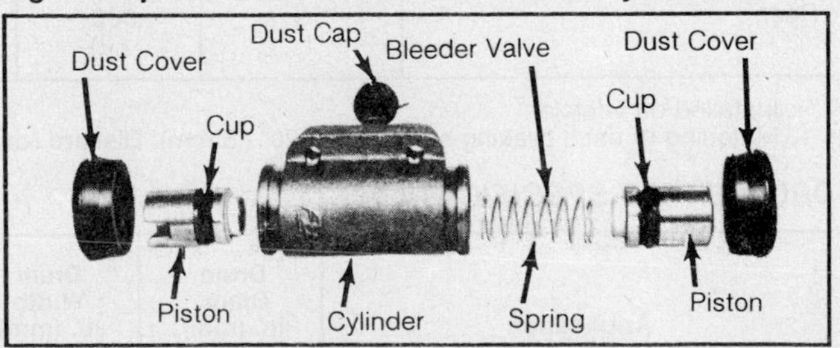
Dust Cap
Bleeder Valve
Dust Cover
Dust Cover
Cup
Cup
Piston
Cylinder
Spring
Piston

BMW (Cont.)

MASTER CYLINDER

NOTE: All master cylinders are similar. Procedures outlined are general.

Disassembly

Push in on primary piston, and remove secondary piston stop screw. Remove snap ring from end of cylinder, and remove primary and secondary piston assemblies and return spring. Disassemble piston assemblies, noting number and position of parts used.

Cleaning & Inspection

Clean all parts in alcohol and inspect for wear or damage. Master cylinder bore diameter is .812" (20.64 mm) on 318i and 320i; .938" (23.81 mm) on 528e, 533i and 633CSi; and .875" (22.23 mm) on 733i.

NOTE: Cylinders with surface defects in bores must be replaced. Do not overhaul.

Fig. 6: Master Cylinder Primary Piston Assembly

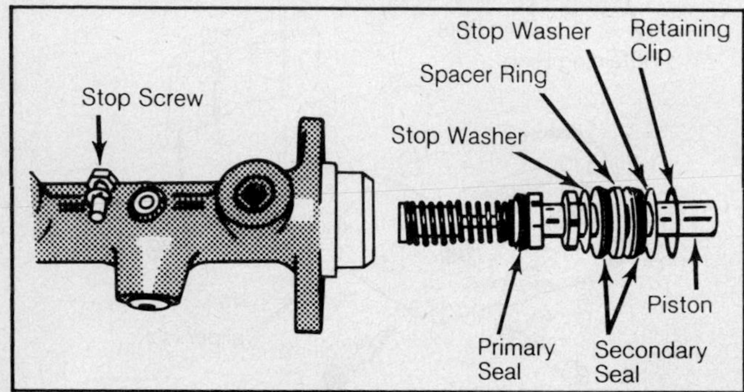
Stop Washer
Retaining Clip
Spacer Ring
Stop Screw
Stop Washer
Piston
Primary Seal
Secondary Seal

Reassembly

Reassemble piston assemblies using thin coating of ATE brake paste. Install piston assemblies into cylinder bore, using a guide sleeve to prevent damage to seals. Install secondary piston stop screw, making sure piston is pushed fully forward before screw is installed and tightened. Install retaining ring in end of master cylinder bore.

Fig. 7: Master Cylinder Secondary (Front) Piston Assy.

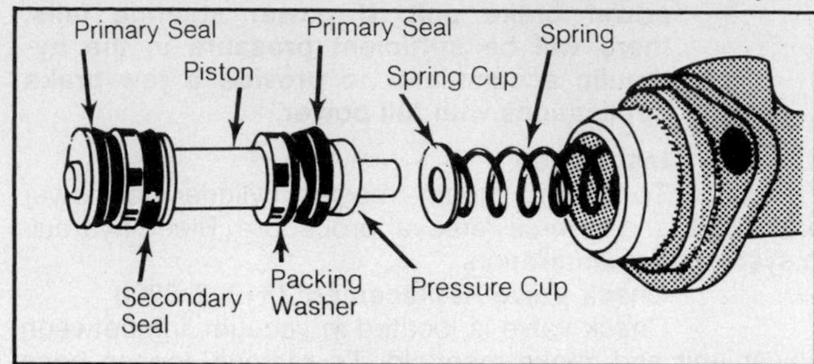
Primary Seal
Primary Seal
Spring
Piston
Spring Cup
Secondary Seal
Packing Washer
Pressure Cup

TIGHTENING SPECIFICATIONS

Application	Ft. Lbs. (N.m)
Caliper Mounting Bolts	
Front	58-69 (79-94)
Rear	43-48 (58-65)
Rotor-to-Wheel Hub	
318i & 320i	36-42 INCH Lbs. (4-5 N.m)
528e, 533i & 633CSi	11-13 (15-18)
733i	23-24 (30-33)

DISC BRAKE ROTOR SPECIFICATIONS

Application	Disc Diameter In. (mm)	Lateral Runout In. (mm)	Parallelism In. (mm)	Original Thickness In. (mm)	Min. Refinish Thickness In. (mm)	Discard Thickness In. (mm)
318i & 320i						
Front	.....	.008 [1] (.2)	.0008 (.02)	.500 (12.7)	[2]	.461 (11.7)
528e & 533i						
Front	.....	.008 [1] (.2)	.0008 (.02)	.866 (20.4)	[2]	.804 (21)
Rear	.....	.008 [1] (.2)	.0008 (.02)	.374 (9.5)	[2]	.331 (8.4)
633CSi						
Front	.....	.008 [1] (.2)	.0008 (.02)	.866 (22)	[2]	.827 (21)
Rear	.....	.008 [1] (.2)	.0008 (.02)	.748 (19)	[2]	.331 (8.4)
733i						
Front	.....	.008 [1] (.2)	.0008 (.02)	.866 (22)	[2]	.827 (21)
Rear	.....	.008 [1] (.2)	.0008 (.02)	.394 (10)	[2]	.331 (8.4)

[1] – Installed on vehicle.
[2] – Matching of each braking surface is .020" (.5 mm). Discard rotor thickness must be observed.

DRUM BRAKE SPECIFICATIONS

Application	Drum Diam. In. (mm)	Drum Width In. (mm)	Max. Drum Refinish Diam. In. (mm)	Wheel Cyl. Diam. In. (mm)	Master Cyl. Diam. In. (mm)
318i & 320i					
Rear	9.84 (250)	.....	9.04 (230)	3/4 (19.05)	.....

Brakes

CHRYSLER CORP. IMPORTS

Challenger, Colt, Colt Pickup, Ram-50 Pickup, Sapporo

DESCRIPTION

Brake system is hydraulically-operated using a master cylinder with a single reservoir and 2 outlets, a vacuum power brake unit, and a proportioning valve (or combination valve) to control braking action. All brake systems are self-adjusting.

Colt models are equipped with pin caliper type front disc brakes. Challenger, Sapporo, and Colt/Ram-50 Pickups are equipped with sliding caliper type front disc brakes.

All 2WD Pickups and 4WD gasoline-powered Pickups use duo-servo type drum brakes. All other models with rear drum brakes use the leading/trailing shoe design. The parking brake cable actuates the rear drum brakes.

Rear disc brakes are available as an option on Challenger and Sapporo models.

COMBINATION & PROPORTIONING VALVES

Different types of proportioning valves are used depending upon vehicle model. Proportioning valve function testing is similar, however, for all models.

Challenger and Sapporo With Rear Disc Brakes

These models use a Blend Proportioning Valve (BPV), with a Red color-coding mark. It is located near front wheels.

The BPV accomplishes 2 functions. It improves braking efficiency by distributing braking force to front and rear wheels. It also increases braking force to rear wheels, when large braking force is required or front brakes fail.

Fig. 1: Sectional View of Combination Valve

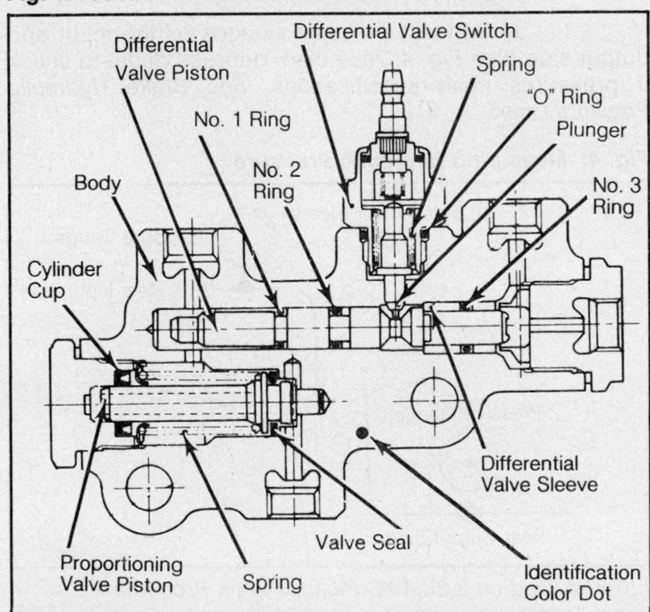
Differential Valve Piston
Differential Valve Switch
Spring
"O" Ring
Plunger
No. 1 Ring
No. 2 Ring
No. 3 Ring
Body
Cylinder Cup
Differential Valve Sleeve
Valve Seal
Proportioning Valve Piston
Spring
Identification Color Dot

Valve shown is for Challenger & Sapporo with rear drum brakes.

Challenger & Sapporo With Rear Drum Brakes

These models use a Combination Valve, identified by a Pink color coding mark. *See Fig. 1.* The valve is located near front wheels.

The combination valve, which includes both a proportioning and differential valve, accomplishes 3 functions. It provides pressure control of rear service brakes, deactivates rear brake pressure control when front service brakes fail, and provides warning in event of trouble.

NOTE: Do not attempt to disassemble combination valve, as its performance is based on the factory setting.

Colt

On Colt models, the valve body contains 2 separate proportioning valves. Each valve must be checked separately. *See Fig. 2.* Valve body is identified with "A150" stamped on plug.

Fig. 2: Colt Valve Body with 2 Proportioning Valves

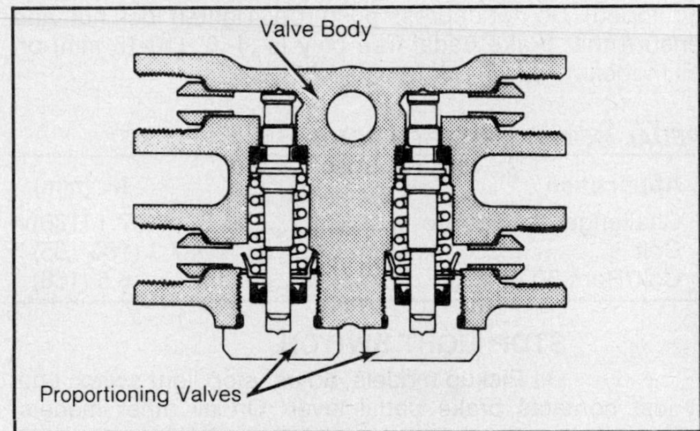
Valve Body
Proportioning Valves

Each valve must be tested separately.

All Pickups Except 4WD Diesel

Gasoline-powered Pickups and all diesel-powered 2WD Pickups use a Blend Proportioning Valve (BPV). *See Fig. 3.* On 2WD models, it is located near rear wheels; on 4WD models, it is located near front wheels.

Fig. 3: Blend Proportioning Valve for Pickups

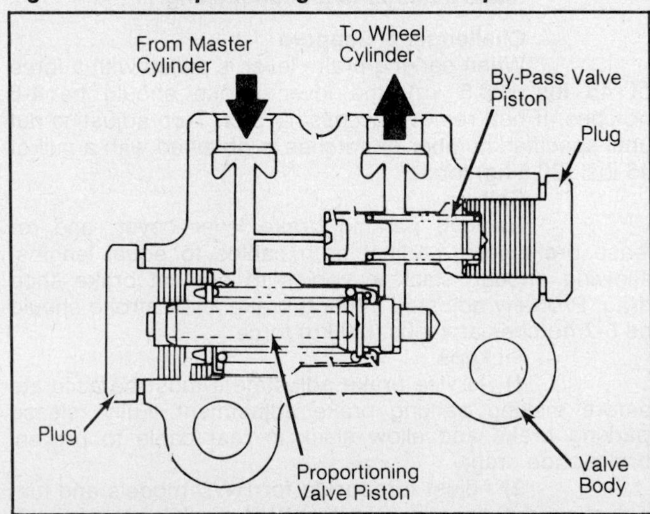
From Master Cylinder
To Wheel Cylinder
By-Pass Valve Piston
Plug
Plug
Proportioning Valve Piston
Valve Body

BPV valve is used on all Pickups except 4WD Diesel.

CHRYSLER CORP. IMPORTS (Cont.)

The BPV accomplishes 2 functions. It improves braking efficiency by distributing braking force to front and rear wheels. It also increases braking force to rear wheels, when large braking force is required or front brakes fail.

4WD Diesel Pickups

All diesel-powered 4WD Pickups use a Load Sensing Proportioning Valve (LSPV), located near the rear wheels. *See Figs. 4 and 5.*

The LSPV provides 3 functions. It responds to vehicle load condition by preventing early lock-up of the front wheels, provides stability during braking, and adds extra fluid pressure control to the rear wheels should the front brake system fail.

ADJUSTMENT

PEDAL HEIGHT & FREE PLAY

Back off stop light switch. To adjust pedal height (distance from top of pedal to floor board), loosen lock nut, and rotate master cylinder push rod (yoke, if equipped). Do not depress push rod. Tighten lock nut, and ensure that brake pedal free play is .4-.6" (10-15 mm) on all models.

PEDAL HEIGHT SPECIFICATIONS

Application	In. (mm)
Challenger & Sapporo	7.1 (180)
Colt	7.1-7.3 (180-185)
Colt/Ram-50 Pickup	6.5 (166)

STOP LIGHT SWITCH

On Pickup models, adjust stop light switch until it just contacts brake pedal lever. On all other models, loosen lock nut and adjust switch-to-pedal arm clearance to .02-.04" (0.5-1.0 mm). Tighten lock nut. Do not depress master cylinder push rod during stop light switch adjustment.

PARKING BRAKE

NOTE: **On all models, if parking brake lever stroke is longer than specified after adjustment, automatic adjuster is malfunctioning.**

Challenger & Sapporo

When parking brake lever is pulled with a force of 45 lbs. (20.5 kg), the lever stroke should be 4-6 notches. If not, remove accessory box. Turn adjusting nut until specified number of notches is obtained with a pull of 45 lbs. (20.5 kg) force.

Colt

Remove parking brake lever cover, and release brake lever. Adjust both cables to equal lengths, allowing enough slack in cables to prevent brake shoe drag. Properly adjusted parking brake lever stroke should be 5-7 notches at 44 lbs. (20 kg) force.

Pickups

1) Service brake adjustment must be accurate before making parking brake adjustment. Fully release parking brake and allow slack in rear cable to prevent brake shoe drag.

2) Adjust turnbuckle for RWD models and turn adjusting nut on equalizer for 4WD models, to obtain a brake lever stroke of 16-17 notches with a 66 lb. (30 kg) setting force.

3) On 2WD models, balancer must be parallel with center line of vehicle. On 4WD models, the equalizing joint must be at right angles to each other.

TESTING

DIFFERENTIAL VALVE SWITCH TEST

Challenger & Sapporo With Rear Drum Brakes

1) Remove bleeder cap from one of the bleeder screws. Connect one end of a vinyl tube to bleeder screw. Place other end in a glass container. Loosen bleeder screw.

2) Connect ohmmeter leads to combination valve's differential valve switch and ground. *See Fig. 1.* Depress brake pedal. If continuity exists, differential valve switch is good.

COMBINATION VALVE & BPV VALVE PRESSURE TEST

NOTE: **On Colt models, the valve body contains 2 proportioning valves. Each must be tested separately.**

Use 2 pressure gauges that measure at least 2000 psi 140.6 (kg/cm²). Hook one gauge to master cylinder rear side and the other to rear wheel cylinder. Pressure readings should be as specified. *See Brake Hydraulic Pressure Chart.* Replace defective part as required. Do not disassemble combination or BPV valves.

LSPV VALVE PRESSURE TEST

NOTE: **The vehicle must be on a level surface, in an unloaded condition, and not supported in any way, except by its own wheels.**

1) Connect pressure gauges to the input and output side. *See Fig. 4.*Once bled, depress pedal to check if pressures meet specifications. *See Brake Hydraulic Pressure Chart.*

Fig. 4: Measuring Hydraulic Pressure

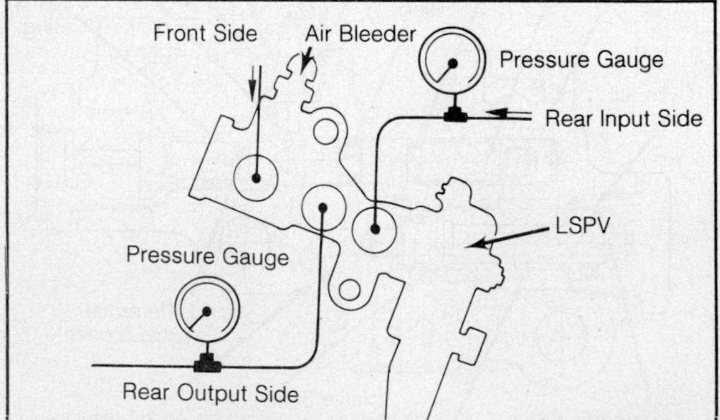
Front Side
Air Bleeder
Pressure Gauge
Rear Input Side
LSPV
Pressure Gauge
Rear Output Side

LSPV is used on 2.3L 4WD Pickups only. Procedure is similar for other valves.

CHRYSLER CORP. IMPORTS (Cont.)

2) With pedal depressed, open bleeder screw of LSPV. If both pressures are equal, the fail safe system is operating. If the pressures are not within specifications, loosen spring support bolt and adjust the length of the sensor spring. *See Fig. 5.*

Fig. 5: Load Sensing Proportioning Valve

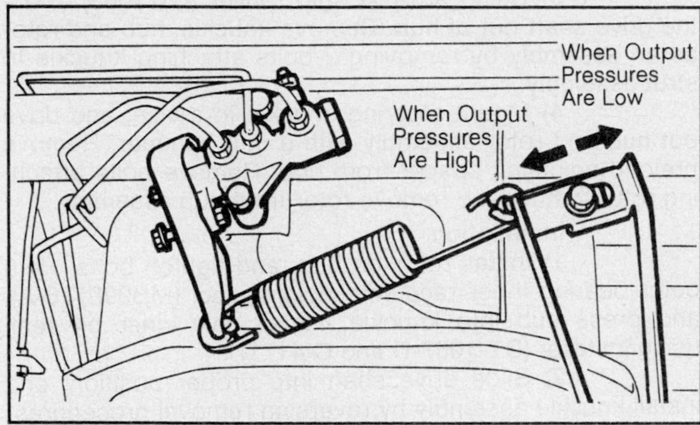
When Output Pressures Are Low
When Output Pressures Are High

Loosen bolt to adjust sensor spring length.

3) If adjustments do not meet specifications, replace LSPV and sensor spring as a set.

SENSOR SPRING LENGTH

Application	In. (mm)
Sensor Spring	7.29-7.31 (185-187)

BRAKE HYDRAULIC PRESSURE CHART

Application	Wheel Cyl. psi (kg/cm^2)	Master Cyl. psi (kg/cm^2)
Challenger & Sapporo		
Rear Disc	556-569 (39-40)	1138 (80)
Rear Drum	569 (40)	569 (40)
	674 (47)	853 (60)
	779 (55)	1138 (80)
Colt	519-590 (37-42)	953 (67)
Diesel 4WD Pickups		
LSPV	410-492 (29-35)	853 (60)
	712-827 (50-58)	1990 (140)
Other Pickups		
BPV		
2WD	437-494 (31-35)	711 (50)
	633-718 (45-51)	996 (70)
	775-860 (55-61)	1138 (80)
4WD	398-455 (28-32)	853 (60)
	604-690 (43-49)	1138 (80)
	747-832 (53-59)	1280 (60)

WARNING LIGHT TEST

To test warning light, if equipped, loosen bleeder screw of 1 wheel cylinder, and depress brake pedal. Warning light should come on. If not, check switch and wire connector.

PROPORTIONING VALVE RESET

Challenger & Sapporo

After repairs on brake system, bleed brake lines. With all lines bled and bleeder valves secured, depress brake pedal hard. This will center valve and warning light should go out.

REMOVAL & INSTALLATION

FRONT DISC BRAKE PADS

Removal (Colt)

1) Raise and support vehicle. Remove front wheel. Remove protector by prying up edge of clip at center of protector. Hold center of "M" clip, detach "M" clip from pad and its ends from retaining pins. Remove clip.

2) Remove retaining pins from caliper, and remove "K" spring. Remove pads and anti-squeal springs from caliper by grasping backing plate area of pads with pliers.

Fig. 6: Installing Spring and Clip on Brake Pads

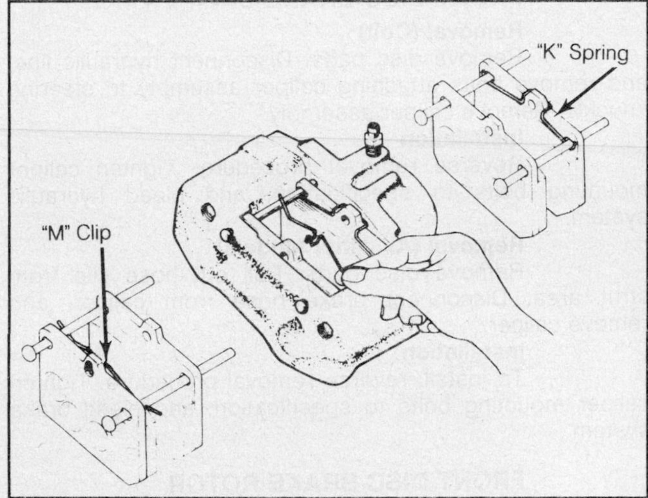
"K" Spring
"M" Clip

Illustration applies to Colt models.

NOTE: Replace all pads (left and right side) at same time.

Installation

Press piston to bottom of bore using a suitable tool. Install disc pads and retaining pins. Install "K" spring and "M" clip, making sure positions are not reversed. *See Fig. 6.* Install pad protector with retaining clips on inner side of caliper.

Removal (All Other Models)

1) Raise and support vehicle. Remove front wheel. Remove spigot pins and pull out stopper plugs.

2) Pull caliper assembly up and down in a diagonal manner and remove from mounting bracket. Remove inner and outer pad clips. Pull pads and anti-squeal shims from caliper support.

Installation

To install, reverse removal procedure. Press piston to bottom of caliper bore prior to pad installation. Ensure pad retaining clips are installed properly. *See Fig. 7.*

CHRYSLER CORP. IMPORTS (Cont.)

Fig. 7: Installing Pad Retaining Clips

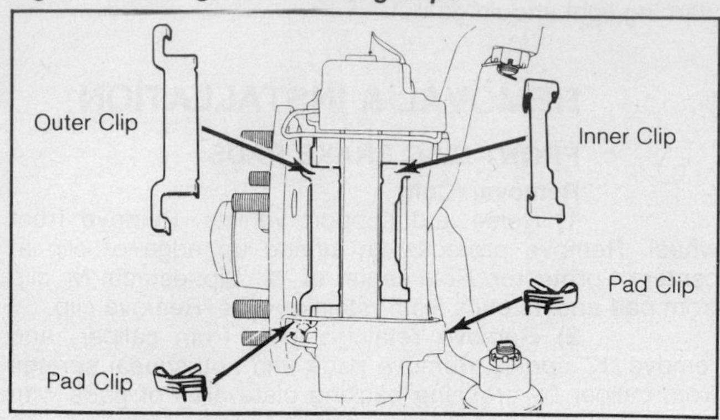
Outer Clip
Inner Clip
Pad Clip
Pad Clip

Illustration applies to Challenger, Pickups & Sapporo.

FRONT DISC BRAKE CALIPER

Removal (Colt)

Remove disc pads. Disconnect hydraulic line, and remove bolts attaching caliper assembly to steering knuckle. Remove caliper assembly.

Installation

Reverse removal procedure. Tighten caliper mounting bolts to specification, and bleed hydraulic system.

Removal (All Other Models)

Remove disc pads. Pull out hose clip from strut area. Disconnect brake hose from caliper, and remove caliper.

Installation

To install, reverse removal procedure. Tighten caliper mounting bolts to specification, and bleed brake system.

FRONT DISC BRAKE ROTOR

Removal (Colt)

1) Remove center cap, loosen drive shaft nut, lift vehicle, and remove wheels. Remove undercover. Remove lower arm ball joint and strut bar from lower arm.

CAUTION: Place ball joint of lower arm on lower arm to prevent damage to the ball joint dust boot.

Fig. 8: Removing Drive Shaft From Transaxle

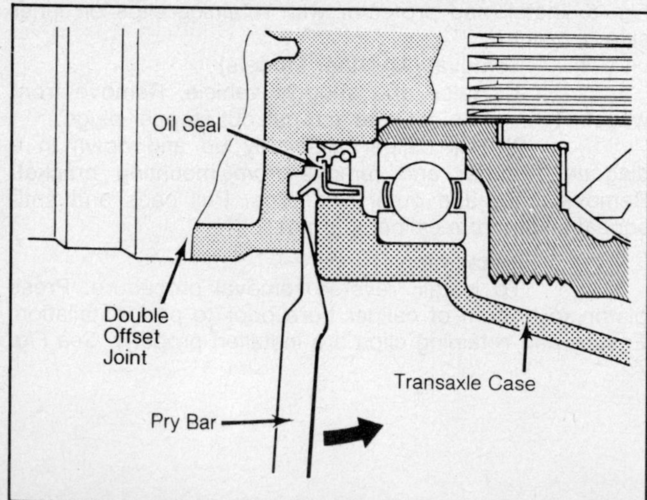
Oil Seal
Double
Offset
Joint
Transaxle Case
Pry Bar

Procedure is shown for Colt model.

2) Drain transaxle fluid, and remove caliper assembly. Insert pry bar between transaxle case and double offset joint outer case. To avoid damaging inner seal, do not insert pry bar more than .28" (7 mm). *See Fig. 8.* Push pry bar toward center of vehicle to remove drive shaft from transaxle.

3) Using an axle shaft puller (CT-1003), force the drive shaft out of hub. Remove knuckle, hub and rotor as an assembly by removing 2 bolts attaching knuckle to strut assembly.

4) Mount steering knuckle in a vise, and drive out hub and rotor assembly with a soft hammer. Remove preload adjusting spacer from hub. Remove bolts attaching rotor to hub, and remove rotor from hub assembly.

Installation

1) Install rotor on hub, and tighten bolts. Hold outer bearing inner race with holding tool (MB990776-A), and press hub into knuckle. Install new inner oil seal, using installer (DT-1007-D and C-4171).

2) Slide drive shaft into proper position, and install knuckle assembly by reversing removal procedures.

NOTE: If removal or replacement of bearings or races is necessary, see articles for Chrysler Corp. Imports – Pickups and 4WD in the SUSPENSION section.

Removal (All Other Models)

With caliper assembly removed, remove hub dust cap, cotter pin, lock nut (if used) and adjusting nut. Pull hub and rotor assembly from spindle using care not to drop outer wheel bearing. Remove hub-to-rotor attaching bolts, and separate rotor from hub.

Installation

To install, reverse removal procedures. Tighten hub-to-rotor bolts. Bleed brake system if necessary, and adjust wheel bearings. *See articles for Chrysler Corp. Imports – Pickups and 4WD in SUSPENSION Section.*

REAR DISC BRAKE PADS

Removal

1) Raise and support vehicle. Remove rear wheels. Remove caliper assembly dust cover. Disconnect

Fig. 9: Positioning of Piston Stopper Groove On Rear Disc Brakes

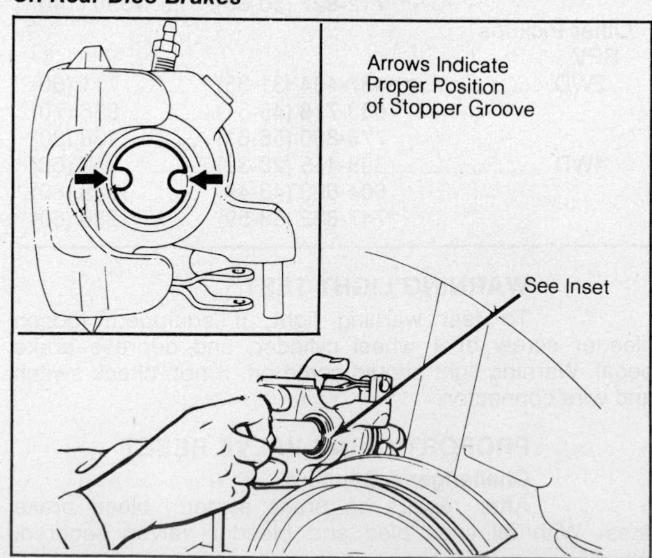
Arrows Indicate
Proper Position
of Stopper Groove
See Inset

parking brake cable from parking brake lever and from bracket.

2) Remove spigot pins and pull out stopper plug. Remove caliper assembly from rotor. Pull pads from caliper support.

Installation

To install, reverse removal procedure. Using a special driver (MB990652), screw the piston into its original position using a clockwise rotation. Ensure piston stopper groove is positioned, so projection on back of pad will securely fit groove. *See Fig. 9.* Pad clips must be installed properly.

NOTE: **Do not use a screwdriver to push piston into original position.**

REAR DISC BRAKE CALIPER

Removal

Remove disc pads. Pull out hose clip from axle housing, and disconnect brake hose from caliper assembly. Remove clevis pin, connecting lever assembly to parking brake cable. Remove stopper plugs. Remove caliper assembly.

Installation

To install, reverse removal procedure, and bleed brake system.

REAR DISC BRAKE ROTOR

Removal

Remove disc pads. Remove caliper support-to-axle housing bolts. Remove caliper support. Remove rotor from axle shaft.

Installation

To install, reverse removal procedure, tightening bolts evenly.

REAR BRAKE SHOES

Removal (Pickups Except Diesel 4WD)

1) Raise and support vehicle. Remove brake drum, return springs, adjusting spring and lever.

2) Remove shoes and adjuster as an assembly, and separate. Remove parking brake cable from lever.

Removal (Diesel 4WD Pickup)

1) Raise and support vehicle. Remove brake drum. Remove shoe return spring, shoe retainer spring and shoe hold-down pin.

2) Remove shoe and lining assembly and shoe and lever assembly. Remove cable from parking lever. Remove brake tube from wheel cylinder and wheel cylinder from backing plate.

3) Remove backing plate together with axle shaft, but do not remove backing plate unless absolutely necessary.

Removal (Challenger & Sapporo)

1) Raise and support vehicle. Remove brake drum and remove hold-down springs. *See Fig. 10.* Disconnect strut-to-shoe spring and upper shoe return spring end from trailing shoe.

2) Remove trailing shoe and lower return spring. Hold adjuster latch down, pull adjuster lever toward center of brake.

3) Remove leading shoe assembly. Remove upper shoe return spring and strut-to-shoe spring.

Removal (Colt)

1) Raise and support vehicle. Remove brake drum, clip spring, shoe return spring, shoe-to-shoe spring and hold-down spring.

2) Remove shoes and adjuster as an assembly and separate. Remove parking brake cable from lever.

Installation (All Models)

1) To install, reverse removal procedure. Apply Lubriplate (or equivalent), to all shoe contact points, adjuster assembly, wheel cylinder, and parking brake lever pin. After pulling lever fully toward center of brake, adjust amount of engagement of adjusting lever with strut. Note that adjusting lever and latch spring differ between right and left sides.

Fig. 10: Exploded View of Rear Brake Assembly for Component Relationship

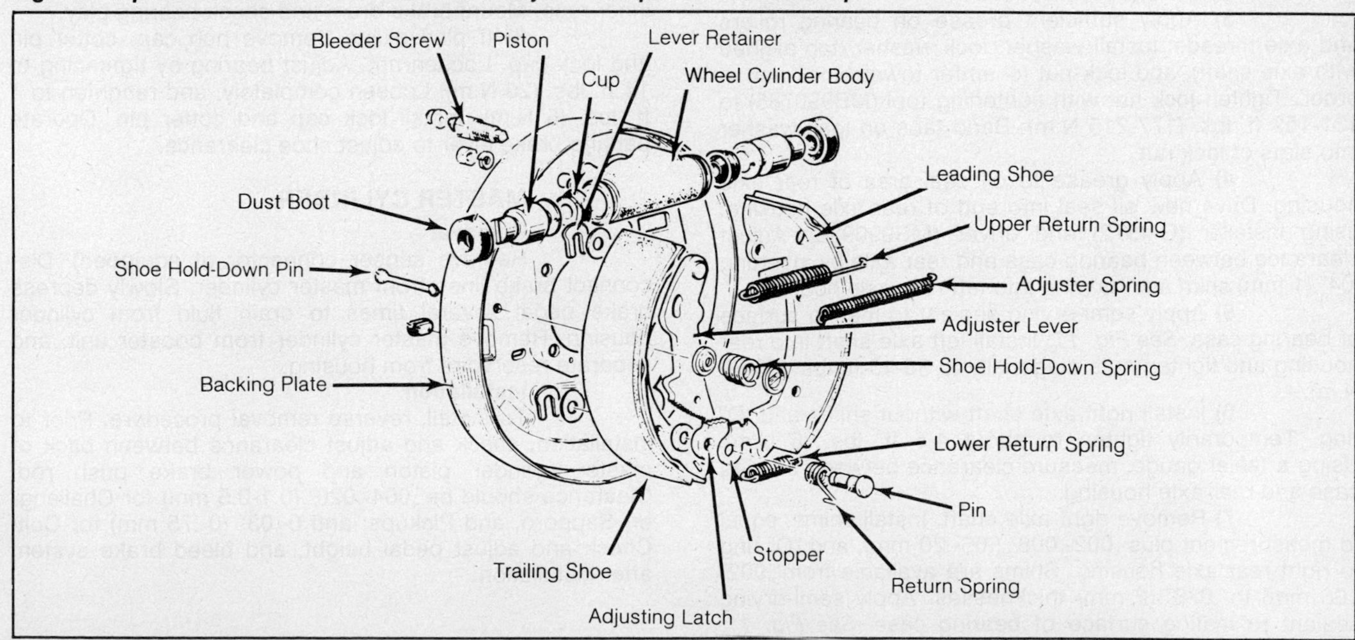

Bleeder Screw
Piston
Lever Retainer
Cup
Wheel Cylinder Body
Leading Shoe
Dust Boot
Upper Return Spring
Shoe Hold-Down Pin
Adjuster Spring
Adjuster Lever
Shoe Hold-Down Spring
Backing Plate
Lower Return Spring
Pin
Stopper
Trailing Shoe
Return Spring
Adjusting Latch

Rear brake assembly for Challenger & Sapporo is shown. Other models are similar.

2) Colt models require check of parking brake cable to ensure it will not advance brake lever when released. Adjuster will malfunction if lever advances.

3) Pickups require check of adjuster after installation is complete. Adjuster lever should mesh with next tooth of adjuster when pulled, and return to original position after wheel has moved one tooth. Adjuster assemblies differ between right and left sides.

REAR AXLE SHAFT BEARING & OIL SEAL

Removal (Except Colt)

1) With drum removed, disconnect brake tube from wheel cylinder. Disconnect bearing case from axle housing end. Remove brake backing plate, bearing case, and axle shaft as an assembly. If axle shaft binds, use slide hammer (C-637) and puller (CT-1003).

2) Remove "O" ring and shims for preloading wheel bearing. Retain shims for reassembly. Use slide hammer (screwdriver for Challenger and Sapporo) and hook attachment to remove oil seal.

3) To remove wheel bearing, remove lock washer and lock nut, using removal tool (MB990785). Remove lock washer and washer. Reinsert lock nut on axle shaft approximately 3 turns. Install puller (MB990787-A) to remove bearing case from axle shaft.

4) Turn nuts with equal pressure to ensure smooth removal of wheel bearing. Using a hammer and drift, drive bearing outer race from bearing case. Remove oil seal from bearing case.

Installation

1) Check axle shaft for .004" (.10 mm) runout. Apply multipurpose type grease (SAE J310a, NLGI 2EP) to outside circumference of bearing outer race. Press race into bearing case using installer (MB990937) and driver (MB990938). Follow same procedure for oil seal, using different installer (MB990935).

2) Slide bearing case and wheel bearing over axle shaft. Apply grease to roller surfaces of bearing inner race. Install rear brake assembly, bearing case and rear inner race to axle shaft. Press bearing inner race onto axle shaft using installer (MB990799).

3) Apply sufficient grease on bearing rollers and axle threads. Install washer, lock washer (tab aligned with axle shaft), and lock nut (chamfer toward lock nut) in order. Tighten lock nut with tightening tool (MB990785) to 131-159 ft. lbs. (177-215 N.m). Bend tabs on lock washer into slots of lock nut.

4) Apply grease to oil seal area of rear axle housing. Drive new oil seal into end of rear axle housing, using installer (C-4572) and driver (MB990938). Adjust clearance between bearing case and rear axle by inserting .04" (1 mm) shim and "O" ring into left rear axle housing.

5) Apply semi-drying sealant to mating surface of bearing case. *See Fig. 11.* Install left axle shaft into rear housing and tighten nuts diagonally to 36-43 ft. lbs. (50-60 N.m).

6) Install right axle shaft without shims and "O" ring. Temporarily tighten to about 4-5 ft. lbs. (6 N.m). Using a feeler gauge, measure clearance between bearing case and rear axle housing.

7) Remove right axle shaft. Install shims, equal to measurement plus .002-.008" (.05-.20 mm), and "O" ring to right rear axle housing. Shims are available from .002" (.05 mm) to .078" (2 mm) thicknesses. Apply semi-drying sealant to mating surface of bearing case. *See Fig. 11.* Install axle into housing, tightening nuts diagonally to 36-43 ft. lbs. (50-60 N.m).

8) Using dial indicator, check axle shaft for .002-.008" (.05-.20 mm) end play. If not correct, use different size shim.

Fig. 11: Applying Sealer for "O" Ring and Shim

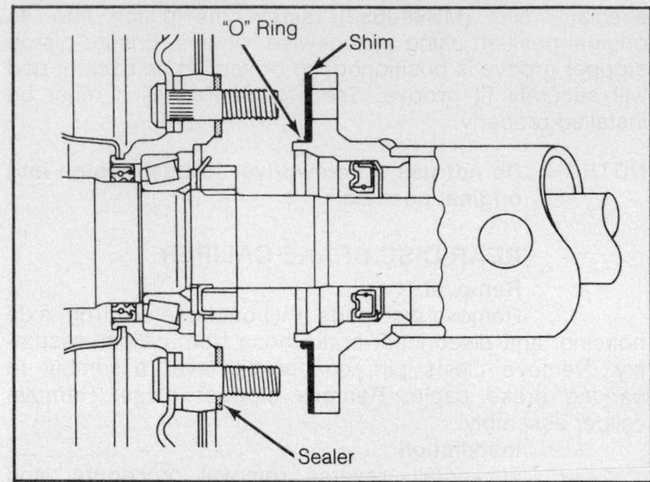
"O" Ring
Shim
Sealer

Apply to mating surface of bearing case.

REAR AXLE HUB BEARING

Removal (Colt)

With brake drum removed, pry out oil seal with screwdriver. Remove grease from inside hub. Remove bearing outer races using a hammer and soft punch.

Installation

1) Install bearing outer races, using installers (MB990926 and MB990928) and driver (MB990938). Use press-fitting force of 4,400 lbs. (2,000 kg) or more. If less force is required, replace entire drum assembly.

2) Install inside bearing inner race. Press new oil seal into end of drum, using installer (MB990926) and driver (MB990938). Apply grease to bearings, oil seal lip and bearing surface of brake drum. Install outside bearing inner race. Mount brake drum and check bearing play.

3) If play exists, remove hub cap, cotter pin and lock cap. Loosen nut. Adjust bearing by tightening to 14 ft. lbs. (20 N.m). Loosen completely, and retighten to 4 ft. lbs. (5 N.m). Install lock cap and cotter pin. Operate parking brake lever to adjust shoe clearance.

MASTER CYLINDER

Removal

Remove sensor connector (if equipped). Disconnect brake lines from master cylinder. Slowly depress brake pedal several times to drain fluid from cylinder housing. Remove master cylinder from booster unit, and separate reservoirs from housing.

Installation

To install, reverse removal procedure. Prior to installation, check and adjust clearance between back of master cylinder piston and power brake push rod. Clearance should be .004-.020" (0.1-0.5 mm) for Challenger, Sapporo, and Pickups; and 0-.03" (0-.75 mm) for Colt. Check and adjust pedal height, and bleed brake system after installation.

CHRYSLER CORP. IMPORTS (Cont.)

POWER BRAKE UNIT CHECK VALVE REPLACEMENT

NOTE: **Test check valve before removal. Pull off vacuum hose on booster side of check valve. Place finger over check valve, and crank engine. Vacuum should be felt.**

Removal

Remove hose clamps from both ends of check valve. Remove check valve clamp and remove check valve.

Installation

Coat both ends of check valve with sealer, and install valve with arrow (identification mark) pointing toward intake manifold side. Install check valve clamp and vacuum hoses, and secure hose clamps.

POWER BRAKE UNIT

Removal

Remove master cylinder and disconnect vacuum hose from power brake unit. Disconnect brake pedal and operating rod of power brake unit. From inside the vehicle, remove 4 nuts, attaching power brake unit to firewall. Remove power brake unit.

Installation

Install power brake unit, and tighten nuts to specifications. Install brake master cylinder.

OVERHAUL

FRONT DISC BRAKE CALIPER

Disassembly (Colt)

Remove caliper attaching bridge bolts. *See Fig. 12.* Separate inner and outer caliper halves, and remove torque plate. Remove retaining ring and dust seal. Apply compressed air to fluid inlet to remove piston. Remove piston seal without damaging caliper bore or seal groove.

Fig. 12: Disassembled View of Disc Brake Caliper

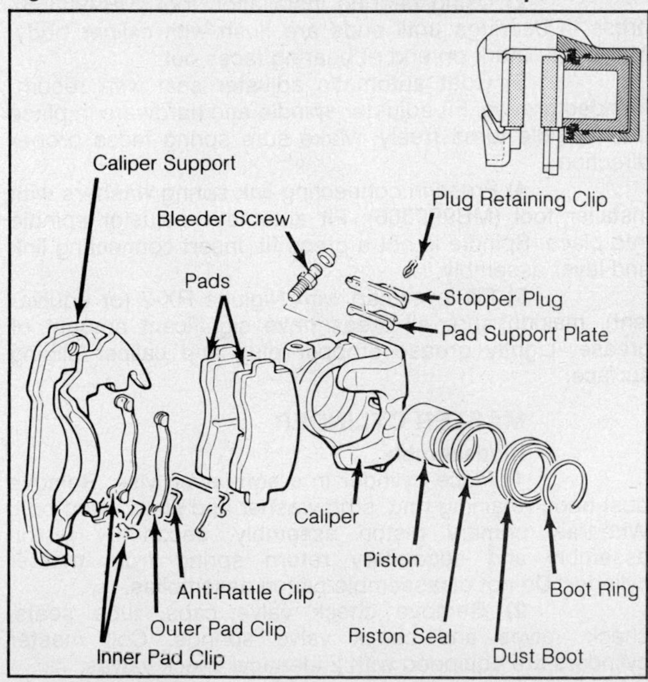
Caliper Support
Plug Retaining Clip
Bleeder Screw
Pads
Stopper Plug
Pad Support Plate
Caliper
Piston
Boot Ring
Anti-Rattle Clip
Outer Pad Clip
Piston Seal
Inner Pad Clip
Dust Boot

Illustration applies to Colt only.

Cleaning & Inspection

Clean all metal parts in alcohol or brake fluid. Clean piston seal in brake fluid or alcohol; clean dust seal and other rubber parts in alcohol only. Inspect caliper bore and piston for wear, damage or rust. Replace parts as necessary. Always replace piston seal and dust seal.

NOTE: **Repair kits contain proper lubricants to be used during reassembly.**

Reassembly

To reassemble, reverse disassembly procedure. Apply rubber grease to piston seal. Apply brake fluid to piston when reassembling. If torque plate was removed from inner caliper half, clean torque plate shaft and shaft bore in caliper. Apply special rubber grease to rubber bushing. Wipe seal inner surface and torque plate shaft before reassembly. Tighten bridge bolts of caliper halves.

NOTE: **Possible cause of increased pedal stroke is insufficient fit between piston and piston seal. Make sure brake pad is removed during this adjustment. Correct by manually levering piston to seat several times. This will create a better fit between piston and seal.**

Disassembly (All Other Models)

Remove dust boot. Apply compressed air to fluid inlet to remove piston. Remove piston seal without damaging caliper bore or seal groove. *See Fig. 13.*

Cleaning & Inspection

Clean all metal parts in alcohol or brake fluid. Clean piston seal in alcohol or brake fluid. Clean dust boot and other rubber parts in alcohol only. Inspect caliper bore and piston for wear, damage or rust. Replace parts as necessary. Always replace piston seal and dust boot.

Fig. 13: Exploded View of Front Disc Brake Caliper

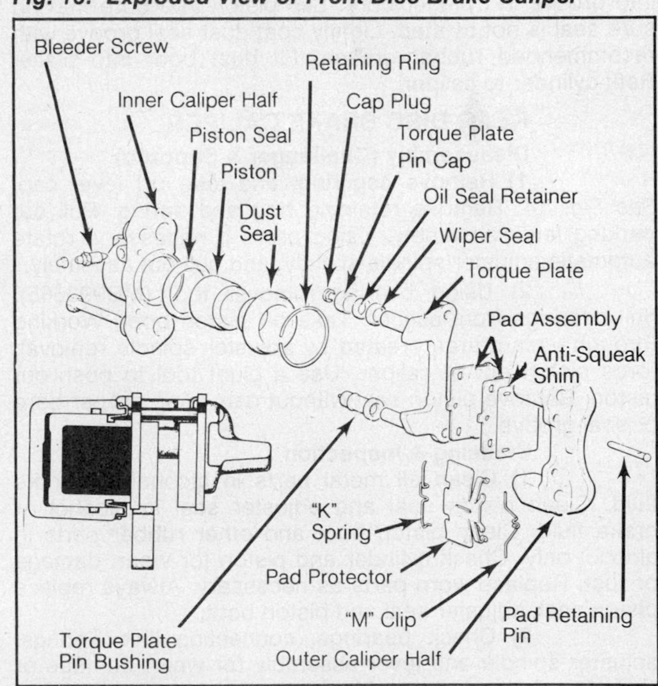
Bleeder Screw
Retaining Ring
Inner Caliper Half
Cap Plug
Piston Seal
Torque Plate Pin Cap
Piston
Dust Seal
Oil Seal Retainer
Wiper Seal
Torque Plate
Pad Assembly
Anti-Squeak Shim
"K" Spring
Pad Protector
"M" Clip
Pad Retaining Pin
Torque Plate Pin Bushing
Outer Caliper Half

Caliper is for Challenger, Sapporo & Pickups.

Fig. 14: Exploded View of Rear Disc Brake Caliper Assembly

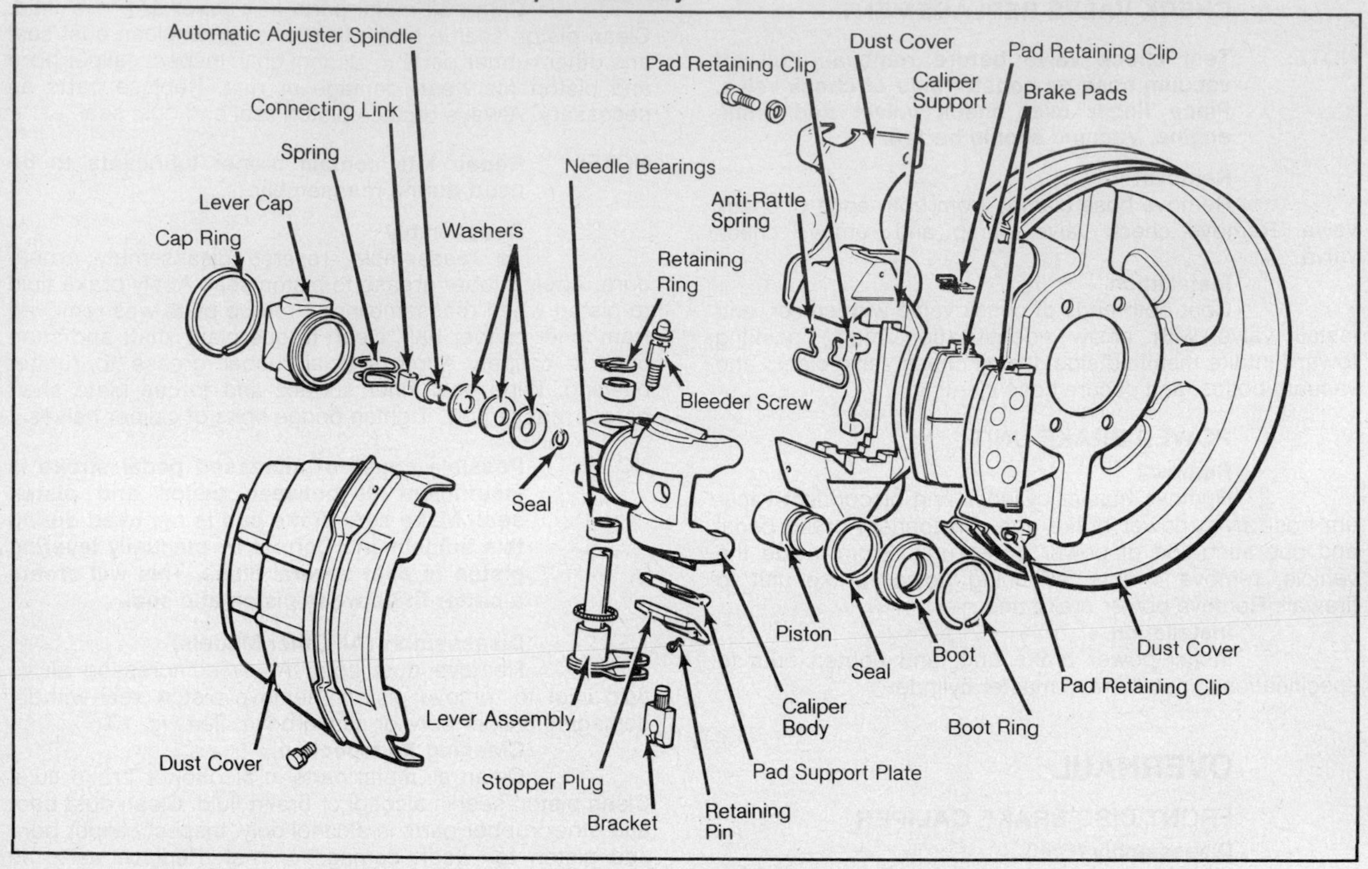
Automatic Adjuster Spindle
Connecting Link
Spring
Lever Cap
Cap Ring
Washers
Needle Bearings
Pad Retaining Clip
Dust Cover
Caliper Support
Pad Retaining Clip
Brake Pads
Anti-Rattle Spring
Retaining Ring
Bleeder Screw
Seal
Piston
Seal
Boot
Dust Cover
Pad Retaining Clip
Caliper Body
Boot Ring
Lever Assembly
Dust Cover
Stopper Plug
Bracket
Retaining Pin
Pad Support Plate

Reassembly

Coat piston seal with rubber grease. Slide seal into groove in cylinder bore. Slip piston into bore making sure seal is not twisted. Lightly coat dust seal groove with recommended rubber grease. Fit dust boot into place. Refit cylinder to caliper.

REAR DISC BRAKE CALIPER

Disassembly (Challenger & Sapporo)

1) Remove cap ring, and take off lever cap. *See Fig. 14.* Remove retaining ring and spring. Pull out parking lever assembly. Using pliers if necessary, rotate automatic adjuster spindle slightly, and pull out assembly.

2) Using bearing remover tool (MB990665), pull bearings from caliper. Take off piston boot. Working through vacant area created by adjuster spindle removal, force piston out of caliper. Use a blunt tool to push out piston. Remove piston seal without damaging caliper bore or seal groove.

Cleaning & Inspection

1) Clean all metal parts in alcohol, or brake fluid. Clean piston seal and adjuster seal in alcohol or brake fluid. Clean piston boot and other rubber parts in alcohol only. Check cylinder and piston for wear, damage or rust. Replace worn parts as necessary. Always replace piston seal, adjuster seal and piston boot.

2) Check bearings, connecting link, springs, adjuster spindle and lever assembly for wear, damage or rust. Check lever assembly for excessive play between shaft and bearing.

Reassembly

1) Lightly coat piston seal and piston with lubricant. Slide piston and seal into place, ensuring seal does not twist in groove. Lubricate boot, and slide boot into position making sure it engages groove in cylinder bore.

NOTE: Repair kit includes recommended lubricants.

2) Using bearing installation tool (MB990665), press in bearings until ends are flush with caliper body. Make sure mark on end of bearing faces out.

3) Coat automatic adjuster seal with recommended grease. Fit adjuster spindle and hardware in place until spindle turns freely. Make sure spring faces proper direction.

4) Press in connecting link spring washers with installer tool (MB990666). Fit automatic adjuster spindle into place. Spindle is not a press fit. Insert connecting link and lever assembly.

5) Fill lever cap with Niglube RX-2 (or equivalent), making sure all areas have significant amount of grease. Lightly grease stopper plug and caliper sliding surface.

MASTER CYLINDER

Disassembly

1) Place cylinder in a soft-jawed vise. Remove dust boot, retaining ring, stop washer and piston stop bolt. Withdraw primary piston assembly, secondary piston assembly and secondary return spring from master cylinder. Do not disassemble piston assemblies.

2) Remove check valve caps, tube seats, check valves and check valve springs. Colt master cylinders are equipped with 2 identical check valves.

Brakes

CHRYSLER CORP. IMPORTS (Cont.)

Cleaning & Inspection

Check bore and piston for wear or damage. Check piston-to-bore clearance. If it exceeds .006" (.15 mm), replace parts as necessary. If parts of primary and secondary piston assemblies or piston cups and springs are found defective, replace components as assemblies.

Fig. 15: Disassembled View of Colt Master Cylinder

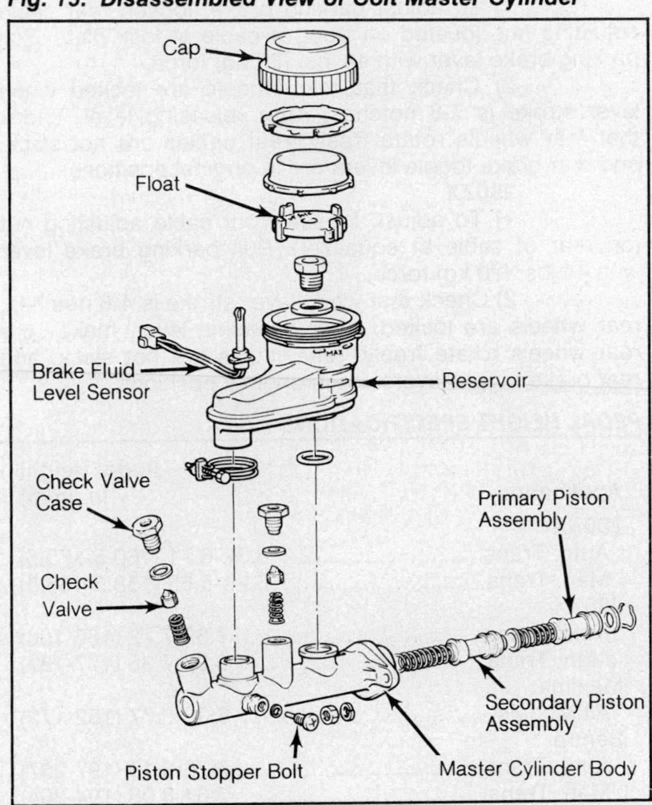

Cap
Float
Brake Fluid
Level Sensor
Reservoir
Check Valve
Case
Primary Piston
Assembly
Check
Valve
Secondary Piston
Assembly
Piston Stopper Bolt
Master Cylinder Body

Reassembly

To reassemble, reverse disassembly procedure. Apply rubber grease to all parts except boots. When assembled, check that return port is not blocked by piston cup, when piston is at return position.

NOTE: Check valves differ between rear disc and rear drum models. Be sure correct check valve is installed.

TIGHTENING SPECIFICATIONS

Application	Ft. Lbs. (N.m)
Rotor-to-Hub Bolts	
Challenger & Sapporo	
Front Wheel	25-29 (34-39)
Rear Wheel	
Steel Rim	51-58 (69-78)
Aluminum Rim	58-72 (78-98)
Colt	29-36 (39-49)
Pickup Models	
2WD	34-38 (46-51)
4WD	36-44 (49-59)
Caliper Mounting Bolts	
Challenger & Sapporo	
Front	51-65 (69-88)
Rear	29-36 (39-49)
Colt	43-58 (59-78)
Pickup Models	51-65 (69-88)
Caliper Bridge Bolts (Colt)	58-69 (78-93)
Front Wheel Drive Components (Colt)	
Drive Shaft Nut	145-188 (196-255)
Knuckle-to-Strut Assembly	54-65 (74-88)
Lower Arm-to-Ball Joint	69-87 (93-118)
Lower Arm-to-Strut Bar	69-87 (93-118)
Knuckle-to-Tie Rod	11-25 (15-33)

DISC BRAKE ROTOR SPECIFICATIONS

Application	Disc Diameter In. (mm)	Lateral Runout In. (mm)	Parallelism In. (mm)	Original Thickness In. (mm)	Min. Refinish Thickness In. (mm)	Discard Thickness In. (mm)
Challenger & Sapporo Front	10.04 (255)	.006 (0.15)	.....	.49 (12.5)	.....	.43 (11.0)
Rear (Optional)	9.72 (247)	.006 (0.15)	.....	.39 (10.0)	.....	.33 (8.4)
Colt	.....	.006 (0.15)	.....	.51 (13.0)	.....	.45 (11.4)
Colt/Ram-50 Pickups	.....	.006 (0.15)	.....	.79 (20.1)	.....	.72 (18.4)

DRUM BRAKE SPECIFICATIONS

Application	Drum Diam. In. (mm)	Drum Width In. (mm)	Max. Drum Refinish Diam. In. (mm)	Brake Cyl. Diam. In. (mm)	Master Cyl. Diam. In. (mm)
Challenger & Sapporo	9.0 (228.6)	.....	9.08 (230.6)	.8125 (20.64)	.875 (22.22)
Colt	7.1 (180)	.....	7.20 (182)	.750 (19.05)	.8125 (20.64)
Colt/Ram-50 Pickup 2.3L 4-Wheel Drive	9.5 (241.3)	.....	9.58 (243.3)	.750 (19.05)	.875 (22.22)
All Others	10 (254)	.....	10.08 (256)	.8125 (20.64)	.875 (22.22)

DATSUN/NISSAN MAXIMA, SENTRA, STANZA 200SX, 280ZX & 280ZX TURBO

DESCRIPTION

All service brake systems are hydraulically-operated using a tandem master cylinder and vacuum power unit.

Federal Maxima and all Sentra, equipped with optional diesel engines, incorporate a vacuum pump to provide vacuum to power brake booster. On Maxima models with diesel engine, a Master-Vac vacuum warning switch is provided. Switch lights brake warning light on dash when vacuum drops lower than specified value.

The 200SX, 280ZX and Maxima brake systems are hydraulically-controlled, dual line type systems, which operate independently on front and rear wheels.

Sentra and Stanza brake systems are hydraulically-controlled, dual line type which operate independently on right front and left rear wheels and left front and right rear wheels.

Front brakes of 200SX are fixed caliper, sliding yoke disc; rear brakes are sliding caliper disc. Front and rear brakes of 280ZX are sliding caliper with vented disc. Front brakes of Maxima Wagon & Sedan, Sentra and Stanza are sliding caliper disc. Rear brakes of Maxima Wagon, Sentra and Stanza are leading/trailing shoe. Maxima Sedan rear brake has sliding caliper rear disc.

Sentra models, equipped with optional diesel engine, have sliding caliper front disc brakes with larger I.D. caliper bore, longer and wider front pads, and larger bore master cylinder than gas engine models. Rear brakes are leading/trailing shoe type with larger diameter and wider linings and drums than gas engine models.

The 200SX, 280ZX and Maxima brake systems are equipped with a Nissan Proportioning valve to prevent premature lockup of rear wheels. Sentra and Stanza brake systems are equipped with a Dual Proportioning valve for pressure control of rear brakes. The 280ZX master cylinder incorporates a brake fluid level gauge.

All service brake systems are self-adjusting. Parking brake is cable-actuated on rear brake systems. On Maxima Wagon, a booster lever is built into rear cable section for better parking brake action.

ADJUSTMENT

BRAKE PEDAL HEIGHT

1) Measure pedal height from pressure face of pedal pad to floor pan insulator, without carpet.

2) To adjust to specification shown in table, loosen brake booster input rod lock nut, and turn input rod to attain proper height. Tighten lock nut and adjust stop light switch. Pedal free play is nonadjustable on all models.

STOP LIGHT SWITCH

1) Stop light switch is located under dash panel at brake pedal. Adjust travel during pedal height adjustment. After obtaining correct pedal height, check clearance and position of stop light switch.

2) To adjust, loosen lock nut and turn switch body. Clearance between brake pedal stopper rubber and threaded end of stop light switch is 0-.04" (0-1 mm) on all models. After adjustment, tighten lock nut.

PARKING BRAKE

200SX, Maxima & Sentra

1) Adjust parking brake by rotating turnbuckle. Rear wheels should lock when brake lever is pulled 7-9 notches (Maxima), 6-7 notches (Sentra) and 7-8 notches (200SX) with 44 lbs. (20 kg.) force.

2) After releasing lever, ensure rear wheels rotate freely, rear cables are not slack, and rear brake toggle levers are in original positions.

Stanza

1) To adjust parking brake, loosen rear cable adjusting nut, located on front of cable at lock plate. Pull parking brake lever with 44 lbs. (20 kg) force.

2) Check that rear wheels are locked when lever stroke is 7-8 notches. After releasing lever, check that rear wheels rotate freely, rear cables are not slack, and rear brake toggle levers are in original positions.

280ZX

1) To adjust, loosen front cable adjusting nut (on rear of cable at equalizer). Pull parking brake lever with 44 lbs. (20 kg) force.

2) Check that when lever stroke is 4-6 notches, rear wheels are locked. After releasing lever, make sure rear wheels rotate freely, rear cables are not slack, and rear brake toggle levers are in original positions.

PEDAL HEIGHT SPECIFICATIONS

Application	Pedal Height In. (mm)
200SX	
Auto. Trans.	6.32-6.71 (160.5-170.5)
Man. Trans.	6.24-6.63 (158.5-168.5)
280ZX	
Auto. Trans.	7.32-7.72 (186-196)
Man. Trans.	6.97-7.36 (177-187)
Maxima	
All Models	6.38-6.77 (162-172)
Sentra	
Auto. Trans.	7.76-8.15 (197-207)
Man. Trans.	7.64-8.03 (194-204)
Stanza	
Auto. Trans.	5.93-6.32 (150.5-160.5)
Man. Trans.	5.85-6.24 (148.5-158.5)

BRAKE WARNING LIGHT

Light indicates parking brake is engaged and also warns of low brake fluid level.

1) Turn ignition switch on. To adjust light operation with parking brake applied, bend switch plate down. Light should come on when brake lever is pulled up 1 notch and go out when lever is released.

2) To check warning light operation with ignition switch on, release parking brake lever and raise master cylinder reservoir cap. Warning light should glow. If not, check switch and wire connector.

BRAKE BLEEDING SEQUENCE

200SX, 280ZX & Maxima

These models must be bled in the following sequence: Master cylinder (bench bleed before installation), right rear wheel, left rear wheel, right front wheel and left front wheel.

Sentra & Stanza

These models must be bled in the following sequence: Master cylinder (bench bleed before installation), right rear wheel, left front wheel, left rear wheel and right front wheel.

DATSUN/NISSAN MAXIMA, SENTRA, STANZA 200SX, 280ZX & 280ZX TURBO (Cont.)

REMOVAL & INSTALLATION

FRONT DISC BRAKE PADS

Removal (200SX)

1) Raise and support vehicle. Remove wheel and tire. Remove retaining pin clip, retaining pins and pad springs.

2) Remove pads and shims from caliper assembly. Note location and condition of pads for proper installation (if reusable).

NOTE: Standard front brake pad thickness is .38" (9.7 mm). Minimum pad thickness is .08" (2 mm).

Installation

1) Clean and apply silicone grease to cylinder body yoke guide groove, yoke sliding contact points, and piston end surface.

CAUTION: When retracting outer piston, do not push piston deep inside of caliper or piston groove will go inside of piston seal and seal could be damaged. If this happens, remove and disassemble caliper. Push piston away from seal and reassemble.

2) Loosen bleeder screw, and push outer piston into cylinder until piston end surface coincides with boot retaining ring end surface. Tighten bleeder screw. Install inner shim and brake pad.

3) Push inner piston into cylinder by pulling on yoke. Install outer shim and pad. Install pad springs, retaining pins, and clips. Depress brake pedal several times to seat pads. Bleed hydraulic system.

Removal (Except 200SX)

1) Raise and support vehicle. Remove wheel and tire. Remove lock pin. Rotate caliper body upward on guide pin.

2) Remove pad retainers, shims and brake pads. Note pad condition and location for proper installation (if reusable).

NOTE: Standard front brake pad thickness is .43" (11 mm) for 280ZX and .39" (10 mm) for Maxima, Sentra and Stanza. Minimum pad thickness is .08" (2 mm) for all models.

Installation

1) Clean piston and area around lock and guide pins. Install inner pad. Seat piston by placing lever through opening in caliper body and pushing piston into bore. Apply brake grease to pad retainer points on caliper assembly. Install outer pad and shims.

2) Install pad retainers. Rotate caliper body down into original position. Install lower lock pin. Tighten bolt, and depress brake pedal several times to seat pads.

FRONT DISC BRAKE CALIPER

Removal

Raise and support vehicle. Remove wheel and tire. Disconnect and plug brake line from caliper. Remove caliper mount bolts. Remove caliper assembly.

Installation

To install, reverse removal procedure. Tighten caliper mount bolts, and bleed hydraulic system.

FRONT DISC BRAKE ROTOR

Removal (200SX, 280ZX & Maxima)

1) Remove caliper assembly as previously described, and hang from frame with wire. Do not disconnect hydraulic line. Remove hub dust cap, "O" ring, cotter pin, adjusting cap, and lock nut.

NOTE: During removal of dust cap, avoid damage to hub dust cap "O" ring.

2) Remove hub/rotor assembly from spindle without dropping washer and outer bearing. Remove washer, outer bearing, grease seal and inner bearing. Replace grease seal whenever hub and rotor are removed. *See Fig. 1*. Remove hub-to-rotor bolts. Separate rotor from hub.

Fig 1: Exploded View of 200SX, 280ZX & Maxima Front Brake Hub & Rotor Assembly

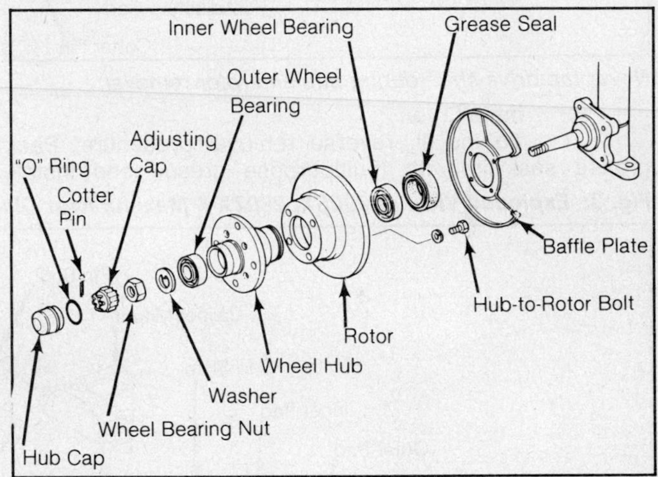
Inner Wheel Bearing
Grease Seal
Outer Wheel Bearing
Adjusting Cap
"O" Ring
Cotter Pin
Baffle Plate
Hub-to-Rotor Bolt
Rotor
Wheel Hub
Washer
Wheel Bearing Nut
Hub Cap

Replace grease seal whenever hub and rotor are removed.

Installation

To install, reverse removal procedure and adjust wheel bearings. *See Wheel Bearing Adjustment in SUSPENSION Section*.

Removal (Sentra & Stanza)

1) Raise and support vehicle. Remove wheel and tire. Remove caliper assembly, and hang from frame with wire. Do not disconnect hydraulic line. Remove cotter pin. Hold hub with tool, and loosen hub nut from drive shaft. Install wheel nuts to avoid damage to studs.

2) Separate wheel hub and rotor from drive shaft end using removal tools (KV40101000 & ST36230000). Remove hub nut once hub and rotor assembly has broken loose from drive shaft. Remove bolts holding wheel hub to rotor. Remove outer grease seal from knuckle and discard. Replace grease seal even if it appears good.

NOTE: During hub removal, do not tap drive shaft or damage will result. See Fig. 2. When replacing wheel bearings with grease seal, knuckle must be removed. Once hub and rotor assembly is installed, check axle end play. Replace spacer in knuckle if any end play is present or bearing preload is lower than specification. Bearing preload, as measured at wheel hub stud: 3.1-10.8 lb. (1.4-4.9 kg).

DATSUN/NISSAN MAXIMA, SENTRA, STANZA 200SX, 280ZX & 280ZX TURBO (Cont.)

Fig. 2: Exploded View of Sentra & Stanza Front Brake Hub & Rotor Assembly

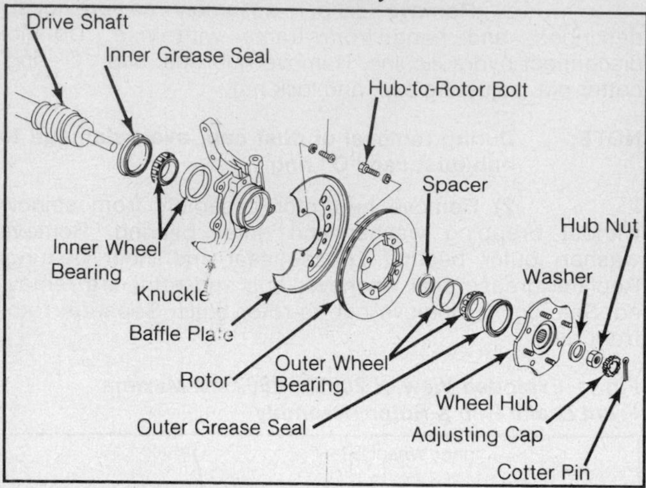
Drive Shaft
Inner Grease Seal
Hub-to-Rotor Bolt
Spacer
Hub Nut
Inner Wheel Bearing
Knuckle
Washer
Baffle Plate
Outer Wheel Bearing
Rotor
Wheel Hub
Outer Grease Seal
Adjusting Cap
Cotter Pin

Never tap drive shaft during hub and rotor removal.

Installation

To install, reverse removal procedure. Pack grease seal lip with multipurpose grease and install. Tighten bolts securing hub-to-rotor. Install on drive shaft. Tighten hub nut. Install new cotter pin.

REAR DISC BRAKE PADS

Removal (200SX, 280ZX & Maxima)

1) Raise and support vehicle. Remove rear wheel and tire. Disconnect parking brake cable. Remove spring retainer. Remove pin bolts.

2) Remove pad springs, pads and pad shim. Note location and condition of pads for proper installation (if reuseable).

NOTE: **Standard rear brake pad thickness is .31" (8 mm) for all models. Minimum pad thickness is .079" (2 mm) for all models.**

Installation

1) To install, reverse removal procedure. Clean area around pin bolts and piston end. Using care not to damage piston boot, retract piston into cylinder body by turning it clockwise.

2) Apply silicone brake grease to caliper sliding surfaces and pad contact area on mounting support. Install pads, shim and pad springs. Tighten cylinder body and outer spring retainer. Connect parking brake cable.

Fig. 3: Exploded View of 200SX, 280ZX & Maxima Rear Disc Brake Caliper

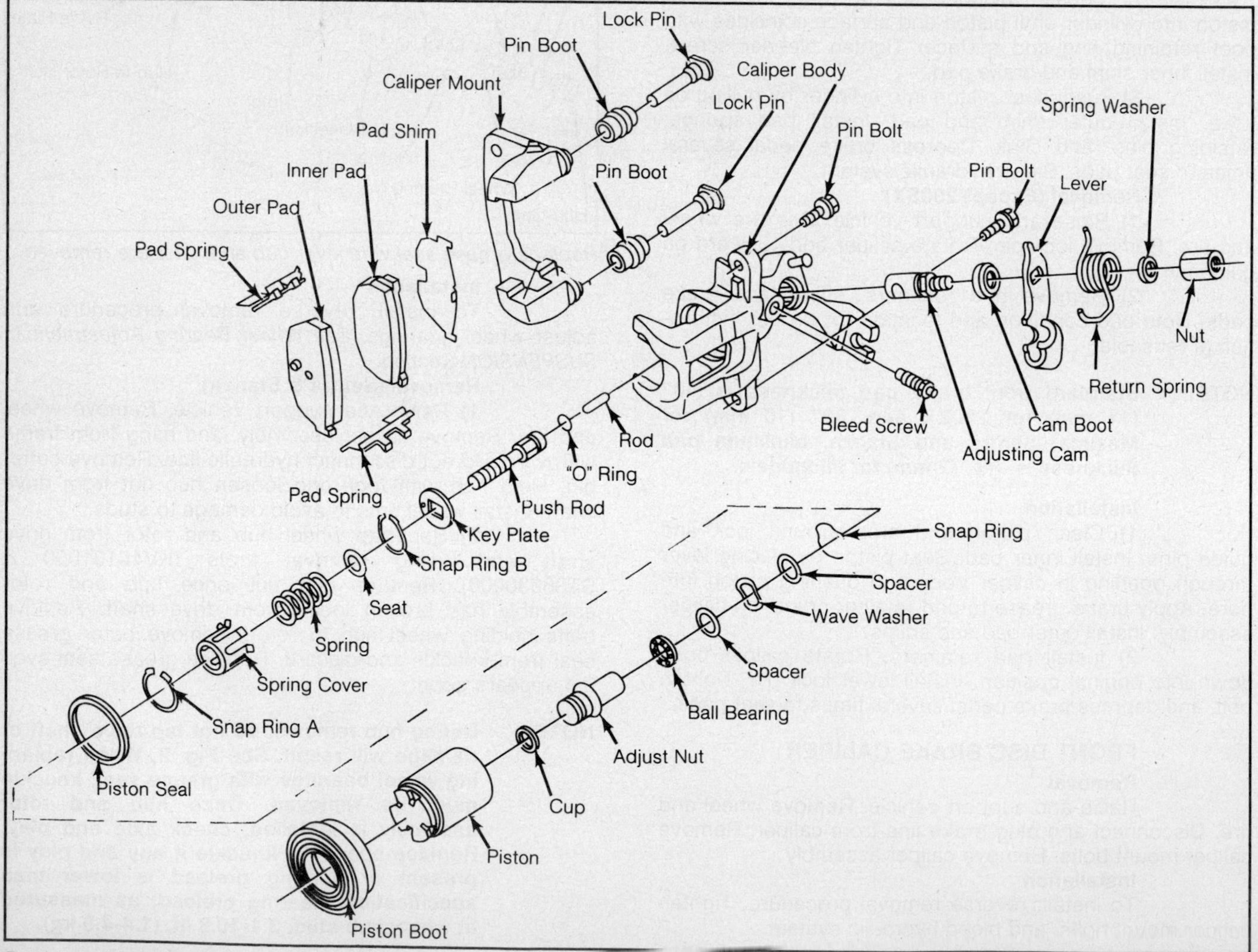

Replace all rubber parts during overhaul.

DATSUN/NISSAN MAXIMA, SENTRA, STANZA 200SX, 280ZX & 280ZX TURBO (Cont.)

REAR DISC BRAKE CALIPER

Removal (200SX, 280ZX & Maxima)

Remove rear wheel and tire. Disconnect hydraulic line from caliper and plug openings. Disconnect parking brake cable. Remove 2 caliper mount bolts and remove caliper assembly.

Installation

To install, reverse removal procedure. Install and tighten hydraulic line and caliper mount bolts. Bleed hydraulic system.

REAR DISC BRAKE ROTOR

Removal (200SX, 280ZX & Maxima)

With caliper removed, rotor can be removed from axle flange.

Installation

Install rotor and caliper assembly. After installation, adjust pad-to-rotor clearance by depressing pedal until pedal stroke is constant.

REAR AXLE SHAFT BEARING & OIL SEAL

Removal (200SX)

1) Raise and support vehicle. Remove rear wheel and tire. Remove caliper assembly and hang by wire. Remove disc brake rotor. Disconnect parking brake cable and brake line.

2) Remove nuts from backing plate, and draw out axle shaft using tool (KV40101000 & ST36230000). Pry out old oil seal and discard.

NOTE: **After installing backing plate and adapter plate, install bearing spacer with chamfer side facing axle shaft flange. Insert wheel bearing with seal side facing axle shaft flange. After axle installation, check end play. Axle shaft end play is .002-.016" (.05-.40 mm).**

Installation

1) To install, reverse removal procedure. Pack cavity between oil seal lips with multipurpose grease, and install using seal driver tool (KV40100300). Insert axle shaft into axle case, using guide tool (ST37840000). Apply multipurpose grease to outer surface of bearing collar.

2) Remove guide when distance between axle flange and bearing is 2.76-3.54" (70-90 mm). Measure gap between caliper adapter and axle case end. Select proper shims so clearance between rear axle end and caliper adapter is 0-.004" (0-.10 mm). Check and adjust axle end play as necessary.

Removal (280ZX & Maxima Sedan)

1) Raise and support vehicle. Remove rear wheel and tire. Remove caliper assembly and hang by wire. Remove disc brake rotor. Disconnect drive shaft from axle shaft. Remove wheel bearing lock nut using rear axle tool (KV40101000) and suitable bar.

2) Draw out axle shaft using rear axle stand tool (KV40101000) and slide hammer (ST36230000). Remove rear axle shaft. Remove companion flange and discard old grease seal.

Installation

1) To install, reverse removal procedure. Clean wheel bearings and inside of axle shaft housing.

NOTE: **Wheel bearings are sealed type. When installing, ensure sealed side of outer bearing faces wheel and that sealed side of inner bearing faces differential. When installing outer bearing to rear axle shaft, use rear axle shaft bearing drift (ST37750000). A mark "N", "M" or "P" is stamped on bearing housing. Select distance piece spacer with mark corresponding to mark on bearing housing. If distance piece is reused, ensure both ends are not collapsed or deformed.**

2) Install new grease seal with tool (ST37710000). Tighten new wheel bearing lock nut. Measure preload and rear axle shaft end play. If proper preload or end play cannot be obtained, disassemble and replace distance piece spacer. Rear axle shaft end play is less than .012" (.30 mm).

Removal (Maxima Wagon)

1) Raise and support vehicle. Remove rear wheel and tire. Remove brake drum. Disconnect parking brake cable and brake line.

2) Remove nuts securing backing plate mount bolts. Remove axle shaft using tools (KV40101000 & ST36230000). Pry out and discard old oil seal.

NOTE: **To remove wheel bearing from axle, first cut collar with cold chisel. Use care not to damage axle shaft. Press wheel bearing and collar off axle with hydraulic press. When installing bearing spacer, make sure chamfered side is facing axle shaft flange. Insert wheel bearing with seal side facing axle shaft flange.**

Installation

1) To install, reverse removal procedure. Pack cavity between sealing lips of new oil seal with multipurpose grease. Install with tool (KV40100300).

2) Install rear axle shaft guide (ST37840000) onto axle shaft, and insert shaft into axle case. Apply multipurpose grease to outer surface of bearing collar. Remove guide when distance between axle flange and bearing is 2.76-3.54" (70-90 mm).

3) Measure gap between backing plate and axle tube end. Select suitable shim(s) so clearance between axle rear end and backing plate is 0-.004" (0-.10 mm). Measure and adjust axle end play as necessary. Axle end play is .008-.020" (.20-.50 mm).

Removal (Sentra & Stanza)

1) Raise and support vehicle. Do not lift at parallel links. Remove rear wheel and tire. Release parking brake.

2) Remove hub cap, cotter pin, adjusting cap and wheel bearing nut. Remove brake drum with outer bearing and washer. Remove grease seal and inner wheel bearing.

Installation

1) To install, reverse removal procedure. Coat inner and outer wheel bearings with multipurpose grease, and place inner bearing in hub.

2) Install new grease seal, coating sealing lips with grease. Adjust wheel bearing preload. *See Wheel Bearing Adjustment in SUSPENSION Section*. Pack hub cap, and coat "O" ring with grease.

MASTER CYLINDER

Removal

Remove heat shield plate, if equipped. Disconnect brake fluid level gauge wiring and hydraulic lines from master cylinder. Remove master cylinder-to-power brake unit mounting nuts. Remove master cylinder from power brake unit.

Installation

Reverse removal procedure. Check pedal height and bleed hydraulic system.

NOTE: **Before removing power brake unit, test check valve. Using brake booster tester, apply 7.9 in. Hg to brake unit side of check valve on 200SX. Apply 19.7 in. Hg to check valve on 280ZX, Maxima, Sentra and Stanza. If pressure drops more than .4 in. Hg in 15 seconds, replace check valve. Also, if valve does not open when pressure is applied to brake unit side of check valve, replace check valve. If valve is not defective, check brake system and vacuum lines for leaks. Repair as needed.**

POWER BRAKE UNIT

Removal

1) Disconnect power unit push rod from brake pedal by removing clevis pin. Disconnect hydraulic lines from master cylinder and vacuum line from power brake unit.

2) Remove master cylinder mounting nuts and master cylinder. Remove nuts attaching power brake unit to firewall. Remove power brake unit from engine compartment.

Installation

1) To install, reverse removal procedure and check push rod length, operating rod length and pedal height. *See Fig. 4*. Push rod on 200SX and Maxima CANNOT be adjusted. If not to specification, replace power brake unit.

Fig. 4: Measuring Push Rod and Operating Rod Lengths

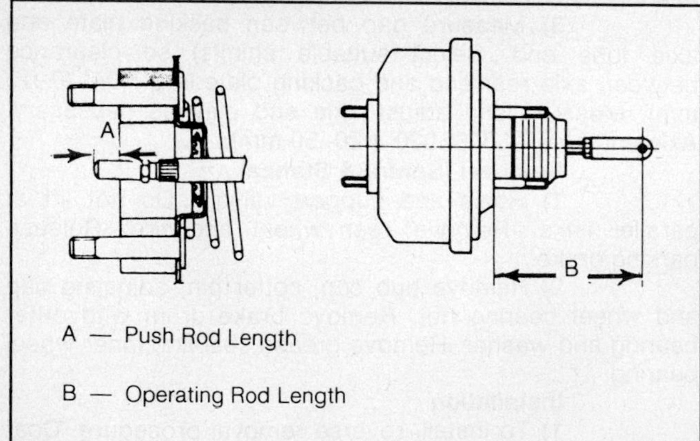
A
B
A — Push Rod Length
B — Operating Rod Length

Push rod on Maxima & 200SX CANNOT be adjusted.

2) Adjust push rod length on 280ZX by turning tip of push rod. Adjust operating rod length by loosening lock nut and turning operating rod to attain proper length. Tighten lock nut and clevis. Bleed hydraulic system.

PUSH ROD & OPERATING ROD LENGTHS

Application	Push Rod In. (mm)	Operating Rod In. (mm)
200SX	5.24 (133)	.4045-.4144 (10.275-10.525)
280ZX	5.63 (143)	.4045-.4144 (10.275-10.525)
Maxima	5.71 (145)	.3652-.4144 (9.275-10.525)
Sentra	5.91 (150)	.4045-.4144 (10.275-10.525)
Stanza	5.12 (130)	.4045-.4144 (10.275-10.525)

CHECK VALVE REPLACEMENT

Check valve is located in vacuum line between intake manifold and power brake unit on firewall. To remove, disconnect retaining clip from firewall. Remove hose clamps, separate hoses from valve, and remove check valve. To install, reverse removal procedure.

OVERHAUL

FRONT DISC BRAKE CALIPER

Disassembly (200SX)

1) With caliper and pads removed, drain fluid from cylinder. Remove gripper pin attaching bolts. Separate yoke and cylinder body. Remove yoke holder from piston.

2) Remove retaining rings and dust seals from pistons. Push both pistons out in one direction. Remove piston seals. Remove gripper, if necessary. *See Fig. 5.*

Fig. 5: Exploded View of 200SX Front Disc Brake Caliper

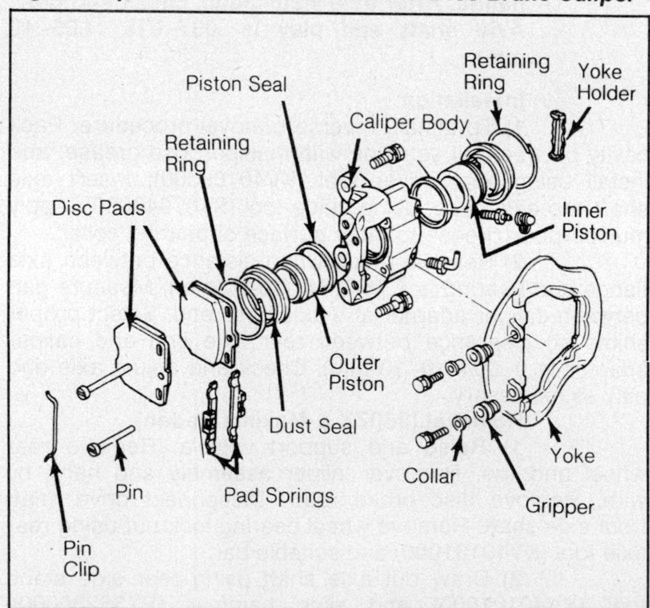
Retaining Ring
Yoke Holder
Piston Seal
Caliper Body
Retaining Ring
Disc Pads
Inner Piston
Outer Piston
Dust Seal
Yoke
Collar
Pin
Pad Springs
Gripper
Pin Clip

No clearance should be present between piston and yoke.

Cleaning & Inspection

1) Clean parts with brake fluid and check components for scoring, rust, wear or damage.

DATSUN/NISSAN MAXIMA, SENTRA, STANZA 200SX, 280ZX & 280ZX TURBO (Cont.)

NOTE: As piston surfaces are plated, pistons must be replaced if corroded or worn. Do not polish with emery cloth. The 200SX front disc brake caliper inside diameter is 2.125" (54 mm). Replace all rubber components during overhaul. Use DOT 3 or higher rated brake fluid in all models.

2) If minor corrosion cannot be removed from cylinder bore with fine emery cloth, cylinder must be replaced. Replace all seals during overhaul.

Reassembly

1) Install piston seals without damaging seals. Coat cylinder bore and pistons with brake fluid. Push outer piston into cylinder until piston end surface coincides with boot retaining ring end surface.

2) Do not force piston groove inside piston seal or damage may result. Push inner piston into cylinder bore by holding cylinder body. Align piston yoke groove with cylinder yoke groove.

3) Apply brake grease to sealing surface of dust seal and install. Clamp seal securely with retaining ring. Install yoke holder to inner piston. Install gripper to yoke. Apply soap and water solution to inner gripper wall. Drive gripper pin into position.

CAUTION: When pressing yoke into yoke holder, be sure to insert yoke vertically so as not to crack or chip yoke holder. If yoke holder is damaged or pressing force is out of specification, replace with new component.

4) Install yoke to yoke-holder by supporting outer piston end. Press yoke into yoke-holder with 44-66 lb. (20-30 kg) force. No clearance should be present between piston and yoke. Install shims, brake pads, springs, pins and clip.

Disassembly
(280ZX, Maxima, Sentra & Stanza)

1) Drain brake fluid from caliper body and clean exterior of caliper assembly. Remove pin bolts and separate caliper body from caliper mount. Remove pad retainers and pads. *See Fig. 6*.

2) Force piston and dust seal out of bore by applying low pressure compressed air to brake inlet.

CAUTION: Gradually increase air pressure so piston does not fly out and cause personal injury or component damage.

Cleaning & Inspection

1) Clean parts with brake fluid and check components for scoring, rust, wear or damage.

NOTE: Front disc brake caliper inside diameter for the 280ZX is 2.386" (60.60 mm); for Maxima, 2.126" (54 mm); for Sentra gas model, 1.894" (48.10 mm); and for Sentra diesel and Stanza models, 2.012" (51.10 mm).

2) If minor corrosion cannot be removed from cylinder bore with fine emery cloth, cylinder must be replaced. Replace all seals during overhaul.

Reassembly

1) Apply brake fluid to sliding portions of piston and caliper bore. Apply rubber grease to inside of dust seals. Install piston seal in bore. Install dust seal on piston and slide piston into caliper bore. Secure dust seal in piston groove and caliper groove.

2) Apply multipurpose grease to subpin rubber bushing, main pin, and subpin. Install seals, subpin rubber bushing, subpin, and main pin. Apply grease to disc pad-to-caliper mount contact portions. Install caliper mount to caliper body.

3) Install caliper assembly without pads or retainer to knuckle spindle. Install upper pin bolt. Install disc pads, shims, retainer and rotate caliper down into position. Install lower pin bolt. When caliper assembly is mounted on vehicle, turn rotor to ensure there is no excessive drag. Install front brake hose and bleed brake system.

Fig. 6: Exploded View of 280ZX Front Disc Brake Caliper

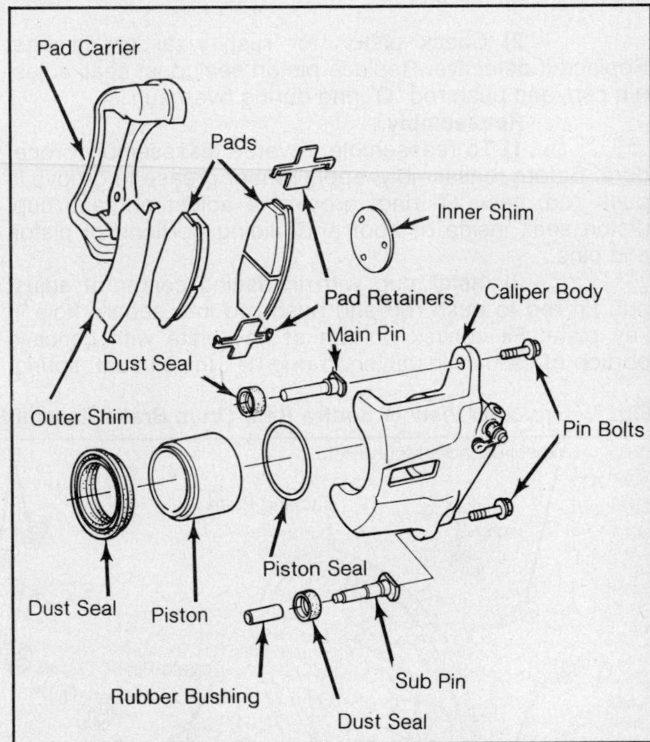
Pad Carrier
Pads
Inner Shim
Pad Retainers
Caliper Body
Main Pin
Dust Seal
Outer Shim
Pin Bolts
Piston Seal
Dust Seal
Piston
Sub Pin
Rubber Bushing
Dust Seal

The 280ZX uses single piston design. Maxima, Sentra & Stanza are similar.

REAR DISC BRAKE CALIPER

Disassembly
(200SX, 280ZX & Maxima Sedan)

1) With caliper removed, remove outer spring retainer and pin bolts. Separate caliper body from caliper mount. *See Fig. 3*. Using long nose pliers or equivalent, pull piston from bore while rotating it in a counterclockwise direction.

2) Disassemble piston by prying off retainer ring. Remove wave washer, spacers, ball bearing and adjuster nut. Remove cup from adjuster nut. To disassemble caliper body, remove snap ring "A" with snap ring pliers. Remove spring cover, spring and seat.

3) Take out snap ring "B" and remove key plate, push rod, and rod. Remove "O" ring from push rod and the piston seal from caliper body. To disassemble parking brake lever, remove return spring, nut, spring washer and lever. Remove adjusting cam and cam boot. Remove pins and pin boots.

DATSUN/NISSAN MAXIMA, SENTRA, STANZA 200SX, 280ZX & 280ZX TURBO (Cont.)

Cleaning & Inspection

1) Clean all parts in brake fluid only. Check caliper bore for wear, rust, corrosion or other damage. Minor deposits or scratches can be removed with fine emery cloth. Check caliper mount for wear, cracks or other damage. Replace if defective.

NOTE: **As piston surfaces are plated, pistons must be replaced if corroded or worn. Do not polish with emery cloth. The rear caliper inside diameter for the 200SX and Maxima is 1.5" (38.2 mm); for 280ZX, 1.685" (42.8 mm). Replace all rubber components during overhaul. Use DOT 3 or higher rated brake fluid in all models.**

2) Check piston for rust, wear or damage. Replace if defective. Replace piston seal, dust seal, adjust nut cup, and push rod "O" ring during overhaul.

Reassembly

1) To reassemble, reverse disassembly procedure. Before reassembly, apply rubber grease to groove in push rod, new "O" ring, groove in adjust nut and cup, piston seal, inside of boot and sliding portions of piston and pins.

2) Install cup with lip facing center of adjust nut. Fit rod to push rod and push rod into square hole in key plate. Fit convex portion of key plate with concave portion of caliper. Install snap ring "B". Install seat, spring, spring cover and snap ring "A" with suitable press and drift.

REAR BRAKE DRUM & LININGS

Disassembly

(Maxima Wagon, Sentra & Stanza)

1) Raise and support vehicle. Remove rear wheel and tire. Remove brake drum. Remove parking brake rear cable. Remove retainer, anti-rattle spring, spring seat, and pin from primary brake shoe.

NOTE: **If brake drum cannot be easily removed, install two 8 x 1.25 mm bolts to pull drum free of axle flange. Alternately turn each bolt until drum works loose. If drum has heavy rust or dirt built up, spray penetrating oil around wheel studs, bolt holes and drum center cutout.**

2) Remove return springs (and clip retainer on Sentra Diesel) and primary shoe. Remove secondary brake shoe and on Stanza, renmove adjuster assembly. *See Fig. 7*. On Maxima, adjuster assembly is on axle housing side of backing plate and does not require removal.

3) On Sentra models, remove toggle lever spring. Remove clip, washer, spacer and toggle pin. Separate toggle lever and shoe. *See Fig. 7*. On all models, note lining condition and location for proper installation (if reusable).

Fig. 7: Exploded View of Sentra Rear Drum Brake Assembly

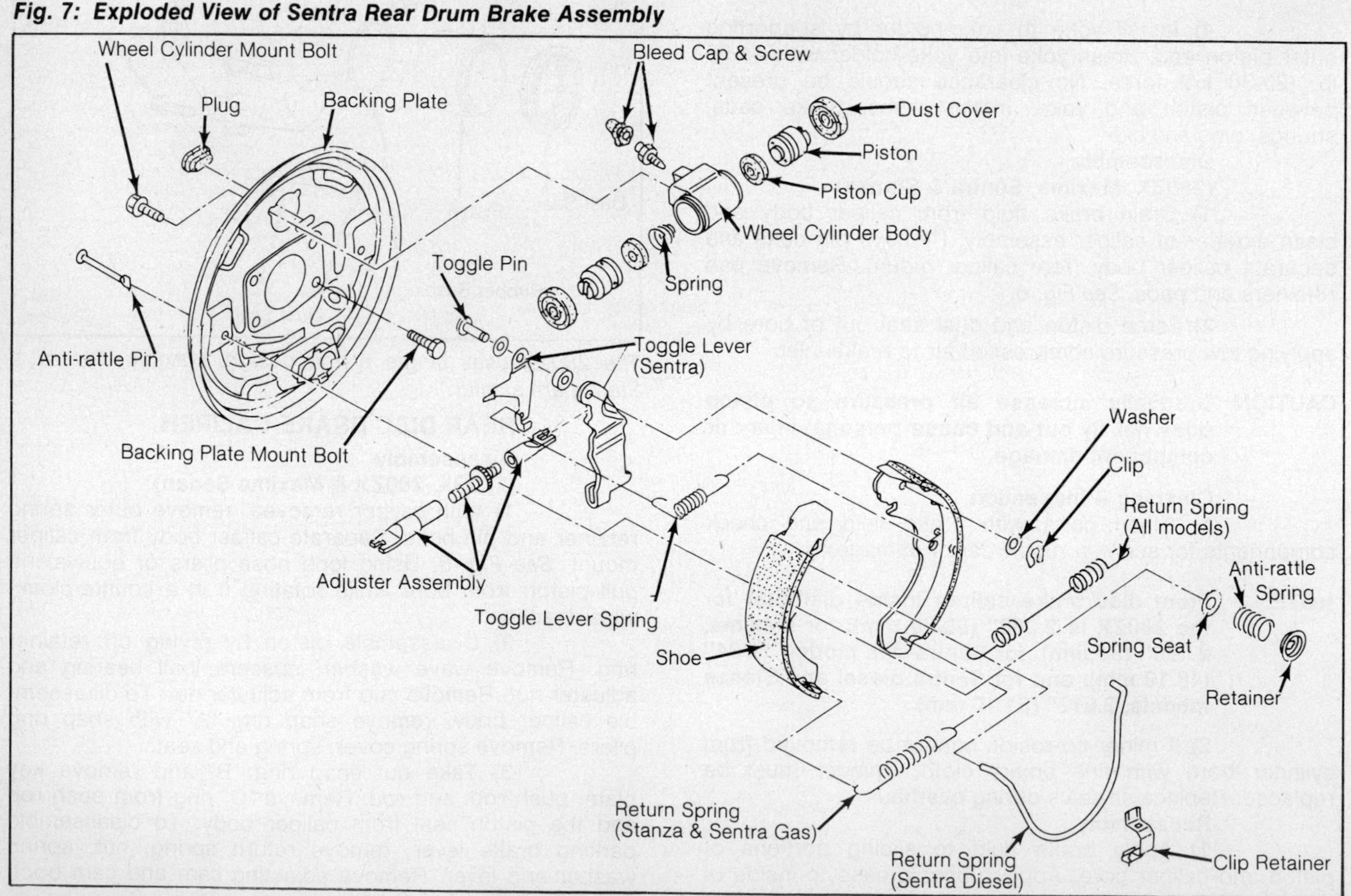
Wheel Cylinder Mount Bolt
Plug
Backing Plate
Bleed Cap & Screw
Dust Cover
Piston
Piston Cup
Wheel Cylinder Body
Toggle Pin
Spring
Anti-rattle Pin
Toggle Lever
(Sentra)
Backing Plate Mount Bolt
Washer
Clip
Return Spring
(All models)
Anti-rattle
Spring
Adjuster Assembly
Toggle Lever Spring
Shoe
Spring Seat
Retainer
Return Spring
(Stanza & Sentra Gas)
Return Spring
(Sentra Diesel)
Clip Retainer

Maxima adjuster is on axle housing side and Stanza adjuster is on drum side of backing plate.

DATSUN/NISSAN MAXIMA, SENTRA, STANZA 200SX, 280ZX & 280ZX TURBO (Cont.)

NOTE: Standard rear brake lining thickness is .157" (4 mm) for Sentra gasoline model, .177" (4.50 mm) for Maxima, and .189" (4.80 mm) for Sentra diesel model and Stanza. Minimum lining thickness is .059" (1.50 mm) for all models.

Reassembly

1) To install, reverse removal procedure. Using brake grease, lubricate all brake shoe sliding surfaces, adjuster nut and rod threads, shoe-to-adjuster contact points and shoe-to-wheel cylinder and anchor.

2) After installing brake shoes, set initial shoe-to-drum clearance to .0091-.0126" (.23-.32 mm) with adjuster. After installation is complete, adjust final shoe-to-drum clearance by operating parking brake several times.

REAR WHEEL CYLINDER

Disassembly

(Maxima Wagon, Sentra & Stanza)

With rear brake linings removed, disconnect hydraulic line and 2 mount bolts. With wheel cylinder removed, remove dust covers, pistons, cups and spring. *See Fig. 4.*

Cleaning & Inspection

Clean all parts in brake fluid. Check cylinder bore and pistons for excessive wear or damage. If piston-to-cylinder clearance is greater than .006" (.15 mm), replace necessary parts. Replace any torn or damaged rubber parts.

NOTE: Wheel cylinders are produced by 2 manufacturers, Nabco and Tokico, and parts are not interchangeable. Rear wheel cylinder inside diameter for Maxima Wagon is .875" (22.2 mm), for Sentra and Stanza, .6875" (17.5 mm). Ensure repair kit matches wheel cylinder. Brake fluid must be DOT 3 or higher rated.

Reassembly

To reassemble, reverse disassembly procedure. Apply brake fluid to cylinder bore, pistons and piston cups. Install parts using fingers only to avoid damage to rubber components.

MASTER CYLINDER

Disassembly

Remove reservoir caps and filters. Drain brake fluid from reservoir. Remove snap ring and stopper bolt. Withdraw stopper, primary piston assembly, secondary piston assembly, and springs. *See Fig. 8.* Remove check valve plugs. Withdraw check valve assemblies.

NOTE: Master cylinders are produced by 2 manufacturers, Nabco and Tokico. Parts are not interchangeable. Make sure repair kit matches cylinder. The 200SX and Maxima models use Nabco parts, 280ZX models use Tokico parts, and Sentra and Stanza use either brand. Brake fluid must be DOT 3 or higher rated.

Cleaning & Inspection

1) Clean all parts in brake fluid. Check components for excessive wear or damage. If piston-to-cylinder clearance exceeds .006" (.15 mm), replace defective part. Caps, gaskets, packing and valves must be replaced during overhaul.

2) Master cylinder inside diameter for 200SX and Maxima models is .875" (22.23 mm); for 280ZX, .9375" (23.81 mm); and for Stanza, .8125" (20.64 mm).

3) Master cylinder small bore inside diameter for Sentra gas model is .75" (19.05 mm) and large bore I.D. is .9375" (23.81 mm). Master cylinder small bore I.D. for Sentra diesel model is .8125" (20.64 mm) and large bore I.D. is 1.00" (25.4 mm). Maximum piston-to-cylinder clearance is .006" (.15 mm).

4) Do not remove reservoir tanks. If tanks are removed for any reason, discard them and install new tanks. Also, do not disassemble brake fluid level gauge in 280XZ master cylinder.

Fig. 8: Exploded View of Master Cylinder Assembly

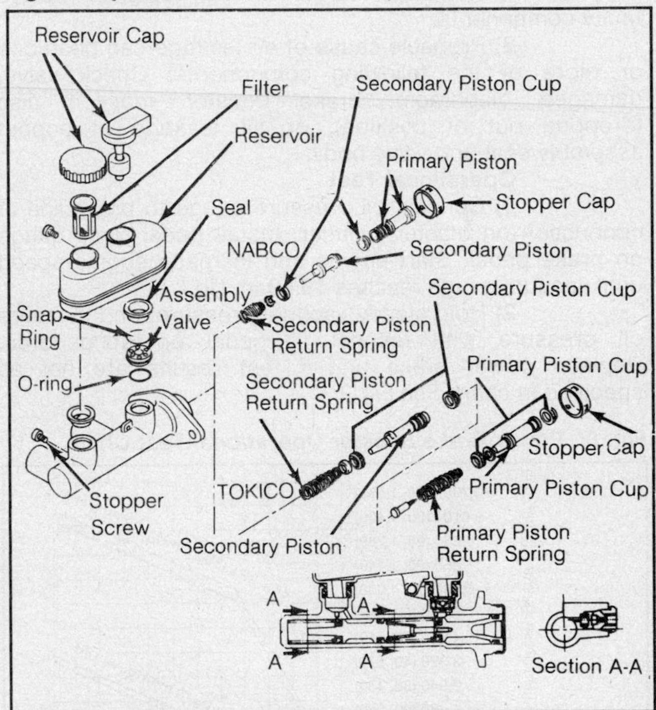
Reservoir Cap
Filter
Secondary Piston Cup
Reservoir
Primary Piston
Stopper Cap
Seal
NABCO
Secondary Piston
Secondary Piston Cup
Snap Ring
Assembly Valve
Secondary Piston Return Spring
Primary Piston Cup
O-ring
Secondary Piston Return Spring
Stopper Cap
TOKICO
Primary Piston Cup
Stopper Screw
Secondary Piston
Primary Piston Return Spring
A
A
A
A
Section A-A

Make sure repair kit matches master cylinder.

Reassembly

To reassemble, reverse disassembly procedure. Apply rubber grease to all rubber parts. To prevent damage, apply brake fluid to remaining parts when assembling.

POWER BRAKE UNIT

Manufacturer does not recommend disassembly of this unit. After air-tight and operational tests, if problem is determined to be in power brake unit, complete assembly must be replaced. Do not disassemble power brake unit.

NOTE: Determine whether source of problem is in power brake unit or check valve. Before reaching final conclusion, inspect check valve.

DATSUN/NISSAN MAXIMA, SENTRA, STANZA 200SX, 280ZX & 280ZX TURBO (Cont.)

POWER BRAKE UNIT TEST

Air Tight Test (No Load)

1) Connect vacuum gauge, in line, between check valve and power brake unit. Start engine and increase engine speed. Do not depress brake pedal. Stop engine when vacuum gauge indicates 19.69 in. Hg. Fifteen seconds after engine is stopped, observe rate of drop in air pressure registered on gauge.

2) If pressure drops more than .98 in. Hg, repair or replace faulty component(s). Probable cause of air leakage can be in one or more of following components: Check valve, push rod seal, valve body and seal, valve plunger seat, damaged piping or joints.

Air Tight Test (Under Load)

1) Repeat step **1)** of No Load test. Fifteen seconds after engine is stopped and brake fully applied, observe rate of drop in air pressure registered on gauge. If pressure drops more than .98 in. Hg, repair or replace faulty components.

2) Probable cause of air leakage can be in one or more of the following components: Check valve, damaged diaphragm, brake booster reaction disc (dropped out of position), or air leakage at poppet assembly seat and valve body.

Operational Test

1) Connect oil pressure gauge to brake line at connection on master cylinder. Install pedal force gauge on brake pedal. Start engine and increase engine speed until vacuum gauge reaches 19.69 in. Hg.

2) Hold steady vacuum pressure, and measure oil pressure with respect to pedal operating force. Replace power brake unit if test results are not as specified in chart. *See Fig 9.*

Fig. 9: Power Brake Booster Operational Test Chart

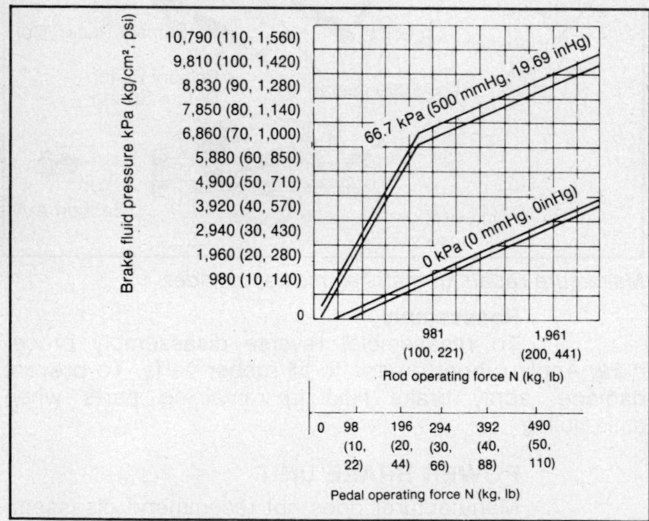
Brake fluid pressure kPa (kg/cm², psi)
10,790 (110, 1,560)
9,810 (100, 1,420)
8,830 (90, 1,280)
7,850 (80, 1,140)
6,860 (70, 1,000)
5,880 (60, 850)
4,900 (50, 710)
3,920 (40, 570)
2,940 (30, 430)
1,960 (20, 280)
980 (10, 140)
0
66.7 kPa (500 mmHg, 19.69 inHg)
0 kPa (0 mmHg, 0inHg)
981 (100, 221)
1,961 (200, 441)
Rod operating force N (kg, lb)
0
98 (10, 22)
196 (20, 44)
294 (30, 66)
392 (40, 88)
490 (50, 110)
Pedal operating force N (kg, lb)

Check the power unit and compare specifications to the chart before replacing the unit.

Check Valve Test

1) Remove check valve and apply vacuum pressure of 19.69 in. Hg to port of check valve on brake booster side. If vacuum pressure drops more than .39 in. Hg in 15 seconds, replace check valve.

2) When 20 psi air pressure is applied to brake power unit side of check valve and valve DOES NOT open, replace check valve.

DIESEL ENGINE BRAKE VACUUM PUMP

Removal (Drive Belt & Pump)

1) Set No. 1 piston to TDC on compression stroke. Ensure grooves in rear plate and drive plate are aligned with each other. Check No. 1 valve is closed. Remove radiator shroud and fan. Remove drive belt, alternator belt, power steering belt, air conditioner belt and power steering pump belt, if equipped.

2) Remove crankshaft damper belt and dust cover. Loosen spring set pin and tensioner shaft. Set tensioner pulley to free tension position and tighten. Mark pump drive belt if necessary and remove. Drain oil from vacuum pump. Manually rotate pump shaft at alternator pulley to discharge any accumulated oil in pump. Disconnect all hoses and remove vacuum pump assembly from rear of alternator.

Inspection

1) Separate center plate and vacuum pump housing. Disconnect check valve assembly. Clean all parts and check for wear or scratches on mating surfaces of rotor-to-pump housing and rotor-to-center plate. Replace any worn components. *See Fig. 10.*

Fig. 10: Exploded View of Diesel Engine Vacuum Pump

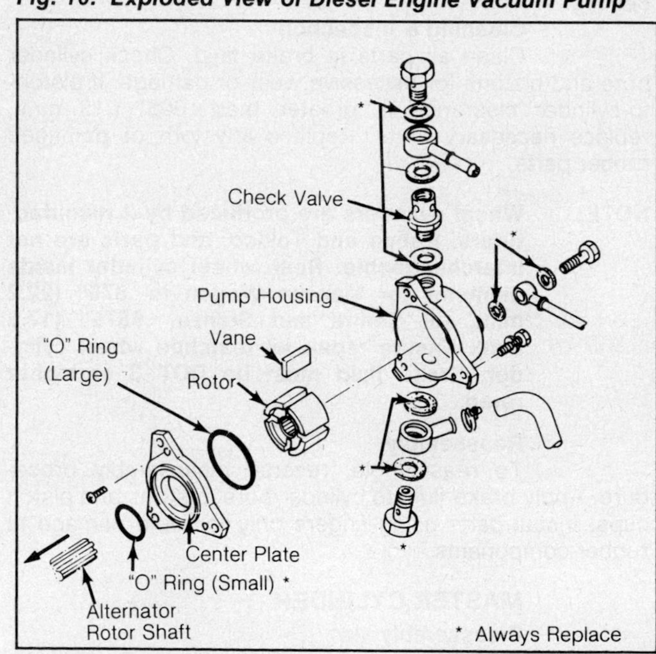
*
Check Valve
Pump Housing
Vane
"O" Ring (Large)
Rotor
Center Plate
"O" Ring (Small) *
Alternator Rotor Shaft
* Always Replace

Replace all "O" rings and any pump vanes that are worn beyond specifications.

2) Check for wear and scratches on pump vanes. Standard vane length is .512-.551" (13-14 mm). Replace as necessary. Check inner wall of pump housing for wear. Standard pump housing inner diameter is 2.244-2.248" (57.00-57.10 mm). Check rotor shaft opening and serrated end of rotor shaft for wear.

3) Inspect check valve locations and copper washers for bending or deformity. Replace components as necessary. Check for air leaks and proper operation of check valves. Replace as necessary. Remove and discard all rubber "O" rings.

Installation

1) To install pump and belt, reverse removal procedure and note the following: Install timing belt. Clean

DATSUN/NISSAN PICKUP & PULSAR

DESCRIPTION

Brake system for all models uses a tandem master cylinder and vacuum power unit. Pickup models are equipped with a hydraulically-controlled, dual line brake system, which operates independently on the front and rear wheels. The Pickup has single cylinder, dual piston, fixed caliper, sliding yoke type front disc brakes.

Pulsar models are equipped with a hydraulically-controlled, dual line brake system. It operates independently on right front and left rear wheel, and left front and right rear wheel. Pulsar models have single piston, sliding caliper, disc brakes.

Rear brake systems are duo-servo drum on Pickup models and leading/trailing drum on Pulsar models.

Pulsar models are equipped with a Dual Proportioning valve to prevent premature rear wheel lock-up. The Nissan Load Sensing Valve (NLSV) on Pickup models is mounted at a 10° incline on frame to change braking power of rear wheels in response to changes in load and brake fluid pressures. All models have parking brake systems, which are cable-operated at rear wheels.

ADJUSTMENT

DRUM BRAKES

Pickup

1) Raise and support vehicle. Release parking brake and remove dust boot from backing plate. Lightly tap adjuster housing and move it forward. Rotate adjuster down with a screwdriver until drum locks.

2) Back off adjuster 12 notches for correct shoe-to-drum clearance. Rotate brake drum by hand and ensure no excessive drag is present. Readjust clearance if necessary. Reinstall rubber boot and lower vehicle.

Pulsar

Drum brakes are self-adjusting. No service adjustment is required.

PEDAL HEIGHT & FREE PLAY

1) Adjust pedal height, measured from pedal pad to floor, to specification shown in table. To adjust, move stop light switch.

2) Loosen operating rod lock nut and turn operating rod to attain proper height. Tighten lock nut and adjust stop light switch. Pedal free play should be .04-.20" (1-5 mm). If specification is exceeded, adjust push rod length.

PEDAL HEIGHT SPECIFICATIONS

Application	In. (mm)
Pickup	6.4-6.8 (163-173)
Pulsar	
Auto. Trans.	7.8-8.2 (197-207)
Manual Trans.	7.6-8.0 (194-204)

STOP LIGHT SWITCH

Stop light switch is located under dash panel at brake pedal. Adjust travel during pedal height adjustment. After obtaining correct pedal height, position stop light switch so that it just contacts brake pedal arm. Tighten lock nut.

PARKING BRAKE

Pickup

1) To adjust, apply parking brake with 44 lbs. (20 kg) force to obtain lever stroke of 6-10 notches. Adjust equalizer link with adjusting nut until rear wheels are locked.

2) Release parking brake. Ensure rear wheels turn freely. After adjustment, parking brake should operate smoothly without noise or drag.

Pulsar

1) Adjust parking brake by rotating turnbuckle. Rear wheels should lock when lever is pulled 6-7 notches with a force of 44 lbs. (20 kg). Release parking brake.

2) Ensure rear wheels turn freely. After adjustment, ensure cables are slack and all parts are in original positions.

BRAKE WARNING LIGHT

1) Light indicates parking brake is engaged. Turn ignition on. To adjust light operation, bend switch plate so that light comes on when brake lever is pulled 1 notch and goes out when lever is released.

2) On all models, light also indicates low fluid level when parking brake is released. To check warning light operation, release parking brake and raise master cylinder reservoir cap. Warning light should glow. If not, check switch and wire connector.

BRAKE SYSTEM BLEEDING SEQUENCE

Pickup

Bleed air from system in the following sequence: Master cylinder, Nissan load sensing valve, left rear wheel, right rear wheel, right front wheel and left front wheel.

Pulsar

Bleed air out of system in the following sequence: Master cylinder, dual proportioning valve, right rear wheel, left front wheel, left rear wheel and right front wheel.

REMOVAL & INSTALLATION

FRONT DISC BRAKE PADS

Removal

1) Raise and support vehicle. Remove tire and wheel. On Pulsar models, remove guide and lock pins and lift off caliper. On Pickup models, remove retaining clip, pad pins and anti-squeal springs.

2) Remove pad retainers, if equipped, inner and outer shims and disc brake pads. Note shim positions for proper installation.

NOTE: **Standard disc brake pad thickness is .382" (9.70 mm) for Pickup models and .394" (10 mm) for Pulsar models. Minimum brake pad thickness is .079" (2 mm) on all models.**

Installation

1) After cleaning, apply silicone grease to cylinder body yoke guide groove, yoke sliding contact points, piston end surface and on Pickup models, guide and lock pins.

2) On Pulsar models, push piston into caliper with finger pressure. Install shims, pad retainers, and brake pads onto caliper support bracket. Install caliper onto bracket and tighten lock and guide pins.

CAUTION: On Pickup models, during reassembly, do not push groove of piston too far inside caliper. Piston seal could be damaged and caliper will have to be disassembled and piston repositioned.

3) On Pickup models, loosen bleeder screw and push outer piston into cylinder until piston end surface coincides with boot retaining ring end surface. Tighten bleeder screw and install inner brake pad.

4) Push inner piston into cylinder by pulling on yoke. Install outer pad, shims, anti-squeal springs, retaining pins and clip. On all models, depress brake pedal several times to seat pads. Bleed hydraulic system, if necessary.

FRONT DISC BRAKE CALIPER

Removal

Raise and support vehicle. Remove tire and wheel. Disconnect hydraulic line from caliper and plug opening. Remove caliper mounting bolts and lift off caliper (also yoke on Pickup).

Installation

To install, reverse removal procedure and bleed hydraulic system.

FRONT DISC BRAKE ROTOR

Removal (4WD Pickup)

1) Raise and support vehicle. Remove tire and wheel. Remove caliper as previously described and hang from frame with wire. Do not disconnect hydraulic line.

2) Set free-running hub to "Lock" position. Remove free-running hub assembly bolts. Remove driven clutch by turning clockwise. Remove hub assembly.

CAUTION: A pin is located inside free-running hub case to lock driven clutch. To remove pin, pull and turn driven clutch, while attracting lock pin with magnet.

3) Remove snap ring and remove drive clutch assembly by turning clockwise. Ensure lock pin is retained without damage.

4) Remove front side rebound bumper. Remove stabilizer bar securing bolt to lower link. Remove bolts fixing drive shaft to differential carrier. Do not remove boots. Remove drive shaft, drawing its outer end out of front wheel.

5) Remove knuckle arm-to-knuckle bolt. Support lower link with jack, and remove upper and lower ball joint nuts. Remove knuckle assembly from upper and lower links.

6) Straighten wheel lock washer and remove lock washer. Using lock nut remover tool (KV40102500), remove lock nut, lock washer and bearing washer. Remove inside grease seal.

7) Push wheel bearing support out of wheel hub. Using puller (KV40101000 & ST36230000), remove knuckle from hub. Remove hub-to-rotor bolts and remove rotor.

Installation

1) Install hub-to-rotor bolts and tighten. Assemble wheel hub and knuckle in reverse order of disassembly, noting the following. Pack cavity of knuckle with wheel bearing grease, and coat all bearings.

2) Install new inner grease seal, drive shaft bearing, bearing support, inner wheel bearing, knuckle, baffle plate, rotor, collar, outer wheel bearing, new outer grease seal, wheel hub, bearing washer, lock washer and lock nut in order.

3) Rotate hub several times to seat bearings, and check bearing preload. Bend lock washer lip up into a

Fig. 1: Exploded View of 4WD Pickup Disc Brake Rotor and Axle Assembly

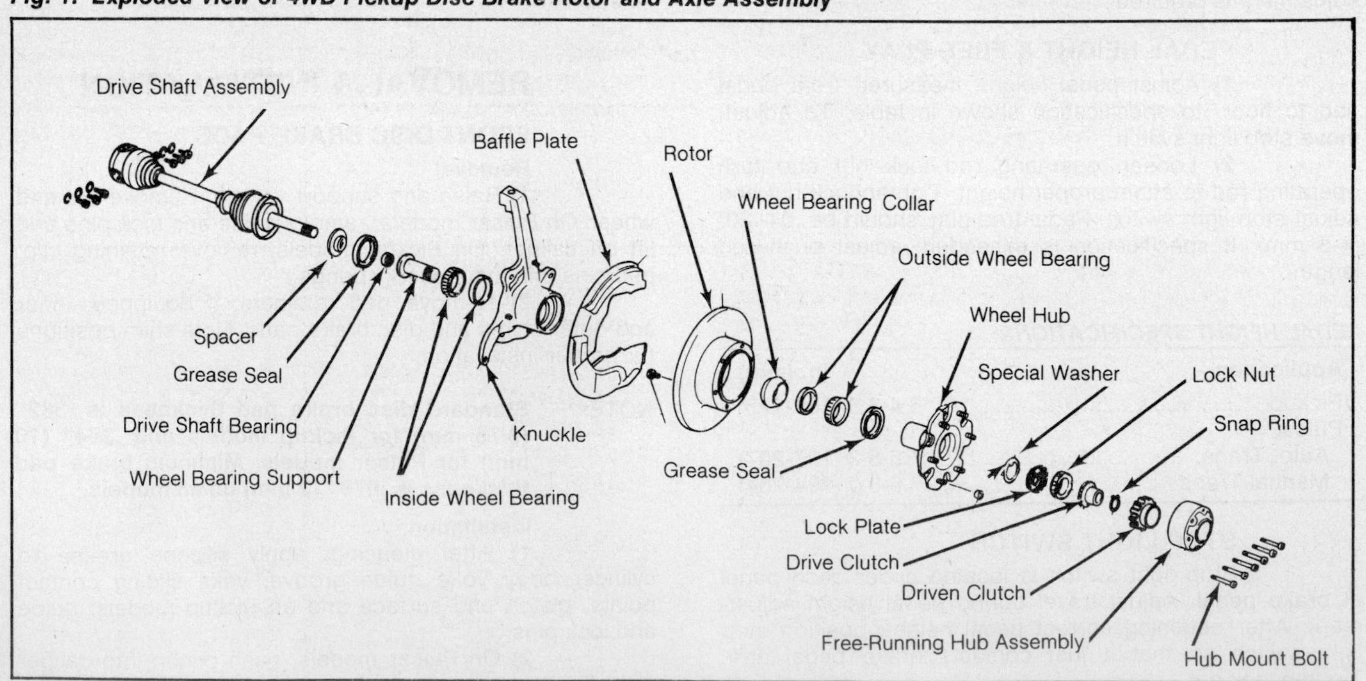
Drive Shaft Assembly
Baffle Plate
Rotor
Wheel Bearing Collar
Outside Wheel Bearing
Wheel Hub
Special Washer
Lock Nut
Snap Ring
Spacer
Grease Seal
Drive Shaft Bearing
Knuckle
Wheel Bearing Support
Inside Wheel Bearing
Grease Seal
Lock Plate
Drive Clutch
Driven Clutch
Free-Running Hub Assembly
Hub Mount Bolt

Whenever rotor has been removed, check drive axle end play upon installation.

DATSUN/NISSAN PICKUP & PULSAR (Cont.)

lock nut groove. Install spindle assembly, and tighten suspension components. After installing drive shaft, check that axle shaft end play is .004-.012" (.1-.3 mm).

4) Adjust axle shaft end play with proper thickness of snap ring. *See Fig. 1.* Mount caliper, tighten, and bleed hydraulic system if necessary.

Removal (2WD Pickup)

1) With caliper removed, remove hub dust cap, "O" ring, cotter pin, adjusting cap and lock nut. Remove hub and rotor assembly from spindle without dropping outer bearing and washer.

2) Remove washer, outer bearing, inner grease seal, inner wheel bearing and hub-to-rotor bolts. Separate hub and rotor.

NOTE: Avoid damaging dust cap "O" ring while removing hub dust cap.

Installation

1) To install, reverse removal procedure. Coat wheel bearings and inside hub with wheel bearing grease. Install new inner grease seal.

2) Tighten hub-to-rotor bolts evenly and adjust wheel bearings. *See Wheel Bearing Adjustment in SUSPENSION Section.* Bleed hydraulic system.

Removal (Pulsar)

1) With caliper removed, remove cotter pin. Remove hub nut from drive shaft end while holding hub with tool. Install wheel nuts to prevent damage to studs during this operation.

2) Using puller (KV40101000 & ST36230000), remove hub and rotor assembly from drive shaft. Remove hub-to-rotor bolts and seperate hub from rotor. Remove outer grease seal, outer wheel bearing and spacer.

Installation

To install, reverse removal procedure. Install new grease seal and pack bearing and hub with wheel bearing grease. Tighten hub-to-rotor bolts and adjust wheel bearings. *See Wheel Bearing Adjustment in SUSPENSION Section.* Bleed hydraulic system.

Fig. 2: Exploded View of Pickup Rear Brake Assembly

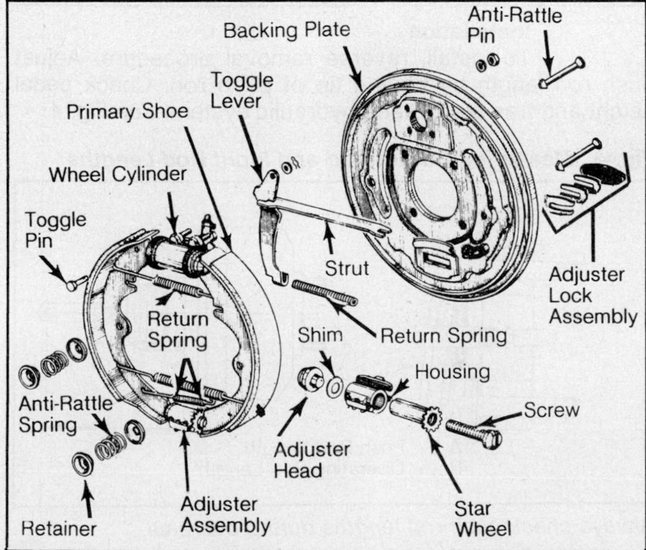
Backing Plate
Anti-Rattle Pin
Toggle Lever
Primary Shoe
Wheel Cylinder
Toggle Pin
Strut
Adjuster Lock Assembly
Return Spring
Shim
Return Spring
Housing
Anti-Rattle Spring
Screw
Adjuster Head
Retainer
Adjuster Assembly
Star Wheel

Remove pin to separate secondary shoe from toggle lever.

REAR BRAKE SHOES

Removal (Pickup)

1) Raise and support vehicle on safety stands. Remove tire and wheel. Loosen parking brake and remove brake drum. Remove retainers, anti-rattle springs, spring seats and anti-rattle pins.

2) Remove 2 lower return springs. Open brake shoe outward, remove upper return spring and extension link. Remove brake shoes. Separate secondary shoe from toggle lever by removing pin. *See Fig. 2.*

NOTE: Standard rear brake lining thickness is .177" (4.50 mm). Minimum lining thickness is .059" (1.50 mm).

Installation

1) To install, reverse removal procedure. Apply brake grease to moving parts of adjuster assembly and all metal contact surfaces of brake shoes.

2) Using spring scale, measure adjuster sliding resistance. Scale should read 11-26 lbs. (5-12 kg). If not, install new adjuster shim.

Removal (Pulsar)

1) Raise and support vehicle. Remove tire and wheel and brake drum. Remove parking brake rear cable from toggle lever. Remove retainers, anti-rattle springs, spring seats and pins. *See Fig. 3.*

Fig. 3: Exploded View of Rear Brake Assembly

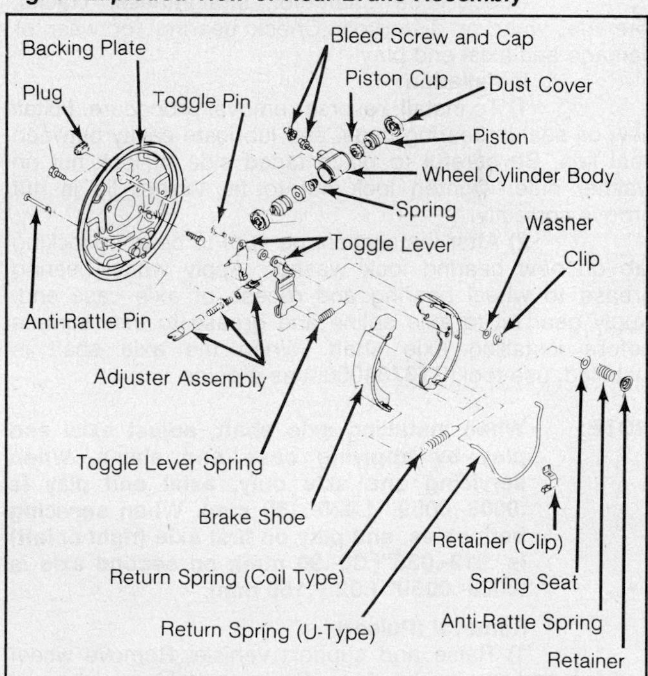
Backing Plate
Bleed Screw and Cap
Piston Cup
Dust Cover
Plug
Toggle Pin
Piston
Wheel Cylinder Body
Spring
Washer
Toggle Lever
Clip
Anti-Rattle Pin
Adjuster Assembly
Toggle Lever Spring
Brake Shoe
Retainer (Clip)
Return Spring (Coil Type)
Spring Seat
Anti-Rattle Spring
Return Spring (U-Type)
Retainer

Rear brake assembly for Pulsar models.

2) Remove return spring retainer, "U" type return spring, coil type return spring, adjuster assembly and brake shoes. Remove clip, washer and primary shoe from toggle lever.

NOTE: Standard rear brake lining thickness is .157" (4 mm). Minimun lining thickness is .059" (1.50 mm). Before installing brake drum, set shoe-to-drum clearance with adjuster to .0091-.0126" (.230-.320 mm). After installa-

DATSUN/NISSAN PICKUP & PULSAR (Cont.)

tion, adjust shoe-to-drum clearance by operating parking brake several times.

Installation

To install, reverse removal procedure. Apply brake grease to all contact points, mating surfaces and adjuster assembly threads. Ensure adjuster operates properly. Adjust shoe-to-drum clearance, and bleed hydraulic system, if necessary.

REAR AXLE SHAFT BEARING & OIL SEAL

Removal (Pickup)

1) Raise and support vehicle. Remove rear wheel and tire. Remove brake drum. Disconnect parking brake cable and hydraulic brake line from backing plate. Remove 4 nuts holding backing plate to rear axle case. Using tools (KV40101000 & ST36230000), pull out axle shaft assembly with backing plate assembly.

2) Remove oil seal from rear axle case. Discard oil seal. Using screwdriver, straighten lock washer securing lock nut on rear axle case side of backing plate. Position axle shaft in vise, using tool (KV40101000).

3) Using tool (ST38020000), remove bearing lock nut. Using hydraulic press and tool (HT72480000), withdraw wheel bearing, bearing cage and backing plate. Remove oil seal in bearing cage of backing plate and discard.

Inspection

Check axle shaft for straightness, cracks, damage, wear or distortion. Check bearing for wear or damage and axial end play.

Installation

1) To install, reverse removal procedure. Install new oil seal in bearing cage, and lubricate cavity between seal lips. Be careful to place faced side of lock nut on washer side. Tighten lock nut to fit washer lip in nut groove correctly.

2) After installation, be sure to bend up locking tab on new bearing lock washer. Apply wheel bearing grease to wheel bearing and recess of axle case end. Apply gear oil to axle spline and grease to seal surface before installing axle shaft. When the axle shaft is installed, use tool (ST37840000) as a guide.

NOTE: **When installing axle shaft, adjust axial end play by applying case end shims. When servicing one axle only, axial end play is .0008-.0059" (.020-.150 mm). When servicing both axles, end play on first axle (right or left) is .012-.035"(.30-.90 mm); on second axle is .0008-.0059" (.020-.150 mm).**

Removal (Pulsar)

1) Raise and support vehicle. Remove wheel and tire and rear brake drum. Release parking brake and remove dust cap without damaging "O" ring. Remove cotter pin, adjusting cap and wheel bearing nut.

2) Remove brake drum without dropping washer and outer wheel bearing. Remove and discard grease seal. Remove inner wheel bearing.

Installation

1) To install, reverse removal procedure. Pack inner and outer wheel bearings with multi-purpose grease. Coat with grease; sealing lips of new oil seal, threaded portion of spindle and contacting surfaces of wheel bearing nut and washer.

2) Install components and adjust wheel bearing preload. Coat "O" ring and pack dust cap with grease and install.

MASTER CYLINDER

Testing

Before removing power brake unit, test check valve. Using a vacuum gauge/tester, apply 19.7 in. Hg to brake unit side of check valve. If pressure drops more than .98 in. Hg in 15 seconds, replace check valve. If valve does not open when pressure is applied to brake unit side of check valve, replace valve. If check valve is not defective, check brake system and vacuum lines for leaks. Replace booster as an assembly.

Removal

Disconnect electrical wiring at cylinder reservoir. Disconnect and plug hydraulic lines at master cylinder. Drain fluid from reservoir. Remove cylinder mounting nuts and master cylinder.

Installation

To install master cylinder, reverse removal procedure. Bleed hydraulic system and check pedal height.

POWER BRAKE UNIT

Removal

With master cylinder removed, disconnect vacuum line from power unit. From inside vehicle, disconnect pedal return spring, push rod from brake pedal and power unit mounting nuts. Remove power unit from engine compartment.

POWER BOOSTER ROD LENGTHS

Application	In. (mm)
Output Rod [1]	
Pickup	.38-.39 (9.75-10)
Pulsar	.40-.41 (10.28-10.53)
Input Rod [2]	
Pickup	10.83 (275)
Pulsar	5.91 (150)

[1] – See measurement "A" in Fig. 4.
[2] – See measurement "B" in Fig. 4.

Installation

To install, reverse removal procedure. Adjust push rod length by turning tip of push rod. Check pedal height and free play. Bleed hydraulic system. *See Fig. 4.*

Fig. 4: Measuring Output Rod and Input Rod Lengths

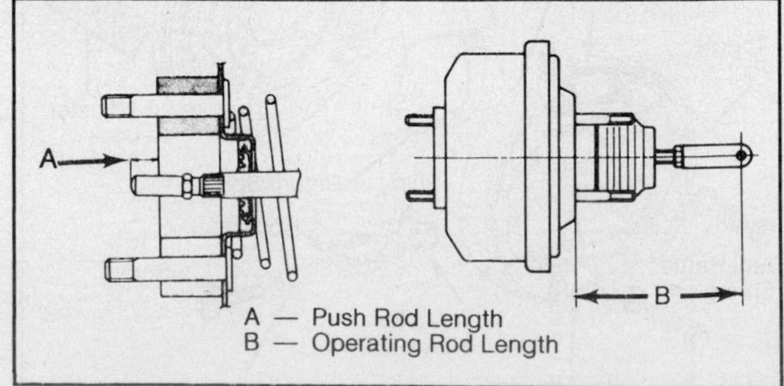
A
B
A — Push Rod Length
B — Operating Rod Length

Always check push rod lengths during overhaul.

DATSUN/NISSAN PICKUP & PULSAR (Cont.)

OVERHAUL

FRONT DISC BRAKE CALIPER

Disassembly (Pickup)

1) With caliper and pads removed, drain any remaining fluid from cylinder. Remove caliper retaining bolts and grippers. Separate yoke and cylinder body.

2) Remove yoke holder, retaining rings and dust seals from both pistons. Push both pistons out in one direction. Note piston locations for proper installation. Remove piston seals. *See Fig. 5.*

Fig. 5: Exploded View of Pickup Front Disc Brake Caliper

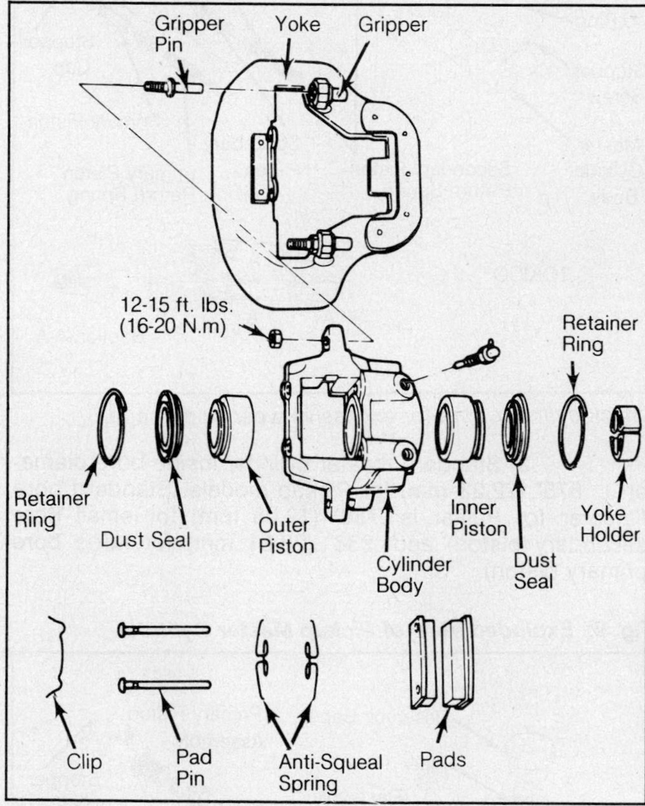
Gripper Pin
Yoke
Gripper
12-15 ft. lbs. (16-20 N.m)
Retainer Ring
Retainer Ring
Dust Seal
Outer Piston
Cylinder Body
Inner Piston
Dust Seal
Yoke Holder
Clip
Pad Pin
Anti-Squeal Spring
Pads

Push both pistons out in one direction.

NOTE: Piston surfaces are plated and must be replaced if corroded or worn. Do not polish with emery cloth. Standard inside diameter for Pickup disc brake caliper is 2.125" (53.98 mm).

Cleaning & Inspection

Clean all parts with brake fluid, and check all components for wear or damage. If minor corrosion cannot be removed from cylinder bore with emery cloth, cylinder must be replaced. All seals must be replaced during overhaul.

Reassembly

1) Install piston seals without damaging seals. Coat cylinder bore and pistons with brake fluid. Push outer piston into cylinder until piston end surface coincides with boot retaining ring end surface.

2) Do not push dust seal groove of piston to far into cylinder bore or piston groove will go inside of piston seal and seal will be damaged. Push inner piston into cylinder bore by holding cylinder body.

3) Apply brake grease to sealing surface of dust seal, and install dust seal; clamping securely with retaining ring. Install yoke holder to inner piston. Install gripper to yoke.

4) Apply soap solution to inner gripper wall and drive gripper pin into position. Install yoke to yoke holder by supporting outer piston end and pressing yoke into yoke holder with 44-66 lb. (20-30 kg) force. No clearance should be present between piston and yoke.

Disassembly (Pulsar)

With caliper and pads removed, drain any remaining fluid from caliper. Push out piston, with dust seal, through brake hose outlet. Remove piston seal. Remove guide and lock pins and boots from torque member.

NOTE: Piston surfaces are plated and must be replaced if corroded or worn. Do not polish with emery cloth. Standard inside diameter for Pulsar disc brake caliper is 1.894" (48.10 mm).

Cleaning & Inspection

Clean parts with brake fluid. Check all components for wear or damage. If minor corrosion cannot be removed from cylinder bore with emery cloth, replace cylinder. Replace piston seals, dust covers and rubber boots during overhaul. *See Fig. 6.*

Fig. 6: Exploded View of Pulsar Front Disc Brake Caliper

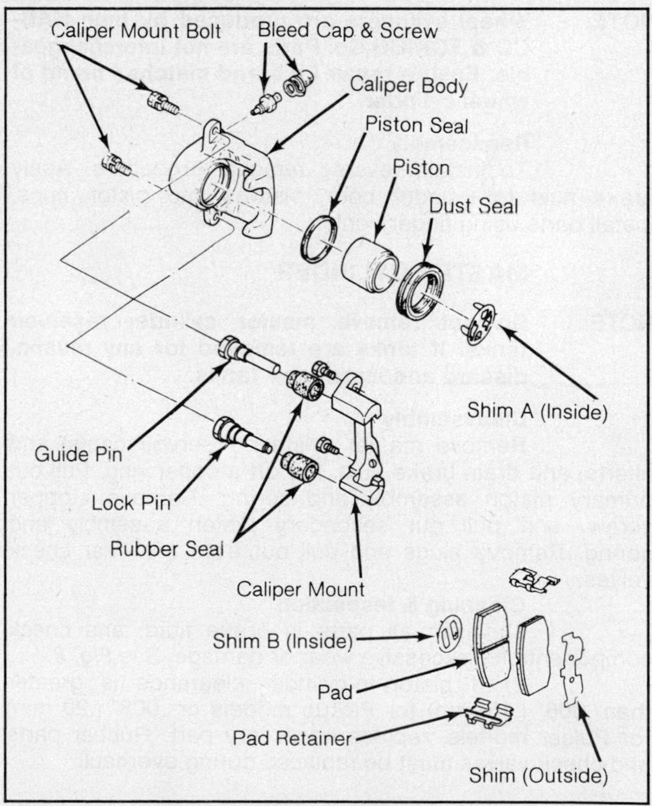
Caliper Mount Bolt
Bleed Cap & Screw
Caliper Body
Piston Seal
Piston
Dust Seal
Shim A (Inside)
Guide Pin
Lock Pin
Rubber Seal
Caliper Mount
Shim B (Inside)
Pad
Pad Retainer
Shim (Outside)

Replace all rubber parts during overhaul.

Reassembly

1) Apply brake fluid to caliper cylinder bore and install piston seal. Lightly coat sliding surfaces and inside of dust seal with rubber grease. With dust seal fitted to piston, insert dust seal into groove on cylinder and insert piston into caliper with finger pressure.

2) Apply rubber grease to guide and lock pin sliding portion. Install lock and guide pin boots. Install lock and guide pins. Attach torque member to caliper body.

REAR WHEEL CYLINDER

Disassembly

With rear wheel cylinder removed, remove dust covers, pistons, cups and springs.

Cleaning & Inspection

Clean all parts in brake fluid and check cylinder bore and pistons for excessive wear or damage. If piston-to-cylinder clearance is greater than .006" (.15 mm), replace necessary parts. Replace any torn or damaged rubber parts. *See Fig. 7.*

Fig. 7: Exploded View of Rear Wheel Cylinder

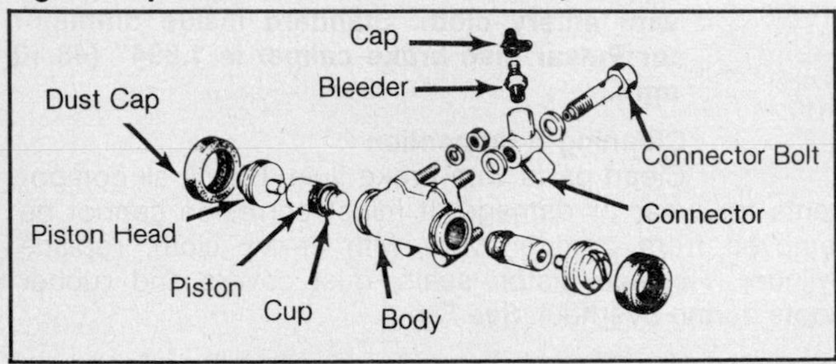
Cap
Bleeder
Dust Cap
Connector Bolt
Connector
Piston Head
Piston
Cup
Body

Replace all rubber parts during overhaul.

NOTE: **Wheel cylinders are produced by both NABCO & TOKICO Co. Parts are not interchangeable. Ensure repair kit brand matches brand of wheel cylinder.**

Reassembly

To install, reverse removal procedure. Apply brake fluid to cylinder bore, pistons and piston cups. Install parts using fingers only.

MASTER CYLINDER

NOTE: **Do not remove master cylinder reservoir tanks. If tanks are removed for any reason, discard and install new tanks.**

Disassembly

Remove master cylinder reservoir cap(s) and filter(s) and drain brake fluid. Pry off stopper ring. Pull out primary piston assembly and spring. Remove stopper screw, and pull out secondary piston assembly and spring. Remove plugs and pull out front and rear check valves.

Cleaning & Inspection

1) Clean all parts in brake fluid, and check components for excessive wear or damage. *See Fig. 8.*

2) If piston-to-cylinder clearance is greater than .006" (.15 mm) for Pickup models or .008" (.20 mm) for Pulsar models, replace necessary part. Rubber parts and check valves must be replaced during overhaul.

NOTE: **Master cylinders are produced by both NABCO or TOKICO Co. Parts are not interchangeable. Ensure repair kit brand matches master cylinder.** ***See Fig. 9.***

Fig. 8: Exploded View of Pulsar Master Cylinder

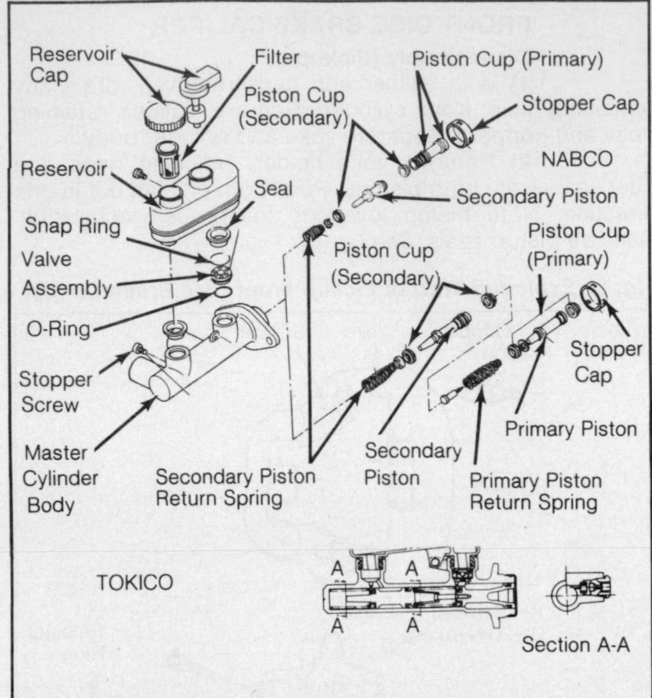
Reservoir Cap
Filter
Piston Cup (Primary)
Piston Cup (Secondary)
Stopper Cap
NABCO
Reservoir
Seal
Secondary Piston
Snap Ring
Piston Cup (Primary)
Piston Cup (Secondary)
Valve Assembly
O-Ring
Stopper Cap
Stopper Screw
Primary Piston
Master Cylinder Body
Secondary Piston Return Spring
Secondary Piston
Primary Piston Return Spring
TOKICO
A
A
A
A
Section A-A

Check cylinder bore for excessive wear or damage.

3) Standard master cylinder inside bore diameter is .875" (22.23 mm) for Pickup models. Standard bore diameter for Pulsar is .750" (19.05 mm) for small bore (secondary piston) and .938" (23.81 mm) for large bore (primary piston).

Fig. 9: Exploded View of Pickup Master Cylinder

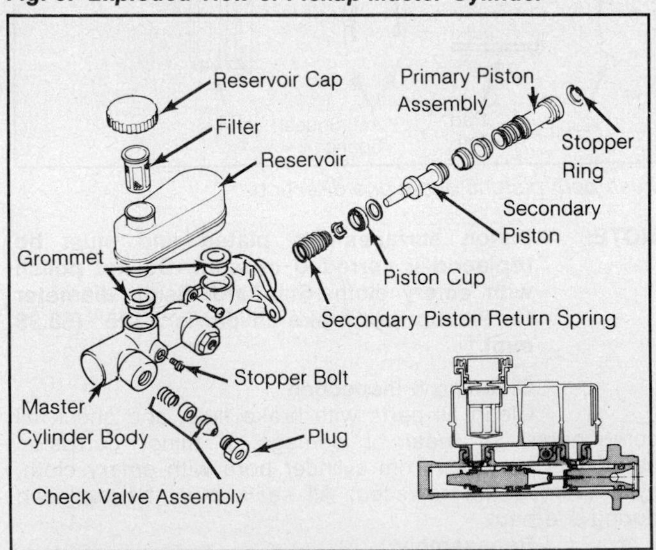
Reservoir Cap
Primary Piston Assembly
Filter
Stopper Ring
Reservoir
Secondary Piston
Grommet
Piston Cup
Secondary Piston Return Spring
Stopper Bolt
Master Cylinder Body
Plug
Check Valve Assembly

Check brand of cylinder for proper repair kit.

Reassembly

Reverse disassembly procedure. Coat all parts with brake fluid (rubber parts with brake grease) when assembling. Check output and input rod length whenever master cylinder is removed. Adjust, as necessary.

DATSUN/NISSAN PICKUP & PULSAR (Cont.)

POWER BRAKE UNIT

Manufacturer does not recommend disassembly of this unit. If a problem is determined to be in booster unit, complete assembly must be replaced.

NOTE: If amount of output rod length adjustment required exceeds .02" (0.5 mm), reaction disc may have been either dislocated or fallen off. Replace power brake booster assembly.

VACUUM PUMP

Disassembly & Reassembly (Diesel Pickup)

Drain oil. Remove and disassemble pump. *See Fig. 10.* Inspect parts for wear or scratches on mating surfaces. Vane length is .512-.551" (13-14 mm). Pump housing inner diameter is 2.244-2.248" (57.00-57.10 mm). Replace worn parts during reassembly.

Fig. 10: Exploded View of Diesel Engine Vacuum Pump

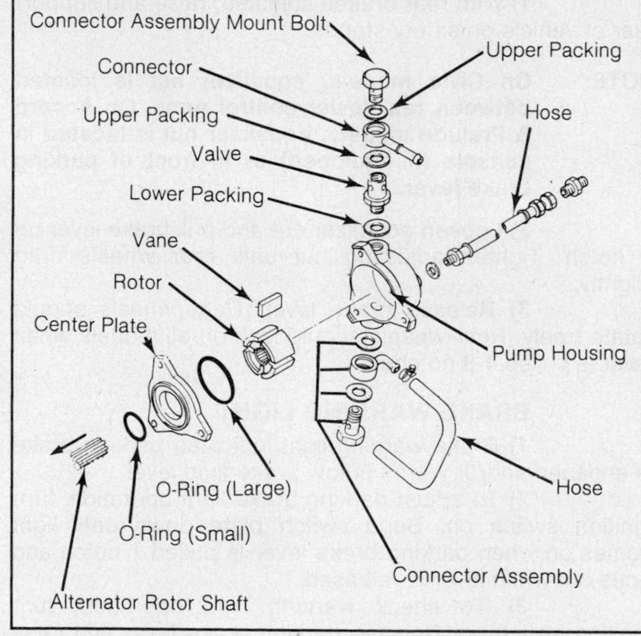
Connector Assembly Mount Bolt
Upper Packing
Connector
Upper Packing
Hose
Valve
Lower Packing
Vane
Rotor
Center Plate
Pump Housing
O-Ring (Large)
Hose
O-Ring (Small)
Connector Assembly
Alternator Rotor Shaft

DUAL PROPORTIONING & NLSV VALVES

Manufacturer does not recommend disassembly of these units. If a problem is determined to be in either valve, complete assembly must be replaced.

TIGHTENING SPECIFICATIONS

Application	Ft. Lbs. (N.m)
Brake Booster Input Rod	
Lock Nut (All)	12-16 (16-22)
Brake Hose Connector (All)	12-14 (16-20)
Caliper-to-Caliper Mount	
Pickup	12-15 (16-21)
Pulsar	16-23 (22-31)
Caliper Mount-to-Knuckle Bolts	
Pickup	53-72 (72-98)
Pulsar	40-47 (54-64)
Drum Brake Backing Plate	
Pickup	39-46 (53-63)
Pulsar	18-25 (25-34)
Hub-to-Drive Shaft Lock Nut	
Pulsar	87-145 (118-196)
Hub-to-Rotor Bolt	
Pickup	28-38 (38-52)
Pulsar	18-25 (25-34)
Pickup (4WD Only)	
Drive Shaft-to-Carrier	20-27 (27-37)
Hub-to-Drive Shaft Lock Nut	108-145 (147-196)
Knuckle Arm-to-Knuckle	53-72 (72-97)
Locking Hub	18-25 (25-34)
Stabilizer Bar-to-Lower Link	12-16 (16-22)
Wheel Nut	87-108 (118-147)
	INCH Lbs. (N.m)
Dual Proportioning Valve Bolt	
Pulsar	34-43 (4-5)
Master Cylinder-to-Brake Booster (All)	70-96 (8-11)
Nissan Load Sensing Valve Bolt	
Pickup	70-96 (8-11)
Secondary Piston Stopper Bolt	
NABCO	13-26 (1.5-2.9)
TOKICO	17-30 (2.0-3.)

DISC BRAKE ROTOR SPECIFICATIONS

Application	Disc Diameter In. (mm)	Lateral Runout In. (mm)	Parallelism In. (mm)	Original Thickness In. (mm)	Min. Refinish Thickness In. (mm)	Discard Thickness In. (mm)
Pickup	10.67 (271)	.0060 (.150)	.0030 (.070)	.492 (12.50)	.413 (10.50)	.413 (10.50)
Pulsar	9.45 (240)	.0028 (.070)	.0012 (.030)	.....	.394 (10.0)	.394 (10.0)

DRUM BRAKE SPECIFICATIONS

Application	Drum Diam. In. (mm)	Drum Width In. (mm)	Max. Drum Refinish Diam. In. (mm)	Wheel Cyl. Diam. In. (mm)	Master Cyl. Diam. In. (mm)
Pickup	10.0 (254)	1.77 (45)	10.06 (255.5)	5/8 (15.88)	7/8 (22.23)
Pulsar	7.09 (180)	1.378 (35)	7.13 (181)	11/16 (17.46)	[1] 3/4 (19.05)

[1] – Master cylinder small bore diameter shown, large bore diameter is 15/16" (23.8 mm).

Brakes

HONDA

Accord, Civic, Prelude

DESCRIPTION

Brake system is hydraulically-operated using a tandem master cylinder and vacuum brake unit. All models are equipped with single piston, floating-caliper front disc brakes and leading/trailing rear drum brakes.

All models use dual-valve combination valves to prevent premature rear wheel lock-up. A brake warning light is mounted on the dash to indicate loss of brake fluid, uneven fluid pressure between brake systems and parking brake engagement. Parking brake is cable-actuated at rear wheels.

TESTING

POWER BRAKE UNIT

Functional Test

1) With engine stopped, depress brake pedal several times, then depress pedal hard and hold pressure for 15 seconds. If pedal sinks, master cylinder, brake line or wheel cylinder is faulty.

2) Start engine with pedal depressed. If pedal sinks slightly, vacuum unit is working. If pedal height does not vary, booster is faulty.

Leak Test

1) Depress brake pedal with engine running, then stop engine. If pedal height does not vary while depressed for 30 seconds, vacuum unit is good. If pedal rises, vacuum unit is faulty.

2) With engine stopped, depress brake pedal several times. Pedal should be low when first depressed. On consecutive applications, pedal height should gradually rise. If pedal height does not vary, check power brake unit's check valve.

Check Valve Test

1) Disconnect both ends of power brake unit's vacuum hose. Check valve is inside hose and cannot be removed.

NOTE: **Mark hose ends for proper reassembly. Power unit will not work if hose ends are reversed.**

2) Using 20 psi (1.4 kg/cm²) air pressure, air should flow from power unit to manifold but not from manifold to power unit.

ADJUSTMENT

REAR DRUM BRAKE SHOES

Rear brake shoes are self-adjusted by brake pedal action. No in-service adjustment is required.

REAR WHEEL SPINDLE NUT

1) Tighten spindle nut to 14-22 ft. lbs. (20-30 N.m) and manually turn brake drum. Loosen spindle nut. Retighten spindle nut to 48 INCH lbs. (5 N.m).

2) Install pin holder with slots as close as possible to hole in spindle. Tighten enough to align slot with hole and install cotter pin.

PEDAL HEIGHT

1) Pedal height is measured from center of pedal pad to floorboard (without carpet or floormat). To adjust, loosen brake light switch lock nut and back switch away from brake pedal arm.

2) Loosen power unit push rod lock nut and rotate push rod to adjust pedal height. On Civic models pedal height is 7.25" (184 mm). On Prelude models pedal height is 7" (176 mm). On Accord models pedal height is 7.36" (187 mm).

3) Tighten lock nut. Reposition and adjust stop light switch. Check for proper brake pedal free play. Free play on all models is .05-.20" (1-5 mm).

STOP LIGHT SWITCH

1) Stop light switch is located under dash, above brake pedal. To adjust, turn switch until plunger is fully depressed (threaded end touching pedal arm pad).

2) Back off switch 1/2 turn and tighten lock nuts. Check that brake lights go off when pedal is released.

PARKING BRAKE

1) With rear brakes adjusted, raise and support rear of vehicle on safety stands.

NOTE: **On Civic models, equalizer nut is located between rear lower control arms. On Accord & Prelude models, equalizer nut is located in console (if equipped) or in front of parking brake lever.**

2) Loosen equalizer nut and pull brake lever up 1 notch. Tighten adjusting nut until rear wheels drag slightly.

3) Release brake lever. Rear wheels should rotate freely. Rear wheels should lock on all models when lever is pulled 4-8 notches.

BRAKE WARNING LIGHT

1) Brake warning light indicates parking brake is engaged and/or warns of low brake fluid level.

2) To adjust parking brake light operation, turn ignition switch on. Bend switch plate down until light comes on when parking brake lever is pulled 1 notch and goes out when lever is released.

3) To check warning light operation, turn ignition switch on. Release parking brake lever and raise master cylinder reservoir cap. Warning light should glow. If not, check switch and wire connector.

MASTER CYLINDER PUSH ROD

1) Using rod bolt adjustment gauge, mount to master cylinder and adjust bolt with top flush to master cylinder piston.

NOTE: **Accord Rod Bolt Adjustment Gauge is No. 07975-SA50000. Civic Gauge is No. 07975-6570000. Prelude Gauge is No. 07975-SA50001.**

2) Remove gauge from master cylinder and place upside down on power brake unit without disturbing adjusting bolt position.

3) Install 4 master cylinder nuts and tighten.

4) Connect power unit in-line with vacuum gauge (0-30 in. Hg) to power brake unit's engine vacuum supply. Start engine and set RPM to allow reading of 20 in. Hg.

HONDA (Cont.)

5) Measure clearance between output rod and adjusting bolt with feeler gauge. If adjustment is needed, loosen star lock nut and turn adjuster to adjust.

6) Push rod-to-piston clearance is 0-.016" (0-.4 mm) for all models.

REMOVAL & INSTALLATION

FRONT DISC BRAKE PADS

Removal (All Except Civic Wagon)

1) Raise and support vehicle. Remove tire and wheel. Remove lower caliper guide pin and pivot caliper body up out of way.

2) Remove pads, pad shim, upper and lower anti-rattle springs, pad spring and pad retainers, where applicable.

NOTE: **Always replace brake pads in sets of four. Keep grease, brake fluid or other contaminants off lining surface. Check and clean rotor as necessary.**

Installation

1) Lubricate shim and all sliding surfaces with high temperature silicone grease. Install 4 small anti-rattle springs on Accord, 2 large anti-rattle springs on Civic, or pad spring and pad retainers on Prelude.

2) Install shim against outer pad and install brake pads. Loosen bleeder screw. Seat piston into caliper bore with finger pressure and tighten bleeder screw.

3) Rotate caliper body down and tighten lower caliper guide pin.

4) Depress brake pedal several times to seat pads. Bleed brakes as necessary.

Removal (Civic Wagon)

1) Raise and support vehicle. Remove tire and wheel. Remove spring clips and guide plates.

2) Remove caliper body and hang from frame with wire. Do not allow caliper to hang from hydraulic line.

3) Remove anti-rattle springs and pad clips, brake pads and shim.

Installation

1) Install anti-rattle springs and pad clips. Lubricate all sliding surfaces and metal side of brake pads with silicone grease. Install pads, with shim against outside shoe.

2) Loosen bleeder screw, and seat piston into caliper bore with finger pressure. Tighten bleeder screw. Install caliper on mounting. Install guide plates and secure with spring pins.

3) Depress brake pedal several times to seat pads. Bleed brakes as necessary.

NOTE: **Disc brake calipers on all models are of the same basic design. Only caliper-to-bracket attachments and anti-rattle springs or clips differ between models.**

FRONT DISC BRAKE CALIPER

Removal

1) Raise and support vehicle. Remove tire and wheel. Disconnect and plug hydraulic line at caliper.

2) On all models except Civic wagon, remove caliper guide pins and remove caliper. On Prelude models; during removal, avoid damage of splash guard on upper caliper bolt side.

3) On Civic Wagon, remove spring pins and guide plates and remove caliper. Remove disc pads, anti-rattle pad clips, anti-rattle springs and shim.

Installation

To install, reverse removal procedure. Replace copper washers when installing brake flex hose and bleed hydraulic system.

DISC BRAKE ROTOR

Removal

1) Raise and support vehicle. Remove wheel and tire. Remove caliper assembly and suspend with wire. Remove rotor retaining screws.

2) Install two 8 x 1.25 x 12 mm bolts in existing holes. To prevent warpage, alternately turn bolts 2 turns until disc can be removed from hub.

Installation

To install, reverse removal procedure. Tighten retaining screws and bleed hydraulic system as necessary.

REAR BRAKE DRUM

Removal

1) Raise and support vehicle. Remove rear wheel. Remove brake drum grease cap, cotter pin and pin retainer.

2) Remove spindle nut, hub washer and outer wheel bearing. Remove brake drum.

NOTE: **If drum is difficult to remove, use slide hammer with hub puller attachment.**

Fig. 1: Exploded View of Civic Rear Brake Assembly

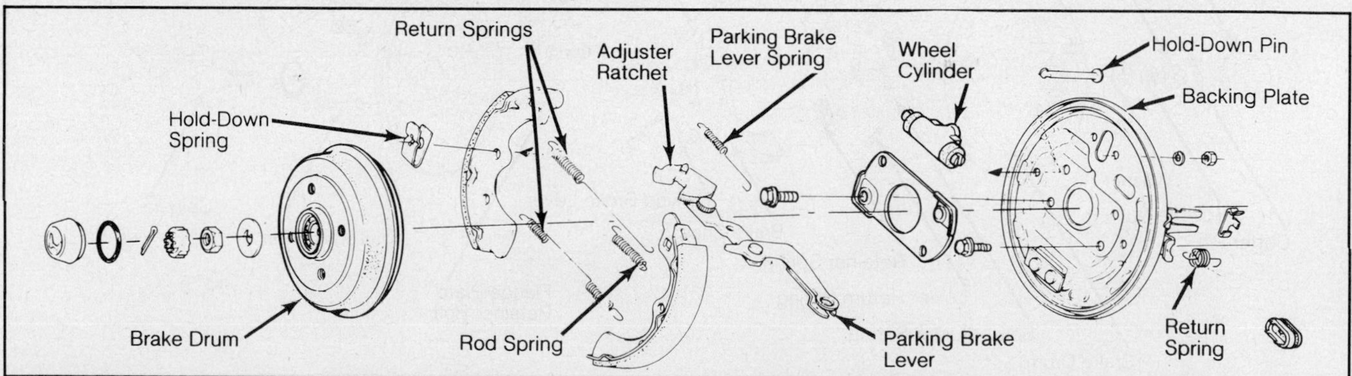
Return Springs
Adjuster Ratchet
Parking Brake Lever Spring
Wheel Cylinder
Hold-Down Pin
Backing Plate
Hold-Down Spring
Brake Drum
Rod Spring
Parking Brake Lever
Return Spring

Upper/lower return springs not interchangeable.

Brakes

HONDA (Cont.)

Installation

To install, reverse removal procedure and tighten axle nut.

NOTE: **All models use same basic rear brake design. Some minor variations may exist between systems.**

REAR BRAKE SHOES

Removal

1) Raise and support vehicle. Remove wheel and tire and brake drum. Remove retaining springs and pins, self-adjuster spring and return springs (note original position of return springs). *See Figs. 1 & 2*.

2) Remove primary brake shoe. Disconnect and remove secondary brake shoe from parking brake lever assembly.

3) Standard rear brake lining thickness is .18" (4.5 mm). Service limit is .08" (2 mm).

NOTE: **Inspect brake shoes for distortion, looseness, nicks, burrs or oil-soaked linings. Repair or replace as necessary.**

Installation

1) Apply light coat of grease to adjuster assembly, sliding surfaces of brake shoes and metal contact areas of backing plate.

2) On all models, upper return spring is identified by long single coil. Lower return spring is identified by short single coil (Prelude & Accord), or long double coil (Civic).

3) To install, reverse removal procedure. Adjust and bleed brakes.

NOTE: **Before installing brake drum, release brake adjuster ratchet with screwdriver. Mark engaged teeth. Install drum and spindle nut. Depress brake pedal, remove drum and ensure ratchet has moved and brakes have self-adjusted.**

MASTER CYLINDER

Removal

1) Drain hydraulic fluid from master cylinder and disconnect hydraulic lines.

2) Remove retaining nuts and master cylinder from power brake unit.

Installation

To install, reverse removal procedure. Bench bleed master cylinder before installation. Install master cylinder and bleed hydraulic system.

POWER BRAKE UNIT

Removal

1) Disconnect vacuum hose at power brake unit and hydraulic lines at master cylinder.

2) Remove cotter pin and clevis pin retaining power brake unit push rod to brake pedal. Remove 4 bolts accessible from inside vehicle) attaching power unit to firewall.

3) Remove power brake unit and master cylinder as an assembly.

Installation

To install, reverse removal procedure. Tighten all bolts and bleed hydraulic system.

REAR AXLE SEAL

Removal

1) Raise and support vehicle. Remove wheel and tire. Remove dust cap, cotter pin, pin retainer, spindle nut, washer and outer wheel bearing.

2) Remove brake drum. Pry grease seal from drum and replace. Inspect outer and inner wheel bearings and replace as necessary.

Installation

To install, reverse removal procedure and adjust rear wheel spindle nut.

Fig. 2: Exploded View of Accord & Prelude Rear Brake Assembly

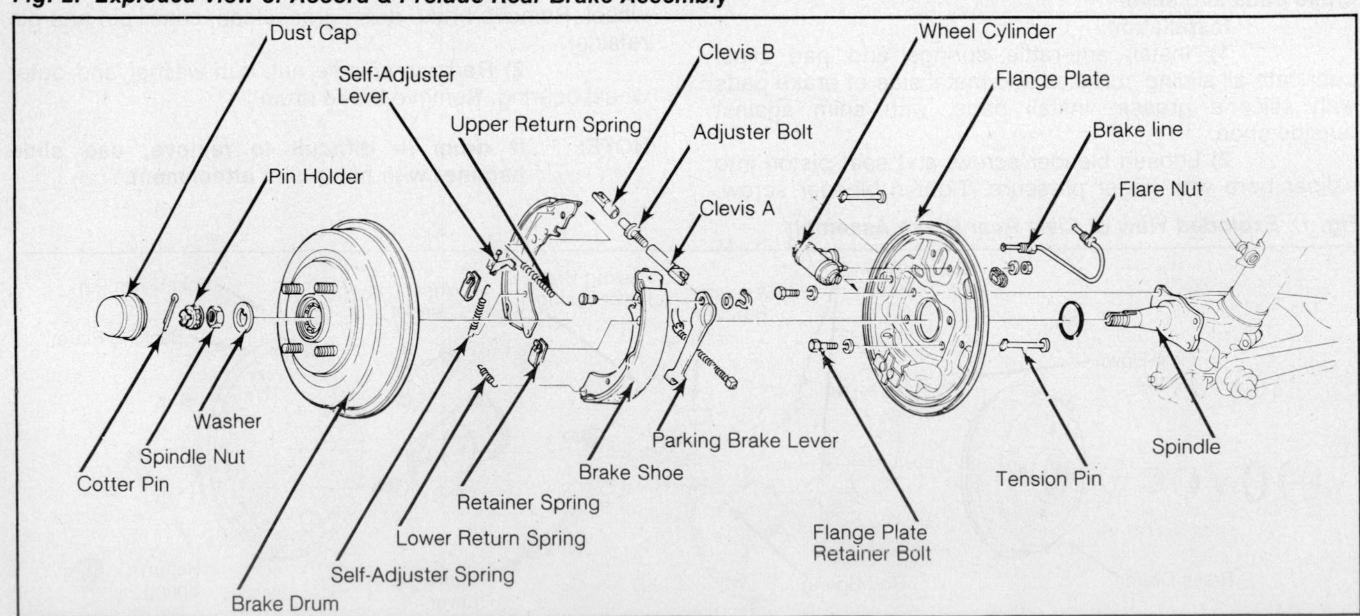

Dust Cap
Self-Adjuster Lever
Upper Return Spring
Clevis B
Adjuster Bolt
Clevis A
Pin Holder
Wheel Cylinder
Flange Plate
Brake line
Flare Nut
Washer
Spindle Nut
Cotter Pin
Parking Brake Lever
Brake Shoe
Retainer Spring
Lower Return Spring
Self-Adjuster Spring
Brake Drum
Flange Plate Retainer Bolt
Tension Pin
Spindle

Insert tensioner pin in retainer spring slot and turn 90° to lock.

HONDA (Cont.)

OVERHAUL

DISC BRAKE CALIPER

Disassembly

1) Remove retaining snap ring (if equipped) and piston dust boot. Place rags in front of piston to prevent damage during removal.

2) Force piston out of caliper bore by applying 30 psi (2.1 kg/cm²) air pressure to brake fluid inlet port. Remove and discard piston square ring seal without damaging cylinder bore. *See Figs. 3 & 4.*

Fig. 3: Exploded View of Front Disc Brake Caliper

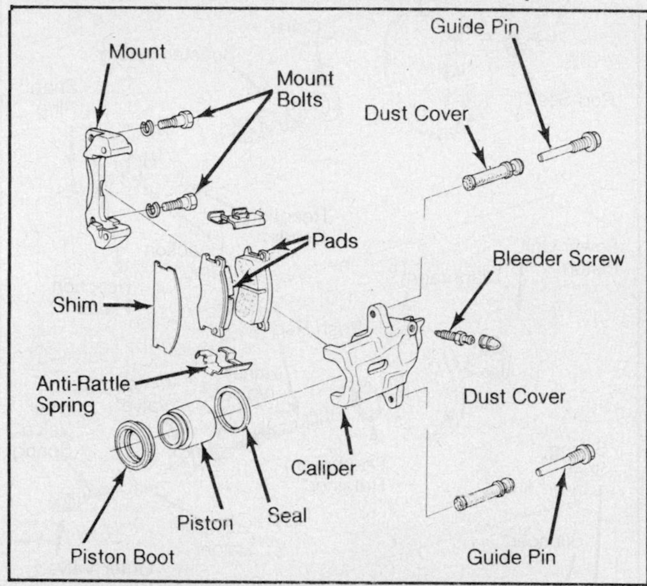
Guide Pin
Mount
Mount Bolts
Dust Cover
Pads
Bleeder Screw
Shim
Anti-Rattle Spring
Dust Cover
Caliper
Seal
Piston
Piston Boot
Guide Pin

Applies to all Civic models except Wagon. Accord and Prelude are similar.

Cleaning & Inspection

1) Wash all parts in clean brake fluid or denatured alcohol, and check for wear or damage.

Fig. 4: Exploded View of Front Disc Brake Caliper

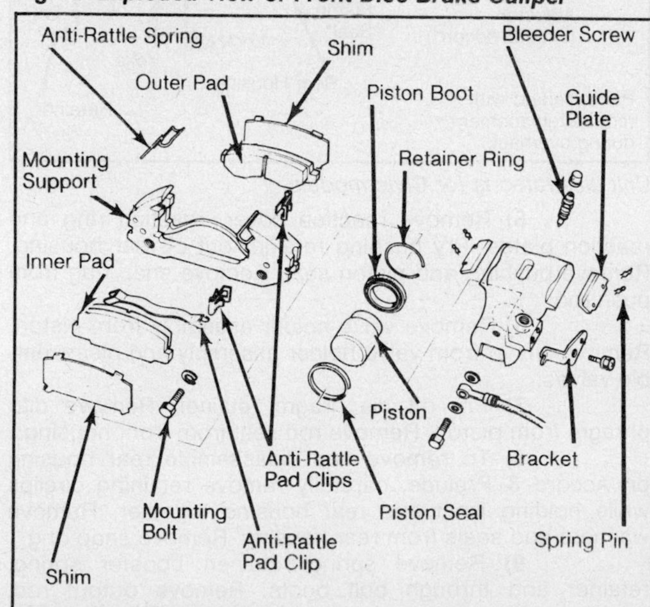
Anti-Rattle Spring
Shim
Bleeder Screw
Outer Pad
Piston Boot
Guide Plate
Mounting Support
Retainer Ring
Inner Pad
Piston
Anti-Rattle Pad Clips
Bracket
Mounting Bolt
Piston Seal
Anti-Rattle Pad Clip
Spring Pin
Shim

Applies to Civic Wagon.

2) Check cylinder bore and pistons for damage. Replace any components that are scratched or scored. Replace all rubber components during overhaul.

3) Standard piston-to-caliper clearance is .001-.005" (.025-.125 mm). Service limit is .010" (.25 mm).

Reassembly

1) Apply brake fluid to caliper bore, piston surface and piston seal. Install piston square ring seal into caliper bore.

2) Apply silicone grease at piston-to-dust seal ridge of piston. Install dust boot onto piston. Seat piston into caliper bore using finger pressure only.

3) Evenly seat outside metal edge of dust seal into caliper. Use care not to buckle or crimp dust seal outer ring.

REAR WHEEL CYLINDER

Disassembly

1) Remove dust covers, pistons and expander spring. Remove cylinder cups from pistons.

2) Remove bleeder cap and screw.

Cleaning & Inspection

1) Wash all parts in clean brake fluid or denatured alcohol, and blow dry with compressed air.

2) Check for wear or damage to pistons and cylinder bore. Replace all rubber components and defective parts.

3) On Civic, standard piston-to-wheel cylinder clearance is .0006-.0030" (.016-.086 mm). Service limit is .0040" (.100 mm).

4) On Accord & Prelude, standard piston-to-wheel cylinder clearance is .0008-.0041" (.020-.105 mm). Service limit is .0040" (.100 mm).

NOTE: **Lips of piston cups must face center of cylinder.**

Reassembly

1) Install cups to pistons and coat cylinder bore, pistons and cups with brake fluid.

2) Apply sealant between wheel cylinder and flange plate whenever separated.

3) Reverse disassembly procedure, and install parts in cylinder bore. Install dust covers securely in cylinder body grooves.

NOTE: **If fluid contamination or corrosion is found, use clean brake fluid to bench bleed master cylinder and bleed hydraulic system. Brake fluid must be DOT 3 rated or better. Do not use gasoline, kerosene, antifreeze, alcohol or any other cleaner containing mineral oil or damage to rubber parts will result.**

MASTER CYLINDER

Disassembly

1) Remove master cylinder and clamp into vise. Remove reservoir cap assembly and drain brake fluid. Loosen retaining clamp and remove reservoir.

2) On Civic models, remove snap ring. Press in on secondary piston assembly, and remove stop bolt. Cover open end of master cylinder with a clean rag.

3) On Accord and Prelude models, remove outer snap ring. Remove washer, secondary cups and secondary piston bushing.

4) Press in on secondary piston assembly, remove stop bolt and inner snap ring.

Brakes

HONDA (Cont.)

Fig. 5: Exploded View of Master Cylinder Assembly

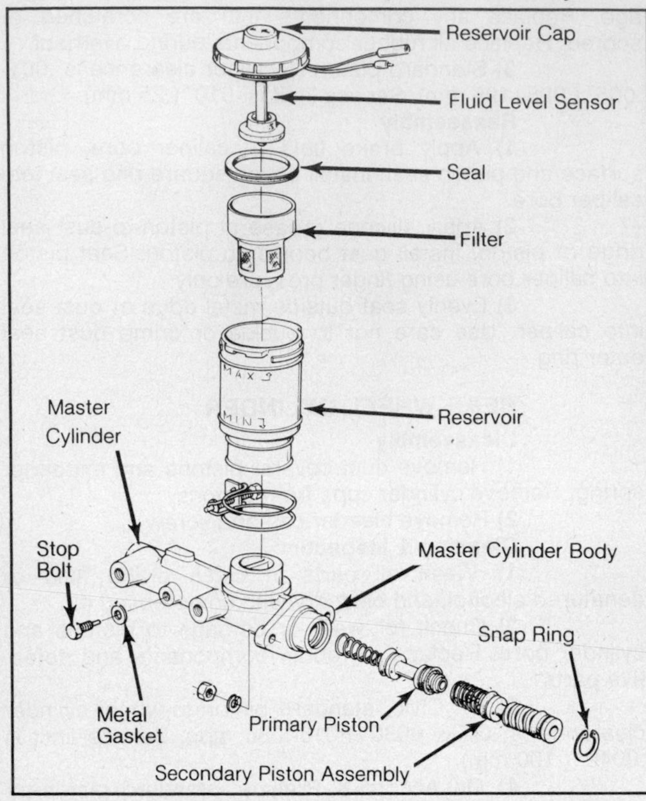
Reservoir Cap
Fluid Level Sensor
Seal
Filter
Master Cylinder
Reservoir
Stop Bolt
Master Cylinder Body
Snap Ring
Metal Gasket
Primary Piston
Secondary Piston Assembly

Replace both piston assemblies whenever disassembled.

5) On all models, place finger over stop bolt hole and secondary outlet port. Remove pistons by applying 30 psi (2.1 kg/cm²) air pressure to primary port. *See Fig. 5*.

6) Piston assemblies must be replaced as complete units if disassembled.

Cleaning & Inspection

1) Wash all parts in clean brake fluid or denatured alcohol, and blow dry. Check for wear or damage to cylinder bore and piston assemblies.

2) Check master cylinder bore-to-piston clearance. Standard clearance is .0008-.0041" (.020-.105 mm). Service limit is .0060" (.150 mm).

Reassembly

1) Coat all parts with brake fluid and reverse disassembly procedure.

2) Use a rotating, twisting motion while pushing pistons into cylinder bore. Use cup guide tool to compress secondary piston, when installing stop bolt with new gasket on Civic models.

3) Install snap ring and bench bleed master cylinder. Check master cylinder push rod-to-piston clearance and adjust before installation.

POWER BRAKE UNIT

NOTE: Although power brake units vary, overhaul procedures are similar for all models.

Disassembly

1) Scribe an index mark across front and rear power brake unit housings for reassembly reference. On Civic models, remove lock spring and lock plate.

2) Drain brake fluid. Remove master cylinder and output rod.

3) To remove and disassemble rear housing on Civic, reinstall master cylinder mount nuts with lock nuts behind them. Tighten nuts against each other on studs.

4) Clamp power brake unit in vise. Tighten vise against locked nuts on studs. Attach brake unit handles (07967-6340000) to rear housing with 4 nuts. Turn rear housing counterclockwise until locking tabs are free of slots on front housing. *See Fig. 6*.

Fig. 6: Exploded View of Power Brake Unit

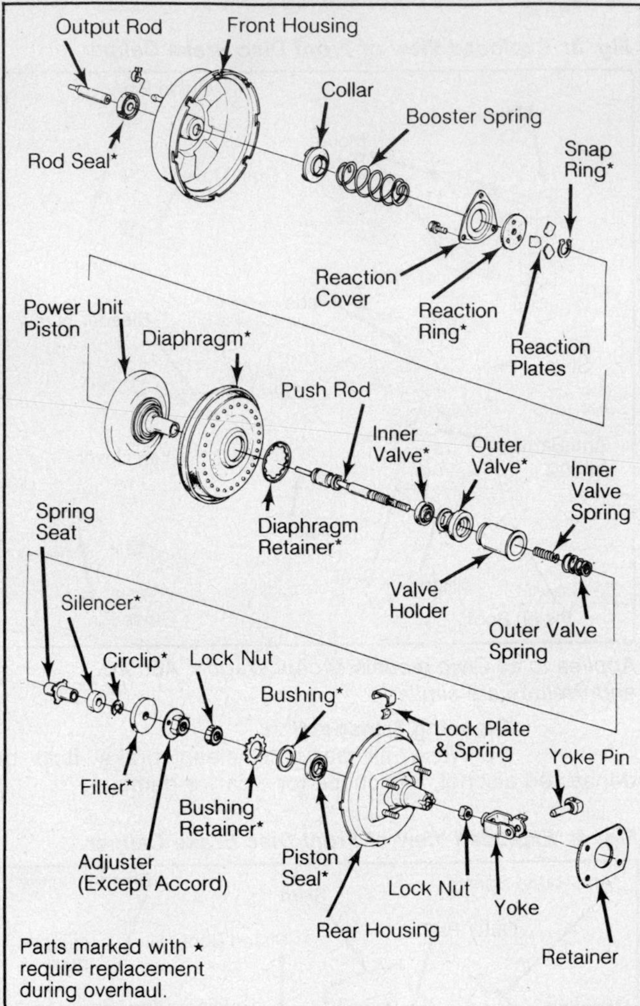
Output Rod
Front Housing
Collar
Booster Spring
Snap Ring*
Rod Seal*
Reaction Cover
Reaction Ring*
Reaction Plates
Power Unit Piston
Diaphragm*
Push Rod
Inner Valve*
Outer Valve*
Inner Valve Spring
Spring Seat
Diaphragm Retainer*
Valve Holder
Outer Valve Spring
Silencer*
Circlip*
Lock Nut
Bushing*
Lock Plate & Spring
Yoke Pin
Filter*
Bushing Retainer*
Adjuster (Except Accord)
Piston Seal*
Lock Nut
Yoke
Rear Housing
Retainer
Parts marked with * require replacement during overhaul.

Unit illustrated is for Civic models.

5) Remove reaction cover, reaction ring and reaction plates. Pry bushing retainer out of rear housing. Remove bushing and piston seal. Remove snap ring from push rod.

6) Remove valve holder assembly from piston. Remove circlip from valve holder assembly and disassemble valves.

7) Pry off diaphragm retainer. Remove diaphragm from piston. Remove rod seal from front housing.

8) To remove and disassemble rear housing on Accord & Prelude, carefully remove retaining circlips while holding front and rear housing together. Remove washers and seals from rear housing. Remove snap ring.

9) Remove spring retainer, booster spring, retainer and through bolt boots. Remove output rod, reaction disc and pushrod seat.

HONDA (Cont.)

10) Remove diaphragm from rear housing. Remove yoke, push rod lock nut, star lock nut, adjuster and filter.

11) Remove snap ring and valve holder assembly. Remove circlip from valve holder assembly and disassemble. *See Fig. 7.*

Fig. 7: Exploded View of Power Brake Unit

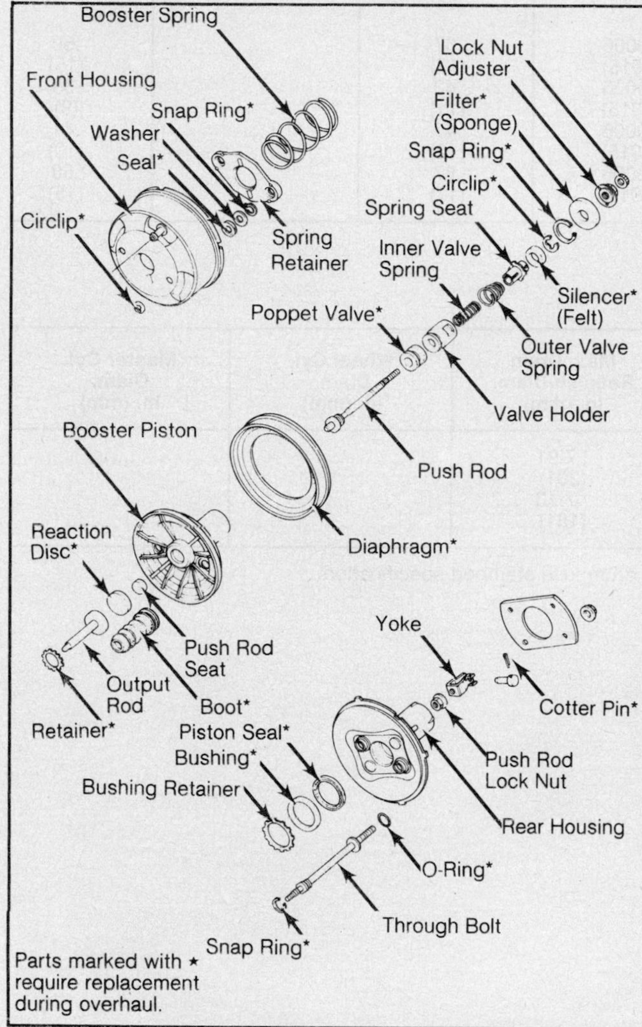
Booster Spring
Lock Nut
Adjuster
Front Housing
Filter*
(Sponge)
Snap Ring*
Washer
Snap Ring*
Seal*
Circlip*
Spring Seat
Circlip*
Spring
Retainer
Inner Valve
Spring
Silencer*
(Felt)
Poppet Valve*
Outer Valve
Spring
Valve Holder
Booster Piston
Push Rod
Reaction
Disc*
Diaphragm*
Yoke
Push Rod
Seat
Output
Rod
Boot*
Cotter Pin*
Retainer*
Piston Seal*
Bushing*
Push Rod
Lock Nut
Bushing Retainer
Rear Housing
O-Ring*
Through Bolt
Snap Ring*
Parts marked with ★ require replacement during overhaul.

Unit for Accord & Prelude is shown.

Cleaning & Inspection

1) Clean all parts in denatured alcohol, and dry with compressed air. Check all parts for wear or damage.

2) Check booster piston for cracks or deformation. Replace all parts as indicated in *Fig. 7*.

Reassembly

1) On Civic, seat inner valve in groove of push rod (note valve direction) and lubricate with silicone grease. Install outer valve on holder.

2) Install push rod through valve holder and seat metal end of outer valve in groove of inner valve. Install inner and outer valve springs, spring seat, and felt silencer into valve holder and secure with circlip.

3) On Accord & Prelude, install poppet valve on valve holder. Install valve holder, inner valve spring, outer valve spring and spring seat on push rod. Install silencer with circlip.

4) Align diaphragm tabs with slots in piston and install. Apply silicone grease to inner and outer piston tube surfaces. Press valve holder assembly into booster piston tube and install snap ring.

5) On all models, slip foam filter over end of push rod. Thread adjuster and lock nut onto shaft but do not tighten.

6) On Civic, slip new diaphragm over piston and press retainer ring into place. Apply silicone grease to inner and outer surfaces of piston tube. Press valve holder in power unit piston tube.

7) On all models, apply silicone grease to piston seal. Install piston seal with lip of seal facing inward. Install bushing in rear housing and drive retainer in until seal bottoms.

8) On Civic, install diaphragm/piston assembly into rear housing. Install snap ring in groove of push rod.

9) Install reaction plates, reaction ring and reaction cover.

NOTE: **Reaction plates must be installed with rounded portion facing reaction ring. Install reaction ring with rubber end facing plates. Apply silicone grease to plates.**

10) Apply silicone grease to sealing lip and in groove of new rod seal. Install rod seal in front housing with flat side of seal inward.

11) On Accord & Prelude, install through bolts, using "O" rings and snap rings. Attach piston to rear housing, aligning tab of piston with slot in rear housing. Install boots on through bolts.

12) Apply silicone grease to bore of piston. Install push rod seat, reaction disc, output rod and retainer. Install booster spring, compress and install spring retainer and snap rings.

13) To complete reassembly, reverse removal procedure. On Civic, check that push rod end comes through front housing bore when assembling.

14) Before installing master cylinder to power brake unit, check master cylinder-to-push rod clearance and adjust as necessary.

TIGHTENING SPECIFICATIONS

Application	Ft. Lbs. (N.m)
Caliper Mount Bracket Bolt	56 (76)
Caliper Guide Pin Bolt	
Accord	20 (27)
Civic Hatchback & Sedan	20 (27)
Prelude	13-14 (18-19)
Flange Plate Mount Bolt	
Accord & Prelude	22 (30)
Civic	40 (54)
Flex Hose-to-Caliper Bolt	25 (34)
Master Cylinder Stop Bolt	
Accord & Prelude	6 (8)
Civic	7 (9.5)
Master Cylinder-to-Power Unit Nut	
Accord & Prelude	5 (7)
Civic	11 (15)
Push Rod Lock Nut	7 (9.5)

Brakes

HONDA (Cont.)

DISC BRAKE ROTOR SPECIFICATIONS

Application	Disc Diameter In. (mm)	Lateral Runout In. (mm)	Parallelism In. (mm)	Original Thickness In. (mm)	Min. Refinish Thickness In. (mm)	Discard Thickness In. (mm)
Accord	7.50 (190)	.006 (.15)	.0006 (.015)	.67 (17)	.....	.60 (15)
Civic						
1500 Hatchback & Sedan	.....	.006 (.15)	.0006 (.015)	.67 (17)	.....	.60 (15)
1300 4-Spd. & Station Wagon	.....	.006 (.15)	.0006 (.015)	.43 (11)	.....	.35 (9)
1300 5-Spd. & Station Wagon	.....	.006 (.15)	.0006 (.015)	.47 (12)	.....	.41 (10)
Prelude	9.10 (231)	.006 (.15)	.0006 (.015)	.67 (17)	.....	.60 (15)

DRUM BRAKE SPECIFICATIONS

Application	Drum Diam. In. (mm)	Drum Width In. (mm)	Max. Drum Refinish Diam. In. (mm)	Wheel Cyl. Diam. In. (mm)	Master Cyl. Diam. In. (mm)
Accord, Prelude & Civic Station Wagon	7.87 (200)	1.40 (35)	[1] 7.91 (201)	.....	.....
Civic (Exc. Station Wagon)	7.87 (200)	1.40 (35)	[1] 7.13 (181)	.....	.....

[1] – If maximum refinish diameter disagrees with specification stamped on drum; use stamped specification.

ISUZU I-MARK

DESCRIPTION

Brake system is hydraulically-operated, using a tandem master cylinder and a vacuum-operated power brake unit. All models are equipped with front disc and rear drum brakes. Rear brakes are leading/trailing type and have a self-adjusting mechanism.

A combination valve is installed in engine compartment, and includes a pressure limiting valve and a differential pressure switch (fail indicator). Parking brakes are cable-operated and operate on rear wheels.

ADJUSTMENT

REAR DRUM BRAKE

1) Raise and support vehicle. Index mark wheel assembly and axle flange, and remove wheel and tire. Remove brake drum.

NOTE: Replace drum brake linings when lining thickness is less than .040 in. (1 mm).

2) Measure inside diameter of brake drum with brake measuring tool (J-21177 or equivalent). Adjust brake shoes to brake drum dimension. Use screwdriver to move automatic adjuster lever toward secondary shoe for diameter increase. To decrease, relieve pressure on latch.

3) Install brake drum and wheel assembly. Lower vehicle.

PARKING BRAKE

Fully release parking brake lever. Check cable for free movement. Remove cable play by turning brake lever rod adjustment nut. Parking brake lever travel should be 8-10 notches.

PEDAL HEIGHT AND FREE PLAY

Adjust pedal free play by turning push rod. Distance between upper face of brake pedal and carpet should be 6.73" (171 mm). Push brake pedal while turning stop light switch so free play is eliminated. Tighten clevis lock nut and stop light switch lock nut.

REMOVAL & INSTALLATION

FRONT DISC PADS

Removal

Raise and support front of vehicle. Remove wheel and tire. Remove clips, pins, retaining spring, pad shims and brake pads.

NOTE: Minimum pad thickness is .067" (1.70 mm).

Installation

1) To install, apply PBC (Poly Butyl Caprysil) grease to caliper inside face and pad pin holes but not to dust seal. Lube both sides of pad shims. *See Fig. 1.* Slightly open bleeder valve. Using piston installer (J-22430), push pistons back into bore. Close valve.

2) Assemble pad shims to brake pads with arrow pointing in direction of normal disc rotation. Install assembly to caliper. Install retaining spring, pins and clips. Install wheels and lower vehicle.

Fig. 1: Pad Shim Lubrication Point

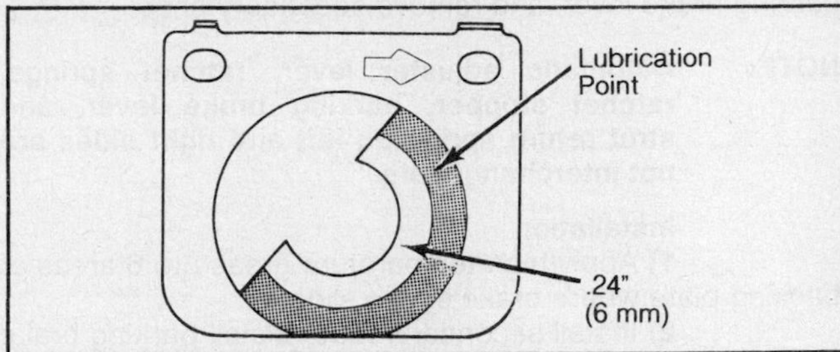
Lubrication
Point
.24"
(6 mm)

Apply PBC grease to both sides of pad shims.

FRONT DISC CALIPER

Removal & Installation

Raise and support vehicle. Remove wheel and tire. Disconnect caliper hose from caliper, and plug to prevent entry of dirt. Remove caliper mounting bolts and caliper. To install, reverse removal procedure. Tighten caliper mounting bolts to 36 ft. lbs. (49 N.m).

FRONT DISC ROTOR

Removal

1) Raise and support vehicle. Remove tire and wheel. Remove caliper and suspend out of way. Do not allow to hang from hydraulic hose. Remove grease cap, cotter key, and spindle nut.

2) Remove hub and disc assembly. Remove hub-to-rotor bolts and remove rotor from hub.

Installation

To install, reverse removal procedure. Tighten hub-to-rotor bolts to 36 ft. lbs. (49 N.m). Adjust wheel bearings. *See Wheel Bearing Adjustment in SUSPENSION Section*. Replace wheel and tire.

FRONT & REAR BRAKE HOSES

Removal

1) Clean dirt from fittings. Using backup wrench on female fitting, disconnect brake hose(s) from fitting. Soak connections with penetrating oil if necessary. Do not bend frame bracket or brake line.

2) Remove "U" clip from female fitting at bracket. Remove hose. Remove junction block on rear axle.

NOTE: Check junction block location to ensure proper remounting when installing rear brake hose(s).

Installation

1) Reverse removal procedure for installation. Tighten all fitting nuts to 12 ft. lbs. (16 N.m). Check hose and line clearance, allowing minimum 3/4" (19 mm) clearance to all vibrating or moving parts.

2) Fill and maintain brake fluid level in reservoir. Bleed brake system.

REAR BRAKE SHOES

Removal

1) Raise and support vehicle. Remove tire and wheel. Remove brake drum. Remove return springs, hold down pins, cups, and springs. *See Fig. 2.*

2) Move automatic adjuster lever all the way in direction of expansion, and disconnect strut. Remove primary shoe. Disconnect parking brake cable from parking brake lever, and remove secondary shoe.

NOTE: **Automatic adjuster lever, ratchet springs, ratchet stopper, parking brake lever, and strut return spring on left and right sides are not interchangeable.**

Installation

1) Apply high-temperature grease to 6 areas of backing plate where brake shoes slide.

2) Install secondary shoe. Install parking brake cable to parking brake lever. Install primary shoe, strut, and automatic adjuster lever.

3) Install return springs, shoe hold-down springs, cups, and pins. Install drum, adjust brake linings as outlined previously. Install wheel and lower vehicle.

Fig. 2: Exploded View of Rear Brake Assembly

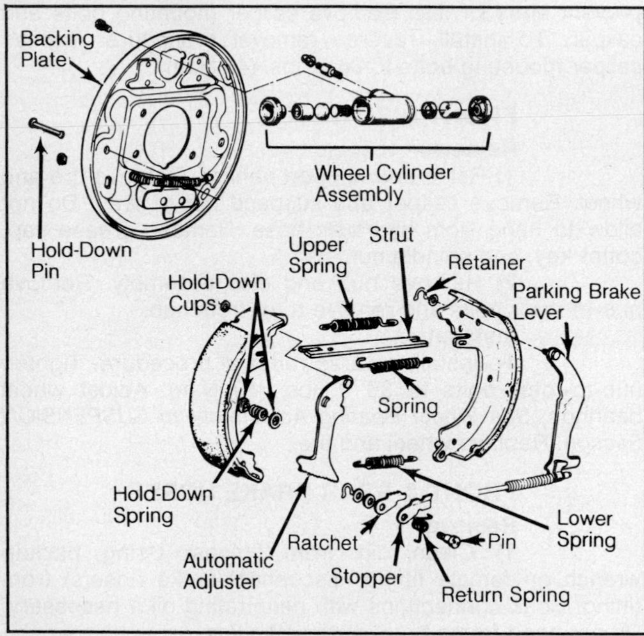
Backing Plate
Wheel Cylinder Assembly
Hold-Down Pin
Upper Spring
Strut
Retainer
Hold-Down Cups
Parking Brake Lever
Spring
Hold-Down Spring
Lower Spring
Ratchet
Pin
Automatic Adjuster
Stopper
Return Spring

Replace all rubber components during repair.

REAR AXLE SHAFT BEARING & OIL SEAL

Removal

1) Raise and support vehicle. Remove wheel and tire and brake drum.

2) Working through access holes in axle shaft flange, remove 4 nuts and washers holding axle shaft bearing retainer.

3) Install axle shaft puller (J-8805-01) coupled with slide hammer (J-2619-01) on axle shaft flange. Remove axle shaft.

4) Using a chisel, remove bearing retaining ring behind bearing on spline side. Prevent metal chips from falling into bearing. Press off bearing with rear pinion bearing remover (J-22912-01).

Inspection

1) Check axle shaft radial runout for .002" (.95 mm). Carefully check axle bearing for rough or brinelled condition, replace as necessary whenever axle seal is removed and replaced.

2) Check axle shaft end play with depth gauge. With backing plate in place, measure depth of rear axle bearing seat in axle housing.

3) Measure width of bearing outer race. The difference between the 2 measurements indicates required thickness of shims. Standard end play is 0-.008" (0-.20 mm). Add or remove shims accordingly to comply with specifications. Shims are only available in .006" (.15 mm) thickness.

NOTE: **No end play will cause loose fit of backing plate.**

Installation

1) Using bearing tool (J-22912-01), press bearing on axle shaft with oil seal groove facing shaft splines. Use care not to wedge bearing retainer-seal between axle shoulder and bearing.

2) Using bearing tool, press on retaining ring with shoulder facing bearing.

3) Coat axle shaft splines with hypoid gear oil, and install shaft into housing. Install lock washers and tighten nuts to 28 ft. lbs. (38 N.m). Install drum, wheel and tire. Remove supports and lower vehicle.

MASTER CYLINDER

Removal

1) Disconnect hydraulic lines from master cylinder. Remove nuts securing master cylinder to power brake unit and support bracket.

2) Remove bolts securing fluid reservoir bracket and remove master cylinder assembly and fluid reservoir.

Installation

1) Place master cylinder and reservoir in position with the fluid reservoir bracket and install bolts securing bracket to inner fender. Install nuts holding master cylinder to power brake unit and tighten support bracket to 10 ft. lbs. (13.5 N.m).

2) Connect front and rear hydraulic lines to master cylinder. Tighten brake line flare nuts to 12 ft. lbs. (16 N.m). Bleed hydraulic system.

POWER BRAKE UNIT

Removal

1) Disconnect hydraulic lines from master cylinder. Cover and plug line ends. Remove master cylinder bracket bolts to cylinder and fender skirt. Remove bracket. Remove vacuum hose clip and hose from check valve.

2) Remove clevis pin and separate clevis from brake pedal arm. Remove power brake unit to dash panel retaining nuts. Lift out power brake unit and master cylinder.

Installation

1) Install master cylinder and power brake unit to dash panel and support bracket. Connect hydraulic lines to master cylinder.

2) Tighten master cylinder to power brake unit nuts, power brake to dash panel nuts, and master cylinder support bracket bolt. Adjust brake pedal height and bleed brake system.

OVERHAUL

FRONT CALIPER

Disassembly

1) With caliper and pads removed, remove dust seal ring and dust seal from each piston. *See Fig. 3.*

ISUZU I-MARK (Cont.)

Install clamp (J-22429) on mounting half of caliper. Remove rim half piston by applying compressed air to brake line connection.

2) Install clamp on rim half of caliper. Remove mounting half piston with compressed air. Remove piston seals from annular grooves in caliper piston bores.

NOTE: Caliper is of integral design and cannot be disassembled. Replace caliper assembly if leak is found at caliper joint.

Fig. 3: Exploded View of Disc Brake Assembly

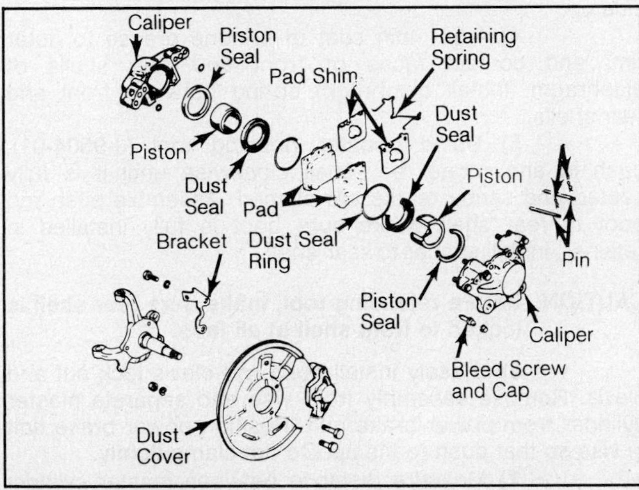
Caliper
Piston Seal
Retaining Spring
Pad Shim
Dust Seal
Piston
Piston
Dust Seal
Pad
Bracket
Dust Seal Ring
Pin
Piston Seal
Caliper
Bleed Screw and Cap
Dust Cover

Caliper is of integral design. Never disassemble.

Reassembly

1) Apply rubber grease to seal and cylinder wall, install new piston seal in cylinder. Carefully install piston to bottom of cylinder bore using finger pressure only.

2) Install dust seal and seal ring. Apply PBC grease to caliper inside face, pad shims (on both sides), and pad pin holes. Do not apply on dust seal. Assemble pad shim to brake pad with arrow pointing in direction of normal disc rotation and install in caliper. Install retaining spring pins and clips.

MASTER CYLINDER

Disassembly

1) Pour brake fluid out of reservoir. Disconnect front and rear rubber hoses from master cylinder, separate fluid reservoir. Place cylinder in vise and remove pipe connector.

2) Remove check valve, spring, and retainer. Push in on primary piston with screwdriver, remove secondary piston stop bolt and snap ring.

3) Remove primary piston assembly, primary piston spring, secondary piston assembly, and secondary piston spring.

NOTE: Primary and secondary piston assemblies are of integral design, never disassemble. Replace assembly as necessary. Always replace piston cups whenever disassembly occurs.

Inspection

Measure master cylinder bore diameter, and outside diameter of primary and secondary pistons. Standard bore diameter is .875" (22.20 mm). Standard clearance is .0010-.0050" (.025-.125 mm). Clearance limit is .006" (.15 mm). Replace cylinder if damage is found or clearance is beyond limit.

NOTE: Brake fluid must be DOT 3 rated or better.

Reassembly

1) Replace all rubber parts and lubricate with clean brake fluid. Assemble the spring check valve, gasket, and pipe connector to the cylinder body. Semi-tighten the pipe connector.

2) Clamp cylinder in soft-jawed, vise and tighten pipe connector to 47 ft. lbs. (64 N.m). Apply rubber grease to bore opening. Using a rotating, twisting motion, install secondary piston spring and secondary piston assembly into cylinder. Install the primary piston spring and primary piston assembly into cylinder, set in position with snap ring.

3) Carefully note the direction of setting when assembling primary and secondary piston assembly into cylinder. Do not force piston into cylinder. Press primary piston into position with screwdriver. Tighten secondary piston stop bolt with new gasket on cylinder body to 14 ft. lbs. (19 N.m).

4) Bench bleed master cylinder. Remount to power brake unit and bleed hydraulic system.

WHEEL CYLINDER

Disassembly

Remove boots, pistons, piston cups, spring, and bleeder screw from the wheel cylinder.

NOTE: Repair or replace cylinder if brake fluid is found behind wheel cylinder boot.

Inspection

Measure wheel cylinder bore and outside diameter of piston. Standard cylinder clearance is .003" (.07 mm). Limit of clearance is .006" (.15 mm). Standard cylinder bore diameter is .812" (20.60 mm).

Reassembly

1) Always use new rubber components when repairing hydraulic system. Lubricate sliding parts of wheel cylinder with clean brake fluid. Assemble into cylinder so piston cups are facing outward. Apply rubber grease to inner face of boots before installing.

2) Install wheel cylinder on backing plate. Tighten bolts to 7 ft. lbs. (9.5 N.m). Tighten brake line nut to 12 ft. lbs. (16 N.m). After brake lining installation, bleed hydraulic system.

POWER BRAKE UNIT

Disassembly

1) With master cylinder and power brake unit removed from vehicle, pour brake fluid out of reservoir. Disconnect front and rear rubber hoses from master cylinder, and separate fluid reservoir. Index mark shell mating surfaces for reassembly reference. Clamp flange of master cylinder assembly loosely in vise with power brake unit up. *See Fig. 4.*

NOTE: Do not tighten vise too tight as damage to flange will result.

2) Remove 4 nuts and spacer from rear shell of power brake unit. Loosen and remove lock nut and clevis from operating rod. Attach booster housing tool (J-9504-01) to rear shell, and carefully turn rear shell

ISUZU I-MARK (Cont.)

counterclockwise. Be careful, shell is under spring pressure. Maintain pressure on rear shell during removal.

3) Remove rear shell and diaphragm return spring. Remove boot from rear shell, and remove diaphragm plate assembly. Remove retainer from rear shell, and remove plate and seal.

4) Remove diaphragm and silencer retainer from diaphragm assembly. Remove valve plunger stopper key, plunger assembly and reaction disc. Remove push rod, retainer, and seal from front shell assembly.

Inspection

Clean and dry disassembled parts. Check diaphragm, boot, and reaction disc for weakening, distortion, or damage, replace as necessary. Check plunger assembly for wear. Replace if worn. Check diaphragm plate, check valve, and vacuum hose for damage, or wear, replace as necessary.

Fig. 4: Exploded View of Power Brake Unit

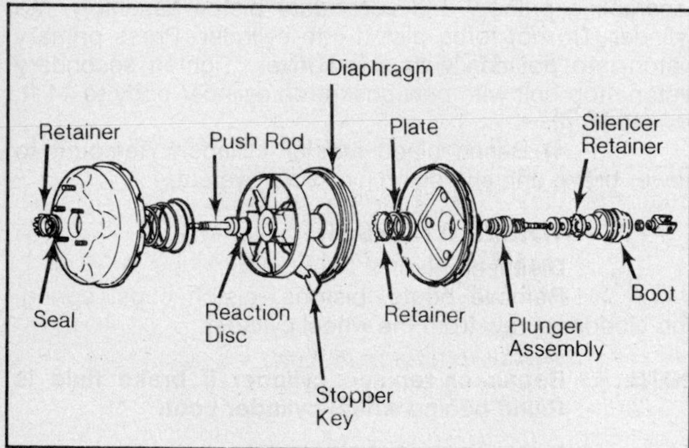
Diaphragm
Retainer
Push Rod
Plate
Silencer Retainer
Seal
Reaction Disc
Retainer
Plunger Assembly
Boot
Stopper Key

Use caution during disassembly, as shell is under spring pressure.

Reassembly

1) Apply silicone grease to sliding faces of parts. Lubricate seal fitting face of rear shell, and lipped portion. Install plate, seal, and retainer. Lubricate outer and inner faces of diaphragm plate, and outer face of poppet valve.

2) Install plunger assembly with filter and silencer, making sure poppet valve is not projecting beyond retainer. Push in on plunger, and install valve plunger stopper key. Lubricate reaction disc and install in diaphragm plate. Install retainer and diaphragm on diaphragm plate.

3) Assemble diaphragm assembly to rear shell, and install boot and clevis. Install seal assembly to front shell. Lubricate sliding face of seal and push rod. Install retainer and push rod. Temporarily secure master cylinder to front shell with nuts and lock washers. Clamp flanged portion of master cylinder loosely in vise with front shell side up.

4) Apply thin coat of silicone grease to outer rim, and contact faces of front and rear shells of diaphragm. Install diaphragm spring between front and rear shells.

5) Using booster housing tool (J-9504-01), push in and rotate rear shell clockwise until it is fully seated and scribe marks are aligned. Assemble push rod boot to rear shell. Make sure boot is fully installed in retainer, install spacer to rear shell.

CAUTION: Before releasing tool, make sure rear shell is locked to front shell at all tabs.

6) Loosely install push rod clevis lock nut and clevis. Remove assembly from vise and separate master cylinder from power brake unit. Position power brake unit in vise so that push rod is up. Do not clamp tightly.

7) Measure distance between master cylinder mounting face of front shell and end of push rod. If necessary, adjust push rod to .733" (18.60 mm). Hold rod at serrated portion and turn threaded end.

TIGHTENING SPECIFICATIONS

Application	Ft. Lbs. (N.m)
Hydraulic Line Flare Nuts	12 (16)
Caliper-to-Steering Knuckle	136 (184)
Rotor-to-Hub	36 (49)
Master Cylinder-to-Power Brake Unit	10 (14)

DISC BRAKE ROTOR SPECIFICATIONS

Application	Disc Diameter In. (mm)	Lateral Runout In. (mm)	Parallelism In. (mm)	Original Thickness In. (mm)	Min. Refinish Thickness In. (mm)	Discard Thickness In. (mm)
I-Mark	.....	.006 (.15)	.....	.394 (10.0)	.354 (9.0)	.338 (8.6)

DRUM BRAKE SPECIFICATIONS

Application	Drum Diam. In. (mm)	Drum Width In. (mm)	Max. Drum Refinish Diam. In. (mm)	Wheel Cyl. Diam. In. (mm)	Master Cyl. Diam. In. (mm)
I-Mark	9.0 (228.6)	.....	[1] 9.04 (229.6)	13/16 (20.6)	7/8 (22.2)

[1] – Drum discard diameter is 9.055" (230 mm).

Brakes

ISUZU IMPULSE

DESCRIPTION

Brake system is hydraulically-operated, using a tandem master cylinder and a vacuum-operated power brake unit. All models are equipped with vented front discs and non-vented rear discs. Calipers are self-adjusting, single piston, floating type on front and rear.

Cable-operated parking brake (on rear wheels) is manually adjusted. A combination valve is installed in engine compartment. It includes a pressure-limiting valve and differential pressure switch (fail indicator).

ADJUSTMENT

PARKING BRAKE

1) Release parking brake lever. Raise and support vehicle. Adjust lining clearance by turning adjuster (through slot in backing plate) until shoe contact is felt when turning wheel. Back adjuster off 6 notches.

2) Check cable for free movement. Adjust parking brake cable where front and rear cables connect. Loosen front lock nut on front cable assembly and turn rear lock nut to adjust. Retighten lock nuts.

3) Proper brake lever travel is 11-12 notches, pulling with force of 66 lbs. (30 kg). After adjustment, check that brakes do not drag.

NOTE: Parking brake cable bolts attaching cable to lever assembly have LEFT-HAND threads.

SERVICE BRAKES

Both front and rear brakes self-adjust each time brakes are firmly applied. If brake pedal moves farther than normal due to lack of adjustment, drive forward and backward a few times, applying brakes intermittently.

Brake pedal should return to normal. If pedal height does not return properly or there is a rapid increase in pedal travel, inspect hydraulic system.

PEDAL HEIGHT AND FREE PLAY

1) Bleed hydraulic system. Adjust power brake unit push rod to obtain 5.63" (143 mm) clearance between lower face of brake pedal and carpet.

2) Adjust clearance between brake switch and pedal to .0039" (0.1 mm). Turn switch in 1/2 turn, then lock in position with floor-to-pedal height readjusted to 5.52" (140 mm).

3) Brake pedal free play is .24-.39" (6-10 mm). Pedal stroke is 2.95" (75 mm) or less.

REMOVAL AND INSTALLATION

DISC BRAKE PADS

Removal (Front & Rear)

1) Raise and support vehicle. Remove wheel and tire. Remove front pads as follows: Remove caliper support bracket sleeve bolts. *See Fig. 1.* Lift off caliper and hang out of the way with wire.

2) Remove rear pads as follows: Disconnect rear brake flex hose at caliper. Remove caliper lock pin, sleeve and sleeve boot. Pivot caliper up, slide off guide pin and remove guide pin boot. *See Fig. 2.*

Fig. 1: Exploded View of Front Disc Brake Assembly

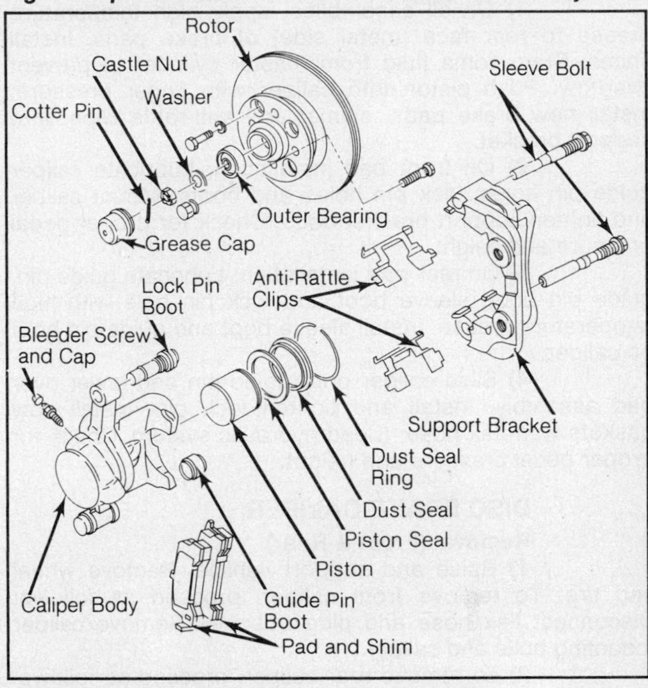
Rotor
Castle Nut
Sleeve Bolt
Washer
Cotter Pin
Outer Bearing
Grease Cap
Anti-Rattle Clips
Lock Pin Boot
Bleeder Screw and Cap
Support Bracket
Dust Seal Ring
Dust Seal
Piston Seal
Piston
Caliper Body
Guide Pin Boot
Pad and Shim

Replace all rubber components during repair.

3) On all assemblies remove anti-rattle clips, brake pads and shims from support bracket. Mark pads for installation, if reusable. Standard front pad thickness is .323" (8.2 mm).

4) Standard rear pad thickness is .39" (10 mm). Minimum front and rear pad lining thickness is .118" (3 mm).

NOTE: Always replace brake pads in sets of four. Keep grease, brake fluid or other contaminants off lining surface. Check and clean rotor as necessary

Fig. 2: Exploded View of Rear Brake Caliper Assembly

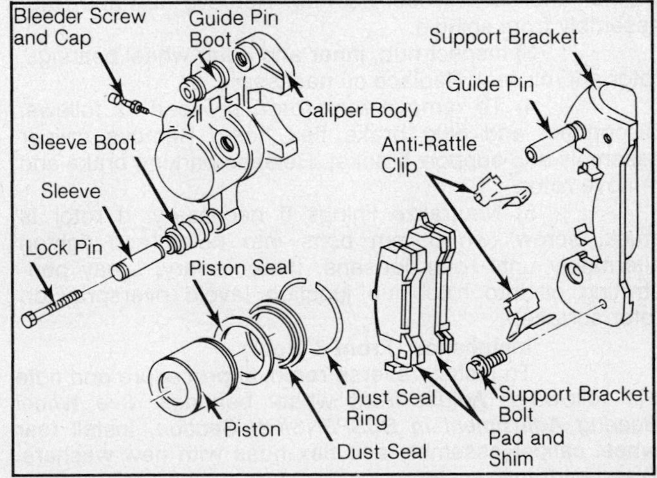
Bleeder Screw and Cap
Guide Pin Boot
Support Bracket
Guide Pin
Caliper Body
Sleeve Boot
Anti-Rattle Clip
Sleeve
Lock Pin
Piston Seal
Dust Seal Ring
Support Bracket Bolt
Piston
Dust Seal
Pad and Shim

Lubricate guide pin, guide pin boot, sleeve boot and lock pin hole.

ISUZU IMPULSE (Cont.)

Installation (Front & Rear)

1) On all assemblies, apply high temperature grease to rear face (metal side) of brake pads. Install shims. Drain some fluid from master cylinder to prevent overflow. Push piston into caliper with finger pressure. Install new brake pads, shims, and anti-rattle clips onto support bracket.

2) On front pad installation; Lubricate caliper guide pin holes, lock pin holes and boots. Mount caliper and tighten support bracket bolts. Check for proper pedal pressure and height.

3) On rear pad installation; Lubricate guide pin, guide pin boot, sleeve boot and lock pin hole with high temperature grease. Install sleeve boot and guide pin boot on caliper.

4) Slide caliper onto guide pin and lower over pad assembly. Install and tighten lock pin. Install new gaskets with flex hose. Bleed hydraulic system. Check for proper pedal pressure and height.

DISC BRAKE CALIPER

Removal (Front & Rear)

1) Raise and support vehicle. Remove wheel and tire. To remove front caliper, proceed as follows: Disconnect flex hose and plug opening. Remove caliper mounting bolts and caliper.

2) To remove rear caliper, proceed as follows: Disconnect brake flex hose at caliper. Remove caliper lock pin, sleeve and sleeve boot. Lift up caliper, slide off guide pin and remove guide pin boot.

Installation (Front & Rear)

To install, reverse removal procedure and note the following: Install new washers on flex hose. Bleed hydraulic system.

DISC BRAKE ROTOR

Removal (Front & Rear)

1) Raise and support vehicle. Remove wheel and tire. To remove front rotor, proceed as follows: Remove caliper assembly and hang out of the way with wire.

2) Remove grease cap, cotter pin, castle nut, washer and outer wheel bearing. Remove hub and rotor assembly from spindle.

3) Inspect hub, inner and outer wheel bearings, rotor and oil seal. Replace as necessary.

4) To remove rear rotor, proceed as follows: Disconnect and plug brake flex hose. Remove caliper assembly and support bracket. Release parking brake and remove rotor.

5) Neutralize linings if necessary. If rotor is stuck, screw two 6 mm bolts into holes and tighten alternately until rotor loosens. If necessary, spray penetrating oil into rotor-hub junction (avoid overspray on rotor surface).

Installation (Front & Rear)

To install, reverse removal procedure and note the following: Adjust front wheel bearings. *See Wheel Bearing Adjustment in SUSPENSION Section*. Install rear wheel caliper assembly and flex hose with new washers. Bleed hydraulic system.

Fig. 3: Master Cylinder, Power Brake Unit and Brake Pedal Bracket Assembly

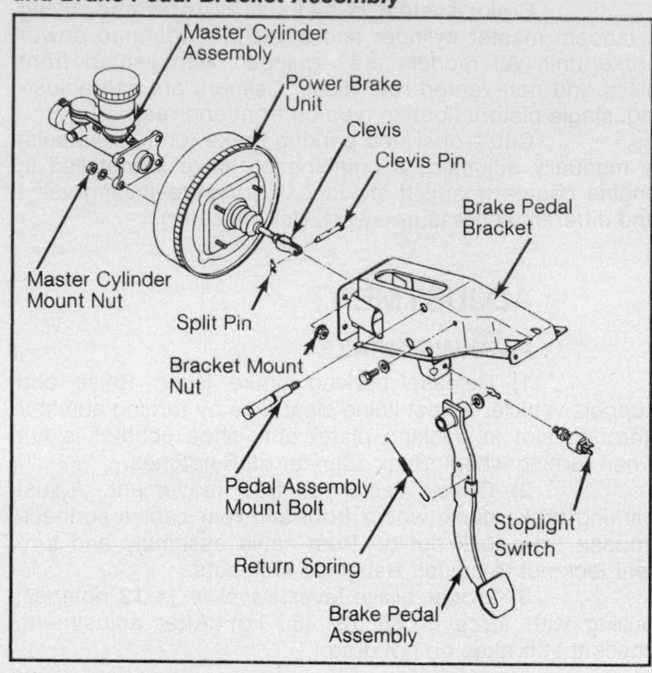
Master Cylinder
Assembly
Power Brake
Unit
Clevis
Clevis Pin
Brake Pedal
Bracket
Master Cylinder
Mount Nut
Split Pin
Bracket Mount
Nut
Pedal Assembly
Mount Bolt
Stoplight
Switch
Return Spring
Brake Pedal
Assembly

Lift out brake pedal bracket as an assembly.

MASTER CYLINDER

Removal

Disconnect hydraulic lines from master cylinder and plug openings. Remove 4 nuts securing master cylinder to power brake unit. Drain brake fluid. Remove master cylinder and gasket. *See Fig. 3*.

Installation

To install, reverse removal procedure, note the following: Replace gasket whenever master cylinder is removed. Tighten hydraulic lines and bleed system.

POWER BRAKE UNIT

Removal

1) Disconnect air duct connector hose and vacuum hose. Remove hydraulic lines from master cylinder and plug ends. Remove split pin and clevis pin. Separate clevis from brake pedal arm.

2) Remove power brake unit-to-dash panel retaining bolts. Lift out power brake unit and master cylinder as an assembly. *See Fig. 3*. Remove master cylinder and gasket from power brake unit.

Installation

1) To install, reverse removal procedure and note the following: Check distance from flange face of power brake unit to end of push rod. Proper distance is .732" (18.6 mm). If measurement is incorrect, adjust with lock nut at end of push rod.

2) Apply sealer to dash panel face and install power brake unit. Install master cylinder with new gasket and bleed hydraulic system. Check and adjust brake pedal height as necessary.

ISUZU IMPULSE (Cont.)

BRAKE PEDAL ASSEMBLY

Removal

1) Remove screws, clips and lap vent duct. Remove steering stay. Remove steering column assembly. Disconnect split pin and remove clevis pin.

2) Remove nuts from dash panel and lift out brake pedal bracket as an assembly. Disconnect return spring and stop light switch. Remove brake pedal assembly. *See Fig. 3*.

Installation

1) To install, reverse removal procedure, noting the following. Install steering column with sealer applied to dash panel fitting face of support bracket.

2) Ensure that all nuts and bolts are properly tightened. Check and adjust brake pedal height as necessary.

REAR AXLE BEARING & SEAL

Removal

1) Raise and support vehicle. Remove disc brake caliper and rotor. Remove 4 axle housing-to-flange plate bolts and separate emergency brake cable from lever.

2) Remove axle shaft using Slide Hammer Tool (J-2619-01) and Axle Shaft Puller Adapter Tool (J-8805-01). Remove axle bearing by applying pressure onto shaft with bench press using Rear Axle Bearing Remover Tool (J-33949).

Installation

1) To install, reverse removal procedure and the note following: Install new "O" ring on outer surface of bearing outer race. Install bearing with "O" ring turned to splined end of axle shaft.

2) Install sleeve with flanged side facing toward ball bearing. Press into position with bench press.

PARKING BRAKE ASSEMBLY

Removal & Installation

See REAR DISC BRAKE ROTOR procedure.

OVERHAUL

DISC BRAKE CALIPER

Disassembly (Front & Rear)

1) On all assemblies, remove caliper, pads, shims, anti-rattle clips and flex hose. On front caliper; disconnect guide pin and lock pin boots. *See Fig. 1*.

2) On rear caliper; disconnect sleeve and guide pin boots. *See Fig. 2*.

3) On all assemblies; remove dust seal ring and dust seal. Place a block of wood between piston and caliper cavity wall. Apply compressed air to force piston from cylinder.

4) Remove and discard piston square ring seal. Remove bleeder screw and cap.

Cleaning & Inspection

Clean brake parts with denatured alcohol or clean brake fluid and blow dry. Check all components for wear, bending, distortion, cracks, corrosion or other abnormal conditions. Replace all rubber parts during repair.

Reassembly (Front & Rear)

1) Apply rubber grease to new piston seal and cylinder wall, and install seal in cylinder. Push piston into cylinder with finger pressure.

2) Lubricate dust seal and seal fitting face of piston. Install dust seal and dust seal ring. Install anti-rattle clips, assemble pad shims to brake pads and install into support bracket.

3) On front caliper; lubricate lock pin boot and guide pin boot with high temperature grease and install.

4) Lubricate lock pin hole and guide pin hole and install sleeve bolts. Replace new washers on flex hose and install. Bleed hydraulic system.

5) On rear caliper; install caliper (slide over guide pin and pivot down into place over pads). Lubricate lock pin hole and install lock pin. Replace new washers on flex hose and install. Bleed hydraulic system.

Fig. 4: Exploded View of Master Cylinder Assembly

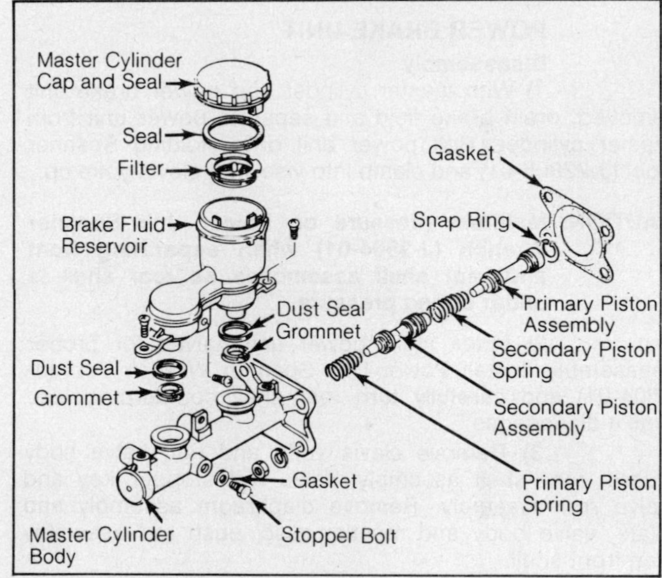

Master Cylinder Cap and Seal
Seal
Filter
Gasket
Snap Ring
Brake Fluid Reservoir
Dust Seal Grommet
Primary Piston Assembly
Secondary Piston Spring
Dust Seal
Grommet
Secondary Piston Assembly
Gasket
Primary Piston Spring
Master Cylinder Body
Stopper Bolt

Replace all rubber parts and gaskets during overhaul.

MASTER CYLINDER

Disassembly

1) With master cylinder and gasket removed, drain brake fluid and place cylinder in vise. Remove 3 screws retaining brake fluid reservoir. Remove reservoir and pull out dust seals and grommets. *See Fig. 4*.

2) Push in on primary and secondary pistons and remove snap ring and stopper bolt. Remove primary and secondary piston assemblies with springs. Remove piston cups (noting direction for proper installation).

Cleaning & Inspection

1) Wash master cylinder components in clean brake fluid or denatured alcohol only. DO NOT use any cleaner containing mineral oil or rubber parts will be damaged. Inspect all parts for wear, distortion, cuts, nicks, corrosion and other abnormal conditions.

2) Remove and replace ALL rubber parts during overhaul. Measure master cylinder bore diameter and outside diameter of primary and secondary pistons.

Brakes

ISUZU IMPULSE (Cont.)

3) Standard bore diameter is .874" (22.2 mm). Standard clearance is .00158-.00493" (.04-.125 mm). Maximum clearance is .00591" (.15 mm).

4) Check return port for restrictions and if necessary, clean and blow away foreign matter with compressed air.

Reassembly

1) Lubricate master cylinder bore with rubber grease. Lubricate piston cups with clean brake fluid. Use care to avoid scratching piston cups when installing piston assemblies.

2) Install short secondary piston spring, secondary piston assembly, primary piston spring and primary piston. Push in on primary piston and install snap ring. Install new gasket and tighten stopper bolt.

3) Stroke pistons in and out to ensure smooth operation and that brake fluid is forced out of front and rear outlets. Install new dust seals and grommets (with flared side ahead). Install brake fluid reservoir. Fill with clean brake fluid and bench bleed.

POWER BRAKE UNIT

Disassembly

1) With master cylinder and power brake unit removed, drain brake fluid and separate power unit from master cylinder. Bolt power unit onto Holding Spanner Tool (J-22805-01) and clamp into vise with clevis yoke up.

CAUTION: **Maintain pressure on Power Unit Spanner Wrench (J-9504-01) when separating front and rear shell assemblies as rear shell is under spring pressure.**

2) Index mark power unit halves for proper reassembly. Install Power Unit Spanner Wrench Tool (J-9504-01) and carefully turn rear shell counterclockwise until it disengages.

3) Remove clevis yoke and nut, valve body guard, rear shell assembly, valve rod stopper key and valve rod assembly. Remove diaphragm assembly and plate, valve body and reaction disc, push rod assembly and front shell.

Cleaning & Inspection

1) Remove, clean and inspect check valve and grommet, replace as necessary. Check diaphragm plate, rotor, push rod, poppet valve and shell for weakening, distortion or damage and replace as necessary.

NOTE: **Clean power brake unit components with denatured alcohol and blow dry using compressed air. Never use any cleaner containing mineral oil or damage to all rubber parts will result.**

2) Inspect valve body seal and replace as necessary. If seal is replaced, carefully note installation position. Apply silicone grease to portions of rear shell in contact with seal. Install seal. Install and secure bearing plate into position with retainer.

NOTE: **Setting position of retainer should not be too deep or too shallow, or air leakage or premature wear of lipped portion will result. Retainer setting position (from outer edge of rear shell) is .512" (13 mm).**

Reassembly

1) Reassemble in reverse order of disassembly and note the following: Apply silicone grease to front and rear shell fitting face of diaphragm and all sliding parts.

2) Insert diaphragm spring into front shell. Apply silicone grease to outer rim and contact faces of diaphragm plate and reaction disc. Assemble power brake components. *See Fig. 5.*

3) Using Power Unit Spanner Wrench (J-9504-01), push in on rear shell and rotate clockwise until fully seated with index marks aligned.

CAUTION: **Before releasing tool, make sure rear shell is locked properly to front shell at all points.**

4) Before installing master cylinder, check for proper distance of push rod from flange face of power

Fig. 5: Exploded View of Power Brake Unit

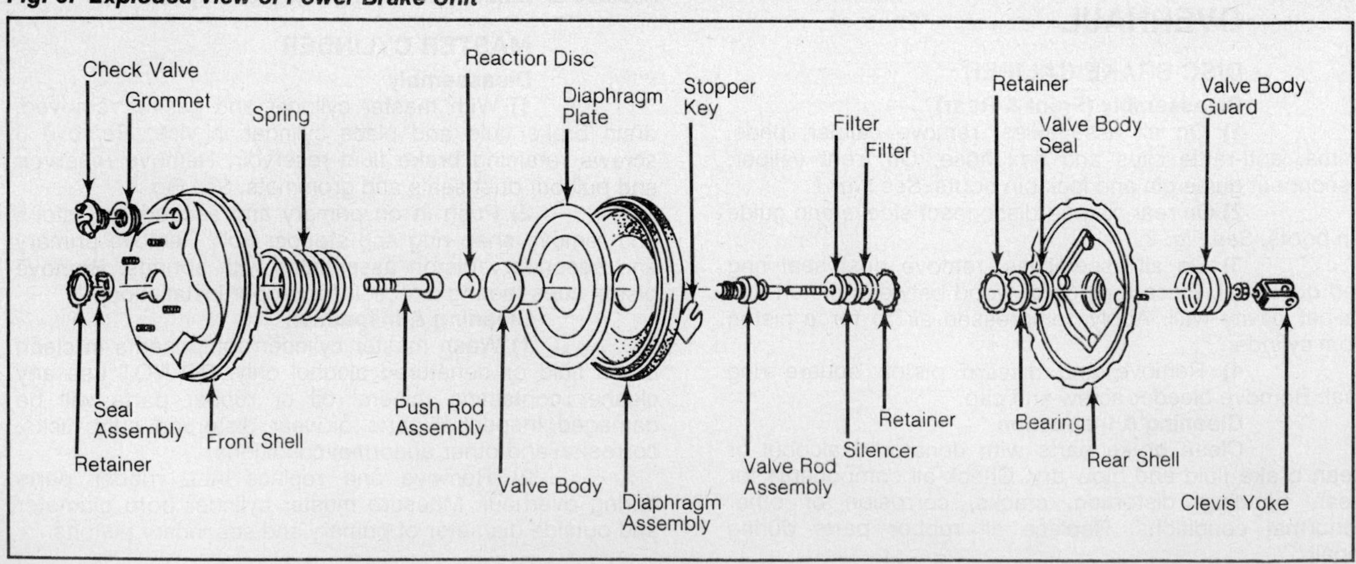
Check Valve
Grommet
Spring
Reaction Disc
Diaphragm Plate
Stopper Key
Filter
Filter
Retainer
Valve Body Seal
Valve Body Guard
Seal Assembly
Retainer
Front Shell
Push Rod Assembly
Valve Body
Diaphragm Assembly
Valve Rod Assembly
Silencer
Retainer
Bearing
Rear Shell
Clevis Yoke

Use caution when disassembling power brake unit as diaphragm spring is under pressure.

ISUZU IMPULSE (Cont.)

unit to end of push rod. If adjustment is needed, loosen lock nut at end of push rod and adjust to .732" (18.6 mm).

5) Install master cylinder to power unit. Install assembly to dash panel (apply sealer to dash panel). Check and adjust brake pedal height as necessary.

Fig. 6: Exploded View of Parking Brake Assembly

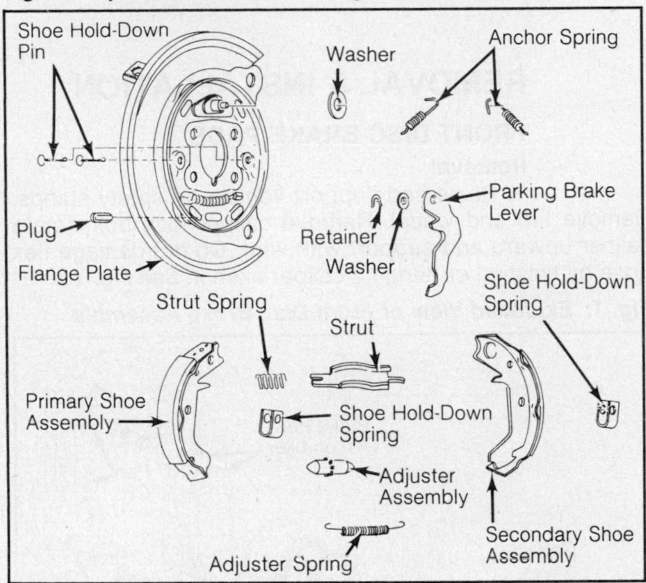

Shoe Hold-Down Pin
Washer
Anchor Spring
Parking Brake Lever
Plug
Retainer
Washer
Flange Plate
Shoe Hold-Down Spring
Strut Spring
Strut
Primary Shoe Assembly
Shoe Hold-Down Spring
Adjuster Assembly
Secondary Shoe Assembly
Adjuster Spring

Burnish in parking brake linings when new linings are installed.

PARKING BRAKE ASSEMBLY

Disassembly

1) With rear caliper and rotor removed, check parking brake assembly for excessive brake dust. Wash off assembly with water and blow dry.

CAUTION: DO NOT breathe airborne asbestos dust.

2) Remove primary and secondary brake shoe hold-down springs and pins. Remove adjuster spring and adjuster, anchor-to-brake shoe springs and washer. Remove strut spring, strut and primary shoe assembly. *See Fig. 6*.

3) Disconnect parking brake cable from parking brake lever and remove secondary shoe assembly with lever attached. If linings are worn, remove "C" clip retainer and wave washer from lever and separate lever from shoe.

Reassembly

1) Apply high temperature grease to anchor pins, adjuster assembly and shoe sliding surfaces of backing plate.

2) If new linings are installed, install "C" clip retainer, wave washer and parking brake lever to secondary shoe. Install primary and secondary shoes to backing plate with shoe hold-down pins and springs. Connect parking brake cable to lever. Install strut and spring.

3) Install adjuster and spring. On left side, install adjuster with wheel toward front and opposite way on right side. Install primary anchor spring and washer. Install secondary anchor spring.

4) Install rotor and adjust linings. Check parking brake cable slack and adjust as necessary.

PARKING BRAKE LININGS

Break-in

Parking brake linings must be burnished in periodically or whenever new linings are installed. Burnish as follows:

1) Drive vehicle at 30 MPH on dry and level road. With parking brake release button pushed in, pull lever with 20 lbs. (9 kg) pressure and drive for 1/4 mile.

2) Repeat procedure 2-3 times, allow linings to cool between applications.

TIGHTENING SPECIFICATIONS

Application	Ft. Lbs. (N.m)
Brake Line (Front)	10-13 (14-18)
Brake Line (Rear)	9-14 (12-19)
Brake Pedal Assembly Bolt	14-22 (19-30)
Caliper Lock Pin (Rear)	13-16 (18-22)
Column-to-Instrument Panel Nut	11-14 (15-19)
Flexible Brake Hose (Front)	24-27 (33-37)
Flexible Brake Hose (Rear)	10-13 (14-18)
Master Cylinder Brake Line	9-14 (12-19)
Master Cylinder-to-Power Unit Nut	8-11 (11-15)
Power Unit Push Rod Nut	8-11 (11-15)
Power Unit-to-Dash Panel Nut	8-11 (11-15)
Second Shaft-to-Universal Joint Bolt	14-22 (19-30)
Stopper Bolt, Master Cylinder	12-14 (16-19)
Support Bracket Bolt (Rear)	35-38 (47-52)
Support Bracket Sleeve Bolt (Front)	25-28 (34-38)
Support Bracket-to-Knuckle Bolt	35-38 (47-52)

DISC BRAKE ROTOR SPECIFICATIONS

Application	Disc Diameter In. (mm)	Lateral Runout In. (mm)	Parallelism In. (mm)	Original Thickness In. (mm)	Min. Refinish Thickness In. (mm)	Discard Thickness In. (mm)
Impulse						
(Front)	9.8 (249.0)	[1] .002 (.05)	.0012 (.03)	.709 (18.0)	.....	.654 (16.6)
(Rear)	10.5 (267.0)	.002 (.05)	.0012 (.03)	.709 (18.0)	.....	.654 (16.6)

[1] – Lateral Runout Limit In. (mm); .0051 (.13)

Brakes

ISUZU P'UP

DESCRIPTION

Brake system uses a dual master cylinder with a single reservoir and a vacuum power brake unit. Front brakes are single piston, floating type disc. Rear brakes are duo-servo type drum. A combination valve, equipped with a fail indicator switch, is used.

If hydraulic pressure varies between front and rear systems, a warning light on instrument panel will light and glow until defect is repaired. Parking brake is cable-actuated on rear brake system.

Rear brakes self-adjust on reverse brake applications. No in-service adjustment is required. Initial adjustment must be made after changing brake linings or if adjuster setting has been changed.

BRAKE WARNING LIGHT

1) A dual warning light is mounted on dash. With ignition switch on, light should glow when parking brake lever is pulled 1 notch and go off when lever is fully released.

2) To check circuit warning sensor, release parking brake. With ignition on, warning light should be off. Open bleed screw on 1 wheel, depress brake pedal. Light should glow. Close bleed screw without releasing pedal. Check fluid level in reservoir.

ADJUSTMENT

REAR DRUM BRAKE SHOES

1) After rear lining replacement, check shoe adjustment. To adjust, raise and support vehicle. Remove brake drum. Measure brake drum diameter with drum-to-brake shoe gauge (J-21177).

2) Transfer gauge to brake shoes. Adjust star wheel until gauge just slides over linings. Install drum. Make final adjustment by alternating forward and reverse brake applications until pedal height remains constant.

PEDAL HEIGHT

1) Pedal height (measured from center of pedal pad to floorboard) should be 6.5-6.9" (164-174 mm). To adjust, disconnect negative battery cable and stop light switch electrical lead.

2) Remove stop light switch from bracket. Rotate push rod to obtain proper pedal height. Install and adjust stop light switch. Install electrical leads.

STOP LIGHT SWITCH

Stop light switch is located under dash, above brake pedal. Loosen lock nut and adjust clearance between switch housing (not actuating pin) and brake pedal tab to .02-.04" (0.5-1 mm). Tighten lock nut.

PARKING BRAKE

NOTE: **Service brake must be properly adjusted prior to parking brake adjustment.**

1) With vehicle on a hoist and parking brake released, loosen lock nut on parking brake cable adjuster. Turn cable adjuster clockwise until actuating lever stopper on each rear brake is lifted completely off flange plate. Apply and release parking brake 3-4 times. Check for slack at right rear wheel stopper. If loose, repeat steps **1)** and **2)**.

3) Parking brake lever stroke should be 12-13 notches when set firmly. Rear wheels should rotate freely with parking brake fully released. If either does not operate as described, repeat steps **1)** and **2)** until proper operation is obtained. Lower vehicle.

REMOVAL & INSTALLATION

FRONT DISC BRAKE PADS

Removal

1) Raise and support vehicle on safety stands. Remove tire and wheel. Remove caliper lock bolt, rotate caliper upward and support with wire. Do not damage flex hose by twisting or hanging caliper from it. *See Fig. 1.*

Fig. 1: Exploded View of Front Disc Brake Assembly

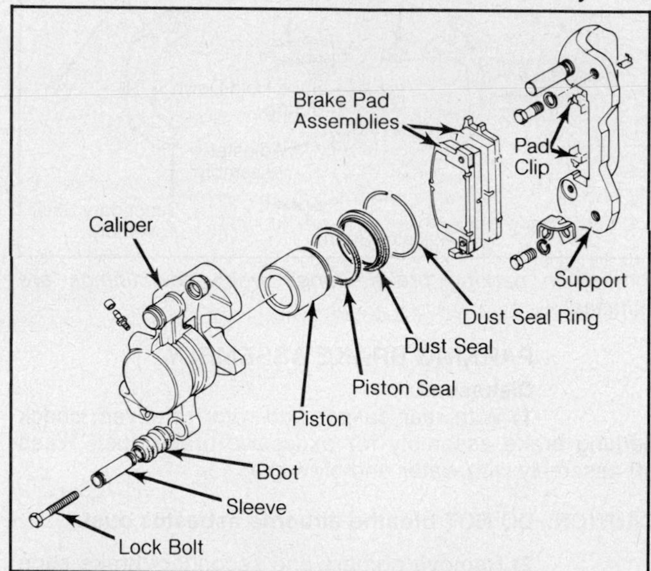
Brake Pad Assemblies
Pad Clip
Caliper
Support
Dust Seal Ring
Dust Seal
Piston Seal
Piston
Boot
Sleeve
Lock Bolt

Lubricate caliper sliding surfaces, shims and rubber boots.

2) Remove pads and shims, marking reusable pads. Remove shoe clips from support. Replace pads if less than .039" (1.0 mm) lining left. Always replace pads in axle sets. Inspect inside of caliper for fluid leakage. Repair as necessary.

Installation

1) To install, reverse removal procedure. Install new pad clips and shims. Apply high temperature brake grease to shims and caliper sliding surfaces.

2) Used pads must be installed in original position. Install pads to supports with wear indicators facing LOWER SIDE.

FRONT DISC BRAKE CALIPER

Removal

1) Raise and support vehicle. Remove tire and wheel. Remove lock bolt from caliper. Disconnect hydraulic flex hose from caliper and plug openings.

2) Disengage guide pin dust boot from guide pin. Raise caliper, and remove from guide pin built into support.

ISUZU P'UP (Cont.)

Installation

1) To install, reverse removal procedure. Apply rubber grease to pad shims, caliper sliding surfaces and inside rubber boots.

2) Install sleeve dust boot on caliper, and insert sleeve into dust boot. Apply rubber grease into guide pin fitting hole in caliper. Install guide pin dust boot on caliper.

3) Clean sliding surface of guide pin. Install caliper and dust boot on guide pin. Secure caliper to support by installing and tightening lock bolt.

4) Flex hose identification stripe must follow a straight line without binding. Hose must not contact moving or vibrating parts. Install wheel and tire. Bleed hydraulic system.

FRONT DISC BRAKE ROTOR

Removal

1) Raise and support vehicle. Remove wheel and tire. Remove caliper support bolts and support. Suspend caliper and support from frame with wire.

2) Remove grease cap, cotter pin, spindle nut retainer and nut.

3) Remove hub and rotor assembly. Separate only if replacing either component. If separated, tighten hub-to-rotor bolts to 36 ft. lbs. (49 N.m).

Installation

1) To install, reverse removal procedures. Adjust wheel bearings. *See appropriate Front Suspension article in SUSPENSION Section*.

2) Tighten caliper support bolts, and bleed hydraulic system as necessary.

REAR BRAKE SHOES

Removal

1) Remove drum. If reusable, mark linings for reassembly reference. Remove shoe return springs, hold-down springs, pins and retainers. Remove adjuster lever spring, adjuster cable and guide plate.

2) Remove adjuster lever and lever hold down spring. Remove brake shoes as an assembly. Separate primary and secondary shoes, adjuster, return spring and strut.

3) Separate parking brake lever and rear cable. Remove clip and washer, and separate brake lever from secondary shoe. *See Fig. 2*. Check behind wheel cylinder boots for excessive leakage. Presence of some fluid is normal and acts as piston lubricant. Repair as necessary.

NOTE: Inspect brake shoes for distortion, looseness, nicks, or oil-soaked linings. Repair or replace as necessary. Replace rear brake linings when thickness is .039" (1 mm) or less.

Installation

1) Apply high temperature grease to sliding surfaces of flange plate, slot in wheel cylinder pistons where brake shoes fit, and anchors.

2) Install parking brake lever to secondary shoe and rear cable to lever. Connect brake shoes together with return spring. Place adjuster screw into position, with star wheel nearest secondary shoe.

3) Install parking brake strut with spring on primary shoe end. Fit shoes to wheel cylinder pistons.

Fig. 2: Exploded View of Rear Drum Brake Assembly

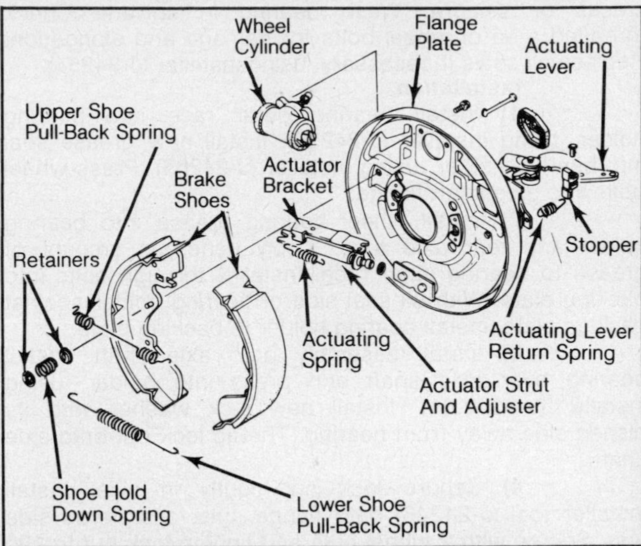
Wheel Cylinder
Flange Plate
Actuating Lever
Upper Shoe Pull-Back Spring
Actuator Bracket
Brake Shoes
Stopper
Retainers
Actuating Spring
Actuating Lever Return Spring
Actuator Strut And Adjuster
Shoe Hold Down Spring
Lower Shoe Pull-Back Spring

Parking brake lever is attached to secondary shoe.

4) Install hold-down springs, self-adjuster assembly and return springs. Install drum and retaining screws. Adjust brakes. Bleed hydraulic system.

REAR AXLE SHAFT BEARING & OIL SEAL

Removal

1) Raise and support vehicle. Remove wheel and tire. Remove brake drum. Disconnect parking brake rear cable from actuator. Disconnect brake line at wheel cylinder. Plug brake line opening.

2) Remove 4 nuts from bearing holder through bolts, located inside of flange plate. Pull out axle shaft assembly including flange plate.

NOTE: Do not strike flange plate with hammer to remove axle shaft. Use tool (J-21579), if shaft cannot be removed by hand.

3) Flatten locking tab on convex lock washer. Mount axle shaft in vise, clamping vise around lock nut. Do not tighten excessively. Install removal tool (J-24246) on flange studs. Lock in position with 2 wheel nuts and turn axle shaft loose from lock nut.

4) Supporting backing plate solidly and holding axle shaft, use light pressure to press lock nut, washer, bearing and holder, and brake backing plate from axle shaft.

5) Remove oil seal from outboard side of bearing holder. Drive off bearing outer race with a drift. Remove wheel bolts from axle flange, using removal tool (J-6627-A).

Inspection

1) Using dial indicator, mounted 13.78" (350 mm) from splined end, check axle shaft for bent condition. Replace if runout exceeds .039" (1 mm).

2) Check axle flange runout by mounting dial indicator so it just touches flange. Rotate axle shaft slowly while observing dial. Replace shaft if runout exceeds .003" (.08 mm).

3) Check all other parts for wear, separation, cracks or seizure. Wash bearing in solvent. Check threaded area of wheel bolts for damage and elongation. Replace oil seals if necessary, using installer (J-24254).

Installation

1) Install bearing outer race into bearing holder, using installer (J-24259). Install new grease seal into bearing holder, using installer (J-24255). Press wheel bolts into axle shaft flange.

2) Install wheel bearing grease into bearing holder and rear axle tube. Apply generous amount of grease to bearing inner race. Install 4 through bolts into backing plate. With oil seal side of bearing holder against backing plate, install bearing holder to backing plate.

3) Install assembly onto axle shaft. Install bearing over axle shaft and press into holder, using installer (J-8609-01). Install new lock washer with its dished side away from bearing. Thread lock nut onto axle shaft.

4) Secure lock nut tightly in vise. Install installer tool (J-24246) onto flange nuts, chamfered side first. Secure with 2 wheel nuts and tighten lock nut to 190 ft. lbs. (258 N.m). Bend over portion of lock washer opposite to locating tab to prevent lock nut from loosening.

5) If only one shaft has been serviced, begin axle shaft installation with step **7)**. If both axles have been serviced, proceed with step **6)**.

6) Insert .079" (2 mm) shim between bearing holder and axle tube end-flange. Insert axle shaft assembly into axle tube. Tighten 4 bearing holder-to-flange bolts to 55 ft. lbs. (75 N.m).

7) Insert remaining axle shaft, assembled without shims, into axle tube until it comes in contact with thrust block in differential. Measure clearance between bearing holder (flange plate) and end-flange (axle tube).

8) Proper shim size is determined by adding .012" (.3 mm) to this measurement. For example, if measured clearance is .081" (2.05 mm), correct shim size is .081" + .012" = .093" (2.05 + .30 = 2.35 mm).

9) Select shim or combination of shims of proper size. Remove axle, and install shim(s) between bearing holder and flange face. Tighten 4 through bolts to 55 ft. lbs. (75 N.m).

10) Complete axle installation. Connect brake line. Install parking brake rear cable, brake drum and wheel and tire. Bleed hydraulic system. Adjust rear brakes, and adjust parking brake tension.

MASTER CYLINDER

Removal

1) Disconnect battery ground cable. Disconnect hydraulic lines at master cylinder. Cover ends to prevent entry of dirt.

2) Remove bracket bolt at front end of cylinder. Remove 4 nuts retaining cylinder to power unit. Remove master cylinder and gasket from power unit.

NOTE: **Master cylinder should be bench-bled before installation. Once remounted, bleed hydraulic system with engine running to prevent damage to push rod seal.**

Installation

To install, reverse removal procedure. Bleed hydraulic system. Monitor fluid level to prevent resevoir from running dry. Adjust pedal height if necessary.

POWER BRAKE UNIT

Removal

1) Disconnect battery ground cable. Remove hydraulic lines at master cylinder, covering ends to prevent entry of dirt. Remove bolts attaching bracket to master cylinder and fender. Remove bracket.

2) Remove vacuum line from power brake unit. Disconnect brake pedal return spring. Remove cotter pin, washer and brake pedal pin that connects push rod clevis.

3) From inside vehicle, remove 4 nuts attaching power brake unit to firewall. Remove power brake unit and master cylinder as an assembly.

Installation

To install, reverse removal procedure, Bleed hydraulic system and adjust pedal height, as necessary.

PARKING BRAKE CABLE ASSEMBLY

Removal

1) Disconnect battery ground cable. Release parking brake front cable at relay lever, located on left side of engine compartment. Keep dust boot on lower end of parking brake handle housing apart from housing.

2) Remove screws attaching handle assembly to instrument panel. Disconnect parking brake light switch harness at switch. Remove parking brake handle and front cable as assembly.

3) To remove front cable, remove parking brake light switch lock nut and remove switch. Release ratchet, totally depress handle and remove cable assembly.

4) To remove rear cable, remove cotter pins, plain washers, waved washers and pins from joint on each side of cable. Disconnect cables on both sides from joint. Disconnect left side cable. Raise cable guides on rear axle case to release from guide bracket. Disconnect right side cable.

Installation

To install, reverse removal procedures. Ensure rear brake system is adjusted properly, Adjust parking brake, as necessary.

OVERHAUL

FRONT DISC BRAKE CALIPER

Disassembly

1) Remove lock bolt from caliper. Disconnect flex hose from caliper. Plug fluid lines. Remove sleeve, sleeve dust boot and guide pin dust boot. Using blunt-pointed instrument, remove dust seal ring and dust seal. *See Fig. 1.*

2) Place a block of wood between piston and caliper cavity wall. Apply compressed air to force piston from cylinder. Remove and discard piston square ring seal.

Cleaning & Inspection

1) Wash all parts in clean brake fluid and dry with filtered, dry, compressed air. Check cylinder bore and piston for wear, scuffing or corrosion. Replace as necessary.

2) Minor imperfections can be removed from caliper bore with crocus cloth or fine emery cloth. Replace dust seal, dust boots and piston square ring seal during overhaul.

ISUZU P'UP (Cont.)

NOTE: Do not polish piston outer surfaces with abrasive. If damaged or badly corroded, replace piston. Brake fluid must be DOT 3 rating or better.

Reassembly

1) Lubricate piston square ring seal with brake fluid or rubber grease. Insert seal into caliper bore. Carefully insert piston into caliper assembly with finger pressure.

2) Apply rubber grease to piston and install dust seal on piston and caliper. Fit seal ring into dust seal.

3) Reverse removal procedure to complete installation, and bleed hydraulic system.

WHEEL CYLINDER

Disassembly

Remove boots from cylinder. Remove pistons, cups and expander spring.

NOTE: Do not remove wheel cylinder unless replacement is necessary. Disassembly, inspection and overhaul may be done while mounted to flange plate.

Cleaning & Inspection

1) Wash parts in clean brake fluid. Inspect cylinder bore and pistons for rust, corrosion or damage. Replace defective parts. Replace ALL rubber parts during overhaul.

2) Check wheel cylinder bore-to-piston clearance. If clearance exceeds .006" (.15 mm), replace wheel cylinder assembly.

Reassembly

1) Lubricate cylinder bore with clean brake fluid. Install spring expander and new cups with flat surfaces toward outside.

2) Install pistons into cylinder with flat surfaces facing center. Do not lubricate pistons, cups or boots prior to installation. Press new boots onto cylinder.

MASTER CYLINDER

Disassembly

1) Remove fluid reservoir cap and filter. Drain brake fluid. Place master cylinder in vise. Push primary piston in completely, and remove stop bolt and gasket on left side of master cylinder.

2) Remove primary piston snap ring. Remove primary and secondary piston assemblies from cylinder bore. *See Fig. 3.*

NOTE: Do not remove reservoirs unless they are to be replaced.

Cleaning & Inspection

1) Wash parts in denatured alcohol (or clean brake fluid). Dry using compressed air. Blow out passages, orifices and valve holes. If slight rust is found, polish clean with crocus cloth or fine emery cloth. Rewash master cylinder and blow dry.

2) Inspect cylinder bore for scoring, pitting or other damage. Check cylinder bore-to-piston clearance. If clearance exceeds .006" (.15 mm), replace master cylinder. Replace all rubber parts and gaskets during overhaul.

Reassembly

1) Lubricate cylinder bore and parts with clean brake fluid or rubber grease. Reverse disassembly procedure.

Fig. 3: Exploded View of Master Cylinder Assembly

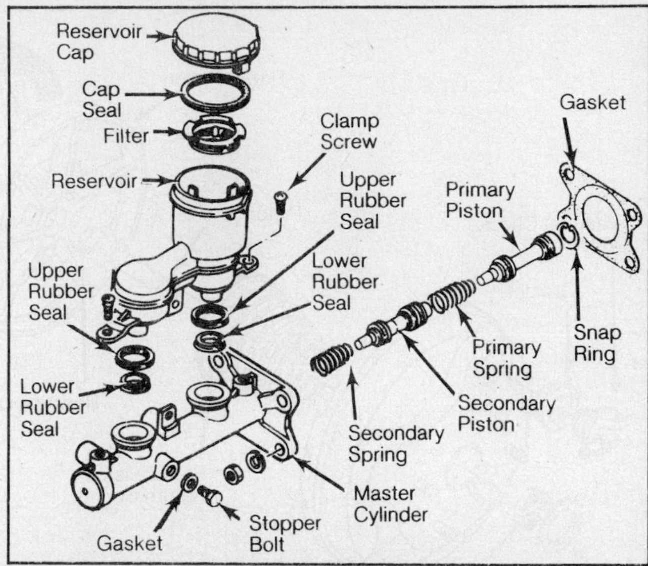
Reservoir Cap
Cap Seal
Filter
Reservoir
Clamp Screw
Upper Rubber Seal
Gasket
Primary Piston
Upper Rubber Seal
Lower Rubber Seal
Snap Ring
Primary Spring
Lower Rubber Seal
Secondary Piston
Secondary Spring
Master Cylinder
Stopper Bolt
Gasket

Replace ALL rubber parts and gaskets during overhaul.

2) Install secondary piston assembly and primary piston assembly, using a gentle twisting, rotating motion to avoid damage to rubber seals. Install snap ring. Depress primary piston, and install piston stopper bolt with new gasket.

NOTE: If fluid contamination or corrosion is found, use clean brake fluid to bench-bleed master cylinder. Do not use any cleaner containing mineral oil or damage to rubber parts will result.

3) Complete reassembly. Bench-bleed master cylinder by installing plugs in outlet ports of cylinder. Fill reservoir with clean brake fluid.

4) Press in and out on primary piston until air bubbles are no longer seen in fluid and pressure is felt when primary piston is depressed. Install master cylinder on power brake unit. Bleed hydraulic system.

POWER BRAKE UNIT

Disassembly

1) Scribe alignment marks on front and rear shells to ensure reassembly in original position. Remove master cylinder reservoir cover assemblies and filters. Drain remaining brake fluid from reservoirs.

2) Clamp flange of master cylinder in vise with power unit up. Remove push rod clevis and lock nut. Remove push rod boot.

NOTE: Spanner wrench (J-9504) must be reworked to fit power brake unit by drilling three 3/8" holes in flat plate to match dash panel mounting studs on power brake unit.

CAUTION: When separating front and rear shell assemblies, maintain pressure on spanner wrench as rear shell is under spring pressure.

3) Place wrench (J-9504) over rear shell mounting studs. Press down on wrench while rotating

ISUZU P'UP (Cont.)

Fig. 4: Exploded View of Power Brake Unit Assembly

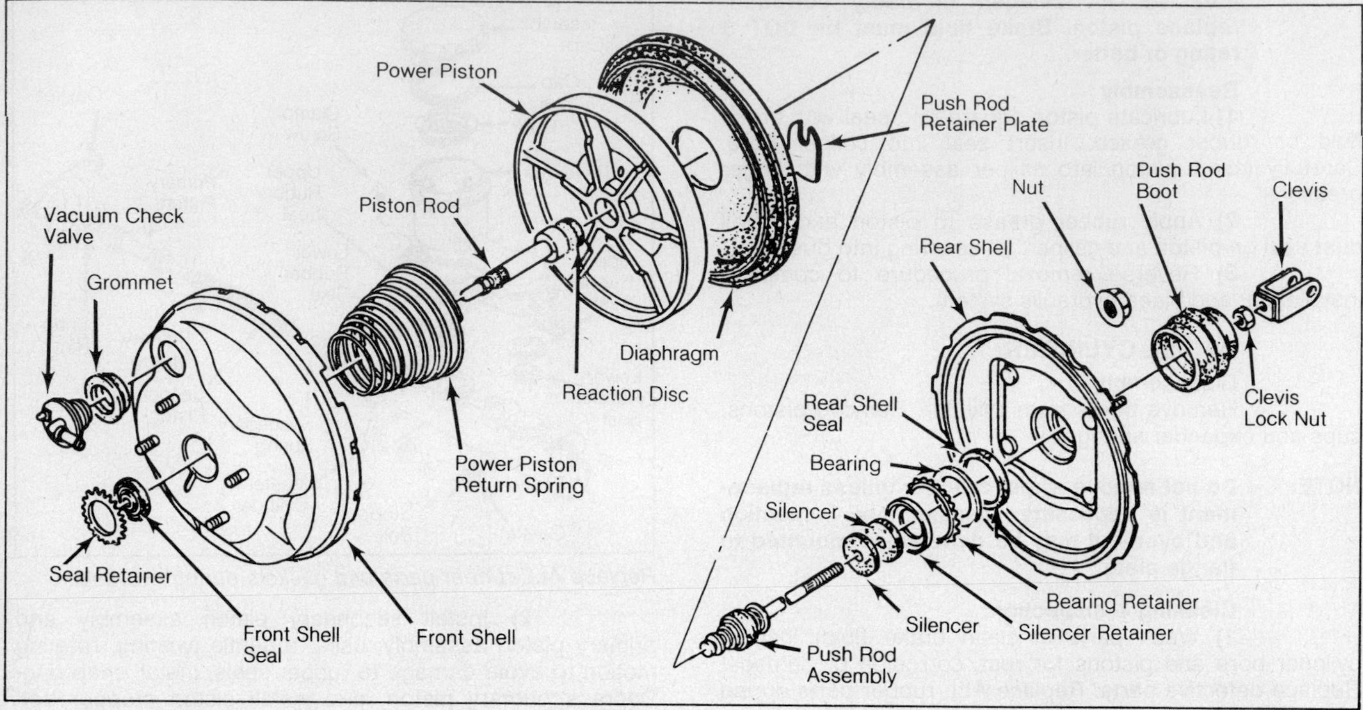
Power Piston
Push Rod Retainer Plate
Piston Rod
Nut
Push Rod Boot
Clevis
Vacuum Check Valve
Rear Shell
Grommet
Diaphragm
Reaction Disc
Clevis Lock Nut
Rear Shell Seal
Bearing
Power Piston Return Spring
Silencer
Seal Retainer
Bearing Retainer
Silencer
Silencer Retainer
Front Shell Seal
Front Shell
Push Rod Assembly

Use denatured alcohol to clean power brake unit components.

counterclockwise. Remove rear shell, piston rod, power piston, return spring and spring retainer. *See Fig. 4*.

4) Remove 4 nuts and lock washers. Separate master cylinder from power unit front shell. Remove and discard gasket.

5) Pry air silencer retainer off power piston. Remove air silencer, filter and rubber diaphragm from power piston.

6) Rotate power piston until push rod retainer slot is down. Press in on rod, allowing retainer to fall out of power piston. Remove push rod assembly and reaction disc.

NOTE: Do not disassemble push rod assembly. If defective, replace complete assembly.

7) If rear shell seal is defective, pry out seal retainer. Remove spacer and seal assembly. If front shell seal is defective, pry out retainer and remove seal.

8) If vacuum check valve is defective, remove and replace with a new valve. Remove grommet.

NOTE: Do not clean parts with a mineral-based solvent.

Cleaning & Inspection

1) Wash all parts in denatured alcohol. Blow dry with compressed air. Inspect inner surface of both shells for wear or damage. Slight rust can be removed with crocus cloth or fine emery cloth.

2) Inspect all parts for cracks, nicks, distortion or other damage. Replace parts as necessary.

Reassembly

1) To reassemble, reverse disassembly procedures. If check valve was removed, install new grommet. Insert check valve into position by rotating back and forth until flanged portion is seated.

2) If front shell seal was removed, apply rubber grease to new seal and seal area of shell. Install seal and retainer in shell with lip of seal facing forward.

3) If rear shell seal was removed, apply rubber grease to rear shell seal area, seal and spacer. Insert seal into rear shell with lip of seal facing forward. Install spacer and retainer. Set retainer to a depth of .264-.276" (6.71-7.01 mm) into rear shell seal area.

4) Apply rubber grease tc lip of piston seal and inner surface of power piston housing. Install push rod and piston assembly into housing. Compress push rod assembly and install retainer plate.

5) Install air filter over push rod. Install air silencer. Seat filter and silencer in housing and install retainer.

6) Install rubber diaphragm over power piston housing, seating diaphragm in housing groove. When installed, rotate one-half turn to assure correct positioning.

7) Temporarily install master cylinder to front shell. Clamp flanged portion of master cylinder in vise with front shell side up. Lubricate face of piston rod, reaction disc and outer rim of diaphragm with rubber grease. Install reaction disc in power piston assembly.

8) In order, assemble rear shell, power piston, piston rod, return spring retainer, return spring and front shell. Using spanner wrench (J-9504), compress return spring and lock rear shell to front shell, ensuring marks made at disassembly are aligned.

CAUTION: Before releasing pressure on spanner wrench, make certain rear shell is locked in place at all tabs.

ISUZU P'UP (Cont.)

9) Assemble push rod boot to rear shell, making sure boot is fully installed on retainer. Loosely install push rod clevis lock nut and clevis.

10) Remove assembly from vise. Remove master cylinder from power unit. Position power unit in vise with piston rod up (Do not clamp parts tightly). Place gauge (J-29759) over piston rod so that legs rest on master cylinder mounting surface.

NOTE: Piston rod must be bottomed in power unit before making adjustment. If necessary, apply 20 in. Hg vacuum at power unit to bottom piston.

11) Piston rod should touch cut out portion of gauge which is .729-.736" (18.5-18.7 mm) away from master cylinder mounting surface. If rod must be adjusted, hold rod at serrated portion and turn threaded end.

TIGHTENING SPECIFICATIONS

Application	Ft. Lbs. (N.m)
Brake Line Nuts	11 (15)
Caliper Lock Bolt	15 (20)
Caliper Support-to-Adapter	64 (87)
Dash Panel Stud Nuts	19 (26)
Flexible Hose-to-Caliper	25 (34)
Flexible Hose-to-Brake Line Nut	11 (15)
Master Cylinder Brake Line Nuts	9 (12)
Master Cylinder Stopper Bolt	13 (18)
Master Cylinder-to-Power Brake Unit	10 (14)
Rear Axle Bearing Holder-to-Flange	55 (75)
Rear Axle Lock Nut	190 (258)
Rotor-to-Hub	36 (49)
Steering Knuckle-to-Adapter	29 (40)
Wheel Cylinder-to-Flange Plate	7.5 (10)

DISC BRAKE ROTOR SPECIFICATIONS

Application	Disc Diameter In. (mm)	Lateral Runout In. (mm)	Parallelism In. (mm)	Original Thickness In. (mm)	Min. Refinish Thickness In. (mm)	Discard Thickness In. (mm)
P'UP	.....	[1] .005 (.13)	.003 (.08)	.492 (12.5)	.453 (11.5)	.437 (11.1)

[1] – Maximum rate of change must not exceed .001" (.03 mm) in 30°.

DRUM BRAKE SPECIFICATIONS

Application	Drum Diam. In. (mm)	Drum Width In. (mm)	Max. Drum Refinish Diam. In. (mm)	Brake Cyl. Diam. In. (mm)	Master Cyl. Diam. In. (mm)
P'UP	10.0 (254.0)	.....	[1] 10.039 (255.0)	1.0 (25.4)	.875 (22.2)

[1] – Drum Replacement Diameter is 10.059" (255.5).

Brakes

JAGUAR XJ6 & XJS

DESCRIPTION

Brake system is 4-wheel disc brakes with tandem master cylinder and power brake unit. Front calipers are 4-piston type; rear calipers are 2-piston type. A combination valve is used to indicate pressure difference between front and rear brake circuits. Parking brake is cable-actuated on rear calipers, and consists of independent disc-mounted pads which act on a rotor.

BRAKE WARNING LIGHT

1) A dual warning light is mounted on instrument panel. Turn ignition on. Parking brake light should glow when parking brake lever is pulled one notch. It should go off when lever is fully released.

2) To check circuit warning sensor, fully release parking brake and ensure light is off (ignition on). Open any bleed screw and light should glow. Close bleed screw, and release and reapply brake pedal. Warning light should go out.

ADJUSTMENT

PARKING BRAKE

Parking Brake Caliper

Caliper is self-adjusting to compensate for pad wear. No adjustment is required.

Parking Brake Cable

1) Fully release parking brake lever. Loosen lock nut on front yoke, and disconnect yoke from bell crank lever at clevis pin.

2) Rotate yoke on adjusting rod so that when yoke is reconnected, there is a slight amount of slack in cable. Reconnect yoke and tighten lock nut.

REMOVAL & INSTALLATION

SERVICE BRAKE DISC PADS

Removal

Raise and support vehicle. Remove wheels and tires. Remove pin clips, pad retaining pins, anti-chatter springs (if equipped) and brake pads. If reuseable, mark all brake pads for proper installation.

Fig. 1: Removing Front Disc Brake Pads

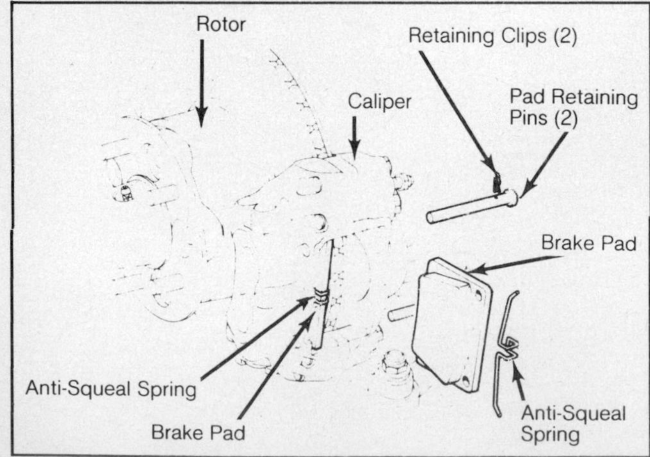
Rotor
Retaining Clips (2)
Caliper
Pad Retaining Pins (2)
Brake Pad
Anti-Squeal Spring
Brake Pad
Anti-Squeal Spring

Check brake pads for proper thickness.

Installation

1) Drain some brake fluid from reservoirs. This will enable caliper pistons to be pushed back into cylinders without overflow at master cylinder.

NOTE: **Minimum pad thickness is 0.2 in. (5.0 mm) for front and rear brake pads.**

2) Push pistons back, insert new pads and springs and replace retaining pins and clips. Check pads for free movement within caliper. Check caliper-to-disc centralization and adjust as necessary. Check reservoirs for correct fluid level and add if needed.

PARKING BRAKE DISC PADS

Removal & Installation

Parking brake caliper must be removed to replace disc pads. Remove and install parking brake disc pads according to instructions for Parking Brake Caliper.

PARKING BRAKE CALIPER

Removal

1) Raise and support vehicle. Remove nuts and bolts attaching rear suspension mounting plate to rear suspension unit. Remove plate from vehicle. Disconnect parking brake cable and return spring from caliper.

2) Remove caliper mounting bolts and release lever. Slide caliper around rotor and remove through hole left by suspension plate. To remove disc pads, remove nut and spring washer securing pads to pad carriers.

Fig. 2: Detail of Parking Brake Caliper Adjustment

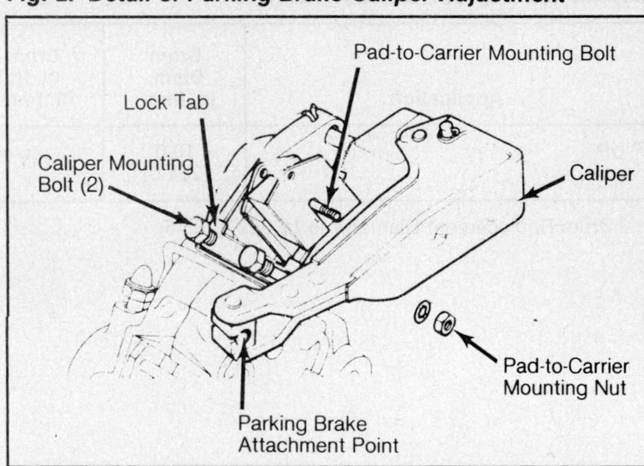
Pad-to-Carrier Mounting Bolt
Lock Tab
Caliper Mounting Bolt (2)
Caliper
Pad-to-Carrier Mounting Nut
Parking Brake Attachment Point

Parking brake caliper clearance should be .75" (19 mm) between the disc pad surfaces.

Installation

1) To install, reverse removal procedure. Adjust caliper if new pads have been installed or if caliper has been overhauled.

2) Adjust by holding one pad carrier stationary and turning remaining carrier until there is a clearance of .75" (19 mm) between disc pad surfaces.

3) Operate caliper actuating lever until adjuster ratchet stops clicking. Install remaining components and check operation of brakes.

SERVICE BRAKE CALIPER

NOTE: **Do not separate caliper halves for repair. If a leak exists between halves, replace caliper.**

JAGUAR XJ6 & XJS (Cont.)

Removal (Front)

1) Raise vehicle and remove wheels. Disconnect caliper fluid line and plug. Disconnect and discard locking wire from mounting bolts. Remove caliper.

NOTE: Check position and number of shims between steering arm and caliper. Replace shims in proper order.

Fig. 3: Removal of Front Disc Brake Caliper

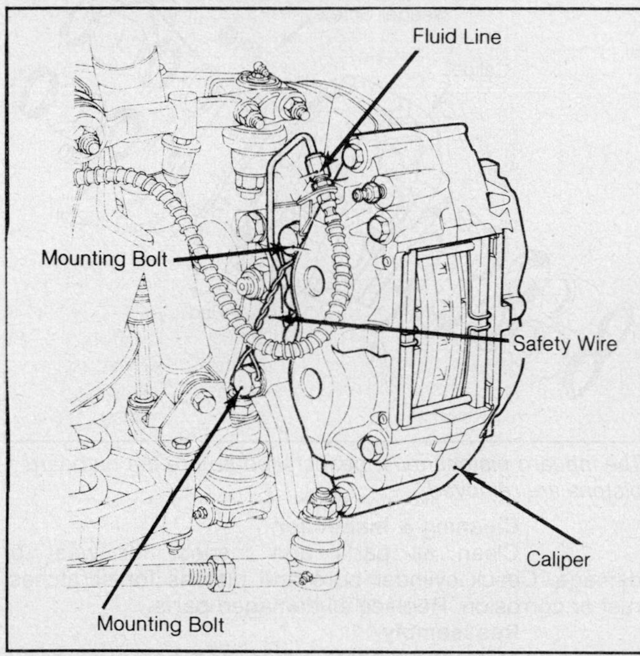
Fluid Line
Mounting Bolt
Safety Wire
Caliper
Mounting Bolt

Disconnecting these components will allow caliper removal.

2) If new caliper is being used, check gap between caliper abutment and rotor face. Gap should be no more than .010" (.25 mm). Gap on upper and lower abutment on same side must be equal. If rotor is not centered, remove one caliper mounting bolt and add or subtract shims as necessary. Repeat procedure on other mounting bolt.

Removal (Rear)

Remove parking brake caliper as previously outlined. Disconnect hydraulic line from caliper and plug line. Disconnect lock wire and mounting bolts. Slide caliper around brake rotor and out hole left by suspension plate.

Installation (Front & Rear)

1) Place caliper in position, install shims (if equipped) and secure bolts. Install safety wire on front and rear mount bolts. Check rotor for centering between caliper. If necessary, adjust shims between drive flange and rotor.

2) If shim adjustment is performed, rear wheel camber must be checked. *See Jaguar Rear Wheel Camber Adjustment in WHEEL ALIGNMENT Section.* To complete installation, reverse removal procedure.

DISC BRAKE ROTOR

Removal (Front)

1) Remove brake caliper as previously outlined. Remove hub-to-rotor attaching bolts and washers. Remove hub dust cap, cotter pin, axle nut and washer from axle stub. Remove hub.

2) Insert punch through access hole in splash shield and lightly tap on it to free water deflector. Remove rotor assembly by sliding it from caliper jaws and over axle stub.

Installation

To install, reverse removal procedure. Pack hub and wheel bearings with grease and adjust wheel bearings. *See Wheel Bearing Adjustment in SUSPENSION Section.*

Fig. 4: Exploded View of Rear Brake Caliper with Detail of Parking Brake Assembly

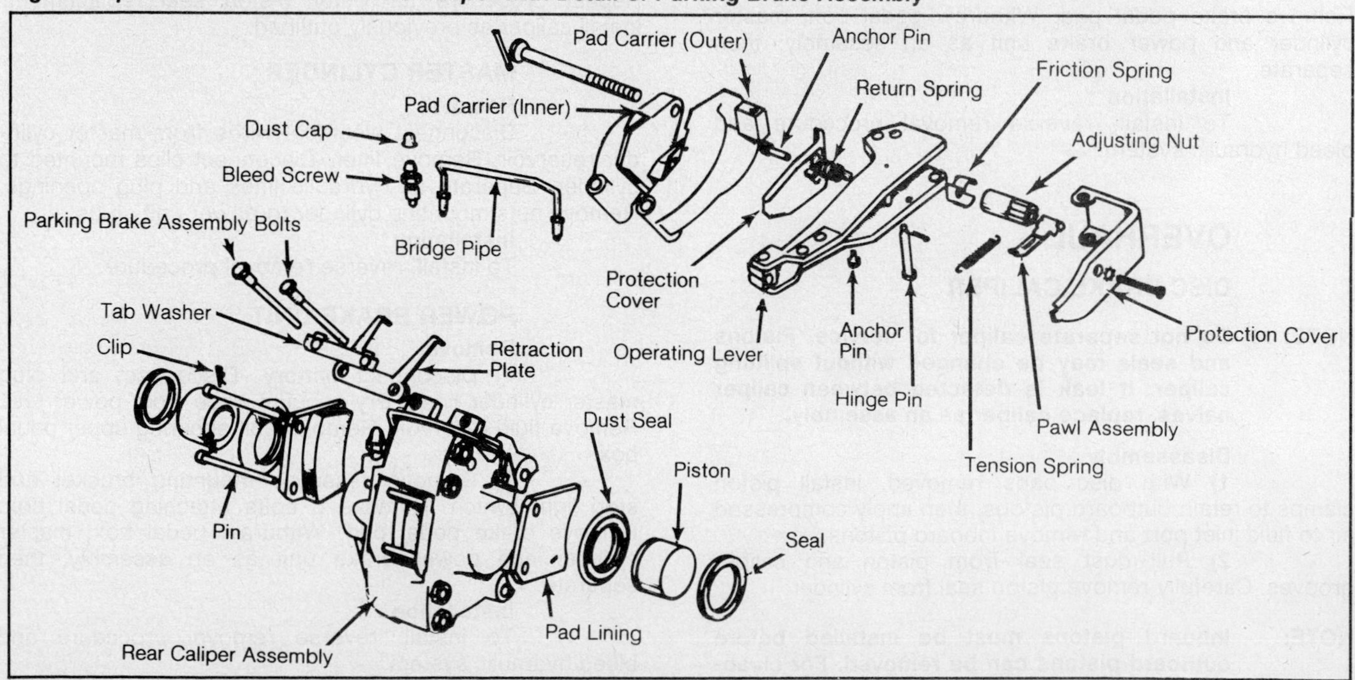
Pad Carrier (Outer)
Anchor Pin
Friction Spring
Return Spring
Pad Carrier (Inner)
Dust Cap
Adjusting Nut
Bleed Screw
Parking Brake Assembly Bolts
Bridge Pipe
Protection Cover
Tab Washer
Anchor Pin
Protection Cover
Clip
Retraction Plate
Operating Lever
Hinge Pin
Pawl Assembly
Dust Seal
Piston
Tension Spring
Pin
Seal
Pad Lining
Rear Caliper Assembly

If leakage is found at caliper halves, do not separate, replace as an assembly.

Removal (Rear)

1) Remove brake caliper as previously outlined. Disconnect shock absorber from lower mount, and remove radius arm locking bolt and lower control arm outer grease fitting.

2) Place stands under hub assembly, and slide radius arm from anchor point. Loosen clamp, and slide boot away from inner universal joint. Remove universal joint-to-rotor attaching bolts, and separate universal joint from rotor.

NOTE: Do not move shims mounted between drive axle flange and brake rotor.

Installation

1) To install, reverse removal procedure. Ensure caliper is centered on rotor. Adjust by adding or removing shims between rotor and drive axle flange.

2) Caliper is centered when gap is not more than .010" (.25 mm). Check rear wheel camber and adjust, if necessary. *See Camber Adjustment in WHEEL ALIGNMENT Section.*

MASTER CYLINDER

Removal

1) Disconnect electrical wires from master cylinder reservoir. Remove filter. Disconnect clips mounted to cylinder.

2) Separate all hydraulic lines and plug openings. Remove nuts mounting cylinder to power unit studs.

Installation

To install, reverse removal procedure.

POWER BRAKE UNIT

Removal

1) Disconnect battery. Disconnect and plug master cylinder lines. Pry vacuum hose from power unit. Remove fluid reservoir.

2) Remove bolt securing upper pedal box. Remove reservoir mounting bracket and stop light switch.

3) Remove 6 bolts attaching pedal box. Remove brake pedal pad. Withdraw pedal box, master cylinder and power brake unit as an assembly; then separate.

Installation

To install, reverse removal procedure and bleed hydraulic system.

OVERHAUL

DISC BRAKE CALIPER

NOTE: Do not separate caliper for service. Pistons and seals may be changed without splitting caliper. If leak is detected between caliper halves, replace caliper as an assembly.

Disassembly

1) With disc pads removed, install piston clamps to retain outboard pistons, then apply compressed air to fluid inlet port and remove inboard pistons.

2) Pull dust seal from piston and caliper grooves. Carefully remove piston seal from cylinder.

NOTE: Inboard pistons must be installed before outboard pistons can be removed. For cleaning purposes, use only clean brake fluid or Castrol/Girling brake cleaning fluid. Do not use denatured alcohol. Wash all parts after cleaning. Always use DOT 3 or higher rated brake fluid.

Fig. 5: 4-Piston Front Disc Brake Caliper Assembly

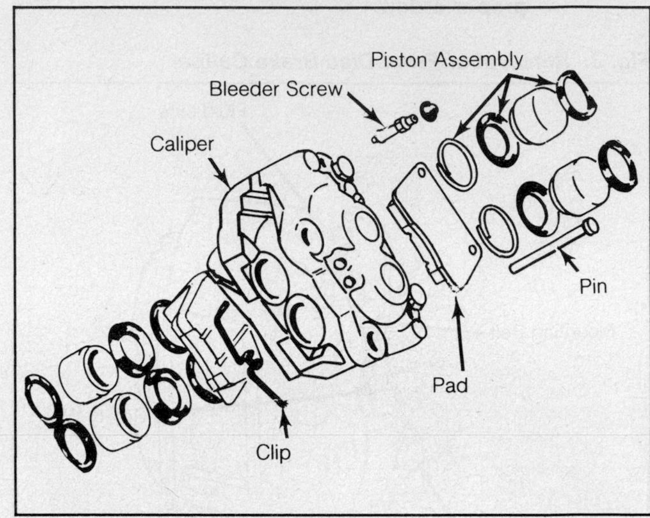
Piston Assembly
Bleeder Screw
Caliper
Pin
Pad
Clip

The inboard pistons must be installed before the outboard pistons are removed.

Cleaning & Inspection

Clean all parts and inspect for wear or damage. Check cylinder bore and pistons for scratches, rust or corrosion. Replace all damaged parts.

Reassembly

1) Coat cylinder, piston and seal with brake fluid before installing. Place piston seal in bore. Install dust seal over cylinder groove, and carefully insert piston through dust seal.

2) Pull dust seal into groove in piston. Use piston clamp to press piston completely into cylinder. Repeat procedure for outer piston seal replacement. Install caliper as previously outlined.

MASTER CYLINDER

Removal

Disconnect electrical wires from master cylinder reservoir. Remove filter. Disconnect clips mounted to cylinder. Separate all hydraulic lines and plug openings. Remove nuts mounting cylinder to power unit studs.

Installation

To install, reverse removal procedure.

POWER BRAKE UNIT

Removal

1) Disconnect battery. Disconnect and plug master cylinder lines. Pry vacuum hose from power unit. Remove fluid reservoir. Remove bolt securing upper pedal box.

2) Remove reservoir mounting bracket and stop light switch. Remove 6 bolts attaching pedal box. Remove brake pedal pad. Withdraw pedal box, master cylinder and power brake unit as an assembly; then separate.

Installation

To install, reverse removal procedure and bleed hydraulic system.

JAGUAR XJ6 & XJS (Cont.)

Fig. 6: Exploded View of Master Cylinder Assembly

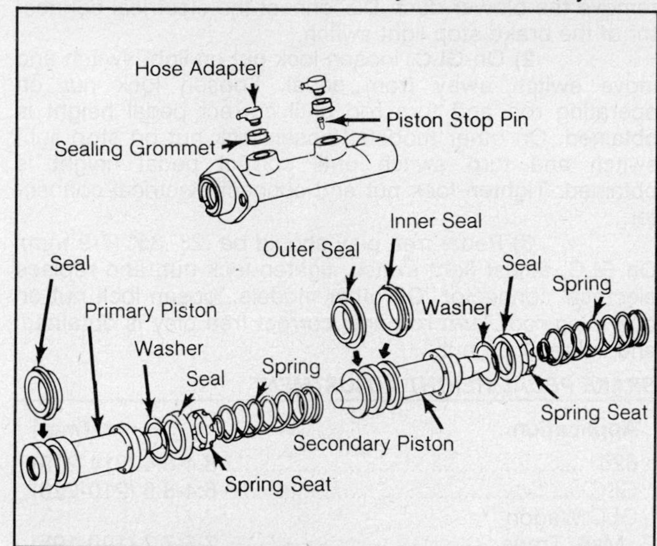
Hose Adapter
Piston Stop Pin
Sealing Grommet
Inner Seal
Outer Seal
Seal
Seal
Spring
Primary Piston
Washer
Washer
Seal
Spring
Spring Seat
Secondary Piston
Spring Seat

Check master cylinder bore for wear.

MASTER CYLINDER

Disassembly

1) With master cylinder removed from vehicle, carefully pry hose adapters from sealing grommets and remove grommets from master cylinder. Push in on primary piston and remove secondary piston stop pin from forward grommet housing.

2) Remove spring lock. Tap flange end of cylinder lightly to remove primary and secondary piston assemblies. Disassemble springs, spring seats, seals and washers from piston assemblies.

NOTE: Master Cylinder standard bore diameter is .937" (23.8 mm).

Cleaning & Inspection

Clean all parts and dry with a lint-free cloth. Inspect pistons and bore for wear, scoring or corrosion. Replace damaged parts as necessary.

Reassembly

1) To reassemble, reverse disassembly procedure. Lubricate all parts with clean brake fluid. Install secondary piston inner seal with lip facing away from primary piston.

2) Install outer seal with lip facing primary piston. Install primary piston seal with lip facing away from spring lock. Install master cylinder and bleed brake system.

POWER BRAKE UNIT

Power brake unit CANNOT be overhauled. If determined defective, replace entire unit.

TIGHTENING SPECIFICATIONS

Application	Ft. Lbs. (N.m)
Brake Line Flare Nuts	
12 mm	12-14 (16-19)
10 mm	6-10 (9-14)
Brake Pedal Box-to-Body	11-13 (15-18)
Brake Pedal Pivot Pin	14-18 (19-24)
Caliper Mounting Bolts	
Front	50-60 (68-82)
Rear	49-55 (67-75)
Flexible Hose-to-Bracket	10-12 (14-16)
Master Cylinder-to-Power Unit	15-20 (21-27)
Power Unit-to-Brake Pedal Box	8-10 (11-14)
Relay Lever Pivot	22-26 (30-35)
Wheel Lug Nut	45 (61)

DISC BRAKE ROTOR SPECIFICATIONS

Application	Disc Diameter In. (mm)	Lateral Runout In. (mm)	Parallelism In. (mm)	Original Thickness In. (mm)	Min. Refinish Thickness In. (mm)	Discard Thickness In. (mm)
XJ6 & XJS						
Front	11.2 (283.8)	.004 (.10)	.....	.945 (24.0)	.....	.895 (22.7)
Rear	10.4 (263.8)	.004 (.10)	.....	.500 (12.7)	.....	0.45 (11.4)

MAZDA

GLC, GLC Wagon, Pickups, RX7, 626

DESCRIPTION

Brake system is hydraulically-operated, using a tandem master cylinder and power brake unit. Front brakes are floating caliper disc. Rear brakes on most models are leading/trailing drums.

Floating caliper rear disc brakes are available on RX7 as an option. Proportioning valves are used on most models to prevent premature lockup of rear wheels.

ADJUSTMENT

REAR DRUM BRAKE SHOES

GLC Wagon, RX7 & Pickups

1) Raise and support rear of vehicle. Release parking brake. Remove rear wheel. Through the hole in the brake drum of the GLC Wagon or on the backing plate of all others, remove the star wheel plug. Insert a flat-tipped screwdriver, and move the star wheel forward until the wheel is locked. *See Fig. 1.*

Fig. 1: Adjusting Rear Brake Shoe-to-Drum Position

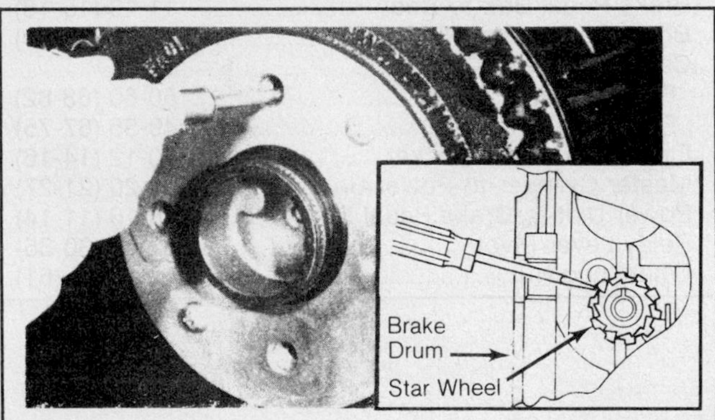
Brake
Drum
Star Wheel

2) On all backing plates, remove the pawl lever hole plug. Insert a flat-tipped screwdriver through hole. Push on the pawl lever self-adjuster, so the star wheel may be moved in the reverse direction.

3) Back off the star wheel about 3 or 4 notches, so the wheel turns freely. Repeat procedure for opposite side. Adjust the parking brake. Install plugs in the adjusting holes.

4) Adjust the parking brake. Install plugs in the adjusting holes.

GLC & 626

1) Raise and support rear of vehicle. Release parking brake. Uncrimp the lock nut and remove it. Remove the brake drum.

2) On the GLC, place a flat-tipped screwdriver between the knurled pin and the quadrant; on the 626, between the adjusting plate and the quadrant of the adjuster. Twist the screwdriver to disengage the teeth. Push the quadrant adjusting lever toward the backing plate.

3) Replace the drum. Install new lock nut and secure by crimping. A few operations of the brake pedal will reset the adjuster. Adjust the parking brake.

PEDAL HEIGHT, FREE PLAY & STOP LIGHT SWITCH

1) Pedal height, measured from firewall to pedal pad center, should be as shown in chart. On the GLC, remove cover under instrument panel. On the 626, remove the blower duct. Disconnect the electrical connector of the brake stop light switch.

2) On GLC, loosen lock nut on light switch and move switch away from pedal. Loosen lock nut on operating rod and turn rod until correct pedal height is obtained. On other models, loosen lock nut on stop light switch and turn switch until correct pedal height is obtained. Tighten lock nut and connect electrical connector.

3) Pedal free play should be .28-.35" (7-9 mm). On GLC, adjust light switch, tighten lock nut, and replace electrical connector. On other models, loosen lock nut on operating rod. Turn rod until correct free play is obtained, and tighten lock nut.

BRAKE PEDAL HEIGHT ADJUSTMENT

Application	In. (mm)
626	8.4-8.6 (214-219)
GLC	8.4-8.6 (210-220)
GLC Wagon	
Man. Trans.	7.5-7.7 (190-195)
Auto. Trans.	7.7-7.9 (195-200)
RX7	7.5-7.7 (190-195)
B2000 & B2200	8.1-8.3 (205-210)

PARKING BRAKE

1) With service brakes properly adjusted, raise and support the rear of the vehicle. Remove parking brake lever boot or console, if necessary. Release the brake lever. Turn the adjusting screw or nut to obtain specified clearance. On Pickups, turn adjusting nut at equalizer under the vehicle.

2) The lever should be pulled with a force of 22 lbs. to obtain a stroke of 3-7 notches on GLC Wagon, 5-9 notches on GLC, 6-8 notches on RX7, 7-9 notches on 626, and 5-10 notches on Pickups.

3) Reinstall brake lever boot or console. Remove supports and lower vehicle. On all models, operate parking brake several times and make sure rear wheels rotate freely.

NOTE: Insure that the rear brakes are not dragging and the parking brake warning light is activated when the lever is pulled 1 notch.

4) On all models, operate parking brake several times and make sure rear wheels rotate freely.

BRAKE WARNING LIGHT

All Models (If Equipped)

1) Light indicates parking brake is engaged and also warns of low fluid level. With engine running, light should glow when parking brake lever is pulled 1 notch and go off when lever is fully released.

2) To check warning light operation with engine running, release parking brake lever and ensure light is off. Raise master cylinder reservoir cap and light should glow. If not, check switch and wire connector.

REMOVAL & INSTALLATION

FRONT DISC BRAKE PADS

Removal

1) Raise and support the front of the vehicle. Remove the wheels. Detach brake hose attachment from shock absorber, if necessary.

MAZDA (Cont.)

2) On RX7, 626, and GLC, remove lower caliper guide pin and pivot caliper body up out of way. On GLC Wagon and Pickups remove locking clips and stopper plates.

3) Remove caliper body and hang from frame with wire. Do not disconnect hydraulic lines. On all models, remove anti-rattle springs (clips), pads, and shims, if equipped.

Installation

1) To install, reverse removal procedure. Before mounting caliper, loosen bleed screw, and seat piston. Tighten bleed screw.

2) After pad installation, depress brake pedal several times to seat pads. Bleed hydraulic system, if required.

NOTE: **Grease pad mounting support, caliper contact area, and shims with special grease (NLGI No. 2 or equivalent).**

REAR DISC BRAKE PADS

Removal (RX7)

1) Raise and support the rear of the vehicle. Remove wheel. Disconnect parking brake cable from caliper. Remove lower caliper attaching bolt.

2) Lift the lower side of caliper. Remove anti-rattle spring. Remove disc brake pads and shims.

Installation

1) Using brake piston wrench (49 FA18 602), turn piston clockwise until piston is inserted into caliper fully.

2) Position piston so that dowel on pad will seat in piston stopper groove. To complete installation, reverse removal procedure.

FRONT DISC BRAKE CALIPER

Removal

1) Raise and support the front of the vehicle. Remove the wheel. Disconnect and plug the fluid line at caliper. On RX7, remove lower caliper bolt, lift the caliper body, and remove by sliding toward the inside of the vehicle.

2) On GLC remove slide pins, return spring, shim, and lift off caliper. On 626 remove caliper mounting bolts and lift off caliper. On GLC Wagon and Pickups, remove locking clips, stopper plates, and anti-rattle spring. Lift off caliper. Remove disc pads as previously described.

Installation

To install, reverse removal procedure and bleed hydraulic system.

REAR BRAKE CALIPER

Removal (RX7)

1) Raise and support the rear of the vehicle. Remove the wheel. Disconnect parking brake cable from caliper.

2) Remove caliper attaching bolt (lower side). Lift up caliper. Slide the caliper toward the inside of the vehicle and remove the caliper. Disconnect the brake hose from the caliper.

Installation

To install caliper, reverse removal procedure and bleed hydraulic system.

FRONT DISC BRAKE ROTOR

Removal (GLC & 626)

1) Raise and support front of vehicle. Remove the wheel. Raise lock nut tab before loosening. Apply brakes to lock hub and remove drive shaft lock nut. Loosen tie rod end nut and separate tie rod end from knuckle using joint puller (49 0118 850C).

2) Disconnect brake line from shock absorber, if necessary. Remove brake caliper assembly from knuckle and support it on a wire. Remove nuts and bolts which couple the knuckle with the ball joint and the shock absorber. Remove knuckle assembly from the ball joint and drive shaft.

3) Separate knuckle from wheel hub, on GLC with puller (49 B001 726) and on 626 with puller (49 G030 725). Make mating marks on hub-to-rotor assembly, detach hub bolts, and separate hub from rotor. *See Fig. 2.*

NOTE: **If drive shaft will not separate from the hub, use bearing puller set (49 0839 425C).**

4) Separate knuckle from wheel hub, on GLC with puller (49 B001 726) and on 626 with puller (49 G030 725). Make mating marks on hub-to-rotor assembly, detach hub bolts, and separate hub from rotor. *See Fig. 2.*

NOTE: **Place wheel hub in a vise with soft jaws to aid disassembly.**

Fig. 2: Removing Wheel Hub From Rotor

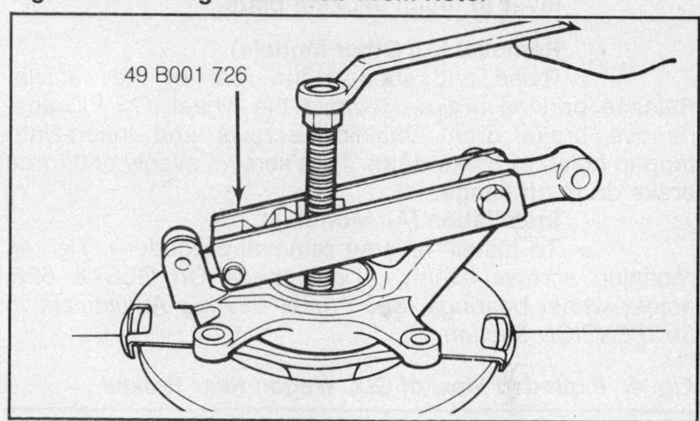
49 B001 726

Tool shown is for GLC; tool for 626 is similar.

Installation

To install, press knuckle on to wheel hub assembly, using spacer selector (49 B001 727) for GLC and (49 G030 728) for 626. *See Fig. 3.* Continue assembly by reversing removal procedures.

Fig. 3: Assembling Wheel Hub to Knuckle

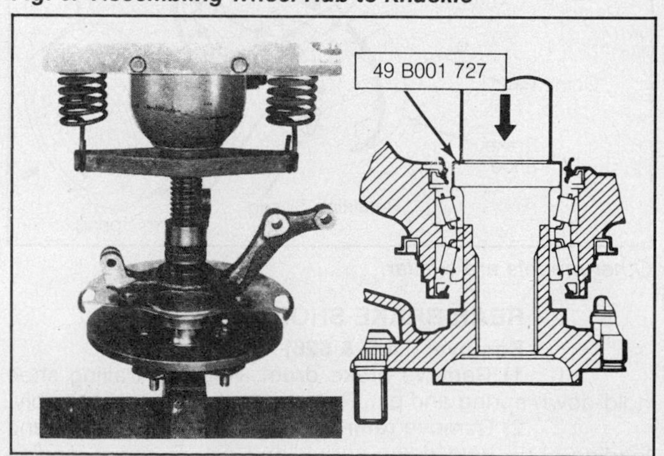
49 B001 727

Procedure is for GLC & 626.

Brakes

MAZDA (Cont.)

Removal (All Other Models)

1) With caliper assembly removed, remove wheel hub grease cap, cotter pin, lock plate and ring adjusting lock nut.

2) Remove thrust washer and outer bearing from hub. Slide hub and rotor assembly from spindle. On Pickups, place wheel in a soft-jawed vise, make mating marks, remove hub-to-rotor bolts, and separate rotor from hub.

Installation

To install, reverse removal procedure, and tighten hub-to-rotor bolts evenly. Adjust wheel bearings. *See Wheel Bearing Adjustment in SUSPENSION Section.*

REAR BRAKE DRUM

Removal (GLC & 626)

Raise and support the rear of the vehicle. Release parking brake. Remove the wheel and grease cap. Clear the staked nut's position, and remove the nut and washer. Remove brake drum.

NOTE: If it is difficult to remove drum, widen the shoe-to-drum clearance by removing the lever stop. If necessary, disconnect the parking brake cable from lever, and move lever to touch backing plate.

Removal (All Other Models)

Raise and support the rear of the vehicle. Release parking brake. Remove the wheel. On Pickups, remove brake drum retaining screws and insert into tapped holes of brake drum. Turn screws evenly and force brake drum off flange.

Installation (All Models)

To install, reverse removal procedure. Tighten retaining screws evenly (if equipped). On GLC & 626, adjust wheel bearings. *See Wheel Bearing Adjustment in SUSPENSION Section.*

Fig. 4: Exploded View of GLC Wagon Rear Brakes

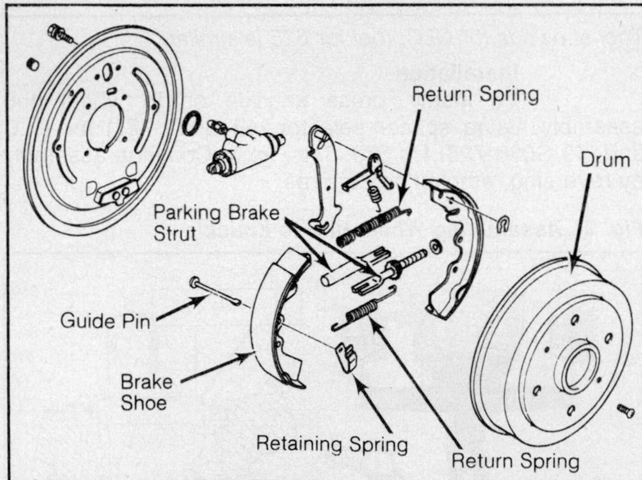
Return Spring
Drum
Parking Brake
Strut
Guide Pin
Brake
Shoe
Retaining Spring
Return Spring

Other models are similar.

REAR BRAKE SHOES

Removal (GLC & 626)

1) Remove brake drum. Remove trailing shoe hold-down spring and pin. Remove trailing shoe assembly

2) Remove return spring, anti-rattle spring, and leading shoe hold down spring and pin. Remove leading shoe assembly.

Installation

To install, reverse removal procedure. Move quadrant until it touches backing plate. Grease contact areas of brake shoes and backing plate. Adjust wheel bearings. *See Wheel Bearing Adjustment in SUSPENSION Section.*

Fig. 5: Moving GLC & 626 Brake Quadrant

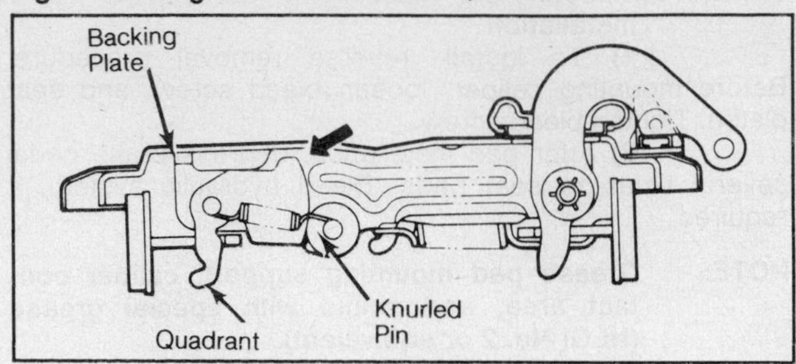
Backing
Plate
Knurled
Pin
Quadrant

To move quadrant, insert a screwdriver between knurled pin and quadrant, twist in direction of arrow.

Removal (All Other Models)

1) With brake drum removed, remove brake shoe return springs, retaining springs and guide pins. Remove brake shoes.

2) Remove parking brake strut and disconnect parking brake cable from operating lever of secondary shoe.

Installation

1) Lubricate adjusting screw threads and contact surfaces of shoes and backing plate with brake grease. Install parking brake operating lever to secondary shoe and secure with clip. Engage operating lever with parking brake cable.

2) Position operating strut between slots of shoes. Mount assembly to backing plate so slots in shoes are toward adjusting screws. Install return springs and retainer springs.

MASTER CYLINDER

Removal

1) Disconnect fluid level sensor coupler, if equipped. Disconnect and plug hydraulic lines at master cylinder to prevent entry of dirt and loss of fluid.

2) Remove nuts attaching master cylinder to firewall or power brake unit and remove master cylinder from vehicle. On RX7, remove proportioning valve by-pass bolt.

Installation

To install, reverse removal procedure and bleed hydraulic system.

POWER BRAKE UNIT

Removal

1) Remove master cylinder from power brake unit before removing power brake unit. Disconnect vacuum line at power brake unit.

NOTE: On GLC, remove cover under instrument panel. On 626, remove the blower duct.

2) From inside vehicle, remove cotter pin and clevis pin attaching push rod to brake pedal, and separate.

3) Remove nuts retaining power unit to fire wall. Remove power brake unit and master cylinder as an

MAZDA (Cont.)

assembly. Separate master cylinder from power brake unit.

Installation

To install, reverse removal procedure and bleed hydraulic system.

OVERHAUL

FRONT DISC BRAKE CALIPER

Disassembly

1) Thoroughly clean exterior of caliper and remove retainer and dust boot. Place a piece of wood in front of piston.

2) Apply compressed air to fluid inlet and remove piston. Tap caliper with plastic hammer, if required. Remove piston seal without damaging caliper bore.

Fig. 6: Exploded View of Pickup Front Disc Brake Caliper

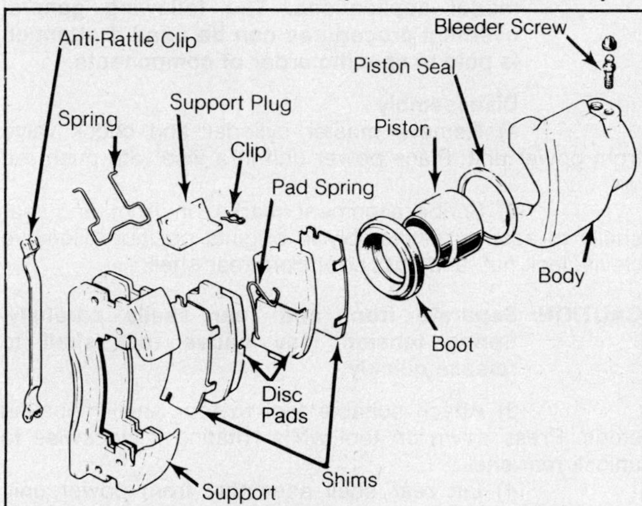

Anti-Rattle Clip
Bleeder Screw
Piston Seal
Support Plug
Spring
Piston
Clip
Pad Spring
Body
Boot
Disc
Pads
Shims
Support

Cleaning & Inspection

1) Wash all parts in alcohol or brake fluid and air dry. Inspect cylinder bore and piston for scoring, scratches or rust. Replace defective parts.

2) Minor damage may be removed with crocus cloth. Always replace dust boot and piston seal when caliper is disassembled.

Fig. 7: Exploded View of RX7 Front Brake Caliper

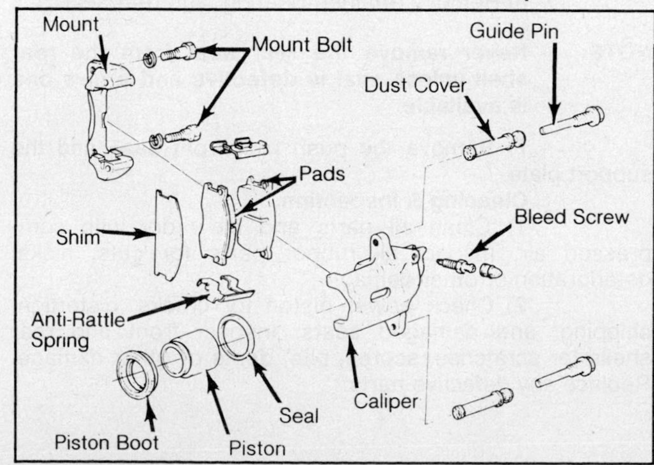

Mount
Mount Bolt
Guide Pin
Dust Cover
Pads
Bleed Screw
Shim
Anti-Rattle
Spring
Seal
Caliper
Piston Boot
Piston

GLC & 626 calipers are similar.

Reassembly

1) Apply clean brake fluid to cylinder bore, piston and piston seal. Seat piston seal in caliper bore.

2) Install piston carefully into cylinder bore and install dust boot and retainer.

REAR DISC BRAKE CALIPER

Disassembly (RX7)

1) Remove dust boot retainer and boot. Turn piston counterclockwise with disc brake piston wrench (49 FA18 602), and screw out piston. Remove piston seal.

2) Remove boot retainer. Slip off boot. Remove snap ring. Compress conical spring in caliper with spring compressor (49 FA18 601), valve spring lifter arm (49 0636 100A), and removing plate (49 E301 144).

3) Remove parking brake crank, torsion spring and strut. Remove adjusting bolt and conical spring assembly. Press out needle roller bearings.

Inspection

1) Clean all parts in brake fluid or alcohol. Air dry parts. Inspect caliper bore for scratches, scoring or rust. Minor damage can be removed by polishing with crocus cloth.

CAUTION: Never use gasoline or kerosene when cleaning caliper parts.

2) Inspect needle roller bearing, strut, adjusting bolt, and parking brake crank for corrosion, wear or damage. Check torsion spring and conical spring for corrosion, weakness or damage.

3) Check piston and sleeve nut for excessive play. It should be within .012-.020" (.3-.5 mm).

Reassembly

1) Assemble the caliper in the reverse order of disassembly. Use new piston and dust seals. Three kinds of grease contained in seal kit must be used.

2) White grease is for caliper slide bolts and mounting bolts. Orange grease is for bearings, adjusting bolt, strut and piston boot. Pink grease is for piston seal.

3) Lubricate the piston and caliper bore with clean brake fluid. Press in needle roller bearing so that arrow on bearing faces outward.

4) Assemble conical spring and adjusting bolt. *See Fig. 8.* Install adjusting bolt assembly, strut and torsion spring in the caliper. Install piston using disc brake wrench, as described under Disc Brake Pad Installation.

Fig. 8: Proper Installation of Conical Spring and Adjusting Bolt

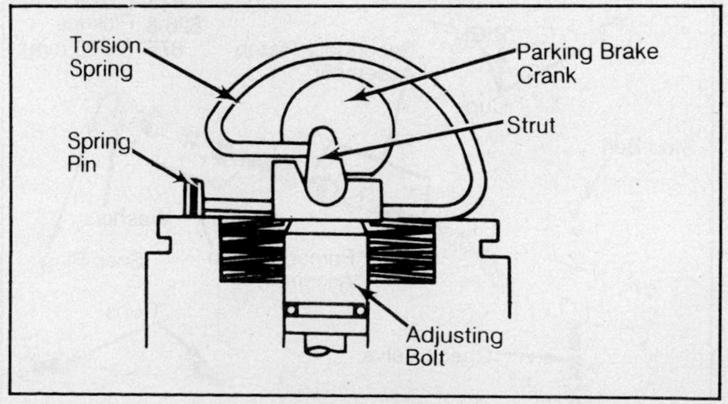

Torsion
Spring
Parking Brake
Crank
Strut
Spring
Pin
Adjusting
Bolt

Apply orange grease, supplied in seal kit, to adjusting bolt.

Brakes

MAZDA (Cont.)

WHEEL CYLINDERS

Disassembly

Remove dust boots. Remove piston assemblies by pressing on cylinder cup to force out filling blocks and return spring.

Cleaning & Inspection

1) Clean all parts in alcohol or brake fluid. Check cylinder bore and pistons for scores, roughness or wear.

2) Check clearance between cylinder bore and pistons. Replace if clearance exceeds .006" (.15 mm). Check cups for deformation. Replace as necessary.

Fig. 9: Exploded View of Wheel Cylinder

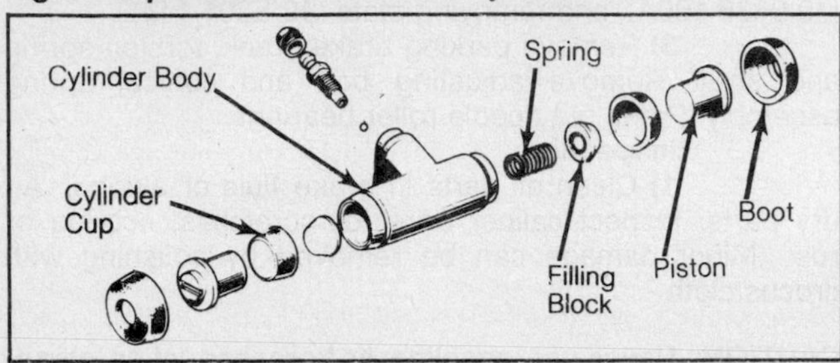
Spring
Cylinder Body
Cylinder Cup
Boot
Filling Block
Piston

Flat side of cylinder cups face outward.

Reassembly

1) Reverse disassembly procedure. Coat all parts with clean brake fluid before reassembly.

2) When installing cylinder cups, make sure flat side of cup faces outward.

MASTER CYLINDER

Disassembly

1) Thoroughly clean outside of master cylinder, and pour out any remaining brake fluid. If equipped, remove reservoir and dust boot. Depress primary piston assembly. *See Fig. 10.*

2) From rear of cylinder bore, remove retaining ring , washer, primary piston assembly, and return spring. Remove stopper bolt and secondary piston by blowing compressed air through the outlet port. *See Fig. 11.*

3) Carefully withdraw secondary piston assembly and return spring. Remove fittings, check valves, and springs.

Fig. 10: Exploded View of Typical Master Cylinder

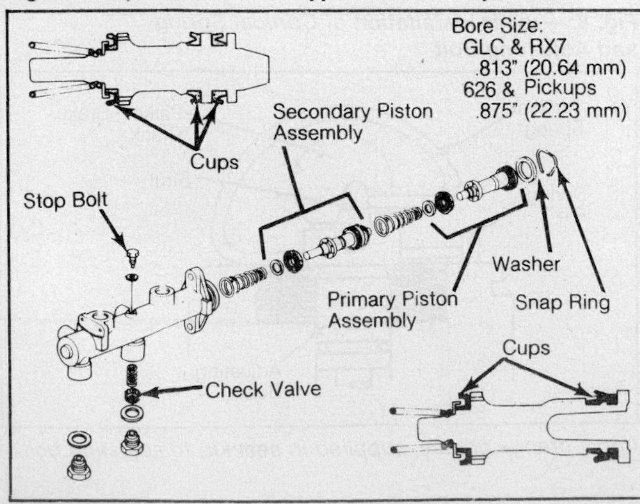
Bore Size:
GLC & RX7
.813" (20.64 mm)
626 & Pickups
.875" (22.23 mm)
Secondary Piston Assembly
Cups
Stop Bolt
Washer
Primary Piston Assembly
Snap Ring
Cups
Check Valve

Some models may vary slightly.

Cleaning & Inspection

1) Clean all parts in alcohol or brake fluid. Check all parts for scoring, roughness or wear. Check piston-to-cylinder clearance.

2) If clearance exceeds .006" (.15 mm), replace parts as necessary. Remove all foreign matter from internal passages and recesses with compressed air.

3) Check cylinder cups for deformation and replace as required.

Reassembly

1) Reverse disassembly procedure. Coat all parts with clean brake fluid before reassembly. Use new gaskets at all hydraulic unions.

2) When assembled, make sure piston cups do not cover compensating ports. Make sure valve with hole in center, faces front side outlet hole.

POWER BRAKE UNIT

NOTE: Power brake units vary slightly between model applications. The following general overhaul procedures can be used if attention is paid to specific order of components.

Disassembly

1) Remove master cylinder and check valve from power unit. Place power unit in a vise with push rod up.

2) Scribe alignment marks on front and rear shells to assure reassembly in original position. Remove clevis, lock nut, and dust boot from rear shell.

CAUTION: Separate front and rear shells carefully. Spring tension may cause rear shell to release quickly.

3) Attach suitable tool to rear shell mounting studs. Press down on tool while rotating it clockwise to unlock rear shell.

4) Lift rear shell assembly from power unit, remove air silencer retainer, and separate diaphragm from power piston assembly. Remove valve rod with plunger assembly from rear shell.

5) Remove lock plate and press the valve rod in to remove the valve retainer key. Remove valve rod and plunger assembly. Remove air silencer and filter.

NOTE: Service the valve rod plungers as an assembly.

6) Remove retainer, bearing, and rear seal.

NOTE: Never remove the rear seal from the rear shell unless seal is defective and a new one is available.

7) Remove the push rod, front seal, and the support plate.

Cleaning & Inspection

1) Clean all parts and blow dry with compressed air. Inspect all rubber parts for cuts, nicks, deterioration or other damage.

2) Check power piston for cracks, distortion, chipping, and damaged seats. Inspect front and rear shells for scratches, scores, pits, dents or other damage. Replace any defective parts.

MAZDA (Cont.)

Reassembly

1) Reverse disassembly procedure. Apply silicone grease to parts before reassembly. When assembling rear shell to front shell, make sure index marks are aligned.

Fig. 11: Exploded View of Typical Power Brake Unit

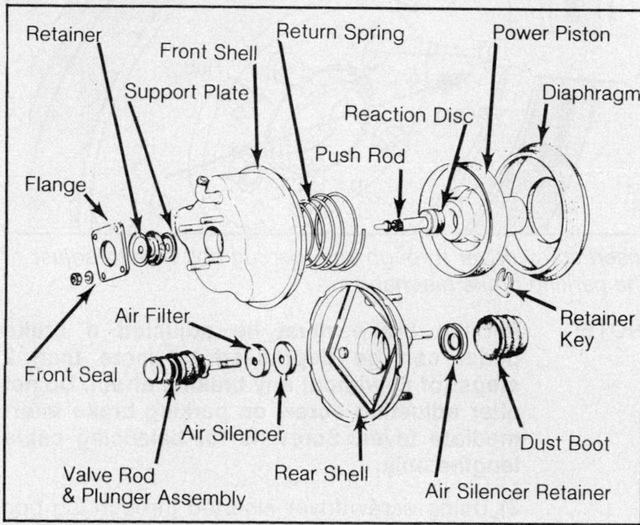

Retainer
Front Shell
Return Spring
Power Piston
Support Plate
Diaphragm
Reaction Disc
Push Rod
Flange
Retainer Key
Air Filter
Front Seal
Air Silencer
Dust Boot
Valve Rod & Plunger Assembly
Rear Shell
Air Silencer Retainer

Some models may vary slightly.

2) Before installing master cylinder to power unit, measure clearance between primary piston and power unit push rod. Clearance on RX7 & GLC Wagon should be .004-.012" (.1-.3 mm).

3) On all other models, clearance should be .004-.020" (.1-.5 mm). If clearance is not to specifications, correct by adjusting push rod length.

TIGHTENING SPECIFICATIONS

Application	Ft. Lbs. (N.m)
Caliper Mounting Bracket	
Pickups	40-47 (55-65)
626	
Upper	18.1 (25)
Lower	21.7 (30)
GLC & GLC Wagon	33-40 (45-55)
Caliper Guide Pin	33-40 (45-55)

DISC BRAKE ROTOR SPECIFICATIONS

Application	Disc Diameter In. (mm)	Lateral Runout In. (mm)	Parallelism In. (mm)	Original Thickness In. (mm)	Min. Refinish Thickness In. (mm)	Discard Thickness In. (mm)
626	7.95 (202)	.004 (.10)	.....	.55 (14)	.....	.51 (13)
GLC	8.94 (227)	.004 (.10)	.....	.433 (11)		.394 (10)
GLC Wagon	9.02 (229)	.002 (.06)	.....	.512 (13)	.....	.472 (12)
RX7						
Front	.....	.004 (.10)	.....	.709 (18)	.....	.669 (17)
Rear	.....	.004 (.10)	.....	.394 (10)	.....	.354 (9)
B2000	10.08 (256)	.004 (.10)	.....	.472 (12)		.433 (11)
B2200	10.08 (256)	.004 (.10)	.....	.787 (20)	.....	.748 (19)

DRUM BRAKE SPECIFICATIONS

Application	Drum Diam. In. (mm)	Drum Width In. (mm)	Max. Drum Refinish Diam. In. (mm)	Wheel Cyl. Diam. In. (mm)	Master Cyl. Diam. In. (mm)
626	7.87 (200)	.....	7.91 (201)	.750 (19)	.875 (22.2)
GLC	7.09 (180)	.....	7.13 (181)	.6875 (17.4)	.8125 (20.6)
GLC Wagon	7.87 (200)	.....	7.91 (201)	.750 (19.0)	.8125 (20.6)
RX7	7.87 (200)	.....	7.91 (201)	.750 (19.0)	.8125 (20.6)
B2000 & B2200	10.23 (260)	.....	10.27 (261)	.875 (22.2)	.875 (22.2)

MERCEDES-BENZ

240D, 300 Series, 380 Series

DESCRIPTION

Service brake system utilizes 4-wheel disc brakes, hydraulically-operated by a tandem or stepped tandem master cylinder and power brake units. Stop screw is on top center of stepped tandem master cylinder and bottom center of tandem master cylinder.

Master cylinders, manufactured by Teves or Bendix, incorporate 2- or 3-chamber reservoirs. A fluid level sensor contact is built into each chamber. A dash panel warning light is activated when brake fluid level is low or when pressure differential between two brake circuits is caused by loss of fluid in one circuit.

Floating type front disc brake calipers are used on the 380 Series; fixed calipers on other models. On 300 Series sedan, rear disc brake caliper has larger inside bore diameter than other models. Parking brakes are cable-actuated, internal expanding shoe-type, housed in rear brake rotors.

All models have brake pad wear indicator and differential pressure warning indicator. Wear indicator for 380 Series operates on inner pads only.

On 300SD and 380 Series, the Anti-Locking Brake System (ABS) is optional. *See Mercedes-Benz Anti-Locking Brake (ABS) System article in this section*.

On diesel models, a vacuum pump is incorporated to supply vacuum to power brake unit.

BRAKE WARNING LIGHT

1) A dual warning light is mounted on dash. Turn ignition on. Light should glow when parking brake lever is pulled 1 notch and go off when lever is fully released.

2) To check circuit warning sensor, turn ignition on, release parking brake, and ensure light is off. Open bleeder screw on one wheel and depress brake pedal. Light should glow.

3) Close bleeder screw, replenish brake fluid and bleed hydraulic system. Check that light goes out after testing. If not, differential pressure pin in master cylinder must be reset.

ADJUSTMENT

PEDAL HEIGHT & FREE PLAY

1) Pedal height, measured from pedal pad to pedal stop, should be 5.9" (150 mm).

2) Loosen lock nuts, and turn stop light switch until correct pedal height is obtained. Tighten lock nuts. Pedal free play should be .20-.60" (5-15 mm).

BRAKE LIGHT SWITCH

Stop light switch is located under dash, above brake pedal. Loosen lock nuts, and adjust switch so that contact button extends .24-.32" (6-8 mm). Tighten lock nuts.

PARKING BRAKE

1) Remove 1 wheel lug bolt at each rear wheel. Raise and support vehicle.

2) Rotate wheel until lug bolt hole is positioned over parking brake adjuster, approximately 45° forward for diagonal swing axle and 90° forward for diagonal swing axle with starting torque compensation. *See Fig. 1.*

Fig. 1: Adjusting Parking Brake Mechanism

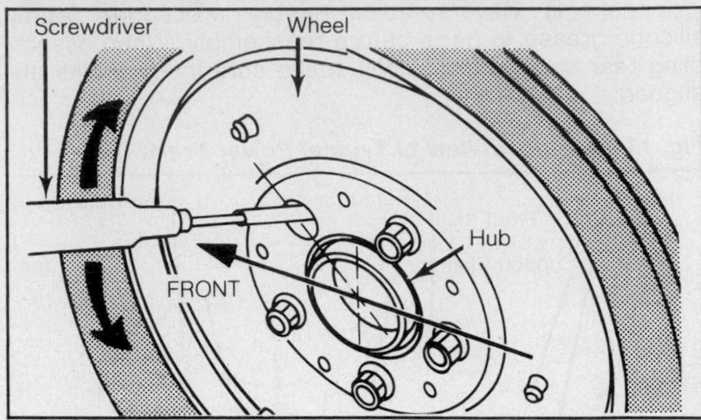
Screwdriver
Wheel
Hub
FRONT

Insert screwdriver through any rear lug bolt hole to adjust the parking brake mechanism.

NOTE: Parking brake must be adjusted if brake pedal can be depressed by more than 2 steps (of 6) without any braking effect. Do not alter adjusting screw on parking brake intermediate lever. Screw is for balancing cable lengths only.

3) Using screwdriver inserted through lug bolt hole, turn adjuster until rear wheel cannot be turned by hand. Back off adjuster until wheel can be turned without drag.

REMOVAL & INSTALLATION

DISC BRAKE PADS

Removal (300SD, 380SEC & 380SEL)

1) Raise vehicle, support with safety stands and remove wheels. Remove upper hex-head caliper bolt.

2) Pull clip of brake pad wear sensor out of plug (by opening cap on plug). Rotate caliper downward and remove disc pads from carrier.

3) Note condition and location of pads for proper assembly (if reuseable).

4) Standard front disc brake pad assembly thickness (including lining backing plate) is .69" (17.5 mm). Standard rear pad assembly thickness is .61" (15.5 mm).

5) Front backing plate thickness is .18" (4.5 mm). Rear backing plate thickness is .20" (5 mm). Minimum pad thickness is .08" (2 mm).

NOTE: All self-locking, hex head bolts should only be used once.

Installation

1) Using cylinder brush, clean disc pad guide surface in caliper. Siphon sufficient fluid from master cylinder reservoir to prevent overflowing. Press piston to bottom of bore.

2) Install disc pads and wear sensor wires. Reverse removal procedure to complete installation. Check that dash light goes out. Reset pin in master cylinder if necessary.

Removal (All Other Models)

1) Raise vehicle, support with safety stands, and remove wheels. If equipped, remove cover plate from caliper, and disconnect wear indicator wires.

2) Drive out retaining pins toward inside of vehicle. On Bendix brakes, retaining pins have locking keys. Remove cross spring.

MERCEDES-BENZ (Cont.)

Fig. 2: Mercedes-Benz Single Piston Disc Brake Caliper

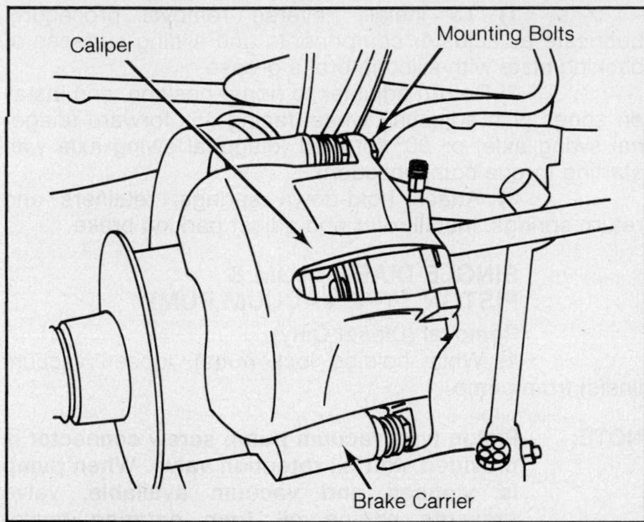
Caliper
Mounting Bolts
Brake Carrier

Brake caliper is used on 300SD, 380SEC & 380SEL.

3) Remove disc pads from caliper assembly. If reusable, note condition and location of pads for proper assembly.

4) Standard front disc brake pad assembly thickness, including lining backing plate, is .69" (17.5 mm). Standard rear pad assembly thickness is .59" (15 mm).

5) Front backing plate thickness is .18" (4.5 mm). Rear backing plate thickness is .20" (5 mm). Minimum pad thickness is .08" (2 mm).

NOTE: All self-locking, hex head bolts should only be used once.

Installation

1) Using cylinder brush, clean disc pad guide surface in caliper. Siphon sufficient fluid from master cylinder reservoir to prevent overflowing. Press pistons to bottom of bores.

2) Apply Molykote to back of disc brake pads. *See Fig. 3*. Install disc pads, cross spring and retaining pins.

Fig. 3: Mercedes-Benz Disc Brake Pad

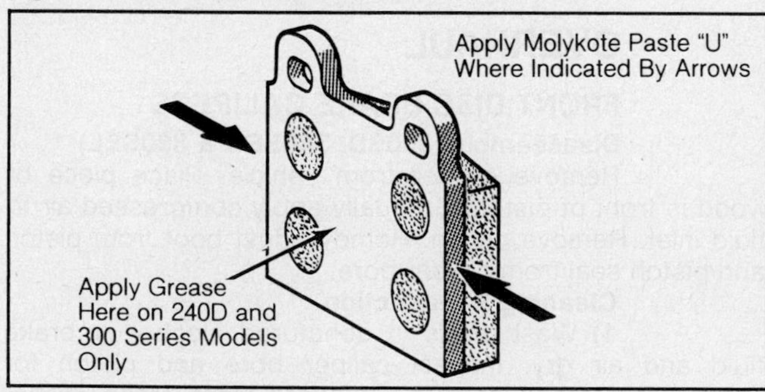
Apply Molykote Paste "U"
Where Indicated By Arrows
Apply Grease
Here on 240D and
300 Series Models
Only

Illustration shows Molykote application points.

3) If equipped, install cover plate, retaining pin locking keys and wear sensor wires. Check that dash light goes out. Reset pin at master cylinder if necessary.

DISC BRAKE CALIPER

Removal

1) Raise and support vehicle. Remove wheel and tire. Disconnect and plug brake lines at caliper assembly.

2) Remove caliper attaching bolts. Remove caliper assembly from vehicle.

Installation

To install, reverse removal procedure. Tighten all nuts and bolts, bleed hydraulic system, and check that dash light goes out. Reset pin in master cylinder if necessary.

DISC BRAKE ROTOR

Removal (Front)

1) With caliper assembly removed, remove hub grease cap. Remove contact spring for radio shielding. Loosen clamping nut socket screw on wheel spindle.

2) Remove clamping nut and washer. Remove wheel hub and rotor assembly. Remove bolts securing hub to rotor, and remove rotor.

Cleaning and Inspection

1) Clean rotor and check for cracks, scoring or excessive wear, replace as necessary.

2) Before installing stock replacement rotor, use solvent to remove nitrocellulose corrosion preventive paint from rotor surface.

Installation

To install, reverse removal procedure. Tighten all bolts and fittings evenly. Bleed hydraulic system, if necessary. Lubricate and adjust wheel bearings. *See Wheel Bearing Adjustment in SUSPENSION Section.*

Removal (Rear)

1) Raise and support vehicle. Remove rear wheel and tire. Disconnect and plug brake lines. Remove caliper assembly.

2) Using rear axle shaft assembly tool (116-589-24-61-00), pull rotor out from axle shaft flange. *See Fig. 4*.

Fig. 4: Assembled View of Rear Rotor & Caliper

Rotor
Rear Axle
Shaft Flange
Dowel Pin
Mounting Pins
Cross Spring
Brake Pad
Caliper

With the caliper removed, the rotor will pull free.

Installation

1) To install, reverse removal procedure. Coat axle splines with high-temperature lubricant. Grease wheel bearings and seal as necessary and install.

2) Tighten all bolts and fittings evenly. Bleed hydraulic system, if necessary.

REAR AXLE SEAL

Removal

1) Raise and support vehicle. Remove rear wheel and tire. Release locking plates. Remove mount bolts and caliper. Hang out of work area by wire.

2) On vehicles with starting torque compensation, disconnect brake hose holder and hang caliper assembly with wire.

3) Loosen and remove .32" (8 mm) bolt or .47" (12 mm) bolt with spacing sleeve and clamping disc at center of rear brake rotor.

4) Using rear axle shaft assembly tool (116-589-24-61-00) or equivalent, remove rotor from rear axle shaft flange. Pry rear axle seal from rotor at inner wheel bearing and discard.

NOTE: **If brake rotor is difficult to free from axle flange, strike outer circumference lightly with plastic hammer. Ensure parking brake is released.**

Installation

1) Coat inside of new axle seal lip and wheel bearings with grease. Install bearings and seal into rear brake rotor.

2) Coat axle splines with heat resistant lubricant, and install rotor. To complete installation, reverse removal procedure.

MASTER CYLINDER

Removal

1) Drain master cylinder brake fluid. Disconnect and plug brake lines. Disconnect electrical wires.

2) Remove bolts securing master cylinder to power brake unit, and remove master cylinder.

Installation

1) Reverse removal procedure. Always replace rubber "O" ring seal between master cylinder and power unit.

2) Bleed hydraulic system, and check complete system for fluid leaks. Check that dash light is out, and reset pin in master cylinder, if necessary.

PARKING BRAKE LININGS

Removal

1) Raise and support vehicle. Remove wheel and tire. Disconnect hydraulic line. Remove caliper and rotor. Turn rear axle flange until one threaded hole faces hold-down spring. Compress spring with spring installer tool (040) and turn 90°.

2) Remove all retainers and hold-down springs. Detach lower return spring, opposite adjuster. Pull brake shoes apart enough to remove over rear axle shaft flange. Detach upper return spring and remove the adjuster.

Cleaning & Inspection

Use brake vacuum cleaner to clear asbestos dust from assembly and check condition of linings and components.

NOTE: **Disc brake rotor inside diameter is 6.30" (160 mm). Parking brake lining width is .98" (25 mm).**

Installation

1) To install, reverse removal procedure. Lubricate all adjuster components and sliding surfaces of backing plate with silicone brake grease.

2) Return adjuster to home position, and install on shoes with adjusting wheel facing 45° forward (diagonal swing axle) or 90° forward (diagonal swing axle with starting torque compensation).

3) Attach hold-down springs, retainers and return springs. Install rotor and adjust parking brake.

SINGLE DIAPHRAGM & PISTON TYPE VACUUM PUMP

Removal (Diesel Only)

1) While holding lock nut(s), loosen vacuum line(s) from pump.

NOTE: **Piston type vacuum pump screw connector is provided with oil retention valve. When pump is stopped and vacuum available, valve prevents engine oil from entering power brake unit.**

2) Detach hex head mount screws from crankcase, and remove vacuum pump and gasket.

Installation

Install vacuum pump with new gasket to crankcase. New gasket thickness is .0078" (.20 mm). Connect vacuum lines and test for proper operation.

DOUBLE DIAPHRAGM VACUUM PUMP

Removal (Diesel Only)

1) Loosen upper radiator hose and drain some coolant. Remove fan, radiator shell and power steering pump V-belt.

2) Loosen vacuum lines from pump. Remove hex head mount screws from crankcase. Remove vacuum pump with toothed intermediate sleeve and gasket.

Installation

1) Clean sealing surfaces, and install pump with new gasket to crankcase. Ensure intermediate sleeve and pump locating pins are properly seated in crankcase.

2) Connect vacuum lines to pump. Install V-belt, radiator shell, fan and hose. Check pump for proper operation.

OVERHAUL

FRONT DISC BRAKE CALIPERS

Disassembly (300SD, 380SEC & 380SEL)

Remove caliper from vehicle. Place piece of wood in front of piston. Gradually apply compressed air to fluid inlet. Remove piston. Remove dust boot from piston and piston seal from caliper bore.

Cleaning & Inspection

1) Wash parts in denatured alcohol or brake fluid and air dry. Inspect caliper bore and piston for scoring, scratches or rust. Standard front brake caliper bore inside diameter is 2.36" (60 mm).

MERCEDES-BENZ (Cont.)

2) Replace dust boot and piston seal when disassembling caliper. Remove small rust deposits in bore with fine emery cloth.

CAUTION: When installing new caliper, check that calipers on same axle have pistons of same diameter. Only identical calipers should be installed on front axle.

Reassembly

Coat piston and caliper bore with ATE brake cylinder paste. Install piston seal into caliper bore. Install piston and dust boot.

Disassembly (240D, 300CD, 300D, 300TD, and 380SL)

NOTE: This procedure also applies to all rear calipers.

1) With caliper removed from vehicle and disc pads removed from caliper, remove dust boot.

2) Hold one piston in place using piston resetting pliers (123 589 00 37 00). Gradually apply compressed air to fluid inlet to remove opposite piston. *See Fig. 5.*

Fig. 5: Disassembled View of Dual Piston Brake Caliper

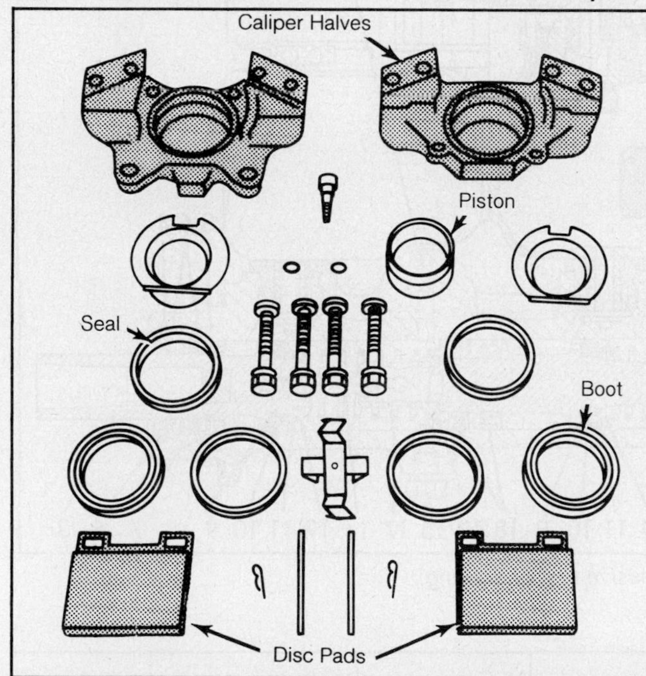
Caliper Halves
Piston
Seal
Boot
Disc Pads

Do not separate caliper halves. Replace as an assembly.

3) Remove piston seal from groove of cylinder bore. Remove remaining piston and seal in same manner.

NOTE: Do not separate caliper halves. Replace only as an assembly. Calipers installed on front axle must be from same manufacturer. Calipers on rear axle may be different only if same brand replacement part is unavailable.

Cleaning & Inspection

1) Check cylinder bores of caliper for wear or damage. Small rust deposits may be removed from caliper bores with polishing cloth.

CAUTION: Do not clean chrome-plated surfaces of pistons with polishing or emery cloth. Damage to surface may result. Remove deposits with soft brass wire brush or rough cleaning cloth. Replace piston, if chrome surface is damaged.

2) Heavy rust deposits or badly scored bore will require replacement of caliper. Rust deposits in front of piston seal groove may be removed with fine emery cloth.

3) Standard front brake caliper bore inside diameter is 2.36" (60 mm). Standard rear caliper bore I.D. (Teves) is 1.49" (38 mm) and rear caliper bore I.D. (Bendix/Girling) is 1.65" (42 mm).

Reassembly

1) Coat piston and caliper bore with ATE brake cylinder paste. Install piston seal into caliper bore and install piston.

NOTE: With caliper installed on diagonal swing axle, elevation on piston faces upward. On diagonal swing axle with starting torque compensation, elevation on piston must be at bottom and project at least .004" (.1 mm) above shield. Use DOT 4 or higher rated brake fluid during overhaul.

2) Check position of piston in caliper with proper piston gauge (000 589 34 23 00 for front or 000 589 35 23 00 for rear).

3) Adjust with piston rotating pliers (000 589 50 37 00). Install dust boot. Install heat shield into piston, with recess in shield fitting into elevation of piston.

REAR DISC BRAKE CALIPER

Overhaul procedure is the same as for the front caliper of 240D, 300CD, 300D, 300TD, and 380SL models.

MASTER CYLINDER

CAUTION: Bendix master cylinder (painted Blue) cannot be overhauled; replace as an assembly only.

Disassembly (Tandem & Stepped Tandemn)

1) On tandem master cylinder, remove reservoir and push piston in. Remove stop screw. Remove push rod piston assembly and "O" ring.

2) Remove lock ring from housing. Remove floating circuit piston, stop washer, 2 vacuum seals and intermediate ring.

3) Remove piston assembly, for floating circuit, by tapping lightly on housing with plastic mallet. *See Fig. 6.*

NOTE: On Teves reservoir only, remove cap, end covers, strainer, splash guard, "O" rings and contact inserts. On Bendix model, remove strainer from cover. Do not remove contact inserts. Always use DOT 4 or higher rated brake fluid during overhaul.

Cleaning & Inspection

1) Clean all parts with denatured alcohol or brake fluid, and flush residue out of housing. Check bore in housing and piston for score marks and rust.

NOTE: Determine whether source of problem is in power brake unit or check valve. Inspect check valve first.

MERCEDES-BENZ (Cont.)

2) Small rust spots in housing may be removed with polishing cloth. Scored or badly rusted parts cannot be repaired, replace complete master cylinder.

3) On tandem models, standard master cylinder inside diameter is .937" (23.81 mm). Maximum bore wear limit is .941" (23.92 mm).

4) On stepped tandem models, standard master cylinder I.D. for push rod circuit is .937" (23.81) and I.D. for floating circuit is .750" (19.05 mm).

5) Maximum master cylinder bore I.D. is .941" (23.92 mm) for push rod circuit and .754" (19.16 mm) for floating circuit.

Reassembly

1) To assemble, reverse disassembly procedure. Coat bore of master cylinder with brake fluid.

2) Install new floating circuit piston assembly. Push in piston assembly and install lock ring.

3)Install new push rod piston assembly. Screw in stopper screw using new copper washer for Gray iron master cylinder or new aluminum washer for light alloy master cylinder.

4) Replace "O" ring to ensure proper vacuum seal at power brake unit. Bleed hydraulic system. Check that dash light is out.

NOTE: **Differential pressure warning indicator reset pin, located at front end of master cylinder, MUST be reset once indicator light in dash panel has been triggered.**

TIGHTENING SPECIFICATIONS

Application	Ft. Lbs. (N.m)
Brake Pressure	
Switch-to-Master Cylinder	11-22 (15-30)
Caliper Mount Bolt	
Front (240D & 300 Series)	83 (113)
Rear	67 (90)
Front (380 Series)	26 (35)
Rear	67 (90)
Hub-to-Rotor Bolt	83 (113)

Fig. 6: Sectional View of Tandem Master Cylinder

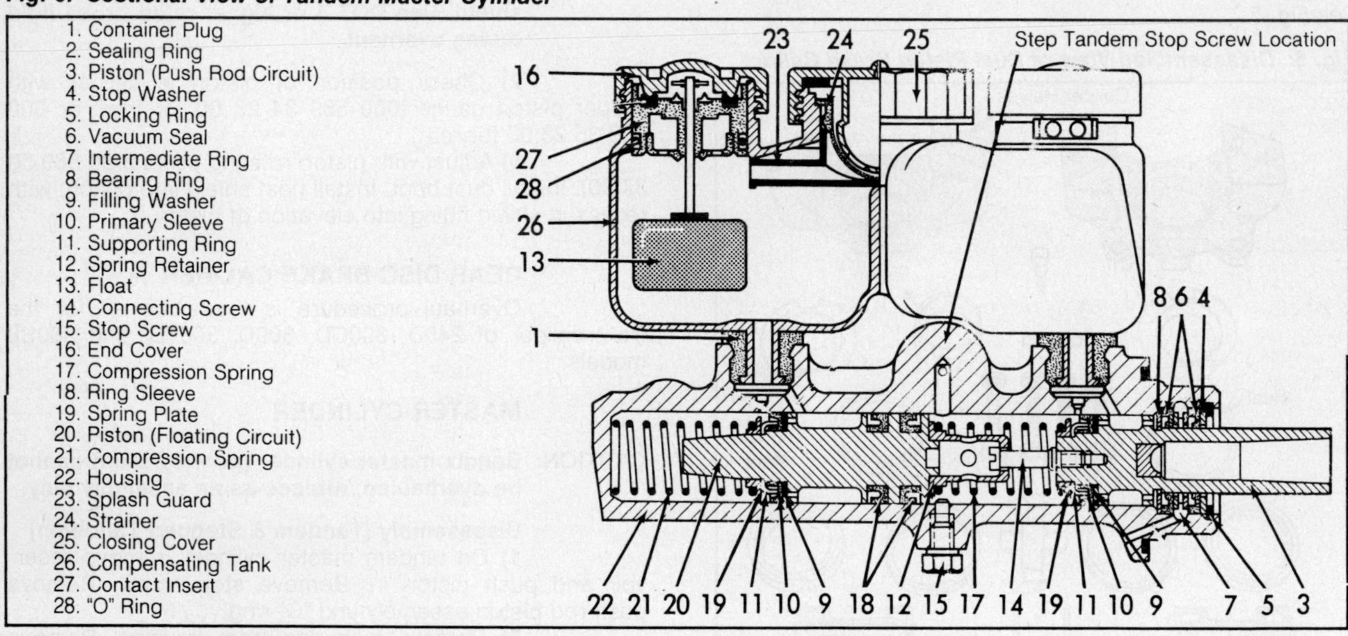
1. Container Plug
2. Sealing Ring
3. Piston (Push Rod Circuit)
4. Stop Washer
5. Locking Ring
6. Vacuum Seal
7. Intermediate Ring
8. Bearing Ring
9. Filling Washer
10. Primary Sleeve
11. Supporting Ring
12. Spring Retainer
13. Float
14. Connecting Screw
15. Stop Screw
16. End Cover
17. Compression Spring
18. Ring Sleeve
19. Spring Plate
20. Piston (Floating Circuit)
21. Compression Spring
22. Housing
23. Splash Guard
24. Strainer
25. Closing Cover
26. Compensating Tank
27. Contact Insert
28. "O" Ring
Step Tandem Stop Screw Location
16 27 28 26 13 1 23 24 25 8 6 4
22 21 20 19 11 10 9 18 12 15 17 14 19 11 10 9 7 5 3

Check the master cylinder bore for proper inside diameter and excessive rust or scoring.

DISC BRAKE ROTOR SPECIFICATIONS

Application	Disc Diameter In. (mm)	Lateral Runout In. (mm)	Parallelism In. (mm)	Original Thickness In. (mm)	Min. Refinish Thickness In. (mm)	Discard Thickness In. (mm)
240D, 300 Series & 380SL						
Front	10.95 (278)	.005 (.12)	.0008 (.02)	.866 (22.0)	.787 (20.0)	.787 (20.0)
Rear	11.0 (279)	.005 (.12)	.0008 (.02)	.394 (10.0)	.327 (8.3)	.327 (8.3)
380 SEC						
Front	11.25 (286)	.005 (.12)	.0008 (.02)	.866 (22.0)	.76 (19.4)	.76 (19.4)
Rear	11.0 (279)	.005 (.12)	.0008 (.02)	.394 (10.0)	.327 (8.3)	.327 (8.3)
380 SEL						
Front	10.95 (278)	.005 (.12)	.0008 (.02)	.866 (22.0)	.76 (19.4)	.76 (19.4)
Rear	11.0 (279)	.005 (.12)	.0008 (.02)	.394 (10.0)	.327 (8.3)	.327 (8.3)

MERCEDES-BENZ ANTI-LOCKING BRAKE (ABS) SYSTEM

DESCRIPTION

The ABS system consists of a hydraulic unit with 3 fast-switching solenoid valves, speed sensors, electronic control unit and a harness with relays and overvoltage protection.

A Yellow warning lamp with ABS symbols, located on the instrument panel, lights when ignition switch is turned on. Like a charge indicator lamp, the ABS warning lamp goes out when engine is running. The ABS system activates after 7.5 MPH is reached.

When vehicle speed is above 3 MPH, built-in test equipment will start a check-up of ABS system. If a fault is found, warning lamp will again light up. When warning lamp lights, ABS is switched off and vehicle will brake without ABS control. The conventional brake system remains operational.

If battery is below 10.5 volts when ignition is switched on and test speed is exceeded, ABS will remain switched off until alternator increases voltage to above 10.5 volts. Warning light will then go out.

Following repair, during which no direct components of ABS were involved, a simple lamp test will be sufficient to check system. Check that lamp goes out after 7 MPH.

NOTE: **The entire ABS system must be checked if repair includes hydraulic unit, electronic control unit, speed sensors or harness, or if units are replaced during repair following an accident. Use BOSCH tester (Model ETT 016.00, Part No. 0084 101 600) in combination with brake test bench.**

OPERATION

HYDRAULIC UNIT

Independent of master cylinder pressure, the hydraulic unit changes fluid pressure to wheel cylinders during regulation. Pressure increase above master cylinder pressure is not possible.

The 3 hydraulic unit solenoid valves control left front, right front and rear brakes. By activating valves with current of varying amperage, brake fluid pressure in individual calipers can be increased, held or decreased.

In pressure "build-up" stage, pressure increases by opening intake valve to pressure supplied by master cylinder.

In pressure "holding" stage, which precedes each "reduction" stage, pressure from hydraulic unit to wheels is constant, because output and input valves in solenoid valve are closed.

During pressure "reduction" stage, brake fluid flows from reservoir to return pump. To maintain fluid volume, pump returns brake fluid into main cylinder against prevailing pressure.

To dampen delivery noise, each circuit is provided with a silencer. Relays for solenoid valves and return pump are on the 12-pole plug socket of the hydraulic unit. A diode is soldered into the socket. Hydraulic unit is connected to ground by a cable.

SPEED SENSOR

Rod-shaped speed sensors (impulse transmitters) are used for measuring wheel speeds. The 3 channel system with 3 speed sensors separately measures wheel speed of each wheel on front axle and both rear wheels.

Speed sensors for front axle are installed on steering knuckles. Speed sensor for rear axle is mounted on rear axle housing. Drive pinion serves to measure speed of rear wheels.

Speed sensors measure wheel speeds by sensing rotor teeth movement. On front axle, rotor teeth are machined into front wheel hub. Speed sensors for front axle are double-edged and have a diameter of .71" (18 mm).

On rear axle, the toothed rotor is pressed on drive pinion. Axles with different axle ratios have gear wheels with different numbers of teeth. Speed sensor for rear axle is single-edged and has diameter of .59" (15 mm).

The speed sensors consist of a magnetic core and coil. Rotation of rotor, located a specific distance from speed sensor, causes an alternating voltage in the coil. This alternating voltage changes frequency in proportion to wheel speed and number of rotor teeth.

ELECTRONIC CONTROL UNIT

Electronic control unit is a 2-board type. Two circuit boards are inside control unit, one above the other, enclosed in light alloy housing. The control unit processes signals of speed sensors and contacts valves in hydraulic unit. Signal conditioning and processing is digital. The electronic control unit is subdivided into signal conditioning section, logic section and safety circuit.

Signal Conditioning Section

In signal conditioning section, signals supplied by speed sensors are converted for logic section. While measuring wheel speed, trouble caused by production tolerances or movements in steering knuckle is prevented by filtering input signals prior to use. Deceleration and acceleration signals obtained from wheel speed signals are processed in logic section.

Logic Section

Logic section of electronic control unit employs wheel slip, wheel speed acceleration and deceleration signals for each controlled front wheel or rear wheels. Output signals of logic section control solenoid valves of hydraulic unit.

Safety Circuit

The safety circuit recognizes faulty signals inside and outside electronic control unit. Safety circuit intervenes in control sequence during extreme driving conditions, such as aquaplaning. When fault is recognized, system is switched off. The condition is indicated to driver by illuminated warning lamp.

The safety circuit continuously monitors battery voltage. If voltage is below specified requirements, system is switched off until voltage is within specified range. In addition to the monitoring function, safety circuit also includes active test cycle section or BITE (Built In Test Equipment).

Test Cycle (BITE)

Test cycle begins when wheel speed in all 3 speed channels exceeds 3 MPH. Test cycle, which is activated by speed sensor voltage, also monitors safety circuit and logic section. The electronic control unit is fed given test signals to check whether correct output signals are available.

MERCEDES-BENZ ANTI-LOCKING BRAKE (ABS) SYSTEM (Cont.)

HARNESS WITH RELAY & OVERVOLTAGE PROTECTION

A supplementary harness for anti-locking brake system is installed. To ensure function of ABS, power is supplied by ignition switch activated relay. An overvoltage protection unit, between battery and relay, protects electronic control unit. The harness is connected to control unit by a 35-pole plug. A harness with 12-pole plug leads to hydraulic unit. Ground cable for hydraulic unit is mounted to inner fender wall.

Front axle speed sensors connect to harness by coaxial cable. Speed sensor cable from steering knuckle-to-coaxial cable routes through tubing to bracket on firewall and on through inner front fender wall.

Rear axle speed sensor connects to harness under rear seat by a cable connector. Two relays are located under hydraulic unit cover. One relay contacts return pump. The other relay flows current to solenoid valves. Diode in plug socket lights instrument panel warning lamp when multi-point plug on control unit is pulled off.

CONTROL CYCLE (ONE WHEEL)

Wheel speed measured by speed sensor provides wheel deceleration and acceleration for electronic control unit. Linking individual wheel speed provides approximate vehicle reference speed.

Comparison of wheel speed with reference speed supplies slip signals. If wheel locks from too much pressure in caliper, a condition recognized by wheel speed sequence (wheel slip), pressure is held constant with no additional increase possible.

If there is a tendency toward locking because constant pressure is still too high, output solenoid valve will open to lower pressure. If pressure is low enough for wheel acceleration, pressure is not lowered but instead held constant.

When re-acceleration of wheel passes a given value, pressure is increased in between by opening input valve in solenoid valve. Signals from control unit allow hydraulic unit to actuate pressure maintenance, reduction and build-up.

Control sequence is repeated during controlled braking until brake pedal is released or until just before vehicle stops.

REMOVAL & INSTALLATION

HYDRAULIC UNIT

Removal

With ignition off, disconnect battery. Remove brake lines from hydraulic unit. Plug openings. Remove hydraulic unit mount bolt and cover. Detach ground strap from pump motor. Remove 12-pole plug socket. Remove mount nuts and hydraulic unit.

NOTE: **Do not loosen sealed center bolt or 2 hex socket bolts next to cover and brake lines.**

Installation

1) To install, reverse removal procedure. Connect brake lines to hydraulic unit fittings. Brake line identification codes are as follows: Code "V" is line from master cylinder to front brake circuit. Code "H" is line from master cylinder to rear brake circuit.

2) Code "L" is line from hydraulic unit to left front brake. Code "R" is line from unit to right front brake. Code "h" is line from unit to rear brakes. Bleed brake system. Check for leaks.

FRONT WHEEL SPEED SENSOR

Removal

1) Remove front wheel and tire. With ignition off, separate coaxial cable in engine compartment. Remove from bracket. Pull cable downward from grommet in wheel housing.

NOTE: **When removing right speed sensor, remove windshield washer reservoir.**

2) Speed sensors have different protective tubes at left and right, identified in holder by "L" or "R". Before installing, ensure NO metal is on magnetic edges of sensor. Coat sensor and steering knuckle bore with Molykote Longterm 2 lubricant.

3) Remove protective tube from cover plate. As they may only be used once, remove hex socket bolt and discard. Pull speed sensor out of steering knuckle bore.

Installation

1) Replace "O" ring on sensor. Mount unit on steering knuckle. Ensure "O" ring is not damaged. Do not force. Attach sensor-to-knuckle with new bolt. Tighten to 72 INCH lbs (8 N.m).

2) Attach protective tube to cover plate. Clip cable into holder. Pull through grommet into engine compartment. Replace "O" ring. Connect coaxial cable. Mount front wheel and tire. Complete test program.

REAR AXLE SPEED SENSOR

Removal

Remove rear seat and backrest. With ignition off, remove cable at connector. Remove clips from cable to sensor. Pull cable down through grommets in frame floor and axle carrier. Remove hex bolt and discard. Remove sensor from rear axle housing.

Installation

To install, reverse removal procedure. Replace "O" ring on sensor. Do not damage "O" ring. Insert sensor into rear axle housing. Using new bolt, attach sensor to rear axle housing and tighten.

ELECTRONIC CONTROL UNIT

NOTE: **Turn ignition off before removing or installing electronic control unit. Unit is located on front wall in engine compartment.**

Removal & Installation

Push back holding springs. Remove electronic control unit from bracket. Actuate lock. Pull plug from unit. To install, reverse removal procedure. When mounting on unit, ensure plug engages audibly in lock.

RELAYS & OVERVOLTAGE PROTECTION

Removal & Installation

Turn ignition off. To replace ABS components, pull units from plug-in. Note location for proper installation. Engine and valve relays are mounted at hydraulic unit. Relays for electronic control unit and overvoltage protection unit are mounted at fusebox. Install by pressing relay or unit into circuit.

MITSUBISHI – EXCEPT STARION

DESCRIPTION

BRAKE SYSTEM

Brake system is hydraulically-operated using a master cylinder with a single reservoir and 2 outlets, a vacuum power brake unit, and a proportioning valve to control braking action. All brake systems are self-adjusting.

All models are equipped with sliding caliper type front disc brakes. All 2WD Pickups and gasoline-powered 4WD Pickups use duo-servo type rear drum brakes. All other models use leading-trailing shoe type rear drum brakes.

The parking brake cable actuates the rear drum brakes.

PROPORTIONING VALVES

Different types of proportioning valves are used depending upon vehicle model. Proportion valve function testing is similar, however, for all models.

Cordia & Tredia

On Cordia and Tredia models, the valve body contains 2 proportioning valves. Each valve must be checked separately.

Fig. 1: Sectional View of 2-Valve Proportioning Valve Body

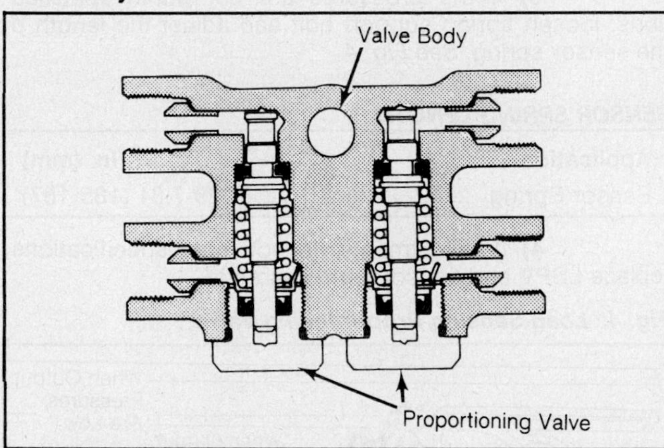
Valve Body
Proportioning Valve

Illustration applies to Cordia and Tredia.

Diesel 4WD Pickups

Diesel-powered 4WD Pickups use a Load Sensing Proportioning Valve (LSPV). On these models, the LSPV, located near the rear wheels, provides 3 functions.

The LSPV responds to vehicle load condition by preventing early lock-up of the front wheels, provides stability during braking, and adds extra fluid pressure control to the rear wheels should the front brake system fail.

All Other Models

Montero, all 2WD Pickups and all gasoline-powered 4WD Pickups use a Blend Proportioning Valve (BPV).

On these models, the BPV accomplishes 2 functions. It improves braking efficiency by distributing braking force to front and rear wheels. It also increases braking force to rear wheels, when large braking force is required or front brakes fail.

Fig. 2: Sectional View of Blend Proportioning Valve

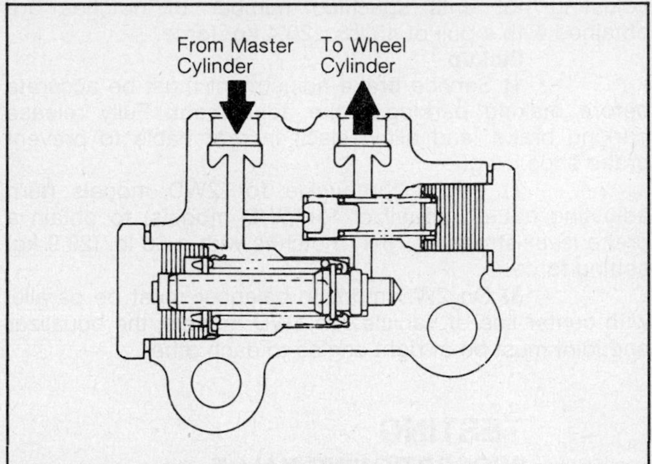
From Master Cylinder
To Wheel Cylinder

Illustration applies to Montero and all Pickups, except 4WD Diesel.

ADJUSTMENT

PEDAL HEIGHT & FREE PLAY

Back off stop light switch. To adjust pedal height (distance from top of pedal to floor board) loosen lock nut, and rotate master cylinder push rod (yoke, if equipped). Do not depress push rod. Tighten lock nut, and ensure that brake pedal free play is .4-.6" (10-15 mm) on all models.

PEDAL HEIGHT SPECIFICATIONS

Application	In. (mm)
Cordia & Tredia	6.9-7.1 (175-180)
Montero	7.5-7.7 (191-196)
Pickups	6.5 (166)

STOP LIGHT SWITCH

On Pickup models, adjust stop light switch until it just contacts brake pedal lever. On all other models, loosen lock nut and adjust switch-to-pedal arm clearance to .02-.04" (0.5-1.0 mm). Tighten lock nut. Do not depress master cylinder push rod during stop light switch adjustment.

PARKING BRAKE

NOTE: If parking brake lever stroke is not to specifications after adjustment, automatic adjuster will malfunction.

Cordia & Tredia

Remove console box and release brake lever. Adjust the cable adjusting nut, allowing enough slack in cables to prevent brake shoe drag. Properly adjusted parking brake lever stroke should be 5-7 notches at 44 lbs. (20 kg) force.

Montero

When parking brake lever is pulled with a force of 45 lbs. (20.4 kg), the lever stroke should be 4-6

MITSUBISHI – EXCEPT STARION (Cont.)

notches. If not, remove accessory box. Turn cable adjusting nut until specified number of notches are obtained with a pull of 45 lbs. (20.4 kg) force.

Pickup

1) Service brake adjustment must be accurate before making parking brake adjustment. Fully release parking brake, and allow slack in rear cable to prevent brake shoe drag.

2) Adjust turnbuckle for 2WD models (turn adjusting nut on equalizer for 4WD models) to obtain a brake lever stroke of 16-17 notches with a 66 lb. (29.9 kg) setting force.

3) On 2WD models, balancer must be parallel with center line of vehicle. On 4WD models, the equalizer and joint must be at right angles to each other.

TESTING

PROPORTIONING VALVE FUNCTION TEST

1) Use 2 pressure gauges that measure at least 2000 psi (140.6 kg/cm²). Attach one gauge to master cylinder rear side, and other gauge to rear wheel cylinder. Depress brake pedal.

2) With master cylinder pressure equal to readings shown in *Brake Hydraulic Pressure Chart*, the wheel cylinders should meet specifications. If not, replace defective part as required. Do not disassemble proportioning valve.

BRAKE HYDRAULIC PRESSURE CHART

Application	Wheel Cyl. psi (kg/cm²)	Master Cyl. psi (kg/cm²)
Cordia (Deluxe)		
& Tredia	325-400 (23-28)	375 (27)
	460-520 (33-37)	725 (51)
	590-690 (42-49)	1175 (83)
Cordia (Standard)	350-425 (25-30)	390 (27)
	500-550 (35-39)	875 (62)
	575-650 (41-46)	1175 (83)
Diesel 4WD Pickup		
LSPV	410-492 (29-35)	853 (60)
	712-827 (50-58)	1990 (140)
Montero &		
Other Pickups		
BPV		
2WD	437-494 (31-35)	711 (50)
	633-718 (45-51)	996 (70)
	775-860 (55-61)	1138 (80)
4WD	398-455 (28-32)	853 (60)
	604-690 (43-49)	1138 (80)
	747-832 (53-59)	1280 (90)

LOAD SENSING PROPORTIONING VALVE TEST

NOTE: **The vehicle must be unloaded, on a level surface, and not supported in any way, except by wheels.**

1) Connect pressure gauges to the input and output side. Once bled, depress pedal to check if pressures meet specifications in *Brake Hydraulic Pressure Chart*.

Fig. 3: Measuring Hydraulic Pressure

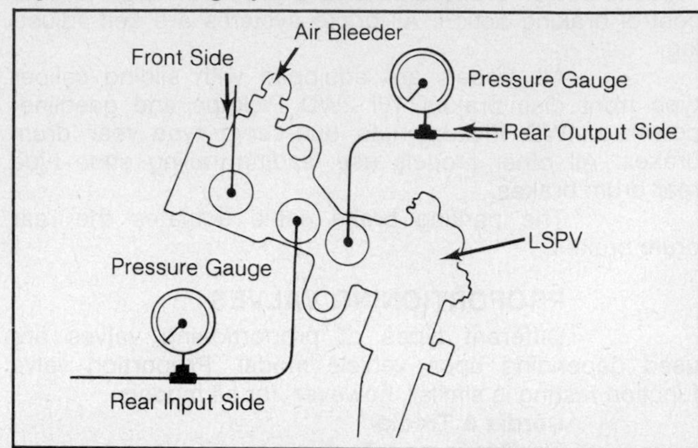
Air Bleeder
Front Side
Pressure Gauge
Rear Output Side
LSPV
Pressure Gauge
Rear Input Side

Illustration applies to 2.3L 4WD Diesel Pickup.

2) With pedal depressed, open bleeder screw of LSPV. *See Fig. 3.* If both pressures are equal, the fail safe system is operating.

3) If the pressures are not within specifications, loosen spring support bolt and adjust the length of the sensor spring. *See Fig. 4.*

SENSOR SPRING LENGTH

Application	In. (mm)
Sensor Spring	7.29-7.31 (185-187)

4) If adjustments do not meet specifications, replace LSPV and sensor spring as a set.

Fig. 4: Load Sensing Proportioning Valve

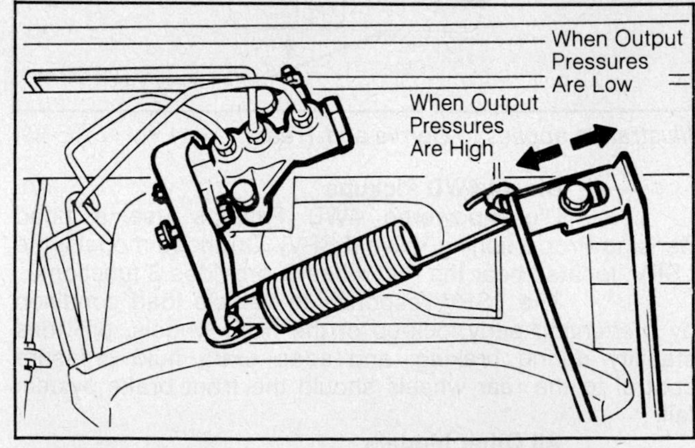
When Output Pressures Are Low
When Output Pressures Are High

Loosen bolt to adjust the sensor spring length.

REMOVAL & INSTALLATION

FRONT DISC BRAKE PADS

Removal (Type AD51, Cordia & Tredia)

1) Raise and support vehicle. Remove front wheel. Remove lock pin and lift caliper body upward.

MITSUBISHI – EXCEPT STARION (Cont.)

Fig. 5: Exploded View of Cordia and Tredia Disc Brake (Type AD51)

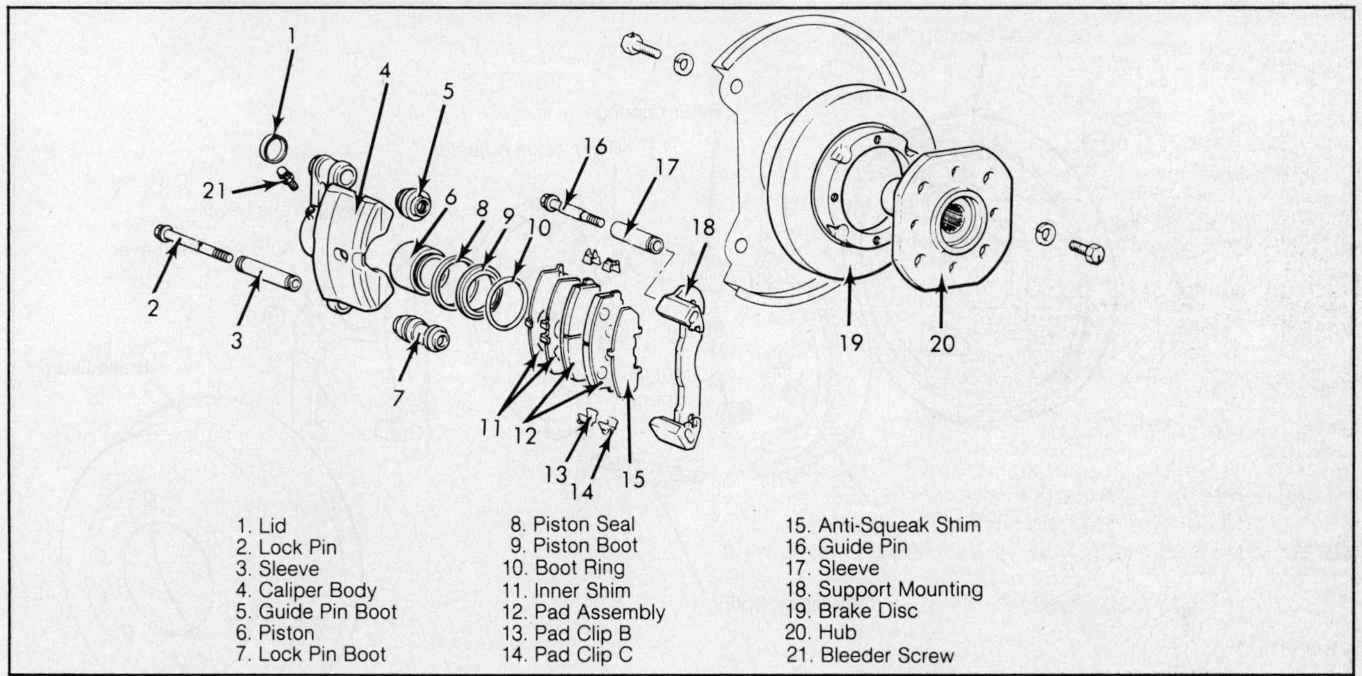
1. Lid
2. Lock Pin
3. Sleeve
4. Caliper Body
5. Guide Pin Boot
6. Piston
7. Lock Pin Boot
8. Piston Seal
9. Piston Boot
10. Boot Ring
11. Inner Shim
12. Pad Assembly
13. Pad Clip B
14. Pad Clip C
15. Anti-Squeak Shim
16. Guide Pin
17. Sleeve
18. Support Mounting
19. Brake Disc
20. Hub
21. Bleeder Screw

CAUTION: Be careful not to remove lock pin's coat of special grease or permit dirt to adhere to it.

2) Support caliper on a wire. Remove inner shim(s), anti-squeak shim, and pad assembly from support mounting. Remove pad clips.

NOTE: Replace all pads (left and right side) at the same time.

Installation

Press piston to bottom of bore. Install pads clips, pad assembly, inner shim(s), and anti-squeak shim onto support mounting. *See Fig. 5.* Lower caliper body and install lock pin.

Removal (Montero & Pickup)

1) Raise and support vehicle. Remove front wheel. Remove spigot pins and pull out stopper plugs.

2) Pull caliper assembly up and down in a diagonal manner, and remove from mounting bracket.

Fig. 6: Installing Pad Retaining Clips

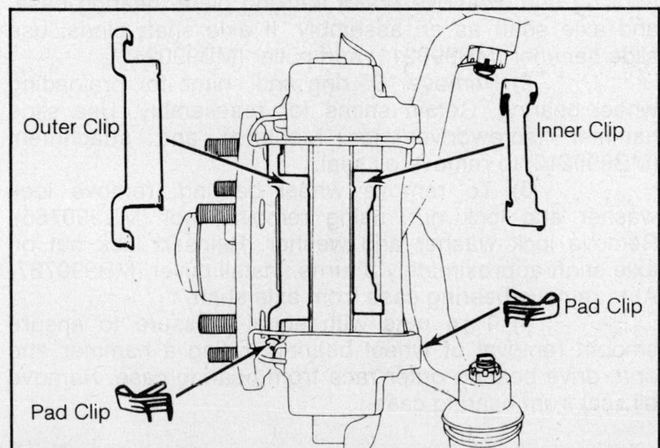
Outer Clip
Inner Clip
Pad Clip
Pad Clip

Illustration applies to Montero and Pickups.

Remove inner and outer pad clips. Pull pads and anti-squeal shims from caliper support.

Installation

To install, reverse removal procedure noting the following: Press piston to bottom of caliper bore prior to pad installation. Ensure pad retaining clips are installed properly. *See Fig. 6.*

FRONT DISC BRAKE CALIPER

Removal (Cordia & Tredia)

Remove disc pads. Disconnect hose connection at strut and hydraulic line. Remove bolts attaching caliper assembly to steering knuckle. Remove caliper assembly.

Installation

To install, reverse removal procedure. Tighten caliper mounting bolts to specification and bleed hydraulic system.

Removal (Montero & Pickup)

Remove disc pads. Pull out hose clip from strut area. Disconnect brake hose from caliper. Remove caliper.

Installation

To install, reverse removal procedure. Tighten bolts to specified torque and bleed brake system.

FRONT DISC BRAKE ROTOR

Removal (Cordia & Tredia)

1) Remove brake assembly and support with a wire. Remove drive shaft from hub.

2) Remove hub and knuckle as an assembly. Place in a soft-jawed vise and disassemble hub and knuckle assembly.

3) Mark the disc and hub, and disassemble.

Installation

Assemble disc and hub by aligning mating marks. Check brake drag torque.

MITSUBISHI – EXCEPT STARION (Cont.)

Fig. 7: Exploded View of Leading/Trailing Shoe Rear Brake Assembly

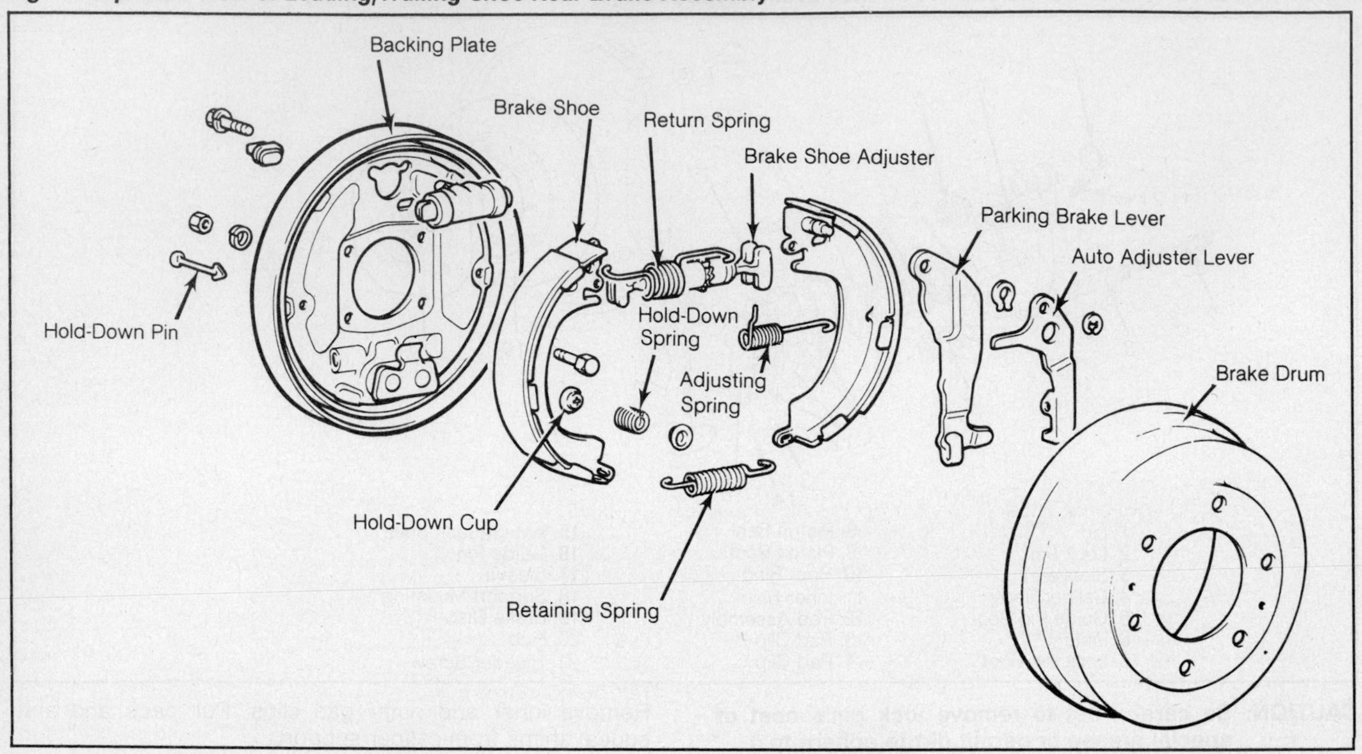
Backing Plate
Brake Shoe
Return Spring
Brake Shoe Adjuster
Parking Brake Lever
Auto Adjuster Lever
Hold-Down Pin
Hold-Down Spring
Adjusting Spring
Brake Drum
Hold-Down Cup
Retaining Spring

Montero and diesel-powered 4WD Pickup are shown. Other models are similar.

Removal (Montero & Pickup)

With caliper assembly removed and supported by a wire, remove front hub assembly from the knuckle. After marking the hub and disc, disassemble the hub from the disc.

NOTE: **If removal or replacement of bearings or races is necessary, see Mitsubishi Pickup and 4WD articles in SUSPENSION Section.**

Installation

To install, reverse removal procedures and tighten to specifications. *See Mitsubishi Pickup and 4WD articles in SUSPENSION Section.*

REAR BRAKE SHOES

Removal (Cordia & Tredia)

1) Raise and support vehicle. Remove brake drum and hold-down springs. Disconnect strut-to-shoe spring and upper shoe return spring end from trailing shoe.

2) Remove shoe hold-down spring and shoe retaining spring. Remove leading shoe.

3) Remove parking brake cable from parking brake lever. Remove trailing shoe.

Removal (Montero & Pickup)

1) Raise and support vehicle. Remove brake drum, return springs, adjusting spring and lever.

2) Remove shoes and adjuster as an assembly, and separate. Remove parking brake cable from lever.

Installation (All Models)

1) To install, reverse removal procedure and note the following: Apply Lubriplate (or equivalent), to all shoe contact points, adjuster assembly, wheel cylinder and parking brake lever pin.

2) Set adjustment lever all the way back. After assembling the brake shoes, install brake drum. Depress brake pedal to adjust shoe clearance. Adjust parking brake.

3) Pickups require check of adjuster after installation is complete. Adjuster lever should mesh with next tooth of adjuster when pulled, and return to original position after wheel has moved one tooth. Adjuster assemblies differ between right and left sides.

REAR AXLE SHAFT BEARING & OIL SEAL

Removal (Montero & Pickup)

1) With drum removed, disconnect brake tube from wheel cylinder. Disconnect bearing case from axle housing end. Remove brake backing plate, bearing case, and axle shaft as an assembly. If axle shaft binds, use slide hammer (MB990211) and puller (MB990241).

2) Remove "O" ring and shims for preloading wheel bearing. Retain shims for reassembly. Use slide hammer (screwdriver for Montero) and attachment (MB990212) to remove oil seal.

3) To remove wheel bearing, remove lock washer and lock nut, using removal tool (MB990785). Remove lock washer and washer. Reinsert lock nut on axle shaft approximately 3 turns. Install puller (MB990787-A) to remove bearing case from axle shaft.

4) Turn nuts with equal pressure to ensure smooth removal of wheel bearing. Using a hammer and drift, drive bearing outer race from bearing case. Remove oil seal from bearing case.

MITSUBISHI – EXCEPT STARION (Cont.)

Installation

1) Check axle shaft for .004" (.10 mm) runout. Apply multipurpose type grease (SAE J310a, NLGI 2EP) to outside circumference of bearing outer race. Press race into bearing case using installer (MB990937) and driver (MB990938). Follow same procedure for oil seal, using different installer (MB990935).

2) Apply grease to the lip of oil seal and to roller surfaces of bearing inner race. Install rear brake assembly, bearing case and rear inner race to axle shaft. Press bearing inner race onto the axle shaft using installer (MB990799).

3) Pack bearing case and axle threads with grease. Install lock washer (tab aligned with axle slot) and lock nut (chamfer toward lock washer). Tighten nut to 130-159 ft. lbs. (180-220 N.m). Bend tabs on lock washer into slots of lock nut.

4) Apply grease to oil seal area of rear axle housing. Drive new oil seal into end of rear axle housing, using installer (MB990930) and driver (MB990938). Adjust clearance between bearing case and rear axle by inserting .04" (1 mm) shim and "O" ring into left rear axle housing.

5) Apply semi-drying sealant to mating surface of bearing case. *See Fig. 8.* Install left axle shaft into rear housing and tighten nuts diagonally to 36-43 ft. lbs. (50-60 N.m).

Fig. 8: Applying Sealer for "O" Ring and Shim

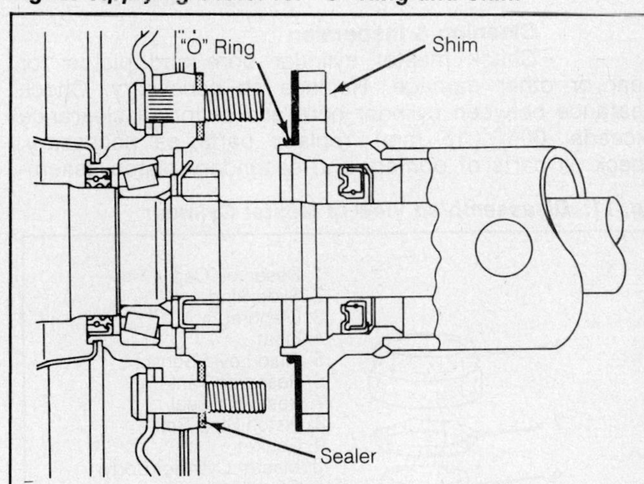
"O" Ring
Shim
Sealer

Apply to mating surface of bearing case.

6) Install right axle shaft without shims and "O" ring. Temporarily tighten to about 4-5 ft. lbs. (6 N.m). Using a feeler gauge, measure clearance between bearing case and rear axle housing.

7) Remove right axle shaft. Install shims, equal to measurement plus .002-.008" (.05-.20 mm), and "O" ring to right rear axle housing. Apply semi-drying sealant to mating surface of bearing case. *See Fig. 8.* Install axle into housing, tightening nuts diagonally to 36-43 ft. lbs. (50-60 N.m).

8) Using dial indicator, check axle shaft for .002-.008" (.05-.20 mm) end play.

REAR AXLE HUB BEARING

Removal (Cordia & Tredia)

With brake drum removed, pry out oil seal with screwdriver. Remove bearing outer races using a hammer and soft punch.

Installation

1) Install bearing outer races, using installers (MB990926 and MB990928) and driver (MB990938). Use press-fitting force of 4,400 lbs. (2,000 kg) or more. If less force is required, replace entire drum assembly.

2) Install inner bearing races. Press oil seal into end of drum, using installer (MB990926) and driver (MB990938). Apply grease to bearings, oil seal lip and inside surface of brake drum. Mount brake drum and check bearing play.

3) If play exists, remove hub cap, cotter pin and lock cap. Loosen nut. Adjust bearing by tightening to 14 ft. lbs. (20 N.m). Loosen completely, and retighten to 4 ft. lbs. (5 N.m). Install lock cap and cotter pin.

MASTER CYLINDER

Removal

Remove sensor connector (if equipped). Disconnect brake lines from master cylinder. Slowly depress brake pedal several times to drain fluid from cylinder housing. Remove master cylinder from booster unit and separate reservoirs from housing.

Installation

Reverse removal procedure. Prior to installation, check and adjust clearance between back of master cylinder piston and power brake push rod. Clearance is .004-.020" (.1-.5 mm) for all models. Adjust pedal height, and bleed brake system after installation.

POWER BRAKE UNIT CHECK VALVE REPLACEMENT

NOTE: Test check valve before removal. Pull off vacuum hose on booster side of check valve.

Fig. 9: Exploded View of Power Brake Unit

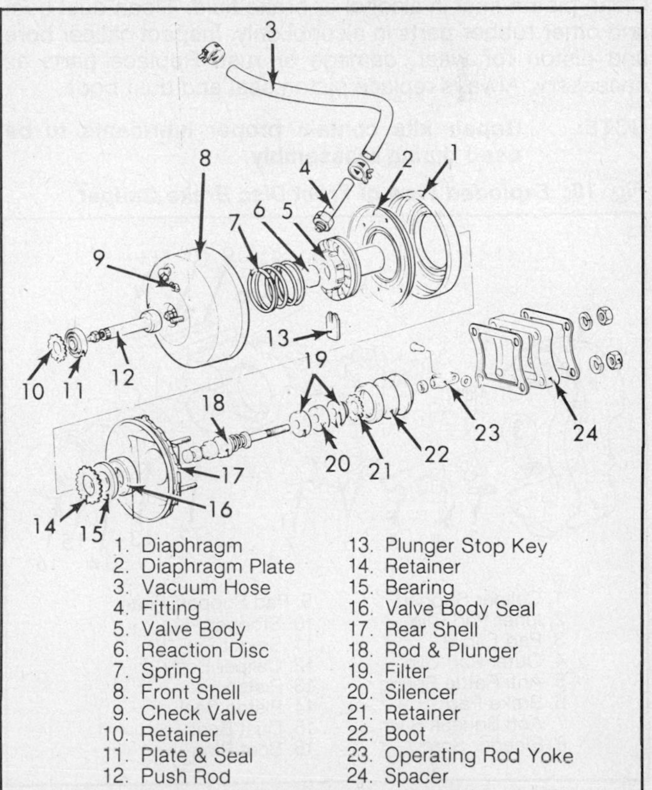
1. Diaphragm
2. Diaphragm Plate
3. Vacuum Hose
4. Fitting
5. Valve Body
6. Reaction Disc
7. Spring
8. Front Shell
9. Check Valve
10. Retainer
11. Plate & Seal
12. Push Rod
13. Plunger Stop Key
14. Retainer
15. Bearing
16. Valve Body Seal
17. Rear Shell
18. Rod & Plunger
19. Filter
20. Silencer
21. Retainer
22. Boot
23. Operating Rod Yoke
24. Spacer

Unit for Cordia, Montero and Tredia is shown.

MITSUBISHI – EXCEPT STARION (Cont.)

Place finger over check valve, and crank engine. Vacuum should be felt.

Removal

Remove hose clamps from both ends of check valve. Remove check valve clamp and remove check valve.

Installation

Coat both ends of check valve with sealer and install valve with arrow (identification mark) pointing toward intake manifold side. Install check valve clamp and vacuum hoses, and secure hose clamps.

POWER BRAKE UNIT

Removal

Remove the brake master cylinder, and disconnect vacuum hose from power brake unit. Disconnect brake pedal and operating rod of power brake unit. Remove 4 nuts, attaching power brake unit to firewall from inside vehicle. Remove power brake unit.

Installation

Install power brake unit, and tighten nuts to specifications. Install brake master cylinder.

OVERHAUL

FRONT DISC BRAKE CALIPER

Disassembly

Remove dust boot. Apply compressed air to fluid inlet to remove piston. Remove piston seal without damaging caliper bore or seal groove.

Cleaning & Inspection

Clean all metal parts in alcohol or brake fluid. Clean piston seal in alcohol or brake fluid. Clean dust boot and other rubber parts in alcohol only. Inspect caliper bore and piston for wear, damage or rust. Replace parts as necessary. Always replace piston seal and dust boot.

NOTE: **Repair kits contain proper lubricants to be used during reassembly.**

Fig. 10: Exploded View of Front Disc Brake Caliper

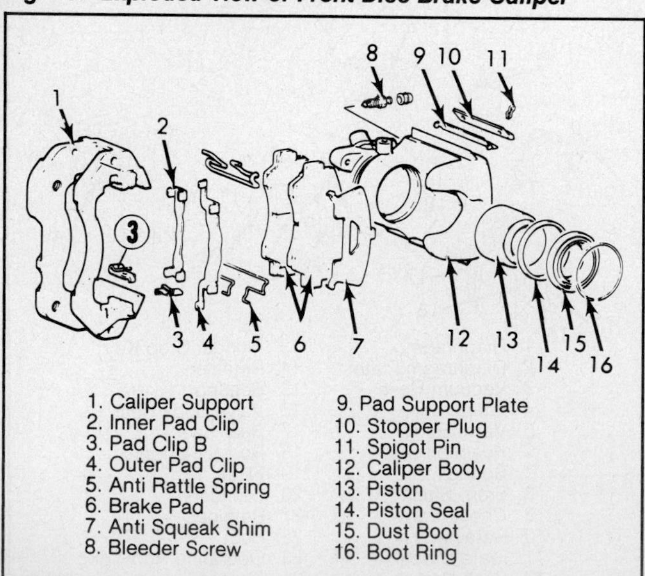
1. Caliper Support
2. Inner Pad Clip
3. Pad Clip B
4. Outer Pad Clip
5. Anti Rattle Spring
6. Brake Pad
7. Anti Squeak Shim
8. Bleeder Screw
9. Pad Support Plate
10. Stopper Plug
11. Spigot Pin
12. Caliper Body
13. Piston
14. Piston Seal
15. Dust Boot
16. Boot Ring

Caliper shown is for Montero and Pickup.

Reassembly

Coat piston seal with rubber grease. Slide seal into groove in cylinder bore. Slip piston into bore making sure seal is not twisted. Lightly coat dust seal groove with recommended rubber grease. Fit dust boot into place. Refit cylinder to caliper.

NOTE: **Possible cause of increased pedal stroke is insufficient fit between piston and piston seal. Correct by manually levering piston to seat several times. This will create a better fit between piston and seal. Make sure brake pad is removed during this procedure.**

MASTER CYLINDER

Disassembly

1) While holding cylinder in a soft-jawed vise, remove dust boot, retaining ring, stop washer and piston stop bolt. Withdraw primary piston assembly, secondary piston assembly and secondary return spring from master cylinder.

2) Remove check valve caps, tube seats, check valves and check valve springs. Colt master cylinders are equipped with 2 identical check valves.

NOTE: **Do not disassemble primary and secondary piston assembly.**

Cleaning & Inspection

Check master cylinder bore and piston for wear or other damage. Replace as necessary. Check clearance between cylinder bore and piston. If clearance exceeds .006" (.15 mm), replace parts as necessary. Check all parts of primary and secondary piston assem-

Fig. 11: Disassembled View of Master Cylinder

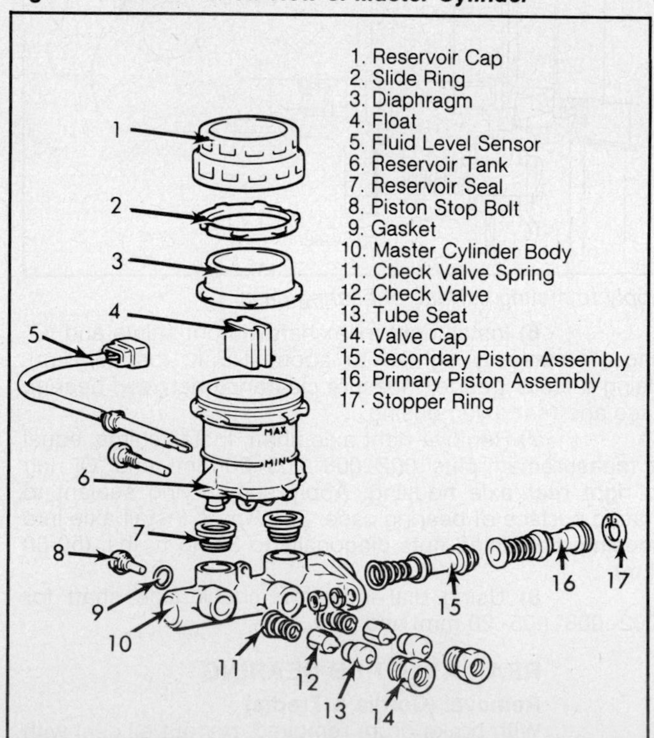
1. Reservoir Cap
2. Slide Ring
3. Diaphragm
4. Float
5. Fluid Level Sensor
6. Reservoir Tank
7. Reservoir Seal
8. Piston Stop Bolt
9. Gasket
10. Master Cylinder Body
11. Check Valve Spring
12. Check Valve
13. Tube Seat
14. Valve Cap
15. Secondary Piston Assembly
16. Primary Piston Assembly
17. Stopper Ring
MAX
MIN

Cylinder for Cordia and Tredia is shown. Other models are similar.

MITSUBISHI – EXCEPT STARION (Cont.)

blies and piston cups and springs. If any parts are found defective, replace components as assemblies.

Reassembly

Reverse disassembly procedure and note the following: Before reassembly, apply rubber grease to all parts (except boots). When assembled, check that return port is not blocked by piston cup, when piston is at return position.

NOTE: **Check valves for rear disc models (Starion) and these rear drum models differ. Be sure correct check valve is properly installed.**

TIGHTENING SPECIFICATIONS

Application	Ft. Lbs. (N.m)
Rotor-to-Hub Bolts	
Cordia & Tredia	29-36 (40-50)
Montero	36-43 (50-60)
Pickup Models	
2WD	34-38 (46-51)
4WD	36-44 (50-59)
Caliper Mounting Bolts	
Cordia & Tredia	58-72 (80-100)
Montero & Pickups	51-65 (69-88)

DISC BRAKE ROTOR SPECIFICATIONS

Application	Disc Diameter In. (mm)	Lateral Runout In. (mm)	Parallelism In. (mm)	Original Thickness In. (mm)	Min. Refinish Thickness In. (mm)	Discard Thickness In. (mm)
Montero & Pickup	10.04 (255)	.006 (0.15)	.....	.79 (20.1)	.....	.72 (18.4)
Cordia & Tredia	9.57 (243)	.006 (0.15)	.....	.51 (13)	.....	.45 (11.4)

DRUM BRAKE SPECIFICATIONS

Application	Drum Diam. In. (mm)	Drum Width In. (mm)	Max. Drum Refinish Diam. In. (mm)	Wheel Cyl. Diam. In. (mm)	Master Cyl. Diam. In. (mm)
Pickup					
2.3L Diesel 4WD	9.5 (241.3)	.....	9.579 (243.3)	3/4 (19.05)	7/8 (22.22)
2.0L & 2.6L 4WD & All 2WD	10 (254)	.....	10.08 (256)	13/16 (20.64)	7/8 (22.22)
Montero	10 (254)	.....	10.08 (256)	13/16 (20.64)	7/8 (22.22)
Cordia & Tredia	8.0 (203)	.....	8.1 (205)	11/16 (17.46)	7/8 (22.22)

MITSUBISHI STARION

DESCRIPTION

Brake system is hydraulically-operated using a master cylinder with a single reservoir and 2 outlets, a vacuum power brake unit and a proportioning valve to control braking action.

The vehicle is equipped with sliding caliper type FS17 front disc brakes and type AD rear disc brakes.

ADJUSTMENT

PEDAL HEIGHT & FREE PLAY

Back off stop light switch. To adjust pedal height (distance from top of pedal to floor board) loosen lock nut, and rotate master cylinder push rod (yoke, if equipped). Do not depress push rod. Tighten lock nut, and ensure that brake pedal free play is .4-.6" (10-15 mm).

PEDAL HEIGHT SPECIFICATIONS

Application	In. (mm)
Starion	7.1 (180)

STOP LIGHT SWITCH

Loosen lock nut and adjust switch-to-pedal arm clearance to .02-.04" (.5-1.0 mm). Tighten lock nut. Do not depress master cylinder push rod during stop light switch adjustment.

PARKING BRAKE

When parking brake lever is pulled with a force of 45 lbs. (20 kg), the lever stroke should be 4-5 notches. If not, remove the center console. Turn the adjusting nut until the specified number of notches is obtained with a pull of 45 lbs. (20 kg).

NOTE: **If parking brake lever stroke is shorter than specified after adjustment, brake dragging will result.**

TESTING

PROPORTIONING VALVE

The proportioning valve is responsible for pressure control of rear service brakes and allows braking should the front service brakes fail. The valve body is identified with "A70" stamped on plug.

Pressure Test

Use 2 pressure gauges that measure at least 1500 psi (105.5 kg/cm²). Hook one gauge to master cylinder rear side and the other to rear wheel cylinder. Depress brake pedal. With master cylinder pressure equal to readings shown in chart, the wheel cylinders should meet specifications. If not, replace defective part as required. Do not disassemble proportioning valve.

BRAKE HYDRAULIC PRESSURE CHART

Application	Master Cyl. psi (kg/cm²)	Wheel Cyl. psi (kg/cm²)
Starion	525 (37)	515-550 (36-39)
	1175 (83)	660-790 (46-56)

Warning Light Test

Loosen bleeder screw on one wheel cylinder and depress brake pedal. Warning light should come on. If not, check switch and wire connector.

Fig. 1: Identifying Proportioning Valve

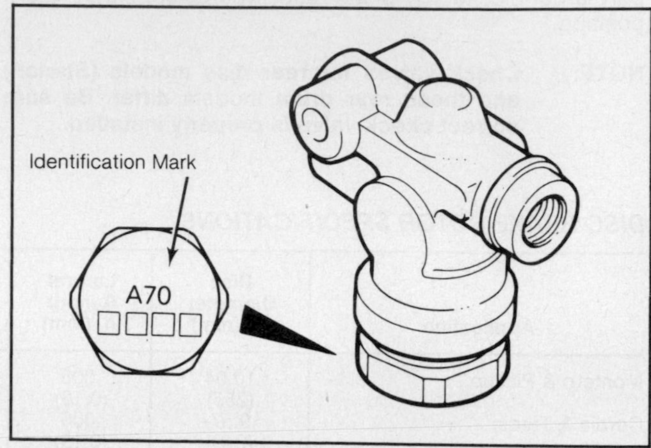
Identification Mark
A70

Identification mark located on plug.

REMOVAL & INSTALLATION

FRONT DISC BRAKE PADS

NOTE: **Replace left and right side pads at same time.**

Removal

1) Raise and support vehicle. Remove front wheel. Remove lower caliper slide pin.

NOTE: **Use care not to remove special grease from slide pin or allow dirt to get in grease.**

2) Pull caliper assembly up and suspend with wire. Remove retainers and brake pads.

Installation

To install, reverse removal procedure. Press piston to bottom of caliper bore prior to pad installation. Ensure pad retaining clips are installed.

FRONT DISC BRAKE CALIPER

Removal

Pull out hose clip from strut area. Disconnect brake hose from caliper, pull out slide pins, and remove caliper.

Installation

To install, reverse removal procedure. Apply new grease to slide pins, install pins and bleed brake system.

FRONT DISC BRAKE ROTOR

Removal

With caliper assembly removed, remove hub dust cap, cotter pin, lock nut (if used) and adjusting nut. Pull hub and rotor assembly from spindle using care not to drop outer wheel bearing. Place in a soft-jawed vise, remove hub-to-rotor attaching bolts and separate rotor from hub.

MITSUBISHI STARION (Cont.)

Installation

To install, reverse removal procedures, tightening hub-to-rotor bolts to specification. Bleed brake system if necessary, and adjust wheel bearings. *See Mitsubishi article in SUSPENSION Section.*

REAR DISC BRAKE PADS

Removal

1) Raise and support vehicle. Remove rear wheels. Disconnect parking brake cable from parking brake lever and from bracket.

2) Remove lower caliper lock pin.

NOTE: **Since the guide pins are coated with a special grease, do not remove the grease or get dirt on it.**

3) Lift caliper assembly from rotor and suspend with wire. Remove retaining clips and pull pads from caliper support.

Installation

To install, reverse removal procedure, and note the following: Using a special driver (MB990652), screw the piston into its original position with a clockwise rotation. Ensure piston stopper groove is positioned properly so projection on back of pad will securely fit groove. *See Fig. 2.* Pad clips must be installed properly.

NOTE: **Do not use a screwdriver to push piston into original position.**

Fig. 2: Positioning of Piston Stopper Groove On Rear Disc Brakes

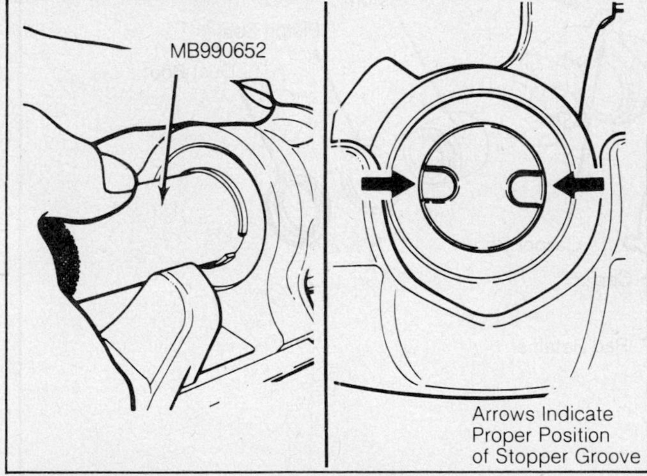
MB990652
Arrows Indicate
Proper Position
of Stopper Groove

Adjust with special driver (MB990652).

REAR DISC BRAKE CALIPER

Removal

Pull out hose clip from axle housing, and disconnect brake hose from caliper assembly. Remove clevis pin connecting lever assembly to parking brake cable. Remove guide pins. Remove caliper assembly.

Installation

To install, reverse removal procedure and bleed brake system

REAR DISC BRAKE ROTOR

Removal

After removing the caliper from the axle, make mating marks and remove the disc from the axle shaft.

Installation

To install, reverse removal procedure, tightening bolts evenly.

REAR AXLE SHAFT BEARING & OIL SEAL

Removal

1) Remove rear disc caliper assembly, and support it out of way. Separate drive shaft from companion flange. Remove axle housing from lower control arm. Remove strut assembly from axle housing. Remove axle shaft assembly. *See Fig. 3.*

Fig. 3: Exploded View of Rear Axle Assembly

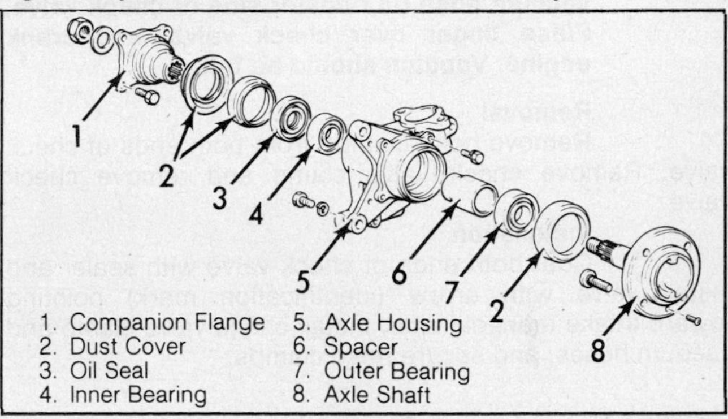
1
2
3
4
5
6
7
2
8
1. Companion Flange
2. Dust Cover
3. Oil Seal
4. Inner Bearing
5. Axle Housing
6. Spacer
7. Outer Bearing
8. Axle Shaft

2) Loosen companion flange mounting nut. Using plastic hammer, tap axle shaft out of axle housing. Use care not to damage oil seal. Remove spacer and dust covers from inside axle housing. Do not remove inner and outer bearings unless they are to be replaced.

3) To replace bearings, cut bearing retainer in 3 places with chisel portion of removal tool (MB990918). Insert 3 claws of removal tool into 3 retainer cuts, turning claws 90° to lock them into place. Place upper end of 3 claws in tool body. Tighten claw nut to secure claws tightly.

4) While holding body by tool handle, tighten center bolt to remove bearing. Using a drift, drive inner bearing and oil seal from axle housing.

Installation

1) Press-fit new outer bearing to axle shaft, with seal side toward flange side of axle shaft. Position new inner bearing so seal side faces companion flange. Press-fit bearing, using installer (MB990932) and driver (MB990938).

2) Apply multipupose grease (SAE J310a, NLGI 2EP) to oil seal area of axle shaft. Using installer (MB990932) and driver (MB990727), press in oil seal until it contacts edge of axle housing.

3) Install dust cover to axle housing. Apply grease to oil seal lip. Insert axle shaft and spacer into housing, and attach companion shaft. Place axle housing in a vise, and tighten companion shaft nut to 188-217 ft. lbs. (260-300 N.m).

4) Measure starting torque of axle shaft for 4 INCH lbs. (.45 N.m) or less. If greater, replace spacer. Complete installation by installing axle housing to lower control arm and strut assembly. Using dial indicator, check axle end play for .031" (.8 mm).

MASTER CYLINDER

Removal

Remove sensor connector (if equipped). Disconnect brake lines from master cylinder. Slowly depress

MITSUBISHI STARION (Cont.)

brake pedal several times to drain fluid from cylinder housing. Remove master cylinder from booster unit and separate reservoirs from housing.

Installation

Reverse removal procedure. Prior to installation, check and adjust clearance between back of master cylinder piston and power brake push rod. Clearance should be .004-.020" (.1-.5 mm). Check and adjust pedal height, and bleed brake system after installation.

POWER BRAKE UNIT CHECK VALVE REPLACEMENT

NOTE: **Test check valve before removal. Pull off vacuum hose on booster side of check valve. Place finger over check valve, and crank engine. Vacuum should be felt.**

Removal

Remove hose clamps from both ends of check valve. Remove check valve clamp and remove check valve.

Installation

Coat both ends of check valve with sealer and install valve with arrow (identification mark) pointing toward intake manifold side. Install check valve clamp and vacuum hoses, and secure hose clamps.

POWER BRAKE UNIT

Removal

Remove the brake master cylinder, and disconnect vacuum hose from power brake unit. *For illustration, see brake article for other Mitsubishi models.* Disconnect brake pedal and operating rod of power brake unit. From inside vehicle, remove 4 nuts attaching power brake unit to firewall. Remove power brake unit.

Installation

To install, reverse removal procedure. Check for push rod-to-master cylinder piston clearance of .004-.020" (.1-.5 mm). Tighten attaching nuts to 6-9 ft. lbs. (8-12 N.m). Install master cylinder.

OVERHAUL

FRONT DISC BRAKE CALIPER

NOTE: **Possible cause of increased pedal stroke is insufficient fit between piston and piston seal. Correct by manually levering piston to seat several times, creating a better fit between piston and seal. Make sure brake pad is removed during this procedure.**

Fig. 4: Exploded View of Model FS17 Front Disc Brake Assembly for Component Relationship

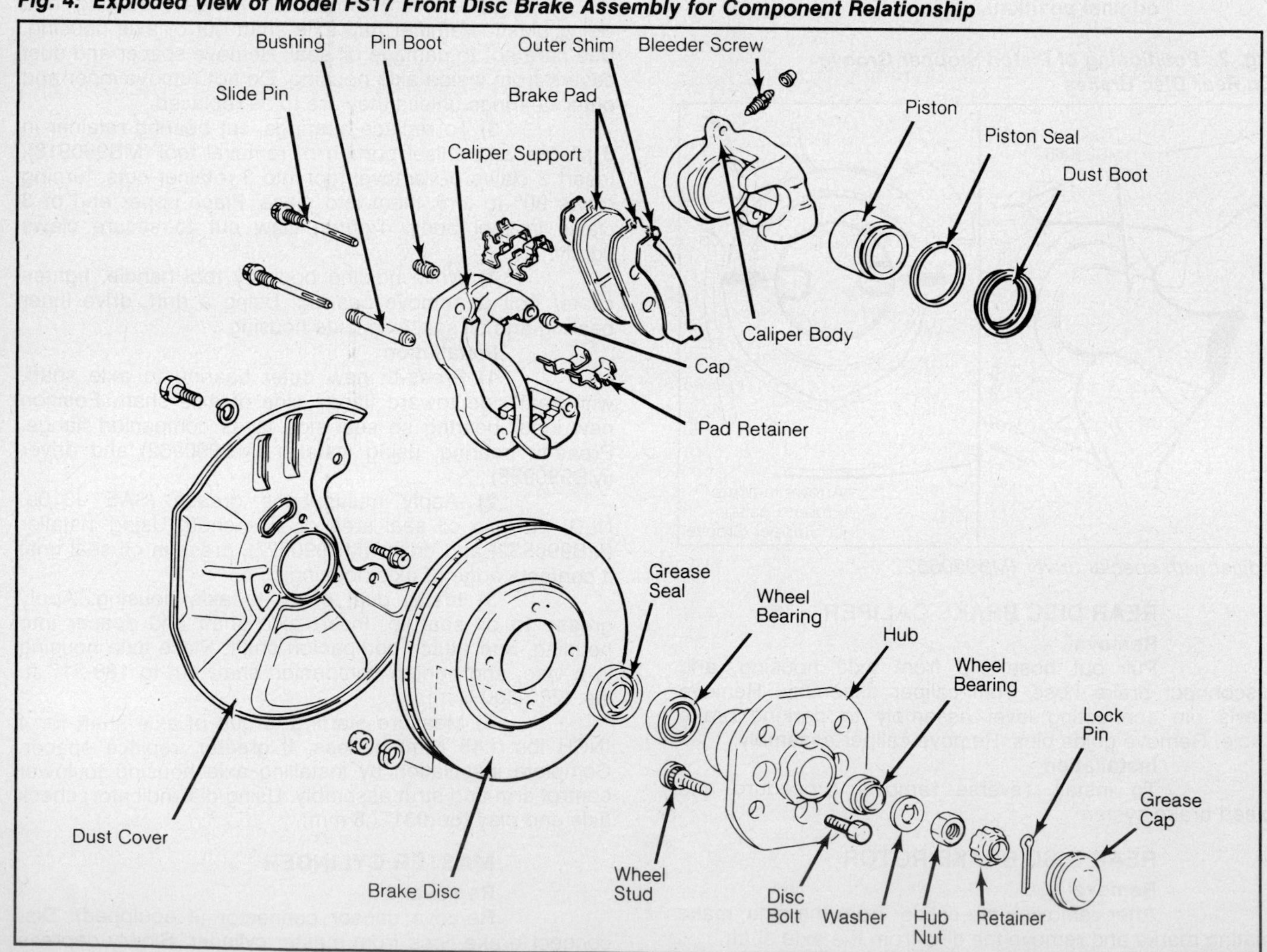
Bushing
Pin Boot
Outer Shim
Bleeder Screw
Slide Pin
Brake Pad
Piston
Piston Seal
Caliper Support
Dust Boot
Caliper Body
Cap
Pad Retainer
Grease Seal
Wheel Bearing
Hub
Wheel Bearing
Lock Pin
Grease Cap
Dust Cover
Brake Disc
Wheel Stud
Disc Bolt
Washer
Hub Nut
Retainer

MITSUBISHI STARION (Cont.)

Disassembly

Remove dust boot. Apply compressed air to fluid inlet to remove piston. Remove piston seal without damaging caliper bore or seal groove.

Cleaning & Inspection

Clean all metal parts and piston seal in alcohol or brake fluid. Clean dust boot and other rubber parts in alcohol only. Inspect caliper bore and piston for wear, damage or rust. Replace parts as necessary. Always replace piston seal and dust boot.

Reassembly

Coat piston seal with rubber grease. Slide seal into groove in cylinder bore. Slip piston into bore making sure seal is not twisted. Lightly coat dust seal groove with recommended rubber grease. Fit dust boot into place. Refit cylinder to caliper.

REAR DISC BRAKE CALIPER

Disassembly

1) Remove cap ring and garter spring, and take off lever cap. *See Fig. 5.* Remove retaining ring. Pull out parking lever assembly. Unscrew automatic adjuster spindle and pull out assembly. Remove piston, piston seal and boot ring.

2) Using bearing remover tool (MB990665), press bearings from caliper. Take off piston boot. Remove the guide pin and lock pin boots.

Cleaning & Inspection

1) Clean all metal parts, piston seal and adjuster seal in alcohol or brake fluid. Clean piston boot and other rubber parts in alcohol only. Check cylinder and piston for wear, damage or rust. Replace worn parts as necessary. Always replace piston seal, adjuster seal, and piston boot.

2) Check bearings, connecting link, springs, adjuster spindle and lever assembly for wear, damage or rust. Check lever assembly for excessive play between shaft and bearing.

Reassembly

1) Lightly coat piston seal and piston with lubricant. Slide piston and seal into place, ensuring seal does not twist in groove. Lubricate boot, and slide boot into position making sure it engages groove in cylinder bore.

NOTE: **Repair kit includes recommended lubricants.**

2) Using bearing installation tool (MB990665), press in bearings until ends are flush with caliper body. Make sure mark on end of bearing faces out.

3) Coat automatic adjuster seal with recommended grease. Fit adjuster spindle and hardware in place until spindle turns freely. Make sure spring faces proper direction.

4) Press in connecting link spring washers with installation tool (MB990666). Fit automatic adjuster spindle into place (spindle is not a press fit). Insert connecting link and lever assembly.

5) Fill lever cap with Niglube RX-2 (or equivalent), making sure all areas have ample grease. Lightly

Fig. 5: Exploded View of Type AD Rear Disc Brake Caliper Assembly

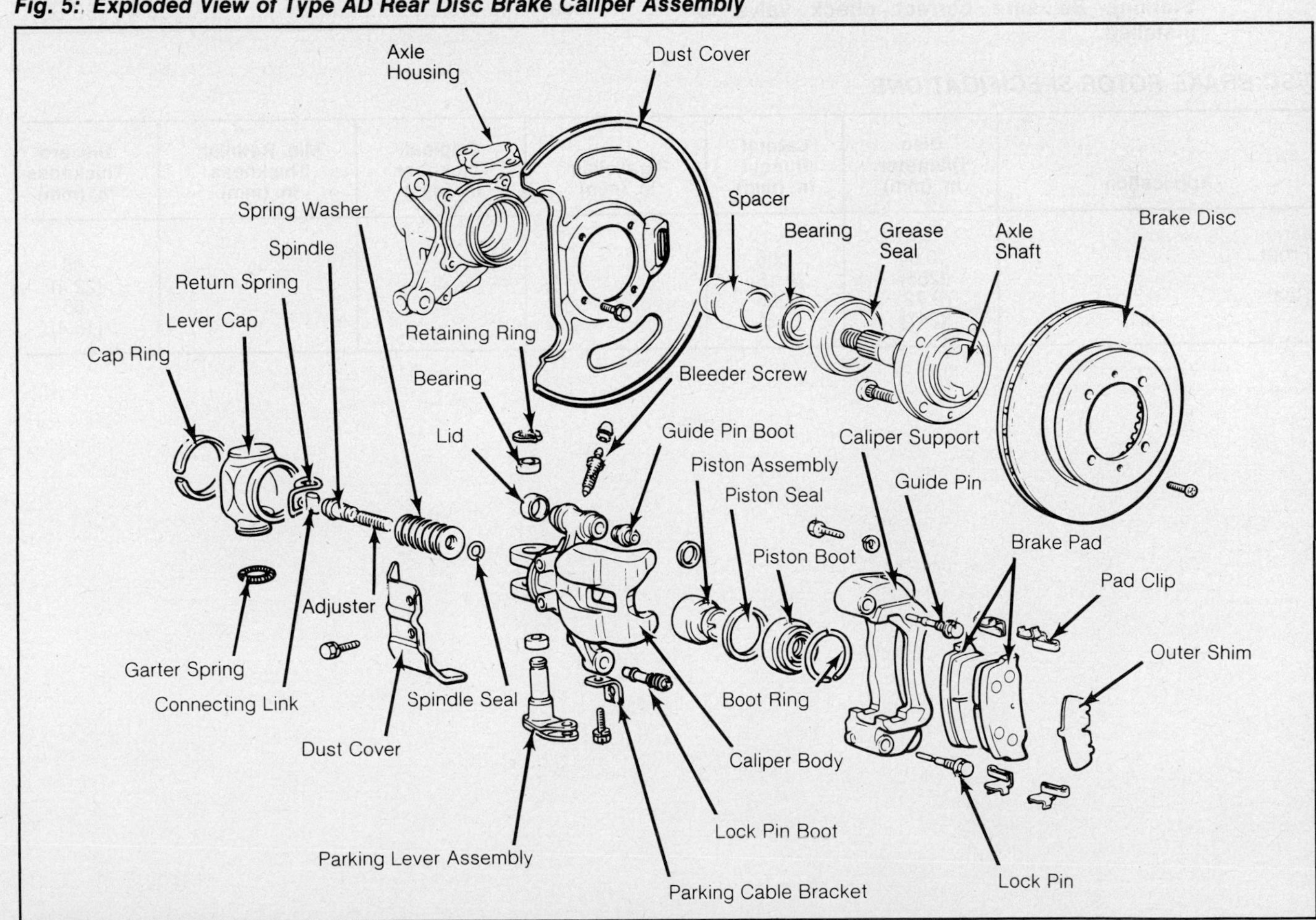
Axle Housing
Dust Cover
Spring Washer
Spindle
Return Spring
Lever Cap
Cap Ring
Retaining Ring
Spacer
Bearing
Grease Seal
Axle Shaft
Brake Disc
Bearing
Bleeder Screw
Lid
Guide Pin Boot
Caliper Support
Piston Assembly
Guide Pin
Piston Seal
Piston Boot
Brake Pad
Pad Clip
Adjuster
Outer Shim
Garter Spring
Connecting Link
Spindle Seal
Boot Ring
Dust Cover
Caliper Body
Lock Pin Boot
Parking Lever Assembly
Parking Cable Bracket
Lock Pin

MITSUBISHI STARION (Cont.)

grease caliper sliding surface. Assembly is ready for installation.

MASTER CYLINDER

Disassembly

1) Place cylinder in a soft-jawed vise. Remove dust boot, retaining ring, stop washer and piston stop bolt. Withdraw primary piston assembly, secondary piston assembly and secondary return spring from master cylinder.

2) Remove check valve caps, tube seats, check valves and check valve springs.

NOTE: **Do not disassemble primary and secondary piston assembly.**

Cleaning & Inspection

Check master cylinder bore and piston for wear or other damage. Replace as necessary. Check clearance between cylinder bore and piston. If clearance exceeds .006" (.15 mm), replace parts as necessary. Check all parts of primary and secondary piston assemblies and piston cups and springs. If any parts are found defective, replace components as assemblies.

Reassembly

Reverse disassembly procedure. Before reassembly, apply rubber grease to all parts (except boots). When assembled, check that the return port is not blocked by piston cup, when piston is at return position.

NOTE: **Check valves differ between rear disc model (Starion) and rear drum models (except Starion). Be sure correct check valve is installed.**

Fig. 6: Disassembled View of Master Cylinder

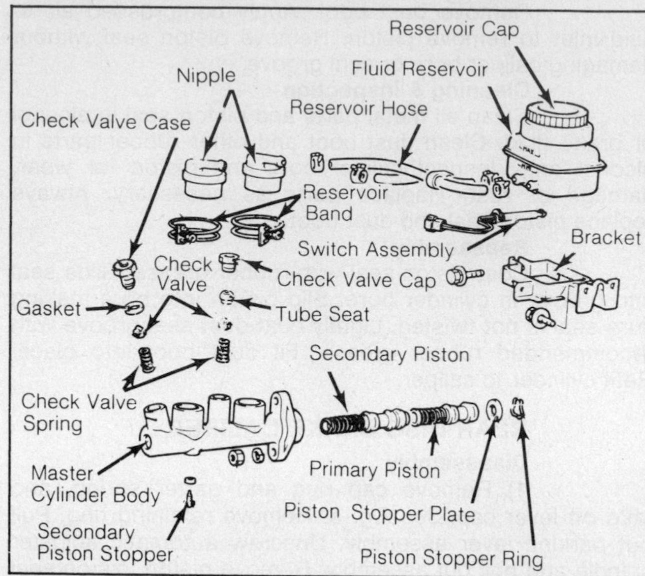
Reservoir Cap
Fluid Reservoir
Nipple
Check Valve Case
Reservoir Hose
Reservoir Band
Switch Assembly
Bracket
Check Valve
Check Valve Cap
Gasket
Tube Seat
Secondary Piston
Check Valve Spring
Master Cylinder Body
Primary Piston
Piston Stopper Plate
Secondary Piston Stopper
Piston Stopper Ring

TIGHTENING SPECIFICATIONS

Application	Ft. Lbs. (N.m)
Starion	
Rotor-to-Hub Bolts (Frt. & Rear)	25-29 (34-40)
Caliper Mounting Bolts	
Front	61-69 (85-95)
Rear	36-43 (50-60)

DISC BRAKE ROTOR SPECIFICATIONS

Application	Disc Diameter In. (mm)	Lateral Runout In. (mm)	Parallelism In. (mm)	Original Thickness In. (mm)	Min. Refinish Thickness In. (mm)	Discard Thickness In. (mm)
Starion						
Front	10.04 (255)	.006 (0.15)	.....	.....	.....	.88 (22.4)
Rear	9.72 (247)	.006 (15)	.....	.....	.....	.65 (16.4)

MITSUBISHI AUTOMATIC BRAKE CONTROL SYSTEM

Starion

DESCRIPTION & OPERATION

The automatic brake control system is designed to provide efficient braking for quick stops on wet or icy road surfaces, to reduce vehicle skidding.

NOTE: If the front wheels become locked, the automatic brake control system will not work.

Fig. 1: Rear Brake Lock-Up Control Component Locations

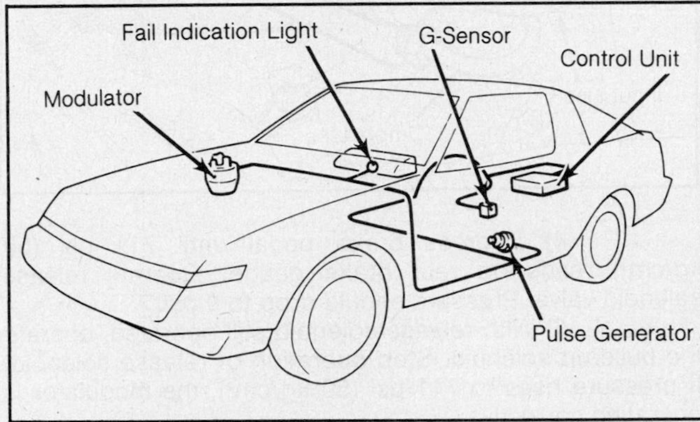
Fail Indication Light
G-Sensor
Control Unit
Modulator
Pulse Generator

PULSE GENERATOR

Pulse generator consists of a permanent magnet, a coil and a rotor. It is located on the transmission speedometer exit port. The frequency of the AC voltage, which is produced by the spinning of the rotor in combination with the coil and magnet, is proportionate to the speed of the wheels.

G-SENSOR

Composed of a differential transformer and printed circuit board, the G-sensor is installed in the floor of the luggage compartment. When braking, the core of the transformer moves and produces a voltage equal to the amount of the displacement of the core, which is the speed reduction.

CONTROL UNIT

The control unit is located inside the luggage compartment. It receives signals from the pulse generator, G-sensor, and the brake switch. Once the signal has been received, it sends the brake fluid pressure control signal to the modulator. It also will detect a malfunction in the control unit or modulator or an open circuit, and return the brake system to conventional operation.

MODULATOR

Located on the right fender wall of the engine compartment, the modulator consists of a pressure control section, a vacuum pressure drive section, and a solenoid valve. It receives signals from the control unit to control the brake fluid pressure for the rear brakes.

FAIL INDICATOR LIGHT

Located on the dash, the indicator lights if the control unit malfunctions.

NOTE: Should a radio transmitter/receiver be installed in the vehicle, the following items should be noted. Install the antenna as far as possible from the control unit (preferably on the front of the vehicle). Keep the coaxial cable at least 12" away from the control unit and only cross the wiring harness at right angles. Keep transmitter output to 10W, and select a cable and an antenna which are electrically matched.

Fig. 2: Rear Brake Lock-up Control System

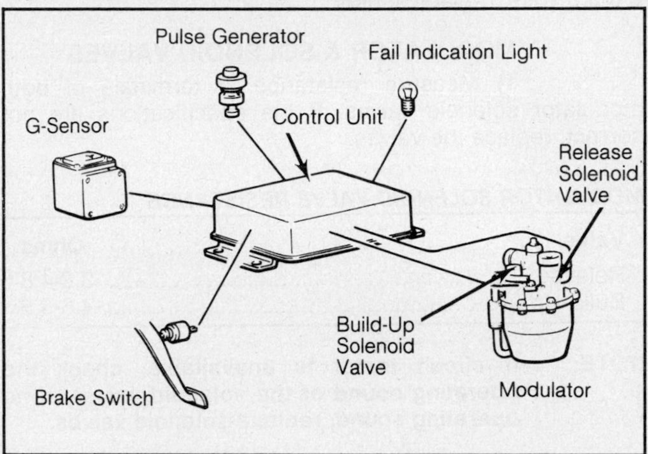
Pulse Generator
Fail Indication Light
G-Sensor
Control Unit
Release Solenoid Valve
Build-Up Solenoid Valve
Brake Switch
Modulator

DIAGNOSIS & TESTING

NOTE: If any problem exists in the system, check all components (including wiring harness) except the control unit. If all components check out, replace the control unit

REAR BRAKE CONTROL SYSTEM QUICK CHECK

1) With vehicle stationary, operate engine for at least 5 seconds. Turn the ignition key to "LOCK" position and step on the brake pedal. Turn the ignition key to "ON" position and confirm the a clicking sound of the operating modulator.

2) Raise rear of vehicle, support on stands, and block front wheels. Warm up engine and place transmission in second gear. Accelerate to a steady 19 MPH.

3) With acclerator held at 19 MPH, step on the brake pedal suddenly. The brakes should attempt to slow the rotation of the rear wheels, then, because fluid is cut-off, the wheels should resume normal rotation.

PULSE GENERATOR

Measure the resistance between generator terminals. If not 600-800 ohms, replace generator. Measure resistance between terminals and case. It should be infinity, if not replace the generator.

G-SENSOR

1) Ensure sensor is mounted correctly. Sensor must be within ±1° of being level, if not, use shims to adjust to level.

NOTE: If any oil leakage occurs with the sensor, replace it.

MITSUBISHI AUTOMATIC BRAKE CONTROL SYSTEM (Cont.)

2) Check voltage between "R" terminal of control unit and ground. If not 7.0-7.5 volts, control unit is faulty.

CAUTION: Set voltmeter at correct range before measurement to prevent damage to control unit.

3) Remove sensor and ground to car body using wire. Place sensor so manufacturer mark is upward. Measure voltage between "G" terminal and ground. If not 4.6-5.0 volts, replace sensor.

MODULATOR & SOLENOID VALVES

1) Measure resistance at terminals of both modulator solenoid valves. If the specifications are not correct, replace the valves.

MODULATOR SOLENOID VALVE RESISTANCE

Valve	Ohms
Release	3.8-4.8
Build-Up	4.5-5.5

NOTE: If circuit tester is unavailable, check the operating sound of the solenoid valves. If no operating sound, replace solenoid valves.

CAUTION: Do not connect battery to solenoid valves for more than 1 minute.

2) Inspect vacuum hoses for malfunction. Check the check valves of the modulator and brake power unit for clogging conditions.

3) Using 2 pressure gauges (with a range of 0-2,500 psi, 0-175.75 kg/cm²), connect one gauge between modulator master cylinder port and master cylinder, and other to modulator rear brake port. Let engine run at idle.

Fig. 4: View of Modulator Connections

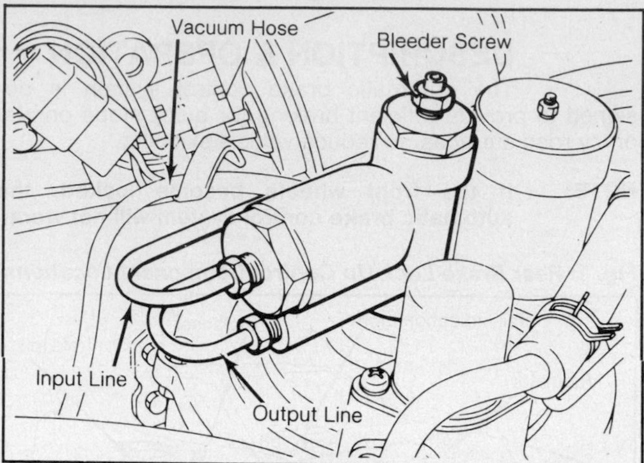

Vacuum Hose
Bleeder Screw
Input Line
Output Line

4) Depress brake pedal until 711 psi (50 kg/cm²) reads on rear brake gauge. Operate release solenoid valve. Pressure should drop to 0 psi.

5) With release solenoid still operated, operate the build-up solenoid. Stop operation of release solenoid. If pressure rises to 711 psi (50 kg/cm²), the modulator is operating correctly.

6) Repeat steps **4)** & **5)**, except do not operate build-up solenoid. When release solenoid operation is cut-off, pressure should rise to 711 psi (50 kg/cm²). If so, the operation is okay.

7) Set both solenoid valves in a non-operating position. Increase pressure on master cylinder by operating brakes. Rear brake port gauge should show pressure of 1,422 psi (100 kg/cm²). Master cylinder gauge should show 1,707 psi (120 kg/cm²). If any test does not meet specifications, replace the modulator.

Fig. 3: Sectional View of Modulator

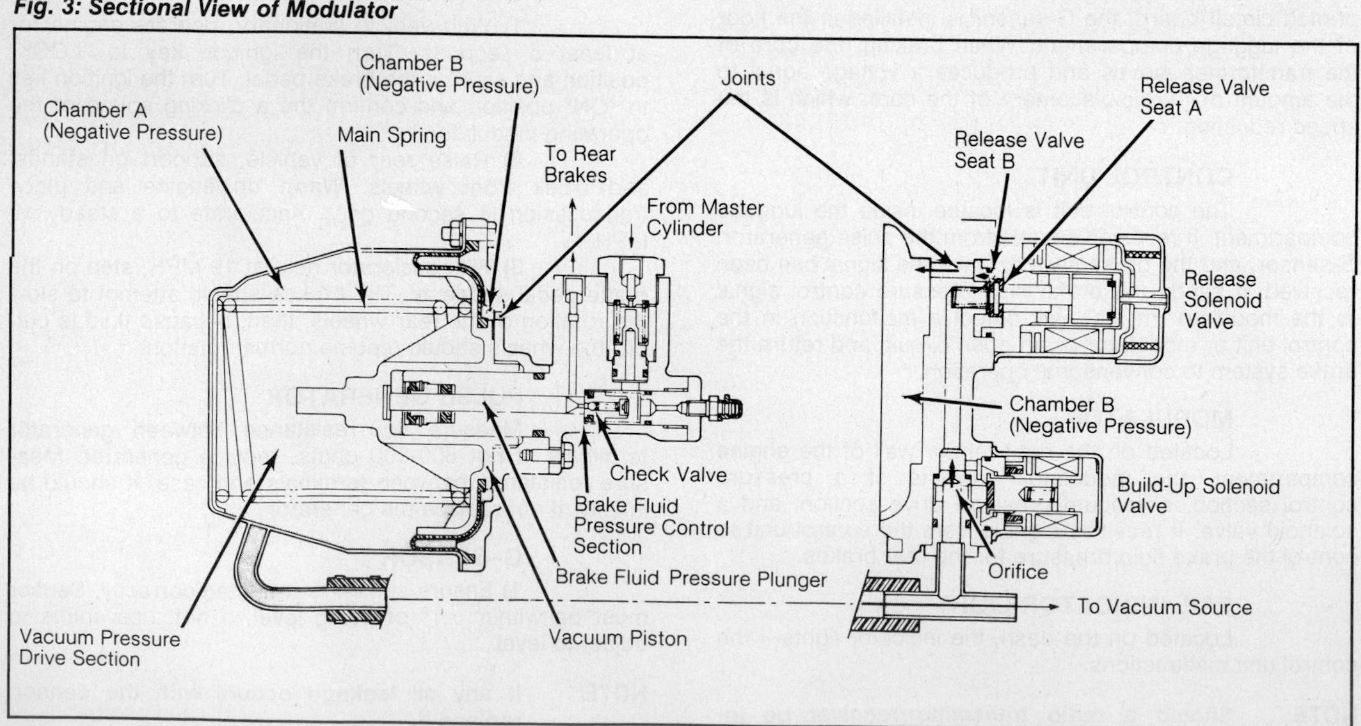

Chamber B
(Negative Pressure)
Joints
Release Valve
Seat A
Chamber A
(Negative Pressure)
Main Spring
Release Valve
Seat B
To Rear
Brakes
From Master
Cylinder
Release
Solenoid
Valve
Chamber B
(Negative Pressure)
Check Valve
Brake Fluid
Pressure Control
Section
Build-Up Solenoid
Valve
Orifice
Brake Fluid Pressure Plunger
To Vacuum Source
Vacuum Pressure
Drive Section
Vacuum Piston

Modulator acts as a rear brake pressure regulator.

MITSUBISHI AUTOMATIC BRAKE CONTROL SYSTEM (Cont.)

STOP LIGHT SWITCH

Be sure the switch is set correctly. To adjust, use a circuit tester to check continuity. Set stop light switch while operating stop lights, by depressing and releasing the brake pedal.

REMOVAL & INSTALLATION

G-SENSOR

Removal

Unbolt sensor from its position on the luggage compartment floor. Do not allow sensor to receive any impact or violent shaking.

Installation

With vehicle on a level surface and unloaded, install sensor making sure it is level within $\pm 1°$. Use appropriate shims to bring to correct level.

PULSE GENERATOR

Removal

Disconnect speedometer cable at pulse generator side and remove pulse generator.

Installation

Reverse removal procedure. To install on a manual transmission, count the number of speedometer driven gear teeth and select the generator sleeve mark which indicates that number of teeth. Align selected mark with reference mark on extension housing. *See Fig. 5.*

Fig. 5: View of Pulse Generator Alignment Marks

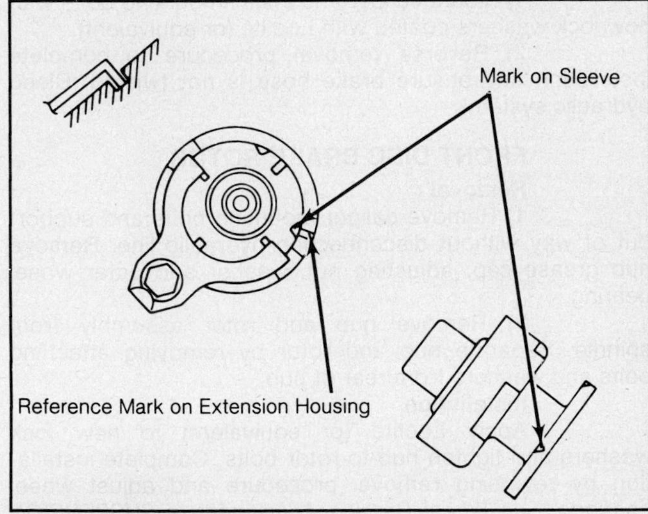
Mark on Sleeve
Reference Mark on Extension Housing

Illustration applies to manual transmission only.

CONTROL UNIT

Removal

Remove the unit from under the high floor side panel on the right side of the luggage compartment. Remove electrical connector.

Installation

To install, reverse removal procedure.

MODULATOR

Removal

Remove heat protector. Remove vacuum hose, brake tubes, and connector for solenoid valves. Remove modulator bracket and then modulator.

Installation

To install, reverse removal procedure.

BRAKE LINE BLEEDING

If brake bleeding is required after any servicing, perform bleeding in sequence as follows: Rear wheel (right side); rear wheel (left side); modulator bleeding screw; and front wheels.

Brakes

PEUGEOT

504, 505, & 604

DESCRIPTION

Brake system is hydraulically-operated, using a tandem master cylinder and power brake unit. The 504 is equipped with sliding-yoke, front disc brakes and rear drum brakes. All other models are equipped with 4-wheel, sliding-yoke, disc brakes.

All models are equipped with a load-actuated compensator to provide equal fluid distribution to front and rear brakes. Parking brake is cable-operated at rear wheels.

ADJUSTMENT

REAR DRUM BRAKE SHOES

1) Raise and support rear of vehicle. To adjust, rotate front adjustment eccentric clockwise until wheel locks, then back off until wheel just turns freely.

2) Repeat procedure for rear adjustment eccentric, but rotate the eccentric counterclockwise.

NOTE: Do not alter the adjustment of brake pedal.

PARKING BRAKE

504

1) Remove center console and raise and support vehicle. Fully release parking brake lever.

2) Loosen lock nut at lever and tighten adjusting screw until wheels are locked with 4-7 notches of lever travel.

3) Tighten lock nut and ensure wheels rotate freely with parking brake fully released.

All Other Models

Parking brake is self-adjusting and requires no in-service adjustment. Normal lever travel should be 7-13 notches.

BRAKE WARNING LIGHT

1) A warning light is mounted on instrument panel. Light will glow to indicate that disc brake pads need replacing, parking brake is engaged, brake fluid is low or malfunction exists in brake system.

2) Light should glow when parking brake lever is pulled 1 notch and go off when lever is fully released (ignition on). To check circuit warning sensor, release parking brake (ignition on) and ensure light is off.

3) Open bleed screw on 1 wheel and depress brake pedal; light should glow. Close bleed screw and replenish brake fluid.

REMOVAL & INSTALLATION

DISC BRAKE PADS

CAUTION: Peugeot uses brake calipers from various manufacturers. Removal and Overhaul procedures may vary slightly. Brake pads and calipers MUST match for each axle application.

Removal

1) Raise and support vehicle under frame. Remove tire and wheel. Disconnect pad wear indicator electrical lead.

2) Remove retaining spring and pins, then remove damper spring and brake pads.

NOTE: Manufacturer recommends applying Permatex "High Tack" adhesive to back portion of brake pads prior to installation.

Installation

1) Remove small amount of brake fluid from master cylinder reservoir. Press piston into cylinder bore.

2) On rear calipers, rotate piston clockwise 1/8 turn before pressing into cylinder. After piston is seated in bore of rear caliper, return piston to original position by rotating counterclockwise 1/8 turn.

3) On all calipers, install brake pads and damper spring. Damper spring of rear caliper MUST be installed with arrow (or hole) at top. On all brake calipers, reconnect pad wear indicator. Bleed hydraulic system.

DISC BRAKE CALIPER

Removal

1) Raise and support vehicle. Remove tire and wheel. Remove brake pads as previously described. Remove and plug hydraulic line from caliper.

2) On rear caliper, disconnect parking brake cable and casing from operating lever. On all calipers, remove mounting bolts and remove caliper assembly.

Installation

1) Mount caliper and install mounting bolts with new lock washers coated with Loctite (or equivalent).

2) Reverse removal procedure to complete installation and ensure brake hose is not twisted. Bleed hydraulic system.

FRONT DISC BRAKE ROTOR

Removal

1) Remove caliper mounting bolts and support out of way without disconnecting hydraulic line. Remove hub grease cap, adjusting nut, washer and outer wheel bearing.

2) Remove hub and rotor assembly from spindle. Separate hub and rotor by removing attaching bolts and washers from rear of hub.

Installation

Apply Loctite (or equivalent) to new lock washers and tighten hub-to-rotor bolts. Complete installation by reversing removal procedure and adjust wheel bearings. *See Wheel Bearing Adjustment in SUSPENSION Section.*

REAR DISC BRAKE ROTOR

Removal

1) Disconnect hydraulic line retaining clip on control arm. Remove pad electrical lead and brake pads.

2) Remove caliper mounting bolts and support caliper out of way without disconnecting hydraulic line. Remove axle shaft nut.

3) Align bearing housing access hole and remove bearing housing bolts. Remove shaft, hub and rotor as an assembly

PEUGEOT (Cont.)

4) Remove drive shaft from hub assembly with puller. Mount hub assembly in a padded vise and install extractor. Remove bearing housing nut with a 35 mm socket.

5) Install extractor and thrust pad and remove bearing housing. Remove hub-to-rotor bolts and separate assembly.

Installation

1) Apply Loctite (or equivalent) to new lock washers and tighten hub-to-rotor bolts. Install bearing housing nut to bearing housing and tighten nut.

2) Mount hub and rotor assembly on bearing housing. Coat drive shaft splines with Molykote 321 (or equivalent) and install drive shaft in hub.

3) Mount shaft, hub and rotor assembly on vehicle. Install new washers coated with Loctite (or equivalent) on bearing housing bolts and tighten bolts.

4) Install axle nut and tighten. Mount caliper and install new washers coated with Loctite (or equivalent) on mounting bolts. Install brake pads.

REAR BRAKE DRUM

Removal

1) Raise and support vehicle. Remove tire and wheel. Slide brake drum off brake assembly.

2) It may be necessary to neutralize brakes by removing backing plate plug and pushing parking brake lever off its seat.

Installation

To install, reverse removal procedure.

REAR BRAKE SHOES

Removal

1) With brake drum removed, remove and discard hold down springs. Remove return springs, separate parking brake linkage from brake shoes.

2) Remove parking brake cable from operating lever. Remove brake shoes. Remove parking brake lever and strut from shoes.

Fig. 1: Rear Brake Assembly for 504 Models

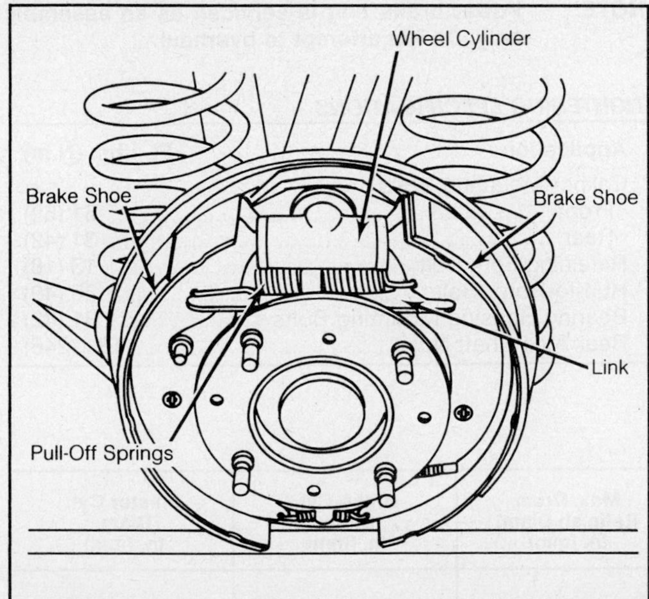
Wheel Cylinder
Brake Shoe
Brake Shoe
Link
Pull-Off Springs

Hold down springs should be replaced when performing rear brake service.

Installation

To install, reverse removal procedure and note: Replace hold down springs during installation and ensure proper operation of parking brake.

MASTER CYLINDER

Removal

1) Using a siphon, drain brake fluid from master cylinder. Disconnect all hydraulic lines from master cylinder.

2) Remove master cylinder-to-power brake unit attaching nuts and lift off master cylinder.

Installation

To install, reverse removal procedure, fill master cylinder with new brake fluid and bleed hydraulic system.

OVERHAUL

FRONT DISC BRAKE CALIPER

Disassembly

1) Clamp caliper assembly in a soft-jawed vise and remove brake pads. Seat pistons in cylinder bore and remove thrust spring and yoke. Remove protector retaining clips and protectors.

2) Remove both pistons from cylinder bore by applying compressed air to inlet port of caliper. Remove nylon spacer on yoke piston. Remove and discard piston seals.

Cleaning & Inspection

1) Clean all parts in denatured alcohol and check cylinder bore and pistons for wear, damage or scoring.

2) If any defects are found, defective parts must be replaced. Replace piston seals during overhaul.

Fig. 2: Disassembling Front Disc Brake Caliper

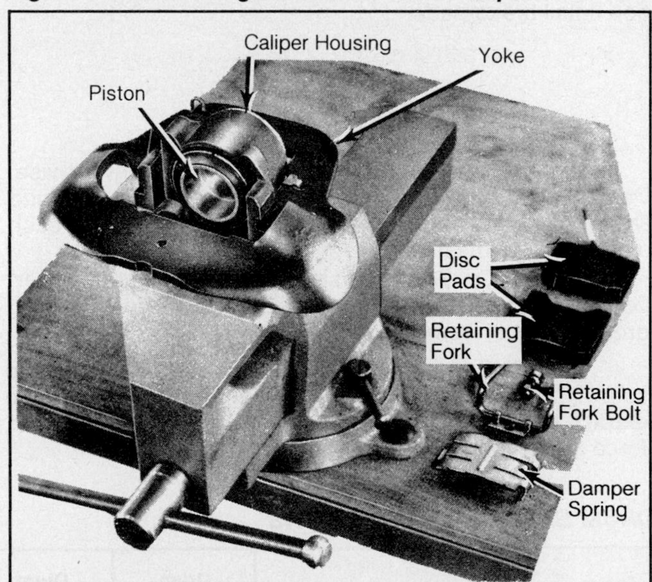
Caliper Housing
Yoke
Piston
Disc Pads
Retaining Fork
Retaining Fork Bolt
Damper Spring

Always replace piston seals after disassembling brake caliper.

Reassembly

1) Lubricate pistons and seals with brake fluid and install seals. Insert pistons in cylinder bore with nylon

PEUGEOT (Cont.)

spacer seated against yoke piston. Install protectors and retaining clips (thin clip on rotor side).

2) Coat yoke and caliper sliding parts with Molykote 321 (or equivalent) and install yoke and thrust spring. Seat pistons in cylinder bore and install brake pads.

REAR DISC BRAKE CALIPER

Disassembly

1) Clamp caliper assembly in a soft-jawed vise and remove brake pads. Rotate piston clockwise 1/8 turn and seat piston assembly in cylinder bore.

2) Remove thrust spring and yoke. Remove parking brake lever return spring. Lift lever and remove nylon spacer. Remove protector retaining clips and protectors.

3) Remove piston assembly from cylinder bore by applying compressed air to inlet port of caliper. Remove and discard piston seals.

Cleaning & Inspection

1) Clean all parts in denatured alcohol and check cylinder bore and piston assembly for wear or damage. If any defects are found, replace defective part.

2) Separate piston assembly and inspect wear compensation assembly. Replace piston seals during overhaul.

Reassembly

1) Lubricate piston assembly and seals with brake fluid and install seals. Insert piston assembly from rear of cyliner assembly without damaging piston seals.

2) Install protectors and retaining clips (thin clip on rotor side). Raise parking brake lever and install nylon spacer. Install return spring.

3) Coat yoke and caliper sliding parts with Molykote 321 (or equivalent) and install yoke and thrust spring.

4) Seat piston assembly in caliper bore, then rotate piston assembly counterclockwise to original position. Intall brake pads.

MASTER CYLINDER

Disassembly

1) Mount master cylinder in a soft-jawed vise. On Lockheed master cylinders, remove reservoir attaching screw from inside each reservoir and separate each reservoir from master cylinder.

2) On Teves master cylinders, separate reservoir from master cylinder by pulling it from sealing grommets. then remove grommets.

3) On all master cylinders, remove piston stop screw. Remove piston circlip and stop washer, then extract primary piston assembly. Using compressed air, force out secondary piston assembly.

Fig. 3: Sectional View of Master Cylinder Assembly

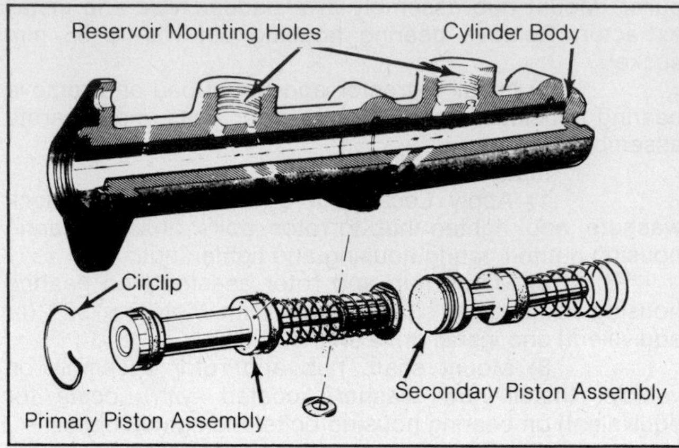
Reservoir Mounting Holes
Cylinder Body
Circlip
Secondary Piston Assembly
Primary Piston Assembly

Illustration shows Teves master cylinder, Lockheed master cylinder is similar.

NOTE: **DO NOT disassemble piston assemblies. If piston or seals are worn or damaged, replace both piston assemblies.**

Cleaning & Inspection

Wash all parts in denatured alcohol and dry with compressed air. Inspect all parts for wear, scoring burrs or corrosion and replace as necessary.

NOTE: **DO NOT polish cylinder bore with emery cloth.**

Reassembly

1) Reverse disassembly procedure and note the following: Coat all parts with clean brake fluid prior to reassembly.

2) After reassembly is completed, push in primary piston several times and ensure it returns fully and smoothly to its stop each time.

POWER BRAKE UNIT

NOTE: **Power brake unit is serviced as an assembly only. Do not attempt to overhaul.**

TIGHTENING SPECIFICATIONS

Application	Ft. Lbs. (N.m)
Caliper Mounting Bolts	
Front	51 (69)
Rear	31 (42)
Retaining Fork Bolt	13 (18)
Hub-to-Rotor Bolts	36 (49)
Bearing Housing Mounting Bolts	31 (42)
Rear Axle Shaft Nut	181 (246)

DRUM BRAKE SPECIFICATIONS

Application	Drum Diam. In. (mm)	Drum Width In. (mm)	Max. Drum Refinish Diam. In. (mm)	Brake Cyl. Diam. In. (mm)	Master Cyl. Diam. In. (mm)
504					
Rear	11.00 (280)	.....	11.06 (281)	55/64 (22)	13/16 (22.6)

PEUGEOT (Cont.)

DISC BRAKE ROTOR SPECIFICATIONS

Application	Disc Diameter In. (mm)	Lateral Runout In. (mm)	Parallelism In. (mm)	Original Thickness In. (mm)	Min. Refinish Thickness In. (mm)	Discard Thickness In. (mm)
504						
Front	.....	.003 (.07)	.0008 (.02)	.502 (12.75)	.443 (11.25)	.423 (10.75)
505						
Front	.....	.003 (.07)	.0008 (.02)	.502 (12.75)	.443 (11.25)	.423 (10.75)
Rear	.....	.003 (.07)	.0008 (.02)	.472 (12.0)	.433 (11.0)	.413 (10.5)
604						
Front	.....	.003 (.07)	.0008 (.02)	.787 (20.0)	.748 (19.0)	.709 (18.0)
Rear	.....	.003 (.07)	.0008 (.02)	.472 (12.0)	.433 (11.0)	.413 (10.5)

PORSCHE

911SC, 928S & 944

DESCRIPTION

Brake system is hydraulically-operated using a tandem master cylinder, and power brake unit. All models are equipped with 4-wheel disc brakes.

All models use a brake warning light to detect pressure drop in brake circuit. The 928S model also has a pad wear sensor.

ADJUSTMENT

BRAKE PEDAL TRAVEL & FREE PLAY

Brake Pedal Travel

1) Pedal travel, measured from pedal pad center to point of brake application, should be 1.19-1.56" (30-40 mm).

2) To adjust pedal travel, loosen operating rod lock nut and rotate rod until correct pedal travel is obtained. Tighten operating rod lock nut.

Pedal Free Play

Pedal free play measured from pedal pad center to floorboard should be 3/8" (10 mm). To adjust, loosen operating rod lock nut, and set to specification. Check pedal travel and tighten operating rod lock nut.

STOP LIGHT SWITCH

All Models

The stop light switch is operated mechanically and located on a bracket above the brake pedal.

1) The distance ("A") between the stop light switch and the brake pedal, when brake pedal is in neutral (off) position, should be .197" (5 mm). *See Fig. 1.*

2) If necessary, change location of stop light switch until specified distance is reached. Tighten and check function.

Fig. 1: Adjusting Stop Light Switch

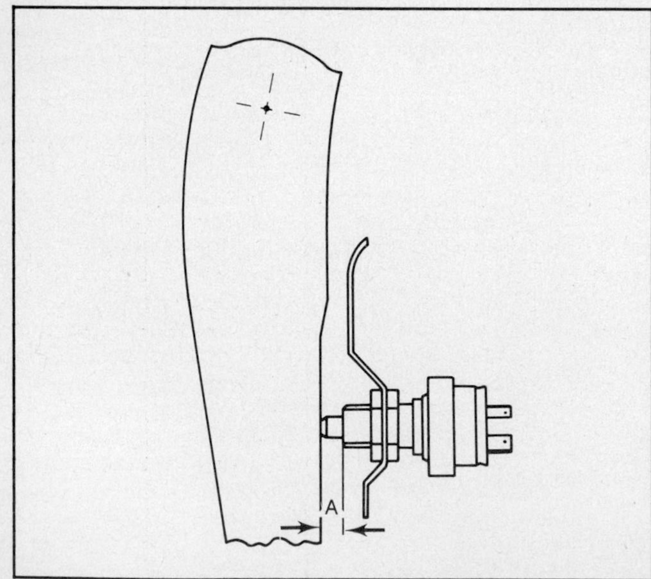
A

Distance "A" is .197" (5 mm).

PARKING BRAKE

4-Wheel Disc (All Models)

1) Raise and support vehicle. Remove tire and wheel. Release parking brake lever. Push caliper pistons and pads into caliper to allow rotor to turn freely.

2) Loosen parking brake cable lock nuts until cable is slack. Working through access hole in parking brake drum, turn star wheel adjuster until rotor cannot be turned by hand.

3) Adjust parking brake cable at rear cable end until it just begins to pull. Tighten lock nuts. Back off star wheel adjuster until rotor turns freely without drag. Repeat operation on opposite wheel. Check parking brake operation.

BRAKE WARNING LIGHT

NOTE: **Warning light will glow after any repair on service brake system, and will not go out until manually reset.**

1) A dual warning light is mounted on instrument panel. Parking brake light should glow when parking brake lever is pulled 1 notch (ignition on), and go off when lever is fully released.

2) Check circuit warning sensor as follows: Fully release parking brake and ensure light is off (ignition on). Open one bleeder screw and depress brake pedal. Warning light should glow.

3) To reset warning light, bleed hydraulic system, and test service brakes. Disconnect and reconnect negative battery cable. Warning lamp should go out.

REMOVAL & INSTALLATION

DISC PADS

NOTE: **Mark disc pads and calipers before removal. If disc pads are to be reused, they must be installed in original position. If only 1 pad (front or rear) needs replacing, all disc pads on same axle must be replaced.**

NOTE: **On 928S models, depending on type, the front axle disc brakes will have either floating frame calipers or floating calipers.**

Removal (928S with Floating Calipers)

1) Raise and support vehicle. Remove tire and wheel. Disconnect pad wear indicator. Remove housing retaining spring by applying pressure in center of spring pushing upward until it disengages in the housing bores.

2) Pull plugs out of guide sleeves and remove guide pins with a 7 mm socket wrench. Pull housing toward outside of car by hand to push back the piston slightly. Remove housing. Pull disc pad out of piston and lay housing aside suspended with wire. Do not disconnect hydraulic line. Remove outer disc pad from holder.

CAUTION: **If fluid level is too high in reservoir, overflow will result when during installation pistons are pushed back into calipers.**

PORSCHE (Cont.)

Removal (All Other Models)

1) Raise and support vehicle. Remove tire and wheel. Disconnect disc pad wear indicator electrical connection (if equipped).

2) Remove retaining pin clip and retaining pins. On 911SC, squeeze spreader spring and remove disc pads.

3) On all other models, remove inside disc pad with pad remover tool. Outside disc pad is guided by a tab on sliding caliper frame. Remove outer disc pad by pushing frame out away from rotor and removing disc pad.

Installation (All Models)

1) Push piston back into caliper using tool (P83), or wooden block. Remove anti-rotation locks (if equipped), and clean all parts with alcohol.

2) Inspect all parts for damage or wear. Ensure piston 20° position is correct using gauge (P84). Install remaining parts in reverse order of removal, replacing parts as necessary.

Fig. 2: Positioning Caliper Piston Using 20° Gauge

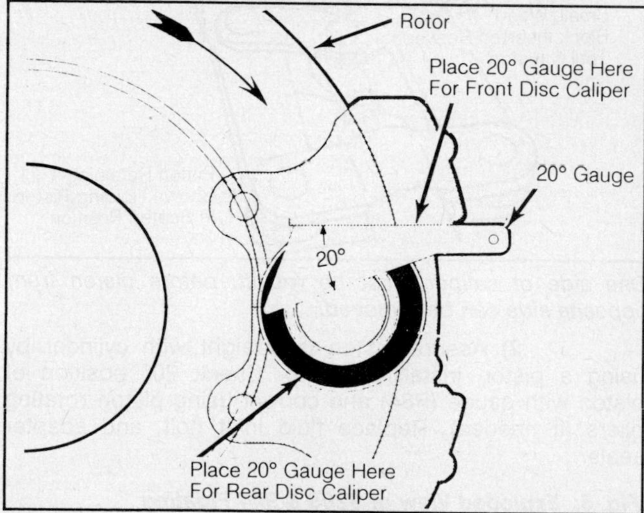
Rotor
Place 20° Gauge Here
For Front Disc Caliper
20° Gauge
20°
Place 20° Gauge Here
For Rear Disc Caliper

Adjustment for all disc brake calipers.

BRAKE CALIPER

CAUTION: When any fluid fitting is disconnected, fluid will drain from reservoir through master cylinder and out open fitting. To avoid this, depress brake pedal far enough so piston cup will pass the compensating (resupply) port.

Removal

1) Raise and support vehicle. Remove tire and wheel. On floating frame calipers, remove disc pads as previously described. Remove splash shield (if equipped).

2) Disconnect and plug hydraulic line. Remove caliper mounting bolts and remove caliper.

Installation

To install, reverse removal procedure and bleed hydraulic system.

BRAKE ROTOR

Removal

1) Raise and support vehicle. Remove tire and wheel. Remove caliper as previously described and hang from frame with wire. Do not disconnect hydraulic line.

2) On front brake rotors, remove dust cap, loosen clamp lock screw, then remove clamp nut and thrust washer. Remove rotor and wheel bearings as an assembly, then separate.

3) On rear brake rotors, remove rotor attaching bolts and remove rotor. Mark rotor and hub for reassembly reference. Remove hub-to-rotor bolts (if equipped), and separate hub from rotor.

NOTE: If rear rotor cannot be removed by hand, insert two 8 mm bolts into attaching screw holes, and alternately tighten bolts to press rotor from hub.

Installation

To install, reverse removal procedure. Bleed hydraulic system and adjust front wheel bearings.

NOTE: Rotors must be installed in original position due to cooling holes and internal ventilation channels. These holes and channels are different for right and left sides.

PARKING BRAKE SHOES (REAR DISC BRAKE ONLY)

Removal

1) Raise and support vehicle. Remove tire and wheel. Remove parking brake drum retaining screws, and remove parking brake drum.

2) Remove parking brake cable attachment from brake shoes. Remove expander shoe retaining springs and pins. Raise upper shoe and remove adjuster and spring. Remove lower shoe retainer and remove parking brake shoes.

Installation

To install, reverse removal procedure.

MASTER CYLINDER

Removal

1) On 911SC, raise and support vehicle. Drain brake fluid from reservoir. Pull back on accelerator pedal to detach pedal from pad.

2) Remove floor mat and floor board. Withdraw boot from master cylinder. Remove underpanel covering front axle.

3) On all models, remove hydraulic lines, electrical connections and reservoir tubes (if equipped). Remove mounting nuts, and remove master cylinder.

Fig. 3: Push Rod-to-Master Cylinder Piston Clearance on 911SC Models

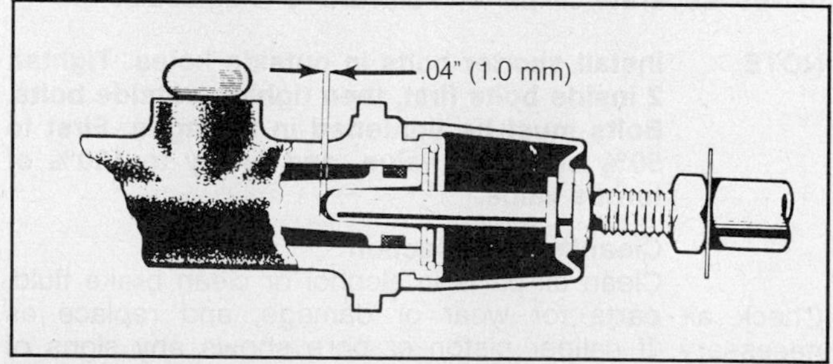
.04" (1.0 mm)

Be sure push rod is correctly installed before checking clearance.

Installation

1) To install, reverse removal procedure, noting the following: On 911SC, be sure push rod is correctly installed and that clearance between push rod, and piston is .04" (1.0 mm).

2) Use a sealing material on cylinder flange to prevent water leakage into driver's compartment. Bleed hydraulic system.

POWER BRAKE UNIT

NOTE: **Before removal, test check valve and power brake unit for operation. To test check valve, pull off vacuum hose, place finger over check valve and crank engine; vacuum should be created. To check power brake unit, push on brake pedal several times with engine stopped. Hold pedal down and start engine. If power brake unit is operating properly, brake pedal will drop slightly.**

Removal

1) With master cylinder removed, disconnect vacuum hose from power brake unit.

2) Remove pin connecting power brake unit operating rod to brake pedal assembly, remove attaching nuts and remove power brake unit from vehicle.

Installation

1) To install, reverse removal procedures noting the following: Apply sealer to power brake unit mounting surface and vacuum line connections.

2) Adjust pedal height and bleed hydraulic system.

OVERHAUL

BRAKE CALIPER

Disassembly (911SC)

1) Clamp caliper, by mounting flange in vise. Remove dust boot retaining ring and dust boot.

2) Install piston retaining tool (P83) to 1 piston, and place thin wooden block between tool and piston to be removed. *See Fig. 5.*

3) Apply light air pressure to fluid inlet hole to remove piston. Remove piston seal from cylinder groove without damaging bore or groove.

4) Repeat procedure for opposite piston after reassembly of first piston.

Separating Caliper Halves

1) Caliper halves should only be separated if "O" ring seals between caliper halves show signs of leakage.

2) To separate, remove bolts attaching caliper halves, separate caliper and discard "O" ring seals.

NOTE: **Install shorter bolts in outside holes. Tighten 2 inside bolts first, then tighten outside bolts. Bolts must be tightened in 2 stages. First to 50% of torque value, and finally to 100% of torque value.**

Cleaning & Inspection

Clean all parts in alcohol or clean brake fluid. Check all parts for wear or damage, and replace as necessary. If caliper piston or bore shows any signs of wear or damage, complete caliper assembly must be replaced.

Reassembly

1) To reassemble, reverse disassembly procedure noting the following: Use new rubber components, dust cover retaining ring and pad retaining plates. Apply brake cylinder paste to piston and cylinder seal.

Fig. 4: Using Air Pressure to Remove 911SC Caliper Piston

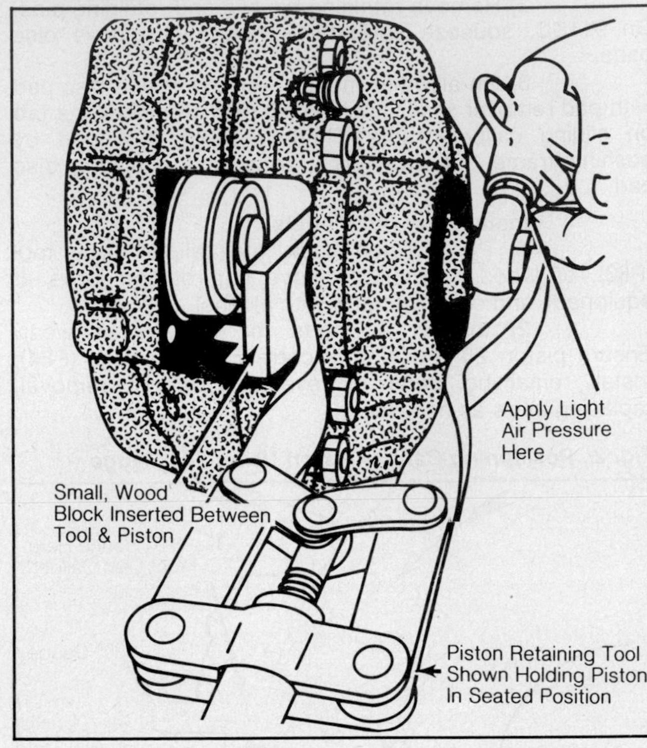
Apply Light
Air Pressure
Here
Small, Wood
Block Inserted Between
Tool & Piston
Piston Retaining Tool
Shown Holding Piston
In Seated Position

One side of caliper must be rebuilt, before piston from opposite side can be removed.

2) Assure piston is straight with cylinder by using a piston installing clamp. Check 20° position of piston with gauge (P84) and correct using piston rotating pliers (if needed). Replace fluid inlet bolt, and adapter seals.

Fig. 5: Exploded View of 928S & 944 Floating Frame Brake Caliper Assembly

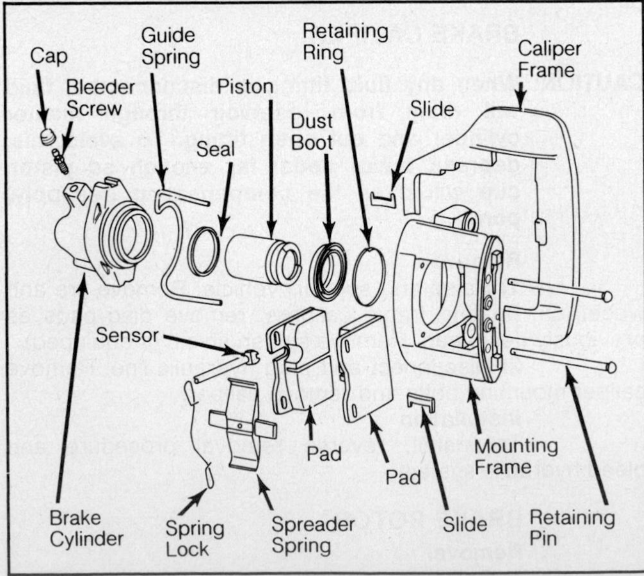
Cap
Guide
Spring
Retaining
Ring
Caliper
Frame
Bleeder
Screw
Piston
Slide
Dust
Boot
Seal
Sensor
Pad
Pad
Mounting
Frame
Brake
Cylinder
Spring
Lock
Spreader
Spring
Slide
Retaining
Pin

Piston seal and dust boot must be replaced if caliper is disassembled.

PORSCHE (Cont.)

Disassembly
(All Exc. 911SC & 928S with Floating Caliper

1) With disc pads removed, press caliper frame off mounting frame. Insert wooden block in caliper frame, and force cylinder assembly off caliper frame with plastic hammer.

2) Remove dust boot retaining ring and dust boot. Force piston out of caliper bore with light air pressure. Remove piston seal from cylinder groove without damaging groove or bore.

Cleaning & Inspection

Clean all parts in alcohol or clean brake fluid. Check all parts for wear or damage, and replace as necessary. If caliper piston or bore show any signs of wear or damage, complete caliper assembly must be replaced.

Reassembly

1) To reassemble, reverse disassembly procedure noting the following: Use new rubber components, dust cover retaining ring, and pad retaining plates.

2) Apply brake cylinder paste to piston, and cylinder seal. Assure piston is straight with cylinder by using piston installing clamp. Check 20° position.

Fig. 6: Exploded View of 928S Floating Caliper Assembly

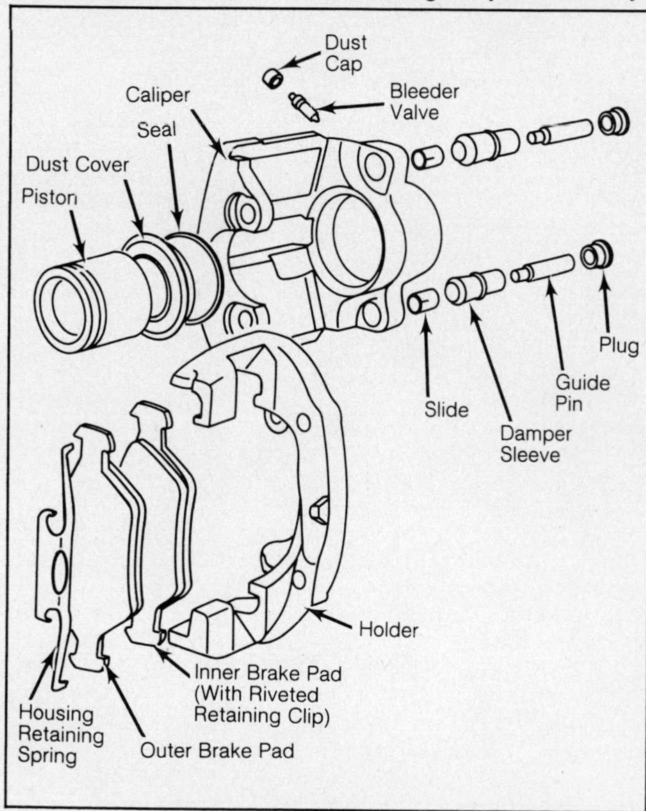
Dust Cap
Bleeder Valve
Caliper
Seal
Dust Cover
Piston
Plug
Guide Pin
Slide
Damper Sleeve
Holder
Inner Brake Pad (With Riveted Retaining Clip)
Housing Retaining Spring
Outer Brake Pad

Disassembly (928S with Floating Caliper)

1) With caliper off holder, remove disc pads. Support a piece of wood on piston and force piston out of caliper bore with light air pressure.

2) Remove piston seal from cylinder groove without damaging groove or bore.

Cleaning & Inspection

Clean all parts in alcohol or clean brake fluid. Check all parts for wear or damage, and replace as necessary. If caliper piston or bore show any signs of wear or damage, complete caliper assembly must be replaced.

Reassembly

1) To reassemble, reverse disassembly procedure noting the following: Use new rubber componants and replace damaged dampers and guides.

2) Apply brake paste to piston, cylinder bore and seal. Push dust cover on inside part of piston so that large diameter sealing lip extends over the piston

3) Press piston into housing. Small diameter sealing lip should settle in groove of piston. Check 20° position.

MASTER CYLINDER

Disassembly

1) Push in on primary piston to remove lock ring, then remove stop plate, and primary piston assembly.

2) Remove piston stop screw. Using compressed air, remove secondary piston. Remove secondary piston support washer, spring seat and return spring.

3) To remove hydraulic warning system assembly, remove sending unit and retaining bolt from master cylinder. Using compressed air, remove pistons and springs.

Cleaning & Inspection

Clean all parts with alcohol. Check all pistons, and cylinders for out-of-round, corrosion or damage. Inspect all other parts for scoring, excessive wear, corrosion or other damage.

Reassembly

1) To reassemble, reverse disassembly procedure noting the following: Lightly coat all parts with brake cylinder paste before installation.

2) Use new "O" ring seals on warning system sending unit and retaining bolt. Tighten all hydraulic lines and fittings. Bleed hydraulic system.

POWER BRAKE UNIT

NOTE: **Manufacturer does not recommend overhaul of power brake unit. Replace as complete assembly, if defective.**

TIGHTENING SPECIFICATIONS

Application	Ft. Lbs. (N.m)
Caliper Mounting Bolts	
911SC	50 (68)
928S & 944	61 (83)
Caliper Housing Bolts (911SC, Front)	43 (58)
Rotor-to Hub Bolts	
911SC	17 (23)
928S	84 INCH Lbs. (10)

Brakes

PORSCHE (Cont.)

DISC BRAKE ROTOR SPECIFICATIONS

Application	Disc Diameter In. (mm)	Lateral Runout In. (mm)	Parallelism In. (mm)	Original Thickness In. (mm)	Min. Refinish Thickness In. (mm)	Discard Thickness In. (mm)
911SC & 944						
Front	.....	.004 (.10)	.0008 (.02)	.807 (20.5)	.751 (19.1)	.728 (18.5)
Rear	.....	.004 (.10)	.0008 (.02)	.787 (20.0)	.732 (18.6)	.708 (18.0)
928S						
Front [1]	.....	.004 (.10)	.0012 (.03)	.787 [2] (20)	.756 (19.2)	.732 (18.6)
Front [3]	.....	.004 (.10)	.0008 (.02)	1.26 (32)	1.23 (31.2)	1.20 (30.6)
Rear	.....	.004 (.10)	.0012 (.03)	.787 (20)	.756 (19.2)	.732 (18.6)

[1] – For floating frame caliper disc.
[2] – For grooved disc is .807" (20.5 mm).
[3] – For floating caliper disc.

RENAULT

18i, Fuego & Le Car

DESCRIPTION

Brake system is hydraulically-operated using a tandem master cylinder and optional power brake unit. All models are equipped with front disc brakes and rear drum brakes.

A pressure limiter valve is installed in rear brake circuit to prevent premature rear wheel lock-up. Parking brake is cable-actuated on rear wheels.

ADJUSTMENT

REAR DRUM BRAKE SHOES

Le Car

Two adjusting lugs are located on backing plate. Using a wrench, turn front lug counterclockwise, and rear lug clockwise until shoes just contact drum. Then back off adjustment until drum rotates freely.

18i & Fuego

Adjust brake shoes by pressing down on brake pedal repeatedly.

BRAKE PEDAL FREE PLAY

Brake pedal free play (measured at pedal pad center) should be .203" (5 mm). To adjust free play, loosen operating rod lock nut and rotate operating rod until specified free play is obtained. Tighten lock nut.

PARKING BRAKE

Le Car

1) Adjust service brakes, then fully release parking brake. Loosen lock nut on adjustment rod. Tighten adjustment nut until lining just meets drum.

2) At this point, parking brake lever travel should be about 6 notches. Tighten lock nut, and check operation.

18i & Fuego

Place vehicle on a lift with parking brake handle released. Screw on equalizer nut until cable deflection between secondary cable, and vehicle chassis is about .74" (20 mm). Check parking brake lever travel. It should move a minimum of 12 notches.

Fig. 1: Le Car Parking Brake Adjustment Points

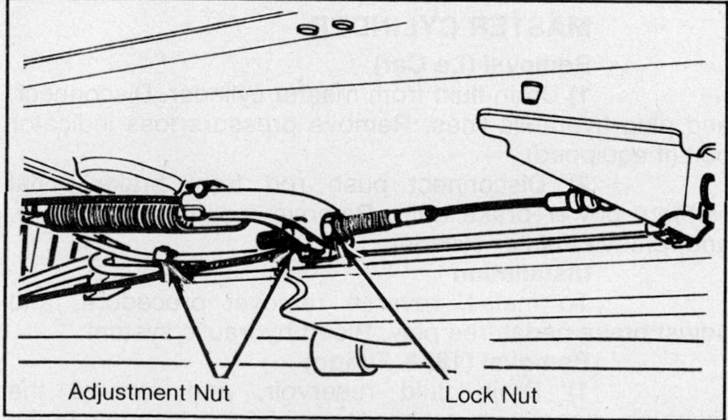
Adjustment Nut
Lock Nut

BRAKE WARNING LIGHT

1) A dual warning light is mounted on instrument panel. Light should glow when parking brake lever is pulled 1 notch and go off when lever is fully released (ignition on).

2) To check circuit warning sensor, release parking brake (ignition on), and ensure light is off. Raise master cylinder reservoir cap; light should glow. If not, check bulb or circuit connections.

REAR BRAKE PRESSURE LIMITER

NOTE: **Limiter must always be checked and adjusted with vehicle on level ground, fuel tank full, trunk empty and driver's seat occupied.**

1) To check limiter, remove 1 rear wheel cylinder bleeder screw, and install a pressure gauge into vacant hole.

2) Bleed system through screw on gauge. Depress brake pedal, and check pressure at wheel cylinder. Pressure on all models should be 405-465 psi (28.5-32.5 kg/cm²).

3) Release lock nut and tighten adjustment nut to increase pressure or loosen it to reduce pressure. Apply brake pedal several times, and recheck adjustment. Remove pressure gauge, and bleed system.

Fig. 2: Pressure Limiter Adjustment Points

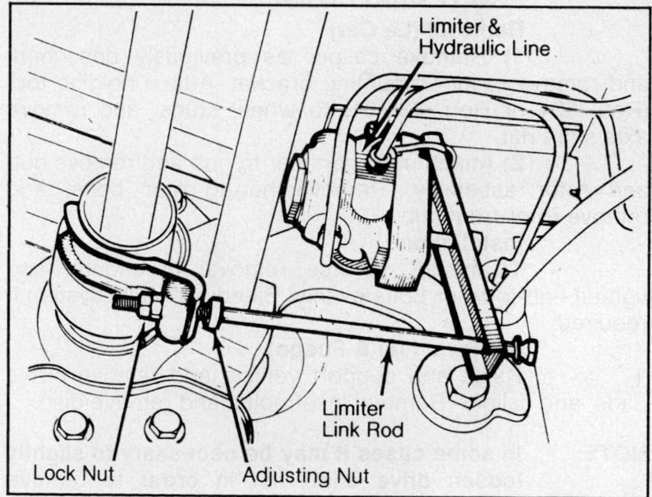
Limiter &
Hydraulic Line
Limiter
Link Rod
Lock Nut
Adjusting Nut

Le Car shown, 18i & Fuego are similar.

REMOVAL & INSTALLATION

FRONT DISC PADS

Removal & Installation (Le Car)

Caliper must be removed to remove brake pads. See Disc Brake Caliper Removal & Installation.

Removal (18i & Fuego)

1) Raise and support vehicle. Disconnect pad wear warning light wires. Take out retaining clip, and remove key.

2) With a screwdriver, gently pry between rotor and caliper at outer pad to push caliper piston back slightly. Remove pads.

Installation

1) Push caliper piston back with clamp. Put the 2 anti-squeal pins in place on new pads.

2) Position pads in caliper bracket, and engage key after having chamfered entry end of key. Install clip on key.

3) Reconnect wear-warning light wires. Press down brake pedal several times to seat pads.

FRONT DISC CALIPER

Removal (Le Car)

1) Raise and support vehicle and remove front wheels. Remove spring clips, and slide keys out of caliper, and mounting bracket.

2) Disconnect brake line fitting from flexible hose, and remove hose retaining clip from body.

3) Remove caliper from mounting bracket, and disconnect flexible hose from caliper. Remove brake pads, and pad spring from caliper.

Installation

To install, reverse removal procedure, and note the following: Install longest pad spring on outside of caliper. Tighten all fittings and bleed hydraulic system.

Removal (18i & Fuego)

Raise and support vehicle, and remove wheel and tire. Remove brake pads. Disconnect hydraulic line. Remove 2 caliper bolts, remove caliper.

Installation

To install, reverse removal procedure, and bleed brake system.

FRONT DISC ROTOR

Removal (Le Car)

1) Remove caliper as previously described, and remove caliper mounting bracket. Attach holding tool (Rou. 604 or Rou. 436-01) to wheel studs, and remove axle shaft nut.

2) Attach slide hammer to hub and remove hub and rotor assembly. Remove hub-to-rotor bolts, and remove rotor from hub.

Installation

To install, reverse removal procedure, and tighten hub-to-rotor bolts evenly. Bleed hydraulic system if required.

Removal (18i & Fuego)

Raise and support vehicle and remove brake pads, and caliper. Remove inset bolts, and remove disc.

NOTE: **In some cases it may be necessary to slightly loosen drive shaft nut in order to remove disc.**

Installation

1) Put the new disc in place on hub and attach with bolts. If necessary, torque drive shaft nut while holding hub with hub locking tool (Rou. 604).

2) Install the caliper, and tighten bolts. Install brake pads.

REAR BRAKE DRUM

Removal (Le Car)

Raise and support vehicle. Remove hub grease cap, cotter pin, nut and washer. Back off brake shoe adjuster. Attach slide hammer, and remove drum.

Installation

To install, reverse removal procedure. Lubricate wheel bearings and adjust. *See Wheel Bearing Adjustment in SUSPENSION Section.*

Removal (18i & Fuego)

1) Loosen parking brake. Remove dust plug from backing plate. Put a screwdriver against parking brake lever and push to free its peg from brake shoe.

2) Loosen lever by pushing toward rear. Remove grease cap, cotter pin, lock nut, drum hub nut, and washer. Remove drum, and outer wheel bearing.

Installation

1) Grease bearings, and place drum in place with outer bearing, drum hub, and nut. Adjust bearings. *See Wheel Bearing Adjustment in SUSPENSION Section.*

2) Install castle lock nut, and cotter pin. Put on grease cap filled with grease. Adjust brake shoes by pressing down on the brake pedal repeatedly. Adjust parking brake. Reinstall dust plug on backing plate.

REAR BRAKE SHOES

Removal

1) Remove wheel, and brake drum from vehicle. Install wheel cylinder clamp, then remove upper brake shoe return spring.

2) Disconnect parking brake cable from actuator lever. Remoe parking brake actuator link, and lower return spring.

3) Unhook shoe hold-down springs, and remove brake shoes.

Installation

To install, reverse removal procedure.

Fig. 3: Exploded View of Brake Shoe Assembly

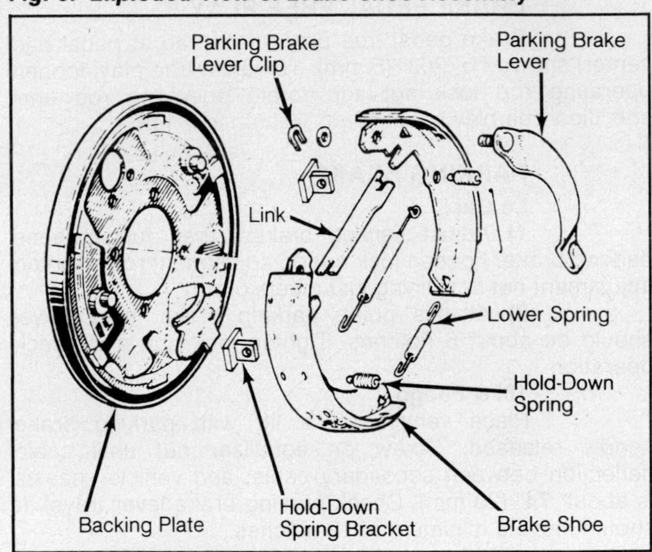
Parking Brake
Lever Clip
Parking Brake
Lever
Link
Lower Spring
Hold-Down
Spring
Backing Plate
Hold-Down
Spring Bracket
Brake Shoe

Le Car shown, 18i & Fuego are similar.

MASTER CYLINDER

Removal (Le Car)

1) Drain fluid from master cylinder. Disconnect, and plug hydraulic lines. Remove pressure loss indicator bolt (if equipped).

2) Disconnect push rod from brake pedal (without power brake unit). Remove mounting hardware, and remove master cylinder.

Installation

To install, reverse removal procedure, and adjust brake pedal free play. Bleed hydraulic system.

Removal (18i & Fuego)

1) Drain fluid reservoir, and remove the reservoir along with rubber hose rings. Unscrew brake lines, and mark their positions on master cylinder.

2) Remove 2 attaching nuts on brake booster. Remove master cylinder.

RENAULT (Cont.)

Installation

1) Check master cylinder operating clearance. The piston rod projection length should be .354" (9 mm). Attach master cylinder to brake booster.

2) Attach hydraulic lines in the following order: Right front wheel, left front wheel, left rear wheel, and right rear wheel. Bleed brake system.

POWER BRAKE UNIT

NOTE: Power brake unit is not serviceable, only the air filter and check valve can be serviced.

Removal (Le Car)

1) Disconnect battery, and remove fluid from master cylinder. Remove engine air cleaner (if necessary).

2) Disconnect hydraulic lines at master cylinder, and remove pressure loss indicator valve bolt (if equipped). Disconnect vacuum hose, and remove clevis from brake pedal.

3) Remove power brake unit attaching nuts from pedal side of firewall. Remove master cylinder and power cylinder as an assembly. Separate master cylinder from power brake unit.

Removal (18i & Fuego)

Remove master cylinder from vehicle. Remove brake pedal push rod adjuster link pin. Remove brake booster attaching nuts on firewall. Remove brake booster from vehicle, saving support spacer.

Installation (All Models)

To install reverse removal procedure, and adjust push rod-to-master cylinder clearance. Clearance should be .36" (9.13 mm) on Le Car and .35" (9.0 mm) on 18i and Fuego. On all models, bleed hydraulic system.

Check Valve Replacement

Check valve is located on power brake unit. To replace, remove vacuum input line, and pull and turn check valve out of power unit. Install new check valve by pushing and turning to seat valve. Reconnect vacuum line.

OVERHAUL

NOTE: Master cylinder, power brake unit, and brake pressure limiter cannot be overhauled.

FRONT CALIPER

Disassembly

1) Remove caliper from vehicle, and remove piston dust cover. Using compressed air introduced through caliper fluid inlet, carefully remove piston from caliper assembly.

2) Remove piston seal from cylinder. On Le Car, use a wedge to slightly spread legs of caliper piston bracket a small amount. Remove caliper stop peg from piston bracket. Slide cylinder assembly from bracket.

Cleaning & Inspection

Clean all parts in denatured alcohol, and inspect for piston and cylinder wear. Replace worn parts as required. Replace all rubber seals during overhaul.

Reassembly

Lubricate cylinder bore, piston, and seals with brake fluid prior to reassembly. To reassemble, reverse disassembly procedure.

WHEEL CYLINDER

Disassembly & Reassembly

Remove dust boots, pistons, cups and spring. Examine components for damage or excessive wear. Replace worn parts as required. Before reassembly, dip pistons and cups in clean brake fluid.

Fig. 4: Exploded View of 18i & Fuego Caliper Assembly

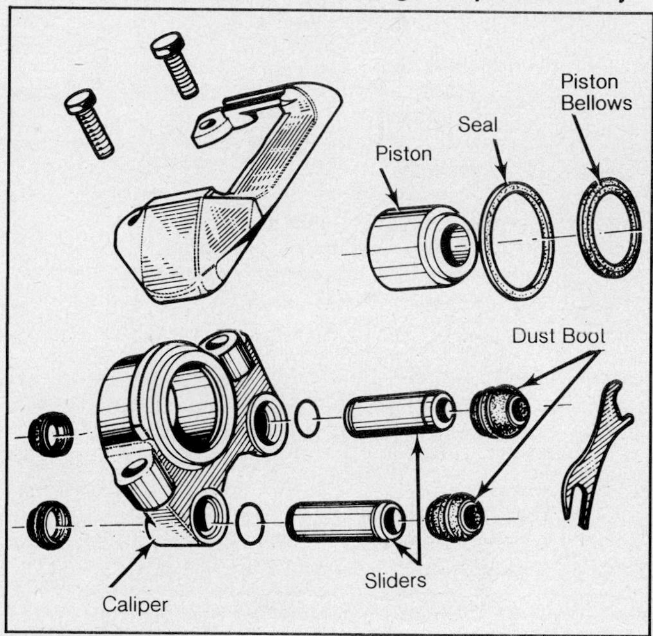
Piston
Bellows
Seal
Piston
Dust Boot
Sliders
Caliper

TIGHTENING SPECIFICATIONS

Application	Ft. Lbs. (N.m)
Caliper Bracket Bolts	
Le Car	50 (68)
18i & Fuego	74 (101)
Caliper Attaching Bolts	
18i & Fuego	144 (60)
Rotor-to-Hub	
Le Car	20 (27)
Drive Shaft Nut	
Le Car	90 (122)
18i & Fuego	185 (252)

DRUM BRAKE SPECIFICATIONS

Application	Drum Diam. In. (mm)	Drum Width In. (mm)	Max. Drum Refinish Diam. In. (mm)	Brake Cyl. Diam. In. (mm)	Master Cyl. Diam. In. (mm)
18i & Fuego	8.996 (228.5)	.....	9.035 (229.5)	55/64 (22)	13/16 (19)
Le Car	7.10 (180)	.....	7.136 (181)	55/64 (22)	13/16 (20.6)

Brakes

RENAULT (Cont.)

DISC BRAKE ROTOR SPECIFICATIONS

Application	Disc Diameter In. (mm)	Lateral Runout In. (mm)	Parallelism In. (mm)	Original Thickness In. (mm)	Min. Refinish Thickness In. (mm)	Discard Thickness In. (mm)
18i & Fuego	9.370 (238)	.003 (.08)	.....	.472 (12)	.....	.433 (11)
Le Car	9.000 (228)	.004 (.10)	.....	.395 (10)	[1]	.354 (9)

[1] — Rotor cannot be machined.

SAAB 900 & 900 TURBO

DESCRIPTION

Brake system is hydraulically-operated by tandem master cylinder and vacuum power brake unit acting on 4-wheel disc brakes. Front brakes have sliding-yoke Girling calipers. Rear brakes are fixed-yoke ATE units. Brake circuit is double-diagonal system (right front, left rear/left front, right rear). Parking brake is cable operated on FRONT caliper assemblies.

Master cylinder contains level sensor, which lights warning lamp on instrument panel if fluid is low. Since cylinder is for both brake and clutch fluid, warning light has dual function. If fluid is leaking, clutch will become inoperative first.

BRAKE WARNING LIGHT

1) Brake warning lights are mounted on instrument panel. Turn on ignition switch. Parking brake light should glow when brake lever is pulled 1 notch and go off when lever is fully released.

2) To check lever indicator circuit, raise master cylinder filler cap. Warning light should glow. If not, check bulb, circuit connections and sensor.

ADJUSTMENT

PARKING BRAKE

1) Before adjusting, apply brake lever several times to stretch cables. Slide seat completely forward for access to adjustment panel in shift lever tunnel. Remove ashtray.

2) To adjust, rotate cable adjusting nuts under plastic cover at rear of parking brake lever. With parking brake off, distance between lever on front caliper and yoke should be .019" (.5 mm).

3) With engine off, slowly pump pedal until foot brake starts to operate. Pull parking brake lever up 5 notches. Continue to pump brake pedal until parking brake operates after being pulled up an additional 2-4 notches.

NOTE: **Parking brake cables are crossed. To adjust left cable, right adjusting nut must be rotated and vice versa.**

REMOVAL & INSTALLATION

DISC BRAKE PADS

Removal (Front)

Raise and support vehicle. Remove tire and wheel. Rotate disc so recess on edge is in line with brake pads. Remove damper spring, pin retaining clip and pad retaining pin. If retaining pin is difficult to remove, tap out using thin punch. Remove brake pads.

NOTE: **Both inner and outer front brake pads are semi-metallic and are interchangeable.**

Installation

1) If necessary, siphon fluid from master cylinder. Rotate direct piston with piston wrench (89 96 043) as piston is pressed into cylinder. Ensure piston movement has not moved dust cover and yoke moves easily in groove on housing.

2) Lubricate grooves with Castrol-45 grease (30 08 612). Fit new pads together with "U" pin retaining clip and damper spring. To complete installation, reverse removal procedure. Adjust parking brake.

Removal (Rear)

Raise and support vehicle. Remove tire and wheel. Tap out brake pad retaining pins using .11" (2.8 mm) drift. Remove retaining spring. Remove brake pads. If required, use extractor (89 95 043).

NOTE: **Inner and outer rear brake pads are asbestos-free organic composition.**

Installation

Using handle of piston tool (89 96 043), push pistons back. Do not overflow master cylinder. Install new pads. Insure piston position is correct. *See Fig. 4.* Fit pad retaining pins and pin retaining clip. To complete installation, reverse removal procedure.

DISC BRAKE CALIPER

Removal

Raise and support vehicle. Remove wheels and tires. Remove brake pads. On front wheel calipers, disconnect parking brake cable from lever on caliper. On all calipers, disconnect hydraulic lines. Plug lines to prevent entry of dirt or loss of fluid. Remove caliper mount bolts and caliper.

Installation

To install, reverse removal procedure. Tighten mount bolts using new locking plate. Bleed hydraulic system. Adjust parking brake cables.

DISC BRAKE ROTOR

Removal

Remove brake pads and suspend caliper out of way. Do not hang from hydraulic line. Remove mount bolts and rotor.

NOTE: **If hub must be removed, use puller (89 96 084). Hub nut torque is 250-266 ft.lbs. (340-360 N.m).**

Installation

To install, reverse removal procedure. Tighten all nuts and bolts. Adjust parking brake if necessary.

MASTER CYLINDER

Removal

1) Remove electrical lead to warning switch on master cylinder. Disconnect clutch master cylinder hose from fluid reservoir. Plug reservoir nipple to prevent fluid loss.

2) Disconnect hydraulic lines from master cylinder. Remove master cylinder-to-power brake unit mount nuts. Lift off master cylinder.

Installation

To install, reverse removal procedure and bleed hydraulic system.

POWER BRAKE UNIT

Removal

1) Remove steering column bearing cover, ashtray and safety padding screw from inside vehicle. Remove safety padding screws from inside engine compartment. Remove center console if equipped.

2) Disconnect electrical leads, hydraulic and vacuum lines from master cylinder and power brake unit. Plug hydraulic lines to prevent fluid loss. Remove cotter pin from brake pedal push rod.

SAAB 900 & 900 TURBO (Cont.)

3) Remove 4 attaching nuts from inside vehicle. Lift off master cylinder and power brake unit as an assembly.

NOTE: Power brake unit is non-serviceable. Replace as a unit. The dome nut on output push rod is set by the factory. Do not adjust.

Installation

To install, reverse removal procedure and bleed hydraulic system.

Check Valve Replacement

Remove hose clamps and check valve from power unit. To install, reverse removal procedure.

Filter Replacement

Remove power brake unit. Remove dust boot and filter retainer. Withdraw silencer and filter from end of unit. To install, cut slit in filter and slip over push rod. Reverse removal procedure. Ensure slots in filter and silencer are 180° apart.

OVERHAUL

CALIPER ASSEMBLY

Disassembly (Girling Type)

1) With caliper removed, mount assembly in soft-jawed vise. Remove parking brake return spring. Separate yoke from caliper assembly. *See Fig. 1*.

2) Remove spring and parking brake lever from yoke. Remove retaining ring and dust boot. With compressed air, force indirect piston from caliper.

3) Press direct piston push rod by hand. Remove piston from caliper. Remove "O" rings and seal rings from caliper bore and pistons.

Cleaning & Inspection

Wash parts, except indirect piston assembly, in clean brake fluid. Dry with lint-free cloth. Inspect for corrosion, damage or wear. Replace defective parts and rubber parts during overhaul.

NOTE: Do not use solvent or brake fluid on indirect piston assembly. Wipe clean only.

Reassembly

1) Replace any worn, damaged or corroded parts. On indirect piston, replace "O" ring on push rod and "O" ring retainer at parking brake lever. Lubricate cylinder bore with brake fluid. Fit new piston seals.

NOTE: Brake fluid must be DOT 4 rated. Do not use DOT 5 Silicone brake fluid in Saab vehicles.

2) Lubricate hole for parking brake lever with grease (89 94 782). Fit anchor plate to push rod. Fit push rod into hole in indirect piston. Ensure recess in anchor plate comes immediately over spring in piston. Lubricate indirect piston. Insert in caliper housing. Yoke recess must be in line with groove in caliper housing.

3) Push direct piston into cylinder. Using brake piston tool (89 96 043), screw together piston and push rod. Push in both pistons until edges of dust cover grooves are flush with caliper. Fit new dust covers and retaining rings. Install yoke spring and parking brake lever to yoke.

4) Brush Castrol-45 grease (30 08 612) on yoke sliding surfaces. Apply grease to seating surface of pad retaining disc in housing. Align yoke guide edges with grooves in caliper housing. Lift parking brake lever. Fit end of axle pin into hole in indirect piston.

5) Ensure yoke fits into recess in indirect piston. Install parking lever return spring. Check clearance between sliding surface of yoke and brake housing. No clearance is allowed on bleeder screw side. Opposite side must have .006"-.012" (.15-.30 mm) clearance. *See Fig. 2.*

Fig. 1: Exploded View of Girling Caliper

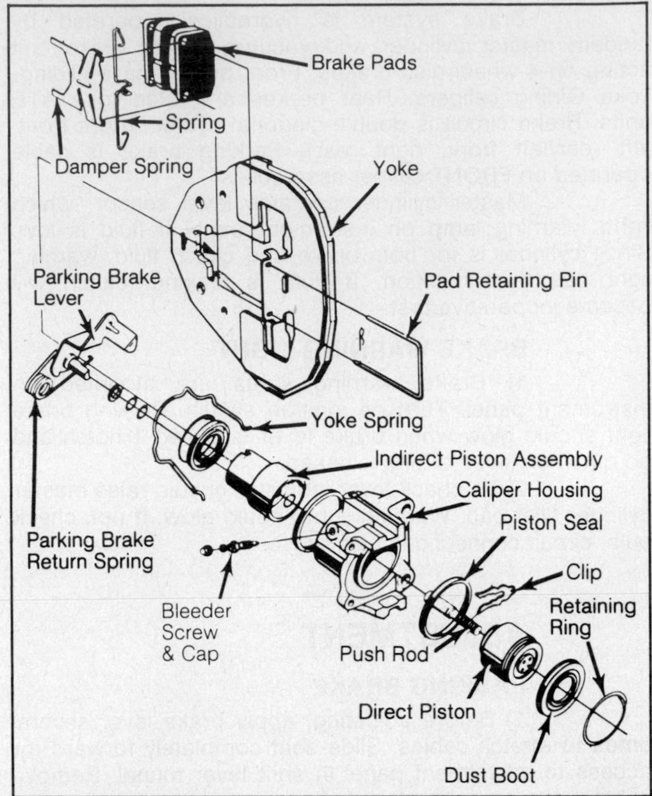
Brake Pads
Spring
Damper Spring
Yoke
Parking Brake Lever
Pad Retaining Pin
Yoke Spring
Indirect Piston Assembly
Caliper Housing
Parking Brake Return Spring
Piston Seal
Clip
Bleeder Screw & Cap
Retaining Ring
Push Rod
Direct Piston
Dust Boot

Ensure recess in anchor plate comes immediately over spring in piston.

Fig. 2: Girling Caliper Clearance Measuring Points

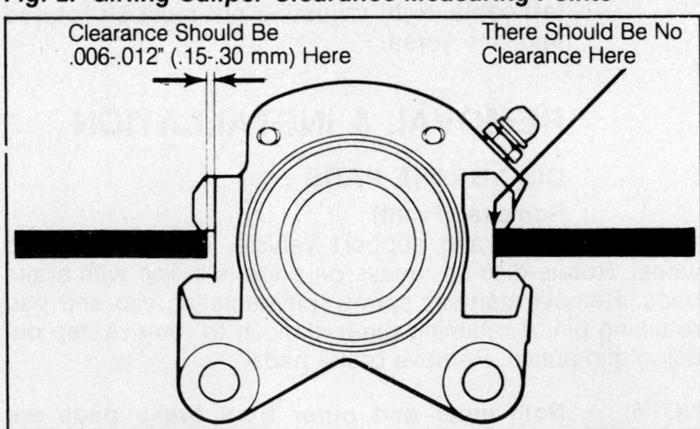
Clearance Should Be .006-.012" (.15-.30 mm) Here
There Should Be No Clearance Here

Align yoke guide edges with grooves in brake housing.

Disassembly (ATE Type)

Remove caliper and pads. Remove dust covers and retaining rings. *See Fig. 3*. Insert wood block between pistons. Apply compressed air to fluid inlet port to force pistons out of cylinder bores. Remove piston seals from bores. Remove bleeder screw. Clean caliper.

SAAB 900 & 900 TURBO (Cont.)

Fig. 3: Exploded View of ATE Caliper

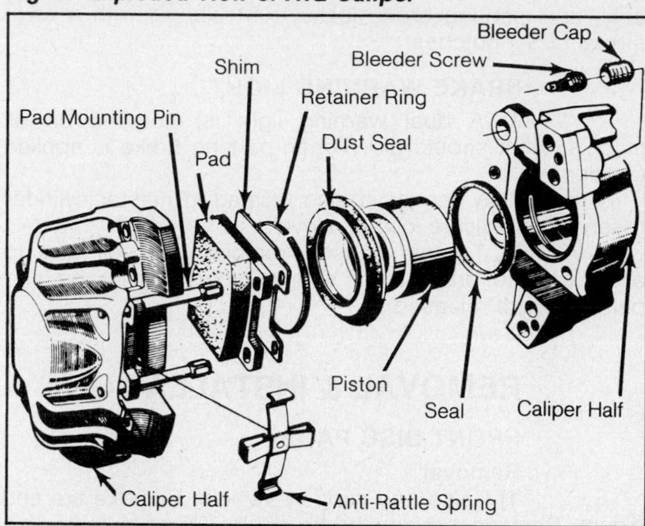
Bleeder Cap
Bleeder Screw
Shim
Retainer Ring
Pad Mounting Pin
Dust Seal
Pad
Piston
Seal
Caliper Half
Caliper Half
Anti-Rattle Spring

Do not separate caliper halves.

Cleaning & Inspection

Wash parts in clean brake fluid. Inspect cylinder bores and pistons for corrosion, damage or wear. Replace defective parts. Replace all rubber parts during overhaul.

Reassembly

1) Coat all parts with clean brake fluid. Install new piston seals in cylinder bores. Carefully install pistons into cylinder bores.

2) Check piston position with template (89 953 42). *See Fig. 4.* Install rubber boots and retaining clips. Install bleeder screw and disc pads.

Fig. 4: Checking ATE Caliper Piston Position

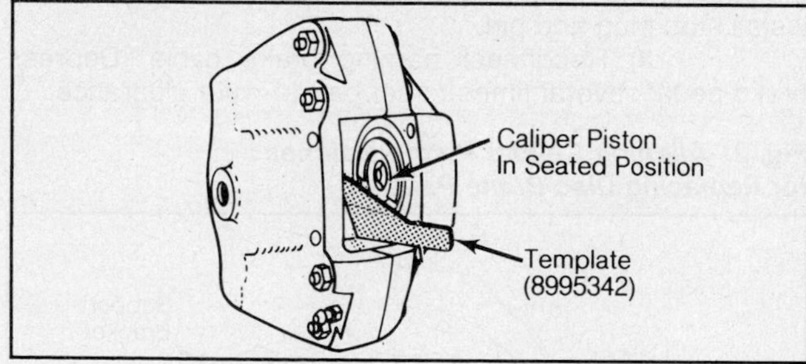
Caliper Piston
In Seated Position
Template
(8995342)

Template gauge must be held against lower surface of caliper.

MASTER CYLINDER

Disassembly

1) With master cylinder removed from vehicle, drain brake fluid from reservoir. Mount cylinder in a soft-jawed vise. Remove retaining pins. Separate reservoir from master cylinder.

2) Remove rubber seals from reservoir mounting holes in cylinder. Push in on primary piston. Pull secondary piston stop pin from forward reservoir mounting hole. *See Fig. 5.*

3) Remove circlip. Take out primary piston assembly and spring. Remove cylinder from vise. Carefully knock against block of wood, or blow out with compressed air, to remove secondary piston assembly and spring.

4) Remove springs and sealing rings from two pistons. Keep pistons and their rings separate so they can be fitted back into cylinders from which removed. Remove brake warning switch from master cylinder. Remove end plug. Lift out warning valve assembly.

NOTE: **When piston seals are removed, note seal lip direction for reassembly reference.**

Cleaning & Inspection

Wash all parts in clean brake fluid and dry with clean, lint-free cloth. Inspect parts for corrosion, damage or wear. Replace defective parts. Replace rubber parts during overhaul.

Reassembly

Reverse disassembly procedure. When installing primary and secondary pistons, coat parts with clean brake fluid. Do not damage seals during installation of pistons. Be sure seals are installed facing in the proper direction.

NOTE: **When installing pistons in master cylinder bore, avoid seal damage. Rotate each spring and piston assembly with twisting motion.**

Fig. 5: Exploded View of Girling Master Cylinder

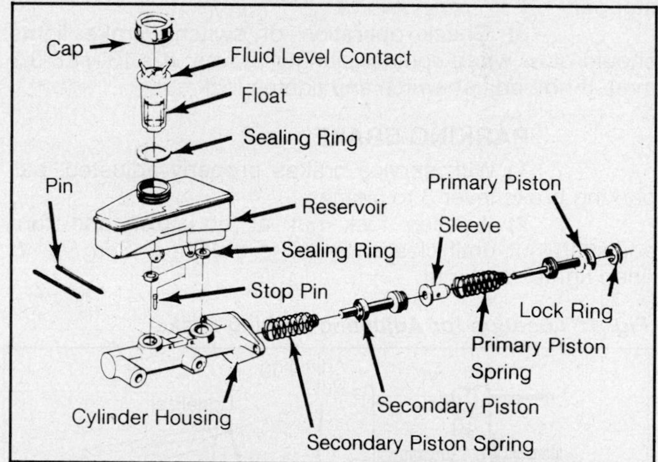
Cap
Fluid Level Contact
Float
Sealing Ring
Pin
Reservoir
Primary Piston
Sleeve
Sealing Ring
Stop Pin
Lock Ring
Primary Piston
Spring
Secondary Piston
Cylinder Housing
Secondary Piston Spring

Inspect cylinder bore for corrosion, damage or wear.

DISC BRAKE ROTOR SPECIFICATIONS

Application	Disc Diameter In. (mm)	Lateral Runout In. (mm)	Parallelism In. (mm)	Original Thickness In. (mm)	Min. Refinish Thickness In. (mm)	Discard Thickness In. (mm)
900 & 900 Turbo						
Front	11.0 (280)	.004 (.10)	.0006 (.015)	.500 (12.7)	.461 (11.7)	.441 (11.2)
Rear	10.6 (269.5)	.004 (.10)	.0006 (.015)	.413 (10.5)	.374 (9.5)	.354 (9.0)

SUBARU 1600 & 1800

DESCRIPTION

Service brake system is a diagonally-split, dual hydraulic circuit with tandem master cylinder and vacuum-suspended type power brake unit. Front brakes are Bendix automatic-adjusting discs. Rear brakes are leading/trailing type drum. Parking brake is mechanically-actuated on FRONT brakes.

ADJUSTMENT

REAR DRUM BRAKE SHOES

1) Raise and support vehicle. Loosen adjuster lock nut and turn adjuster until wheel locks.

2) Back off adjusting nut 180°. Clearance between drum and shoes should be .004-.006" (.10-.15 mm).

PEDAL HEIGHT & FREE PLAY

1) Brake pedal height (measured from floorboard to pedal pad center) should be 5.3-5.9" (135-150 mm).

2) To adjust pedal height, loosen stop light switch lock nut and position out of way.

3) Loosen brake operating rod lock nut and turn operating rod until correct pedal height is obtained. Tighten operating rod lock nut.

4) Adjust brake pedal free play to .20-.43" (5-11 mm) with stop light switch. Tighten stop light switch lock nut.

STOP LIGHT SWITCH

1) Stop light switch is located under instrument panel, above brake pedal.

2) To adjust stop light switch, loosen lock nut and position switch so contact plunger touches pedal arm stopper.

3) Check operation of switch. Brake lights should glow when contact plunger moves .07-.13" (1.8-3.3 mm). If not, adjust switch and tighten lock nut.

PARKING BRAKE

1) With service brakes properly adjusted, pull parking brake lever 3 to 5 times.

2) Loosen lock nut at equalizer and turn adjusting nut until clearance "A" is obtained. *See Fig. 1.* Then tighten lock nut.

Fig. 1: Location for Adjusting Parking Brake

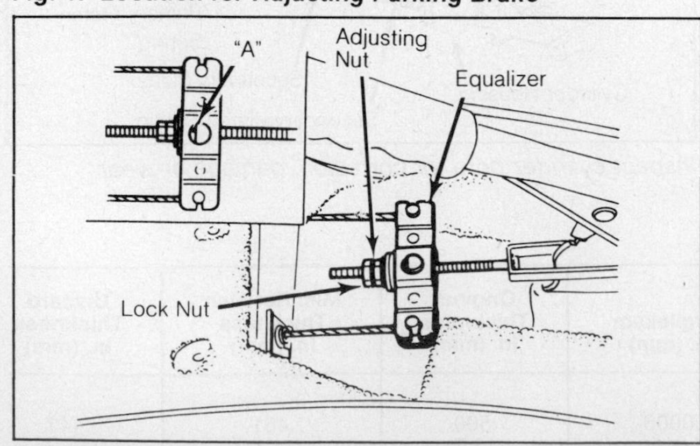
"A"
Adjusting Nut
Equalizer
Lock Nut

Clearance at "A" should be .02" (.5 mm).

3) Depress service brake pedal slightly (repeatedly) until parking brake locks front wheels with a lever stroke of 3-4 notches.

BRAKE WARNING LIGHT

1) A dual warning light is mounted on all models. Light should glow when parking brake is applied (ignition on).

2) A sensor is also located in master cylinder reservoir to indicate low fluid level.

3) To test sensor, remove reservoir cap to allow float to drop. Light should glow (ignition on and parking brake released).

REMOVAL & INSTALLATION

FRONT DISC PADS

Removal

1) Raise and support vehicle. Remove tire and wheel. Remove parking brake cable. Remove lower pin and stop plug.

2) Rotate caliper body up away from the disc. Remove pads, clips and shims from caliper support bracket.

NOTE: **Do not press on brake pedal after the pads have been removed. Do not disconnect hydraulic line.**

Installation

1) Turn piston clockwise with piston wrench to seat piston in caliper bore and align notches. *See Fig. 2.* After turning and seating piston, check piston boot for twist. If twisted, use a strip driver to correct.

2) Install shim on outer pad only (if required), then install clips and pads. Rotate caliper body down and install stop plug and pin.

3) Reconnect parking brake cable. Depress brake pedal several times to set pad-to-rotor clearance.

Fig. 2: Aligning Caliper Piston Notches for Replacing Disc Brake Pads

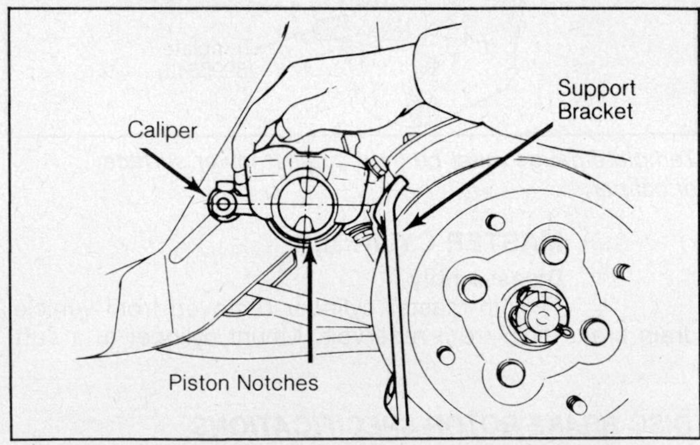
Caliper
Support Bracket
Piston Notches

Using a piston wrench, turn piston clockwise to align.

FRONT DISC CALIPER

Removal

1) Raise and support vehicle. Remove tire and wheel. Remove pads as previously described.

2) Disconnect and plug hydraulic line at caliper and remove parking brake cable. Remove caliper assem-

SUBARU 1600 & 1800 (Cont.)

bly. DO NOT remove support bracket unless rotor is being removed.

Installation

Apply silicone grease to lock pin and guide pin. Install caliper assembly, pads and parking brake cable. Install hydraulic line, then bleed hydraulic system.

FRONT DISC ROTOR

Removal

1) Raise and support vehicle. Remove tire and wheel. Remove disc pads as previously described.

2) Remove caliper assembly and hang from frame with wire. DO NOT disconnect hydraulic line. Remove caliper mounting bracket bolts and bracket.

3) Remove cotter pin and nut from axle shaft. Using a puller, pull rotor and hub assembly from axle. Remove hub-to-rotor bolts and separate rotor from hub.

NOTE: Replace mounting bracket when rotor is replaced.

Installation

To install, reverse removal procedure and tighten hub-to-rotor bolts evenly. Depress brake pedal several times to seat pads.

REAR BRAKE DRUM

Removal

1) Raise and support vehicle. Remove tire and wheel. Remove dust cap, nut and wheel bearing components (2WD).

Fig. 3: Exploded View of Rear Drum Brake Assembly

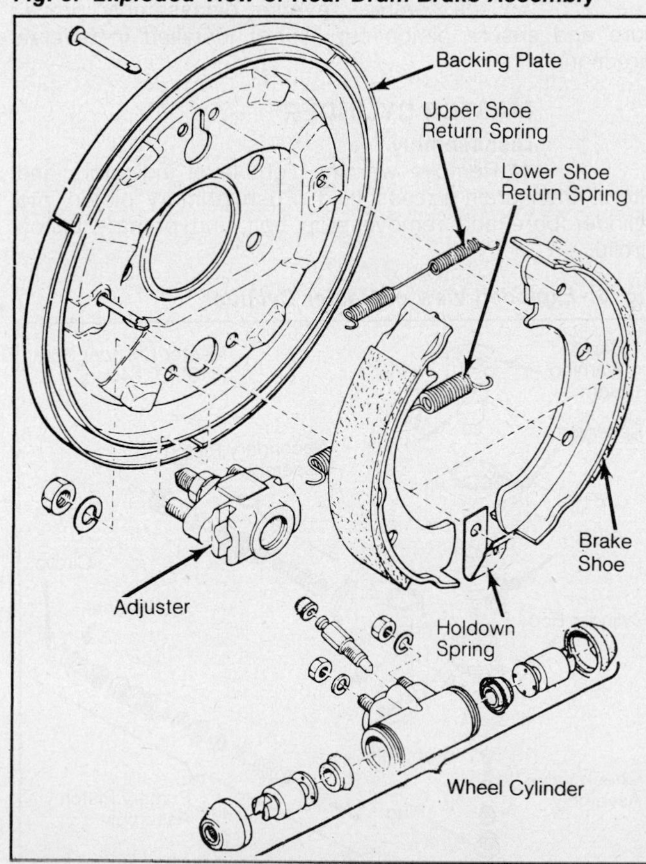
Backing Plate
Upper Shoe Return Spring
Lower Shoe Return Spring
Brake Shoe
Adjuster
Holdown Spring
Wheel Cylinder

Lower brake return spring is larger in diameter.

2) Remove cotter pin and castle nut on 4-wheel drive. Remove brake drum. Loosen brake adjustment if necessary and use puller if required to pull off brake drum.

Installation

To install, reverse removal procedure and adjust wheel bearings. *See Wheel Bearing Adjustment in SUSPENSION Section.*

REAR BRAKE SHOES

Removal

1) With brake drum removed, remove and plug hydraulic lines from wheel cylinder. Remove backing plate bolts and backing plate assembly.

2) Separate shoes from backing plate by removing hold down springs. Disconnect lower end first and then remove upper end from cylinder. Separate return springs from shoes. *See Fig. 3.*

Installation

1) To install, reverse removal procedure and note the following: Return springs are installed with coils on inside of shoe assemblies (next to backing plate).

2) Return springs are not interchangeable. Lower spring is larger in diameter. Adjust brakes and bleed hydraulic system.

MASTER CYLINDER

Removal

1) Siphon brake fluid from reservoir. Disconnect warning light level connection. Remove hydraulic lines.

2) Remove retaining nuts and remove master cylinder from power brake unit.

Installation

To install, reverse removal procedure and bleed hydraulic system.

POWER BRAKE UNIT

Removal

1) From inside vehicle, remove clevis pin and snap pin. Disconnect push rod from brake pedal. Remove power brake retaining nuts from firewall.

2) Remove nuts connecting hydraulic lines from master cylinder. Remove master cylinder retaining nuts. Disconnect vacuum hose at power brake unit and wiring harness from master cylinder.

3) Position master cylinder to one side without damaging hydraulic lines. Remove power brake unit.

Installation

To install, reverse removal procedure and bleed hydraulic system.

OVERHAUL

FRONT CALIPER

Disassembly

1) Thoroughly clean exterior of caliper with clean brake fluid. Remove outer pad clip and bleeder screw. Remove dust boot retainer and dust boot.

2) Apply compressed air to fluid inlet and force piston out of caliper bore. Carefully remove guide pin boot and piston seal.

3) Remove parking brake lever cap ring and lever cap, then remove snap ring from lever and spindle assembly.

SUBARU 1600 & 1800 (Cont.)

4) Mount caliper assembly in soft-jawed vise and install puller (925471000) to release spring washer tension. *See Fig. 5.*

5) With spring tension released, pull out lever and spindle. Remove puller and remove connecting link, return spring, spindle and cone spring.

Fig. 4: Exploded View of Front Disc Caliper Assembly

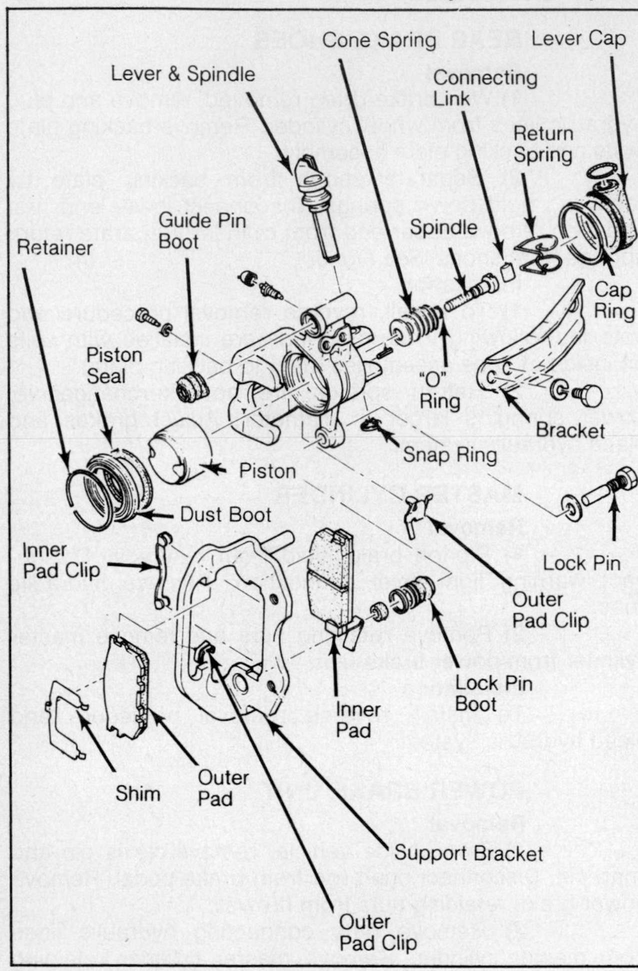

Cone Spring
Lever Cap
Lever & Spindle
Connecting Link
Return Spring
Guide Pin Boot
Spindle
Retainer
Cap Ring
Piston Seal
"O" Ring
Bracket
Snap Ring
Piston
Dust Boot
Inner Pad Clip
Lock Pin
Outer Pad Clip
Lock Pin Boot
Inner Pad
Shim
Outer Pad
Support Bracket
Outer Pad Clip

Replace piston seals if caliper is disassembled.

Cleaning & Inspection

Clean all components with brake fluid and ensure that inner cylinder wall is not scratched or corroded. Replace any damaged parts.

Reassembly

1) Coat piston seal with silicone grease and insert into cylinder by hand. Coat piston, piston boots and cylinder wall with brake fluid.

2) Hand insert piston. Install boot and retainer. Lightly coat spindle and "O" ring with silicone grease.

3) Insert spindle and install spring washers with puller (925471000). Lubricate and install connecting link (thick side in spindle head slot).

4) Install lever and spindle assembly. Be sure to force in the hooked portion of the return spring into the groove of the lever and spindle as shown in *Fig. 5.*

5) Remove puller. Install snap ring at end of lever and spindle. Install lever cap and cap retainer.

6) Clean fitting hole of guide pin in caliper body. Evenly tap guide pin boot into fitting hole. Make sure boot is not damaged.

NOTE: **Whenever the guide pin boot is removed, always replace it with a new one.**

Fig. 5: Removal & Installation of Lever & Spindle

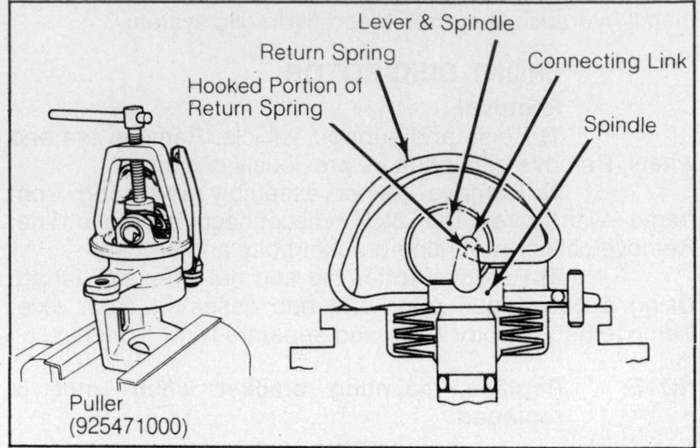

Lever & Spindle
Return Spring
Connecting Link
Hooked Portion of Return Spring
Spindle
Puller (925471000)

Place caliper in soft-jawed vise.

REAR WHEEL CYLINDER

Disassembly

Remove boot and take out piston with cup. DO NOT separate cup unless replacement is available.

Cleaning & Inspection

Clean all parts in brake fluid only. If cylinder is out of round or burred, replace as an assembly; DO NOT hone.

Reassembly

To reassemble, reverse disassembly procedure and ensure piston cup is not installed in reverse direction.

MASTER CYLINDER

Disassembly

1) Remove warning light level indicators and filters, then drain excess fluid. Push primary piston into cylinder bore and remove stop bolt and primary piston circlip.

Fig. 6: Exploded View of Master Cylinder

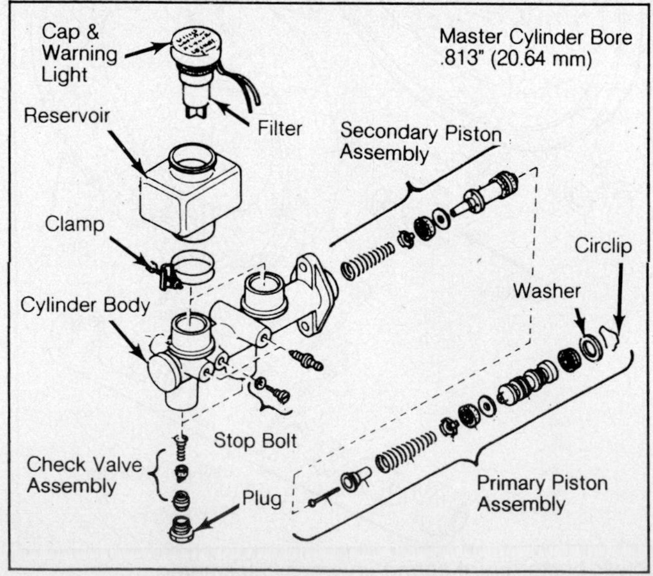

Cap & Warning Light
Master Cylinder Bore .813" (20.64 mm)
Reservoir
Filter
Secondary Piston Assembly
Clamp
Circlip
Washer
Cylinder Body
Stop Bolt
Check Valve Assembly
Plug
Primary Piston Assembly

Do not hone master cylinder.

SUBARU 1600 & 1800 (Cont.)

2) Remove stop washer and gasket, then remove primary and secondary piston assemblies. Remove check valve plug and valve assembly.

NOTE: **Do not disassemble piston assemblies. Piston cup replacement requires replacement of piston assemblies. Removal of fluid reservoir requires installation of new reservoir.**

Cleaning & Inspection

1) Clean all components in brake fluid. Inspect cylinder bore for smoothness and roundness. Replace cylinder if scored or out of round.

2) DO NOT hone cylinder. Check piston-to-cylinder clearance, and replace master cylinder if clearance is excessive or parts are worn.

Reassembly

To reassemble master cylinder, reverse disassembly procedure.

POWER BRAKE UNIT

Manufacturer does not recommend disassembly of this unit. Replace as complete assembly.

TIGHTENING SPECIFICATIONS

Application	Ft. Lbs. (N.m)
Caliper Lock Pin	12-17 (16-24)
Support Bracket Mounting Bolts	36-51 (49-69)
Backing Plate Mounting Bolts	34-43 (46-58)

DISC BRAKE ROTOR SPECIFICATIONS

Application	Disc Diameter In. (mm)	Lateral Runout In. (mm)	Parallelism In. (mm)	Original Thickness In. (mm)	Min. Refinish Thickness In. (mm)	Discard Thickness In. (mm)
1600 & 1800	7.24 (184)	.004 (.10)	.....	.492 (12.5)	.....	.394 (10)

DRUM BRAKE SPECIFICATIONS

Application	Drum Diam. In. (mm)	Drum Width In. (mm)	Max. Drum Refinish Diam. In. (mm)	Brake Cyl. Diam. In. (mm)	Master Cyl. Diam. In. (mm)
1600 & 1800	7.09 (180)	.....	7.17 (182)	.625 [1] (15.87)	.813 (20.64)

[1] – Diameter for Station Wagon and BRAT is .690" (17.46 mm).

TOYOTA

Camry, Celica, Corolla, Cressida, Land Cruiser, Pickup, Starlet, Supra & Tercel

DESCRIPTION

Brake systems are hydraulically-actuated, using a tandem master cylinder, and vacuum power brake unit. Power units vary among models. Land Cruiser models use a separate vacuum pump to provide vacuum to power brake unit.

Cressida (if installed) & Supra are equipped with 4-wheel disc brakes, with an intricate rear wheel drum type parking brake. Most other models are equipped with front disc and rear drum brakes. A load sensing proportioning valve is installed in rear circuit of all Pickup & Land Cruiser models.

Rear brakes on all models are self-adjusting. All parking brakes are cable-actuated and operate on rear brakes, except Land Cruiser when equipped with a center brake located at rear of transfer case.

NOTE: **Brake caliper applications vary among models. Check and compare calipers with those shown in this article for correct service procedures.**

ADJUSTMENTS

DRUM BRAKES

1) Raise and support vehicle on safety stands. Release parking brake and ensure wheel rotates freely. Remove plug from adjusting hole.

2) Turn adjusting screw with adjusting tool until wheel cannot be turned. Depress brake pedal and ensure drum is locked.

3) On Land Cruiser, back off adjuster 4-5 notches or until wheel turns with slight drag. On all other models, back off adjuster 10-12 notches or until wheel turns freely.

BRAKE PEDAL HEIGHT

1) Brake pedal height is measured from center of brake pedal to asphalt sheet under carpet. To adjust clearance, loosen stop light switch and lock nut on brake pedal push rod.

2) Adjust pedal height by turning push rod. After setting pedal height, tighten lock nut, adjust switch, and tighten switch lock nut. *See Fig. 1.*

BRAKE PEDAL HEIGHT

Application	In. (mm)
Camry	7.4-7.8 (187-197)
Celica & Supra	6.0-6.5 (154-164)
Corolla	6.5-6.9 (164-174)
Cressida	6.1-6.5 (154-165)
Land Cruiser	
Hardtop (FJ40)	8.5 (215)
Sta. Wagon (FJ60)	7.6 (192)
Pickup	6.2-6.6 (157-167)
Starlet	6.91-6.95 (175-177)
Tercel	7.3-7.6 (184-194)

BRAKE PEDAL FREE PLAY

1) Pedal free play is distance brake pedal travels before initial resistance of power brake push rod is contacted.

2) To adjust pedal free play, stop engine and depress brake pedal several times to exhaust vacuum from power brake unit.

3) Place a straightedge beside brake pedal and depress pedal down with fingers until initial resistance is felt. *See Fig. 1.*

Fig. 1: Measuring Pedal Height and Free Play

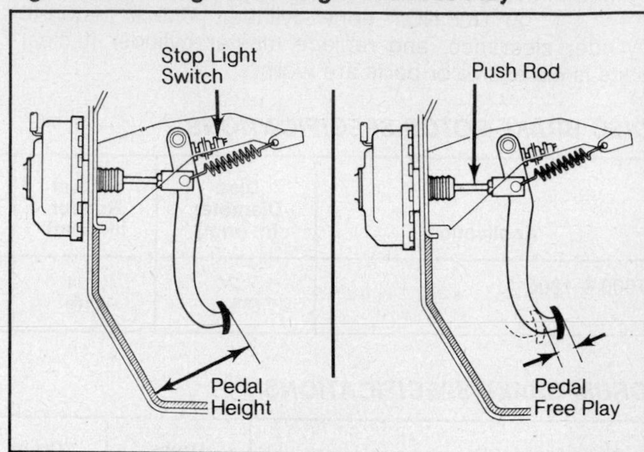
Stop Light
Switch
Push Rod
Pedal
Height
Pedal
Free Play

Make measurement from asphalt sheet.

4) Free play for all models should be .12-.24" (3-6 mm).

5) If pedal travel is not as specified, adjust pedal height, start engine, and confirm free play measurement. Check brake pedal height.

PARKING BRAKE

NOTE: **Before adjusting parking brake, operate parking brake lever several times. Pull parking brake and count number of notches lever travels. If lever travel meets specifications, do not adjust parking brake. All models require adjustment of service brakes before adjusting parking brake. After adjustment recheck lever travel.**

All Models Except Cressida, Land Cruiser & Pickup

1) If parking brake lever travel is not as specified, remove rear console (if equipped), release parking brake, loosen lock nut, and turn adjusting screw on lever until lever travel is correct.

2) Tighten lock nut and install console (if equipped). Wheels should be locked when parking brake is applied and rotate freely when lever is released.

Cressida

1) If parking brake lever travel is not as specified, release parking brake and loosen lock nut on turnbuckle located under vehicle on right side cable.

2) Rotate turnbuckle until .39" (10 mm) of threaded cable end is inside turnbuckle.

3) Tighten lock nut. Remove slack from rear cables by loosening lock nut on equalizer and turning adjusting nut. Tighten lock nut.

TOYOTA (Cont.)

4) Wheels should be locked when parking brake is applied and rotate freely when lever is released.

Land Cruiser

1) Fully release parking brake and turn adjusting cam on back of backing plate (at rear of transfer case), until brake shoes are seated against drum.

2) Back off adjusting cam 1 notch at a time until drum locks when parking brake is applied and spins freely when released.

3) After adjusting brake shoes, adjust parking brake travel by turning cable adjusting nut.

4) Wheels should be locked when parking brake is applied and rotate freely when lever is released.

Pickup

1) If parking brake lever travel is not as specified, adjust parking brake AFTER adjusting service brakes.

2) To adjust parking brake on 2WD models, release parking brake and turn adjusting nut on intermediate lever (under vehicle) until lever travel is correct.

3) Wheels should be locked when parking brake is applied and rotate freely when lever is released.

4) To adjust parking brake on 4WD models, release parking brake and loosen lock nut of bell crank stopper screw on operating lever on rear of backing plate.

5) Turn bell crank stopper screw until no play is evident at operating lever, then loosen screw one turn. Tighten stopper screw lock nut. Tighten 1 adjusting nut on intermediate lever while loosening other nut, until lever travel is correct.

6) Tighten both adjusting nuts. After lever travel adjustment is made, note operating lever stopper screw, it MUST contact backing plate when lever is released.

PARKING BRAKE ADJUSTMENT

Application	Notches
Land Cruiser	
Hardtop (FJ40)	
With Center Brake	3-6
Without	8-10
Sta. Wagon (FJ60)	7-9
Starlet	3-6
Tercel	
4x2	5-8
4x4	6-8
Pickup	7-15
All Other Models	4-7

STOP LIGHT SWITCH

Stop light switch is located under dash, above brake pedal. To adjust, loosen lock nuts and adjust switch so contact button just touches brake pedal. Tighten lock nut and check pedal height.

BRAKE WARNING LIGHT

1) A dual warning light is mounted on dash of all vehicles except Pickup (single warning light).

2) On all models, light should glow when parking brake lever is pulled 1 notch and go off when lever is fully released (ignition on).

3) To check circuit warning on all models (except Pickup), release parking brake (ignition on) and ensure light is off.

4) Open bleeder screw on 1 wheel and depress brake pedal, light should glow. Close bleeder screw, replenish brake fluid, and bleed hydraulic system.

LOAD SENSING PROPORTIONING VALVE (LSPV)

Land Cruiser & Pickup

1) Mounted near the rear axle, LSPV is used to control braking characteristics according to rear axle load condition.

LOAD SENSING PROPORTIONING VALVE SPECIFICATIONS

Application	[1] Lbs. (kg) (Including Vehicle Weight)
Land Cruiser	
FJ40	2,535 (1,150)
FJ60	2,646 (1,200)
Pickup	
2WD	1,323 (600)
4WD	1,433 (650)

[1] – Weight includes vehicle weight.

2) Install a load proportioning gauge (09705-29017 or 09709-29017) to front caliper and another to rear wheel cylinder.

3) Depress brake pedal and raise pressure on front gauge to 711 psi (50 kg/cm²). DO NOT depress brake pedal more than 1 time and do not release pedal while setting front pressure reading.

4) After 2 seconds, rear brake pressure should be 398-540 psi (28-38 kg/cm²) on Pickup and 498-640 psi (35-45 kg/cm²) on Land Cruiser.

5) Depress brake pedal further to raise front brake pressure to 1138 psi (80 kg/cm²) on Pickup and 1422 psi (100 kg/cm²) on Land Cruiser.

6) Rear brake pressure should be 525-725 psi (37-51 kg/cm²) on Pickup and 725-925 psi (51-65 kg/cm²) on Land Cruiser.

7) If pressure readings do not meet specifications, adjust load sensing proportioning valve by adjusting length of lower shackle. *See Fig. 2.*

Fig. 2: Adjusting Load Sensing Proportioning Valve

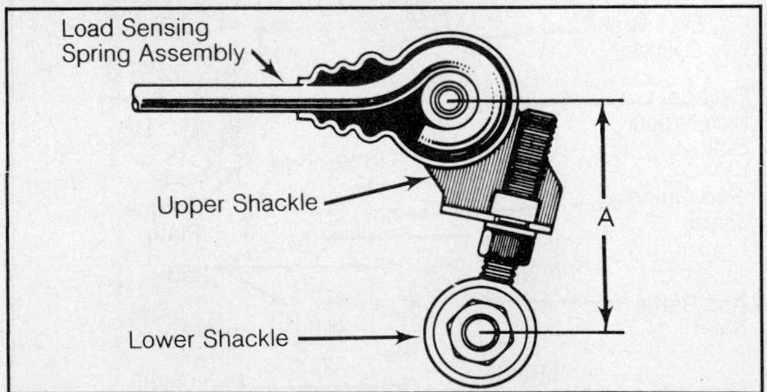
Load Sensing
Spring Assembly
Upper Shackle
A
Lower Shackle

Turning the lower shackle one turn changes pressure reading 8.5 psi (.6 kg/cm²).

8) If rear pressure is low, lengthen distance "A". If rear pressure is high, shorten distance. Repeat test procedure and check pressure readings.

9) If rear pressures do not conform to specifications after adjusting lower shackle, loosen valve body retaining nuts and reposition valve body. If rear pressure is high, raise valve body.

10) If pressure is low, lower valve body. Tighten nuts and adjust length of lower shackle to standard length.

11) Standard length for 4WD pickup should be 4.72" (120 mm) and 3.07" (78 mm) for all other models. Repeat test procedure and check pressures.

12) If pressures do not meet specifications, position valve body in uppermost position and depress brake pedal to obtain readings shown on Load Sensing Proportioning Valve Pressures table. If measured value does not meet specifications shown in table, replace valve assembly.

LOAD SENSING PROPORTIONING VALVE PRESSURES

Application	Front Reading psi (kg/cm²)	Rear Reading psi (kg/cm²)
Pickup	71 (5)	71 (5)
	711 (50)	280-337 (19.7-23.7)
	1138 (80)	424-509 (29.8-35.8)
Land Cruiser	71 (5)	71 (5)
	365 (25)	148-205 (10.4-14.4)
	835 (60)	312-411 (21.9-28.9)

REMOVAL & INSTALLATION

NOTE: **Front disc calipers used on Toyota vehicles may vary between manufacturer and model. Refer to appropriate illustrations to assist in identification of caliper.**

FRONT DISC BRAKE PADS

Removal (Celica, Starlet, Supra and Tercel)

1) Raise and support vehicle. Remove tire and wheel. Remove bottom installation bolt and lift up cylinder. Insert bolt into torque plate to secure cylinder.

Fig. 3: Exploded View of Front Disc Brake Used On Celica and Supra

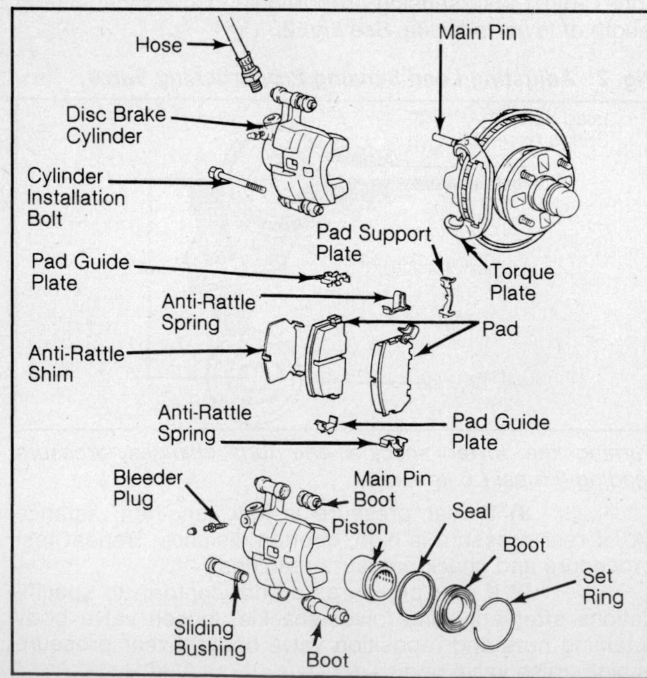
Hose
Main Pin
Disc Brake Cylinder
Cylinder Installation Bolt
Pad Support Plate
Pad Guide Plate
Torque Plate
Anti-Rattle Spring
Pad
Anti-Rattle Shim
Anti-Rattle Spring
Pad Guide Plate
Bleeder Plug
Main Pin Boot
Seal
Piston
Boot
Set Ring
Sliding Bushing
Boot

When reassembling, apply grease to cylinder guides.

2) Remove pads and anti-squeal shim. *See Fig. 3.* Remove anti-rattle springs, pad guide plates, and support plate.

Installation

1) Install new items: pad support plate, pad guide plates, anti-rattle springs, brake pads, and anti-squeal shim.

NOTE: **Install outside pad so wear indicator is at top side and place anti-squeal shim toward the inside of the pad.**

2) Remove bolt from torque plate and lower cylinder over brake pads. Install cylinder installation bolt.

Removal ("K" Type, Cab and Chassis Pickup)

1) Raise and support front of vehicle. Remove tire and wheel. To remove cylinder, remove guide plates, cylinder support springs, and pad support plates.

2) Remove cylinder with outer pad attached and suspend from frame without disconnecting hydraulic line.

3) Remove outer pad and anti-rattle spring. Remove inner pad from cylinder mount. *See Fig. 4.*

Fig. 4: Exploded View of "K" Type Disc Brake Used on Cab and Chassis Pickup

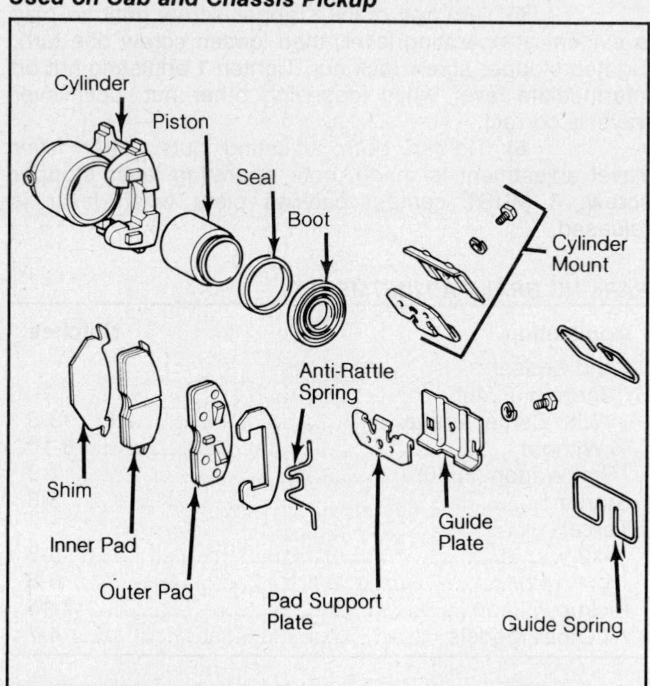
Cylinder
Piston
Seal
Boot
Cylinder Mount
Anti-Rattle Spring
Shim
Inner Pad
Outer Pad
Guide Plate
Pad Support Plate
Guide Spring

When assembling, apply rubber grease to piston seal.

Installation

1) Clean piston and cylinder assembly, open bleeder screw if necessary. Install inner pad and shim to cylinder mount.

2) Install outer pad, shim (if equipped), and anti-rattle spring on caliper. Apply brake grease to cylinder guides.

3) Install cylinder (with outer pad installed) over inner pad. Then install pad support plates, cylinder support springs, and guide plates. Torque bolts.

NOTE: **Larger side of support springs MUST face away from vehicle.**

TOYOTA (Cont.)

Removal S-16 Type (Standard Pickup)

Raise and support vehicle. Remove tire and wheel. Remove clip, pins, anti-rattle spring, brake pads, and anti-squeal shims. Lift off caliper. *See Fig. 5.*

Fig. 5: Exploded View of S-16 Type Disc Brake Used on Standard Pickup

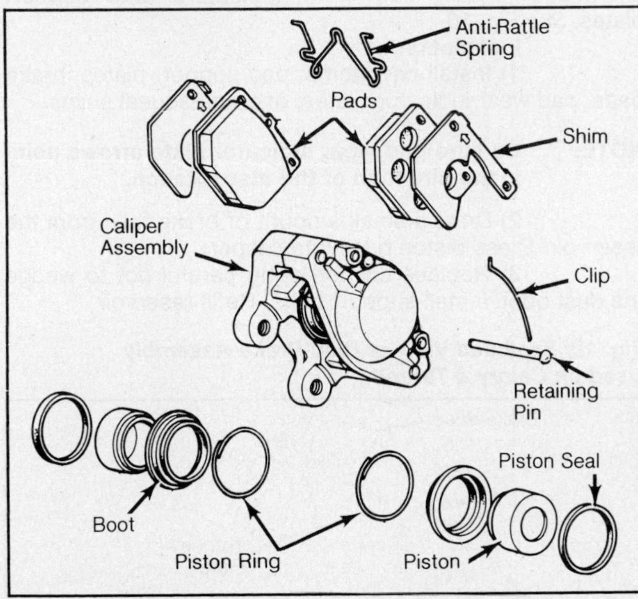
Anti-Rattle Spring
Pads
Shim
Caliper Assembly
Clip
Retaining Pin
Piston Seal
Boot
Piston Ring
Piston

Install anti-squeal shim on piston side only.

Installation

1) Coat anti-squeal shims with brake grease. Remove small amount of brake fluid from master cylinder reservoir. Push pistons into cylinder bore.

2) Install shims with arrows pointing in direction of forward rotation of disc. Install brake pads, anti-squeal shims, anti-rattle springs, pins, and clip. Refill master cylinder reservoir.

Fig. 6: Exploded View of Toyota or Sumitomo Type Disc Brake Used on Corolla

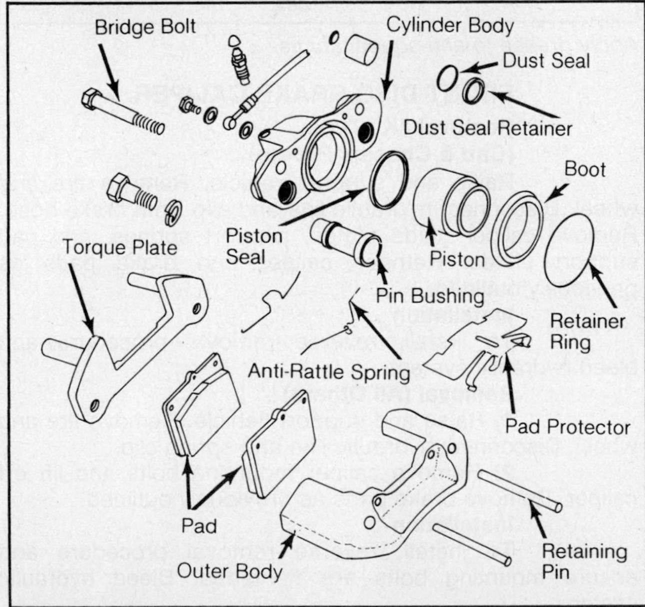
Bridge Bolt
Cylinder Body
Dust Seal
Dust Seal Retainer
Boot
Torque Plate
Piston Seal
Piston
Pin Bushing
Retainer Ring
Anti-Rattle Spring
Pad Protector
Pad
Retaining Pin
Outer Body

Install shims with arrows pointing in direction of forward rotation of disc.

Removal (Corolla)

Raise and support vehicle. Remove tire and wheel. Remove pad protector, anti-rattle springs, hole pins, brake pads, and anti-squeal shims. Clean dirt from pin portion of torque plate. *See Fig. 6.*

NOTE: **Before installation, clean lining of both pads with sandpaper.**

Installation

To install, clean piston assembly and seat piston in cylinder bore. Insert new pads, new anti-squeal shims, hole pin, anti-rattle springs, and pad protector.

Removal (Cressida)

Raise and support vehicle. Remove tire and wheel. Remove cylinder sub (bottom) slide pin. Lift up cylinder, remove pads, anti-squeal shim, and pad support plate. *See Fig. 7.*

Installation

1) Install new pad support plates. Siphon a small amount of brake fluid from master cylinder reservoir. Seat piston in cylinder bore.

2) Install new brake pads, pad wear indicators, and anti-squeal shim. Lower claiper, be careful not to damage cylinder boot. Install slide pin.

Fig. 7: Exploded View of Cressida Disc Brake

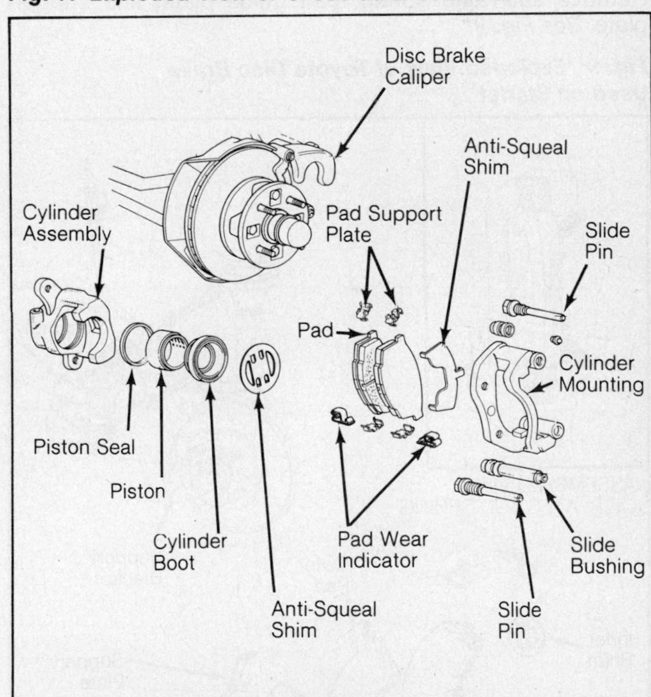
Disc Brake Caliper
Anti-Squeal Shim
Cylinder Assembly
Pad Support Plate
Slide Pin
Pad
Cylinder Mounting
Piston Seal
Piston
Cylinder Boot
Pad Wear Indicator
Slide Bushing
Anti-Squeal Shim
Slide Pin

Apply grease to slide pins.

Removal S-12+8 Type (Land Cruiser & 4WD Pickup)

Raise and support vehicle. Remove tire and wheel. Remove clip, retaining pins, and anti-rattle spring. Pull disc pads from caliper cavity. *See Fig. 8.*

Installation

Siphon small amount of brake fluid from master cylinder reservoir. Seat pistons into cylinder bores. Install new brake pads, anti-rattle spring, retaining pins, and clip. Refill master cylinder reservoir.

TOYOTA (Cont.)

Fig. 8: Exploded View of S-12+8 Type Disc Brake Assembly Used on Land Cruiser and 4WD Pickup

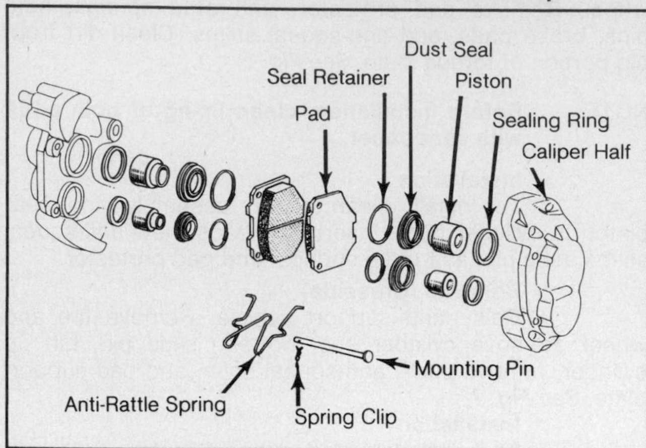
Dust Seal
Seal Retainer
Piston
Pad
Sealing Ring
Caliper Half
Mounting Pin
Anti-Rattle Spring
Spring Clip

Apply grease to slide pins.

Removal (Starlet)

1) Raise and support vehicle. Remove tire and wheel. Remove cylinder mounting bolts and suspend caliper without disconnecting hydraulic line.

2) Remove brake pads and anti-squeal shim. Remove anti-rattle spring, pad guide plate, and support plate. *See Fig. 9.*

Fig. 9: Exploded View of Toyota Disc Brake Used on Starlet

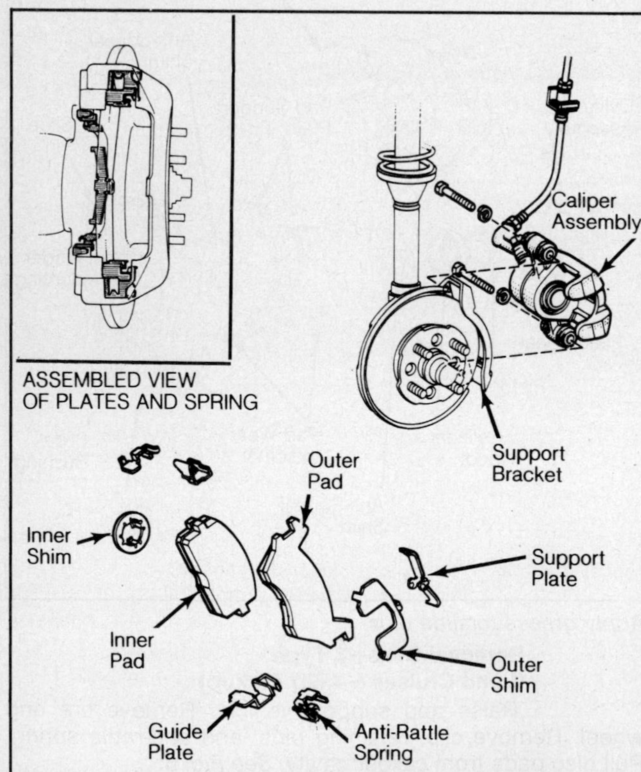
Caliper Assembly
ASSEMBLED VIEW OF PLATES AND SPRING
Support Bracket
Outer Pad
Inner Shim
Support Plate
Inner Pad
Outer Shim
Guide Plate
Anti-Rattle Spring

Observe position of anti-squeal shims.

Installation

1) Install new items in reverse order: support plate, pad guide plate, anti-rattle springs, and brake pads.

2) Draw out a small amount of brake fluid from master cylinder reservoir. Seat piston in cylinder bore. Assemble the anti-squeal shim to the piston. Install caliper and tighten bolts. Refill master cylinder reservoir.

Removal (Camry & Tercel)

1) Raise and support front of vehicle. Remove tire and wheel. Remove the two installation bolts, lift off caliper, and support without disconnecting hydraulic hose.

2) Remove anti-squeal springs, brake pads, anti-squeal shims, pad wear indicators, and support plates. *See Fig. 10.*

Installation

1) Install new items: pad support plates, brake pads, pad wear indicator plates, and anti-squeal shims.

NOTE: Be sure pad wear indicator plate arrows point in the direction of the disc rotation.

2) Draw a small amount of brake fluid from the reservoir. Press piston back into caliper.

3) Replace caliper being careful not to wedge the dust boot. Install support bolts. Refill reservoir.

Fig. 10: Exploded View of Disc Brake Assembly Used on Camry & Tercell

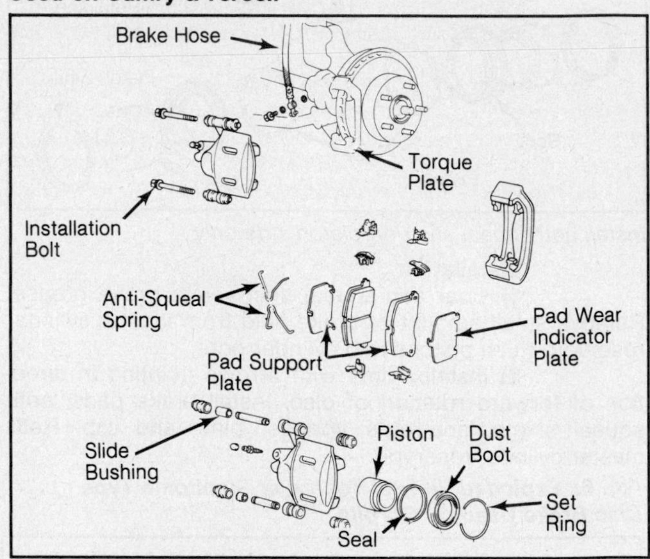
Brake Hose
Torque Plate
Installation Bolt
Anti-Squeal Spring
Pad Wear Indicator Plate
Pad Support Plate
Slide Bushing
Piston
Dust Boot
Set Ring
Seal

Apply grease to anti-squeal shims.

FRONT DISC BRAKE CALIPER

Removal "K" Type (Cab & Chassis Pickup)

Raise and support vehicle. Remove tire and wheel. Disconnect hydraulic line and clip from brake hose. Remove caliper guide plates, support springs, and pad support plates. Remove caliper and brake pads as previously outlined.

Installation

To install, reverse removal procedure and bleed hydraulic system.

Removal (All Others)

1) Raise and support vehicle. Remove tire and wheel. Disconnect hydraulic line and spring clip.

2) Remove caliper mounting bolts and lift off caliper. Remove brake pads as previously outlined.

Installation

To install, reverse removal procedure and ensure mounting bolts are tightened. Bleed hydraulic system.

TOYOTA (Cont.)

FRONT DISC BRAKE ROTOR

Removal (Land Cruiser & 4WD Pickup)

1) Raise and support vehicle. Remove wheel and caliper assembly. Remove flange or free wheel hub and snap ring. Remove free wheel mounting nuts.

2) Using a tapered punch, tap on slits of cone washers to remove them. To remove the flange (if equipped), install and tighten two bolts in threaded holes.

3) To remove axle hub with disc, release lock washer with a screwdriver. Using tool SST 09607-60020, remove lock nut. Remove second lock washer and adjusting nut. Remove thrust washer, outer bearing, and axle hub with disc.

4) Press hub bolts out of the axle hub. Remove the two retaining bolts and separate disc from the hub.

NOTE: Free wheel hub control handle must be set to "FREE" position for removal.

Installation

To install, reverse removal procedure. Adjust wheel bearings. *See Wheel Bearing Adjustment in SUSPENSION Section.*

Removal (Camry & Tercel)

1) Raise and support vehicle. Remove tire and wheel. Remove torque plate from the knuckle. Remove caliper assembly as previously described and suspend from frame without disconnecting hydraulic line.

2) Remove the hub nuts of the temporarily installed disc and seperate the disc from the axle hub.

Installation

Install disc and loosely install hub nuts. Install torque plate and caliper assembly. Install wheel and lower vehicle.

Removal (All Others)

1) Raise and support vehicle. Remove tire and wheel. Remove caliper. Remove hub grease cap, cotter pin, washer, and castellated nut. Carefully remove outer wheel bearing.

2) Remove rotor and hub assembly. Place alignment marks on rotor and hub for reassembly reference. Remove hub-to-rotor bolts and separate hub from rotor.

Installation

To install, reverse removal procedure and adjust wheel bearings. *See Wheel Bearing Adjustment in SUSPENSION Section.*

REAR DISC BRAKE PADS

Removal (Cressida)

Remove pad protector, anti-rattle springs, hole pins, brake pads, and anti-squeal shims. *See Fig. 11.*

Installation

Push piston into cylinder. Install new brake pads and anti-squeal shims. Install hole pins, anti-rattle springs, and pad protector.

Removal (Supra)

1) Raise and support rear of vehicle. Remove tire and wheel. Remove caliper installation bolt.

2) Lift caliper and insert bolt into torque plate hole to secure cylinder. Remove brake pads, anti-squeal shim, anti-rattle springs, pad guide plates, and support plate. *See Fig. 12.*

Installation

Press piston into cylinder body. Install new brake pads and anti-squeal shim. Install all items in reverse order. Remove bolt from torque plate and lower caliper. Install caliper installation bolt.

Fig. 11: Exploded View Cressida Rear Disc Brake

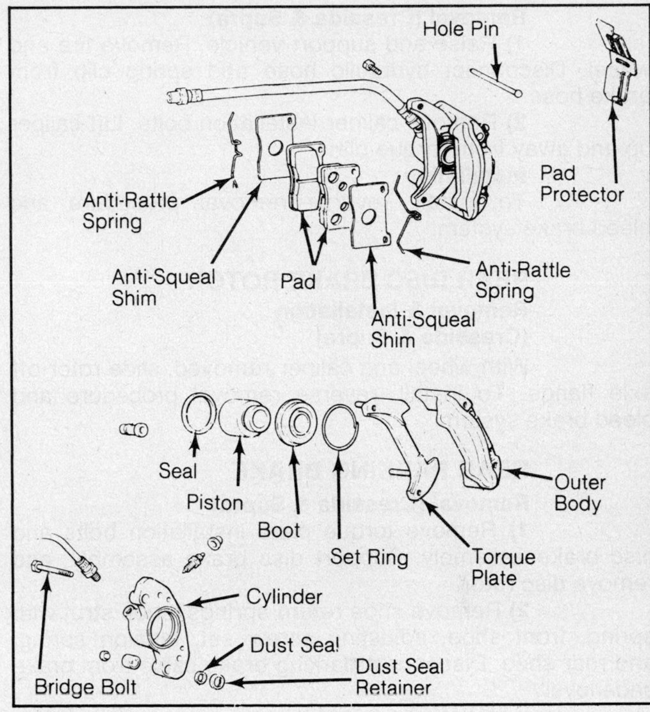
Hole Pin
Pad Protector
Anti-Rattle Spring
Anti-Squeal Shim
Pad
Anti-Rattle Spring
Anti-Squeal Shim
Seal
Piston
Boot
Set Ring
Outer Body
Torque Plate
Cylinder
Dust Seal
Dust Seal Retainer
Bridge Bolt

Apply grease to shims and pins.

Fig. 12: Exploded View Supra Rear Disc Brake

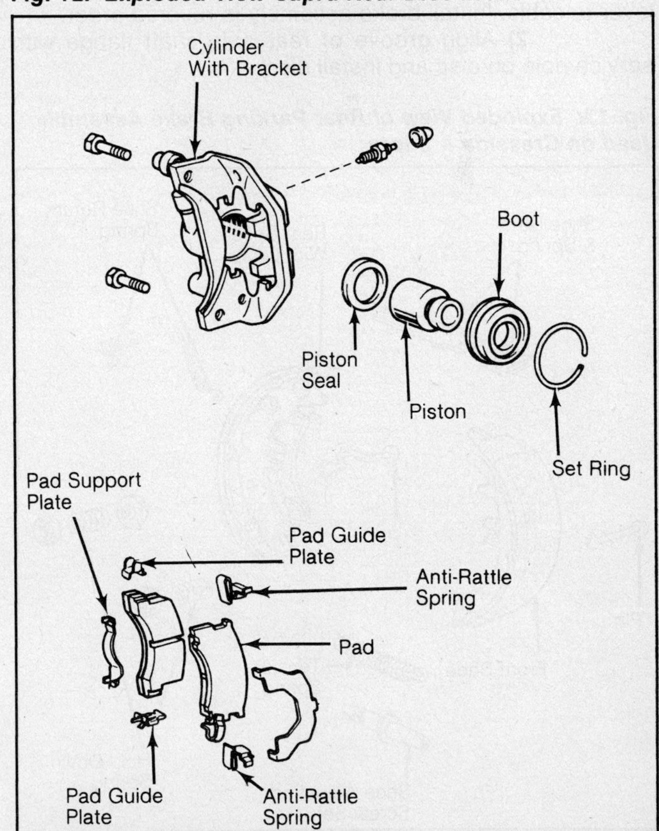
Cylinder With Bracket
Boot
Piston Seal
Piston
Set Ring
Pad Support Plate
Pad Guide Plate
Anti-Rattle Spring
Pad
Pad Guide Plate
Anti-Rattle Spring

Apply grease to shim.

NOTE: Install outside pad so wear indicator is at the bottom.

REAR DISC BRAKE CALIPER

Removal (Cressida & Supra)

1) Raise and support vehicle. Remove tire and wheel. Disconnect hydraulic hose and spring clip from brake hose.

2) Remove caliper installation bolts. Lift caliper up and away from torque plate.

Installation

To install, reverse removal procedure and bleed brake system.

REAR DISC BRAKE ROTOR

Removal & Installation (Cressida & Supra)

With wheel and caliper removed, slide rotor off axle flange. To install, reverse removal procedure and bleed brake system.

REAR PARKING BRAKE

Removal (Cressida & Supra)

1) Remove torque plate installation bolts and disc brake assembly. Support disc brake assembly, and remove disc rotor.

2) Remove shoe return springs, shoe strut with spring, front shoe, adjusting screw set, tension spring, and rear shoe. Disconnect parking brake cable from brake shoe lever.

Installation

1) Apply non-melting grease to sliding surfaces of shoes and adjusting screw set. Connect parking brake lever to cable. Install brake assembly in reverse order.

2) Align groove of rear axle shaft flange with service hole on disc and install disc.

Fig. 13: Exploded View of Rear Parking Brake Assembly Used on Cressida & Supra

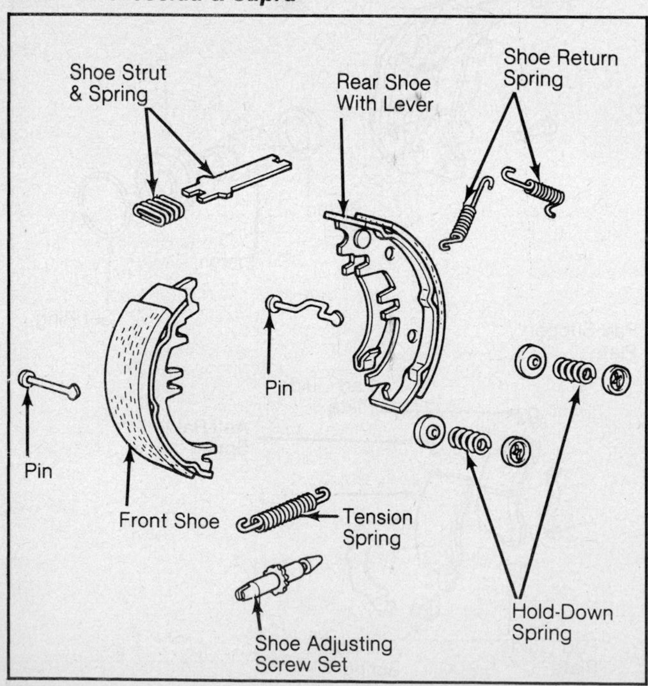
Shoe Strut & Spring
Rear Shoe With Lever
Shoe Return Spring
Pin
Pin
Front Shoe
Tension Spring
Shoe Adjusting Screw Set
Hold-Down Spring

Apply grease to sliding surfaces and adjusting screw set.

NOTE: Before installation, polish surfaces of shoes and disc with sandpaper.

REAR BRAKE DRUM

Removal (Tercel)

1) Raise and support vehicle. Remove tire and wheel. Remove grease cap, cotter pin, lock nut, and bearing nut.

2) Remove brake hub together with outer bearing and thrust washer.

Installation

1) To install, pack bearings, fill inside of axle hub, and grease cap with "MP" grease. Install brake hub by reversing removal procedures.

2) Snug down bearing nut, then loosen until hub can be turned by hand.

Removal (All Other Models)

1) Raise and support vehicle. Remove tire and wheel. Remove set screws from brake drum (if equipped).

2) Pull drum from axle flange. It may be necessary to loosen brake adjustment before removing drum.

Installation

1) On all models, set brake shoe-to-drum clearance by measuring inside diameter of brake drum and diameter of brake shoes.

2) Turn brake adjuster until difference between diameters is .02" (.6 mm). Install brake drum and adjust brakes if required.

BRAKE SHOES

Removal (Standard Pickup)

1) With brake drum removed, remove return spring and adjuster. Remove front hold-down spring and pin. Remove front shoe and anchor spring.

2) Remove rear hold-down spring, pin, and rear shoe. Remove strut and spring from adjusting lever.

3) Disconnect parking brake cable from lever. Using a screwdriver, remove "C" washers retaining parking brake lever and adjuster lever to rear shoe. Remove levers from shoe.

Fig. 14: Exploded View of Standard Pickup Rear Brake

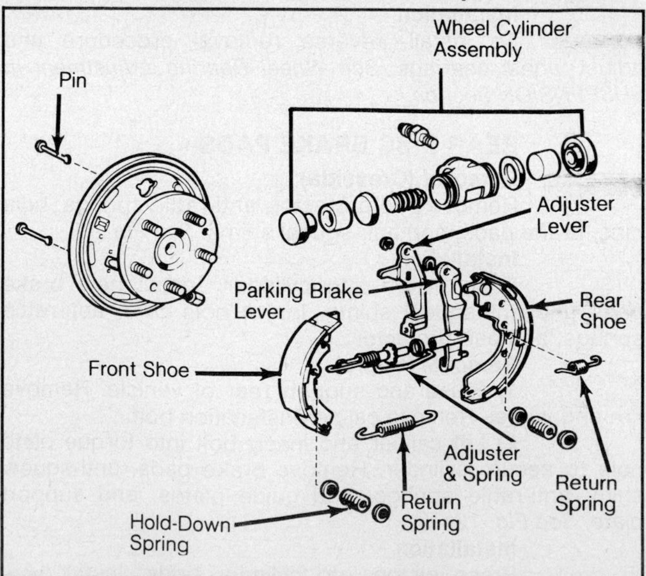
Wheel Cylinder Assembly
Pin
Adjuster Lever
Parking Brake Lever
Rear Shoe
Front Shoe
Adjuster & Spring
Return Spring
Return Spring
Hold-Down Spring

When reassembling, install new "C" washers.

Installation

1) To install, reverse removal procedure and note the following: Install parking brake lever and adjuster lever to rear shoe with new "C" washers.

2) After installation of brake assembly, move adjuster back and forth to ensure adjusting bolt moves. If not, check installation of brake assembly. Bleed hydraulic system.

NOTE: **When installing new brake shoes, install new "C" washers on parking brake lever, coat wheel cylinder cups with rubber grease, apply non-melt grease to the sliding areas of backing plate and automatic adjuster.**

Removal (Land Cruiser)

With brake drum removed, remove tensioner spring and hold-down springs. Remove tension spring from bell crank. Remove brake shoes and disengage parking brake lever.

Installation

Position brake shoes over wheel cylinders with front return spring hooked on inner side of shoe. Install hold-down springs. Connect return spring and tensioner spring. Adjust and bleed brakes.

Fig. 15: Exploded View of Land Cruiser Rear Brake

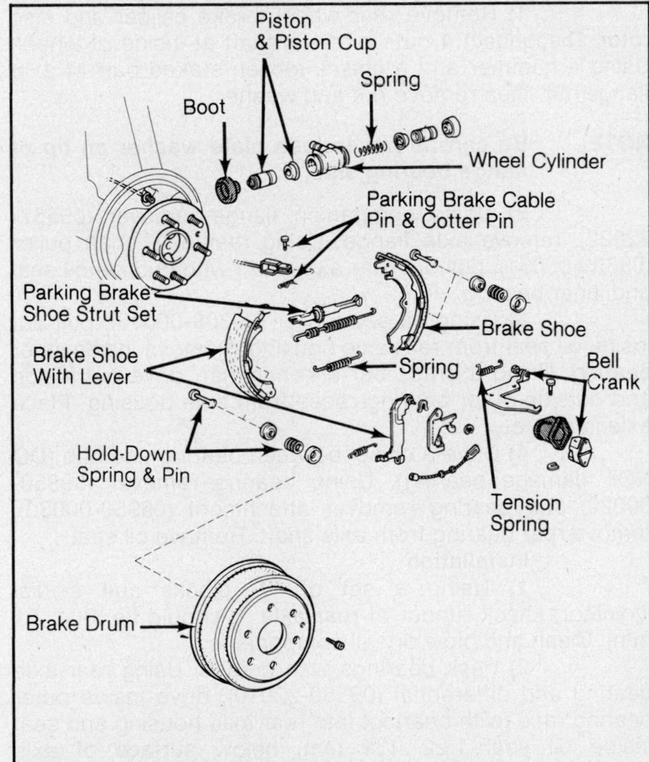
Piston
& Piston Cup
Spring
Boot
Wheel Cylinder
Parking Brake Cable
Pin & Cotter Pin
Parking Brake
Shoe Strut Set
Brake Shoe
Brake Shoe
With Lever
Spring
Bell
Crank
Hold-Down
Spring & Pin
Tension
Spring
Brake Drum

Install new bell crank "C" washer.

Removal (Cab & Chassis Pickup & 4WD Pickup)

1) With brake drum removed, remove upper return springs. Remove adjuster cable, cable guide, adjuster lever, and anchor plate.

2) Remove adjuster lever tension springs and strut. Remove hold-down springs and pins. Pull brake shoes from backing plate, separate adjusting mechanism and return spring.

3) Disconnect parking brake cable from lever. Mount rear shoe in vise and remove "C" washer retaining parking brake lever to shoe. Remove parking brake lever.

Installation

1) To install, reverse removal procedure and note the following: Adjuster mechanisms are not interchangeable. Left-hand thread – right wheel, right-hand thread – left wheel.

2) After installation of brake assembly, pull adjusting cable backward and release, adjusting bolt should move. If not, check installation of brake assembly. Install drum and adjust brakes.

Fig. 16: Exploded View of Cab and Chassis and 4WD Pickup Rear Brake

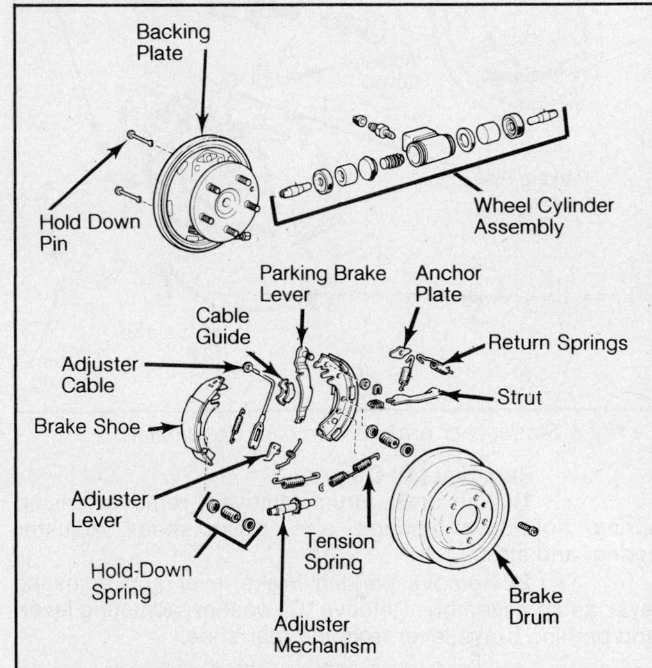
Backing
Plate
Hold Down
Pin
Wheel Cylinder
Assembly
Parking Brake
Lever
Anchor
Plate
Cable
Guide
Adjuster
Cable
Return Springs
Strut
Brake Shoe
Adjuster
Lever
Hold-Down
Spring
Tension
Spring
Adjuster
Mechanism
Brake
Drum

Adjusting mechanisims are not interchangable.

Removal (Camry, Starlet and Tercel)

1) With brake drum removed, remove return spring. Remove hold-down springs and pins. Disconnect front shoe from parking brake strut and disconnect lower spring.

2) Remove front shoe. Disconnect parking brake lever return spring. Remove rear shoe from backing plate and disconnect parking brake cable from lever.

3) Remove "C" washer, adjusting lever, and parking brake lever from rear shoe. Remove "C" washer retaining parking brake lever on adjusting lever and separate levers.

Installation

1) Install parking brake lever onto adjusting lever with NEW "C" washer. Install lever assembly on rear shoe and retain in position temporarily with NEW "C" washer.

2) Measure clearance between adjusting lever and rear shoe. Remove "C" washer and install correct shim(s) which will give a clearance of 0-.014" (0-.35 mm). Install and stake "C" washer, ensure that lever moves.

3) Complete installation by reversing removal procedure and note the following: Adjuster mechanisms are not interchangeable. Left-hand thread – left wheel,

TOYOTA (Cont.)

right-hand thread – right wheel. Install drum and bleed hydraulic system.

NOTE: Shims are available in 6 sizes: .008" (.2 mm), .012" (.3 mm), .016" (.4 mm), .020" (.5 mm), .024" (.6 mm), and .035" (.9 mm). Shims may be installed in pairs to provide proper clearance.

Fig. 17: Exploded View of Tercel Rear Brake

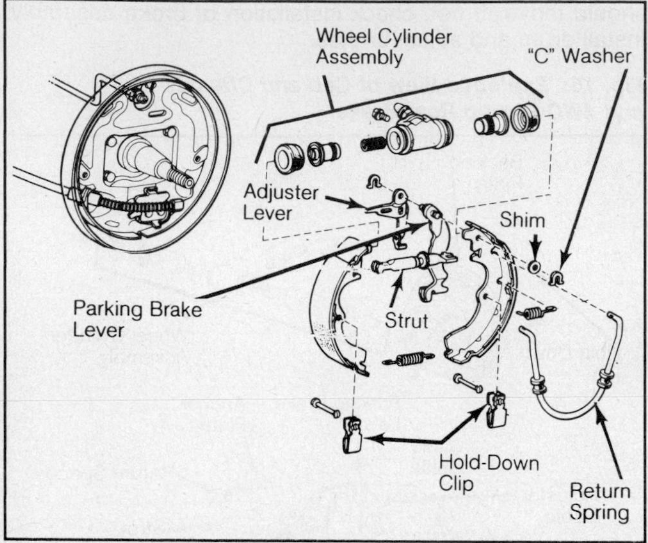
Wheel Cylinder Assembly
"C" Washer
Adjuster Lever
Shim
Parking Brake Lever
Strut
Hold-Down Clip
Return Spring

Camry & Starlet rear brake assemblies are similar.

Removal (All Others)

1) With brake drum removed, remove tension spring, hold-down springs, pins, brake shoes, adjuster spring, and strut.

2) Remove parking brake lever and adjusting lever as an assembly. Remove "C" washer, adjusting lever, and parking brake lever from the rear shoe.

Fig. 18: Exploded View of Rear Brake Used on Celica, Corolla, and Cressida

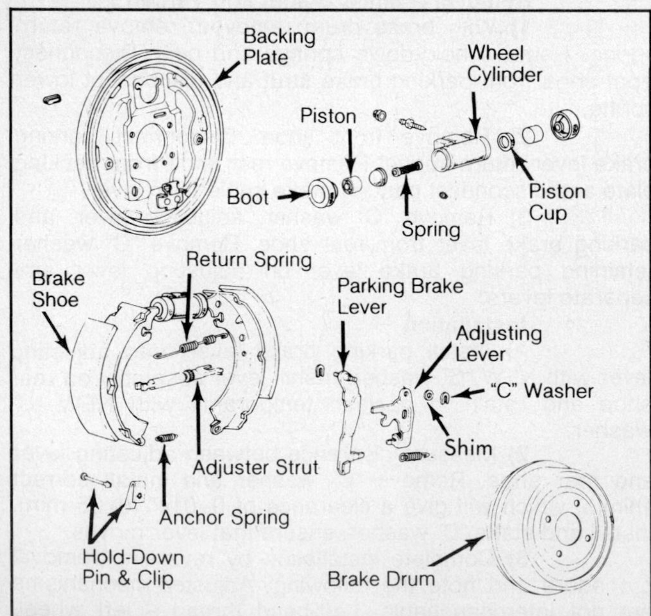
Backing Plate
Wheel Cylinder
Piston
Boot
Spring
Piston Cup
Return Spring
Brake Shoe
Parking Brake Lever
Adjusting Lever
"C" Washer
Shim
Adjuster Strut
Anchor Spring
Hold-Down Pin & Clip
Brake Drum

When reassembling, install new "C" washers.

Installation

1) Install adjusting lever and parking brake lever to rear shoe with NEW "C" washer. Measure clearance between lever and shoe.

2) Remove "C" washer, and install correct shim(s) which will give a clearance of 0-.014" (0-.35 mm). Install and stake "C" washer, ensure that lever moves.

3) Complete installation by reversing removal procedure and note the following: Adjuster mechanisms are not interchangeable. Left-hand thread – right wheel, right-hand thread – left wheel. Install drum and bleed hydraulic system.

REAR BRAKE WHEEL CYLINDER

Removal (All Drum Brake Models)

With brake drum and shoes removed, disconnect hydraulic line from wheel cylinder. Remove mounting bolts and remove wheel cylinder.

Installation

To install, reverse removal procedure. Adjusting mechanisms on many models are not interchangeable. Install adjusting mechanism to the wheel from which it was removed.

REAR WHEEL BEARING AND OIL SEAL REPLACEMENT

Removal (Celica, Cressida and Supra)

1) Remove rear wheel, brake caliper and disc rotor. Disconnect 4 nuts of drive shaft at inside of wheel. Using a hammer and a chisel, loosen staked part of axle flange nut, then remove nut and washer.

NOTE: Be careful not to lose plate washer on tip of flange bearing side.

2) Using companion flange remover (09557-22022), remove axle flange. Using rear axle shaft puller (09520-00031), pull out rear axle shaft with outside oil seal and inner bearing.

3) Using oil seal puller (09308-00010), pull out inside oil seal from rear axle housing. Remove inside inner bearing. Using a brass bar and hammer, drive out inside and outside outer bearing races from axle housing. Place axle in a vise.

4) Drive a chisel between bearing and hub (DO NOT damage bearing). Using bearing remover (09950-00020) and bearing remover attachment (09950-00030), remove rear bearing from axle shaft. Remove oil seal.

Installation

1) Using a set of "V" blocks and a dial indicator, check runout of rear axle. It should be .004" (.1 mm). Clean and blow dry all components.

2) Pack bearings with grease. Using rear axle bearing and differential (09550-22010), drive inside outer bearing race (with bearing) into rear axle housing and seat inside oil seal 1.22" (31 mm) below surface of axle housing.

3) Using rear axle bearing and differential (09550-22010), drive outside outer bearing race into rear axle housing. Pack inside of axle housing with grease. Coat outside of new spacer with grease and install into housing. Install new outside inner bearing.

4) Using rear axle bearing and differential (09550-22010), drive new outside oil seal .217" (5.5 mm) for Cressida or .236" (6 mm) for all others below outer surface of axle housing. Install rear axle shaft and plate washer into rear housing.

TOYOTA (Cont.)

5) Using companion flange remover/replacer (09557-22022), draw axle shaft into rear axle housing. Using rear axle shaft puller (09520-00031) to hold axle shaft, install new axle flange nut and torque to 22-36 ft. lbs. (30-49 N.m), revolve shaft back and forth to snug down.

6) Using a torque wrench, check rotation resistance and torque to 58 ft. lbs. (77 N.m). Using a torque wrench, check preload rotation. It should be .9-3.5 In. lbs. (.1-.4 N.m).

7) If preload is less than specification, retighten flange nut 5-10° at a time until a maximum torque of 145 ft. lbs. (197 N.m) is reached. Stake flange nut with a punch. Connect drive shaft and torque nuts to 44-57 ft. lbs. (60-77 N.m). Install rear brake and wheel.

Removal (Corolla, Cressida, Starlet and Tercel)

1) With wheel and brake drum removed, remove 4 backing plate nuts. Using rear axle shaft puller (09520-00031), remove rear axle. Inspect maximum runout of rear axle for Cressida of .059" (1.5 mm), for all others .079" (2 mm).

2) Maximum flange runout for Cressida is .004" (.1 mm), for all others is .008" (0.2 mm). Using a grinder, grind down inner bearing retainer of axle shaft and cut off with a chisel and hammer.

3) Using rear axle shaft bearing remover (09527-21011) for Cressida and Starlet or rear axle shaft bearing remover (09527-20011) for all others and an arbor press, remove bearing from axle shaft. Using oil seal puller (09308-00010), pull oil seal from axle housing.

Installation

1) Install outer bearing retainer and new bearing on axle shaft. Using a rear axle shaft bearing replacer (09515-21010) for Cressida and Starlet or rear axle shaft bearing remover (09515-20010) for all others and an arbor press, press bearing onto axle shaft.

2) Heat new inner bearing retainer to about 302° F (150° C) in an oil bath. While it is still hot, face non-beveled side toward bearing and press onto axle shaft, using rear axle shaft bearing replacer (09515-21010) for Cressida or rear axle shaft bearing replacer (09515-20010) for all others.

NOTE: **When installing hot inner bearing retainer, make sure there is no oil or grease on the axle shaft.**

3) Apply grease to lips of new oil seal. Using rear axle shaft oil seal replacer (09517-30010) for Cressida or rear axle shaft oil seal replacer (09517-12010) for all others, drive seal .197" (4.9 mm) for Corolla wagon, .232" (5.9 mm) for Corolla, .236" (6 mm) for Cressida or .220" (5.6 mm) for all others below outer edge of housing.

4) With bearing retainer and gasket assembly on axle shaft, align and position with notches facing down. Install axle shaft into housing and torque mounting nuts to 44-53 ft. lbs. (60-72 N.m). Complete installation by reversing removal procedures.

Removal (Land Cruiser – Semi Floating)

Drain differential and remove cover plate. Remove pinion shaft pin from differential, then draw out pinion shaft and spacer. Push axle shaft to center of vehicle and remove axle shaft lock. Pull axle shaft from axle housing. Using axle shaft bearing remover (09514-35011), pull wheel bearing and seal from axle housing at same time.

Installation

Using rear wheel bearing replacer (09515-35010), drive new wheel bearing and oil seal into axle housing. To complete installation, reverse removal procedures.

Removal (Land Cruiser – Full Floating)

1) Remove nuts and washers from axle flange. Install bolts in holes provided in flange and tighten to remove axle. Using oil seal puller (09308-00010), pull oil seal from axle housing.

2) Using adjusting nut remover/installer (09509-25011), remove adjusting nut and lock plate from axle hub. Remove inside oil seal with a screwdriver. Using a brass drift, remove inside and outside outer races. Clean parts in solvent and blow dry.

Installation

1) Using axle hub and drive pinion bearing (09608-35013), install new outer bearing races and inside oil seal into hub. Pack hub with grease. Install inner bearings to hub and place hub on wheel spindle. Install lock plate.

2) Using adjusting nut remover/installer (09509-25011), torque adjusting nut to 43 ft. lbs. (58 N.m), then loosen nut until it can be rotated by hand. Using a spring gauge, adjust preload by adjusting to 5.7-12.6 lbs. (25-56 N.).

3) Align 1 slot of axle housing with 1 slot of adjusting nut, install 2 lock screws at 90° to aligned slots and torque lock screws to 35-60 In. lbs. (4-7 N.m). Check preload with spring gauge. Install axle shaft and torque flange nuts to 21-25 ft. lbs. (28-34 N.m). Complete installation by reversing removal procedure.

Removal (Pickup)

1) Remove parking brake clip and clamp bolt from frame. Disconnect parking brake cable from equalizer. On 4WD, remove pin and disconnect parking brake cable from bell crank lever. Remove wheel and brake drum.

2) Remove differential drain plug and drain oil. Disconnect brake tube from wheel cylinder. Remove 4 backing plate nuts from behind backing plate. Pull out rear axle together with backing plate.

3) Remove snap ring on back side of axle. Attach rear axle shaft puller (09521-25011) to backing plate and use an arbor press to push axle from backing plate. Use a dial indicator to check runout of axle, maximum shaft runout is .079" (2 mm) and maximum flange runout is .008" (.2 mm).

4) Using oil seal puller (09308-00010), pull outer oil seal from bearing case. Using front hub/drive pinion bearing (09608-30011) and front hub/drive pinion collar (09515-30010), press bearing from bearing case.

5) Inspect bearing case, if necessary replace it. Using oil seal puller (09308-00010), pull inside oil seal from axle housing. Clean parts with solvent and compressed air.

Installation

1) Using front hub/drive pinion bearing (09608-30011), drive a new oil seal into axle housing and bearing case. Using front hub/drive pinion bearing (09608-35012) and front hub/drive pinion collar (09515-30010), press new bearing into bearing case.

2) Slide axle shaft into backing plate. Using an arbor press and front hub/drive pinion collar (09515-30010), press axle shaft into backing plate.

3) Install snap ring to axle shaft. Install rear axle shaft into axle housing and secure with 4 nuts.

Torque backing plate to 44-57 ft. lbs. (60-77 N.m). Complete installation by reversing removal procedures.

FRONT WHEEL BEARING AND OIL SEAL REPLACEMENT

Removal (Camry and Tercel)

1) Remove cotter pin, bearing lock nut cap and bearing lock nut (depress brake pedal when removing lock nut). Remove brake caliper and suspend on a wire. Disconnect disc. Remove cotter pin and nut from tie rod end.

2) Using universal puller (09950-20014) for Camry or pitman arm puller (09610-20012) for Tercel, pull tie rod end from steering knuckle. Place match marks on lower shock absorber bracket and camber adjust cam.

3) Remove bolts and nuts to separate steering knuckle and shock absorber. Remove 2 bolts holding ball joint to steering knuckle and separate. Pull axle hub from drive shaft and cover drive boot with a cloth.

4) Place steering knuckle in a vise and remove dust deflector with a screwdriver. Using oil seal puller (09308-00010), pull inner oil seal out of steering knuckle.

5) Using snap ring pliers, remove snap ring from steering knuckle hole. Remove 3 bolts holding brake dust cover. Using universal puller (09950-20014), push axle hub off of steering knuckle.

NOTE: **If axle hub is removed, be sure to replace outer oil seal.**

6) Remove bearing inner race from bearing. Using universal puller (09950-20014), pull inside outer bearing race from axle hub. Remove disc brake dust cover. Using oil seal puller (09308-00010), pull oil seal out of steering knuckle.

7) Using an arbor press, oil filter wrench (09228-22020) and universal puller (09950-20014) for Tercel, install outside inner race on bearing and press bearing out of steering knuckle.

Installation

1) Using an arbor press and steering knuckle oil seal replacer (09608-32010) for Camry or transmission rear bearing replacer (09309-35010) for Tercel, press new bearing into steering knuckle. Place outside inner bearing race on outside bearing.

2) Using steering knuckle oil seal replacer (09608-32010) and rear suspension bushing (09710-14012) for Camry or rear wheel bearing replacer (09515-35010) for Tercel, drive new oil seal into steering knuckle. Apply sealer to dust cover and steering knuckle connection and assemble.

3) Place inner race on inside bearing. Assemble hub and steering knuckle. Using an arbor press, oil filter wrench (09228-22020) and countershaft bearing replacer (09310-35010), press bearing tightly against shoulder of hub. Install snap ring into hole of steering knuckle.

NOTE: **DO NOT interchange outer and inner races when installing bearings.**

4) Using steering knuckle oil seal replacer (09608-32010) and rear suspension bushing (09710-14012) for Camry or transmission rear bearing replacer (09309-35010) for Tercel, drive new inside oil seal into steering knuckle

NOTE: **When installing inside oil seal, tap seal to -.004-.004" (-.1-.1 mm) for Camry or .126-.134" (3.2-3.4 mm) for Tercel below end surface of steering knuckle.**

5) Using crankshaft rear oil seal replacer (09223-41020) for Camry or transmission/transfer bearing replacer (09316-60010) for Tercel, drive new dust onto steering knuckle.

6) To complete installation, reverse removal procedures. When installing steering knuckle with axle hub to lower arm, torque to 83 ft. lbs. (113 N.m) for Camry or 59 ft. lbs. (80 N.m) for Tercel.

7) When installing steering knuckle to shock absorber, align match marks of camber adjust cam and torque bolts to 152 ft. lbs. (206 N.m) for Camry or 105 ft. lbs. (142 N.m) for Tercel. When assembling brake caliper to steering knuckle, torque to 57-83 ft. lbs. (77-113 N.m).

8) When connecting tie rod end to steering knuckle, torque to 36 ft. lbs. (49 N.m) for Camry or 29-43 ft. lbs. (39-58 N.m) for Tercel. To install wheel bearing lock nut, depress brake pedal, torque nut to 137 ft. lbs. (186 N.m).

Removal (Land Cruiser and Pickup)

1) Using a flare wrench (09751-36011), disconnect brake tube and remove brake disc caliper. If equipped with a flange, remove cap from flange, snap ring, mounting nuts and washers. To remove flange, place 2 bolts in holes on flange and tighten, flange will come off.

2) If equipped with free wheel hub, set control handle to "FREE", remove mounting bolts and pull off cover, then remove snap ring. Using a screwdriver, release lock washer.

3) Using a 2" socket (09607-60020), remove lock nut, lock washer and adjusting nut. Remove axle hub with disc, thrust washer and outer bearing. Using a screwdriver, pry out oil seal. Using a brass bar, drive out bearing races.

Installation

1) Clean all parts with solvent and compressed air. Using axle hub and drive pinion bearing (09608-35013), drive new bearing races into hub. Pack new bearings with grease. Coat inside of hub with grease.

2) Install inside inner bearing and oil seal. Install axle hub on spindle. Install outer inner bearing and thrust washer. Install adjusting nut and torque to 43 ft. lbs. (58 N.m). Turn hub right and left 2 or 3 times. Loosen nut and retighten to 35-60 In. lbs. (4-7 N.m).

3) Use spring tension gauge to check preload of 6.2-12.6 lbs. (27.6-56 N.). Install lock washer and nut. Using a 2" socket (09607-60020), torque nut to 58-72 ft. lbs. (77-98 N.m). Secure lock nut by bending outward, 1 lock washer tooth.

4) Place gasket on hub and install flange or free wheel hub. Torque 6 attaching nuts to 21-25 ft. lbs. (28-34 N.m). Install bolt in axle shaft and pull it out. Install snap ring, remove bolt and install cap (if equipped with flange) or cover (if equipped with free wheel hub). Install brake caliper and wheel.

CENTER PARKING BRAKE

Removal (Land Cruiser)

1) Disconnect front of drive shaft and support with wire in out-of-way position. Place vehicle in forward drive, secure parking brake and foot brake, remove drum

TOYOTA (Cont.)

mounting nut, and slide drum off splines.

2) Remove return springs, tension springs, hold-down springs, and pins. Disconnect parking brake cable from shoes.

Installation

To install, reverse removal procedure and note: Make sure lower tension spring is installed so it lies between back plate and shoes. Tighten drum mounting nut and adjust parking brake.

MASTER CYLINDER

Removal & Installation

Disconnect electrical lead (if equipped). Disconnect and plug hydraulic lines. Remove master cylinder-to-power brake unit mounting nuts. Remove master cylinder. To install, reverse removal procedures and bleed brake system.

VACUUM PUMP

Removal (Land Cruiser)

Disconnect vacuum line from pump assembly. Disconnect and plug oil lines. Remove mounting nuts and gently pry pump off studs. Tap with a plastic hammer, if necessary.

Installation

To install, reverse removal procedure and note: Run engine at idle speed. Loosen screw at vacuum pump outlet and check that oil is circulating.

POWER BRAKE UNIT

Removal & Installation

Remove master cylinder assembly from vehicle. Disconnect push rod clevis at brake pedal. Remove power booster attaching hardware and booster assembly from vehicle. To install, reverse removal procedure.

LOAD SENSING PROPORTIONING VALVE

Removal (Land Cruiser & Pickup)

1) Raise and support vehicle. Disconnect No. 2 shackle from bracket. Disconnect and plug hydraulic lines from load sensing valve. Remove clip from brake hose.

2) Remove mounting bolts from valve bracket and remove LSPV assembly. Separate valve body from bracket. *See Fig. 19.*

NOTE: **DO NOT disassemble valve body. If adjustments cannot be made, replace valve body.**

1) To install, reverse removal procedure and note the following: Apply rubber grease to all rubbing areas.

2) Install new rubber plate on valve body side of spring. Adjust length of upper and lower shackle to original height.

3) After installation, position valve body so valve piston lightly contacts load sensing spring. Bleed hydraulic system and check brake pressures.

NOTE: **DO NOT mistake valve side of load sensing spring for shackle side.**

OVERHAUL

NOTE: **When overhauling caliper, wheel cylinder, or master cylinder assemblies, replace all rubber components. If cylinder bores are pitted or scored more than a light honing will repair, replace entire assemblies.**

Fig. 19: Exploded View of Load Sensing Proportioning Valve

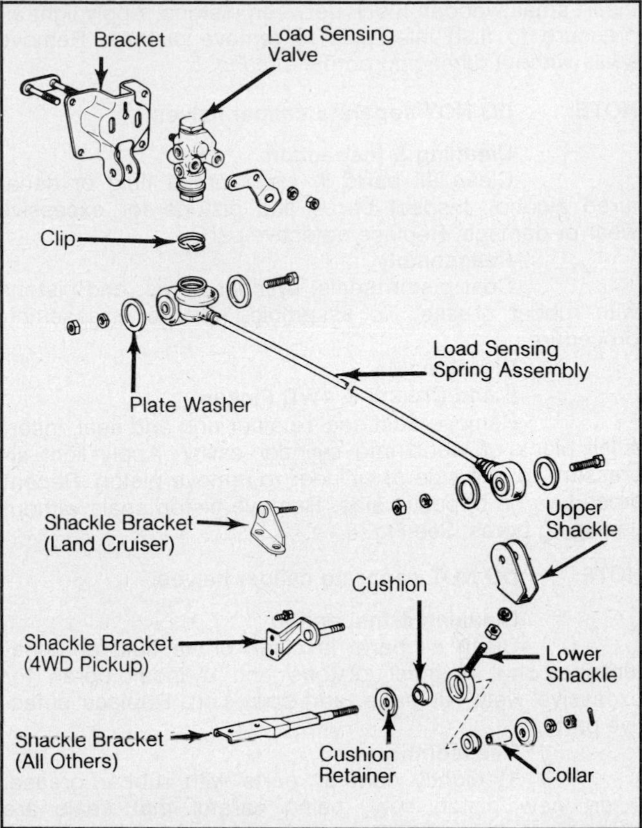

Bracket
Load Sensing Valve
Clip
Plate Washer
Load Sensing Spring Assembly
Shackle Bracket (Land Cruiser)
Upper Shackle
Cushion
Shackle Bracket (4WD Pickup)
Lower Shackle
Shackle Bracket (All Others)
Cushion Retainer
Collar

Do not disassemble valve body.

DISC BRAKE CALIPER

Disassembly (Corolla)

1) Loosen both bridge bolts (caliper half mounting bolts) and separate cylinder casting from outer body. Pull out torque plate. Remove retainer ring and boot.

2) Force light air pressure through fluid inlet port to remove piston. From caliper, remove following: piston seal, bushings, hole plug, retainers, and dust seals. *See Fig. 6.*

Cleaning & Inspection

1) Clean all parts in alcohol or clean brake fluid. Inspect parts for excessive wear or damage. Replace defective parts.

2) If torque plate pins are excessively worn or pin weld parts are abnormally corroded, replace caliper.

Reassembly

1) After ensuring torque plate pins and bushing bores are clean, coat with grease furnished in repair kit. Coat piston seals and cylinder bore with rubber grease.

2) Fit dust seal, retainers, and bushings to cylinder. Fit piston seal on cylinder and push piston in by hand. Install dust boot and ring.

3) Reassemble torque plate pins in cylinder body. Make sure torque plate is free to slide smoothly. Install bridge bolts and tighten.

Disassembly (Standard Pickup)

Remove dust boot set ring and dust boot. Insert small wooden block between pistons. Apply light air pressure to fluid inlet port to remove pistons. Remove seals without damaging bores. *See Fig. 5.*

NOTE: DO NOT separate caliper halves.

Cleaning & Inspection

Clean all parts in clean brake fluid or denatured alcohol. Inspect bores and pistons for excessive wear or damage. Replace defective parts.

Reassembly

Coat piston seals, cylinder bores, and pistons with rubber grease. To assemble, reverse disassembly procedure.

Disassembly (Land Cruiser & 4WD Pickup)

Remove dust seal retainer ring and seal. Insert small block of wood into cylinder cavity. Apply light air pressure to one side of cylinder to remove piston. Repeat procedure on opposite side. Remove piston seals without damaging bores. *See Fig. 8.*

NOTE: DO NOT separate caliper halves.

Cleaning & Inspection

Clean all parts in clean brake fluid or denatured alcohol. Inspect pistons and cylinder bores for excessive wear, damage, and corrosion. Replace defective parts.

Reassembly

1) Lightly coat all parts with rubber grease. Insert new piston seal, being careful that seals are properly seated in grooves.

2) Fit piston and slide dust seal into position. With dust seal seated, install retainer ring.

Disassembly (Cressida & Supra Rear Caliper)

1) Remove the two bridge bolts and seperate caliper halves (for Cressida, remove torque plate). Remove dust boot set ring and boot.

2) Remove piston from cylinder with a little compressed air. Remove piston seal from cylinder groove without damaging cylinder bore. *See Fig. 11 & 12.*

Cleaning & Inspection

Wash all parts in clean brake fluid or denatured alcohol. Inspect all parts for excessive wear, damage, and corrosion. Replace defective parts.

Reassembly

Coat all parts with rubber grease. Install piston seal into cylinder bore. Install piston into cylinder bore. Install dust boot and retaining ring (for Cressida, install torque plate). Reassemble caliper halves and torque bridge bolts.

Disassembly (All Others)

Remove retainer ring (if equipped) and boot. Apply light air pressure to fluid inlet port to remove piston from cylinder. Remove seal from cylinder without damaging bore. *See Figs. 3, 4, 7, 9, 20.*

Cleaning & Inspection

Clean all parts in clean brake fluid or denatured alcohol. Inspect bore and piston for excessive wear or damage. Replace defective parts.

Reassembly

Coat piston, seal, and cylinder bore with rubber grease before reassembly. To reassemble, reverse disassembly procedure and note the following: On "K" type, install seal, fit boot to piston, fit boot to cylinder, and push piston into cylinder bore.

Fig. 20: Exploded View of Starlet Caliper Assembly

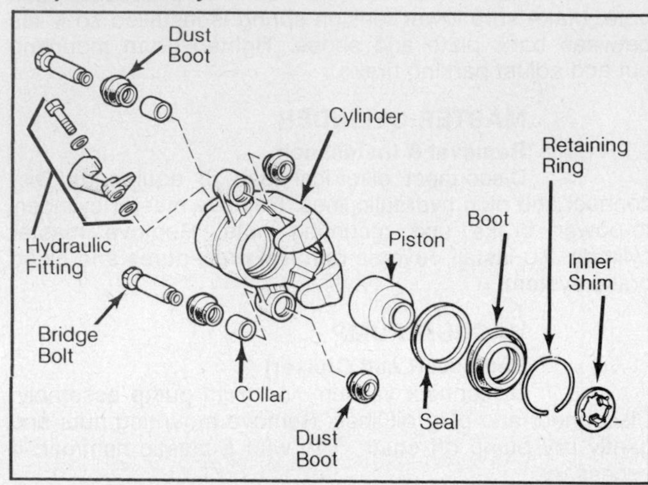
Dust
Boot
Cylinder
Retaining
Ring
Boot
Piston
Hydraulic
Fitting
Inner
Shim
Bridge
Bolt
Collar
Seal
Dust
Boot

MASTER CYLINDER

Disassembly

1) Remove reservoir, hose, and switch. Mount cylinder in a soft-jawed vise. Remove dust boot and check valves.

2) Push pistons into cylinder bore and remove stop bolt. Remove snap ring and withdraw piston assemblies.

3) Remove unions, outlet plugs, and other external components. Disassemble piston assemblies by removing springs, retainers, and cups. *See Fig. 21.*

Cleaning & Inspection

Wash all parts in clean brake fluid or denatured alcohol. Inspect for wear, damage, and corrosion. Replace defective parts as required.

Reassembly

To assemble, reverse disassembly procedure using all new rubber parts and lubricate all components with clean brake fluid.

VACUUM PUMP

Disassembly (Land Cruiser)

1) Drive dowel pins from end cover toward case. Separate end cover. Continue to drive dowels through case and stop when flush with end frame.

2) Remove end frame with pins still fitted. Remove both "O" rings and discard. Slide rotor and blades from case.

Inspection

1) Inspect end cover and casing for damage or wear. Casing bore must not be worn beyond 2.29" (5.8 mm). Check rotor-to-valve shaft spline play.

2) Rotor wear must not exceed .095" (2.4 mm). Inspect rotor blades for the following wear limits: height .46" (11.6 mm), length 1.374" (34.91 mm), and width .272" (6.9 mm).

3) Check end frame bushing and oil seal. Bushing bore must not exceed .635" (16.13 mm). Replace oil seal by driving out and pressing in new one.

TOYOTA (Cont.)

Fig. 21: Exploded View of Master Cylinders With Detail of Each Model's Piston Assemblies Shown

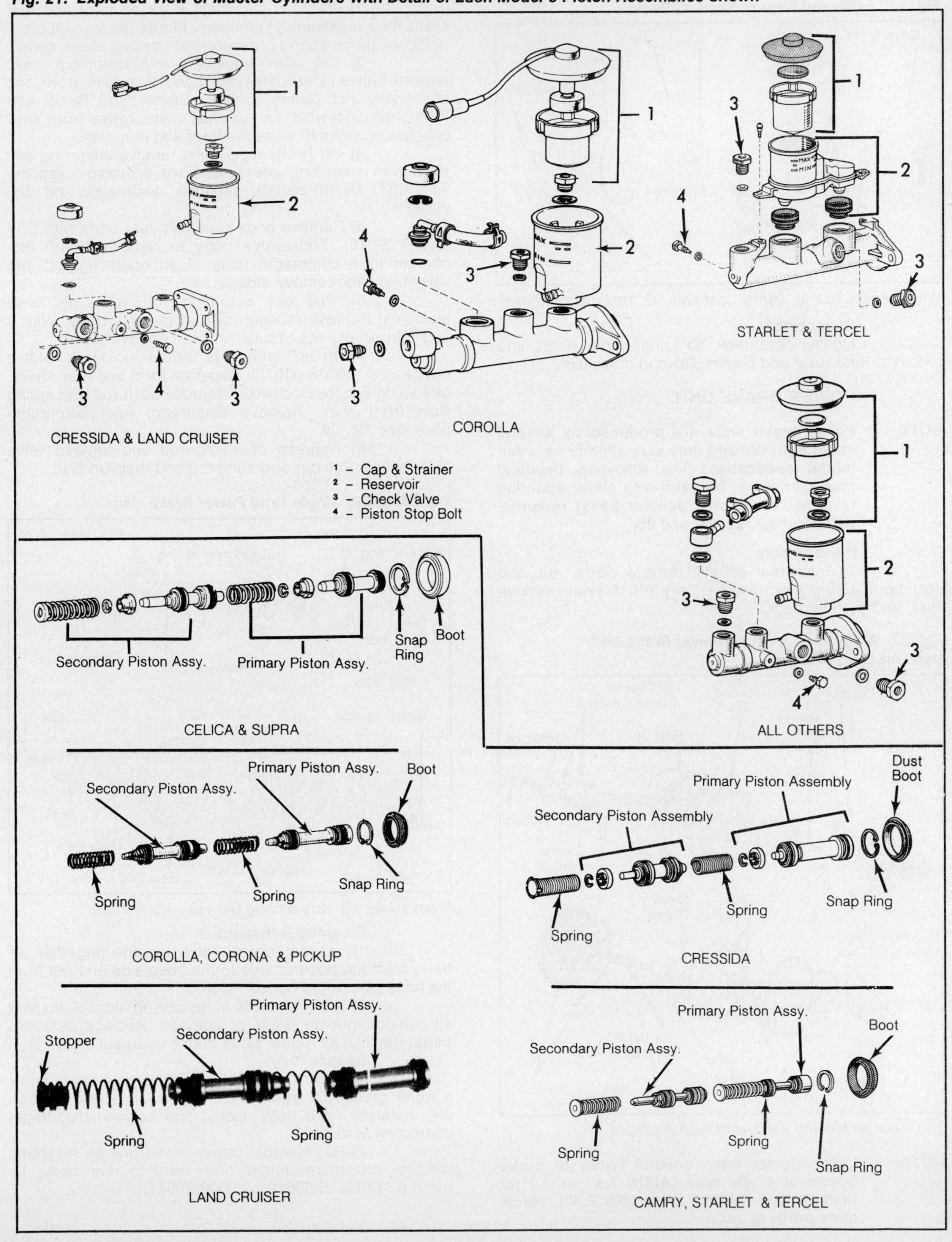
CRESSIDA & LAND CRUISER
COROLLA
STARLET & TERCEL
ALL OTHERS
1 – Cap & Strainer
2 – Reservoir
3 – Check Valve
4 – Piston Stop Bolt
Secondary Piston Assy.
Primary Piston Assy.
Snap Ring
Boot
CELICA & SUPRA
Primary Piston Assembly
Secondary Piston Assembly
Dust Boot
Spring
Snap Ring
CRESSIDA
COROLLA, CORONA & PICKUP
Stopper
LAND CRUISER
CAMRY, STARLET & TERCEL

TOYOTA (Cont.)

Fig. 22: Exploded View of Vacuum Pump

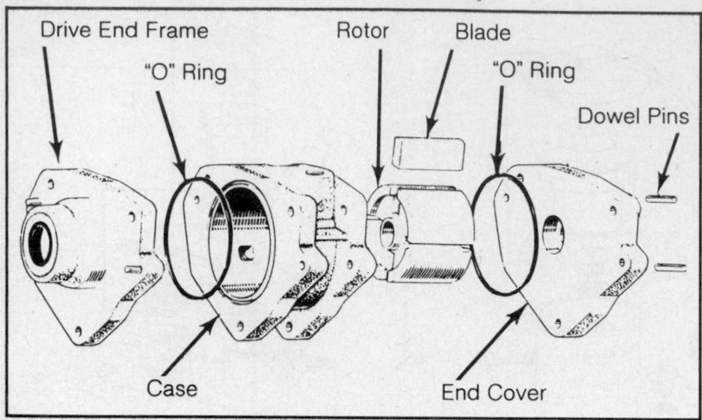
Drive End Frame
"O" Ring
Rotor
Blade
"O" Ring
Dowel Pins
Case
End Cover

When reassembling, lightly coat new "O" rings with grease.

Reassembly

Lightly coat new "O" rings and insert into grooves. Refit rotor and blades. Drive in dowel pins.

POWER BRAKE UNIT

NOTE: Power brake units are produced by several manufacturers and may vary slightly between model application. The following overhaul procedures can be used with minor attention to detail of specific booster being repaired. Refer to Figs. 23, 24, and 25.

Disassembly

1) From rear of unit, remove clevis, nut, and dust boot. Using a screwdriver, pry off retainer, remove filter and silencer pack.

Fig. 23: AISIN Tandem Type Power Brake Unit Used on Land Cruiser

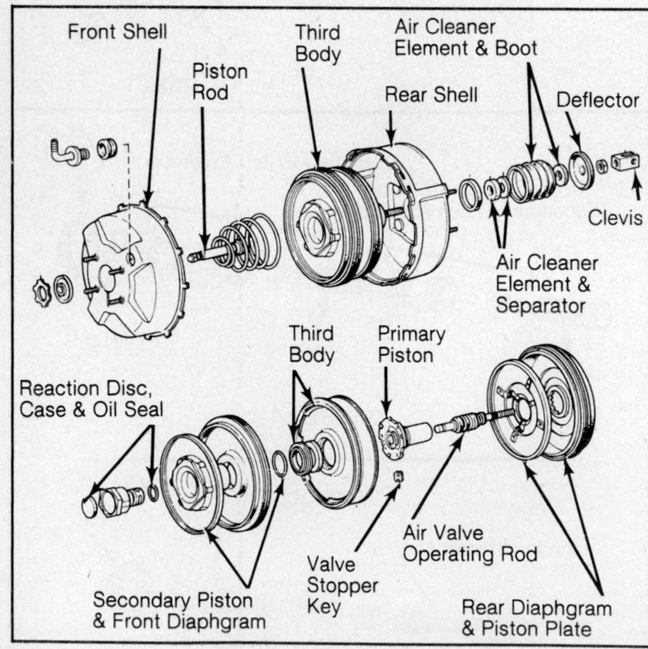
Front Shell
Piston Rod
Third Body
Air Cleaner Element & Boot
Rear Shell
Deflector
Clevis
Air Cleaner Element & Separator
Third Body
Primary Piston
Reaction Disc, Case & Oil Seal
Air Valve Operating Rod
Valve Stopper Key
Secondary Piston & Front Diaphgram
Rear Diaphgram & Piston Plate

Lubricate all moving parts with silicon grease.

NOTE: Land Cruiser uses several types of brake boosters: single type (AISIN 7.5" or 9.0")or tandem type (AISIN 7.5" or JKC 7.5"). Tercel uses AISIN or JKC.

2) Place an alignment mark on front and rear shells for a reassembly reference. Mount unit in support to prevent internal spring pressure from forcing shells apart.

3) On units equipped with clamping band, remove bolt and nut. Remove band, separate front and rear shells. For Camry, Corolla, Starlet, and Tercel turn front shell clockwise. On all other units, rotate front shell counterclockwise to separate front and rear shells.

4) On AISIN type units, remove snap ring and plate with snap ring pliers. Remove diaphragm retainer with SST (09736-30020), seperate diaphragm and diaphragm plate.

5) Remove body seal from rear body with SST (09308-00010). Turn valve body to remove it and diaphragm from diaphragm plate. Push operating rod into valve body and remove stopper key.

6) Pull out operating rod with the three elements. Remove reaction disc from valve body. With a screwdriver, pry out circular ring and remove seal.

7) On JKC type units, mount booster in holding device SST (09738-00020). Seperate fornt and rear shells, by turning counterclockwise. Remove push rod and spring from front shell. Remove diaphragm from diaphragm plate. *See Fig. 25.*

8) Depress operating rod and remove valve stopper key. Pull out operating rod and reaction disc.

Fig. 24: AISIN Single Type Power Brake Unit

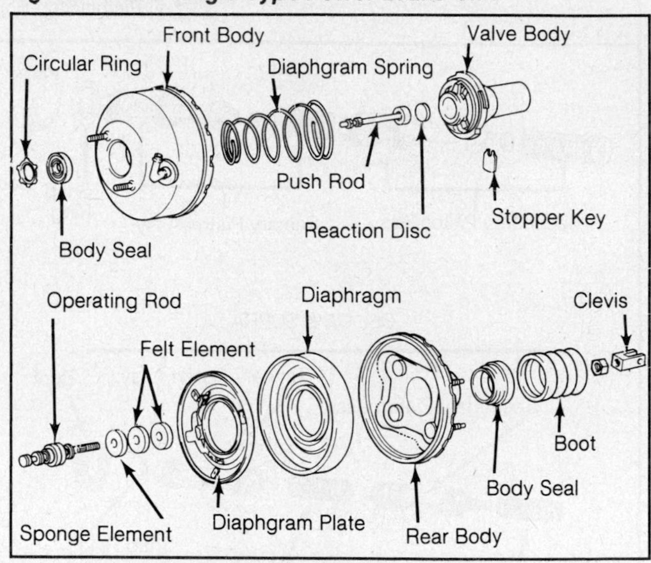
Front Body
Valve Body
Circular Ring
Diaphgram Spring
Push Rod
Stopper Key
Reaction Disc
Body Seal
Operating Rod
Diaphragm
Clevis
Felt Element
Boot
Body Seal
Sponge Element
Diaphgram Plate
Rear Body

Front shells will vary among the various vehicles.

Cleaning & Inspection

1) Inspect check valve by ensuring that air flows from the booster side to the hose side and not from the hose side to the booster side.

2) Wash all parts in denatured alcohol. Inspect all components for wear or damage. Replace defective parts. Replace all rubber parts during overhaul.

Reassembly

1) Before assembly of AISIN type units, apply silicone grease to front seals, rear shell seals, reaction disc surface, valve body sliding surface, and diaphragm contacting surface.

2) Reassemble power brake unit by reversing removal procedure. Install body seal to rear body, by using SST (09515-30010 & 09608-20011).

TOYOTA (Cont.)

Fig. 25: JKC Tandem Type Power Brake Unit

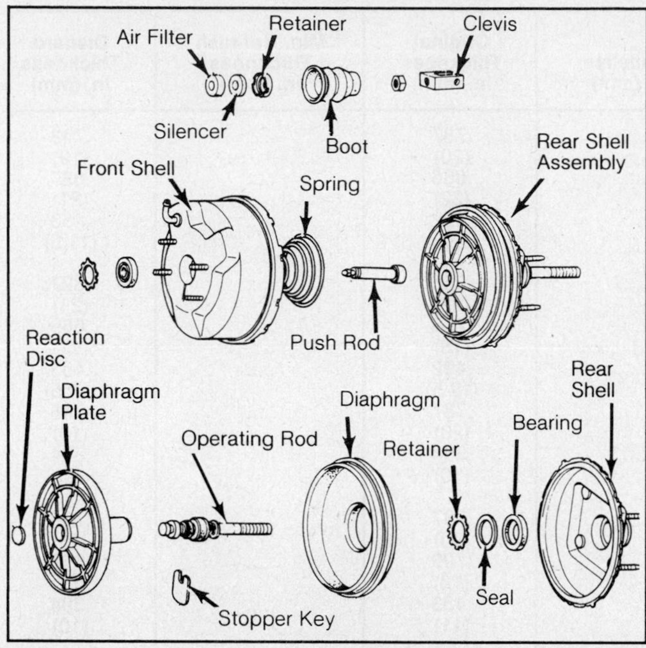
Air Filter
Retainer
Clevis
Silencer
Boot
Rear Shell Assembly
Front Shell
Spring
Reaction Disc
Push Rod
Rear Shell
Diaphragm Plate
Diaphragm
Bearing
Operating Rod
Retainer
Seal
Stopper Key

Apply silicone grease to all sliding surfaces.

3) Mount front body on SST (09738-00020). Install diaphragm spring, push rod, diaphragm plate, and rear body. Compress unit and turn counterclockwise until alignment marks match.

4) Before assembling JKC type units, grease all moving parts with silicon grease and install in reverse order. Place SST (09753-30010) in vise and install reaction disc case.

Fig. 26: Adjusting Push Rod Clearance With Gauge

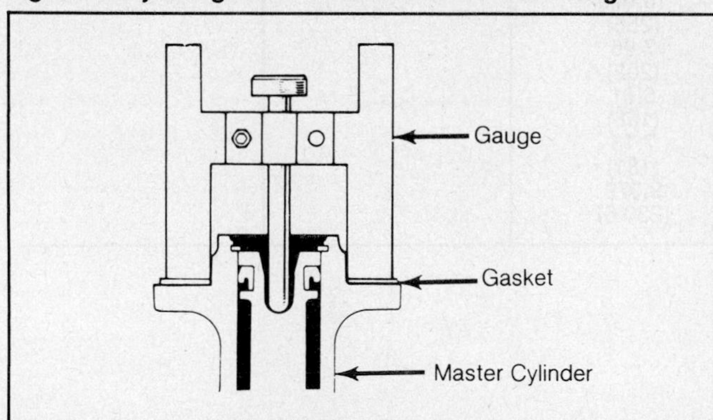
Gauge
Gasket
Master Cylinder

Check with gasket installed, if equipped.

5) Install front diaphragm and No. 2 piston to reaction case, by aligning the notched holes at a right angle. Install retainer and clip. To assemble unit, install rear shell, compress, and turn shell to lock.

6) After installation, adjust push rod length using depth gauge (09737-00010). Place gauge on master cylinder (with gauge gasket installed, if equipped) and turn pin until tip touches piston. *See Fig. 26.*

7) Without disturbing gauge setting, turn gauge upside down on power brake unit. Adjust length of push rod by turning lock nut until clearance between gauge and tip of push rod is obtained. Under no vacuum, clearance should be .004-.020" (.1-.5 mm).

TIGHTENING SPECIFICATIONS

Application	Ft. Lbs. (N.m)
Caliper Mounting Bolts	
2WD Pickup	68-86 (92-117)
4WD Pickup	54-76 (73-103)
Land Cruiser	73-108 (99-147)
Cressida (Rear)	29-39 (39-53)
Caliper Bracket-to-Steering Knuckle	
Cab & Chassis Pickup	80-126 (109-171)
Camry & Tercel	70 (95)
Celica	58-75 (77-102)
Cressida	68-86 (92-117)
Starlet	29-54 (39-73)
Supra	44-57 (60-77)
Caliper Bracket-to-Suspension Arm	
Supra (Rear)	29-39 (39-53)
Caliper-to-Caliper Bracket	
Camry & Tercel	18 (24)
Celica & Supra (Front & Rear)	12-17 (16-23)
Caliper Bridge Bolts	
Corolla	58-68 (79-92)
Cressida	37-43 (50-58)
Caliper Guide-to-Caliper Bracket	
Cab & Chassis Pickup	29-44 (39-60)
Supra	29-39 (39-53)
Hub-to-Rotor Bolts	
Cab & Chassis Pickup, Celica & Supra	40-54 (54-73)
All Others	29-39 (39-53)
Tercel Suspension Components	
Axle Nut	137 (186)
Lower Arm-to-Crossmember	51-65 (69-88)
Lower Arm-to Steering Knuckle	59 (80)
Stabilizer Bar	66-90 (89-122)
Steering Knuckle-to-Shock	105 (142)
Strut Bar	64 (87)
Tie Rod End	29-43 (39-58)

TOYOTA (Cont.)

DISC BRAKE ROTOR SPECIFICATIONS

Application	Disc Diameter In. (mm)	Lateral Runout In. (mm)	Parallelism In. (mm)	Original Thickness In. (mm)	Min. Refinish Thickness In. (mm)	Discard Thickness In. (mm)
Cab & Chassis Pickup & Celica	.....	.006 (.15)	.....	.787 (20)	.....	.748 (19)
Camry	.....	.006 (.15)	.....	.866 (22)	.....	.827 (21)
Corolla	.....	.006 (.15)	.....	.492 (12.5)	.....	.453 (11.5)
Cressida						
Front	.....	.006 (.15)	.....	.866 (22)	.....	.827 (21)
Rear	.....	.006 (.15)	.....	.709 (18)	.....	.669 (17)
Pickup (Except Cab & Chassis)	.....	.006 (.15)	.....	.492 (12.5)	.....	.453 (11.5)
Land Cruiser	.....	.005 (.12)	.....	.787 (20)	.....	.748 (19)
Starlet	.....	.006 (.15)	.....	.394 (10)	.....	.354 (9)
Supra						
Front	.....	.006 (.15)	.....	.787 (20)	.....	.748 (19)
Rear	.....	.006 (.15)	.....	.709 (18)	.....	.669 (17)
Tercel	.....	.006 (.15)	.....	.433 (11)	.....	.394 (10)

DRUM BRAKE SPECIFICATIONS

Application	Drum Diam. In. (mm)	Drum Width In. (mm)	Max. Drum Refinish Diam. In. (mm)	Wheel Cyl. Diam. In. (mm)	Master Cyl. Diam. In. (mm)
Camry	7.87 (200)	.....	7.91 (201)	.....	.....
Land Cruiser	11.61 (295)	.....	11.69 (297)	.....	.....
Pickup	10.00 (254)	.....	10.079 (256)	.....	.....
Starlet	7.87 (200)	.....	7.95 (202)	.....	.....
Supra	6.57 (167)	.....	6.61 (168)	.....	.....
Tercel	7.09 (180)	.....	7.13 (181)	.....	.....
All Others	9.0 (228.6)	.....	9.079 (230.6)	.....	.....

VOLKSWAGEN

Jetta, Rabbit, Rabbit GTI, Rabbit Pickup, Scirocco, Quantum & Vanagon

DESCRIPTION

Brake systems are hydraulically-actuated, using a tandem master cylinder and optional power brake unit. All models are equipped with front disc brakes, and self-adjusting rear drum brakes.

Jetta, Rabbit, Rabbit GTI and Rabbit Pickup models are equipped with a brake proportional valve. All other models are equipped with a pressure regulator in rear brake circuit to avoid rear wheel lock-up. All models are equipped with cable-actuated parking brake, which operates on rear brakes.

ADJUSTMENT

PEDAL FREE PLAY

NOTE: **Pedal free play is adjusted at the power brake unit on all models. Power brake unit (if equipped) must be removed to adjust free play.**

STOP LIGHT SWITCH

All Models

Stop light switch is located under dash, above brake pedal. To adjust, loosen lock nuts and adjust switch so distance between brake pedal arm and switch body is .20-.24" (5-6 mm). Tighten lock nuts. *See Fig. 1.*

Fig. 1: Adjusting Stop Light Switch

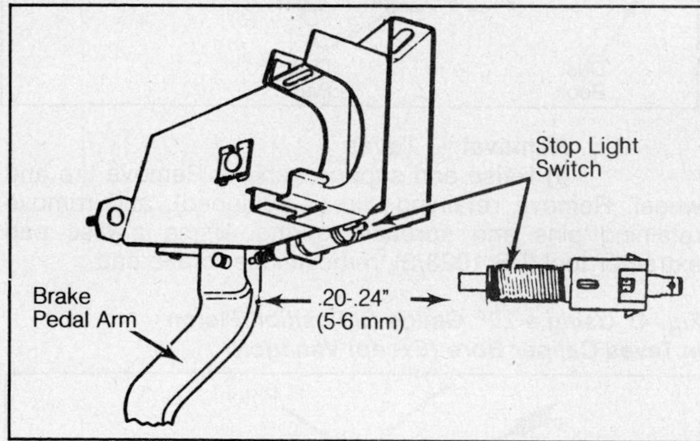
Stop Light
Switch
Brake
Pedal Arm
.20-.24"
(5-6 mm)

PARKING BRAKE

Vanagon

1) Raise and support vehicle. Ensure rear brakes are properly adjusted. From under vehicle, loosen parking brake cable lock nut(s).

2) Pull parking brake handle up 2-4 notches, and tighten cable adjusting nut(s) until rear wheels lock.

3) Tighten lock nut(s), and ensure rear wheels rotate freely with parking brake fully released.

All Models Except Vanagon

1) Raise and support vehicle. Ensure rear brakes are properly adjusted. Pull back rubber (plastic) boot at base of parking brake handle, and loosen parking brake cable lock nuts.

2) Pull handle up 2 notches, and tighten each adjusting nut until rear wheels lock. Tighten lock nuts and refit boot. Ensure rear wheels rotate freely with parking brake fully released.

BRAKE WARNING LIGHT

1) A dual warning light is mounted on dash. Turn ignition on. Light should glow when parking brake lever is pulled 1 notch, and go off when lever is fully released.

2) To check circuit warning operation, turn ignition on. Release parking brake and ensure light is off.

3) Open bleeder screw on 1 wheel, and depress brake pedal. Light should glow. Close bleeder screw, replenish brake fluid, and bleed hydraulic system.

NOTE: **Jetta, Rabbit, Rabbit GTI and Rabbit Pickup models are equipped with warning sensor, which is connected to brake proportioning valve. This sensor DOES NOT indicate fluid level in master cylinder. All other models are equipped with sensor which indicates fluid level in reservoir.**

BRAKE PROPORTIONING VALVE

Jetta, Rabbit, Rabbit GTI & Rabbit Pickup

1) Valve is located below master cylinder. Using two 1500 psi gauges, connect one to left front caliper and other to right rear wheel cylinder. Bleed gauges and depress brake pedal several times.

2) Apply brake pedal until front gauge reads indicated pressure for first reading in Brake Pressure Chart. Record rear gauge reading. Increase pedal pressure until front gauge reads indicated pressure for second reading.

3) Record rear gauge reading. Remove gauges, and bleed hydraulic system. If pressures do not meet specifications, replace proportioning valve.

BRAKE PRESSURE REGULATOR

Scirocco & Quantum

1) Regulator is located on right rear frame on Quantum, and left rear frame on Scirocco. With vehicle empty and fuel tank full, load driver's seat to 165 lbs. Bounce car several times, and allow vehicle to settle normally.

2) Measure distance from top of tire rim to lower edge of fender lip (both sides). Attach spring tensioners to hold vehicle in settled position. *See Fig. 2.*

3) Raise and support vehicle. Check measurement, and adjust tension if required. Using two 1500 psi gauges, connect one to left front caliper, and other to right rear wheel cylinder. Bleed gauges.

4) Pump pedal several times. Depress brake pedal until front gauge reads indicated pressure for first reading in Brake Pressure Chart. Record rear gauge reading. Increase pedal pressure until front gauge reads indicated pressure for second reading. Record rear gauge reading.

5) If both pressures were high on rear wheel, loosen regulator clamp bolt, and REDUCE spring tension. INCREASE spring tension if pressures were too low. Replace pressure regulator if spring adjustment does not correct pressures.

NOTE: **Do not adjust spring tension with brake pedal depressed.**

VOLKSWAGEN (Cont.)

Fig. 2: Tensioner Installed to Shock Absorber Mount

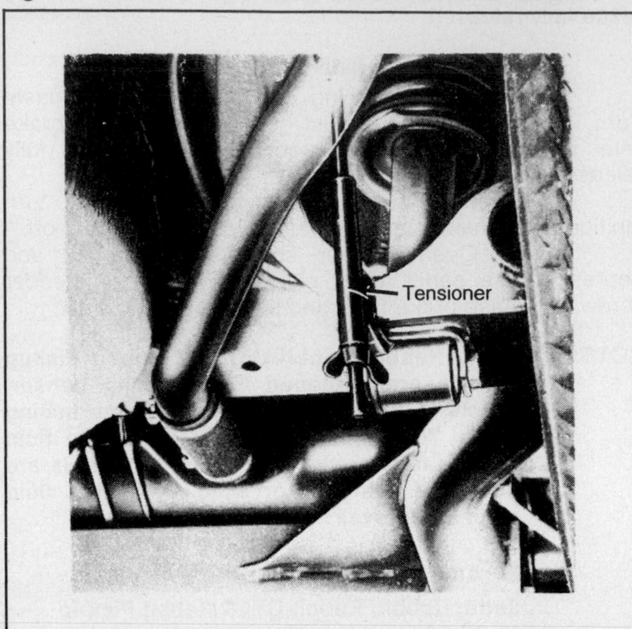
Tensioner

Tensioners will keep vehicle in a settled position.

Vanagon

1) Regulator is mounted on right rear frame. Raise and support vehicle. Connect two 1500 psi gauges, one to left front caliper, and other to left rear wheel cylinder. Bleed gauges, and depress brake pedal several times.

2) Remove regulator attaching nuts. Remove regulator from mounting studs. Depress brake pedal until front gauge reads indicated pressure for first reading in Brake Pressure Chart.

3) Maintain pressure, and tilt front of regulator down at a 30° angle. Increase pedal pressure until front gauge reads indicated pressure for second reading. Record rear gauge reading.

NOTE: Do not damage brake lines when tilting regulator.

4) If pressures are as specified in Brake Pressure Chart, return and secure regulator to proper position. Remove gauges, and bleed hydraulic system. If pressures are not as specified, replace regulator.

BRAKE PRESSURE CHART

Application	Front Gauge psi (kg/cm²)	Rear Gauge psi (kg/cm²)
Rabbit Pickup		
1st Reading	725 (51)	536-594 (38-42)
2nd Reading	1450 (102)	826-899 (58-63)
Quantum		
1st Reading	725 (51)	457-566 (32-40)
2nd Reading	1450 (102)	725-914 (51-64)
Vanagon		
1st Reading	725 (51)	725 (51)
2nd Reading	1450 (102)	798-943 (56-66)
All Other Models		
1st Reading	725 (51)	449-507 (32-36)
2nd Reading	1450 (102)	768-826 (54-58)

REMOVAL & INSTALLATION

FRONT DISC BRAKE PADS

NOTE: Teves, Girling or Kelsey-Hayes calipers may be used on front disc brakes. Quantum is equipped with new type Girling calipers. Disc pads are interchangeable between Teves and Girling calipers only.

Fig. 3: Teves Disc Brake Assembly (Vanagon)

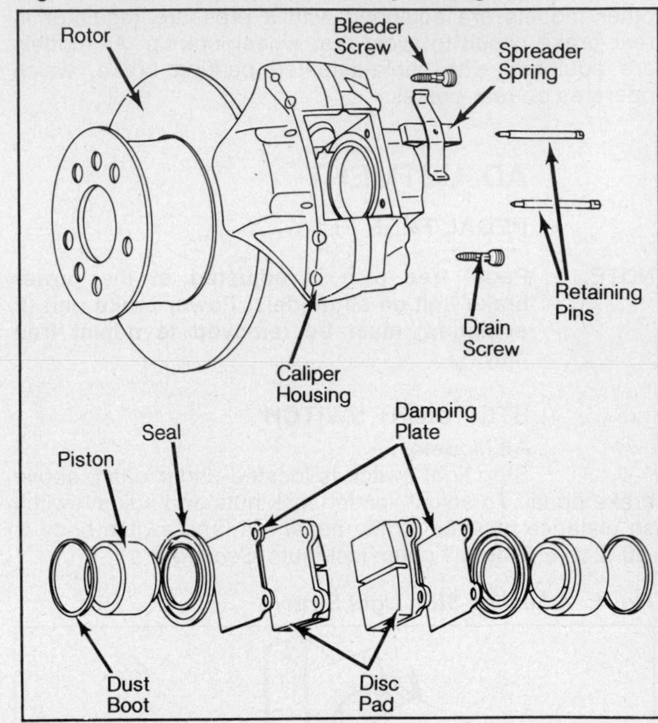
Rotor
Bleeder Screw
Spreader Spring
Retaining Pins
Drain Screw
Caliper Housing
Seal
Damping Plate
Piston
Dust Boot
Disc Pad

Removal - Teves

1) Raise and support vehicle. Remove tire and wheel. Remove retaining clip (if equipped), and remove retaining pins and spreader spring. Using a disc pad extractor tool (US 1023/3), remove inner brake pad.

Fig. 4: Using a 20° Gauge to Position Piston in Teves Caliper Bore (Except Vanagon)

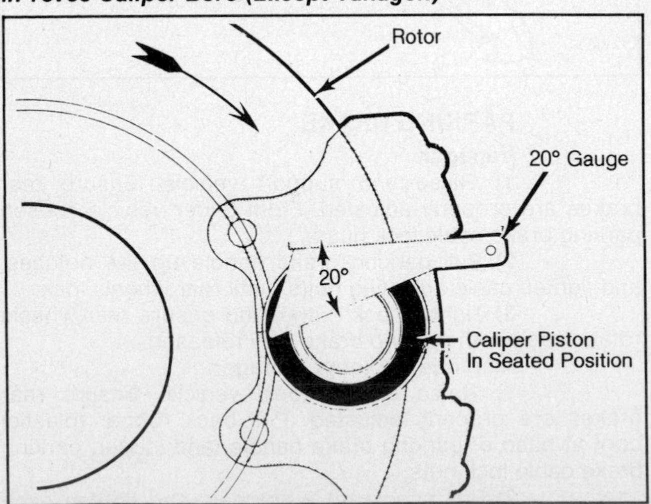
Rotor
20° Gauge
20°
Caliper Piston
In Seated Position

Measured from top side of caliper.

VOLKSWAGEN (Cont.)

2) Separate outer pad from notch in piston. Then extract outer brake pad. Remove damping plates. Replace brake pads if thickness is less than .08" (2 mm) on Vanagon or .25" (6 mm) on all other models.

Installation

1) Siphon small amount of brake fluid from master cylinder reservoir. Seat piston in caliper bore with compressor tool (US 1023/4). Check position of piston.

2) On Vanagon, notches in piston must face bottom of caliper. Rotate with pliers (US 1023/2) if required. On all other models, use 20° gauge (US 1023/1) to position piston. *See Fig. 4*.

3) Install noise dampening plates with lugs engaged in piston recesses. Install brake pads, and new spreader spring. Install retaining pins, and clips (if equipped). Depress brake pedal several times to set pad-to-rotor clearance.

Fig. 5: Teves Disc Brake Assembly (Except Vanagon)

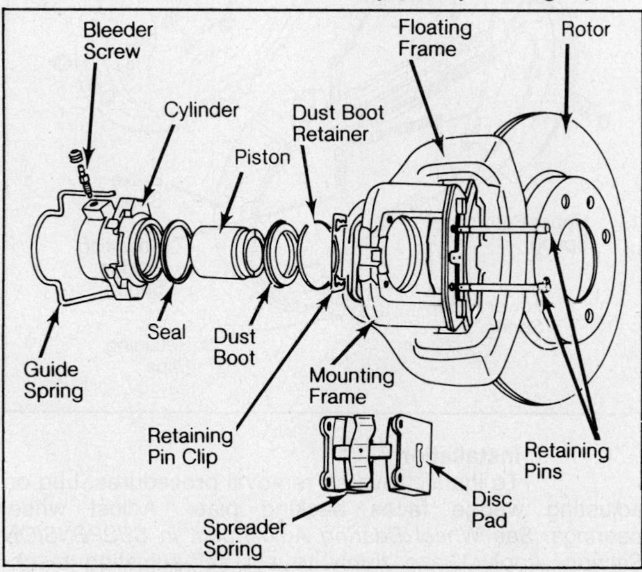
Bleeder Screw
Floating Frame
Rotor
Cylinder
Dust Boot Retainer
Piston
Seal
Dust Boot
Guide Spring
Mounting Frame
Retaining Pin Clip
Retaining Pins
Disc Pad
Spreader Spring

Install new spreader spring when disc pads are replaced.

Removal - Girling (Except Quantum)

1) Raise and support vehicle. Remove tire and wheel, and remove spreader spring. Remove pin retaining bolt (pin clips), and remove pad pins.

2) Using brake pad extractor tool (US 1023/3), remove pads and damping plates (if equipped). Replace brake pads if thickness of friction material is less than .08" (2 mm).

Installation

1) Remove small amount of brake fluid from reservoir. Seat pistons in caliper bore with compressor tool (US 1023/4). Install pads, and damping plates (if equipped). Damping plates must be installed with arrows pointing toward forward wheel rotation.

2) Attach spreader spring. If stamped with an arrow, install spring with arrow pointing down. Install pad pins, and new pin retaining bolt (pin clips). Depress brake pedal several times to adjust pad-to-rotor clearance.

Removal - Girling (Quantum)

1) Raise and support vehicle. Remove tire and wheel. Remove small amount of brake fluid from reservoir. Using hand pressure, seat piston in housing by pushing caliper toward outer bearing.

2) Remove lower caliper mounting bolt while holding guide pin head with open end wrench. Rotate caliper body upward and remove pads. Replace pads if lining is less than .28" (7 mm).

Installation

To install, reverse removal procedure and install new lower mounting bolt. Depress brake pedal several times to adjust pad-to-rotor clearance.

Removal - Kelsey-Hayes

1) Raise and support vehicle. Remove tire and wheel. Remove anti-rattle springs and guide pins.

2) Remove caliper and suspend with wire. Do not allow caliper to hang from hydraulic line. Remove pads. Replace pads if lining is less than .28" (7 mm).

Installation

1) Insert pads in caliper support (inner pad is identified by chamfered ends). Remove brake fluid from reservoir and seat piston with compressor tool (US 1023/4).

2) Position caliper on support. Lube guide pins with silicone grease and install with long pin on top. Install anti-rattle springs.

3) Depress brake pedal several times to adjust pad-to-rotor clearance.

DISC BRAKE CALIPER

Removal

1) Raise and support vehicle. Remove tire and wheel. Disconnect brake line from caliper and plug opening.

2) Bend back locking tabs (if equipped) on mounting bolts. Remove caliper mounting bolts, and take off caliper assembly.

Installation

To install, reverse removal procedure, using new lock plates and mounting bolts.

DISC BRAKE ROTOR

Removal (Vanagon)

1) Raise and support vehicle. Remove wheel and tire. Remove and suspend brake caliper. Remove grease cap, and loosen peen nut.

2) Remove wheel bearing hardware. Pull hub and rotor from spindle without dropping bearing.

Removal (Except Vanagon)

Raise and support vehicle. Remove wheel and tire. Remove caliper and suspend with wire. Remove countersunk screw from between 2 wheel bolt holes. Pull rotor off hub.

Installation (All Models)

To install, reverse removal procedure. On Vanagon, adjust wheel bearings. *See Wheel Bearing Adjustment in SUSPENSION Section.*

REAR BRAKE DRUM

CAUTION: Loosen and tighten spindle nut only with wheels on the ground.

Removal (Vanagon)

1) Remove dust cap, cotter pin and loosen castellated nut. Raise and support vehicle. Remove tire and wheel.

2) Release parking brake at equalizer, and back off adjuster. Remove drum retaining screws. Install puller (OTC 827-B or equivalent) and remove drum.

NOTE: Drum must rotate freely during removal.

VOLKSWAGEN (Cont.)

Installation

To install, reverse removal procedure and ensure drum retaining screws are tight. Adjust parking brake and depress brake pedal several times to set self-adjusting mechanism.

Removal (Except Vanagon)

1) Raise and support vehicle. Remove 1 wheel bolt. Through wheel bolt hole, push adjusting wedge up against stop with a screwdriver.

2) Reinstall wheel bolt. Remove grease cap, cotter pin, nut lock and nut. Remove drum assembly from spindle without dropping thrust washer or outer bearing.

Installation

1) To install, reverse removal procedure and adjust wheel bearings. *See Wheel Bearing Adjustment in SUSPENSION Section.*

2) Apply brake pedal firmly several times to set self-adjusting mechanism.

BRAKE SHOES

Removal (Vanagon)

1) With wheel and drum removed, remove hold-down springs, and pins. Disconnect parking brake cable from lever on brake shoe. Remove lower return spring, and adjuster spring.

2) Move brake shoes out of lower support, and remove return springs. Remove brake shoes as an assembly from backing plate without pulling pistons out of wheel cylinder.

3) Separate brake shoes, and disconnect parking brake lever from brake shoe. Remove lower support bolts and support.

Fig. 6: Vanagon Rear Brake Assembly

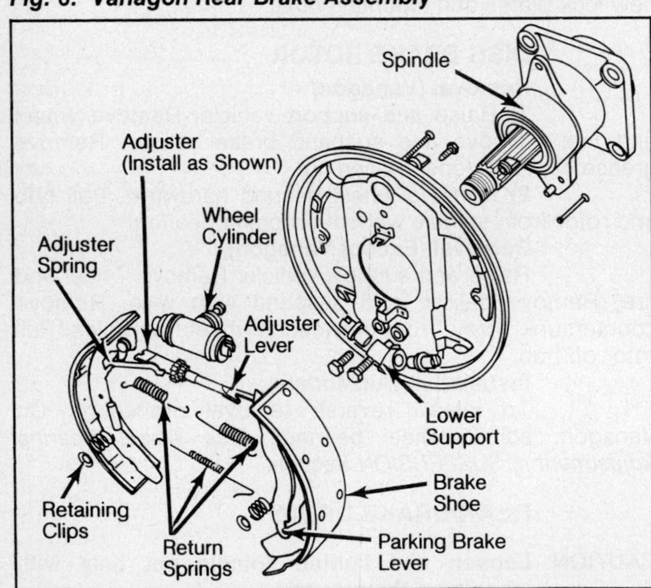
Spindle
Adjuster
(Install as Shown)
Wheel
Cylinder
Adjuster
Spring
Adjuster
Lever
Lower
Support
Brake
Shoe
Retaining
Clips
Return
Springs
Parking Brake
Lever

Installation

1) To install, reverse removal procedure. After installing brake shoes, adjust brake shoes by setting distance (measured from outer surface of each brake lining) to 9.87" (250.7 mm).

2) Adjust parking brake at equalizer (there must not be any free play between parking brake lever on brake shoe and adjusting rod). Install brake drum and depress brake pedal several times to set self-adjusting mechanism.

Removal (Except Vanagon)

1) With drum removed, remove hold-down springs and pins. Remove brake shoes from anchor pins. Remove lower return spring.

2) Disconnect parking brake cable from lever. Disconnect adjusting wedge spring and upper return spring. Remove brake shoes.

3) Place adjuster strut and shoe in vise, and remove tension spring. Separate shoe and components.

Fig. 7: Rear Brake Assembly (Except Vanagon)

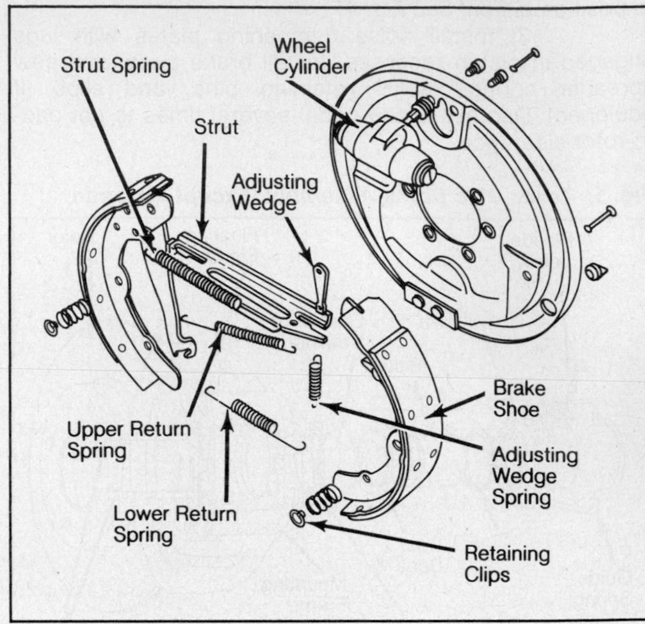
Strut Spring
Wheel
Cylinder
Strut
Adjusting
Wedge
Brake
Shoe
Upper Return
Spring
Adjusting
Wedge
Spring
Lower Return
Spring
Retaining
Clips

Installation

To install, reverse removal procedures. Lug on adjusting wedge faces backing plate. Adjust wheel bearings. *See Wheel Bearing Adjustment in SUSPENSION Section*. Apply brake firmly to set self-adjusting mechanism.

REAR AXLE SHAFT BEARING & GREASE SEAL

Removal

1) Remove brake drum and wheel hub. Remove brake line from wheel cylinder and remove brake backing plate. Remove axle shaft from constant velocity joint. Remove bearing housing from trailing arm.

2) Press shaft from bearing housing using removal tool (VW411). Using screwdriver, pry grease seals from bearing housing. Remove inner race of outer wheel bearing. Remove spacer sleeve.

3) Using a brass drift, drive outer bearing from bearing housing. Press out inner wheel bearing with removal tools (VW412 and VW244b).

Installation

1) Press inner bearing in until seated, using installer tools (VW407, VW472, and VW401). Install circlip against inner bearing. Grease bearing. Grease outer bearing, and fill space between inner and outer bearings with multipurpose grease.

2) Install spacer sleeve. Press outer bearing into bearing housing, using installer tools (VW407, VW472 and VW401). Install inner race of outer bearing, using installer (VW240a).

VOLKSWAGEN (Cont.)

3) Install grease seals in bearing housing, using installer tool (VW240a). Press in flush with bearing housing on wheel side and against circlip on flange side.

4) Press axle shaft into bearing housing, using installer tools (VW412, 30-100, and VW402). Attach bearing housing to trailing arm.

5) Connect axle shaft to constant velocity joint. Reinstall brake backing plate and attach brake line to wheel cylinder. Install wheel hub and brake drum.

6) Install axle nut on axle shaft. With wheels on ground, tighten nut to 253 ft. lbs. (350 N.m). Insert new cotter pin. Bleed brakes.

MASTER CYLINDER

NOTE: **Removal and installation of all master cylinders is basically the same. The following variations may apply: Location of cylinder, removal of wheel for accessibility, number of fluid connections, and number of electrical connections.**

Removal (Vanagon)

1) Remove instrument panel. Then drain or siphon fluid from master cylinder reservoir. Disconnect fluid lines and electrical connections from master cylinder.

2) Remove vacuum lines from power brake unit. Remove pedal and bracket assembly. Disconnect brake push rod from brake pedal.

3) Remove power brake unit and master cylinder assembly from pedal bracket. Remove master cylinder-to-power brake unit attaching bolts and remove master cylinder.

Installation

To install, reverse removal procedure. Install a new "O" ring between master cylinder and power brake unit. Adjust brake push rod length. *See Power Brake Unit.* Bleed hydraulic system.

Removal (Except Vanagon)

1) Drain or siphon fluid from reservoir. Raise and support vehicle. Remove cover plate (if equipped). Disconnect fluid lines and electrical connections at master cylinder.

2) On models without power unit, remove brake push rod from brake pedal. Remove master cylinder-to-power brake unit attaching bolts and remove master cylinder.

NOTE: **If spacers are used on attaching bolts, do not drop or lose spacers.**

Installation

To install, reverse removal procedure. Install a new "O" ring between master cylinder and power brake unit. After installation, bleed hydraulic system.

POWER BRAKE UNIT

Function Test

1) With engine off, depress and release brake pedal several times to exhaust vacuum. Depress and hold pedal. Start engine. Pedal should fall slightly, then hold.

2) Replace booster assembly if check valve is operative, and no defects or leaks are present in vacuum or hydraulic systems.

Removal (Vanagon)

Remove instrument panel, and separate power brake unit from master cylinder as previously described.

Installation

1) To install, reverse removal procedure. Before installing brake push rod to brake pedal, adjust push rod length.

2) To adjust push rod length (measured from power unit flange to centerline of push rod clevis), loosen lock nut, and turn push rod until distance is 4.39" (111.5 mm). Tighten lock nut. Complete installation, and bleed hydraulic system.

Removal (Except Vanagon)

1) Remove master cylinder from power brake unit as previously described. Disconnect brake push rod from brake pedal.

2) Disconnect vacuum lines from power brake unit. Remove mounting nuts from firewall, and remove power brake unit.

Installation

To install, reverse removal procedure. Always replace damping ring, washer, filter and "O" ring. Slots in damping washer, and filter must be offset 180°.

CHECK VALVE

Function Test

1) Check valve is located in vacuum line between power brake unit, and intake manifold. Blowing into large diameter side should unseat valve.

2) Valve must seat when test is performed on opposite side. Replace defective valve.

VACUUM BOOSTER
CIS FUEL-INJECTED MODELS ONLY

1) An adjustable or non-adjustable vacuum booster is installed to increase vacuum to power brake unit. To check booster, warm engine until oil reaches 140°F.

2) Install "T" connector between distributor vacuum unit and intake manifold. Gauge should read 7.4 in. Hg vacuum with engine idling. If not, check vacuum lines for leaks.

3) If vacuum is as specified in step **2)**, check booster as follows: Remove and plug hose from right side of booster. Loosen lock nut (if equipped), and install vacuum gauge and hose.

4) Gauge should read 11.8 in. Hg vacuum with engine idling. Adjust screw in or out to obtain correct reading (if equipped). Replace defective booster.

VACUUM PUMP (DIESEL ONLY)

Removal & Installation

Remove vacuum lines from upper housing. Remove unit from engine block. To install, reverse removal procedure, and replace "O" ring at mounting base.

OVERHAUL

DISC BRAKE CALIPER

Disassembly – Teves & Girling (Vanagon)

1) Remove disc pads and damping plates as previously described. Clamp mounting flange in a soft-jawed vise, and remove dust boot retainer (if equipped), and dust boot.

2) Install piston retainer clamp (US 1023/5) on 1 piston. Insert wooden block in caliper, and force piston

VOLKSWAGEN (Cont.)

out using compressed air. Repeat procedure for opposite piston. Remove piston seals without damaging bore.

Cleaning & Inspection

Clean all parts in brake fluid. Check piston and caliper bore for wear or damage. Replace as necessary. Do not separate caliper halves. Caliper assembly must be replaced if halves are separated. Replace all parts included in repair kit.

Reassembly

1) Apply light coat of brake paste to piston and seal. Fit seal in groove, install piston in bore and press into bore with piston installer clamp (US 1023/5). Lightly coat inside of dust boot with brake paste, and fit to piston.

2) Using press clamp (VW 442), press dust cap onto bore groove and seat piston. Install dust boot retainer (if equipped). Install damping plates. Repeat procedure for other piston.

NOTE: Ensure pistons are properly seated, and piston damping plates are properly installed on Teves calipers.

Disassembly – Teves (Except Vanagon)

1) Remove disc pads as previously described. Press caliper frame off floating frame. Insert wooden block in floating frame and drive cylinder and guide spring off with brass drift.

2) Remove piston retaining ring and dust seal. Protect piston with wooden block, and force piston out with compressed air. Remove piston seal without damaging bore.

Cleaning & Inspection

Clean all parts in brake fluid. Check piston and bore for wear or damage. Replace as necessary. Replace all parts included in repair kit.

Fig. 8: Girling Disc Brake Assembly (Vanagon)

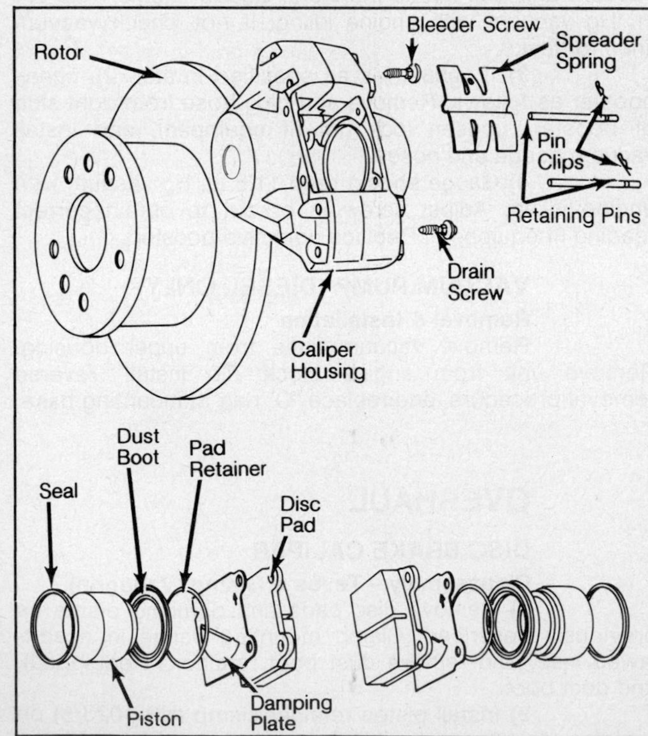
Bleeder Screw
Rotor
Spreader Spring
Pin Clips
Retaining Pins
Drain Screw
Caliper Housing
Dust Boot
Pad Retainer
Seal
Disc Pad
Piston
Damping Plate

Do not separate caliper halves.

Fig. 9: Girling Disc Brake Assembly (Except Vanagon & Quantum)

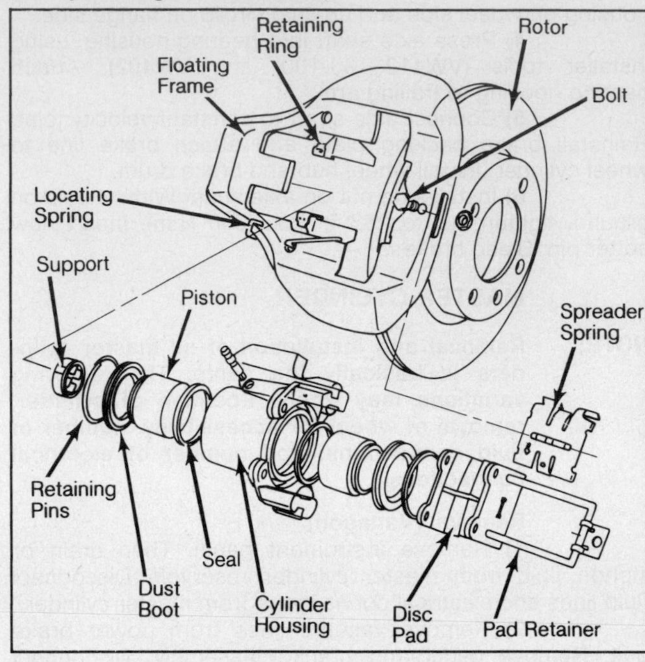
Retaining Ring
Rotor
Floating Frame
Bolt
Locating Spring
Support
Piston
Spreader Spring
Retaining Pins
Seal
Dust Boot
Cylinder Housing
Disc Pad
Pad Retainer

Reassembly

1) Reverse disassembly procedure. Coat piston with brake paste. Use a vise to seat piston.

2) Use a brass drift to fit brake cylinder to floating frame. Make sure both grooves in mounting frame are pushed over ribs on floating frame. Make sure piston is properly positioned. *See Fig. 4*.

Disassembly – Girling (Except Quantum)

1) Press cylinder out of frame. Remove dust boot, and retaining ring from each piston.

2) Clamp mounting flange in a soft-jawed vise, and force pistons out of bore using compressed air. Remove piston seals without damaging bore.

Cleaning & Inspection

Clean all parts in brake fluid. Check piston and caliper bore for wear or damage. Replace as necessary. Replace all parts included in repair kit.

Reassembly

To reassemble, reverse disassembly procedure. Coat pistons and seals with brake paste before refitting.

Disassembly – Girling (Quantum)

1) Place caliper in soft-jawed vise. insert wooden block in caliper and force piston out using compressed air.

2) Remove dust seal. Remove piston seal without damaging bore.

Cleaning & Inspection

Clean all parts in brake fluid. Check piston and caliper bore for wear or damage. Replace as necessary. Replace all parts included in repair kit.

Reassembly

1) Install piston seal in bore. Slide dust seal on piston. Lubricate piston and cylinder bore with brake paste.

2) Install piston and insert inner lip of dust seal into groove of caliper bore. Press piston in as far as it will

VOLKSWAGEN (Cont.)

Fig. 10: Girling Disc Brake Assembly (Quantum)

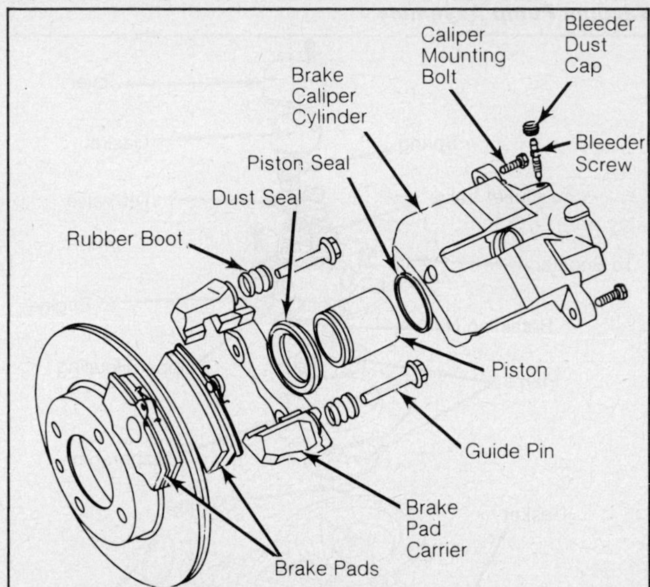
Caliper
Mounting
Bolt
Bleeder
Dust
Cap
Brake
Caliper
Cylinder
Bleeder
Screw
Piston Seal
Dust Seal
Rubber Boot
Piston
Guide Pin
Brake
Pad
Carrier
Brake Pads

Note new-type caliper for Quantum.

Fig. 11: Exploded View of Master Cylinder

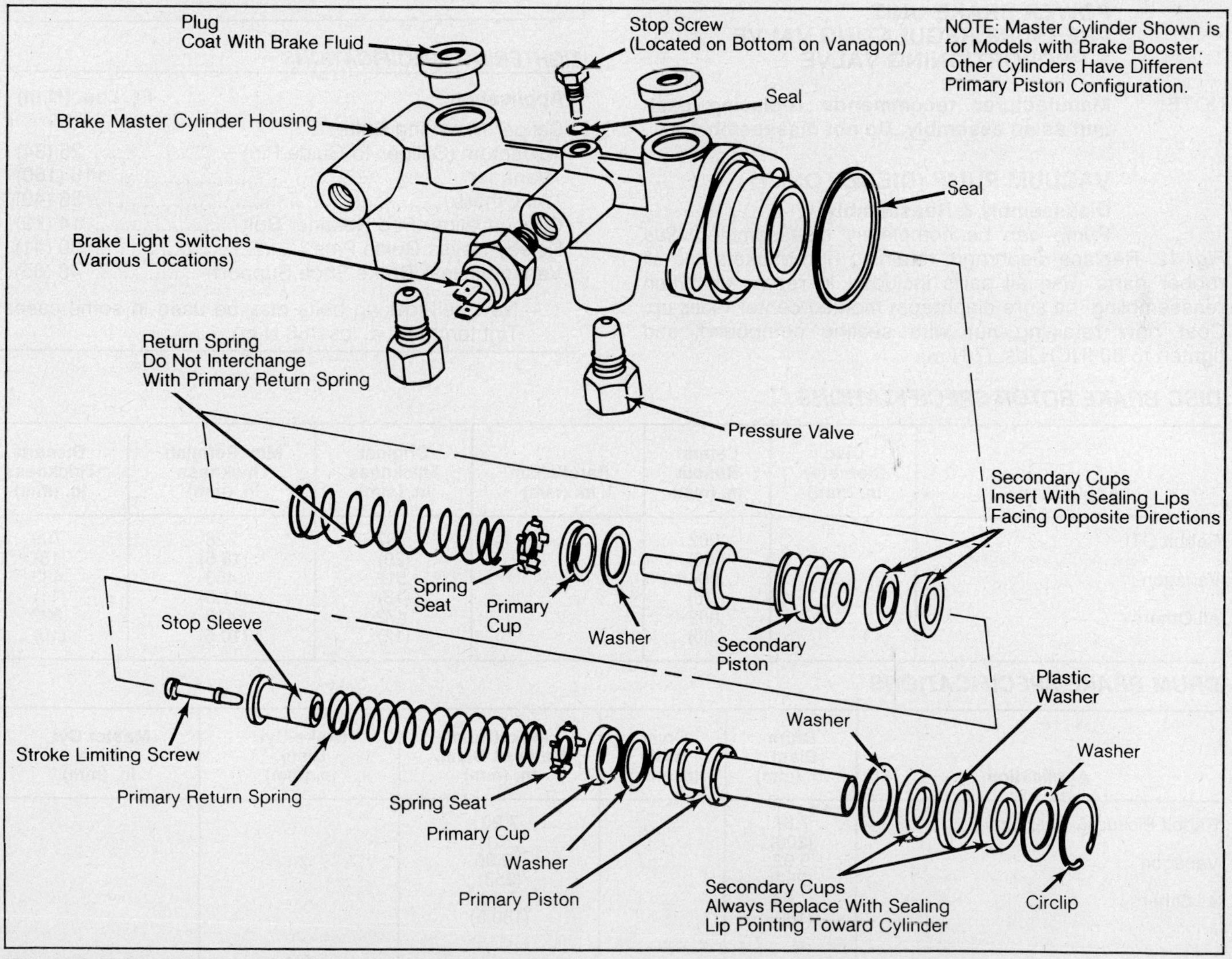

Plug
Coat With Brake Fluid
Stop Screw
(Located on Bottom on Vanagon)
NOTE: Master Cylinder Shown is for Models with Brake Booster. Other Cylinders Have Different Primary Piston Configuration.
Seal
Brake Master Cylinder Housing
Seal
Brake Light Switches
(Various Locations)
Return Spring
Do Not Interchange
With Primary Return Spring
Pressure Valve
Secondary Cups
Insert With Sealing Lips
Facing Opposite Directions
Spring
Seat
Primary
Cup
Washer
Secondary
Piston
Stop Sleeve
Plastic
Washer
Washer
Washer
Stroke Limiting Screw
Primary Return Spring
Spring Seat
Primary Cup
Washer
Primary Piston
Secondary Cups
Always Replace With Sealing
Lip Pointing Toward Cylinder
Circlip

Master cylinder shown is for models with brake booster.

go with tool (US 1023/4). When completly inserted, outer lip of dust seal must slip into groove in piston.

Disassembly – Kelsey-Hayes

1) Disconnect brake hose from caliper. Remove caliper from support assembly. Remove anti-rattle springs and guide pins. Remove support from spindle.

2) Remove dust boot from piston. Place wooden block in caliper housing, and force piston out of cylinder using compressed air.

3) Remove piston seal without damaging bore. Remove guide pins and bushings, if required.

Cleaning & Inspection

Clean all parts in brake fluid. Check cylinder bore and piston for wear or corrosion. Replace defective part. Replace all parts included in repair kit.

Reassembly

1) Coat seals, dust boot, cylinder bore and piston with brake paste. Coat guide pins with silicone grease.

2) Reverse disassembly procedure. Seat dust boot with brass drift. Long guide pin is installed in top hole of caliper housing.

VOLKSWAGEN (Cont.)

MASTER CYLINDER

NOTE: Master cylinders differ in external design and primary piston configuration between power assist, and non-power assist models. Disassembly procedures are the same.

Disassembly

1) Remove dust boot (if equipped), and piston stop screw. Remove circlip and washer.

2) Tap open end of cylinder and remove piston assemblies. Remove all external mountings and hardware from cylinder.

Cleaning & Inspection

Clean all parts with brake fluid or denatured alcohol. Check cylinder bore and pistons for wear. Replace as complete assembly if defective. Replace all rubber parts during overhaul and use all parts included in repair kit.

Reassembly

1) Reverse disassembly procedure. Coat primary piston shaft with lubricant supplied in repair kit. Coat pistons and cups with brake paste.

2) Do not interchange return springs or piston cups. (Teves secondary cups are identified by chamfer and groove.)

POWER BRAKE UNIT PRESSURE REGULATING VALVE & PROPORTIONING VALVE

NOTE: Manufacturer recommends replacing each unit as an assembly. Do not disassemble.

VACUUM PUMP (DIESEL ONLY)

Disassembly & Reassembly

Pump can be completely disassembled. *See Fig. 12*. Replace diaphragm retaining nut, gaskets and all rubber parts. Use all parts included in repair kit. When reassembling, be sure diaphragm molded center faces up. Coat new retaining nut with sealing compound, and tighten to 60 INCH lbs. (7 N.m).

Fig. 12: Exploded View of Diesel Engine Vacuum Pump Assembly

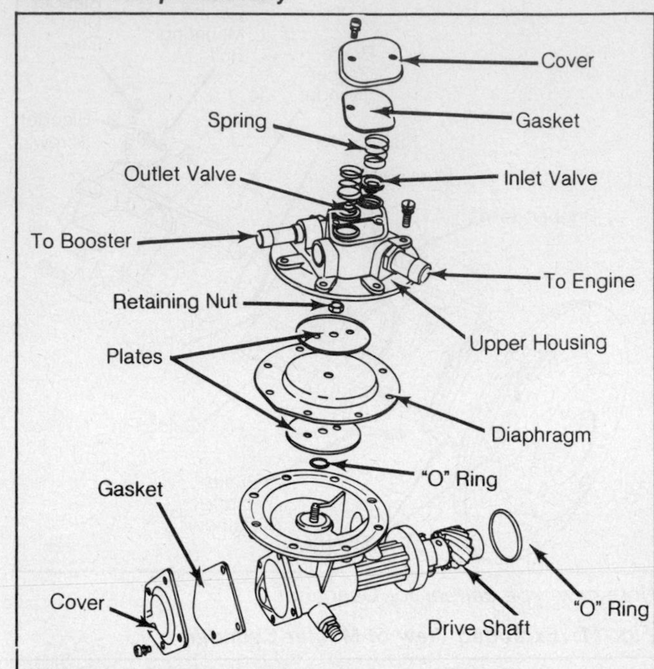
Cover
Gasket
Spring
Outlet Valve
Inlet Valve
To Booster
To Engine
Retaining Nut
Upper Housing
Plates
Diaphragm
"O" Ring
Gasket
Cover
"O" Ring
Drive Shaft

TIGHTENING SPECIFICATIONS

Application	Ft. Lbs. (N.m)
Caliper Mounting Bolts [1]	
Quantum (Caliper-to-Guide Pin)	25 (34)
Vanagon	116 (160)
All Others	36 (49)
Girling Caliper Pad Retainer Bolt	14 (19)
Kelsey-Hayes Guide Pins	30 (41)
Vanagon Rear Brake Shoe Support	48 (65)

[1] – New self-locking bolts may be used in some cases. Tighten to 50 ft. lbs. (68 N.m).

DISC BRAKE ROTOR SPECIFICATIONS

Application	Disc Diameter In. (mm)	Lateral Runout In. (mm)	Parallelism In. (mm)	Original Thickness In. (mm)	Min. Refinish Thickness In. (mm)	Discard Thickness In. (mm)
Rabbit GTI	.....	.002 (.06)	.....	.787 (20)	.728 (18.5)	.709 (18)
Vanagon	.....	.004 (.10)	.....	.512 (13)	.453 (11.5)	.433 (11)
All Others	.....	.002 (.06)	.....	.472 (12)	.413 (10.5)	.393 (10)

DRUM BRAKE SPECIFICATIONS

Application	Drum Diam. In. (mm)	Drum Width In. (mm)	Max. Drum Refinish Diam. In. (mm)	Brake Cyl. Diam. In. (mm)	Master Cyl. Diam. In. (mm)
Rabbit Pickup & Quantum	7.87 (200)	.....	7.90 (201)	.....	.....
Vanagon	9.92 (252)	.....	[1] 9.96 (253)	.....	.....
All Others	7.08 (180)	.....	7.10 (180.5)	.....	.....

[1] – Use oversize linings after turning drum .020" (0.50 mm).

VOLVO

DL, GL, Turbo, 760 GLE

DESCRIPTION

Volvo models, except some late production 760 GLE models, may be equipped with Girling calipers on all 4 wheels or with Girling front calipers and ATE rear calipers. Some late production 760 GLE models may be equipped with Bendix calipers on all 4 wheels. Service brakes are hydraulically-operated by a tandem master cylinder and vacuum power brake unit.

Master cylinder distributes hydraulic pressure to distribution/warning valve. Distribution/warning valve equally distributes hydraulic pressure to each circuit. One circuit is for lower front caliper pistons and right rear caliper. Other circuit is for upper front caliper pistons and left rear caliper.

If hydraulic pressure differs between circuits, dash-mounted light will glow. Each rear brake line has a pressure valve to prevent rear wheel lock-up. Parking brake is mechanically-operated on rear wheel mounted, internal brake shoes.

ADJUSTMENT

PEDAL HEIGHT

Brake pedal height should be equal to clutch pedal height. To adjust, loosen lock nut, remove cotter pin and turn push rod until pedal height is equal. Replace cotter pin and tighten lock nut. Pedal travel should be 5.7-6.5" (145-165 mm).

NOTE: Pedal travel can only be measured during brake bleeding operation. See Hydraulic System Bleeding article in this section.

STOP LIGHT SWITCH

DL, GL & Turbo

1) Stop light switch is located under instrument panel, in front of brake pedal. To adjust, loosen retaining screws, and position switch so contact plunger just contacts pedal arm.

2) Measureable distance from switch body to pedal arm should be .08-.24" (2-6 mm). Tighten retaining screws.

760 GLE

Remove soundproofing on left side of center console. Adjust switch so that brake light goes on when pedal is depressed about .30-.55" (8-14 mm).

PARKING BRAKE

NOTE: Adjust parking brake when full application stroke of brake lever exceeds 3 or 4 notches.

DL, GL & Turbo

1) Remove center console rear ash tray, then working through ash tray hole, loosen parking brake cables adjusting screw until cables are slack.

2) Raise and support rear of vehicle, then remove wheels. Align hole in parking brake drum with starwheel adjuster.

3) Tighten starwheel until drum can just be rotated by hand, then back off adjuster until drum just rotates freely. Install rear wheels.

4) Tighten parking brake cable adjusting screw until parking brake is fully applied when lever is pulled 2 or 3 notches. Install ash tray and lower vehicle.

760 GLE

1) Remove cover at rear of center console. Remove adjusting screw by carefully tapping on spring sleeve with a hammer and screwdriver.

2) Adjust cable so that parking brake is fully applied by 3rd-4th notch. Replace cover.

BRAKE WARNING LIGHTS

Brake Failure Light

1) This light will glow if pressure differential is exceeded or fluid level is low. Light will continue to glow until problem is corrected.

2) Check calipers, hydraulic lines, master cylinder, power brake unit and vacuum pump for defects and repair as needed.

Parking Brake Light

This light should glow when parking brake lever is pulled 1 notch, and go out when fully released (ignition on).

REMOVAL & INSTALLATION

DISC PADS

Removal

1) Raise and support vehicle. Remove tire and wheel. On Girling calipers, remove lock clip; then, remove 1 lock pin while holding damper spring in place. Remove springs and other lock pin.

2) On ATE calipers, drive out upper guide pin, and remove tensioning spring. Drive out lower guide pin. Remove disc pads from caliper with pad extractor tool (2917).

3) On Bendix calipers, slacken lower sliding pin and lift up caliper. Remove pads. On all calipers, replace pads in sets if lining thickness is less than 1/8" (3 mm). If pads are to be reinstalled, mark for reference.

Installation

1) Siphon small amount of fluid from master cylinder reservoir. On ATE and Girling calipers, seat pistons in caliper bore with piston tool (2809).

2) On Bendix calipers, install brake pads. Check that spring is located correctly in caliper. Check rubber boots. Position brake caliper and reinstall lower sliding pin.

3) On ATE rear calipers, check piston position by installing template (SV02919). Piston recess should incline 20° in relation to lower guide area on caliper. If distance from one recess to the other *(Measurement "A" in Fig. 1)* exceeds .04" (1 mm), adjust position.

4) Install new pads, install intermediate plates (if equipped) or damper washers (if equipped) in original positions. On Girling calipers, install one lock pin; then, install damper springs and other lock pin.

5) Install new lock clips on pins. On ATE calipers, tap 1 guide pin into position, and install new tensioning spring. Install other guide pin while holding tensioning spring in position.

NOTE: Install damper washers with small contact face toward pad. DO NOT install intermediate plates in calipers equipped with damper washers.

Fig. 1: Checking ATE Rear Caliper Piston Angle

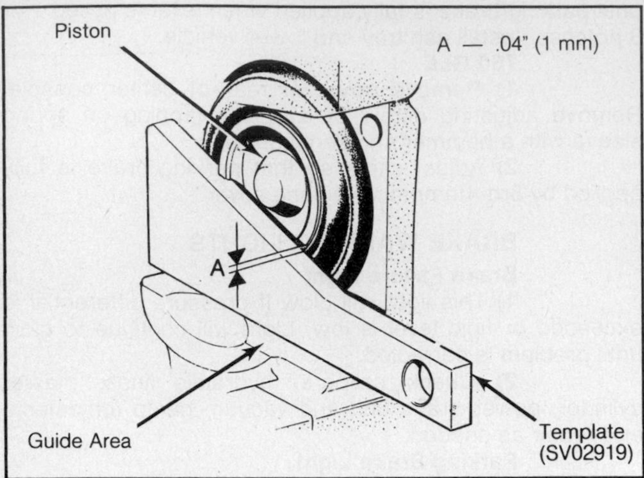
Piston
A — .04" (1 mm)
A
Guide Area
Template
(SV02919)

Piston recess should incline 20° in relation to lower guide area on caliper.

CALIPER ASSEMBLY

Removal

1) Raise and support vehicle, and remove wheel. Disconnect brake line connections at caliper, and cap lines to prevent entry of foreign matter.

2) Remove caliper mounting bolts and lift caliper from mounting bracket.

Installation

1) Position caliper assembly on mounting bracket, and install attaching bolts. After installing bolts, check clearance between disc pads and rotor on both sides of rotor.

2) Maximum deviation between sides should not exceed .004" (.10 mm) on front calipers or .010" (.25 mm) on rear calipers.

3) If clearance is not within specifications, correct by adding shims to caliper. Connect hydraulic lines and bleed hydraulic system.

DISC BRAKE ROTOR

Removal

1) With caliper assembly removed, mount a dial indicator and check rotor runout. Runout must not exceed .004" (.10 mm).

2) Measure rotor thickness through one revolution. Thickness variance must not exceed .0008" (.02 mm). Unscrew rotor lock bolts and pull rotor from hub.

Installation

To install, reverse removal procedure.

REAR AXLE SEAL & BEARING

Removal (DL, GL & Turbo)

1) Remove rear wheels and collision guards. Disconnect brake line and bracket from axle housing. Remove caliper and support to side with wire, being careful not to damage brake line. Make sure parking brake is fully released.

2) Remove brake rotor set screws. Take off rotors, tapping with soft mallet if necessary. Remove parking brake shoes, unhooking retaining springs. Disconnect parking brake cables by driving out lock pin at lever.

3) Remove bolts for bearing retainer through holes in axle flange. Remove axle shaft using puller (2709). Pry inner seal from housing. Press bearing and snap ring off axle shaft. Remove oil seal.

Installation

1) Pack new bearing and new seal lip groove with high temperature wheel bearing grease. Place bearing retainer and oil seal on axle shaft. Press new bearing and new snap ring onto axle shaft. Always use a new snap ring. Narrow side of taper fits into axle housing.

2) Clean axle housing and drive in new inner seal. Install axle shaft and tighten bearing retainer bolts. Install parking brake shoes and reconnect cables. Install rotors and tighten set screws.

3) Check parking brake adjustment. Install brake caliper, pads, and collision guard, if used. Reconnect brake line and bracket to axle housing. Install wheels and tighten lug nuts.

Removal (760 GLE)

1) Remove rear wheel. Remove caliper and suspend from coil spring. Remove brake disc and pads. Remove axle shaft retaining plate. Using brake disc, fit nuts with flat side towards disc and pull out axle shaft.

2) Using long screwdriver, remove seal. Clean interior of rear axle tube. Remove bearing and lock ring.

Installation

1) Using press tool (5212), lift up seal and retaining plate on drive shaft so that split press plate can be installed on bearing. Place press yoke on top of press plate. Ensure that press plate opening is at 90° angle to press yoke opening.

2) Grease new bearing between inner and outer races until grease protrudes on other side. Grease new inner and outer seals. Fill space between seal lips with grease. Position retaining plate and seal correctly on axle shaft.

3) Install greased bearing and lock ring. Place bearing ring (5242) under bearing and lock ring. Position axle shaft in press. Put 2 "V" blocks under bearing ring ensuring that blocks do not touch axle shaft.

4) Use bearing installer (1801) to press on shaft. Using drift (5243) and handle (1801), install inner seal. Install and tighten axle shaft and retaining plate assembly with brake pad retaining springs.

5) Install parking brake shoes, brake disc and caliper. Ensure that disc clears parking brake shoes. Adjust parking brake cable.

PARKING BRAKE SHOES

Removal (DL, GL & Turbo)

1) Remove center console rear ash tray and loosen parking brake cable adjusting nut until cables are slack. Raise and support rear of vehicle and remove wheels.

2) Remove caliper (without disconnecting hydraulic line) and support out of way, then remove rotor. Remove brake shoe return springs and lift off shoes and adjuster.

Installation

1) Reverse removal procedure and note the following: Replace brake drum (rotor) if out-of-round more than .008" (.2 mm).

2) Apply a thin coat of heat-resistant graphite grease to brake shoe sliding surfaces and to adjusting starwheel. After installation, adjust parking brake.

VOLVO (Cont.)

Fig. 2: Exploded View of Parking Brake Assembly

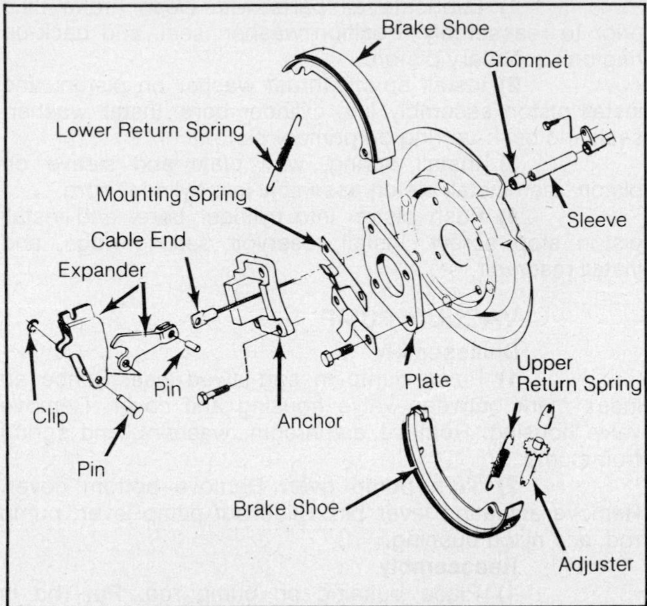
Brake Shoe
Grommet
Lower Return Spring
Mounting Spring
Sleeve
Cable End
Expander
Pin
Plate
Upper
Return Spring
Clip
Anchor
Pin
Brake Shoe
Adjuster

DL, GL and Turbo models shown, 760 GLE models similar.

Removal (760 GLE)

1) Remove cover at rear of center console. Remove adjusting screw by carefully tapping on spring sleeve with a hammer and screwdriver. Unscrew adjusting screw so that cables are slackened.

2) Raise vehicle and remove rear wheels. Remove brake caliper and hang is up with a steel wire on rear spring to avoid damaging brake hose. Remove brake disc. Unhook rear return spring and remove brake shoes.

Installation

1) Smear thin layer of heat resistant graphite grease on brake shoe lining surfaces. Assemble brake shoes. Using new bolts, install rear return spring, brake disc and caliper.

2) Ensure that disc rotates with touching brake pads. Install wheels. Adjust parking brake cable. Lower vehicle.

MASTER CYLINDER

Removal

Disconnect hydraulic lines at master cylinder and cap openings to prevent entry of foreign matter. Remove cylinder attaching nuts, and remove cylinder assembly from vehicle.

Installation

To install, reverse removal procedure. Bleed hydraulic system.

POWER BRAKE UNIT

Removal (DL, GL & Turbo)

Remove master cylinder, Disconnect vacuum hose. Remove soundproofing on left side of center console. Disconnect pressure rod from brake pedal. Remove 4 nuts and power brake unit.

Installation

On 9" units, apply sealing compound to contact surface on firewall. Fit other types with sealing ring. Reverse removal procedure to complete installation.

Removal (760 GLE)

1) Disconnect master cylinder and move it aside. Leave brake pipes attached to master cylinder. Disconnect vacuum hose. Using screwdriver, pry out check valve from unit. Remove fuel filter and move it aside.

2) Disconnect vacuum pump and move it aside. Remove soundproofing on left side of center console. Disconnect push rod from brake pedal. Remove 4 nuts and power brake unit. Rmeove check valve seal and check for damage.

Installation

Install seal in power brake unit and ensure that it is correctly seated. Remove sealing ring (1272078-5) and install on new power brake unit. To complete installation, reverse removal procedure.

Check Valve Replacement

Disconnect vacuum hose from check valve. Using 2 screwdrivers, lever out check valve. Remove seal. Fit new seal ensuring that flange is properly aligned in cylinder. Smear seal with grease. Press valve carefully into place. Ensure that seal does not move out of position. Reconnect vacuum hose so that highest point is attached to valve.

VACUUM PUMP

Removal & Installation

Disconnect hoses at vacuum pump, and remove mounting bolts and pump. Clean mating surfaces to remove gasket material, and install new gasket. Reverse removal procedure to complete installation.

OVERHAUL

BRAKE CALIPER

Disassembly

1) With caliper removed from vehicle, remove disc pads, piston dust covers, and retaining clips.

2) Insert wooden block into caliper housing and apply compressed air at fluid inlet ports to force pistons out of caliper.

3) Remove piston seals from cylinder bore with blunt tool without damaging cylinder bore. Open bleeder screw.

NOTE: **DO NOT separate caliper halves.**

Cleaning & Inspection

Clean all parts in brake fluid or alcohol. Inspect cylinder bores for scoring, rust, or corrosion; replace if defective. Replace rubber seals and dust covers during overhaul.

Reassembly

1) Coat all parts with clean brake fluid, and install new piston seals in cylinder bores. Carefully install pistons into cylinder bores.

2) Check piston position on ATE rear brake calipers. Install rubber dust boots and retaining clips. Close bleeder screw and install disc pads.

VOLVO (Cont.)

Fig. 3: Girling Front Caliper Assembly

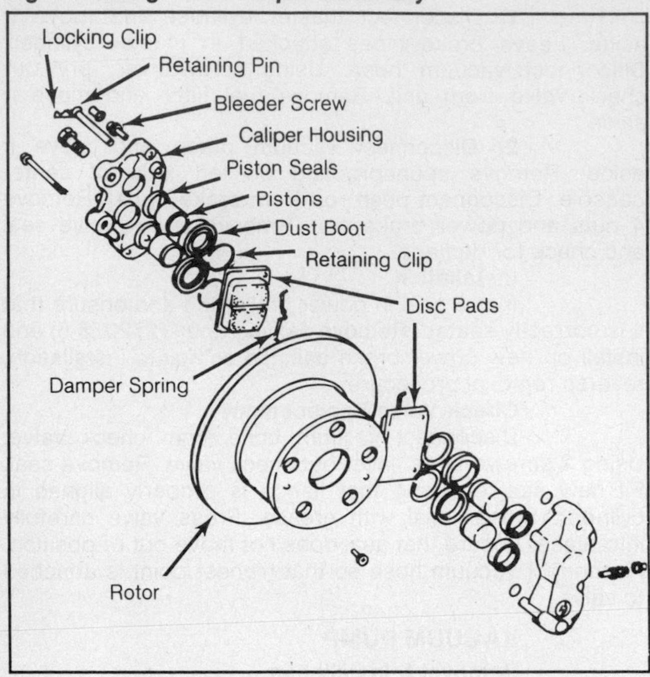
Locking Clip
Retaining Pin
Bleeder Screw
Caliper Housing
Piston Seals
Pistons
Dust Boot
Retaining Clip
Disc Pads
Damper Spring
Rotor

MASTER CYLINDER

Disassembly

1) Remove master cylinder from vehicle, and clamp mounting flange in a vise. Remove reservoir from cylinder, and remove rubber sealing rings.

2) Remove piston stop screw, and remove retainer ring from end of cylinder bore. Remove pistons from cylinder bore.

Cleaning & Inspection

Wash all parts in clean brake fluid or alcohol, and blow dry with compressed air. Inspect cylinder bore for scratches, rust, or corrosion. Replace if defective. Replace both pistons with connector sleeve as an assembly.

Reassembly

1) Lubricate all parts with clean brake fluid prior to reassembly. Position washer, seal, and back-up ring on secondary piston.

2) Install spring thrust washer on piston, and install piston assembly into cylinder bore. Install washer, seal, and back-up ring on primary piston.

3) Install spring, with plate and sleeve on piston; then install piston assembly into cylinder bore.

4) Push piston into cylinder bore, and install piston stop screw. Install reservoir sealing rings, and install reservoir.

VACUUM PUMP

Disassembly

1) Place pump in soft-jawed vise. Scribe an index mark between valve housing and cover. Remove valve housing. Remove diaphragm, washers, and spring from pump.

2) Turn pump over. Remove bottom cover. Remove actuating lever pin. Slide out pump lever, pump rod, and nylon bushing.

Reassembly

1) Place bushing on pump rod. Put rod in pump housing. Fit lever and pin. Install bottom cover and gasket.

2) Place washer and "O" ring on diaphragm screw. Lightly coat end of screw with thread locking compound.

3) Install diaphragm assembly. Insert valve housing and align with index mark. Fit valves and seals. Make sure domed side of disc faces diaphragm. Install valve housing cover with spring and gasket.

TIGHTENING SPECIFICATIONS

Application	Ft. Lbs. (N.m)
Axle Shaft & Retaining plate	29 (40)
Front Caliper Mounting Bolts	74 (100)
Rear Caliper Mounting Bolts	43 (58)

Fig. 4: ATE Rear Caliper Assembly

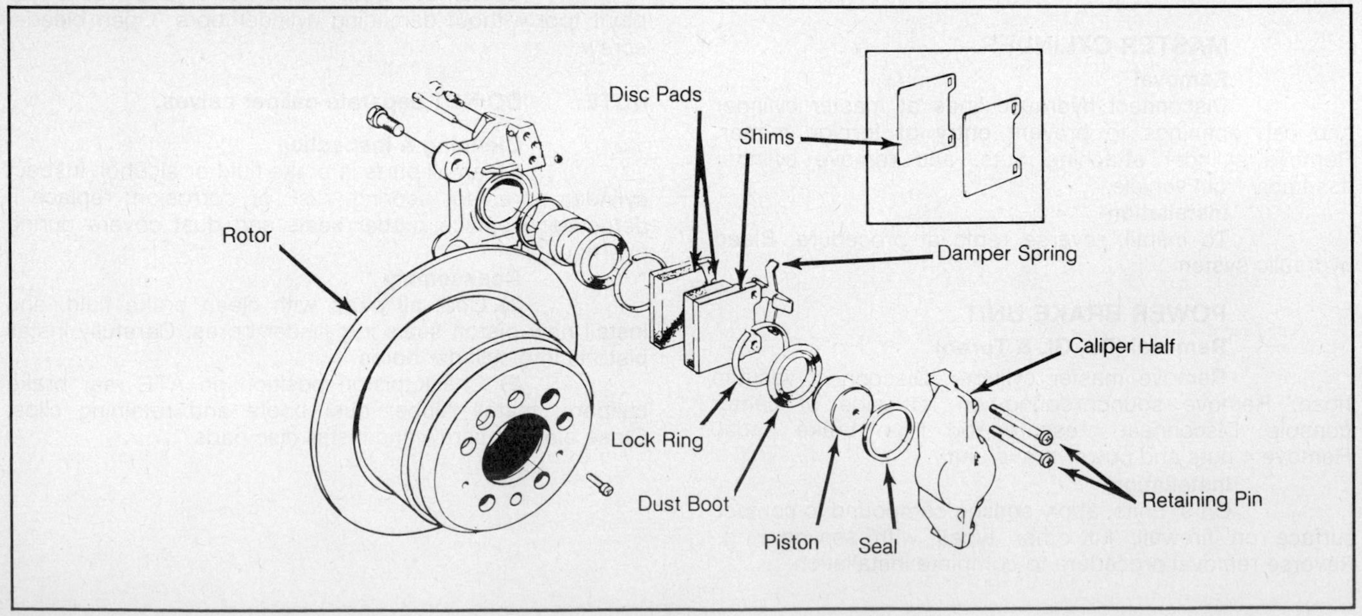
Disc Pads
Shims
Rotor
Damper Spring
Caliper Half
Lock Ring
Dust Boot
Piston
Seal
Retaining Pin

Replace rubber seals and dust covers if caliper is disassembled.

VOLVO (Cont.)

Fig. 5: Girling Rear Caliper Assembly

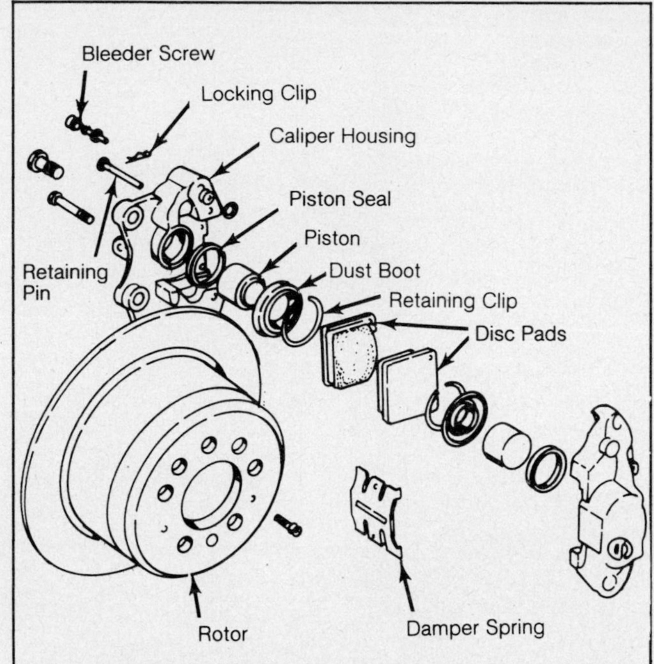
Bleeder Screw
Locking Clip
Caliper Housing
Piston Seal
Piston
Retaining Pin
Dust Boot
Retaining Clip
Disc Pads
Rotor
Damper Spring

Fig. 6: Master Cylinder Assembly

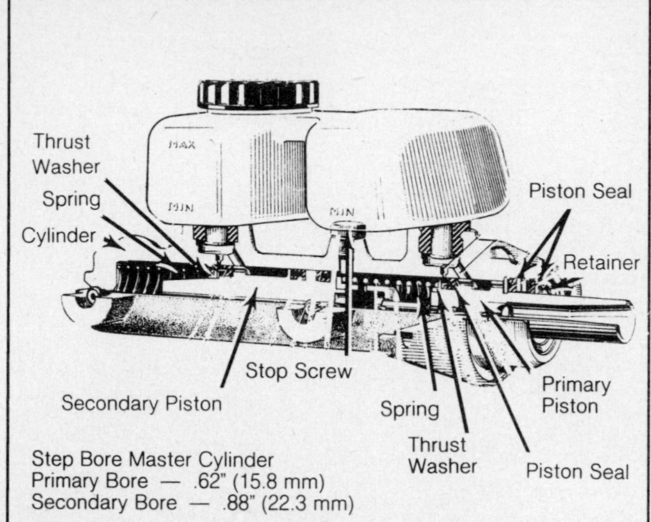
Thrust Washer
Spring
Cylinder
Piston Seal
Retainer
Stop Screw
Secondary Piston
Spring
Primary Piston
Thrust Washer
Piston Seal
Step Bore Master Cylinder
Primary Bore — .62" (15.8 mm)
Secondary Bore — .88" (22.3 mm)

Do not hone master cylinder.

DISC BRAKE ROTOR SPECIFICATIONS

Application	Disc Diameter In. (mm)	Lateral Runout In. (mm)	Parallelism In. (mm)	Original Thickness In. (mm)	Min. Refinish Thickness In. (mm)	Discard Thickness In. (mm)
DL & GL						
Front	.....	.004 (.10)	.0008 (.02)	.563 (14.3)	.557 [1] (14.1)	.....
Rear	.....	.004 (.10)	.0008 (.02)	.378 (9.6)	.331 (8.4)	.....
Turbo & 760 GLE						
Front	.....	.004 (.10)	.0008 (.02)	.945 (24.0)	.990 [1] (22.8)	.....
Rear	.....	.004 (.10)	.0008 (.02)	.378 (9.6)	.331 (8.4)	.....

[1] – Minimum refinish thickness is stamped on all rotors. Adhere to stamped specifications.

SECTION 10

WHEEL ALIGNMENT

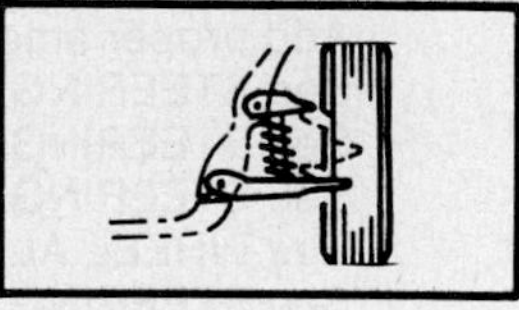

CONTENTS

NOTE: ALSO SEE GENERAL INDEX.

Wheel Alignment

TROUBLE SHOOTING

CONDITION	POSSIBLE CAUSE	CORRECTION
Premature Tire Wear	Improper tire inflation	Check tire pressure
	Front alignment out of tolerance	See Adjustments in WHEEL ALIGNMENT
	Suspension components worn	See SUSPENSION
	Steering system components worn	See STEERING
	Improper standing height	See RIDING HEIGHT SPECIFICATIONS
	Uneven or sagging springs	See Coil Springs in SUSPENSION
	Bent wheel	See WHEEL ALIGNMENT
	Improper torsion bar adjustment	See SUSPENSION
	Loose or worn wheel bearings	See Wheel Bearing Adj. in SUSPENSION
	Worn or defective shock absorbers	Replace shock absorbers
	Tires out of balance	Check tire balance
Pulls to One Side	Improper tire inflation	Check tire pressure
	Brake dragging	See BRAKES
	Mismatched tires	See WHEEL ALIGNMENT
	Broken or sagging spring	See SUSPENSION
	Broken torsion bar	See SUSPENSION
	Power steering valve not centered	See STEERING
	Front alignment out of tolerance	See Adjustments in WHEEL ALIGNMENT
	Defective wheel bearing	See Wheel Bearings in SUSPENSION
	Uneven sway bar links	See SUSPENSION
	Frame bent	Check for frame damage
	Steering system bushing worn	See STEERING
	Idler arm bushing too tight	See STEERING LINKAGE
Hard Steering	Idler arm bushing too tight	See STEERING LINKAGE
	Ball joint tight or seized	See Ball Joint Checking in SUSPENSION
	Steering linkage too tight	See STEERING LINKAGE
	Power steering fluid low	Add proper amount of fluid
	Power steering drive belt loose	See STEERING
	Power steering pump defective	See STEERING
	Steering gear out of adjustment	See STEERING
	Incorrect wheel alignment	See WHEEL ALIGNMENT
	Damaged steering gear	See STEERING
	Damaged suspension	See SUSPENSION
	Bent steering knuckle or supports	See SUSPENSION
Vehicle "Wanders"	Strut rod or control arm bushing worn	See SUSPENSION
	Loose or worn wheel bearings	See Wheel Bearings in SUSPENSION
	Improper tire inflation	Check tire pressure
	Stabilizer bar missing or defective	See SUSPENSION
	Wheel alignment out of tolerance	See Adjustment in WHEEL ALIGNMENT
	Broken spring	See SUSPENSION
	Defective shock absorbers	Replace shock absorbers
	Worn steering & suspension components	See SUSPENSION
Front End Shimmy	Tire out of balance/round	Check tire balance
	Excessive wheel runout	See WHEEL ALIGNMENT
	Insufficient or improper caster	See WHEEL ALIGNMENT
	Worn suspension or steering components	See SUSPENSION
	Defective shock absorbers	Replace shock absorbers
	Wheel bearings worn or loose	See Wheel Bearing Adj. in SUSPENSION
	Power steering reaction bracket loose	See STEERING
	Steering gear box (rack) mounting loose	See STEERING
	Steering gear adjustment loose	See STEERING
	Worn spherical joints	See SUSPENSION
Toe-In Not Adjustable	Lower control arm bent	See SUSPENSION
	Frame bent	Check frame for damage
Camber Not Adjustable	Control arm bent	See SUSPENSION
	Frame bent	Check frame for damage
	Hub & bearing not seated properly	See SUSPENSION

Wheel Alignment

SPECIFICATIONS

WHEEL ALIGNMENT SPECIFICATIONS

Application	Caster (Degrees)	Camber (Degrees)	Toe-In (Inches)	TOE-OUT ON TURNS (Degrees)	
				Inner	Outer
Alfa Romeo					
Spider 2.0	1 1/2±1/2	1/3±1/2	1/8	.....	.....
GTV-6 2.5					
Front	3±1/2	-1±1/2	1/8	.....	.....
Rear	[2]	0±1/2 [2]	0±1/6 [2]	.....	.....
Audi					
4000 & Coupe					
Front	0 to 1 [2]	-1/6 to -1 1/6	0 to 1/3 [1]	20 1/2	20
Rear	[2]	-1 1/3 to -2/3	0 to 2/3 [1]		
5000					
Front	5/6±2/3	-1/2±1/2	Out 1/6 to In 1/12 [1]	18 3/4	20
Rear	[2]	-1/2±2/3	1/4±1/6 [3]		
BMW					
318i					
Front	8 7/8±1/2	-2/3±1/2	5/64±1/64	20	18 1/3
Rear	.....	-1 2/3	5/64±1/32		
320i					
Front	8 1/3±1/2	0±1/2	3/64 to 3/32	20	19 3/4
Rear	[2]	-2 1/3±1/2	0 to 5/64		
528e					
Front	8 1/4±1/2	-1/3±1/2	5/64±1/64	20	18 1/2
Rear	[2]	-2±1/2	5/64±1/32		
533i					
Front	8 1/4±1/2	-1/3±1/2	5/64±1/64	20	18 1/2
Rear		-2 1/3±1/2	5/64±1/64		
633CSi					
Front	8 1/4±1/2	-1/3±1/2	5/64±1/64	20	18 1/2
Rear	[2]	-2 1/3±1/2	5/64±1/32		
733i					
Front	9±1/2	0±1/2	0±1/16	20	18 1/2
Rear	[2]	-1 1/2±1/2	5/64±1/32		
Chrysler Corp. Imports					
Colt	5/6±1/3	1/2±1/2 [2]	Out 5/64 to In 5/32	33±1 1/2	29 5/16
Colt & Ram-50 Pickups					
2WD	2 1/2±1	1±1/2	5/64±5/16	37	30 1/2
4WD	2±1	1±1/2	5/64±5/16	30 3/5	28
Challenger & Sapporo	2 2/3±1/2	1 1/6±1/2 [2]	0 to 9/32	37±1	32
Datsun/Nissan					
Maxima					
Front	2 7/8 to 4 1/2 [2]	-1/3 to 1 1/6 [2]	Out 3/64 to In 3/64	20	18 2/3
Rear	[2]	1 to 2 1/2	Out 7/64 to In 9/32		
Pickup					
2WD	5/6 to 1 5/6	0 to 1	1/5 to 9/32	20	18 1/2
4WD	1 1/6 to 2 1/6	0 to 1	1/5 to 9/32	18 1/2	18
Pulsar	2/3 to 2 1/4 [2]	-1/2 to 1 [2]	0 to 5/64	.....	.....
Sentra	3/4 to 2 1/4 [2]	-1/2 to 1 [2]	7/64 to 1/5	20	17 1/2
Stanza					
Front	2/3 to 2 1/6 [2]	-3/4 to 3/4 [2]	0 to 5/64	20	18 1/2
Rear	[2]	0 to 1 1/2 [2]	Out 1/5 to In 19/64		
200SX	1 3/4 to 3 1/4 [2]	-2/3 to 5/6 [2]	0 to 5/64	20	18 5/8
280ZX					
Front	4 1/6 to 5 2/3 [2]	-1/2 to 1 [2]	3/64 to 7/64	20	18
Rear	[2]	0 to 1 1/3	0 to 5/64		
Honda					
Accord					
Front	1 5/12±1 [2]	0±1 [2]	0±1/8	....	....
Rear			0 to 5/32		
Civic					
Front	2 1/20±1 [4]	0±1 [2]	5/64±5/64	....	....
Rear			0 to 5/32		
Prelude					
Front	0±1/2	0±1	0±1/8	....	....
Rear			5/64±5/64		

[1] – Toe-in given in degrees.
[2] – Not adjustable.
[3] – Before chassis No. EN 096670, From chassis No. EN 096670 1/6±1/12.
[4] – Wagon caster in degrees are 1 1/3±1.

Wheel Alignment

SPECIFICATIONS (Cont.)

WHEEL ALIGNMENT SPECIFICATIONS

Application	Caster (Degrees)	Camber (Degrees)	Toe-In (Inches)	TOE-OUT ON TURNS (Degrees)	
				Inner	Outer
Isuzu					
I-Mark	3 2/3 to 6 1/6 [2]	-1 to 2/3	5/32 to 5/64	.....	.....
Impulse	3 1/2 to 6 [2]	-1 to 1/2 [2]	0 to 1/8	.....	.....
P'UP	1/2±1/2	1/2±1/2	5/64±5/64	.....	.....
Jaguar					
XJ6					
Front	3 1/4±1/4	-1/2±1/4	0 to 1/8	....	....
Rear	[2]	-3/4±1/4	0±1/32		
XJS					
Front	3 1/2±1/4	-1/2±1/4	0 to 1/8	....	....
Rear	[2]	-3/4±1/4			
Mazda					
B2000 & B2200 Pickups	1	1/3 to 1 1/4	0 to 1/64	.....	.....
GLC	2±2/3 [2]	1±1/2	0±1/8 [4]	.....	.....
GLC Wagon	1 to 2 1/3 [2]	1/4 to 1 1/4 [2]	0 to 9/32	.....	.....
RX7	3 2/3±1/2 [6]	1±1/2	0 to 9/32	.....	.....
626	1 2/3±2/3	1/3±1/2	1/8±1/8 [7]	.....	.....
Mercedes-Benz					
240D	8 3/4±1/2	0±1/6	1/8±3/64	....	....
300 & 380 Series	9 3/4±1/2	0±1/6	3/16±3/64	20	18 1/2
Mitsubishi					
Cordia & Tredia	4/5±1/2	5/12±1/2	0±1/16	.....	.....
Montero	2 11/12±1/2	1±1/2	5/64 to 23/64	.....	.....
Pickup	2 1/2±1 [8]	1±1/2	5/64 to 23/64	.....	.....
Starion					
Front	5 1/3	0 [2]	Out 5/64 to In 1/5	.....	.....
Rear	[2]	-1/3 [2]	0±5/64		
Peugeot					
504	2 1/6 to 3 1/6	0 to 1	5/32 to 5/16	.....	.....
505					
Front	3 to 4	0 to 1 1/3	1/4 to 25/64	.....	.....
Rear	[2]	-1 to 0	7/64 to 21/64		
604					
Front	3 to 4	-1 1/4 to -1/4	5/32 to 5/16	.....	.....
Rear	[2]	-2 to -1	5/64 to 5/16		
Porsche					
911SC					
Front	6 1/12±1/4	1/2±1/6	1/4±1/12 [1]	20	19 1/2
Rear	[2]	-1±1/6	1/6±1/6 [1]		
928S					
Front	3 1/2 to 4	-1/2±1/6	1/4±1/12 [1]	.....	.....
Rear	[2]	-2/3±1/6	1/6±1/12 [1]		
944					
Front	2 1/2±1/4	-2/3±1/4	1/6±1/12 [1]	20	19
Rear	[2]	-1±2/3	0 to +1/6 [1]		
Renault					
Fuego & Fuego Turbo					
Front	3±1/2	0±1/2 [2]	3/64±3/64	.....	.....
Rear	[2]	0 to 1/2 [2]	0 to 1/4 [1]		
Le Car					
Front	11±1/2	1/2±1/2	3/64 to 3/16	.....	.....
Rear	[2]	0 to 1 1/2	0 to 5/32		
18i					
Front	2±1/2	0±1/2 [2]	1/6±1/6 [1]	.....	.....
Rear	[2]	0±1/2 [2]	0±1/8 [1]		
Saab					
900 & 900 Turbo	1±1/2 [5]	1/2±1/2	5/64±1/32	20 3/4	20

[1] – Toe-in given in degrees.
[2] – Not adjustable.
[3] – 1 1/6±2/3 for Turbo
[4] – Same for rear.
[5] – For power steering models, 2±1/2.
[6] – Left side only, right side specifications are 4 1/6±1/2
[7] – Rear specifications are 0±1/8
[8] – For 4WD models, 2±1/2

Wheel Alignment

SPECIFICATIONS (Cont.)

WHEEL ALIGNMENT SPECIFICATIONS

Application	Caster (Degrees)	Camber (Degrees)	Toe-In (Inches)	TOE-OUT ON TURNS (Degrees)	
				Inner	Outer
Subaru					
1600, 1800 & 1800 Turbo					
Hatchback, Sedan, Hardtop					
Front	-1 1/6 to 2/3	3/4 to 2 1/4	3/64 ± 3/64	.....	.....
Rear	[2]	-3/4 to 3/4	Out 1/8 to In 1/8		
Station Wagon					
Front	-5/6 to 2/3	1 to 2 1/2	3/64 ± 3/64	.....	.....
Rear	[2]	-3/4 to 3/4	Out 1/8 to In 1/8		
Hatchback 4-WD					
Front	-1 1/4 to 1/4	1 2/3 to 3 1/6	Out 3/16 to 3/64	.....	.....
Rear	[2]	-3/4 to 3/4	Out 1/8 to In 1/8		
Station Wagon 4-WD, Brat					
Front	-1 1/2 to 1/12	1 2/3 to 3 1/6	Out 3/16 to 3/64	.....	.....
Rear	[2]	-1/2 to 1 1/12	Out 1/8 to In 1/8		
Toyota					
Camry					
Front					
Manual Steering	1 ± 1/2	1/2 ± 1/2	0 ± 5/32	22 1/3	20
Power Steering	2 1/2 ± 1/2	1/2 ± 1/2	5/64 ± 5/32	22 1/4	20
Rear		1/2 ± 1/2	0 ± 5/64		
Celica					
Front	3 1/3 ± 2/3	1 ± 3/4 [2]	5/32 ± 5/32	37	32
Rear		1/10 ± 3/4 [2]	0 ± 5/64		
Corolla	1 3/4 ± 3/4	1 ± 3/4 [2]	3/64 ± 5/32	20 1/3	20
Cressida					
Front	2 1/2 ± 3/4	3/4 ± 3/4	7/64 ± 5/32	38	31
Rear		1/3 ± 3/4 [2]	Out 5/64 ± 5/32		
Land Cruiser	1 ± 3/4	1 ± 3/4	3/64 ± 5/64	32	30
Pickup					
1/2 Ton	1 ± 3/4	1 1/12 ± 3/4	5/64 ± 5/32	36	29
3/4 Ton	1/2 ± 3/4	1 1/12 ± 3/4	5/64 ± 5/32	36	29
4WD	3 1/2 ± 3/4	1 ± 3/4	3/64 ± 5/32	30 1/2	29
Starlet	2 ± 3/4	2/3 ± 3/4 [2]	5/64 ± 5/32	37 1/3	33 5/6
Supra					
Front	4 1/6 ± 3/4	5/6 ± 3/4	7/64 ± 5/32	37 1/2	30 3/4
Rear		1/10 ± 3/4	0 ± 5/32		
Tercel					
2WD					
Front					
Manual Steering	1 1/6 ± 1/2	1/3 ± 1/2	0 ± 3/64	21 1/2	20
Power Steering	2 2/3 ± 1/2	1/3 ± 1/2	0 ± 3/64	21	20
Rear		-1/12 ± 1/2 [2]	0 ± 5/64		
4WD	2 5/12 ± 1/2	5/6 ± 1/2	0 ± 3/64	21	20
Volkswagen					
Jetta, Rabbit & Scirocco					
Front	1 1/3 to 2 1/3	-1/6 to 5/6	Out 1/12 to Out 1/2 [1]	22	20
Rear	[2]	-2/3 to -1 5/6 [2]	Out 1/6 to In 5/6 [1]		
Rabbit Pickup					
Front	5/6 to 1 5/6 [2]	-1/6 to 5/6	Out 1/12 to Out 1/2 [1]	21 1/2	20
Rear	[2]	-1 to 1 [2]	Out 1 to In 1 [1,2]		
Quantum					
Front	1/2 ± 1/2 [2]	-2/3 ± 1/2	1/6 ± 1/6 [1]	21	20
Rear	[2]	-1 2/3 ± 1/3 [2]	5/12 ± 1/4 [1,2]		
Vanagon					
Front	7 1/4 ± 1/4	0 ± 1/2	1/3 ± 1/2 [1]	24 1/2	20
Rear	[2]	-5/6 ± 1/2	0 ± 1/3 [1]		
Volvo					
DL & GL	3 to 4 [2]	1 to 1 1/2	1/8	20 3/4	20
Turbo	3 to 4 [2]	1/4 to 3/4	1/8	20 4/5	20
760 GLE	4.5 to 5.5	1/4 to 5/8	1/8		

[1] – Toe-in given in degrees.
[2] – Not adjustable.

Radial Tire Lead

Some alignment problems involving "lead" or pull to one side have been caused by off-center belts on radial tires. To diagnose this problem, inflate tires to recommended pressure and drive vehicle in both directions on an uncrowned road. Observe and note any "lead", then switch front tires and road test again. If "lead" is corrected, without roughness, leave tires in position. If roughness results, replace tires. If "lead" reverses, install a known good tire on one side and repeat road test. If "lead" remains, install a known good tire in place of other front tire. If "lead" remains, recheck alignment. It may be necessary to adjust caster so that leading side is 1° more positive than other side.

Wheel Alignment

ALFA ROMEO

ADJUSTMENT

TIRE INFLATION (COLD)

Before attempting to check or adjust wheel alignment, make sure that tires are properly inflated. Refer to manufacturer's specifications given inside the back cover of owner's manual.

CAMBER

GTV-6 2.5

Adjust camber by loosening inner side of lower suspension arm and shim as required. Adding or removing one shim will result in 1/4° of adjustment. Maximum difference between right and left wheels should not exceed 2/3°.

Rear camber specifications are supplied by manufacturer but are not adjustable. If not to specifications, check suspension for wear or damage and repair or replace as necessary.

Spider 2.0

Camber is preset at factory and cannot be adjusted. If not to specifications, check suspension for wear or damage and repair or replace components as necessary.

CASTER

All Models

Adjust caster by turning the adjuster on the front upper wishbone strut rod connected between the steering spindle and chassis. Change the length of strut rod until specifications are meet. On the GTV-6 2.5 rotating adjuster one complete turn will result in 3/4° of adjustment.

TOE-IN

All Models

Loosen lock nuts on tie rods and turn until proper toe-in is obtained. Rotating tie rod one complete turn will give approximately .14" (3.5 mm) of adjustment. After specifications are meet, tighten lock nuts and check toe-in.

On GTV-6 2.5, rear toe-in specifications are supplied by manufacturer but are not adjustable. If not to specifications, check suspension for wear or damage and repair or replace as necessary.

AUDI

ADJUSTMENT

TIRE INFLATION (COLD)

Before attempting to check and adjust wheel alignment, ensure tires are properly inflated. Tire sizes and pressures can be found in owners manual for all models.

NOTE: **Vehicles must not be loaded down with passengers or any weight that would cause vehicle to lean or sag, which will affect riding height.**

CASTER

All Models

Caster angle is not adjustable. If caster is not within specification, check suspension components for excessive wear or damage. Replace components as necessary to bring caster into specifications.

CAMBER

4000

1) With vehicle properly positioned on alignment rack, measure camber angle. If not within specifications, loosen ball joint mounting bolts on control arm and install tool (US 4490).

2) Tighten adjusting nut to break ball joint loose from control arm. *See Fig. 1.* When tool nut is loosened, weight of vehicle will move wheel to negative camber. After adjustment, retorque ball joint bolts to 47 ft. lbs. (64 N.m) and remove tool.

5000

Work under hood and loosen the upper strut mounting nuts. Place a socket over suspension strut nut. Move strut around in slots until camber is correct. Tighten nuts to 14 ft. lbs. (19 N.m).

Fig. 1: Camber Adjusting Tool for Audi 4000

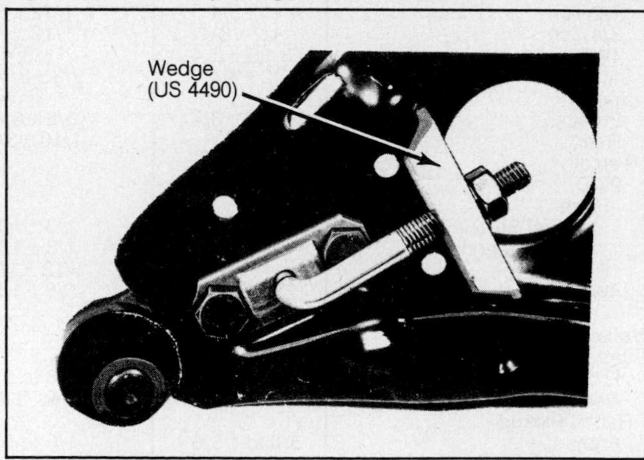
Wedge
(US 4490)

TOE-IN

4000

1) On 4-cylinder models, adjustments are done on only one side. Loosen clamp and lock nut on adjustable tie rod. Turn tie rod and set to specifications. On 5-cylinder models, steering gear centering tool (3075) must be used. Center steering gear, attach tool by removing bolt from spacer on chain of tool and inserting it through hole (marked with L) on tool and tighten to steering gear. *See Fig. 2.* Loosen clamps and jam nuts on both tie rods and set to specifications.

2) Tighten locking components. If necessary, remove steering wheel and reposition so wheel spokes are horizontal when front wheels point straight-ahead.

AUDI (Cont.)

Fig. 2: Steering Gear Centering Tool

Steering Gear
Centering Tool (3075)

NOTE: Remove tool from 5-cylinder models by reversing installation procedures.

5000

1) Loosen adjustable tie rod jam nuts. Rotate threaded collar until specifications are reached.

2) Tighten locking components. If necessary, remove steering wheel and reposition so wheel spokes are horizontal when front wheels point straight-ahead.

BMW

ADJUSTMENT

TIRE INFLATION (COLD)

Before attempting to check and adjust wheel alignment, ensure tires are properly inflated. Tire sizes and pressures can be found in owner's manual.

CASTER & CAMBER

Caster & Camber is not adjustable. Before checking caster and camber, vehicle must be in loaded condition. *See Vehicle Loading Table.* If caster or camber are not within specifications, check suspension components for damage and repair or replace as necessary.

TOE-IN

Before checking toe-in, vehicle must be in loaded condition. *See Vehicle Loading Table.* Position steering gear to straight ahead and make sure that the marks on steering gear housing and steering shaft are aligned. If not within specifications, loosen tie rod clamps and turn tubes until correct toe-in is obtained. Tighten clamping bolts and make sure dust covers are not twisted.

VEHICLE LOADING TABLE

Application	[1] Lbs. (kg)
Each Front Seat	150 (68)
Rear Seat	150 (68)
Luggage Compartment	46 (21)

[1] – Fuel tank full.

CHRYSLER CORP. IMPORTS

ADJUSTMENT

TIRE INFLATION (COLD)

Before attempting to check and adjust wheel alignment, ensure tires are properly inflated. Tire sizes and pressures can be found in owner's manual.

CASTER

Pickups (2WD & 4WD)

Adjust by turning eccentrics on upper arm shaft. A half turn of upper arm shaft will cause .049" (1.25 mm) front or rear movement of upper arm shaft, resulting in 1/4° change in caster adjustment

All Other Models

Caster, as a general rule, requires no adjustment. However, slight adjustment can be made by moving strut bar nut until specified caster angle is obtained.

CAMBER

Pickups (2WD & 4WD)

To adjust camber, on 2WD vehicles, hold upper arm shaft-to-crossmember bolt in position and remove nut from engine compartment side. Adjust number of shims between upper arm shaft and crossmember. On 4WD vehicles, adjust number of shims between upper arm shaft and arm post of side frame.

NOTE: Adjust caster before adjusting camber.

All Other Models

Camber requires no adjustment. Steering knuckle is integral with strut assembly and camber is preset at the factory. If camber is not within specifications, check suspension components for damage.

TOE-IN

Colt FWD & 4WD Pickups

1) Position wheels in straight ahead position. Loosen tie rod turnbuckles and adjust toe-in to specifications. On Colt, remove outer bellows clip to prevent twisting of bellows.

2) The same amount of adjustment should be made to both tie rods. Tighten tie rod end lock nuts and reinstall bellows clip (Colt).

Wheel Alignment

CHRYSLER CORP. IMPORTS (Cont.)

All Other Models

1) Position wheels in straight ahead position. If toe-in is not to specifications, loosen locking nut on left tie rod turnbuckle. Rotate buckle until toe-in is within specifications. Tighten lock nut.

2) After adjusting toe-in, check difference in lengths of left and right tie rods. If difference exceeds .20" (5 mm), remove right tie rod and adjust length until difference is .20" (5 mm) or less. Readjust toe-in to specifications.

DATSUN/NISSAN

ADJUSTMENT

TIRE INFLATION (COLD)

Before attempting to check or adjust wheel alignment, make sure that tires are properly inflated. Refer to manufacturer's specifications given in owner's manual.

CASTER & CAMBER

Pickup (2WD & 4WD)

1) Adjust caster and camber by increasing or decreasing thickness of shims, inserted between upper link spindle and upper link mounting bracket.

2) Caster adjustment affects camber adjustment, if you change caster specification, camber specification is also changed.

3) Total thickness of shims must be within .236" (6.0 mm) and must not collectively total more than 3 individual shims. Difference of total thickness between front and rear must be within .079" (2.0 mm).

All Other Models

Caster and camber is preset at factory and cannot be adjusted. If not to specifications, check suspension for wear or damage and repair or replace components as necessary.

TOE-IN

All Models

Place wheels in straight-ahead position, then make sure steering wheel and steering gear are also in straight-ahead position. Adjust toe-in by varying the length of steering tie rods. Loosen lock nuts and rotate rods evenly until toe-in is within specifications.

HONDA

ADJUSTMENT

TIRE INFLATION (COLD)

Before checking or adjusting wheel alignment or riding height, make sure tires are correctly inflated. Refer to manufacturer's specifications located on the drivers door or on left rear door jamb on 4-Door Sedan and Wagon models.

RIDING HEIGHT

Measure from top of wheel opening to floor, car must be empty and parked on level surface. If front height measurement is not within specifications, check rear height before attempting to repair front suspension. *See Riding Height Specifications table.*

RIDING HEIGHT SPECIFICATIONS

Application	Front In. (mm)	Rear In. (mm)
Accord		
Hatchback	25.9 (658)	25.2 (639)
Sedan	25.9 (658)	25.0 (636)
Civic		
Hatchback/Sedan		
1300		
Without A/C	25.6 (650)	25.3 (643)
With A/C	25.0 (635)	25.2 (640)
1500		
Without A/C	25.6 (650)	25.3 (643)
With A/C	25.3 (643)	25.4 (645)
Wagon		
Without A/C	25.6 (650)	26.3 (668)
With A/C	25.3 (643)	26.3 (668)
Prelude	25.6 (650)	25.3 (642)

CASTER

Accord & Civic

Caster is nonadjustable. If alignment is not within specifications, inspect for excess wear or damaged parts and replace as necessary.

Prelude

NOTE: **Alignment adjustments must be carried out in this order: camber, caster and toe-in.**

1) Remove spindle nut and install wheel alignment tool (07410-0010200), install gauge on spindle and install a set of turning radius gauges under front tires. Check caster angle.

2) Loosen 16 mm nuts on front beam radius rods and adjust by turning lock nut on the end of radius rod as required. To increase turn counterclockwise and to decrease turn clockwise. Tighten bolts, remove gauge and reinstall spindle nut.

CAMBER

Accord & Civic

Camber is nonadjustable. If alignment is not within specifications, inspect for excess wear or damaged parts and replace as necessary.

Prelude

1) To adjust camber, wheels must be in a straight ahead position, leave gauge on spindle and check camber.

2) Loosen upper arm nuts so ball joint slides freely. Adjust camber and tighten upper arm nuts to 40 ft. lbs. (55 Nm).

Wheel Alignment

HONDA (Cont.)

TOE-IN

Front

1) Loosen jam nuts at each end of tie rods. Turn tie rod until toe-in is within specifications. Use same procedure for both sides.

2) To center steering wheel after toe-in has been adjusted, turn both tie rods in same direction until steering wheel (spokes) are centered. Tighten jam nuts.

NOTE: Reposition tie rod boot if twisted or displaced after adjustment.

Rear

1) Release emergency brake. Loosen lock nuts while holding adjusting bolts on radius arm. Rotate adjusting bolt to meet specifications, then tighten lock nuts.

2) On Accord models, each notch on cam plate is equal to .20" (5 mm). On Civic models, each notch on cam plate is equal to .63" (16 mm). On Prelude models manufacturer did not specify measurements for cam plate.

NOTE: Notches on cam plate are for reference only. Do not use notches to equalize adjustments on rear radius rods.

ISUZU

ADJUSTMENT

TIRE INFLATION (COLD)

Before attempting to check or adjust wheel alignment, make sure tires are properly inflated. Refer to owner's manual for manufacturer's specifications. Check front end for loose parts.

CASTER

I-Mark

1) Realign the washers located between legs of upper control arm. One 1/8" (3 mm) thickness washer and one 3/8" (9.5 mm) thickness washer must be used as a couple for caster adjustment.

2) The combination that the total thickness of front and rear equals is 1/2" (12.7 mm). Only minimal changes to caster can be accomplished this way.

Impulse

Adjustment is built into front end and is not adjustable. Check for the cause of trouble if car is out of alignment and replace parts as necessary.

P'UP (2WD & 4WD)

Loosen and turn lock nuts on strut rods to specifications. Tighten and check alignment. Shims should not be used for adjustments.

CAMBER

I-Mark

Adjust by removing the upper upper ball joint, rotating it 180° and reinstalling ball joint. Approximately 1° of camber may be obtained.

Impulse

Adjustment is built into front end and is not adjustable. Check for the cause of trouble if car is out of alignment and replace parts as necessary.

P'UP (2WD & 4WD)

Adjust by adding or subtracting equal amount of shims from front and rear of bolts on upper control arm. Pivot shaft may also be inverted to aid in camber adjustment.

TOE-IN

All Models

Center steering wheel, loosen jam nuts on tie rods and turn tie rods until toe-in is within specifications. Tighten tie rod jam nuts and check wheel alignment.

NOTE: On I-Mark models make sure rubber bellows is not twisted after any maintenance is completed.

JAGUAR

ADJUSTMENT

TIRE INFLATION (COLD)

Before attempting to check or adjust wheel alignment, make sure tires are properly inflated. Refer to owner's manual for manufacturer's specifications.

RIDING HEIGHT

Front

1) Check that vehicle is full of fuel, oil, water and on level surface. Press down on front bumper and slowly release, then lift up on bumper and slowly release. This will settle front suspension.

2) Measure distance between center of outer headlight and floor on both sides of vehicle. Height should be 24.6" (611 mm) minimum. To adjust height, install or remove spring spacers from front coil springs.

NOTE: Spring spacers are 1/8" (3.2 mm) thick and will change riding height approximately 5/16" (7.9 mm).

Rear

1) Check that vehicle is full of fuel, oil and water. Roll vehicle forward 3 car lengths on level surface to settle rear suspension system.

2) Measure distance between lower surface of rear crossmember and floor on both sides of vehicle. Correct height should be 7.2-7.7" (182.6-195.4 mm). If height is not within specifications, check all bushings and bearing points of rear suspension. If the cause can not be found replace all 4 rear springs as a complete set.

JAGUAR (Cont.)

PREPARATION FOR CASTER & CAMBER ADJUSTMENT

1) Ensure vehicle is on level surface. Compress front suspension and insert tool (BLT5024 or fabricated tool) as shown in *Fig. 1.* under upper control arms, adjacent to control arm rubber stops and over brackets welded to bottom of control arms.

Fig. 1: Dimensions for Fabricating Setting Tools

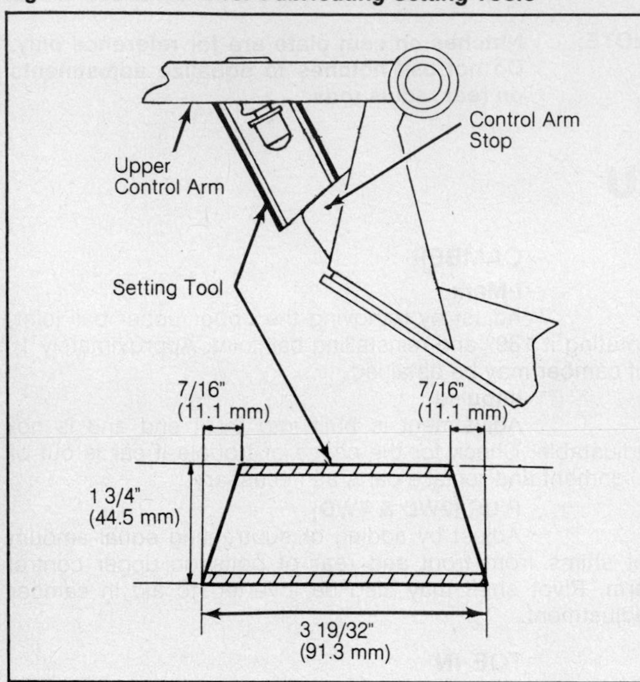

Control Arm
Stop
Upper
Control Arm
Setting Tool
7/16"
(11.1 mm)
7/16"
(11.1 mm)
1 3/4"
(44.5 mm)
3 19/32"
(91.3 mm)

2) Compress rear suspension and install setting links (JD25B) to lock rear suspension in place. *See Fig. 2.* Vehicle is now locked in half-loaded condition and caster and camber can be checked and adjusted.

Fig. 2: Rear Suspension in Locked Position with Tool

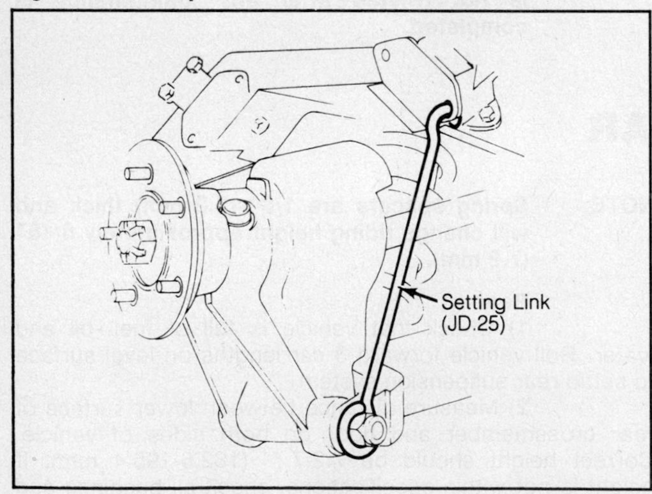

Setting Link
(JD.25)

CASTER

1) Adjust by moving shims on front and rear of upper control arm ball joint until caster is within specifications.

2) To increase caster, loosen bolts securing upper ball joint and move shims from rear of ball joint to front of ball joint. To decrease caster, reverse procedure. Transposing one shim 1/16" (1.6 mm) thick will alter the castor angle approximately 1/4°. Tighten ball joint attaching bolts and recheck caster angle.

CAMBER

Front

1) Place wheels in straight-ahead position. Measure camber angle.

2) Adjust by adding or subtracting shims. *See Fig. 3.* Adding shims increases camber angle. Make sure same number of shims are used on each bolt. Adding a 1/16" (1.6 mm) shim will alter camber angle by approximately 1/4°

Fig. 3: Adjustment Shim Location for Front Camber

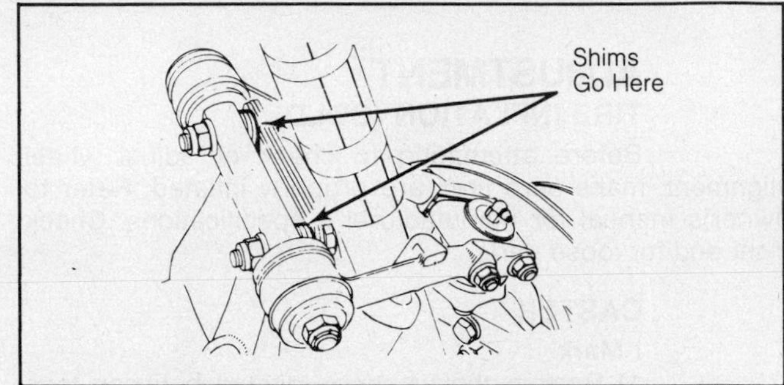

Shims
Go Here

Place equal numbers of shims on each side.

Rear

1) To adjust, remove suspension setting links (JD25B), raise and support rear of vehicle and remove wheels. Loosen nuts securing half-shaft to brake disc.

2) Add or remove shims as required to bring camber angle within specifications. Addition of one shim, 1/64" (.5 mm) will alter camber position 1/4°. Replace parts, remove car from stands and check camber angle.

Fig. 4: Adjustment Shim Location for Rear Camber

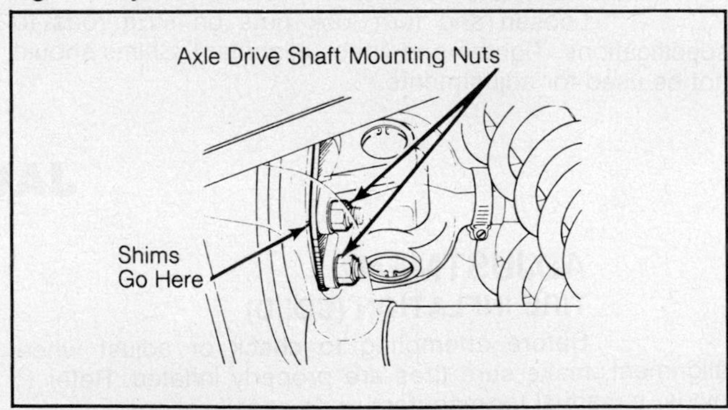

Axle Drive Shaft Mounting Nuts
Shims
Go Here

TOE-IN

1) Place wheels in straight ahead position. Remove grease nipple from rack adjuster nut. Put centralizing tool (12279) into locating hole. Push tool onto back of rack bar.

2) Slowly turn steering wheel until tool drops into back of rack bar. Measure toe-in. If toe-in is not within specifications, adjust by loosening steering link lock nuts and rotating adjuster sleeves equal amounts, as necessary. Tighten lock nuts, remove centralizing tool, install grease nipple and recheck toe-in.

MAZDA

ADJUSTMENT

TIRE INFLATION (COLD)

Before attempting to check or adjust wheel alignment, make sure tires are properly inflated. Refer to manufacturer's specifications given in owner's manual.

CASTER

GLC

Caster is not adjustable. If caster is not to specifications, inspect suspension for excessive wear or damage. Replace components as necessary.

RX7 & 626

1) Caster and camber angles are adjusted together by changing position of strut support. Remove 4 nuts attaching strut support to fender apron.

2) Raise front of vehicle and support with jack stands. Press strut downward and change position of support according to *Table and Fig. 1*.

3) Tighten strut support mounting nuts. Lower vehicle and recheck caster and camber.

MacPHEARSON STRUT SUPPORT TABLE

Strut Position	Caster	Camber
A 0°	0°	0°
B 90°	1/2°	0°
C 180°	1/2°	1/2°
D 270°	0°	1/2°

Fig. 1: RX7 & 626 Caster & Camber Adjustment Using MacPhearson Strut Support

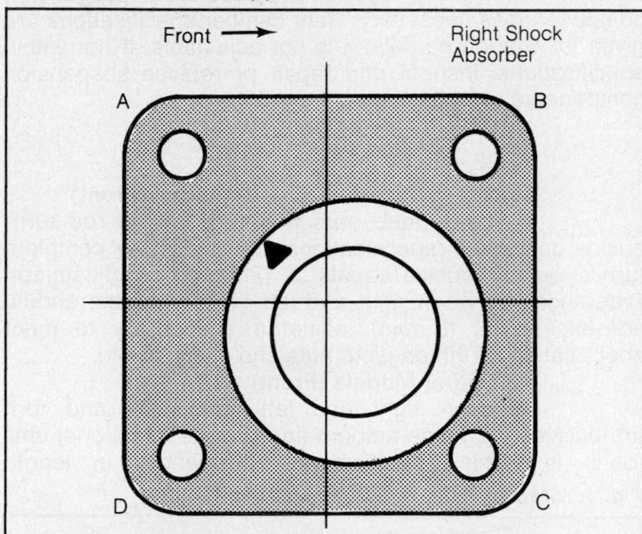
Front
Right Shock Absorber
A
B
C
D

Pickups

Change shims between upper control arm shaft and support bracket or turn upper control arm shaft until specifications are obtained.

CAMBER

NOTE: **On GLC wagon, camber is not adjustable. If camber is not within specifications, inspect suspension for excessive wear or damage. Replace components as necessary.**

GLC

1) Raise front end, support with jack stands and open hood.

2) Remove 2 mounting nuts holding strut support to fender apron. Push mounting block down, turn 180° and tighten mounting nuts. Note a triangular shaped mark on mounting block. Rotating mark away from engine changes camber to the negative side and opposite direction the opposite happens. Check camber angle.

RX7 & 626

NOTE: **See procedure given under RX7 & 626 Caster adjustment.**

Pickups

Change shims between upper arm shaft and support bracket until specifications for camber are within limits.

TOE-IN

626 (Front)

Loosen lock nuts and turn tie rods equal amounts. Both tie rods are right-threaded, to increase turn right tie rod toward front of vehicle and to decrease turn left one toward rear of vehicle by the same amount. One full turn equals .24" (6 mm). If boot is twisted or dented, loosen band and straighten boot.

All Other Models (Front)

1) Raise front of vehicle. Turn wheels by hand and mark a line in center of each tire tread. Place vehicle in straight-ahead position and lower vehicle to ground.

2) Measure distance between marked lines at both front and rear of wheel. Make sure measurements are made equal distances from ground.

3) Loosen lock nuts and turn tie rods until adjustment is correct. Tighten lock nuts with bolts horizontal and below rod. This procedure will prevent interference with center link.

GLC FWD & 626 (Rear)

1) Release emergency brake. Mark front and back of tire at same height as center of wheel. Mark center lower section of crossmember. Points marked on tires and crossmember form a triangle and are reference points for adjusting rear toe-in.

2) Turn spacer (star wheel) to make the points from rear of tire to center of crossmember equal. *See Fig. 2.* Turn both right and left spacers the same amount to adjust toe-in.

Fig. 2: GLC & 626 Star Wheel Adjustment

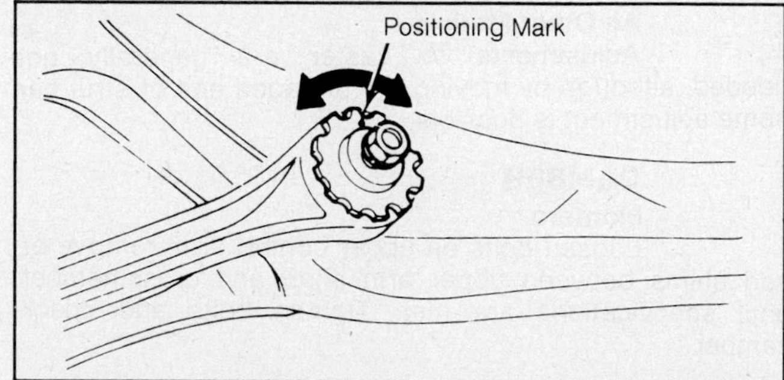
Positioning Mark

3) On GLC only, check parallelism of body and rear wheel. Use existing mark on rear of tire and hole on each side member. Measure from hole on one side to tire on the other. Repeat using other hole and tire. If measurements are not equal, loosen 2 crossmember mounting nuts on each side. Move crossmember so measurement is within .2" (5 mm).

Wheel Alignment

MERCEDES-BENZ

ADJUSTMENT

TIRE INFLATION (COLD)

Before attempting to check or adjust wheel alignment, make sure tires are properly inflated. Refer to manufacturer's specifications given in owner's manual.

CASTER

1) Test under loaded condition. Load vehicle with 2 weights of 143 lbs. (65 kg) on rear seat and a full tank of fuel. If caster is not to specifications, loosen lock nut on eccentric bolt on front side of lower control arm.

2) To adjust, rotate eccentric bolt until caster angle is within specifications. Hold eccentric bolt in place and tighten lock nut.

CAMBER

1) Test under loaded condition. Load vehicle with 2 weights of 143 lbs. (65 kg) on front seat, 1 similar weight on rear seat and a full tank of fuel. If camber is not within specifications, loosen lock nut of eccentric bolt on rear side of lower control arm.

2) To adjust, rotate eccentric bolt until camber is within specifications. Hold eccentric bolt in place and tighten lock nut.

TOE-IN

1) Place wheels in straight ahead position. If toe-in is not within specifications, adjust by loosening jam nuts on outer tie rods.

2) Rotate tie rods to obtain specified toe-in. Make sure tie rods are adjusted equally. Tighten jam nuts on tie rods and check wheel alignment.

MITSUBISHI

ADJUSTMENT

TIRE INFLATION (COLD)

Before attempting to check or adjust wheel alignment, make sure tires are properly inflated. Specifications are listed on a label attached near striker on driver's side of vehicle on all vehicles except on Tredia models. Location on Tredia is on the lower corner of driver's door.

CASTER

Montero

1) Remove upper control arm from crossmember. *See appropriate removal procedure in suspension section.*

2) Working from top side of control arm, turn arm shaft. To reduce caster rotate top side of shaft away from ball joint and the opposite direction to increase caster.

3) Install control arm and check caster.

Pickup (2WD & 4WD)

Loosen and turn eccentrics on upper control arm shaft. A half turn will result in a 1/4° of caster adjustment. Tighten eccentrics and check caster.

All Other Models

Adjustments to caster are generally not needed, although by moving the threaded end of strut bar some adjustment is possible.

CAMBER

Montero

Loosen bolts on upper control arm, remove or add shims between upper arm shaft and crossmember until specifications are met. Tighten bolts and check camber.

Pickup (2WD)

Hold upper arm shaft to crossmember bolt and remove nut from engine compartment side. Remove or add shims between shaft and crossmember until specifications are met. A .39" (1 mm) adjustment will provide approximately 1/4° of camber adjustment. Tighten bolts and check camber.

Pickup (4WD)

Adjust by changing amount of shims between upper arm shaft and arm post of side frame. A .39" (1 mm) adjustment will provide approximately 1/4° of camber adjustment.

All Other Models

Camber is not adjustable. If not within specifications, inspect and repair or replace front suspension components as necessary. Rear camber specifications are given for Starion models, it is not adjustable. If not within specifications, inspect and repair or replace suspension components as necessary.

TOE-IN

Montero, Pickup (2WD) & Starion (Front)

Loosen jamb nuts and turn left tie rod turnbuckle until toe-in specifications are meet. One complete turn of left turnbuckle equals .3" (7.5 mm) of adjustment. Differences between right and left tie rod lengths should not exceed .2" (5 mm), adjust as necessary to meet specifications. Tighten jamb nuts and check toe-in.

All Other Models (Front)

Loosen right and left jamb nuts and turn turnbuckles the same amount (in opposite directions) until toe-in is within specifications. Differences in length

Fig. 1: Starion Rear Toe-in Adjustment Cam

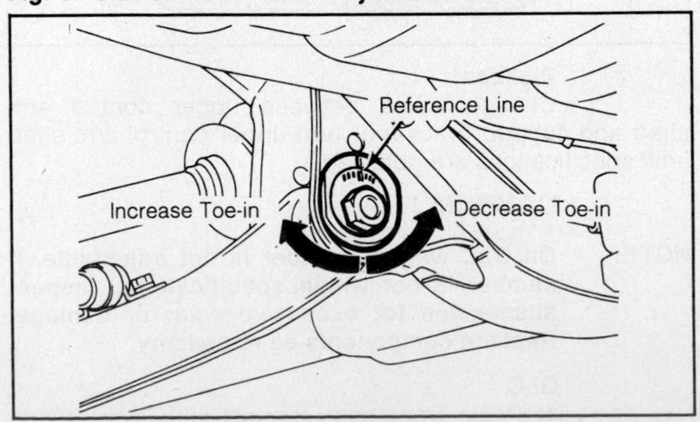
Reference Line
Increase Toe-in
Decrease Toe-in

MITSUBISHI (Cont.)

between right and left tie rod should not exceed .2" (5 mm), adjust as necessary to meet specifications. On Cordia and Tredia, each half turn of turnbuckle is equal to .24" (6 mm) of adjustment. On Pickups (4WD), a half turn of each turnbuckle will change the total toe-in approximately .3" (7.5 mm).

Starion (Rear)

Adjustments are made by moving crossmember to lower control arm mounting bolts. Loosen lock nut and turn mounting bolt until toe-in is correct. *See Fig. 1.* Turn right and left mounting bolts equally. Movement of one division on scale per side will change total toe-in approximately .08" (2 mm).

PEUGEOT

ADJUSTMENT

TIRE INFLATION (COLD)

Before attempting to check or adjust wheel alignment, make sure tires are properly inflated. Refer to manufacturer's specifications given in owner's manual.

CAMBER & CASTER

Camber and caster are not adjustable. If alignment is not within specifications, inspect for damaged suspension parts and repair or replace as necessary.

TOE-IN

1) Position wheels in straight-ahead position. If toe-in is not to specifications, loosen jam nuts or nuts on clamps of tie rod ends.

2) Rotate tie rods simultaneously in either direction necessary to obtain specified toe-in. Tighten tie rod jam nuts or nuts on clamps making sure that boot is not twisted. Recheck toe-in.

PORSCHE

ADJUSTMENT

TIRE INFLATION (COLD)

Before attempting to check or adjust wheel alignment, make sure tires are properly inflated. Refer to manufacturer's specifications given in owner's manual.

RIDING HEIGHT

NOTE: Check riding height with fuel tank full, spare tire and jack in vehicle.

911SC (Front)

1) Checking or adjusting riding height must only be performed with vehicle on level floor. Mark center of front wheel hub cap (grease retainer cup).

Fig. 1: Front Suspension Riding Height Measuring Points for 911SC

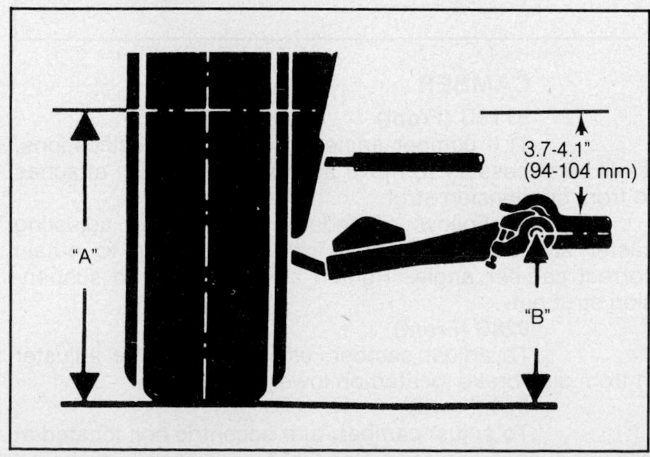
3.7-4.1"
(94-104 mm)
"A"
"B"

2) Jounce vehicle several times to settle suspension. Measure distance "A" and "B" shown in *Fig. 1.* Difference between measurements should be 3.7-4.1" (94-104 mm).

3) To adjust, loosen or tighten torsion bar adjusting bolt until correct height is obtained. Jounce vehicle several times and recheck height. Make sure difference between right and left side measurements does not exceed .20" (5.1 mm).

928S (Front)

1) Checking or adjusting riding height must only be performed with vehicle on level floor. Place wheels in straight ahead position.

2) Measure distance from boss (on forward underside of lower control arm) to floor. Distance should be approximately 7.48" (190 mm). Height is determined by the coil springs and corrections can be made by placing spacers underneath lower spring retainers (a maximum of two spacers per spring) or the replacement of coil springs.

944 (Front)

1) Checking or adjusting riding height must only be performed with vehicle on level floor. Place front wheels in straight ahead position.

2) Measure from upper edge of bumper to floor. Measurement must be 19.75-21.25" (502-542 mm).

3) Adjustments are made by changing front springs, if front riding height is not to specifications.

911SC (Rear)

1) To check riding height, vehicle must be on level floor. Mark center of rear wheel. Jounce vehicle several times to settle suspension. Measure distance "A" shown in *Fig. 2.*

2) Distance "A" plus 1.26-1.65" (32-42 mm) equals "B"; however, distance "B" is difficult to measure because torsion bar is mounted off center in its rubber

Wheel Alignment

PORSCHE (Cont.)

bushing. Therefore it is necessary to measure distance "B1" and add .585" (14.9 mm), radius of bushing. This total should equal "B".

3) After calculating "B", difference between "A" and "B" should be 1.26-1.65" (32-42 mm). Difference in height from left to right should not exceed .20" (5.1 mm). If values are not within specifications, check front height and rear torsion bar adjustment. Correct as necessary.

Fig. 2: Rear Suspension Riding Height Measuring Points for 911SC

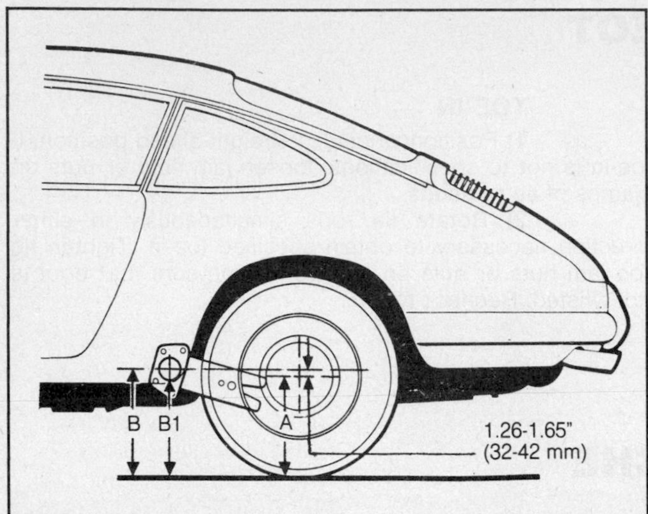
B
B1
A
1.26-1.65"
(32-42 mm)

928S (Rear)

1) Checking or adjusting riding height must only be performed with vehicle on level floor. Place front wheels in straight ahead position.

2) Measure distance from lower edge of crossmember (below camber adjusting cam) to floor. Distance should be 6.81-7.20" (173-183 mm).

3) To adjust vehicle upward, turn coil spring adjusting nut (located at under side of lower spring retainer) clockwise. Rear height must be adjusted to match front height. For example, if front height is .394" (10 mm) too high, rear height must be raised .394" (10 mm).

Fig. 3: Location of 944 Rear Riding Height & Camber Adjusting Bolts

Mounting Bolt
Eccentric Bolt

944 (Rear)

1) Checking or adjusting riding height must only be performed with vehicle on level floor. Place front wheels in straight ahead position.

2) Rear height is adjusted with 2-piece spring struts without removal of torsion bars.

3) Loosen joint between spring strut and trailing arm and adjust to specified value by turning camber eccentric. *See Fig. 3.*

CASTER

911SC

1) If caster angle is not within specifications, it will be necessary to remove adjuster plate which attaches to front suspension strut.

2) Remove enough front compartment carpet to allow access to top of each suspension strut. Mark position of each movable plate, located below each Allen screw.

3) Loosen each screw and upper suspension strut nut. Move assembly lengthwise to obtain correct caster angle. Tighten all 3 screws and suspension strut nut.

928S

Caster is adjusted at eccentric located on lower control arm. To adjust caster, use eccentric closest to brake disc.

944

To adjust caster, move the rear control arm mount from side-to-side. *See Fig. 4.*

Fig. 4: 944 Caster Adjustment Location

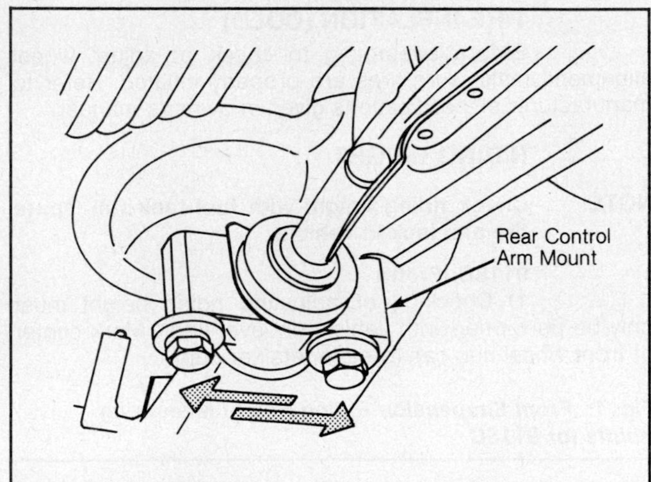
Rear Control
Arm Mount

CAMBER

911SC (Front)

1) If camber angle is not within specifications, it will be necessary to move adjuster plate which attaches to front suspension strut.

2) Follow procedure outlined for adjusting caster and move assembly from side-to-side to obtain correct camber angle. Tighten all 3 screws and suspension strut nut.

928S (Front)

To adjust camber, use 2nd eccentric adjuster in from disc brake located on lower control arm.

944 (Front)

To adjust camber, turn eccentric bolt located at base of suspension strut. *See Fig. 5.*

PORSCHE (Cont.)

Fig. 5: 944 Front Camber Eccentric Bolt Location

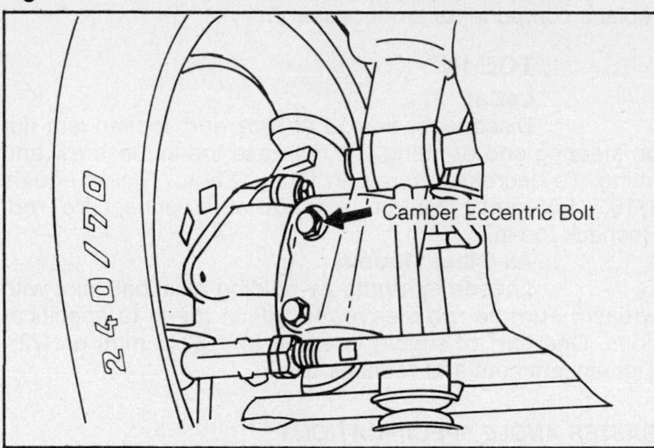
Camber Eccentric Bolt
240/70

911SC (Rear)

1) To obtain correct camber angle at rear wheels, it is necessary to adjust rear torsion bars first. *See Torsion Bar Adjustment.*

2) Loosen nuts on retaining bolts and on eccentric at rear axle flange. *See Fig. 6.* Turn camber eccentric until camber angle is within specifications. Tighten retaining nuts and eccentric nut.

Fig. 6: 911SC Rear Camber Adjustment Points

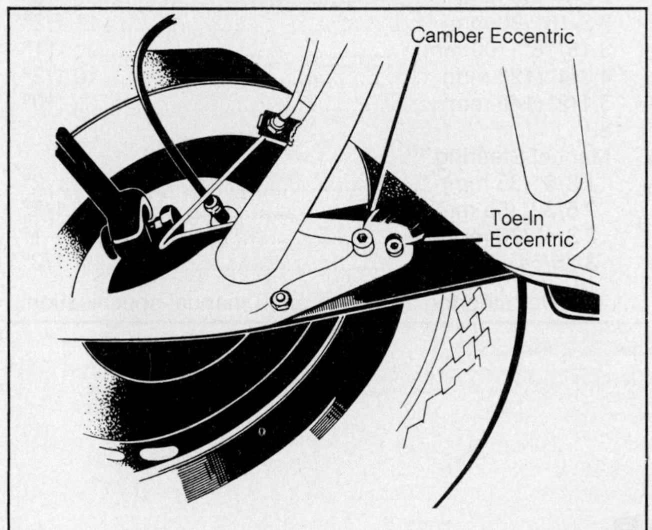
Camber Eccentric
Toe-In
Eccentric

928S (Rear)

To adjust camber, use eccentric bolt located on inner control arm mount.

944 (Rear)

To adjust, loosen joint between spring strut and trailing arm. Bring camber to specification by turning eccentric.

TOE-IN

All Models (Front)

Place front wheels in straight-ahead position. Adjust left and right tie rods equally to obtain specified setting. Coat each tie rod with anti-corrosive compound after adjustment.

911SC (Rear)

To adjust rear wheel toe-in, loosen nuts on retaining bolts and adjusting eccentrics at rear axle flange. Turn toe-in eccentric until toe-in is set to specifications. Hold eccentric stationary and tighten all lock nuts.

928S (Rear)

To adjust rear toe-in, use eccentric bolt located on front control arm mount.

944 (Rear)

To adjust toe-in, reposition control arm flange in slots of spring plate. Use of adjusting tool (9171) is suggested.

TORSION BAR ADJUSTMENT

911SC (Rear)

1) Place torsion bar into transverse tube with inner end splines first. Slip radius arm onto outer end splines of torsion bar.

2) Place leveling tool (VW 261) on lower edge of door opening and adjust level so bubble is in center of glass.

3) Check adjustment (degrees) of free hanging radius arm with same leveling tool. If not to specifications, adjust by turning torsion bar and radius arm in opposite directions. Adjustment of both radius arms must each equal 36 3/4° ± 1/4°.

RENAULT

ADJUSTMENT

TIRE INFLATION (COLD)

Before attempting to check or adjust wheel alignment or riding height, make sure tires are properly inflated. Refer to manufacturer's specifications given in owner's manual.

RIDING HEIGHT

NOTE: **Riding height should be set with fuel tank full and without additional weight in vehicle.**

Front

1) Checking or adjusting riding height can only be performed with vehicle on level floor. To calculate front riding height, measure distance from floor to center of wheel (H1) and distance from floor to front side member (H2) in line with wheel centers. *See Fig. 1.*

2) Subtract the 2 measurements (H1 from H2). Variation between right and left sides should not exceed 3/8" (9.5 mm). To adjust front riding height, mark position of torsion bar in bracket. Remove and rotate torsion bar until correct riding height is obtained.

RENAULT (Cont.)

Rear

1) On all models, rear riding height is calculated by measuring from floor to center of wheel (H4). On LeCar measure from floor to the punched out hole in rear side member (H5). On Fuego and 18i measure between floor and center of front bolt at side arms (H5). *See Fig. 1.*

2) The variation between right and left sides should not exceed 3/8" (9.5 mm). Adjust rear riding height in same manner as front riding height.

Fig. 1: Measurement Location Points For Riding Height

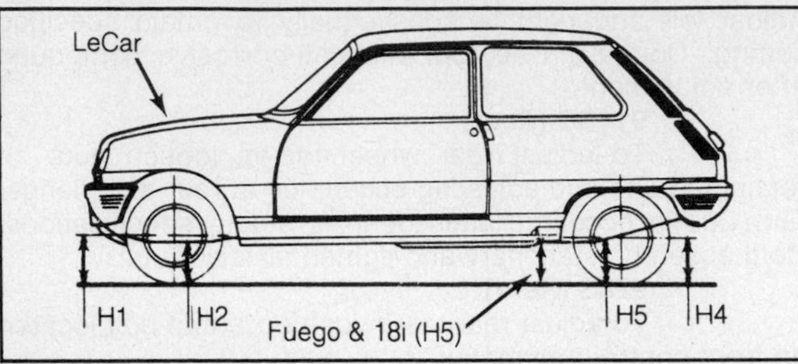
LeCar
H1
H2
Fuego & 18i (H5)
H5
H4

CASTER

Fuego & Fuego Turbo

Check riding height first since caster angle may change if riding height is not to specifications. Caster is adjustable by turning tierods, one turn is equal to 1/4°.

Le Car

Loosen both lower control arm mounting bolts and add or remove shims to adjust caster to specifications. The addition or removal of one shim equals about 1° change in caster angle.

NOTE: **Never use more than 2 shims between bushing and side member. Always check steering box height after caster adjustment.**

18i

Vehicle riding height controls caster angle. Caster is not adjustable.

CAMBER

All Models

Vehicle riding height controls camber. Camber angle is not adjustable. If not within specifications, inspect front suspension for wear or damage and repair or replace components as necessary.

TOE-IN

LeCar

Disconnect tie rod at rack end, loosen jam nut on steering end of fitting. To increase toe-in, unscrew end fitting. To decrease, screw in fitting. Each 1/2 turn equals 1/16" (1.5 mm). Tighten jam nut and connect tie rod. Recheck toe-in.

All Other Models

Loosen jam nuts by holding axial ball joint with wrench. Turn tie rod sleeves to adjust toe-in to specifications. One turn of sleeve is equal to 1/8" (3 mm) or 1/2°. Tighten jam nuts and recheck toe-in.

CASTER ANGLE SPECIFICATIONS

Difference Between H2 & H5	Caster Angle
Fuego & Fuego Turbo	
3/4" (20 mm)	3° 1/2'
1 3/8 (35 mm)	3°
2 5/32" (55 mm)	2° 1/2'
2 3/4" (70 mm)	2°
Le Car	
1 9/16" (40 mm)	12 1/2°
2 3/8" (60 mm)	12°
3 3/16" (80 mm)	11 1/2°
3 15/16" (100 mm)	11°
4 3/4" (120 mm)	10 1/2°
5 1/2" (140 mm)	10°
18i	
Manual Steering [1]	
1 3/8" (35 mm)	2°
2 5/32" (55 mm)	1 1/2°
2 3/4" (70 mm)	1°
3 35/64" (90 mm)	1/2°

[1] – Power steering add 1° to each manual specification.

SAAB

ADJUSTMENT

TIRE INFLATION (COLD)

Before attempting to check or adjust wheel alignment, make sure tires are properly inflated. Refer to manufacturer's specifications given in owner's manual.

CASTER

Add or remove shims under upper control arm bushing brackets. Changing shims from front to rear bracket increases caster angle. Moving shims from rear to front decreases caster angle.

NOTE: **Same shim thicknesses removed from front must be placed under rear and vice versa. Change in caster also affects camber.**

CAMBER

Add or remove same number of shims under upper control arm bushing brackets. Increasing shims under both brackets reduces camber angle and removing shims under both increases camber.

NOTE: **Always add or remove same thickness of shims at front and rear or caster angle will be affected.**

TOE-IN

1) With wheels in straight ahead position, loosen outer bellows clip and tie rod jam nuts. Turn adjustable sleeves until correct toe-in is obtained. Tighten

SAAB (Cont.)

Fig. 1: Tie Rod Length Measurement, Vehicle with Power Steering

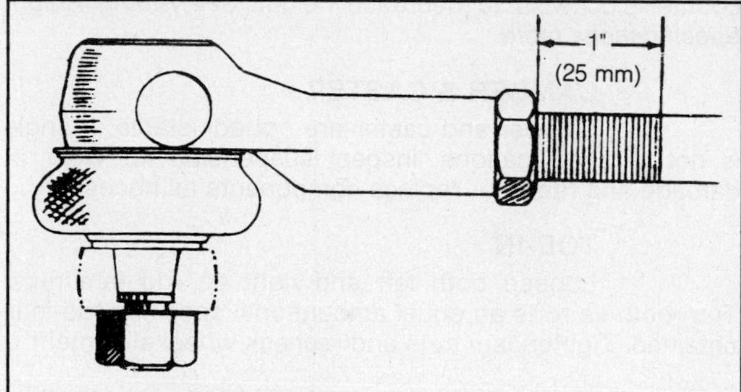
1"
(25 mm)

jam nuts and recheck toe-in, make sure both tie rods are the same length.

2) After adjustment of toe-in, measure thread width of tie rod. Manual steering must not exceed 15/16" (24 mm) or 1" (25 mm) for power steering models. The maximum difference between measurements of both sides must not exceed 3/16" (5 mm).

SUBARU

ADJUSTMENT

TIRE INFLATION (COLD)

Before attempting to check or adjust wheel alignment, make sure tires are properly inflated. Refer to manufacturer's specifications given in owner's manual.

RIDING HEIGHT

Front (All Models)

Place vehicle on level floor. Measure distance between floor and front end of lower control arm at center of inboard attaching bolt. Adjust clearance by turning nuts on both sides of strut until specified height is obtained. Turn both nuts on one side of strut the same amount. *See Riding Height Specifications table.*

Rear (2WD)

1) Riding height is adjusted by changing the angle between trailing arm center line and markings on outer bracket. *See Fig. 1.* Trailing arm and outer bracket have full serrations around torsion bar mounting hole, while torsion bar has 1 missing serration, thus allowing torsion bar to be inserted at any angle.

Fig. 1: Installed View of Torsion Bar Outer End Attachment

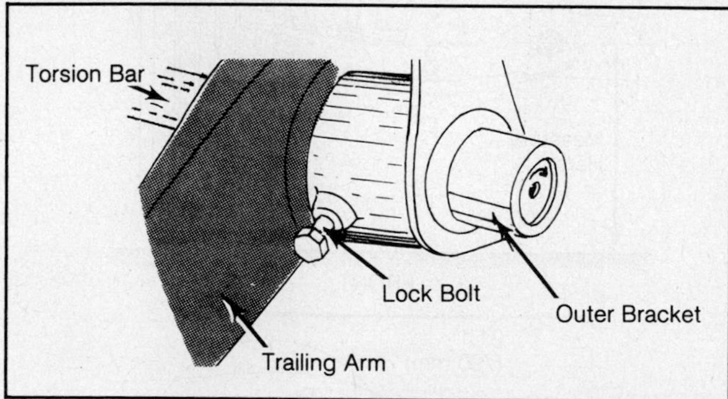
Torsion Bar
Lock Bolt
Outer Bracket
Trailing Arm

2) To increase riding height, turn outer end and inner end of torsion bar in direction opposite to cast-in arrow on outer end of bar. Height changes .20" (5 mm) with each shift in serration.

3) Initially set vehicle rear riding height by inserting torsion bar with its missing serrations aligned with markings on outer bracket surface and trailing arm inner surface. This should equal the approximate riding height. *See Riding Height Specifications table.*

4) Measure riding height at lower face of crossmember to floor and determine numbers of teeth to be shifted on inner and/or outer serrations.

NOTE: Vehicle must be in unloaded condition.

5) At top of shock absorber, remove bolt attaching shock to body. Raise rear of vehicle and remove wheel. Remove lock bolt of outer bushing. Remove bolts connecting outer and inner arms with brake drum supported by a jack to prevent brake hose damage.

6) Place alignment mark on outer bushing, crossmember and torsion bar for reassembly reference. Measure vertical distance between end of outer arm and vehicle body. Pull out outer arm and torsion bar until inner serration is completely disengaged.

RIDING HEIGHT SPECIFICATIONS

Application	Front In. (mm)	Rear In. (mm)
1600 & 1800 2WD		
Wagon	9.65-10.63 (245-270)	11.02-11.81 (280-300)
All Others	9.45-10.43 (240-265)	10.24-11.02 (260-280)
1600 & 1800 4WD		
Hatchback		
GL	10.63-11.61 (270-295)	12.80-13.58 (325-345)
STD	10.43-11.42 (265-290)	12.60-13.39 (320-340)
Wagon		
DL	10.43-11.42 (265-290)	13.19-13.98 (335-355)
GL	10.63-11.61 (270-295)	13.39-14.17 (340-360)

7) Rotate torsion bar and outer arm to shift matching of inner serration by appropriate pitches and engage inner serration with crossmember. Pull outer arm from torsion bar and rotate outer arm in opposite direction to shift matching of outer serration by appropriate pitches.

Wheel Alignment

SUBARU (Cont.)

NOTE: Do not disengage inner serration of torsion bar from crossmember.

8) Install outer arm to torsion bar and crossmember, then measure vertical distance between end of outer arm and vehicle body. Change in this distance shows half of change in riding height clearance caused by adjustment.

9) Install bolts connecting outer and inner arms. Repeat adjustment procedure on opposite wheel. Install shock absorbers and outer bushing lock bolt. Install wheels and lower vehicle. Check rear riding height adjustment. If correct, tighten lock bolt on outer bushing. If incorrect, repeat adjustment on each wheel.

Rear (4WD)

Place vehicle on level floor. Measure distance between floor and lowest point of crossmember pipe. Adjust clearance by turning adjusting bolt (through service hole in floor) clockwise to increase riding height and counter-clockwise to decrease height. *See Riding Height Specifications table.*

CAMBER & CASTER

Camber and caster are not adjustable. If angle is not to specifications, inspect suspension for wear or damage and repair or replace components as necessary.

TOE-IN

Loosen both left and right tie rod jam nuts. Turn both tie rods an equal amount until specified toe-in is obtained. Tighten jam nuts and recheck wheel alignment.

TOYOTA

ADJUSTMENT

TIRE INFLATION (COLD)

Before attempting to check or adjust wheel alignment, make sure tires are properly inflated. Refer to manufacturer's specifications given in owner's manual.

RIDING HEIGHT

Before adjusting wheel alignment, check riding height. Riding height must be checked with vehicle on level floor. Bounce vehicle serveral times and allow suspension to settle. Check riding height measurement as shown in *Fig. 1 and 2.* If riding height is not within specifications listed in *Riding Height Specifications table*, check and repair or replace suspension components.

RIDING HEIGHT SPECIFICATIONS

Application	Front In. (mm)	Rear In. (mm)
Camry	8.52 (216.5)	10.26 (260.5)
Celica	9.1 (232)	9.4 (240)
Corolla	9.1 (232)	9.1 (232)
Cressida		
Sedan	8.94 (227)	10.63 (270)
Wagon	9.17 (233)	9.57 (243)
Pickup		
1/2 Ton (2WD)		
7.00x14	10.3 (262)	11.4 (288)
E78x14	10.0 (254)	11.1 (281)
ER78x14	9.9 (251)	10.7 (271)
205/70SRx14	9.5 (242)	10.3 (262)
3/4 Ton (2WD)	11.0 (278)	12.0 (305)
Starlet	9.02 (229)	9.11 (232)
Supra	8.8 (225)	10.4 (265)
Tercel		
2WD	8.0 (206)	11.3 (290)
4WD	9.2 (235)	10.7 (273.5)

CAMBER & CASTER

Camry

Adjust camber by loosening shock absorber nut and turning camber adjustment cam. Camber will change about 1/3° with each graduation of cam. Adjust caster by increasing or decreasing the number of spacers on stabilizer bar. Caster will change 1/2° with each .16 in. (4 mm) spacer, do not install more than two spacers.

Pickup (2WD)

Adjust camber and caster by adding or removing shims between upper control arm shaft and front suspension crossmember.

Land Cruiser & Pickup (4WD)

Camber and caster are not adjustable. If not within specifications, inspect and repair or replace front suspension components as necessary.

Starlet

Camber is not adjustable, check for bent or worn parts and replace as necessary. To adjust caster, add or subtracting spacers on stabilizer bar. Do not install more than two spacers.

Fig. 1: Riding Height Measurement Points for Pickup (2WD) Models

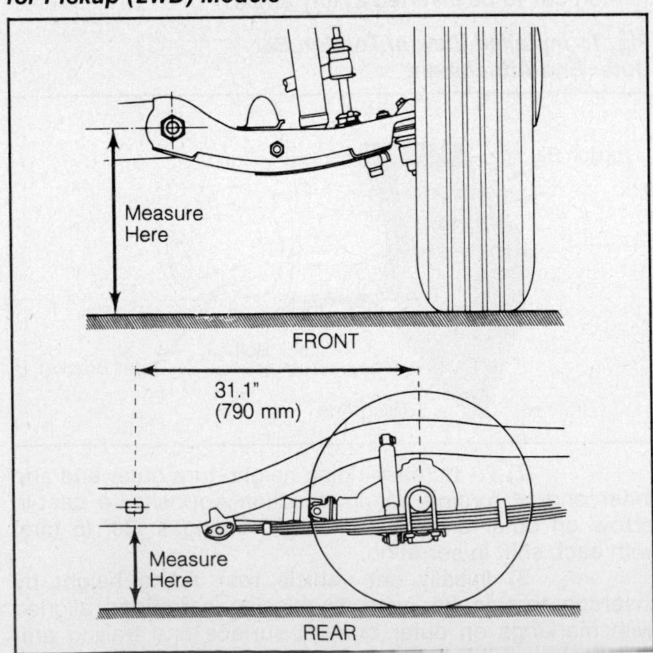
Measure
Here
FRONT
31.1"
(790 mm)
Measure
Here
REAR

TOYOTA (Cont.)

Fig. 2: Riding Height Measurement Points for All Models (Except Pickup & Land Cruiser)

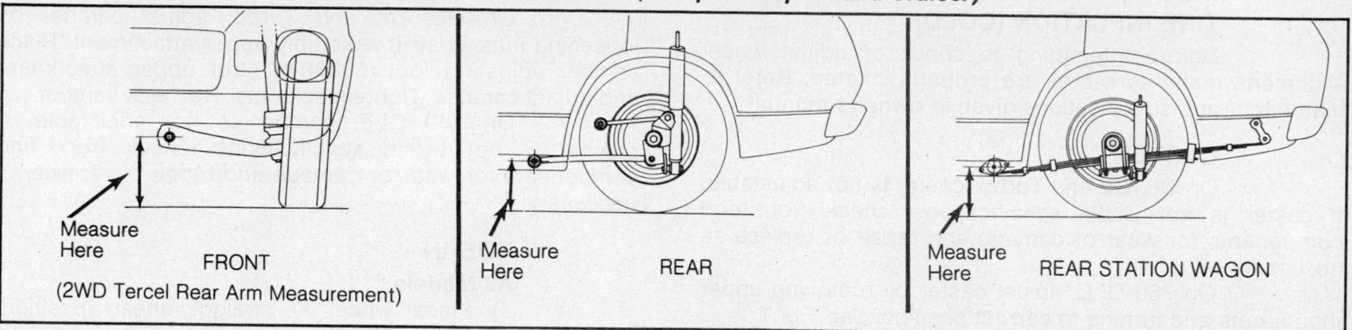
Measure Here
FRONT
(2WD Tercel Rear Arm Measurement)
Measure Here
REAR
Measure Here
REAR STATION WAGON

Tercel

Adjust camber by turning camber adjustment cam. Loosen shock absorber nut and turn cam. Camber will change about 1/3° with each graduation of cam. Caster adjustment is only possible if an increase is needed, if caster reading is above specification, no adjustment is possible.

All Other Models

If caster angle is not within specifications, adjust by loosening nuts on strut rod and turning nuts to lengthen or shorten strut rod.

NOTE: Camber angle is not adjustable, check front end for bent or worn parts and replace as necessary.

TOE-IN

All Models

Make sure wheels are positioned straight ahead, remove rack boot clips, loosen tie rod clamp bolts and rotate adjusting sleeves an equal amount until correct toe-in is obtained. Position clamp bolts at right angles to slot in tie rod, tighten bolts and install rack boot clips making sure that boot is not twisted.

VOLKSWAGEN

ADJUSTMENT

TIRE INFLATION (COLD)

Before attempting to check or adjust wheel alignment, make sure tires are properly inflated. Refer to manufacturer's specifications given in owner's manual.

CASTER

Vanagon

Adjust by changing length of strut bar at crossmember mount. After adjusting caster, check and adjust camber.

NOTE: Proper sequence for adjustments are caster, camber and toe-in.

All Other Models

Caster angle is not adjustable. If not within specifications, inspect front suspension for wear or damage and repair or replace components as necessary.

CAMBER

Quantum (Front)

1) Loosen ball joint mounting nuts on control arm.

2) Insert camber adjusting lever (US 4471) in proper holes on control arm and move ball joint until proper camber is obtained.

3) Tighten nuts and check camber.

Vanagon (Front)

Loosen nut on upper control arm shaft and rotate shaft until camber angle is set to specifications. Tighten nut and recheck camber.

All Other Models (Front)

Loosen nuts and bolts of suspension strut-to-steering knuckle. Turn eccentric bolt (upper mounting bolt) until specified camber angle is obtained. Tighten mounting bolts and recheck camber.

Vanagon (Rear)

Loosen outer bolt on trailing arm and adjust camber by using a screwdriver to move trailing arm up or down. Tighten trailing arm bolt and recheck camber.

All Other Models (Rear)

Rear camber is not adjustable. If camber angle is not within specifications, inspect rear suspension for wear or damage and repair or replace components as necessary.

TOE-IN

Vanagon (Front)

Set steering gear to center position by counting the number of turns. Lug on rubber washer of pinion shaft must be aligned with notch in steering gear housing. Loosen jam nuts and rotate both tie rods equal amounts until toe-in specifications are obtained. Tighten jam nuts. Steering wheel must be centered on steering shaft and dust boots must not be twisted on tie rods. If steering wheel is not in center position, remove and center on splines.

All Other Models (Front)

Place wheels in straight ahead position. Loosen jam nuts on adjustable tie rod end. Hold axle boot to avoid twisting. Adjust tie rod until specified toe-in is obtained. Tighten jam nut and recheck toe-in.

Vanagon (Rear)

Loosen inner bolt on trailing arm. Using a screwdriver, adjust toe-in by moving trailing arm forward or rearward until correct toe-in specification is obtained. Tighten trailing arm inner bolt.

All Other Models (Rear)

Toe-in is not adjustable. If toe-in is not within specifications, inspect rear suspension for wear or damage and repair or replace components as necessary.

Wheel Alignment

VOLVO

ADJUSTMENT

TIRE INFLATION (COLD)

Before attempting to check or adjust wheel alignment, make sure tires are properly inflated. Refer to manufacturer's specifications given in owner's manual

CASTER

On GL, DL and Turbo, caster is not adjustable. If caster is not within specifications, check front end components for wear or damage and repair or replace as necessary.

On 760 GLE, adjust caster by removing upper mount nuts and turning to correct position. *See Fig. 1.*

Fig. 1: 760 GLE Caster Location Adjustments

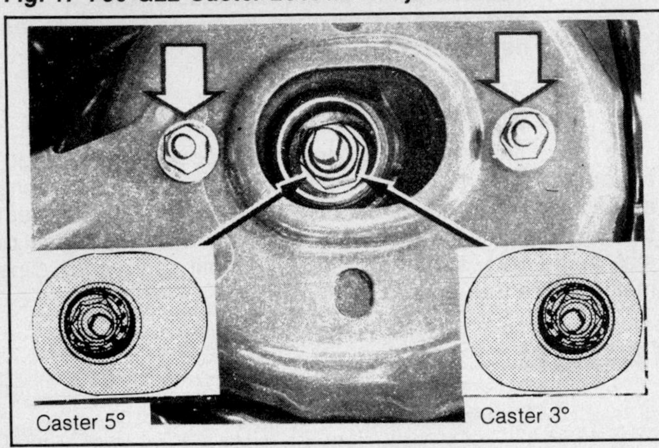
Caster 5°
Caster 3°

CAMBER

On GL, DL and Turbo, adjust camber by loosening nuts at strut assembly upper attachment. Place camber adjusting tool (5038) at strut upper attachment and adjust camber. Tighten lock nuts. Recheck camber.

On 760 GLE, camber is not adjustable. If camber is not within specifications, check front end components for wear or damage and repair or replace as necessary.

TOE-IN

All Models

1) Place wheel in straight ahead position. Loosen jam nuts on tie rods. Loosen outer clamps on rubber dust boot.

2) Turn tie rods until toe-in is within specifications. Make sure length of each tie rod does not differ more than .08" (2 mm). On GL, DL and Turbo, measure difference between wrench grip on tie rod and jam nut. On 760 GLE, measure difference between lock nut and edge of screw thread.

NOTE: Manufacturer recommends rustproofing threads and nuts after adjustments have been made.

3) Check steering wheel position and adjust if necessary. Adjustments are made by removing steering wheel and repositioning it to proper location.

WHEEL LUG NUT TORQUES – ALL MODELS

WHEEL LUG NUT TIGHTENING SPECIFICATIONS

Application	Ft. Lbs. (N.m)
Alfa Romeo	65-79 (88-107)
Audi	
4000	65 (90)
5000	80 (108)
BMW	72-80 (100-110)
Chrysler Corp. Imports	
Pickups	51-57 (69-78)
All Others	
Aluminum Wheels	58-72 (78-97)
Steel Wheels	51-58 (69-78)
Datsun/Nissan	
Pickups	87-108 (118-147)
All Others	58-78 (78-98)
Honda	
Accord & Prelude	80 (110)
Civic	58 (80)
Isuzu	
I-Mark	
Aluminum Wheels	86 (117)
Steel Wheels	50 (68)
Impulse	80-94 (108-127)
P'UP	65 (88)
Jaguar	45-65 (61-88)
Mazda	
Pickup	58-65 (80-90)
All Others	65-87 (90-120)
Mercedes-Benz	80 (108)
Mitsubishi	
Aluminum Wheels	57-72 (80-100)
Steel Wheels	50-57 (70-80)
Peugeot	
504 & 505	45 (60)
604	63 (85)
Porsche	
Aluminum Wheels	94 (130)
Steel Wheels	80 (110)
Renault	
LeCar	40 (54)
All Others	59 (80)
Saab	65-80 (88-108)
Subaru	58-72 (78-98)
Toyota	
Camry	76 (103)
All Others	66-86 (89-116)
Volkswagen	
Vanagon	123 (170)
All Others	66 (90)
Volvo	
GL, DL & Turbo	75-95 (100-130)
760 GLE	63 (85)

Jacking & Hoisting

ALL MANUFACTURERS

NOTE: **These illustrations are not intended to represent exact structure of each vehicle's frame, underbody or body outline. They are presented only to give the mechanic some point of reference.**

FRAME & UNDERBODY

The following illustrations indicate areas (parts) of the underbody and frame which may be used to raise and support the vehicle, using either floor jack or hoist. These points are indicated by shaded areas on the frame. *See Fig. 1: Sample Illustration.*

OUTERBODY

Those points designated on the outline of the body were specifically designed to facilitate the use of the vehicle's own jack. These jacking points are indicated by circular dots on the outline of the body. *See Fig. 1: Sample Illustration.* If floor jack or hoist is employed, extreme care should be exercised to avoid damaging the outer body shell.

Fig. 1: Sample: Jacking & Hoisting Points (Typical Illustration)

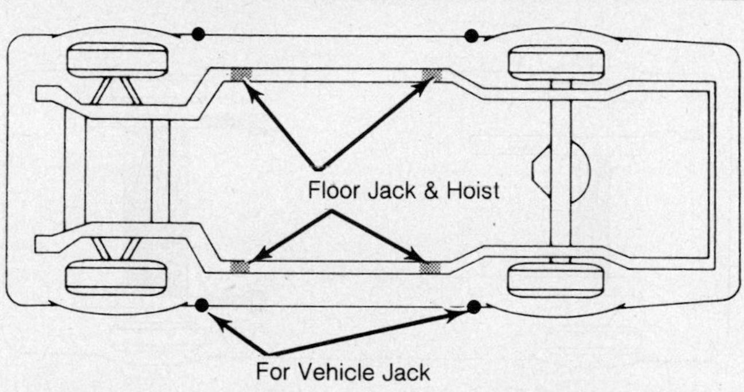
Floor Jack & Hoist
For Vehicle Jack

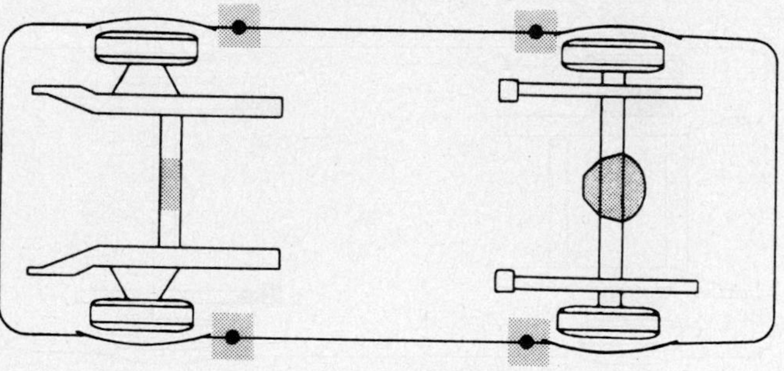

Alfa Romeo Spider 2.0

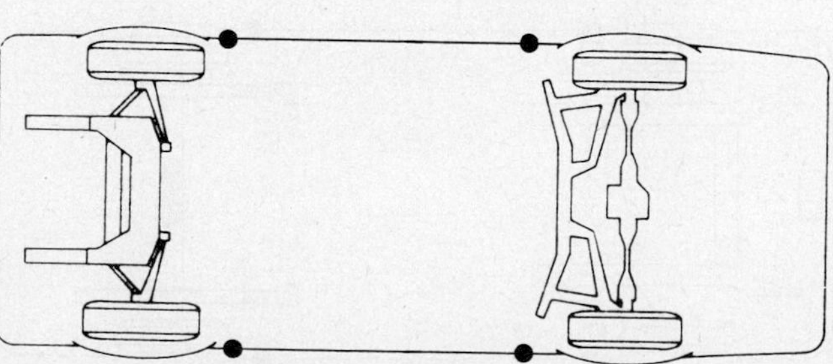

Alfa Romeo GTV-6 2.5

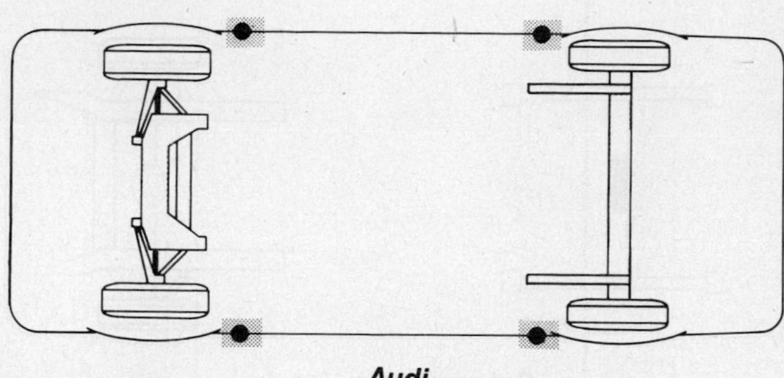

Audi

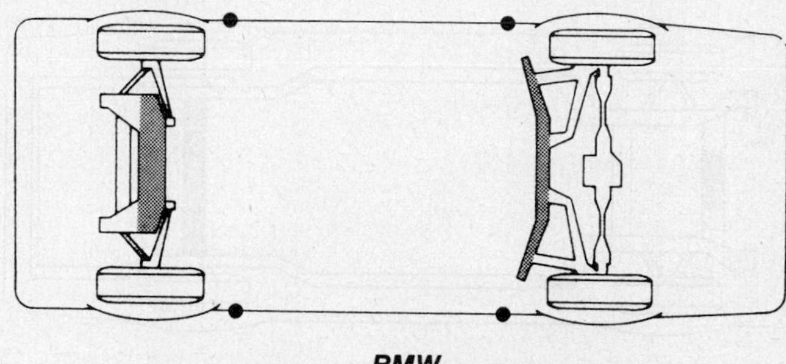

BMW

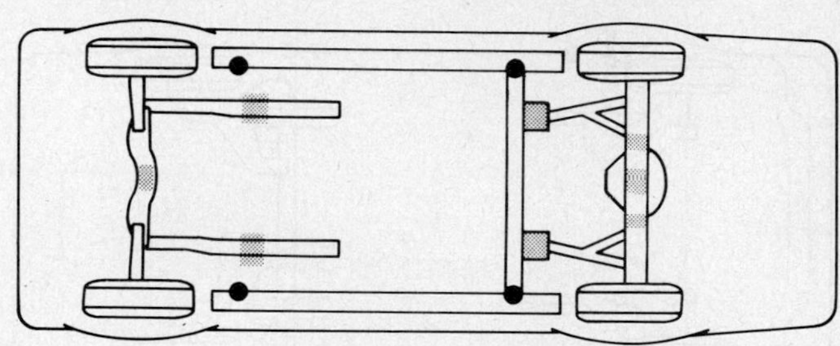

Challenger & Sapporo

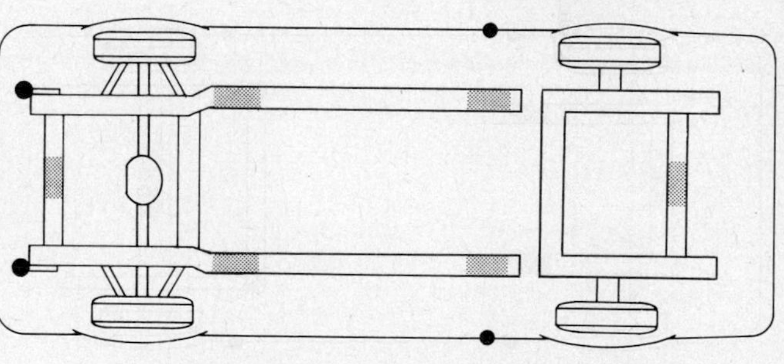

Colt Hatchback

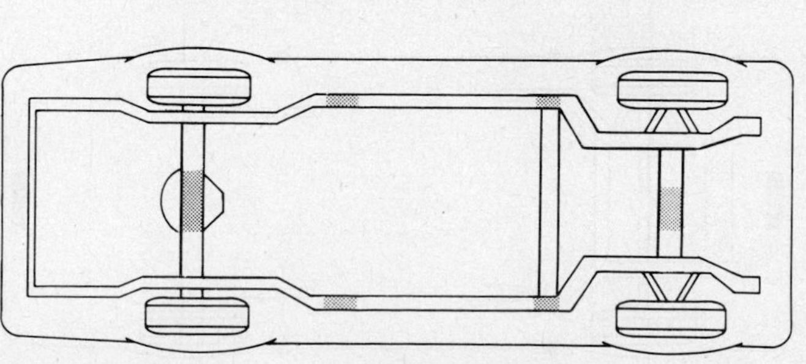

Colt & Ram 50 Pickups

Jacking & Hoisting

ALL MANUFACTURERS (Cont.)

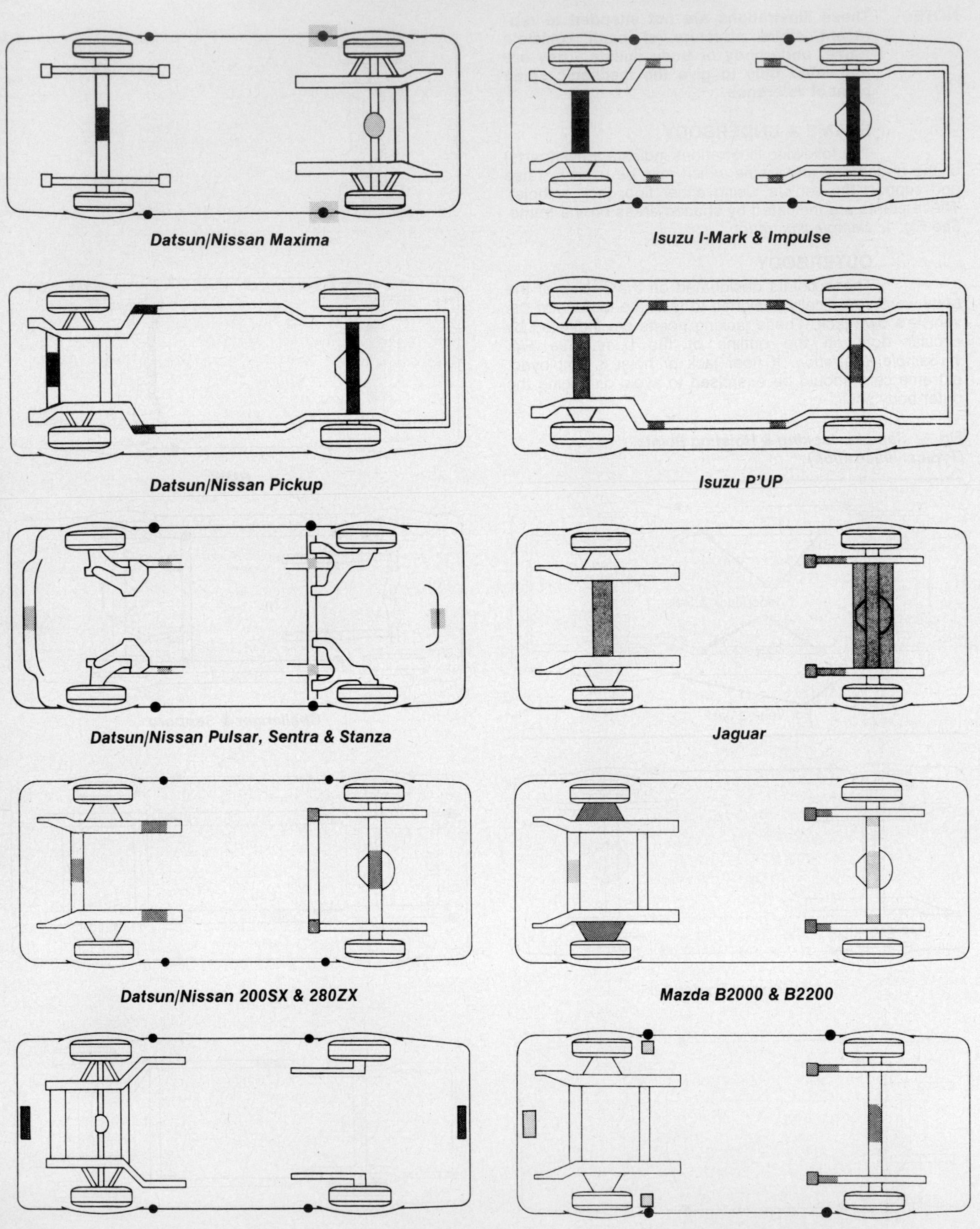
Datsun/Nissan Maxima
Isuzu I-Mark & Impulse
Datsun/Nissan Pickup
Isuzu P'UP
Datsun/Nissan Pulsar, Sentra & Stanza
Jaguar
Datsun/Nissan 200SX & 280ZX
Mazda B2000 & B2200
Honda
Mazda GLC & 626

Jacking & Hoisting

ALL MANUFACTURERS (Cont.)

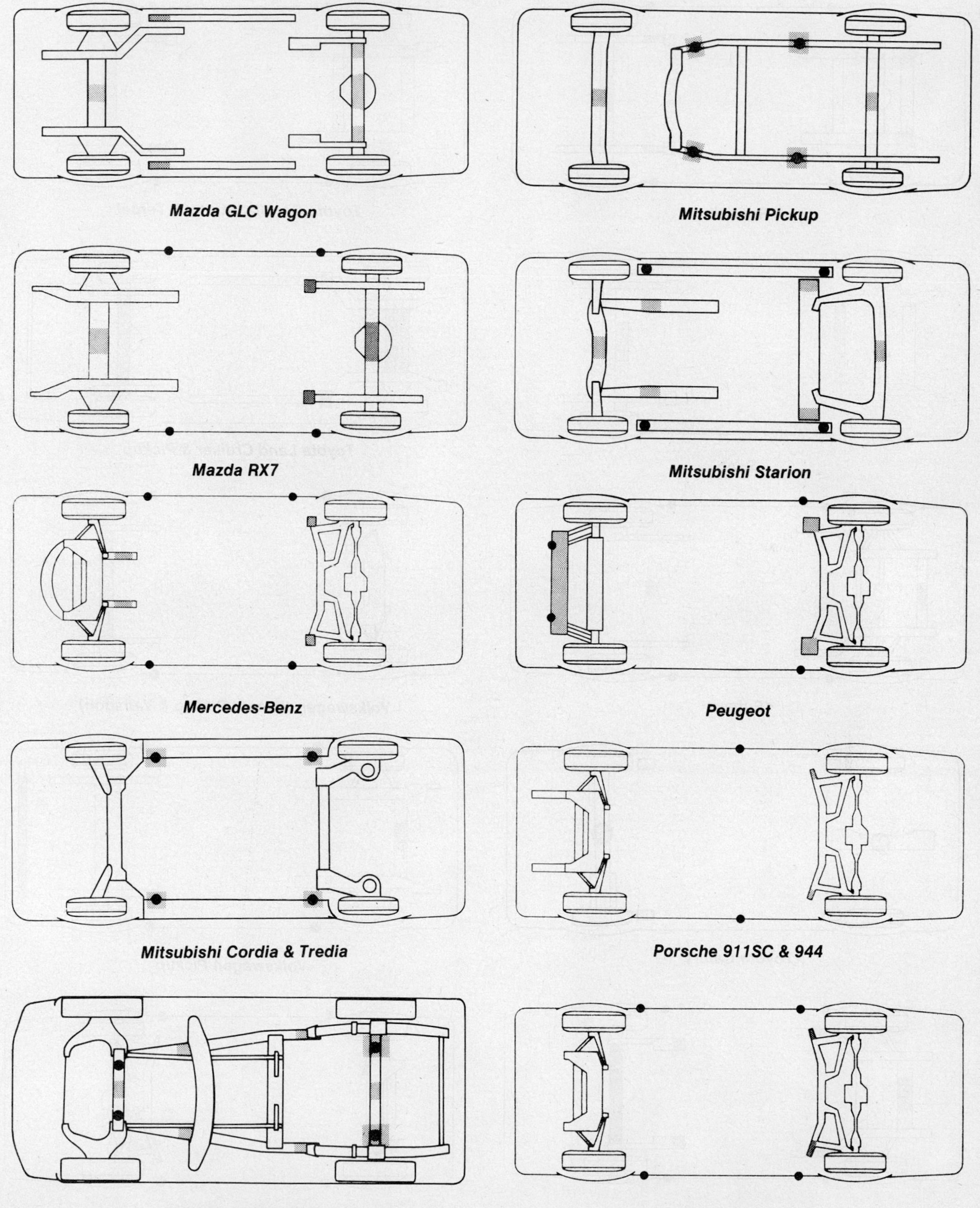
Mazda GLC Wagon
Mitsubishi Pickup
Mazda RX7
Mitsubishi Starion
Mercedes-Benz
Peugeot
Mitsubishi Cordia & Tredia
Porsche 911SC & 944
Mitsubishi Montero
Porsche 928S

Jacking & Hoisting

ALL MANUFACTURERS (Cont.)

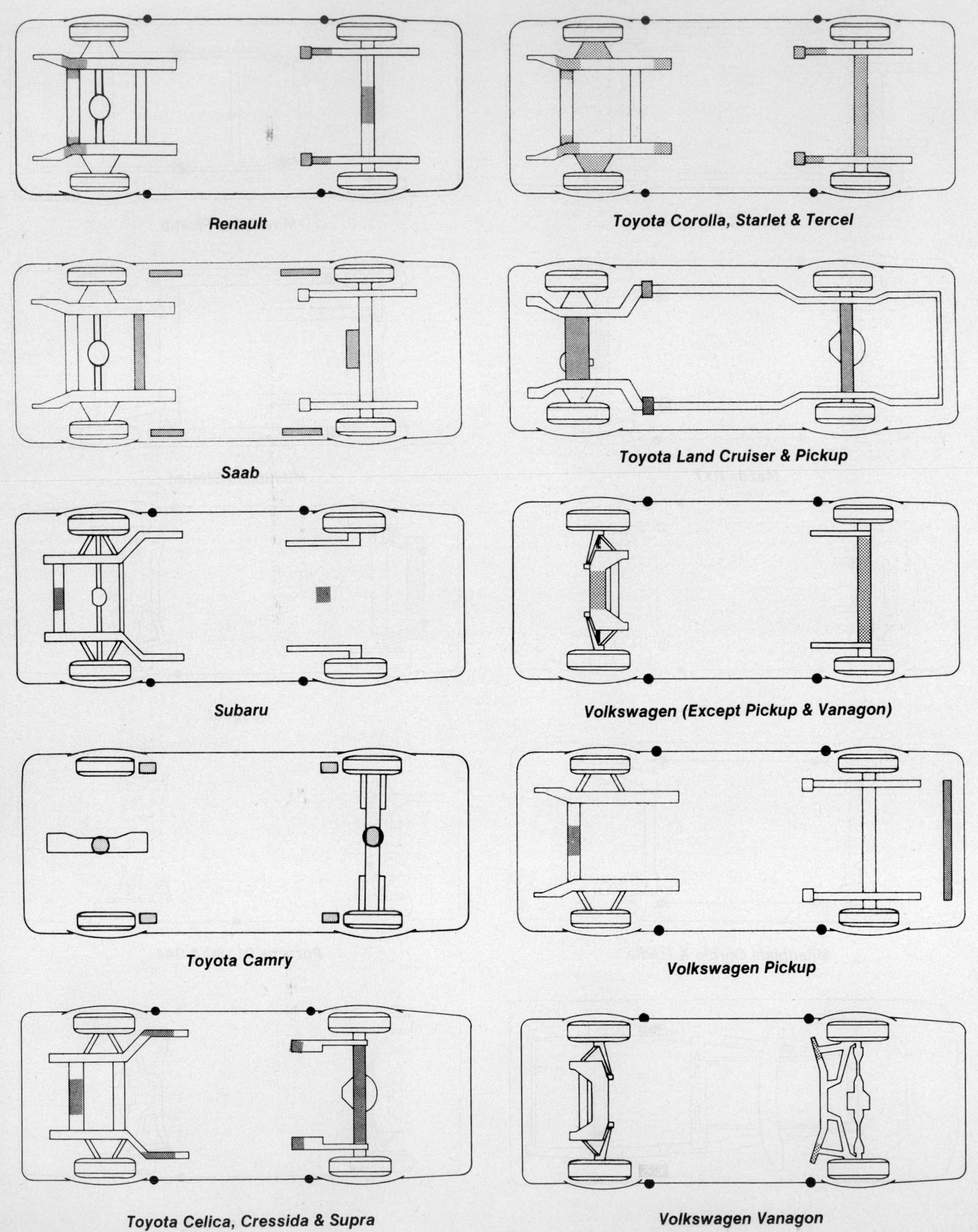

Renault

Toyota Corolla, Starlet & Tercel

Saab

Toyota Land Cruiser & Pickup

Subaru

Volkswagen (Except Pickup & Vanagon)

Toyota Camry

Volkswagen Pickup

Toyota Celica, Cressida & Supra

Volkswagen Vanagon

Jacking & Hoisting

ALL MANUFACTURERS (Cont.)

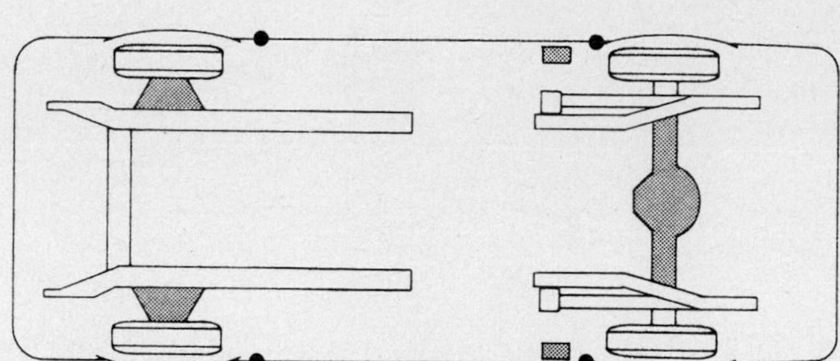

Volvo DL, GL & Turbo

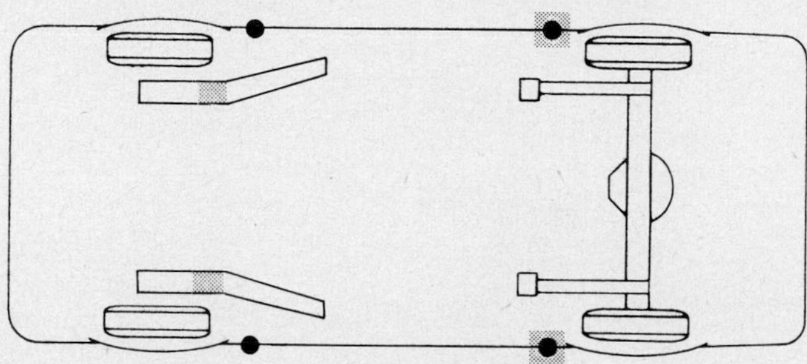

Volvo 760 GLE

SECTION 11

SUSPENSION

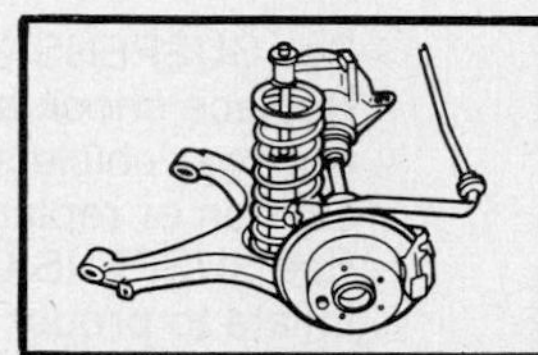

CONTENTS

TROUBLE SHOOTING

FRONT SUSPENSION

REAR SUSPENSION

AUTOMATIC LEVEL CONTROL

NOTE: **ALSO SEE GENERAL INDEX.**

Suspension

TROUBLE SHOOTING

CONDITION	POSSIBLE CAUSE	CORRECTION
Hard Steering	Tire pressure too low	Check tire pressure
	Front wheels out of alignment	See Adjustments in WHEEL ALIGNMENT
	Lower control arm ball joint seized	See Ball Joint Checking in SUSPENSION
Vehicle Pulls to One Side	Crossmember broken, cracked or loose	Tighten or replace as necessary
	Left and right side wheel base uneven	Check for sagging springs or broken shock
	Loose or worn wheel bearings	See Wheel Bearings in SUSPENSION
	Loose wheel lug nuts	Tighten to specifications
Steering Wheel Wander	Ball joint worn	See Ball Joint Checking in SUSPENSION
	Lower control arm and strut worn	See SUSPENSION
	Pivot bolt (shaft) loose or worn	Tighten or replace as necessary
Body Roll	Stabilizer broken or damaged	See SUSPENSION
	Shock absorbers worn	Replace shock absorbers
Noise	Coil spring broken	See SUSPENSION
	Bad shock absorber	Replace shock absorber
	Insufficient lubrication	Service vehicle suspension
	Components loose or worn	Tighten or replace as necessary
	Damaged wheel bearing	See SUSPENSION
	Improper tire pressure	Inflate to proper pressure
Steering Hard to Control	Broken front coil spring	See SUSPENSION
	Defective shock absorber	Replace shock as necessary
	Loose control arm bushings	See SUSPENSION
	Strut assembly loose	See SUSPENSION
	Improper tire pressure	Inflate to proper pressure
	Front end out of alignment	See WHEEL ALIGNMENT
	Damaged suspension links	See SUSPENSION

AUDI

Coupe, Quattro, 4000, 5000

DESCRIPTION

Front suspension is a MacPherson strut independent type system. The system consists of a strut assembly, control arm and stabilizer bar. The strut assembly attaches to the inner fender panel shock tower and steering knuckle.

The 5000 uses a contol arm/ball joint combination connected to the frame by 1 bushing. Stabilizer bar is attached to control arm and connected to subframe by 2 brackets. On all other models, the lower control arm is connected at the frame by 2 bushings and to the steering knuckle by a replaceable ball joint.

Fig. 1: Exploded View of Audi Front Suspension

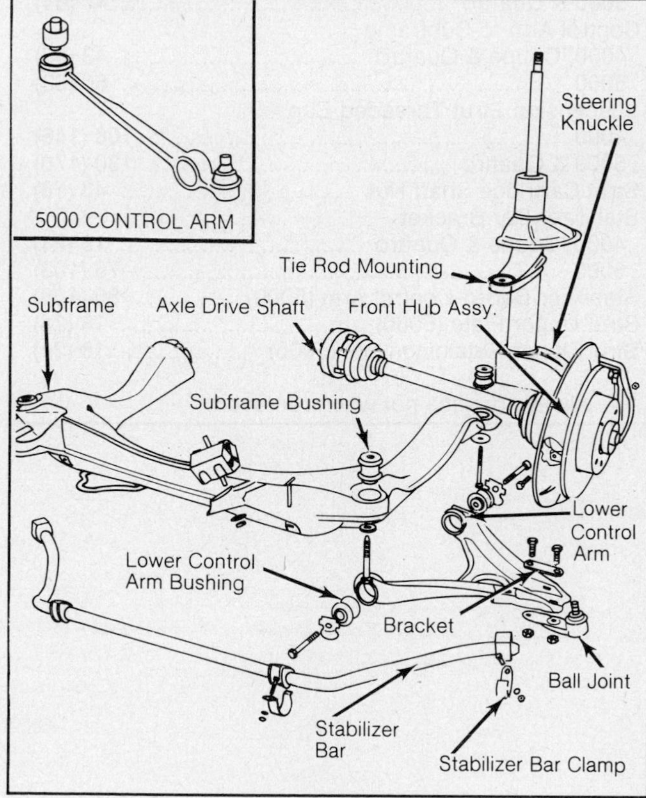
5000 CONTROL ARM
Steering Knuckle
Tie Rod Mounting
Subframe
Axle Drive Shaft
Front Hub Assy.
Subframe Bushing
Lower Control Arm
Lower Control Arm Bushing
Bracket
Ball Joint
Stabilizer Bar
Stabilizer Bar Clamp

ADJUSTMENTS

WHEEL ALIGNMENT SPECIFICATIONS & PROCEDURES

See Wheel Alignment Specifications and Procedures in WHEEL ALIGNMENT Section.

WHEEL BEARING ADJUSTMENT

No adjustment is required.

BALL JOINT CHECKING

Inspect ball joints for wear or excessive play. Replace as necessary. On 5000 models, the entire control arm assembly must be replaced.

REMOVAL & INSTALLATION

BALL JOINT

Removal

1) To remove ball joint, remove retaining bolt from steering knuckle and lower control arm enough for ball joint to clear steering knuckle.

2) On 4000 and Coupe, mark position of and remove 2 ball joint-to-control arm retaining bolts and remove ball joint. On 5000, with stabilizer removed, remove bolt retaining control arm-to-frame and remove control arm. Control arm/ball joint assembly must be replaced as a unit.

Installation

To install, reverse removal procedure.

STRUT CARTRIDGE

Removal (5000 Only)

1) With vehicle resting on floor at full curb weight, remove cartridge attaching nut. Mark and remove 3 spring strut mounting (camber adjustment) nuts and remove plate.

2) Turn steering to center cartridge piston rod in upper spring retainer. Working through side and top of coil spring, remove washer, bump stop and cover. Install threaded cap removing tool (2069) over cartridge shaft and remove cap. Pull cartridge through hole in strut tower.

Installation

To install, reverse removal procedure. Adjust alignment as required.

STRUT ASSEMBLY

NOTE: **When removing strut assembly from 5000, install strut tool (2070) before removing. Mount tool retaining plate, tighten spindle and spindle nut until seated.**

NOTE: **During any removal and installation procedure, if axle nut is removed or installed, do so with vehicle resting on floor at full curb weight.**

Removal

1) Loosen axle nut. Raise and support vehicle. Remove wheel assembly. Without detaching brake hose or line, unbolt caliper, remove brake hose bracket and suspend caliper out of way. Remove rotor.

2) Remove stabilizer bar. Disconnect ball joint from steering knuckle. Press off tie rod end. Using puller attached to hub studs, press stub axle from hub.

3) While supporting strut assembly at bottom remove attaching nut(s) at strut tower. Remove strut assembly.

Disassembly

1) With strut assembly on bench, attach spring compressor to coil spring and compress enough to remove upper strut rod retaining nut. Remove strut top plate.

2) Slowly release tension from coil spring and remove spring. With cap removal tool (2069), remove threaded cap from top of strut cartridge. Remove strut cartridge.

Front Suspension

AUDI (Cont.)

Fig. 2: Exploded View of 4000 Strut Assembly

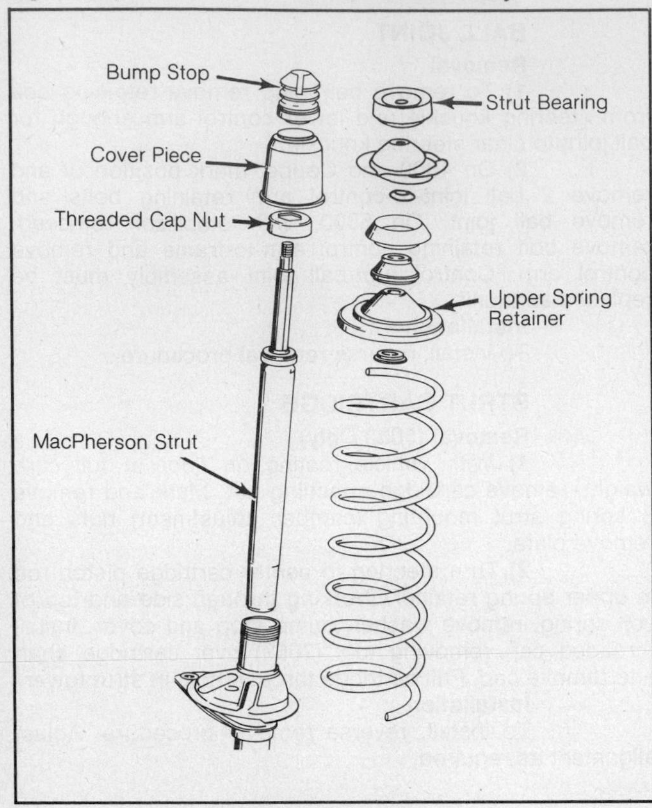
Bump Stop
Strut Bearing
Cover Piece
Threaded Cap Nut
Upper Spring
Retainer
MacPherson Strut

Other models are similar.

Reassembly & Installation

1) To reassemble and install, reverse disassembly and removal procedure. On 5000 models, be sure damping ring locating tabs are mated with indentations on upper spring retainers. Drive axle splines must be grease-free.

2) Apply a narrow ring of locking compound around outer end of drive shaft splines, and allow 1 minute to dry before installing. Tighten drive axle nut with vehicle resting on floor. Check and adjust alignment as required.

WHEEL BEARINGS

Removal

Remove strut assembly from vehicle. Press wheel hub from steering knuckle. Remove bearing retaining snap rings, and press wheel bearing from knuckle. Use bearing puller to remove inner race from wheel hub.

NOTE: Whenever wheel bearing is replaced, a new race must be used.

Installation

To install, reverse removal procedure.

CAUTION: When installing hub, be sure that press contacts only the inner bearing race.

LOWER CONTROL ARM

Removal

1) Raise and support front of vehicle. Place additional support under strut assembly.

2) Remove stabilizer bar. Loosen control arm-to-frame mounting bolt(s). Disconnect ball joint from steering knuckle. Remove control arm-to-frame mounting bolt(s), and remove control arm.

Installation

To install, reverse removal procedure. Check and adjust wheel alignment as required.

TIGHTENING SPECIFICATIONS

Application	Ft. Lbs. (N.m)
Axle Nut [1]	
4000 & Coupe	167 (226)
5000 & Quattro	203 (275)
Ball Joint Bracket Nuts	47 (64)
Ball Joint-to-Strut Nut	
4000 & Coupe	36 (49)
5000 & Quattro	47 (64)
Control Arm-to-Subframe	
4000, Coupe & Quattro	43 (58)
5000	60 (83)
Suspension Strut Threaded Cap	
4000	108 (146)
5000 & Quattro	130 (176)
Strut Cartridge Shaft Nut	43 (58)
Stabilizer Bar Bracket	
4000, Coupe & Quattro	18 (24)
5000	76 (103)
Stabilizer Bar-to-Control Arm (5000)	80 (108)
Strut Upper Plate (5000)	18 (24)
Strut Upper Retaining Nuts (5000)	18 (24)

[1] – Always replace nut when removed.

BMW

318i, 320i, 528e, 533i, 633CSi, 733i

DESCRIPTION

All BMW models use independent MacPherson strut front suspension systems. The front suspension systems consist of vertically mounted strut assemblies directly attached to steering knuckles. The steering knuckles are connected to axle carriers (crossmembers) through lower control arms.

A stabilizer bar is used on all models. The stabilizer bar is attached to the strut assembly on the 528e, 533i and 633CSi. The stabilizer bar is connected to the lower control arm on the 318i, 320i and 733i. Strut rods are installed on all models except the 318i and 320i.

Fig. 1: BMW 320i Front Suspension Assembly

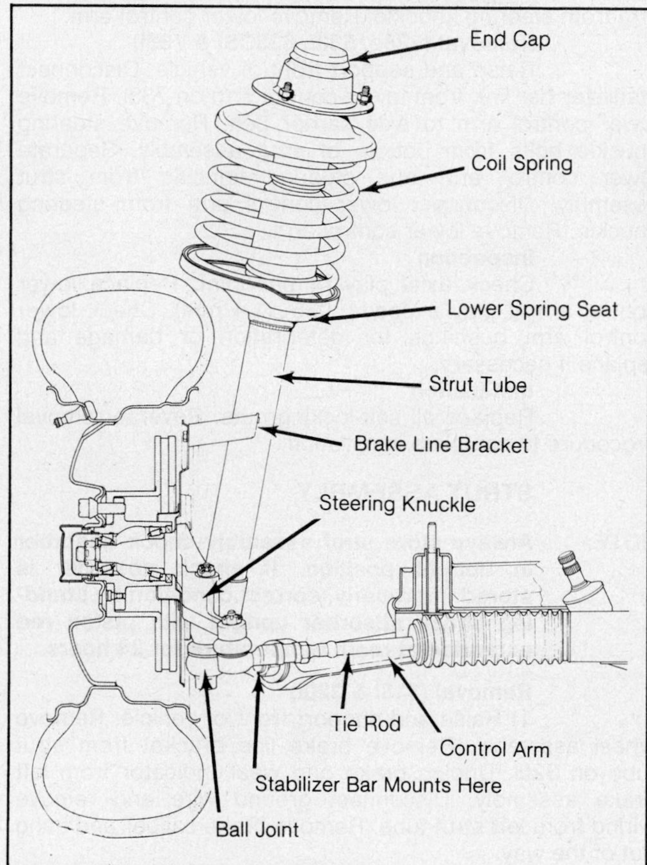
End Cap
Coil Spring
Lower Spring Seat
Strut Tube
Brake Line Bracket
Steering Knuckle
Tie Rod
Control Arm
Stabilizer Bar Mounts Here
Ball Joint

ADJUSTMENTS

WHEEL ALIGNMENT SPECIFICATIONS & PROCEDURES

See Wheel Alignment Specifications and Procedures in WHEEL ALIGNMENT section.

WHEEL BEARING ADJUSTMENT

320i & 733i

Tighten castle nut to 22-24 ft. lbs. (30-33 N.m) while rotating hub assembly. Rotate hub assembly at least 2 more times. Loosen castle nut until bearing end play is noticed. Tighten castle nut to a maximum of 24 INCH lbs. (3 N.m). If necessary, turn back (loosen) castle nut to allow cotter pin installation. Washer between castle nut and bearing should move easily and without noticeable resistance.

BALL JOINT CHECKING

Check axial play of ball joint. Replace lower control arm if play exceeds .055" (1.4 mm).

REMOVAL & INSTALLATION

WHEEL BEARING

NOTE: **BMW recommends that wheel bearing not be reused on 318i once it is removed.**

Removal (318i, 528e, 533i & 633CSi)

1) Raise and support front of vehicle. Remove wheel assembly. Unplug brake pad wear indicator if left side caliper is to be removed. Remove disc brake caliper and hang out of the way. Remove hex head screw from rotor. Remove brake rotor and hub cap.

2) Unlock collar nut with a chisel and remove nut. Remove washer on 528e, 533i and 633CSi. Pull off hub/wheel bearing assembly. If 318i bearing inner race remains on stub axle, bend back dust guard and pull off bearing inner race.

Installation

Install new dust guard. Press hub/wheel bearing assembly. Install washer on 528e, 533i and 633CSi. Install collar nut and lock into place. *See TIGHTENING SPECIFICATIONS in this article.* Reverse removal procedure to complete installation.

Removal (320i & 733i)

1) Raise and support front of vehicle. Remove wheel assembly. Unplug brake pad wear indicator if left side caliper is to be removed. Disconnect brake line bracket from strut assembly. Remove disc brake caliper and hang out of the way.

2) Remove hub cap, cotter pin, castle nut, washer and outer bearing. Remove hub and rotor assembly. Remove shaft seal and inner bearing. Remove bearing outer races if required.

Installation

Press bearing outer races into hub. Pack wheel bearings. Coat hub cavity and bearing outer races with grease and install inner bearing. Coat shaft seal with grease (graphite grease on 320i) and press in until flush. Reverse removal procedure to complete installation and adjust wheel bearings. *See WHEEL BEARING ADJUSTMENT in this article.*

FRONT SUSPENSION ASSEMBLY

CAUTION: **Strut assemblies must not be allowed to tilt, sag or drop during front suspension assembly removal as ball joint sockets may be damaged.**

Removal (318i & 320i)

1) Raise and support front of vehicle. Remove wheel assemblies. Remove brake line bracket from strut tubes on 320i. Disconnect ground wire and brake pad wear indicator from left brake assembly. Remove wiring from left strut tube on 318i. Remove brake calipers and hang them out of the way.

Front Suspension

BMW (Cont.)

2) Remove steering gear shaft pinch bolt and disconnect steering shaft. Disconnect power steering lines from steering gear and plug openings on 318i. Remove lower control arm bracket bolts on 318i. Remove heat shield from right lower control arm bracket on 318i. Remove stabilizer bar brackets on 320i.

3) Disconnect engine damper from axle carrier. Remove engine mount-to-axle carrier nuts. Loosen top of right engine mount on 318i. Attach engine sling and suspend engine with hoist. Support axle carrier with a floor jack. Remove nuts from top of strut assemblies. Remove axle carrier bolts and carefully lower front suspension assembly.

Fig. 2: BMW 528e, 533i and 633CSi Front Suspension

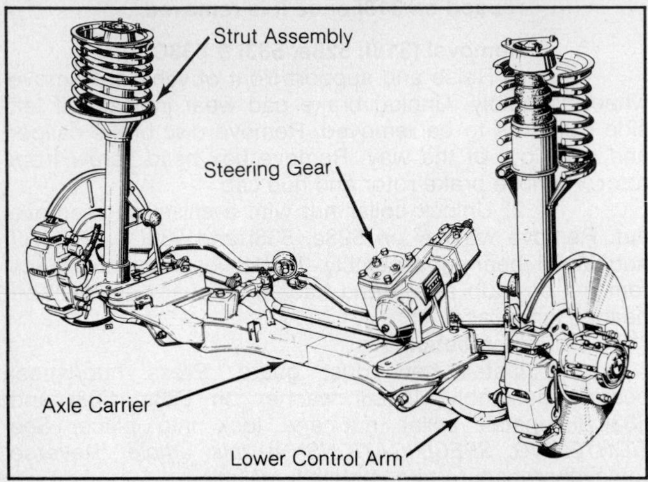
Strut Assembly
Steering Gear
Axle Carrier
Lower Control Arm

Removal (528e, 533i, 633CSi & 733i)

1) Raise and support front of vehicle. Remove wheel assemblies. Remove engine splash guard on 528e, 533i and 633CSi. Remove brake line bracket and clamp from strut assemblies on 733i. Disconnect ground wire and brake pad wear indicator from left brake assembly on 733i. Remove brake calipers and hang them out of the way.

2) Disconnect ground wire and brake pad wear indicator from left brake assembly on 528e, 533i and 633CSi. Remove wiring from left strut tube on 528e and 633CSi. Disconnect steering linkage from steering gear arm. Remove steering gear mount bolts and hang steering gear.

3) Disconnect strut rods and remove stabilizer bar brackets on 528e, 533i and 633i. Remove engine mount-to-axle carrier nuts. Loosen top of right engine mount on 528e, 533i and 633CSi. Partially drain radiator and disconnect top radiator hose from engine on 633CSi and 733i.

4) Attach engine sling and suspend engine with hoist. Support axle carrier with a floor jack. Remove nuts from top of strut assemblies. Remove axle carrier bolts and carefully lower front suspension assembly.

Installation

1) Replace all self-locking nuts. Engine mount pin must engage in hole properly. Position wheels straight ahead on 318i and 320i. Alignment marks on steering gear housing and steering gear shaft must be aligned on 318i. Alignment mark on dust boot must be located between alignment marks on steering gear housing on 320i.

2) Pinch bolt must fit in groove of steering gear shaft on 318i and 320i. Check stabilizer bar and engine dampener bushings for deterioration or damage on 318 and 320i. Bleed cooling system on 633CSi and 733i. Bleed power steering pump on 318i. Reverse removal procedure to complete installation and check wheel alignment.

LOWER CONTROL ARM

Removal (318i)

Raise and support front of vehicle. Remove lower control arm bracket bolts. Disconnect stabilizer bar link from stabilizer bar. Remove lower control arm ball joint nut and knock ball joint loose with a plastic hammer. Disconnect lower control arm from steering knuckle. Remove lower control arm.

Removal (320i)

Raise and support front of vehicle. Remove stabilizer bar from lower control arm. Remove lower control arm to axle carrier bolt. Disconnect lower control arm from steering knuckle. Remove lower control arm.

Removal (528e, 533i, 633CSi & 733i)

Raise and support front of vehicle. Disconnect stabilizer bar link from lower control arm on 733i. Remove lower control arm to axle carrier bolt. Remove steering knuckle bolts from bottom of strut assembly. Separate lower control arm and steering knuckle from strut assembly. Disconnect lower control arm from steering knuckle. Remove lower control arm.

Inspection

Check axial play of ball joint. Replace lower control arm if play exceeds .055" (1.4 mm). Check lower control arm bushings for deteriration or damage and replace if necessary.

Installation

Replace all self-locking nuts. Reverse removal procedure to complete installation.

STRUT ASSEMBLY

NOTE: Always store strut assembly shock absorber in upright position. If shock absorber is stored improperly, correct condition by standing shock absorber upright with piston rod extended at room temperature for 24 hours.

Removal (318i & 320i)

1) Raise and support front of vehicle. Remove wheel assembly. Remove brake line bracket from strut tube on 320i. Unplug brake pad wear indicator from left brake assembly. Disconnect ground wire and remove wiring from left strut tube. Remove brake caliper and hang out of the way.

2) Disconnect stabilizer bar link from stabilizer bar on 318i. Disconnect stabilizer bar from lower control arm on 320i. Disconnect lower control arm and steering linkage from steering knuckle. Remove lower control arm-to-axle carrier bolt on 320i. Support strut assembly. Remove nuts from top of strut assembly and remove strut.

Removal (528e, 533i 633CSi & 733i)

1) Raise and support front of vehicle. Remove wheel assembly. Remove brake line bracket and clamp from strut tube on 733i. Unplug brake pad wear indicator from left brake assembly. Disconnect ground wire and remove wiring from left strut tube on 528e, 533i and 633CSi. Remove brake caliper and hang out of the way.

2) Disconnect stabilizer bar link from strut tube on 528e, 533i and 633CSi. Disconnect stabilizer bar link from lower control arm on 733i. Remove steering knuckle bolts from bottom of strut assembly. Support strut

BMW (Cont.)

assembly. Remove nuts from top of strut assembly and remove strut.

Disassembly

1) Compress coil spring. Remove end cap, spring retainer nut and small diameter washer. Slowly release spring compressor and remove centering plate, insulator, large diameter washer, upper spring retainer, rubber ring and coil spring.

2) Remove damper washer, rubber damper and dust sleeve from shock absorber piston rod. Remove threaded ring using ring remover (31 3 150). Slide out shock absorber. Pour out used oil.

Reassembly

1) Replace shock absorber with one of same code, if shock absorber is to be replaced. Fill strut tube with SAE 30 oil. *See SHOCK ABSORBER OIL QUANTITY table in this article.*

2) Fit shock absorber into tube and tighten threaded ring. Use a rubber ring with 2 beads for coil springs with red color code. Ends of coil spring must rest on shoulders of lower and upper spring retainers. Reverse disassembly procedure to complete reassembly.

Installation

Replace all self-locking nuts. Reverse removal procedure to complete installation.

STABILIZER BAR

Removal (318i & 320i)

Raise and support front of vehicle. Disconnect stabilizer bar links and remove left lower control arm bracket bolts on 318i. Disconnect stabilizer bar from lower control arm and remove left lower control arm to axle carrier bolt on 320i. Remove stabilizer bar brackets and remove stabilizer bar.

Removal (528e, 533i, 633CSi & 733i)

Raise and support front of vehicle. Disconnect stabilizer bar from stabilizer bar links on 528e, 533i and 633CSi. Disconnect stabilizer bar links from lower control arm on 733i. Remove stabilizer bar brackets and remove stabilizer bar.

Installation

Inspect bushings for deterioration or damage and replace if necessary. Reverse removal procedure to complete installation.

STRUT ROD

Removal (528e, 533i, 633CSi & 733i)

Raise and support front of vehicle. Remove front wheel assembly. Remove steering knuckle bolts from bottom of strut assembly. Disconnect strut rod from steering knuckle. Remove strut rod pivot bolt and remove strut rod.

Installation

Remove grease and dirt from ball joint bore. Reverse removal procedure to complete installation.

SHOCK ABSORBER OIL QUANTITY

Application	Ounces (cc)
318i	0.7-0.9 (20-25)
320i	1 (30)
528e, 533i & 633CSi	1-1.2 (30-35)
733i	1.7 (50)

TIGHTENING SPECIFICATIONS

Application	Ft. Lbs. (N.m)
Axle Carrier-to-Body	
733i	53-59 (73-81)
All Other Models	31-35 (43-48)
Control Arm-to-Axle Carrier	
320i	60-66 (81-89)
528e, 533i & 633CSi	52-63 (72-87)
733i	58-65 (80-90)
Control Arm Ball Joint	
318i Only	55-69 (75-94)
Control Arm Bracket Bolt	
318i Only	29-34 (39-46)
Control Arm Castle Nut	
318i, 320i & 733i	43-51 (58-69)
528e, 533i & 633CSi	54-69 (73-94)
Engine Mount-to-Axle Carrier	
8 mm Nuts	18-20 (24-27)
10 mm Nuts	31-33 (42-45)
Spring Retainer Nut	
733i	56-62 (76-84)
All Other Models	43-53 (58-72)
Stabilizer Bar Bracket	
320i	35-38 (47-52)
All Other Models	16-17 (22-23)
Stabilizer Bar-to-Control Arm	
320i	51-66 (69-89)
733i	
8 mm Nuts	18-20 (24-27)
10 mm Nuts	35-39 (47-53)
Stabilizer Bar Links	
318i	29-34 (39-46)
528e & 533i (Yellow Plating)	14-17 (19-23)
528e, 533i & 633CSi (White Plating)	22-26 (30-35)
Steering Knuckle Bolts	
528e, 533i & 633CSi	55-69 (75-94)
733i	58-65 (79-88)
Steering Linkage Castle Nut	25-29 (34-39)
Steering Gear	
733i	31-35 (42-47)
All Other Models	
10 mm Bolts	29-34 (39-46)
12 mm Bolts	52-63 (71-85)
Steering Gear Arm Pinch Bolt	16-17 (22-23)
Strut Assembly-to-Body	16-17(22-23)
Threaded Ring	87-101 (117-137)
Wheel Hub Shaft Nut	
318i	188-203 (254-275)
528e, 533i & 633CSi	166-203 (230-280)

Front Suspension

CHRYSLER CORP. IMPORTS & MITSUBISHI FWD

Chrysler Corp. Imports: Colt
Mitsubishi: Cordia & Tredia

DESCRIPTION

Colt, Cordia and Tredia use a vertically-mounted MacPherson strut independent type front suspension. It consists of a strut assembly, lower control arm, strut rod and stabilizer bar. The strut assembly is mounted to the fender panel shock tower and steering knuckle arm.

Fig. 1: Exploded View of Colt & Mitsubishi FWD Front Suspension

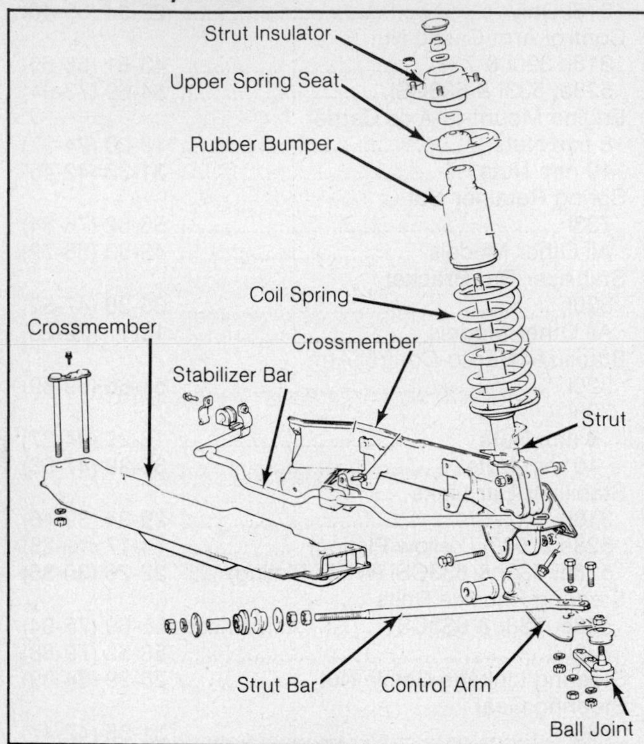

Strut Insulator
Upper Spring Seat
Rubber Bumper
Coil Spring
Crossmember
Crossmember
Stabilizer Bar
Strut
Strut Bar
Control Arm
Ball Joint

ADJUSTMENTS

WHEEL ALIGNMENT SPECIFICATIONS & PROCEDURES

See the Wheel Alignment Specifications and Procedures in the WHEEL ALIGNMENT Section.

WHEEL BEARING

NOTE: **On Mitsubishi, the wheel bearing adjustment is pre-set and can not be adjusted. On Colt, adjust wheel bearing by selecting proper spacer.**

Colt

1) Remove steering knuckle arm, with hub assembly, from vehicle. Mount in vise. Remove hub assembly and inside bearing inner race from knuckle. If hard to remove, tap hub off with soft hammer. Remove bearing spacer and brake rotor from hub.

2) Remove outside bearing inner race with hammer and drift. Pry out inside and outside oil seals. Remove bearing outer races. Inspect for damaged or seized bearings, cracked hub or knuckle, loose fitting hub-to-inner race or knuckle-to-outer race. Replace components if damaged or fit is loose.

3) Install outer races of inside and outside bearings into knuckle. Select bearing spacer before installing hub. Ensure dial indicator, service tool and inner bearing race surfaces are clean before mounting components.

4) Install Front Hub Spacer Select Gauge service tool (MB990959) onto bearing races. Lightly tighten nut "B" until spacer gauge face contacts inside bearing inner race. Tighten nut "A" about 5 turns. Install dial indicator onto service tool and set pointer onto tool surface. *See Fig. 2.*

Fig. 2: Installation of Front Hub Spacer Select Guage

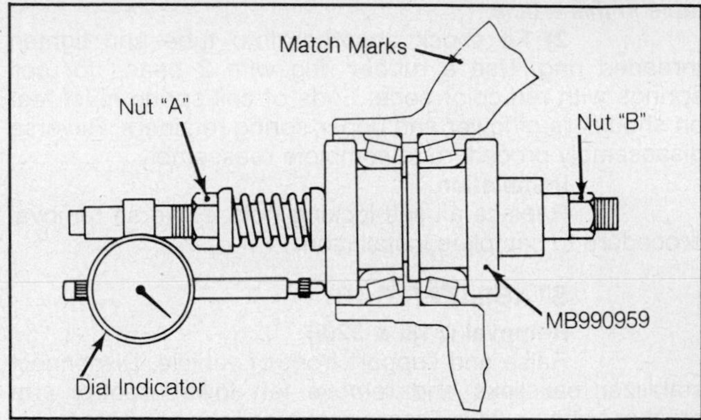

Match Marks
Nut "A"
Nut "B"
MB990959
Dial Indicator

Note dial indicator gauge mount position and pointer location on the spacer gauge.

BEARING SPACER SELECTION

Indicator Reading In. (mm)	Spacer Color	Spacer Thickness In. (mm)
.020-.023 (.52-.58)	Pink	.2236 (5.68)
.023-.025 (.58-.64)	Green	.2260 (5.74)
.025-.028 (.64-.70)	Red	.2283 (5.80)
.028-.030 (.70-.76)	White	.2307 (5.86)
.030-.032 (.76-.82)	None	.2330 (5.92)
.032-.035 (.82-.88)	Yellow	.2354 (5.98)
.035-.037 (.88-.94)	Blue	.2378 (6.04)
.037-.039 (.94-1.00)	Orange	.2402 (6.10)
.039-.042 (1.02-1.06)	Light Green	.2425 (6.16)
.042-.044 (1.06-1.12)	Brown	.2449 (6.22)
.044-.046 (1.12-1.18)	Grey	.2472 (6.28)
.046-.049 (1.18-1.24)	Navy Blue	.2496 (6.34)
.049-.051 (1.24-1.30)	Vermilion	.2520 (6.40)
.051-.054 (1.30-1.36)	Purple	.2543 (6.46)

CHRYSLER CORP. IMPORTS & MITSUBISHI FWD (Cont.)

5) Rotate spacer gauge tool and hub assembly several times to seat bearing. Set the dial indicator to zero. Loosen nut "B" until pointer of dial indicator stops. Read dial displacement.

NOTE: The dummy spacer of spacer gauge is .197" (5 mm) in thickness.

6) Select needed bearing spacer according to *Bearing Spacer Selection table*. Remove spacer gauge, dial indicator and bearing inner races from knuckle. Apply grease to knuckle, oil seals and bearings. Evenly tighten hub and brake disc. Place outside bearing inner race on outer race.

7) Install outside oil seal using seal installer tool (DT-1007-D & C-4171). While holding outside bearing inner race with Front Axle Base service tool (MB990776-A), press hub into knuckle arm. Insert selected new spacer into knuckle. Press inside bearing inner race into hub using service tool. Install inside oil seal using installer tool.

REMOVAL & INSTALLATION

WHEEL BEARINGS

Removal

1) Remove knuckle and hub assembly. On Colt, mount assembly in vise and, using a soft hammer, separate by tapping hub from knuckle. Remove bearing spacer and rotor from hub.

2) Remove outside bearing inner race, using a hammer and drift. Pry out inner and outer oil seals. Remove bearing outer race with a hammer and drift.

3) On Mitsubishi models, Do not strike the hub/knuckle assembly with hammer to separate or bearing will be damaged. Separate hub from knuckle using service tools (MB990998 & 991001). Secure knuckle in vise. Remove brake rotor from hub.

4) Remove outer bearing race from hub using service tools (MB990339, MB990370 & MB990781). Pry out oil seal from knuckle and discard. Drive out outer race from hub using long drift and hammer. If either race needs replacement, they must be replaced as a set.

NOTE: On Mitsubishi models, check identification marks on bearings and hub are correct. Do not use bearing or hub which has no identification marks.

Installation

1) On Colt, to install, refer to Wheel Bearing Adjustment procedure. To install on Mitsubishi models, place outside bearing inner race into knuckle. Apply grease to seal lip and hub contact surface.

2) Drive in hub side oil seal using seal installer tools (MB990934 & MB990938). Place inner bearing in knuckle. Tighten hub-to-knuckle nut to 144-188 ft. lbs. (200-260 N.m). Rotate hub to seat bearing. Measure total preload.

3) Standard preload is 18.2 IN.lbs. (2 N.m) or less. If total preload is 0 IN. lbs. (0 N.m), measure hub axial play. Standard hub axial play is .004" (.10 mm). If total preload and hub axial play are not within specifications with nut tightened to 144-188 ft. lbs. (200-260 N.m), recheck component installation. Complete installation by reversing removal procedure.

BALL JOINT

NOTE: Always replace dust cover whenever ball joint is removed or knuckle is separated from joint.

Removal

1) Raise and support vehicle. Remove wheel assembly. If necessary for clearance, remove brake caliper assembly, rotor with hub and dust cover. Do not hang caliper assembly by hydraulic hose, use wire hook.

2) On Colt, remove ball joint-to-knuckle arm mount nut. Disconnect ball joint from knuckle using ball joint fork tool (MB990778) and hammer. Disconnect ball joint from control arm by removing 2 mount bolts.

3) On Mitsubishi models, disconnect stabilizer bar and strut rod from lower control arm. Loosen ball joint nut and detach joint from knuckle arm using fork tool (MB990778) and hammer.

4) Detach control arm-to-crossmember mount bolt and remove lower control arm from vehicle. Disconnect ball joint from control arm by first removing dust cover.

5) Remove snap ring and discard. Install control arm/ball joint assembly in hydraulic press. Press out joint using attaching plate, ball joint removal/installer tool (MB990800) and control arm support tool (MB991005).

Inspection

1) Check for damaged joint dust cover, deformed or cracked lower control arm, cracks or deterioration of lower arm bushings, loose ball joint and proper joint starting and/or turning torque.

2) Standard starting torque for Colt is 9 ft. lbs. (12 N.m). Since joint requires a large initial starting torque, measure torque after ball joint has been seated.

3) Standard turning torque is 2.2-4.3 ft. lbs. (3-6 N.m). On Mitsubishi models, standard turning torque is 78.1 IN. lbs. (8.8 N.m). Replace components as necessary.

Installation

1) On Colt, after joint is mounted to lower arm, install plain washer under joint inner mount bolt head. Tighten mount bolts to final torque. Lubricate and/or replace dust cover as necessary.

2) Install knuckle arm, brake rotor/hub assembly and related components in reverse of removal procedure. Preload lower control arm with jack or lower vehicle to the ground and final tighten strut rod and stabilizer bar mount bolts. Check for correct front end alignment.

3) On Mitsubishi models, press ball joint into control arm using service tools. Fit new snap ring into groove of ball joint case and check for tight fit. Install new dust cover using proper size end of control arm support tool. Drive on until cover makes contact with snap ring.

4) Install lower arm to crossmember, ensuring that it does not become twisted. Install and tighten control arm mount bolt. Loosely install stabilizer bar and strut rod with new bushings if needed. Final tighten mount bolts with no load on vehicle. Check for correct front end alignment.

STRUT ASSEMBLY

Removal

1) Raise and support vehicle. Remove wheel assembly. Disconnect brake line bracket from strut assembly. Remove 2 lower mount bolts attaching strut assembly-to-knuckle arm.

2) Separate strut assembly from the knuckle arm. Remove 4 nuts attaching strut-to-fender panel shock tower. Remove strut assembly from vehicle.

Disassembly

1) Mount strut assembly in vise. Compress spring with coil spring compressor tool (L-4514 for Colt & MB990987 for Mitsubishi models). While holding upper spring seat with spanner tool (MB990775), remove nut at top end of strut to remove insulator.

2) On Colt, remove spring seat, spring and rubber bumper. On Mitsubishi models, with insulator detached, remove spring seat, spring upper pad, bumper rubber, coil spring and spring lower pad from strut assembly.

3) Check for fluid leakage. If necessary to disassemble sub-assembly, place vertically in vise. Before disassembly of strut tube, remove dirt from outside of strut. Prevent dirt entry into cylinder or fluid during overhaul:

NOTE: Mitsubishi shock absorber is filled with Nitrogen gas. Do not disassemble. Replace shock as an assembly.

4) On Colt, lower piston rod assembly to bottom of cylinder. Using spanner tool, remove oil seal nut and discard. Drain shock absorber fluid. Using a small screwdriver, pull out square "O" ring and discard. Slowly draw piston rod assembly out of cylinder.

Inspection

1) Check strut insulator bearing for wear, damage or looseness. The bearing is integrated with insulator. If defective, replace insulator as an assembly.

2) Check rubber components and coil spring for damage or deterioration. Inspect strut for cracks, damage, oil leakage, bent piston rod assembly and unusual noise.

Reassembly

1) On Colt, apply fluid to all sliding surfaces of piston rod and cylinder assemblies. To avoid damage to piston ring, press together with fingers only.

2) Assemble unit by sliding piston rod assembly along cylinder wall and into cylinder assembly. Assemble cylinder and piston rod assemblies to the strut and fill with proper amount of new shock absorber fluid.

NOTE: Air inside cylinder must be expelled while filling strut with fluid. Move piston assembly slowly as fluid is poured in. It may take a short time to complete filling. Use 8 oz. (240 cc) of shock absorber fluid for dry shock fill limit.

3) With piston guide flange located at top, lower piston guide over piston rod. Insert new square "O" ring between the guide and strut outer cylinder. Do not wrinkle or cock it in bore.

4) Apply fluid to lip of new oil seal assembly. Place cover tool (CT-1111B) over threads of piston rod assembly and install new oil seal nut. Tighten oil seal nut assembly until end surface contacts strut.

NOTE: Coil springs have color marks to indicate spring identification and load classification. Ensure when springs are replaced, markings are for appropriate vehicle.

5) Install coil spring. Extend piston rod assembly and install strut components. Align "D" shaped hole in center of spring upper seat with flat dent on piston rod shaft.

6) Align locating holes or grooves in upper and lower seats with spring locating pins. Remove spring compressor. Hold seat with service tool and install insulator by attaching new self-locking nut. Pack strut insulator bearing with grease and install dust cap.

7) On Mitsubishi models, install new shock absorber assembly. Mount spring lower pad to strut. Assemble by completing steps **5)** and **6)**.

Installation

To install, reverse removal procedure. Check that strut assembly and knuckle mating surfaces are clean to ensure tight fit. Tighten lower strut mount bolts and new top mount bolt to specification. After installation, check front end alignment.

LOWER CONTROL ARM

Removal

1) Raise and support vehicle. Remove wheel assembly. Remove front brake components and rotor/hub assembly for clearance, if necessary.

2) On Colt, disconnect ball joint from control arm but do not disconnect joint from steering knuckle. Remove strut rod from lower control arm.

3) Remove lower control arm pivot bolt from crossmember and remove control arm assembly. Do not remove ball joint from knuckle unless boot is loose or damaged or operation is improper.

4) On Mitsubishi models, disconnect strut rod and stabilizer bar from lower control arm. Loosen ball joint nut. Separate joint from knuckle using fork tool (MB990778) and hammer. Remove control arm from crossmember.

NOTE: Do not remove control arm bushings unless necessary.

5) To remove lower control arm bushing, install control arm assembly on hydraulic press. Using bushing removal/installer tools (MB990996, MB990997 & MB991005) or equivalent, press bushing out of control arm.

Installation

Using service tools, press in new bushing until it contacts the end surface of control arm. On all models, install lower control arm. Reverse remove procedure to complete installation. Check for proper front end alignment.

STEERING KNUCKLE ARM

Removal

1) Raise and support vehicle. Remove wheel assembly. On Colt, remove engine under cover (if equipped). On all models, remove disc brake caliper assembly from knuckle.

2) Hang brake components away from work area with wire hook. On Colt, detach ball joint from knuckle, remove drive shaft and separate from hub if necessary. *See Drive Axle Removal in FWD Axle Shafts & CV Joints in DRIVE AXLE Section.*

NOTE: Replace retainer ring each time drive shaft is removed. Prevent spacer from falling out of place. Check position and type for reassembly reference.

CHRYSLER CORP. IMPORTS & MITSUBISHI FWD (Cont.)

3) Disconnect tie rod end from knuckle using service tool (MB990635) or equivalent. Remove 2 bolts attaching knuckle-to-strut housing. Remove hub/knuckle assembly from vehicle. If necessary, separate hub from knuckle by mounting in vise and tapping hub with soft hammer.

4) On Mitsubishi models, disconnect lower ball joint from knuckle arm. Remove stabilizer bar and strut rod from control arm. Detach tie rod end from knuckle using service tool (MB990635). Remove drive axle from hub. *See Drive Axle Removal in FWD Axle Shafts & CV Joints in DRIVE AXLE Section.*

5) Remove knuckle and hub as an assembly from strut assembly. Separate knuckle from hub, if necessary, using service tools (MB990998 & MB991001). Do not strike hub and knuckle with hammer to separate or bearing will be damaged.

Installation

To install, reverse removal procedure.

STABILIZER BAR & STRUT ROD

Removal

1) Raise and support vehicle. Disconnect each end of stabilizer bar from control arms. Remove stabilizer brackets and/or mount bolts from body and bar from vehicle. Remove strut rod nut, outer end washer, collar and outer bushing from body bracket.

NOTE: **Inner and outer strut rod bushings are different, note bushing shape and location for reassembly reference. Always use new bushings and self-locking nuts.**

2) Detach strut rod mount bolt from control arm and remove rod with inner bushing and end washer. Check for bent or damaged stabilizer bar and/or strut rod.

3) Strut rod bend limit is .12" (3 mm) or less for Colt and .01" (.25 mm) for Mitsubishi models. Check all bushings for wear and deterioration. Replace damaged parts as necessary.

Installation

1) To install, reverse removal procedure. Check strut rod identification marks before installation. For Colt, left rod identification is a Red mark. Right rod has White mark.

2) Final tighten strut rod and stabilizer bar nuts with vehicle resting at curb height. Ensure strut rod end-to-lock nut distance is correct. On Colt, distance between strut rod end and lock nut is 3.17" (80.5 mm).

3) On Mitsubishi models, ensure strut rod end-to-lock nut distance and stabilizer bar mount bolt end-to-nut distance is correct. Distance between stabilizer bar mount bolt end and nut is .31-.39" (8-10 mm).

4) Distance between strut rod end and lock nut is 3.07" (78 mm). Final tighten strut rod mount bolts with no load on vehicle. After installation, check front end alignment.

TIGHTENING SPECIFICATIONS

Application	Ft. Lbs. (N.m)
Ball Joint-to-Control Arm	69-87 (93-118)
Ball Joint-to-Knuckle	40-51 (54-69)
Control Arm-to-Crossmember	69-87 (93-118)
Disc Rotor-to-Hub	29-36 (39-49)
Drive Axle Nut	145-188 (196-255)
Stabilizer Bar-to-Strut Bar	4-5 (5-6)
Stabilizer Bar-to-Crossmember	22-29 (29-39)
Strut Bar-to-Control Arm	69-87 (93-118)
Strut Bar-to-Crossmember	54-61 (74-83)
Strut-to-Knuckle	54-65 (74-88)
Tie Rod End-to-Knuckle	11-25 (15-33)

CHRYSLER CORP. IMPORTS & MITSUBISHI RWD EXCEPT PICKUPS

Chrysler Corp. Imports: Challenger & Sapporo
Mitsubishi: Starion

DESCRIPTION

The front suspension is a MacPherson strut type. The strut assembly and knuckle arm are integrated. The strut upper end is attached to a strut assembly mounting bracket in the front fender wheel housing. The strut lower end is attached to the steering knuckle arm by a ball joint.

ADJUSTMENTS

WHEEL ALIGNMENT SPECIFICATIONS & PROCEDURES

See Wheel Alignment Specifications and Procedures in WHEEL ALIGNMENT Section.

WHEEL BEARING

While spinning hub and rotor by hand, tighten spindle nut to 15 ft. lbs. (20 N.m) to seat bearings. Back off nut and retighten to 4 ft. lbs. (5 N.m). Install nut retainer, cotter pin and dust cap. Do not back off nut more than 15° to accommodate cotter pin. If holes cannot be aligned within 15°, repeat procedure.

Fig. 1: View of Front Suspension for Chrysler Corp. Imports and Mitsubishi RWD Models (Except Pickups)

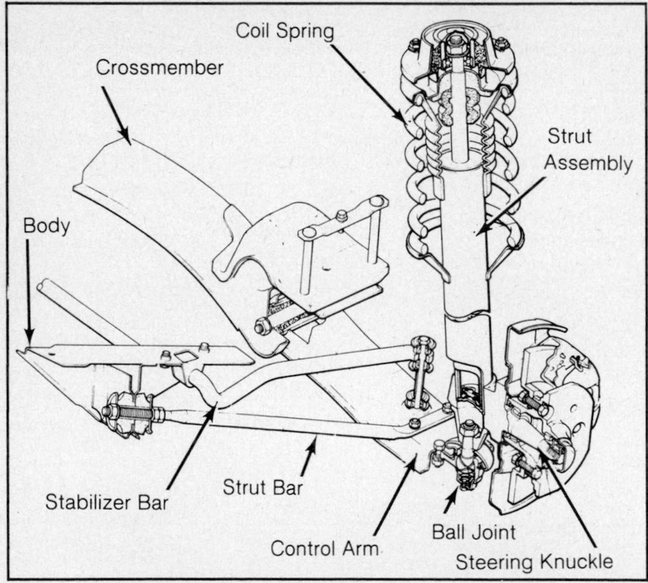
Coil Spring
Crossmember
Strut Assembly
Body
Stabilizer Bar
Strut Bar
Ball Joint
Control Arm
Steering Knuckle

REMOVAL & INSTALLATION

WHEEL BEARINGS

Removal

1) Raise and support vehicle. Remove front wheel assembly. Remove brake caliper assembly and support out of way with wire.

2) Remove dust cap, cotter pin, nut retainer, nut and outer bearing. Remove hub and rotor assembly. Pry out inner grease seal and discard.

3) Remove inner bearing. If necessary, drive out bearing races, from inside-to-outside, by tapping uniformly around inside diameter of race lip with long drift punch.

Installation

1) To install, reverse removal procedure. Replace new bearing races by tapping into place using long drift and old bearing race for Chrysler Corp. Import models.

2) For Mitsubishi models, use service tools (MB990927 for outer race and MB990931 for inner race with handle MB990938) or punch and old race. Ensure race is fully seated in hub.

3) Always replace inner grease seal. Apply grease to seal lip and bearing races. Pack wheel bearings with grease. Adjust according to *Wheel Bearing Adjustment* procedures.

BALL JOINT

Removal

1) Remove front wheel assembly. Remove caliper support, with caliper assembly and brake hose, from disc brake adapter. Support components out of way with wire hook.

2) If necessary, detach stabilizer bar and strut rods from lower control arm. Disconnect tie rod end from steering knuckle arm using service tool (C-3894-A for Chrysler Corp. Import models and MB990635 for Mitsubishi).

3) Remove bolts attaching strut-to-steering knuckle arm. Tap bolts with plastic hammer to disconnect. Remove bolts attaching ball joint-to-control arm. Remove ball joint and steering knuckle arm from vehicle.

4) Loosen self-locking nut but do not remove. On Chrysler Corp. Import models, disconnect ball joint from steering knuckle by tapping on nut with a plastic hammer. On Mitsubishi models, use service tool (MB990635) to detach ball joint from knuckle arm.

Installation

1) When installing ball joint, always use new dust cover and self-locking nut. To install, reverse removal procedure. If necessary, install stabilizer bar and strut rods.

2) Ensure strut rods are straight and identification marks are in proper positions. Left side has "L" or white mark and right side has "R" or no mark. After installation, check front end alignment.

STRUT ASSEMBLY

Removal

1) Raise and support vehicle. Remove wheel assembly. Disconnect and remove brake hose at strut and wheel house brackets. Remove caliper support, front hub with brake disc, dust cover and disc brake adapter.

2) Disconnect strut assembly from the wheel house strut assembly mount bracket and the steering knuckle arm. Remove strut assembly from vehicle.

Disassembly

1) Mount assembly in vise. Compress coil spring using compressor tool (L-4514 for Chrysler Corp. Imports & MB990987 for Mitsubishi) or equivalent. After removing dust cap, hold spring upper seat with strut tool (CT-1112 for Chrysler Corp. Imports & MB990564 for Mitsubishi). Remove strut rod nut and strut insulator.

CHRYSLER CORP. IMPORTS & MITSUBISHI RWD EXCEPT PICKUPS (Cont.)

2) Remove spacer with spring upper seat, rubber bumper, dust cover, rubber helper seat (if equipped) and coil spring. Before disassembly of strut tube, remove dirt from outside of strut. Prevent dirt entry into cylinder or fluid during overhaul. Hold strut vertically.

3) On Chrysler Corp. Import models, lower piston rod assembly to bottom of cylinder. Use strut tool (CT-1112) to remove oil seal assembly. Drain shock absorber fluid. Using a small screwdriver, pull out square "O" ring and discard. Slowly draw piston rod assembly out of cylinder.

NOTE: Mitsubishi shock absorber is filled with Nitrogen gas. Do not disassemble it unless necessary for replacement. Replace shock inner parts as a kit.

4) On Mitsubishi models, drill .16" (4 mm) or less diameter hole, at 2-2.4" (50-60 mm) down from top of strut, in the strut to bleed the nitrogen gas. Remove the ring nut using service tool (MB990564). Remove shock absorber assembly from strut.

Fig. 2: Exploded View of Chrysler Corp. Imports & Mitsubishi MacPherson Strut Assemblies

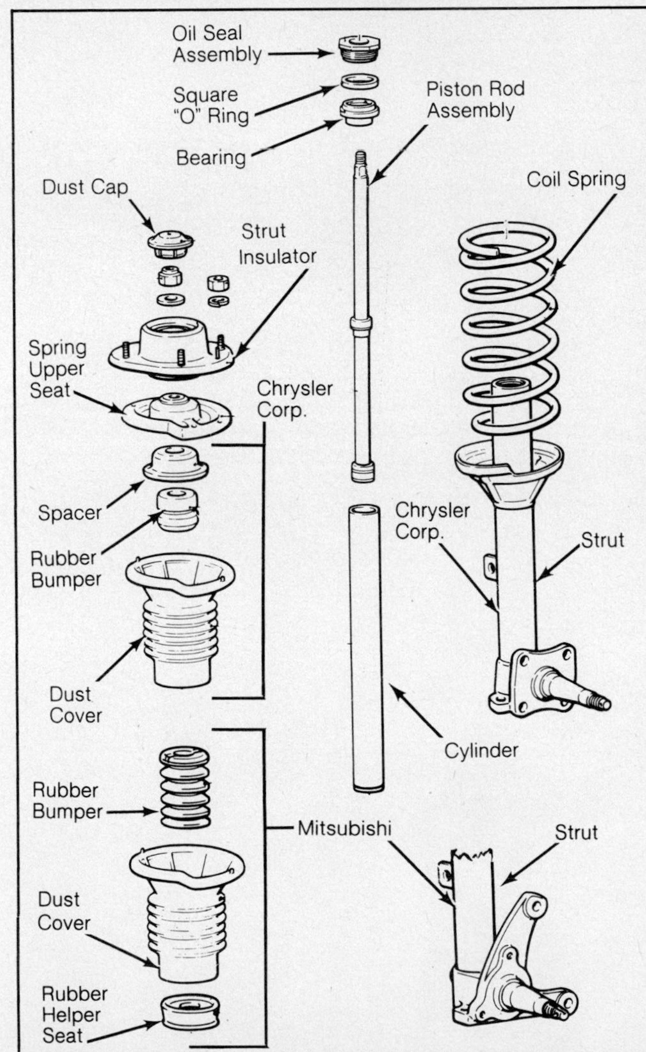
Oil Seal Assembly
Square "O" Ring
Bearing
Piston Rod Assembly
Dust Cap
Coil Spring
Strut Insulator
Spring Upper Seat
Chrysler Corp.
Spacer
Rubber Bumper
Chrysler Corp.
Strut
Dust Cover
Cylinder
Rubber Bumper
Mitsubishi
Strut
Dust Cover
Rubber Helper Seat

Front strut assemblies are similar; differences in the dust cover, bumpers and strut shown.

Inspection

1) Check strut insulator bearing for wear, damage or looseness. The bearing is integrated with insulator. If defective, replace insulator as an assembly. On Chrysler Corp. Import models, check oil seal assembly for wear and damage.

2) On all models, check rubber components and coil spring for damage or deterioration. Inspect strut for cracks, damage, oil leakage, bent piston rod assembly and unusual noise. Bend limit of piston rod assembly is .008" (.20 mm). Replace components as necessary.

Reassembly

1) On Chrysler Corp. Import models, apply strut fluid to all sliding surfaces of piston rod and cylinder assemblies. To avoid damage to piston ring, press together with fingers only.

2) Assemble unit by sliding piston rod assembly along cylinder wall and into cylinder assembly. Assemble cylinder and piston rod assemblies to the strut and fill with proper amount of new shock absorber fluid.

NOTE: Air inside cylinder must be expelled while filling strut with fluid. Move piston assembly slowly as fluid is poured in. It may take a short time to complete filling. Use 14 oz. (426 cc) of shock absorber fluid.

3) With bearing assembly flange located at top, lower piston rod assembly until flange contacts cylinder assembly end. Insert new square "O" ring between bearing assembly and strut. Do not wrinkle or cock it in bore.

4) Apply fluid to lip of new oil seal assembly. Place cover tool (CT-1111B) over threads of piston rod assembly and slip oil seal over rod. Tighten oil seal assembly until end surface contacts strut.

NOTE: Coil springs have color marks to indicate spring identification and load classification. Ensure when springs are replaced, markings are for appropriate vehicle.

5) Install coil spring. Extend piston rod assembly and install strut components. Ensure spacer is attached to spring upper seat with a heat resistant drying adhesive before installing. Align "D" shaped hole in center of spring upper seat with flat dent on piston rod shaft.

6) Align locating holes or grooves in upper and lower seats with spring locating pins. Remove spring compressor. Hold seat with service tool and install insulator by attaching new self-locking nut. Pack strut insulator bearing with grease and install dust cap.

7) On Mitsubishi models, install new shock absorber assembly into strut and tighten ring nut with service tool. Attach label, furnished with shock absorber, over drilled hole to prevent water entry. Assemble by completing steps **5)** and **6)**.

Installation

Apply semi-drying sealer to flanged mating surfaces of strut assembly and knuckle arm before mounting. To install, reverse removal procedure. Ensure strut assembly is installed with strut insulator guide pin located in hole in strut assembly mount bracket. Tighten new top mount bolt to specification. After installation, check front end alignment.

CHRYSLER CORP. IMPORTS & MITSUBISHI RWD EXCEPT PICKUPS (Cont.)

LOWER CONTROL ARM

Removal

1) Raise and support vehicle. Remove wheel assembly. On Chrysler Corp. Import models, disconnect bolts mounting stabilizer bar, strut rod and ball joint from control arm.

2) Disconnect idler arm bracket from body. Move steering linkage toward the back for clearance. Remove control arm-to-crossmember bolt and remove control arm from vehicle.

3) On Mitsubishi models, disconnect stabilizer bar and strut rod from lower control arm. Detach tie rod from knuckle arm using service tool (MB990635).

4) Remove strut assembly from knuckle arm. Remove control arm assembly, with knuckle arm, from crossmember. Remove knuckle arm from ball joint using service tool (MB990635).

NOTE: **Do not remove control arm bushings unless necessary.**

5) To remove lower control arm bushing, install control arm assembly on hydraulic press. Using 1.3" (30 mm) outside diameter pipe and removal/installer tool (CT-1131A) for Chrysler Corp. Imports or removal/installer tools (MB990828, MB990868 & MB990799) for Mitsubishi, press bushing out of control arm.

Installation

1) On Chrysler Corp. Import models, use 1.57" (40 mm) inside diameter pipe and service tool to press in new bushing until it contacts the end surface of control arm. On Mitsubishi models, press in new bushing and install knuckle arm using service tools.

2) On all models, install lower control arm. Apply sealer to flange mating surfaces of strut assembly and steering knuckle arm. Install strut assembly, stabilizer bar, strut rod and remaining components.

3) Tighten the control arm shaft and stabilizer bar nuts with vehicle resting at curb height. Ensure the stabilizer bar mount bolt end-to-lock nut surface distance is correct. After installation, check front end alignment.

STABILIZER BAR & STRUT ROD

Removal

1) Raise and support vehicle. Disconnect each end of stabilizer bar from control arms. Remove stabilizer brackets from body and bar from vehicle. Remove strut rod nut, outer end washer, collar and outer bushing from body bracket.

NOTE: **Inner and outer strut rod bushings are different, note bushing shape and location for reassembly reference. Always use new bushings and self-locking nuts.**

2) Detach strut rod mount bolt from control arm and remove rod with inner bushing and end washer. Check for bent or damaged stabilizer bar and/or strut rod. Strut rod bend limit is .12" (3 mm) or less. Check all bushings for wear and deterioration. Replace damaged parts as necessary.

Installation

1) To install, reverse removal procedure. Check strut rod identification marks before installation. Left rod mark is "L" or White mark. Right rod mark is "R" or no mark. Final tighten strut rod and stabilizer bar nuts with vehicle resting at curb height.

2) Ensure strut rod and stabilizer bar mount bolt end-to-lock nut distance is correct. Distance between stabilizer bar mount bolt end and nut is .59-.67" (15-17 mm). Distance between strut rod end and lock nut is 3.2" (81 mm). After installation, check front end alignment.

TIGHTENING SPECIFICATIONS

Application	Ft. Lbs. (N.m)
Ball Joint-to-Steering Knuckle	43-52 (59-70)
Control Arm-to-Crossmember	58-69 (78-94)
Control Arm-to-Ball Joint	43-52 (59-70)
Hub-to-Rotor	25-29 (34-39)
Stabilizer-to-Control Arm	7-14 (10-20)
Stabilizer Bracket	6-9 (8-12)
Strut Assembly Top End Nut	43-57 (59-70)
Strut Rod-to-Control Arm	43-52 (59-70)
Strut Rod-to-Bracket	54-61 (74-83)
Strut-to-Steering Knuckle	58-72 (78-98)
Tie Rod End-to-Steering Knuckle	25-32 (34-44)

CHRYSLER CORP. IMPORTS & MITSUBISHI – 2WD PICKUPS

DESCRIPTION

A wishbone independent front suspension with coil springs is used. Coil springs are mounted between the upper and lower control arms. A strut rod is used to control lower control arm front-to-rear movement. Damping is provided by 2 shock absorbers. A stabilizer bar is also used.

Fig. 1: View of 2WD Front Suspension

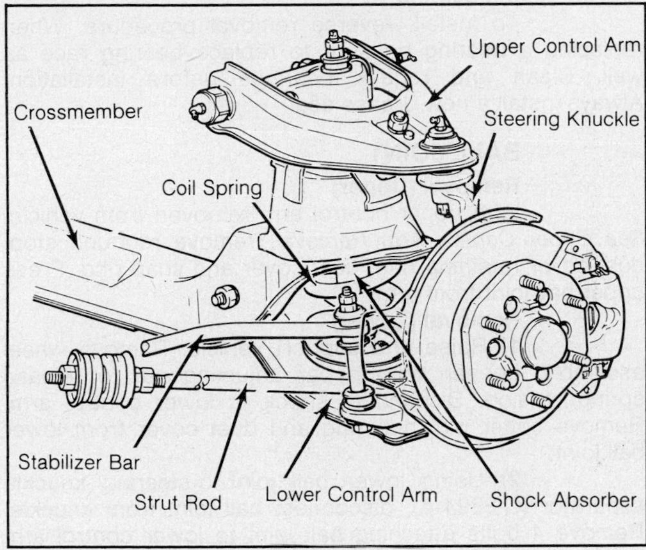
Upper Control Arm
Crossmember
Steering Knuckle
Coil Spring
Stabilizer Bar
Strut Rod
Lower Control Arm
Shock Absorber

ADJUSTMENT

WHEEL ALIGNMENT SPECIFICATIONS & PROCEDURES

See Wheel Alignment Specifications & Procedures in WHEEL ALIGNMENT Section.

WHEEL BEARING

While turning hub, tighten adjusting nut to 22 ft. lbs. (29 N.m) to seat bearings. Loosen nut, and retighten to 6 ft. lbs. (8 N.m). Install cotter pin, but do not loosen nut more than 30° to accommodate cotter pin. If holes cannot be aligned within 30°, repeat procedure.

REMOVAL & INSTALLATION

WHEEL BEARING

Removal

Raise and support vehicle. Remove wheel assembly. Remove caliper assembly and support out of way. Remove dust cap, cotter pin, nut, washer and outer bearing. Remove rotor and hub assembly from spindle. Remove grease seal from back side of hub and remove inner bearing.

Installation

Clean and repack both bearings. Lightly grease lip of grease seal and install inner bearing and seal. To finish installation, reverse removal procedure.

BALL JOINT

Removal (Upper)

1) To remove upper ball joint, raise and support vehicle. Raise lower control arm to level position with a floor jack. Remove upper ball joint-to-steering knuckle nut and separate knuckle from ball joint using a ball joint separator fork.

2) Remove 2 bolts attaching upper control arm shaft to crossmember and remove control arm from vehicle. Retain camber shims for reassembly. Remove rebound stop, dust cover retaining ring, dust cover and snap ring and press ball joint from arm.

Removal (Lower)

1) To remove lower ball joint, raise and support vehicle. Raise lower control arm to level position with a floor jack. Remove nut attaching lower ball joint to steering knuckle and separate knuckle from ball joint using a ball joint separator fork.

2) Remove dust cover retaining ring and dust cover from ball joint. Remove 3 bolts attaching ball joint to control arm and remove ball joint from vehicle.

Installation (Upper & Lower)

To install, reverse removal procedure.

LOWER CONTROL ARM & COIL SPRING

Removal

1) Raise and support vehicle. Loosen strut rod adjusting nut at frame. Disconnect stabilizer bar and strut rod from control arm. Remove shock absorber. Raise lower control arm to level position with a floor jack.

2) Remove lower ball joint-to-steering knuckle nut. Separate lower ball joint from knuckle using a ball joint separator fork. Lower arm to relieve coil spring tension and remove coil spring. Remove lower arm pivot shaft, and remove arm.

Installation

To install, reverse removal procedure. Be sure to tighten lower control arm with vehicle resting at curb height.

UPPER CONTROL ARM

Removal & Installation

Remove and install upper control arm as outlined in *Upper Ball Joint Removal & Installation.*

TIGHTENING SPECIFICATIONS

Application	Ft. Lbs. (N.m)
Shock Absorber-to-Lower Arm	6-8 (8-11)
Shock Absorber-to-Crossmember	9-13 (12-17)
Lower Arm Shaft Nut	40-54 (54-73)
Ball Joint-to-Lower Arm	22-30 (30-41)
Upper Ball Joint-to-Knuckle	44-65 (59-88)
Lower Ball Joint-to-Knuckle	87-130 (118-176)
Upper Arm Shaft-to-Crossmember	73-86 (99-117)
Strut Bar-to-Lower Arm	51-61 (69-83)

CHRYSLER CORP. IMPORTS & MITSUBISHI – 4WD MODELS

Colt Pickup, Ram-50 Pickup
Mitsubishi Pickup, Montero

DESCRIPTION

A wishbone design is used for the front suspension. This consists of the upper arms, lower arms, shock absorbers, and torsion bars. Long enlarged springs are utilized for the torsion bars, and in addition, the front axle on these models is composed of a differential carrier, housing tube, inner shaft and 2 drive shafts.

Fig. 1: Exploded View of 4WD Front Suspension

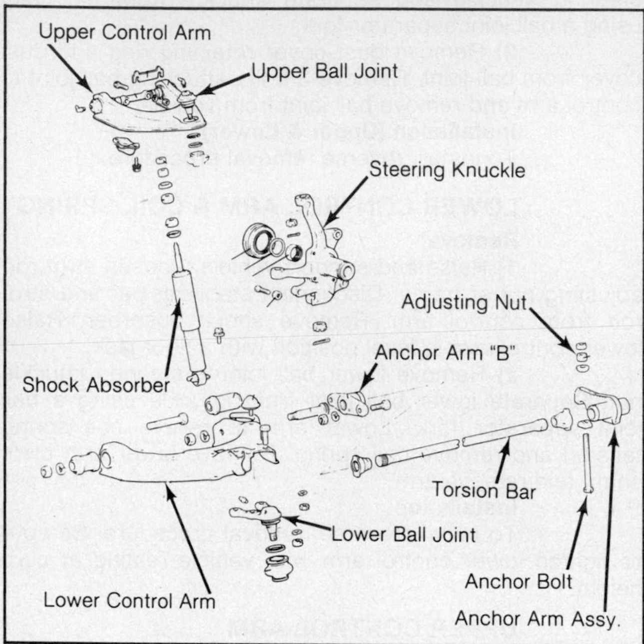
Upper Control Arm
Upper Ball Joint
Steering Knuckle
Adjusting Nut
Anchor Arm "B"
Shock Absorber
Torsion Bar
Lower Ball Joint
Anchor Bolt
Lower Control Arm
Anchor Arm Assy.

ADJUSTMENT

WHEEL ALIGNMENT SPECIFICATIONS & PROCEDURES

See Wheel Alignment Specifications & Procedures in WHEEL ALIGNMENT Section.

WHEEL BEARING

1) Remove free-wheeling hub assembly. Remove snap ring from end of axle shaft. Unbolt lock washer from lock nut and remove. Using a spanner socket, tighten lock nut to 95-145 ft. lbs. (130-200 N.m). Loosen and retighten to 18 ft. lbs. (25 N.m). Back nut off 30° and reinstall lock washer.

2) If lock washer and lock nut holes do not line up, align holes by loosening nut not more than 20°. Reinstall free-wheeling hub assembly.

REMOVAL & INSTALLATION

WHEEL BEARING

Removal

1) Remove caliper assembly with brake hose attached. Remove free-wheeling hub, lock washer attaching bolts and lock washer.

2) Remove lock nut with a spanner socket. Remove front hub assembly from steering knuckle, together with inner and outer bearings.

3) Remove outer bearing inner race. Remove grease seal from back side of hub and remove inner bearing inner race.

Inspection

Check bearings and races for seizure, discoloration, cracks and rough raceway surfaces.

Installation

To install, reverse removal procedure. When replacing a bearing be sure to replace bearing race as well. Clean and repack bearings before installation. Always install a new grease seal.

BALL JOINT

Removal (Upper)

With upper control arm removed from vehicle, *See Upper Control Arm Removal,* remove rebound stop, dust cover retaining ring, dust cover and snap ring. Press upper ball joint from arm.

Removal (Lower)

1) Raise and support vehicle. Remove wheel assembly. Loosen torsion bar adjusting nut to release spring tension. Disconnect shock at lower control arm. Remove cotter pin, nut, ring and dust cover from lower ball joint.

2) Using lower ball joint-to-steering knuckle separator (C-3894-A), disconnect ball joint from knuckle. Remove 4 bolts attaching ball joint to lower control arm and remove joint from vehicle.

Installation (Upper & Lower)

To install, reverse removal procedure. Adjust riding height with torsion bar adjusting nut. When pressing upper ball joint into upper arm, line up mating mark on ball joint with that on arm.

STEERING KNUCKLE

Removal

1) Raise and support vehicle. Remove wheel, caliper and hub assembly. Loosen torsion bar adjusting nut to release spring tension. Disconnect shock absorber at lower control arm.

2) Remove tie rod end attaching nut and disconnect tie rod end from knuckle. Remove cotter pins and ball joint-to-steering knuckle nuts from upper and lower ball joints.

3) Using lower ball joint-to steering knuckle separator (C-3894-A), separate ball joint from knuckle. Separate upper ball joint from steering knuckle using separator (MB990635) and remove knuckle from drive shaft.

Installation

To install, reverse removal procedure.

TORSION BAR

Removal

1) Raise and support vehicle. Support lower control arm with a floor jack. Disconnect torsion bar dust covers from anchor arm assembly and anchor arm B, respectively.

2) Put a mark on torsion bar in alignment with mark on anchor arm B. Loosen adjusting nut and pull torsion bar out of anchor arm B. It may be necessary to remove anchor arm assembly to facilitate removal of torsion bar.

CHRYSLER CORP. IMPORTS & MITSUBISHI – 4WD MODELS (Cont.)

Installation

To install, reverse removal procedure. Be sure to align marks. Adjust riding height with torsion bar adjusting nut.

CONTROL ARM

Removal (Upper)

1) Raise and support vehicle. Remove wheel assembly. Loosen torsion bar adjusting nut to release spring tension. Remove shock absorber. Discharge brake fluid and disconnect brake hose from crossmember.

2) Remove nut holding upper ball joint to knuckle. Using ball joint separator (MB990635), disconnect ball joint from knuckle. With rope, tie tool to upper arm to prevent bouncing when ball joint is disconnected.

3) Unbolt arm from crossmember and remove arm from vehicle. Retain alignment shims for use during assembly.

NOTE: **Do not turn upper arm shaft, because caster will change.**

Removal (Lower)

1) Raise and support vehicle. Remove wheel assembly. Remove front skid plate and under cover, if equipped. Remove torsion and stabilizer bars. Disconnect shock absorber from lower control arm.

2) Remove lower ball joint-to-knuckle retaining nut. Separate ball joint from knuckle using separator (C-3894-A). Remove control arm mounting bolts and remove arm from vehicle.

Installation (Upper & Lower)

To install, reverse removal procedure. Tighten lower control arm bolts with vehicle resting at riding height. Align as needed.

TIGHTENING SPECIFICATIONS

Application	Ft. Lbs. (N.m)
Ball Joint-to-Lower Arm	40-54 (54-73)
Free Wheeling Hub Body	37-43 (50-58)
Free Wheeling Hub Cover	8-10 (11-14)
Upper Arm-to-Frame	73-86 (99-117)
Lower Arm-to-Frame	101-116 (137-157)
Upper Ball Joint-to-Knuckle	44-65 (60-88)
Lower Ball Joint-to-Knuckle	87-130 (118-176)
Shock Absorber-to-Lower Arm	6-8 (8-11)
Stabilizer Bracket	6-8 (8-11)

Front Suspension

DATSUN/NISSAN MAXIMA, 200SX & 280ZX

DESCRIPTION

A MacPherson type strut suspension is used, consisting of a vertically-mounted strut, lower control arm, stabilizer bar, and compression rod. Compression rod is mounted between lower control arm and chassis. Stabilizer bar is mounted to front chassis member, and is connected at end of lower control arm.

Strut assembly consists of a shock absorber built into strut tube, a coil spring mounted on outside of strut tube with an integral wheel spindle. Strut assembly is mounted at top to chassis frame by a thrust bearing, and at bottom to lower control arm by a ball joint.

ADJUSTMENTS

WHEEL ALIGNMENT SPECIFICATIONS & PROCEDURES

See Wheel Alignment Specifications & Procedures in WHEEL ALIGNMENT section

WHEEL BEARING

Tighten spindle nut to specifications. Spin wheel, and retighten spindle nut. Loosen nut according to specification and tighten to align cotter pin hole.

WHEEL BEARING ADJUSTMENT

Application [1]	Torque Ft. Lbs. (N.m)	Loosen
All Models	18-22 (25-29)	60°

[1] – Figures given are for new wheel bearings.

BALL JOINT CHECKING

Remove lower control arm. Use appropriate gauge, and attach it to top of ball joint stud nut. Measure force (in INCH lbs.) required to turn ball joint stud. If measurement is not within specifications, replace ball joint.

BALL JOINT TURNING TORQUE

Application	New INCH Lbs. (N.m)	Used INCH Lbs. (N.m)
280ZX	22-69 (2.5-7.8)	13 (1.5) Or Less
All Others	35-87 (3.9-9.8)	[1] 35 (3.9) Or Less

[1] – 17-69 Inch Lbs. (2.0-7.8 N.m) on 200SX.

REMOVAL & INSTALLATION

WHEEL BEARING

Removal

1) Raise vehicle, and support with safety stands. Remove wheel assembly. Remove caliper, and support out of the way. Remove dust cap, cotter pin, adjusting cap, and wheel bearing nut.

2) Remove wheel hub with rotor. Remove retaining bolts, and separate wheel hub from rotor. Pry out wheel bearing, washers, and grease seals. Drive out bearing races.

Installation

To install, reverse removal procedures. Make sure bearing races are fully seated. Pack hub, cap, and bearings thoroughly with grease. Lubricate contact surface of grease seals, threaded part of spindle, and bearing washer-to-bearing contact face before final assembly. Adjust wheel bearings.

LOWER CONTROL ARM & BALL JOINT

Removal

1) Raise vehicle, and support with safety stands. Remove wheel assembly. Detach tie rod at ball socket. Remove steering knuckle arm bolts, and separate arm from bottom of strut.

Fig. 1: Exploded View of Maxima Front Suspension

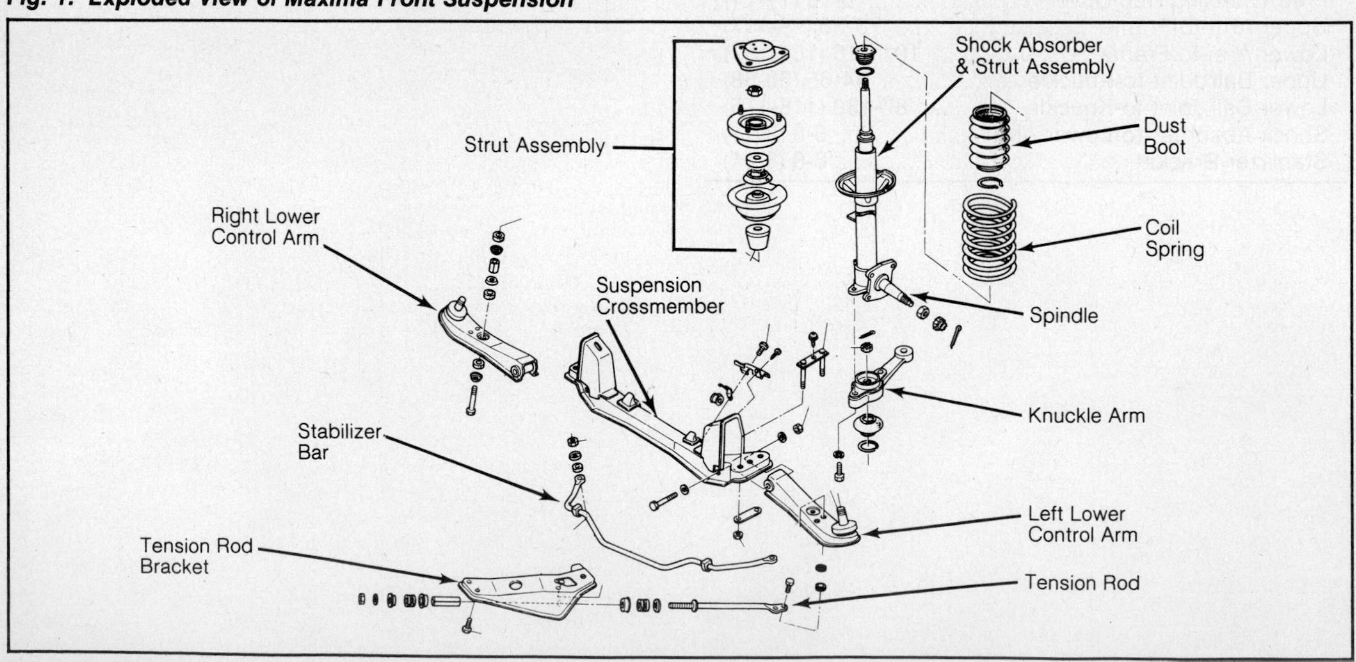
Shock Absorber & Strut Assembly
Strut Assembly
Dust Boot
Right Lower Control Arm
Coil Spring
Suspension Crossmember
Spindle
Knuckle Arm
Stabilizer Bar
Left Lower Control Arm
Tension Rod Bracket
Tension Rod

All other models are similar.

DATSUN/NISSAN MAXIMA, 200SX & 280ZX (Cont.)

2) Separate compression rod and stabilizer bar from lower control arm. Remove bolt connecting lower control arm to crossmember. Remove lower control arm with ball joint and knuckle arm.

3) Place arm in vise, loosen control arm ball joint bolts, and remove ball joint (Except Maxima). On Maxima models, ball joint is attached to steering knuckle. Place steering knuckle arm in vise, and press out ball joint. Remove bushing from lower control arm.

Installation

Press bushing into control arm, (Except Maxima). On Maxima models, press ball joint into steering knuckle. To install lower control arm, reverse removal procedure. Do not tighten nuts and bolts to final torque until weight of vehicle is on front wheels.

SPRING & STRUT ASSEMBLY

Removal

1) Raise and support front of vehicle. Remove wheel assemblies. Detach brake hose from bracket on front strut (if required). Remove caliper assembly retaining bolts and remove caliper from axle.

2) Remove bolts holding strut to knuckle arm. Detach knuckle arm from bottom of strut. If necessary, pry lower control arm away from strut to ease removal. Remove strut assembly.

3) Support strut assembly with a jack stand and remove upper nuts. Remove strut assembly from vehicle.

Disassembly

1) Thoroughly clean strut assembly. Place assembly in holding fixture (KV48100300) or equivalent, and clamp fixture in vise.

2) With spring compressor (HT71730000) or equivalent, press spring down just far enough to permit turning of strut mounting insulator. Remove self-locking nut.

NOTE: **Be sure spring tool evenly engages on at least 3 coils. Do not hit piston rod of strut with spring tool.**

3) Take out strut insulator, bearing, dust seal, upper spring seat, spring and rubber bumper.

4) Push piston rod down until it bottoms. Remove gland packing using gland wrench (ST35500001) or equivalent. Remove "O" ring from top of piston rod guide and lift out piston rod and cylinder.

NOTE: **The piston rod, piston rod guide and cylinder are furnished as a matched set with precision mating surfaces.**

Reassembly

1) Install strut outer casing onto holding fixture (KV48100300). Install cylinder and piston rod assembly (shock absorber kit) in outer casing.

2) Where present, remove piston rod guide from cylinder. Pour in specified amount of new fluid (outer casing).

STRUT OIL REPLACEMENT CAPACITY

Application	Fl. Oz. (cc)
Maxima, 200SX	11.0 (325)
280ZX	9.3 (275)

3) Install piston rod guide (bushing), taking care not to damage guide with threaded portion of rod. On 280ZX, install new "O" ring over rod guide. Lube inner edge of sealing lips of gland packing, and install with gland packing guide (ST35520000).

4) To correctly bleed strut assembly, stand strut vertically with spindle end down. Pull piston rod up to end of stroke. Turn strut assembly until spindle end is up, and depress piston rod to end of stroke.

5) Repeat several times, until there is no variation of pressure between pushing and pulling piston rod.

6) Pull piston rod fully out, and install rubber bumper. Place spring on lower spring seat, and compress with proper tool (HT71730000) or equivalent. Lubricate dust seal, and install dust cover, spring seat, dust seal, mounting bearing, and insulator.

7) Install new self-locking nut hand tight only. Tighten to specification after unit is installed in vehicle. To prevent entry of dirt, apply a thick coat of multi-purpose grease around upper seal.

8) After positioning spring between upper and lower seats, release spring compressor slowly. Raise rubber bumper to upper spring seat.

Installation

To install, reverse removal procedures.

COMPRESSION & STABILIZER BARS

Removal

1) Raise vehicle, and support with safety stands. Remove wheel assembly. Remove splash guard, and back off nuts securing compression rod to mounting bracket.

2) Remove bolts attaching compression rod to lower control rod. Remove nuts securing stabilizer bar to connecting rod. Remove stabilizer bracket bolts and brackets. Remove stabilizer bar.

Installation

To install, reverse removal procedures.

TIGHTENING SPECIFICATIONS

Application	Ft. Lbs. (N.m)
Stabilizer Bar Bracket Bolts	
200SX	23-31 (31-42)
Maxima, 280ZX	20-27 (26-36)
Compression Rod-to-Lower Control Arm	
200SX	37-44 (50-60)
Maxima, 280ZX	33-40 (44-54)
Compression Rod Nut	33-40 (44-54)
Gland Packing Nut	
Maxima, 200SX	72-87 (98-118)
280ZX	72-94 (98-127)
Strut Self-Locking Nut	43-54 (59-74)
Lower Control Arm-to-Crossmember	
200SX	46-55 (63-75)
Maxima, 280ZX	58-80 (78-108)
Ball Joint-to-Lower Control Arm	
200SX	37-44 (50-60)
Maxima, 280ZX	33-40 (44-54)
Knuckle Arm-to-Strut	53-72 (72-97)
Ball Joint-to-Knuckle Arm	
All Models	71-88 (96-120)
Tie Rod Ball Joint	
200SX	22-51 (20-69)
Maxima, 280ZX	40-72 (54-98)

Front Suspension

DATSUN/NISSAN PICKUP

DESCRIPTION

Front suspension is an independent type with upper and lower control arms which are connected by ball joints. This suspension also incorporates a tosion bar which connects to lower control arm outer end and a stabilizer bar. A double-acting shock absorber is also used. *See Fig. 1.*

ADJUSTMENTS

WHEEL ALIGNMENT SPECIFICATIONS & PROCEDURES

See Wheel Alignment Specifications & Procedures in WHEEL ALIGNMENT Section.

WHEEL BEARING

2WD Models

1) Tighten hub nut to 25-29 ft. lbs. (34-39 N.m). Rotate hub serveral times in both directions to seat bearings. Retorque hub nut. Turn hub nut back 45°.

2) Install adjusting cap and tighten only enough to align hole for cotter pin. Install new cotter pin and measure bearing preload and axial play. Measure preload with pull gauge on one of the wheel studs.

3) Axial play should be less than .003" (.08 mm) and preload should be less than 2.6 lbs. (1.18 kg) with old parts and 6.4 lbs. (2.90 kg) with new parts. If not to specifications, repeat procedures until correct readings are obtained.

4WD Models

1) Raise vehicle and support with safety stands. Remove free-running hubs and brake pads. Measure wheel bearing preload and axial play.

2) If end play exceeds .004-.012" (.1-.3 mm) or preload exceeds 2.2-9.5 lbs. (1.0-4.31 kg), bearings require adjustment.

3) To adjust bearing preload, replace wheel bearing collar with a thicker one (stamped number is higher by one) when preload is too high, or a thinner one (stamped number is lower by one) when preload is too low. *See Wheel Bearing Removal in this article for procedures.*

Fig. 1: Exploded View of 2WD Pickup Front Suspension

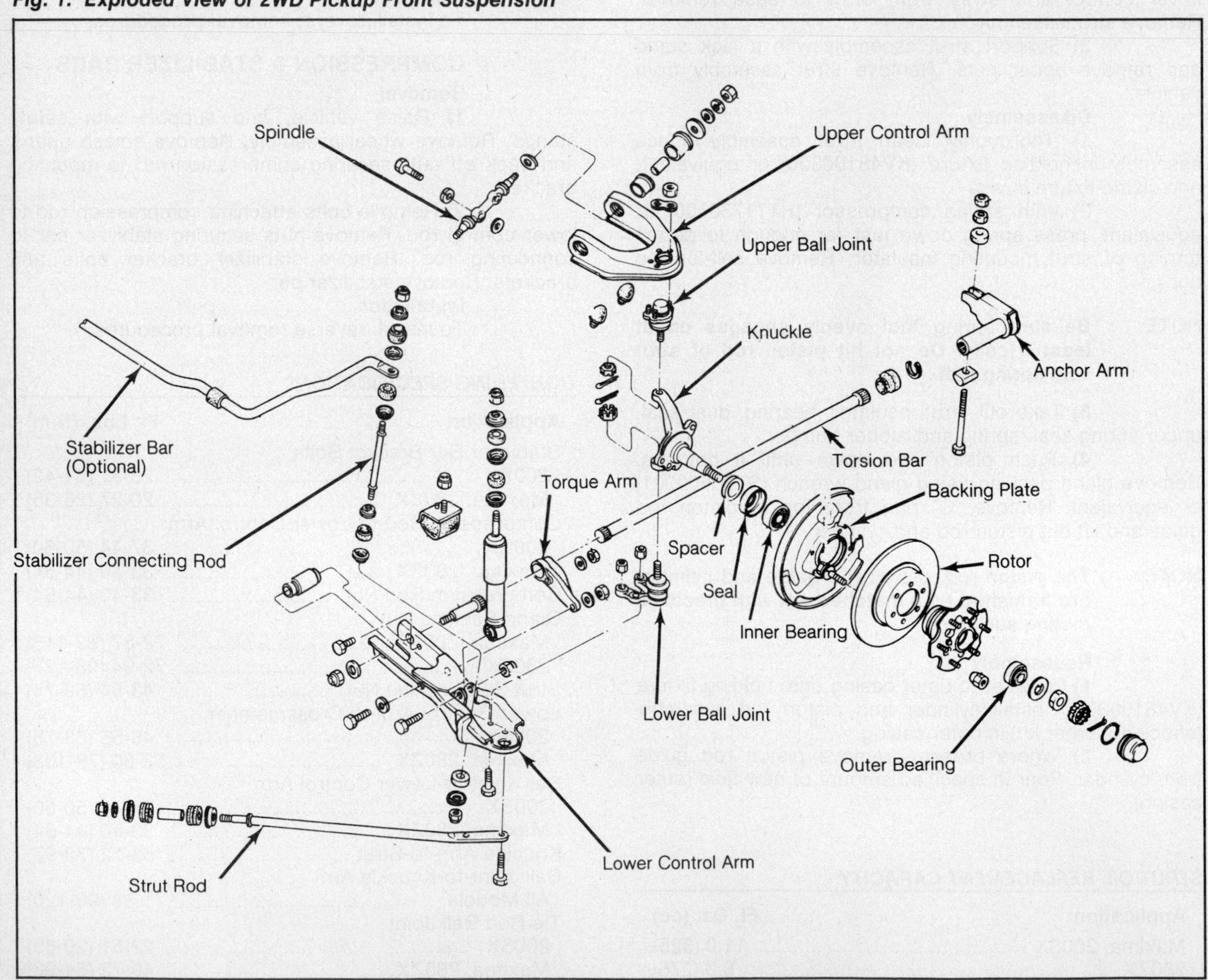
Spindle
Upper Control Arm
Upper Ball Joint
Knuckle
Anchor Arm
Stabilizer Bar
(Optional)
Torsion Bar
Torque Arm
Backing Plate
Stabilizer Connecting Rod
Spacer
Rotor
Seal
Inner Bearing
Lower Ball Joint
Outer Bearing
Lower Control Arm
Strut Rod

DATSUN/NISSAN PICKUP (Cont.)

BALL JOINT CHECKING

Upper Ball Joint

With ball joint removed from vehicle and stud nut in place, check stud turning torque. If torque does not meet specifications of 8.7-43.4 INCH lbs. (1.0-4.9 N.m), ball joint should be replaced. If dust cover is excessivly cracked, replace ball joint.

Lower Ball Joint

Check ball joint end play in axial direction. If play exceeds .004-.039" (.1-1.0 mm) joint should be replaced. If dust cover is cracked, replace ball joint.

REMOVAL & INSTALLATION

WHEEL BEARING, HUB & KNUCKLE

Removal (2WD)

1) Raise vehicle and support with safety stands. Remove wheel assembly. Remove caliper and support out of the way. Remove dust cap, cotter pin, adjusting cap and hub nut.

2) Remove hub and rotor. Remove outside bearing inner race and washer. Remove hub-to-rotor retaining bolts and separate hub form rotor. Remove wheel bearings and grease seals. Drive out bearing outer races.

3) Remove knuckle arm and backing plate. Loosen ball joint retaining nuts. Using separator tool (ST29020001) separate ball joints from knuckle. Using a floor jack raise lower control arm. Remove retaining nuts from ball joints.

Removal (4WD)

1) Raise vehicle and support with safety stands. Remove wheel assembly. Remove caliper and support out of the way. Remove free-running hub assembly. Remove snap ring, drive clutch and stabilizer connecting rod bolt from lower control arm.

2) Remove bolts retaining drive shaft to differential, do not remove boots. Remove drive shaft from knuckle. Turn steering wheel all the way to the right to remove right shaft and all the way to left to remove left shaft.

3) Remove knuckle arm retaining bolt. Loosen ball joint retaining nuts. Using separator tool (ST29020001), separate ball joints from steering knuckles. Using a floor jack raise lower control. Remove retaining nuts from ball joints. Remove steering knuckle.

4) Straighten tangs on lock washer. Remove lock nut with removal tool (KV40102500), remove lock-washer and special washer. Push wheel bearing support from wheel hub.

5) Separate knuckle from hub with puller. Remove wheel bearing collar and drive out inside bearing outer race. Separate wheel hub from rotor.

6) Strike wheel hub projection against wood block to loosen bearing and press off bearing. Remove drive shaft bearing from wheel bearing support with drift.

Installation (All Models)

1) To install, reverse removal procedures. On 4WD models, check wheel bearing adjustment as previously described before installing complete assembly in vehicle.

2) On all models, always use new lock washers, grease seals, and cotter pins.

UPPER CONTROL ARM & BALL JOINT

Removal

1) Raise vehicle and support with safety stands. Remove wheel assembly. Using a floor jack raise lower control arm.

2) Remove cotter pin and nut from upper ball joint and separate ball joint from steering knuckle with separator tool.

Fig. 2: Exploded View of 4WD Front Axle Assembly

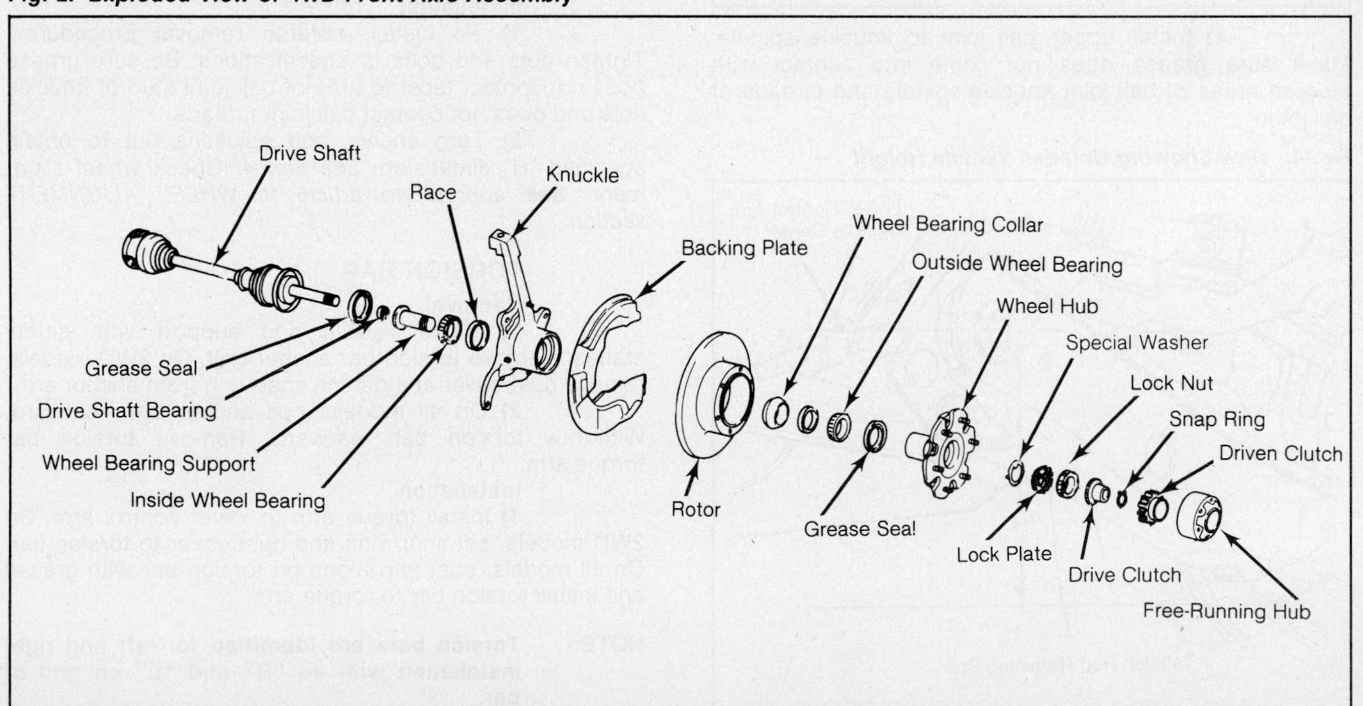
Drive Shaft
Race
Knuckle
Backing Plate
Wheel Bearing Collar
Outside Wheel Bearing
Wheel Hub
Special Washer
Lock Nut
Snap Ring
Driven Clutch
Grease Seal
Drive Shaft Bearing
Wheel Bearing Support
Inside Wheel Bearing
Rotor
Grease Seal
Lock Plate
Drive Clutch
Free-Running Hub

DATSUN/NISSAN PICKUP (Cont.)

3) Loosen bolts retaining upper ball joint to upper control arm and remove ball joint.

4) Remove bolts retaining upper link spindle. Remove spindle and upper control arm. Collect all camber adjusting shims.

5) Remove nuts and washers at both ends of upper link spindle. Place assembly on a vise and press upper link spindle from one end.

6) Remove rubber bushing. Press from other end and remove other bushing. Remove spindle from upper control arm.

Installation

1) Apply a soapy solution to rubber bushings and press bushings into place from outside of control arm. Flange of bushing should securely contact end of control end surface of upper control arm collar.

2) Insert upper control arm spindle and inner washers. Install inner washers with rounded edges facing inward. Press in other bushing as described in step **1)**. Temporarily tighten nuts. Install upper ball joint.

3) Install upper control arm to frame. Tighten upper control arm spindle with camber adjusting shims. After fitting, check dimensions "A" and "B". *See Fig. 3.* Dimension "A" should be 5.34-5.42" (135.6-137.6 mm), "B" should be 1.114" (28.3 mm).

Fig. 3: Upper Control Arm Spindle Dimensions

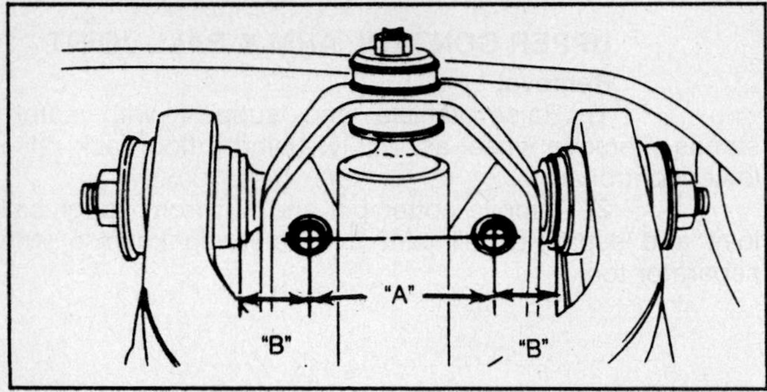
"A"
"B"
"B"

4) Install upper ball joint to knuckle spindle. Make sure grease does not come into contact with tapered areas of ball joint knuckle spindle and threads of ball joint.

Fig. 4: View Showing Unladen Vehicle Height

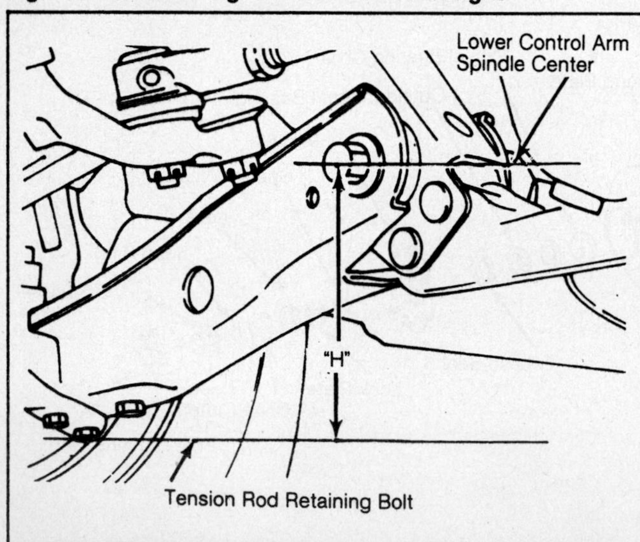
Lower Control Arm
Spindle Center
"H"
Tension Rod Retaining Bolt

5) Install wheel assembly. Lower vehicle and check riding height "H" of lower control arm. *See Fig. 4.* Check wheel alignment. *See appropriate article in WHEEL ALIGNMENT section.*

LOWER CONTROL ARM & BALL JOINT

Removal

1) Raise vehicle and support with safety stands. Remove wheel assembly. Remove torsion bar, and disconnect lower end of shock absorber from control arm.

2) Press out lower ball joint from knuckle. Disconnect stabilizer bar connecting rod from frame. Remove torque arm from lower control arm.

3) Remove lower control arm spindle from control arm and remove control arm from frame. Remove lower ball joint nuts and bolts. Remove ball joints from control arm.

4) Using drift (KV40102000), drive out lower control arm bushings. *See Fig. 5.*

Fig. 5: Removing Bushings from Lower Control Arm

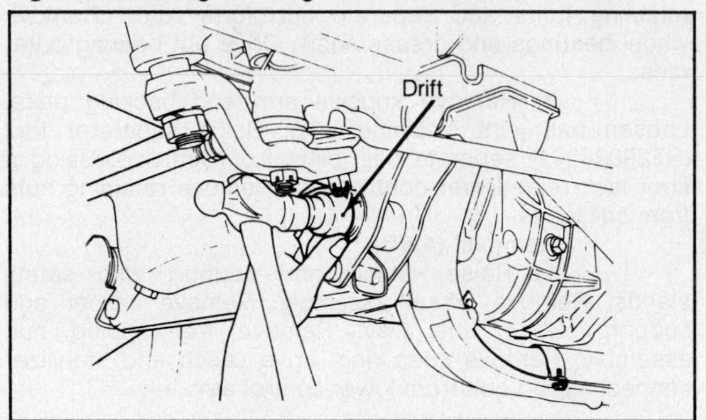
Drift

Installation

1) To install, reverse removal procedures. Tighten nuts and bolts to specifications. Be sure grease does not contact tapered area of ball joint stud or knuckle hole and does not contact ball joint threads.

2) Turn anchor bolt adjusting nut to obtain specified "H" dimension. *See Fig. 4.* Check wheel alignment. *See appropriate article in WHEEL ALIGNMENT section.*

TORSION BAR

Removal

1) Raise vehicle and support with safety stands. Remove torsion bar anchor bolt. On 2WD models, remove dust cover and detach snap ring from anchor arm.

2) On all models, pull anchor arm rearward. Withdraw torsion bar rearward. Remove torsion bar torque arm.

Installation

1) Install torque arm to lower control arm. On 2WD models, set snap ring and dust cover to torsion bar. On all models, coat serrations on torsion bar with grease and install torsion bar to torque arm.

NOTE: **Torsion bars are identified for left and right installation with an "R" and "L" on end of bar.**

DATSUN/NISSAN PICKUP (Cont.)

2) Install anchor arm to serrations on torsion bar. Install adjusting bolt to anchor arm. On 2WD models, install snap ring and dust cover to anchor arm.

3) On all models, tighten adjusting bolt to obtain specified dimension "A" when bar is in contact with rubber bumper. *See Fig. 6.*

Fig. 6: Measuring Points Shown for Installation of Anchor Pin

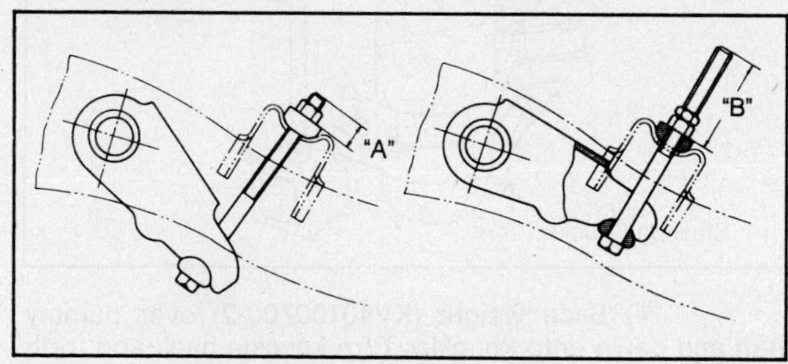
"A"
"B"

4) Temporarily adjust anchor arm adjusting bolt to obtain dimensions "B" and install lock nut. *See Fig. 6.* On 2WD models, install snap ring and dust cover to anchor arm.

5) On all models, lower vehicle and turn anchor arm adjusting nut to obtain specified "H" dimension with vehicle unladen. *See Fig. 4.*

DIMENSIONS FOR SETTING TORSION BAR

Application	In. (mm)
Dimension "A"	.28-.67 (7-17)
Dimension "B"	2.36-2.76 (60-70)
Dimension "H"	
2WD	4.88-5.08 (124-129)
4WD	5.28-5.47 (134-139)

STABILIZER BAR

Removal

Remove nut retaining stabilizer connecting rod to lower control arm. Remove bolt retaining stabilizer mounting bracket to frame. Remove nut retaining stabilizer and connecting rod and remove these parts.

Installation

To install, reverse removal procedures. The white mark on stabilizer bar can be seen from both sides of the vehicle when properly installed.

STRUT ROD

Removal

Remove bolts retaining strut rod to lower control arm and separate these parts. Remove nut retaining strut rod to bracket. Remove rod bushings, collar, and washers.

Installation

To install, reverse removal procedures. Swing strut rod a few times to settle bushings and washers. Do not allow grease or oil to contact rubber bushings.

TIGHTENING SPECIFICATIONS

Application	Ft. Lbs. (N.m)
Anchor Bolt	22-30 (30-41)
Shock Absorber Upper Nut	12-16 (16-22)
Shock Absorber Lower Nut	22-30 (30-41)
Knuckle Arm-to-Knuckle	53-72 (72-97)
Upper Control Arm Spindle Nut	56-76 (76-103)
Upper Control Arm	
Spindle-to-Frame	80-108 (109-147)
Upper Ball Joint-to-Control Arm	12-16 (16-22)
Upper Control Arm-to-Knuckle	
2WD	87-123 (118-167)
4WD	43-72 (59-98)
Stabilizer Bar	12-16 (16-22)
Strut Rod-to-Frame	87-116 (118-157)
Strut Rod-to-Lower Control Arm	28-38 (38-52)
Torque Arm-to-Lower Control Arm	
Inner Nut	26-33 (35-45)
Outer Nut	20-27 (27-37)
Drive Shaft-to-Differential (4WD)	20-27 (27-37)
Free-Running Hub Bolts (4WD)	18-25 (25-34)

DATSUN/NISSAN PULSAR, SENTRA & STANZA

DESCRIPTION

All models use a MacPherson strut type front suspension system. Shock absorbers are built into each strut tube.

Upper end of strut is mounted to inner fender panel. Lower end is connected by a ball joint to lower control arm. Control arm mounts to subframe. Steering knuckle is removable from strut. Knuckle bolts to strut and has a hole for axle drive shafts to pass through.

ADJUSTMENTS

WHEEL ALIGNMENT SPECIFICATIONS & PROCEDURES

See Wheel Alignment Specifications and Procedures in WHEEL ALIGNMENT Section

WHEEL BEARING

1) Loosen hub nut and tighten to specifications. Preload is measured with a pull scale attached to one of the wheel studs. Force required should be 3.1-10.8 lbs. (13.7-48.1 N). If preload is not to specifications, bearing spacer must be replaced.See Bearing Removal.

2) If any axial end-play is present in wheel bearing, or bearing preload is below specification, replace spacer with a smaller one. If bearing preload is greater than specification, a larger spacer must be installed.

BALL JOINT CHECKING

1) With ball joint removed and stud nut in place, check turning torque required to turn stud. On Stanza and Pulsar models, if force required is less than 8.7 INCH lbs. (1.0 N.m) on a used joint, it should be replaced.

2) On Sentra models, if force required is less than 4.3 INCH lbs. (.5 N.m) on used joint, it should be replaced. Check end play with dial indicator at stud end. If end play exceeds .059" (1.5 mm), replace ball joint.

REMOVAL & INSTALLATION

WHEEL BEARING

Removal

1) Raise and support vehicle. Remove wheel and tire. Remove caliper assembly and wire out of way. Remove cotter pin and loosen (do not remove) hub nut from drive shaft.

2) Remove steering knuckle. Remove bolts retaining wheel hub to rotor. Using hub tools (KV40101000 & ST36230000), separate rotor from hub. Remove and discard old grease seal.

2) Press wheel bearing from hub. Remove wheel bearing from steering knuckle. Drive out bearing race with a brass drift fitted through notches in knuckle.

Installation

1) Pack wheel bearings with grease. Install new grease seal and install inner and outer bearing races.

2) Place outer bearing on base (KV40100700-3) and place steering knuckle over it so bearing seats in outer race.

3) Slide inner bearing over dummy shaft (KV40100700-1). Place shaft bearing in knuckle with end of shaft in outer bearing and inner bearing in inner race.

Fig. 1: Determining Required Spacer Thickness

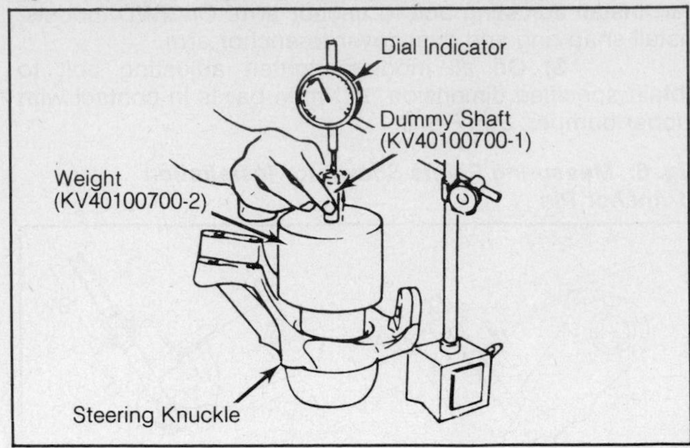
Dial Indicator
Dummy Shaft
(KV40100700-1)
Weight
(KV40100700-2)
Steering Knuckle

4) Slide weight (KV40100700-2) over dummy shaft and down onto knuckle. Turn knuckle back and forth to seat bearing. Assemble dial indicator with contact button resting on top of dummy shaft.

5) Zero indicator. Pull upward on shaft until it reaches end of travel, rotate 1 revolution and record maximum deflection of indicator needle.

6) To determine required spacer thickness, add recorded dial indicator reading to metric thickness dimension stamped on side of flange on end of dummy shaft.

7) Select required spacer. Spacers are available in 18 sizes, ranging from .291-.293" (7.38-7.44 mm) to .331-.333" (8.40-8.46 mm) in .002" (.05 mm) increments. For size identification, spacers are numbered "05" (smallest size) through "22" (largest size).

8) Pack bearings with bearing grease. Install outer grease seal and press outer bearing onto stub axle.

9) Install spacer and press inner bearing onto stub axle and knuckle assembly until it just bottoms. Install inner seal. To complete installation, reverse removal procedures.

NOTE: **Wheel bearings must be replaced in complete sets, including both bearings and races.**

BALL JOINT

Removal

Raise vehicle and support with safety stands. Remove wheel assembly. Remove drive shaft and remove ball joint stud nut. Remove bolts retaining ball joint to lower control arm. Using ball joint tool (HT72520000), seperate ball joint from steering knuckle, do not damage ball joint dust cover.

NOTE: **Do not to damage ball joint dust cover.**

Installation

To install, reverse removal procedures. Make sure new cotter pin is installed. Replace ball joint dust cover, if cracked or damaged.

CONTROL ARM

Removal

1) Raise vehicle and support with safety stands. Remove wheel assembly. Remove bolts retaining lower control arm to ball joint.

DATSUN/NISSAN PULSAR, SENTRA & STANZA (Cont.)

Fig. 2: Exploded View of Sentra Front Suspension

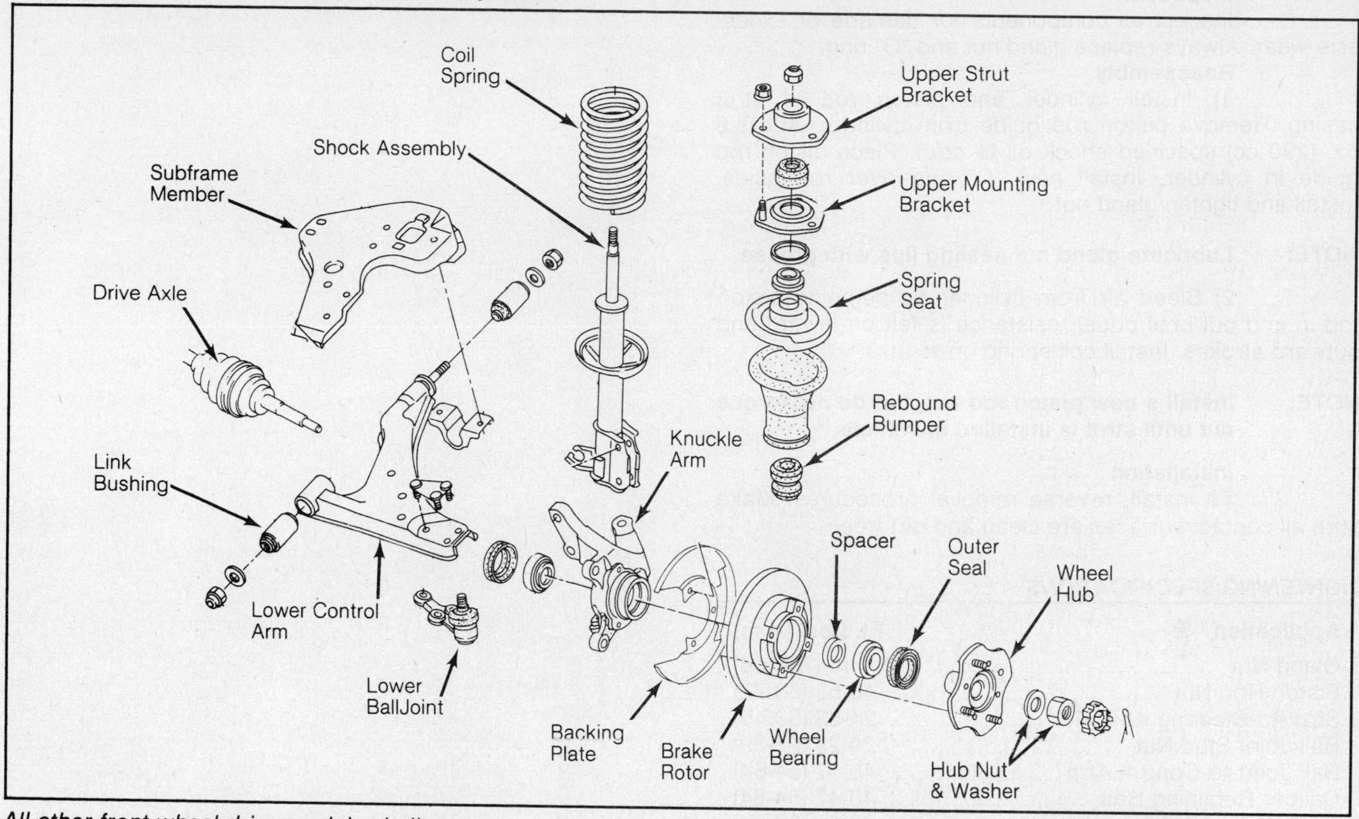
Coil Spring
Shock Assembly
Subframe Member
Drive Axle
Link Bushing
Lower Control Arm
Lower BallJoint
Backing Plate
Brake Rotor
Knuckle Arm
Upper Strut Bracket
Upper Mounting Bracket
Spring Seat
Rebound Bumper
Spacer
Outer Seal
Wheel Hub
Wheel Bearing
Hub Nut & Washer

All other front wheel drive models similar.

2) Take off nut retaining stabilizer bar to control arm. Disconnect control arm from subframe by removing retaining bolts.

Inspection

Inspect arm for distortion. Replace control arm bushings using a press. Make sure new bushings extend evenly on both sides of hole.

Installation

To install, reverse removal procedures. Control arm bolts must be tightened with weight of vehicle on floor.

STEERING KNUCKLE

Removal

1) Raise vehicle and support with safety stands. Remove wheel assembly. Disconnect and plug brake line. Remove brake caliper. Remove axle nut.

2) Using a puller (HT72520000), remove stub axle and brake rotor assembly from axle shaft. Disconnect ball joint and support control arm. Remove bolts retaining steering knuckle to strut.

Installation

To install, reverse removal procedures.

STABILIZER BAR

Removal

1) Raise vehicle and support with safety stands. Support subframe with floor jack. Disconnect exhaust pipe from exhaust manifold and front body mount.

2) Disconnect transmission control linkage and transmission support rod at transmission. Remove stabilizer-to-control arm nuts. Loosen, but do not remove, subframe retaining bolts.

3) Lower subframe just enough to allow removal of stabilizer bar clamp bolts from subframe. Remove stabilizer bar from vehicle.

Installation

To install, reverse removal procedures. Replace any bushing that is worn or cracked.

STRUT ASSEMBLY

Removal

1) Raise vehicle and support with safety stands. Remove wheel assembly. Working from inside engine compartment, remove cap and loosen lock nut retaining piston rod.

2) Disconnect brake line and plug opening. Detach tie rod from steering knuckle. Place safety stand under control arm for support.

3) Remove bolts retaining strut to steering knuckle. Remove nuts keeping upper portion of strut to inner fender panel. Remove strut and coil spring assembly from vehicle.

Disassembly

1) Place strut in a vise. Using a spring compressor, slightly compress coil spring. Remove piston rod nut and all upper mounting hardware.

2) Push piston rod into cylinder until it bottoms. Remove gland nut. Remove "O" ring. Slowly lift out piston rod and cylinder as a unit.

3) Drain all fluid from inner cylinder and strut casing. Discard inner cylinder. Flush strut casing with solvent.

DATSUN/NISSAN PULSAR, SENTRA & STANZA (Cont.)

Inspection

Inspect all components for damage or excessive wear. Always replace gland nut and "O" ring.

Reassembly

1) Install cylinder and piston rod in strut casing. Remove piston rod guide from cylinder. Add 9.8 oz. (290 cc) specified shock oil to strut. Place piston rod guide in cylinder. Install new "O" ring over rod guide. Install and tighten gland nut.

NOTE: Lubricate gland nut sealing lips with grease.

2) Bleed air from cylinder by pumping piston rod in and out until equal resistance is felt on inward and outward strokes. Install coil spring on strut.

NOTE: Install a new piston rod nut, but do not torque nut until strut is installed in vehicle.

Installation

To install, reverse removal procedures. Make sure all contact surfaces are clean and dirt free.

TIGHTENING SPECIFICATIONS

Application	Ft. Lbs. (N.m)
Gland Nut	58-116 (79-158)
Piston Rod Nut	46-53 (63-72)
Strut-to-Steering Knuckle	24-33 (33-45)
Ball Joint Stud Nut	20-29 (27-39)
Ball Joint-to-Control Arm	40-47 (54-64)
Caliper Retaining Bolt	40-47 (54-64)
Control Arm Retaining Nut	42-51 (57-69)
Stabilizer Bar	6-9 (8-12)
Axle Shaft Nut	
Sentra & Pulsar	87-145 (118-197)
Stanza	145-203 (197-276)

HONDA

Accord, Civic, Prelude

DESCRIPTION

The Accord and Civic use a MacPherson strut front suspension. The strut assembly consists of an inner shock absorber and a coil spring, surrounding the outside upper portion of the strut tube.

The bottom of the strut assembly is attached to the steering knuckle and lower control arm. A stabilizer bar is attached to the lower control arm. On Accord models, a strut rod is attached to the lower control arm.

The Honda Prelude uses an independent double wish-bone strut assembly. The suspension system consists of a vertically-mounted strut assembly. The bottom end of the strut is bolted to the steering knuckle.

The steering knuckle is attached to the upper and lower control arms by ball joints. A stabilizer bar and strut rod is attached to the lower control arm.

ADJUSTMENT

WHEEL ALIGNMENT SPECIFICATIONS & PROCEDURES

See Wheel Alignment Specifications & Procedures in WHEEL ALIGNMENT Section.

WHEEL BEARINGS

Wheel bearings are not adjustable.

BALL JOINT CHECKING

1) Raise front of vehicle and support with safety stands. Attach dial indicator to lower control arm, with indicator tip on steering knuckle near ball joint. Place pry bar between lower control arm and steering knuckle.

Fig. 1: Civic Front Suspension

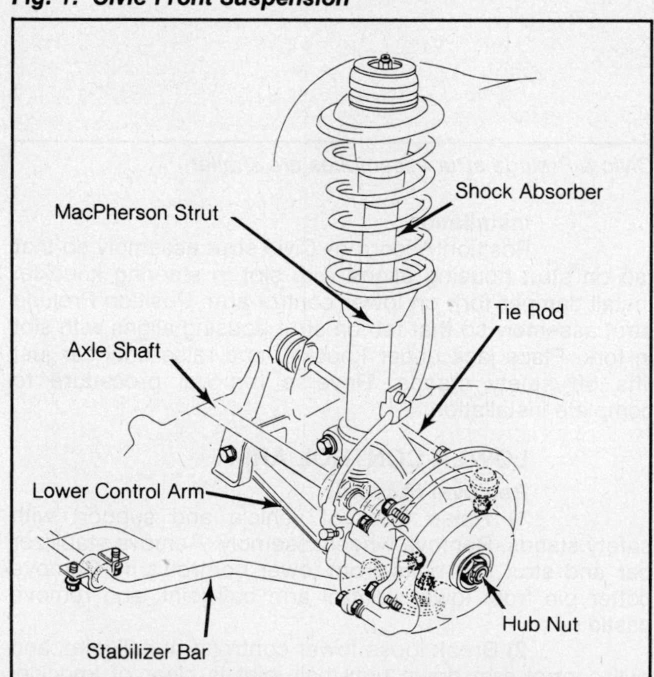
Shock Absorber
MacPherson Strut
Tie Rod
Axle Shaft
Lower Control Arm
Hub Nut
Stabilizer Bar

Accord and Prelude front suspensions are similar.

2) Push on pry bar, and observe movement on dial indicator. Movement should not exceed .020" (0.5 mm). Replace lower control arm on Accord or Civic, if ball joint exceeds wear limit. Replace ball joint on Prelude, if ball joint exceeds wear limit. *See Ball Joint in this article.*

REMOVAL & INSTALLATION

WHEEL BEARING

Removal

1) Remove steering knuckle. *See Steering Knuckle in this article.* Remove splash guard, snap ring, outboard bearing inner race and bearing. Flip knuckle over, remove inboard dust seal, inboard bearing inner race and bearing.

2) Press bearing outer race out of knuckle. Remove outboard bearing inner race from hub using bearing puller. Remove outboard dust seal from hub. Wash knuckle and hub throughly before reassembly.

Installation

1) Pack wheel bearings before installation. Apply grease to outer race and both inner races. Press bearing outer race into knuckle. Pressure required must not exceed 5000 lbs. (2268 kg). Install outboard bearing and inner race in knuckle.

2) Install snap ring in knuckle groove. Pack grease in groove and around sealing lip of outboard dust seal. Drive outboard dust seal into knuckle, until flush with knuckle surface.

3) Install splash guard and turn knuckle upside down. Install inboard bearing and inner race. Place front hub in tool fixture and position knuckle. Press hub into knuckle. Pressure required must not exceed 4000 lbs. (1814 kg).

4) Pack grease in groove and around sealing lip of inboard dust seal. Drive inboard dust seal into knuckle. Reverse removal procedure to complete installation.

BALL JOINT

Removal (Lower)

1) Remove steering knuckle. *See Steering Knuckle in this article.* Remove dust boot snap ring and remove dust boot. Remove ball joint snap ring, and tighten ball joint nut on ball joint remover (07965-SB00100).

2) Position ball joint removal base (07965-SB00200) between ball joint housing and knuckle. Press ball joint out of knuckle.

Installation

1) Position ball joint in steering knuckle. Position ball joint installer (07965-SB00100) on ball joint. Position ball joint installation base (07965-SB00300) on end of ball joint housing. Press ball joint into knuckle.

2) Install ball joint snap ring. Install dust boot and dust boot snap ring. Reverse removal procedure to complete installation.

STEERING KNUCKLE

Removal (Accord and Civic)

1) Pry nut lock tab away from spindle and loosen hub nut. Raise front of vehicle and support with safety stands. Remove wheel assembly and hub nut. Remove caliper and hang caliper out of way.

HONDA (Cont.)

2) Remove disc brake retaining screws on Accord. Screw two 8 x 1.25 x 12 mm bolts into disc to push it away from hub. Turn each screw 2 turns at a time to prevent cocking disc.

3) Remove cotter pin from tie-rod ball joint, and remove castle nut. Break loose tie-rod ball joint, and lift tie-rod out of knuckle. Remove cotter pin from lower control arm ball joint, and remove castle nut. Break loose lower control arm ball joint, and pull control arm down until ball joint is clear of knuckle.

4) Remove strut assembly locking bolt, and tap knuckle down until it comes off strut. Pull knuckle/hub assembly off axle. Remove splash guard screws, and press hub out of knuckle. Use care not to distort splash guard.

Removal (Prelude)

1) Pry nut lock tab away from spindle, and loosen hub nut. Raise front of vehicle and support with safety stands. Remove wheel assembly and hub nut. Remove caliper and hang caliper out of way.

2) Remove disc brake retaining screws. Screw two 8 x 1.25 x 12 mm bolts into disc to push it away from hub. Turn each screw 2 turns at a time to prevent cocking disc.

3) Remove cotter pin from tie-rod ball joint, and remove castle nut. Break loose tie-rod ball joint, and lift tie-rod out of knuckle. Remove cotter pin from lower control arm ball joint, and remove castle nut. Break loose lower control arm ball joint, and pull control arm down until ball joint is clear of knuckle.

4) Remove upper ball joint shield. Remove cotter pin from upper ball joint, and remove castle nut. Break loose upper ball joint. Pull knuckle/hub assembly off axle. Remove splash guard screws and press hub out of knuckle. Taking care not to distort splash guard.

Installation

Reverse removal procedure to complete installation. Use new hub nut, and stake after torquing.

STRUT ASSEMBLY

Removal (Accord & Civic)

1) Raise front of vehicle and support with safety stands. Remove wheel assembly and brake hose clamp from strut. Remove caliper and hang caliper out of way. Remove stabilizer bar from lower control arm on Accord.

2) Remove strut assembly locking bolt, and tap knuckle down until it comes off strut. Remove cap and nuts from top of strut on Accord. Remove cap and self-locking nut from top of strut on Civic. Remove strut assembly.

Removal (Prelude)

Raise front of vehicle and support with safety stands. Remove wheel assembly and strut locking bolt. Remove damper fork bolt and remove damper fork. Remove cap and nuts from top of strut. Remove strut assembly.

Disassembly

Compress strut assembly spring and remove spring seat nut. Slowly release spring compressor and lift spring off. Disassemble strut assembly, noting relative position of assembled parts. *See Fig. 2.*

Reassembly

Check spring tension. Check parts for deterioration or damage. Check shock absorber for leaks and proper operation. Replace worn or damaged parts. Coat Accord or Civic needle bearings with grease. Position Prelude mounting base so that one of the studs aligns with tab on strut housing. Reverse disassembly procedure.

Fig. 2: Accord Strut Assembly

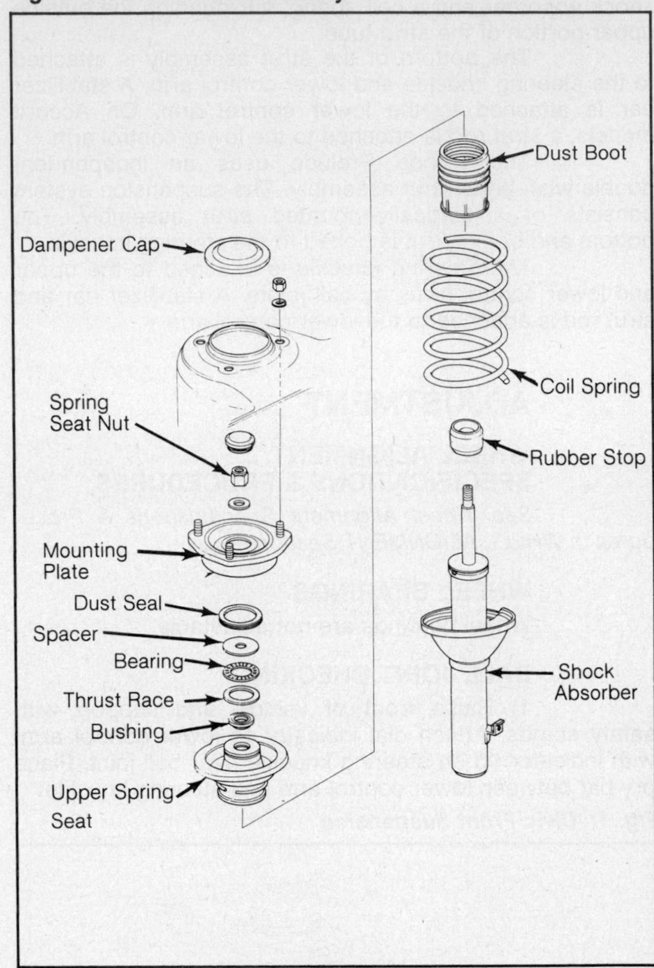
Dust Boot
Dampener Cap
Coil Spring
Spring Seat Nut
Rubber Stop
Mounting Plate
Dust Seal
Spacer
Bearing
Shock Absorber
Thrust Race
Bushing
Upper Spring Seat

Civic & Prelude strut assemblies are similar.

Installation

Position Accord or Civic strut assembly so that tab on strut housing aligns with slot in steering knuckle. Install damper fork on lower control arm. Position Prelude strut assembly so that tab on strut housing aligns with slot in fork. Place jack under knuckle, and raise until car just lifts off safety stands. Reverse removal procedure to complete installation.

LOWER CONTROL ARM

Removal (Accord)

1) Raise front of vehicle and support with safety stands. Remove wheel assembly. Remove stabilizer bar and strut rod bolts from lower control arm. Remove cotter pin from lower control arm ball joint, and remove castle nut.

2) Break loose lower control arm ball joint, and pull control arm down until ball joint is clear of knuckle. Remove lower control arm pivot bolt and remove control arm.

HONDA (Cont.)

Removal (Civic)

1) Raise front of vehicle and support with safety stands. Remove wheel assembly. Remove bushing nut and washer from stabilizer bar. Remove cotter pin from lower control arm ball joint, and remove castle nut.

2) Break loose lower control arm ball joint, and pull control arm down until ball joint is clear of knuckle. Remove lower control arm pivot bolt, and remove control arm.

Removal (Prelude)

1) Raise front of vehicle and support with safety stands. Remove wheel assembly. Remove damper fork and strut rod bolts. Remove bushing nut and washer from stabilizer bar.

2) Remove cotter pin from lower control arm, and remove castle nut. Break loose lower control arm ball joint, and pull arm down until ball joint is clear of knuckle. Remove lower control arm pivot bolt, and remove control arm.

Installation

Check parts for deterioration or damage. Replace worn or damaged parts. Reverse removal procedure to complete installation.

UPPER CONTROL ARM

Inspection (Prelude Only)

Raise front of vehicle and support with safety stands. Remove wheel assembly. Rock the upper ball joint front-to-back with a force of approximately 65 lbs. (30 kg). Replace upper arm bushings if there is any play.

Fig. 3: Prelude Upper Control Arm

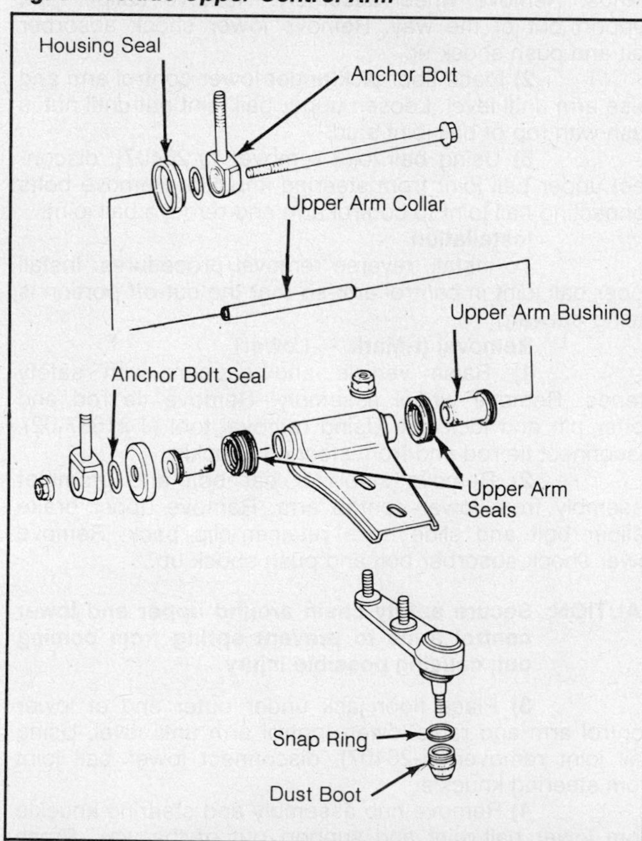
Housing Seal
Anchor Bolt
Upper Arm Collar
Upper Arm Bushing
Anchor Bolt Seal
Upper Arm Seals
Snap Ring
Dust Boot

Apply sealer to underside of bolt head, threads and nut.

Removal

1) Raise front of vehicle and support with safety stands. Remove wheel assembly. Remove cotter pin from upper ball joint, and remove castle nut.

2) Break loose upper control arm ball joint, and push arm up until ball joint is clear of knuckle. Remove anchor bolt nuts, and remove upper control arm.

Disassembly

Clamp upper control arm in vise by anchor bolts. Remove upper control arm bolt, anchor bolts and seals. Reposition upper control arm in vise, and remove upper arm collar and bushings.

Reassembly

Coat ends and insides of upper arm bushings with grease. Coat the sealing lips of the upper arm bushing seals with grease. Apply sealer to underside of upper control arm bolt head, threads and bolt nut. Reverse disassembly procedure.

Installation

Reverse removal procedure to complete installation. Check camber and adjust if necessary.

TIGHTENING SPECIFICATIONS

Application	Ft. Lbs. (N.m)
Wheel Hub Nut	
Accord & Prelude	137 (186)
Civic	134 (182)
Ball Joint	
Accord & Prelude	[1] 40 (54)
Civic	25 (34)
Control Arm-to-Crossmember	
Accord	36 (49)
Civic & Prelude	40 (54)
Spring Seat Nut	
Accord	33 (45)
Civic	17 (23)
Prelude	22 (30)
Strut-to-Knuckle	
Accord	47 (64)
Civic	36 (49)
Prelude	32 (44)
Strut-to-Body	
Accord (3 Nuts)	28 (38)
Civic (1 Nut)	33 (45)
Prelude (3 Nuts)	29 (39)
Stabilizer-to-Control Arm	
Accord	16 (22)
Civic	32 (44)
Prelude	60 (81)
Stabilizer-to-Body	
Accord & Prelude	16 (22)
Civic	37 (50)
Tie Rod End-to-Knuckle	32 (44)
Strut Rod-to-Control Arm	
Accord & Prelude	40 (54)
Strut Rod-to-Body	
Accord & Prelude	32 (44)
Anchor Bolt-to-Body	60 (81)
Upper Control Arm Bolt	40 (54)

[1] – Prelude upper ball joint 32 ft. lbs. (44 N.m)

Front Suspension

ISUZU I-MARK & IMPULSE

DESCRIPTION

Both models use independent type front suspension consisting of upper and lower control arms with steering knuckle mounted between control arms by means of ball joints. Upper control arm pivots on shaft bolt through crossmember; lower arm pivots on shaft bolts (2) through crossmember and frame.

A coil spring is mounted between lower control arm and crossmember. Shock absorber is hydraulic, double-action type mounted between upper control arm and inner fender panel. A stabilizer bar is used to enhance stability and riding comfort. Impulse models are also equipped with a strut rod on the lower control arm.

Fig. 1: Exploded View of Isuzu Front Suspension

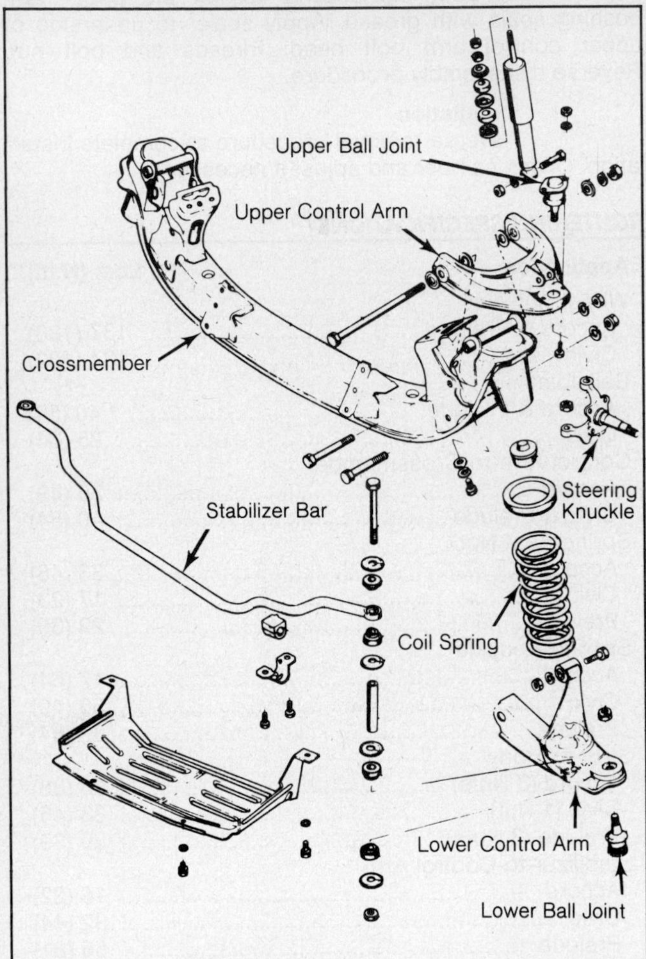
Upper Ball Joint
Upper Control Arm
Crossmember
Steering Knuckle
Stabilizer Bar
Coil Spring
Lower Control Arm
Lower Ball Joint

Illustration applies to I-Mark only.

ADJUSTMENT

WHEEL ALIGNMENT SPECIFICATIONS & PROCEDURES

See Wheel Alignment Specifications & Procedures in WHEEL ALIGNMENT Section.

WHEEL BEARING ADJUSTMENT

1) Raise vehicle and support with safety stands. Remove grease cap and cotter pin. Loosen spindle nut. Tighten spindle nut to 22 ft. lbs. (30 N.m) while rotating wheel to seat bearings.

2) Back off nut completely and tighten finger tight. Install new cotter pin. Tighten nut as needed to align slot in nut with hole in spindle.

BALL JOINT CHECKING

Check ball joints for excessive movement or play. If axial play of lower ball joint exceeds .040" (1.0 mm) it should be replaced.

REMOVAL & INSTALLATION

WHEEL BEARING

Removal

1) Raise vehicle and support with safety stands. Remove wheel assembly. Remove brake caliper and support out of the way. Remove grease cap, cotter pin hub nut and washer.

2) Remove outer wheel bearing. Remove hub/rotor assembly. Pry out inner grease seal and remove inner wheel bearing. Remove wheel bearing races, if necessary.

Installation

To install, reverse removal procedures. Adjust wheel bearings. *See WHEEL BEARING ADJUSTMENT in this article.*

BALL JOINT

Removal (Upper)

1) Raise vehicle and support with safety stands. Remove wheel assembly. Remove caliper and support out of the way. Remove lower shock absorber bolt and push shock up.

2) Place floor jack under lower control arm and raise arm until level. Loosen upper ball joint nut until nut is flush with top of ball joint stud.

3) Using ball joint remover (J-26407), disconnect upper ball joint from steering knuckle. Remove bolts connecting ball joint to control arm and remove ball joint.

Installation

To install, reverse removal procedures. Install upper ball joint in control arm so that the cut-off portion is facing outward.

Removal (I-Mark – Lower)

1) Raise vehicle and support with safety stands. Remove wheel assembly. Remove tie rod end cotter pin and lock nut. Using removal tool (J-21687-02), disconnect tie rod end from steering knuckle.

2) Remove stabilizer bar bolt and grommet assembly from lower control arm. Remove upper brake caliper bolt and slide hose retainer clip back. Remove lower shock absorber bolt and push shock up.

CAUTION: Secure safety chain around upper and lower control arms to prevent spring from coming out, causing possible injury.

3) Place floor jack under outer end of lower control arm and raise lower control arm until level. Using ball joint remover (J-26407), disconnect lower ball joint from steering knuckle.

4) Remove hub assembly and steering knuckle from lower ball joint and support out of the way. Press lower ball joint from control arm using ball joint remover (J-9519-03).

ISUZU I-MARK & IMPULSE (Cont.)

Installation

To install, reverse removal procedures.

Removal (Impulse – Lower)

Raise and support vehicle. Remove front wheels. Remove brake caliper and rotor. Remove ball joint stud nut. Separate ball joint from steering knuckle. Remove ball joint-to-lower control arm bolt and remove ball joint.

Installation

To install, reverse removal procedure. Tighten lower ball joint assembly-to-control arm bolt to 27 ft. lbs. (37 N.m).

SHOCK ABSORBER

Removal

Raise vehicle and support with safety stands. Remove wheel assembly. Remove lower shock absorber retaining bolt from upper control arm. Remove upper retaining nut from inside engine compartment and remove shock absorber.

Installation

To install, reverse removal procedures.

STEERING KNUCKLE

Removal

1) Raise vehicle and support with safety stands. Remove wheel assembly. Remove lower shock absorber attaching bolt and push shock up. Remove brake caliper and support out of the way.

2) Disconnect tie rod end from steering knuckle. Remove grease cap, cotter pin, hub nut and washer. Remove hub/rotor assembly. Remove dust plate retaining bolts and remove dust plate from knuckle.

3) With floor jack positioned under outer end of lower control arm, raise arm until level and support. Loosen upper and lower ball joint nuts and disconnect ball joints from knuckle. Remove steering knuckle.

Installation

To install, reverse removal procedures. Attach dust plate to knuckle before installing knuckle to ball joints.

LOWER CONTROL ARM

Removal

1) Raise vehicle and support with safety stands. Remove wheel assembly. Disconnect tie rod end from steering knuckle. Remove lower shock absorber bolt.

2) Disconnect stabilizer bar from lower control arm. Remove brake caliper and support out of the way. Place jack under outer end of lower control arm and lift until level.

CAUTION: Secure coil spring to upper control arm with safety chain to prevent accidental release of spring.

3) Separate lower ball joint ball joint from steering knuckle. Remove hub, rotor and steering knuckle assembly.

4) Slowly lower jack supporting control arm and remove spring. Remove control arm pivot bolts and remove control arm.

Installation

To install, reverse removal procedures. Do not tighten control arm pivot bolts to specifications until installation is complete. When compressing spring, attach safety chain between spring and upper control arm.

UPPER CONTROL ARM

Removal

1) Raise vehicle and support with safety stands. Remove wheel assembly. Remove brake caliper and support out of the way. Remove lower shock absorber bolt and push shock up.

2) With floor jack positioned under outer end of lower control arm, raise arm until level and support. Loosen upper ball joint nut and disconnect ball joint from knuckle.

3) Remove bolts connecting ball joint to control arm and remove ball joint. Remove upper control arm pivot shaft bolt and remove arm.

Installation

1) To install, reverse removal procedures. When installing ball joint, be sure that the cut off side of mounting flange is towards outside of vehicle.

2) Do not tighten pivot shaft bolt to specification until installation is otherwise complete.

3) When installing control arm, make sure that the smaller washer is installed on the inside of the front arm and the larger washer is installed on the inside of the rear arm.

STABILIZER BAR

Removal

Raise vehicle and support with safety stands. Remove engine splash guard. Remove stabilizer bar bolt and grommet assemblies from lower control arms. Remove stabilizer support clamps from body and remove stabilizer bar.

Installation

To install, reverse removal procedures.

TIGHTENING SPECIFICATIONS

Application	Ft. Lbs. (N.m)
Brake Caliper-to-Steering Knuckle	36 (49)
Lower Ball Joint-to-Steering Knuckle	58 (79)
Lower Control Arm-to-Crossmember	47 (64)
Shock Absorber-to-Control Arm	29 (39)
Tie Rod-to-Steering Knuckle	29 (39)
Upper Ball Joint-to-Steering Knuckle	47 (64)
Upper Control Arm-to-Ball Joint	29 (39)
Upper Control Arm-to-Crossmember	47 (64)

ISUZU P'UP

DESCRIPTION

P'UP trucks are equipped with a short arm-long arm, independent front suspension. The front suspension consists of a torsion bar, upper and lower control arms, a strut bar, a steering knuckle assembly and a stabilizer bar. The forward end of the torsion bar is attached to the lower control arm, the aft end is attached to the height control arm.

The short upper control arm pivots on a shaft mounted to frame. The long lower control arm pivots on a bolt (shaft on 4WD) mounted to crossmember. Ball joints connect the steering knuckle assembly to upper and lower control arms. A stabilizer bar is used between lower control arm and frame. The strut bar controls fore and aft movement of front suspension.

ADJUSTMENT

WHEEL ALIGNMENT SPECIFICATIONS & PROCEDURES

See Wheel Alignment Specifications & Procedures in WHEEL ALIGNMENT Section.

WHEEL BEARING ADJUSTMENT

1) Raise and support vehicle. Remove hub cap, grease cup, cotter pin and nut retainer. Remove locking hub assembly on 4WD models.

2) Rotate wheel and tighten spindle nut to 22 ft. lbs. (30 N.m). Rotate wheel 2 to 3 turns and loosen spindle nut. Tighten spindle nut finger tight so that hub has no free play.

3) Make sure that brake pads are not in contact with brake rotor. Attach a spring scale and measure starting torque. Tighten spindle nut so that spring scale reads 1.8-2.6 lbs. (0.8-1.2 kg). Perform procedure to both front wheels. Install remaining hardware to complete wheel bearing adjustment.

BALL JOINT CHECKING

Replace lower control arm ball joint if play exceeds 0.06" (1.5 mm). Replace upper control arm, if upper ball joint play exceeds 0.06" (1.5 mm).

REMOVAL & INSTALLATION

WHEEL BEARING

Removal (2WD)

1) Raise and support vehicle. Remove wheel assembly. Remove brake caliper and hang out of the way. Remove grease cup, cotter pin, nut retainer and spindle nut.

2) Remove hub/rotor assembly. Remove outer wheel bearing. Remove shaft seal and inner bearing. Remove bearing races, if necessary.

Removal (4WD)

1) Raise and support vehicle. Remove locking hub assembly. Remove wheel assembly. Remove brake caliper and hang out of the way.

2) Remove lock washer and remove hub nut. Remove hub/rotor assembly. Remove outer wheel bearing. Remove shaft seal, retaining ring and inner wheel bearing. Remove bearing races, if necessary.

Installation

Reverse removal procedure to complete installation. Adjust wheel bearings. *See WHEEL BEARING ADJUSTMENT in this article.*

BALL JOINT

Removal (2WD)

Remove cotter pin and castle nut. Disconnect ball joint from steering knuckle assembly. Remove bolts attaching ball joint to lower control arm and remove ball joint.

Removal (4WD)

1) Raise and support vehicle. Remove wheel assembly. Loosen torsion bar adjusting bolts. Disconnect strut bar from lower control arm. Remove torsion bar. *See TORSION BAR in this article.*

2) Disconnect stabilizer bar from lower control arm. Disconnect tie rod ends. Remove cotter pin and castle nut. Disconnect ball joint from steering knuckle assembly. Remove bolts attaching ball joint to lower control arm.

3) Remove lower shock absorber bolt. Remove locking hub assembly. Slide off steering knuckle assembly from drive axle and support steering knuckle. Remove ball joint.

Installation

Mount ball joint to lower control arm. Tighten bolts attaching ball joint to lower control arm. Reverse removal procedure to complete installation. Lubricate ball joint.

UPPER CONTROL ARM

Removal

1) Raise and support vehicle. Remove wheel assembly. Remove shock absorber dust cover on 2WD models. Remove upper ball joint cotter pin and castle nut. Support lower control arm and steering knuckle assembly. Disconnect upper control arm ball joint from steering knuckle assembly.

2) Note number and placement of shims between upper control arm pivot shaft and frame. Remove bolts from upper pivot shaft. Remove shock absorber upper retaining nut, retainer and rubber grommet on 2WD models. Compress shock absorber on 2WD models. Remove upper control arm.

Inspection

Check upper control arm and pivot shaft for cracks, distortion or thread damage. Check pivot shaft bushings for wear or damage, replace if necessary. Replace upper control arm, if upper ball joint play exceeds 0.06" (1.5 mm).

Bushing Replacement

Remove bolts from ends of pivot shaft. Remove lock washer, flat washer and plate. Press out pivot shaft and bushings. Reverse removal procedure to install bushings.

Installation

Install ball joint stud through steering knuckle. Tighten castle nut and install cotter pin. Reverse removal procedure to complete installation.

LOWER CONTROL ARM

Removal

1) Raise and support vehicle. Remove wheel assembly. Remove strut bar. *See STRUT BAR in this article.* Disconnect stabilizer bar from lower control arm. Remove torsion bar. *See TORSION BAR in this article.*

2) Disconnect shock absorber from lower control arm. Remove bolts attaching ball joint to lower control arm. Remove lower control arm pivot bolt (shaft on 4WD) and remove lower control arm.

Inspection

Check lower control arm and pivot bolt (shaft on 4WD) for cracks, distortion or thread damage. Check pivot bushing for wear or damage, replace if necessary.

Fig. 1: Exploded View of 2WD Front Suspension

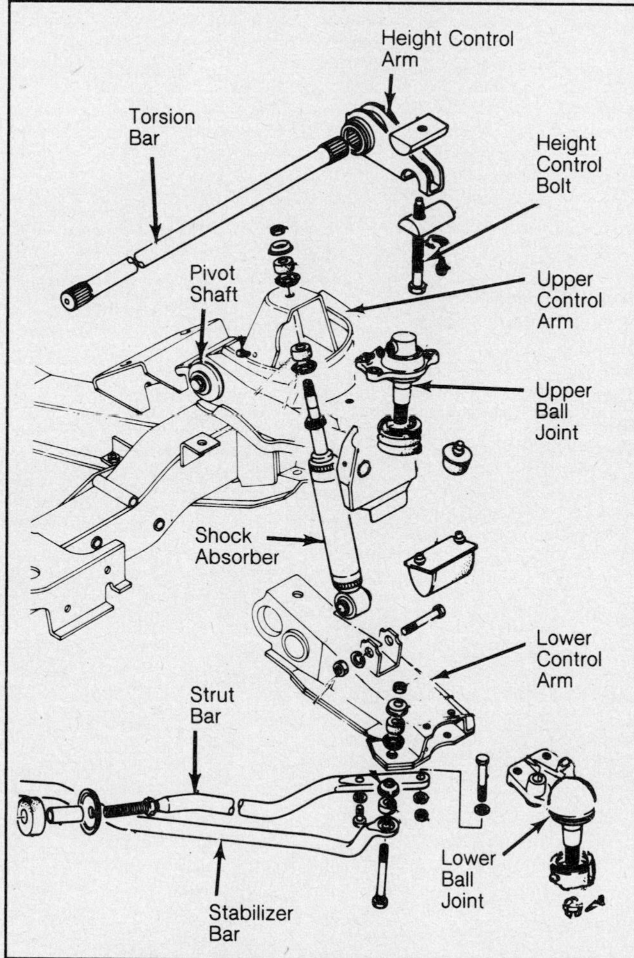

Height Control Arm
Torsion Bar
Height Control Bolt
Pivot Shaft
Upper Control Arm
Upper Ball Joint
Shock Absorber
Lower Control Arm
Strut Bar
Lower Ball Joint
Stabilizer Bar

Front suspension of 4WD is similar.

Installation

Attach ball joint to lower control arm before lower control arm is attached to frame. Reverse removal procedure to complete installation. Adjust riding height. *See Riding Height article in WHEEL ALIGNMENT Section.*

SHOCK ABSORBER

Removal

Raise and support vehicle. Remove shock absorber dust cover on 2WD models. Remove shock absorber retainer nut, retainer and rubber grommet. Disconnect shock absorber from lower control arm and remove shock absorber.

Installation

Slide shock absorber into position. Reverse removal procedure to complete installation.

STABILIZER BAR

Removal

Raise and support vehicle. Disconnect stabilizer bar from lower control arm. Remove stabilizer bar brackets and remove bar.

Installation

Inspect grommets and bushings for wear or damage and replace if necessary. Reverse removal procedure to complete installation.

TORSION BAR

Removal

Raise and support vehicle. Remove stopper plate on 2WD models. Remove adjusting bolt from height control arm. Mark position and remove height control arm from torsion bar and bracket frame. Mark position and remove torsion bar from lower control arm.

Inspection

Check torsion bar for bending or damage, replace if necessary. Check height control arm for cracks or distortion, replace if necessary.

Installation

1) Grease serrated portions of torsion bar. Raise lower control arm to position rubber bumpers in contact with lower control arm. Insert front end of torsion bar into control arm. Grease portion of height control arm which fits into frame.

2) Install height control arm so its end reaches height control arm adjusting bolt. Turn height control adjusting bolt to position marked during removal. Check riding height. *See Riding Height article in WHEEL ALIGNMENT Section.* Install stopper plate on 2WD models.

STRUT BAR

NOTE: **Correct caster angle can be maintained by marking position of frame nuts on threaded part of strut bar.**

Removal

Raise and support vehicle. Remove nuts, washers and rubber bushing from front side of strut bar. Remove bolts attaching strut bar to lower control arm. Remove strut bar.

Installation

1) Install washers and bushing on aft side of strut bar. Insert strut bar through frame bracket. Install bushing and washers on front side of strut bar. Install one frame nut, but do not tighten.

2) Install strut bar to lower control arm and tighten attaching bolts. Lower vehicle and tighten frame nut. Install second frame nut and tighten.

STEERING KNUCKLE

Removal (2WD)

1) Raise and support vehicle. Remove wheel assembly. Remove brake caliper and hang out of the way. Remove grease cup, cotter pin, nut retainer and spindle nut. Remove hub/rotor assembly. Remove tie rod end link attaching bolts and move aside.

2) Remove bolts attaching dust shield and adapter. Remove cotter pin and castle nut from upper and

Front Suspension

ISUZU P'UP (Cont.)

lower ball joint. Disconnect steering knuckle from ball joints and remove steering knuckle.

Removal (4WD)

1) Raise and support vehicle. Remove locking hub assembly. Remove bolts attaching steering knuckle, dust shield and adapter.

2) Remove cotter pin and castle nut from upper and lower ball joint. Disconnect steering knuckle from ball joints and remove steering knuckle.

Installation

Reverse removal procedure to complete installation. Adjust wheel bearings. *See WHEEL BEARING ADJUSTMENT in this article.*

TIGHTENING SPECIFICATIONS

Application	Ft. Lbs. (N.m)
Stabilizer Bar-to-Frame	55 (75)
Stabilizer Bar-to-Lower Control Arm	7 (10)
Strut Bar-to-Lower Control Arm	51 (69)
Strut Bar-to-Frame	58-72 (78-98)
Upper Control Arm Pivot Shaft Bushings	87 (118)
Upper Control Arm Pivot Shaft-to-Frame	75 (102)
Lower Control Arm-to-Crossmember	
2WD	90 (122)
Lower Control Arm-to-Frame Bracket	
4WD	97 (132)
Ball Joint-to-Lower Control Arm	51 (69)
Ball Joint Castle Nuts	75 (102)
Shock Absorber (Upper End)	14 (19)
Shock Absorber (Lower End)	45 (61)
Rotor-to-Hub	36 (49)

Front Suspension

JAGUAR

XJ6, XJS

DESCRIPTION

Front suspension consists of upper and lower control arms, double acting hydraulic shock absorbers, coil springs, stabilizer bar and steering knuckles. The upper control arms are mounted inboard to fulcrum shafts and are mounted outboard to steering knuckles by upper ball joint.

Lower control arms are mounted inboard to crossmember and outboard to steering knuckles by lower ball joint. Coil springs are mounted between lower control arms and crossmember. Shock absorbers are attached at bottom of lower control arms and at the top to body. Stabilizer bar is attached to lower control arms and crossmember.

Fig. 1: Sectional View of Front Suspension Assembly

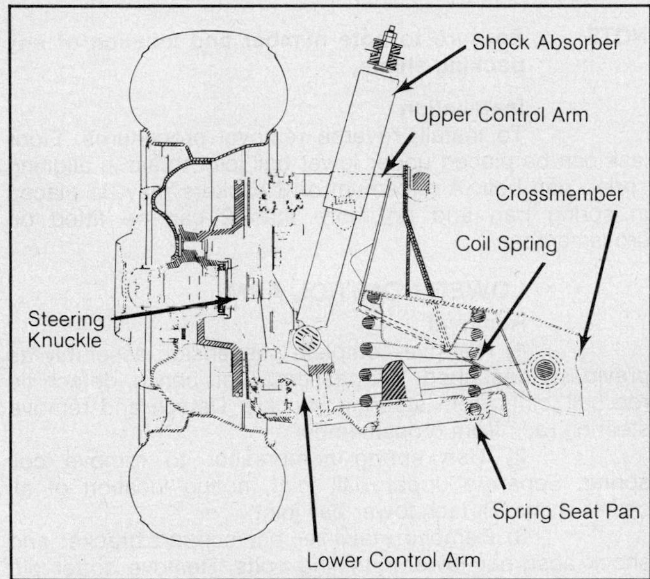
Shock Absorber
Upper Control Arm
Crossmember
Coil Spring
Steering Knuckle
Spring Seat Pan
Lower Control Arm

ADJUSTMENT

WHEEL ALIGNMENT SPECIFICATIONS & PROCEDURES

See Wheel Alignment Specifications and Procedures in WHEEL ALIGNMENT Section.

WHEEL BEARING

While rotating hub, tighten nut until no end play is evident. Loosen nut a maximum of 120° to line up cotter pin and install new pin. Check end play with dial indicator. If end play is not .002-.006" (.05-.015 mm), adjust hub nut until correct end play is obtained.

BALL JOINT CHECKING

Inspect ball joints for any signs of excessive wear or damage. Replace as needed. Lower ball joint can be adjusted with shims. These shims are not to be used to compensate for worn ball joints, and are designed to provide adjustment during overhaul reassembly only.

REMOVAL & INSTALLATION

WHEEL BEARING

Removal

1) Raise vehicle and support with safety stands. Remove wheel assembly. Remove hub to rotor attaching bolts through holes in hub.

2) Remove grease cap, cotter pin, hub nut and washer. Remove hub. Remove grease seal and wheel bearings. Drive out bearing races.

Installation

To install, reverse removal procedures.

LOWER BALL JOINT

Removal

1) Raise vehicle and support with safety stands. Remove wheel assembly. Disconnect brake line from caliper and plug openings. Disconnect tie rod from steering arm.

2) Twist stub axle carrier to gain access to bolts securing upper ball joint to control arm and remove bolts. Note position and number of shims.

3) Remove nut retaining lower ball joint to control arm. Use ball joint removal tool (JD 24) separate ball joint from control arm. Remove assembly from vehicle.

Disassembly

Pry back tab washers and remove screws retaining ball pin cap. Lift out ball pin. Release clip and remove upper socket from stub axle. Clean all components and inspect for excessive wear or damage.

Reassembly

1) Install new upper socket to stub axle. Fit lip of boot clip in recess in ball joint socket. Lip must be near lower face of clip. Install new boot to clip and attach with plastic retaining ring. Grease new ball pin and put into position.

2) Put ball pin cap into vise and cut out lower ball joint socket. Clean shavings and fit new socket. Refit shims and replace ball cap. Fit set screws with lock tabs and tighten, continually checking ball joint movement.

3) If ball pin is loose in socket, remove shims. If pin is excessively tight, add shims until movement is correct. Movement should be slightly stiff.

Fig. 2: Exploded View of Lower Ball Joint

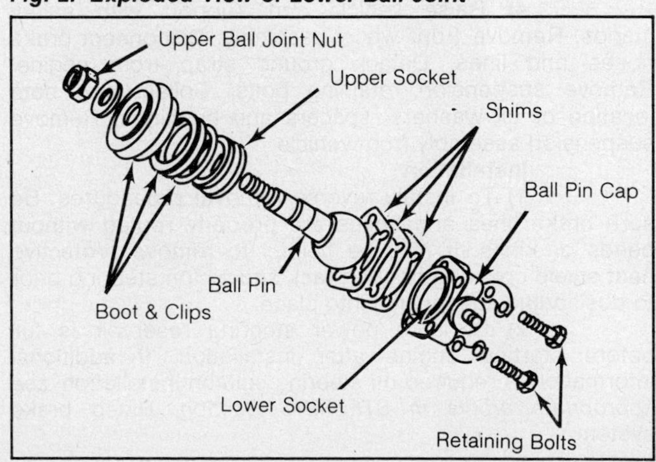
Upper Ball Joint Nut
Upper Socket
Shims
Ball Pin Cap
Ball Pin
Boot & Clips
Lower Socket
Retaining Bolts

Front Suspension

JAGUAR (Cont.)

Installation

Insert ball joint in lower control arm and tighten lock nut. Align stub axle with upper control arm, and insert bolts with heads facing forward. Make sure packing pieces and shims are properly installed. Reconnect tie rod. Attach brake lines and bleed brakes. Check alignment.

UPPER BALL JOINT

NOTE: **Upper control arm ball joint cannot be overhauled. If ball joint is excessively worn, assembly must be replaced.**

Removal

1) Raise vehicle and place on safety stands. Remove wheel assembly. Turn steering to full lock position. Wire stub axle to crossmember to prevent tension on brake hose when ball joint is separated.

2) Remove bolt retaining upper ball joint to control arm. Note number of shims and position of packing pieces. Remove ball joint lock nut and using ball joint removal tool (JD 24) separate ball joint from control arm. Remove assembly from vehicle. Withdraw ball joint from stub axle.

Installation

Apply grease to replacement ball joint and place in position in stub axle. Hold ball joint against taper fit washer and tighten retaining nut. Refit upper control arm retaining bolts and caster shims, with bolt heads facing forward. Check wheel alignment.

FRONT SUSPENSION ASSEMBLY

Removal

1) Disconnect battery and remove air cleaners. Disconnect the upper end of shock absorber. Drain and discard power steering fluid. Disconnect and plug power steering inlet and outlet hoses.

2) Remove nuts securing engine mounts to brackets on frame crossmember. Disconnect rear crossmember retaining bolts, and separate stabilizer bar from link. Turn steering column until pinch bolt holding lower "U" joint to pinion shaft is accessible. Remove pinch bolt.

3) Return steering to straight ahead position. Set ignition to "LOCK" and remove key. Separate lower steering column from upper universal joint, and separate from pinion shaft.

4) Raise vehicle and support with safety stands. Remove front wheel assembly. Disconnect brake hoses and lines. Detach ground strap from engine. Remove suspension retaining bolts. Collect and note location of all washers, spacers and bushings. Remove suspension assembly from vehicle

Installation

1) To install, reverse removal procedures. Be sure brake lines and hoses are properly routed without bends or kinks. It may be helpful to remove protective heat shield covering boot on rack and pinion steering prior to positioning suspension into place.

2) Be sure power steering reservoir is full before starting engine after installation. If additional information is required on steering column installation, *see appropriate article in STEERING Section.* Bleed brake system.

SHOCK ABSORBERS

Removal

Detach upper shock absorber retaining bolts. Raise vehicle and support with safety stands. Remove wheel assembly, (if necessary for access to lower mounting). Remove lower shock absorber retaining bolts and remove from vehicle.

Installation

To install, reverse removal procedure.

COIL SPRINGS

Removal

1) Raise vehicle and support with safety stands. Remove wheel assembly. Fit a spring compressor (JD 6D & adaptor JD 6D 1) and collapse spring coil enough to allow load on pan seat to be relieved.

2) Remove hardware mounting spring pan to lower control arm. Slightly loosen spring compressor and remove complete assembly.

NOTE: **Be sure to note number and location of any packing shims.**

Installation

To install, reverse removal procedures. Floor jack can be placed under lower ball joint to aid in aligning spring pan bolt. A maximum of 3 packers may be placed in spring pan and no more than 2 can be fitted on crossmember.

LOWER CONTROL ARM

Removal

1) Remove complete suspension assembly as previously described. With assembly on bench, detach tie rod ball joints from steering knuckle. Detach and remove steering rack from crossmember.

2) Use spring compressor to remove coil spring. Separate upper ball joint, noting location of all caster shims. Detach lower ball joint.

3) Remove stabilizer bar support bracket and shock absorber lower retaining bolts. Remove cotter pin and pivot shaft nut. Drive pivot shaft from crossmember and collect spacers. Remove lower control arm.

Installation

To install, reverse removal procedure. Do not tighten pivot shaft nut until vehicle is resting on floor at full curb weight.

UPPER CONTROL ARM

Removal

1) Raise vehicle and support with safety stands. Remove wheel assembly. Detach upper ball joint from control arm. Note number of all caster adjusting shims present.

2) Wire steering knuckle to coil spring and remove bolts holding upper control arm pivot shaft to vehicle. Note number and location of camber adjusting shims. Remove control arm from vehicle. *See Fig. 3.*

JAGUAR (Cont.)

Fig. 3: Upper Control Arm Mounting Points

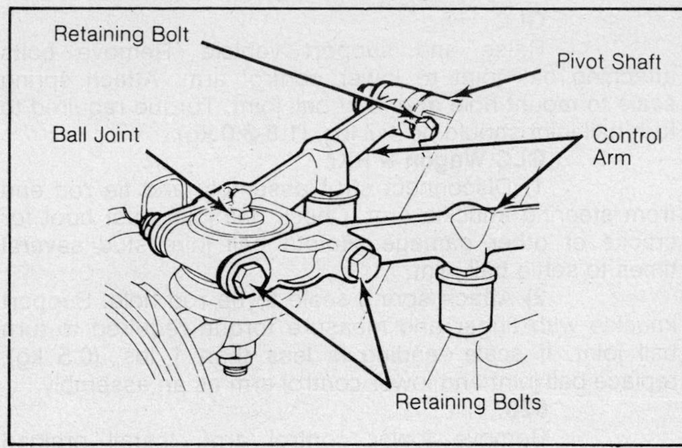
Retaining Bolt
Pivot Shaft
Ball Joint
Control Arm
Retaining Bolts

Installation

To install, reverse removal procedures. Check wheel alignment.

STABILIZER BAR

Removal

Raise vehicle and support with safety stands. Remove wheel assemblies. Detach both ends of stabilizer bar from links. Remove both brackets from frame. Remove all bushings from bar. Detach 1 tie rod end from steering knuckle and remove stabilizer from vehicle.

Installation

To install, reverse removal procedures. Fully tightening stabilizer bar-to-link nuts after vehicle is resting on floor.

TIGHTENING SPECIFICATIONS

Application	Ft. Lbs. (N.m)
Upper Pivot Shaft-to-Crossmember	49-55 (67-75)
Upper Ball Joint-to-Arm	26-32 (35-44)
Pivot Shaft-to-Upper Arm	45-55 (61-75)
Pivot Shaft-to-Lower Arm	32-50 (44-68)
Upper Shock Absorber	27-32 (37-44)
Lower Shock Absorber	45-50 (61-68)
Spring Pan	27-32 (37-44)
Stabilizer-to-Link	14-18 (19-24)
Tie Rod Nut	35-50 (48-68)

Front Suspension

MAZDA – EXCEPT PICKUPS

DESCRIPTION

Mazda uses independent front suspension with MacPherson type struts. Strut assemblies mount between lower control arms and upper fender panels. Strut assemblies consist of inner shock absorbers and coil springs surrounding outside of strut tube housing.

The steering knuckle is connected to lower control arm and strut. Lower control arms pivot at crossmember and are connected by ball joints to steering knuckle. Some models are equipped with a stabilizer bar. Strut rods are installed on RX7 to maintain alignment and stability.

ADJUSTMENT

WHEEL ALIGNMENT SPECIFICATIONS & PROCEDURES

See Wheel Alignment Specifications & Procedures in WHEEL ALIGNMENT Section.

WHEEL BEARING ADJUSTMENT

GLC

NOTE: **Tighten selector nut by 35 ft. lb. (48 N.m) increments. Ensure that steering knuckle can be turned smoothly by hand each time nut is tightened.**

1) Install wheel bearings and spacer in steering knuckle. Attach spacer selector (49 B001 727) to steering knuckle. Tighten selector nut to 145 ft. lbs. (197 N.m). Attach spring scale to steering knuckle lower caliper mounting hole. Measure and record preload.

2) Preload should be 1.7-6.9 INCH lbs. (0.2-0.8 N.m). If preload is not within specifications, the spacer must be changed. There are 21 spacers available from .2474" (6.285 mm) to .2794" (7.085 mm) in steps of .0016" (.04 mm). Select spacer that will keep preload within specifications.

3) If preload is too high, increase spacer thickness. If it is too low, decrease spacer thickness. Changing spacer thickness by one number will change preload by about 1.7-3.5 INCH lbs. (0.2-0.4 N.m). Spacer number is stamped on outer edge of spacer. Check preload after new spacer is installed.

GLC Wagon & RX7

1) Raise and support vehicle. Remove brake caliper and hang out of the way. Remove brake caliper adapter on RX7. Remove grease cap, cotter pin and nut lock. Tighten spindle nut to 18-22 ft. lbs. (24-30 N.m).

2) Turn hub a few times to seat bearings. Loosen nut. Install one wheel bolt and attach spring scale. Gradually tighten spindle nut until a preload reading of 1.0-1.4 lbs. (.45-.64 kg) is obtained.

626

1) Tighten drive axle lock nut by hand. Attach a spring scale to wheel hub stud. Measure hub rotation starting torque with no preload on wheel bearing. Install brake caliper assembly. Have an assistant depress brake pedal to keep hub/rotor assembly from turning.

2) Tighten drive axle lock nut to 116-174 ft. lbs. (160-240 N.m). Remove brake caliper assembly. Measure hub rotation starting torque. Bearing preload must not be greater than 4.4 lbs. (2.0 kg) from that of first reading, as measured in step one.

BALL JOINT CHECKING

GLC

Raise and support vehicle. Remove bolts attaching ball joint to lower control arm. Attach spring scale to mount hole at end of ball joint. Torque required to turn ball joint should be 4-7 lbs. (1.8-3.0 kg).

GLC Wagon & RX7

1) Disconnect strut assembly and tie rod end from steering knuckle arm. Check ball joint dust boot for cracks or other damage. Rotate ball joint stud several times to settle ball joint.

2) Attach spring scale to tie rod hole. Support knuckle with finger and measure torque required to turn ball joint. If scale reading is less than 1 lbs. (0.5 kg), replace ball joint and lower control arm as an assembly.

626

Remove lower control arm. Install preload attachment (49 0180 510B) to ball joint stud. Ball joint turning torque should be 1.5-2.5 ft. lbs. (2.0-3.0 N.m).

REMOVAL & INSTALLATION

WHEEL BEARING

Removal (GLC)

1) Raise and support vehicle. Remove wheel assembly. Have an assistant depress brake pedal to keep hub/rotor assembly from turning. Remove drive axle lock nut. Disconnect tie rod end from steering knuckle. Disconnect brake line from strut assembly.

2) Remove brake caliper and hang out of the way. Remove bolts attaching steering knuckle to strut assembly. Remove bolts attaching ball joint to lower control arm. Remove steering knuckle and ball joint as an assembly. Remove ball joint from steering knuckle.

3) Remove wheel hub using wheel hub puller (49 B001 726). Remove outer bearing inner race from wheel hub with attachment (49 F401 368) and bearing remover (49 F401 365). Remove wheel bearing outer races, if required.

Installation

Adjust wheel bearings prior to installation. *See WHEEL BEARING ADJUSTMENT in this article.* To install, reverse removal procedures.

Removal (GLC Wagon & RX7)

1) Raise and support vehicle. Remove wheel assembly. Remove brake caliper and hang out of the way. Remove brake caliper adapter on RX7. Remove grease cap, cotter pin, nut lock and spindle nut.

2) Remove washer and outer wheel bearing. Remove hub/rotor assembly. Remove grease seal and inner wheel bearing. Remove wheel bearing outer races, if required.

Installation

To install, reverse removal procedures. Adjust wheel bearings. *See WHEEL BEARING ADJUSTMENT in this article.*

Removal (626)

1) Raise and support vehicle. Remove wheel assembly. Disconnect tie rod end from steering knuckle. Disconnect stabilizer bar from lower control arm. Have an assistant depress brake pedal to keep hub/rotor assembly from turning. Remove drive axle lock nut.

2) Disconnect brake line from strut assembly. Remove brake caliper and hang out of the way. Remove bolt attaching ball joint to steering knuckle. Remove bolts attaching steering knuckle to strut assembly. Remove steering knuckle.

3) Remove wheel hub using wheel hub puller (49 G030 725) and attachment (49 G030 727). Remove snap ring. Remove wheel bearing from steering knuckle with attachment (49 G030 728). Remove wheel bearing outer races, if required.

Installation

To install reverse removal procedures. Adjust wheel bearings. *See WHEEL BEARING ADJUSTMENT in this article.*

LOWER CONTROL ARM

Removal (GLC & 626)

Raise and support vehicle. Remove wheel assembly. Remove splash shield and disconnect stabilizer bar on 626. Remove bolt attaching steering knuckle to lower control arm ball joint. Remove lower control arm pivot/bracket bolts and remove lower control arm.

Installation

To install, reverse removal procedure. Tighten lower control arm pivot/bracket bolts to specified torque with vehicle resting on ground.

Removal (GLC Wagon & RX7)

Raise and support vehicle. Remove wheel assembly. Remove bolts attaching steering knuckle arm to strut assembly. Disconnect tie rod end. Disconnect stabilizer bar. Disconnect strut rod on RX7. Remove steering knuckle arm. Remove lower control arm pivot bolt and remove lower control arm.

Fig. 1: RX7 Front Suspension

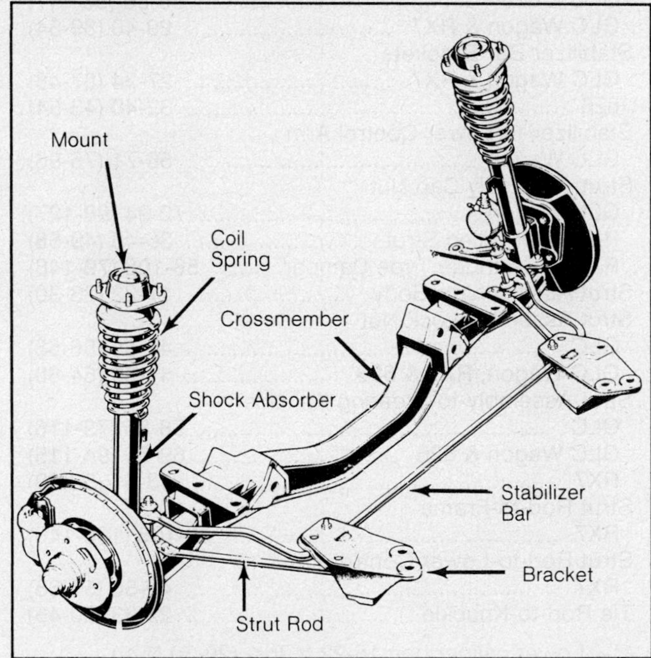
Mount
Coil Spring
Crossmember
Shock Absorber
Stabilizer Bar
Bracket
Strut Rod

Installation

To install, reverse removal procedure. Tighten lower control arm pivot bolt to specified torque with vehicle resting on ground.

STRUT ASSEMBLY

NOTE: **Loosen lock nut before removing strut assembly on 626.**

Removal (GLC & 626)

Raise and support vehicle. Remove wheel assembly. Disconnect brake line from strut assembly. Remove bolts attaching steering knuckle to strut assembly. Remove nuts attaching strut assembly and remove strut.

Fig. 2: Exploded View of GLC Wagon Front Suspension

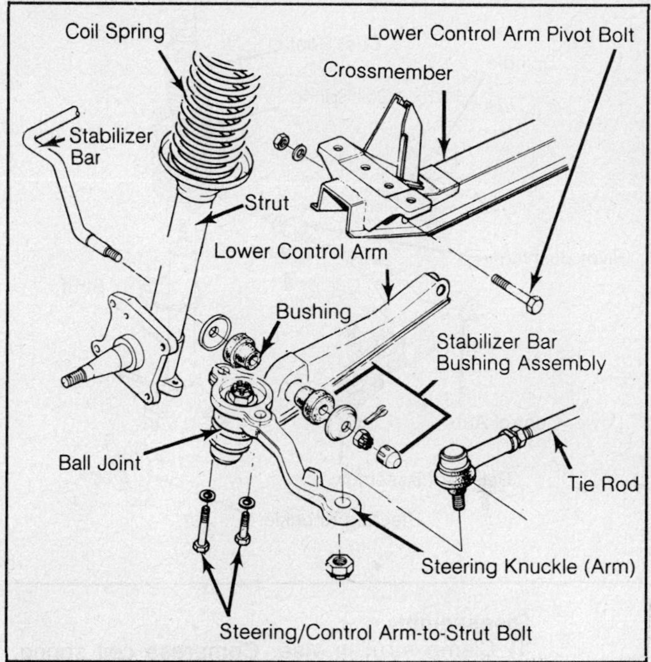
Coil Spring
Lower Control Arm Pivot Bolt
Crossmember
Stabilizer Bar
Strut
Lower Control Arm
Bushing
Stabilizer Bar Bushing Assembly
Ball Joint
Tie Rod
Steering Knuckle (Arm)
Steering/Control Arm-to-Strut Bolt

Disassembly

Clamp strut in vise. Compress coil spring. Remove cap, lock nut and washer from top of piston rod. Remove strut assembly mount, thrust bearing and spring seat. Remove coil spring, dust boot and damper.

Inspection

Check strut tube for cracks or damage. Check rubber parts for deterioration or damage. Inspect coil spring for signs of fatigue or damage. Replace parts as needed.

Reassembly

Install coil spring and remaining hardware in reverse order of disassembly.

Installation

To install, reverse removal procedures. Install strut assembly with triangle pointed toward center of vehicle on GLC. Install strut assembly mount so that positioning mark aligns with rear stud on 626.

Removal (GLC Wagon & RX7)

NOTE: **Note position of triangle on top of strut assembly before removing strut assembly on RX7.**

1) Raise and support vehicle. Remove wheel assembly. Remove brake caliper and hang out of the way. Remove grease cap, cotter pin, nut lock and spindle nut. Remove washer and outer wheel bearing. Remove hub/rotor assembly.

2) Remove backing plate. Disconnect brake line from strut assembly. Remove bolts attaching steering knuckle arm to strut assembly. Remove nuts attaching strut assembly and remove strut.

Front Suspension

MAZDA – EXCEPT PICKUPS (Cont.)

Fig. 3: Exploded View of GLC Front Suspension

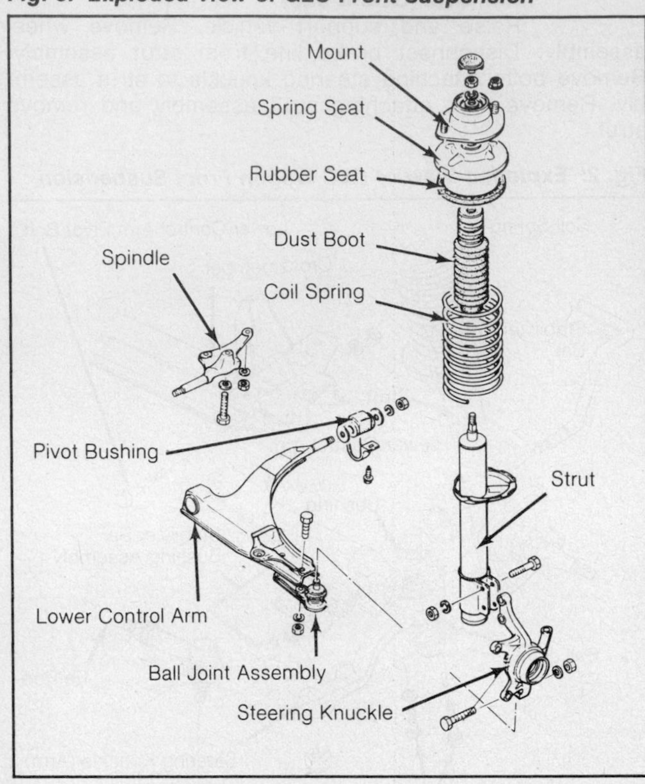
Mount
Spring Seat
Rubber Seat
Dust Boot
Spindle
Coil Spring
Pivot Bushing
Strut
Lower Control Arm
Ball Joint Assembly
Steering Knuckle

Disassembly

1) Clamp strut in vise. Compress coil spring. Remove cap, lock nut and washer from top of piston rod. Remove strut assembly mount, thrust bearing and spring seat. Remove coil spring, dust boot and damper.

2) Remove cap nut and seal. Pry "O" ring from piston guide rod. Pull piston rod and pressure tube assembly out of strut tube. Remove strut from vise and drain fluid, if used.

NOTE: Do not remove piston rod, guide or base valve from pressure tube. Service as a complete assembly only.

Inspection

Check strut tube for cracks or damage. Check rubber parts for deterioration or damage. Inspect coil spring for signs of fatigue or damage. Replace parts as needed.

Reassembly

1) Clamp strut in vise. Insert pressure tube and piston rod assembly into strut tube. Fill strut tube with shock absorber fluid, if used. *See STRUT RESERVOIR VOLUME table in this article.*

2) Fit pilot (49 0259 590) over threads of piston rod. Apply grease to lip of oil seal and insert cap nut through pilot onto piston rod. Tighten cap nut and pull out piston rod. Seat piston and torque cap nut. Install coil spring and remaining hardware in reverse order of disassembly.

Installation

1) To install, reverse removal procedures. Place triangle in its original position on RX7. Adjust wheel bearings. *See WHEEL BEARING ADJUSTMENT in this article.* Measure the distance between level ground and headlights on RX7.

2) The difference between headlights should not exceed 0.59" (15mm). If height is not within specifications, adjust the difference by inserting adjusting plates between mount and front suspension tower. Do not use more than two adjusting plates on one side.

STRUT RESERVOIR VOLUME

Application	Ounces (cc)
RX7	7.61 (225)
GLC Wagon	8.5 (250)

TIGHTENING SPECIFICATIONS

Application	Ft. Lbs. (N.m)
Backing Plate-to-Steering Knuckle	
GLC Wagon & RX7	25-33 (34-45)
Ball Joint-to-Lower Control Arm	
GLC	32-40 (43-54)
Ball Joint-to-Steering Knuckle	
GLC & 626	32-40 (43-54)
GLC Wagon	43-58 (58-79)
RX7	43-51 (58-69)
Brake Caliper Adapter-to-Strut	
RX7	25-33 (34-45)
Brake Caliper Bolts	
GLC, GLC Wagon & RX7	33-40 (45-54)
626 [1]	12-18 (16-24)
Drive Axle Lock Nut	
GLC & 626	116-174 (157-235)
Lower Control Arm-to-Frame	
GLC & 626 [2]	69-86 (93-117)
GLC Wagon & RX7	29-40 (39-54)
Stabilizer Bar Brackets	
GLC Wagon & RX7	27-34 (37-46)
626	32-40 (43-54)
Stabilizer-to-Lower Control Arm	
GLC Wagon	56-71 (76-96)
Strut Assembly Cap Nut	
GLC Wagon	72-94 (98-127)
RX7 w/Oil Filled Strut	36-43 (49-58)
RX7 w/Cartridge Type Damper	58-108 (79-146)
Strut Assembly-to-Body	17-22 (23-30)
Strut Assembly Lock Nut	
GLC	41-50 (56-68)
GLC Wagon, RX7 & 626	47-59 (64-80)
Strut Assembly-to-Steering Knuckle	
GLC	58-86 (79-116)
GLC Wagon & 626	69-85 (94-115)
RX7	43-51 (58-69)
Strut Rod-to-Frame	
RX7	80-108 (108-146)
Strut Rod-to-Lower Control Arm	
RX7	40-50 (54-68)
Tie Rod-to-Knuckle	22-33 (30-45)

[1] – Lower caliper bolt 15-22 ft. lbs. (20-30 N.m).
[2] – GLC rear control arm bracket 43-54 ft. lbs. (58-73 N.m).

MAZDA PICKUPS

B2000, B2200

DESCRIPTION

Mazda uses independent type front suspension. Suspension consists of upper and lower control arms. Wheel spindle mounted between upper and lower control arms by means of ball joints.

Upper control arm pivots on a shaft attached to frame. Lower control arm pivots on a shaft mounted to crossmember. A coil spring is mounted between lower control arm and frame.

Shock absorber is double-action type, mounted between lower control arm and frame inside coil spring. A stabilizer bar is connected to the lower control arm on each side by bushings and links.

Fig. 1: Exploded View of Front Suspension Assembly

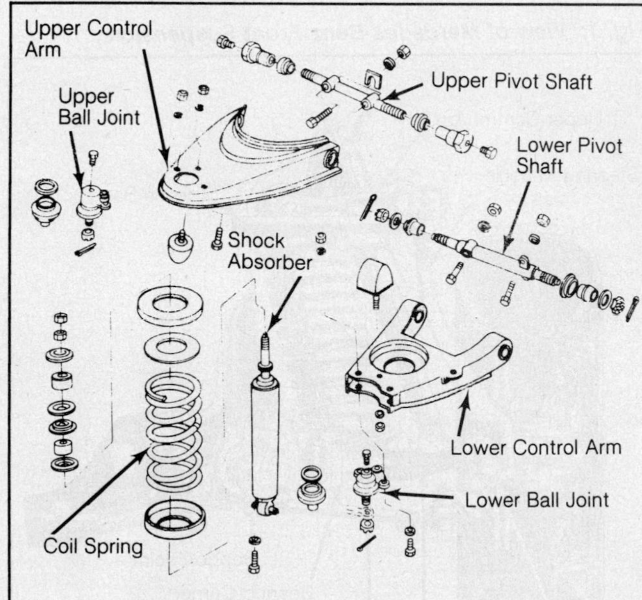
Upper Control Arm
Upper Ball Joint
Upper Pivot Shaft
Lower Pivot Shaft
Shock Absorber
Lower Control Arm
Lower Ball Joint
Coil Spring

ADJUSTMENTS

WHEEL ALIGNMENT SPECIFICATIONS & PROCEDURES

See Wheel Alignment Specifications & Procedures in WHEEL ALIGNMENT Section.

WHEEL BEARING ADJUSTMENT

Raise and support vehicle. Remove wheel assembly. Tighten spindle nut to 18-22 ft. lbs. (25-30 N.m). Rotate hub a few times to seat bearing. Loosen adjusting nut slightly until it can be turned by hand. Using a spring scale on one of the hub bolts, set preload to 1.3-2.5 lbs. (.59-1.1 kg).

BALL JOINT CHECKING

Check revolving torque of ball joint by using spring scale and measuring amount of pull to move ball joint stud. Revolving torque of lower ball joint should be 6-11 lbs. (2.7-5.0 kg). Revolving torque of upper ball joint should be 2.2-8.4 lbs. (1.0-3.8 kg).

REMOVAL & INSTALLATION

WHEEL BEARING

Removal

Raise and support vehicle. Remove wheel assembly. Remove brake caliper and support out of the way. Remove grease cap, cotter pin, lock and hub nut. Remove washer and outer bearing. Remove hub/rotor assembly. Remove grease seal and inner bearing.

Installation

To install, reverse removal procedures.

SHOCK ABSORBER

Removal

Remove nut, rubber bushing and washer attaching upper end of shock absorber to crossmember. Remove lower retaining bolts holding shock absorber to lower control arm, and remove shock absorber from vehicle.

Installation

To install, reverse removal procedures.

UPPER AND LOWER CONTROL ARM, COIL SPRING & BALL JOINTS

Removal

1) Raise and support vehicle. Remove wheel assembly. Remove front shock absorber. Remove stabilizer bar. Support lower control arm with floor jack. Disconnect upper and lower ball joint from steering knuckle.

2) Remove nuts and bolts retaining upper arm shaft to support bracket. Note the number and location of adjusting shims for reassembly. Slowly lower the lower control arm with floor jack and remove coil spring.

3) Remove nuts and bolts retaining lower control arm to frame. Remove lower control arm. Remove bolts retaining ball joints and remove ball joints, if necessary.

Installation

To install, reverse removal procedures. When replacing the coil spring, install adjusting plate(s) as needed to obtain equal road clearance on right and left sides. Never use more than 2 adjusting plates on any one side.

TIGHTENING SPECIFICATIONS

Application	Ft. Lbs. (N.m)
Ball Joint-to-Knuckle	51-65 (69-88)
Ball Joint-to-Lower Control Arm	60-70 (81-95)
Ball Joint-to-Upper Arm	14-20 (19-27)
Upper & Lower Control Arm-to-Frame	54-69 (73-94)
Stabilizer-to-Control Arm	18-26 (24-35)
Stabilizer Bracket	12-17 (16-23)

Front Suspension

MERCEDES-BENZ – EXCEPT 380 SERIES

DESCRIPTION

Mercedes-Benz uses independent front suspension, consisting of upper and lower control arms, coil springs, shock absorbers, steering knuckles and a stabilizer bar. Steering knuckle is connected at top and bottom by ball joints.

ADJUSTMENTS

WHEEL ALIGNMENT SPECIFICATIONS & PROCEDURES

See Wheel Alignment Specifications and Procedures in WHEEL ALIGNMENT Section.

WHEEL BEARING

1) While rotating hub, tighten clamp nut until hub can just be turned. Loosen clamp nut and release bearing tension by striking steering knuckle spindle with soft mallet.

2) Using a dial indicator, check wheel bearing end play. End play should be .0004-.0008" (.01-.02 mm). Adjust clamp nut until end play is within limits. Tighten socket bolt of clamp nut. Washer between outer bearing and clamp nut should rotate when light pressure is applied.

BALL JOINT CHECKING

Check ball joint lateral and vertical movement. If any measureable lateral movement is observed, replace ball joint. Correct excessive or insufficient vertical movement by adding or removing washers.

REMOVAL & INSTALLATION

WHEEL BEARING

Removal

Raise and support vehicle. Remove wheel and caliper assemblies. Remove dust cap. Loosen hex screw of clamp nut and remove clamp nut. Together with outer wheel bearing, remove hub and rotor assembly. Remove grease seal to access inner wheel bearing.

Installation

Replace any parts that show signs of wear. Clean and repack both bearings. Clean hub of old grease and install inner bearing and new grease seal into hub. Complete reassembly by reversing removal procedure and adjust bearing according to *WHEEL BEARING ADJUSTMENT* procedure.

STEERING KNUCKLE

Removal

1) Raise vehicle and support with safety stands under outer edge of lower control arms. Remove wheel assemblies.

2) Detach steering knuckle arm from steering knuckle. Remove caliper from steering knuckle and support out of the way. Remove hub.

3) Loosen brake hose holder on backing plate. Remove nut from upper ball joint and separate from steering knuckle.

4) Remove nut from lower ball joint. Rotate upper end of steering knuckle slightly outward, and use a ball joint separator fork to detach steering knuckle from lower ball joint. Remove knuckle from vehicle.

Installation

To install, reverse removal procedure.

COIL SPRING

Removal

1) Disconnect upper shock mount. Raise and support vehicle. Remove wheel assembly and attach coil spring compressor.

2) Tighten spring compressor while raising floor jack under lower control arm to assist in compressing spring. Slowly lower floor jack and remove the coil spring and rubber mounting.

Installation

1) Position rubber mount on coil spring. With spring compressed, position in vehicle. Slowly release spring, being sure it rests in mounting groove.

2) Install wheel assembly and lower vehicle to floor. Attach upper shock absorber mount.

Fig. 1: View of Mercedes-Benz Front Suspension

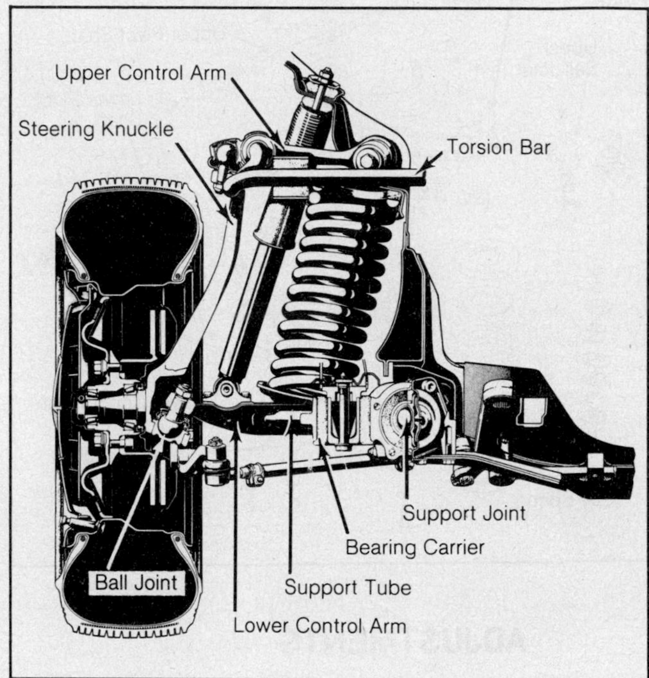
Upper Control Arm
Steering Knuckle
Torsion Bar
Support Joint
Bearing Carrier
Ball Joint
Support Tube
Lower Control Arm

UPPER CONTROL ARM

Removal

1) Raise vehicle and support under outer edge of lower control arms with safety stands.

CAUTION: Loosen hex nuts on ball joints with coil spring installed ONLY WHEN SUPPORTING STANDS ARE UNDER LOWER CONTROL ARM AND NOT BODY. If jack cannot be so positioned, remove coil spring.

2) Remove upper ball joint nut. Using separator tool, detach ball joint from steering knuckle arm. Wire steering knuckle to frame so it will not drop.

3) Remove upper control arm support from stabilizer bar and from body. Remove upper control arm.

Installation

1) Position upper control arm in vehicle and install control arm-to-body bolt. Connect upper ball joint to steering knuckle.

MERCEDES-BENZ – EXCEPT 380 SERIES (Cont.)

2) Mount stabilizer bar support to upper control arm, attaching bolt loosely. Lower vehicle to floor and tighten all bolts to specifications. Check wheel alignment.

LOWER CONTROL ARM

Removal

1) Loosen top shock absorber mount. Remove lower mount and remove shock absorber. Raise vehicle and support with safety stands under outer edge of lower control arms.

2) Remove wheel assembly. Remove coil spring as previously described. Detach tie rod end from steering knuckle arm.

3) Mark position of lower control arm eccentric bolt and bushing to crossmember for reference at reassembly.

4) Remove bolts holding brake support to frame. Remove lower control arm eccentric bolt. Detach lower ball joint from control arm. Remove lower control arm with brake support.

Installation

1) Mount lower control arm to ball joint. Position control arm bushing to frame. Attach brake support to frame.

2) Install coil spring. Install shock absorber, loosely. Install wheel assembly and lower vehicle to floor.

3) Tighten shock absorber mountings. Position eccentric bolt to original position and tighten to specifications. Attach tie rod end to steering knuckle arm. Check wheel alignment.

SUSPENSION ASSEMBLY

Removal

1) Disconnect upper shock mount. Raise vehicle and support with safety stands under outer edge of lower control arms. Remove wheel assembly.

2) Remove coil spring, as previously outlined. Use separator fork to remove tie rod end from steering knuckle arm.

3) Detach flexible brake hose from brake line at connection on fender well. Loosen plug connection of brake lining wear indicator on caliper. Remove bolts holding brake support to frame.

4) Support front axle half. Mark position of lower control arm. Remove eccentric bolt.

5) Remove stabilizer bar support from upper control arm. Remove bolt holding upper control arm bushing to body. Remove suspension assembly.

Installation

1) Position suspension in vehicle and mount upper control arm to body and stabilizer bar, but do not fully tighten bolts.

2) Raise opposite side of vehicle as required to obtain proper stabilizer bar position. Attach upper control arm to frame crossmember.

3) Attach brake support to frame. Reconnect brake line to hose and connect plug connection of caliper wear indicator. Install coil spring.

4) Install shock absorber loosely. Attach tie rod end to steering knuckle arm. Bleed brake system. Install wheel assembly and lower vehicle to floor.

5) Place eccentric bolt of camber adjustment to original position and tighten. Tighten upper control arm-to-body bolt and stabilizer bar-to-control arm support bolt.

6) Tighten shock absorber mounting bolts. Check axle riding height and wheel alignment.

STABILIZER BAR

Removal

1) Raise and support vehicle. Place safety stands under lower control arms. Remove wheels. Detach upper control arm support from stabilizer bar.

2) Remove master cylinder and booster. Remove heater hoses, air cleaner, regulator linkage, vacuum lines and electrical wiring as required to allow clearance for stabilizer bar removal.

3) Remove stabilizer bar mounting brackets and bushings. Remove end covers and stabilizer bar.

Fig. 2: Stabilizer Bar Mounting Location

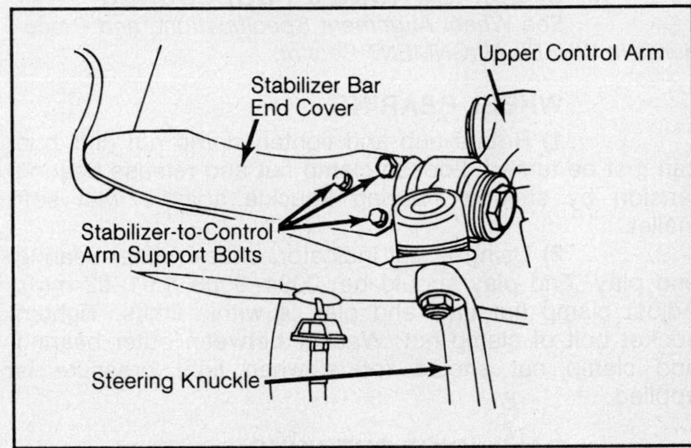
Upper Control Arm
Stabilizer Bar
End Cover
Stabilizer-to-Control
Arm Support Bolts
Steering Knuckle

Installation

1) Position stabilizer bar in vehicle and loosely attach bar support to upper control arm.

2) Position rubber bushings on stabilizer bar, with splits facing against frame. Install brackets loosely.

3) Attach left and right end covers and replace all hoses, linkage, wiring and brake components removed. Install wheel assemblies and lower vehicle.

4) Tighten stabilizer bar-to-control arm support bolt. Tighten mounting brackets. Check wheel alignment.

TIGHTENING SPECIFICATIONS

Application	Ft. Lbs. (N.m)
Shock Absorber Lower Mount	18 (24)
Stabilizer Bar Bracket Bolts	18 (24)
Steering Linkage Bolts	25 (34)
Steering Knuckle Arm Bolts	58 (79)
Upper Control Arm Eccentric Bolts	43 (58)
Lower Control Arm Eccentric Bolts	87 (118)
Upper Ball Joint Nut	43 (58)
Lower Ball Joint Nut	58 (79)

MERCEDES-BENZ 380 SERIES

DESCRIPTION

Front suspension assembly is a coil spring type, having separately mounted coil springs and shock absorbers between upper and lower control arms. Other front suspension components include steering knuckle, tie rods and a stabilizer bar. Steering knuckle is attached at top and bottom with ball joints.

ADJUSTMENTS

WHEEL ALIGNMENT SPECIFICATIONS & PROCEDURES

See Wheel Alignment Specifications and Procedures in WHEEL ALIGNMENT Section.

WHEEL BEARING

1) Rotate hub and tighten clamp nut until hub can just be turned. Loosen clamp nut and release bearing tension by striking steering knuckle spindle with soft mallet.

2) Using a dial indicator, check wheel bearing end play. End play should be .0004-.0008" (.01-.02 mm). Adjust clamp nut until end play is within limits. Tighten socket bolt of clamp nut. Washer between outer bearing and clamp nut should rotate when light pressure is applied.

BALL JOINT CHECKING

Check ball joint lateral and vertical movement. If any measurable lateral movement is observed, replace ball joint. Correct excessive or insufficient vertical movement by adding or removing washers.

REMOVAL & INSTALLATION

SHOCK ABSORBER

Removal

With vehicle on floor, detach upper and lower shock absorber mountings. Compress shock absorber to gain clearance and remove from vehicle.

NOTE: **Shock absorber attachments are not to be loosened or tightened unless vehicle is resting on floor or axle is supported enough to simulate full vehicle load.**

Installation

To install, reverse removal procedure.

WHEEL BEARING

Removal

Raise and support vehicle. Remove wheel and caliper assemblies. Remove dust cap. Loosen hex screw of clamp nut and remove clamp nut. Together with outer wheel bearing, remove hub and rotor assembly. Remove grease seal to access inner wheel bearing.

Installation

Replace any parts that show signs of wear. Clean and repack both bearings. Clean hub of old grease and install inner bearing and new grease seal into hub. Complete reassembly by reversing removal procedure and adjust wheel bearing. *See WHEEL BEARING ADJUSTMENT.*

COIL SPRING

Removal

1) Loosen lower shock absorber mounting and stabilizer bar connecting linkage. Raise vehicle and support with safety stands. Remove wheel assembly.

2) Mark position of lower control arm eccentric bolts on inner end of arm for reinstallation reference. Attach and engage coil spring compressor. Remove eccentric bolts.

3) Place cradle support beneath lower control arm directly below coil spring position. Slowly lower cradle support, allowing inner end of control arm to drop down, and remove coil spring.

Installation

To install, reverse removal procedure, fully tightening stabilizer bar mountings and lower shock absorber mounting after vehicle is resting on floor.

STEERING KNUCKLE

Removal

1) Install coil spring compressor on spring. Raise vehicle and support with safety stands. Remove wheel assembly.

2) Remove bolt holding steering knuckle arm to steering knuckle. Detach flexible brake hose from brake line and plug openings. Remove caliper.

NOTE: **On some models, it may be possible to remove caliper from rotor and support it out of the way, without detaching brake hose. This will eliminate necessity of bleeding brake system after installation.**

3) Remove nuts from upper and lower ball joint studs. Disconnect both ball joints from steering knuckle. Remove steering knuckle.

Installation

To install, reverse removal procedure, bleed brakes and check wheel alignment.

UPPER CONTROL ARM

Removal

1) Attach spring compressor to coil spring. Raise vehicle and support with safety stands. Remove wheel assembly. Shock absorber remains installed.

2) Remove bolt holding steering knuckle to steering knuckle arm. Detach brake hose from brake line and plug openings.

3) Remove nuts from upper and lower ball joint studs. Using separator tool, detach upper ball joint from steering knuckle.

4) Remove both upper control arm mounting nuts and remove arm.

Installation

To install, reverse removal procedure. Bleed brakes and check wheel alignment.

LOWER CONTROL ARM

Removal

1) Loosen and detach lower shock absorber mounting. Raise vehicle and support with safety stands. Remove wheel assembly.

MERCEDES-BENZ 380 SERIES (Cont.)

2) Detach steering knuckle arm from steering knuckle. Separate brake hose from brake line and plug openings. Remove coil spring as previously described.

3) Remove nuts from upper and lower ball joint studs. Detach lower control arm from lower ball joint. Remove control arm.

Installation

To install, reverse removal procedure. Bleed brake system. Tighten shock absorber mounting bolts after vehicle is resting on floor. Check wheel alignment.

STABILIZER BAR

Removal

Loosen stabilizer bar connecting linkage from both lower control arms. Remove stabilizer bar-to-frame mounting brackets and remove stabilizer bar.

NOTE: Stabilizer bar attachments are not to be loosened or tightened unless vehicle is resting on floor or axle is supported enough to simulate full vehicle load.

Installation

To install, reverse removal procedure.

TIGHTENING SPECIFICATIONS

Application	Ft. Lbs. (N.m)
Shock Absorber Lower Mount	14 (19)
Upper & Lower Ball Joint Nut	29 (39)
Tie Rod End Nut	14 (19)
Lower Control Arm-to-Frame	130 (176)
Steering Arm-to-Steering Knuckle	57 (77)
Upper Control Arm Clamping Bolt	21 (28)
Upper Control Arm-to-Body	60 (81)

Front Suspension

PEUGEOT

DESCRIPTION

An independent front suspension is used, with MacPherson type struts. Wheels are supported by steering knuckles that are attached to the strut assemblies. Lower control arms are attached to bottom of steering knuckles by lower ball joints.

Inner ends of control arms pivot on front crossmember. Attached to the lower control arms are strut rods that run forward to mounting points on front crossmember. The tops of the vertical suspension strut assemblies are attached to inner fender panels.

Coil springs surround the strut assembly. Hydraulic shock absorbers are built into strut assemblies. A stabilizer bar is mounted to the frame and connected at the ends to the lower control arm.

ADJUSTMENTS

WHEEL ALIGNMENT SPECIFICATIONS & ADJUSTMENTS

See Wheel Alignment Specifications and Adjustments in WHEEL ALIGNMENT Section.

WHEEL BEARING

Raise vehicle and support with safety stands. Rotate wheel or hub and tighten spindle nut to 29 ft. lbs. (39 N.m) on 505 and 604 models, or 22 ft. lbs. (30 N.m) on 504 models. On all models, loosen spindle nut and retighten to 7 ft. lbs. (10 N.m).

REMOVAL & INSTALLATION

WHEEL BEARING

Removal

1) Raise vehicle and support with safety stands. Remove wheel assembly. Remove brake cylinder and support out of the way.

2) Remove hub dust cap and nut. Remove wheel hub. If inner bearing remains on spindle, remove with puller as necessary.

3) On 504 models with angular contact ball bearings, remove hub nut "O" ring and wipe grease from hub. On all models, access inner bearing by removing grease seal.

Installation

To install, reverse removal procedure. Clean and repack bearings. When replaceing a bearing, replace bearing race also. Always treat bearings and races as matched sets.

LOWER BALL JOINT

Removal

1) If ball joint assembly is removed, ball joint must be replaced with new assembly. With suspension strut assembly removed from vehicle and using a gear puller, remove control arm from strut assembly. Install assembly in removal/installation clamp (8.0906H).

2) Raise and break off 2 tabs of lock washer. Place removal/installer tool (8.0616F) on ball joint and unscrew ball joint.

Installation

Lubricate threads of new ball joint assembly. Make certain that locating tabs of new lock washer are in place. Torque ball joint assembly to specifications. To complete installation, reverse removal procedure.

STRUT ASSEMBLY

Removal

1) Raise vehicle and support with safety stands under front crossmember. Remove wheel assembly. Remove brake caliper and support out of the way.

2) Separate tie rod end from knuckle. Disconnect stabilizer bar at mounting on lower control arm. Remove control arm pivot bolt nut and tap bolt out. Remove nut mounting strut rod to control arm.

3) Place a floor jack under steering knuckle and remove bolts retaining strut to inner fender panel. Hold spring by one coil and lower floor jack to remove strut assembly.

Disassembly

1) Install strut holder and spring compressor on strut assembly. Mount assembly horizontally in vise and compress spring.

2) Hold shock absorber piston rod and remove top nut and retainer. Slowly release tension on spring. Remove upper spring seat assembly, coil spring and rubber boot from shock absorber rod.

3) Mount strut assembly vertically in vise. Remove shock absorber gland nut. Pull up slowly on piston rod and remove piston rod assembly.

4) Remove support cup with rod seal, thrust washer, upper spring and bushing "O" ring from piston rod.

5) Pry bumper and lower spring seat off strut housing. Take strut housing from vise and drain hydraulic fluid. Unscrew strut housing and remove compensator valve.

Fig. 1: Components That Must be Disconnected Prior to Strut Assembly Removal

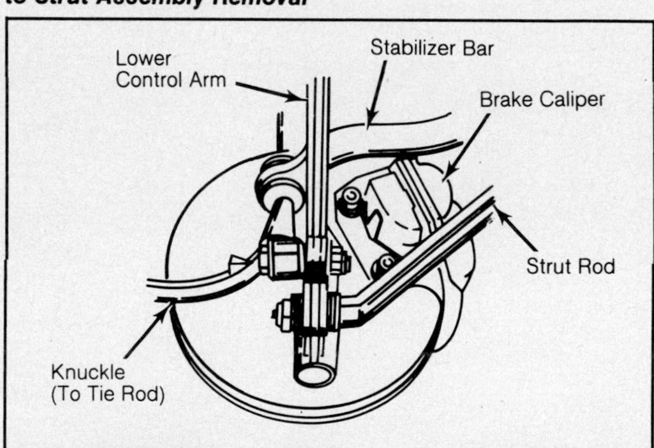
Lower
Control Arm
Stabilizer Bar
Brake Caliper
Strut Rod
Knuckle
(To Tie Rod)

Cleaning & Inspection

Clean and inspect all parts for wear or damage. During overhaul, replace all indicated components in *Figs. 2 and 3*.

Reassembly

1) Mount strut vertically in vise. Install recoil bumper with lower spring seat. Install compensator valve to shock absorber tube by lightly tapping with rubber mallet.

2) Clean valve, shock absorber tube and shock absorber inner housing with compressed air. Fit shock

PEUGEOT (Cont.)

absorber tube to strut housing. Fill shock absorber with 10 oz. (504 and 604) or 11 oz. (505) of Esso Oleofluid 40X (or equivalent).

3) Slowly insert piston rod assembly into shock absorber tube. Clearance between upper shock absorber housing and upper bushing must be .12" (3 mm).

4) Install new "O" Ring. Install upper spring and thrust washer (convex side up). Install new piston rod seal to cup. Position cup and seal over rod and force assembly down until thrust washer engages spring.

5) Tighten gland nut. Check rod rotation and operation. Install rubber dust boot. Fully extend piston rod and place holding clamp between bottom of dust boot and shock absorber cap nut.

6) Place housing horizontally in vise. Fit new seal to bearing thrust plate. Reassemble upper spring seat components as shown in *Figs. 2 and 3.* Install coil spring and upper spring seat.

7) Install and tighten spring compressor until retainer and new locking nut can be installed. Tighten nut while holding rod.

Installation

1) Install assembled strut assembly by guiding it into position while raising steering knuckle with floor jack. Install upper retaining bolts. Retainer must be parallel with centerline of vehicle.

2) Fit thrust washer, cup, and bushing to strut rod. Slide strut rod into control arm. Install bushing cup and new stop nut.

Fig. 2: Peugeot 504 and 604 Strut Assembly and Spring Seat Components

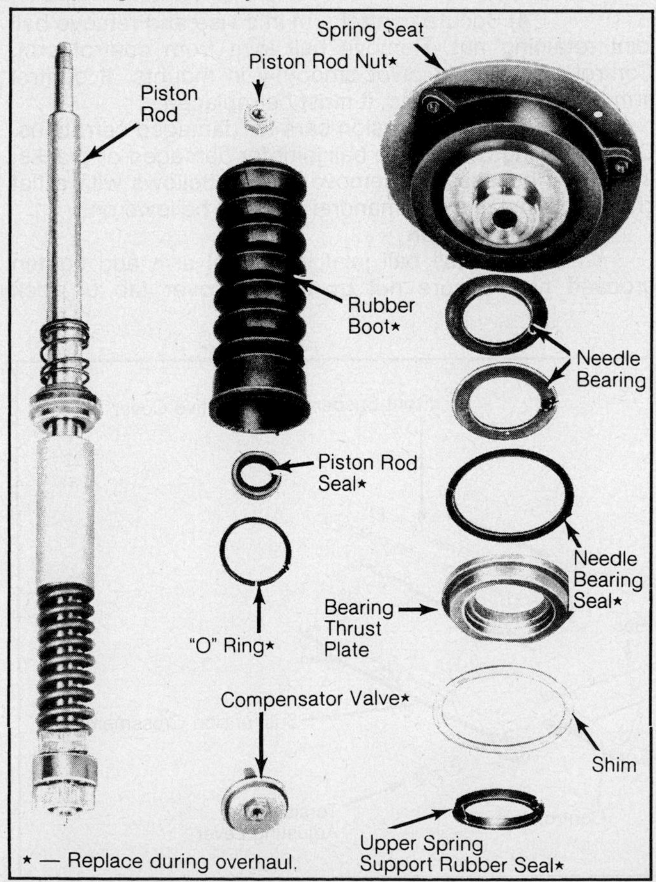
Spring Seat
Piston Rod Nut*
Piston Rod
Rubber Boot*
Needle Bearing
Piston Rod Seal*
"O" Ring*
Bearing Thrust Plate
Needle Bearing Seal*
Compensator Valve*
Shim
Upper Spring Support Rubber Seal*
* — Replace during overhaul.

Fig. 3: Peugeot 505 Strut Assembly and Spring Seat Components

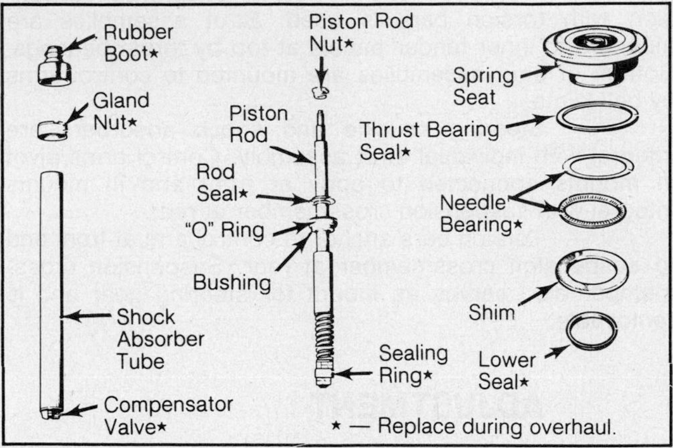
Rubber Boot*
Piston Rod Nut*
Spring Seat
Gland Nut*
Piston Rod
Thrust Bearing Seal*
Rod Seal*
Needle Bearing*
"O" Ring
Bushing
Shim
Shock Absorber Tube
Sealing Ring*
Lower Seal*
Compensator Valve*
* — Replace during overhaul.

3) With bolt head facing rearward, insert pivot bolt into position between control arm and front crossmember. Do not tighten nut. Refit stabilizer bar (nut end forward) to lower control arm. Install new washer and nut but do not tighten.

4) Connect tie rod end to knuckle and tighten nut. Clean brake disc and refit brake caliper. Tighten retaining bolts after placing a few drops of Loctite (or equivalent) on washers.

5) Install wheel assembly and lower vehicle. Install strut rod. Tighten all nuts with vehicle resting at riding height.

STABILIZER BAR

Removal

With vehicle resting on floor, remove 2 bolts retaining stabilizer bar near front crossmember. Disconnect both links mounting stabilizer bar at connecting links. Remove bar from vehicle.

Installation

Fit cup, spacer, and bushing to control link. Install stabilizer retaining bolts and spacers.

TIGHTENING SPECIFICATIONS

Application	Ft. Lbs. (N.m)
Shock Absorber Piston Nut	33 (45)
Shock Absorber Housing Nut	58 (79)
Knuckle-to-Control Arm Nut	33 (45)
Knuckle-to-Tie Rod Nut	31 (42)
Strut Rod-to-Control Arm Nut	33 (45)
Stabilizer Bar-to-Control Arm	33 (45)
Control Arm Pivot Bolts	33 (45)
Ball Joint	123 (167)

Front Suspension

PORSCHE 911SC

DESCRIPTION

Independent MacPherson strut type suspension with torsion bars is used. Strut assemblies are mounted to inner fender panels at top by thrust bearings. Bottom of strut assemblies are mounted to control arms by ball joints.

Steering knuckle and shock absorbers are integral with individual strut assembly. Control arms pivot in mounts connected to body at front and in mounts integral with suspension crossmember at rear.

Torsion bars anchor to control arm at front and to suspension crossmember at rear. Suspension crossmember also serves as mount for steering gear and is removable.

ADJUSTMENT

WHEEL ALIGNMENT SPECIFICATIONS & PROCEDURES

See Wheel Alignment Specifications & Procedures in WHEEL ALIGNMENT section.

WHEEL BEARING

1) Tighten hub nut while rotating wheel to seat bearings. Back off nut until thrust washer can be moved sideways with light pressure from a screwdriver.

2) Spindle nut should be tight enough to prevent any wheel hub axial play. Tighten pinch bolt, making sure that hub nut does not change position.

BALL JOINT CHECKING

Check lower ball joints for any signs of unusual wear, damage or excessive play. If any is found, ball joint must be replaced.

REMOVAL & INSTALLATION

WHEEL BEARING

Removal

1) Raise vehicle and support with safety stands. Remove wheel assembly. Disconnect brake line from caliper. Remove caliper. Remove grease cap, loosen hub nut pinch bolt.

2) Remove hub nut and remove wheel bearing thrust washer. Remove hub and rotor assembly from vehicle.

3) Press out outer wheel bearing (depending on equipment used, it may be necessary to separate rotor from hub), heat wheel hub to 250-300° F (120-150° C) and press out inner bearing and grease seal. Press out bearing races.

NOTE: **Always replace bearings and races as matched sets.**

Installation

To install, reverse removal procedures.

CONTROL ARM & BALL JOINT

Removal

1) Raise vehicle and support with safety stands, under body. Remove wheel assembly. Remove adjusting screw from torsion bar lever and remove lever.

2) Disconnect strut assembly from control arm. Remove rear control arm retaining bolt at suspension crossmember.

3) Remove bolts securing front control arm mount to body. Slide control arm with torsion bar out of suspension crossmember.

NOTE: **If both control arms are being removed, reinstall rear control arm mounting bolt in suspension crossmember before removing opposite side.**

4) Secure control arm in a vise and remove ball joint retaining nut. Remove ball joint from control arm. Control arm should pivot smoothly in mounts. If control arm binds or is distorted, it must be replaced.

5) Inspect torsion bars for damaged serrations. Check sealing bellows on ball joint for damaged or cracks, (replace if necessary). Remove sealing bellows with a flat chisel and install using mandrel to press bellows on.

Installation

1) Install ball joint in control arm and tighten grooved nut. Secure nut by bending over tab on lock

Fig. 1: Exploded View of Front Suspension Assembly

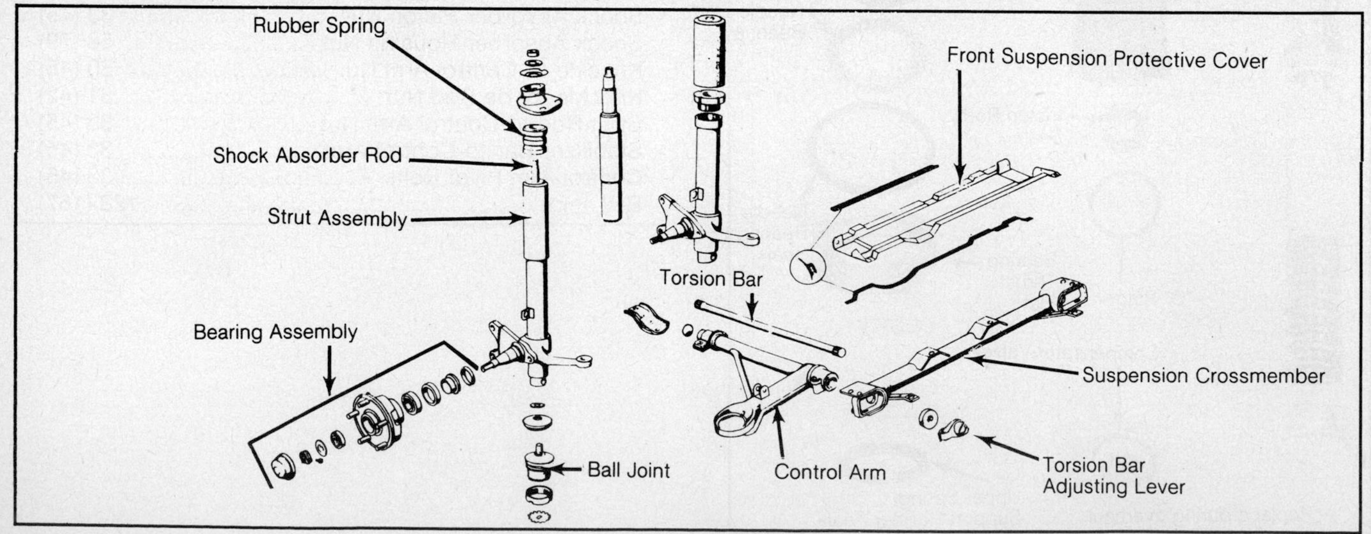
Rubber Spring
Shock Absorber Rod
Strut Assembly
Bearing Assembly
Torsion Bar
Front Suspension Protective Cover
Suspension Crossmember
Ball Joint
Control Arm
Torsion Bar
Adjusting Lever

PORSCHE 911SC (Cont.)

washer. Grease entire torsion bar and install in control arm.

2) Place control arm in proper position in vehicle and tighten retaining bolts (front to rear). Install strut assembly on ball joint and tighten retaining bolt. Push down on control arm until it contacts stops. Install torsion bar seal and adjusting lever.

3) Slide adjusting lever against torsion bar until it reaches stop. Grease adjusting bolt threads and install in lever. Make sure closing cover is correctly seated against adjusting lever.

4) Install control arm protective cover. Install wheel assembly. Lower vehicle and check riding height and wheel alignment.

STRUT ASSEMBLY

Removal

1) Raise vehicle and support with safety stands, under body. Remove wheel assembly. Remove brake rotor and brake caliper.

NOTE: If necessary, refer to appropriate article in BRAKE SYSTEM section.

2) Remove tie rod end strut nut and separate tie rod end from steering arm. Unscrew adjusting screw from torsion bar adjusting lever and remove lever.

3) Remove ball joint retaining bolt at bottom of strut assembly and push control arm down to separate strut assembly from ball joint.

4) From inside luggage compartment, remove center nut from upper strut assembly mount. Remove lock washer, tab washer and strut assembly.

5) Mark position of pressure plates on fender panel and remove Allen head bolts and pressure plates. Remove thrust bearing and support.

NOTE: Thrust bearing can be removed without completely removing strut assembly by disconnecting upper mount and pulling down on control arm to separate from thrust bearing.

Installation

1) Install thrust bearing and support. Place pressure plates in proper position and tighten Allen head bolts. Inspect strut assembly for leaks, if leak is discovered, strut assembly must be replaced.

2) Push rod to bottom of stroke, if flange does not bottom out against strut tube, replace strut assembly. There should be no variation of pressure when pushing in or pulling out on rod.

3) Install strut assembly in proper position in vehicle. Install hollow rubber spring, new lock washer, and tighten nut. Fit strut assembly to ball joint and tighten nut.

NOTE: Make sure steel washer is between ball joint and stud.

4) Push control arm lever down to stop and install adjusting lever on torsion bar. Grease threads of adjusting screw with grease and install screw. Make sure closing cover is correctly seated against adjusting lever.

5) Install tie rod and retighten nut. Install remaining components. *See appropriate article in BRAKE SYSTEM section*. Tighten all nuts and bolts, bleed brake system, check riding height, and wheel alignment.

SUSPENSION CROSSMEMBER

Removal

1) Raise vehicle and support with safety stands, under vehicle body. Remove front axle protective cover. Remove steering gear bolts from crossmember.

2) Remove rear control arm retaining bolts. Remove suspension crossmember. Place crossmember on level surface and check for distortion. Inspect for cracks or damage, (replace if necessary).

Installation

1) Place crossmember in proper position in vehicle and install control arm retaining bolts. Install steering gear bolts and tighten.

2) Install front suspension protective cover. Lower vehicle. Check riding height and wheel alignment.

STABILIZER BAR

Removal

Remove stabilizer shackles. Unbolt stabilizer lever retaining nuts and extract lever. Remove stabilizer mounting cover hardware and gently pry cover from vehicle.

Installation

1) Check all rubber grommets for signs of wear, (replace if necessary). Coat rubber parts with lubricant. Reinstall stabilizer mounting cover, center stabilizer, and tighten attaching bolts.

2) Seat stabilizer lever in position so stabilizer protrudes approximately .118" (3 mm) beyond lever. Tighten retaining nuts and install shackles.

AXLE ASSEMBLY

Removal

1) Disconnect brake hose and plug openings. Disconnect stabilizer bar at crossmember. Remove tie rod shield. Remove bolts at carrier and control arm brackets.

2) Place floor jack under crossmember. Disconnect steering shaft. Remove upper strut mounting hardware. Carefully pull front axle assembly from vehicle.

Installation

To install, reverse removal procedure.

TIGHTENING SPECIFICATIONS

Application	Ft. Lbs. (N.m)
Strut Assembly-to-Ball Joint Securing Bolt	47 (64)
Strut Assembly Thrust Bearing	58 (79)
Pressure Plate Allen Head Bolts	34 (46)
Front Control Arm Mount	34 (46)
Control Arm & Suspension Crossmember Retaining Bolt	65 (88)
Steering Gear Bolts	34 (46)
Ball Joint-to-Control Arm Grooved Nut	108 (147)
Front Protective Clamp Allen Head Bolt	32 (44)
Suspension Protective Cover-to-Body Bolts	34 (46)
Suspension Protective Cover-to-Crossmember Bolts	11 (15)
Tie Rod End Strut Nuts	32 (44)

Front Suspension

PORSCHE 928S

DESCRIPTION

Front suspension used is an independent MacPherson strut type suspension. It consists of a strut assembly, surrounded by a coil spring. This assembly is connected at top to inner fender panel and at bottom to lower control arm.

Lower control arm connects at outer end to steering knuckle through a ball joint. At inner end of the "T" shaped control arm, bushings connect arm to frame member.

An upper control arm is attached by ball joint to steering knuckle and by pivot shaft to frame member. A stabilizer bar is connected by a link to lower mounting of strut assembly.

Fig. 1: Exploded View of Front Suspension Assembly

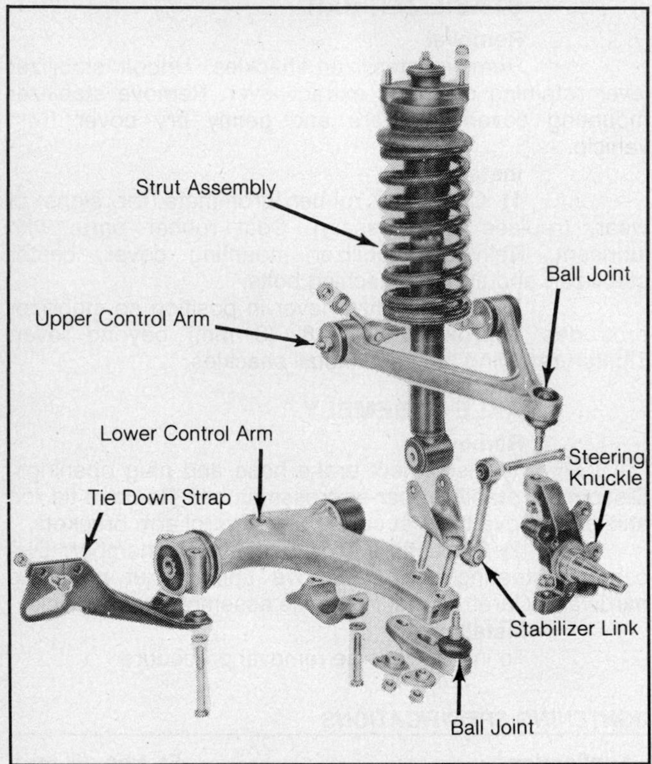
Strut Assembly
Ball Joint
Upper Control Arm
Lower Control Arm
Steering Knuckle
Tie Down Strap
Stabilizer Link
Ball Joint

ADJUSTMENTS

WHEEL ALIGNMENT SPECIFICATIONS & PROCEDURES

See Wheel Alignment Specifications and Procedures in WHEEL ALIGNMENT section.

WHEEL BEARING

1) Tighten hub nut while rotating wheel to seat bearing. Back off nut until thrust washer can be moved sideways with light pressure from a screwdriver.

2) Bearing adjustment should be tight enough to prevent any wheel hub axial play. Tighten pinch bolt, making sure that hub nut does not change position.

BALL JOINT CHECKING

Check ball joint and seal for signs of abnormal or excessive wear, damage or play, (replace if necessary).

REMOVAL & INSTALLATION

WHEEL BEARING

Removal

1) Raise vehicle and support with safety stands. Remove wheel assembly. Remove grease cap, loosen pinch bolt and remove hub nut. Remove thrust washer and outer wheel bearing.

2) Remove brake caliper and support out of the way. Remove hub and rotor assembly. Pry out inner grease seal and remove inner bearing.

3) Remove hub-to-rotor retaining bolts and separate hub from rotor. Heat wheel hub to 250-300°F (120-150°C) and press out inner and outer bearing races.

Installation

To install, reverse removal procedures. Wheel hub must be heated as in removal before installing bearing races. Always replace wheel bearings and races in matched sets. Adjust wheel bearings.

BALL JOINT

Removal (Upper)

1) Raise vehicle and support with safety stands. Remove wheel assembly. Remove caliper and support out of the way.

2) Remove castle nut from ball joint. Using removal tool (VW 267), press ball joint from steering knuckle and remove from control arm.

Installation

1) Install new ball joint into control arm and place stud into steering knuckle. Load ball joint by prying down on upper control arm to keep ball studs from turning and to facilitate installation of flange nut.

2) While prying down, install castle nut and tighten to specifications. To complete installation, reverse removal procedures.

Removal (Lower)

1) Raise vehicle and support with safety stands. Remove wheel assembly. Remove caliper and support out of the way.

2) Remove castle from ball joint. Using removal tool (VW 267), press ball joint from steering knuckle. Remove bolts retaining ball joint to lower contol arm. Remove ball joint.

Installation

To install, reverse removal procedures.

STRUT ASSEMBLY & UPPER CONTROL ARM

Removal

1) Remove retaining nuts from strut assembly to inner fender panel (located in engine compartment). Raise vehicle and support with safety stands. Remove wheel assembly.

2) Unscrew castle nut and use removal tool (VW 267), separate upper control arm ball joint from steering knuckle. Remove nuts holding upper control arm pivot shaft to body.

3) Remove strut lower retaining bolt and remove strut assembly and upper control arm from vehicle.

Disassembly

1) Place strut assembly in vise and attach coil spring compressor. Apply enough tension to coil spring to allow removal of top nut, washer and mounting plate.

Front Suspension

PORSCHE 928S (Cont.)

2) Release spring compressor. Remove upper spring retainer, coil spring and components from piston rod. Mark position of lower spring retainer to shock absorber for proper reassembly reference.

Reassembly

1) Reassemble strut assembly components in reverse order of disassembly. If replacing coil spring, be sure proper weight class springs are used.

2) If replacing lower spring retainer, coil spring or shock absorber, position of spring retainer to shock absorber must be determined.

3) Install assembly in vehicle by attaching upper retainers. Position upper end of spring against upper retainer stop. Position lower retainer and turn until against stop. Mark position. Remove strut assembly back to vise and complete reassembly.

Installation

To install, reverse removal procedure.

TIGHTENING SPECIFICATIONS

Application	Ft. Lbs. (N.m)
Upper Control Arm-to-Body	101 (137)
Lower Control Arm-to-Body	
Front	61 (83)
Rear	87 (118)
Stabilizer Bar-to-Body	33 (45)
Stabilizer Link Nut	61 (83)
Ball Joints-to-Steering Knuckle	61 (83)

Front Suspension

PORSCHE 944

DESCRIPTION

Independent MacPherson type struts are used. Lower control arms mount with a ball joint to steering knuckle.

Back branch of control arm mounts to frame with "U" clamp around control arm pivot shaft. Front branch attaches to frame with bushings and pivot bolt. Strut assembly mounts at top to body and at bottom to steering knuckle. The 944 has an alloy crossmember to hold engine, steering, and front control arm mounts.

Front stabilizer bar is 20 mm in diameter. A 21.5 mm stabilizer is optional. Koni shock absorbers are also available as optional equipment.

ADJUSTMENTS

WHEEL ALIGNMENT SPECIFICATIONS & PROCEDURES

See Wheel Alignment Specifications and Procedures in WHEEL ALIGNMENT section.

WHEEL BEARING

1) Tighten hub nut while rotating wheel to seat bearings. Back off nut until thrust washer can be moved sideways with light pressure from a screwdriver.

2) Hub nut should be tight enough to prevent any wheel hub axial play. Tighten pinch bolt, making sure that hub nut does not change position.

BALL JOINT CHECKING

1) Measure distance between upper edge of control arm and lower edge of steering knuckle using a vernier caliper.

2) Place a lever under ball joint and pry upward. Record any movement. New ball joints should have no end play. Wear limit for older ball joints is .1" (2.5 mm).

REMOVAL & INSTALLATION

WHEEL BEARING

Removal

1) Raise vehicle and support with safety stands. Remove wheel assembly. Remove grease cap and loosen pinch bolt. Remove hub nut, washer, and outer wheel bearing.

2) Remove brake caliper and support out of the way. Remove hub and rotor assembly. Pry off inner grease seal and remove inner bearing. Drive out bearing races, (if necessary or if bearings are to be replaced).

Installation

If bearing or race is bad, replace in matched sets. Do not use new bearings with old bearing races. To install, reverse removal procedures. Adjust wheel bearings.

CONTROL ARM & BALL JOINT

Removal

1) Raise vehicle and support with safety stands, so suspension is free. Remove wheel assembly. Remove caliper and support out of the way.

2) Remove bolt retaining ball joint in bottom of steering knuckle. Pull ball joint out of steering knuckle.

3) If control arm is not being removed, drill through ball joint rivets with 15/64" (6 mm) drill bit. Chisel off rivet heads. Fit new ball joint into slot on control arm and install bolts so heads are on top of control arm.

4) If control arm is being removed, take out mounting pivot bolt and "U" clamp housing inner pivot pin. Slide out control arm. For ball joint replacement, refer to step **3)**.

Fig. 1: Replacing Ball Joint on Lower Control Arm

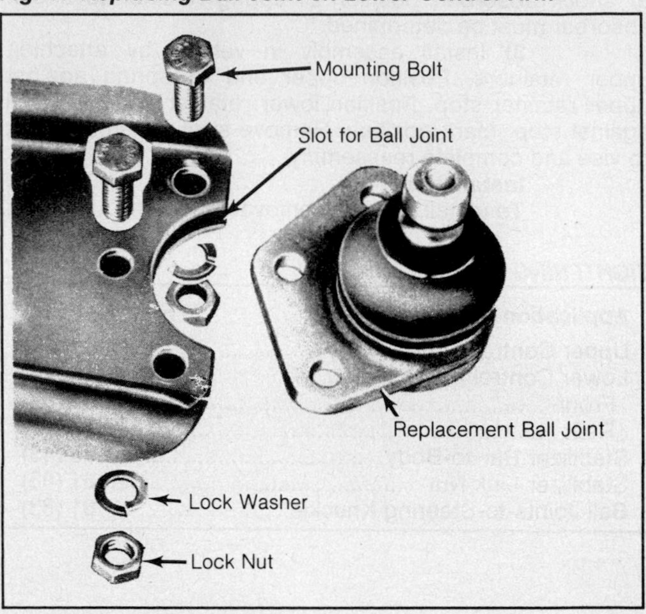
Mounting Bolt
Slot for Ball Joint
Replacement Ball Joint
Lock Washer
Lock Nut

Lower control arm does not have to be removed to replace ball joint.

Inspection

Check control arm bushings. If bushings are bad, replace by pressing out worn bushings. Select new bushings and press into position. Make sure new bushings do not twist when seating into position.

Installation

To install, reverse removal procedures.

STRUT ASSEMBLY

Removal

1) Raise vehicle and support with safety stands, so suspension hangs free. Remove wheel assembly. Remove caliper and support out of the way.

2) Remove bolts mounting suspension strut to steering knuckle. Note that top bolt is one used to adjust wheel camber.

3) Pry strut off of steering knuckle. Support front suspension. Working inside engine compartment, remove upper strut retaining nuts. Remove assembly from vehicle.

Disassembly

1) Using spring compressor, slightly collapse coil spring on strut. Remove shock absorber piston rod nut. Remove upper components from strut tube. *See Fig. 2.*

2) Slowly release spring pressure and remove coil spring. Lift off rubber buffer and protective sleeve.

3) Hold shock absorber upright and work piston rod through entire stroke several times. Equal pressure must be felt in both directions. Remove cap nut and take out inner shock absorber.

PORSCHE 944 (Cont.)

Fig. 2: Exploded View of Suspension Strut Assembly

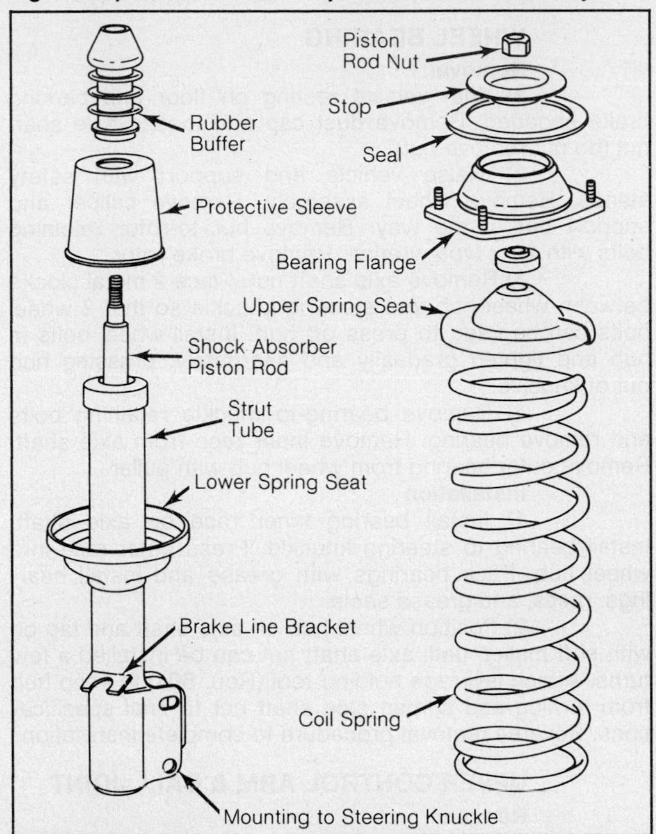
Piston
Rod Nut
Stop
Rubber
Buffer
Seal
Protective Sleeve
Bearing Flange
Upper Spring Seat
Shock Absorber
Piston Rod
Strut
Tube
Lower Spring Seat
Brake Line Bracket
Coil Spring
Mounting to Steering Knuckle

Fig. 3: Exploded View of Front Suspension

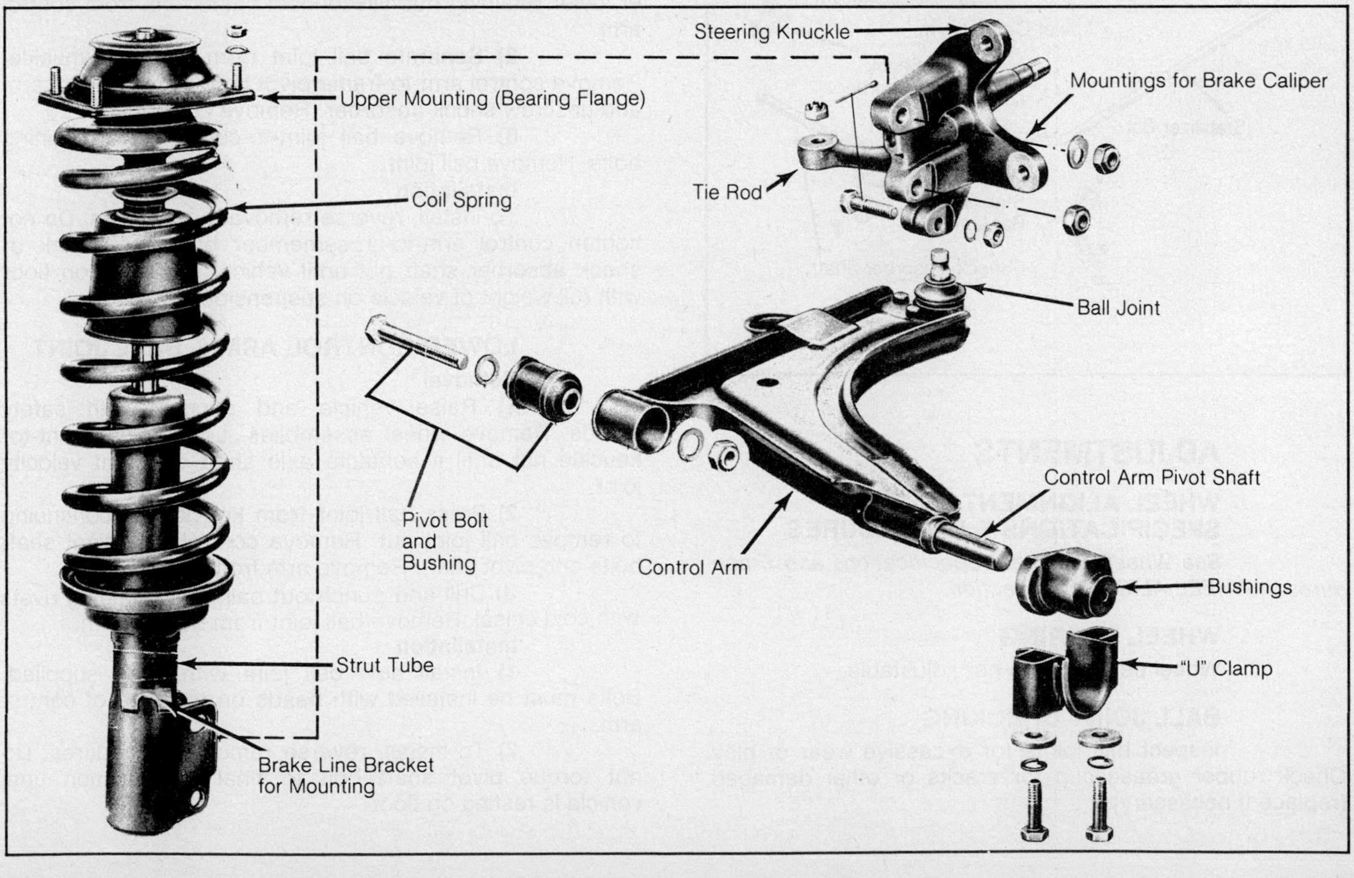

Steering Knuckle
Mountings for Brake Caliper
Upper Mounting (Bearing Flange)
Tie Rod
Coil Spring
Ball Joint
Control Arm Pivot Shaft
Pivot Bolt and Bushing
Control Arm
Bushings
Strut Tube
"U" Clamp
Brake Line Bracket for Mounting

Reassembly

1) Place shock absorber in strut tube and install cap nut. Slide on protective sleeve and buffer. Position coil spring into lower seat.

2) If new coil spring is being installed, ensure that paint stripe color code matches that of spring on opposite side.

3) Fit coil spring to compressor and collapse coil enough to allow piston rod threads to be exposed after upper mounting hardware is installed. Tighten piston rod lock nut. Release spring pressure.

Installation

To install, reverse removal procedures. Check wheel alignment.

TIGHTENING SPECIFICATIONS

Application	Ft. Lbs. (N.m)
Control Arm-to-Crossmember	40-54 (54-73)
"U" Clamp Bolts	33 (46)
Tie Rod Castle Nut	22-36 (30-49)
Strut Piston Rod Nut	56-58 (76-79)
Strut-to-Steering Knuckle	72 (98)
Upper Strut Mount	15-21 (20-29)
Ball Joint-to-Control Arm Replacement Bolts	18 (24)
Ball Joint Nut	36-43 (49-58)

Front Suspension

RENAULT FUEGO & 18i

DESCRIPTION

An independent front suspension system is used. Coil springs surround shock absorbers. Front suspension utilizes upper and lower control arms.

Shock absorbers are mounted to inner fender panels at top and to upper controls arm at the bottom.

Wheel hub and rotor are supported by a steering knuckle which is mounted between the control arms with ball joints. A stabilizer bar is used to aid vehicle control and stability.

Fig.1: Exploded View of Front Suspension

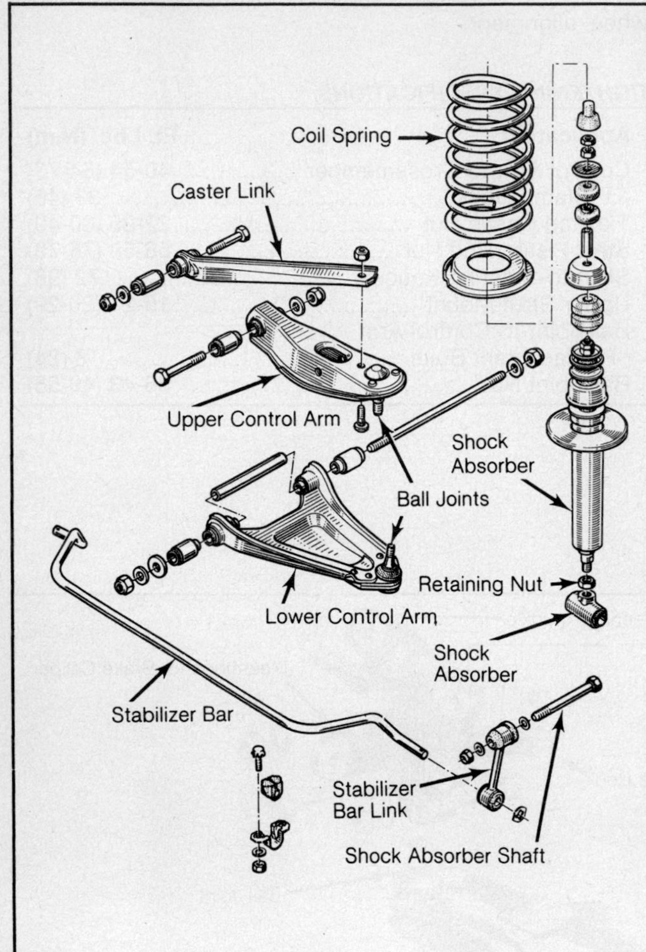
Coil Spring
Caster Link
Upper Control Arm
Shock Absorber
Ball Joints
Retaining Nut
Lower Control Arm
Shock Absorber
Stabilizer Bar
Stabilizer Bar Link
Shock Absorber Shaft

ADJUSTMENTS

WHEEL ALIGNMENT SPECIFICATIONS & PROCEDURES

See Wheel Alignment Specifications and Procedures in WHEEL ALIGNMENT section.

WHEEL BEARING

Wheel bearings are not adjustable.

BALL JOINT CHECKING

Inspect ball joints for excessive wear or play. Check rubber grease cup for cracks or other damaged, (replace if necessary).

REMOVAL & INSTALLATION

WHEEL BEARING

Removal

1) With vehicle resting on floor and parking brake engaged. Remove dust cap and loosen axle shaft nut (do not remove nut).

2) Raise vehicle and support with safety stands. Remove wheel assembly. Remove caliper and support out of the way. Remove hub-to-rotor retaining bolts with Torx type wrench. Remove brake rotor.

3) Remove axle shaft nut. Place 2 metal blocks between wheel hub and steering knuckle so that 2 wheel bolts can be used to press off hub. Install wheel bolts in hub and tighten gradually and alternately, pressing hub out of knuckle.

4) Remove bearing-to-knuckle retaining bolts and remove bearing. Remove inner race from axle shaft. Remove outer bearing from wheel hub with puller.

Installation

1) Install bearing inner race on axle shaft. Install bearing to steering knuckle. Press outer race into wheel hub. Pack bearings with grease and install bearings, races, and grease seals.

2) Position wheel hub on axle shaft and tap on with soft mallet, until axle shaft nut can be installed a few turns. Attach leverage holding tool (Rou. 604) to keep hub from turning and tighten axle shaft nut to final specifications. Reverse removal procedure to complete installation.

UPPER CONTROL ARM & BALL JOINT

Removal

1) Raise vehicle and support with safety stands. Remove wheel assemblies. Loosen shock absorber lower retaining nut. Disconnect caster link from control arm.

2) Separate ball joint from steering knuckle. Remove control arm-to-frame pivot bolt. Raise control arm and unscrew shock absorber. Remove control arm.

3) Remove ball joint-to-control arm retaining bolts. Remove ball joint.

Installation

To install, reverse removal procedures. Do not tighten control arm-to-crossmember bolt, caster link or shock absorber shaft nut until vehicle is resting on floor with full weight of vehicle on suspension.

LOWER CONTROL ARM & BALL JOINT

Removal

1) Raise vehicle and support with safety stands. Remove wheel assemblies. Loosen ball joint-to-knuckle nut until it contacts axle shaft constant velocity joint.

2) Press ball joint from knuckle by continuing to remove ball joint nut. Remove control arm pivot shaft bolts and pivot shaft. Remove arm from vehicle

3) Drill and punch out ball joint retaining rivets with cold chisel. Remove ball joint from control arm.

Installation

1) Install new ball joint with bolts supplied. Bolts must be installed with heads on top side of control arm.

2) To install, reverse removal procedures. Do not torque pivot shaft bolt to final specification until vehicle is resting on floor.

RENAULT FUEGO & 18i (Cont.)

NOTE: Since the ball joint-to-control arm nut is used to press out ball joint, a new nut must be used upon reassembly.

SHOCK ABSORBER & COIL SPRING

Removal

1) Raise vehicle and support under control arms with floor jack. Remove wheel assemblies.

2) Install spring compressor with clamps over next-to-last upper coil of spring. Lubricate threaded ends of clamps. Install nuts hand tight only.

3) Lower jack until coil spring separates from upper spring mounting cup. Spring should now turn by hand. Loosen shock absorber shaft nut but do not remove bolt.

4) Remove upper shock retaining nut. Loosen lower shock retaining nut. Remove shock absorber, coil spring and tool.

5) Install inside type coil spring compressor and tighten to release spring compressor clamps. Loosen compressor and remove spring.

Fig. 2: Shock Absorber & Coil Spring Removal

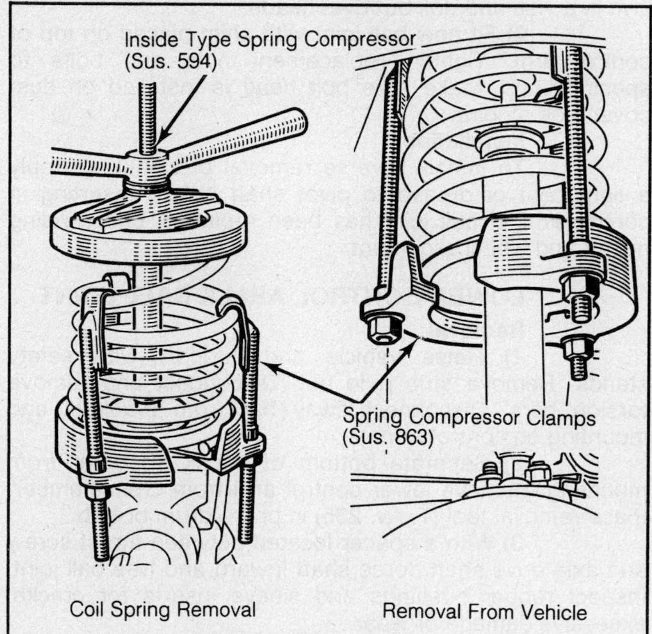
Inside Type Spring Compressor
(Sus. 594)
Spring Compressor Clamps
(Sus. 863)
Coil Spring Removal
Removal From Vehicle

Installation

1) Compress spring with inside compressor and install compressor clamps. Remove inside compressor. Install shock absorber with coil spring and compressor.

2) Raise floor jack and tighten shock absorber. Back off nut 1 turn. Install upper shock absorber bushings and cups in same position as before removal. Install upper nut hand tight.

3) Lower vehicle completely and jounce up and down a few times to settle suspension. Tighten upper nut, lower retaining nut and shaft nut to final specifications. Remove spring compressor.

STABILIZER BAR

Removal

1) Raise vehicle and support with safety stands. Remove engine undercover. Remove stabilizer bar clamp-to-frame bushing bolts.

2) Remove shock absorber shaft nut and stabilizer bar link retainer. Remove stabilizer bar with links and bushings.

Installation

To install, reverse removal procedures. Tighten bolts to specification only after vehicle is resting on floor.

TIGHTENING SPECIFICATIONS

Application	Ft. Lbs. (N.m)
Axle Shaft Nut	185 (252)
Shock Absorber Retaining Nut	30 (41)
Shock Absorber Shaft Nut	59 (80)
Shaft-to-Shock Absorber	44 (60)
Caster Link-to-Upper Control Arm	59 (80)
Upper Control Arm-to-Frame	65 (88)
Lower Control Arm-to-Frame	65 (88)
Upper Ball Joint-to-Steering Knuckle	48 (65)
Lower Ball Joint-to-Steering Knuckle	48 (65)
Stabilizer Bar Clamp-to-Frame	11 (15)

Front Suspension

RENAULT LE CAR

DESCRIPTION

Le Car uses independent type suspension, consisting of upper and lower control arms. Stub axles are mounted in steering knuckle, between upper and lower control arms held by ball joints.

Upper control arm pivots on shaft attached to frame. Lower arm pivots on shaft secured to the crossmember. Shock absorbers mount to body brackets at top and control arms at the bottom.

Fig. 1: Cutaway View of Front Suspension

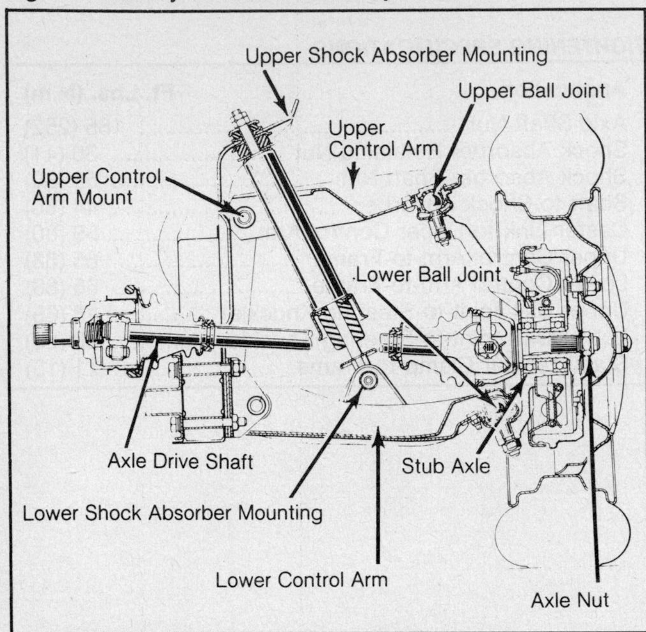
Upper Shock Absorber Mounting
Upper Ball Joint
Upper Control Arm
Upper Control Arm Mount
Lower Ball Joint
Axle Drive Shaft
Stub Axle
Lower Shock Absorber Mounting
Lower Control Arm
Axle Nut

ADJUSTMENT

WHEEL ALIGNMENT SPECIFICATIONS & PROCEDURES

See Wheel Alignment Specifications & Procedures in WHEEL ALIGNMENT section.

WHEEL BEARING

No adjustment is necessary on wheel bearings. Tighten stub axle nuts to specifications.

BALL JOINT CHECKING

Inspect ball joints for excessive wear or play, (replace if necessary).

REMOVAL & INSTALLATION

WHEEL BEARING

Removal

1) Raise vehicle and support with safety stands. Remove wheel assembly. Remove caliper and bracket. Attach leverage holding tool (Rou. 604) to keep rotor from turning and loosen stub axle nut.

2) Attach slide hammer to wheel studs and remove hub and rotor. Remove hub-to-rotor retaining bolts. Separate hub from rotor. Pull outer bearing from inside of hub.

3) Disconnect tie rod end from steering knuckle. Disconnect control arm ball joints from knuckle. Remove knuckle. Remove bearing cover from inside of knuckle. Press out inner bearing.

Installation

To install, reverse removal procedures. Use sealer when installing bearing cover to knuckle. Assemble hub and rotor to steering knuckle and install to stub axle as a complete assembly.

UPPER CONTROL ARM & BALL JOINT

Removal

1) Take out overflow tank and remove ignition coil. Using removal tool (T. AV. 476) disconnect upper ball joint. Remove nut from inboard edge of pivot shaft.

2) Place a lock nut on outer end of pivot shaft and turn retaining nut to remove shaft. Pivot shaft will clear brake lines. Remove control arm from vehicle. Inspect rubber bushings for cracks or distortion, (replace if necessary).

Replacement (Bushings & Ball Joints)

1) Use a press and mandrel to remove and replace worn bushings. To replace ball joint, place control arm in a vise and drill out rivet heads.

2) Fit new ball joint with shim placed on top of control arm. Tighten replacement nuts and bolts to specifications. Make sure bolt head is installed on dust cover side of joint.

Installation

To install, reverse removal procedures. Apply a light coat of grease to pivot shaft before inserting in control arm. If ball joint has been replaced, check riding height and wheel alignment.

LOWER CONTROL ARM & BALL JOINT

Removal

1) Raise vehicle and support with safety stands. Remove stub axle nut. Disconnect and remove torsion bars. Disconnect sway bar from brackets and mounting on control arm.

2) Separate bottom of shock absorber from mounting. Remove lower control arm from crossmember. Place removal tool (T. Av. 235) in brake drum or hub.

3) With a spacer located between thrust screw and axle drive shaft, force shaft inward and free ball joint. Inspect rubber bushings and sleeve inserts for cracks, excessive damage or wear.

NOTE: Make sure axle drive shaft is not removed.

Replacement (Bushings & Ball Joints)

1) Use a mandrel and press to replace bushings. Make sure each bushing is centered and has adequate protrusion out each side of control arm.

2) Place control arm in holding fixture. Chisel or drill out rivet heads. Remove nuts, (if necessary). Separate joint from control arm.

3) Fit new ball joint into control arm. Make sure bolt heads face dust cover side. Tighten to specifications.

Installation

To install, reverse removal procedures. Make sure castor adjusting shims are under bushing. Check riding height and wheel alignment.

RENAULT LE CAR (Cont.)

SHOCK ABSORBER

Removal

Raise vehicle and support with safety stands. Remove lock nut, retaining nut, and bushing attaching shock absorber to upper bracket. Remove lower retaining bolt holding shock absorber to lower control arm. Remove shock absorber from vehicle.

Installation

To install, reverse removal procedure.

STUB AXLE

Removal

1) Raise vehicle and support with safety stands. Remove wheel assembly. Remove hub and disc assembly. Using removal tool (T. Av. 476). Disconnect upper and lower ball joints.

2) Separate tie rod end. Using a slide hammer withdraw drum/hub assembly. Make sure axle drive shaft does not drop.

Installation

Install stub axle into position while guiding ball joints into position. Pull drive shaft into carrier housing. To complete installation, reverse removal procedures.

TORSION BAR

Removal

1) Slide seat forward and tilt. Loosen lock nut and turn cam screw counterclockwise to zero. Raise vehicle and support with safety stands. Remove dust cover from adjusting lever.

Fig. 2: Exploded View of Torsion Bar Assembly

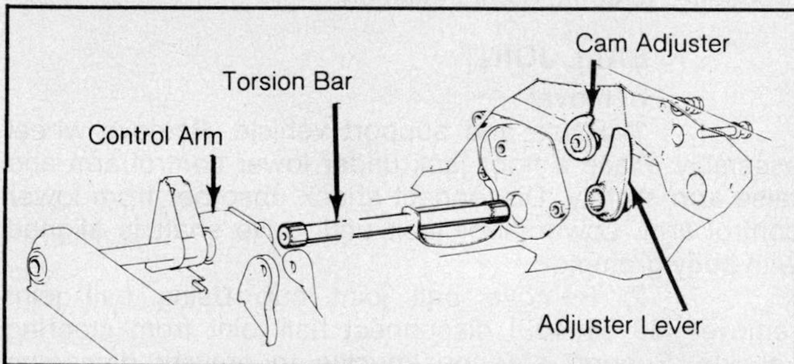
Cam Adjuster
Torsion Bar
Control Arm
Adjuster Lever

2) Install removal tool (545) on adjusting lever. From inside vehicle, remove lever housing attachment bolts. Remove housing cover cam assembly from adjusting lever. Slowly release pressure on wrench.

Fig. 3: Scribing Marks on Floor Crossmember

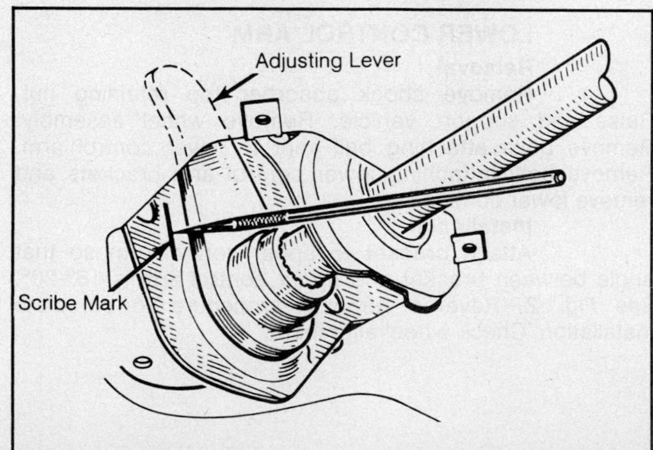
Adjusting Lever
Scribe Mark

3) Index mark position of adjusting lever with floor crossmember. Mark position of torsion bar on lower arm anchor sleeve. Disconnect stabilizer bar brackets.

4) Remove bar from arm and check that mark made on lower arm anchor sleeve is aligned with punch mark on torsion bar. If punch marks do not align, count number of revolutions and spines displaced to align marks.

Installation

1) Lightly grease torsion bar ends. Reassemble cover seal, cam housing, and adjusting lever over torsion bar. Insert bar into lower control arm, aligning index mark made during removal.

Fig. 4: Lower Arm Anchor Sleeve Scribe Mark

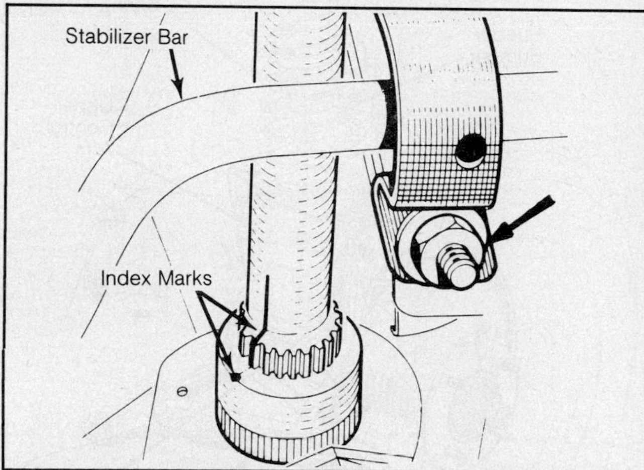
Stabilizer Bar
Index Marks

2) Install adjusting lever on splines, aligning with mark on floor crossmember. Place adjusting lever 3/8-3/4" (10-20 mm). *See Fig. 5.* Insert wrench (545) and take up tension on bar.

3) Center the cover by resetting cam. Hold assembly with vise grips and insert retaining bolts. Adjust under body height by turning adjusting cams.

Fig. 5: Position of Adjusting Lever

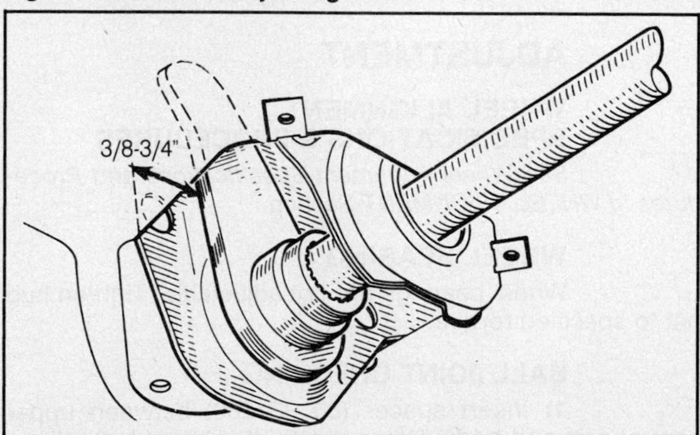
3/8-3/4"

TIGHTENING SPECIFICATIONS

Application	Ft. Lbs. (N.m)
Lower Shock Absorber Bolt	30 (41)
Lower Ball Joint	40 (54)
Upper Ball Joint	25 (34)
Lower Control Arm Nuts	75 (102)
Stub Axle Nut	90 (122)

Front Suspension

SAAB 900 & 900 TURBO

DESCRIPTION

Independent double wishbone front suspension consists of transversely mounted control arms, vertically mounted coil springs and specially designed double-acting shock absorbers.

The downward stroke of the lower control arm is limited by the shock absorber. The coil spring is mounted between the upper control arm and wheel housing. The lower spring seat is attached by a rubber bushing to the upper control arm.

Fig. 1: Saab 900 & 900 Turbo Front Suspension

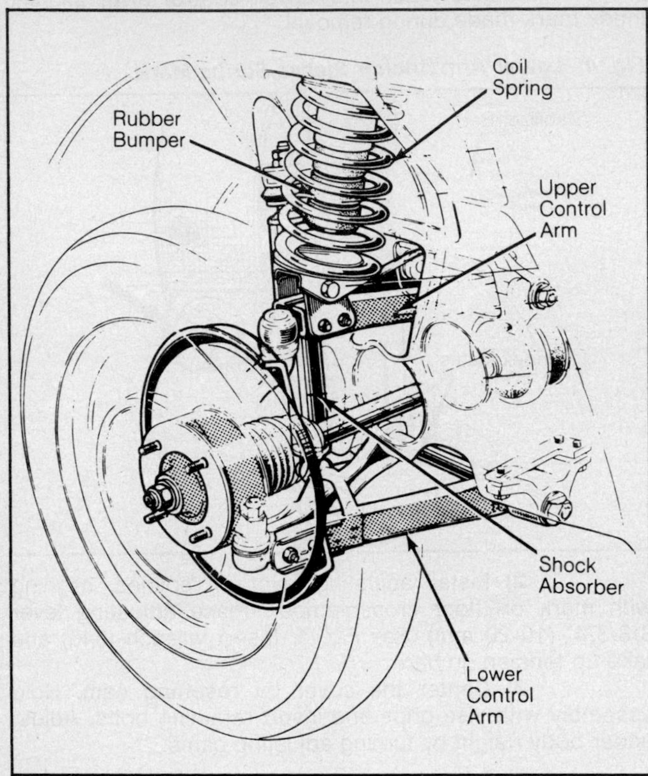
Coil
Spring
Rubber
Bumper
Upper
Control
Arm
Shock
Absorber
Lower
Control
Arm

ADJUSTMENT

WHEEL ALIGNMENT SPECIFICATIONS & PROCEDURES

See Wheel Alignment Specifications and Procedures in WHEEL ALIGNMENT Section.

WHEEL BEARING

Wheel bearings are not adjustable. Tighten hub nut to specified torque.

BALL JOINT CHECKING

1) Insert spacer (83 93 209) between upper control arm and body. Using a pair of channel lock pliers, compress ball joint. Check ball joint axial play. Maximum axial play should be .08" (2.0 mm).

2) Apply pressure between lower control arm and vertical link, to check radial play. Maximum radial play should be .04" (1.0 mm). Check ball joint seals for wear or damage, replace if necessary.

REMOVAL & INSTALLATION

WHEEL BEARING

Removal

1) Insert spacer (83 93 209) between upper control arm and body. Loosen hub nut. Raise and support vehicle. Remove wheel assembly. Remove brake pads, using the recesses in edge of disc brake rotor. Remove brake caliper and hang out of the way. Remove disc brake rotor.

2) Using ball joint remover (89 95 409) disconnect tie rod from steering knuckle assembly. Remove bolts attaching ball joint to upper and lower control arms. Remove the steering knuckle assembly by pulling it off drive shaft and control arms.

3) Press hub out of steering knuckle assembly. Pull inner bearing race off hub. If there are no groves for puller, chisel off race. Remove snap rings from steering knuckle assembly and press out bearing.

Installation

NOTE: Pressing hub out of steering knuckle assembly damages the wheel bearing, always replace bearing.

1) Lubricate steering knuckle bearing recess in with Molycote Paste G. Install snap ring in inner groove of steering knuckle assembly. Press bearing against snap ring.

2) Install outer snap ring and press hub into bearing. Lubricate drive shaft splines with Molycote Paste G and insert steering knuckle assembly. Reverse removal procedure to complete installation.

BALL JOINT

Removal

1) Raise and support vehicle. Remove wheel assembly. Place a floor jack under lower control arm and raise arm slightly. Disconnect shock absorber from lower control arm. Lower floor jack until drive shaft is aligned with body grommet.

2) Remove ball joint nut. Using ball joint remover (89 95 409) disconnect ball joint from steering knuckle. Support steering knuckle to prevent damaging brake hose, if upper ball joint is being removed. Remove bolts attaching ball joint to control arm and remove ball joint.

Installation

Replace self-locking nuts on ball joint attaching bolts. Reverse removal procedure to complete installation.

LOWER CONTROL ARM

Removal

Remove shock absorber top retaining nut. Raise and support vehicle. Remove wheel assembly. Remove bolts attaching ball joint to lower control arm. Remove bolts attaching lower control arm brackets and remove lower control arm.

Installation

Attach bracket to upper control arm so that angle between bracket and upper control arm is 16°-20°. *See Fig. 2.* Reverse removal procedure to complete installation. Check wheel alignment.

SAAB 900 & 900 TURBO (Cont.)

Fig. 2: Lower Control Arm Bracket Angle

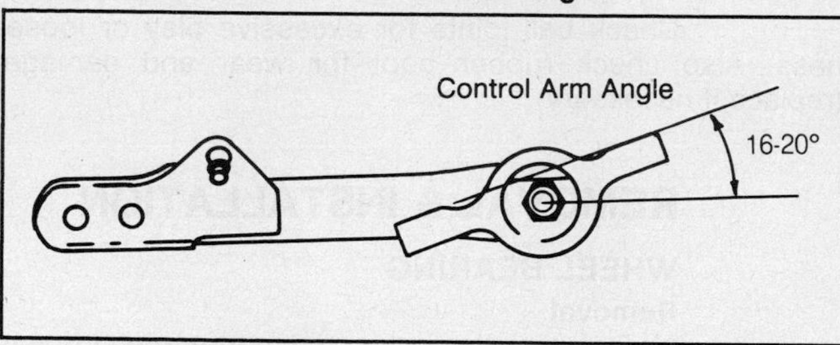
Control Arm Angle
16-20°

UPPER CONTROL ARM

NOTE: **Engine must be removed prior to removing left upper control arm.**

Removal

1) Remove shock absorber top retaining nut. Raise and support vehicle. Remove wheel assembly. Compress coil spring using spring compressor (89 95 839) and remove coil spring.

2) Remove bolts attaching ball joint to upper control arm. Support steering knuckle to prevent damaging brake hose. Remove bolts attaching upper control arm bracket and remove upper control arm. Note amount and location of shims.

Installation

1) Attach bracket to upper control arm so that angle between bracket and upper control arm is 60°-64°. *See Fig. 3.* Install shims between upper control arm bracket and body.

2) Check that ring and rubber bumper in upper spring seat are in position. Replace self-locking nuts on ball joint attaching bolts. Reverse removal procedure to complete installation. Check wheel alignment.

Fig. 3: Upper Control Arm Bracket Angle

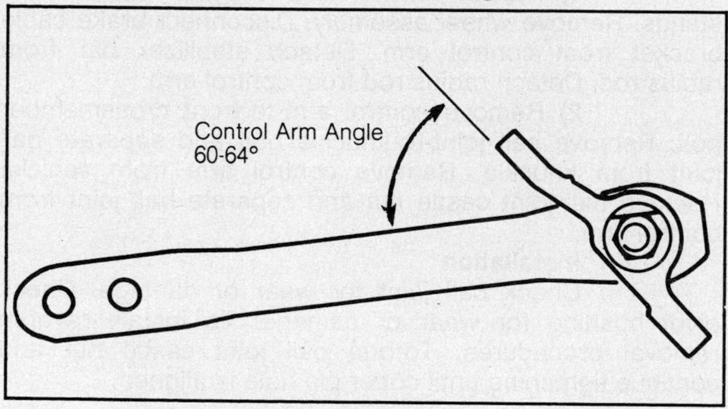
Control Arm Angle
60-64°

SHOCK ABSORBER

Removal

Remove shock absorber top retaining nut. Raise and support vehicle. Remove wheel assembly. Place a floor jack under lower control arm and raise arm slightly. Disconnect shock absorber from lower control arm and remove shock absorber.

NOTE: **Used shock absorbers require special handling to prevent personal injury. Drill a hole 3/8-5/8" (10-15 mm) from edge of pressure chamber before discarding shock absorber.**

Installation

Hold shock absorber in upright position and pump shock absorber for a few full strokes to bleed air from shock absorber. Reverse removal procedure to complete installation.

TIGHTENING SPECIFICATIONS

Application	Ft. Lbs. (N.m)
Hub Nut	213-227 (289-308)
Bracket-to-Lower Control Arm Nuts	70-77 (95-105)
Bracket-to-Upper Control Arm Nuts	54-66 (73-90)
Lower Shock Absorber Mount	70 (95)
Tie Rod End-to-Steering Knuckle	35-44 (47-60)

Front Suspension

SUBARU 1600, 1800 & 1800 TURBO

DESCRIPTION

Front suspension is a MacPherson strut type, using a hydraulic shock absorber inside a strut tube. Strut tube is surrounded by coil spring.

Strut is secured at top to the body and at the bottom to steering knuckle. Steering knuckle pivots on ball joint attached to lower control arm. Lower control arms are attached to front crossmember.

Radius rods are bolted to lower control arms and attached to rear crossmember with rubber bushings, washers and nuts. A stabilizer bar is attached to rear crossmember and to radius rods with clamps and rubber bushings.

Fig. 1: Exploded View of Front Suspension

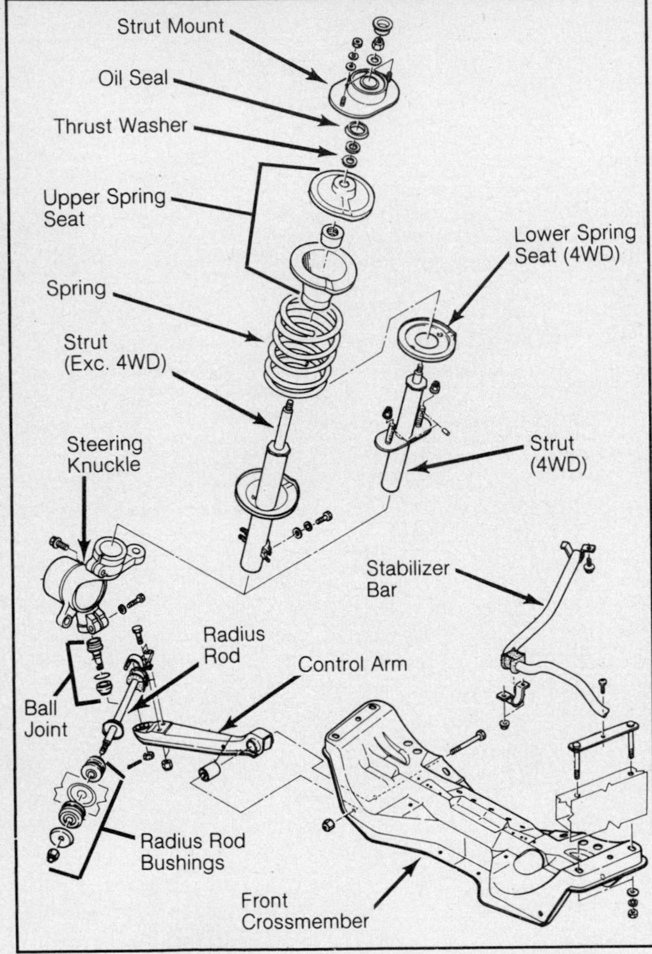
Strut Mount
Oil Seal
Thrust Washer
Upper Spring Seat
Lower Spring Seat (4WD)
Spring
Strut (Exc. 4WD)
Steering Knuckle
Strut (4WD)
Stabilizer Bar
Radius Rod
Control Arm
Ball Joint
Radius Rod Bushings
Front Crossmember

ADJUSTMENTS

WHEEL ALIGNMENT SPECIFICATIONS & PROCEDURES

See Wheel Alignment Specifications and Procedures in WHEEL ALIGNMENT section.

WHEEL BEARING

Wheel bearing is not adjustable. Tighten hub nut to 145 ft. lbs. (197 N.m). If cotter pin hole is not aligned, tighten further a maximum of 30° to align hole. Install cotter pin.

BALL JOINT CHECKING

Check ball joints for excessive play or looseness. Also check rubber boot for wear and damage, (replace if necessary).

REMOVAL & INSTALLATION

WHEEL BEARING

Removal

1) Remove dust cap and cotter pin. Loosen hub nut and wheel lug nuts. Raise vehicle and support with safety stands.

2) Disconnect parking brake cable from lever at brake caliper. Remove clip of outer part of parking brake cable and disconnect cable from caliper.

3) Remove retaining bolts to brake caliper assembly, and support assembly out of the way. Remove damper strut retaining bolts. Remove cotter pin and castle nut of tie rod end. Remove tie rod from knuckle arm housing using a puller.

4) Remove retaining bolt and separate transverse link from housing. Disconnect strut from housing. Remove castle nut on housing and remove disc and hub assembly from axle shaft.

5) Remove disc shield by removing retaining bolt. Attach puller tool (921121000) to housing and turn tool handle to pull housing off axle shaft.

6) Using a soft mallet and aluminum or brass bar, tap on inner race to remove outer bearing and outer race to remove inner bearing.

Installation

To install, reverse removal procedure.

LOWER CONTROL ARM & BALL JOINT

Removal

1) Raise vehicle and support with safety stands. Remove wheel assembly. Disconnect brake cable bracket from control arm. Detach stabilizer bar from radius rod. Detach radius rod from control arm.

2) Remove control arm-to-front crossmember bolt. Remove ball joint-to-knuckle bolt and separate ball joint from knuckle. Remove control arm from vehicle. Remove ball joint castle nut and separate ball joint from control arm.

Installation

Check ball joint for wear or damage. Check pivot bushing for wear or damage. To install, reverse removal procedures. Torque ball joint castle nut and continue tightening until cotter pin hole is aligned.

FRONT SUSPENSION

Removal

1) Raise vehicle and support with safety stands. Remove wheel assemblies. Remove parking brake cable hanger from tie rod end. Remove cable end from caliper lever.

2) Remove outer cable clip from caliper. Remove cable bracket from housing. Remove cable mounting bracket from lower control arm. Disconnect brake hose from brake line and plug line.

3) Drive out spring pins from inner ends of drive axles nearest transaxle housing. Remove self-locking nut and bolt holding control arm to crossmember. Pull control arm downward from crossmember.

SUBARU 1600, 1800 & 1800 TURBO (Cont.)

4) Use separator tool to separate tie rod end from steering knuckle arm. Detach radius rod from rear crossmember. Remove stabilizer bar brackets.

5) Remove upper strut assembly retaining nuts. Pull drive shaft from transaxle. Remove suspension assembly from vehicle.

Installation

1) To install, reverse removal procedures. Be sure to align spring pin holes in drive axle before installing.

2) When installing strut top mount, be sure stud marked "FRONT" is forward on Sedan, Hatchback and Hardtop models, and stud marked "VAN/4WD" is forward on Station Wagon and 4WD models.

3) When installing stabilizer, be sure slit in bushing is facing downward in clamp. Replace all self-locking nuts. Before installing radius rod bushing, soak it in soapy solution or rubber lubricant to assist installation.

4) When installing castellated nuts on ball joints, tighten nut, as required, beyond specified torque setting to align cotter pin hole. Always use new spring pins for attaching inner end of drive shaft. Bleed brake system.

STRUT ASSEMBLY

Removal

1) Raise vehicle and support with safety stands. Remove wheel assembly. Disconnect brake hose from brake line, strut and brake caliper. Plug all brake line openings.

2) Remove strut-to-knuckle bolts and pull strut out of knuckle. Remove upper strut retaining nuts. Remove strut from vehicle.

Disassembly

1) Place strut in spring compressor holding fixture (925651000) and place in horizontal position. Compress spring until upper seat is separated from coil spring.

2) Use wrench portion of tool to hold upper mounting plate while removing self-locking nut from top end of strut. Remove thrust washer, oil seal and thrust bearing.

3) Remove the upper spring seat from rod. Carefully remove tension from coil spring and remove tool and spring from strut.

Reassembly

To reassemble, reverse disassembly procedures, replacing self-locking nut with a new one. Place small amount of grease on thrust washer.

Installation

1) To install, reverse removal procedures. Be sure upper strut mounting plate is facing in proper direction as described under "Front Suspension" installation procedure in this article.

2) When reattaching brake line and hose, be sure to allow enough clearance from wheel apron. Bleed brake system.

STABILIZER BAR

Removal

Raise vehicle and support with safety stands. Remove clamps securing stabilizer bar to radius rod. Remove clamps attaching stabilizer bar to rear crossmember.

Installation

Check all bushings for wear or damage and replace as necessary. Check stabilizer bar for possible cracking. To install, reverse removal procedures.

TIGHTENING SPECIFICATIONS

Application	Ft. Lbs. (N.m)
Ball Joint-to-Control Arm	29 (39)
Ball Joint-to-Knuckle	22-29 (30-39)
Control Arm-to-Crossmember	40-47 (54-64)
Lower Strut End-to-Knuckle	22-29 (30-39)
Radius Rod-to-Rear Crossmember	51-62 (69-84)
Stabilizer Bracket Nuts	13-16 (18-22)
Strut-to-Piston Rod Nut	43-54 (58-73)
Tie Rod End Ball Joint Nut	18-22 (24-30)
Upper Strut Retaining Nuts	22-29 (30-39)
Hub Nut	145 (197)

Front Suspension

TOYOTA CAMRY & TERCEL

DESCRIPTION

Vehicles are equipped with front wheel drive and independent front suspension. Vertically mounted MacPherson type strut assemblies are used. Coil springs surround the strut tubes.

Struts are mounted at top of inner fender and steering knuckle at bottom. Tie rod ends connect rack and pinion steering to steering knuckle. A ball joint connects knuckle to control arm which attaches to frame crossmember.

Stabilizer bar attaches to control arm and crossmember in front of wheels. Strut rod attaches to steering knuckle and chassis to the rear of front wheels.

Fig. 1: Exploded View of Suspension Components

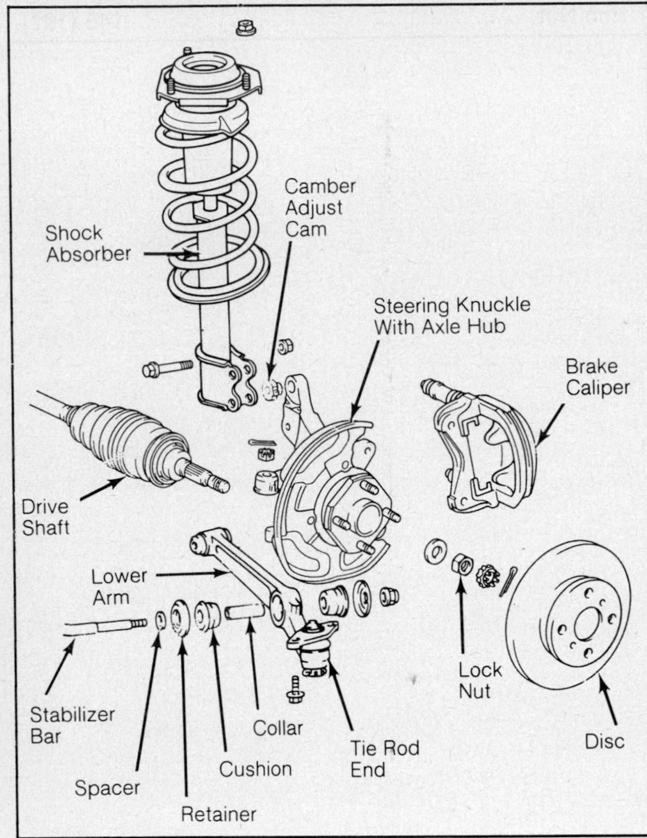
Camber
Adjust
Cam
Shock
Absorber
Steering Knuckle
With Axle Hub
Brake
Caliper
Drive
Shaft
Lower
Arm
Stabilizer
Bar
Lock
Nut
Collar
Tie Rod
End
Disc
Cushion
Spacer
Retainer

ADJUSTMENT

WHEEL ALIGNMENT SPECIFICATIONS & PROCEDURES

See Wheel Alignment Specifications & Procedures in WHEEL ALIGNMENT section.

WHEEL BEARING

Wheel bearings are not adjustable. Whenever bearings are removed, replace with new bearings and races.

BALL JOINT CHECKING

1) Raise vehicle and place wooden block 7.09-7.87" (180-200 mm) in height under one front wheel assembly. Lower floor jack until there is about half the load on front coil springs.

2) Place safety stand under vehicle. Insure that front wheel assemblies are in a straight ahead position and block them. Move lower arm up and down.

3) Ball joint maximum vertical play is .10" (3.0 mm). Ball joint is serviceable as a unit only. If worn or damaged, replace ball joint. Repeat in same manner for other side.

REMOVAL & INSTALLATION

WHEEL BEARING

Removal

1) Remove cotter pin, bearing lock nut cap and bearing lock nut (depress brake pedal when removing lock nut). Remove brake caliper and suspend on a wire. Disconnect disc. Remove cotter pin and nut from tie rod end.

2) Using universal puller (09950-20014) for Camry or pitman arm puller (09610-20012) for Tercel, pull tie rod end from steering knuckle. Place match marks on lower strut bracket and camber adjust cam.

3) Remove bolts and nuts to separate steering knuckle and strut. Remove 2 bolts holding ball joint to steering knuckle and separate. Using universal puller (09950-20014), pull axle hub from drive shaft and cover drive boot with a cloth.

4) Place steering knuckle in a vise and remove dust deflector with a screwdriver. Using oil seal puller (09308-00010), pull inner oil seal out of steering knuckle.

5) Using snap ring pliers, remove snap ring from steering knuckle hole. Remove 3 bolts holding brake dust cover. Using universal puller (09950-20014), push axle hub off of steering knuckle.

NOTE: **If axle hub is removed, be sure to replace outer oil seal.**

6) Remove bearing inner race from bearing. Using universal puller (09950-20014), pull inside outer bearing race from axle hub. Remove disc brake dust cover. Using oil seal puller (09308-00010), pull oil seal out of steering knuckle.

7) Using an arbor press, oil filter wrench (09228-22020) and universal puller (09950-20014) for Tercel, install outside inner race on bearing and press bearing out of steering knuckle.

Installation

1) Using an arbor press and steering knuckle oil seal replacer (09608-32010) for Camry or transmission rear bearing replacer (09309-35010) for Tercel, press new bearing into steering knuckle. Place outside inner bearing race on outside bearing.

2) Using steering knuckle oil seal replacer (09608-32010) and rear suspension bushing (09710-14012) for Camry or rear wheel bearing replacer (09515-35010) for Tercel, drive new oil seal into steering knuckle. Apply sealer to dust cover and steering knuckle connection and assemble.

3) Place inner race on inside bearing. Assemble hub and steering knuckle. Using an arbor press, oil filter wrench (09228-22020) and countershaft bearing

TOYOTA CAMRY & TERCEL (Cont.)

replacer (09310-35010), press bearing tightly against shoulder of hub. Install snap ring into hole of steering knuckle.

NOTE: **DO NOT interchange outer and inner races when installing bearings.**

4) Using steering knuckle oil seal replacer (09608-32010) and rear suspension bushing (09710-14012) for Camry or transmission rear bearing replacer (09309-35010) for Tercel, drive new oil seal into steering knuckle.

NOTE: **When installing inside oil seal, tap seal below end surface of steering knuckle to a depth of -.004" to +.004" (-.1 mm to +.1 mm) for Camry or to .126-.134" (3.2-3.4 mm) for Tercel.**

5) Using crankshaft rear oil seal replacer (09223-41020) for Camry or transmission and transfer bearing replacer (09316-60010) for Tercel, drive new dust onto steering knuckle. To complete installation, reverse removal procedures.

6) When installing steering knuckle with axle hub to control arm, torque to 83 ft. lbs. (113 N.m) for Camry or 59 ft. lbs. (80 N.m) for Tercel. When installing steering knuckle to strut, align match marks of camber adjust cam and torque bolts to 152 ft. lbs. (206 N.m) for Camry or 105 ft. lbs. (142 N.m) for Tercel.

7) When assembling brake caliper to steering knuckle, torque to 57-83 ft. lbs. (77-113 N.m). When connecting tie rod end to steering knuckle, torque to 36 ft. lbs. (49 N.m) for Camry or 29-43 ft. lbs. (39-58 N.m) for Tercel. To install wheel bearing lock nut, depress brake pedal, torque nut to 137 ft. lbs. (186 N.m).

CONTROL ARM & BALL JOINT

Removal

1) Place vehicle on jack stands. Remove 2 bolts holding ball joint to steering knuckle and separate. Remove stabilizer bar nut, retainer and cushion from lower control arm. Raise opposite wheel until vehicle lifts of jack stand.

2) Loosen control arm bolt, pry control arm and pull out bolt. Disconnect control arm from stabilizer. Using universal puller (09950-20014), remove ball joint from control arm.

NOTE: **When removing control arm, temporarily install ball joint nut to keep ball joint from falling out.**

Installation

1) Place ball joint in control arm bushing. Install nut and torque to 67 ft. lbs. (91 N.m) for Camry or 51-65 ft. lbs. (69-88 N.m) for Tercel. Replace cotter pin. To complete installation, reverse removal procedure.

2) Torque control arm to steering knuckle to 83 ft. lbs. (113 N.m) for Camry or 59 ft. lbs. (80 N.m) for Tercel. Torque stabilizer bar-to-control arm to 86 ft. lbs. (117 N.m) for Camry or 66-90 ft. lbs. (89-122 N.m) for Tercel. Torque control arm bolt-to-body to 83 ft. lbs. (113 N.m).

CONTROL ARM BUSHING

Removal

1) Before removing control arm bushing, cut off excess rubber from tip of control arm bushing. Using a hammer and a chisel, bend bushing flange inward.

2) Using a pair of pliers, bend in and pull off flange. Using an arbor press and rear suspension bushing remover and replacer (09726-32010), press bushing from control arm.

Installation

When installing control arm bushing, there must be no oil or grease on bushing or arm boss. Using an arbor press and rear suspension bushing remover and replacer (09726-32010), press bushing into control arm boss.

STRUT ASSEMBLY

Removal

NOTE: **With Camry, disconnect brake tube at strut, remove 2 clips and 2 "E" rings. Move disconnected brake tubes away from strut.**

1) Place match marks on strut lower bracket and camber adjustment cam. Remove 2 nuts and bolts and separate strut from steering knuckle. From inside engine compartment, remove dust cover from strut mount.

2) Loosen strut suspension support nut. Remove 3 nuts from top of strut support. Remove strut from vehicle.

CAUTION: **When removing strut cover drive shaft boot with a cloth for protection.**

Disassembly

1) Install a bolt and nut to clamp at bottom of strut and secure bottom of strut in a vise. Using front coil spring compressor (09727-22031), compress coil spring. Hold suspension support and remove strut rod top nut.

2) Relieve pressure on spring and remove spring. Remove suspension support, spring seat, upper insulator, spring and dust cover.

Inspection

1) Inspect for leakage, damage or deformation. Replace any damaged parts. Pull up shock absorber piston rod at even speed to see if tension is even throughout length of pull.

2) Abruptly move piston up and down .20-.39" (5-10 mm) to see if there is a change in tension. Inspect for cracks in bearing knuckle area.

Installation

1) To install, reverse removal procedures. Using front coil spring compressor (09727-22031), compress coil spring. Install strut to body and torque to 17 ft. lbs. (23 N.m) for Tercel.

2) Install strut to steering knuckle and torque bolts to 105 ft. lbs. (142 N.m). Torque new suspension support nut to 36 ft. lbs. (49 N.m) for Tercel. Check wheel alignment.

STABILIZER BAR

Removal

Remove engine under cover. Remove stabilzer bar brackets from crossmember. Remove both ends of stabilizer bar from control arms, noting bushing positioning. Remove stabilizer bar.

Installation

To install, reverse removal procedures.

SUSPENSION CROSSMEMBER

Removal

1) Raise vehicle and support with safety stands. Disconnect steering intermediate shaft pinch bolt.

Front Suspension

TOYOTA CAMRY & TERCEL (Cont.)

Remove engine under cover and detach tie rod end from steering knuckle.

2) Remove stabilizer bar. Remove control arm pivot bolt. Remove steering link housing brackets. Remove steering assembly from vehicle.

3) Remove engine retaining nuts and support engine from below. Remove lower crossmember retaining bolts. Remove crossmember.

Installation

To install, reverse removal procedures. For the left side, raise control arm with floor jack, to install crossmember. Lower vehicle and bounce before tightening lower arm pivot bolts. Check wheel alignment.

TIGHTENING SPECIFICATIONS

Application	Ft. Lbs. (N.m)
Camry	
Ball Joint-to-Control Arm	83 (113)
Control Arm-to-Body	83 (113)
Control Arm-to-Steering Knuckle	83 (113)
Control Arm-to-Stabilizer	86 (117)
Strut Top Support Nut	34 (46)
Stabilizer Bar Bracket	83 (113)
Steering Knuckle-to-Strut	152 (206)
Strut-to-Upper Mount	27 (37)
Tie Rod End-to-Steering Knuckle	36 (49)
Tercel	
Ball Joint-to-Control Arm	59 (80)
Control Arm-to-Body	83 (113)
Control Arm-to-Steering Knuckle	59 (80)
Control Arm-to-Stabilizer	66-90 (89-122)
Strut Top Support Nut	36 (49)
Stabilizer Bar Bracket	32 (44)
Steering Knuckle-to-Strut	105 (142)
Strut-to-Upper Mount	17 (23)
Tie Rod End-to-Steering Knuckle	29-43 (39-58)

TOYOTA CELICA, COROLLA, CRESSIDA, STARLET & SUPRA

DESCRIPTION

An independent MacPherson type strut suspension is used. Suspension consists of vertically mounted strut assemblies, control arms, strut rods and a stabilizer bar.

Individual strut assembly is mounted at top to inner fender and at bottom to control arm by means of a ball joint. Strut assembly consists of a shock absorber built into strut tube and a coil spring mounted on outside of strut tube. Steering knuckle is integral with bottom of strut tube.

A strut rod is mounted between control arm and frame. A stabilizer bar is mounted to front frame members and connected at ends to control arms.

Fig. 1: Assembled View of Corolla Suspension Assembly

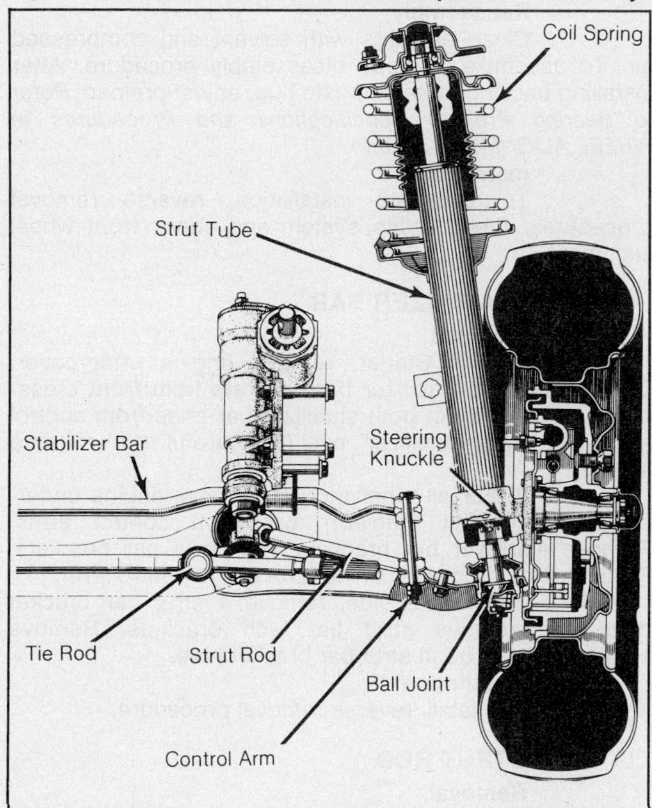
Coil Spring
Strut Tube
Stabilizer Bar
Steering Knuckle
Tie Rod
Strut Rod
Ball Joint
Control Arm

Other models are similar.

ADJUSTMENT

WHEEL ALIGNMENT SPECIFICATIONS & PROCEDURES

See Wheel Alignment Specifications & Procedures in WHEEL ALIGNMENT section.

WHEEL BEARING

Tighten nut to 22 ft. lbs. (30 N.m), while turning hub to seat bearings. Loosen hub nut until it can be turned with fingers. Tighten nut finger tight using a socket without a handle. If not aligned for cotter pin installation, tighten until installation is possible. Hub preload should be within specifications listed in Bearing Preload Specifications table.

BEARING PRELOAD SPECIFICATIONS

Application	Lbs. (kg)
Corolla	.7-1.5 (.3-.7)
Celica, Cressida, Starlet & Supra	.8-1.9 (.36-.86)

BALL JOINT CHECKING

1) Raise vehicle and place wooden block 7.09-7.87" (180-200 mm) in height under one front wheel assembly. Lower floor jack until there is about half the load on front coil springs.

2) Place safety stand under vehicle. Insure that front wheel assemblies are in a straight ahead position and block them. Move control arm up and down.

3) Ball joint's maximum vertical play is .09" (3.0 mm). Ball joint is serviceable as a unit only. If worn or damaged, replace ball joint. Repeat in same manner for other side.

REMOVAL & INSTALLATION

WHEEL BEARING

Removal

1) Raise vehicle and support with safety stands. Remove wheel assembly. Remove dust cap, cotter pin, nut lock and loosen hub nut.

2) Remove caliper retaining bolts. Remove caliper and support out of way. Remove hub nut, thrust washer, outer bearing and axle hub assembly. Using a screwdriver, remove oil seal from hub.

3) Remove inner bearing. Using a brass bar and a hammer, drive both bearing races out of axle hub. Clean parts with solvent and compressed air.

Installation

1) Using front hub bearing replacer (09608-30021) for Celica, Cressida and Supra or front hub/drive pinion bearing set (09608-20011) for Corolla and Starlet, drive new bearing races into place. Place grease in new bearing, inside hub and grease cap.

2) Place inside inner bearing in axle hub. Using front hub/drive pinion bearing set (09608-20011) for Celica, Corolla and Starlet or front hub bearing replacer (09608-30021) for Cressida and Supra, install oil seal.

3) To complete install, reverse removal procedure. Adjust preload of wheel bearing. Torque wheel nut to 22 ft. lbs. (30 N.m).

CONTROL ARM

Removal

1) Raise vehicle and support with safety stands. Remove wheel assembly. Remove 2 bolts holding steering knuckle to shock absorber, push control arm down and disconnect steering knuckle from shock absorber. Remove cotter pin and nut holding steering knuckle to tie rod.

2) Using tie rod end puller (09611-22012), disconnect tie rod from steering knuckle. Remove nut, retainer and cushion from stabilizer bar at control arm. Remove stabilizer bar. On all models except Starlet, disconnect strut bar.

3) Remove bolt holding control arm to crossmember and remove control arm. Remove cotter pin and

Front Suspension

TOYOTA CELICA, COROLLA, CRESSIDA, STARLET & SUPRA (Cont.)

nut holding ball joint to control arm. Using ball joint puller (09628-10011) for Starlet, press ball joint from control arm and steering knuckle.

4) For all others, use an arbor press, to press ball joint and control arm from steering knuckle. Use a screwdriver to remove ball joint dust cover ring set and dust cover.

Disassembly

For Starlet, use front suspension bushing remover/replacer (09710-10010) to remove bushing from control arm. For all others, use lower suspension arm bushing remover/replacer (09726-12021) to remove bushing from control arm.

Fig. 2: Ball Joint and Dust Cover

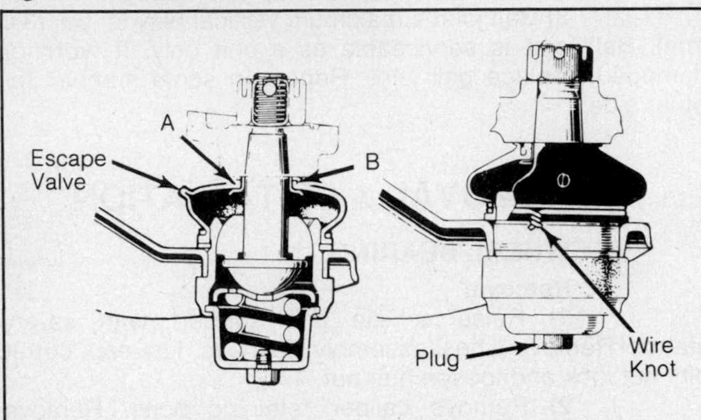
A
B
Escape
Valve
Plug
Wire
Knot

Reassembly

1) Using an arbor press and front suspension bushing remover/replacer (09710-10010) for Starlet or lower suspension arm bushing remover/replacer (09726-12021) for all others, press new bushing into control arm. Apply ball joint grease to points "A" and "B" of new dust cover. *See Fig. 2.*

2) Install dust cover with escape valve facing rear of vehicle. Wind wire twice around dust cover and bend wire knot down, facing to rear of ball joint. Remove plug and install grease fitting. Fill ball joint with grease. Remove fitting and install plug.

Installation

To install, reverse removal procedures. Torque all nuts and bolts to specifications. Check alignment of front wheels.

STRUT ASSEMBLY

Removal

1) Raise vehicle and support with safety stands. Remove wheel assembly. Disconnect brake line and flexible hose. Plug brake line openings. Remove 3 nuts retaining top of strut assembly to vehicle.

2) Remove 2 bolts retaining lower end of strut tube to steering knuckle. Pull down on control arm and remove strut assembly (with brake and axle hub assembly attached) from vehicle.

Disassembly

1) Mount shock absorber overhaul (09720-00010) to strut assembly and install assembly in a vise (clamp portion of holding fixture in vise). Remove 2 brake hoses and caliper.

2) Remove grease cap, cotter pin, lock cap, nut, thrust washer and outer bearing. Remove disc and axle assembly from wheel spindle. Remove backing plate.

3) Using front coil spring compressor (09727-22031), compress coil spring. Using front spring upper seat holder (09729-22021), to support top nut of strut assembly, remove nut. Remove suspension support dust cover, suspension support, spring seat and spring.

NOTE: Do not attempt to disassemble piston rod and valve.

Inspection

1) Inspect for leakage, damage or deformation. Replace any damaged parts. Pull up shock absorber piston rod at even speed to see if tension is even throughout length of pull.

2) Abruptly move piston up and down .20-.39" (5-10 mm) to see if there is a change in tension. Inspect for cracks in bearing knuckle area.

Reassembly

Clean all parts with solvent and compressed air. To assemble, reverse disassembly procedure. After installing backing plate and axle hub, adjust preload. *Refer to Bearing Preload Specifications and Procedures in WHEEL ALIGNMENT section.*

Installation

To complete installation, reverse removal procedures. Bleed brake system and check front wheel alignment.

STABILIZER BAR

Removal

1) For Starlet, remove engine undercover. Disconnect both stabilizer bar brackets from front crossmember. Disconnect both stabilizer bar ends from control arms. Remove stabilizer bar (be careful not to lose spacer).

2) For all other models, remove engine undercover. Disconnect stabilizer bar from control arms. Remove stabilizer bar brackets from strut bar brackets. Remove 2 nuts/bolts retaining strut bar to control arm.

3) On one side, remove 4 strut bar bracket bolts and remove strut bar with brackets. Remove stabilizer bar through strut bar bracket hole.

Installation

To install, reverse removal procedure.

STRUT ROD

Removal

Except for Starlet, raise vehicle and support with safety stands, under vehicle body. Remove nut, washer, retainer, and rubber grommet from front of strut rod bracket. Remove 2 nuts/bolts connecting strut rod to control arm. Remove rod from vehicle.

NOTE: Do not attempt to loosen staked nut.

Installation

Check distance between staked nut and center of bolt hole. Distance should be 14.64" (371.9 mm) on Corolla, 15.64" (397.2 mm) on Cressida, 14.53" (369.1 mm) on Supra and 15.16" (385.2 mm) on Celica. To complete installation, reverse removal procedures and torque all fasteners.

NOTE: If adjustment of strut bar is necessary, staked nut may be loosened and correct adjustment made.

Front Suspension

TOYOTA CELICA, COROLLA, CRESSIDA, STARLET & SUPRA (Cont.)

TIGHTENING SPECIFICATIONS

Application	Ft. Lbs. (N.m)
Ball Joint-to-Steering Knuckle	51-65 (69-88)
Control Arm-to-Crossmember [1]	
Corolla	51-65 (69-88)
Starlet	42-56 (57-76)
All Other Models	66-94 (89-127)
Control Arm-to-Stabilizer Bar	
Starlet	66-90 (89-122)
All Others	11-15 (15-20)
Control Arm-to-Strut Rod	
Corolla	29-39 (39-53)
All Other Models	44-53 (60-72)
Stabilizer Bar Bracket-to-Crossmember	
Celica	11-15 (15-20)
Starlet	29-39 (39-53)
All Others	8-11 (11-15)
Steering Knuckle-to-Shock Absorber	
Corolla	51-65 (69-88)
All Other Models	58-86 (79-117)
Steering Knuckle-to-Tie Rod	37-50 (50-68)
Strut Bar Bracket-to-Body	29-39 (39-53)
Strut Rod-to-Bracket	
Celica & Corolla	55-79 (75-107)
All Others	66-86 (89-117)
Strut Assembly-to-Body	
Corolla	11-15 (15-20)
Starlet	15-21 (20-28)
All Others	22-32 (30-43)
Shock Absorber Top Nut	29-39 (39-53)

[1] – With vehicle at full curb weight.

Front Suspension

TOYOTA PICKUP

DESCRIPTION

An independent front suspension with torsion bars is used. Wheel is supported by steering knuckle mounted between upper and lower control arms by ball joints.

Upper and lower control arms pivot on shafts connected to frame. Torsion bars mount in anchor arms at frame and in torque arms mounted to lower control arms.

Strut bars mount at frame and at lower control arm ends. Shock absorbers mount between lower control arms and frame. A stabilizer bar is mounted to frame and connected at ends to lower control arms.

ADJUSTMENT

WHEEL ALIGNMENT SPECIFICATIONS & PROCEDURES

See Wheel Alignment Specifications & Procedures in WHEEL ALIGNMENT section.

WHEEL BEARING

1) Tighten outer bearing nut to 22 ft. lbs. (30 N.m). Turn hub right and left 2 or 3 times. Loosen hub nut until it can be turned by hand.

2) Using a socket without handle, tighten hub nut as tight as possible by hand. Using a spring tension gauge, check bearing preload. Bearing preload should be 1.3-4.0 lbs. (5.8-17.8 N).

3) Adjust preload by turning hub nut, recheck preload. If preload is excessive, loosen hub nut and recheck. Install nut lock, new cotter pin and dust cap.

BALL JOINT CHECKING

Raise vehicle with floor jack. Lift at lower control arm until wheel assembly is off floor. Move wheel assembly up and down. Maximum ball joint vertical movement should not exceed .091" (2.3 mm). Inspect ball joint dust cover for wear or damage, replace if necessary.

REMOVAL & INSTALLATION

WHEEL BEARING

Removal

Raise vehicle and support with safety stands. Remove wheel assembly. Remove dust cap, cotter pin and nut lock. Remove brake tube (at junction and plug ends), caliper and support out of way. Remove hub nut, thrust washer, outer bearing and hub. Using a screwdriver, remove grease seal from back of hub and inner bearing.

Installation

To install, reverse removal procedures.

UPPER CONTROL ARM & BUSHING

Removal

1) Raise vehicle by placing floor jack under control arm. Place stands under frame and leave floor jack in place. Remove wheel assembly. Remove brake tube (at junction and plug ends), cotter pin, castle nut and washer from upper ball joint.

2) Using ball joint puller (09610-20011), separate ball joint from steering knuckle. Remove 3 nuts from upper control arm and remove ball joint.

3) Remove upper control arm shaft bolts/washers and camber adjusting shims (noting size and number of shims). Remove control arm shaft and control arm. If necessary, press bushings from control arm using suspension bushing remover/installer (09710-30020).

NOTE: When installing bushings, use soapy water to aid installation.

Fig. 1: Exploded View of Pickup Front Suspension

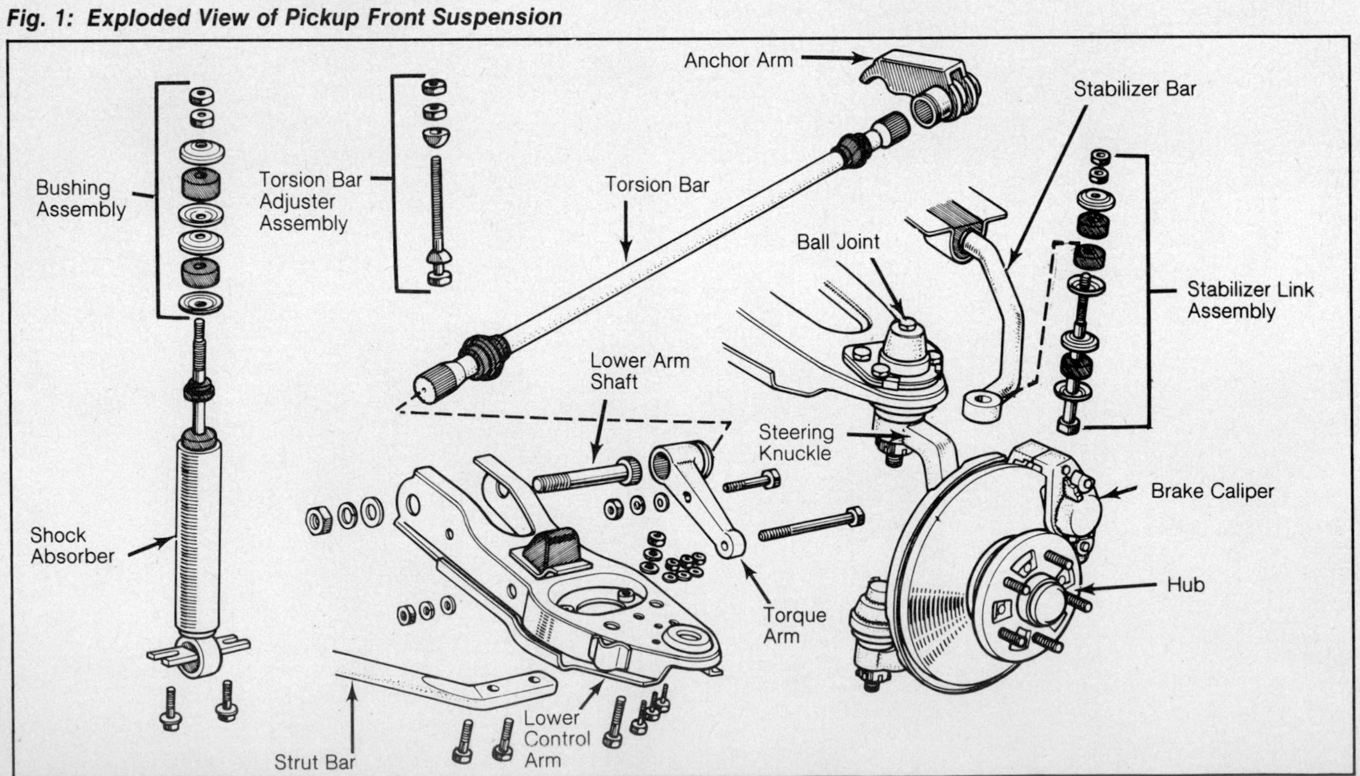

Anchor Arm
Stabilizer Bar
Bushing Assembly
Torsion Bar Adjuster Assembly
Torsion Bar
Ball Joint
Stabilizer Link Assembly
Lower Arm Shaft
Steering Knuckle
Brake Caliper
Shock Absorber
Hub
Torque Arm
Lower Control Arm
Strut Bar

Front Suspension

TOYOTA PICKUP (Cont.)

Fig. 2: Exploded View of Upper Control Arm Assembly

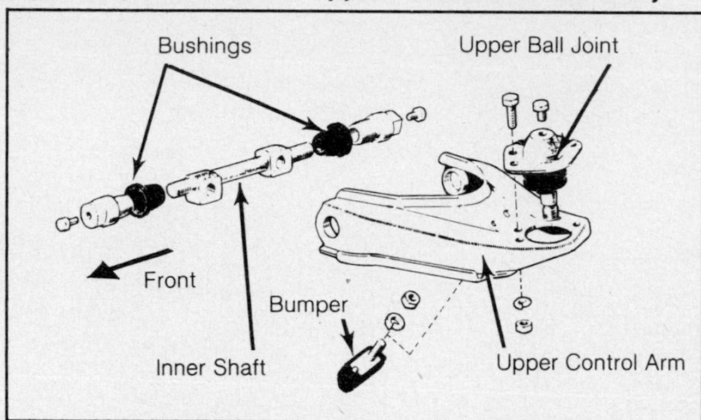
Bushings
Upper Ball Joint
Front
Bumper
Inner Shaft
Upper Control Arm

Installation

1) Inspect all components for wear or distortion. If replacing bushings, use suspension bushing remover/installer (09710-30020) to press bushings into upper control arm. Install upper control arm shaft with offset mounting hole to front.

2) To complete installation, reverse removal procedures. Make sure wheel alignment shims are installed in correct position. Check wheel alignment.

LOWER CONTROL ARM & BUSHING

Removal

1) Raise vehicle and support with safety stands. Remove wheel assembly. Remove torsion bar and shock absorber. Disconnect stabilizer bar and strut bar from lower control arm.

2) Remove 3 nuts and separate lower ball joint from lower control arm. Remove torque arm and lower arm shaft from lower control arm. Pull down and remove lower control arm from vehicle.

3) If necessary, remove lower control arm bushing. Using bushing remover/installer (09726-35010), press bushing from crossmember.

NOTE: Excess rubber on rear side of bushing will be cut off as it is drawn from mounting hole.

Installation

1) If lower control arm bushing is being replaced, apply soapy water to bushing and mounting hole. Using bushing remover/installer (09726-35010), press new bushing into crossmember mounting hole.

2) To complete installation, reverse removal procedures. Tighten lower arm mount nut to specifications after vehicle has been lowered to floor and bounced to align suspension. Check wheel alignment.

BALL JOINTS

Removal

1) When removing upper ball joint, disconnect brake tube at junction on lower control arm and plug tubes. Remove cotter pin, castle nut and washer from ball joint. Using ball joint puller (09610-20011), push ball joint from steering knuckle. Remove 3 nuts holding ball joint to upper control arm and remove ball joint.

2) When removing lower ball joint, use a jack to support lower control arm. Remove cotter pin, castle nut and washer from ball joint. Using ball joint puller (09628-62010), push lower ball joint from steering knuckle. Remove 3 nuts from lower control arm and remove ball joint.

Installation

To install, reverse removal procedures. After installing upper ball joint, bleed front brake system.

STABILIZER BAR

Removal

Remove 1 torsion bar spring. Remove nuts, cushions and bolts retaining both sides of stabilizer bar to lower control arms. Remove both stabilizer bar bushings and brackets from frame. Remove stabilizer bar.

Installation

To install, reverse removal procedures. Adjust torsion bar spring tension. *Refer to TORSION BAR section.*

STRUT BAR

Removal

Place match marks on threaded portion of strut bar. Remove nut from strut bar bracket. Remove bolts holding strut bar to lower control arm. Remove strut bar.

Installation

To install, reverse removal procedures.

STEERING KNUCKLE

Removal

1) Raise vehicle and support with safety stands. Remove wheel assembly. Disconnect brake tube from brake caliper and plug openings. Remove caliper from knuckle.

2) Remove dust cap, cotter pin and nut lock. Remove hub nut, thrust washer, inner bearing and axle hub with rotor. Remove knuckle arm and dust cover.

3) Remove cotter pins and castle nuts from ball joint studs. Using a ball joint puller (09628-62010), separate ball joints from steering knuckle. Remove steering knuckle.

Installation

To install, reverse removal procedure. Check wheel alignment.

TORSION BAR

Removal

1) Raise vehicle and support with safety stands. Remove wheel assembly. Remove torsion bar boots at both ends. Place match marks on torsion bar, anchor arm and torsion arm for correct spline alignment at reassembly. Remove adjuster bolt, lock nut.

2) Measure distance from end of adjuster bolt to lower face of adjusting nut. Record distance for use during installation. Place a floor jack under anchor arm and raise slightly. Remove adjusting nut, lower floor jack slowly. Remove anchor arm and torsion bar.

Inspection

Inspect all parts for wear or damage. Check all splines carefully. Note that left and right torsion bars are not interchangeable.

Installation

1) Grease splines prior to installation. When reusing old torsion bar, align marks on torsion bar with marks on torsion arm and anchor arm, then install.

2) When using new torsion bar, raise vehicle and block wheel assembly up to height of 7.09-7.87" (180-200 mm). Lower jack until clearance between spring bumper on lower arm and frame is .51" (13 mm).

NOTE: Place safety stands under vehicle.

Front Suspension

TOYOTA PICKUP (Cont.)

3) Install new torsion bar so adjusting bolt protrusion is .31-1.10" (7.87-27.94 mm) for 1/2 ton vehicles and .43-1.22" (11-31 mm) for 3/4 ton vehicles. Remove block from under wheel and lower front of vehicle until it rests on stands.

4) Tighten adjusting nut until bolt protrudes 2.72-3.50" (69-89 mm). On either old or new torsion bar, grease boot lips and install boots to torsion arm and anchor arm.

5) Remove stands and bounce vehicle several times to settle suspension. Adjust vehicle to standard height with adjusting nut. *See Riding Height Specifications in WHEEL ALIGNMENT section.* Use 2 wrenches to tighten lock nut.

NOTE: If bolt protrusion is NOT 2.72-3.50" (69-89 mm), change position of anchor arm spline and reassemble.

SHOCK ABSORBER

Removal

1) Raise vehicle and support with safety stands. Remove wheel assembly. Remove 2 nuts retaining shock absorber to bracket. Remove washers and cushions from shaft of shock absorber.

2) Remove bolts securing shock absorber to lower control arm. Fully compress shock absorber, tilt forward, rotate 90° and remove from vehicle.

Installation

To install, reverse removal procedures.

TIGHTENING SPECIFICATIONS

Application	Ft. Lbs. (N.m)
Lower Ball Joint-to-Arm (8 mm)	15-21 (20-29)
Lower Ball Joint-to-Arm (10 mm)	29-39 (39-53)
Lower Ball Joint-to Steering Knuckle	87-122 (118-166)
Upper Ball Joint-to-Arm	15-21 (20-29)
Upper Ball Joint-to Steering Knuckle	66-94 (90-128)
Lower Arm-to-Frame	145-216 (197-293)
Upper Arm Shaft-to-Frame	51-65 (69-88)
Upper Arm-to-Shaft	62-79 (84-107)
Shock Absorber-to-Bracket	14-22 (19-30)
Shock Absorber-to-Lower Arm	11-15 (15-20)
Stabilizer-to-Lower Arm	8-11 (11-15)
Strut Bar-to-Lower Arm	55-75 (75-102)
Torsion Bar-to-Lower Arm	29-39 (39-53)

Front Suspension

VOLKSWAGEN — EXCEPT VANAGON

DESCRIPTION

Vehicles are equipped with front wheel drive and MacPherson strut type independent front suspension. Axles are supported by lower control arms and vertically-mounted strut assemblies.

Strut assemblies consist of double action shock absorbers mounted inside strut tubes. With coil springs mounted over the outside of the tube.

The top portion of strut is attached to inner fender panel and lower portion is attached directly to steering knuckle. Tie rods are connected to steering knuckle.

ADJUSTMENT

WHEEL ALIGNMENT SPECIFICATIONS & PROCEDURES

See Wheel Alignment Specifications & Procedures in WHEEL ALIGNMENT section.

WHEEL BEARING

Wheel bearings are pressed into bearing housing and no adjustment is required.

BALL JOINT CHECKING

1) Raise vehicle and support with safety stands. Turn steering wheel to one side. Install lever so that ball joint spring may be compressed.

2) With spring compressed, position a vernier caliper with lower jaw on ball joint stud and upper jaw on top of clamping bolt for ball joint stud. Note reading.

3) Slowly release tension from spring and note travel of caliper. This reading indicates ball joint play. If play exceeds .040" (1 mm) for new ball joints or .100" (2.5 mm) for used ball joints, replace ball joints.

REMOVAL & INSTALLATION

WHEEL BEARING

Removal

1) Remove strut assembly from vehicle as described in Strut Assembly. Press bearings out of hub.

NOTE: **The wheel bearing is destroyed when pressed out of the hub. Once either the wheel hub or bearing has been removed from suspension strut, a new bearing must be installed.**

2) Remove circlips inside bearing housing (one at each end of bearing). Using a press sleeve, apply pressure to bearing outer race. Press out bearing toward outboard end of bearing housing.

Installation

To install, reverse removal procedure.

LOWER CONTROL ARM & BALL JOINT

Removal

1) Raise vehicle and support with safety stands, under vehicle body. Remove nut and clamp bolt retaining ball joint in bottom of steering knuckle.

2) Force ball joint out of steering knuckle, (ball joint can be replaced while control arm is in vehicle). Leave control arm hanging in mounts at subframe.

Fig. 1: Exploded View of Suspension Components

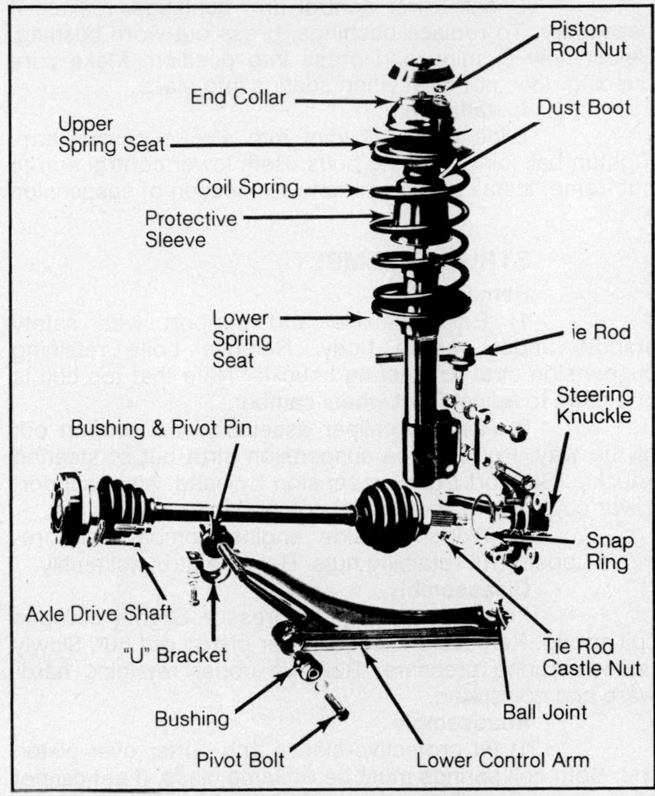

Piston Rod Nut
End Collar
Dust Boot
Upper Spring Seat
Coil Spring
Protective Sleeve
Lower Spring Seat
ie Rod
Steering Knuckle
Bushing & Pivot Pin
Snap Ring
Axle Drive Shaft
Tie Rod Castle Nut
"U" Bracket
Ball Joint
Bushing
Pivot Bolt
Lower Control Arm

3) If control arm is not being removed, drill out ball joint rivets with a 9/32" (7 mm) drill. After drilling rivets it still may be necessary to chisel off rivet heads. Remove ball joint.

4) If control arm is being removed, take out pivot bolt and "U" bracket housing inner pivot pin. Slide out control arm.

NOTE: **On vehicles equipped with automatic transmissions, engine may have to be slightly raised to gain access to pivot bolts.**

Fig. 2: New Ball Joint Installation on Lower Control Arm

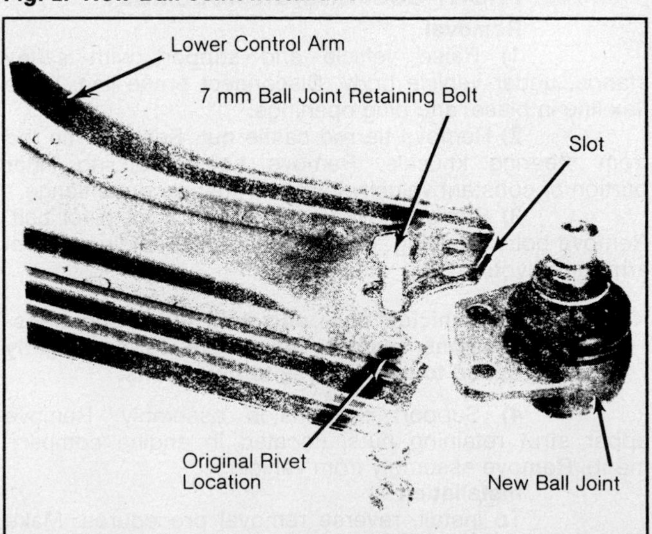

Lower Control Arm
7 mm Ball Joint Retaining Bolt
Slot
Original Rivet Location
New Ball Joint

Inspection

Check lower control arm bushings, replace if necessary. To replace bushings, press out worn bushing. Select new bushing and press into position. Make sure bushing does not twist when seating into place.

Installation

Slide new ball joint into slot in control arm. Tighten ball joint retaining bolts. Refit lower control arm to subframe. Install ball joint into lower section of suspension strut.

STRUT ASSEMBLY

Removal

1) Raise vehicle and support with safety stands, under vehicle body. Remove bolts retaining suspension strut to steering knuckle. Note that top bolt is one used to adjust front wheel camber.

2) Remove caliper assembly and support out of the way. Pry or force suspension strut out of steering knuckle. Support front suspension by hand. Also, support lower control arm and related components.

3) Working inside engine compartment, remove upper strut retaining nuts. Remove strut assembly.

Disassembly

Fit strut to spring compressor. Slightly collapse coil spring. Remove shock absorber piston rod nut. Slowly release spring pressure. Remove upper retaining hardware and coil spring.

Reassembly

1) Fit protective sleeve and buffer over piston rod. Both coil springs must be of same class. If set cannot be matched, both springs will have to be replaced. Springs are color coded.

2) Position coil spring into lower spring seat. Install the upper spring retainer. Fit entire assembly into spring compressor and collapse coil gradually until all the threaded portion of piston rod is exposed.

3) Install bearing, rubber bumper and remaining upper retaining components. Hold piston rod and tighten piston and lock nut.

Installation

To install, reverse removal procedures. Check wheel alignment.

FRONT SUSPENSION ASSEMBLY

Removal

1) Raise vehicle and support with saftey stands, under vehicle body. Disconnect brake line, leave flex line in place, and plug openings.

2) Remove tie rod castle nut. Separate tie rod from steering knuckle. Remove bolts retaining inner portion of constant velocity joint to transaxle drive flange.

3) Remove lower control arm front pivot bolt. Remove bolts retaining "U" shaped bracket holding control arm rear pivot.

NOTE: **On vehicles equipped with automatic transmissions, engine may have to be slightly raised to gain access to pivot bolts.**

4) Support suspension assembly. Remove upper strut retaining nuts, (located in engine compartment). Remove assembly from vehicle.

Installation

To install, reverse removal procedures. Make sure convex side of thrust washer faces pivot bolt head.

TIGHTENING SPECIFICATIONS

Application	Ft. Lbs. (N.m)
Axle Nut	173 (235)
Axle Drive Shaft-to-Transaxle	32 (44)
Ball Joint Clamp Bolt-to Steering Knuckle	36 (49)
Control Arm-to-Subframe	50 (68)
New Ball Joint-to-Control Arm	18 (24)
Piston Rod Nut	58 (79)
Pivot Pin "U" Bracket	32 (44)
Suspension Strut-to-Steering Knuckle	58 (79)
Suspension Strut-to-Inner Fender	14 (19)
Tie Rod Castle Nut	22 (30)

Front Suspension

VOLKSWAGEN VANAGON

DESCRIPTION

Front suspension is an indepenent type consisting of upper and lower control arms and ball joints connected to steering knuckles. With shock absorbers surrounded by coil springs.

Strut rods are attached to chassis and lower control arms, and a stabilizer bar is attached to chassis and strut rod.

ADJUSTMENT

WHEEL ALIGNMENT SPECIFICATIONS & PROCEDURES

See Wheel Alignment Specifications and Procedures in WHEEL ALIGNMENT section.

WHEEL BEARING

Tighten hub nut firmly to seat bearing while turning hub. Wheel bearing is correctly adjusted when thrust washer can be moved slightly with a screwdriver and finger pressure. After adjustment, peen flange of hub nut into stub axle shaft recess.

Fig. 1: Exploded View of Front Suspension

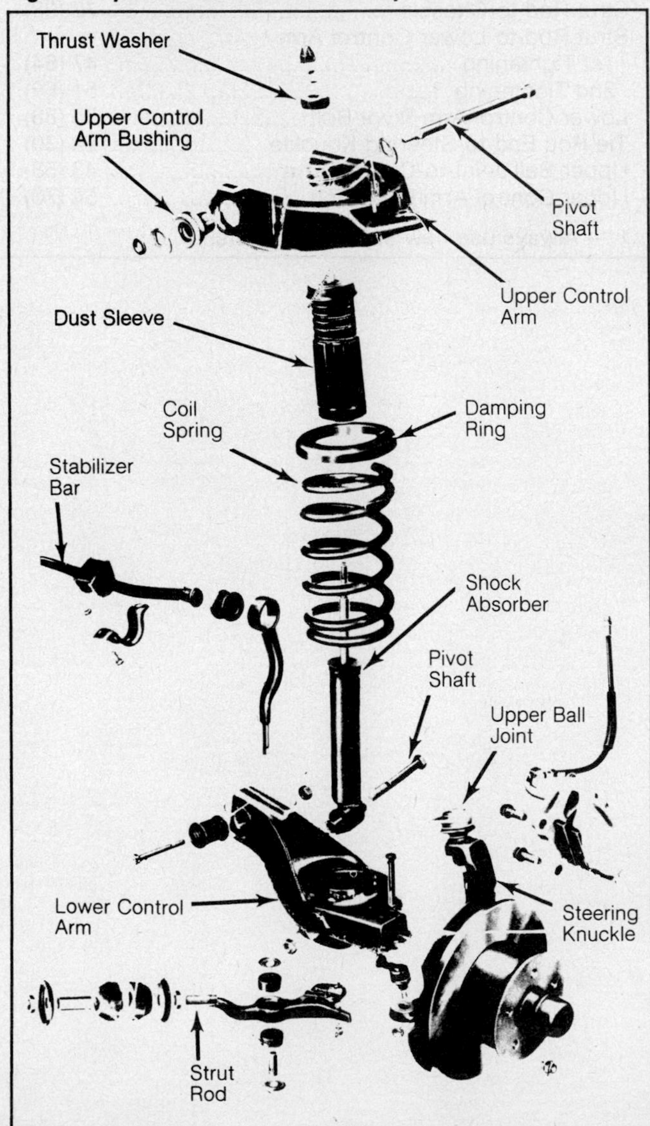

Thrust Washer
Upper Control Arm Bushing
Pivot Shaft
Upper Control Arm
Dust Sleeve
Coil Spring
Damping Ring
Stabilizer Bar
Shock Absorber
Pivot Shaft
Upper Ball Joint
Lower Control Arm
Steering Knuckle
Strut Rod

BALL JOINT CHECKING

Inspect ball joint for wear or excessive play. Replace ball joints as necessary.

REMOVAL & INSTALLATION

WHEEL BEARING

Removal

1) Raise vehicle and support with safety stands. Remove wheel assembly. Remove dust cap. Pry flange on hub nut out of recess in shaft and loosen hub nut.

2) Remove caliper and support out of the way. Remove hub nut, washer, outer bearing and hub. Remove seal and inner bearing from hub.

Installation

To install, reverse removal procedure.

BALL JOINT

Removal

1) Remove steering knuckle from vehicle. *See Lower Control Arm, Steering Knuckle & Coil Spring Removal* in this article. Remove self-locking nuts retaining ball joints to steering knuckle.

2) Using special tool (VW 267a), press lower ball joint adapter off of ball joint. Remove circlip and press out lower ball joint. Press upper ball joint out with same tool.

Installation

1) Press in ball joints with flat side of shoulder facing spindle. Attach adapter loosely to lower ball joint. Do not tighten adapter fully.

2) Adapter must be aligned with control arm when steering knuckle is installed or rubber boot will tear. Install steering knuckle on vehicle. Tighten ball joints and adapter with new self-locking nuts.

LOWER CONTROL ARM, STEERING KNUCKLE & COIL SPRING

Removal

1) Raise and support with safety stands. Remove wheel assembly. Detach stabilizer bar from strut rod.

2) Remove nuts retaining strut rod, steering knuckle, and lower control arm together. Remove caliper and brake hose bracket. Support caliper out of the way.

NOTE: **Strut rod length determines caster angle. If setting at body mounting is changed, caster must be readjusted.**

3) Separate tie rod end from steering knuckle. Remove upper ball joints from control arms. Remove steering knuckle.

4) Loosen shock absorber mounting on lower control arm. Support lower control arm with a floor jack, and pull out shock absorber bolt from lower control arm.

5) Lower floor jack slowly and remove coil spring. Remove lower control arm pivot bolt and remove control arm from vehicle.

Bushing Replacement

Using press and adapters, press out old bushings and press in replacements.

Front Suspension

VOLKSWAGEN VANAGON (Cont.)

Installation

1) Install lower control arm to vehicle with pivot bolt. Position coil spring so straight end is at bottom.

2) Attach damping ring to spring with tape. Install spring in control arm spring depression.

3) Lift control arm with a floor jack and attach shock absorber lower mount. Attach steering knuckle to control arm.

4) Attach strut rod to steering knuckle and control arm lower connection. Install stabilizer bar, tie rod end, and brake caliper.

NOTE: When installing strut rod bolts, spring washers go under bolt heads. Always use new self-locking nuts.

5) Install wheel assembly. Lower vehicle. Turn wheel to full-lock position and check distance between wheel and brake hose. Bend bracket as necessary to adjust distance to 1" (25 mm).

SHOCK ABSORBER

Removal

1) Raise vehicle and support with safety stands. Loosen shock absorber lower retaining bolt.

2) Lower vehicle to floor and remove retaining bolt. Raise vehicle and remove shock absorber upper mounting hardware. Remove shock absorber from vehicle.

Installation

When lifting vehicle with shock absorber disconnected, avoid damaging upper ball joint.

UPPER CONTROL ARM

Removal

1) Raise vehicle and support with safety stands. Remove wheel assembly. Remove bolts retaining upper ball joint to upper control arm.

2) Swing steering knuckle carefully to one side. Note the position of upper control arm pivot shaft and remove from control arm. Remove control arm from vehicle.

Bushing Replacement

Note the position of and grind off spot welds retaining bushings. Using press and adapters, press out old bushing and press in replacements. Secure bushing with spot welds in noted locations. Clean up welds and paint surface.

Installation

Lubricate pivot shaft with grease. Install upper control arm to body and position pivot shaft as noted during removal. Install ball joint to upper control arm. Install wheel assembly and lower vehicle.

NOTE: Flat on pivot shaft must be vertical and face center of vehicle. Larger side of eccentric washer faces down.

STABILIZER BAR

Removal

Disconnect stabilizer bar from strut rod. Remove bolts retaining bracket to chassis. Remove stabilizer bar.

Installation

To install, reverse removal procedures.

STRUT ROD

Removal

Disconnect stabilizer bar from strut rod. Remove nuts retaining strut rod, steering knuckle, and lower control arm together. Remove hardware mounting strut rod to chassis. Remove strut rod from vehicle.

Installation

To install, reverse removal procedures. Check wheel alignment.

NOTE: When attaching strut rod, steering knuckle, and lower control arm, spring washers are to be installed under bolt heads. Always use new self-locking nuts.

TIGHTENING SPECIFICATIONS

Application	Ft. Lbs. (N.m)
Ball Joint Self-Locking Nuts [1]	80 (109)
Brake Caliper-to-Bracket	115 (156)
Shock Absorber Top Nut	22 (30)
Stabilizer Bracket-to-Chassis	14 (19)
Stabilizer-to-Strut Rod	22 (30)
Strut Rod-to-Chassis	72 (98)
Strut Rod-to-Lower Control Arm [1]	
1st Tightening	47 (64)
2nd Tightening	51 (69)
Lower Control Arm Pivot Bolt	65 (88)
Tie Rod End-to-Steering Knuckle	22 (30)
Upper Ball Joint-to-Control Arm	43 (58)
Upper Control Arm Pivot Bolt	54 (73)

[1] — Always use new self-locking nuts.

VOLVO

DESCRIPTION

MacPherson strut type suspension is used. Suspension consists of a vertically mounted strut assembly. Strut assembly is mounted to chassis frame at top. Lower end of strut assembly is mounted to a ball joint which is bolted to lower control arm.

Steering knuckle is an integral part of strut assembly. Strut assembly consists of a shock absorber built into strut tube. The coil spring surrounds the outside of strut tube, and the spindle is integral with bottom of strut assemble. A stabilizer bar connects the control arms through rubber mounted links.

ADJUSTMENT

WHEEL ALIGNMENT SPECIFICATIONS & PROCEDURES

See Wheel Alignment Specifications & Procedures in WHEEL ALIGNMENT Section.

WHEEL BEARING

While rotating hub, tighten hub nut to 42 ft. lbs. (57 N.m). Loosen nut 1/2 turn, then tighten by hand (no tools). Check for hub rotating freely with no end play. If necessary to align cotter pin holes, loosen nut and install new cotter pin (recheck end play).

BALL JOINT CHECKING

Maximum axial play for lower ball joint is .12" (3 mm). Maximum radial play for lower ball joint is .02" (.5 mm). If specifications are exceeded, replace ball joint.

Fig. 1: Exploded View of Suspension Assembly

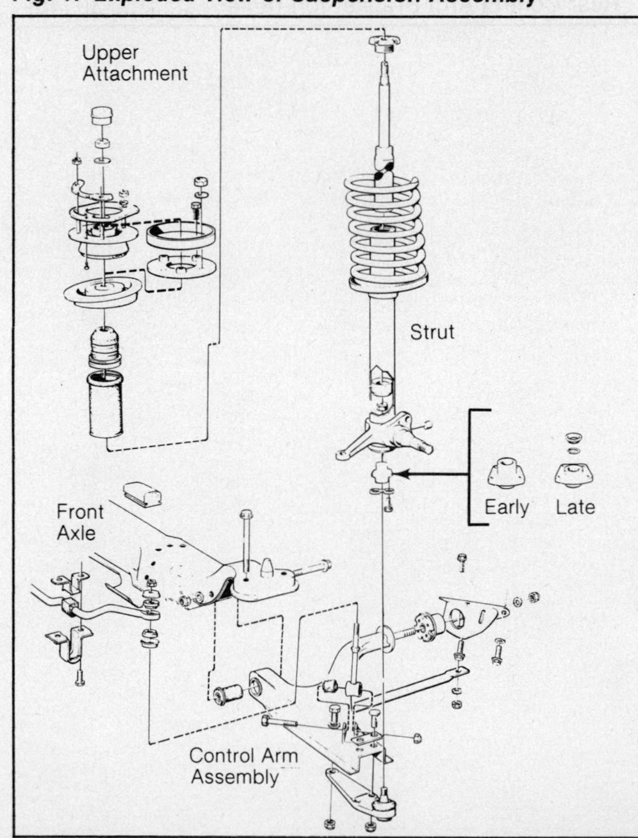
Upper Attachment
Strut
Early
Late
Front Axle
Control Arm Assembly

Illustration applies to all models except 760 GLE.

REMOVAL & INSTALLATION

WHEEL BEARING

Removal & Installation

1) Raise vehicle and support with safety stands. Remove wheel assembly. Remove dust cap. Remove cotter pin and loosen hub nut. Remove caliper retaining bolts.

2) Remove caliper and support out of the way. Remove hub nut, washer, outer bearing, and hub. Remove seal and inner bearing from hub. To install, reverse removal procedure.

BALL JOINT

Removal & Installation (760 GLE)

Raise and support vehicle. Remove front wheels. Remove sway bar-to-control arm bolt and ball joint nut. Separate ball joint from control arm. Remove ball joint-to-strut bolts and remove ball joint. Using new bolts coated with Loctite, install ball joint on strut. Tighten all nuts and bolts to specification.

Removal (All Others)

Raise and support vehicle. Remove front wheels. Remove ball joint-to-strut bolts. Remove ball joint-to-control arm nuts. Remove center ball joint retaining nut and press ball joint out of retainer.

CAUTION: Ball joints for the right and left sides are different sizes.

Installation

Remove grease from ball joint stud. Press new ball joint into retainer and tighten center nut to specification. Using new lock bolts, install ball joint on strut. Tighten to specification. Tighten ball joint bracket-to-control arm nuts to specification.

CONTROL ARM

Removal (760 GLE)

1) Raise and support vehicle. Remove front wheels. Remove ball joint stud nut, sway bar link, and control arm strut bolt from control arm. Separate ball joint from control arm.

2) Remove control arm from crossmember. If necessary, press out bushing.

Installation

Install control arm in crossmember. Do not tighten nut. Assemble ball joint, sway bar link, and control arm strut to control arm. Tighten all nuts and bolts to specfications. Install front wheels and lower vehicle to ground. Tighten control arm nut to specification.

Removal (All Others)

1) Raise and support vehicle. Remove front wheels. Disconnect stabilizer bar from control arm. Disconnect ball joint from control arm. Remove front retaining bolt from control arm.

2) Remove bracket attaching rear of control arm to chassis. Remove control arm from vehicle. Separate control arm from bracket. If control arm bushing is being replaced, press out using adapter sleeve (5085) and driver (5091).

Installation

1) Inspect all components for wear or damage. Use adapter sleeve (5085) and driver (5084) to install new bushings, (if necessary). Assemble control arm to bracket. Install control arm nut finger tight.

Front Suspension

VOLVO (Cont.)

2) Install bracket, with control arm to chassis, do not tighten bolts. Install front retaining bolt for control arm, do not tighten. Install ball joint to control arm and tighten bolts.

3) Position a floor jack under control arm and raise so coil spring is compressed. Connect stabilizer bar to link. Tighten control arm retaining nuts and bolts to specifications. Install wheel assembly.

SHOCK ABSORBER

Removal (760 GLE)

1) Raise and support vehicle. Remove front wheels. Separate tie rod end from steering knuckle. Place floor jack under control arm. Remove sway bar link and brake line bracket.

2) Remove upper shock absorber cover. Loosen shock absorber nut a few turns while holding center of strut rod with tool (5036). Mark position of upper mount to maintain wheel alignment. *See Fig. 2.*

Fig. 2: Removing Center Nut From Strut Assembly

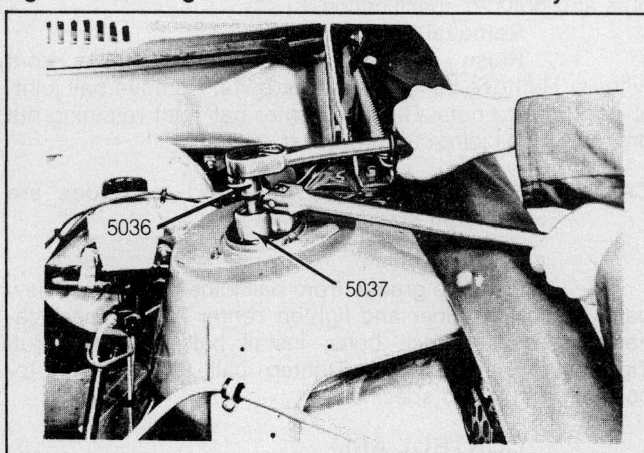
5036
5037

3) Lower floor jack. Guide strut out of strut tower. Attach spring compressor. Remove nut and lift off upper mount, spring retainer, and bumper. Unscrew shock absorber retaining nut using tool (5039 or 5173). Pull out shock absorber.

Installation

1) Install new shock absorber and tighten nut to specification. Install bumper, spring retainer, and upper mount. Tighten nut a few turns. Remove spring compressor. Install strut in tower and tighten mounting nuts.

2) Tighten shock absorber nut to specifications. Assemble remaining suspension parts in reverse order of removal.

Removal (All Others)

1) Raise and support vehicle. Remove wheel assembly. Loosen shock absorber retaining nut on strut assembly using tool (5039). Place floor jack under control arm. Disconnect tie rod from steering knuckle and sway bar link from control arm.

2) Remove brake line bracket. Remove cover over shock absorber center nut. Loosen center nut several turns. *See Fig. 2.* To maintain wheel alignment, place reference marks between plate and top of shock tower.

3) Lower jack and guide strut assembly out of shock tower. Using a spring compressor, compress coil spring. Remove center shock absorber nut. Remove upper mount, spring seat, and rubber bumper.

4) Remove coil spring with spring compressor attached. Unscrew shock absorber retaining nut using tool (5039 or 5173). Pull out shock absorber.

Installation

1) Install new shock absorber and tighten retaining nut with adapter tool (5039). Pull shock absorber spindle to fully extended position. Install coil spring onto strut assembly making sure spring end is properly aligned on strut bracket.

2) Install rubber bumper and install spring seat on coil spring. Guide strut assembly into upper mount and shock absorber spindle through upper mount. Install nut but do not tighten.

3) Guide strut assembly into shock tower. Position strut in tower and tighten mount bolts. Tighten center shock absorber nut to specification. Replace remaining components in reverse order of removal.

TIGHTENING SPECIFICATIONS

Application	Ft. Lbs. (N.m)
760 GLE	
Ball Joint Stud Nut	44 (60)
Ball Joint-to-Strut Assembly	22 (30)
Control Arm-to-Control Arm Strut	70 (95)
Shock Absorber Nut (Center)	111 (150)
Shock Absorber-to-Strut Nut	119 (160)
All Other Models	
Ball Joint Stud Nut	44 (60)
Ball Joint Bracket-to-Control Arm	85 (116)
Ball Joint-to-Strut Strut Assembly	17 (23)
Control Arm Retaining Bolts	
Front	55 (75)
Rear	40 (54)
Rear Control Arm Bracket-to-Frame	30 (40)

Rear Suspension

AUDI COUPE, 4000 & 5000

DESCRIPTION

Rear suspension on Audi Coupe, 4000 and 5000 consists of coil springs, shock absorbers, transverse rod and trailing arms. Some design differences occur between models.

On 5000, the coil spring is mounted directly on the rear axle, and the shock absorber is mounted separately. *See Fig. 1.* Transverse rod mounts behind axle beam. Top end of shock absorber is a stud type mount, incorporating a rubber damper assembly.

On Coupe and 4000, the coil spring and shock absorber are combined into a MacPherson strut type assembly. A transverse rod is also used, and mounts diagonally in front of the axle beam. *See Fig. 2.*

Fig. 1: Exploded View of 5000 Rear Suspension

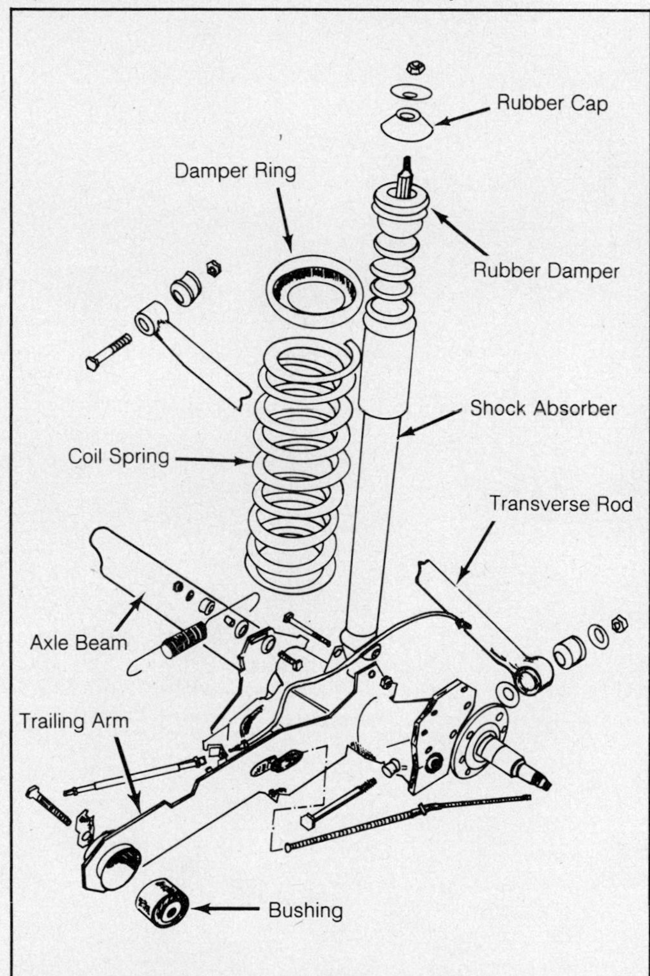
Rubber Cap
Damper Ring
Rubber Damper
Shock Absorber
Coil Spring
Transverse Rod
Axle Beam
Trailing Arm
Bushing

ADJUSTMENTS

WHEEL ALIGNMENT SPECIFICATIONS & PROCEDURES

Rear wheel alignment is not adjustable.

WHEEL BEARING

Remove grease cap, cotter pin and castle nut. While turning wheel tighten nut firmly to seat bearing. Back nut off until washer can be moved from side to side with tip of screwdriver. Install castle nut, new cotter pin and grease cap.

REMOVAL & INSTALLATION

SHOCK ABSORBERS

NOTE: **Remove and install shock absorbers one at a time. Do not allow rear axle to hang from body mounts only.**

Removal (Coupe & 4000)

Loosen trunk sheet metal trim, and remove shock absorber top protective cap. Remove upper mounting nut. Raise vehicle, remove lower mounting bolts, and remove shock absorber.

Removal (5000)

Remove top shock absorber mounting. Remove lower mounting and shock.

Installation (All Models)

To install, reverse removal procedure.

REAR AXLE ASSEMBLY

Removal (Coupe & 4000)

1) Raise and support vehicle with safety stands. Remove wheel assemblies. Disconnect muffler hangers. Lower and secure muffler and tailpipe.

2) Remove nut on parking brake linkage equalizer bar. Pry cable sleeves out of brackets. Remove parking brake cables from brackets.

Fig. 2: Exploded View of Coupe & 4000 Rear Suspension

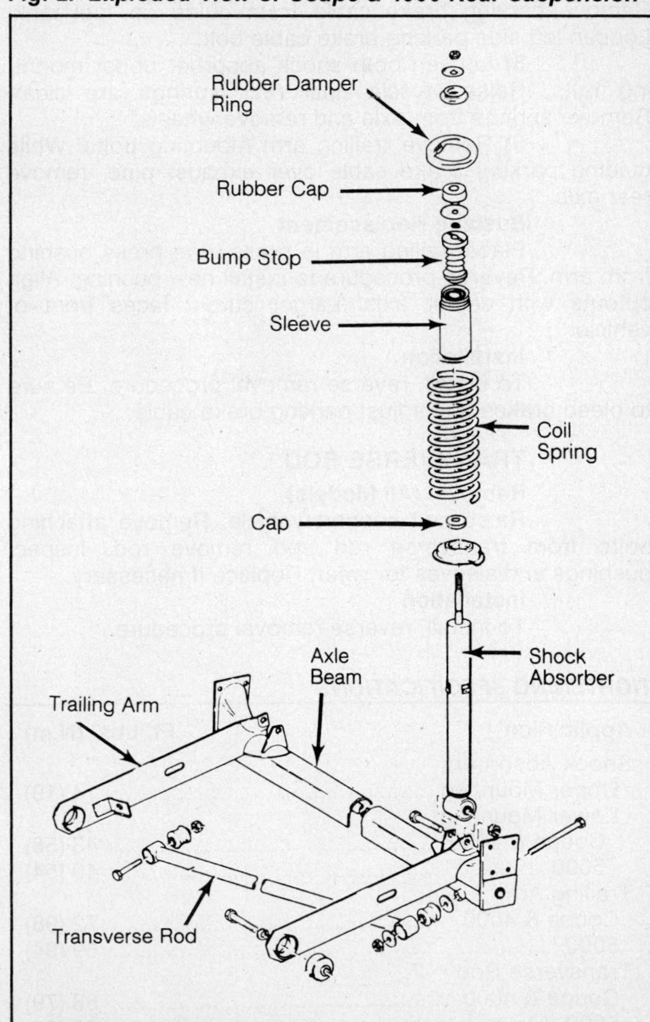
Rubber Damper
Ring
Rubber Cap
Bump Stop
Sleeve
Coil
Spring
Cap
Shock
Absorber
Axle
Beam
Trailing Arm
Transverse Rod

Rear Suspension

AUDI COUPE, 4000 & 5000 (Cont.)

3) Disconnect brake hoses and plug lines. Remove nuts from trailing arm mounting bolts, leaving bolts in place. Disconnect spring from brake pressure regulator.

4) Remove transverse rod mounting bolt, shock absorber mounting bolts and trailing arm mounting bolts. Remove rear axle assembly while guiding parking brake cable over muffler and tailpipe.

Bushing Replacement

Place trailing arm in press and press bushing from arm. Reverse procedure to install new bushing. Make sure bushing slots are positioned horizontally in trailing arm.

Installation

To install, reverse removal procedure. Be sure to bleed and adjust brakes as needed.

Removal (5000)

1) Raise and support vehicle with safety stands. Loosen wheel bolts, and transverse rod mounting bolt at body, but DO NOT remove. Disconnect right brake hose at steel line. Plug openings.

2) Disconnect brake pressure regulator spring at lower mounting bolt of shock absorber. Disconnect left brake hose at steel line, and plug openings.

3) Loosen parking brake compensator nut, and disconnect parking brake cable. Remove exhaust system at rear and lower vehicle.

4) Remove right fuel tank retaining strap. Remove parking brake cable from guide on fuel tank. Loosen left side parking brake cable bolt.

5) Loosen both shock absorber upper mounting nuts. Raise vehicle until rear springs are clear. Remove springs from axle and remove wheels.

6) Remove trailing arm mounting bolts. While guiding parking brake cable over exhaust pipe, remove rear axle.

Bushing Replacement

Place trailing arm in press, and press bushing from arm. Reverse procedure to install new bushing. Align cutouts with center axis. Larger cutout faces front of vehicle.

Installation

To install, reverse removal procedure. Be sure to bleed brakes and adjust parking brake cable.

TRANSVERSE ROD

Removal (All Models)

Raise and support vehicle. Remove attaching bolts from transverse rod and remove rod. Inspect bushings and sleeves for wear. Replace if necessary.

Installation

To install, reverse removal procedure.

TIGHTENING SPECIFICATIONS

Application	Ft. Lbs. (N.m)
Shock Absorbers	
Upper Mounting	14 (19)
Lower Mounting	
Coupe & 4000	43 (58)
5000	40 (54)
Trailing Arm	
Coupe & 4000	72 (98)
5000	69 (94)
Transverse Rod	
Coupe & 4000	58 (79)
5000	65 (88)

Rear Suspension

BMW

318i, 320i, 528e, 533i, 633CSi, 733i

DESCRIPTION

All BMW models use independent, trailing control arm rear suspension systems. Vertically mounted MacPherson type struts assemblies are used on all models except the 318i. Shock absorbers with separate barrel shaped coil springs are used on the 318i. A stabilizer bar is used on all models except the 320i.

Fig. 1: BMW 318i Rear Suspension

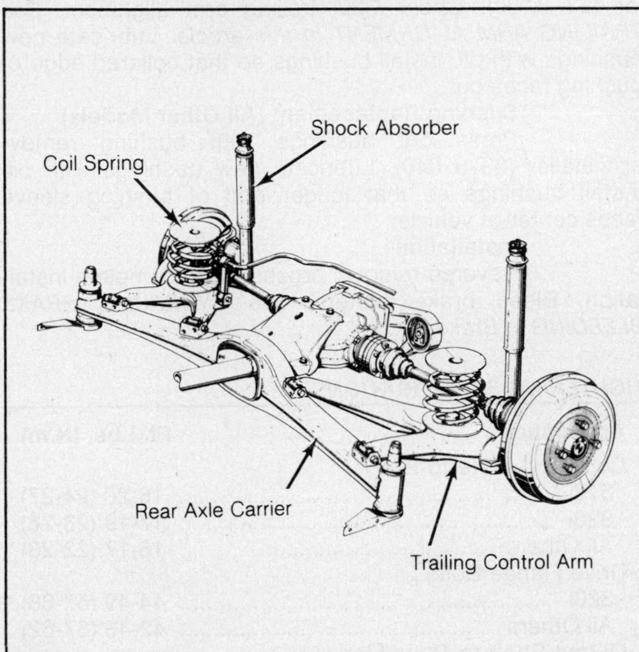
Shock Absorber
Coil Spring
Rear Axle Carrier
Trailing Control Arm

ADJUSTMENTS

WHEEL ALIGNMENT SPECIFICATIONS & PROCEDURES

See Wheel Alignment Specifications and Procedures in WHEEL ALIGNMENT Section.

TRAILING CONTROL ARM ALIGNMENT

320i Only

Place trailing control arm in alignment fixture (Special Tools 33 3 001, 33 3 003, 33 3 004, 33 3 009 and 33 3 011). Swing trailing control arm to correct position and push in dowel pins (33 3 005 and 33 3 006) by hand. If dowel pins cannot be inserted, trailing control arm is distorted and must be replaced.

WHEEL BEARING ADJUSTMENT

320i Only

1) Measure and record length of spacer. Install inner wheel bearing. Measure distance from outer wheel bearing surface to inner wheel bearing outer race. Subtract bearing surface measurement from spacer measurement and determine total clearance.

2) Subtract wheel bearing axial play .004" (0.1 mm) from total clearance and determine locating ring thickness. Install a locating ring equal to locating ring thickness to obtain correct wheel bearing clearance.

REMOVAL & INSTALLATION

WHEEL BEARING

Removal (320i)

1) Raise and support vehicle. Remove hub cap, cotter pin and castle nut. Remove wheel assembly. Remove hex head screw and remove brake drum. Pull of drive flange. Disconnect output shaft at drive flange and hang out of the way.

2) Install castle nut flush with end of rear axle shaft and knock shaft out with soft mallet. Remove outer wheel bearing and shaft seal. Remove locating ring and spacer. Remove inner wheel bearing and shaft seal.

Installation

Reverse removal procedure to complete installation and adjust wheel bearings. *See WHEEL BEARING ADJUSTMENT in this article.*

Removal (318i)

1) Raise and support vehicle. Remove wheel assembly. Remove lock plate and nut. Disconnect output shaft at drive flange and hang out of the way. Press output shaft out using output shaft remover (33 2 110). Remove hex head screw and remove brake drum.

2) Drive out rear axle shaft using driver (33 4 010). Remove snap ring and remove wheel bearing with puller. Remove inner bearing shell from rear axle shaft with puller, if necessary.

Removal (528e, 533i, 633CSi & 733i)

1) Raise and support vehicle. Disconnect output shaft at drive flange and suspend out of the way. Remove brake caliper bolts and remove brake caliper. Remove hex head screw and remove rotor.

2) Remove lock plate. Remove collar nut with nut remover (33 4 000). Pull off drive flange. Install collar nut flush with end of shaft and knock shaft out with soft mallet.

3) Remove snap ring and remove wheel bearing with puller. Remove inner bearing shell from rear axle shaft with puller, if necessary.

Installation (318i, 528e, 533i, 633CSi & 733i)

Reverse removal procedure to complete installation. Tighten collar nut. Drive in lock plate with driver (33 4 060) on 528e, 533i, 633CSi and 733i. Use driver (33 4 050) on 318i.

SHOCK ABSORBER

NOTE: Always store shock absorbers in upright position. If shock absorbers are stored improperly, correct condition by storing shock absorbers in upright position with piston rod extended at room temperature for 24 hours.

Removal (318i)

Raise and support vehicle. Support trailing control arm. Partially remove trunk trim panel. Disconnect shock absorber centering plate. Remove shock absorber and gasket.

Installation

Ensure that centering plate gasket is in place. Replace all self-locking nuts. Reverse removal procedure to complete installation.

COIL SPRING

Removal (318i)

1) Raise and support vehicle. Disconnect exhaust assembly and hang out of the way. Disconnect

Rear Suspension

BMW (Cont.)

final drive rubber mount and push down. Hold down trailing control arm with a wedge of wood or similar item.

2) Disconnect stabilizer bar. Support trailing control arm and disconnect shock absorber. Lower trailing control arm and remove coil spring.

Installation

Replace coil spring with one of same color code, if coil spring is to be replaced. Install correct rubber rings. Reverse removal procedure to complete installation.

STRUT ASSEMBLY

Removal

Raise and support vehicle. Support trailing control arm. Disconnect strut assembly from trailing control arm. Paritally remove trunk trim. Disconnect strut assembly centering plate. Remove strut assembly and gasket.

Disassembly

Remove end cap. Compress coil spring. Remove spring retainer nut and washer. Slowly release spring compressor. Remove centering plate, spring, cap, snap ring, damper and dust sleeve.

Reassembly

Reverse disassembly procedure. Before releasing spring compressor make sure that coil spring ends are in openings provided in centering plate and lower spring retainer.

Installation

Replace all self-locking nuts. Reverse removal procedure to complete installation.

Fig. 2: BMW 528e Rear Suspension

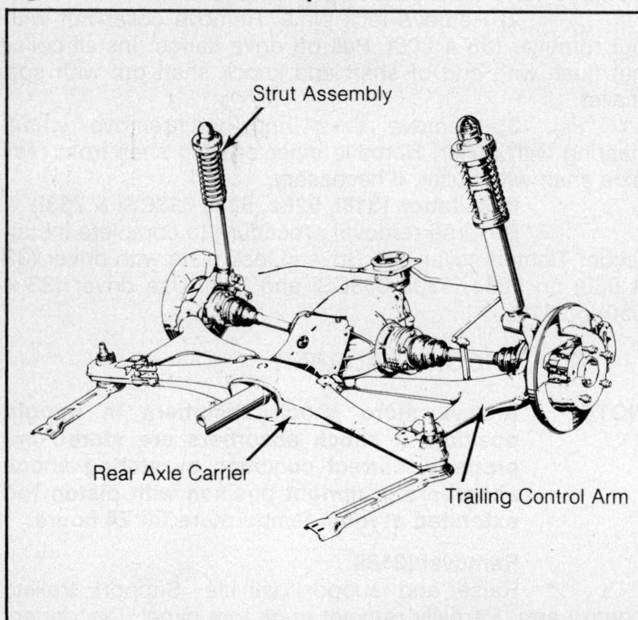
Strut Assembly
Rear Axle Carrier
Trailing Control Arm

TRAILING CONTROL ARM

Removal (320i)

1) Raise and support vehicle. Remove hub cap, cotter pin and castle nut. Disconnect parking brake cable at parking brake lever. Disconnect output shaft from rear axle shaft. Remove wheel assembly.

2) Disconnect strut assembly. Disconnect brake hose at brake line bracket. Remove trailing arm-to-axle carrier bolts, pull out brake cable and remove trailing arm.

Removal (318i, 528e, 533i, 633CSi & 733i)

1) Raise and support vehicle. Remove wheel assembly. Apply parking brake and disconnect output shaft from drive flange. Release parking brake and remove parking brake lever.

2) Remove a small amount of brake fluid from master cylinder. Disconnect brake hose at brake line bracket. Disconnect stabilizer bar. Remove trailing arm-to-axle carrier bolts. Disconnect strut assembly and remove trailing arm.

Bushing Replacement (318i & 320i)

Pull out bushings with bushing remover/installer (33 3 50). Check 320i trailing arm alignment. *See TRAILING ARM ALIGNMENT in this article.* Lubricate new bushings with oil. Install bushings so that collared edge of bushing faces out.

Bushing Replacement (All Other Models)

Press out bushings with bushing remover/installer (33 3 040). Lubricate new bushings with oil. Install bushings so that longer end of bushing sleeve faces center of vehicle.

Installation

Reverse removal procedure to complete installation. Bleed brake system. *See HYDRAULIC BRAKE BLEEDING in Brake Section.*

TIGHTENING SPECIFICATIONS

Application	Ft. Lbs. (N.m)
Centering Plate-to-Body	
318i	18-20 (24-27)
320i	17-19 (23-26)
All Others	16-17 (22-23)
Drive Flange Bolts	
320i	44-49 (57-66)
All Others	42-46 (57-62)
Output Shaft-to-Drive Flange	
318i (Collar Nut)	140-152 (190-206)
320i (Castle Nut)	295-346 (400-469)
All Others (Collar Nut)	169-188 (229-254)
Shock Absorber-to-Arm	
318i Only	52-63 (71-85)
Spring Retainer Nut	
320i	16-17 (22-23)
528e, 533i & 633CSi	16-18 (22-24)
733i	18-22 (24-30)
Strut Assembly-to-Arm	
320i	60-66 (81-89)
All Others	94-103 (127-140)
Trailing Control Arm Bolts	
320i	60-66 (81-89)
All Others	48-54 (65-73)

Rear Suspension

CHRYSLER CORP. IMPORTS & MITSUBISHI FWD

DESCRIPTION

An independent type rear suspension is used on the Colt. It consists of an integral axle/control arm combination with both sides working independently.

The assembly is attached to the frame with 2 shock absorbers and 2 fixtures at opposite ends of the axle tube. Support is provided by 2 coil springs and some models feature a stabilizer bar.

Fig. 1: Exploded View of Colt Rear Suspension

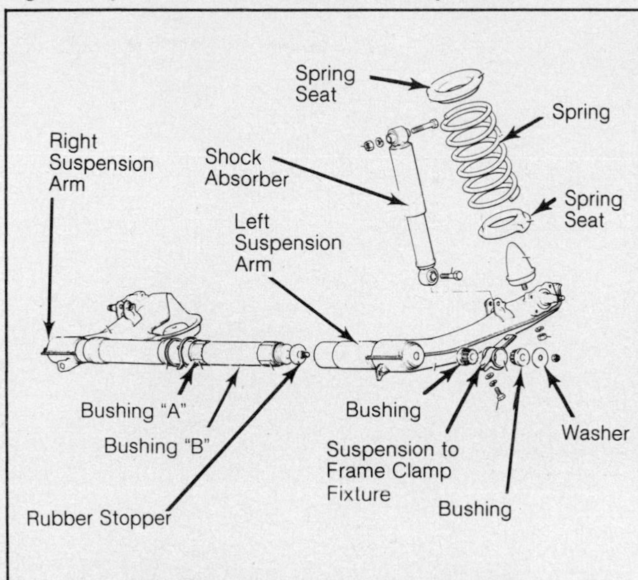

Spring Seat
Spring
Right Suspension Arm
Shock Absorber
Spring Seat
Left Suspension Arm
Bushing "A"
Bushing "B"
Bushing
Washer
Suspension to Frame Clamp Fixture
Bushing
Rubber Stopper

ADJUSTMENT

WHEEL ALIGNMENT SPECIFICATIONS & PROCEDURES

Rear alignment is not adjustable.

WHEEL BEARING ADJUSTMENT

Remove dust cap, cotter pin and nut retainer. While turning wheel or drum, tighten adjusting nut to 14 ft. lbs. (20 N.m). Loosen nut and retighten to 4 ft. lbs. (5 N.m). Reinstall dust cap, cotter pin and nut retainer.

REMOVAL & INSTALLATION

WHEEL BEARING

Removal

Raise and support vehicle. Remove wheel assembly. Remove drum by removing dust cap, cotter pin, nut retainer, nut, washer and outer bearing. Pry grease seal from drum and remove inner bearing.

Installation

Clean grease from inside of drum and bearings. Repack inner and outer bearings. Install inner bearing and grease seal. Install outer bearing and retaining parts. Adjust bearing preload and install nut retainer, cotter pin and dust cap.

REAR SUSPENSION ASSEMBLY

Removal

1) Raise and support vehicle. Remove wheel and brake assemblies. Remove muffler. Raise suspension with floor jack and keep it slightly raised. Disconnect shock absorbers from suspension arms.

2) Lower suspension enough to remove coil springs. Disconnect brake hoses at suspension arm. Remove fixture bolts holding suspension to body and remove suspension assembly.

Disassembly

1) Before fixtures are removed, make alignment marks on fixtures and suspension arms for reference at reassembly.

2) On vehicles equipped with stabilizer bar, put aligning mark on each end of stabilizer bar in alignment with punch mark on stabilizer bar bracket, before disassembling suspension.

3) Remove nuts at both ends of suspension arm to remove fixtures and rubber bushings. Remove dust cover clamp. Separate suspension into right and left arms. Remove stabilizer from bracket. Leave dust cover attached to right suspension arm to protect lip from damage.

4) Remove rubber stopper from right arm. Remove bushing "A" with a cold chisel and hammer. Working through small hole at end of arm, punch bushing "B" out of arm with a drift and hammer. *See Fig. 2.*

Fig. 2: Removal of Bushing "B"

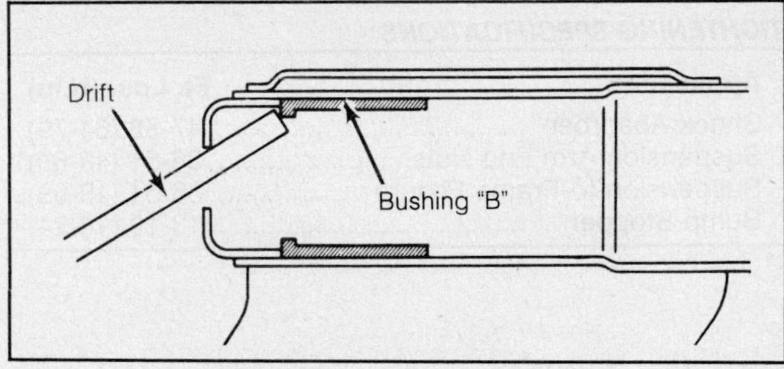

Drift
Bushing "B"

Inspection

Check for bent or damaged suspension arm, broken dust cover, damaged rubber stopper, damaged bushing and worn or damaged rubber bushings.

Reassembly

1) Apply grease to inside of left suspension arm and to all outside surfaces of bushings "A" and "B". Using special tool (MB990779 and MB990780), drive bushing "B" in until notch on bar reaches end of suspension arm. Using tool without bar, drive in bushing "A". *See Fig. 3.*

2) Install dust cover on right arm. Apply grease to surface of right arm and install rubber stopper. Slowly push right and left suspension arms together and wipe away any excess grease.

3) If equipped with stabilizer bar, align marks on bar and bracket. Install rubber bushings, fixtures and washers. Ensure toothed side of washer faces bushing.

4) After aligning fixtures with arm according to alignment marks, tighten nuts. Be sure fixture angle is set at 30°. Pack grease into dust cover and lips, and secure dust cover with clamp.

Installation

To install, reverse removal procedure. Be sure to bleed brakes. Check upper and lower spring seats for proper installation.

Rear Suspension

CHRYSLER CORP. IMPORTS & MITSUBISHI FWD (Cont.)

Fig. 3: Installation of Bushings "A" & "B"

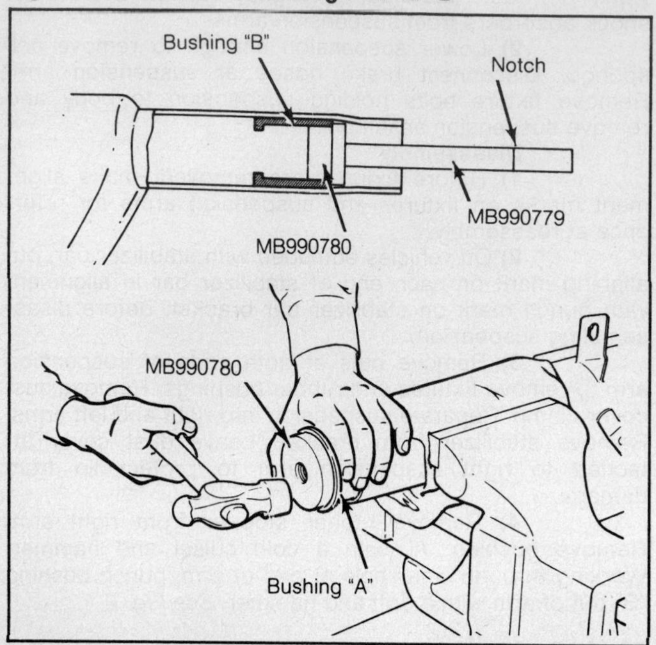
Bushing "B"
Notch
MB990779
MB990780
MB990780
Bushing "A"

TIGHTENING SPECIFICATIONS

Application	Ft. Lbs. (N.m)
Shock Absorber	47-58 (64-79)
Suspension Arm End Nuts	36-51 (49-69)
Suspension-to-Frame Fixture	36-51 (49-69)
Bump Stopper	13-18 (18-24)

Rear Suspension

CHRYSLER CORP. IMPORTS — RWD MODELS

Challenger, Sapporo

DESCRIPTION

Rear suspension is of the 4-link coil spring type. Lower arm and upper control arm are attached to rear axle housing brackets and to body with individual bushings. Shock absorbers attach to body and to rear axle housing.

Fig. 1: Exploded View of Rear Suspension

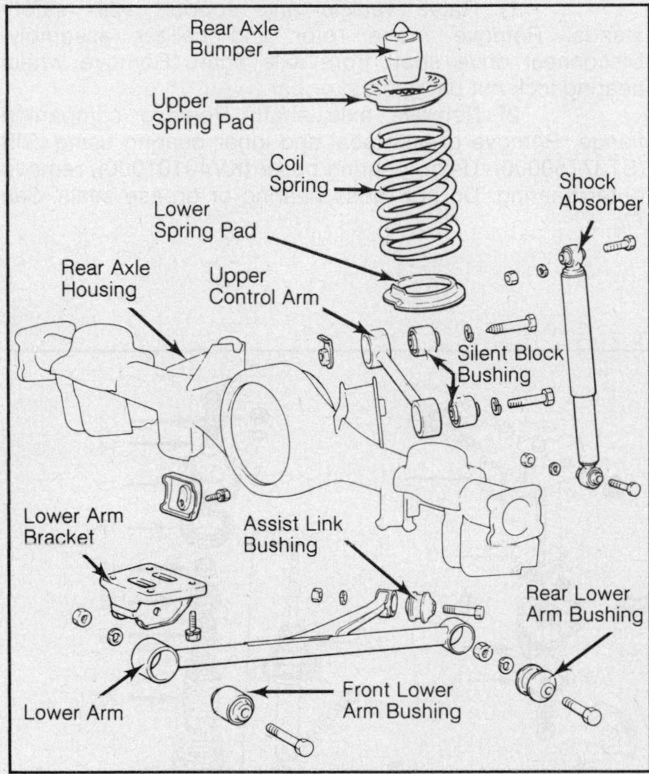
Rear Axle Bumper
Upper Spring Pad
Coil Spring
Shock Absorber
Lower Spring Pad
Rear Axle Housing
Upper Control Arm
Silent Block Bushing
Lower Arm Bracket
Assist Link Bushing
Rear Lower Arm Bushing
Front Lower Arm Bushing
Lower Arm

REMOVAL & INSTALLATION

WHEEL BEARING

Removal

1) Raise and support vehicle on safety stands. Remove wheel assembly. Remove brake disc (drum if equipped). On models with disc brakes, remove caliper support together with parking brake cable and caliper assembly (brake hose connected), and support out of the way.

2) Remove brake disc. On all models, utilizing hole in flange of rear axle shaft, remove bolts attaching bearing outer retainer to rear axle housing. Pull rear axle shaft from housing. Remove oil seal with a screw driver.

3) Remove bearing inner retainer by grinding down retainer to a thickness of .04-.06" (1.0-1.5 mm). Using a chisel, make a cut in the ground section of bearing retainer. Remove split bearing retainer.

4) Using axle bearing puller (CT-1120), remove rear wheel bearing from rear axle shaft.

Installation

To install, reverse removal procedure.

COIL SPRING & SHOCK ABSORBER

Removal

1) Raise vehicle and support body on safety stands. Place a floor jack under rear axle assembly, and raise axle assembly slightly.

2) Remove upper and lower shock absorber bolts, and remove shock absorber. Lower jack, and let axle assembly hang down. Remove coil spring.

Installation

1) Install coil springs so that spring ends contact spring stops in upper and lower spring pad.

2) Install shock absorbers, and loosely tighten bolts. Lower vehicle to floor, and tighten shock absorber attaching bolts.

LOWER ARM & UPPER CONTROL ARM

Removal

1) Raise vehicle, and support body with safety stands. Place a floor jack under rear axle assembly, and raise slightly. Remove upper control arm attaching bolts, and remove upper control arm.

2) If equipped with rear drum brakes, remove parking brake rear cable from lower arm. Remove bolts that attach lower arm to rear axle housing and to bracket attached to body. Remove lower arms.

Bushing Replacement

1) Use an arbor press to replace any damaged or deteriorated bushing in lower arms or upper control arm.

2) When new bushing is pressed into place, be sure that bushing extends out each end of arm equally.

Installation

1) Support rear axle housing with a floor jack. Install lower arms, being sure that right and left arms are installed on their proper sides.

2) Install upper control arm and attaching bolts. If equipped with drum brakes, reconnect parking brake cable to lower arm.

TIGHTENING SPECIFICATIONS

Application	Ft. Lbs. (N.m)
Bearing Retainer-to-Housing	25-36 (34-49)
Lower Arm-to-Lower Arm Bracket	94-108 (127-146)
Lower Arm-to-Axle Housing	
Inner Bracket	47-58 (64-79)
Outer Bracket	94-108 (127-146)
Shock Absorber Attaching Bolts	47-58 (64-79)
Upper Control Arm Bolts	94-108 (127-146)

Rear Suspension

DATSUN/NISSAN MAXIMA & 280ZX

DESCRIPTION

Rear suspension is of the semi-trailing arm, independent type. The rear wheel is supported by a MacPherson type strut assembly and a semi-trailing arm. The upper end of the strut is attached directly to the upper body. The lower end of the strut is attached to the end of the semi-trailing arm.

The differential gear carrier is installed directly to the suspension subframe with a differential mounting bracket and insulator. The semi-trailing arm is installed on the subframe with rubber bushings and pivot bolts. The rear wheel bearing housing and lower strut mount bracket are welded to the end of the semi-trailing arm. A stabilizer bar is used for added suspension control.

ADJUSTMENTS

WHEEL ALIGNMENT SPECIFICATIONS & PROCEDURES

See Wheel Alignment Specifications & Procedures in WHEEL ALIGNMENT Section

WHEEL BEARING

Wheel bearings are adjusted by using a spacer sleeve between sealed wheel bearing and bearing housing. Rear wheel hub must be disassembled in order to adjust preload and rear axle shaft end play.

REMOVAL & INSTALLATION

WHEEL BEARING

Removal

1) Raise vehicle and support with safety stands. Remove brake rotor and caliper assembly. Disconnect drive shaft from axle shaft. Remove wheel bearing lock nut using breaker bar.

2) Remove axle shaft. Remove companion flange. Remove grease seal and inner bearing using drift (ST37750000). Using bearing puller (KV40101000), remove outer bearing. Do not reuse bearing or grease seals. *See Fig. 2.*

Fig. 1: Exploded View of Maxima & 280ZX Rear Suspension

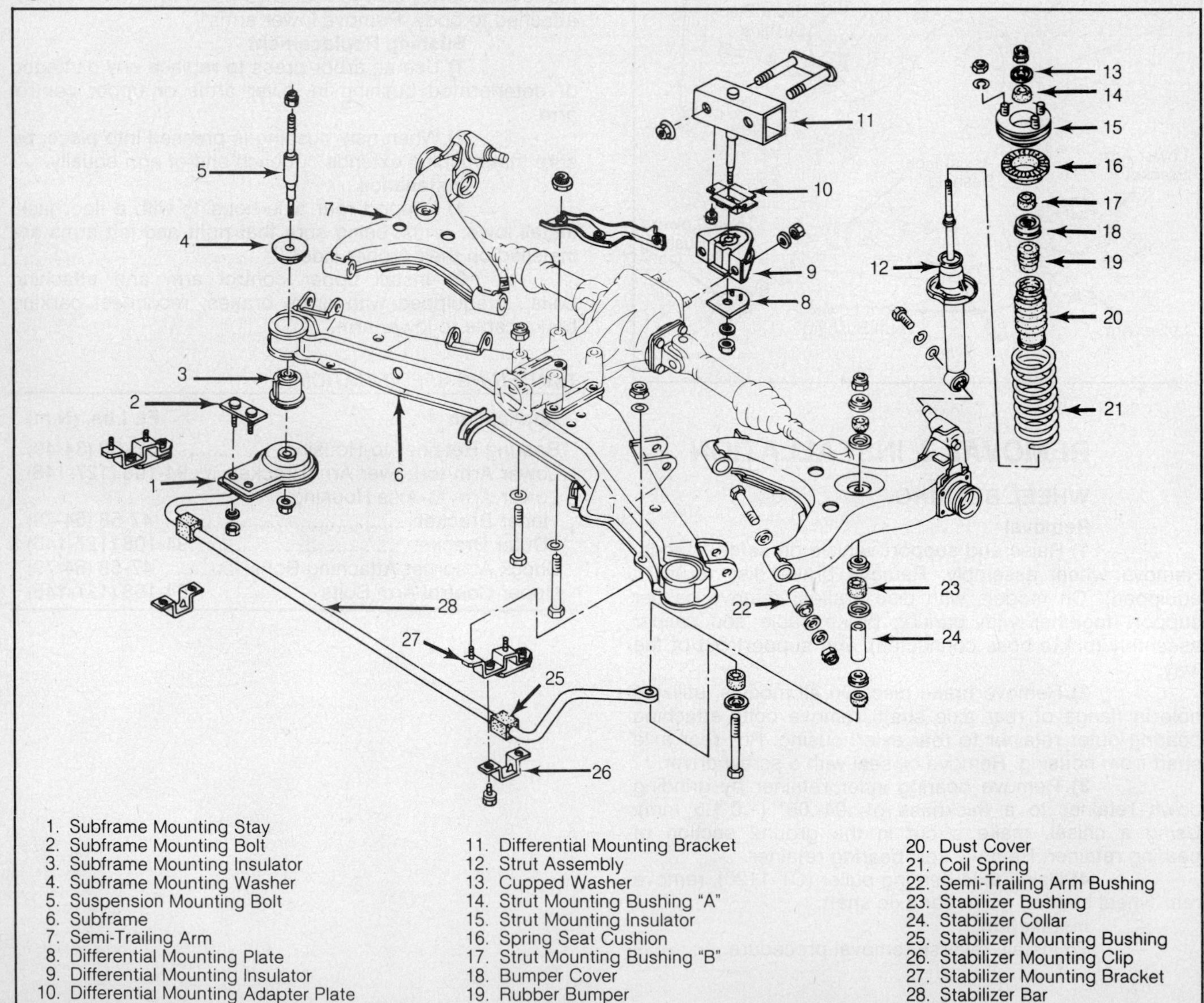
1. Subframe Mounting Stay
2. Subframe Mounting Bolt
3. Subframe Mounting Insulator
4. Subframe Mounting Washer
5. Suspension Mounting Bolt
6. Subframe
7. Semi-Trailing Arm
8. Differential Mounting Plate
9. Differential Mounting Insulator
10. Differential Mounting Adapter Plate
11. Differential Mounting Bracket
12. Strut Assembly
13. Cupped Washer
14. Strut Mounting Bushing "A"
15. Strut Mounting Insulator
16. Spring Seat Cushion
17. Strut Mounting Bushing "B"
18. Bumper Cover
19. Rubber Bumper
20. Dust Cover
21. Coil Spring
22. Semi-Trailing Arm Bushing
23. Stabilizer Bushing
24. Stabilizer Collar
25. Stabilizer Mounting Bushing
26. Stabilizer Mounting Clip
27. Stabilizer Mounting Bracket
28. Stabilizer Bar

Rear Suspension

DATSUN/NISSAN MAXIMA & 280ZX (Cont.)

Installation

1) Install wheel bearings, use bearing drift (ST37750000) to install outer bearing. Match mark stamped on housing and on spacer sleeve and install sleeve.

NOTE: Wheel bearings are sealed type. Sealed side of outer bearing must face the wheel and sealed side of inner bearing must face differential.

2) Install grease seal using seal installer (ST37710000). Tighten new bearing lock nut and measure preload and rear axle shaft end play.

3) Torque wheel bearing lock nut to specifications. Check wheel bearing preload. Preload should be 2.6 lbs. (12 N.m) or less. Rear axle shaft end play should be .012" (0.3 mm).

4) If correct preload and shaft end play cannot be obtained, disassemble again and replace bearing spacer sleeve.

Fig. 2: Exploded Veiw of 280ZX Rear Axle Bearings

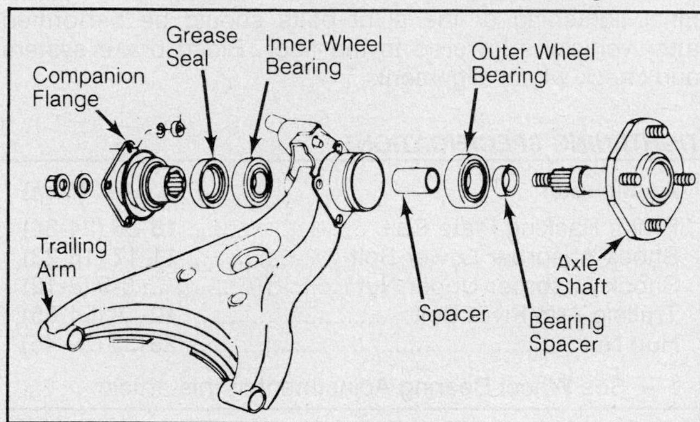
Grease Seal
Inner Wheel Bearing
Outer Wheel Bearing
Companion Flange
Trailing Arm
Axle Shaft
Spacer
Bearing Spacer

Maxima models similar.

STRUT & COIL SPRING

Removal

1) Raise rear of vehicle and support with safety stands. Support semi-trailing arm with hydraulic floor jack. Open trunk lid, remove cover and nuts securing strut assembly to body.

2) Lower floor jack gradually. Disconnect strut by removing bolt at semi-trailing arm. Remove strut from vehicle.

Disassembly

NOTE: Set spring compressor only on spring. Make sure spring compressor is properly secured to strut.

For coil spring removal, mark position of shock absorber mounting insulator and lower end pin for proper reassembly. Using spring compressor (ST35651001), compress spring until mounting insulator can be turned by hand. Remove self-locking nut on strut shaft. Release spring compressor and remove coil spring.

Reassembly

Reverse disassembly procedure using a new self-locking nut on strut shaft.

Installation

Install strut assembly to upper body. Connect lower end of strut to semi-trailing arm and tighten bolt to specifications.

SEMI-TRAILING ARM

Removal

1) Raise vehicle and support with safety stands. Remove wheel assemblies. Disconnect brake tube from hose at semi-trailing arm and brake assembly. Remove brake line and disconnect hand brake cable from caliber. Disconnect axle shaft from stub shaft by removing flange bolts.

2) Remove stabilizer bar bolt and related hardware. On 280ZX models, remove brake rotor and caliper assembly. Disconnect strut from semi-trailing arm. Disconnect semi-trailing arm from subframe by removing pivot bolts. Remove semi-trailing arm from vehicle.

Installation

To install, reverse removal procedures. Replace all self-locking nuts. Tighten semi-trailing arm-to-subframe bolts to specifications only after installing wheels and lowering vehicle to floor. Bleed and adjust brakes.

REAR SUSPENSION ASSEMBLY

Removal

1) Raise and support vehicle with safety stands. Remove wheel assemblies. Remove heat shield from front of fuel tank. Remove rear exhaust pipe and muffler. Mark flange of propeller shaft and companion flange. Remove propeller shaft.

2) Disconnect and plug rear brake hoses at semi-trailing arm. Place a floor jack under center of suspension and differential assembly. Disconnect hand brake cables and lower strut ends.

3) Remove subframe nuts at body. Remove differential mount lock nut. Lower rear suspension assembly and remove from under vehicle.

Disassembly

1) Disconnect axle shafts from differential and stub shafts. Remove differential assembly from subframe. Remove pivot bolts and semi-trailing arms.

2) Insulator bushings can be removed with removal/installing tool (ST38280000).

Reassembly & Installation

Reassemble and install in reverse order of disassembly and removal. Final tightening of semi-trailing arm pivot bolt lock nuts should be done after vehicle has been lowered to the floor. All self-locking nuts should be replaced, if they were removed.

TIGHTENING SPECIFICATIONS

Application	Ft. Lbs. (N.m)
Wheel Bearing Lock Nut	181-240 (245-325)
Differential Mount Lock Nut	87-108 (118-146)
Propeller Shaft-to-Flange	25-33 (34-45)
Semi-Trailing Arm Pivot Nuts	58-72 (79-98)
Stabilizer Bar-to-Semi-Trailing Arm	12-15 (16-20)
Strut Lower Mount Bolt	43-58 (58-79)
Strut Upper Mount Nut	22-29 (30-39)
Subframe-to-Body Nuts	58-72 (79-98)

Rear Suspension

DATSUN/NISSAN PULSAR, SENTRA & STANZA

DESCRIPTION

Rear suspension is of the trailing arm, independent type and consists of a coil spring, shock absorber and trailing arm.

The forward end of the trailing arm pivots at the body and is suspended by the coil spring. The shock absorber mounts adjacent to the spring and controls trailing arm vertical movement.

ADJUSTMENTS

WHEEL ALIGNMENT SPECIFICATIONS & PROCEDURES

Wheel alignment is not adjustable.

WHEEL BEARING

Tighten hub nut to 29-33 ft. lbs. (39-44 N.m). Rotate hub serveral times to seat bearings. Turn hub nut back 90° and install new cotter pin. Hub nut may be tightened 15° to align cotter pin hole. Preload of wheel hub must be less than 3.1 lbs. (13.7 N). If not within specifications, readjust wheel bearings.

Fig. 1: Exploded View of Rear Suspension

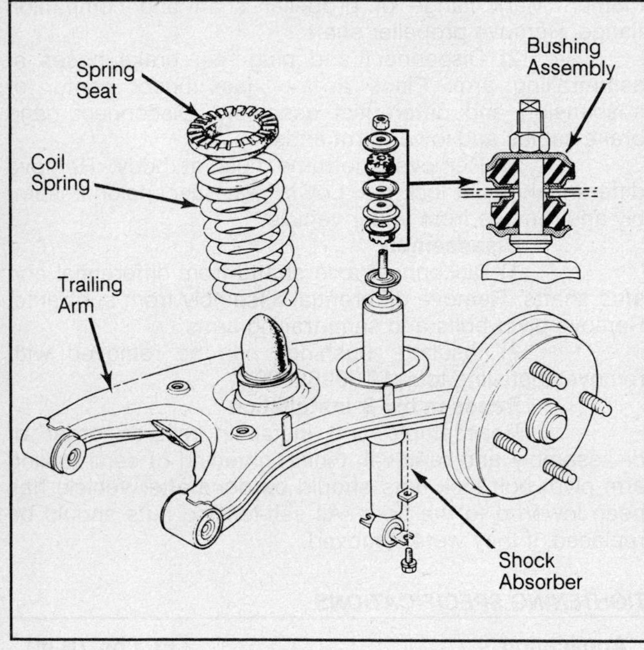
Spring Seat
Bushing Assembly
Coil Spring
Trailing Arm
Shock Absorber

REMOVAL & INSTALLATION

SHOCK ABSORBER

Removal

Raise vehicle and support with safety stands. Remove wheel assembly. Support lower end of trailing arm with a hydraulic floor jack. Remove nut and bolts from shock absorber ends. Lower jack slowly and remove shock absorber.

Installation

To install, reverse removal procedures.

COIL SPRING

Removal

Raise vehicle and support with safety stands. Remove wheel assembly. Support lower end of trailing arm with a floor jack. Remove shock absorber. Lower trailing arm and remove coil spring.

Installation

To install, reverse removal procedures.

TRAILING ARM

Removal

1) Raise vehicle and support with safety stands. Place a floor jack under lower end of trailing arm. Remove wheel assembly. Disconnect parking brake cable.

2) Remove dust cap, cotter pin and hub nut. Remove brake drum with bearings. Disconnect and plug brake line. Remove brake assembly.

3) Remove shock absorber and coil spring. Remove pivot nuts and bolts. Remove trailing arm. Inspect pivot bushings and replace as necessary.

Installation

To install, reverse the removal procedures. Final tightening of the pivot bolts should be performed after vehicle is lowered to the floor. Bleed brake system and check wheel alignment.

TIGHTENING SPECIFICATIONS

Application	Ft. Lbs. (N.m)
Brake Backing Plate Bolt	18-25 (24-34)
Shock Absorber Lower Bolt	11-17 (15-23)
Shock Absorber Upper Nut	6-9 (8-12)
Trailing Arm Pivot Bolt	40-48 (54-65)
Hub Nut [1]	29-33 (39-45)

[1] – See Wheel Bearing Adjustment in this article.

Rear Suspension

DATSUN/NISSAN 200SX

DESCRIPTION

Rear suspension is a coil spring and 4-link type, consisting of coil springs, shock absorbers, stabilizer bar and links which control axle movement.

Fig. 1: Exploded View of 200SX Rear Suspension

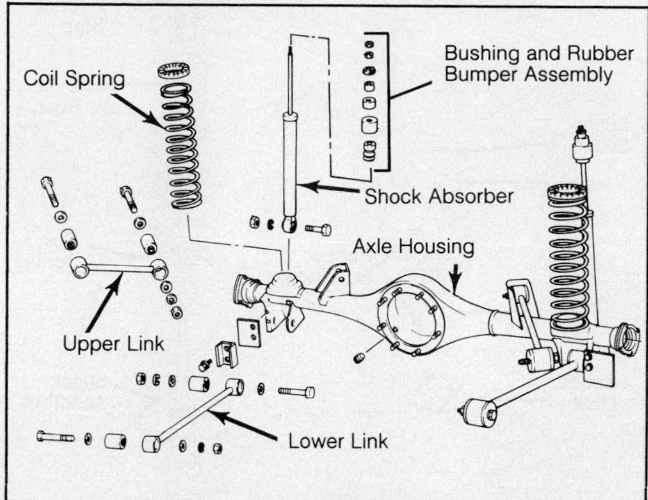

Coil Spring
Bushing and Rubber Bumper Assembly
Shock Absorber
Axle Housing
Upper Link
Lower Link

REMOVAL & INSTALLATION

SHOCK ABSORBER

Removal

From inside vehicle, remove upper shock absorber nut. Remove lower shock absorber bolt from bracket. Remove shock absorber.

Installation

To install, reverse removal procedure.

COIL SPRING

Removal

1) Block front wheels. Raise and support rear of vehicle with safety stands at frame. Support center of differential with floor jack.

2) Remove wheel assembies. Remove shock absorber mount bolts from axle assembly. Lower axle assembly slowly, and remove coil springs as they are extended.

Installation

To install, reverse removal procedure.

STABILIZER BAR

Removal

1) Remove clamp bolts retaining stabilizer bar to lower link arms. Remove rubber bushings and lower stabilizer bar.

2) Check stabilizer bar for deformation or cracks. Check rubber parts for deterioration or cracks. Replace parts as neccessary.

Installation

To install, reverse removal procedures. Be careful not to confuse left from right sides of stabilizer bar.

REAR AXLE ASSEMBLY

Removal

1) Block front wheels. Raise and support rear of vehicle with safety stands at frame. Support center of differential with floor jack. Remove wheel assemblies.

2) Disconnect propeller shaft, brake hose, and parking brake cable adjuster. Remove lower shock absorber mounting bolts.

3) Lower floor jack slowly, and remove coil springs. Raise jack to original position. Remove bolts securing upper and lower links at axle housing. Lower floor jack slowly, and remove axle assembly from under vehicle.

Installation

To install, reverse removal procedure. When tightening link arms, be sure wheels are on the ground.

LINK ASSEMBLY

NOTE: **If rear axle assembly is not being removed, do not remove more than 1 link at a time.**

Removal

If equipped, remove stabilizer bar. Remove bolts from each link end, and remove link assembly.

Inspection

Inspect link bushings for wear or damage. Replace as necessary.

Installation

To install, reverse removal procedure. When tightening link arms, be sure both wheels are on the ground.

TIGHTENING SPECIFICATIONS

Application	Ft. Lbs. (N.m)
Link Assembly Bolts	51-58 (69-78)
Propeller Shaft Flange Bolts	17-24 (23-32)
Shock Absorber Lower Nuts	51-58 (69-78)
Shock Absorber Upper Nuts	11-14 (15-19)

Rear Suspension

HONDA

Accord, Civic (Exc. Wagon), Prelude

DESCRIPTION

The Honda rear suspension uses independent MacPherson type struts. The suspension consists of a vertically mounted strut, a lower control arm, and a rear hub carrier. A radius rod is installed on Accord and Prelude. A radius arm is used on Civic. The Civic 1500S and Prelude are equipped with a rear stabilizer bar.

ADJUSTMENTS

WHEEL ALIGNMENT SPECIFICATIONS & PROCEDURES

See Wheel Alignment Specifications and Procedures in WHEEL ALIGNMENT Section.

REMOVAL & INSTALLATION

STRUT ASSEMBLY

CAUTION: Block front wheels before raising vehicle.

Removal (Accord)

Raise rear of vehicle and support with safety stands. Remove wheel assembly. Disconnect and plug brake line. Remove brake drum and disconnect parking brake cable. Remove strut assembly locking bolt and top mounting nuts. Remove strut assembly.

Removal (Civic)

Raise rear of vehicle and support with safety stands. Remove wheel assembly. Disconnect and plug brake line. Disconnect parking brake cable. Loosen lower control arm pivot bolt. Loosen forward bolt on radius arm. Remove strut assembly locking bolt and top mounting nuts. Remove strut assembly.

Removal (Prelude)

Raise rear of vehicle and support with safety stands. Remove wheel assembly. Disconnect and plug brake line. Remove stabilizer bar. Loosen lower control arm pivot bolt. Loosen radius rod nut and hub carrier bolt. Remove strut assembly locking bolt and remove strut from hub carrier. Remove top mounting nuts and remove strut assembly.

Disassembly

Compress strut assembly spring and remove spring seat nut. Slowly release spring compressor and lift spring off. Disassemble strut assembly, noting relative position of assembled parts. *See Fig. 1.*

Reassembly

Check spring tension. Check parts for deterioration or damage. Check shock absorber for leaks and proper operation. Replace worn or damaged parts. Install strut assembly mount base with "OUT" mark aligned with index mark on strut tube on Prelude. Reverse disassembly procedure.

Installation

1) Position top of strut assembly. Align tab on strut tube with slot in hub carrier and tighten locking bolt. Install lower control arm and radius arm/rod loosely in place. Place jack under hub carrier and raise until car just lifts off safety stands.

Fig. 1: Accord Rear Strut Assembly

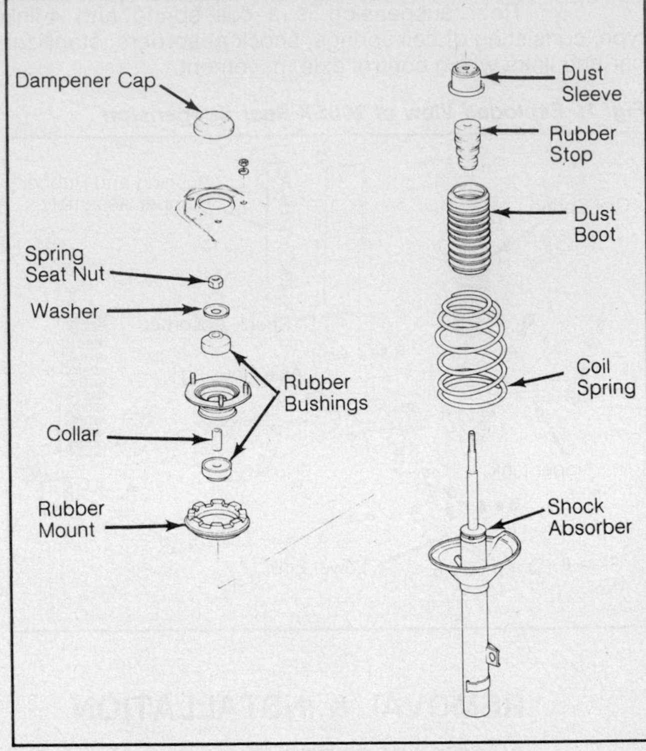
Dampener Cap
Dust Sleeve
Rubber Stop
Dust Boot
Spring Seat Nut
Washer
Rubber Bushings
Coil Spring
Collar
Rubber Mount
Shock Absorber

Civic & Prelude strut assemblies are similar.

2) Tighten lower control arm and radius arm/rod adjusting bolts. Reverse removal procedure to complete installation. Bleed brake system and check rear wheel alignment.

WHEEL HUB CARRIER

Removal (Accord)

1) Raise rear of vehicle and support with safety stands. Remove wheel assembly and brake drum. Disconnect parking brake cable. Disconnect and plug brake line. Remove backing plate assembly.

2) Remove radius rod bolt and remove radius rod. Remove strut assembly locking bolt and separate hub carrier. Remove hub carrier bolt and remove hub carrier.

Removal (Civic)

1) Raise rear of vehicle and support with safety stands. Remove wheel assembly and brake drum. Disconnect parking brake cable. Disconnect and plug brake line. Remove backing plate assembly.

2) Remove stabilizer bar on Civic 1500S. Remove radius arm bolts and remove radius arm. Remove strut assembly locking bolt and separate hub carrier. Remove hub carrier bolt and remove hub carrier.

Removal (Prelude)

1) Raise rear of vehicle and support with safety stands. Remove wheel assembly and brake drum. Disconnect parking brake cable. Disconnect and plug brake line. Remove stabilizer bar.

2) Remove backing plate assembly. Remove radius rod bolts and remove radius rod. Remove strut assembly locking bolt and remove strut from hub carrier. Remove hub carrier hub bolt and remove carrier.

Installation

1) Align tab on strut tube with slot in hub carrier and tighten locking bolt. Install lower control arm

Rear Suspension

HONDA (Cont.)

and radius arm/rod loosely in place. Place jack under hub carrier and raise until car just lifts off safety stands.

2) Tighten lower control arm and radius arm/rod adjusting bolts. Reverse removal procedure to complete installation. Bleed brake system and check rear wheel alignment.

Fig. 2: Civic Rear Suspension

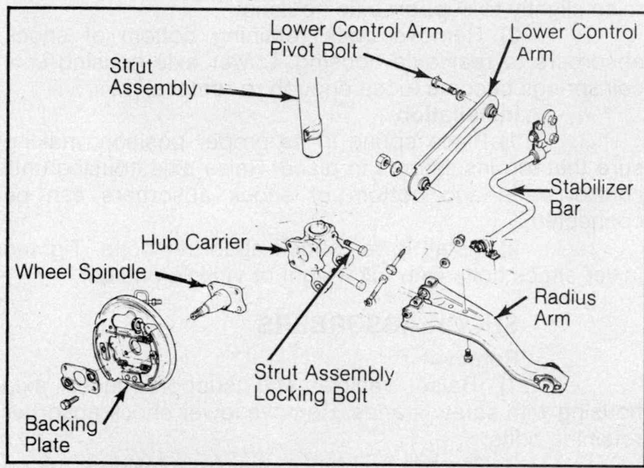
Lower Control Arm
Pivot Bolt
Lower Control
Arm
Strut
Assembly
Stabilizer
Bar
Hub Carrier
Wheel Spindle
Radius
Arm
Strut Assembly
Locking Bolt
Backing
Plate

Rear stabilizer bar is used on Civic 1500S only.

RADIUS ARM/ROD

Removal

Raise rear of vehicle and support with safety stands. Remove stabilizer bar from radius arm on Civic 1500S. Remove bolt(s) attaching radius arm/rod to hub carrier. Remove adjusting bolt(s) attaching radius arm/rod to body bracket.

Inspection

Check parts for deterioration or damage. Replace worn or damaged parts.

Installation

Check parts for deterioration or damage. Replace worn or damaged parts. Reverse removal procedure to complete installation.

Fig. 3: Prelude Rear Suspension

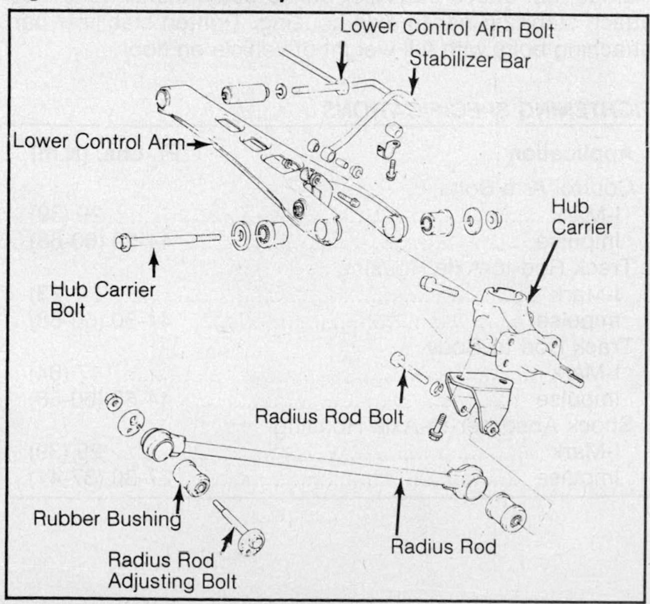
Lower Control Arm Bolt
Stabilizer Bar
Lower Control Arm
Hub
Carrier
Hub Carrier
Bolt
Radius Rod Bolt
Rubber Bushing
Radius Rod
Radius Rod
Adjusting Bolt

Accord rear suspension is similar.

CONTROL ARM

Removal

1) Raise rear of vehicle and support with safety stands. Remove wheel assembly and brake drum. Disconnect parking brake cable. Disconnect and plug brake line. Remove backing plate assembly. Remove stabilizer bar on Civic 1500S and Prelude.

2) On all models, remove radius arm bolts and remove radius rod. Remove strut assembly locking bolt and separate hub carrier. Remove hub carrier bolt and remove hub carrier. Remove lower control arm pivot bolt and remove lower control arm.

Inspection

Check parts for deterioration or damage. Replace worn or damaged parts.

Installation

1) Position top of strut assembly. Align tab on strut tube with slot in hub carrier and tighten locking bolt. Install lower control arm and radius arm/rod loosely in place. Place jack under hub carrier and raise until car just lifts off safety stands.

2) Tighten lower control arm and radius arm/rod adjusting bolts. Reverse removal procedure to complete installation. Bleed brake system and check rear wheel alignment.

STABILIZER BAR

Removal (Civic 1500S & Prelude)

Remove stabilizer bar-to-radius arm bolts on Civic. Remove stabilizer bar-to-lower control arm bolts on Prelude. Remove bolts attaching stabilizer bar to body. Remove stabilizer bar from vehicle.

Installation

Check parts for deterioration or damage. Replace worn or damaged parts. Reverse removal procedure to complete installation

TIGHTENING SPECIFICATIONS

Application	Ft. Lbs. (N.m)
Hub Carrier Bolt	
Accord & Prelude	60 (81)
Civic	40 (54)
Lower Control Arm Pivot Bolt	40 (54)
Radius Arm-to-Body	
Civic	61 (83)
Radius Arm-to-Hub Carrier	
Civic	
Inner Nut	40 (54)
Outer Bolt	72 (98)
Radius Rod-to-Body	
Accord & Prelude	61 (83)
Radius Rod-to-Hub Carrier	
Accord & Prelude	50 (68)
Spring Seat Nut	
Accord & Civic	33 (45)
Prelude	40 (54)
Stabilizer Bar	16 (22)
Strut Assembly Locking Bolt	
Accord & Prelude	40 (54)
Civic	36 (49)
Strut Assembly Mounting Nuts	16 (22)

Rear Suspension

ISUZU I-MARK & IMPULSE

DESCRIPTION

The rear suspension is of link type and consists mainly of a track rod, control arms, coil springs, shock absorbers and a stabilizer bar on some models.

The track rod is connected to the rear axle housing and to the body. Control arms are connected to the body and rear axle housing to control front and rear movement of the rear axle. Shock absorbers are connected to the rear wheel arch and to rear axle housing.

Fig. 1: Exploded View of I-Mark Rear Suspension

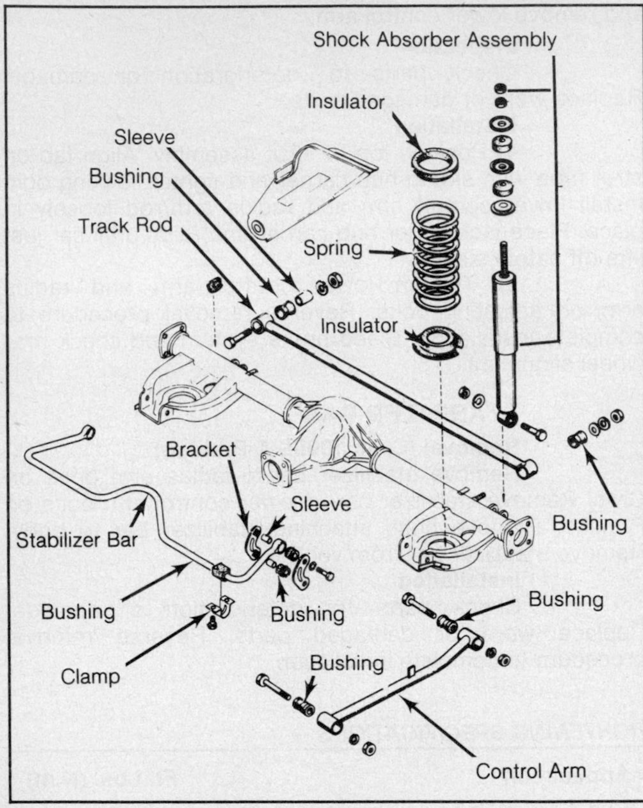
Shock Absorber Assembly
Insulator
Sleeve
Bushing
Track Rod
Spring
Insulator
Bracket
Sleeve
Bushing
Stabilizer Bar
Bushing
Bushing
Bushing
Clamp
Bushing
Control Arm

Impulse rear suspension is similar.

REMOVAL & INSTALLATION

TRACK ROD

Removal

Raise vehicle and support under rear axle housing. Remove bolt that attaches track rod to body. Remove nut that attaches track rod to rear axle housing. Remove track rod.

Installation

Install track rod to rear axle housing and to body. Tighten track rod attaching bolts with full weight of vehicle on floor.

CONTROL ARMS

Removal

Raise vehicle and support under rear axle housing with safety stands. Remove bolts attaching control arms to rear axle housing. Remove bolts attaching control arms to body. Remove control arms.

Installation

Install control arms to body and to rear axle housing. Tighten control arm bolts with full weight of vehicle on floor.

COIL SPRING

NOTE: **Do not stress brake hose when lowering axle housing.**

Removal

1) Raise vehicle and support with safety stands. Place a floor jack under rear axle housing and raise slightly to support axle housing.

2) Remove bolts retaining bottom of shock absorbers to rear axle housing. Lower axle housing until coil springs become loose enough to remove.

Installation

1) Place spring in its proper position, making sure that top insulator is in place. Raise axle housing until control arms and bottom of shock absorbers can be connected.

2) Install lower shock absorber bolts. Tighten lower shock bolts with full weight of vehicle on floor.

SHOCK ABSORBERS

Removal

1) Raise vehicle and support under axle housing with safety stands. Remove lower shock absorber retaining bolts.

2) Remove fuel tank cover from inside trunk on I-Mark. Remove upper shock absorber retaining nuts. Remove shock absorber.

Installation

1) Install upper end of shock absorber. Install upper shock absorber retaining nuts.

2) Install fuel tank cover in trunk on I-Mark. Install lower shock absorber attaching bolts. Remove safety stands and lower vehicle.

STABILIZER BAR

Removal

Raise vehicle and support with safety stands. Remove bolts attaching stabilizer bar-to-axle housing brackets. Remove clamps attaching stabilizer bar to body. Remove stabilizer bar.

Installation

Install rubber bushings on stabilizer bar. Install clamps that attach stabilizer bar to body. Install bolts that attach stabilizer bar to axle housing. Tighten stabilizer bar attaching bolts with full weight of vehicle on floor.

TIGHTENING SPECIFICATIONS

Application	Ft. Lbs. (N.m)
Control Arm Bolts	
I-Mark	29 (39)
Impulse	44-50 (60-68)
Track Rod-to-Axle Housing	
I-Mark	54 (73)
Impulse	44-50 (60-68)
Track Rod-to-Body	
I-Mark	47 (64)
Impulse	44-50 (60-68)
Shock Absorber-to-Axle Housing	
I-Mark	29 (39)
Impulse	27-30 (37-41)

Rear Suspension

JAGUAR

XJ6, XJS

DESCRIPTION

Jaguar uses independent coil spring type rear suspension. Outer bearing carrier and hub assembly is supported by control arms at bottom and utilizes drive axles as upper support.

Suspension is controlled by 4 coil spring/shock absorber assemblies, 2 mounted at each rear wheel. Movement of lower control arms is controlled by radius arms connected to control arms at rear and to chassis members at front.

Fig. 1: Jaguar Rear Suspension Assembly

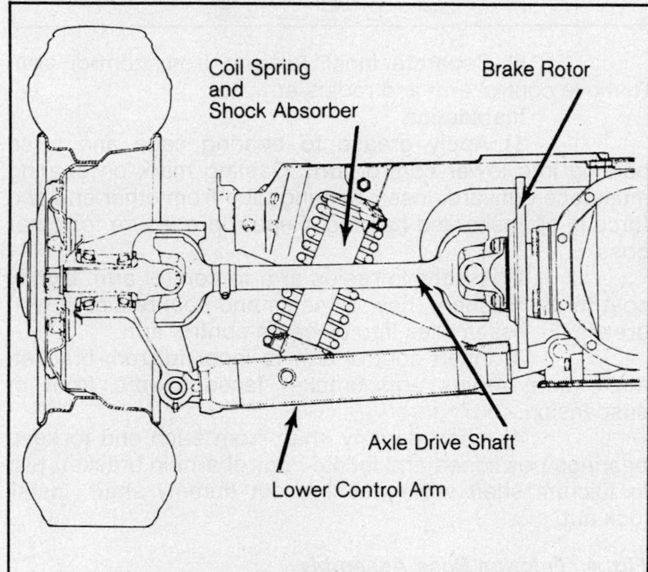
Coil Spring
and
Shock Absorber
Brake Rotor
Axle Drive Shaft
Lower Control Arm

ADJUSTMENTS

WHEEL ALIGNMENT SPECIFICATIONS & PROCEDURES

See Wheel Alignment Specifications and Procedures in WHEEL ALIGNMENT Section.

WHEEL BEARING & END FLOAT

Wheel bearing and end float adjustment, is controlled by a spacer located next to the universal joint on the hub shaft. Spacers are available in thicknesses from .109 to .151" (2.77 to 3.84 mm) in .003" (.076 mm) steps. End float is normally .001-.003" (.026-.076 mm) and must be corrected if it exceeds .005" (.127 mm) by changing the spacer for a thicker one.

NOTE: **If vehicle is equipped with a limited slip differential, do not run engine with vehicle in gear with 1 wheel off the floor.**

Checking

1) Raise vehicle and support with safety stands. Remove wheel assembly. Tap hub towards vehicle. Clamp dial indicator mount to hub carrier web. Stylus of dial indicator must contact hub flange. Note reading of dial indicator.

2) Using 2 levers between hub and hub carrier boss, press hub outwards. Take care not to damage water thrower. Note reading on dial indicator.

3) The difference between dial indicator readings represents end float of hub bearings. If this exceeds .005" (.127 mm) install thicker spacer.

Adjustment

1) Remove cotter pin. Remove hub nut and washer from end of axle shaft. Remove fulcrum shaft grease nipple from hub carrier. Place thread protector (JD 1C 7) on end of drive shaft.

2) Mount hub puller (JD 1D) on rear hub. Withdraw hub and carrier from drive shaft and remove hub puller and thread protector. Remove spacer from drive shaft and measure thickness. Using a .006" (.15 mm) thicker spacer will reduce end float by .001" (.026 mm).

3) Clean drive shaft splines. Place selected spacer on drive shaft. Apply Loctite (Stud Lock) to outer two thirds of drive axle splines. To complete installation, reverse removal procedures.

REMOVAL & INSTALLATION

WHEEL BEARING

Removal

1) Remove as previously described in Adjustments, steps **1)** and **2)**. Pry out oil seal retainers from fulcrum shaft housing and remove seals, bearings, distance tubes, and shims.

2) Mount hub carrier in vice and drift out bearing cups from fulcrum shaft housing. Using press, remove hub assembly from carrier. Drift out inner hub bearing cup with seal and bearing, from hub carrier.

3) Drift out bearing cup. Using hand press, remove outer bearing from hub. Remove oil seal track from hub shaft and clean and inspect all parts.

Installation

To install, reverse removal procedures.

COIL SPRING & SHOCK ABSORBER

Removal

1) Raise vehicle and support at lift points with safety stands. Position floor jack under control arm. Remove bolt retaining top of shock absorbers to suspension assembly crossmember.

2) Remove nuts retaining shock absorbers to lower mount. Using a drift, remove mounting piece. Withdraw shock absorber and coil spring assembly.

3) Using spring compressor and adaptor (SL 14 & JD 11B), collapse spring until collets and spring seat can be removed. Release pressure and separate shock absorber from spring.

Installation

To install, reverse removal procedures.

RADIUS ROD

Removal

1) Raise vehicle and support with safety stands, forward of radius arms. Remove wheel assembly. Remove bolt and spring washer securing safety strap to body. Remove safety wire and bolt securing radius arm to body, remove safety strap.

2) Remove forward lower shock absorber retaining pin. Using a punch, remove pin rearward. Bend tab washer and remove bolt retaining radius arm to control arm.

Rear Suspension

JAGUAR (Cont.)

Fig. 2: Installed Position of Radius Arm

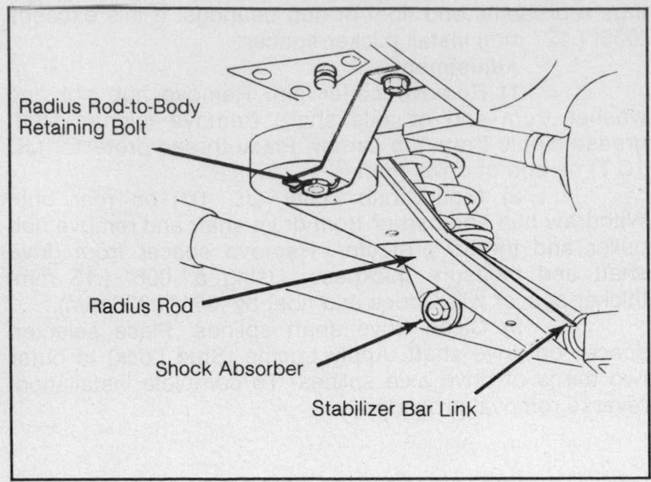

Radius Rod-to-Body
Retaining Bolt
Radius Rod
Shock Absorber
Stabilizer Bar Link

Installation

Replace any damaged radius arm bushings. When pressing bushings into radius arm, bushing should protrude from each side equal amounts. To complete installation, reverse removal procedure.

REAR SUSPENSION ASSEMBLY

Removal

1) Raise vehicle and support with safety stands, forward of radius arms. Remove wheel assemblies. Place floor jack (with adaptor to hold suspension assembly) under rear suspension.

2) Disconnect intermediate exhaust pipes at both ends and remove from vehicle. Support rear mufflers out of the way. Disconnect radius arm-to-body mounting hardware.

3) Separate brake line union from body bracket. Disconnect brake lines at flexible hoses and plug openings. Disconnect propeller shaft at differential and lower out of the way.

4) Release parking brake. Disconnect parking brake cable from junction at rear suspension assembly. Remove suspension bracket nuts. Lower suspension assembly to floor and slide from vehicle.

NOTE: Suspension mount bushings are replaced in pairs.

Installation

To install, reverse removal procedures. Bleed brake system and check wheel alignment.

LOWER CONTROL ARM

Removal

1) Raise vehicle and support with safety stands, placed ahead of radius arms. Remove wheel assembly.

2) Remove lock nut and drift out bearing carrier fulcrum shaft. Fit dummy shaft for support. Collect shims and all seal retainers.

3) Lift bearing carrier up, clear of control arm. Keep carrier in position with heavy wire attached to crossmember. Separate radius arm from body.

4) Remove bolts retaining support plate to crossmember and inner fulcrum brackets. Separate shock absorber at upper mount. Drift out pivot pin.

Fig. 3: Bolts & Set Screws Retaining Support Plate to Crossmember & Inner Fulcrum Brackets

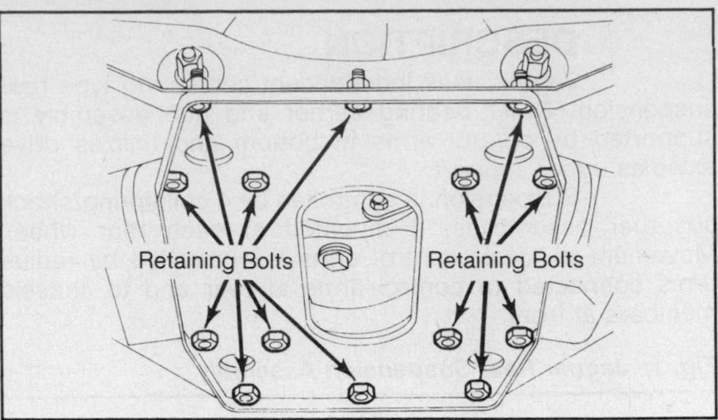

Retaining Bolts
Retaining Bolts

5) Separate inner fulcrum from control arm. Remove control arm and radius arm.

Installation

1) Apply grease to bearing cage and force bearing into lower control arm. Casting mark on bearing must face outward. Insert bearing tube from other end and force in opposite end bearing. Repeat procedure for other boss.

2) Assemble radius arm to control arm. Lightly coat thrust washers, new oil seals and seal retainers with grease. Fit assemblies into place on control arm.

3) Insert control arm to inner fulcrum bracket. Make sure radius arm bracket faces toward front of suspension.

4) Insert dummy shaft from each end to keep bearings positioned and locate control arm in bracket. Slip in fulcrum shaft while pushing out dummy shaft. Install lock nut.

Fig. 4: Fulcrum Boss Assembly

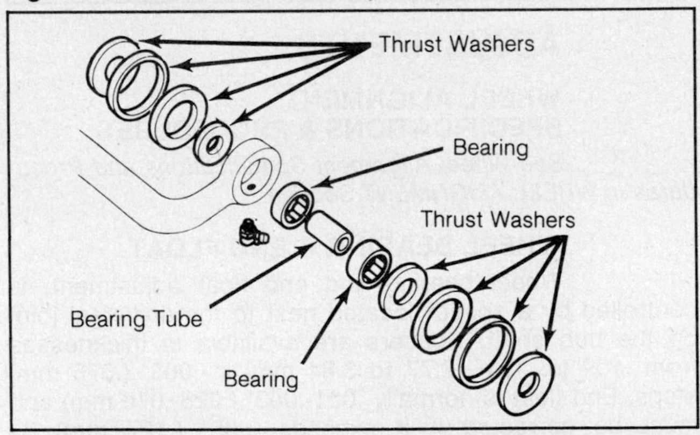

Thrust Washers
Bearing
Thrust Washers
Bearing Tube
Bearing

5) To complete installation, reverse removal procedure.

TIGHTENING SPECIFICATIONS

Application	Ft. Lbs. (N.m)
Inner Fulcrum Shaft	45-50 (61-68)
Radius Rod-to-Body	40-45 (54-61)
Radius Rod-to-Control Arm	60-70 (81-95)
Shock Absorbers	32-36 (44-49)
Stabilizer Bar Bracket-to-Body	14-18 (19-24)
Support Plate-to-Crossmember & Inner Fulcrum	60-65 (81-88)

MAZDA – EXCEPT GLC WAGON & PICKUPS

DESCRIPTION

Mazda GLC and 626 rear suspension consists of vertically mounted MacPherson type struts, trailing arms and laterally mounted links. All components attach to rear wheel hub. A stabilizer bar is used in some models.

The RX7 rear suspension consists of upper and lower control links, vertically mounted shock absorbers and coil springs. A 3-piece Watts linkage is used to control side-to-side movement. A stabilizer bar is installed in some models.

Fig. 1: RX7 Rear Suspension Assembly

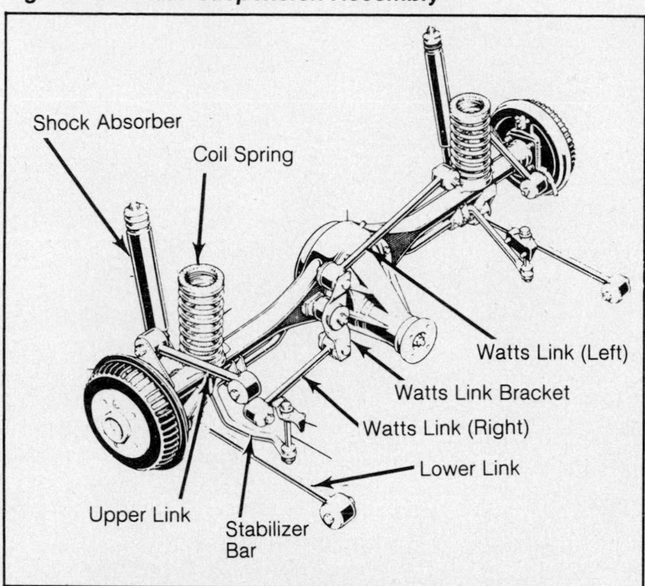
Shock Absorber
Coil Spring
Watts Link (Left)
Watts Link Bracket
Watts Link (Right)
Lower Link
Upper Link
Stabilizer Bar

Fig. 2: GLC Rear Suspension Assembly

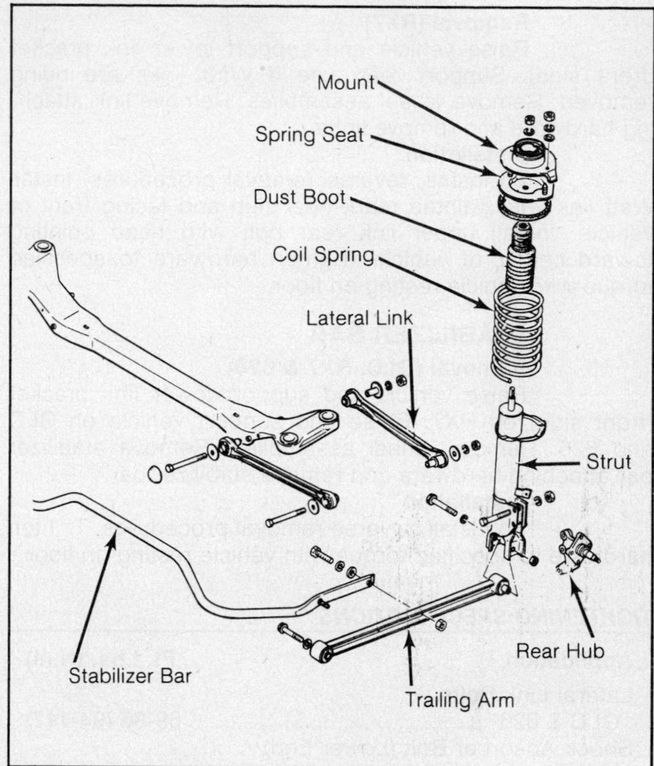
Mount
Spring Seat
Dust Boot
Coil Spring
Lateral Link
Strut
Rear Hub
Stabilizer Bar
Trailing Arm

626 rear suspension is similar.

REMOVAL & INSTALLATION

COIL SPRING

Removal (RX7)

Raise vehicle and support lower link brackets (front side). Remove wheel assemblies. Support rear axle housing. Disconnect shock absorber lower end. Disconnect upper and lower link pivot bolts at axle housing. Disconnect front end of stabilizer bar, if used. Disconnect Watt links at axle housing. Slowly lower rear axle and remove coil springs.

Installation

To install, reverse removal procedures. Install coil spring with painted mark pointing toward rear of vehicle. Install left hand shock absorber lower end attaching bolt with head pointing toward center of vehicle. Tighten hardware to specified torque with vehicle resting on floor.

SHOCK ABSORBER

Removal (RX7)

Raise vehicle and support lower link bracket (front side). Remove wheel assembly. Remove side trim in luggage compartment and disconnect shock absorber upper end. Disconnect shock absorber lower end and remove shock sbsorber.

Installation

To install, reverse removal procedures. Install left hand shock absorber lower end attaching bolt with head pointing toward center of vehicle.

STRUT ASSEMBLY

Removal (GLC & 626)

Remove trunk side trim on GLC. Remove rear seat and trim on 626. Remove mount nuts. Raise and support vehicle. Remove wheel assembly. Disconnect brake hose from strut assembly. Disconnect trailing arm and lateral link from strut assembly on GLC. Disconnect rear hub and remove strut.

Disassembly

Clamp strut in vise. Compress coil spring. Remove lock nut, washer and mount. Remove spring seat, rubber seat (GLC only), dust boot, coil spring and damper.

Assembly

Check parts for deterioration or damage. Replace parts, if necessary. Install coil spring and remaining hardware in reverse order of disassembly.

Installation

To install, reverse removal procedures. Adjust rear wheel toe-in.

TRAILING ARMS & LATERAL LINKS

Removal (GLC & 626)

1) Raise and support vehicle. Remove fuel tank on 626. Disconnect stabilizer bar from trailing arm on GLC. Disconnect stabilizer bar from lateral links on 626.

2) Remove bolt attaching trailing arm to rear hub. Remove trailing arm pivot bolt and remove arm. Remove bolt attaching lateral link to rear hub. Remove lateral link pivot bolt and remove link.

Installation

Check parts for deterioration or damage. Replace parts, if necessary. To install, reverse removal procedures. Adjust rear wheel toe-in.

Rear Suspension

MAZDA – EXCEPT GLC WAGON & PICKUPS (Cont.)

UPPER/LOWER LINKS & WATT LINKS

Removal (RX7)

Raise vehicle and support lower link bracket (front side). Support rear axle if Watt links are being removed. Remove wheel assemblies. Remove link attaching hardware and remove links.

Installation

To install, reverse removal procedures. Install Watt link with painted mark near hub and facing front of vehicle. Install upper link rear bolt with head pointing toward center of vehicle. Tighten hardware to specified torque with vehicle resting on floor.

STABILIZER BAR

Removal (GLC, RX7 & 626)

Raise vehicle and support lower link bracket (front side) on RX7. Raise and support vehicle on GLC and 626. Remove wheel assemblies. Remove stabilizer bar attaching hardware and remove stabilizer bar.

Installation

To install, reverse removal procedures. Tighten hardware to specified torque with vehicle resting on floor.

TIGHTENING SPECIFICATIONS

Application	Ft. Lbs. (N.m)
Lateral Link Bolts	
GLC & 626	69-86 (94-117)
Shock Absorber Bolt (Lower End)	
RX7	47-59 (64-80)
Stabilizer Bar Brackets	
RX7	27-38 (37-52)
Stabilizer-to-Trailing Arm	
GLC	23-34 (31-46)
Strut Assembly-to-Body	
GLC & 626	17-22 (23-30)
Strut Assembly-to-Hub	
GLC	40-50 (54-68)
626	69-86 (94-117)
Strut Assembly Lock Nut	
GLC & 626	41-59 (56-80)
Trailing Arm Bolt (Front)	
GLC	43-54 (58-73)
626	27-40 (37-54)
Trailing Arm Bolt (Rear)	
GLC & 626	40-50 (54-68)
Upper/Lower Link Bolts	
RX7	56-76 (76-103)
Watt Link-to-Body/Bracket	
RX7	47-59 (64-80)
Watt Link Bracket-to-Axle	
RX7	56-76 (76-103)

Rear Suspension

MERCEDES-BENZ

240D, 300 Series, 380 Series

NOTE: For 300TD components not covered in this article, see Automatic Level Control article in this section.

DESCRIPTION

Mercedes-Benz rear suspension is independent type with coil springs and semi-trailing arms. Rear axle carrier is mounted to body at 3 points and supports rear axle assembly. Axle shafts serve as upper control arms to rear wheels.

Wheel hubs are supported by semi-trailing arms which run forward to pivot points on rear axle carrier and body. Shock absorbers are mounted inside of coil springs, attached to body on top and to semi-trailing arms on bottom. Stabilizer bar is mounted to body and to wheel hubs at ends.

ADJUSTMENTS

WHEEL ALIGNMENT SPECIFICATIONS & ADJUSTMENTS

See Wheel Alignment Specifications & Adjustments in WHEEL ALIGNMENT Section.

REMOVAL & INSTALLATION

SHOCK ABSORBER

Removal (Except 300TD)

1) Shock absorbers should be removed only when vehicle is resting on wheels or when semi-trailing arm is supported. On vehicles with coupe top, remove top and open flap.

2) On all models, remove rear seat and backrest. Remove locking lever from top flap and unscrew lining. Remove nut and rubber ring of upper shock mount. Remove lower shock mount on semi-trailing arm. Remove shock absorber in a downward direction.

Installation

To install, reverse removal procedure.

COIL SPRING

Removal

1) Remove shock absorbers as previously outlined. Raise vehicle and support with safety stands. Raise semi-trailing arm until approximately level.

2) Using spring compressor, compress coil spring. Carefully lower semi-trailing arm and remove spring with rubber mounting.

Installation

To install, reverse removal procedure.

REAR SUSPENSION & AXLE

REMOVAL

1) Raise vehicle and support with safety stands. Remove wheel assemblies. Disconnect exhaust system. Detach parking brake control cables at frame and compensating lever.

2) Loosen clamp nut and disconnect drive shaft intermediate bearing from frame. Disconnect rear of drive shaft and slide forward, out of centering position.

NOTE: On 3-piece drive shaft, loosen front clamp nut only.

3) Remove shock absorber and coil spring as previously described. Detach and plug brake lines. Disconnect stabilizer bar holding clamps.

4) Place floor jack under rear suspension. Disconnect supporting plates and front and rear rubber mounts from frame. Carefully lower jack and remove rear suspension from vehicle.

5) Remove rear rubber mount from axle. When lowering and removing rear suspension, be sure cover plates of disc brakes are not damaged.

Installation

To install, reverse removal procedure.

Fig. 1: Rear Suspension Trailing Arm, Differential & Axle Carrier

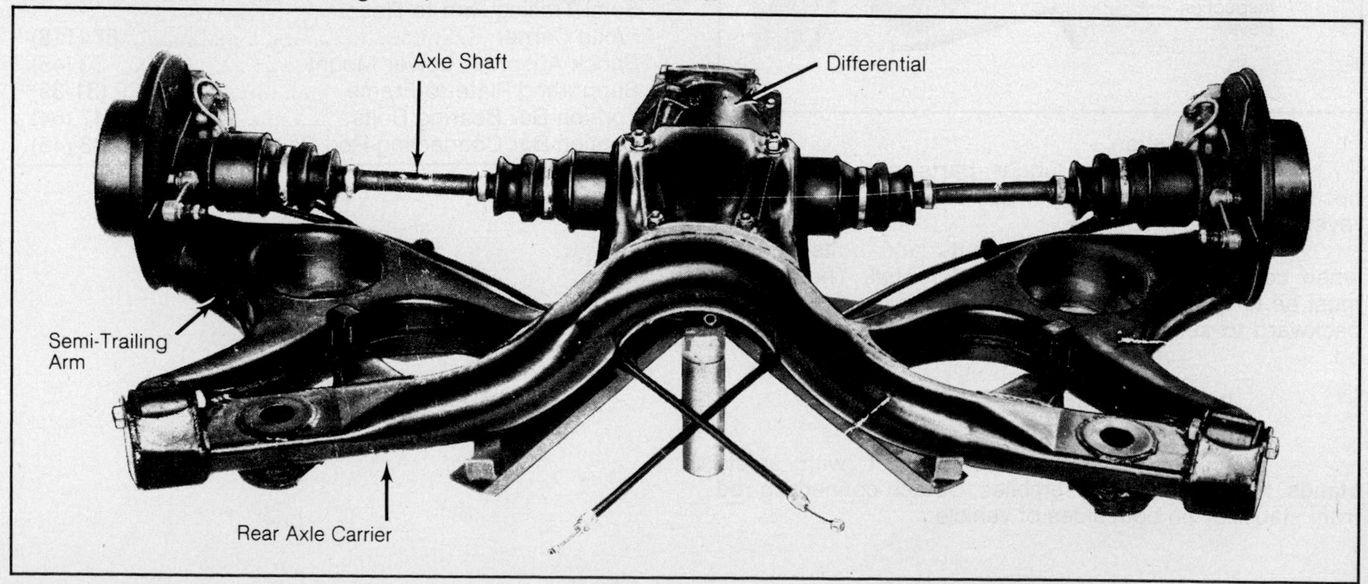
Axle Shaft
Differential
Semi-Trailing Arm
Rear Axle Carrier

Rear Suspension

MERCEDES-BENZ (Cont.)

DIFFERENTIAL WITH AXLE SHAFTS

Removal

1) Drain fluid from differential. Detach brake caliper from right rotor and support out of the way. Remove axle shaft-to-flange attaching bolts (both sides) and force rear shafts out of shaft flanges.

NOTE: **It may be necessary to loosen right shock absorber upper mount and lower semi-trailing arm to deflection stop.**

2) If required, remove exhaust system. Loosen clamp nut and detach drive shaft intermediate bearing from frame. Remove drive shaft from differential and push from centering alignment.

NOTE: **On 3-piece drive shaft, loosen front clamp nut only.**

3) Support differential with floor jack and support tool (115 589 35 63 00). Disconnect rear rubber mount from body. Disconnect differential from rear axle carrier. Lower floor jack and remove differential with axle shaft.

CAUTION: **When moving differential with axle shafts, make sure that axle shafts are supported and do not drop down, as this might damage inner joints.**

Fig. 2: Proper Washer Placement for Rear Axle Carriers without Spot Welds

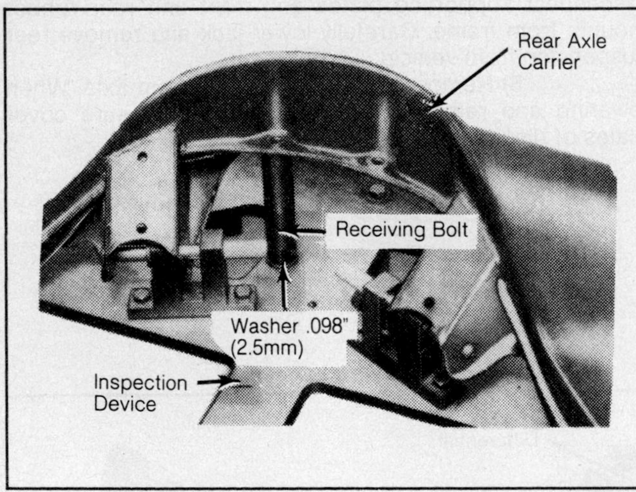
Rear Axle
Carrier
Receiving Bolt
Washer .098"
(2.5mm)
Inspection
Device

Installation

1) Check all rubber parts and replace as necessary. To install differential with rear axle shafts, reverse removal procedure.

2) Tighten down all nuts and bolts, except when connecting drive shaft to differential. These bolts must be torqued after vehicle has been rolled forward and backward to seat parts. Install exhaust system, if removed.

REAR STABILIZER BAR

Removal

1) Raise vehicle and support with safety stands. Remove wheel assemblies. Detach connecting rod from stabilizer on both sides of vehicle.

2) Remove stabilizer bar holding brackets. Loosen exhaust pipe mounts (rubber rings) and lower slightly. Remove stabilizer bar in a downward direction

Fig. 3: Stabilizer Bar and Mounting Locations

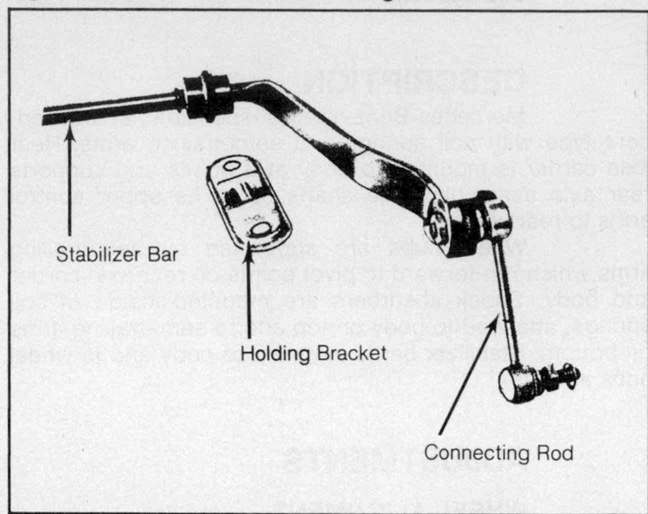
Stabilizer Bar
Holding Bracket
Connecting Rod

Installation

To install, reverse removal procedure.

NOTE: **When installing rear stabilizer bar, ensure that bend of bar is pointing upward.**

TIGHTENING SPECIFICATIONS

Application	Ft. Lbs. (N.m)
Axle Shaft-to-Axle Shaft Flange	69 (94)
Brake Caliper Bolts	23-29 (31-39)
Differential-to-Rear Axle Carrier	72 (98)
Drive Shaft Clamp Nut	
2-Piece	145 (197)
3-Piece	
Front	23-29 (31-39)
Rear	145 (197)
Front Rubber Mounts-to-Frame	29 (39)
Rear Rubber Mount-to-End Cover	101 (137)
Rear Rubber Mount-to-Frame	18 (24)
Semi-Trailing Arm-to-Rear Axle Carrier	87 (118)
Shock Absorber Lower Mount	33 (45)
Supporting Plate-to-Frame	23-29 (31-39)
Torsion Bar Bearing Bolts	47 (64)
Torsion Bar Connecting Rod Ball Joints	33 (45)

MITSUBISHI STARION

Starion

DESCRIPTION

The rear suspension system is an independent type consisting of 2 lower control arms mounted to a rear suspension support and rear crossmember. The control arms are connected to each other by a stabilizer bar mounted to the rear suspension support. The shock absorber strut assemblies are mounted to each lower control arm and upper frame bracket.

REMOVAL & INSTALLATION

WHEEL BEARING

Removal

1) Raise and support vehicle on safety stands. Remove rear wheel assembly. Disconnect parking brake cable from rear brake caliper assembly. Remove rear caliper assembly, caliper support and rotor. Support caliper assembly away from work area with wire.

2) Check axle shaft end play and replace inner and/or outer bearing as necessary. Scribe index marks on flange yoke and companion flange. Remove 4 drive shaft flange yoke-to-companion flange mount bolts. Separate drive shaft from flange.

3) Remove drive shaft from differential carrier using slide hammer service tools (MB990211 & MB990906) or equivalent. Do not damage oil seal with drive shaft spline during removal. Remove all nuts and bolts retaining axle housing to lower control arm.

4) Remove shock strut assembly from axle housing. Remove axle shaft/housing assembly. Mount assembly in vise and loosen the companion flange mount bolt. Tap the axle shaft out of the axle housing using a plastic hammer. Remove the spacer and dust covers from inside axle housing.

CAUTION: Do not remove inner and outer bearings unless necessary for replacement.

5) To remove axle shaft bearing, cut bearing retainer in 3 places with chisel. Insert claws of bearing puller set service tool (MB990918) into the three places cut in retainer and turn tool 90° to lock claws in place.

6) Fit claws into slots of service tool body and tighten claw nut to secure claws tightly. Hold body of service tool with handle. Tighten center bolt to remove the axle shaft bearing. To remove inner bearing and seal from axle housing, drive bearing and seal from housing using long drift and hammer.

Installation

1) Install new axle shaft bearing by press fitting outer bearing onto the axle shaft. Check that seal side of the outer bearing faces flange side of axle shaft. Apply grease to the inside surface of axle housing.

2) Position new inner bearing so seal side faces the companion flange. Press fit bearing using service tools (MB990932 & MB990938). Apply grease to oil seal contact area of axle housing.

3) Using service tool (MB990727), press new oil seal into axle housing until it contacts the edge of housing. Install dust cover onto axle housing. Apply grease to oil seal lip. Insert axle shaft and spacer into axle housing.

4) Attach axle flange. Mount axle housing in vise and tighten companion flange mount nut to specification. Measure axle shaft starting torque. Standard axle shaft starting torque is 4 IN. lbs. (.5 N.m). If starting torque exceeds specification, replace spacer.

5) Install axle housing onto lower control arm and strut assembly. Install drive shaft flange-to-companion flange mount bolts. Tighten all components to specification. Ensure axle shaft end play is within service limit. Install dial indicator with pointer mounted to axle shaft flange.

6) Push axle shaft in and zero dial gauge. Pull shaft out and read indicator reading for end play. Standard axle shaft end play is .031" (.80 mm). If end play is not within limits, replace bearing or recheck new bearing mounting position.

REAR SUSPENSION ASSEMBLY

Removal

1) Raise and support vehicle at a minimum of two feet from the ground. Remove rear wheel assembly. Using rope or wire, support strut assembly to the crossmember. Support the rear suspension assembly with a wooden block and jack.

2) Disconnect drive shaft from torque tube. Remove center exhaust pipe and main muffler. Disconnect parking brake cable from rear disc brake and lower control arm.

3) Disconnect brake hose from rear floor. Remove strut assembly upper mount bolts located under side trim in rear hatch area. Remove crossmember mount bolts.

4) Detach front support mount bolts and nuts. Lower jack slowly and carefully remove suspension assembly from vehicle. Ensure all wires, cables and hoses are detached before assembly removal.

Fig. 1: Mitsubishi Starion Rear Suspension Assembly

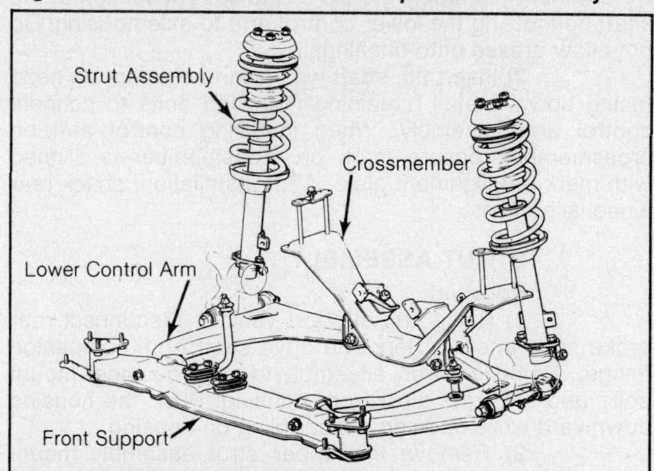
Strut Assembly
Crossmember
Lower Control Arm
Front Support

Support suspension assembly while removing mount bolts.

Installation

To install rear suspension assembly, reverse removal procedures.

LOWER CONTROL ARM

Removal

1) Raise and support vehicle. Remove rear wheel assembly. Disconnect parking brake cable from

MITSUBISHI STARION (Cont.)

lower control arm. Disconnect stabilizer bar. Remove all nuts and bolts connecting lower control arm-to-axle housing.

2) Remove nuts and bolts connecting lower control arm-to-front suspension support. Detach lower control arm from crossmember and remove from vehicle. Inspect bushings for wear and deterioration. Check for bent or broken lower control arm.

3) Remove lower control arm bushing "A" using service tools (MB990848, MB990884 & MB990890). Remove bushing "B" using service tools (MB990883, MB990885 & MB990890). Press out bushing "C" using service tools (MB990897 & MB990892). *See Fig. 2.*

Fig. 2: Exploded View of Rear Lower Control Arm

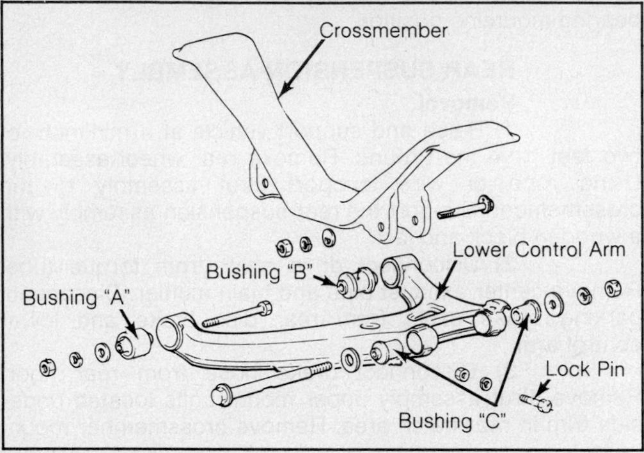
Crossmember
Lower Control Arm
Bushing "B"
Bushing "A"
Lock Pin
Bushing "C"

Take care not to deform the lower control arm during the removal and installation procedures.

Installation

1) Press bushings into control arm using service tools. Do not deform control arm during assembly. Before installing, apply grease to the cut out section of the shaft connecting the lower control arm to axle housing. Do not allow grease onto bushings.

2) Insert the shaft with reference mark on head facing down. Install remaining nuts and bolts to connect control arm assembly. When installing control arm on crossmember, ensure mark on crossmember is aligned with mark on alignment plate. After installation, check rear wheel alignment.

STRUT ASSEMBLY

Removal

1) Raise and support vehicle. Disconnect rear brake hose at strut. Separate drive shaft from companion flange. Remove strut assembly-to-axle housing mount bolts and separate strut from housing. Push the housing downward while opening the coupling on housing.

2) Remove the upper strut assembly mount bolts from under side trim in rear hatch area. Remove strut assembly. Mount strut assembly in vise. Compress spring using service tool (MB990987).

3) While holding spring seat, remove top nut using service tool (MB990899). Remove strut insulator, spring seat, dust cover, rubber helper and seat. *See Fig. 3.*

Inspection

Check all strut components for cracks, damage or deterioration. Inspect strut assembly for oil leakage and piston rod for bend. Replace components as necessary.

Fig. 3: Exploded View of Shock Absorber Strut Assembly

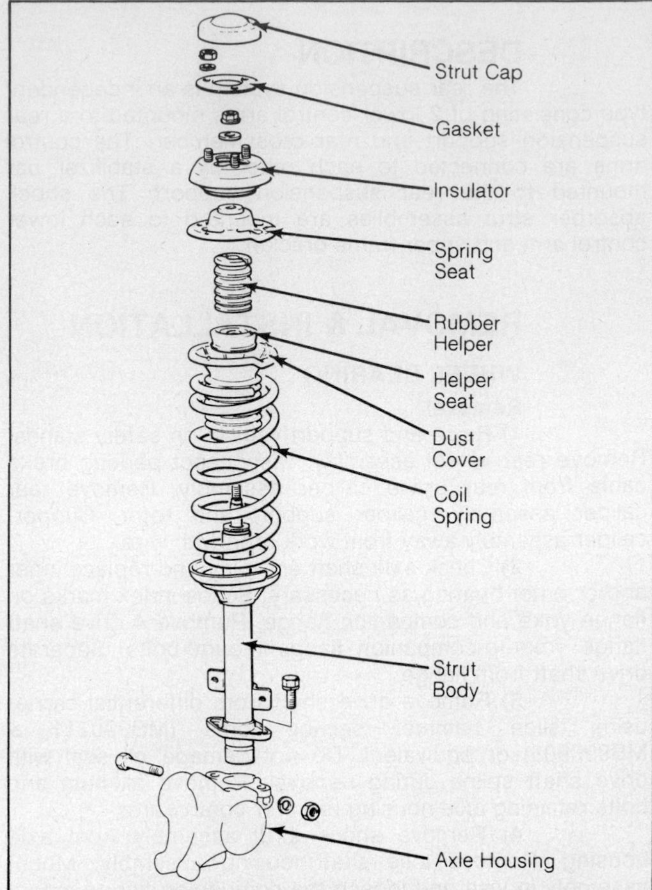
Strut Cap
Gasket
Insulator
Spring Seat
Rubber Helper
Helper Seat
Dust Cover
Coil Spring
Strut Body
Axle Housing

NOTE: **Coil springs are color coded for identification and load classification with paint marks on coils. Be sure to use spring with proper color code for vehicle.**

Installation

1) With spring compressed, position coil spring into seat of strut. Install rubber helper seat, rubber helper and dust cover onto strut. Align D-shaped hole in spring seat with flat on piston rod. Align projections on dust cover with holes on spring seat.

2) Install strut insulator and loosely install top end nut. Align studs in insulator with bracket at lower end of strut. Hold spring seat and tighten top end nut.

3) After checking spring is aligned in the top and bottom seats, remove compressor tool. Position rubber helper with thick sided portion up. Apply semi-drying sealant to top surface of the insulator. Note that gasket is factory installed.

4) To complete installation, reverse removal procedure. Before and after coupling drive shaft to companion flange, move drive shaft in axial direction to check that it does not slip out of differential gear carrier.

FRONT SUSPENSION SUPPORT

Removal

1) Raise and support vehicle. Remove rear wheel assembly. Detach center exhaust pipe. Remove stabilizer bar brackets from front support. Remove nuts and bolts connecting lower control arm to front support.

MITSUBISHI STARION (Cont.)

2) Support torque tube with jack. Remove bolts connecting torque tube to front support. Detach nut, bolt and lower stopper from each end of front support and remove front support. *See Fig. 4*.

Fig. 4: Exploded View of Suspension Front Support

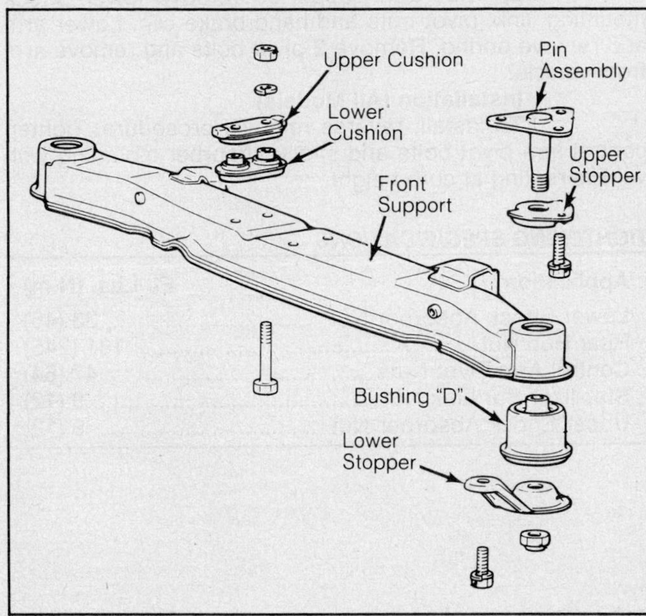

Upper Cushion
Pin Assembly
Lower Cushion
Upper Stopper
Front Support
Bushing "D"
Lower Stopper

3) Check support for damage and bushings for wear and deterioration. Note bushing position for reassembly reference. Replace bushing "D" using service tool (MB990882). During installation, align holes in bushing with notch in support.

Installation

To install front support, reverse removal procedure. Measure rear wheel alignment after assembly.

CROSSMEMBER

Removal

1) Raise and support vehicle. Remove rear wheel assembly. Remove lower control arms. Remove nuts connecting rear support insulator to crossmember and rear support.

2) Support differential with jack. Detach nuts at each end of crossmember and remove crossmember from vehicle. Check crossmember for cracks or damage. Inspect rear supports and insulators for deterioration, cracks or damage. Replace components as necessary.

Installation

1) Align the positions of projections on rear supports to the holes in differential carrier. Mount rear supports to carrier. Loosely mount rear support insulators to rear supports. Raise crossmember. Be sure insulator studs are aligned with crossmember.

2) Install nuts at each end of crossmember. Align positions of projections of rear support insulators to the holes in rear supports and tighten to specification. Install lower control arms. Complete installation by reversing removal procedure. After installation, check rear wheel alignment.

TIGHTENING SPECIFICATIONS

Application	Ft. Lbs. (N.m)
Lock Pin	11-14 (15-20)
Lower Control Arm-to-Crossmember Mount Nut	94-108 (130-150)
Lower Control Arm-to-Axle Housing Mount Nut	51-58 (70-80)
Lower Stopper Nut	51-61 (70-85)
Lower Stopper Bolt	29-36 (40-50)
Stabilizer Bar Bracket Bolt	22-29 (30-40)
Stabilizer Bar Mount Bolt	7-14 (10-20)
Strut Top Nut	18-25 (25-35)
Strut Top End Nut	51-65 (70-90)
Strut Assembly-to-Axle Housing	36-51 (50-70)
Upper Stopper Bolt	51-61 (70-85)

Rear Suspension

PEUGEOT

DESCRIPTION

An independent rear suspension utilizing trailing arms and coil springs is used. Rear hub is supported by lower control arms which pivot on axle crossmember.

Coil springs are mounted between suspension crossmember at top and control arm at bottom. Hydraulic shock absorbers are located inside coil spring. A stabilizer bar is mounted to frame and connected to control arms.

Fig. 1: Assembled View of Peugeot Rear Suspension

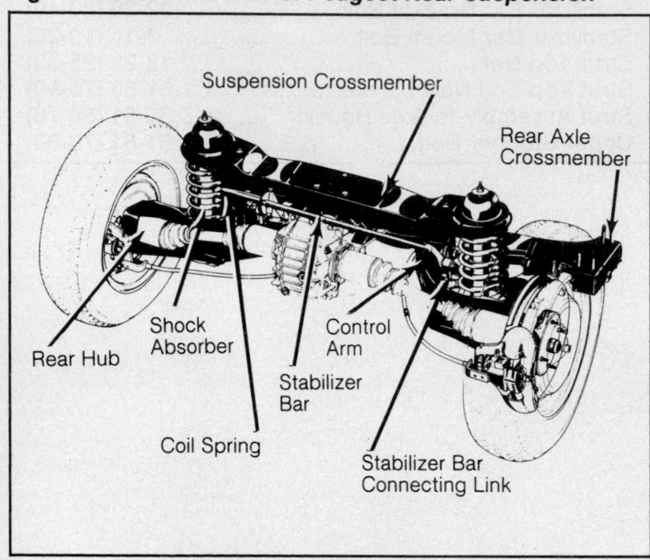
Suspension Crossmember
Rear Axle Crossmember
Shock Absorber
Control Arm
Rear Hub
Stabilizer Bar
Coil Spring
Stabilizer Bar Connecting Link

REMOVAL & INSTALLATION

SHOCK ABSORBER

Removal

From inside luggage compartment, remove lock nut at top of shock absorber while holding shock to prevent rotation. On control arm, remove lower pivot bolts and remove shock absorber.

Installation

To install, reverse removal procedures. Use new rubber washers and lock nut. Tighten upper retaining bolt first, then tighten lower mount to specifications.

COIL SPRING & CONTROL ARM

Removal (504 & 604)

1) Raise vehicle and support with safety stands, under rear crossmember. Remove wheel assemblies. Disconnect hydraulic line from control arms. Remove calipers retaining bolts and support calipers out of way.

2) Remove drive shaft nut. Remove bearing housing bolts and pull shaft, hub, and disc assemblies from arms. Raise the lower arm with a floor jack to compress spring. Remove shock absorber.

3) Disconnect parking brake cables from lower arms. Remove stabilizer connecting link nuts at lower arms. Remove metal cup and rubber mount and refit nut to prevent upper parts from falling inside arms.

4) Unscrew rear arm pivot nuts and carefully lower floor jack. Remove spring and upper rubber mount. Remove rear arm pivots and remove trailing arm.

Removal (505)

1) Raise and support vehicle. Place floor jack under control arm and coil spring to be removed. Unclip brake hose and disconnect metal line from hose. Remove stub axle, hub and drive shaft assembly.

2) With arm supported remove lower shock mounting, link, pivot nuts and hand brake clip. Lower arm and remove spring. Remove 2 pivot bolts and remove arm from vehicle.

Installation (All Models)

To install, reverse removal procedure. Tighten control arm pivot bolts and shock absorber mounting with vehicle resting at curb height.

TIGHTENING SPECIFICATIONS

Application	Ft. Lbs. (N.m)
Lower Shock Absorber Nut	33 (45)
Rear Hub Nut	181 (245)
Control Arm Pivot Nuts	47 (64)
Stabilizer Bar Link Nut	9 (12)
Upper Shock Absorber Nut	9 (12)

Rear Suspension

PORSCHE 911SC

DESCRIPTION

Independent torsion bar type rear suspension is used. Torsion bars are mounted inside rear cross-member tube and anchored in center by a splined hub. Outer end of torsion bars mount into splined hubs integral with spring plates which connect at ends to control arms.

Control arms pivot in mounts integral with body and also serve as rear wheel bearing carriers. Hydraulic shock absorbers are mounted between control arms and inner fender panel. A stabilizer bar is installed on some models.

ADJUSTMENT

WHEEL ALIGNMENT SPECIFICATIONS & PROCEDURES

See Wheel Alignment Specifications & Procedures in WHEEL ALIGNMENT section.

WHEEL BEARING

Wheel bearings are not adjustable.

REMOVAL & INSTALLATION

SHOCK ABSORBER

Removal

1) Raise vehicle and support with safety stands, in a position so weight of vehicle is still on rear wheels. Remove rubber cap from upper mount (accessible from inside engine compartment).

2) Remove nut from shock absorber. Remove bolt securing shock absorber to control arm. Remove shock absorber. Remove rod cover and rubber buffer from shock absorber.

Installation

1) Inspect rubber buffer for wear or cracking, (replace if necessary). Make sure that stop disc grooves face bottom of shock absorber when assembling.

2) Install rubber buffer and cover. Reverse removal procedure to install remaining components. Tighten upper and lower mounts.

Fig. 1: Exploded View of Porsche Rear Suspension

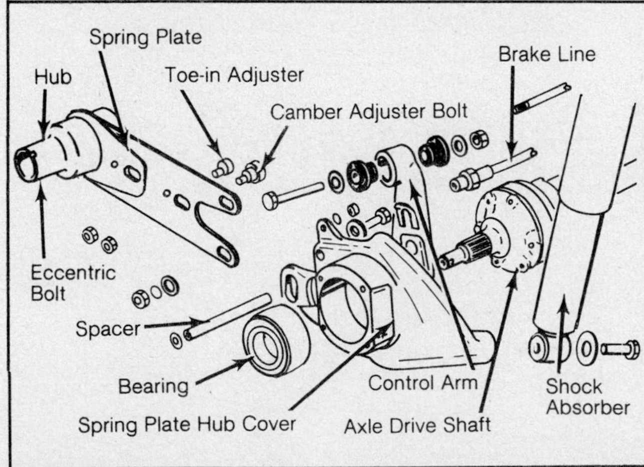
Spring Plate
Hub
Toe-in Adjuster
Camber Adjuster Bolt
Brake Line
Eccentric Bolt
Spacer
Bearing
Spring Plate Hub Cover
Control Arm
Axle Drive Shaft
Shock Absorber

CONTROL ARM

Removal

1) Raise vehicle and support with safety stands, under vehicle body. Remove wheel assemblies. Detach brake system components from rear wheel hub. *See Porsche article in BRAKES section.*

2) Remove axle hub cotter pin and nut. Remove Allen head bolts from axle shaft flanges and remove axle shafts. Using a driver, remove wheel hub from control arm.

3) Remove cotter pin and nut from parking brake cable and pull cable out toward center of vehicle. Remove bolts securing parking brake assembly to control arm and remove assembly.

4) Raise torsion bar spring plate to take tension from shock absorber. Remove lower shock absorber mount. Remove bolts securing spring plate to control arm.

5) Disconnect brake hose from bracket on control arm. Remove nut from control arm pivot bolt and drive bolt out with a punch. Remove control arm from vehicle.

Installation

To install, reverse removal procedures. Use new self-locking nuts and tighten all bolts and nuts. Check riding height, wheel alignment, and bleed brake system.

TORSION BAR & SPRING PLATE

Removal

1) Raise vehicle and support with safety stands, under vehicle body. Remove wheel assembly. Raise torsion bar spring plate. Remove lower shock absorber retaining bolt.

2) Remove bolts securing spring plate to control arm. Pull back on control arm to separate from spring plate. Remove torsion bar hub cover bolts.

3) Remove hub cover by prying off with a screwdriver. Remove torsion bar tensioner tool. Remove plug from body.

4) Remove spring plate and withdraw torsion bar. If torsion bar is broken, opposite side torsion bar will have to be removed in order to drive out broken piece.

Installation

1) Inspect all components for wear or damage, (replace if necessary). Coat torsion bar with lithium grease before installing. Torsion bars are marked left and right, (install accordingly).

2) Coat rubber components with glycerin paste. Install torsion bar and spring plate in correct position.

3) To adjust torsion bars, use protractor (VW261), place onto lower edge of door sill. Adjust protractor so that bubble in glass tube marked "Axle Housing/Angle" is in the center.

4) Reset glass tube carrier by value specified. Place protractor onto spring plate and adjust to .448-.488" (11-12 mm) by turning eccentric screw on spring plate.

NOTE: **Difference between right and left measurement must not exceed .20" (5 mm).**

5) Install hub cover and start bolts that are accessible. Raise spring plate until remaining bolt can be installed. Reverse removal procedures for remaining components. Check rear wheel alignment.

Rear Suspension

PORSCHE 911SC (Cont.)

TIGHTENING SPECIFICATIONS

Application	Ft. Lbs. (N.m)
Axle Shaft Allen Head Bolts	
M8-12K	31 (42)
M10-8G	34 (46)
M10 x 55-12K	60 (82)
Camber Adjusting Bolt	43 (58)
Control Arm Pivot Bolt	87 (118)
Hub Nut	235 (320)
Lower Shock Absorber Mount	54 (73)
Spring Plate-to-Control Arm Bolts	65 (88)
Torsion Bar Hub Cover Bolts	34 (46)
Tracking Adjusting Bolt	36 (49)

Rear Suspension

PORSCHE 928S

DESCRIPTION

Porsche 928S rear suspension is a MacPherson strut type indepenent suspension. Strut assembly consist of a coil spring surrounding a strut tube with an inner shock absorber.

Strut is mounted at bottom to the rear wheel hub and lower control arm and at top to vehicle body. An upper control arm is also incorporated. A stabilizer bar is connected by a link to the lower control arm.

ADJUSTMENTS

WHEEL ALIGNMENT SPECIFICATIONS & PROCEDURES

See Wheel Alignment Specifications and Procedures in WHEEL ALIGNMENT section.

REMOVAL & INSTALLATION

REAR SUSPENSION ASSEMBLY

Removal

1) Raise vehicle and support with safety stands. Detach axle shaft from differential by removing Allen head bolts.

2) Detach caliper from rotor. Remove countersunk screws and take off rotor. Remove parking brake shoes and spreader lever. Pull parking brake cable out of guide in hub assembly.

3) Remove hub assembly with upper control arm attached after removing control arm retaining bolt.

4) Remove lower control arm retaining nuts and bolts. Remove control arm from vehicle. Remove stabilizer bar and link, (if necessary).

Installation

To install, reverse removal procedures.

Fig. 1: Exploded View of Rear Suspension

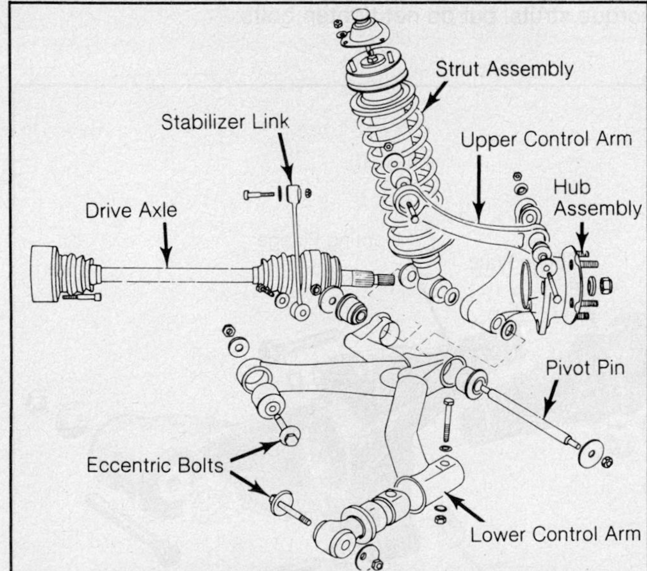
Strut Assembly
Stabilizer Link
Upper Control Arm
Hub Assembly
Drive Axle
Pivot Pin
Eccentric Bolts
Lower Control Arm

STRUT ASSEMBLY

Removal

1) Working from luggage compartment, remove retaining nuts from upper strut mounting plate. Raise vehicle and support with safety stands. Remove wheel assembly.

2) While holding rear nut, remove front nut from pivot pin of lower control arm (it may be necessary to double-nut the shaft end with another M14 x 1.5 Nut). Remove pivot pin.

3) Remove stabilizer bar link from its attachment at lower control arm to gain additional clearance. Remove strut assembly from vehicle.

Disassembly

1) Attach a coil spring compressor to coil spring and compress enough to allow removal of top piston rod nut. Loosen coil spring compressor slowly, and remove coil spring.

2) Lift off cover pieces, unscrew adjusting nut and remove threaded sleeve.

Reassembly

Reassemble in reverse of disassembly procedures. *See Fig. 2.*

Installation

To install, reverse removal procedures.

Fig. 2: Disassembled View of Suspension Strut Assembly

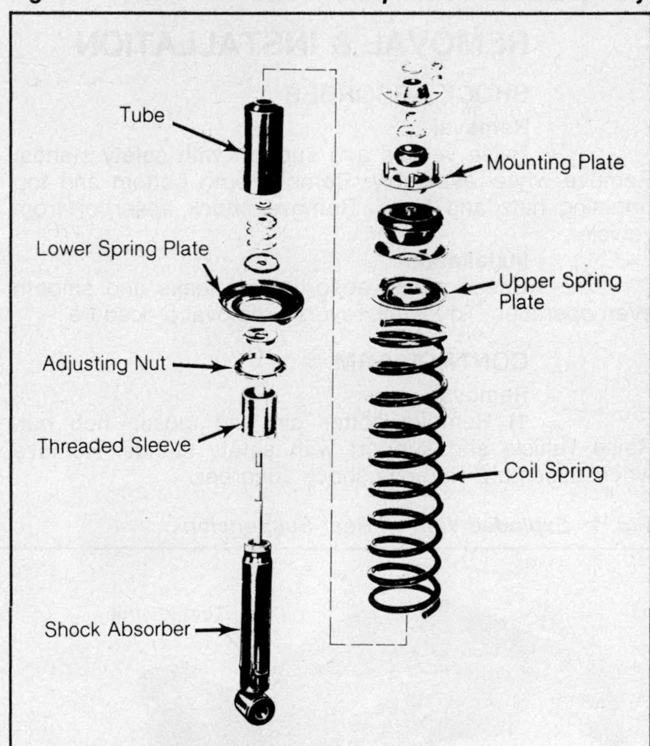
Tube
Mounting Plate
Lower Spring Plate
Upper Spring Plate
Adjusting Nut
Threaded Sleeve
Coil Spring
Shock Absorber

TIGHTENING SPECIFICATIONS

Application	Ft. Lbs. (N.m)
Caliper-to-Hub Bolt	61 (83)
Hub-to-Stub Axle	333 (453)
Lower Control Arm-to-Hub	101 (137)
Lower Control Arm-to-Link Pin	61 (83)
Shock Absorber-to-Upper Strut Mount	42 (57)
Stabilizer Bar-to-Body	33 (45)
Stabilizer Bar-to-Link	33 (45)
Stabilizer Link-to-Control Arm	33 (45)
Upper Control Arm-to-Crossmember	33 (45)
Upper Control Arm-to-Hub	33 (45)
Upper Strut Mount-to-Body Nuts	33 (45)

Rear Suspension

PORSCHE 944

DESCRIPTION

Independent torsion bar type rear suspension is used. Torsion bars mount in rear crossmember tube and anchor in center of tube by a splined hub. Outer ends of torsion bar mount into splined hubs integral with spring plates.

Spring plates are bolted to control arm flange. Control arms pivot in mounts on crossmember tube and are integral with stub axle housing. Hydraulic shock absorbers mount on control arm and to upper body.

ADJUSTMENTS

WHEEL ALIGNMENT SPECIFICATIONS & PROCEDURES

See Wheel Alignment Specifications and Procedures in WHEEL ALIGNMENT section.

WHEEL BEARING

Information not available from manufacturer.

REMOVAL & INSTALLATION

SHOCK ABSORBER

Removal

Raise vehicle and support with safety stands. Remove wheel assembly. Remove both bottom and top retaining nuts and bolts. Remove shock absorber from vehicle.

Installation

Check shock absorber for leaks and smooth even operation. To install, reverse removal procedure.

CONTROL ARM

Removal

1) Remove cotter pin and loosen hub nut. Raise vehicle and support with safety stands. Remove wheel assembly. Remove shock absorber.

2) Remove bolts retaining axle drive shaft to stub axle. Separate axle drive shaft from stub axle and wire out of way.

3) Use protective cap to cover exposed end of axle drive shaft. Remove caliper and plug brake line. Disconnect parking brake.

4) Index mark spring plate in relation to a point on control arm. Remove control arm pivot bolt and remove arm from vehicle.

Installation

To install, reverse removal procedure. Tighten pivot bolt and lock in place by staking edge to metal shoulder on bracket. Align spring plate marks with those on control arm. Bleed brake system.

CROSSMEMBER TUBE

Removal

1) Raise vehicle and support with safety stands. Remove wheel assemblies. Disconnect parking brake cable from lever. Remove cable.

2) Disconnect and remove rear portion of exhaust system from catalytic converter. Remove transaxle retaining nuts. Support transaxle with a chain by attaching ends to frame.

3) Disconnect shock absorbers from control arms. Support control arms with jacks or safety stands. Remove stabilizer bar links. Mark location of spring plate on control arm. Remove camber eccentric and retaining bolts between spring plate and control arm flange.

4) Remove parking brake retaining straps from spring plates. Reattach shock absorbers temporarily. Remove control arm pivot bolts.

5) Disconnect parking brake cable from crossmember tube. Remove crossmember lower retaining bolts. Remove torque strut bolts from upper mounts. Remove crossmember tube.

Installation

1) Apply rubber lubricant to lower mount bushings. Install crossmember tube with lower retaining bolts. Remove upper mounts from body and install on torque struts, but do not tighten bolts.

Fig. 1: Exploded View of Rear Suspension

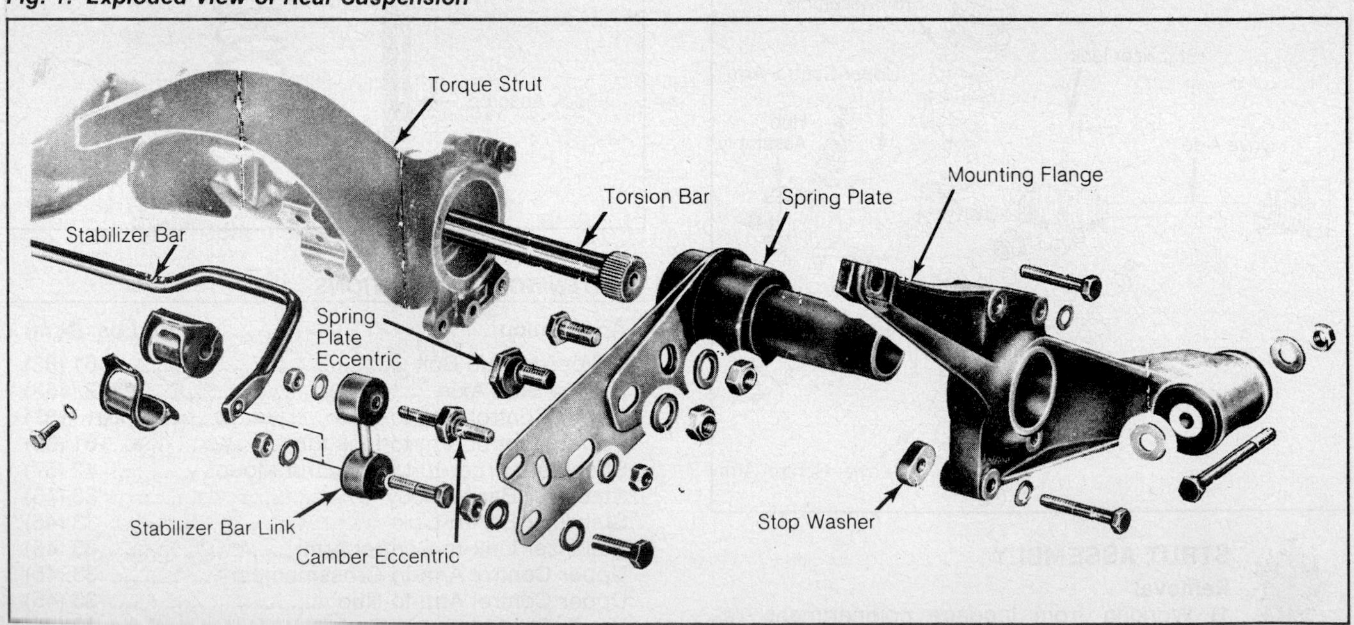
Torque Strut
Torsion Bar
Spring Plate
Mounting Flange
Stabilizer Bar
Spring
Plate
Eccentric
Stabilizer Bar Link
Camber Eccentric
Stop Washer

Rear Suspension

PORSCHE 944 (Cont.)

2) Install control arms with pivot bolts. Disconnect shock absorber from control arm. Install control arm to spring plate, but do not tighten bolts. Reinstall shock absorber to control arm.

3) Install upper retaining bolts to body approximately 2-3 threads deep. Tighten torque strut-to-mount bolts. Tighten all remaining mount bolts.

4) Lower transaxle and remove support chain. Install and tighten transaxle retaining nuts. Reinstall parking brake cables and retainers. Install wheel assemblies and lower vehicle.

5) Check and adjust rear axle alignment. After alignment, raise vehicle and remove rear wheel assemblies. Tighten all nuts and bolts to specification. Install stabilizer bar links.

TORSION BARS & SPRING PLATES

Removal

With crossmember tube removed and placed in a vise, remove mounting flange bolts and flange. Pry off spring plate. Remove spring plate and withdraw torsion bars. Left and right torsion bars are not interchangeable.

Installation

1) Position crossmember tube so that flat surface of torque strut is horizontal. Using a protractor (VW 261) and a straight edge, measure any deviation from horizontal and record that figure.

2) Add 23 2/3" to recorded figure for setting spring plate angle. Set protractor at indicated angle and turn spring plate or torsion bar until bubble in level is centered.

3) Install mounting flange, using rubber lubricant, using the short bolts, until the long bolt with stop washer can be inserted. Install mounting flange-to-torque strut bolt temporarily.

4) Compress spring plate with floor jack or compression tool (VW 655/3). Install spring plate stop washer and tighten bolt slightly. Remove tool allowing spring plate to position stop washer. Tighten all flange bolts.

TIGHTENING SPECIFICATIONS

Application	Ft. Lbs. (N.m)
Control Arm Camber Eccentric	65 (88)
Control Arm-to-Spring Plate	75 (102)
Mounting Flange-to-Body	51 (69)
Mounting Flange-to-Crossmember	33 (45)
Mounting Flange-to-Upper Mount	33 (45)
Shock Absorber-to-Body	44 (60)
Spring Plate Height Eccentric	177 (241)
Stabilizer Bar Link	33 (45)
Torque Strut Mount-to-Body	33 (45)
Torque Strut Mount-to-Strut	17 (23)
Upper Mount-to-Body	33 (45)

Rear Suspension

RENAULT FUEGO & 18i

DESCRIPTION

The trailing axle shaft used on rear suspension, is supported by a center arm and 2 side arms. The pivot points are mounted in rubber bushings. A stabilizer bar is welded at each end to the side arms. Coil springs surround the shock absorbers.

Fig. 1: Exploded View of Rear Suspension

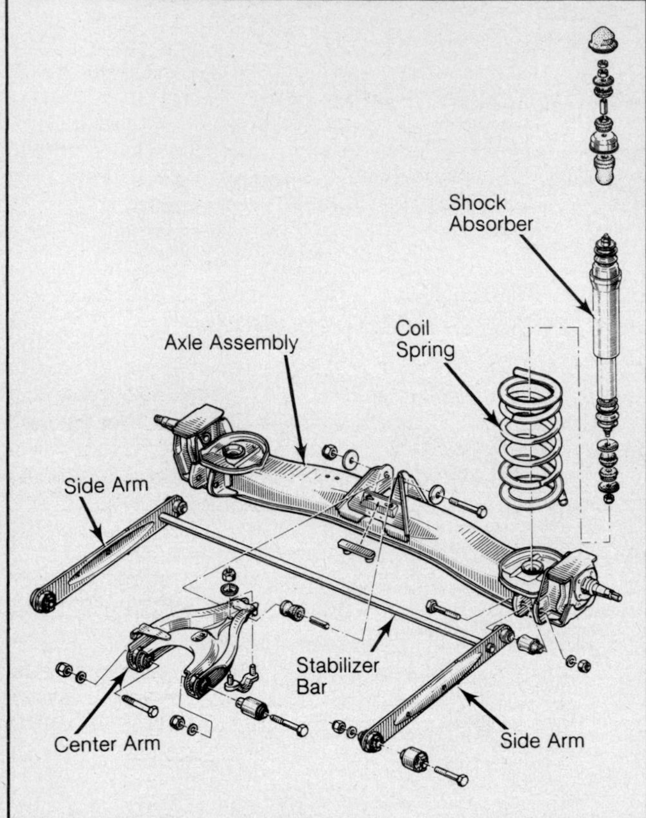
Shock Absorber
Coil Spring
Axle Assembly
Side Arm
Stabilizer Bar
Center Arm
Side Arm

ADJUSTMENTS

WHEEL ALIGNMENT SPECIFICATIONS & PROCEDURES

See Wheel Alignment Specifications and Procedures in WHEEL ALIGNMENT section.

WHEEL BEARING

Tighten hub nut to 22 ft. lbs. (30 N.m) while rotating brake drum. Lightly tap side of brake drum with a soft mallet. Loosen nut 1/6 turn. Attach a dial indicator to brake drum with indicator tip on axle. Check bearing end play. End play should be .001" (.03 mm) or less. Adjust bearing end play by turning hub nut.

REMOVAL & INSTALLATION

WHEEL BEARING

Removal

1) Raise vehicle and support with safety stands. Remove wheel assembly. Release parking brake. Loosen secondary cables of parking brake so that lever may be drawn back.

2) Remove dust plug from backing plate and disengage automatic adjuster. Insert a screwdriver through backing plate and hole in brake shoe, push in against parking brake lever to disengage catch. Push the lever towards the rear.

3) Remove hub dust cap, cotter pin, and lock nut. Remove hub nut and washer. Remove brake drum, outer bearing, and seal. Using bearing removal tool (Rou. 370-02), place centering sleeve on axle.

4) Install 2 half casings in place and clamp assembly with retaining ring. Remove inner bearing from axle with assembly and extractor tool (Mot. 49). Remove grease seal deflector with extractor tool.

Installation

1) Slide new deflector onto axle and drive in place using hub nut and installer sleeve (Rou. 737-01). Mount inner bearing onto axle using sleeve of extractor tool (Rou. 370-02), and hub nut.

2) Install outer bearing race. Install new grease seal using installer tool (Rou. 770). Pack inside of hub with grease and coat bearing rollers. Install hub, outer bearing, washer, and hub nut. Adjust bearings. To complete installation, reverse removal procedures.

AXLE ASSEMBLY

Removal

1) Raise vehicle and support with safety stands. Remove wheel assemblies. Remove lower shock absorber retaining nuts and push shock absorber up as far as possible. Remove flexible brake lines from limiter.

2) Pull down on rear axle and remove coil springs. Remove the 2 side arm nuts and drive out bolts. Disconnect parking brake cables at adjuster and remove them from retaining bracket.

3) Place floor jack under rear axle shaft. Disconnect brake limiter valve. Remove 2 center arm bolts from body. Lower axle assembly away from vehicle.

Installation

To install, reverse removal procedures. Lubricate all bolts with grease before installing. Tighten all bolts with full weight of vehicle on floor. Bleed brake system.

SIDE ARMS

Removal

Raise vehicle and support with safety stands. Disconnect parking brake cables. Remove retaining bolts from side arms to body and rear axle assembly. Remove side arms and stabilizer bar as an assembly.

Installation

To install, reverse removal procedures. Lubricate all bolts with grease before installation. Tighten all bolts with full weight of vehicle on floor.

CENTER CONTROL ARM

Removal

Raise vehicle and support with safety stands. Disconnect brake limiter at control rod. Remove retaining nuts holding center arm and axle assembly. Remove nuts and bolts that retain center arm to body. Remove center arm.

Installation

To install, reverse removal procedures. Lubricate all bolts with grease before installation. Tighten all nuts and bolts with full weight of vehicle on floor. Check alignment of limiter valve.

SHOCK ABSORBER & COIL SPRING

Removal

1) Remove cover and upper shock absorber retaining nuts from inside luggage compartment. Raise vehicle on hoist and remove wheel assemblies. Remove lower shock absorber retaining nuts.

2) Remove brake hose clips from rear axle. Compress shock absorber by hand and carefully work shock absorber and coil spring from vehicle.

Installation

To install, reverse removal procedures.

TIGHTENING SPECIFICATIONS

Application	Ft. Lbs. (N.m)
Center Arm-to-Axle	30 (41)
Center Arm-to-Body	59 (80)
Center Arm Clamp Nuts	11 (15)
Side Arm-to-Axle	30 (41)
Side Arm-to-Body	26 (35)
Shock Absorber Nuts	
Lower	22 (30)
Upper	11 (15)

Rear Suspension

RENAULT LE CAR

DESCRIPTION

Le Car rear suspension system is torsion bar type with trailing arms. Trailing arms are mounted off chassis and have torsion bars connected to inboard edge.

ADJUSTMENT

WHEEL ALIGNMENT SPECIFICATIONS & PROCEDURES

See Wheel Alignment Specifications and Procedures in WHEEL ALIGNMENT section.

WHEEL BEARING

Tighten stub axle nut to 25 ft. lbs. (34 N.m) while rotating drum. Loosen stub axle nut 1/4 turn. Attach dial indicator to brake drum with indicator tip on stub axle shaft. End play should be .0004-.002" (.01-.05 mm). Adjust end play by turning stub axle nut.

REMOVAL & INSTALLATION

WHEEL BEARING

Removal

1) Raise vehicle and support with safety stands. Remove wheel assembly. Remove brake drum and retain outer bearing. Remove oil seal and races.

2) Using bearing puller/installer (Rou. 370-02), assemble locating sleeve onto stub axle. Assemble half shells in position. The thinner end fits around the washer. Support complete assembly with sleeve.

3) Attach protective tool (Rou. 15-01) to stub axle. Remove bearing assembly using puller tool (B. Vi. 28-01). Check stub axle for wear and/or seizure.

Installation

1) Use bearing and sleeve from tool (Rou. 370-02) to perform installation. Using mandrel install bearing track races. Use a 1 13/16" (46 mm) diameter for the outer bearing and 2" (51 mm) for the inner bearing.

2) Install seal using a 2 1/4" (58 mm) diameter mandrel. Coat inside of hub with bearing grease and slide hub onto axle. Replace outer bearing, thrust washer and nut. To complete installation, reverse removal procedures.

TRAILING ARM

Removal

1) Raise vehicle and support with safety stands. Disconnect and remove sway bar. Remove shock absorber. Disconnect brake lines and plug openings.

2) Put torsion bar adjusting cams in zero position. Remove bars from both sides. Remove retaining bolts and slide complete arm assembly from vehicle.

Inspection

Check all bushings and spacers for obvious signs of wear or damage. Use puller and/or mandrel with press, to replace bushings.

Installation

To install, reverse removal procedures. Bleed brake system. Recheck brake pressure equalizer. Check wheel alignment.

Fig. 1: Trailing Arm and Torsion Bar Assembly

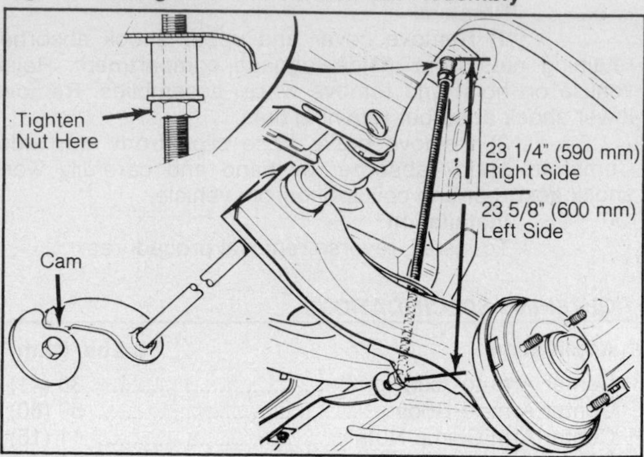

Tighten
Nut Here
23 1/4" (590 mm)
Right Side
23 5/8" (600 mm)
Left Side
Cam

Fabricated tool is constructed by using all thread and welding nuts together.

TORSION BAR

Removal

1) Raise vehicle and support with safety stands. Loosen lock nut on cam and adjust until cam is zeroed. Remove shock absorber.

2) Fit fabricated tool where shock absorber has been removed. *See Fig. 1.* Tighten nut until adjuster lever is raised from cam. Remove torsion bar.

NOTE: **Before installing torsion bar, adjust nut on frabricated tool to 23 1/4" (590 mm), right side and/or 23 5/8" (600 mm), left side. This will allow torsion bar to be inserted.**

Installation

1) Put adjuster lever so it touches cam. Lightly coat torsion bar splines with grease, insert into lever and arm.

2) Tighten cam lock nut. Take off tool. Install shock absorber. Lower vehicle. Measure under body riding height. *See Riding Height in WHEEL ALIGNMENT section.*

SHOCK ABSORBER

Removal

Work from inside trunk and remove upper retaining nuts. Raise vehicle and support with safety stands. Remove lower retaining nut and take off shock absorber.

Installation

To install, reverse removal procedure. Make sure upper mounting is attached first.

TIGHTENING SPECIFICATIONS

Application	Ft. Lbs. (N.m)
Trailing Arm Bolts	
Outer	30 (41)
Inner	55 (75)
Shock Absorber Nuts	60 (82)

SAAB 900 & 900 TURBO

DESCRIPTION

Rear suspension is a rigid axle with coil springs. Rear axle is straight tube with stub axles press fitted into ends. Axle is mounted to body by 2 lower control arms, which are connected at rear to the axle tube and to the body at front.

Rear links are also used which mount rearward from stub axle assembly to body. A cross bar is mounted from right side of axle and attaches to body support in center. Coil springs are mounted between lower control arms and body. Shock absorbers are used and are attached between lower control arms and body.

Fig. 1: Saab 900 & 900 Turbo Rear Suspension

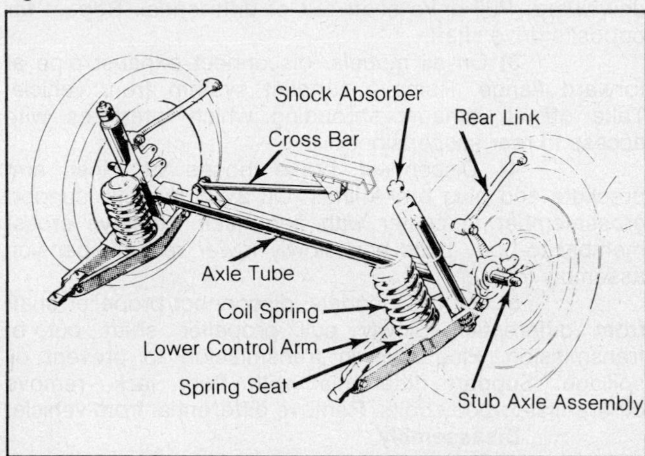
Shock Absorber
Rear Link
Cross Bar
Axle Tube
Coil Spring
Lower Control Arm
Spring Seat
Stub Axle Assembly

ADJUSTMENT

WHEEL ALIGNMENT SPECIFICATIONS & PROCEDURES

See Wheel Alignment Specifications and Procedures in WHEEL ALIGNMENT Section.

WHEEL BEARING

Tighten hub nut to 36 ft. lbs. (49 N.m) to seat bearings. Loosen hub nut. Tighten hub nut to 1.5-3.0 ft. lbs. (2-4 N.m). Lock hub nut into place by bending locking collar into slot.

REMOVAL & INSTALLATION

NOTE: **Do not lift vehicle with jack applied directly to rear axle tube.**

WHEEL BEARING

Removal

1) Raise and support vehicle. Remove wheel assembly. Remove brake caliper and hang out of the way. Remove disc brake rotor. Pry out dust cap. Bend back locking collar and remove hub nut and washer.

2) Remove hub using puller (89 96 084). Remove seal ring with screwdriver. Remove inner bearing races. Drive out outer bearing races, if necessary.

Installation

Reverse removal procedure to complete installation. Adjust wheel bearing. *See WHEEL BEARING ADJUSTMENT in this article.*

COIL SPRING

Removal

1) Apply hand brake and loosen wheel lug nuts. Raise and support vehicle. Remove wheel assembly. Support control arm with floor jack. Slightly raise arm and disconnect lower end of shock absorber.

2) Support rear axle with safety stand to prevent sudden drop of axle. Disconnect control arm from body. Lower control arm and remove spring, spring support and rubber spacer.

Installation

Replace self-locking nuts that attach control arm to body. Reverse removal procedure to complete installation.

AXLE ASSEMBLY

Removal

1) Raise vehicle and support with safety stands, under vehicle body. Remove wheel assemblies. Disconnect rear brake hoses and plug. Lower shock absorber attachments and cross bar.

2) Position a floor jack under rear axle, lower axle and remove rear springs. Remove bolts from spring link rear bushings and remove axle assembly from vehicle.

Installation

1) To install, reverse removal procedures. When repositioning axle tube, do not place floor jack in center of axle tube. Either use 2 floor jacks (one at each end) or 1 floor jack and 1 safety stand.

2) Do not tighten bushings until vehicle weight is on suspension to ensure bushings are aligned correctly. Cross bar-to-body retaining bolt must be installed with nut facing forward. Bleed brake system.

SHOCK ABSORBER

Removal (Standard Type)

Raise vehicle and support with safety stands, under vehicle body. Remove wheel assembly. Disconnect shock absorber from upper and lower mounting brackets. Remove shock absorber.

Installation

Bleed air from shock absorber before installing by holding shock upright and working it through full cycle several times. Reverse removal procedure to install shock.

Removal (Pneumatic Type)

1) Raise vehicle and support with safety stands, under vehicle body. Remove wheel assembly. Support axle with safety stand to prevent sudden drop of axle.

2) Raise control arm with a floor jack placed under axle. Remove shock retaining nuts and control arm-to-rear axle mounting bolts. Lower control arm and remove shock.

NOTE: **Used shock absorbers require special handling to prevent personal injury. Drill a hole 3/8-5/8" (10-15 mm) from the edge of pressure chamber before discarding.**

Installation

To install, reverse removal procedures.

Rear Suspension

SUBARU 1600, 1800 & 1800 TURBO

DESCRIPTION

Rear suspension is of the independent type and utilizes semi-trailing arms and torsion bars. A crossmember, which contains the torsion bars, is attached to body.

The semi-trailing arms attach to crossmember at inner pivot points and to torsion bar ends at outer pivot points. Shock absorbers are mounted between body and semi-trailing arms.

On 4WD models a center control arm has been added to crossmember, which simplifies adjustment of riding height.

Fig. 1: 2WD Suspension and Components

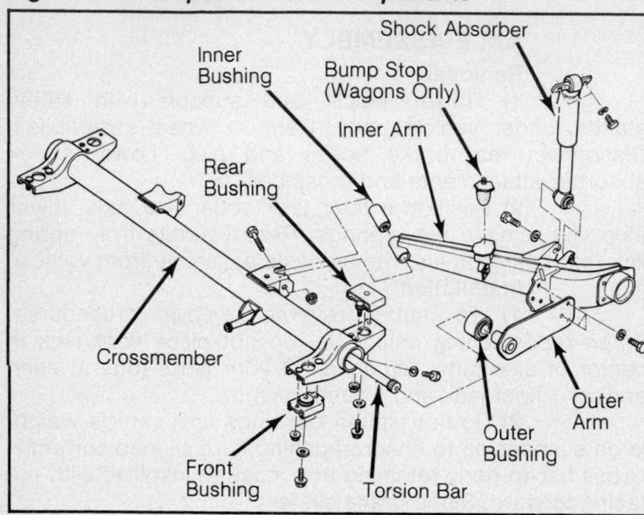
Shock Absorber
Inner Bushing
Bump Stop (Wagons Only)
Inner Arm
Rear Bushing
Crossmember
Outer Arm
Outer Bushing
Front Bushing
Torsion Bar

4WD models are similar.

ADJUSTMENT

WHEEL ALIGNMENT SPECIFICATIONS & PROCEDURES

See Wheel Alignment Specifications and Procedures in WHEEL ALIGNMENT section.

WHEEL BEARING

2WD Models

Tighten hub nut to 36 ft. lbs. (49 N.m). Turn back nut a small amount and rotate brake drum serveral times to seat bearings. Turn back nut 1/10 to 1/8 turn to obtain correct starting torque. Correct starting torque is 2.0-3.2 lbs. (8.9-14.2 N). Adjust starting torque by turning hub nut.

4WD Models

Wheel bearings are not adjustable. Tighten hub nut to 145 ft. lbs. (197 N.m). If cotter pin hole is not aligned, tighten further a maximum of 30° to align hole. Install new cotter pin.

REMOVAL & INSTALLATION

WHEEL BEARING

Removal

1) Raise vehicle and support with safety stands. Remove wheel assembly. Remove dust cap and cotter pin. Remove hub nut and hub assembly from axle shaft.

2) Using a soft mallet and aluminum or brass bar, tap on inner race to remove outer bearing and outer race to remove inner bearing.

Installation

To install, reverse removal procedure.

REAR SUSPENSION ASSEMBLY

Removal

1) Remove shock absorber upper retaining bolts. Raise vehicle and support with safety stands. Remove wheel assemblies.

2) On 4WD models, drive spring pins out of axle drive shaft ends. Disconnect outer CV joint from spindle by pushing inner CV joint inward and brake drum downward. Pull drive shaft out of differential. Repeat for opposite drive shaft.

3) On all models, disconnect exhaust pipe at forward flange. Remove exhaust system from vehicle. Take off all exhaust shrouding which interferes with access to rear suspension.

4) Disconnect brake hoses at inner arm brackets and plug brake lines. On 2WD models, support crossmember at center with floor jack. Remove crossmember-to-body bolts and slowly lower rear suspension assembly to floor.

5) On 4WD models, disconnect propeller shaft from differential. Slowly pull propeller shaft out of transmission. Plug hole in transmission to prevent oil spillage. Support differential with floor jack, remove differential-to-body bolts. Remove differential from vehicle.

Disassembly

1) Remove shock absorbers from trailing arms. Scribe a mark on outer arm and crossmember for reassembly reference. Loosen outer bushing lock bolts.

2) Remove bolts attaching outer arm to inner arm. Pull outer arm and torsion bar out of crossmember. Repeat for opposite side.

CAUTION: Take care not to twist or bend torsion bar while removing.

3) Remove torsion bar from outer arm. Remove inner arm-to-crossmember bolt. Remove inner arm. If inner bushing is worn or damaged, press it out of inner arm, (replace if necessary).

Reassembly

To reassemble, reverse disassembly procedures. When installing torsion bar and outer arm, align scribe marks made during disassembly to achieve correct outer arm angle.

Installation

To install, reverse removal procedures. Tighten outer bushing lock bolts with vehicle on floor. Bleed brake system and check wheel alignment.

TIGHTENING SPECIFICATIONS

Application	Ft. Lbs. (N.m)
Crossmember-to-Body Bolts	87-108 (118-147)
Differential Retaining Nuts (4WD)	51-58 (69-79)
Inner Arm-to-Crossmember Bolts	54-69 (73-94)
Outer Bushing Lock Bolts	23-29 (31-39)
Outer-to-Inner Arm Bolts	87-101 (118-137)
Propeller Shaft Bolts (4WD)	13-18 (18-24)

TOYOTA IRS – CAMRY & TERCEL

DESCRIPTION

The rear suspension system utilizes MacPherson Struts, which fasten to axle carrier and wheel housing. Camry has a double type wheel bearing consisting of 1 outer race and with 2 inner races.

Camry uses a rear disc brake system, designed with the axle shaft nut facing the inside of the vehicle. Tercel uses a rear drum brake system, designed with the axle shaft nut facing the outside of the vehicle.

Connected to each axle carrier are 2 suspension arms and 1 strut rod. Intergral with rear suspension arm is an adjustable cam, which controls the toe of the rear wheels.

ADJUSTMENTS

WHEEL ALIGNMENT SPECIFICATIONS & PROCEDURES

See Wheel Alignment Specifications and Procedures in WHEEL ALIGNMENT section.

WHEEL BEARING

NOTE: To adjust axle shaft nut for Camry, axle hub MUST be removed from axle carrier.

Tighten hub nut to 22 ft. lbs. (30 N.m) and turn hub several times. Loosen nut until it can be turned by hand, use ONLY a socket without a handle. Tighten axle shaft nut until preload is 0.9-2.2 lbs. (4-9.8 N). Turn nut until correct preload is obtained.

NOTE: When rotating hub, make certain there is no brake drag.

Fig. 1: Toyota Camry Rear Axle Components

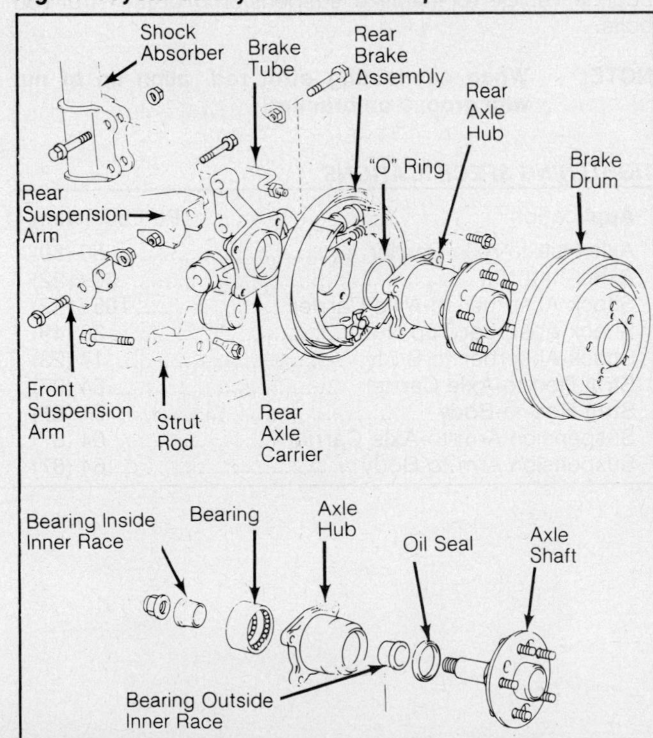
Shock Absorber
Brake Tube
Rear Brake Assembly
Rear Axle Hub
"O" Ring
Brake Drum
Rear Suspension Arm
Front Suspension Arm
Strut Rod
Rear Axle Carrier
Bearing Inside Inner Race
Bearing
Axle Hub
Oil Seal
Axle Shaft
Bearing Outside Inner Race

Tercel uses a drum brake system.

REMOVAL & INSTALLATION

AXLE HUB, CARRIER & SHAFT

Removal

1) Raise vehicle and remove rear wheel. Using a micrometer, check bearing play in axial direction, it should be less than .002" (.05 mm). Disconnect brake tube at brake caliper for Camry or wheel cylinder for Tercel and plug tube openings.

2) For Tercel, remove grease cap, cotter pin, nut lock and axle nut. Remove thrust washer, inner bearing and brake hub/drum assembly. Using a screwdriver, remove oil seal and inside bearing inner race.

3) Using rear hub bearing remover/installer (09608-16010) and front hub and drive pinion bearing remover/installer (09608-20011), drive bearing outer races from brake drum. Remove 4 bolts retaining axle hub for Camry or axle shaft for Tercel to axle carrier.

4) Remove axle hub for Camry or axle shaft for Tercel. For Camry, remove "O" ring. For both models, remove nuts/bolts holding axle carrier to strut rod, shock absorber, front and rear suspension arms. Remove axle carrier.

5) For Camry, use a hammer and a chisel to loosen staked part of axle nut and remove axle nut. Using universal puller (09950-20014), remove axle shaft from axle hub. Remove inside bearing inner race. Using universal puller (09950-20014), remove outside bearing inner race from axle shaft.

6) Remove oil seal. Place outside bearing inner race in bearing of axle hub. Using an arbor press, oil filter wrench (09228-22020) and upper ball joint dust cover replacer (09636-20010), press bearing from axle hub. Clean all parts with solvent and compressed air.

Installation

1) For Camry, apply grease around bearing outer race. Using transmission and transfer bearing replacer (09316-60010), press new bearing into axle hub. Place inside bearing inner race on axle hub bearing.

2) Using countershaft bearing replacer (09310-35010), drive new oil seal into axle hub. Place new oil seal and new outside bearing inner race on axle shaft.

3) Using upper ball joint dust cover replacer (09636-20010) and oil filter wrench (09228-22020), press inner race with axle hub onto axle shaft. Check preload. Torque and stake axle nut.

4) For Tercel, use rear hub bearing remover/installer (09608-16010) and front hub and drive pinion bearing remover/installer (09608-20011) to drive new outer races and oil seal into hub. Pack grease into new bearings, grease cap and center of hub.

5) For both models, place axle carrier in mounting position. Install and torque nuts/bolts holding axle carrier to shock absorber. Install (DO NOT torque) nuts/bolts to front and rear suspension arm (install lip of nut into hole on suspension arm).

6) Install (DO NOT torque) nut/bolt holding axle carrier to strut rod (insert lip of nut into groove on bracket). For Camry, install new "O" ring to axle carrier.

7) Using 4 bolts, install axle hub assembly for Camry or axle shaft for Tercel and torque bolts. Install brake caliper for Camry. For Tercel, install brake drum-/hub assembly, inner bearing, thrust washer and nut. Adjust preload an install nut lock, cotter pin and grease cap.

TOYOTA IRS – CAMRY & TERCEL (Cont.)

8) For both models, connect brake tube to wheel cylinder or caliper and bleed brake system. Lower vehicle to ground and bounce to stabilize suspension. With weight of vehicle on suspension, torque setting bolts. Check rear wheel alignment.

SHOCK ABSORBER & COIL SPRING

Removal

1) Raise vehicle and support with safety stands. Remove wheel assembly. Disconnect brake tube at wheel cylinder and at junction on shock absorber. Remove flexible brake hose at shock absorber and plug openings.

2) Remove suspension support cover and loosen nut (DO NOT remove nut) holding suspension support to shock absorber. Remove 2 nuts/bolts holding shock absorber to axle carrier. Disconnect shock absorber.

3) Remove 3 nuts holding shock absorber to body and remove shock absorber. Reinstall a nut/bolt or socket between axle carrier bottom mounting flanges of shock absorber and secure in a vise.

4) Using front coil spring compressor (09727-22031), compress coil spring. Remove nut holding suspension support to shock absorber. Remove suspension support, coil spring, insulator and bumper. DO NOT disassemble shock absorber.

CAUTION: **When replacing a shock absorber, drill a hole .39" (10 mm) above top of mounting at base of shock absorber to relieve high pressure gas.**

Installation

To install, reverse removal procedures. Align coil spring end in hollow portion of spring seat. Align suspension support with lower bracket of shock absorber. *See Fig. 2.* Bleed rear brake system. Check alignment of rear wheels.

Fig. 2: Aligning Shock Absorber Suspension Support

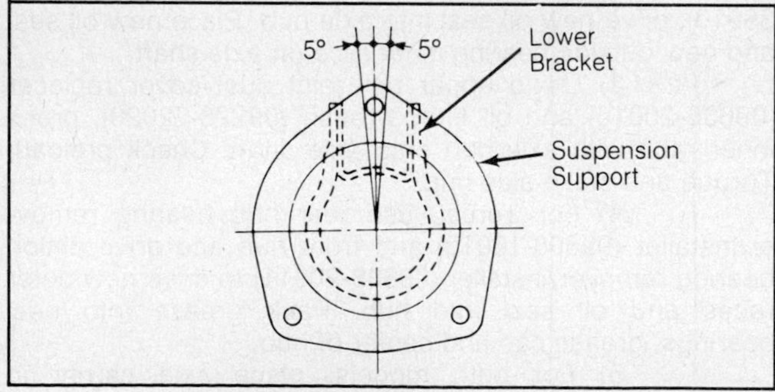
5°
5°
Lower Bracket
Suspension Support

SUSPENSION ARM

Removal

1) Raise vehicle and support with safety stands. Remove nuts/bolts holding rear suspension arms to axle carrier. Record match mark of cam plate of rear suspension arm at body mounting bracket.

NOTE: **When loosening cam, turn bolt ONLY.**

2) Remove cam and bolt holding rear suspension arm to body and remove rear suspension arm. Remove nut/bolt holding front suspension arm to body mounting bracket. Remove front suspension arm.

Installation

1) Connect (DO NOT torque) front suspension arm to body and axle carrier with nuts/bolts. Install (DO NOT torque) rear suspension arm to body with cam (align cam plate mark) and bolt.

NOTE: **When installing front suspension arm to body, make sure lip of nut is resting on bracket flange, NOT over it. When connecting front suspension arm to axle carrier, insert lip of nut into hole on suspension.**

2) Install (DO NOT torque) rear suspension arm to axle carrier with nut/bolt. Remove jack stands and bounce vehicle to stabilize suspension. Torque bolts with vehicle resting on suspension. Check rear wheel alignment.

Bushing Replacement

To remove bushing from suspension arm, use rear suspension bushing remover/replacer (09726-32010) and an arbor press to press out bushing.

Installation

Using rear suspension bushing remover/replacer (09726-32010) and an arbor press, press new bushing into suspension arm.

NOTE: **DO NOT use lubricant bushings to be pressed into suspension arms.**

STRUT ROD

Removal

Raise vehicle and place on jack stands. Remove wheel. Remove nuts/bolts holding strut rod to axle carrier and to body. Remove strut rod.

Installation

Install (DO NOT torque) strut rod to body and to axle carrier with nuts/bolts. Remove jack stands and bounce vehicle to stabilize suspension. Torque strut rod bolts.

NOTE: **When connecting strut rod, align lip of nut with groove on bracket.**

TIGHTENING SPECIFICATIONS

Application	Ft. Lbs. (N.m)
Axle Hub-to-Axle Carrier	59 (80)
Axle Shaft Nut	90 (122)
Shock Absorber-to-Axle Carrier	105 (142)
Shock Absorber Top Nut	36 (49)
Shock Absorber-to-Body	17 (23)
Strut Rod-to-Axle Carrier	64 (87)
Strut Rod-to-Body	64 (87)
Suspension Arm-to-Axle Carrier	64 (87)
Suspension Arm-to-Body	64 (87)

Rear Suspension

TOYOTA CELICA, COROLLA, CRESSIDA, STARLET & TERCEL

DESCRIPTION

Coil spring type suspension is used, utilizing upper and lower control rods as pivot supports. Coil springs are mounted between axle and chassis member.

Shock absorbers are connected to axle housing and to chassis member. A lateral control rod is mounted to rear axle housing and to mount at side of body. A stabilizer bar attached to chassis with end links and at axle with brackets.

Fig. 1: Toyota Rear Suspension Components

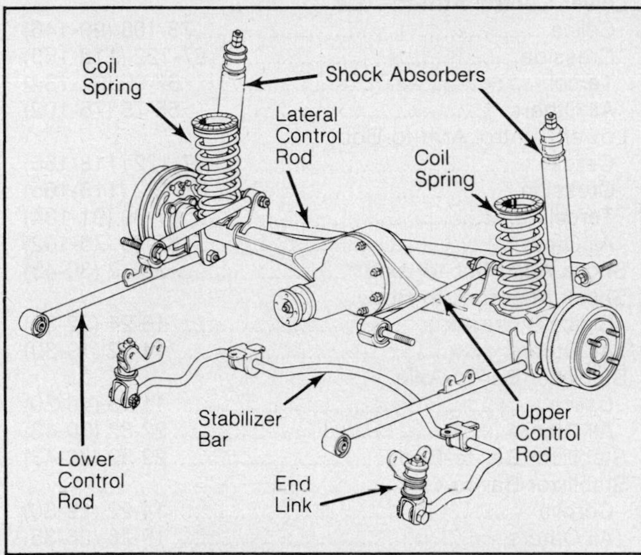

Coil
Spring
Shock Absorbers
Lateral
Control
Rod
Coil
Spring
Stabilizer
Bar
Upper
Control
Rod
Lower
Control
Rod
End
Link

Starlet does not use the lateral control rod.

ADJUSTMENTS

WHEEL ALIGNMENT SPECIFICATIONS & PROCEDURES

See Wheel Alignment Specifications and Procedures in WHEEL ALIGNMENT section.

REMOVAL & INSTALLATION

WHEEL BEARING

Removal

1) Raise vehicle and place on jack stands. Remove wheel and brake drum. Remove 4 backing plate nuts. Using rear axle shaft puller (09520-00031), pull rear axle from axle housing.

CAUTION: When pulling axle shaft from axle housing, be careful not to damage oil seal.

2) Inspect axle shaft for maximum shaft runout of .079" (2 mm) and maximum flange runout of .008" (.2 mm). To remove inner bearing retainer of axle shaft, use a grider to grind down a side of retainer. Using a chisel and a hammer, cut off retainer and remove from shaft.

3) Using an arbor press and rear axle shaft bearing remover (09527-20011) press bearing from axle shaft. Using oil seal puller (09308-00010), pull oil seal from axle housing.

Installation

1) Using rear axle shaft bearing replacer (09515-20010), press new bearing onto axle shaft. Place new bearing retainer in an oil bath and heat to 302° F (150° C). While bearing retainer is still hot, use rear axle shaft bearing replacer (09515-20010) to press bearing retainer onto axle shaft.

NOTE: When pressing bearing retainer onto axle shaft, face non-beveled side toward bearing.

2) Using rear axle shaft oil seal replacer (09517-12010), drive new oil seal .22" (5.6 mm) below bottom surface of wheel bearing seat. When replacing axle shaft, align gasket and gasket retainer with internal notches facing down. Install 4 backing plate nuts and torque. To complete installation, reverse removal procedures.

SHOCK ABSORBER

Removal

Raise vehicle and support with jack stands. Remove nut retaining shock absorber to rear axle housing. Remove nut holding shock absorber to body and remove shock absorber.

NOTE: When removing shock absorber from body, use an adjustable wrench to hold shock absorber shaft.

Installation

To install, reverse removal procedures.

COIL SPRING

Removal

1) Raise vehicle and support body with jack stands. Leave floor jack under axle housing. Remove nut/bolt holding shock absorber to rear axle housing. If replacing shock absorber, remove nuts, collars and cushion from shock absorber body mount.

NOTE: When removing shock absorber from body, use an adjustable wrench to hold shock absorber shaft.

2) Remove stabilizer bar bushing brackets from axle housing. Disconnect lateral control rod from axle housing and body. Begin to lower axle housing. As axle housing is being lowered, remove coil spring and upper/lower insulators.

CAUTION: As axle housing is being lowered, be careful not to pull brake line and parking brake cable.

Installation

To install, reverse removal procedure. DO NOT torque lateral control rod fasteners. Lower vehicle to ground and bounce to stabilize suspension. Torque control rod fasteners.

STABILIZER BAR

Removal

1) Raise vehicle and support on jack stands. Remove stabilizer bushing brackets from rear axle

Rear Suspension

TOYOTA CELICA, COROLLA, CRESSIDA, STARLET & TERCEL (Cont.)

housing. Remove nut, cushions and retainers from stabilizer bar end links.

2) Remove end links from brackets. Remove stabilizer bar with end links from vehicle. Remove cotter pin, nut, bolt, collar, cushion and end links from stabilizer bar.

Installation

To install, reverse removal procedures.

LATERAL CONTROL ROD

Removal

Raise vehicle and support rear axle housing with jack stands. Remove nuts/bolts, washers and bushings holding lateral control rod to axle housing and to body. Remove lateral control rod.

Installation

To install, reverse removal procedure. DO NOT torque fasteners. Lower vehicle to ground and bounce to stabilize suspension. Raise axle housing and torque fasteners of lateral control rod.

UPPER & LOWER CONTROL RODS

Removal

Raise vehicle and support body with jack stands. Support rear axle housing with floor jack. Remove nuts/bolts holding upper control rod to body and to axle housing. Remove upper control rod. Remove nuts/bolts holding lower control rod to body and to rear axle housing. Remove lower control rod.

Bushing Replacement

Using an arbor press and rear suspension bushing set (09710-14012), press bushing from or into lateral control rod.

NOTE: When removing or installing bushing, press or pull from chamfered side.

Installation

To install, reverse removal procedures. DO NOT torque fasteners. Lower vehicle to ground and bounce vehicle to stabilize suspension. Raise axle housing until body is free from jack stands. Torque nuts/bolts of control rods.

TIGHTENING SPECIFICATIONS

Application	Ft. Lbs. (N.m)
Axle Shaft Mounting Nuts	44-53 (60-72)
Lateral Control Rod-to-Axle	
Celica & Cressida	30-55 (41-75)
All Others	37-57 (50-77)
Lateral Control Rod-to-Body	
Celica & Cressida	51-65 (69-88)
Corolla	55-75 (75-102)
All Others	67-99 (91-134)
Lower Control Arm-to-Axle	
Celica	73-108 (99-146)
Cressida	87-122 (118-165)
Tercel	67-99 (91-134)
All Others	55-75 (75-102)
Lower Control Arm-to-Body	
Celica	87-122 (118-165)
Cressida	87-122 (118-165)
Tercel	67-99 (91-134)
All Others	55-75 (75-102)
Shock Absorber-to-Axle	22-32 (30-43)
Shock Absorber-to-Body	
Celica & Cressida	16-24 (22-33)
All Others	14-22 (19-30)
Stabilizer Bar-to-Axle	
Celica	11-15 (15-20)
All Others	22-32 (30-43)
Stabilizer Bar-to-Body	22-32 (30-43)
Stabilizer Bar-to-Link	
Corolla	14-22 (19-30)
All Others	19-26 (26-35)
Upper Control Arm-to-Axle	
Celica	73-108 (99-146)
Corolla	55-75 (75-102)
Tercel	67-99 (91-134)
All Others	87-122 (118-165)
Upper Control Arm-to-Body	
Celica	87-122 (118-165)
Corolla	55-75 (75-102)
Tercel	67-99 (91-134)
All Others	87-122 (118-165)

Rear Suspension

TOYOTA SUPRA

DESCRIPTION

Rear Suspension is an independent, coil spring type. The suspension arms are mounted by bushings and pivot bolts to body and are supported by coil springs and shock absorbers. The stabilizer bar attaches to the differential support member and suspension arms.

ADJUSTMENTS

WHEEL ALIGNMENT SPECIFICATIONS & PROCEDURES

See Wheel Alignment Specifications and Procedures in WHEEL ALIGNMENT section.

WHEEL BEARING

Tighten hub nut to 22-36 ft. lbs. (30-49 N.m). Rotate axle back and forth to snug down. Measure preload rotation resistance, it should be .9-3.5 INCH lbs. (.1-.4 N.m). Torque hub nut to 58 ft. lbs. (79 N.m). Check preload rotation. Maximum torque of hub nut is 145 ft. lbs. (197 N.m).

NOTE: **Turn hub flange 1 turn every 6 seconds and measure preload. If preload is less than .9-3.5 INCH lbs. (.1-.4 N.m), retighten hub nut 5-10° at a time until preload is reached.**

REMOVAL & INSTALLATION

SHOCK ABSORBER & COIL SPRING

Removal

1) Raise vehicle, support body with safety stands and leave a floor jack under suspension arm. Remove brake hose clips and plug openings. Disconnect nut, cushion and retainer of stabilizer bar and remove from suspension arm. Remove 4 nuts holding drive shaft to axle hub flange.

2) Remove bolt holding shock absorber to suspension arm and disconnect shock absorber. If replacing shock absorber, use a screwdriver to hold shaft and remove nut retaining shock absorber to body. Remove shock absorber. Lower suspension arm. Remove coil spring and insulators.

Installation

To install, reverse removal procedures (DO NOT torque fasteners). After installation, lower and bounce vehicle to stabilize suspension. Torque fasteners.

WHEEL BEARING

Removal

1) Raise vehicle and support on safety stands. Remove rear wheel. Remove 4 mounting nuts and remove drive shaft from axle shaft flange. Remove brake caliper and disc rotor.

2) Using a hammer and a chisel, loosen staked part of axle shaft nut. Remove nut and washer. Using companion flange remover/installer (09557-22022), remove axle flange from axle shaft.

NOTE: **When removing axle flange, be careful not to lose plate washer on tip of flange bearing side.**

3) Using rear axle shaft puller (09520-00031), remove axle shaft with oil seal and outside bearing. Using oil seal puller (09308-00010), remove inside oil seal and bearing.

4) Using a brass bar, drive inside and outside bearing outer races from axle housing. To remove bearing from axle shaft, drive a chisel between bearing and hub to provide working clearance.

5) Using bearing remover (09950-00020) and bearing remover attachment (09950-00030), remove outside bearing from axle shaft. Remove oil seal from axle shaft.

Fig. 1: Exploded View of Rear Suspension

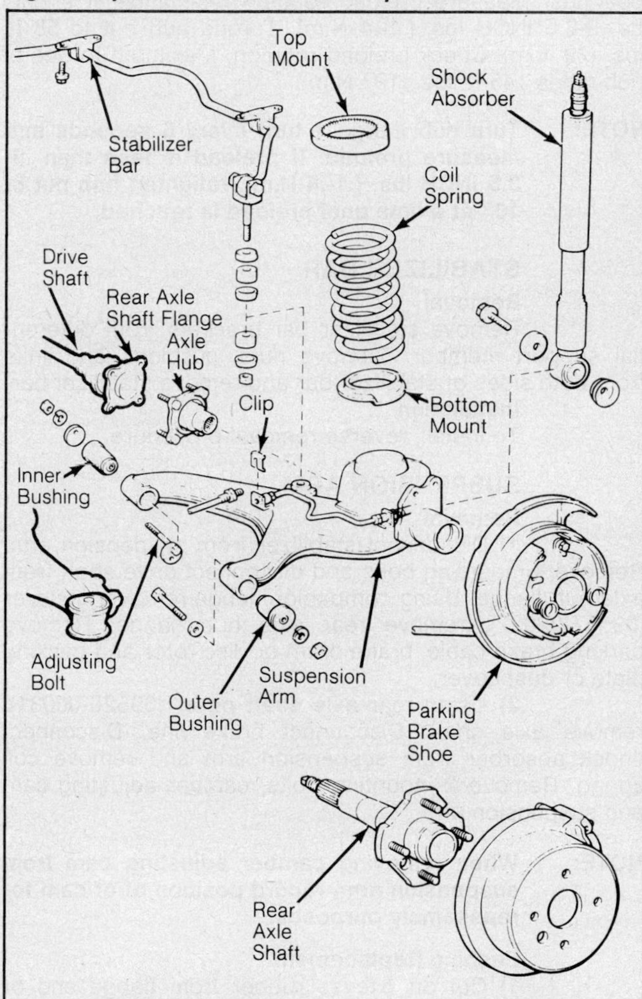
Top Mount
Shock Absorber
Stabilizer Bar
Coil Spring
Drive Shaft
Rear Axle Shaft Flange
Axle Hub
Clip
Bottom Mount
Inner Bushing
Adjusting Bolt
Suspension Arm
Outer Bushing
Parking Brake Shoe
Rear Axle Shaft

Inspection

Using a dial micrometer and 2 "V" blocks, check axle shaft runout. Maximum runout is .004" (.1 mm). Clean parts with solvent or compressed air.

Installation

1) Pack new bearings with grease. Using rear axle bearing and differential (09550-22010, No. 2 & 4), drive new inside bearing outer race into axle housing. Install inside bearing.

2) Using rear axle bearing and differential (09550-22010, No. 2 & 5), drive new inside oil seal to a depth of 1.22" (31 mm). Using rear axle bearing and

Rear Suspension

TOYOTA SUPRA (Cont.)

differential (09550-22010, No. 2 & 5), drive new outside bearing outer race into axle housing.

3) Pack inside of axle housing and new spacer with grease. Install spacer into axle housing. Install outside bearing. Using rear axle bearing and differential (09550-22010, No. 2 & 5), drive new oil seal to a depth of .236" (6 mm).

4) To complete installation, reverse removal procedures. Using companion flange remover/installer (09550-22022), Draw axle shaft into axle housing. Using rear axle shaft puller (09520-00031), torque new axle shaft nut to 22-36 ft. lbs. (30-49 N.m).

5) Rotate axle shaft back and forth to seat bearings. Measure preload rotation resistance, it should be .9-3.5 INCH lbs. (.1-.4 N.m). Torque hub nut to 58 ft. lbs. (79 N.m). Check preload rotation. Maximum torque of hub nut is 145 ft. lbs. (197 N.m).

NOTE: Turn hub flange 1 turn every 6 seconds and measure preload. If preload is less than .9-3.5 INCH lbs. (.1-.4 N.m), retighten hub nut 5-10° at a time until preload is reached.

STABILIZER BAR

Removal

Remove stabilizer bar brackets from differential support member. Remove nuts, cushions and links from both sides of stabilizer bar and remove stabilizer bar.

Installation

To install, reverse removal procedure.

SUSPENSION ARM

Removal

1) Disconnect stabilizer from suspension arm. Remove 4 mounting bolts and disconnect drive shaft from axle hub flange. Using companion flange remover/installer (09557-22022), remove rear axle hub flange. Remove parking brake cable, brake drum or disc rotor and backing plate or dust cover.

2) Using rear axle shaft puller (09520-00031), remove axle shaft. Disconnect brake line. Disconnect shock absorber from suspension arm and remove coil spring. Remove 2 mounting bolts, camber adjusting cam and suspension arm.

NOTE: When removing camber adjusting cam from suspension arm, record position of of cam for reassembly purposes.

Bushing Replacement

1) Cut off excess rubber from flange end of bushing. Using a hammer and a chisel, bend flange inward. Using a pair of pliers, bend and pull off flange tips.

2) Using rear suspension bushing (09710-22040, No. 4 & 5), press outer bushing from suspension arm. Using rear suspension bushing (09710-22040, N0. 5 & 6), press new bushings into suspension arm.

NOTE: DO NOT allow grease or oil to get on bushing.

Installation

Install camber adjusting cam to suspension arm and align to correct mark. To complete installation, reverse removal procedures (DO NOT torque fastners). Lower and bounce vehicle several times to align suspension. Torque fasteners. Check and adjust rear wheel alignment. Bleed brake system.

TIGHTENING SPECIFICATIONS

Application	Ft. Lbs. (N.m)
Drive Shaft-to-Axle Hub Flange	44-57 (60-77)
Shock Absorber-to-Body	14-22 (19-30)
Shock Absorber-to-Suspension Arm	22-32 (30-43)
Stabilizer Bar-to-Suspension Arm	11-15 (15-20)
Suspension Arm Inside Bushing	73-97 (99-132)
Suspension Arm Outside Bushing	84-108 (114-146)

VOLKSWAGEN JETTA, RABBIT & SCIROCCO

DESCRIPTION

Rear suspension is a link type with MacPherson type suspension struts. Suspension uses control arms and torsion beam for stabilization. Control arm and torsion beam are combined as one unit.

Shock absorbers are mounted inside suspension strut tubes, with coil springs surrounding the outside of the tube. Struts are attached to control arm at the bottom and to vehicle body at the top.

ADJUSTMENTS

WHEEL ALIGNMENT SPECIFICATIONS & PROCEDURES

See Wheel Alignment Specifications & Procedures in WHEEL ALIGNMENT section.

WHEEL BEARING

Tighten hub nut to 7.5 ft. lbs. (10 N.m), while rotating brake drum by hand. Determine the bearing play by testing the force needed to move thrust washer. Light pressure should move thrust washer. Turn hub nut until correct pressure is obtained.

REMOVAL & INSTALLATION

STRUT ASSEMBLY

Removal

1) With vehicle on floor. Take off plastic cap covering strut upper retaining nuts. Remove nuts.

2) Slowly raise vehicle until weight is off spring. Remove bolt retaining lower end of strut shock absorber to axle beam mount. Raise vehicle until strut can be removed.

Fig. 1: Exploded View of Rear Suspension Components

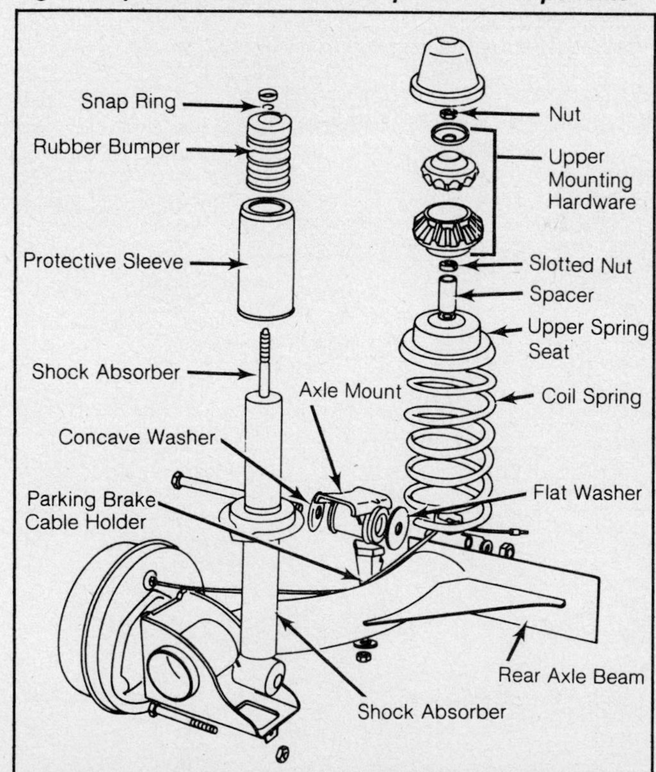

Snap Ring
Rubber Bumper
Protective Sleeve
Shock Absorber
Concave Washer
Parking Brake Cable Holder
Axle Mount
Nut
Upper Mounting Hardware
Slotted Nut
Spacer
Upper Spring Seat
Coil Spring
Flat Washer
Rear Axle Beam
Shock Absorber

Disassembly

Place strut assembly in vise. Hold piston rod and remove strut retaining nut. Take off components down to slotted nut. Remove slotted nut. Take off spacer and coil spring.

Inspection

Hand check shock absorbers for even resistance through entire piston stroke. Worn shock absorbers cannot be overhauled. If coil spring is being replaced, ensure that paint stripe color code on replacement spring matches original spring code.

Reassembly

1) Fit protective cap on shock absorber. Install rubber buffer, with small diameter end downward. Insert snap ring and washer.

2) Place spring into lower seat. Fit upper retainer with spacer sleeve. Tighten slotted nut retaining piston rod. Put on upper mounting hardware and tighten piston rod.

Installation

To install, reverse removal procedures.

SUSPENSION ASSEMBLY

Removal

1) With vehicle on floor. Disconnect upper strut mount. Raise vehicle and support with safety stands.

2) Disconnect parking brake at holder near axle mount. Disconnect and plug brake lines. Leave flex hose attached to suspension.

3) Separate brake pressure regulator spring from axle beam, (if equipped). Remove both nuts retaining axle beam on each side to body.

Installation

1) If axle beam mounting has been removed, use *Fig. 2* to correctly adjust mounting pad. If pad is not correctly aligned, torsional preload of mounting bushings will be incorrect.

2) Position rear suspension on body. Install nuts retaining axle beam to body. Raise wheel and guide upper end of strut into body mount.

3) Connect parking brake cables. Connect brake lines. Lower vehicle and tighten upper strut retaining nuts. Bleed brake system.

AXLE BEAM PIVOT BUSHING

Removal

1) This procedure is for replacing bushing with axle beam installed. Raise vehicle and support with safety stands under vehicle body.

2) With no pressure on beam, remove nuts retaining axle beam to body and tap out pivot bolt.

3) Press out bushing. Select new bushing and press bushing into place.

Installation

Loosely install mounting on axle beam. Concave washer and bolt head must face toward outside of vehicle. Bolt head must recess into washer. Align mount as shown in *Fig. 2*. Tighten pivot bolt nut. Lower Vehicle.

VOLKSWAGEN JETTA, RABBIT & SCIROCCO (Cont.)

Fig. 2: Correct Alignment of Axle Beam Mounting Pad

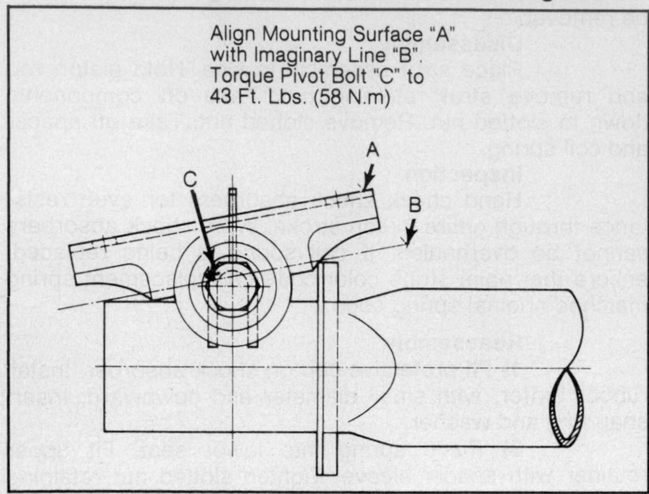
Align Mounting Surface "A" with Imaginary Line "B". Torque Pivot Bolt "C" to 43 Ft. Lbs. (58 N.m)
A
B
C

TIGHTENING SPECIFICATIONS

Application	Ft. Lbs. (N.m)
Coil Spring Retainer-to-Piston Rod	14 (19)
Rear Axle Beam-to-Mounting Pad	43 (58)
Rear Axle Mounting-to-Body	32 (44)
Shock Absorber-to-Axle Beam	32 (44)
Shock Absorber-to-Body	26 (35)
Shock Absorber Slot Nut	15 (20)

Rear Suspension

VOLKSWAGEN VANAGON

DESCRIPTION

Rear suspension is independent, coil spring type. Trailing arms mount in front to pivot brackets having provision for caster and toe-in adjustment.

Shock absorber mounts at top to chassis and at bottom to rear of trailing arm. Coil spring mounts to trailing arm and chassis in spring seats ahead of shock absorber. Drive shafts run through trailing arms and attach to inside of wheel hub.

ADJUSTMENT

WHEEL ALIGNMENT SPECIFICATIONS & PROCEDURES

See Wheel Alignment Specifications & Procedures in WHEEL ALIGNMENT section.

WHEEL BEARING

Wheel bearings require no adjustment.

REMOVAL & INSTALLATION

TRAILING ARMS

Removal

1) Raise vehicle and support with safety stands. Remove wheel assembly. Support trailing arm with a floor jack.

2) Remove nuts attaching brake drum and axle hub assembly to trailing arm. Using hex wrench, remove hex screws at axle shaft-to-transaxle joint.

3) Pull axle shaft and brake drum assembly through trailing arm and remove from vehicle. Remove shock absorber lower retaining bolt and slowly lower floor jack.

4) Remove coil spring and spring seats. Note relative position of trailing arm in mounting brackets. Remove pivot bolts. Remove trailing arm from vehicle.

Bushing Replacement

1) Using bushing remover (VW 442), adapter (30-14), and a threaded rod, pull bushing out of trailing arm. Coat washer with oil and place between nut and tool.

2) Coat hole in trailing arm, installer tool (3053), and bushing with soapy solution. Pull bushing in until sleeve contacts tool. Wait about 30 seconds before removing tool. Bushing should seat itself. If necessary, press edge of bushing out.

Installation

1) To install, reverse removal procedure. Depressions in spring seats must be aligned with ends of coil spring.

2) Align depression in lower spring seat with depression in trailing arm. Install trailing arm at noted position in bracket. Check wheel alignment.

Removal

Raise vehicle and support with safety stands. Support trailing arm with a floor jack. Remove shock absorber retaining bolts and shock absorber. Slowly lower floor jack. Remove coil spring and spring seats.

NOTE: **If only coil spring is to be removed, remove only one shock absorber mounting.**

Fig. 1: Exploded View of Rear Suspension

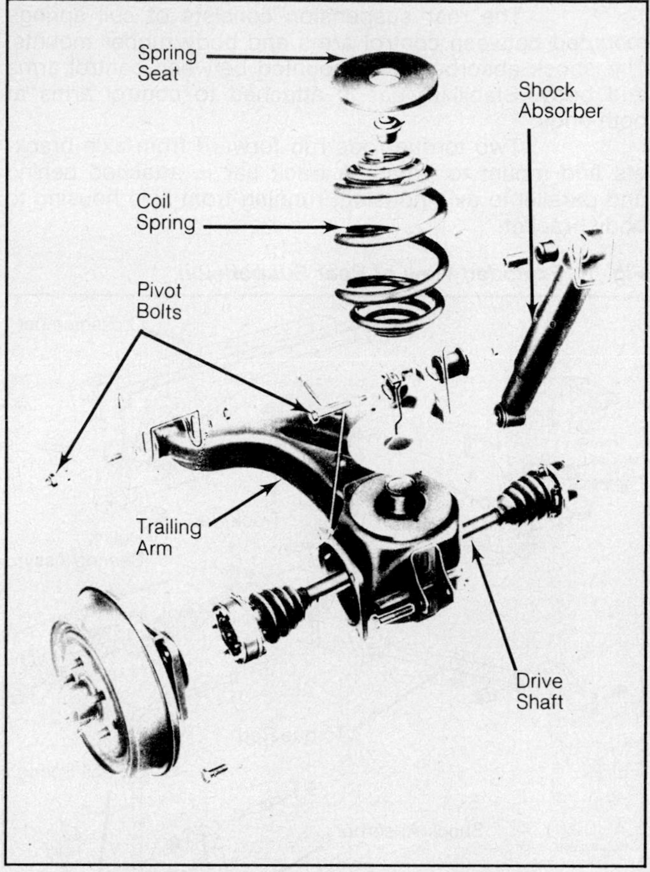

Spring Seat
Shock Absorber
Coil Spring
Pivot Bolts
Trailing Arm
Drive Shaft

Bushing Replacement

Press out bushings in shock absorber. File off any sharp edges on sleeve before installation. Coat parts with soapy solution. Press sleeve 1/2 way into bushing using vise. Using press, fully push bushing and sleeve into shock absorber.

Installation

To install reverse removal procedure. End of the coil spring must fit in spring seat depression. Depression in lower spring seat should fit into depression in trailing arm.

TIGHTENING SPECIFICATIONS

Application	Ft. Lbs. (N.m)
Drive Shaft Hex Screws	33 (45)
Hub Assembly-to-Trailing Arm	101 (137)
Lower Shock Absorber Retaining Bolt	65 (88)
Trailing Arm Pivot Bolts	76 (103)
Axle Nut	360 (488)

Rear Suspension

VOLVO DL, GL & TURBO

DESCRIPTION

The rear suspension consists of coil springs mounted between control arms and body rubber mounts. The shock absorbers are mounted between control arms and body. Stabilizer bar is attached to control arms at both ends.

Two torque rods run forward from axle brackets and mount to frame. A track bar is attached behind and parallel to axle housing, running from axle housing to body bracket.

Fig. 1: Exploded View of Rear Suspension

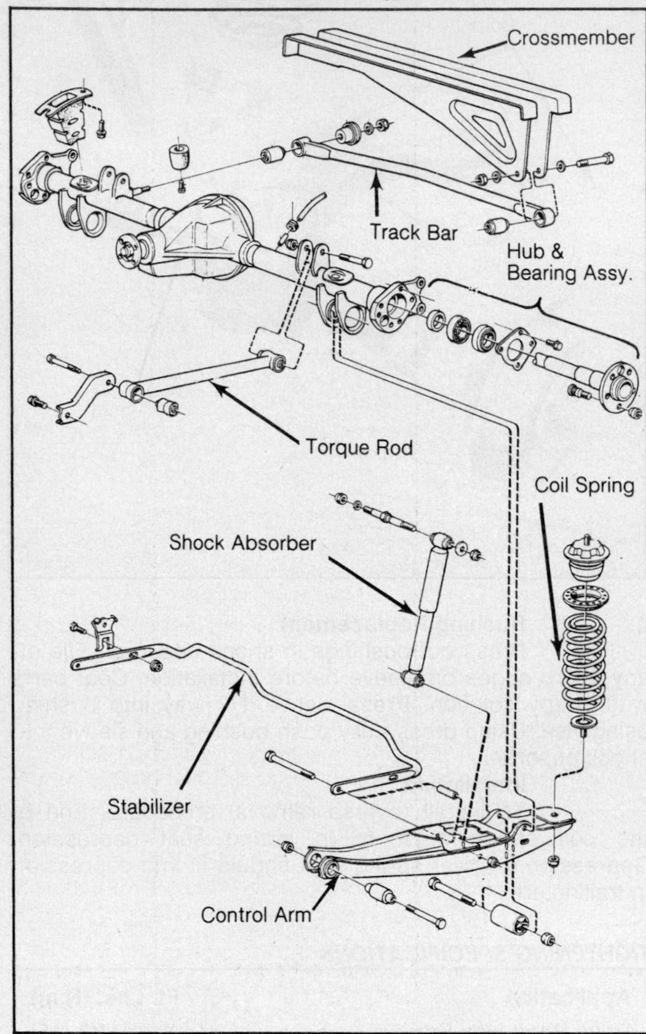
Crossmember
Track Bar
Hub &
Bearing Assy.
Torque Rod
Coil Spring
Shock Absorber
Stabilizer
Control Arm

REMOVAL & INSTALLATION

WHEEL BEARING

Removal

1) Raise vehicle and remove wheel. Remove collision guard from brake caliper. Remove brake tube (plug openings) from rear wheel brake caliper and suspend caliper out of way.

2) Remove 2 bolts holding brake caliper to axle housing and remove brake caliper. Remove brake disc. Using brake spring pliers, unhook and remove parking brake springs.

3) Using a .12" (3 mm) punch, drive out lock pin holding parking brake cable to lever. Disconnect parking brake cable from lever. Remove 4 bolts holding rear axle shaft bearing retainer and 2 brake shoe retaining springs to axle housing.

4) Using a slide hammer puller and axle shaft attachment (2709), pull axle shaft from axle housing. Using a slide hammer puller and oil seal attachment (2337), pull oil seal from axle housing.

5) Place axle shaft in rear axle shaft bearing remover/installer (2838), position tool between bearing and seal. Press bearing and bearing retainer from axle shaft (discard bearing retainer). Clean parts with solvent and/or compressed air.

Installation

1) Using oil seal adapter (5009) and oil seal driver (1801), drive new oil seal into axle housing. Using rear axle shaft bearing remover/installer (2838) and bearing adapter (5010), press new bearing and bearing retainer onto axle shaft.

2) Install axle shaft to axle housing. Install 2 brake shoe retaining springs and 4 bolts to axle shaft bearing retainer. Torque bearing retainer bolts. To complete installation, reverse removal procedures.

COIL SPRING

Removal

1) Raise vehicle and support with safety stands. Remove wheel assembly. Place floor jack under rear axle housing and raise axle until spring compresses. Using spring compressor (5040), compress spring until shock absorber can be detached.

2) Disconnect lower end of shock absorber. Remove spring lower retaining nut. Lower floor jack and remove coil spring.

Installation

To install, reverse removal procedures. Make sure rubber spring support is in correct position.

SHOCK ABSORBER

Removal

Raise vehicle and support with safety stands. Remove wheel assembly. Use floor jack to raise rear axle. Using spring compressor (5040), compress spring until shock absorber can be detached. Remove upper and lower shock absorber retaining nuts. Remove shock absorber.

Installation

To install, reverse removal procedures. Make sure spacer sleeve is in correct position.

CONTROL ARM

Removal

1) Raise vehicle and support with safety stands. Position floor jack under axle and raise until spring compresses. Using spring compressor (5040), compress spring until shock absorber can be detached.

2) Disconnect shock absorber from control arm. Remove coil spring lower retaining nut. Remove coil spring. Remove control arm retaining bolts. Remove control arm.

Installation

1) Install retaining bolts at front and rear end of control arm (DO NOT torque). Install coil spring and lower plate retaining nut.

2) Raise axle while guiding coil spring into position. Attach shock absorber lower mount. Lower vehicle to floor and tighten control arm bolts.

VOLVO DL, GL & TURBO (Cont.)

STABILIZER BAR

Removal

Raise vehicle and support with safety stands, under vehicle body. With a floor jack, raise axle to take load off shock absorbers. Disconnect stabilizer bar mounts and remove stabilizer bar from vehicle.

Installation

Install stabilizer bar in position on brackets (DO NOT torque fasteners). Install lower end of shock absorber. Position stabilizer bar so it settles in bracket. Torque fasteners.

TORQUE RODS & TRACK BAR

Removal

Raise vehicle and support with safety stands. Disconnect track bar and torque rods from body and axle mountings. Inspect bushings and sleeves for wear or damage, replace if necessary.

Installation

To install, reverse removal procedures.

TIGHTENING SPECIFICATIONS

Application	Ft. Lbs. (N.m)
Bearing Retainer-to-Axle Housing	22-36 (30-49)
Control Arm-to-Body	80 (110)
Coil Spring-to-Body	32 (43)
Coil Spring-to-Control Arm	14 (19)
Control Arm-to-Rear Axle	90 (125)
Shock Absorber Bolts	62 (84)
Stabilizer Bar	
M10 Bolts	33 (45)
M12 Bolts	62 (84)
Torque Rod Bolts	62 (84)
Track Bar-to-Axle	44 (60)
Track Bar-to-Body	62 (84)
Wheel Nuts	85 (115)

Rear Suspension

VOLVO 760 GLE

DESCRIPTION

The "Constant Track" rear suspension consists of coil springs, self-leveling gas-filled shocks, and a live axle located by longitudinal control arms. A stabilizer bar is attached to both trailing arms. Also, a pair of trailing torque rods connect the differential to a subframe.

Fig. 1: Exploded View of 760 GLE Rear Suspension

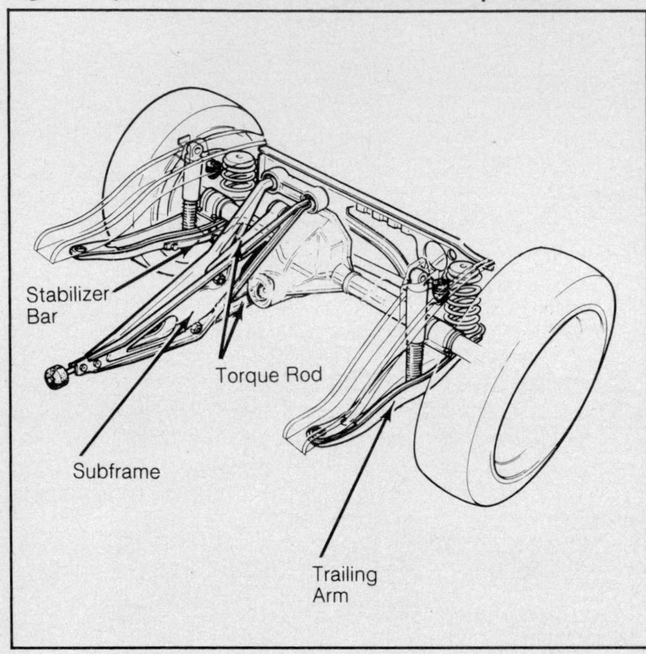
Stabilizer Bar
Torque Rod
Subframe
Trailing Arm

REMOVAL & INSTALLATION

COIL SPRINGS

Removal & Installation

1) Raise and support vehicle. Remove rear wheels. Remove disc brake calipers and place aside. Do not disconnect brake lines.

2) Disconnect drive shaft from differential. Place jack stands under coil spring ends of trailing arms. Remove stabilizer bar bolts from trailing arms. Remove shock absorber.

3) Lower rear axle to unload springs. Remove coil springs. To install, reverse removal procedure.

TRAILING ARMS & BUSHINGS

Removal

Remove coil spring as previously described. Remove rear trailing arm bracket and support rubbers. Remove front trailing arm bracket and lift out trailing arm. Press front bushings out of trailing arms.

Installation

1) Press new bushings in trailing arms with bushing tapered hole facing up. Bushing must be evenly spaced in trailing arm. Attach front of trailing arms and brackets. Do not tighten nuts yet.

2) Place rubber supports on rear axle. Smear ends with petroleum jelly. Guide spring into position on trailing arm. Lift up trailing arm and install shock absorber and stabilizer bar. Do not tighten nuts.

3) Install rear trailing arm bracket and rubber support. Tighten nuts to specifications. Tighten stabilizer bar and lower shock bolt to specification. Tighten front trailing arm bracket to specification. Continue installation in reverse of removal procedure.

TORQUE RODS & BUSHINGS

Removal

Raise and support vehicle. Remove torque rod(s). Press out front and rear support bushings.

Installation

1) Smear edges of rod with petroleum jelly and press in new bushings. Install torque rods with longer rod in lower position. Attach rear end 1st. Do not tighten bolts yet.

2) Install front end of torque rod. It may be necessary to remove subframe front mount to install front end of torque rod. Tighten front end of torque rod to specification. Tighten subframe front mount and rear of torque rod to specifications.

SUBFRAME BUSHINGS

Remove

1) Raise and support vehicle. Remove front subframe mount bolts and pry out mount. Tap out front bracket with a hammer and drift. Remove torque rod front retaining bolts, cross link, and parking brake cable clamp.

2) Insert a bolt in front mount. Pull outsub frame by placing a "C" clamp on chassis member and behind bolt. Tighten clamp and pull out subframe from rear bushsings.

3) Remove rear mounting bracket from body. Press bushings from rear mounting bracket.

Installation

1) Coat edges of rear mount bushings with petroleum jelly. Press bushings in rear mount bracket. Install rear mount bracket. Install rear of subframe in mount.

2) Install front end of torque rods and cross link. Do not tighten bolts yet. Install new bushing on front mount. Install front mount in vehicle with beveled edges vertical.

3) Tighten front mounting bracket bolts to specification. Tighten front end of torque rod to specification.

TIGHTENING SPECIFICATIONS

Application	Ft. Lbs. (N.m)
Front Trailing Arm Bracket	
Bolt	35 (48)
Nut	63 (85)
Shock Bolts	63 (85)
Stabilizer Bar-to-Trailing Arm	35 (48)
Subframe Front Mount Bolts	63 (85)
Torque Rod Bolts	103 (140)
Trailing Arm Rear Bracket	33 (45)

Automatic Level Control

MERCEDES-BENZ 300TD

DESCRIPTION

The 300TD rear suspension uses an automatic leveling system. The system contains a hydraulic pump, reservoir, leveling valve, pressure reservoir and special combination shock absorber/suspension struts.

The leveling valve lever, which is connected to the torsion bar, has 3 position: neutral, filling and return flow.This positioning of the leveling valve lever, due to the load in vehicle, controls amount of fluid in the special shock absorber which raises or lowers rear of vehicle to maintain a level attitude.

OPERATION

As rear of vehicle is lowered due to added weight, the leveling valve lever raises to the filling position. This allows fluid to flow from pump to pressure reservoir then to special shock absorber, through check valves.

This added fluid will raise the rear of the vehicle until the leveling valve lever is moved back to the neutral position. When the added weight is removed, rear of vehicle raises which moves the leveling lever to the return flow position.

This allows the fluid in the special shock absorber to drain back into the reservoir until the leveling lever is back in the neutral position and the vehicle is level.

TESTING

HYDRAULIC OIL PUMP & LEVELING VALVE

NOTE: **These tests can only be performed on a ready-to-drive vehicle. Check leveling valve for leaks during test. In case of leaks on valve housing parting surface, install new "O" ring.**

1) Make sure that hydraulic oil is cold before starting test. Disconnect connecting bar at leveling valve lever. Tighten leveling valve housing screws.

CAUTION: **Do not loosen clamping screw retaining lever on valve control shaft.**

2) Attach an oil drain line to bleed screw and release pressure in system by opening bleed screw. Remove bleed screw and attach pressure tester (126 589 02 21 00) directly to leveling valve via 3 or 4-way distribution fitting.

3) Push leveling valve lever up into filling position. Run engine at idle (800-1000 RPM) for a short time and observe pressure reading on tester. Pressure should read 1885 psi (132.5 kg/cm²) minimum.

NOTE: **Perform this test quickly to avoid damage to components.**

4) Turn off engine. Move leveling valve lever down to return flow position and observe base pressure reading. After a stabilization period of 5 minutes, repeat test procedure. Leave pressure tester connected at least 4 hours and observe.

NOTE: **Base pressure must not drop after the stabilization period. This also applies to extended periods, such as overnight.**

5) Bleed base pressure at bleed screw, disconnect tester and install bleed screw. Fill level control system by running engine at medium RPM's and pushing leveling valve lever up into filling position for approximately 30 seconds.

6) Turn off engine. Reconnect connecting bar at leveling valve lever. Check reservoir oil level. Oil level should be between "Max." and "Min." for unloaded vehicle, "Min." for loaded vehicle.

Fig. 1: Mercedes-Benz 300TD Level Control Rear Suspension System

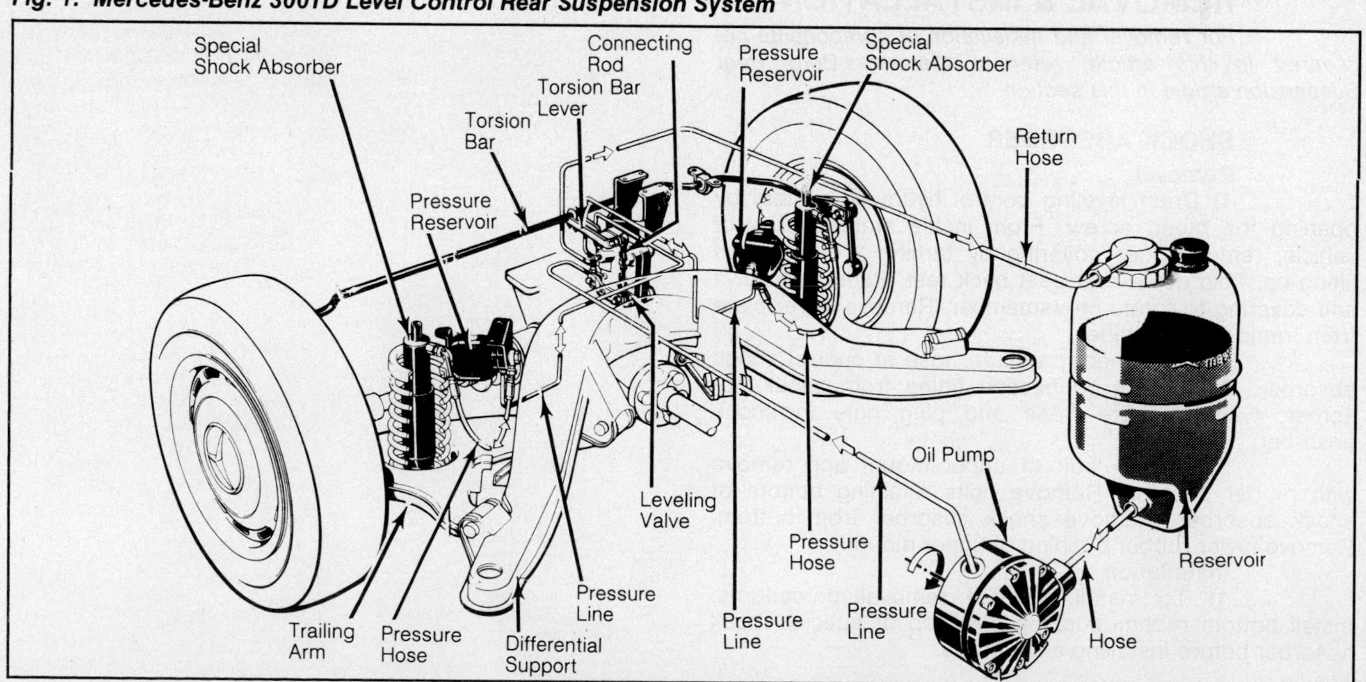
Special Shock Absorber
Connecting Rod
Torsion Bar Lever
Torsion Bar
Pressure Reservoir
Pressure Reservoir
Special Shock Absorber
Return Hose
Oil Pump
Leveling Valve
Pressure Hose
Reservoir
Pressure Line
Trailing Arm
Pressure Hose
Differential Support
Pressure Line
Pressure Line
Hose

Automatic Level Control

MERCEDES-BENZ 300TD (Cont.)

PRESSURE RESERVOIR

NOTE: This test can be performed only on a ready-to-drive vehicle.

1) Disconnect connecting bar at leveling valve. Push leveling valve lever down to return flow position. Release pressure in system by opening bleed screw, and remove bleed screw.

2) Connect pressure tester to leveling valve. Disconnect pressure line from leveling valve to pressure reservoir and from leveling valve to left and right pressure reservoirs (near special shock absorbers).

3) Plug lines with couplings and bleed screws. Attach pressure hose from gauge to either right or left pressure reservoir.

4) Push leveling valve lever down to return flow position. Run engine at idle speed. Push leveling valve lever up to filling position and observe pressure gauge.

5) Gas pressure in reservoir is indicated at point where pressure gauge needle changes from indication of a gradual pressure increase to an indication of rapid increase. This increase is caused when oil pressure exceeds gas pressure.

6) Gas pressure should be 304-363 psi (21.4-25.5 kg/cm²) for new pressure reservoirs, and a minimum of 217 psi (15.2 kg/cm²) for used pressure reservoirs. Repeat this test for the other reservoir.

7) Disconnect pressure tester, install bleed screw and reconnect pressure lines to pressure reservoirs. Run engine at medium RPM and push leveling valve lever up to filling position for approximately 30 seconds to fill control system.

8) Turn off engine. Reconnect connecting bar at leveling valve lever. With engine off, check oil reservoir oil level. Oil level should be between "Max." and "Min." for unloaded vehicle, "Min." for loaded vehicle.

REMOVAL & INSTALLATION

For removal and installation of components not covered in this article, refer to Mercedes-Benz Rear Suspension article in this section.

SHOCK ABSORBER

Removal

1) Drain leveling control hydraulic system by opening the bleed screw. From inside storage area of vehicle, remove floor covering by turning "T" lever and lifting up. Fold down rear seat back rest. Remove screws and covering to frame crossmember. Remove cover plate from frame crossmember.

2) Disconnect pressure hose at special shock absorber. Disconnect connection fitting from shock absorber. Cap pressure hose and plug hole in shock absorber.

3) Loosen bolt of upper mount and remove with rubber bushing. Remove bolts retaining bottom of shock absorber. Remove shock absorber from bottom. Remove lower rubber bushing of upper mount.

Installation

1) To install, reverse removal procedures. Install bottom rubber bushing onto top of special shock absorber before installing into vehicle.

2) Plugged hole in shock absorber must point toward frame crossmember and mounting pin must protrude through bore in frame crossmember.

3) Make sure all bolts and fittings are tight and reservoir is full. Fill leveling valve by starting engine and moving leveling lever up to filling position. Check leveling suspension system for proper operation.

TIGHTENING SPECIFICATIONS

Application	Ft. Lbs. (N.m)
Ball Joint-to-Spring Strut	48 (65)
Fitting at Pressure Reservoir	32 (44)
Lower Retaining Bolt	33 (45)
Pressure Hose-to-Shock Absorber Fitting	25 (34)
Shock Absorber Fitting-to-Shock Absorber	15 (20)
Spherical Mount on Shock Absorber	48 (65)
Upper Retaining Bolt	22 (30)

SECTION 12

STEERING

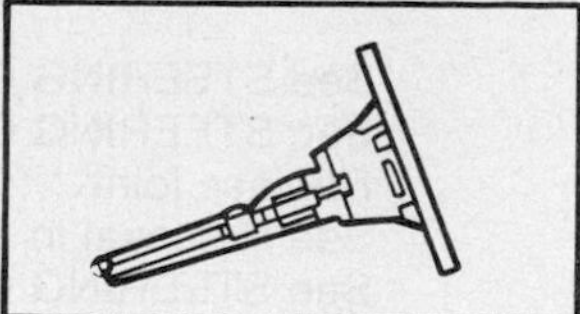

CONTENTS

TROUBLE SHOOTING

STEERING WHEEL & COLUMN SWITCHES

STEERING COLUMNS

STEERING GEARS & LINKAGE

POWER STEERING

NOTE: **ALSO SEE GENERAL INDEX.**

Steering

STANDARD STEERING COLUMN TROUBLE SHOOTING

CONDITION	POSSIBLE CAUSE	CORRECTION
Noise in Column	Coupling pulled apart	See STEERING COLUMNS
	Column not correctly aligned	See STEERING COLUMNS
	Broken lower joint	Replace joint
	Horn contact ring not lubricated	See Removal in STEERING WHEEL
	Bearings not lubricated	See STEERING COLUMNS
	Bearing worn or broken	Replace bearing and lubricate
	Shaft snap ring not properly seated	Reseat or replace snap ring
	Plastic spherical joint not lubricated	See STEERING COLUMNS
	Shroud or housing loose	Tighten holding screws
	Lock plate retaining ring not seated	See STEERING COLUMNS
	Loose sight shield	Tighten holding screws
High Steering Shaft Effort	Column assembly misaligned	See STEERING COLUMNS
	Improperly installed dust shield	Adjust or replace
	Damaged upper or lower bearing	Replace bearings
	Tight steering universal joint	See STEERING COLUMNS
High Shift Effort	Column is out of alignment	See STEERING COLUMNS
	Improperly installed dust shield	Adjust or replace
	Seals or bearings not lubricated	See STEERING COLUMNS
	Ignition switch screws too long	Replace with new shorter screws
	Neutral switch screws too long	Replace with new shorter screws
	Mounting bracket screws too long	Replace with new shorter screws
	Burrs on shift tube	Remove burrs or replace tube
	Lower bowl bearing assembled wrong	See STEERING COLUMNS
	Shift tube bent or broken	Replace as necessary
	Improper adjustment of shift levers	See STEERING COLUMNS
Improper Trans. Shifting	Sheared shift tube joint	Replace as necessary
	Sheared lower shaft lever weld joint	Replace as necessary
	Improper shift lever adjustment	See STEERING COLUMNS
	Improper gate plate adjustment	See STEERING COLUMNS
Excess Play in Column	Instrument panel bracket bolts loose	Tighten bolts and check bracket
	Broken weld nut on jacket	See STEERING COLUMNS
	Instrument bracket capsule sheared	See STEERING COLUMNS
	Column bracket/jacket bolts loose	Tighten bolts and check bracket
Steering Locks in Gear	Release lever mechanism damaged	See STEERING COLUMNS

TILT STEERING COLUMN TROUBLE SHOOTING

CONDITION	POSSIBLE CAUSE	CORRECTION
Steering Wheel Loose	Excess clearance in support	Check and replace if necessary
	Excess clearance in housing/pivot pin	Check and replace if necessary
	Damaged anti-lash spring in spheres	See TILT STEERING COLUMNS
	Upper bearing not seated properly	See TILT STEERING COLUMNS
	Upper bearing inner race seal missing	Replace if necessary
	Improperly adjusted tilt/telescopic lock	See adjustment in STEERING COLUMNS
	Loose support screws	Tighten and check bracket
	Bearing preload spring missing/broken	Replace spring
	Housing loose on jacket	Tighten and/or replace screws
Play in Column Mount	Loose support screws	Tighten and check bracket
	Loose shoes in housing	See TILT STEERING COLUMNS
	Loose tilt head pivot pins	See TILT STEERING COLUMNS
	Loose shoe lock pin in support	See TILT STEERING COLUMNS
Housing Scraping on Bowl	Bowl bent or out of round	See STEERING WHEEL removal
Wheel Will Not Lock	Shoe seized on its pivot pin	See TILT STEERING COLUMNS
	Shoe may have burrs/dirt in them	Clean or replace
	Shoe lock spring weak/broken	Replace if necessary

TILT STEERING COLUMN TROUBLE SHOOTING (Cont.)

CONDITION	POSSIBLE CAUSE	CORRECTION
Wheel Fails to Return	Pivot pins are bound up	Clean or replace
	Wheel tilt spring is damaged	See TILT STEERING COLUMNS
	Turn signal switch wires too tight	Loosen and check operation
Noise When Tilting	Upper tilt bumpers worn	Replace if necessary
	Tilt spring rubbing in housing	Adjust and check operation
Hard Steering	Incorrect tire pressure	Inflate to proper pressure
	Lack of lubricant in steering linkage	Service Steering, Suspension and Linkage
	Improper front end alignment	See WHEEL ALIGNMENT
	Improper steering gear adjustment	See STEERING

MANUAL STEERING GEAR TROUBLE SHOOTING

CONDITION	POSSIBLE CAUSE	CORRECTION
Rattle or Chucking Noise in Rack and Pinion	Rack and pinion mounting bracket loose	Tighten all mounting bolts
	Lack of/or incorrect lubricant	See RACK & PINION STEERING
	Pitman arm loose on shaft	See STEERING
	Steering gear mounting bolts loose	Tighten all mounting bolts
Excessive Play	Front wheel bearing improperly adjusted	See FRONT SUSPENSION
	Loose or worn steering linkage	See STEERING LINKAGE
	Loose or worn ball joints	See FRONT SUSPENSION
	Loose or worn steering gear shaft	See STEERING
	Steering arm loose on gear shaft	See STEERING
	Incorrect front wheel alignment	See WHEEL ALIGNMENT
	Steering gear housing bolts loose	Tighten all mounting bolts
	Steering gear adjustment too loose	See adjustment in STEERING
	Steering arms loose on knuckles	Tighten and check steering linkage
	Rack and pinion mounting loose	Tighten all mounting bolts
	Rack and pinion out of adjustment	See adjustment in STEERING
	Tie rod end loose	Tighten and check steering linkage
	Steering wheel loose	See STEERING
	Excessive Pitman shaft-to-ball nut lash	See STEERING
Poor Returnability	Lack of lubricant in ball joint or linkage	Lubricate and service systems
	Binding in linkage or ball joints	See STEERING LINKAGE and SUSPENSION
	Improper front end alignment	See WHEEL ALIGNMENT
	Improper steering gear adjustment	See STEERING
	Improper tire pressure	Inflate to proper pressure
Excessive Vertical Motion	Improper tire pressure	Inflate to proper pressure
	Tires, wheels or rotors out of balance	Balance tires then check wheels and rotors
	Worn or faulty shock absorbers	Check and replace if necessary
	Loose tie rod ends or steering	Tighten or replace if necessary
	Improper wheel alignment	See WHEEL ALIGNMENT
	Loose or worn wheel bearings	See SUSPENSION
Steering Pulls to One Side	Improper tire pressure	Inflate to proper pressure
	Mismatched front tires	Rotate or replace if necessary
	Wheel bearings not adjusted properly	See FRONT SUSPENSION
	Bent or broken suspension components	See FRONT SUSPENSION
	Improper wheel alignment	See WHEEL ALIGNMENT
	Brakes dragging	See BRAKES
Instability	Low or uneven tire pressure	Inflate to proper pressure
	Loose or worn wheel bearings	See FRONT SUSPENSION
	Loose or worn idler arm bushing	See FRONT SUSPENSION
	Loose or worn strut bushings	See FRONT SUSPENSION
	Incorrect front wheel alignment	See WHEEL ALIGNMENT
	Steering gear not centered	See STEERING
	Springs or shock absorbers inoperative	Check and replace if necessary
	Improper cross shaft	See STEERING

Steering

POWER STEERING TROUBLE SHOOTING

CONDITION	POSSIBLE CAUSE	CORRECTION
Rattle or Chucking Noise in Steering	Pressure hoses touching engine parts	Adjust to proper clearance
	Loose Pitman shaft	Adjust or replace if necessary
	Tie rods ends or Pitman arm loose	Tighten and check system
	Rack and pinion mounts loose	Tighten all mounting bolts
	Free play in worm and piston assembly	See STEERING
	Loose sector shaft or thrust bearing adjustment	See STEERING
	Free play in pot coupling	See STEERING
	Worn shaft serrations	See STEERING
Growl in Steering Pump	Excessive pressure in hoses	Restriction in hoses see POWER STEERING
	Scored pressure plates	See POWER STEERING
	Scored thrust plates or rotor	See POWER STEERING
	Extreme wear of cam ring	See POWER STEERING
Rattle in Steering Pump	Vanes not installed properly	See POWER STEERING PUMPS
	Vanes sticking in rotor slots	See POWER STEERING PUMPS
Swish Noise in Pump	Defective flow control valve	See POWER STEERING PUMPS
Groan in Steering Pump	Air in fluid	See POWER STEERING PUMPS
	Poor pressure hose connection	Tighten and check, replace if necessary
Squawk When Turning	Damper "O" ring on valve spool cut	See POWER STEERING PUMPS
Moan or Whine in Pump	Pump shaft bearing scored	Replace bearing and fluid
	Air in fluid or fluid level low	See POWER STEERING PUMPS
	Hose or column grounded	Check and replace if necessary
	Cover "O" ring missing or damaged	See POWER STEERING PUMPS
	Valve cover baffle missing or damaged	See POWER STEERING PUMPS
	Interference of components in pump	See POWER STEERING PUMPS
	Loose or poor bracket alignment	Correct or replace if necessary
Hissing When Parking	Internal leakage in steering gear	Check valve assembly first
Chirp in Steering Pump	Loose or worn power steering belt	Adjust or replace if neceesary
Buzzing When Not Steering	Noisy pump	See POWER STEERING PUMPS
	Free play in steering shaft bearing	See STEERING
	Bearing loose on shaft serrations	See STEERING
Clicking Noise in Pump	Pump slippers too long	See POWER STEERING PUMPS
	Broken slipper springs	See POWER STEERING PUMPS
	Excessive wear or nicked rotors	See POWER STEERING PUMPS
	Damaged cam contour	See POWER STEERING PUMPS
Poor Return of Wheel	Wheel rubbing against turn signal	See STEERING WHEEL SWITCHES
	Flange rubbing steering gear adjuster	See STEERING
	Tight or frozen steering shaft bearing	See STEERING
	Steering Gear out of adjustment	See Adjustment in STEERING
	Sticking or plugged spool valve	See POWER STEERING PUMPS
	Improper front end alignment	See WHEEL ALIGNMENT
	Wheel bearings worn or loose	See FRONT SUSPENSION
	Ties rods or ball joints binding	Check and replace if necessary
	Intermediate shaft joints binding	See STEERING
	Kinked pressure hoses	Correct or replace if necessary
	Loose housing head spanner nut	See POWER STEERING
	Damaged valve lever	See POWER STEERING
	Sector shaft adjusted too tight	See adjustment in POWER STEERING
	Worm thrust bearing adjusted too tight	See adjustment in POWER STEERING
	Reaction ring sticking in cylinder	See POWER STEERING
	Reaction ring sticking in housing head	See POWER STEERING
	Steering pump internal leakage	See POWER STEERING PUMPS
	Steering gear-to-column misalignment	See STEERING COLUMNS
	Lack of lubrication in linkage	Service front suspension
	Lack of lubrication in ball joints	Service front suspension

POWER STEERING TROUBLE SHOOTING (Cont.)

CONDITION	POSSIBLE CAUSE	CORRECTION
Increased Effort When Turning Wheel Fast Foaming, Milky Power Steering Fluid, Low Fluid Level or Low Pressure	High internal pump leakage	See POWER STEERING PUMPS
	Power steering pump belt slipping	Adjust or replace if necessary
	Low fluid level	Check and fill to proper level
	Engine idle speed to low	Adjust to correct setting
	Air in pump fluid system	See POWER STEERING PUMPS
	Pump output low	See POWER STEERING PUMPS
	Steering gear malfunctioning	See STEERING
Wheel Surges or Jerks	Low fluid level	Check and fill to proper level
	Loose fan belt	Adjust or replace if necessary
	Insufficient pump pressure	See POWER STEERING PUMPS
	Sticky flow control valve	See POWER STEERING PUMPS
	Linkage hitting oil pan at full turn	See STEERING LINKAGE
Kick Back or Free Play	Air in pump fluid system	See POWER STEERING PUMPS
	Worn poppet valve in steering gear	See POWER STEERING
	Excessive over center lash	See POWER STEERING
	Thrust bearing out of adjustment	See POWER STEERING
	Free play in pot coupling	See POWER STEERING PUMPS
	Steering gear coupling loose on shaft	See POWER STEERING PUMPS
	Steering disc mounting bolts loose	Tighten or replace if necessary
	Coupling loose on worm shaft	Tighten or replace if necessary
	Improper sector shaft adjustment	See POWER STEERING
	Excessive worm piston side play	See POWER STEERING
	Damaged valve lever	See POWER STEERING
	Universal joint loose	Tighten or replace if necessary
	Defective rotary valve	See POWER STEERING
No Power When Parking	Sticking flow control valve	See POWER STEERING PUMPS
	Insufficient pump pressure output	See POWER STEERING PUMPS
	Excessive internal pump leakage	See POWER STEERING PUMPS
	Excessive internal gear leakage	See POWER STEERING PUMPS
	Flange rubs against gear adjust plug	See STEERING COLUMN
	Loose pump belt	Adjust or replace if necessary
	Low fluid level	Check and add proper amount of fluid
	Engine idle too low	Adjust to correct setting
	Steering gear-to-column misaligned	See STEERING
No Power Left Turns	Left turn reaction seal "O" ring worn	See POWER STEERING
	Left turn reaction seal damaged/missing	See POWER STEERING
	Cylinder head "O" ring damaged	See POWER STEERING PUMPS
No Power Right Turns	Column pot coupling bottomed	See STEERING
	Right turn reaction seal "O" ring worn	See POWER STEERING
	Right turn reaction seal damaged	See POWER STEERING
	Internal leakage through piston end plug	See STEERING
	Internal leakage through side plugs	See STEERING
Lack of Effort in Turning	Left and/or right reaction seal worn	Replace, see POWER STEERING
	Left and/or right reaction oil passageway not drilled	Check housing and cylinder head
	Left and/or right reaction seal sticking in cylinder head	See POWER STEERING
Wanders to One Side	Front end alignment incorrect	See WHEEL ALIGNMENT
	Unbalanced steering gear valve	See STEERING
Low Pressure Due to Steering Pump	Flow control valve stuck or inoperative	See POWER STEERING
	Pressure plate not flat against cam ring	See POWER STEERING PUMPS
	Extreme wear of cam ring	Replace and check adjustments
	Scored plate, thrust plate or rotor	See POWER STEERING PUMPS
	Vanes not installed properly	See POWER STEERING PUMPS
	Vanes sticking in rotor slots	See POWER STEERING PUMPS
	Cracked/broken thrust or pressure plate	See POWER STEERING PUMPS

AUDI

REMOVAL & INSTALLATION

STEERING WHEEL & HORN

Removal

Disconnect battery ground cable. Using hand pressure, pull off steering wheel center pad. Make sure horn leads (carbon brushes) slide out of recess in steering wheel on 5000 models. Remove steering wheel nut. Using wheel puller, remove steering wheel.

Installation

To install, reverse removal procedure.

TURN SIGNAL, DIMMER & WIPER/WASHER

Removal (4000)

Disconnect battery ground cable. Remove steering wheel. Unscrew 3 steering column switch housing screws. Pull housing off column tube. Disconnect electrical wires from switch housing. Remove mounting screws and switches.

Installation

To install, reverse removal procedure.

TURN SIGNAL, DIMMER, HAZARD & WIPER/WASHER

Removal (5000)

Disconnect battery ground cable. Remove steering wheel. Working through hole in bottom of column shroud, release mounting and take off shroud. Disconnect electrical wire connectors. Remove switch mounting screws. Lift out switches.

Installation

To install, reverse removal procedure.

STEERING COLUMN LOCK

Removal (Power Steering)

Remove column cover and switches. Remove lock washer and contact ring. With key in ignition, remove bolt and lock assembly.

Fig. 1: Audi 5000 Steering Wheel Assembly

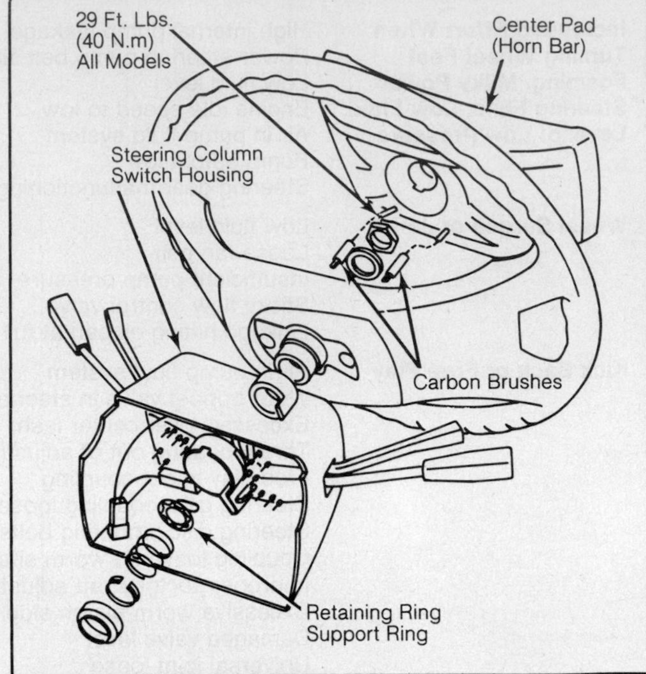
29 Ft. Lbs.
(40 N.m)
All Models
Center Pad
(Horn Bar)
Steering Column
Switch Housing
Carbon Brushes
Retaining Ring
Support Ring

Audi 4000 models are similar.

Installation

To install, reverse removal procedure.

Removal (All Others)

Remove column cover. Disconnect electrical wires from back of ignition switch. With key in ignition, drill out shear bolts. Remove lock from column.

Installation

Make sure lugs on steering lock engage column tube. Tighen mounting bolts until heads shear off. To complete installation, reverse removal procedure.

BMW

REMOVAL & INSTALLATION

STEERING WHEEL

Removal

Disconnect battery ground cable. Place wheels in straight-ahead position. Pry steering wheel cover off to expose wheel mounting nut. Index mark wheel and main shaft. Remove mounting nut. Pull off steering wheel.

Installation

To install, reverse removal procedure. Align reference marks made during removal.

HORN CONTROLS

Removal

Using small screwdriver, carefully pry off horn button. Remove contact spring. Remove 2 slip ring mounting screws and slide slip ring off steering wheel.

Installation

To install, reverse removal procedure. Ensure slip ring engages recessed contact point. Ensure contact pins of contact ring face down.

Fig. 1: Slip Ring Mounting Screw Removal

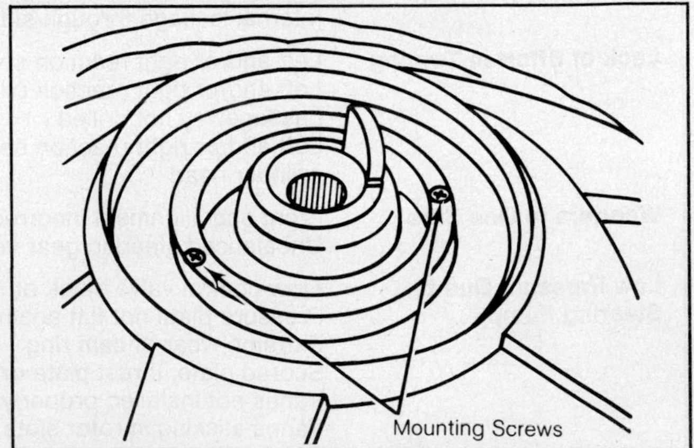
Mounting Screws

BMW (Cont.)

TURN SIGNAL, DIMMER SWITCH & WIPER/WASHER

Removal

1) Disconnect battery ground cable. Loosen bottom center instrument panel trim. Remove 3 mounting screws and pull down lower shroud. Remove steering wheel as previously outlined.

2) Separate wiring from switch plate. Remove switch mounting screws. Slide off switches with harness.

Installation

To install, reverse removal procedure and note: Ensure steering wheel aligns with reference marks. Center turn signal assembly. Finger on canceling cam must face toward center. Distance between switch and finger should be about .118" (3 mm). *See Fig. 2.*

Fig. 2: Canceling Cam and Finger Alignment

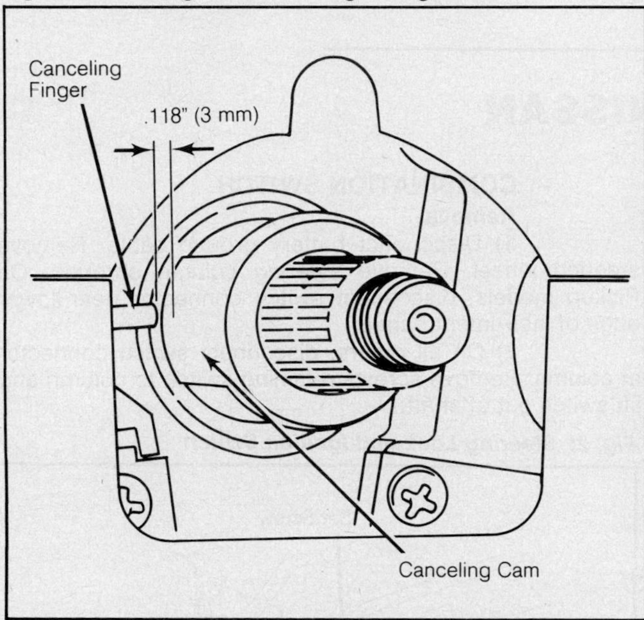
Canceling Finger
.118" (3 mm)
Canceling Cam

Finger on canceling cam must face toward center.

IGNITION SWITCH

Removal

Disconnect battery ground cable. Remove turn signal mounting screws and pull off lower plastic shroud. Remove turn signal, dimmer and wiper/washer switches. Unscrew and remove flasher relay. Remove hollow set screw. Slide out ignition switch.

Installation

To install, reverse removal procedure and note following: Turn ignition key all the way back before inserting. Set ignition switch at "O" position before installing.

Fig. 3: Location of Shear Bolts

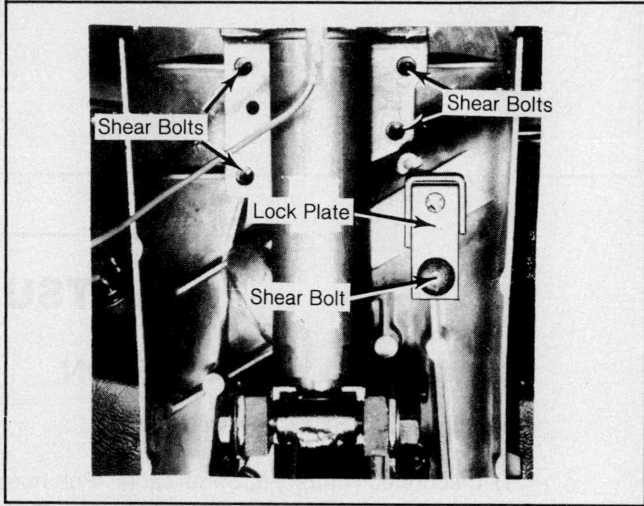
Shear Bolts
Shear Bolts
Lock Plate
Shear Bolt

View looking up from under steering column.

STEERING LOCK

Removal

1) Disconnect battery ground cable. Remove steering wheel. Remove upper and lower steering column shrouds. Disconnect and remove turn signal, dimmer and wiper/washer switch plate.

2) Remove shear bolts from switch plate with chisel. Remove set screw on outside of steering column tube. Pull out ignition switch. Remove steering lock plate shear bolt. Pull out steering lock.

Installation

To install, reverse removal procedure.

CHRYSLER CORP. IMPORTS

REMOVAL & INSTALLATION

STEERING WHEEL & COMBINATION SWITCH

Removal

1) Disconnect battery ground cable. Remove horn pad. Mark main shaft and steering wheel for reassembly reference. Remove steering wheel nut. Remove steering wheel with puller (DT-1001-A).

2) Remove column cover. Disconnect electrical connections at base of steering column. Remove retaining screws and pull combination switch out.

Installation

1) Install combination switch and retaining screws. Connect electrical connections at base of column and route harness along center of tube.

2) To install, place front wheels in straight ahead position. On Challenger, Colt and Sapporo models, align cancel pins of column switch with holes in bottom of steering wheel.

3) On all models, refit steering wheel with index marks aligned. Tighten nut and install horn pad.

CHRYSLER CORP. IMPORTS (Cont.)

Fig. 1: Installation of Chrysler Corp. Steering Wheel

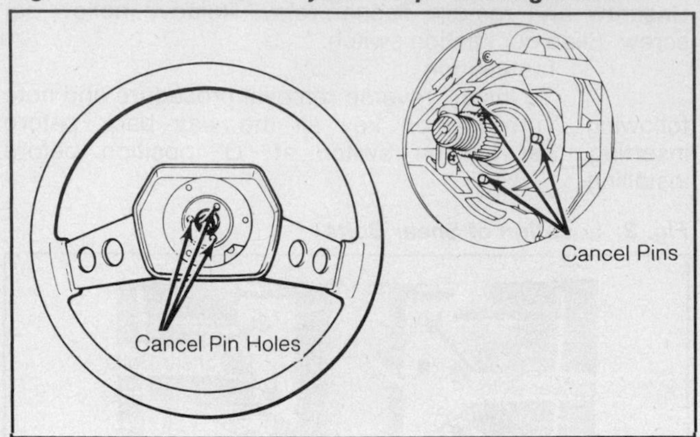
Cancel Pins
Cancel Pin Holes

STEERING LOCK

Removal

With steering wheel removed, remove column levers and switches. Cut slot in mounting pad screws and bracket with hack saw. Remove screws and steering wheel lock.

Installation

To install, reverse removal procedures. Install new bracket and screws.

DATSUN/NISSAN

REMOVAL & INSTALLATION

STEERING WHEEL & HORN PAD

Removal

1) Disconnect battery ground cable. Pull horn pad off steering wheel. Remove horn wire. Remove retaining nut. Mark steering wheel and column shaft.

2) Using puller (ST27180001), remove steering wheel. Do not hammer on steering wheel. Pounding will cause damage to collapsible steering column.

Installation

To install, reverse removal procedures. Grease all sliding components. Match index marks made during removal. Check operation.

Fig. 1: Steps for Removing and Installing Steering Wheel and Combination Switch

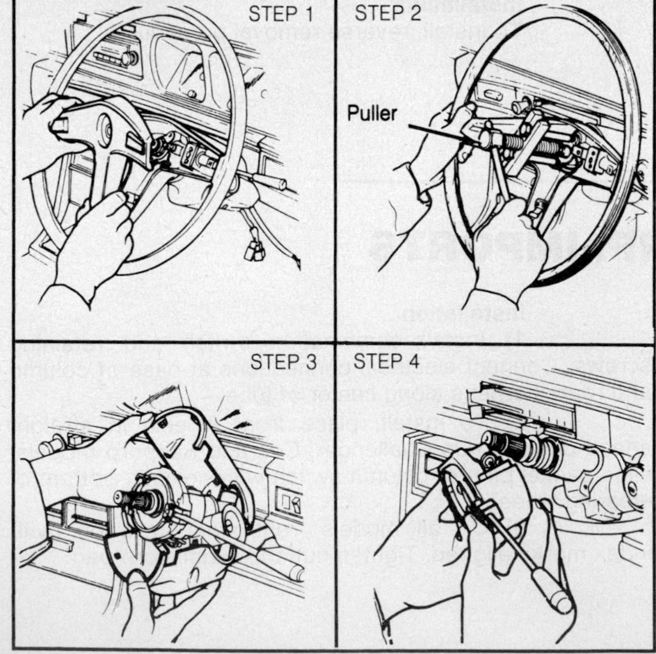
STEP 1
STEP 2
Puller
STEP 3
STEP 4

COMBINATION SWITCH

Removal

1) Disconnect battery ground cable. Remove steering wheel. Remove steering column shrouds. On Pickup models, disconnect switch connector near lower edge of instrument panel.

2) On all others, disconnect switch connector at column. Remove screws retaining switch to column and lift switch out of shaft.

Fig. 2: Steering Lock and Ignition Switch

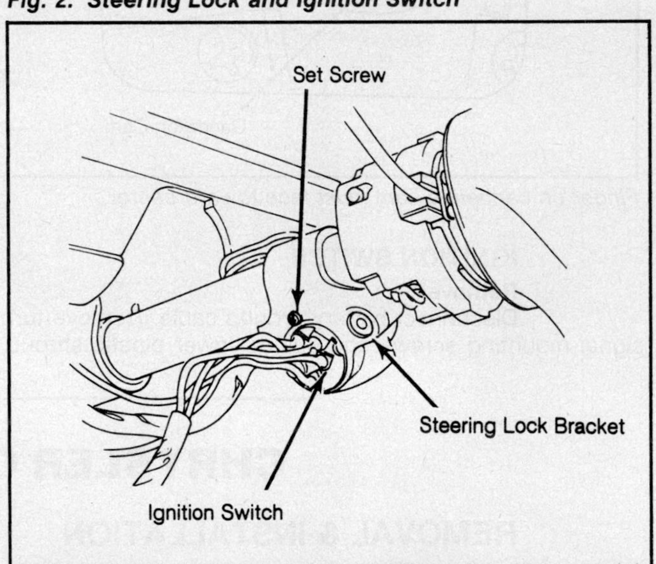
Set Screw
Steering Lock Bracket
Ignition Switch

Remove small set screw to remove ignition switch.

Installation

To install, reverse removal procedures. Make sure switch tab locates in hole in column.

HAZARD WARNING SWITCH

Removal

Disconnect battery ground cable. Remove mounting screws and steering column shrouds. Discon-

DATSUN/NISSAN (Cont.)

nect lead wires at connector. Remove retaining screws and take switch out of shroud.

Installation

To install, reverse removal procedures.

STEERING LOCK & IGNITION SWITCH

Removal

1) Disconnect battery ground cable. Remove steering column shroud. Drill out shear bolts. Separate steering lock from column shaft.

2) If ignition switch is to be removed, separate electrical connector. Remove small set screw retaining switch body. Remove switch.

Installation

To install, reverse removal procedures. Fit ignition switch to lock mechanism before installing lock.

HONDA

REMOVAL & INSTALLATION

HORN PAD & STEERING WHEEL

Removal

1) Disconnect battery ground cable. Pull out and remove steering wheel horn pad. With wheels in straight-ahead position, mark position of steering wheel to shaft. Remove retaining nut.

2) Remove steering wheel with puller. Steering wheel components should be disassembled and replaced, if necessary.

Installation

To install, reverse removal procedures. Ensure wheels are straight-ahead and marks made at removal are aligned.

COMBINATION SWITCH

Removal

1) Disconnect battery ground cable. Remove steering pad. Remove column shrouding. Disconnect electrical connectors and remove steering wheel. Remove retaining screws and lift out combination switch.

2) Washer/wiper switch can be separated from turn signal switch. Do not drop or lose turn signal cancel cam key when removing combination switch.

Installation

To install, reverse removal procedures. Insert lug on turn signal switch assembly into recess in steering column. Turn signal cancel key lugs must fit into recess in steering wheel. Horn switch spring terminal must touch contact ring.

HAZARD SWITCH

Switch is located in top column shrouding. Remove top shrouding, disconnect electrical wires and remove switch from mounted position.

NOTE: **Accord models also have an indicator light switch located in the upper column shrouding. Switch, when depressed, will allow all indicator lights to function. Procedures for Hazard switch apply.**

STEERING LOCK & IGNITION SWITCH

Removal

1) Remove steering column upper and lower shrouding. Disconnect ignition switch electrical wiring at lower end of steering column.

2) Center punch shear bolts. Drill out shear head bolts and extract from lock bracket. Remove ignition switch.

Installation

Insert new ignition switch. Hand tighten new shear bolts. Check switch operation at this time. Tighten shear bolts. Reconnect switch electrical leads.

Fig. 1: Exploded View of Steering Column Components

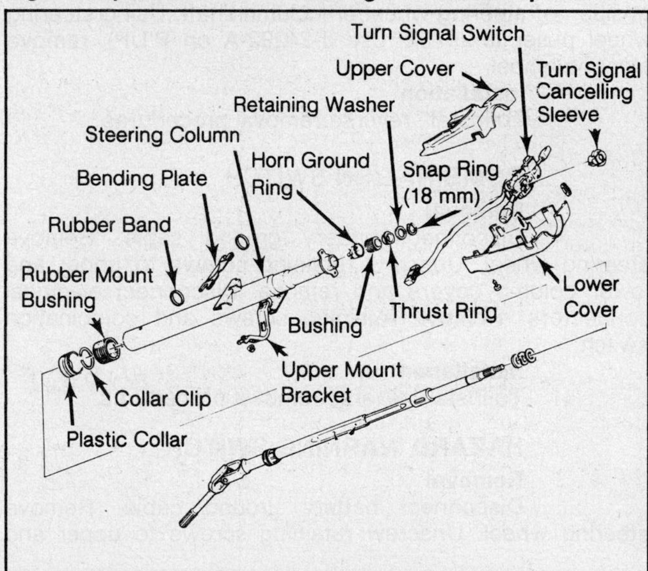

Turn Signal Switch
Upper Cover
Turn Signal Cancelling Sleeve
Retaining Washer
Steering Column
Horn Ground Ring
Snap Ring (18 mm)
Bending Plate
Rubber Band
Rubber Mount Bushing
Lower Cover
Thrust Ring
Bushing
Upper Mount Bracket
Collar Clip
Plastic Collar

Civic model is shown; others are similar.

ISUZU

REMOVAL & INSTALLATION

CAUTION: **Steering shaft is an energy absorbing unit. During any service operation, avoid hammering, jarring, or leaning on any portion of column.**

HORN PAD & STEERING WHEEL

Removal

1) Disconnect battery ground cable. Remove retaining screws on back of steering wheel. Remove horn pad. Disconnect horn wires.

ISUZU (Cont.)

Fig. 1: Disassembled View of Isuzu I-Mark Steering Wheel Assembly

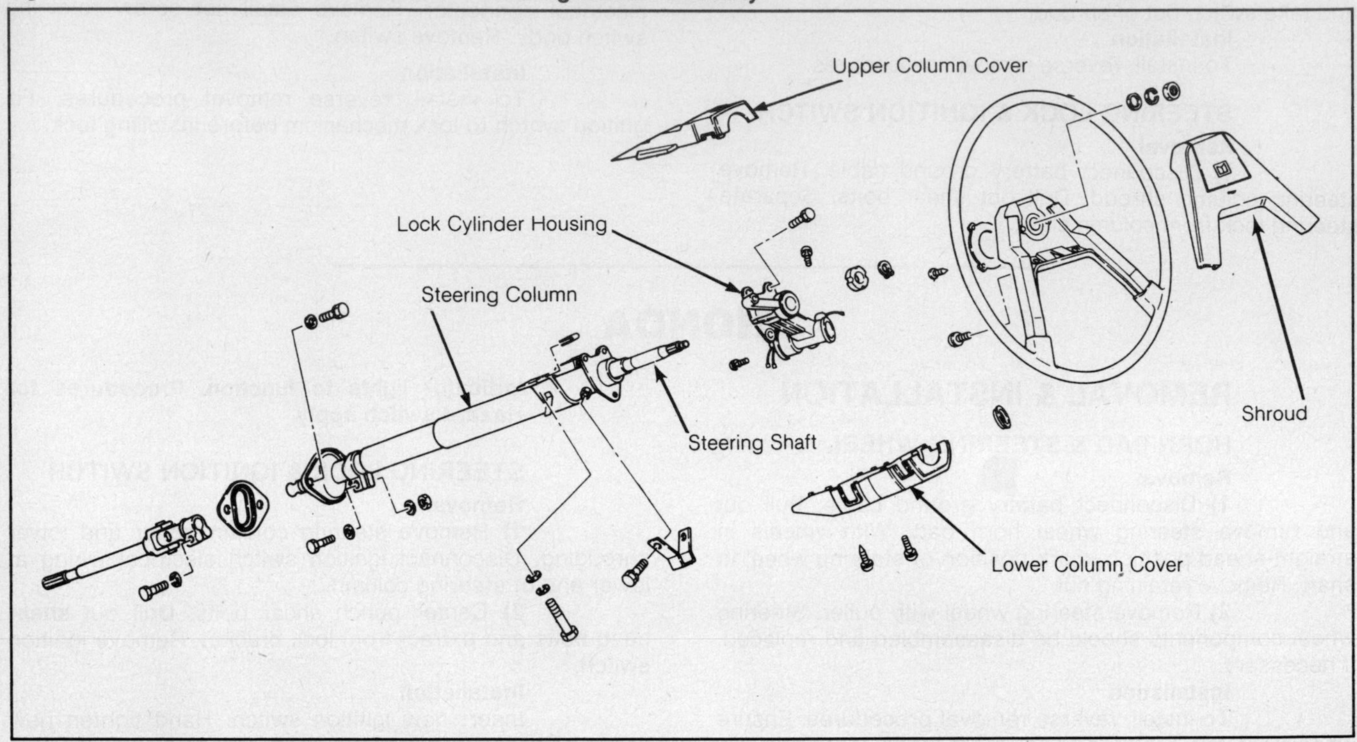
Upper Column Cover
Lock Cylinder Housing
Steering Column
Steering Shaft
Shroud
Lower Column Cover

P'UP steering wheel assembly is similar.

2) Unscrew steering wheel retaining nut. Mark position of steering wheel on column shaft. Using steering wheel puller (J-29752; use J-24292-A on P'UP), remove steering wheel.

Installation

To install, reverse removal procedures.

COMBINATION SWITCH

Removal

Disconnect battery ground cable. Remove steering wheel. Unscrew retaining screws to upper and lower column covers and remove. Disconnect electrical connectors. Remove retaining screws and combination switch.

Installation

To install, reverse removal procedures.

HAZARD WARNING SWITCH

Removal

Disconnect battery ground cable. Remove steering wheel. Unscrew retaining screws to upper and lower column covers and remove. Disconnect electrical connectors. Remove retaining screws. Remove combination switch and hazard warning switch.

Installation

To install, reverse removal procedures.

STEERING LOCK & IGNITION SWITCH

Removal (I-Mark & Impulse)

Disconnect battery ground cable. Remove steering wheel and column covers. Remove snap ring, washer and retaining bolts on column flange. Remove ignition switch and steering lock assembly.

Installation

To install, reverse removal procedures.

Removal (P'UP)

Disconnect battery ground cable. Remove steering wheel. Remove upper and lower column covers. Disconnect ignition switch wiring connector. Remove switch cover. Remove ignition switch ring nut and switch.

Installation

To install, reverse removal procedures.

JAGUAR

REMOVAL & INSTALLATION

HORN PAD & STEERING WHEEL

Removal

1) Set front wheels in straight-ahead position. Mark position on steering wheel and column shaft. Remove screws retaining lower switch cover. Detach cover.

2) Working from below, remove clamp bolt retaining split collet adapter to steering column. *See Fig. 1*. Loosen lock nut on set screw and loosen screw 2 turns. Remove steering wheel, complete with hand lock nut, impact rubber bumper, collet adapter and shaft.

Disassembly

1) Remove self-tapping screws from lower face of steering wheel boss and lift off padded horn

JAGUAR (Cont.)

Fig. 1: Components Located Behind Steering Wheel

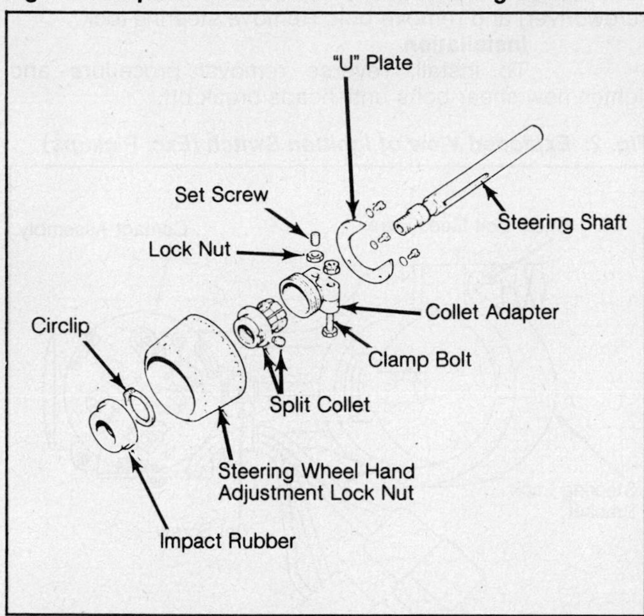
"U" Plate
Set Screw
Steering Shaft
Lock Nut
Collet Adapter
Circlip
Clamp Bolt
Split Collet
Steering Wheel Hand
Adjustment Lock Nut
Impact Rubber

Collect split collet and save for reassembly.

contact. Unscrew nylon nut from top of steering wheel shaft and carefully remove it. Remove horn contact tube.

2) Remove self-locking nut and plain washer which retain steering wheel. Carefully pull steering wheel from shaft. Collect both halves of split cone.

Reassembly

To reassemble horn pad and steering wheel, reverse disassembly procedures.

Installation

To install, reverse removal procedures. Be sure that front wheels are always kept in straight-ahead position. When tightening collet clamp, tighten grub screw finger tight. Snug down lock nut and tighten clamp bolt.

STEERING LOCK

Removal

Take off upper column shrouding. Using a center punch, make several dimples in shear bolt and rotate bolt out.

Installation

To install, reverse removal procedure.

IGNITION SWITCH

Removal

Disconnect battery ground cable. Separate column shrouding from switch side. Disengage retaining ring holding ignition switch in housing. Disconnect ignition switch wiring at multi-pin connector. Remove switch and harness.

Installation

To install, reverse removal procedure.

COMBINATION SWITCH

Removal

1) Disconnect battery cable. Take off steering column lower shroud. Remove steering wheel as previously outlined. Remove steering column upper shroud and cover from below instrument panel.

2) Loosen pinch bolt and pull combination switch assembly from steering column. Disconnect electrical wiring. Hazard flasher can now be separated by disconnecting wires, depressing tangs and pushing switch through mounting plate.

Installation

To install, reverse removal procedures.

Fig. 2: Combination Switch Location and Assembly

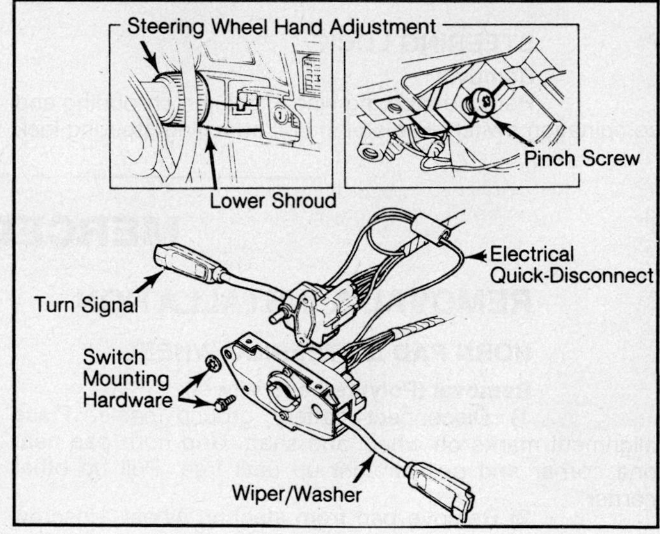
Steering Wheel Hand Adjustment
Pinch Screw
Lower Shroud
Electrical
Quick-Disconnect
Turn Signal
Switch
Mounting
Hardware
Wiper/Washer

MAZDA

REMOVAL & INSTALLATION

STEERING WHEEL & COMBINATION SWITCH

Removal

1) Disconnect battery ground cable. Pull off horn cap. Place front wheels in straight-ahead position. Index mark column shaft and steering wheel.

2) Remove steering column shrouding. Disconnect electrical connectors. To disconnect electrical connections on RX7, remove air duct at base of steering column.

3) On all models, remove steering shaft stop ring, cancel cam and spring. Remove retaining screws and combination switch assembly.

NOTE: **Wiper switch can be removed with combination switch or separated from it.**

Installation

To install, reverse removal procedures.

IGNITION SWITCH

Removal

1) Remove steering wheel as previously outlined. Remove column shrouding. Remove combination switch. Disconnect electrical connector.

2) Remove screw attaching switch contact housing to steering lock body and slide out contact housing. *See Fig. 2.*

MAZDA (Cont.)

Fig. 1: Typical Mazda Steering Wheel Assembly

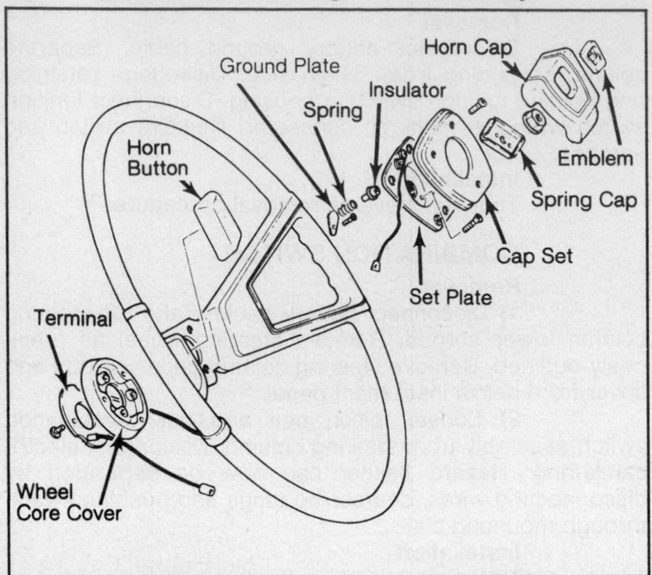
Horn Cap
Ground Plate
Insulator
Spring
Horn Button
Emblem
Spring Cap
Cap Set
Set Plate
Terminal
Wheel Core Cover

Installation
To install, reverse removal procedure.

STEERING LOCK
Removal
Remove steering wheel, column shrouding and combination switch. File slot in bolt attaching steering lock body to column shaft (in order to remove bolt with screwdriver) and remove bolt. Remove steering lock.

Installation
To install, reverse removal procedure and tighten new shear bolts until heads break off.

Fig. 2: Exploded View of Ignition Switch (Exc. Pickups)

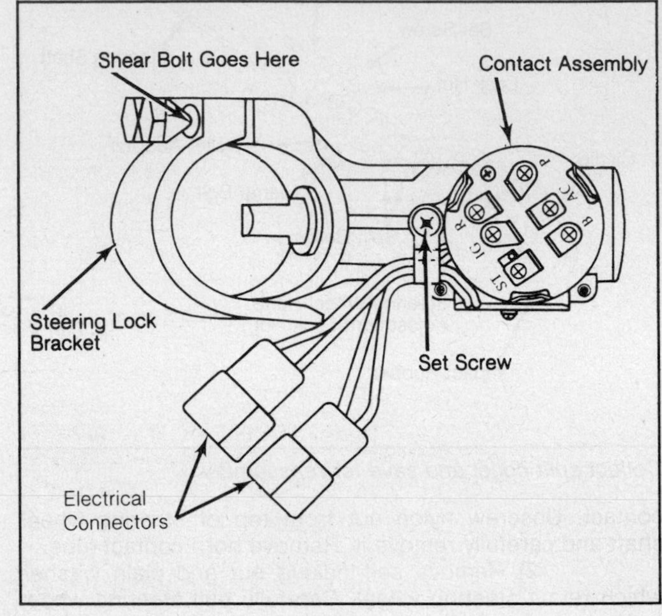
Shear Bolt Goes Here
Contact Assembly
Steering Lock Bracket
Set Screw
Electrical Connectors

MERCEDES-BENZ

REMOVAL & INSTALLATION

HORN PAD & STEERING WHEEL

Removal (Polyurethane Wheel)

1) Disconnect battery ground cable. Place alignment marks on wheel and shaft. Grip horn pad near one corner and pull straight up until free. Pull up other corner.

2) Remove pad from steering wheel. Unscrew retaining nut, remove spring washer and pull steering wheel from shaft.

Installation
To install, reverse removal procedures.

Removal (Plastic Wheel)

1) Disconnect battery ground cable. Remove vehicle emblem from horn pad. Unscrew steering wheel retaining nut and pull wheel from shaft with pad still attached.

2) Unscrew hex nuts on backside of wheel. Separate steering wheel from pad.

NOTE: **Horn wire is still attached to steering wheel, so care must be taken to avoid breaking it.**

3) Detach horn wire from contact ring. Remove steering wheel. Remove countersunk screws from steering wheel hub and centering pad of contact ring.

4) Remove horn ring from steering wheel. Remove locking ring from hub of pad. Remove slip ring.

Installation
To install, reverse removal procedures. Ensure wheels are kept in straight-ahead position and that steering wheel spokes are horizontal.

Fig. 1: Mercedes-Benz Steering Wheel with Cover Removed

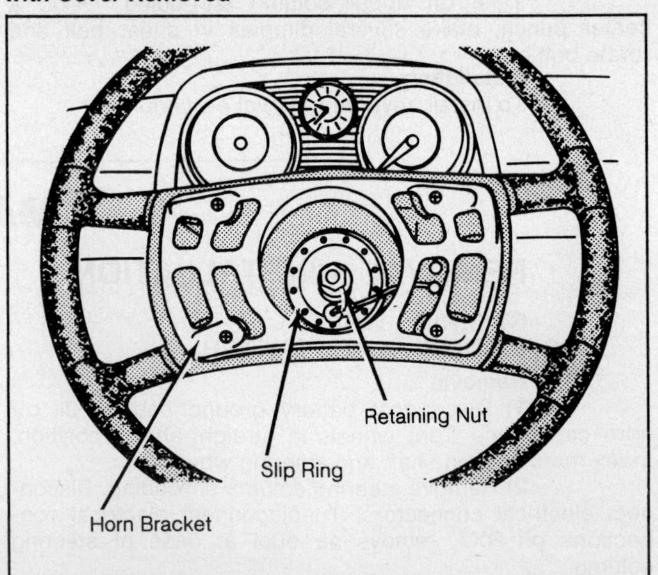
Retaining Nut
Slip Ring
Horn Bracket

MITSUBISHI

REMOVAL & INSTALLATION

STEERING WHEEL & COMBINATION SWITCH

Removal

1) Disconnect battey ground cable. Remove horn pad. Remove steering wheel nut. Using steering wheel puller, remove steering wheel. *See Fig. 1*.

NOTE: **If equipped with tilt steering, handle must be in lowest position before removing steering wheel.**

2) Remove column cover. Disconnect electrical connections on column. Remove retaining screws and pull combination switch out.

Installation

To install, reverse removal procedures.

COLUMN LOCK & IGNITION SWITCH

Removal

With steering wheel removed, remove column levers and switches. Cut slot in mounting pad screws and bracket with hack saw. Remove screws and steering column lock/ignition switch.

Installation

To install, reverse removal procedures. Install new bracket and shear bolts.

Fig. 1: Steering Wheel Removal

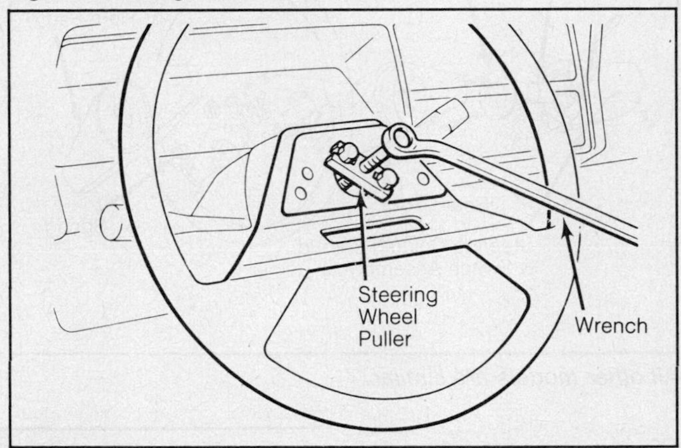
Steering
Wheel
Puller
Wrench

PORSCHE

REMOVAL & INSTALLATION

HORN PAD & STEERING WHEEL

Removal (911SC)

1) Align front wheels in straight-ahead position. Disconnect battery ground cable. Grasp horn pad and rotate counterclockwise while pushing in.

CAUTION: **Do not apply excessive or striking forces to the steering wheel or steering column.**

2) When horn pad is free, lift from steering wheel and disconnect horn contact finger.

3) Loosen steering wheel retaining nut. Mark position of steering wheel to steering shaft. Attach puller and remove steering wheel.

Installation

To install, reverse removal procedures. Lightly lubricate horn contact finger with electrical contact grease before installation.

Removal (928S)

Disconnect battery ground cable. Place wheels in straight-ahead position. Remove horn pad. Disconnect horn wires. Index mark steering wheel and column shaft. Unscrew retaining nut. Remove steering wheel.

Installation

Align index marks and replace steering wheel so spokes are horizontal. Install retaining nut. Fit horn wires into place in pad. Press horn pad onto retaining pins.

Removal (944)

Disconnect battery ground cable. Using hand pressure, lift up horn pad. Unscrew wheel retaining nut. Pull wheel upward and off shaft.

CAUTION: **Do not apply excessive or striking forces to the steering wheel or steering column.**

Installation

To install, reverse removal procedures.

COMBINATION SWITCH

Removal (928S)

1) Disconnect battery ground cable. Remove steering wheel. Remove cover from under steering column switch. Remove steering column switch retaining screw.

2) Remove instrument cover retaining screws. Maneuver instrument cover until electrical wires can be disconnected. Remove column switch.

Installation

To install, reverse removal procedures.

Removal (944)

1) Disconnect battery ground cable. Using hand pressure, lift up steering pad. Remove steering wheel retaining nut. Pull steering wheel off shaft.

CAUTION: **Do not apply excessive or striking forces to the steering wheel or steering column.**

2) Remove shroud from around switch housing. Pull up on switch plate and disconnect electrical wires.

3) Remove entire switch assembly, separate wiper/washer switch from turn signal switch by taking out screw that retains them together.

Installation

1) Refit switches together with screw. Slide switch assemblies back into place, refitting spacer at same time.

2) Make sure spacer is driven in until there is a distance of 1.7" (42.5 mm) from face (top edge) of spacer to top edge of shaft.

3) This distance will ensure there is .08-.15" (2-4 mm) between steering wheel and steering column

PORSCHE (Cont.)

Fig. 1: Exploded View of Porsche 944 Steering Wheel

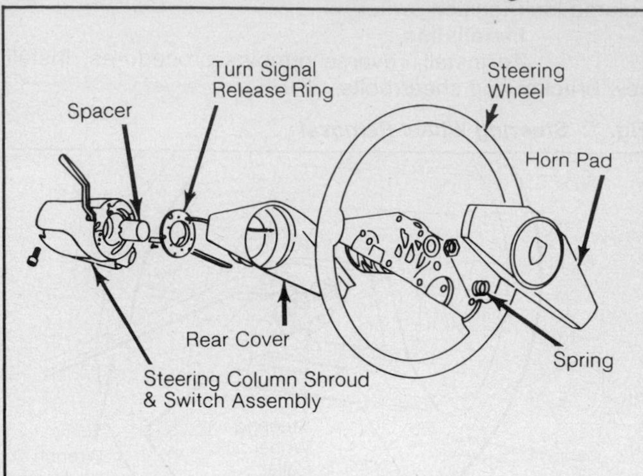
Turn Signal Release Ring
Steering Wheel
Spacer
Horn Pad
Rear Cover
Spring
Steering Column Shroud & Switch Assembly

All other models are similar.

switches. Reverse removal procedures to install remaining components.

STEERING COLUMN LOCK, KEY CYLINDER & IGNITION SWITCH

Removal

1) Remove combination switch as previously outlined. Drill out shear bolts. Disconnect ignition switch wiring.

2) Disengage snap ring and slide out switch housing with bearing. Using pointed tool (scribe), push cylinder lock retainer in to release cylinder.

3) With key inserted and retainer depressed, pull cylinder from housing. Remove ignition switch set screw. Remove ignition switch back from housing.

Installation

To install, reverse removal procedure.

RENAULT

REMOVAL & INSTALLATION

HORN PAD & STEERING WHEEL

Removal (LeCar)

Disconnect battery ground cable. Remove horn pad. Remove steering wheel nut. Using puller (Dir. 21A) remove steering wheel.

Installation

To install, reverse removal procedures.

Removal (Fuego & 18i)

1) Disconnect battery ground cable. Remove horn pad. Remove steering column protective housings. Remove steering wheel nut. Install puller plate tool (Dir. 372) behind steering wheel.

2) Using center punch, make center point mark in center of steering column shaft. Connect puller tool (Mot. 49) to puller plate.

3) Using wrench, turn puller shaft until steering wheel is pulled from steering shaft.

Installation

1) Position steering wheel on steering shaft. Install steering wheel nut and tighten.

2) Using center punch, notch edge of steering column shaft to lock the nut in place. To complete installation, reverse removal procedures.

TURN SIGNAL & LIGHTING SWITCH

Removal (LeCar)

1) Disconnect battery ground cable. Remove instrument panel housing retaining screws and remove housing. *See Fig. 2.*

2) Remove switch retaining screws. Disconnect electrical connectors. Remove switch.

Installation

To install, reverse removal procedures.

COMBINATION SWITCH

Removal (Fuego & 18i)

1) Disconnect battery ground cable. Remove steering wheel. Remove steering column protective housings.

Fig. 1: Removing Steering Wheel on Fuego & 18i

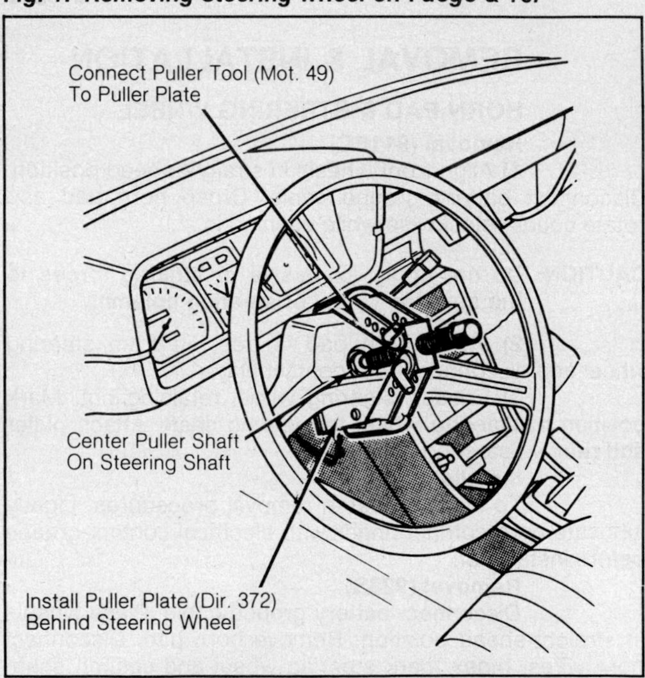
Connect Puller Tool (Mot. 49) To Puller Plate
Center Puller Shaft On Steering Shaft
Install Puller Plate (Dir. 372) Behind Steering Wheel

2) Remove switch retaining bolts and screw. Disconnect electrical connectors. Remove switch.

Installation

To install, reverse removal procedures.

NOTE: Turn signal and windshield wiper switch are one unit and cannot be separated. If one is defective, both must be replaced. Headlight switch may be replaced separately and removed from combination switch by removing retaining pin.

RENAULT (Cont.)

Fig. 2: Location of Switch Assembly Retaining Screws

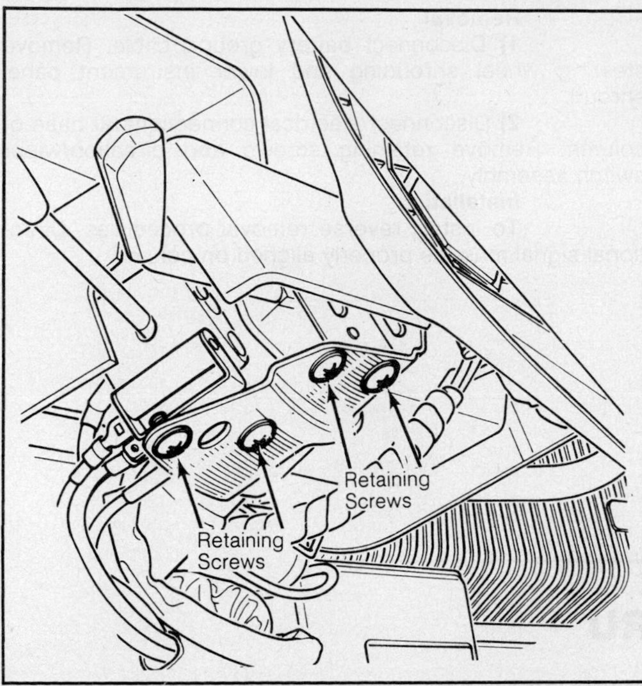
Retaining
Screws
Retaining
Screws

IGNITION SWITCH

Removal (LeCar)

1) Disconnect battery ground cable. Remove shroud from around switch assembly. Disconnect electrical connections.

2) Turn ignition switch to "G" (Garage) position and remove switch. Remove set screw and press in retaining catch with small punch. Push switch body from rear to release it. *See Fig. 3.*

Installation

To install, reverse removal procedures.

Removal (Fuego & 18i)

1) Disconnect battery ground cable. Remove steering wheel. Remove steering column protective housings.

2) Disconnect electrical connections. Turn key to "Park" position and remove ignition switch and key.

Installation

To install, reverse removal procedures.

COLUMN LOCK

Removal (All Models)

1) Remove ignition switch and lock assembly from column. Turn key to "Stop" position.

2) Remove 2 rear bracket retaining screws. Slide lock assembly toward rear and remove.

Installation

To install, reverse removal procedures.

Fig. 3: Le Car Ignition Switch Removal

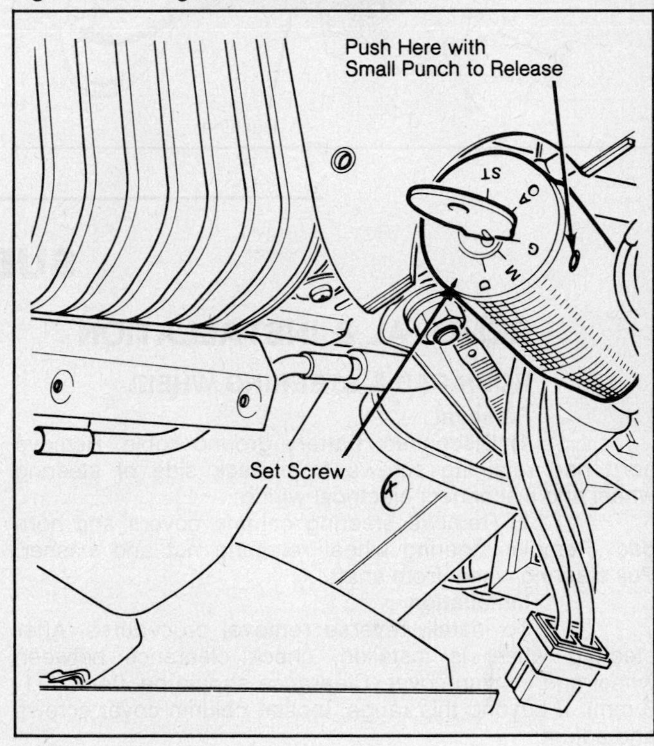
Push Here with
Small Punch to Release
Set Screw
ST
OA
G
M
D

SAAB

Fig. 1: Using Puller to Remove Steering Wheel

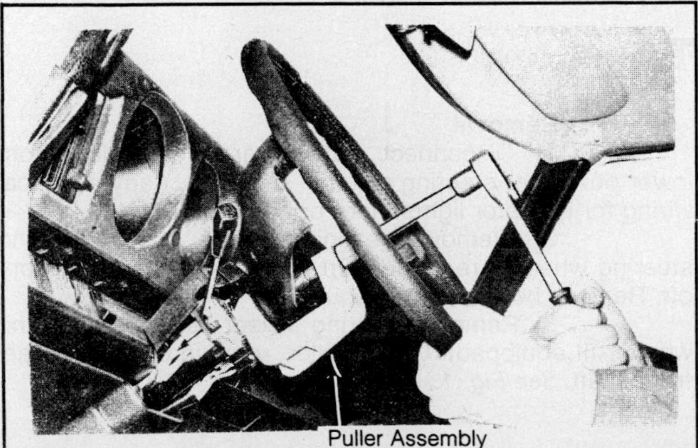
Puller Assembly

REMOVAL & INSTALLATION

HORN CONTROL & STEERING WHEEL

Removal

1) Disconnect battery ground cable. Remove bottom cover retaining screws and cover. On standard steering wheel, remove retaining screws from behind steering wheel. Remove pad and horn contact.

2) On 3-spoke wheel, lift pad from spokes. Reach under and disconnect horn leads while supporting pad.

3) On all models, mark position of steering wheel to shaft. Remove retaining nut and washer. Remove wheel from shaft with wheel puller.

Installation

To install, reverse removal procedures.

SAAB (Cont.)

Fig. 2: Exploded View of Steering Wheel Assembly

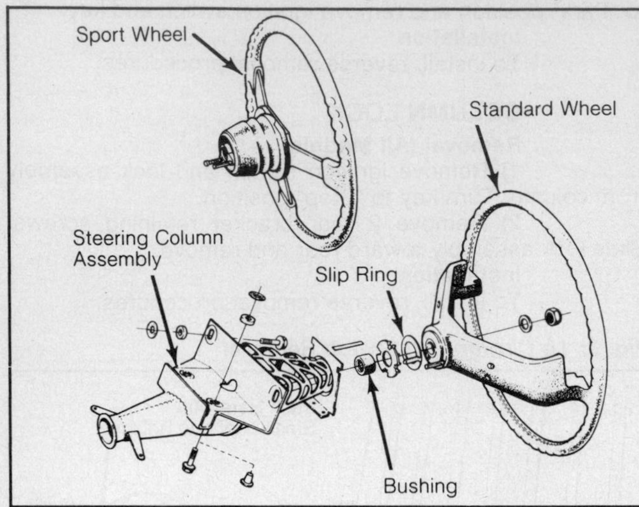
Sport Wheel
Standard Wheel
Steering Column Assembly
Slip Ring
Bushing

COMBINATION SWITCH

Removal

1) Disconnect battery ground cable. Remove steering wheel shrouding and lower instrument panel shroud.

2) Disconnect electrical connections at base of column. Remove retaining screws and direction/wiper switch assembly.

Installation

To install, reverse removal procedures. Directional signal must be properly aligned on column.

SUBARU

REMOVAL & INSTALLATION

HORN PAD & STEERING WHEEL

Removal

1) Disconnect battery ground cable. Remove horn pad retaining screws from back side of steering wheel and disconnect electrical wiring.

2) Remove steering column covers and horn pad. Remove steering wheel retaining nut and washer. Pull steering wheel from shaft.

Installation

To install, reverse removal procedures. After steering wheel is installed, check clearance between wheel and column cover. Clearance should be .04-.12" (1-3 mm). If beyond this range, loosen column cover screws and adjust.

COMBINATION SWITCH

Removal

Remove steering wheel as previously described. Remove hazard warning knob from steering column. Remove switch retaining screws. Remove switch from steering column.

Installation

To install, reverse removal procedures.

Fig. 1: View of Combination Switch With Steering Wheel Removed

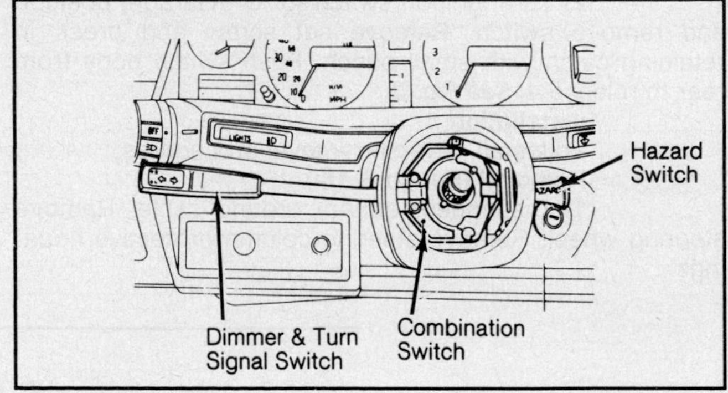
Hazard Switch
Dimmer & Turn Signal Switch
Combination Switch

TOYOTA

REMOVAL & INSTALLATION

STEERING WHEEL

NOTE: Steering wheel removal procedure is a general one. It should be noted that all steps may not apply to every model.

CAUTION: Some models are equipped with collapsible type steering. Do not apply excessive pressure or impact to mainshaft.

Removal

1) Disconnect battery ground cable. From lower portion of steering column, disconnect any electrical wiring for indicator lights, horn or dimmer switch.

2) Remove retaining screws from behind steering wheel (if required). On some models, pad will pry off. Remove horn wires (if required).

3) Remove steering wheel retaining nut and washer (if equipped). Using puller, remove steering wheel from shaft. *See Fig. 1.*

TOYOTA (Cont.)

Fig. 1: Using Puller to Remove Steering Wheel

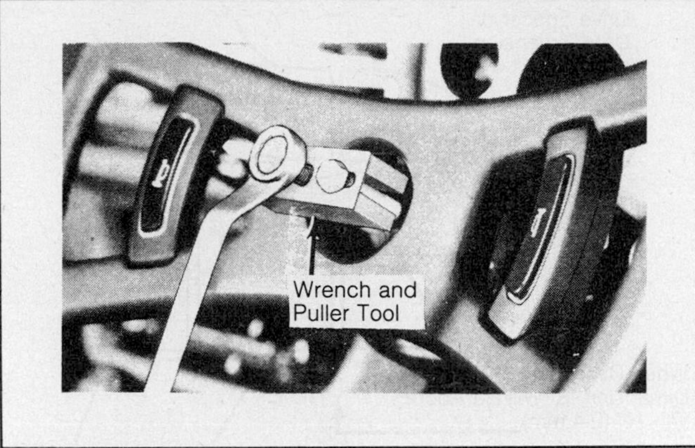
Wrench and
Puller Tool

Front wheels should be in straight-ahead position.

Installation

To install, reverse removal procedures.

COMBINATION SWITCH

Removal

1) After removing steering wheel as previously outlined, combination switch may be removed by detaching steering column covers.

2) Remove retaining screws from face of switch assembly. Unplug necessary electrical connectors.

Installation

To install, reverse removal procedures. Make sure all electrical connections are properly made. Check cancelling operation of turn signal switch.

COLUMN LOCK & IGNITION SWITCH

Removal

1) Disconnect battery ground cable. Remove steering wheel as previously outlined.

NOTE: **Steering wheel removal is optional if only ignition switch portion is being removed. Removal of wheel makes access to this operation easier.**

2) Remove screws retaining upper and lower column covers and disconnect any electrical couplings not detached during steering wheel removal.

NOTE: **On some models, access to ignition switch for its removal is gained by removing lower cover only. It is easier to perform this operation, however, by removing both cover halves.**

3) Remove turn signal switch assembly (only if column lock assembly is being removed). Remove main-shaft bearing retainer and snap ring (if required).

4) Insert key and turn ignition to "ACC" position. Using pointed tool to press down stop pin on side of cylinder, free mechanism and pull cylinder from housing. *See Fig. 2.*

5) On Celica and Supra models, remove snap ring on main shaft. On all other models, lock is part of upper column bearing assembly. Remove bolts retaining upper bearing assembly and slide off column.

Installation

1) To install, reverse removal procedures.

2) Fit key cylinder so ignition switch and cylinder will be aligned in "ACC" position. Insert into housing and check for proper locking operation and key movement.

3) Replace all other components (combination switch assembly, bearing retainer, steering wheel) as removed. Check for proper turn signal cancelling operation and smoothness of steering wheel movement.

Fig. 2: Disengaging Key Cylinder from Position on Mainshaft

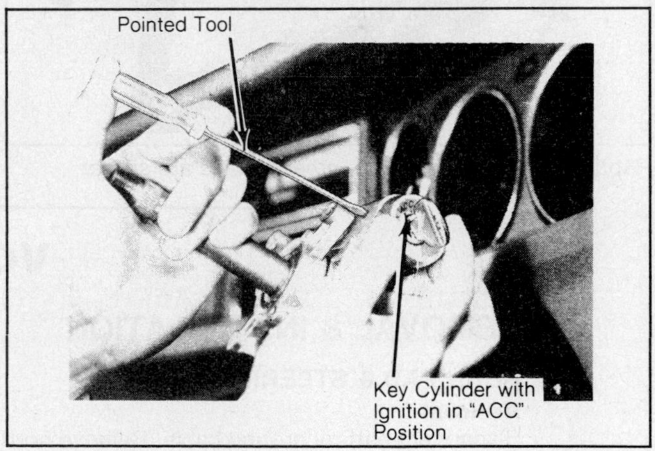
Pointed Tool
Key Cylinder with
Ignition in "ACC"
Position

VOLKSWAGEN

REMOVAL & INSTALLATION

HORN PAD & STEERING WHEEL

Removal

Disconnect battery ground cable. Carefully pry off horn pad and disconnect electrical connectors. Remove steering wheel retaining nut and washer, if equipped. Using puller remove wheel from shaft.

Installation

To install, reverse removal procedures.

CAUTION: **Steering column has collapsible section. Care must be used when working with steering not to damage assembly.**

COMBINATION SWITCH

Removal

1) Disconnect battery ground cable. Remove steering wheel as previously outlined. Remove screws retaining switch assembly to steering lock mechanism.

2) Force switch assembly toward instrument panel and remove spacer sleeve. Pull up on switch assembly and disconnect electrical wires. Remove switch and separate windshield wiper lever from dimmer/turn signal lever.

Installation

Refit switches together with screw and spacer sleeve. Slide switch assembly onto column and hook up wires. Install spacer sleeve. *See Fig. 2.*

VOLKSWAGEN (Cont.)

COLUMN LOCK & IGNITION SWITCH

Removal

1) Disconnect battery ground cable. Remove steering wheel and combination switch as previously outlined. If necessary, drill .125" (3.18 mm) hole in cylinder to gain access to cylinder release pin. *See Fig. 3.*

2) Insert pin through hole and press down spring holding lock cylinder in housing. It may be necessary to insert key to pull out cylinder.

3) To remove ignition switch, remove locking mechanism shear bolts and remove switch housing. Remove set screw on back side of switch, near wire connector. Remove ignition switch.

Installation

To install, reverse removal procedures. Before shearing bolt head, set clearance between steering wheel and switch to .08-.12" (2-3 mm).

Fig. 1: Typical Volkswagen Steering Wheel

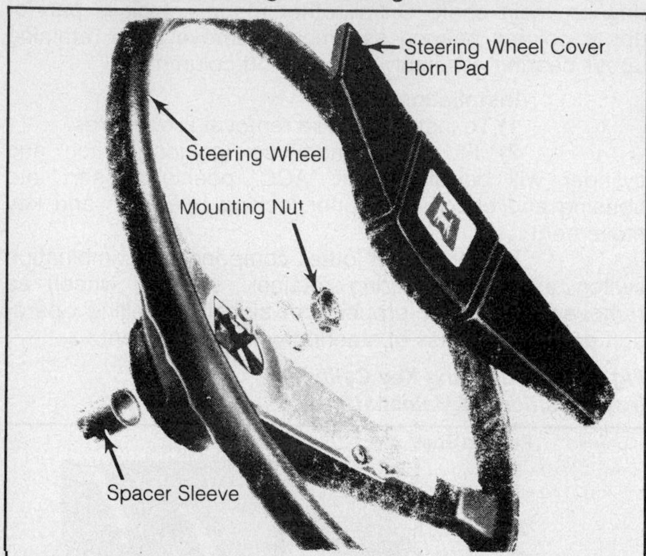
Steering Wheel Cover
Horn Pad
Steering Wheel
Mounting Nut
Spacer Sleeve

Rabbit and Scirocco shown, other models are similar.

Fig. 2: Dimensions for Installing Spacer Sleeve

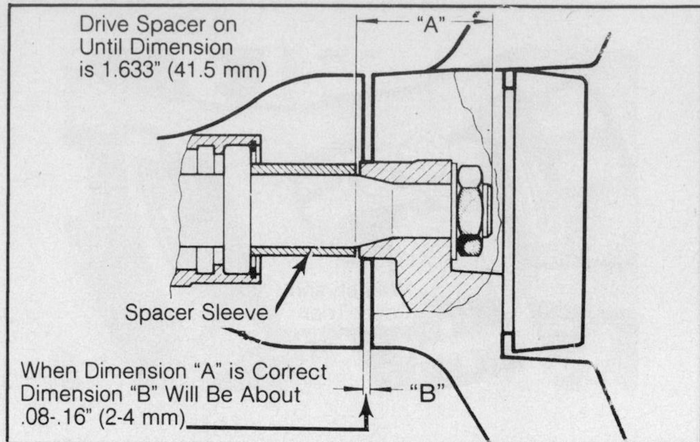
Drive Spacer on
Until Dimension
is 1.633" (41.5 mm)
"A"
Spacer Sleeve
When Dimension "A" is Correct
Dimension "B" Will Be About
.08-.16" (2-4 mm)
"B"

Fig. 3: Location for Drilling into Lock Cylinder

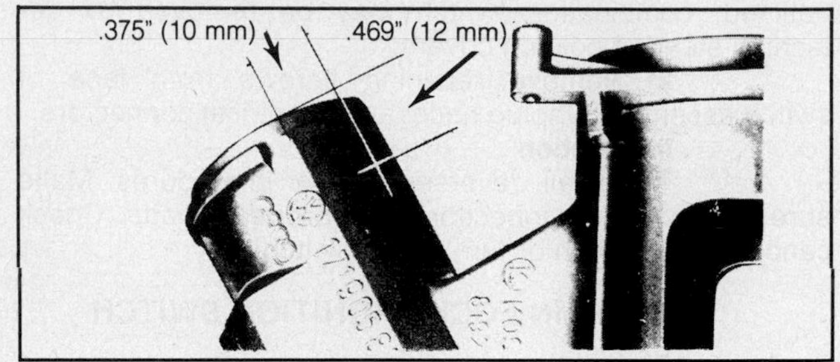
.375" (10 mm)
.469" (12 mm)

VOLVO

REMOVAL & INSTALLATION

HORN PAD & STEERING WHEEL

Removal

Disconnect battery ground cable. Remove horn pad by squeezing top and bottom towards center of pad and unfolding upper edge of pad. Disconnect electrical wires and remove steering wheel nut. Pull off steering wheel.

Installation

To install, reverse removal procedure.

Fig. 1: Removing Steering Wheel

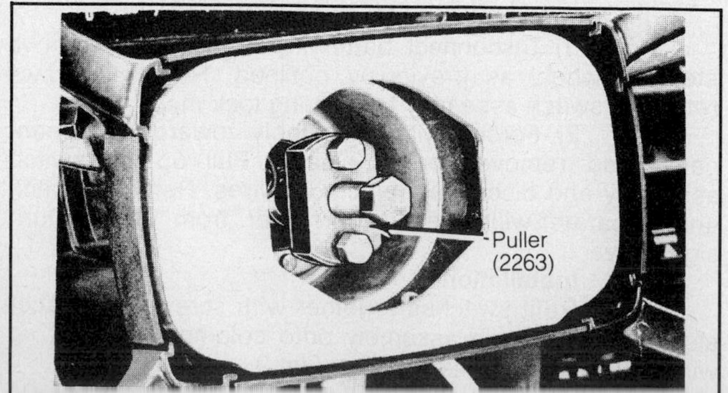
Puller
(2263)

TURN SIGNAL & WIPER SWITCHES

NOTE: **Steering wheel does not have to be removed to remove combination switch, however, removal of switch is easier with steering wheel removed.**

Removal

Disconnect battery ground cable. Remove column covers from steering column. Disconnect electrical connectors from switches and remove switches.

Installation

To install, reverse removal procedure.

IGNITION SWITCH & STEERING LOCK

Removal

1) Disconnect battery ground cable. Remove steering wheel and column covers. Remove turn signal and wiper switches. Remove upper bearing spring and race.

2) Drill out center of shear bolts and remove with screw extractor. Remove lock assembly. Disconnect electrical connections and remove ignition switch.

Installation

To install, reverse removal procedure and note: Position front of lock assembly 3.81" (97 mm) from upper end of steering column.

Steering Columns

AUDI 4000

DESCRIPTION

Audi 4000 model uses a 2-piece safety steering column with slip joint flange connection. Steering column is supported by column tube and steering lock assembly.

REMOVAL & INSTALLATION

STEERING COLUMN

Removal

1) Disconnect battery ground cable. Remove steering wheel and column switches. *See Audi under Steering Wheels & Column Switches in this section*.

2) From under hood, remove clamp bolt attaching steering shaft clamp to steering gear pinion shaft. Remove column cover bolts and steering column covers. *See Fig. 1*.

3) Pry lock washer off steering shaft. Remove spring. Remove contact ring and steering lock assembly. Remove support ring from column tube. *See Fig. 1*. Center punch shear bolt attaching column tube to dash. Drill out shear bolt. Remove socket head screw attaching column tube to dash.

4) From inside vehicle, force dust boot out of floor board. Remove steering column tube and shaft as an assembly.

Fig. 1: Exploded View of Upper Steering Column

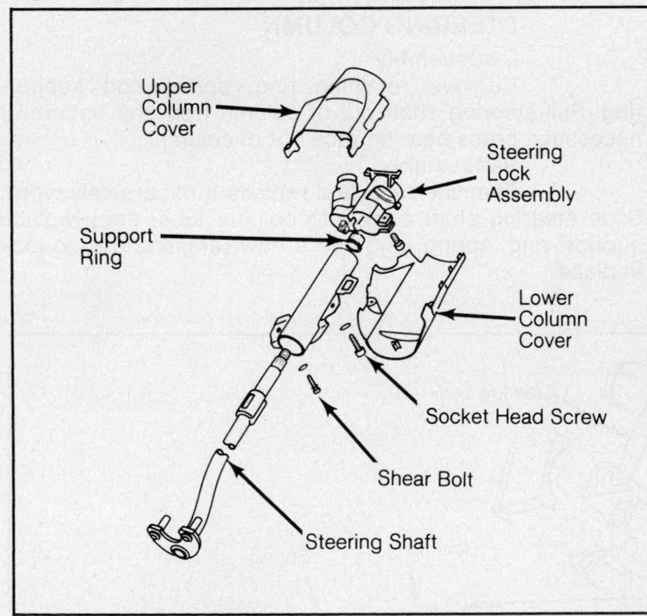
Upper Column Cover
Steering Lock Assembly
Support Ring
Lower Column Cover
Socket Head Screw
Shear Bolt
Steering Shaft

Installation

1) Install assembled steering column into vehicle. Install shear bolt and socket head bolt finger tight. Push dust boot into floor board until seated. Place clamp onto steering gear pinion shaft. Place support ring into column tube.

2) Install steering lock assembly on steering column. Install contact ring, spring and new lock washer. Tighten socket head screw. Tighten shear bolt until head snaps off.

3) Install upper and lower column covers. Install column switches and steering wheel. *See Audi under Steering Wheels & Column Switches in this section*.

OVERHAUL

STEERING COLUMN

Disassembly

1) On lower steering shaft, remove clamp bolt attaching lower flange tube to upper flange tube. Separate flange tubes and remove bearing flange, bearing, support ring, spring and washer. *See Fig. 2*.

2) Push upper flange tube toward steering shaft until components can be separated. Remove flange tube bushings with plastic bushings. *See Fig. 2*.

Fig. 2: Exploded View of Lower Steering Column

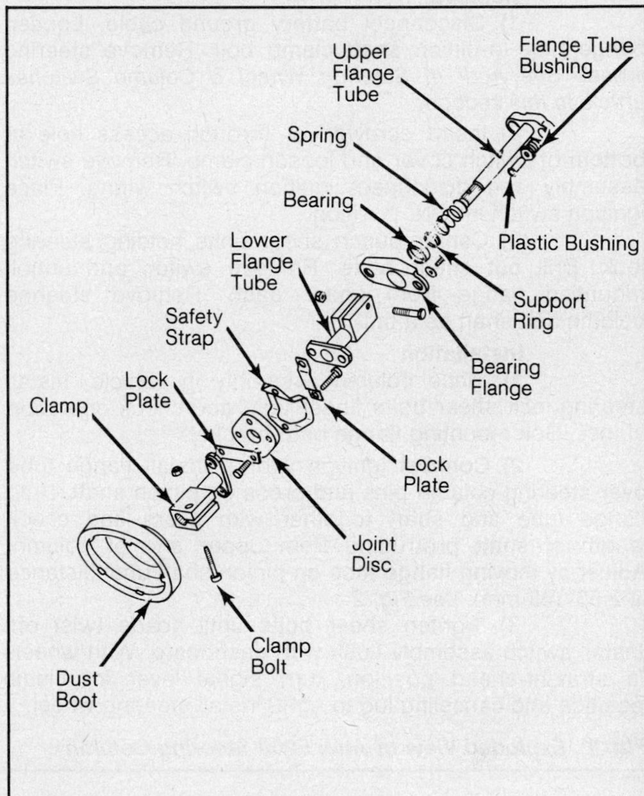
Upper Flange Tube
Flange Tube Bushing
Spring
Bearing
Plastic Bushing
Lower Flange Tube
Support Ring
Safety Strap
Bearing Flange
Lock Plate
Clamp
Lock Plate
Joint Disc
Clamp Bolt
Dust Boot

3) Remove lower flange tube-to-clamp bolts. Separate lower flange tube from clamp. Inspect joint disc, safety strap and lock plates for damage or wear.

4) On steering shaft, slide column tube off steering shaft. Inspect steering shaft, support ring and steering lock assembly for wear or damage. Replace components as necessary. *See Fig. 1*.

Reassembly

To reassemble steering column, reverse disassembly procedure. Press flange tube bushing and plastic bushing in by hand.

TIGHTENING SPECIFICATIONS

Application	Ft. Lbs. (N.m)
Clamp Bolt	22 (30)
Lock Plate Bolts	18 (24)
Lower Flange Tube Bolt	22 (30)
Socket Head Screw	14 (19)
Steering Wheel Nut	29 (39)

Steering Columns

AUDI 5000

DESCRIPTION

Audi 5000 has a 2-piece steering column/shaft assembly. Steering shaft has offset slip joint engaging flange tube. In a collision, gear box and flange tube may move rearward, but force will not be transmitted through upper column shaft. Locking device prevents steering wheel from turning when ignition key is removed.

REMOVAL & INSTALLATION

STEERING COLUMN

Removal

1) Disconnect battery ground cable. Loosen flange tube-to-pinion shaft clamp bolt. Remove steering wheel. *See Audi in Steering Wheel & Column Switches article in this section.*

2) Insert screwdriver through access hole at bottom of switch cover and loosen clamp. Remove switch assembly and disconnect ignition switch wiring. Place ignition switch in "ON" position.

3) Center punch shear bolts holding steering lock. Drill out shear bolts. Remove switch and unbolt mounting flange from under dash. Remove steering column and shaft as a unit.

Installation

1) Place column assembly in vehicle. Install steering lock shear bolts finger tight and check operation of lock. Bolt mounting flange onto bracket.

2) Connect ignition wiring. Install flange tube over steering column pins and press on pinion shaft. Hold flange tube and shaft together with pliers and check length of shaft protruding from upper end of column. Adjust by moving flange tube on pinion shaft until distance is 2.56" (65 mm). *See Fig. 2.*

3) Tighten shear bolts until heads twist off. Install switch assembly flush with dashboard. With wheels in straight-ahead position, turn signal lever in middle position and canceling lug to right, install steering wheel.

4) Tighten steering wheel nut. Gap between wheel and switch assembly should be .118" (3 mm). Adjust if necessary and tighten flange clamp bolt on pinion shaft.

Fig. 2: Steering Shaft Installation Measurement

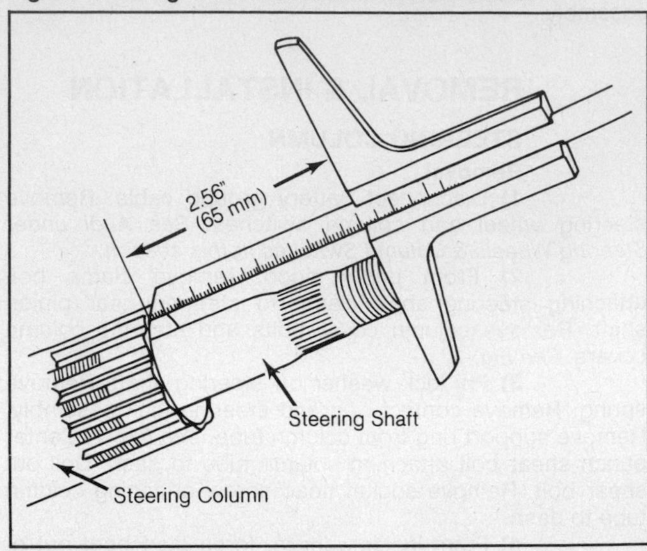
2.56"
(65 mm)
Steering Shaft
Steering Column

OVERHAUL

STEERING COLUMN

Disassembly

Remove retaining ring, spring and support ring. Pull steering shaft out of column from the bottom. If necessary, press bearing race out of column.

Reassembly

Examine race and replace if excessively worn. Slide steering shaft back into column tube, then replace support ring, spring, and use a new retaining ring to lock in place.

Fig. 1: Exploded View of Audi 5000 Steering Column

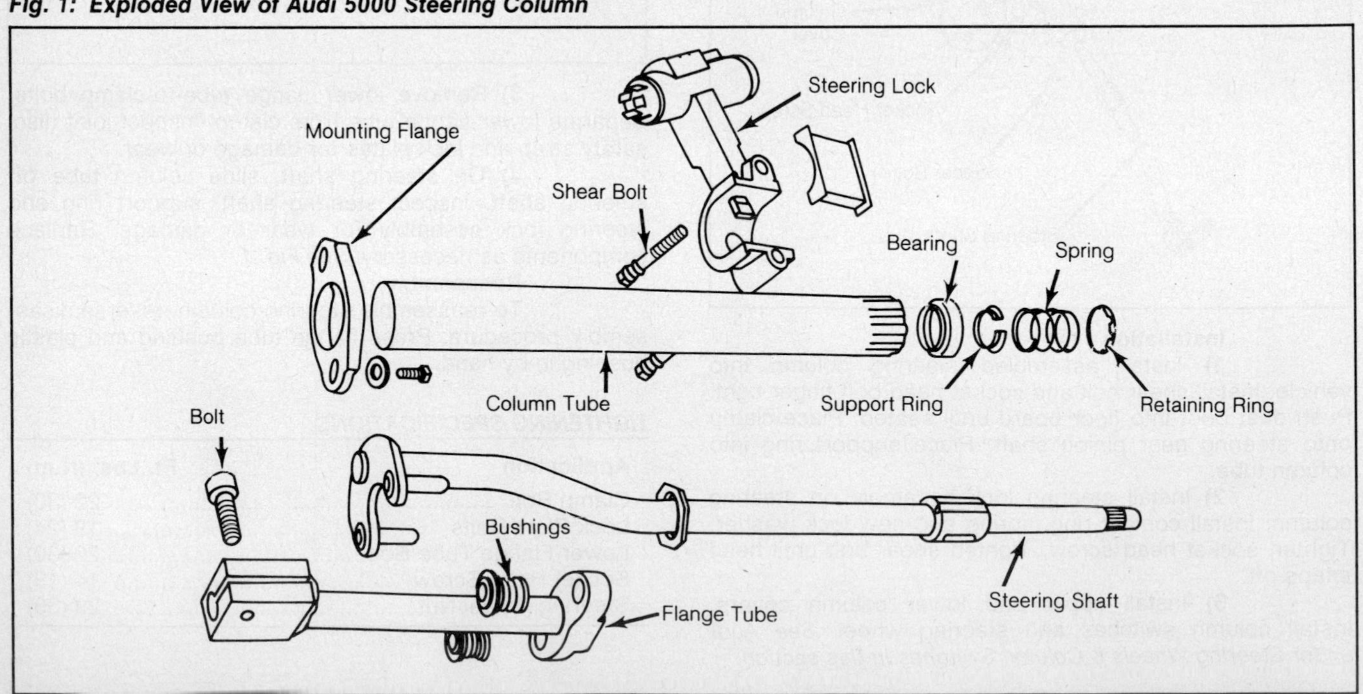
Steering Lock
Mounting Flange
Shear Bolt
Bearing
Spring
Column Tube
Support Ring
Retaining Ring
Bolt
Bushings
Steering Shaft
Flange Tube

Steering Columns

BMW

DESCRIPTION

Steering column consists of a padded steering wheel with horn contact, turn signal/dimmer switch, windshield wiper/washer switch and an anti-theft steering column lock/ignition switch.

Columns on 528e, 533i, 633CSi and 733i are telescoping, while 318i and 320i column is fixed in position. Column is connected to steering gear by universal joints and flexible coupling.

REMOVAL & INSTALLATION

STEERING COLUMN

Removal (318i & 320i)

1) Disconnect battery ground cable. Remove lower half of steering column casing. Lift off pad from center of steering wheel and remove steering wheel. *See BMW in Steering Wheel & Column Switches article in this section*.

2) Remove windshield wiper/washer and turn signal/dimmer switches at switch plate. Remove flasher relay. Loosen set screw and pull out ignition switch.

3) Detach steering shaft at universal joint next to firewall in engine compartment. Loosen casing tube clamp at base of tube in driver's compartment. Drill or chisel off shear head bolts holding steering column to instrument panel. Remove steering column.

4) Lower bearing may be replaced by driving shaft and bearing out from top. Remove snap ring, split ring and bearing.

Installation

1) To install, reverse removal procedure and note the following: Upper column casing and tube must be aligned prior to tightening. When installing turn signal switch, wheels must point straight-ahead.

2) Turn signal switch must be in center position. Finger on canceling cam must point to center. Adjust switch so finger is about .12" (3 mm) from canceling cam.

3) When reinstalling lower bearing, stem of split ring must face bearing and snap ring must fit in locking groove.

Removal (528e, 533i & 633CSi)

1) Disconnect battery ground cable. Remove steering wheel. *See BMW in Steering Wheel & Column Switches article in this section*. Detach lower half of housing below column. Remove turn signal/dimmer and wiper/washer switches.

2) Remove steering shaft bearing holder at top of column. Loosen adjusting nut and mark position of upper and lower shafts. Carefully pry steering shaft bearing from top of column and pull shaft out from above.

3) To remove upper outer tube, disconnect horn. Drill or chisel off switch plate shear screws and disconnect wiring harnesses. Loosen clamp bolt and support screws, then slide down lower outer tube. Lift up outer casing and pull out outer tube.

Installation

To install, reverse removal procedure noting the following: Prior to tightening clamp bolt, ensure that distance from centerline of clamp bolt to end of upper outer tube is 2.05-2.16" (52-55 mm). Align upper and lower steering shaft marks and tighten adjusting nut.

Fig. 1: Outer Tube and Clamp Bolt (528e, 533i & 633CSi)

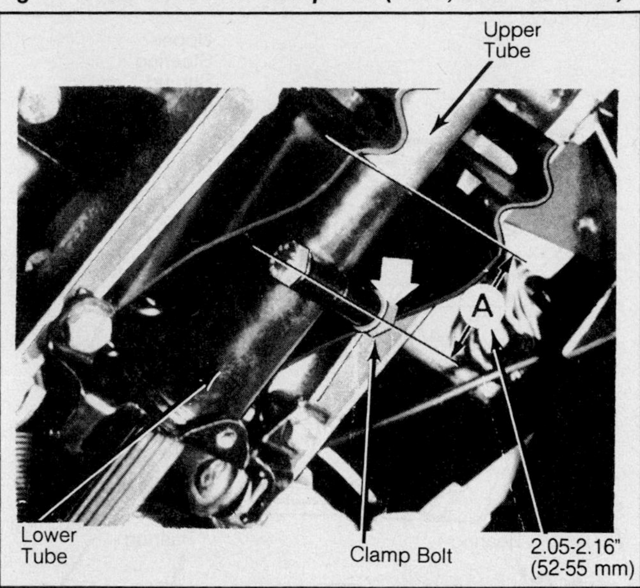
Upper
Tube
A
Lower
Tube
Clamp Bolt
2.05-2.16"
(52-55 mm)

Ensure distance is correct before tightening bolt.

Fig. 2: Upper Steering Shaft and Bearing (All Models Except 733i)

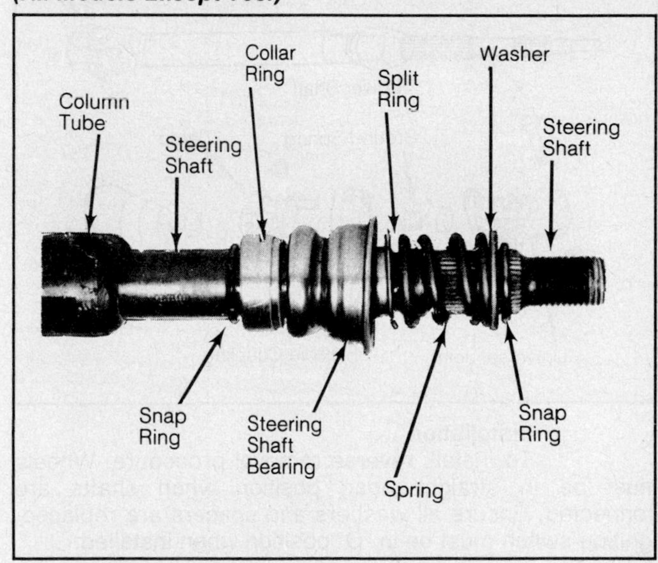
Collar
Ring
Washer
Split
Ring
Column
Tube
Steering
Shaft
Steering
Shaft
Snap
Ring
Steering
Shaft
Bearing
Snap
Ring
Spring

Removal (733i)

1) Disconnect battery ground cable. Remove steering wheel. Remove lower instrument panel cover and steering column housing. Disconnect switches and remove all wiring and ignition switch.

2) Remove clamp bolt and detach lower shaft. Remove 5 bolts holding column assembly to dash and pedal bracket. Remove upper shroud and shaft. Disconnect lower shaft from clamp in engine compartment and pull into passenger compartment.

3) Remove inner steering shaft by taking off collar, snap ring, washer, spring, and lock ring. Pry out upper bearing with screwdrivers. Pry out lower bearing and remove shaft. Remove snap ring, collar, ring and bearing.

Steering Columns

BMW (Cont.)

Fig. 3: Exploded View of Steering Column (733i)

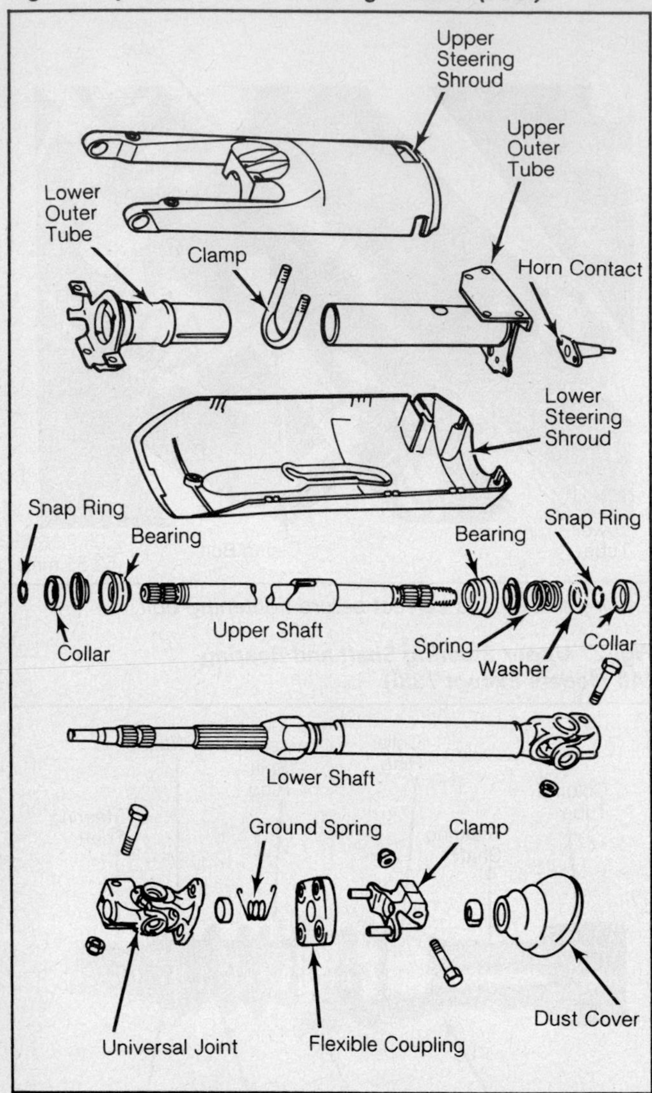
Upper
Steering
Shroud
Upper
Outer
Tube
Lower
Outer
Tube
Clamp
Horn Contact
Lower
Steering
Shroud
Snap Ring
Bearing
Bearing
Snap Ring
Collar
Upper Shaft
Spring
Collar
Washer
Lower Shaft
Ground Spring
Clamp
Dust Cover
Universal Joint
Flexible Coupling

Installation

To install, reverse removal procedure. Wheels must be in straight-ahead position when shafts are connected. Ensure all washers and spacers are replaced. Ignition switch must be in "O" position when installed.

TIGHTENING SPECIFICATIONS

Application	Ft. Lbs. (N.m)
Casing Tube Clamp Bolt	
318i & 320i	12-14 (16-19)
528e, 533i & 633CSi	16-17 (22-23)
Column Bracket-to-Dashboard	16 (22)
Column-to-Housing	10 (14)
Lower-to-Upper Shaft Bolt (733i only)	18 (24)
Steering Wheel Nut	51-61 (70-85)
Universal Joint-to-Steering Shaft	18-20 (24-27)

Steering Columns

CHRYSLER CORP. IMPORTS FWD MODELS

Colt

DESCRIPTION

Collapsible steering system is a 2-piece (upper and lower) column shaft, joined by collapsible (bellows type) section. Bellows section contracts axially under impact without affecting turning motion.

REMOVAL & INSTALLATION

STEERING COLUMN

Removal

1) Remove steering wheel. *See Chrysler Corp. Imports in Steering Wheel & Column Switches article in this section*. Remove steering column cover. Pull out column switch connectors. Pull switch out toward steering wheel end.

NOTE: When removing steering column as an assembly, leave all connector clamps intact.

Fig. 1: Exploded View of Steering Column

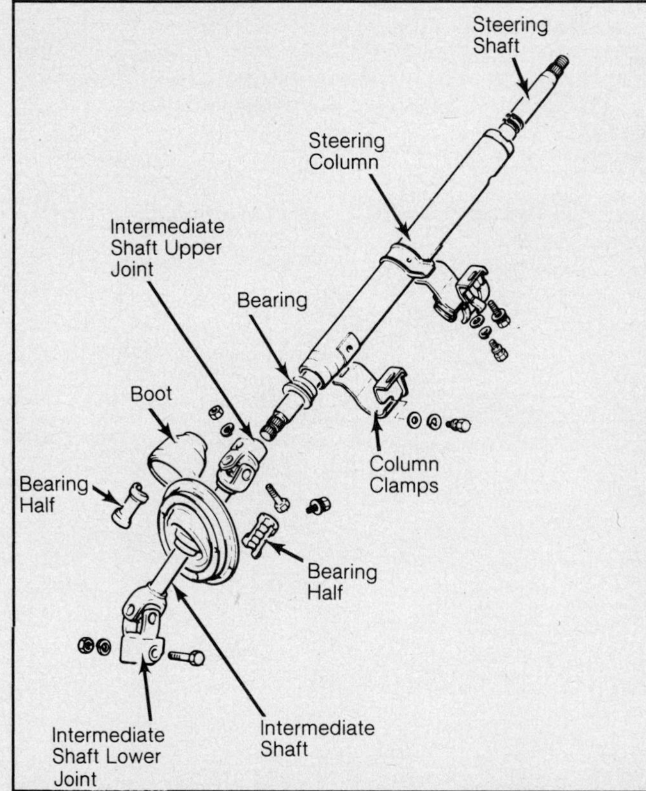
Steering Shaft
Steering Column
Intermediate Shaft Upper Joint
Bearing
Boot
Bearing Half
Column Clamps
Bearing Half
Intermediate Shaft Lower Joint
Intermediate Shaft

2) Remove steering shaft upper coupling bolt. Remove bolts retaining steering column brackets to frame. Disconnect steering shaft from coupling (inside vehicle). Remove steering column assembly.

3) Remove intermediate shaft lower coupling bolt (at steering gear). Remove dust cover retaining bolts. Remove intermediate shaft (with dust cover) toward inside of vehicle.

Installation

1) Install dust cover to intermediate shaft. Make sure bearing side of cover faces steering shaft side of intermediate shaft. *See Fig. 2 & 3.*

Fig. 2: Determining Correct Intermediate Shaft Installation Position

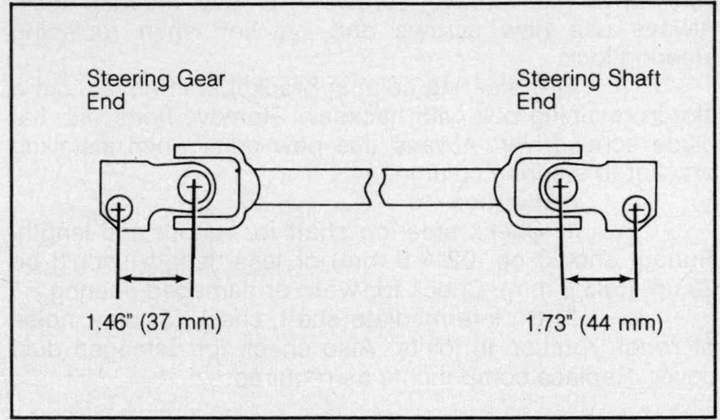
Steering Gear End
Steering Shaft End
1.46" (37 mm)
1.73" (44 mm)

2) Apply grease to bearing and dust cover. Install bearing (2-piece) into dust cover. Attach intermediate shaft lower joint to steering gear and temporarily tighten dust cover bolts. Now tighten lower joint clamp bolt.

Fig. 3: Dust Cover and Bearing Installation

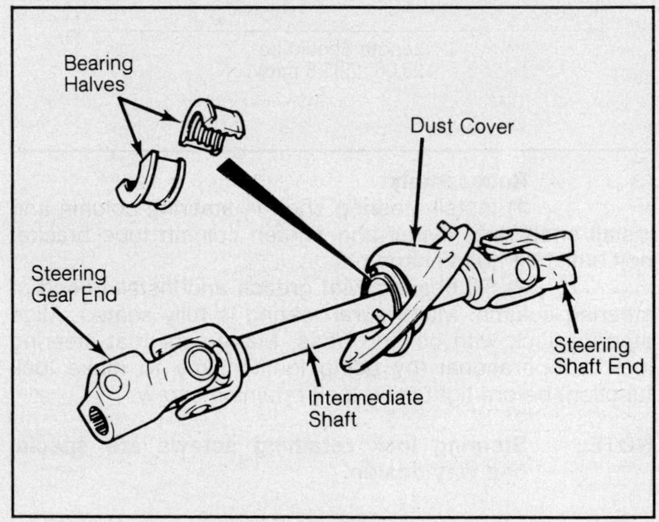
Bearing Halves
Dust Cover
Steering Gear End
Steering Shaft End
Intermediate Shaft

3) Connect intermediate shaft upper joint to steering shaft. Attach steering column brackets to dash. Tighten clamp bolt of intermediate shaft and column bracket bolts.

4) Loosen dust cover bolts and position dust cover so no clearance exists between joint and dust cover sliding surfaces. Tighten dust cover bolts. Adjust steering wheel position if necessary.

OVERHAUL

STEERING COLUMN

Disassembly

1) Remove the 2-piece bearing from dust cover of intermediate shaft. Remove dust cover from intermediate shaft.

2) Remove snap ring from steering shaft (steering wheel end). Unlock steering wheel lock (with ignition key). Remove steering shaft from column by lightly tapping shaft with soft mallet.

CHRYSLER CORP. IMPORTS FWD MODELS (Cont.)

3) If steering lock is to be removed, cut a slot in retaining screws with hacksaw. Use a flat blade screwdriver to remove screws. Remove steering lock. Always use new screws and bracket when replacing steering lock.

4) If steering column bracket is removed, cut a slot in retaining bolt with hacksaw. Remove bolts with flat blade screwdriver. Always use new bolts when installing bracket to steering column.

Inspection

1) Check steering shaft for runout and length. Runout should be .02" (.5 mm) or less, length should be 23.06" (585.8 mm). Check for worn or damaged bearing.

2) On intermediate shaft, check for play, noise or rough rotation in joints. Also check for damaged dust cover. Replace components as required.

Fig. 4: Check Steering Shaft for Length and Damage

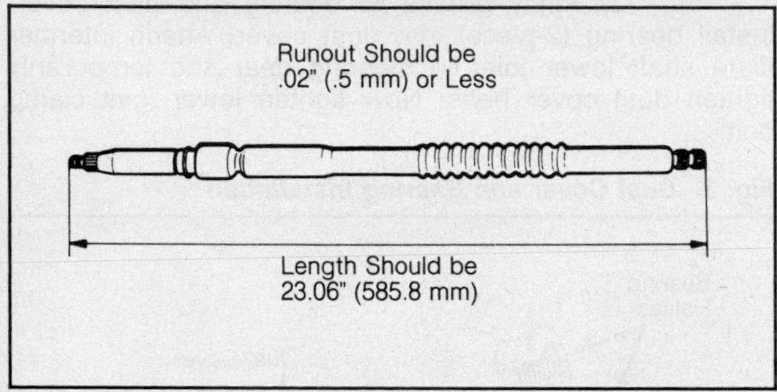
Runout Should be
.02" (.5 mm) or Less
Length Should be
23.06" (585.8 mm)

Reassembly

1) Install steering shaft in steering column and install snap ring. Install and tighten column tube bracket bolt until bolt head snaps off.

2) Fill bearing with grease and install in end of steering column. Make sure bearing is fully seated. Align steering lock with column boss. Make sure that steering lock is operational (by using ignition key to make lock function) before tightening lock retaining screw.

NOTE: **Steering lock retaining screws are special one way design.**

TIGHTENING SPECIFICATIONS

Application	Ft. Lbs. (N.m)
Clamp Joint Bolts	
Upper and Lower	11-14 (15-19)
Steering Wheel Nut	25-32 (34-44)
Column Support Bracket Bolts	7 (10)

Steering Columns

CHRYSLER CORP. IMPORTS RWD MODELS

Challenger, Colt Pickup, Ram-50 Pickup & Sapporo

DESCRIPTION

The steering column consists of a 2-piece shaft joined by a collapsible section. This section contracts under impact without affecting turning. The upper column cover has slits, allowing it to collapse under impact.

REMOVAL & INSTALLATION

STEERING COLUMN

NOTE: **Do not jar or lean on column when servicing.**

Removal

1) Remove air cleaner. Unbolt clamp connecting steering shaft to gear box. If vehicle is equipped with A/C, do this step from underneath vehicle.

2) On 4WD Pickups, slide lower shaft boot up and remove joint assembly-to-gear box clamp bolt. Disconnect joint assembly from steering shaft.

3) On all models, remove horn pad, steering wheel nut, and remove steering wheel using a puller. Loosen tilt lock lever or knob and lower the column. Remove column cover and floor dust cover.

4) Unplug column switch connectors, leaving clamps intact, and pull out switch toward shaft end. Remove tilt bracket, then remove column.

Installation

1) Insert steering shaft from inside vehicle. Connect joint assembly to steering shaft and gear box (4WD Pickups). Connect shaft to steering gear housing main shaft with bolt hole facing down. Tighten clamp bolt. Attach tilt bracket to pedal support member.

2) Apply sealer to dust cover bolt holes. Install dust cover to body. Install column switch and route and secure wiring harness along column tube. Reconnect switch connectors and install column cover.

3) Make sure wheels are straight and steering wheel lock is locked. Install steering wheel, tighten nut and install horn pad.

OVERHAUL

STEERING COLUMN

Disassembly

1) Remove clamp bolt and remove column tube and joint cover. Make a slit in steering lock bracket bolt head and column support bolt head and remove lock and support.

Fig. 1: Exploded View of Challenger & Sapporo Steering Column Components

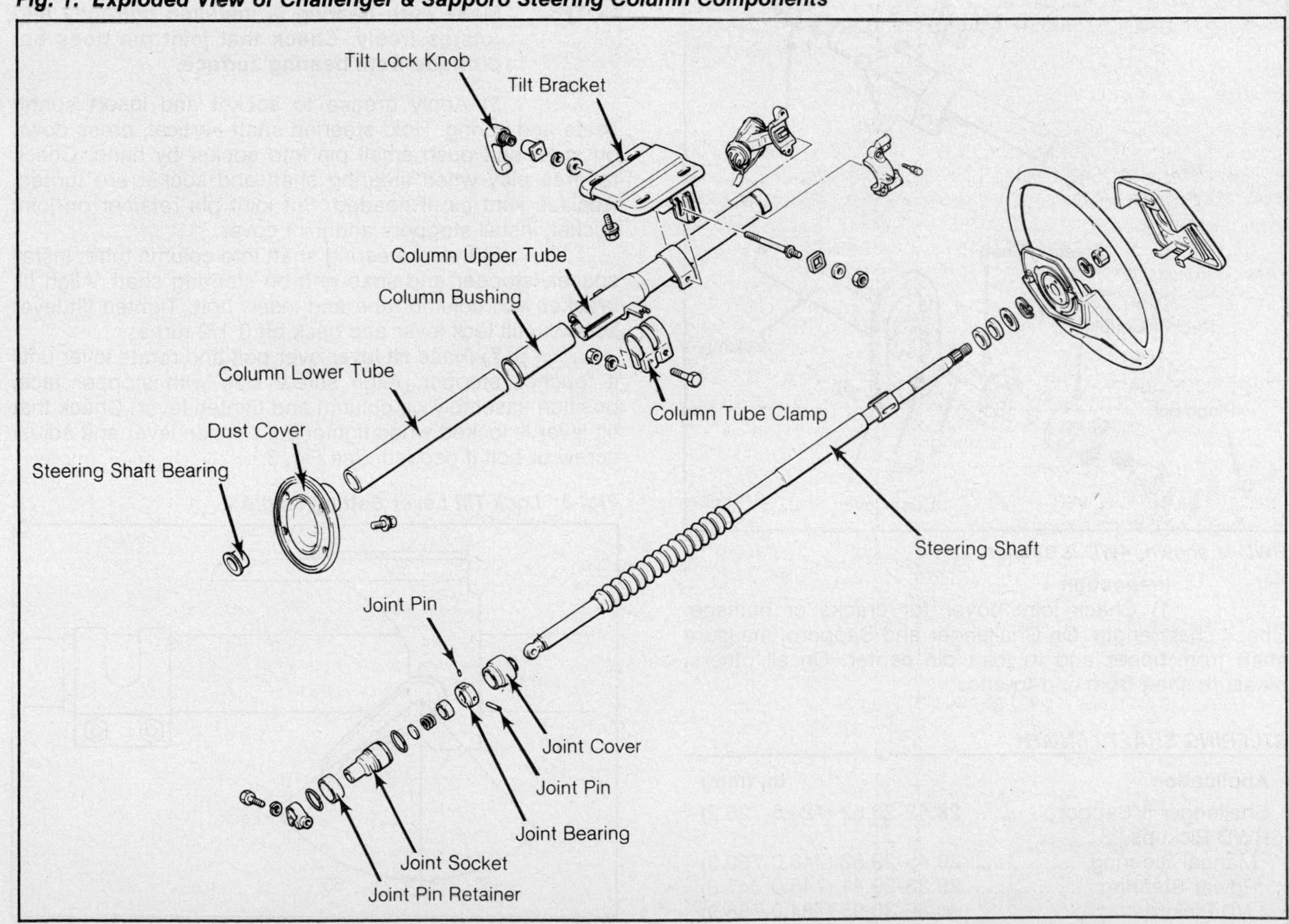
Tilt Lock Knob
Tilt Bracket
Column Upper Tube
Column Bushing
Column Lower Tube
Dust Cover
Steering Shaft Bearing
Column Tube Clamp
Steering Shaft
Joint Pin
Joint Cover
Joint Pin
Joint Bearing
Joint Socket
Joint Pin Retainer

Steering Columns

CHRYSLER CORP. IMPORTS RWD MODELS (Cont.)

2) Remove snap ring from upper shaft (upper and lower shaft snap rings on 4WD Pickups). Remove shaft (with dust seal and bushing) from column tube.

3) On RWD Pickups, remove yoke and rubber coupling from steering shaft lower end. Remove rubber band from dust seal and move seal to expose retainer caulking. Drill caulking and remove retainer with a drift. Remove rubber band, dust cover, dust seal and bushing from shaft.

NOTE: Do not remove pin from steering shaft. Do not disassemble socket.

4) On 4WD Pickups, slide dust cover to lower shaft side. Separate lower and upper shafts. Remove pipe, spring and upper boot from upper shaft. Remove dust cover and lower boot from lower shaft.

5) On Challenger and Sapporo, slide off joint socket cover toward shaft. Remove stoppers and retainer toward socket. With shaft upright, press down on shaft and remove small retaining pin with a magnet. Do not drive out pin. Remove joint socket. Remove large retaining pin only if necessary, using a hand press.

Fig. 2: Exploded View of Pickup Steering Column

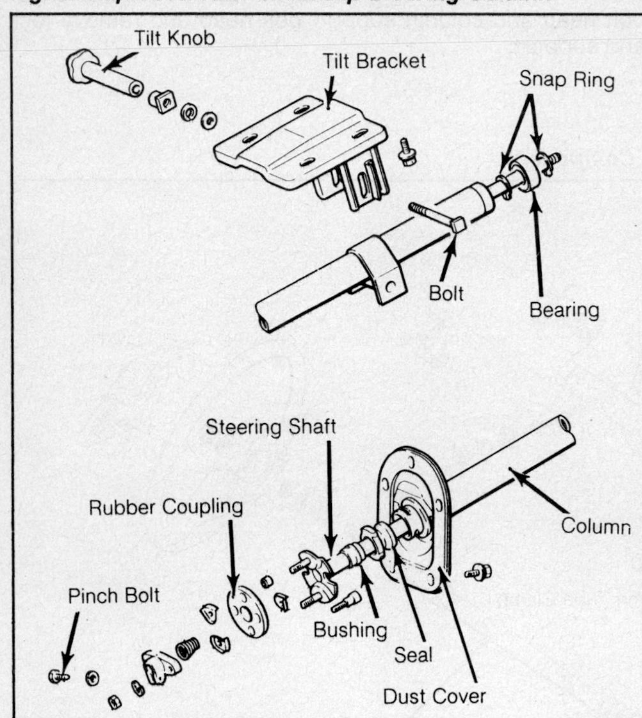
Tilt Knob
Tilt Bracket
Snap Ring
Bolt
Bearing
Steering Shaft
Rubber Coupling
Column
Pinch Bolt
Bushing
Seal
Dust Cover

RWD is shown, 4WD is similar.

Inspection

1) Check joint cover for cracks or damage. Check shaft length. On Challenger and Sapporo, measure shaft from upper end to joint pin center. On all others, measure shaft from end-to-end.

STEERING SHAFT LENGTH

Application	In. (mm)
Challenger & Sapporo	28.52-28.62 (724.5-726.9)
RWD Pickups	
Manual Steering	29.45-29.53 (748.0-750.0)
Power Steering	29.33-29.41 (745.0-747.0)
4WD Pickups	30.86-30.95 (784.0-786.0)

2) On RWD and 4WD Pickups, check steering shaft-to-column bearing clearance. Clearance should be .0004-.0020" (.010-.050 mm). Check steering coupling for damage. On 4WD Pickups, check upper and lower universal joints for play or sticking. Check upper and lower boots and dust cover for damage.

3) On all models, check steering shaft distortion using a dial indicator. Shaft should not be bent more than .020" (.50 mm). Check tilt bracket for deformation or cracks. Check collapsible tube for damage.

4) Hold lower end of steering shaft and move upper shaft to check for free play between upper and lower shaft splines. Check upper and lower column bearings for wear or damage. On Challenger and Sapporo, check column bushing for wear.

Reassembly (Challenger and Sapporo)

1) Install column tube bushings onto upper and lower column tubes until bushing stop seats in column tube end. Tighten column tube clamp bolt.

2) Coat inside of steering shaft bearing with grease. Coat outside of bearing with adhesive and install bearing into lower column tube.

3) Align column tube hole with wheel lock guide dowel to install steering wheel lock. Insert key and check for lock proper operation. Tighten shear bolts until bolt heads twist off.

4) Install joint bearing (flanged surface facing up) onto shaft lower end. Rotate bearing 90° and insert large pin.

NOTE: Make sure bearing is installed correctly and rotates freely. Check that joint pin does not protrude from bearing surface.

5) Apply grease to socket and insert spring seats and spring. Hold steering shaft vertical, press down on shaft and push small pin into socket by hand. Check for free play when steering shaft and socket are turned. Replace joint pin if needed. Put joint pin retainer on joint socket, install stoppers and joint cover.

6) Insert steering shaft into column tube. Install spacer, stopper and snap ring on steering shaft. Align tilt bracket with column tube and insert bolt. Tighten tilt lever screw to tilt lock lever and back off 3 1/2 turns.

7) Place tilt lever over bolt and rotate lever until it touches stopper. Align screw side with stopper face, position assembly on column and tighten lever. Check that tilt lever is locked when tightened. Loosen lever and adjust screw or bolt if needed. *See Fig. 3.*

Fig. 3: Lock Tilt Lever Setting Angle

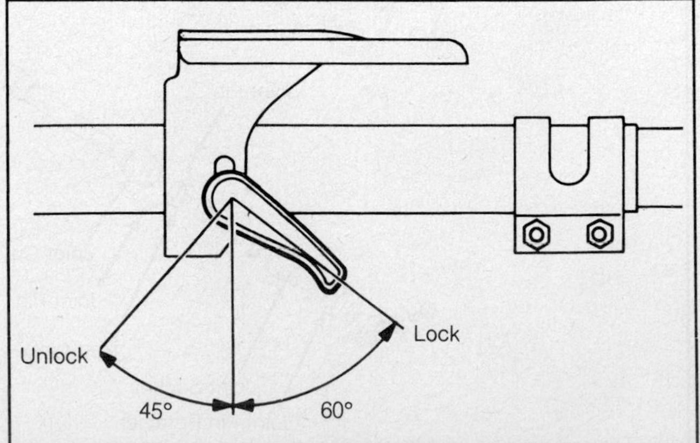
Unlock
Lock
45°
60°

CHRYSLER CORP. IMPORTS RWD MODELS (Cont.)

Reassembly (Colt Pickup and Ram-50 Pickup)

1) On 4WD models, assemble upper and lower boots to shafts, but not to universal joints. Install dust cover over lower shaft. Grease upper and lower shafts and serrated part of pipe. Assemble spring and pipe to upper shaft.

2) Tilt lower shaft 10° from upper shaft and insert lower shaft into pipe until 2.36" (60 mm) of splines remain. Rotate lower shaft clockwise until pipe plate and upper shaft plate are aligned. Push lower shaft into upper shaft until 1.38" (35 mm) of splines remain.

NOTE: **When inserting lower shaft, make sure there is no play in serrated part of pipe. After joining shafts, make sure upper and lower shaft yokes are within 5° of each other.**

3) Align boot arrows with yoke slits to assemble upper and lower boots to universal joints.

4) On all models, align column tube hole with wheel lock guide dowel and install lock. Insert ignition key and check lock operation. Tighten lock bracket shear bolts until bolt heads twist off.

5) Attach column support to tube and tighten support shear bolts until bolt heads twist off. Install joint cover to column, making sure clamp bolt faces up. *See Fig. 4.* Tighten clamp bolt.

Fig. 4: Installing Joint Cover to Column (Colt Pickup & Ram-50 Pickup)

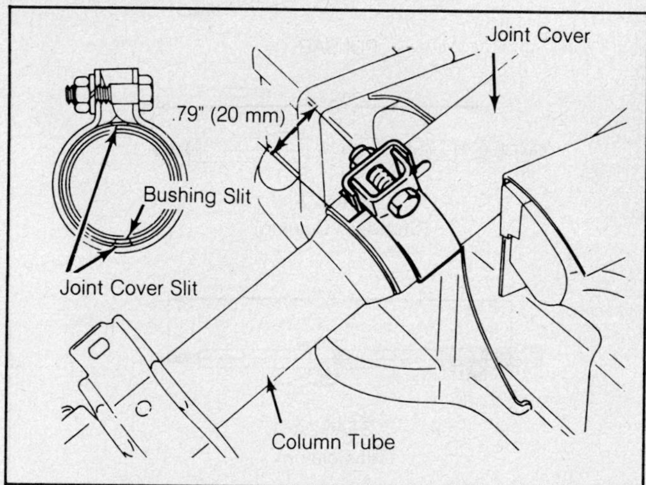
Joint Cover
.79" (20 mm)
Bushing Slit
Joint Cover Slit
Column Tube

6) Apply grease to bearing roller surfaces of column tube and inside dust cover grommet. Install steering shaft bushing, dust seal, dust cover, rubber band and retainer in order.

7) Install springs and sliders on steering shaft. Fill inside of socket with grease and install retainer on socket, making sure punch marks are aligned. Stake retainer at two points with a punch. Fill inside of dust cover with grease and install dust cover over socket.

8) Install rubber band on dust cover. Apply grease to horn ground spring seats and attach coupling and yoke to steering shaft.

TIGHTENING SPECIFICATIONS

Application	Ft. Lbs. (N.m)
Joint Assembly-to Gear Box (4WD)	24 (33)
Steering Shaft Clamp	
Challenger & Sapporo	17 (23)
Steering Shaft-to-Joint (4WD)	24 (33)
Steering Wheel Nut	29 (39)

Steering Columns

DATSUN/NISSAN – EXCEPT 280ZX, 280ZX TURBO & PICKUP

DESCRIPTION

Steering columns are collapsible on impact. A flexible coupling and 2 universal joints (1 joint or flexible coupling on 200SX) connect steering column and gear assembly. A tilt steering column is available.

Fig. 1: Maxima, Pulsar, Sentra & Stanza Steering Column Assembly

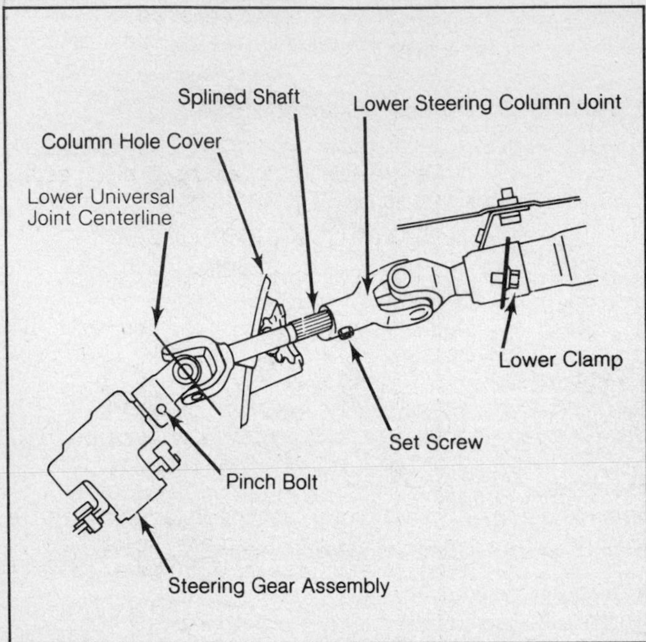
Splined Shaft
Lower Steering Column Joint
Column Hole Cover
Lower Universal
Joint Centerline
Lower Clamp
Set Screw
Pinch Bolt
Steering Gear Assembly

200SX uses one universal joint or flexible coupling.

REMOVAL & INSTALLATION

STEERING COLUMN

Removal

1) Disconnect battery negative cable. Remove horn pad and column shaft nut. Remove steering wheel with a puller. Remove clamp bolt securing column lower universal joint or flexible coupling to stub or worm shaft (Maxima and 200SX). On all other models, remove column lower universal joint.

2) On all models, remove steering column shell cover. Separate turn signal switch assembly and combination light switch from column.

3) Remove heater ducts. Remove jacket tube bracket from floorboard (Maxima and 200SX). Remove column mounting bolts and column from interior side.

STEERING COLUMN DIMENSIONS

Models	[1] "A" In. (mm)
Maxima	15.95 (405.2)
Pulsar	23.37-23.43 (593.6-595.2)
Sentra	18.95-19.07 (481.3-484.3)
Stanza	
Std. Column	24.21-24.25 (615.0-616.0)
Tilt Column	26.02-26.06 (661.0-662.0)
200SX	
Manual Steering	7.05 (179.0)
Power Steering	7.09 (180.0)

[1] – See Fig. 2 for measuring points.

Inspection

Check column bearings for smooth operation. If necessary, lubricate bearings with grease. Check jacket tube for deformation or breaks. Replace parts as required. If vehicle has been in a collision, check column dimension "A" in Steering Column Dimensions Table. *See Fig. 2.*

Installation (Maxima)

1) Set wheels straight ahead. Connect lower joint to pinion, making sure pinion punch mark faces rear of vehicle. Install column into lower joint, making sure clamp bolt faces lower joint notch. Loosely tighten column mounting bracket to support column upper end.

2) Install and tighten jacket tube bracket and lower joint securing bolt. Tighten column mounting bracket. Install steering wheel on column shaft and tighten

Fig. 2: Datsun/Nissan Steering Column Measuring Points

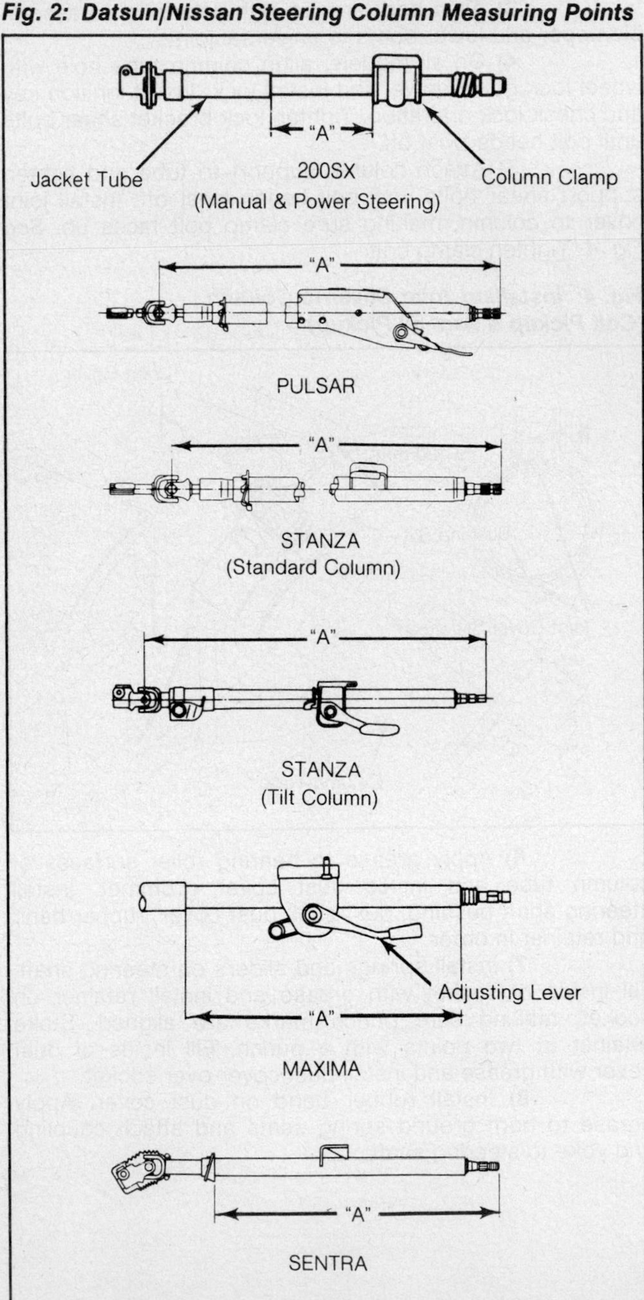
"A"
Jacket Tube
200SX
(Manual & Power Steering)
Column Clamp
"A"
PULSAR
"A"
STANZA
(Standard Column)
"A"
STANZA
(Tilt Column)
Adjusting Lever
"A"
MAXIMA
"A"
SENTRA

DATSUN/NISSAN – EXCEPT 280ZX, 280ZX TURBO & PICKUP (Cont.)

Fig. 3: Datsun/Nissan Collapsible Steering Column

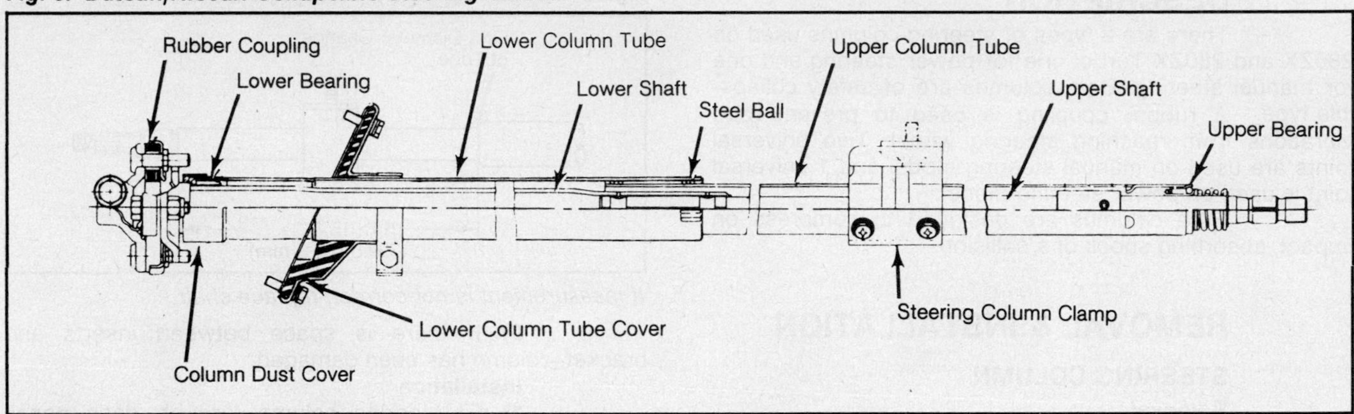
Rubber Coupling
Lower Bearing
Lower Column Tube
Lower Shaft
Steel Ball
Upper Column Tube
Upper Shaft
Upper Bearing
Steering Column Clamp
Lower Column Tube Cover
Column Dust Cover

Bolt locations differ between models.

nut. Check horn, turn wheel lock-to-lock and check centering and turning ease.

Installation (200SX)

1) Remove column band and install centering band (power steering models). Set wheels straight ahead. Connect column to stub or worm shaft, making sure punch mark at column shaft upper end faces upward. Loosely tighten stub or worm shaft securing bolts to support column upper end.

2) Loosely tighten column mounting bracket. Install jacket tube bracket to floorboard. Tighten stub or worm shaft securing bolts, then tighten column mounting bracket bolts.

3) Remove centering band and install column band (power steering models). Install steering wheel on column shaft and tighten nut. Check horn, turn wheel lock-to-lock and check centering and turning ease.

Installation (All Other Models)

To install, reverse removal procedure, noting the following: Loosely tighten lower bracket and joint clamp bolts until column is installed, then tighten bolts. After installing steering wheel, check horn, wheel centering and turning ease.

OVERHAUL

STEERING COLUMN

Overhaul is not recommended for 200SX models. If damaged, replace steering column as an assembly.

Disassembly (Maxima, Pulsar, Sentra & Stanza)

Be sure steering lock is unlocked. Remove jacket tube bracket and column mounting bracket if necessary. Remove snap ring and spring (Maxima) from steering column shaft. Remove washer and pull column shaft from bottom of jacket tube. Remove "O" ring from column shaft.

Reassembly

Inspect jacket tube and column shaft for excessive wear or damage. Coat column upper and lower bearings with grease. Install new "O" ring. Slide column shaft into column tube from bottom. Compress spring using wire around coils before installing (Maxima). Install washer and new snap ring (rounded face toward upper bearing). Make sure column shaft rotates easily in tube.

TIGHTENING SPECIFICATIONS

Application	Ft. Lbs. (N.m)
Coupling-to-Worm Shaft	
200SX	29-36 (39-49)
Lower Joint-to-Column	
Pulsar	17-22 (24-29)
Sentra	22-29 (29-39)
Stanza	23-31 (31-42)
Lower Joint-to-Coupling	
Maxima	29-36 (39-49)
Lower Joint-to-Gear	
Maxima	24-28 (32-38)
Pulsar	17-22 (24-29)
Sentra	22-29 (29-39)
Stanza	23-31 (31-42)
Steering Column Mounting Bolts	
Maxima & 200SX	9-13 (12-18)
Pulsar, Sentra & Stanza	7-10 (10-14)
Steering Wheel Nut	
Maxima, Stanza & 200SX	27-38 (37-52)
Pulsar & Sentra	29-40 (39-54)

Steering Columns

DATSUN/NISSAN 280ZX & 280ZX TURBO

DESCRIPTION

There are 2 types of steering columns used on 280ZX and 280ZX Turbo, one for power steering and one for manual steering. Both columns are of safety collapsible type. A rubber coupling is used to prevent road vibrations from reaching steering wheel. Two universal joints are used on manual steering model and 1 universal joint is used on power steering model.

Both columns are designed to compress on impact, absorbing shock of a collision.

REMOVAL & INSTALLATION

STEERING COLUMN

Removal

NOTE: During service procedure involving steering assembly, do not hammer or exert extreme pressure on steering column or damage to collapsible section may result.

Fig. 1: Manual Steering Upper and Lower Shaft Assembly

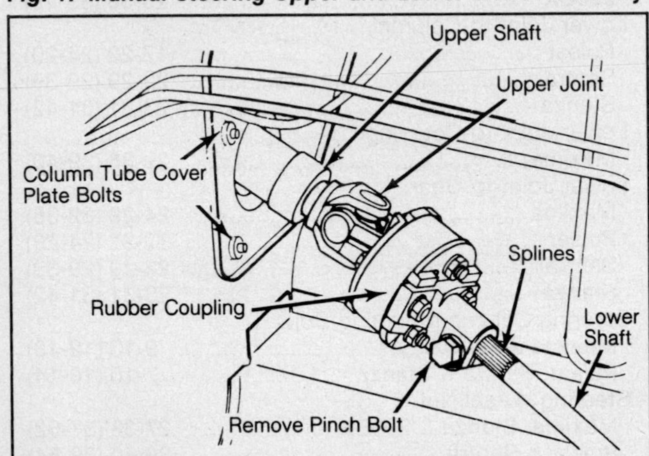
Upper Shaft
Upper Joint
Column Tube Cover
Plate Bolts
Splines
Rubber Coupling
Lower
Shaft
Remove Pinch Bolt

Remove pinch bolt and pull column through firewall.

1) On models with power steering, remove bolt retaining stub shaft to rubber coupling. On models with manual steering, remove bolt retaining lower joint to rubber coupling.

2) On all models, remove steering wheel. *See Datsun/Nissan in Steering Wheel & Column Switches article in this section*. Remove column tube bracket and cover from dash panel. Remove column mounting bracket and remove column assembly from passenger compartment side.

Inspection

1) Check all steering components for free, smooth rotation. Inspect jacket tube for deformation or breakage (replace if necessary).

2) Check column shaft spring for proper tension. Free length is 1.075" (27.3 mm), loaded length is .059" @ 66 lbs. (15 mm @ 29.9 kg).

3) Measure distance from upper end of tube collapsible section to first diameter change of tube. *See Fig. 2*. Measurement should be 15.73-15.77" (399.5-400.6 mm).

4) If measurement is not correct, tube has been crushed and should be replaced. Inspect inserts in column support clamp.

Fig. 2: Measuring Points on Collapsible Column

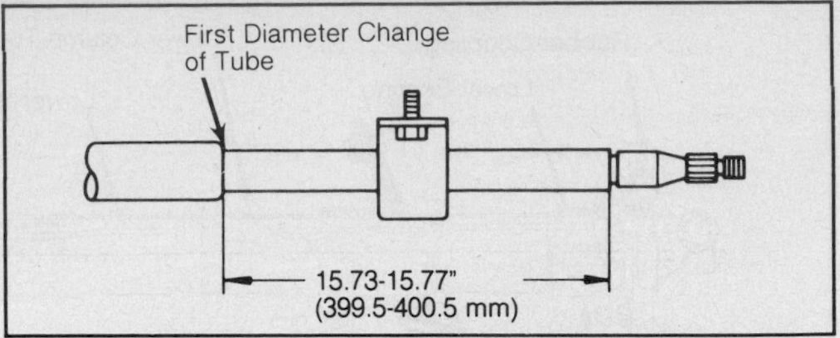
First Diameter Change
of Tube
15.73-15.77"
(399.5-400.5 mm)

If measurement is not correct, replace shaft.

5) If there is space between inserts and bracket, column has been damaged.

Installation

1) Fit steering column through dash panel. Install steering column onto stub shaft (power steering) or onto lower joint (manual steering).

2) Set front wheels in straight-ahead position. Line up slits of universal joints with punch mark on upper end of steering shaft (punch mark should be on top).

3) Connect column and tighten bolts. After installation, ensure steering wheel rotates smoothly.

Fig. 3: Manual Steering Lower Shaft and Pinion Gear

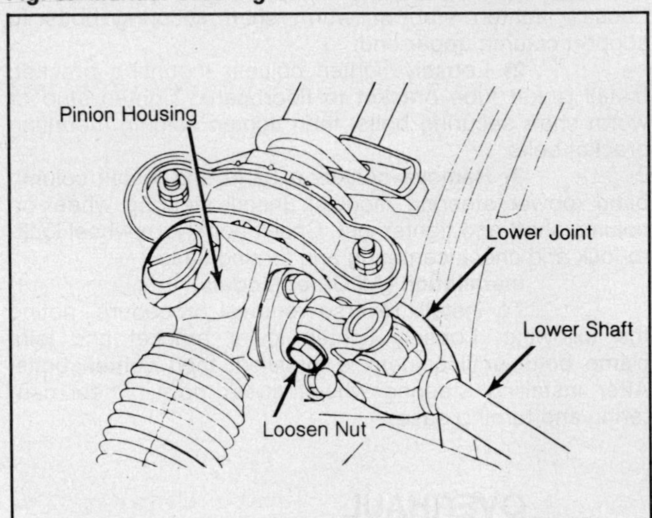
Pinion Housing
Lower Joint
Lower Shaft
Loosen Nut

Remove bolt retaining stub shaft to rubber coupling.

OVERHAUL

Refer to Inspection in this article for description of components which may be replaced. If damage to collapsible section is suspected, steering column replacement is recommended.

TIGHTENING SPECIFICATIONS

Application	Ft. Lbs. (N.m)
Column Clamp Bolt	9-13 (12-18)
Coupling-to-Column Shaft	12-14 (16-19)
Lower Joint-to-Pinion Gear	29-36 (39-49)
Lower Joint-to-Rubber Coupling	17-20 (23-27)
Stub Shaft-to-Coupling	24-28 (33-38)
Steering Wheel Nut	29-36 (39-49)

Steering Columns

DATSUN/NISSAN PICKUP

DESCRIPTION

Pickup steering columns are safety collapsible type. Columns are supported by column bracket at dash and attached to floor pan by floor bracket. Steering shaft uses a universal joint and is attached to gearbox by a flexible rubber coupling.

REMOVAL & INSTALLATION

STEERING COLUMN

Removal

1) Remove rubber coupling to gearbox bolt. Remove steering wheel. *See Datsun/Nissan in Steering Wheel & Column Switches article in this section.*

2) Remove steering column shell covers. Remove combination switch assembly. Remove heater duct from under dash (around steering column).

3) Remove column bracket and floor bracket. Remove steering column assembly through passenger compartment.

NOTE: **During service procedure involving the steering assembly, do not hammer or exert extreme pressure on steering column or damage to the collapsible section may result.**

Installation

1) Place wheels in straight-ahead position. Install steering column assembly through passenger compartment. Attach rubber coupling to gear box, make sure punch mark on upper end of steering shaft faces up.

Fig. 1: Exploded View of Manual Steering Column

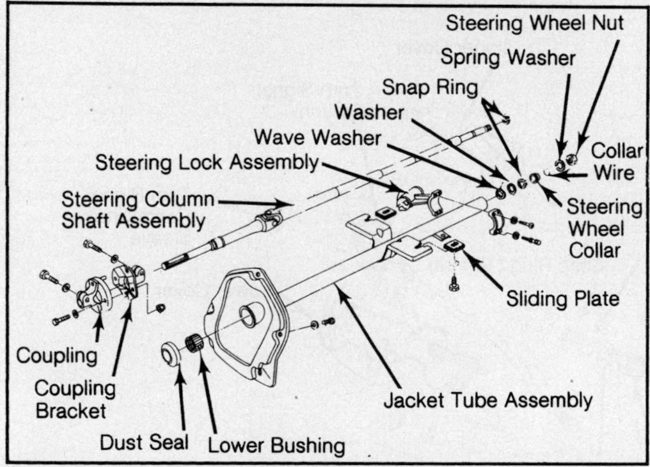
Steering Wheel Nut
Spring Washer
Snap Ring
Washer
Wave Washer
Steering Lock Assembly
Collar
Wire
Steering Column Shaft Assembly
Steering Wheel Collar
Sliding Plate
Coupling
Coupling Bracket
Jacket Tube Assembly
Dust Seal
Lower Bushing

2) Loosely install column bracket bolts. Loosely install floor pan bracket bolts. With column and floor bracket bolts installed, tighten rubber coupling bolt.

3) Tighten column bracket bolts and then floor pan bracket bolts. Complete installation in reverse order of removal. Make sure steering wheel turns smoothly.

OVERHAUL

STEERING COLUMN

Disassembly

1) Remove rubber coupling assembly. On steering lock assembly, drill out shear type screws, install screw extractor, and remove screws.

2) Disconnect and remove steering lock. Remove snap ring (discard ring) and separate each part. Remove dust seal and lower bushing.

Inspection

1) Check column bearings for damage or unevenness. Check jacket tube for damage, replace if necessary.

2) If vehicle has had a light collision, check dimensions "A", "B", and "C". *See Fig. 2.* If they are not within specifications, replace steering column as an assembly.

Fig. 2: Measuring Points for Checking Steering Column Lengths

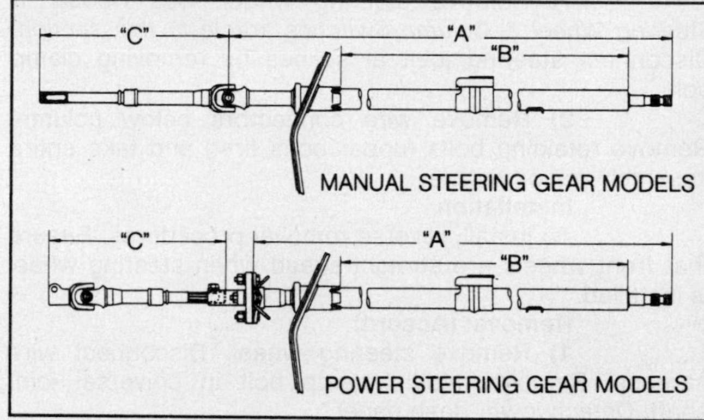
"C"
"A"
"B"
MANUAL STEERING GEAR MODELS
"C"
"A"
"B"
POWER STEERING GEAR MODELS

Use Steering Column Measurements table with illustration.

STEERING COLUMN MEASUREMENTS

Model	"A" In. (mm)	"B" In. (mm)	"C" In. (mm)
Manual			
2-WD	33.57-33.65 (852.7-854.7)	23.76-23.84 (603.6-605.6)	13.33-13.41 (338.7-340.7)
4-WD	33.57-33.65 (852.7-854.7)	23.76-23.84 (603.6-605.6)	11.81-11.89 (300.1-302.1)
Power			
2-WD			
Diesel	30.83-30.91 (783.0-785.0)	23.76-23.84 (603.6-605.6)	9.84-9.92 (250.0-252.0)
Gas	32.01-32.09 (813.0-815.0)	23.76-23.84 (603.6-605.6)	8.68-8.76 (220.4-222.4)
4-WD	32.01-32.09 (813.0-815.0)	23.76-23.84 (603.6-605.6)	10.20-10.28 (259.2-261.2)

Reassembly

To reassemble, reverse order of disassembly procedures. Apply grease to column bearings and other moving parts. Be careful not to damage remote control lever bracket. Always use new snap rings.

TIGHTENING SPECIFICATIONS

Application	Ft. Lbs. (N.m)
Rubber Coupling Bolt	29-36 (39-49)
Column Support Bracket	6-8 (8-11)
Steering Wheel Nut	29-36 (39-49)

Steering Columns

HONDA

DESCRIPTION

Steering columns are mounted with an impact absorbing plate on upper bracket that deforms under pressure.

Plastic bracket collar at lower end of column allows assembly to slide, and double universal joints absorb impact without the need for collapsing column.

REMOVAL & INSTALLATION

STEERING COLUMN

Removal (Civic & Prelude)

1) Remove steering wheel. *See Honda in Steering Wheel & Column Switches article in this section.* Disconnect steering joint at splines by removing clamp bolt.

2) Remove wire connectors below column. Remove retaining bolts (upper bolts first) and take entire assembly out of vehicle.

Installation

To install, reverse removal procedures. Ensure that front wheels are straight-ahead when steering wheel is installed.

Removal (Accord)

1) Remove steering wheel. Disconnect wire harness. Remove middle clamp bolt in universal joint shaft. Detach lower dash panel.

2) Remove nuts retaining column to mounting brackets (remove upper nuts first). Remove column from vehicle.

NOTE: **If steering wheel has been removed, ignition switch must be in "LOCK" position to retain steering shaft during column removal.**

Installation

1) Insert column in vehicle. Slide upper half of connector on bottom end of steering shaft. Install top bolt across flat part of shaft. Loosely install upper bracket nuts.

2) Pull down on column to seat bending plate against hook. Connect bottom connector to gearbox shaft, install bolt and tighten. Loosely install lower bracket.

3) Tighten upper and lower bracket nuts. To complete installation, reverse removal procedures.

OVERHAUL

STEERING COLUMN

Disassembly

1) Remove steering wheel and column switchs. *See Honda in Steering Wheel & Column Switches article in this section*.

2) Remove rubber bands, bending plate and upper mounting plate. On Civic and Prelude models, remove snap ring and steering shaft washer from upper end of steering shaft.

3) Turn ignition switch to "I" position on Prelude or "ACC" position on Civic. On all models, remove plastic collar, shaft bushing and column hanger bushing.

4) Pull steering shaft out from bottom end of column. Remove thrust ring, bushing and horn ring from top end of column.

Fig. 1: Exploded View of Civic and Prelude Steering Column

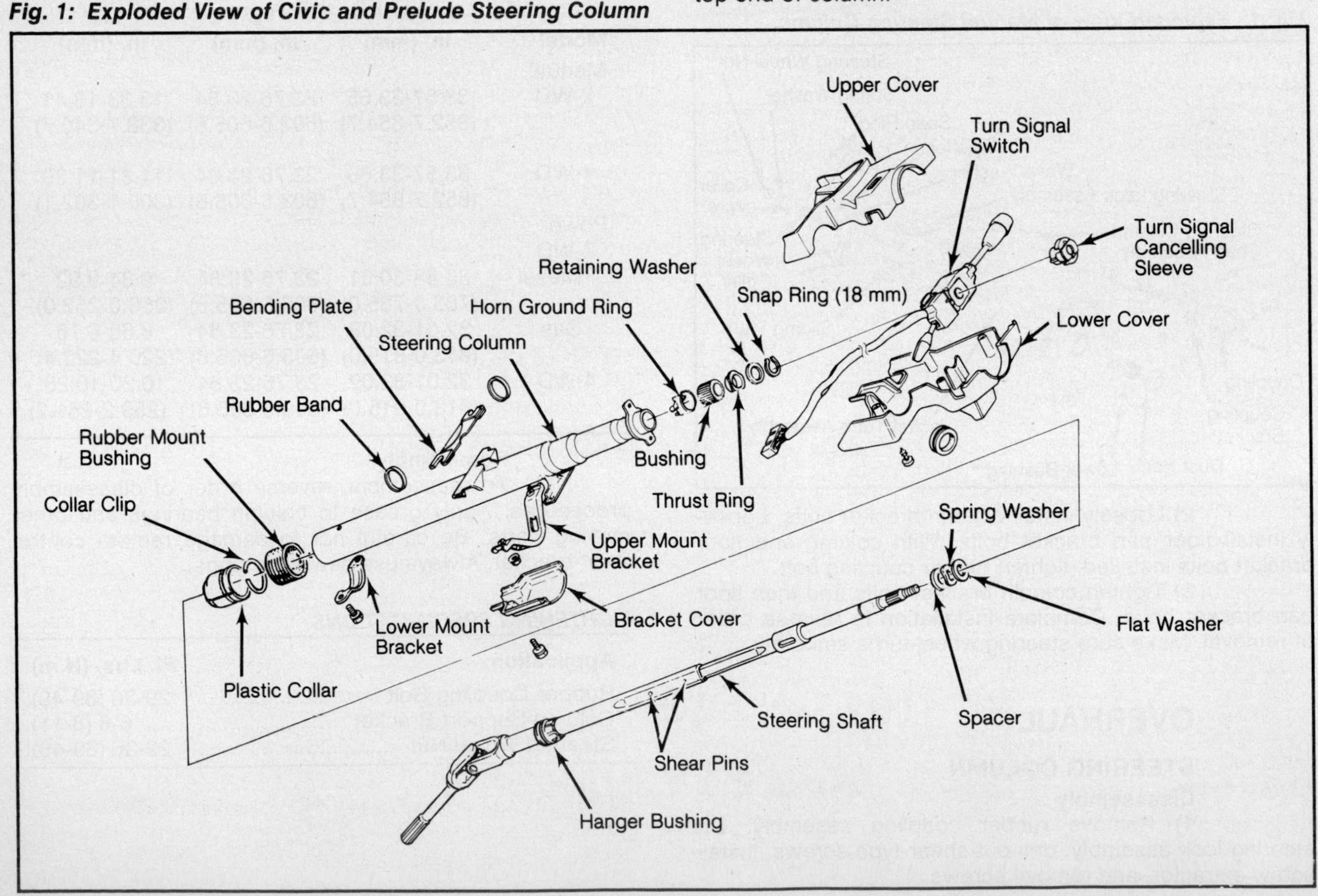
Upper Cover
Turn Signal Switch
Turn Signal Cancelling Sleeve
Retaining Washer
Snap Ring (18 mm)
Bending Plate
Horn Ground Ring
Lower Cover
Steering Column
Rubber Band
Rubber Mount Bushing
Bushing
Collar Clip
Thrust Ring
Spring Washer
Upper Mount Bracket
Bracket Cover
Lower Mount Bracket
Flat Washer
Plastic Collar
Steering Shaft
Spacer
Shear Pins
Hanger Bushing

Steering Columns

HONDA (Cont.)

Fig. 2: Exploded View of Accord Steering Column

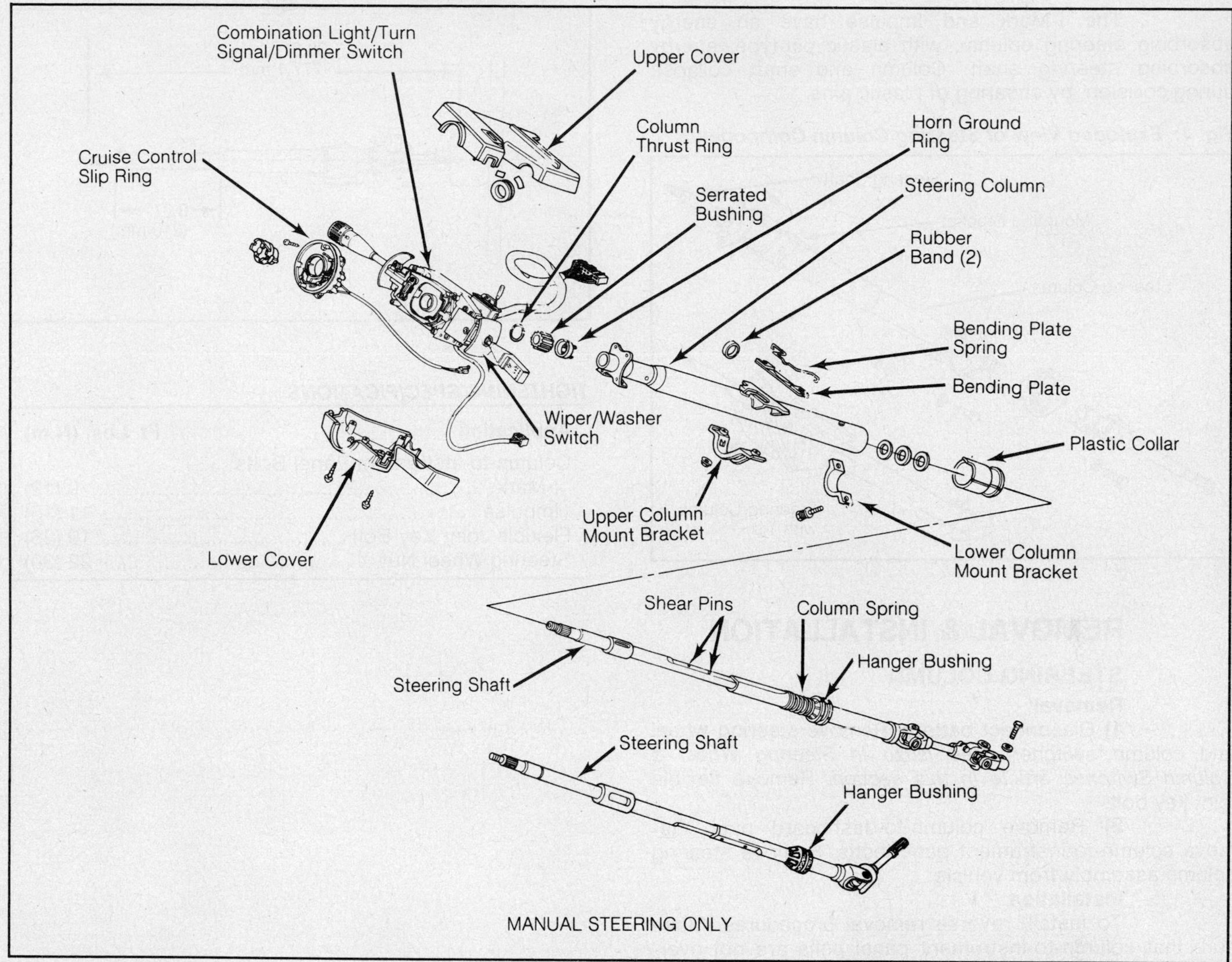

Combination Light/Turn Signal/Dimmer Switch
Upper Cover
Cruise Control Slip Ring
Column Thrust Ring
Horn Ground Ring
Serrated Bushing
Steering Column
Rubber Band (2)
Bending Plate Spring
Bending Plate
Plastic Collar
Wiper/Washer Switch
Upper Column Mount Bracket
Lower Column Mount Bracket
Lower Cover
Shear Pins
Column Spring
Hanger Bushing
Steering Shaft
Steering Shaft
Hanger Bushing
MANUAL STEERING ONLY

5) On Accord models with power steering, remove rubber stop, plastic collar, washer, spring, washer and snap ring before pulling steering shaft out of bottom end of steering column.

Reassembly

1) Install horn ground ring, serrated bushing and thrust ring in steering column. Flat sides of thrust ring should be aligned with slots in steering column.

2) Grease top end of steering shaft and carefully insert in column. Be careful not to bend horn ground ring. Fill bottom of column with grease and install plastic hanger bushing.

3) Align tab in column with cut-away in bushing. On Accord models with power steering, install snap ring, washer, spring and washer before installing plastic hanger bushing.

4) On all models, install plastic collar to bottom of column, align round projection on inside of collar with hole in column. On Accord models with power steering, install rubber stop. On Civic and Prelude models, install snap ring to top end of steering shaft.

5) On Accord models, attach connector shaft universal joint to steering shaft so clamp bolt rests at bottom of machined flat of steering shaft. Tighten clamp bolt.

NOTE: **On Accord models, place ignition switch in the "O" position to prevent shaft from sliding out during installation.**

6) Install column switchs. Use rubber bands to assemble upper bracket and bending plate to steering column. Bending plate should fit under hook on column with arrow mark facing out and pointing down. Install upper and lower covers.

TIGHTENING SPECIFICATIONS

Application	Ft. Lbs. (N.m)
Column Bracket Bolts	
Upper	9 (12)
Lower	16 (22)
Universal Clamp Bolts	22 (30)
Steering Wheel Nut	36 (50)

Steering Columns

ISUZU I-MARK & IMPULSE

DESCRIPTION

The I-Mark and Impulse have an energy absorbing steering column, with plastic pin-type, energy absorbing steering shaft. Column and shaft collapse during collision, by shearing of plastic pins.

Fig. 1: Exploded View of Steering Column Components

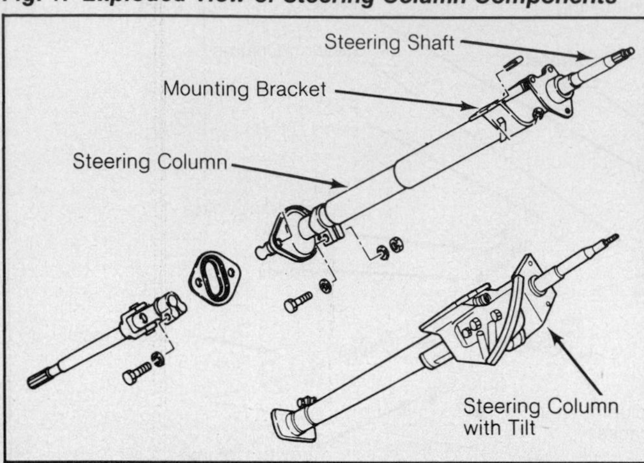
Steering Shaft
Mounting Bracket
Steering Column
Steering Column
with Tilt

Fig. 2: Steering Column Length Measurement Points

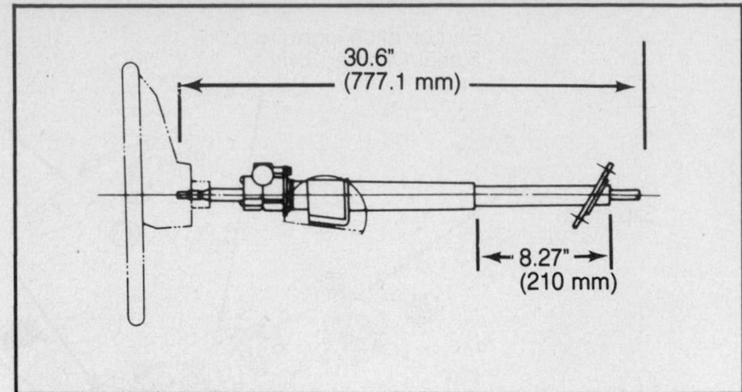
30.6"
(777.1 mm)
8.27"
(210 mm)

TIGHTENING SPECIFICATIONS

Application	Ft. Lbs. (N.m)
Column-to-Instrument Panel Bolts	
I-Mark	9 (12)
Impulse	11 (15)
Flexible Joint Key Bolt	19 (26)
Steering Wheel Nut	22 (30)

REMOVAL & INSTALLATION

STEERING COLUMN

Removal

1) Disconnect battery. Remove steering wheel and column switches. *See Isuzu in Steering Wheel & Column Switches article in this section.* Remove flexible joint key bolt.

2) Remove column-to-dashboard nuts. Remove column-to-instrument panel bolts. Remove steering column assembly from vehicle.

Installation

To install, reverse removal procedures. Make sure that column-to-instrument panel bolts are not overtightened.

OVERHAUL

STEERING COLUMN

Disassembly

NOTE: **On tilt steering models, steering column and steering shaft have been integrated and cannot be disassembled.**

Remove snap ring, washer and retaining bolts from column flange. Remove ignition lock cylinder housing. Using screwdriver, pry out lower column rubber bushing. Remove steering shaft from column.

Inspection

Measure steering shaft from end-to-end. Total length of steering shaft should be 30.6" (777.1 mm). Measure lower half of steering column. *See Fig. 2*. Lower half of column should be 8.27" (210 mm) in length.

Reassembly

To reassemble, reverse disassembly.

Steering Columns

ISUZU P'UP

DESCRIPTION

Column is fastened to steering gear through a flexible coupling. During impact of predetermined loads, energy absorbing shaft will collapse by shearing plastic pins.

REMOVAL & INSTALLATION

NOTE: **Before beginning removal and installation, inspect steering shaft shear pins. If steering shaft plastic pins have been sheared, shaft will rattle when struck lightly from side.**

STEERING COLUMN

Removal

1) Disconnect battery ground cable. Remove horn cover and spring. Remove steering column shrouding and hazard warning light switch. Remove combination switch. Remove steering wheel. *See Isuzu P'UP in Steering Wheel & Column Switches article in this section.*

2) Working inside engine compartment, remove upper coupling clamp pinch bolt from steering shaft flexible coupling.

3) Scribe reference mark across steering shaft and coupling clamp to ensure proper installation. Disconnect combination and ignition switch wiring at harness connector.

4) Remove steering column-to-instrument panel bolts. Separate rubber coupling from steering shaft.

5) Slide steering column toward inside of passenger compartment and remove from vehicle.

Installation

To install, reverse removal procedures. Make sure to align reference mark on steering shaft to mark on coupling clamp.

FLEXIBLE COUPLING

Removal

1) Raise vehicle and support with safety stands. Remove coupling through bolts and lock nuts. Remove pinch bolts on upper and lower flanges of coupling.

2) Remove column bracket retaining bolts. Pull steering column rearward approximately 2.0" (51 mm). Remove upper coupling flange, coupling, and lower coupling flange.

Installation

Install lower coupling flange. Install coupling and upper coupling flange. To complete installation, reverse removal procedure.

TIGHTENING SPECIFICATIONS

Application	Ft. Lbs. (N.m)
Column-to-Instrument Panel	13 (18)
Column-to-Worm Shaft Clamp	22 (30)
Coupling Through Bolts	18 (24)
Shaft Coupling Clamp	22 (30)
Steering Wheel Nut	22 (30)

Fig. 1: Exploded View of P'UP Steering Column Assembly

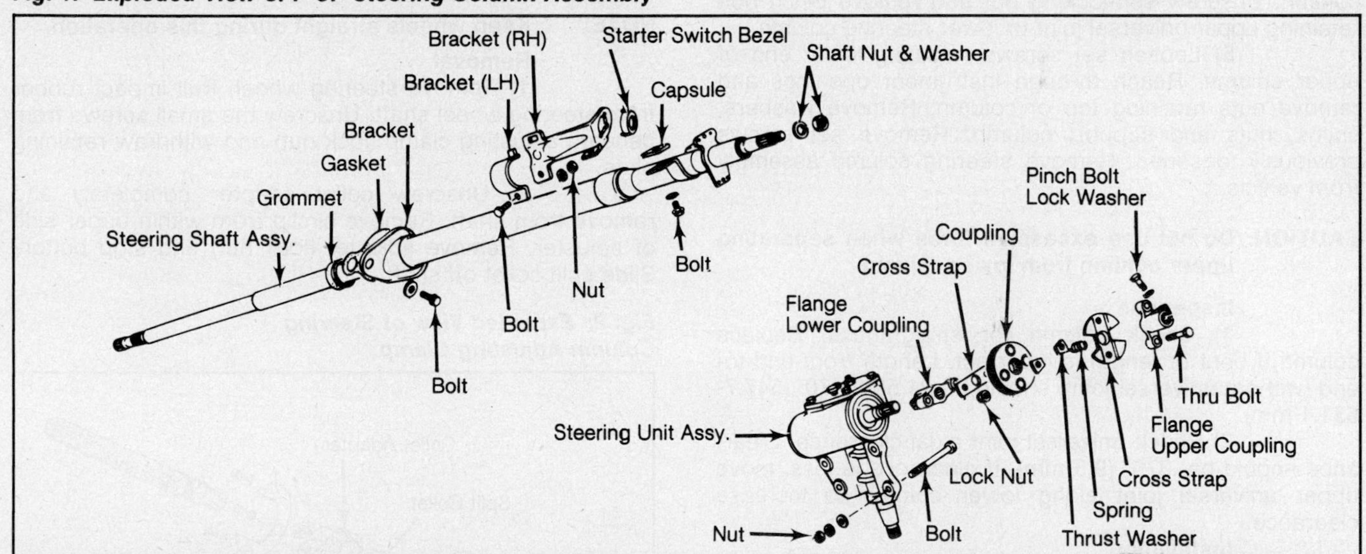

Bracket (RH)
Starter Switch Bezel
Shaft Nut & Washer
Bracket (LH)
Capsule
Bracket
Gasket
Grommet
Steering Shaft Assy.
Bolt
Nut
Bolt
Bolt
Pinch Bolt
Lock Washer
Coupling
Cross Strap
Flange
Lower Coupling
Thru Bolt
Flange
Upper Coupling
Steering Unit Assy.
Lock Nut
Cross Strap
Spring
Nut
Bolt
Thrust Washer

Avoid impact to steering wheel at all times.

Steering Columns

JAGUAR XJ6 & XJS

DESCRIPTION

The upper and lower steering columns are collapsible. The collapse points are retained by nylon plugs which shear on impact, allowing steering wheel and columns to move forward.

The upper column consists of 2 sliding shafts. The lower column consists of 2 sliding shafts, retained by nylon plugs. The column shaft is supported by 2 prelubricated roller bearings.

REMOVAL & INSTALLATION

UPPER STEERING COLUMN

Removal

1) Disconnect battery ground cable. Remove steering wheel. *See Steering Wheel & Column Switches article in this section.* Remove speedometer casing. Behind speedometer, unscrew knurled nut from bracket.

2) Disconnect speedometer drive cable. Disconnect trip odometer reset control cable by unscrewing knurled nut. Press on instrument panel bezel, rotate speedometer clockwise until it releases, and remove from panel. Remove headlight warning light and instrument lights.

3) Press instrument bezel and rotate counterclockwise until tachometer releases. Disconnect electrical plug and socket. Remove ground lead. Remove instrument light holder.

4) Remove trim panel below the upper steering column. Disconnect electrical switch connections (socket and plug connections). Detach horn contact at upper column. Unscrew self-locking nut and remove pinch bolt retaining upper universal joint to lower steering column.

5) Loosen set screws retaining lower end of upper column. Reach through instrument openings and remove nuts retaining top of column. Remove washers, shims, nuts and support column. Remove set screws previously loosened. Remove steering column assembly from vehicle.

CAUTION: Do not use excessive force when separating upper column from lower column.

Inspection

1) Check column for straightness. Replace column if bent or length is incorrect. Length from end-to-end (without universal joint) should be 21.56-21.70" (547.7-551.1 mm).

2) Check universal joint axial clearance. Clearance should be .375" (9.5 mm). If clearance is less, move upper universal joint along lower column to increase clearance.

Installation

1) Install universal joint and/or adjusting clamp (if removed). To complete installation, reverse removal procedure.

2) Check self-canceling operation of turn signal. Make sure that steering wheel spokes are horizontal when wheels are straight. Refit steering wheel as needed.

LOWER STEERING COLUMN

Removal

1) Raise vehicle and remove pinch bolt retaining lower universal joint to pinion shaft. Remove pinion shaft heat shield. Lower vehicle. Remove lower parcel shelf. Remove both pinch bolts from upper universal joint.

2) Unscrew upper column lower retaining screws. Pull lower column from upper universal joint. Raise vehicle. Remove lower universal joint from pinion shaft and remove lower steering column.

Fig. 1: Disconnecting Lower Steering Column from Pinion Shaft

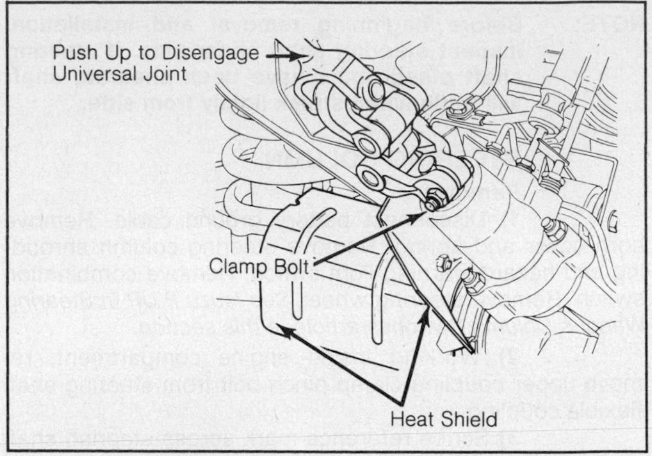
Push Up to Disengage Universal Joint
Clamp Bolt
Heat Shield

Installation

To install, reverse removal procedure. Make sure there is a gap of .375" (9.5 mm) between lower universal joint sections.

STEERING COLUMN ADJUSTING CLAMP

NOTE: Keep wheels straight during this operation.

Removal

1) Remove steering wheel. Pull impact rubber from steering wheel shaft. Unscrew the small screws from beneath adjusting clamp (lock nut) and withdraw retaining plate.

2) Unscrew collet adapter completely and remove from shaft. Remove circlip from within upper side of adjuster. Remove adjuster (lock nut) and stop button. Slide split collet off shaft.

Fig. 2: Exploded View of Steering Column Adjusting Clamp

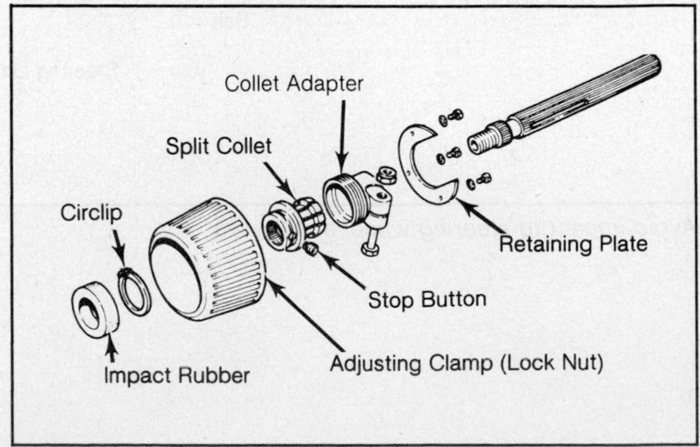
Collet Adapter
Split Collet
Circlip
Retaining Plate
Stop Button
Adjusting Clamp (Lock Nut)
Impact Rubber

JAGUAR XJ6 & XJS (Cont.)

Installation

Clean parts thoroughly and remove burrs with a file. Lightly lubricate all enclosed metal components. To install, reverse removal procedure.

STEERING COLUMN LOWER SEAL

Removal

1) Remove upper steering column, as previously outlined. Loosen hose clip attaching upper sealing sleeve to lower column. Remove clip and sleeve.

2) Remove screws retaining seal retainer to instrument panel. Slide seal, retainer and sealing sleeve up and off lower column.

Installation

1) Fit assembly of sealing sleeve, seal and retainer over lower column end. Insert and tighten retaining set screws.

2) Slide second sealing sleeve, flanged end first, over lower column up to first sealing sleeve. Position hose clip, but do not tighten.

3) Move second sealing sleeve about .25" (6 mm) toward dash, to preload it against first sealing sleeve. Secure with hose clip. Replace upper column assembly.

OVERHAUL

UPPER & LOWER STEERING COLUMNS

NOTE: **No adjustments or overhaul procedures are given by the manufacturer. If components are damaged, replace column.**

TIGHTENING SPECIFICATIONS

Application	Ft. Lbs. (N.m)
Column-to-Brackets	14-18 (19-24)
Steering Wheel	25-32 (34-44)
Universal Joint Bolts	14-18 (19-24)

Steering Columns

MAZDA B2000 & B2200 PICKUPS, GLC & 626

DESCRIPTION

Steering columns incorporate a collapsible steering shaft. Columns use plastic shear pins to absorb collision impact. Steering shaft is connected directly to steering gear by a universal joint.

REMOVAL & INSTALLATION

STEERING COLUMN

Removal

1) Disconnect battery ground cable. Remove horn cap. Remove steering wheel with steering wheel puller. *See Mazda in Steering Wheel & Column Switches article in this section*. Disconnect combination switch coupler and remove switch.

2) Remove dust boot. Remove universal joint bolts on intermediate shaft. Remove intermediate shaft from engine compartment side.

3) Remove upper and lower steering column mounting bolts. Remove steering column.

4) On Pickup models, remove upper column bolts. Remove floor plate bolts and slide floor plate back. Disconnect steering column universal joint. Remove steering column.

Installation

To install, reverse removal procedures. Make sure there is clearance between column cover and steering wheel.

OVERHAUL

STEERING COLUMN

NOTE: Do not hammer or exert pressure on column. Collapsible section may be damaged.

Disassembly

Remove column and switches. Clamp column jacket in vise. Turn steering shaft to remove.

Inspection & Reassembly

Check all components for damage or wear. Check steering shaft for bends, damage or sheared plastic pins. On 626, check shaft length for 23.86-23.94" (606.1-608.1mm). *See inset in Fig. 1*. To reassemble, reverse disassembly procedures. Grease steering shaft, bushings and bearings.

TIGHTENING SPECIFICATIONS

Application	Ft. Lbs. (N.m)
GLC & 626	
Steering Universal Joints	13-20 (18-28)
Column Brackets	12-17 (16-23)
Steering Wheel	29-36 (40-50)
Tilt Lever Bolt (626 Only)	13-20 (18-28)
Pickups	
Steering Universal Joint	13-20 (18-28)
Column Bracket	12-19 (16-27)
Steering Wheel	22-29 (30-40)

Fig. 1: 626 & GLC Steering Columns

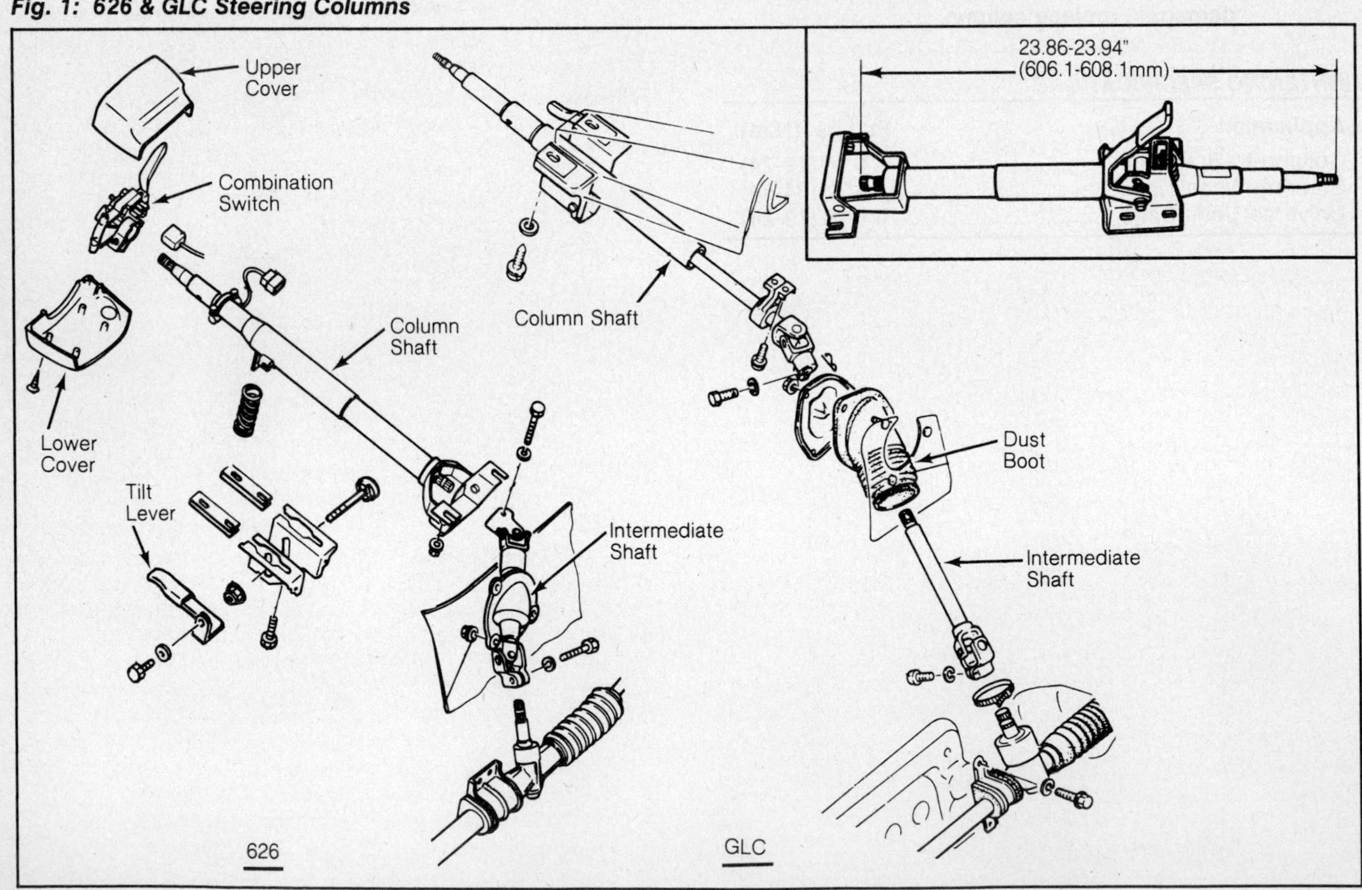

23.86-23.94"
(606.1-608.1mm)
Upper Cover
Combination Switch
Column Shaft
Column Shaft
Lower Cover
Tilt Lever
Intermediate Shaft
Dust Boot
Intermediate Shaft
626
GLC

Pickup steering column does not use intermediate shaft. See 626 column shaft measurement in inset.

Steering Columns

MAZDA GLC WAGON & RX7

DESCRIPTION

Steering columns used on these models incorporate a collapsible steering shaft.

REMOVAL & INSTALLATION

STEERING COLUMN

Removal

1) Disconnect battery ground cable. Remove horn cap. Remove steering wheel with steering wheel puller. *See Mazda in Steering Wheel & Column Switches article in this section.* Remove steering column covers. Disconnect combination switch coupler and remove switch.

NOTE: Do not hammer or exert extreme pressure on steering column, as damage to collapsible section may result.

2) Remove lock assembly. Remove steering column mounting bolts. Remove steering column jacket.

3) Disconnect center link from pitman arm using puller (49-0118-850C). Remove pitman arm from sector shaft using puller (49-0223-695E).

4) Remove steering gear housing attaching bolts. Remove steering gear housing assembly through engine compartment. *See Fig. 1.*

Inspection

Check all components for damage or wear. Check steering shaft for bend or damage.

Installation

To install, reverse removal procedures. Make sure there is clearance between column cover and steering wheel.

TIGHTENING SPECIFICATIONS

Application	Ft. Lbs. (N.m)
Column Bracket Bolts	12-17 (16-23)
Steering Wheel Nut	29-36 (40-50)
Steering Gear Housing to Frame	32-40 (44-55)
Pitman Arm to Sector Shaft	58-87 (80-120)
Pitman Arm to Center Link	22-33 (30-45)

Fig. 1: GLC Wagon Steering Column

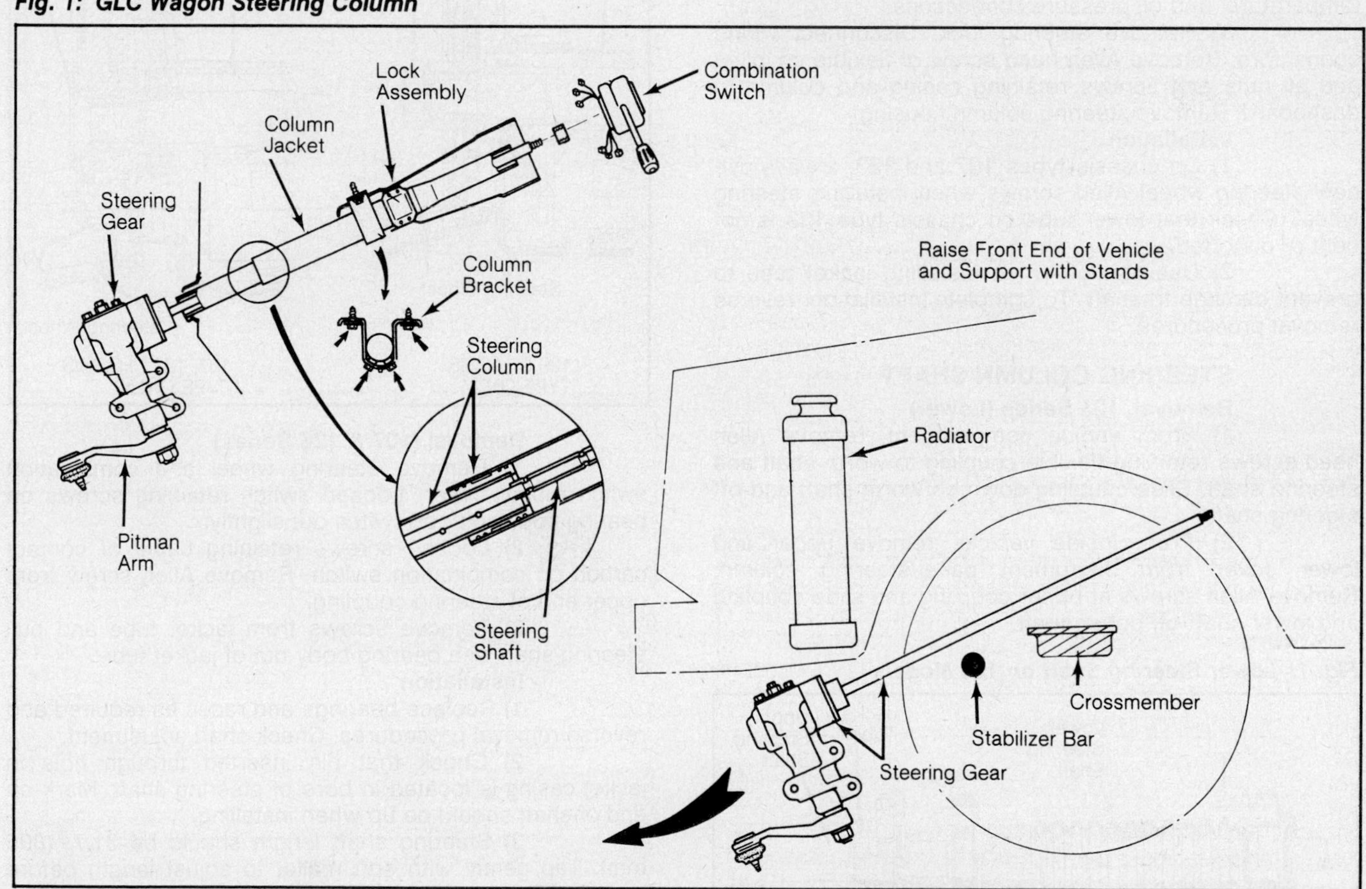
Lock Assembly
Combination Switch
Column Jacket
Steering Gear
Column Bracket
Raise Front End of Vehicle and Support with Stands
Steering Column
Radiator
Pitman Arm
Steering Shaft
Crossmember
Stabilizer Bar
Steering Gear

RX7 steering column is similar.

Steering Columns

MERCEDES-BENZ

DESCRIPTION

Steering column assembly includes an impact absorbing steering wheel, upper and lower column shafts and flexible coupling. Lower shaft on 123 Series models is corrugated for additional impact protection.

CHASSIS IDENTIFICATION CODES

Application	Chassis Type
380SL	107
240D, 300D, 300CD & 300TD	123
300SD, 380SEL & 380 SEC	126

STEERING COLUMN

Removal

1) On 123 series, remove screws retaining upper and lower cover on instrument panel and remove covers. On all models, disconnect battery. Remove steering wheel. *See Mercedes-Benz in Steering Wheel & Column Switches article in this Section.*

2) Remove instrument cluster by pulling outward as far as possible and loosening tachometer, temperature, and oil pressure connections.

3) Remove steering lock. Disconnect wiring connectors. Remove Allen head screw of flexible coupling and all nuts and screws retaining casing and column to dashboard. Remove steering column housing.

Installation

1) On chassis types 107 and 123, always use new steering wheel Allen screws when installing steering wheel. Check that lower tube on chassis type 123 is not bent or distorted.

2) Use caution when installing jacket tube to prevent damage to shaft. To complete installation, reverse removal procedures.

STEERING COLUMN SHAFT

Removal, 123 Series (Lower)

1) From engine compartment, remove Allen head screws retaining flexible coupling to worm shaft and steering shaft. Slide coupling down on worm shaft and off steering shaft.

2) From inside vehicle, remove upper and lower cover from instrument panel/steering column. Remove Allen screws at upper coupling and slide coupling and lower shaft off upper shaft.

Fig. 1: Lower Steering Shaft on 123 Models

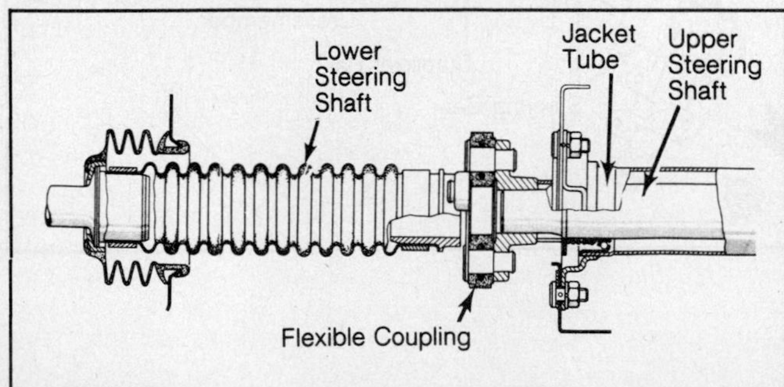
Lower Steering Shaft
Jacket Tube
Upper Steering Shaft
Flexible Coupling

When disassembled check shaft for bend or distortion.

Installation

To install, lubricate inner lips of bellows seal or firewall and reverse removal procedures.

NOTE: **Wheels must be in straight-ahead position and notch on upper shaft must point directly upward during installation.**

Removal, 123 Series (Upper)

1) With column out of vehicle, remove combination switch. Remove jacket tube casing. Remove spacing ring from steering shaft.

2) Remove gripper ring, compression spring, supporting ring and ball bearing from steering shaft. Knock steering shaft upward out of jacket tube with soft mallet.

Installation

Inspect and replace bearings and races, if necessary. Reverse removal procedure and reinstall upper steering shaft.

Fig. 2: Sectional View of Mercedes-Benz Steering Column and Steering Shaft

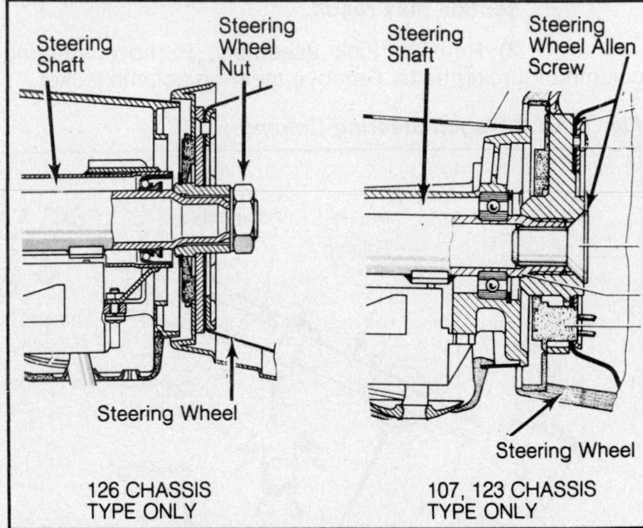
Steering Shaft
Steering Wheel Nut
Steering Shaft
Steering Wheel Allen Screw
Steering Wheel
Steering Wheel
126 CHASSIS TYPE ONLY
107, 123 CHASSIS TYPE ONLY

Removal (107 & 126 Series)

1) Remove steering wheel and combination switch rubber cover. Loosen switch retaining screws on bearing body and pull switch out slightly.

2) Loosen screws retaining cable of contact carbon on combination switch. Remove Allen screw from upper end of steering coupling.

3) Remove screws from jacket tube and pull steering shaft with bearing body out of jacket tube.

Installation

1) Replace bearings and races as required and reverse removal procedures. Check shaft adjustment.

2) Check that pin inserted through hole in jacket casing is located in bore of steering shaft. Mark on end of shaft should be up when installing.

3) Steering shaft length should be 31.7" (805 mm). Tap gently with soft mallet to adjust length before installation.

TIGHTENING SPECIFICATIONS

Application	Ft. Lbs. (N.m)
Flexible Coupling (Allen)	18 (24)
Steering Wheel	
107, 123	59 (80)
126	37 (50)

Steering Columns

MITSUBISHI FWD MODELS

Cordia & Tredia

DESCRIPTION

Collapsible steering system is a 2-piece upper-lower column shaft, joined by collapsible bellows-type section. Bellows section contracts axially under impact without affecting turning motion.

REMOVAL & INSTALLATION

STEERING COLUMN

Removal

1) Remove steering wheel. *See Mitsubishi in Steering Wheel & Column Switches article in this section.* Remove steering column cover. Pull out column switch connectors. Pull switch out toward steering wheel end.

NOTE: **When removing steering column as an assembly, leave all connector clamps intact.**

2) Remove steering shaft upper coupling bolt. Remove bolts retaining steering column brackets to frame. Disconnect steering shaft from coupling inside vehicle. Remove steering column assembly.

3) On vehicles with tilt steering, lower steering column assembly toward floor by removing bolts which secure lower bracket and tilt bracket. Remove bolt which holds steering shaft to joint assembly. Remove steering column assembly.

4) Remove intermediate shaft lower coupling bolt at steering gear. Remove dust cover retaining bolts. Remove intermediate shaft, with dust cover, toward inside of vehicle.

Installation

1) Install dust cover to intermediate shaft. Make sure bearing side of cover faces steering shaft side of intermediate shaft.

2) Apply grease to bearing and dust cover. Install 2-piece bearing into dust cover. Attach intermediate shaft lower joint to steering gear and temporarily tighten dust cover bolts. Now tighten lower joint clamp bolt.

Fig. 2: Dust Cover and Bearing Installation

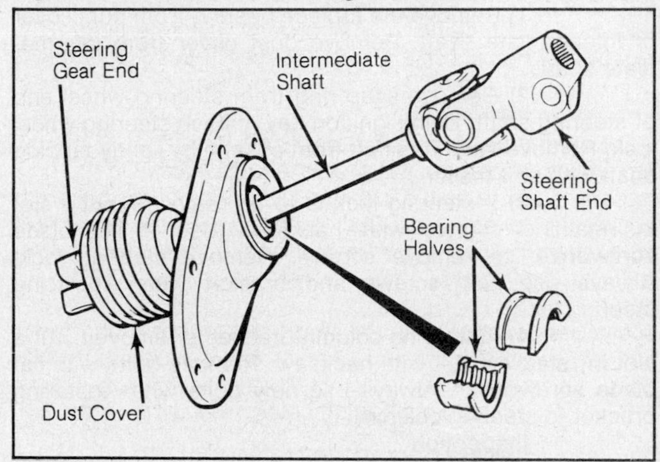
Steering Gear End
Intermediate Shaft
Steering Shaft End
Bearing Halves
Dust Cover

Fig. 1: Exploded View of Steering Columns

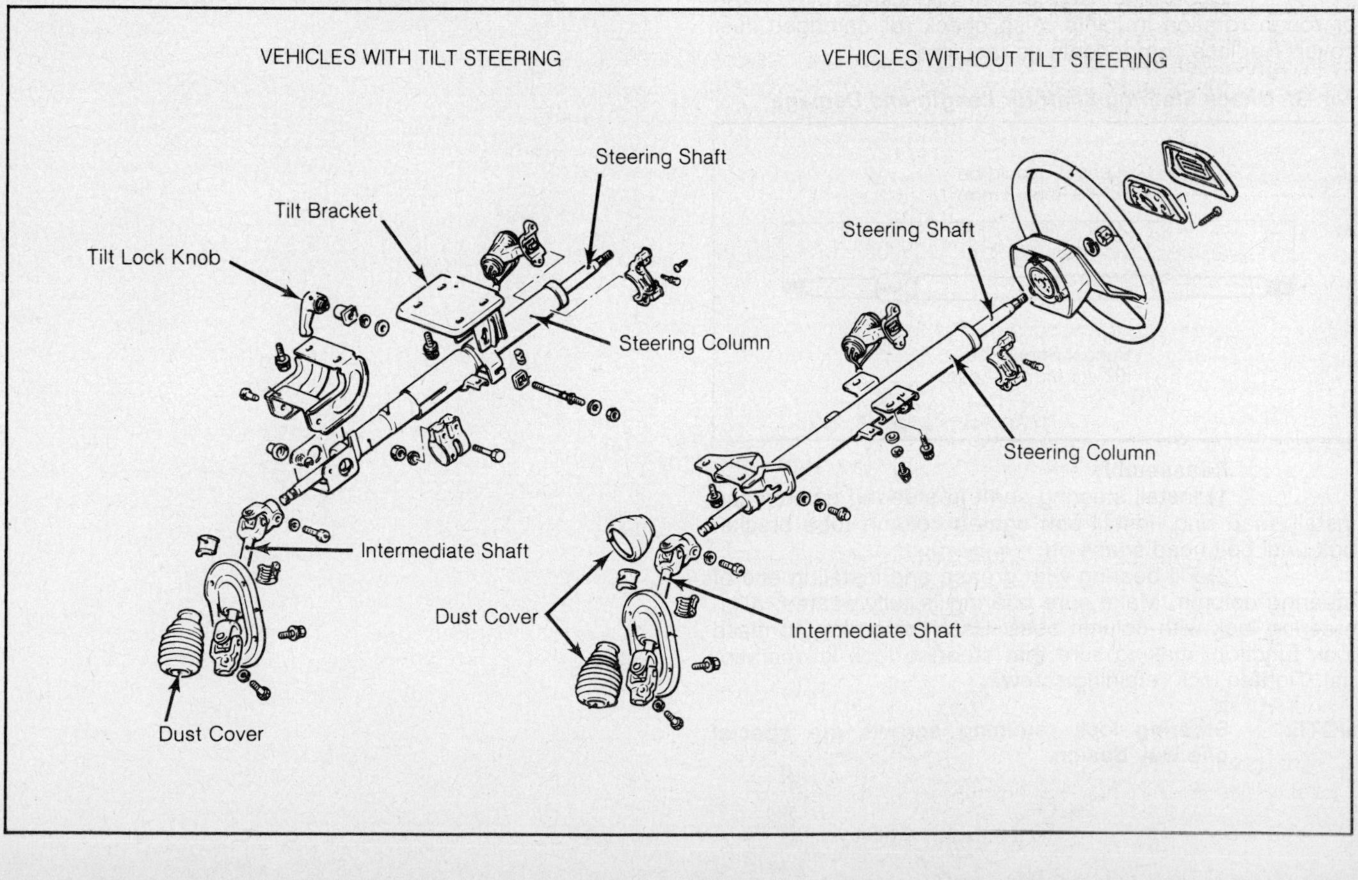

VEHICLES WITH TILT STEERING
VEHICLES WITHOUT TILT STEERING
Steering Shaft
Tilt Bracket
Tilt Lock Knob
Steering Column
Intermediate Shaft
Dust Cover
Steering Shaft
Steering Column
Dust Cover
Intermediate Shaft

Steering Columns

MITSUBISHI FWD MODELS (Cont.)

3) Connect intermediate shaft upper joint to steering shaft. Attach steering column brackets to dash. Tighten clamp bolt of intermediate shaft and column bracket bolts.

4) Loosen dust cover bolts and position dust cover so no clearance exists between joint and dust cover sliding surfaces. Tighten dust cover bolts. Adjust steering wheel position if necessary.

OVERHAUL

STEERING COLUMN

Disassembly

1) Remove the 2-piece bearing from dust cover of intermediate shaft. Remove dust cover from intermediate shaft.

2) Remove snap ring from steering wheel end of steering shaft. Using ignition key, unlock steering wheel lock. Remove steering shaft from column by lightly tapping shaft with soft mallet.

3) If steering lock is to be removed, cut a slot in retaining screws with hacksaw. Use a flat blade screwdriver to remove screws. Remove steering lock. Always use new screws and bracket when replacing steering lock.

4) If steering column bracket is removed, cut a slot in retaining bolt with hacksaw. Remove bolts with flat blade screwdriver. Always use new bolts when installing bracket to steering column.

Inspection

1) Check steering shaft for runout and length. Runout should be .02" (.5 mm) or less, length should be 21.89" (556.2 mm). Check for worn or damaged bearing.

2) On intermediate shaft, check for play, noise or rough rotation in joints. Also check for damaged dust cover. Replace components as required.

Fig. 3: Check Steering Shaft for Length and Damage

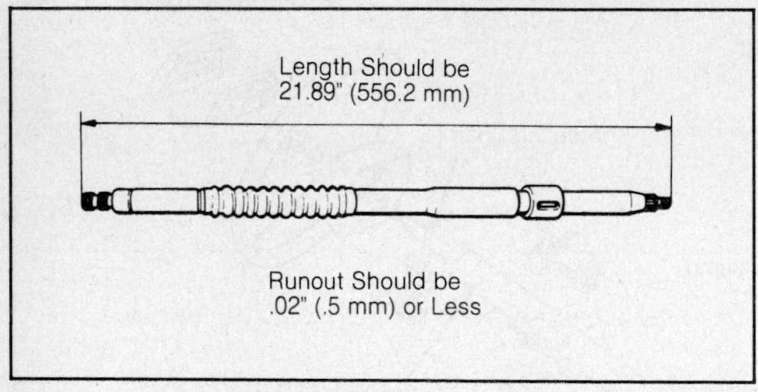
Length Should be
21.89" (556.2 mm)
Runout Should be
.02" (.5 mm) or Less

Reassembly

1) Install steering shaft in steering column and install snap ring. Install and tighten column tube bracket bolt until bolt head snaps off.

2) Fill bearing with grease and install in end of steering column. Make sure bearing is fully seated. Align steering lock with column boss. Use ignition key to make lock function, making sure that steering lock is operational. Tighten lock retaining screw.

NOTE: Steering lock retaining screws are special one way design.

TIGHTENING SPECIFICATIONS

Application	Ft. Lbs. (N.m)
Joint Bolts	
Upper and Lower	22-25 (30-35)
Steering Wheel Nut	25-32 (34-44)
Column Support Bracket Bolts	7 (10)

Steering Columns

MITSUBISHI RWD MODELS

Montero, Pickups, Starion

DESCRIPTION

The steering column consists of a 2-piece shaft joined by a collapsible section. This section contracts under impact without affecting turning. Upper column cover has slits, allowing it to collapse under impact.

REMOVAL & INSTALLATION

STEERING COLUMN

NOTE: Do not jar or lean on column when servicing.

Removal

1) Remove air cleaner. Unbolt clamp connecting steering shaft to gear box. If vehicle is equipped with A/C, do this step from underneath vehicle.

2) On 4WD Pickups and Montero, slide lower shaft boot up and remove joint assembly-to-gear box clamp bolt. Disconnect joint assembly from steering shaft.

3) On all models, remove horn pad, steering wheel nut, and remove steering wheel using a puller. *See Mitsubishi in Steering Wheel & Column Switches article in this section.* Loosen tilt lock lever or knob and lower the column. Remove column cover and floor dust cover.

4) Unplug column switch connectors, leaving clamps intact, and pull out switch toward shaft end. Remove tilt bracket, then remove column.

Installation

1) Insert steering shaft from inside vehicle. Connect joint assembly to steering shaft and gear box (4WD Pickups & Montero). Connect shaft to steering gear housing main shaft with bolt hole facing down. Tighten clamp bolt. Attach tilt bracket to pedal support member.

2) Apply sealer to dust cover bolt holes. Install dust cover to body. Install column switch and route and secure wiring harness along column tube. Reconnect switch connectors and install column cover.

3) Make sure wheels are straight and steering wheel lock is locked. Install steering wheel, tighten nut and install horn pad.

OVERHAUL

STEERING COLUMN

Disassembly

1) Remove clamp bolt and remove column tube and joint cover. Make slit in steering lock bracket bolt head and column support bolt head and remove lock and support.

2) Remove snap ring from upper shaft (upper and lower shaft snap rings on 4WD Pickups). Remove shaft (with dust seal and bushing) from column tube.

Fig. 1: Exploded View of Starion Steering Column Components

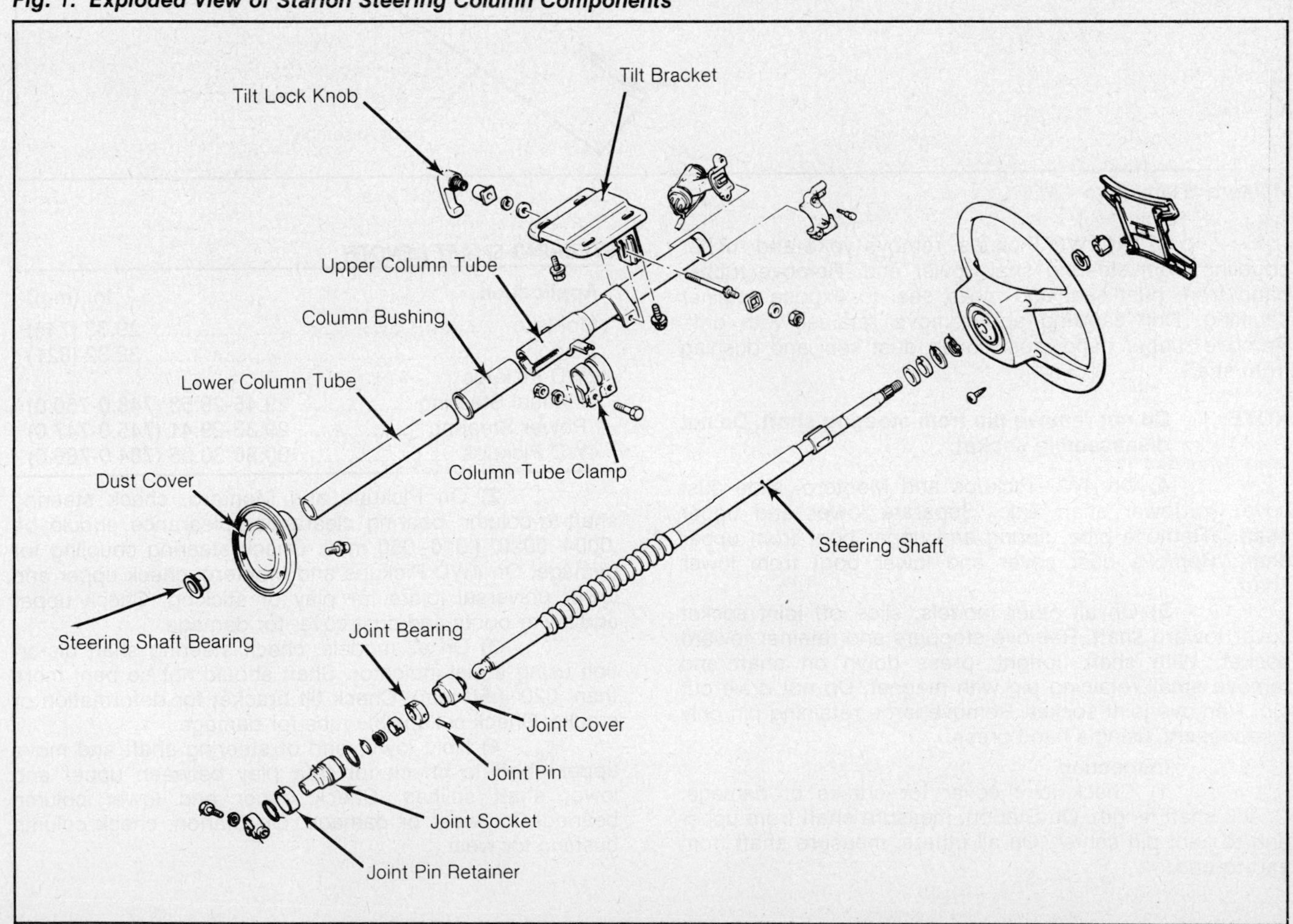
Tilt Bracket
Tilt Lock Knob
Upper Column Tube
Column Bushing
Lower Column Tube
Column Tube Clamp
Dust Cover
Steering Shaft
Steering Shaft Bearing
Joint Bearing
Joint Cover
Joint Pin
Joint Socket
Joint Pin Retainer

MITSUBISHI RWD MODELS (Cont.)

Fig. 2: Exploded View of 2WD & 4WD Pickup Steering Columns

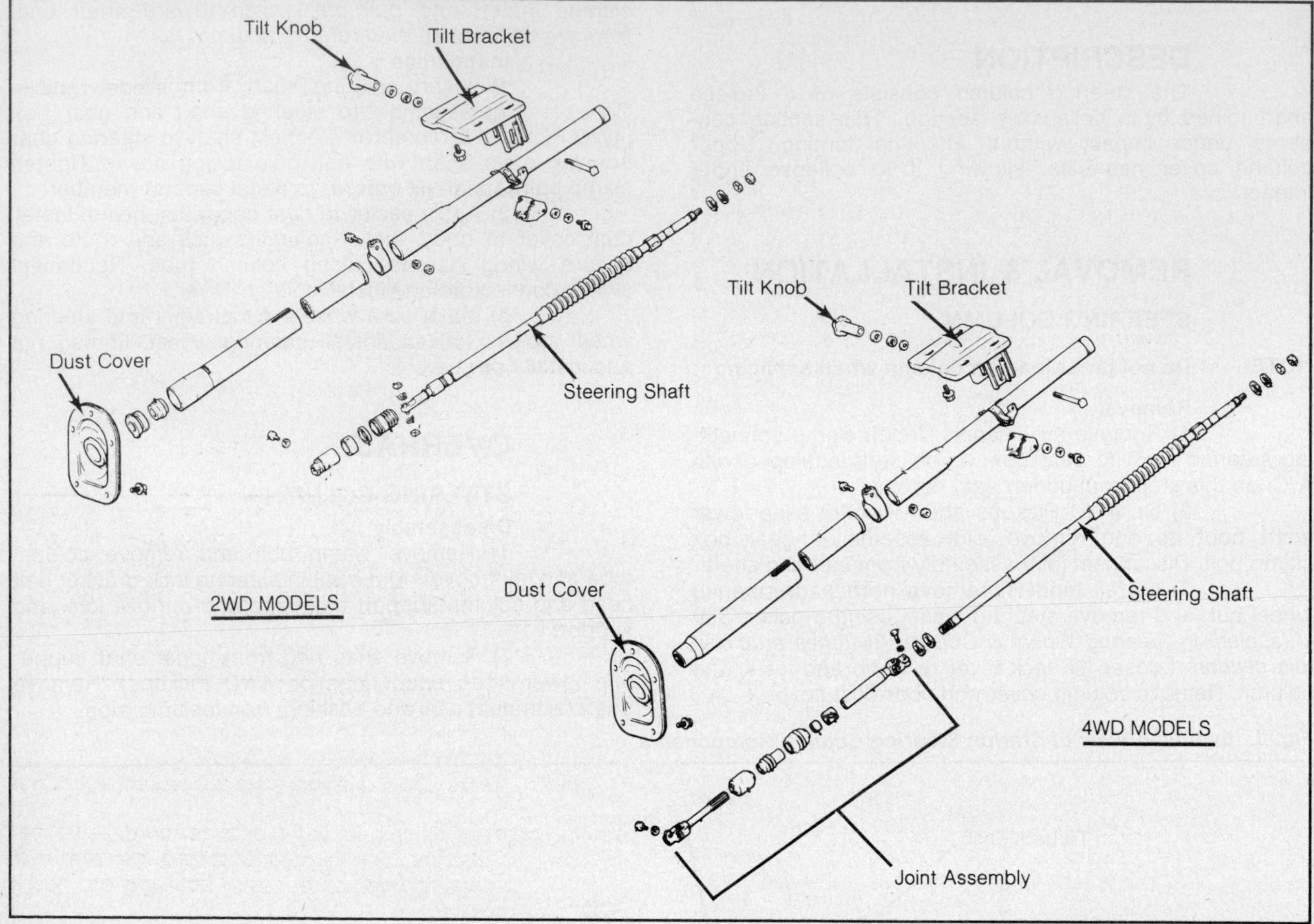
Tilt Knob
Tilt Bracket
Dust Cover
Steering Shaft
2WD MODELS
Tilt Knob
Tilt Bracket
Dust Cover
Steering Shaft
4WD MODELS
Joint Assembly

Montero is similar to 4WD.

3) On 2WD Pickups, remove yoke and rubber coupling from steering shaft lower end. Remove rubber band from dust seal and move seal to expose retainer caulking. Drill caulking and remove retainer with drift. Remove rubber band, dust cover, dust seal and bushing from shaft.

NOTE: **Do not remove pin from steering shaft. Do not disassemble socket.**

4) On 4WD Pickups and Montero, slide dust cover to lower shaft side. Separate lower and upper shafts. Remove pipe, spring and upper boot from upper shaft. Remove dust cover and lower boot from lower shaft.

5) On all other models, slide off joint socket cover toward shaft. Remove stoppers and retainer toward socket. With shaft upright, press down on shaft and remove small retaining pin with magnet. Do not drive out pin. Remove joint socket. Remove large retaining pin only if necessary, using a hand press.

Inspection

1) Check joint cover for cracks or damage. Check shaft length. On Starion, measure shaft from upper end to joint pin center. On all others, measure shaft from end-to-end.

STEERING SHAFT LENGTH

Application	In. (mm)
Montero	29.33 (745)
Starion	32.32 (821)
2WD Pickups	
Manual Steering	29.45-29.53 (748.0-750.0)
Power Steering	29.33-29.41 (745.0-747.0)
4WD Pickups	30.86-30.95 (784.0-786.0)

2) On Pickups and Montero, check steering shaft-to-column bearing clearance. Clearance should be .0004-.0020" (.010-.050 mm). Check steering coupling for damage. On 4WD Pickups and Montero, check upper and lower universal joints for play or sticking. Check upper and lower boots and dust cover for damage.

3) On all models, check steering shaft distortion using a dial indicator. Shaft should not be bent more than .020" (.50 mm). Check tilt bracket for deformation or cracks. Check collapsible tube for damage.

4) Hold lower end of steering shaft and move upper shaft to check for free play between upper and lower shaft splines. Check upper and lower column bearings for wear or damage. On Starion, check column bushing for wear.

Steering Columns

MITSUBISHI RWD MODELS (Cont.)

Reassembly (Starion)

1) Install column tube bushings onto upper and lower column tubes until bushing stop seats in column tube end. Tighten column tube clamp bolt.

2) Coat inside of steering shaft bearing with grease. Coat outside of bearing with adhesive and install bearing into lower column tube.

3) Align column tube hole with wheel lock guide dowel to install steering wheel lock. Insert key and check for lock proper operation. Tighten shear bolts until bolt heads twist off.

4) Install joint bearing (flanged surface facing up) onto shaft lower end. Rotate bearing 90° and insert large pin.

NOTE: **Make sure bearing is installed correctly and rotates freely. Check that joint pin does not protrude from bearing surface.**

5) Apply grease to socket and insert spring seats and spring. Hold steering shaft vertical, press down on shaft and push small pin into socket by hand. Check for free play when steering shaft and socket are turned. Replace joint pin if needed. Put joint pin retainer on joint socket, install stoppers and joint cover.

6) Insert steering shaft into column tube. Install spacer, stopper and snap ring on steering shaft. Align tilt bracket with column tube and insert bolt. Tighten tilt lever screw to tilt lock lever and back off 3 1/2 turns.

7) Place tilt lever over bolt and rotate lever until it touches stopper. Align screw side with stopper face, position assembly on column and tighten lever. Check that tilt lever is locked when tightened. Loosen lever and adjust screw or bolt if needed. *See Fig. 3.*

Fig. 3: Lock Tilt Lever Setting Angle

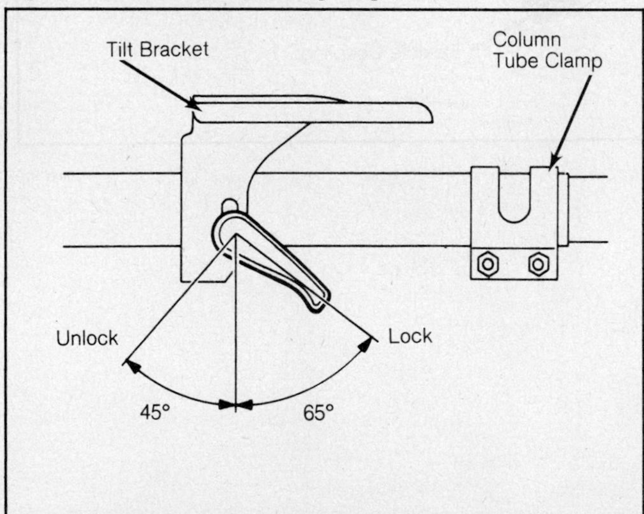
Tilt Bracket
Column
Tube Clamp
Unlock
Lock
45°
65°

Reassembly (Montero & Pickups)

1) On 4WD & Montero models, assemble upper and lower boots to shafts, but not to universal joints. Install dust cover over lower shaft. Grease upper and lower shafts and serrated part of pipe. Assemble spring and pipe to upper shaft.

2) Tilt lower shaft 10° from upper shaft and insert lower shaft into pipe until 2.36" (60 mm) of splines remain. Rotate lower shaft clockwise until pipe plate and upper shaft plate are aligned. Push lower shaft into upper shaft until 1.38" (35 mm) of splines remain.

NOTE: **When inserting lower shaft, make sure there is no play in serrated part of pipe. After joining shafts, make sure upper and lower shaft yokes are within 5° of each other.**

3) Align boot arrows with yoke slits to assemble upper and lower boots to universal joints.

4) On all models, align column tube hole with wheel lock guide dowel and install lock. Insert ignition key and check lock operation. Tighten lock bracket shear bolts until bolt heads twist off.

5) Attach column support to tube and tighten support shear bolts until bolt heads twist off. Install joint cover to column, making sure clamp bolt faces up. Tighten clamp bolt.

6) Apply grease to bearing roller surfaces of column tube and inside dust cover grommet. Install steering shaft bushing, dust seal, dust cover, rubber band and retainer in order.

7) Install springs and sliders on steering shaft. Fill inside of socket with grease and install retainer on socket, making sure punch marks are aligned. Stake retainer at two points with a punch. Fill inside of dust cover with grease and install dust cover over socket.

8) Install rubber band on dust cover. Apply grease to horn ground spring seats and attach coupling and yoke to steering shaft.

TIGHTENING SPECIFICATIONS

Application	Ft. Lbs. (N.m)
Flexible Coupling Bolts	23 (32)
Joint Assembly-to Gear Box (4WD)	24 (33)
Steering Shaft Clamp	
Starion	17 (23)
Steering Shaft-to-Joint (4WD)	24 (33)
Steering Wheel Nut	29 (39)

Steering Columns

PEUGEOT

DESCRIPTION

Steering column consists of an upper and lower steering shaft connected by a universal joint. A flexible coupling at steering shaft lower end helps absorb road shocks.

Steering column contains a steering lock, turn signal/horn switch, headlight dimmer/washer switch and, on some models, a speed control switch.

REMOVAL & INSTALLATION

STEERING COLUMN

Removal

1) Disconnect battery ground cable. Remove bolt connecting steering shaft flexible coupling to gear box. Remove horn pad, steering wheel nut and steering wheel. Mark relative position of steering wheel to shaft.

2) Remove steering column trim panels to access column mounting bolts. Disconnect all switch connectors. Remove column cover-to-floor pan bolts.

3) Remove lower column retaining bolts, then remove upper column retaining bolts. Pull steering column out from passenger compartment.

Fig. 1: Dimensions for Making Clearance Gauge for 504 Models Only

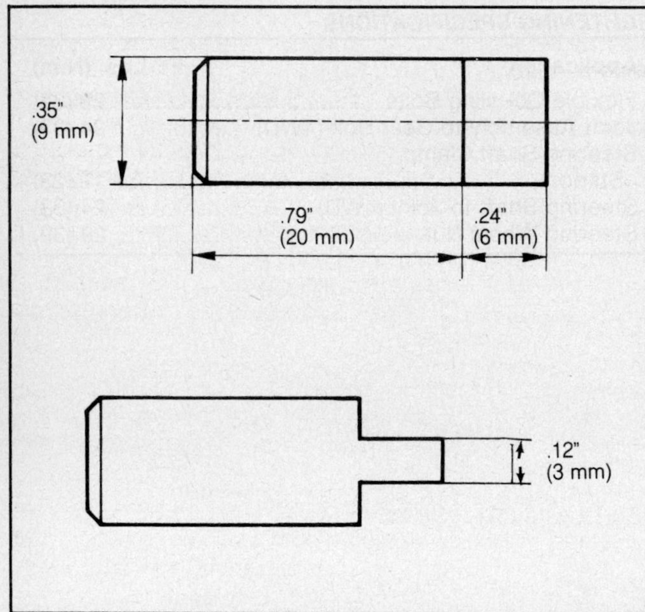
.35"
(9 mm)
.79"
(20 mm)
.24"
(6 mm)
.12"
(3 mm)

Installation

1) To install column, reverse removal procedure, noting the following: Place front wheels in straight-ahead position. Install column assembly from passenger compartment and align lower shaft with flexible coupling. Tighten column mounting bolts.

2) On 504 models, insert a fabricated clearance gauge into recess at flexible coupling and tighten pinch bolt. *See Fig. 1.* Remove gauge. On all models, make sure all switches are installed and operate properly. Install column trim covers and steering wheel.

Fig. 2: Peugeot Steering Column Assembly (504 Shown, 505 and 604 Similar)

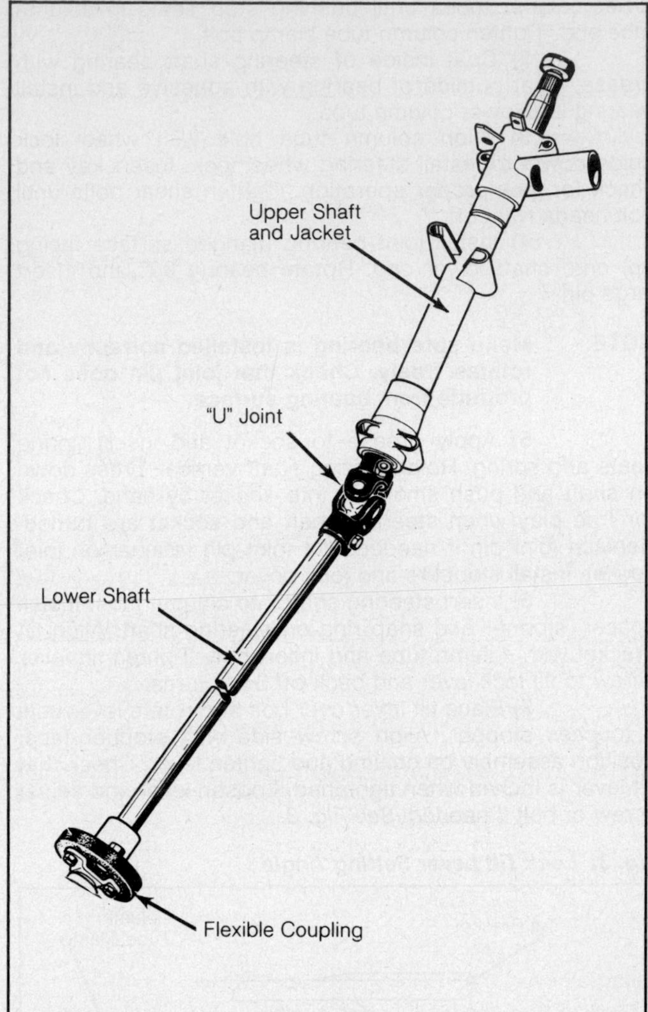
Upper Shaft
and Jacket
"U" Joint
Lower Shaft
Flexible Coupling

Steering Columns

PORSCHE 911SC, 928S & 944

DESCRIPTION

The steering column on Porsche models is a 3-piece, energy-absorbing unit. Intermediate shaft connects to steering rack and shaft with 2 universal joints.

The steering shaft offset design and the steering column collapsible section provide energy-absorbing protection.

An energy-absorbing steering wheel with rebound chambers and padded horn pad provides additional protection.

REMOVAL & INSTALLATION

STEERING COLUMN ASSEMBLY

Removal (911SC)

1) Disconnect battery ground cable. Remove blower, ducting and steering shaft cover. Remove universal joint retaining bolt.

2) From driver's compartment, remove knee strip, light switch and tachometer. Drill or grind off shear bolts retaining ignition switch/steering lock in panel mounting.

3) Lift off horn pad and remove steering wheel. Detach wire connection and remove steering column switch assembly with steering shaft and tube.

Installation

To install, reverse removal procedure. Tighten attaching shear bolts until heads break off.

Removal (928S)

1) Remove universal joint set screws and remove joint. Remove intermediate shaft cover (if equipped). Disconnect battery ground cable at body.

2) Push electric seats (if equipped) rearward. Remove horn pad and horn wires. Mark steering wheel position on steering shaft. Remove steering wheel.

3) Remove trim covers under instrument cowl and column switch. Remove instrument cowl mounting bolts. Remove column switch mounting bolt. Lift instrument cowl and disconnect connector.

4) Pull off instrument cowl switch knobs, compress spring clips and pull out switches and plugs. Remove ignition lock cover. Pull out plugs (mark for reinstallation) from guides and remove instrument cowl.

5) Remove plugs from ignition switch. Disconnect steering wheel height control spring. Remove steering shaft circlip and support. Remove column tube bracket mounting bolts.

6) Pull up column tube slightly, then carefully push down steering and intermediate shafts against steering shaft mount stop. Remove column tube.

Installation

To install, reverse removal procedure, noting the following: Using spacer tool (9208), make a .3" (8 mm) gap between steering gear and universal joint. If vehicle is equipped with long universal joint, gap will be smaller. Steering gear may need lowering to install long universal joint.

Removal (944)

1) Disconnect battery ground cable and remove horn pad. Remove steering wheel. Remove upper universal joint retaining bolt.

2) Disconnect wiring plugs from rear of switches. Drill out casing tube shear bolts. Remove upper steering column and switches as an assembly.

Installation

1) Lubricate rubber bearing and slide bearing support on casing tube about .8" (20 mm). Install column switch on casing tube, loosely tighten bolts.

2) Slide casing tube with bearing support and column switch on steering column. Install bearing support screws. Loosely tighten casing tube shear bolts.

3) Drive spacer sleeve on steering column until sleeve is 1.67" (42.5 mm) from steering column face. Tighten column switch Allen bolt and bearing support mounting screws.

4) Mount propeller shaft on steering gear. Make sure shaft is free of tension. Reposition casing tube if needed. Check that play between steering wheel and column is .08-.16" (2-4 mm). Tighten shear bolts until heads break off.

OVERHAUL

STEERING COLUMN ASSEMBLY

Disassembly (911SC)

1) With column out of vehicle and switches removed from column, drive steering shaft out of tube. Remove shaft lower end circlip and lower ball bearing.

2) Press Seeger ring out of steering shaft tube top end. Remove ball bearing and contact ring.

Reassembly

1) Install ball bearing against circlip at steering column lower end and seat bottom circlip against bearing. Circlip must seat in recessed groove.

Fig. 1: Exploded View of 944 Steering Column

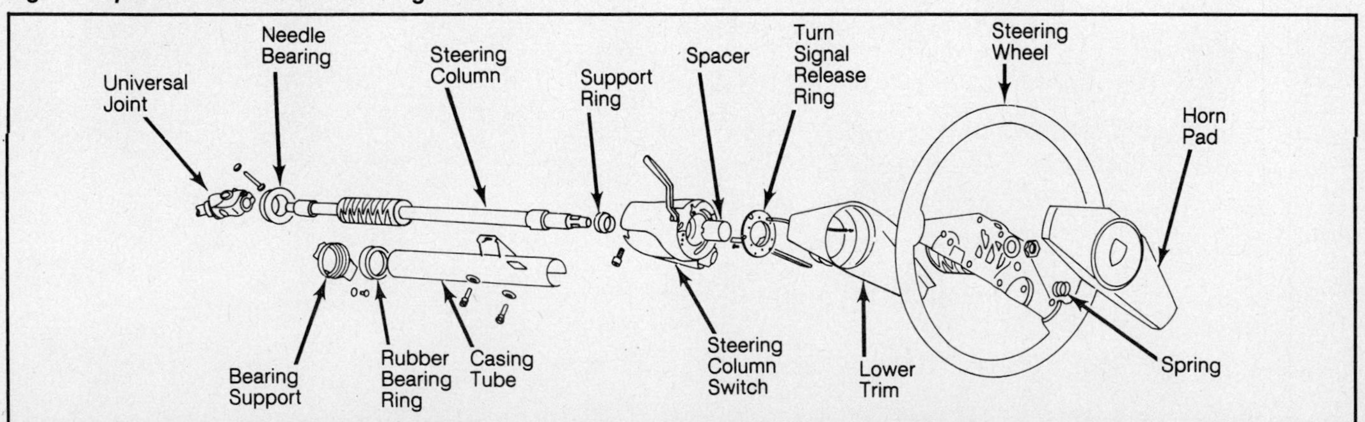
Universal Joint
Needle Bearing
Steering Column
Support Ring
Spacer
Turn Signal Release Ring
Steering Wheel
Horn Pad
Bearing Support
Rubber Bearing Ring
Casing Tube
Steering Column Switch
Lower Trim
Spring

Steering Columns

PORSCHE 911SC, 928S & 944 (Cont.)

2) Place contact ring and upper bearing together on steering shaft. Using a pipe, drive bearing into place on shaft. Pipe should contact inner race only. To complete reassembly, reverse disassembly procedure.

3) Pipe should contact inner race only. To complete reassembly, reverse disassembly procedure.

Disassembly (928S)

1) With steering wheel unlocked and circlip and support removed, pull intermediate and steering shaft down and out of column tube. Remove universal joint set screw and disconnect intermediate shaft from steering shaft with a mallet.

2) If steering shaft has 3 bearings, remove only center bearing if damaged, using a pipe. Replacement bearings are not available. Drive upper steering shaft from tube.

Reassembly

Press in upper steering shaft bearing with pressure pad (VW 433). Bearing collar should face column opening for switch. Lubricate column tube inside and center bearing sleeve (if installed) and insert steering shaft into tube from below. To complete reassembly, reverse disassembly procedure.

Disassembly (944)

No disassembly procedure is given by the manufacturer.

TIGHTENING SPECIFICATIONS

Application	Ft. Lbs. (N.m)
Universal Joint Bolts	18-25 (24-34)
Steering Wheel Nut	
911SC	54 (73)
928S	37 (50)
944	33 (45)

Steering Columns

RENAULT FUEGO, FUEGO TURBO, LeCAR & 18i

DESCRIPTION

Renault models have a collapsible column. Two column sections are joined by a universal joint. The upper column sliding section compresses on impact. The column lower end connects to the steering gear pinion flange with a flexible coupling or universal joint.

REMOVAL & INSTALLATION

STEERING COLUMN

Removal

1) Disconnect battery negative cable. Remove column housings and horn pad. Mark steering wheel position on shaft for installation. Remove steering wheel using a puller.

2) Remove combination switch. Disconnect universal joint. On LeCar, remove instrument panel and fuse box and disconnect flexible coupling (retain rubber spacer).

3) Make sure steering wheel lock is unlocked. Remove column clamps and column. To remove lower shaft, remove both universal joints, rubber sleeve and lower shaft.

Fig. 1: Exploded View of Renault Steering Column

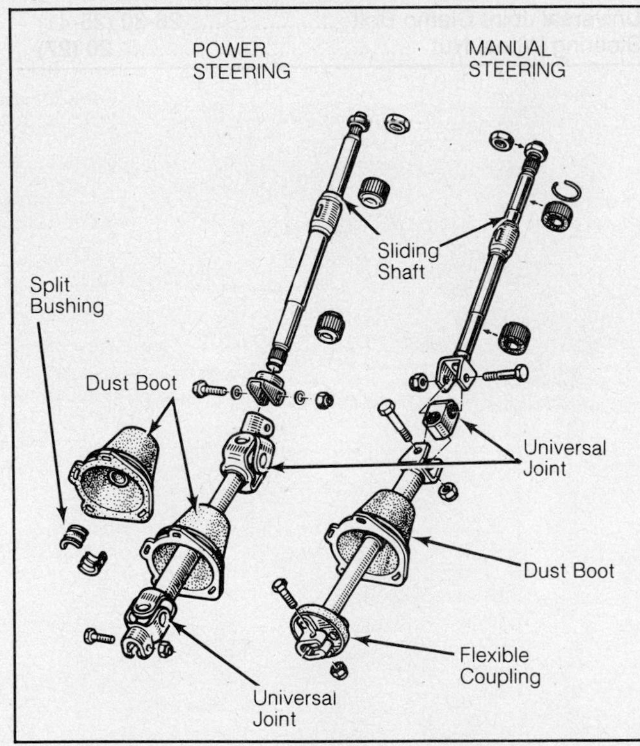
POWER
STEERING
MANUAL
STEERING
Sliding
Shaft
Split
Bushing
Dust Boot
Universal
Joint
Dust Boot
Flexible
Coupling
Universal
Joint

Installation

To install, reverse removal procedure, noting the following: On Fuego, Fuego Turbo and 18i, check lower shaft length. Replace shaft if length is incorrect. On vehicles with manual steering, align each shaft with universal joint, then tighten corresponding joint bolt. *See Fig. 2.*

LOWER STEERING SHAFT LENGTH

Application	In. (mm)
All Fuego	9.68-9.77 (246.0-248.0)
18i	
Manual Steering	12.68 (322.0)
Power Steering	11.93 (303.0)

Fig. 2: Aligning Shafts With Universal Joint

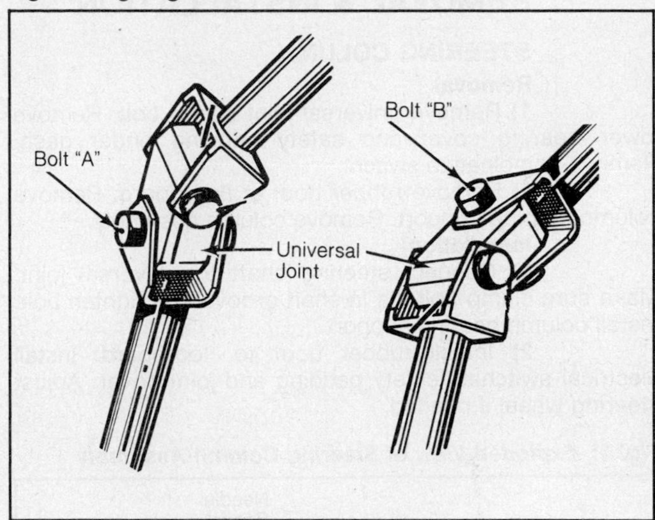
Bolt "B"
Bolt "A"
Universal
Joint

Tighten bolt "A", turn wheel 1/4 turn and tighten bolt "B".

OVERHAUL

REPLACING BUSHINGS

Disassembly

Tap steering shaft upper end until lower bushing comes out of column tube. Remove snap ring from top of column tube and carefully pry out bushing with screwdriver.

Reassembly

1) On LeCar and 18i, coat new bushing with grease. Position lower split bushing on steering shaft. Below split bushing, fit an old bushing which has been turned down .08" (2 mm) in diameter.

2) Insert lower bushing by pulling steering shaft upward. Push shaft back slightly to remove used bushing. Using a sleeve, replace upper bushing. Install snap ring.

3) On all Fuego models, coat bushings with grease and drive in new lower bushing using a sleeve. Place new upper bushing on shaft. Slide shaft into column and center it in lower bushing.

4) Insert shaft lower end in universal joint. Align slot with shaft flat. Install key bolt. Drive in upper bushing using a sleeve. Install snap ring.

TIGHTENING SPECIFICATIONS

Application	Ft. Lbs. (N.m)
Steering Wheel Nut	33 (45)
Universal Joint Bolt (All Fuego)	26 (35)

Steering Columns

SAAB 900 & 900 TURBO

DESCRIPTION

Steering column collapses on frontal impact. Steering shaft mounts in 2 needle bearing assemblies in column support. Column support mounts to a crossmember under dash. An intermediate shaft, with universal joints at each end, transmits steering shaft movement to steering gear.

REMOVAL & INSTALLATION

STEERING COLUMN

Removal

1) Remove universal joint clamp bolt. Remove lower bearing cover and safety padding under dash. Remove combination switch.

2) Remove rubber boot at floorboard. Remove column bearing support. Remove column assembly.

Installation

1) Connect steering shaft to universal joint. Make sure clamp bolt fits in shaft groove and tighten bolt. Install column bearing support.

2) Install rubber boot to floorboard. Install electrical switches, safety padding and joint cover. Adjust steering wheel if needed.

Fig. 1: Exploded View of Steering Column Assembly

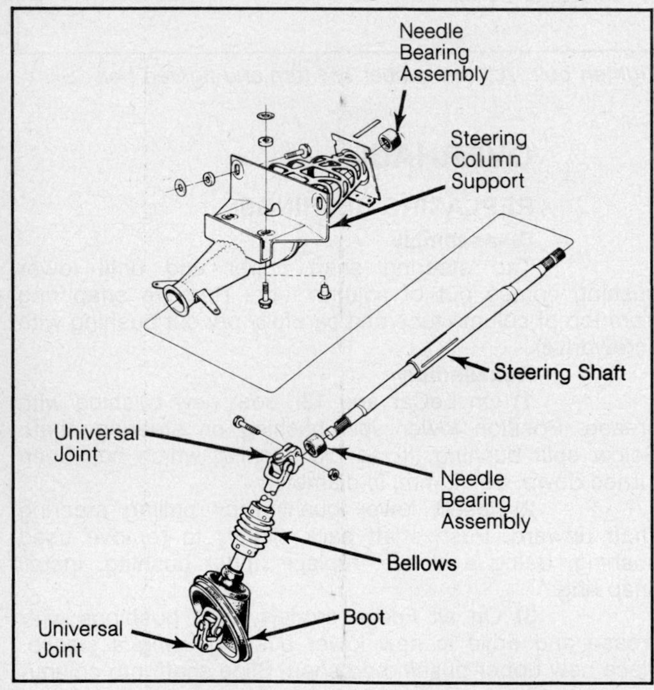
Needle Bearing Assembly
Steering Column Support
Steering Shaft
Universal Joint
Needle Bearing Assembly
Bellows
Boot
Universal Joint

INTERMEDIATE SHAFT BELLOWS

Removal

Remove cover under dash. Remove universal joint clamp bolt. Unbolt column tube from dash. Pull steering shaft from intermediate shaft. Remove grommet. Cut off old bellows.

Installation

1) Lubricate bellows installer cone (89 95 813) with petroleum jelly. Position cone against joint. Ease new bellows over cone and joint. Insert grommet in bellows hole.

2) Connect steering shaft to intermediate shaft. Make sure universal joint clamp bolt fits in shaft groove and tighten bolt.

3) Attach steering column to dash. Check steering wheel position and adjust if needed. Fit bellows to floorboard. Replace cover under dash.

OVERHAUL

STEERING COLUMN

Disassembly

Remove steering wheel. *See Saab in Steering Wheel & Column Switches in this section.* Pull steering shaft out of tube. Remove rubber bushings with needle bearing assemblies.

NOTE: **Replacement of needle bearing assemblies is the only overhaul procedure possible.**

Reassembly

To reassemble steering column, reverse disassembly procedure.

TIGHTENING SPECIFICATIONS

Application	Ft. Lbs. (N.m)
Universal Joint Clamp Bolt	26-30 (35-41)
Steering Wheel Nut	20 (27)

SUBARU 1600, 1800 & 1800 TURBO

DESCRIPTION

Energy-absorbing steering shaft collapses on impact. Steering column connects to the steering gear with a universal joint. An anti-theft locking mechanism prevents steering shaft from turning when key is removed. A tilt steering wheel is available on GL models.

Fig. 1: Subaru Manual Steering Column Assembly

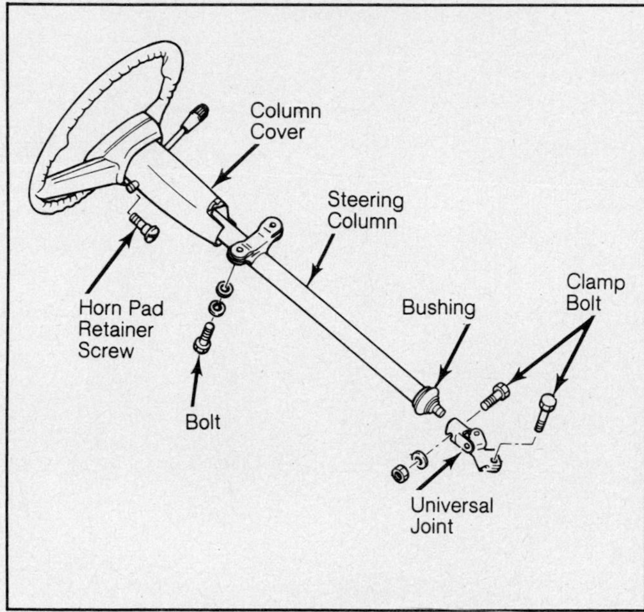
Column
Cover
Steering
Column
Clamp
Bolt
Horn Pad
Retainer
Screw
Bushing
Bolt
Universal
Joint

REMOVAL & INSTALLATION

STEERING COLUMN

Removal

1) Disconnect battery negative cable. Remove universal joint clamp bolt and separate shaft from joint.

2) Remove trim panel and unplug all wiring connectors to steering column switches. Remove steering shaft bolt from instrument panel and pull steering column from floorboard.

Installation

Insert column through floorboard into universal joint. Install column bolt into instrument panel and tighten. Connect all electrical connections. Tighten universal joint clamp bolt.

TILT MECHANISM

Removal

1) Disconnect tension cords. Set wheel fully up. Remove cords and balance springs. Remove universal joint clamp bolt. Loosen lower bearing screws and remove universal joint shaft and bearing downward as a unit.

2) Remove snap ring, washer, "O" ring, bearing and housing from universal joint shaft. Remove ignition switch bolts. Detach switch and universal joint shaft from tilt bracket.

3) Remove inner stop ring from ignition switch using a sharp screwdriver. Remove inner needle bearing and race. Remove inner spring washer. Remove outer stop ring, washer, needle bearing and race. Remove outer spring washer.

4) Remove tilt lever spring and plate. Remove lock gear and lever as an assembly. Remove lever snap ring, washer and shaft. Remove tilt bracket pivot bolt and bushing. Remove tilt bracket. Remove lock gear shaft and lever shaft.

Installation

1) Apply grease to shaft lower bearing surface. Install bearing, "O" ring, washer and snap ring onto steering shaft. Install springs in ignition switch grooves.

2) Install inner and outer needle bearings and races into ignition switch. Install inner stop ring and outer stop ring and washer. Apply grease to inside of inner and outer needle bearings.

3) Install universal joint shaft to ignition switch, making sure 2.29-2.30" (58.1-58.4 mm) of shaft smooth section protrudes from ignition switch. Turn shaft to make sure it operates smoothly.

4) Apply grease to column friction surface at tilt bracket. Install wave washer and tilt bracket. Apply grease to tilt bracket bushing and shaft. Install bushing, shaft, washer and snap ring.

5) Install pivot bolt to column. Temporarily attach lock gear shaft and tilt lever shaft to column. Apply grease to both shafts. Insert lock gear guide pin into tilt lever groove. Install tilt lever and lock gear to their shafts.

6) Apply grease to lock and sector gear teeth and roller surfaces. Attach spacer to lock gear. Install plate, aligning holes with pivot bolt, lock gear shaft and lever shaft.

7) Temporarily tighten pivot bolt, lock gear shaft and lever shaft. Apply grease to lever spring and install tube on spring. Install spring to tilt lever and plate.

8) Move lever up and down and adjust clearance between lever and plate cutout portion to .16-.31" (4-8 mm). Tighten nuts. Guide universal joint through tilt bracket hole.

9) Install ignition switch. Install steering shaft into column tube lower end until universal joint serration reaches tube. Align shaft bearing and tube holes and install lock washer and set screw. Tighten universal joint clamp bolt.

10) Apply grease to balance springs. Install tubes on springs. Install springs and tension cords. Make sure tilt lever is locked at each position when operated.

11) Install combination switch. Clamp ignition and combination switch harnesses. Install column covers. Attach clips to column bracket and install column to body.

OVERHAUL

STEERING COLUMN

Disassembly

1) Remove horn pad retaining screw (2-spoke wheel) or screws (4-spoke wheel) from behind wheel. Pull down horn pad to remove. On soft-type steering wheel, lift up horn pad from front.

2) Remove steering wheel. *See Subaru in Steering Wheel and Column Switches in this section.* Remove column covers, combination switch and horn brush.

3) Remove lower bearing screws. Pull out shaft with bearing downward. Remove snap ring, washer, "O" ring and bearing.

SUBARU 1600, 1800 & 1800 TURBO (Cont.)

Inspection

1) Make sure universal joint has no play in any direction. Replace if necessary. Flex universal joint and check for binding. Replace if yawing torque exceeds 4 INCH Lbs. (.58 N.m).

Fig. 2: Cross Section of Lower Steering Shaft

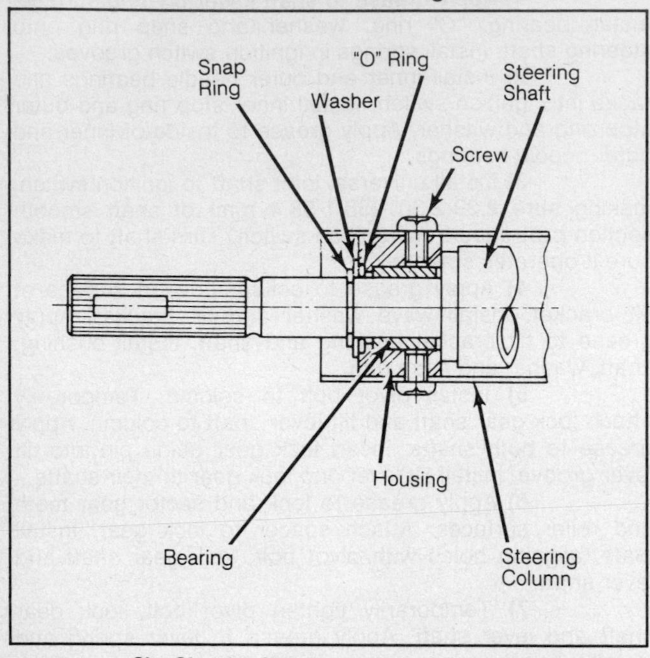
Snap Ring
"O" Ring
Washer
Steering Shaft
Screw
Housing
Bearing
Steering Column

2) Check plastic washer for damage, and serration for wear. Check steering shaft length. Standard shaft length should be 33.74-33.82" (857.0-859.0 mm). Shaft length for tilt column should be 25.35-25.43" (644.0-646.0 mm).

3) Check shaft runout. Runout for elliptical part should be less than 1.28" (32.5 mm). Runout for upper end of shaft should be less than .047" (1.2 mm). Runout for shaft collar (standard wheel) should be less than .024" (.6 mm). Replace steering shaft if not within specifications. Check bearings for damage and replace if needed.

Reassembly

To reassemble, reverse disassembly procedure. Apply grease to shaft sliding section at lower and upper bearing and horn brush. With steering wheel in place, check clearance between wheel and cover. If clearance exceeds .04-.12" (1.0-3.0 mm), loosen column cover screws and adjust cover.

TIGHTENING SPECIFICATIONS

Application	Ft. Lbs. (N.m)
Column Bracket Bolt	14-22 (19-30)
Steering Wheel Nut	22-29 (30-39)
Universal Joint Bolt	16-19 (22-26)

Steering Columns

TOYOTA CAMRY & COROLLA

DESCRIPTION

Columns used on Camry and Corolla models are collapsible 2-piece design. Columns use plastic shear pins to absorb collision impact. Sliding yoke connects steering shaft to steering gear.

REMOVAL & INSTALLATION

STEERING COLUMN

Removal

1) Disconnect battery ground cable. Remove steering wheel. *See Toyota in Steering Wheel & Column Switches article in this Section.* Remove sliding yoke.

2) On both models, remove instrument panel cover (under column). On Camry remove heater duct below column.

3) Remove upper and lower column covers. Remove combination switch. Remove column bracket bolts and floor hole cover bolts. Remove steering column from inside vehicle.

Installation

To install, reverse removal procedures. Make sure steering wheel is horizonal when wheels are in straight-ahead position.

OVERHAUL

STEERING COLUMN

Disassembly

1) Remove retainer and snap ring from upper end of steering column. Remove mounting bolts from hole cover plate.

2) Pull column tube off steering shaft from upper end of shaft. Remove upper bracket from column tube.

Inspection

1) Check all components for damage or wear. Check steering shaft for bend or damage. Check column for sheared plastic pins.

2) Check upper bracket for proper operating lock mechanism. If necessary, upper bracket bearing can be replaced.

Reassembly

1) To reassemble steering column, reverse disassembly procedures. Make sure to grease steering shaft, bushings and bearings.

2) Also make sure lock on upper bracket operates properly and steering shaft is not binding in column tube.

TIGHTENING SPECIFICATIONS

Application	Ft. Lbs. (N.m)
Column Bracket (Breakaway)	
Camry	14-22 (19-30)
Corolla	22-33 (30-45)
Sliding Yoke Bolt	22-28 (30-38)
Steering Wheel	22-29 (30-39)

Fig. 1: Exploded View of Camry and Corolla Steering Column

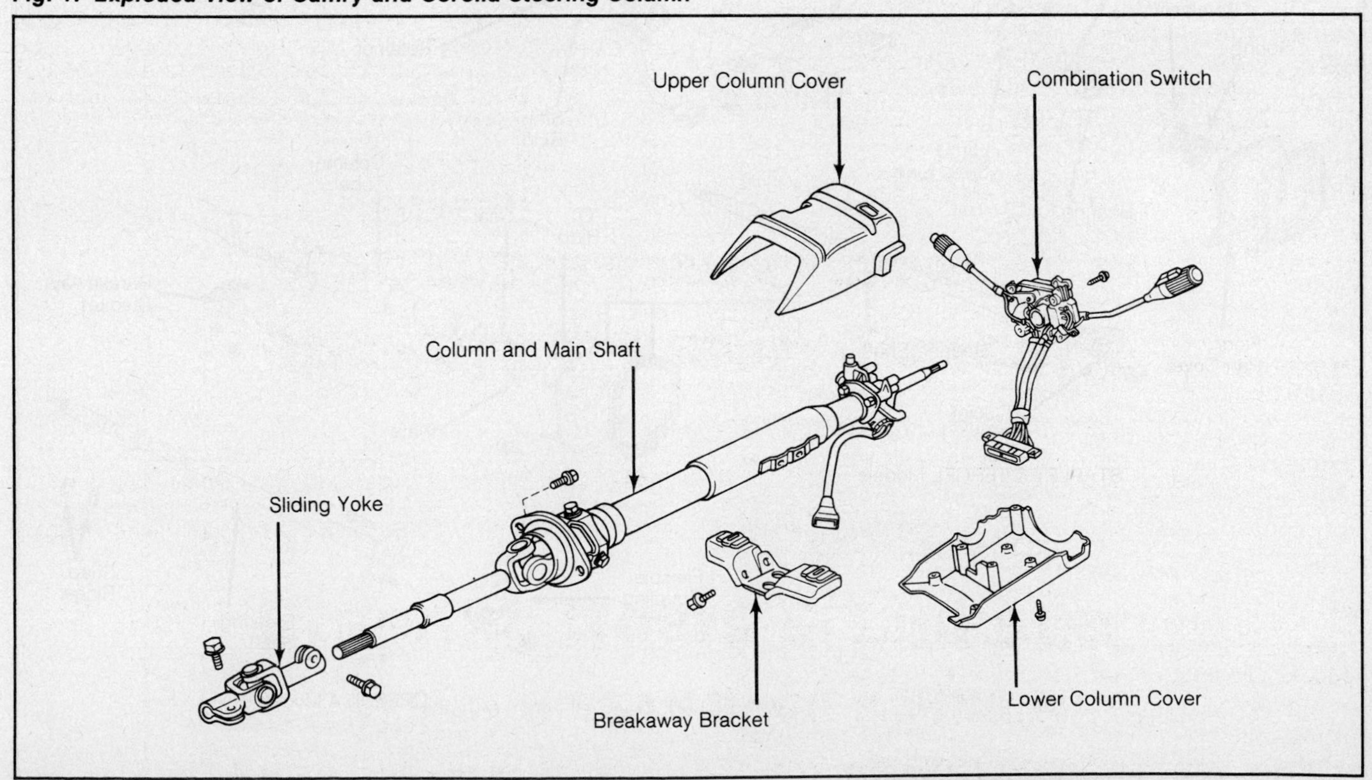
Upper Column Cover
Combination Switch
Column and Main Shaft
Sliding Yoke
Breakaway Bracket
Lower Column Cover

Steering Columns

TOYOTA CRESSIDA, LAND CRUISER, PICKUP, STARLET & TERCEL

DESCRIPTION

Steering columns used on these models are of collapsible 2-piece design. Columns use shear pins to absorb collision impact. Steering shaft is connected directly to steering gear with flexible couplings on Cressida models.

Starlet, Tercel and Pickup models use intermediate steering shafts. On 2WD Pickup models, intermediate shaft is connected to steering gear by a flexible coupling. On Land Cruiser, Starlet, Tercel and 4WD Pickup models, intermediate shaft is connected to steering gear and to main steering shaft by universal joints.

NOTE: **For models with Tilt Wheel steering columns, see Tilt Wheel Steering Columns article in this section.**

REMOVAL & INSTALLATION

STEERING COLUMN

Removal

1) Disconnect battery ground cable. Remove steering wheel. *See Toyota in Steering Wheel & Column Switches article in this section.* On Cressida models, remove fuse box cover, lower instrument trim panel and heater duct (located under steering column).

2) On all models, remove upper and lower steering column covers. Remove combination switch. On Land Cruiser, Starlet, Tercel and 4WD Pickups, mark position of "U" joints-to-shafts and remove intermediate steering shaft.

3) On all other models, mark position of flexible coupling-to-steering gear and remove flexible coupling bolt. Remove floor pan cover bolts and column bracket bolts. Remove steering column toward inside of vehicle.

NOTE: **Remove steering column with intermediate shaft attached on 2WD Pickup models.**

Installation

To install steering column, reverse removal procedures. Make sure "U" joint and flexible coupling alignment marks (made upon removal) are correctly aligned.

Fig. 1: Exploded View of Cressida, Starlet and Tercel Steering Columns

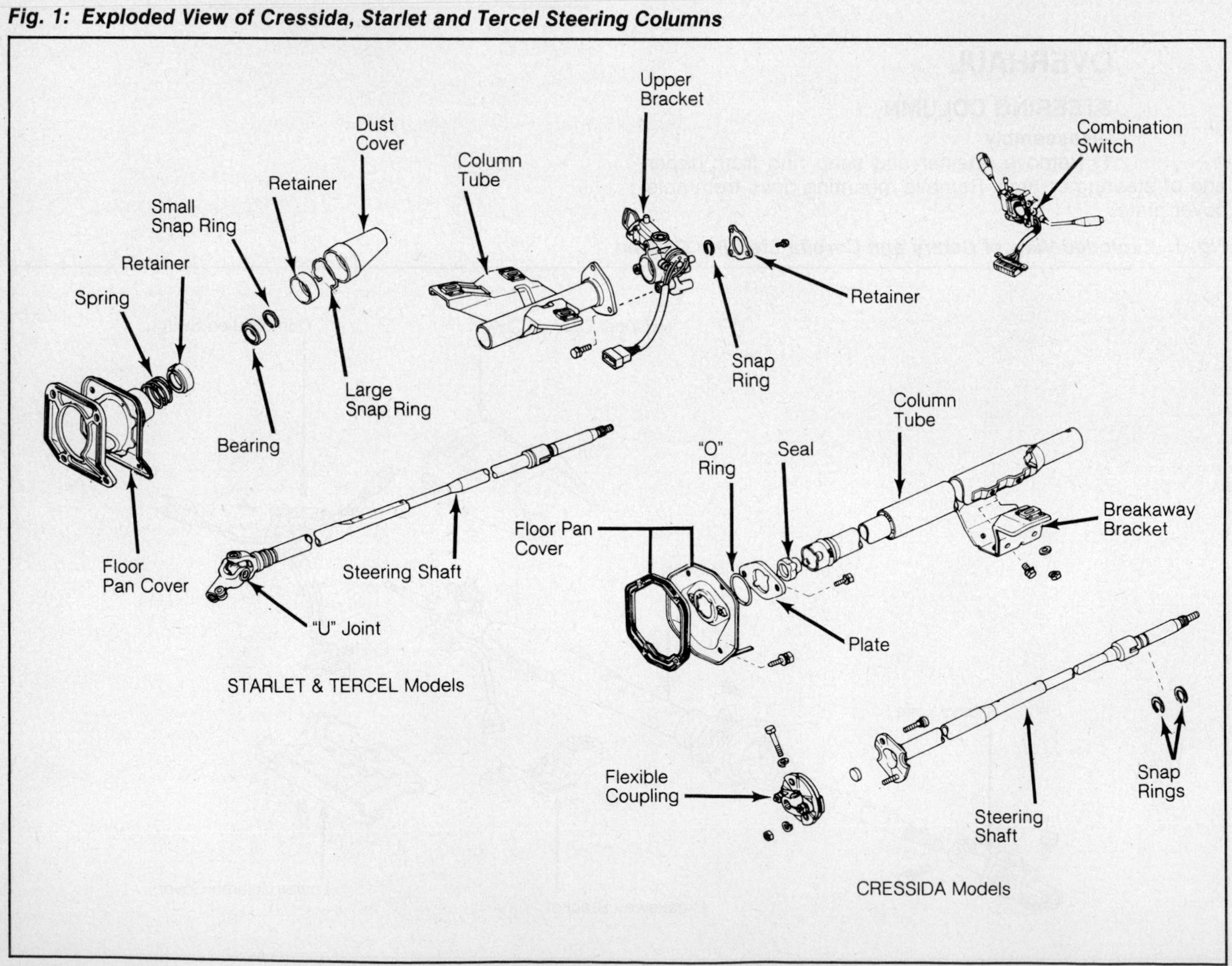
Upper
Bracket
Dust
Cover
Column
Tube
Combination
Switch
Retainer
Small
Snap Ring
Retainer
Spring
Retainer
Snap
Ring
Large
Snap Ring
Bearing
Column
Tube
"O"
Ring
Seal
Breakaway
Bracket
Floor Pan
Cover
Floor
Pan Cover
Steering Shaft
"U" Joint
Plate
STARLET & TERCEL Models
Flexible
Coupling
Snap
Rings
Steering
Shaft
CRESSIDA Models

TOYOTA, CRESSIDA, LAND CRUISER, PICKUP, STARLET & TERCEL (Cont.)

OVERHAUL

STEERING COLUMN

Disassembly

1) Remove bearing retainer and snap ring from upper end of column tube. On Starlet and Tercel models, remove upper bracket from column tube. On all models, pull steering shaft out bottom of column tube.

2) On 2WD Pickups, mark main steering shaft-to-intermediate shaft position. Remove snap ring and separate intermediate shaft from steering shaft. Be careful not to lose bearing blocks (located on intermediate shaft).

3) On Cressida and 2WD Pickups, remove flexible coupling from steering shaft. On all models (except Starlet and Tercel), remove upper bracket from column tube.

4) On Starlet and Tercel models, remove dust cover, compress shaft toward floor pan cover and remove large snap ring.

5) Remove spring retainer, and again compress shaft to remove small snap ring. Remove bearing, spring retainer and spring. Remove floor pan cover from steering shaft.

6) On all other models, separate floor pan cover from column tube plate and be careful not to damage "O" ring (dust seal on Land Cruiser and 4WD Pickup models). On Cressida, remove bracket from column tube. Remove plate and seal from bottom of column tube.

7) On 2WD Pickups, remove plate spring, bearing retainers and bearing from bottom of column tube. On Land Cruiser and 4WD Pickups, remove bolt from column support tube clamp.

8) Remove column support tube from column tube. Remove snap ring and bearing from column support tube.

Inspection

1) Inspect all components for wear or damage. Check bearings for smooth operation. Check steering shafts for collision damage. Check steering lock mechanism (located in upper bracket) for proper operation. Replace components as necessary.

2) On 2WD Pickups, temporarily assemble main steering shaft to intermediate shaft and measure amount of radial play between shafts. Allowable limit is .0024" (.06 mm). Replace pin and bearing blocks, if necessary.

NOTE: **If replacing pin and bearing blocks, make sure new bearing blocks have the small anti-rattle rubber inserts installed before assembling intermediate shaft to main steering shaft, otherwise steering shafts will rattle when installed in vehicle.**

3) On Land Cruiser and Starlet, Tercel and 4WD Pickups, check "U" joints for excessive axial play. Maximum play is .002" (.05 mm). Replace "U" joint, if necessary.

Reassembly

1) To reassemble steering columns, reverse disassembly procedures. Grease main steering shaft and all bearings.

2) Make sure marks made to flexible couplings and to "U" joints are aligned. Make sure steering column and shafts do not bind after installation.

TIGHTENING SPECIFICATIONS

Application	Ft. Lbs. (N.m)
Column Bracket	15-22 (20-30)
Flexible Coupling	15-22 (20-30)
Steering Wheel	22-29 (30-39)
"U" Joint Bolts	22-33 (30-45)

Fig. 2: Exploded View of Land Cruiser & Pickup Steering Columns

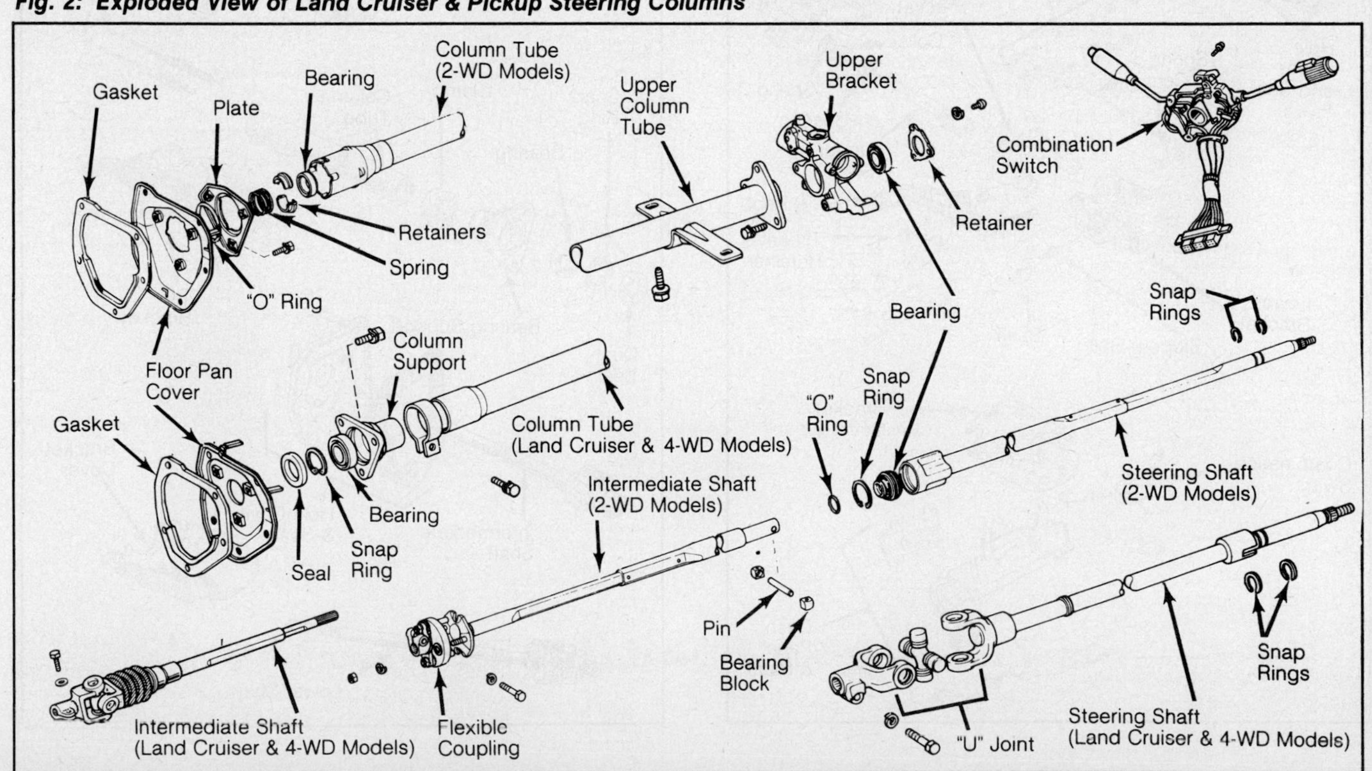
Column Tube
(2-WD Models)
Bearing
Gasket
Plate
Upper
Column
Tube
Upper
Bracket
Combination
Switch
Retainers
Spring
Retainer
"O" Ring
Bearing
Snap
Rings
Column
Support
Floor Pan
Cover
Gasket
Column Tube
(Land Cruiser & 4-WD Models)
"O"
Ring
Snap
Ring
Steering Shaft
(2-WD Models)
Bearing
Intermediate Shaft
(2-WD Models)
Seal
Snap
Ring
Pin
Bearing
Block
Snap
Rings
Intermediate Shaft
(Land Cruiser & 4-WD Models)
Flexible
Coupling
"U" Joint
Steering Shaft
(Land Cruiser & 4-WD Models)

Steering Columns

TOYOTA CELICA, COROLLA, CRESSIDA, LAND CRUISER, PICKUP & SUPRA – TILT WHEEL

DESCRIPTION

Tilt steering wheels incorporate an upper steering shaft attached, by a universal joint, with an intermediate steering shaft. These shafts are held in place by upper and lower brackets.

Brackets are pinned together so that upper bracket will move up or down. Upper bracket is locked in place by pawl attached to lever. Steering columns are collapsible type.

REMOVAL & INSTALLATION

STEERING COLUMN

Removal

1) Disconnect battery ground cable. Remove steering wheel pad. Mark steering shaft and wheel for installation. Remove steering wheel. *See Toyota in Steering Wheel & Column Switches article in this section.* Remove dash panels and pads, if necessary. On models with air conditioning, remove air duct under steering column.

2) Remove column bracket covers. Remove turn signal or combination switch. From under hood, disconnect steering shaft universal joint from steering gear (on passenger vehicles) or from lower steering shaft (on Land Cruiser and Pickup models).

3) Be sure to mark universal joint and shaft for installation. Remove bolts from column hole cover. Remove column support bracket bolts. Remove steering column from vehicle.

Installation

1) Install steering column in vehicle and tighten column bracket bolts finger tight. Install column hole cover bolts. Tighten column bracket bolts.

2) Make sure alignment marks are aligned on universal joints, then tighten clamp bolts. Install turn signal or combination switch. Install bracket covers, dash panels and pads. Install air ducts (if equipped).

3) Install steering wheel and steering wheel pad. Make sure alignment marks on steering shaft and steering wheel are aligned.

Fig. 1: Exploded View of Passenger Car Tilt Steering Column

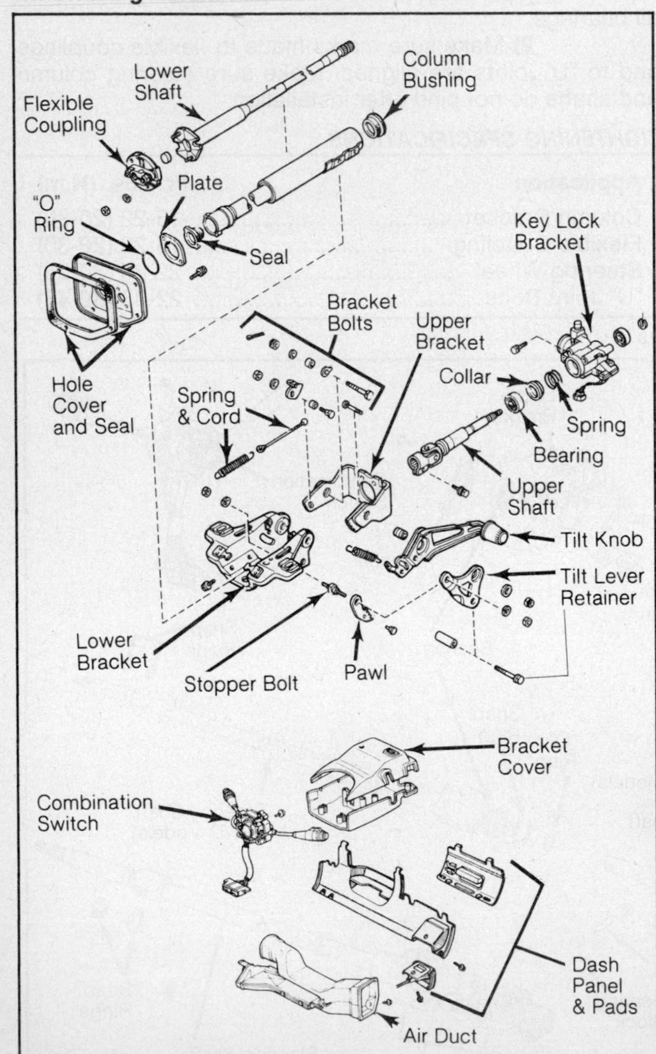
Lower Shaft
Column Bushing
Flexible Coupling
Plate
"O" Ring
Seal
Key Lock Bracket
Bracket Bolts
Upper Bracket
Hole Cover and Seal
Spring & Cord
Collar
Spring
Bearing
Upper Shaft
Tilt Knob
Tilt Lever Retainer
Lower Bracket
Stopper Bolt
Pawl
Bracket Cover
Combination Switch
Dash Panel & Pads
Air Duct

Fig. 2: Exploded View of Land Cruiser & Pickup Tilt Wheel Steering Column

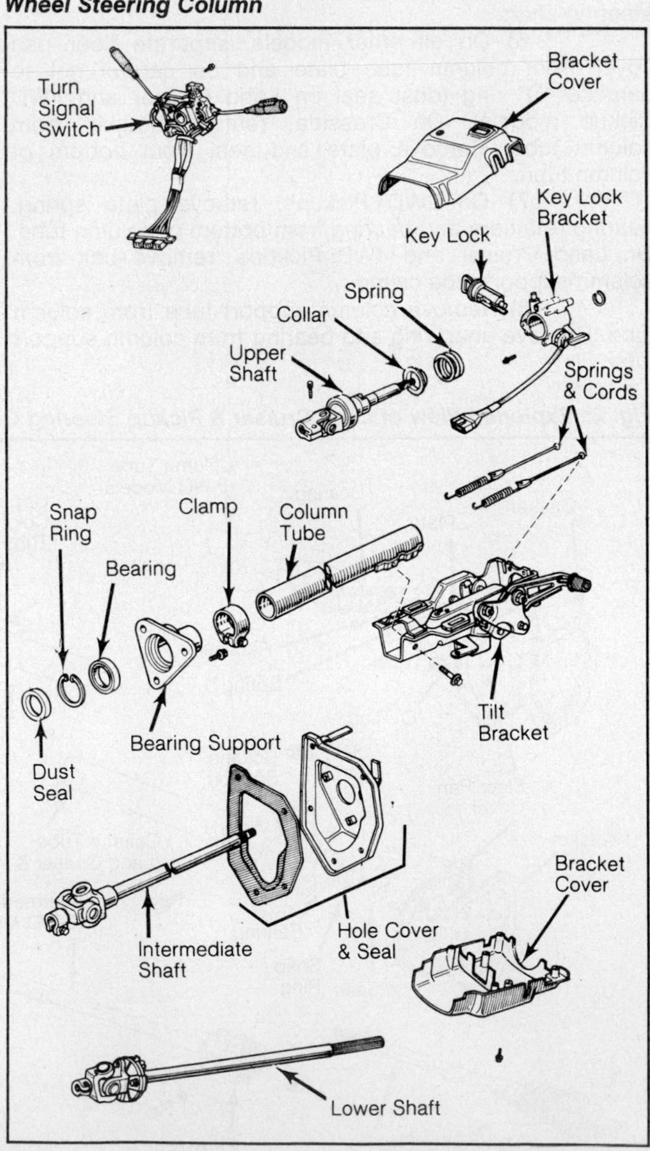
Turn Signal Switch
Bracket Cover
Key Lock Bracket
Key Lock
Spring
Collar
Upper Shaft
Springs & Cords
Snap Ring
Clamp
Column Tube
Bearing
Tilt Bracket
Dust Seal
Bearing Support
Intermediate Shaft
Hole Cover & Seal
Bracket Cover
Lower Shaft

TOYOTA CELICA, COROLLA, CRESSIDA, LAND CRUISER, PICKUP & SUPRA – TILT WHEEL (Cont.)

OVERHAUL

STEERING COLUMN

Disassembly

1) On Land Cruiser and Pickup models, remove ignition key cylinder. On all models, remove tension springs and cords. Mark universal joint and lower steering shaft.

2) Remove clamp bolt and lower steering shaft. Remove hole cover from column. Remove snap ring from upper steering shaft.

3) Remove reclining pawl release pin and steering pawl. Drive out serrated bolt with soft mallet. Remove reclining pawl set bolt.

Fig. 3: Exploded View of Tilt Wheel Bracket

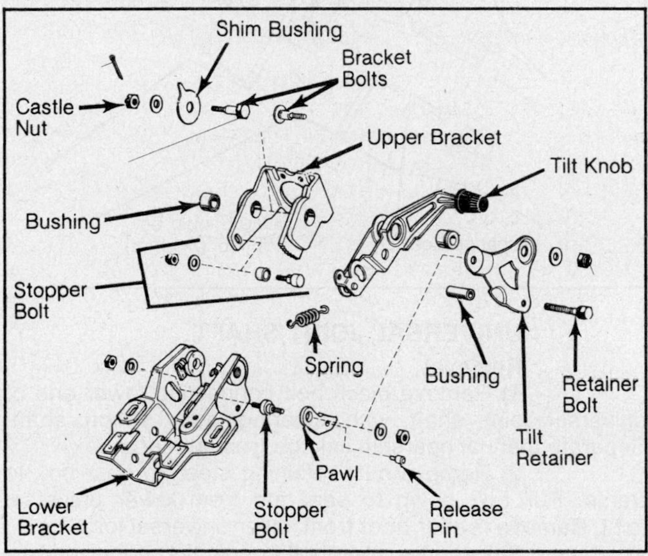

Shim Bushing
Bracket Bolts
Castle Nut
Upper Bracket
Tilt Knob
Bushing
Stopper Bolt
Spring
Bushing
Retainer Bolt
Tilt Retainer
Pawl
Lower Bracket
Stopper Bolt
Release Pin

Inspection

1) Check upper bracket for damage. Check upper bearing for rotating smoothness. Check steering shafts for bending, damaged splines or damaged universal joints.

2) Check tilt bracket for worn bushings, damaged pawl, broken or damaged breakaway brackets. Check column tube for bending or other damage. Repair or replace components as necessary.

Reassembly

Reassemble in reverse order of disassembly procedures. Make sure all bushings, bearings, shims and bolts are not damaged or worn.

TIGHTENING SPECIFICATIONS

Application	Ft. Lbs. (N.m)
Castle Nut	11-21 (15-28)
Flexible Coupling	15-21 (20-28)
Steering Wheel Nut	22-28 (30-38)
Support Bracket	
Land Cruiser & Pickup	11-15 (15-20)
All Others	14-22 (19-30)
Support Bracket-to-Column	11-15 (15-20)
Tilt Lever Retainer Bolt	11-15 (15-20)
Tilt Steering Support Stopper Bolt	6-8 (8-11)
Universal Joint Clamp Bolt [1]	15-21 (20-28)

[1] – Tighten clamp bolt at steering gear on Land Cruiser and Pickup to 22-32 ft. lbs. (30-44 N.m).

Steering Columns

VOLKSWAGEN JETTA, RABBIT, PICKUP & SCIROCCO

DESCRIPTION

Swing-away steering column is held by a clamp and leaf spring. On impact the universal joint shaft pushes steering column against the leaf spring. The spring allows the column to disengage and swing away.

REMOVAL & INSTALLATION

STEERING COLUMN

NOTE: Do not remove steering shaft before removing column from vehicle.

Removal

1) Disconnect battery ground cable. Remove steering wheel. *See Volkswagen in Steering Wheel & Column Switches article in this section.*

2) Remove bolt and screw from switch housing recess. Tilt switch unit toward instrument panel. Pry off spacer sleeve on steering column.

3) Pull up switch unit to disconnect wires. Remove switch unit from column. Disconnect steering shaft from universal joint shaft. Disconnect brake pedal push rod.

4) Separate clutch pedal from actuating cable under instrument panel. Push down leaf spring retainer clip with a screwdriver and disengage it from mounting slot.

5) Remove bolts retaining column under instrument panel. Punch and drill out shear bolts. Pull column assembly from vehicle.

Fig. 1: Exploded View of Steering Column Assembly

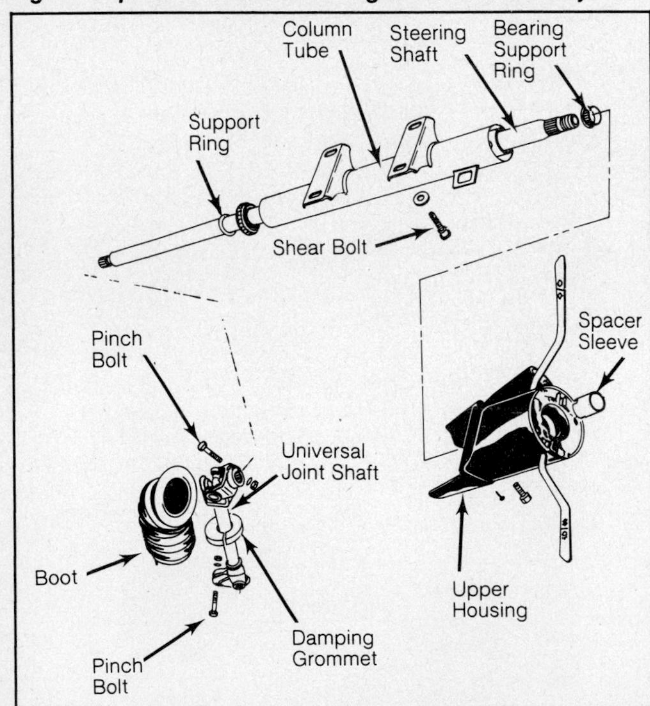
Column Tube
Steering Shaft
Bearing Support Ring
Support Ring
Shear Bolt
Pinch Bolt
Spacer Sleeve
Universal Joint Shaft
Boot
Upper Housing
Damping Grommet
Pinch Bolt

Bearing Replacement

Drive steering shaft from column. Remove bearings. Press in steering shaft and new bearings. Do not press in shaft with more than 100-200 lbs. (45-90 kg) force.

Installation

To install, reverse removal procedure. Make sure front wheels point straight-ahead before tightening pinch bolt. Before fitting column switch unit, install spacer. *See Fig. 2.* Adjust both brake pedal and clutch pedal height.

Fig. 2: Spacer Sleeve Adjustment Dimensions

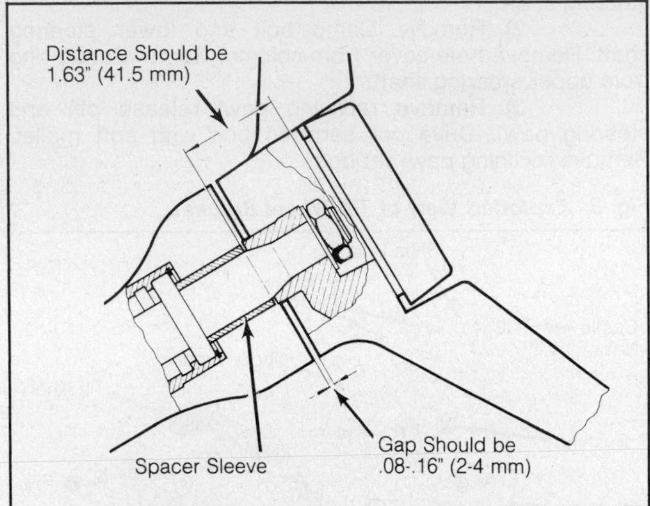
Distance Should be
1.63" (41.5 mm)
Spacer Sleeve
Gap Should be
.08-.16" (2-4 mm)

UNIVERSAL JOINT SHAFT

Removal

1) Remove pinch bolt connecting lower end of universal joint shaft with steering gear pinion shaft. Separate manual gearshift linkage from steering box.

2) Remove nuts retaining steering gear box to frame. Pull box down to separate from lower universal joint. Remove rubber boot from lower universal joint.

3) Remove pinch bolt connecting upper universal joint to steering shaft. Pull down joint and remove shaft with universal joints.

Installation

1) Fit universal joint to steering shaft. Make sure steering shaft notch aligns with lower universal joint slot.

2) Install boot and damping grommet. Fit steering gear box to frame while guiding pinion shaft into lower universal joint. Loosely tighten gear box nuts.

3) Position front wheels straight ahead. Align pinion shaft and universal joint. Tighten pinch bolt. Tighten gear box nuts. Connect manual gearshift linkage to gear box. Check linkage operation.

TIGHTENING SPECIFICATIONS

Application	Ft. Lbs. (N.m)
Steering Column-to-Instrument Panel	
Retaining Bolt	15 (20)
Shear Bolts	[1]
Steering Wheel Nut	37 (50)
Pinch Bolts	22 (30)

[1] – Tighten until bolt head snaps off.

VOLKSWAGEN QUANTUM

DESCRIPTION

The Quantum uses a 2-piece, collapsible steering column. A flange connects lower column to upper column.

REMOVAL & INSTALLATION

STEERING COLUMN

Removal

1) Disconnect battery ground cable. Remove steering wheel and column switches. *See Volkswagen in Steering Wheels & Column Switches article in this section.*

2) From under hood, remove clamp bolt retaining steering shaft clamp to steering gear pinion shaft. Remove column cover bolts and steering column covers. *See Fig. 1.*

Fig. 1: Exploded View of Upper Steering Column

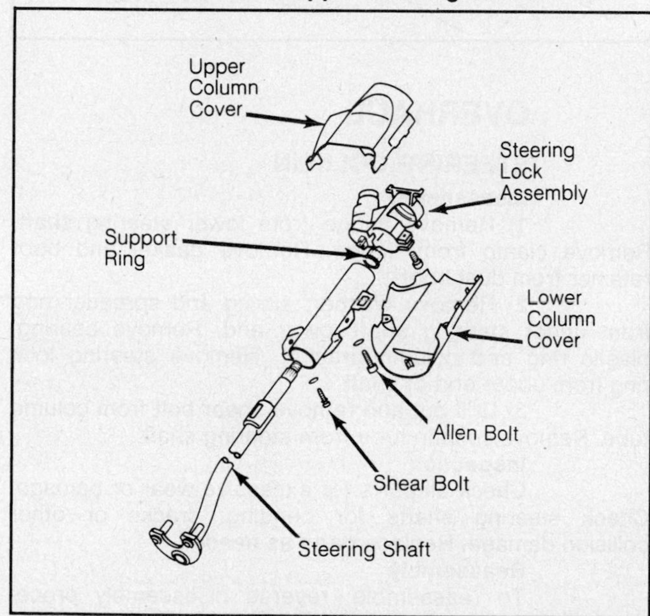

Upper Column Cover
Steering Lock Assembly
Support Ring
Lower Column Cover
Allen Bolt
Shear Bolt
Steering Shaft

3) Pry lock washer off steering shaft. Remove spring. Remove contact ring and steering lock assembly. Remove support ring from column tube. *See Fig. 1.*

4) Punch and drill out shear bolt retaining column tube to dash. Remove Allen bolt. Remove dust boot from floorboard. Remove steering column tube and shaft as an assembly.

Installation

1) Install assembled steering column into vehicle. Install shear bolt and Allen bolt finger tight. Seat dust boot into floorboard. Place clamp onto steering gear pinion shaft.

2) Place support ring into column tube. Install steering lock assembly on steering column. Install contact ring, spring and new lock washer. Tighten Allen bolt. Tighten shear bolt until head snaps off.

3) Install upper and lower column covers. Install column switches and steering wheel. *See Volkswagen in Steering Wheels & Column Switches article in this section.*

OVERHAUL

STEERING COLUMN

Disassembly

1) Remove lower flange tube clamp bolt from lower steering shaft. Separate flange tubes and remove bearing flange, bearing, support ring, spring and washer. *See Fig. 2.*

Fig. 2: Exploded View of Lower Steering Column

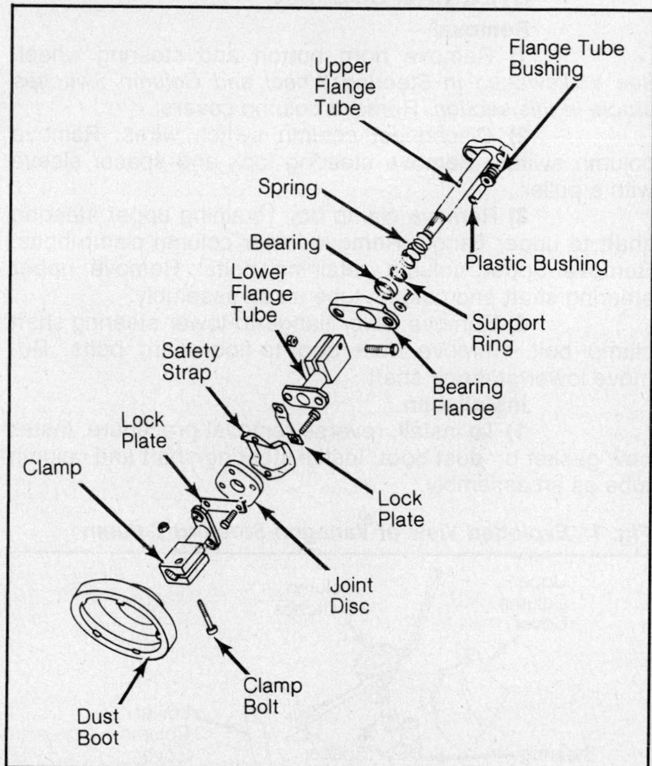

Upper Flange Tube
Flange Tube Bushing
Spring
Bearing
Plastic Bushing
Lower Flange Tube
Support Ring
Safety Strap
Bearing Flange
Lock Plate
Clamp
Lock Plate
Joint Disc
Clamp Bolt
Dust Boot

2) Push upper flange tube toward steering shaft until components can be separated. Remove flange tube bushings with plastic bushings. *See Fig. 2.*

3) Remove joint disc bolts and pinion clamp bolt. Check joint disc, safety strap and lock plates for damage or wear.

4) Slide column tube off steering shaft. Check steering shaft, support ring and steering lock assembly for wear or damage. Replace components as necessary. *See Fig. 1.*

Reassembly

To reassemble steering column, reverse disassembly procedure. Press flange tube bushing and plastic bushing in by hand.

TIGHTENING SPECIFICATIONS

Application	Ft. Lbs. (N.m)
Clamp Bolt	22 (30)
Lock Plate Bolts	18 (24)
Lower Flange Tube Bolt	22 (30)
Allen Bolt	15 (20)
Steering Wheel Nut	29 (39)

Steering Columns

VOLKSWAGEN VANAGON

DESCRIPTION

Volkswagen Vanagon uses an energy-absorbing, 2-piece steering column. Column is attached to dash with brackets and to floorboard with a boot flange. Lower steering shaft connects to the transfer gear with a flange.

REMOVAL & INSTALLATION

STEERING COLUMN

Removal

1) Remove horn button and steering wheel. *See Volkswagen in Steering Wheel and Column Switches article in this section.* Remove column covers.

2) Disconnect column switch wires. Remove column switch. Remove steering lock and spacer sleeve with a puller.

3) Remove clamp bolt retaining upper steering shaft to upper flange. Remove lower column clamp bolts. Remove upper column retaining bolts. Remove upper steering shaft and column tube as an assembly.

4) Remove lower flange-to-lower steering shaft clamp bolt. Remove dust boot-to-floorboard bolts. Remove lower steering shaft.

Installation

1) To install, reverse removal procedure. Install new gasket on dust boot. Install steering shaft and column tube as an assembly.

Fig. 1: Exploded View of Vanagon Steering Column

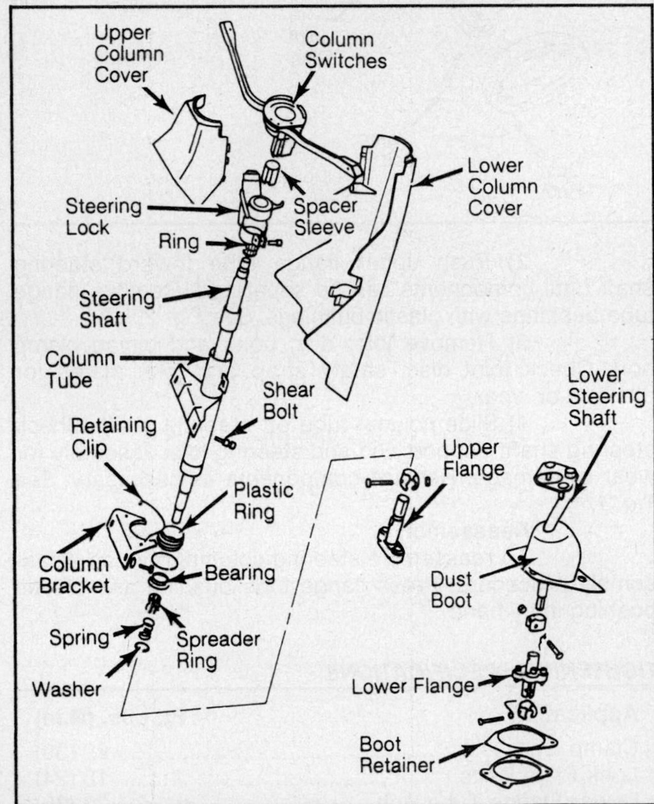
Upper Column Cover
Column Switches
Lower Column Cover
Steering Lock
Spacer Sleeve
Ring
Steering Shaft
Column Tube
Shear Bolt
Lower Steering Shaft
Retaining Clip
Upper Flange
Plastic Ring
Column Bracket
Bearing
Dust Boot
Spring
Spreader Ring
Washer
Lower Flange
Boot Retainer

2) When installing steering lock and spacer sleeve, clamp lower steering shaft to upper flange with clamp tool (VW 267a).

3) Make sure distance from top of column tube to top of upper steering shaft (with steering wheel and nut installed) is 1.634" (41.5 mm). Space between column switch and steering wheel should be .079-157" (2-4 mm). *See Fig. 2.*

Fig. 2: Measurements for Installing Spacer Sleeve

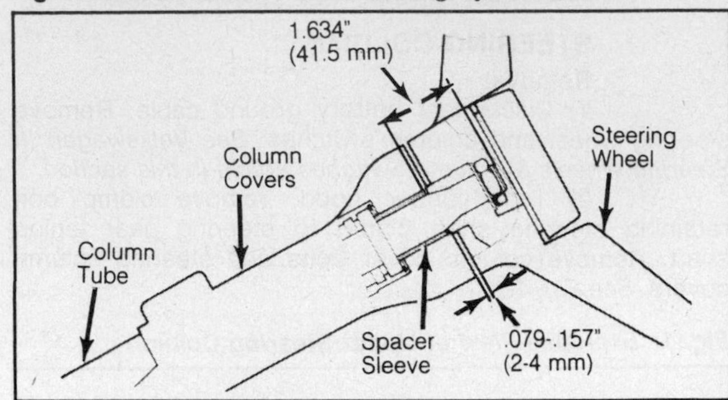
1.634"
(41.5 mm)
Column Covers
Steering Wheel
Column Tube
Spacer Sleeve
.079-.157"
(2-4 mm)

OVERHAUL

STEERING COLUMN

Disassembly

1) Remove flange from lower steering shaft. Remove clamp from flange. Remove gasket and boot retainer from dust boot.

2) Remove washer, spring and spreader ring from upper steering shaft lower end. Remove bearing, plastic ring and column bracket. Remove steering lock ring from upper end of shaft.

3) Drill out and remove shear bolt from column tube. Remove column tube from steering shaft.

Inspection

Check all parts for excessive wear or damage. Check steering shafts for bending, cracks or other collision damage. Replace parts as needed.

Reassembly

To reassemble, reverse disassembly procedure. Assemble steering lock, spacer sleeve and ring before installing to steering shaft. Tighten shear bolt until head snaps off.

TIGHTENING SPECIFICATIONS

Application	Ft. Lbs. (N.m)
Clamp Bolts	15 (20)
Lower Bracket Bolts	18 (24)
Steering Wheel Nut	37 (50)

VOLVO

DESCRIPTION

Steering column upper and lower sections are joined by a flange. On frontal impact, flange breaks from upper column. Upper column is carried in 2 ball bearings in jacket tube. Lower end of steering column connects to steering shaft with a flange.

REMOVAL & INSTALLATION

STEERING COLUMN

Removal (760 GLE)

1) Disconnect battery ground cable. Remove clamp bolts and snap rings from upper and lower steering shaft joints. Push steering shaft toward cowl and remove.

2) Remove steering wheel, column covers and switches. *See Volvo in Steering Wheel & Column Switches in this section.* Remove trim panels and heater duct under dash.

3) Punch and drill out column lock shear bolts. Remove lower bearing plate attaching bolts and column support bolts.

4) Turn ignition key to "II" position and remove column lock retaining screw. Press in tab under lock and remove lock. Remove key and wiring connector. Remove column guide from bracket. Remove column.

Bearing Replacement

1) To replace lower bearing, clamp steering shaft in soft-jawed vise and remove bearing race with a hammer and open end wrench. Grease inside of race and install so flats align with shaft flats. Race should be 1.98" (50.3 mm) from shaft flat end.

2) Check that upper column length is between 28.59-28.67" (726.2-728.2 mm). If length is incorrect, replace shaft.

3) To replace upper bearing, press bearing housing toward shaft. Remove snap ring, plastic cone, beaing housing, metal cone, washer, spring and washer.

4) Using a punch, tap out inner race and then outer race. Install new bearing with drift (2724) and handle (1801). Install washer, spring, washer and metal cone.

Fig. 1: Steering Wheel Lock Position

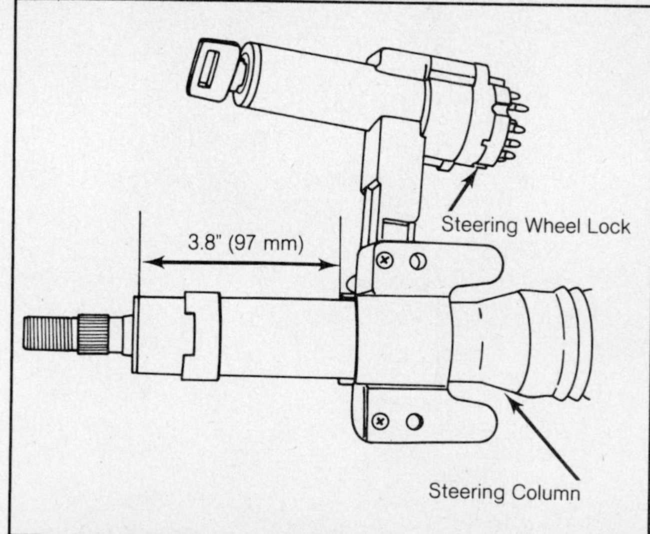
3.8" (97 mm)
Steering Wheel Lock
Steering Column

Make sure lock is properly positioned.

5) Temporarily place 2 flat washers between upper washer and metal cone, on each side of shaft. Install bearing housing and plastic cone (facing housing). Install snap ring. Remove 2 flat washers.

Installation

To install, reverse removal procedure. Tighten new shear bolts (until heads break off) after installing column lock bracket and lower bearing plate.

Removal (All Other Models)

1) Disconnect battery ground cable. Disconnect upper joint from upper and lower steering shafts. Remove steering wheel, column covers and switches. *See Volvo in Steering Wheel & Column Switches in this section.*

2) Under dash, remove trim panel and console side panel. Disconnect connector at steering lock. Drill lock retaining screws and remove with screw extractor. Remove defroster duct.

3) Remove column lower bracket. Pull column toward seat and remove firewall seal. Remove column and lock as an assembly.

Installation

1) Install lock so upper edge is 3.8" (97 mm) from upper edge of column. *See Fig. 1.* Make sure both plastic guides and spacers are in place. Washers must face downward.

2) Insert column through firewall. Install shear bolts and column clamp, but do not tighten them.

3) Adjust column position so lock protrudes .53-.65" (13.5-16.5 mm) from dash, measured at lock position "II". Column must not contact upper attachment plastic guides. Adjust dash beam if needed.

4) Tighten column clamp and bracket bolts. Install defroster duct. Install firewall seal. Loosely install upper joint on steering shaft. Install lower steering shaft flange to upper joint.

5) Check distance between lower steering shaft shoulder and upper joint. Distance should be .40-.75" (10-19 mm). If distance is incorrect, pull up lower joint cover, loosen joints and move lower shaft up or down.

6) Check distance between steering wheel and upper column cover. If clearance is not .04-.08" (1-2 mm), pull up lower joint cover, loosen lower joint and move lower shaft up or down.

7) To complete installation, reverse removal procedure. Tighten shear bolts until heads break off. If needed, place 1 or 2 flat washers between steering wheel and upper bearing spring to stop rattling.

TIGHTENING SPECIFICATIONS

Application	Ft. Lbs. (N.m)
Steering Wheel Nut	
760 GLE	21-27 (28-37)
All Others	33-55 (45-75)
Upper Joint	
760 GLE	15 (20)
All Others	14-22 (19-30)
Lower Joint	
760 GLE	15 (20)
All Others	13-21 (18-28)

AUDI 4000 RACK & PINION

DESCRIPTION

Audi 4000 uses manual rack and pinion steering. Rack housing mounts to the crossmember. Tie rods on 4-cylinder models adjust on left side only. Tie rods on 5-cylinder models adjust on both sides.

ADJUSTMENT

RACK ADJUSTMENT

1) Loosen lock nut on steering gear cover. Hand tighten adjusting screw until it touches thrust washer. Hold screw and tighten lock nut.

2) Readjust if steering is too tight or does not center itself. If gear rattles when vehicle is driven, adjustment is too loose.

CAUTION: Do not turn gear hard against either lock when vehicle is raised off ground or damage may result.

REMOVAL & INSTALLATION

STEERING GEAR

Removal

1) Remove both tie rod mounting bolts from rack. Pry tie rods off steering gear.

2) Using a screwdriver, push dust cap to inside of vehicle. Loosen column lower flange tube mounting bolt and pry off clamp. Remove seal ring.

3) Drive column lower flange off gear using a brass drift. Remove gear mounting bolts from body. Turn wheels to right lock and remove steering gear through opening in right wheel well.

Installation

1) Install steering gear to vehicle.

2) Attach tie rods to tie rod bracket. Install bracket to steering drive pawl. Install steering drive pawl to steering gear rack. Install seal ring.

3) Install clamp and attach column to steering gear. Push cap from inside vehicle onto steering gear.

Fig. 1: Cross Sectional View of Pinion Shaft with Rack Adjustment

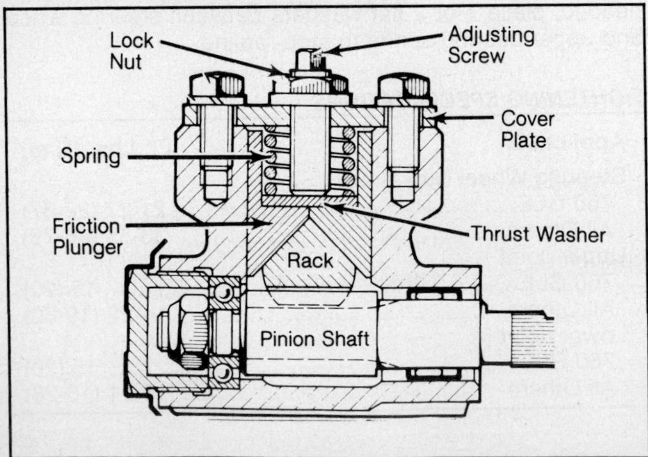
Lock Nut
Adjusting Screw
Cover Plate
Spring
Friction Plunger
Thrust Washer
Rack
Pinion Shaft

STEERING DAMPER

NOTE: Replace steering damper if unit is defective. Do not overhaul damper.

OVERHAUL

NOTE: Manufacturer does not recommend overhaul of this rack and pinion steering unit. If unit is defective, replace as an assembly.

Fig. 2: Exploded View of Audi 4000 Rack and Pinion Assembly

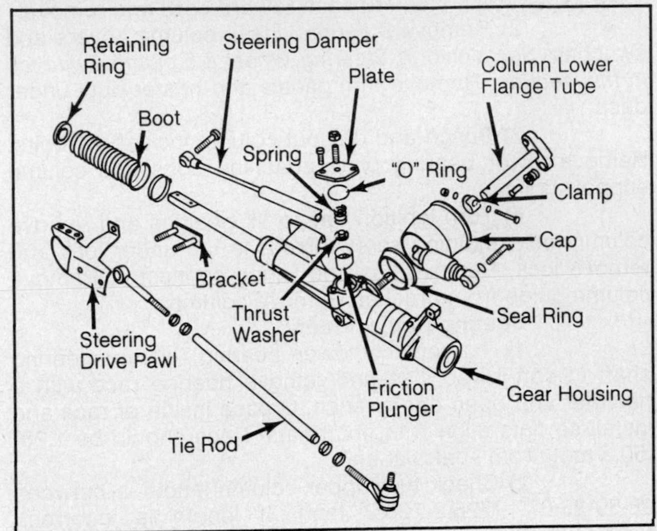
Retaining Ring
Steering Damper
Plate
Column Lower Flange Tube
Boot
Spring
"O" Ring
Clamp
Cap
Bracket
Thrust Washer
Seal Ring
Steering Drive Pawl
Friction Plunger
Gear Housing
Tie Rod

TIGHTENING SPECIFICATIONS

Application	Ft. Lbs. (N.m)
Flange Tube Clamp Bolt	18 (25)
Tie Rod End Ball Joint Nut	22 (30)
Tie Rod End-to-Tie Rod	30 (40)

BMW 320i RACK & PINION

DESCRIPTION

A ZF manual rack and pinion gear with hydraulic steering damper is used.

ADJUSTMENT

Steering gear assembly should be removed for proper adjustment. *See Adjustment in Overhaul section in this article.*

REMOVAL & INSTALLATION

STEERING GEAR

Removal

Raise vehicle and remove front wheels. Disconnect tie rods from steering knuckles using a puller. Detach steering gear mounting bolts at front axle support. Remove pinch bolt from steering shaft and pull steering gear from universal coupling.

Installation

To install, reverse removal procedure, noting the following: Wheels must point straight ahead. Mark on dust seal must align between marks on steering gear box.

OVERHAUL

STEERING GEAR

Disassembly

1) Mount gear in holding fixture (32 1 100) in a vise. Bend open right lock plate and slide rack in up to stop. Detach damper at holder.

2) Using tie rod remover (32 2 110), detach right tie rod at rack. Loosen bellows clamp and slide bellows off housing. Move rack in far enough to apply tie rod remover (32 2 100) to left side of rack. Loosen clamp and slide back bellows onto rack. Bend open lock plate and detach left tie rod at rack.

3) Remove cap from pinion housing. Remove cotter pin holding set screw. Unscrew set screw with special socket (32 1 040) and remove spring retainer and spring. Lift rack to remove pressure pad and "O" ring from pinion housing.

4) Remove pinion shaft dust cover, "V" lock ring and notched ring. Remove pinion shaft set screw with special socket (32 1 040). Remove "O" ring and washer.

5) Clamp drive pinion spline in soft-jawed vise. Remove drive pinion from housing by tapping housing with mallet. Remove circlip from pinion shaft and press ball bearing off drive pinion shaft.

Fig. 1: Exploded View of BMW Rack & Pinion Steering Gear Assembly

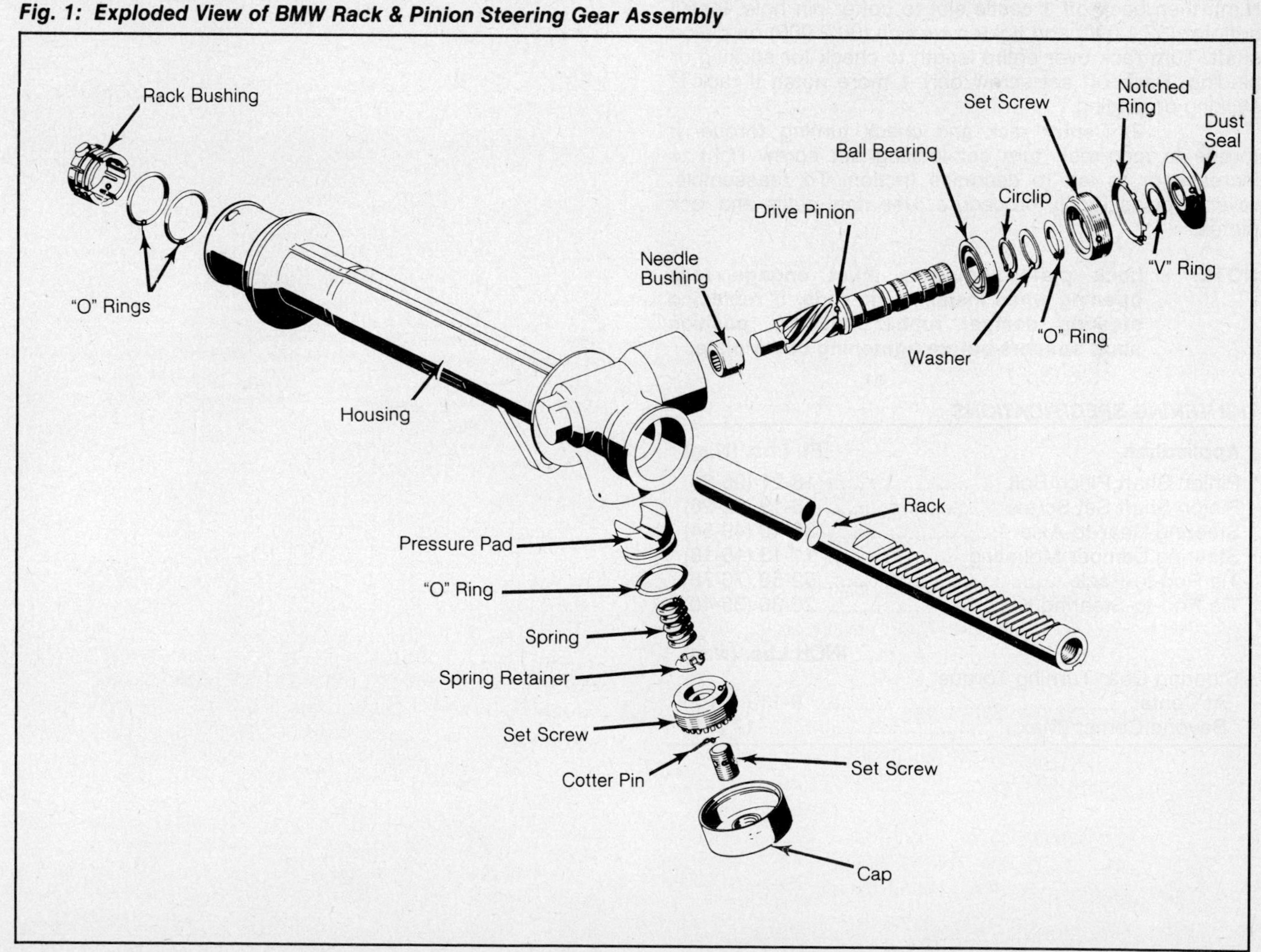
Rack Bushing
"O" Rings
Housing
Set Screw
Notched Ring
Dust Seal
Ball Bearing
Circlip
Drive Pinion
"V" Ring
Needle Bushing
"O" Ring
Washer
Rack
Pressure Pad
"O" Ring
Spring
Spring Retainer
Set Screw
Cotter Pin
Set Screw
Cap

BMW 320i RACK & PINION (Cont.)

6) Needle bearing can be removed from housing with screw-type puller (Kukko 00 8 510). Remove rack bushings from housing by prying bushings out with 2 screwdrivers.

Reassembly

1) Place new "O" rings on rack bushings and install bushings in steering box. Locking tabs must engage in housing lock holes. Drive needle bearing, flat side down, into box using a mandrel.

2) Press ball bearing onto drive pinion with closed end facing spline. Install circlip. Apply thick coat of grease to splined surface of rack and thin coating to remainder of surface. Insert rack into box. Dip assembled pinion shaft in grease and install in box. Install plastic washer and "O" ring to pinion shaft.

3) Tighten set screw with special socket. Insert "V" ring up to groove and press notched ring up to stop. Center rack in housing. Right end of rack should extend 3.031" (77 mm) beyond housing. Place dust seal on shaft so mark on seal is between marks on housing. Place "O" ring into pressure pad and slide pad into steering box.

4) Place spring and retainer on pressure pad. Tighten notched set screw against stop, then back off socket head set screw until it extends about 1/2" (13 mm) above edge of housing.

Adjustment

1) Tighten notched set screw to 4 ft. lbs. (5 N.m), then back off 1 castle slot to cotter pin hole. Install adaptor (32 1 000) and tighten wrench (00 2 000) on pinion shaft. Turn rack over entire length to check for sticking or binding. Back off set screw only 1 more notch if rack is sticking or binding.

2) Center rack and check turning torque. If torque is incorrect, turn self-locking set screw right to increase or to left to decrease friction. To reassemble, reverse disassembly procedure. Use new seals and lock plates.

NOTE: Lock plate shoulders must engage rack opening when installing tie rods. If replacing steering damper rubber bushing, position short spacers before tightening cover plate.

TIGHTENING SPECIFICATIONS

Application	Ft. Lbs. (N.m)
Pinion Shaft Pinch Bolt	18-21 (25-28)
Pinion Shaft Set Screw	16-19 (22-26)
Steering Gear-to-Axle	36-40 (49-54)
Steering Damper Mounting	11-13 (15-18)
Tie Rod-to-Rack	52-58 (70-78)
Tie Rod-to-Steering Knuckle	26-30 (35-40)
	INCH Lbs. (N.m)
Steering Gear Turning Torque	
At Center	8-11 (.9-1.2)
Beyond Center (Max.)	17 (1.9)

CHRYSLER CORP. IMPORTS & MITSUBISHI RACK & PINION

Colt, Cordia, Tredia

DESCRIPTION

Rack and pinion type steering is mounted by rubber insulators to crossmember. Adjustment is provided for pinion gear preload.

Pinion shaft is coupled to the steering shaft. Tie rods connect end of rack to steering arms of front wheels.

ADJUSTMENT

See Overhaul procedure in this article.

REMOVAL & INSTALLATION

Removal

1) Raise and support front of vehicle. Remove wheels. Remove coupling bolt from pinion shaft joint.

2) Using puller (C-3894-A), disconnect tie rod ends from knuckle arms. On Cordia and Tredia, remove right sub-member from No. 2 crossmember. On all models, remove mount bolts at crossmember. Remove rack and pinion assembly (from right side on Cordia and Tredia).

Installation

Install in reverse order of removal. Check wheel alignment.

OVERHAUL

NOTE: Before disassembly, measure rack starting force and pinion starting torque in neutral (straight ahead) position for reassembly reference.

Disassembly

1) With rack and pinion assembly mounted in soft-jawed vise, remove boot clamp and rubber boot. Remove tie rod staking with a chisel. Then, use a wrench to remove tie rod assemblies.

2) Remove yoke plug lock nut, and using an Allen wrench, remove yoke adjusting screw. Remove yoke spring, rubber cushion and support yoke. Carefully pry out oil seal.

3) Remove snap ring and remove pinion and bearing. Remove snap ring retaining bearing to shaft and press off bearing. Remove rack from left side of housing to avoid damage from rack teeth during removal.

Inspection

1) Check rubber boots for wear or damage. Check for loose or damaged ball bearings and pinion needle bearings. Check for loose rack bushing, inadequate contact between rack and rack support. Check for deteriorated yoke spring.

Fig. 2: Colt Rack and Pinion Identification Marks

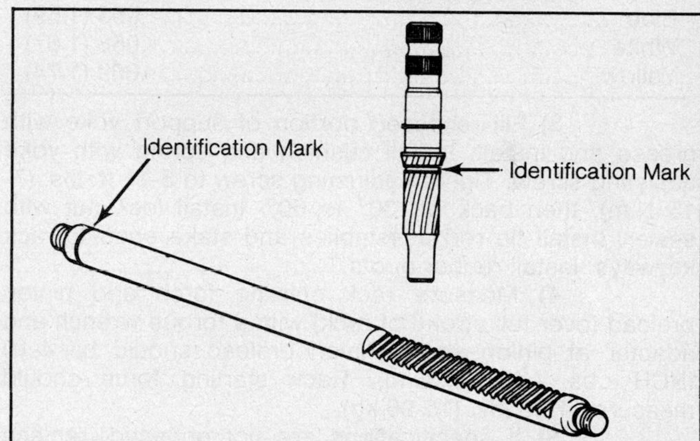
Identification Mark
Identification Mark

Pinion with 6 teeth is shown.

Fig. 1: Exploded View of Rack and Pinion Steering

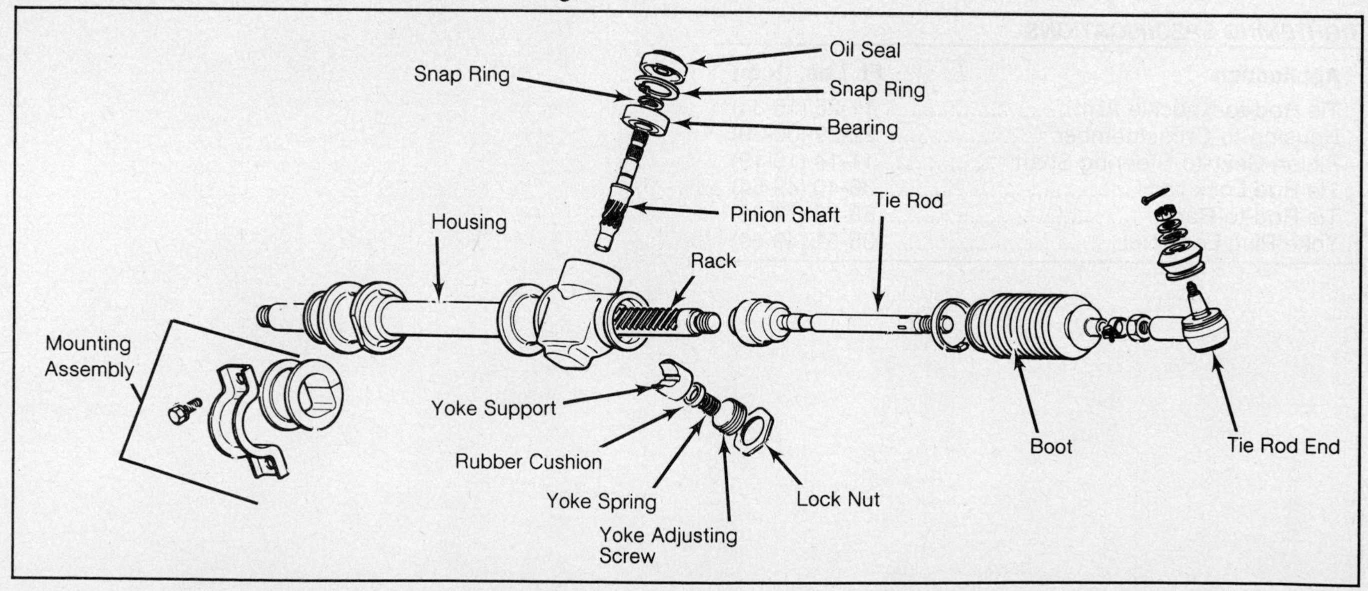
Oil Seal
Snap Ring
Snap Ring
Bearing
Pinion Shaft
Tie Rod
Housing
Rack
Mounting Assembly
Yoke Support
Rubber Cushion
Yoke Spring
Yoke Adjusting Screw
Lock Nut
Boot
Tie Rod End

CHRYSLER CORP. IMPORTS & MITSUBISHI RACK & PINION (Cont.)

2) On Colt, inspect rack and pinion for identification marks. Rack and pinion sets with an identification mark have a 6-tooth pinion and are for Rally and Luxury Sport models. Rack and pinion sets without an identification mark have a 5-tooth pinion and are for all other models.

Reassembly & Adjustment

1) Always replace tie rods on Colt. Use grease on all friction surfaces during assembly. Do not plug air passage of housing bushing with grease. Using bearing installer (MB990783), press bearing onto pinion. Install snap ring.

2) Insert rack into gear housing from the left side. Mesh the pinion gear with the rack. Select and install a snap ring that eliminates axial play. *See Pinion Bearing Snap Ring chart.* Coat new oil seal with grease and install.

PINION BEARING SNAP RINGS

Snap Ring Color	In. (mm)
Blue	.063 (1.59)
White	.066 (1.67)
Yellow	.069 (1.74)

3) Fill recessed portion of support yoke with grease and install. Install cushion and spring with yoke adjusting screw. Tighten adjusting screw to 5-11 ft. lbs. (7-15 N.m), then back off 30° to 60°. Install lock nut with sealer. Install tie rod assemblies and stake ends to rack keyways. Install rubber boots.

4) Measure rack starting force and pinion preload (over full stroke of rack) with a torque wrench and adapter at pinion shaft. Pinion preload should be 4-10 INCH Lbs. (.44-1.1 N.m). Rack starting force should measure 11-66 lbs. (15-90 kg).

5) If specifications are not obtained, replace yoke spring and rubber cushion and readjust. Install rack and pinion assembly on crossmember. Connect tie rod ends to steering knuckles and pinion shaft to steering shaft coupler. Check wheel alignment.

TIGHTENING SPECIFICATIONS

Application	Ft. Lbs. (N.m)
Tie Rod-to-Knuckle Arm	11-25 (15-34)
Housing-to-Crossmember	22-29 (30-39)
Pinion Gear-to-Steering Shaft	11-14 (15-19)
Tie Rod Lock Nut	36-40 (49-54)
Tie Rod-to-Rack	58-72 (79-98)
Yoke Plug Lock Nut	36-51 (49-69)

CHRYSLER CORP. IMPORTS & MITSUBISHI RECIRCULATING BALL

Challenger; Colt, Ram-50, & Mitsubishi Pickups; Sapporo, Montero & Starion Turbo

NOTE: **Challenger, Sapporo and Starion Turbo models are equipped with power-assisted recirculating ball. Linkage is similar for all models.**

DESCRIPTION

Steering system uses a recirculating ball gear of variable ratio. This type of gear minimizes gear ratio at the straight-ahead position, resulting in high stability at center. Gear ratio increases as the wheel is turned from center, allowing easy maneuvering.

REMOVAL & INSTALLATION

STEERING GEAR

Removal & Installation (Pickups Only)

Remove steering shaft-to-steering gear clamp bolt. Disconnect steering shaft from gear box main shaft. Remove cotter pin and lock nut from pitman arm, if equipped. Using puller (C-3894-A), separate pitman arm and tie rod from relay rod. Remove gear box from frame. Remove pitman arm nut and pull pitman arm from cross shaft with puller (CT-1106). To install, reverse removal procedure.

TIE ROD ASSEMBLY

Removal

Remove cotter pin and lock nut from tie rod end. Using puller (C-3894-A), disconnect tie rod ends from steering knuckles. Unscrew tie rod ends from tie rod.

Installation

1) Grease tie rod end dust cover and coat lower edge of cup with packing sealer before installation. Temporarily install tie rod ends to tie rods.

2) Distance from center-to-center of tie rod ends should be 13.31" (338 mm) for Challenger and Sapporo; 12.85" (326.4 mm); for Starion and Montero; 14.78" (375.5 mm) left tie rod and 14.84" (377 mm) right tie rod on Pickup models.

3) Amount of threads showing on each side of tie rod sleeve should be equal. Install tie rods to vehicle and check toe-in. *See WHEEL ALIGNMENT Section.*

Fig. 1: Exploded View Showing Steering Linkage Components

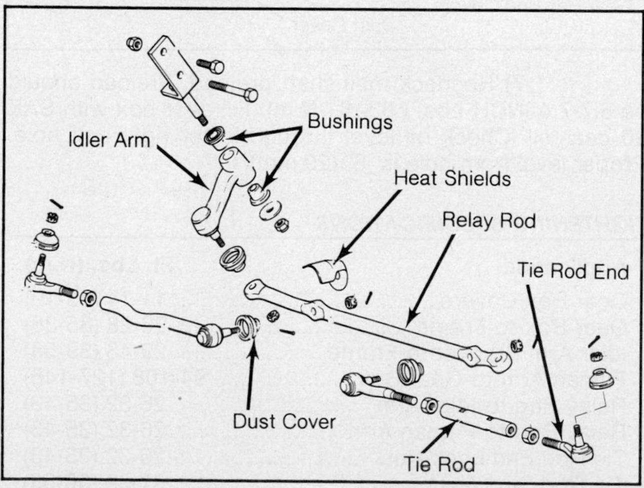
Bushings
Idler Arm
Heat Shields
Relay Rod
Tie Rod End
Dust Cover
Tie Rod

RELAY ROD

Removal

Remove cotter pins and lock nuts, if equipped. Using puller (C-3894-A), disconnect tie rod ends from steering knuckle arms. Detach pitman arm and idler arm, using the same puller. Remove relay rod.

Installation

To install, reverse removal procedure, noting the following: Ensure dust covers are well greased and that lower edge of covers are coated with packing sealer. After installation, ensure relay rod-to-idler arm and relay rod-to-pitman arm clearance is .15-.17" (3.8-4.3 mm).

IDLER ARM

Removal

Using puller (C-3894-A), disconnect idler arm from relay rod. Remove idler arm assembly from frame.

NOTE: **Do not disassemble idler arm and support unless absolutely necessary.**

Installation

1) Apply soapy water to bushings and idler arm. Push bushings into arm, using a vise if necessary.

2) Grease bracket shaft and inner surface of bushing, then insert shaft into idler arm. Install washer with knurled side toward bushing and, using a new self-locking nut, tighten to specification. Idler arm turning torque should be 2.2-6.5 INCH Lbs. (.2-.7 N.m).

PITMAN ARM

Removal

Remove steering gear. Using the puller (C-3894-A), disconnect pitman arm from cross shaft.

Installation

To install, reverse removal procedure and note the following: Ensure slit on cross shaft aligns with pitman arm mark.

OVERHAUL

STEERING GEAR

Disassembly (Pickups Only)

1) Prior to disassembly, record starting torque of mainshaft for guide during reassembly. Remove breather plug and drain gear oil. Remove upper cover bolts. Loosen adjusting screw lock nut and turn screw in 2 or 3 turns.

2) Set gear in center position (mainshaft and cross shaft in straight ahead position). Tap bottom of cross shaft with plastic hammer. Remove cross shaft and upper cover as an assembly. Do not damage cross shaft oil seal.

3) Mount upper cover in soft-jawed vise and separate upper cover and cross shaft by turning adjusting screw. Keep spacer for reassembly. Mount steering gear

CHRYSLER CORP. IMPORTS & MITSUBISHI RECIRCULATING BALL (Cont.)

in soft-jawed vise and remove end cover and mainshaft adjusting shims. Measure and record thickness of shims. Carefully remove mainshaft, ball nut assembly and bearings. Pry out oil seals.

CAUTION: Do not disassemble the mainshaft and ball nut assembly.

Inspection

Check components for excess wear or free play. If rough rotation or excess play is found in mainshaft or ball nut, replace both as an assembly. Do not force ball nut to either end of mainshaft.

Reassembly & Adjustment

1) Coat oil seal lips with grease and install. Mount steering gear in soft-jawed vise. Hold mainshaft in horizontal position and install into housing. Install gasket, original shims and end cover.

2) Tighten cover screws and measure mainshaft preload with adapter (CT-1108). If less or greater than 3.0-4.8 INCH Lbs. (.34-.54 N.m), reduce or increase shim thickness to obtain proper preload. *Refer to Mainshaft Shim Thickness table.* Remove cover bolts, apply adhesive and tighten.

MAINSHAFT SHIM THICKNESS

Shim No.	In. (mm)
1	.0020 (.05)
2	.0024 (.06)
3	.0030 (.07)
4	.0040 (.10)
5	.0080 (.20)
6	.0120 (.30)
7	.0200 (.50)

3) Install adjusting screw and original spacer in groove on upper end of cross shaft. Use spacers to adjust axial play of cross shaft to 0-.002" (0-.05 mm). *Refer to Cross Shaft Spacer Thickness table.*

CROSS SHAFT SPACER THICKNESS

Spacer No.	In. (mm)
1	.077 (1.95)
2	.079 (2.00)
3	.081 (2.05)
4	.083 (2.10)

4) Apply small quantity of oil to ball nut, cross shaft gear and shaft. Lightly coat oil seal lip with grease. Insert cross shaft into housing so it meshes with ball nut rack. Do not damage bushing and oil seal. Coat upper cover bolts with adhesive. Install cover and tighten bolts.

5) Install pitman arm on cross shaft with mating marks aligned. Finger tighten pitman arm nut. Remove breather cap and inject small amount of gear oil to lubricate bearing parts and teeth of each shaft.

6) Tighten adjusting screw until it contacts gear teeth. Move pitman arm from side-to-side 3-5 times. Mount dial indicator so indicator tip is touching end of pitman arm. Move pitman arm by hand to measure steering gear backlash when mainshaft, cross shaft and pitman arm are in straight ahead position. Loosen adjusting screw to increase backlash and tighten to decrease backlash.

Fig. 2: Exploded View Showing Components of Recirculating Ball & Nut Manual Steering Gear Box

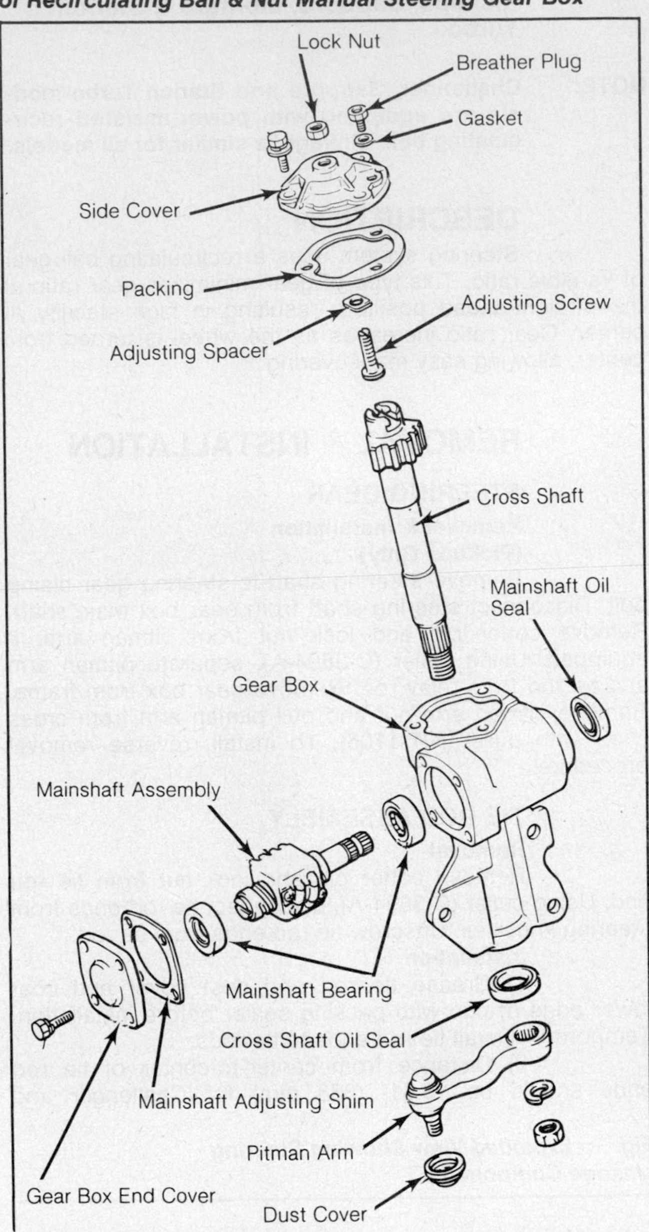
Lock Nut
Breather Plug
Gasket
Side Cover
Packing
Adjusting Screw
Adjusting Spacer
Cross Shaft
Mainshaft Oil Seal
Gear Box
Mainshaft Assembly
Mainshaft Bearing
Cross Shaft Oil Seal
Mainshaft Adjusting Shim
Pitman Arm
Gear Box End Cover
Dust Cover

7) Recheck mainshaft preload. Preload should be 5.7-7.4 INCH Lbs. (.63-.81 N.m). Fill gear box with SAE 90 gear oil. Check oil level through lower right bolt hole. Proper level from hole is .8" (20 mm).

TIGHTENING SPECIFICATIONS

Application	Ft. Lbs. (N.m)
Gear Box Covers	11-14 (15-19)
Gear Box-to-Frame	26-28 (35-38)
Idler Arm Bracket-to-Frame	29-43 (39-58)
Pitman Arm-to-Gear Box	94-108 (127-146)
Relay Rod-to-Idler Arm	26-32 (35-43)
Relay Rod-to-Pitman Arm	26-32 (35-43)
Tie Rod End Lock Nuts	26-32 (35-43)
Tie Rod Stud Nuts	37-39 (50-53)

Steering Gears & Linkage

DATSUN/NISSAN RACK & PINION

280ZX, Maxima, Pulsar, Sentra, Stanza

DESCRIPTION

Steering assembly is a direct-acting rack and pinion system. Unit consists of a rack bar and toothed pinion, both working in the plain bearing of the rack housing.

Backlash is held to zero by the retainer and retainer spring.

REMOVAL & INSTALLATION

Removal

1) Raise and support front of vehicle. Remove tie rod from steering knuckle. Loosen steering gear mounting bolts.

2) On 280ZX and Maxima models, loosen bolt attaching lower joint shaft to rubber coupling.

3) On all models, remove bolts attaching steering column to lower joint. Remove steering gear and linkage assembly.

NOTE: **On 280ZX models, raise front engine mount approximately 1/2" (with jack) before trying to remove steering gear.**

Installation

Install in reverse order of removal procedure. Check wheel alignment. For wheel alignment procedures, *see Datsun/Nissan in WHEEL ALIGNMENT section*.

ADJUSTMENT

NOTE: **Adjustments are performed during gear assembly process. See Overhaul as outlined.**

OVERHAUL

DISASSEMBLY

Steering Gear

1) Clamp steering gear and linkage in a padded vise. Remove both dust boot clamps. Flatten lock plate. Loosen inner joint lock nut and remove tie rod from rack.

NOTE: **Do not disassemble inner joint assembly and tie rod socket assembly.**

2) Loosen adjuster lock nut and remove retainer adjust screw. Remove retainer spring and steering gear retainer out of steering gear housing.

3) Remove oil seal and pry off snap ring from steering gear housing. Remove steering pinion assembly and rack from steering gear housing.

Pinion Gear

Pry off snap ring securing pinion bearing from pinion gear. Press bearing from pinion gear, then remove inner snap ring from pinion gear.

INSPECTION

Check rack and pinion gear for wear or damage, replace if necessary. Inspect tie rod inner socket

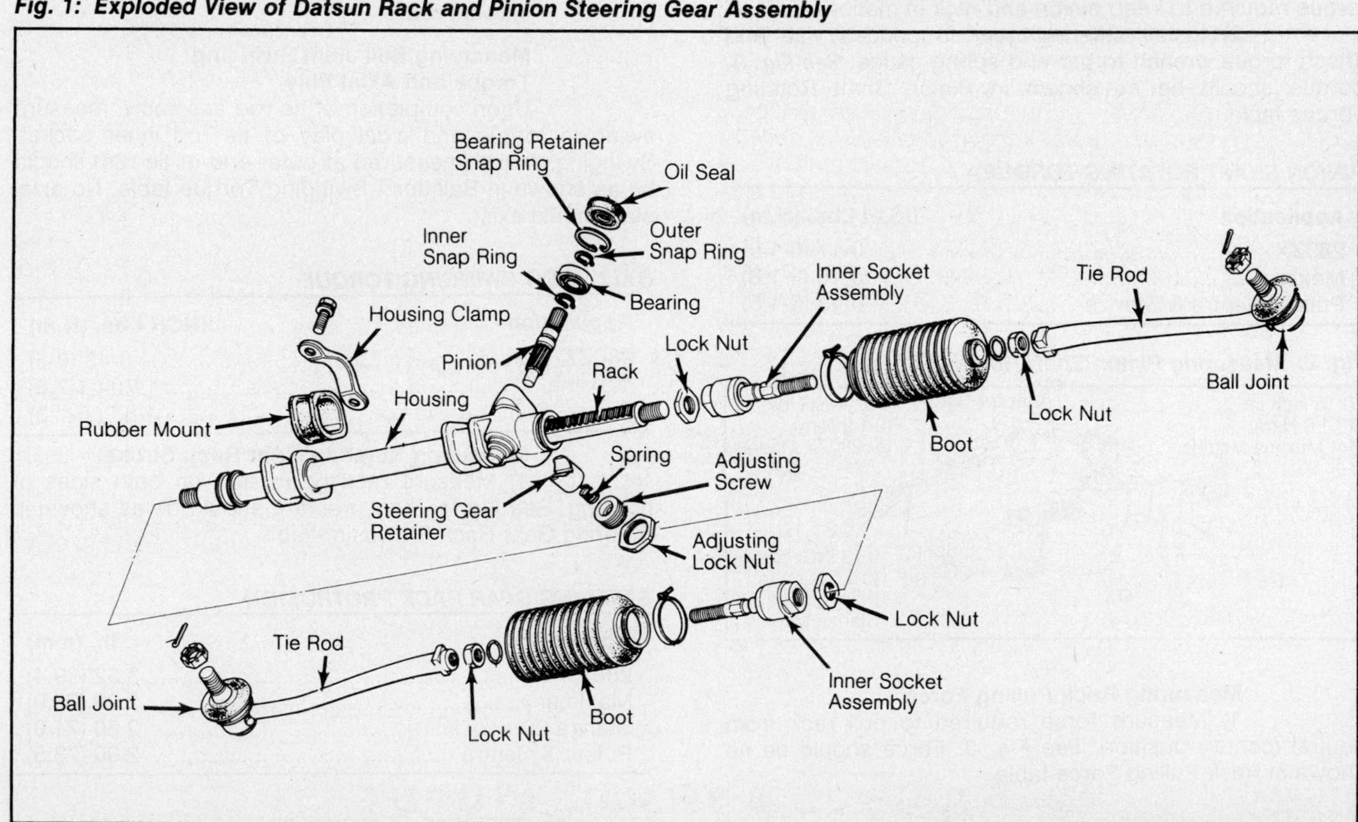
Bearing Retainer
Snap Ring
Oil Seal
Inner
Snap Ring
Outer
Snap Ring
Bearing
Housing Clamp
Pinion
Rack
Lock Nut
Inner Socket
Assembly
Tie Rod
Ball Joint
Lock Nut
Boot
Housing
Rubber Mount
Spring
Adjusting
Screw
Steering Gear
Retainer
Adjusting
Lock Nut
Lock Nut
Tie Rod
Ball Joint
Lock Nut
Boot
Inner Socket
Assembly

Fig. 1: Exploded View of Datsun Rack and Pinion Steering Gear Assembly

DATSUN/NISSAN RACK & PINION (Cont.)

for smooth operation and for excessive looseness, replace if necessary. Replace all oil seals.

REASSEMBLY AND ADJUSTMENT

Pinion Gear

1) Install inner snap ring to pinion gear and then press bearing onto pinion gear. Install outer snap ring onto pinion gear.

2) Outer snap ring thickness should be selected so that bearing play is less than .004" (.1 mm).

Steering Gear

1) On all models, clamp steering gear in padded vise. Coat rack teeth and friction surfaces of rack with grease. Install rack into housing from pinion gear side and make sure rack teeth are facing correct direction.

2) Install pinion gear (coated with grease), make sure pinion gear teeth and rack teeth mesh properly. Make sure rack protrudes same amount from each end of housing.

3) Install snap ring to steering gear housing (snap ring retains pinion bearing in place). Snap ring thickness should be selected so that pinion gear movement is less than .004" (.1 mm). Pack grease seal with grease and install. Make sure pinion assembly rotates smoothly.

4) Apply grease to steering gear retainer and insert gear retainer and retainer spring into housing. Turn adjusting screw in and install lock nut.

5) Fully tighten adjusting screw then back off approximately 10-15°. Apply liquid sealant around lock nut and tighten lock nut.

Pinion Shaft Rotating Torque

1) With steering gear assembled, measure torque required to keep pinion and rack in motion.

2) Install steering gear in padded vise and attach torque wrench to bar and spring gauge. *See Fig. 2.* Torque should be as shown in Pinion Shaft Rotating Torque table.

PINION SHAFT ROTATING TORQUE

Application	INCH Lbs. (N.m)
280ZX	0-17 (0-1.9)
Maxima	0-16 (0-1.8)
Pulsar, Sentra & Stanza	0-13 (0-1.5)

Fig. 2: Measuring Pinion Shaft Rotating Torque

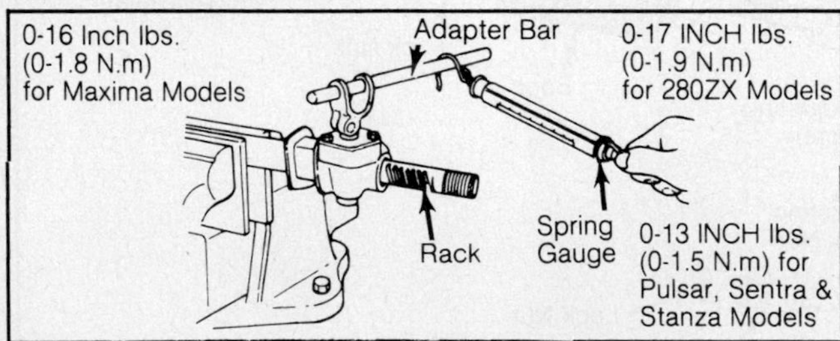
0-16 Inch lbs.
(0-1.8 N.m)
for Maxima Models
Adapter Bar
0-17 INCH lbs.
(0-1.9 N.m)
for 280ZX Models
Rack
Spring
Gauge
0-13 INCH lbs.
(0-1.5 N.m) for
Pulsar, Sentra &
Stanza Models

Measuring Rack Pulling Force

1) Measure force required to pull rack from neutral (center) position. *See Fig. 3.* Force should be as shown in Rack Pulling Force table.

RACK PULLING FORCE

Application	Lbs. (kg)
280ZX	0-22 (0-10)
Maxima	22-36 (10-16)
Pulsar & Sentra	22-31 (10-14)
Stanza	13-29 (6-13)

Fig. 3: Measuring Steering Gear Rack Pulling Force

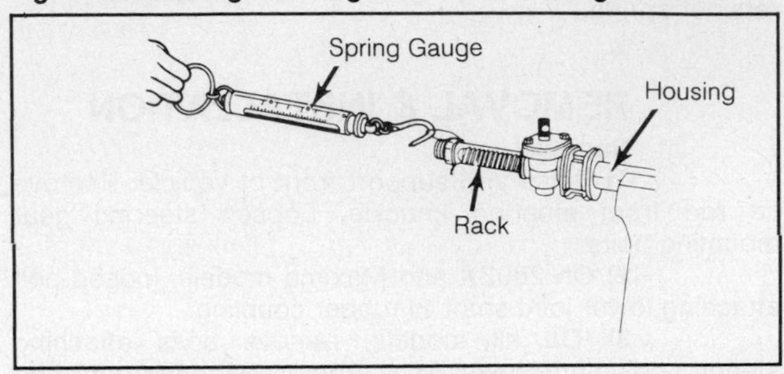
Spring Gauge
Housing
Rack

2) Install rubber boot and clamp onto tie rod. Thread lock nut over threaded portion of rack. Apply grease to sliding surfaces of tie rod inner socket and spring seat.

3) Install tie rod assembly to rack end, together with inner spring and spring seat. Screw inner socket portion until ball seat reaches rack end and then tighten lock nut.

NOTE: On 280ZX models, tie rod for left side is marked with an "L". No mark is used for right side tie rod.

Measuring Ball Joint Swinging Torque and Axial Play

Upon completion of tie rod assembly, measure swinging torque and axial play of tie rod inner socket. Swinging torque (measured at outer end of tie rod) should be as shown in Ball Joint Swinging Torque table. No axial play should exist.

BALL JOINT SWINGING TORQUE

Application	INCH Lbs. (N.m)
280ZX	0-43 (0-5)
Maxima	1-70 (.1-7.8)
Pulsar, Sentra & Stanza	4-65 (.5-7.3)

Measuring Steering Gear Rack Stroke

1) Measure rack protrusion on both sides of housing. See Fig. 4. Measurement should be as shown in Steering Gear Rack Protrusion table.

STEERING GEAR RACK PROTRUSION

Application	In. (mm)
280ZX	3.52 (89.4)
Maxima	2.99 (76.0)
Stanza	2.80 (71.0)
Pulsar & Sentra	2.90 (73.5)

DATSUN/NISSAN RACK & PINION (Cont.)

Fig. 4: Measuring Steering Gear Rack Stroke

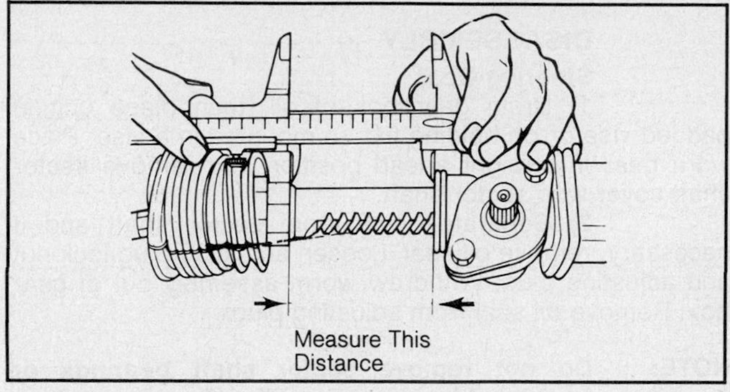
Measure This
Distance

2) Attach boot and clamps. Insert grease nipples at both ends of housing and lubricate gear assembly until a small amount of grease appears at boot outlet hole.

Tie Rod Length

Adjust tie rod length so that distance from outer side of lock nut to end of boot mounting groove is as shown in Tie Rod Length table. *See Fig. 5.*

TIE ROD LENGTH

Application	In. (mm)
280ZX	1.16 (29.5)
Maxima	1.42 (36.0)
Pulsar & Sentra	6.93 (176.0)
Stanza	1.68 (42.6)

Fig. 5: Adjusting Steering Gear Tie Rod Length

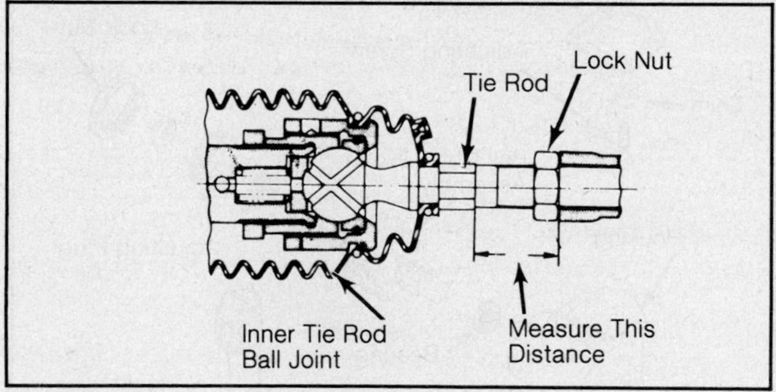
Lock Nut
Tie Rod
Inner Tie Rod
Ball Joint
Measure This
Distance

TIGHTENING SPECIFICATIONS

Application	Ft. Lbs. (N.m)
Tie Rod-to-Steering Knuckle	22-36 (29-49)
Gear Housing Clamp Bolt	43-58 (59-78)
Pinion Adjusting Lock Nut	29-43 (4-6)
Tie Rod-to-Socket Lock Nut	
Maxima & 280ZX	58-72 (79-98)
All Others	27-34 (37-46)

DATSUN/NISSAN RECIRCULATING BALL

200SX & Pickup

DESCRIPTION

The steering gear used on these vehicles is a recirculating ball type. The worm shaft is joined to the steering shaft by a rubber shock-absorbing coupling.

The steering linkage is a relay design, with the steering gear attached by a pitman arm to one end of the center link (cross shaft), while the other end of the center link moves on the idler arm.

REMOVAL & INSTALLATION

STEERING GEAR

Removal

1) Remove bolt holding worm shaft to rubber coupling. Remove nut holding gear arm to sector shaft and remove steering gear arm from sector shaft.

2) Remove bolts securing steering gear housing to body side member. Remove steering gear housing from vehicle.

Installation

To install, reverse removal procedure, aligning markings on pitman arm with markings on sector shaft.

STEERING LINKAGE

Removal

1) Jack up front of vehicle and support with stands. Detach both outer tie rod ends from steering knuckles.

2) Separate cross shaft from idler arm and pitman arm, then remove cross shaft and tie rods as an assembly. Idler assembly may be removed from side member, if necessary to replace bushing.

Installation

To install, reverse removal procedure, noting the following: Set tie rod end length to the prescribed setting, then check wheel alignment. *See Datsun/Nissan article in WHEEL ALIGNMENT section.*

TIE ROD SETTINGS

Application	In. (mm)
200SX [1]	2.80 (71.0)
Pickup [2]	
2WD	13.07 (332.0)
4WD	10.83 (275.0)

[1] – Measured between lock nuts.
[2] – Measured from center-to-center of tie rod ball studs.

ADJUSTMENT

NOTE: **Steering gear adjustments are performed during reassembly. See Overhaul as outlined below.**

OVERHAUL

DISASSEMBLY

Steering Gear

1) Drain gear box of oil, then place unit in padded vise or on holding fixture mounted in a vise. Place worn gear in straight ahead position and remove sector shaft cover with sector shaft.

2) Separate cover from sector shaft and if necessary, remove oil seal. Loosen adjusting plug lock nut and adjusting plug. Withdraw worm assembly out of gear box. Remove oil seal from adjusting plug.

NOTE: **Do not remove sector shaft bearings or bushings from housing. If defective, replace housing assembly. Do not disassemble ball nut; replace, if necessary, with worm shaft assembly. Do not let ball nut bottom out on either end of worm shaft, or damage to ball guides will result.**

INSPECTION

Inspect gear teeth on sector shaft and ball nut for wear or damage; replace as necessary. Check bearings for wear or roughness during rotation. Ensure ball nut moves smoothly over its entire length of travel.

Fig. 1: Exploded View of Recirculating Ball Steering Gear Assembly

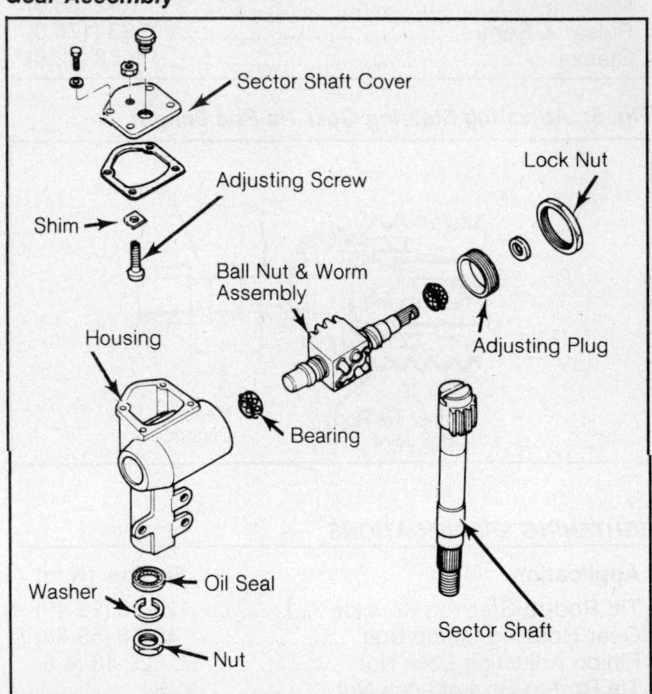
Sector Shaft Cover
Lock Nut
Adjusting Screw
Shim
Ball Nut & Worm Assembly
Housing
Adjusting Plug
Bearing
Oil Seal
Washer
Sector Shaft
Nut

REASSEMBLY & ADJUSTMENT

Steering Gear

Lubricate bearings, gear and all other moving parts with gear oil. Apply grease to oil seal lip and press seal into adjusting plug.

DATSUN/NISSAN RECIRCULATING BALL (Cont.)

Worm Bearing Preload

1) Rotate worm shaft a few times to settle assembly. Attach torque wrench to worm shaft and measure bearing preload (initial turning torque).

2) Tighten adjusting plug until preload of 3.5-5.2 INCH lbs. (.4-.6 N.m) is obtained. With preload adjusted, apply sealer to lock nut and tighten lock nut. Recheck preload.

Fig. 2: Measuring Steering Gear Initial Turning Torque to Check Worm Gear Preload

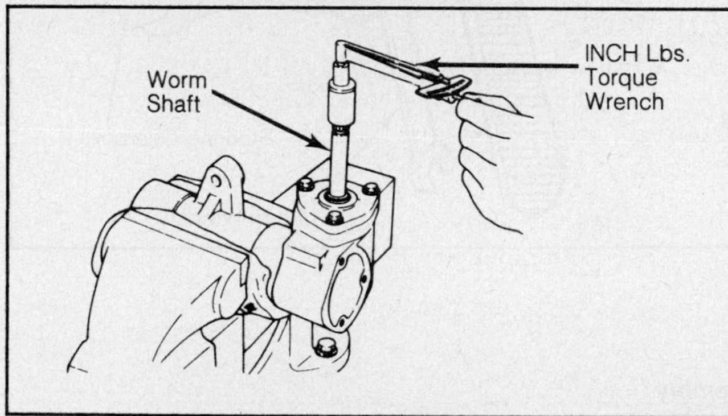
Worm Shaft
INCH Lbs. Torque Wrench

Sector Shaft End Play

Insert adjusting screw into "T" groove of sector shaft and adjust end play between shaft and screw head to less than .0004-.0012" (.01-.03 mm).

Fig. 3: Insert Feeler Gauge into Sector Shaft to Measure Sector Shaft-to-Adjusting Screw End Play

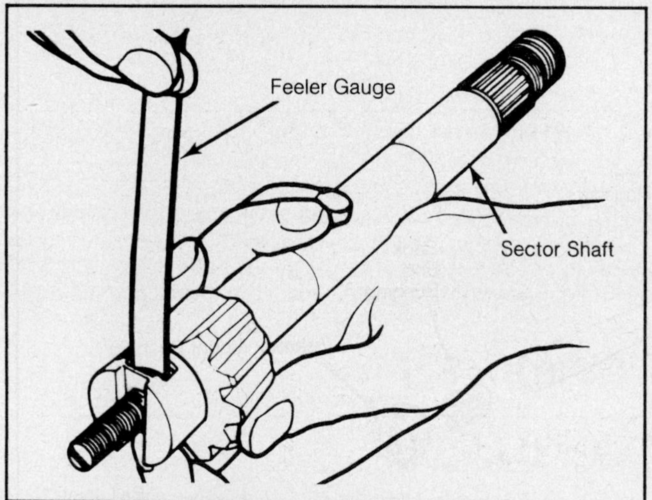
Feeler Gauge
Sector Shaft

End play is decreased by installing shims.

Steering Gear Preload

1) Coat oil seal contact surface with gear oil and press seal to steering gear housing. Install cover to sector shaft (with adjusting screw). Place worm gear in center position, then install sector gear to gear housing (with gasket) and tighten bolts. Fill gear box with gear oil.

2) Install torque wrench to worm shaft. Tighten sector shaft adjusting screw while measuring total gear turning torque (preload). Total preload should be less than 10.9 INCH Lbs. (1.2 N.m).

NOTE: Always adjust preload by tightening adjusting screw, never by loosening.

TIGHTENING SPECIFICATIONS

Application	Ft. Lbs. (N.m)
Adjusting Plug Lock Nut	181-231 (246-314)
Gear Housing-to-Frame	
Pickup	62-71 (84-96)
200SX	38-46 (52-62)
Sector Shaft Adjusting Screw Lock Nut	22-29 (29-39)
Sector Shaft-to-Gear Arm	94-108 (127-147)
Sector Shaft Cover Bolt	11-18 (15-25)
Worm Shaft-to-Rubber Coupling	29-36 (39-49)

HONDA RACK & PINION

DESCRIPTION

Rack and pinion steering mounts by rubber insulators to crossmember. Adjustment is provided for pinion gear preload. Pinion shaft couples to the steering shaft. Tie rods connect rack ends to steering arms.

ADJUSTMENT

NOTE: Adjust rack piston whenever steering gear assembly is removed and installed.

STEERING WHEEL TURNING FORCE

Raise and support front of vehicle, so front wheels are off ground. Attach spring gauge to steering wheel rim at spoke. Turn wheel with spring gauge. If reading is more than 3.3 lbs. (1.5 kg), turn rack piston adjusting screw until turning force is correct.

Fig. 1: Steering Gearbox Adjustment

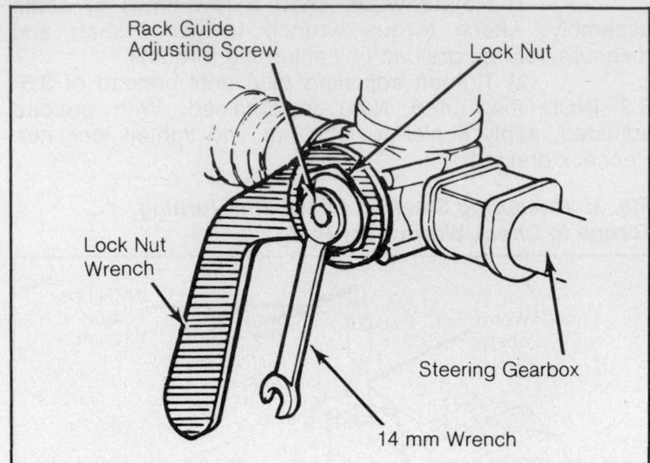
Rack Guide
Adjusting Screw
Lock Nut
Lock Nut
Wrench
Steering Gearbox
14 mm Wrench

Fig. 2: Exploded View of Honda Rack & Pinion Steering Gear Assembly

Outer Dust Seal
Pinion Dust Seal
35 mm Snap Ring
External Snap Ring
Bearing
Pinion
Needle Bearing
Rack Piston
Pressure Spring
Lock Nut
"O" Ring
Piston
Screw
Gear
Housing
Rack
End
Bushing
Gearbox Mount Bushing
Rack
Ball Joint
Seal
Castle Nut
Bellow Clamp
Circlip
Tie Rod Stop Washer
Tie Rod Lock Washer
Tie Rod
Dust Boot
Lock Nut
Tie Rod End

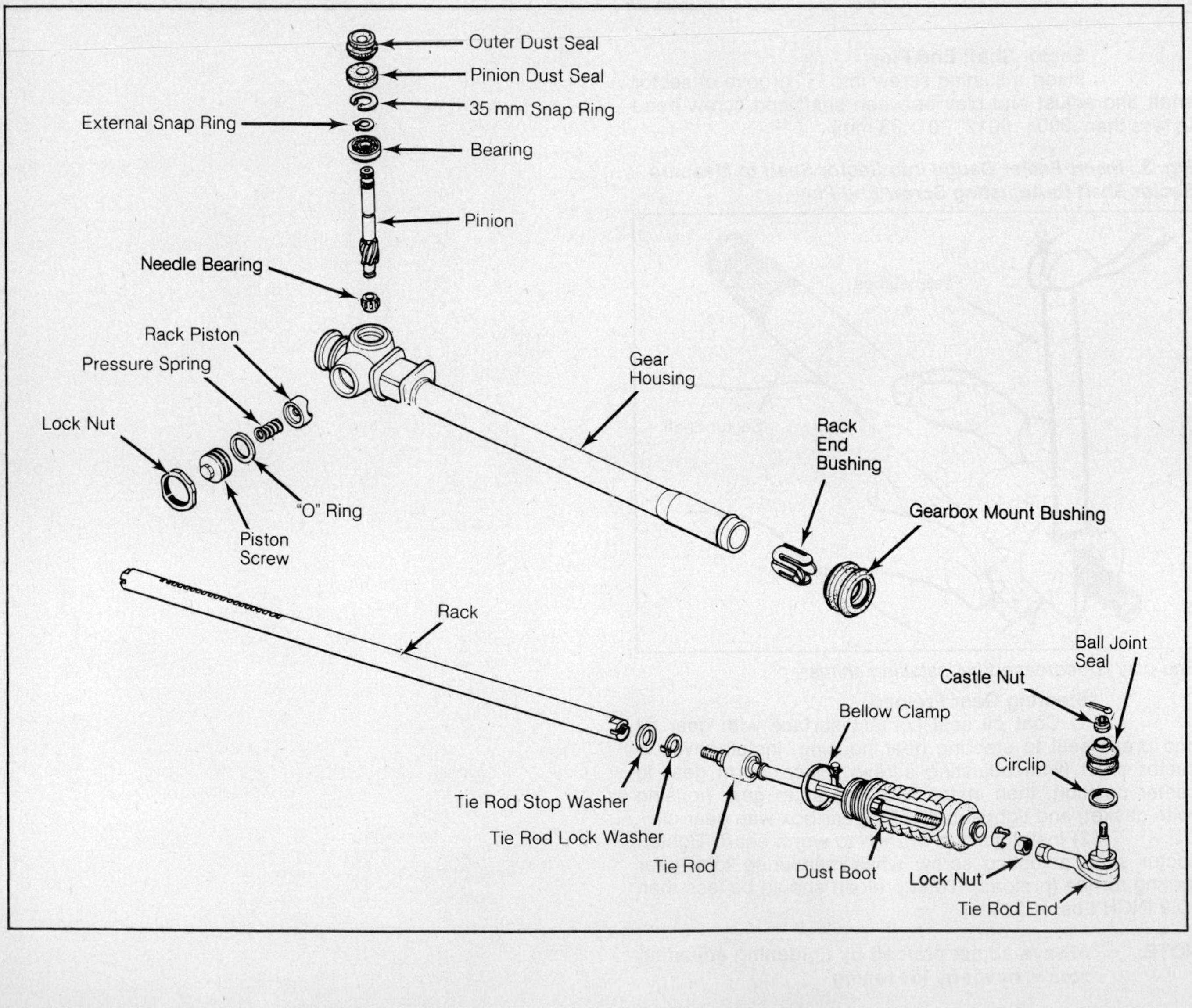

HONDA RACK & PINION (Cont.)

RACK PISTON ADJUSTMENT

Loosen rack screw lock nut. Tighten rack guide adjusting screw until lightly bottomed then back off screw 45°. Tighten lock nut and recheck steering wheel turning force.

REMOVAL & INSTALLATION

STEERING GEAR

Removal (Accord)

1) Remove steering shaft connector bottom bolt. Pull connector off pinion shaft. Raise and support front of vehicle. Remove front wheels.

2) Remove cotter pins and ball joint nuts. Using a ball joint remover, remove tie rod ends from steering knuckles.

3) Place manual transmission in 1st or 3rd and remove shift rod yoke bolt. Remove engine crossmember. Disconnect shift lever torque arm from manual transmission.

4) Remove exhaust manifold-to-header pipe nuts. Push rack to extreme right (simulate a left turn). Remove gearbox brackets. Lower the gearbox so pinion shaft end comes out of frame hole.

5) Rotate gearbox 180° forward until pinion shaft points rearward. Move gear right until left tie rod clears exhaust pipe. Remove through left side of vehicle.

Removal (Civic)

1) Raise and support front of vehicle. Remove front wheels. Remove cotter pins and ball joint nuts. Using a ball joint remover, remove tie rod ends from steering knuckles.

2) Remove bottom bolt from steering shaft connector. Remove gearbox mounting bracket and bolts. Drop gearbox straight down until pinion is free of connector. Rotate gearbox 180° and remove it through opening in left side of vehicle.

Removal (Prelude)

1) Remove steering shaft connector bottom bolt. Pull connector up off pinion shaft. Raise vehicle and remove front wheels. Remove cotter pins and ball joint nuts. Using ball joint remover, remove tie rod ends from steering knuckles.

2) Remove crossmember. Disconnect shift rod and extension from manual transmission. On automatic transmission models, remove shift cable guide from floor and pull shift cable down by hand.

3) Remove exhaust manifold-to-header pipe nuts and header pipe bracket nuts. Push rack to extreme right (simulate a left turn) and remove gearbox brackets.

4) Lower the gearbox enough so pinion shaft end comes out frame hole. Rotate gearbox forward until pinion shaft points rearward. Slide gearbox right until left tie rod clears exhaust pipe. Remove through left side of vehicle.

Installation (All Models)

To install, reverse removal procedure. Check steering gear operation for smoothness after installation.

OVERHAUL

STEERING GEAR

Disassembly

1) Place steering gear in a vise. Loosen boot clamps and pull dust boots away from gearbox ends. Unbend tie rod lock washers.

2) Hold rack with a wrench and unscrew tie rods. Remove rack guide adjuster lock nut, adjuster screw, washer, spring and piston.

3) Remove pinion boot, pinion dust seal and snap ring. Remove pinion from gearbox. Slide rack out of gearbox.

Inspection

Check all parts for wear or damage. Replace parts as needed.

Rack End Bushing Replacement

Apply grease to inside of rack end bushing. Do NOT fill slots with grease. Align bushing round projections with gearbox holes and install bushing. Slide gearbox mount bushing onto gearbox.

Reassembly

To reassemble, reverse disassembly procedure. Use new lock washers and stop washers on tie rods. Fill boots with grease and gently squeeze them to bleed out air.

TIGHTENING SPECIFICATIONS

Application	Ft. Lbs. (N.m)
Adjusting Screw Lock Nut	18 (24)
Ball Joint Nut	32 (43)
Tie Rod End Lock Nut	32 (43)

Steering Gears & Linkage

ISUZU RACK & PINION

I-Mark

DESCRIPTION

Steering gear assembly is a rack and pinion type. The steering gear pinion shaft, connected to steering column lower end, transmits steering wheel turning motion to tie rods and steering knuckles.

ADJUSTMENT

STEERING GEAR ADJUSTMENT

Position front wheels straight ahead with steering wheel centered. Turn adjusting screw into gear housing and tighten to 3.7 ft. lbs. (5 N.m). Loosen adjusting screw and tighten to same torque. Loosen and tighten adjusting screw again. Back off adjusting screw 1/12 turn. Tighten lock nut.

Fig. 1: Exploded View of I-Mark Rack & Pinion Steering

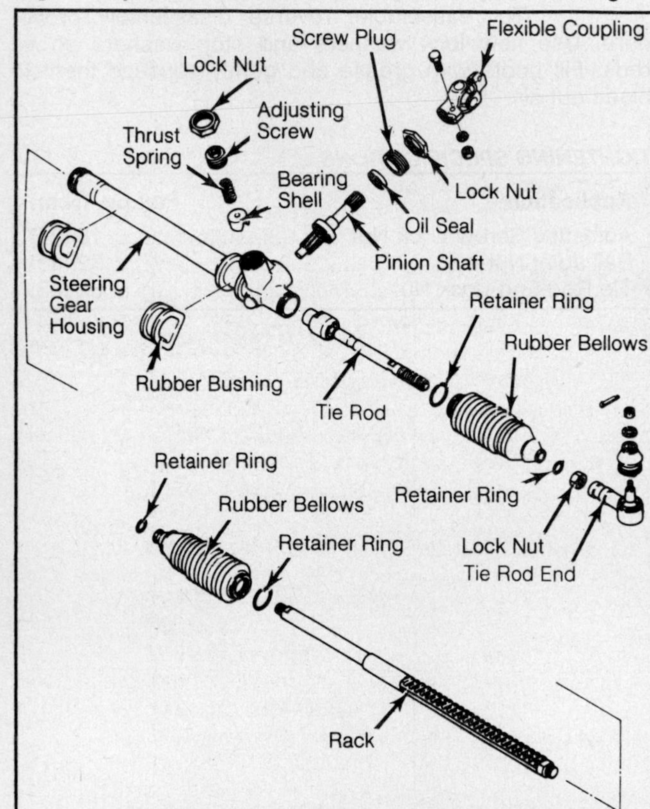

Screw Plug
Flexible Coupling
Lock Nut
Adjusting Screw
Thrust Spring
Bearing Shell
Lock Nut
Oil Seal
Pinion Shaft
Steering Gear Housing
Retainer Ring
Rubber Bellows
Rubber Bushing
Tie Rod
Retainer Ring
Rubber Bellows
Retainer Ring
Retainer Ring
Lock Nut
Tie Rod End
Rack

REMOVAL & INSTALLATION

STEERING GEAR

Removal

1) Raise and support vehicle. Remove splash shield. Remove steering shaft coupling bolt. Remove both tie rod end cotter keys and castle nuts. Using tie rod puller, disconnect tie rod ends from steering knuckles.

2) Disconnect steering gear housing from crossmember. Expand steering shaft coupling and remove steering gear assembly from car.

Installation

Position wheels straight ahead with steering wheel centered. To install, reverse removal procedure. Check toe-in.

OVERHAUL

STEERING GEAR

Disassembly

1) Clamp steering gear assembly in a soft-jawed vise. Disconnect tie rod ends from tie rods. Remove retainer rings from rubber bellows. Remove bellows from steering gear housing and ball joint.

2) Disconnect ball joint from rack. Loosen adjusting screw lock nut. Remove adjusting screw, thrust spring and bearing shell from adjusting screw opening.

3) Remove lock nut and screw plug from steering gear housing. Do not turn pinion to end position. Pull pinion and rack from steering gear housing.

Reassembly

1) Clamp steering gear assembly in a soft-jawed vise. Coat all moving parts with gear lubricant. Insert long (toothless) end of rack into short end of housing until rack is centered in housing.

NOTE: **Make sure gear lubricant does not clog air channels in metal bushings. If air channels are blocked, a vacuum in bellows may draw bellows into rack teeth.**

2) Center pinion on rack. Insert pinion shaft into gear, making sure pinion center tooth meshes with rack center tooth. Install screw plug and lock nut.

3) Place bearing shell into gear housing. Assemble thrust spring, adjusting screw and lock nut on gear assembly. Adjust gear as previously outlined.

4) Check pinion shaft starting torque. If starting torque is incorrect, adjust adjustment screw, but not more than 1/12 of a turn. Tighten lock nut.

5) Screw ball joints onto rack ends. Assemble tie rod ends to tie rods and tighten lock nuts. Lubricate axial joint on bellows with grease. Slide bellows onto axial joint and gear housing. Attach retaining rings. Check that bellows is not twisted.

TIGHTENING SPECIFICATIONS

Application	Ft. Lbs. (N.m)
Adjusting Screw Lock Nut	58 (79)
Column-to-Instrument Panel Nut	11 (15)
Flexible Coupling Bolt	19 (26)
Tie Rod Ball Housing	65 (88)
Tie Rod End-to-Knuckle Nut	29 (39)
Tie Rod End Lock Nut	47 (64)
Screw Plug	58 (79)
Screw Plug Lock Nut	72 (98)
Steering Gear Housing Clamp Bolt	14 (19)
	INCH Lbs. (N.m)
Pinion Shaft Starting Torque	3.4-12 (.38-1.36)

ISUZU P'UP RECIRCULATING BALL

DESCRIPTION

STEERING GEAR

Steering gear is a recirculating ball type. A worm gear on steering shaft lower end engages with ball nut through recirculating balls. Adjustment is provided for backlash between sector gear and ball nut by a tapered sector gear. Adjustment screw is on sector shaft.

Fig. 1: Exploded View of Recirculating Ball Steering Gear Assembly

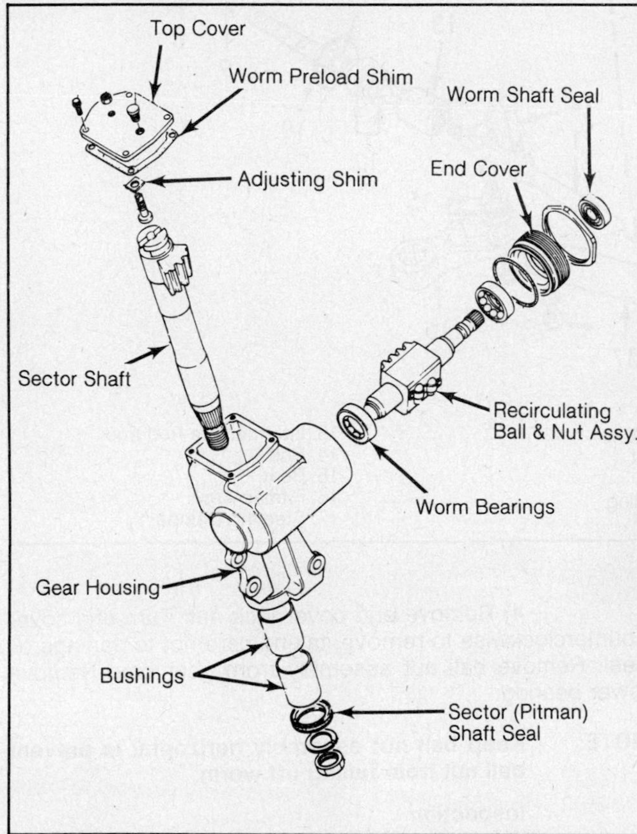
Top Cover
Worm Preload Shim
Worm Shaft Seal
Adjusting Shim
End Cover
Sector Shaft
Recirculating Ball & Nut Assy.
Worm Bearings
Gear Housing
Bushings
Sector (Pitman) Shaft Seal

STEERING LINKAGE

A splined pitman arm connects to an adjustable center link on RWD models or nonadjustable center link on 4WD models. Center link attaches to the idler arm and then to tie rods. Idler arm attaches to frame by a bracket. Tie rods are nonadjustable on RWD models, but adjustable on 4WD models.

ADJUSTMENT

PRELOAD & LASH

1) Disconnect battery ground cable. Raise and support front of vehicle. Remove pitman arm nut and mark position of pitman arm to shaft. Remove pitman arm using puller. Remove horn shroud and spring.

NOTE: Do not turn wheel hard against stop, as damage to ball guides may result.

2) Turn steering wheel gently against one stop, then turn back half way. To measure bearing drag, attach torque wrench to steering wheel nut and rotate 90°.

NOTE: Use a torque wrench with a maximum scale of 50 INCH Lbs. (6 N.m).

3) Adjust sector lash by turning steering wheel from one stop to the other. Turn wheel back exactly halfway to center. Turn sector adjusting screw clockwise to eliminate backlash between ball nut and sector gear. Tighten lock nut.

Fig. 2: Adjusting Sector Gear Lash

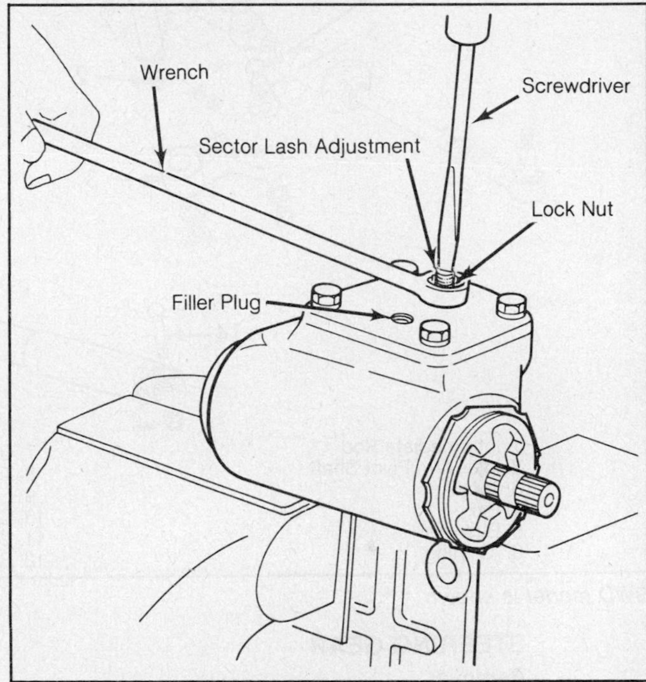
Wrench
Screwdriver
Sector Lash Adjustment
Lock Nut
Filler Plug

Turn adjusting screw clockwise to remove cover.

4) Check torque at steering wheel nut, taking highest reading as steering wheel turns through center. Torque should be 4.3-8.7 INCH Lbs. (.5-1.0 N.m).

5) If torque is incorrect, loosen lock nut and readjust sector screw. Tighten lock nut and recheck torque at steering wheel. If torque is more than 8.7 INCH Lbs. (1 N.m), turn adjusting screw counterclockwise. Turn adjuster lock nut clockwise.

6) Reassemble pitman arm to sector shaft, lining up marks made during removal. Tighten pitman arm-to-sector shaft nut. Install horn spring and shroud. Connect battery cable.

REMOVAL & INSTALLATION

STEERING LINKAGE

Removal

1) Raise and support vehicle. Disconnect tie rod ball joints from steering knuckle. Remove pitman arm-to-sector shaft nut and lock washer. Mark relative position of pitman arm-to-sector shaft and remove pitman arm from shaft.

2) Remove idler arm-to-pivot shaft nut and lock washer. Remove idler arm from pivot shaft. Unscrew pivot arm from bracket and remove pivot arm. Remove bracket.

Installation

To install steering linkage, reverse removal procedure. Align marks on pitman arm and sector shaft.

ISUZU P'UP RECIRCULATING BALL (Cont.)

Fig. 3: Exploded View of Steering Linkage

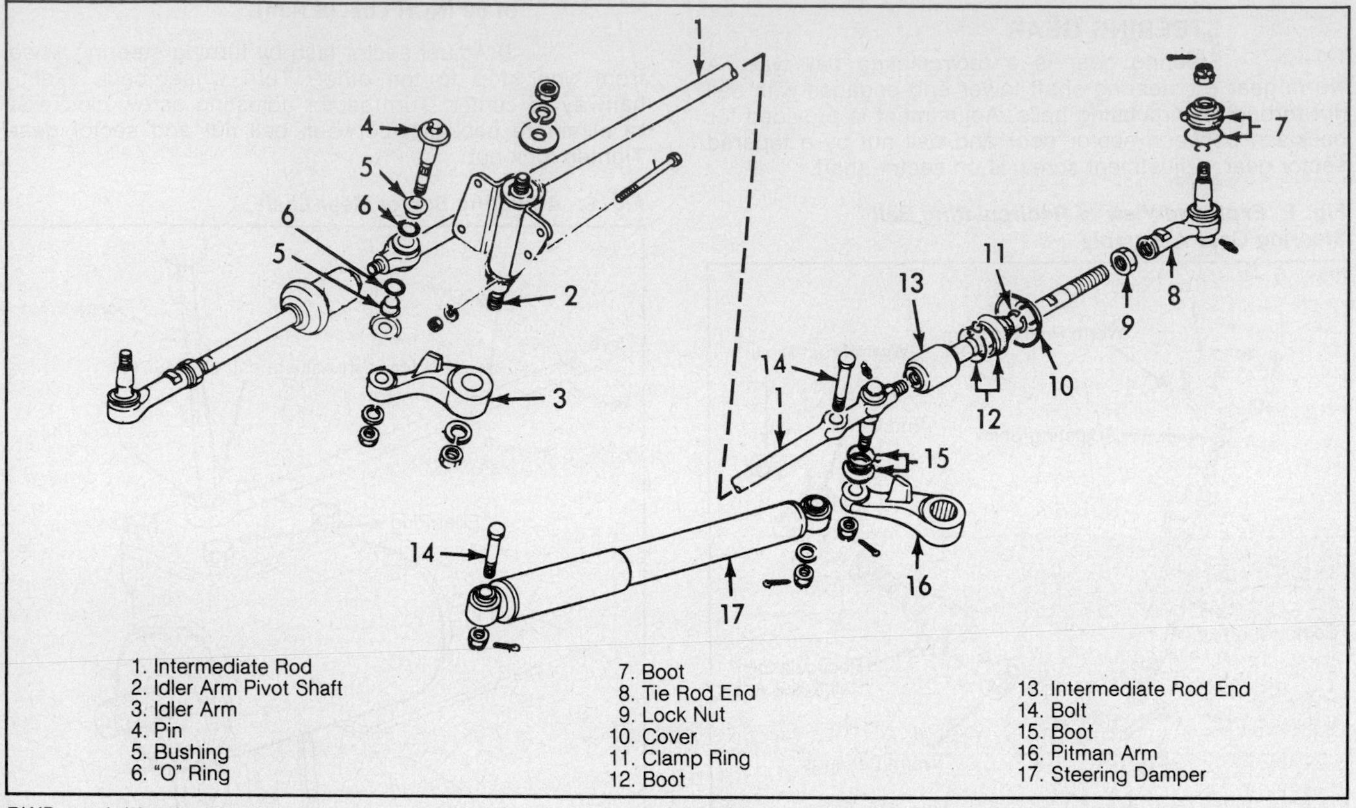
1
2
3
4
5
6
7
8
9
10
11
12
13
14
15
16
17
1. Intermediate Rod
2. Idler Arm Pivot Shaft
3. Idler Arm
4. Pin
5. Bushing
6. "O" Ring
7. Boot
8. Tie Rod End
9. Lock Nut
10. Cover
11. Clamp Ring
12. Boot
13. Intermediate Rod End
14. Bolt
15. Boot
16. Pitman Arm
17. Steering Damper

RWD model is shown.

STEERING GEAR

Removal

1) Raise and support vehicle. Remove pitman arm nut and mark relative position of pitman arm to sector shaft. Using a puller, remove pitman arm from shaft.

2) Remove splash shield. Remove lower clamp-to-flexible coupling bolts. Remove steering gear-to-frame bolts and remove steering gear.

Installation

1) Position gear and start (do not tighten) gear mounting bolts. Install clamp-to-coupling bolts and tighten.

2) Tighten gear mounting bolts. Install pitman arm to shaft, aligning index marks. Install splash shield.

OVERHAUL

STEERING GEAR

NOTE: **If parts other than bearings, covers or seals are worn, replace entire worm and ball nut assembly.**

Disassembly

1) Mark coupling relation to worm shaft. Disconnect flexible coupling from worm shaft. Drain gear box through filler plug hole.

2) Remove adjustment screw lock nut. Turn adjustment screw counterclockwise to remove preload between sector gear and ball nut rack.

3) Remove top cover bolts. Center worm shaft. Remove top cover and sector shaft, holding sector shaft straight ahead. Do not drive shaft off gear box.

4) Remove end cover lock nut. Turn end cover counterclockwise to remove, taking care not to damage oil seal. Remove ball nut assembly from gear box. Remove lower bearing.

NOTE: **Keep ball nut assembly horizontal to prevent ball nut from falling off worm.**

Inspection

Wash all parts in solvent. Check steering shaft for bending. Check ball nut teeth for dents and wear. Check bearings for wear or damage. Check splined sections for dents or damage. Check ball nut operation on worm shaft. Check sector shaft and shaft teeth for wear or damage.

Reassembly & Adjustment

1) Insert lower bearing into gear box. Install worm shaft assembly in gear box. Check lower end of worm shaft for proper fit in lower bearing.

2) Assemble upper bearing onto worm shaft. Install adjusting shims between gear housing and end cover. Lubricate "O" ring and install into end cover. Lubricate oil seal lip and install cover over worm shaft without damaging seal.

3) Screw in end cover until torque required to rotate worm shaft is between 2.6-5.2 INCH Lbs. (.3-.6 N.m). *See Fig. 4.* If torque is incorrect, add or remove shims as needed.

4) Insert adjusting screw with shim into sector shaft slot. Check clearance between adjusting screw head and sector shaft. Screw should slide freely in slot, with no more than .004" (.10 mm) clearance. If clearance is incorrect, adjust with shims.

ISUZU P'UP RECIRCULATING BALL (Cont.)

Fig. 4: Measuring Steering Gear Starting Torque

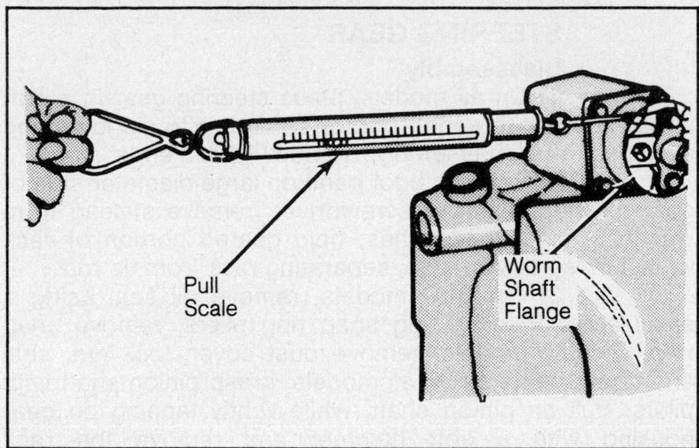
Pull
Scale
Worm
Shaft
Flange

5) Apply lubricant to bushing and oil seal. Bring ball nut to center of worm and insert sector shaft into gear box. Engage shaft center tooth with worm center tooth.

6) Install top cover while turning adjusting screw counterclockwise. Tighten lock nut. Check that worm turns more than 5 turns from lock-to-lock. If not, reinstall sector shaft.

7) Check that total gear preload (starting torque) is between 4.3-8.7 INCH Lbs. (.5-1.0 N.m). *See Fig. 4.* Turn adjusting screw if preload is incorrect. Tighten lock nut.

8) Connect sector shaft to pitman arm (align marks made during removal) and tighten pitman arm nut. Install coupling on worm shaft. Adjust end cover setting so clearance between coupling and end cover is .15-.22" (3.8-5.6 mm). Install pinch bolt. Fill gear box with .5 pint of lubricant.

PITMAN SHAFT SEAL REPLACEMENT

NOTE: Replacement can be done without removing steering gear.

1) Raise and support vehicle. Remove pitman arm as previously outlined. Clean area around seal. Pry out old seal, being careful not to damage housing bore.

NOTE: Check gear lubricant for contamination. If contaminated, overhaul gear.

2) Coat new seal with gear lubricant and tap into position. Install pitman arm. Lower vehicle and check gear lubricant level.

TIGHTENING SPECIFICATIONS

Application	Ft. Lbs. (N.m)
Ball Joint Nut	44 (60)
Center Link Lock Nut	89 (121)
Idler Arm Nut	89 (121)
Sector Lash Nut	15-22 (20-30)
Pitman Arm Nut	162 (220)
	INCH Lbs. (N.m)
Sector Lash Adjustment	4.3-8.7 (.5-1.0)
Total Steering Gear Preload	4.3-8.7 (.5-1.0)
Worm Bearing Preload	2.6-5.2 (.3-.6)

MAZDA RACK & PINION

GLC FWD & 626

DESCRIPTION

Rack and pinion type steering is mounted by rubber insulators to crossmember. Adjustment is provided for pinion gear preload.

Pinion shaft is coupled to steering shaft and tie rods connect end of rack to steering arms of front wheels.

ADJUSTMENT

NOTE: **Adjustments are performed during reassembly portion of overhaul procedure. See Overhaul procedure in this article.**

REMOVAL & INSTALLATION

STEERING GEAR

Removal

1) Raise front of vehicle and support with stands. Remove front wheels. Disconnect tie rod ends from steering knuckles.

2) Remove band securing rubber boot to steering gear. Pull boot upward and remove bolt and washer securing steering shaft-to-pinion coupler.

3) Remove steering gear bracket bolts. Remove steering gear and linkage through left tie rod hole.

Installation

To install, reverse removal procedure.

Fig. 1: Exploded View of GLC Steering Gear Assembly

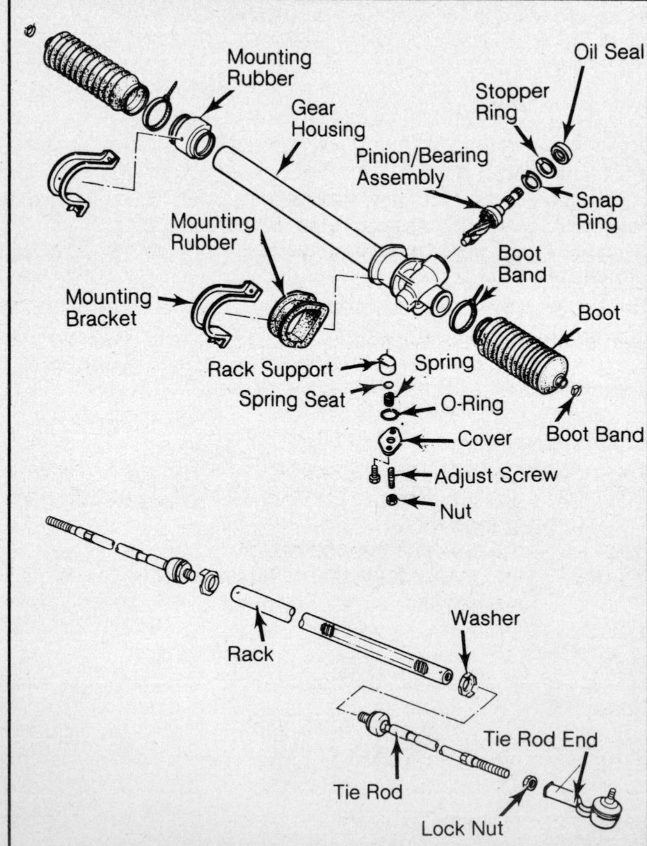
Mounting Rubber
Oil Seal
Gear Housing
Stopper Ring
Pinion/Bearing Assembly
Snap Ring
Mounting Rubber
Boot Band
Mounting Bracket
Boot
Rack Support
Spring
Spring Seat
O-Ring
Cover
Boot Band
Adjust Screw
Nut
Washer
Rack
Tie Rod End
Tie Rod
Lock Nut

OVERHAUL

STEERING GEAR

Disassembly

1) On all models, place steering gear in a soft jaw vise. Mark threaded portion of tie rod to aid in setting alignment after reassembly. Remove tie rod ends.

2) Remove boot band on large diameter side of gear housing. Using a screwdriver, remove staking from washer. Using 2 wrenches, hold geared portion of rack while turning tie rod side, separating rack from tie rod.

3) On GLC models, remove oil seal using a small screwdriver. Using snap ring pliers, remove snap ring. On 626 models, remove dust cover, lock nut, seal and upper bearing. On all models, grasp pinion shaft with pliers. Pull on pinion shaft, while lightly tapping on gear housing with a soft hammer and remove the rack assembly from housing.

Fig. 2: Exploded View of 626 Steering Gear Assembly

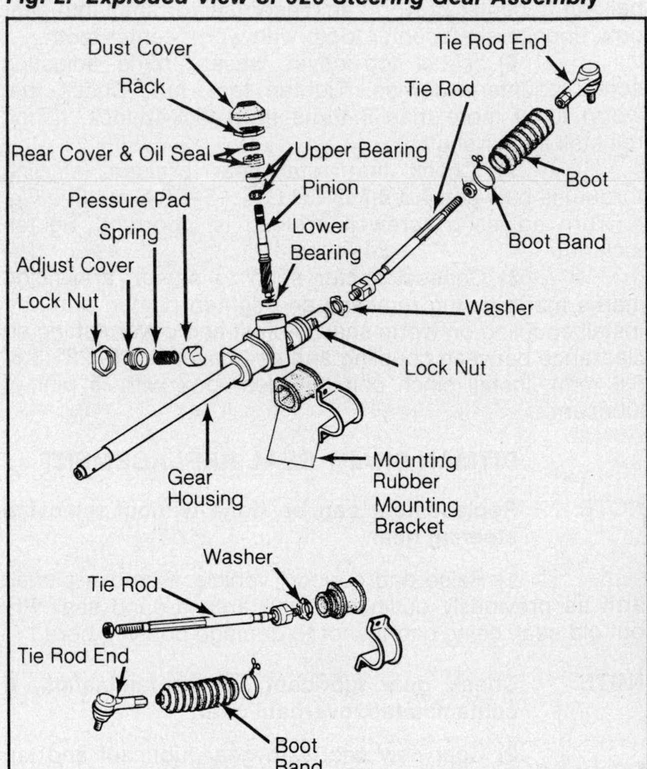
Dust Cover
Tie Rod End
Rack
Tie Rod
Rear Cover & Oil Seal
Upper Bearing
Boot
Pinion
Pressure Pad
Spring
Lower Bearing
Boot Band
Adjust Cover
Lock Nut
Washer
Lock Nut
Gear Housing
Mounting Rubber
Mounting Bracket
Washer
Tie Rod
Tie Rod End
Boot Band

4) On 626 models, the lower bearing can be removed if necessary. Remove bearing by heating the housing with hot water, about 176° F (80° C). After housing is heated, remove bearing by tapping the end of housing.

Inspection

Check rubber boots, ball bearings and tooth surface of rack for wear or damage. Check sliding surface of rack support and gear housing for cracks or damage. Check tie rod ball joints for smooth operation.

NOTE: **If part(s) of rack and gear assembly are found to be defective, entire gear assembly must be replaced.**

Reassembly (GLC)

1) Apply lithium grease to the following parts: Ball bearing, roller bearing on pinion, inside of gear

MAZDA RACK & PINION (Cont.)

housing, lip of oil seal, sliding and backing surface of rack support, sliding surface of rack bushings, rack pinion teeth and ball joint of tie rods.

2) Carefully insert rack with non-tooth side into pinion side of housing. Install pinion and bearing assembly making sure rack teeth and pinion are meshed properly.

NOTE: **If fit between housing and bearing is too tight, strike outer ring of bearing lightly while carefully checking the meshing of rack and pinion.**

3) Install snap ring in housing groove. Install stopper with protruded portion being placed in gap of snap ring. Position a new seal in housing. Using a hammer, tap lightly on seal until seal is flush with end surface of housing.

4) Turn adjusting screw until tightening torque increases suddenly. Unscrew adjusting screw 0-15° and tighten screw with lock nut. To complete reassembly, reverse disassembly procedure.

5) Measure pinion gear preload using a spring scale and attachment (49 0180 510B). Install attachment to gear shaft.

6) Hook spring scale to attachment and turn it at a speed of 1 revolution per 1 to 2 seconds. Scale should read 1.3-2.6 lbs. (.6-1.2 kg).

Reassembly (626)

1) Apply lithium grease to the following parts: Upper and lower bearing, inside of gear housing, lip of oil seal, sliding and backing surface of rack support, sliding surface of rack bushings, rack pinion teeth and ball joint of tie rods.

2) If lower bearing was removed, use pinion to press the bearing into place, making sure of bearing direction. Carefully install the rack. Insert pinion with the notched edge of rack at the central position of pinion. *See Fig. 3.* Apply grease to upper bearing and rear cover and install.

3) Apply sealant to threaded part of cover. Install upper bearing and rear cover. Adjust pinion so that torque is about 4.32 INCH lbs (.5 N.m). Rotate pinion left and right so the bearing becomes seated.

NOTE: **Do not install oil seal at this point.**

4) Measure pinion gear preload using a spring scale and attachment (49 0180 510B). Install attachment to gear shaft. Scale should read 1.1 lb. (.5 kg). Loosen rear cover and adjust pinion torque to 1.74-2.60 INCH lbs. (.2-.3 N.m). Tighten lock nut to 58-72 ft. lbs. (80-100 N.m). Recheck pinion torque, readjust if necessary.

Fig. 3: Location of Pinion-To-Rack

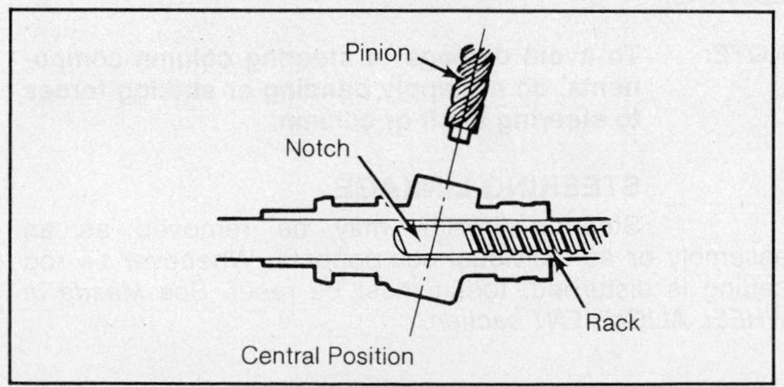
Pinion
Notch
Rack
Central Position

5) Install pressure pad and spring. Coat adjustment cover with a sealant and install, torque to 7.2 ft. lbs. (10 N.m). Tighten lock nut to 29-43 ft. lbs. (40-60 N.m).

6) Measure pinion torque using a spring scale and attachment (49 0180 510B). Pinion torque specifications in the neutral position are .6-.9 INCH lbs (.7-1 N.m) and in any other postion .6-1.3 INCH lbs. (.7-1.5 N.m). *See Fig. 3.*

7) To complete reassembly, install new oil seal and dust cover and reverse disassembly procedure.

TIGHTENING SPECIFICATIONS

Application	Ft. Lbs. (N.m)
Shaft-to-Pinion Bolt	13-20 (18-27)
Mounting Bracket Bolt	23-34 (32-47)
Tie Rod Locknut	
GLC	25-30 (35-40)
626	50-58 (70-80)
Tie Rod & Rack	
GLC	43-58 (60-80)
626	58-72 (80-100)

MAZDA RECIRCULATING BALL

B2000 & B2200 Pickups, GLC Wagon, RX7

DESCRIPTION

Steering gear is a recirculating ball type with a variable ratio, depending on turning angle of sector shaft. The worm gear and steering shaft are an integral (non-separable) unit.

Steering linkage is basically the same for all models, having a non-adjustable center link, 2 adjustable tie rods, an idler arm assembly, and pitman arm.

ADJUSTMENT

NOTE: **Adjustments are performed during assembly portion of overhaul. See Overhaul procedure in this article.**

REMOVAL & INSTALLATION

STEERING GEAR

Removal (B2000 & B2200 Pickups)

1) Remove steering wheel and column, *See Mazda under Steering Wheel & Column Switches in this section.* Remove air cleaner and brake master cylinder. On column shift models remove the lower bracket from the selection rod and shift rod.

2) Raise front end and disconnect center link from pitman arm using appropriate puller. Remove bolts and nuts holding steering gear to frame and remove steering gear.

Fig. 1: Exploded View of Steering Gear Assembly (B2000 and B2200 Pickups)

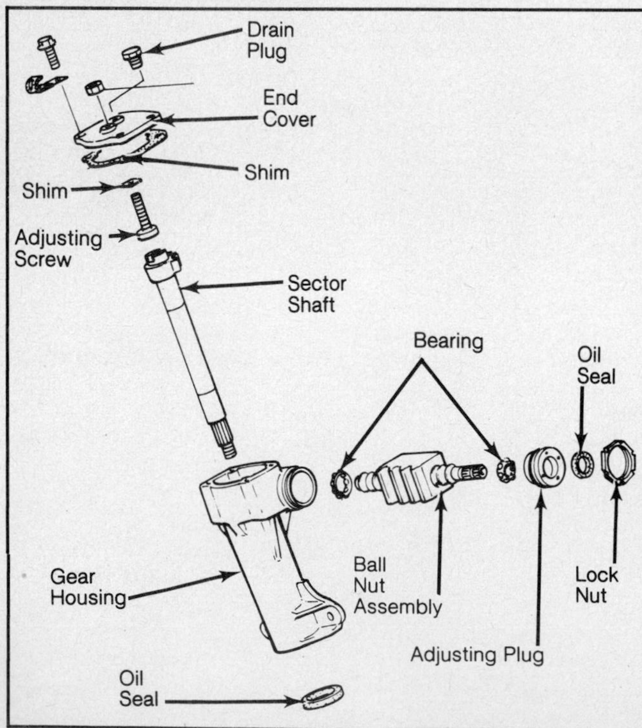
Drain Plug
End Cover
Shim
Shim
Adjusting Screw
Sector Shaft
Bearing
Oil Seal
Gear Housing
Ball Nut Assembly
Lock Nut
Adjusting Plug
Oil Seal

Removal (GLC Wagon)

1) Disconnect negative battery cable. Remove steering wheel and switches. *See Mazda under Steering Wheel & Column Switches in this section.* Remove bolts holding column to dash. Loosen dust cover screws, any other column bolts and pull column jacket off shaft.

2) With vehicle raised, disconnect center link from pitman arm with puller. Remove steering gear mounting bolts and pull gear forward after raising vehicle.

Fig. 2: Exploded View of Steering Gear Assembly (GLC Wagon and RX7 Models)

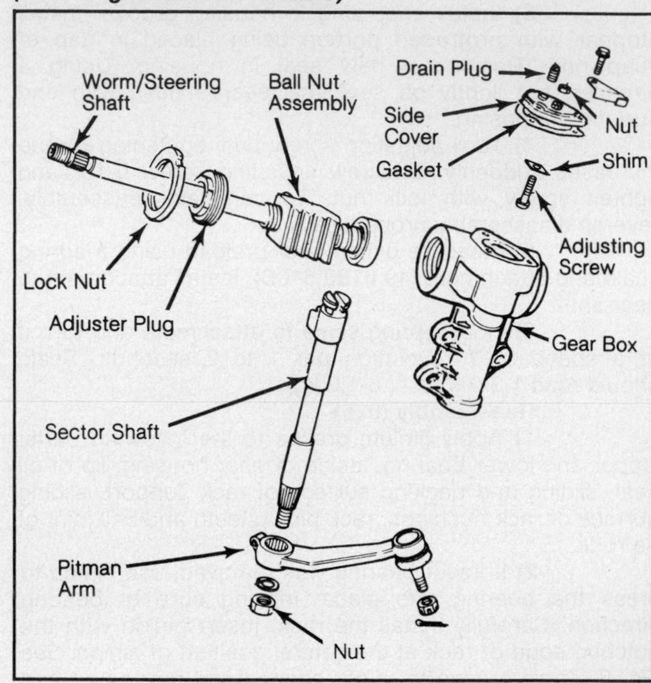
Drain Plug
Worm/Steering Shaft
Ball Nut Assembly
Side Cover
Nut
Gasket
Shim
Adjusting Screw
Lock Nut
Adjuster Plug
Gear Box
Sector Shaft
Pitman Arm
Nut

Removal (RX7)

1) Disconnect negative battery cable. Remove steering wheel and switches. *See Mazda under Steering Wheel & Column Switches in this section.* Remove hood, steering column covers and air duct. Disconnect couplers of combination switch and remove the switch assembly.

2) Raise and support front of vehicle. Disconnect pitman arm and center link. Remove nuts and bolts retaining steering gear housing to body. Remove steering gear assembly from vehicle through engine compartment.

Installation (All Models)

To install, reverse removal procedure, ensuring any shims which were removed are installed in original positions.

NOTE: **To avoid damage to steering column components, do not apply bending or striking forces to steering shaft or column.**

STEERING LINKAGE

Steering linkage may be removed as an assembly or as individual components. Whenever tie rod setting is disturbed, toe-in must be reset. *See Mazda in WHEEL ALIGNMENT section.*

MAZDA RECIRCULATING BALL (Cont.)

OVERHAUL

DISASSEMBLY

Steering Gear

1) On all models, drain gear oil from housing. Remove pitman arm from sector shaft, if not removed previously. Remove sector shaft adjusting screw lock nut. Remove side cover attaching bolts and remove side cover by turning adjusting screw clockwise.

2) Remove sector shaft adjusting screw and shim from sector shaft. Remove sector shaft carefully to avoid damage to oil seal.

3) On B2000 and B2200 models, remove lock ring, adjusting plug with oil seal, outer bearing, worm ball nut assembly and inner bearing.

4) On GLC Wagon and RX7 models, remove ball nut/worm gear adjusting plug lock nut. Then remove adjusting plug and withdraw ball nut, worm gear and steering shaft assembly from gear housing.

INSPECTION

1) Check the action of ball nut assembly on the worm gear. If movement is not smooth for full length of travel, replace worm and ball nut assembly. Worm and ball nut are not serviced separately.

2) Check worm bearings and cups, sector shaft gear surface, and oil seal. Check clearance between sector shaft and housing bore. Clearance should be .004" (.1 mm) or less. If any component is defective, replace it.

Fig. 3: Checking Sector Shaft Adjusting Screw End Clearance

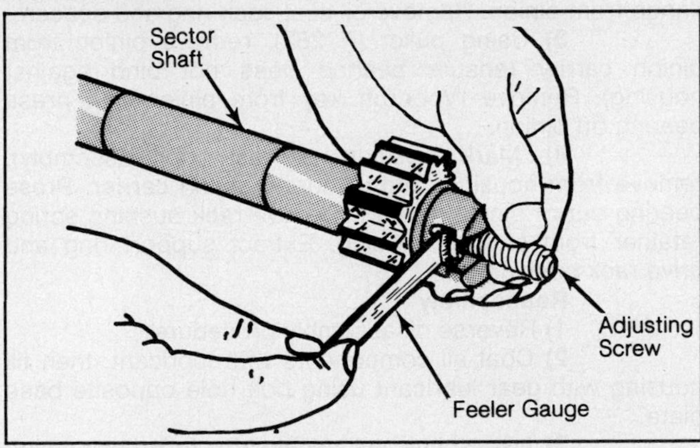
Sector Shaft
Adjusting Screw
Feeler Gauge

REASSEMBLY & ADJUSTMENT

Steering Gear

Replace oil seals if necessary. Insert worm gear, ball nut assembly into gear housing. Check preload of worm ball nut.

Worm Bearing Preload

1) Ckeck preload (without sector shaft) with a spring scale and 3.9" (10 cm) attachment, preload reading should be .44-1.10 lbs. (.2-.5 kg).

2) Loosen lock nut and tighten or loosen adjusting srcrew if preload is not to specifications. Tighten lock nut securely.

Sector Shaft End Play

1) Check clearance between sector shaft adjusting screw and sector shaft. Insert shim so that final clearance will be .004" (.1 mm) or less. Insert sector shaft with ball nut. *See Fig. 4.*

Fig. 4: Aligning Sector Shaft to Ball Nut

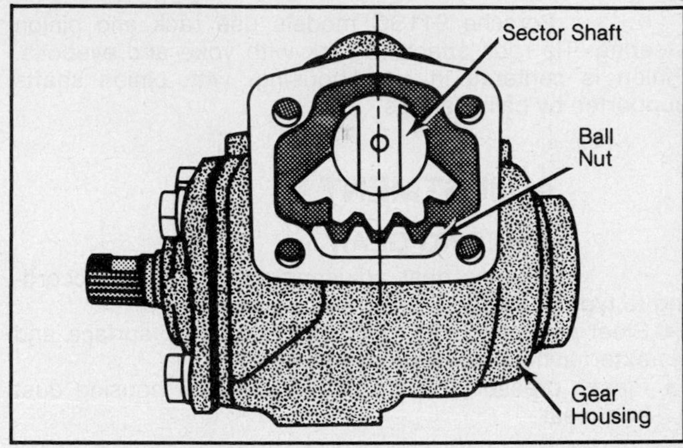
Sector Shaft
Ball Nut
Gear Housing

2) Insert adjusting screw and shim in sector shaft. Place side cover and gasket over adjusting screw and turn adjusting screw until cover is in place, then install cover bolts.

Steering Gear Backlash

1) Install pitman arm to sector shaft. Install and tighten retaining nut. Measure pitman arm backlash. If necessary, turn sector adjusting screw until zero backlash is obtained.

2) Tighten adjusting screw lock nut, taking care not to disturb backlash adjustment.

3) Check worm shaft rotating torque. Attach an INCH lb. torque wrench to steering shaft upper end. If not to specifications, adjust as necessary. *See Final Worm Bearing Preload table.* Fill gear housing with lubricant (API GL-4 SAE 90).

FINAL WORM BEARING PRELOAD

Application	INCH Lbs. (N.m)
B2000 & B2200	5.2-7.8 (.57-.86)
RX7	1.3-2.7 (.14-.30)
GLC Wagon	5.2-10.4 (.6-1.2)

TIGHTENING SPECIFICATIONS

Application	Ft. Lbs. (N.m)
Pitman Arm-to-Sector Shaft	
GLC Wagon, B2000 & B2200	58-87 (80-120)
RX7	108-130 (150-180)
Tie Rod Lock Nut	
B2000 & B2200	22-33 (30-45)
GLC Wagon & RX7	51-58 (70-80)

PORSCHE 911SC RACK & PINION

DESCRIPTION

Porsche 911SC models use rack and pinion steering. Tie rods attach to rack with yoke and eyebolts. Pinion is centered in rack housing. with pinion shafts supported by ball bearings.

ADJUSTMENT

STEERING GEAR

Steering gear adjusting methods vary according to type of steering rack pressure block:

- Steel pressure block with plastic contact surface and external housing dust boot seat.
- Plastic pressure block with no external housing dust boot seat.

Fig. 1: Adjusting Nut with Cover

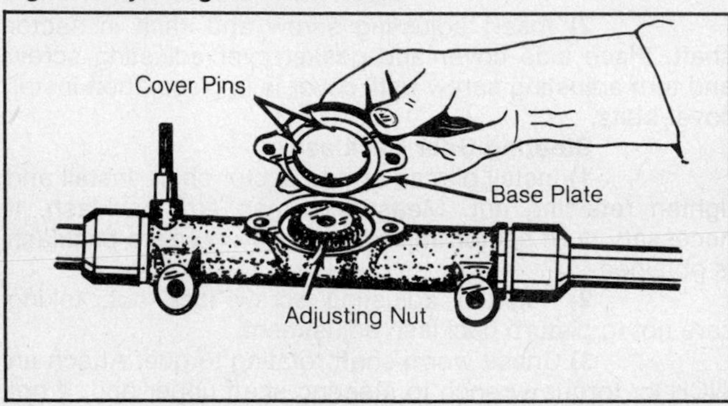
Cover Pins
Base Plate
Adjusting Nut

Steel Pressure Block Type

1) With housing assembly in padded vise, detach base plate. Tighten adjusting nut seating contact. Back nut off contact by 3 teeth.

NOTE: Base plate has integral pins which may be used as a wrench for this adjustment.

2) Check steering gear drag at pinion flange, using an INCH lb. torque wrench. A measurement of 7 INCH lbs. (.8 N.m) should be obtained. If beyond this measurement, loosen adjusting nut.

3) If this measurement is not less than 3.5 INCH lbs. (.39 N.m), do not retighten adjusting nut. Install base plate with gasket.

NOTE: When installing base plate, pin in plate must fit easily between teeth of adjusting nut. If necessary, move nut slightly.

Plastic Pressure Block Type

Remove base plate and tighten adjusting nut until 7 INCH lbs. (.8 N.m) torque is obtained, using method as previously described. Install base plate with gasket.

REMOVAL & INSTALLATION

STEERING GEAR

Removal

1) Remove bottom bolt attaching universal joint to pinion shaft. Remove nuts and detach tie rod ball joints from steering knuckles.

2) Remove steering housing retaining bolts and extract entire steering housing from right side of vehicle. Detach track rods from rack.

Fig. 2: Plastic Pressure Block Housing Assembly

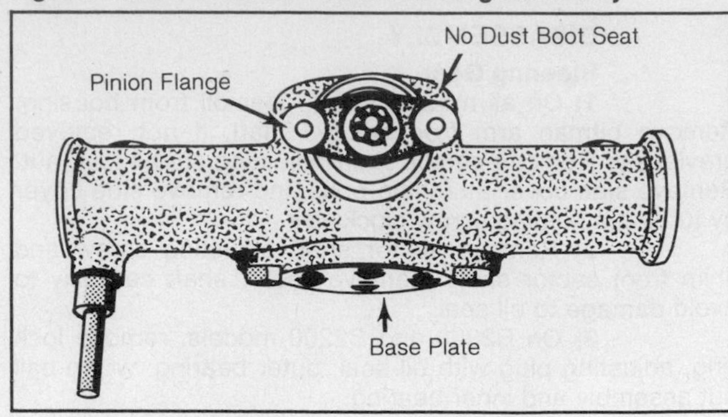
No Dust Boot Seat
Pinion Flange
Base Plate

Installation

To install, reverse removal procedures noting that indentation in pinion shaft must line up with bolt hole in lower universal joint.

OVERHAUL

STEERING GEAR

Disassembly

1) Mount steering housing in padded vise and remove base plate retaining bolts. Unscrew adjusting nut (base plate may be used as wrench). Remove pressure block and spring.

2) Move steering rack to either lock position and remove castellated nut. Using puller (P 293), remove flange from pinion. Remove oil seal, lock ring and spacer.

3) Using puller (P 282), remove pinion from pinion carrier (ensure bearing does not bind against housing). Remove Woodruff key from pinion and press bearing off pinion.

4) Mark position of rack (for assembly), remove from housing, and withdraw pinion carrier. Press bearing out of pinion carrier. Remove rack bushing spring retainer from end of housing. Extract support ring and drive rack bushing out.

Reassembly

1) Reverse disassembly procedure.

2) Coat all components with lubricant, then fill housing with gear lubricant using bolt hole opposite base plate.

3) Use shims, as necessary, to adjust pinion axial play to zero.

EYEBOLT

Disassembly

1) Clamp gear into special tool (P 285b) without washers.

2) Remove clamps on outer end of bellows and pull bellows off holder.

3) Loosen bellows holder with hook spanner and unscrew eyebolt and bellows holder.

Inspection

Check eyebolt, bellows and clamps for visible wear. Replace as required.

Reassembly

1) Mount bellows on housing. Screw bellows holder on eyebolt. Coat eyebolt threads and rack face end with sealer. Install eyebolts.

PORSCHE 911SC RACK & PINION (Cont.)

CAUTION: Eyebolt must be installed in precise position to ensure free movement of steering components and exact guiding of track rod.

2) Attach steering gear, without washers, to original holding tool (P 285b). Locating pins should slide easily into eyebolts, with flattened end resting against outer pin.

3) Tighten bellows holder. Clamp bellows to gear assembly.

Fig. 3: Exploded View of 911SC Steering Gear Assembly

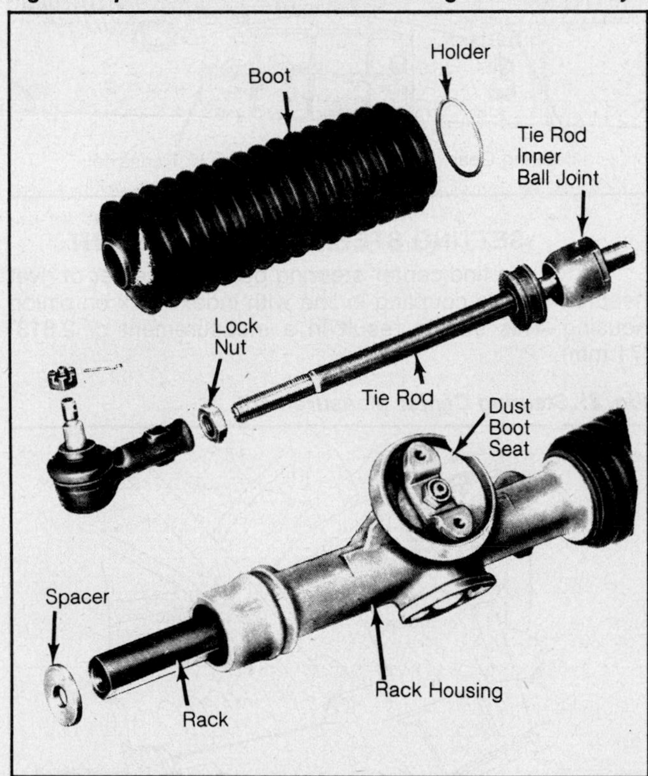
Holder
Boot
Tie Rod
Inner
Ball Joint
Lock
Nut
Tie Rod
Dust
Boot
Seat
Spacer
Rack Housing
Rack

TIGHTENING SPECIFICATIONS

Application	Ft. Lbs. (N.m)
Housing-to-Crossmember	34 (46)
Tie Rod-to-Steering Knuckle	33 (45)
"U" Joint Coupling	23 (31)

RENAULT RACK & PINION

Le Car

DESCRIPTION

Vehicles are fitted with a rack and pinion steering gear, which has direct steering linkage (tie rods) to each front wheel. Steering housing is mounted to front crossmember and connected to steering column through a flexible coupling.

ADJUSTMENT

STEERING GEAR HEIGHT (TOE-OUT)

NOTE: **This adjustment must be performed whenever steering gear is removed or replaced.**

1) Place vehicle on lift, or alignment rack, with front wheels on radius gauges. Attach a brake press to pedal (to prevent rolling movement of wheels). Set steering at center point and lock in position with holding tool (MS. 504) attached to steering wheel.

2) Load front of vehicle until measurement from centerline of front wheel to bottom of lower frame member (at front wheel) is 4.313" (110 mm). Mount scale boards (T. Av. 552) on side of body so distance from wheel center to board is 51.188" (1300 mm). *See Fig. 1.*

3) Mount measuring tools on both front wheels of vehicle so pointers are in line with crosses on scale boards. Remove load from vehicle (and raise with jack if necessary) so position is 3.125" (79 mm) higher than loaded position. Pointer should move to 6-7.75 on scale board. If not, steering gear must be adjusted.

Fig. 1: Measurements for Steering Gear

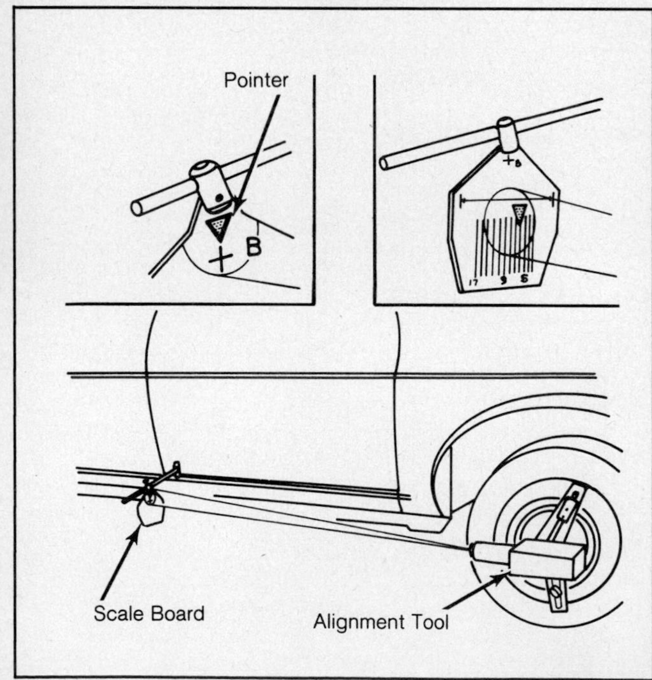
Pointer
B
Scale Board
Alignment Tool

4) Slotted shims are used to adjust steering gear. Position of slot in shim varies to move gear up and down. To replace or adjust shims, remove transaxle cover. Loosen steering gear bolts and remove adjusting shims. *See Fig. 2.*

Fig. 2: Location of Adjustment Shim

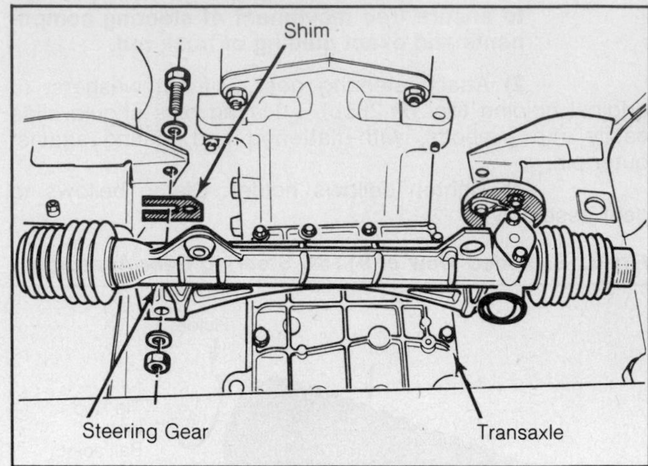
Shim
Steering Gear
Transaxle

SETTING STEERING CENTER POINT

To find center steering point, set center of rivet head on flexible coupling in line with index mark on pinion housing. This should result in a measurement of 2.813" (71 mm).

Fig. 3: Steering Center Measurement

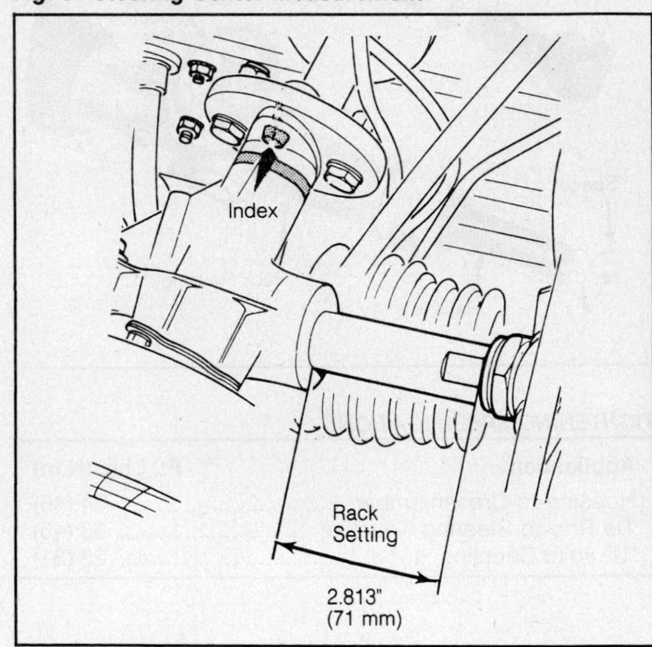
Index
Rack
Setting
2.813"
(71 mm)

REMOVAL & INSTALLATION

STEERING GEAR

Removal

1) Remove spare tire and disconnect battery. Remove air cleaner and cooling fan relay, without disconnecting wiring. Remove governor, connector, valve and air pump pipe. Remove air filter bracket bolts and place assembly on engine.

2) Remove air pump filter. Remove steering shaft flexible coupling bolts and gear mounting bolts. Disconnect tie rod ends and remove steering gear. Mark shim location to reinstall in correct position.

RENAULT RACK & PINION (Cont.)

Installation

To install, reverse removal procedure, noting the following: Coat tie rod end connections with grease. Check condition of bellows and clamps. Align tie rod connecting bolts horizontally. After steering gear is installed, check height setting and alignment.

OVERHAUL

STEERING GEAR

Disassembly

1) Loosen rack and lock nut. Remove rack end fitting, opposite pinion, noting the number of turns required. Take off bellows, circlip, and thrust washer. Pry out rubber washer.

Fig. 4: Exploded View of Steering Gear Assembly

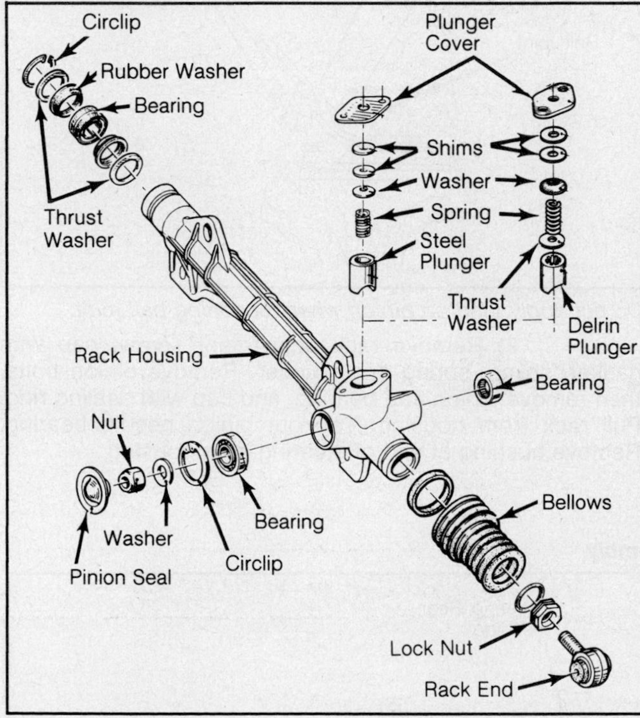

Circlip
Rubber Washer
Bearing
Thrust Washer
Plunger Cover
Shims
Washer
Spring
Steel Plunger
Thrust Washer
Delrin Plunger
Rack Housing
Bearing
Nut
Washer
Pinion Seal
Bearing
Circlip
Bellows
Lock Nut
Rack End

2) Make a bearing removal tool by drilling two .156" (4 mm) holes, 1.063" (27 mm) apart in a piece of steel strap. Turn two .125" (3 mm) screws into old bearing and turn pinion shaft to remove bearing.

Fig. 5: Removal of Rack Bearing

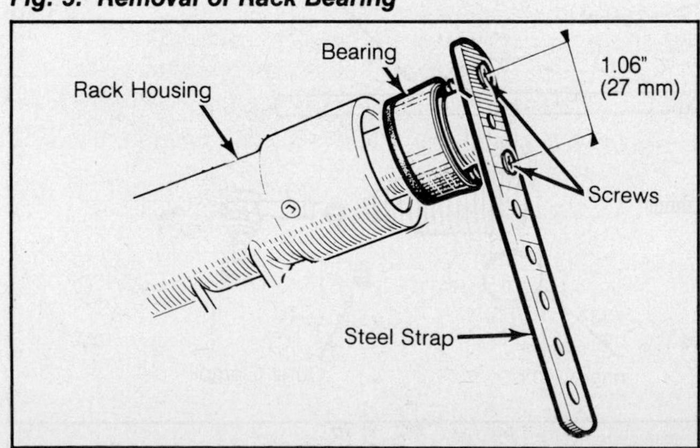

Bearing
Rack Housing
1.06"
(27 mm)
Screws
Steel Strap

3) Remove plunger cover, washers, spring and plunger. Pry out pinion seal plug, then remove pinion nut and washer. Pull out pinion and rack. Remove circlip and tap out bearings.

Inspection

Clean all parts with soft cloth and check for excessive wear or damage. Replace parts if necessary.

Reassembly & Adjustment

1) Tap pinion bearings into place. Replace thrust washers, rubber rings and bushing in end of rack housing. Be sure slot is clear, and refit circlip. Spread Molykote grease over rack and pinion, then center rack in housing and install pinion. Replace washer, nut, and seal.

2) Grease plunger, spring and washers, and replace in housing. Fabricate a dial indicator bracket using a spare plunger cover. Drill a hole in the center and weld on a flange to hold indicator outer shaft. *See Fig. 6.*

Fig. 6: Tool for Rack Play Measurement

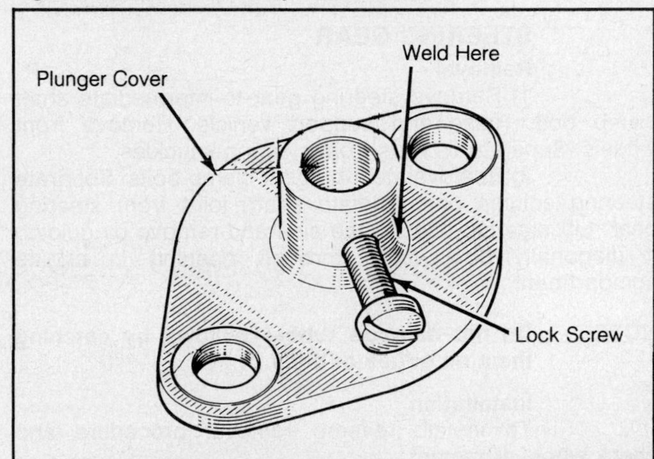

Weld Here
Plunger Cover
Lock Screw

3) Measure plunger movement while turning pinion. Set rack at position of greatest measurement, then reset dial indicator to zero. Pry rack back and forth without moving from position, and measure play on indicator.

4) Select a shim .0016" (.04 mm) smaller than measured play, then remove spare cover, insert shim, and replace plunger cover. Tighten cover bolts to specification.

TIGHTENING SPECIFICATIONS

Application	Ft. Lbs. (N.m)
Flexible Coupling Bolts	11 (15)
Gear-to-Frame Bolts	25 (34)
Pinion Nut	7.5 (10)
Plunger Cover Bolts	7.5 (10)
Tie Rod-to-Rack Bolts	25 (34)

SAAB RACK & PINION

900 & 900 Turbo

DESCRIPTION

Steering gear is rack and pinion type. Rack is protected from dirt by rubber bellows. The pinion and bearing are assembled as a unit and uses an adjustable spring-loaded plunger.

The gear is oil-lubricated. The steering linkage is a direct link from the steering rack to the steering knuckles, consisting of tie rods and enclosed ball joint.

ADJUSTMENT

See Overhaul procedure in this article.

REMOVAL & INSTALLATION

STEERING GEAR

Removal

1) Remove steering gear-to-intermediate shaft clamp bolt. Raise and support vehicle. Remove front wheels. Separate tie rods from steering knuckles.

2) Remove steering gear clamp bolts. Separate steering column (intermediate shaft) joint from steering gear. Lift steering gear to the side and remove by guiding it diagonally downwards through opening in engine compartment.

NOTE: **Do not damage rubber bellows by catching them on edges of body.**

Installation

To install, reverse removal procedure and check wheel alignment.

OVERHAUL

DISASSEMBLY

Steering Gear

1) Remove tie rod ends and rubber bellows. Drill out tab from groove on ball joint, using a .16" (4 mm) drill bit. Mount toothed end of rack in soft-jawed vise. Using spanner wrench (89 96 472), remove ball joint. *See Fig.* 2. DO NOT apply load on pinion when loosening ball joint.

Fig. 2: Removing Ball Joint

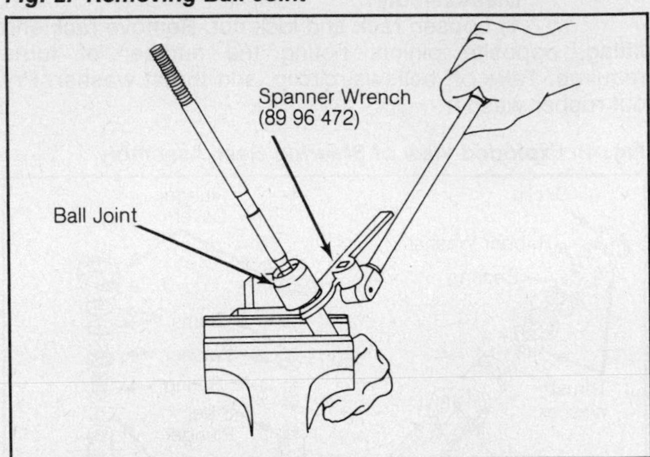
Spanner Wrench
(89 96 472)
Ball Joint

Do not apply load on pinion when loosening ball joint.

2) Remove rack adjustment screw, cap with gasket, shims, spring and plunger. Remove pinion bolts, then remove pinion and bearing, and cap with sealing ring. Pull rack from housing. Tap out pinion needle bearing. Remove bushing at end of steering gear housing.

Fig. 1: Exploded View of Saab Rack & Pinion Steering Gear Assembly

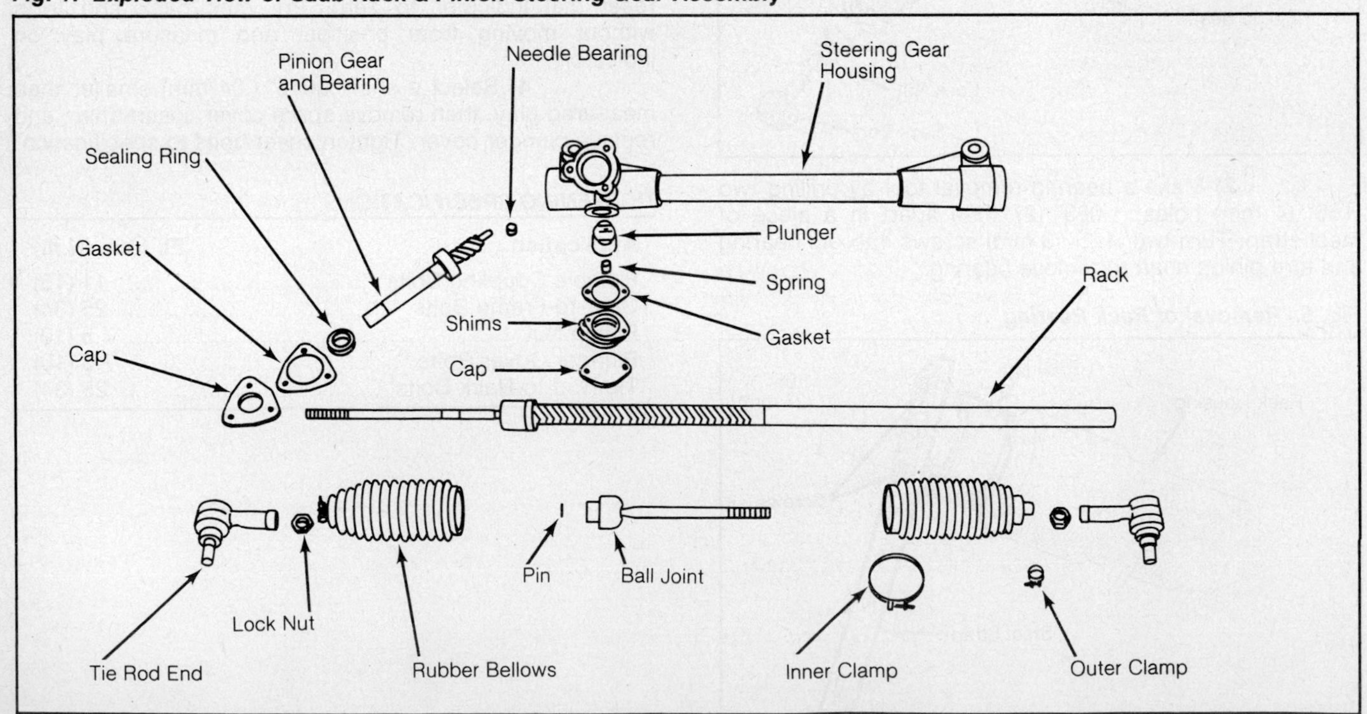
Pinion Gear
and Bearing
Needle Bearing
Steering Gear
Housing
Sealing Ring
Plunger
Gasket
Spring
Rack
Shims
Gasket
Cap
Cap
Pin
Ball Joint
Lock Nut
Tie Rod End
Rubber Bellows
Inner Clamp
Outer Clamp

SAAB RACK & PINION (Cont.)

NOTE: The bearing is factory fitted to the pinion shaft and cannot be replaced separately. Pinion and bearing must be replaced as an assembly.

REASSEMBLY AND ADJUSTMENT

Steering Gear

1) Ensure all parts are thoroughly cleaned and lubricated before proceeding with reassembly. Insert bushing at end of steering gear housing. Install and seat needle bearing in housing.

2) Mount toothed end of rack in soft-jawed vise. Screw ball joint onto rack end. If old ball joint is being reused, existing lock mark must be rotated 90° from original position by installing a special spacer between rack and ball joint.

3) Using spanner wrench (89 96 472) and torque wrench, tighten ball joint to 80-94 ft. lbs. (108-127 N.m). DO NOT apply load on pinion when tightening ball joint. Lock ball joint in position by bending tab into groove in rack.

4) Insert rack into housing, then install pinion with bearing, gasket, sealing ring (coated with chassis grease) and cap. Apply thread sealing compound to through bolt and install pinion bolts.

Radial Play

1) Adjust radial play of rack as follows: Insert plunger without spring and gasket, then attach cap with bolts (finger tight only).

2) Measure clearance between cap and housing. To this measurement add .002-.006" (.05-.15 mm) to allow for play between plunger and cap after assembly. Shims are available in thicknesses of .005", .0075" and .010" (.13 mm, .19 mm and .25 mm).

3) This total thickness will be the thickness of gasket and shims required. Measure shims and gasket together, then remove cap and install plunger, spring, shims, gasket and cap. Check rack for free movement by rotating pinion with 12-point 18 mm socket attached to splines on pinion shaft.

Fig. 3: Measuring Cap-to-Gear Housing Clearance

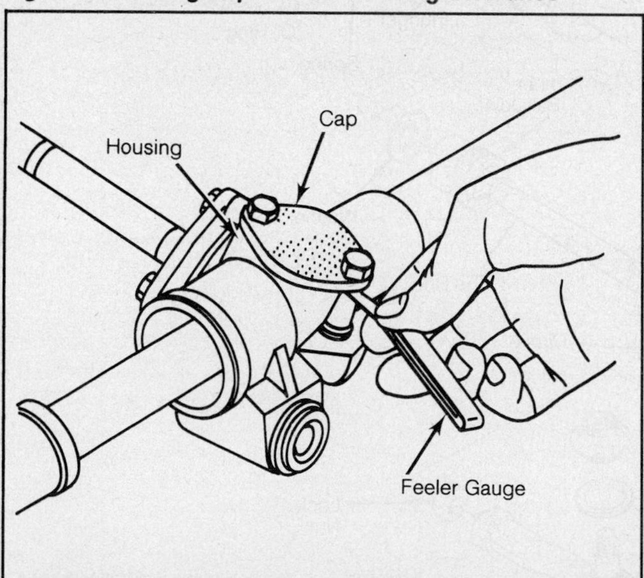
Cap
Housing
Feeler Gauge

Pinion Rotating Torque

1) Measure pinion rotating torque. Using a torque wrench and a 12-point 18 mm socket, rotate pinion through full travel of rack. Pinion torque should be 7-24 ft. lbs. (10-33 N.m).

2) Attach bellows after lubricating contact area between bellows and tie rod with silicone grease. Attach both inner clamps.

3) Stand gear on end and pour 5.0 oz. of EP 90 gear oil into bellows. Attach outboard bellows with clamps. Screw on lock nuts and mount tie rod assemblies.

NOTE: Outer clamps should be protected with rubber caps.

TIGHTENING SPECIFICATIONS

Application	Ft. Lbs. (N.m)
Ball Joint	80-94 (108-127)
Lower Joint Clamp Bolt	26-30 (35-41)
Steering Gear Clamp Bolts	44-60 (60-81)
Tie Rod End	35-44 (47-60)
Tie Rod Lock Nut	44-60 (60-81)

SUBARU RACK & PINION

1600 & 1800

DESCRIPTION

Steering gear, mounted on crossmember, is a rack and pinion type, with backlash automatically adjusted. Pinion is connected to steering shaft by a flexible rubber coupling.

Steering knuckle arms are connected to rack by tie rods which are threaded onto ball joint studs at each end of rack.

ADJUSTMENT

NOTE: **Adjustments are performed during gear assembly process. See Overhaul as outlined.**

REMOVAL & INSTALLATION

STEERING GEAR

Removal

1) Disconnect negative battery terminal. Raise and support front of vehicle. Remove both front wheels. Disconnect ball joints from steering knuckles.

2) Disconnect flexible coupling from pinion gear. Remove hot air stove from exhaust manifold and air cleaner. Disconnect exhaust manifold and pull down out of way. Remove rubber boot protector.

3) Remove bolts attaching steering gear housing to crossmember. Lower gear housing until pinion gear is disconnected from flexible coupling. Rotate gear housing backwards and remove gear housing from left side.

Fig. 1: Exploded View of Subaru Rack & Pinion Steering Gear Assembly

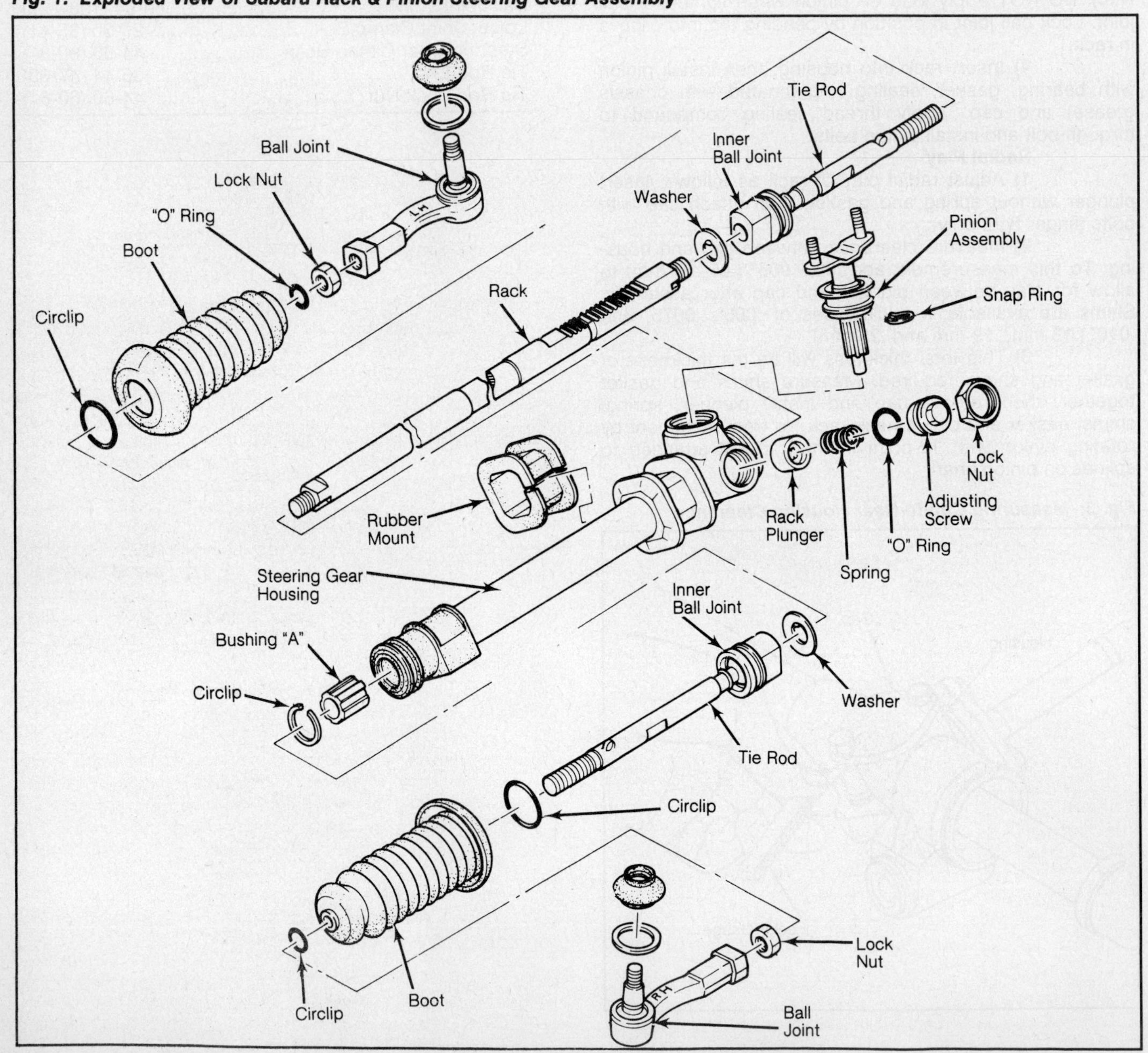
Tie Rod
Inner Ball Joint
Ball Joint
Lock Nut
Washer
"O" Ring
Pinion Assembly
Boot
Rack
Snap Ring
Circlip
Lock Nut
Adjusting Screw
Rubber Mount
Rack Plunger
"O" Ring
Steering Gear Housing
Spring
Inner Ball Joint
Bushing "A"
Circlip
Washer
Tie Rod
Circlip
Lock Nut
Circlip
Boot
Ball Joint

SUBARU RACK & PINION (Cont.)

Installation

1) To install steering gear assembly, reverse removal procedures and note the following. Tighten left steering gear housing bracket first.

2) Tighten ball joint nuts to specifications, then turn a maximum of 1/6 turn to align cotter pin hole.

OVERHAUL

DISASSEMBLY

Steering Gear

1) Place steering gear housing in a padded vise. Loosen lock nuts and remove ball joints from rods. Remove "O" rings from outside of rubber boots, then remove rubber boots.

2) Straighten tab on inner ball joint lock washer, then loosen lock nut and remove inner ball joint from rack. Repeat procedure for other inner ball joint.

3) Remove rack plunger lock nut, adjusting screw, spring and rack plunger. Remove pinion gear oil seal from steering gear housing. Remove pinion gear large snap ring from housing.

4) Remove pinion gear from steering gear housing. Pull rack out of steering gear housing, from pinion side. Remove pinion gear small snap ring (located on pinion gear).

5) Press bearing off pinion gear, then remove oil seal and large snap ring.

6) Remove clip from gearbox. Remove bushing "A" from the end of gearbox unit by using a aluminum drift.

INSPECTION

1) Check for bent rack. Place rack ends in "V" blocks and attach dial indicator so plunger rests on center of rack. Rotate rack and note deflection of gauge.

2) Maximum deflection should be less than .004" (.1 mm). Replace if not to specifications. Check all other steering gear components and replace if worn, scored or damaged.

Fig. 2: View Showing Method of Centering Rack in Gear Housing

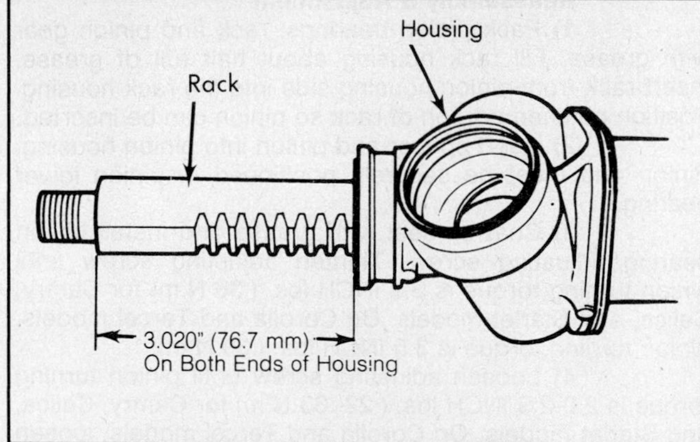
Housing
Rack
3.020" (76.7 mm)
On Both Ends of Housing

REASSEMBLY AND ADJUSTMENT

Steering Gear

1) Press bushing "A" into gearbox and install clip. Apply grease to bushing "A". If pinion gear was disassembled, slide large snap ring on pinion. Install new oil seal, then press on new bearing. Install small snap ring to pinion gear.

2) Grease toothed and sliding portions of rack and install rack into steering gear housing, from pinion side. Locate rack in housing so that 3.02" (76.7 mm) of rack protrudes from each end of housing.

Fig. 3: Cross Sectional View of Pinion Gear and Rack Showing Lubrication Points and Backlash Adjustment

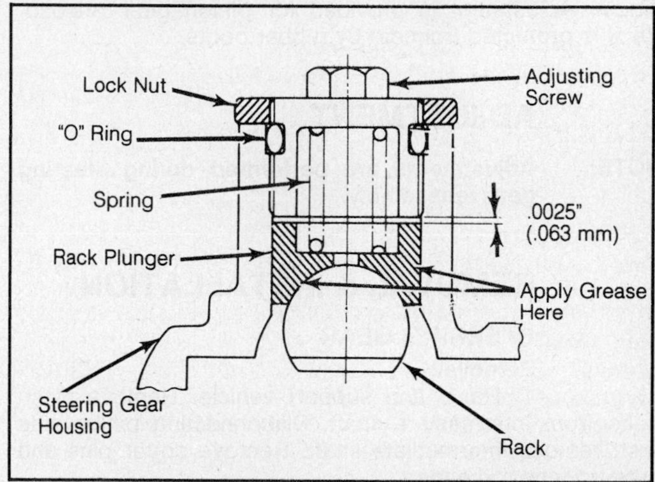
Lock Nut
Adjusting Screw
"O" Ring
Spring
.0025" (.063 mm)
Rack Plunger
Apply Grease Here
Steering Gear Housing
Rack

3) Grease pinion gear teeth and install into steering gear housing. Flange on pinion gear should be out of line of straight ahead position by 36° when meshed with rack teeth properly.

4) Install large snap ring, of pinion gear, to steering gear housing. Measure amount of pinion gear end play. End play should be less than .012" (.3 mm).

5) If end play is not to specifications, check for worn snap rings, bearing or steering gear housing. Replace components as necessary.

6) With pinion gear end play correct, press oil seal into steering gear housing. Grease rack plunger cavity. Install rack plunger, spring, adjusting screw and lock nut. Adjust rack plunger backlash.

7) Adjust backlash by turning adjusting screw in until torque increases sharply. Back adjusting screw off 1/24 turn (15°). Tighten lock nut to 29-43 ft. lbs. (39-58 N.m).

8) Install tie rod inner ball joint lock washer to rack. Grease inner ball joint and install to rack. Bend lock washer over flat area on inner ball joint.

9) Grease inside lip of rubber boot (large end) and install boot to steering gear housing. Install "O" ring to boot outer end.

10) Install ball joints and lock nuts to tie rods. Make sure ball joints are installed on correct end of steering gear. Left ball joint is marked "LH", right ball joint is marked "RH".

11) Make sure steering gear operates properly and smoothly. Check pinion rotating torque in straight ahead position. Rotating torque should be .8-1.1 ft. lbs. (.11-1.5 N.m).

TIGHTENING SPECIFICATIONS

Application	Ft. Lbs. (N.m)
Ball Joint Nut	18-25 (24-34)
Gear-to-Crossmember	33-40 (45-54)
Rack Plunger Lock Nut	29-43 (39-58)
Tie Rod-to-Ball Joint Lock Nut	58-65 (79-88)
Tie Rod Inner Ball Joint Lock Nut	58 (79)

TOYOTA RACK & PINION

Camry, Celica, Corolla, Starlet & Tercel

DESCRIPTION

Steering assembly is a direct-acting rack and pinion system. This unit consists of a rack bar and toothed pinion. Adjustment is provided for pinion gear preload. Rack is protected from dirt by rubber boots.

ADJUSTMENT

NOTE: **Adjustments are performed during steering gear reassembly.**

REMOVAL & INSTALLATION

STEERING GEAR

Removal

1) Raise and support vehicle. Remove pinch bolts from intermediate shaft. Disconnecting pinion side first, remove intermediate shaft. Remove cotter pins and nuts from tie rod ends.

2) Separate tie rod ends from steering knuckles. Remove rack housing brackets, taking care not to damage rack boots. Remove steering gear.

Installation

To install, reverse removal procedure. Check toe-in. *See WHEEL ALIGNMENT Section*.

OVERHAUL

STEERING GEAR

Disassembly

1) Place steering gear in a vise and mark rack end threaded areas for reassembly reference. Remove tie rods, spring clips, rack end dust seals, and rack boot clamps. Remove rack boots.

NOTE: **Left and right tie rod ends, rack boots and rack ends are different and should be marked accordingly.**

2) Unstake claw washers and remove rack ends. Remove rack guide screw lock nut, guide screw and spring. Remove rack guide by pulling out with needle-nose pliers.

3) Remove pinion bearing adjusting screw lock nut and pinion bearing adjusting screw.

4) Pull rack completely through pinion housing side and align notched portion of rack with pinion. Pull pinion and upper pinion bearing out of pinion housing. Remove rack from pinion housing side without rotating it.

Inspection

1) Check all parts for damage or deterioration. Check for play in rack ends and tie rod end ball joints. Check pinion teeth surfaces for wear or damage.

2) If pinion oil seal must be replaced, drive it in until it protrudes .020" (0.5 mm) from tip of pinion bearing adjusting screw.

3) If pinion upper bearing must be replaced, remove with a puller. Drive new bearing on.

Fig. 1: Exploded View of Toyota Rack and Pinion Steering Gear Assembly

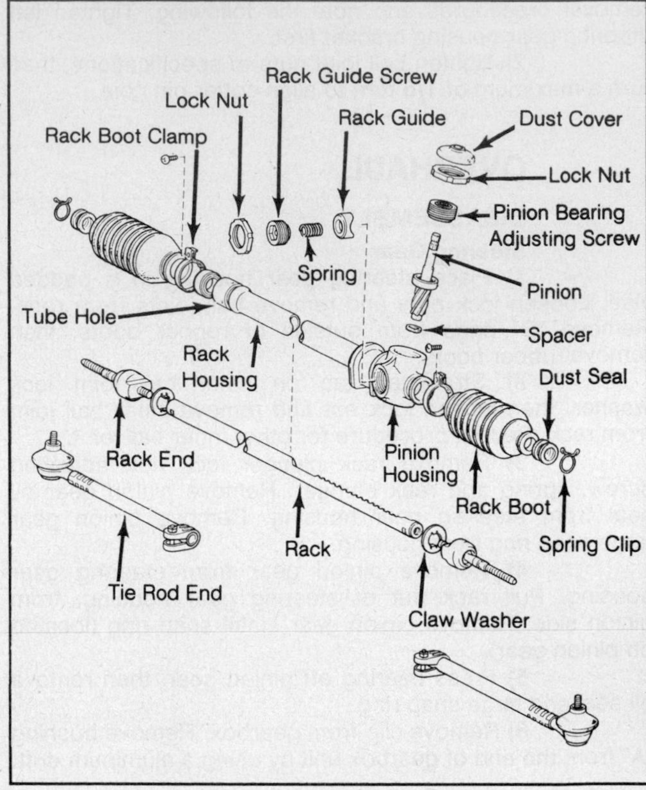
Rack Guide Screw
Lock Nut
Rack Guide
Dust Cover
Rack Boot Clamp
Lock Nut
Pinion Bearing Adjusting Screw
Spring
Pinion
Tube Hole
Spacer
Rack Housing
Dust Seal
Rack End
Pinion Housing
Rack Boot
Rack
Spring Clip
Tie Rod End
Claw Washer

NOTE: **Seal side of bearing faces down.**

4) If pinion lower bearing must be replaced, heat rack to at least 176°F (80°C). Tap bearing out with plastic hammer. Reheat pinion housing and drive in new bearing.

5) Check rack for runout and tooth wear. Runout must not exceed .012" (0.3 mm). If rack bushing must be replaced, remove with puller. Press in new bushing.

Reassembly & Adjustment

1) Pack pinion bearings, rack and pinion gear with grease. Fill rack housing about half full of grease. Insert rack from pinion housing side into the rack housing. Position notched portion of rack so pinion can be inserted.

2) Insert spacer and pinion into pinion housing. Pinion end must be securely positioned in pinion lower bearing.

3) Coat oil seal with grease and install pinion bearing adjusting screw. Tighten adjusting screw until pinion turning torque is 3.2 INCH lbs. (.36 N.m) for Camry, Celica, and Starlet models. On Corolla and Tercel models, pinion turning torque is 3.5 INCH lbs. (.39 N.m).

4) Loosen adjusting screw until pinion turning torque is 2.0-2.9 INCH lbs. (.22-.33 N.m) for Camry, Celica, and Starlet models. On Corolla and Tercel models, loosen adjusting screw until turning torque is 1.7-2.6 INCH lbs. (.19-.29 N.m).

5) On all models, apply liquid sealer to adjusting screw lock nut and housing contact points. Tighten lock nut to 73-94 ft. lbs. (99-127 N.m).

TOYOTA RACK & PINION (Cont.)

6) Recheck pinion turning torque. It should be 2.0-2.9 INCH lbs. (.22-.33 N.m) on Camry and Celica models. Starlet models should be 1.4-2.1 INCH lbs. (.16-.24 N.m). Corolla and Tercel models should be 1.3-2.2 INCH lbs. (.15-.25 N.m).

7) Mesh rack and pinion. Coat rack guide with grease. Install rack guide, spring and rack guide screw. Using torque wrench and guide screw wrench, tighten guide screw to 18 ft. lbs. (24 N.m).

8) Loosen screw about 90° from tightened position on Celica, Corolla, and Tercel models. Loosen screw 25-30° on Camry and Starlet models.

9) On all models, measure pinion turning torque and adjust by turning guide screw. Acceptable range is 8.7-11.3 INCH lbs. (.98-1.27 N.m) for Camry, Celica, Corolla, and Tercel models. On Starlet models, 6.1-7.8 INCH lbs. (.69-.88 N.m).

10) Apply liquid sealer to lock nut and housing contact points, and using torque wrench and lock nut wrench, tighten lock nut to 44-57 ft. lbs. (59-77 N.m). Recheck total preload with a full stroke of the rack.

11) Apply grease to rack end ball joints. Align claw washer with rack groove and tighten rack end into housing. Stake claw washer.

12) Coat rack end dust seal with grease. Clear rack housing tube hole of any grease. Install rack boots. Spring clips must have bends facing outward.

13) Rack boot clamp on pinion housing side should have a gap of .19-.24" (5-6 mm) but tube side clamp should have no gap.

14) Rotate pinion and check rack stroke. Rack stroke should be 4.80" (122.0 mm). There should be no contour change of rack boots during this operation. Install tie rod ends in original position.

TIGHTENING SPECIFICATIONS

Application	Ft. Lbs. (N.m)
Intermediate Shaft Pinch Bolts	22-28 (30-38)
Pinion Bearing Adjusting	
Screw Lock Nut	73-94 (99-127)
Rack Guide Screw Lock Nut	44-57 (59-77)
Rack End-to-Rack	
Celica	66-86 (89-117)
All Others	51-72 (69-98)
Rack Housing Bracket-to-Body	22-32 (30-44)
Tie Rod-to-Knuckle	37-50 (50-68)
Tie Rod-to-Rack End	11-14 (15-19)

TOYOTA LAND CRUISER RECIRCULATING BALL

DESCRIPTION

STEERING GEAR

Steering gear mechanism is of the recirculating ball type. Gear mounts off a bracket that is attached to frame.

Adjustment screws are provided for backlash and preload. Initial preload is achieved with shims.

STEERING LINKAGE

Steering linkage consists of a Pitman arm, relay rod, tie rod, damper, center arm and drag link.

Tie rod and relay rod are adjustable to correct wheel alignment.

ADJUSTMENT

NOTE: Adjustments are performed during reassembly after overhaul. For adjustments, refer to Overhaul in this article.

REMOVAL & INSTALLATION

STEERING GEAR

Removal

1) Scribe mating marks on all steering shaft couplings to aid in reassembly.

2) Remove dust cover, joint cover, relay rod end and pitman arm. Remove intermediate shaft coupling clamp bolt and shaft.

3) Remove steering gear mounting bolts. Remove gear from frame.

Installation

To install, reverse removal procedure and tighten all mounting bolts.

Fig. 1: Toyota Land Cruiser Steering Gear

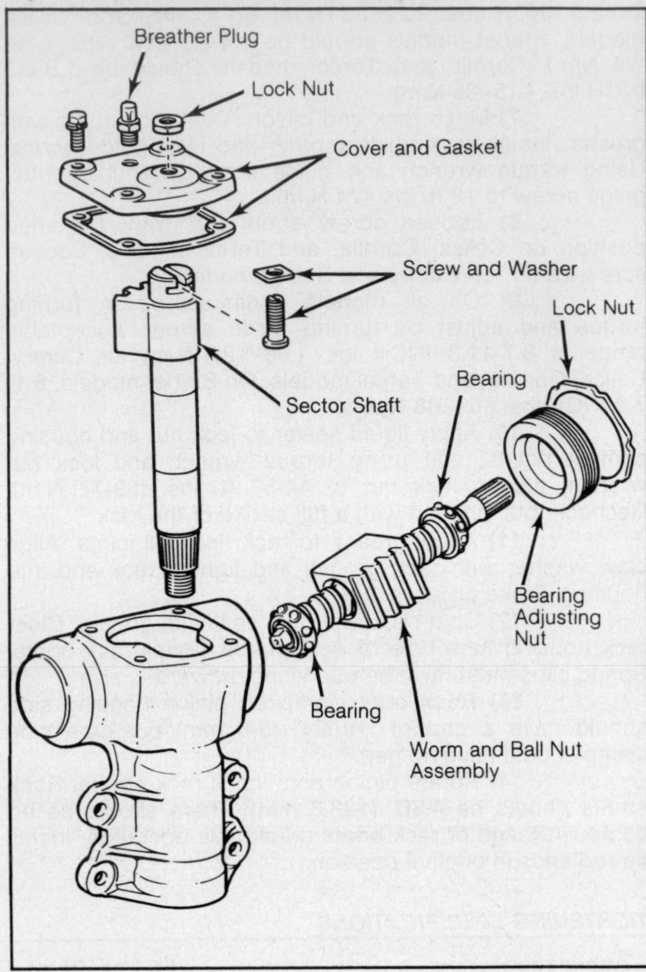
Breather Plug
Lock Nut
Cover and Gasket
Screw and Washer
Lock Nut
Bearing
Sector Shaft
Bearing Adjusting Nut
Bearing
Worm and Ball Nut Assembly

Fig. 2: Toyota Land Cruiser Front Steering Linkage

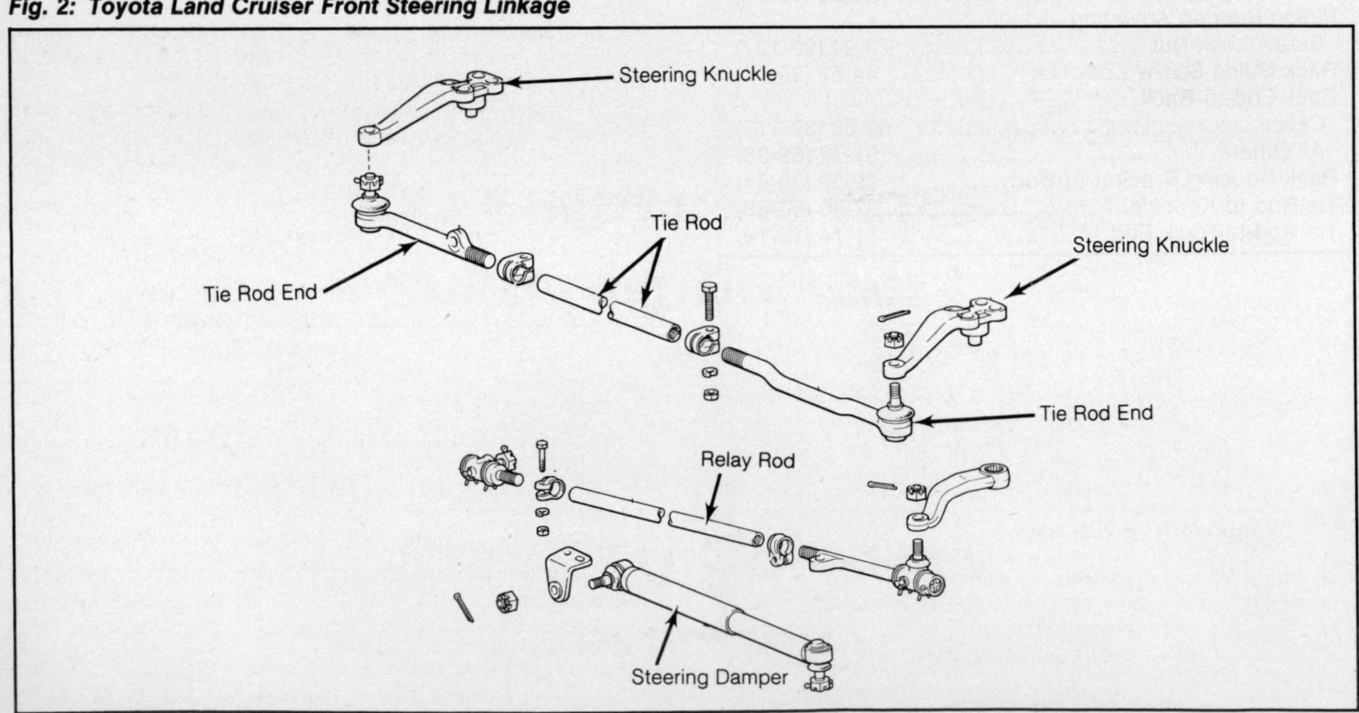
Steering Knuckle
Tie Rod
Tie Rod End
Steering Knuckle
Tie Rod End
Relay Rod
Steering Damper

TOYOTA LAND CRUISER RECIRCULATING BALL (Cont.)

STEERING LINKAGE

Removal

1) Raise and support front of vehicle, then remove front wheels. Index mark relative position of pitman arm to sector shaft and remove arm, using puller. Disconnect steering drag link from steering center arm.

2) Disconnect tie rod ends from both sides. Disconnect relay rod from steering center arm, then remove tie rod assembly with relay arm assembly.

3) Disconnect end of steering damper from bracket on crossmember. Loosen and remove center arm from bracket (with steering damper). Remove steering center arm bracket from frame.

Installation

To install, reverse removal procedure and note the following: Adjust tie rod, relay rod and drag link as shown in *Fig. 3*.

Fig. 3: Adjustment Lengths for Installation of Tie Rod, Relay Rod and Drag Link

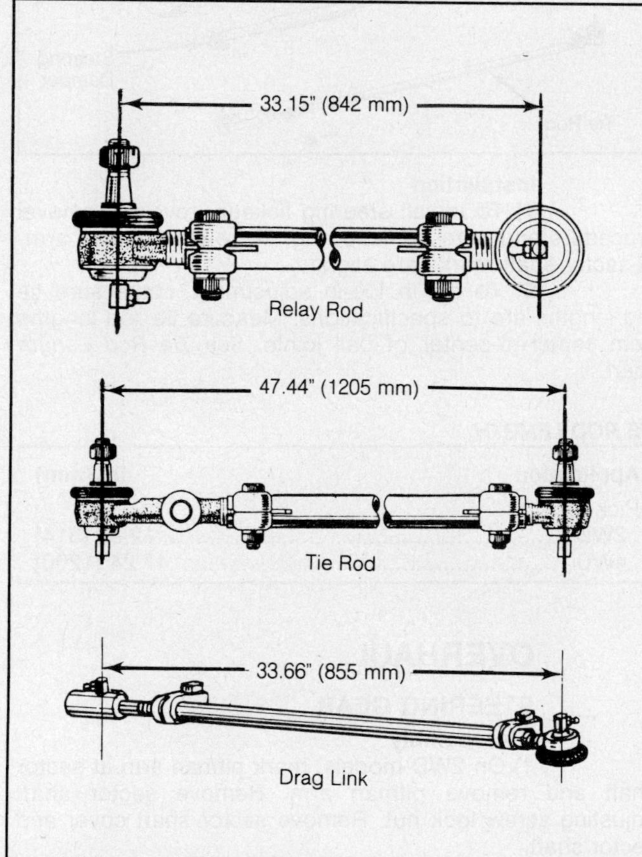

33.15" (842 mm)
Relay Rod
47.44" (1205 mm)
Tie Rod
33.66" (855 mm)
Drag Link

OVERHAUL

Disassembly

1) Screw in sector shaft adjusting screw to remove the end cover and gasket. Drain gear lubricant, then secure housing in a vise. With sector shaft positioned at rotational center, remove the sector shaft by tapping the bottom end with a plastic hammer.

2) Loosen the lock nut and remove the worm bearing adjusting nut. Take out worm assembly, keeping bearings in sequence. Do not attempt to disassemble worm assembly.

Inspection

1) Wash all disassembled parts and inspect for wear or damage; replace as necessary. If inner or outer races are scored or pitted, replace as required.

2) Inspect sector shaft and bushings for wear. If replacement is necessary, use a press to remove and replace bushings.

3) Hone bushings until clearance between bushing and sector shaft is .0004-.0024" (.009-.060 mm). Install new oil seal.

4) Measure sector shaft thrust clearance, then select thrust washer that provides a minimum clearance between sector shaft and adjustment screw of .0020" (.051 mm).

Reassembly

1) Install cover with same number of shims that were removed, then tighten bolts.

NOTE: **When tightening cover bolts, keep checking worm to ensure that it will turn freely.**

2) Using a pull scale, measure initial (starting) worm bearing preload for 3.0-5.6 INCH lbs. (.33-.62 N.m). If preload is not within specifications, correct by selecting proper thickness shim(s).

3) Position worm ball nut at center, then insert sector shaft ensuring ball nut and sector mesh together at center. Loosen ball adjusting bolt all the way and install cover.

4) Set worm shaft preload to 6.9-9.5 INCH lbs. (.76-1.0 N.m) with adjusting bolt. Make sure measurement is made with meshing positioned at center.

5) Install pitman arm and check backlash. There should be zero backlash when worm is rotated within 45° to either side. Tighten adjustment screw lock nut and recheck preload.

TIGHTENING SPECIFICATIONS

Application	Ft. Lbs. (N.m)
Gear Box Bracket	29-40 (39-54)
Pitman Arm Nut	119-141 (162-192)
Sector End Cover Bolts	22-32 (30-44)
Worm Bearing Cap	22-32 (30-44)

Steering Gears & Linkage

TOYOTA PICKUP RECIRCULATING BALL

DESCRIPTION

STEERING GEAR

Steering gear is a variable ratio, recirculating ball type. Ball bearings circulate within grooves in worm and nut. As worm shaft turns, ball nut moves up or down, turning the sector shaft and pitman arm.

STEERING LINKAGE

Linkage consists of an idler arm, center relay rod, adjustable tie rods, and steering knuckles. Pickups also use a steering damper attached to center relay rod.

The connection between each component is by ball joints. Linkage assembly is connected to steering gear by a pitman arm.

Fig. 1: Exploded View of Steering Linkage

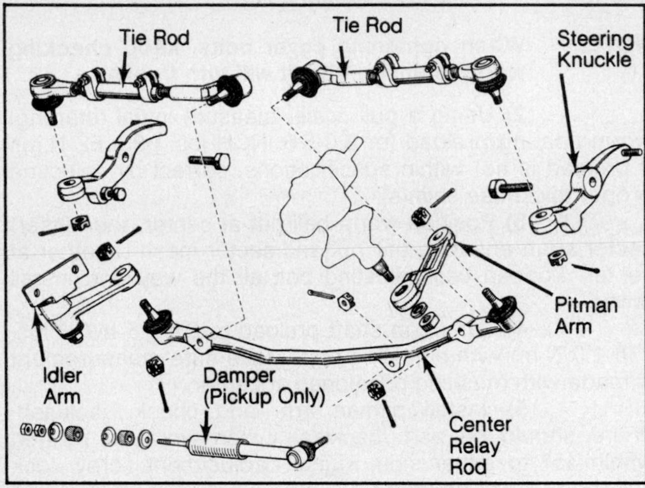
Tie Rod
Tie Rod
Steering
Knuckle
Pitman
Arm
Idler
Arm
Damper
(Pickup Only)
Center
Relay
Rod

Illustration does not apply to 4WD models.

ADJUSTMENT

See Overhaul in this article.

REMOVAL & INSTALLATION

STEERING GEAR

Removal

1) Mark steering gear shaft at flexible coupling or universal joint and remove coupling. Mark steering gear shaft at pitman arm. Disconnect pitman arm from steering gear.

2) Remove steering gear bolts from frame and disconnect steering gear from steering shaft as gear is removed.

Installation

To install steering gear, reverse removal procedures. Make sure marks made upon removal are aligned upon installation.

STEERING LINKAGE

Removal

1) On 2WD Pickup, mark pitman arm at sector shaft. Use a puller to disconnect pitman arm from sector shaft and tie rod ball joints from steering knuckles. Disconnect steering damper from crossmember. Remove idler arm bracket bolts. Remove steering linkage assembly from vehicle.

2) On 4WD Pickup, mark pitman arm at sector shaft and disconnect pitman arm. Disconnect steering damper from front axle. Remove steering knuckle-to-front axle bolts and remove steering linkage assembly from vehicle.

Fig. 2: Exploded View of 4WD Steering Linkage

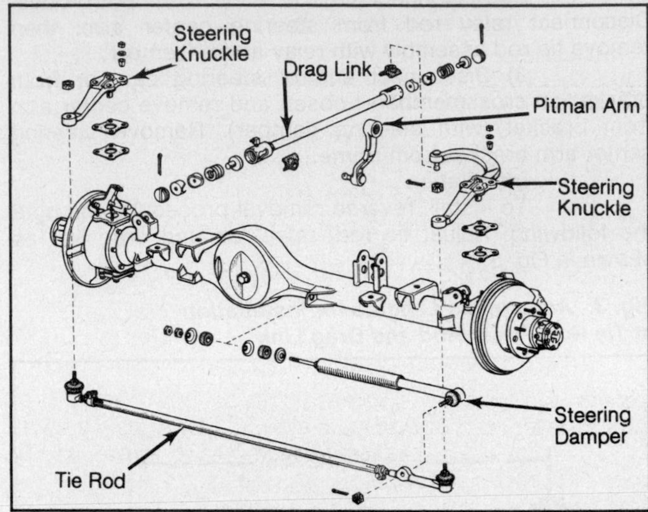
Steering
Knuckle
Drag Link
Pitman Arm
Steering
Knuckle
Steering
Damper
Tie Rod

Installation

1) To install steering linkage, reverse removal procedure and note the following. Make sure pitman arm-to-sector shaft marks are aligned.

2) To aid in toe-in adjustment, make sure tie rod lengths are to specifications. Measure tie rod lengths from center-to-center of ball joints. *See Tie Rod Length* chart.

TIE ROD LENGTH

Application	In. (mm)
Pickup	
2WD	12.36 (314)
4WD	47.24 (1200)

OVERHAUL

STEERING GEAR

Disassembly

1) On 2WD models, mark pitman arm at sector shaft and remove pitman arm. Remove sector shaft adjusting screw lock nut. Remove sector shaft cover and sector shaft.

2) Be careful not to lose adjusting screw and shim. Remove worm assembly lock nut, adjusting screw and oil seal. Remove worm assembly and bearings. *See Fig. 3.*

NOTE: **Do not disassemble ball nut from worm. If recirculating ball assembly has damaged or worn components, replace entire assembly.**

3) On 4WD models, mark pitman arm at sector shaft and remove pitman arm. Remove sector shaft adjusting screw lock nut. Remove sector shaft cover and sector shaft. Remove worm assembly cover and shims. Remove worm assembly with bearings. *See Fig. 4.*

TOYOTA PICKUP RECIRCULATING BALL (Cont.)

Fig. 3: Exploded View of 2WD Steering Gear Assembly

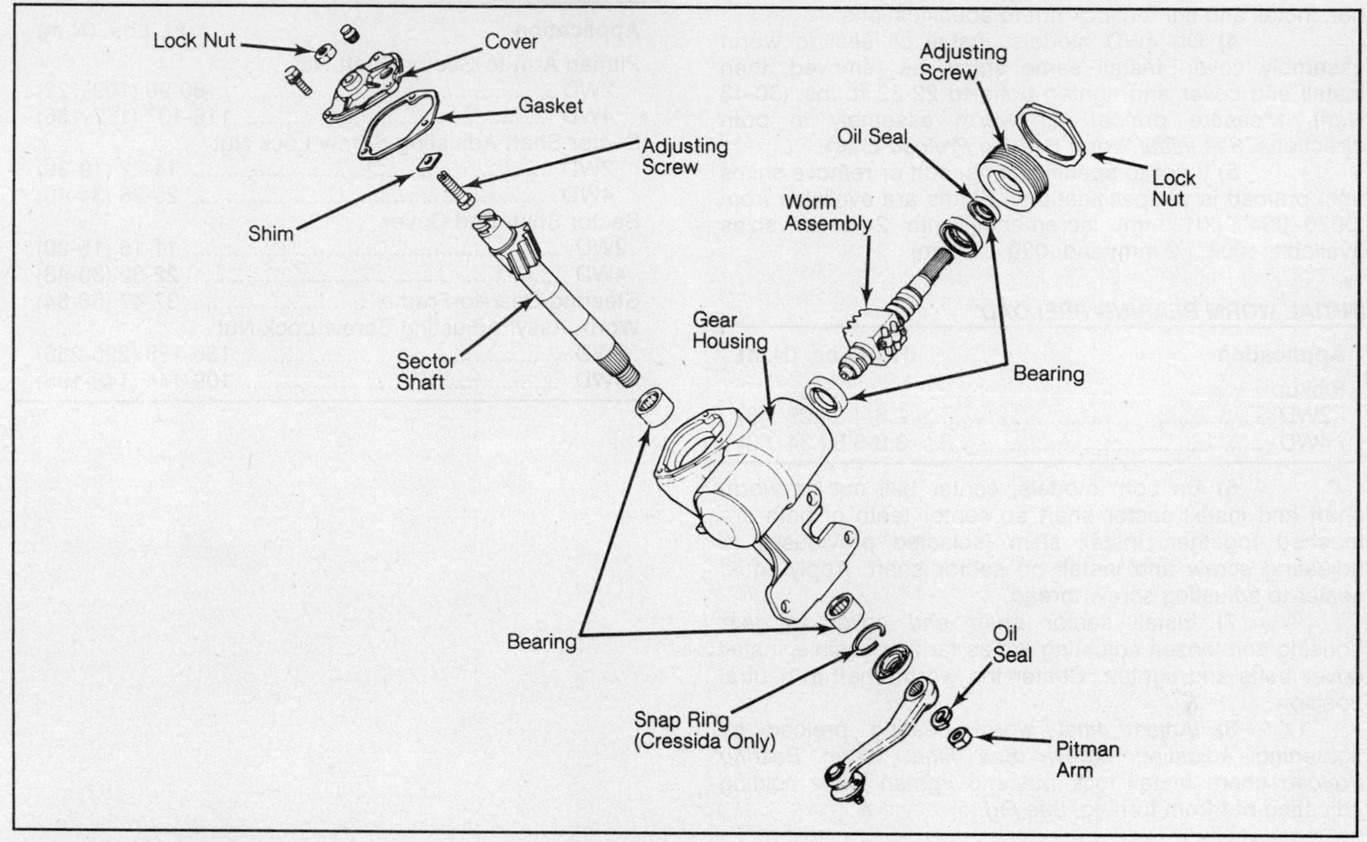
Lock Nut
Cover
Gasket
Adjusting Screw
Shim
Sector Shaft
Adjusting Screw
Oil Seal
Lock Nut
Worm Assembly
Gear Housing
Bearing
Bearing
Oil Seal
Snap Ring (Cressida Only)
Pitman Arm

Inspection

1) Check all components for excessive wear or damage. Measure clearance between adjusting screw (with shim installed) and sector shaft. Maximum clearance should be .002" (.05 mm).

2) If clearance is not to specifications, shims are available from .0787" (2.00 mm) to .0866" (2.20 mm) in .0016" (.04 mm) increments.

Fig. 4: Exploded View of 4WD Steering Gear Assembly

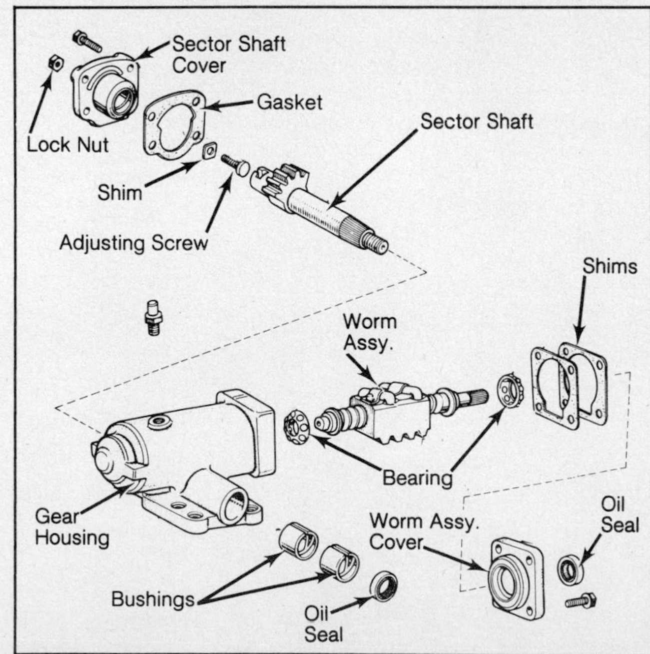
Sector Shaft Cover
Gasket
Lock Nut
Sector Shaft
Shim
Adjusting Screw
Shims
Worm Assy.
Bearing
Gear Housing
Worm Assy. Cover
Oil Seal
Bushings
Oil Seal

3) Check worm bearings and races for pitting and smooth operation. Replace if necessary. Replace oil seal. On 2WD models, replace end cover bushing and needle bearings if necessary.

4) On 4WD models, measure sector shaft diameter. Minimum diameter is 1.258" (31.95 mm). Measure sector shaft bushings (in gear housing) for clearance between sector shaft and bushings. Maximum clearance is .004" (.1 mm).

5) If clearance exceeds specifications and sector shaft is not worn, replace bushings in gear housing and hone to obtain standard clearance of .0004-.0024" (.01-.06 mm).

6) On 4WD models, inspect end cover bushing for wear or damage. Standard oil clearance should be .0004-.0024 (.009-.060 mm). If not, replace bushing.

CAUTION: When checking worm gear and ball nut, do not let ball nut bottom out on either end of worm gear. If ball nut bottoms out, damage to worm assembly will occur.

7) On both models, hold worm assembly up at an angle so ball nut will travel down worm gear (full travel) and check for smooth operation. Replace worm assembly if any damage is found or operation is not smooth.

Reassembly & Adjustment

1) Grease all bearings and sliding portions of gear assembly. Install bearings on worm assembly. Install worm assembly to gear housing.

2) On 2WD models, install oil seal and adjusting nut. Tighten nut while rotating worm gear to seat bearings. Loosen adjusting nut, then tighten while measuring preload. *See Initial Worm Bearing Preload* chart.

Steering Gears & Linkage

TOYOTA PICKUP RECIRCULATING BALL (Cont.)

3) With preload to specification, hold adjusting nut, install and tighten lock nut to specifications.

4) On 4WD models, install oil seal to worm assembly cover. Install same shims as removed, then install end cover and tighten bolts to 22-32 ft. lbs. (30-43 N.m). Measure preload of worm assembly in both directions. *See Initial Worm Bearing Preload* chart.

5) If not to specifications, add or remove shims until preload is to specifications. Shims are available from .0020-.004" (.01 mm) increments, with 2 larger sizes available; .008" (.2 mm) and .020" (.5 mm).

INITIAL WORM BEARING PRELOAD

Application	INCH Lbs. (N.m)
Pickup	
2WD	2.6-4.3 (.29-.48)
4WD	3.0-5.6 (.34-.63)

6) On both models, center ball nut on worm shaft and install sector shaft so center teeth of both are meshed together. Install shim (selected previously) to adjusting screw and install on sector shaft. Apply liquid sealer to adjusting screw thread.

7) Install sector shaft end cover to gear housing and loosen adjusting nut as far as possible. Install cover bolts and tighten. Center the worm shaft in neutral position.

8) Adjust final worm bearing preload by tightening adjusting screw. *See Final Worm Bearing Preload* chart. Install lock nut and tighten while holding adjusting nut from turning. *See Fig. 5.*

FINAL WORM BEARING PRELOAD

Application	INCH Lbs. (N.m)
Pickup	
2WD	6.9-9.1 (.78-1.03)
4WD	6.9-9.5 (.78-1.07)

9) Install pitman arm and nut (aligning mating marks). Attach dial indicator so plunger touches end of pitman arm. Sector shaft should have no backlash when measured at any point 100° on either side of centered position.

Fig. 5: Measuring Final Worm Bearing Preload

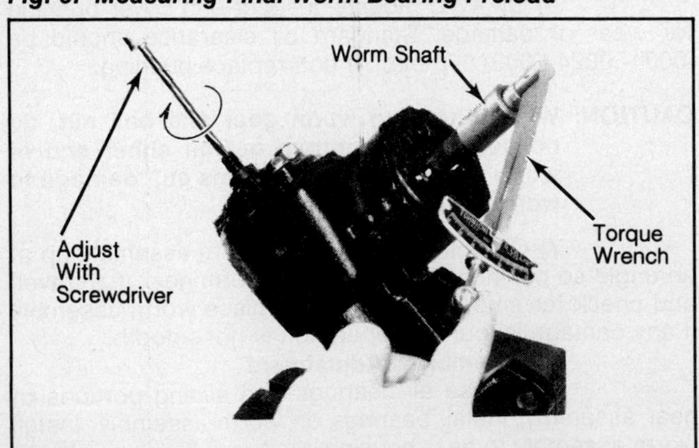
Worm Shaft
Adjust
With
Screwdriver
Torque
Wrench

TIGHTENING SPECIFICATIONS

Application	Ft. Lbs. (N.m)
Pitman Arm-to-Sector Shaft Nut	
2WD	80-90 (109-122)
4WD	116-137 (157-186)
Sector Shaft Adjusting Screw Lock Nut	
2WD	14-22 (19-30)
4WD	25-36 (34-49)
Sector Shaft End Cover	
2WD	11-15 (15-20)
4WD	22-32 (30-43)
Steering Gear-to-Frame	37-47 (50-64)
Worm Assy. Adjusting Screw Lock Nut	
2WD	166-188 (226-256)
4WD	109-144 (148-195)

Steering Gears & Linkage

VOLKSWAGEN JETTA, RABBIT, PICKUP & SCIROCCO RACK & PINION

DESCRIPTION

Steering gear is a rack and pinion type. Tie rods attach to ends of rack. Racks are mounted with "U" bolts and rubber bushings.

REMOVAL & INSTALLATION

STEERING GEAR

Removal

1) Disconnect shift linkage bearing plate from rack housing. Loosen pinch bolts on steering shaft. Remove shaft from pinion.

2) Disconnect tie rod ends from steering linkage, using puller. Remove mounting bolts and remove rack with tie rods attached.

Installation

1) To install, reverse removal procedures. Correctly align and insert pinion shaft with steering shaft lower universal joint before securing steering gear housing clamp bolts.

2) Connect tie rod outer ends to steering linkage. Tighten upper and lower universal joint pinch bolts. Connect and adjust shift linkage bearing plate to gear housing.

ADJUSTMENT

RACK & TIE RODS

1) Center rack in housing so rack protrudes an equal amount from each end of housing. *See Fig. 1.*

Fig. 1: Centering Rack in Steering Gear Housing

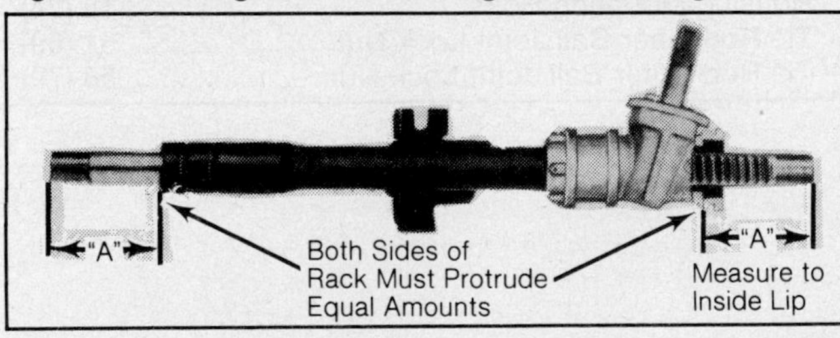
"A"
Both Sides of
Rack Must Protrude
Equal Amounts
"A"
Measure to
Inside Lip

2) If replacing the non-adjustable left tie rod with adjustable type, adjust tie rod length "D" to 14.92" (379 mm).

3) Screw tie rods onto rack and adjust to specified dimensions without moving rack from center position. When adjustment is correct, secure tie rods with jam nuts and install rubber boots. *See Fig. 2.*

TIE ROD SPECIFICATIONS

Application	Dimension "B"	Dimension "C"
Man. Trans	2.72" (69 mm)	2.72" (69 mm)
Auto. Trans.	2.64" (67 mm)	2.72" (69 mm)

Fig. 2: Installation Adjustment of Tie Rods on Rack

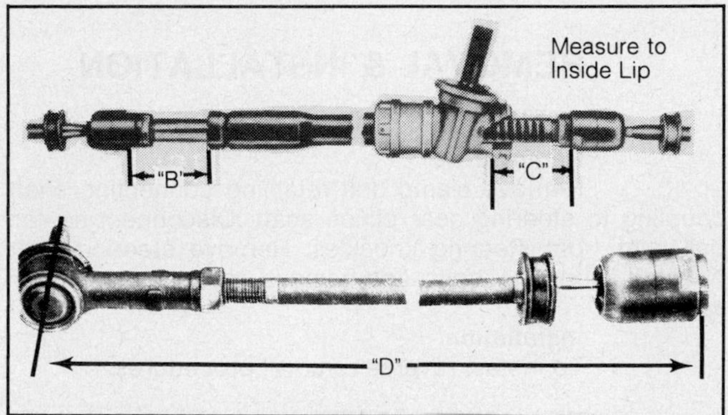
Measure to
Inside Lip
"B"
"C"
"D"

STEERING DRIVE

Loosen pinion shaft adjusting screw lock nut. Turn adjusting bolt until it just contacts thrust washer. Tighten lock nut.

TIGHTENING SPECIFICATIONS

Application	Ft. Lbs. (N.m)
Gear Box Rubber Mounting Bolts	22 (30)
Tie Rod End Jam Nut	29 (39)
Tie Rod End-to-Steering Arm	22 (30)
Universal Joint Pinch Bolt	22 (30)

Fig. 3: Disassembled View of Rack & Pinion Steering Gear Assembly

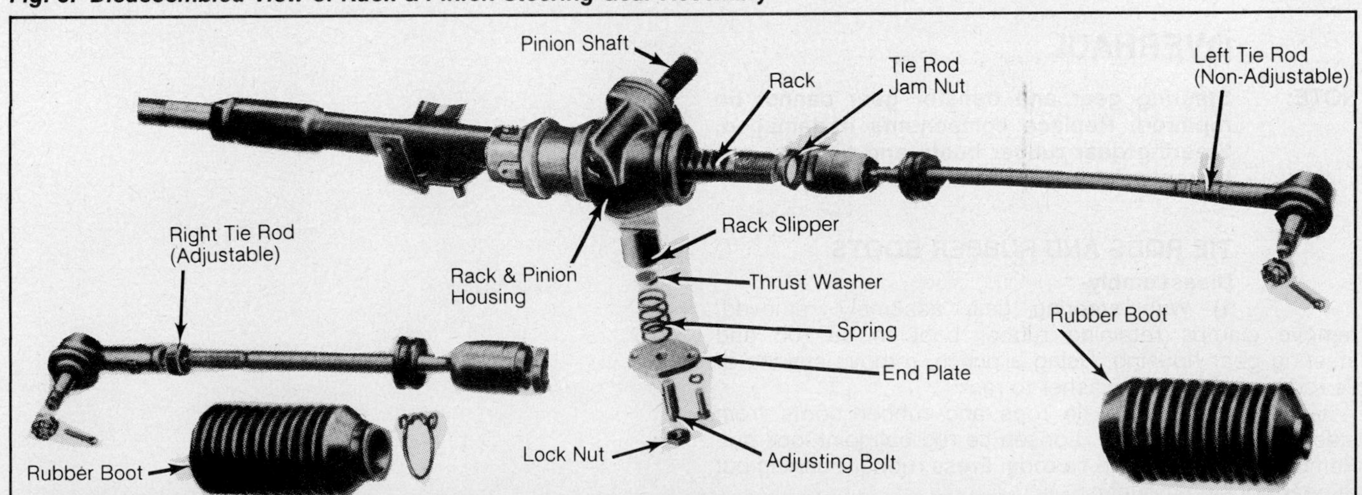
Pinion Shaft
Rack
Tie Rod
Jam Nut
Left Tie Rod
(Non-Adjustable)
Right Tie Rod
(Adjustable)
Rack Slipper
Rack & Pinion
Housing
Thrust Washer
Spring
End Plate
Rubber Boot
Lock Nut
Adjusting Bolt
Rubber Boot

VOLKSWAGEN VANAGON RACK & PINION

DESCRIPTION

Volkswagen Vanagon models use a rack and pinion steering gear. A transfer gear is used to connect steering shaft to steering gear.

Tie rods are connected to rack and directly to steering knuckle, with ball joints. Both tie rods are adjustable for toe-in.

ADJUSTMENT

STEERING GEAR

NOTE: Steering gear is not adjustable on these models. If gear is damaged or does not operate properly, complete unit must be replaced.

REMOVAL & INSTALLATION

STEERING GEAR

Removal

Remove clamp bolt retaining connecting shaft coupling to steering gear pinion shaft. Disconnect tie rod ball joint from steering knuckles. Remove steering gear housing mounting bolts and remove steering gear from vehicle.

Installation

To install, reverse removal procedures.

TRANSFER GEAR

Removal

Remove clamp bolt retaining connecting shaft coupling to transfer gear shaft. Remove clamp bolt retaining lower steering shaft flange to transfer gear shaft. Remove transfer gear retaining bolts. Remove transfer gear.

Installation

To install, reverse removal procedures.

NOTE: During installation of steering gear and/or transfer gear, always replace rubber couplings in connecting shaft and steering shaft lower flange.

OVERHAUL

NOTE: Steering gear and transfer gear cannot be repaired. Replace components if damaged. Steering gear rubber boots and tie rods can be replaced.

TIE RODS AND RUBBER BOOTS

Disassembly

1) With steering gear assembly removed, remove clamps retaining rubber boot to tie rod and steering gear housing. Using a punch, remove staking of tie rod inner ball joint washer to rack.

2) Remove tie rods and rubber boots from steering gear assembly. Loosen tie rod ball joint lock nut. Remove ball joints from tie rods. Press rubber bushing out of gear housing mounting.

Fig. 1: Exploded View of Steering Gear and Transfer Gear

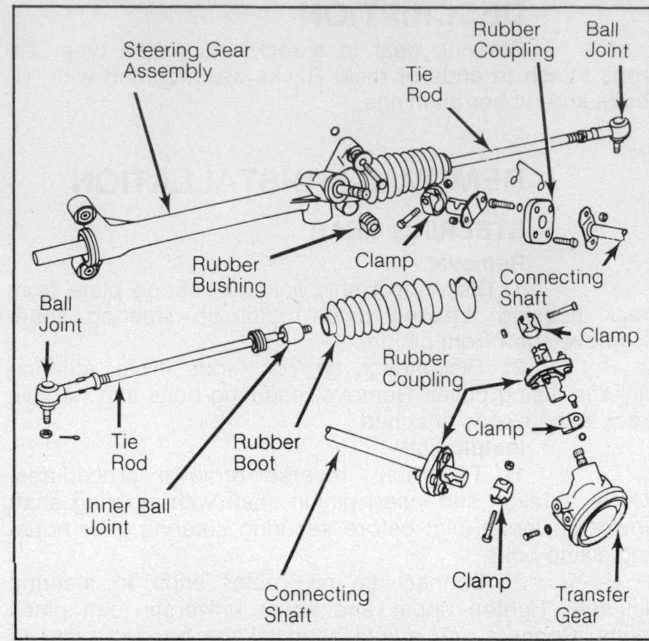
Steering Gear Assembly
Rubber Coupling
Ball Joint
Tie Rod
Rubber Bushing
Clamp
Connecting Shaft
Ball Joint
Clamp
Rubber Coupling
Clamp
Tie Rod
Rubber Boot
Inner Ball Joint
Connecting Shaft
Clamp
Transfer Gear

Reassembly

To reassemble tie rods and rubber boots, reverse disassembly procedures. After tightening tie rod inner ball joints, stake washer to groove in rack.

TIGHTENING SPECIFICATIONS

Application	Ft. Lbs. (N.m)
Clamp Bolts	14 (19)
Housing Mounting Bolts	18 (24)
Tie Rod Inner Ball Joint Lock Nut	51 (69)
Tie Rod Outer Ball Joint Lock Nut	58 (79)

AUDI POWER-ASSISTED RACK & PINION

Coupe & 4000

DESCRIPTION

Power-assisted rack and pinion steering system consists of a vane pump, rotary piston pinion gear assembly and an oil reservoir.

The vane pump draws fluid from the reservoir and supplies it to the flow control valve. The control valve supplies fluid to the proper side of the rack piston when the steering wheel is turned.

The belt-driven pump mounts on the front of the engine. The reservoir is near the firewall.

LUBRICATION

CAPACITY

1 qt. (.95L)

FLUID TYPE

ATF Dexron

FLUID LEVEL CHECK

Remove reservoir cover, start engine and check fluid level. Fluid level should be at mark on upper inside of reservoir.

HYDRAULIC SYSTEM BLEEDING

1) With engine at idle, check that fluid is at proper level. Turn steering wheel lock-to-lock several times quickly. Do not force wheel against locks.

2) Continue until fluid level remains at reservoir mark. Make sure no bubbles appear in reservoir when steering wheel is turned. Shut off engine and check that oil level does not rise more than 3/8" (9.5 mm) above mark.

OIL FILTER REPLACEMENT

Remove outer cover, gasket and spring from reservoir. Remove inner filter cover and filter insert. Install new filter insert. Replace old filter cover, spring, gasket, and top cover. Check fluid level.

NOTE: Oil filter insert must be replaced whenever repairs are made to power steering system.

Fig. 1: Exploded View of Power Steering Gear

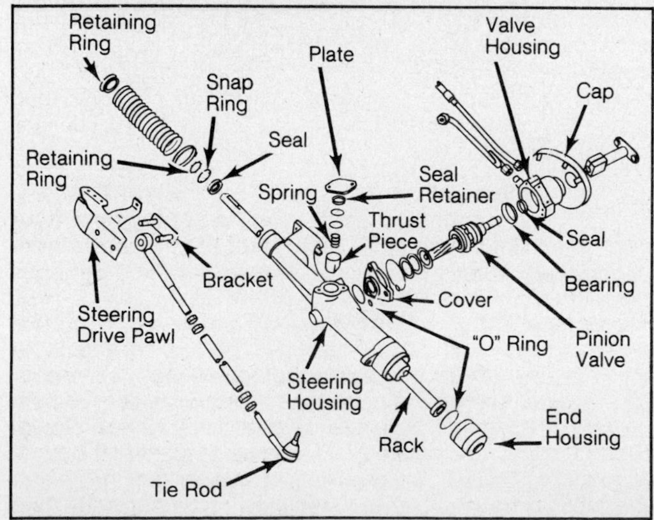
Retaining Ring
Plate
Valve Housing
Snap Ring
Cap
Seal
Retaining Ring
Seal Retainer
Spring
Thrust Piece
Seal
Bracket
Bearing
Cover
Steering Drive Pawl
"O" Ring
Pinion Valve
Steering Housing
End Housing
Rack
Tie Rod

ADJUSTMENT

PUMP BELT

Loosen bolts holding pump to brackets. Turn adjusting nut on bracket until belt deflection is 3/8" (9.5 mm) at center of belt. Tighten nuts to specifications.

TESTING

SYSTEM PRESSURE TEST

1) Connect pressure gauge (US1074/2) between pressure hose and pressure pipe of valve housing, with pressure gauge valve open. Run engine at idle.

2) Turn steering wheel lock-to-lock several times. Check pressure. Pressure should be 986-1189 psi (69-84 kg/cm²). If pressure is not within limits, replace steering gear.

PUMP PRESSURE TEST

1) With pressure gauge installed, start engine and let it idle. Close gauge valve (for no longer than 5 seconds) and check pressure. Pressure should be 986-1189 psi (69-84 kg/cm²).

2) If pressure differs, check limiting valve by inspecting bores in valve and piston for obstructions. Check that piston moves freely in housing. Install new valve if needed.

LEAKAGE TEST

1) With engine idling, turn steering wheel to full lock and hold. Inspect all connections and tighten if needed. If leak shows at steering pinion, replace housing seal and both intermediate cover seals.

2) If pinion shaft seal is leaking, fluid will have entered gear housing. Check for fluid by loosening outer clamp on right steering boot and pushing in boot. If seal is leaking, disassemble steering gear and replace all seals.

REMOVAL & INSTALLATION

STEERING GEAR

Removal

1) Drain fluid from system. Disconnect pressure and return pipes from valve housing. Disconnect lower steering shaft from pinion shaft. Move cap out of the way.

2) Remove steering drive pawl and tie rod bracket nuts. Disconnect tie rods from bracket. Remove bolts attaching gear housing to body. Remove gear housing.

Installation

To install, reverse removal procedure. Install one tie rod to steering gear and start bolts before installing other tie rod.

VANE PUMP

Removal

Remove vane pump belt. Disconnect pressure and suction lines from pump and cover openings. Remove retaining bolts from bracket and lift pump from engine.

Installation

To install, reverse removal procedure. Adjust belt deflection to 3/8" (9.5 mm) at center. After installing

Power Steering

AUDI POWER-ASSISTED RACK & PINION (Cont.)

Fig. 2: View of Vane Pump Assembly

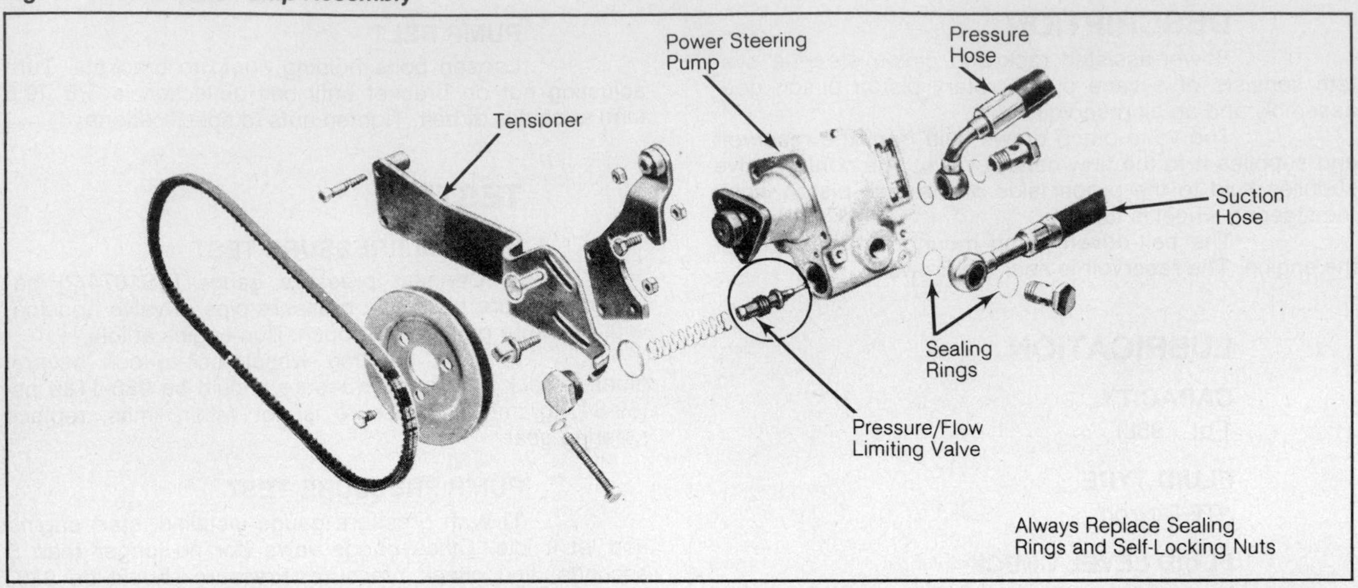
Power Steering
Pump
Pressure
Hose
Tensioner
Suction
Hose
Sealing
Rings
Pressure/Flow
Limiting Valve
Always Replace Sealing
Rings and Self-Locking Nuts

Only pressure/flow limiting valve can be replaced.

pressure and suction lines, start engine, turn steering wheel to full lock and check for connection leaks.

OVERHAUL

Before disassembling steering gear, check output and system pressure. Use all parts in repair kit (811 498 020) and always use new self-locking nuts.

VALVE HOUSING SEAL

Disassembly

1) Remove attaching bolts from valve housing and remove housing. Remove pinion gear and intermediate cover.

2) Remove "O" rings from intermediate cover (1 on each side). Clamp housing in padded vise and drive out oil seal from the back.

3) Install new "O" rings on the intermediate cover. Install new seals in valve. Make sure that housing seal lip faces intermediate cover. Replace both intermediate cover "O" rings.

Reassembly

To install, reverse removal procedure. Protect pinion teeth on shaft when replacing intermediate cover. Do not damage "O" rings during installation.

STEERING GEAR

Disassembly

1) With steering gear assembly removed from vehicle, remove pinion valve housing. Remove pinion valve assembly. Remove plate, seal retainer, spring, and thrust piece from steering housing.

2) Remove retaining ring, clamp and boot from steering housing. Remove retaining ring and snap ring from steering housing.

3) Remove end housing and "O" ring from steering housing. Pull rack out of steering housing. Using oil seal puller, remove oil seal from steering housing.

Reassembly

1) To install new oil seal to steering housing, place oil seal on flat surface and push sleeve (available in repair kit 811 498 020) into oil seal. Slide rack into steering housing.

2) Slide oil seal with sleeve over rack and into steering housing using seal installers (VW 426 and VW 416b). Remove sleeve. Install snap ring and retaining ring.

3) Install end housing with new "O" ring. Install thrust piece, spring, "O" ring, seal retainer, and plate. Install clamp, boot, and retaining ring. Install pinion valve assembly as previously outlined.

TIGHTENING SPECIFICATIONS

Application	Ft. Lbs. (N.m)
End Housing	37 (50)
Pressure Pipe	29 (39)
Return Pipe	
On Pump	29 (39)
On Valve Housing	22 (30)
Valve Housing Bolts	15 (20)

AUDI 5000 POWER-ASSISTED RACK & PINION

DESCRIPTION

A power-assisted rack and pinion steering gear is used. The system consists of a vane pump, rotary piston pinion gear assembly and an oil reservoir.

The vane pump draws fluid from the reservoir and supplies it to the flow control valve. The control valve supplies fluid to the proper side of the rack piston as the steering wheel is turned.

The belt-driven pump mounts at the front of the engine. The reservoir is near the firewall.

LUBRICATION

CAPACITY

1 qt. (.95L)

FLUID TYPE

ATF Dexron

FLUID LEVEL CHECK

Remove reservoir cover, start engine and check fluid level. Fluid level should be at mark on upper inside of reservoir.

HYDRAULIC SYSTEM BLEEDING

1) Start engine and let it idle. Check that fluid is at proper level. Turn steering wheel lock-to-lock several times quickly. Do not force wheel against lock. Continue until fluid level remains at reservoir mark.

Fig. 1: Exploded View of Steering Gear Assembly

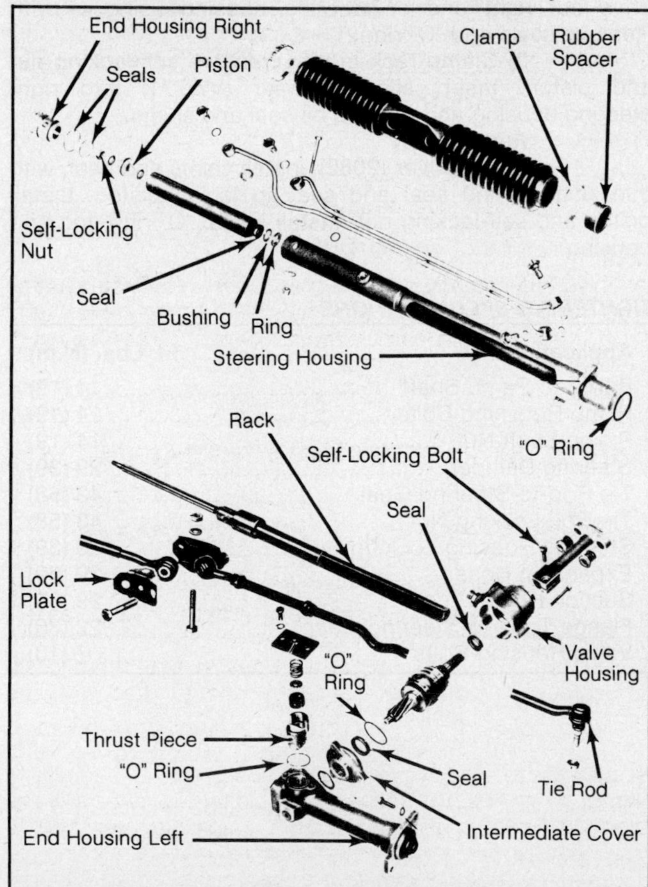
End Housing Right
Seals
Piston
Clamp
Rubber Spacer
Self-Locking Nut
Seal
Bushing
Ring
Steering Housing
Rack
Self-Locking Bolt
"O" Ring
Seal
Lock Plate
Valve Housing
"O" Ring
Thrust Piece
"O" Ring
Seal
Tie Rod
End Housing Left
Intermediate Cover

2) Make sure that no bubbles appear in reservoir when steering wheel is turned. Shut off engine and check that fluid level does not rise more than 3/8" (9.5 mm) above mark.

OIL FILTER REPLACEMENT

Remove outer cover, gasket and spring from reservoir. Remove inner filter cover and filter insert. Install new filter. Replace filter cover, spring, gasket and cover. Check fluid level.

NOTE: **Oil filter insert must be replaced whenever repairing power steering system.**

ADJUSTMENT

PUMP BELT

Loosen nuts on pump mounting bracket. Turn adjusting nut on bracket until belt deflection is 3/8" (9.5 mm) at center. Tighten nuts.

STEERING GEAR

Loosen lock nut on steering gear. Hand tighten adjusting screw until it touches thrust plate. Hold adjusting screw and tighten lock nut. Check adjustment with engine idling. Readjust if necessary.

Fig. 2: Steering Gear Adjustment

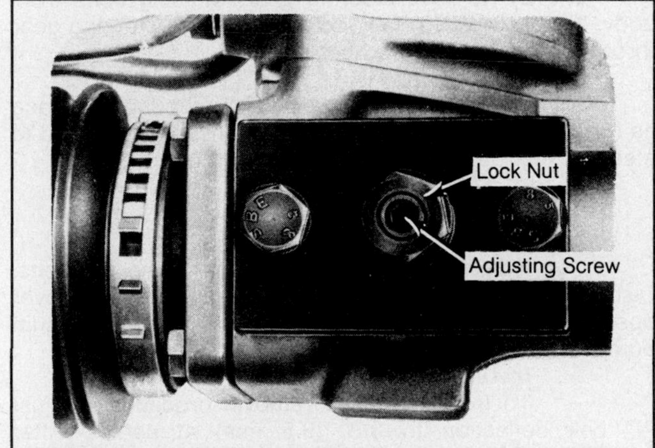
Lock Nut
Adjusting Screw

No play should be felt.

TESTING

SYSTEM PRESSURE TEST

1) Connect pressure gauge (US1070) between expansion hose and valve housing connecting pipe, with valve open. Run engine at idle. Turn steering wheel lock-to-lock several times.

2) Check pressure. Correct pressure is 986-1189 psi (68-84 kg/cm²). If pressure is incorrect, replace steering gear.

PUMP PRESSURE TEST

1) With pressure gauge installed, start engine and let it idle. Close valve (no longer than 5 seconds) and check pressure.

AUDI 5000 POWER-ASSISTED RACK & PINION (Cont.)

2) Correct pressure is 986-1189 psi (69-84 kg/cm²). If pressure is incorrect, check pressure/flow limiting valve. If valve is good, replace steering pump.

3) To check limiting valve, inspect piston and valve bores for obstructions. Check that piston moves freely in housing. Install new valve if needed.

LEAKAGE TEST

1) With engine idling, turn steering wheel to full lock and hold. Inspect all connections and tighten if needed. If leak shows at steering pinion, replace pinion housing seal and intermediate cover seals.

2) If piston rod is leaking, fluid has entered steering housing. Check for fluid by loosening outer clamp on right steering boot and pushing in boot. If seal is leaking, disassemble steering gear and replace all seals.

REMOVAL & INSTALLATION

STEERING GEAR

Removal

1) Drain fluid from system. Disconnect pressure hose and return line. Cap openings. Remove tie rod lock plate and both tie rod retaining bolts.

2) Separate tie rods from steering gear. Disconnect steering damper. Disconnect flange tube clamp from steering gear. Remove flange tube from steering shaft.

3) Remove steering gear retaining bolts from body. Turn wheels to right lock and remove steering gear through opening in right wheel well.

Installation

To install, reverse removal procedure. Replace tie rod lock plate before reinstallation. Install one tie rod to steering gear before installing other tie rod.

VANE PUMP

Removal

Remove alternator and vane pump "V" belts. Disconnect pressure and suction lines from pump. Cover openings. Remove retaining bolts from bracket and lift pump from engine.

Installation

To install, reverse removal procedure. Adjust "V" belt deflection to 3/8" (9.5 mm) at center. After reinstalling pressure and suction lines, start engine. Turn steering wheel to full lock and check for connection leaks.

OVERHAUL

NOTE: **Steering gear overhaul is not recommended. Leaking seals can be replaced if gear is removed. Check system output and pressure before removing steering gear.**

PINION HOUSING SEAL

Disassembly

1) Remove retaining bolts from valve housing and remove housing. Remove pinion gear and intermediate cover.

2) Remove "O" rings from intermediate cover. Drive out intermediate cover oil seal. Clamp housing in padded vise and drive out oil seal from the back.

3) Install new seals from the inside cover and housing. Make sure housing seal lip faces intermediate cover, and cover seal lip faces valve housing. Replace both intermediate cover "O" rings.

Reassembly

To install, reverse removal procedure. Protect pinion teeth on shaft when replacing intermediate cover. Do not damage "O" rings during reinstallation.

Fig. 3: Steering Housing Oil Seal

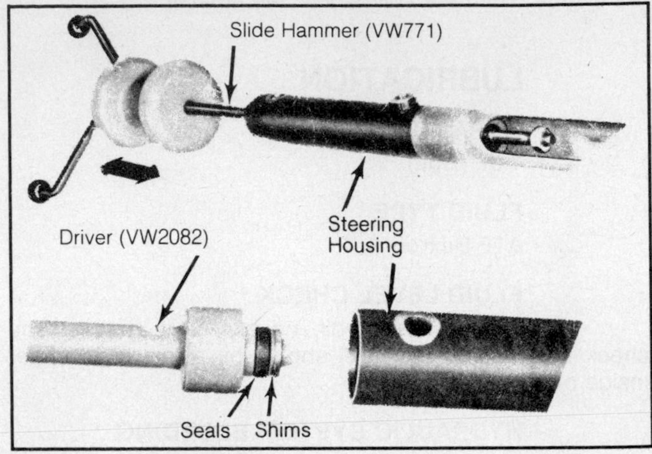
Slide Hammer (VW771)
Steering
Housing
Driver (VW2082)
Seals
Shims

Remove one seal from each side.

STEERING HOUSING SEAL

Disassembly

1) With steering gear removed from vehicle, drive out right end of steering housing using a drift. Remove seals and "O" ring.

2) Clamp rack in vise, remove self-locking nut and piston. Insert slide hammer (VW771) into right steering housing and remove oil seal and shims.

Reassembly

Using driver (2082), install shims and seal, with thin shim behind seal and seal lip facing piston. Install piston and self-locking nut. Install seals, "O" ring and end housing.

TIGHTENING SPECIFICATIONS

Application	Ft. Lbs. (N.m)
Pulley-to-Pump Shaft	14 (19)
Pump Retaining Bolts	14 (19)
Pinion Shaft Nut	14 (19)
Steering Damper	29 (39)
Tie Rod-to-Steering Gear	43 (58)
Tie Rod Locking Nut	43 (58)
Steering Housing Locking Nut	29 (39)
Expansion Hose	29 (39)
Suction Hose	29 (39)
Flange Tube-to-Steering Gear	22 (30)
Valve Housing Bolts	7 (10)

BMW 318i POWER-ASSISTED RACK & PINION

DESCRIPTION

A ZF power-assisted rack and pinion steering gear is used. A belt-driven vane pump draws fluid from the reservoir and supplies it to the control valve. The control valve supplies fluid to the proper side of the rack piston as the steering wheel is turned. System provides manual steering control (higher effort) if hydraulic pressure fails.

LUBRICATION

FLUID TYPE

ATF Dexron

FLUID LEVEL CHECK

Check fluid level with engine off. Fluid must be between marks on dipstick.

HYDRAULIC SYSTEM BLEEDING

Check fluid level. Start engine and let it idle. Turn steering wheel gently against each lock 2 times. Turn off engine. Recheck fluid level. Add fluid if needed.

TESTING

PUMP PRESSURE TEST

1) Detach steering gear pressure line and connect pressure tester (32 4 000). Connect tester pressure line to gear. Make sure valve closest to gear pressure line is closed.

2) Open second valve and bleed power steering. Shut second valve (no longer than 10 seconds). Read pressure. Pressure should be 1280-1422 psi (90-100 kg/cm²). If pressure is not within limits, check drive belt tension. Recheck pump pressure. If pressure is still incorrect, replace pump.

SYSTEM PRESSURE TEST

Connect pressure tester as previously outlined. Use a spring scale to pull steering wheel against lock with a 22 lb. (10 kg) force. Read pressure. If pressure is less than previously measured pump pressure, replace steering gear.

Fig. 1: Assembled View of 318i Power Steering Rack

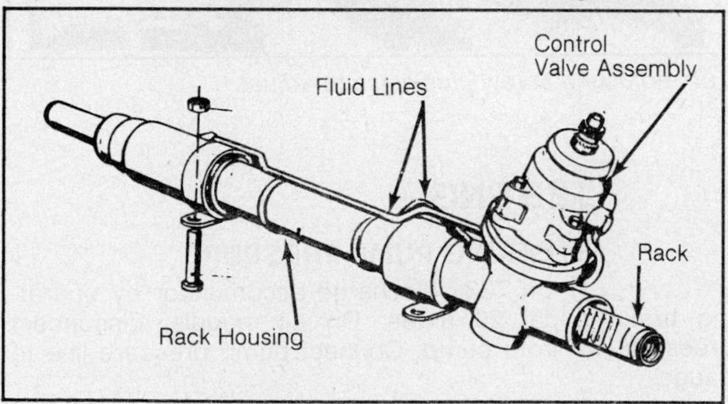
Control
Valve Assembly
Fluid Lines
Rack
Rack Housing

REMOVAL & INSTALLATION

STEERING GEAR

Removal

1) Raise vehicle and remove front wheels. Remove steering shaft-to-pinion clamp bolt. Loosen steering shaft coupling clamp bolt. Press steering shaft off pinion and remove.

2) Detach fluid pressure and return lines and plug connections. Disconnect tie rod ends from knuckles. Disconnect steering gear at crossmember.

Installation

To install, reverse removal procedure, noting the following: Replace fluid line connector seals. Mount gear to rear holes of crossmember. Fill and bleed system.

VANE PUMP

Removal

Disconnect fluid lines and plug connections. Loosen adjusting bracket nut and remove drive belt from pump. Remove pump mounting bolts and remove pump.

Installation

To install, reverse removal procedure, noting the following: Replace fluid line connector seals. Tighten drive belt before tightening mounting bolts. Fill and bleed system.

OVERHAUL

NOTE: **Manufacturer gives no overhaul procedure for gear or pump. Replace gear or pump if defective.**

BMW POWER-ASSISTED RECIRCULATING BALL

528e, 533i, 633CSi, 733i

DESCRIPTION

STEERING GEAR

Power steering gear consists of a gear housing containing a sector shaft with sector gear, a power piston with gear teeth inside of piston which is in constant mesh with sector shaft teeth.

A worm shaft connects steering shaft to power piston through a universal joint coupling. The worm shaft is geared to the piston through recirculating ball contact. The steering valve is incorporated into upper end of worm gear assembly.

STEERING PUMP

Power steering pump is a high pressure, belt driven, vane type pump. A fluid reservoir incorporating a filter element supplies hydraulic fluid to pump. Pump maintains hydraulic pressure to power steering gear assembly.

LUBRICATION

CAPACITY

528e and 633CSi 1.25 qt. (1.2L).
733i 2.1 qt. (2.0L).

FLUID TYPE

ATF Dexron II.

FILTER REPLACEMENT

528e & 633CSi

Remove reservoir cap. Remove spring and filter cover. Replace filter.

733i

Remove reservoir cap. Remove nut, washer, spring, fine mesh filter screen and filters. Clean fine mesh filter screen and replace filters.

ADJUSTMENT

PUMP BELT

Loosen adjustment bolts and shift pump to tighten belt. Adjustment is correct when it is possible to press in belt 0.2-0.4" (5-10 mm) with the thumb.

Fig. 1: Power Steering Belt Adjustment Locations

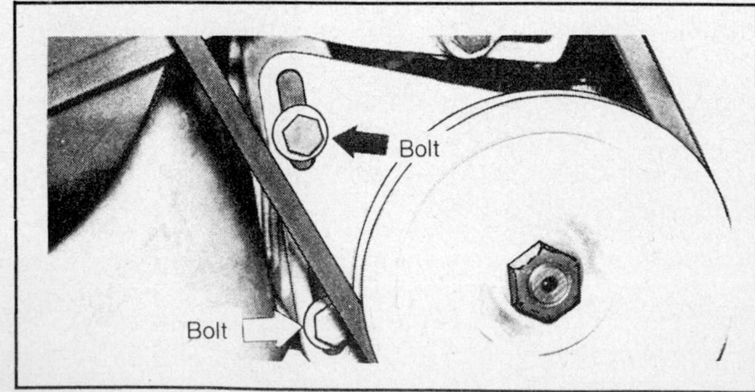
Bolt
Bolt

Adjustment is made using thumb pressure only.

HYDRAULIC SYSTEM BLEEDING

1) Power steering system must be bled whenever system is opened, or oil level falls so low that the vane type pump picks up air. Fill reservoir to upper mark with fluid.

2) Turn engine over with starter and continue to add fluid. When oil level no longer falls, start and run engine at idle speed.

3) Turn steering wheel rapidly from lock to lock and back until no further air bubbles rise in reservoir. Stop engine on 733i and operate brake pedal to discharge hydraulic accumulator.

4) On all models, during and after operation, fluid level must remain at upper mark.

SECTOR SHAFT

Adjustment (In Vehicle)

1) Position wheels straight ahead. Remove cotter pin and castle nut from tie-rod. Press off center tie-rod from steering arm. Remove BMW emblem from steering wheel.

2) Turn wheel counterclockwise 1 turn from center. Install torque wrench on nut, turn wheel clockwise and read frictional torque. Torque should be 2.7-3.5 INCH lbs. (.31-.40 N.m).

3) To adjust, turn steering wheel counterclockwise from center 1 turn. Loosen lock nut on steering gear.

4) Turn adjusting screw clockwise until correct torque is reached when passing through center position. Tighten lock nut and recheck adjustment.

Fig. 2: Sector Shaft Adjusting Screws

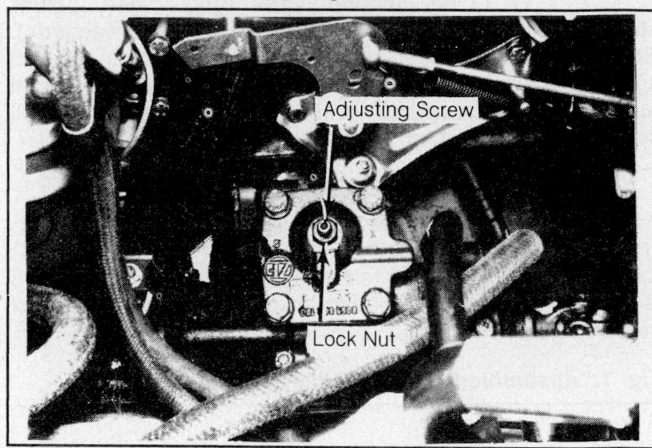
Adjusting Screw
Lock Nut

Turn adjusting screw clockwise to adjust.

TESTING

STEERING PUMP PRESSURE

1) On 733i, discharge accumulator by operating brake pedal 20 times. On all models, disconnect pressure line from pump. Connect pump pressure line to gauge.

2) Disconnect pressure line from control regulator and connect it to pressure gauge. Shut cut-off valve on gauge. Open shut-off valve on pressure line *See Fig. 6.*

3) Bleed system with engine running at idle. After bleeding, close valve in pressure line for 10 seconds

BMW POWER-ASSISTED RECIRCULATING BALL (Cont.)

Fig. 3: Cross-Sectional View of Power Steering Gear Assembly

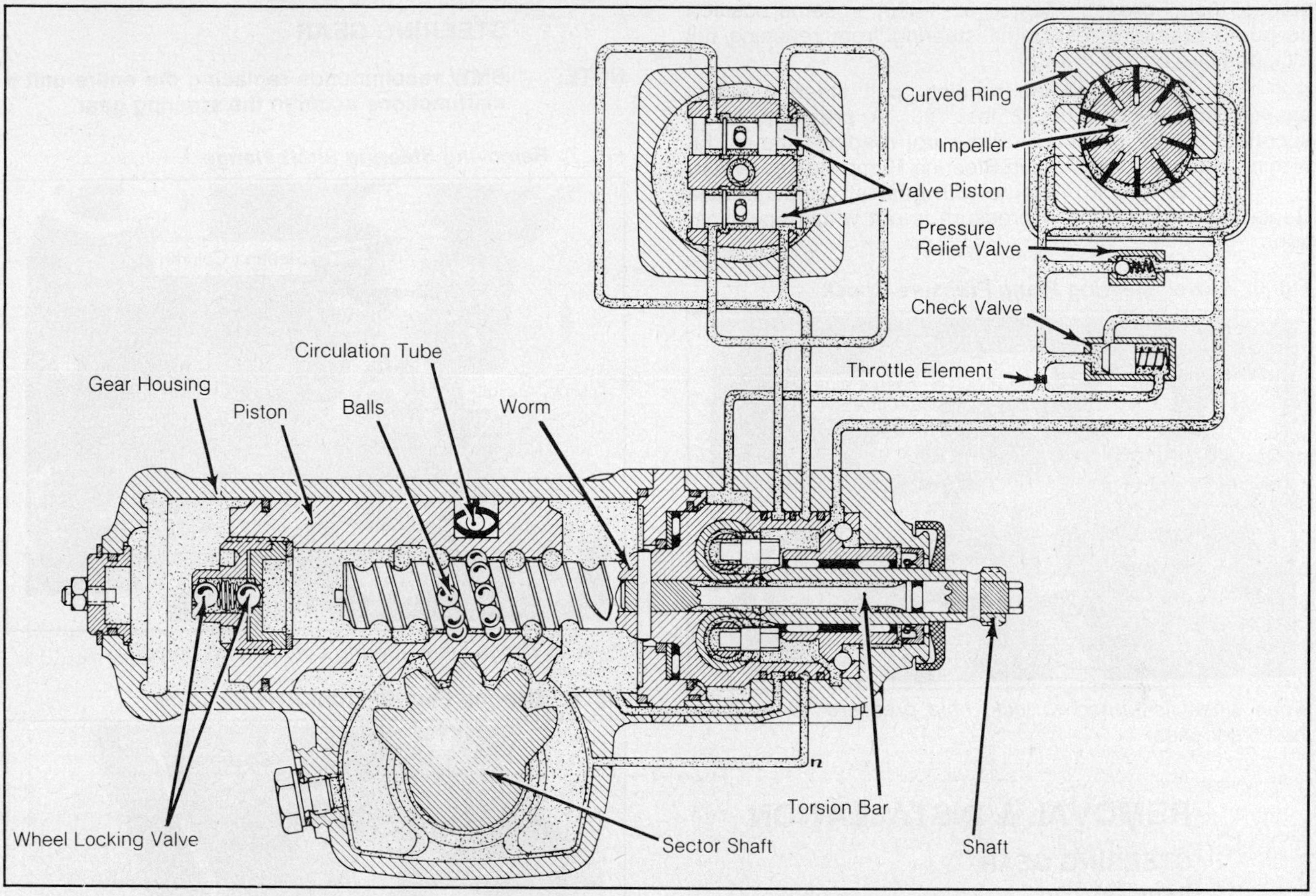

Fig. 4: Cross-Sectional View of Power Steering Pump.

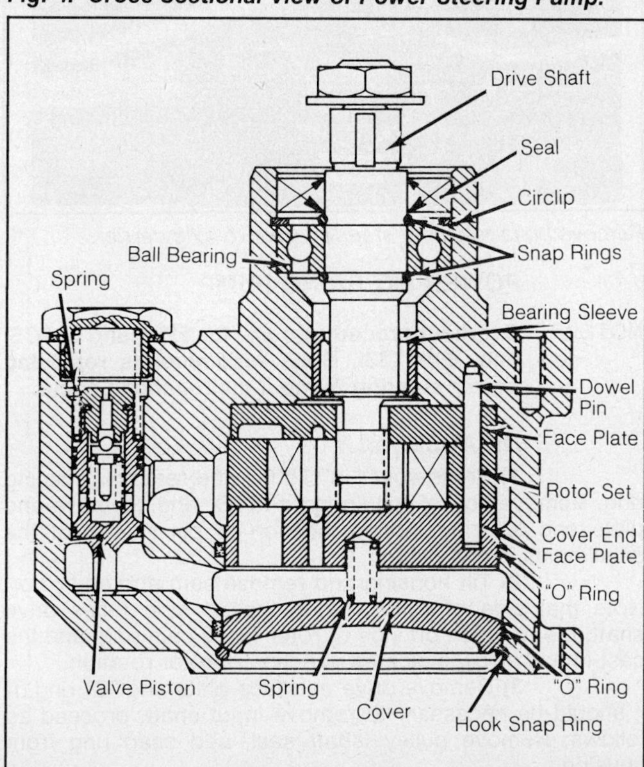
Drive Shaft
Seal
Circlip
Ball Bearing
Snap Rings
Spring
Bearing Sleeve
Dowel Pin
Face Plate
Rotor Set
Cover End Face Plate
"O" Ring
Valve Piston
Spring
Cover
"O" Ring
Hook Snap Ring

maximum and read pressure. On all models except 733i, pressure should be 1422-1564 psi. (100-110 kg/cm²).

4) On 733i, pressure should be 1849-1991 psi. (130-140 kg/cm²). If pressure is not within limits, check belt tightness. Repair or replace pump if belt adjustment does not remedy problem.

STEERING GEAR PRESSURE

NOTE: Perform Steering Pump Pressure test before performing this test.

Fig. 5: Power Steering Pump Pressure Gauge Installation

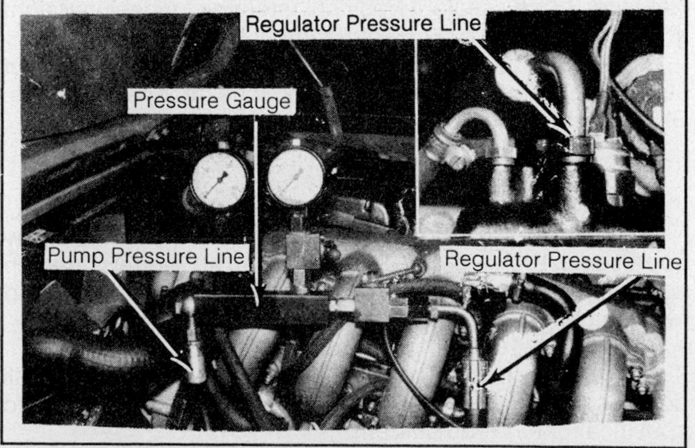
Regulator Pressure Line
Pressure Gauge
Pump Pressure Line
Regulator Pressure Line

Bleed system with engine idling.

BMW POWER-ASSISTED RECIRCULATING BALL (Cont.)

1) Raise vehicle and support with safety stands. Install pressure tester (32-4-000), in same position as pump pressure test. Limit steering from reaching full lock position by 1/2-3/4 turn.

2) With engine running, pull steering wheel against final lock with 22 lbs. (98 N) pressure for 5 seconds. Read pressure. Pressure reading should be within specifications given in Steering Pump Pressure test.

3) Check pressure with gear at opposite lock. Replace steering gear, if pressure is not within specifications.

Fig. 6: Power Steering Pump Pressure Check

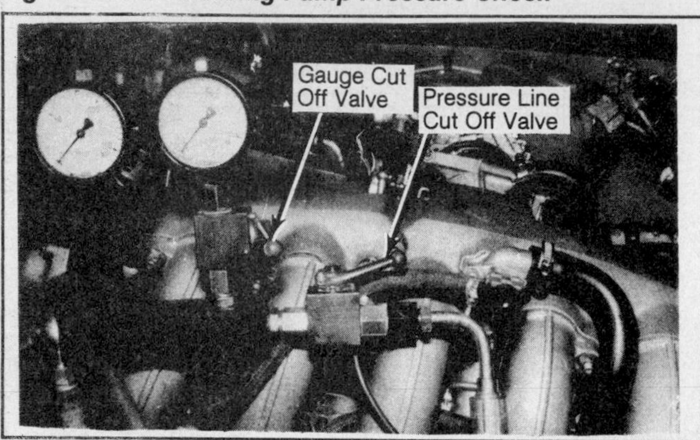
Gauge Cut
Off Valve
Pressure Line
Cut Off Valve

When wheel is turned to lock, hold pressure for no more than 5 seconds.

REMOVAL & INSTALLATION

STEERING GEAR

Removal

1) Turn steering to full left lock. On 733i, discharge hydraulic accumulator by depressing brake pedal 20 times. On all models, detach pressure and return hoses from steering gear and cap openings.

CAUTION: Do not reuse fluid drained from system.

2) Remove cotter pin and nut from tie rod end. Separate tie rod from steering arm. Remove bolt from locking groove of steering shaft. *See Fig. 7.* Push up pivot flange with steering column. Detach steering gear from front axle carrier.

Installation

1) To install, reverse removal procedures. Replace hose seals. Position steering wheel straight ahead. Align marks on pivot flange with steering shaft.

2) Make sure bolt is in locking groove of steering shaft. Tighten all connections to specifications. Bleed system.

STEERING PUMP

Removal

On 733i, discharge hydraulic accumulator by depressing brake pedal 20 times. On all models, detach hoses from pump. Loosen pump retaining bolts and remove belt. Remove retaining bolts and remove pump.

Installation

To install, reverse removal procedures. Install hoses so that they do not rub on engine carrier. Torque to specifications. Bleed system.

OVERHAUL

STEERING GEAR

NOTE: BMW recommends replacing the entire unit if malfunctions occur in the steering gear.

Fig. 7: Removing Steering Shaft Flange

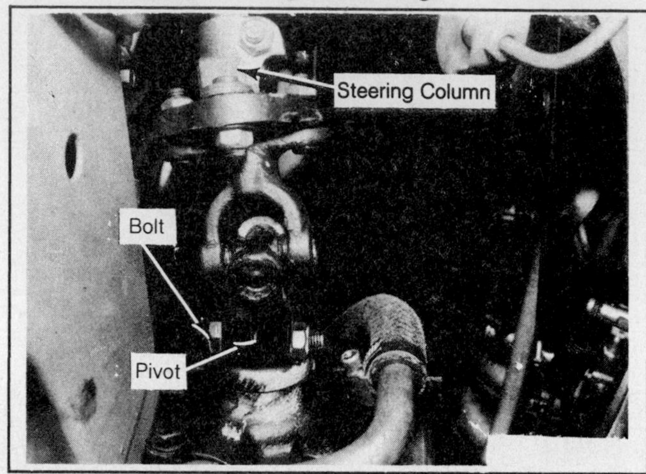
Steering Column
Bolt
Pivot

Push up flange with steering column and detach.

Fig. 8: Steering Gear-to-Front Axle Removal

Bolts

Remove bolts retaining steering gear to axle carrier.

POWER STEERING PUMP

NOTE: Overhaul procedures are for 528e and 633CSi only. For 733i, BMW recommends replacing power steering pump if malfunctions occur.

DISASSEMBLY

1) Press cover in slightly and remove retaining ring. Remove cover, coil spring and "O" ring. Remove end plate and "O" ring, noting location of pin in one of the small holes in end plate.

2) Tilt housing and remove cam ring and rotor. Note that side of rotor with recessed hole faces drive shaft, the rounded off side of rotor faces cam ring, and the cast-in half arrow indicates direction of rotor rotation.

3) Remove drive end face plate and "O" ring. If it should be necessary to remove input shaft, proceed as follows: Remove pulley, shaft seal, and snap ring from housing.

BMW POWER-ASSISTED RECIRCULATING BALL (Cont.)

Fig. 9: Pin Location Inside of Pump Housing

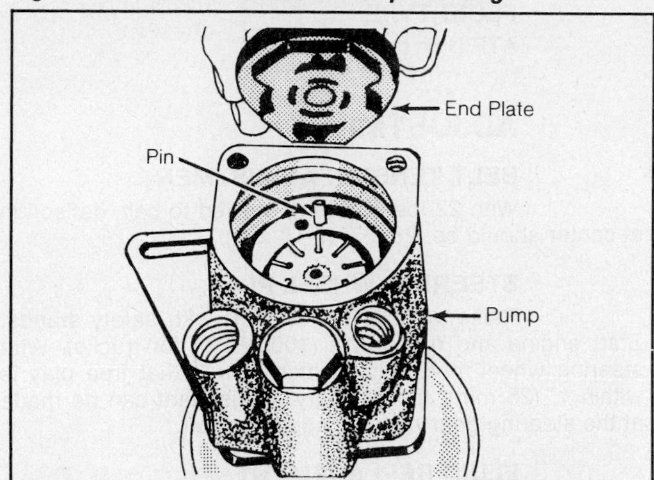
End Plate
Pin
Pump

Note which hole pin is located in when disassembling.

4) Remove circlip and press ball bearing off of shaft. Using a mandrel, press bearing sleeve out of housing.

5) Remove plug from pressure valve bore. Remove coil spring and valve piston. Note that threaded section on valve piston faces coil spring.

Fig. 10: Mark Showing Direction of Rotation

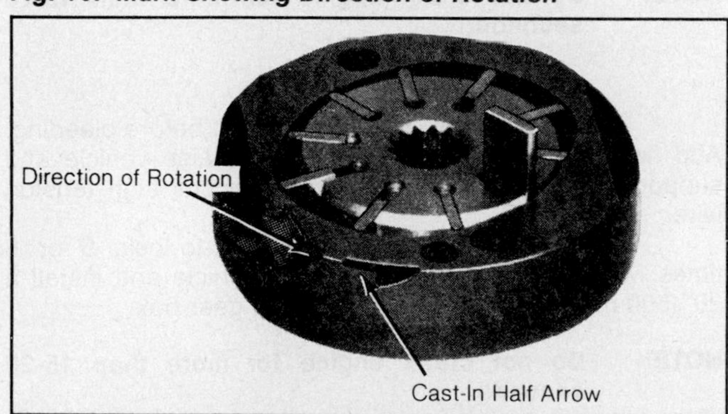
Direction of Rotation
Cast-In Half Arrow

The rounded off side of rotor faces cam ring.

CAUTION: Do not alter length of coil spring or thickness of plug sealing ring.

6) The valve tolerance group (1 or 2) is stamped into housing adjacent to pressure valve bore and valve barrel should be scribed with one or two marks (lines) agreeing with group number stamped into housing.

NOTE: If valve must be replaced, install valve of same tolerance group.

CAUTION: When disassembling piston, do not clamp across sliding surfaces.

7) Clean and inspect all parts. Clean restrictor insert in pump outlet passage. Valve piston may be disassembled for cleaning. A pressure valve is located inside valve piston (flow limit valve).

8) Thickness of washers determines cut-in range of pressure valve. Maximum pump pressure should not be more than 10% below value stated on plate attached to pump.

REASSEMBLY

To reassemble, reverse disassembly procedure, replacing all seals and worn components.

TIGHTENING SPECIFICATIONS

Application	Ft. Lbs. (N.m)
Steering Gear to Front Axle	33-35 (45-48)
Worm End Cover	25 (34)
Sector Shaft End Cover	
528e, 633SCi	23 (31)
733i	50 (68)
Adjusting Screw Counternut	22 (30)
Steering Pump Mounting	17 (23)
Hose Connections	33-37 (45-50)

Power Steering

CHRYSLER CORP. IMPORTS & MITSUBISHI POWER-ASSISTED RECIRCULATING BALL

Challenger; Colt, Mitsubishi, & Ram-50 Pickups; Montero, Sapporo, & Starion Turbo

DESCRIPTION

POWER STEERING GEAR BOX

The power steering gear box displaces fluid to provide hydraulic pressure assist when turning. A torsion bar transmits road feel to the driver.

A one-piece rack piston nut is geared to the cross shaft. An adjusting screw on the shaft maintains backlash between the shaft and the rack piston.

Fig. 1: Exploded View of Chrysler Corp. Power Steering Gear

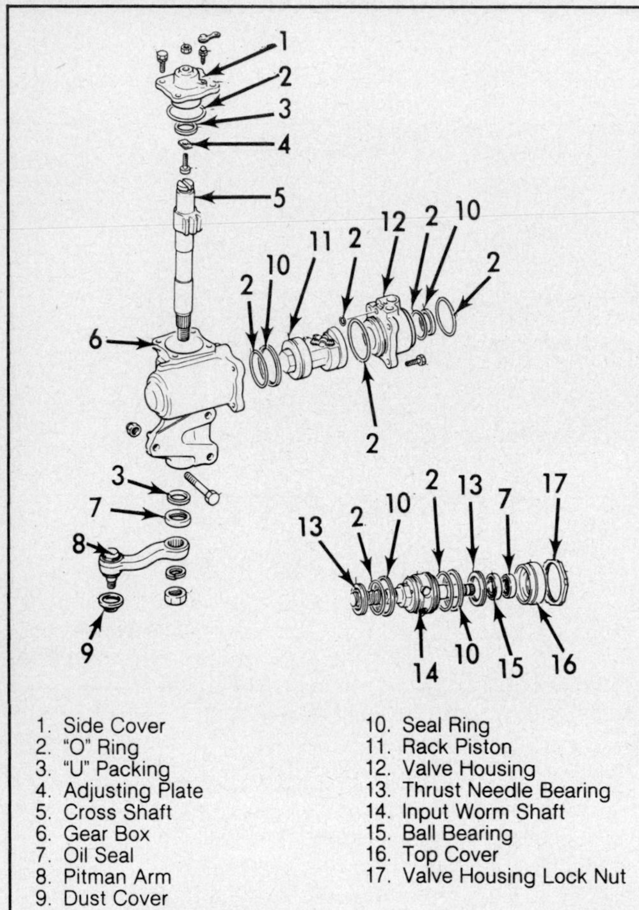
1
2
3
4
5
6
2
10
11
2
12
2
10
2
2
3
7
8
9
13
2
10
2
13
7
17
14
10
15
16
1. Side Cover
2. "O" Ring
3. "U" Packing
4. Adjusting Plate
5. Cross Shaft
6. Gear Box
7. Oil Seal
8. Pitman Arm
9. Dust Cover
10. Seal Ring
11. Rack Piston
12. Valve Housing
13. Thrust Needle Bearing
14. Input Worm Shaft
15. Ball Bearing
16. Top Cover
17. Valve Housing Lock Nut

POWER STEERING PUMP

Depending on model, 2 different types of pumps are used. Pickups with 2.6L engine, use a type "A" pump with retaining ring holding pump end plate to body. The pump has a separate reservoir. All other models use a type "B" pump with oval fill neck. Pulley is held to drive shaft with a bolt.

LUBRICATION

CAPACITY

1.1 qt. (1.07L)

FLUID TYPE

ATF Dexron II

ADJUSTMENT

BELT TENSION ADJUSTMENT

With 22 lbs. (9.98 kg) applied to belt, deflection at center should be .28-.37" (7-10 mm).

STEERING WHEEL PLAY

Raise vehicle and support with safety stands. Start engine and run at idle (1000 RPM for trucks). With steering wheel in center position, check that free play is within 1" (25 mm). If necessary, adjustment can be made at the steering gear housing adjusting bolt.

FLUID REPLACEMENT

1) Disconnect suction hose at reservoir and drain fluid. Disconnect pressure hose at pump and drain fluid. Disconnect coil high tension wire.

2) Raise vehicle and support with safety stands. Turn steering wheel lock-to-lock several times while cranking engine to drain fluid from gear box. Reconnect all hoses and fill power steering system with fluid. Bleed system.

NOTE: Do not crank engine for more than 15-20 seconds.

AIR BLEEDING

1) Make sure reservoir is filled before bleeding. Add fluid as needed during bleeding. Raise vehicle and support with safety stands. Disconnect coil high tension wire.

2) Turn steering wheel lock-to-lock, 5 or 6 times, while cranking engine. Lower vehicle and install a 20" (500 mm) hose to bleeder screw of gear box.

NOTE: Do not crank engine for more than 15-20 seconds.

3) Place other end of hose in a container. Connect coil wire. Start engine and idle. Turn steering wheel to left lock and loosen bleeder screw. Repeat this until no more bubbles appear in container (from hose).

4) Remove hose and tighten bleeder screw. Check fluid level, add fluid if necessary. Turn steering wheel lock-to-lock and note that fluid level in reservoir does not change more than .12-.16" (3-4 mm).

CAUTION: Abrupt rising of fluid level after engine is shut off signals incomplete bleeding. Repeat procedure as needed.

FLUID PRESSURE TESTING

1) Remove pressure hose from oil pump and attach adapter for pressure gauge (C-3309-E). Tighten to 22-29 ft. lbs. (30-39 N.m).

2) Start engine and place thermometer in reservoir. Close the gauge valve fully 3 times to bleed air from gauge. Check fluid level and add if necessary.

3) When oil temperature reaches 170°F (76.6°C) for Pickups, or 122°F (50°C) for all other models, check pressure.

CHRYSLER CORP. IMPORTS & MITSUBISHI POWER-ASSISTED RECIRCULATING BALL (Cont.)

Fig. 2: Exploded View of Power Steering Pump

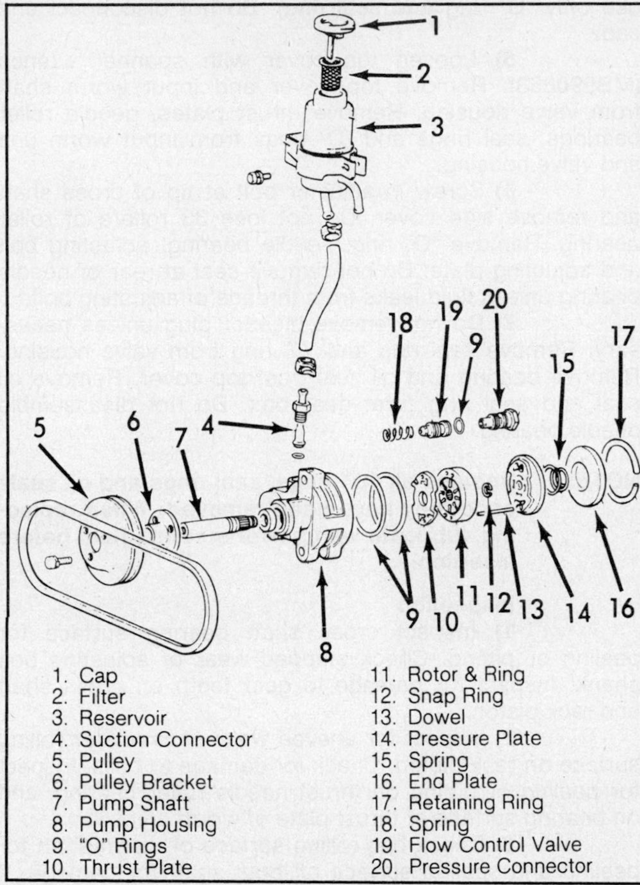
1. Cap
2. Filter
3. Reservoir
4. Suction Connector
5. Pulley
6. Pulley Bracket
7. Pump Shaft
8. Pump Housing
9. "O" Rings
10. Thrust Plate
11. Rotor & Ring
12. Snap Ring
13. Dowel
14. Pressure Plate
15. Spring
16. End Plate
17. Retaining Ring
18. Spring
19. Flow Control Valve
20. Pressure Connector

Type "A" shown, used on Pickup models with 2.6L engine.

Fig. 3: Exploded View of Power Steering Pump

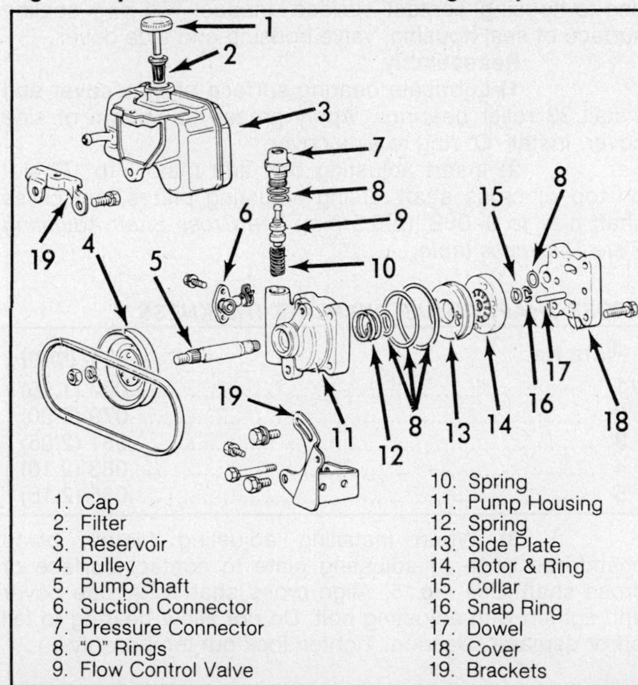
1. Cap
2. Filter
3. Reservoir
4. Pulley
5. Pump Shaft
6. Suction Connector
7. Pressure Connector
8. "O" Rings
9. Flow Control Valve
10. Spring
11. Pump Housing
12. Spring
13. Side Plate
14. Rotor & Ring
15. Collar
16. Snap Ring
17. Dowel
18. Cover
19. Brackets

Type "B" shown, used on all other models.

4) With valve closed, Pickup and Montero pumps should read 1099-1200 psi (77-84 kg/cm²). All other pumps pressure should be 1067-1210 psi (75-85 kg/cm²).

5) Valve open pressure for both types of pumps should be 142 psi (10 kg/cm²) or less. Reinstall pressure hose, taking care not to twist hose or interfere with adjacent parts.

CAUTION: Do not keep shut-off valve closed more than 3 seconds at a time. Do not keep steering wheel turned more than 10 seconds at a time.

REMOVAL & INSTALLATION

POWER STEERING GEAR BOX

Removal

1) On passenger cars and Montero, disconnect pressure and suction hoses from gear box. Raise and support vehicle on safety stands. On all models, remove steering shaft-to-steering gear clamp bolt. Disconnect steering shaft from gear box.

2) Remove cotter pin and lock nut from pitman arm, if equipped. Using puller (C-3894-A), disconnect tie rod and pitman arm from relay rod.

3) On Pickup models, remove air cleaner and under cover. Disconnect pressure and suction hoses from gear box. On Pickup models with automatic transmission, remove throttle linkage and shield. On Pickup models with manual transmission, remove starter.

4) On all models, move fuel line aside. Remove gear box bolts and gear box. Remove pitman arm nut. Using puller (CT-1106), remove pitman arm from gear box.

Installation

1) To install, reverse removal procedure. When connecting cross shaft to pitman arm, align slit of cross shaft tip to marking of pitman arm.

2) Ensure that clearance between bolt hole at the bottom of the gear box and pitman arm is .73-93" (18.5-23.6 mm).

POWER STEERING PUMP

Removal (Challenger & Sapporo)

Loosen pulley and pump bolts. Remove belt and pulley. Disconnect and plug pressure and suction hoses. Remove pump retaining bolts and remove pump with reservoir.

Removal (Montero & Starion Turbo)

1) Loosen pump bolts and remove belt. Remove reservoir cap. Using a container to catch fluid, disconnect return hose at reservoir and drain fluid.

2) Raise front of vehicle and support on safety stands. Disconnect coil high tension wire. Crank engine several times to drain fluid from system. Disconnect pressure hose from pump. Remove pulley. Remove pump bolts and remove pump with reservoir.

Removal (Pickups with 2.6L Engine)

Disconnect and plug pressure and suction hoses. Loosen pump brace and remove belt and pulley. Remove pump bolts and remove pump.

Removal (All Other Pickups)

1) Remove reservoir cap and disconnect return hose at reservoir to drain fluid. On models with 2.0L engine, disconnect coil high tension wire. On models with 2.3L diesel engine, remove fuel cut valve connector at

CHRYSLER CORP. IMPORTS & MITSUBISHI POWER-ASSISTED RECIRCULATING BALL (Cont.)

injection pump. On all models, crank engine several times to drain fluid from gear box.

2) On models with 2.0L engine, disconnect and plug pressure and return hoses at pump. Loosen pump bolts. Remove belt and pulley. Remove pump bolts and pump. Separate reservoir from pump.

3) On models with 2.3L diesel engine, disconnect and plug suction and return hoses at pump. Remove reservoir. Disconnect and plug pressure hose at pump. Loosen pump bolts. Remove belt and pulley. Remove pump bolts and pump.

Installation (All Models)

To install, reverse removal procedure. Check oil pump bracket for slack and tighten, if necessary. Fill and bleed reservoir. Start engine after installation and run at 2000 RPM for 5 minutes to check for fluid leaks.

OVERHAUL

POWER STEERING GEAR BOX

Disassembly

1) Drain fluid from gear box. Loosen adjusting lock nut and remove. Remove side cover bolts and screw in the adjusting bolt 2 or 3 turns. With gear in neutral position, tap bottom of cross shaft with plastic hammer and remove. Do not damage cross shaft splines and oil seal.

2) Mount valve housing in vise and remove housing lock nut with spanner wrench (MB990852). Hold rack piston stationary and remove valve housing and rack piston assembly. Do not hold housing with rack pointing down as rack may slide off housing.

3) Place valve housing in vise and move rack piston up and down to check backlash between circulator balls and rack piston gutter. Turn the rack piston fully into the valve housing and loosen 2 turns to measure backlash. Service limit is .008" (.2 mm). If backlash exceeds limit, replace ball screw unit and rack piston as an assembly.

Fig. 4: Measuring Backlash of Gutter and Ball

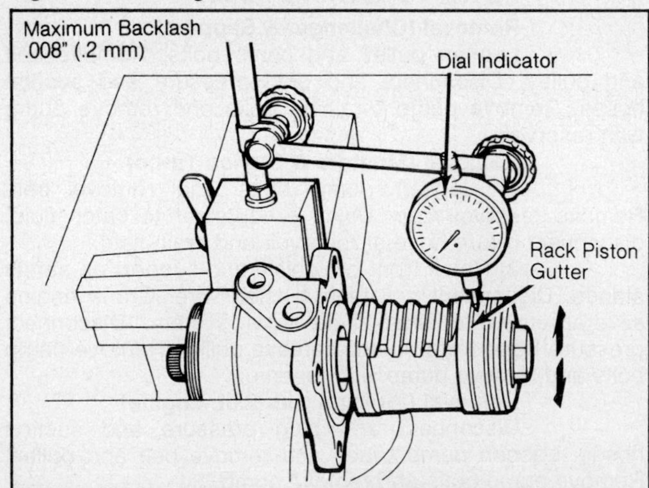
Maximum Backlash
.008" (.2 mm)
Dial Indicator
Rack Piston
Gutter

Maximum service limit is .008" (.2 mm).

4) Remove rack piston by turning counterclockwise. Do not lose 26 circulator balls (except 4WD Pickups). Remove "O" ring, seal ring, steel balls, circulators and circulator holder from rack piston (4WD Pickups use only "O" ring and seal ring). Do not disconnect end cap.

5) Loosen top cover with spanner wrench (MB990853). Remove top cover and input worm shaft from valve housing. Remove thrust plates, needle roller bearings, seal rings and "O" rings from input worm unit and valve housing.

6) Screw in adjuster bolt at tip of cross shaft and remove side cover. Do not lose 33 rollers of roller bearing. Remove "O" ring, needle bearing, adjusting bolt and adjusting plate. Do not remove seal at rear of needle bearing unless fluid leaks from threads of adjusting bolt.

7) Do not remove bleeder plug unless necessary. Remove seal ring and "O" ring from valve housing. Remove bearing and oil seal from top cover. Remove oil seal and seal ring from gear box. Do not disassemble needle bearing.

NOTE: **Replace all "O" rings, seal rings and oil seals once they have been removed. When replacing, lubricate with power steering fluid before insertion.**

Inspection

1) Inspect cross shaft bearing surface for peeling or pitting. Check stepped wear of adjusting bolt shank. Inspect for damage to gear teeth on cross shaft and rack piston.

2) Inspect for uneven wear of circulator rolling surface on rack piston. Check for damage to balls. Inspect for peeling or pitting on thrust needle roller bearing, and on bearing surface of thrust plate of worm unit.

3) Check ball rolling surface of worm shaft for peeling and sealing surface of input shaft for damage. If thrust bearing or thrust plate is defective, replace both as a set.

4) Inspect valve housing for damage to seal ring-to-housing contact surface. Inspect "O" ring sealing surface of seal housing, valve housing and side cover.

Reassembly

1) Lubricate bearing surface of side cover and install 33 roller bearings. Apply grease to bottom of side cover. Install "O" ring to side cover.

2) Insert adjusting bolt and plate into "T" slot on top of cross shaft. Using adjusting plates, set cross shaft play to 0-.002" (0-0.5 mm) *See Cross Shaft Adjusting Plate Thickness table.*

CROSS SHAFT ADJUSTING PLATE THICKNESS

Plate No.	In. (mm)
1	.077 (1.95)
2	.079 (2.00)
3	.081 (2.05)
4	.083 (2.10)
5	.085 (2.15)

3) When installing adjusting plates, place chamfered edge of adjusting plate to contact surface of cross shaft. *See Fig. 5.* Align cross shaft with side cover and tighten with adjusting bolt. Do not allow bearing to fall off or damage seal ring. Tighten lock nut temporarily.

CHRYSLER CORP. IMPORTS & MITSUBISHI POWER-ASSISTED RECIRCULATING BALL (Cont.)

Fig. 5: Adjusting Cross Shaft

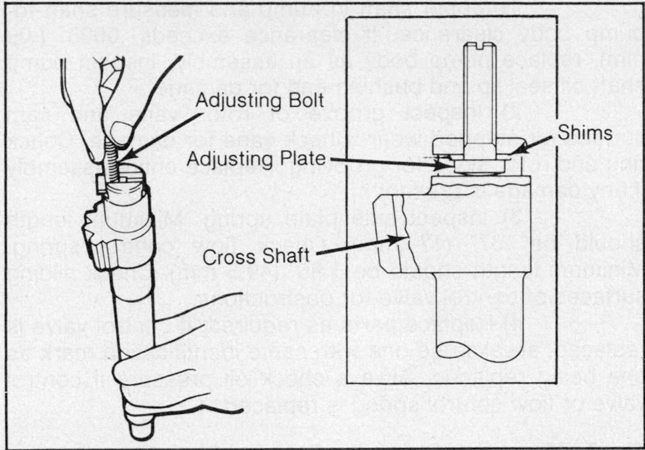
Adjusting Bolt
Shims
Adjusting Plate
Cross Shaft

Place chamfered edge of adjusting plate to contact surface of cross shaft.

4) Apply grease to oil seal lip. Press oil seal and ball bearing into top cover. Apply grease to "U" packing and lip of oil seal and press into gear box.

5) Install "O" ring and seal ring to input worm shaft. Install thrust plate, needle bearing, and thrust plate in that order onto input worm shaft. Install "O" ring and seal ring (compressed into hear shape) into valve housing groove.

6) Install input worm shaft to valve housing. Install thrust plate, needle roller bearing and thrust plate in that order to top cover.

NOTE: **Install thinner thrust plate to top cover side.**

7) Temporarily tighten top cover to valve housing using spanner wrench (MB990853). Make sure thrust plate and needle bearing are aligned. Attach spring tension gauge to spanner wrench and tighten cover 14-19 lbs. (6.4-8.6 kg). Then loosen cover to zero lbs. (zero kg). *See Fig. 6*. Check input worm shaft for uniform rotation.

Fig. 6: Tightening Top Cover

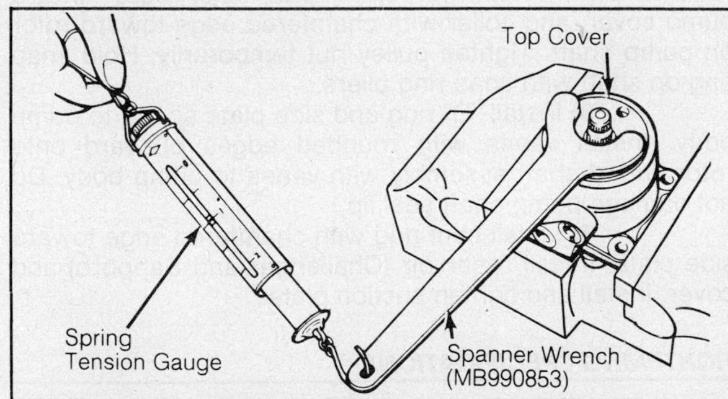
Top Cover
Spring
Tension Gauge
Spanner Wrench
(MB990853)

Tighten to 14-19 lbs. (6.4-8.6 kg), then back off to zero lbs. (zero kg).

8) Using preload socket (CT-1108) and INCH Lb. torque wrench, measure and record input worm shaft starting torque. Gradually tighten top cover until input worm shaft starting torque is 1.8-2.7 INCH Lbs. (.2-.3 N.m) greater than recorded value. Using spanner wrench (MB990852) and torque wrench, tighten valve housing nut without rotating top cover.

9) Again measure input worm shaft starting torque while turning input worm shaft. If starting torque is not 2.2-5.6 INCH Lbs. (.3-.6 N.m), loosen valve housing nut and repeat steps **7)** and **8)**. Install "O" ring and seal ring to rack piston without forcing. Insert rack piston into input worm shaft until piston touches worm shaft end.

10) Rotate worm shaft and align ball running surface with ball insertion hole. Insert 19 balls into hole by pushing lightly with a brass rod (except 4WD models). After installation, make sure that ball-to-rack piston clearance is .5" (13 mm). *See Fig. 7*. If clearance is excessive, a ball has entered wrong groove. Remove rack piston and reinstall balls.

NOTE: **Do not rotate input worm shaft and rack piston. Balls may enter wrong grooves.**

Fig. 7: Installing Circulator Balls to Rack Piston

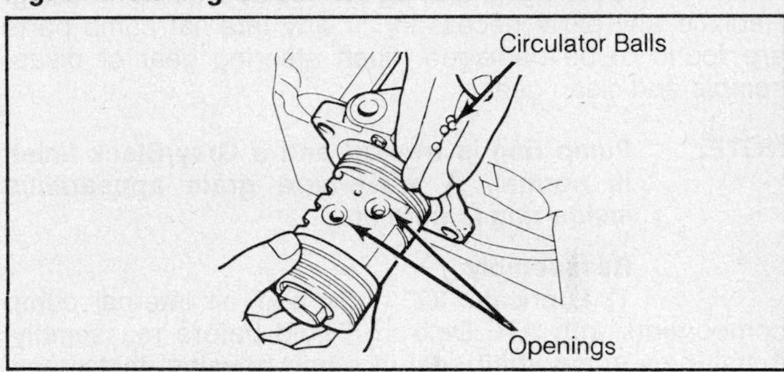
Circulator Balls
Openings

Use brass rod to push balls into position on all models except 4WD.

11) Insert 7 more balls with grease to prevent them from falling. Insert circulator and holder to rack piston and tighten. Mount gear box in vise and install valve housing and rack piston. Tighten valve housing. Rotate input worm shaft to move rack piston to center (neutral) position.

NOTE: **Do not force rack piston into housing. Seal ring may be damaged by edge of gear housing.**

12) Apply a thin coating of automatic transmission fluid to teeth and shaft of rack piston. Apply grease to oil seal lip. Wrap serration of cross shaft with vinyl tape to avoid damage when installing. Install cross shaft and side cover to gear box. Do not rotate side cover for installation to prevent damage to "O" ring. Tighten side cover.

13) Using preload socket (CT-1108), measure starting torque of input worm shaft. Adjust to 4.3-7.8 INCH lbs. (.5-.9 N.m) by turning cross shaft adjusting bolt. Tighten lock nut. Make sure valve housing and rack piston unit operates smoothly.

14) Connect cross shaft to pitman arm. Ensure slit on cross shaft tip aligns with groove on pitman arm. On Challenger and Sapporo, make sure clearance between center of lower steering gear box bolt hole and pitman arm is .7-.9" (18-23 mm).

POWER STEERING PUMP

Disassembly

(Type "A" – Pickups with 2.6L Engine)

1) Remove pulley bracket with puller. Remove suction tube connector. Remove pressure connector.

CHRYSLER CORP. IMPORTS & MITSUBISHI POWER-ASSISTED RECIRCULATING BALL (Cont.)

Using small punch inserted in hole of pump housing (opposite flow control valve hole) to compress retaining ring, pry end plate retaining ring out pump housing.

2) Remove end plate and "O" ring. Remove flow control valve and spring. Tap on pump shaft with plastic hammer enough to loosen pressure plate. Remove pressure plate, pump shaft, ring, vanes and rotor.

3) Remove pump shaft retaining ring and discard. Remove rotor and thrust plate from shaft. Remove 2 dowel pins from housing. Pry pump shaft seal out of housing and discard.

Inspection

1) Check flow control valve, rotor and ring, end plates and pump shaft for damage, scoring or excessive wear. Inspect pump housing for cracks or signs of visual damage. Check "O" ring seats for scratches or burrs.

2) Inspect pump shaft bushing, in pump housing. If bushing is damaged, replace pump housing. Replace any parts necessary. If any internal pump parts are found to be damaged, flush steering gear or disassemble and clean gear.

NOTE: Pump ring is treated and a Gray/Black finish is normal. A wave-type grain appearance inside ring is normal.

Reassembly

1) Lubricate "O" rings and all internal pump components with ATF Dexron II fluid before reassembly. Install new pump shaft seal in pump housing. Install new pressure plate "O" ring to 3rd groove from end of pump housing. Insert both dowel pins into pump housing.

2) Install thrust plate and rotor to pump shaft. Install new snap ring to pump shaft. Make sure rotor is installed with countersunk side toward thrust plate.

3) Install pump shaft into pump housing, making sure thrust plate slides over dowel pins properly. Install pump ring into pump housing, over dowel pins and with arrow on ring toward rear of pump housing.

4) Install vanes in rotor and make sure rounded edge of vanes face outward. Install pressure plate into pump housing and over dowel pins. Seat plate by depressing about .06" (1.6 mm) over "O" ring. Make sure circular depression (for spring) is toward rear of housing.

5) Install new "O" ring in 2nd groove from rear of pump housing. Place end plate spring in pressure plate groove. Press end plate into pump housing. Depress end plate just enough to install retaining ring. Make sure retaining ring seats properly. Press pulley bracket onto shaft.

Disassembly
(Type "B" – All Except 2.6L Pickups)

1) Drain fluid. Remove suction plate bolts. Remove reservoir from pump on Challenger and Sapporo. Mount pump in a soft-jawed vise. Remove pump cover bolts and cover. Tap the shaft with a plastic hammer.

2) Take out the cam ring, 10 vanes, shaft assembly, side plate spring and 4 "O" rings. Remove snap ring from shaft assembly and remove collar, rotor and side plate from shaft.

3) Pry oil seal out of pump body. Remove pressure connector and take out control valve assembly, flow control spring and 2 "O" rings. Do not disassemble control valve assembly.

Inspection

1) Mount shaft in pump and measure shaft-to-pump body clearance. If clearance exceeds .0035" (.09 mm), replace pump body as an assembly. Inspect pump shaft oil seal lip and bushing end for damage.

2) Inspect groove of rotor vane and cam surface for stepped wear. Check vane for damage. Check ring and rotor sides for grooving. Replace entire assembly if any damage is present.

3) Inspect side plate spring. Minimum length should be .67" (17 mm). Check flow control spring. Minimum length should be 1.95" (49.5 mm). Check sliding surfaces of control valve for obstructions.

4) Replace parts as required. If control valve is replaced, always use one with same identification mark as one being replaced. Always check oil pressure if control valve or flow control spring is replaced.

Fig. 8: Measuring Clearance Between Shaft and Pump Body

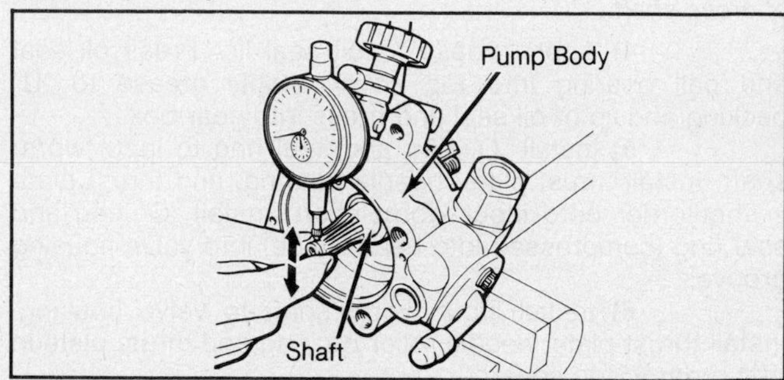
Pump Body
Shaft

Maximum service limit is .0035" (.09 mm).

Reassembly

1) Lubricate "O" rings and all internal pump components with ATF Dexron II before reassembly. Install flow control valve spring and control valve in pump body. Install and tighten pressure connector. Depress control valve to check for smooth operation. Apply grease to lip of oil seal and press into pump body.

2) Install side plate with chamfered edge toward rotor, rotor with chamfered inner bore toward pump cover, and collar with chamfered edge toward rotor on pump shaft. Tighten pulley nut temporarily. Hold snap ring on shaft with snap ring pliers.

3) Install "O" ring and side plate spring to pump body. Install vanes with rounded edges outward onto rotor. Insert shaft assembly with vanes to pump body. Do not damage pump shaft seal lip.

4) Install cam ring with chamfered edge toward side plate. Install reservoir (Challenger and Sapporo) and cover. Install and tighten suction plate.

TIGHTENING SPECIFICATIONS

Application	Ft. Lbs. (N.m)
Gear-to-Frame	40-47 (54-64)
Oil Pump Cover	22-29 (30-39)
Pitman Arm-to-Cross Shaft	94-109 (128-148)
Pressure Hose	22-29 (30-39)
Suction Hose	29-36 (39-49)
Side Cover	33-40 (45-46)
Valve Housing	33-40 (45-46)
Valve Housing Lock Nut	130-166 (178-226)

DATSUN/NISSAN POWER-ASSISTED RACK & PINION

Maxima, 280ZX, & 280ZX Turbo

DESCRIPTION

Power steering is rack and pinion cam gear type. System consists of a rack and pinion steering gear, steering pump, reservoir and flexible connecting lines.

Fig. 1: View of Power Steering Assembly

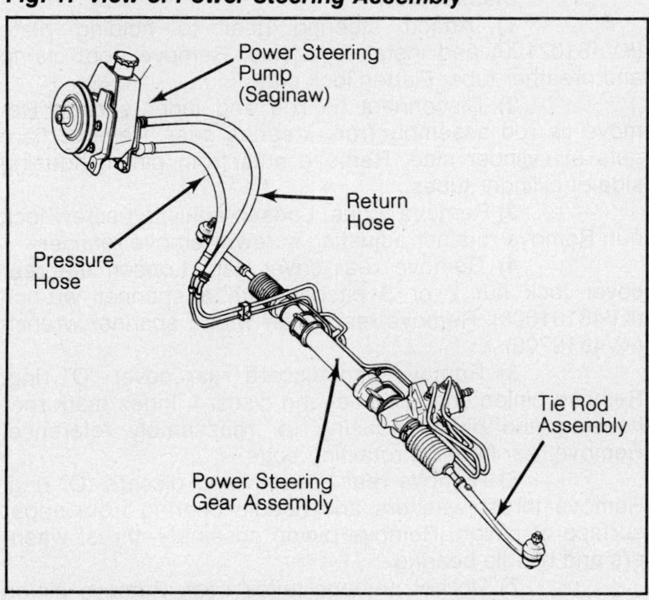
Power Steering
Pump
(Saginaw)
Return
Hose
Pressure
Hose
Tie Rod
Assembly
Power Steering
Gear Assembly

Pump is belt driven from crankshaft

LUBRICATION

CAPACITY

Saginaw Pump 1.4 qt. (1.3L).
Atsugi Pump Type "B" 1.0 qt. (.9L).

FLUID TYPE

ATF Dexron

NOTE: **Normal operating temperature for power steering fluid is 140-176°F (60-80°C).**

ADJUSTMENTS

HYDRAULIC SYSTEM BLEEDING

1) Raise vehicle and support with safety stands. Turn steering wheel quickly to lock-to-lock positions until fluid level no longer decreases and bubbles do not appear.

2) Start engine and idle for 2-3 minutes. Accelerate engine under no load 2-3 times. Let engine idle and quickly turn wheel lock-to-lock until air bubbles no longer appear.

NOTE: **Do not hold steering wheel at lock position for more than 15 seconds. Ensure no unusual noises appear from system.**

HYDRAULIC SYSTEM PRESSURE TEST

1) Disconnect pressure line at pump and connect pressure gauge and shut-off valve. Gauge must be between valve and pump. Open valve, check fluid level, and run engine for about 5 seconds.

2) Check fluid level and restart engine. Turn steering wheel lock-to-lock several times to expel air from system and bring fluid temperature up.

3) Check pressure quickly with wheel turned to full lock position (both left and right). Pressure at idle should be 950-1120 psi (67-79 kg/cm²).

NOTE: **Do not hold steering wheel in lock position for more than 15 seconds.**

4) If incorrect, close valve. If pressure is now too low or high, pump is fualty. If pressure is okay, steering gear is faulty.

BELT TENSION

With 22 lbs. (10 kg) pressure on belt, deflection at center should be .31-.47" (8-12 mm).

STEERING WHEEL TURNING FORCE

1) Park vehicle on a dry, level surface. Set parking brake. Bring hydraulic fluid up to normal operating temperature.

2) Attach a spring scale and check steering wheel turning force with wheel one turn from straight ahead.

3) Force should be less than 5.5-6.6 lbs. (24.5-29.4 N.m). If not, remove steering gear and check turning force of pinion gear.

PINION ROTATING FORCE & RACK STARTING FORCE

1) Install gear to holding plate (KV48102100) and install in a vise. Disconnect cylinder tube and drain fluid. Attach torque wrench to pinion and measure turning force.

2) Turning force should be less than 8 INCH lbs. (.9 N.m) average and less than 13 INCH lbs. (1.5 N.m) maximum. Attach spring scale to rack end to measure rack starting force. Force should be 28-42 lbs. (12.5-19.0 kg).

NOTE: **If either force is incorrect, adjust retainer screw. If adjustment cannot be made correctly, replace steering gear.**

REMOVAL & INSTALLATION

STEERING GEAR

Removal

1) Raise vehicle and support with safety stands. Disconnect hose clamp fixing bolt. Disconnect flare nut at steering gear. Drain fluid. Remove hose clamp from steering gear mounting bracket.

2) Detach side ball studs from knuckle arm with ball joint remover (HT72520000). Loosen steering gear retaining bolts.

3) Loosen bolt retaining lower joint to pinion gear. Draw out lower joint from pinion gear. Remove bolt retaining steering gear housing to suspension cross-member. Remove steering gear and linkage.

Installation

To install, reverse removal procedures. Install lower joint on steering gear. *See Fig. 2.* Tighten steering gear retaining bolts.

DATSUN/NISSAN POWER RACK & PINION (Cont.)

Fig. 2: Steering Shaft to Pinion Gear Lower Joint Attachment

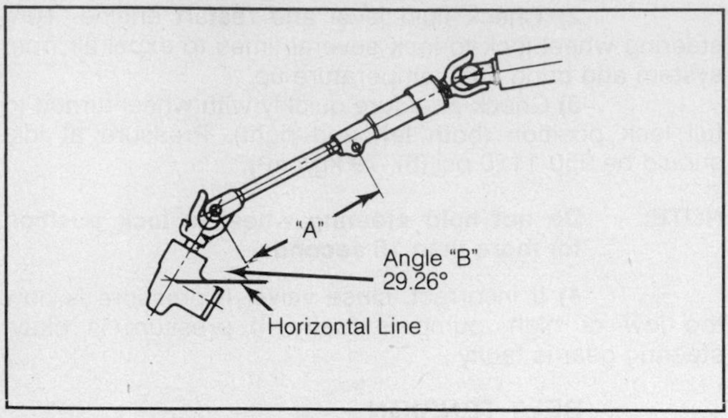
"A"
Angle "B"
29.26°
Horizontal Line

Dimension "A" should equal 6.52" (165 mm).

STEERING PUMP

Removal

1) Loosen power steering pump pulley lock nut. Turn adjusting bolt counterclockwise to loosen pump belt.

2) Remove belt. Disconnect pressure hose flare nut at power steering pump. Drain fluid. Remove hose clamp. Remove pump retaining bolts and pump.

3) Remove flare nuts at steering gear. Remove hose clamps at suspension member. Remove hose from steering gear.

Installation

To install, reverse removal procedures. After pump is installed, bleed system and adjust belt tension.

OVERHAUL

POWER STEERING GEAR

NOTE: **Before disassembling, measure pinion rotating force and rack starting force. If they cannot be adjusted properly, replace steering gear.**

Disassembly

1) Attach steering gear to holding plate (KV48102100) and install in a vise. Remove boot clamp and breather tube. Flatten lock plate.

2) Disconnect tie rod and inner socket. Remove tie rod assembly from steering gear. Remove flare nuts at cylinder side. Remove nuts from pinion housing side of cylinder tubes.

3) Remove tubes. Loosen adjusting screw lock nut. Remove retainer adjusting screw. Remove retainer.

4) Remove rear cover cap. Loosen the rear cover lock nut 2 or 3 pitches with a spanner wrench (KV48101600). Remove rear cover with a spanner wrench (KV4810700).

5) Remove and discard rear cover "O" ring. Remove pinion shaft oil seal and discard. Index mark rear housing and pinion housing for reassembly reference. Remove rear housing retaining bolts.

6) Remove rear housing and discard "O" ring. Remove thrust washers and needle bearing from upper surface of pinion. Remove pinion assembly, thrust washers and needle bearing.

7) Do not damage teflon seal. Remove pinion bearing and pinion oil seal. Put index mark on housing

Fig. 3: Exploded View of Power Rack & Pinion Steering Gear

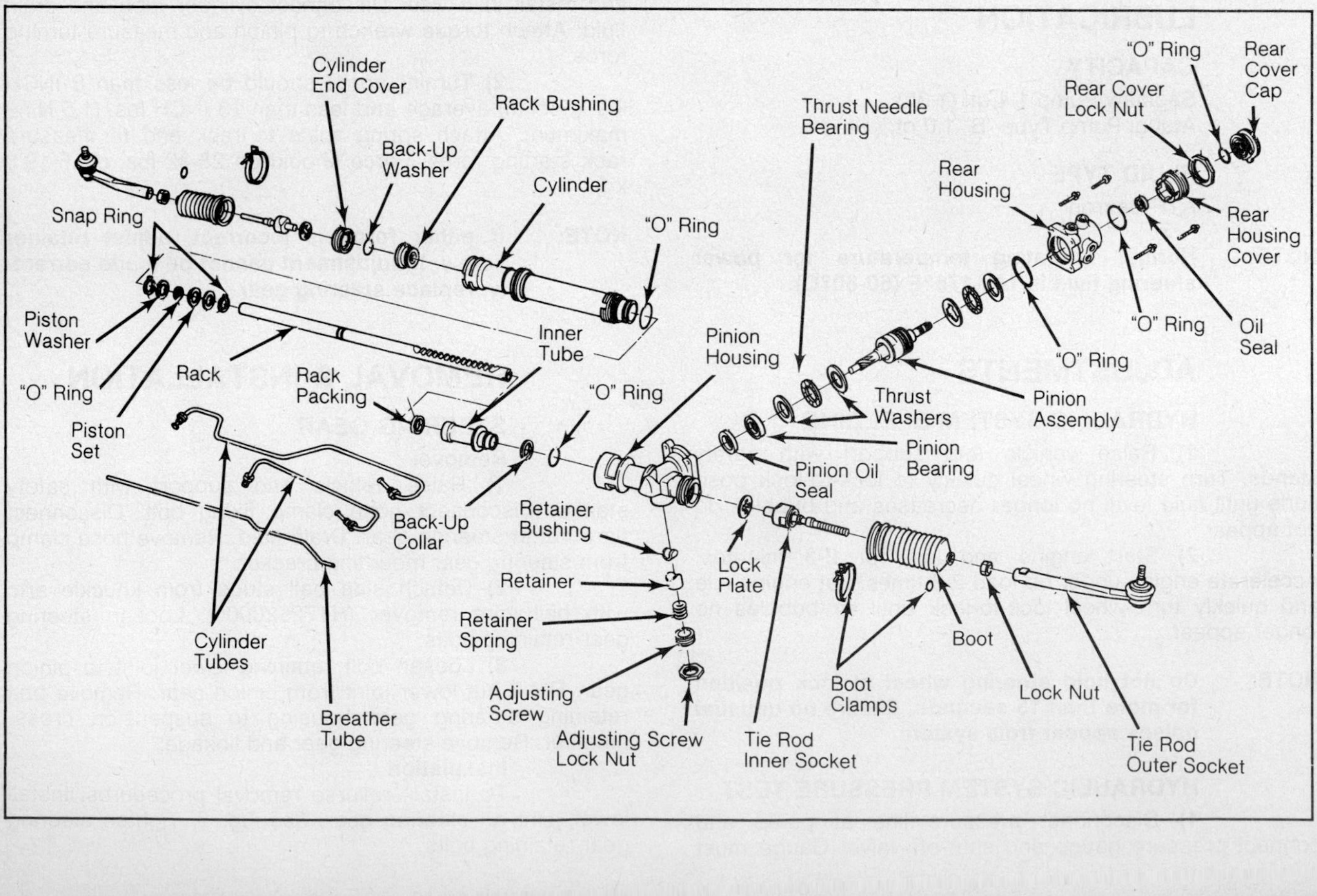

Cylinder End Cover
Rack Bushing
Back-Up Washer
Cylinder
Snap Ring
"O" Ring
Piston Washer
Rack
"O" Ring
Piston Set
Rack Packing
Inner Tube
"O" Ring
Pinion Housing
Back-Up Collar
Retainer Bushing
Retainer
Retainer Spring
Adjusting Screw
Adjusting Screw Lock Nut
Cylinder Tubes
Breather Tube
Thrust Needle Bearing
"O" Ring
Rear Cover Lock Nut
Rear Cover Cap
Rear Housing
Rear Housing Cover
"O" Ring
Oil Seal
"O" Ring
Pinion Assembly
Thrust Washers
Pinion Bearing
Pinion Oil Seal
Lock Plate
Boot
Boot Clamps
Lock Nut
Tie Rod Inner Socket
Tie Rod Outer Socket

DATSUN/NISSAN POWER RACK & PINION (Cont.)

and cylinder. Disconnect cylinder lock nut with lock nut wrench (KV48101800).

8) Separate cylinder from pinion housing. Remove rack bushing and discard. Remove cylinder "O" ring and discard.

9) Remove inner tube. Remove "O" ring and inner tube collar from inner tube. Remove rack packing and back-up collar.

Inspection

1) Thoroughly clean all parts in automatic transmission fluid and blow dry. Replace all oil seals, "O" rings and snap rings.

2) Inspect all steering gear components. Replace steering gear assembly as a unit if components are worn or damaged.

NOTE: **When assembling power steering gear, apply automatic transmission fluid to "O" rings, seals and moving parts.**

Reassembly

1) Install new "O" ring to inner tube. Attach back-up collar to inner tube and press new rack packing into place. Use less than 1320 lbs. (600 kg) force. Install inner tube.

NOTE: **To prevent damage, wrap cellophane tape around rack end edge and affected piston areas.**

2) Install new snap ring to rack. Install piston component parts to rack. Apply a coat of grease to rack surface. Install new "O" ring to cylinder.

3) Position cylinder on pinion housing and align index marks. Be careful not to damage Teflon ring. Tighten cylinder lock nut with lock nut wrench (KV48101800).

4) Attach new back-up washer and tighten end cover with cylinder holder (KV48101900). Press new pinion oil seal into pinion housing.

5) Apply coat of grease to oil seal lip. Attach thrust washers, thrust bearings and needle bearing. Apply grease to bearing. Position rack with equal protrusion at ends and with teeth facing pinion at right angles.

6) Install pinion so that punch mark on pinion shaft is located exactly on rear side as it is mounted in vehicle. Apply coat of grease to rack and pinion gear.

7) Install new "O" ring to rear housing. Install housing by aligning index marks. Tighten housing. Install new pinion shaft oil seal and press into rear housing cover. Install second "O" ring to cover.

8) Fit rear housing lock nut approximately 10 pitches down on rear housing cover. Completely tighten rear housing cover to pinion housing. Turn back cover 1 turn from that position.

9) Turn pinion shaft lock-to-lock several times and measure pinion rotating force. Force should be 0.1-0.2 ft. lbs. (.15-.25 N.m). Tighten rear cover lock nut with rear cover wrench (KV48101700).

10) Apply a coat of grease to contact surface of rack and install retainer to pinion housing. Install retainer spring and fully tighten adjusting screw. Turn back screw 20-25° and tighten lock nut.

11) Measure and adjust pinion rotating force and rack starting force. See Adjustments in this article. Temporarily tighten flare nut at rear housing side and then at cylinder side. Tighten to final torque.

12) Fit inner socket to rack end with new lock plate. Be sure lock plate tab enters groove at end portion of rack so rack and inner socket fit snugly. Tighten inner socket and bend lock plate at 2 cut-outs.

NOTE: **To prevent damage to boot, remove burrs after bending plate.**

13) Screw in tie rod outer socket until distance between boot and outside of lock nut is 1.68" (42.7 mm). Measure rack stroke. Stroke should be 2.76" (70 mm). Apply sealant to contact surfaces between boot, cylinder and breather.

14) Install boot as shown in *Fig. 4.* Set breather tube. Locate clamp bolt opposite breather tube and tighten. Ensure rack moves smoothly, boot is not deformed, and that clamp is held tightly in place.

Fig. 4: Boot and Rack Positioning

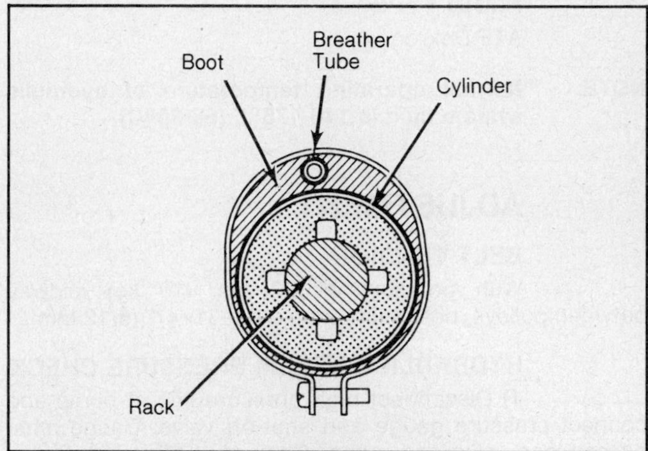
Breather
Tube
Boot
Cylinder
Rack

Apply sealant to contact surfaces.

POWER STEERING PUMP

NOTE: **Manufacturer does not recommend overhaul of power steering pump. Replace as a unit if defective.**

TIGHTENING SPECIFICATIONS

Application	Ft. Lbs. (N.m)
Side Rod-to-Knuckle Arm	40-47 (54-64)
Gear Housing Clamp Bolt	25-33 (34-45)
Lower Joint-to-Pinion Gear	24-48 (33-65)
Lower Joint-to-Rubber Coupling	29-36 (39-49)
Pressure Hose-to-Pump	29-36 (39-49)
Hose Connector-at-Steering Gear	29-36 (39-49)
Pump Mounting Bolt	20-27 (27-37)
Cylinder Lock Nut	58-72 (79-98)
Retainer Adjusting Screw Lock Nut	29-43 (39-58)
Rear Cover Lock Nut	58-72 (79-98)
Flare Nuts	29-36 (39-49)

Power Steering

DATSUN/NISSAN POWER RECIRCULATING BALL

200SX

DESCRIPTION

Power steering is composed of a power steering pump with separate reservoir, steering gear and connecting hoses. Power steering gear is an integral unit consisting of a spool valve and power cylinder (worm shaft ball nut assembly) connected to the sector shaft. Power steering gear is pressure operated by the pump through the connecting lines.

LUBRICATION

CAPACITY

200SX 1.3 qts. (1.2L)

FLUID TYPE

ATF Dexron

NOTE: **Normal operating temperature of hydraulic system fluid is 140-176°F (60-80°C)**

ADJUSTMENT

BELT TENSION

With pressure of 22 lbs. (10 kg) midway between pulleys, deflection should be .31-.47" (8-12 mm).

HYDRAULIC SYSTEM PRESSURE CHECK

1) Disconnect high pressure line at pump and connect pressure gauge and shut-off valve. Gauge must be between valve and pump. Open shut-off valve. Check fluid level and bleed air.

2) Run engine for about 5 seconds. Check fluid level and restart engine. Turn steering wheel from lock-to-lock several times to expel air from system.

3) Allow fluid to reach normal operating temperature. Turn wheel to full lock position and check pressure. It should be 740-910 psi (52-64 kg/cm²) at idle.

CAUTION: **Do not hold at lock position for more than 15 seconds.**

4) If pressure is incorrect, slowly close shut-off valve. If pressure is too low or high, the pump is faulty. If pressure is now okay, steering gear is faulty.

HYDRAULIC SYSTEM BLEEDING

1) Check fluid level in reservoir. Raise vehicle and support with safety stands. With engine off, turn steering wheel from lock-to-lock ten times. Check fluid level and add if necessary. Start engine and run until fluid is hot. Stop engine and recheck level.

2) Run engine for 3-5 seconds. Recheck fluid level, then turn steering wheel from lock-to-lock ten times. Repeat until all air is bled from system. If air cannot be completely bled, hold wheel at lock position for 5 seconds and check for fluid leakage.

BACKLASH

On Vehicle

1) Place vehicle on level dry floor. Inflate tires to specified pressure. Run engine until power steering fluid is at normal operating temperature.

2) With steering wheel in straight ahead (centered) position, turn steering wheel 1 complete turn (360°). Attach spring gauge to outer rim of wheel and measure turning force.

3) Turning force should be 6.6-7.7 lbs. (3.0-3.5 kg) for 200SX. If turning force is not to specifications, remove steering gear. Check turning force of steering gear.

Off Vehicle

1) With steering gear removed from vehicle, mount gear to a plate that can be clamped in a vise (special tool KV48100301). Turn worm shaft (where steering shaft connects) all the way from left to right several times. Center steering gear, then turn one full turn in enither direction.

2) Attach a torque wrench to worm shaft splines and measure turning force of steering gear one turn from center position. Torque should be less than 10 INCH lbs. (1.2 N.m). Turn worm shaft back to center position and measure torque.

3) Torque at this point should be .9-3.5 INCH lbs. (.1-.4 N.m) more than torque measured one turn from center position. If not, loosen adjusting bolt lock nut.

4) Turn adjusting bolt (clockwise) until correct turning torque specification is obtained. If the correct turning torque cannot be obtained, replace steering gear.

REMOVAL & INSTALLATION

STEERING GEAR

Removal

1) Remove bolt from universal joint to worm shaft. Disconnect fluid lines and wire lines up to prevent fluid spillage. Remove nut and washer from sector shaft.

2) Remove pitman arm from sector shaft using a puller. Remove steering gear mounting bolts. Remove steering gear from vehicle.

Installation

To install, reverse removal procedures. Align 4 grooves in gear arm serrations with 4 projections of sector shaft serrations. Install and tighten lock nut.

STEERING PUMP

Removal

Remove air duct. Loosen pump pulley adjusting nut. Remove belt. Loosen fluid lines at pump and block off fittings. Lift oil pump and reservoir. Disconnect hoses from pump. Remove clamps on crossmember to remove hoses.

Installation

To install, reverse removal procedures.

OVERHAUL

NOTE: **Overhaul of steering gear is limited to oil seal replacement. If any further repair is necessary, replace entire steering gear assembly. Always check turning torque before disassembly.**

ADJUSTING SCREW SEAL REPLACEMENT

Remove adjusting screw lock nut. Remove "O" ring from lock nut. Grease new "O" ring and insert in lock

DATSUN/NISSAN POWER RECIRCULATING BALL (Cont.)

nut. Replace lock nut and adjust steering gear turning torque.

NOTE: Always use new copper washer when adjusting screw lock nut is removed.

SECTOR SHAFT SEAL REPLACEMENT

Disassembly

1) With steering gear assembly mounted in a vise, set sector shaft to center position. DO NOT loosen adjusting screw lock nut. Remove sector shaft cover bolts. Using a mallet, tap sector shaft out approximately 3/4" (.75 mm).

NOTE: Wrap a piece of stiff plastic film around the sector shaft, approximately the same diameter as the sector shaft and approximately 8" (200 mm) long. This will prevent bearings from falling into gear housing.

2) Pull sector shaft from gear housing while at same time pushing plastic film into gear housing. Remove dust seal, snap ring, special large washer, and oil seal. Remove "O" ring from sector shaft cover.

Reassembly

1) Install new oil seal and special large washer. Install snap ring with radiused side of washer facing into gear housing. Press dust seal into gear housing.

2) Coat "O" ring with petroleum jelly. Install "O" ring in sector shaft cover. Make sure worm shaft and rack piston is in centered position.

Fig. 1: Exploded View of Datsun Power Steering Gear

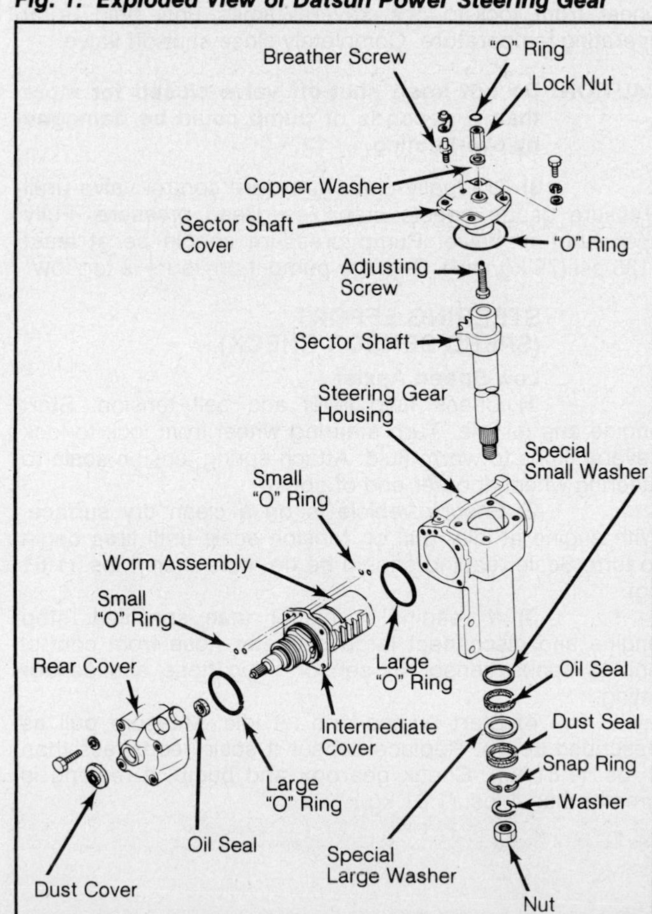
Breather Screw
"O" Ring
Lock Nut
Copper Washer
Sector Shaft Cover
"O" Ring
Adjusting Screw
Sector Shaft
Steering Gear Housing
Special Small Washer
Small "O" Ring
Worm Assembly
Small "O" Ring
Rear Cover
Large "O" Ring
Oil Seal
Dust Seal
Intermediate Cover
Snap Ring
Washer
Large "O" Ring
Oil Seal
Special Large Washer
Dust Cover
Nut

3) Wrap splined and threaded portions of sector shaft with tape to prevent damage to oil seal. Slowly insert sector shaft into gear housing, pushing plastic film out and being careful not to damage oil seal.

4) Install sector shaft fully. Remove plastic and tighten sector shaft cover bolts evenly. Check and adjust steering gear turning torque.

REAR HOUSING SEAL REPLACEMENT

Disassembly

1) Install steering gear assembly to mounting plate and place in a vise. Loosen rear cover bolts approximately .20" (5 mm). Do not remove bolts.

2) Turn sector shaft clockwise slightly to raise intermediate cover through piston.

3) Place piston and worm shaft in center position and remove sector shaft. See Sector Shaft Seal Replacement for removal procedures. Remove rear housing bolts and pull out rear housing with intermediate cover and worm gear assembly.

NOTE: When worm assembly is removed, piston may turn and come off under its own weight. Hold piston to prevent this. Do not damage Teflon ring at piston end when removing.

4) Turn worm assembly upside down and lightly tap worm shaft against bench to remove rear housing.

5) Remove rear housing oil seal. Remove large and small "O" rings from both sides of intermediate cover.

Reassembly

1) Lubricate rear housing oil seal with multipurpose grease. Apply pertoleum jelly on intermediate cover "O" rings. Install seal and "O" rings. Install worm assembly into rear housing then into gear housing. Do not tilt ball bearings.

CAUTION: As worm assembly is installed, Teflon ring will be compressed. Be careful not to damage it on corner of sector hole.

2) Be sure worm assembly is level. If bolts are tightened with worm assembly tilted, seals will be damaged. Tighten rear cover bolts in a crisscross pattern. Install sector shaft. See Sector Shaft Seal Replacement for installation procedures.

3) Make sure steering gear operates smoothly. Check and adjust turning torque.

TIGHTENING SPECIFICATIONS

Application	Ft. Lbs. (N.m)
Hose-to-Gear Housing	36-51 (49-69)
All Cover Bolts	20-24 (27-33)
Sector Shaft-to-Pitman Arm Nut	94-108 (128-147)
Gear-to-Body	36-51 (49-69)

Power Steering

HONDA POWER-ASSISTED RACK & PINION

Accord, Prelude

DESCRIPTION

Power steering is rack and pinion with the power assist proportional to both vehicle speed and steering load. Power assist is high when vehicle speed is low and reduces as vehicle speed increases.

The system consists of a power rack and pinion steering gear, steering pump, fluid filter/reservoir, control unit, vehicle speed sensor and cooler lines and hoses.

Fig. 1: View of Accord Power Steering System

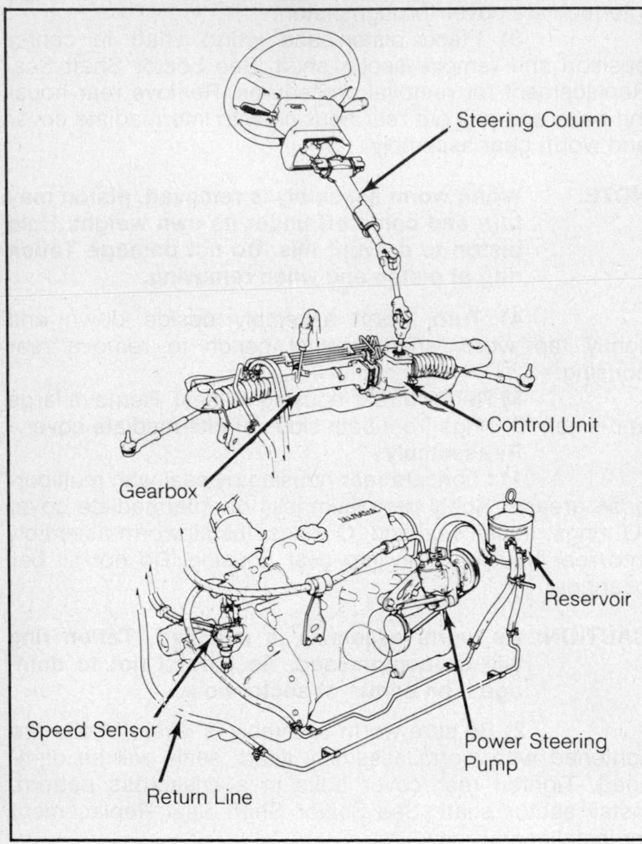
Steering Column
Control Unit
Gearbox
Reservoir
Speed Sensor
Power Steering
Pump
Return Line

Prelude uses same components in a slightly different arrangement.

LUBRICATION

HYDRAULIC SYSTEM LUBRICANT

CAPACITY

Reservoir - .7 qts. (.7L)
System - 1.5 qts (1.4L)

FLUID TYPE

Honda power steering fluid only.

CAUTION: Using ATF or other manufacturer's power steering fluid, will cause damage to system.

FLUID AND OIL RESERVOIR/FILTER REPLACEMENT

NOTE: Fluid reservoir/filter should be replaced if system is open for repair or if water or dirt gets in fluid.

1) To drain, disconnect return hose from gearbox at reservoir and place end in container. Start engine, run at idle and turn steering wheel lock-to-lock several times until fluid flow stops. Shut off engine.

2) Discard fluid. Replace reservoir/filter, if necessary. Fill reservoir to upper level mark. Start engine and run at fast idle. Turn steering wheel from lock-to-lock several times to bleed air from system. Recheck fluid level.

ADJUSTMENTS

BELT TENSION

Measure pump belt deflection midway between pulleys while pushing on belt with about 22 lbs. (9.98 kg) pressure. Deflection should be .75-1.0" (18-22 mm) on Accord, .75-.87" (18-22 mm) on Prelude.

PUMP PRESSURE CHECK

1) Check fluid level and belt tension. Adjust if necessary. Disconnect outlet hose from pump. Install pressure gauge set (07406-0010000). Fully open shut-off and pressure control valves.

2) Start engine and let idle. Turn steering wheel from lock-to-lock several times until fluid is at operating temperature. Completely close shut-off valve.

CAUTION: Do not keep shut-off valve closed for more than 5 seconds or pump could be damaged by overheating.

3) Gradually close pressure control valve until pressure gauge needle stabilizes. Read pressure. Fully open shut-off valve. Pump pressure should be at least 1135 psi (79 kg/cm²). Replace pump if pressure is too low.

STEERING EFFORT (SPEED SENSOR CHECK)

Low Speed Assist

1) Check fluid level and belt tension. Start engine and let idle. Turn steering wheel from lock-to-lock several times to warm fluid. Attach spring tension scale to steering wheel at outer end of spoke.

2) Ensure vehicle is on a clean dry surface. With engine at idle, pull on tension scale until tires begin to turn. Scale reading should be no more than 4 lbs. (1.81 kg).

3) If reading is higher than specified, stop engine and disconnect large diameter hose from control unit to speed sensor at sensor. Plug hose and sensor fitting.

4) Start engine and let idle. Measure pull as described above. Replace sensor if scale reads less than 4 lbs. (1.81 kg). Check gearbox and pump, if reading is greater than 4 lbs. (1.81 kg.).

HONDA POWER-ASSISTED RACK & PINION (Cont.)

Simulated High Speed Assist

1) Check fluid level and belt tension. Start engine and turn steering wheel from lock-to-lock to warm fluid. Stop engine and disconnect all 3 sensor hoses at speed sensor.

2) Connect special by-pass tool (07406-0010100) to the 3 hoses. This tool connects 2 hoses from cut-off valve and control unit to reservoir hose and simulates driving speeds over 30 MPH.

3) Attach spring tension scale to outer end of spoke. With vehicle on clean dry floor, start engine and let idle. Pull on tension scale until tires begin to turn.

4) Replace speed sensor if turning force is 11 lbs. (4.98 kg) or more. If turning force is less than 11 lbs. (4.98 kg), speed sensor is okay. Check sensor feed line for restriction first, then check pump and gearbox.

STEERING SHAFT

1) Adjustment is necessary only when installing column. It is not necessary if steering column was lowered for gauge or wiring access, without loosening connector bolt.

2) Properly adjusted shaft should move in .039" (1 mm), when steering wheel is turned left and out .039" (1 mm) when turned right, for a total movement of 2 mm.

3) Remove steering wheel and turn signal cancelling sleeve. Install adjustment guide (07573-6920001) on top end of steering shaft, as far as possible. Guide should bottom against turn signal switch.

Fig. 2: Installing Steering Shaft Adjustment Guide

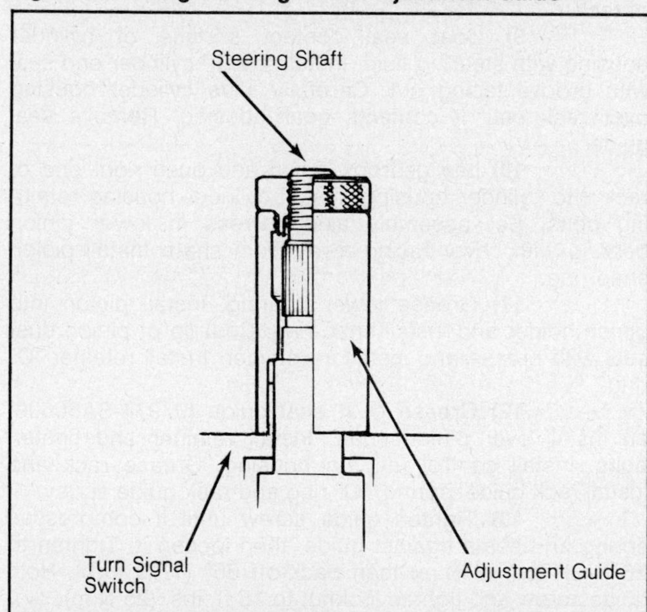
Steering Shaft
Turn Signal Switch
Adjustment Guide

Install guide as far as possible. Guide should bottom on turn signal switch.

4) Remove boot from base of steering column. Loosen top bolt in steering shaft-to-pinion shaft connector assembly. Ensure lower connector bolt is tight. Pull down on top half of connector and tighten top bolt.

5) Ensure adjustment guide is seated against turn signal switch. Remove adjustment guide. Install boot, cancelling sleeve and steering wheel. Align lugs on cancelling sleeve with grooves on steering wheel hub. Tighten steering shaft nut.

RACK GUIDE

1) Loosen lock nut on rack guide screw, using wrench (07916-SA50000). Turn guide screw until it compresses spring and seats against guide.

2) Loosen screw slightly, then tighten to 26 INCH lbs. (3 N.m). Back off screw 35° (1/10 turn). Hold guide screw and tighten lock nut. Check steering effort.

REMOVAL & INSTALLATION

CONTROL UNIT

Removal

Drain fluid. Remove gearbox shield. Thoroughly clean control unit, lines and gearbox with solvent. Blow dry. Disconnect and plug lines from control unit. Remove 2 control unit-to-gear housing bolts and remove control unit.

Installation

To install, reverse removal procedures. Coat new "O" rings with grease. Fill reservoir to upper mark with fluid. Bleed air from system and check for leaks.

GEARBOX

Removal

1) Turn steering wheel completely to left. Remove boot from base of steeering column and remove lower steering column-to-pinion connector bolt. Slide connector off pinion shaft.

2) Drain fluid and remove gearbox shield. Thoroughly clean dirt from control unit, lines and gearbox, with solvent. Blow dry. Remove front wheels. Separate tie rods from steering knuckles.

3) Remove center beam. On Accord with 5-speed transmission, remove bolt from shift rod clevis and disconnect shift rod. Disconnect shift lever torque arm from transmission.

4) On Accord with automatic transmission, push molded rubber cushion on control cable up and out on its support bracket. On Prelude, remove control cable holder and exhaust pipe hanger nuts.

5) On all models, disconnect header pipe from manifold. Disconnect and plug lines from control unit. Remove gearbox mounting brackets. Pull gearbox down so pinion shaft clevis clears frame. Move gearbox to the right, until tie rod drops free. Lower it out of car to the left.

Installation

Reverse removal procedure to install, noting tightening specifications. Use new gasket and lock nuts on header pipe. Install new cotter pins on tie-rod ends. Adjust steering shaft. *See Steering Shaft Adjustment.* Fill system with new fluid. Bleed air from system and check for leaks.

STEERING PUMP

Removal

Drain fluid. Disconnect inlet, outlet and return hoses at pump. Remove belt by loosening pump pivot and adjusting bolts. Remove pump retaining bolts and pump.

Installation

To install, reverse removal procedures. Adjust belt tension and fill reservoir with new fluid. Bleed air from system and check for leaks.

Power Steering

HONDA POWER-ASSISTED RACK & PINION (Cont.)

SPEED SENSOR

Removal

Lift up speedometer cable boot. Remove retaining clip and pull out cable. Disconnect and plug speed sensor hoses. Loosen speedometer gear set bolt and remove speed sensor.

Installation

After replacing sensor, turn steering wheel from lock-to-lock several times, with engine idling, to bleed air from system.

OVERHAUL

GEARBOX

Disassembly

1) Remove control unit as previously described. Carefully clamp gearbox in a vise. Loosen bands and pull boots away from end of gearbox. Unbend tie rod lock washers. Unscrew tie rods.

2) Push right end of rack back into cylinder housing to avoid damaging seal surface. Remove lock nut and remove rack guide screw. Remove snap-ring securing pinion lower ball bearing.

3) Lightly tap pinion to remove it from gear housing. Remove snap-ring separating pinion and lower ball bearing. Remove 4 bolts holding cylinder housing-to-gear housing. Slide cylinder housing off rack.

4) Remove rack bushing, spring and end seal from cylinder housing. Remove cylinder seal retainer, cylinder cap and steering rack from gear housing. Remove retainer washer and "O" ring from cylinder end of gear housing.

5) Remove pinion dust seal retainer bolts from gear housing and remove dust seal and "O" ring from retainer. Check upper pinion bearing for excessive play or contaminated grease.

6) If replacement is necessary, remove snap-ring and pinion holder from gear housing. Drive out bearing. Inspect needle bearings in pinion holder and gear housing for wear or damage. Replace as necessary.

7) Remove cylinder barrel and seal retainer from rack. Remove two "O" rings from cylinder cap on seal retainer. Remove "O" ring and snap-ring from seal retainer. Slide cylinder cap off seal retainer.

8) Carefully pry "white" cylinder end seal from seal retainer. Carefully remove piston ring from rack. Remove "O" ring, located under piston ring on rack.

Inspection

Replace any parts with damaged sliding surfaces. Note that rack, pinion housing and gearbox are matched and must be replaced as a unit. Always replace "O" rings, seals and gear housing washer when reassembling.

Reassembly

NOTE: Always coat new "O" rings with grease during installation.

1) Pack new upper pinion bearing with grease. If installing new bearing, use driver (07949-6110000). Apply grease to pinion holder and gear housing needle bearings. Install pinion holder in gear housing and retain with snap-ring.

2) Set gear housing aside. Install new "O" ring on rack with narrow edge facing away from rack. Apply steering fluid to guide tool (07974-SA50100). Slide guide tool, large end first, onto rack.

3) Slide new piston ring over guide tool and into piston groove, over "O" ring. Coat piston and sizing tool (07974-SA50200) with steering fluid. Slide tool onto rack and over piston ring. Slide and rotate sizing tool over piston ring to break-in new ring.

4) Grease and install "O" rings on cylinder cap. Slide cylinder cap onto seal retainer and install snap-ring and "O" ring. Grease sliding surface of new "white" cylinder end seal. Install seal with grooved end facing out.

CAUTION: Both cylinder end seals are same size but are not interchangeable; white seal goes in end of seal retainer, black seal in end of cylinder housing.

5) Install new "O" ring and retainer washer into gear housing. Install seal retainer into gear housing. Stand housing on end with flange end up. Coat cylinder end seal slider tool (07974-SA50300) with grease.

6) Make sure tool's surface isn't damaged. Set seal slider over seal, in end of retainer. Coat rack and fill teeth with grease. Insert rack into seal retainer, making sure rack teeth do not face slot in seal slider tool.

7) Pull slider tool out of seal retainer. Spread ends and remove from rack. Coat inside surface of cylinder barrel with steering fluid. Slide cylinder barrel over rack until it seats against seal retainer.

8) Install cylinder spring over rack. Coat rack bushing with steering fluid and install on spring. Grease end seal guide tool (07074-SA50400) and slip it, onto end of rack.

9) Coat seal contact surface of cylinder housing with steering fluid. Install "black" cylinder end seal with groove facing out. Carefully slide cylinder housing over rack until it contacts gear housing. Remove seal guide.

10) Lay gearbox down and push right end of rack into cylinder housing. Install cylinder housing retaining bolts. Set assembly aside. Press in lower pinion bearing with cover facing away from shaft. Install pinion snap-ring.

11) Grease lower bearing, install pinion into pinion holder and install snap-ring. Coat lip of pinion dust seal with grease and install in retainer. Install retainer "O" ring.

12) Grease dust seal guide (07974-SA50600) an install over pinion shaft. Install retainer and tighten bolts. Install control unit on housing. Grease rack and install rack guide, spring, "O" ring and rack guide screw.

13) Tighten guide screw until it compresses spring and seats against guide, then loosen it. Tighten to 26 INCH lbs. (3 N.m) then back-off 35° (1/10 turn). Hold guide screw and tighten locknut to 18 ft. lbs. (25 N.m).

14) Reverse removal procedure to complete installation. Tighten all fasteners to specifications and adjust steering shaft. *See Steering Shaft Adjustment.* Add fluid, bleed system and check for leaks.

POWER STEERING PUMP

Front Seal Replacement
Without Disassembling Pump

1) Remove pump from vehicle. Hold pulley with spanner wrench, remove pulley nut and pulley with hub.

HONDA POWER-ASSISTED RACK & PINION (Cont.)

Loosen front cover bolts diagonally and remove cover. Pry out seal with a screwdriver.

2) Ensure oil passage in front cover is not clogged. Install new seal using a 19 mm socket. Install front cover bolts and diagonally tighten to specifications. Reinstall pulley and tighten nut to specifications.

3) Position torque wrench on pulley nut and rotate pump to measure preload. Preload should be 35 INCH lbs. (4 N.m). Install belt and adjust as previously described. Add fluid, bleed air from system and check for leaks.

Disassembly

NOTE: Overhaul of Honda power steering pump is limited to replacement of front cover, control valve, pulley hub and seals.

1) Remove pump from vehicle and mount in vise. Hold pulley with spanner wrench and remove nut. If pulley is damaged, separate pulley from hub. Loosen front cover bolts and remove cover. Pry seal out of front cover.

2) Remove plunger housing from pump housing. Remove plungers and gears. Separate pump housing from port housing. Remove inlet-outlet fitting from port housing. Remove "O" rings, filter, spring and control valve from port housing.

Inspection

1) Ensure oil passage in front cover is not clogged. Inspect control valve and filter. Check valve for wear, burrs or damage to edges of groove. Slip valve into bore and check for smooth movement. Replace valve if necessary.

2) Pressure check control valve. Attach a hose to hex side of control valve and submerge valve in steering fluid or solvent. Using no more than 3 psi (.21 kg/cm²), blow into hose and check for leakage.

3) If leak is found, disassemble and clean valve. Replace any shims found during disassembly. Retest for leakage. Replace valve if leak persists. Note if valve has an identification mark to determine correct replacement valve.

Reassembly

1) Reverse disassembly procedure to reassemble, noting the following. Align plunger cut-outs before installing. *See Fig. 3.* Apply grease to all "O" rings and seals before installing.

Fig. 3: Aligning Plunger Cut-outs

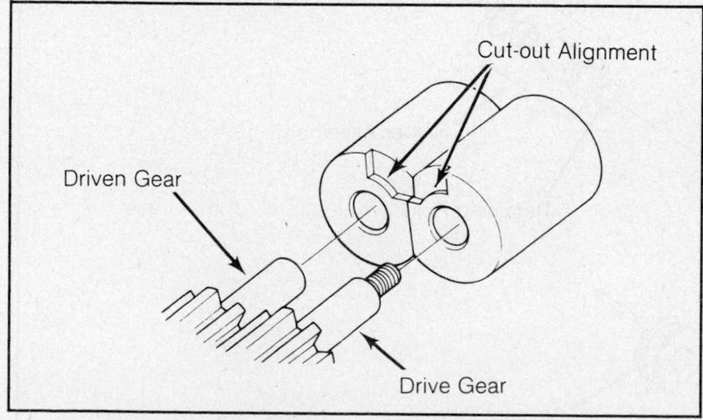
Cut-out Alignment
Driven Gear
Drive Gear

2) Lubricate gears and shafts with steering fluid. Install seal guide (07974-SA50500) over shaft of drive gear before installing front cover. Tighten front cover bolts diagonally to specifications.

3) Test pump preload by rotating pump, using a torque wrench on pulley nut. Preload should be 35 INCH lbs. (4 N.m). Install pump on vehicle. Adjust belt tension. Add fluid, bleed air from system and check for leaks.

TIGHTENING SPECIFICATIONS

Application	Ft. Lbs. (N.m)
Center Beam	16 (22)
Gearbox Mounting Brackets	16 (22)
Header Pipe	36 (50)
Pulley Nut	33 (45)
Pump Front Cover	22 (30)
Pump Pivot Bolt	36 (50)
Rack Guide Screw Lock Nut	18 (24)
Shift Rod Clevis	16 (22)
Tie Rod Nuts	54 (75)
	INCH Lbs. (N.m)
Shift Rod Torque Arm	97 (11)

ISUZU POWER-ASSISTED RACK & PINION

Impulse

DESCRIPTION

Power-assisted rack and pinion steering system consists of a vane pump, rotary valve assembly, and an oil reservoir.

The vane pump draws fluid from the reservoir and supplies it to the valve assembly. The rotary valve in the valve assembly supplies fluid to the proper side of the rack piston when the steering wheel is turned.

The belt-driven pump mounts on the front of the engine. The reservoir is near the firewall.

LUBRICATION

CAPACITY

Capacity is 1.5 pints (.7L).

FLUID TYPE

ATF Dexron

ADJUSTMENTS

HYDRAULIC SYSTEM BLEEDING

Fill fluid reservoir. Raise and support vehicle. Start engine. Turn steering wheel lock-to-lock 3 or 4 times. System is free of air when there is no buzz in hydraulic line. Also, fluid level should not increase with wheels in straight ahead position and engine stopped.

BACKLASH

Install the 7 shims from the overhaul kit in the steering housing. Install valve housing assembly and tighten to specification. Measure the clearance between mating faces of steering housing and valve housing.

Fig. 1: Exploded View of Isuzu Power-Assisted Rack & Pinion

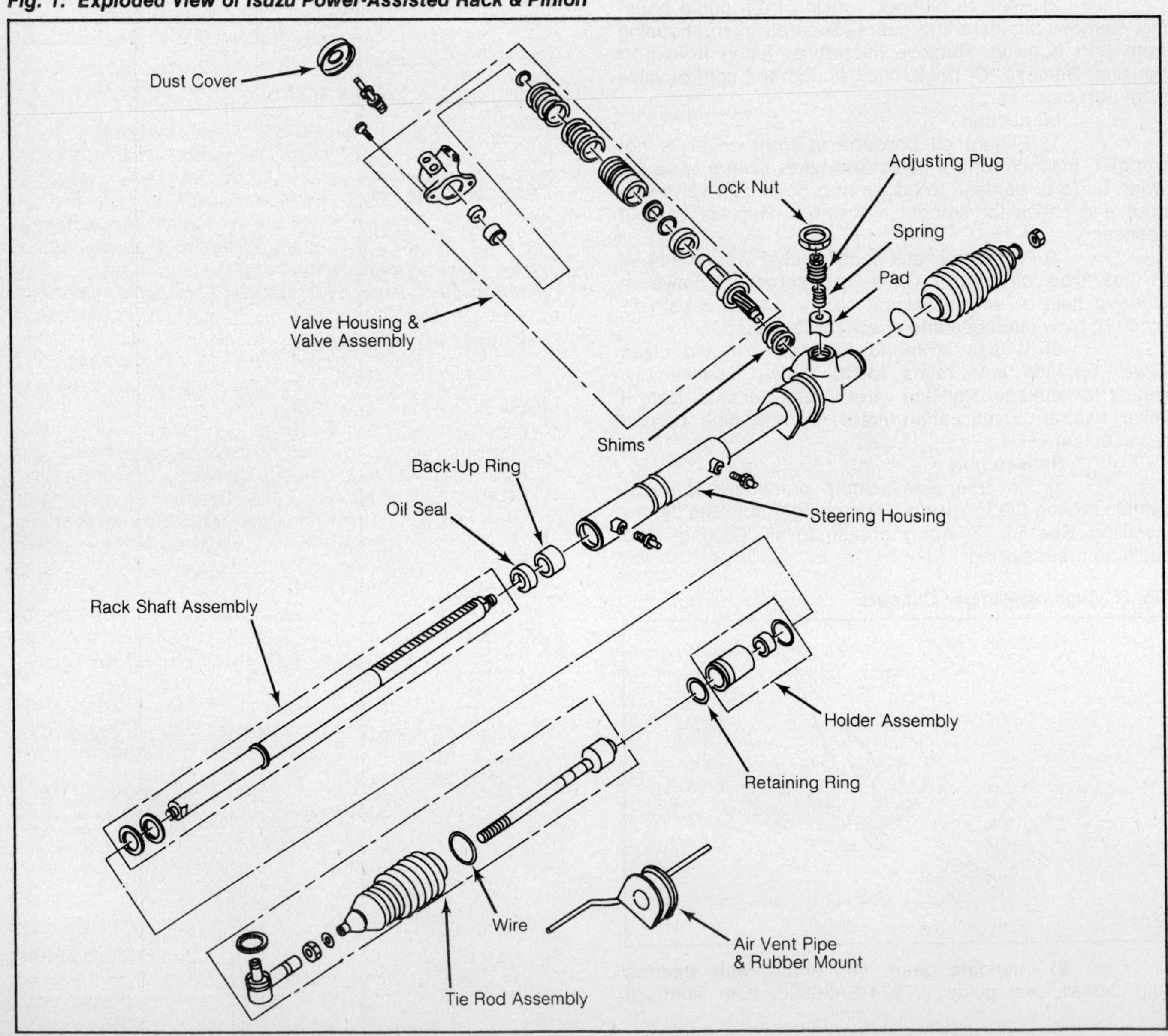
Dust Cover
Adjusting Plug
Lock Nut
Spring
Pad
Valve Housing &
Valve Assembly
Shims
Back-Up Ring
Oil Seal
Steering Housing
Rack Shaft Assembly
Holder Assembly
Retaining Ring
Wire
Air Vent Pipe
& Rubber Mount
Tie Rod Assembly

ISUZU POWER-ASSISTED RACK & PINION (Cont.)

TESTING

STEERING PUMP PRESSURE

1) Install pressure gauge (J-29877-A) with shut-off valve between steering gear and power steering pump. Connect the gauge hose furthest from the shut-off valve to the back of the power steering pump.

2) Fill fluid reservoir and bleed air from system. Open shut-off valve. Start engine. Set idle speed to 1500 RPM.

3) Measure fluid pressure when steering wheel is turned to lock in both direction. Pressure should be 925-1067 psi (65-75 kg/cm²).

4) If pressure is higher than specified, oil pressure relief valve in power steering pump is defective. If pressure is lower than specified, place steering wheel in straight ahead position.

5) Close stop valve completely. Hold engine speed at 1500 RPM. If pressure is now normal, steering gear is defective. If pressure is still low, power steering pump is defective.

REMOVAL & INSTALLATION

STEERING GEAR

Removal & Installation

1) Raise and support vehicle. Remove front wheels, disc brake calipers (do not disconnect lines), and rotors. Separate tie rod ends from steering arms. Separate steering column from steering gear.

2) Note installed position of power steering fluid lines. Disconnect and plug lines. Remove gear-to-frame mounts and lift off steering gear. To install, reverse removal procedure. Bleed air from system.

POWER STEERING PUMP

Removal & Installation

Remove engine undercover. Loosen pump bracket and remove drive belt from pulley. Disconnect and plug power steering fluid lines. Remove pump mounting bolts and lift out pump.

OVERHAUL

STEERING GEAR

CAUTION: To prevent distortion or damage to steering gear housing, do not overtighten when clamping in vise.

Disassembly

1) Place steering gear in vise. Move dust boots toward tie rod end. Hold rack with wrench and unscrew tie rod. Mark position of stub shaft relative to rack shaft. Remove valve housing and valve assembly.

2) Note number of shims removed. Shims will be used to for adjusting backlash between rack shaft and pinion if rack shaft, valve housing, and valve assembly are to be reused.

3) Remove rack retaining ring by inserting a pin punch into the hole at the outer circumference of steering gear housing. Carefully remove oil seals, rack shaft, and back-up ring. Remove seal ring from rack shaft.

4) Remove valve assembly from valve housing. Remove sleeve from stub shaft. Remove all "O" rings and seals from sleeve. Drive oil seal out of valve housing.

Inspection

1) Inspect all parts for excessive wear or damage. Replace cylinder assembly if the inner wall is scored or damaged. Sleeve and rotor are precision-machined must be replaced assembly if damaged.

2) Replace the track-rod assembly if any play is felt when moving the ball on tie rod. Clean all parts with compressed air before assembly.

Assembly

1) Using special tool (J-33997-7), install center oil seal on stub shaft with seal lip toward rotor. Replace all seals and "O" rings on sleeve and valve assembly.

2) Assemble sleeve and valve assembly. Pin on sleeve must be properly fitted into groove at rear end of oil seal. Install retaining ring. Install oil seal and ball bearing in end of valve housing. Install valve assembly in valve housing.

3) Place new seal ring, back-up ring, holder assembly, and oil seal on rack shaft. Lubricate all seals with clean ATF and install rack shaft in cylinder. Distance between tip of rack shaft and end of housing should be approximately 3".

4) Install original valve assembly shims in the steering housing. If valve housing assembly, valve assembly, rack shaft, or steering housing has been replaced, new shims will have to installed and backlash adjusted at this time. *See Adjustments* in this article.

5) Install valve housing with oil pipe fitting face turned toward the adjusting plug opening. Recess for pinch bolt at serrated portion of stub shaft must be pointed away from the adjusting plug opening.

6) Tighten valve housing bolt to specification. Install adjusting pad, spring, and plug in steering housing. Tighten adjusting plug to 5.4 ft. lbs. (7.3 N.m) then back off 30-35°. Install lock nut.

7) Install tie rods on rack ends. Tighten to specification. Install boots.

POWER STEERING PUMP

Disassembly

1) Clamp pump in vise. Remove front bolts and carefully remove front body assembly from rear assembly. Carefully disassembly front body side assembly.

2) To remove drive shaft from front body, tap on splined end with plastic hammer. Remove oil seal from pump body.

3) Remove "O" rings, flow control valve, pressure sensing valve, and springs from rear body.

Inspection

Inspect all parts for scoring, wear, or damage. The main and sub cartridge assembly in the front body are precision finished and must be replace together if worn or damaged. Pressure sensing valve and flow control valve must also be replaced if defective. Check drive shaft for excessive runout.

Reassembly

1) Wash all parts in solvent and blow dry with compressed air. Lubricate parts with ATF before reassembly. Install "O" rings, flow control valve, and pressure sensing valve in rear body.

ISUZU POWER-ASSISTED RACK & PINION (Cont.)

Fig. 2: Exploded View of Isuzu Power Steering Pump

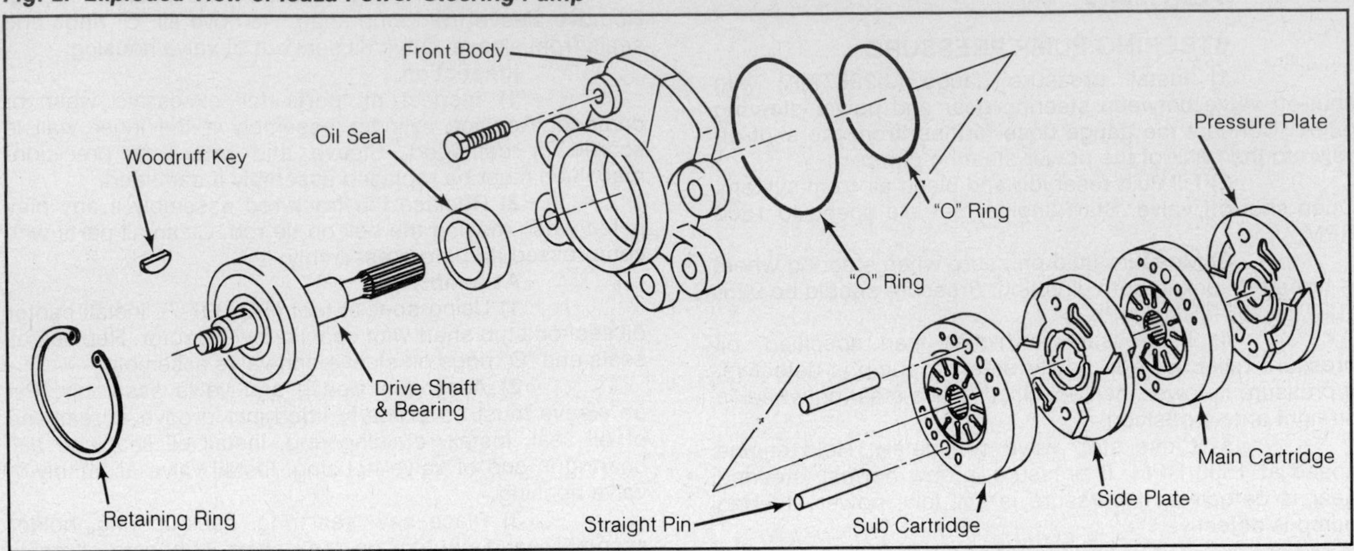
Front Body
Oil Seal
Woodruff Key
Pressure Plate
"O" Ring
"O" Ring
Drive Shaft & Bearing
Main Cartridge
Side Plate
Retaining Ring
Straight Pin
Sub Cartridge

2) Install oil seal and drive shaft with bearing into front body. Assemble front body side main and sub cartridges and side plates. Set chamfered face of main cartridge to rear body side.

3) Install front body assembly into rear body assembly. Install bolts and tighten to specification.

TIGHTENING SPECIFICATIONS

Application	Ft. Lbs. (N.m)
Pump Front-to-Rear Body Bolts	36-43 (49-58)
Tie Rod-to-Rack	58-72 (79-98)
Valve Housing-to-Steering Gear Bolt	15-22 (20-30)

ISUZU POWER ASSISTED RECIRCULATING BALL

P'UP

DESCRIPTION

The power assisted recirculating ball steering system on the P'UP consists of the power steering gear assembly, hydraulic pump, and hydraulic lines.

The power steering gear is an integral type. It consists of the conventional ball-screw type steering gear combined with a rotary and torsion bar type control valve and power cylinder.

The oil pump is a constant delivery vane type and is belt driven. The pump and gear assemblies are connected by hoses.

LUBRICATION

CAPACITY

1.1 qts. (1L)

FLUID TYPE

ATF (Dexron)

ADJUSTMENTS

BELT

The power steering belt is adjusted by rotating the pump body on mounting bolts. Belt should have .4 in. (1 mm) of deflection when measured. *See Fig. 1.*

Fig. 1: Checking Power Steering Pump Belt Adjustment

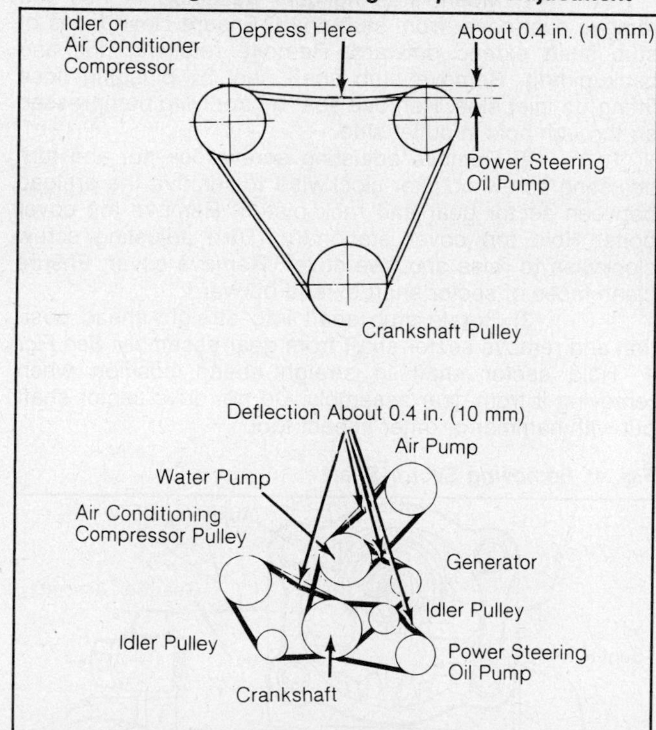
Idler or
Air Conditioner
Compressor
Depress Here
About 0.4 in. (10 mm)
Power Steering
Oil Pump
Crankshaft Pulley
Deflection About 0.4 in. (10 mm)
Air Pump
Water Pump
Air Conditioning
Compressor Pulley
Generator
Idler Pulley
Idler Pulley
Power Steering
Oil Pump
Crankshaft

Measure deflection at locations indicated.

SYSTEM BLEEDING

1) Raise front end of vehicle so that the wheels are off the ground. Fill fluid reservoir. With engine off, turn steering wheel lock-to-lock several times. Recheck fluid level. Refill fluid if necessary.

2) With engine at idle, turn steering wheel lock-to-lock several times. Recheck fluid level and add fluid if necessary. Lower vehicle to ground and turn steering wheel lock-to-lock with engine at idle.

NOTE: **Avoid holding steering wheel at full lock position for more than 10 seconds or fluid temperature will increase sharply.**

3) With steering wheel in straight ahead position and engine off, look for fluid rising in reservoir. If fluid rises, air is trapped in system. Repeat bleeding procedure in step **2)**. Check fluid in reservoir. Check fluid joints for leakage.

SECTOR GEAR BACKLASH

NOTE: **Sector Gear Backlash adjustment is part of steering gear reassembly procedure.**

Fig. 2: Exploded View of Power Steering Gear Assembly

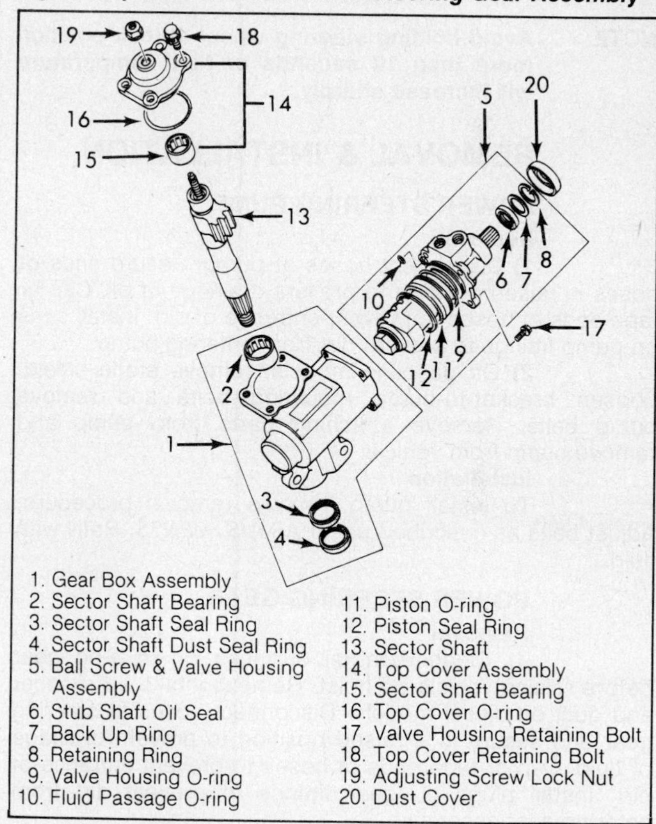
19
18
14
16
15
5
20
13
8
6
7
10
17
9
12
11
2
1
3
4

1. Gear Box Assembly
2. Sector Shaft Bearing
3. Sector Shaft Seal Ring
4. Sector Shaft Dust Seal Ring
5. Ball Screw & Valve Housing Assembly
6. Stub Shaft Oil Seal
7. Back Up Ring
8. Retaining Ring
9. Valve Housing O-ring
10. Fluid Passage O-ring
11. Piston O-ring
12. Piston Seal Ring
13. Sector Shaft
14. Top Cover Assembly
15. Sector Shaft Bearing
16. Top Cover O-ring
17. Valve Housing Retaining Bolt
18. Top Cover Retaining Bolt
19. Adjusting Screw Lock Nut
20. Dust Cover

TESTING

HYDRAULIC SYSTEM TESTING

1) With engine not running, disconnect pressure hose from pump. Install gauge (J-29877) and shut-off valve in hose using extra hose. Gauge capacity should exceed 1250 psi (88 kg/cm²). Pressure gauge must be connected between valve and pump.

2) Bleed system by holding gauge beneath fluid reservoir with shut-off valve open. Check fluid level in reservoir with engine idling. Refill if necessary. Turn steering wheel from lock-to-lock several times until

ISUZU POWER ASSISTED RECIRCULATING BALL (Cont.)

thermometer indicates that hydraulic fluid has reached a temperature of 122°-140° F (50°-60° C).

NOTE: **To prevent scrubbing flat spots on tires, do not turn steering wheel more than 5 times without moving vehicle.**

3) When checked with engine running at 1500 RPM and valve closed, fluid pressure must be 1065-1210 psi (75-85 kg/cm²). If fluid is not at specified pressure, oil pump is malfunctioning.

NOTE: **DO NOT leave shut-off valve fully closed more than 15 seconds or pump may be damaged internally.**

4) If step **3)** indicates that pump pressure is to specifications, open valve fully to test steering gear assembly. With engine running, turn steering gear lock-to-lock and note oil pressure. If steering gear assembly is okay, pressure will be 1065-1210 psi (75-85 kg/cm²). If pressure is not to specification, steering gear may require repair.

NOTE: **Avoid holding steering wheel at lock position more than 10 seconds or fluid temperature will increase sharply.**

REMOVAL & INSTALLATION

POWER STEERING PUMP

Removal

1) Disconnect hoses at pump. Secure ends of hoses in raised position to prevent drainage of oil. Cap or tape ends of hoses to prevent entrance of dirt. Install caps on pump fittings to prevent dirt from entering pump.

2) On gasoline models, remove stone shield. Loosen bracket-to-pump mounting bolts and remove pump belts. Remove attaching parts from pump and remove pump from vehicle.

Installation

To install pump, reverse removal procedure. Adjust belts as described under *ADJUSTMENTS*. Refill with fluid.

POWER STEERING GEAR

Removal

1) Clean external surfaces of steering gear before raising vehicle on hoist. Remove intake air silencer and duct on diesel models. Disconnect hoses at steering gear and secure in a raised position to prevent drainage of fluid. Cap or tape ends of hoses to prevent entrance of dirt. Install plugs on gear fittings to prevent dirt from entering gear assembly.

NOTE: **Before removing steering shaft coupler from stub shaft on gear assembly, mark location of coupler to shaft.**

2) Remove pinch bolt on the universal joint. Remove 2 steering column-to-instrument panel bolts. Disconnect universal joint from stub shaft by pulling column and shaft approximately 2 in. (50 mm) in toward cab.

3) Remove pitman arm nut and washer. Remove pitman arm from shaft with puller (J-29107). Remove engine stone shield. Remove steering gear-to-frame attaching bolts and remove gear assembly from vehicle.

Installation

To install steering gear, reverse removal procedure. Replace locking nuts and bolts and torque to specification. Refill system with fluid and bleed system.

OVERHAUL

POWER STEERING GEAR

NOTE: **Avoid clamping steering gear in vise by power cylinder portion. Internal damage to cylinder may result.**

Fig. 3: Incorrect Clamping of Power Steering Gear Assembly

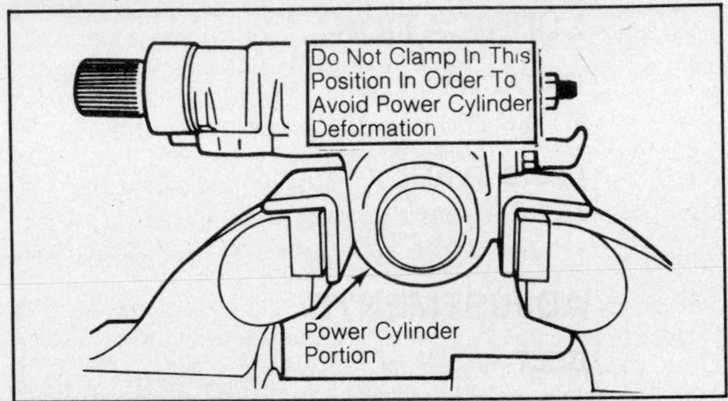
Do Not Clamp In This Position In Order To Avoid Power Cylinder Deformation
Power Cylinder Portion

Gear assembly must be clamped by the sector shaft portion to prevent damage.

Disassembly

1) Mount steering gear assembly in vise and remove dust cover from stub shaft. Ensure clean faces of stub shaft extend outward. Remove retaining ring and backup ring. Remove stub shaft seal by plugging hose fitting on inlet side. Remove seal by applying compressed air through hole in outlet side.

2) Remove adjusting screw lock nut and turn adjusting screw counter-clockwise to remove the preload between sector gear and rack piston. Remove top cover bolts. Hold top cover stationary. Turn adjusting screw clockwise to raise and free cover. Remove cover. Ensure clean faces of sector shaft extend outward.

3) Rotate stub shaft into straight-ahead position and remove sector shaft from gear assembly. *See Fig. 4.* Hold sector shaft in straight-ahead position when removing it from gear assembly. Do not drive sector shaft out with hammer or other impact tool.

Fig. 4: Removing Sector Shaft

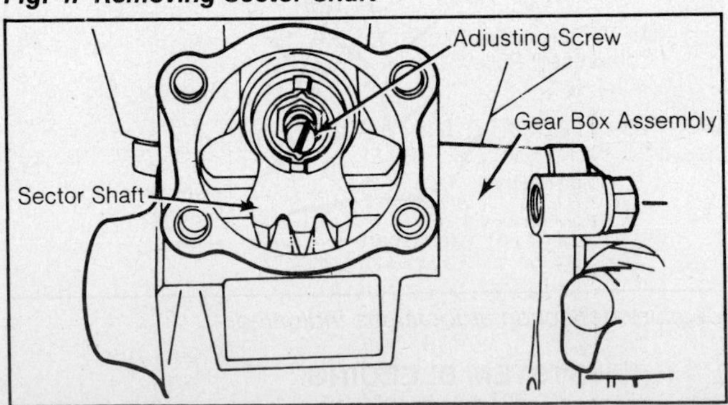
Adjusting Screw
Gear Box Assembly
Sector Shaft

DO NOT use hammer or other impact tool to remove sector from steering gear.

ISUZU POWER ASSISTED RECIRCULATING BALL (Cont.)

NOTE: **Always keep ball screw and valve housing assembly in a horizontal position. When held vertically, rack piston will fall off onto the end of worm. This causes rack piston to slip out of end of worm shaft and the balls to fall apart.**

4) Remove 4 bolts retaining valve housing to gear box. Remove ball screw and valve housing assembly from gear assembly. Remove valve housing O-rings, piston seal ring with O-ring and top cover O-ring. Remove sector shaft seals using a wire. Discard them as new parts are installed at reassembly.

Inspection

Wash disassembled parts in clean solvent before inspection. Check all gear assembly parts for wear or chipping or other damage. If any internal parts are damaged, entire ball screw and valve housing parts should be replaced as an assembly. Oil seal, O-rings, hose fitting and dust cover may be replaced individually.

Reassembly

1) If sector shaft bearing was removed, install new bearing into top cover and gear box housing.

NOTE: **Install bearing flush with recessed face of housing and with name on bearing facing out.**

2) Install sector shaft seal ring and dust seal ring in gear box and apply a thin coat of grease to lip of seals. Apply a thin coat of grease to rack piston O-ring and install it to rack piston carefully to prevent twisting. Install seal ring to rack piston over O-ring by expanding it. *See Fig. 5.* Apply a coat of grease to entire circumference of seal ring.

Fig. 5: Installing Rack Piston Seals

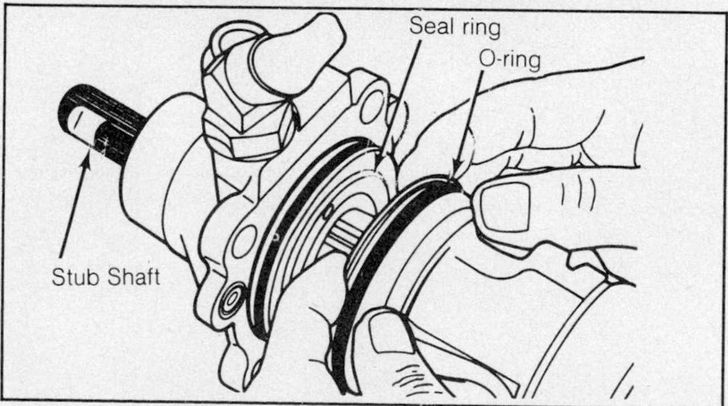
Seal ring
O-ring
Stub Shaft

3) Apply a thin coat of grease to valve housing O-ring and top cover O-ring and install O-rings to grooves carefully to prevent twisting. Insert ball screw and housing assembly into gear assembly, while keeping it horizontal. Install valve housing retaining bolts.

4) Install new stub shaft oil seal into valve housing using seal driver (J-26508). Install backup ring, retaining ring and dust cover in order just mentioned. The backup ring and retaining ring should be installed so that its face with rounded outer circumference is turned to oil seal.

5) If hose was removed, install hose fitting to valve housing with a new O-ring. Tape sector shaft spline to protect seal rings. Install sector shaft, aligning sector and rack in the straight-ahead position. *See Fig. 4.*

6) Thread adjusting screw into top cover. Turn adjusting screw counterclockwise until the top cover contacts gear box. Continue for 2 more turns and install cover bolts.

7) Check if sector and rack are installed properly by turning the stub shaft lock-to-lock. Sector and rack are installed properly if stub shaft turns more than 4 turns.

8) Adjust backlash between rack piston and sector by placing relative parts in a straight-ahead position and rotating stub shaft with a torque wrench and socket. Starting torque is normal if reading of torque wrench is within 5.2-7.8 ft. lbs. (0.6-0.9 N.m) when stub shaft begins to rotate sector shaft from rest.

9) If reading of wrench deviates from specified range, make adjustment by turning adjusting screw. Backlash is decreased when screw is turned clockwise. install new lock nut when backlash is adjusted.

POWER STEERING PUMP

Disassembly

Remove components from pump in this order: Pulley, End Plate Retaining Ring, End Plate, Pressure Plate Spring, Pump Cartridge and Shaft, Pressure Plate, Cam, Retaining Ring, Rotor, Vane Thrust Plate and Dowel Pins, O-rings, Control Valve Assembly, Oil Seal and Pump Housing. *See Fig. 6.*

Fig. 6: Exploded View of Power Steering Pump

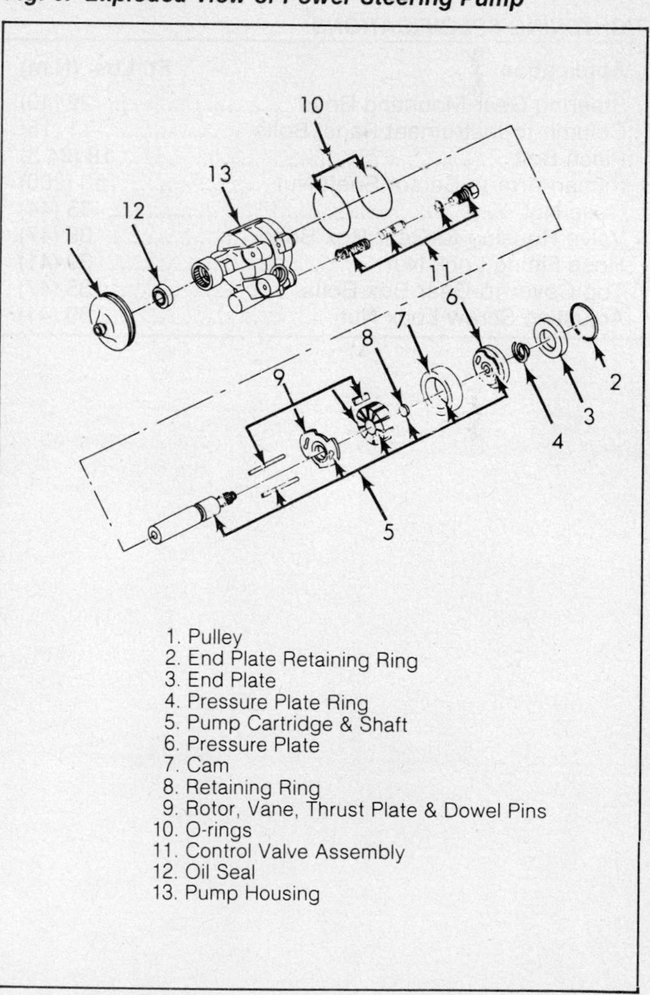
10
13
12
1
11
6
7
8
9
2
3
4
5
1. Pulley
2. End Plate Retaining Ring
3. End Plate
4. Pressure Plate Ring
5. Pump Cartridge & Shaft
6. Pressure Plate
7. Cam
8. Retaining Ring
9. Rotor, Vane, Thrust Plate & Dowel Pins
10. O-rings
11. Control Valve Assembly
12. Oil Seal
13. Pump Housing

Inspection

1) Check that groove in rotor is free from excessive wear and that vane slides smoothly. When part

ISUZU POWER ASSISTED RECIRCULATING BALL (Cont.)

replacement becomes necessary, pump cartridge should be replaced as an entire assembly.

2) Check that sliding faces of vanes are free from wear. When part replacement becomes necessary, pump cartridge should be replaced as an entire assembly.

3) Check that innner face of cam should have a trace of uniform contact without a sign of wear. When part replacement becomes necessary, pump cartridge should be replaced as an entire assembly.

4) Check pressure plate and thrust plate that sliding faces of parts must be free from step wear which may be felt with finger nail. Parts may be reused after lapping face.

5) Check that sliding face of valve is free of burrs and damage. Parts with minor scores may be reused after making corrections with emery cloth (#800 or finer).

6) Oil seal sliding faces must be free from a step wear which may be felt by a finger nail. Needle bearing face must be free from disintegration and wear.

Reassembly

To reassemble pump, reverse order of disassembly procedure. Install new seals. Install pulley using a press.

TIGHTENING SPECIFICATIONS

Application	Ft. Lbs. (N.m)
Steering Gear Mounting Bolts	29 (40)
Column-to-Instrument Panel Bolts	11 (15)
Pinch Bolt	18 (24.5)
Pitman Arm-to-Sector Shaft Nut	160 (200)
Hose Nut	33 (44)
Valve Housing-to-Gear Box Bolts	35 (47)
Hose Fitting Lock Nut	30 (41)
Top Cover-to-Gear Box Bolts	35 (47)
Adjusting Screw Lock Nut	30 (41)

JAGUAR POWER-ASSISTED RACK & PINION

DESCRIPTION

Vehicles are equipped with a power-assisted rack and pinion type steering system. The system consists of 2 main components.

The rack and pinion steering gear and the power assist pump. The 2 components are connected by flexible fluid lines. The power assist pump and fluid reservoir are combined.

LUBRICATION

FLUID TYPE

ATF Dexron II

ADJUSTMENTS

CONTROL VALVE & PINION

1) Connect a 100 psi (7 kg/cm²) pressure gauge into pump return line, start engine and allow to idle. Pressure reading should be approximately 40 psi (2.8 kg/cm²). Turn steering gear left and right a small amount.

CAUTION: Excessive turning of steering gear will cause damage to pressure gauge.

2) Pressure should increase equal amounts as wheel is turned in either direction. A slight fall in pressure occurring before rise in pressure indicates a defective control valve. Stop and restart engine. Check that steering does not kick to one side.

HYDRAULIC SYSTEM

1) Connect a 1500 psi (100 kg/cm²) pressure gauge to pump pressure line, start engine and allow to idle.

2) Turn steering to full lock and exert pressure on steering gear. Pressure should be 1100-1200 psi (77.5-84.4 kg/cm²) at idle.

NOTE: If pressure is below 1100 psi (77.5 kg/cm²) at idle, but rises with engine speed increase, problem is either a defective pump control valve or internal leakage in rack and pinion.

3) If system pressure readings were not to specifications, connect a shut-off valve (JD. 10-2) between pump and pressure gauge. This will isolate steering pump from steering gear and determine if problem is in gear or pump. *See Fig. 2.*

4) With shut-off valve open, start engine and allow steering fluid to reach normal operating temperature. Close shut-off valve and repeat pressure tests.

NOTE: Do not keep shut-off valve closed for more than 5 seconds at a time, otherwise fluid will overheat and damage to system could occur.

5) If test pressures are not to specifications, fault is in steering gear. If test pressures are still not to specifications, fault is in pump. See Overhaul in this article.

Fig. 1: Exploded View of Jaguar Power-Assisted Rack and Pinion Steering Gear

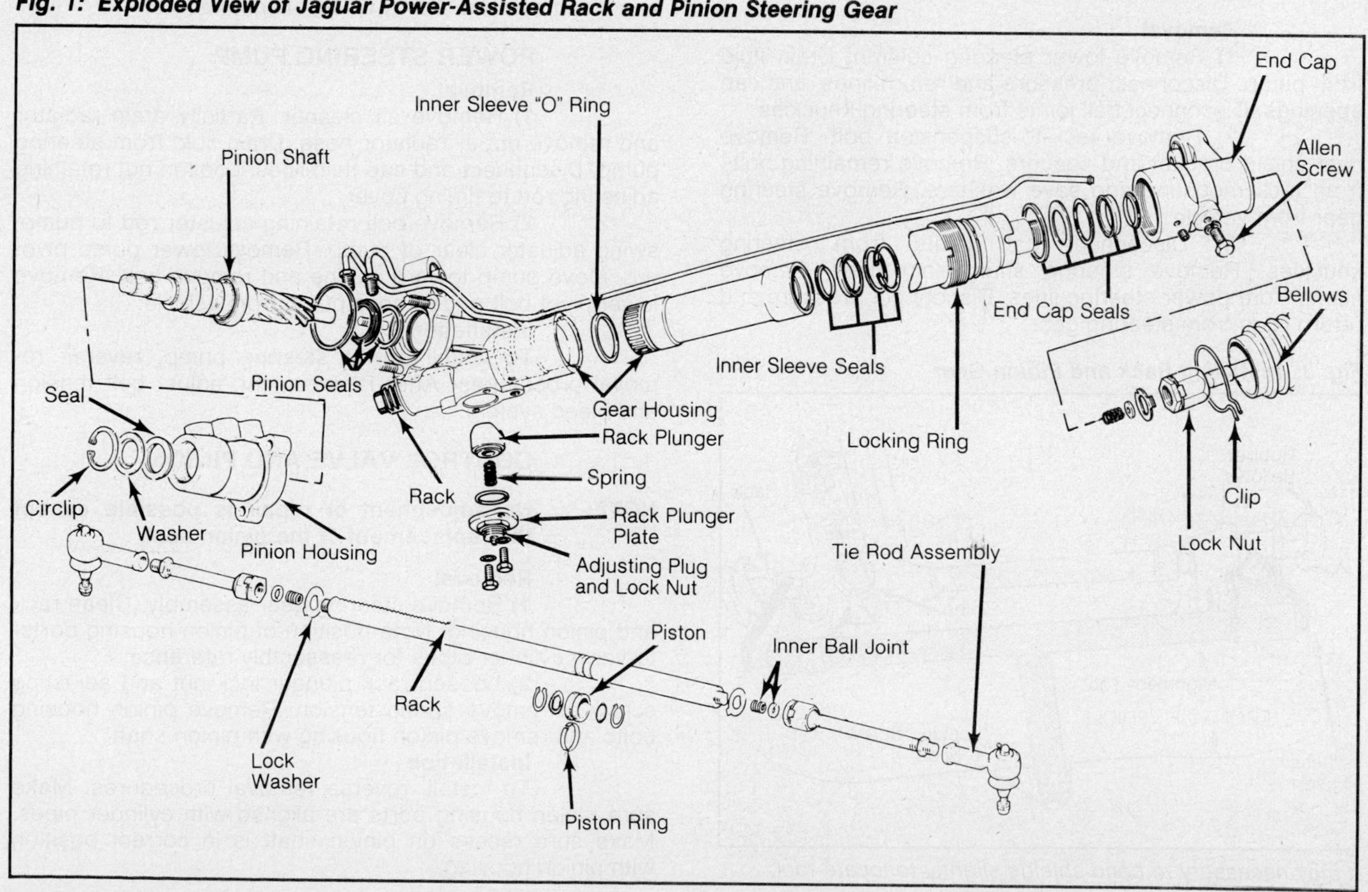
End Cap
Inner Sleeve "O" Ring
Pinion Shaft
Allen Screw
Bellows
End Cap Seals
Inner Sleeve Seals
Seal
Pinion Seals
Gear Housing
Rack Plunger
Locking Ring
Spring
Rack
Circlip
Clip
Rack Plunger Plate
Washer
Pinion Housing
Lock Nut
Tie Rod Assembly
Adjusting Plug and Lock Nut
Piston
Inner Ball Joint
Rack
Lock Washer
Piston Ring

JAGUAR POWER-ASSISTED RACK & PINION (Cont.)

Fig. 2: Pressure Gauge and Shut-Off Valve Connections

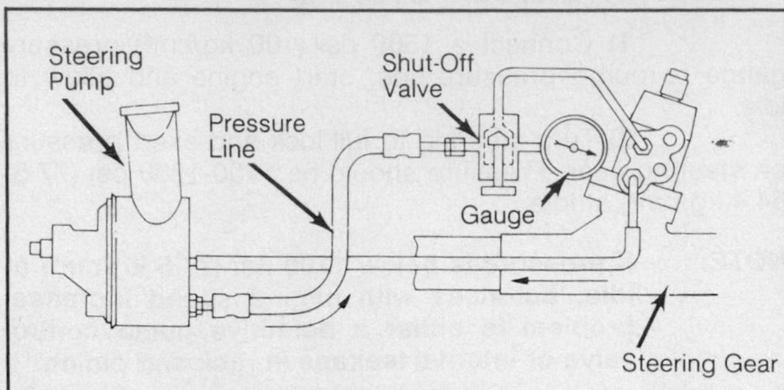
Steering
Pump
Shut-Off
Valve
Pressure
Line
Gauge
Steering Gear

By adding a shut-off valve you can isolate steering pump from steering gear.

SYSTEM BLEEDING

1) Turn wheels to full left lock, add fluid to "COLD" level mark on dipstick. Start engine and idle. Turn steering wheel lock-to-lock to expel air. Check fluid level.

2) Straighten wheels and run engine for several minutes. Turn off engine, check fluid level. Fluid should be up to "HOT" mark on dipstick.

REMOVAL & INSTALLATION

STEERING GEAR

NOTE: **The amount and location of all washers and spacers must be noted for correct installation.**

Removal

1) Remove lower steering column. Drain fluid from pump. Disconnect pressure and return lines, and cap openings. Disconnect ball joints from steering knuckles.

2) Remove rack-to-suspension bolt. Remove heat shield bracket and spacers. Remove remaining bolts from rack mounting and save washers. Remove steering gear from vehicle.

3) Disconnect ball joints from steering knuckles. Remove steering shaft from gear. Remove clamp from power steering lines. Disconnect pressure and return lines from steering gear.

Fig. 3: Installing Rack and Pinion Gear

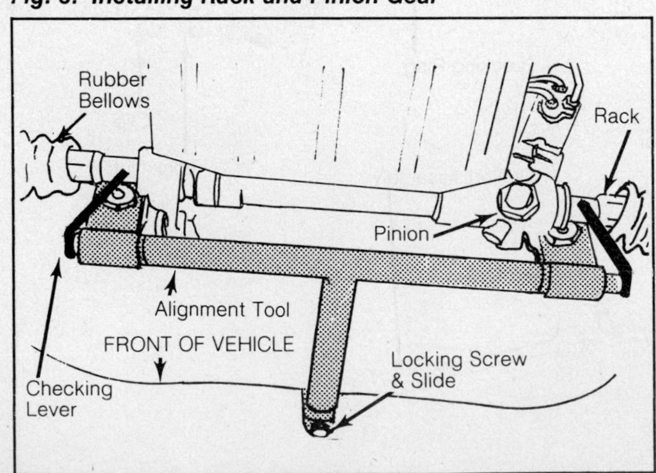
Rubber
Bellows
Rack
Pinion
Alignment Tool
FRONT OF VEHICLE
Locking Screw
& Slide
Checking
Lever

It may necessary to bend shields slightly to locate tool.

4) Drain fluid and cap openings. Remove nuts and bolts attaching steering gear to sub frame. Position a jack under sub frame. Remove bolts attaching sub frame-to-frame.

5) Lower sub frame until rear mounting bolts just clear sub frame. Turn steering to full right lock. Move steering gear to right until left tie rod clears. Remove steering gear from vehicle.

Installation

1) Position rack against mounting brackets and center lugs on bracket. Insert shims between lug and bracket to insure a gap of .05" (1.3 mm) on both sides of rack lug and mounting bracket.

2) Insert retaining bolts but do not tighten. Repeat centering procedure on upper and lower mountings on pinion side of rack. Make sure heat shield mounting bracket is located on upper mounting bolt.

3) Remove clip retaining rubber bellows to rack housing and fold bellows back to expose inner ball joints. Install attachment brackets, of alignment tool (JD.36A), over large hex head bolts on lower control arms.

4) It may be necessary to bend shields slightly to locate tool correctly. *See Fig. 3.* Release locking screw and slide collar along tool to front of suspension unit until slot engages front weld flange of crossbeam.

5) Lock slide in this position. Rotate alignment tool until legs rest on tie rods. To adjust slack, loosen lock nut of single bolt mounting and raise or lower same side of rack assembly.

6) Remove tool, fully tighten rack mounting lock nuts. Reposition bellows and secure clips. On all models, reinstall tie rods and power steering hoses. Refill and bleed system. Check wheel alignment.

POWER STEERING PUMP

Removal

1) Remove air cleaner. Partially drain radiator and remove upper radiator hose. Drain fluid from steering pump. Disconnect and cap fluid lines. Loosen nut retaining adjusting rod to timing cover.

2) Remove bolt retaining adjuster rod to pump, swing adjuster clear of pump. Remove lower pump pivot nut. Move pump toward engine and remove belt. Remove lower pivot bolt and remove pump from vehicle.

Installation

To install power steering pump, reverse removal procedures. After replacement, adjust belt tension and bleed system.

CONTROL VALVE AND PINION

NOTE: **No adjustment or repair is possible except the replacement of the pinion seal.**

Removal

1) Remove steering gear assembly. Clean rack and pinion housing. Note position of pinion housing ports-to-valve cylinder pipes for reassembly reference.

2) Loosen rack plunger lock nut and adjusting screw to remove spring tension. Remove pinion housing bolts and remove pinion housing with pinion shaft.

Installation

To install, reverse removal procedures. Make sure pinion housing ports are aligned with cylinder pipes. Make sure recess on pinion shaft is in correct position with pinion housing.

JAGUAR POWER-ASSISTED RACK & PINION (Cont.)

OVERHAUL

RACK ASSEMBLY

Disassembly

1) Clean rack and pinion housing, drain assembly of fluid. Remove clips attaching bellows to tie rods and fold bellows back, exposing tie rod inner ball joint.

2) Straighten lock tab of tie rod inner ball joint. Remove tie rods from rack by loosening lock nut on inner ball joint. Note position of pinion housing-to-valve cylinder pipes, remove pipes. Remove air transfer pipe.

3) Remove Allen screw from end cap. Remove locking ring from end housing. remove end housing. Remove rack plunger lock nut, adjusting nut, spring and plunger. Remove pinion housing cover. Remove pinion housing from rack housing.

4) Remove pinion from pinion housing. Remove snap ring, washer and seal from pinion housing. Remove rack from rack housing. Remove porting adapter and slide porting ring along cylinder until feed hole is exposed.

5) Using a scribe (or similar tool) pry seal until seal can be removed from cylinder with a hooked wire. Remove all seals, "O" rings and sleeves from rack housing.

NOTE: Do not remove seals from pinion piston.

Inspection

1) Clean all parts in solvent and dry. Do not wipe dry as lint could contaminate parts and cause malfunction when assembled. Check all parts for excessive wear, scratches, nicks or scoring. Replace parts as necessary.

2) Check rack teeth and pinion teeth for chips, burrs and other damage. Always replace all "O" rings and seals upon reassembly. Check rubber bellows for cracks, splits or holes, replace as necessary.

Reassembly

1) Lubricate all "O" rings, seals and sleeves before installation. Also lubricate all moving parts before installation. Install seal and "O" ring to end housing.

2) Install new center feed porting adapter to porting ring. Position ring to allow conical seating on adapter to engage with seating on cylinder and tighten.

3) Install rack seal over rack teeth up against piston. Install anti-extrusion ring to recess in back of rack seal. Lubricate inside of rack housing and grease rack. Insert rack into rack housing with firm steady pressure until seal seats against abutment face.

4) Make sure piston ring collapses and enters rack housing without damage. Install new seal, washer and snap ring to pinion housing. Install new pinion valve seal to pinion shaft (located against pinion bearing).

5) Lubricate pinion shaft, piston seals, and bearing. Carefully install pinion shaft to pinion housing, tap gear end of shaft lightly to make sure it is seated.

6) Grease pinion teeth and small journal of pinion. Install pinion and housing (use new gasket) to rack housing. Make sure rack teeth and pinion teeth mate correctly.

7) Make sure pinion housing ports are correctly aligned so cylinder-to-valve pipes can be installed. Install seals to end housing.

8) Install end housing-to-rack housing and screw locking ring into end housing just enough to hold mounting feet in parallel alignment.

9) With end housing and mounting feet in alignment, tighten locking ring. Install rack plunger, spring, adjusting plug and lock nut. Tighten adjusting plug, while moving rack through full stroke, until rack is hard to move.

10) Back off adjusting nut just enough to obtain a smooth rack movement (approximately 1/8 turn). Tighten lock nut while holding adjusting plug from turning.

Fig. 4: Rack End Play Adjustment

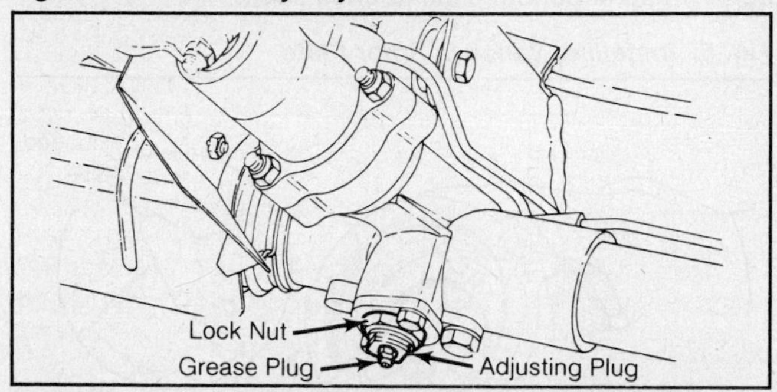
Lock Nut
Grease Plug
Adjusting Plug

To obtain smooth rack movement, back off 1/8 turn.

11) Install air transfer pipe and cylinder-to-valve pipes. Place bellows onto tie rods, small opening towards outer ball joint. Install tie rod inner ball joint to rack. Make sure lock washer tab is aligned with slot in rack end.

12) Pull rack out until rack teeth can be held in soft-jawed vise. Tighten tie rod inner ball joint lock nut. Repeat procedure for other tie rod. Bend lock washer tab into rack slots with punch.

13) Place 1 to 2 oz. of grease into each bellows, attach bellows to rack housing and tie rod with wire clips. Remove plug in rack plunger adjusting plug and install grease nipple.

14) Using a hand grease gun, fill with approximately 5 strokes of the grease gun. Remove grease nipple and install plug.

POWER STEERING PUMP

Disassembly

1) Remove rear mounting plate and pulley from pump. Remove front mounting plate from pump and clean pump body. Remove pressure outlet union and mounting plate studs from rear of pump.

2) Tip pump and remove flow control valve and spring. Place pump in padded vise and tap pump casing from body. Remove "O" rings from pump body and magnet from flange.

3) With pin punch, push retaining ring free from groove and lever from body. Remove spring retaining plate and spring. Remove "O" ring from recess in pump body.

4) Remove Woodruff key from shaft. Tap roller spindle toward body. Remove pump assembly from body. Remove "O" ring from recess in pump body. Remove dowel pins.

Cleaning and Inspection

1) Clean all parts with lint-free cloth. Replace all "O" rings and seals. Check all parts for scratches, nicks, burrs or excessive wear.

JAGUAR POWER-ASSISTED RACK & PINION (Cont.)

2) Replace rotor ring and vanes if excessive wear or chatter marks are present. Check flow control valve for free movement in bore. Lubricate all parts with power steering fluid before reassembly.

3) Check interference fit between pump shaft and pulley. Replace parts if interference fit is less than .001" (.025 mm) or more than .0026" (.066 mm).

Reassembly

1) Lubricate drive shaft seal and fit into pump shaft housing. Fit "O" ring to lower recess in pump body. Place dowel pins in locating holes. With cutaway face uppermost, fit bottom plate to drive shaft.

Fig. 5: Installing Vanes in Rotor Plate

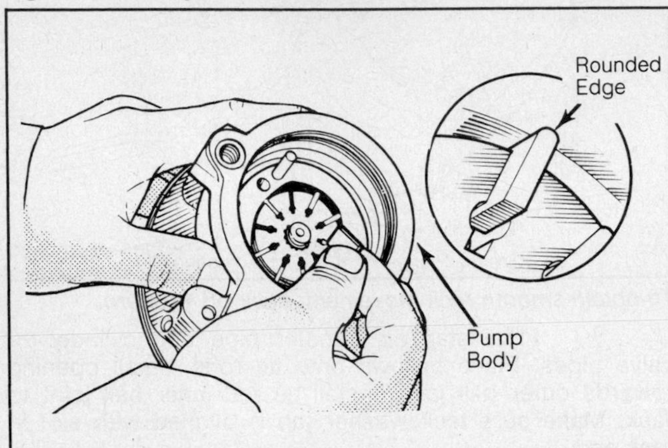
Rounded Edge
Pump Body

Rounded end of vanes face out.

2) Fit rotor over splines of drive shaft (countersunk face towards thrust plate) and secure with snap ring. Insert vanes in rotor with curved edge out.

3) Fit drive shaft and rotor to pump body. Make sure dowel pins locate through smallest holes of bottom plate. With arrow towards rear of housing, place pump ring chamber over rotor and dowel pins.

4) With spring recess up, fit chamber top plate over dowel pins. Push complete pump assembly home. Fit "O" ring into upper recess of pump body. Fit spring to recess in top plate.

5) Place retaining plate over spring and push into body. Fit "O" rings to port recess, and large "O" ring to outside pump body and magnet to flange.

6) Place pump casing over body. Locate mounting studs into outer casing and into pump body. Place outer casing over pump body. Tighten mounting studs.

7) Install spring and flow control valve. Fit pressure outlet union. Place Woodruff key in drive shaft spindle. Install pulley and mounting plates. Refill system with fluid and bleed system.

TIGHTENING SPECIFICATIONS

Application	Ft. Lbs. (N.m)
Center Feed Porting Adapter Ring	22-25 (30-34)
Pump High Pressure Fitting	25-40 (34-54)
Rack Housing End Plate Lock Ring	80-90 (109-122)
Rack Housing Mounting Bolts	49-55 (67-75)
Tie Rod Inner Ball Joint Lock Nut	45-55 (61-75)

Fig. 6: Exploded View of Power Steering Pump

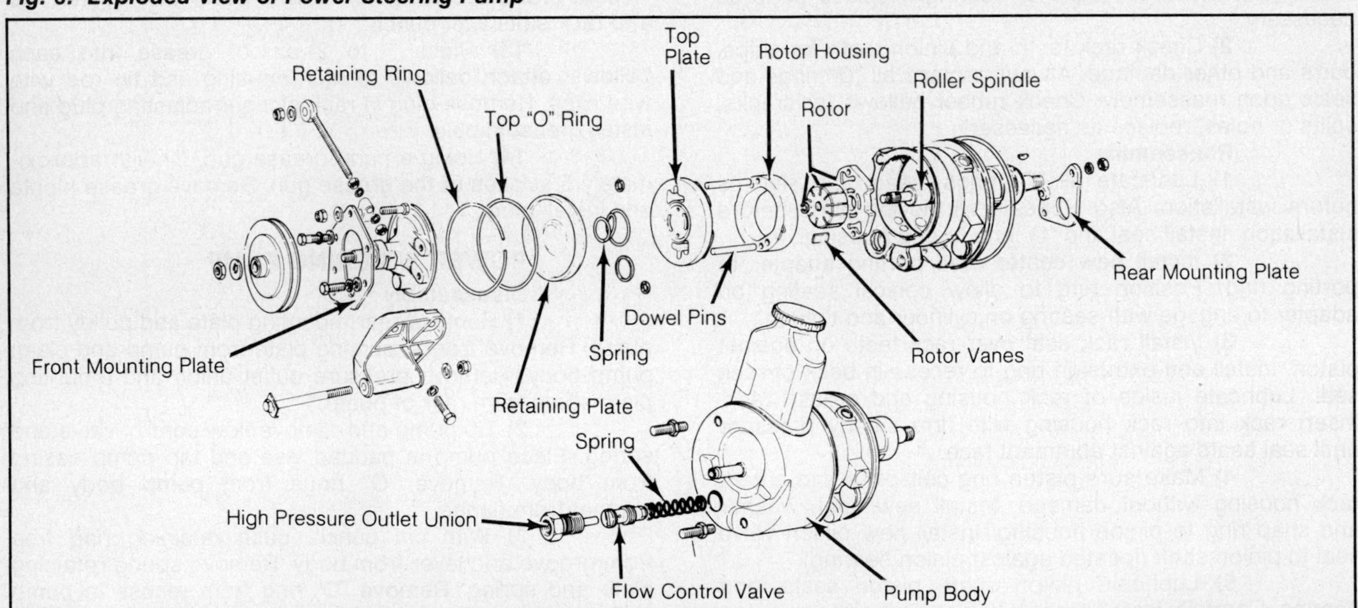
Top Plate
Rotor Housing
Retaining Ring
Roller Spindle
Top "O" Ring
Rotor
Rear Mounting Plate
Dowel Pins
Front Mounting Plate
Spring
Rotor Vanes
Retaining Plate
Spring
High Pressure Outlet Union
Flow Control Valve
Pump Body

MAZDA POWER-ASSISTED RACK & PINION

GLC FWD & 626

DESCRIPTION

Vehicles are equipped with a power-assisted rack and pinion type steering system. The system consists of 2 main components.

The rack and pinion steering gear and the power assist pump. The 2 components are connected by flexible fluid lines. The power assist pump and fluid reservoir are combined.

FLUID TYPE

ATF Type F

HYDRAULIC FLUID FILLING

Fluid levels should be checked before engine is started and when fluid is still cool. To check and fill, remove the fluid level gauge on oil pump assembly and check fluid level. If fluid is needed, fill with approved fluid through the gauge tube and recheck. Do not overfill.

ADJUSTMENTS

HYDRAULIC FLUID BLEEDING

1) Raise front of vehicle and support with safety stands. Turn steering wheel completely to the left and right several times. Add fluid as required. Repeat this process until fluid level no longer decreases.

NOTE: **Do not start engine for first step.**

2) Start engine and let it idle. Turn steering wheel completely to left and right several times. Check fluid level and add fluid as necessary. Continue this process until there is no longer a decrease in fluid level.

HYDRAULIC SYSTEM PRESSURE TEST

1) Connect a pressure gauge between steering pump and steering gear. *See Fig. 1.* Bleed any air from system.

Fig. 1: Presure Gauge Test Set Up

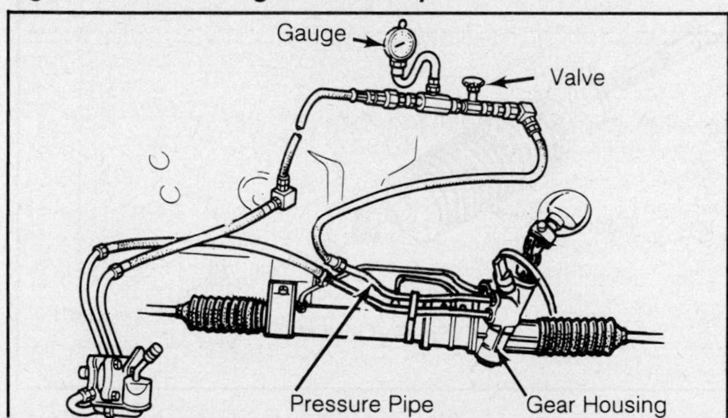
Gauge
Valve
Pressure Pipe
Gear Housing

Put gauge set valve on gear housing side.

2) Open valve on gauge, start engine and turn steering wheel back and forth to increase fluid temperature. To measure fluid pressure generated by the oil pump, completely close the gauge valve for 15 seconds and increase engine speed to 1,000-1,500 RPM.

NOTE: **Leaving gauge valve closed for more than 15 seconds will increase fluid temperature and could adversely affect the oil pump.**

3) To measure the fluid pressure generated at the gear housing, first open the gauge valve completely, increase engine speed to 1,000-1,500 RPM and turn steering wheel all the way to the left and right. Do not keep steering wheel fully turned for more than 10 seconds. The correct gear housing fluid pressure limit is 924 psi (6,500 kpa) at a temperature of 122-140°F (50-60°C).

4) If the oil pump must be replaced, replace it as a complete assembly.

REMOVAL & INSTALLATION

Removal

1) Raise front of vehicle and support with safety stands. Remove front tires and check oil seal for damage.

2) Remove tie rod nuts and disconnect ball studs from spindle using appropriate ball joint removal tool. Remove splash shield.

3) Remove lock bolt from bottom of the steering column and the pinion. Disconnect power steering hoses at steering gear and install plugs in hose to protect against contamination.

4) Remove steering gear mounting bolts, gear assembly and linkage.

Installation

To install reverse removal procedure. After installation bleed air from system, check fluid level and check system for leaks. Check and adjust toe-in.

POWER STEERING PUMP

Removal

Raise front of vehicle and support with safety stands. Remove splash shield, alternator and belt. Disconnect the pressure switch and the power steering lines from pump. Cap lines to prevent contamination. Remove bolts holding pump assembly on bracket and remove pump.

NOTE: **On GLC models it is necessary to disconnect the air cleaner duct.**

Installation

Reverse removal procedures to install. After installation, adjust belt tension, bleed air from steering system and check for leaks.

OVERHAUL

STEERING GEAR

Disassembly (GLC)

1) Secure steering gear in a soft jaw vise. Remove boot clips and boots. Remove rack end, note that both washer and damper ring are taken out at the same time.

2) Remove pressure lines, bracket and mounting rubber. Use a screwdriver to remove the oil seal. Remove valve case and gasket at the same time.

3) Loosen lock nut on back side of gear assembly and remove the adjustment cover, spring and pressure pad. Loosen lock nut on the bottom side of pinion and remove the plug and thrust washer. Remove

MAZDA POWER-ASSISTED RACK & PINION (Cont.)

Fig 2: Exploded View of GLC Gear Assembly

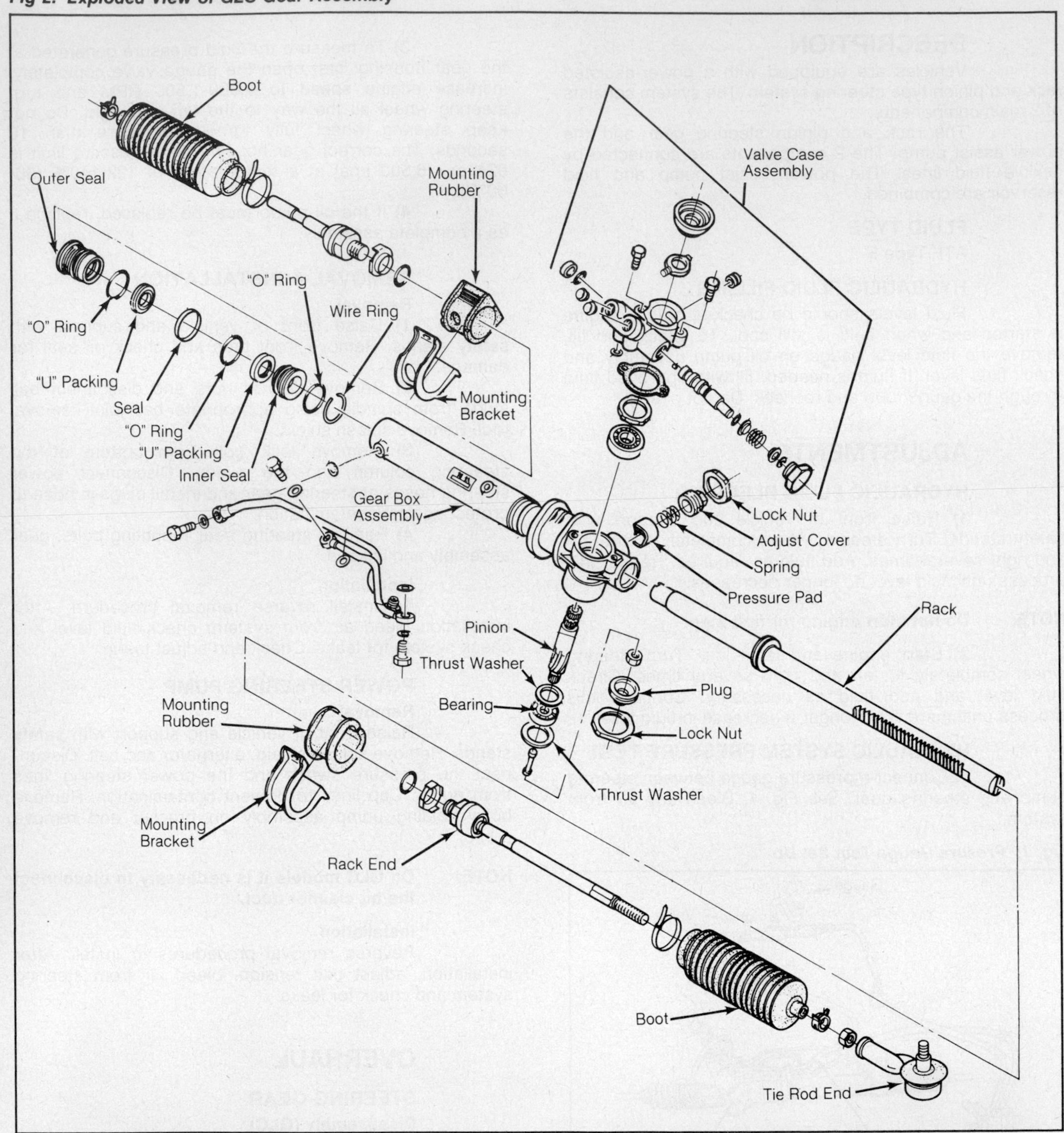
Boot
Outer Seal
"O" Ring
"U" Packing
Seal
"O" Ring
"U" Packing
Inner Seal
"O" Ring
Wire Ring
Mounting Rubber
Mounting Bracket
Gear Box Assembly
Valve Case Assembly
Lock Nut
Adjust Cover
Spring
Pressure Pad
Rack
Pinion
Thrust Washer
Bearing
Plug
Lock Nut
Thrust Washer
Mounting Rubber
Mounting Bracket
Rack End
Boot
Tie Rod End

the spacer and ball bearing on the opposite side at the same time. Remove the pinion.

4) Slowly pull out the rack and outer seal. Remove wire ring and inner seal.

Disassembly (626)

1) Secure steering gear in a soft jaw vise. Mark threaded portion of tie rod ends as a guide for installation and remove tie rod ends, boot bands and boots.

2) Turn gear all the way to the left and remove lock nut. Remove tie rods after securing toothed part in soft jaw vise. Remove spring pins from pin holes with a pair of pliers.

3) Remove the oil seal by threading the rack bushing assembly 2 or 3 turns onto the gear housing, plug the return line with a finger and then blow compressed air in from the pressure line forcing the oil seal to the end of rack bushing assembly. Remove rack assembly and oil seal together. Remove snap ring with snap ring pliers.

4) Remove gear from vise, place it on a press. *See Fig. 1.* Push on pinion to remove control valve assembly from housing.

MAZDA POWER-ASSISTED RACK & PINION (Cont.)

Fig. 3: Exploded View of 626 Gear Assembly

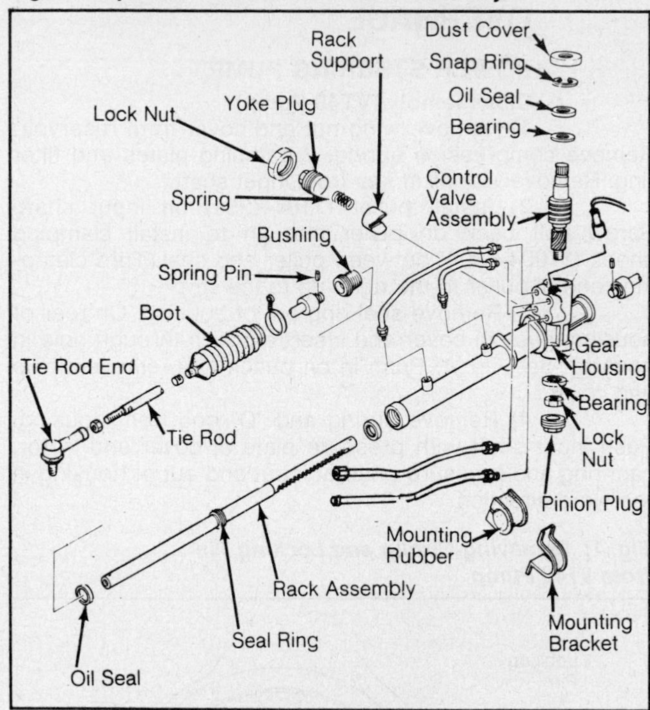
Rack Support
Dust Cover
Snap Ring
Oil Seal
Bearing
Lock Nut
Yoke Plug
Control Valve Assembly
Spring
Bushing
Spring Pin
Boot
Gear Housing
Tie Rod End
Bearing
Tie Rod
Lock Nut
Pinion Plug
Mounting Rubber
Rack Assembly
Mounting Bracket
Seal Ring
Oil Seal

5) Attach protector (49 G030 595) to the rack in order to cover teeth and remove rack.

Fig 4: Removing Control Valve Assembly

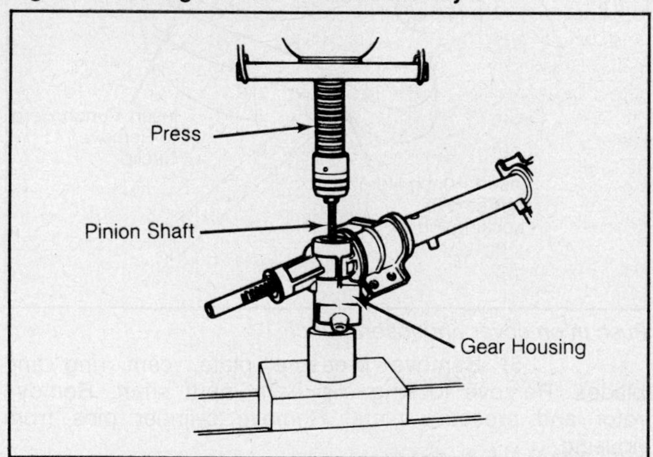
Press
Pinion Shaft
Gear Housing

NOTE: **If protector is not used, the oil seal within housing will be damaged.**

6) Remove seal and "O" ring with a small screwdriver. Carefully fit a new "O" ring into groove and seal ring into ring groove by hand. Remove bearing.

Inspection

Clean all parts. Inspect for wear or damage. Replace parts if problems are found. If any part of the gear assembly is damaged, replace as a complete gear assembly. If the teeth of the rack are worn or damaged, replaced rack assembly as one unit.

Reassembly (GLC)

1) Before assembly, coat or fill the following parts with a lithium base grease: pinion teeth, pinion installation position of gear housing, sliding parts, rear surface of rack support, rack teeth, tie rod ball joints and inside right and left boots.

2) Secure gear assembly in a soft jaw vise. Install outer seal on non-tooth side of rack and install rack in gear box. Install wire ring and inner seal.

3) Install pinion, insert thrust bearing with its slide surface (gray colored) side facing bearing. Set the ball bearing and spacer at opposite side. Install plug, tighten to 29-36 ft. lbs. (40-50 N.m) and back off 10-20° and install lock nut.

4) Install pressure pad and spring. Tighten to 29-36 ft. lbs. (40-50 N.m) and back off 40-60°, install lock nut. Install gasket and valve case in gear box. Lightly tap in oil seals.

5) Check operation torque of pinion with a torque wrench. Proper operation torque of pinion is 4.3-9.5 ft. lbs. (.5-1.1 N.m). Install return lines, use a new copper washers. Install rack ends and boots.

Reassembly (626)

1) Before assembly, coat or fill the following parts with a lithium base grease: pinion teeth, pinion installation position of gear housing, sliding parts, rear surface of rack support, rack teeth, tie rod ball joints and inside right and left boots.

2) Secure gear assembly in a soft jaw vise. Coat piston seal ring with ATF type F. Attach protector (49 G030 595) to rack and install to gear housing. Install oil seal, rack and bushing assembly.

3) Check that rack and pinion gear are correctly meshed. Coat the control valve, bearing and seal with ATF. Install control valve, bearing and oil seal assembly by tapping with a piece of pipe. Install snap ring with snap ring pliers.

4) Loosley tighten rack support, spring, yoke plug and lock nut. Secure toothed end of rack in a vise and tighten tie rod to specifications. Tap new spring pin in place.

5) Install bearing and torque lock nut to 29-36 ft. lbs (40-50 N.m). Apply sealant to pinion plug and install. Tighten yoke plug to 48 INCH lbs. (5.5 N.m) and loosen and retighten. Repeat this several times and after final torque loosen plug 45°.

6) Measure pinion rotation torque with a preload attachment (49 0180 510B) and a spring gauge. The proper pinion rotation torque (spring gauge reading) is 17.6-42.3 oz.(500-1,200 g). Complete reassembly by installing return lines, tie rod boots and tie rods.

TIGHTENING SPECIFICATIONS

Application	Ft. Lbs. (N.m)
Mounting Bracket Bolts	23-34 (32-47)
Tie Rod Lock Nut	51-58 (70-80)
Rack-to-Tie Rod	
GLC	43-58 (60-80)
626	58-72 (80-100)

Power Steering

MERCEDES-BENZ POWER-ASSISTED RECIRCULATING BALL

DESCRIPTION

Power steering system is composed of power steering pump, steering gear and connecting hoses. Both ZF and VT49 type pumps are used. Pumps have integral reservoirs. Some of these pumps are made of a light alloy material. The light alloy pumps are interchangeable with the cast iron type.

All power steering pumps are engine driven vane type with a control valve. The purpose of the power steering gear pump is to supply fluid (under pressure) to the steering gear.

Steering gear has integral piston/steering nut. Fluid pressure to each side of piston/steering nut is controlled by a control valve which is moved by a lever from steering column shaft. Steering system has a digressive action. Boost is relatively weak in the central range, and increases as steering resistance increases.

LUBRICATION

CAPACITY

1.6 qts. (1.5L)

FLUID TYPE

ATF (Automatic Transmission Fluid)

REMOVAL & INSTALLATION

POWER STEERING PUMP

Removal

1) Remove power steering tank cover, spring and damping plate. Drain tank with a syringe. Disconnect high pressure and return hoses and cap openings.

2) Loosen retaining bolts and push pump towards engine, remove "V" belts from pulley. Remove retaining bolts. Remove pressure pump with carrier.

Installation

To install, reverse removal procedures. Fill system with recommended fluid.

POWER STEERING GEAR

NOTE: The stop for the full lock position is incorporated into the housing itself. This gear can be recognized by an "A" stamped on housing.

Removal

1) Drain fluid from power steering pump. Disconnect and plug pressure line and return line from steering gear. Remove retaining bolts from steering coupling.

2) Remove rear exhaust system. On 380 models, remove left hand exhaust pipe at manifold. On all models, disconnect center link and tie rod from pitman arm. Remove bolts retaining steering gear to frame.

3) Force steering gear from steering column shaft, in a downward direction. Drain fluid from steering gear. Remove steering coupling and pitman arm from gear (be sure to mark pitman shaft-to-pitman arm position for proper assembly).

Installation

To install, reverse removal procedures. Replace locking nuts and bolts, tighten to specifications. Fill system with recommended fluid.

OVERHAUL

POWER STEERING PUMP

Disassembly (VT49 Pump)

1) Remove wing nut and cover from reservoir. Remove compression spring, 2 damping plates and filter ring. Remove Woodruff key from input shaft.

2) Install puller (1104-7251) on input shaft. Screw bolt back on puller enough to install clamping shoes (11004-6304) between puller and seal. Turn clamping cone of puller to the right, up to the stop.

3) Remove seal ring out of housing. On rear of housing, push in cover and insert a punch through hole in housing. *See Fig. 1.* Push in on punch and remove circlip and cover.

4) Remove spring and "O" ring from housing. Push input shaft with pressure plate at cover end, rotor, cam ring and pressure plate at input end out of housing in rearward direction.

Fig. 1: Removing Circlip and Locking Pin from VT49 Pump

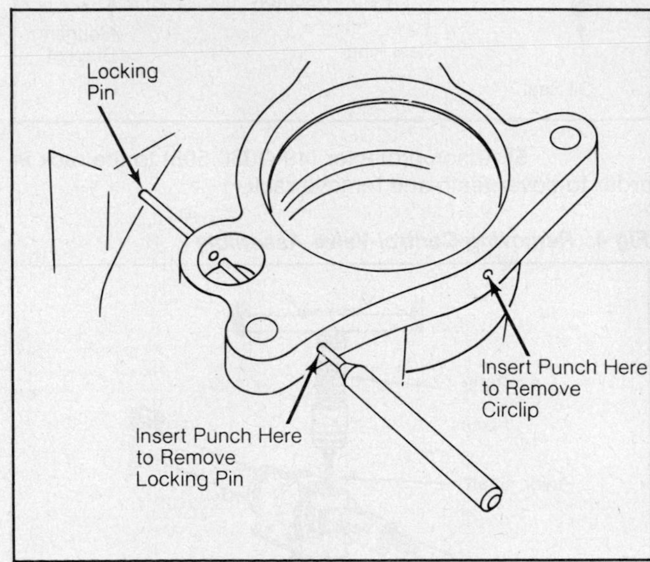
Locking Pin
Insert Punch Here to Remove Circlip
Insert Punch Here to Remove Locking Pin

Push in on cover and insert punch.

5) Remove pressure plate, cam ring and blades. Remove locking clip from input shaft. Remove rotor and pressure plate. Remove cylinder pins from housing.

6) Using a punch, knock out locking pins in housing. *See Fig. 1.* Remove closing plug, volume control valve and compression spring from housing.

7) Clamp volume control valve in vise and disassemble valve. Check spacer washer, valve cone and compression spring.

Inspection

Check pressure plates, input shaft, and bearing bushing for wear. Check blades for easy sliding in rotor. Check surfaces of volume control valve and bore in pump housing for wear or damage.

NOTE: Never replace volume control valve only, replace power steering pump.

Reassembly

To install, reverse removal procedures. Fill system with recommended fluid.

MERCEDES-BENZ POWER-ASSISTED RECIRCULATING BALL (Cont.)

Disassembly (ZF Pump)

1) Remove Woodruff key from input shaft. Install puller (1104-7251) on shaft. Screw bolt back on puller enough to install clamping shoes (1104-6304) between puller and seal.

2) Turn clamping core of puller to the right, up to the stop. Remove tool, seal and washer from housing. Remove knurled nut and cover from housing. Remove retaining and compression springs.

3) Remove upper damping plate, filter ring, and lower damping plate. On rear of housing, push in cover plate. Using a screwdriver, remove circlip and cover. Remove "O" ring, compression spring, and pressure plate.

4) Remove rotor with blades from input shaft and "O" ring and cam ring. Remove lock ring from forward end of shaft. Press out input shaft from rear of housing.

5) Remove circlip from shaft. Remove bearing by pressing off toward rear of shaft. Remove needle bearing from housing. Remove closing plug from housing.

6) Remove compression spring and volume control valve. Clamp volume control valve in vise, disassemble and check spacer washers, ball, and compression spring.

Inspection

Check pressure plates, input shaft, bearing housing, and bushing for wear. Check blades for easy sliding in rotor. Check surfaces of volume control valve and bore in pump housing for wear or damage.

NOTE: **Never replace volume control valve only, replace power steering pump.**

Reassembly

To install, reverse removal procedures. Fill system with recommended fluid.

POWER STEERING GEAR

Disassembly

1) Attach steering gear to an assembly plate (116 589 01 59 00). Remove lock nut from adjusting screw. Remove copper seal ring. Remove bolts attaching pitman shaft cover to steering case.

2) With steering in center position, turn adjusting screw clockwise. This forces pitman shaft, with housing, from steering gear case. Remove pitman shaft with cover.

Fig. 2: Sectional View of Adjusting Screw

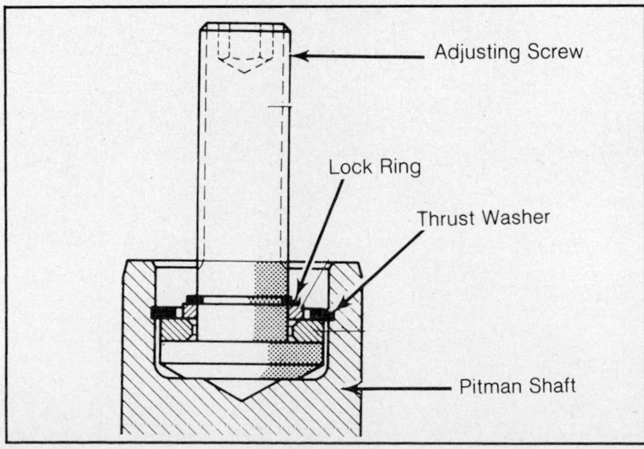
Adjusting Screw
Lock Ring
Thrust Washer
Pitman Shaft

To adjust, first center steering.

3) Remove "O" rings from cover. Remove lock ring and seal ring. Remove lock ring from pitman shaft. Remove adjusting screw with thrust washers. *See Fig. 2.*

4) Remove bolts retaining bearing cap to steering gear case. Turn worm gear counterclockwise until bearing cap is forced out of steering gear case.

NOTE: **Balls will fall out of ball guide if worm gear is turned too far.**

5) Remove bearing cap and worm gear with piston/steering nut from steering gear case. Unscrew worm gear with bearing cap from piston/steering nut. Do not lose circulator balls.

6) Remove "O" ring from bearing cap and attach bearing cap to an assembly fixture.

7) Unscrew slotted nut, using hook wrench, from bearing insert. Remove bearing insert from bearing cap using spanner wrench. *See Fig. 3.*

Fig. 3: Removing Bearing Insert from Bearing Cap

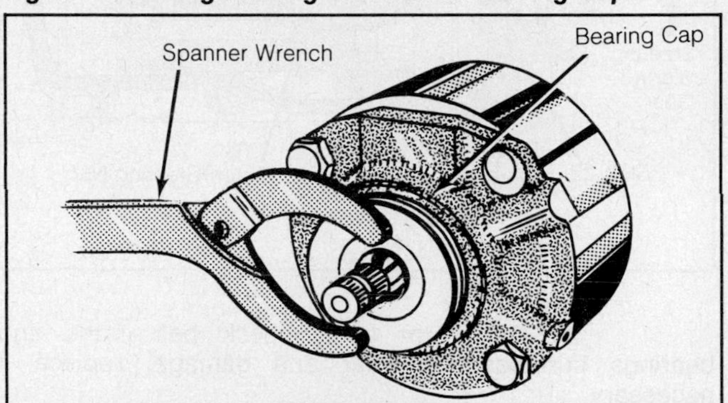
Spanner Wrench
Bearing Cap

Assembly must be held in a fixture.

8) Remove steering worm and washer from bearing cap. Remove roller cage from steering worm, along with seal and "O" rings.

9) Remove bearing and disc from bearing cap. Remove bolts, clamp, and both ball guide halves from piston/steering nut.

Fig. 4: Removing Worm Gear Nut from Piston Nut

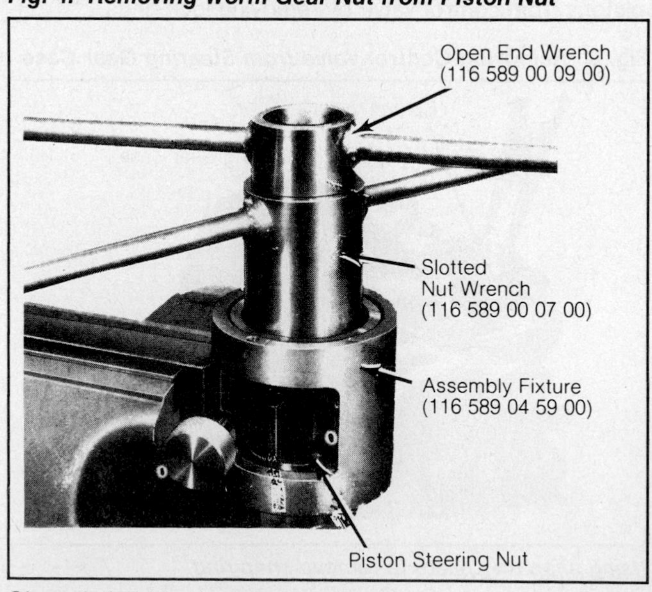
Open End Wrench
(116 589 00 09 00)
Slotted
Nut Wrench
(116 589 00 07 00)
Assembly Fixture
(116 589 04 59 00)
Piston Steering Nut

Clamp is held in vise.

MERCEDES-BENZ POWER-ASSISTED RECIRCULATING BALL (Cont.)

10) Using clamp and tools, remove worm gear nut from piston/steering nut. *See Fig. 4.* Remove seal ring and "O" ring from worm gear nut.

11) Remove bearings from piston/steering nut. Remove lock ring, cover and control valve from steering gear case. *See Fig. 5.*

Fig. 5: Cross Sectional View of Steering Gear

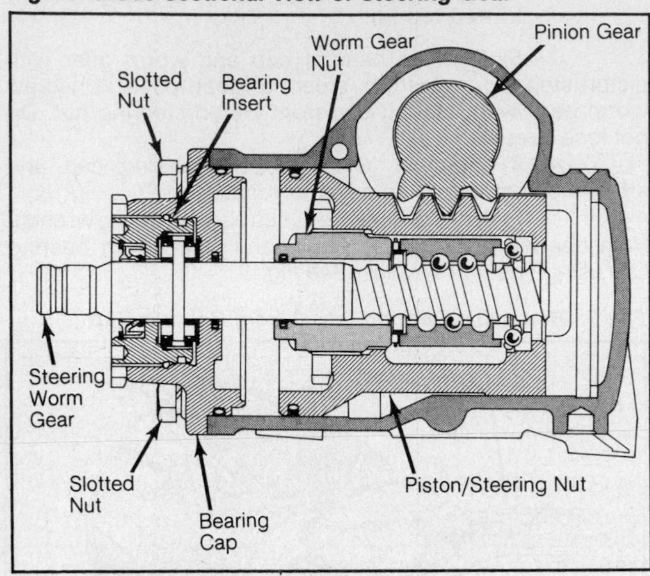

Worm Gear Nut
Pinion Gear
Slotted Nut
Bearing Insert
Steering Worm Gear
Slotted Nut
Bearing Cap
Piston/Steering Nut

Inspection

1) On worm gear, check ball paths and bearings surfaces for wear and damage, replace if necessary.

2) On piston/steering nut, remove seal rings, "O" rings, bearings and races. Remove worm gear nut. Inspect for wear or damage and replace as necessary.

3) Check pitman shaft for wear or damage on bearing surfaces. Check for bent or warped shaft and replace as necessary. Check steering case, cover, and bearing insert for wear or damage, replace as necessary.

4) On control valve, check reaction piston in control valve for free movement. If necessary remove pistons from control valve by removing lock rings.

Fig. 6: Removing Control Valve from Steering Gear Case

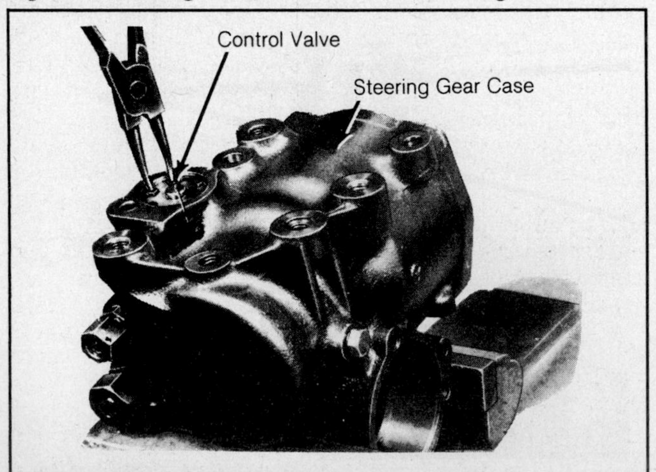

Control Valve
Steering Gear Case

Using snap ring pliers to remove snap ring

Reassembly

To reassemble, reverse disassembly procedure. Replace all "O" rings and sealing rings. Adjust gear to specifications.

STEERING SPECIFICATIONS

Application	Dimensions
Steering Wheel Free Play	1" (25 mm) Maximum
Pump Circulation Pressure	28.4-71.0 psi (2.0-5.0 kg/cm²)
Number of Balls in Ball Circuit	24
End Play of Pump Shaft	
New	.028" (.71 mm) Maximum
Used	.039" (.99 mm) Maximum

TIGHTENING SPECIFICATIONS

Application	Ft. Lbs. (N.m)
Steering Gear-to-Frame	50-57 (68-78)
Pitman Arm-to-Pitman Shaft	116-145 (158-197)
Slotted Nut-to-Bearing Cap	101-115 (137-156)
Adjusting Screw Nut	22-25 (30-34)
Pump Housing Bolts	25-29 (34-39)

PEUGEOT POWER-ASSISTED RACK & PINION

DESCRIPTION

Vehicles are equipped with a power-assisted rack and pinion type steering system. The system consists of 2 main components, rack and steering gear, and the power-assisted pump.

Steering gear and pump are connected by flexible lines. Power steering pump has an integral reservoir on 504 and 604 models. The 505 model has a separate reservoir.

LUBRICATION

CAPACITY

504 and 604 models .69 qts. (.66L)
505 models .74 qts. (.70L)

ADJUSTMENTS

SYSTEM BLEEDING

Fill reservoir to full mark on dipstick. Start engine and turn steering wheel from lock-to-lock several times (to expel all air). Recheck fluid level and refill as required.

REMOVAL & INSTALLATION

STEERING GEAR

Removal

1) Drain steering system and disconnect pressure lines between pump and gear. Disconnect bolt at flexible coupling. Disconnect tie rod ball joints at steering knuckle.

2) On 604 models, remove rear bolts form front crossmember and install longer bolts. Remove front crossmember from bolts. Loosen rear bolts until a gap of approximately 1.5" (40 mm) exists between crossmember and frame.

3) On all models, remove steering gear to crossmember mounting bolts. Remove bolt retaining power cylinder to crossmember. On 604 models, remove safety clips from pins on steering gear.

4) On all models, remove steering gear from vehicle by pulling gear backwards and down.

Installation

1) To install, reverse removal procedures. When installing crossmember on 604 models, make sure steering column is correctly aligned with power assisted steering valve.

2) Use new nuts when installing ball joints. Bleed steering system after installation. Check wheel alignment.

POWER STEERING PUMP

Removal

1) Remove air cleaner and connecting hoses. Remove pressure lines from pump. Loosen drive belt tensioner bolts and remove drive belt.

2) Remove pump retaining bolts. On 505 models, disconnect hose from reservoir to pump. On all models, remove pump from vehicle.

3) On 504 models, remove pump pulley with gear puller (555 TAX). On 505 models, remove pulley by removing bolts retaining pulley to pump.

4) On 604 models, on pumps with extractor groove, use extractor tool (80706 H1, H2, H5) and pull pulley out as far as possible. Tap pulley off with mallet. On 604 models without extractor groove, use gear puller (555 TAX) and remove pulley.

Installation

To install, reverse removal procedures. Make sure hose connections are clean before installing. Fill system with fluid. Bleed system. See System Bleeding in this article.

OVERHAUL

POWER STEERING PUMP

Manufacturer does not recommend overhaul of power steering pump.

POWER STEERING GEAR

Disassembly

1) Clean steering gear assembly before starting disassembly. Place steering gear assembly in a padded vise. Disconnect pressure lines from power cylinder and plug all openings.

Fig. 1: Peugeot Power-Assisted Rack and Pinion Steering Gear

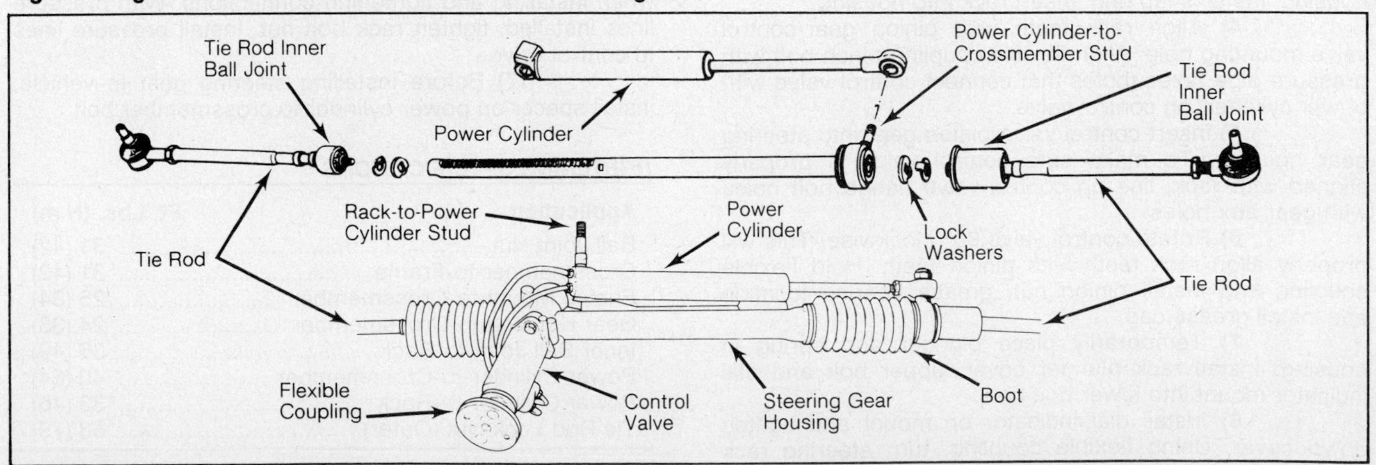
Tie Rod Inner
Ball Joint
Power Cylinder-to-
Crossmember Stud
Tie Rod
Inner
Ball Joint
Power Cylinder
Tie Rod
Rack-to-Power
Cylinder Stud
Power
Cylinder
Lock
Washers
Tie Rod
Flexible
Coupling
Control
Valve
Steering Gear
Housing
Boot

PEUGEOT POWER-ASSISTED RACK & PINION (Cont.)

NOTE: Do not disconnect pressure lines from control valve if valve is to be reused. Do not loosen lock nut on power cylinder attaching joint.

2) Remove nut retaining power cylinder to rack. Remove power cylinder. Loosen lock nut on right tie rod inner ball joint. Disconnect tie rod from rack.

3) If control valve is to be replaced, remove pressure line connections.

NOTE: Be careful not to bend or twist lines connecting control valve to power cylinder.

4) Remove left boot clamp and push boot toward steering gear. Disconnect left tie rod inner ball joint from rack. Remove rack piston cover, spring and rack piston from steering gear housing.

5) Remove control valve bearing cap cover and nut. Remove bolts retaining control valve-to-steering gear. Remove control valve from gear housing.

6) Withdraw rack from housing. Remove snap ring and remove pinion gear bearing.

7) If control valve is to be rebuilt, proceed by removing flexible coupling. Remove snap ring and thrust washer. Withdraw control valve piston from control valve housing.

NOTE: Do not tap on shaft to aid removal or damage to shaft will occur. Do not remove piston rotor segments from shaft.

8) From control valve housing, remove snap ring, scraper seal and oil seal.

Inspection

1) Check steering gear housing and rack for any damage, scoring or any signs of excessive wear. Check control valve housing and shaft for damage, wear or scoring.

2) Replace components as necessary. Always replace all washers, nuts, seals, and bearings when reassembling steering gear.

Reassembly

1) If control valve was disassembled, install oil seal (soaked in oil) to piston/pinion gear assembly with seal lip facing pinion gear. Install piston in control valve.

2) Install thrust washer and snap ring on pinion end of control valve housing. Install oil seal, scraper ring, and snap ring on flexible coupling end of valve housing.

3) Install flexible coupling to control valve housing. Install new pinion gear bearing into steering gear housing. Install snap ring. Insert rack into housing.

4) Align rack teeth with pinion gear/control valve mounting hole. Align flexible coupling pinch bolt with pressure pipe holes (holes that connect control valve with power cylinder) on control valve.

5) Insert control valve/pinion gear into steering gear housing. To make sure control valve is properly aligned with rack, line up control valve flange bolt holes with gear box holes.

6) Rotate control valve 90° clockwise. This will properly align rack teeth with pinion teeth. Hold flexible coupling and install pinion nut, grease bearing location and install grease cap.

7) Temporarily place plunger and spring in housing. Install rack plunger cover, upper bolt and dial indicator mount into lower bolt hole.

8) Install dial indicator on mount and tighten down cover. Using flexible coupling, turn steering rack from lock-to-lock and zero dial indicator on maximum deflection indicated.

9) Using lever, push steering rack in direction of plunger and record dial indicator reading. Remove dial indicator, rack cover and rack plunger from housing.

10) Install stop to rack plunger and lay straight edge over stop and plunger. Select shim pack to eliminate clearance between stop and straight edge.

Fig. 2: Measuring Steering Rack Plunger Clearance

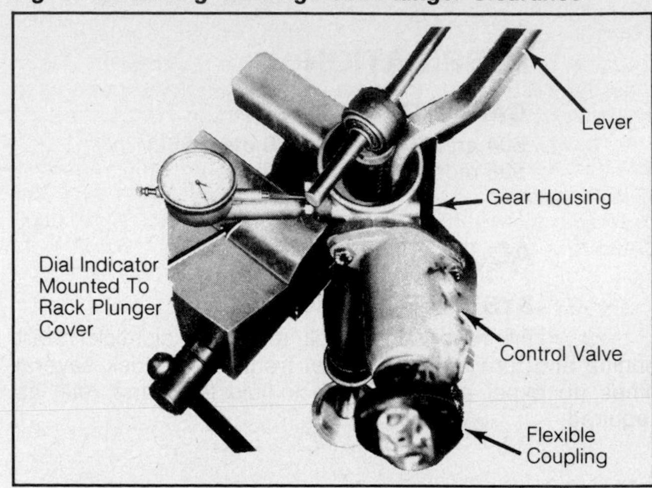
Lever
Gear Housing
Dial Indicator
Mounted To
Rack Plunger
Cover
Control Valve
Flexible
Coupling

Plunger clearance should be .002-.006" (.05-.15 mm).

11) Steering rack plunger clearance should be .002-.006" (.05-.15 mm) at maximum point along rack travel. To obtain required clearance, subtract .004" (.1 mm) from dial indicator reading obtained in step **8)**.

12) Measurement indicates the thickness of shim washers needed in plunger. Install shim pack selected, stop and spring to rack plunger. Install rack plunger assembly to gear housing.

13) Install grease nipple to cover. Install cover over rack plunger assembly and tighten bolts. Install rubber boots, with clamps, to steering gear housing.

14) Push boots out of way when installing tie rod inner ball joints. Install stop plate and lock washer. Install tie rod inner ball joints to rack.

15) Insert bolt into power cylinder. Attach power cylinder to bolt on rack end and tighten nut finger tight. Install pressure pipes from control valve to power cylinder.

16) Do not bend or deform pressure lines when installing and tightening connections. With pressure lines installed, tighten rack bolt nut. Install pressure lines to control valve.

17) Before installing steering gear in vehicle, install spacer on power cylinder to crossmember bolt.

TIGHTENING SPECIFICATIONS

Application	Ft. Lbs. (N.m)
Ball Joint Nut	31 (42)
Crossmember-to-Frame	31 (42)
Engine Mount-to-Crossmember	25 (34)
Gear Housing-to-Crossmember	24 (33)
Inner Ball Joint-to-Rack	36 (49)
Power Cylinder-to-Crossmember	40 (54)
Power Cylinder-to-Rack	33 (45)
Tie Rod Lock Nut (Outer)	58 (79)

PORSCHE POWER-ASSISTED RACK & PINION

928S

DESCRIPTION

A power-assisted rack and pinion steering gear is used as standard equipment on Porsche 928S models. The power assistance decreases with engine speed to provide a better road feel at high speeds.

The system consists of a belt driven vane pump mounted on the engine, a fluid reservoir located in the left front engine compartment, and a rotary piston pinion steering gear.

LUBRICATION

FLUID TYPE

ATF Dexron

FLUID LEVEL CHECK

Remove reservoir cap and start engine. Check that fluid level is up to embossed mark on inside of reservoir.

Fig. 1: Disassembled View of Power Steering Gear

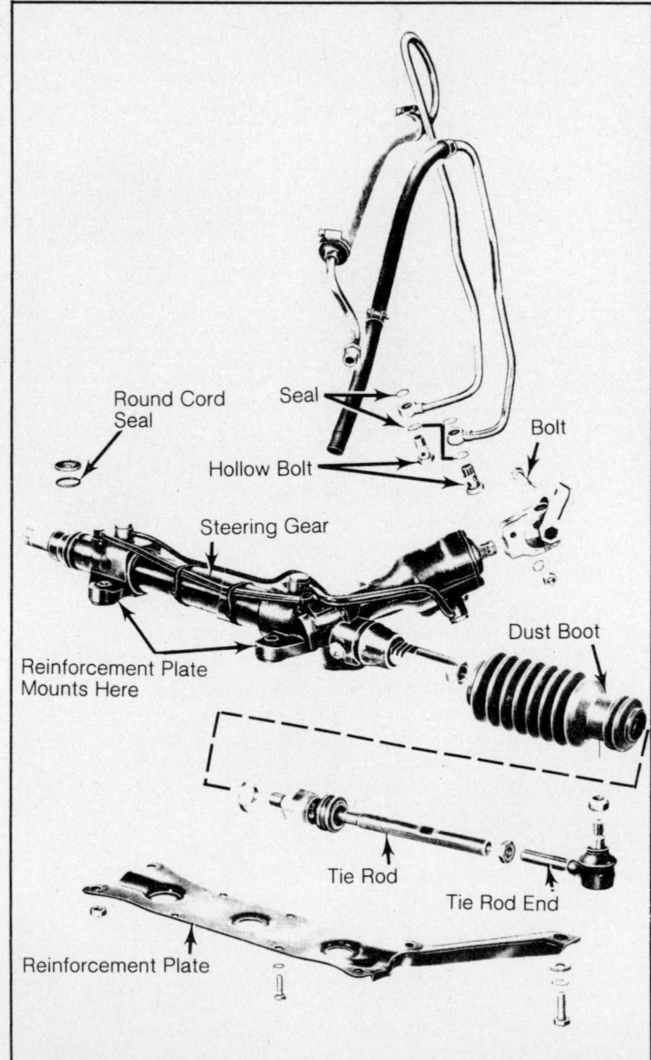
Round Cord Seal
Seal
Bolt
Hollow Bolt
Steering Gear
Dust Boot
Reinforcement Plate Mounts Here
Tie Rod
Tie Rod End
Reinforcement Plate

ADJUSTMENTS

HYDRAULIC SYSTEM BLEEDING

1) Start engine, set to idle. Check fluid level. Turn steering wheel lock to lock several times quickly. Do not turn wheel harder than necessary.

2) Check fluid and add if needed. No air bubbles should rise in reservoir. Shut off engine.

3) Check that fluid level does not rise more than 3/8" (9.5 mm). If level rises, repeat procedure.

PUMP BELT

Check belt deflection at center of belt between pump pulley and crankshaft pulley. Correct deflection is 3/8" (9.5 mm). Adjust by loosening pump mounting bolts and moving pump.

PRESSURE CHECK

1) Unscrew bolts from stabilizer bushings. Pull stabilizer down to expose pressure line hollow bolt. Detach pressure line at steering gear. Pull down on line.

2) Connect a 4 1/2 ft. long hose to pressure line with hollow bolt and adapter. Attach hose with pressure gauge between steering gear and pressure line.

3) Bleed system. Run engine at idle speed and close pressure gauge valve. Check pressure gauge reading. Pressure should be 986-1189 psi (69-84 kg/cm²).

NOTE: **Do not keep valve closed for more than 5 seconds.**

4) With pressure gauge valve open, turn wheel lock-to-lock and hold in lock position at a force of 22 lbs. (9.97 kg). Read pressure gauge. Pressure should be 986-1189 psi (69-84 kg/cm²).

SYSTEM LEAKS

With engine running, turn steering to full lock position and hold. This produces maximum pressure in lines. Check all hose connections and tighten, if necessary.

REMOVAL & INSTALLATION

STEERING GEAR

Removal

1) Drain fluid from system. Raise vehicle and support with safety stands. Press out tie rods with standard extractor. Remove bolt retaining hose strap, and pull back hose and harness.

2) Remove bolts from stabilizer bar mounts. Allow stabilizer to hang down. Disconnect pressure and return lines from steering gear.

3) Remove bolts retaining reinforcement plate on engine crossmember. Loosen self-locking nuts on steering gear, but do not remove.

4) Remove bolt on universal joint which connects to steering intermediate shaft and pull off shaft. Remove lock nuts on steering gear and lower steering gear off studs on engine crossmember.

Installation

To install, reverse removal procedures. Position steering intermediate shaft correctly and install bolt to universal shaft. Add fluid to reservoir. Check for leaks after reinstalling. Check wheel alignment.

PORSCHE POWER-ASSISTED RACK & PINION (Cont.)

Fig. 2: Steering Intermediate Shaft Removal

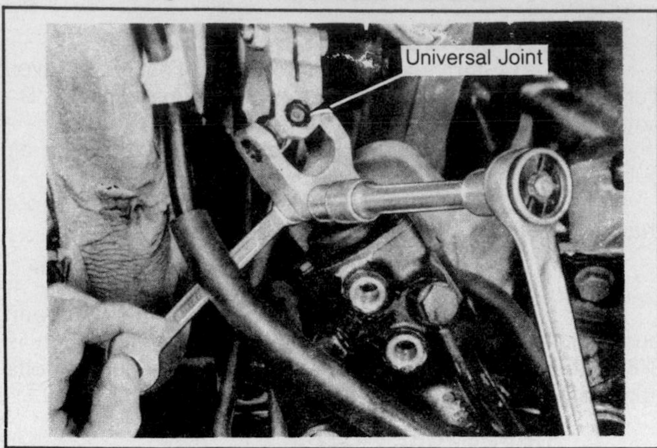
Universal Joint

Hold bolt on backside of universal joint with wrench.

STEERING PUMP

Removal

1) Detach intake hose from air cleaner on left side. Drain fluid from reservoir. Remove splash shield. Loosen front bolts on pump, but do not remove.

2) Remove rear bolt from pump. Remove "V" belt. Take off upper left section of drive belt cover. Disconnect pressure hose from pump.

3) Loosen clip holding suction hose and remove hose. Remove front bolts holding pump. Remove pump.

Installation

1) To install, reverse removal procedures. Install pressure hose so that not more than 1" (25 mm) is provided between inner wheel well and hose when pump is installed.

2) If hose is too close to exhaust manifold it could slip from its holder. Adjust belt tension, add fluid and bleed system. Check for leaks.

OVERHAUL

Manufacturer does not recommend disassembly or overhaul of power steering gears or pumps.

TIGHTENING SPECIFICATIONS

Application	Ft. Lbs. (N.m)
Tie Rod-to-Steering Arm	61 (83)
Tie Rod-to-Steering Rack	108 (147)
Tie Rod End-to-Tie Rod	33 (45)
Universal Joint-to-Steering Column	17 (23)
Steering Rack-to-Crossmember	33 (45)
Pressure/Return Lines-to-Steering Rack	22 (30)

RENAULT POWER-ASSISTED RACK & PINION

Fuego, 18i

DESCRIPTION

Power steering is an integrated power cylinder type rack and pinion. Steering box serves as a power cylinder body and rack serves as rod.

Power steering consists of a rack and pinion steering gear and a power-assist pump connected by flexible lines. Pump has a separate reservoir mounted next to air cleaner.

Fig. 1: View of Renault Power Steering Assembly

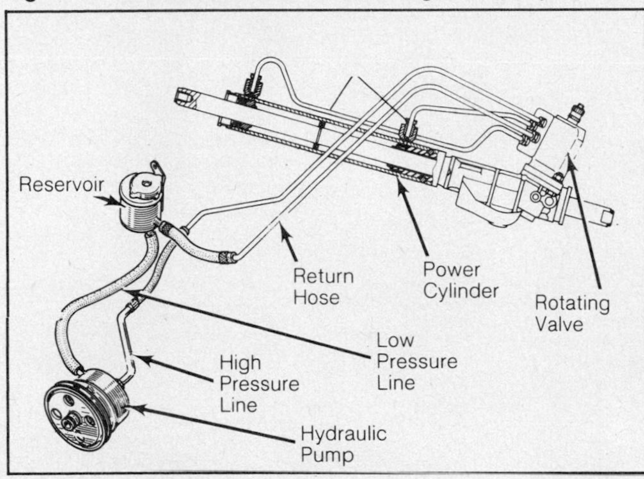
Reservoir
Return Hose
Power Cylinder
Rotating Valve
Low Pressure Line
High Pressure Line
Hydraulic Pump

LUBRICATION

CAPACITY

1.2 qts. (1.1L)

FLUID TYPE

ATF Dexron II

BELT TENSION ADJUSTMENT

Run engine for 10 minutes. Measure deflection with gauge (Ele. 346). Deflection should be .21-.25" (5.5-6.6 mm).

HYDRAULIC SYSTEM FILLING AND BLEEDING

Fill reservoir completely. Gently turn steering wheel lock-to-lock. Refill reservoir to top. Start engine and turn wheel lock-to-lock. Refill reservoir. Oil level should be visible in the bottom of filter in opening.

HYDRAULIC SYSTEM PRESSURE TEST

1) Place a clamp on pump lower pressure hose. Disconnect high pressure line. Insert connector (Dir. 803) between high pressure line and pump. Connect pressure gauge (Fre. 214-04).

2) Disconnect clamp from hose. Bring up oil level in reservoir and turn on engine. Pressure should be 72-102 psi (5.1-7.2 kg/cm²) when steering wheel is not turned. If at idle pressure is too great, valve is defective.

3) If during acceleration pressure is too low, regulator is defective. With wheel turned to lock position, pressure should be 725-943 psi (51-66 kg/cm²).

4) Difference between sides must not exceed 72 psi (5.1 kg/cm²). If it does, valve is defective. If pressure is too low but gauge needle does not move, check for loose belt, defective valve or internal leak in power cylinder.

ADJUSTMENT

RACK PLUNGER

1) Raise vehicle and support with saftey stands. Unlock plunger adjusting nut by straightening out nut lock collar. Tighten adjusting nut to 8 ft. lbs. (11 N.m).

2) Wheel should now be tight when turned. Loosen adjusting nut 1/4 turn. Wheel should now turn without resistance. Relock nut in 2 opposite notches of collar by bending down on nut lock collar.

Fig. 2: Adjusting Nut and Locking Collar

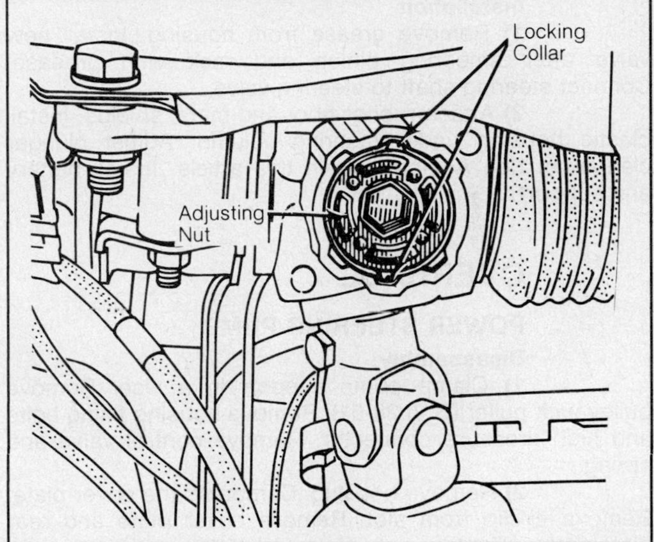
Locking Collar
Adjusting Nut

Unlock nut by straightening collar.

REMOVAL & INSTALLATION

STEERING GEAR

Removal

1) Clamp hoses on steering reservoir. Disconnect lines from rotating valve. Raise and support front of vehicle. Remove tie rod end nuts. Remove ball joint cones from stub axle carriers.

2) Disconnect steering universal joint, index marking position to steering pinion splines. Remove rack housing retaining bolts from crossmember. Remove steering rack through hole on cowl side.

3) If rack and pinion assembly is to be replaced, ball joints on stub axle carrier side must be saved. Loosen lock nut by holding axial ball joint with a wrench. Unscrew ball joints counting turns for reassembly reference.

Installation

Place steering arm ball joints in position noted when removed. Install assembly to vehicle. To complete installation, reverse removal procedures. Bleed hydraulic system. Check wheel alignment.

RENAULT POWER-ASSISTED RACK & PINION (Cont.)

POWER STEERING PUMP

Removal

Place a clamp on pump input line. Disconnect input line and high pressure line. Loosen idler bolt and pump retaining bolt. Remove pump from vehicle.

Installation

To install, reverse removal procedures. Fill and bleed hydraulic system.

POWER STEERING VALVE

Removal

1) Remove battery and support. Remove shields attached with plastic clips to firewall. Push boot towards passenger compartment. Remove plastic housing under steering column.

2) Disconnect steering column shaft from steering valve. Remove from firewall. From under vehicle loosen steering plunger adjusting nut. Remove valve retaining bolts and remove valve from housing.

Installation

1) Remove grease from housing. Install new valve after smearing pinion and rack with greease. Connect steering shaft to steering valve.

2) Attach rubber boot and metal shields. Install plastic housing under steering column. Adjust plunger clearance. See Adjustments in this article. Install battery and support.

OVERHAUL

POWER STEERING PUMP

Disassembly

1) Clamp pump support in a vise. Remove pulley with puller (B.Vi.28-01). Remove housing fixing bolts and high pressure connector. Remove control valve and spring.

2) Remove housing. Compress the cover plate. Remove circlip from slot. Remove cover plate and rear plate spring. Remove rear plate and stator.

3) Remove positioning pins. Remove shaft and rotor. Save the 10 blades. Separate the rotor from the shaft by removing circlip. Remove shaft seal.

Reassembly

Replace all gaskets and seals. Lubricate all parts with automatic transmission fluid. Clean and install the magnet on the body of pump. Be careful of the direction of blades when installing magnet. To complete assembly, reverse disassembly procedure.

TIGHTENING SPECIFICATIONS

Application	Ft. Lbs. (N.m)
Ball Joint Nut	30 (41)
Tie Rod Lock Nut	26 (35)

SAAB POWER-ASSISTED RACK & PINION

900 & 900 Turbo

DESCRIPTION

Power steering is available as optional equipment. The assembly consists of a rack and pinion steering gear with a servo valve which regulates the oil flow to a servo plunger on the rack.

The hydraulic pressure is generated by an oil pump which is driven by a belt attached to the crankshaft pulley. The pump is integrated in a steel container that also serves as the hydraulic reservoir. In addition to pump unit itself, the pump also contains a control valve which regulates oil pressure and flow.

LUBRICATION

FLUID TYPE

General Motors power steering fluid. Do not use ATF type fluid.

REMOVAL & INSTALLATION

POWER STEERING GEAR

Removal

1) Clean areas around hydraulic connections and disconnect return and pressure lines from steering gear. Plug lines and steering gear to prevent dirt from entering system and also prevent fluid from draining out.

2) Remove steering gear-to-intermediate shaft clamp bolt. Raise and support vehicle. Remove front wheel assemblies. Separate tie rods from steering knuckles.

3) Remove steering gear retaining bolts. Separate steering column (intermediate shaft) joint from steering gear. Lift steering gear to the side and remove by guiding it diagonally downward through opening in engine compartment.

Installation

To install, reverse removal procedure. Tie rod ends are to be connected after gear assembly has been fully installed. Check wheel alignment.

OVERHAUL

POWER STEERING GEAR

Disassembly

1) With steering gear removed from vehicle, remove lock nuts and tie rod ends. Remove rubber bellows and breather tube. Remove hydraulic lines from steering valve and steering housing.

2) Remove lock nut, adjusting nut, spring and piston from steering housing. Remove pinion dust cap.

3) Hold pinion from rotating (11/16" socket will fit splines of pinion) and remove pinion lock nut. Remove dust cover lock ring from upper pinion.

4) Press pinion (with spool valve) out of steering gear. The bearing, support, seal, and dust cover seal will come out with the pinion.

Fig. 1: Exploded View of Power Steering Components

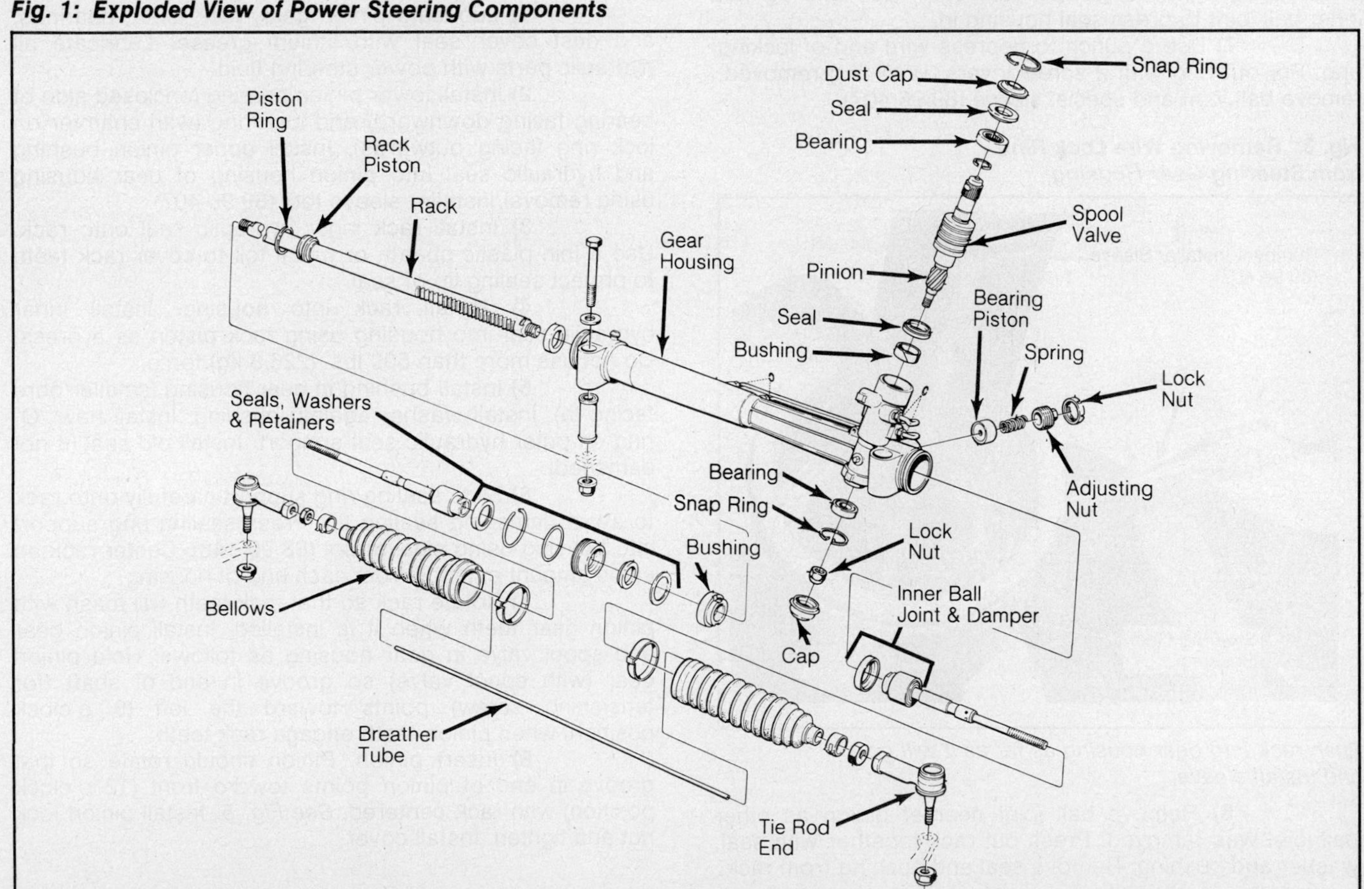
Snap Ring
Dust Cap
Seal
Bearing
Piston Ring
Rack Piston
Rack
Spool Valve
Gear Housing
Pinion
Bearing Piston
Seal
Bushing
Spring
Lock Nut
Seals, Washers & Retainers
Adjusting Nut
Bearing
Snap Ring
Bushing
Lock Nut
Bellows
Inner Ball Joint & Damper
Cap
Breather Tube
Tie Rod End

SAAB POWER-ASSISTED RACK & PINION (Cont.)

Fig. 2: Removing Pinion Lock Nut from Pinion Gear and Spool Valve

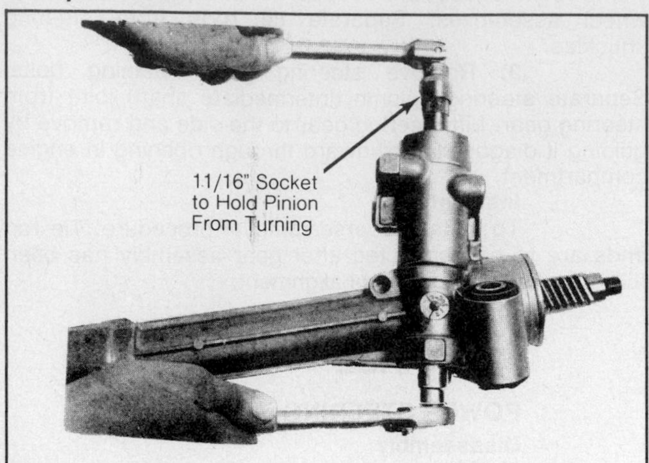
11/16" Socket
to Hold Pinion
From Turning

Wrap tape around serrations. Place socket over taped end to hold shaft.

NOTE: Do not use a hammer to remove pinion or damage to pinion, spool valve and/or housing could result.

5) Remove inner ball joint furthest from pinion by clamping rack in a soft-jawed vise. Push plastic sleeve out of the way and unscrew ball joint.

6) Remove lock ring in end of gear housing as follows: Push rack into gear housing as far as it will go. Install special sleeve (89 96 407) over rack and tighten inner ball joint to press seal housing in.

7) Use a punch to depress wire end of locking ring. Pry out ring with 2 screwdrivers. With ring removed, remove ball joint and special sleeve (89 96 407).

Fig. 3: Removing Wire Lock Ring from Steering Gear Housing

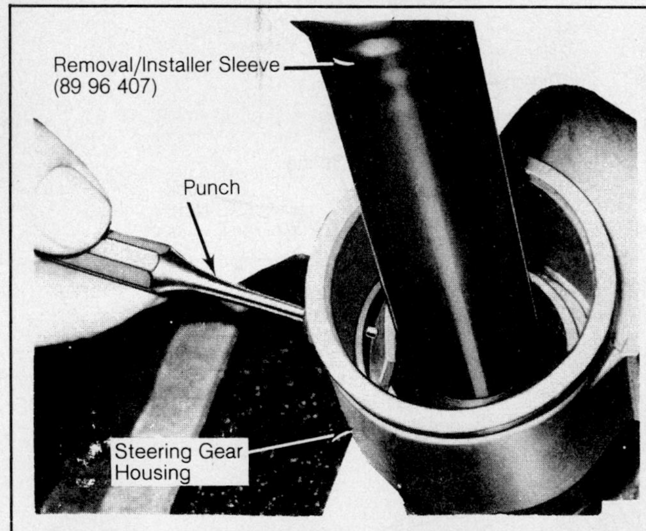
Removal/Installer Sleeve
(89 96 407)
Punch
Steering Gear
Housing

Push rack into gear housing as far as it will go and install sleeve.

8) Remove ball joint nearest pinion as other ball joint was removed. Press out rack together with seal, washer and bushing. Remove seal and bushing from rack.

9) Make sure there are no burrs on rack to damage seal or bushing before removing.

10) Remove inner rack using seal removal/installer tool (89 96 399) and a long punch or rod. Insert tool lips under seal. From other end of housing, insert long rod and drive seal out.

11) Remove lock ring and lower pinion bearing. Remove sealing ring and bushing from top of pinion housing.

Fig. 4: Removing Inner Rack Seal Using Removal/Installer Tool and Long Rod

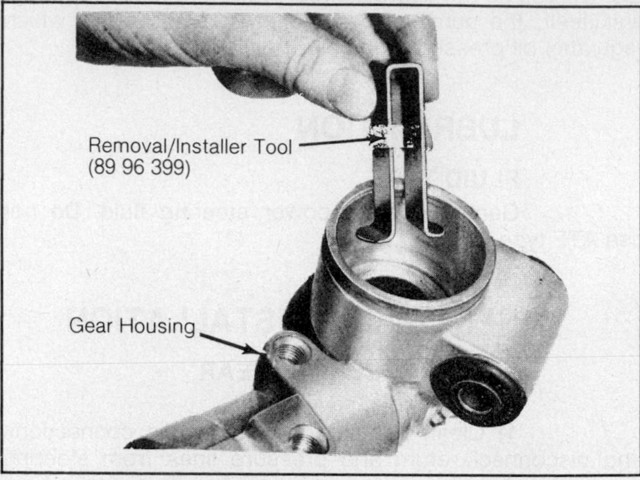
Removal/Installer Tool
(89 96 399)
Gear Housing

From other end of housing insert long rod to drive out seal.

Reassembly

1) Lubricate pinion gear, rack teeth, bearings, and dust cover seal with lithium grease. Lubricate all hydraulic parts with power steering fluid.

2) Install lower pinion bearing (enclosed side of bearing facing downward) and lock ring (with chamfer on lock ring facing outwards). Install upper pinion bushing and hydraulic seal into pinion housing of gear housing using removal/installer sleeve tool (89 96 407).

3) Install rack inner hydraulic seal onto rack. Use a thin plastic sheath or metal foil to cover rack teeth to protect sealing lip of seal.

4) Install rack into housing. Install inner hydraulic seal into housing using rack piston as a press. Do not use more than 500 lbs. (226.8 kg) force.

5) Install bushing in gear housing (smaller bore facing in). Install washer against bushing. Install new "O" ring on outer hydraulic seal support. Install old seal (if not damaged).

6) Slide sealing ring support carefully onto rack to avoid damaging sealing lip. Press sealing ring support into housing using sleeve tool (83 90 148). Center rack so same amount extends from each end of housing.

7) Rotate rack so that rack teeth will mesh with pinion gear teeth when it is installed. Install pinion gear and spool valve in gear housing as follows: Hold pinion gear (with spool valve) so groove in end of shaft (for tensioning screw) points toward the left (9 o'clock position) when pinion teeth engage rack teeth.

8) Insert pinion. Pinion should rotate so that groove in end of pinion points toward front (12 o'clock position) with rack centered. *See Fig. 5.* Install pinion lock nut and tighten. Install cover.

SAAB POWER-ASSISTED RACK & PINION (Cont.)

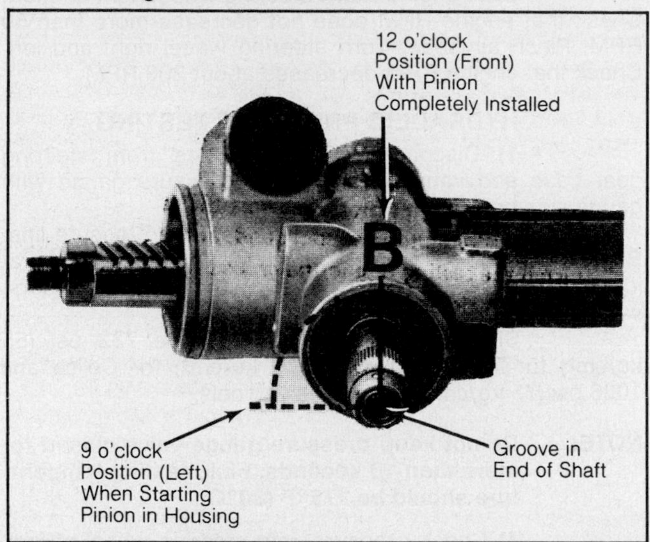
12 o'clock
Position (Front)
With Pinion
Completely Installed
B
9 o'clock
Position (Left)
When Starting
Pinion in Housing
Groove in
End of Shaft

Fig. 5: Installing Pinion Gear and Spool Valve Into Gear Housing With Rack Installed

9) Install washer, needle bearing, sealing ring, dust cover, and lock ring onto top of pinion gear (spool valve). Protect seal lips with tape or plastic sleeve over splines of pinion.

10) Install bearing piston, spring and adjusting nut in gear housing. Tighten adjusting nut until bearing piston firmly contacts rack. Back off adjusting nut 30-50°. Install and tighten lock nut.

11) Install plastic sleeves (end stops) and inner ball joints, with tie rods, to rack ends. Hold rack in soft-jawed vise and tighten ball joints. Lock inner ball joints by tapping tab on ball joint into rack. DO NOT use pinion as support when loosening or tightening ball joints.

12) Install lock ring for sealing ring support in end of gear housing. Turn pinion until inner ball joint presses against sealing ring support. Press in support and, at same time, install sealing ring in groove with thin screwdriver. Install rubber bellows, breathing tube and hydraulic lines.

TIGHTENING SPECIFICATIONS

Application	Ft. Lbs. (N.m)
Tie Rod End	37-44 (50-60)
Pinion Gear Lower Lock Nut	22-34 (30-46)
Bearing Piston Lock Nut	48-55 (65-75)
Inner Ball Joint-to-Rack	59-72 (80-98)
Tie Rod End	44-60 (60-81)
Steering Gear Clamp Bolt	44-60 (60-81)

TOYOTA POWER-ASSISTED RACK & PINION

Camry, Celica, Corolla, Supra & Tercel

DESCRIPTION

POWER STEERING PUMP

The power steering pump is a vane-type pump. Pump components include an engine-driven eccentric rotor with vane plates, an eccentric cam ring and flow control valve to regulate maximum oil pressure and amount of oil flow.

Vane plates (fitted in slotted grooves) are pressed against cam ring surface by pressure produced in adjoining slots. As rotor rotates, space between the rotor and cam ring changes, which produces oil pressure.

POWER RACK & PINION STEERING GEAR

Power rack and pinion steering gear consists of a frame mounted rack and pinion assembly, a flow control valve and high pressure tubes. Rotary motion of steering pinion is converted to sideways movement through meshing of rack and pinion teeth. Flow control valve regulates hydraulic pressure in proportion to the steering effort.

LUBRICATION

CAPACITY

Corolla .73 qt. (.70L)
All Other Models .83 qt. (.80L)

FLUID TYPE

ATF Dexron

ADJUSTMENTS

BELT TENSION ADJUSTMENT

Use belt tension gauge and adjust belt tension to 100-150 lbs. (45-68 kg) for new belt or to 60-100 lbs. (27-68 kg) for used belt.

SYSTEM BLEEDING

1) Raise vehicle and support with safety stands. Fill fluid to proper level in vane pump reservoir. Turn wheels fully in both directions and recheck fluid level.

2) Start engine and let idle. Turn steering from lock-to-lock 2 or 3 times. Lower vehicle. Run engine at 1000 RPM or less. Turn wheel from lock-to-lock 2 or 3 times. Center steering wheel.

3) If fluid level does not rise and no foaming of fluid is evident, bleeding is complete. If level rises, or foaming is evident, repeat procedure until air is released.

FLUID REPLACEMENT

Raise vehicle and support with safety stands. Disconnect return hose and drain fluid into container. Turn steering wheel from lock-to-lock while draining. Cap reservoir return tube. Fill reservoir with fluid. Start engine and run for 1 to 2 seconds. Stop engine and refill reservoir. Repeat 4 or 5 times, or until no more air is in fluid. Reconnect return hose. Add fresh fluid and bleed system.

AIR CONTROL VALVE TESTING

Start engine. Turn steering wheel right and left. Check that engine RPM does not decrease more than 50 RPM. Pinch air hose. Turn steering wheel right and left. Check that engine RPM decreases about 200 RPM.

HYDRAULIC PRESSURE TESTING

1) Disconnect pressure lines from steering gear case and vane pump. Attach pressure gauge with gauge side connected to vane pump.

2) Attach valve side of gauge to pressure line. Bleed air from system and check fluid level. With engine at idle, check fluid pressure reading with pressure gauge valve closed.

3) Correct pressure should be 782 psi (55 kg/cm²) for Tercel, 1024 psi (72 kg/cm²) for Celica and 1066 psi (75 kg/cm²) for all other models.

NOTE: **Do not keep pressure gauge valve closed for more than 10 seconds. Fluid testing temperature should be 176°F (80°C).**

4) Check pressure with steering wheel at lock position and pressure valve open. Pressure should be 782 psi (55 kg/cm²) for Tercel, 1024 psi (72 kg/cm²) for Celica and 1066 psi (75 kg/cm²) for all other models.

5) Measure pressure with engine at idle and again at 3000 RPM. Pressure difference should be less than 71 psi (5 kg/cm²). If more, check flow control valve.

6) With vehicle on flat surface, turn steering wheel to center position. With engine idling, measure steering turning force at steering wheel outer rim, in both directions.

7) Turning force should not exceed 12.0 lbs. (5.5 kg) on Corolla and Tercel, or 8.8 lbs. (4.0 kg) on all other models.

REMOVAL & INSTALLATION

POWER STEERING PUMP

Removal

Loosen pulley retaining nut before removing drive belt. Disconnect and plug oil lines at pump housing. Drain fluid. Disconnect air control valve hoses (if equipped). Remove pump retaining bolts. Remove pump.

NOTE: **Keep disconnected hoses plugged and elevated to prevent fluid from draining out.**

Installation

To install, reverse removal procedures. Adjust drive belt tension and bleed system.

POWER RACK & PINION STEERING GEAR

Removal

1) Raise front of vehicle and support with safety stands. Position steering wheel so front wheels point straight ahead. Remove pinch bolts from sliding yoke and remove.

2) Mark tie rod ends and remove. Use a puller to disconnect tie rod ends from steering knuckles. Disconnect oil lines.

TOYOTA POWER-ASSISTED RACK & PINION (Cont.)

Fig. 1: Exploded View of Toyota Power Steering Pump Assemblies

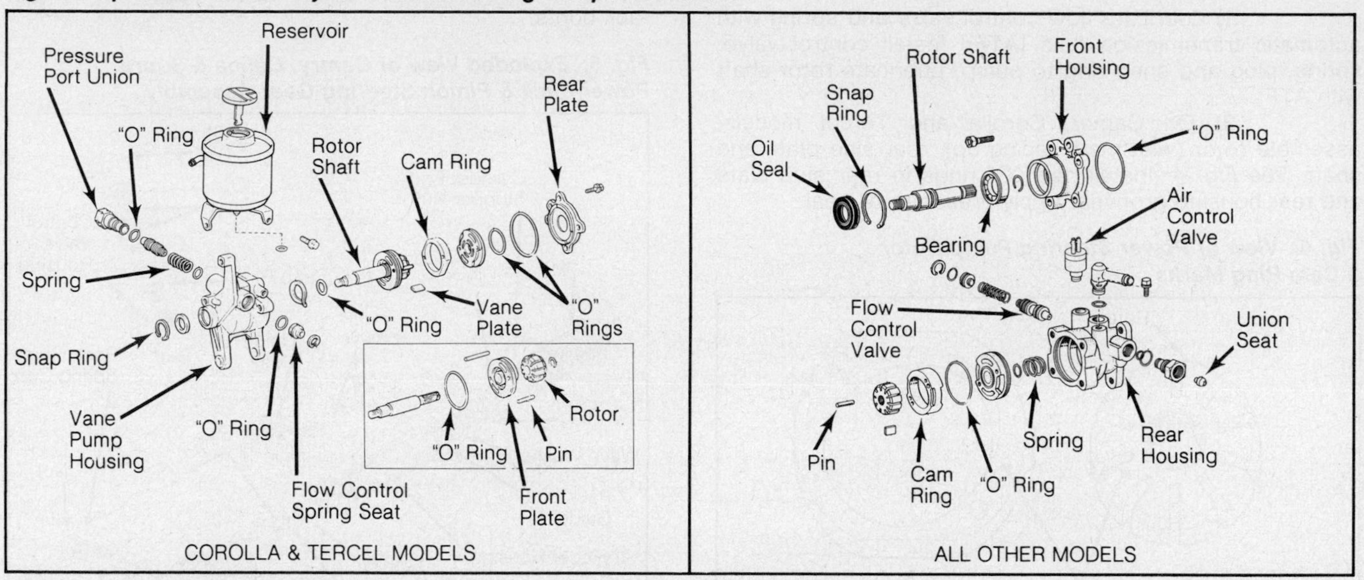
Reservoir
Pressure Port Union
"O" Ring
Rear Plate
Rotor Shaft
Cam Ring
Spring
"O" Ring
Vane Plate
"O" Rings
Snap Ring
Rotor
Vane Pump Housing
"O" Ring
"O" Ring
Pin
Flow Control Spring Seat
Front Plate
COROLLA & TERCEL MODELS
Rotor Shaft
Front Housing
Snap Ring
"O" Ring
Oil Seal
Air Control Valve
Bearing
Flow Control Valve
Union Seat
Spring
Rear Housing
Pin
Cam Ring
"O" Ring
ALL OTHER MODELS

3) On Camry models, remove lower crossmember retaining bolts. Remove lower crossmember. Remove transmission control cables for manual transmission (if equipped). Remove rack and pinion housing brackets, taking care not to damage rack boots. On all models, remove assembly.

Installation

To install, reverse removal procedure and check toe-in. *See WHEEL ALIGNMENT Section for specifications and procedures.*

OVERHAUL

POWER STEERING PUMP

Disassembly

1) Mount power steering pump in vise. Remove air control valve (if equipped). Remove union from rear housing. Remove reservoir from pump (if equipped). Index mark front and rear housings for reassembly reference. Remove front housing bolts.

2) Tap off front housing with plastic mallet. Be careful that vane plates, rotor and cam plate do not fall out. Remove ring cam, rotor and vane plates. Clamp front housing in a vise. Using chisel, pry off oil seal.

3) Remove snap ring. With plastic mallet, lightly tap the rotor shaft out of front housing and tap bottom of rear housing. Remove rear plate and spring.

4) Temporarily install a bolt into plug. Push bolt in and remove snap ring. Pull out bolt with plug. Remove spring and control valve by hand.

Inspection

1) Check all parts for wear or damage and replace as necessary. Check oil clearance between pump housing bushing and rotor shaft. *See Fig. 2.* If difference is greater than .0028" (.07 mm), replace complete pump assembly.

2) Check that bearings operate smoothly. If necessary, press out old bearing and press in new bearing.

3) Measure difference between cam ring and rotor. Maximum difference should be .0024" (.06 mm). If necessary, replace cam ring with one with the same letter stamped on the rotor.

Fig. 2: Checking Pump Housing Bushing to Rotor Shaft Clearance

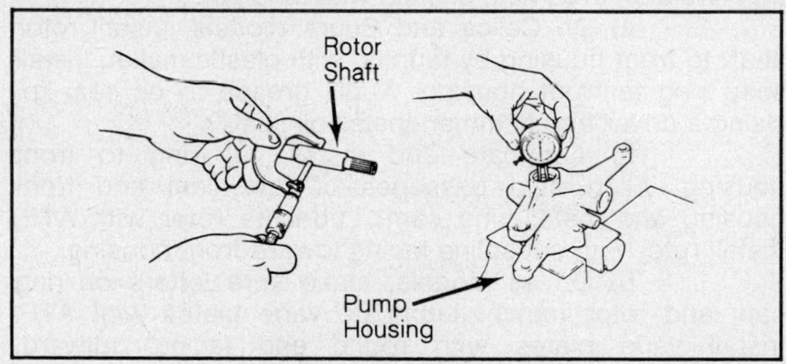
Rotor Shaft
Pump Housing

4) Check vane plates for wear or damage. Dimensions of the vane plate should be .589 x .307 x .067" (14.97 x 7.80 x 1.70 mm) for Celica and Supra, or .590 x .319 x .070" (14.99 x 8.10 x 1.79 mm) for Camry, Corolla and Tercel models.

5) Maximum clearance between vane plate and rotor groove is .0024" (.06 mm) for Celica and Supra, or .0011" (.028 mm) for Camry, Corolla and Tercel models.

6) Check flow control valve for leakage with compressed air. *See Fig. 3.*. Control valve spring should be 1.85-1.97" (47-50 mm) long.

Fig. 3: Checking Flow Control Valve

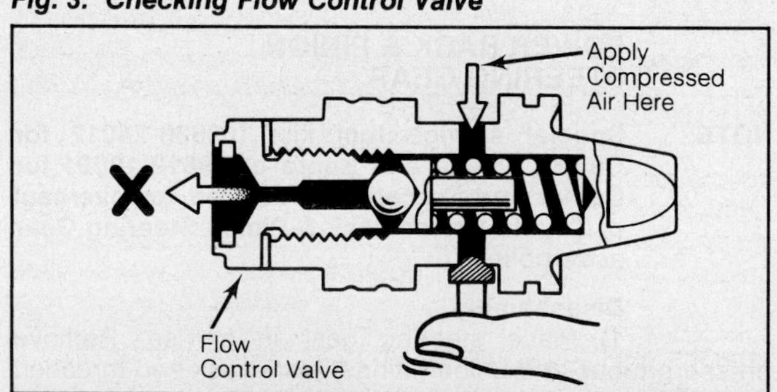
Apply Compressed Air Here
X
Flow Control Valve

TOYOTA POWER-ASSISTED RACK & PINION (Cont.)

Reassembly

1) Lubricate flow control valve and spring with automatic transmission fluid (ATF). Install control valve, spring, plug and snap ring to pump. Lubricate rotor shaft with ATF.

2) On Camry, Corolla and Tercel models, assemble rotor (with mark facing up), rear side plate and shaft. *See Fig. 4.* Install new "O" rings in rear side plate and rear housing grooves. Apply grease to oil seal.

Fig. 4: View of Power Steering Pump Rotor & Cam Ring Marks

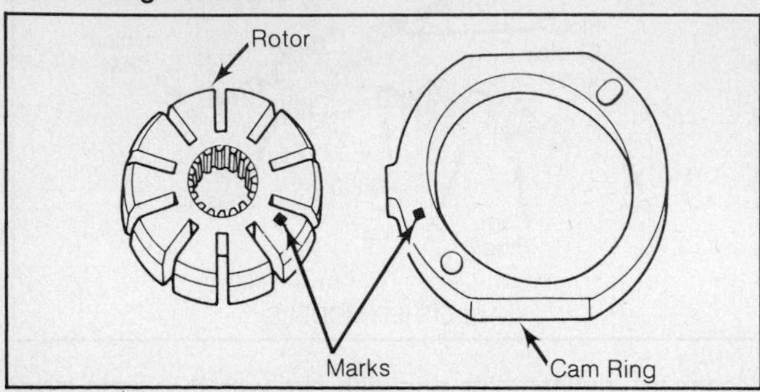

Rotor
Marks
Cam Ring

3) Install wave washer and long straight pin. Use a plastic hammer to tap rotor assembly in place. Install short pin. Install cam ring with the mark facing outward and large hole aligned with long pin.

4) On Celica and Supra models, install rotor shaft to front housing by tapping with plastic mallet. Install snap ring to front housing. Apply grease to oil seal lip. Using a driver and hammer, install oil seal.

5) Lubricate and install "O" ring to front housing. Align fluid passages of ring cam and front housing and install ring cam. Lubricate rotor with ATF. Install rotor with cut spline facing toward front housing.

6) On all models, make sure letters on ring cam and rotor match. Lubricate vane plates with ATF. Install vane plates with round end facing outward. Lubricate and install "O" ring (if equipped) to rear plate.

7) Place rear plate on the ring cam with pin holes aligned with pins. On Celica and Supra models, place spring on the rear plate. Align marks on front and rear housings and install.

8) Half tighten front and rear housing retaining bolts. Clamp rear housing in vise. Tighten housing bolts evenly 3 or 4 times. Lubricate and install "O" ring to union.

9) Insert and tighten union. Check to ensure rotor shaft operates smoothly. Install pulley nut and check rotating torque. Torque should be less than 2.4 INCH lbs. (2.7 N.m). Install air control valve and/or reservoir (if equipped).

POWER RACK & PINION STEERING GEAR

NOTE: Special service tool kits (09630-24012 for Camry, Celica and Supra or 09612-10091 for Camry and Tercel) are required for overhaul of Toyota Power Rack & Pinion Steering Gear assemblies.

Disassembly

1) Place steering gear in a vise. Remove pressure tubes and union fittings. Mark rack end threaded areas for reassembly reference. Remove tie rods, spring clips, rack end dust seals and rack boot clamps. Remove rack boots.

Fig. 5: Exploded View of Camry, Celica & Supra Power Rack & Pinion Steering Gear Assembly

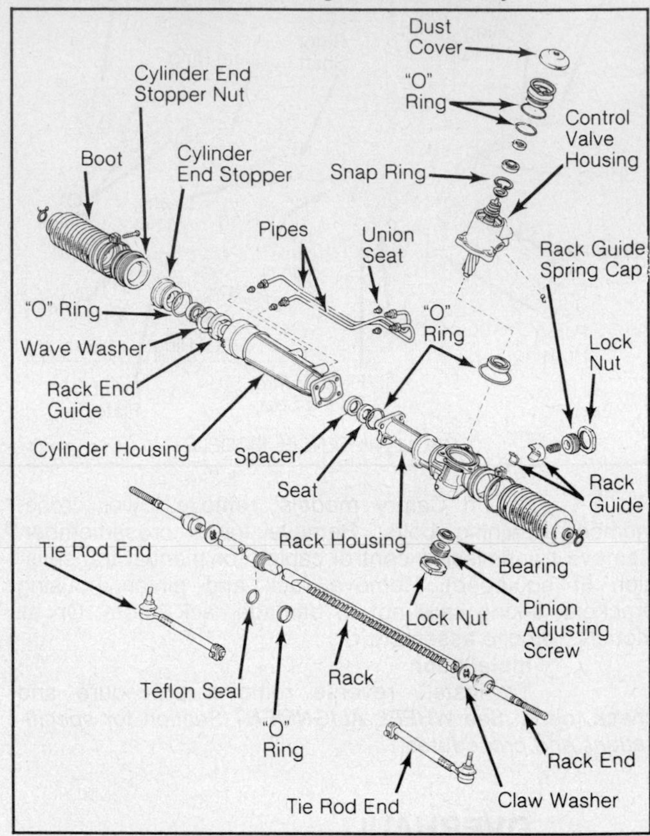

Dust Cover
Cylinder End Stopper Nut
"O" Ring
Control Valve Housing
Boot
Cylinder End Stopper
Snap Ring
Pipes
Union Seat
Rack Guide Spring Cap
"O" Ring
"O" Ring
Wave Washer
Lock Nut
Rack End Guide
Cylinder Housing
Spacer
Seat
Rack Guide
Tie Rod End
Rack Housing
Bearing
Lock Nut
Pinion Adjusting Screw
Teflon Seal
Rack
"O" Ring
Rack End
Tie Rod End
Claw Washer

Fig. 6: Exploded View of Corolla & Tercel Power Rack & Pinion Steering Gear Assembly

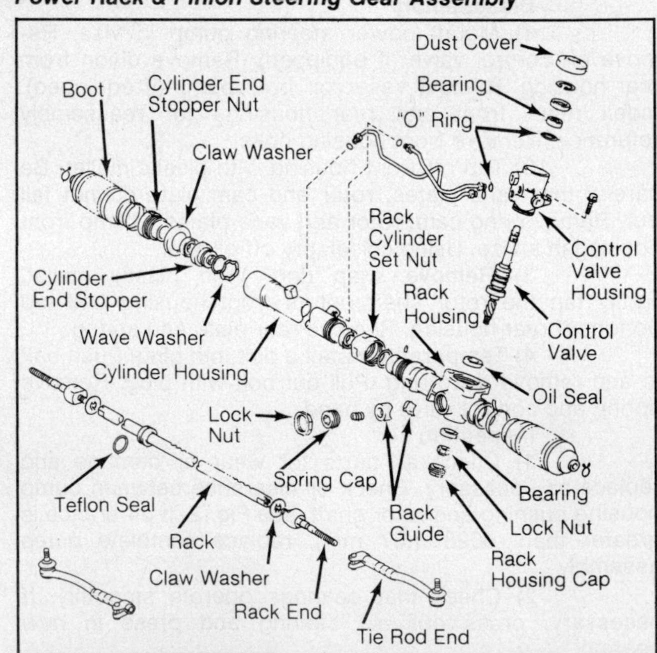

Dust Cover
Boot
Cylinder End Stopper Nut
Bearing
"O" Ring
Claw Washer
Rack Cylinder Set Nut
Control Valve Housing
Cylinder End Stopper
Rack Housing
Wave Washer
Control Valve
Cylinder Housing
Oil Seal
Lock Nut
Spring Cap
Bearing
Teflon Seal
Rack Guide
Lock Nut
Rack
Rack Housing Cap
Claw Washer
Rack End
Tie Rod End

TOYOTA POWER-ASSISTED RACK & PINION (Cont.)

NOTE: Left and right tie rod ends, rack boots and rack ends are different and should be marked accordingly.

2) Unstake claw washers and remove rack ends. Remove rack guide spring cap lock nut, spring cap and spring. Remove rack guide and seat by pulling out with needle-nose pliers.

3) On Corolla and Tercel models, remove rack housing cap. Hold the control valve shaft with tool (09616-00010) and remove the self locking nut.

4) On all models, remove control valve dust cover. Place alignment marks on the control valve housing and remove. Remove the "O" ring. Remove control valve from housing.

5) On Camry, Celica and Supra models, remove pinion bearing adjusting screw lock nut and pinion bearing adjusting screw. On all models, remove the cylinder end stopper nut.

6) On Corolla and Tercel models, place alignment mark on rack housing and rack cylinder. Unstake the rack cylinder set nut. Using a plastic hammer, tap the rack, end stopper and wave washer out of the rack cylinder.

7) On Camry, Celica and Supra models, remove the rack housing bolts. Remove the rack housing, "O" ring and spacer. Insert service tool into rack cylinder to protect oil seal lip. Pull rack completely through cylinder. Remove components from rack and remove service tool from cylinder.

Inspection

1) Check all parts for damage or deterioration. Check steering rack for runout. Maximum runout is .0059" (.15 mm) for Corolla, or .012" (.30 mm) for all other models.

2) If required, rack cylinder oil seal may be replaced. On Corolla and Tercel models, reinstall the rack cylinder set nut. Install the rack and cylinder end stopper into the rack cylinder. Press the rack cylinder oil seal out. To install, drive in seal about 1.18" (30 mm) from edge of rack cylinder.

3) On all other models, drive rack cylinder seal from cylinder with seal driver (09620-3310). Drive in seal until round surface of driver (09620-3310) is flush with edge of rack cylinder.

4) If control valve bearing and seal must be replaced, remove snap ring. Remove the oil seal. Use a brass drift and hammer to remove the bearing. Drive new bearing on. Install new seal and snap ring.

5) If pinion lower bearing must be replaced, remove snap ring (if equipped). Press bearing out. On Camry, Celica and Supra models, press in the new bearing. Install new seal and retain with snap ring.

6) On Corolla and Tercel models, use hammer to install new lower pinion bearing. Use the rack housing cap to seat the bearing. Remove the rack housing cap.

7) On all models, if necessary, replace teflon ring seal on rack, cylinder end stopper seal and valve cap seal.

NOTE: Special service tools are required to install the teflon seals.

Reassembly & Adjustment

1) Coat lower pinion bearing, rack and control valve pinion gears with grease. Coat rack guides and housing with grease. Coat all other seals and "O" rings with ATF. Install special tools on rack to protect cylinder seals. On Camry, Celica and Supra models, install seat and spacer. Insert rack into the rack cylinder. Position notched portion of rack so control valve can be inserted.

2) On Camry, Celica and Supra models, install special tools to protect cylinder end stopper seals. Install cylinder end stopper to cylinder. Install seal, spacer and "O" ring between cylinder and housing. Install cylinder to housing and tighten bolts. Coat cylinder end stopper nut with sealer. Tighten nut and stake nut to rack cylinder.

3) On Corolla and Tercel models, insert rack into rack cylinder. Install wave washer with cylinder end stopper into rack cylinder. Install new "O" ring and pin in housing. Align marks and tighten rack housing nut. Use hammer and chisel to stake nut.

4) On all models, apply grease to rack ends. Align claw washer with rack groove and tighten rack ends into housing. Stake claw washer.

5) Assemble control valve. Install new "O" ring into rack housing. On Celica and Supra models, install spring seat and spring. Coat control valve bolts with sealer.

6) On all models, install control valve. Align control valve housing mark with rack housing mark and tighten bolts.

7) On Camry models, install the control valve bearing. Measure and record the frictional force on the control valve shaft. Apply sealer and install the control valve adjusting cap. Torque cap to 11 ft. lbs. (15 N.m).

8) Loosen cap and adjust preload to frictional force (previously measured), plus .87-1.74 INCH lbs. (.10-.19 N.m). Coat control valve adjusting cap lock nut with sealer and tighten.

9) To adjust total preload, install rack seat, rack guide and spring. Apply sealer to spring cap and torque to 18 ft. lbs. (24 N.m). Back off spring cap 12°. *See Fig. 7.* Turn the control valve shaft right and left 2 times.

Fig. 7: Initial Rack & Pinion Preload Setting

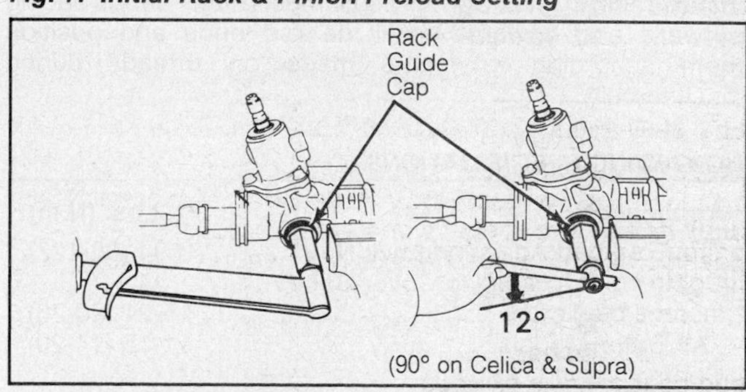
Rack
Guide
Cap
12°
(90° on Celica & Supra)

10) Install torque wrench to control valve shaft and tighten spring cap until a preload of 7.8-10.4 INCH lbs. (.90-1.17 N.m) is obtained. *See Fig. 8.*

11) On Celica and Supra models, apply sealer and install the control valve shaft adjusting cap. Torque cap to 11 ft. lbs. (15 N.m). Back off adjusting nut 10°.

12) Measure control valve shaft preload with torque wrench. Preload should be 3.9-5.6 INCH lbs. (.44-.63 N.m). If not, readjust. Coat control valve adjusting cap lock nut with sealer and tighten. Recheck control valve shaft preload. If required, readjust preload.

13) To adjust total preload, install rack seat, rack guide and spring. Apply sealer to spring cap and torque to 18 ft. lbs. (24 N.m). Back off spring cap 90°. *See*

TOYOTA POWER-ASSISTED RACK & PINION (Cont.)

Fig. 7. Measure total preload with torque wrench. *See Fig. 8.* Total preload should be 7.8-10.4 INCH lbs. (.90-1.17 N.m). Apply sealer to the lock nut and tighten. Recheck total preload and readjust if necessary.

Fig. 8: Setting Rack & Pinion Total Preload

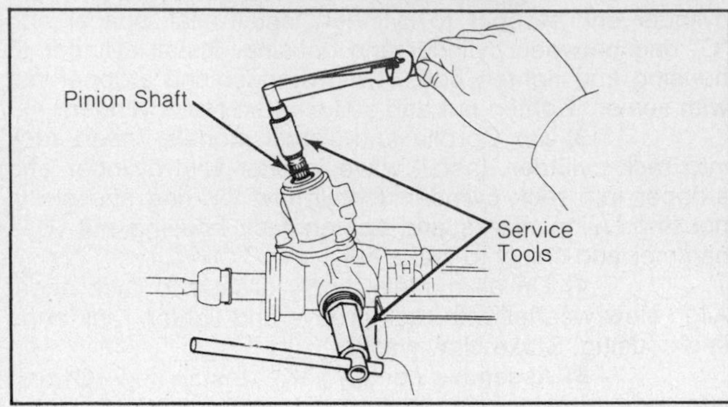
Pinion Shaft
Service
Tools

Tighten rack guide cap in small amounts, until total preload is obtained.

14) On Corolla and Tercel models, install self locking control valve nut. Apply sealer to the rack housing cap. Stake rack housing cap in 2 places.

15) Install the rack guide, spring and cap. To adjust the total preload, use service tool to hold steering shaft and tighten rack guide spring cap to 18 ft. lbs. (24 N.m). Back off the rack guide spring cap 12°. *See Fig. 7.*

16) Turn the control valve shaft right and left 2 times. Loosen the rack guide spring cap until no preload is felt. Install a torque wrench to the control valve shaft. Tighten the rack guide spring cap until a total preload of 6.9-11.3 INCH lbs. (.77-1.27 N.m) is obtained. *See Fig. 8.* Apply sealer to the lock nut and tighten. Recheck total preload and readjust if necessary.

17) Install oil pipes. Coat rack end dust seal with grease. Clear rack housing tube hole of any grease. Install rack boots. Spring clips must have bends facing outward and upward. Install tie rod ends and position them according to marks made on threads during disassembly.

TIGHTENING SPECIFICATIONS

Application	Ft. Lbs. (N.m)
Control Shaft Adjusting Lock Nut	73-94 (98-127)
Control Shaft Housing Cover Bolts	
Corolla & Tercel	15-21 (20-28)
All Other Models	11-15 (14-20)
Control Valve Lock Nut	
Corolla & Tercel	15-21 (20-28)
Cylinder End Stopper Nut	
Corolla & Tercel	87 (116)
All Other Models	109-144 (145-192)
Cylinder Set Nut	
Corolla & Tercel	102-122 (136-163)
Pump Housing Bolts	30-40 (41-54)
Pump Pully Nut	26-39 (35-52)
Rack Guide Adjusting Cap Lock Nut	44-53 (58-70)
Rack Housing-to-Cylinder Housing	
Camry, Celica & Supra	11-15 (14-20)
Steering Assembly-to-Body	
Camry & Tercel	43 (57)
Celica & Supra	29-39 (38-53)
Corolla	22-32 (29-43)

TOYOTA POWER-ASSISTED RECIRCULATING BALL

Cressida, Land Cruiser & Pickup

DESCRIPTION

POWER STEERING PUMP

Cressida and Pickup power steering pump uses an engine-driven rotor with vane plates, an eccentric cam ring and flow control valve to regulate maximum oil pressure and amount of oil flow.

Land Cruiser power steering pump components include an engine-driven eccentric rotor, a fixed ring having 6 slotted grooves with 6 slippers, and a flow control valve to regulate maximum oil pressure and amount of oil flow.

Slippers or vane plates (fitted in each slotted groove) are pressed against rotor or cam ring surface by pressure produced in adjoining slots or by spring tension. As rotor rotates, space between the rotor and ring changes, which produces oil pressure.

POWER STEERING GEAR

Power steering gear consists of 2 mechanisms. One converts steering wheel torque to cross shaft torque by means of a worm and power piston nut. The other detects hydraulic pressure developed by vane pump, and controls this pressure in proportion to the steering effort.

LUBRICATION

CAPACITY

4WD Pickup .91 qt. (.86L)
All Other Models .88 qt. (.84L)

FLUID TYPE

ATF Dexron

ADJUSTMENTS

BELT TENSION ADJUSTMENT

1) On Land Cruiser, apply 22 lbs. (10 kg) pressure, belt deflection between idler pulley and pump pulley should be .43-.55" (11-14 mm).

2) On all other models, use belt tension gauge and adjust belt tension to 100-150 lbs. (45-68 kg) for new belt or to 60-100 lbs. (27-68 kg) for used belt.

SYSTEM BLEEDING

1) Raise vehicle and support with safety stands. Fill fluid to proper level in vane pump reservoir. Turn wheels fully in both directions and recheck fluid level.

2) Start engine and let idle. Turn steering from lock-to-lock 2 or 3 times. Lower vehicle. Run engine at 1000 RPM or less. Turn wheel from lock-to-lock 2 or 3 times. Center steering wheel.

3) If fluid level does not rise and no foaming of fluid is evident, bleeding is complete. If level rises, or foaming is evident, repeat procedure until air is released.

FLUID REPLACEMENT

Raise vehicle and support with safety stands. Disconnect return hose and drain fluid into container. Turn steering wheel from lock-to-lock while draining. On Cressida model, cap reservoir return tube. Fill reservoir with fluid. Start engine and run for 1 to 2 seconds. Stop engine and refill reservoir. Repeat 4 or 5 times, or until no more air is in fluid. On all models, reconnect return hose, add fresh fluid and bleed system.

AIR CONTROL VALVE TESTING

Start engine. Turn steering wheel right and left. Check that engine RPM does not decrease more than 50 RPM. Pinch air hose. Turn steering wheel right and left. Check that engine RPM decreases about 200 RPM.

HYDRAULIC PRESSURE TESTING

1) Disconnect pressure lines from steering gear case and vane pump. Attach pressure gauge with gauge side connected to vane pump.

2) Attach valve side of gauge to pressure line. Bleed air from system and check fluid level. With engine at idle, check fluid pressure reading with pressure gauge valve closed.

3) Correct pressure should be 882 psi (62 kg/cm²) for 4WD Pickup and 1024 psi (72 kg/cm²) for all other models.

NOTE: **Do not keep pressure gauge valve closed for more than 10 seconds. Fluid testing temperature should be 176°F (80°C).**

4) Check pressure with steering wheel at lock position and pressure valve open. Pressure should be 882 psi (62 kg/cm²) for 4WD Pickup and 1024 psi (72 kg/cm²) for all other models.

5) Measure pressure with engine at idle and again at 3000 RPM. Pressure difference should be less than 71 psi (5 kg/cm²). If more, check flow control valve.

6) With vehicle on flat surface, turn steering wheel to center position. With engine idling, measure steering turning force at steering wheel outer rim over a full rotation on both sides of center point.

7) Turning force should not exceed 8.8 lbs. (4.0 kg) on Cressida, 13.2 lbs. (6.0 kg) on Land Cruiser, or 7.7 lbs. (3.5 kg) on Pickup models.

REMOVAL & INSTALLATION

POWER STEERING PUMP

Removal

Loosen pulley retaining nut before removing drive belt. Disconnect and plug oil lines at pump housing. Disconnect air control valve hose on Cressida models. Remove pump retaining bolts. Remove pump.

NOTE: **Keep disconnected hoses plugged and elevated to prevent fluid from draining out.**

Installation

To install, reverse removal procedures. Adjust drive belt tension and bleed system.

POWER STEERING GEAR

Removal

1) Disconnect and plug pressure and return lines at gear housing. Mark steering gear shaft to flexible coupling or universal joint. Disconnect flexible coupling or universal joint.

TOYOTA POWER-ASSISTED RECIRCULATING BALL (Cont.)

2) Mark pitman arm to sector shaft. Disconnect pitman arm. Disconnect steering gear housing from heat shield on Land Cruiser. Remove steering gear retaining bolts. Remove steering gear.

Installation

To install, reverse removal procedures. Align all marks during installation. Bleed system and perform pressure test.

OVERHAUL

POWER STEERING PUMP

Disassembly

1) Mount power steering pump in vise. Remove union from rear housing. Remove reservoir from pump (if equipped). Index mark front and rear housings for reassembly reference. Remove front housing bolts.

2) Use plastic mallet to tap off front housing. Ensure that vane plates, rotor and cam plate do not fall out. Remove ring cam, rotor and vane plates. Clamp front housing in a vise. Use chisel to pry off oil seal.

3) Remove snap ring. With plastic mallet, lightly tap the rotor shaft out of front housing and tap bottom of rear housing. Remove rear plate and spring.

4) Install a bolt into plug. Push bolt and remove snap ring. Pull out bolt and remove plug. Remove spring and control valve by hand.

Inspection

1) Check all parts for wear or damage and replace as necessary. Check oil clearance between bushing and rotor shaft. Maximum clearance is .0028" (.07 mm). Check that bearings operate smoothly.

2) If necessary, press out old bearing and press in new bearing. Measure difference between cam ring and rotor. Maximum difference should be .0024" (.06 mm).

3) Dimensions of the vane plate should be .589 x .307 x .067" (14.97 x 7.80 x 1.70 mm). Maximum clearance between vane plate and rotor groove is .0024" (.06 mm).

4) Check flow control valve for leakage with compressed air. Control valve spring should be 1.85-1.97" (47-50 mm) long.

Reassembly

1) Lubricate flow control valve and spring with automatic transmission fluid (ATF). Install control valve, spring, plug and snap ring to pump. Lubricate rotor shaft with ATF.

2) Install to front housing by tapping with plastic mallet. Install snap ring to front housing. Apply grease to oil seal lip. Using a driver and hammer, install oil seal.

3) Lubricate and install "O" ring to front housing. Align fluid passages of ring cam and front housing and install ring cam. Lubricate rotor with ATF. Install rotor with cut spline facing toward front housing.

4) Make sure letters on ring cam and rotor match. Lubricate vane plates with ATF. Install vane plates with round end facing outward. Lubricate and install 2 "O" rings to rear plate.

5) Place rear plate on the ring cam with pin holes aligned with pins. Place spring on the rear plate. Align marks on front and rear housings and install.

6) Half tighten front and rear housing retaining bolts. Clamp rear housing in vise. Tighten housing bolts evenly 3 or 4 times. Lubricate and install "O" ring to union.

7) Insert and tighten union. Check to ensure rotor shaft operates smoothly. Install pulley nut and check

Fig. 1: Exploded View of Toyota Power Steering Pump Assemblies

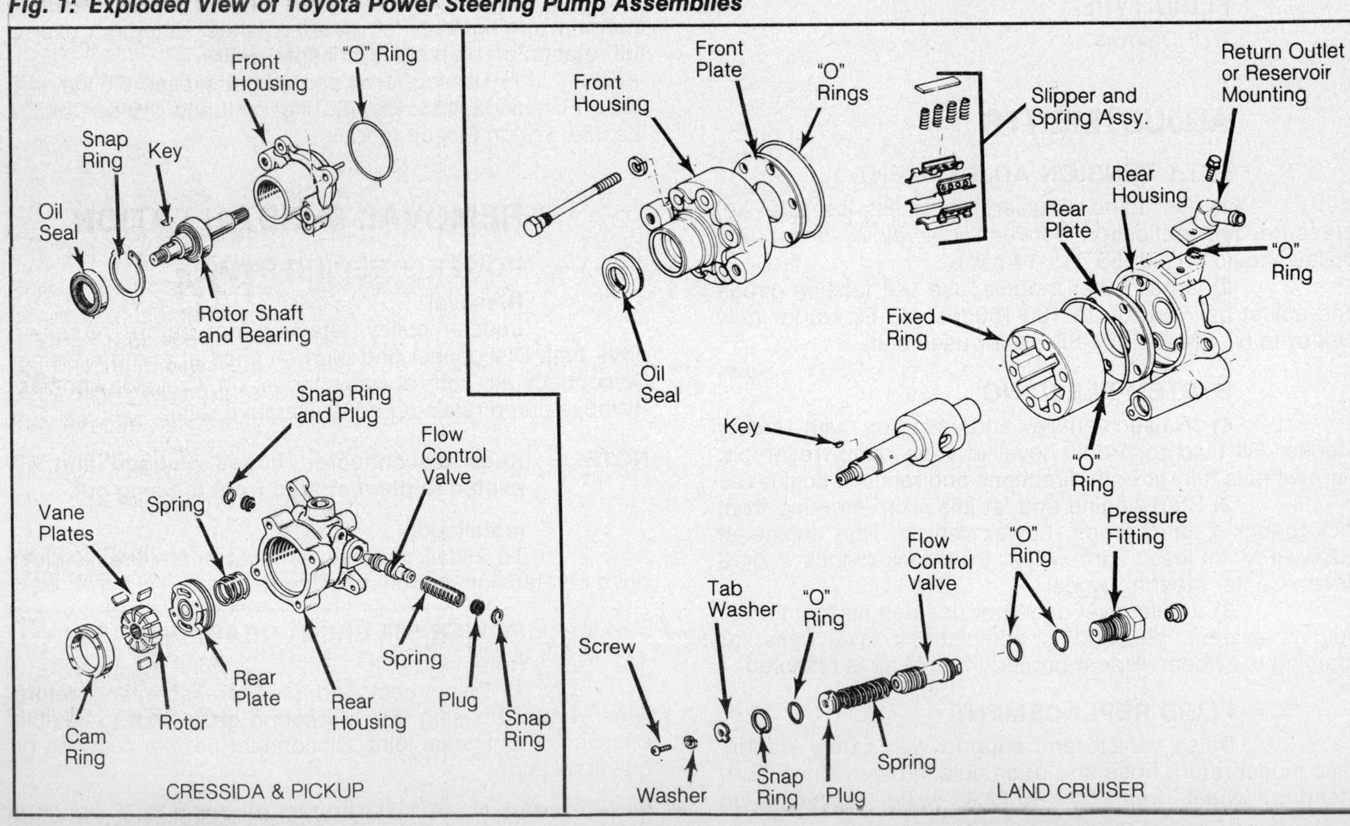
Front Housing
"O" Ring
Snap Ring
Key
Oil Seal
Rotor Shaft and Bearing
Snap Ring and Plug
Flow Control Valve
Vane Plates
Spring
Spring
Cam Ring
Rotor
Rear Plate
Rear Housing
Plug
Snap Ring
CRESSIDA & PICKUP
Front Plate
Front Housing
"O" Rings
Slipper and Spring Assy.
Return Outlet or Reservoir Mounting
Rear Housing
Rear Plate
"O" Ring
Fixed Ring
Oil Seal
Key
"O" Ring
Pressure Fitting
Flow Control Valve
"O" Ring
Tab Washer
"O" Ring
Screw
Washer
Snap Ring
Plug
Spring
LAND CRUISER

TOYOTA POWER-ASSISTED RECIRCULATING BALL (Cont.)

rotating torque. Torque should be less than 24 INCH lbs. (2.7 N.m).

POWER STEERING GEAR

Disassembly

1) Attach gear housing to holding fixture and mount in a vise. Remove sector shaft adjusting screw lock nut and sector shaft cover bolts.

2) Turn sector shaft adjusting screw clockwise until cover is removed. Remove sector shaft by tapping bottom end with mallet.

3) Remove valve housing-to-gear housing bolts. Hold power piston nut with hand and turn worm shaft clockwise. Remove valve assembly and power piston from gear housing.

Fig. 2: Using Gauge to Check Ball Clearance

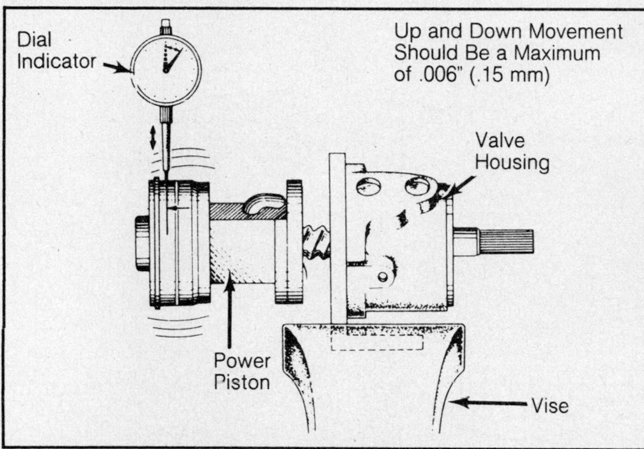
Dial Indicator
Up and Down Movement Should Be a Maximum of .006" (.15 mm)
Valve Housing
Power Piston
Vise

Maximum up and down movement is .006" (.15 mm).

CAUTION: Ensure that power piston nut does not come off worm shaft. Do not disassemble valve body or remove power piston from worm shaft.

Fig. 3: Using Dial Indicator to Check Sector Shaft Thrust Clearance

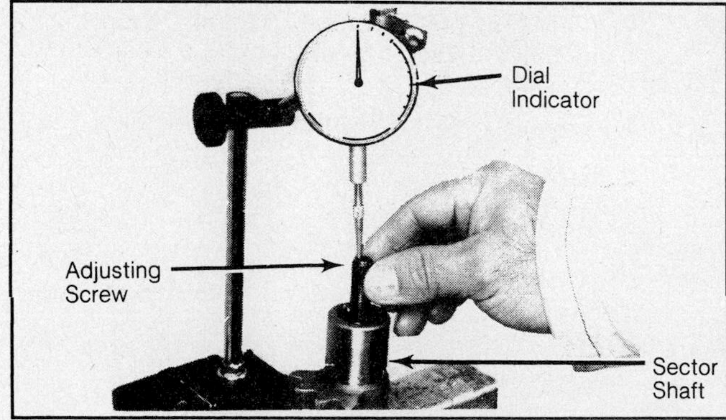
Dial Indicator
Adjusting Screw
Sector Shaft

Remove stake on adjusting nut to adjust sector shaft.

4) Install valve assembly in vise. Using a dial indicator measure ball clearance. If clearance exceeds .006" (.15 mm) replace valve assembly. Install sector shaft in a vise.

5) Using dial indicator, check sector shaft adjusting screw for thrust clearance of .001-.002" (.03-.05 mm). To adjust thrust clearance, remove stake on adjusting nut. Turn adjusting nut to obtain correct thrust clearance.

6) Temporarily install valve assembly in gear housing and install retaining bolts. Using lock nut tool, remove lock nut and adjusting bolt from gear assembly.

7) Remove and replace as needed, oil seal, "O" ring, and bearing assembly. Install lock nut and tighten. Remove valve assembly from gear housing.

Cleaning & Inspection

1) Clean all parts in solvent and dry. Coat all sliding parts, "O" rings, and Teflon rings with power steering fluid upon reassembly.

Fig. 4: Exploded View of Power Steering Gear Assembly

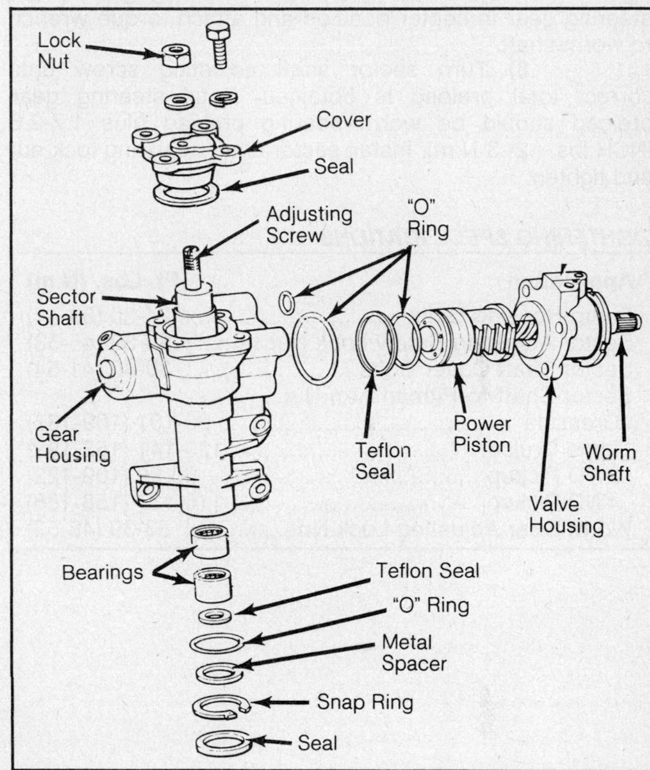
Lock Nut
Cover
Seal
Adjusting Screw
"O" Ring
Sector Shaft
Gear Housing
Teflon Seal
Power Piston
Worm Shaft
Valve Housing
Bearings
Teflon Seal
"O" Ring
Metal Spacer
Snap Ring
Seal

2) Inspect sector shaft for peeling or pitting at ball rolling surface. Check power piston nut mesh with sector shaft. Look for damaged tooth surfaces or ball rolling surfaces.

3) Gear housing bearings must be replaced if bearing rollers are pitted or peeled. Also replace housing bearings if it was noticed that sector shaft bearing surfaces had been scored or pitted.

4) Remove Teflon ring and "O" ring from gear housing. Using needle bearing removal tool, remove needle bearings.

Reassembly

1) Install needle bearings with longer edge of outer race facing outwards. Make sure that top end aligns with housing end surface.

2) Install lower bearing so it is positioned .93" (23.6 mm) away from housing inner end surface on Land Cruiser, or .76" (19.4 mm) on all other models.

3) Install "O" ring and Teflon ring to power piston. Install large and small "O" rings to gear housing. Install power piston assembly to gear housing. Tighten bolts.

TOYOTA POWER-ASSISTED RECIRCULATING BALL (Cont.)

4) To adjust worm shaft preload, loosen lock nut and install adjusting wrench to adjusting plug. Install torque wrench to worm shaft and tighten adjusting plug to obtain 3.5-5.6 INCH lbs. (.4-.6 N.m) preload.

5) Hold adjusting plug and tighten lock nut. Wrap tape around spline area of sector shaft. Align sector shaft gear teeth with power piston teeth (centered) and insert sector shaft into gear housing.

6) Do not turn sector shaft during installation, as damage to "O" ring could result. Install sector shaft cover, with seal, to sector shaft adjusting screw.

7) Turn screw counterclockwise until cover will fit completely down on gear housing. Install bolts and tighten. To adjust total preload of steering gear, place steering gear in center position and attach torque wrench to worm shaft.

8) Turn sector shaft adjusting screw until correct total preload is obtained. Total steering gear preload should be worm bearing preload plus 1.7-2.6 INCH lbs. (.2-.3 N.m). Install sector shaft adjusting lock nut and tighten.

TIGHTENING SPECIFICATIONS

Application	Ft. Lbs. (N.m)
Pump Housing Bolts	24-30 (33-41)
Sector Adjusting Screw Lock Nut	33-39 (45-53)
Sector Shaft Cover Bolts	30-40 (41-54)
Sector Shaft-to-Pitman Arm Nut	
Cressida	80-101 (109-137)
Land Cruiser	120-141 (163-192)
2WD Pickup	80-90 (109-122)
4WD Pickup	116-137 (158-186)
Worm Gear Adjusting Lock Nut	33-39 (45-53)

VOLKSWAGEN POWER-ASSISTED RACK & PINION

Jetta, Quantum, Rabbit, Rabbit Pickup, & Scirocco

DESCRIPTION

The system consists of a vane pump, rotary piston pinion gear assembly and an oil reservoir. The vane pump draws fluid from the reservoir and supplies it to the flow control valve. The control valve supplies fluid to the proper side of the rack-piston when the steering wheel is turned.

The pump is belt driven and is mounted on the front of the engine. The reservoir is located near the firewall.

LUBRICATION

CAPACITY

1 qt. (.95L)

FLUID TYPE

ATF Dexron

FLUID LEVEL CHECK

Remove reservoir cover, start engine and check fluid level. Fluid level should be at mark on upper inside of reservoir.

HYDRAULIC SYSTEM BLEEDING

1) Start engine and allow to idle. Check that fluid is at proper level. Turn steering wheel lock-to-lock several times quickly.

2) Continue until fluid level remains at reservoir mark. Make sure that no bubbles appear in reservoir when steering wheel is turned. Shut off engine and check that oil level does not rise more than 3/8" (9.5 mm) above mark.

OIL FILTER REPLACEMENT

Remove outer cover, gasket and spring from reservoir. Remove inner filter cover and filter insert. Replace filter. Install new filter, replace old filter cover, spring, gasket, and top cover. Check fluid level.

Fig. 1: Exploded View of Power Steering Gear

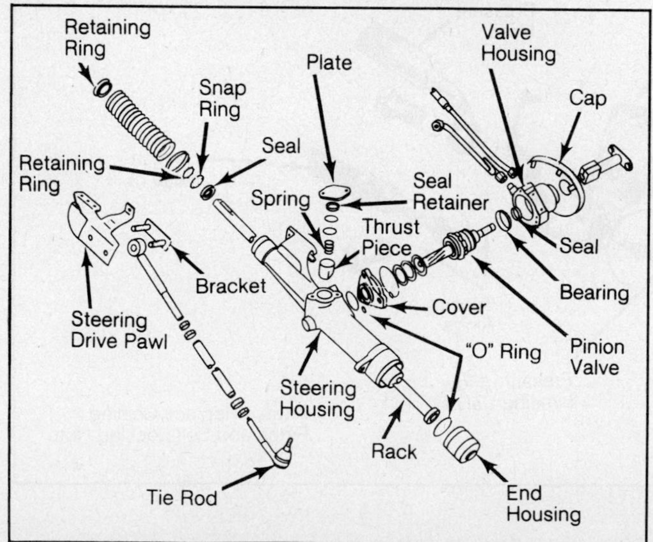
Retaining Ring
Snap Ring
Plate
Valve Housing
Cap
Seal
Retaining Ring
Spring
Seal Retainer
Thrust Piece
Seal
Bracket
Bearing
Cover
Steering Drive Pawl
"O" Ring
Pinion Valve
Steering Housing
Rack
Tie Rod
End Housing

NOTE: Oil filter insert must be replaced whenever repairs are made to power steering system.

ADJUSTMENT

PUMP BELT

Quantum

Loosen nuts on pump mounting bracket. Turn adjusting bolt on bracket until belt deflection is 3/8" (9.5 mm) at center of belt. Tighten nuts to specifications.

All Others

Belt tension is adjusted by means of shims between inner and outer pump pulley. Adjust tension so that deflection at center of belt is .4-.5" (10-12 mm) under thumb pressure.

STEERING GEAR

Quantum

Loosen lock nut on steering gear. Hand tighten adjusting screw until it just touches thrust plate. Hold adjusting screw and tighten lock nut. Check adjustment with engine idling. No play should be felt. Readjust if necessary.

TESTING

SYSTEM PRESSURE TEST

1) Install pressure gauge (US1074/2) between pressure hose and pressure pipe of valve housing, with pressure gauge valve open. Run engine at idle. Turn steering wheel lock-to-lock several times.

2) Pressure should be 986-1189 psi (69-84 kg/cm²) on Quantum. All other models should be 1100-1200 psi (77.33-84.36 kg/cm²). If pressure is not within limits, check pump pressure. If pump is good, replace steering gear.

PUMP PRESSURE TEST

1) With pressure gauge installed, start engine and idle. Close valve (for no longer than 5 seconds). Pressure should be 986-1189 psi (69-84 kg/cm²) on Quantum and 1100-1200 psi (77.83-84.36 kg/cm²).

2) If pressure differs, check limiting valve by inspecting bores in valve and piston for obstructions. Check that piston moves freely in housing. Install new valve, if necessary.

LEAK TEST

1) With engine idling, turn steering wheel to full lock and hold in position. Inspect all connections and tighten, if necessary. If leak shows at steering pinion, replace housing seal and both intermediate cover seals.

2) If pinion shaft seal is leaking, fluid will have entered gear housing. Check for fluid by loosening outer clamp on right steering boot and pushing boot in. If seal is leaking, disassemble steering gear. Replace all seals.

REMOVAL & INSTALLATION

STEERING GEAR

Removal

1) Drain fluid from system. Disconnect pressure and return pipes from valve housing. Disconnect

VOLKSWAGEN POWER-ASSISTED RACK & PINION (Cont.)

lower steering shaft from pinion shaft. Disconnect tie rods from bracket. Remove bolts retaining gear housing to body.

2) On all except Quantum, remove rear motor/transmission mount and exhaust pipe. Remove gear housing.

Installation

To install, reverse removal procedures. To facilitate tie rod installation, install one tie rod to steering gear and tighten before installing other tie rod.

VANE PUMP

Removal

Remove alternator and vane pump belts. Disconnect pressure and suction lines from pump and cover openings. Remove retaining bolts from bracket and lift pump from engine.

Installation

To install, reverse removal procedures. Adjust belt deflection. Start engine. Turn steering wheel to full lock and check for leaks in connections.

OVERHAUL

Before disassembling steering gear, check output and system pressure. Always use all parts in repair kit (811 498 020) and always use new self-locking nuts.

PINION HOUSING SEAL

Removal (Quantum)

1) Remove retaining bolts from pinion valve housing and remove housing. Mark position of pinion gear relative to rack. Remove pinion gear and intermediate cover. Remove "O" rings from intermediate cover (1 on each side).

2) Anchor housing in padded vise and drive out oil seal from back. Install new seals. Make sure seal lip on housing seal faces intermediate cover. Replace both intermediate cover "O" rings.

Installation

To install, reverse removal procedures. Protect pinion teeth on shaft when replacing intermediate cover. Do not damage "O" rings during installation.

NOTE: **On all models except Quantum, manufacturer recommends replacement of steering gear if pinion or piston-rod seals are leaking.**

STEERING GEAR

Disassembly (Quantum)

1) Remove steering gear assembly from vehicle. Remove pinion valve housing. Remove pinion valve assembly. Remove plate, seal retainer, spring, and thrust piece from steering housing.

2) Remove retaining ring, clamp and boot from steering housing. Remove retaining ring and snap ring from steering housing.

3) Remove end housing and "O" ring from steering housing. Pull rack out of steering housing. Using oil seal puller, remove oil seal from steering housing.

Reassembly

1) To install oil seal on steering housing, place oil seal on flat surface and push sleeve (available in repair kit 811 498 020) into oil seal. Slide rack into steering housing.

2) Slide oil seal with sleeve over rack and into steering housing using installer tools (VW 426 and VW 4166). Remove sleeve. Install snap ring and retaining ring.

3) Install end housing with new "O" ring. Lock in place with 2 punch marks 180° apart. Install thrust piece, spring, "O" ring, seal retainer, and plate. Install clamp, boot, and retaining ring. Install pinion valve assembly as previously described.

TIGHTENING SPECIFICATIONS

Application	Ft. Lbs. (N.m)
End Housing	37 (50)
Pressure-Flow Limiting Valve Cap	42 (57)
Pressure Pipe	29 (39)
Return Pipe	
On Pump	29 (39)
On Valve Housing	22 (30)
Tie Rod-to-Steering Arm	32 (44)
Valve Housing Bolts	15 (20)

Fig. 2: View of Vane Pump Assembly

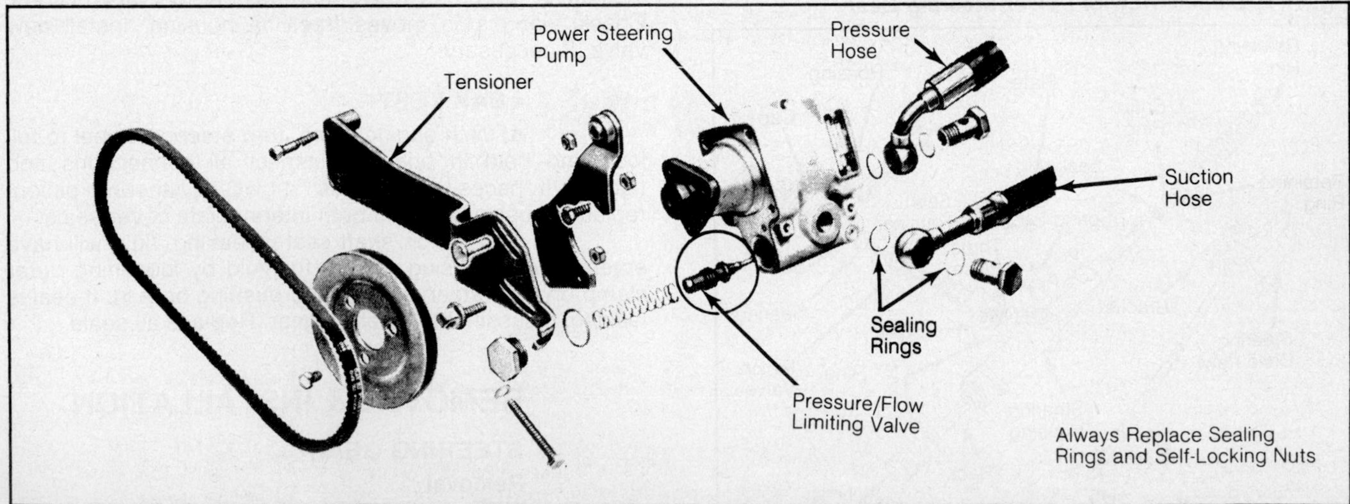
Power Steering Pump
Tensioner
Pressure Hose
Suction Hose
Sealing Rings
Pressure/Flow Limiting Valve
Always Replace Sealing Rings and Self-Locking Nuts

Only pressure/flow limiting valve can be replaced.

Power Steering

VOLVO POWER-ASSISTED RACK & PINION

DESCRIPTION

Power steering is rack and pinion type. All 760 GLE and some DL, GL and Turbo models use a cam gear type with aluminum housing. Other DL, GL and Turbo models use a ZF gear type with removable valve housing.

Steering consists of the rack and pinion steering gear and a power-assist pump interconnected with flexible lines. A separate reservoir is attached to the power steering pump.

LUBRICATION

CAPACITY

DL, GL & Turbo .75 qts. (.7L)
760 GLE 1 qt. (1L)

FLUID TYPE

ATF (Automatic Transmission Fluid)

STEERING GEAR FILLING

Remove inner clamp on right side rubber bellows, and using a suction gun, fill gear with recommended lubricant through side of bellows. Reinstall clamp. Carefully compress bellows so some fluid will flow to other side.

HYDRAULIC FLUID FILLING

Fill the reservoir with approved fluid, start engine and allow to idle, adding fluid as level drops.

ADJUSTMENTS

HYDRAULIC FLUID BLEEDING

1) Fill the reservoir with approved fluid, start engine and allow to idle, adding fluid as level drops. Turn steering wheel from lock-to-lock in a slow even motion to allow the pump to operate at low pressure.

2) Continue turning steering wheel until fluid in reservoir is almost free of air bubbles. Check that fluid is at the level mark. Install reservoir cap.

SERVO BALANCE

Pre-Adjustment Testing

1) On all models, connect a pressure gauge between steering pump and steering gear. *See Fig. 1.* Make sure fluid in reservoir is at level mark. Place pressure gauge so it can be seen from the driver's seat.

2) Remove steering wheel impact guard on 760 GLE models by lifting lower edge and pulling out. On all other models, remove by compressing sides slightly. On all models, install a torque wrench on steering wheel nut.

3) With engine at idle, turn steering wheel (using torque wrench) slowly to the right. Read torque when pressure reaches 171 psi (12 kg/cm²) on cam gear type, 285 psi (20 kg/cm²) for ZF steering gear.

4) Repeat operation turning wheel to left. Torque should be 2.6-3.3 ft. lbs. (3.5-4.5 N.m) as gear approaches specified pressure.

5) Difference between both sides must not exceed 9 INCH lbs. (1 N.m) on cam gear type. Difference must not exceed 4.4 INCH lbs. (.5 N.m) on ZF steering gear.

Fig. 1: Pressure Gauge Test Set Up

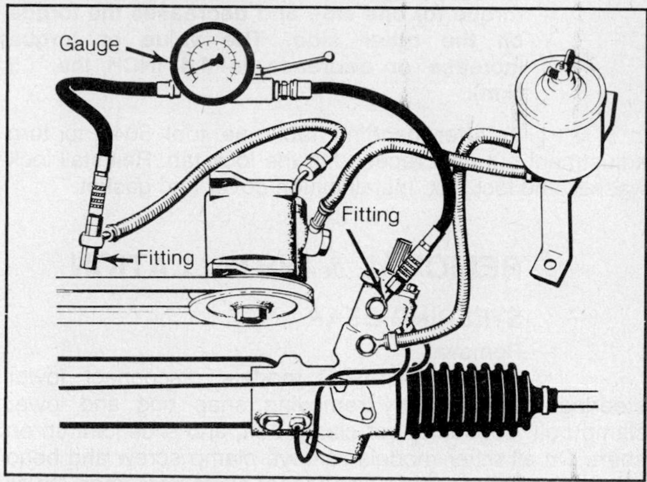
Gauge
Fitting
Fitting

Make sure fluid level is at full mark when testing.

6) If difference exceeds specifications on 760 GLE models, the steering gear must be reconditioned or a new one installed. Adjustments can be made on DL, GL and Turbo models if specifications are not meet. Adjust with the following adjustment procedure.

Cam Gear Type Adjustment (DL, GL & Turbo Models)

1) Turn off engine and remove lock nut and washer from lower pinion bearing. Lock washer will have 1 tab bent down to lock adjustment nut (bearing race). *See Fig. 2.*

Fig. 2: Adjusting Lock Washer on Cam Gear Type Power Steering

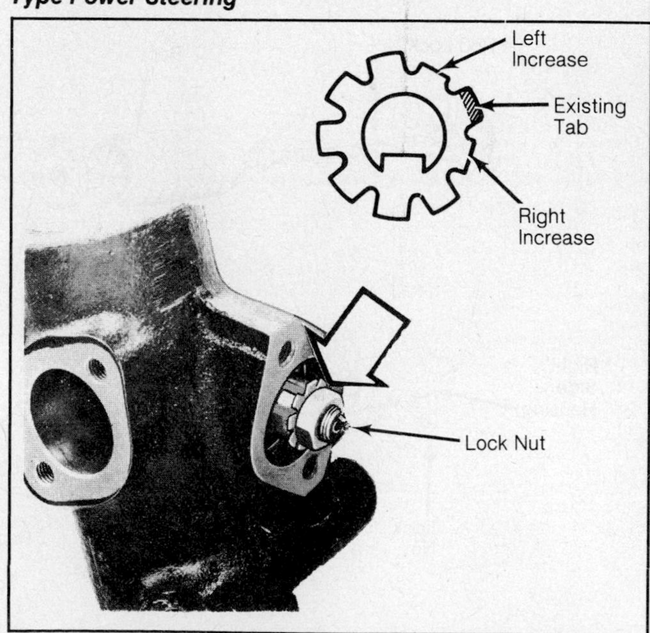
Left
Increase
Existing
Tab
Right
Increase
Lock Nut

Only 1 tab should be bent down to lock adjustment nut.

2) To increase torque for left side, straighten existing bent tab and bend first tab to left. To increase torque for right side, bend first tab to right.

VOLVO POWER-ASSISTED RACK & PINION (Cont.)

NOTE: Changing tabs increases the amount of torque for one side and decreases the torque on the other side. The value of torque increase or decrease is 4.4 INCH lbs. (.5 N.m).

3) After bending tab, use tool 5049 to turn adjustment nut until recess fits the lock tab. Reinstall lock washer and lock nut. Install pinion cover and gasket.

REMOVAL & INSTALLATION

STEERING GEAR

Removal

1) On 760 GLE models disconnect lower steering gear shaft by removing snap ring and lower clamp bolt. Loosen upper clamp bolt, and slide joint up on shaft. On all other models remove clamp screw and bend flange apart slightly and disconnect shaft from gear. On all models, raise vehicle and support with safety stands. Remove wheel assembies.

2) Remove tie rod nuts and disconnect ball studs from spindle using appropriate ball joint removal tool. Remove splash guard.

3) Disconnect hoses at steering gear and install plugs in hose connections to protect against contamination.

4) On 760 GLE remove anti-roll bar mounting brackets from side members and move out of way. Remove steering gear bolts and lower steering gear. On all other models remove steering gear bolts and pull gear down until free of steering shaft flange. Remove steering gear on left side of vehicle.

Installation

1) To install, reverse removal procedures. Make sure recess on pinion shaft is aligned toward lock bolt opening in flange.

2) Install right side "U" bolt and flange, but do not tighten. Install and tighten left side bolts. Tighten right side "U" bolt.

3) Connect steering rods. Make sure rods are same length. Difference should not exceed 1/16" (2 mm). Install lock bolt on flange and reconnect hoses. Install splash shield and tires.

POWER STEERING PUMP

Removal

Remove pivot bolts on bracket and bolt on belt tensioning bracket. Place a container below pump to receive drained fluid, disconnect hydraulic connections at pump, remove pump.

Installation

To install, reverse removal procedures. Fill and bleed the system.

Fig. 3: Exploded View of Cam Gear Type Power Steering Assembly

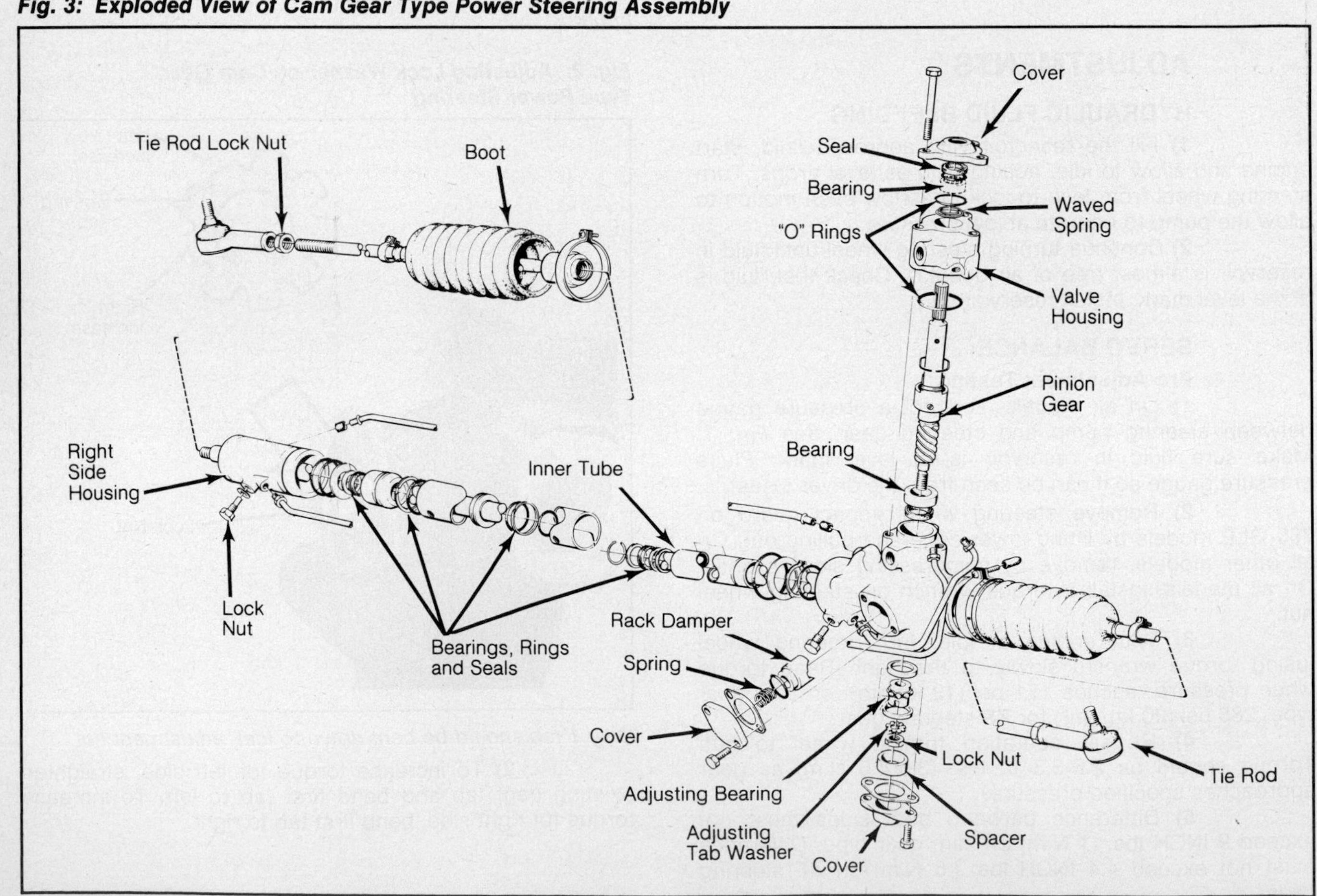
Cover
Seal
Bearing
Waved Spring
"O" Rings
Valve Housing
Pinion Gear
Bearing
Tie Rod Lock Nut
Boot
Right Side Housing
Inner Tube
Lock Nut
Bearings, Rings and Seals
Rack Damper
Spring
Cover
Lock Nut
Tie Rod
Adjusting Bearing
Adjusting Tab Washer
Spacer
Cover

VOLVO POWER-ASSISTED RACK & PINION (Cont.)

OVERHAUL

STEERING GEAR

Disassembly (Cam Gear Type)

1) Remove hose clamps holding rubber bellows. Cut clamps and remove equalizer tube and 2 pressure tubes. Attach steering gear to fixture (5046) and fasten with "U" bolt.

2) Drain fluid from rack by slowly turning pinion back and forth in full strokes. Place rack in center position. Check inner and outer ball joints for excessive wear.

3) Remove outer clamp and pull back boot. Clean grease from rack and ball joint areas. Using a 1 1/4" (32 mm) spanner and adjustable wrench, remove left steering rod. Loosen right side rod.

4) Remove locking wire for cage on right side. Turn end housing clockwise. Wire will protrude through hole in tube. Hold pinion stationary and apply compressed air to remove end housing and bushing.

5) Remove right steering rod. Remove end housing plastic ring and bushing. Remove cover, shims, spring and piston of pre-tension device. Remove pinion lock cover, lock washer and gaskets.

6) Using a hook spanner, remove spacer (inner) sleeve. Bend back lock washer, hold pinion shaft and remove nut. Valve should not move. Remove inner bearing race, ball cage and lower race using sleeve (5049).

7) Remove dust seal, valve housing cover, and "O" ring. Remove spring, valve housing and pinion gear. Remove "O" ring. Carefully pull out rack on right side. Remove upper bushing and seal for pinion gear using extractor (1819).

8) If damaged, remove inner race for pinion bearing using 2 screwdrivers. Carefully tap out rack rod seal ring and spacer sleeve from steering gear tube.

NOTE: **Ensure that inner surface of tube is not damaged by scratches.**

9) Use a 1 1/16" (27 mm) socket and 2 long extensions inserted through housing. Place bearing in soft-jawed vise and pry out seal. If damaged, or if vehicle has been driven more than 25,000 miles, remove seal ring.

Inspection

1) Clean all parts. Inspect for wear or damage. If pinion control valves or housing are damaged, parts should be replaced as an assembly.

2) Should right rack bushing require replacement, complete rack sleeve should be replaced. Replace all seals, "O" rings, and valve housing cover when reassembling.

Reassembly

1) Install seal and "O" ring to right side rack sleeve. Seal lips should face down. Lubricate seal lips before installation and use a socket to press in.

2) Install "O" ring and Teflon ring to piston seal. Install seal ring in pinion housing with handle and drift (1801 and 5184). Seal ring lip must face up.

3) Make sure bearing turns freely on pinion shaft. Install to pinion housing with handle and drift. Fit spacer washer from the rack toothed side. Cover rack teeth with tape and lubricate with automatic transmission fluid.

4) Install seal with lips facing inward. Install tapered spacer washer with taper facing seal ring. Install second spacer washer. Remove tape and push 2 spacer washers together.

5) Fill rack teeth with lubricant (Volvo P/N 1 116 001-1). With teeth facing up, insert rack into tube. As seal ring enters tube, apply pressure on rack.

6) Seal ring and distance washers will lock into position in tube. Looking through inner high pressure hole, line up Teflon ring with center of hole.

7) Pull rack rod back until it is positioned flush with pinion housing left side. DO NOT pull rack further back. Cover threads and edge of rack with tape.

8) Install rack sleeve with seal facing to the right. Take care not to damage sleeve outer "O" ring against lock wire groove. Install plastic spacer in rack with bevelled edge toward seal.

9) Remove tape. Place sleeve on rack with tool recess facing steering rod end. Turn sleeve to line up hole in lock sleeve with elongated hole in tube.

10) Using a new lock wire, install wire in lock wire groove. Slowly turn sleeve counterclockwise until end of locking wire is positioned inside elongated hole in tube.

11) If removed, install inner race for pinion lower bearing. Pack pinion gear with lubricant. Install rack rod in housing.

12) With pinion in place, rack should protrude 2 1/8" (55 mm) from housing when flat of lock bolt is in positions shown. *See Fig. 4.*

Fig. 4: Positioning Rack Rod Pinion

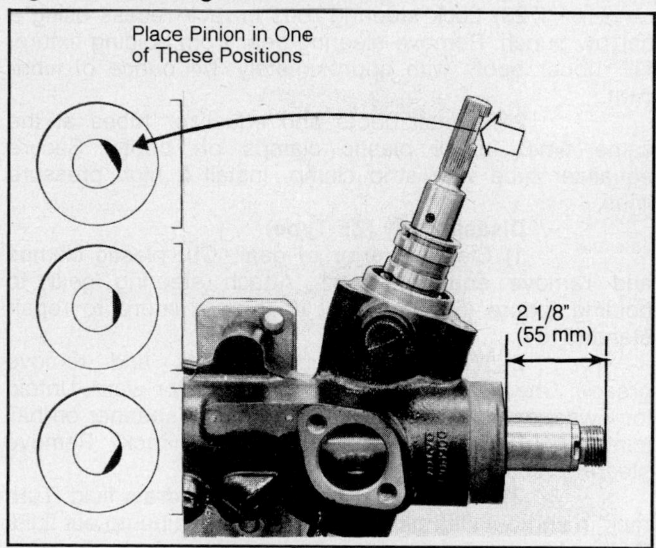
Place Pinion in One
of These Positions
2 1/8"
(55 mm)

Pinion gear should be filled with grease.

NOTE: **Be careful when installing pinion not to damage valve.**

13) Use pinion bearing sleeve (5049) to screw on inner bearing. Shaft end should protrude 23/64" (9 mm). Install outer race for lower pinion bearing.

14) Install spacer sleeve on top of bearing race. Screw in sleeve until it bottoms. Place lock washer in position on housing and finger tighten bolts.

VOLVO POWER-ASSISTED RACK & PINION (Cont.)

15) Bend down lock washer tab which is lined up with one of the recesses on sleeve. Remove bolts and washer. Install "O" ring in lower part of valve housing.

16) Install valve housing, being careful not to damage housing or pinion valve. Install coil spring with large end facing down. Using cover installing sleeve (5182) place "O" ring in position.

17) As cover is installed, make sure that coil spring is not squeezed under cover. Install dust seal. Install lock washer and nut. Use pinion shaft socket (5179) to hold pinion when tightening nut. Do not lock with washer tab.

18) Measure preload piston clearance. Place piston without "O" ring in housing. Measure clearance between piston and housing. Use a feeler gauge and ruler.

19) Press piston against rack, while sliding rack back and forth. Note maximum clearance. Select shim with thickness .002-.006" (.05-.15 mm) greater than thickness noted in step **18).**

20) Place spring in position. Install shims and gasket, with gasket closest to aluminum housing. Install cover and tighten. Measure pinion torque with pinion shaft socket and torque gauge (9177).

21) Crank rack back and forth between rack end positions. Correct torque should be 8-15 INCH lbs. (.9-1.7 N.m). If torque in any position is excessive, stop rack in that position and readjust preload.

22) If rack binds with preload removed, rack is warped and must be replaced. Use a spanner on ball joint and support rack end with a large adjustable wrench to install steering rods.

23) Lock steering rods in rack recess using a narrow punch. Remove steering gear from holding fixture. Fill rubber boots with approximately 3/4 ounce of lubricant.

24) Install boots and equalizer tubes at the same time. Install plastic clamps on boots. Secure equalizer tube with strip clamp. Install 2 high pressure lines.

Disassembly (ZF Type)

1) Clean exterior of gear. Cut plastic clamps and remove equalizer tube. Attach steering gear to holding fixture (5046). Install gear and fixture to repair stand (5154).

2) Disconnect rubber boots and remove grease. Check inner and outer ball joints for wear. Unfold lock washer tab. Using a 1 1/16" (27 mm) spanner on ball joint and large adjustable wrench on rack. Remove steering rods.

3) Remove pressure lines and drain fluid. Turn rack in and out with pinion socket (5179) to pump out fluid. Remove preload piston by removing cover, washer, spring and piston. Remove rubber dust cover from pinion shaft.

4) Remove pinion housing cover with seal and "O" ring. Lift out pinion with upper roller bearing. Remove lower washer and needle bearing. Index mark position of center tube on housing. Do not use a punch to mark center tube.

5) Remove "O" ring from center tube. Only remove lock ring, if lock collar is damaged and needs to be replaced. Check rubber seal, replace if necessary.

6) Withdraw bearing from outer (right) tube end. First remove Teflon bushing with a screwdriver. Tap out seal with a 1 1/16" (27 mm) socket and a short extension.

7) Using seal extractor under washer, remove Teflon bushing, seal, and washer from right housing. Remove seal and "O" ring from top cover.

8) Remove depressor and "O" ring from preload piston. Remove Teflon seal rings from pinion valve assembly.

Inspection

Clean all parts and inspect for wear or damage. Replace as necessary.

Reassembly

1) If removed, lubricate needle bearing with lubricant (Volvo P/N 1 161 001-1). Install to pinion housing with drift. Bearing bottom should be flush with housing.

2) Install bearing race (bevelled edge down), needle bearing and bearing race to pinion housing. Do not use lubricant at this time. *See Fig. 5.*

Fig. 5: Installing Pinion Bearings and Races

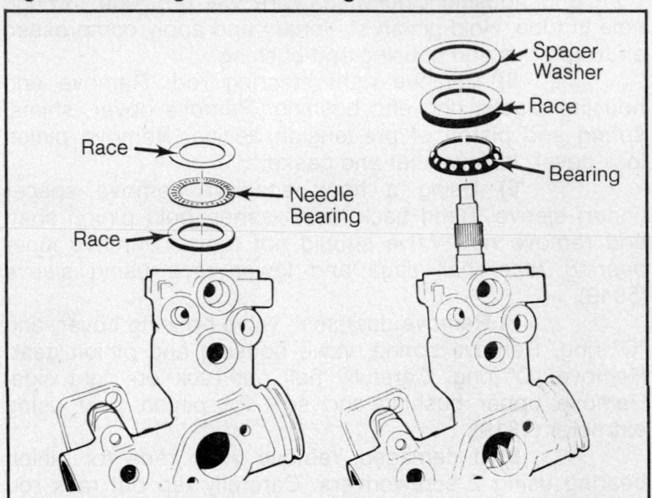
Spacer
Washer
Race
Race
Bearing
Needle
Bearing
Race

Race is installed with beveled edge down.

NOTE: **Before installing any seals, preload of pinion bearing must be checked.**

3) Install pinion assembly without seals. Install bearing, race and spacer washer to pinion. *See Fig. 5.* Install pinion housing cover. Tighten cover bolts to 7 ft. lbs. (10 N.m).

4) To adjust pinion, tie a string around shaft. Attach a spring gauge and measure turning force. Force should be 3.7-6.4 lbs. (1.7-2.9 kg). Adjust by replacement of spacer washer. *See Fig. 5.*

5) Washers are available in increments of .0004" (.01 mm) from .075" (1.91 mm) to .10" (2.45 mm). Remove pinion with bearings and spacers.

6) Install 4 rubber "O" rings in valve body grooves. Install 4 Teflon rings over "O" rings.

NOTE: **Green Teflon ring must be installed as indicated by arrow in Fig. 6.**

7) Install pinion housing seal in housing with lips up. Fill lubricant in space between seal lips. Use drift (5184) and handle (1801) to install.

8) Install spacer ring to housing with cone end in, grooved end out. Install bronze bushing in spacer (inner) tube with chamfered side down.

VOLVO POWER-ASSISTED RACK & PINION (Cont.)

Fig. 6: Installing Green Teflon Ring to Pinion

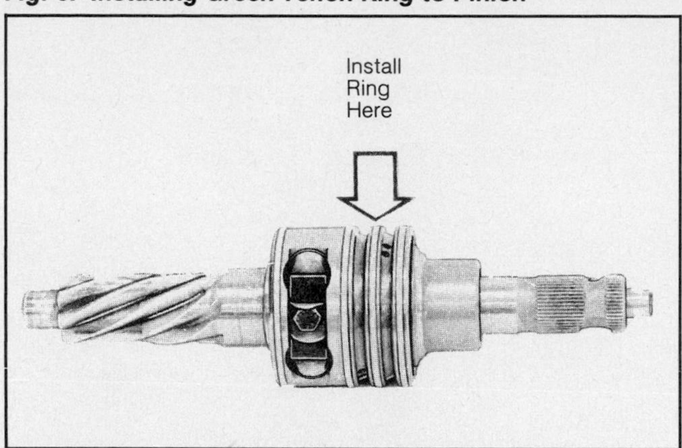
Install
Ring
Here

Ring must be installed at arrow.

9) Fill lubricant in space between seal lips and install seal in spacer tube with lips up. Use drift and handle. If removed, install replacement spacer washer and lock ring to tube (only if removed).

10) Install lock ring with notch (for wrench) facing center of tube. Smear threads and lock ring with lubricant. Install "O" ring. Lubricate Teflon bushing with ATF and install. Install spacer.

11) Grease seal lip and install with lip facing up. Use drift (5184) and adapter (5269) with extension pieces and install. Install Teflon ring and "O" ring to tube. Fill snap ring grooves and coat surrounding area with wheel bearing grease.

12) Slide tube into steering rack from smooth end and pass quickly over snap ring. Install "O" ring and piston ring to piston. Collar threads should be lubricated before installation.

13) Adjust steering rack so it protrudes 2 1/16" (53 mm) from edge of housing. Fill pinion teeth with lubricant. Install bearing washer with bevelled edge down.

14) Attach thrust washer and thrust bearing to valve body with grease. *See Fig. 5.* Hold pinion with flat surface in line with upper high pressure outlet and insert to housing.

15) As the pinion enters housing, it will turn. When fully seated, the flat surface should be parallel to flat surface of housing. Rack must not have moved. Install bearing, race and spacer washer of predetermined thickness. *See Fig. 5.*

16) Fill top cover seal lips with lubricant. Install seal on drift (2863) with seal lips toward tool. Remove screw and cone. Tap seal in cover. Oil "O" ring with automatic transmission fluid and install.

17) Install cover on sleeve (5182), with cone attached. Remove cone. Install cover. Tighten bolts. Install dust seal. Insert preload piston without "O" ring.

18) Be sure Teflon insert is on piston. Set up preload measuring fixture (5865) using cover bolt hole and a 8 x45 mm bolt. Assemble tool with the preload spring between bolt head and bolt. Adjust for slight preload.

19) Move gear lock-to-lock and make sure it does not jam. With micrometer measure distance between housing face and piston stop. Check measurement at 3 different points on steering rack. Subtract .004-.006" (0.1-.15 mm) from smallest reading obtained. Select washer of that thickness.

20) Washers are available in thickness of .083-.114" (2.1-2.90 mm) in increments of .0019" (.05 mm). Remove press tool (5865). Lubricate "O" ring and install on preload piston. Install spacer washer and piston spring.

21) Fill space around spring with lubricant. Apply sealant on cover sealing surface. Install and tighten cover. Install and tighten pressure lines. Make sure "O" rings seat correctly. Using spanner and adjustable wrench.

22) Install steering rods. Bend back steering rod locks. Install boots. Fill each boot with approximately 3/4 ounce of lubricant. Install boot clamps. Install equalizer tube and plastic clamps.

TIGHTENING SPECIFICATIONS

Application	Ft. Lbs. (N.m)
Pinion Cover	
Cam Gear	14 (19)
ZF	7 (10)
Preload Device Cover	
Cam Gear	13 (18)
ZF	15 (20)
Line Fitting (ZF)	15 (20)
Valve Housing Cover	15 (20)

SECTION 13

TRANSMISSION SERVICING

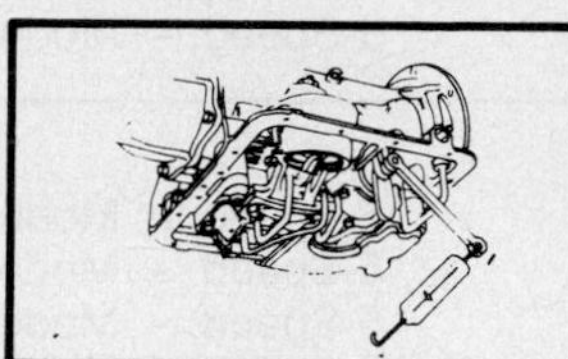

CONTENTS

MANUAL TRANSMISSION APPLICATION

AUTOMATIC TRANSMISSION APPLICATION

MANUAL TRANSMISSION SERVICING

AUTOMATIC TRANSMISSION SERVICING

NOTE: ALSO SEE GENERAL INDEX.

Transmission Application

MANUAL TRANSMISSIONS

MANUFACTURER & MODEL	TRANSMISSION MODEL
ALFA ROMEO	
Spider 2.0 & GTV-6 2.5	5-Speed
AUDI	
4000 Series	5-Speed – Model 014 Transaxle
Coupe & 5000S Series	5-Speed – Model 093 Transaxle
Quattro	5-Speed – Model 5H Transaxle
BMW	
318i, 320i, 528e, 533i, 633CSi & 733i	5-Speed – Borg-Warner
CHRYSLER CORP. IMPORTS	
Colt & Ram-50 Pickups (2WD)	4-Speed – Model KM130
	5-Speed – Model KM132
Colt & Ram-50 Pickups (4WD)	4-Speed – Model KM130
	5-Speed – Model KM132
Colt	4-Speed – Model KM160 Transaxle
	4- x 2-Speed – Model KM165 Transaxle
Challenger & Sapporo	5-Speed – Model KM 132
DATSUN/NISSAN	
Maxima & 200SX	5-Speed – Model FS5W71B
280ZX	5-Speed – Model FS5W71B
280ZX Turbo	5-Speed – Model FS5R90A
Pickup (2WD & 4WD)	4-Speed – Model F4W71B
	5-Speed – Model FS5W71B
Pulsar	5-Speed – Model RS5F30A Transaxle
Sentra	4-Speed – Model RN4F30A Transaxle
	5-Speed – Model RS5F30A Transaxle
Stanza	5-Speed – Model RS5F31A Transaxle
HONDA	
Accord	5-Speed – Model GK Transaxle
Civic	4-Speed – Model GJ Transaxle
	5-Speed – Model GM Transaxle
Prelude	5-Speed – Model GM Transaxle
ISUZU	
I-Mark	4-Speed – Model MSG-4K
	5-Speed – Model MSG-5K
Impulse	5-Speed – Model MSG-5K
P'UP (2WD)	4-Speed – Model MSG-4K
	5-Speed – Model MSG-5K
P'UP (4WD)	4-Speed – Model MSG-4ET
MAZDA	
GLC Wagon, B2000 Pickup & B2200 Pickup	4- & 5-Speed
GLC	4- & 5-Speed – Transaxle
RX7	5-Speed
626	5-Speed – Transaxle
MERCEDES-BENZ	
240D	4-Speed – Model GL 68/20A
MITSUBISHI	
Cordia & Tredia	4- x 2-Speed – Model KM165 Transaxle
	5-Speed – Model KM162 Transaxle
Montero	5-Speed – Model KM132

Transmission Application

MANUAL TRANSMISSIONS (Cont.)

MANUFACTURER & MODEL	TRANSMISSION MODEL
MITSUBISHI Cont.	
Pickup (2WD)	4-Speed – Model KM130
	5-Speed – Model KM132
Pickup (4WD)	4-Speed – Model KM130
	5-Speed – Model KM132
Starion	5-Speed – Model KM132
PEUGEOT	
504 & 505 Diesel	4-Speed
505 Series	5-Speed
604	5-Speed
PORSCHE	
911SC	5-Speed – Model 915/63 Transaxle
928S	5-Speed – Model G28.05 Transaxle
944	5-Speed – Model 016 K Transaxle
RENAULT	
Fuego	5-Speed – Model NG3 Transaxle
Fuego Turbo	5-Speed – Model NG1 Transaxle
LeCar	4-Speed – Model 354-35 Transaxle
18i	4-Speed – Model 352 Transaxle
	5-Speed – Model 395 Transaxle
SAAB	
900 Series	5-Speed – Model G Transaxle
SUBARU	
1600, 1800 & 1800 (4WD)	4- & 5-Speed – Transaxle
TOYOTA	
Camry	5-Speed – Transaxle
Celica, Cressida, & Supra	5-Speed – Model W58
Corolla	4-Speed – Model T41
	5-Speed – Model T50
Land Cruiser	4-Speed – Model H42
Pickup (Diesel)	5-Speed – Model G52
Pickup (2WD Gas)	4-Speed – Model W42
	5-Speed – Model W52
Pickup (4WD Gas)	4-Speed – Model L45
	5-Speed – Model L52
Starlet	4-Speed – Model K40
	5-Speed – Model K50
Tercel (2WD)	4-Speed – Model Z44 Transaxle
	5-Speed – Model Z52 Transaxle
Tercel (4WD)	5-Speed – Model Z52F Transaxle
VOLKSWAGEN	
Jetta, Quantum, Rabbit & Scirocco	4-Speed – Model Transaxle
	5-Speed – Model 020 Transaxle
Rabbit Hatchback & Pickup	4-Speed – Transaxle
	5-Speed – Transaxle
Vanagon (Gas)	
1.9L	4-Speed – Model 091/1 Transaxle
2.0L	4-Speed – Model 091 Transaxle
Vanagon (Diesel)	4-Speed – Model 091 Transaxle
	5-Speed – Model 094 Transaxle
VOLVO	
All Models	4-Speed – Model M46

Transmission Application

AUTOMATIC TRANSMISSIONS

MANUFACTURER & MODEL	[1] TRANSMISSION MODEL
AUDI	
Coupe & 5000 Series	Model 087 Transaxle
4000 Series	Model 089 Transaxle
BMW	
318i, 320i, 528e, 533i, 633CSi & 733i	Model ZF 3 HP 22
CHRYSLER CORP. IMPORTS	
Challenger & Sapporo	Torqueflite – Model MA904A
Colt	Mitsubishi – Model KM170 Transaxle
Colt Pickup & Ram-50 Pickup	2WD – Torqueflite Model MA904A
	4WD – Torqueflite Model MA904A
DATSUN/NISSAN	
Maxima	JATCO – Model L4N71B
Pickup	JATCO – Model 3N71B
Pulsar & Stanza	JATCO – Model RL3F01A
Sentra	
Diesel	JATCO – Model RN3F01A
Gas	JATCO – Model RL3F01A
200SX	JATCO – Model L3N71B
280ZX	JATCO – Model L3N71B
280ZX Turbo	JATCO – Model 3N71B
HONDA	
Accord & Prelude	1500 Engine – Model AK Transaxle
Civic	1300 Engine – Model AJ Transaxle
	1500 Engine – Model AM Transaxle
ISUZU	
I-Mark, Impulse & P'UP	Model AW03-55
JAGUAR	
XJ6	Borg-Warner – Model 66
XJS	GM Turbo Hydra-Matic – Model 400
MAZDA	
GLC & 626	Mazda – Model F3A Transaxle
GLC Wagon	JATCO – Model L3N71B
RX7	JATCO – Model 3N71B
MERCEDES-BENZ	
240D	MB – Model W4B025 4-Speed
300 & 380 Series	MB – Model W4A040 4-Speed
MITSUBISHI	
Cordia & Tredia	Mitsubishi – Model KM171 Transaxle
Pickup	2WD – Torqueflite Model MA904A
	4WD – Mitsubishi Model KM146 Transaxle
PEUGEOT	
504, 505 & 604	Model ZF 3 HP 22
PORSCHE	
928S	Model A22 Transaxle
944	Model 087 Transaxle

1 – Unless otherwise specified, all models use 3 forward gears.

Transmission Application

AUTOMATIC TRANSMISSIONS (Cont.)

MANUFACTURER & MODEL	[1] TRANSMISSION MODEL
RENAULT	
Fuego & 18i	Renault – Model 4139-65 Transaxle
SAAB	
900 Series	Borg-Warner – Model 37 Transaxle
SUBARU	
1800	
2WD	Gunma Model C
4WD & Turbo	Gunma Model F
TOYOTA	
Camry	Model A140E Transaxle
Celica	Model A40D
Corolla	Model A40D & A41
Cressida & Supra	Model A43DE
Pickup	Model A43D
Tercel	Model A55 Transaxle
VOLKSWAGEN	
Jetta, Pickup, Rabbit & Scirocco	Model 010 Transaxle
Quantum	Model 089 Transaxle
Vanagon	Model 090 Transaxle
VOLVO	
760 GLE	Aisin-Warner Model AW71
All Others	Borg-Warner Model 55

[1] – Unless otherwise specified, all models use 3 forward gears.

Manual Transmission Servicing

ALFA ROMEO

GTV-6 2.5, Spider 2.0

LUBRICATION

SERVICE INTERVALS

Inspect transmission lubricant level at 20,000, 60,000, and 100,000 miles. Oil does not have to be changed.

FLUID LEVEL

Check lubricant level at fill hole. Lubricant should be level with bottom of fill hole.

FLUID TYPE

Hypoid SAE 85W/90.

FLUID CAPACITY

GTV-6 2.5 5-Speed - 2.9 qts. (2.7L)
Spider 2.0 5-Speed - 1.9 qts. (1.85L)

ADJUSTMENTS

LINKAGE

Both models use floor-mount shifters with no external adjustment.

AUDI

Coupe, Quattro, 4000, 4000S Series & 5000S Series

LUBRICATION

SERVICE INTERVALS

Inspect transmission lubricant level when vehicle is serviced. Oil does not have to be changed.

FLUID LEVEL

Check lubricant level at fill hole. Lubricant should be slightly below bottom of fill hole.

FLUID TYPE

Hypoid SAE 80 or SAE 80W/90.

FLUID CAPACITY

Coupe 5-Speed 093 - 1.7 qts. (1.6L)
Quattro 5-Speed 5H - 3.8 qts. (3.6L)
4000 Series 5-Speed 014 - 1.7 qts. (1.6L)
5000S Series 5-Speed 093 - 2.75 qts. (2.6L)

ADJUSTMENT

GEAR LEVER

All (Except Quattro)

1) Place gear shift lever in "Neutral". Loosen shift rod clamp nut. Check that shift finger slides freely on shift rod. Remove shift lever knob and rubber shift boot.

2) Align holes of gear shift lever housing and shift lever bearing housing. Install Shift Lever Adjustment Tool (3057), with locating pin toward front. Push shift lever into 5th/Rev cutout position of tool.

3) Tighten lower screw on tool, move shift lever and slide to right stop. Tighten upper screw on tool. Push shift lever to 3rd/4th position cutout of tool and align shift rod and finger. Tighten clamp nut and remove tool.

4) Push shift lever into 1st gear and press to left stop. Shift lever must spring back to right. Place lever in 5th gear position, push shift lever to right stop and release, shift lever must spring back to left. Tighten shift rod clamp nut and remove adjustment tool. Reinstall shift boot and shift lever knob.

NOTE: If gearshift lever does not spring back after moving in extreme directions, move gearshift lever housing slightly sideways in slots.

Quattro

NOTE: Make certain adjusting rod maintains a center-to-center distance of 5.27" (134 mm).

1) Position lever in "Neutral". Loosen shift rod clamp nut (rod must move freely) between front and rear shift rods. Loosen stop plate retaining bolts and align holes in stop plate with bearing support. Tighten bolts.

2) Install Shift Adjustment Tool (3048), tighten clamp nut, and remove adjusting tool. Push shift lever to left stop and release, lever must spring back. Push shift lever to right stop and release, lever must spring back.

NOTE: If gearshift lever does not spring back after moving in extreme directions, move gearshift lever housing slightly sideways in slots.

3) To adjust center differential lock, disengage lock and push in plastic bracket on servo. Pull outer cable to rear and install clip in front groove in outer cable.

NOTE: Lock can ONLY be engaged with sufficient vacuum. It may be necessary to run engine to check lock operation. To engage lock with engine "OFF", turn driveshaft or one rear wheel.

4) To adjust rear differential lock, note following: Press out clevis pin on servo. Loosen operating lever clamping bolt and turn operating shaft clockwise. Pull servo clevis out, install clevis pin, and tighten clamping bolt of operating lever.

Manual Transmission Servicing

BMW

318i, 320i, 528e, 533i, 633CSi & 733i

LUBRICATION

SERVICE INTERVALS

Inspect transmission lubricant level when vehicle is serviced. Change transmission oil at first 600 miles, then at every 30,000 mile intervals thereafter.

FLUID LEVEL

Check lubricant at fill hole. Lubricant should be to bottom of fill plug hole.

FLUID TYPE

SAE 80W (API GL-4, in cold climates use HD)

FLUID CAPACITY

318i 5-Speed – 1.4 qts. (1.2L)
320i 5-Speed – 1.6 qts. (1.5L)
All Others 5-Speed – 1.7 qts. (1.6L)

ADJUSTMENT

LINKAGE

All models use floor-mount shifter with no external linkage. No adjustment is provided.

CHRYSLER CORP. IMPORTS

Challenger, Colt, Colt Pickup, Ram-50 Pickup & Sapporo

LUBRICATION

SERVICE INTERVALS

Check the fluid level every 30,000 miles.

FLUID LEVEL

Check lubricant level at fill hole. Lubricant must be at bottom of fill hole.

FLUID TYPE

Transaxle–Hypoid SAE 75W/85W (API GL-4)
Transmission–Hypoid SAE 80W (API GL-4)

FLUID CAPACITY

Challenger & Sapporo KM132 – 2.4 qts. (2.3L)
Colt
4-Speed KM160 – 2.2 qts. (2.1L)
4- x 2-Speed KM165 – 2.2 qts. (2.1L)
Colt & Ram-50 Pickup (2WD & 4WD)
4-Speed KM130 – 2.2 qts. (2.1L)
5-Speed KM132 – 2.4 qts. (2.3L)
Transfer Case – 2.2 qts. (2.1L)

NOTE: **KM130 (4-Speed) transmission with transfer case is referred to as KM144; KM132 (5-Speed) transmission with transfer case is referred to as KM145.**

ADJUSTMENT

LINKAGE

4-Speed Transaxle

To adjust range selector control, place selector in "E" position, loosen adjustment nut and establish .2" (5 mm) free play at top of selector control handle. After adjustment, tighten adjustment nut. For shift lever, no linkage adjustment is required.

4- & 5-Speed Transmissions

Shifter is integral with transmission housing and has no external linkage. No adjustment is required.

DATSUN/NISSAN

Maxima, Pickup, Pulsar, Sentra, Stanza, 200SX, 280ZX, & 280ZX Turbo

LUBRICATION

SERVICE INTERVALS

Add or replace oil level every 15,000 miles.

FLUID LEVEL

Lubricant level should be to bottom of fill hole.

FLUID TYPE

Hypoid SAE 80W/90 (API GL-4)

FLUID CAPACITY

Maxima, 280SX & 280SX Turbo 5-Speed
FS5W71B – 2.13 qts. (2.0L)
FS5R90A – 2.0 qts. (1.9L)
Pickup (2WD & 4WD)
4-Speed F4W71B – 1.8 qts. (1.7L)
5-Speed FS5W71B – 2.1 qts. (2.0L)
Transfer Case – 1.5 qts. (1.4L)
Pulsar 5-Speed RS5F30A – 2.7 qts. (2.5L)
Sentra
4-Speed RN4F30A – 2.4 qts. (2.3L)
5-Speed RS5F30A – 2.9 qts. (2.7L)
Stanza 5-Speed RS5F31A – 2.9 qts. (2.7L)
200SX 5-Speed FS5W71B – 2.0 qts. (1.9L)

DATSUN/NISSAN (Cont.)

ADJUSTMENT

LINKAGE

NOTE: **All RWD models have a floor shift which has no external linkage and requires no adjustment.**

Pulsar, Sentra & Stanza

1) Loosen selector stopper bolts. Place transaxle in "1st" gear. Slide selector stopper to establish clearance of .039" (1 mm) between control lever and select stopper. *See Fig. 1.*

2) Tighten bolts. After adjustment, shift control lever to be sure no binding or dragging exists.

Fig. 1: Control Lever Adjustment

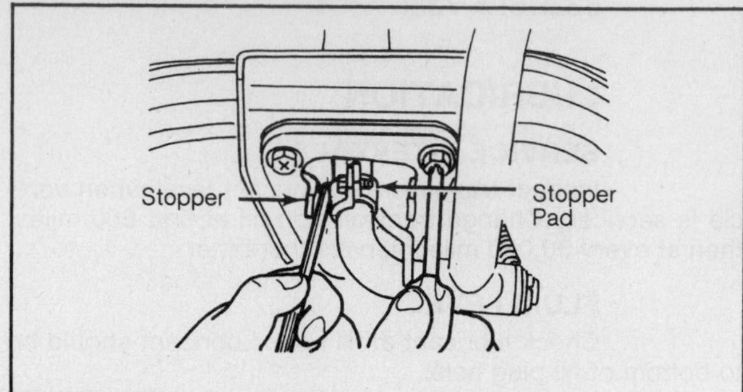

Stopper
Stopper Pad

Place shifter in 1st gear.

HONDA

Accord, Civic & Prelude

LUBRICATION

SERVICE INTERVALS

Change lubricant every 30,000 miles.

FLUID LEVEL

Check lubricant level at transmission fill hole. Lubricant should be to bottom of filler hole.

FLUID TYPE

SAE 10W/40 engine oil rated SE.

FLUID CAPACITY

Accord 5-Speed GK – 2.5 qts. (2.4L)
Civic
4-Speed GJ – 2.6 qts. (2.5L)
5-Speed GM – 2.6 qts. (2.5L)
Prelude 5-Speed GM – 2.6 qts. (2.5L)

ADJUSTMENT

LINKAGE

No external adjustments required.

ISUZU

I-Mark, Impulse & P'UP

LUBRICATION

SERVICE INTERVALS

Replace lubricant after first 7,500 miles and every 30,000 miles thereafter. Check lubricant every 7,500 miles or 12 months, whichever comes first.

FLUID LEVEL

Check lubricant level at fill hole. Lubricant should be to bottom edge of fill hole.

FLUID TYPE

I-Mark, P'UP & Transfer Case
Below 50° F (10° C) SAE 10W/30 engine oil.
0°-90° F (–18°-32° C) SAE 30 engine oil.
Above 50° F (10° C) SAE 40 engine oil.
Impulse
Under 90° F (32° C) SAE 5W/30SF engine oil.
Above 90° F (32° C) SAE 40 engine oil.

FLUID CAPACITY

I-Mark
4-Speed MSG-4K – 1.4 qts. (1.3L)
5-Speed MSG-5K – 1.6 qts. (1.5L)
Impulse 5-Speed MSG-5K – 1.6 qts. (1.5L)
P'UP
2WD
4-Speed MSG-4K – 1.4 qts. (1.3L)
5-Speed MSG-5K – 1.6 qts. (1.5L)
P'UP
4WD 4-Speed MSG-4ET – 1.3 qts. (1.2L)

ADJUSTMENT

LINKAGE

Shift linkage is integral with transmission housing and requires no external adjustment.

Manual Transmission Servicing

MAZDA

B2000 & B2200 Pickups, GLC, GLC Wagon, RX7 & 626

LUBRICATION

SERVICE INTERVALS

Replace lubricant every 30,000 miles and check lubricant level every 7,500 miles.

FLUID LEVEL

GLC & 626

Remove speedometer cable and driven gear from transaxle case. Use "L" and "F" marks on speedometer gear housing to check lubricant level. If necessary, add oil through this opening.

All Others

Check lubricant level at fill hole. Lubricant level should be to bottom of fill hole.

FLUID TYPE

Hypoid SAE 80W/90 (API GL-4 or GL-5)

FLUID CAPACITY

B2000 & B2200
4-Speed – 1.6 qts. (1.5L)
5-Speed – 1.8 qts. (1.7L)
GLC – 3.4 qts. (3.2L)
GLC Wagon
4-Speed – 1.4 qts. (1.3L)
5-Speed – 1.8 qts. (1.7L)
RX7 – 2.1 qts. (2.0L)
626 – 3.6 qts. (3.4L)

ADJUSTMENT

LINKAGE

No external linkage adjustment is required.

MERCEDES-BENZ

240D

LUBRICATION

SERVICE INTERVALS

Transmission fluid has to be changed at first 800-1000 miles and 5000 miles of operation. Thereafter check and replenish fluid every 15,000 miles.

FLUID LEVEL

Check lubricant level at fill hole. Lubricant should be up to bottom of fill hole.

FLUID TYPE

Automatic Transmission Fluid (ATF)
Type A Suffix A

FLUID CAPACITY

4-Speed GL 68/20A – 1.4 qts. (1.3L)

ADJUSTMENT

LINKAGE

1) Disconnect shift rods at shift lever. Align 3 intermediate levers at bottom of shift bracket by inserting a centering pin. *See Fig. 1.*

Fig. 1: View Showing Shift Lever Adjustment

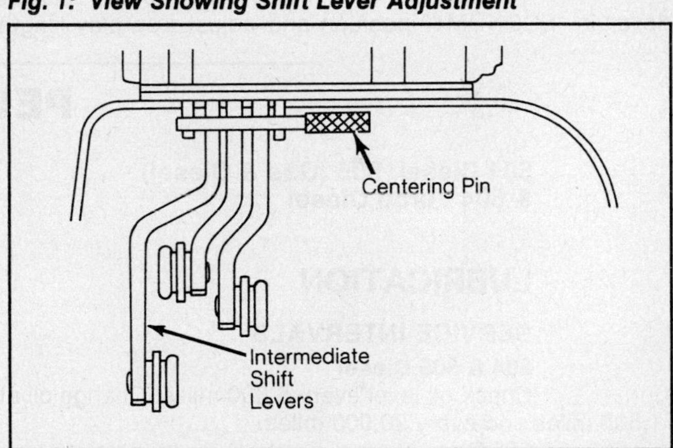
Centering Pin
Intermediate
Shift
Levers

2) Place transmission in "NEUTRAL". Adjust shift rods so they will fit into their respective holes in intermediate levers without tension. Install lock pins, remove centering pin and check for proper operation.

MITSUBISHI

Cordia, Montero, Pickups, Starion & Tredia

LUBRICATION

SERVICE INTERNVALS

2WD Pickup

Inspect and replenish oil every 30,000 miles or 12 months, whichever comes first.

All Others

Replace oil every 30,000 miles or 12 months.

FLUID LEVEL

Lubricant should be up to bottom of fill hole.

FLUID TYPE

Hypoid SAE 75W/85W or 80W (API GL-4)

MITSUBISHI (Cont.)

FLUID CAPACITY

Cordia & Tredia
- 4- x 2-Speed KM165 – 2.2 qts. (2.1L)
- 5-Speed KM162 – 2.2 qts. (2.1L)

Montero
- 5-Speed KM132 – 2.3 qts. (2.2L)
- Transfer Case – 2.3 qts. (2.2L)

Pickup (2WD & 4WD)
- 4-Speed KM130 – 2.2 qts. (2.1L)
- 5-Speed KM132 – 2.4 qts. (2.3L)
- Transfer Case – 2.3 qts. (2.2L)

Starion KM132 – 2.4 qts. (2.3L)

NOTE: **KM130 (4-Speed) transmission with transfer case is referred to as KM144; KM132 (5-Speed) transmission with transfer case is referred to as KM145.**

ADJUSTMENT

LINKAGE

Cordia & Tredia

To adjust selector cable length, place selector lever in "ECONOMY" position and adjust free play length to .20" (5 mm). Tighten adjuster nut. Install selector switch so mating marks are in a straight line and selector switch is on "ECONOMY" position. Operate lever to make sure lever operates correctly. *See Fig. 1.*

Fig. 1: Selector Switch Position

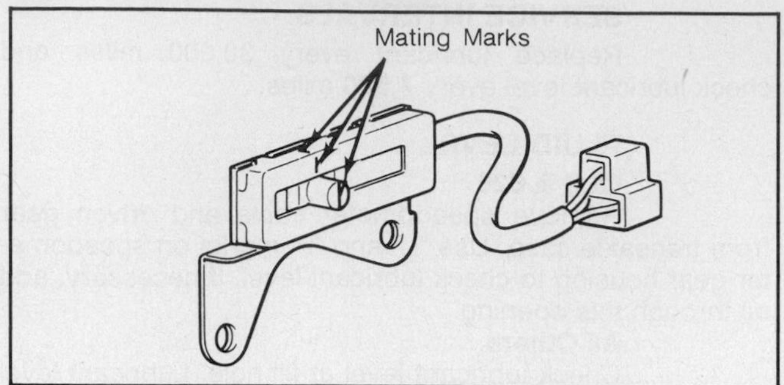
Mating Marks

Selector lever must be in "ECONOMY" position.

All Others

No external linkage adjustment is required.

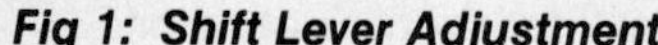

PEUGEOT

504 Diesel, 505 (Gas & Diesel) & 604 Turbo Diesel

LUBRICATION

SERVICE INTERVALS

504 & 505 Diesel

Check oil level every 5,000 miles. Change oil at 1,500 miles and every 20,000 miles.

505 Gas

Check oil level every 7,500 miles. Change oil at 1,500 miles and every 22,500 miles.

604 Turbo Diesel

Check oil level every 3,000 miles. Change oil at first 1,500 miles and every 15,000 miles.

FLUID LEVEL

Transmission oil fill plug is located on side of transmission. Lubricant should be at bottom edge of hole.

FLUID TYPE

SAE 10W/40 engine oil (API grade CC)

Fig 1: Shift Lever Adjustment

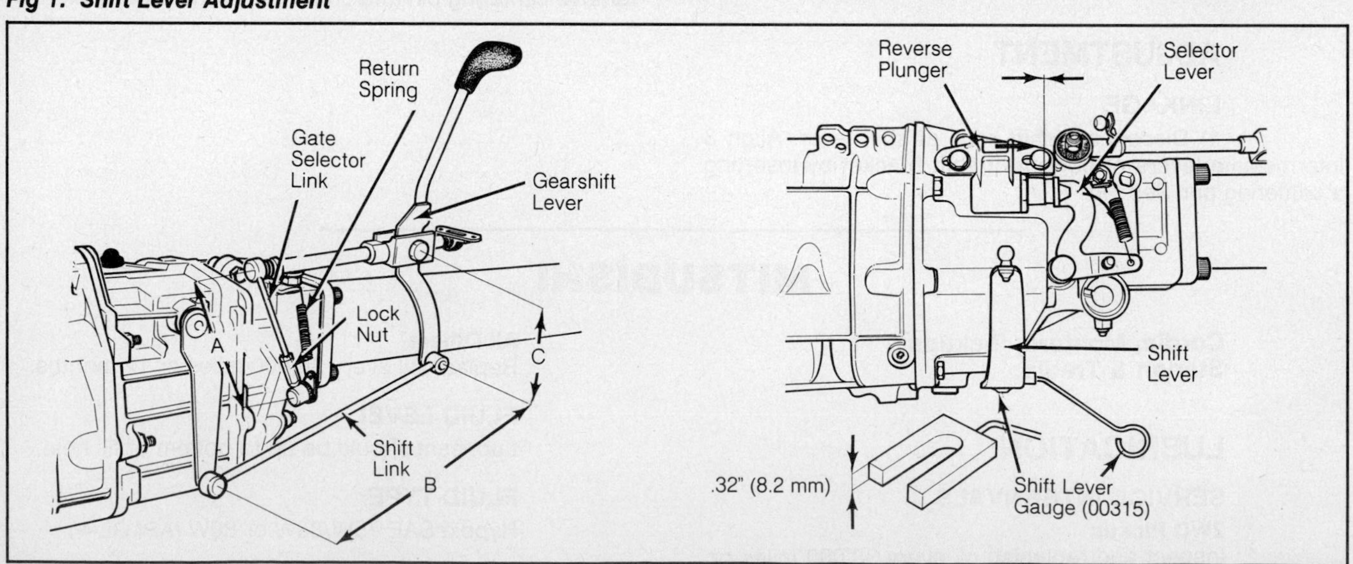
Return Spring
Gate Selector Link
Gearshift Lever
Lock Nut
A
C
Shift Link
B
Reverse Plunger
Selector Lever
Shift Lever
.32" (8.2 mm)
Shift Lever Gauge (00315)

PEUGEOT (Cont.)

FLUID CAPACITY

504 & 505 Diesel
- 4-Speed – 1.2 qts. (1.1L)
- 5-Speed – 1.8 qts. (1.7L)

505 Series & 604
- 5-Speed – 1.8 qts. (1.7L)

ADJUSTMENT

LINKAGE

4-Speed

Install Shift Lever Gauge (00315) and place shift lever in correct position. *See Fig. 1.* Loosen reverse plunger bolts and place reverse plunger against selector lever. Tighten 2 bolts and remove gauge.

4- & 5-Speed

Lubricate ball sockets. Install shift link with center-to-center dimension "B" of 11.22" (285 mm) for 4-Speed; 11" (280 mm) for 5-Speed. *See Fig. 1.* Adjust gate selector link with center-to-center dimension "A" to 4.37" (111 mm). Holding ball sockets in proper directions, tighten lock nut. Install gate selector link with fixed ball socket side mounted to gearshift lever.

NOTE: Gearshift lever dimension "C" is 3.11" (79 mm) for 4-Speed and 4.13" (105 mm) for 5-Speed.

PORSCHE

911SC, 928S & 944

LUBRICATION

SERVICE INTERVALS

911SC

Check lubricant level and clean magnetic drain plug at first 1,000 miles. Check lubricant level every 15,000 miles and replace every 30,000 miles.

928S

Check lubricant level and clean magnetic drain plug at first 1,000 miles. Check lubricant level every 15,000 miles and replace every 30,000 miles.

944

Change oil and clean magnetic drain plug at first 1,250 miles. Check and correct oil level every 15,000 miles. Change oil every 30,000 miles.

FLUID LEVEL

Oil level should be to bottom of fill hole.

FLUID TYPE

911SC Hypoid SAE 90W (API GL-5)
928S Hypoid SAE 75W/90 (API GL-5)
944 Hypoid SAE 80 (API GL-4)

FLUID CAPACITY

911SC 5-Speed 915/63 – 3.2 qts. (3.0L)
928S 5-Speed G28.05 – 4 qts. (3.8L)
944 5-Speed 016K – 2.7 qts. (2.6L)

ADJUSTMENT

LINKAGE

No adjustment required.

RENAULT

Fuego, Fuego Turbo, LeCar & 18i

LUBRICATION

SERVICE INTERVALS

Change lubricant after first 1,000 miles and at 12,000 mile intervals thereafter.

FLUID LEVEL

Check lubricant level at fill hole. Lubricant should be even with bottom of hole.

FLUID TYPE

Hypoid SAE 80 (API GL-5)

FLUID CAPACITY

Fuego 5-Speed NG3 – 2.1 qts. (2.0L)
Fuego Turbo 5-Speed NG1 – 2.1 qts. (2.0L)
LeCar 4-Speed 354-35 – 1.9 qts. (1.8L)
18i
- 4-Speed 352 – 2.0 qts. (1.9L)
- 5-Speed 395 – 2.0 qts. (1.9L)

ADJUSTMENT

LINKAGE

LeCar

1) Place shift lever in 3rd gear. Press shift lever toward 1st-2nd gear position. Use slotted holes in stop plate to visually check clearance between end of shift lever and stop plate. Clearance should be 1/8" (3 mm).

2) Adjustments are made by placing washers between the stop plate and floor panel. The tolerance of the reverse stop should be 3/16 - 9/32" (5-7 mm) when the end of the shift lever is resting against stop plate.

Fuego, Fuego Turbo & 18i

1) Place shift lever in Neutral position. Loosen lock nut on yoke so shift linkage turns freely. Put transmission lever at transmission case exit, against 3rd-4th gear line.

2) Place a .079" (2 mm) shim (4-Speed) or a .394" (10 mm) shim (5-Speed) between the end piece of the shift linkage and the surface of the housing. Tighten yoke nut. Make sure that clearance between end piece and lever housing is the same as the shim.

RENAULT (Cont.)

Fig 1: Setting LeCar Shift Lever Dimension

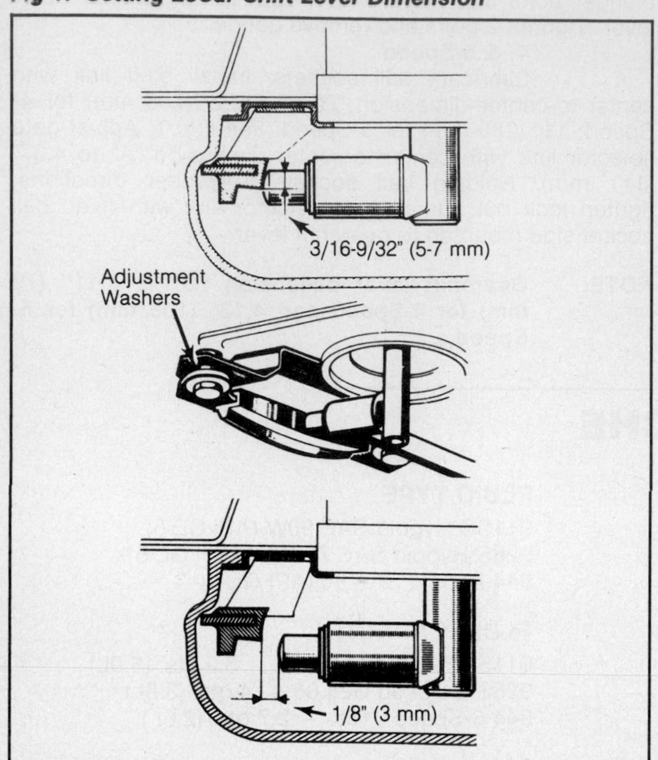
3/16-9/32" (5-7 mm)
Adjustment
Washers
1/8" (3 mm)

Fig. 2: 18i Shift Lever Adjustment

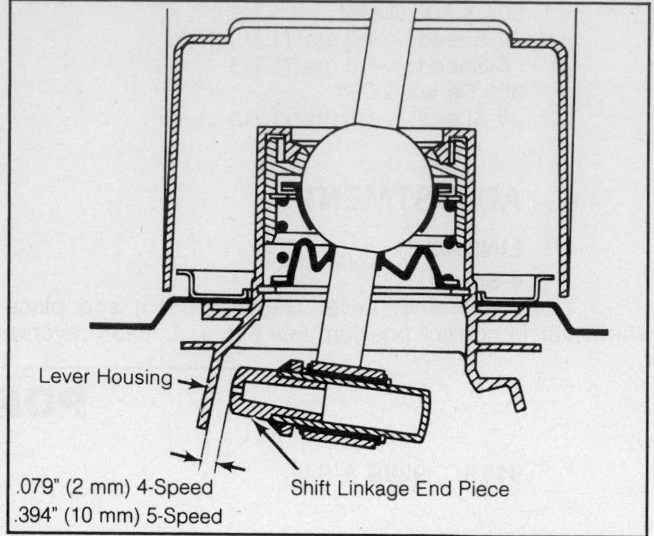
Lever Housing
.079" (2 mm) 4-Speed
.394" (10 mm) 5-Speed
Shift Linkage End Piece

SAAB

900 & 900 Turbo

LUBRICATION

SERVICE INTERVALS

Change transmission lubricant and clean magnetic drain plug at first 1,000 miles. Check and adjust lubricant every 7,500 miles thereafter, except 900 Turbo, which should be checked every 5,000 miles.

FLUID LEVEL

Check fluid level with dipstick located in engine compartment. Fluid level should be between "Min" and "Max" marks on dipstick.

FLUID TYPE

SAE 10W/30 engine oil

FLUID CAPACITY

5-Speed G – 2.6 qts. (2.5L)

ADJUSTMENT

LINKAGE

1) Select reverse gear. Loosen clamp on the gear shift rod joint so that the gear shift rod can be moved in the joint.

2) Lock gear lever in reverse by inserting a 6 mm Allen wrench into the apertures in the gear lever housing and gear shift rod. The apertures are accessible once the gear lever console cover has been loosened and removed rearward.

3) Check that reverse gear is fully engaged. Tighten clamp on gear shift rod joint. Torque to 12-16 ft. lbs. (16-22 N.m).

SUBARU

1600, 1800 & 1800 4WD

LUBRICATION

SERVICE INTERVALS

Replace lubricant at first 1,000 miles and every 30,000 miles thereafter. Check lubricant level every 15,000 miles.

FLUID LEVEL

Check lubricant level at dipstick located in engine compartment. Transmission and differential (transaxle) are lubricated through a common oil supply.

FLUID TYPE

SAE (API GL-5) engine oil
SAE 90W above 30°F (0°C)
SAE 85W from -30°F (-34°C)

Manual Transmission Servicing

SUBARU (Cont.)

FLUID CAPACITY

2WD 4- & 5-Speed - 2.9 qts. (2.7L)
4WD 4-Speed - 3.2 qts. (3.0L)

ADJUSTMENT

LINKAGE

All models use shift linkage which does not require external adjustment.

If equipped with dual-range, confirm that lower surface of drive selector grip is approximately 1.57" (40 mm) from rod cover surface. If dimension is beyond adjustment distance, readjust positioning plate.

TOYOTA

Camry, Celica, Corolla, Cressida, Land Cruiser, Pickup, Starlet, Supra & Tercel

LUBRICATION

SERVICE INTERVALS

Check lubricant level every 15,000 miles. No fluid change is required.

FLUID LEVEL

Check lubricant level at fill hole. Lubricant should be to bottom of hole.

FLUID TYPE

Camry ATF Dexron II
Land Cruiser
SAE 90W (API GL-4 or GL-5)
Pickup
2WD & Diesel
SAE 75W/90 (API GL-4 or GL-5)
4WD & Transfer
SAE 80W/90 (API GL-4 or GL-5)
Tercel (API Hypoid GL-5)
Above 0° F (-18° C) SAE 80W/90 or 90W
Below 0° F (-18° C) SAE 80W/90 or 80W
All Others
SAE 80W/90 (API GL-4 or GL-5)
SAE 75W/90 (API GL-4 or GL-5)

FLUID CAPACITY

Camry 4-Speed - 2.7 qts. (2.6L)
Celica, Cressida, & Supra
5-Speed W58 - 2.5 qts. (2.4L)
Celica, Cressida, & Supra
5-Speed W58 - 2.5 qts. (2.4L)
Land Cruiser
4-Speed H42 - 3.3 qts. (3.1L)
Transfer Case - 2.6 qts. (2.5L)
Pickup (2WD)
4-Speed W42 - 2.9 qts. (2.6L)
5-Speed W52 - 2.7 qts. (2.6L)
Pickup (4WD)
4-Speed L45 - 2.1 qts. (2.0L)
5-Speed L52 - 1.9 qts. (1.8L)
Transfer Case - 1.7 qts. (1.6L)
Pickup Diesel G52 - 2.3 qts. (2.2L)
Starlet
4-Speed K40 - 2.6 qts. (2.5L)
5-Speed K50 - 2.6 qts. (2.5L)
Tercel (2WD)
4-Speed Z44 - 3.5 qts. (3.3L)
5-Speed Z52 - 4.1L (3.9L)
Tercel (4WD) 5-Speed Z52F - 4.1 qts. (3.9L)

ADJUSTMENT

LINKAGE

Camry

To adjust cable stroke, loosen shift lever adjusting nut and install a .20" (5 mm) guide pin into shift lever hole (rotate turn buckle to align shift lever hole and shift lever support hole). Tighten adjusting lock nut and remove guide pin. Install console.

All Others

No adjustment required.

VOLKSWAGEN

Jetta, Pickup, Quantum, Rabbit, Rabbit Hatchback, Scirocco & Vanagon

LUBRICATION

SERVICE INTERVALS

No oil changes are required. Check oil every 15,000 miles.

FLUID LEVEL

Check oil level through fill plug hole in side of transmission. Oil level should be to bottom of hole.

FLUID CAPACITY

Jetta, Quantum, Rabbit, & Scirocco
4- & 5-Speed 020 - 2.1 qts. (2.0L)
Rabbit Hatchback & Pickup
4-Speed - 1.6 qts. (1.5L)
5-Speed - 2.1 qts. (2.0L)
Vanagon (Gas)
1.9L 4-Speed 091/1 - 3.2 qts. (3.0L)
2.0L 4-Speed 091 - 3.7 qts. (3.5L)
Vanagon (Diesel)
4-Speed 091 - 3.7 qts. (3.5L)
5-Speed 094 - 4.2 qts. (4.0L)

VOLKSWAGEN (Cont.)

FLUID TYPE

Hypoid SAE 80W or 80W/90 (API GL-4)

ADJUSTMENT

LINKAGE

Jetta, Pickup, Rabbit, Quantum & Scirocco

1) Loosen bolts holding lever housing, and pull boot off of housing. Loosen shift rod clamp bolt so selector lever moves freely on shift rod. Adjust shift finger in center of lock out plate so that an equal distance is obtained on both sides of the shift finger. *See Fig. 1.*

Fig. 1: Correct Position of Shift Finger

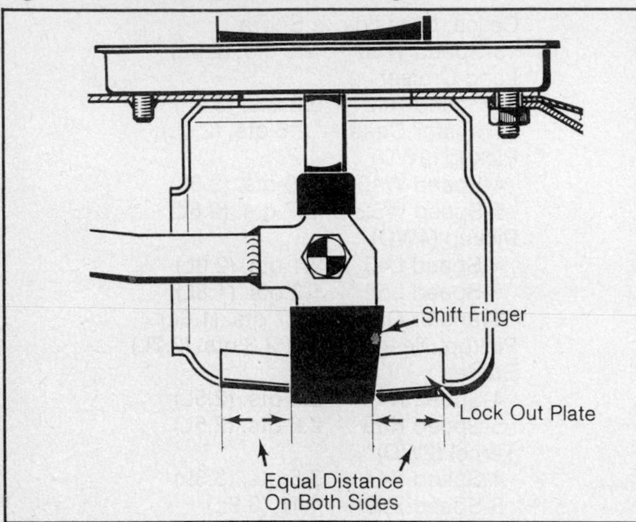
Shift Finger
Lock Out Plate
Equal Distance
On Both Sides

2) Adjust shift rod end so that a distance of 3/4" (20 mm) for 4-Speed models, or 9/32" (15 mm) for 5-Speed models exists between shift finger and stop plate. *See Fig. 2.* Tighten shift rod clamp. Shift through gears and check for proper engagement.

Vanagon

1) Place shift lever in Neutral position. Align holes of upper lever bearing plate with holes in lower lever bearing plate.

2) Loosen shift rod clamp so selector lever moves freely on shift rod. Remove spare tire. Move shift finger of front shift rod to center of rubber stop in housing.

Fig. 2: Adjusting Shift Finger Distance

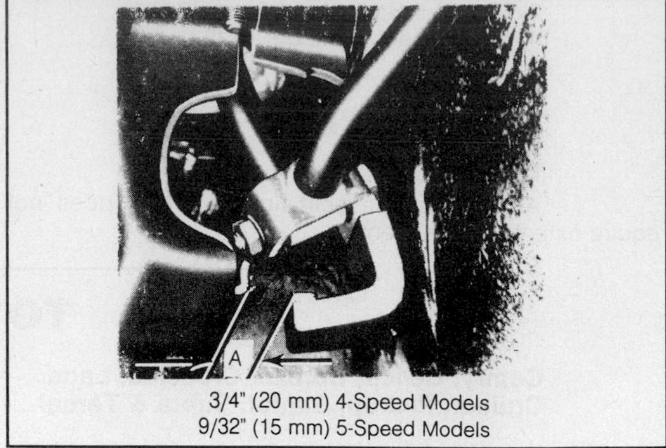
A
3/4" (20 mm) 4-Speed Models
9/32" (15 mm) 5-Speed Models

3) Adjust shift rod end so that a distance of 3/4" (20 mm) exists between shift rod end and stop plate. Check for proper operation.

GEAR SHIFT LEVER

Jetta, Pickup, Rabbit, Quantum & Scirocco

Move the lever bearing assembly on its elongated bolt holes until the round holes indicated in *Fig. 3* are perfectly aligned with the corresponding round holes in lever plate and housing.

Fig. 3: Adjusting Shift Lever All Models (Except Vanagon)

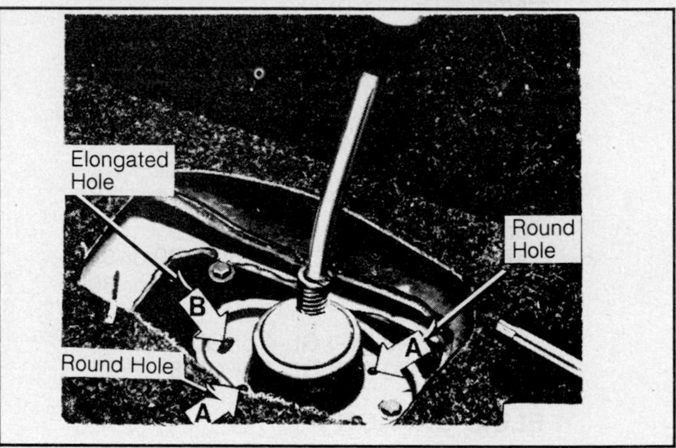
Elongated Hole
Round Hole
B
A
Round Hole
A

VOLVO

DL, Diesel, GL, Turbo,
760 GLE & 760 GLE Turbo Diesel

LUBRICATION

SERVICE INTERVALS

Replace transmission oil at first 600-1200 miles ONLY. Check every 7,500 miles thereafter.

FLUID LEVEL

Check lubricant level at fill hole. Oil should be up to bottom of fill hole. When adding oil, allow sufficient time for oil to flow into overdrive unit.

FLUID TYPE

F or G Automatic Transmission Fluid (FLM)

FLUID CAPACITY

4-Speed M46 – 2.4 qts. (2.3L) (With overdrive)

ADJUSTMENT

No external linkage adjustment is required.

AUDI

4000 & 5000 Series
IDENTIFICATION

TRANSMISSION CODES

Application	Code
4000S & 4000S Turbo Diesel	089
Coupe, 5000S, 5000 Turbo, & 5000 Turbo Diesel	087

LUBRICATION

SERVICE INTERVALS

Check fluid in automatic transmission and final drive every 15,000 miles. Change fluid in transmission every 30,000 miles.

FLUID LEVEL

When checking fluid levels, be sure vehicle is level, place selector lever in "N" position and apply parking brake. Run engine at idle until fluid is lukewarm.

Automatic Transaxle

Pull out dipstick and wipe clean. Reinsert dipstick, make sure ring of dipstick handle is parallel to engine when fully seated. Fluid level should be between the 2 marks, but not above or below marks.

NOTE: **It takes approximately 1 pint of ATF to bring level from lower to upper mark on dipstick.**

Final Drive

1) When checking final drive, remove fill plug on side of assembly and note fluid level. It should be even with bottom of plug hole.

2) If fluid level in final drive is higher than filler plug, it indicates ATF has possibly entered the final drive. If too low, hypoid oil may have entered transmission. If level is too high, hypoid oil in final drive must be changed.

FLUID TYPE

Transaxle
Automatic Transmission Fluid (ATF)
Dexron or Dexron II
Final Drive
Hypoid oil SAE 90 (API GL-5)

FLUID CAPACITY

Transaxle
3.2 qts. (3.0L)
Final Drive
4000S, 4000S Turbo Diesel, & Coupe
.8 qts. (.75L)
5000S, 5000 Turbo, & 5000 Turbo Diesel
1.1 qts. (1.0L)

DRAINING & REFILLING

Transaxle

1) After removing plug and draining fluid, pan should be removed and thoroughly cleaned with lint-free cloths. Reinstall pan using new gasket, tightening bolts in a criss-cross pattern. Tighten to 14 ft. lbs. (19 N.m), checking torque twice at 5-10 minute intervals as gasket settles.

2) Add 3.2 qts. (3.0L) of specified ATF. Start engine and select all shift lever positions while keeping vehicle stationary. Drive a short road test until fluid is lukewarm. Check fluid lever and top off so that level is between upper and lower marks on dipstick.

Final Drive

Remove drain plug and allow hypoid gear oil to drain. Replace drain plug and fill housing to proper level.

ADJUSTMENT

SECOND GEAR BAND

Loosen lock nut and tighten adjusting screw to 87 INCH lbs. (10 N.m). Loosen and retorque to 43 INCH lbs. (5 N.m). Turn adjusting screw out 2 1/2 turns and tighten lock nut.

Fig. 1: Location of Second Gear Band Adjusting Screw

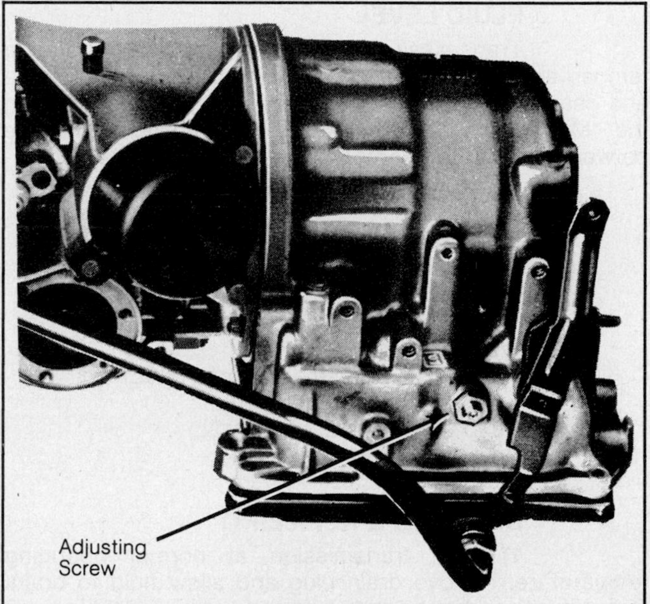
Adjusting
Screw

THROTTLE LINKAGE

NOTE: **This adjustment applies to 5000 series.**

1) Ensure that throttle is in idle position and loosen clamping bolt on push rod at transaxle end. Hold transaxle selector lever in "Neutral" position and tighten bolt.

2) Remove stop and intermediate piece from under accelerator pedal. Attach 2 nuts to M8 X 135 bolt so that distance from top of bolt to bottom of nuts is 4 7/8" (124 mm).

3) Install bolt in place of pedal stop so bottom of pedal rests on bolt head. Adjust slack out of accelerator cable with adjusting nut on transmission bracket. Replace accelerator pedal stop.

NEUTRAL SAFETY SWITCH

1) Remove console and shift selector. Loosen cable clamp nut and move lever on transaxle into "PARK" position. Tighten cable clamp nut to 72 INCH lbs. (8 N.m).

2) Adjust neutral safety switch by moving forward or rearward so that engine can only be started in "NEUTRAL" or "PARK" positions and tighten mounting screws. Reinstall console.

BMW

318i, 320i, 528e, 533i, 633CSi & 733i

IDENTIFICATION

TRANSMISSION CODES

Application	Code
All Models	ZF 3 HP-22

LUBRICATION

SERVICE INTERVALS

Check fluid level at least at every oil change. Drain and refill transmission every 30,000 miles.

FLUID LEVEL

Transmission must be at normal operating temperature with vehicle on a level surface, engine at idle and gear selector in "Park". Fluid level should be between the "MAX" and "MIN" marks on the dipstick. Distance between marks represents .42 qts. (.40L).

FLUID TYPE

Automatic Transmission Fluid
Dexron or Dexron II

FLUID CAPACITY

With Oil Cooler
318i, 320i, & 528e - 6.4 qts. (6.0L)
All Others - 7.5 qts. (7.0L)
Deep Oil Pan - 2.3 qts. (2.2L)
Standard - 2.1 qts. (2.0L)

DRAINING & REFILLING

1) With transmission at normal operating temperature, remove drain plug and allow fluid to drain. Remove oil pan bolts and tap on pan to break seal loose.

2) Remove oil screen and clean or replace as necessary. Clean oil pan. Reinstall filter screen and oil pan. Fill transmission with new transmission fluid.

Fig. 1: BMW Shift Linkage Adjustment

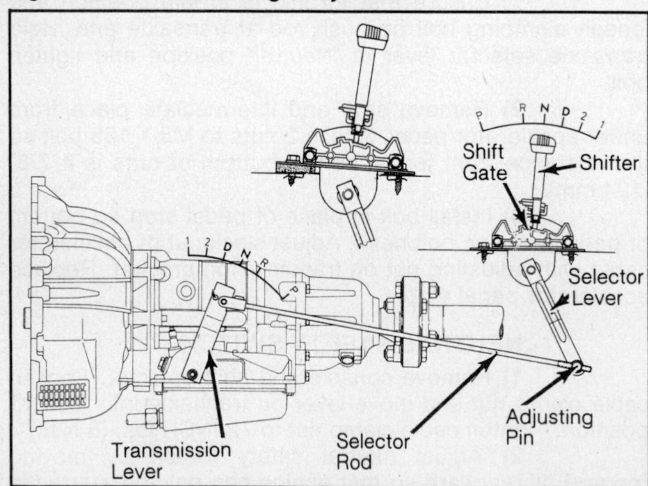
P R N D 2 1
Shift Gate
Shifter
1 2 D N R P
Selector Lever
Adjusting Pin
Transmission Lever
Selector Rod

Place shifter in "NEUTRAL" position to make rod adjustments.

ADJUSTMENT

SHIFT LINKAGE

1) Check tightness of shift console lever before adjusting. Disconnect selector rod from lever at adjustment pin. Move transmission shifter lever to "NEUTRAL" position. Press shifter against shift gate stop.

2) Alter length of selector rod with adjusting pin until adjusting pin aligns with hole in selector lever. Shorten selector rod by 1 turn of adjusting pin. Attach selector rod, adjusting pin and selector lever together.

THROTTLE CABLE & KICKDOWN STOP

320i

1) With accelerator cable properly adjusted and transmission in "NEUTRAL" position, turn adjusting screw until throttle cable clearance is .010-.030" (.25-.75 mm).

2) Depress accelerator to kickdown stop. Clearance should now be 1.71-2.20" (43.5-55 mm). If not, adjust kickdown stop screw. *See Fig. 2.*

Fig. 2: Throttle Cable and Kickdown Stop Adjustment

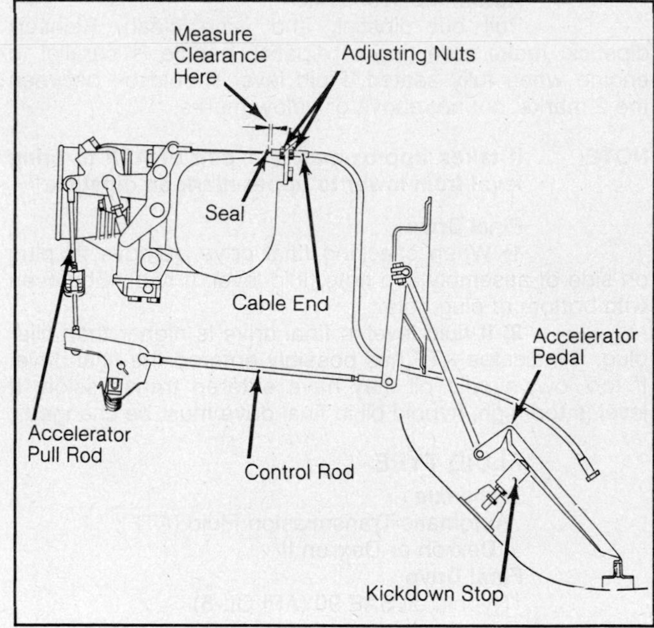
Measure Clearance Here
Adjusting Nuts
Seal
Cable End
Accelerator Pedal
Accelerator Pull Rod
Control Rod
Kickdown Stop

Model 733i is shown. Other models (Exc. 320i) are similar.

318i, 528e, 633CSi & 733i

1) On model 733i, adjust accelerator pull rod length to 16.93" (430 mm). *See Fig. 3.* With throttle at idle, adjust cable housing nuts to give .010-.030" (.25-.76 mm) clearance between seal and cable housing end. Loosen kickdown stop nut and screw throttle stop in all the way.

2) Depress accelerator pedal until transmission pressure point is felt. Loosen throtle stop until it just touches pedal. Tighten lock nut. Press accelerator pedal completely down and adjust control rod so that clearance from seal to cable end is 1.7-2.0" (43-51 mm).

NEUTRAL SAFETY SWITCH

Neutral safety switch is connected with selector lever and a relay. If not operating properly, check relay and selector adjustment.

CHRYSLER CORP. IMPORTS

Challenger, Colt, Colt Pickup, Ram-50 Pickup & Sapporo

IDENTIFICATION

TRANSMISSION CODES

Application	Code
Challenger & Sapporo	MA904A
Colt	KM170
Colt & Ram-50 Pickups	
2WD	MA904A
4WD	[1] KM146

[1] – Includes MA904A transmission and transfer case.

LUBRICATION

SERVICE INTERVALS

Change fluid and filter every 30,000 miles; if under severe usage, change more often. Fluid level should be checked every 6 months. For Colt transaxle, check fluid level every 15,000 miles.

FLUID LEVEL

1) Park vehicle on level area. Oil must be at normal operating temperature, parking brake engaged and engine at idle. Place select lever in each gear, momentarily.

2) Place selector in "N" position and clean area around dipstick tube. Ensure that fluid level is between lower and upper marks, but never over upper mark. Add or drain fluid as necessary.

CAUTION: If severe darkening of the fluid and a strong odor is noted, fluid and filter should be changed and bands adjusted.

FLUID TYPE

Automatic Transmission Fluid (ATF)
Dexron II
Transfer Case - API GL-4 & -5 SAE 90

FLUID CAPACITY

Torqueflite
MA904A - 7.2 qts. (6.8L)
Mitsubishi
KM170 - 6.0 qts. (5.7L)
KM146 - 9.5 qts. (9.0L)

NOTE: Fluid capacity for KM146 transmission includes MA904A transmission and transfer case.

DRAINING & REFILLING

Mitsubishi KM146 & Torqueflite MA904A

1) Carefully remove oil pan and drain fluid. Install new filter on bottom of valve body. Clean oil pan, replace gasket and install oil pan. Pour 4 qts. (3.8L) of specified fluid through filler tube. Start engine and allow to idle for 2 minutes.

2) Shift transmission into each position, ending in "N" position. Check fluid level with engine running at idle and add sufficient fluid to bring level to "ADD 1 PINT" mark. Recheck fluid level after transmission is at normal operating temperature.

Mitsubishi KM170

1) Remove drain plugs from both differential and pan and drain fluid. *See Fig. 1.* If replacing filter, remove bolts and lower oil pan. Install new filter on bottom of valve body. Replace pan gasket and install pan.

2) Tighten differential plug to 22-25 ft. lbs. (30-34 N.m) and pan plug to 18-21 ft. lbs. (24-28 N.m). Ensure that dipstick hole area is clean and pour in approximately 4.2 qts. (4.0L) of "DEXRON II" fluid.

3) Run engine for 2 minutes at idle. Shift transmission to each position, ending in "N" position. Add sufficient fluid to reach lower mark. After reaching normal operating temperature, fluid should be between upper and lower marks of "HOT" range.

Fig. 1: Mitsubishi KM170 Drain Plug Locations

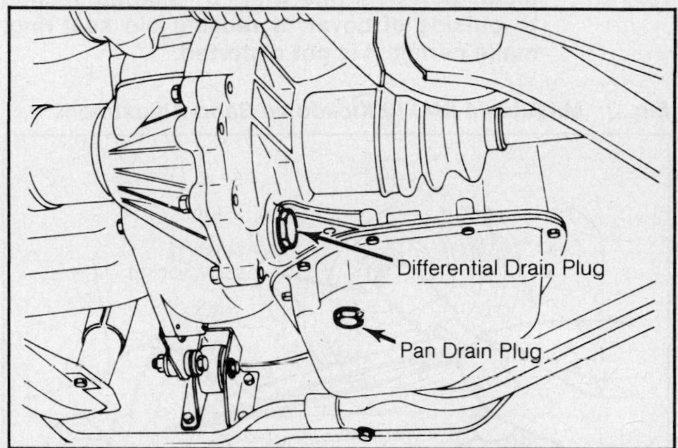
Differential Drain Plug
Pan Drain Plug

ADJUSTMENT

FRONT (KICKDOWN) BAND

Mitsubishi KM146 & Torqueflite MA904A

1) Front (kickdown) band adjuster screw is located on left side of transmission case. To adjust band, loosen and back off lock nut about 5 turns. Check that adjuster screw turns freely.

Fig. 2: Mitsubishi KM146 & Torqueflite MA904A Front (Kickdown) Band Adjusting Screw Location

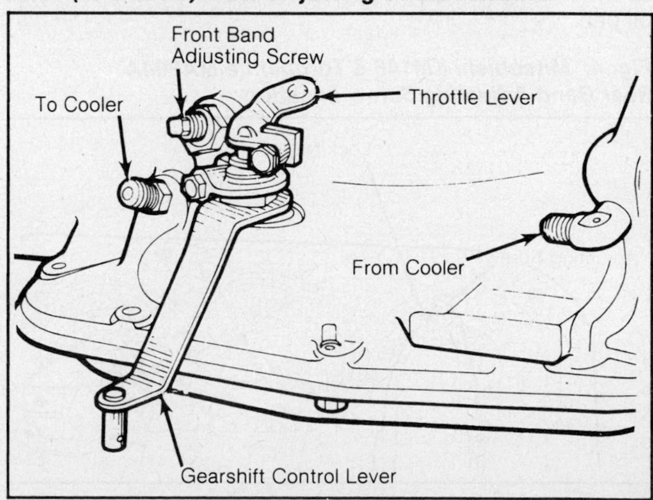
Front Band
Adjusting Screw
To Cooler
Throttle Lever
From Cooler
Gearshift Control Lever

CHRYSLER CORP. IMPORTS (Cont.)

2) Using wrench (C-3380-A) with adapter (C-3705), tighten band adjuster screw to 52 INCH lbs. (5.9 N.m). *See Fig. 2.*

3) If adapter (C-3705) is not used, tighten adjuster screw to 51 INCH lbs. (5.8 N.m), which is the true torque. Back off adjusting screw 3 1/2 turns, hold adjuster screw and tighten lock nut to 37 ft. lbs. (50 N.m).

Mitsubishi KM170

1) Clean all dirt from kickdown servo cover and remove snap ring. Remove cover and loosen lock nut. Hold servo piston from turning and tighten adjusting screw to 88 INCH lbs. (10 N.m) and back it off.

2) Repeat torquing twice to seat kickdown band against drum. Tighten adjusting screw to 44 INCH lbs. (5 N.m) and back off 3 1/2 turns. Hold screw and tighten lock nut. Install cover and snap ring.

NOTE: Install new seal ring with "D" shaped section to outside of cover. If reusing old seal ring, make certain it is not distorted.

Fig. 3: Mitsubishi KM170 Kickdown Band Adjustment

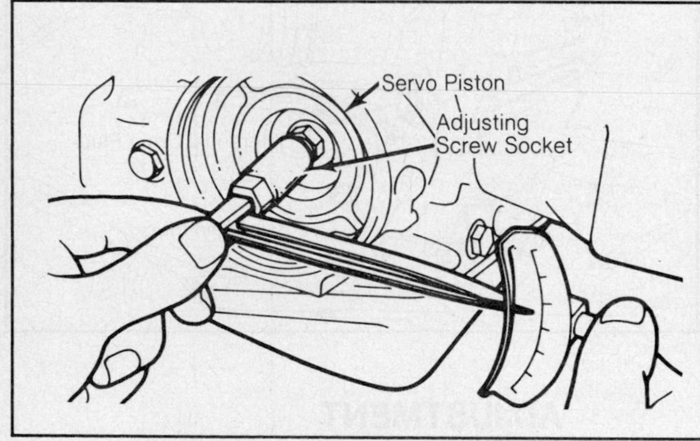
Servo Piston
Adjusting
Screw Socket

Hold piston and turn adjusting screw.

REAR BAND

Mitsubishi KM146 & Torqueflite MA904A

1) Remove oil pan. Loosen lock nut and adjusting screw at servo end of lever and tighten screw to 43 INCH lbs. (4.9 N.m) of torque.

2) Back off screw 7 turns. Hold adjusting screw and tighten lock nut to 29 ft. lbs. (40 N.m). Reinstall oil pan.

Fig. 4: Mitsubishi KM146 & Torqueflite MA904A Rear Band Adjusting Screw Location

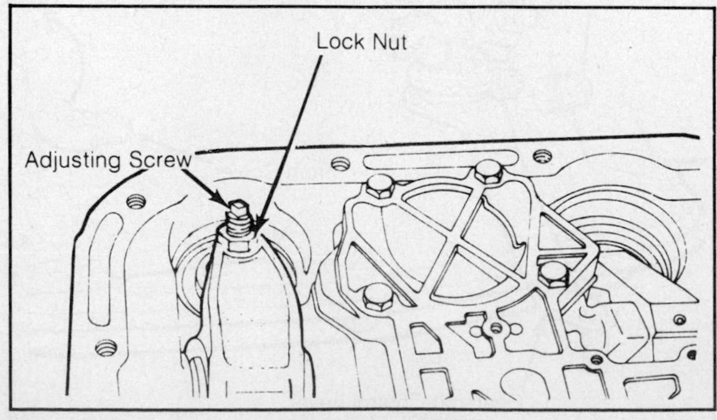
Lock Nut
Adjusting Screw

Oil pan must be removed for adjustment.

TRANSMISSION THROTTLE CONTROL

Mitsubishi KM146 & Torqueflite MA904A

1) With engine at normal operating temperature and idle speed set correctly, loosen bolt retaining throttle rod "C" to "B". Lightly push throttle rod "A" or transmission throttle lever and rod toward idle stop and set rods to "IDLE" position.

2) Tighten bolt retaining rod "B" to "C". Open throttle to "WIDE OPEN" position. Make sure that transmission lever moves from "IDLE" to "WIDE OPEN" position (total movement 47.5° to 54°). Some play should still exist in throttle lever stroke at wide open throttle.

Fig. 5: Mitsubishi KM146 & Torqueflite MA904A Throttle Rod Adjustment

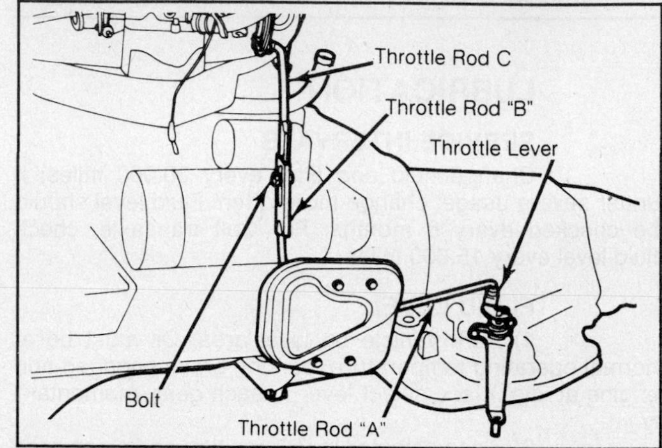
Throttle Rod C
Throttle Rod "B"
Throttle Lever
Bolt
Throttle Rod "A"

Make sure that transmission lever moves from "IDLE" to "WIDE OPEN" position.

Mitsubishi KM170

1) Ensure that carburetor throttle lever is at "CURB IDLE" position, engine is at operating temperature, and fast idle condition has been reset. Raise cover "B" and loosen cable bracket mounting bolt.

Fig. 6: Mitsubishi KM170 Throttle Cable Adjustment

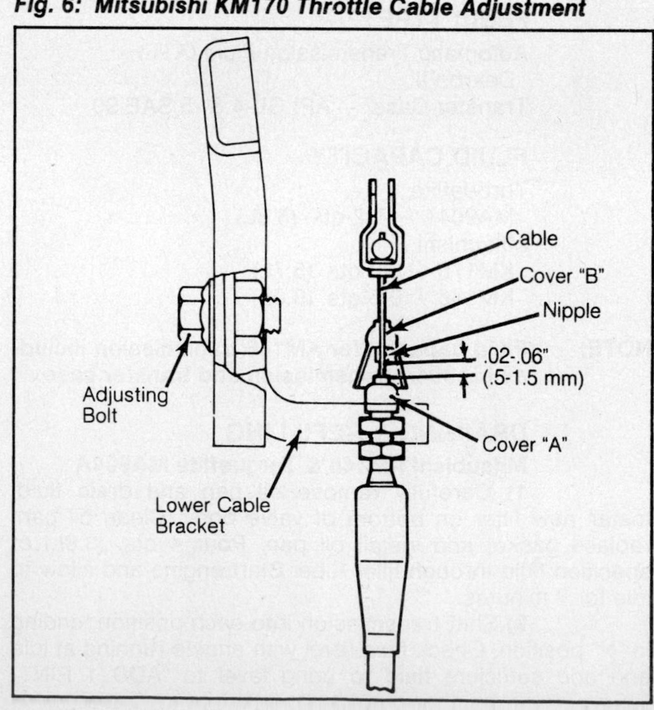
Cable
Cover "B"
Nipple
.02-.06"
(.5-1.5 mm)
Adjusting
Bolt
Cover "A"
Lower Cable
Bracket

CHRYSLER CORP. IMPORTS (Cont.)

2) Move lower cable bracket until distance between nipple and top cover "A" of throttle cable is adjusted to .02-.06" (.5-1.5 mm). *See Fig. 6.* Tighten lower cable bracket mounting bolt.

3) With throttle lever in "WIDE OPEN" position, pull cable upward to ensure freedom of cable movement.

SHIFT LINKAGE

Mitsubishi KM146 & Torqueflite MA904A

1) Remove shift handle by loosening set screw and pulling off handle. For Challenger & Sapporo, place selector lever in "N" and turn adjusting cam in top of lever until surface "A" of cam is flush with end of selector lever "B". *See Fig. 7.*

Fig. 7: Mitsubishi KM146 & Torqueflite MA904A Adjusting Selector Cam Rod On Automobiles

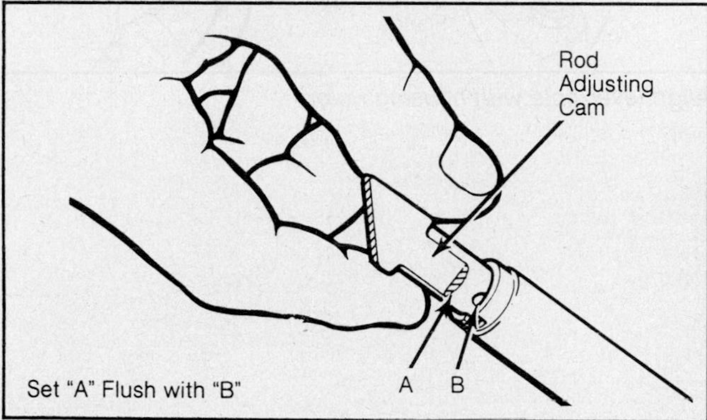

Rod Adjusting Cam
Set "A" Flush with "B"
A
B

Adjust surface "A" flush with surface "B".

2) For Pickups, place selector lever in "N" and turn adjusting cam in top of lever until surface "A" of cam is flush with push button. *See Fig. 8.*

Fig. 8: Mitsubishi KM146 & Torqueflite MA904A Adjusting Selector Cam Rod On Pickups

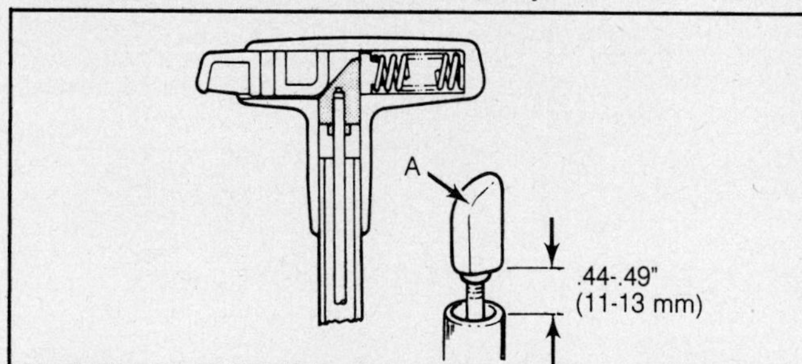

A
.44-.49"
(11-13 mm)

Rod cam surface "A" and push button must be flush.

3) Loosen lock nut at connection of rod and arm at transmission. Place transmission lever arm in "N". Place selector lever in "N" and tighten lock nut to adjust control rod length.

Mitsubishi KM170

1) Place selector in "N" position. Loosen set screw retaining handle to lever. Depress selector knob and turn handle to give .008-.035" (.2-.9 mm) clearance between selector lever end pin and detent plate. *See Fig. 9.*

2) When knob button is on driver's side, tighten set screw. With selector lever and neutral safety switch in "N" position, turn adjusting nuts at cable end until slack is removed from control cable.

Fig. 9: Adjusting Selector Lever On Mitsubishi KM170 Transaxle

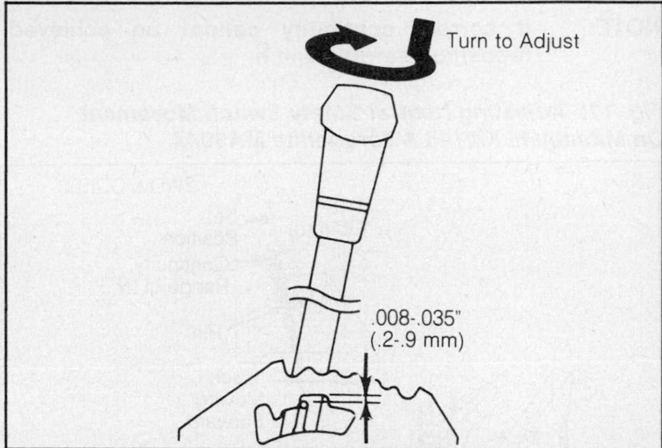

Turn to Adjust
.008-.035"
(.2-.9 mm)

To adjust, depress knob and turn handle.

NOTE: **After adjustment, confirm that every selector position of position indicator is set properly and that selector position indicator turns "RED" on proper setting.**

NEUTRAL SAFETY SWITCH

Mitsubishi KM146 & Torqueflite MA904A

NOTE: **Safety switch is located under shift lever console and is operated by shift lever. In addition to the neutral safety switch function, switch also operates back-up lights and seat belt warning system.**

1) To adjust switch, remove console, loosen switch attaching screws, and place selector lever in "N" position. For Challenger and Sapporo, align mating marks of switch with that of rod pin position. *See Fig. 10.* For Pickups, slide switch back and forth to measure contact range of "N" position. *See Fig. 11.*

Fig. 10: Positioning Neutral Safety Switch On Mitsubishi KM146 & Torqueflite MA904A

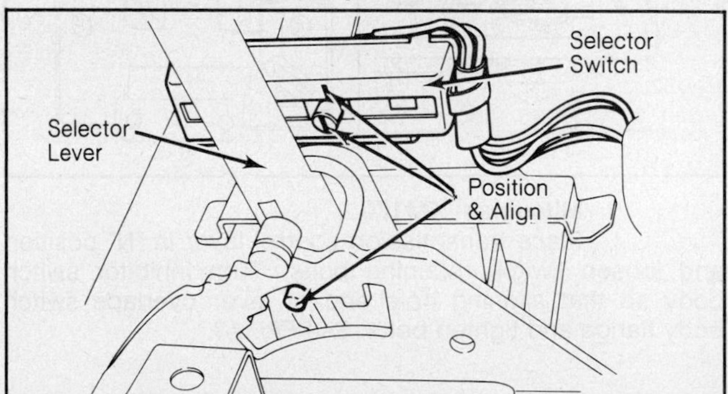

Selector Switch
Selector Lever
Position & Align

Place shift lever in "N" and align switch mark with rod indicator.

2) Temporarily install switch and adjust so there is .06" (1.5 mm) for Challenger, Sapporo, and 2WD Pickup, .1" (2.5 mm) for 4WD Pickup, side clearance between selector lever and switch. *See Fig. 12.* Set selector lever in "P", "R", and "N" positions and check

CHRYSLER CORP. IMPORTS (Cont.)

continuity of terminals. After confirming continuity, tighten switch attaching screws and reinstall console.

NOTE: If correct continuity cannot be achieved, reposition safety switch.

Fig. 11: Adjusting Neutral Safety Switch Movement On Mitsubishi KM146 & Torqueflite MA904A

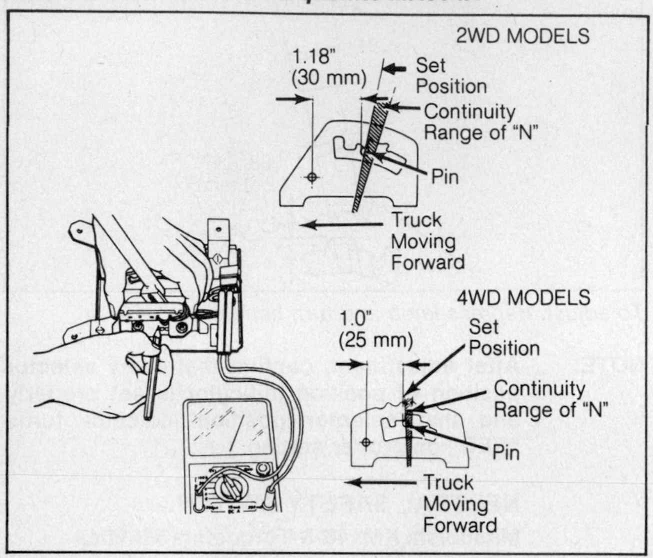

2WD MODELS
1.18"
(30 mm)
Set
Position
Continuity
Range of "N"
Pin
Truck
Moving
Forward
4WD MODELS
1.0"
(25 mm)
Set
Position
Continuity
Range of "N"
Pin
Truck
Moving
Forward

Connect tester to switch terminals (BY-BY) and move switch back and forth to check continuity.

Fig. 12: Adjusting Torqueflite Neutral Safety Switch On Mitsubishi KM146 & Torqueflite MA904A

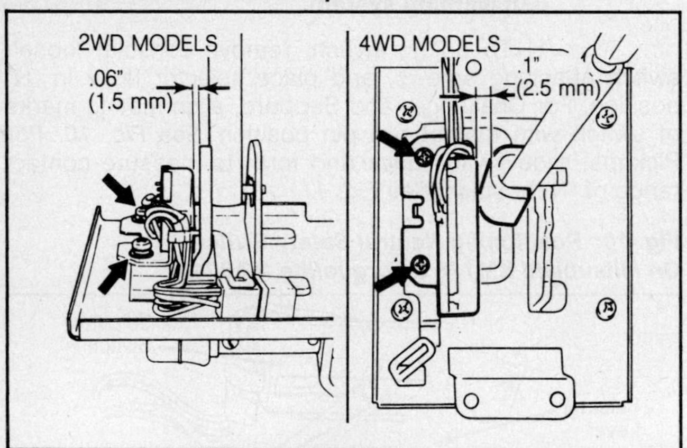

2WD MODELS
.06"
(1.5 mm)
4WD MODELS
.1"
(2.5 mm)

Mitsubishi KM170

Place transmission control lever in "N" position and loosen switch retaining bolts. Turn inhibitor switch body so that aligning hole end of lever overlaps switch body flange and tighten bolts. *See Fig. 13.*

Fig. 13: Adjusting Neutral Safety Switch On Mitsubishi KM170 Transaxle

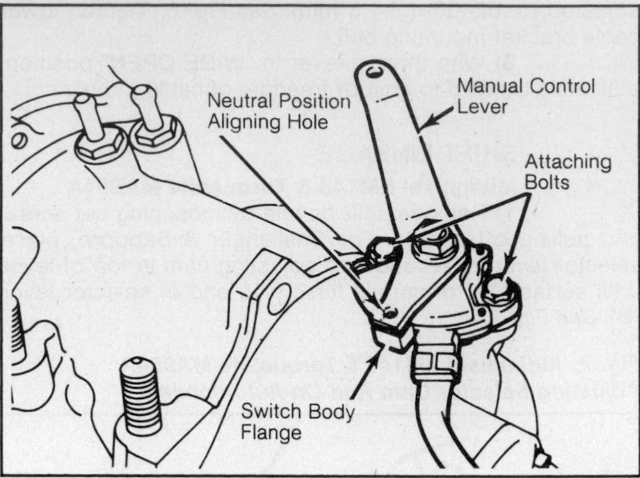

Neutral Position
Aligning Hole
Manual Control
Lever
Attaching
Bolts
Switch Body
Flange

Align lever hole with housing hole.

DATSUN/NISSAN

Maxima, Pickup, Pulsar, Sentra, Stanza, 200SX, 280ZX & 280ZX Turbo

IDENTIFICATION

TRANSMISSION CODES

Application	Code
FWD	
Pulsar & Stanza	RL3F01A
Sentra	
Diesel	RN3F01A
Gas	RL3F01A
RWD	
Maxima	L4N71B
Pickup	3N71B
200SX	L3N71B
280ZX	L3N71B
280ZX Turbo	3N71B

LUBRICATION

SERVICE INTERVAL

Inspect fluid level every 15,000 miles or 12 months. If under severe usage, change every 30,000 miles or 24 months.

FLUID LEVEL

Transaxle & Transmission

1) Check fluid with engine and transmission at normal operating temperatures (this is reached after several minutes of driving). With vehicle standing level and at idle, shift transmission through all positions and return to "P" position.

2) Clean area around dipstick. Remove dip stick, wipe clean, insert and withdraw. Level should be between "H" and "L" marks, if not, add as necessary.

NOTE: **Normal fluid should be clear with a pink color and should not have a strong odor.**

Transfer Case

Oil level should be at bottom of fill hole.

NOTE: **If fluid has a strong, burned odor or is dark in color, overheating and internal wear may be indicated. If milky in appearance, moisture from cooling system or road may have entered the system. Foamy or excessively bubbled fluid indicates overfilling and aeration.**

FLUID TYPE

Automatic Transmission Fluid (ATF)
Dexron
Transfer Case SAE 80W/90 (API GL-4)

FLUID CAPACITY

FWD
RL3F01A - 6.4 qts. (6.0L)
RN3F01A - 6.4 qts. (6.0L)

RWD
3N71B - 5.9 qts. (5.5L)
L3N71B - 6.5 qts. (6.1L)
L4N71B - 7.4 qts. (7.0L)
Transfer Case 1.5 qts. (1.4L)

DRAINING & REFILLING

Transaxle & Transmission

1) Loosen oil pan bolts and allow ATF to drain. Remove oil pan and clean pan and screen thoroughly. Install pan using a new gasket. Add fluid through filler tube.

2) Run engine at idle speed for about 2 minutes, then at fast idle (1200 RPM) for several more minutes, until normal operating temperatures are reached. Shift transmission through all gears and return to "P" (Park). Check fluid level and add to obtain appropriate level.

ADJUSTMENT

BRAKE BAND

Transmission

Loosen piston stem lock nut and tighten piston stem (adjusting screw) to 106-132 INCH lbs. (12-15 N.m). Back off piston stem 2 turns. While holding servo piston stem stationary, tighten lock nut to 177 INCH lbs. (20 N.m).

Transaxle

Loosen locknut. Torque anchor end pin to 35-53 INCH lbs. (4-6 N.m). Back off anchor end pin 2 1/2 turns. Tighten lock nut (while holding anchor pin), to 141-195 INCH lbs. (16-22 N.m).

SHIFT LINKAGE

RWD

1) Starting in "P" position, shift through all positions to "1" position. If detents cannot be felt or pointer is improperly aligned, linkage must be adjusted.

2) Place shift lever in "D" position and loosen lock nuts on rod. Turn lock nuts until pointer aligns properly and all detents can be felt. Tighten lock nuts and recheck positions, ensuring that full detent is felt in "P" position.

NOTE: **If unable to adjust, grommets at ends of rod may be worn or damaged and require replacement.**

FWD

1) Place control lever at "P" position. Connect control cable end to manual lever of transaxle unit and tighten control cable retaining bolts. Move control lever from "P" to "1".

2) Make sure that control lever can move smoothly and without any sliding noise. Place control lever at "P". Make sure that control lever locks at "P". Remove lock nut at control cable and loosen adjusting nut. Connect control cable to trunnion.

3) Adjust and tighten adjusting nut. Install and tighten lock nut. Move control lever from "P" to "1" again. Make sure that control lever can move smoothly and without sliding noise. Apply grease to spring washer.

DATSUN/NISSAN (Cont.)

KICKDOWN SWITCH

RWD

Kickdown switch is located at top of accelerator pedal post. A "click" should be heard just before accelerator bottoms out when depressed. If not, loosen switch lock nut and adjust.

NOTE: Do not allow switch to close too soon, for downshift will occur at part throttle.

NEUTRAL SAFETY SWITCH

1) Switch operates back-up lights and prevents starting except in "P" or "N". To adjust, ensure that transmission is in "N" with lever at transmission in vertical position.

2) Remove alignment hole screw at bottom of switch and loosen retaining bolts. Move switch until alignment pin, .08" (2 mm) for RWD or .098" (2.5 mm) for FWD, can be inserted in rotor. Tighten retaining bolts and replace alignment hole screw.

Fig. 1: Adjusting Neutral Safety Switch

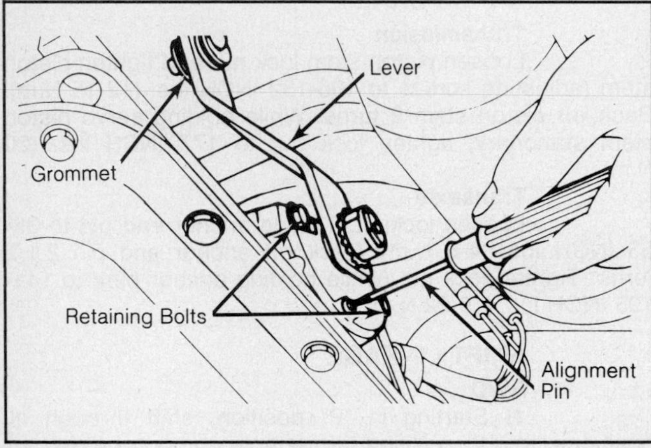
Lever
Grommet
Retaining Bolts
Alignment
Pin

Safety switch for transaxle is similar.

HONDA

Accord, Civic & Prelude

IDENTIFICATION

TRANSMISSION CODES

Application	Code
Accord & Prelude	Model AK Transaxle
Civic	
1300 Engine	Model AJ Transaxle
1500 Engine	Model AM Transaxle

LUBRICATION

SERVICE INTERVALS

Check fluid level at every oil change. Transmission fluid should be changed at 15,000 miles, then every 30,000. No filter service or band adjustment is required.

FLUID LEVEL

1) With vehicle on level floor and at normal operating temperature, stop engine. Clean area around dipstick and unscrew dipstick. Remove dipstick and wipe clean, then insert into hole but do not screw down.

2) Remove dipstick and check level. Fluid should be between upper and lower marks. Add fluid as necessary.

FLUID TYPE

Automatic Transmission Fluid (ATF) Dexron

FLUID CAPACITY

Dry Fill – 5.2 qts (4.9L)
Refill – 2.6 qts. (2.5L)

DRAINING & REFILLING

1) Ensure that operating temperature is up to normal and remove transmission drain plug. Use new gasket and replace drain plug when fluid is drained.

2) Fill with about 2 qts. (1.9L) of fluid through dipstick hole and check level. Add fluid to bring to upper mark on dipstick.

NOTE: Refill capacity will always be slightly less than specified capacity due to fluid remaining in recesses of housing and converter.

ADJUSTMENT

SHIFT CONTROL CABLE

1) Ensure that reverse gear engages. Remove center console. Place shift lever in "D" position. Remove lock clip and control cable pin. Check that hole in cable end is aligned with holes in selector lever arm.

2) If not, loosen lock nuts on control cable and adjust as required. Tighten lock nuts and install pin with lock clip. If pin does not go in easily, further adjustment is required. Check gear operation. *See Fig. 1.*

THROTTLE CONTROL CABLE & BRACKET

1) Ensure that engine is warmed to normal operating temperature and cable securing clamps are in position. Disconnect control cable from lever and lay end on top of shock absorber tower.

2) Using throttle gauge (07974-6890300), adjust cable control bracket so that distance between

Fig. 1: Shift Control Cable Alignment

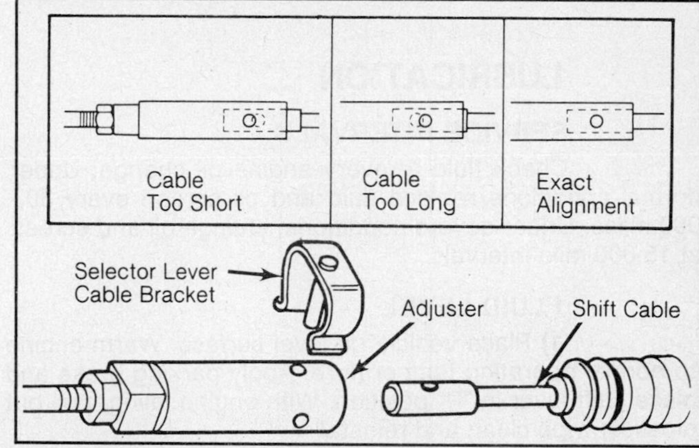
Cable Too Short
Cable Too Long
Exact Alignment
Selector Lever Cable Bracket
Adjuster
Shift Cable

bracket and lever is 3.29" (83.5 mm). Depress accelerator until there is no slack in carburetor throttle cable.

3) Adjust distance between control cable end and nut "A" to 3.3" (84.5 mm). Install cable and tighten lock nut "B", ensuring that lock nut "A" does not turn. *See Fig. 2.*

Fig. 2: Throttle Cable & Bracket Adjustment

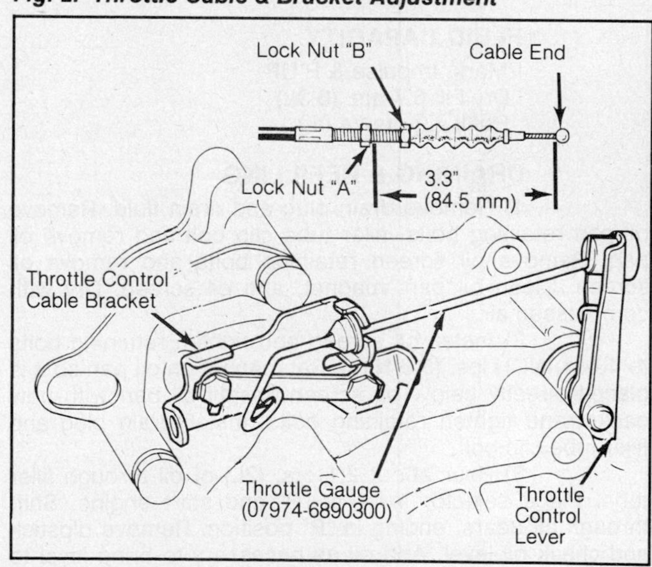
Lock Nut "B"
Cable End
Lock Nut "A"
3.3"
(84.5 mm)
Throttle Control Cable Bracket
Throttle Gauge (07974-6890300)
Throttle Control Lever

SAFETY SWITCH

Place safety switch slider and shift selector lever in "N" position. Slip switch over actuator pin and secure with 2 bolts and lock washers. Move selector lever through positions and check switch continuity in various positions.

ISUZU

I-Mark, Impulse & P'UP

IDENTIFICATION

TRANSMISSION CODES

Application	Code
I-Mark, Impulse & P'UP	AW03-55

LUBRICATION

SERVICE INTERVALS

Check fluid at every engine oil change. Under normal conditions replace fluid and oil screen every 30,-000 miles. Under severe conditions, change oil and screen at 15,000 mile intervals.

FLUID LEVEL

1) Place vehicle on level surface. Warm engine to normal operating temperature. Apply parking brake and place shift lever in "P" position. With engine idling, pull out dipstick, wipe clean and reinstall.

2) Remove dipstick and check level reading. Fluid level should be between the 2 dimples indicating "Hot" range. If not, add sufficient fluid to bring fluid to proper level.

FLUID TYPE

Automatic Transmission Fluid (ATF)
Dexron II

FLUID CAPACITY

I-Mark, Impulse & P'UP
Dry Fill 6.7 qts. (6.3L)
Refill 4.2 qts. (4.0L)

DRAINING & REFILLING

1) Remove drain plug and drain fluid. Remove oil pan retaining bolts, filler tube clip bolt and remove oil pan. Remove oil screen retaining bolts and remove oil screen. Clean oil pan, magnet, and oil screen. Dry with compressed air.

2) Install oil screen and tighten retaining bolts to 43-51 INCH lbs. (5-6 N.m). Set magnet on oil pan so it is placed directly below oil screen. Install oil pan with new gasket and tighten retaining bolts. Install drain plug and filler tube clip bolt.

3) Pour about 2.1 qts. (2L) of oil through filler tube. Place selector lever in "P" and start engine. Shift through all gears, ending in "P" position. Remove dipstick and check oil level. Add oil as necessary to bring level to correct mark on dipstick.

ADJUSTMENTS

THROTTLE VALVE CABLE

Gasoline Engine

1) Loosen throttle valve cable adjusting nuts. Ensure that carburetor throttle adjusting screw is in contact with stopper for normal idling.

2) Adjust setting of outer cable, using adjusting nuts, so that distance between upper face of rubber boot on outer cable and cable stopper on inner cable is .04-.06" (.8-1.5 mm). Tighten adjusting nuts. *See Fig. 1.*

Fig. 1: Gasoline Throttle Valve Cable Adjustment

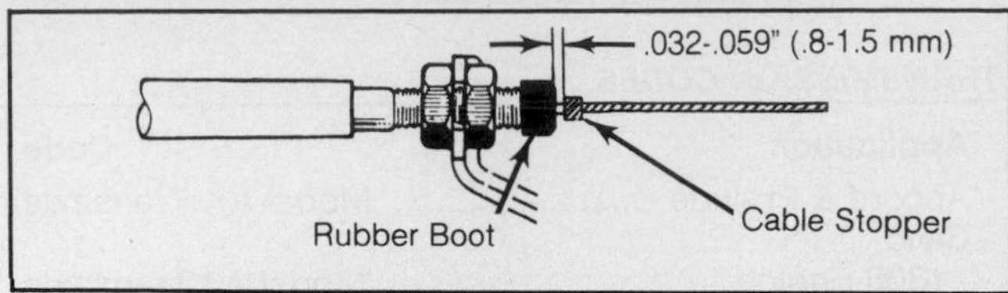
.032-.059" (.8-1.5 mm)
Rubber Boot
Cable Stopper

3) Tighten adjusting nuts. Check that stroke of inner cable from normal idling position to wide open throttle is 1.30-1.36" (32.9-33.9 mm).

Diesel Engine

1) Loosen throttle valve cable adjusting nuts. With accelerator pedal fully depressed, ensure that injection pump lever is in contact with maximum speed adjust screw.

2) Hold lever in this position. Adjust setting of outer cable, using adjusting nuts, so that distance between end of rubber boot on outer cable and cable stopper on inner cable is .0-.04" (0-1 mm). *See Fig. 2.*

Fig. 2: Diesel Throttle Valve Cable Adjustment

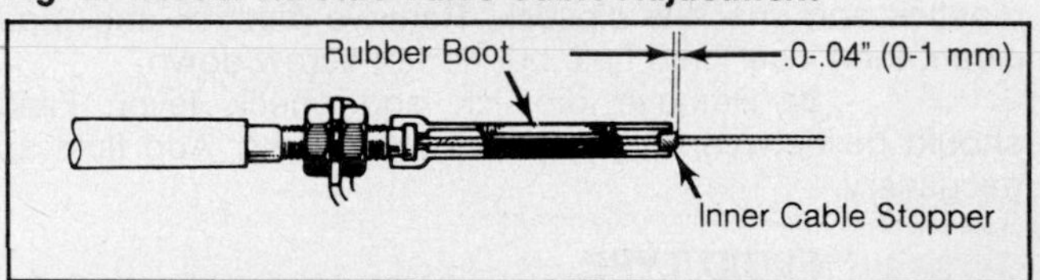
Rubber Boot
.0-.04" (0-1 mm)
Inner Cable Stopper

3) Tighten adjusting nuts. Check that stroke of inner cable from normal idling position to wide open throttle is 1.30-1.36" (32.9-33.9 mm).

SHIFT LINKAGE

I-Mark & Impulse

1) Loosen shift control rod adjusting nuts on transmission. Turn manual shaft fully clockwise as viewed from right side of transmission. Turn back to 3rd stop and set shaft in "N" position.

2) With transmission in "N", check that manual shift lever is in vertical position. Hold manual shaft in position and place shift lever in "N".

3) To remove play, tighten adjusting nuts with control shaft lever pushed rearward together with shift control lever. Road test vehicle to ensure that shift lever moves properly and transmission operates smoothly.

P'UP

1) Loosen control rod lock nuts on transmission. Turn manual shaft on transmission counterclockwise, as viewed from left side as far as it will go. Back off 3 stops to "N" position.

2) Hold shaft in this position and place shift lever in "N" position. Holding levers in this position, push shift control lever rearward to remove all play. Tighten lock nuts. Check for proper movement of shift control lever.

NEUTRAL SAFETY SWITCH

Loosen switch retaining screws (near base of selector lever). Place selector lever in "N". Bring the center of the switch moving piece into alignment with the line scribed on the steel case of the switch. Tighten retaining screws. Ensure that vehicle will only start in "P" or "N" position.

JAGUAR

XJ6 & XJS

IDENTIFICATION

TRANSMISSION CODES

Application	Code
XJ6	Borg-Warner 66
XJS	GM THM 400

LUBRICATION

SERVICE INTERVALS

Check fluid level at first 1,000 miles and then every 7,500 miles. Change fluid and filter at 30,000 mile intervals.

FLUID LEVEL

1) Park vehicle, bring engine and transmission to normal operating temperature. Apply hand brake and position gear selector in all ranges and return to "P" position.

2) Withdraw and wipe off dipstick, check fluid level. If necessary, add fluid to reach "MAX" level on "HOT" side of dipstick. After adding, repeat checking procedure to make sure overfilling has not occurred.

FLUID TYPE

XJ6 – Automatic Transmission Fluid (ATF) Type "G"
XJS – Automatic Transmission Fluid (ATF) Dexron II

FLUID CAPACITY

XJ6 – Dry Fill 8.4 qts. (8.0L)
XJS – Dry Fill 9.6 qts. (9.1L)

DRAINING & REFILLING

XJ6 (Borg-Warner 66)

1) Place drain pan under transmission. Detach dipstick/filler tube and drain oil. Remove pan bolts and pan. Remove and discard filter and gasket.

2) Ensure that oil pan is clean and install filter and pan, using new gaskets. Replace dipstick/filler tube and add approximately 2 qts. (1.9L). Proceed as in Fluid Level.

NOTE: Since converter is not drained, fluid required will be less than specified in Fluid Capacity.

XJS (GM THM 400)

1) Remove vacuum capsule clamp and bolt. Disconnect capsule and drain oil. Reconnect capsule and clamp to transmission.

2) Disconnect right side of intermediate exhaust pipe and tie aside. Remove crash bracket. Remove oil pan bolts, oil pan and gasket. Clean and replace oil pan using a new gasket. Complete installation by reversing removal proceedures.

ADJUSTMENT

FRONT BAND

XJ6 (Borg-Warner 66)

1) Remove nut retaining selector lever to selector shaft and remove lever. Loosen lock nut retaining band adjuster screw and loosen adjuster 2 or 3 turns.

2) Tighten adjuster to 60 INCH lbs. (7 N.m). Back off screw 3/4 turn. Tighten lock nut while holding adjuster and replace covers and carpet.

NOTE: No front band adjustment on XJS (GM THM 400) transmission.

REAR BAND

XJ6 (Borg-Warner 66)

1) Loosen lock nut and rear band adjusting screw 2 or 3 turns, ensuring that adjusting screw rotates freely in case.

2) Tighten adjusting screw to 60 INCH lbs. (7 N.m). Back off 3/4 turn. Tighten lock nut while holding adjusting screw.

NOTE: No rear band adjustment on XJS (GM THM – 400) transmission.

THROTTLE CABLE

XJ6 (Borg-Warner 66)

1) Engine must be correctly tuned before attempting transmission throttle adjustment. Using Allen wrench, remove plug from transmission and connect pressure gauge to transmission with adapter.

Fig. 1: XJ6 Transmission Throttle Cable Adjustment

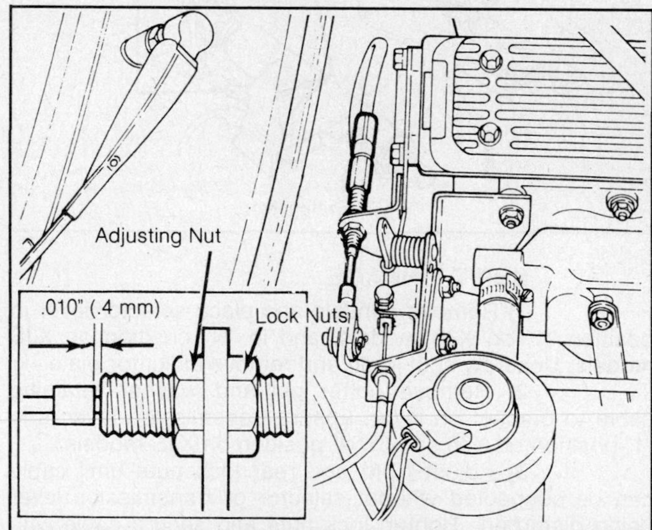
Adjusting Nut
.010" (.4 mm)
Lock Nuts

Ferrule crimped on inner cable should be .060" (.4 mm) from threaded portion of outer cable.

2) Feed gauge hose through passenger window, keeping hose clear of exhaust pipe. Block wheels and apply hand and foot brake. Run engine to normal operating temperature.

JAGUAR (Cont.)

3) With transmission selector in "D" position, pressure gauge should read 60-75 psi (4.2-5.3 kg/cm²) at idle speed. Increase engine speed to 1200 RPM. Gauge should now read 75-115 psi (5.3-8.1 kg/cm²).

4) If correct pressure is not obtained, switch engine off and place transmission in "N". Loosen lock nut on downshift cable, and adjust nut on outer cable to alter pressure. *See Fig. 1.*

5) When pressure is correct, tighten cable lock nut, reinstall plug using new sealing compound. Road test vehicle.

NOTE: **Increasing length of cable increases pressure. Decreasing length decreases pressure.**

DETENT DOWNSHIFT SWITCH

XJS (GM THM 400)

1) With ignition on, check that power is available at input terminal (Green wire). With one lead of test light grounded, connect other lead to output terminal (Green/White wire).

2) Fully depress accelerator and depress switch arm. If light still does not operate, replace switch. If switch is OK, loosen switch screws. Move switch towards cable until at full throttle opening, light operates. Tighten switch screws and recheck.

Fig. 2: XJS Detent Downshift Switch Adjustment

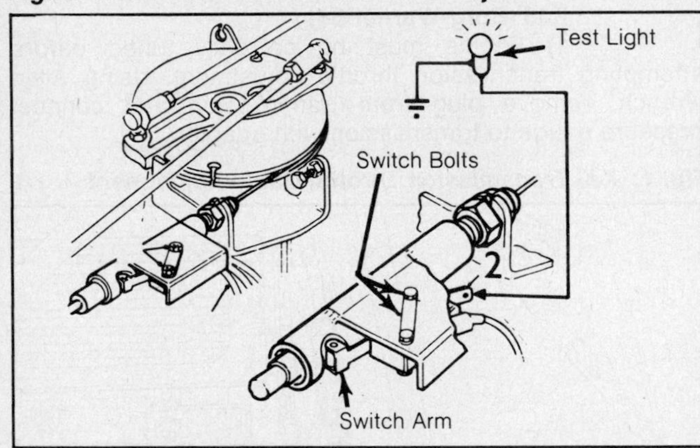
Test Light
Switch Bolts
Switch Arm

SHIFT LINKAGE

1) Remove console and place selector lever in position "1" on XJ6 models, and in "N" position on XJS models. Unscrew shift knob and remove indicator plate.

2) Remove cotter pin and washer retaining cable to bracket on lever. Ensure transmission lever is in "1" position on XJ6 and in "N" position on XJS models.

3) Adjust front and rear lock nuts until cable can be connected without selector or transmission lever being disturbed. Tighten lock nuts and secure cable with new cotter pin. Reinstall selector plate and shift knob.

NEUTRAL SAFETY SWITCH

1) Remove selector indicator and position electric window switch panel away from console. Move control panel to gain access to cigar lighter wiring and door lock switch wiring. Disconnect these wires after noting positions for reassembly.

Fig. 3: Jaguar Shift Linkage

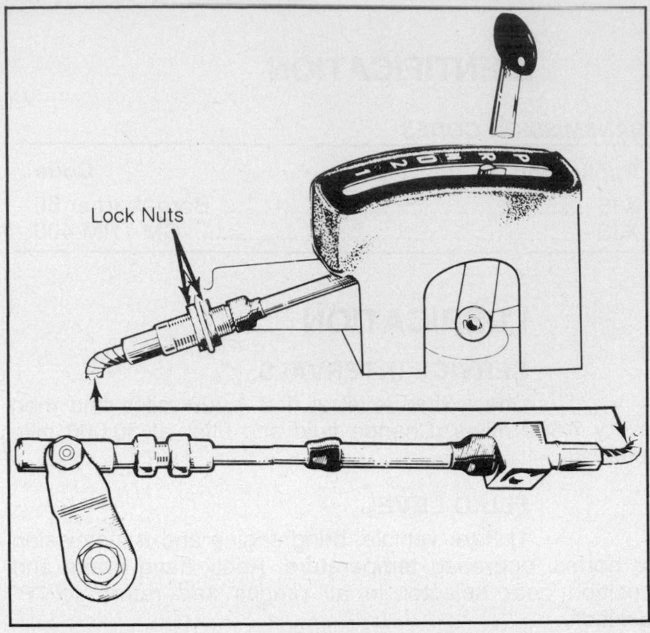
Lock Nuts

2) Remove control panel. Disconnect feed wire to switch and connect powered test light to terminal. Place selector lever in "N" position and loosen lock nuts which secure the switch. Adjust switch until test light operates.

3) Tighten switch lock nuts and check that light remains on with lever in "P", and goes off with lever in any driving positions. Remove test light, reconnect feed wire, and reinstall all removed parts.

Fig. 4: Neutral Safety Switch Adjustment

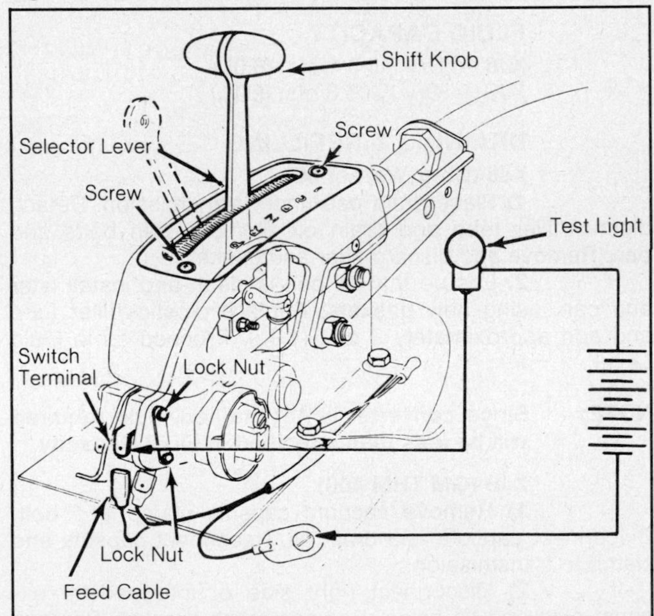
Shift Knob
Screw
Selector Lever
Screw
Test Light
Switch Terminal
Lock Nut
Lock Nut
Feed Cable

MAZDA

GLC, GLC Wagon, RX7 & 626

IDENTIFICATION

TRANSMISSION CODES

Application	Codes
GLC & 626	F3A
GLC Wagon	L3N71B
RX7	3N71B

LUBRICATION

SERVICE INTERVALS

Inspect automatic transmission fluid level every 7,500 miles or 8 months.

FLUID LEVEL

1) Check fluid with vehicle on level floor. Apply parking brake firmly and run engine approximately 2 minutes at 1200 RPM.

2) With engine running at normal idle, move selector lever through all gears, pausing at each gear to allow for engagement.

3) Return to "P" position and leave engine running. Wipe area clean around dipstick filler tube and remove dipstick.

4) Wipe dipstick clean, reinsert, withdraw, and note reading. If between "L" and "F" marks, level is satisfactory. If not, add fluid.

FLUID TYPE

Automatic Transmission Fluid (ATF)
Type "F"

FLUID CAPACITY

GLC & 626 Transaxle – 6.0 qts. (5.7L)
GLC Wagon Transmission – 6.0 qts. (5.7L)
RX7 Transmission – 6.6 qts. (6.2L)

DRAINING & REFILLING

Transmission

1) If draining and refilling is required for any operation, remove pan bolts and allow fluid to drain. Remove pan and gasket, (discard gasket).

2) Clean pan thoroughly and reinstall new gasket, tightening pan bolts to 36-60 INCH lbs. (4-9 N.m). Add fluid, make sure not to overfill.

Transaxle

1) Drain oil by removing drain plug on bottom of differential. Remove speedometer driven gear and oil pan. Clean oil pan. Replace oil pan and speedometer driven gear.

2) Replace oil through oil filler tube. Place selector lever in "P", warm engine, and check oil level. Oil level must not be higher than "F" on gauge.

ADJUSTMENT

BRAKE BAND

All Models

1) Oil pan must be removed on GLC Wagon & 626 to adjust brake band. Loosen servo piston stem lock nut and back off a few turns.

2) Using a torque wrench, tighten servo piston stem to 108-132 INCH lbs. (12-15 N.m), then back off piston stem 2 turns.

Fig. 1: GLC Wagon and 626 Transmission Brake Band Adjustment

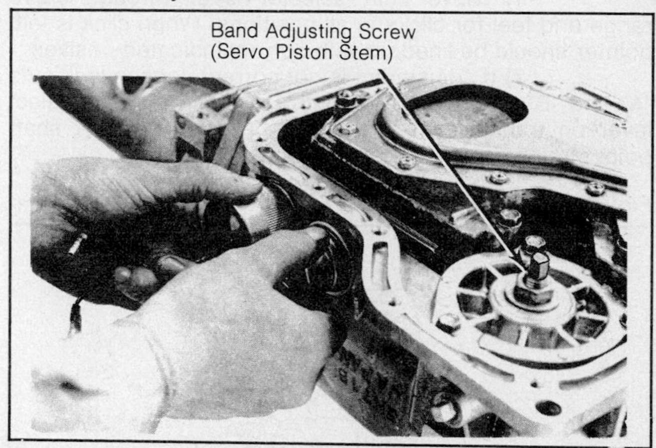

Band Adjusting Screw
(Servo Piston Stem)

3) Hold piston stem in this position and tighten lock nut to 132-348 INCH lbs. (15-39 N.m) on RWD models. On GLC & 626 FWD models, tighten lock nut to 41-59 ft. lbs. (56-80 N.m).

Fig. 2: RX7 Transmission Brake Band Adjustment

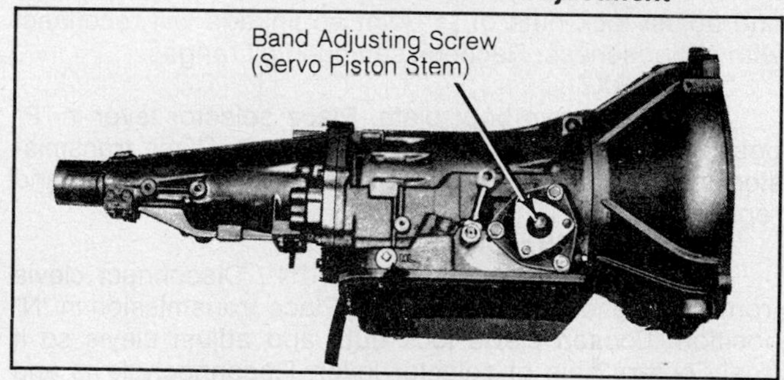

Band Adjusting Screw
(Servo Piston Stem)

KICKDOWN SWITCH & DOWNSHIFT SOLENOID

All Models

1) Depress accelerator pedal to limit. Near wide open throttle, click should be heard from solenoid. Switch must operate at or after 7/8 of pedal travel.

2) If not, loosen switch retaining nut and adjust switch to engage when pedal is at 7/8 of its full travel, tighten retaining nut and check solenoid.

Fig. 3: Kickdown Switch and Downshift Solenoid

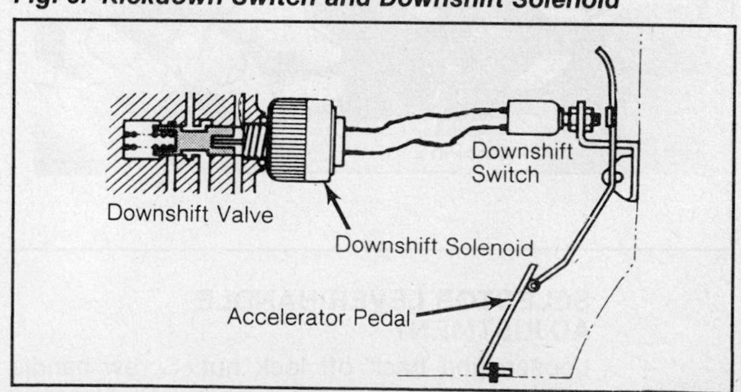

Downshift Switch
Downshift Valve
Downshift Solenoid
Accelerator Pedal

MAZDA (Cont.)

SHIFT LINKAGE

NOTE: **Before linkage is adjusted, be sure engine idle is properly set.**

GLC & 626

1) Move shift selector lever through entire range and feel for clicks in all positions. When click is felt, pointer should be lined up with correct indicated position.

2) If adjustment is not correct, loosen lock nuts "A" and "B" of "T" joint on control rod. Place range select lever on transaxle in "N" position (slot of selector shaft point straight up and detent engages). *See Fig. 4.*

Fig. 4: GLC & 626 FWD Shift Linkage Adjustment

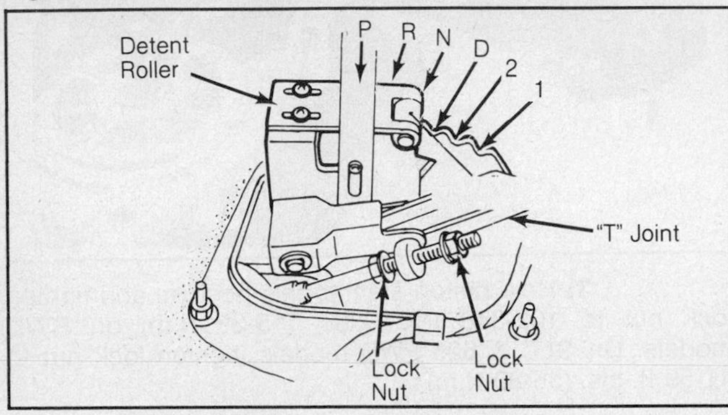
Detent Roller
P
R
N
D
2
1
"T" Joint
Lock Nut
Lock Nut

3) Position shift selector lever in "N" position and adjust lock nuts of "T" joint so linkage will reconnect with no looseness. Recheck setting in all ranges.

RX7

Remove boot plate. Place selector lever in "P" position. Loosen selector lever plate bolt. Place transmission in "P" position. Tighten selector lever plate bolt and replace boot.

GLC Wagon

Place selector lever in "N". Disconnect clevis from lower end of selector lever. Place transmission in "N" position. Loosen clevis lock nuts and adjust clevis so it freely enters hole of selector lever. Reconnect clevis and check shifting operation. *See Fig. 5.*

Fig. 5: GLC Wagon Transmission Shift Linkage

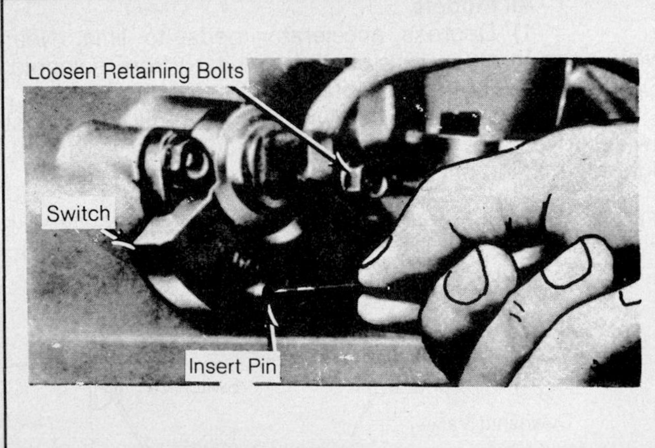
Loosen Retaining Bolts
Switch
Insert Pin

SELECTOR LEVER HANDLE ADJUSTMENT

Loosen and back off lock nut. Screw handle fully down until no play exists in the push button. Unscrew handle 1 complete turn at a time until smooth shifting operation is obtained. Tighten lock nut.

NEUTRAL SAFETY SWITCH

GLC Wagon & RX7

1) After checking and adjusting shift linkage, place the transmission lever in the "N" position. On GLC Wagon ONLY, remove transmission manual lever retaining nut and lever.

2) Loosen safety switch retaining bolts. Remove screw from alignment pin hole at bottom of switch.

3) Rotate switch and insert a .078" (2 mm) diameter alignment pin through the alignment hole and into hole of internal rotor. Tighten switch retaining bolts and remove alignment pin.

4) Reinstall alignment pin hole screw. On GLC Wagon ONLY, reinstall transmission manual lever and retaining nut. Check operation of switch. The engine should only start in "N" or "P" position.

Fig. 6: Adjusting Neutral Safety Switch On GLC Wagon & RX7 Transmissions

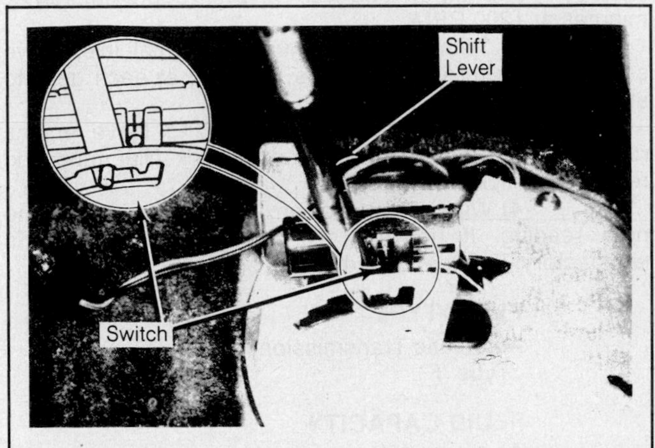
Shift Lever
Switch

MITSUBISHI

Cordia, Pickups & Tredia

IDENTIFICATION

TRANSMISSION CODES

Application	Codes
Cordia & Tredia	KM171
Pickup	
2WD	MA904A
4WD	[1] KM146

[1] – Includes MA904A transmission and transfer case

LUBRICATION

SERVICE INTERVAL

Check oil level every 15,000 miles. Change oil every 30,000 miles or if under severe usage, change every 15,000 miles.

FLUID LEVEL

1) Position vehicle on a level surface and set parking brake. Run engine at idle. Move selector lever through all positions, ending in "N".

2) With engine at normal operating temperature, remove dipstick and wipe with a clean cloth, and check oil level. Oil level must be between "FULL" and "ADD" mark of dipstick.

CAUTION: If severe darkening of the fluid and a strong odor is noted, fluid and filter should be changed and bands adjusted.

FLUID TYPE

Transaxle & Transmission
Dexron II (ATF)
Transfer Case
SAE 75W/85W (API GL-4)

FLUID CAPACITY

Cordia & Tredia
KM171 - 6.1 qts. (5.8L)
Pickup
2WD MA904A - 7.2 qts. (6.8L)
4WD KM146 - 9.5 qts. (9.0L)
Transfer Case 2.3 qts. (2.2L)

NOTE: KM146 transmission fluid capacity includes MA904A transmission and transfer case.

DRAINING & REFILLING

Mitsubishi KM146 & Torqueflite MA904A

1) Carefully remove oil pan and drain fluid. Install new filter on bottom of valve body. Clean oil pan, replace gasket and install oil pan. Pour 4 qts. (3.8L) of specified fluid through filler tube. Idle engine for 2 minutes.

2) Shift transmission into each position, ending in "N" position. Check fluid level with engine running at idle and add sufficient fluid to bring level to "ADD 1 PINT" mark. Recheck fluid level after transmission is at normal operating temperature. *See Fluid Level in this article.*

Mitsubishi KM171

1) Remove drain plugs from both differential and oil pan and drain fluid. If replacing filter, remove bolts and lower oil pan. Install new filter on bottom of valve body. Replace pan gasket and install pan.

2) Tighten differential plug to 22-25 ft. lbs. (30-34 N.m) and pan plug to 18-21 ft. lbs. (24-28 N.m). Ensure that dipstick hole area is clean and pour in approximately 4.2 qts. (4.0L) of "DEXRON II" fluid.

3) Run engine for 2 minutes at idle. Shift transmission to each position, ending in "N" position. After reaching normal operating temperature, fluid should be between upper and lower marks of "HOT" range.

ADJUSTMENT

FRONT (KICKDOWN) BAND

Mitsubishi KM146 & Torqueflite MA904A

1) Front (kickdown) band adjuster screw is located on left side of transmission case. To adjust band, loosen and back off lock nut about 5 turns.

2) Using wrench (C-3380-A) with adapter (C-3705), tighten band adjuster screw to 52 INCH lbs. (5.9 N.m). *See Fig. 1.*

3) If adapter (C-3705) is not used, tighten adjuster screw to 51 INCH lbs. (5.8 N.m), which is the true torque. Back off adjusting screw 3 1/2 turns, hold adjuster screw and tighten lock nut to 37 ft. lbs. (50 N.m).

Fig. 1: Mitsubishi KM146 & Torqueflite MA904A Front (Kickdown) Band Adjusting Screw Location

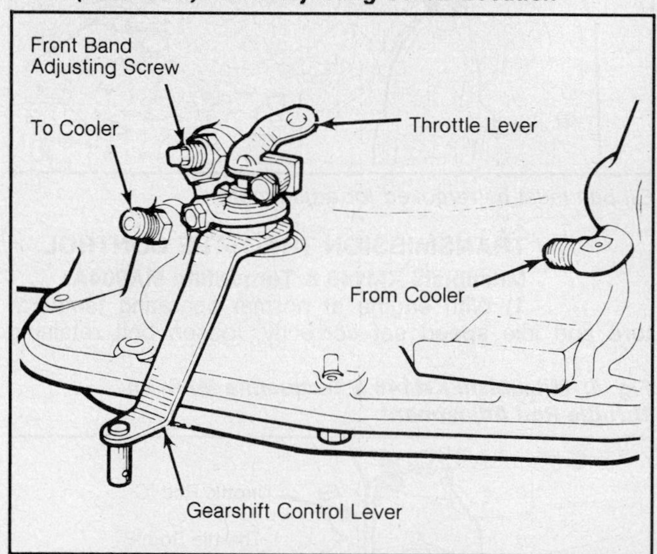
Front Band
Adjusting Screw
To Cooler
Throttle Lever
From Cooler
Gearshift Control Lever

Mitsubishi KM171

1) Clean all dirt from kickdown servo cover and remove snap ring. Remove cover and loosen lock nut. Hold servo piston from turning and tighten adjusting screw to 88 INCH lbs. (10 N.m) and back it off.

2) Repeat torquing twice to seat kickdown band against drum. Tighten adjusting screw to 44 INCH lbs. (5 N.m) and back off 3 1/2 turns. Hold screw and tighten lock nut. Install cover and snap ring.

NOTE: Install new seal ring with "D" shaped section to outside of cover. If reusing old seal ring, make certain it is not distorted.

MITSUBISHI (Cont.)

Fig. 2: Mitsubishi KM171 Kickdown Band Adjustment

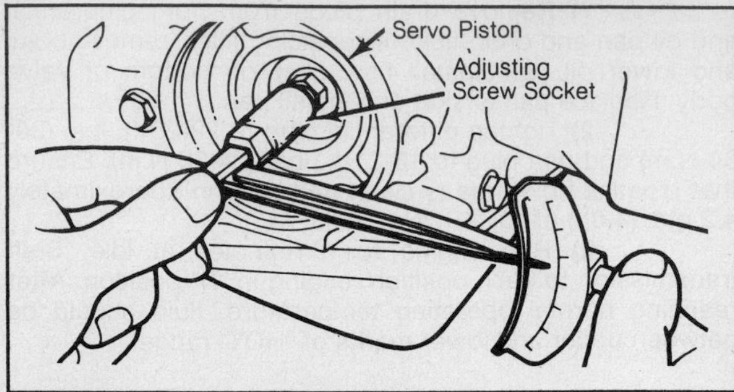
Servo Piston
Adjusting
Screw Socket

Hold piston and turn adjusting screw.

REAR BAND

Mitsubishi KM146 & Torqueflite MA904A

1) Remove oil pan. Loosen lock nut and adjusting screw at servo end of lever and tighten screw to 43 INCH lbs. (4.9 N.m) of torque.

2) Back off screw 7 turns. Hold adjusting screw and tighten lock nut to 29 ft. lbs. (40 N.m). Reinstall oil pan.

Fig. 3: Mitsubishi KM146 & Torqueflite MA904A Rear Band Adjusting Screw Location

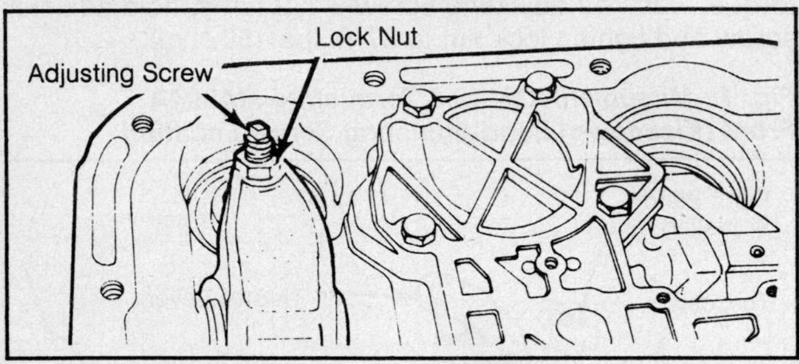
Lock Nut
Adjusting Screw

Oil pan must be removed for adjustment.

TRANSMISSION THROTTLE CONTROL

Mitsubishi KM146 & Torqueflite MA904A

1) With engine at normal operating temperature and idle speed set correctly, loosen bolt retaining throttle rod "C" to "B". Lightly push throttle rod "A" toward idle stop and set rods to "IDLE" position.

Fig. 4: Mitsubishi KM146 & Torqueflite MA904A Throttle Rod Adjustment

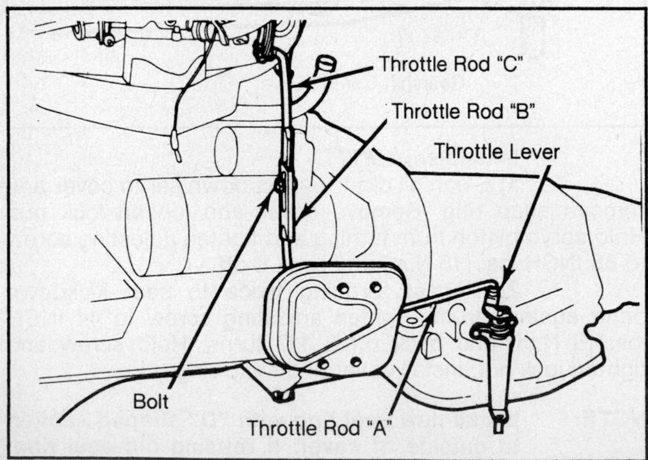
Throttle Rod "C"
Throttle Rod "B"
Throttle Lever
Bolt
Throttle Rod "A"

Make sure that transmission lever moves from "IDLE" to "WIDE OPEN" position.

2) Tighten bolt retaining rod "B" to "C". Open throttle to "WIDE OPEN" position. Make sure that transmission lever moves from "IDLE" to "WIDE OPEN" position (total movement 47.5° to 54°). Some play should still exist in throttle lever stroke at wide open throttle.

Mitsubishi KM171

1) Ensure that carburetor throttle lever is at "CURB IDLE" position, engine is at operating temperature, and fast idle condition has been reset. Raise cover "B" and loosen cable bracket mounting bolt.

2) Move lower cable bracket until distance between nipple and top cover "A" of throttle cable is adjusted to .02-.06" (.5-1.5 mm). *See Fig. 5.* Tighten lower cable bracket mounting bolt.

3) With throttle lever in "WIDE OPEN" position, pull cable upward to ensure freedom of cable movement.

Fig. 5: Mitsubishi KM171 Throttle Cable Adjustment

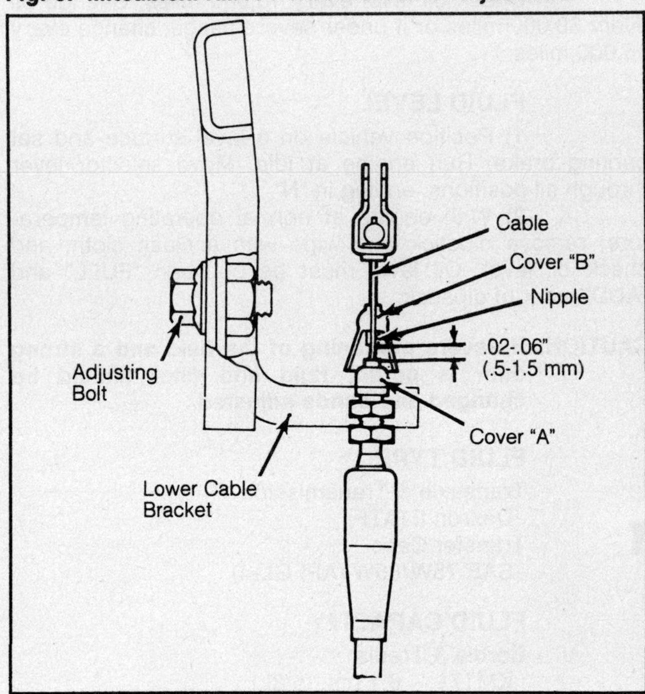
Cable
Cover "B"
Nipple
.02-.06"
(.5-1.5 mm)
Adjusting
Bolt
Cover "A"
Lower Cable
Bracket

Pull back cover "B" to loosen bracket nut.

SHIFT LINKAGE

Mitsubishi KM146 & Torqueflite MA904A

1) Remove shift handle by loosening set screw and pulling off handle. Place selector lever in "N" and turn

Fig. 6: Adjusting Selector Rod Cam On Mitsubishi KM146 & Torqueflite MA904A

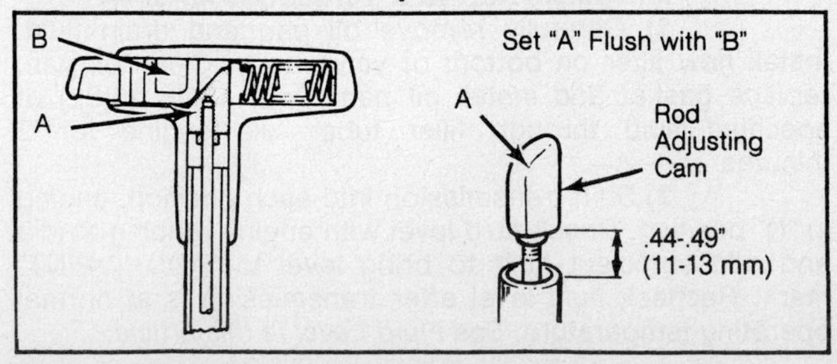
B
Set "A" Flush with "B"
A
A
Rod
Adjusting
Cam
.44-.49"
(11-13 mm)

Rod cam surface "A" and push button must be flush.

MITSUBISHI (Cont.)

adjusting cam in top of lever until surface "A" of cam is flush with push button. *See Fig. 6.*

2) Loosen lock nut at connection of rod and arm at transmission. Place transmission lever arm in "N". Place selector lever in "N" and tighten lock nut to adjust control rod length.

Mitsubishi KM171

1) Place selector in "N" position. Loosen set screw retaining handle to lever. Push selector knob and turn handle to give .008-.035" (.2-.9 mm) clearance between selector lever end pin and detent plate. *See Fig. 7.*

Fig. 7: Adjusting Selector Lever On Mitsubishi KM171 Transaxle

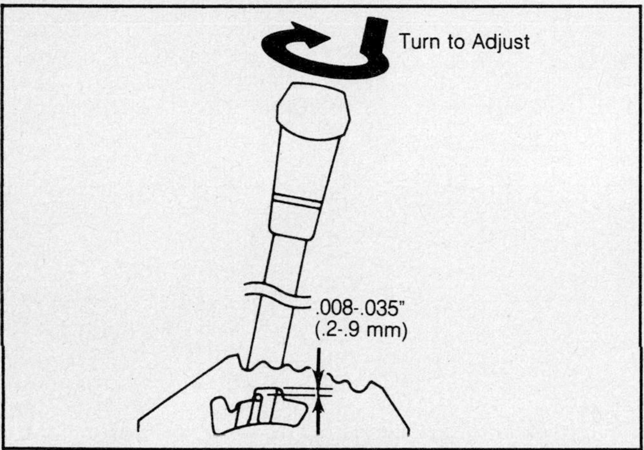
Turn to Adjust
.008-.035"
(.2-.9 mm)

To adjust, depress knob and turn handle.

2) When knob button is on driver's side, tighten set screw. With selector lever and neutral safety switch in "N" position, turn adjusting nuts at cable end until slack is removed from control cable.

NOTE: **After adjustment, confirm that every selector position of position indicator is set properly.**

Fig. 8: Adjusting Neutral Safety Switch Movement On Mitsubishi KM146 & Torqueflite MA904A

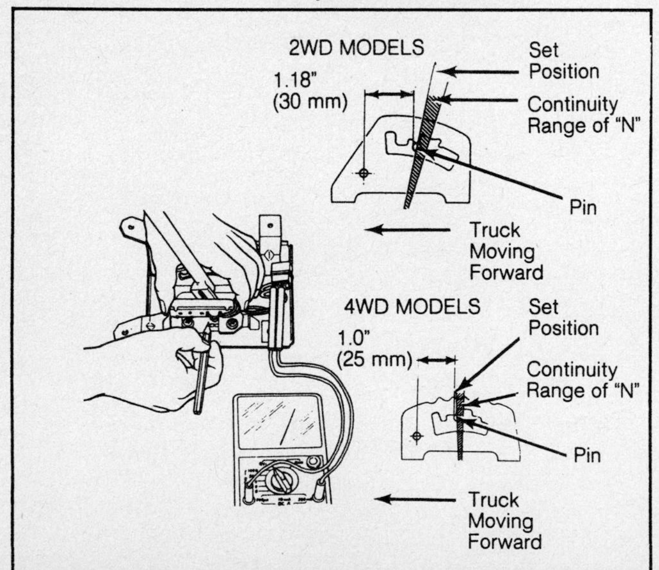
2WD MODELS
Set Position
1.18"
(30 mm)
Continuity Range of "N"
Pin
Truck Moving Forward
4WD MODELS
Set Position
1.0"
(25 mm)
Continuity Range of "N"
Pin
Truck Moving Forward

Connect tester to switch terminals (BY-BY).

NEUTRAL SAFETY SWITCH

Mitsubishi KM146 & Torqueflite MA904A

NOTE: **Safety switch is located under shift lever console and is operated by shift lever. This switch also operates back-up lights and seat belt warning system.**

1) To adjust switch, remove console, loosen switch attaching screws, and place selector lever in "N" position. Slide switch back and forth to measure contact range of "N" position. *See Fig. 8.*

2) Install switch and adjust so there is .06" (1.5 mm) for 2WD Pickup and .1" (2.5 mm) for 4WD Pickup, side clearance between selector lever and switch. *See Fig. 9.* Set selector lever in "P", "R", and "N" positions and check continuity of terminals. After confirming continuity, tighten switch attaching screws and reinstall console.

NOTE: **If correct continuity cannot be achieved, reposition safety switch.**

Fig. 9: Adjusting Neutral Safety Switch On Mitsubishi KM146 & Torqueflite MA904A

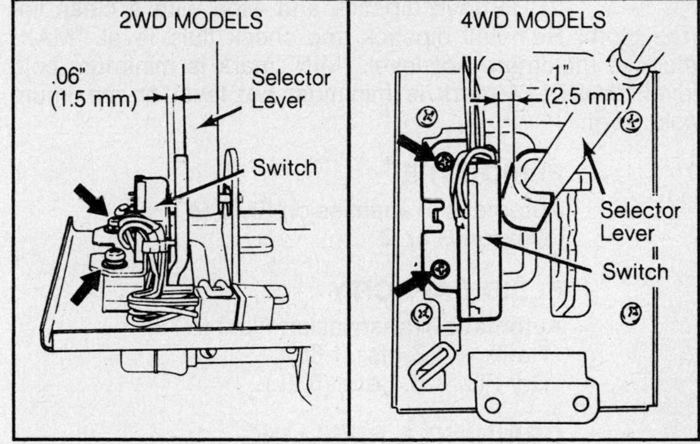
2WD MODELS
.06"
(1.5 mm)
Selector Lever
Switch
4WD MODELS
.1"
(2.5 mm)
Selector Lever
Switch

Mitsubishi KM171

Place transmission control lever in "N" position and loosen switch retaining bolts. Turn inhibitor switch body so that aligning hole end of lever overlaps switch body flange and tighten bolts. *See Fig. 10.*

Fig. 10: Adjusting Neutral Safety Switch On Mitsubishi KM171 Transaxle

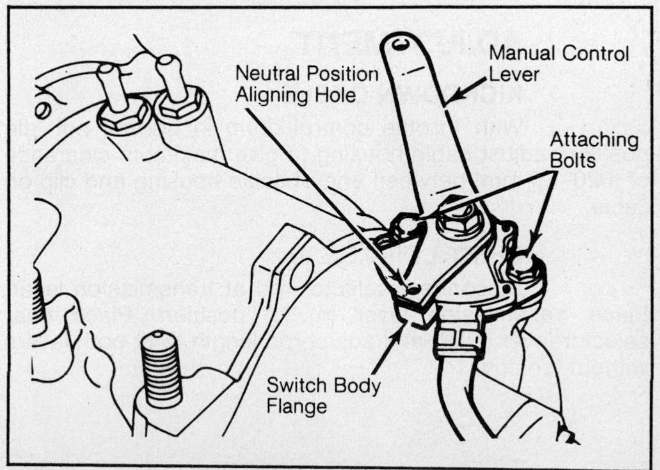
Neutral Position Aligning Hole
Manual Control Lever
Attaching Bolts
Switch Body Flange

Align lever hole with housing hole.

PEUGEOT

504, 505 & 604

IDENTIFICATION

TRANSMISSION CODES

Application	Codes
504, 505 & 604	ZF 3HP 22

LUBRICATION

SERVICE INTERVALS

Check transmission level at every oil change. Drain and refill transmission every 30,000 miles or 2 years, whichever comes first. In severe driving conditions change fluid at 12,500 miles.

FLUID LEVEL

1) Position vehicle on level floor and have engine at operating temperature. Apply parking brake, move selector lever through all positions ending in "P".

2) Remove dipstick and wipe with a clean lint free cloth. Reinstall dipstick and check fluid level. "MAX" mark is maximum hot level. "MIN" mark is minimum cold level. "MIDDLE" mark is minimum hot level or maximum cold level.

FLUID TYPE

Automatic Transmission Fluid (ATF)
Dexron B or D

FLUID CAPACITY

Automatic Transmission Fluid (ATF)
Refill – 1.7 qts. (1.6L)
Dry Fill – 5.4 qts. (5.2L)

DRAINING & REFILLING

1) Have engine at normal operating temperature. Remove drain plug from transmission oil pan, allow all fluid to drain and install drain plug. Pour approximate amount of fluid as listed in Fluid Capacity.

2) Start and run engine at normal idle. Shift selector lever through all positions, check fluid level, add fluid as needed. DO NOT overfill.

ADJUSTMENT

KICKDOWN CABLE

With throttle control drum in normal hot idle position, adjust cable housing to give maximum clearance of .020" (.5 mm) between end of cable housing and clip on cable.

SHIFT LINKAGE

Disconnect selector rod at transmission lever. Place transmission lever in "N" position. Place gear selector lever in "N" and adjust rod length to fit both levers without tension.

NEUTRAL SAFETY SWITCH

Engine should start in "N" or "P" positions only. To adjust, install or remove shims at base of switch until proper operation is achieved.

PORSCHE

928S & 944

IDENTIFICATION

TRANSMISSION CODES

Application	Code
928S	A22
944	087

LUBRICATION

SERVICE INTERVALS

Check fluid level every 15,000 miles. Change fluid and filter every 30,000 miles.

FLUID LEVEL

1) With vehicle on level floor, run engine until normal operating temperatures are reached. Shift selector lever to "N" or "P" position.

2) The fluid level is checked visually through the transparent reservior, located at the rear end of the transmission. Oil level must be between the 2 marks. Do not overfill.

FLUID TYPE

Automatic Transmission Fluid (ATF)
DEXRON B

FLUID CAPACITY

928S
Dry Fill - 6.3 qts. (6.0L)
Refill - 5.8 qts. (5.5L)
944
Dry Fill - 6.3 qts. (6.0L)
Oil cooler requires - .9 qts. (.8L)
Refill - 3.0 qts. (2.8L)

DRAINING & REFILLING

1) Place vehicle on level surface with engine at normal operating temprature. From oil pan, unscrew oil filler tube bolt and coupling nut on 928S (tube connector on 944) and turn tube so it can drain.

2) Turn crankshaft to expose converter drain plug. Remove drain plug. Remove oil pan and replace oil filter. Reverse removal procedures. *Refer to FLUID LEVEL in this article.*

ADJUSTMENT

SELECTOR LEVER

944

1) Move selector lever to "P" position. Loosen nut on clamping sleeve for selector lever cable. Move operating lever on transmission to "P" position (against stop). *See Fig. 1.*

2) Tighten nut on clamping sleeve. Move selector through all positions with engine running, engagement should be felt after 5 seconds.

Fig. 1: 944 Selector Lever Adjusting Point

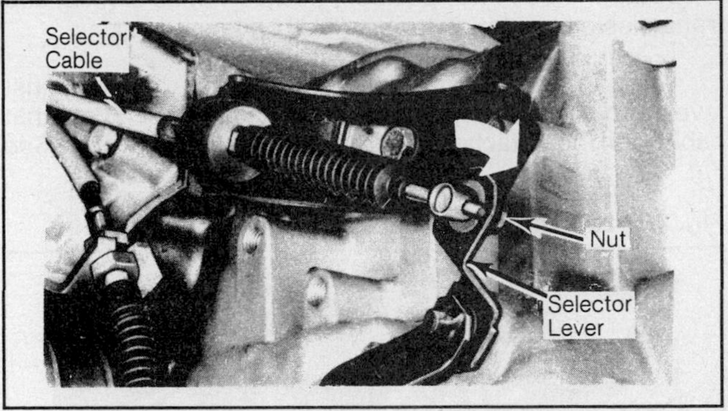
Selector Cable
Nut
Selector Lever

928S

1) Place selector lever in "N" position. Detach cable from operating lever on transmission. Place selector lever (on transmission) in "N" position.

2) Adjust cable so that socket attaches to operating lever without tension and reattach cable to lever. *See Fig. 2.*

Fig. 2: 928S Selector Lever Adjusting Point

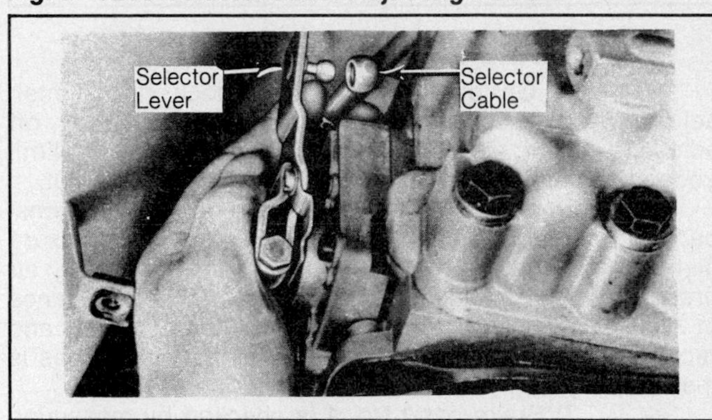
Selector Lever
Selector Cable

NEUTRAL SAFETY SWITCH

944

Starter should operate only in "P" or "N" positions. If starter operates in any other position, remove selector lever gate and loosen retaining bolts on safety switch. Adjust switch as necessary.

928S

Move selector lever to "N" position. Loosen adjusting screw, insert .157" (4 mm) pin through drive dog into hole in case. Tighten adjusting screw and remove locating pin. Check to see that engine starts in "N" or "P" positions only.

THROTTLE PRESSURE CABLE

944

1) Completely screw in mounting nut for cable sleeve on transmission bracket and ball socket, for transmission lever and mount. Relax cable sleeve on firewall and long cable sleeve on cam plate bracket.

2) Place and position cable around cam plate. Adjust long cable sleeve until clamping nipple is positioned in opening without tension. Adjust accelerator pedal cable to sleeve control without tension.

PORSCHE (Cont.)

3) When cable is adjusted correctly, accelerator pedal will be in idle position, throttle will be closed, and transmission operating lever will be on lower step.

928S

Detach cable at transmission lever. Adjust lever with adjusting bolt "A" after loosening bolt "B" so that cable can be attached without tension or free play. *See Fig. 3.*

Fig. 3: 928S Throttle Cable Pressure Adjustment

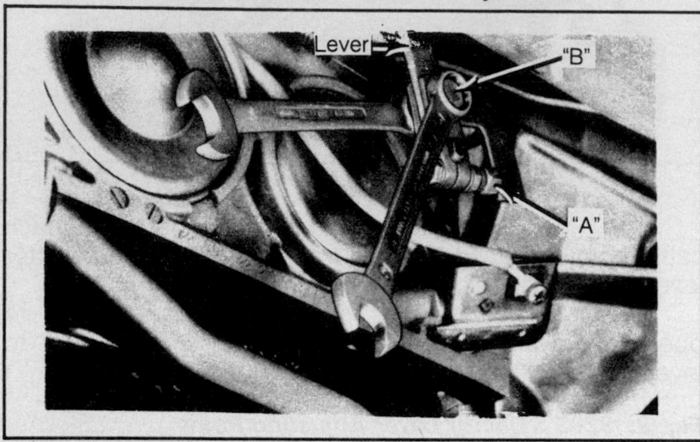
Lever
"B"
"A"

BRAKE BANDS

1) On all models. loosen lock nut, tighten adjusting screw to 84 INCH lbs. (10 N.m). Back off adjusting screw and retighten to 48 INCH lbs. (5 N.m). Loosen adjusting screw 1 3/4 turns and tighten lock nut.

2) On 928S models, there are 2 additional bands to adjust and they are adjusted with pins. Measure distance of free play for piston No. 2 by applying air pressure to No. 2 release port. *See Fig. 4.* Check distance at "B", then apply air pressure to No. 2 apply port and recheck distance "B". The difference of both distances is the free play.

3) Brake band No. 1 is checked by measuring the distance at "A". Apply air pressure to No. 1 apply port and recheck distance "A". The difference of both measurements is the free play. Free play of both bands should be .118-.157" (3-4 mm). Adjustments are made with adjustment pins.

Fig. 4: 928S Brake Band Measurement

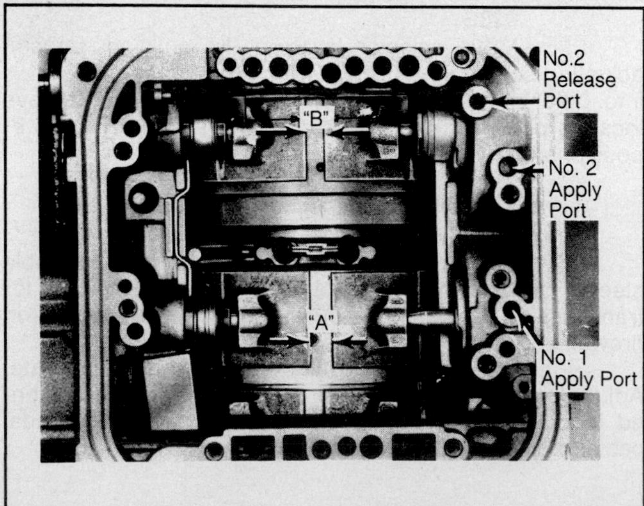
No.2 Release Port
"B"
No. 2 Apply Port
"A"
No. 1 Apply Port

RENAULT

Fuego & 18i

IDENTIFICATION

TRANSMISSION CODES

Application	Codes
Fuego & 18i	4139-65

LUBRICATION

SERVICE INTERVALS

Check fluid every 6,000 miles. Change fluid at first 1,000 miles and every 30,000 miles thereafter.

FLUID LEVEL

1) With vehicle on level floor, place selector lever in "P" position. Apply parking brake and start engine. Allow engine to idle. Remove dipstick, wipe clean, replace, and remove again.

2) With engine at normal operating temperature, fluid level should be between "Mini Hot" and "Maxi Hot" marks. With fluid level at ambient temperatures, level should be between "Mini Cold" marks.

NOTE: If level is not correct, add fluid to bring level to correct mark, do not overfill.

FLUID TYPE

Automatic Transmission Fluid (ATF)
Dexron II

FLUID CAPACITY

Dry Fill – 5.2 qts. (5.0L)
Refill – 2.7 qts. (2.5L)

ADJUSTMENTS

KICKDOWN SWITCH

Make sure that the accelerator cable has sufficient play to allow a .12-.16" (3-4 mm) movement in the stop sleeve when accelerator pedal is completely depressed. Make sure that cover is in position to prevent tarnishing of contacts. *See Fig. 1.*

Fig. 1: Adjusting Kickdown Switch

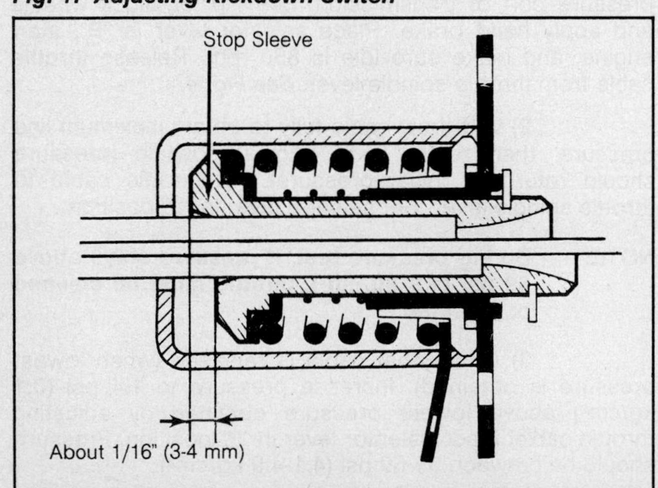
Stop Sleeve
About 1/16" (3-4 mm)

Adjust kickdown switch before adjusting other components.

ACCELERATOR CABLE

Depress accelerator fully to wide open throttle. Adjust accelerator cable to obtain .080" (2 mm) compression of spring in the cable stop. *See Fig. 2.*

Fig. 2: Adjusting Accelerator Cable

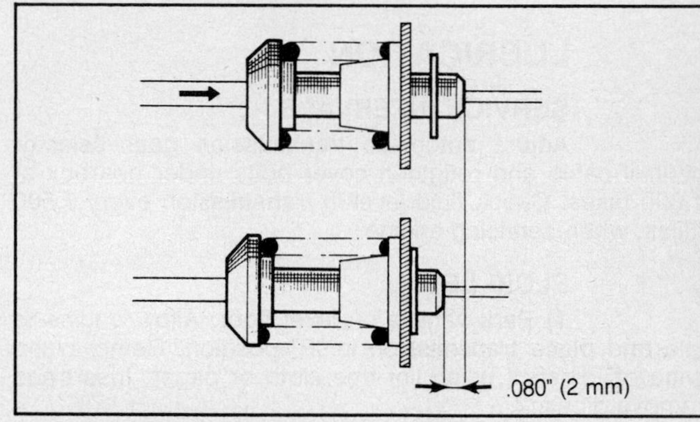
.080" (2 mm)

Make sure kickdown switch is functioning correctly.

GOVERNOR CABLE

Adjust cable adjusters on both governor and throttle sides to midway. Adjust cable stop to obtain a clearance of .008-.028" (.20-.70 mm). *See Fig. 3.*

Fig. 3: Adjusting Governor Cable.

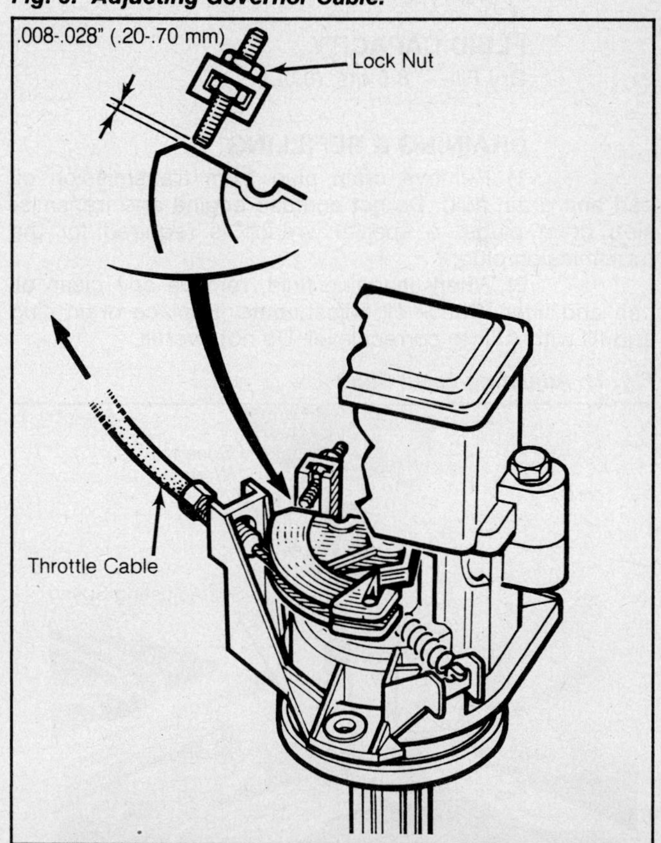
.008-.028" (.20-.70 mm)
Lock Nut
Throttle Cable

All other components must be operating properly before adjusting governor.

SAAB

900 Series

IDENTIFICATION

TRANSMISSION CODES

Application	Transmission (Code)
All Models	Borg-Warner (37)

LUBRICATION

SERVICE INTERVALS

Adjust automatic transmission gear selector control cable and retigthen cover bolts under gearbox at 1,000 miles. Check fluid level in transmission every 7,500 miles, when servicing engine.

FLUID LEVEL

1) Park vehicle on level floor. Allow engine to idle and place transmission in "P" position. Remove and wipe off dipstick using lint free cloth or paper. Insert and remove dipstick.

2) Fluid level should be between the maximum and minimum marks on the dipstick. Be sure to read hot or cold markings on dipstick, depending on transmission oil temperature. Do not overfill.

FLUID TYPE

Automatic Transmission Fluid (ATF)
Ford Type "F"

FLUID CAPACITY

Dry Fill - 8.5 qts. (8.0L)

DRAINING & REFILLING

1) Remove drain plug from transmission oil pan and drain fluid. Do not confuse engine and transmission drain plugs. A special wrench is required for the transmission plug.

2) When changing fluid, remove and clean oil pan and filter. Check all adjustments. Replace drain plug and fill with ATF to correct level. Do not overfill.

Fig. 1: Adjusting Front Band

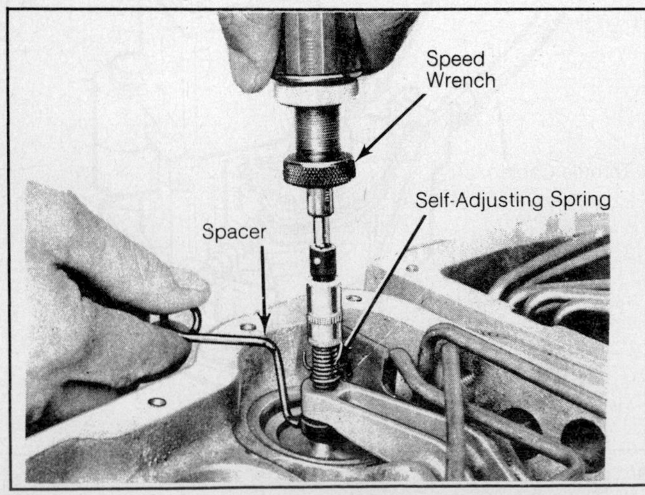
Speed Wrench
Self-Adjusting Spring
Spacer

Pan must be removed to adjust front band.

ADJUSTMENT

FRONT BAND

Up To Serial No. 001-1700 & 002-1800

Drain fluid and remove oil pan. Place a .25" (6.35 mm) thick Spacer Tool (8790073) between adjusting screw and boss on servo piston. Tighten adjusting screw to 9 INCH lbs. (1 N.m). Back off screw 1 turn and while holding in position, tighten lock nut. *See Fig. 1.*

From Serial No. 001-1701 & 002-1801

Drain fluid and remove oil pan. Place a .35" (8.9 mm) thick Spacer Tool between adjusting screw and boss on servo piston. Tighten adjusting screw to 9 INCH lbs. (1 N.m) and while holding in position (DO NOT back off screw), tighten lock nut. *See Fig. 1.*

REAR BAND

Rear band adjusting screw is located outside transmission housing on left side. To adjust band, loosen lock nut a few turns and tighten adjusting screw to 106-124 INCH lbs. (12-14 N.m). Back screw off 1 1/4 turn and hold in position while tightening lock nut. *See Fig. 2.*

Fig. 2: Adjusting Rear Band

Torque Wrench
Square Socket

Adjustment is made on left side of transmission.

TRANSMISSION THROTTLE CABLE

1) Connect a precision pressure gauge to pressure port of transmission. *See Fig. 3.* Block wheels and apply hand brake. Place selector lever in "P", start engine, and make sure idle is 850 rpm. Release throttle cable from throttle spindle lever. *See Fig. 4.*

2) Withdraw cable fully to obtain maximum line pressure, then return it to original position (pressure should return to initial pressure). Fit throttle cable to throttle spindle lever. Set selector lever in "D" position.

NOTE: During pressure test, if pressure stays above 69 psi (4.9 kg/cm²), throttle must be cleaned or adjusted.

3) Check that cable is released (when lowest pressure is obtained). Increase pressure to 1.4 psi (0.1 kg/cm²) above lowest pressure obtained by adjusting throttle cable. Place selector lever in "P" position. Pressure should be between 59-69 psi (4.1-4.9 kg/cm²).

SAAB (Cont.)

Fig. 3: Pressure Gauge Connecting Point for Throttle Pressure Test

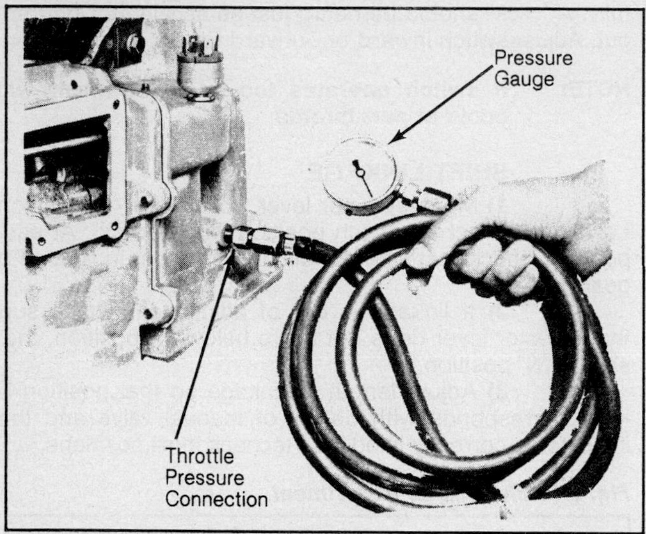
Pressure
Gauge
Throttle
Pressure
Connection

SHIFT LINKAGE

1) To check linkage adjustment, depress pawl button and move lever slightly back and forth until a "click" can be heard and you feel the selector valve lock in the "N" position.

2) Release pawl button and selector lever should now be in "N" position. To adjust, loosen cable attachment at lever with Allen wrench and extend while selector valve is locked in "N" position. Move lever to position pawl in notch on selector segment and tighten cable set screw.

Fig. 4: Shift Selector Segment with "N" Detent

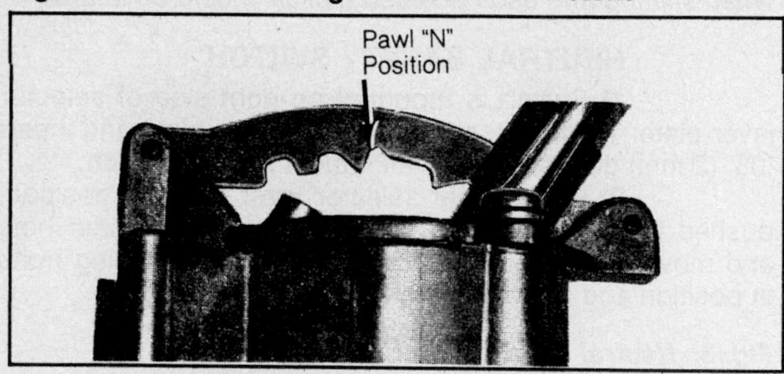
Pawl "N"
Position

NEUTRAL SAFETY SWITCH

Place selector lever in "N" position. Loosen securing screws. Rotate switch housing to line up lever with mark on switch housing. Tighten securing screws.

SUBARU

1800 & 1800 Turbo

IDENTIFICATION

TRANSMISSION CODES

Application	Transmission (Code)
1800 2WD	Model Gunma (C)
1800 4WD & Turbo	Model Gunma (F)

LUBRICATION

SERVICE INTERVALS

Check fluid level in transmission every 5 months or 15,000 miles, whichever comes first. Transmission fluid should be changed every 30,000 miles and band adjusted as necessary.

FLUID LEVEL

1) Normal operating temperature for fluid is 140-176°F (60-80°C) and is reached after driving for 10 minutes or idling for 25 minutes. With vehicle parked on level floor and at normal operating temperature.

2) Set transmission selector lever in "P" position with engine idling. Remove dipstick and clean with lint-free cloth. Insert and remove dipstick, note fluid level and add through dipstick hole to bring to full mark. When filling transmission, do not overfill.

FLUID TYPE

Automatic Transmission Fluid (ATF)
Dexron

FLUID CAPACITY

1800 – 5.9-6.3 qts. (5.6-6.0L)
1800 4WD & Turbo – 6.3-6.8 qts. (6.0-6.4L)

NOTE: **Fluid capacity of transfer case is part of 1800 4WD and Turbo specification.**

DRAINING & REFILLING

Remove drain plug and drain fluid. Replace drain plug and fill transmission with about 4 quarts of ATF. Start engine and check fluid level with engine idling. Add fluid as necessary, do not overfill.

ADJUSTMENT

REAR BAND

Loosen lock nut on band adjusting screw and tighten screw to 78 INCH lbs. (9 N.m). Loosen screw 2 turns and hold in position while tightening lock nut.

Fig. 1: Rear Band Adjustment

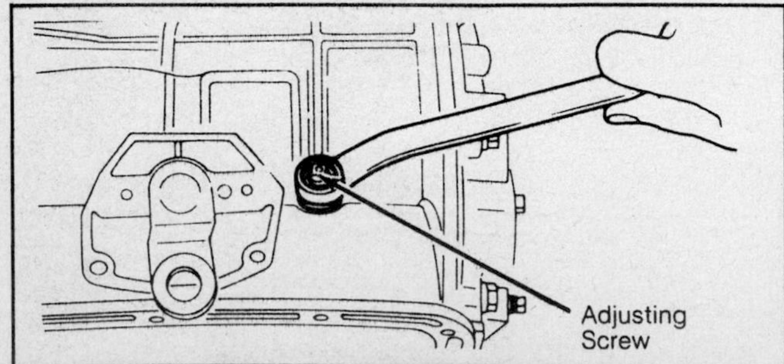
Adjusting
Screw

Adjustment is made at left side of transaxle.

KICKDOWN SWITCH

Switch ignition "ON" and depress accelerator fully. A "click" should be heard just as accelerator bottoms out. Adjust switch inward or outward for proper operation.

NOTE: **If switch operates too soon, downshift will occur at part throttle.**

SHIFT LINKAGE

1) Move selector lever from "P" to "1" position. Lever should set into each position with a "click". At each position, check that selector dial gives proper indication of gear position.

2) If linkage is out of adjustment, make sure that selector lever does not move below "1" position, then shift to "N" position.

3) Adjust length of linkage so that position of lever corresponds with detent of manual valve and that indicator is correctly lined up. Recheck in all positions.

Fig. 2: Shift Linkage Adjustment

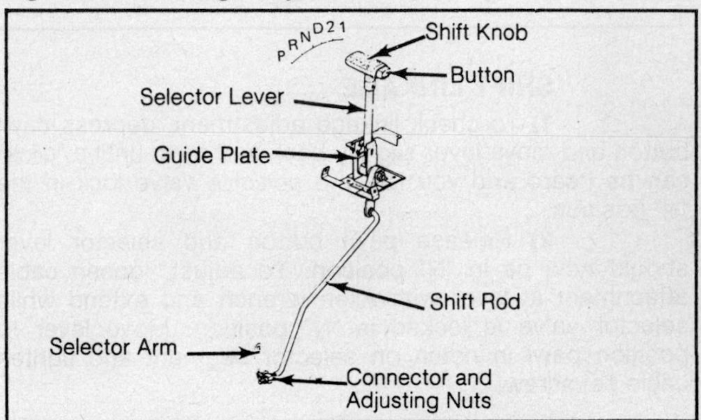
PRND21
Shift Knob
Button
Selector Lever
Guide Plate
Shift Rod
Selector Arm
Connector and
Adjusting Nuts

When shifting into each position a click should be heard.

NEUTRAL SAFETY SWITCH

1) Switch is mounted on right side of selector lever plate. To adjust, remove switch from plate and insert .08" (2 mm) diameter pin in alignment hole on switch.

2) Ensure that selector lever is in "N" position, pushed lightly toward "P". Match locator to bracket hole and moving plate pin to arm hole. Tighten retaining bolts in position and remove alignment pin.

Fig. 3: Neutral Safety Switch Adjustment

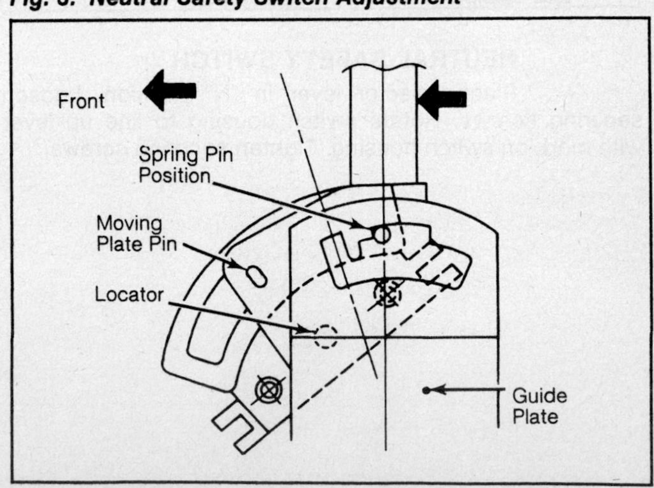
Front
Spring Pin
Position
Moving
Plate Pin
Locator
Guide
Plate

Insert a .08" (2 mm) diameter pin to align hole in switch.

TOYOTA

Camry, Celica, Corolla, Cressida, Supra, Tercel & Pickup

IDENTIFICATION

TRANSMISSION CODES

Application	Code
Camry (FWD)	A140E
Celica (RWD)	A40D
Corolla (RWD)	A40D & A41
Cressida & Supra (RWD)	A43DE
Pickup (RWD)	A43D
Tercel (FWD)	A55

LUBRICATION

SERVICE INTERVALS

Check transmission fluid every 15,0000 miles. In servere conditions change transmission fluid every 15,-000 miles.

FLUID LEVEL

Check transmission fluid level with engine idling. Shift each gear from "P" through "L" and back to "P". Fluid level should be within cold or hot ranges marked on dipstick. Do not overfill.

FLUID TYPE

A40D, A43D, & A43DE
Type "F" (AFT)
A41, A55, & A140E
Dexron II (AFT)

FLUID CAPACITY

Camry
Dry – 6.3 qts. (6.0L)
Refill – 2.5 qts. (2.4L)
Celica
Dry Fill – 6.7 qts. (6.3L)
Refill – 2.5 qts. (2.4L)
Corolla
A40D
Dry – 6.2 qts. (5.9L)
Refill – 2.5 qts. (2.4L)
A41
Dry – 5.8 qts. (5.5L)
Refill – 2.4 qts. (2.3L)
Cressida, Pickup, & Supra
Dry Fill – 6.9 qts. (6.5L)
Refill – 2.5 qts. (2.4L)
Tercel
Dry Fill – 4.8 qts. (4.5L)
Refill – 2.5 qts. (2.4L)

DRAINING & REFILLING

1) Remove drain plug and drain fluid. Remove oil pan retaining bolts. Remove oil pan and filter screens. Clean filter screens and dry with compressed air. Install screens, oil pan, and a new pan gasket.

2) Repeat tightening several times until torque remains constant, taking care not to over tighten bolts. Replace drain plug and fill transmission with approximately 2 quarts of ATF fluid. Start engine and select all gears. Check fluid level and add additional fluid as necessary. Do not overfill.

ADJUSTMENTS

FLOOR SHIFTER LINKAGE

Place transmission shift lever in "N" position and adjust shift rod until shift lever indicates "N" position correctly. Holding shift selector lightly toward "R" position, tighten lock nuts. Check that all ranges are correctly engaged.

Fig. 1: Floor Shift Linkage Assembly

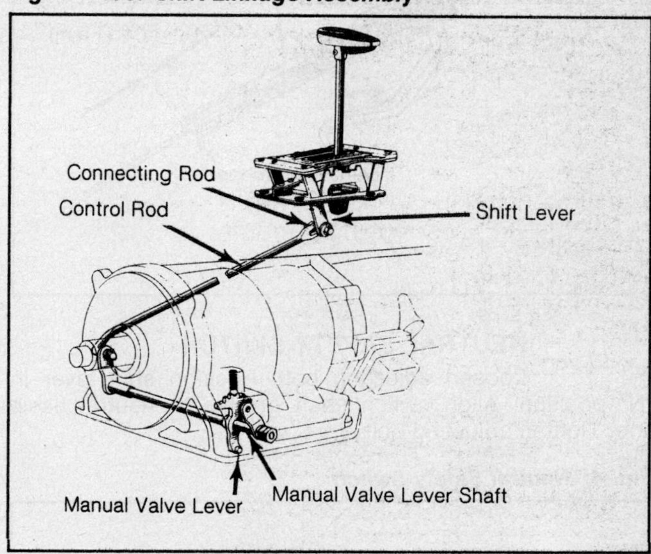
Connecting Rod
Control Rod
Shift Lever
Manual Valve Lever
Manual Valve Lever Shaft

THROTTLE CABLE

Remove air cleaner. Check throttle cable bracket and linkage for looseness or bending. Depress accelerator to wide open throttle position. Adjust cable housing so distance between rubber boot end and inner cable stopper is .04" (1 mm). Tighten lock nut.

Fig. 2: Adjusting Throttle Cable

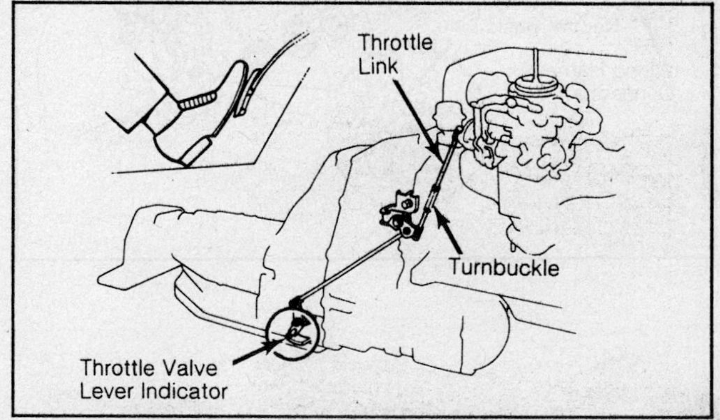
Throttle
Link
Turnbuckle
Throttle Valve
Lever Indicator

TOYOTA (Cont.)

THROTTLE LINK

Tercel

1) Remove air cleaner. Check throttle cable bracket and linkage for looseness or bending. Depress accelerator to wide open throttle position.

2) Adjust linkage by turning turnbuckle until throttle valve lever indicator lines up with mark on transmission case. Tighten lock nut.

Fig. 3: Tercel Throttle Link Adjustment

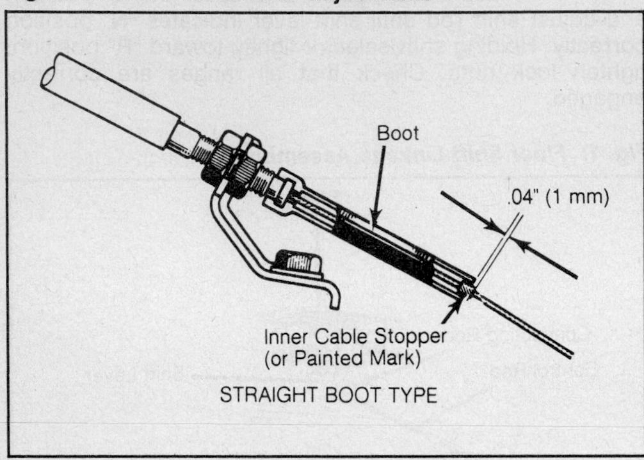
Boot
.04" (1 mm)
Inner Cable Stopper
(or Painted Mark)
STRAIGHT BOOT TYPE

NEUTRAL SAFETY SWITCH

Loosen adjusting bolt. Position shift lever in "N" position. Align switch shaft groove to neutral basic line. Tighten adjusting bolt.

Fig. 4: Neutral Safety Switch

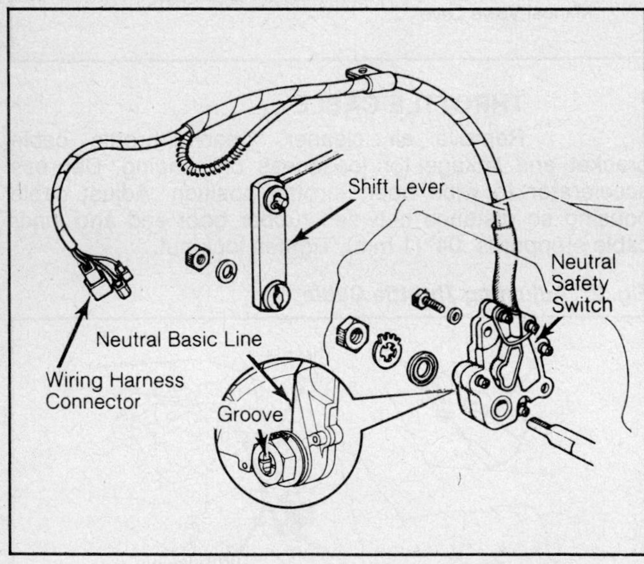
Shift Lever
Neutral
Safety
Switch
Neutral Basic Line
Wiring Harness
Connector
Groove

VOLKSWAGEN

Jetta, Rabbit, Pickup,
Quantum, Scirocco & Vanagon

IDENTIFICATION

TRANSMISSION CODES

Appication	Code
Jetta, Rabbit, Pickup & Scirocco	010
Quantum	089
Vanagon	090

LUBRICATION

SERVICE INTERVALS

Check fluid level every 15,000 miles. Change fluid every 30,000 miles under normal conditions, or every 15,000 miles under heavy duty conditions.

FLUID LEVEL

With transmission warm and engine idling in neutral, check that ATF fluid is between marks on dipstick. The ring shaped handle should be in a vertical position when checking level. The difference in fluid quantity between upper and lower marks is only .4 qts. (.37L).

FLUID TYPE

Automatic Transmission Fluid (ATF)
Dexron or Dexron II

FLUID CAPACITY

All Models
Dry Fill – 6.4 qts. (6.0L)
Refill – 3.2 qts. (3.0L)

DRAINING & REFILLING

1) Remove drain plug from oil pan and allow as much fluid to drain as possible. Remove oil pan and filter screen. Clean screen and air dry with compressed air. Do not use cleaning rags to dry filter screen.

2) Replace oil pan and screen using new gasket. Tighten oil pan bolts to 168 INCH lbs. (19 N.m) in a diagonal pattern. Wait 5 minutes for gasket to compress and retighten bolts. Repeat several times until bolts remain at proper torque value. Do not over tighten.

3) Fill transmission with 2.5 qts. (2.4L) of ATF fluid. Warm up transmission fluid and top-up to proper level, as in Fluid Level.

ADJUSTMENT

BRAKE BAND

With transmission in a horizontal position adjust brake band. Tighten 2nd gear brake band adjusting screw to 84 INCH lbs. (10 N.m). Loosen adjusting screw, then tighten again to 48 INCH lbs. (5 N.m). Back off screw 2 1/2 turns, then tighten lock nut to 168 INCH lbs. (19 N.m).

Fig. 1: Brake Band Adjusting Location

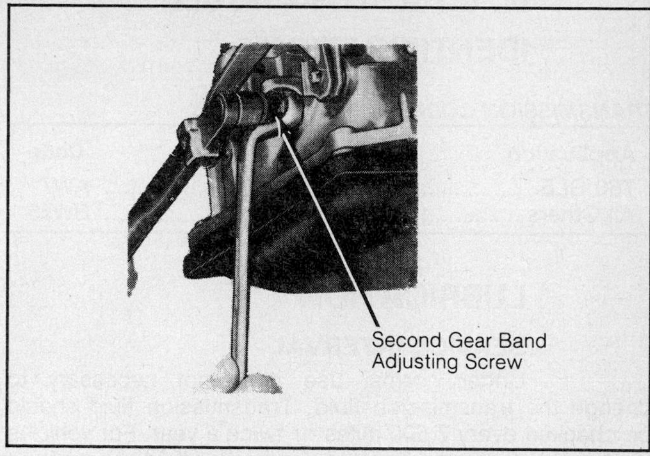
Second Gear Band
Adjusting Screw

KICKDOWN SWITCH

Vanagon

Rotate throttle lever open until there is a gap of .040-.060" (1.0-1.5 mm) between lever and stop. Adjust position of switch so it operates with throttle lever in this position.

SELECTOR LEVER CABLE

Jetta, Rabbit, Pickup, & Scirocco

Place transmission in "P" position. Loosen nut for clamping pin which retains selector cable to operating lever on transaxle. Ensure that selector lever and operating lever are in "P" position. Tighten cable clamping nut to 72 INCH lbs. (8 N.m).

Quantum

Place shift selector lever into "P" position. Loosen clamping nut and press shift lever on transmission into park. Tighten nut on cable clamp to 72 INCH lbs. (8 N.m).

Vanagon

Place transmission lever in "P" position. Loosen bolt which retains shift rod to operating lever on transaxle. Ensure that selector lever and operating lever are in "P" position. Push shift rod to rear and tighten bolt.

NEUTRAL SAFETY SWITCH

Neutral safety switch is located in shift console. Remove console cover and adjust switch so that it makes contact only in "P" and "N" positions.

VOLVO

DL, GL, GL Turbo & 760 GLE

IDENTIFICATION

TRANSMISSION CODES

Application	Code
760 GLE	AW71
All Others	BW55

LUBRICATION

SERVICE INTERVAL

Under normal use it is not necessary to change the transmission fluid. Transmission fluid should be checked every 7,500 miles or twice a year. For vehicles in heavy duty service, transmission fluid should be changed every 25,000 miles.

FLUID LEVEL

1) Position vehicle on level floor. Apply parking brake and shift selector lever into "P" position. Start engine and let idle. Shift selector lever through all gears pausing 4-5 seconds for engagement at each position.

2) Return selector lever to "P". Wait 2 minutes, then remove dipstick. Wipe dipstick off with lint free cloth and reinsert. Withdraw dipstick and check reading. Level must be between "MIN" and "MAX" marks. If not, add (or remove) fluid to obtain correct level.

FLUID TYPE

Automatic Transmission Fluid (ATF)
Type "F" or "G"

FLUID CAPACITY

BW55
- Dry
  - With Overdrive – 7.8 qts. (7.4L)
  - Without Overdrive – 7.1 qts. (6.8L)
- Refill – 3.2 qts (3L)

AW71 – 7.9 qts. (7.5L)

ADJUSTMENT

THROTTLE & KICKDOWN CABLES

1) Transmission cable should be stretched in idle position. Distance between clip and sheath should be .010-.040" (.25-1.0 mm). *See Fig. 1.*

2) Pull transmission cable out by hand approximately .39-.59" (10-15 mm), and release. A distinct "click" should be heard from transmission, indicating cable moves freely and throttle cam returns to initial position.

3) Depress accelerator pedal completely. The transmission cable should travel 1.992-2.024" (47-55 mm), from idle position to full throttle position. *See Fig. 1.*

GEAR SELECTOR

1) Press on gear selector and check that clearance from "D" to stop is approximately the same as from "2" to stop. If clearance is incorrect, control rod needs adjustment.

2) Adjustment is made by turning clevis in or out on control rod. Maximum visible thread length permitted is 1.1" (28 mm).

Fig. 1: Checking Throttle Controls

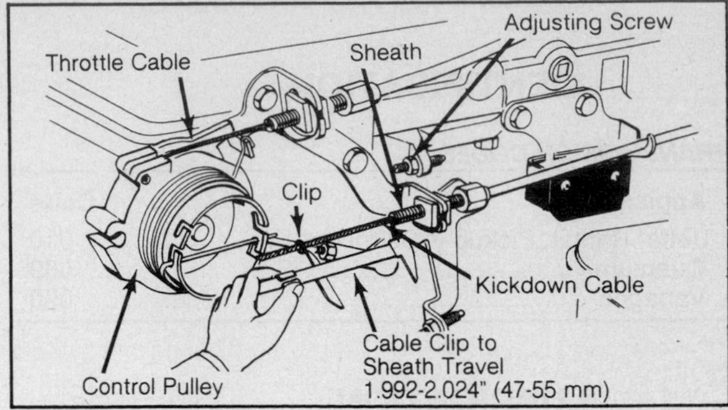
Adjusting Screw
Throttle Cable
Sheath
Clip
Kickdown Cable
Cable Clip to
Sheath Travel
1.992-2.024" (47-55 mm)
Control Pulley

3) Increasing rod length reduces position "D" clearance. Decreasing rod length increases position "D" clearance. Shift to position "1" then to position "P" for recheck. *See Fig. 2.*

Fig. 2: Gear Selector Adjustment

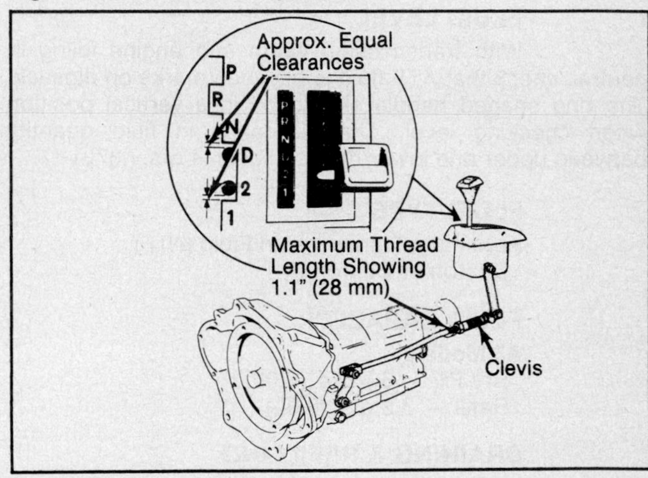
Approx. Equal
Clearances
P
R
N
D
2
1
Maximum Thread
Length Showing
1.1" (28 mm)
Clevis

NEUTRAL SAFETY SWITCH

1) Switch is located at and directly controlled by the gear shift control lever. Place selector lever in "P" position. Adjust neutral safety switch to set "P" mark at center of switch lever.

2) Place selector lever in "N" position. Confirm "N" mark is at center of switch lever. Move selector lever from "P" to "1" and back again.

3) Check that control pin does not slide out of switch lever. *See Fig. 3.* Check that engine only starts in "P" and "N", and that the back-up lights illuminate in position "R" only.

Fig. 3: Adjusting Neutral Safety Switch

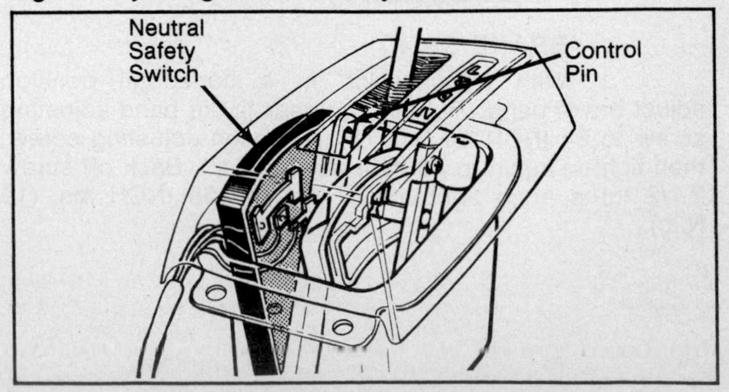
Neutral
Safety
Switch
Control
Pin

Latest Changes & Corrections

FOR 1983 & EARLIER MODELS

TUNE-UP

1 PEUGEOT 4-CYLINDER GASOLINE MODELS: INCORRECT FIRING ORDER AND DISTRIBUTOR ROTATION ILLUSTRATION – In some editions of the Imported Car Service and Repair Manual and Imported Emission Control Service and Repair Manual, an incorrect Peugeot illustration is shown. This illustration is for Peugeot Firing Order and Distributor Rotation, and shows an incorrect cylinder numbering and distibutor rotation. Instead of cylinder numbering 1-2-3-4 from front-to-rear, it should be 4-3-2-1 from front-to-rear. In addition, the distributor rotation should be clockwise, instead of counterclockwise. The correct illustration appears below.

Peugeot 505 Firing Order & Distributor Rotation

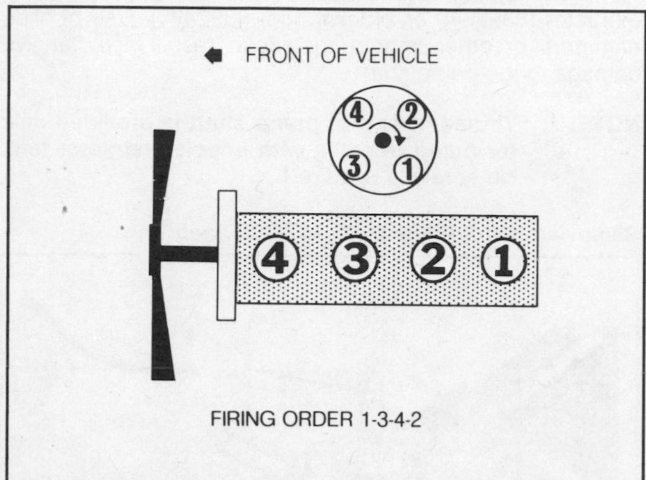
FRONT OF VEHICLE
4
2
3
1
4
3
2
1
FIRING ORDER 1-3-4-2

2 1981-83 SAAB MODELS: INCORRECT DISTRIBUTOR LOCATION ILLUSTRATION – In the 1981-82 Imported Car Service and Repair Manual and the 1982-83 Imported Car Emission Control Service and Repair Manual, there is an incorrect Saab illustration. The illustration in the Tune-Up article showing Saab Firing Order and Distributor Rotation shows the distributor at the left side of the engine. This is incorrect. The distributor is located at the front of the engine on Saab models.

Saab Firing Order and Distributor Rotation

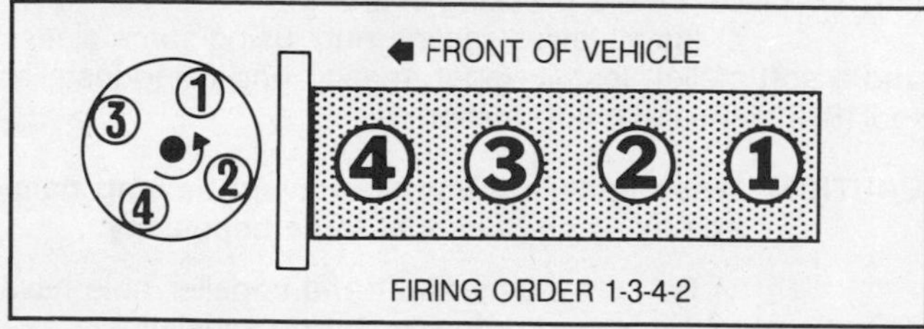
FRONT OF VEHICLE
3
1
2
4
4
3
2
1
FIRING ORDER 1-3-4-2

FUEL SYSTEMS

3 1981 BOSCH AFC FUEL INJECTION: JAPANESE MODELS: INCORRECT OHMMETER READING ON AIR FLOW METER TEST CHART – On page 2-81, in the 1981 Imported Car Service and Repair Manual and page 347 in the 1981 Imported Car Emission Control Service and Repair Manual, shows an incorrect ohmmeter reading in the Air Flow Meter Resistance Chart. The last word on bottom line should read "Infinity" instead of "Continuity".

4 1982-83 DATSUN/NISSAN MAXIMA DIESEL MODELS: CORRECTION TO INJECTION PUMP INSTALLATION INSTRUCTIONS – The note for installation of the diesel fuel injection pump is incorrect in the Fuel Systems Section of the 1982 Imported Car Service and Repair Manual and the 1982-83 Imported Car Emission Control Service and Repair Manual.

The following note is incorrect as it appears in these manuals:

NOTE: **There are two grooves and two aligning marks on the drive gear. Use the groove and mark without the "A" marking to position the gear.**

Use the following note for correct information:

NOTE: **There are two grooves and three drive belt aligning marks on the drive gear. Use the groove and aligning mark with the "B" marking to position the gear.**

5 TOYOTA COROLLA MODELS WITH AISAN CARBURETOR: INCORRECT ENGINE IDENTIFICATION – In the 1983 Imported Car Emission Manual, the engine usage was incorrectly identified. On pages 370-372 of the Aisan Carburetor article, the carburetor is for 4A-C engines not 3T-C engines formerly used in Corolla models. The carburetor information given in the article is correct, only the engine identification is wrong.

ELECTRICAL

6 1981-83 BMW MODELS WITH TRIP COMPUTER: JUMP STARTING PRECAUTIONS – BMW models with trip computers can be extensively damaged using normal starting procedures, unless a fuse is removed from the fuse block prior to connecting the battery jumper cables. On 1983 633CSi models, the fuse is number 27. On 1983 733i models, the fuse is number 21. On all other models, the fuse is number 5.

The fuse block is located under the hood on the fender well with a clear plastic cover over the fuse block. If the fuse is not removed prior to jump starting, the car may not start, or the trip computer may be permanently damaged. Repairing a trip computer may cost as much as $1,000. If there is any doubt about the proper procedure or fuse, do not jump start the car.

7 1983 MITSUBISHI STARION TURBO MODELS: FUSES & CIRCUIT BREAKERS – Fuse protected circuits was omitted in the Fuses and Circuit Breakers section of the 1983 Import Car Service and Repair Manual. The fuses are numbered 1-5 on one side and 6-12 on the other side, from top to bottom. Circuits protected are:

1 - 10A Dome Light
2 - 15A Stop Lights
3 - 15A Hazard Flashers
4 - 10A Headlight Pop-Up Motors
5 - 15A Tail Lights
6 - 20A Heater
7 - 15A Horn
8 - 15A Wiper
9 - 10A Radio
10 - 10A Gauges

Latest Changes & Corrections

FOR 1983 & EARLIER MODELS (Cont.)

11 - 10A Turn Signals
12 - 10A Backup Lights

In-Line Fuses

In-line fusible links are located at the main battery cable, at the relay box near the inner right front wheel fender and the left front inner fender.

ENGINES

8 ALL AUDI MODELS WITH 100 LS ENGINE: DIAMETER PISTON CLEARANCE AND CONNECTING ROD DIAMETER SPECIFICATIONS - On Audi models using the 100 LS engine, the piston clearance should be .0012" (.030 mm). The connecting rod diameter should be 1.8898" (48.000 mm).

9 1977-1982 FIAT STRADA, 128 & X1/9 ENGINE: TIGHTENING SPECIFICATION TABLE - In the 1977-82 Imported Car Service and Repair Manuals, the camshaft housing tightening specification is missing from the tightening specification table. Tighten the camshaft housing nuts to 14.5 ft. lbs. (19 N.m).

10 1976-79 HONDA CIVIC CVCC & ACCORD 4-CYLINDER ENGINE: INCORRECT VALVE TIMING PROCEDURE - In the 1976-79 Imported Car Service and Repair Manual, Valve Timing procedure, the text says to: "Align TDC mark on flywheel. Rotate camshaft until Woodruff key is pointing straight up and timing marks on pulley are parallel with top of cylinder head. *See Fig.*" The accompanying illustration shows the timing marks parallel with the cylinder head. This procedure and illustration are incorrect.

The correct procedure, is to rotate crankshaft until TDC mark on flywheel or driveplate is aligned with index mark. "UP" mark on camshaft gear should be at the 11 o'clock position and timing mark aligned with arrow on cylinder head.

Camshaft Alignment Marks for Honda Civic & Accord Valve Timing Procedure

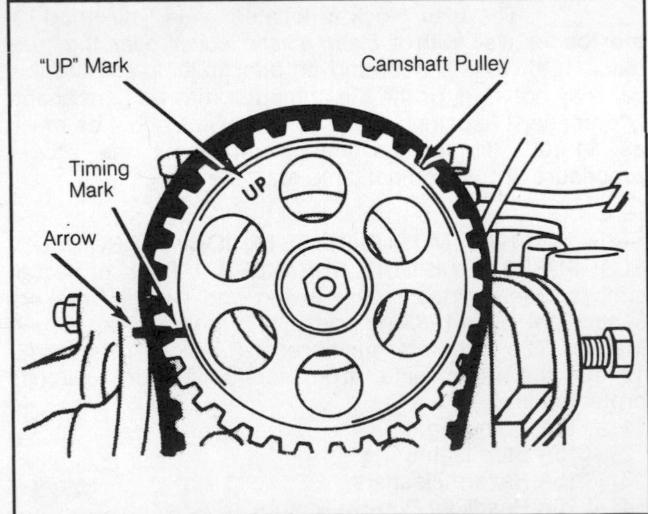
"UP" Mark
Camshaft Pulley
Timing Mark
Arrow
UP

11 1980-81 HONDA CIVIC: INCORRECT TIGHTENING SPECIFICATIONS - The connecting rod and main bearing tightening specifications are incorrect. The connecting rod bolts should be tightened to 21 ft. lbs. (28 N.m). The main bearings should be tightened to 29 ft. lbs. (39 N.m) on 1.3L engines or 33 ft. lbs. (44 N.m) on 1.5L engines.

12 ALL 1978-80 SAAB MODELS: USE SPECIAL TOOLS WHEN REMOVING WATER PUMP TO PREVENT SHAFT GEAR DAMAGE - Under no circumstances should slide hammers or similar tools be used to remove water pumps on 1978-80 models. If special tools are not used, gear teeth damage may occur to pump shaft and idler shaft. To remove and install water pump:

1) Drain coolant. Disconnect negative battery cable. Remove intake manifold. Remove alternator and alternator bracket. Remove bolts and remove water pump cover.

2) Remove water pump, using water pump extractor (8392649 or older model 8392490). Use of slide hammers or other impact tools can result in expensive damage to the pump shaft.

NOTE: Threaded end of pump shaft is provided only for pump removal with special extractor tool. No screw is required.

Removing Water Pump from 1978-80 Saab

83 92 649

3) Press pump shaft (with bearing and lock ring) into engine block, using sleeve (8390551) along with extractor (8392649 or 8392490). Make sure that teeth mesh in place, before pressing in shaft.

4) Install lower sealing ring, using same sleeve and a soft mallet. Install upper sealing ring using installer tool (8390536) and a soft mallet.

CAUTION: When installing impeller, avoid bearing damage by using minimum force necessary.

5) Be sure pump shaft and impeller hole have been thoroughly cleaned before installing impeller.

6) Press impeller in place with sleeve (8392524) and extractor (8392649 or 8392490). Turn pressing screw 90° at a time, then loosen it. Repeat procedure until impeller is pressed fully into place.

NOTE: To check proper impeller positioning and clearance, place a bead of cement on impeller blade. Install water pump cover. Remove cover and cement should not appear flattened.

FOR 1983 & EARLIER MODELS (Cont.)

7) Install gasket and water pump cover. Replace other engine components previously removed.

CLUTCHES

13

1983 VOLVO 760 GLE WITH DIESEL ENGINE: CLUTCH CABLE VIBRATIONS AND NOISE – This condition may be corrected by installation of a new design clutch cable (1272229-4) and vibration damper (1330433-2).

1) To replace, raise the vehicle on a hoist. Disconnect the return spring and slacken the lock nut. Remove the vibration damper and rubber pad. Disconnect the clutch cable.

2) From under the dash. Remove the floor padding. Remove the washer and rubber pad. Disconnect the clutch cable from the pedal assembly.

3) Check the rubber pad for cracks and replace if necessary. Install the clutch cable to the pedal assembly. Install the cable retaining spring with the opening facing down.

4) Install the clutch cable to the clutch fork. Install the new design vibration damper. Depress the clutch pedal 3 times. Press the clutch fork forward. Adjust the clutch free play to .04-.12" (1-3 mm). Tighten the lock nut.

BRAKES

14

1983 SAAB 900 MODELS: FRONT BRAKES KNOCK IN REVERSE OR RATTLE – This condition may be corrected by modification to the brake pad retaining "U-Pin".

Remove the wheel. Remove the "U-Pin" from the brake pads. Bend the "U-Pin" 2.69-2.77" (68.5-70.5 mm) from the back side of the "U-Pin". Bend both ends 2°30' so the ends will point downward when installed.

Modified Brake Pad Retaining "U-Pin"

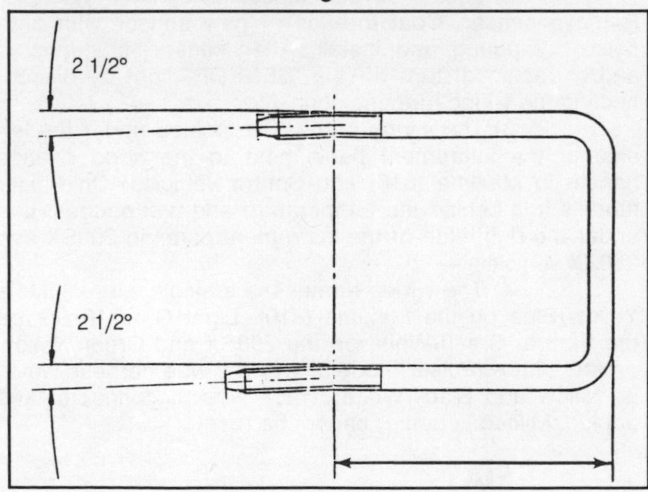
2 1/2°
2 1/2°

1980-83 RESET PROCEDURES — ALL MANUFACTURERS

ALFA ROMEO

1) Every 30,000 miles on Spider 2.0 and 60,000 on GTV-6 2.5, a light on the dash will light, as a reminder to replace the sensor. The system should be checked and the oxygen sensor replaced.

2) From underneath vehicle remove oxygen sensor. Coat new oxygen sensor threads with anti-seize compound before installation. Do not get any compound into slots of sensor.

3) To turn off light on Spider 2.0, locate mileage counter in engine compartment on left side. Remove plastic cover by drilling through shank of attaching screws. Remove cover, then rotate and press button. Reinstall cover using new screws.

AUDI

1) EGR light will come on every 15,000 miles of operation. After EGR system is checked, and any defects corrected, reset mileage counter.

2) Every 30,000 miles a reminder light in the dashboard will light indicating that the emissions system should be checked and the oxygen sensor (if equipped) replaced.

3) Locate oxygen sensor on exhaust manifold and follow lead wire (Green) to connecting plug. Disconnect plug. Remove oxygen sensor. Coat threads of new sensor with anti-seize compound. Install sensor. Do not allow any of the anti-seize compound to get in slots of sensor. Reconnect wire.

4) To turn off reminder light, trace speedometer cable to the mileage counter control box (below left side of instrument panel). The control box is installed in line with the cable. Press White button on box and check that reminder light has gone out.

Fig. 1: Resetting Audi Mileage Counter

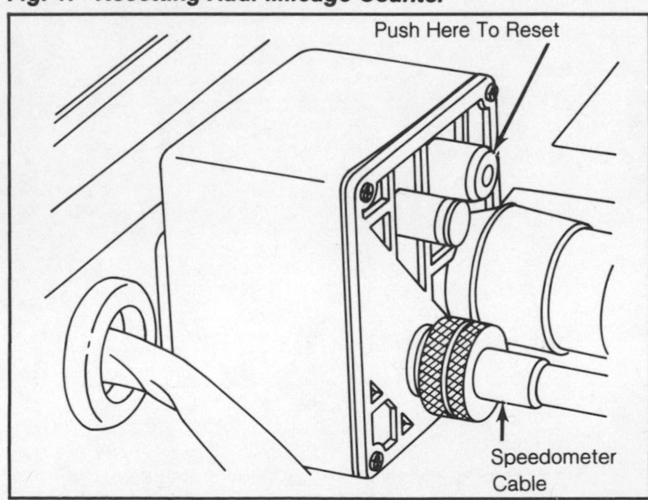
Push Here To Reset
Speedometer
Cable

Press White button to reset counter.

BMW

1) Every 30,000 miles (25,000 on 528i) the "OXYGEN" light in the dash will light as a reminder to replace the oxygen sensor. Trace wire from oxygen sensor to plug and disconnect. Remove oxygen sensor. With a light coat of copper paste applied to threads, install new sensor.

NOTE: **On 528e and 1983 633CSI models, pull the protective metal plate off before removing the oxygen sensor.**

2) On all except 528e and 1983 633CSI, reset the interval switch. Trace speedometer cable to switch, mounted on the frame rail left of transmission. Switch is in-line with speedometer cable. Press White reset button. Check light on dash to be sure that it has gone out.

3) On 528e models and 1983 633CSI, the interval switch cannot be reset. Lift display panel out of dash, turn it over and remove the bulb for "OXYGEN" light.

Fig. 2: Location of BMW Interval Switch

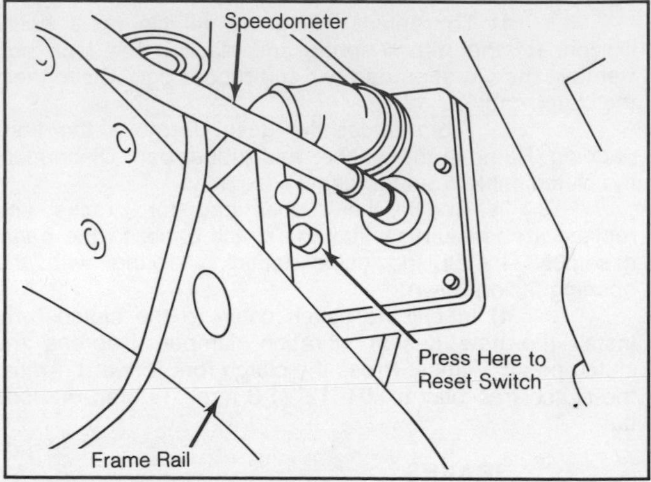
Speedometer
Press Here to
Reset Switch
Frame Rail

Trace speedometer cable to switch and press White button to reset.

DATSUN/NISSAN

1) Datsun/Nissan Maxima (810), Pulsar, Sentra, 200SX and 280ZX models utilize an oxygen sensor. After 30,000 miles of operation, the oxygen sensor warning light in the dash will come on. This light indicates that the sensor should be inspected. If sensor is faulty, it must be replaced.

2) Locate oxygen sensor on exhaust manifold. Remove sensor. Coat threads of new sensor with anti-seize compound and install. After sensor is inspected and/or replaced, turn off the "SENSOR" light by disconnecting the wiring harness connector.

3) The wiring harness is located under the left side of the instrument panel next to the hood release handle in Maxima (810) and Sentra vehicles. On Pulsar models it is behind the temperature and fuel gauges. It is under the right side of the instrument panel in 200SX and 280ZX vehicles.

4) The wiring harness is a single wire which is Yellow/Blue on the Maxima (810), Light Green/Black on the Sentra, Green/White on the 200SX and Green/Yellow on the 280ZX. Pulsar models have a 2 wire harness which is Yellow and Black/White. Trace wire to connector and unplug. Mileage counter cannot be reset.

FIAT

1) All Fiats with fuel injection are equipped with an oxygen sensor. After 30,000 miles of operation, a warning light in the dash will light, indicating that the sensor must be replaced.

2) Locate sensor in exhaust manifold and trace wire to first connector. Disconnect wire and remove sensor. Apply anti-seize compound to threads of new sensor and install.

1980-83 RESET PROCEDURES — ALL MANUFACTURERS (Cont.)

3) Reset mileage counter. First, locate switch unit. On Brava, the switch is located behind the dash on the left hand side and on Strada, under the dash between the glove box and the radio.

4) On Spider 2000, the switch is located under the left side of the dash, above the accelerator pedal and on X 1/9, behind the center console.

5) To reset switch, cut the cap screw retaining wire and remove screw. Insert small screwdriver through housing and press switch contact. This resets switch and turns out "EX GAS SENSOR" light. Install the cap screw and secure with new wire.

Fig. 3: Fiat Oxygen Sensor Switch Unit

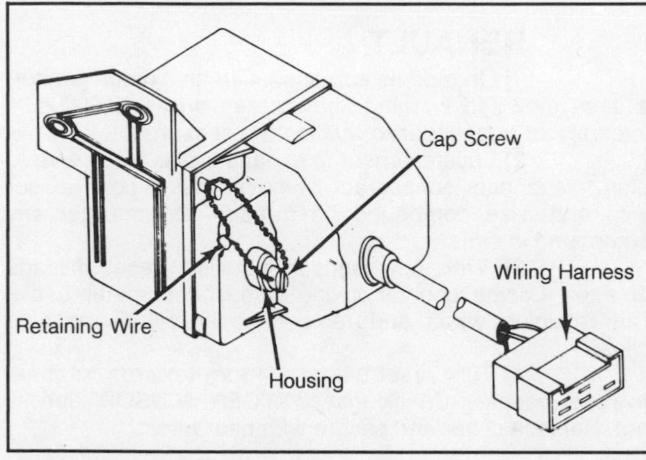

Cap Screw
Wiring Harness
Retaining Wire
Housing

Reset switch at 30,000 mile intervals.

JAGUAR

1) All fuel-injected Jaguars are equipped with an oxygen sensor. When the warning light on the dash comes on (at 30,000 mile intervals), replace the sensor.

2) Remove sensor from exhaust pipe and install a new sensor. Coat threads of new sensor with anti-seize compound before installation.

3) After replacing sensor, locate the interval counter (in-line with speedometer cable). Reset counter using key (BLT-5007) supplied in kit with new sensor.

4) Models with electronic speedometers have a mileage counter in the trunk. Counter is behind the left side trim adjacent to the wheel arch. The reset button is White.

MERCEDES-BENZ

1) When the "OX-SENSOR" light comes on (at 30,000 miles) the oxygen sensor must be replaced. Remove sensor from exhaust pipe and install new sensor with anti-seize compound applied to threads.

2) On 280 series vehicles, locate mileage counter in-line with the speedometer cable, under instrument panel. Disconnect wiring plug from counter and leave disconnected. No reset switch is provided.

3) On 380 series vehicles, the instrument cluster must be partially removed. Insert a hooked steel wire between right side of cluster and dashboard. Turn hook to engage cluster and pull cluster out of spring retaining clips. Remove bulb from lower corner of cluster. Press cluster back into position. No reset switch is provided.

Fig. 4: Mercedes-Benz 280 Mileage Counter

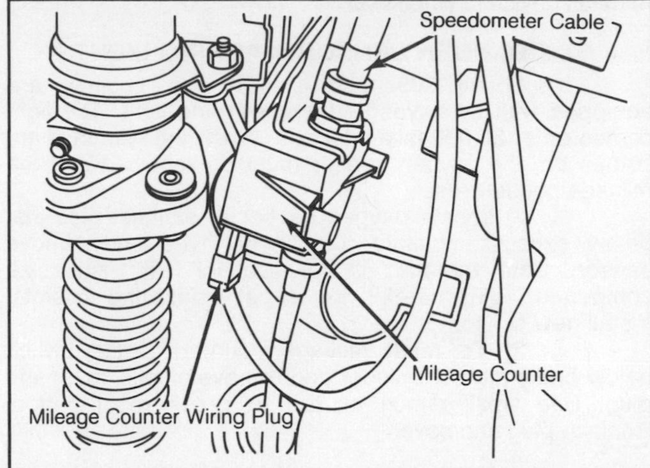

Speedometer Cable
Mileage Counter
Mileage Counter Wiring Plug

Disconnect wiring plug to turn off "OX-SENSOR" light.

PEUGEOT

EGR WARNING LIGHT

1) All 1980 604 models are equipped with an "EGR" warning light. The light comes on at 12,500 mile intervals as determined by a mileage counter. When light comes on, perform EGR service. After service, reset mileage counter.

2) To reset mileage counter, unbolt the maintenance switch from inside of left front wheelwell. Pull down switch without disconnecting speedometer cables.

3) Remove covers (outer and inner) from counter and turn reset button counterclockwise until reaching a stop point. This resets counter to zero. Check

Fig 5: Resetting Peugeot Mileage Counter

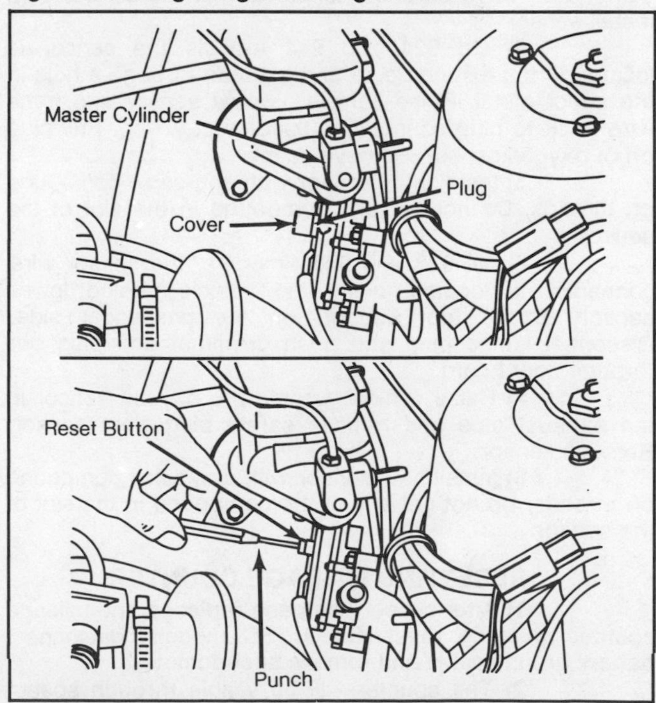

Master Cylinder
Plug
Cover
Reset Button
Punch

Use small punch or probe to push reset button.

1980-83 RESET PROCEDURES — ALL MANUFACTURERS (Cont.)

that warning light has gone out. Replace covers and reinstall device in wheelwell.

OXYGEN SENSOR WARNING LIGHT

1) All 505 models with gas engines are equipped with an oxygen sensor warning light. The light comes on at 30,000 mile intervals. When the warning light comes on, the oxygen sensor must be replaced and the mileage counter reset.

2) Locate oxygen sensor in exhaust pipe just below exhaust manifold. Disconnect wire and remove sensor. Coat threads of new sensor with anti-seize compound, being careful not to get compound in slots. Install new sensor.

3) To reset mileage counter, locate switch below brake master cylinder and remove plastic cover and plug. Use small punch or rod to press reset button. Replace plug and cover.

PORSCHE

All models are equipped with an oxygen sensor. On all except the 944, an "OXS" light in the dash comes on at 30,000 mile intervals as a reminder to replace the sensor. It is recommended by Porsche that the oxygen sensor in the 944 be replaced every 60,000 miles, however, no warning light is provided on this model.

REPLACING OXYGEN SENSOR

1) ON 911SC models, locate oxygen sensor plug on left side of engine compartment, just below ignition coil. Disconnect wire at plug and push grommet and plug through hole.

2) Raise vehicle. Remove left rear wheel. Remove exhaust shield. Locate oxygen sensor on exhaust manifold and pull safety plug off of sensor. Remove sensor.

3) Coat threads of new sensor with anti-seize compound, using care not to get any in the sensor slot. Install sensor.

4) On 924 and 944 models the sensor is located in the exhaust pipe and extends through a hole in the sheet metal. Raise vehicle. Locate sensor and trace wire back to plug connector. Disconnect wiring. Pull plug off of oxygen sensor. Remove sensor.

5) Install new sensor with anti-seize compound on threads. Do not get any compound in the slot of the sensor.

6) On 928 and 928S models, the sensor wire connector is located inside the vehicle behind lower section of the foot support on the passenger side. Disconnet wiring plug and push grommet and plug out through floor board.

7) Raise vehicle. Locate the oxygen sensor in the exhaust pipe and remove safety plug from sensor. Remove sensor.

8) Install new sensor with anti-seize compound on threads. Do not get any of the compound in the slot of the sensor.

RESETTING MILEAGE COUNTER

1) After sensor has been replaced, the mileage counter must be reset. On 911SC models, disconnect battery ground cable and remove speedometer.

2) The counter will be visible through speedometer mounting hole. Use a thick piece of wire or a thin rod to press White reset button. Push button all the way in against stop. Check that warning light has gone out.

3) On 924 models the mileage counter is located on the left engine mount. After removing oxygen sensor (vehicle still raised), locate the counter and use a thick wire or thin metal rod to push in reset button. Be sure to push button in all the way to stop. Check that "OXS" light is out.

4) On 928 models the counter is located on the floor, to the right of the passenger seat. Remove the counter cover retaining screw and cover. Press reset button all the way in against stop. Make sure that warning light is out.

RENAULT

1) On models equipped with an oxygen sensor, a dash mounted warning light comes on at 30,000 mile intervals as a reminder to replace the sensor.

2) Locate sensor in exhaust pipe. Trace wire to plug, disconnect sensor and remove. Install new sensor with anti-seize compound on threads. Do not get any compound in slots.

3) With new sensor installed, reset mileage counter. Locate counter in-line with speedometer cable. Cut retaining wires and remove cover by disengaging clips.

4) Turn reset button 1/4 turn towards "o" mark to reset counter. Check that "OXYGEN SENSOR" light is out. Replace cover and secure with new wires.

Fig. 6: Resetting Renault Mileage Counter

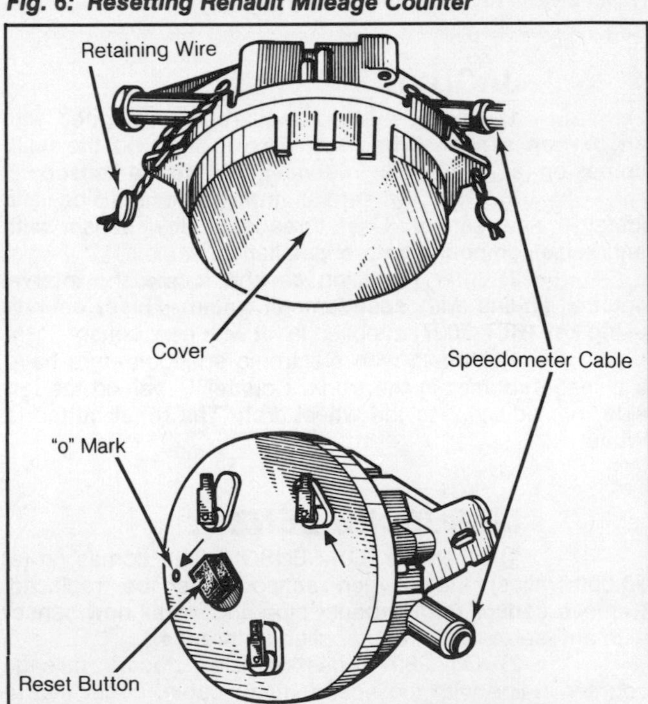
Retaining Wire
Cover
Speedometer Cable
"o" Mark
Reset Button

Remove cover. Turn reset button counterclockwise 1/4 turn.

SAAB

1) All gasoline engine equipped models use an oxygen sensor as part of the exhaust emissions system.

1980-83 RESET PROCEDURES — ALL MANUFACTURERS (Cont.)

The "EXH" maintenance light on the dash comes on every 30,000 miles. The oxygen sensor should be replaced at this time.

2) Locate oxygen sensor on exhaust manifold and remove. Apply anti-seize compound to threads of new sensor, being careful not to get any compound in slots of sensor. Install sensor.

3) To reset mileage counter for "EXH" light, press reset button on counter unit. The unit is located at flasher relay under instrument panel. Reach under guard panel, locate unit, and press reset button (next to single wire connection).

Fig. 7: Resetting Saab Mileage Counter

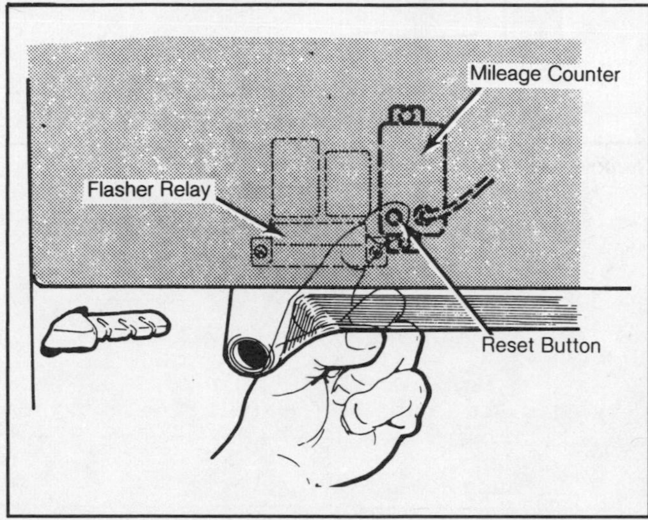
Mileage Counter
Flasher Relay
Reset Button

Press reset button located next to single wire connection.

TOYOTA

1) On Diesel Pickups, an instrument panel maintenance reminder light will come on at 50,000 miles (60,000 on 1982-3 models). The engine timing belt should be replaced at this time. After belt is replaced, remove rubber grommet from speedometer bezel and reset speedometer counter by pressing reset switch.

Fig. 8: Resetting Speedometer Counter On Toyota Diesel Pickups

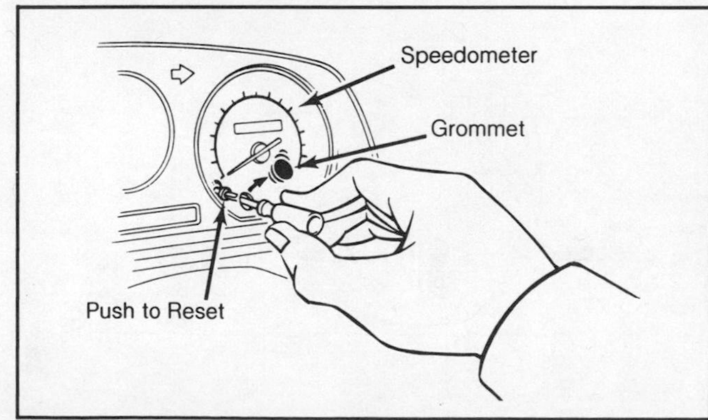
Speedometer
Grommet
Push to Reset

Remove rubber grommet. Reset counter.

2) All 1980 Supra, Cressida and all 1981 models with gasoline engines (except Starlet) are equipped with an oxygen sensor. At 30,000 mile intervals, a mileage counter activates a warning light in the dash. The oxygen sensor must be inspected at this time.

3) On vehicles with High Altitude Compensation (HAC), disconnect vacuum hose between HAC valve and check valve. Plug check valve. On vehicles with a Vacuum Control Valve (VCV), disconnect the lower vacuum line (from VCV to vacuum connector) and plug connector.

4) Warm engine to normal operating temperature. Locate service connector on left fender, near ignition coil. Remove rubber cap and connect a voltmeter to connector with positive probe at "Ox" terminal and negative probe at "E" terminal.

5) Run engine at 2500 RPM for 90 seconds. Maintain engine speed and check needle on voltmeter. It should fluctuate between 0 and 7 volts at least 8 times in a 10 second period. If not, check all hose connections and wiring. If no other fault is found, replace oxygen sensor.

6) To reset warning light, remove cancel switch from top of left kick panel, except Cressida. Remove small panel next to steering column on Cressida models. Pry open the tab and move switch to the opposite position.

Fig. 9: Testing Toyota Oxygen Sensor

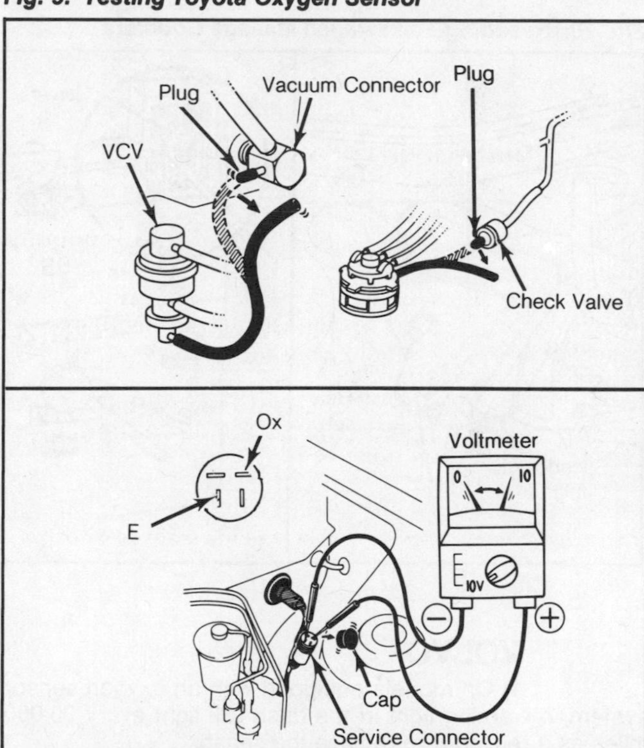
Plug
Vacuum Connector
Plug
VCV
Check Valve
Ox
Voltmeter
E
Cap
Service Connector

Disconnect and plug vacuum lines as shown. Attach voltmeter and observe needle fluctuations.

TRIUMPH

1) All fuel-injected Triumphs are equipped with an oxygen sensor. When the warning light on the dash comes on (at 30,000 mile intervals), replace the sensor.

2) Remove sensor from exhaust pipe and install a new sensor. Coat threads of new sensor with anti-seize compound before installation.

3) After replacing sensor, locate the interval counter (in-line with speedometer cable). Reset counter using key (BLT-5007) supplied in kit with new sensor.

1980-83 RESET PROCEDURES — ALL MANUFACTURERS (Cont.)

VOLKSWAGEN

EGR MAINTENANCE LIGHT

Check EGR system operation every 15,000 miles ("EGR" light will come on). After system check, reset mileage counter.

OXYGEN SENSOR WARNING LIGHT

Replace oxygen sensor when "OXS" light comes on (30,000 miles). Coat threads of new sensor with anti-seize compound, ensuring that no compound gets into slots on sensor. With new sensor installed, reset the mileage counter.

RESETTING MILEAGE COUNTER

1) On some models, remove instrument panel cover plate. Reach into opening at top left corner of speedometer and pull release arm to reset counter. Left arm resets EGR, right arm resets oxygen sensor.

2) On other models, locate mileage counter (on firewall, in-line with speedometer cable) and push White reset button. Check maintenance light to ensure that it is out.

Fig. 10: Resetting Volkswagen Mileage Counters

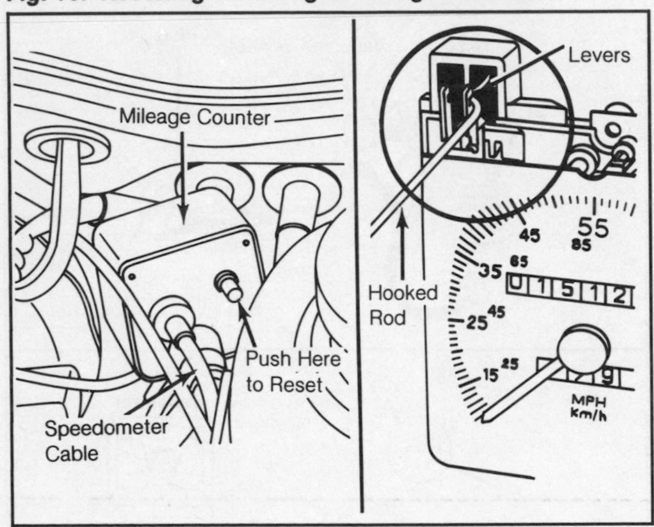
Mileage Counter
Push Here to Reset
Speedometer Cable
Levers
Hooked Rod
45
55
85
35
65
25
45
15
25
0 1 5 1 2
7 9
MPH
km/h

VOLVO

1) On models equipped with an oxygen sensor system, a warning light in the dash will light every 30,000 miles as a reminder to replace the sensor.

2) Remove old sensor from exhaust manifold. Apply anti-seize compound to threads of new sensor and install. Do not allow any of the compound to get on the slotted part of the sensor.

3) On 760 GLE models, the reminder light is connected to the electronic speedometer gauge. Resetting procedure is not available from manufacturer at time of publication.

4) On all other models, locate the mileage counter in-line with the speedometer cable. Remove retaining screw and switch cover. Press reset button. Check that the reminder light in the dash has gone out. Replace switch cover.

Fig. 11: Resetting Volvo Mileage Counter

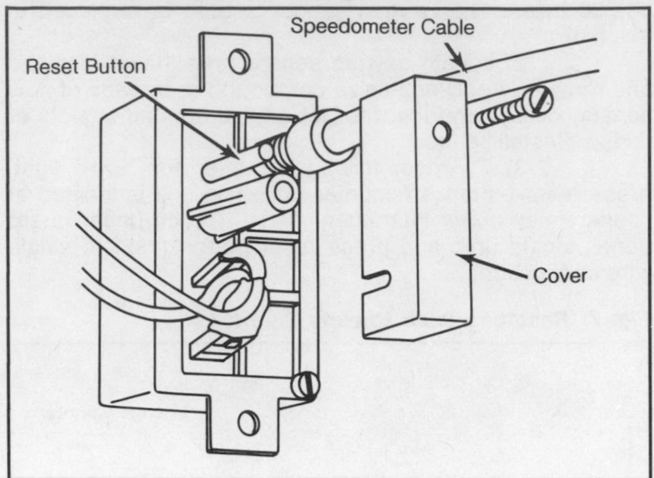
Speedometer Cable
Reset Button
Cover

Remove switch cover and press reset button.